Holt Algebra 2 Features Quicklist

S0-BAC-424

HOLT MATH

	SEE PAGE(S)
PROVEN INSTRUCTIONAL DESIGN	
• Consistent lesson format of **Example, Solution, Check It Out** provides a logical instructional approach.	90-93
• Step-by-step examples and color-coded explanations help students become independent learners.	97-99
• Know-it Notes indicate key concepts for students to remember and correspond to entries in the students' **Know-it Notebook.**	119, 159
• Exercises matched to examples mean no homework surprises!	100
COMPREHENSIVE DIFFERENTIATED INSTRUCTION	
• Reaching All Learners includes strategies for adapting the material for all types of learners.	TE 98
• English Language Learners identifies strategies particularly effective with this group of students.	TE 129
• Geometry Labs allow students to explore math concepts through manipulatives.	58-59
• Technology Labs assist students in the use of graphing calculators, spreadsheets, and dynamic geometry software.	113-114
• Reteach, Practice, Challenge, Reading Strategies, and Problem Solving reduced images make selecting worksheets quick and easy.	TE 110-111
• Teaching Tips provide suggestions for addressing various learning styles.	TE 152
• Additional Examples offer more classroom review for struggling students.	TE 116
• Assignment Guide recommends homework assignments based on student ability.	TE 138
• Power Presentations are editable PowerPoint® presentations for every lesson as well as extra examples and quizzes.	TE 156
BUILT-IN ASSESSMENT AND INTERVENTION	
• Are You Ready? at the beginning of each chapter assesses students' prerequisite skills..	87
• Ready to Go On? diagnoses students' skill development within the chapter.	133
• Check It Out and Try This questions enable students to check their understanding after every example and activity.	92, 104
• Questioning Strategies aid on-the-spot intervention with questions crafted to assess student comprehension.	TE 116
• Common Error Alert helps teachers anticipate potential pitfalls for students.	TE 127
• Alternative Assessment provides options to monitor student progress.	TE 131
• Chapter Test assesses students' mastery of concepts and skills.	170

	SEE PAGE(S)
READING AND WRITING MATH FOR COMPREHENSION	
• Reading and Writing Math lessons help students develop strong communication skills as they master math concepts.	89
• Reading Math and Writing Math hints appear throughout each chapter to help students use the language of math.	99,150
• Write About It exercises require students to explain a math concept or procedure.	139
• Journal suggestions encourage students to write about math.	TE 123
• Think and Discuss questions in every lesson extend and enrich student knowledge.	127
• Graphic Organizers in every lesson help students organize and remember key information.	137
• Glossary contains definitions and illustrations of key mathematical terms in English and Spanish.	S118-161
ENGAGING CONNECTIONS AND APPLICATIONS	
• Links spark student interest by giving them the opportunity to apply math skills to other disciplines and the real world.	95, 111, 155
• Connecting Algebra to Geometry provides review and application of previously learned geometry concepts.	104, 122
• Career Path relates math concepts to the real world.	277
• Problem Solving on Location	176-177
INTEGRATED TEST PREP	
• Countdown to Testing prepares students for state tests with daily practice questions.	C4-C27
• Test Prep and Spiral Review provide daily practice of new and previously taught skills in standardized test format.	112
• Test Prep Doctor addresses specific test-taking strategies related to the lesson.	TE 140
• Multi-Step Test Prep uses real-world scenarios to develop higher order thinking skills	102, 132
• Test Tackler targets specific test-taking strategies to help students become savvy test-takers.	172-173
• College Entrance Exam Practice provides practice for college entrance exams such as the SAT and ACT.	171
• Standardized Test Prep provides cumulative assessment in standardized test format.	174-175
STUDENT SUPPORT	
• Study Guide: Preview prepares students for the concepts they will learn in the chapter and connects the concepts to the real world.	88
• Student to Student shares advice from other students on how to approach the math in the lesson.	117
• Extra Practice directs students to additional, immediate practice of lesson concepts.	101, S6, S33
• Homework Help Online provides stepped out solutions and additional practice for students as they work independently. (go.hrw.com Homework Help Online KEYWORD: MB7 2-5)	161
• Study Guide: Review highlights each lesson's vocabulary and key skills and offers additional examples and practice exercises.	166-169

INDIANA TEACHER'S EDITION

HOLT

Algebra 2

Edward B. Burger
David J. Chard
Earlene J. Hall
Paul A. Kennedy
Steven J. Leinwand
Freddie L. Renfro
Dale G. Seymour
Bert K. Waits

HOLT, RINEHART AND WINSTON
A Harcourt Education Company
Orlando • Austin • New York • San Diego • London

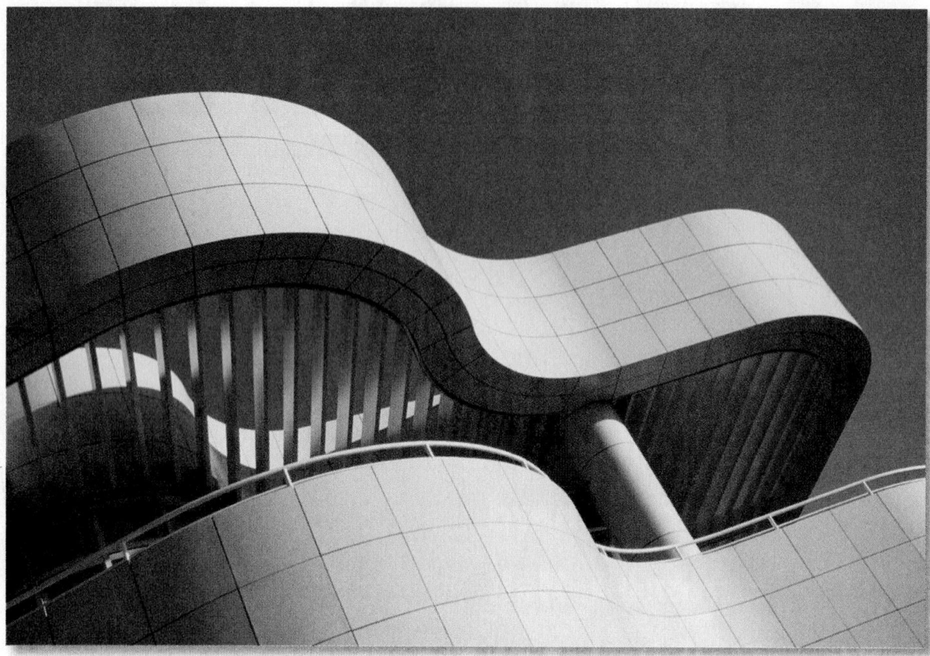

Cover Photography: Getty Center, Los Angeles, CA. © Richard Cummins/SuperStock

Printed in the United States of America

ISBN 978-0-547-25895-9

ISBN 0-547-25895-x

1 2 3 4 5 0868 13 12 11 10 09

Algebra 2 Teacher's Edition

Contents in Brief

Chapter Teacher Material

Student Handbook

Contributing Authors

Linda Antinone
Fort Worth, TX

Ms. Antinone teaches mathematics at R. L. Paschal High School in Fort Worth, Texas. She has received the Presidential Award for Excellence in Teaching Mathematics and the National Radio Shack Teacher award. She has coauthored several books for Texas Instruments on the use of technology in mathematics.

Carmen Whitman
Pflugerville, TX

Ms. Whitman travels nationally helping districts improve mathematics education. She has been a program coordinator on the mathematics team at the Charles A. Dana Center, and has served as a secondary math specialist for the Austin Independent School District.

Indiana Teacher Reviewers

Kathy Bartley
Highland High School
Highland, IN

Mr. John M. Bogner
Highland High School
Highland, IN

Heather Lee Hart
Center Grove High School
Greenwood, IN

Letitia McCallister
Hamilton Southeastern High School
Fishers, IN

Janice Mitchener
Carmel High School
Carmel, IN

Angela Moreman
Creekside Middle School
Mathematics Dept Chair
Carmel, IN

Kathleen Robeson
Fishers High School
Fishers, IN

Vicki Tribul
Carmel High School
Carmel, IN

Reviewers

Mary Anderson
Mathematics Department Chair
Community High School District 99 South
Downers Grove, IL

Dave Barker
Mathematics Department Chair
Los Alamitos High School
Los Alamitos, CA

MaryLane Blomquist
Mathematics Department Chair
Kewaskum High School
Kewaskum, WI

William L. Bonney
Mathematics Department Chair
Ballard High School
Seattle, WA

Suzanne Castren
Mathematics Teacher
Williamsville South High School
Williamsville, NY

Lala Geraldine Chambers, NBCT
Mathematics Department Chair
Forest Hill High School
Jackson, MS

Joan Chrismer-McNatt
Mathematics Teacher
Clear Creek High School
League City, TX

Roy L. Conwell, Jr.
Mathematics Department Chair
Sam Houston High School
Houston, TX

Patricia Daley
Mathematics Teacher, retired
Fairfield High School
Fairfield, CT

Mohamad Elkhatib
Mathematics Department Chair
Jones High School
Houston Community College Instructor
Houston, TX

Marti Freihofer
Mathematics Department Chair
Scott High School
Taylor Mill, KY

Mary Gesino
Mathematics Department Co-Chair
R. L. Turner High School
Carrollton, TX

Marilyn Gutman
Mathematics Department Chair
Mayfield High School
Las Cruces, NM

Jim Harrington
Supervisor of Mathematics
Omaha Public Schools
Omaha, NE

Marieta W. Harris
Mathematics Specialist
Memphis, TN

Jere Hassberger, PhD
Mathematics Department Chair
Saline High School
Saline, MI

James Patrick Herrington
Mathematics Department Chair
O'Fallon Township High School
O'Fallon, IL

Margie Hill
District Coordinating Teacher for Mathematics, K-12
Blue Valley USD 229
Overland Park, KS

Dr. Douglas Lohnas
Director of Mathematics
Niskayuna Central School District
Niskayuna, NY

Brenda Lynch
Mathematics Department Chair
Montgomery High School
Montgomery, TX

Dr. Charlotte May
Mathematics Teacher
Austin ISD
Austin, TX

Ruth Harbin Miles
K–12 Coordinator of Mathematics
Olathe USD 233
Olathe, KS

Saundra Paschal
Mathematics Department Chair
Lake View High School
San Angelo, TX

Carolyn Randolph
Mathematics Department Chair
Academic Director
Kendrick High School
Columbus, GA

Sarah Ritch
Mathematics Department Chair
Hebron High School
Carrollton, TX

Paul Schwiegerling
Gifted Mathematics Program
SUNY at Buffalo
Buffalo, NY

Katie Smith
Mathematics Department Chair
Berea High School
Greenville, SC

Stephanie Turner
Former Mathematics Teacher
Colleyville Heritage High School
Colleyville, TX

Field Test Participants

Gerri Chambers-McGee
Forest Hill High School
Jackson, MS

Stephanie Cundiff
Mesa Ridge High School
Colorado Springs, CO

Eddie Hancock
Navasota High School
Navasota, TX

Brenda Lynch
Montgomery High School
Montgomery, TX

Lisa Pope
Jacobs High School
Cincinnati, OH

Niki Robinson
Navasota High School
Navasota, TX

Piper Singleton
Pershing High School
Detroit, MI

Dierdre M. Watkins
Dunwoody High School
Dunwoody, GA

THE 6–12 MATH SERIES YOU CAN COUNT ON

HOLT MATH

You can count on **Holt Algebra 2** for

1

Built-in Assessment and Intervention. Prescribe the resources your students need when they need them in order to lead your students to success.

2

Comprehensive Differentiated Instruction. Ensure all students have the opportunity to succeed with strategies designed to reach students of all learning styles and skill levels.

3

Success on High-Stakes Tests. Prepare students for success on test day with standards-based test preparation that's embedded into daily lessons.

4

Integrated Technology that Enhances Learning. Motivate your students to excel and manage your classroom with maximum effectiveness using Holt technology.

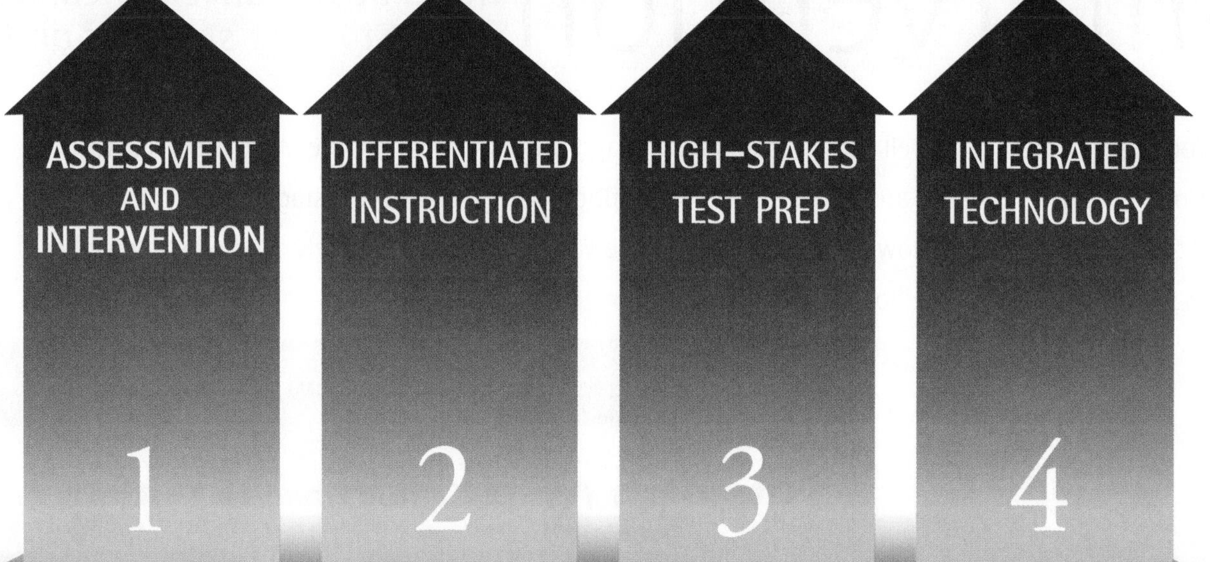

Built for Student Success... from the Ground Up

Every student is unique with individual strengths and weaknesses. Starting with *Holt Mathematics* and *Pre-Algebra* for middle school through *Holt Algebra 1, Geometry,* and *Algebra 2,* Holt provides the instruction and resources you need to reach and teach every one of your students. Whether it's an alternative approach to a lesson, a modification for a visual learner, or extra practice with basic skills, Holt has what you need to help all of your students succeed.

> *"Deep and abstract ideas are challenging to all, but the challenge should be a pleasurable one that students want to conquer."*
>
> – Dr. Edward B. Burger, Holt author

Program Highlights

Count on Holt Algebra 2 for

Built-in assessment and intervention

1

Holt's at-a-glance system makes it easy to keep students on track.

You need to know how well your students understand the lesson BEFORE they take the test. With *Holt Algebra 2*, informal and formal assessment options are given at every stage within the chapter. Intervention resources allow you to reteach or review material without merely sending students back to previous lessons in the book.

- **Assess Prior Knowledge** to make sure all students start the chapter on solid footing.

  Intervene with alternate teaching strategies and basic skills review in **Are You Ready? Intervention and Enrichment.**

- **Formative Assessment** to diagnose skill development within the chapter.

  Intervene with **Ready to Go On?, Lesson Tutorial Videos, Homework Help Online,** and more.

- **Summative Assessment** to allow students to demonstrate their mastery of the concepts.

  Intervene with **Reteach** and **Lesson Tutorial Videos.**

OPTIONS • RESOURCE OPTIONS • RESOURCE OPTIONS • RESOURCE OPTIONS

ONGOING ASSESSMENT and INTERVENTION

	DIAGNOSE	PRESCRIBE
Assess Prior Knowledge	**Before Chapter 2** Diagnose readiness for the chapter. **Are You Ready?** SE p. 73	Prescribe intervention. ***Are You Ready? Intervention*** pp. 48, 51, 55, 58, 60
Formative Assessment	**Before Every Lesson** Diagnose readiness for the lesson. **Warm Up** TE, every lesson	Prescribe intervention. **Reteach** CRB, Ch. 11
	During Every Lesson Diagnose understanding of lesson concepts. **Check It Out!** SE, every example **Think and Discuss** SE, every lesson **Write About It** SE, every lesson **Journal** TE, every lesson	Prescribe intervention. **Questioning Strategies** TE, every example **Reading Strategies** CRB, every lesson ***Success for ELL*** ***Lesson Tutorial Videos***
	After Every Lesson Diagnose mastery of lesson concepts. **Lesson Quiz** TE, every lesson **Alternative Assessment** TE, every lesson **Test Prep** SE, every lesson ***Test and Practice Generator***	Prescribe intervention. **Reteach** CRB, every lesson **Problem Solving** CRB, every lesson **Test Prep Doctor** TE, every lesson ***Homework Help Online***
	Before Chapter 2 Testing Diagnose mastery of concepts in the chapter. **Ready to Go On?** SE pp. 113, 147 **Multi-Step Test Prep** SE pp. 112, 146 **Section Quizzes** AR pp. 160–161 ***Test and Practice Generator***	Prescribe intervention. ***Ready to Go On? Intervention*** pp. 21-46 ***Scaffolding Questions*** TE pp. 112, 146
	Before High Stakes Testing Diagnose mastery of benchmark concepts. **College Entrance Exam Practice** SE p. 157 **Standardized Test Prep** SE pp. 160–161 ***State Test Prep CD-ROM***	Prescribe intervention. ***College Entrance Exam Practice*** pp. 23-29 ***State Test Prep Workbook*** pp. 20-27
Summative Assessment	**After Chapter 2** Check mastery of chapter concepts. **Multiple-Choice Tests (Forms A, B, C)** **Free-Response Tests (Forms A, B, C)** **Performance Assessment** AR ***Test and Practice Generator*** Check mastery of benchmark concepts. **AYP State Tests** **College Entrance Exams**	Prescribe intervention. **Reteach** CRB, every lesson ***Lesson Tutorial Videos*** Chapter 2 Prescribe intervention. ***State Test Prep Workbook*** pp. 20-27 ***College Entrance Exam Practice*** pp. 23-29

KEY: SE = *Student Edition* TE = *Teacher's Edition* CRB = *Chapter Resource Book* AR = *Assessment Resources* Available online Available on CD-ROM

72B

When students are struggling they don't want to keep rereading the same lesson in the hope that eventually it will make sense. They need to try a new approach to the lesson. That's at the core of the assessment and intervention system in *Holt Algebra 2.*

Name ______________ Date ________ Class ________

SKILL 68 **Are You Ready?**
Solve One-Step Equations

To solve a one-step equation, do the inverse of whatever operation is being done to the variable. Remember, because it is an equation, what is done to one side of the equation must also be done to the other side.

Solve an addition equation using subtraction.	Solve a subtraction equation using addition.
$x + 5 = 15$ $\underline{-5 \quad -5}$ $x \quad = 10$	$x - 8 = -3$ $\underline{+8 \quad +8}$ $x \quad = 5$
Solve a multiplication equation using division.	**Solve a division equation using multiplication.**
$7x = 42$ $\frac{7x}{7} = \frac{42}{7}$ $x = 6$	$\frac{x}{12} = -3$ $12 \cdot \frac{x}{12} = -3 \cdot 12$ $x = -36$

Practice on Your Own
Solve.

1. $m - 5 = 9$ ______
2. $\frac{h}{6} = -3$ ______
3. $6x = 54$ ______
4. $b + 15 = 25$ ______
5. $4y = -12$ ______
6. $k + 9 = -3$ ______
7. $p - 7 = -2$ ______
8. $\frac{t}{3} = 7$ ______
9. $\frac{x}{4} = -1$ ______
10. $5 + h = 16$ ______
11. $-12x = -24$ ______
12. $r - 2 = -9$ ______

Check
Solve.

13. $3x = 15$ ______
14. $c - 11 = 1$ ______
15. $d + 9 = 5$ ______
16. $\frac{s}{6} = -5$ ______
17. $z - 2 = -17$ ______
18. $\frac{w}{4} = 12$ ______
19. $-10b = 120$ ______
20. $x + 99 = 100$ ______

Copyright © by Holt, Rinehart and Winston. All rights reserved. 148 Holt Algebra 2

Are You Ready?
Intervention and Enrichment

- Diagnoses mastery of prerequisite skills
- Strengthens student weaknesses with direct instruction, conceptual models, and scaffolded practice
- Enriches every chapter with critical thinking activities
- Available in print, on CD-ROM, and online

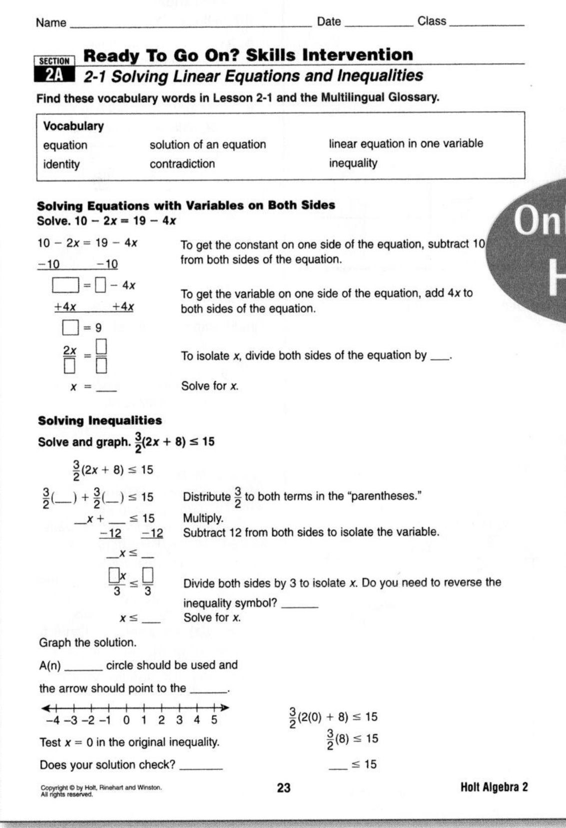

Name ______________ Date ________ Class ________

SECTION 2A **Ready To Go On? Skills Intervention**
2-1 Solving Linear Equations and Inequalities

Find these vocabulary words in Lesson 2-1 and the Multilingual Glossary.

Vocabulary		
equation	solution of an equation	linear equation in one variable
identity	contradiction	inequality

Solving Equations with Variables on Both Sides
Solve. $10 - 2x = 19 - 4x$

$10 - 2x = 19 - 4x$ — To get the constant on one side of the equation, subtract 10 from both sides of the equation.
$\underline{-10 \qquad -10}$
$\square = \square - 4x$ — To get the variable on one side of the equation, add $4x$ to both sides of the equation.
$\underline{+4x \qquad +4x}$
$\square = 9$
$\frac{2x}{\square} = \frac{\square}{\square}$ — To isolate x, divide both sides of the equation by ___.
$x =$ ___ — Solve for x.

Solving Inequalities
Solve and graph. $\frac{3}{2}(2x + 8) \le 15$

$\frac{3}{2}(2x + 8) \le 15$
$\frac{3}{2}(\_\_) + \frac{3}{2}(\_\_) \le 15$ — Distribute $\frac{3}{2}$ to both terms in the "parentheses."
$\_x + \_\_ \le 15$ — Multiply.
$\underline{-12 \quad -12}$ — Subtract 12 from both sides to isolate the variable.
$\_x \le \_\_$
$\frac{\square x}{3} \le \frac{\square}{3}$ — Divide both sides by 3 to isolate x. Do you need to reverse the inequality symbol? ______
$x \le$ ___ — Solve for x.

Graph the solution.
A(n) ______ circle should be used and the arrow should point to the ______.

−4 −3 −2 −1 0 1 2 3 4 5

Test $x = 0$ in the original inequality.
Does your solution check? ______

$\frac{3}{2}(2(0) + 8) \le 15$
$\frac{3}{2}(8) \le 15$
___ ≤ 15

Copyright © by Holt, Rinehart and Winston. All rights reserved. 23 Holt Algebra 2

Only from Holt!

Ready to Go On?
Intervention and Enrichment

- Diagnoses mastery of newly taught skills
- Addresses deficiencies with alternative instruction and practice
- Checks student progress with post tests
- Available in print, on CD-ROM, and online

> *"Closing the gaps in academic achievement among students from different social divisions (class, ethnicity, gender, language) will require research-based instructional interventions."*
>
> **— Dr. Earlene J. Hall, Holt author**

Program Highlights

Count on Holt Algebra 2 for

Comprehensive differentiated instruction

Reach all learners in your classroom—no matter what their skill levels or learning styles are.

Not all students "get it" at the same time or in the same way. *Holt Algebra 2* accommodates the students in your classroom with different skill levels and those whose learning styles benefit from different approaches.

With leveled practice and tests, content presented in a variety of media, and teaching strategies built in at point-of-use, helping all of your students succeed has never been easier.

- **Teaching Tips** make your teaching more adaptable to the range of learning styles in your classroom.
- **Know-It! Notes** indicate key concepts for students to remember and correspond to entries in the students' **Know It Notebook.**
- **Reaching All Learners** recommends alternative approaches to the lesson at point-of-use.

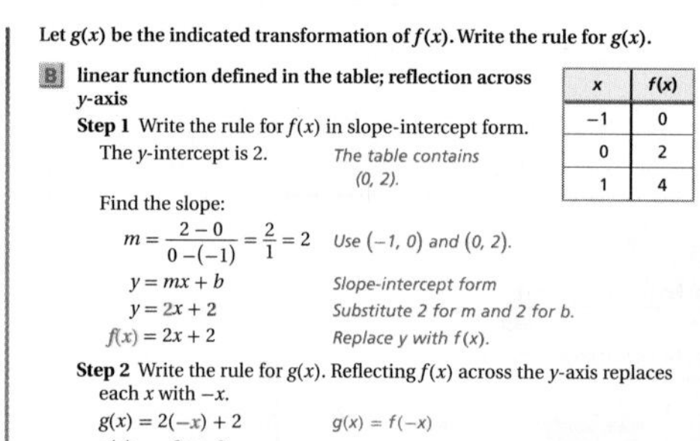

Let $g(x)$ be the indicated transformation of $f(x)$. Write the rule for $g(x)$.

B linear function defined in the table; reflection across y-axis

x	$f(x)$
−1	0
0	2
1	4

Step 1 Write the rule for $f(x)$ in slope-intercept form.

The y-intercept is 2. *The table contains (0, 2).*

Find the slope:

$m = \frac{2-0}{0-(-1)} = \frac{2}{1} = 2$ *Use (−1, 0) and (0, 2).*

$y = mx + b$ *Slope-intercept form*

$y = 2x + 2$ *Substitute 2 for m and 2 for b.*

$f(x) = 2x + 2$ *Replace y with f(x).*

Step 2 Write the rule for $g(x)$. Reflecting $f(x)$ across the y-axis replaces each x with $-x$.

$g(x) = 2(-x) + 2$ $g(x) = f(-x)$

$g(x) = -2x + 2$

Check Graph $f(x)$ and $g(x)$ on a graphing calculator. The graphs are symmetric about the y-axis. ✓

CHECK IT OUT! Let $g(x)$ be the indicated transformation of $f(x)$. Write the rule for $g(x)$.

1a. $f(x) = 3x + 1$; translation 2 units right $g(x) = 3(x-2) + 1$

1b. linear function defined in the table; a reflection across the x-axis $g(x) = -(x+2)$

x	−1	0	1
y	1	2	3

Stretches and compressions change the slope of a linear function. If the line becomes steeper, the function has been stretched vertically or compressed horizontally. If the line becomes flatter, the function has been compressed vertically or stretched horizontally.

Know It! Note

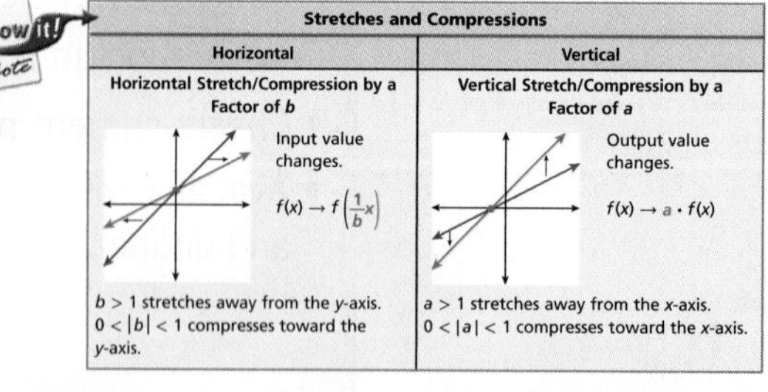

Stretches and Compressions

Horizontal	Vertical
Horizontal Stretch/Compression by a Factor of b	Vertical Stretch/Compression by a Factor of a
Input value changes. $f(x) \to f\left(\frac{1}{b}x\right)$	Output value changes. $f(x) \to a \cdot f(x)$
$b > 1$ stretches away from the y-axis. $0 < \lvert b \rvert < 1$ compresses toward the y-axis.	$a > 1$ stretches away from the x-axis. $0 < \lvert a \rvert < 1$ compresses toward the x-axis.

2-6 Transforming Linear Functions **135**

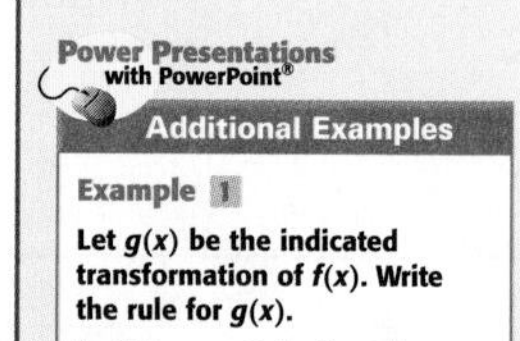

Additional Examples

Example 1

Let $g(x)$ be the indicated transformation of $f(x)$. Write the rule for $g(x)$.

A. $f(x) = x - 2$, horizontal translation right 3 units
$g(x) = x - 5$

B. linear function defined in the table; reflection across x-axis

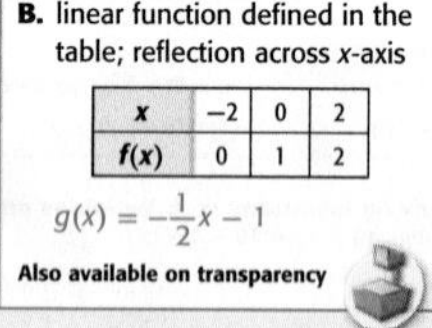

x	−2	0	2
$f(x)$	0	1	2

$g(x) = -\frac{1}{2}x - 1$

Also available on transparency

INTERVENTION Questioning Strategies

EXAMPLE 1

- Does the slope change when a linear function is translated?
- How does a reflection change the function rule?

Teaching Tip **Multiple Representations** Introduce students to *function notation* to record the transformed function. For a horizontal shift, $g(x) = f(x-h)$. For a vertical shift, $g(x) = f(x) + k$. For a reflection across the y-axis, $g(x) = f(-x)$, and for a reflection across the x-axis, $g(x) = -f(x)$. For a horizontal stretch or compression, $g(x) = f\left(\frac{1}{b}x\right)$, and for a vertical stretch or compression, $g(x) = a \cdot f(x)$.

2 Teach

Guided Instruction

Encourage students to compare and contrast horizontal and vertical shifts in translations of linear functions. Repeat with reflections across the axes and with transformations that stretch and compress. Have students note both the similarities and the differences. Elicit that each transformation is a rule that tells how the parent linear function is changed.

Reaching All Learners

Through Kinesthetic Experience

Have students model the translations and reflections using a pencil to represent a linear function on a coordinate plane. Have students move the pencil up and down, right and left to see how the y-intercept changes in vertical and horizontal shifts while the slope remains the same. Students can use a pair of pencils to model reflections.

HOLT MATH

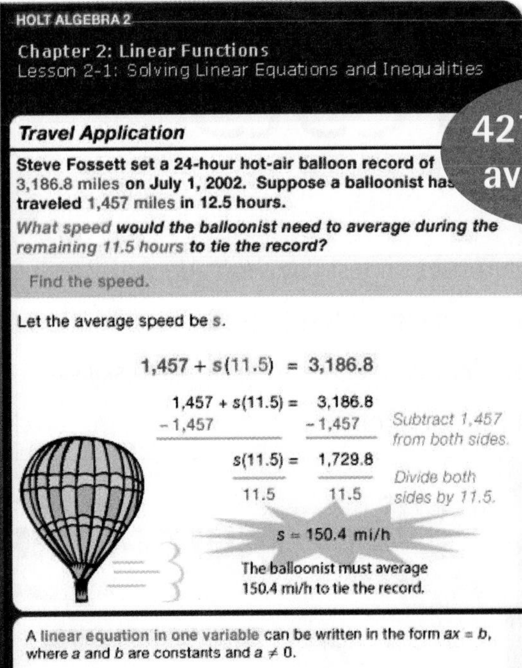

HOLT ALGEBRA 2
Chapter 2: Linear Functions
Lesson 2-1: Solving Linear Equations and Inequalities
Travel Application
Steve Fossett set a 24-hour hot-air balloon record of 3,186.8 miles on July 1, 2002. Suppose a balloonist has traveled 1,457 miles in 12.5 hours.
What speed would the balloonist need to average during the remaining 11.5 hours to tie the record?
Find the speed.
Let the average speed be s.
1,457 + s(11.5) = 3,186.8
Subtract 1,457 from both sides.
s(11.5) = 1,729.8
Divide both sides by 11.5.
s = 150.4 mi/h
The balloonist must average 150.4 mi/h to tie the record.
A linear equation in one variable can be written in the form ax = b, where a and b are constants and a ≠ 0.

427 videos available!

Lesson Tutorial Videos

- Illustrate every example!
- Your students' personal take-home tutor
- Reach your visual and auditory learners
- Available online or on CD-ROM

Only from Holt!

IDEA Works! Special Education CD-ROM

- Modified tests, quizzes, and worksheets
- Adapted format for students with special needs

LESSON 1-1 **Practice A**

Variables and Expressions

Write each algebraic expression in words.

> **algebraic expression**
> a mathematical phrase that contains operations, numbers, and/or variables

1. $a + 3$ ______

2. $2x$ ______

3. $5 - y$ ______

4. $\frac{n}{4}$ ______

5. Clint runs c miles.
Brenda runs 2 miles more than Clint.
Write an expression for the number of miles Brenda runs. ______

Evaluate each expression for $a = 2$ and $b = 6$.
The first one has been started for you.

> **evaluate**
> replace the variable with a number

6. $a + b$ — 2 + ___ = ______

7. $b - a$ ______

8. ab ______

"Key to effective instructional design is differentiated levels of support or scaffolding to support student learning when and where they need it." — Dr. David J. Chard, Holt author

Program Highlights

Count on **Holt** Algebra 2 for

Success on High-Stakes Tests

3

Test prep that covers the basics AND develops higher order thinking

Integrated test prep means no surprises on test day. *Holt Algebra 2* includes lesson and cumulative review in standardized test format throughout every lesson and chapter to develop student confidence in test-taking skills—without taking time away from core content.

Multi-Step Test Prep uses real-world scenarios to develop higher order thinking skills.

Test Prep and **Spiral Review** provide daily practice of new and previously taught skills in standardized test format.

CHAPTER 2

MULTI-STEP TEST PREP

SECTION 2A

Linear Equations and Inequalities

Sailing Away Crossing the Atlantic Ocean in a sailboat is a prestigious feat that many sailors attempt. Some of the speed records for the west-to-east trip from New York to England are shown in the table.

Transatlantic Sailing Records (New York to England)			
Yacht	Year	Country	Average Speed (knots)
Atlantic	1905	USA	10.02
Royale II	1986	France	15.47
Jet Services V	1990	France	18.62
PlayStation	2001	USA	25.78

1. The length of the course that each yacht sailed, from the Ambrose Light Tower in New York to Lizard Point in England, is 3364 statute miles. How much longer did the *Atlantic* take to complete the trip than the *PlayStation*?
2. Dolphins can swim about 20 statute miles per hour. If a dolphin were racing against each of the yachts in the table, in which place would the dolphin finish?
3. Graph the distance in nautical miles that the *PlayStation* could cover over a period from 0 to 48 hours. The sailing distance from New York to Florida is 947 nautical miles. Use your graph to estimate how long it would take the *PlayStation* to make this trip.
4. In 1980, the *Paul Ricard* broke the *Atlantic's* record for time crossing the Atlantic Ocean. The *Paul Ricard* finished the crossing in 10 days, 5 hours, and 14 minutes. Write a linear equation that describes the distance in nautical miles that the *Paul Ricard* covered as a function of time in hours.
5. Write and graph an inequality to show the possible distance d in statute miles that the *Atlantic* could cover in t hours. Is the point $(7.5, 85)$ a solution to the inequality? Explain the meaning of this point in the context of the problem.

Unit Conversions
$1 \text{ knot} = \frac{1 \text{ nautical mi}}{1 \text{ h}}$
1 nautical mi = 1.15 statute mi
1 statute mi = 5280 ft

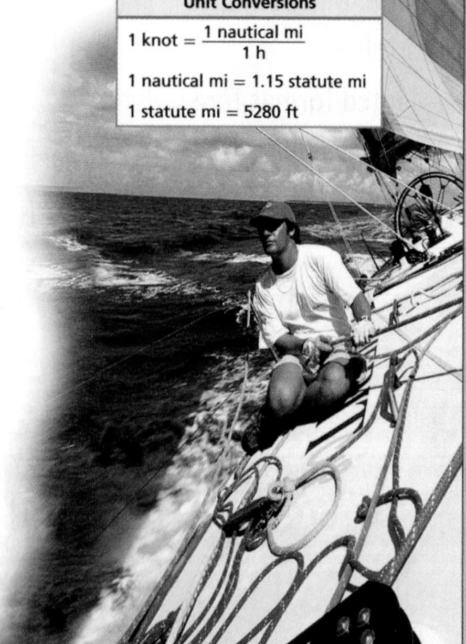

132 *Chapter 2 Linear Functions*

Program Highlights

HOLT MATH

CUMULATIVE ASSESSMENT, CHAPTERS 1–2

Multiple Choice

1. For which function is $g(-3) > g(5)$?
   - (A) $g(x) = 5x - 9$
   - (B) $g(x) = x^2 - 12$
   - (C) $g(x) = (x + 5)^2$
   - (D) $g(x) = (x - 9)^2$

2. A television commercial claims that 4 out of every 5 dentists surveyed preferred Freshen tooth... to the leading brand. If 120 dentists in the ... preferred Freshen, how many dentists parti... in the survey?
   - (F) 30
   - (G) 96
   - (H) 150
   - (J) 180

3. Which is an equation of a line with a slope ... that passes through (−2, 7)?
   - (A) $y = -3x - 1$
   - (B) $y = -3x + 1$
   - (C) $y = -3x + 13$
   - (D) $y = -\frac{1}{3}x + 1$

4. Which of the following shows the graph of $y + \frac{3}{4}x \geq 2$?

(F) 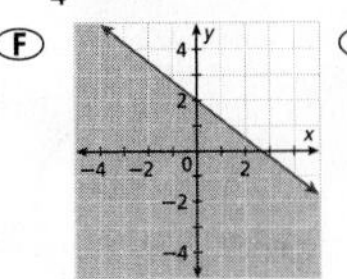

(H) 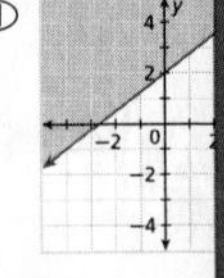

(G) 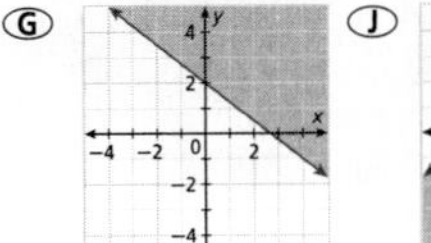

(J)

5. In which of the following number sets does −3 NOT belong?
   - (A) Integers
   - (B) Rational numbers
   - (C) Real numbers
   - (D) Whole numbers

6. What is a reasonable slope of the line of best fit of the salary data for teachers in a New York school district, as shown in the table below?

174 Chapter 2 Linear Functions

Standardized Test Prep provides a cumulative assessment in standardized test format.

CHAPTER 2

Standardized Test Strategies

Gridded Response: Write Gridded Responses

To answer a gridded-response test item, you must write your answer correctly in the top of the provided grid and fill in the bubbles accurately, or the item will be marked as incorrect. Answers may be gridded using several correct formats.

The answer to a gridded-response item is always a *whole number,* a *fraction,* or a *decimal.* Non-numerical signs and symbols, such as units of measure, the percent sign, the degree sign, the negative sign, variables, and commas, cannot be gridded.

EXAMPLE 1

Gridded Response: Solve the equation. $25 - 3(5x - 4) = 32$

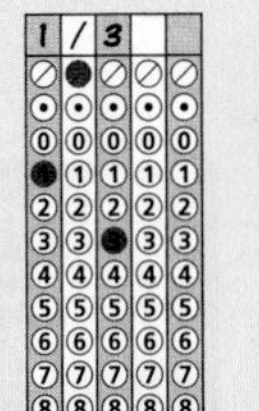

$$25 - 3(5x - 4) = 32$$
$$25 - 15x + 12 = 32$$
$$-15x = -5$$
$$x = \frac{5}{15} = \frac{1}{3}$$

Grid $\frac{1}{3}$ or its rounded decimal equivalent 0.333 or .3333:

Write your answer in the boxes at the top of the grid.
Put only a digit, the fraction bar, or the decimal point in each box.

Put the first digit of your answer in the box on the left OR put the last digit of your answer in the box on the right. Do not leave a blank box in the middle of an answer.

Shade the bubble of each digit or symbol in its corresponding column.

EXAMPLE 2

Gridded Response: Find the slope of the line that passes through (−2, −5) and (8, 10).

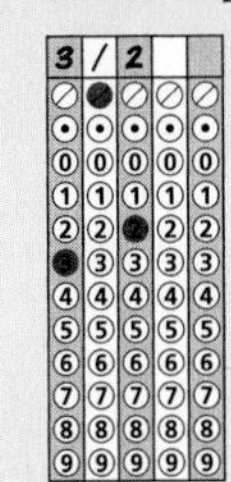

$$m = \frac{y_2 - y_1}{x_2 - x_1} = \frac{10-(-5)}{8-(-2)} = \frac{15}{10} = 1\frac{1}{2}$$

The slope of the line is $1\frac{1}{2}$, but a mixed number must be converted to either a decimal or an improper fraction before the answer can be written on the grid.

Grid the answer 1.5 or $\frac{3}{2}$ following the instructions in Example 1.

172 Chapter 2 Linear Functions

Test Tackler targets specific test-taking strategies to help students become savvy test-takers.

> "Assessment should enhance mathematics learning. What we assess and how we assess it communicates what we value." – Steven J. Leinwand, Holt author

Program Highlights

Count on Holt Algebra 2 for

Integrated Technology that enhances learning

4

Resources help you manage your classroom and motivate students to take learning one step further.

Holt Algebra 2 empowers you with key management and presentation tools that help you meet the needs of a broad range of students.

Interactive Answers and Solutions CD-ROM allows teachers to create a screen of selected answers and access complete solutions.

One-Stop Planner® CD-ROM with Test and Practice Generator contains everything you need to plan and manage your lessons in one place.

- All print ancillaries
- Customizable lesson plans
- Holt Calendar Planner®
- Holt PuzzlePro®
- ExamView Test and Practice Generator

Transparencies CD-ROM

- Includes **Countdown to Testing Transparencies** and daily **Teaching Transparencies**
- Available in print or on CD-ROM

more than 1000 transparencies!

Power Presentations CD-ROM contains colorful, animated, editable presentations for every lesson.

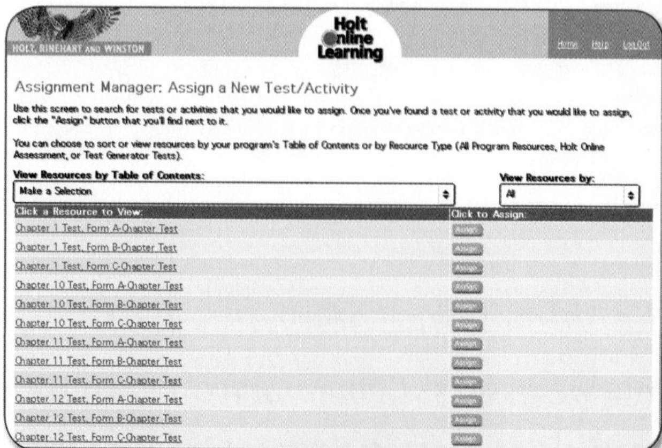

Holt Online Assessment

- Diagnoses individual student performance by standards and textbook objectives
- Automatically assigns resources to strengthen students' skills
- Tracks student progress in one easy-to-manage reporting system

With *Holt Algebra 2* technology, students get all the help they need, any time they need it. Interactive features and online tools make the math more meaningful to deepen student understanding.

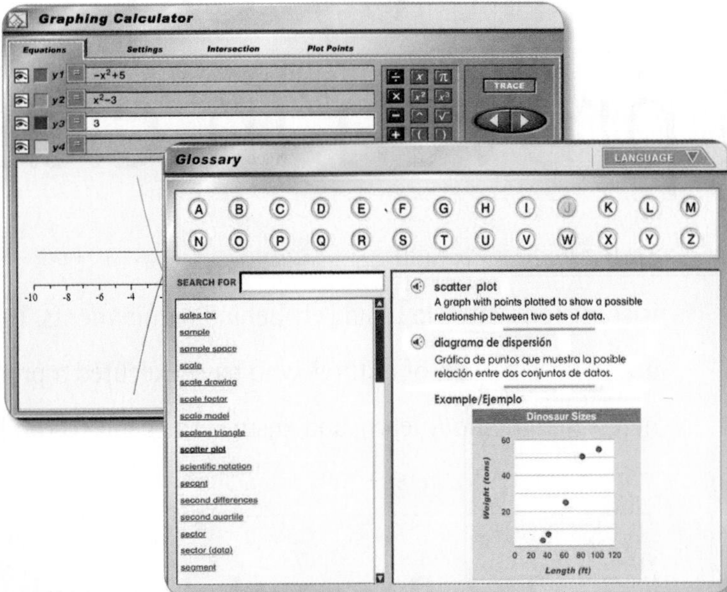

Premier Online Edition makes math come alive!

- Lesson Tutorial Videos
- Interactive practice with feedback
- Online study tools

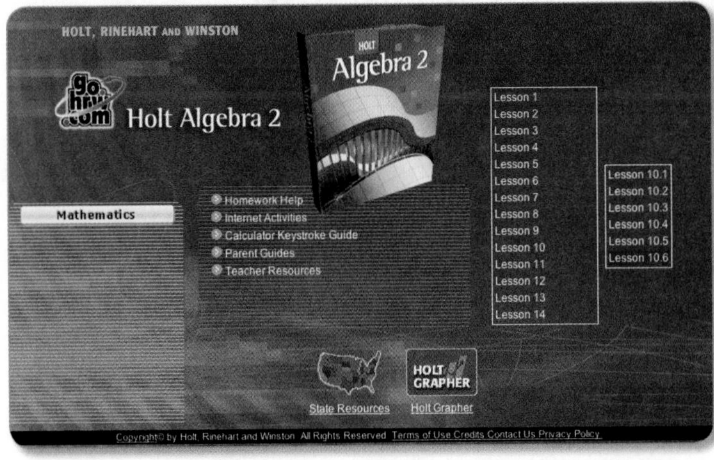

go.hrw.com gives students easy access to lesson resources.

- Homework Help Online
- Intervention and enrichment exercises
- Online games and projects

Student One Stop CD-ROM solves the backpack problem.

- Entire *Student Edition*
- Workbooks
- Intervention and enrichment exercises

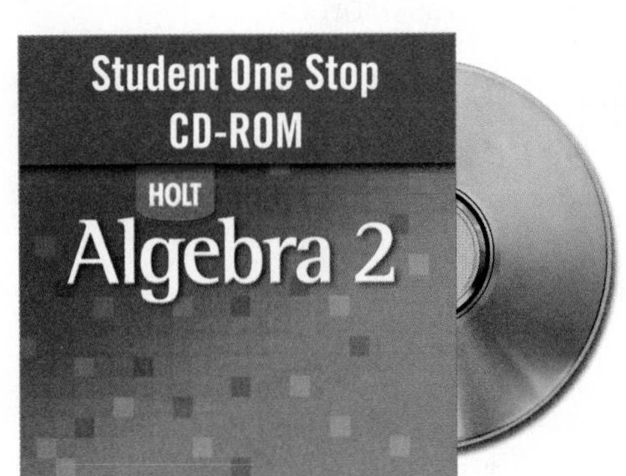

> "*Technology, when used appropriately, can improve students' mathematical understanding and problem-solving skills.*"
>
> **– Dr. Bert K. Waits, Holt author**

Program Highlights

Count on **Holt Algebra 2** to be

Grounded in research, built by experts, proven in classrooms

Holt Algebra 2 is built on a solid foundation of research, proven to work in the classroom, and is consistent with No Child Left Behind requirements. This research is backed by the expertise of a world-class team of authors who have executed a program that makes students *want* to learn, helps them *actually* learn, and ensures their success on high-stakes tests.

The Research Underlying the Program

Holt established a pattern of interaction with the educational community throughout all stages of the program's development.

Needs Assessment

- Teacher Interviews
- University Faculty Interviews
- Federal, State, and Local Agencies
- Advisory Panels
- Task Forces
- Academic Conferences
- Surveys with Teachers, Sales, Administrators

Pedagogical Research

- Thorough
- Effective
- Scientifically-Based

Program Development

- Classroom Observation
- Field Testing of Prototypes
- Reviewed by Program and Field Consultants
- Reviewed by Teachers and Administrators

Program Validation

- User Surveys
- Student and Teacher Appraisals
- Field Consultant and Sales Reports

Program Effectiveness

- Post-Implementation Effectiveness Studies
- Valid and Reliable Test

Edward B. Burger, Ph.D.
Professor of Mathematics and Chair | Williams College, MA

Student Engagement

“Learning should be fun. Deep and abstract ideas are challenging to all, but the challenge should be a pleasurable one that students want to conquer. Thus we offer levity throughout the *Holt Algebra 1/Geometry/Algebra 2* series— jokes for the teachers to share with their students and entertaining antics on the accompanying videos, mixing mathematical insights with laughs. There is no better student than the student who wants to learn. In this program we worked hard to make learning fun so students enjoy the journey and, as a result, attain a deeper understanding of the mathematics they explore.

The mathematics is developed in a meaningful manner with student readers in mind. Questions such as "What would resonate with real high school students today?" were asked at every stage of the writing.”

SUPPORTING RESEARCH

Ames, R., & Ames, C. (Eds.). (1984). *Research on motivation in education: Vol. 1. Student motivation.* New York: Academic Press.

Brewster, Cori, and Jennifer Fager. (2000). *Increasing Student Engagement and Motivation: From Time-on-Task to Homework.* Portland, Ore.: Northwest Regional Educational Laboratory.

David J. Chard, Ph.D.
Associate Dean, Curriculum and Academic Programs | University of Oregon

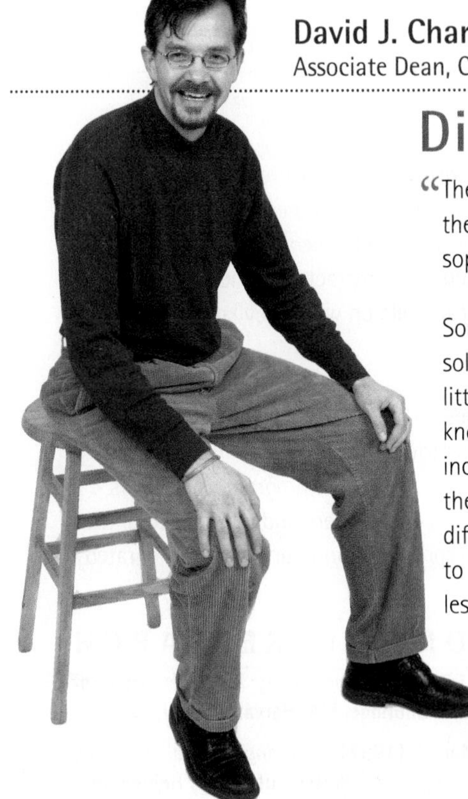

Differentiated Instruction

“The *Holt Algebra 1/Geometry/Algebra 2* series is designed to assist teachers in helping all their students learn conceptual knowledge, skills, and strategies essential to understanding sophisticated mathematics.

Some students often require substantial assistance in developing strategies for problem solving, while others may already have the knowledge necessary to solve problems with little support. In this program, the instructional framework builds the background knowledge essential for ensuring that all students are able to understand and solve increasingly complex problems. Scaffolding in this program takes many forms. For example, the program presents content starting with simple examples and progressing to more difficult content and applications. In addition, the program offers frequent opportunities to review, alternative lessons to help students who did not master content in introductory lessons, and additional examples for extended instruction.”

SUPPORTING RESEARCH

Bransford, J. D., Brown, A. L., & Cocking, R. R. (Eds.). (2000). *How people learn: Brain, mind, experience, and school.* Washington, DC: National Research Council.

Gersten, R., Chard, D. J., Baker, S., et al. (2005). *A meta-analysis of research on mathematics instruction for students with learning disabilities.* Signal Hill, CA: Instructional Research Group.

Earlene J. Hall, Ed.D
Mathematics Supervisor | Detroit Public Schools

Intervention

"Traditionally, mathematics intervention has been offered in an 'extraction type format'. In this series, Holt has provided teachers a tool kit of strategies that address closing the achievement gap through the use of an innovative intervention system. The *Holt Algebra 1/Geometry/Algebra 2* series provides intervention at the point of misconception. An ongoing assessment and intervention system in each chapter allows the teacher to diagnose, monitor, and assess students' mastery of the mathematical concepts throughout the chapters.

Within each lesson, at each stage of the developing concept, this program offers teachers scaffolding intervention questions and instructional examples that focus on comprehension of the mathematics content by students impacted by language barriers."

SUPPORTING RESEARCH

All Students Reaching The Top : Strategies for Closing Academic Achievement Gaps. A Report of the National Study Group for the Affirmative Development of Academic Ability. (2004)

Resnick, L. B. , & Klopfer, L.E. (1989). *Toward the Thinking Curriculum: Current Cognitive Research.*

Paul A. Kennedy, Ph.D.
Professor, Department of Mathematics | Colorado State University

Algebraic Thinking

" Students learn best when they are provided with opportunities to link present learning to concrete knowledge. This area in which learning occurs, in between the concrete and the abstract, is what Vygotsky calls the "zone of proximal development." Our sequence empowers students to make the transition from concrete to abstract with the notion that "abstractions" become new "concretes" so that they can build on what they know to develop true algebraic thinking.

The *Holt Algebra 1/Geometry/Algebra 2* series focuses on multiple representations—verbal, numerical, graphical, and symbolic. The series provides students with many opportunities to work with multiple representations throughout the program. This allows them to move fluidly among representations, deepening their understanding of algebra. The notion of "doing and undoing," or moving from one representation to another, is integrated throughout the program."

SUPPORTING RESEARCH

Vygotsky, L.S. (1978). *Mind and society: The development of higher mental processes.* Cambridge, MA: Harvard University Press.

Driscoll, Mark J. (1997). *Fostering algebraic thinking.* **Portsmouth, NH.; Heinemann.**

HOLT MATH

Steven J. Leinwand
Principal Research Analyst, American Institutes for Research | Washington, DC

Assessing Student Understanding

"As the mathematics curriculum has broadened to encompass communicating and conceptualizing, problem solving and reasoning, so too must our traditional view of assessment broaden. To reflect today's curriculum and more accurately determine students' progress, assessment should be an integral part of the teaching and learning process. Questioning strategies, such as those found in the *Holt Algebra 1/Geometry/Algebra 2* series, can be integral to daily assessment, along with lesson quizzes.

Additionally, assessment should provide opportunities for students to evaluate, reflect upon, and improve their work. The **Are You Ready?** feature allows students to determine if they have the skills to complete the chapter successfully. And more importantly, **Ready to Go On?** provides several opportunities during the course of the chapter for students to see how well they understand the material and to work several times in a chapter to improve their work before the Chapter Test (rather than after)."

SUPPORTING RESEARCH

NCTM Assessment Standards Working Groups (1995). *Assessment Standards for School Mathematics.* National Council of Teachers of Mathematics. Reston, VA.

National Research Council (1989). *Everybody Counts.* Washington, DC; National Academy Press.

Freddie L. Renfro
Former Director of Mathematics Instruction K–12 | Texas City Independent School District

Differentiated Instruction

"Imagine a classroom where diversity in learning is the norm, and the teacher responds to the learners' needs with flexible strategies, open dialogue, and ongoing assessment.

Every child is unique. Finding ways to tailor instruction to meet individual student needs in the classroom can be a manageable task with the right support. In the *Holt Algebra 1/Geometry/Algebra 2* series, we promote differentiated instruction by including activities that address a variety of learning styles: discovery learning, the use of concrete examples, and student interaction, to name a few.

The *Teacher's Edition* offers suggestions for differentiated assessment as well so that students have the opportunity to demonstrate their understanding in a manner that reflects their learning style."

SUPPORTING RESEARCH

Tomlinson, C. (1999). *The differentiated classroom: Responding to the needs of all learners.* Alexandria, VA: Association for Supervision and Curriculum Development.

Willis, S. and Mann, Larry. (2000). *Differentiating instruction.* Alexandria, VA: Association for Supervision and Curriculum Development.

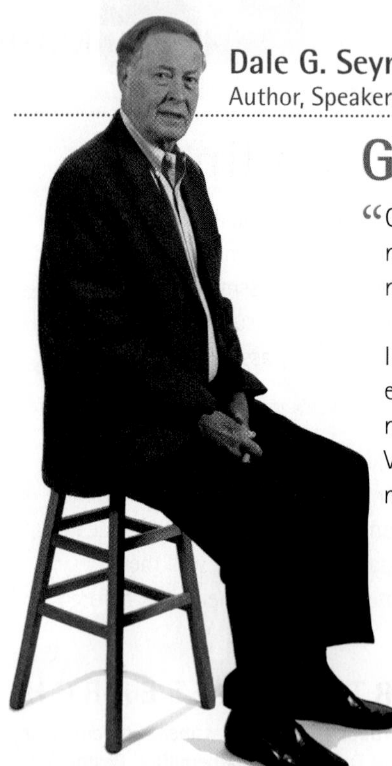

Dale G. Seymour
Author, Speaker, Publisher, and Former Mathematics Teacher | Founder, Creative Publications

Geometry Instructional Design

"Connections in mathematics are key to understanding and appreciating the beauty of mathematics. These connections need to be demonstrated so that students can view mathematics as an integrated whole.

In the *Holt Algebra 1/Geometry/Algebra 2* series we use graphical illustrations to help students envision complex mathematical concepts. Many students can comprehend a difficult concept more quickly if they see it as a whole rather than attempt to understand it as an abstraction. Visualizations in the textbook as well as in the series' accompanying posters enable students to make connections among interrelated ideas."

SUPPORTING RESEARCH

Fuys, D., Geddes, D., & Tischler, R. (1988). The van Hiele model of thinking in geometry among adolescents. *Journal for Research in Mathematics Education.*

Gagatsis, A. & Patronis, T. (1990, February). Using geometrical models in a process of reflective thinking in learning and teaching mathematics. *Educational Studies in Mathematics, 21, 1, 29-54.*

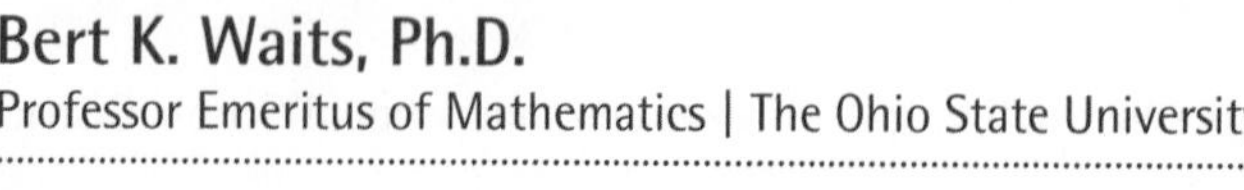

Bert K. Waits, Ph.D.
Professor Emeritus of Mathematics | The Ohio State University

Technology to Enhance Learning

"Research has demonstrated that technology, when used appropriately, can improve students' mathematical understanding and problem-solving skills. Similarly, technological tools can help teachers challenge students to use and understand mathematics in real-world scenarios.

The *Holt Algebra 1/Geometry/Algebra 2* series presents a balanced approach to learning. We stress that students must utilize all available tools, including mental and paper-and- pencil skills and technology, in the mathematics-learning process. This series uses technology not as an end in itself, but rather as a means for understanding and application. Current research supports this use of computer software including spreadsheets, dynamic geometry software, and graphing calculators."

SUPPORTING RESEARCH

Graham, A.T., & J.O.J. Thomas. (2000). Building a versatile understanding of algebraic variables with a graphic calculator. *Educational Studies in Mathematics,* 41 (3), 265-282.

Hallar, Jeannie C., & Karen Norwood. (1999). The effects of a graphing-approach intermediate algebra curriculum on students' understanding of function. *Journal for Research in Mathematics Education,* 30 (2), 220-226.

Holt Algebra 2
Program Components

Student Edition
Student One Stop CD-ROM
Premier Online Edition
Teacher's Edition

Assessment and Intervention
Are You Ready? Intervention and Enrichment
Assessment Resources
Ready to Go On? Intervention and Enrichment

Differentiated Instruction
Algebra Lab Activities
Alternate Openers: Explorations Transparencies
IDEA Works! Special Education CD-ROM
Lesson Tutorial Videos
Manipulatives Kit
Multilingual Glossary
Posters
Premier Online Edition
Student One Stop CD-ROM
Success for English Language Learners
Technology Lab Activities

Workbooks
Homework and Practice Workbook
Know-It Notebook
Problem Solving Workbook
State Test Prep Workbook

Spanish Resources
Holt Algebra 2 Summary and Review
Lesson Tutorial Videos with Spanish closed captioning

Anytime, Anyplace Professional Development: Building a Community of Learners

High-Stakes Test Prep
Countdown to Testing Transparencies
Holt College Entrance Exam Practice for Mathematics
Holt Mathematics State Test Prep for Middle School and High School CD-ROM
State Test Prep Workbook

Integrated Technology
Are You Ready? Intervention and Enrichment CD-ROM
Chapter Resources CD-ROM
Holt Mathematics State Test Prep for Middle School and High School CD-ROM
IDEA Works! Special Education CD-ROM
Interactive Answers and Solutions CD-ROM
Lesson Tutorial Videos CD-ROM
One-Stop Planner with Test and Practice Generator and State-Specific Resources CD-ROM
Power Presentations CD-ROM
Premier Online Edition
Ready to Go On? Intervention and Enrichment CD-ROM
Student One Stop CD-ROM
Technology Lab Activities
Transparencies CD-ROM

Teaching Resources
Chapter Resource Books
Interactive Answers and Solutions CD-ROM
Know-It Notebook Teacher's Guide with Transparencies
Lesson Plans
Lesson Transparencies Volumes 1-4
One-Stop Planner with Test and Practice Generator and State-Specific Resources CD-ROM
Power Presentations CD-ROM
Solutions Key
Transparencies CD-ROM

State flower, Peony

State bird, Cardinal

State capitol, Indianapolis

Explanation of Correlation

The following document is a correlation of ***Holt Algebra 2*** to Indiana's Academic Standards for Mathematics, Algebra II. The format for this correlation follows the same basic format established by Indiana's Academic Standards for Mathematics, modified to accommodate the addition of page references. The correlation provides a cross-reference between the skills in the standards and representative page numbers where those skills are taught or assessed.

The references contained in this correlation reflect Holt's interpretation of the Mathematics standards outlined in the Indiana curriculum.

Indiana's Academic Standards for Mathematics, Algebra II

STANDARD 1 – RELATIONS AND FUNCTIONS			
A2.1.1	Find the zeros, domain and range of a function.	**SE**	44-48, 55, 56, 67, 333-339, 428, 432, 507, 531, 532, 593, 594-599, 636, 661, 669, 686, 991, 1000
A2.1.2	Use and interpret function notation, including evaluation of functions represented by tables, graphs, words, equations, or a set of ordered pairs.	**SE**	51-57, 60-66, 67-73, 134-140, 158-163, 460-465, 537-544, 654-661, 662-669, 672-679, 682-688, 698-705, 990-997, 998-1003
A2.1.3	Recognize and describe the relationships among the solutions of an equation, the zeros of a function, the x-intercepts of a graph, and the factors of a polynomial expression.	**SE**	438-444, 445-451, 455-459
STANDARD 2 – LINEAR AND ABSOLUTE VALUE EQUATIONS, INEQUALITIES AND FUNCTIONS			
A2.2.1	Solve systems of three linear equations and inequalities in three variables by substitution and elimination.	**SE**	220-226

A2.2.2	Solve problems that can be modeled using systems of linear equations containing up to three variables, interpret the solutions and determine whether the solutions are reasonable.	**SE** 222-225, 273, 274, 275, 290-293
A2.2.3	Graph piecewise-defined functions.	**SE** 663-667, 670-671, 672
A2.2.4	Solve equations and inequalities involving the absolute value of a linear function.	**SE** 150-156, 157
STANDARD 3 – QUADRATIC EQUATIONS AND FUNCTIONS		
A2.3.1	Define, add, subtract, multiply and divide complex numbers. Represent complex numbers, and the addition, subtraction and absolute value of complex numbers, in the complex plane.	**SE** 351, 382-389
A2.3.2	Solve quadratic equations in the complex number system.	**SE** 351-355, 357, 358, 361, 362, 363
A2.3.3	Analyze, describe and sketch graphs of quadratic functions including the lines of symmetry.	**SE** 314, 315-321, 323-330
A2.3.4	Determine how the graph of a parabola changes if *a*, *b* and *c* changes in the equation $y = a(x - b)^2 + c$. Find an equation for a parabola given sufficient information.	**SE** 315-322, 337
A2.3.5	Solve problems that can be modeled using quadratic equations and functions, interpret the solutions and determine whether the solutions are reasonable.	**SE** 327, 328, 329, 335, 338, 339, 346, 347, 353, 361, 362, 376-380, 698, 702-705
STANDARD 4 – POLYNOMIAL EQUATIONS AND FUNCTIONS		
A2.4.1	Analyze, describe and sketch graphs of polynomial functions by examining intercepts, zeros, domain and range and end behavior.	**SE** 452, 453-459
A2.4.2	Use the binomial theorem to expand binomial expressions raised to positive integer powers.	**SE** 416-420, 837-843
A2.4.3	Perform arithmetic operations, including long division and division with remainders, on polynomials by others of equal or lower degree.	**SE** 407-408, 410, 414-420, 422-427
A2.4.4	Factor polynomials completely and solve polynomial equations by factoring.	**SE** 430-435, 438-440, 442-444
A2.4.5	Use graphing technology to find approximate solutions for polynomial equations.	**SE** 438, 439, 446
A2.4.6	Solve problems that can be represented or modeled using polynomial equations, interpret the solutions and determine whether the solutions are reasonable.	**SE** 432, 433, 440, 448, 449, 456-458, 467-470, 701-705

A2.4.7	Find a polynomial function of lowest degree with real coefficients given its roots and use the relationship between solutions of an equation, zeros of a function *x*-intercepts of a graph and factors of a polynomial expression to solve problems.	**SE** 445, 447, 449, 450

STANDARD 5 – RATIONAL AND RADICAL EXPRESSIONS, EQUATIONS AND FUNCTIONS

A2.5.1	Analyze, describe and sketch graphs of rational functions by examining intercepts, zeros, domain and range and asymptotic and end behavior.	**SE** 591, 592-599
A2.5.2	Add, subtract, multiply, divide, reduce and evaluate rational expressions with polynomial denominators. Simplify rational expressions, including expressions with negative exponents in the denominator.	**SE** 577-582, 583-590
A2.5.3	Understand the properties of rational exponents and use the properties to simplify, multiply, divide and find powers of expressions containing negative and fractional exponents. Relate expressions containing rational exponents to the corresponding radical expressions.	**SE** 611-617
A2.5.4	Analyze, describe and sketch graphs of square root and cube root functions by examining intercepts, zeros, domain and range and end behavior.	**SE** 619-627
A2.5.5	Solve equations that contain radical expressions and identify extraneous roots when they occur.	**SE** 628-635
A2.5.6	Solve problems that can be modeled using equations involving rational and radical functions, including problems of direct and inverse variation. Interpret the solutions and determine whether the solutions are reasonable.	**SE** 571-575, 587-589, 602, 605, 607, 622, 624, 626, 631, 632, 633, 634, 699, 702-705

STANDARD 6 – EXPONENTIAL AND LOGARITHMIC FUNCTIONS

A2.6.1	Analyze, describe and sketch graphs of exponential functions by examining intercepts, zeros, domain and range and asymptotic and end behavior.	**SE** 490-496, 531-536
A2.6.2	Know that the inverse of an exponential function is a logarithm, use laws of exponents to derive laws of logarithms, and use the inverse relationship between exponential functions and logarithms and the laws of logarithms to solve problems.	**SE** 505-511, 512-519, 522-528, 532-535, 553, 555-556, 558, 621

A2.6.3	Solve exponential and logarithmic equations.	**SE** 522-528, 533
A2.6.4	Solve problems that can be modeled using exponential and logarithmic equations, interpret the solutions and determine whether the solutions are reasonable using technology as appropriate.	**SE** 523, 526-528, 533-535, 540-543, 545-551, 699-700, 702-705
STANDARD 7 – SEQUENCES AND SERIES		
A2.7.1	Write the recursive formula for arithmetic and geometric sequences and find specific terms of arithmetic and geometric sequences.	**SE** 879-881, 884-886, 891, 892, 895-897
A2.7.2	Write the formula for the general term for arithmetic and geometric sequences and make connections to linear and exponential functions.	**SE** 862-868
A2.7.3	Find partial sums of arithmetic and geometric series.	**SE** 870-875, 877, 882-885, 893-897
A2.7.4	Solve problems involving applications that can be modeled using sequences and finite arithmetic and geometric series, interpret the solutions, and determine whether the solutions are reasonable using spreadsheets as appropriate.	**SE** 864-867, 872-873, 874, 875, 883-886, 894-897
STANDARD 8 – DATA ANALYSIS AND PROBABILITY		
A2.8.1	Use the relative frequency of a specified outcome of an event to estimate the probability of the out come and apply the law of large numbers in simple examples.	**SE** 809
A2.8.2	Determine the probability of simple events involving independent and dependent events and conditional probability. Analyze probabilities to interpret odds and risk of events.	**SE** 811-818
A2.8.3	Know and apply the characteristics of the normal distribution. Identify settings in which the normal distribution may be useful. Determine whether a set of data appears to be uniform, skewed or normally distributed. Use the empirical rule to find probabilities that an event will occur in a specific interval that can be described in terms of one, two or three standard deviations about the mean.	**SE** 846-847
A2.8.4	Use permutations, combinations, and other counting methods to determine the number of ways that events can occur and to calculate probabilities including the probability of compound events.	**SE** 794-800, 819-825

Process Standards *(* denotes NCTM process standards)*		**Citations** *(The process standards are found throughout the textbook. The page citations listed below are some of the many examples.)*
Problem Solving*		
Build new mathematical knowledge through problem solving.	**SE**	10–11, 17, 265, 328–330, 463–465, 541, 624, 676–678, 726–728, 798–800, 822, 895, 933, 995, 1011
Solve problems that arise in mathematics and in other contexts.	**SE**	121, 308–309, 228, 268, 348, 501–504, 520, 615–617, 740–742, 922, 956, 974, 1011–1013
Apply and adapt a variety of appropriate strategies to solve problems.	**SE**	25, 101, 202, 226, 344, 418, 442, 534–536, 597–599, 627, 686–688, 823–824, 833, 896, 933–934, 1001–1003
Monitor and reflect on the process of mathematical problem solving.	**SE**	11, 34, 95, 197, 264, 321, 353, 426, 547, 606, 625, 632, 667, 739, 747, 756, 833, 897, 932
Reasoning and Proof*		
Recognize reasoning and proof as fundamental aspects of mathematics.	**SE**	16, 72, 110, 120, 188, 329, 379, 456, 528, 533, 596, 614, 615, 626, 633, 677, 754, 765, 822, 841, 965, 994, 1025
Make and investigate mathematical conjectures.	**SE**	12, 210, 249, 267, 468, 519, 528, 665, 725, 734, 806, 835, 875, 898, 935
Develop and evaluate mathematical arguments and proofs.	**SE**	23, 195, 203, 281, 346, 388, 419, 464, 527, 573, 580, 634, 701, 727, 771, 866, 940, 955, 1032
Select and use various types of reasoning and methods of proof.	**SE**	64, 147, 188, 251, 283, 427, 201, 217, 330, 409, 508, 515, 676, 765, 797, 964, 1010
Communication*		
Organize and consolidate their mathematical thinking through communication.	**SE**	71, 112, 380, 510, 623, 755–757, 832, 883, 903, 996, 1006
Communicate their mathematical thinking coherently and clearly to peers, teachers, and others.	**SE**	49, 145, 372, 543, 581, 604, 678, 763, 842, 873, 946, 1025
Analyze and evaluate the mathematical thinking and strategies of others.	**SE**	29, 93, 252, 346, 352, 419, 432, 518, 525, 598, 685, 693, 727, 814, 840, 865, 947–948, 1001
Use the language of mathematics to express mathematical ideas precisely.	**SE**	30–31, 196, 256, 327, 427, 527, 633–635, 749, 765, 799, 834, 868, 953

Connections*		
Recognize and use connections among mathematical ideas.	SE	94, 186, 389, 518, 659–661, 705, 815–817, 865, 904–907, 949, 955, 1031–1033
Understand how mathematical ideas interconnect and build on one another to produce a coherent whole.	SE	13, 204, 469–471, 576, 666–668, 772–774, 884–886, 1017–1019
Recognize and apply mathematics in contexts outside of mathematics.	SE	110, 197, 212, 390, 472, 548–550, 605–607, 680, 702–704, 758, 788, 789, 826, 844, 888, 923, 1034, 1046
Representation*		
Create and use representations to organize, record, and communicate mathematical ideas.	SE	185, 250–252, 332, 497, 658, 697, 836, 1017
Select, apply, and translate among mathematical representations to solve problems.	SE	149, 282–284, 338, 429, 591, 696, 818, 843, 942, 1003
Use representations to model and interpret physical, social, and mathematical phenomena.	SE	132, 164, 608, 636, 648–649, 706, 776, 807–809, 908, 1004, 1047
Estimation and Mental Computation		
Know and apply appropriate methods for estimating the results of computations.	SE	18, 25, 40, 64, 96, 101, 147, 155, 188, 216, 251, 347, 411, 450, 495, 510, 575, 576, 616, 687, 694, 695, 741, 773, 817, 834, 842, 875, 934, 972, 996, S56
Use estimation to decide whether answers are reasonable.	SE	37, 103, 522, 526
Decide when estimation is an appropriate strategy for solving a problem.	SE	25, 37, 64, 101, 147, 251, 347, 450, 495, 616773
Determine appropriate accuracy and precision of measurement in problem situations.	SE	25, 39, 99, 101, 418, 442, 833, 896
Use properties of numbers and operations to perform mental computation.	SE	16-17, 506-507, 509, 714
Recognize when the numbers involved in a computation allow for a mental computation strategy.	SE	16-17, 506-507, 509, 714
Technology		
Technology should be used as a tool in mathematics education to support and extend the mathematics curriculum.	SE	33, 113-114, 157, 227, 286, 314, 332, 452, 497, 530, 591, 670-671, 697, 767, 810, 878, 942, 1006
Technology can contribute to concept development, simulation, representation, communication, and problem solving.	SE	41, 71, 107, 143, 144, 187, 256, 278, 329, 334, 347, 367, 372, 376, 412, 419, 443, 518, 544, 634, 657, 700, 701, 703, 705, 722-724, 768, 784, 831, 841, 897, 898, 1012, 1025, 1032, 1033
The challenge is to ensure that technology supports-but is not a substitute for the development of skills with basic operations, quantitative reasoning, and problem-solving skills.	SE	157, 227, 286, 332-452, 497, 591, 697, 942, 1006

Fast Track to ECA

ALGEBRA 2

45-minute classes

This sequence was created as a guide to assist you in covering all the necessary Indiana Academic Standards indicators before the state test administration.

Chapter 1

Day 1	Day 2	Day 3	Day 4	Day 5	Day 6		
1-6 Lesson	1-7 Lesson	1-8 Algebra Lab 1-8 Lesson	1-9 Lesson	Chapter 1 Review	Chapter 1 Test		

Chapter 2

Day 7	Day 8	Day 9	Day 10	Day 11	Day 12	Day 13	
2-6 Lesson	2-6 Lesson Connecting Algebra to Data Analysis	2-8 Lesson	2-8 Lesson	2-9 Technology Lab 2-9 Lesson	Chapter 2 Review	Chapter 2 Test	

Chapter 3

Day 14	Day 15						
3-6 Lesson	3-6 Technology Lab						

Chapter 4

Day 16	Day 17	Day 18	Day 19	Day 20	Day 21	Day 22	Day 23
4-4 Lesson	4-4 Lesson	4-5 Lesson	4-5 Lesson	4-5 Technology Lab	4-6 Lesson	4-6 Lesson	Extension
Day 24	**Day 25**						
Chapters 3 and 4 Review	Chapters 3 and 4 Test						

Chapter 5

Day 26	Day 27	Day 28	Day 29	Day 30	Day 31	Day 32	Day 33
5-1 Technology Lab 5-1 Lesson	5-1 Lesson	5-2 Lesson	Connecting Algebra to Previous Courses 5-3 Technology Lab	5-3 Lesson	5-4 Lesson	5-4 Lesson Connecting Algebra to Geometry	5-5 Lesson
Day 34	**Day 35**	**Day 36**	**Day 37**	**Day 38**	**Day 39**	**Day 40**	
5-6 Lesson	5-8 Lesson	5-8 Lesson	5-9 Lesson	5-9 Lesson	Chapter 5 Review	Chapter 5 Test	

Chapter 6

Day 41	Day 42	Day 43	Day 44	Day 45	Day 46	Day 47	Day 48
6-1 Lesson	Connecting Algebra to Number Theory 6-2 Lesson	6-2 Lesson Connecting Algebra to Geometry	6-3 Lesson	6-3 Lesson	6-4 Algebra Lab 6-4 Lesson	6-4 Lesson	6-5 Lesson

Chapter 6 (continued)

Day 49	Day 50	Day 51	Day 52	Day 53	Day 54	Day 55	Day 56
6-6 Lesson	6-6 Lesson	6-7 Technology Lab 6-7 Lesson	6-7 Lesson	6-8 Lesson	6-9 Lesson	Chapter 6 Review	Chapter 6 Test

Chapter 7

Day 57	Day 58	Day 59	Day 60	Day 61	Day 62	Day 63	Day 64
7-1 Lesson	7-1 Lesson	7-3 Lesson	7-4 Lesson	7-4 Lesson	7-5 Lesson	7-5 Lesson	Connecting Algebra to Probability 7-6 Technology Lab
Day 65	**Day 66**	**Day 67**	**Day 68**	**Day 69**	**Day 70**		
7-6 Lesson	7-6 Lesson	7-7 Lesson	7-8 Lesson	Chapter 7 Review	Chapter 7 Test		

Chapter 8

Day 71	Day 72	Day 73	Day 74	Day 75	Day 76	Day 77	Day 78
8-1 Algebra Lab	8-1 Lesson	8-2 Lesson	8-3 Lesson	8-4 Technology Lab 8-4 Lesson	8-4 Lesson	8-5 Lesson	8-5 Lesson
Day 79	**Day 80**	**Day 81**	**Day 82**	**Day 83**	**Day 84**		
Connecting Algebra to Geometry 8-7 Lesson	8-7 Lesson	8-8 Lesson	8-8 Lesson	Chapter 8 Review	Chapter 8 Test		

Chapter 9

Day 85	Day 86	Day 87	Day 88	Day 89	Day 90	Day 91	Day 92
9-1 Lesson	9-1 Lesson	9-2 Lesson	9-2 Technology Lab	9-3 Lesson	9-4 Lesson	Connecting Algebra to Geometry	9-6 Technology Lab
Day 93	**Day 94**	**Day 95**	**Day 96**				
9-6 Lesson	9-6 Lesson	Chapter 9 Review	Chapter 9 Test				

Chapter 11

Day 97	Day 98	Day 99	Day 100	Day 101	Day 102	Day 103	Day 104
11-1 Lesson	11-3 Lesson	11-4 Lesson	11-6 Lesson	11-6 Lesson	Extension	Chapter 11 Review	Chapter 11 Test

Chapter 12

Day 105	Day 106	Day 107	Day 108	Day 109	Day 110	Day 111	Day 112
12-1 Lesson	Connecting Algebra to Geometry	12-2 Lesson	12-2 Technology Lab	12-3 Lesson	12-3 Lesson	12-4 Lesson	12-4 Lesson
Day 113	**Day 114**						
Chapter 12 Review	Chapter 12 Test						

Chapter 14

Day 115	Day 116	Day 117	Day 118	Day 119	Day 120		
14-1 Lesson	14-1 Lesson	14-2 Lesson	14-2 Lesson	Chapter 14 Review	Chapter 14 Test		

Fast Track to ECA

ALGEBRA 2

90-minute classes

This sequence was created as a guide to assist you in covering all the necessary Indiana Academic Standards indicators before the state test administration.

Chapter 1

Day 1	Day 2	Day 3					
1-6 Lesson 1-7 Lesson	1-8 Algebra Lab 1-8 Lesson 1-9 Lesson	Chapter 1 Review Chapter 1 Test					

Chapter 2

Day 4	Day 5	Day 6	Day 7				
2-6 Lesson Connecting Algebra to Data Analysis	2-8 Lesson	2-9 Technology Lab 2-9 Lesson	Chapter 2 Review Chapter 2 Test				

Chapter 3

Day 8							
3-6 Lesson 3-6 Technology Lab							

Chapter 4

Day 9	Day 10	Day 11	Day 12	Day 13			
4-4 Lesson	4-5 Lesson	4-5 Technology Lab 4-6 Lesson	4-6 Lesson Extension	Chapter 3 and 4 Review Chapter 3 and 4 Test			

Chapter 5

Day 14	Day 15	Day 16	Day 17	Day 18	Day 19	Day 20	
5-1 Technology Lab 5-1 Lesson	5-2 Lesson Connecting Algebra to Previous Courses	5-3 Technology Lab 5-3 Lesson	5-4 Lesson Connecting Algebra to Geometry	5-5 Lesson 5-6 Lesson	5-8 Lesson 5-9 Lesson	Chapter 5 Review Chapter 5 Test	

Chapter 6

Day 21	Day 22	Day 23	Day 24	Day 25	Day 26	Day 27	Day 28
6-1 Lesson Connecting Algebra to Number Theory 6-2 Lesson	6-2 Lesson Connecting Algebra to Geometry 6-3 Lesson	6-3 Lesson 6-4 Algebra Lab 6-4 Lesson	6-4 Lesson 6-5 Lesson	6-6 Lesson	6-7 Technology Lab 6-7 Lesson	6-8 Lesson 6-9 Lesson	Chapter 6 Review Chapter 6 Test

Chapter 7

Day 29	Day 30	Day 31	Day 32	Day 33	Day 34	Day 35	
7-1 Lesson	7-3 Lesson 7-4 Lesson	7-4 Lesson 7-5 Lesson	7-5 Lesson Connecting Algebra to Probability 7-6 Technology Lab	7-6 Lesson	7-7 Lesson 7-8 Lesson	Chapter 7 Review Chapter 7 Test	

Chapter 8

Day 36	Day 37	Day 38	Day 39	Day 40	Day 41	Day 42	
8-1 Algebra Lab 8-1 Lesson	8-2 Lesson 8-3 Lesson	8-4 Technology Lab 8-4 Lesson	8-5 Lesson	Connecting Algebra to Geometry 8-7 Lesson	8-8 Lesson	Chapter 8 Review Chapter 8 Test	

Chapter 9

Day 43	Day 44	Day 45	Day 46	Day 47	Day 48		
9-1 Lesson	9-2 Lesson 9-2 Technology Lab	9-3 Lesson 9-4 Lesson	Connecting Algebra to Geometry 9-6 Technology Lab	9-6 Lesson	Chapter 9 Review Chapter 9 Test		

Chapter 11

Day 49	Day 50	Day 51	Day 52				
11-1 Lesson 11-3 Lesson	11-4 Lesson 11-6 Lesson	11-6 Lesson Extension	Chapter 11 Review Chapter 11 Test				

Chapter 12

Day 53	Day 54	Day 55	Day 56	Day 57			
12-1 Lesson Connecting Algebra to Geometry	12-2 Lesson 12-2 Technology Lab	12-3 Lesson	12-4 Lesson	Chapter 12 Review Chapter 12 Test			

Chapter 14

Day 58	Day 59	Day 60					
14-1 Lesson	14-2 Lesson	Chapter 14 Review Chapter 14 Test					

correlated to

Indiana

Academic Standards for Mathematics, *Algebra II*

CONTENTS

IN2

State bird, Cardinal

State flower, Peony

Indiana's Academic Standards for Mathematics, *Algebra II*

STANDARD 1:

FUNCTIONS

A2.1.1 Find the zeros, domain and range of a function.

A2.1.2 Use and interpret function notation, including evaluation of functions represented by tables, graphs, words, equations or set of ordered pairs.

A2.1.3 Recognize and describe the relationships among the solutions of an equation, the zeros of a function, the x-intercepts of a graph, and the factors of a polynomial expression.

STANDARD 2:

LINEAR AND ABSOLUTE VALUE EQUATIONS, INEQUALITIES AND FUNCTIONS

A2.2.1 Solve systems of linear equations and inequalities in three variables by substitution and elimination.

A2.2.2 Solve problems that can be modeled using systems of linear equations containing up to three variables, interpret the solutions, and determine whether the solutions are reasonable.

A2.2.3 Graph piecewise-defined functions.

A2.2.4 Solve equations and inequalities involving the absolute value of a linear function.

Indianapolis at night

Indiana
The Hoosier State

STANDARD 3:

QUADRATIC EQUATIONS AND FUNCTIONS

A2.3.1 Define, add, subtract, multiply and divide complex numbers. Represent complex numbers, and the addition, subtraction and absolute value of complex numbers, in the complex plane.

A2.3.2 Solve quadratic equations in the complex number system.

A2.3.3 Analyze, describe, and sketch graphs of quadratic functions including the lines of symmetry.

A2.3.4 Determine how the graph of a parabola changes if a, b, and c changes in the equation $y = a(x - b)^2 + c$. Find an equation for a parabola given sufficient information.

A2.3.5 Solve problems that can be represented modeled using quadratic equations and functions, interpret the solutions and determine whether the solutions are reasonable.

STANDARD 4:

POLYNOMIAL EXPRESSIONS, EQUATIONS AND FUNCTIONS

A2.4.1 Analyze, describe and sketch graphs of polynomial functions by examining intercepts, zeros, domain and range and end behavior.

A2.4.2 Use the binomial theorem to expand binomial expressions raised to positive integer powers.

A2.4.3 Perform arithmetic operations, including long division, on polynomials by others of equal or lower degree.

A2.4.4 Factor polynomials completely and solve polynomial equations by factoring.

A2.4.5 Use graphing technology to find approximate solutions for polynomial equations.

A2.4.6 Solve problems that can be represented or modeled using polynomial equations, interpret the solutions and determine whether the solutions are reasonable.

A2.4.7 Find a polynomial function of lowest degree with real coefficients given its roots and use the relationship between solutions of an equation, zeros of a function, x-intercepts of a graph and factors of a polynomial expression to solve problems.

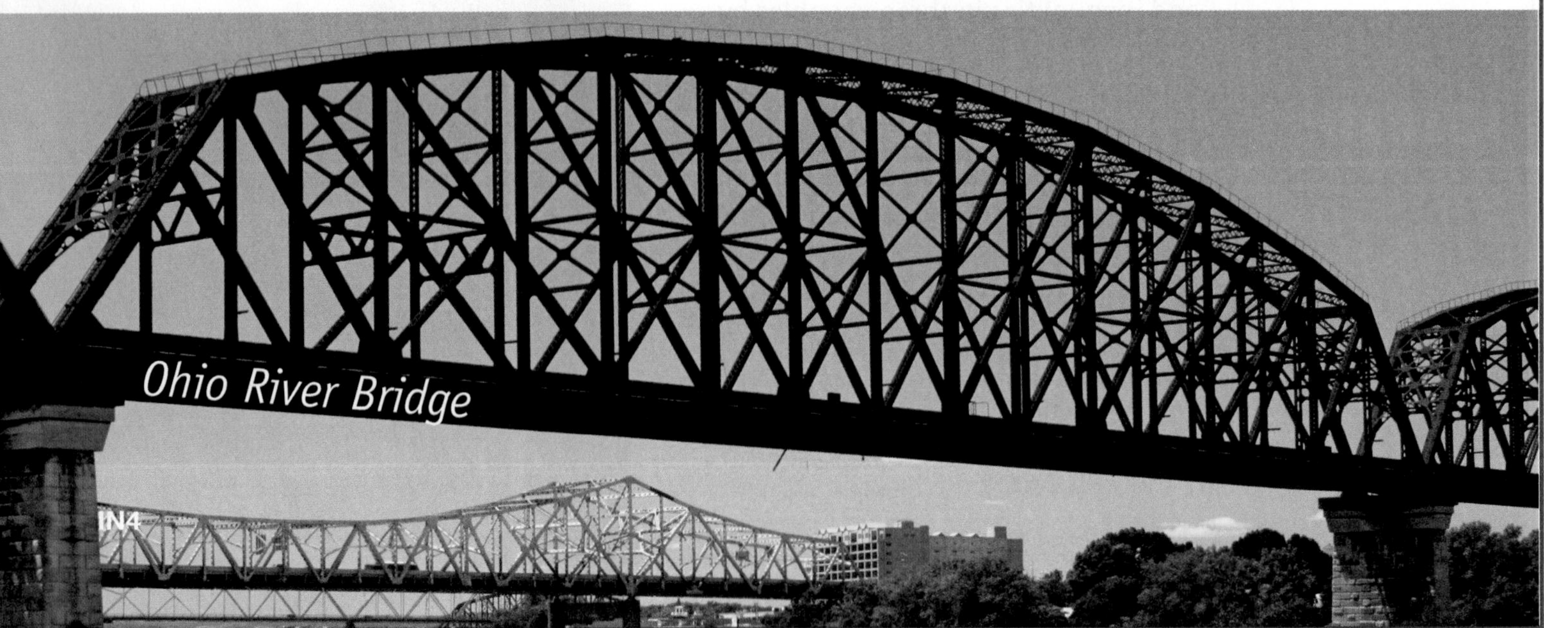

STANDARD 5:

RATIONAL AND RADICAL EXPRESSIONS, EQUATIONS AND FUNCTIONS

A2.5.1 Analyze, describe and sketch graphs of rational functions by examining intercepts, zeros, domain and range, and asymptotic and end behavior.

A2.5.2 Add, subtract, multiply, divide, reduce and evaluate rational expressions with polynomial denominators. Simplify rational expressions, including expressions with negative exponents in the denominator.

A2.5.3 Understand the properties of rational exponents and use the properties to simplify, multiply, divide, and find powers of expressions containing negative and fractional exponents. Relate expressions containing rational exponents to the corresponding radical expressions.

A2.5.4 Analyze, describe and sketch graphs of square root and cube root functions by examining intercepts, zeros, domain and range and end behavior.

A2.5.5 Solve equations that contain radical expressions and identify extraneous roots when they occur.

A2.5.6 Solve problems that can be modeled using equations involving rational and radical functions, including problems of direct and inverse variation. Interpret the solutions and determine whether the solutions are reasonable.

STANDARD 6:

EXPONENTIAL AND LOGARITHMIC FUNCTIONS

A2.6.1 Analyze, describe and sketch graphs of exponential functions by examining intercepts, zeros, domain and range, and asymptotic and end behavior.

A2.6.2 Know that the inverse of an exponential function is a logarithm, use laws of exponents to derive laws of logarithms, and use the inverse relationship between exponential functions and logarithms and laws of logarithms to solve problems.

A2.6.3 Solve exponential and logarithmic equations.

A2.6.4 Solve problems that can be modeled using exponential and logarithmic equations, interpret the solutions and determine whether the solutions are reasonable using technology as appropriate.

State capitol, Indianapolis

IN5

STANDARD 7:

SEQUENCES AND SERIES

A2.7.1 Write the recursive formula for arithmetic and geometric sequences and find specific terms of arithmetic and geometric sequences.

A2.7.2 Write the formula for the general term for arithmetic and geometric sequences and make connections to linear and exponential functions.

A2.7.3 Find partial sums of arithmetic and geometric series.

A2.7.4 Solve problems involving applications that can be modeled using sequences and finite arithmetic and geometric series, interpret the solutions, and determine whether the solutions are reasonable using spreadsheets as appropriate.

STANDARD 8:

DATA ANALYSIS AND PROBABILITY

A2.8.1 Use the relative frequency of a specified outcome of an event to estimate the probability of the outcome and apply the law of large numbers in simple examples.

A2.8.2 Determine the probability of simple events involving independent and dependent events and conditional probability. Analyze probabilities to interpret odds and risk of events.

A2.8.3 Know and apply the characteristics of the normal distribution. Identify settings in which the normal distribution may be useful. Determine whether a set of data appears to be uniform, skewed or normally distributed. Use the empirical rule to find probabilities that an event will occur in a specific interval that can be described in terms one, two or three standard deviations about the mean.

A2.8.4 Use permutations, combinations, and other counting methods to determine the number of ways that events can occur and to calculate probabilities, including the probability of compound events.

PROCESS STANDARDS

(denotes NCTM process standards)*

Problem Solving*

- Build new mathematical knowledge through problem solving.
- Solve problems that arise in mathematics and in other contexts.
- Apply and adapt a variety of appropriate strategies to solve problems.
- Monitor and reflect on the process of mathematical problem solving.

Reasoning and Proof *

- Recognize reasoning and proof as fundamental aspects of mathematics.
- Make and investigate mathematical conjectures.
- Develop and evaluate mathematical arguments and proofs.
- Select and use various types of reasoning and methods of proof.

Communication*

- Organize and consolidate their mathematical thinking through communication.
- Communicate their mathematical thinking coherently and clearly to peers, teachers, and others.
- Analyze and evaluate the mathematical thinking and strategies of others.
- Use the language of mathematics to express mathematical ideas precisely.

Connections*

- Recognize and use connections among mathematical ideas.
- Understand how mathematical ideas interconnect and build on one another to produce a coherent whole.
- Recognize and apply mathematics in contexts outside of mathematics.

Representation*

- Create and use representations to organize, record, and communicate mathematical ideas.
- Select, apply, and translate among mathematical representations to solve problems.
- Use representations to model and interpret physical, social, and mathematical phenomena.

Estimation and Mental Computation

- Know and apply appropriate methods for estimating the results of computations.
- Use estimation to decide whether answers are reasonable.
- Decide when estimation is an appropriate strategy for solving a problem.
- Determine appropriate accuracy and precision of measurement in problem situations.
- Use properties of numbers and operations to perform mental computation.
- Recognize when the numbers involved in a computation allow for a mental computation strategy.

Technology

- Technology should be used as a tool in mathematics education to support and extend the mathematics curriculum.
- Technology can contribute to concept development, simulation, representation, communication, and problem solving.
- The challenge is to ensure that technology supports-but is not a substitute for the development of skills with basic operations, quantitative reasoning, and problem-solving skills.

IN7

Preparing for ECA

Holt Algebra 2 provides many opportunities for you to prepare for standardized tests, such as the ECA.

Test Prep Exercises

Use the Test Prep Exercises for daily practice of standardized test questions in various formats.

Multiple Choice—choose your answer.

Numeric Response—write open-ended responses that are scored with a 2-point rubric.

Extended Response—write open-ended responses that are scored with a 4-point rubric.

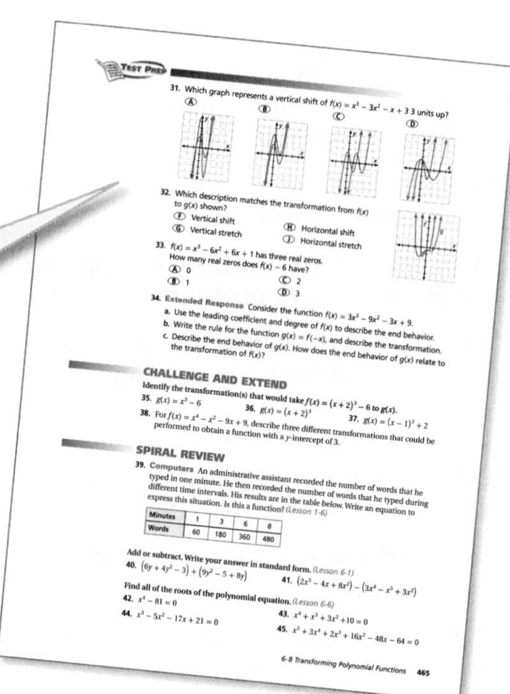

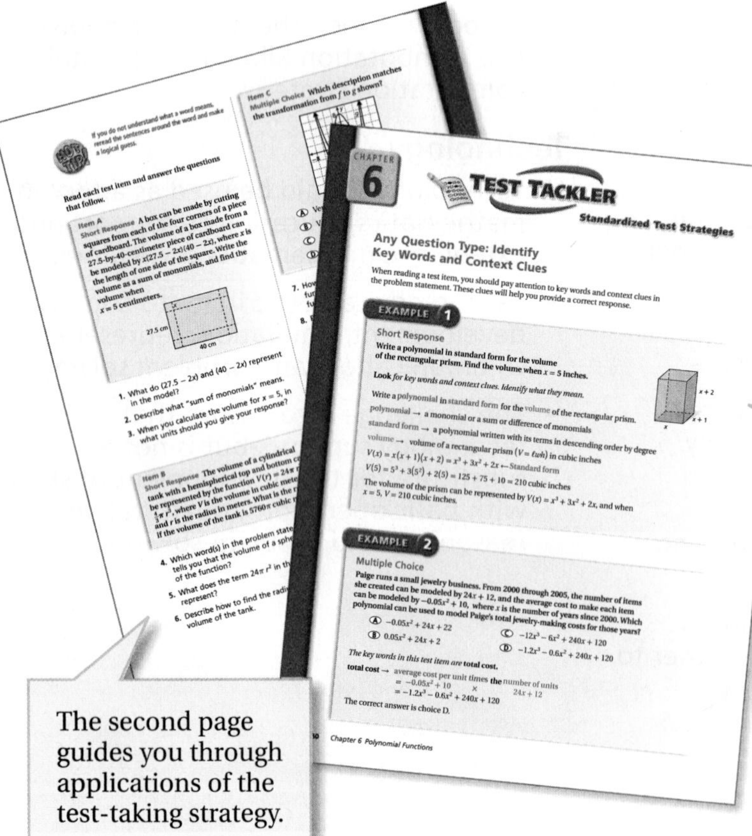

Test Tackler

Use the Test Tackler to become familiar with and practice test-taking strategies.

The first page of this feature explains and shows an example of a test-taking strategy.

The second page guides you through applications of the test-taking strategy.

IN8

ECA Test Prep

Use the ECA Test Prep to apply test-taking strategies.

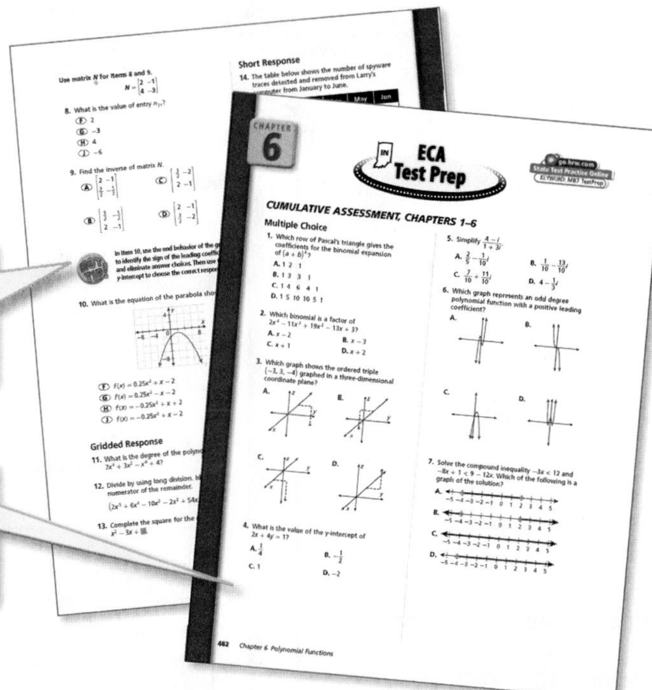

The Hot Tip provides test-taking tips to help you succeed on your tests.

These pages include practice with multiple choice, short answer, and extended response test items.

Countdown to ECA

Use the Countdown to ECA to practice for the Indiana End-of-Course Assessment everyday.

There are 24 pages of practice for the ECA. Each page is designed to be used in a week so that all practice will be completed before the ECA is given.

Each week's page has five practice test items, one for each day of the week.

Test-Taking Tips

- Get plenty of sleep the night before the test. A rested mind thinks more clearly and you won't feel like falling asleep while taking the test.
- Draw a figure when one is not provided with the problem. If a figure is given, write any details from the problem on the figure.
- Read each problem carefully. As you finish each problem, read it again to make sure your answer is reasonable.
- Review the formula sheet that will be supplied with the test. Make sure you know when to use each formula.
- First answer problems that you know how to solve. If you do not know how to solve a problem, skip it and come back to it when you have finished the others.
- Use other test-taking strategies that can be found throughout this book, such as working backward and eliminating answer choices.

Countdown to ECA

Day 1:
Part A: $A = (x + 2)^2 - 36$ square units; the side length of the larger square is $x + 2$, so the area is $(x + 2)^2$. The side length of the smaller square is 6, so the area is $6^2 = 36$. The shaded area is the area of the larger square minus the area of the smaller square, or $(x + 2)^2 - 36$ square units.

Part B: 36 square units; each triangular part of the shaded area is an isosceles right triangle with a hypotenuse of 6. The length of each leg is $\frac{6}{\sqrt{2}}$. The area of each triangle is $\frac{1}{2}\left(\frac{6}{\sqrt{2}}\right)\left(\frac{6}{\sqrt{2}}\right) = 9$ square units, so the are of the four shaded triangles is $4(9) = 36$ square units.

Day 2: C

Day 3: 1.875 hours;

$\frac{1}{3} + \frac{1}{5} = \frac{1}{t}$

$\frac{5}{15} + \frac{3}{15} = \frac{1}{t}$

$\frac{8}{15} = \frac{1}{t}$

$t = \frac{15}{8} = 1.875$

Day 4: A

Day 5: D

Countdown to ECA

WEEK 1

DAY 1

Extended Response The figure shows a square within a square.

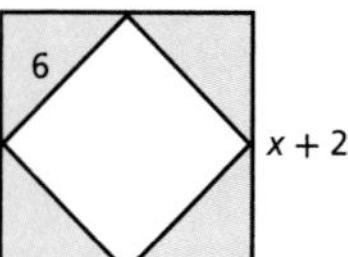

Part A Write an expression for the shaded area in square units in terms of x. Show or explain your work.

Part B The vertices of the smaller square are the midpoints of the sides of the larger square. Find the shaded area. Show or explain your work.

DAY 2

A furniture store sells a piece of furniture that comes in 4 different types of wood and 3 different sizes. How many variations of this piece of furniture are possible?

A. 6

B. 7

C. 12

D. 16

DAY 3

Short Answer You own a catering business and it takes you 3 hours to do the prep work for an event. It takes your friend 5 hours to complete the prep work for the same event.

The equation $\frac{1}{3} + \frac{1}{5} = \frac{1}{t}$ is used to find the amount of time it will take to do the prep work if you and your friend work together. How long will it take you and your friend to complete the prep work? Show or explain your work.

DAY 4

Which of the following describes the solutions of $x^2 + 7x - 6 = -2x + 4$?

A. Discriminant is 121 and two real solutions.

B. Discriminant is 73 and two real solutions.

C. Discriminant is 0 and one real solution

D. Discriminant is –41 and two imaginary solutions.

DAY 5

Simplify the expression $5(x^2 + 4x) + 3(x + 6)$.

A. $12x^2 + 6$

B. $12x^2 + 18$

C. $5x^2 + 7x + 6$

D. $5x^2 + 23x + 18$

Day	Indiana's Core Standards for Mathematics Algebra II
1	3. Quadratic Equations and Functions
2	8. Combinatorics and Probability
3	5. Rational Functions
4	3. Quadratic Equations and Functions
5	4. Polynomial Equations and Functions

Countdown to ECA — WEEK 2

DAY 1

Extended Response Justin and Emily are making trail mix. Justin buys 2 bags of peanuts and 3 bags of raisins for $13.00. Emily buys 3 bags of peanuts and 4 bags of raisins for $18.00. Let p be the price of one bag of peanuts and r by the price of one bag of raisins.

Part A Write equations to represent the total cost for each person.

Part B Graph the equations.

Part C Explain the meaning of the intersection of the two lines in terms of the real-world situation. Justify your answer.

DAY 2

What is the value of i^{16}?

A. $-i$

B. -1

C. i

D. 1

DAY 3

Which expression is equivalent to $\frac{12x^4y^8}{9xy^4}$?

A. $\frac{4}{3}xy^2$

B. $\frac{4}{3}xy^4$

C. $\frac{4}{3}x^3y^4$

D. $\frac{4}{3}x^4y^2$

DAY 4

The restaurant specials for the evening are a chicken entrée, a fish entrée, and a beef entrée. With each entrée you can choose corn, peas, or squash for your vegetable, and also choose soup or salad. What is the probability that the next order received will be chicken with squash and a salad?

A. $\frac{1}{3}$

B. $\frac{3}{8}$

C. $\frac{1}{8}$

D. $\frac{1}{18}$

DAY 5

Short Answer Maureen, Erin, Amy, and Cindy are on the school cross-country team. They practice everyday after school. What is the probability that Amy then Erin will finish practice first? Show or explain your work.

Countdown to ECA

Day 1: A

Part A: Price of one bag of peanuts: p
Price of one bag of raisins: r
Cost of Justin's purchase: $13
Cost of Emily's purchase: $18
Justin: $2p + 3r = 13$
Emily: $3p + 4r = 18$

Part B:

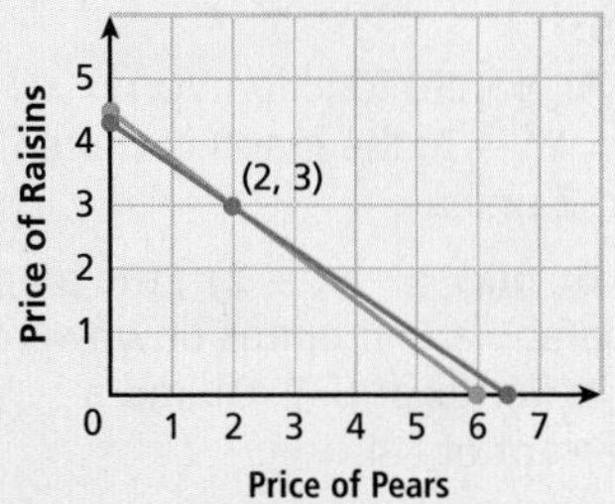

Part C: The intersection represents the prices of each kind of bag. Each bag of peanuts cost $2 and each bag of raisins cost $3.

Day 2: D

Day 3: C

Day 4: D

Day 5: $\frac{1}{12}$;

Probability that Amy will finish first: $\frac{1}{4}$

Probability that Erin will finish second: $\frac{1}{3}$

Probility that Amy then Erin will finish practice first: $\frac{1}{4} \cdot \frac{1}{3} = \frac{1}{12}$

Day	Indiana's Core Standards for Mathematics Algebra II
1	1. Linear and Absolute Value Equations and Inequalities
2	2. Complex Numbers
3	5. Rational Functions
4	8. Combinatorics and Probability
5	8. Combinatorics and Probability

Countdown to ECA

Day 1: A

Day 2: -1; $(-i)^2 = \left(-\sqrt{-1}\right)^2$
$= \left(-1 \cdot \sqrt{-1}\right)^2 = (-1)^2 \cdot \left(\sqrt{-1}\right)^2$
$= 1 \cdot (-1) = -1$

Day 3: B

Day 4: B

Day 5:
Part A: parent function: $f(x) = x^2$; $g(x) = x^2 - 2$; the graph is shifted down 2 units.

Part B: $h(x) = -(x + 2)^2$; the graph is a parabola that opens downward, with its vertex at $(-2, 0)$ and a y-intercept of -4.

Countdown to ECA — WEEK 3

DAY 1

What is the quotient of $4 + 3i$ and $6 - 2i$ as a complex number in standard form?

A. $\frac{9}{20} + \frac{13}{20}i$

B. $\frac{9}{20} + 26i$

C. $\frac{3}{4} + \frac{1}{4}i$

D. $\frac{3}{4} + \frac{13}{20}i$

DAY 2

Short Answer What is the value of $(-i)^2$? Show or explain your work.

DAY 3

For what value of c does the equation have exactly one real solution?

$$x^2 - 2x + c = 0$$

A. $\frac{1}{4}$

B. 1

C. 2

D. 4

DAY 4

Which of the following is the quadratic equation with the solutions 6 and –2?

A. $y = x^2 + 6x - 2$

B. $y = x^2 - 4x - 12$

C. $y = x^2 + 4x - 12$

D. $y = x^2 - 8x + 12$

DAY 5

Extended Response

Part A What is the parent function of the function shown in the graph? Write the equation of the graph shown and describe the transformation.

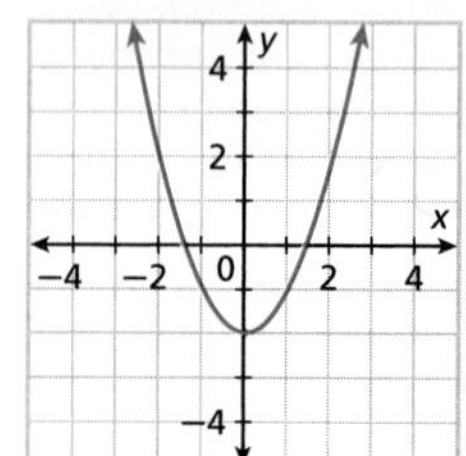

Part B The same parent function is reflected across the x-axis, then translated left two units. Write the equation and describe or draw the graph.

Day	Indiana's Core Standards for Mathematics Algebra II
1	2. Complex Numbers
2	2. Complex Numbers
3	3. Quadratic Equations and Functions
4	3. Quadratic Equations and Functions
5	3. Quadratic Equations and Functions

Countdown to ECA — WEEK 4

DAY 1

Which is equivalent to $\frac{x^3 - 81x}{x + 9}$?

A. $x + 9$

B. $x^2 + 9$

C. $x - 9$

D. $x^2 - 9x$

DAY 2

Short Answer What is the product of $(5 + 8i)$ and $(-3 - 2i)$ as a complex number in standard form? Show or explain your work.

DAY 3

What are the solutions of $x^2 + 6x + 10 = -3$?

A. $-3 \pm \sqrt{22}$

B. $-3 \pm 4i$

C. $-3 \pm 2i$

D. 1, 7

DAY 4

Extended Response

Part A Simplify the expression $\left(\frac{6x^2y^4}{x^4y^2}\right)^3$ using only positive exponents. Show each step.

Part B Rewrite the given expression using negative exponents, and simplify. Show each step. Explain why the two simplified expressions are equivalent.

DAY 5

Which of the following is a quadratic function that passes through the given points of $(-8, 0)$, $(-3\ 0)$, and $(-2, 12)$?

A. $y = x^2 + 11x + 24$

B. $y = x^2 - 15x - 22$

C. $y = 2x^2 + 22x + 48$

D. $y = 3x^2 - 15x + 24$

Countdown to ECA

Day 1: D

Day 2: $1 - 34i$; $(5 + 8i)(-3 - 2i) = -15 - 10i - 24i + 16 = 1 - 34i$

Day 3: C

Day 4:
Part A: $\frac{216y^6}{x^6}$; $\left(\frac{6x^2y^4}{x^4y^2}\right)^3 = \frac{6^3x^6y^{12}}{x^{12}y^6} = \frac{216y^6}{x^6}$

Part B: $216x^{-6}y^6$; $\left(\frac{6x^2y^4}{x^4y^2}\right)^3 = (6^3x^6y^{12})\cdot(x^{-12}y^{-6}) = 216x^{-6}y^6$; the expressions are equivalent because x^{-6} is equivalent to $\frac{1}{x^6}$.

Day 5: C

Day	Indiana's Core Standards for Mathematics Algebra II
1	4. Polynomial Equations and Functions
2	2. Complex Numbers
3	3. Quadratic Equations and Functions
4	3. Quadratic Equations and Functions
5	3. Quadratic Equations and Functions

Countdown to ECA

Day 1: B

Day 2: $\frac{x+6}{x-8}$; $\frac{x^2+10x+24}{x^2-4x-32} = \frac{(x+4)(x+6)}{(x+4)(x-8)} = \frac{x+6}{x-8}$

Day 3: C

Day 4: C

Day 5:

Part A: $f(x) = 8x^2 - 4$ has a minimum with a value of -4.

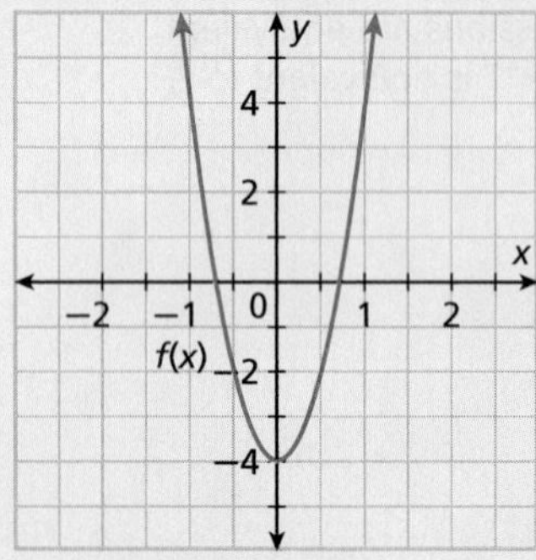

Part B: $f(x)$ in comparison to $g(x)$ is translated 4 units down and vertically stretched by a factor of 8.

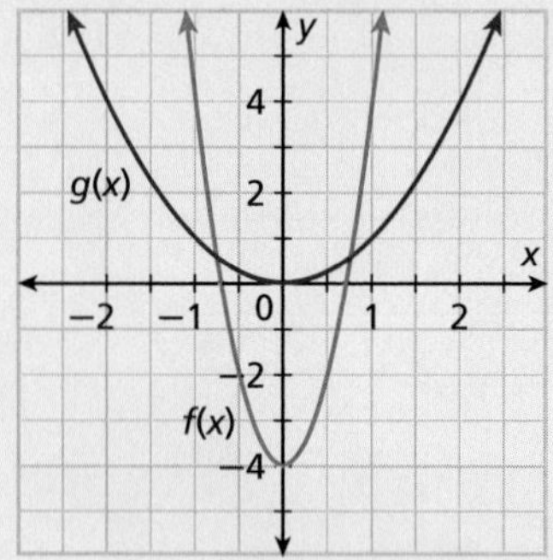

Countdown to ECA — WEEK 5

DAY 1

Which graph best represents the function $f(x) = x^2$?

A.  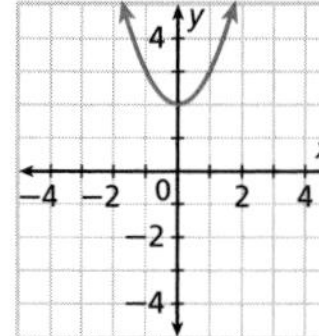

B.  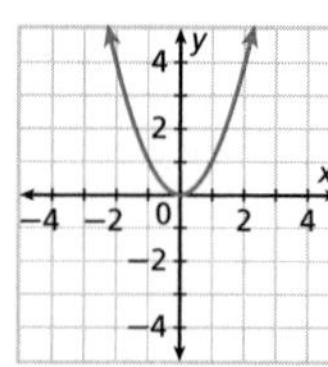

C. 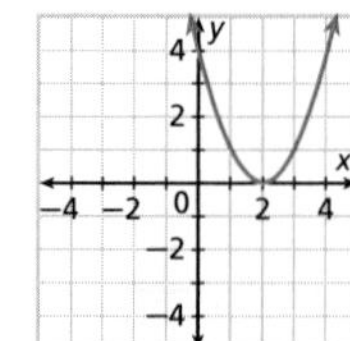

D. 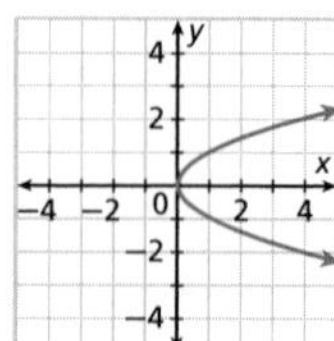

DAY 2

Short Answer Which is equivalent to $\frac{x^2+10x+24}{x^2-4x-32}$? Show or explain your work.

DAY 3

Simplify: $(a^2 + 3a - 2) - (2a^2 + 4)$.

A. $3a^2 + 3a - 6$

B. $-a^2 + 3a - 2$

C. $-a^2 + 3a - 6$

D. $-a^2 + 3a + 2$

DAY 4

What are the solutions to the polynomial equation $x^3 - 3x^2 - 16x + 48 = 0$

A. $-4, -3$

B. $-3, 4$

C. $-4, 3, 4$

D. $3, 16$

DAY 5

Extended Response Consider the function $f(x) = 8x^2 - 4$.

Part A Does the graph of $f(x) = 8x^2 - 4$. have a maximum or minimum, and what is its value?

Part B How does the graph of $f(x) = 8x^2 - 4$. compare with $g(x) = x^2$?

Day	Indiana's Core Standards for Mathematics Algebra II
1	3. Quadratic Equations and Functions
2	5. Rational Functions
3	4. Polynomial Equations and Functions
4	4. Polynomial Equations and Functions
5	3. Quadratic Equations and Functions

Countdown to ECA — WEEK 6

DAY 1

Short Answer What is the solution to the polynomial equation $8p^4 - 216p = 0$? Show or explain your work.

DAY 2

The probability that it will rain on Thursday is 0.4 and the probability that it will rain on Friday is 0.75. What is the probability of rain on Thursday and Friday?

A. 0.3 **B.** 0.35

C. 0.58 **D.** 0.79

DAY 3

Extended Response Consider the following graph of a polynomial function.

Part A Estimate the coordinates of any local minimums, local maximums, and zeros.

Part B Make sure to label each point as to if it corresponds to a minimum, maximum, or zero.

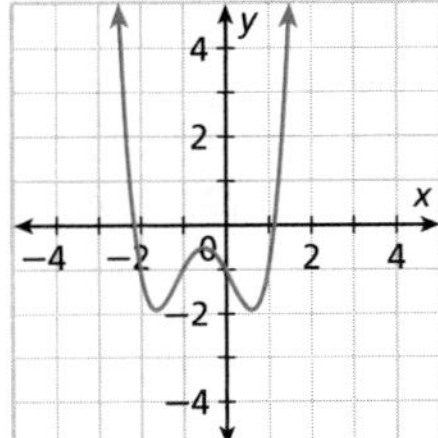

DAY 4

The volume of a square pyramid is given by the formula $V = \frac{1}{3}Bh$, where B is the area of the base and h is the height. What is the volume of a square pyramid whose height is $2x - 6$ and base side length is $3x + 1$?

A. $2x^2 - \frac{16}{3}x - 2$

B. $6x^3 - 14x^2 - \frac{34}{3}x - 2$

C. $9x^3 - 21x^2 - 17x - 3$

D. $18x^3 - 42x^2 - 34x - 6$

DAY 5

There are 12 chips in a blue bag. The chips are numbered 1 through 12. You randomly select two chips without replacement. What is the probability that the first chip is a prime number and the second chip is a multiple of 4?

A. $\frac{1}{12}$ **B.** $\frac{1}{11}$

C. $\frac{2}{11}$ **D.** $\frac{5}{12}$

COUNTDOWN TO ECA

Day 1: 0 and 3;
$8p^4 - 216p = 0$
$8p(p^3 - 27) = 0$
$8p = 0$
$p = 0$
and
$p^3 - 27 = 0$
$p^3 = 27$
$p = 3$

Day 2: A

Day 3:
Part A: – Part B: zeros: (–2.1, 0) and (1.1, 0); local minimums: (.6, –2) and (–1.6, –2); local maximum: (–0.5, –0.5)

Day 4: B

Day 5: B

Day	Indiana's Core Standards for Mathematics Algebra II
1	4. Polynomial Equations and Functions
2	8. Combinatorics and Probability
3	4. Polynomial Equations and Functions
4	3. Quadratic Equations and Functions
5	8. Combinatorics and Probability

Countdown to ECA

Day 1:
Part A:

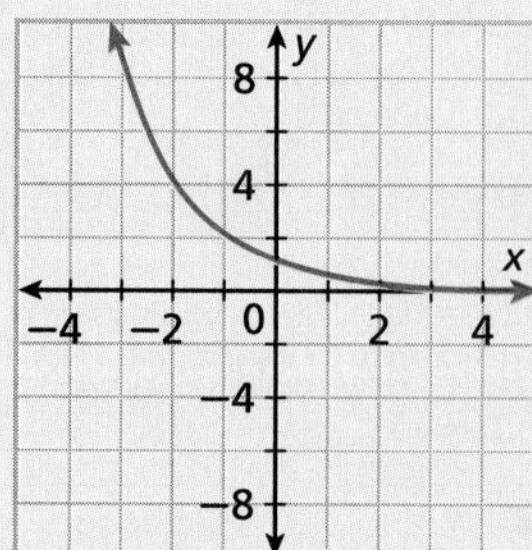

Part B:

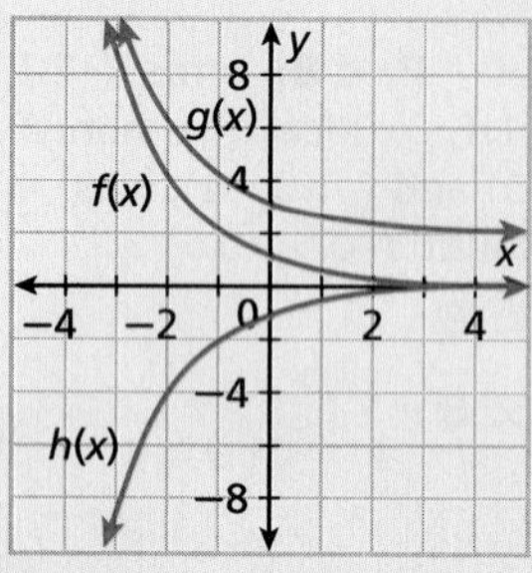

Part C: Both graphs from part B have the same parent function $f(x)$ from part A. The first function $g(x)$ has been shifted vertically 2 units from $f(x)$, and the second function $h(x)$ is the reflection of $f(x)$ over the x-axis.

Day 2: C

Day 3: C

Day 4: B

Day 5: The graph of $y = 0.8\log_6 (x + 3)$ crosses the x-axis at $x = -2$.

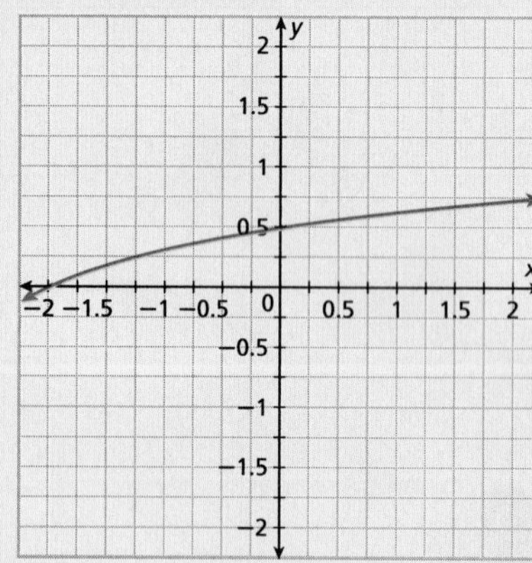

Countdown to ECA — WEEK 7

DAY 1

Extended Response

Part A Graph the function $f(x) = \frac{1}{2}^{x}$.

Part B On the same grid, graph the functions $g(x) = \frac{1}{2}^{x} + 2$ and $h(x) = -\left(\frac{1}{2}^{x}\right)$.

Part C Describe the relationship between the graphs in **Part B** and the graph in **Part A.**

DAY 2

What is the solution of $\log_5 (4x + 1) = 3$?

A. $x = 3.5$

B. $x = 3.75$

C. $x = 31$

D. $x = 31.25$

DAY 3

Which best illustrates the Associative Property?

A. $3x^2 + 5x^2 - 6 = 3x^2 - 6 + 5x^2$

B. $x^2(3 + 5) - 6 = (3x^2 + 5x^2) - 6$

C. $3x^2 + (5x^2 - 6) = (3x^2 + 5x^2) - 6$

D. $3x^2 + (5x^2 - 6) = (-6 + 3x^2) + 5x^2$

DAY 4

Which of the following is equivalent to $5 \log_3 x - 7 \log_3 y$?

A. $\log_3 \frac{x^5}{y^7}$

B. $\log_3 \frac{y^7}{x^5}$

C. $\log_3 \frac{5^x}{7^y}$

D. $\log_3 \frac{7^y}{5^x}$

DAY 5

Short Answer Where does the graph of $y = 0.8 \log_6 (x + 3)$ cross the x-axis? Show or explain your work.

Day	Indiana's Core Standards for Mathematics Algebra II
1	6. Exponential and Logarithmic Equations
2	6. Exponential and Logarithmic Equations
3	4. Polynomial Equations and Functions
4	6. Exponential and Logarithmic Equations
5	6. Exponential and Logarithmic Equations

DAY 1

What is the domain of the function $y = |x - 1|$?

A. $\{y \mid y \geq 0\}$

B. $\{x \mid x \geq 0\}$

C. Positive integers

D. All real numbers

DAY 2

Which of the following logarithmic expressions is equivalent to $\log_5 \frac{a^7 b}{c^3}$?

A. $\log_5 a^7 - \log_5 b - 3 \log_5 c$

B. $7 \log_5 a + \log_5 b - 3 \log_5 c$

C. $7 \log_5 ab - 3 \log_5 c$

D. $\log_5 \frac{a^7}{c^3} - \log_5 b$

DAY 3

Extended Response Use the rectangular prism below and its given dimensions to answer the following parts.

Part A Write an equation for the volume of the prism.

Part B Solve the equation from **Part A** to find the possible values of x if the volume of the prism is 40 cubic units. Show or explain your work.

Part C Verify that there is only one real solution for x by showing the other two solutions are non-real. Show or explain your work.

DAY 4

What is the solution of $\log_6 2x - 2 \log_6 2 = \log_6 5$?

A. $x = 10$

B. $x = \frac{9}{2}$

C. $x = \frac{7}{2}$

D. $x = \frac{3}{2}$

DAY 5

Short Answer Teresa has two identical CD binders that are partly filled with CDs.

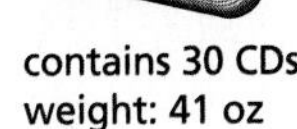

contains 30 CDs
weight: 41 oz

contains 75 CDs
weight: 66.5 oz

How much does each binder weigh when empty, to the nearest ounce? Show or explain your work.

COUNTDOWN TO ECA

Day 1: D

Day 2: B

Day 3:
Part A: $V = 2x(x - 1)(x - 4)$

Part B: 5
$2x(x - 1)(x - 4) = 40$
$2x^3 - 10x^2 + 8x - 40 = 0$
$x^3 - 5x^2 + 4x - 20 = 0$
$x^2(x - 5) + 4(x - 5) = 0$
$(x - 5)(x^2 + 4) = 0$
$x = 5$ and $x^2 = -4$

Part C: From previous work in **Part B**, $x^2 = -4$, therefore, $x = \pm 4i$ which are two non-real solutions.

Day 4: A

Day 5: 24 oz; if the weight of the binders is b and the weight of each CD is c, then $b + 30c = 41$ and $b + 75c = 66.5$. Multiply the first equation by -1 and add the two equations to get $45c = 25.5$. Divide by 45 to get $c = 0.5\overline{6}$. Substitute into the first equation and solve to get $b = 24$.

Day	Indiana's Core Standards for Mathematics Algebra II
1	1. Linear and Absolute Value Equations and Inequalities
2	6. Exponential and Logarithmic Equations
3	4. Polynomial Equations and Functions
4	6. Exponential and Logarithmic Equations
5	1. Linear and Absolute Value Equations and Inequalities

Countdown to ECA

Day 1: A

Day 2: $-7 \le x \le 7$;
$2 - |x| \ge -5$
$-|x| \ge -7$
$|x| \le 7$
$-7 \le x \le 7$

Day 3:
Part A: $p(x) = 49.99(0.91)^t$
Part B: \$34.28; find $p(4)$.
Part C: $t = 5$

Day 4: D

Day 5: B

Countdown to ECA — WEEK 9

DAY 1

Simplify the expression $\left(\frac{x^{16}}{y^{12}}\right)^{1/4}$.

A. $\frac{x^4}{y^3}$

B. $\frac{x^3}{y^4}$

C. $\sqrt[3]{x^4}$

D. $\sqrt[4]{x}$

DAY 2

Short Answer Determine the solution of the absolute value inequality $2 - |x| \ge -5$? Show or explain your work.

DAY 3

Extended-Response In 2001, the cost of high-speed internet provided by a certain company was \$49.99. During the next 5 years, the price decreased an average of 9% each year.

Part A Write a model giving the average price p (in dollars) of internet t years after 2001. show or explain your work.

Part B What was the price of internet in 2005?

Part C For what value of t in the domain does the price p have a meaningful minimum?

DAY 4

Which expression is equivalent to $\frac{11x^2}{2x} + \frac{7}{x^2}$?

A. $\frac{18x^2}{2x^3}$

B. $\frac{11x^4 + 7x^2}{2x^3}$

C. $\frac{x^2(11x + 7)}{2x}$

D. $\frac{11x^3 + 14}{2x^2}$

DAY 5

What absolute value inequality is graphed below?

A. $|x + 6| \ge 7$

B. $|x + 6| \ge 8$

C. $|x - 6| \le 7$

D. $|x - 6| \le 8$

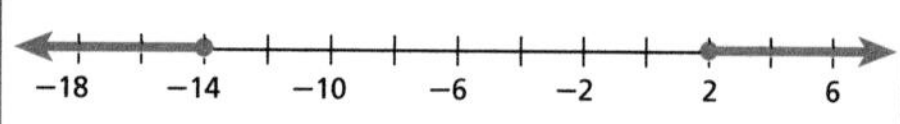

Day	Indiana's Core Standards for Mathematics Algebra II
1	5. Rational Functions
2	1. Linear and Absolute Value Equations and Inequalities
3	6. Exponential and Logarithmic Equations
4	5. Rational Functions
5	1. Linear and Absolute Value Equations and Inequalities

Countdown to ECA

WEEK 10

DAY 1

Which expression is equivalent to $\frac{25x^2}{5x-4} - \frac{16}{5x-4}$?

A. $\frac{9x^2}{5x-4}$ **B.** $\frac{5x^2-4}{5x-4}$

C. $5x + 4$ **D.** 5

DAY 2

The population *P* of a town was 5200 in 2001 and has increased by 5% per year since then. Which exponential growth model gives the town's population in terms of *t*, where t is the number of years since 2001?

A. $P = 1.05(5200)^t$

B. $P = 0.5(5200)^t$

C. $P = 5200(1.05)^t$

D. $P = 5200(0.05)^t$

DAY 3

Extended Response

Part A Graph the equations below.

$f(x) = 3x^2 - 1$

$g(x) = 3(x - 1)^2$

Part B Explain the relationship between the two graphs and between their equations.

DAY 4

Short Answer An ice cream shop has 45 flavors of ice cream. A customer would like to order 3 scoops of different kinds of ice cream. How many different ways can the customer order the 3 scoops? Show or explain your work.

DAY 5

Simplify the expression $\sqrt[3]{\frac{x^{15}}{y^6}}$.

A. $\frac{x^{45}}{y^{18}}$

B. $\sqrt[3]{\frac{x^5}{y^2}}$

C. x^3

D. $\frac{x^5}{y^2}$

Countdown to ECA

Day 1: C

Day 2: C

Day 3:
Part A:

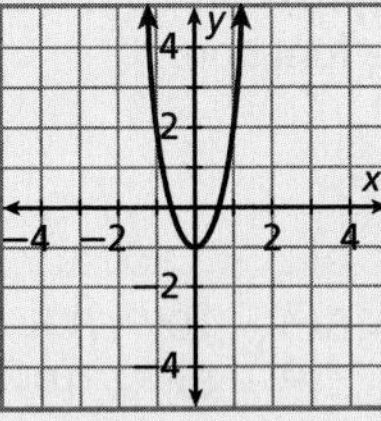

$f(x) = 3x^2 - 1$

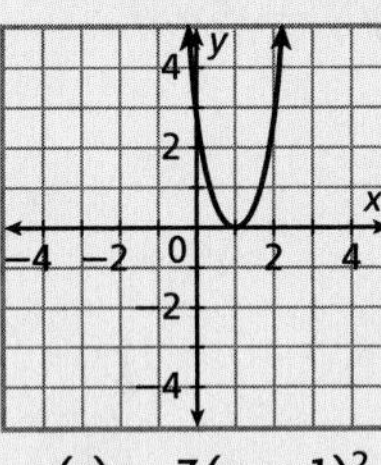

$g(x) = 3(x - 1)^2$

Part B: Both graphs have the same parent function, $y = x^2$. Both graphs are stretched vertically by a factor of 3. $f(x)$ is shifted down 1 unit, and $g(x)$ is shifted right 1 unit. In $f(x)$, the 1 is subtracted from the entire function, but in $g(x)$, the 1 is subtracted only from *x*.

Day 4: 14,190;

$_{45}C_3 = \frac{45!}{(45 - 3)!3!} = 14,190$

Day 5: D

Day	Indiana's Core Standards for Mathematics Algebra II
1	5. Rational Functions
2	6. Exponential and Logarithmic Equations
3	3. Quadratic Equations and Functions
4	8. Combinatorics and Probability
5	5. Rational Functions

COUNTDOWN TO ECA

Day 1: $y \leq 0$; the parent function is $f(x) = |x|$, which has a range of $y \geq 0$. The function is reflected across the y-axis, so the range becomes $y \leq 0$. The horizontal translation and vertical compression do not affect the range of the function.

Day 2: B

Day 3:

Part A: $P = 6x^2 + 10y^3$; $P = 3x^2 + 5y^3 + 3x^2 + 5y^3 = 6x^2 + 10y^3$

Part B: $A = 15x^2y^3$; $A = (3x^2)(5y^3) = 15x^2y^3$

Day 4: B

Day 5: A

Countdown to ECA — WEEK 11

DAY 1

Short Answer What is the range of the function $f(x) = -\frac{1}{4}|x-2|$? Show or explain your work.

DAY 2

Which expression is equivalent to $\frac{x^2 - 9}{x^2 + 7x + 12} \bullet \frac{x^2 - 2x - 24}{x^2 - 9x + 18}$?

A. $\frac{x + 3}{x - 6}$ **B.** 1

C. $\frac{x - 4}{x^2 - 36}$ **D.** $x + 3$

DAY 3

Extended Response The figure below is a rectangle with measurements as shown.

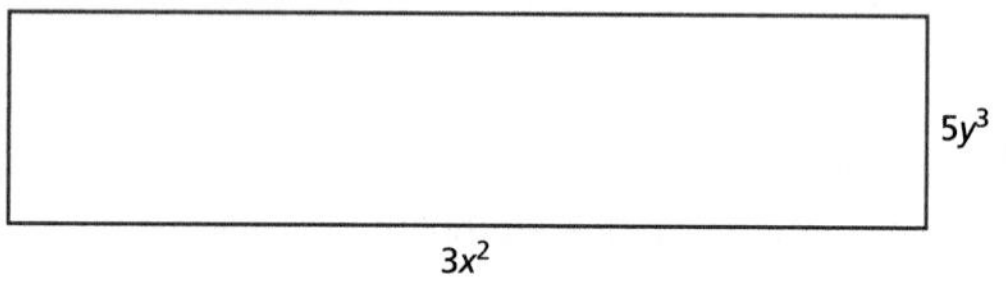

Part A Write an expression for the perimeter of the rectangle. Show or explain your work.

Part B Write an expression for the area of the rectangle. Show or explain your work.

DAY 4

The interest is compounded continuously at an annual rate of 4% on a money market account at your local bank. If you make an initial deposit of \$3500, what will be the balance after 2 years?

A. \$3642.83

B. \$3791.50

C. \$5221.38

D. \$7789.39

DAY 5

A coffee shop sells about 50 bagels each day at a price of \$1 each. For each \$0.10 increase in price, where x is the number of times the price has been increased, about 5 fewer bagels are sold. What is the equation that models the revenue R for this situation?

A. $R(x) = (1 + 0.1x)(50 - 5x)$

B. $R(x) = (1 - 0.1x)(50 + 5x)$

C. $R(x) = 50x + 0.1x - 5$

D. $R(x) = 50 - 0.5x$

Day	Indiana's Core Standards for Mathematics Algebra II
1	1. Linear and Absolute Value Equations and Inequalities
2	5. Rational Functions
3	4. Polynomial Equations and Functions
4	6. Exponential and Logarithmic Equations
5	3. Quadratic Equations and Functions

Countdown to ECA — WEEK 12

DAY 1

How is the graph of $g(x) = |x| - 4$ transformed from the graph of $f(x) = |x|$?

A. The graph of f is translated 4 units up.

B. The graph of f is translated 4 units down.

C. The graph of f is translated 4 units right.

D. The graph of f is translated 4 units left.

DAY 2

Short Answer Given that $f(x)$ is a quadratic function, find the missing value in the table. Show or explain your work.

x	2	4	6	8
$f(x)$	3	−1	−6	?

DAY 3

Extended Response

Part A Describe the graph shown. Include the domain, range, x- and y-intercepts, vertex, and axis of symmetry.

Part B Write the equation of the graph in the form $y = ax^2 + bx + c$, in factored form, and in transformation form.

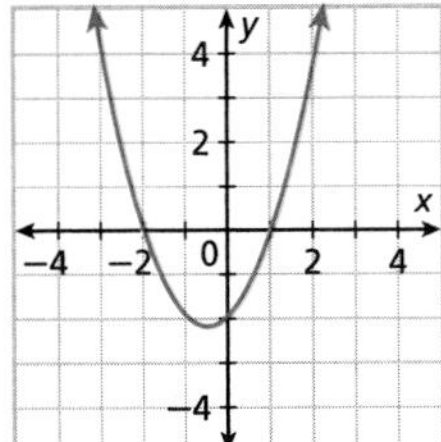

DAY 4

What is the domain of the function $f(x) = -\frac{1}{2}|x - 4|$?

A. All real numbers

B. $x < 0$

C. $x \geq -2$

D. $x > 4$

DAY 5

How is the graph of $g(x) = 2(x + 1)^2$ transformed from the graph of $f(x) = x^2$?

A. The graph of f is translated 2 units left and 1 unit up.

B. The graph of f is vertically compressed by a factor of $\frac{1}{2}$ and translated 1 unit left.

C. The graph of f is vertically stretched by a factor of 2 and translated 1 unit up.

D. The graph of f is vertically stretched by a factor of 2 and translated 1 unit left.

Countdown to ECA

Day 1: B

Day 2: −12; if the function is quadratic, then the sequence of second differences is constant. The sequence of first differences is −4, −5, ..., so the next value must be −6 in order for the second differences to equal 1. Thus, the next value in the table must be 6 less than the value before, or −12.

Day 3:

Part A: The graph is a parabola. The domain is all real numbers, and the range is $y \geq -2.25$. The x-intercepts are −2 and 1, and the y-intercept is −1. The vertex is (−0.5, −2.25), and the axis of symmetry is $x = -0.5$.

Part B: The equation of the graph can be written as $y = x^2 + x - 2$, $y = (x + 2)(x - 1)$, or $y = (x + 0.5)^2 - 2.25$.

Day 4: A

Day 5: D

Day	Indiana's Core Standards for Mathematics Algebra II
1	1. Linear and Absolute Value Equations and Inequalities
2	3. Quadratic Equations and Functions
3	3. Quadratic Equations and Functions
4	1. Linear and Absolute Value Equations and Inequalities
5	3. Quadratic Equations and Functions

Countdown to ECA

Day 1: B

Day 2: Start with the parent function $f(x) = x^2$. Shift the parent function to the right 7 units, then up 3 units.

Day 3: B

Day 4: D

Day 5:
Part A: The graph is a parabola that opens downward. The domain is $0 \leq t \leq 2.5$, which represents the time interval that the ball is in the air. The range is $0 \leq h \leq 25$, which represents the possible heights of the ball. The t-intercepts are 0 and 2.5, which represent the times at which the ball is on the ground. The h-intercept is 0, which represents the height at time 0.

Part B: The maximum height of the graph is 25. This means that the football is never higher than 25 feet off the ground.

Countdown to ECA — WEEK 13

DAY 1

Given the functions $f(x) = (x^2 + 3)$ and $g(x) = (2x - 5)$, find $g \bullet f$.

A. $x^2 + 2x - 2$

B. $2x^3 - 5x^2 + 6x - 15$

C. $3x^3 - 2x^2 - 15$

D. $2x^3 + x - 15$

DAY 2

Extended Response The height in feet of a football t seconds after it is kicked is given by $h(t) = -16t^2 + 40t$.

Part A Describe the graph of the function. Include the domain, range, and intercepts, and what each characteristic represents.

Part B What is the maximum height of the graph? Explain what this means in the context of the problem.

DAY 3

Which situation is best represented by the data?

t	0	0.5	1	1.5	2	2.5
$f(t)$	112	108	96	76	48	12

A. The distance decreases by 4 miles for every 30 seconds traveled.

B. The height of an object above ground decreases nonlinearly over time.

C. As the time increases, the speed of a car increases at a constant rate.

D. As the time increases, the distance traveled decreases at a constant rate.

DAY 4

Which function is equivalent to $f(x) = 30x^2 + 2x - 56$?

A. $f(x) = (3x - 4)(5x + 14)$

B. $f(x) = 2(3x + 4)(5x - 7)$

C. $f(x) = (6x - 4)(5x + 7)$

D. $f(x) = 2(3x - 4)(5x + 7)$

DAY 5

Short Answer Describe how to graph the function $f(x) = (x - 7)^2 + 3$.

Day	Indiana's Core Standards for Mathematics Algebra II
1	4. Polynomial Equations and Functions
2	3. Quadratic Equations and Functions
3	3. Quadratic Equations and Functions
4	3. Quadratic Equations and Functions
5	3. Quadratic Equations and Functions

Countdown to ECA — WEEK 14

DAY 1

Extended Response

Part A Solve the equation $0 = x^2 + 7x - 26$ by completing the square.

Part B Explain each step.

DAY 2

Which quadratic equation has nonreal solutions?

A. $x^2 - 8x + 16 = 0$

B. $4x^2 - 12x + 9 = 0$

C. $-x^2 + 4x - 5 = 0$

D. $x^2 - 3x - 7 = 0$

DAY 3

The function $P = (h - 3)^2 + 174$ models the power, in megawatts, generated between midnight and noon by a power plant, where h represents hours after midnight. How would the graph of the function change if the minimum power generated increased to 250 megawatts?

A. The vertex would change to (3, 250).

B. The vertex would change to (250, 174).

C. The graph of the function would be reflected over the x-axis.

D. The graph of the function would be horizontally compressed.

DAY 4

Short Answer The length x of a rectangle is 6 feet longer than its width. What is a reasonable domain for the function that represents the area of the rectangle? Show or explain your work.

DAY 5

Consider the following functions.

$g(x) = x - 3$

$h(x) = \frac{x^2}{x - 3}$

What is $h(g(x))$?

A. $\frac{x^2 - 6x + 9}{x - 6}$

B. $\frac{x^2 - 9}{x - 6}$

C. $\frac{x^2 - 3}{x - 3}$

D. $\frac{x - 3}{x - 6}$

COUNTDOWN TO ECA

Day 1: $x > 6$; the width of the rectangle must be greater than 0, so if the length is 6 feel longer than the width, then the length must be greater then 6.

Day 2: C

Day 3: A

Day 4:
Part A: $x = -3.5 \pm \sqrt{38.25}$

Part B:
Step 1: Add 26 to both sides.
$26 = x^2 + 7x$
Step 2: Multiply the coefficient of x by $\frac{1}{2}$, and square the result. Add this number to both sides.
$26 + 12.25 = x^2 + 7x + 12.25$
Step 3: Write the expression on the right as a perfect square.
$38.25 = (x + 3.5)^2$
Step 4: Take the square root of both sides.
$\pm\sqrt{38.25} = x + 3.5$
Step 5: Subtract 3.5 from both sides.
$x = -3.5 \pm \sqrt{38.25}$

Day 5: A

Day	Indiana's Core Standards for Mathematics Algebra II
1	3. Quadratic Equations and Functions
2	3. Quadratic Equations and Functions
3	3. Quadratic Equations and Functions
4	3. Quadratic Equations and Functions
5	5. Rational Functions

Countdown to ECA

Day 1: B

Day 2:
Part A: x: number of adults
y: number of children
$x + y = 150$
$12x + 7y = 1610$

Part B: 112 adults and 38 children;
Solve $x + y = 150$ for y.
$y = 150 - x$
Substitute $y = 150 - x$ into
$12x + 7y = 1610.$
$12x + 7(150 - x) = 1610$
$12x + 1050 - 7x = 1610$
$5x + 1050 = 1610$
$5x = 560$
$x = 112$
$y = 150 - 112 = 38$

Day 3: $x = -1, y = 5\ z = -2$

Day 4: A

Day 5: D

Countdown to ECA — WEEK 15

DAY 1

Which exponential function is modeled by the graph below?

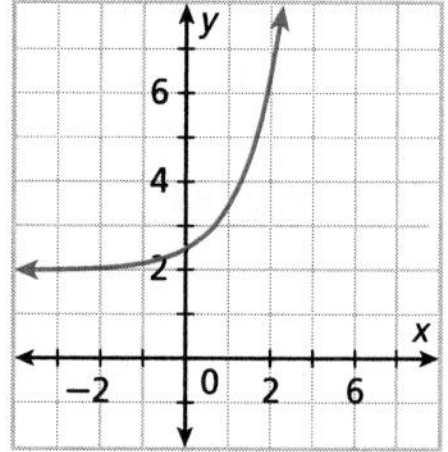

A. $y = 2 \cdot 3^x + 0.5$

B. $y = 0.5 \cdot 3^x + 0.5$

C. $y = (2.5)^x$

D. $y = 2 \cdot 3^x + 2$

DAY 2

Extended Response At the local theater, 150 people attended a matinee performance. Adults paid $12 per ticket and children paid $7 per ticket. The theater took in $1610.

Part A Write a system of equations to model the given information.

Part B How many adults and children attended the matinee? Show or explain your work.

DAY 3

Short Answer Solve the following system of equations. Show or explain your work.

$2x + 4y - 8z = 34$

$4x - 2y - 6z = -2$

$4x - 2y + 2z = -18$

DAY 4

The diameter of the globe in the school library is $2x + 10$. What is the globe's surface area?

A. $16\pi x^2 + 160\pi x + 400\pi$

B. $16\pi x^2 + 80\pi x + 100x$

C. $4\pi x^2 + 80\pi x + 400\pi$

D. $4\pi x^2 + 40\pi x + 100\pi$

DAY 5

Which of the following describes the solutions of $3x^2 + 8x + 7$?

A. one real solution

B. two real solutions

C. one imaginary solution

D. two imaginary solutions.

Day	Indiana's Core Standards for Mathematics Algebra II
1	6. Exponential and Logarithmic Equations
2	1. Linear and Absolute Value Equations and Inequalities
3	1. Linear and Absolute Value Equations and Inequalities
4	3. Quadratic Equations and Functions
5	3. Quadratic Equations and Functions

Countdown to ECA — WEEK 16

DAY 1

Short Answer What are the solutions of the equation $3x^2 - 6x - 7 = 0$? Show or explain your work.

DAY 2

Which function best represents the data in the table?

x	−2	−1	0	1	2	3
$f(x)$	25	13	5	1	1	5

A. $f(x) = 2x^2 - 6x + 5$

B. $f(x) = -2x^2 - 6x + 8$

C. $f(x) = x^2 - 6x + 5$

D. $f(x) = 2x^2 - 9x + 5$

DAY 3

The graph can be used to determine the solutions to which quadratic equation?

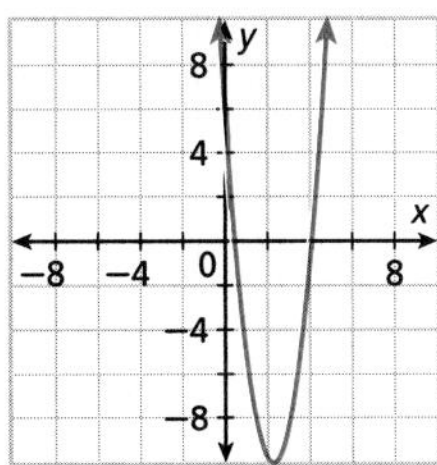

A. $x^2 - 5x + 4 = 0$

B. $3x^2 - 7x + 2 = 0$

C. $3x^2 - 13x + 4 = 0$

D. $3x^2 - 8x + 4 = 0$

DAY 4

Extended Response At the beginning of a basketball game, the referee tosses the ball into the air with an initial velocity of 24 feet per second. The ball's initial height is 5 feet above the floor.

Part A Write an inequality in terms of time t that can be used to find the time interval for which the height of the ball is greater than 10 feet. Show or explain your work.

Part B Solve the inequality. Show or explain your work.

DAY 5

The function $P = -16(c - 25)^2 + 10{,}000$ models the profit the student council makes from a dance, where c is the cost per ticket in dollars. How does the graph of the function change if the maximum profit is made by selling the tickets for $40?

A. The graph of the function would be reflected over the y-axis.

B. The vertex would change to $(25, 40)$.

C. The vertex would change to $(40, 10{,}000)$.

D. The graph of the function would not change.

Countdown to ECA

Day 1: $\frac{3 \pm \sqrt{30}}{3}$; by the Quadratic Formula, $x = \frac{6 \pm \sqrt{36 - 4(3)(-7)}}{6} = \frac{6 \pm \sqrt{120}}{6} = \frac{6 \pm 2\sqrt{30}}{6} = \frac{3 \pm \sqrt{30}}{3}$

Day 2: A

Day 3: C

Day 4:
Part A: $-16t^2 + 24t + 5 > 10$; the height of the ball is given by the equation $h(t) = -16t^2 + 24t + 5$. The inequality $-16t^2 + 24t + 5 > 10$ represents the time when the height is greater than 10 feet.

Part B: $0.25 < t < 1.25$; the graph of the function $h(t) = -16t^2 + 24t + 5$ is above the graph of $h = 10$ over the interval $0.25 < t < 1.25$.

Day 5: C

Day	Indiana's Core Standards for Mathematics Algebra II
1	3. Quadratic Equations and Functions
2	3. Quadratic Equations and Functions
3	3. Quadratic Equations and Functions
4	3. Quadratic Equations and Functions
5	3. Quadratic Equations and Functions

Countdown to ECA

Day 1:
Part A:

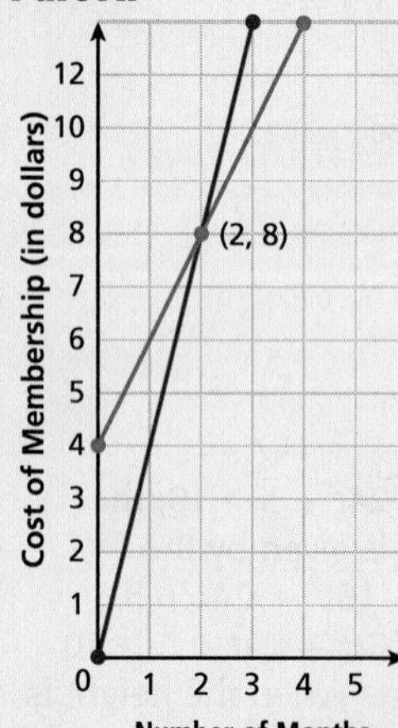

Part B: Monthly memberships; Monthly memberships cost \$12 by the third month, whereas annual memberships cost \$10.

Part C: Annual memberships: The cost of annual memberships changes from $g(x) = 2x + 4$ to $g(x) = 3x + 4$. Annual memberships cost \$40 by the twelfth month, whereas monthly memberships cost \$48.

Day 2: A

Day 3: A

Day 4: 105; $\frac{7!}{1!2!4} = 105$

Day 5: C

Countdown to ECA — WEEK 17

DAY 1

Extended Response The Rowing Club offers both monthly and annual memberships. Monthly memberships are described by the cost function $f(x) = 4x$, whereas annual memberships are described by $g(x) = 2x + 4$. The cost (in dollars) is dependent on x month(s) of membership.

Part A Graph both $f(x)$ and $g(x)$.

Part B Based on the graph, which type of membership is more expensive by the third month?

Part C By increasing the monthly rate of annual memberships to \$3 per month, which type of membership is more cost effective for one year? Show or explain your work.

DAY 2

In chemistry, $pH = -\log[H^+]$, where $[H^+]$ is the hydrogen ion concentration of a solution in moles per liter. What is $[H^+]$ of a carbonated soda if its pH is 1.5?

A. $10^{-1.5}$

B. $10^{1.5}$

C. $-\log 1.5$

D. $-\log(-1.5)$

DAY 3

For which of the following equations does y vary inversely with x?

A. $xy = 17$

B. $y = 3x^4 - 2$

C. $\frac{y}{x} = 24$

D. $y = x + 1$

DAY 4

Short Answer Wilson has 1 quarter, 2 dimes, and 4 pennies in his pocket. What is the number of distinguishable permutations of the coins in Wilson's pocket? Show or explain your work.

DAY 5

The graph represents which parent function?

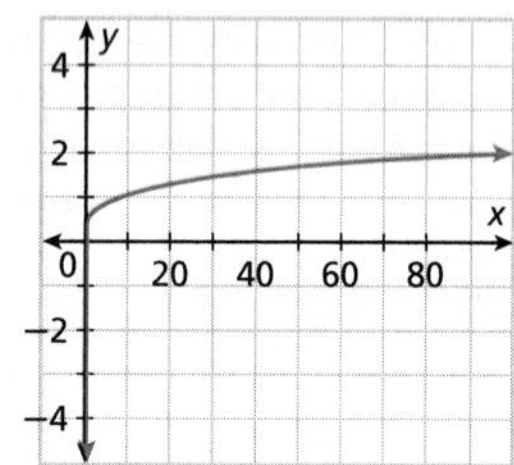

A. $y = x^2$

B. $y = x$

C. $y = \log x$

D. $y = e^x$

Day	Indiana's Core Standards for Mathematics Algebra II
1	1. Linear and Absolute Value Equations and Inequalities
2	6. Exponential and Logarithmic Equations
3	5. Rational Functions
4	8. Combinatorics and Probability
5	6. Exponential and Logarithmic Equations

Countdown to ECA — WEEK 18

DAY 1

Short Answer What is the sum of $(2x^6 + 7x^2 + 1) + (x^6 - 5x^2 - 3)$?

Show or explain your work.

DAY 2

Which ordered pair is NOT a solution of the exponential inequality shown in the graph?

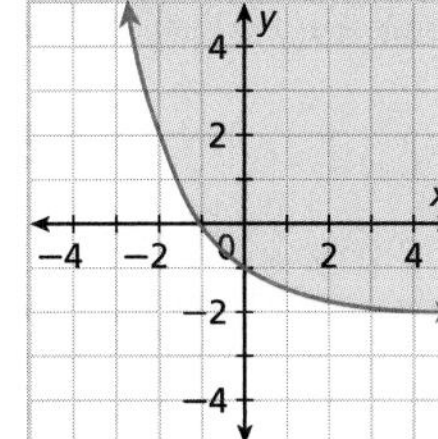

A. (2, −2)

B. (5, 1)

C. (3, 3)

D. (0, 4)

DAY 3

Extended Response Utilize the table below to answer the following questions.

x	−1	0	2
y	10	7	13

Part A What is the quadratic function for the graph that passes through the given points? Show or explain your work.

Part B Determine the value of y when $x = 5$.

DAY 4

Which function represents the graph of $f(x) = \ln x$ translated 2 units right and 5 units up?

A. $g(x) = \ln(x + 2) - 5$

B. $g(x) = \ln(x + 5) - 2$

C. $g(x) = \ln(x - 2) + 5$

D. $g(x) = \ln(x - 5) + 2$

DAY 5

Which of the following is equivalent to $-\frac{2}{3m} \div \frac{12}{9n}$?

A. $-\frac{n}{2m}$

B. $-\frac{24}{27mn}$

C. $\frac{8}{9mn}$

D. $\frac{-2m}{n}$

Countdown to ECA

Day 1: $3x^6 + 2x^2 - 2$;
$(2x^6 + 7x^2 + 1) + (x^6 - 5x^2 - 3) =$
$2x^6 + x^6 + 7x^2 - 5x^2 + 1 - 3 =$
$3x^6 - 2x^2 - 2$

Day 2: A

Day 3:
Part A: $y = 2x^2 - x + 7$
From the table, you can determine that the y-intercept of the quadratic function is 7. Now substitute the coordinates (−10, 10) and (2, 13) into the quadratic function.
For (−1, 10),
$10 = a(-1)^2 + b(-1) + 7$
$10 = a - b + 7$
$3 = a - b$
For (2, 13),
$13 = a(2)^2 + b(2) + 7$
$13 = 4a + 2b + 7$
$6 = 4a + 2b$
$3 = 2a + b$
Now solve the first equation for a.
$a = 3 + b$
Substitute into the second equation and solve for b.
$3 = 2(3 + b) + b$
$3 = 6 + 2b + b$
$3 = 6 + 3b$
$-3 = 3b$
$b = -1$
$a = 3 - b = 2$
$y = 2x^2 - x + 7$
Now solve for a.
$a = 3 - 1 = 2$
$y = 2x^2 - x + 7$

Part B: 52

Day 4: C

Day 5: A

Day	Indiana's Core Standards for Mathematics Algebra II
1	4. Polynomial Equations and Functions
2	6. Exponential and Logarithmic Equations
3	3. Quadratic Equations and Functions
4	6. Exponential and Logarithmic Equations
5	5. Rational Functions

Countdown to ECA

Day 1:
Part A: $f(x) = \frac{1}{2}(4)^x$;
Substitute the points (1, 2) and (3, 32) into $f(x) = ab^x$.
For (1, 2),
$2 = ab$
For (3, 32),
$32 = ab^3$
Now use a proportion to solve for b.
$\frac{2}{32} = \frac{ab}{ab^3}$
$\frac{1}{16} = \frac{1}{b^2}$
$b^2 = 16$
$b = 4$
Solve for a using $2 = ab$.
$2 = a4$
$a = \frac{1}{2}$
$f(x) = \frac{1}{2}(4)^x$
Part B: 8192

Day 2: 15;
$x(x - 11) = 60$
$x^2 - 11x - 60 = 0$
$(x + 4)(x - 15) = 0$
$x + 4 = 0$
$x = -4$
$x - 15 = 0$
$x = 15$
Since length of the rectangle is a positive number, then $x = 15$.
Day 3: C
Day 4: C
Day 5: B

Countdown to ECA — WEEK 19

DAY 1

Extended Response

Part A Find the exponential function $f(x) = ab^x$ whose graph passes through the points (1, 2) and (3, 32). Show or explain your work.

Part B What is $f(7)$?

DAY 2

Short Answer The area of the rectangle is 60. What is the value of x? Show or explain your work.

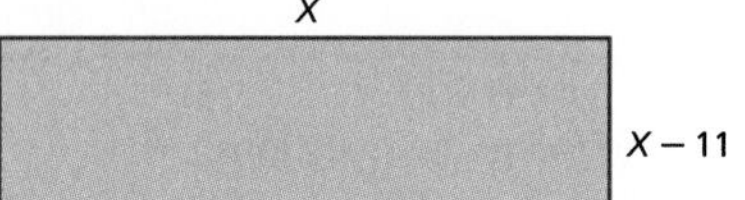

DAY 3

A value of a car that cost $20,000 when new decreases at a rate of 5% each year. What is the value of the car after 4 years?

A. $4,000
B. $16,000
C. $16,290
D. $19,600

DAY 4

Simplify: $4(p^3 - 2p^2) + 5(-3p^2 - 6)$.

A. $4p^3 - 17p^2 - 6$
B. $p^3 - 11p^2 - 30$
C. $4p^3 - 23p^2 - 30$
D. $4p^3 - 11p^2 - 6$

DAY 5

Look at the sequence below.

115, 104, 93, 82, ...

What is the 10th term of the sequence?

A. 27
B. 16
C. –6
D. –17

Day	Indiana's Core Standards for Mathematics Algebra II
1	6. Exponential and Logarithmic Equations
2	3. Quadratic Equations and Functions
3	6. Exponential and Logarithmic Equations
4	4. Polynomial Equations and Functions
5	7. Sequences and Series

Countdown to ECA — WEEK 20

DAY 1

Short Answer What is the value of x given that $\log(x^3 - 21x) - \log(x) = 2$? Show or explain your work.

DAY 2

Extended Response Martha invested \$12,000 and earned \$840 in interest in one year. She invested some of the money in an account that pays 8% per year and the rest of it in an account that pays 5% per year.

Part A Write a system of equations and solve it to find the amount she invested at each rate.

Part B How much would Martha have had to invest at each rate to have earned \$960 in interest?

DAY 3

The Richter scale measures earthquakes using the equation $R = 0.67\log(0.37E) + 1.46$, where R is the Richter magnitude and E is the energy (in kilowatt-hours) released. How much energy is released in an earthquake with a Richter scale measure of 4.5?

A. about 2950 kilowatt-hours

B. about 34,400 kilowatt-hours

C. about 93,100 kilowatt-hours

D. about 101,000 kilowatt-hours

DAY 4

Which function represents a reflection of $f(x) = 2^x$ across the y-axis?

A. $g(x) = -2^x$ **B.** $g(x) = \left(\frac{1}{2}\right)^x$

C. $g(x) = 2^{-x}$ **D.** $g(x) = \left(\frac{1}{x}\right)^2$

DAY 5

Which equation is equivalent to $12^{-x} = 24$?

A. $\log_{24} 12 = x$ **B.** $\log_x 24 = 12$

C. $\log_{12} 24 = -x$ **D.** $\log_{-x} 12 = 24$

Countdown to ECA

Day 1: $x = 11$;

$\log(x^3 - 21x) - \log(x) = 2$

$\log \frac{x^3 - 21x}{x} = 2$

$\log x^2 - 21 = 2$

$10^{\log x^2 - 21} = 10^2$

$x^2 - 21 = 100$

$x^2 = 121$

$x = 11$

Day 2:

Part A: \$8000 at 8% and \$4000 at 5%;

$$\begin{cases} x + y = 12{,}000 \\ 0.08x + 0.05y = 840 \end{cases}$$

Multiply the second expression by -20 to get $-1.6x - y = -16{,}800$. Combine with the second equation to get $-0.6x = -4800$. Divide both sides by -0.6 to get $x = 8000$. Substitute 8000 for x into the first equation and solve to get $y = 4000$.

Part B: \$12,000 at 8% and \$0 at 5%;

$$\begin{cases} x + y = 12{,}000 \\ 0.08x + 0.05y = 960 \end{cases}$$

Multiply the second expression by -20 to get $-1.6x - y = -19{,}200$. Combine with the second equation to get $-0.6x = -7200$. Divide both sides by -0.6 to get $x = 12{,}000$.

Day 3: C

Day 4: B

Day 5: C

Day	Indiana's Core Standards for Mathematics Algebra II
1	6. Exponential and Logarithmic Equations
2	1. Linear and Absolute Value Equations and Inequalities
3	6. Exponential and Logarithmic Equations
4	6. Exponential and Logarithmic Equations
5	6. Exponential and Logarithmic Equations

Countdown to ECA

Day 1:
Part A: 17

Part B: arithmetic; there is a common difference of 4.

Part C: $a_n = 4n - 3$;
$a_n = a_1 + (n - 1)d$
Substitute $a_1 = 1$ and $d = 4$;
$a_n = 1 + (n - 1)4$.
Simplify; $a_n = 1 + 4n - 4 = 4n - 3$

Day 2: B

Day 3: 512
$a_n = a_1r^{n-1}$
$a_2 = a_1r^{2-1}$
$8 = 2r$
$r = 4$
$a_n = 2(4)^{n-1}$
$a_2 = 2(4)^{5-1}$
$a_5 = 2(4)^4 = 512$

Day 4: B
Day 5: A

Countdown to ECA — WEEK 21

DAY 1

Extended Response Use the following sequence to answer the parts below.

1, 5, 9, 13, . . .

Part A What is the next term in this sequence?

Part B Identify the sequence as arithmetic or geometric and include how you came to that conclusion.

Part C Write a rule to find the *n*th term of the sequence.

DAY 2

Which function represents a translation of $f(x) = 2^x$ six units right?

A. $g(x) = 2^x - 6$

B. $g(x) = 2^{x-6}$

C. $g(x) = 2^x + 6$

D. $g(x) = 2^{x+6}$

DAY 3

Short Answer The second term of a geometric sequence is 8 and the first term is 2. What is the fifth term? Show or explain your work.

DAY 4

Find a rule for the *n*th term of the following arithmetic sequence.

$a_3 = 40$, $a_5 = 62$, $a_8 = 95$, $a_{11} = 128$

A. $a_n = 8(n + 5)$

B. $a_n = 11n + 7$

C. $a_n = 10(8n + 0.5)$

D. $a_n = 14n - 2$

DAY 5

Which quadratic function is represented by the graph?

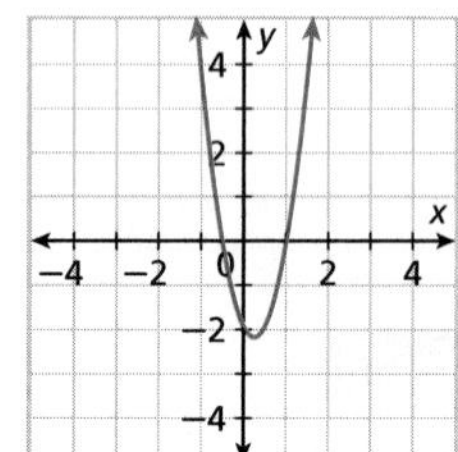

A. $f(x) = 4x^2 - 2x - 2$

B. $f(x) = x^2 - 2$

C. $f(x) = (x + 1)(x - 1)$

D. $f(x) = (x - 2)^2 - 2$

Day	Indiana's Core Standards for Mathematics Algebra II
1	7. Sequences and Series
2	6. Exponential and Logarithmic Equations
3	7. Sequences and Series
4	7. Sequences and Series
5	3. Quadratic Equations and Functions

Countdown to ECA — WEEK 22

DAY 1

Find a rule for the *n*th term of the following geometric sequence.

$a_2 = 21, a_5 = 567, a_7 = 5103, a_{10} = 137{,}781$

A. $a_n = \frac{44 - n}{n}$

B. $a_n = 81(7)^{n-1}$

C. $a_n = 63(81)^n$

D. $a_n = 7(3)^{n-1}$

DAY 2

Extended Response Bobby is on a biking trip that consists of 55 miles on paved roads and 18 miles on unpaved roads. He is able to bike twice as fast on paved roads as unpaved roads.

Part A Write a funcation that represents the total time in hours $T(x)$ that Bobby needs to complete the trip in terms of his average speed on unpaved roads x in miles per hour. Show or explain your work.

Part B Rewrite the function in the form of an inverse variation function $T(x) = \frac{k}{x}$, where k is the constant of variation. Describe the relationship of Bobby's speed on unpaved roads to the total time T.

DAY 3

Which of the following represents the series $\frac{3}{4} + \frac{9}{16} + \frac{27}{64} + \frac{81}{256} + \frac{243}{768}$?

A. $\sum_{i=1}^{\infty}\left(\frac{1}{4}\right)^i$

B. $\sum_{i=1}^{\infty}\left(\frac{1}{4}\right)^{i+1}$

C. $\sum_{i=1}^{5}\left(\frac{3}{4}\right)^i$

D. $\sum_{i=1}^{5}\left(\frac{3}{4}\right)^{i+1}$

DAY 4

Short Answer An arithmetic sequence has a sixth term of 27 and common difference of 3. What is the second term of the sequence? Show or explain your work.

DAY 5

What is the relationship between the graph of the function $y = x^2 - 4x$ and the graph of its inverse?

A. Reflection across the line $y = x$

B. Translation of 4 units down

C. 180° rotation about the origin

D. Vertical stretch by a factor of 4

Countdown to ECA

Day 1: D

Day 2:

Part A: $T(x) = \frac{55}{2x} + \frac{18}{x}$;

let x be Bobby's speed on unpaved roads. Then the time it takes him to ride 18 miles on unpaved roads is $\frac{18}{x}$. His speed on paved roads is twice as fast, or $2x$. So the time it takes him to ride 55 miles on paved roads is $\frac{55}{2x}$. Thus, the total length of time for the trip is $T(x) = \frac{55}{2x} + \frac{18}{x}$.

Part B: $T(x) = \frac{45.5}{x}$;

$T(x) = \frac{27.5}{x} + \frac{18}{x} = \frac{45.5}{x}$, so the constant of variation is 45.5. Thus, the total length of time of his trip in hours is 45.5 times his speed on unpaved roads in miles per hour.

Day 3: C

Day 4: $a_2 = 15$;

$a_n = a_1 + (n - 1)d$

$a_6 = a_1 + (6 - 1)(3)$

$27 = a_1 + (5)(3)$

$27 = a_1 + 15$

$a_1 = 12$

$a_n = 12 + (n - 1)(3)$

$a_n = 12 + 3n - 3$

$a_n = 9 + 3n$

$a_2 = 9 + 3(2) = 9 + 6 = 15$

Day 5: A

Day	Indiana's Core Standards for Mathematics Algebra II
1	7. Sequences and Series
2	5. Rational Functions
3	7. Sequences and Series
4	7. Sequences and Series
5	3. Quadratic Equations and Functions

Countdown to ECA

Day 1: $\sum_{i=1}^{6} 3i + 5$; The difference between each term of the series is three.

Day 2: A

Day 3: A

Day 4:

Part A: $f(x) = \frac{1}{(x-3)(x+3)}$; the only values of x that would make the denominator equal to 0 are −3 and 3, so the domain of f is all real numbers except −3 and 3.

Part B: $g(x) = \sqrt{9 - x^2}$; the domain of the function is all values of x for which $9 - x^2 \geq 0$. Subtract x^2 from both sides to get $9 \geq x^2$. This inequality is true for all values of x between −3 and 3, so the domain of g is $-3 \leq x \leq 3$.

Day 5: B

Countdown to ECA — WEEK 23

DAY 1

Short Answer Represent the following arithmetic series by writing it using sigma notation. Show or explain your work.

$8 + 11 + 14 + 17 + 20 + 23$

DAY 2

A tennis player uses a racket 4 feet off the ground to hit a tennis ball directly upward with an initial vertical velocity of 20 feet per second. Which expression shows how long the ball will be in the air before hitting the ground?

A. $\frac{-20 + \sqrt{656}}{-32}$ seconds

B. $\frac{-20 + \sqrt{656}}{-32}$ seconds

C. $\frac{-20 + \sqrt{244}}{-32}$ seconds

D. $\frac{-20 + \sqrt{244}}{-32}$ seconds

DAY 3

The first four terms of a sequence are

6561, 2187, 729, 243, ...

Find the explicit and recursive rules for the given sequence.

A. $a_n = 6561\left(\frac{1}{3}\right)^{n-1}$

$a_1 = 6561,\ a_n = \frac{1}{3}a_{n-1}$

B. $a_n = 6561 - 2187^{n-1}$

$a_1 = 6561,\ a_n = \frac{1}{9}a_{n-1}$

C. $a_n = 243\ (3)^n$

$a_1 = 243,\ a_n = 3a_{n-1}$

D. $a_n = 243^n + 729^{n-1}$

$a_1 = 243,\ a_n = 3a_{n-1}$

DAY 4

Extended Response

Part A Write an equation of a function whose domain is all real numbers except −3 and 3. Show or explain your work.

Part B Write an equation of a function whose domain is $-3 \leq x \leq 3$. Show or explain your work.

DAY 5

What is the rule for the nth term of the sequence?

4, 8, 16, 32, ...

A. $a_1 = 4,\ a_n = a_{n-1} + 4$

B. $a_1 = 4,\ a_n = 2a_{n-1}$

C. $a_1 = 4,\ a_n = 4a_{n-1}$

D. $a_1 = 4,\ a_n = a_{n-1}$

Day	Indiana's Core Standards for Mathematics Algebra II
1	7. Sequences and Series
2	8. Combinatorics and Probability
3	7. Sequences and Series
4	5. Rational Functions
5	7. Sequences and Series

Countdown to ECA WEEK 24

DAY 1

Which graph can be used to determine the solution of $x^2 = \sqrt{2x}$?

A.
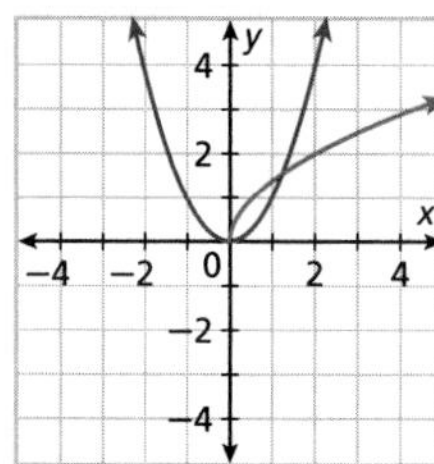

B.
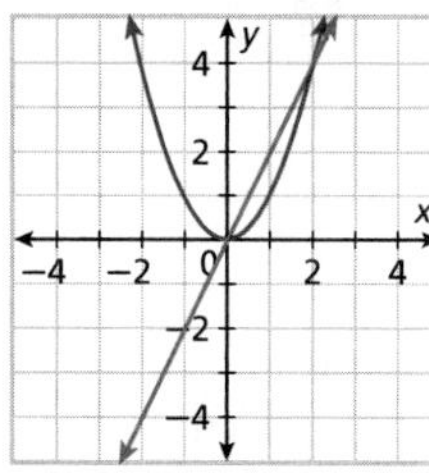

C.
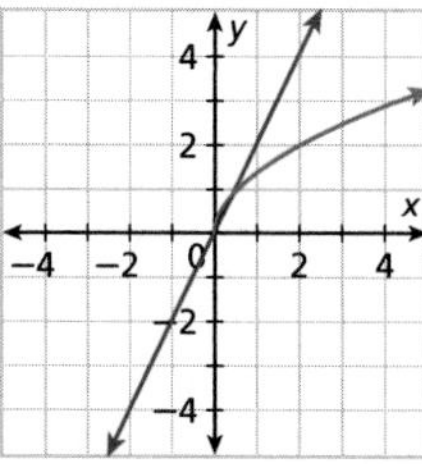

D.
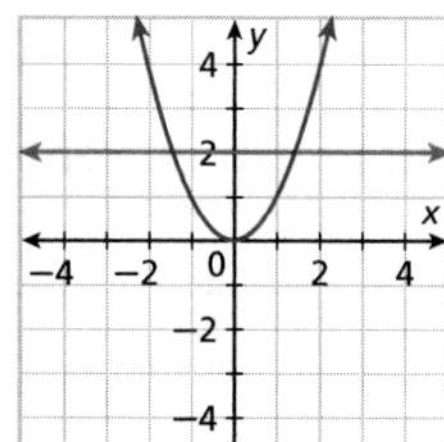

DAY 2

Find the sum of the geometric series $\sum_{i=1}^{4} 3\left(\frac{1}{4}\right)^{i-1}$.

A. $\frac{255}{64}$

B. $\frac{85}{64}$

C. $\frac{3}{256}$

D. $\frac{81}{256}$

DAY 3

The population of Warren County is 55,000 and is growing at a rate of 3.8% per decade. Which of the following expressions represents the population of Warren County after n decades?

A. $55{,}000(3.8)^n$

B. $55{,}000(1.38)^n$

C. $55{,}000(1.038)^n$

D. $55{,}000 + (3.8)^n$

DAY 4

Short Answer What value of x makes the equation $3 = 1 + \log(2x)$ true? Show or explain your work.

DAY 5

Extended Response Consider the following sequence.

27, 9, 3, 1, ...

Part A What is the rule for the nth term of the sequence? Show or explain your work.

Part B Find the 8th term of the sequence.

COUNTDOWN TO ECA

Day 1: A

Day 2: A

Day 3: C

Day 4: 50; subtract 1 from both sides to get $2 = \log(2x)$. Write in exponential form as $10^2 = 2x$. Divide both sides by 2 to get $50 = x$.

Day 5:

Part A: $a_n = 27\left(\frac{1}{3}\right)^{n-1}$;
The sequence is a geometric sequence with a common ratio of $\frac{1}{3}$ and first term of 27.

Part B: $\frac{1}{81}$; $a_8 = 27\left(\frac{1}{3}\right)^{8-1} = 27\left(\frac{1}{3}\right)^7 = 27\left(\frac{1}{2187}\right) = \frac{1}{81}$

Day	Indiana's Core Standards for Mathematics Algebra II
1	3. Quadratic Equations and Functions
2	7. Sequences and Series
3	6. Exponential and Logarithmic Equations
4	6. Exponential and Logarithmic Equations
5	7. Sequences and Series

Math Testing and Critical Thinking Skills

What Are Critical Thinking Skills?

Critical thinking skills are not a new phenomenon on the education scene. In 1956, Benjamin Bloom published a book that listed critical thinking skills in the form of a taxonomy as shown in the illustration below.

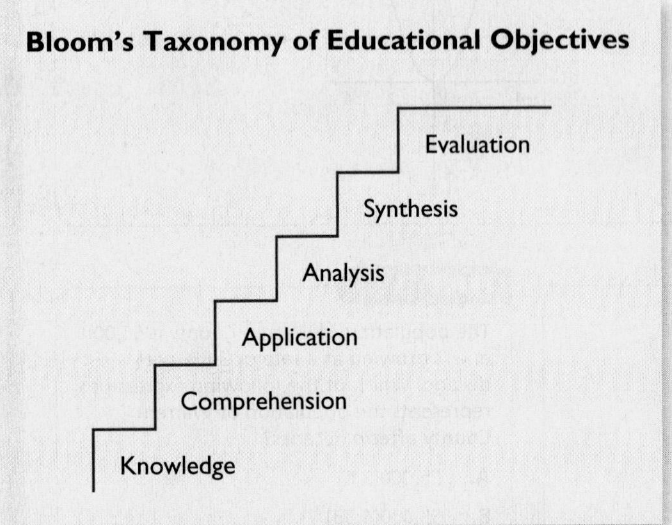

- **Knowledge** is the simplest level of education objectives and is not considered a higher-order thinking skill. It requires the learner to remember information without having to fully understand it. Tasks that students perform to demonstrate knowledge are recalling, identifying, recognizing, citing, labeling, listing, reciting, and stating.

EXAMPLES

1. *What is the formula for the area of a trapezoid?*
2. *What quadrant is the point (2, −6) located in?*
3. *What is the reciprocal of* $\frac{2}{3}$*?*

IN34

- **Comprehension** is not considered a higher-order thinking skill either. Learners demonstrate comprehension when they paraphrase, describe, summarize, illustrate, restate, or translate. Information isn't useful unless it's understood. Students can show they've understood by restating the information in their own words or by giving an example of the concept.

  EXAMPLES

  1. *Explain the difference between the points (4, 5) and (5, 4).*
  2. *Interpret the information in the graph below.*
  3. *Give an example of an irrational number.*

Many teachers tend to focus the most on knowledge and comprehension—and the tasks performed at these levels are important because they provide a solid foundation for the more complex tasks at the higher levels of Bloom's pyramid.

However, offering students the opportunity to perform at still higher cognitive levels provides them with more meaningful contexts in which to use the information and skills they have acquired, thus allowing them to more easily retain what they have learned.

When teachers incorporate **application, analysis, synthesis,** and **evaluation** as objectives, they allow students to utilize **higher-order thinking skills.**

- **Application** involves solving, transforming, determining, demonstrating, and preparing. Information becomes useful when students apply it to new situations—predicting outcomes, estimating answers—this is application.

  EXAMPLES

  1. *Organize the forms of pollution from most damaging to least damaging.*
  2. *Using the scale of 1 inch equals 200 miles, determine the point-to-point distance between Boston and Atlanta.*
  3. *Put the information below into a bar graph.*

- **Analysis** includes classifying, comparing, making associations, verifying, seeing cause-and-effect relationships, and determining sequences, patterns, and consequences. You can think of analysis as taking something apart in order to better understand it. Students must be able to think in categories in order to analyze.

EXAMPLES

1. *What math skills do you use when reading a circle graph?*
2. *Use the function table to write a rule for y in terms of x.*
3. *How can you use the LCM of 3 and 5 to find the sum of* $\frac{1}{3}$ *and* $\frac{1}{5}$*?*

- **Synthesis** requires generalizing, predicting, imagining, creating, making inferences, hypothesizing, making decisions, and drawing conclusions. Students create something which is new to them when they use synthesis. It's important to remember, though, that students can't create until they have the skills and information they have received in the comprehension through analysis levels.

EXAMPLES

1. *Make a scale drawing of your classroom.*
2. *Write a word problem that can be represented by the equation* $3 + y = 5$*.*
3. *Poll your classmates about their favorite breakfast food and display your results in an appropriate graph.*

- **Evaluation** involves assessing, persuading, determining value, judging, validating, and solving problems. Evaluation is based on all the other levels. When students evaluate, they make judgments, but not judgments based on personal taste. These judgments must be based on criteria. It is important for students to evaluate because they learn to consider different points of view and to know how to validate their judgments.

EXAMPLES

1. *Which of the following describes the correct way to round* $-3\frac{7}{8}$*?*
2. *Based on the ratios of protein to serving size and fat to serving size, which muffin do you think is healthier? Explain.*
3. *Do you think the statistics given in the article are accurate? Why or why not?*

IN36

Why is it Important for Students to Work with Higher-Order Thinking Skills?

For one thing, if students can determine the levels of questions that will appear on their tests, they will be able to study using appropriate strategies. Bloom's leveling of questions provides a useful structure in which to categorize test questions, since tests will characteristically ask questions within particular levels.

Also, thinking is a skill that can be taught. When you have students practice answering questions at all the levels of Bloom's taxonomy, you are helping to scaffold their learning. Information just becomes trivia unless that information is understood well enough to build more complicated concepts or generalizations. When students can comprehend—not just recall—the information, it becomes useful for future problem solving or creative thought. Think of information as a building material—like a board. It could be used to build something, but it is just useless litter unless you understand how to make use of it.

Below are some question stems you—or your students—could use to create questions for each of the levels of higher-order thinking:

Application

1. Make a diagram to show ________.
2. Use (a formula, manipulatives, mental math, a problem solving strategy, etc.) to find ________.
3. (Find, determine, calculate, compute, etc.) ________.
4. Explain how the (principle, theorem, concept) is evident in ________.
5. In what way is ________ a ______?

Analysis

1. Which (strategies, operations, etc.) would you use to solve this problem?
2. Find a pattern in ____________.
3. What other (properties, rules, definitions) are similar? Explain.
4. Compare and contrast ____________.
5. How does the value of ________ affect the value of ________?

IN37

Synthesis

1. Write a problem that can be solved by _________ .
2. Use information in (your science book, a newspaper article, etc.) to write a problem.
3. Create a new way to classify ______.
4. Design your own _______to show ______.
5. Create a new way to _________.

Evaluation

1. Is (an answer, an estimate, etc.) reasonable? Explain.
2. Do you have enough information to solve this problem?
3. Which _______ best represents _________?
4. Which solution method (is most efficient, is most accurate, gives the most information, etc.)?
5. What is the important information in this problem?

IN38

Gridded-Response Questions

Some questions require you to place your answer in a special grid. This type of question is called "gridded response" and may be identified by a special logo on your test. Answers to these questions may be whole numbers, fractions, or decimals.

Work the problem and find an answer. Then write your answer in the grid provided. There is often more than one correct way to write your answer in the response grid.

When filling in your grid, make your marks heavy and dark. Fill in the circles completely, but do not shade outside the circles. Do not make any stray marks on or outside of your grid.

If your answer does not fit in the grid, you may need to write your answer in another form. If your answer still does not fit, read the question again. Be sure that you understand the problem. Check your work for possible errors.

Sample Question

A bowl of fruit contains 3 oranges, 4 apples, and 3 bananas. If Amy chooses 1 piece of fruit at random, what is the probability that she will choose an apple?

Sample Correct Answers

Write your answer in the answer boxes at the top of the grid.

Fill in the corresponding circle under each box.

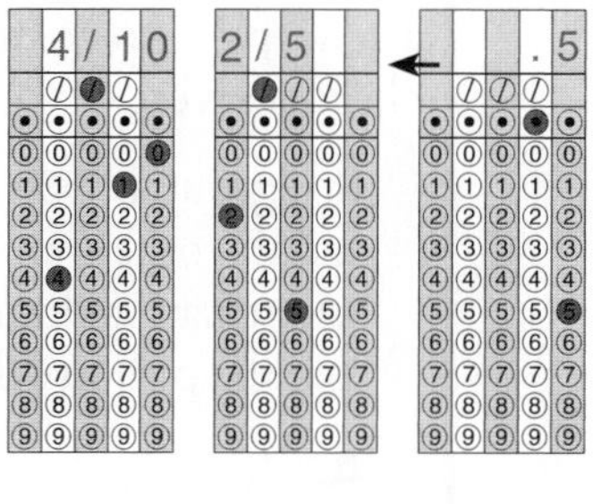

4/10   2/5   .5

Write a decimal point or fraction bar in the answer boxes if it is part of your answer. Shade the decimal point or fraction bar circle below this answer box.

Notice in the sample answers above that you may write your answers as either fractions or decimals. However, you may **not** write mixed numbers, such as $13\frac{1}{4}$, in a response grid. If you tried to fill in $13\frac{1}{4}$, it would be read as $\frac{131}{4}$ and would be counted as wrong. If your answer is a mixed number, write it as an improper fraction $\left(\frac{53}{4}\right)$ or as a decimal (13.25) before filling in your grid.

IN39

Multiple-Choice Questions

The most common type of test question is multiple choice.

To answer questions on a multiple-choice test, you will most likely fill in an answer sheet. It is very important to fill in your answer sheet correctly. When shading in circles, make your marks heavy and dark. Fill in the circles completely, but do not shade outside the circles. Do not make any stray marks on your answer sheet.

Questions on a multiple-choice test may require an understanding of number and operations, algebra, geometry, measurement, and data analysis and probability. Drawings, grids, or charts may be included for certain types of questions.

Read each question carefully and work the problem. You may be allowed to use blank space in the test booklet to write your calculations. Choose your answer from among the answer choices given, and fill in the corresponding circle on your answer sheet.

If your answer is not one of the choices, read the question again. Be sure that you understand the problem. Check your work for possible errors.

Sample Question

Try the following practice question to prepare for taking a multiple-choice test. Choose the best answer from the choices given.

In a group of 30 students, 27 are middle school students, and the others are high school students. If one person is selected at random from this group, what is the probability that the person selected will be a high school student?

A. $\frac{1}{30}$

B. $\frac{1}{10}$

C. $\frac{3}{10}$

D. $\frac{9}{10}$

IN40

Think About the Solution

First consider the total number of people in the group (30). If 27 out of 30 are middle school students, how many are high school students? (3) If one person is selected at random, there is a probability of 3 out of 30 that the person will be a high school student. This can be written as a ratio (3:30), a fraction $\left(\frac{3}{30}\right)$, a decimal (0.1), or a percent (10%). None of these solutions is listed as one of the choices, so you must look for a solution that is equivalent. The fraction $\frac{3}{30}$ can be simplified to $\frac{1}{10}$. Since $\frac{1}{10}$ is given as one of your answer choices, B is the correct response.

Indicate your response by filling in the circle that contains B.

Test-Taking Tip

Sometimes you can find the best solution to a test question by understanding what is wrong with some of the choices. Read the sample question again. Why are A, C, and D incorrect?

Response A is $\frac{1}{30}$. You might think A is correct because there are 30 people and you are selecting 1. However, this answer indicates that only 1 of the 30 people is a high school student. Since that is not what the problem states, A cannot be correct.

Response C is $\frac{3}{10}$. This answer indicates that 3 out of 10 people are high school students. The numerator is correct, since there are three high school students in the group. However, the denominator must show the relationship 3 out of 30. C is not correct.

Response D is $\frac{9}{10}$. If you chose D, read the problem again. The problem asks you to find the probability that a high school student will be selected. Answer D would be the best choice if you wanted to find the probability that a *middle school student* will be selected, but D does not match the question that was asked.

IN41

Foundations for Functions

Tools for Success

A2.1.1 Find the zeros, domain and range of a function.
A2.1.2 Use and interpret function notation, including evaluation of functions represented by tables, graphs, words, equations or a set of ordered pairs.

Linear Functions

Tools for Success

A2.1.2 Use and interpret function notation, including evaluation of functions represented by tables, graphs, words, equations or a set of ordered pairs.

A2.2.4 Solve equations and inequalities involving absolute value of a linear function.

Linear Systems

Tools for Success

Reading Math 191
Writing Math 181, 188, 196, 203, 210, 217, 225
Vocabulary 179, 180, 186, 194, 202, 209, 216, 232

Know-It Notes 184, 206, 220
Graphic Organizers 185, 194, 201, 208, 216, 224
Homework Help Online 186, 194, 202, 209, 216, 224

Test Prep Exercises 188–189, 196–197, 203–204, 211, 218, 226
Multi-Step Test Prep 188, 196, 203, 210, 212, 217, 225, 228
College Entrance Exam Practice 237
Test Tackler 238
ECA Test Prep 240

IN46

A2.2.1 Solve systems of equations and inequalities in three variables by substitution and elimination.

Matrices

CHAPTER 4

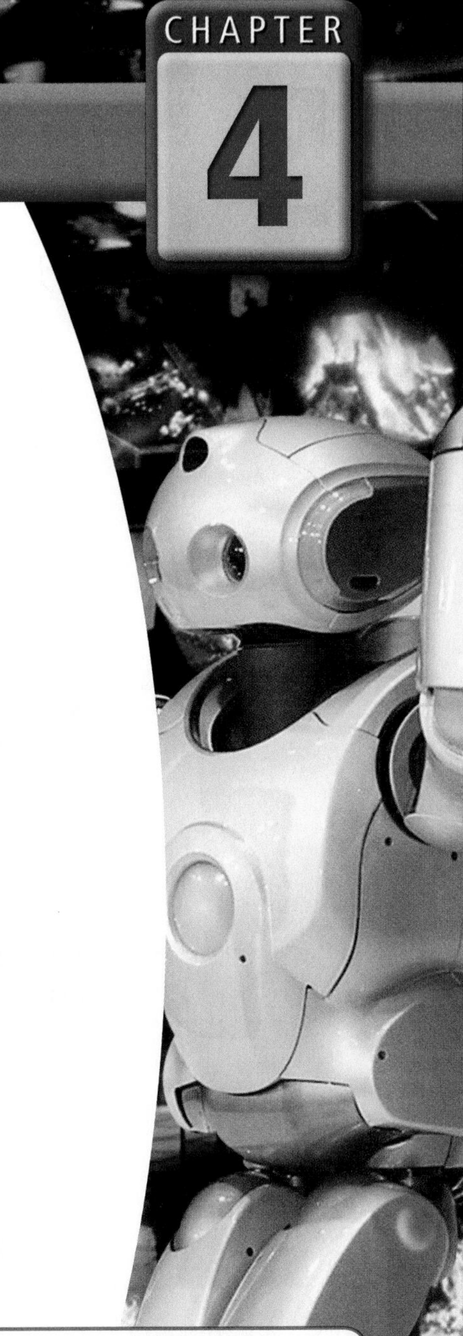

Tools for Success

A2.2.2 Solve problems that can be modeled using systems of linear equations up to three variables, interpret the solutions, and determine whether the solutions are reasonable.

CHAPTER 5

Quadratic Functions

go.hrw.com
Online Resources
KEYWORD: MB7 TOC

Tools for Success

Reading Math 334, 341, 367, 375

Writing Math 321, 329, 339, 347, 354, 362, 372, 380, 388

Vocabulary 311, 312, 320, 328, 338, 345, 353, 361, 370, 377, 386, 392

Study Strategy 313

Know-It Notes 315, 316, 317, 318, 319, 323, 324, 326, 327, 334, 336, 337, 341, 342, 343, 344, 350, 352, 356, 358, 360, 366, 370, 377, 382, 385

Graphic Organizers 319, 327, 337, 344, 351, 352, 360, 370, 377, 385

Homework Help Online 320, 328, 338, 345, 353, 361, 370, 377, 386

Test Prep Exercises 322, 330, 340, 347–348, 355, 363, 373, 381, 389

Multi-Step Test Prep 321, 329, 339, 347, 354, 362, 364, 372, 378, 388, 390

College Entrance Exam Practice 397

Test Tackler 398

ECA Test Prep 400

IN48

A2.1.1 Find the zeros, domain and range of a function.
A2.3.1 Define, add, subtract, multiply and divide complex numbers. Represent complex numbers, and the addition, subtraction and absolute value of complex numbers, in the complex plane.
A2.3.2 Solve quadratic equations in the complex number system.
A2.3.3 Analyze, describe, and sketch graphs of quadratic functions including the lines of symmetry.
A2.3.5 Solve problems that can be represented modeled using quadratic equations and functions, interpret the solutions, and determine whether the solutions are reasonable.

Polynomial Functions

CHAPTER 6

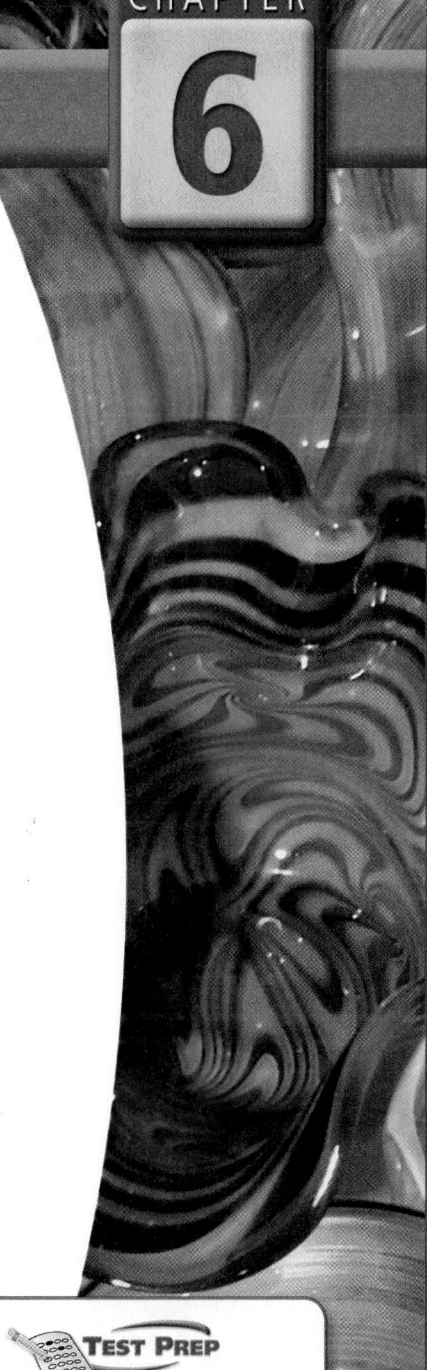

Tools for Success

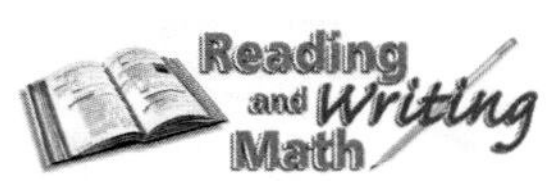

IN49

A2.1.2 Use and interpret function notation, including evaluation of functions represented by tables, graphs, words, equations or a set of ordered pairs.
A2.4.1 Analyze, describe and sketch graphs of polynomial functions by examining intercepts, zeros, domain and range and end behavior.
A2.4.3 Perform arithmetic operations, including long division and division with remainders, on polynomials by others of equal or lower degree.
A2.4.4 Factor polynomials completely and solve polynomial equations by factoring.
A2.4.6 Solve problems that can be represented or modeled using polynomial equations, interpret the solutions, and determine whether the solutions are reasonable.
A2.4.7 Find a polynomial function of lowest degree with real coefficients given its roots and use the relationship between solutions of an equation, zeros of a function, x-intercepts of a graph and factors of a polynomial expression to solve problems.

CHAPTER 7

go.hrw.com
Online Resources
KEYWORD: MB7 TOC

Exponential and Logarithmic Functions

Tools for Success

Reading Math 489, 505
Writing Math 489, 495, 503, 510, 518, 527, 535, 543, 550
Vocabulary 487, 488, 493, 501, 509, 526, 534, 548, 554

Know-It Notes 506, 512, 513, 514, 532, 537, 538
Graphic Organizers 493, 501, 508, 515, 525, 533, 541, 547
Homework Help Online 493, 501, 509, 516, 526, 534, 541, 548

Test Prep Exercises 495–496, 503–504, 510–511, 519, 528, 536, 544, 550
Multi-Step Test Prep 494–495, 502–503, 510, 517–518, 520, 527–528, 535, 543, 550, 552
College Entrance Exam Practice 559
Test Tackler 560
ECA Test Prep 562

IN50

A2.1.1 Find the zeros, domain and range of a function.
A2.1.2 Use and interpret function notation, including evaluation of functions represented by tables, graphs, words, equations or a set of ordered pairs.
A2.6.1 Analyze, describe and sketch graphs of exponential functions by examining intercepts, zeros, domain and range, and asymptotic and end behavior.
A2.6.2 Know that the inverse of an exponential function is a logarithm, use laws of exponents to derive laws of logarithms, and use the inverse relationships between exponential functions and logarithms, and the laws of logarithms to solve problems.
A2.6.3 Solve exponential and logarithmic equations.
A2.6.4 Solve problems that can be modeled using exponential and logarithmic equations, interpret the solutions and determine whether the solutions are reasonable using technology as appropriate.

Rational and Radical Functions

CHAPTER 8

Tools for Success

IN51

A2.5.1 Analyze, describe and sketch graphs of rational functions by examining intercepts, zeros, domain and range, and asymptotic and end behavior.
A2.5.2 Add, subtract, multiply, divide, reduce and evaluate rational expressions with polynomial denominators. Simplify rational expressions, including expressions with negative exponents in the denominator.
A2.5.3 Understand the properties of rational exponents and use the properties to simplify, multiply, divide, and find powers of expressions containing negative and fractional exponents. Relate expressions containing rational exponents to the corresponding radical expressions.
A2.5.4 Analyze, describe and sketch graphs of square root and cube root functions by examining intercepts, zeros, domain and range and end behavior.
A2.5.5 Solve equations that contain radical expressions and identify extraneous roots when they occur.
A2.5.6 Solve problems that can be modeled using equations involving rational and radical functions, including problems of direct and inverse variation. Interpret the solutions, and determine whether the solutions are reasonable.

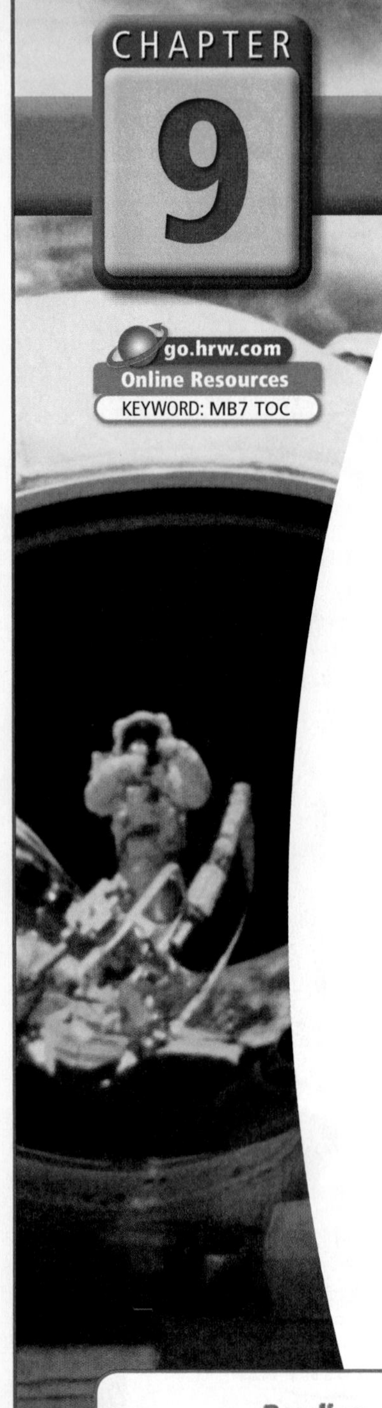

Properties and Attributes of Functions

Tools for Success

A2.1.2 Use and interpret function notation, including evaluation of functions represented by tables, graphs, words, equations or a set of ordered pairs.
A2.2.3 Graph piecewise-defined functions.

Conic Sections

Tools for Success

Probability and Statistics

Tools for Success

A2.4.2 Use the binomial theorem to expand binomial expressions raised to positive integer powers.
A2.8.2 Determine the probability of simple events involving independent and dependent events and conditional probability. Analyze probabilities to interpret odds and risk of events.
A2.8.3 Use permutations, combinations, and other counting methods to determine the number of ways that events can occur and to calculate probabilities including the probability of compound events.

Sequences and Series

Tools for Success

A2.7.1 Write the recursive formula for arithmetic and geometric sequences and find specific terms of arithmetic and geometric sequences.

A2.7.2 Write the formula for the general term for arithmetic and geometric sequences and make connections to linear and exponential functions.

A2.7.3 Find partial sums of arithmetic and geometric series.

Trigonometric Functions

Tools for Success

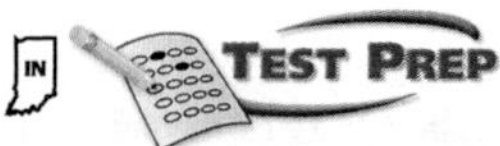

Trigonometric Graphs and Identities

Tools for Success

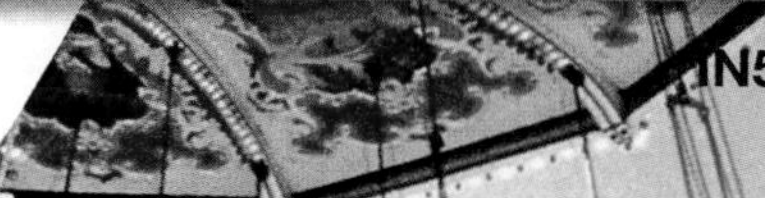

A2.1.2 Use and interpret function notation, including evaluation of functions represented by tables, graphs, words, equations or a set of ordered pairs.

How to Study Algebra 2

This book has many features designed to help you learn and study effectively. Becoming familiar with these features will prepare you for greater success on your exams.

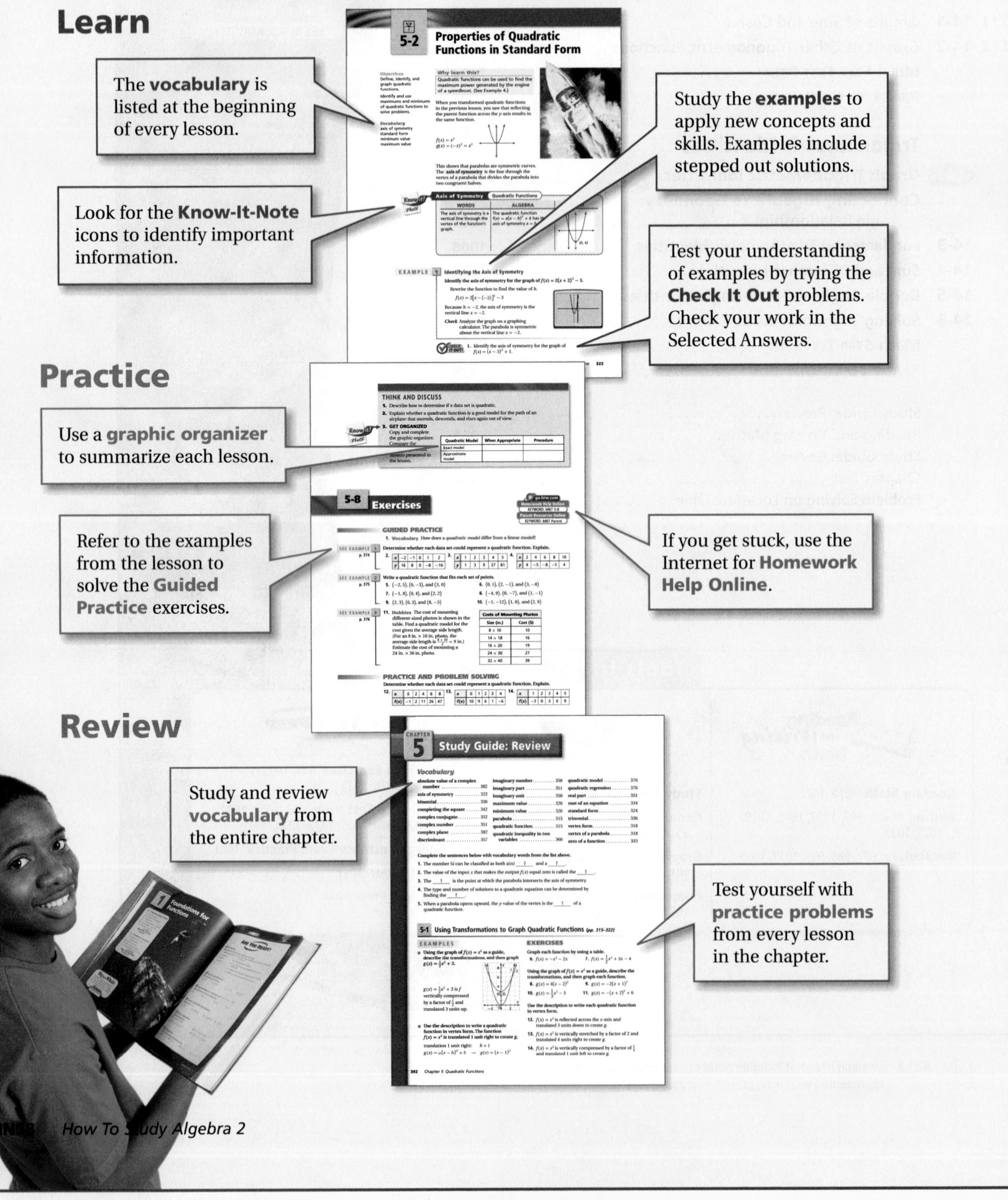

Learn
The vocabulary is listed at the beginning of every lesson.
Study the examples to apply new concepts and skills. Examples include stepped out solutions.
Look for the Know-It-Note icons to identify important information.
Test your understanding of examples by trying the Check It Out problems. Check your work in the Selected Answers.
Practice
Use a graphic organizer to summarize each lesson.
Refer to the examples from the lesson to solve the Guided Practice exercises.
If you get stuck, use the Internet for Homework Help Online.
Review
Study and review vocabulary from the entire chapter.
Test yourself with practice problems from every lesson in the chapter.
5-2 Properties of Quadratic Functions in Standard Form
5-8 Exercises
Chapter 5 Study Guide: Review

Focus on Problem Solving

The Problem Solving Plan

Mathematical problems are a part of daily life. You need to use a good problem-solving plan to be a good problem solver. The plan used in this textbook is outlined below.

UNDERSTAND the Problem

You must first make sure you understand the problem you are asked to solve.

- **What are you asked to find?** Restate the question in your own words.
- **What information is given?** Identify the key facts given in the problem.
- **What information do you need?** Determine which facts are needed to answer the question.
- **Do you have all the information needed?** Determine if you need further information.
- **Do you have too much information?** Determine if there is unnecessary information and eliminate it from your list of key facts.

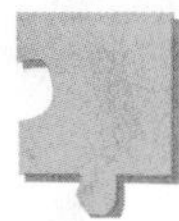

Make a PLAN

Plan how to use the information you are given.

- **What problem solving strategy would best fit this problem?** Choose an appropriate problem solving strategy and decide how you will use it.
- **Have you solved similar problems?** Think about similar problems you have solved successfully.

SOLVE

Use your plan to solve the problem. Show the steps in the solution. Write a final statement that gives the solution to the problem.

LOOK BACK

Check your answer against the original problem.

- **Have you answered the original question?** Make sure you have answered the original question.
- **Is the answer reasonable?** The answer must make sense in relation to the question.
- **Are your calculations correct?** Check to make sure your calculations are accurate.
- **Can you use another strategy or solve the problem in another way?** Using another strategy is a good way to check your answer.

Who Uses Mathematics?

The Career Path features are a set of interviews with young adults who are either preparing for or just beginning in different career fields. These people share what math courses they studied in high school, how math is used in their field, and what options the future holds. Also, many exercises throughout the book highlight the different skills used in various career fields.

Career Path

go.hrw.com
Career Resources Online
KEYWORD: MB7 Career

Career Applications

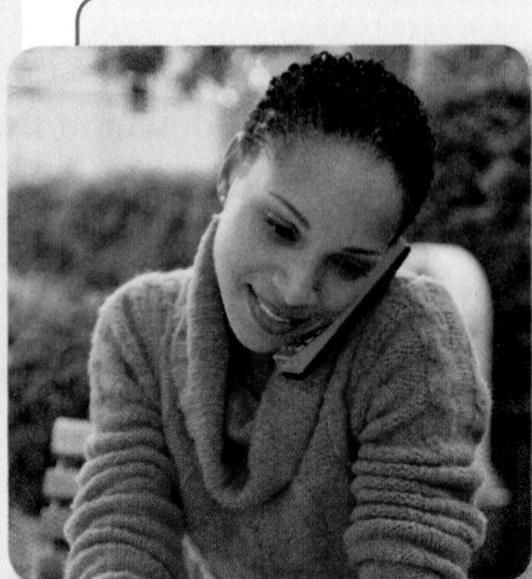

ECONOMIST *p. 277*
Economists help people prepare for the future by analyzing political and business trends and data, and then making predictions. Look on page 277 to learn about the type of training you need for this career path.

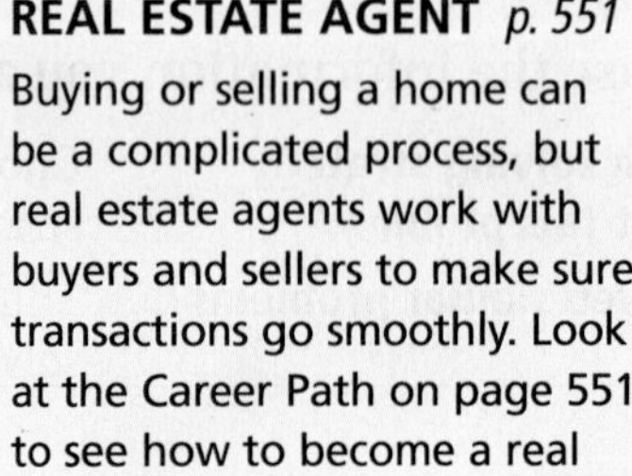

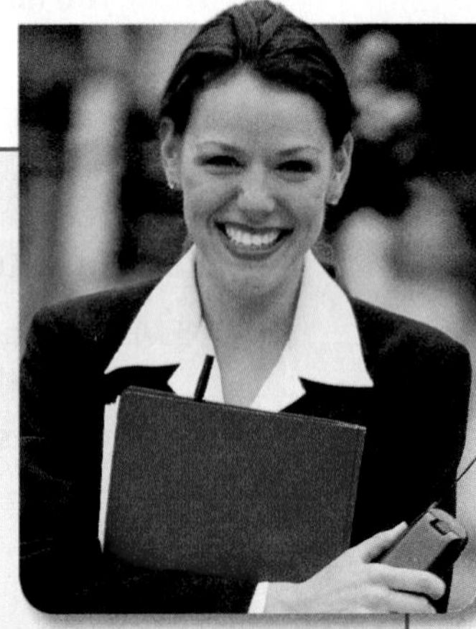

REAL ESTATE AGENT *p. 551*
Buying or selling a home can be a complicated process, but real estate agents work with buyers and sellers to make sure transactions go smoothly. Look at the Career Path on page 551 to see how to become a real estate agent.

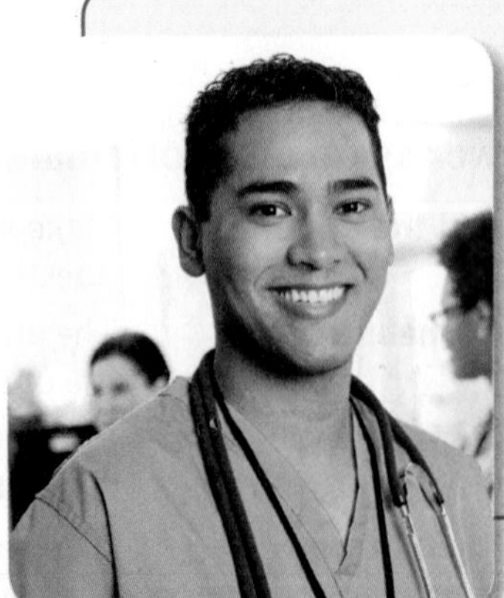

NURSING STUDENT *p. 877*
The demand for nurses is expected to increase in the future because doctors and patients alike depend on their assistance and expertise. The Career Path on page 877 describes what it is like to be a nursing student.

IN60

Focus on Problem Solving

The Problem Solving Plan

Mathematical problems are a part of daily life. You need to use a good problem-solving plan to be a good problem solver. The plan used in this textbook is outlined below.

UNDERSTAND the Problem

You must first make sure you understand the problem you are asked to solve.

- **What are you asked to find?** Restate the question in your own words.
- **What information is given?** Identify the key facts given in the problem.
- **What information do you need?** Determine which facts are needed to answer the question.
- **Do you have all the information needed?** Determine if you need further information.
- **Do you have too much information?** Determine if there is unnecessary information and eliminate it from your list of key facts.

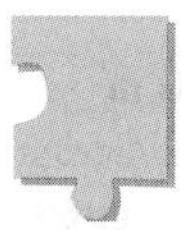

Make a PLAN

Plan how to use the information you are given.

- **What problem solving strategy would best fit this problem?** Choose an appropriate problem solving strategy and decide how you will use it.
- **Have you solved similar problems?** Think about similar problems you have solved successfully.

SOLVE

Use your plan to solve the problem. Show the steps in the solution. Write a final statement that gives the solution to the problem.

LOOK BACK

Check your answer against the original problem.

- **Have you answered the original question?** Make sure you have answered the original question.
- **Is the answer reasonable?** The answer must make sense in relation to the question.
- **Are your calculations correct?** Check to make sure your calculations are accurate.
- **Can you use another strategy or solve the problem in another way?** Using another strategy is a good way to check your answer.

Foundations for Functions

Section 1A: Properties and Operations	Section 1B: Introduction to Functions
1-1 Sets of Numbers	1-6 Relations and Functions
1-2 Properties of Real Numbers	1-7 Function Notation
Connecting Algebra to Geometry The Pythagorean Theorem	1-8 Algebra Lab Chess Translations
1-3 Square Roots	1-8 Exploring Transformations
1-4 Simplifying Algebraic Expressions	1-9 Introduction to Parent Functions
1-5 Technology Lab Explore Negative Exponents	
1-5 Properties of Exponents	

Pacing Guide for 45-Minute Classes

Chapter 1

Countdown to Testing Weeks 1, 2

DAY 1	DAY 2	DAY 3	DAY 4	DAY 5
1-1 Lesson	1-2 Lesson	Connecting Algebra to Geometry 1-3 Lesson	1-3 Lesson 1-4 Lesson	1-4 Lesson 1-5 Technology Lab
DAY 6	**DAY 7**	**DAY 8**	**DAY 9**	**DAY 10**
1-5 Lesson	Multi-Step Test Prep Ready to Go On?	1-6 Lesson	1-7 Lesson	1-8 Algebra Lab 1-8 Lesson
DAY 11	**DAY 12**	**DAY 13**	**DAY 14**	
1-8 Lesson	1-9 Lesson	Multi-Step Test Prep Ready to Go On?	Chapter 1 Test	

Pacing Guide for 90-Minute Classes

Chapter 1

DAY 1	DAY 2	DAY 3	DAY 4	DAY 5
1-1 Lesson 1-2 Lesson	Connecting Algebra to Geometry 1-3 Lesson 1-4 Lesson	1-4 Lesson 1-5 Technology Lab 1-5 Lesson	Multi-Step Test Prep Ready to Go On? 1-6 Lesson	1-7 Lesson 1-8 Algebra Lab 1-8 Lesson
DAY 6	**DAY 7**			
1-8 Lesson 1-9 Lesson	Multi-Step Test Prep Ready to Go On? Chapter 1 Test			

ONGOING ASSESSMENT and INTERVENTION

	DIAGNOSE	PRESCRIBE
Assess Prior Knowledge	**Before Chapter 1**	
	Diagnose readiness for the chapter. ***Are You Ready?*** SE p. 3	Prescribe intervention. ***Are You Ready? Intervention*** Skills 11, 16, 18, 55, 79
Formative Assessment	**Before Every Lesson**	
	Diagnose readiness for the lesson. **Warm Up** TE, every lesson	Prescribe intervention. **Skills Bank** SE pp. S46–S73 **Reteach** CRB, Ch. 1
	During Every Lesson	
	Diagnose understanding of lesson concepts. **Check It Out!** SE, every example **Think and Discuss** SE, every lesson **Write About It** SE, every lesson **Journal** TE, every lesson	Prescribe intervention. **Questioning Strategies** TE, every example **Reading Strategies** CRB, every lesson ***Success for ELL*** pp. 1–18
	After Every Lesson	
	Diagnose mastery of lesson concepts. **Lesson Quiz** TE, every lesson **Alternative Assessment** TE, every lesson **Test Prep** SE, every lesson ***Test and Practice Generator***	Prescribe intervention. **Reteach** CRB, every lesson **Problem Solving** CRB, every lesson **Test Prep Doctor** TE, every lesson ***Homework Help* Online**
	Before Chapter 1 Testing	
	Diagnose mastery of concepts in the chapter. **Ready to Go On?** SE pp. 43, 75 **Multi-Step Test Prep** SE pp. 42, 74 **Section Quizzes** AR pp. 5–6 ***Test and Practice Generator***	Prescribe intervention. ***Ready to Go On? Intervention*** pp. 2–22 **Scaffolding Questions** TE pp. 42, 74
	Before High Stakes Testing 	
	Diagnose mastery of benchmark concepts. **College Entrance Exam Practice** SE p. 81 **Standardized Test Prep** SE pp. 84–85 ***State Test Prep* CD-ROM**	Prescribe intervention. ***College Entrance Exam Practice*** ***State Test Prep Workbook***
Summative Assessment	**After Chapter 1**	
	Check mastery of chapter concepts. **Multiple-Choice Tests (Forms A, B, C)** **Free-Response Tests (Forms A, B, C)** **Performance Assessment** AR pp. 7–20 ***Test and Practice Generator***	Prescribe intervention. **Reteach** CRB, every lesson ***Lesson Tutorial Videos*** Chapter 1
	Check mastery of benchmark concepts. **AYP State Tests** **College Entrance Exams**	Prescribe intervention. ***State Test Prep Workbook*** ***College Entrance Exam Practice***

KEY: **SE** = *Student Edition* **TE** = *Teacher's Edition* **CRB** = *Chapter Resource Book* **AR** = *Assessment Resources*  Available on CD-ROM  Available online

CHAPTER 1

Supporting the Teacher

Chapter 1 Resource Book

Practice A, B, C
pp. 3–5, 11–13, 19–21, 27–29, 35–37, 43–45, 51–53, 59–61, 67–69

Reading Strategies ELL
pp. 10, 18, 26, 34, 42, 50, 58, 66, 74

Reteach
pp. 6–7, 14–15, 22–23, 30–31, 38–39, 46–47, 54–55, 62–63, 70–71

Problem Solving
pp. 9, 17, 25, 33, 41, 49, 57, 65, 73

Challenge
pp. 8, 16, 24, 32, 40, 48, 56, 64, 72

Parent Letter pp. 1–2

Transparencies

Lesson Transparencies, Volume 1 .... Chapter 1
- Teaching Tools
- Warm Ups
- Teaching Transparencies
- Additional Examples
- Lesson Quizzes

Alternate Openers: Explorations 1–9

Countdown to Testing 1–4

Know-It Notebook .... Chapter 1
- Graphic Organizers

Teacher Tools

Power Presentations®
Complete PowerPoint® presentations for Chapter 1 lessons

Lesson Tutorial Videos®
Holt authors Ed Burger and Freddie Renfro present tutorials to support the Chapter 1 lessons.

One-Stop Planner®
Easy access to all Chapter 1 resources and assessments, as well as software for lesson planning, test generation, and puzzle creation

IDEA Works!®
Key Chapter 1 resources and assessments modified to address special learning needs

Lesson Plans .... pp. 1–9

Solutions Key .... Chapter 1

Algebra Posters

TechKeys

Lab Resources

Project Teacher Support

Parent Resources 

Workbooks

Homework and Practice Workbook
Teacher's Guide .... Chapter 1

Know-It Notebook
Teacher's Guide .... pp. 5–35

Problem Solving Workbook
Teacher's Guide .... pp. 1–9

State Test Prep
Teacher's Guide

Technology Highlights for the Teacher

Power Presentations

Dynamic presentations to engage students. Complete PowerPoint® presentations for every lesson in Chapter 1.

2-1 Solving One-Step Equations

Isolate a variable by using inverse operations which "undo" operations on the variable.

An equation is like a balanced scale. To keep the balance, perform the same operation on both sides.

Inverse Operations	
Operation	**Inverse Operation**
Addition	Subtraction
Subtraction	Addition

One-Stop Planner

Easy access to Chapter 1 resources and assessments. Includes lesson-planning, test-generation, and puzzle-creation software.

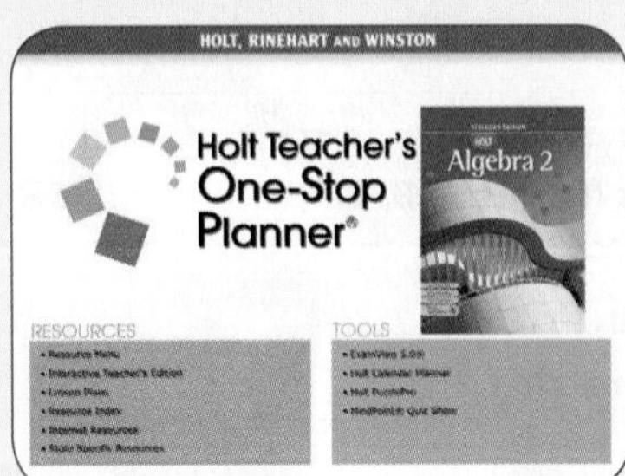

Premier Online Edition

Chapter 1 includes Tutorial Videos, Lesson Activities, Lesson Quizzes, Homework Help, and Chapter Project.

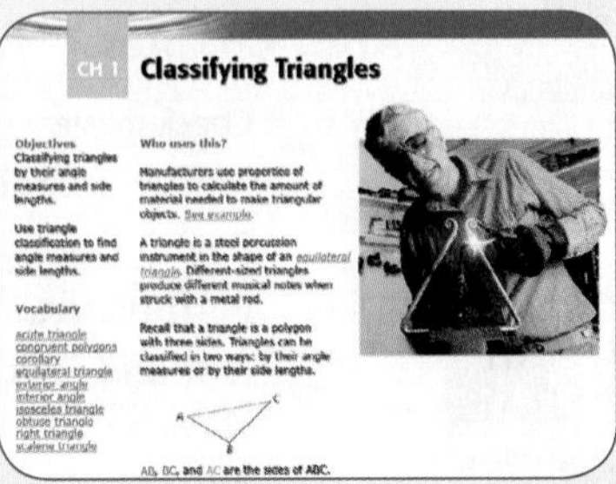

KEY: **SE** = *Student Edition* **TE** = *Teacher's Edition*  = English Language Learners  Available on CD-ROM 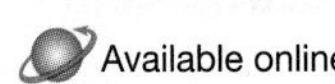 Available online

Reaching All Learners

Resources for All Learners

Algebra Lab Activities .... Chapter 1
Technology Lab Activities .... Chapter 1
Homework and Practice Workbook .... pp. 1–9
Know-It Notebook .... Chapter 1
Problem Solving Workbook .... pp. 1–9

DEVELOPING LEARNERS

Practice A .... CRB, every lesson
Reteach .... CRB, every lesson
Inclusion .... TE p. 45
Questioning Strategies .... TE, every example
Modified Chapter 1 Resources .... *IDEA Works!*
Homework Help Online

ON-LEVEL LEARNERS

Practice B .... CRB, every lesson
Multiple Representations .... TE pp. 18, 45
Modeling .... TE pp. 22, 60

ADVANCED LEARNERS

Practice C .... CRB, every lesson
Challenge .... CRB, every lesson
Reading and Writing Math EXTENSION .... TE p. 5
Multi-Step Test Prep EXTENSION .... TE pp. 42, 74
Critical Thinking .... TE p. 29

English Language Learners

ENGLISH LANGUAGE LEARNERS

***Are You Ready?* Vocabulary** .... SE p. 3
Vocabulary Connections .... SE p. 4
Lesson Vocabulary .... SE pp. 6, 21, 34, 44, 51, 59, 67
Vocabulary Exercises .... SE pp. 10, 24, 38, 47, 54, 63, 70
Vocabulary Review .... SE p. 76
English Language Learners .. TE pp. 5, 7, 8, 9, 22, 35, 37, 45, 64
Reading Strategies .... CRB, every lesson
Success for English Language Learners .... pp. 1–18
Multilingual Glossary

Reaching All Learners Through...

Inclusion .... TE p. 45
Visual Cues .... TE pp. 20, 69
Auditory Cues .... TE pp. 8, 28, 45, 52
Kinesthetic Experience .... TE pp. 22, 55
Concrete Manipulatives .... TE p. 7
Multiple Representations .... TE pp. 18, 45
Modeling .... TE pp. 22, 60
Cooperative Learning .... TE p. 68
Critical Thinking .... TE p. 29
Test Prep Doctor .... TE pp. 13, 19, 26, 32, 41, 50, 56, 73, 81, 82, 84
Common Error Alerts .... TE pp. 9, 15, 23, 31, 35, 37, 39, 45, 55, 61
Scaffolding Questions .... TE pp. 42, 74

Technology Highlights for Reaching All Learners

Lesson Tutorial Videos

Starring Holt authors Ed Burger and Freddie Renfro! Live tutorials to support every lesson in Chapter 1.

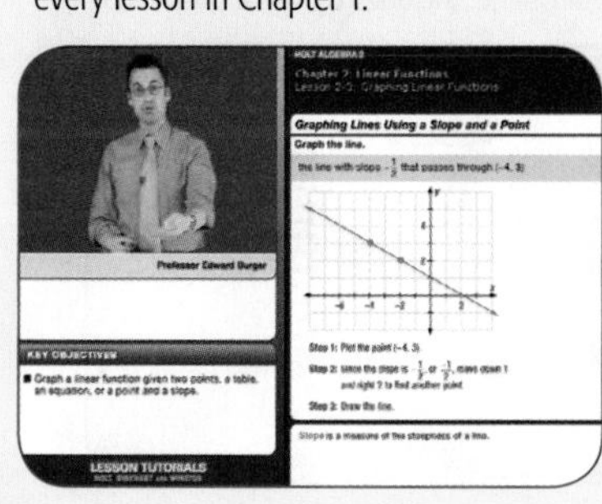

Multilingual Glossary

Searchable glossary includes definitions in English, Spanish, Vietnamese, Chinese, Hmong, Korean, and 4 other languages.

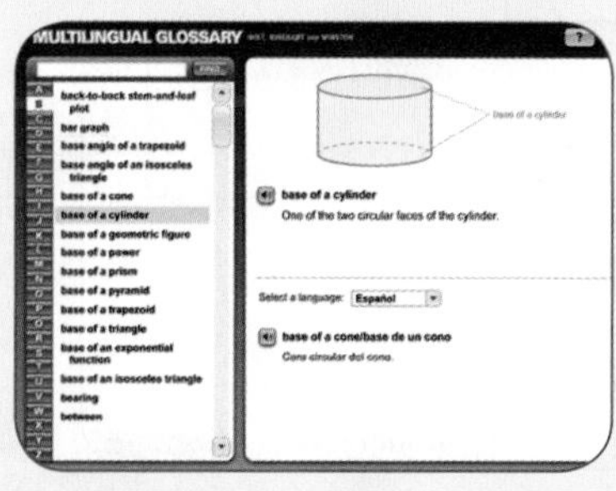

Online Interactivities

Interactive tutorials provide visually engaging alternative opportunities to learn concepts and master skills.

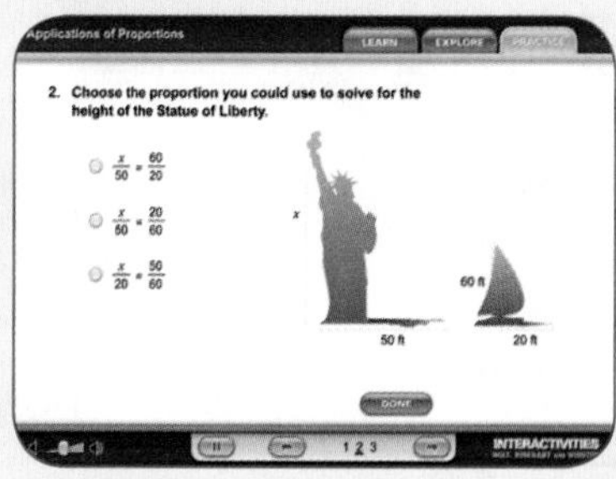

KEY: **SE** = *Student Edition* **TE** = *Teacher's Edition* **CRB** = *Chapter Resource Book* Available on CD-ROM Available online

CHAPTER 1

Ongoing Assessment

Assessing Prior Knowledge

Determine whether students have the required prerequisite concepts and skills for success in Chapter 1.

Are You Ready? SPANISH .... SE p. 3
Warm Up .... TE, every lesson

Test Preparation

Provide review and practice for Chapter 1 and standardized tests.

Multi-Step Test Prep .... SE pp. 42, 74
Study Guide: Review .... SE pp. 76–79
Test Tackler .... SE pp. 82–83
Standardized Test Prep .... SE pp. 84–85
College Entrance Exam Practice .... SE p. 81
***Countdown to Testing* Transparencies** 1–4
State Test Prep Workbook
***State Test Prep* CD-ROM**
IDEA Works!

Alternative Assessment

Assess students' understanding of Chapter 1 concepts and combined problem-solving skills.

Chapter 1 Project .... SE p. 2
Alternative Assessment .... TE, every lesson
Performance Assessment .... AR pp. 19–20
Portfolio Assessment .... AR p. xxxiv

Daily Assessment

Provide formative assessment for each day of Chapter 1.

Questioning Strategies .... TE, every example
Think and Discuss .... SE, every lesson
Check It Out! Exercises .... SE, every example
Write About It .... SE, every lesson
Journal .... TE, every lesson
Lesson Quiz .... TE, every lesson
Alternative Assessment .... TE, every lesson
Modified Lesson Quizzes .... *IDEA Works!*

Weekly Assessment

Provide formative assessment for each week of Chapter 1.

Multi-Step Test Prep .... SE pp. 42, 74
Ready to Go On? .... SE pp. 43, 75
Cumulative Assessment .... SE pp. 84–85
Test and Practice Generator .... *One-Stop Planner*

Formal Assessment

Provide summative assessment of Chapter 1 mastery.

Section Quizzes .... AR pp. 5–6
Chapter 1 Test .... SE p. 80
Chapter Test (Levels A, B, C) .... AR pp. 7–18
• Multiple Choice • Free Response
Cumulative Test .... AR pp. 21–24
Test and Practice Generator .... *One-Stop Planner*
Modified Chapter 1 Test .... *IDEA Works!*

Technology Highlights for Ongoing Assessment

Are You Ready? 

Automatically assess readiness and prescribe intervention for Chapter 1 prerequisite skills.

Ready to Go On?

Automatically assess understanding and prescribe intervention for Sections 1A and 1B.

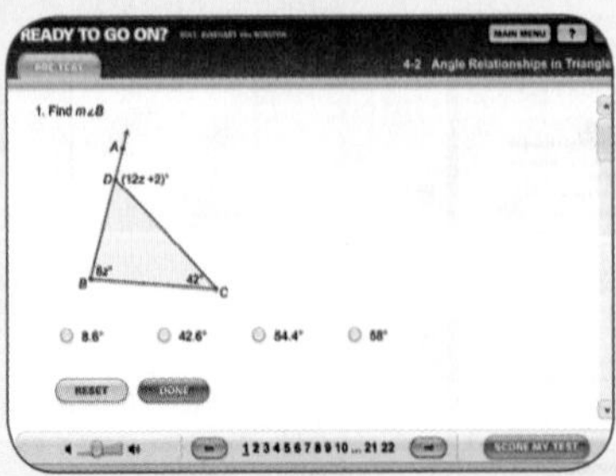

Test and Practice Generator

Use Chapter 1 problem banks to create assessments and worksheets to print out or deliver online. Includes dynamic problems.

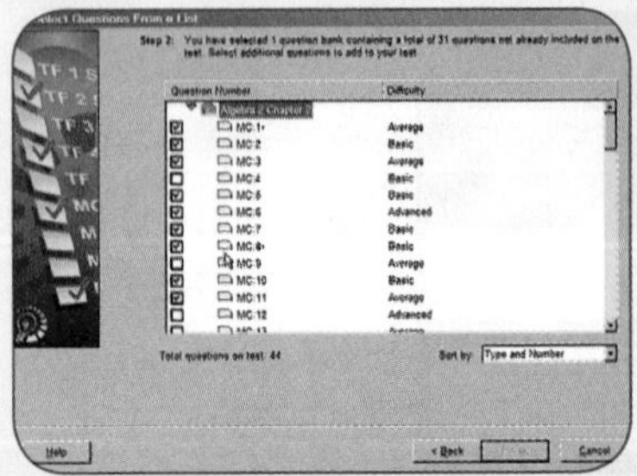

KEY: **SE** = *Student Edition* **TE** = *Teacher's Edition* **AR** = *Assessment Resources* SPANISH Spanish version available; Available on CD-ROM; Available online

CHAPTER 1

Formal Assessment

Three levels (A, B, C) of multiple-choice and free-response chapter tests are available in the *Assessment Resources.*

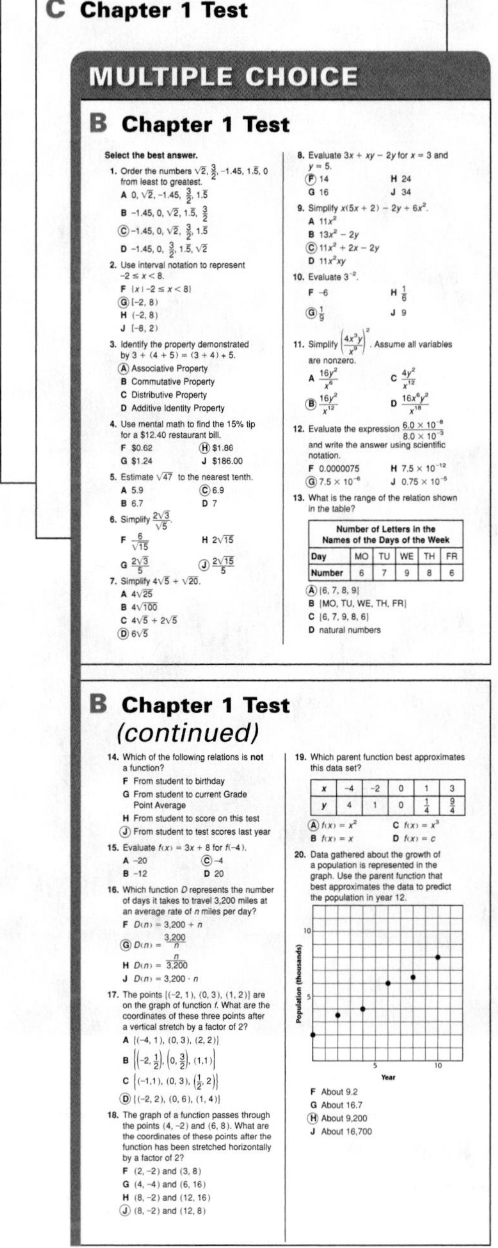

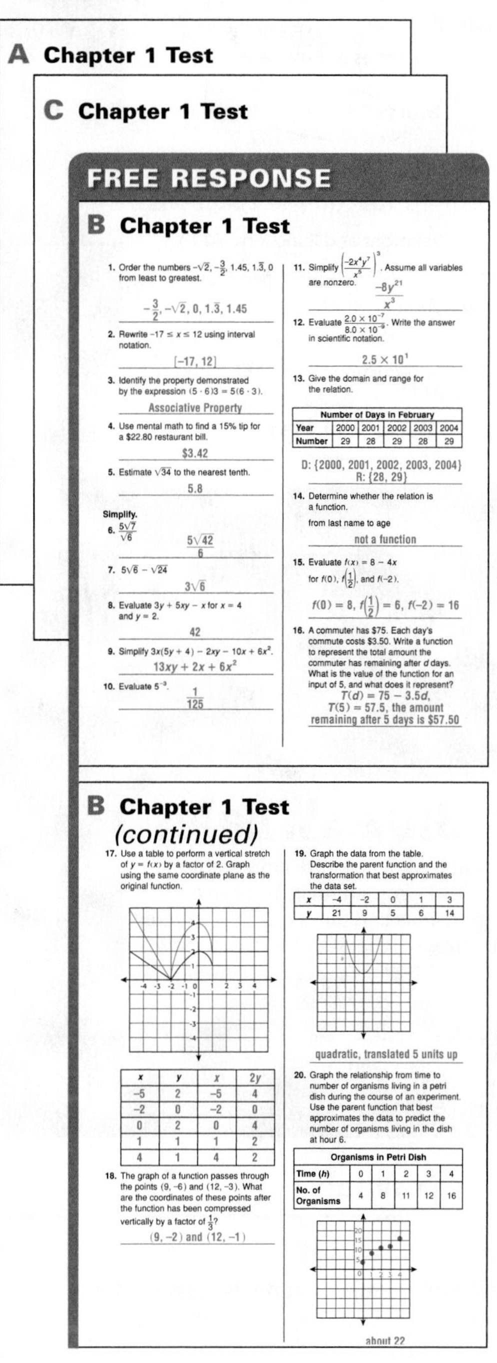

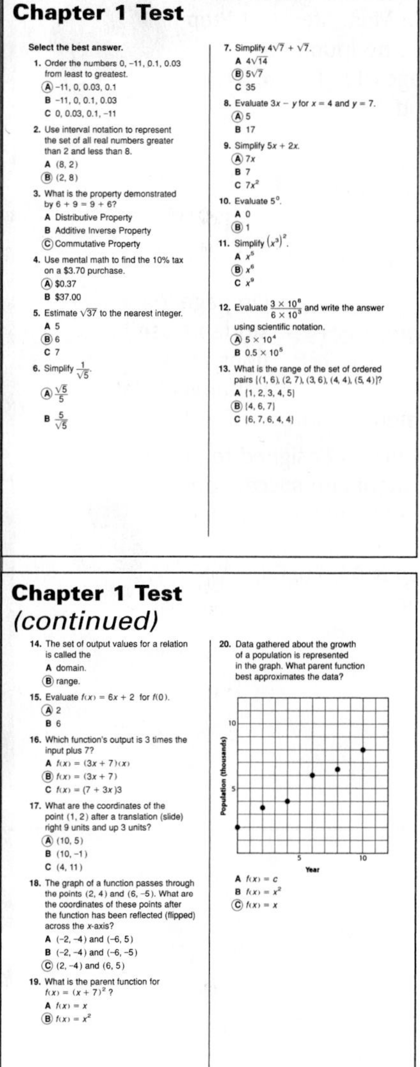

Test & Practice Generator
One-Stop Planner®

Create and customize Chapter 1 Tests. Instantly generate multiple test versions, answer keys, and practice versions of test items.

CHAPTER 1

SECTION 1A
Properties and Operations

On page 42, students use algebraic operations and properties of real numbers to analyze data involving the Moon.

Exercises designed to prepare students for success on the Multi-Step Test Prep can be found on pages 11, 18, 25, 31, and 40.

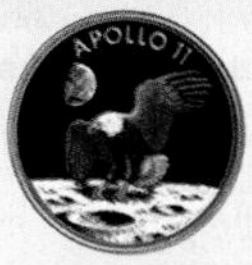

SECTION 1B
Introduction to Functions

On page 74, students use functions to explore patterns in Native American art.

Exercises designed to prepare students for success on the Multi-Step Test Prep can be found on pages 49, 56, 64, and 71.

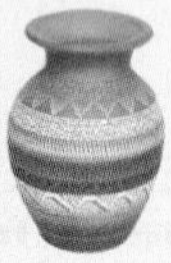

CHAPTER 1

Foundations for Functions

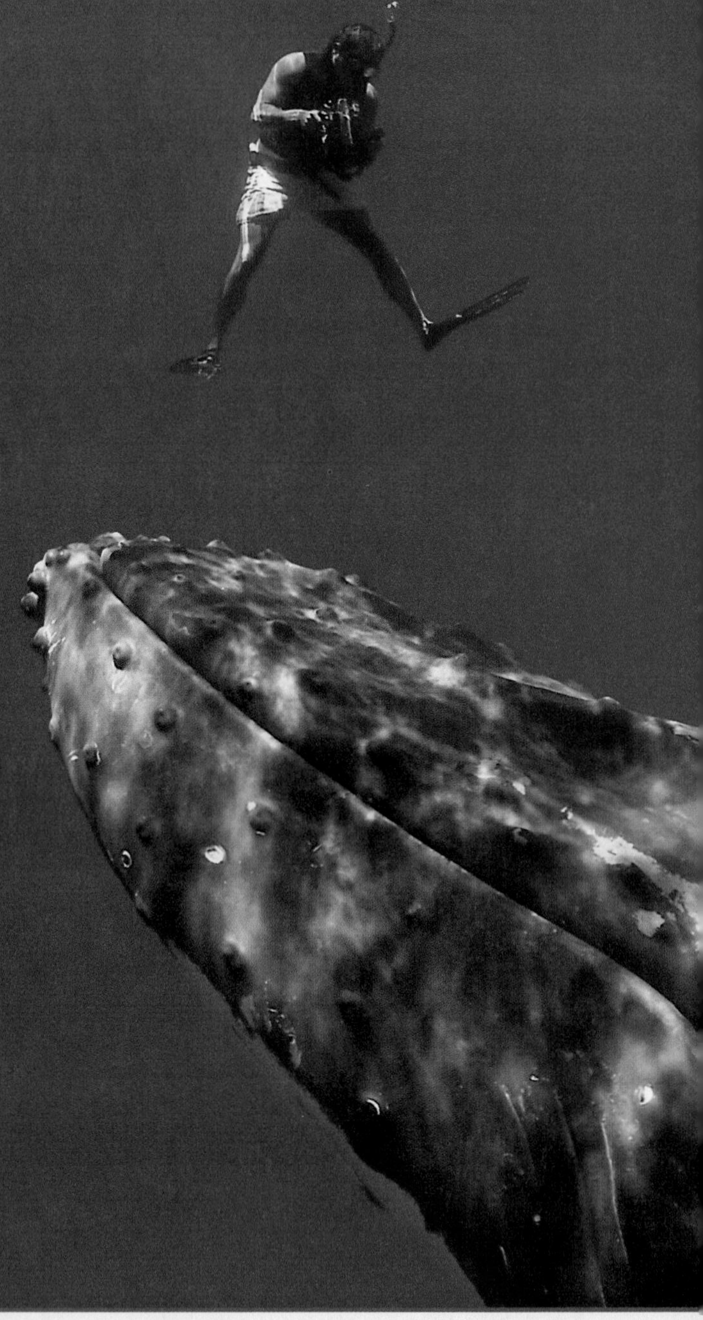

Big as a Whale

Humpback whales are among the world's largest animals. You can use expressions and functions to compare the sizes of whales to various objects.

go.hrw.com
Chapter Project Online
KEYWORD: MB7 ChProj

Big as a Whale

About the Project

In the Chapter Project, students research the sizes of whales, including such measures as length and girth. Students then use the data to write expressions and functions, such as a function for estimating the number of students it would take to hug a whale with a given girth. In addition, students use scientific notation to express measurements related to whales.

Project Resources

All project resources for teachers and students are provided online.

Materials:

- measuring tape or meterstick

ARE YOU READY?

Vocabulary

Match each term on the left with a definition on the right.

1. algebraic expression D
2. opposites C
3. origin A
4. variable E

A. the point in the coordinate plane where the x-axis and the y-axis intersect
B. a value that does not change
C. two numbers that are equal distances from zero on a number line
D. a mathematical phrase that contains one or more variables
E. a symbol that represents a quantity that can change

Fractions and Decimals

Write each fraction as a decimal.

5. $\frac{3}{10}$ 0.3 6. $\frac{3}{5}$ 0.6 7. $-\frac{4}{3}$ $-1.\overline{3}$ 8. $5\frac{3}{4}$ 5.75

Graph Numbers on a Number Line

Graph each number on the same number line.

9. 3.5 10. -4 11. $-\frac{12}{4}$ 12. $3.\overline{3}$

Compare and Order Real Numbers

Compare using $<$ or $>$.

13. $\frac{5}{6}$ ■ $\frac{2}{3}$ $>$ 14. $3\frac{7}{9}$ ■ $3\frac{10}{12}$ $<$ 15. -0.38 ■ -0.3 $<$ 16. $-\frac{15}{8}$ ■ -2 $>$

Order of Operations

Simplify each expression.

17. $14 \div 2(-3) + 1$ -20
18. $8^2 - (-12) + 15 \div 3$ 81
19. $-2(25 - 21)^2 + 11$ -21
20. $3\left(\frac{21 - 9}{6} - 1\right) \div 2$ $\frac{3}{2}$, or 1.5

Ordered Pairs

Graph each point on the same coordinate plane.

21. $(0, 2)$ 22. $(-3, 1)$ 23. $(2, -1)$ 24. $(-3, -2)$

Answers

21–24.

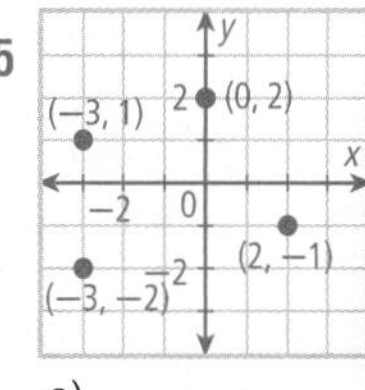

CHAPTER 1

ARE YOU READY?

Organizer

Objective: Assess students' understanding of prerequisite skills.

Prerequisite Skills

- Fractions and Decimals
- Graph Numbers on a Number Line
- Compare and Order Real Numbers
- Order of Operations
- Ordered Pairs

Assessing Prior Knowledge

Diagnose and Prescribe

Use this page to determine whether intervention is necessary or whether enrichment is appropriate.

Resources

***Are You Ready? Intervention and Enrichment* Worksheets**

***Are You Ready?* CD-ROM**

***Are You Ready?* Online**

my.hrw.com

ARE YOU READY?

Diagnose and Prescribe

NO INTERVENE

Prerequisite Skill	*Are You Ready? Intervention*, Chapter 1 Worksheets	CD-ROM	Online
Fractions and Decimals	Skill 11	Activity 11	Diagnose and Prescribe Online
Graph Numbers on a Number Line	Skill 18	Activity 18	
Compare and Order Real Numbers	Skill 16	Activity 16	
Order of Operations	Skill 55	Activity 55	
Ordered Pairs	Skill 79	Activity 79	

YES ENRICH

Organizer

Objective: Help students organize the new concepts they will learn in Chapter 1.

Online Edition
Multilingual Glossary

Resources

Puzzle Pro
One-Stop Planner®

***Multilingual Glossary* Online**

go.hrw.com
KEYWORD: MB7 Glossary

Answers to *Vocabulary Connections*

Possible answers:

1. *Submarine, subroutine, subscript, subzero,* and *subterranean;* these words all mean "below" or "underneath" something.
2. The elements in a mathematical set are probably the fundamental components of the set.
3. A hammer can hit nails into wood (and pull nails out), and a photocopier makes photocopies.
4. To transform something means to change it into something different. A mathematical transformation probably changes numbers into different ones.

CHAPTER 1

Study Guide: Preview

Where You've Been

Previously, you

- used properties of real numbers.
- simplified numeric expressions using the order of operations and exponents.
- used variables, expressions, and equations to represent situations.

In This Chapter

You will study

- using sets of numbers and their properties.
- simplifying algebraic expressions and expressions with exponents.
- using functions and their graphs to represent situations.

Where You're Going

You can use the skills in this chapter

- to quickly calculate tips and discounts in your head.
- to build a foundation for calculus classes.
- to observe patterns and relationships in science and social studies.

Key Vocabulary/Vocabulario

domain	el dominio
element	el elemento
function	la función
parent function	la función elemental
radical symbol	el símbolo de radical
range	el rango
set	el conjunto
subset	el subconjunto
transformation	la transformación

Vocabulary Connections

To become familiar with some of the vocabulary terms in the chapter, consider the following. You may refer to the chapter, the glossary, or a dictionary if you like.

1. The word **subset** begins with the prefix *sub-*. List some other words that begin with *sub-*. What do all of these words have in common?
2. **Element** comes from the Latin word *elementum*, which was used to refer to any one of the four basic substances believed to compose the entire universe (air, water, fire, and earth). What might *element* refer to in a set of numbers?
3. One meaning of the word **function** is "to perform." Give examples of specific machines or tools and the *functions* they perform.
4. What does the word *transform* mean? What do you think a mathematical **transformation** involves?

4 Chapter 1

Study Strategy: Use Your Book for Success

Understanding how your textbook is organized will help you locate and use helpful information.

Pay attention to the **margin notes.** Know-It Note icons point out key information. Helpful Hints, Remember notes, and Caution notes help you understand concepts and avoid common mistakes.

Helpful Hint
A replacement set a set of numbers t can be substituted

Remember!
Terms that are written without a coefficient have

Caution!
In the expression -5^2, 5 is the base because the nega

The **Glossary** is found in the back of your textbook. Use it as a resource when you need the definition of an unfamiliar word or property.

The **Index** is located at the end of your textbook. Use it to locate the page where a particular concept is taught.

The **Skills Bank** is found in the back of your textbook. These pages review concepts from previous math courses, including geometry skills.

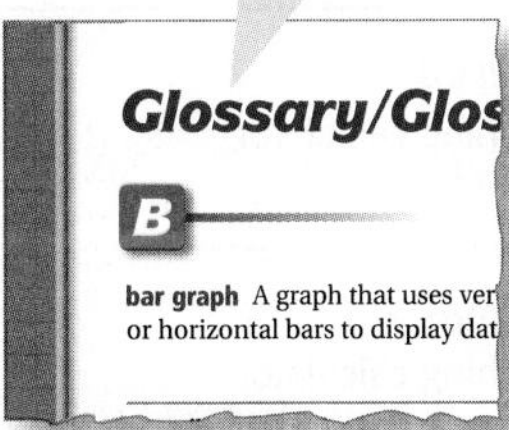

Glossary/Glos
B
bar graph A graph that uses ver
or horizontal bars to display dat

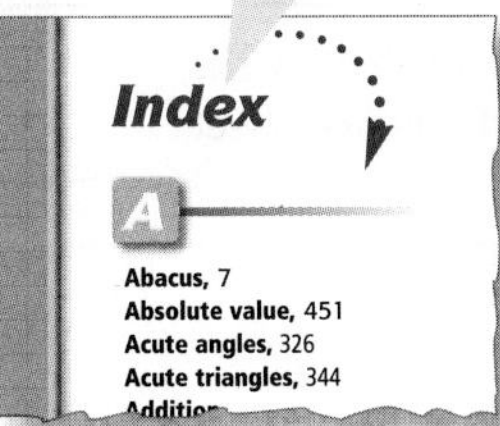

Try This

Use your textbook for the following problems.

1. Use the index to find the page where each term is defined.
   a. range b. translation c. scientific notation
2. In Lesson 1-4, what fact about coefficients does the **Remember** margin note point out?
3. Use the glossary to find the definition of each term.
   a. set b. parent function c. principal root

Reading and Writing Math CHAPTER 1

Organizer

Objective: Help students apply strategies to understand and retain key concepts.

Resources

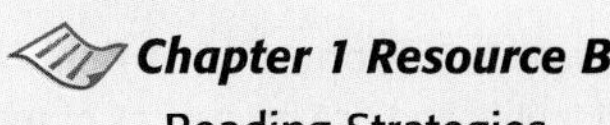

Reading Strategies

ENGLISH LANGUAGE LEARNERS

Study Strategy: Use Your Book for Success

Discuss Students will be able to use their book more efficiently if they know where information is in the book and how it is organized.

Reinforce to students that their books are organized in a way to make learning easier and more interesting.

Point out that reviewing the table of contents before beginning a chapter will give them an idea of what they will be learning. The table of contents can also help them locate information about a specific topic.

Extend As students work through Chapter 1, have them look up in the glossary all vocabulary words introduced in the chapter. Ask them to use the index to see that the vocabulary words will be used throughout the book.

Encourage students to explore their book as they proceed to discover the information it contains.

Answers

1a. p. 44 (Lesson 1-6)
b. p. 59 (Lesson 1-8)
c. p. 36 (Lesson 1-5)

2. Terms written without a coefficient have a coefficient of 1.

3a. a collection of items called elements
b. the simplest function with the defining characteristics of the family
c. the positive root of a number, indicated by the radical sign

SECTION

1A Properties and Operations

One-Minute Section Planner

Lesson	Lab Resources	Materials
Lesson 1-1 Sets of Numbers • Classify and order real numbers. ☑ SAT-10 ☑ NAEP ☑ ACT ☑ SAT ☑ SAT Subject Tests		**Optional** set of coins or other sortable items
Lesson 1-2 Properties of Real Numbers • Identify and use properties of real numbers. ☑ SAT-10 ☑ NAEP ☑ ACT ☐ SAT ☑ SAT Subject Tests		**Optional** poster board, markers
Lesson 1-3 Square Roots • Estimate square roots. • Simplify, add, subtract, multiply, and divide square roots. ☑ SAT-10 ☑ NAEP ☑ ACT ☑ SAT ☑ SAT Subject Tests	***Algebra Lab Activities*** 1-3 Algebra Lab	**Optional** pattern blocks (MK), graph paper, centimeter cubes (MK)
Lesson 1-4 Simplifying Algebraic Expressions • Simplify and evaluate algebraic expressions. ☑ SAT-10 ☑ NAEP ☑ ACT ☑ SAT ☑ SAT Subject Tests		**Optional** cups, water, sand
1-5 Technology Lab Explore Negative Exponents • Explore negative exponents. ☑ SAT-10 ☑ NAEP ☑ ACT ☑ SAT ☐ SAT Subject Tests	***Technology Lab Activities*** 1-5 Lab Recording Sheet	**Required** graphing calculator
Lesson 1-5 Properties of Exponents • Simplify expressions involving exponents. • Use scientific notation. ☑ SAT-10 ☑ NAEP ☑ ACT ☑ SAT ☑ SAT Subject Tests		**Optional** graphing calculator

MK = *Manipulatives Kit*

Section Overview

Sets of Numbers — Lesson 1-1

Understanding subsets of real numbers and ways to express them is critical in the study of algebra.

Subsets of Real Numbers

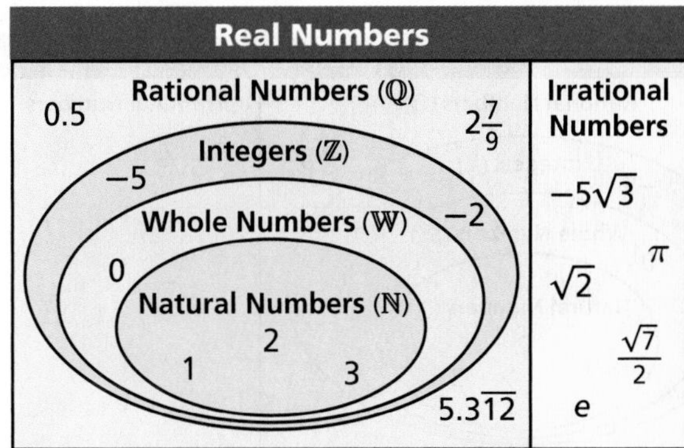

Sets of Numbers

Number Line: −2 −1 0 1 2 3 4

Words: real numbers greater than 0 and less than or equal to 3

Interval Notation: $(0, 3]$

Set-Builder Notation: $\{x \mid 0 < x \leq 3\}$

Properties of Real Numbers — Lessons 1-2, 1-3

Knowing the properties of real numbers helps students simplify expressions and calculate more quickly.

Property	Example
Additive Identity Property	$5 + 0 = 5$
Mutiplicative Identity Property	$5 \cdot 1 = 5$
Additive Inverse Property	$3 + (-3) = 0$
Mutiplicative Inverse Property	$\frac{3}{5} \cdot \frac{5}{3} = 1$
Distributive Property	$3(4 + 5) = 3(4) + 3(5)$

Property	Example
Closure Property	$7.4 + 3.2 = 10.6 \in \mathbb{R}$
Commutative Property	$3 + 2 = 2 + 3$
Associative Property	$2(3 \cdot 4) = (2 \cdot 3)4$
Product Property of Square Roots	$\sqrt{2} \cdot \sqrt{8} = \sqrt{16} = 4$
Quotient Property of Square Roots	$\sqrt{\frac{4}{9}} = \frac{\sqrt{4}}{\sqrt{9}} = \frac{2}{3}$

Simplifying Algebraic Expressions — Lessons 1-4, 1-5

Simplifying and evaluating expressions are essential algebra skills.

Evaluating and Simplifying Expressions

Evaluate $x^2 + 2x$ for $x = 3$.

$$x^2 + 2x$$
$$(3)^2 + 2(3)$$
$$15$$

Simplify by using properties of exponents.

$$\left(\frac{ab^4}{b^7}\right)^2 = \frac{a^2b^8}{b^{14}} = \frac{a^2}{b^6}$$

Simplify by combining like terms.

$$3x^2 + 2x^2 = 5x^2$$

Scientific notation: **Simplify** $\frac{2.3 \times 10^{-6}}{4.6 \times 10^{-2}}$.

$$\frac{2.3 \times 10^{-6}}{4.6 \times 10^{-2}} = 0.5 \times 10^{-4} = 5.0 \times 10^{-5}$$

1-1 Organizer

Pacing: Traditional 1 day
Block $\frac{1}{2}$ day

Objective: Classify and order real numbers.

Online Edition
Tutorial Videos

Countdown to Testing Week 1

Power Presentations with PowerPoint®

Warm Up

Write in decimal form.

1. $-\frac{9}{2}$ -4.5 **2.** $\frac{2}{3}$ $0.\overline{6}$

3. Write $\sqrt{2}$ as a decimal approximation. ≈ 1.414

Order from least to greatest.

4. 10, −5, −10, 0, 5
−10, −5, 0, 5, 10

5. 0.1, 1.1, 0.01, 0.11, 0.009
0.009, 0.01, 0.1, 0.11, 1.1

Also available on transparency

Math Humor

Q: Why do the other numbers refuse to take $\sqrt{2}$, $\sqrt{3}$, and $\sqrt{5}$ seriously?

A: They're completely irrational.

1-1 Sets of Numbers

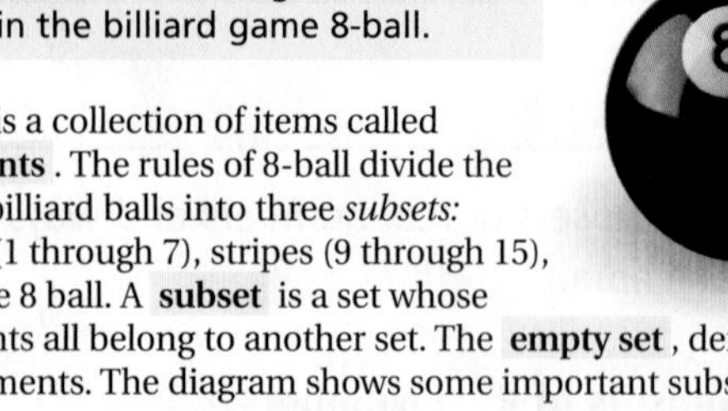

Objective
Classify and order real numbers.

Vocabulary
set
element
subset
empty set
roster notation
finite set
infinite set
interval notation
set-builder notation

Why learn this?
Sets can be used to organize the balls used in the billiard game 8-ball.

A **set** is a collection of items called **elements**. The rules of 8-ball divide the set of billiard balls into three *subsets:* solids (1 through 7), stripes (9 through 15), and the 8 ball. A **subset** is a set whose elements all belong to another set. The **empty set**, denoted ∅, is a set containing no elements. The diagram shows some important subsets of the real numbers.

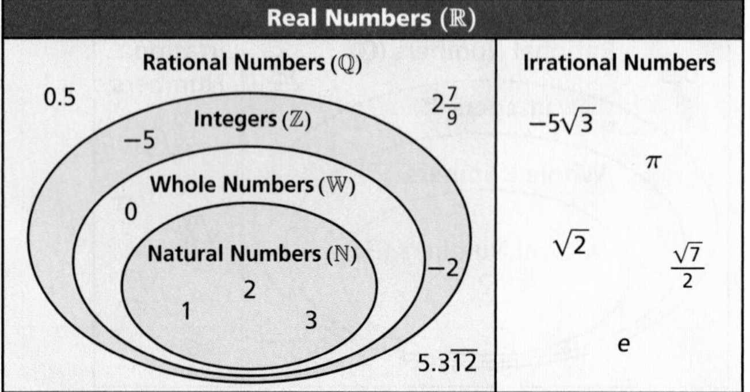

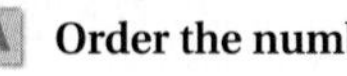

Note the symbols for the sets of numbers.
ℝ: real numbers
ℚ: rational numbers
ℤ: integers
𝕎: whole numbers
ℕ: natural numbers

Rational numbers can be expressed as a quotient (or *ratio*) of two integers, where the denominator is not zero. The decimal form of a rational number either terminates, such as $\frac{1}{2} = 0.5$, or repeats, such as $-\frac{4}{3} = -1.\overline{3} = -1.333\ldots$.

Irrational numbers, such as $\sqrt{2}$ and π, *cannot* be expressed as a quotient of two integers, and their decimal forms do not terminate or repeat. However, you can approximate these numbers using terminating decimals.

EXAMPLE 1 Ordering and Classifying Real Numbers

Consider the numbers $0.\overline{6}$, $\sqrt{2}$, 0, $-\frac{5}{2}$, and 0.5129.

A Order the numbers from least to greatest.

Write each number as a decimal to make it easier to compare them.

$\sqrt{2} \approx 1.414$ *Use a decimal approximation for $\sqrt{2}$.*

$-\frac{5}{2} = -2.5$ *Rewrite $-\frac{5}{2}$ in decimal form.*

$-2.5 < 0 < 0.5129 < 0.666\ldots < 1.414$ *Use < to compare the numbers.*

The numbers in order from least to greatest are $-\frac{5}{2}$, 0, 0.5129, $0.\overline{6}$, and $\sqrt{2}$.

State Resources

go.hrw.com
State Resources Online
KEYWORD: MB7 Resources

1 Introduce

EXPLORATION

Sets of Numbers

A set is a group of items, such as a group of numbers. For example, the numbers that appear on a telephone keypad form a set. The items in a set are called elements.

1. One method of describing a set is to list its elements inside a pair of braces, { }. Use this notation to write the set of numbers found on a telephone keypad.
2. You can also describe a set by describing its properties. Describe the set of numbers found on a telephone keypad without listing them.
3. List four numbers that are NOT included in the set you described in Problem 2.

THINK AND DISCUSS

4. **Explain** how terms such as natural numbers, whole numbers, and integers can help you describe a set.
5. **Describe** the set of numbers that appear on a football field.

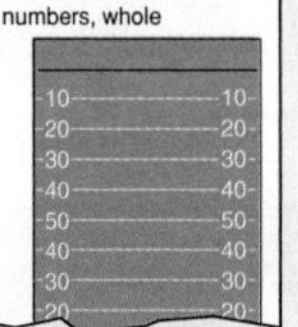

Motivate

List subsets of the natural numbers, such as even numbers, prime numbers, or natural numbers less than 100. Challenge students to describe the subsets in mathematical terms, for example, "The subset of even numbers is the set of natural numbers that are multiples of 2." This will begin to develop the set-builder notation taught in this lesson.

Explorations and answers are provided in the *Explorations* binder.

Consider the numbers $0.\overline{6}$, $\sqrt{2}$, 0, $-\frac{5}{2}$, and 0.5129.

B **Classify each number by the subsets of the real numbers to which it belongs. Use a table to classify the numbers.**

Number	Real ($\mathbb{R}$)	Rational ($\mathbb{Q}$)	Integer ($\mathbb{Z}$)	Whole ($\mathbb{W}$)	Natural ($\mathbb{N}$)	Irrational
$-\frac{5}{2}$	✓	✓				
0	✓	✓	✓	✓		
0.5129	✓	✓				
$0.\overline{6}$	✓	✓				
$\sqrt{2}$	✓					✓

CHECK IT OUT! Consider the numbers -2, π, -0.321, $\frac{3}{2}$, and $-\sqrt{3}$.

1a. Order the numbers from least to greatest. **1a.** $-2, -\sqrt{3}, -0.321, \frac{3}{2}, \pi$

1b. Classify each number by the subsets of the real numbers to which it belongs. -2: $\mathbb{R}, \mathbb{Q}, \mathbb{Z}$; $-\sqrt{3}$: $\mathbb{R}$, irrational; -0.321: $\mathbb{R}, \mathbb{Q}$; $\frac{3}{2}$: $\mathbb{R}, \mathbb{Q}$; π: $\mathbb{R}$, irrational

There are many ways to represent sets. For instance, you can use words to describe a set. You can also use **roster notation**, in which the elements of a set are listed between braces, { }.

Words	Roster Notation
The set of billiard balls is numbered 1 through 15.	{1, 2, 3, 4, 5, 6, 7, 8, 9, 10, 11, 12, 13, 14, 15}

A set can be *finite* like the set of billiard ball numbers or *infinite* like the natural numbers {1, 2, 3, 4...}. A **finite set** has a definite, or finite, number of elements. An **infinite set** has an unlimited, or infinite, number of elements.

Helpful Hint

The Density Property states that between any two real numbers there is another real number. So any interval that includes more than one point contains infinitely many points.

Many infinite sets, such as the real numbers, cannot be represented in roster notation. There are other methods of representing these sets. For example, the number line represents the set of all real numbers.

The set of real numbers between 3 and 5, which is also an infinite set, can be represented on a number line or by an inequality.

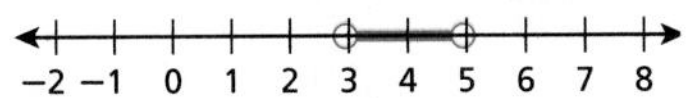

$3 < x < 5$

An interval is the set of all numbers between two endpoints, such as 3 and 5. In **interval notation** the symbols [and] are used to include an endpoint in an interval, and the symbols (and) are used to exclude an endpoint from an interval.

(3, 5) *The set of real numbers between but not including 3 and 5*

An interval that extends forever in the positive direction goes to infinity (∞), and an interval that extends forever in the negative direction goes to negative infinity (−∞).

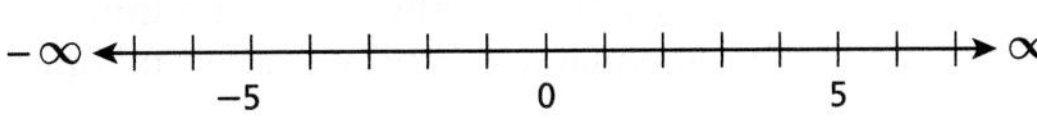

Power Presentations with PowerPoint®

Additional Examples

Example 1

Consider the numbers $2.\overline{3}$, π, $\sqrt{5}$, $-\frac{11}{2}$, and 2.7652.

A. Order the numbers from least to greatest.

$-\frac{11}{2}$, $\sqrt{5}$, $2.\overline{3}$, 2.7652, π

B. Classify each number by the subsets of the real numbers to which it belongs.

$-\frac{11}{2}$: $\mathbb{R}, \mathbb{Q}$; $\sqrt{5}$: $\mathbb{R}$, irrational; 2.7652: $\mathbb{R}, \mathbb{Q}$; $2.\overline{3}$: $\mathbb{R}, \mathbb{Q}$; π: $\mathbb{R}$, irrational

Also available on transparency

INTERVENTION
Questioning Strategies

EXAMPLE 1

- Why do you write all the numbers in decimal form?
- How can you tell if a number belongs to the set of rational numbers?

Teaching Tip **Reading Math** The symbols $\mathbb{N}$, $\mathbb{W}$, and $\mathbb{R}$ are taken directly from the names of the numbers being described. $\mathbb{Q}$ is used for the set of rational numbers because these numbers can be represented by fractions, or quotients. The use of $\mathbb{Z}$ for the set of integers comes from the German word *zahlen*, which means *to count*. **ENGLISH LANGUAGE LEARNERS**

Teaching Tip **Math Background** Although π is irrational, it is difficult to prove that this is true. Johann Lambert first proved the irrationality of π in 1761. He showed that if x is a nonzero rational number, then tan x cannot be rational. Because tan $\frac{\pi}{4} = 1$, which is rational, $\frac{\pi}{4}$ must be irrational.

2 Teach

Guided Instruction

Before ordering and classifying real numbers, review with students how to order decimal numbers. Ensure that students know the meanings of inequality and set symbols before introducing set-builder notation.

Reaching All Learners
Through Concrete Manipulatives

Present the students with a collection of items, such as U.S. coins. Have students name some properties of the items and then sort the items into subsets based on these properties. Properties may include having a value greater than 5 cents or having a building on the back.

Power Presentations with PowerPoint®

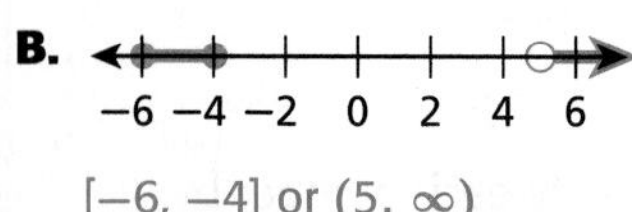

Additional Examples

Example 2

Use interval notation to represent each set of numbers.

A. $7 < x \leq 12$ $(7, 12]$

B. 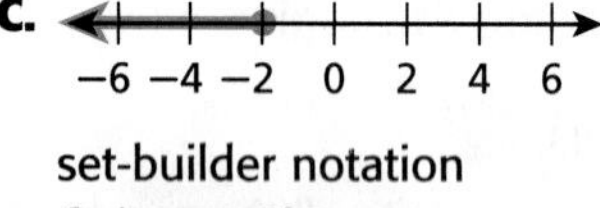

$[-6, -4]$ or $(5, \infty)$

Example 3

Rewrite each set in the indicated notation.

A. $\{x \mid x > -5.5, x \in \mathbb{Z}\}$; words
integers greater than -5.5

B. positive multiples of 10; roster notation
$\{10, 20, 30, \ldots\}$

C. (number line from −6 to 6)

set-builder notation
$\{x \mid x \leq -2\}$

Also available on transparency

INTERVENTION
Questioning Strategies

EXAMPLE 2

- How do you know when to use square brackets or parentheses?
- Why is *or* used instead of *and* to indicate that a set includes more than one interval?

EXAMPLE 3

- What are the similarities and differences among roster, interval, and set-builder notation?
- What are the advantages of having multiple representations to describe the same data set?

Because ∞ and −∞ are not numbers, they cannot be included in a set of numbers, so parentheses are used to enclose them in an interval. The table shows the relationship among some methods of representing intervals.

Methods of Representing Intervals

Words	Number Line	Inequality	Interval Notation
Numbers less than 3	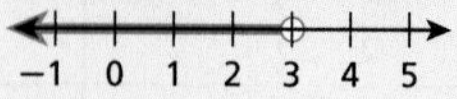 −1 0 1 2 3 4 5	$x < 3$	$(-\infty, 3)$
Numbers greater than or equal to −2	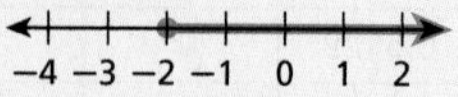 −4 −3 −2 −1 0 1 2	$x \geq -2$	$[-2, \infty)$
Numbers between 2 and 4	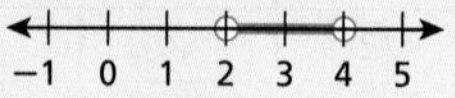 −1 0 1 2 3 4 5	$2 < x < 4$	$(2, 4)$
Numbers 1 through 3	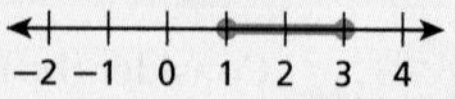 −2 −1 0 1 2 3 4	$1 \leq x \leq 3$	$[1, 3]$

EXAMPLE 2 Interval Notation

Use interval notation to represent each set of numbers.

A $4 \leq x < 6$

$[4, 6)$ *4 is included, but 6 is not.*

B 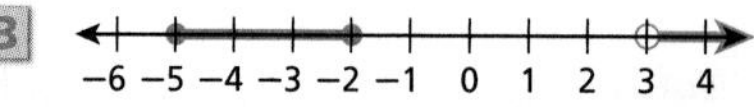

There are two intervals graphed on the number line.

$[-5, -2]$ *−5 and −2 are included.*

$(3, \infty)$ *3 is not included, and the interval continues forever in the positive direction.*

$[-5, -2]$ or $(3, \infty)$ *The word "or" is used to indicate that a set includes more than one interval.*

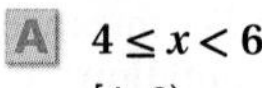

CHECK IT OUT! **Use interval notation to represent each set of numbers.**

2a. (number line from −4 to 4) $(-\infty, -1]$

2b. $x \leq 2$ or $3 < x \leq 11$ $(-\infty, 2]$ or $(3, 11]$

Reading Math

The symbol ∈ means "is an element of." So $x \in \mathbb{N}$ is read "*x* is an element of the set of natural numbers," or "*x* is a natural number."

Another way to represent sets is *set-builder notation.* **Set-builder notation** uses the properties of the elements in the set to define the set. Inequalities and the element symbol (∈) are often used in set-builder notation. The set of striped-billiard-ball numbers, or $\{9, 10, 11, 12, 13, 14, 15\}$, is represented below in set-builder notation.

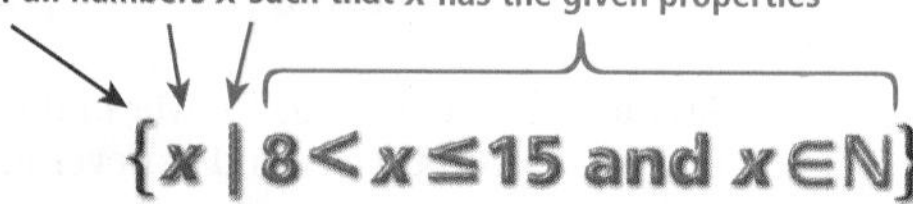

Read the above as "the set of all numbers *x* such that *x* is greater than 8 and less than or equal to 15 and *x* is a natural number."

Teaching Tip

Auditory Have students practice reading aloud expressions in set-builder notation to reinforce the meaning of the symbols in them. For example, the answer to **Example 3C** can be read as, "the set of all numbers *x* such that *x* is greater than −3 and less than or equal to 5."

ENGLISH LANGUAGE LEARNERS

Some representations of the same sets of real numbers are shown.

Methods of Set Notation			
Words	**Roster Notation**	**Interval Notation**	**Set-Builder Notation**
All real numbers except 1	Cannot be written in roster notation	$(-\infty, 1)$ or $(1, \infty)$	$\{x \mid x \neq 1\}$
Positive odd numbers	$\{1, 3, 5, 7, \ldots\}$	Cannot be notated using interval notation	$\{x \mid x = 2n - 1$ and $n \in \mathbb{N}\}$
Numbers within 3 units of 2	Cannot be written in roster notation	$[-1, 5]$	$\{x \mid -1 \leq x \leq 5\}$

EXAMPLE 3 Translating Between Methods of Set Notation

Rewrite each set in the indicated notation.

A $\{x \mid x = 2n$ **and** $n \in \mathbb{N}\}$; **words**

positive even numbers

B **numbers and symbols on a telephone keypad; roster notation**

$\{0, 1, 2, 3, 4, 5, 6, 7, 8, 9, *, \#\}$ *The order of elements is not important.*

C 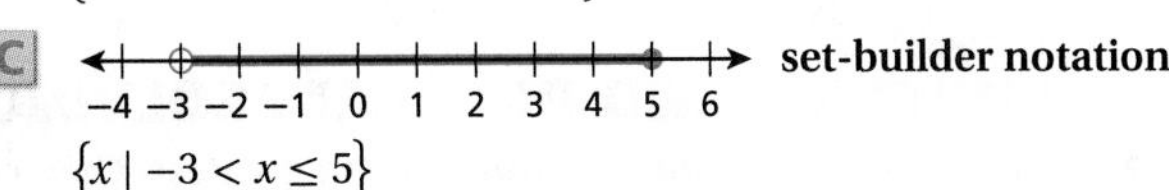 **set-builder notation**

$\{x \mid -3 < x \leq 5\}$

Rewrite each set in the indicated notation.

3a. $\{2, 4, 6, 8\}$; words **even numbers between 1 and 9**

3b. $\{x \mid 2 < x < 8$ and $x \in \mathbb{N}\}$; roster notation $\{3, 4, 5, 6, 7\}$

3c. $[99, \infty)$; set-builder notation $\{x \mid x \geq 99\}$

THINK AND DISCUSS

1. Compare interval notation with roster notation. Is it possible to have a set that can be represented by both methods?
2. Explain whether it is possible to name a number that belongs to both the set of integers and the set of irrational numbers.

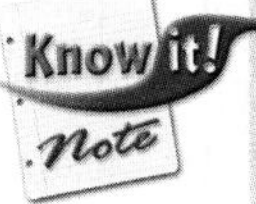

3. **GET ORGANIZED** Copy and complete the graphic organizer. In each box, show the correct notation for each set.

Set	Roster Notation	Interval Notation	Set-Builder Notation
1, 2, 3, 4, and 5			
$-2 \leq n \leq 2$			
Whole numbers less than 3			

Students may confuse (3, 5) used as interval notation with (3, 5) used as an ordered pair. Reinforce to students that common symbols can be used in multiple mathematical contexts. Encourage them to pay attention to the context.

Reading Math The use of *or*, as opposed to *and*, in the set-builder examples may confuse students. Reinforce that *or* means that the values must be in at least one of the intervals (and possibly both).

ENGLISH LANGUAGE LEARNERS

3 Close

Summarize

Review the Venn diagram showing the subsets of the real numbers, and cite examples of each type. Review the methods of set notation outlined in the lesson, highlighting similarities and differences among the methods.

ONGOING ASSESSMENT

and INTERVENTION 

***Diagnose Before* the Lesson**
1-1 Warm Up, TE p. 6

***Monitor During* the Lesson**
Check It Out! Exercises, SE pp. 7–9
Questioning Strategies, TE pp. 7–8

***Assess After* the Lesson**
1-1 Lesson Quiz, TE p. 13
Alternative Assessment, TE p. 13

Answers to *Think and Discuss*

Possible answers:

1. Interval notation is used to indicate infinite sets of real numbers over an interval. Roster notation is used to indicate finite or infinite sets that follow a pattern (such as multiples of 2); no.
2. No; any integer n can be expressed in the form $\frac{n}{1}$, which is a rational number.
3. See p. A2.

1-1 Exercises

Assignment Guide

Assign *Guided Practice* exercises as necessary.

Basic 12–25, 40–42, 44, 52, 62–66, 72–76

Average 12–25, 30–52, 62–66, 69–76

Advanced 12–20 even, 22–45, 52–76

Homework Quick Check

Quickly check key concepts.

Exercises: 12, 16, 18, 20, 41, 42

Answers

2. $\sqrt{7}, 3\sqrt{2}, 4\frac{3}{5}, 4.\overline{6}, 5.125$; $\sqrt{7}$: $\mathbb{R}$, irrational; $3\sqrt{2}$: $\mathbb{R}$, irrational; $4\frac{3}{5}$: $\mathbb{R}, \mathbb{Q}$; $4.\overline{6}$: $\mathbb{R}, \mathbb{Q}$; 5.125: $\mathbb{R}, \mathbb{Q}$

3. $-\frac{100}{4}, -6.897, \frac{1}{8}, \sqrt{4}, \sqrt{6}$; $-\frac{100}{4}$: $\mathbb{R}, \mathbb{Q}, \mathbb{Z}$; -6.897: $\mathbb{R}, \mathbb{Q}$; $\frac{1}{8}$: $\mathbb{R}, \mathbb{Q}$; $\sqrt{4}$: $\mathbb{R}, \mathbb{Q}, \mathbb{Z}, \mathbb{W}, \mathbb{N}$; $\sqrt{6}$: $\mathbb{R}$, irrational

4. $-\sqrt{3}, -1\frac{1}{3}, 1.\overline{3}, \frac{\pi}{2}, \sqrt{5}$; $-\sqrt{3}$: $\mathbb{R}$, irrational; $-1\frac{1}{3}$: $\mathbb{R}, \mathbb{Q}$; $1.\overline{3}$: $\mathbb{R}, \mathbb{Q}$; $\frac{\pi}{2}$: $\mathbb{R}$, irrational; $\sqrt{5}$: $\mathbb{R}$, irrational

State Resources

go.hrw.com
State Resources Online
KEYWORD: MB7 Resources

1-1 Exercises

go.hrw.com
Homework Help Online
KEYWORD: MB7 1-1
Parent Resources Online
KEYWORD: MB7 Parent

GUIDED PRACTICE

1. **Vocabulary** Braces, { }, are used in __?__. (*interval notation* or *roster notation*) **roster notation**

SEE EXAMPLE 1 p. 6

Order the given numbers from least to greatest. Then classify each number by the subsets of the real numbers to which it belongs.

2. $3\sqrt{2}, \sqrt{7}, 5.125, 4\frac{3}{5}, 4.\overline{6}$
3. $-\frac{100}{4}, -6.897, \sqrt{4}, \frac{1}{8}, \sqrt{6}$
4. $\sqrt{5}, \frac{\pi}{2}, -\sqrt{3}, 1.\overline{3}, -1\frac{1}{3}$

SEE EXAMPLE 2 p. 8

Use interval notation to represent each set of numbers.

5. $-10 < x \le 10$ **$(-10, 10]$**
6. 
−15 −10 −5 0 5
$(-\infty, -5)$
7. $1 \le x < 20$ or $x > 30$ **$[1, 20)$ or $(30, \infty)$**

SEE EXAMPLE 3 p. 9

Rewrite each set in the indicated notation.

8. $\{x \mid x = 1 + \frac{1}{2}(n - n) \text{ and } n \in \mathbb{N}\}$; words **one**
9. 
−6 −4 −2 0 2 4 6
set-builder notation **$\{x \mid -5 \le x < 3\}$**
10. $\{0, 5, 10, 15, 20, \ldots\}$; words **nonnegative integer multiples of 5**
11. integers from -5 to 5; roster notation **$\{-5, -4, -3, -2, -1, 0, 1, 2, 3, 4, 5\}$**

PRACTICE AND PROBLEM SOLVING

Independent Practice	
For Exercises	See Example
12–14	1
15–17	2
18–21	3

Extra Practice
Skills Practice p. S4
Application Practice p. S32

Order the given numbers from least to greatest. Then classify each number by the subsets of the real numbers to which it belongs.

12. $2.33, 5.\overline{5}, 2\sqrt{5}, -\frac{4}{5}, -0.75$
13. $\frac{1}{2}, -2, -\sqrt{2}, \frac{\sqrt{2}}{3}, -1.\overline{25}$
14. $-\sqrt{9}, 2\pi, -1, 5.\overline{12}, -\frac{7}{2}$

Use interval notation to represent each set of numbers.

15. $x \ne 5$ **$(-\infty, 5)$ or $(5, \infty)$**
16. $-15 < x < 0$ **$(-15, 0)$**
17. 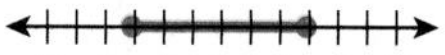
−6 −4 −2 0 2 4 6
$[-3, 3]$

Rewrite each set in the indicated notation.

18. $(-\infty, 3]$ or $(5, 11]$; words
19. positive multiples of 11; roster notation
20. 
−4 −3 −2 −1 0 1 2 3 4
words
21. $\{-9, -7, -5, -3, -1\}$; set-builder notation

Chemistry Use the table for Exercises 22–25.

22. Order the given elements from least to greatest atomic mass. **22. lithium, aluminum, sulfur, chlorine, calcium**
23. Which subset of the real numbers best describes the atomic masses of these elements? Choose from $\mathbb{R}, \mathbb{Q}, \mathbb{Z}, \mathbb{W}$, and $\mathbb{N}$. **$\mathbb{Q}$**
24. Which subset of the real numbers best describes the ionic charges of these elements? Choose from $\mathbb{R}, \mathbb{Q}, \mathbb{Z}, \mathbb{W}$, and $\mathbb{N}$. **$\mathbb{Z}$**
25. Explain why interval notation cannot be used to represent the set of atomic masses given.

Elements from the Periodic Table

Element	Atomic Mass (amu)	Ionic Charge
Aluminum	26.982	+3
Calcium	40.078	+2
Chlorine	35.4527	−1
Lithium	6.941	+1
Sulfur	32.066	−2

Answers

12. $-\frac{4}{5}, -0.75, 2.33, 2\sqrt{5}, 5.\overline{5}$; $-\frac{4}{5}$: $\mathbb{R}, \mathbb{Q}$; -0.75: $\mathbb{R}, \mathbb{Q}$; 2.33: $\mathbb{R}, \mathbb{Q}$; $2\sqrt{5}$: $\mathbb{R}$, irrational; $5.\overline{5}$: $\mathbb{R}, \mathbb{Q}$
13. $-2, -\sqrt{2}, -1.\overline{25}, \frac{\sqrt{2}}{3}, \frac{1}{2}$; -2: $\mathbb{R}, \mathbb{Q}, \mathbb{Z}$; $-\sqrt{2}$: $\mathbb{R}$, irrational; $-1.\overline{25}$: $\mathbb{R}, \mathbb{Q}$; $\frac{\sqrt{2}}{3}$: $\mathbb{R}$, irrational; $\frac{1}{2}$: $\mathbb{R}, \mathbb{Q}$
14. $-\frac{7}{2}, -\sqrt{9}, -1, 5.\overline{12}, 2\pi$; $-\frac{7}{2}$: $\mathbb{R}, \mathbb{Q}$; $-\sqrt{9}$: $\mathbb{R}, \mathbb{Q}, \mathbb{Z}$; -1: $\mathbb{R}, \mathbb{Q}, \mathbb{Z}$; $5.\overline{12}$: $\mathbb{R}, \mathbb{Q}$; 2π: $\mathbb{R}$, irrational
18. less than or equal to 3 or greater than 5 and less than or equal to 11
19. $\{11, 22, 33, 44, 55, 66, 77, \ldots\}$
20. less than -3 or greater than 0
21. $\{x \mid -9 \le x \le -1$ and x is odd$\}$
25. Possible answer: Interval notation is used for ranges of numbers, but the set of atomic masses is a list of numbers.

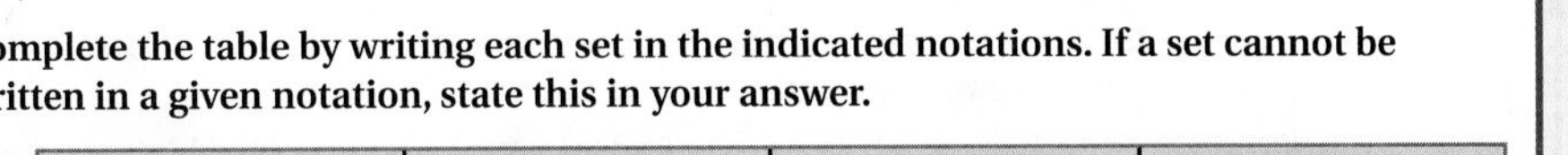

Complete the table by writing each set in the indicated notations. If a set cannot be written in a given notation, state this in your answer.

	Words	Roster Notation	Interval Notation	Set-Builder Notation
26.	?	$\{-2, -4, -6, -8, \ldots\}$	?	?
27.	?	?	$[-4, 8)$	?
28.	Even numbers between 27 and 39	?	?	?
29.	?	?	?	$\{x \mid 0 < x < 1\}$

Express each set of numbers using interval notation and set-builder notation.

30. 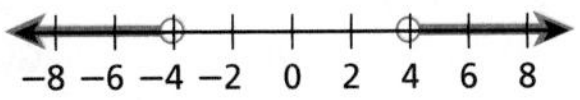 [number line: −8 −6 −4 −2 0 2 4 6 8]
31. 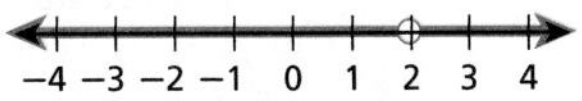 [number line: −4 −3 −2 −1 0 1 2 3 4]
32. $x \leq 2$ or $3 < x < 5$
33. numbers between 1 and 10
34. numbers more than 2 units from 8
35. $x \neq 5$ and $x \leq 10$

Tell whether each statement is true or false. If false, give a counterexample.

36. Every natural number is an integer. true
37. Every real number is irrational.
38. Every integer is a whole number.
39. Every integer is NOT irrational. true

Sports Use the table of soccer ball sizes for Exercises 40–42.

Soccer Ball Sizes			
Size	3	4	5
Weight (oz)	11–12	12–13	14–16
Circumference (in.)	23–24	25–26	27–28
Age of Player	Under 8	8–12	Over 12

40. Identify the size of each ball:
    soccer ball A: 4.36 in. radius
    soccer ball B: 7.54 in. diameter
    soccer ball C: 276.2 in^3 volume
41. Use set-builder notation to represent the weight range for each soccer ball size.
42. Use interval notation to represent the age range for each soccer ball size.
43. **Critical Thinking** The product of an irrational number and a rational number is an irrational number. Explain why this means that no matter how precisely you measure the diameter of a soccer ball, your calculation for its circumference will NEVER be a rational number.

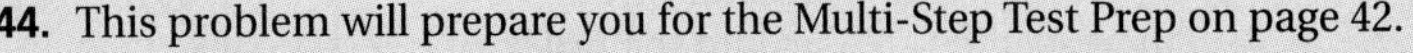

MULTI-STEP TEST PREP

44. This problem will prepare you for the Multi-Step Test Prep on page 42.

Distances in space are often measured in astronomical units (AU). One AU is defined as the average distance between Earth and the Sun.

a. To which subsets of the real numbers do the numbers in the table belong?
b. Order the bodies from least to greatest average distance from Earth.
c. For a given speed, would it take longer to make a round-trip to Venus or a one-way trip to Mars? Explain.

Average Distances from Earth	
Body	**Distance (AU)**
Mars	$\frac{97}{186}$
Mercury	$\frac{117}{310}$
Moon	0.0026
Venus	0.2774

MULTI-STEP TEST PREP Exercise 44 involves classifying and comparing distances between planets. This exercise prepares students for the Multi-Step Test Prep on page 42.

Answers

32. $(-\infty, 2]$ or $(3, 5)$; $\{x \mid x \leq 2 \text{ or } 3 < x < 5\}$
33. $(1, 10)$; $\{x \mid 1 < x < 10\}$
34. $(-\infty, 6)$ or $(10, \infty)$; $\{x \mid x < 6 \text{ or } x > 10\}$
35. $(-\infty, 5)$ or $(5, 10]$; $\{x \mid x < 5 \text{ or } 5 < x \leq 10\}$
37. False; possible answer: 3 is real but not irrational.
38. False; possible answer: −4 is an integer but not a whole number.
40. A: size 5; B: size 3; C: size 4
41. $\{x \mid 11 \leq x \leq 12\}$; $\{x \mid 12 \leq x \leq 13\}$; $\{x \mid 14 \leq x \leq 16\}$
42. $(0, 8)$; $[8, 12]$; $(12, \infty)$
43. Possible answer: The circumference is always irrational because it is the product of an irrational number, π, and a rational number, the diameter d.

44 a. $\mathbb{R}$, $\mathbb{Q}$

b. Moon, Venus, Mercury, Mars

c. The round-trip to Venus would take longer because twice the average distance between Earth and Venus is about 0.555 AU and the average distance between Earth and Mars is about 0.522 AU.

Answers

26. negative even numbers; cannot be expressed in interval notation; $\{x \mid x < 0 \text{ and } x \text{ is even}\}$
27. numbers greater than or equal to −4 and less than 8; cannot be expressed in roster notation; $\{x \mid -4 \leq x < 8\}$
28. $\{28, 30, 32, 34, 36, 38\}$; cannot be expressed in interval notation; $\{x \mid 27 < x < 39 \text{ and } x \text{ is even}\}$
29. numbers greater than 0 and less than 1; cannot be expressed in roster notation; $(0, 1)$
30. $(-\infty, -4)$ or $(4, \infty)$; $\{x \mid x < -4 \text{ or } x > 4\}$
31. $(-\infty, 2)$ or $(2, \infty)$; $\{x \mid x \neq 2\}$

1-1 PRACTICE A

1-1 PRACTICE C

1-1 PRACTICE B

Order the given numbers from least to greatest. Then classify each number by the subsets of the real numbers to which it belongs.

1. $\frac{2}{3}$, $6.1\overline{7}$, $\sqrt{28}$, $-3\frac{1}{8}$, -4.9

   $-4.9, -3\frac{1}{8}, \frac{2}{3}, \sqrt{28}, 6.1\overline{7}$; $-4.9, -3\frac{1}{8}, \frac{2}{3}$, and $6.1\overline{7}$ are rational numbers, and $\sqrt{28}$ is an irrational number.

2. 5π, $-6\sqrt{3}$, $\frac{-8}{3}$, $4.\overline{615}$, 0

   $-6\sqrt{3}, \frac{-8}{3}, 0, 4.\overline{615}, 5\pi$; 0 is a whole number and an integer; 0, $\frac{-8}{3}$, and $4.\overline{615}$ are rational numbers; 5π and $-6\sqrt{3}$ are irrational numbers.

Rewrite each set in the indicated notation.

3. negative multiples of 3; set-builder notation

   $\{x \mid x = -3n \text{ and } n \text{ is a natural number}\}$

4. $[-4, 0)$ or $(10, 21)$; words

   All real numbers between −4 and 0 or between 10 and 21 including −4 but excluding 0, 10, and 21

5. 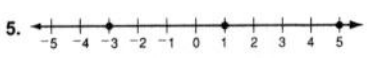 [number line: −5 −4 −3 −2 −1 0 1 2 3 4 5]

   roster notation

   $\{-3, 1, 5\}$

6. 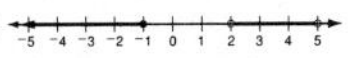 [number line: −5 −4 −3 −2 −1 0 1 2 3 4 5]

   set-builder notation

   $\{x \mid x \leq -1 \text{ or } 2 < x < 5\}$

The length of a necktie is generally in the range [52, 58] inches. The width of a tie is in the range [2.75, 3.5] inches. Use this information for Exercises 7–8.

7. Represent the range of the length of neckties in roster notation. Assume that all neckties come in whole-inch lengths.

   $\{52, 53, 54, 55, 56, 57, 58\}$

8. Represent the range of the width of neckties in set-builder notation.

   $\{x \mid 2.75 \leq x \leq 3.5\}$

Answers

46. 

47. 

48. 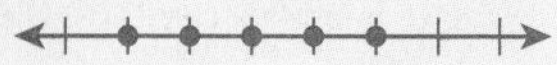

49. 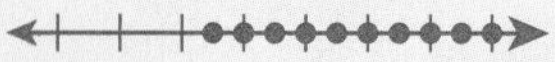

50. 

51. 

52a. {talc, gypsum, calcite, fluorite, apatite}

b. 5

c. Neither; possible answer: quartz is harder than window glass, but apatite is softer than window glass.

56. No; possible answer: square roots of some numbers are not irrational. $\sqrt{9} = 3$ and 3 is rational.

57a. interior designer, police officer, pediatric nurse, marine biologist, astronaut

b. The order would not change.

c. The order would not change.

d. {46,000, 52,900, 59,800, 79,350, 106,950}

58. Possible answer: rational: $\frac{5}{2}$; irrational: $\frac{\sqrt{2}}{2}$; 5 is in the set.

59. Possible answer: rational: 6; irrational: $6\sqrt{3}$; 5 is in the set.

60. Possible answer: rational: 11; irrational: $4\sqrt{5}$; 5 is in the set.

61. Possible answer: rational: $3\frac{2}{3}$; irrational: π; 5 is not in the set.

62. Possible answer: Mathematical and everyday sets are similar because they are both made up of elements. They are different because mathematical sets can be infinite.

45. Use interval notation to express the set of numbers NOT represented on the number line. $(-\infty, -1]$ or $(3, 6)$ or $[9, \infty)$

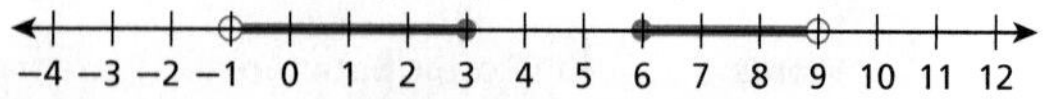

Use a number line to represent each set.

46. $-4 < x \le 4$ or $x > 5$

47. numbers within 6 units of 5

48. $\{-10, -5, 0, 5, 10\}$

49. $\{x \mid x = \frac{1}{2}n \text{ and } n \in \mathbb{N}\}$

50. numbers more than 5 units from −3

51. $(-\infty, 2)$ or $[-1.75, 1.75]$ or $(2, \infty)$

52. Geology The Mohs scale of hardness gives the increasing order of hardness for minerals. The greater the hardness number, the harder the mineral is. Window glass has a hardness of about 5.5 on the Mohs scale.

a. Use roster notation to represent the set of minerals that are softer than window glass.

b. How many elements does the set of minerals that are harder than window glass have?

c. Explain whether {apatite, diamond, topaz, quartz} is a subset of the set of minerals harder than window glass, the set of minerals softer than window glass, or neither.

Mohs Scale of Hardness	
Talc	1
Gypsum	2
Calcite	3
Fluorite	4
Apatite	5
Orthoclase	6
Quartz	7
Topaz	8
Corundum	9
Diamond	10

Identify which of the real numbers best describes each situation. Choose from $\mathbb{R}$, $\mathbb{Q}$, $\mathbb{Z}$, $\mathbb{W}$, and $\mathbb{N}$.

53. the number of stops a train makes during a trip $\mathbb{N}$

54. the cumulative grade point average for a student $\mathbb{Q}$

55. the squares of the set of integers $\mathbb{W}$

56. Critical Thinking Are all square roots irrational numbers? Explain.

57. Careers The graph shows several median salaries by profession.

a. Order the professions by salary from least to greatest.

b. **What if...?** If each salary were increased by $5000, would the order from part **a** change?

c. **What if...?** If each salary were increased by 15%, would the order from part **a** change?

d. Use roster notation to represent the set of salaries from part **c**.

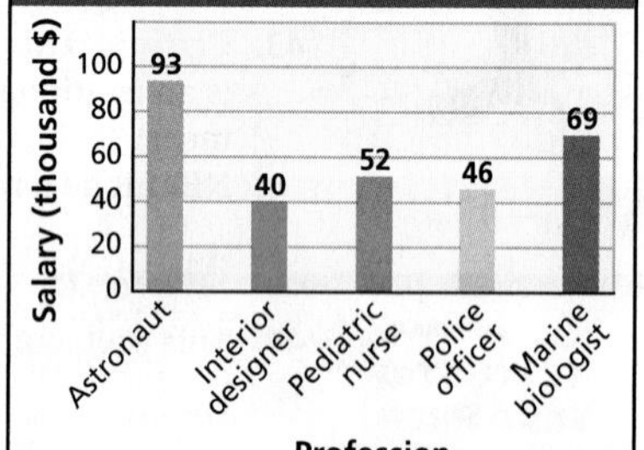

Identify one rational number and one irrational number that belongs to each set. Then explain whether the number 5 is an element of the set.

58. $\{x \mid x = 5c \text{ and } 0 < c \le 1\}$

59. $-1 < x \le 1$ or $x > 4$

60. numbers within 4 units of 9

61. $(3, 5)$

62. Write About It People use sets of tools and eat on sets of dishes. How are mathematical sets similar to and different from such everyday sets?

1-1 READING STRATEGIES

There are many different ways to represent the same interval.

Representing Intervals				
Number Line	Inequality	Interval Notation	Set-Builder Notation	Words
	$x > 2$	$(2, \infty)$	$\{x \mid x > 2\}$	Numbers greater than 2
	$x \le 2$	$(-\infty, 2]$	$\{x \mid x \le 2\}$	Numbers less than or equal to 2
	$x \ne 2$	$(-\infty, 2)$ OR $(2, \infty)$	$\{x \mid x \ne 2$ and $x \in \mathbb{R}\}$	All real numbers except 2
	$-1 < x < 1$ OR $3 \le x \le 4$	$(-1, 1)$ OR $[3, 4]$	$\{x \mid -1 < x < 1$ OR $3 \le x \le 4\}$	Numbers between −1 and 1 or from 3 to 4

Brackets [ ] include the endpoints. Parentheses ( ) do not include endpoints.

Use words to describe each interval.

1. $\{x \mid x \ge -3\}$

   x is greater than or equal to −3.

2. $(-6, 4)$

   x is between −6 and 4.

3. $(\infty, -1]$

   x is less than or equal to −1.

4. $\{x \mid x \ne 0 \text{ and } x \in \mathbb{R}\}$

   x is any real number except 0.

5. $[-10, -5]$ OR $[-2, \infty)$

   x is any number from −10 to −5 or *x* is greater than or equal to −2.

1-1 RETEACH

As you move from left to right on a number line, the numbers increase. Use a number line to help you order real numbers.

Order from least to greatest:

$\sqrt{11}, -2.\overline{6}, \frac{1}{2}, -\frac{\pi}{2}, 2.354.$

Use a calculator to approximate $\sqrt{11}$ and $-\frac{\pi}{2}$ as decimals:

$\sqrt{11} \approx 3.32$ and $-\frac{\pi}{2} \approx -1.57.$

Plot each point on a number line.

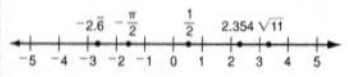

Read the numbers from left to right on the number line.

From least to greatest, the order is $-2.\overline{6}, -\frac{\pi}{2}, \frac{1}{2}, 2.354, \sqrt{11}$.

Order the given numbers from least to greatest. Use a number line to help you.

1. $\pi, -1.\overline{9}, 2\frac{2}{3}, -0.456$, and $\sqrt{3}$

   $\pi \approx 3.14$, $2\frac{2}{3} \approx 2.67$, and $\sqrt{3} \approx 1.73$

   $-1.\overline{9}, -0.456, \sqrt{3}, 2\frac{2}{3}, \pi$

2. $-1.75, 1, \frac{1}{5}, 1.55$, and $-\sqrt{5}$

   $\frac{1}{5} =$ 0.2

   $-\sqrt{5} \approx$ −2.24

   $-\sqrt{5}, -1.75, \frac{1}{5}, 1, 1.55$

3. $\sqrt{6}, -2.\overline{63}, -4.36, 2\sqrt{3}$, and $-\frac{1}{6}$

   $\sqrt{6} \approx$ 2.45

   $2\sqrt{3} \approx$ 3.46

   $-\frac{1}{6} \approx$ −0.17

   $-4.36, -2.\overline{63}, -\frac{1}{6}, \sqrt{6}, 2\sqrt{3}$

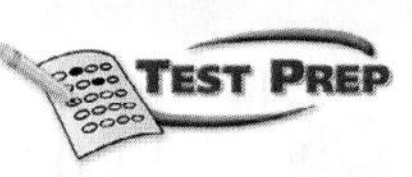

TEST PREP

63. Which of the following is NOT equivalent to 4?
Ⓐ $\sqrt{16}$ Ⓑ $3-(-1)$ Ⓒ $\frac{12}{3}$ ⒹⓄ $2(-2)$

64. Which list is in order from least to greatest?
Ⓕ $\frac{3}{7}, 0.5, \frac{\sqrt{3}}{2}$ Ⓖ $0.5, \frac{3}{7}, \frac{\sqrt{3}}{2}$ Ⓗ $\frac{3}{7}, \frac{\sqrt{3}}{2}, 0.5$ Ⓙ $\frac{\sqrt{3}}{2}, 0.5, \frac{3}{7}$

65. Which set best describes the numbers graphed on the number line?

−3 −2 −1 0 1 2 3

Ⓐ $\{-2, -1.5, 0.5, 1.5\}$ Ⓒ $\{-\frac{6}{3}, -1.\overline{3}, \frac{3}{4}, \sqrt{2}\}$
Ⓑ $\{-\sqrt{4}, -\frac{5}{3}, 0.\overline{3}, 1\frac{1}{2}\}$ Ⓓ $\{-1\frac{1}{3}, 0.\overline{3}, 1.5, 2\}$

66. Which statement can be determined from the diagram?
Ⓕ Every isosceles triangle is equilateral.
Ⓖ Every triangle is either right or isosceles.
Ⓗ No right triangles are isosceles.
Ⓙ No right triangles are equilateral.

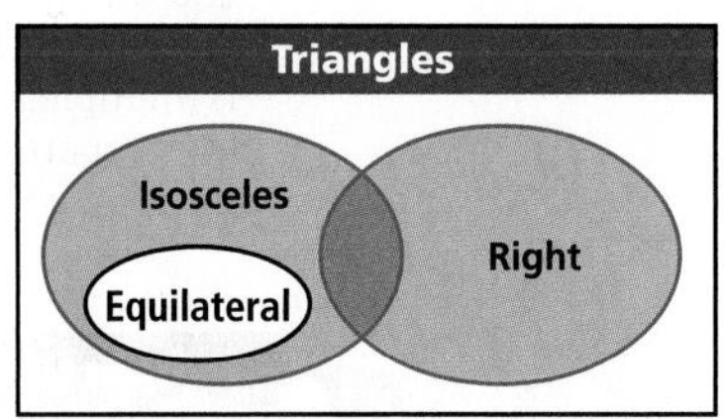

CHALLENGE AND EXTEND

Explain whether each set is finite or infinite. Then identify the subsets of the real numbers to which the set belongs.

67. values in dollars of U.S. coins finite; $\mathbb{Q}$
68. $\{0.\overline{3}, 0.\overline{6}, 1, 1.\overline{3}, \ldots\}$ infinite; $\mathbb{Q}$

finite; $\mathbb{Q}$, $\mathbb{Z}$, $\mathbb{W}$, $\mathbb{N}$ 69. U.S. Postal Service 5-digit zip codes
70. $\{x \mid x = \frac{c}{4} \text{ and } c \in \mathbb{Z}\}$ infinite; $\mathbb{Q}$

71. The symbol π is used to represent the irrational number 3.14159265358.... The fraction $\frac{22}{7}$ and the decimal 3.14 are approximations of π. Possible answers:
  a. Find a rational number between 3.14 and π. 3.141
  b. Find a rational number between $\frac{22}{7}$ and π. 3.142

SPIRAL REVIEW

Use the rectangular prism for Exercises 72–74. *(Previous course)*

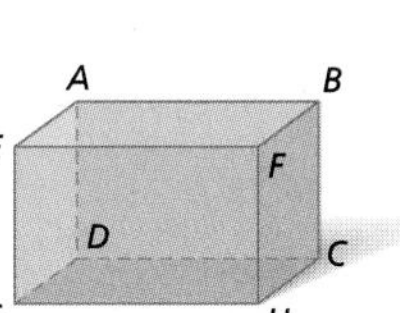
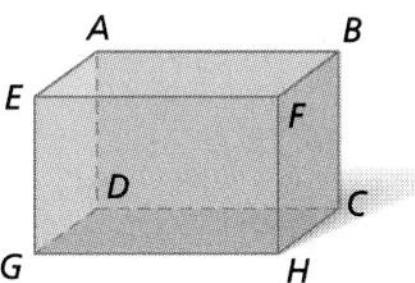

72. Name two edges that intersect to form a right angle.
73. Name two faces that model parallel planes.
74. Name two faces that model perpendicular planes.
75. Debra went shopping with three bills in her wallet. She returned home from shopping with less than \$1.00 in her wallet. She made purchases of \$21.49, \$11.59, and \$12.95, all with 6.5% sales tax. What bills did Debra have in her wallet when she went shopping? *(Previous course)*

\$20, \$20, and \$10

76. The Wildcat pep squad is enlarging the Wildcats' team logo to create a square banner. The ratio of the side length of the logo shown to the side length of the banner is 1:120. What is the area of the banner in square centimeters? *(Previous course)* 197,136 cm²

3.7 cm

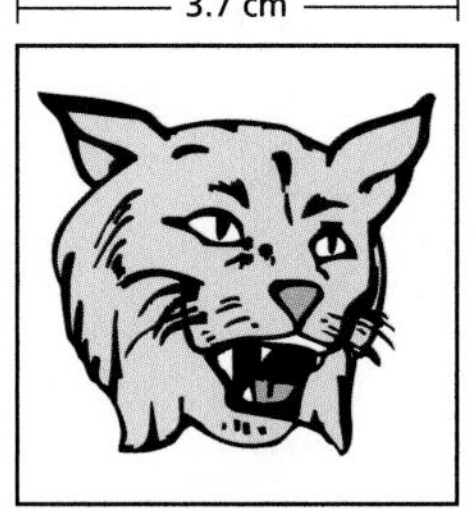

clipart.com

1-1 PROBLEM SOLVING

Ari is comparing the density of some common substances. Density measures how compact a substance is. Use the data in the table for Exercises 1–3.

Substance	Density (kg/m^3)
Air	$1\frac{3}{10}$
Copper	8.9
Helium	$\frac{9}{50}$
Hydrogen	0.09
Milk	1030
Olive oil	900

1. Ari begins by ordering the densities from least to greatest. Write his ordered list.
   $0.09; \frac{9}{50}; 1\frac{3}{10}; 8.9; 900; 1030$
2. Should Ari use roster, interval, or set-builder notation to represent his data? Why?
   roster notation; cannot be written in interval or set-builder notation
3. Which subset of the real numbers best describes the densities given in the table? Choose from $\mathbb{R}$, $\mathbb{Q}$, $\mathbb{Z}$, and $\mathbb{N}$.
   $\mathbb{Q}$

Choose the letter for the best answer.

4. Jean wrote the possible readings on the speedometer of her new car in set-builder notation. Which could be what she wrote?
   A $\{x \mid 0 > x > 120\}$
   B $\{x \mid x = 10n \text{ and } n \le 12\}$
   C $\{10, 20, 30, 40, 50, \ldots, 120\}$
   Ⓓ $\{x \mid 0 \le x \le 120\}$
5. Members of the Booster Club are designing a calendar of the school year to sell as a fund raiser. They begin by making a roster of the possible number of days in a month. Which shows the roster?
   F $\{30, 31\}$
   G $\{x \mid 28 \le x \le 31\}$
   Ⓗ $\{28, 29, 30, 31\}$
   J $\{x \mid x \ge 28 \text{ and } x \in \mathbb{N}\}$

Tell whether each statement is true or false. If false, give a counterexample.

6. Trish and Alex are comparing the populations of different cities in Texas. Alex says the population of a city is always an integer.
   True; number of people must be a whole number and all whole numbers are integers.
7. Neil and Sandy are cutting out circles as decorations. Sandy comments that the distance around a circle is always a rational number.
   False; possible answer: $C = \pi(5)$

1-1 CHALLENGE

The set $A = \{2, 4, 6, 8\}$ is a subset of the even natural numbers. Each element of set A is an even natural number. The set $B = \{2, 3, 4, 5, 6\}$ is not a subset of the even natural numbers. Set B contains the odd numbers 3 and 5 which are not in the set of even natural numbers.

Consider the empty set ∅ which can also be written as { }. It is the set with no elements. Is ∅ a subset of the even natural numbers as well? If yes, then every element in ∅ must be an even natural number. If no, then there must be an element in this set that is not an even natural number. Since there are no elements in ∅ that are not even natural numbers, ∅ must be a subset of the set of even natural numbers.

For Exercises 1–4 it may help to list all the subsets.

1. How many subsets does set $E = \{5\}$ have? 2
2. How many subsets does set $F = \{5, 10\}$ have? 4
3. How many subsets does set $G = \{5, 10, 15\}$ have? 8
4. How many subsets does set $H = \{5, 10, 15, 20\}$ have? 16
5. What pattern do you see developing in the number of subsets for each set?
   For each additional element in the set, the number of subsets doubles.
6. How many subsets are there for a set of 8 elements? Explain your reasoning.
   256; Possible answer: I kept doubling the number of subsets from 4 elements to 8 elements.
7. How many subsets would there be for a set of n elements? 2^n

Set T has 5 elements.

8. How many subsets of set T have 5 elements? 1
9. How many subsets of set T have 4 elements? 5
10. How many subsets of set T have 3 elements? 10
11. How many subsets of set T have 2 elements? 10
12. How many subsets of set T have 1 element? 5
13. How many subsets of set T have 0 elements? 1
14. Where have you seen this sequence of numbers before?
    Pascal's Triangle

TEST PREP DOCTOR In **Exercise 64,** encourage students to use $\frac{1}{2}$, or 0.5, as a reference. For example, since $\frac{3}{7} < \frac{3.5}{7}$, $\frac{3}{7} < \frac{1}{2}$. Thus **G** and **J** are eliminated. Similarly, $\frac{\sqrt{3}}{2} > \frac{1}{2}$, so **H** is eliminated.

Answers

Possible answers:

72. $\overline{AB}$ and $\overline{BC}$
73. *AEGD* and *BFHC*
74. *AEGD* and *ABFE*

Journal

Have students describe familiar objects in terms of nested subsets and Venn diagrams. (A nested subset is a subset of a subset.) For example, a boy is a human, a mammal, an animal, and so on. Challenge students to create as many levels of nesting as they can.

ALTERNATIVE ASSESSMENT

Have students create examples of sets that cannot be described in roster or interval notation. Have them use set-builder notation to describe the sets and explain why the other notation methods fail.

Power Presentations with PowerPoint®

1-1 Lesson Quiz

Consider the numbers $3.\overline{1}$, π, 3, and 3.5729.

1. Order the numbers from least to greatest. $3, 3.\overline{1}, \pi, 3.5729$
2. Classify each number by the subsets of the real numbers to which it belongs.
   3: $\mathbb{R}$, $\mathbb{Q}$, $\mathbb{Z}$, $\mathbb{W}$, $\mathbb{N}$; $3.\overline{1}$: $\mathbb{R}$, $\mathbb{Q}$; 3.5729: $\mathbb{R}$, $\mathbb{Q}$; π: $\mathbb{R}$, irrational

Use interval notation to represent each set of numbers.

3. $-8 < x \le -1$ $(-8, -1]$
4. −6 −4 −2 0 2 4 6
   $[-5, 1)$ or $[3, \infty)$
5. Rewrite the set $\{x \mid x = 5n, n \in \mathbb{N}\}$ in words.
   positive multiples of 5

Also available on transparency

1-2 Organizer

Pacing: Traditional 1 day
Block $\frac{1}{2}$ day

Objective: Identify and use properties of real numbers.

Online Edition
Tutorial Videos

Countdown to Testing Week 1

Power Presentations with PowerPoint®

Warm Up

Simplify.

1. $-5 + 5$ 0 **2.** $-7\left(\frac{1}{-7}\right)$ 1

3. $\frac{1}{2}(3.62)$ 1.81

4. Find 10% of $61.70. $6.17

5. Find the reciprocal of -4. $\frac{1}{-4}$

Also available on transparency

Math Fact !!

There is evidence of both the Indian and Mayan cultures using the number zero by 650 C.E. By contrast, zero was not widely used as a number in Europe until centuries later.

1-2 Properties of Real Numbers

Objective
Identify and use properties of real numbers.

Why learn this?
You can use properties of real numbers to quickly calculate tips in your head. (See Example 3.)

"The tax and tip I understand, but what's this charge for shipping and handling?"

Andrew Toos/CartoonResource.com

The four basic math operations are addition, subtraction, multiplication, and division. Because subtraction is addition of the opposite and division is multiplication by the reciprocal, the properties of real numbers focus on addition and multiplication.

Know it! Note

Properties of Real Numbers Identities and Inverses

For all real numbers n,

WORDS	NUMBERS	ALGEBRA
Additive Identity Property The sum of a number and 0, the additive identity, is the original number.	$3 + 0 = 3$	$n + 0 = 0 + n = n$
Multiplicative Identity Property The product of a number and 1, the multiplicative identity, is the original number.	$\frac{2}{3} \cdot 1 = \frac{2}{3}$	$n \cdot 1 = 1 \cdot n = n$
Additive Inverse Property The sum of a number and its opposite, or additive inverse, is 0.	$5 + (-5) = 0$	$n + (-n) = 0$
Multiplicative Inverse Property The product of a nonzero number and its reciprocal, or multiplicative inverse, is 1.	$8 \cdot \frac{1}{8} = 1$	$n \cdot \frac{1}{n} = 1\ (n \neq 0)$

Recall from previous courses that the opposite of any number a is $-a$ and the reciprocal of any nonzero number a is $\frac{1}{a}$.

EXAMPLE 1 Finding Inverses

Find the additive and multiplicative inverse of each number.

A -9

additive inverse: 9 — *The opposite of -9 is $-(-9) = 9$.*

Check $-9 + 9 = 0$ ✔ — *The Additive Inverse Property holds.*

multiplicative inverse: $\frac{1}{-9}$ — *The reciprocal of -9 is $\frac{1}{-9}$.*

Check $-9 \cdot \left(\frac{1}{-9}\right) = 1$ ✔ — *The Multiplicative Inverse Property holds.*

State Resources

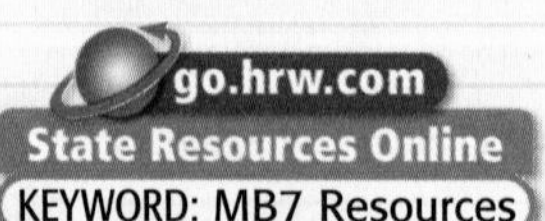

go.hrw.com
State Resources Online
KEYWORD: MB7 Resources

1 Introduce

EXPLORATION

1-2 Properties of Real Numbers

You may use a calculator to help you with the following problems.

Tell whether each statement is true or false.

1. $6 + (-2) = (-2) + 6$
2. $8 - (-2) = (-2) - 8$
3. $5 - 4 - 1 = 1 - 4 - 5$
4. $20 \div 5 \div 2 = 2 \div 5 \div 20$
5. $3(7) = 7(3)$
6. $7 + 3 + 2 = 2 + 7 + 3$
7. $9 \div 3 = 3 \div 9$
8. $10 \cdot 20 \cdot 30 = 30 \cdot 20 \cdot 10$
9. Based on your answers to Problems 1–8, for which operations (addition, subtraction, multiplication, and division) does the order of the numbers make a difference in the result?

Tell whether each statement is true or false.

10. $(8 \div 4) \div 2 = 8 \div (4 \div 2)$
11. $(9 + 4) + 3 = 9 + (4 + 3)$
12. $(5 - 4) - 1 = 5 - (4 - 1)$
13. $21 \cdot (32 \cdot 43) = (21 \cdot 32) \cdot 43$
14. Based on your answers to Problems 10–13, for which operations (addition, subtraction, multiplication, and division) does the grouping of the numbers make a difference in the result?

THINK AND DISCUSS

15. **Discuss** how the properties you explored above might help you find $13 \cdot 20 \cdot 5$ by using mental math.
16. **Discuss** whether it would matter which operation you did first if you had more than one operation in a problem.

Motivate

Ask students what number you could add to 8 to total 0. -8 Ask what number you could multiply by 8 to get 0. 0 Then ask what number you could multiply by 8 to get 1. $\frac{1}{8}$ Explain that special properties of real numbers can be used to find sums that equal 0 and products that equal 0 or 1.

Explorations and answers are provided in the *Explorations* binder.

Find the additive and multiplicative inverse of each number.

B $\frac{4}{5}$

additive inverse: $-\frac{4}{5}$ — *The opposite of $\frac{4}{5}$ is $-\frac{4}{5}$.*

multiplicative inverse: $\frac{5}{4}$ — *The reciprocal of $\frac{4}{5}$ is $\frac{5}{4}$.*

Find the additive and multiplicative inverse of each number.

1a. 500 **-500; $\frac{1}{500}$** **1b.** -0.01 **0.01; -100**

Properties of Real Numbers — **Addition and Multiplication**

For all real numbers a and b,

WORDS	NUMBERS	ALGEBRA
Closure Property The sum or product of any two real numbers is a real number.	$2 + 3 = 5$ $2(3) = 6$	$a + b \in \mathbb{R}$ $ab \in \mathbb{R}$
Commutative Property You can add or multiply real numbers in any order without changing the result.	$7 + 11 = 11 + 7$ $7(11) = 11(7)$	$a + b = b + a$ $ab = ba$
Associative Property The sum or product of three or more real numbers is the same regardless of the way the numbers are grouped.	$(5 + 3) + 7 = 5 + (3 + 7)$ $(5 \cdot 3)7 = 5(3 \cdot 7)$	$(a + b) + c = a + (b + c)$ $(ab)c = a(bc)$
Distributive Property When you multiply a sum by a number, the result is the same whether you add and then multiply or whether you multiply each term by the number and then add the products.	$5(2 + 8) = 5(2) + 5(8)$ $(2 + 8)5 = (2)5 + (8)5$	$a(b + c) = ab + ac$ $(b + c)a = ba + ca$

Reading Math

Based on the Closure Property, the real numbers are said to be *closed* under addition and *closed* under multiplication.

EXAMPLE 2 Identifying Properties of Real Numbers

Identify the property demonstrated by each equation.

A $(3\sqrt{3} + 5)2 = (3\sqrt{3})2 + (5)2$ — *The 2 has been distributed to each term.*

Distributive Property

B $(3 + 6) + (-6) = 3 + [6 + (-6)]$ — *The numbers have been regrouped.*

Associative Property of Addition

Identify the property demonstrated by each equation.

2a. $9\sqrt{2} = (\sqrt{2})9$ **2b.** $9(12\pi) = (9 \cdot 12)\pi$

You can apply the properties of real numbers to simplify numeric expressions and solve problems mentally.

COMMON ERROR ALERT

Students may attempt to distribute addition over multiplication. For example, they may incorrectly write $a + (b \cdot c)$ as $(a + b) \cdot (a + c)$. Use a concrete example with $a = 1$, $b = 2$, and $c = 3$ to show them that this does not work.

Power Presentations with PowerPoint®

Additional Examples

Example 1

Find the additive and multiplicative inverse of each number.

A. 12 $-12; \frac{1}{12}$

B. $-\frac{9}{4}$ $\frac{9}{4}; -\frac{4}{9}$

Example 2

Identify the property demonstrated by each equation.

A. $2 \cdot 3.9 = 3.9 \cdot 2$
Comm. Prop. of Mult.

B. $3(2\sqrt{8}) = (3 \cdot 2)\sqrt{8}$
Assoc. Prop. of Mult.

Also available on transparency

INTERVENTION

Questioning Strategies

EXAMPLE 1

- What is the sum of a number and its opposite?
- What is the product of a number and its reciprocal?

EXAMPLE 2

- Which property states a fact about addition and multiplication at the same time?

Answers to *Check It Out!*

2a. Comm. Prop. of Mult.
2b. Assoc. Prop. of Mult.

2 Teach

Guided Instruction

Students may be familiar with many of the terms and properties in this lesson. Emphasize the terms *identity* and *inverse* because both will be very important in the study of algebra. Review the properties with students. Carefully work through **Example 3** to show students how using the properties of real numbers can make calculations easier.

Reaching All Learners

Through Graphic Organizers

Have students create posters displaying one or more of the properties of real numbers in words, numbers, and algebra. Place the posters in the classroom for the students to reference throughout the course.

Power Presentations with PowerPoint®

Additional Examples

Example 3

Use mental math to find 5% tax on a \$42.40 purchase. \$2.12

Example 4

Classify each statement as sometimes, always, or never true. Give examples or properties to support your answers.

A. $a \cdot b = a$ when $b = 3$
sometimes true; true if $a = 0$; false if $a \neq 0$, as in $1 \cdot 3 \neq 1$

B. $3(a + 1) = 3a + 3$ always true by the Distributive Property

Also available on transparency

INTERVENTION Questioning Strategies

EXAMPLE 3

- How do properties of real numbers help you in this example?
- Why is finding 10% the same as moving the decimal point left one place?

EXAMPLE 4

- Is one example enough to prove that a statement is always or never true?

Answers to *Check It Out!*

4a. always true by the Additive Inverse Property

4b. sometimes true; possible answer: true when $a = 0$, $b = 1$, and $c = 2$; false when $a = 1$, $b = 2$, and $c = 3$

EXAMPLE 3 *Consumer Economics Application*

Use mental math to find a 15% tip for the bill shown.

Think: $15\% = 10\% + 5\%$

$(10\% + 5\%)24.80$

$10\%(24.80) + 5\%(24.80)$ — *Distributive Property*

Think: Find 10% of \$24.80

$10\%(24.80) = 2.480 = 2.48$ — *Move the decimal point left 1 place.*

Think: $5\% = \frac{1}{2}(10\%)$

$\frac{1}{2}(2.48) = 1.24$ — *5% is half of 10% so find half of 2.48.*

$2.48 + 1.24 = 3.72$ — *Add 10% of 24.80 to 5% of 24.80.*

A 15% tip for a meal that totaled \$24.80 is \$3.72.

CHECK IT OUT! 3. Use mental math to find a 20% discount on a \$15.60 shirt. **\$3.12**

EXAMPLE 4 Classifying Statements as Sometimes, Always, or Never True

Classify each statement as sometimes, always, or never true. Give examples or properties to support your answer.

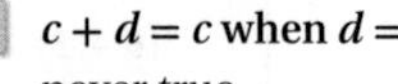

A $c + d = c$ when $d = 2$
never true
counterexample: $1 + 2 \neq 1$

By the Additive Identity Property, $c + 0 = c$, so $c + d = c$ is only true when $d = 0$, not when $d = 2$.

B $a - c = c - a$
sometimes true
true example: $5 - 5 = 5 - 5$
false example: $5 - 2 \neq 2 - 5$

True and false examples exist. The statement is true when $a = c$ and false when $a \neq c$.

CHECK IT OUT! **Classify each statement as sometimes, always, or never true. Give examples or properties to support your answer.**

4a. $a + (-a) = b + (-b)$ **4b.** $a - (b + c) = (a - b) + (a - c)$

THINK AND DISCUSS

1. Explain whether the Commutative Property applies to subtraction and division.
2. Tell why zero has no multiplicative inverse.
3. **GET ORGANIZED** Copy and complete the graphic organizer. In each box, write an example of the property indicated.

Property	Addition	Multiplication
Identity		
Inverse		
Associative		
Commutative		
Distributive		

3 Close

Summarize

Check students' understanding of the properties by asking them if the following are true or false for real values of the variables.

$n + 0 = n$ true $n \cdot 0 = n$ false

$n + (-n) = 1$ false $n \cdot \frac{1}{n} = 1$ true

$a \cdot (b \cdot c) = (a \cdot b) \cdot c$ true

$a + (b \cdot c) = (a + b) \cdot (a + c)$, where $(a \neq 0)$ false

$a(b + c) = ab + ac$ true

ONGOING ASSESSMENT and INTERVENTION

***Diagnose Before* the Lesson**
1-2 Warm Up, TE p. 14

***Monitor During* the Lesson**
Check It Out! Exercises, SE pp. 15–16
Questioning Strategies, TE pp. 15–16

***Assess After* the Lesson**
1-2 Lesson Quiz, TE p. 19
Alternative Assessment, TE p. 19

Answers to *Think and Discuss*

Possible answers:

1. No; the Commutative Property does not apply to subtraction or division because the order in subtraction and division is essential.
2. The product of 0 and another number is always 0, so you cannot multiply 0 by any number and get a product of 1.
3. See p. A2.

1-2 Exercises

go.hrw.com
Homework Help Online
KEYWORD: MB7 1-2
Parent Resources Online
KEYWORD: MB7 Parent

GUIDED PRACTICE

SEE EXAMPLE 1 p. 14

Find the additive and multiplicative inverse of each number.

1. -36 $36; -\frac{1}{36}$
2. -0.05 $0.05; -20$
3. $2\sqrt{2}$ $-2\sqrt{2}; \frac{1}{2\sqrt{2}}$
4. $\frac{2}{5}$ $-\frac{2}{5}; \frac{5}{2}$
5. $-\frac{1}{500}$ $\frac{1}{500}; -500$
6. 0.25 $-0.25; 4$

SEE EXAMPLE 2 p. 15

Identify the property demonstrated by each equation.

7. $3(2\sqrt{5}) = (3 \cdot 2)\sqrt{5}$
8. $x + 7y = 7y + x$
9. $\frac{1}{3}(28)(9) = \frac{1}{3}(9)(28)$

SEE EXAMPLE 3 p. 16

Use mental math to find each value.

10. cost of 3 items at \$2.55 each **\$7.65**
11. a $33\frac{1}{3}$% discount on a \$21.99 item **\$7.33**

SEE EXAMPLE 4 p. 16

Classify each statement as sometimes, always, or never true. Give examples or properties to support your answer.

12. $20a + 20b = 5(4a + 4b)$
13. $a \div b = b \div a$
14. $a + (bc) = (a + b)(a + c)$

PRACTICE AND PROBLEM SOLVING

Independent Practice

For Exercises	See Example
15–20	1
21–23	2
24–25	3
26–27	4

Extra Practice
Skills Practice p. S4
Application Practice p. S32

Find the additive and multiplicative inverse of each number.

15. -2.5 $2.5; -\frac{2}{5}$
16. 0.75 $-0.75; \frac{4}{3}$
17. 2π $-2\pi; \frac{1}{2\pi}$
18. $-\frac{2}{3}$ $\frac{2}{3}; -\frac{3}{2}$
19. $\frac{1}{20}$ $-\frac{1}{20}; 20$
20. 6231 $-6231; \frac{1}{6231}$

Identify the property demonstrated by each equation.

21. $z(x - y) = zx - zy$
22. $4abc = 4acb$
23. $(a + 0) + b = a + b$

Use mental math to find each value.

24. 9% sales tax on a \$150 purchase **\$13.50**
25. cost of 5 items at \$1.96 each **\$9.80**

Classify each statement as sometimes, always, or never true. Give examples or properties to support your answer.

26. $a - (b - c) = a - b + c$
27. $ab\left(\frac{1}{ab}\right) = 0$ for $a \neq 0$ and $b \neq 0$

Shopping **Use the advertisement for Exercises 28–31. Write an expression to represent each total cost and then simplify it.**

28. cost of 2 pencil sets and 3 paintbrush sets
$2(8.88) + 3(14.99) = \$62.73$
29. cost of 4 acrylic paints minus a refund for 2 pencil sets
$4(11.99) - 2(8.88) = \$30.20$
30. cost of 4 paintbrush sets at a 15% discount
$4(0.85)(14.99) = 50.966 \approx \$50.97$
31. cost of 3 sketch books at a 10% discount and 5 acrylic paints at a 25% discount
$3(0.9)(9.96) + 5(0.75)(11.99) = 71.8545 \approx \$71.85$

1-2 Exercises

Assignment Guide

Assign *Guided Practice* exercises as necessary.

If you finished Examples **1–2**
Basic 15–23, 35–40
Average 15–23, 35–40, 57
Advanced 15–23, 35–40, 57

If you finished Examples **1–4**
Basic 15–34, 41–42, 50–56, 59–65
Average 15–43, 50–65
Advanced 15–65

Homework Quick Check
Quickly check key concepts.
Exercises: 18, 22, 24, 26, 42

Answers

7. Assoc. Prop. of Mult.
8. Comm. Prop. of Add.
9. Comm. Prop. of Mult.
12. always true by the Distributive Property
13. sometimes true; possible answer: true when $a = b$; false when $a = 1$ and $b = 2$
14. sometimes true; possible answer: true when $a = 0$; false when $a = 1$, $b = 2$, and $c = 3$
21. Distributive Property
22. Comm. Prop. of Mult.
23. Additive Identity Property
26. always true by the Distributive Property
27. never true by the Multiplicative Inverse Property

State Resources

Multiple Representations In **Exercise 34,** remind students that an increase of 20% results in 120%, or 1.2 times, the original amount.

Exercise 50 involves using the properties of modular arithmetic. This exercise prepares students for the Multi-Step Test Prep on page 42.

Answers

35. 5; Assoc. Prop. of Add.
36. $\frac{11}{15}x$; Comm. Prop. of Add.
37. 0; Additive Identity Property
38. 5; Distributive Property
39. $\frac{5}{4}$; Multiplicative Inverse Prop.
40. a; Comm. Prop. of Mult.
41. yes; Distributive Property
42. Possible answer: Find the ticket price, which is 60% of \$185. 10% of \$185 is \$18.50, so 60% of \$185 is (6)18.50, or \$111.00. Add \$28 for fees and surcharge: \$111 + \$28 = \$139.
43. Possible answer: The set of integers is made up of the set of natural numbers, their additive inverses, and the additive identity. The set of rational numbers is made up of the set of numbers that can be expressed as a ratio of two natural numbers, their additive inverses, and the additive identity.
44. Assoc. Prop. of Add.; Additive Inverse Prop.
45. Multiplicative Identity Prop.

Estimation Use the map for Exercises 32–34.

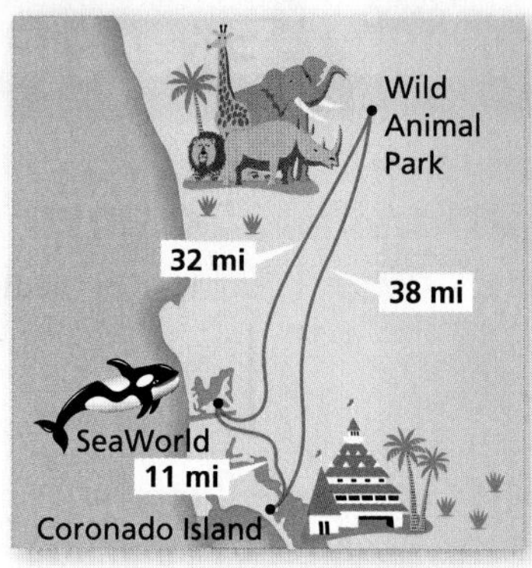

A San Diego tour van starts at Coronado Island, stops at SeaWorld, then at the Wild Animal Park, and then returns to Coronado Island.

32. Estimate how long it would take the van to make one loop at an average speed of 40 mi/h. **≈ 2 h**
33. **Multi-Step** The tour van gets 8 mi/gal, and the gas tank holds 24 gal. Estimate the number of loops the tour van can make on one tank. **≈ 2 loops**
34. **What if...?** The van adds another stop that increases the length of its loop by 20%. Estimate the number of loops the van could make in one 10 h day if it averaged 40 mi/h. **≈ 4 loops**

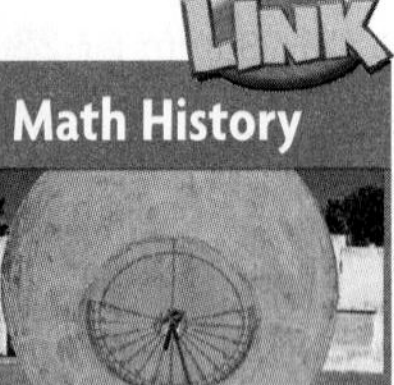

Math History

Brahmagupta, an Indian mathematician (598–668), was one of the first to use zero as a number. He was also head of the ancient astronomical observatory at Ujjain, India. The photo shows a sundial from the observatory at Ujjain.

Complete each statement, and state the property illustrated.

35. $(10 + ■) + 23 = 10 + (5 + 23)$
36. $12 + \frac{11}{15}x = ■ + 12$
37. $j + ■ = j$
38. $5 \cdot 4 + 5 \cdot 3 = ■ \cdot (4 + 3)$
39. $\frac{4}{5} \cdot ■ = 1$
40. $ab = b■$

41. **Consumer Economics** A store is offering a 25% discount on every item purchased. To find the total discount on a purchase, Gary found the sum of the prices and then multiplied the sum by $\frac{1}{4}$. Maria found the total discount by multiplying each price by $\frac{1}{4}$ and then adding the discounts. Do both methods give the same result? Use properties of real numbers to explain why or why not.
42. **Travel** The base price for an airplane ticket from Austin to Houston is \$185. The final price includes an additional \$16 for airport fees and a \$12 fuel surcharge. José purchased a ticket online for 40% off the base price. Explain how to use mental math to find José's final price to the nearest dollar.
43. **Critical Thinking** Use the terms *additive inverse* and *additive identity* to define the set of integers and the set of rational numbers in terms of the set of natural numbers. For example, the set of whole numbers is made up of the set of natural numbers and the additive identity.

Identify which properties make each statement true for all real values of *c*.

44. $-c + (c + 4) = 4$
45. $(10c) \cdot 1 = 10c$
46. $3(2 + c) = (c + 2)3$
47. $4c + 5 = 4(c + 2) - 3$
48. $\frac{1}{2}(1 - 5c) = \frac{-5c + 1}{2}$
49. $8 - 16c = 8(1 - 2c)$

50. This problem will prepare you for the Multi-Step Test Prep on page 42.

Astronauts use a 24-hour clock to tell time. The 24-hour cycle is an example of *modular arithmetic,* arithmetic performed on a circle. The circle shows mod 24. You can perform arithmetic by moving around the circle. For example, 22 + 8 = 6 in mod 24, because if you move 8 units clockwise from 22, you end up at 6.

a. What is 18 + 13 in mod 24?
b. Is addition commutative in mod 24? Give an example to support your answer.
c. Is addition associative in mod 24? Give an example to support your answer.

1-2 PRACTICE A

1-2 PRACTICE C

1-2 PRACTICE B

Find the additive and multiplicative inverse of each number.

1. −6 — $6; \frac{-1}{6}$
2. $3\frac{1}{4}$ — $-3\frac{1}{4}; \frac{4}{13}$
3. −0.7 — $0.7; \frac{-10}{7}$

Identify the property demonstrated by each equation.

4. $x(a - b) = ax - bx$ — Distributive
5. $m + (n + 6) = (n + 6) + m$ — Commutative
6. $4(gh) = (4g)h$ — Associative
7. $\frac{-\sqrt{5}}{w} \cdot \frac{w}{-\sqrt{5}} = 1$ — Multiplicative Inverse

Use mental math to find each value.

8. 5% rebate on a \$150 cell phone — \$7.50
9. cost of 8 items at \$12.98 each — \$103.84

Classify each statement as sometimes, always, or never true. Give examples or properties to support your answer.

10. $d + (-d) = 0$ — Always; Additive Inverse
11. $a + (bc) = (a + b) \cdot (a + c)$ — Never; $1 + (2 \cdot 3) \neq (1 + 2) \cdot (1 + 3)$

Use the table for Exercises 12–14. Write an expression to represent each total cost and then simplify it.

School Supply Store	
Item	Price
Notebook	\$1.79
Pen	\$2.89
Binder	\$3.19

12. cost of 2 pens and 3 notebooks — 2(\$2.89) + 3(\$1.79) = \$11.15
13. cost of 1 binder and 5 notebooks — 5(\$1.79) + \$3.19 = \$12.14
14. cost of 3 notebooks at 20% discount, a binder at 25% discount, and 2 pens — 3(1.79 − 0.36) + (3.19 − 0.80) + 2(2.89) = \$12.46

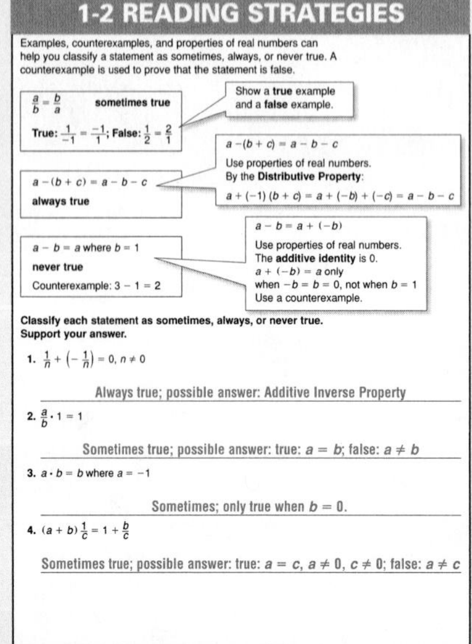

1-2 READING STRATEGIES

Examples, counterexamples, and properties of real numbers can help you classify a statement as sometimes, always, or never true. A counterexample is used to prove that the statement is false.

$\frac{a}{b} = \frac{b}{a}$ sometimes true
True: $\frac{1}{-1} = \frac{-1}{1}$; False: $\frac{1}{2} = \frac{2}{1}$
Show a **true** example and a **false** example.

$a - (b + c) = a - b - c$
always true
$a - (b + c) = a - b - c$
Use properties of real numbers.
By the **Distributive Property**:
$a + (-1)(b + c) = a + (-b) + (-c) = a - b - c$

$a - b = a$ where $b = 1$
never true
Counterexample: 3 − 1 = 2
$a - b = a + (-b)$
Use properties of real numbers.
The **additive identity** is 0.
$a + (-b) = a$ only when $-b = b = 0$, not when $b = 1$
Use a counterexample.

Classify each statement as sometimes, always, or never true. Support your answer.

1. $\frac{1}{n} + \left(-\frac{1}{n}\right) = 0, n \neq 0$ — Always true; possible answer: Additive Inverse Property
2. $\frac{a}{b} \cdot 1 = 1$ — Sometimes true; possible answer: true: $a = b$; false: $a \neq b$
3. $a \cdot b = b$ where $a = -1$ — Sometimes; only true when $b = 0$.
4. $(a + b)\frac{1}{c} = 1 + \frac{b}{c}$ — Sometimes true; possible answer: true: $a = c, a \neq 0, c \neq 0$; false: $a \neq c$

1-2 RETEACH

Properties of Addition	Examples
Additive Identity 0 is the additive identity.	$4 + 0 = 4$ $n + 0 = 0 + n = n$
Additive Inverse The sum of a number and its opposite is 0.	$8 + (-8) = 0$ $n + (-n) = 0$
Closure Property The sum of any two real numbers is a real number.	$3 + 5 = 8$ $a + b \in \mathbb{R}$
Commutative Property The order does not change the sum.	$6 + 12 = 12 + 6$ $a + b = b + a$
Associative Property The grouping does not change the sum.	$(2 + 5) + 9 = 2 + (9 + 5)$ $(a + b) + c = a + (b + c)$

The additive inverse of 8 is −8. The additive inverse of −8 is 8.

Find the additive inverse of each number.

1. 20 — 20 + (−20) = 0
2. −36 — −36 + (36) = 0
3. −7.9 — −7.9 + (7.9) = 0
4. $\frac{2}{3}$ — $-\frac{2}{3}$
5. $\sqrt{3}$ — $-\sqrt{3}$
6. $-\frac{3}{4}$ — $\frac{3}{4}$

Identify the property of addition demonstrated by each equation.

7. $x + 0 = x$ — Additive Identity
8. $(2 + m) + 5n = 2 + (m + 5n)$ — Associative Property
9. $4r + 6s = 6s + 4r$ — Commutative Property
10. $\pi + (-\pi) = 0$ — Additive Inverse
11. $c + (-2) = -2 + c$ — Commutative
12. $1 = 0 + 1$ — Additive Identity

51. **Business** A television repair store was offering a 5% discount on parts and a 5% discount on labor. An employee placed a sign in the store window that read "Receive 10% off of your total costs." Use properties of real numbers to explain whether the sign was correct.

52. **Write About It** Explain the difference between the reciprocal of a number and the opposite of a number. Be sure to discuss the relationship between the signs of the numbers.

TEST PREP

53. Which equation illustrates the Associative Property of Multiplication?
   - Ⓐ $12(8 \cdot 9) = 12(9 \cdot 8)$
   - Ⓑ $12 + (8 + 9) = 12 + (9 + 8)$
   - Ⓒ $12 + (9 + 8) = (12 + 9) + 8$
   - Ⓓ $12(9 \cdot 8) = (12 \cdot 9)8$ (circled)

54. Let a and b be real numbers such that $a \neq b$. Which statement is sometimes true?
   - Ⓕ $a\left(\frac{1}{b}\right) = 1$
   - Ⓖ $a - b = 0$
   - Ⓗ $a(1) = b$
   - Ⓙ $a = 4 + b$ (circled)

55. Let c and d represent real numbers such that $c \neq 0$ and $d \neq 0$. Which expression represents the multiplicative inverse of $\frac{2c}{d}$?
   - Ⓐ $-\frac{2c}{d}$
   - Ⓑ $-\frac{2d}{c}$
   - Ⓒ $\frac{d}{2c}$ (circled)
   - Ⓓ $\frac{c}{2d}$

56. **Short Response** Show two different methods of simplifying $4(1 + 3)$. Justify each step by using the order of operations or properties of real numbers.

CHALLENGE AND EXTEND

57. A positive real number n is 4 times its multiplicative inverse. What is the value of n? 2

58. Consider the four pairs of algebraic expressions below.

   $a + b$ and $b + a$ $\quad a - b$ and $b - a$ $\quad a \cdot b$ and $b \cdot a$ $\quad a \div b$ and $b \div a$

   a. For $a = 3$ and $b = 5$, perform each pair of calculations. Identify which pairs result in a natural number for both calculations.

   b. If a and b are natural numbers, which pairs of algebraic expressions always represent natural numbers? $a + b$ and $b + a$; $a \cdot b$ and $b \cdot a$

   c. Under which operations is the set of natural numbers closed? addition and multiplication

   d. Under which operations is the set of integers closed? addition, subtraction, and multiplication

SPIRAL REVIEW

59. Mr. Connelly planted a 12 ft × 8 ft garden last summer. He wants to increase the size to 16 ft × 10 ft this summer. Find the percent increase in the area of his garden to the nearest tenth. *(Previous course)* 66.7%

Use the following numbers for Exercises 60–62: 0.89, $\sqrt{9}$, −2, $-\frac{1}{3}$, π, −0.125, $3.\overline{09}$, 0, and $-4\sqrt{2}$. Identify each of the following. *(Lesson 1-1)*

60. greatest value π

61. least value $-4\sqrt{2}$

62. irrational numbers $-4\sqrt{2}$, π

Write the inequality $-10 < x \leq 0$ using the indicated method. If the method is not possible, write "cannot be notated." *(Lesson 1-1)*

63. interval notation $(-10, 0]$

64. set-builder notation $\{x \mid -10 < x \leq 0\}$

65. roster notation cannot be notated

TEST PREP DOCTOR In **Exercise 53,** students who chose **C** may not have carefully read the question. **C** illustrates the Associative Property of Addition, but the question asks for that property of multiplication.

Answers

46. Comm. Prop. of Add.; Comm. Prop. of Mult.

47. Distrib. Prop.; Assoc. Prop. of Add.

48. Distrib. Prop.; Comm. Prop. of Add.

49. Distrib. Prop.

50a. 7

b. yes; possible answer: $9 + 19 = 4$ mod 24, $19 + 9 = 4$ mod 24

c. yes; possible answer: $5 + (12 + 20) = 5 + 8 = 13$ mod 24, $(5 + 12) + 20 = 17 + 20 = 13$ mod 24

51. Possible answer: By the Distributive Property, the savings is 5%, not 10%. 5%(labor) + 5%(parts) = 5%(labor + parts) = 5%(total)

Journal

Have students write each of the properties of real numbers using their own words and the form that they understand best.

ALTERNATIVE ASSESSMENT

Have students state the identity and inverse properties in this lesson and give examples of them.

Power Presentations with PowerPoint®

1-2 Lesson Quiz

Find the additive and multiplicative inverse of each number.

1. −15 $\quad 15; \frac{1}{-15}$

2. $\frac{2}{7}$ $\quad -\frac{2}{7}; \frac{7}{2}$

Identify the property demonstrated by each equation.

3. $2 + \sqrt{3} = (\sqrt{3}) + 2$
   Comm. Prop. of Add.

4. $\pi \cdot (2 + \sqrt{8}) = (\pi \cdot 2) + (\pi \cdot \sqrt{8})$
   Distributive Property

5. Use mental math to find a 15% tip for a $64.20 bill. $9.63

Also available on transparency

1-2 PROBLEM SOLVING

Three friends eat together at a restaurant. Their bill is shown at right. Use mental math for Exercises 1–4.

Lou's Fine Foods	
Milk (2)	$3.00
Cajun boil	$8.50
Gumbo (bowl)	$4.25
Salad	$3.75
Subtotal	$19.50
Sales tax	$1.66
TOTAL	$21.16

1. Luke and Willy split one order of the Cajun boil, and they each have a glass of milk. What is Luke's cost for his food and drink? $5.75

2. Laska has a bowl of gumbo and a salad. What is her share of the 8.5% sales tax? $0.68

3. The group decides to leave double the sales tax as the tip and to divide that amount evenly among themselves. What is Willy's share of the tip? $1.11

4. Explain how you would use mental math and the subtotal to find the amount of a 20% tip. Possible answer: Take 10% of the subtotal, which is $1.95. Then double it to get 20%, $3.90.

A music store advertises CDs at 15% off the marked price. There is a 6% sales tax added for each purchase. Use mental math to help you choose the letter for the best answer.

5. Todd buys a two-disk set marked $14.95 and a single CD marked $10.95. What is the total of his bill?
   - Ⓐ $23.34
   - B $24.90
   - C $26.01
   - D $27.45

6. Hedy buys 6 CDs marked "3 for $25." What is her total bill?
   - F $41.60
   - G $42.50
   - Ⓗ $45.05
   - J $50.50

7. Pedro's total before tax is $66.00. How much tax does he pay?
   - A $9.96
   - B $6.60
   - Ⓒ $3.96
   - D $3.36

8. Gail and Pam decide to share the cost of a three-disk set marked $35.00. What is Pam's share of the total?
   - F $14.50
   - Ⓖ $15.77
   - H $29.75
   - J $31.54

52. Possible answer: Opposites are used for addition. A number and its opposite have different signs. Reciprocals are used for multiplication. A number and its reciprocal have the same sign.

56. $4(1 + 3) = 4(4) = 16$ by the order of operations; $4(1 + 3) = 4(1) + 4(3) = 4 + 12 = 16$ by the Distributive Property

58a. $3 + 5 = 5 + 3 = 8$; $3 - 5 = -2$, $5 - 3 = 2$; $3 \cdot 5 = 5 \cdot 3 = 15$; $3 \div 5 = 0.6$, $5 \div 3 = 1.\overline{6}$; the pair $3 + 5$ and $5 + 3$ and the pair $3 \cdot 5$ and $5 \cdot 3$

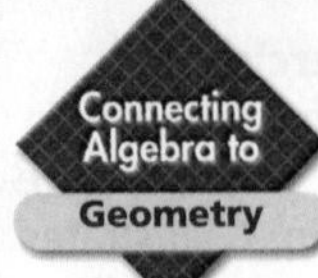

Organizer

See Skills Bank page S60

Pacing:
Traditional $\frac{1}{2}$ day
Block $\frac{1}{4}$ day

Objective: Apply square roots to solve problems involving the Pythagorean Theorem.

Teach

Remember

Students review the definitions of right angle, right triangle, hypotenuse, and leg.

INTERVENTION For additional review and practice of the Pythagorean Theorem, see Skills Bank page S60.

Visual Point out that the illustration shows a square on each side of the right triangle. Have students find the areas of these squares to confirm the Pythagorean Theorem.

Close

Assess

Have students copy any triangle on the page and name its vertices *D, E,* and *F,* with the right angle at *F.* Have students state the Pythagorean Theorem using the names of the sides.

State Resources

The Pythagorean Theorem

Connecting Algebra to Geometry

See Skills Bank page S60

The three sides of a right triangle are related. If you know two of the side lengths, you can find the third.

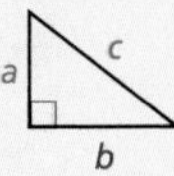

In a right triangle, the side opposite the right angle is the longest side and is called the hypotenuse. The other two sides are called the legs

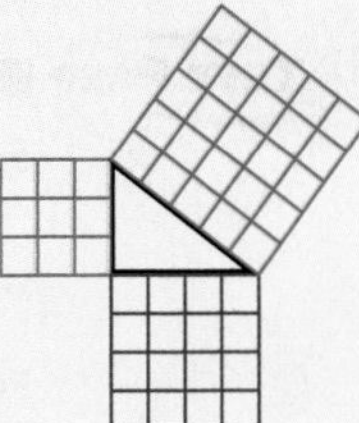

The Pythagorean Theorem
If a triangle is a right triangle with legs of length a and b and hypotenuse of length c, then $a^2 + b^2 = c^2$.

Example

Find the unknown side length in the right triangle.

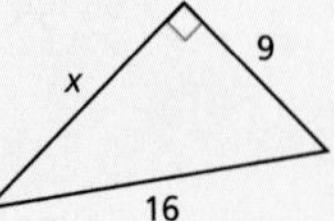

Step 1 The unknown side length is marked with an x. Use the Pythagorean Theorem to write an equation relating the side lengths. Remember that the hypotenuse c is the side opposite the right angle.

$a^2 + b^2 = c^2$

$x^2 + 9^2 = 16^2$ *Use 9 for either side a or side b.*

Step 2 Square the given side lengths and solve for x. Use a calculator to approximate the square root.

$x^2 + 81 = 256$

$x^2 + 81 - 81 = 256 - 81$ *Subtract 81 from both sides.*

$x^2 = 175$

$\sqrt{x^2} = \sqrt{175}$ *Take the square root of both sides.*

$x \approx 13.23$

Try This

Find the unknown side length in each right triangle. Round your answer to the nearest hundredth.

1. 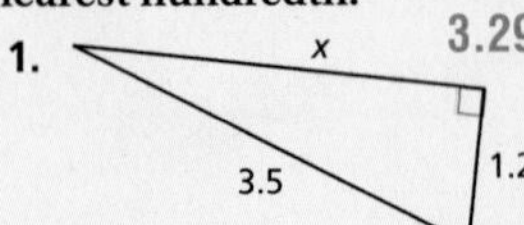

3.29

2. 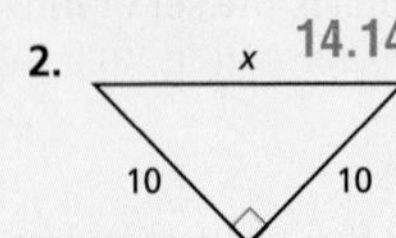

14.14

3. 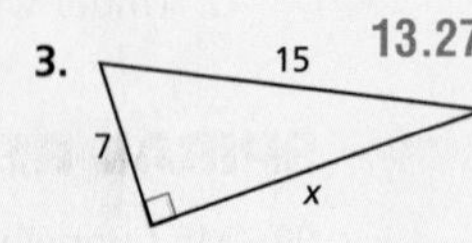

13.27

4. The set {3, 4, 5} is an example of a Pythagorean triple, three numbers that satisfy the Pythagorean Theorem. Show that {20, 21, 29} is a Pythagorean triple. $20^2 + 21^2 = 400 + 441 = 841 = 29^2$

5. The converse of the Pythagorean Theorem states that if the three sides of a triangle satisfy the Pythagorean Theorem, then the triangle is a right triangle. Is a triangle with sides of 36 ft, 77 ft, and 85 ft a right triangle? Explain.

6. Find the diagonal of a square with 10 cm sides. (*Hint:* See Problem 2.) $\approx$ 14.14 cm

7. $\triangle PQR$ is isosceles with altitude $\overline{QS}$. Find the length of the altitude if the side lengths of the triangle are 20, 20, and 8. $\approx$ 19.60

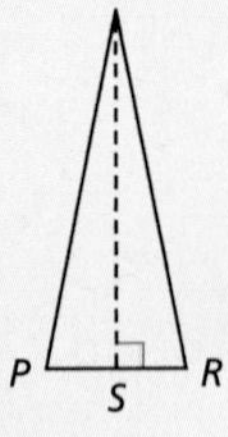

Answers

5. yes;
$36^2 + 77^2 = 1296 + 5929 = 7225 = 85^2$

1-3 Square Roots

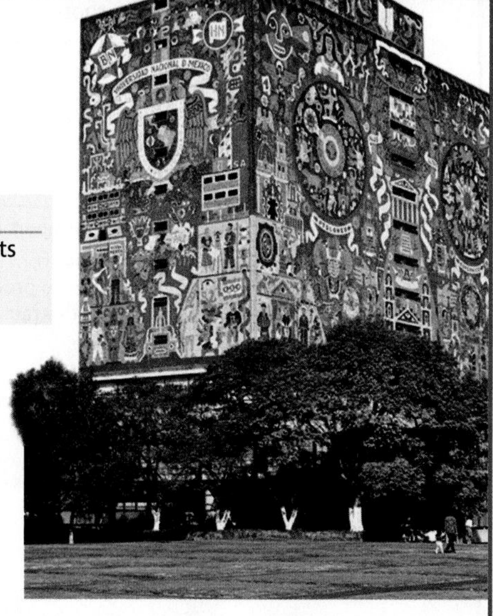

Objectives
Estimate square roots.
Simplify, add, subtract, multiply, and divide square roots.

Vocabulary
radical symbol
radicand
principal root
rationalize the denominator
like radical terms

Who uses this?
Mosaic artists can use square roots to calculate dimensions based on certain areas.

The largest mosaic in the world is located on the exterior walls of the central library of the Universidad Nacional Autónoma de México in Mexico City. It covers an area of 4000 square meters. If it were laid out as a square, you could use square roots to find its dimensions. (See Exercise 42.)

The side length of a square is the square root of its area. This relationship is shown by a **radical symbol** ($\sqrt{\ }$). The number or expression under the radical symbol is called the **radicand**. The radical symbol indicates only the positive square root of a number, called the **principal root**. To indicate both the positive and negative square roots of a number, use the plus or minus sign (±).

$$\sqrt{25} = 5 \qquad -\sqrt{25} = -5 \qquad \pm\sqrt{25} = \pm 5 = 5 \text{ or } -5$$

Numbers such as 25 that have integer square roots are called *perfect squares*. Square roots of integers that are not perfect squares are irrational numbers. You can estimate the value of these square roots by comparing them with perfect squares. For example, $\sqrt{5}$ lies between $\sqrt{4}$ and $\sqrt{9}$, so it lies between 2 and 3.

EXAMPLE 1 Estimating Square Roots

Estimate $\sqrt{34}$ to the nearest tenth.

$\sqrt{25} < \sqrt{34} < \sqrt{36}$ *Find the two perfect squares that 34 lies between.*

$5 < \sqrt{34} < 6$ *Find the two integers that $\sqrt{34}$ lies between.*

Because 34 is closer to 36 than to 25, $\sqrt{34}$ is closer to 6 than to 5.

Try 5.8: $5.8^2 = 33.64$ *Too low, try 5.9.*

$5.9^2 = 34.81$ *Too high*

Because 34 is closer to 33.64 than to 34.81, $\sqrt{34}$ is closer to 5.8 than to 5.9.

$\sqrt{34} \approx 5.8$

Check On a calculator $\sqrt{34} \approx 5.830951895 \approx 5.8$ rounded to the nearest tenth. ✔

1. Estimate $-\sqrt{55}$ to the nearest tenth. −7.4

1-3 Organizer

Pacing: Traditional 1 day
Block $\frac{1}{2}$ day

Objectives: Estimate square roots.
Simplify, add, subtract, multiply, and divide square roots.

Algebra Lab
In *Algebra Lab Activities*

Online Edition
Tutorial Videos, Interactivity

Countdown to Testing Week 1

Power Presentations with PowerPoint®

Warm Up

Round to the nearest tenth.

1. 3.14 3.1 **2.** 1.97 2.0

Find each square root.

3. $\sqrt{16}$ 4 **4.** $\sqrt{625}$ 25

Write each fraction in simplest form.

5. $\frac{24}{72}$ $\frac{1}{3}$ **6.** $\frac{169}{182}$ $\frac{13}{14}$

Simplify.

7. $\frac{1}{3} \cdot \frac{5}{3}$ $\frac{5}{9}$ **8.** $\frac{12}{18} \cdot \frac{6}{21}$ $\frac{4}{21}$

Also available on transparency

Math Humor

Teacher: Let's find the square root of 1 million.

Student: Don't you think that's a bit too radical?

1 Introduce

EXPLORATION

1-3 Square Roots

You can use a calculator to help you investigate some properties of square roots. To enter square roots, press 2nd x^2.

√(25) 5

1. Find the value of each expression in the table. Round to the nearest thousandth.

Expression	Value	Expression	Value
$\sqrt{3} \cdot \sqrt{5}$		$\sqrt{15}$	
$\sqrt{7} \cdot \sqrt{2}$		$\sqrt{14}$	
$\sqrt{50} \cdot \sqrt{2}$		$\sqrt{100}$	

2. Based on your answers to Problem 1, what can you say about $\sqrt{a} \cdot \sqrt{b}$?
3. Find the value of each expression in the table. Round to the nearest thousandth.

Expression	Value	Expression	Value
$\frac{\sqrt{15}}{\sqrt{5}}$		$\sqrt{3}$	
$\frac{\sqrt{60}}{\sqrt{12}}$		$\sqrt{5}$	
$\frac{\sqrt{100}}{\sqrt{4}}$		$\sqrt{25}$	

4. Based on your answers to Problem 3, what can you say

Motivate

Draw three squares on the board and label them as having areas of 25, 100, and 75 square units. Ask students to find the side lengths of the first two squares. 5 units and 10 units Ask students how they might find the side length of the third square. Explain that they need square roots to do this.

Explorations and answers are provided in the *Explorations* binder.

State Resources

go.hrw.com
State Resources Online
KEYWORD: MB7 Resources

Power Presentations with PowerPoint®

Additional Examples

Example 1

Estimate $\sqrt{27}$ to the nearest tenth. 5.2

Example 2

Simplify each expression.

A. $\sqrt{32}$ $4\sqrt{2}$

B. $\sqrt{\frac{25}{36}}$ $\frac{5}{6}$

C. $\sqrt{3} \cdot \sqrt{12}$ 6

D. $\frac{\sqrt{500}}{\sqrt{5}}$ 10

Also available on transparency

INTERVENTION

Questioning Strategies

EXAMPLE 1

- How do you find the pair of integers closest to the value of the square root?
- How do you choose the value in the tenths place?

EXAMPLE 2

- What kind of factor do you look for when simplifying radicals?
- How do you know when a square-root expression is completely simplified?

Reading Math Point out that an expression such as $\sqrt{17}$ is read "the square root of 17." Even though the radical symbol indicates the positive square root, the word *positive* is often left out when the expression is read aloud.

ENGLISH LANGUAGE LEARNERS

Square roots have special properties that help you simplify, multiply, and divide them.

Properties of Square Roots

For $a \geq 0$ and $b > 0$,

WORDS	NUMBERS	ALGEBRA
Product Property of Square Roots The square root of a product is equal to the product of the square roots of the factors.	$\sqrt{12} = \sqrt{4 \cdot 3} = \sqrt{4} \cdot \sqrt{3} = 2\sqrt{3}$ $\sqrt{8} \cdot \sqrt{2} = \sqrt{8 \cdot 2} = \sqrt{16} = 4$	$\sqrt{ab} = \sqrt{a} \cdot \sqrt{b}$ $\sqrt{a} \cdot \sqrt{b} = \sqrt{ab}$
Quotient Property of Square Roots The square root of a quotient is equal to the quotient of the square roots of the dividend and the divisor.	$\sqrt{\frac{25}{16}} = \frac{\sqrt{25}}{\sqrt{16}} = \frac{5}{4}$ $\frac{\sqrt{18}}{\sqrt{2}} = \sqrt{\frac{18}{2}} = \sqrt{9} = 3$	$\sqrt{\frac{a}{b}} = \frac{\sqrt{a}}{\sqrt{b}}$ $\frac{\sqrt{a}}{\sqrt{b}} = \sqrt{\frac{a}{b}}$

Notice that these properties can be used to combine quantities under the radical symbol or separate them for the purpose of simplifying square-root expressions. A square-root expression is in simplest form when the radicand has no perfect-square factors (except 1) and there are no radicals in the denominator.

EXAMPLE 2 **Simplifying Square-Root Expressions**

Simplify each expression.

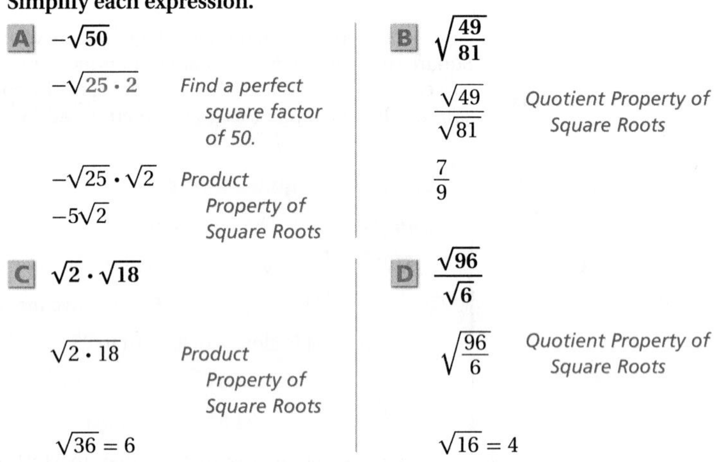

A $-\sqrt{50}$

$-\sqrt{25 \cdot 2}$ *Find a perfect square factor of 50.*

$-\sqrt{25} \cdot \sqrt{2}$ *Product Property of Square Roots*

$-5\sqrt{2}$

B $\sqrt{\frac{49}{81}}$

$\frac{\sqrt{49}}{\sqrt{81}}$ *Quotient Property of Square Roots*

$\frac{7}{9}$

C $\sqrt{2} \cdot \sqrt{18}$

$\sqrt{2 \cdot 18}$ *Product Property of Square Roots*

$\sqrt{36} = 6$

D $\frac{\sqrt{96}}{\sqrt{6}}$

$\sqrt{\frac{96}{6}}$ *Quotient Property of Square Roots*

$\sqrt{16} = 4$

CHECK IT OUT! **Simplify each expression.**

2a. $\sqrt{48}$ $4\sqrt{3}$ **2b.** $\sqrt{\frac{36}{16}}$ $\frac{3}{2}$ **2c.** $\sqrt{5} \cdot \sqrt{20}$ 10 **2d.** $\frac{\sqrt{147}}{\sqrt{3}}$ 7

If a fraction has a denominator that is a square root, you can simplify it by **rationalizing the denominator**. To do this, multiply both the numerator and denominator by a number that produces a perfect square under the radical sign in the denominator.

2 Teach

Guided Instruction

Before investigating square roots, ensure that students recall how to find the area of a square. Have students brainstorm examples of perfect squares. Knowing which numbers are perfect squares will aid students throughout the lesson. Point out to students that rationalizing the denominator of a square-root expression is a skill which will be used later in calculus.

Reaching All Learners

Through Modeling

Have students represent the first 15 perfect squares on graph paper by drawing squares whose areas correspond to the numbers. Then have them represent the square roots of these 15 perfect squares ($\sqrt{1}$, $\sqrt{4}$, $\sqrt{9}$, and so on) on a number line. This will provide students with a visual representation of the nature of square roots as well as a list of perfect squares they can reference when needed.

Through Kinesthetic Experience

Have students use manipulatives such as pattern blocks or centimeter cubes to build models of perfect squares. These can be found in the Manipulatives Kit (MK). Challenge them to build the largest square possible with a limited number of manipulatives.

EXAMPLE 3 Rationalizing the Denominator

Simplify by rationalizing each denominator.

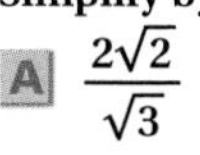

A $\dfrac{2\sqrt{2}}{\sqrt{3}}$

$\dfrac{2\sqrt{2}}{\sqrt{3}} \cdot \dfrac{\sqrt{3}}{\sqrt{3}}$ *Multiply by a form of 1.*

$\dfrac{2\sqrt{2 \cdot 3}}{3}$ *$\sqrt{3} \cdot \sqrt{3} = 3$*

$\dfrac{2\sqrt{6}}{3}$

B $\dfrac{\sqrt{8}}{\sqrt{18}}$

$\dfrac{\sqrt{8}}{\sqrt{18}} \cdot \dfrac{\sqrt{2}}{\sqrt{2}}$ *Multiply by a form of 1.*

$\dfrac{\sqrt{8 \cdot 2}}{6}$ *$\sqrt{18} \cdot \sqrt{2} = 6$*

$\dfrac{\sqrt{16}}{6} = \dfrac{4}{6} = \dfrac{2}{3}$ *$\sqrt{16} = 4$*

CHECK IT OUT! Simplify by rationalizing each denominator.

3a. $\dfrac{3\sqrt{5}}{\sqrt{7}}$ $\dfrac{3\sqrt{35}}{7}$ **3b.** $\dfrac{5}{\sqrt{10}}$ $\dfrac{\sqrt{10}}{2}$

Square roots that have the same radicand are called **like radical terms**.

Like Radicals	$\sqrt{2}$ and $3\sqrt{2}$	$-6\sqrt{15}$ and $7\sqrt{15}$	$\sqrt{ab^2}$ and $4\sqrt{ab^2}$
Unlike Radicals	$2\sqrt{5}$ and $\sqrt{2}$	$\sqrt{x}$ and $\sqrt{3x}$	$\sqrt{xy^2}$ and $\sqrt{x^2y}$

To add or subtract square roots, first simplify each radical term and then combine like radical terms by adding or subtracting their coefficients.

EXAMPLE 4 Adding and Subtracting Square Roots

Add or subtract.

A $5\sqrt{2} + 3\sqrt{2}$

$(5 + 3)\sqrt{2}$

$8\sqrt{2}$

B $5\sqrt{3} - \sqrt{12}$

$5\sqrt{3} - \sqrt{4 \cdot 3}$ *Simplify radical terms.*

$5\sqrt{3} - 2\sqrt{3}$

$(5 - 2)\sqrt{3}$ *Combine like radical terms.*

$3\sqrt{3}$

CHECK IT OUT! Add or subtract.

4a. $3\sqrt{5} + 10\sqrt{5}$ $13\sqrt{5}$ **4b.** $\sqrt{80} - 5\sqrt{5}$ $-\sqrt{5}$

THINK AND DISCUSS

1. Compare $3\sqrt{50}$ with $5\sqrt{18}$.
2. Give two different ways to simplify $\sqrt{16} \cdot \sqrt{4}$.
3. **GET ORGANIZED** Copy and complete the graphic organizer. Write examples of each operation with square roots.

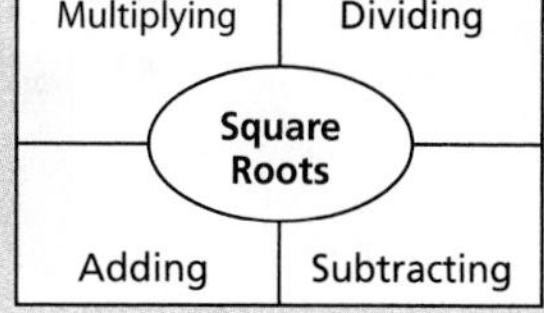

COMMON ERROR ALERT

Students may apply properties incorrectly. For example, they may write $\sqrt{a+b} = \sqrt{a} + \sqrt{b}$. Show students some numerical counter-examples to explain why this statement is not true.

Power Presentations with PowerPoint®

Additional Examples

Example 3

Simplify by rationalizing each denominator.

A. $\dfrac{3\sqrt{5}}{\sqrt{2}}$ $\dfrac{3\sqrt{10}}{2}$

B. $\dfrac{\sqrt{2}}{\sqrt{8}}$ $\dfrac{1}{2}$

Example 4

Add or subtract.

A. $9\sqrt{3} + 7\sqrt{3}$ $16\sqrt{3}$

B. $6\sqrt{5} - \sqrt{20}$ $4\sqrt{5}$

Also available on transparency

INTERVENTION
Questioning Strategies

EXAMPLE 3

- How do you choose what to multiply by to rationalize a denominator?
- Does rationalizing a denominator always remove all radicals from an expression? Explain.

EXAMPLE 4

- What property of real numbers are you using when you add or subtract square roots?

3 Close

Summarize

Have students walk you through simplifying an example, such as $\frac{2\sqrt{3}}{\sqrt{6}}$. $\sqrt{2}$ This type of example will review rationalizing the denominator, simplifying square roots, and writing fractions in simplest form.

ONGOING ASSESSMENT and INTERVENTION

Diagnose ***Before*** **the Lesson**
1-3 Warm Up, TE p. 21

Monitor ***During*** **the Lesson**
Check It Out! Exercises, SE pp. 21–23
Questioning Strategies, TE pp. 22–23

Assess ***After*** **the Lesson**
1-3 Lesson Quiz, TE p. 26
Alternative Assessment, TE p. 26

Answers to *Think and Discuss*

Possible answers:

1. Both are equal to $15\sqrt{2}$.
2. $\sqrt{16} \cdot \sqrt{4} = 4 \cdot 2 = 8$ or $\sqrt{16} \cdot \sqrt{4} = \sqrt{64} = 8$
3. See p. A2.

1-3 Exercises

go.hrw.com
Homework Help Online
KEYWORD: MB7 1-3
Parent Resources Online
KEYWORD: MB7 Parent

GUIDED PRACTICE

1. **Vocabulary** The number under the square root symbol is the __?__. (*radicand* or *radical*) **radicand**

SEE EXAMPLE 1 p. 21

Estimate to the nearest tenth.

2. $\sqrt{75}$ **8.7**
3. $\sqrt{20}$ **4.5**
4. $-\sqrt{93}$ **−9.6**
5. $\sqrt{13}$ **3.6**

SEE EXAMPLE 2 p. 22

Simplify each expression.

6. $-\sqrt{300}$ **$-10\sqrt{3}$**
7. $\sqrt{24} \cdot \sqrt{6}$ **12**
8. $\frac{\sqrt{72}}{\sqrt{2}}$ **6**
9. $\sqrt{80}$ **$4\sqrt{5}$**

SEE EXAMPLE 3 p. 23

Simplify by rationalizing each denominator.

10. $\frac{1}{\sqrt{2}}$ **$\frac{\sqrt{2}}{2}$**
11. $\frac{5\sqrt{6}}{-\sqrt{3}}$ **$-5\sqrt{2}$**
12. $\frac{\sqrt{50}}{\sqrt{12}}$ **$\frac{5\sqrt{6}}{6}$**
13. $\frac{\sqrt{3}}{-\sqrt{21}}$ **$-\frac{\sqrt{7}}{7}$**

SEE EXAMPLE 4 p. 23

Add or subtract.

14. $6\sqrt{7} + 7\sqrt{7}$ **$13\sqrt{7}$**
15. $5\sqrt{32} - 15\sqrt{2}$ **$5\sqrt{2}$**
16. $4\sqrt{5} + \sqrt{245}$ **$11\sqrt{5}$**
17. $-\sqrt{50} + 6\sqrt{2}$ **$\sqrt{2}$**

PRACTICE AND PROBLEM SOLVING

Independent Practice

For Exercises	See Example
18–21	1
22–29	2
30–33	3
34–37	4

Extra Practice
Skills Practice p. S4
Application Practice p. S32

Estimate to the nearest tenth.

18. $\sqrt{60}$ **7.7**
19. $-\sqrt{15}$ **−3.9**
20. $\sqrt{47}$ **6.9**
21. $\sqrt{99}$ **9.9**

Simplify each expression.

22. $\sqrt{162}$ **$9\sqrt{2}$**
23. $-\sqrt{\frac{1}{121}}$ **$-\frac{1}{11}$**
24. $\sqrt{\frac{50}{9}}$ **$\frac{5\sqrt{2}}{3}$**
25. $-2\sqrt{10} \cdot \sqrt{8}$ **$-8\sqrt{5}$**
26. $\frac{\sqrt{288}}{\sqrt{8}}$ **6**
27. $\sqrt{85} \cdot \sqrt{5}$ **$5\sqrt{17}$**
28. $\frac{2\sqrt{126}}{\sqrt{14}}$ **6**
29. $-\sqrt{189}$ **$-3\sqrt{21}$**

Simplify by rationalizing each denominator.

30. $\frac{2}{\sqrt{3}}$ **$\frac{2\sqrt{3}}{3}$**
31. $\frac{3\sqrt{27}}{2\sqrt{6}}$ **$\frac{9\sqrt{2}}{4}$**
32. $-\frac{18}{\sqrt{6}}$ **$-3\sqrt{6}$**
33. $\frac{\sqrt{11}}{5\sqrt{132}}$ **$\frac{\sqrt{3}}{30}$**

Add or subtract.

34. $4\sqrt{3} - 9\sqrt{3}$ **$-5\sqrt{3}$**
35. $\sqrt{112} + \sqrt{63}$ **$7\sqrt{7}$**
36. $\sqrt{8} - 15\sqrt{2}$ **$-13\sqrt{2}$**
37. $\sqrt{12} + 7\sqrt{27}$ **$23\sqrt{3}$**
38. $\sqrt{45} + \sqrt{20}$
39. $5\sqrt{28} - 2\sqrt{7}$
40. $2\sqrt{48} + 2\sqrt{12}$
41. $\sqrt{150} - 8\sqrt{6}$

42. **Art** The largest mosaic in the world is on the walls of the central library of the Universidad Nacional Autónoma de México in Mexico City. The mosaic depicts scenes from the nation's history and covers an area of 4000 m^2. If the entire mosaic were on one square wall, what would its dimensions be? **≈ 63.25 m by 63.25 m**

Geometry Each figure below is made from squares. Given the area of each figure, find its perimeter to the nearest tenth.

43.

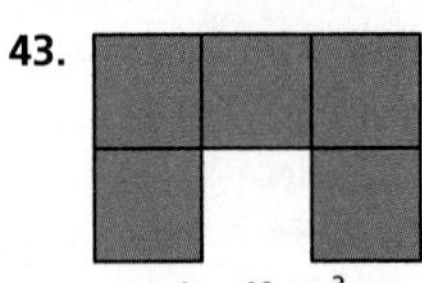

33.9 cm

$A = 40$ cm^2

44. **54.2 ft**

$A = 90$ ft^2

45. **99.0 in.**

$A = 300$ in^2

Assignment Guide

Assign *Guided Practice* exercises as necessary.

If you finished Examples **1–2**
- **Basic** 18–29, 47
- **Average** 18–29, 46–47
- **Advanced** 18–29, 46–47

If you finished Examples **1–4**
- **Basic** 18–47, 57–61, 66–71, 75–85
- **Average** 18–53, 57–61, 65–72, 75–85
- **Advanced** 18–45, 54–85

Homework Quick Check
Quickly check key concepts.
Exercises: 18, 22, 26, 30, 36, 42

Teaching Tip

Geometry In **Exercises 43–45,** remind students that the *perimeter* is the sum of the side lengths of a figure.

Answers

38. $5\sqrt{5}$
39. $8\sqrt{7}$
40. $12\sqrt{3}$
41. $-3\sqrt{6}$

State Resources

go.hrw.com
State Resources Online
KEYWORD: MB7 Resources

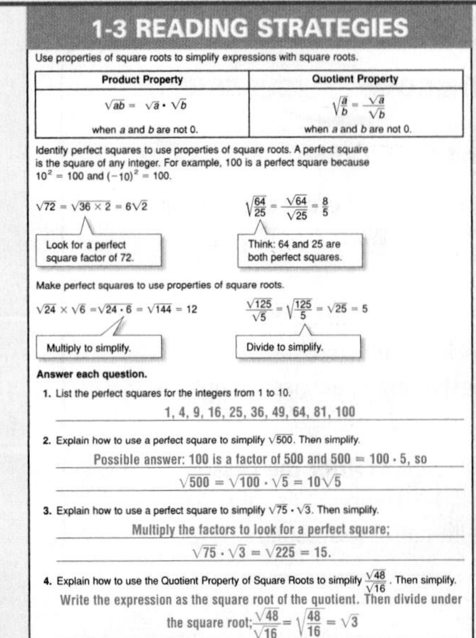

1-3 READING STRATEGIES

Use properties of square roots to simplify expressions with square roots.

Product Property	Quotient Property
$\sqrt{ab} = \sqrt{a} \cdot \sqrt{b}$ when a and b are not 0.	$\sqrt{\frac{a}{b}} = \frac{\sqrt{a}}{\sqrt{b}}$ when a and b are not 0.

Identify perfect squares to use properties of square roots. A perfect square is the square of any integer. For example, 100 is a perfect square because $10^2 = 100$ and $(-10)^2 = 100$.

$\sqrt{72} = \sqrt{36 \times 2} = 6\sqrt{2}$ — Look for a perfect square factor of 72.

$\sqrt{\frac{64}{25}} = \frac{\sqrt{64}}{\sqrt{25}} = \frac{8}{5}$ — Think: 64 and 25 are both perfect squares.

Make perfect squares to use properties of square roots.

$\sqrt{24} \times \sqrt{6} = \sqrt{24 \cdot 6} = \sqrt{144} = 12$ — Multiply to simplify.

$\frac{\sqrt{125}}{\sqrt{5}} = \sqrt{\frac{125}{5}} = \sqrt{25} = 5$ — Divide to simplify.

Answer each question.

1. List the perfect squares for the integers from 1 to 10.
   1, 4, 9, 16, 25, 36, 49, 64, 81, 100
2. Explain how to use a perfect square to simplify $\sqrt{500}$. Then simplify.
   Possible answer: 100 is a factor of 500 and $500 = 100 \cdot 5$, so $\sqrt{500} = \sqrt{100} \cdot \sqrt{5} = 10\sqrt{5}$
3. Explain how to use a perfect square to simplify $\sqrt{75} \cdot \sqrt{3}$. Then simplify.
   Multiply the factors to look for a perfect square; $\sqrt{75} \cdot \sqrt{3} = \sqrt{225} = 15$.
4. Explain how to use the Quotient Property of Square Roots to simplify $\frac{\sqrt{48}}{\sqrt{16}}$. Then simplify.
   Write the expression as the square root of the quotient. Then divide under the square root; $\frac{\sqrt{48}}{\sqrt{16}} = \sqrt{\frac{48}{16}} = \sqrt{3}$

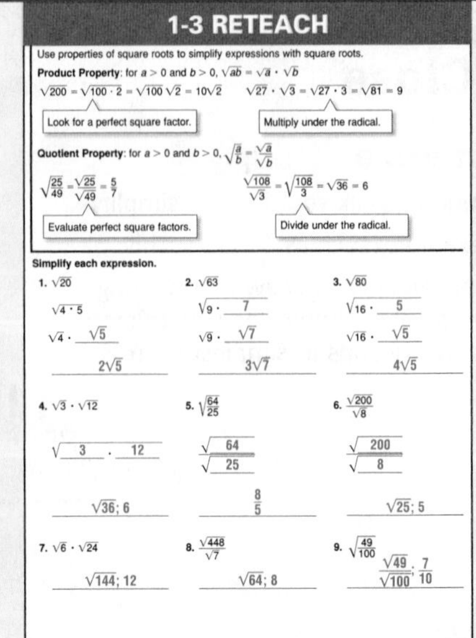

1-3 RETEACH

Use properties of square roots to simplify expressions with square roots.

Product Property: for $a > 0$ and $b > 0$, $\sqrt{ab} = \sqrt{a} \cdot \sqrt{b}$

$\sqrt{200} = \sqrt{100 \cdot 2} = \sqrt{100}\sqrt{2} = 10\sqrt{2}$ — Look for a perfect square factor.

$\sqrt{27} \cdot \sqrt{3} = \sqrt{27 \cdot 3} = \sqrt{81} = 9$ — Multiply under the radical.

Quotient Property: for $a > 0$ and $b > 0$, $\sqrt{\frac{a}{b}} = \frac{\sqrt{a}}{\sqrt{b}}$

$\sqrt{\frac{25}{49}} = \frac{\sqrt{25}}{\sqrt{49}} = \frac{5}{7}$ — Evaluate perfect square factors.

$\frac{\sqrt{108}}{\sqrt{3}} = \sqrt{\frac{108}{3}} = \sqrt{36} = 6$ — Divide under the radical.

Simplify each expression.

1. $\sqrt{20}$
   $\sqrt{4 \cdot 5}$
   $\sqrt{4} \cdot$ __$\sqrt{5}$__
   __$2\sqrt{5}$__
2. $\sqrt{63}$
   $\sqrt{9 \cdot \underline{7}}$
   $\sqrt{9} \cdot$ __$\sqrt{7}$__
   __$3\sqrt{7}$__
3. $\sqrt{80}$
   $\sqrt{16 \cdot \underline{5}}$
   $\sqrt{16} \cdot$ __$\sqrt{5}$__
   __$4\sqrt{5}$__
4. $\sqrt{3} \cdot \sqrt{12}$
   $\sqrt{\underline{3} \cdot \underline{12}}$
   __$\sqrt{36}$; 6__
5. $\sqrt{\frac{64}{25}}$
   $\frac{\sqrt{\underline{64}}}{\sqrt{\underline{25}}}$
   __$\frac{8}{5}$__
6. $\frac{\sqrt{200}}{\sqrt{8}}$
   $\frac{\sqrt{\underline{200}}}{\sqrt{\underline{8}}}$
   __$\sqrt{25}$; 5__
7. $\sqrt{6} \cdot \sqrt{24}$
   __$\sqrt{144}$; 12__
8. $\frac{\sqrt{448}}{\sqrt{7}}$
   __$\sqrt{64}$; 8__
9. $\sqrt{\frac{49}{100}}$
   __$\frac{\sqrt{49}}{\sqrt{100}}$; $\frac{7}{10}$__

127.28 ft **46. Sports** A baseball diamond is a square with an area of 8100 square feet. The length of the diagonal of any square is equal to $\sqrt{2}$ times its side length. Find the distance from home plate to second base (the length of the diagonal) to the nearest hundredth of a foot.

47. Estimation A painter's canvas will cover 600 square inches. Estimate the dimensions of a square wall mural that is the size of 4 complete canvases. Explain your thinking.

Simplify each expression.

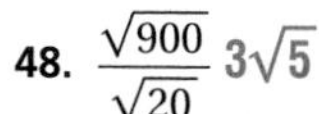

48. $\frac{\sqrt{900}}{\sqrt{20}}$ $3\sqrt{5}$

49. $3\sqrt{50} \cdot 3\sqrt{8}$ 180

50. $-3\sqrt{2} + \sqrt{18}$ 0

51. $2\sqrt{5} - 5\sqrt{2}$ $2\sqrt{5} - 5\sqrt{2}$

52. $\frac{4\sqrt{6} + 3\sqrt{2}}{\sqrt{6}}$ $4 + \sqrt{3}$

53. $\frac{3\sqrt{7} + 1}{\sqrt{5}}$ $\frac{3\sqrt{35} + \sqrt{5}}{5}$

54. $\frac{4\sqrt{10} - \sqrt{90}}{\sqrt{2}}$ $\sqrt{5}$

55. $\frac{4\sqrt{32}}{\sqrt{5}}$ $\frac{16\sqrt{10}}{5}$

56. $\frac{3 + 2\sqrt{7}}{\sqrt{7}}$ $\frac{3\sqrt{7}}{7} + 2$

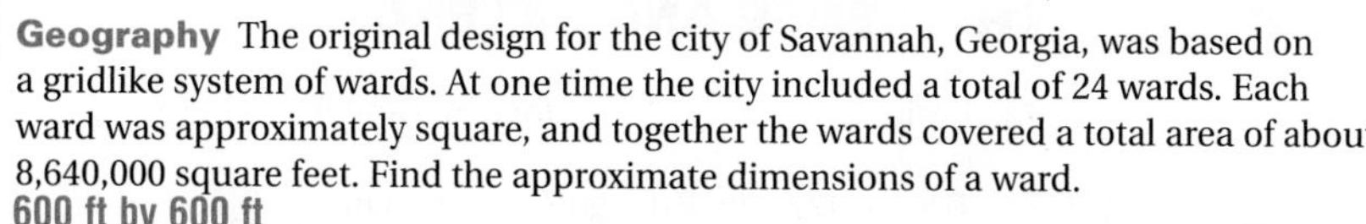

LINK

Geography

Savannah, Georgia, was the first American city to include squares and wards.

Source: www.pps.org/gps

57. Geography The original design for the city of Savannah, Georgia, was based on a gridlike system of wards. At one time the city included a total of 24 wards. Each ward was approximately square, and together the wards covered a total area of about 8,640,000 square feet. Find the approximate dimensions of a ward. 600 ft by 600 ft

Measurement **Use the table for Exercises 58–61. Find the side length, to the nearest tenth of a foot, of a square with the given area.**

58. 10 acres 660.0 ft

59. 2 mi^2 7467.3 ft

60. 5 hectares 733.5 ft

61. 6.2 km^2 8167.7 ft

Unit of Area	Square Feet
Acre	43,560
Hectare	107,600
Square kilometer	10,760,000
Square mile	27,880,000

Determine whether each statement is sometimes, always, or never true for positive integers *a* and *b*. Give examples to support your conclusion.

62. $\sqrt{a} + \sqrt{b} = \sqrt{ab}$

63. $\frac{\sqrt{ab}}{\sqrt{a}} = \sqrt{b}$

64. $a\sqrt{b} + a\sqrt{b} = 2ab$

65. Critical Thinking Given that $\sqrt{2 + 2} = 2$, does $\sqrt{a + a} = a$? Explain.

66. Write About It Find the value of $\sqrt{2}$ on your calculator. Square this value by entering the number and pressing x^2 and ENTER. Is the result 2? Explain why or why not.

MULTI-STEP TEST PREP

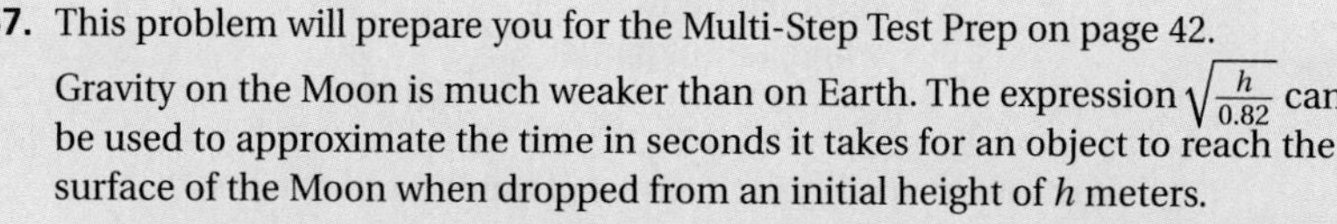

67. This problem will prepare you for the Multi-Step Test Prep on page 42.

Gravity on the Moon is much weaker than on Earth. The expression $\sqrt{\frac{h}{0.82}}$ can be used to approximate the time in seconds it takes for an object to reach the surface of the Moon when dropped from an initial height of *h* meters.

a. How long would it take for an object dropped from a height of 50 meters to land on the Moon? $\approx$ 7.81 s

b. The expression $\sqrt{\frac{h}{4.89}}$ can be used to model the time it takes to reach Earth's surface from a height of *h* meters. How long would it take for an object dropped from a height of 50 meters to land on Earth? $\approx$ 3.20 s

MULTI-STEP TEST PREP Exercise 67 involves evaluating formulas containing square roots. This exercise prepares students for the Multi-Step Test Prep on page 42.

Answers

47. About 50 in. by 50 in.; 4 canvases would cover a total of 2400 in^2, which is approximately 2500 in^2; $\sqrt{2500} = 50$, so the sides are about 50 in.

62. sometimes true; possible answer: true when both *a* and *b* equal 4, but false when *a* equals 5 and *b* equals 3

63. Always true; possible answer: when $a = 4$ and $b = 9$, $\frac{\sqrt{4(9)}}{\sqrt{4}} = \frac{\sqrt{36}}{\sqrt{4}} = \frac{6}{2} = 3 = \sqrt{9}$.

64. sometimes true; possible answer: true for $a = 2$ and $b = 1$, but false for $a = 2$ and $b = 4$

65. no; for example, $\sqrt{3 + 3} = \sqrt{6} \neq 3$

66. Possible answer: no; $\sqrt{2}$ is an irrational number but is rounded by the calculator. The square of the rounded number does not equal 2.

1-3 PROBLEM SOLVING

A downtown public park has a design of three square fountains. The fountains are arranged so that they create a perspective illusion. The area covered by the largest fountain is 144 square yards. Use this information for Exercises 1–3.

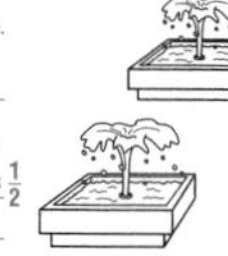

1. The area covered by the smallest fountain is one-fourth the area covered by the largest fountain. What is the side length of the smallest fountain? 6 yd

2. How does the side length of the smallest fountain compare to the side length of the largest fountain? The side length of the smallest fountain is $\frac{1}{2}$ the side length of the largest fountain.

3. The area covered by the middle fountain is $2\frac{1}{4}$ times the area covered by the smallest fountain. What is the side length of the middle fountain? 9 yd

There is a rectangular vacant lot between Ken's house and his school. The dimensions of the lot are 125 ft by 35 ft. Choose the letter for the best answer.

4. Instead of walking along the length and width of the lot, Ken sometimes takes a shortcut and walks along the diagonal. What is the difference in distance between Ken walking along the sidewalk or taking a shortcut?
   (A) 30 ft C 160 ft
   B 130 ft D 190 ft

5. Ken gets a job mowing the lot. He charges $30 to mow a square lot 35 feet long. At the same rate, about what will he charge to mow this lot?
   F $60 (H) $107
   G $84 J $1050

6. The owner of the lot divides it into 3 garden plots. Two of the plots have an area of 1225 square feet each. What could be the dimensions of the third plot?
   A 125 ft by 125 ft
   B 75 ft by 35 ft
   (C) 55 ft by 35 ft
   D 35 ft by 35 ft

7. Ken has a job mowing a park that is made up of 6 congruent square areas separated by paths. The total area of the park is 1734 square yards. What is the approximate length of the side of each square?
   F 145 yd H 42 yd
   G 132 yd (J) 17 yd

1-3 CHALLENGE

Triangle *ABC* is an equilateral triangle with side length *s*. Draw a line from vertex *A* that is perpendicular to the opposite side. Label that point of intersection *D*.

1. Use the Pythagorean Theorem to find the length of $\overline{AD}$ in terms of *s*. $\frac{s\sqrt{3}}{2}$ units

2. Find the area of triangle *ABC* in terms of *s*. $\frac{s^2\sqrt{3}}{4}$ square units

Equilateral triangle *UVW* has side length of 9 units.

3. Find the area of triangle *UVW*. $\frac{81\sqrt{3}}{4}$ square units

An equilateral triangle is centered on each side of triangle *UVW*. The result is a 6-point star. This star is made up of 12 separate line segments

4. Find the length of each of the 12 segments. 3 units

5. Find the area of the star. $\frac{108\sqrt{3}}{4}$ square units

Again an equilateral triangle is centered on each side of the star. The new figure has 18 points.

6. Find the length of each segment in this figure. 1 unit

7. Find the area of this figure. $\frac{120\sqrt{3}}{4}$ square units

If this process were to continue forever, it would generate a figure known as the Koch Snowflake. The snowflake could be contained entirely within a circle.

8. Find the radius of the circle. $3\sqrt{3}$ units

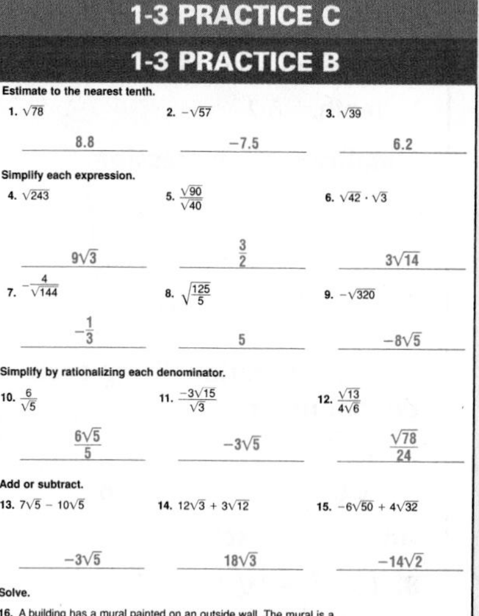

1-3 PRACTICE A

1-3 PRACTICE C

1-3 PRACTICE B

Estimate to the nearest tenth.

1. $\sqrt{78}$ 8.8
2. $-\sqrt{57}$ −7.5
3. $\sqrt{39}$ 6.2

Simplify each expression.

4. $\sqrt{243}$ $9\sqrt{3}$
5. $\frac{\sqrt{90}}{\sqrt{40}}$ $\frac{3}{2}$
6. $\sqrt{42} \cdot \sqrt{3}$ $3\sqrt{14}$
7. $-\frac{4}{\sqrt{144}}$ $-\frac{1}{3}$
8. $\sqrt{\frac{125}{5}}$ 5
9. $-\sqrt{320}$ $-8\sqrt{5}$

Simplify by rationalizing each denominator.

10. $\frac{6}{\sqrt{5}}$ $\frac{6\sqrt{5}}{5}$
11. $\frac{-3\sqrt{15}}{\sqrt{3}}$ $-3\sqrt{5}$
12. $\frac{\sqrt{13}}{4\sqrt{6}}$ $\frac{\sqrt{78}}{24}$

Add or subtract.

13. $7\sqrt{5} - 10\sqrt{5}$ $-3\sqrt{5}$
14. $12\sqrt{3} + 3\sqrt{12}$ $18\sqrt{3}$
15. $-6\sqrt{50} + 4\sqrt{32}$ $-14\sqrt{2}$

Solve.

16. A building has a mural painted on an outside wall. The mural is a square with an area of 14,400 ft^2. What is the width of the mural? 120 ft

TEST PREP DOCTOR + In Exercise 69, students who chose **F** may have stopped after finding the length of one side of the square. Students who chose **G** may have the perimeter formula wrong. The correct choice is **H.**

Journal

Challenge students to describe a real-world situation in which they would need to estimate a square root. Suggest that they consider situations in which they would need to estimate a side length of a square or a radius of a circle when given the area.

ALTERNATIVE ASSESSMENT

Present students with the statement $\sqrt{\frac{a}{b}} = \frac{\sqrt{ab}}{b}$. Have them determine whether the statement is sometimes, always, or never true for positive integers a and b by using the properties of square roots.

always true: $\sqrt{\frac{a}{b}} = \frac{\sqrt{a}}{\sqrt{b}} \cdot \frac{\sqrt{b}}{\sqrt{b}} = \frac{\sqrt{ab}}{b}$

Power Presentations with PowerPoint®

1-3 Lesson Quiz

1. Estimate $\sqrt{45}$ to the nearest tenth. 6.7

Simplify each expression.

2. $\sqrt{72}$ $6\sqrt{2}$
3. $\sqrt{\frac{49}{81}}$ $\frac{7}{9}$
4. $\sqrt{5} \cdot \sqrt{20}$ 10
5. $\frac{\sqrt{48}}{\sqrt{3}}$ 4

Simplify by rationalizing each denominator.

6. $\frac{5\sqrt{7}}{\sqrt{6}}$ $\frac{5\sqrt{42}}{6}$
7. $\frac{42}{\sqrt{6}}$ $7\sqrt{6}$

Add or subtract.

8. $13\sqrt{7} - 7\sqrt{7}$ $6\sqrt{7}$
9. $5\sqrt{3} + \sqrt{48}$ $9\sqrt{3}$

Also available on transparency

TEST PREP

68. Which expression is NOT equivalent to the others?
    Ⓐ $\sqrt{20}$ Ⓑ $\sqrt{8} \cdot \sqrt{5}$ Ⓒ $2\sqrt{10}$ Ⓓ $\frac{5\sqrt{8}}{\sqrt{5}}$

69. What is the approximate perimeter of a square with an area of 30 square meters?
    Ⓕ 5.5 m Ⓖ 11 m Ⓗ 22 m Ⓙ 30 m

70. Which list is in order from least to greatest?
    Ⓐ $\sqrt{\frac{9}{4}}, \sqrt{4}, 2\sqrt{2}, 2.5$
    Ⓒ $0, \sqrt{\frac{1}{4}}, \frac{1}{4}, \sqrt{1}$
    Ⓑ $\sqrt{25}, 5.1, 2\sqrt{5}, 6$
    Ⓓ $\frac{1}{\sqrt{2}}, 1, \sqrt{2}, 2$

71. **Gridded Response** By the Pythagorean Theorem, the length d of a diagonal of a rectangle is given by $d = \sqrt{\ell^2 + w^2}$. Find the length in feet of diagonal $\overline{AC}$ to the nearest tenth. **8.9**

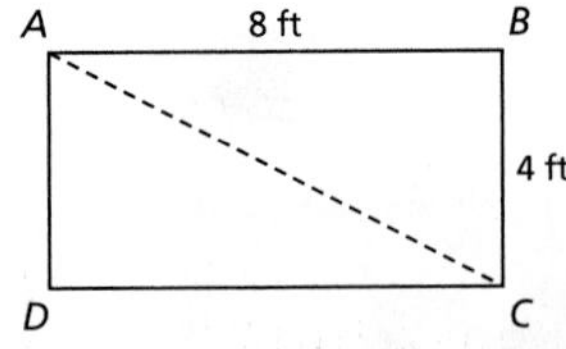

CHALLENGE AND EXTEND

72. Evaluate $\frac{a\sqrt{b} - 3a\sqrt{5ab}}{3\sqrt{b}}$ for $a = 5$ and $b = 6$. $-\frac{70}{3}$

73. **Geometry** The Pythagorean Theorem relates the side lengths a and b of a right triangle to the length of its hypotenuse c, with the formula $a^2 + b^2 = c^2$.

6√2 in. | 6 in. | 6√5 in. | 6 in. | 12 in.

a. Use the Pythagorean Theorem to determine the unknown dimensions of the triangle.

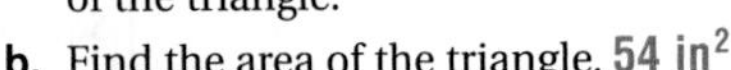

b. Find the area of the triangle. **54 in^2**

c. Find the perimeter of the triangle. $18 + 6\sqrt{2} + 6\sqrt{5}$ **in.**

74. Simplify $\frac{\sqrt{x^3y^5}}{x^2\sqrt{48y^3}}$. Assume all variables are positive. $\frac{y\sqrt{3x}}{12x}$

SPIRAL REVIEW

Identify the three-dimensional figure from the net shown. *(Previous course)*

75.  **tetrahedron or triangular pyramid**

76. 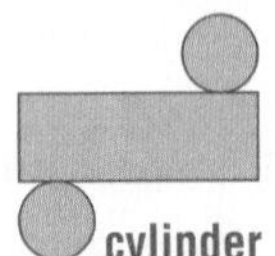 **cylinder**

77. 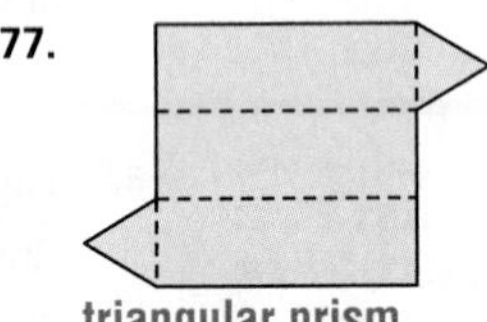 **triangular prism**

Write an inequality for each set of numbers. *(Lesson 1-1)*

78. $(-7, 1]$ $-7 < x \le 1$
79. $(1.5, 8)$ $1.5 < x < 8$
80. $[2, 12]$ $2 \le x \le 12$
81. $\left(\frac{3}{4}, \frac{5}{2}\right)$ $\frac{3}{4} < x < \frac{5}{2}$

Identify the property demonstrated by each equation. *(Lesson 1-2)*

82. $(a \cdot 1)b = ab$
83. $(x + y) + z = z + (x + y)$
84. $8p(q) = 8(pq)$
85. $st + 3s = s(t + 3)$

82. Identity Property of Multiplication **83. Commutative Property of Addition**

Answers

84. Assoc. Prop. of Mult.
85. Distributive Prop.

1-4 Simplifying Algebraic Expressions

Objective
Simplify and evaluate algebraic expressions.

Why learn this?
You can model the total points scored in a basketball game by using an algebraic expression.

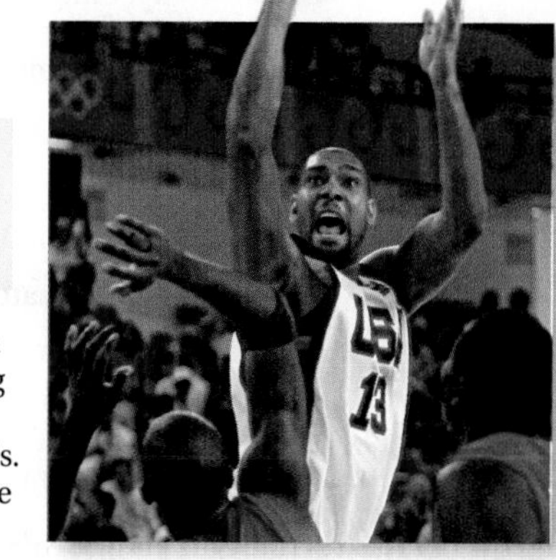

There are three different ways in which a basketball player can score points during a game. There are 1-point free throws, 2-point field goals, and 3-point field goals. An algebraic expression can represent the total points scored during a game.

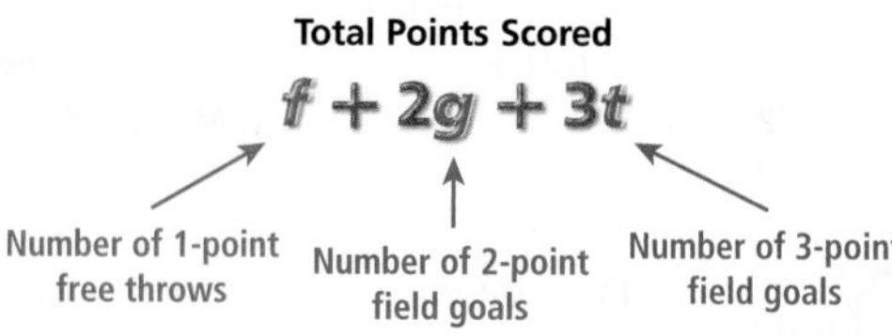

To translate a real-world situation into an algebraic expression, you must first determine the action being described. Then choose the operation that is indicated by the type of action and the context clues.

Action	Operation	Possible Context Clues
Combine	Add	How many total?
Combine equal groups	Multiply	How many altogether?
Separate	Subtract	How many more? How many remaining?
Separate into equal groups	Divide	How many in each group?

EXAMPLE 1 Translating Words into Algebraic Expressions

Write an algebraic expression to represent each situation.

A **the distance remaining for a runner after m miles of a 26.2-mile marathon**

$26.2 - m$ *Subtract m from 26.2.*

B **the number of hours it takes to fly 1800 miles at an average rate of n miles per hour**

$\frac{1800}{n}$ *Divide 1800 by n.*

Write an algebraic expression to represent each situation.

1a. Lucy's age y years after her 18th birthday $18 + y$

1b. The number of seconds in h hours $3600h$

1-4 Organizer

Pacing: Traditional 1 day
Block $\frac{1}{2}$ day

Objective: Simplify and evaluate algebraic expressions.

Online Edition
Tutorial Videos

Countdown to Testing Week 1

Power Presentations with PowerPoint®

Warm Up

List words that indicate each operation. Possible answers:

1. addition *sum, and, total*

2. multiplication *times, product*

Evaluate each expression.

3. $3x$ for $x = 2$ 6

4. $5x - 4 - 3x$ for $x = 7$ 10

Simplify each expression.

5. $3(2x)$ $6x$

6. $4(x + y)$ $4x + 4y$

Also available on transparency

Math Humor

Surgeon: Nurse! I have so many patients! Who do I work on first?

Nurse: Simple. Use the order of operations.

1 Introduce

EXPLORATION

1-4 Simplifying Algebraic Expressions

Whenever you simplify numerical or algebraic expressions, it is important to perform the operations in the correct order.

Simplify each expression. In each case, think about the order in which you should do the operations.

1. $(7 + 2)^2 - 5$
2. $[(2 - 10) + (4 - 1)]^2$
3. $3 - 5(21 - 19)^3$
4. $[(3^3 - 1) \div 13]^2$
5. Check your answers to Problems 1–4 by entering each expression into a graphing calculator.
6. The order of operations tells you the sequence in which you should perform operations. Fill in the flow chart by arranging the steps given below in the correct order.

Order of Operations
1.
2.
3.
4.

THINK AND DISCUSS

7. Explain how you can use the order of operations to evaluate $x^2 - (x + y)$ when $x = -3$ and $y = 4$.
8. Discuss whether $x - (y + 1)$ and $x - y + 1$ are equivalent expressions. How does the order of operations determine the

Motivate

Use objects to model combining like terms. For example, 3 cups of water added to 2 cups of water equals 5 cups of water. Unlike terms may be demonstrated with the same cups filled with different materials. Since 2 cups of water and 3 cups of sand cannot be combined into water or sand, they represent unlike terms.

Explorations and answers are provided in the *Explorations* binder.

State Resources

go.hrw.com
State Resources Online
KEYWORD: MB7 Resources

Power Presentations with PowerPoint®

Additional Examples

Example 1

Write an algebraic expression to represent each situation.

A. the number of apples in a basket of 12 after n more are added $12 + n$

B. the number of days it will take to walk 100 miles if you walk M miles per day $\frac{100}{M}$

Example 2

Evaluate each expression for the given values of the variables.

A. $2x - xy + 4y$ for $x = 5$ and $y = 2$ 8

B. $q^2 + 4qr - r^2$ for $r = 3$ and $q = 7$ 124

Also available on transparency

INTERVENTION
Questioning Strategies

EXAMPLE 1

- What words tell you which operation to use?
- Could there be more than one way to represent a situation with an algebraic expression?

EXAMPLE 2

- What might be a good way to remember the order of operations?
- Why is there an order of operations?

To evaluate an algebraic expression, substitute a number for each variable and simplify by using the order of operations. One way to remember the order of operations is by using the mnemonic PEMDAS.

Order of Operations
1. Parentheses and grouping symbols
2. Exponents
3. Multiply and Divide from left to right.
4. Add and Subtract from left to right.

EXAMPLE 2 Evaluating Algebraic Expressions

Evaluate each expression for the given values of the variables.

A $x + 3xy - 2y$ for $x = 4$ and $y = 7$

$(4) + 3(4)(7) - 2(7)$ *Substitute 4 for x and 7 for y.*

$4 + 84 - 14$ *Multiply from left to right.*

74 *Add and subtract from left to right.*

B $b^2z - 2bz + z^2$ for $b = 6$ and $z = 2$

$(6)^2(2) - 2(6)(2) + (2)^2$ *Substitute 6 for b and 2 for z.*

$36(2) - 2(6)(2) + 4$ *Evaluate exponential expressions.*

$72 - 24 + 4$ *Multiply from left to right.*

52 *Add and subtract from left to right.*

2. Evaluate $x^2y - xy^2 + 3y$ for $x = 2$ and $y = 5$. -15

Recall that the terms of an algebraic expression are separated by addition or subtraction symbols. *Like terms* have the same variables raised to the same exponents. Constant terms are like terms that always have the same value.

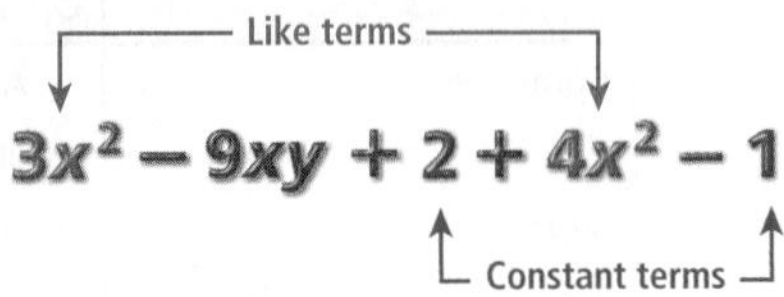

To simplify an algebraic expression, combine like terms by adding or subtracting their coefficients. Algebraic expressions are equivalent if they contain exactly the same terms when simplified.

EXAMPLE 3 Simplifying Expressions

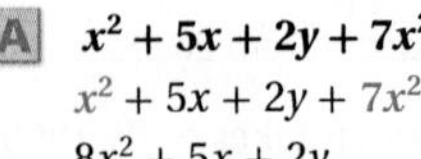

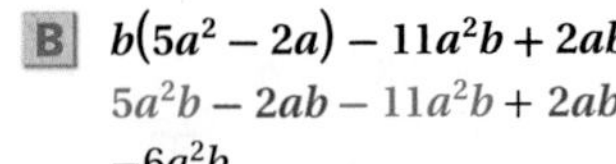

Terms that are written without a coefficient have an understood coefficient of 1. $x^2 = 1x^2$

Simplify each expression.

A $x^2 + 5x + 2y + 7x^2$

$x^2 + 5x + 2y + 7x^2$ *Identify like terms.*

$8x^2 + 5x + 2y$ *Combine like terms.* $1x^2 + 7x^2 = 8x^2$

B $b(5a^2 - 2a) - 11a^2b + 2ab$

$5a^2b - 2ab - 11a^2b + 2ab$ *Distribute, and identify like terms.*

$-6a^2b$ *Combine like terms.* $-2ab + 2ab = 0$

3. Simplify the expression $-3(2x - xy + 3y) - 11xy$. $-6x - 8xy - 9y$

2 Teach

Guided Instruction

Before simplifying expressions, carefully review the Distributive Property. As the lesson proceeds, demonstrate how combining like terms is equivalent to using the Distributive Property.

Emphasize that simplifying and evaluating algebraic expressions are critical skills for success in the study of algebra.

Reaching All Learners
Through Auditory Cues

Have small groups list as many key words and actions as they can for each operation. For example, addition may be indicated by *sum, total, plus, more, together,* etc. Have each group write a sentence using each key word. You may want to have the groups share their results with the entire class.

Through Modeling

Give students several algebraic expressions. Then have them write a real-world situation that can be modeled by each expression. For example, the expression $12d - 4$ could model the number of eggs a chef has if she originally had d dozen and then used 4 in a recipe.

Student to Student

Checking Simplified Expressions

Nadia Torres
Madison High School

To check that I simplified an expression correctly, I substitute the same numbers into both expressions. If I get the same value for each expression, my answer is probably correct.

Original Expression		*Simplified Expression*
$3x + 5y - 2x$		$x + 5y$
$3(2) + 5(3) - 2(2)$	*Use $x = 2$ and $y = 3$.*	$2 + 5(3)$
$6 + 15 - 4$	*Multiply.*	$2 + 15$
17	*They are equal.*	17

EXAMPLE 4 *Transportation Application*

Holly's hybrid car gets 45 miles per gallon on the highway and 25 miles per gallon in the city.

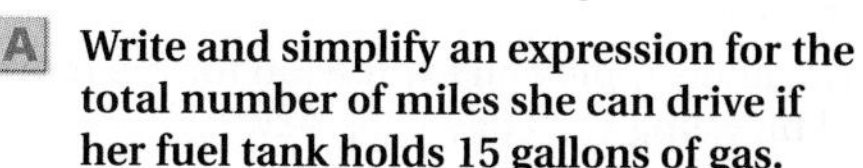

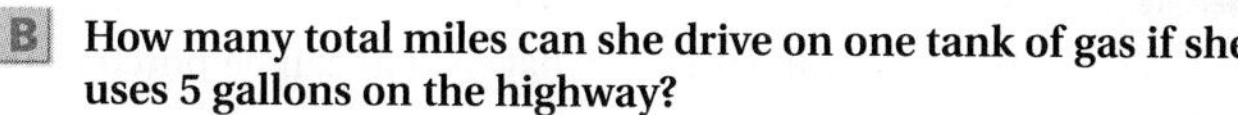

A **Write and simplify an expression for the total number of miles she can drive if her fuel tank holds 15 gallons of gas.**

Let h be the number of gallons used on the highway. Then $15 - h$ is the remaining number of gallons used in the city.

$45h + 25(15 - h) = 45h + 375 - 25h$ *Distribute 25.*

$= 20h + 375$ *Combine like terms.*

B **How many total miles can she drive on one tank of gas if she uses 5 gallons on the highway?**

Evaluate $20h + 375$ for $h = 5$.

$20(5) + 375 = 475$

Holly can travel 475 miles if she uses 5 gallons on the highway.

CHECK IT OUT! **4.** A travel agent is selling 100 discount packages. He makes $50 for each Hawaii package and $80 for each Cancún package.

$8000 - 30h$ **a.** Write an expression to represent the total the agent will make selling a combination of the two packages.

$7160 **b.** How much will he make if he sells 28 Hawaii packages?

THINK AND DISCUSS

1. Tell how many addition or subtraction symbols an expression with five terms will have. Explain.
2. Explain how adding like terms involves the Distributive Property.

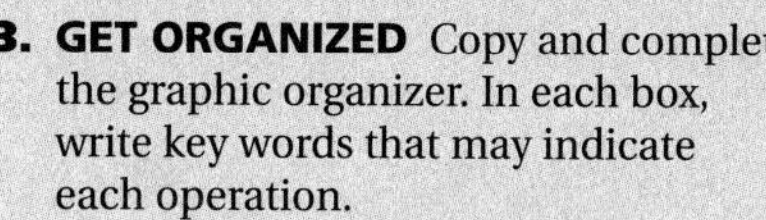

3. **GET ORGANIZED** Copy and complete the graphic organizer. In each box, write key words that may indicate each operation.

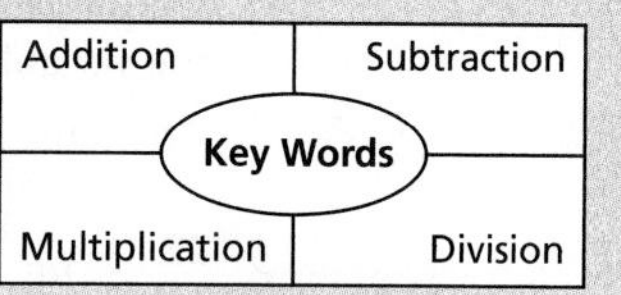

Power Presentations with PowerPoint®

Additional Examples

Example 3

Simplify each expression.

A. $3x^2 + 2x - 3y + 4x^2$
$7x^2 + 2x - 3y$

B. $j(6k^2 + 7k) + 9jk^2 - 7jk$
$15jk^2$

Example 4

Apples cost $2 per pound, and grapes cost $3 per pound.

a. Write and simplify an expression for the total cost if you buy 10 lb of apples and grapes combined. $30 - A$

b. What is the total cost if 2 lb of the 10 lb are apples? $28

Also available on transparency

INTERVENTION

Questioning Strategies

EXAMPLE 3

- Why are x and x^2 not like terms?
- How does combining like terms use the Distributive Property?

EXAMPLE 4

- How do you choose the variable in the expression?
- How do you set up the expression to find the total?

Teaching Tip **Critical Thinking** In **Example 4,** students represent one quantity in terms of another to avoid having two variables. You may want to emphasize this strategy by giving them some other examples (for instance, the acute angles in a right triangle measure x and $(90 - x)$ degrees).

3 Close

Summarize

Ask students if the following are like or unlike terms.

$4xy^2$ and $-7xy^2$ like

$2xy^2$ and $2x^2y$ unlike

1 and −8 like

$3x$ and $\left(\frac{1}{\sqrt{5}}\right)x$ like

$7xy$ and $4yx$ like

Ongoing Assessment and INTERVENTION

***Diagnose Before* the Lesson**
1-4 Warm Up, TE p. 27

***Monitor During* the Lesson**
Check It Out! Exercises, SE pp. 27–29
Questioning Strategies, TE pp. 28–29

***Assess After* the Lesson**
1-4 Lesson Quiz, TE p. 32
Alternative Assessment, TE p. 32

Answers to *Think and Discuss*

Possible answers:

1. An expression with 5 terms will have 4 addition or subtraction symbols, 1 separating each pair of terms.
2. When you add like terms such as $3x + 4x$, you can use the Distributive Property to rewrite the sum. In this case, the sum becomes $(3 + 4)x$. This expression can be simplified to $7x$.
3. See p. A2.

1-4 Exercises

Assignment Guide

Assign *Guided Practice* exercises as necessary.

If you finished Examples **1–2**
- **Basic** 9–14
- **Average** 9–14, 24–25
- **Advanced** 9–11, 24–25, 39–42

If you finished Examples **1–4**
- **Basic** 9–19, 24–30, 34–38, 44–53
- **Average** 9–19, 24–38, 43–53
- **Advanced** 9–53

Homework Quick Check
Quickly check key concepts.
Exercises: 9, 11, 15, 19, 29

Teaching Tip **Science Link** For **Exercise 8,** you may want to explain to students that a *Calorie* is the amount of heat required to raise the temperature of 1 kg of water by 1°C. It is derived from the Latin word *calor,* meaning "heat."

Teaching Tip **Geometry** In **Exercise 9,** make sure students know that the sum of the measures of an angle and its *supplement* is 180°.

State Resources

1-4 Exercises

go.hrw.com
Homework Help Online
KEYWORD: MB7 1-4
Parent Resources Online
KEYWORD: MB7 Parent

GUIDED PRACTICE

SEE EXAMPLE 1 p. 27

Write an algebraic expression to represent each situation.

1. the cost of c containers of yogurt at \$0.79 each **$0.79c$**
2. the area of a rectangle with length ℓ meters and width 8 meters **8ℓ**

SEE EXAMPLE 2 p. 28

Evaluate each expression for the given values of the variables.

3. $a^2 + b^2 - 2ab$ for $a = 5$ and $b = 8$ **9**
4. $\dfrac{3xy}{x^2 - 9y + 2}$ for $x = 2$ and $y = 4$ **$-\dfrac{4}{5}$**

SEE EXAMPLE 3 p. 28

Simplify each expression.

5. $-8a + 9 - 5a + a$ **$-12a + 9$**
6. $-2(2x + y) - 7x + 2y$ **$-11x$**
7. $1 + (ab - 5a)5 - b^2$ **$1 + 5ab - 25a - b^2$**

SEE EXAMPLE 4 p. 29

8. **Athletics** Regan runs and bicycles every day for a total of 60 minutes. Her body uses 9 Calories per minute during running and 7 Calories per minute during bicycling.
   a. Write and simplify an expression for the total Calories Regan uses running and bicycling each day. **$2r + 420$**
   b. How many Calories does she use on a day when she runs for 20 minutes? **460 Calories**

PRACTICE AND PROBLEM SOLVING

Independent Practice	
For Exercises	See Example
9–10	1
11–14	2
15–18	3
19	4

Extra Practice
Skills Practice p. S4
Application Practice p. S32

Write an algebraic expression to represent each situation.

9. the measure of the supplement of an angle whose measure is $x°$ **$(180 - x)°$**
10. the number of \$0.60 bagels that can be purchased with d dollars **$\dfrac{d}{0.60}$**

Evaluate each expression for the given values of the variables.

11. $6c - 3c^2 + d^3$ for $c = 5$ and $d = 3$ **-18**
12. $y^2 - 2xy^2 - x$ for $x = 2$ and $y = 3$ **-29**
13. $3a^2b - ab^3 + 5$ for $a = 5$ and $b = 2$ **115**
14. $\dfrac{2s - t^2}{st^2}$ for $s = 5$ and $t = 3$ **$\dfrac{1}{45}$**

Simplify each expression.

15. $-x - 3y + 4x - 9y + 2$ **$3x - 12y + 2$**
16. $-4(-a + 3b) - 3(a - 5b)$ **$a + 3b$**
17. $5 - (3m + 2n)$ **$5 - 3m - 2n$**
18. $x(4 + y) - 2x(y + 7)$ **$-10x - xy$**
19. **Home Economics** Enrique is baking muffins and bread. He wants to bake a total of 10 batches. Each batch of muffins bakes for 30 minutes, and each batch of bread bakes for 50 minutes. Let m represent the number of batches of muffins.
    a. Write an expression for the total time required to bake a combination of muffins and bread if each batch is baked separately. **$500 - 20m$**
    b. If Enrique makes 2 batches of muffins, how long will it take to bake all 10 batches? **460 min or 7 h 40 min**

Simplify each expression. Then evaluate the expression for the given values of the variables.

20. $-a(a^2 + 2a - 1)$ for $a = 2$ **$-a^3 - 2a^2 + a$; -14**
21. $(2g - 1)^2 - 2g + g^2$ for $g = 3$ **$5g^2 - 6g + 1$; 28**
22. $\dfrac{u^2 - v^2}{uv}$ for $u = 4$ and $v = 2$ **$\dfrac{3}{2}$**
23. $\dfrac{a^2 - 2(b^2 - a)}{2 + a}$ for $a = 3$ and $b = 5$ **$\dfrac{a^2 - 2b^2 + 2a}{2 + a}$; -7**

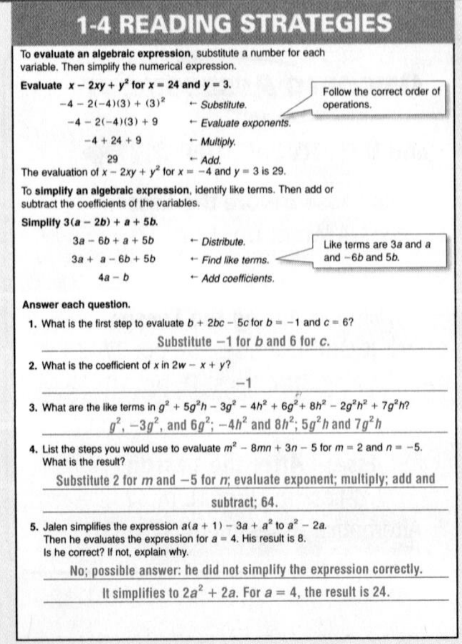

1-4 READING STRATEGIES

To **evaluate an algebraic expression**, substitute a number for each variable. Then simplify the numerical expression.

Evaluate $x - 2xy + y^2$ for $x = 24$ and $y = 3$.

$-4 - 2(-4)(3) + (3)^2$ ← *Substitute.*
$-4 - 2(-4)(3) + 9$ ← *Evaluate exponents.*
$-4 + 24 + 9$ ← *Multiply.*
29 ← *Add.*

Follow the correct order of operations.

The evaluation of $x - 2xy + y^2$ for $x = -4$ and $y = 3$ is 29.

To **simplify an algebraic expression**, identify like terms. Then add or subtract the coefficients of the variables.

Simplify $3(a - 2b) + a + 5b$.

$3a - 6b + a + 5b$ ← *Distribute.*
$3a + a - 6b + 5b$ ← *Find like terms.*
$4a - b$ ← *Add coefficients.*

Like terms are $3a$ and a and $-6b$ and $5b$.

Answer each question.

1. What is the first step to evaluate $b + 2bc - 5c$ for $b = -1$ and $c = 6$?
   Substitute -1 for b and 6 for c.
2. What is the coefficient of x in $2w - x + y$?
   -1
3. What are the like terms in $g^2 + 5g^2h - 3g^2 - 4h^2 + 6g^2 + 8h^2 - 2g^2h^2 + 7g^2h$?
   g^2, $-3g^2$, and $6g^2$; $-4h^2$ and $8h^2$; $5g^2h$ and $7g^2h$
4. List the steps you would use to evaluate $m^2 - 8mn + 3n - 5$ for $m = 2$ and $n = -5$. What is the result?
   Substitute 2 for m and -5 for n; evaluate exponent; multiply; add and subtract; 64.
5. Jalen simplifies the expression $a(a + 1) - 3a + a^2$ to $a^2 - 2a$. Then he evaluates the expression for $a = 4$. His result is 8. Is he correct? If not, explain why.
   No; possible answer: he did not simplify the expression correctly. It simplifies to $2a^2 + 2a$. For $a = 4$, the result is 24.

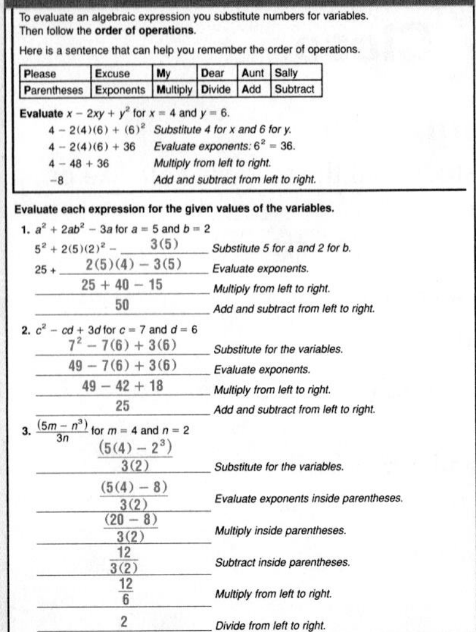

1-4 RETEACH

To evaluate an algebraic expression you substitute numbers for variables. Then follow the **order of operations**.

Here is a sentence that can help you remember the order of operations.

Please	Excuse	My	Dear	Aunt	Sally
Parentheses	Exponents	Multiply	Divide	Add	Subtract

Evaluate $x - 2xy + y^2$ for $x = 4$ and $y = 6$.

$4 - 2(4)(6) + (6)^2$ *Substitute 4 for x and 6 for y.*
$4 - 2(4)(6) + 36$ *Evaluate exponents: $6^2 = 36$.*
$4 - 48 + 36$ *Multiply from left to right.*
-8 *Add and subtract from left to right.*

Evaluate each expression for the given values of the variables.

1. $a^2 + 2ab^2 - 3a$ for $a = 5$ and $b = 2$
   $5^2 + 2(5)(2)^2 -$ **$3(5)$** *Substitute 5 for a and 2 for b.*
   $25 +$ **$2(5)(4) - 3(5)$** *Evaluate exponents.*
   $25 + 40 - 15$ *Multiply from left to right.*
   50 *Add and subtract from left to right.*
2. $c^2 - cd + 3d$ for $c = 7$ and $d = 6$
   $7^2 - 7(6) + 3(6)$ *Substitute for the variables.*
   $49 - 7(6) + 3(6)$ *Evaluate exponents.*
   $49 - 42 + 18$ *Multiply from left to right.*
   25 *Add and subtract from left to right.*
3. $\dfrac{(5m - n^3)}{3n}$ for $m = 4$ and $n = 2$
   $\dfrac{(5(4) - 2^3)}{3(2)}$ *Substitute for the variables.*
   $\dfrac{(5(4) - 8)}{3(2)}$ *Evaluate exponents inside parentheses.*
   $\dfrac{(20 - 8)}{3(2)}$ *Multiply inside parentheses.*
   $\dfrac{12}{3(2)}$ *Subtract inside parentheses.*
   $\dfrac{12}{6}$ *Multiply from left to right.*
   2 *Divide from left to right.*

Copy and complete each table. Identify which expressions are equivalent for the given values of x.

24.

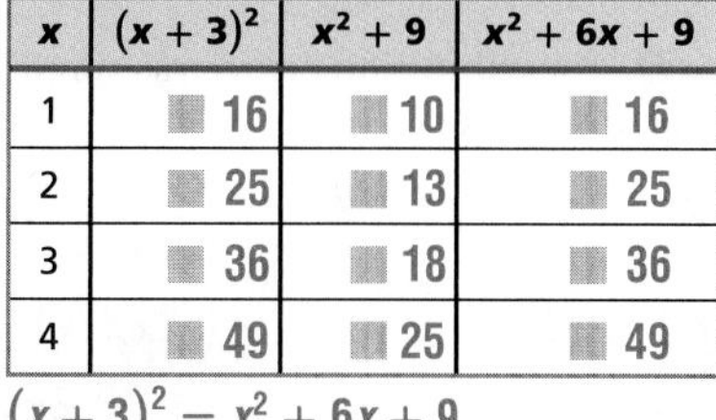

x	$(x+3)^2$	x^2+9	x^2+6x+9
1	16	10	16
2	25	13	25
3	36	18	36
4	49	25	49

$(x+3)^2 = x^2 + 6x + 9$

25.

x	$(x-4)^2$	x^2+16	$x^2-8x+16$
1	9	17	9
2	4	20	4
3	1	25	1
4	0	32	0

$(x-4)^2 = x^2 - 8x + 16$

Super Bowl

The average cost of producing a 30-second television commercial was more than $370,000 in 2003.

Source: Mediapost.com

26. **Super Bowl** The cost for a 1-minute commercial during the first Super Bowl was $85,000. The cost per 30-second commercial during Super Bowl XXXVIII was $2,300,000.

a. Write expressions to represent the cost of an m-minute commercial during the first Super Bowl and during Super Bowl XXXVIII.

b. If a commercial cost $170,000 during the first Super Bowl, how much would it have cost during Super Bowl XXXVIII? How do the costs compare?

c. About 60 million viewers watched the first Super Bowl, and about 800 million watched Super Bowl XXXVIII. Write expressions to represent how much an m-minute commercial cost per 1000 viewers during each Super Bowl.

d. What was the cost per 1000 viewers of a 2-minute commercial during each Super Bowl? How do the costs compare?

Geometry Write and simplify an expression for the perimeter of each figure.

27. $7a + 4b$

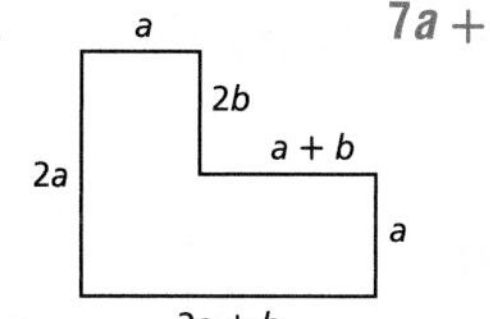

28. $3x^2 + 6x - 1$

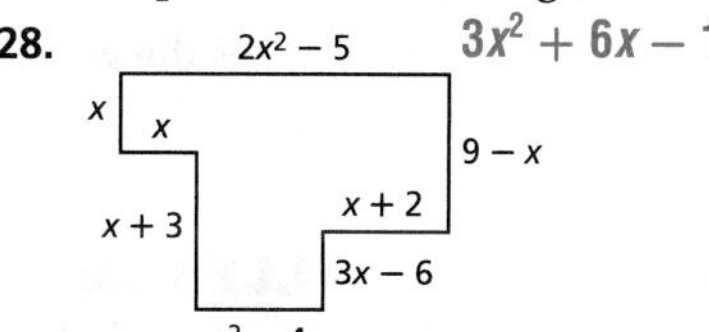

29. **Travel** The Dane family is going on a 15-day vacation to travel and visit relatives. They budget $100 per day when visiting relatives and $275 per day when traveling.

a. Write an expression for the total budgeted cost of the vacation if they visit relatives for d days. $4125 - 175d$

b. What is the budgeted cost if they stay with relatives for 5 days? $3250

c. How does this cost change for each additional day they stay with relatives? They save $175 per day.

MULTI-STEP TEST PREP

30. This problem will prepare you for the Multi-Step Test Prep on page 42.

While Neil Armstrong and Buzz Aldrin walked on the Moon, the *Apollo 11* command module completed 1 orbit every 119 minutes.

a. Write an expression for the time in minutes needed to complete n orbits.

b. Modify your expression from part **a** so that it represents the time in hours needed to complete n orbits.

c. The *Apollo 11* module made 30 orbits. For how many hours did it orbit the Moon?

d. Estimate the number of orbits the *Apollo 11* module would make in 1 week if it continued at the same rate.

In **Exercise 31,** students may treat the first term on the right side of the equation as $(-2x)^2$ rather than $-2x^2$. Reinforce that the order of operations states that exponents are evaluated before multiplication.

MULTI-STEP TEST PREP **Exercise 30** involves using expressions for orbital times. This exercise prepares students for the Multi-Step Test Prep on page 42.

Answers

26a. $85{,}000m$; $4{,}600{,}000m$

b. $9,200,000; Super Bowl XXXVIII cost about 54 times as much.

c. $1.42m$ and $5.75m$ per 1000 viewers

d. $2.84 and $11.50; Super Bowl XXXVIII cost about 4 times as much.

30a. $119n$

b. $\frac{119n}{60}$

c. 59.5 h

d. $\approx$ 85 orbits

1-4 PROBLEM SOLVING

To find out how much water a dripping showerhead wastes, Marisa catches the drips in a measuring cup. She collects a cup of water in 6 minutes.

1. Write and simplify an expression for the number of cups of water wasted in t minutes. $\frac{t}{6}$

2. How much water does this showerhead waste in an hour? 10 c

3. How many minutes will it take for this showerhead to waste a gallon of water? 96 min or 1.6 h

4. Write expressions for the amount of water, in cups and in gallons, that the dripping showerhead wastes in d days. $240d$ cups or $15d$ gallons

Choose the letter for the best answer.

5. Van budgets $12 a day for groceries for weekdays and $15 a day for weekend days. Which expression could be used to find his grocery budget for w weeks?
   (A) $w(12 \cdot 5 + 15 \cdot 2)$
   B $7w(12 + 15)$
   C $12w + 15w$
   D $17w$

6. The Spanish Club is planning to make a quilt for the annual fund-raiser. The quilt design includes 30 blue triangles, each with a base of 4 inches and a height of h inches, and 20 blue squares that are each s inches on a side. Which expression could be used to find the total area of blue fabric needed?
   F $(30 \cdot 4)h + 20s$
   (H) $60h + 20s^2$
   G $120h + 20s$
   J $240sh$

7. Susanne wrote the expression $25 + 0.15m$ for the monthly cost of her cell phone where m is the number of minutes she uses. What will her bill be this month if she makes 55 minutes of calls?
   A $8.25
   C $63.25
   (B) $33.25
   D $80.00

8. The width of a rectangle is $3g^2$. The length of the rectangle is $h^2 - 2h + 5$. Which represents the area of the rectangle?
   F $3g^2 + h^2 - 2h + 15$
   G $3g^2h^2 + 6gh - 15g^2$
   H $18g^2h^2 - 6gh$
   (J) $3g^2h^2 - 6g^2h + 15g^2$

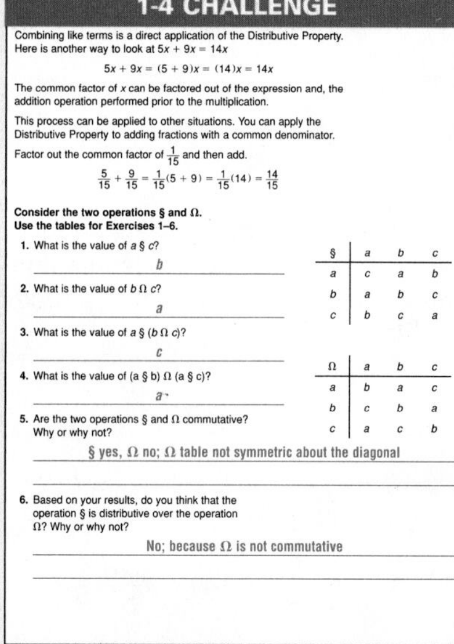

1-4 CHALLENGE

Combining like terms is a direct application of the Distributive Property. Here is another way to look at $5x + 9x = 14x$

$$5x + 9x = (5 + 9)x = (14)x = 14x$$

The common factor of x can be factored out of the expression and, the addition operation performed prior to the multiplication.

This process can be applied to other situations. You can apply the Distributive Property to adding fractions with a common denominator.

Factor out the common factor of $\frac{1}{15}$ and then add.

$$\frac{5}{15} + \frac{9}{15} = \frac{1}{15}(5 + 9) = \frac{1}{15}(14) = \frac{14}{15}$$

Consider the two operations § and Ω.
Use the tables for Exercises 1–6.

§	a	b	c
a	c	a	b
b	a	b	c
c	b	c	a

Ω	a	b	c
a	b	a	c
b	c	b	a
c	a	c	b

1. What is the value of a § c? b

2. What is the value of b Ω c? a

3. What is the value of a § (b Ω c)? c

4. What is the value of (a § b) Ω (a § c)? a

5. Are the two operations § and Ω commutative? Why or why not? § yes, Ω no; Ω table not symmetric about the diagonal

6. Based on your results, do you think that the operation § is distributive over the operation Ω? Why or why not? No; because Ω is not commutative

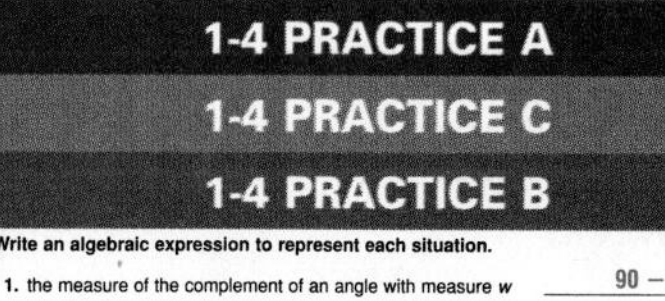

1-4 PRACTICE A

1-4 PRACTICE C

1-4 PRACTICE B

Write an algebraic expression to represent each situation.

1. the measure of the complement of an angle with measure w — $90 - w$

2. the number of eggs in d cartons that each hold 1 dozen eggs — $12d$

Evaluate each expression for the given values of the variables.

3. $4t - 3s^2 + s^3$ for $t = -2$ and $s = -3$ — -62

4. $\frac{5wp + 2w}{3wp^2}$ for $w = 4$ and $p = -1$ — -1

Simplify each expression.

5. $-(4r - 3t) + 6r - t$ — $2r + 2t$

6. $5(a + b) - 6(2a + 3b)$ — $-7a - 13b$

Simplify each expression. Then evaluate the expression for the given values of the variables.

7. $-2(d - 3c) + 4d + c$ for $d = 0$ and $c = -2$ — -14

8. $-3f(2 - 3f + 4g) + g$ for $f = -1$ and $g = 1$ — 28

Solve.

9. Marco delivers newspapers on the weekend. He delivers s newspapers on Saturday and $4s$ newspapers on Sunday. He earns $0.15 for each paper he delivers.
   a. Write an expression for the total amount of money Marco earns each weekend. $0.15(5s)$
   b. Evaluate your expression for $s = 50$. $37.50
   c. Write an expression for the amount of money Marco earns in a year if he delivers the same number of papers every weekend. $0.15(260s)$

10. A tank holds 500 gallons of water. It starts out full, then 10 gallons are released every minute.
   a. Write an expression for the number of gallons in the tank after m minutes. $500 - 10m$
   b. Write an expression for the number of gallons in the tank after m minutes if 2 gallons are *also* added every minute. $500 - 8m$

In **Exercise 38**, students who chose **A** may have squared $3x$. Students who chose **B** may have switched the values for the variables. Students who chose **D** may have forgotten to apply the exponent.

Journal

Have students create and share with the class their own mnemonic devices to remember the order of operations. Suggest that they write a sentence using words starting with the letters *P, E, M, D, A,* and *S*.

ALTERNATIVE ASSESSMENT

Have students evaluate $5x + 3y - 11x$ for several values of x and y. Then have them evaluate $-3(2x - y)$ for the same values of x and y. Have students justify their results.

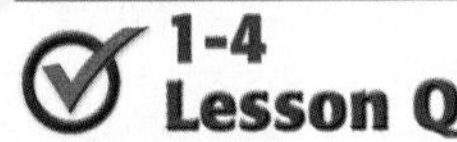

1-4 Lesson Quiz

Write an algebraic expression to represent each situation.

1. the number of cards in a 52-card deck after n cards are dealt $52 - n$
2. the number of days in W weeks $7W$
3. Evaluate $rq^2 + 3qr + r^2$ for $r = 5$ and $q = 2$. 75
4. Simplify $5h^2 + 4k + 7h - 4h^2$. $h^2 + 4k + 7h$

Jake has only nickels and dimes in his pocket.

5. Write and simplify an expression for the total value if Jake has 20 coins.
   Possible answer: \$2 – (\$0.05)N
6. How much does he have if he has 7 nickels? \$1.65

Also available on transparency

For each equation find the value of y when $x = -3, -2, 0, 2,$ and 3.

31. $y = -2x^2 + 5x - 7$ **32.** $y = -\frac{3x + 9}{x^2 - 1}$ **33.** $y = x^3 - 11x + 1$

34. ERROR ANALYSIS The expression below was simplified two different ways. Which is incorrect? Explain the error.

A	B
$-2x(4x - y)$	$-2x(4x - y)$
$= (-2x)(4x) + 2x(-y)$	$= (-2x)(4x) + (-2x)(-y)$
$= -8x^2 - 2xy$	$= -8x^2 + 2xy$

A; the minus sign was not distributed in the second step.

35. Write About It What property of real numbers relates addition and multiplication, and how does it relate them?

TEST PREP

36. Which expression is NOT equivalent to the others?
Ⓐ $-2x(1 - 3x)$ Ⓑ $2(3x - 1)x$ Ⓒ $(3x - 1)2x$ Ⓓ $6x^2 + 2x$ (D circled)

37. Which expression is greatest when $s = 10$?
Ⓕ Number of inches in s feet Ⓗ Number of days in s weeks
Ⓖ Number of minutes in s hours (G circled) Ⓙ Number of inches in s yards

38. What is the value of $3x(y - 1)^2$ when $x = 4$ and $y = 3$?
Ⓐ 576 Ⓑ 81 Ⓒ 48 (C circled) Ⓓ 24

CHALLENGE AND EXTEND

Find the value of a for which the expression $2a - 5$ has the given value.

39. 11 **8** **40.** -5 **0** **41.** 39 **22** **42.** 225 **115**

43. Consider the expression $\frac{3(x + 2)^2}{(x - 1)(x - 3)}$.
a. Evaluate the expression for $x = 0, 1, 2, 3, 4,$ and 5. 4; undefined; -48; undefined; 36; $\frac{147}{8}$
b. Identify the values of x for which the expression cannot be evaluated. 1 and 3
c. Use your results from part **b** to identify the set of reasonable values for x. $\{x \mid x \neq 1 \text{ and } x \neq 3\}$

SPIRAL REVIEW

Name the three-dimensional figure that has the given shapes as its faces. *(Previous course)*

44. three rectangles and two triangles **triangular prism**
45. one square and four triangles **square pyramid**

Classify each number by the subsets of the real numbers to which it belongs. *(Lesson 1-1)*

46. 0 $\mathbb{Q}, \mathbb{Z}, \mathbb{W}$ **47.** $\frac{5}{16}$ $\mathbb{Q}$ **48.** -6.5 $\mathbb{Q}$ **49.** $3\sqrt{2}$ irrational

Simplify each expression. *(Lesson 1-3)*

50. $\sqrt{\frac{52}{25}}$ $\frac{2}{5}\sqrt{13}$ **51.** $\sqrt{24} + \sqrt{6}$ $3\sqrt{6}$ **52.** $\frac{4\sqrt{27}}{18}$ $\frac{2\sqrt{3}}{3}$ **53.** $\sqrt{28} \cdot \sqrt{7}$ 14

Answers

31. $-40; -25; -7; -5; -10$
32. $0; -1; 9; -5; -\frac{9}{4}$
33. $7; 15; 1; -13; -5$
35. Distributive Property; possible answer: the Distributive Property says that multiplying by a sum is the same as adding products.

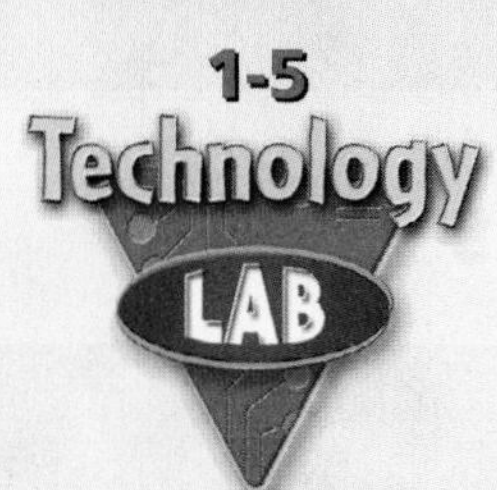

Explore Negative Exponents

You can use the caret key [^] to evaluate powers with a graphing calculator by entering (base) [^] (exponent).

Use with Lesson 1-5

Activity

Use a table to evaluate 10^x and 10^{-x} for $x = 0, 1, 2, 3, 4,$ and 5.

1. Press [Y=] and enter **10** [^] **X** for **Y1** and **10** [^] [(-)] **X** for **Y2**. Note that the calculator key for a negative sign [(-)] is different from the calculator key for subtraction [–].

2. Press [2nd] [WINDOW] (TBLSET) to select the **TABLE SETUP** menu. Set the starting value, **TblStart**, to 0 and the step value, **ΔTbl**, to 1 so that the difference between each x-value in the table will be 1.

3. Press [2nd] [GRAPH] (TABLE) to view the table of values for 10^x and 10^{-x}.

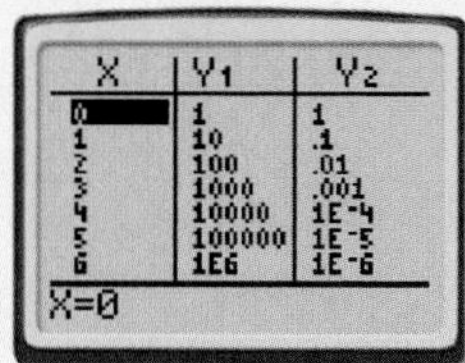

X	Y1	Y2
0	1	1
1	10	.1
2	100	.01
3	1000	.001
4	10000	1E-4
5	100000	1E-5
6	1E6	1E-6

X=0

Try This

Use a table to evaluate each pair of expressions for the given x-values.

1. 2^x and 2^{-x} for $x = -2, -1, 0, 1,$ and 2
2. 3^x and 3^{-x} for $x = -4, -3, -2, -1,$ and 0
3. 4^x and 4^{-x} for $x = -2, -1, 0, 1,$ and 2
4. 5^x and 5^{-x} for $x = -4, -2, 0, 2,$ and 4
5. Use a table to compute 2^{-x} and $\frac{1}{2^x}$ for $x = 0, 1, 2, 3, 4,$ and 5. Explain what you notice.
6. **Make a Conjecture** Use the tables you created for Problems 1–5 to calculate the product of **Y1** and **Y2** for each value of x. Then make a conjecture about the product of a^x and a^{-x} for any nonzero value of a.
7. **Make a Conjecture** For what values of x is $2^{-x} > 2^x$?

Answers to *Try This*

1. Y1 = 2^x, Y2 = 2^{-x}

X	Y1	Y2
-2	.25	4
-1	.5	2
0	1	1
1	2	.5
2	4	.25
3	8	.125
4	16	.0625

X=-2

2. Y1 = 3^x, Y2 = 3^{-x}

X	Y1	Y2
-4	.01235	81
-3	.03704	27
-2	.11111	9
-1	.33333	3
0	1	1
1	3	.33333
2	9	.11111

X=-4

3. Y1 = 4^x, Y2 = 4^{-x}

X	Y1	Y2
-3	.01563	64
-2	.0625	16
-1	.25	4
0	1	1
1	4	.25
2	16	.0625
3	64	.01563

X=-3

4. Y1 = 5^x, Y2 = 5^{-x}

X	Y1	Y2
-4	.0016	625
-2	.04	25
0	1	1
2	25	.04
4	625	.0016
6	15625	6.4E-5
8	390625	2.6E-6

X=-4

5. The expressions are equal for all values of x.

X	Y1	Y2
0	1	1
1	.5	.5
2	.25	.25
3	.125	.125
4	.0625	.0625
5	.03125	.03125
6	.01563	.01563

X=0

6. The product is always 1.
7. $\{x \mid x < 0\}$

Organizer

Use with Lesson 1-5

Pacing:
Traditional $\frac{1}{2}$ day
Block $\frac{1}{4}$ day

Objective: Explore negative exponents.

Materials: graphing calculator

Online Edition
Graphing Calculator, TechKeys

Countdown to Testing Week 1

Resources

Technology Lab Activities
1-5 Lab Recording Sheet

Teach

Discuss

Encourage students to look for patterns in powers with positive and negative exponents.

Close

Key Concept

The pattern of powers indicates that a base raised to a negative exponent is equal to the reciprocal of the base raised to the opposite, positive, exponent.

Assessment

Journal Have students explain how to evaluate a power with a negative exponent by using the reciprocal of a power with a positive exponent.

State Resources

go.hrw.com
State Resources Online
KEYWORD: MB7 Resources

1-5 Organizer

Pacing: Traditional 1 day
Block $\frac{1}{2}$ day

Objectives: Simplify expressions involving exponents.

Use scientific notation.

Online Edition
Tutorial Videos

Countdown to Testing Week 2

Power Presentations with PowerPoint®

Warm Up

Simplify.

1. $4 \cdot 4 \cdot 4$ 64
2. $\frac{1}{2 \cdot 2 \cdot 2 \cdot 2}$ $\frac{1}{16}$
3. $\frac{10 \cdot 10 \cdot 2}{10}$ 20
4. $\left(\frac{2}{3}\right)^2$ $\frac{4}{9}$ 5. $\frac{1}{4^2}$ $\frac{1}{16}$
6. 10^5 100,000
7. 3×10^4 30,000

Also available on transparency

Math Humor

Q: Why won't Goldilocks drink a glass of water with 8 pieces of ice in it?

A: It's too cubed.

1-5 Properties of Exponents

Objectives
Simplify expressions involving exponents.

Use scientific notation.

Vocabulary
scientific notation

Who uses this?
Astronomers use exponents when working with large distances such as that between Earth and the Eagle Nebula. (See Example 5.)

In an expression of the form a^n, a is the base, n is the exponent, and the quantity a^n is called a power. The exponent indicates the number of times that the base is used as a factor.

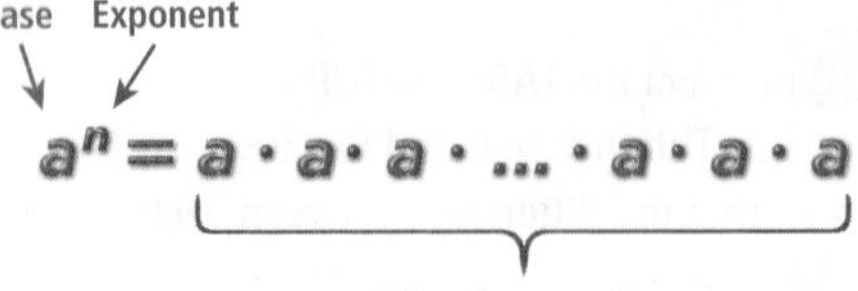

Reading Math

A *power* includes a base and an exponent. The expression 2^3 is a power of 2. It is read "2 to the third power" or "2 cubed."

When the base includes more than one symbol, it is written in parentheses.

Exponential Form	Base	Expanded Form
$-2x^3$	x	$-2(x \cdot x \cdot x)$
$-(2x)^3$	$2x$	$-(2x)(2x)(2x)$
$(-2x)^3$	$-2x$	$(-2x)(-2x)(-2x)$

EXAMPLE 1 Writing Exponential Expressions in Expanded Form

Write each expression in expanded form.

A $(4y)^3$

$(4y)^3$ *The base is 4y, and the exponent is 3.*

$(4y)(4y)(4y)$ *4y is a factor 3 times.*

B $-a^2$

$-a^2$ *The base is a, and the exponent is 2.*

$-(a \cdot a) = -a \cdot a$ *a is a factor 2 times.*

C $2y^2(x-3)^3$

$2y^2(x-3)^3$ *There are two bases: y and x − 3.*

$2(y)(y)(x-3)(x-3)(x-3)$ *y is a factor 2 times, and x − 3 is a factor 3 times.*

CHECK IT OUT! **Write each expression in expanded form.**

1a. $(2a)^5$ **1b.** $3b^4$ **1c.** $-(2x-1)^3y^2$

1a. $(2a)(2a)(2a)(2a)(2a)$ 1b. $3 \cdot b \cdot b \cdot b \cdot b$ 1c. $-(2x-1)(2x-1)(2x-1) \cdot y \cdot y$

State Resources

go.hrw.com
State Resources Online
KEYWORD: MB7 Resources

1 Introduce

EXPLORATION

1-5 Properties of Exponents

You can use a calculator to help you investigate some properties of exponents. Use the ^ key to indicate an exponent.

1. Find the value of each expression in the table.

Expression	Value	Expression	Value
$2^2 \cdot 2^3$		2^5	
$4^3 \cdot 4^3$		4^6	
$10^2 \cdot 10^5$		10^7	

2. Based on your answers to Problem 1, what can you say about $a^m \cdot a^n$?
3. Find the value of each expression in the table.

Expression	Value	Expression	Value
$\frac{2^5}{2^2}$		2^3	
$\frac{5^3}{5^1}$		5^2	
$\frac{10^6}{10^3}$		10^3	

4. Based on your answers to Problem 3, what can you say about $\frac{a^m}{a^n}$?

Motivate

Introduce exponents by presenting powers of 10. Multiply 10 by 10 repeatedly until students begin to see a pattern. As the numbers become very large, have students consider whether they can use patterns to write the large numbers more conveniently.

Explorations and answers are provided in the *Explorations* binder.

Zero and Negative Exponents

For all nonzero real numbers a and b and integers n,

WORDS	NUMBERS	ALGEBRA
Zero Exponent Property A nonzero quantity raised to the zero power is equal to 1.	$100^0 = 1$	$a^0 = 1$
Negative Exponent Property A nonzero base raised to a negative exponent is equal to the reciprocal of the base raised to the opposite, positive exponent.	$7^{-2} = \left(\frac{1}{7}\right)^2 = \frac{1}{7^2}$ $\left(\frac{3}{2}\right)^{-4} = \left(\frac{2}{3}\right)^4$	$a^{-n} = \left(\frac{1}{a}\right)^n = \frac{1}{a^n}$ $\left(\frac{a}{b}\right)^{-n} = \left(\frac{b}{a}\right)^n$

EXAMPLE 2 Simplifying Expressions with Negative Exponents

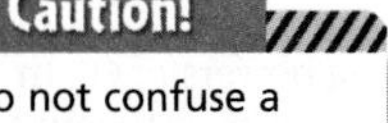

Caution! Do not confuse a negative exponent with a negative expression.
$a^{-n} \neq -a^n \neq \frac{1}{-a^n}$

Simplify each expression.

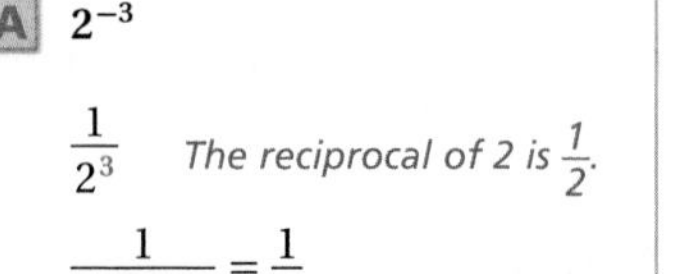

A 2^{-3}

$\frac{1}{2^3}$ *The reciprocal of 2 is $\frac{1}{2}$.*

$\frac{1}{2 \cdot 2 \cdot 2} = \frac{1}{8}$

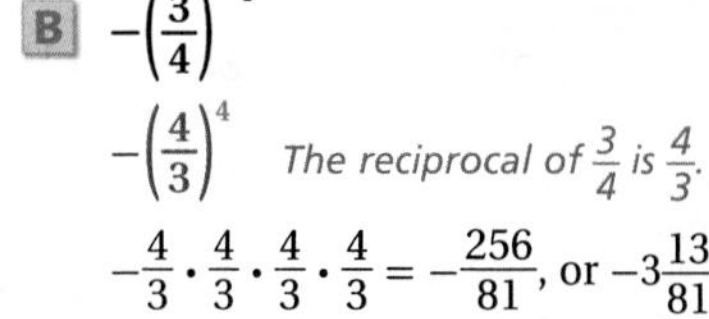

B $-\left(\frac{3}{4}\right)^{-4}$

$-\left(\frac{4}{3}\right)^4$ *The reciprocal of $\frac{3}{4}$ is $\frac{4}{3}$.*

$-\frac{4}{3} \cdot \frac{4}{3} \cdot \frac{4}{3} \cdot \frac{4}{3} = -\frac{256}{81}$, or $-3\frac{13}{81}$

CHECK IT OUT! Simplify each expression.

2a. $\left(\frac{1}{3}\right)^{-2}$ 9

2b. $(-5)^{-5}$ $-\frac{1}{3125}$

You can use the properties of exponents to simplify powers.

Properties of Exponents

For all nonzero real numbers a and b and integers m and n,

WORDS	NUMBERS	ALGEBRA
Product of Powers Property To multiply powers with the same base, add the exponents.	$4^3 \cdot 4^2 = 4^{3+2} = 4^5$	$a^m \cdot a^n = a^{m+n}$
Quotient of Powers Property To divide powers with the same base, subtract the exponents.	$\frac{3^7}{3^2} = 3^{7-2} = 3^5$	$\frac{a^m}{a^n} = a^{m-n}$
Power of a Power Property To raise one power to another, multiply the exponents.	$(4^3)^2 = 4^{3 \cdot 2} = 4^6$	$(a^m)^n = a^{m \cdot n}$
Power of a Product Property To find the power of a product, apply the exponent to each factor.	$(3 \cdot 4)^2 = 3^2 \cdot 4^2$	$(ab)^m = a^m b^m$
Power of a Quotient Property To find the power of a quotient, apply the exponent to the numerator and denominator.	$\left(\frac{3}{5}\right)^2 = \frac{3^2}{5^2}$	$\left(\frac{a}{b}\right)^m = \frac{a^m}{b^m}$

2 Teach

Guided Instruction

Review the properties carefully with students, moving from numeric examples to the algebraic formulas. Emphasize that negative exponents do not represent negative quantities. Students may be familiar with scientific notation, so focus on using this notation to make difficult calculations easier.

Reaching All Learners

Through Number Sense

Computer calculations are based on binary numbers—those used in a number system based on 2 rather than 10. A byte is a unit of computer memory that consists of 8 binary digits. A kilobyte is defined as 1024 bytes. Have students use powers of 2 to see why the kilobyte has been defined as $1024 = 2^{10}$ bytes instead of $1000 = 10^3$ bytes. As an extension, challenge students to find the number of bytes in a megabyte. 1,048,576

COMMON ERROR ALERT

Students may mistakenly include a coefficient or negative sign when evaluating a power such as $3x^2$ or $-y^2$. Emphasize that the exponent applies only to the variable in these situations. Use $(3x)^2$ and $(-y)^2$ to illustrate the differences.

Power Presentations with PowerPoint®

Additional Examples

Example 1

Write each expression in expanded form.

A. $(5z)^2$ $(5z)(5z)$

B. $-s^4$ $-s \cdot s \cdot s \cdot s$

C. $3h^3(k+3)^2$
$3(h)(h)(h)(k+3)(k+3)$

Example 2

Simplify each expression.

A. 3^{-2} $\frac{1}{9}$

B. $\left(\frac{2}{3}\right)^{-2}$ $\frac{9}{4}$

Also available on transparency

INTERVENTION

Questioning Strategies

EXAMPLE 1

- In **Example 1A,** what is the base of the power? What is the exponent?
- In **Example 1B,** why is there only one negative sign in the expanded form?
- How do you know the number of times to use the base as a factor?

EXAMPLE 2

- Do expressions with negative exponents always simplify to a negative number? Explain.

Teaching Tip **Reading Math** Remind students that a *square* with side length ℓ has area ℓ^2. A *cube* with side length ℓ has volume ℓ^3. This helps explain the use of the terms *squared* and *cubed.* ENGLISH LANGUAGE LEARNERS

Power Presentations with PowerPoint®

Additional Examples

Example 3

Simplify each expression. Assume all variables are nonzero.

A. $3z^7(-4z^2)$ $-12z^9$

B. $\left(\frac{yz^3}{z^5}\right)^3$ $\frac{y^3}{z^6}$

Example 4

Simplify each expression. Write the answer in scientific notation.

A. $\frac{4.5 \times 10^{-5}}{1.5 \times 10^6}$ 3.0×10^{-11}

B. $(2.6 \times 10^4)(8.5 \times 10^7)$ 2.21×10^{12}

Also available on transparency

INTERVENTION

Questioning Strategies

EXAMPLE 3

- Which powers in each expression have the same base?
- How are the properties of exponents used in each step?

EXAMPLE 4

- How can you multiply a number by a power of 10 by moving the decimal point of the number?
- In scientific notation, what conditions must the number multiplied by a power of 10 meet?

An algebraic expression is *simplified* when it contains no negative exponents, no grouping symbols, and no like terms.

EXAMPLE 3 Using Properties of Exponents to Simplify Expressions

Simplify each expression. Assume all variables are nonzero.

A $2x^3(-5x)$

$2 \cdot (-5) \cdot x^3 \cdot x^1$

$-10x^{3+1}$ *Product of Powers*

$-10x^4$ *Simplify.*

B $\left(\frac{ab^4}{b^7}\right)^2$

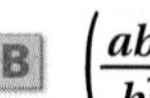

$(ab^{4-7})^2 = (ab^{-3})^2$ *Quotient of Powers*

$a^2(b^{-3})^2$ *Power of a Product*

$a^2b^{(-3)(2)}$ *Power of a Power*

$a^2b^{-6} = \frac{a^2}{b^6}$ *Negative Exponent Property*

CHECK IT OUT! **Simplify each expression. Assume all variables are nonzero.**

3a. $(5x^6)^3$ $125x^{18}$ **3b.** $(-2a^3b)^{-3}$ $-\frac{1}{8a^9b^3}$

Remember!

When you multiply by a power of 10, move the decimal to the right if the exponent is positive. Move the decimal to the left if the exponent is negative.

Scientific notation is a method of writing numbers by using powers of 10. In scientific notation, a number takes the form $m \times 10^n$, where $1 \le m < 10$ and n is an integer.

Scientific Notation	Move the decimal	Standard Notation
1.275×10^7	Right 7 places	12,750,000
3.5×10^{-7}	Left 7 places	0.00000035

You can use the properties of exponents to calculate with numbers expressed in scientific notation.

EXAMPLE 4 Simplifying Expressions Involving Scientific Notation

Simplify each expression. Write the answer in scientific notation.

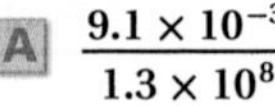

A $\frac{9.1 \times 10^{-3}}{1.3 \times 10^8}$

$\left(\frac{9.1}{1.3}\right) \times \left(\frac{10^{-3}}{10^8}\right)$ $\frac{a \cdot b}{c \cdot d} = \frac{a}{c} \cdot \frac{b}{d}$

7.0×10^{-11} *Divide 9.1 by 1.3 and subtract exponents: $-3 - 8 = -11$.*

B $(3.5 \times 10^8)(5.2 \times 10^5)$

$(3.5)(5.2) \times (10^8)(10^5)$

18.2×10^{13} *Multiply 3.5 and 5.2 and add exponents: $8 + 5 = 13$.*

1.82×10^{14} *Because $18.2 > 10$, move the decimal point left 1 place and add 1 to the exponent.*

CHECK IT OUT! **Simplify each expression. Write the answer in scientific notation.**

4a. $\frac{2.325 \times 10^6}{9.3 \times 10^9}$ 2.5×10^{-4} **4b.** $(4 \times 10^{-6})(3.1 \times 10^{-4})$ 1.24×10^{-9}

Teaching Tip

Math Background A *googol* is 10^{100}. A *googolplex* is $10^{10^{100}}$, or 1 followed by a googol of zeros. Challenge students with the following problem: How many miles long would a sheet of paper need to be for someone to write a googolplex in standard form? Assume that each digit is $\frac{1}{8}$ inch wide and that the number is written in a single row of digits.
about 1.97×10^{94} miles

EXAMPLE 5 Problem-Solving Application

PROBLEM SOLVING

Light travels through space at a speed of about 3×10^5 kilometers per second. How many minutes does it take light to travel from the Sun to Jupiter?

Distances from the Sun	
Object	Approximate Average Distance from Sun (m)
Mercury	5.8×10^{10}
Venus	1.1×10^{11}
Earth	1.5×10^{11}
Mars	2.3×10^{11}
Jupiter	7.8×10^{11}
Saturn	1.4×10^{12}
Uranus	2.9×10^{12}
Neptune	4.5×10^{12}
Pluto	5.9×10^{12}

1 Understand the Problem

The **answer** will be the time it takes for light to travel from the Sun to Jupiter.

List the important information:

- The speed of light in space is 3×10^5 kilometers per second.
- The distance from the Sun to Jupiter is 7.8×10^{11} meters.

2 Make a Plan

Use the relationship: rate, or speed, equals distance divided by time.

$$\text{speed} = \frac{\text{distance}}{\text{time}}, \text{ so time} = \frac{\text{distance}}{\text{speed}}$$

3 Solve

First, convert the speed of light from $\frac{\text{kilometers}}{\text{second}}$ to $\frac{\text{meters}}{\text{minute}}$.

$$3 \times 10^5 \frac{\cancel{\text{km}}}{\cancel{\text{s}}}\left(\frac{10^3\text{ m}}{1\cancel{\text{ km}}}\right)\left(\frac{60\cancel{\text{ s}}}{1\text{ min}}\right)$$

There are 1000, or 10^3, meters in every kilometer and 60 seconds in every minute.

$$(3 \cdot 60) \times (10^5 \cdot 10^3)\frac{\text{m}}{\text{min}}$$

$$180 \times 10^8 \frac{\text{m}}{\text{min}} = 1.8 \times 10^{10}\frac{\text{m}}{\text{min}}$$

Use the relationship between time, distance, and speed to find the number of minutes it takes light to travel from the Sun to Jupiter.

$$\text{time} = \frac{\text{distance}}{\text{speed}} = \frac{7.8 \times 10^{11}\text{ m}}{1.8 \times 10^{10}\frac{\text{m}}{\text{min}}}$$

$$\frac{m}{\left(\frac{m}{min}\right)} = \cancel{m}\left(\frac{min}{\cancel{m}}\right) = min$$

$$= 4.\overline{3} \times 10 \text{ min} \approx 43.33 \text{ min}$$

It takes light approximately 43.33 minutes to travel from the Sun to Jupiter.

4 Look Back

Light traveling at 3×10^5 km/s for $43.33(60) \approx 2600$ seconds travels a distance of $780{,}000{,}000 = 7.8 \times 10^8$ km, or 7.8×10^{11}m. The answer is reasonable.

CHECK IT OUT!

5. How many minutes does it take light to travel from the Sun to Earth? $\approx$ **8.33 min**

COMMON ERROR ALERT

After performing a computation in scientific notation, students may forget to rewrite the answer with only one nonzero digit in front of the decimal point. Remind them that scientific notation is always written in this way.

Power Presentations with PowerPoint®

Additional Examples

Example 5

Using the table on page 37, determine the number of minutes, on average, that it takes light to travel from the Sun to Pluto. about 328 min

Also available on transparency

INTERVENTION

Questioning Strategies

EXAMPLE 5

- Why is multiplying by $\left(\frac{10^3\text{ m}}{1\text{ km}}\right)$ the same as multiplying by 1?
- Why does $\frac{\text{m}}{\left(\frac{\text{m}}{\text{min}}\right)} = \text{min}$?
- Why is scientific notation used in this problem?

Teaching Tip **Communicating Math** Have students practice reading scientific notation expressions aloud. In addition to helping students become more familiar with scientific notation, it will demonstrate that reading 3.5×10^{-7} is easier than reading 0.00000035.

ENGLISH LANGUAGE LEARNERS

3 Close

Summarize

Have students name the property or properties of exponents shown in each statement.

$8^3 \cdot 8^4 = 8^7$ Product of Powers Prop.

$(4^{-5})^3 = \frac{1}{4^{15}}$ Power of a Power Prop.; Negative Exponent Prop.

$8^0 = 1$ Zero Exponent Prop.

$\frac{9^4}{9^6} = \frac{1}{9^2}$ Quotient of Powers Prop.

$5^2 = \frac{15^2}{3^2}$ Power of a Quotient Prop.

$15^2 = 3^2 \cdot 5^2$ Power of a Product Prop.

$5^{-3} = \frac{1}{5^3}$ Negative Exponent Prop.

ONGOING ASSESSMENT and INTERVENTION

Diagnose ***Before*** **the Lesson**
1-5 Warm Up, TE p. 34

Monitor ***During*** **the Lesson**
Check It Out! Exercises, SE pp. 34–37
Questioning Strategies, TE pp. 35–37

Assess ***After*** **the Lesson**
1-5 Lesson Quiz, TE p. 41
Alternative Assessment, TE p. 41

Answers to *Think and Discuss*

Possible answers:

1. The Product and Quotient of Powers Properties both require the same base.
2. Move the decimal point so that there is one nonzero digit in front of it. Use the number of places moved for the exponent of 10. If you moved the decimal point left, use a positive exponent. If you moved the decimal point right, use a negative exponent.
3. See p. A2.

THINK AND DISCUSS

1. Tell which properties of exponents apply only to expressions with the same base.
2. List the steps for writing a number in scientific notation.

3. **GET ORGANIZED** Copy and complete the graphic organizer by providing a numerical and algebraic example of each property.

Property	Numerical Example	Algebraic Example
Product of Powers		
Quotient of Powers		
Power of a Power		
Power of a Product		
Power of a Quotient		

1-5 Exercises

Assignment Guide

Assign *Guided Practice* exercises as necessary.

If you finished Examples **1–3**
Basic 22–33, 39–41, 45–47
Average 22–33, 39–41, 45–47, 56–58, 89
Advanced 22–33, 39–41, 45–50, 56–61, 89

If you finished Examples **1–5**
Basic 22–47, 51–55, 62–86, 91–96
Average 22–55, 62–86, 89–96
Advanced 22–96

Homework Quick Check

Quickly check key concepts.
Exercises: 22, 26, 30, 34, 37, 43, 71

State Resources

1-5 Exercises

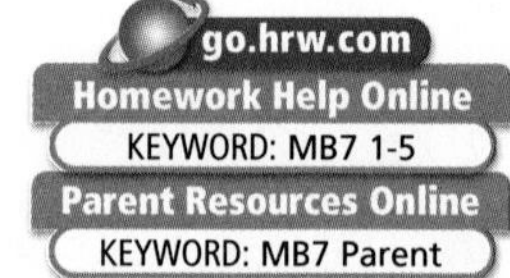

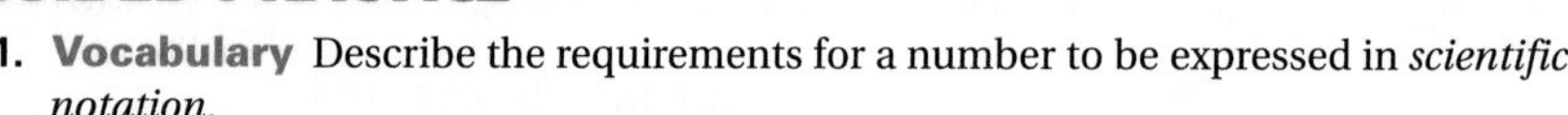

GUIDED PRACTICE

1. **Vocabulary** Describe the requirements for a number to be expressed in *scientific notation.*

SEE EXAMPLE 1 p. 34

Write each expression in expanded form.

2. $4(a-b)^2$ 3. $(12xy)^4$ 4. $-s^3(-2t)^5$ 5. $\left(-\frac{1}{2}d\right)^3$

SEE EXAMPLE 2 p. 35

Simplify each expression.

6. $\left(-\frac{3}{5}\right)^{-2}$ $\frac{25}{9}$ 7. 5^0 1 8. $\left(\frac{2}{3}\right)^{-3}$ $\frac{27}{8}$ 9. 10^{-1} $\frac{1}{10}$

SEE EXAMPLE 3 p. 36

Simplify each expression. Assume all variables are nonzero.

10. $(-3a^2b^3)^2$ $9a^4b^6$ 11. $c^3d^2(c^{-2}d^4)$ cd^6 12. $\frac{5uv^6}{u^2v^2}$ $\frac{5v^4}{u}$ 13. $10\left(\frac{y^5}{x^2}\right)^2$ $\frac{10y^{10}}{x^4}$

14. $-2s^{-3}t(7s^{-8}t^5)$ $-\frac{14t^6}{s^{11}}$ 15. $-4m(mn^2)^3$ $-4m^4n^6$ 16. $\frac{(4b)^2}{2b}$ $8b$ 17. $\frac{x^{-1}y^{-2}}{x^3y^{-5}}$ $\frac{y^3}{x^4}$

SEE EXAMPLE 4 p. 36

Simplify each expression. Write the answer in scientific notation.

18. $(2.2 \times 10^5)(4.5 \times 10^{11})$ 9.9×10^{16} 19. $\frac{7.8 \times 10^8}{2.6 \times 10^{-3}}$ 3×10^{11} 20. $\frac{16 \times 10^{-3}}{4.0 \times 10^4}$ 4×10^{-7}

SEE EXAMPLE 5 p. 37

21. **Technology** Nanotechnology is a branch of engineering that works with devices that are smaller than 100 nanometers. The width of one string on the playable nanoguitar created by scientists at Cornell University in 2003 is 2.0×10^{-7} meters. If the width of a human hair is about 80 microns, how many nanoguitar strings would have the same width as a human hair? (*Hint:* 1 micron $= 10^{-6}$ meters) 400

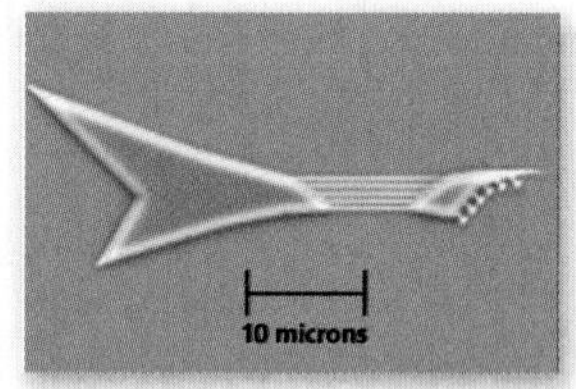

Answers

1. Possible answer: a number between 1 and 10 multiplied by an integer power of 10
2. $4(a-b)(a-b)$
3. $(12xy)(12xy)(12xy)(12xy)$
4. $-s \cdot s \cdot s(-2t)(-2t)(-2t)(-2t)(-2t)$
5. $\left(-\frac{1}{2}d\right)\left(-\frac{1}{2}d\right)\left(-\frac{1}{2}d\right)$

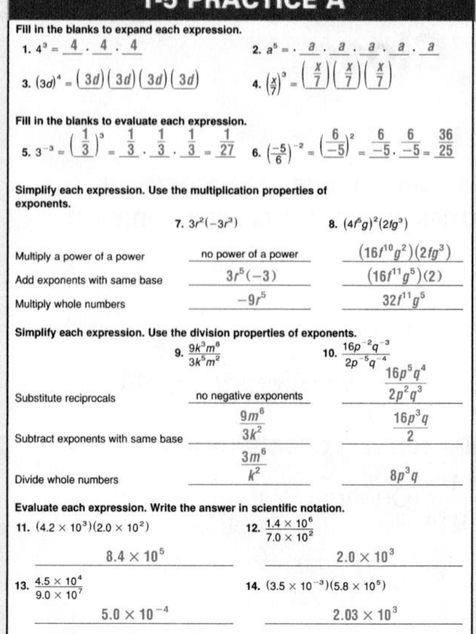

1-5 PRACTICE A

Fill in the blanks to expand each expression.

1. $4^3 = 4 \cdot 4 \cdot 4$
2. $a^5 = \cdot\ a \cdot a \cdot a \cdot a \cdot a$
3. $(3d)^4 = (3d)(3d)(3d)(3d)$
4. $\left(\frac{x}{7}\right)^3 = \left(\frac{x}{7}\right)\left(\frac{x}{7}\right)\left(\frac{x}{7}\right)$

Fill in the blanks to evaluate each expression.

5. $3^{-3} = \left(\frac{1}{3}\right)^3 = \frac{1}{3} \cdot \frac{1}{3} \cdot \frac{1}{3} = \frac{1}{27}$
6. $\left(\frac{-5}{6}\right)^{-2} = \left(\frac{6}{-5}\right)^2 = \frac{6}{-5} \cdot \frac{6}{-5} = \frac{36}{25}$

Simplify each expression. Use the multiplication properties of exponents.

	7. $3r^2(-3r^3)$	8. $(4f^5g)^2(2fg^3)$
Multiply a power of a power	no power of a power	$(16f^{10}g^2)(2fg^3)$
Add exponents with same base	$3r^5(-3)$	$(16f^{11}g^5)(2)$
Multiply whole numbers	$-9r^5$	$32f^{11}g^5$

Simplify each expression. Use the division properties of exponents.

	9. $\frac{9k^3m^8}{3k^5m^2}$	10. $\frac{16p^{-2}q^{-3}}{2p^{-5}q^{-4}}$
Substitute reciprocals	no negative exponents	$\frac{16p^5q^4}{2p^2q^3}$
Subtract exponents with same base	$\frac{9m^6}{3k^2}$	$\frac{16p^3q}{2}$
Divide whole numbers	$\frac{3m^6}{k^2}$	$8p^3q$

Evaluate each expression. Write the answer in scientific notation.

11. $(4.2 \times 10^3)(2.0 \times 10^2)$ 8.4×10^5
12. $\frac{1.4 \times 10^6}{7.0 \times 10^2}$ 2.0×10^3
13. $\frac{4.5 \times 10^4}{9.0 \times 10^7}$ 5.0×10^{-4}
14. $(3.5 \times 10^{-3})(5.8 \times 10^5)$ 2.03×10^3

PRACTICE AND PROBLEM SOLVING

Independent Practice

For Exercises	See Example
22–25	1
26–29	2
30–33	3
34–36	4
37	5

Extra Practice

Skills Practice p. S4

Application Practice p. S32

Write each expression in expanded form.

22. $(m+2n)^3$ $(m+2n)(m+2n)(m+2n)$ **23.** $5x^3$ $5 \cdot x \cdot x \cdot x$ **24.** $(-9fg)^3h^4$ $(-9fg)(-9fg)(-9fg) \cdot h \cdot h \cdot h \cdot h$ **25.** $2a(-b^2-a)^2$ $2a(-b^2-a)(-b^2-a)$

Simplify each expression.

26. $(-4)^{-2}$ $\frac{1}{16}$ **27.** $\left(-\frac{3}{4}\right)^{-1}$ $-\frac{4}{3}$ **28.** $\left(-\frac{5}{2}\right)^{-3}$ $-\frac{8}{125}$ **29.** -6^0 -1

Simplify each expression. Assume all variables are nonzero.

30. $\frac{-100s^3t^{-5}}{25s^{-2}t^6}$ $-\frac{4s^5}{t^{11}}$ **31.** $(-x^4y^2)^5$ $-x^{20}y^{10}$ **32.** $(16u^4v^6)^{-2}$ $\frac{1}{256u^8v^{12}}$ **33.** $8a^2b^5(-2a^3b^2)$ $-16a^5b^7$

Simplify each expression. Write the answer in scientific notation.

34. $(3.2 \times 10^6)(1.7 \times 10^{-4})$ **35.** $\frac{5.1 \times 10^4}{3.4 \times 10^{-5}}$ **36.** $(6.8 \times 10^3)(9.5 \times 10^5)$

37. Computer Science A computer with a 5.4 GHz microprocessor can make 5.4×10^9 calculations in one second. If a total of 5.02×10^{11} calculations are required to convert a given MP3 file to audio, how many minutes will the computer take to convert the file? Round your answer to the nearest hundredth. **1.55 min**

38. Biology A king cobra bite is fatal to a mouse if the mouse receives at least 0.00173 gram of venom per kilogram of its body mass. What is the smallest amount, in grams, of king cobra venom that will be fatal to a mouse with a mass of 0.02 kilogram? Express your answer in scientific notation. 3.46×10^{-5} **g**

LINK Biology

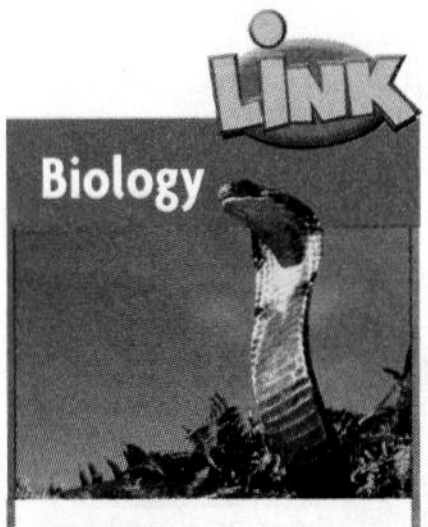

King cobras are native to Asia. They may grow more than 12 feet in length and feed primarily on other snakes.

Order each list from least to greatest by first rewriting each number with a base of 2.

39. $8^2, 4^1, 2^5, 16^{-2}$ **40.** $2^{-1}, -4^3, 4^2, 8^{-2}$ **41.** $-8^2, 4^0, 16^1, 2^{-2}$

42. Multi-Step There are approximately 1.3×10^{15} gallons of water in Lake Michigan. If a faucet is leaking at a rate of 1.5 ounces per minute, how many years would it take for the amount of water that has leaked to be equivalent to the volume of Lake Michigan? (*Hint:* 1 gallon = 128 ounces) $\approx 2.11 \times 10^{11}$ **yr**

Geometry Write and simplify an expression for the volume of each figure.

43. $3m^5n^4$

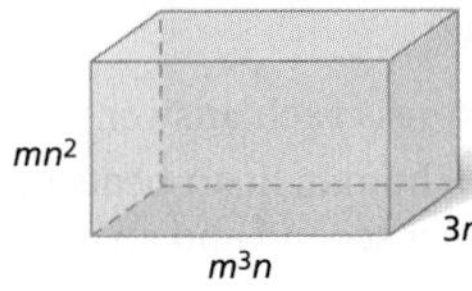

44. πa^5b^3c

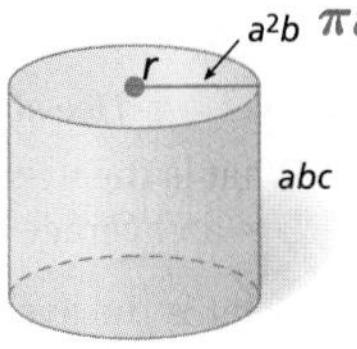

Simplify each expression. Assume all variables are nonzero.

45. $\frac{27x^3y}{18x^2y^4}$ $\frac{3x}{2y^3}$ **46.** $\left(\frac{3a^3b}{2a^{-1}b^2}\right)^2$ $\frac{9a^8}{4b^2}$ **47.** $12a^0b^5(-2a^3b^2)$ $-24a^3b^7$

48. $\frac{72a^2b^3}{-24a^2b^5}$ $-\frac{3}{b^2}$ **49.** $\left(\frac{5mn}{-3m^2}\right)^{-2}$ $\frac{9m^2}{25n^2}$ **50.** $6x^5y^3(-3x^2y^{-1})$ $-18x^7y^2$

Measurement Calculate each of the following.

51. number of square inches in a square yard **1296**

52. number of square centimeters in a square meter **10,000**

53. number of cubic inches in a cubic foot **1728**

54. number of cubic meters in a cubic kilometer 10^9

COMMON ERROR ALERT

In **Exercise 30,** students may make sign errors with exponents in fractions. Remind students that a power can be moved from the numerator to the denominator, or vice versa, as long as the sign of the exponent is switched.

Teaching Tip **Science Link** In **Exercise 37,** the unit GHz is used. This unit is read "gigahertz" and represents 1 billion hertz, or cycles per second.

Teaching Tip **Geometry** For **Exercises 43** and **44,** remind students that the formula for the volume of a rectangular prism is $V = \ell wh$ and the formula for the volume of a cylinder is $V = \pi r^2 h$.

Answers

34. 5.44×10^2

35. 1.5×10^9

36. 6.46×10^9

39. $2^6, 2^2, 2^5, 2^{-8}$; $16^{-2}, 4^1, 2^5, 8^2$

40. $2^{-1}, -2^6, 2^4, 2^{-6}$; $-4^3, 8^{-2}, 2^{-1}, 4^2$

41. $-2^6, 2^0, 2^4, 2^{-2}$; $-8^2, 2^{-2}, 4^0, 16^1$

1-5 PRACTICE B

Write each expression in expanded form.

1. $-3x^5$ $-3 \cdot x \cdot x \cdot x \cdot x \cdot x$

2. $(j-3k)^3$ $((j-3k)j-3k)(j-3k)$

3. $7t^2(-4r)^4$ $7 \cdot t \cdot t(-4r)(-4r)(-4r)(-4r)$

Evaluate each expression.

4. $-(-2)^{-4}$ $\frac{-1}{16}$

5. $\left(\frac{5}{8}\right)^{-2}$ $\frac{64}{25}$

6. $\left(-\frac{3}{2}\right)^{-3}$ $-\frac{8}{27}$

Simplify each expression. Assume all variables are nonzero.

7. $\frac{68f^5g^{-3}}{4f^{-3}g^6}$ $\frac{17f^8}{g^9}$

8. $(-4a^3b^7)^{-2}$ $\frac{1}{16a^6b^{14}}$

9. $6m^4n^9(-3m^2n^3)^{-2}$ $\frac{2n^3}{3}$

Evaluate each expression. Write the answer in scientific notation.

10. $(7.2 \times 10^{-5})(4.5 \times 10^3)$ 3.24×10^{-1}

11. $\frac{1.7 \times 10^5}{3.4 \times 10^9}$ 5.0×10^{-5}

12. $(7.8 \times 10^8)(2.8 \times 10^{11})$ 2.184×10^{20}

Solve.

13. The A-1 Moving and Storage Company sells crates that measure x^2y units wide, x units long, and y^2 units tall. Find the volume of the crate. x^3y^3 cubic units

14. The average lifespan for an adult living today is about 82 years. Some scientists believe that people born in the early part of this century may live up to 150 years. Calculate the number of minutes an 82-year-old and a 150-year-old could live. Round to the nearest million. Record the difference in scientific notation. 43 million; 79 million; 3.6×10^7

15. A movie made 6.7×10^7. It took 250 hours to film it. How much money was earned for each hour of filming? Write your answer in scientific notation. 2.68×10^5

1-5 PRACTICE C

Write and simplify an expression for the volume of each figure.

1.

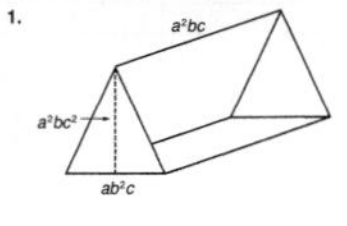

V = area of base × height

$\frac{1}{2}a^5b^4c^4$ cubic units

2.

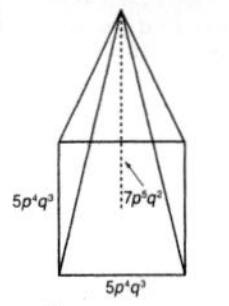

$V = \frac{1}{3}$ area of base × height

$\frac{175p^{13}q^8}{3}$ cubic units

Simplify each expression. Assume all variables are nonzero.

3. $(-5x^5y^{-3}z^8)^3$ $-\frac{125x^{15}z^{24}}{y^9}$

4. $7g^2h^3(-2h^5k^0)^{-3}$ $-\frac{7g^2}{8h^{12}}$

5. $\left(\frac{24m^7n^3}{4mn^{-5}}\right)^{-2}$ $\frac{1}{36m^{12}n^{16}}$

One cubic foot of pennies is 49,152 pennies. Use this fact for Exercises 6–8. Write your answers in scientific notation rounded to the nearest tenth.

6. The Empire State Building in New York City has an approximate volume of 3.7×10^7 ft³. About how many pennies would fit in the Empire State Building? 1.8×10^{12}

7. If the Sears Tower in Chicago were filled with pennies, it would hold about 2.6×10^{12} pennies. What is the approximate volume of the Sears Tower? 5.3×10^7 ft³

8. Think about covering the entire earth with two layers of pennies. The total number of pennies needed could be stacked in a cube that measures 2.73×10^4 ft on each side. How many pennies are in this cube? 1.0×10^{18}

Exercise 55 involves using scientific notation to represent the velocity of spacecraft. This exercise prepares students for the Multi-Step Test Prep on page 42.

Math Background
Exercise 75 refers to 0^0 as undefined. It is one of seven similar indeterminate forms, which are 0^0, $\frac{0}{0}$, $0 \cdot \infty$, $\frac{\infty}{\infty}$, $\infty - \infty$, ∞^0, and 1^∞. Students may have already encountered some of these.

Answers

67. $\approx 2.84 \times 10^9$ beats
68. $\approx 6.31 \times 10^8$ breaths
69. $\approx 1.27 \times 10^5$ hairs
70. Power of a Power Property
71. Power of a Product Property or Power of a Power Property
72. Quotient of Powers Property
73. Power of a Quotient Property or Power of a Power Property
74. 1 million $= 10^6$, so 3.8 million $= 3.8 \times 10^6$. The word *million* can be represented by the expression 10^6.
75. Possible answer: $0^0 = 0^{2-2} = \frac{0^2}{0^2} = \frac{0}{0}$, but division by zero is undefined.
76. 2.997×10^{-7}
77. 6.5×10^{-15}
78. 1.995×10^{-4}
79. 3.5×10^{14}
80. 2.51×10^{-7}
81. 1.1346×10^{24}
82. Possible answer: First compare exponents. Since $9 > 8$, 1.23×10^9 is greater than 4.56×10^8. If the exponents are equal, compare the initial factors. Since $1.23 < 4.56$, 1.23×10^7 is less than 4.56×10^7.

55. This problem will prepare you for the Multi-Step Test Prep on page 42.

The *Apollo 11* took approximately 102 hours and 45 minutes to get to the Moon, which is located about 384,500 km from Earth.

a. What was the average speed of the *Apollo 11* to the nearest kilometer per hour? **3742 km/h**

b. In theory, spaceships of the future might be able to travel at the speed of light, 3×10^5 km/s. How many times as fast is this than the average speed of the *Apollo 11*? $\approx$ **288,608 times as fast**

c. How long would it take future space travelers traveling at the speed of light to get to the Moon? $\approx$ **1.28 s**

Simplify each expression. Assume all variables are nonzero.

56. $-9a^2b^6(-7ab^{-4})$ $\mathbf{63a^3b^2}$

57. $\dfrac{14x^{-2}y^3}{-8x^{-5}y^5}$ $\mathbf{-\dfrac{7x^3}{4y^2}}$

58. $-\left(\dfrac{20x^6}{2x^2}\right)^3$ $\mathbf{-1000x^{12}}$

59. $\left(10x^{-2}y^0z^{-3}\right)^2$ $\mathbf{\dfrac{100}{x^4z^6}}$

60. $\left(-3a^2b^{-1}\right)^{-3}$ $\mathbf{-\dfrac{b^3}{27a^6}}$

61. $\left(8m^4n^{-2}\right)\left(-3m^{-2}n\right)^0$ $\mathbf{\dfrac{8m^4}{n^2}}$

Geography Use the map for Exercises 62–66. Identify which country fits the description, and then find its population density, or population per square mile, to the nearest tenth.

62. greatest population **China; 130.2**
63. median area **Laos; 25.6**
64. median population **Thailand; 126.3**
65. least area **Vietnam; 615.6**
66. second smallest population **Cambodia; 74.0**

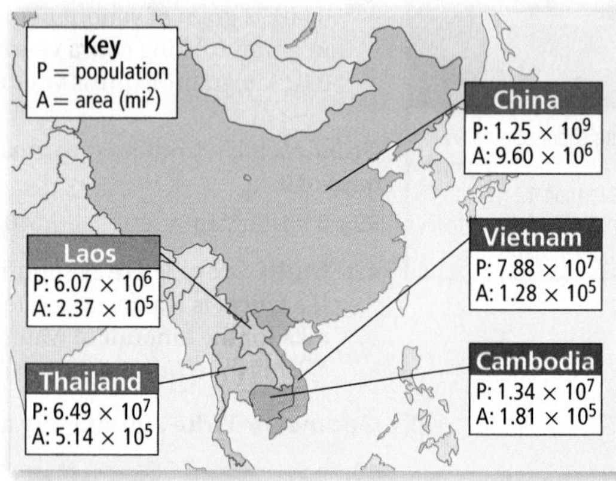

Estimation Use scientific notation to express each answer.

67. What is the average number of times a human heart beats in an average lifetime? Use an average rate of 1.2 heartbeats per second and an average lifespan of 75 years.

68. What is the average number of breaths a person takes in a lifetime? Use an average rate of 16 breaths per minute and an average lifespan of 75 years.

69. What is the average number of hairs on a human head? Use an average of 254 hairs per square centimeter and an average scalp size of 500 square centimeters.

Identify the property of exponents illustrated in each equation.

70. $\left(x^5\right)^3 = x^{15}$

71. $\left(m^2n^5\right)^4 = m^8n^{20}$

72. $\dfrac{3a^3}{a^{-2}} = 3a^5$

73. $\left(\dfrac{st^5}{s^3}\right)^4 = \dfrac{s^4t^{20}}{s^{12}}$

74. **Language** Statements such as "The population of the country is 3.8 million" are commonly used to describe large numbers. Express this value in scientific notation and explain the relationship between the mathematical representation of the number and the words used to describe it.

75. **Critical Thinking** Use the Quotient of Powers Property to show why 0^0 is undefined.

1-5 READING STRATEGIES

Compare these properties of exponents. For each statement, m and n are exponents, a and b are bases. Bases are nonzero real numbers.

Same Base	Different Bases
$a^m \cdot a^n = a^{m+n}$	$(ab)^m = a^mb^m$
$\frac{a^m}{a^n} = a^{m-n}$	$\left(\frac{a}{b}\right)^m = \frac{a^m}{b^m}$
$a^{-n} = \left(\frac{1}{a}\right)^n = \frac{1}{a^n}$	$\left(\frac{a}{b}\right)^{-n} = \left(\frac{b}{a}\right)^n = \frac{b^n}{a^n}$
$(a^m)^n = a^{m \cdot n}$	

To simplify an expression with exponents:

- use properties
- eliminate grouping symbols
- rewrite all negative exponents as positive exponents
- combine like terms

Complete each statement.

1. In g^5, ___ g ___ is the base and ___ 5 ___ is the exponent.
2. Write a power with base 6 and exponent 8. ___ 6^8 ___
3. How would you find the product of k^u and k^v? Give an example with numbers. $k^u \cdot k^v = k^{u+v}$; $2^2 \cdot 2^4 = 2^6$
4. Express h to the negative 7 power in 2 different ways. h^{-7}, $\frac{1}{h^7}$
5. In which expression are the bases the same: x^3y^3 or xx^5? ___ xx^5 ___
6. Which expression has different bases: $-2p^3(3s^3)$ or $-4p^2(5p^5)$? ___ $-2p^3(3s^3)$ ___
7. Which expression is not simplified: $\frac{3a^3}{b^2}$ or $\frac{2a^5}{a^2}$? Explain. Then simplify. $\frac{2a^5}{a^2}$ is not simplified because a is a like term; $2a^3$.
8. Explain how to simplify $\left(\frac{x}{y}\right)^{-2}$. Use the Negative Exponent and Power of a Quotient Properties: $\left(\frac{x}{y}\right)^{-2} = \left(\frac{y}{x}\right)^2 = \frac{y^2}{x^2}$.

1-5 RETEACH

Write: Expanded Form	Write: Exponent Form	Read
$a \cdot a$	a^2	a squared
$a \cdot a \cdot a$	a^3	a cubed
$a \cdot a \cdot a \cdot a$	a^4	a to the fourth power
$a \cdot a \cdot \ldots \cdot a$	a^n	a to the nth power

$-4x^5 = -4(x \cdot x \cdot x \cdot x \cdot x)$
$-(4x^5) = -(4x)(4x)(4x)(4x)(4x)$
$(-4x)^5 = (-4x)(-4x)(-4x)(-4x)(-4x)$
$4x^3(y+6)^2 = 4(x)(x)(x)(y+6)(y+6)$

List the factors to expand exponential expressions.

Zero Exponent Property: $a^0 = 1$; a is not zero $\quad 38^0 = 1$

Negative Exponent Property: $a^{-n} = \frac{1}{a^n}$ and $\left(\frac{a}{b}\right)^{-n} = \left(\frac{b}{a}\right)^n$; a is not zero.

$3^{-4} = \frac{1}{3^4} = \frac{1}{3 \cdot 3 \cdot 3 \cdot 3} = \frac{1}{81}$

$\left(\frac{2}{5}\right)^{-3} = \left(\frac{5}{2}\right)^3 = \frac{5}{2} \cdot \frac{5}{2} \cdot \frac{5}{2} = \frac{125}{8}$

Write each expression in expanded form.

1. $-8c^3$ $\quad -8(c \cdot c \cdot c)$
2. $(3xy)^4$ $\quad (3xy)(3xy)(3xy)(3xy)$
3. $a^3(b-c)^2$ $\quad a \cdot a \cdot a(b-c)(b-c)$

Evaluate each expression.

4. 6^{-1} $\quad \frac{1}{6}$
5. 10^0 $\quad 1$
6. 12^{-2} $\quad \frac{1}{144}$
7. $(-4)^{-3}$ $\quad -\frac{1}{64}$
8. $\left(\frac{1}{7}\right)^{-2}$ $\quad 49$
9. $\left(\frac{3}{4}\right)^{-3}$ $\quad \frac{64}{27}$
10. -5^0 $\quad -1$
11. $\left(\frac{-2}{5}\right)^2$ $\quad \frac{4}{25}$
12. $-\left(\frac{1}{3}\right)^{-2}$ $\quad -9$

Graphing Calculator The key sequence 2nd , (EE) on a calculator is used for scientific notation. To enter the number 2.8×10^5 into your calculator, you would enter 2.8 2nd , (EE) 5. The calculator screen will display 2.8E5. Use your calculator to find the value of each expression.

76. $(3.7 \times 10^{-3})(8.1 \times 10^{-5})$
77. $\dfrac{2.08 \times 10^{-8}}{3.2 \times 10^{6}}$
78. $(4.75 \times 10^{2})(4.2 \times 10^{-7})$
79. $\dfrac{8.4 \times 10^{9}}{2.4 \times 10^{-5}}$
80. $\dfrac{17.068 \times 10^{-4}}{6.8 \times 10^{3}}$
81. $(1.83 \times 10^{13})(6.2 \times 10^{10})$

82. **Write About It** How can you tell which of two numbers written in scientific notation is greater? Use examples to explain your answer.

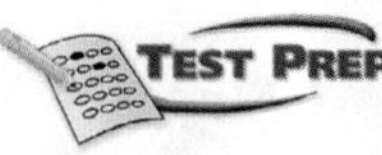

TEST PREP

83. Which number is greatest?
   (A) 0.000025 (B) 2.5×10^{-6} (C) 2.5×10^{-4} (D) 2.5×10^{-5}

84. Which number is expressed correctly in scientific notation?
   (F) 11×10^5 (G) 58.5×10^4 (H) 0.245×10^{-7} (J) 7.25×10^0

85. Which expression is equivalent to $(-5)(-5)(-5)(-5)(-5)(-5)$?
   (A) 5^{-6} (B) $(-5)^{-6}$ (C) $(-5)^6$ (D) -5^6

86. If a and c are nonzero, which expression is equivalent to $\dfrac{a^4b^{-3}}{a^2c^0}$?
   (F) $\dfrac{a^2}{b^3c}$ (G) $\dfrac{a^2c}{b^3}$ (H) $\dfrac{a^{-2}}{b^{-3}c}$ (J) $\dfrac{a^2}{b^3}$

CHALLENGE AND EXTEND

Simplify each expression. Write your answer in scientific notation.

87. $\left(\dfrac{7.82 \times 10^6}{5.48 \times 10^8}\right)^2$ $\approx 2.0363 \times 10^{-4}$
88. $\left[(6.18 \times 10^7)(2.05 \times 10^8)\right]^2$ $\approx 1.61 \times 10^{32}$
89. Give examples of numbers that are greater than 1 when raised to the exponent -2. Make a generalization about the types of numbers that are greater than 1 when raised to a negative exponent.
90. Notice that $2^4 = 4^2$. For whole numbers a and b such that $a < b$, give three examples of values of a and b such that $a^b > b^a$ and three examples such that $a^b < b^a$.

SPIRAL REVIEW

91. When two people play the game rock, paper, scissors, each person's hand simultaneously shows the player's choice of rock, paper, or scissors. What is the probability that both players will make the same choice? *(Previous course)* $\frac{1}{3}$

Complete each statement. *(Lesson 1-2)*

92. $\frac{1}{3} \cdot \blacksquare = 1$ 3
93. $4(-3 + \blacksquare) = -12 + 32$ 8
94. $0 = \sqrt{7} + \blacksquare$ $-\sqrt{7}$

Evaluate each expression for the given values of the variables. *(Lesson 1-4)*

95. $\dfrac{2mn}{n^2 - 2n + 5m}$ for $n = -1$ and $m = 3$ $-\frac{1}{3}$
96. $2x(9y - x^2)$ for $x = -3$ and $y = 10$ -486

1-5 PROBLEM SOLVING

Joan made a presentation to her technology class about the history of the Internet. Use the data in her table for Exercises 1–6.

Number of Internet Users (estimated)		
Year	U.S.	World
1992	4.5×10^6	1.2×10^7
1993	5.5×10^6	1.5×10^7
1994	8.5×10^6	1.75×10^7
1995	2.0×10^7	2.37×10^7
1996	3.0×10^7	5.5×10^7
1997	4.5×10^7	1.01×10^8
1998	7.3×10^7	1.6×10^8
1999	1.02×10^8	2.7×10^8
2000	1.24×10^8	3.85×10^8
2001	1.43×10^8	4.99×10^8
2002	1.64×10^8	5.44×10^8

1. About how many million Internet users were there in the world in 1997? 101 million
2. When did the estimated number of Internet users in the United States show the greatest increase? 1998 to 1999
3. What was the first year the number of Internet users in the United States exceeded 10 million? 1995
4. During which year was there about the same number of Internet users in the United States as in the world? 1995
5. During which two years was the number of Internet users in the world almost double the number of Internet users in the United States? 1994, 1996
6. By what factor did the number of Internet users increase in the United States from 1992 to 2002? 36.4

Choose the letter for the best answer.

7. In 1790 the population of the United States was about 3.9×10^6. By 2000 the population had grown to around 2.8×10^8. By what factor did the population increase?
   A 720
   (B) 72
   C 7.2
   D 0.72
8. Lee is packing three congruent storage boxes. Each box is $2b^3$ high, b^4 long, and $3b^{-2}$ wide. Which expression gives the total volume of the 3 boxes?
   F $6b^5$
   G $4b^7$
   (H) $18b^5$
   J $12b^7$

1-5 CHALLENGE

Compare the expressions -3^2 and $(-3)^2$. How are they different? In the expression -3^2, the base is 3 and the exponent is 2. Only 3 is squared, not -3. Think of -3^2 as $(-1)3^2$. In the expression $(-3)^2$, the base is -3 since the value is shown in parentheses. Evaluating each expression gives $-3^2 = -9$ and $(-3)^2 = 9$.

1. Evaluate -5^3 and $(-5)^3$. -125 and -125
2. Evaluate -2^4 and $(-2)^4$. -16 and 16
3. Write a general rule for $-a^n$ and $(-a^n)$ where $a > 0$.
   Possible answer: $-a^n$ is always negative; $(-a)^n$ is negative if n is odd and positive if n is even.

Insert parentheses to make each equation true or determine that the equation is true as written.

4. $-5^2 + 11 + 14 = 0$
   True as written
5. $-3^2 + 81 - 3^4 - 3^2 = 0$
   $(-3)^2 + 81 - 3^4 - 3^2 = 0$
6. $4x^2 + 36x^4y^4 - 6(x^2y^2)^2 - 2x^2 = 0$
   $4x^2 + 36x^4y^4 - (6(x^2y^2))^2 - (2x)^2 = 0$
7. $-12a^3 + 2b^2 + 1728a^3 - 2b^2 - 2b^2 = 0$
   $-(12a)^3 + (2b)^2 + 1728a^3 - 2b^2 - 2b^2 = 0$
8. $2g^2 + 2h^3 - 4^0 + 24 = 25$
   $(2g^2 + 2h^3 - 4)^0 + 24 = 25$
9. $4p^0 + 81^1 - 9^2 - 2^2 = 0$
   True as written
10. $-12abc^0 - 25d^2 + 34ab^0 + 5d^2 = 2$
    $(-12abc)^0 - 25d^2 + (34ab)^0 + (5d)^2 = 2$

TEST PREP DOCTOR In **Exercise 85,** students who chose **A** or **B** may be unclear on the meaning of a negative exponent. Those who chose **D** forgot to use parentheses to show that the negative sign is part of the base. The correct choice is **C.**

Answers

89. Possible answer: $\left(\frac{1}{2}\right)^{-2}$, $(0.7)^{-2}$, $\left(-\frac{2}{5}\right)^{-2}$; numbers between -1 and 1, excluding 0, are greater than 1 when raised to the exponent -2.
90. Possible answer: $2^3 < 3^2$, $1^3 < 3^1$, $0^2 < 2^0$; $3^4 > 4^3$, $2^5 > 5^2$, $4^5 > 5^4$

Journal

Have students explain how scientific notation is useful for converting measurements.

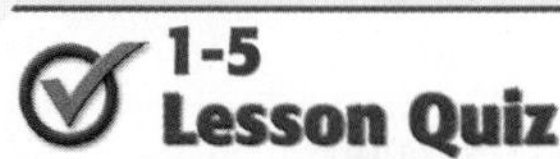

ALTERNATIVE ASSESSMENT

Have students create a numerical example to demonstrate each of the properties of exponents studied in this lesson.

Power Presentations with PowerPoint®

1-5 Lesson Quiz

Simplify each expression.

1. 4^{-3} $\frac{1}{64}$
2. $\left(\frac{2}{5}\right)^{-3}$ $\frac{125}{8}$

Simplify each expression. Assume all variables are nonzero.

3. $8y^6(-6y^3)$ $-48y^9$
4. $\left(\frac{kj^4}{j^7}\right)^4$ $\frac{k^4}{j^{12}}$

Simplify each expression. Write the answer in scientific notation.

5. $\dfrac{4.8 \times 10^{-7}}{1.2 \times 10^3}$ 4.0×10^{-10}
6. If light travels about 3×10^5 kilometers per second, about how many kilometers does it travel in 1 day? Write the answer in scientific notation. 2.592×10^{10} km

Also available on transparency

SECTION 1A MULTI-STEP TEST PREP

Organizer

Objective: Assess students' ability to apply concepts and skills in Lessons 1-1 through 1-5 in a real-world format.

Online Edition

Resources

Algebra II Assessments
www.mathtekstoolkit.org

Problems	Text Reference
1	Skills Bank page S57
2–3	Lesson 1-1
4–5	Lessons 1-3, 1-4
6	Lesson 1–5

Answers

1. 12:50 P.M. EDT, July 24, 1969
2. more than $\frac{1}{6}$ of Earth's gravity

3a. $\mathbb{R}, \mathbb{Q}, \mathbb{Z}, \mathbb{W}, \mathbb{N}$

b. $\mathbb{R}, \mathbb{Q}$

c. $\mathbb{R}, \mathbb{Q}$

4. ≈ 2.96 s
5. ≈ 7.29 s
6. ≈ 49 Moons

State Resources

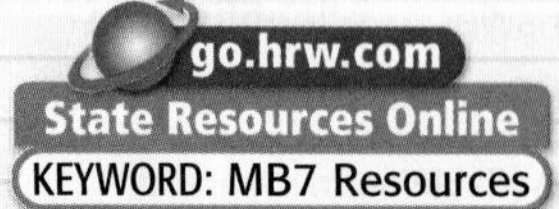
go.hrw.com
State Resources Online
KEYWORD: MB7 Resources

CHAPTER 1

MULTI-STEP TEST PREP

SECTION 1A

Properties and Operations

Man on the Moon On July 20, 1969, the U.S. *Apollo 11* lunar module landed on the Moon. A few hours later, Neil Armstrong was the first human to set foot on the Moon's surface. The *Apollo 11* mission led to many scientific discoveries about Earth's nearest neighbor.

	Earth	Moon
Mean Diameter (km)	12,742	3476
Volume (km^3)	1.08321×10^{12}	2.199×10^{10}
Mass (kg)	5.9736×10^{24}	7.349×10^{22}
Mean Density (kg/m^3)	5515	3342
Surface Gravity (m/s^2)	9.78	1.64
Escape Velocity (km/s)	11.2	2.38

1. *Apollo 11* was launched at 9:32 A.M. eastern daylight time (EDT) on July 16, 1969. The mission lasted 195 h 18 min. What was the date and time when the mission ended?
2. The gravity on the Moon is about $\frac{1}{6}$ of Earth's gravity. Based on the data in the table, is the actual surface gravity on the Moon less than or greater than $\frac{1}{6}$ of Earth's surface gravity? Explain.
3. Classify the numbers in the indicated row of the table by the sets of the real numbers to which they belong.
   a. mean diameter b. surface gravity c. escape velocity
4. The expression $\sqrt{\frac{h}{0.82}}$ can be used to approximate the time in seconds it takes for an object to reach the surface of the Moon when dropped from a height of h meters. The *Apollo 11* lunar module was about 7.2 meters tall. Suppose Neil Armstrong jumped from the top of the lunar module. How long would it have taken him to land on the surface of the Moon?
5. The expression $\sqrt{\frac{h}{4.89}}$ can be used to model the time it takes to reach Earth's surface from a height of h meters. To the nearest tenth of a second, how much longer would it take for an object to fall from a height of 125 m to the surface on the Moon than it would take on Earth?
6. Approximately how many Moons would it take to equal the volume of Earth?

INTERVENTION

Scaffolding Questions

1. How can you change units from hours and minutes to days, hours, and minutes? Divide the number of hours by 24. The whole number part of the quotient gives the number of days.
2. How can you write a fraction as a decimal? Divide the numerator by the denominator.
3. What are some of the subsets of the real numbers? Possible answer: rational numbers, irrational numbers, integers, whole numbers, and natural numbers

4–5. How do you evaluate the expression for a given value of h? Substitute the height for h. Then perform the division and find the square root of the quotient.

6. What information from the table do you need to solve this problem? the volume of Earth and the volume of the Moon

Extension

Approximately how many Moons would it take to equal the mass of Earth?
≈ 81 Moons

Quiz for Lessons 1-1 Through 1-5

1-1 Sets of Numbers

Order the given numbers from least to greatest. Then classify each number by the subsets of the real numbers to which it belongs.

1. $2.5, -3\frac{1}{3}, \sqrt{5}, -\frac{4}{5}, 0.\overline{75}$
2. $\sqrt{3}, -\frac{\pi}{2}, \frac{5}{6}, -1.\overline{15}, -2$

Rewrite each set in the indicated notation.

3. $\{x \mid -4 \le x < 2\}$; interval notation $[-4, 2)$
4. 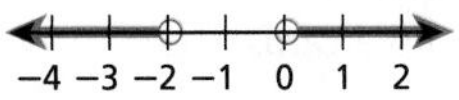 (number line from −4 to 2, open circles at −2 and 0, shaded left of −2 and right of 0) set-builder notation $\{x \mid x < -2 \text{ or } x > 0\}$

1-2 Properties of Real Numbers

Identify the property demonstrated by each equation.

5. $3(2a + b) = 3(2a) + 3b$
6. $21 + 0 = 21$
7. $(2\pi)r = 2(\pi r)$
8. Use mental math to find the amount of a 12% shipping fee for an item that costs \$250. Explain your steps.

1-3 Square Roots

9. A rental company rents portable dance floors in three different sizes: 75 square feet, 125 square feet, and 150 square feet. Estimate the dimensions of each square dance floor to the nearest tenth of a foot. Then identify which of the three sizes is the largest dance floor that would fit in a room 11 feet wide and 13 feet long.

Simplify each expression.

10. $-\sqrt{72}$ $\;-6\sqrt{2}$
11. $5\sqrt{12} + 9\sqrt{3}$ $\;19\sqrt{3}$
12. $\frac{-4\sqrt{10}}{\sqrt{2}}$ $\;-4\sqrt{5}$
13. $\sqrt{32} \cdot \sqrt{6}$ $\;8\sqrt{3}$

1-4 Simplifying Algebraic Expressions

Evaluate each expression for the given values of the variables.

14. $\frac{a^2}{3} + \frac{ab}{4}$ for $a = 3$ and $b = -4$ $\;0$
15. $\frac{d^2}{2cd}$ for $c = -1$ and $d = 2$ $\;-1$

Simplify each expression.

16. $2x^2 - 3y + 5x^2 - x^2$ $\;6x^2 - 3y$
17. $3(x + 2y) - 5x + y$ $\;-2x + 7y$

1-5 Properties of Exponents

Simplify each expression. Assume all variables are nonzero.

18. $(x^{11}y^{-2})^4$ $\;\frac{x^{44}}{y^8}$
19. $\frac{-3s^3t^2}{s^{-2}t^8}$ $\;\frac{-3s^5}{t^6}$
20. $4(a^2b^6)^{-3}$ $\;\frac{4}{a^6b^{18}}$
21. $\left(\frac{m^4}{-5m^{-2}n^3}\right)^2$ $\;\frac{m^{12}}{25n^6}$
22. The atomic mass of an element from the periodic table is the mass, in grams, of one *mole*, or 6.02×10^{23} atoms. Suppose a sample of oxygen contains 4.515×10^{26} atoms. How many moles of oxygen atoms are in the sample? 750 moles

READY TO GO ON? SECTION 1A

Organizer

Objective: Assess students' mastery of concepts and skills in Lessons 1-1 through 1-5.

Resources

Assessment Resources

Section 1A Quiz

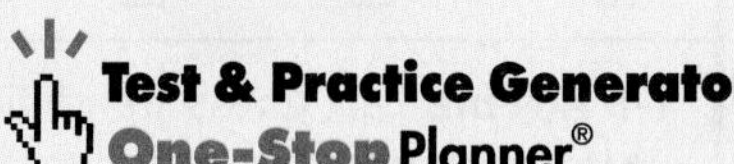

Test & Practice Generator

One-Stop Planner®

INTERVENTION Resources

Ready to Go On? Intervention and Enrichment **Worksheets**

Ready to Go On? **CD-ROM**

Ready to Go On? **Online**

my.hrw.com

Answers

1–2, 5–9. See p. A15.

READY TO GO ON?

Diagnose and Prescribe

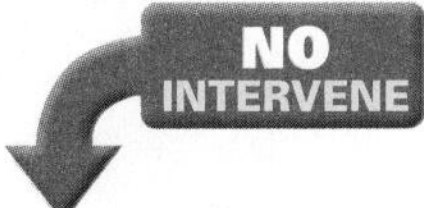

Ready to Go On? Intervention	*Ready to Go On? Intervention,* Section 1A		
	Worksheets	CD-ROM	Online
Lesson 1-1	1-1 Intervention	Activity 1-1	Diagnose and Prescribe Online
Lesson 1-2	1-2 Intervention	Activity 1-2	
Lesson 1-3	1-3 Intervention	Activity 1-3	
Lesson 1-4	1-4 Intervention	Activity 1-4	
Lesson 1-5	1-5 Intervention	Activity 1-5	

YES
ENRICH

Ready to Go On? Enrichment, **Section 1A**

Worksheets

CD-ROM

Online

SECTION
1B Introduction to Functions

One-Minute Section Planner

Lesson	Lab Resources	Materials
Lesson 1-6 Relations and Functions • Identify the domain and range of relations and functions. • Determine whether a relation is a function. ☐ SAT-10 ☑ NAEP ☐ ACT ☑ SAT ☑ SAT Subject Tests		**Optional** note cards, tape
Lesson 1-7 Function Notation • Write functions using function notation. • Evalute and graph functions. ☐ SAT-10 ☑ NAEP ☑ ACT ☑ SAT ☑ SAT Subject Tests		**Optional** graph paper, rulers (MK)
1-8 Algebra Lab Chess Translations • Use chess to explore transformations. ☐ SAT-10 ☐ NAEP ☑ ACT ☑ SAT ☑ SAT Subject Tests	***Algebra Lab Activities*** 1-8 Lab Recording Sheet	**Optional** chessboard and chess pieces
Lesson 1-8 Exploring Transformations • Apply transformations to points and sets of points. • Interpret transformations of real-world data. ☐ SAT-10 ☑ NAEP ☑ ACT ☑ SAT ☑ SAT Subject Tests		**Optional** graph paper, twist ties or small pieces of wire
Lesson 1-9 Introduction to Parent Functions • Identify parent functions from graphs and equations. • Use parent functions to model real-world data and make estimates for unknown values. ☑ SAT-10 ☑ NAEP ☑ ACT ☑ SAT ☑ SAT Subject Tests	***Technology Lab Activities*** 1-9 Technology Lab	**Optional** note cards, graph paper, graphing calculator

MK = *Manipulatives Kit*

Section Overview

Functions — Lessons 1-6, 1-7

Functions describe the relationship between a set of input values and a set of output values. They can be represented in several ways.

Mapping Diagram

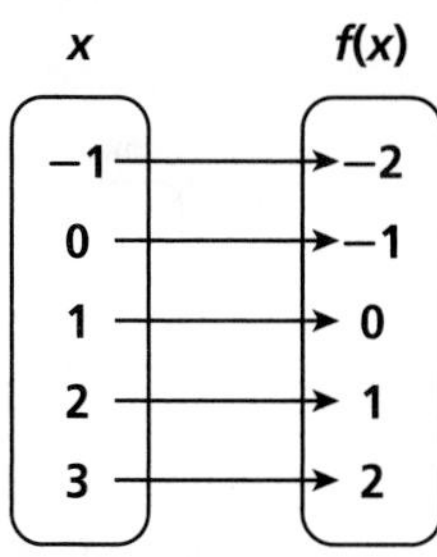

Table

x	−1	0	1	2	3
$f(x)$	−2	−1	0	1	2

Ordered Pairs

(−1, −2) (0, −1), (1, 0), (2, 1), (3, 2)

Function Notation

$f(x) = x - 1$

Graph

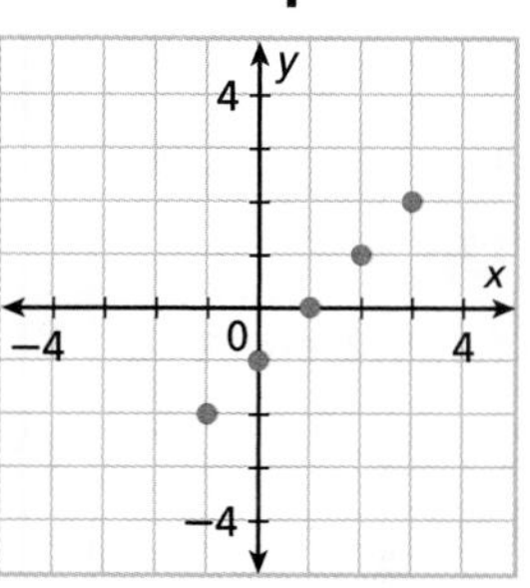

Functions associate each element in a **domain** with exactly one element in a **range.**

Transformations and Parent Functions — Lessons 1-8, 1-9

Identifying parent functions and their transformations helps students classify and make generalizations about functions.

The graphs of points or functions can be **transformed** in several ways.

Translation

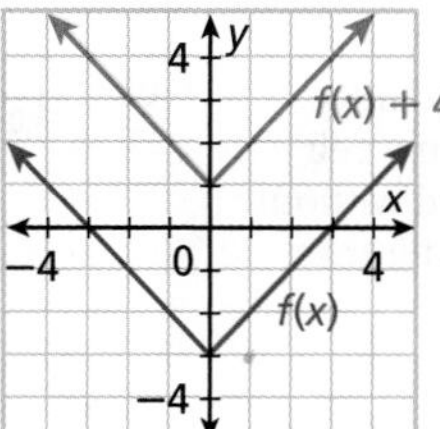

Reflection

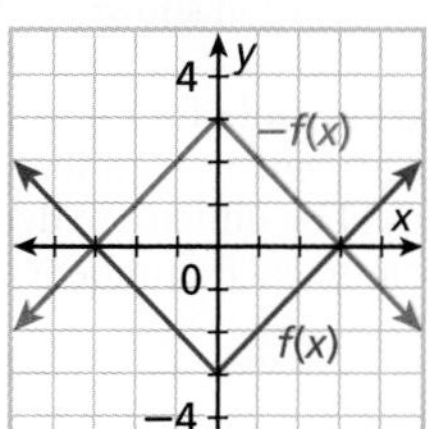

Stretch

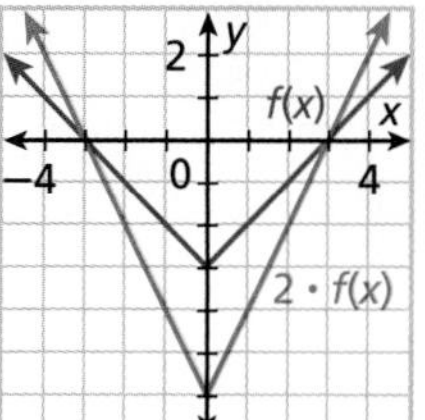

Compression

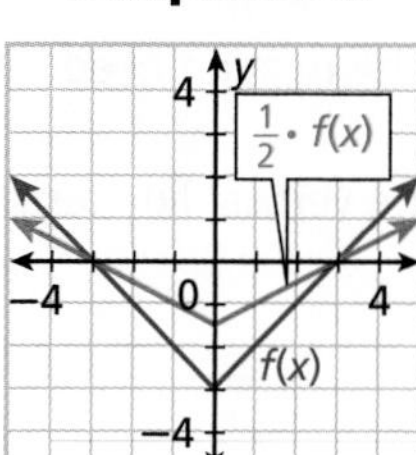

Functions can be grouped based on their **parent functions.** Some parent functions follow:

Linear Function

$f(x) = x$

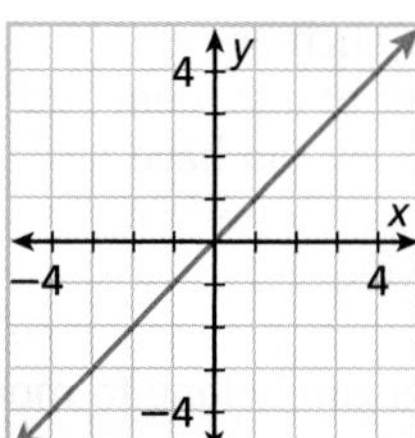

Quadratic Function

$f(x) = x^2$

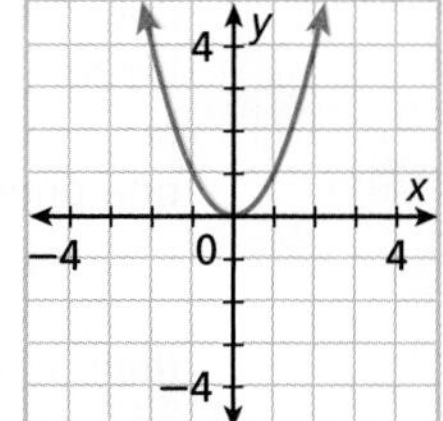

Cubic Function

$f(x) = x^3$

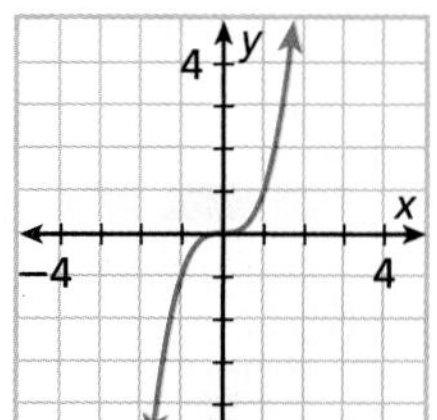

Square-Root Function

$f(x) = \sqrt{x}$

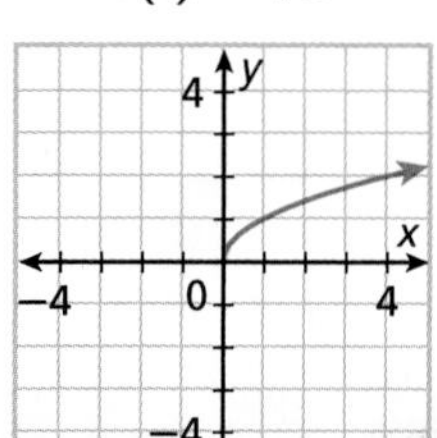

1-6 Organizer

Pacing: Traditional 1 day
Block $\frac{1}{2}$ day

Objectives: Identify the domain and range of relations and functions.

Determine whether a relation is a function.

Online Edition
Tutorial Videos

Countdown to Testing Week 2

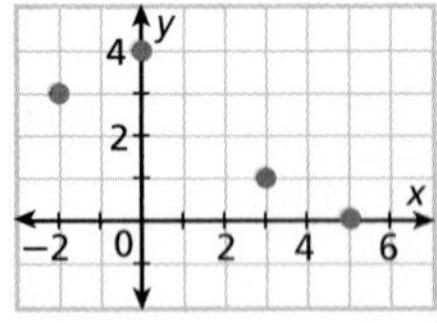

Power Presentations with PowerPoint®

Warm Up

Use the graph for Problems 1–2.

1. List the x-coordinates of the points. −2, 0, 3, 5
2. List the y-coordinates of the points. 3, 4, 1, 0

Also available on transparency

Math Humor

Q: Why did the relation need a math tutor?

A: It failed the vertical-line test.

1-6 Relations and Functions

A2.1.1 Find the zeros, domain and range of a function.

Objectives
Identify the domain and range of relations and functions.

Determine whether a relation is a function.

Vocabulary
relation
domain
range
function

Why learn this?
The relationship between the numbers and the letters on the keys of a cell phone can be described using relations.

When you create a text message on a cell phone, you enter letters by pressing the numbered keys that they appear on. For instance, you would press the 2 key to enter an *A*, *B*, or *C*. This relationship can be represented by a mapping diagram or a set of ordered pairs.

Mapping Diagram

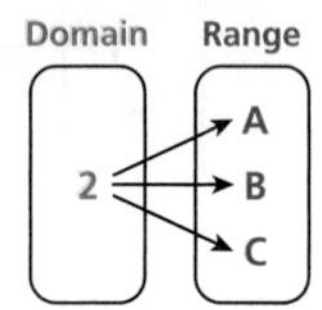

Set of Ordered Pairs

{(2, A), (2, B), (2, C)}

$(x, y) \rightarrow$ (input, output) $\rightarrow$ (domain, range)

A **relation** is a pairing of input values with output values. It can be shown as a set of ordered pairs (x, y), where x is an input and y is an output.

The set of input values for a relation is called the **domain**, and the set of output values is called the **range**.

EXAMPLE 1 Identifying Domain and Range

Give the domain and range for the relation shown.

Helpful Hint

Notice that the rate 2¢ appears twice in the table but is listed only once in the set of range values. When the domain or range of a relation is listed, each value is listed only once.

First-Class Stamp Rates						
Year	1900	1920	1940	1960	1980	2000
Rate (¢)	2	2	3	4	15	33

List the set of ordered pairs:

$\{(1900, 2), (1920, 2), (1940, 3), (1960, 4), (1980, 15), (2000, 33)\}$

Domain: $\{1900, 1920, 1940, 1960, 1980, 2000\}$ *The set of x-coordinates*

Range: $\{2, 3, 4, 15, 33\}$ *The set of y-coordinates*

D: $\{-2, -1, 0, 1, 2, 3\}$
R: $\{-3, -2, -1, 0, 1, 2\}$

1. Give the domain and range for the relation shown in the graph.

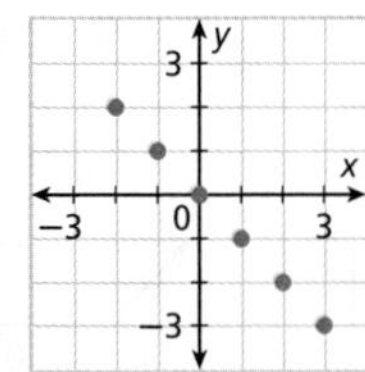

Suppose you are told that a person entered a word into a text message using the numbers 6, 2, 8, and 4 on a cell phone. It would be difficult to determine the word without seeing it because each number can be used to enter three different letters.

State Resources

go.hrw.com
State Resources Online
KEYWORD: MB7 Resources

1 Introduce

EXPLORATION

1-6 Relations and Functions

A [blank] is a pairing of values that can be written as a set of ordered pairs. A [blank] is a special type of relation. Use the information below to explore what makes a function different from other types of relations.

Functions

x	y
0	1
1	1
2	1
3	1

x	y
0	2
2	1
5	−1
9	−4

x	y
−2	3
0	2
2	4
4	5

Not Functions

x	y
0	1
0	2
1	3
1	4

x	y
1	−5
2	−4
3	−5
1	−4

x	y
−2	1
2	4
2	−4
−2	−1

1. Examine the x-values in the tables. Make a conjecture about the x-values in a function.
2. Does your conjecture apply to y-values as well? Explain.
3. Use your conjecture to determine whether the ordered pairs in each table represent a function.

a.

x	−2	−1	0	−1	−2
y	5	4	3	2	1

b.

x	−2	−1	0	1	2
y	3	5	7	5	3

THINK AND DISCUSS

Motivate

Start students thinking about the relationships between two quantities, such as a student and his or her phone number or a student and his or her height. Ask them if they can have more than one phone number or height. Possible answer: At any given time, a student can have more than one phone number, but only one height. Then ask them if a phone number can belong to more than one person. yes

Explorations and answers are provided in the *Explorations* binder.

Number	{Number, Letter}
	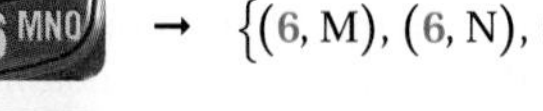 {(6, M), (6, N), (6, O)}
2 ABC	{(2, A), (2, B), (2, C)}
	{(8, T), (8, U), (8, V)}
	{(4, G), (4, H), (4, I)}

The numbers 6, 2, 8, and 4 each appear as the first coordinate of three different ordered pairs.

However, if you are told to enter the word *MATH* into a text message, you can easily determine that you must use the numbers 6, 2, 8, and 4, because each letter appears on only one numbered key.

{(M, 6), (A, 2), (T, 8), (H, 4)} *The first coordinate is different in each ordered pair.*

A relation in which the first coordinate is never repeated is called a *function*. In a **function**, there is only one output for each input, so each element of the domain is mapped to exactly one element in the range.

Although a single input in a function cannot be mapped to more than one output, two or more different inputs can be mapped to the same output.

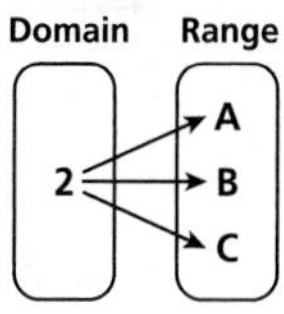

Not a function: The relationship from number to letter is *not* a function because the domain value 2 is mapped to the range values A, B, and C.

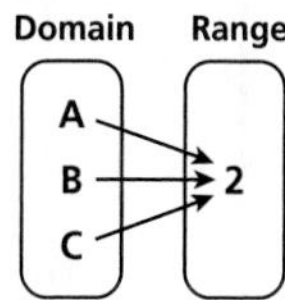

Function: The relationship from letter to number is a function because each letter in the domain is mapped to only one number in the range.

EXAMPLE 2 Determining Whether a Relation Is a Function

Determine whether each relation is a function.

Instant Rice Cooking Times				
Servings	2	4	6	8
Cooking Time (min)	5	8	10	11

There is only one cooking time for each number of servings. The relation from number of servings to cooking time is a function.

 **from last name to Social Security number**

A last name, such as Smith, from the domain would be associated with many different Social Security numbers. The relation from last name to Social Security number is not a function.

Determine whether each relation is a function.

2a.

Shoe Prices			
Size	7	8	9
Price ($)	35	35	35

function

2b. from the number of items in a grocery cart to the total cost of the items in the cart
not a function

2 Teach

Guided Instruction

In this lesson, students use various representations to determine whether a given relation is a function. Emphasize that a function is a special type of relation—one that assigns exactly one domain value to each range value.

Inclusion Point out that *domain* ends in the letters *in* and *input* begins with the letters *in.* Students can use this mnemonic to remember that the domain represents the input values.

ENGLISH LANGUAGE LEARNERS

Reaching All Learners

Through Multiple Representations

Give each student a card or piece of paper containing a relation. These should include ordered pairs, mapping diagrams, tables, graphs, and words. Write "Function" and "Not a Function" on the board and place an example under each. Have each student use a piece of tape to place his or her card in the correct category.

COMMON ERROR ALERT

Students may be confused by relations and functions, especially when data are presented in tables. Encourage students to represent the data in a mapping diagram to see whether each domain element is associated with a unique range element.

Power Presentations with PowerPoint®

Additional Examples

Example 1

Give the domain and range for this relation: {(100, 5), (120, 5), (140, 6), (160, 6), (180, 12)}.

D: {100, 120, 140, 160, 180}

R: {5, 6, 12}

Example 2

Determine whether each relation is a function.

A. from the items in a store to their prices on a certain date function

B. from types of fruits to their colors not a function

Also available on transparency

INTERVENTION

Questioning Strategies

EXAMPLE 1

- Why is the order of the numbers in an ordered pair important?
- Can you think of other examples of relations in which an element of the domain is associated with more than one element of the range?

EXAMPLE 2

- How are relations and functions similar, and how are they different?
- Are all functions relations? Are all relations functions?

Auditory Example 2 provides language that is helpful when students use it consistently: a function maps elements *from* the domain *to* the range. This concept will be used frequently. Practicing the usage of *from* and *to* aloud now will aid students throughout the course.

ENGLISH LANGUAGE LEARNERS

Power Presentations with PowerPoint®

Additional Examples

Example 3

Use the vertical-line test to determine whether each relation is a function. If not, identify two points a vertical line would pass through.

A.

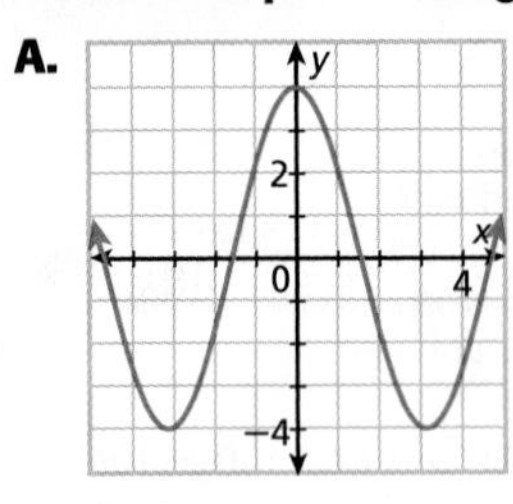

function

B.

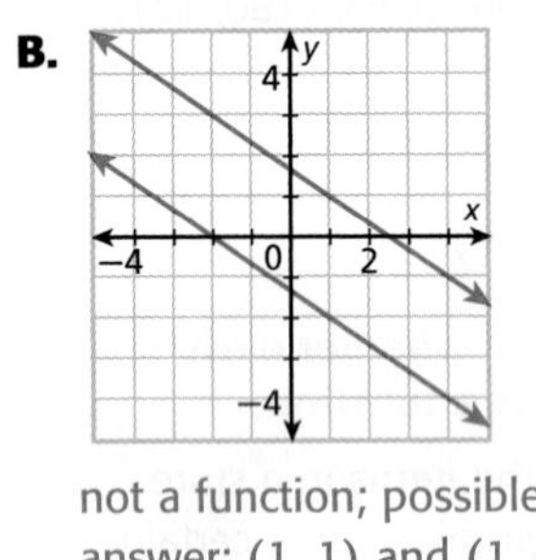

not a function; possible answer: (1, 1) and (1, −2)

Also available on transparency

INTERVENTION
Questioning Strategies

EXAMPLE 3

- How does the vertical-line test apply to the definition of a function?
- Could a horizontal-line test be used to determine whether a relation is a function? Explain.

Every point on a vertical line has the same x-coordinate, so a vertical line cannot represent a function. If a vertical line passes through more than one point on the graph of a relation, the relation must have more than one point with the same x-coordinate. Therefore the relation is not a function.

Know it! Note

Vertical-Line Test

WORDS	EXAMPLES	
If any vertical line passes through more than one point on the graph of a relation, the relation is not a function.	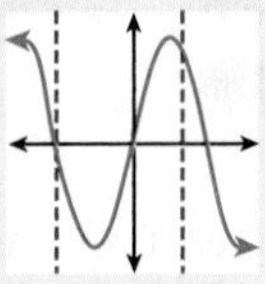 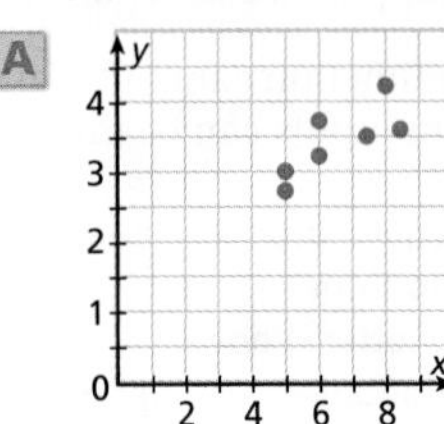 Function	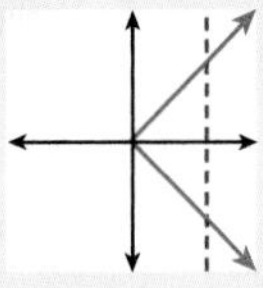 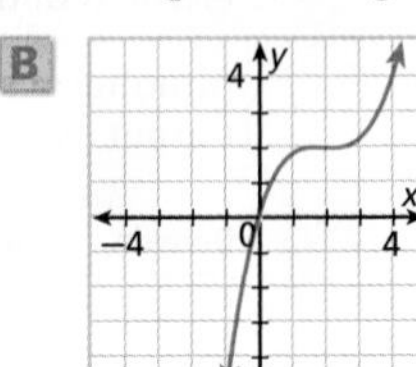 Not a Function

EXAMPLE 3 Using the Vertical-Line Test

Use the vertical-line test to determine whether each relation is a function. If not, identify two points a vertical line would pass through.

A

This is *not* a function. A vertical line at $x = 6$ would pass through $(6, 3.25)$ and $(6, 3.75)$.

B

This *is* a function. Any vertical line would pass through only one point on the graph.

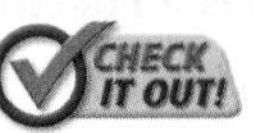

Use the vertical-line test to determine whether each relation is a function. If not, identify two points a vertical line would pass through.

3a.

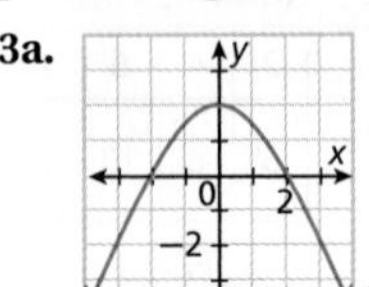

function

3b.

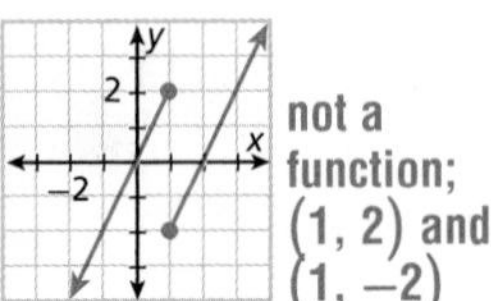

not a function; (1, 2) and (1, −2)

THINK AND DISCUSS

1. Name four different ways to represent a relation or function.
2. Explain why the vertical-line test works.
3. **GET ORGANIZED** Copy and complete the graphic organizer. In each box, give an example of a table, a graph, and a set of ordered pairs.

Know it! Note

Relation
Function

3 Close

Summarize

Review the definition of a function with students. Emphasize that the outputs, or y-values, may repeat but that x-values may not. Explain that the vertical-line test visually reinforces this. Point out that the relationship between time and position serves as a good example of a function because you cannot be in two places at the same time.

ONGOING ASSESSMENT and INTERVENTION

Diagnose ***Before*** **the Lesson**
1-6 Warm Up, TE p. 44

Monitor ***During*** **the Lesson**
Check It Out! Exercises, SE pp. 44–46
Questioning Strategies, TE pp. 45–46

Assess ***After*** **the Lesson**
1-6 Lesson Quiz, TE p. 50
Alternative Assessment, TE p. 50

Answers to *Think and Discuss*

Possible answers:

1. ordered pairs, table, mapping diagram, and graph
2. Any point that is above another on a vertical line has the same input values but different output values, such as (2, 4) and (2, 1).
3. See p. A2.

1-6 Exercises

go.hrw.com
Homework Help Online
KEYWORD: MB7 1-6
Parent Resources Online
KEYWORD: MB7 Parent

GUIDED PRACTICE

1. **Vocabulary** The set of output values of a function is its __?__. (*domain* or *range*) range

SEE EXAMPLE 1 p. 44

Give the domain and range for each relation.

2. 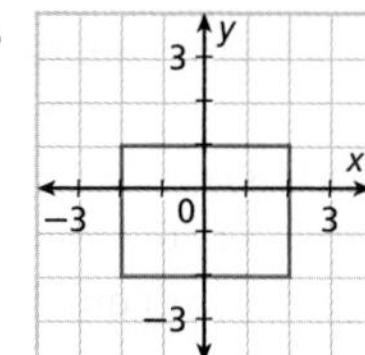

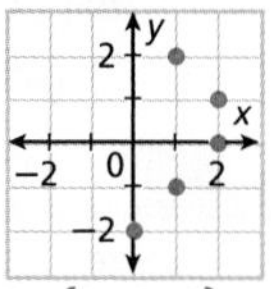

D: {0, 1, 2}
R: {−2, −1, 0, 1, 2}

3.

Average Movie Ticket Price	
Year	Price
2000	$5.39
2001	$5.65
2002	$5.80
2003	$6.03

D: {2000, 2001, 2002, 2003}
R: {5.39, 5.65, 5.80, 6.03}

SEE EXAMPLE 2 p. 45

Determine whether each relation is a function.

4.

Math Test Scores				
Name	Jan	Helen	Luke	Soren
Score	90	84	88	84

function

5. from car models to car colors
not a function

SEE EXAMPLE 3 p. 46

Use the vertical-line test to determine whether each relation is a function. If not, identify two points a vertical line would pass through.

6. 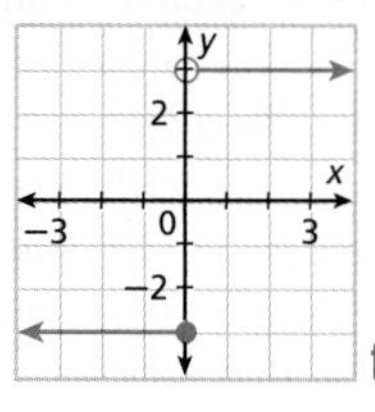

not a function; possible answer: (2, 1) and (2, 0)

7. 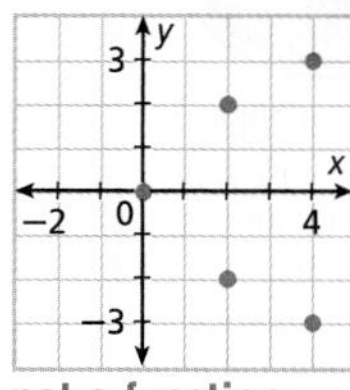

function

8.

not a function; possible answer: (2, 2) and (2, −2)

PRACTICE AND PROBLEM SOLVING

Independent Practice	
For Exercises	See Example
9–10	1
11–12	2
13–15	3

Extra Practice
Skills Practice p. S5
Application Practice p. S32

Give the domain and range for each relation.

9.

Basketball Points Scored				
Player	Irene	Anna	Lea	Kate
Points	22	12	16	12

D: {Irene, Anna, Lea, Kate}
R: {12, 16, 22}

10. 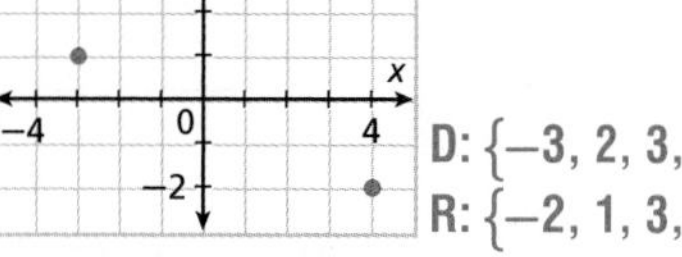

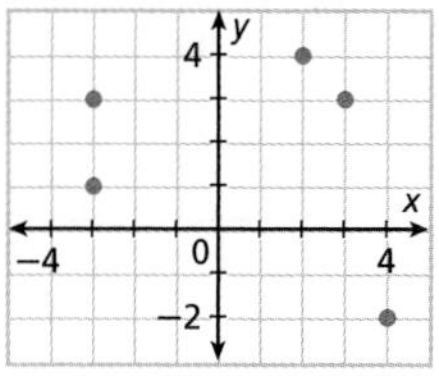

D: {−3, 2, 3, 4}
R: {−2, 1, 3, 4}

Determine whether each relation is a function.

11.

Women's Glove Sizes			
Size	S	M	L
Maximum Hand Length (in.)	6.5	7.5	8.5

function

12. 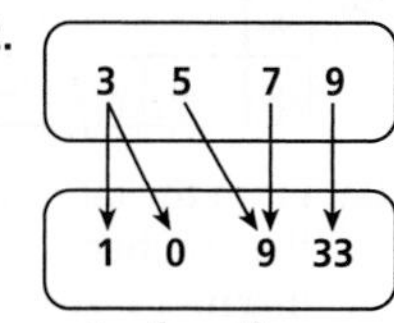

not a function

1-6 Exercises

Assignment Guide

Assign *Guided Practice* exercises as necessary.

If you finished Examples **1–3**
Basic 9–21, 30, 38–41, 43–46, 51–61
Average 9–30, 38–47, 51–61
Advanced 9–21, 30–61

Homework Quick Check
Quickly check key concepts.
Exercises: 10, 12, 14, 16, 39

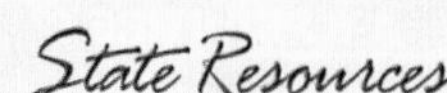

Answers

16. D: {−5, 0, 5}; R: {−5, 0, 5}

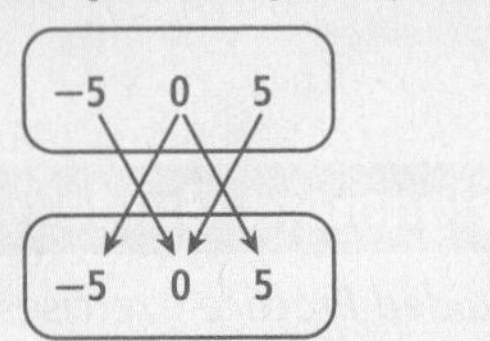

17. D: {−2, −1, 0, 1, 2}; R: {−2, 0, 2}

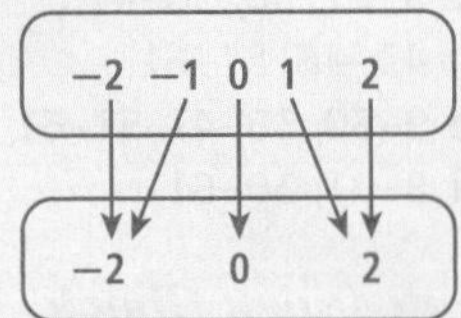

18. D: {−2, −1, 1, 3}; R: {−3, 0, 3}

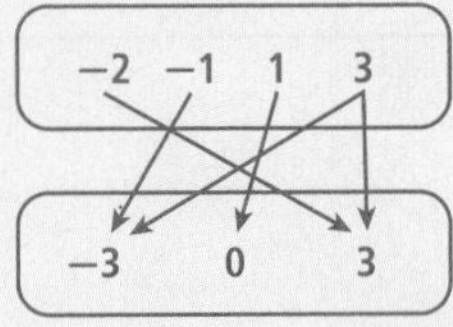

19. D: {jumbo, extra large, large, medium}; R: {1.75, 2, 2.25, 2.5}

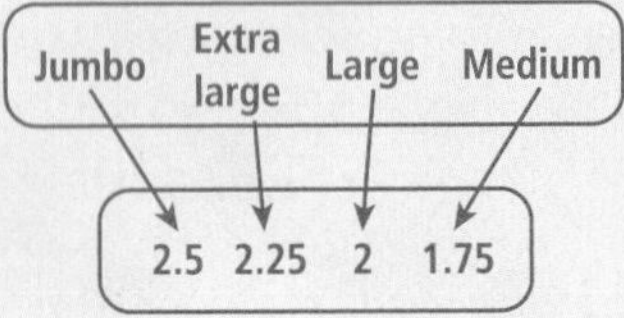

22. D: {−1, 0, 1, 2, 3}; R: {−1, 1, 3}; function

23. D: {a, b, c, d}; R: {1, 2, 4}; function

24. D: {7}; R: {1, 2, 3, 4, 6}; not a function

25. D: {1, 3, 5, 7, 9}; R: {3}; function

26. D: {−3, −1, 0, 3}; R: {−4, −3, −2, −1, 0}; not a function

27. D: {3, 4, 5, 6, 7}; R: {−1, 2, 3}; function

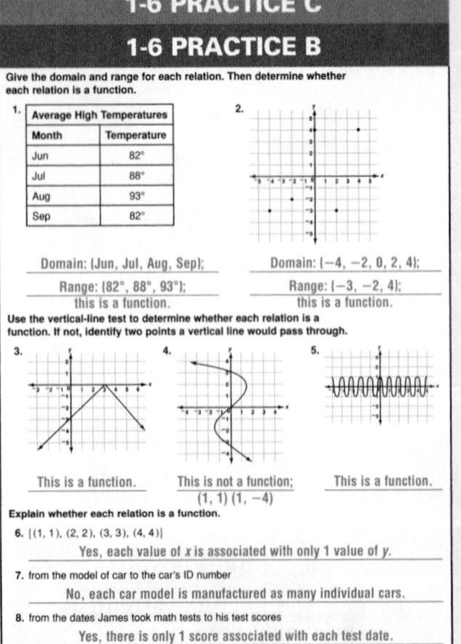

1-6 PRACTICE A

1-6 PRACTICE C

1-6 PRACTICE B

Give the domain and range for each relation. Then determine whether each relation is a function.

1.

Average High Temperatures	
Month	Temperature
Jun	82°
Jul	88°
Aug	93°
Sep	82°

Domain: {Jun, Jul, Aug, Sep}; Range: {82°, 88°, 93°}; this is a function.

2. Domain: {−4, −2, 0, 2, 4}; Range: {−3, −2, 4}; this is a function.

Use the vertical-line test to determine whether each relation is a function. If not, identify two points a vertical line would pass through.

3. This is a function.
4. This is not a function; (1, 1) (1, −4)
5. This is a function.

Explain whether each relation is a function.

6. {(1, 1), (2, 2), (3, 3), (4, 4)} Yes, each value of x is associated with only 1 value of y.

7. from the model of car to the car's ID number No, each car model is manufactured as many individual cars.

8. from the dates James took math tests to his test scores Yes, there is only 1 score associated with each test date.

Use the vertical-line test to determine whether each relation is a function. If not, identify two points a vertical line would pass through.

13.

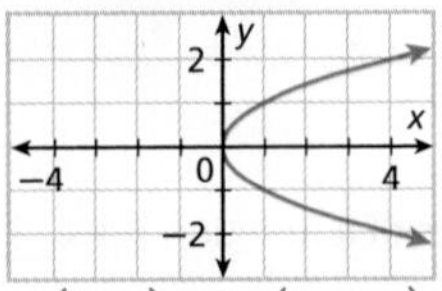

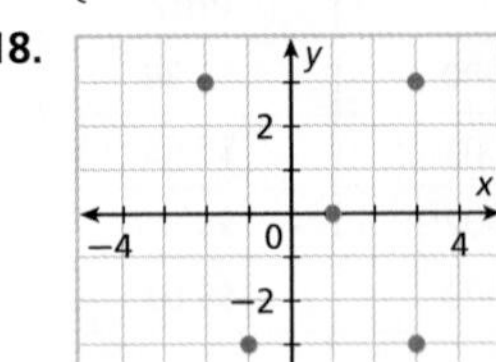

not a function; possible answer: (1, 1) and (1, −1)

14.

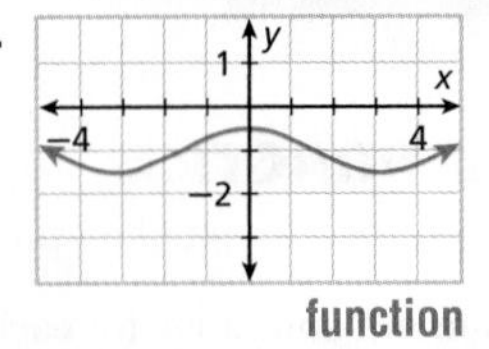

function

15.

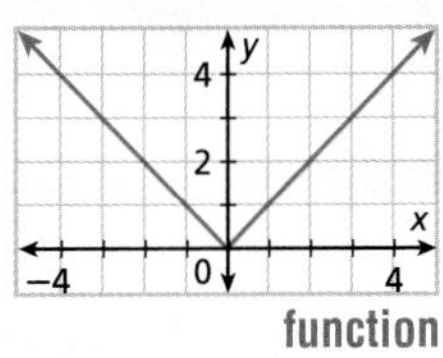

function

Give the domain and range of each relation and make a mapping diagram.

16. $\{(-5, 0), (0, -5), (5, 0), (0, 5)\}$

17. $\{(-2, -2), (-1, -2), (0, 0), (1, 2), (2, 2)\}$

18.

19.

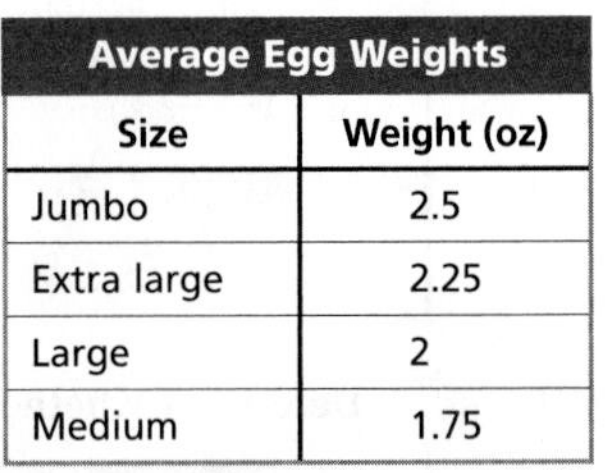

Average Egg Weights	
Size	Weight (oz)
Jumbo	2.5
Extra large	2.25
Large	2
Medium	1.75

LINK

Money

By the end of 2004, there were more than 17.6 billion state quarters in circulation.

Source: www.usmint.gov

20. from each unique letter in the word *seven* to the number that represents the position of that letter in the alphabet D: {e, n, s, v}; R: {5, 14, 19, 22}

21. **Money** In 1999 the U.S. Mint began releasing quarters to commemorate each of the 50 states. The release schedule specified that each year for a total of 10 years, new quarters commemorating 5 different states would be released. Explain whether each relation is a function.

a. from each year to the number of states with new quarters released in that year function

b. from each state to the year its quarter is released function

c. from each year to the states with new quarters released in that year not a function

d. from each year to the total number of states with quarters released by the end of that year function

e. from the number of new quarters released each year to the year not a function

Give the domain and range of each relation. Then explain whether the relation is a function.

22.

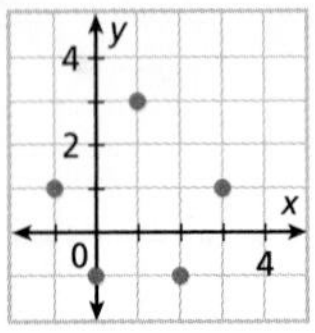

23.

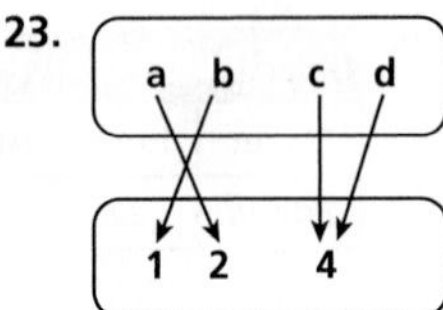

24. $\{(7, 1), (7, 2), (7, 3), (7, 4), (7, 6)\}$

25. $\{(9, 3), (7, 3), (5, 3), (3, 3), (1, 3)\}$

26.

x	3	0	0	−1	−3
y	−4	−3	−1	−2	0

27.

x	7	6	5	4	3
y	−1	2	−1	2	3

28. From the months of the year to the number of days in that month in a non-leap year

29. From day of the week to the number of hours in that day

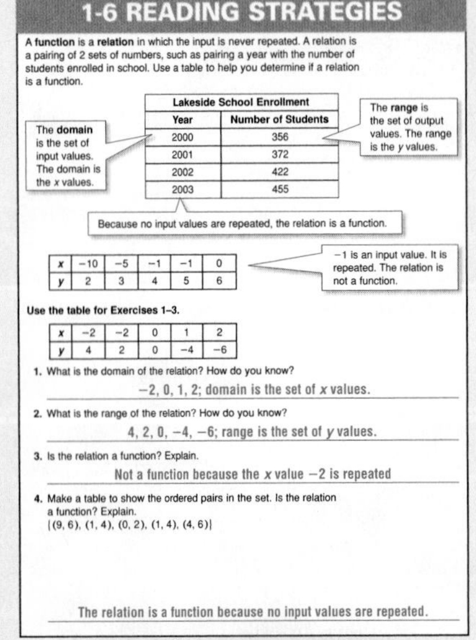

1-6 READING STRATEGIES

A **function** is a relation in which the input is never repeated. A relation is a pairing of 2 sets of numbers, such as pairing a year with the number of students enrolled in school. Use a table to help you determine if a relation is a function.

Lakeside School Enrollment	
Year	Number of Students
2000	356
2001	372
2002	422
2003	455

The domain is the set of input values. The domain is the x values.

The range is the set of output values. The range is the y values.

Because no input values are repeated, the relation is a function.

x	−10	−5	−1	−1	0
y	2	3	4	5	6

−1 is an input value. It is repeated. The relation is not a function.

Use the table for Exercises 1–3.

x	−2	−2	0	1	2
y	4	2	0	−4	−6

1. What is the domain of the relation? How do you know? −2, 0, 1, 2; domain is the set of x values.
2. What is the range of the relation? How do you know? 4, 2, 0, −4, −6; range is the set of y values.
3. Is the relation a function? Explain. Not a function because the x value −2 is repeated
4. Make a table to show the ordered pairs in the set. Is the relation a function? Explain. {(9, 6), (1, 4), (0, 2), (1, 4), (4, 6)}

The relation is a function because no input values are repeated.

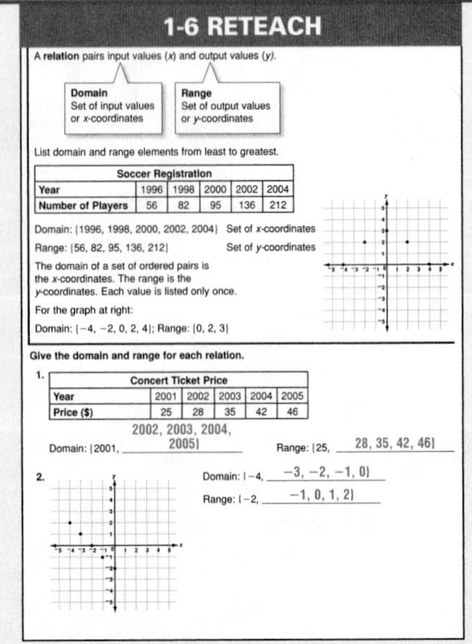

1-6 RETEACH

A **relation** pairs input values (x) and output values (y).

Domain: Set of input values or x-coordinates

Range: Set of output values or y-coordinates

List domain and range elements from least to greatest.

Soccer Registration					
Year	1996	1998	2000	2002	2004
Number of Players	56	82	95	136	212

Domain: {1996, 1998, 2000, 2002, 2004} Set of x-coordinates

Range: {56, 82, 95, 136, 212} Set of y-coordinates

The domain of a set of ordered pairs is the x-coordinates. The range is the y-coordinates. Each value is listed only once.

For the graph at right:

Domain: {−4, −2, 0, 2, 4}; Range: {0, 2, 3}

Give the domain and range for each relation.

1.

Concert Ticket Price					
Year	2001	2002	2003	2004	2005
Price ($)	25	28	35	42	46

Domain: {2001, 2002, 2003, 2004, 2005} Range: {25, 28, 35, 42, 46}

2. Domain: {−4, −3, −2, −1, 0} Range: {−2, −1, 0, 1, 2}

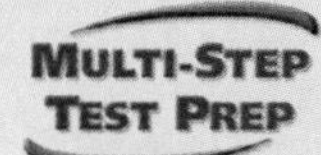

30. This problem will prepare you for the Multi-Step Test Prep on page 74.
   a. The relation (0, 20), (−20, 0), (0, −20), and (20, 0) can be plotted to produce the vertices of a shape very common in Native American art. What shape is this?
   b. Does this relation represent a function? Why or why not?
   c. What is the domain of this relation?
   d. What is the range of this relation?

Explain whether the relation from A to B is a function, the relation from B to A is a function, or both are functions.

	A	B	
31.	Date of birth	Person	B to A
32.	Thumbprint	Person	both
33.	Area code	State	A to B
34.	Amount of sales tax	Purchase total	both
35.	Sales tax percentage	Purchase total	B to A
36.	Jersey number	NFL football player	B to A
37.	Jersey number	current Cleveland Browns player	both

38. **///ERROR ANALYSIS///** Identify which statement is incorrect. Explain the error.

(A) The relation {(−1, 9), (0, 8), (0, 7), (1, 6)} is a function.

(B) The relation {(4, 5), (5, 5), (6, 5), (7, 5)} is a function.

Carpentry Use the table for Exercises 39–41.

Common Wire Nail Data			
Size	Length (in.)	Gauge	Number (per lb)
2d	1	15	876
3d	$1\frac{1}{4}$	14	568
4d	$1\frac{1}{2}$	$12\frac{1}{2}$	316
5d	$1\frac{3}{4}$	$12\frac{1}{2}$	271
6d	2	$11\frac{1}{2}$	181

No; the relation is not a function. 39. If you know the gauge of a nail, can you determine its size? What does this indicate about the relation from gauge to size?

40. Identify the pattern in the nail lengths as size increases. Does the pattern indicate that the relation from length to size is a function?

41. Consider the relation from nail size to the number of nails per pound.
   a. Does the relation represent a function?
   b. Explain the relationship between a nail's size and its average weight.
   c. Confirm your answer to part **b** by finding the average weight for each nail size. (*Hint:* 1 pound = 16 ounces)

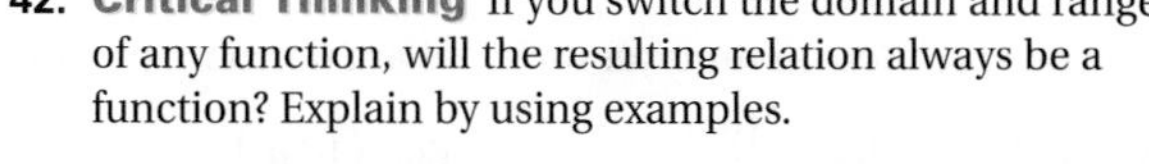

42. **Critical Thinking** If you switch the domain and range of any function, will the resulting relation always be a function? Explain by using examples.

43. **Write About It** Explain how you would determine whether each of the following represents a function: a set of ordered pairs, a mapping diagram, and a graph.

Exercise 30 involves plotting points to determine whether a relation is a function. This exercise prepares students for the Multi-Step Test Prep on page 74.

Answers

28. D: {January, February, March, April, May, June, July, August, September, October, November, December}; R: {28, 30, 31}; function
29. D: {Monday, Tuesday, Wednesday, Thursday, Friday, Saturday, Sunday}; R: {24}; function

30a. a diamond or a square
   b. No; (0, 20) and (0, −20) are on the same vertical line.
   c. {−20, 0, 20}
   d. {−20, 0, 20}

38. Possible answer: Statement A is incorrect. The input value 0 is paired with 2 output values, which violates the definition of a function.

40. Lengths increase in increments of $\frac{1}{4}$ inch; the relation is a function.

41a. Yes, the relation is a function.
   b. It is a function.
   c. 2d: ≈0.0183 oz;
   3d: ≈0.0282 oz;
   4d: ≈0.0506 oz;
   5d: ≈0.0590 oz;
   6d: ≈0.0884 oz

42. Possible answer: No; switching the domain and range of the function {(0, 2), (1, 2)} results in {(2, 0), (2, 1)}. There is more than 1 output for the input 2. The resulting relation is not a function.

43. Possible answers: Set of ordered pairs: Look for a duplicate x-coordinate. Mapping diagram: Look for 2 arrows starting at one domain value. Graph: Use the vertical-line test.

1-6 PROBLEM SOLVING

In order to make a nutrition plan, Richard wants to compare different types of milk. Use the table for Exercises 1–7.

MILK FACTS (1 cup)			
A	B	C	D
Type	Calories	Carbo-hydrates (g)	Saturated Fat (g)
Whole	146	11	4.4
2%	122	11.4	3.1
1%	102	12.2	1.5
Nonfat	83	12.2	0.3

1. Is the relation from calories to saturated fat a function? Explain why or why not.
   Yes; each calorie value has only one fat value.
2. Is the relation from calories to carbohydrates a function? Explain why or why not.
   Yes; each calorie value has only one carbohydrate value.
3. Is the relation from carbohydrates to calories a function? Explain why or why not.
   No; the carbohydrate value 12.2 has two calorie values, 102 and 83.

Choose the letter for the best answer.

4. Richard is drawing graphs of some of the relations from the table above. Which of these graphs fails the vertical-line test if he graphs the data as follows?
   A column B along the x-axis, column C along the y-axis
   B column D along the x-axis, column B along the y-axis
   C column D along the x-axis, column C along the y-axis
   (D) column C along the x-axis, column B along the y-axis
5. For the function (B, D) that relates calories to saturated fat, which column shows the domain?
   F column A
   (G) column B
   H column C
   J column D
6. Which column shows the range of a function that relates the type of milk to the number of calories?
   A column A
   (B) column B
   C column C
   D column D
7. Richard makes a mapping diagram from each type of milk to the number of students in his class of 25 who prefer that type of milk. Which is the best statement about this diagram?
   F It is a relation, but not a function.
   G It is a function, but not a relation.
   (H) It is a function and a relation.
   J It is not a relation or a function.

1-6 CHALLENGE

A relation is said to be **reflexive** if for every element r in the relation, the ordered pair (r, r) is in the relation. For example, if 3 is an element in a relation, then the relation is reflexive if the ordered pair (3, 3) is in the relation.

A relation is said to be **symmetric** if whenever the ordered pair (r, s) is in the relation, then (s, r) is also in the relation. For example, if (5, 6) is an ordered pair in a relation, then the relation is symmetric if the ordered pair (6, 5) is in the relation.

A relation is said to be **transitive** if whenever the ordered pairs (r, s) and (s, t) are in the relation, then the ordered pair (r, t) is in the relation. For example, if (3, 7) and (7, 12) are ordered pairs in a relation, then the relation is transitive if the ordered pair (3, 12) is in the relation.

Any relation that has all 3 properties is called an **equivalence relation**.

The following relations are described in words. Use these relations for Exercises 1–4.

V is a set of ordered pairs such that each first element is a factor of each second element, and every element in the relation is a whole number.

W is a set of ordered pairs such that each first element is congruent to each second element, and every element in the relation is a geometric figure.

X is a set of ordered pairs such that each first element is a multiple of each second element, and every element in the relation is a whole number.

Y is a set of ordered pairs such that each first element is greater than each second element, and every element in the relation is a whole number.

Z is a set of ordered pairs such that each first element is similar to each second element, and every element in the relation is a geometric figure.

1. Which of the relations are reflexive? Explain why the other relations are not reflexive.
   V, W, X, Z; Y: (3, 3) does not exist because 3 is not greater than 3.
2. Which of the relations are symmetric? Explain why the other relations are not symmetric.
   W, Z; V: 10 is a factor of 20, but 20 is not a factor of 10; X: 8 is a multiple of 4 but 4 is not a multiple of 8; Y: 3 > 2 but 2 is not greater than 3.
3. Which of the relations are transitive? Explain why the other relations are not transitive.
   V, W, X, Y, Z
4. Which, if any, of the relations are equivalence relations? W, Z

TEST PREP DOCTOR In **Exercise 44,** students who chose **A** may have noticed repeated elements in the range. Encourage students to look for repeated elements in the domain to determine which is not a function.

Answers

48. Not one to one; each y-value may correspond to more than one x-value.
49. One to one; each length in feet corresponds to only one length in inches.

Journal

Have students explain which representation helps them best understand when a relation is a function.

ALTERNATIVE ASSESSMENT

Have students create an example of a function and a relation that is not a function. Have them justify their answers using mapping diagrams, graphs, or tables.

Power Presentations with PowerPoint®

1-6 Lesson Quiz

1. Give the domain and range for this relation: {(10, 5), (20, 5), (30, 5), (60, 100), (90, 100)}. D: {10, 20, 30, 60, 90}; R: {5, 100}

Determine whether each relation is a function.

2. from each person in class to the number of pets he or she has function
3. from city to zip code not a function

Use the vertical-line test to determine whether the relation is a function. If not, identify two points a vertical line would pass through.

4. 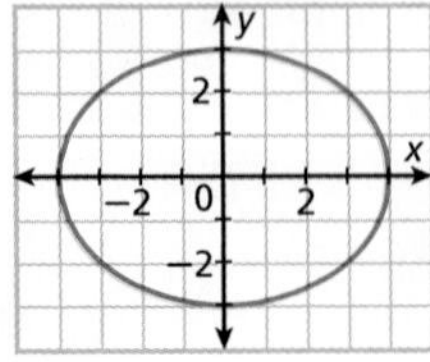

not a function; possible answer: (3, 2) and (3, −2)

Also available on transparency

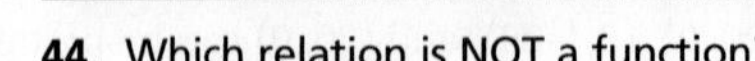

TEST PREP

44. Which relation is NOT a function?

Ⓐ $\{(0, 1), (1, 0), (2, 0), (3, 1)\}$ Ⓒ $\{(1, 1), (2, 2), (3, 3), (4, 4)\}$

Ⓑ $\{(-1, 5), (-2, 4), (-2, 3), (-3, 2)\}$ Ⓓ $\left\{\left(2, \frac{1}{2}\right), \left(4, \frac{1}{4}\right), \left(8, \frac{1}{8}\right), \left(16, \frac{1}{16}\right)\right\}$

45. Which set represents the domain of $\{(99, -2), (99, -3), (96, -4), (96, -5)\}$?

Ⓕ $\{96, 99\}$ Ⓗ $\{-2, -3, -4, -5\}$

Ⓖ All negative integers Ⓙ $\{-2, -3, -4, -5, 96, 99\}$

46. Which is an element of the range of the graphed function?

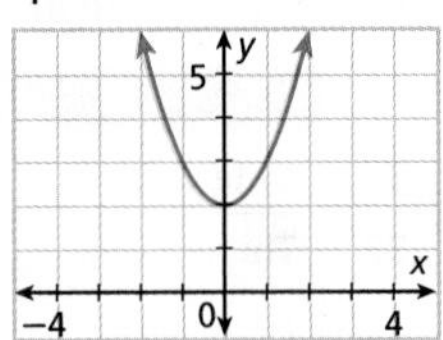

Ⓐ −2
Ⓑ 0
Ⓒ 1
Ⓓ 4

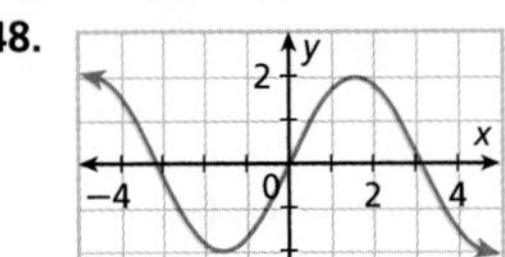

CHALLENGE AND EXTEND

47. Find the conditions for a and b that make $\{(a, b), (-a, b), (2a, b), (a^2, b)\}$ a function. $b \in \mathbb{R}$ and $a \neq \{-1, 0, 1, 2\}$

A *one-to-one function* is a function in which each output corresponds to only one input. Explain whether each function is one to one.

48. 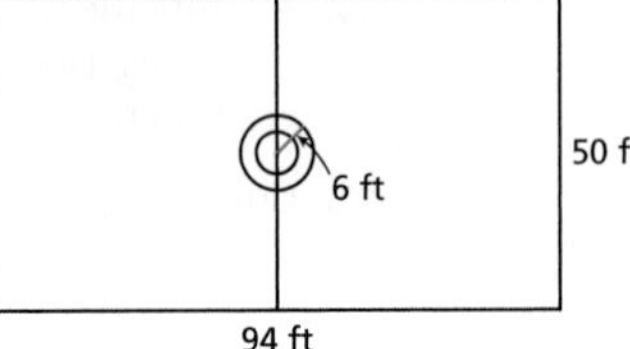

49. from length in inches to length in feet

50. Find the conditions for a and b that make $\left\{(2, b), (3, ab), \left(4, \frac{ab}{2}\right)\right\}$ a one-to-one function. $a \neq \{0, 1, 2\}$ and $b \neq \{0\}$

SPIRAL REVIEW

Use the diagram of the basketball court for Exercises 51–53. *(Previous course)*

51. What is the perimeter of the basketball court? 288 ft
52. What is the area of the basketball court? 4700 ft²
53. To the nearest tenth, what is the area of the outermost circle at center court? $36\pi \approx 113.1$ ft²

Estimate to the nearest tenth. *(Lesson 1-3)*

54. $\sqrt{42}$ 6.5 55. $\sqrt{22}$ 4.7 56. $-\sqrt{8}$ −2.8 57. $\sqrt{90}$ 9.5

Simplify each expression. Assume all variables are nonzero. *(Lesson 1-5)*

58. $(-3y^4)^3$ $-27y^{12}$ 59. $\frac{(10w^2)^2}{5w^5}$ $\frac{20}{w}$ 60. $(4c^6d^2)^2$ $16c^{12}d^4$ 61. $\left(\frac{x^3}{z}\right)^7$ $\frac{x^{21}}{z^7}$

1-7 Function Notation

A2.1.2 Use and interpret function notation, including evaluation of functions represented by tables, graphs, words, equations or a set of ordered pairs.

Objectives
Write functions using function notation.

Evaluate and graph functions.

Vocabulary
function notation
dependent variable
independent variable

Why learn this?

Function notation can be used to indicate the distance traveled by a Japanese bullet train. (See Example 3.)

Some sets of ordered pairs can be described by using an equation. When the set of ordered pairs described by an equation satisfies the definition of a function, the equation can be written in **function notation**.

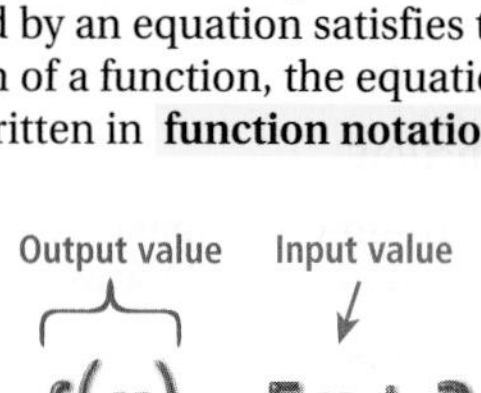

f of *x* equals 5 times *x* plus 3.

Output value   Input value

$$f(1) = 5(1) + 3$$

f of 1 equals 5 times 1 plus 3.

The function described by $f(x) = 5x + 3$ is the same as the function described by $y = 5x + 3$. And both of these functions are the same as the set of ordered pairs $(x, 5x + 3)$.

$$y = 5x + 3 \rightarrow (x, y) \rightarrow (x, 5x + 3)$$
$$f(x) = 5x + 3 \rightarrow (x, f(x)) \rightarrow (x, 5x + 3)$$

Notice that $y = f(x)$ for each x.

The graph of a function is a picture of the function's ordered pairs.

Caution!

$f(x)$ is *not* "f times x" or "f multiplied by x." $f(x)$ means "the value of f at x." So $f(1)$ represents the value of f at $x = 1$.

EXAMPLE 1 Evaluating Functions

For each function, evaluate $f(0)$, $f\left(\frac{1}{2}\right)$, and $f(-2)$.

A $f(x) = 7 - 2x$

Substitute each value for x and evaluate.

$f(0) = 7 - 2(0) = 7$

$f\left(\frac{1}{2}\right) = 7 - 2\left(\frac{1}{2}\right) = 6$

$f(-2) = 7 - 2(-2) = 11$

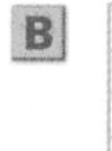

B

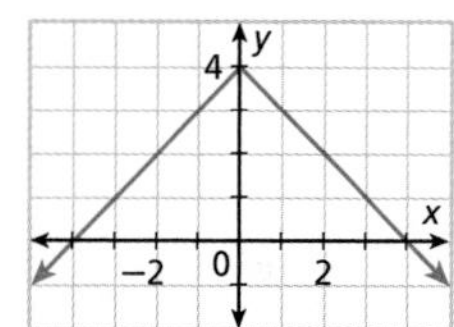

Use the graph to find the corresponding y-value for each x-value.

$f(0) = 4 \quad f\left(\frac{1}{2}\right) = 3\frac{1}{2} \quad f(-2) = 2$

CHECK IT OUT! For each function, evaluate $f(0)$, $f\left(\frac{1}{2}\right)$, and $f(-2)$.

1a. $f(x) = x^2 - 4x$ 0; $-\frac{7}{4}$; 12 **1b.** $f(x) = -2x + 1$ 1; 0; 5

1-7 Organizer

Pacing: Traditional 1 day
Block $\frac{1}{2}$ day

Objectives: Write functions using function notation.

Evaluate and graph functions.

Online Edition
Tutorial Videos

Countdown to Testing Week 2

Power Presentations with PowerPoint®

Warm Up

Evaluate.

1. $5x - 2$ when $x = 4$ 18
2. $3x^2 + 4x - 1$ when $x = 5$ 94
3. $2x + 4\sqrt{x}$ when $x = 16$ 48
4. $2 - t^2$ when $t = \frac{1}{2}$ $1\frac{3}{4}$
5. Give the domain and range for this relation: {(1, 1), (−1, 1), (2, 4), (−2, 4), (−3, 9), (3, 9)}.
D: {−3, −2, −1, 1, 2, 3}
R: {1, 4, 9}

Also available on transparency

Math Humor

Parent: Did you study your algebra lesson at the family reunion?

Student: Sure, it was a function with relations.

State Resources

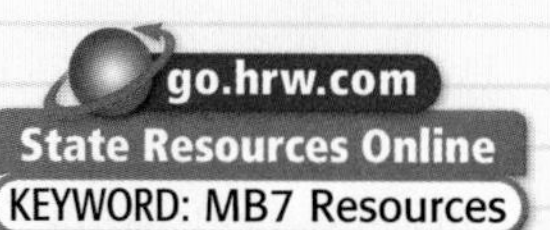

1 Introduce

EXPLORATION

1-7 Function Notation

Felicia is driving to see her parents. When she starts, she is at mile marker 50 on the interstate. She drives at an average speed of 60 mi/h. In the table, t stands for time in hours, and d(t) stands for the mile marker number at time t.

t	d(t)
0	d(0) = 50
0.5	
1	d(1) = 110
1.5	
2	

1. Complete the table to show the mile marker where Felicia is at each half hour.

You can also use a calculator to determine Felicia's location at various times. Enter the function rule by pressing Y= and entering **50 + 60X** as shown. Then press 2nd MODE (QUIT) to return to the home screen. Select the function you entered by pressing VARS, scrolling right to **Y-VARS,** selecting **1:Function,** and choosing **1:Y1.** You can evaluate the function for any x-value by entering a value in parentheses, as shown.

Plot1 Plot2 Plot3
\Y1 = 50+60X
\Y2 =
\Y3 =

Y1(2)
170

2. Use your calculator to find **Y1(3.5).**
3. Explain what **Y1(3.5)** represents.
4. Felicia's exit is at mile marker 362. Determine how many hours it will take her to get there.

THINK AND DISCUSS

Motivate

Ask students to consider the total cost of n items at \$2.50 each, or $c = 2.50n$. Ask them how much several different numbers of items would cost. Explain that the total cost is a function of the number of items purchased. Explain to them that you can show this mathematically using function notation: $c(n) = 2.50n$.

Explorations and answers are provided in the *Explorations* binder.

Power Presentations with PowerPoint®

Additional Examples

Example 1

For each function, evaluate $f(0)$, $f\left(\frac{1}{2}\right)$, and $f(-2)$.

A. $f(x) = 8 + 4x$ 8; 10; 0

B.

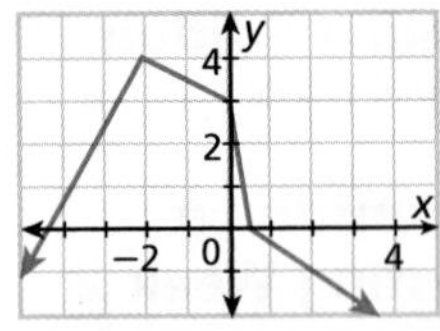

3; 0; 4

Example 2

Graph each function.

A. $\{(0, 4), (1, 5), (2, 6), (3, 7), (4, 8)\}$

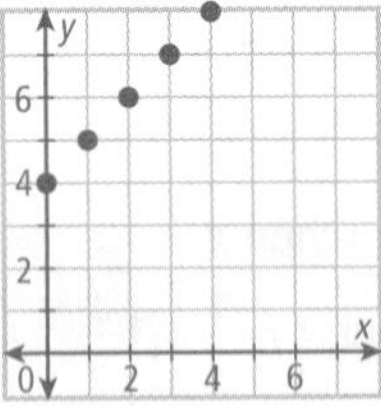

B. $f(x) = 3x - 1$

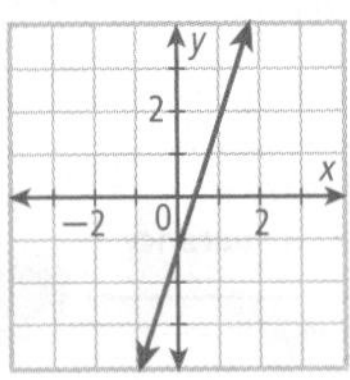

Also available on transparency

INTERVENTION

Questioning Strategies

EXAMPLE 1

- How do you use a graph to find a y-value?
- How is evaluating a function similar to evaluating an expression?

EXAMPLE 2

- Why is one graph a line and the other a set of points?
- How do you know which set of values to plot on the horizontal axis and which set to plot on the vertical axis?

In the notation $f(x)$, f is the *name* of the function. The output $f(x)$ of a function is called the **dependent variable** because it *depends* on the input value of the function. The input x is called the **independent variable**. When a function is graphed, the independent variable is graphed on the horizontal axis and the dependent variable is graphed on the vertical axis.

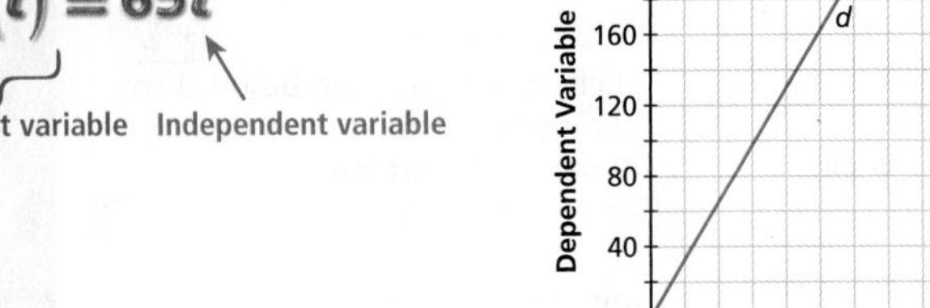

EXAMPLE 2 Graphing Functions

Graph each function.

A The diagram shows the maximum recommended heart rate for women by age.

Graph the points.

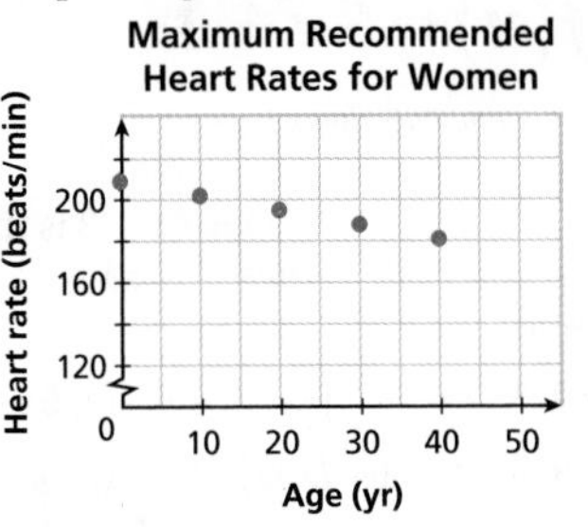

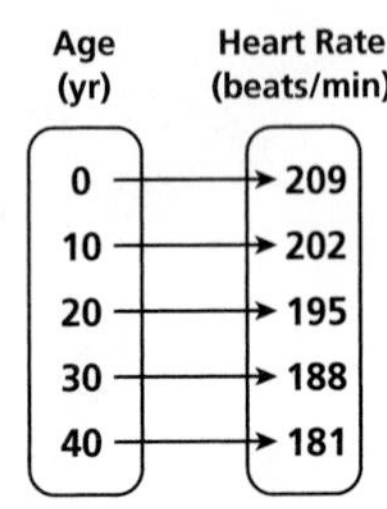

Do not connect the points, because the values between the given points have not been defined.

Reading Math

A function whose graph is made up of unconnected points is called a *discrete* function.

B The maximum recommended heart rate h for men is a function of age a and can be calculated with $h(a) = 214 - 0.8a$.

Make a table.

a	$214 - 0.8a$	$h(a)$
0	$214 - 0.8(0)$	214
20	$214 - 0.8(20)$	198
40	$214 - 0.8(40)$	182
60	$214 - 0.8(60)$	166
80	$214 - 0.8(80)$	150

Graph the points.

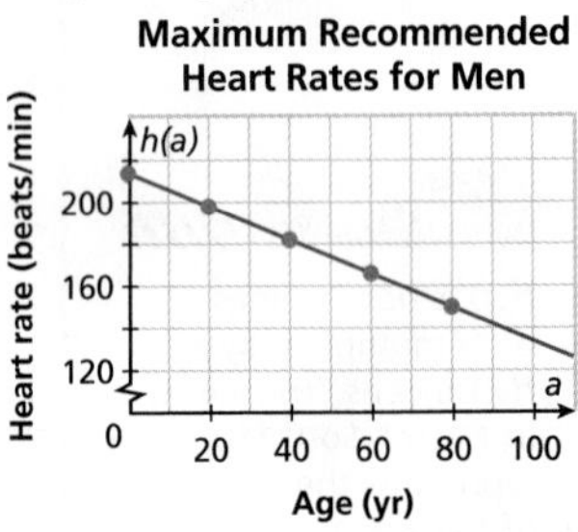

Connect the points with a line because the function is defined for $0 \le a \le 100$.

CHECK IT OUT! Graph each function.

2a.

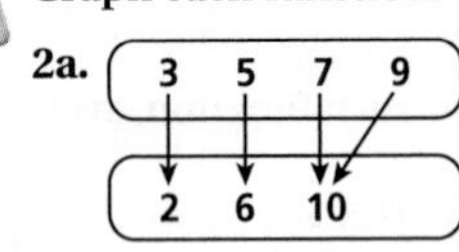

2b. $f(x) = 2x + 1$

2 Teach

Guided Instruction

In this lesson, students are introduced to function notation as they evaluate and graph functions. Help students make a connection between evaluating an algebraic expression and evaluating a function. Point out that many real-world functions are restricted to a reasonable domain of nonnegative values. Therefore, only nonnegative values need to be included on the horizontal axes of the graphs of these functions.

Reaching All Learners

Through Auditory Cues

Create a function and unusual input values, and have students read the equation with the input substituted. For example, $f(x) = 3x - 1$ and "f of Jessie equals 3 times Jessie minus 1" or "f of blue equals 3 times blue minus 1." This will not only get students more comfortable with the usage but also prepare them for more complex concepts.

The algebraic expression used to define a function is called the function rule. The function described by $f(x) = 5x + 3$ is defined by the function rule $5x + 3$. To write a function rule, first identify the independent and dependent variables.

EXAMPLE 3 ***Transportation Application***

The Japanese bullet train that travels from Tokyo to Kyoto averages about 156 km/h. The distance from Tokyo to Kyoto is 380 km.

a. Write a function to represent the distance remaining on the trip after a certain amount of time.

Time traveled is the independent variable, and distance remaining is the dependent variable.

Let t be the time in hours and let d be the distance in kilometers remaining on the trip.

Write a word equation to represent the problem situation. Then replace the words with expressions.

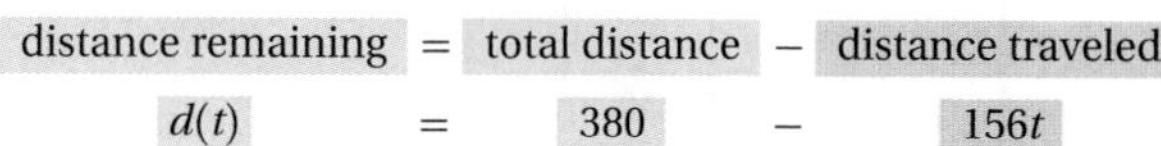

distance remaining	=	total distance	−	distance traveled
$d(t)$	=	380	−	$156t$

b. What is the value of the function for an input of 1.5, and what does it represent?

$d(1.5) = 380 - 156(1.5)$ *Substitute 1.5 for t and simplify.*

$d(1.5) = 146$

The value of the function for an input of 1.5 is 146. This means that there are 146 kilometers remaining in the trip after 1.5 hours.

A local photo shop will develop and print the photos from a disposable camera for $0.27 per print.

3a. Write a function to represent the cost of photo processing. $f(x) = 0.27x$

3b. What is the value of the function for an input of 24, and what does it represent?

6.48; the price to develop 24 prints, in dollars

THINK AND DISCUSS

1. Identify a reasonable domain for the function in Example 3. Explain your answer.

2. Explain three things you can determine about a function from the notation $g(t)$.

3. GET ORGANIZED Copy and complete the graphic organizer. In each blank, fill in the missing portion of the label.

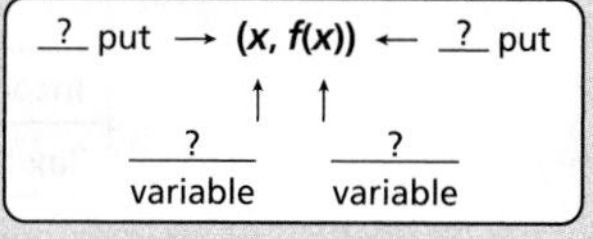

Answers to *Check It Out!*

2a.

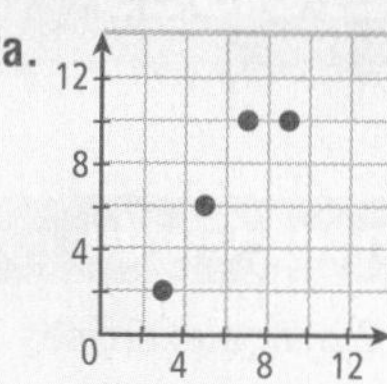

2b.

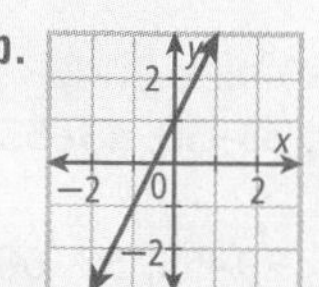

Power Presentations with PowerPoint®

Additional Examples

Example 3

A carnival charges a $5 entrance fee and $2 per ride.

a. Write a function to represent the total cost after taking a certain number of rides. $c(r) = 5 + 2r$

b. What is the value of the function for an input of 12, and what does it represent? 29; the cost in dollars of taking 12 rides

Also available on transparency

INTERVENTION
Questioning Strategies

EXAMPLE 3

- How do you know which variable is dependent?
- Why is the order of operations important in evaluating a function?

3 Close

Summarize

Review the language and notation of the lesson. In particular point out that $f(x)$ is read "f of x" and that $f(-2)$ means to evaluate the function rule by substituting −2 into that expression.

ONGOING ASSESSMENT

and INTERVENTION

***Diagnose Before* the Lesson**
1-7 Warm Up, TE p. 51

***Monitor During* the Lesson**
Check It Out! Exercises, SE pp. 51–53
Questioning Strategies, TE pp. 52–53

***Assess After* the Lesson**
1-7 Lesson Quiz, TE p. 57
Alternative Assessment, TE p. 57

Answers to *Think and Discuss*

Possible answers:

1. A reasonable domain is $[0, \frac{380}{156}]$ h because time cannot be negative and the train completes the trip in $\frac{380}{156}$ h.
2. The name of the function is g, the independent variable is t, and the dependent variable is $g(t)$.
3. See p. A2.

1-7 Exercises

Assignment Guide

Assign *Guided Practice* exercises as necessary.

If you finished Examples **1–3**
Basic 12–22, 33–38, 43–53, 59–66
Average 12–22, 29–55, 59–66
Advanced 12–66

Homework Quick Check
Quickly check key concepts.
Exercises: 13, 15, 18, 20, 22, 33

Answers

8.
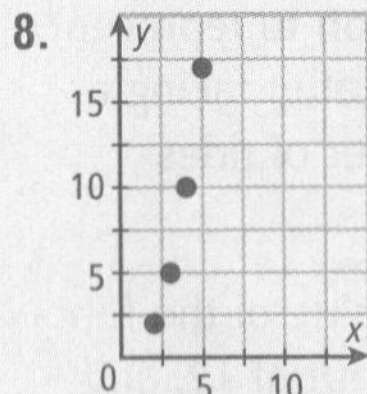

9.
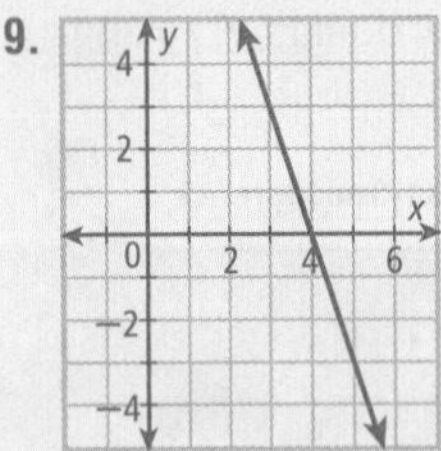

10.
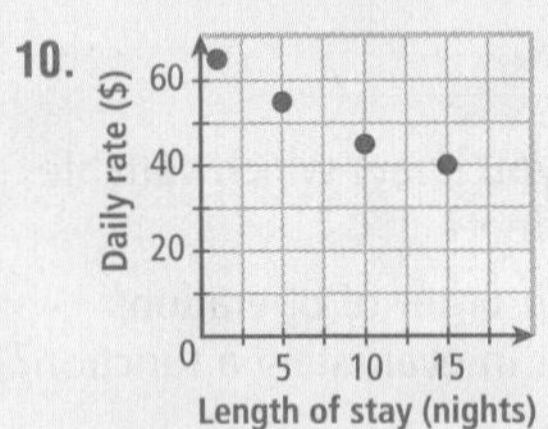

State Resources

1-7 Exercises

GUIDED PRACTICE

1. **Vocabulary** In function notation, the variable x is generally used to represent the __?__ variable. (*dependent* or *independent*) **independent**

SEE EXAMPLE 1 p. 51

For each function, evaluate $f(0)$, $f(1.5)$, and $f(-4)$.

2. $f(x) = 3x - 4$
3. $f(x) = x^2 + 9$
4. $f(x) = 3x^2 - x + 2$

2. −4; 0.5; −16
3. 9; 11.25; 25
4. 2; 7.25; 54

5.
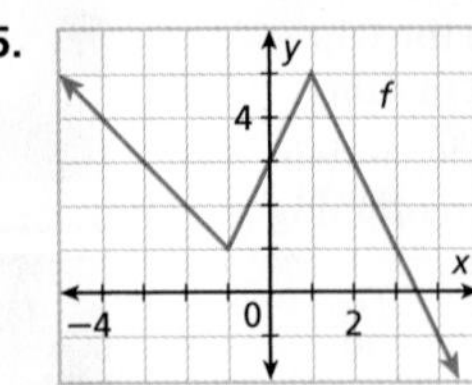
3; 4; 4

6.
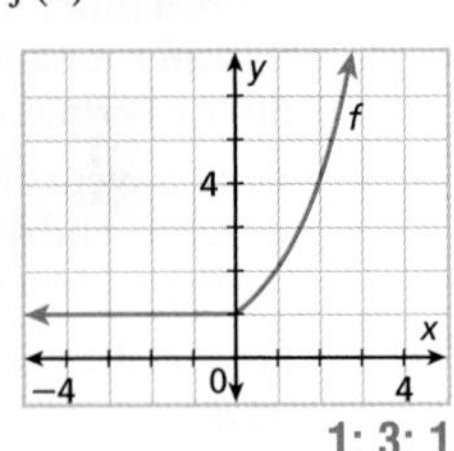
1; 3; 1

7.
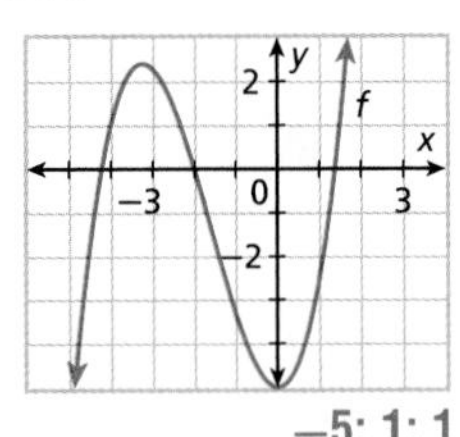
−5; 1; 1

SEE EXAMPLE 2 p. 52

Graph each function.

8.
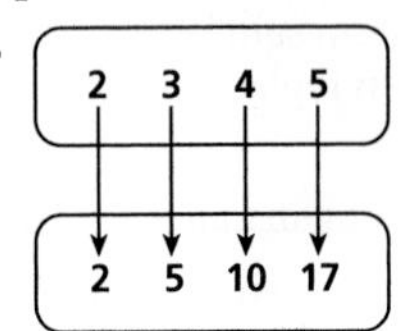

9. $g(x) = -3x + 12$

10.
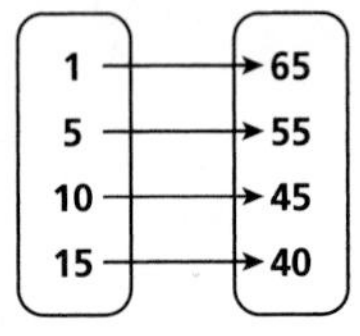

SEE EXAMPLE 3 p. 53

11. **Business** A furniture company misprinted a sales ad for a living room set but honors the advertised price. For each customer who purchases the living room set, the company suffers a loss of \$125. Write a function to represent the company's total loss. What is the value of the function for an input of 50, and what does it represent? **$f(x) = 125x$; 6250; the loss if 50 customers purchase the living room set, in dollars**

PRACTICE AND PROBLEM SOLVING

Independent Practice	
For Exercises	See Example
12–17	1
18–20	2
21	3

Extra Practice
Skills Practice p. S5
Application Practice p. S32

For each function, evaluate $f(0)$, $f\left(\frac{3}{2}\right)$, and $f(-1)$.

12. $f(x) = 7x - 4$
13. $f(x) = -x^2 + x$
14. $f(x) = -2x^2 + 1$

15.
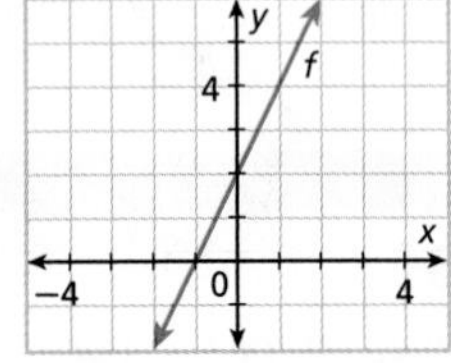

16.
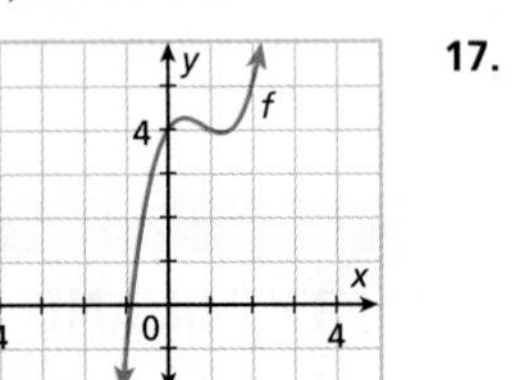

17.
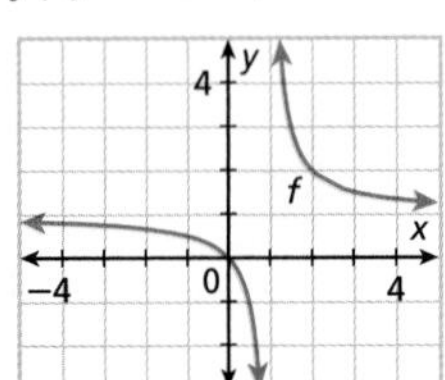

Graph each function.

18.

2003 Federal Income Tax Rates					
Income (\$)	25,000	50,000	75,000	100,000	150,000
Tax Rate (%)	15	25	28	28	33

19. $f(x) = \sqrt{x}$ for $x \geq 0$

20. $f(x) = \frac{1}{2}x + 1$ for $-6 < x < 6$

Answers

12. $-4; \frac{13}{2}; -11$
13. $0; -\frac{3}{4}; -2$
14. $1; -\frac{7}{2}; -1$
15. 2; 5; 0
16. 4; 4; −1
17. $0; 3; \frac{1}{2}$

18.
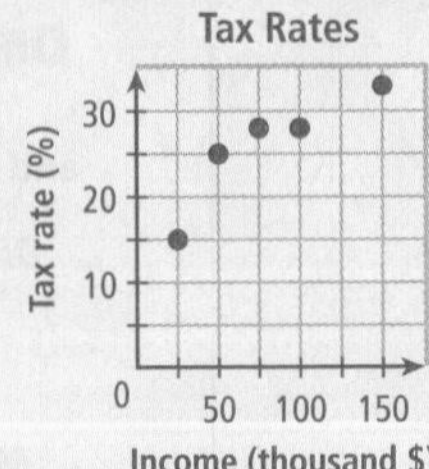

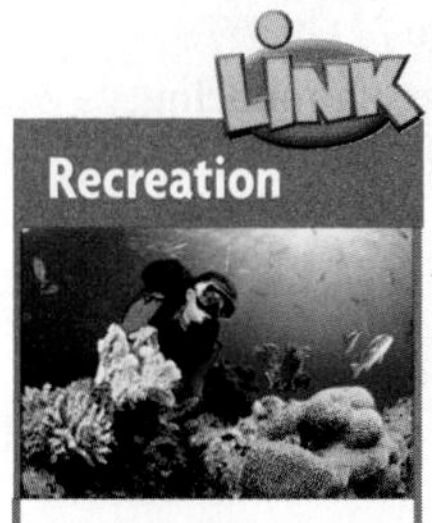

Recreation

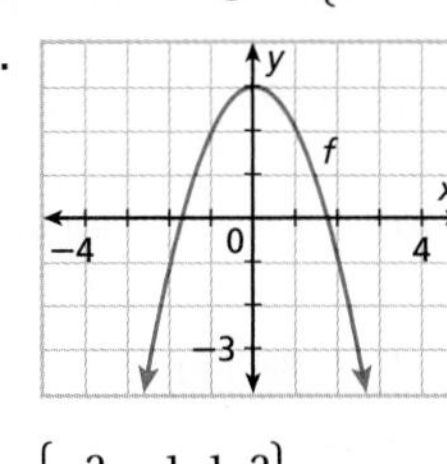

At a depth of 33 feet, a scuba diver is exposed to approximately twice the pressure he or she would experience at the surface.

21. **Safety** In a certain county, the fines for speeding in a school zone are \$160 plus an additional \$4 for every mile per hour over the speed limit. Write a function to represent the speeding fines. What is the value of the function for an input of 8, and what does it represent?

22. **Recreation** In order to scuba dive safely, divers must be aware that the water pressure in the ocean is a function of depth. The water pressure increases by 0.445 pounds per square inch (psi) for each foot of depth. The pressure at the surface is 14.7 psi. Write a function to represent water pressure. What is the value of the function for an input of 50, and what does it represent?

A set of input values is sometimes referred to as the *replacement set* for the independent variable. Evaluate each function for the given replacement set.

23. $f(x) = 3x - 6; \left\{-3.5, -1, \frac{1}{4}, 2, 11\right\}$

24. $f(x) = x(1 - 2x); \left\{-8, \frac{2}{3}, 1, 9, 4\right\}$

25. $f(x) = \frac{2x - 1}{3}; \left\{-4, 0, \frac{1}{2}, 5\right\}$

26. $f(x) = (x - 1)^2 + 4; \left\{-6, -\frac{3}{2}, 1, 4\right\}$

27.

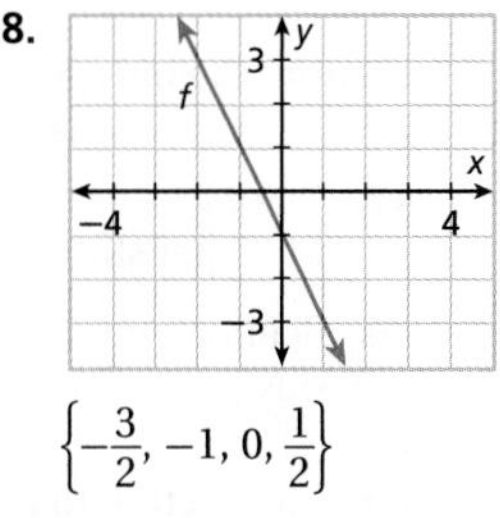

$\{-2, -1, 1, 2\}$

28.

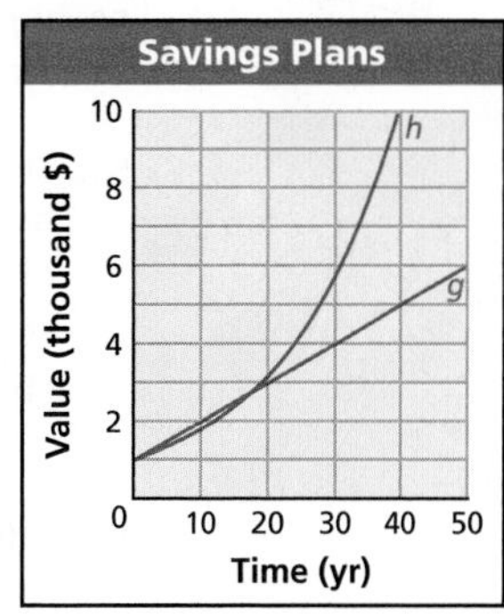

$\left\{-\frac{3}{2}, -1, 0, \frac{1}{2}\right\}$

Explain what a reasonable domain and range would be for each situation. Then explain why the situation represents a function.

29. the number of boxes of kitchen tile that must be purchased to cover a floor with an area of A square feet

30. the number of horseshoes needed to shoe h horses

31. the vertical position of a diver in relation to the surface of the pool t seconds after diving from a 10-meter platform into a 16-foot-deep pool (*Hint:* 1 meter ≈ 3.28 feet)

32. the temperature in degrees Fahrenheit at an Antarctic research station h hours after 12:00 A.M.

Banking **The graph at right shows the functions that represent two different savings plans. Use the graph for Exercises 33–37.**

Savings Plans

33. If t represents time in years, for what value of t will h have a value of \$7500? What does this value of t represent?

34. Use function notation to represent the value of each savings plan at 25 years. Estimate these values.

35. For what value of t is $g(t)$ approximately equal to $\frac{1}{2}h(t)$? Explain what this value of t represents.

36. Approximately how many years will it take for each savings plan to double from its original value?

37. What is the value of $h(40) - g(40)$, and what is its real-world meaning?

COMMON ERROR ALERT

In **Exercise 19,** students may have difficulty graphing the function due to their choice of input values. Encourage students to choose reasonable values before attempting to graph—in this case, perfect squares such as 0, 1, 4, and 9.

Teaching Tip **Kinesthetic** For **Exercises 27** and **28,** encourage students to find the output values by using a ruler (MK) to help them envision a vertical line from the x-value to the graph of the function and then a horizontal line from that point on the graph to the y-axis.

Answers

19.

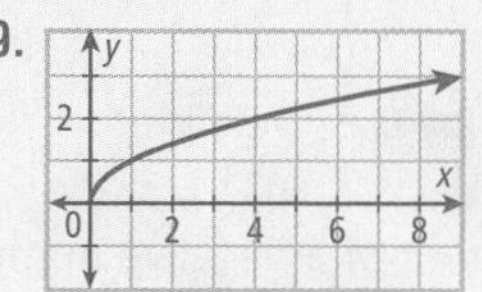

20.

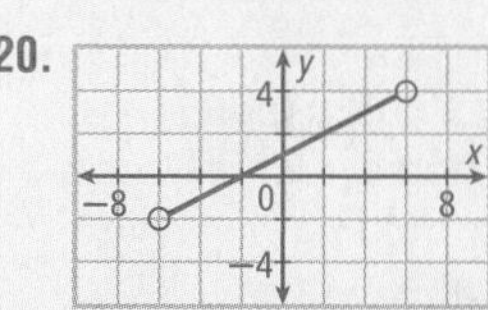

21. $f(m) = 160 + 4m$; 192; a fine of \$192 for driving 8 mi/h over the speed limit

22. $p = 14.7 + 0.445d$; 36.95; pressure in psi at a depth of 50 ft

23. −16.5; −9; −5.25; 0; 27

24. $-136; -\frac{2}{9}; -1; -153; -28$

25. $-3; -\frac{1}{3}; 0; 3$

26. $53; 10\frac{1}{4}; 4; 13$

1-7 PRACTICE A

1-7 PRACTICE C

1-7 PRACTICE B

For each function, evaluate $f(-1)$, $f(0)$, $f\left(\frac{3}{2}\right)$.

1. $g(x) = -4x + 2$ — $6, 2, -4$
2. $h(x) = x^2 - 3$ — $-2, -3, -\frac{3}{4}$
3. $f(x) = 3x^2 + x$ — $2, 0, 8\frac{1}{4}$
4. $f(x) = \frac{x}{2} - 1$ — $-\frac{3}{2}, -1, -\frac{1}{4}$

Graph each function. Then evaluate $f(-2)$ and $f(0)$.

5. $f(x) = x^2 - 4$
6. $f(x) = -\frac{3}{2}x + 1$

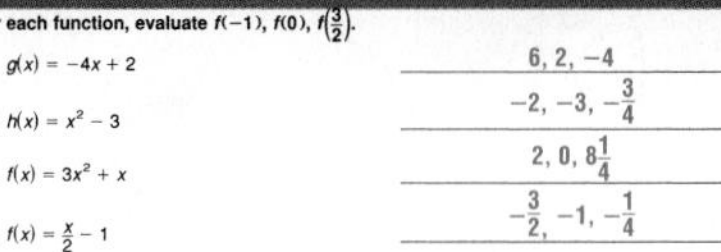

0, −4　　4, 1

Solve.

7. On one day the value of \$1.00 U.S. was equivalent to 0.77 euro. On the same day \$1.00 U.S. was equivalent to \$1.24 Canadian. Write a function to represent the value of Canadian dollars in euros. What is the value of the function for an input of 5 rounded to the nearest cent, and what does it represent?
$f(c) = \frac{0.77c}{1.24}$; $f(5) = 3.10$; the value of \$5 Canadian is equivalent to 3.10 euros.

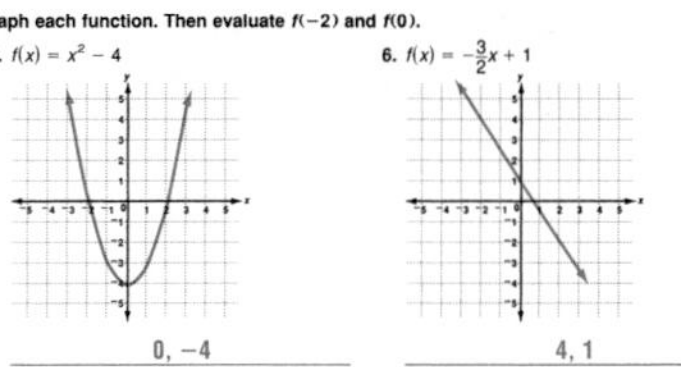

8. PC Haven sells computers at a 15% discount on the original price plus a \$200 rebate. Write a function to represent the final price of a computer at PC Haven. What is the value of the function for an input of 2500, and what does it represent?
$f(p) = 0.85p - 200$; $f(2500) = 1925$; \$1925 is the final, discounted price of a computer with an original price of \$2500.

Answers

27. −1; 2; 2; −1

28. 2; 1; −1; −2

29. D: $\{A \mid A \geq 0\}$; R: $\{y \mid y \in \mathbb{W}\}$; possible answer: for every area, there is only 1 appropriate number of boxes of tile.

30. D: $\{h \mid h \in \mathbb{W}\}$; R: $\{y \mid y \geq 0$ and is a multiple of $4\}$; possible answer: the situation represents a function because each horse needs exactly 4 shoes.

31. D: $\{t \mid t \geq 0\}$;
R: $\{y \mid -16 < y \leq 32.8\}$; possible answer: for every time, the diver can be in only 1 place.

32. Possible answer: D: $\{h \mid h \geq 0\}$; R: $\{y \mid -130 < y < 60\}$; for every time, there is only one temperature reading for a given thermometer.

33. $t = 35$; the number of years it takes for plan h to reach a value of \$7500

34. $h(25) \approx 4400$; $g(25) \approx 3500$

35. $t = 40$; the time when plan g is worth $\frac{1}{2}$ the value of plan h

36. h: 12 years; g: 10 years

37. $h(40) - g(40) = 5000$; the difference in the value of the plans after 40 years

Exercise 38 involves using a function to determine cost. This exercise prepares students for the Multi-Step Test Prep on page 74.

Exercise 51 may be solved more efficiently by reading the answer choices first and then finding $h(1)$, $h(2)$, $h(3)$, and $h(4)$ before selecting the answer. Once these values are known, it becomes clear that **H** is the only correct choice.

Answers

38a. \$612.50

b. 78 pots

c. a line starting at (0, 175) and rising to the right

39. When $x = 3$, $f(x) = \frac{1}{x-3} = \frac{1}{0}$, but division by 0 is undefined.

40. For $-5 < x < 1$, $g(x)$ is the square root of a negative number, which is not defined for real numbers.

41. For $-5 < x < 0$, x represents negative hours, and distance traveled would be negative.

42. (2, 8) and (3, 11)

43. independent: number of shirts; dependent: total cost; domain: $x \geq 15$

44. independent: hospital charges; dependent: the amount Belinda pays; domain: $x \geq 0$

45.

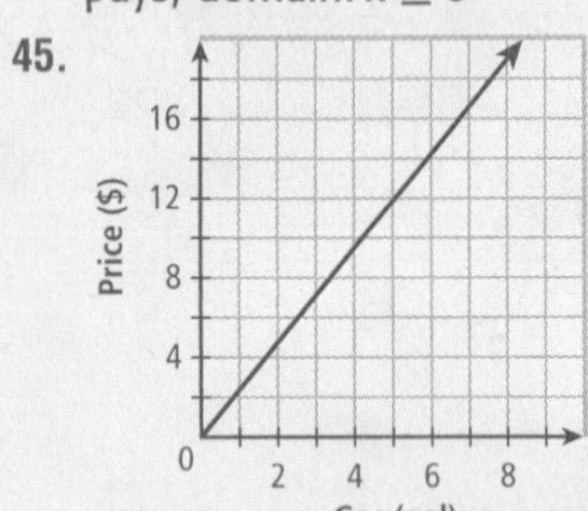

46.

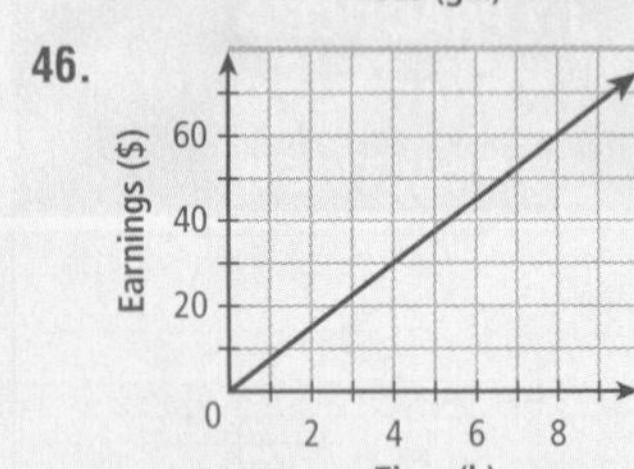

47.

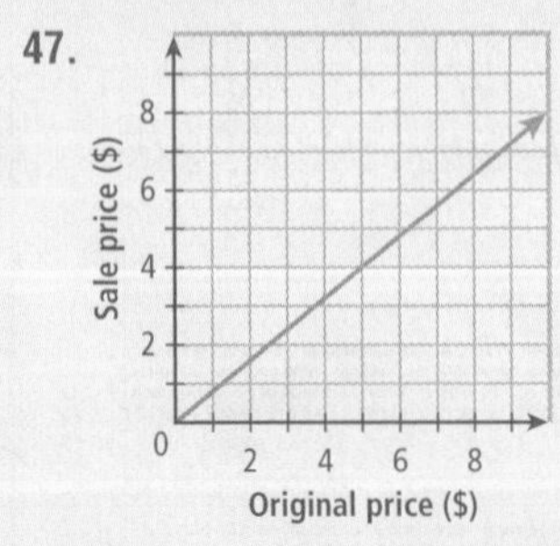

48. For graph, see p. A15.

38. This problem will prepare you for the Multi-Step Test Prep on page 74.
    a. The function $c(p) = 175 + 3.5p$ can be used to define the cost of producing up to 200 ceramic pots. If the materials are \$175 and the additional cost to produce each pot is \$3.50, how much will it cost to produce 125 pots?
    b. How many pots can be produced if the budget is limited to \$450?
    c. What would the graph of this function look like?

Critical Thinking **For Exercises 39–41, explain why $-5 < x < 5$ is not a reasonable domain for each function.**

39. $f(x) = \dfrac{1}{x-3}$

40. $g(x) = \sqrt{x-1}$

41. $f(x)$ is the distance traveled in x hours at a rate of 55 mi/h.

42. If $f(2) = 8$ and $f(3) = 11$, name two points that lie on the graph of f.

Identify the independent and dependent variable for each situation. Then state a reasonable domain.

43. As long as a minimum of 15 shirts are ordered, the cost for an order of T-shirts is \$4.25 per shirt.

44. Belinda's medical insurance states that she must pay the first \$500 for a hospital stay plus 15% of the remaining charges.

Write a function to represent each situation. Graph your function.

45. The price for a tank of gasoline is \$2.37 per gallon. $f(x) = 2.37x$

46. Raul earns \$7.50 per hour for baby-sitting. $f(x) = 7.5x$

47. The sale price is 20% off of the original price. $f(x) = 0.8x$

48. Leona's weekly salary is \$250 plus 5% of her total sales for the week. $f(x) = 250 + 0.05x$

49. **Write About It** Explain what is meant by reasonable domain and range. Give examples.

50. If $f(x) = 5 - 3x$ and $g(x) = 12x + 2$, which statement is NOT true?
    (A) $f(0) > g(0)$ (B) $g(5) > f(5)$ (C) $f(1) > g(1)$ (D) $f(-1) > g(-1)$

51. The function $h(t) = 20t - 5t^2$ gives the height of an object t seconds after it has been thrown into the air. Which statement is true?
    (F) The height at 4 seconds is the same as the height at 2 seconds.
    (G) The height at 2 seconds is less than the height at 3 seconds.
    (H) The height at 3 seconds is the same as the height at 1 second.
    (J) The height at 4 seconds is greater than the height at 1 second.

52. A function is described by the equation $f(x) = -3x^2 + 12$. If the replacement set for the independent variable is $\{1, 3, 4, 9, 10\}$, which is an element of the corresponding set for the dependent variable?
    (A) 1 (B) 3 (C) 4 (D) 9

53. **Gridded Response** Given $f(x) = 3(x-2)^2 + 4$, find $f(-1)$. 31

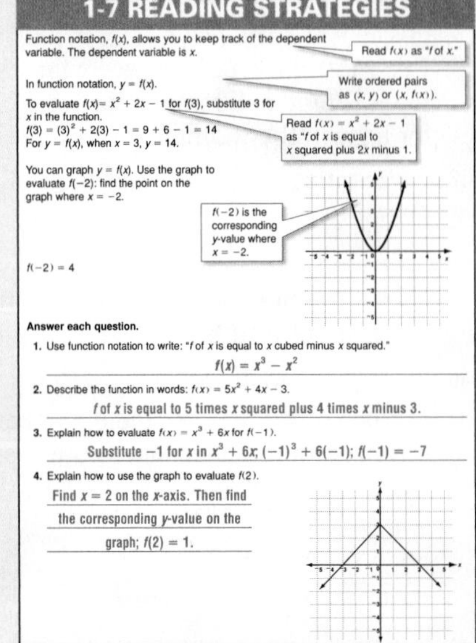

1-7 READING STRATEGIES

Function notation, $f(x)$, allows you to keep track of the dependent variable. The dependent variable is x.

Read $f(x)$ as "f of x."

In function notation, $y = f(x)$.

Write ordered pairs as (x, y) or $(x, f(x))$.

To evaluate $f(x) = x^2 + 2x - 1$ for $f(3)$, substitute 3 for x in the function.
$f(3) = (3)^2 + 2(3) - 1 = 9 + 6 - 1 = 14$
For $y = f(x)$, when $x = 3$, $y = 14$.

Read $f(x) = x^2 + 2x - 1$ as "f of x is equal to x squared plus $2x$ minus 1.

You can graph $y = f(x)$. Use the graph to evaluate $f(-2)$: find the point on the graph where $x = -2$.

$f(-2)$ is the corresponding y-value where $x = -2$.

$f(-2) = 4$

Answer each question.

1. Use function notation to write: "f of x is equal to x cubed minus x squared."
   $f(x) = x^3 - x^2$
2. Describe the function in words: $f(x) = 5x^2 + 4x - 3$.
   f of x is equal to 5 times x squared plus 4 times x minus 3.
3. Explain how to evaluate $f(x) = x^3 + 6x$ for $f(-1)$.
   Substitute -1 for x in $x^3 + 6x$; $(-1)^3 + 6(-1)$; $f(-1) = -7$
4. Explain how to use the graph to evaluate $f(2)$.
   Find $x = 2$ on the x-axis. Then find the corresponding y-value on the graph; $f(2) = 1$.

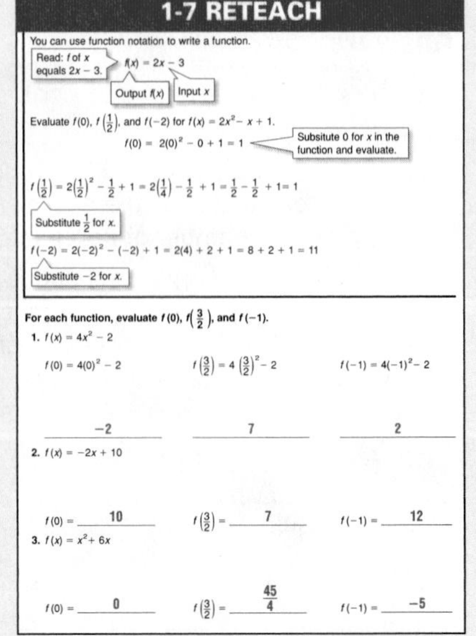

1-7 RETEACH

You can use function notation to write a function.

Read: f of x equals $2x - 3$. $f(x) = 2x - 3$ Output $f(x)$ Input x

Evaluate $f(0)$, $f\left(\frac{1}{2}\right)$, and $f(-2)$ for $f(x) = 2x^2 - x + 1$.

$f(0) = 2(0)^2 - 0 + 1 = 1$ Subsitute 0 for x in the function and evaluate.

$f\left(\frac{1}{2}\right) = 2\left(\frac{1}{2}\right)^2 - \frac{1}{2} + 1 = 2\left(\frac{1}{4}\right) - \frac{1}{2} + 1 = \frac{1}{2} - \frac{1}{2} + 1 = 1$

Substitute $\frac{1}{2}$ for x.

$f(-2) = 2(-2)^2 - (-2) + 1 = 2(4) + 2 + 1 = 8 + 2 + 1 = 11$

Substitute -2 for x.

For each function, evaluate $f(0)$, $f\left(\frac{3}{2}\right)$, and $f(-1)$.

1. $f(x) = 4x^2 - 2$
   $f(0) = 4(0)^2 - 2$ $f\left(\frac{3}{2}\right) = 4\left(\frac{3}{2}\right)^2 - 2$ $f(-1) = 4(-1)^2 - 2$
   -2 7 2
2. $f(x) = -2x + 10$
   $f(0) =$ 10 $f\left(\frac{3}{2}\right) =$ 7 $f(-1) =$ 12
3. $f(x) = x^2 + 6x$
   $f(0) =$ 0 $f\left(\frac{3}{2}\right) = \frac{45}{4}$ $f(-1) =$ -5

CHALLENGE AND EXTEND

Determine each value for the given function. Simplify your answer.

54. $f(2c)$ for $f(x) = \sqrt{x^3}$ $2c\sqrt{2c}$

55. $g\left(-\frac{h}{4}\right)$ for $g(x) = \frac{6x + h}{2x}$, where $h \neq 0$ 1

56. $h(t^2 + 3t)$ for $h(x) = 4x + 7t$ $4t^2 + 19t$

57. $r(t^4)$ for $r(x) = \sqrt{x^2 + \left(\frac{2}{x}\right)^2}$ $\frac{\sqrt{t^{16} + 4}}{t^4}$

58. Geometry The area of a triangle is $\frac{1}{2}$ the product of its base length b and its height h.

a. If $b = 4$, explain whether the equation for the area of a triangle represents a function. Yes; for each value of h, there is only one value of A.

b. Explain whether the equation that represents the area of a triangle is a function for the domain $\{(b, h) \mid b > 0 \text{ and } h > 0\}$. function; possible answer: any combination of values for b and h gives only one possible value of A.

SPIRAL REVIEW

Simplify each expression. Assume all variables are nonzero. *(Lesson 1-4)*

59. $4(x + 2) - x(y - 8)$ $12x - xy + 8$

60. $(2a)^2 + 6a^2$ $10a^2$

61. $\frac{3c - 10 + 2c}{5c}$ $\frac{c - 2}{c}$

62. $s(s + 7) - 4s$ $s^2 + 3s$

Name the conditions for b that would make each set of ordered pairs a function. *(Lesson 1-6)*

63. $\{(1, 2), (6, 0), (0, 1), (-8, b)\}$ b is any value.

64. $\{(b, 2), (0, 3), (5, 4), (-3, 5)\}$ $b \neq -3, 0, \text{ or } 5$

Determine whether each relation is a function. *(Lesson 1-6)*

65. $\left\{(-1, -5), (-2, 0.5), (-4, 5), \left(-5, \frac{1}{2}\right)\right\}$ yes

66. $\{(-1, 3), (-1, 4), (-1, 5), (-1, 6)\}$ no

Career Path

go.hrw.com
Career Resources Online
KEYWORD: MB7 Career

Adam Leung
Radio announcer

Q: What math classes did you take in high school?

A: I took Algebra 1, Geometry, and Algebra 2.

Q: What are some of your duties as an announcer?

A: During the day, I read the traffic reports and the news in addition to playing music. On weekends, I have more freedom to play music and take calls from listeners.

Q: How is math used in your job?

A: I've got to be sure all the scheduled music, ads, news, and traffic reports are covered in my shift. I use math to calculate how much time I need. I also use math to help create contests.

Q: What are your plans for the future?

A: I'll probably continue to work as an announcer for a while. After that, I'd like to become a station manager or a radio engineer. Engineers are responsible for making sure all the equipment at the station works properly.

Answers

49. Possible answer: A domain and range are reasonable if they make sense for the problem situation. For example, a domain that includes negative values is not reasonable for a problem involving the number of boxes of kitchen tile required to cover a floor with area A.

Journal

Have students explain in their own words how they determine which is the dependent variable and which is the independent variable when writing a function.

ALTERNATIVE ASSESSMENT

Give students a simple real-world relationship, such as the following: The cost of renting a car is a flat fee of \$20 plus \$30 per day. Have students write a function using the proper notation, evaluate it for several values, and graph it.

Power Presentations with PowerPoint®

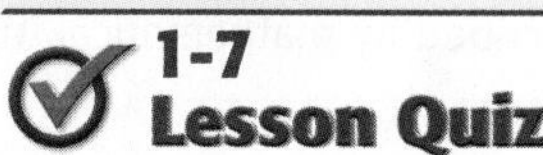

1-7 Lesson Quiz

For each function, evaluate $f(0)$, $f\left(\frac{1}{2}\right)$, and $f(-2)$.

1. $f(x) = 9 - 6x$ 9; 6; 21

2. [graph] 4; 6; 0

3. Graph $f(x) = 4x + 2$.

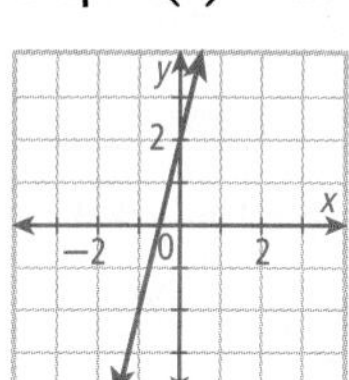

4. A painter charges \$200 plus \$25 per can of paint used.

a. Write a function to represent the total charge for a certain number of cans of paint. $t(c) = 200 + 25c$

b. What is the value of the function for an input of 4, and what does it represent? 300; total charge in dollars if 4 cans of paint are used

Also available on transparency

1-7 PROBLEM SOLVING

Juan is analyzing cell phone plans. The graph shows two plans he is considering. Use the graph for Exercises 1–4.

1. For which value of x does each function have a value of \$40? Plan A, 100 min; plan B, 0 min

2. The graphs of the functions cross at $x = 150$. Explain what this represents. Possible answer: For 150 min the two plans cost the same amount.

3. Use function notation and estimation to represent the value of each function for 200 minutes. Plan A, \$53; plan B, \$50

4. Juan expects to use about 300 minutes per month. Which plan should he buy? Why? Plan B; costs less than plan A for 300 minutes

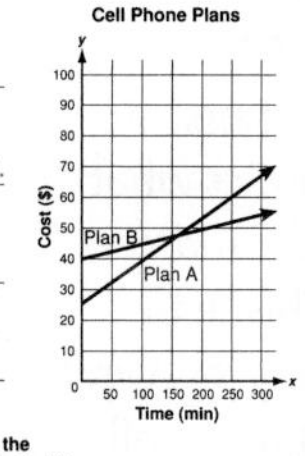

In September, Harley puts \$1035 that he earned during the summer in a bank account to use during the school year for his personal expenses. He budgets d dollars a month for expenses. Choose the letter for the best answer.

5. Which shows a function representing the amount left in his account after 4 months?
   (A) $f(d) = \$1035 - 4d$
   B $f(d) = \$1035 - d$
   C $f(d) = (\$1035 - 4)d$
   D $f(d) = \frac{\$1035}{4d}$

6. Harley writes the function $g(a) = \frac{\$1035}{9} - a$ to show his monthly budgeted amount remaining in a month when a, the actual amount he spends, is less than the amount of his budget. What is the value of this function for a month when he spends \$87.50?
   F \$12.50
   (G) \$27.50
   H \$115.00
   J \$202.50

7. Fay uses the function $f(x) = \frac{3}{2}x + 1$ to find the number of boxes of tile to buy for each 10 square feet of floor. How many boxes of tiles does she need to cover 600 square feet?
   A 901 boxes
   B 401 boxes
   (C) 91 boxes
   D 41 boxes

8. Rasheed uses the function $f(e) = 4e$ to find the distance around a square barbecue pit. What is the length of the side of the pit that has a perimeter of 55.2 ft?
   (F) 13.8 ft
   G 27.6 ft
   H 110.4 ft
   J 220.8 ft

1-7 CHALLENGE

You can think of a function as a process. The process has an input, the independent variable. That independent variable is put into the function, processed, and then output as the dependent variable.

So $f(x) = 3x + 7$ defines the process performed by the function f. The variable, x, is input, multiplied by 3, and then 7 is added to the result. The output is the result of the process.

Consider the functions $f(x) = 2x - 3$ and $g(x) = x^2 + x - 5$.

1. Describe the process of the functions f and g in words. f takes a number, doubles it, and subtracts 3; g squares a number, adds the same number, and subtracts 5.

2. Evaluate $f(5x^2)$. $10x^2 - 3$

3. Evaluate $g(2x)$. $4x^2 + 2x - 5$

A combination of the functions $f(x)$ and $g(x)$ form a composite function, $f(g(x))$. In $f(g(x))$ the output of $g(x)$ is used as the input for $f(x)$.

4. Which function or process is performed first in the composite function $f(g(x))$? g

5. Evaluate the composite function $f(g(x))$ and simplify your result. $2x^2 + 2x - 13$

6. Evaluate the composite function $g(f(x))$ and simplify your result. $4x^2 - 10x + 1$

7. Is it true that $f(g(x)) = g(f(x))$? No

A common function used in math is the difference quotient.

$$\frac{f(x + h) - f(x)}{h}$$

8. Evaluate the difference quotient for the function f and simplify your result. 2

9. Evaluate the difference quotient for the function g and simplify your result. $2x + h + 1$

Organizer

Use with Lesson 1-8

Pacing:
Traditional $\frac{1}{2}$ day
Block $\frac{1}{4}$ day

Objective: Use chess to explore transformations.

Materials: chessboard, chess pieces

Resources

Algebra Lab Activities
1-8 Lab Recording Sheet

Teach

Discuss

Have students consider a chessboard as an example of a coordinate plane.

Close

Key Concept

The movement, or translation, of points on a coordinate plane can be described by mathematical rules.

Assessment

Journal Have students describe the similarities and differences between chessboard locations and points in the coordinate plane.

Answers *to Try This*

1. a1, a2, b2, c1, and c2
2. a7, b7, c7, d6, d8, and e7

3–8. See p. A15.

State Resources

Use with Lesson 1-8

Chess Translations

You can use the game of chess to explore transformations.

A chessboard consists of 64 squares arranged into 8 rows (numbered 1 through 8) and 8 columns (lettered *a* through *h*). Each square is named by its column letter and row number. For instance, the square in the lower left corner is **a1.**

Chessboard Notation

	a	b	c	d	e	f	g	h
8								h8
7				♜		♝		h7
6	♞							h6
5				♞				
4								
3	a3							
2	a2							
1	a1	♚						

Selected Rules of Movement	
Bishop	Diagonally any number of squares
King	One square in any direction
Knight	L-shape: two squares horizontally or vertically and then one square perpendicularly
Rook	Horizontally or vertically any number of squares

You move each chess piece by applying the rules of movement. Pieces of the same color cannot move onto a space occupied by another piece, and the knight is the only piece that can jump over other pieces.

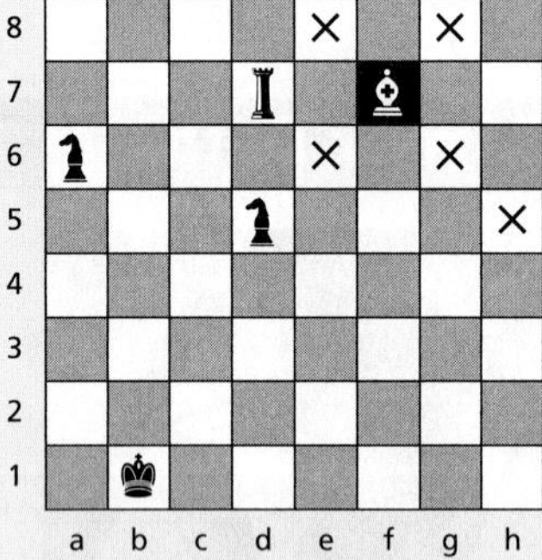

Activity

Use the chessboard at right to name all possible locations of the bishop on f7 after one move.

The bishop can move diagonally any number of spaces, but it cannot move into or through any other pieces.

The bishop at f7 can move to any of the marked spaces: e6, e8, g6, g8, or h5.

Try This

Use the chessboard from the activity to name all possible locations of each piece after one move.

1. the king on b1
2. the rook on d7
3. the knight on a6

Use the chessboard from the activity to name all possible locations of each piece after two moves.

4. the king on b1
5. the rook on d7
6. the knight on a6
7. **Critical Thinking** In the last move of a chess game a knight is moved to d5. What are the possible squares that it came from?
8. **Make a Conjecture** Explain the connection between the position labeling in chess and points in the coordinate plane.

Teacher to Teacher

I like to have students use the graphing calculator to explore translations of different functions. I have them graph a parent function and a translation of the parent function, such as the functions $y = x$ and $y = x + 3$ or the functions $y = \sqrt{x}$ and $y = \sqrt{x} + 5$.

After graphing a few pairs, students are able to predict what the translation will be and can verify by graphing. This activity also allows students to preview the parent functions they will be learning in this course.

Stephanie Turner
Colleyville, TX

1-8 Exploring Transformations

A2.1.2 Use and interpret function notation, including evaluation of functions represented by tables, graphs, words, equations or a set of ordered pairs.

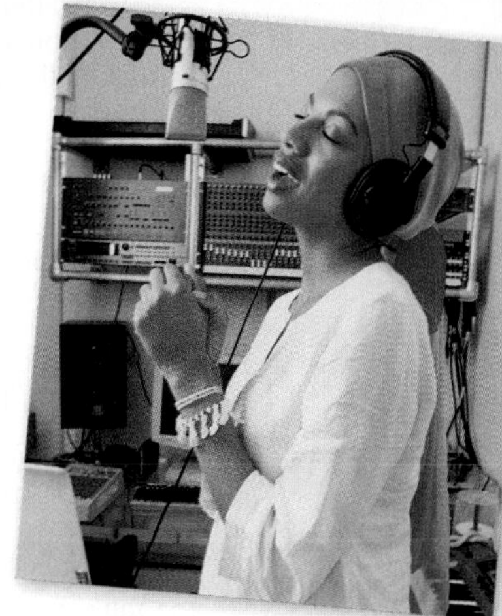

Objectives
Apply transformations to points and sets of points.

Interpret transformations of real-world data.

Vocabulary
transformation
translation
reflection
stretch
compression

Why learn this?
Changes in recording studio fees can be modeled by transformations. (See Example 4.)

A **transformation** is a change in the position, size, or shape of a figure. A **translation**, or slide, is a transformation that moves each point in a figure the same distance in the same direction.

EXAMPLE 1 Translating Points

Perform the given translation on the point $(2, -1)$. Give the coordinates of the translated point.

A **4 units left**

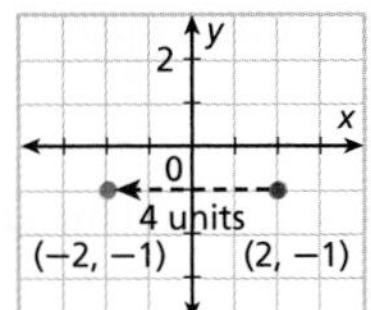

Translating $(2, -1)$ 4 units left results in the point $(-2, -1)$.

B **2 units right and 3 units up**

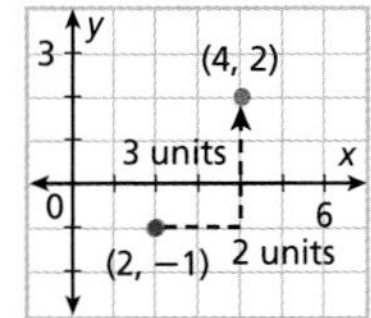

Translating $(2, -1)$ 2 units right and 3 units up results in the point $(4, 2)$.

Perform the given translation on the point $(-1, 3)$. Give the coordinates of the translated point.

1a. 4 units right
$(3, 3)$

1b. 1 unit left and 2 units down
$(-2, 1)$

Notice that when you translate **left or right,** the ***x*-coordinate** changes, and when you translate **up or down,** the ***y*-coordinate** changes.

Translations

Horizontal Translation	Vertical Translation
Each point shifts *right* or *left* by a number of units.	Each point shifts *up* or *down* by a number of units.
(1, 2) (4, 2), 3 units. The x-coordinate changes. $(1, 2) \to (1 + 3, 2)$; $(x, y) \to (x + h, y)$	(1, 4), 2 units, (1, 2). The y-coordinate changes. $(1, 2) \to (1, 2 + 2)$; $(x, y) \to (x, y + k)$
left if $h < 0$ right if $h > 0$	down if $k < 0$ up if $k > 0$

1-8 Organizer

Pacing: Traditional $1\frac{1}{2}$ days
Block $\frac{3}{4}$ day

Objectives: Apply transformations to points and sets of points.

Interpret transformations of real-world data.

Online Edition
Tutorial Videos

Countdown to Testing Week 2

Power Presentations with PowerPoint®

Warm Up

Plot each point.

1. $A(0, 0)$ **2.** $B(5, 0)$
3. $C(-5, 0)$ **4.** $D(0, 5)$
5. $E(0, -5)$ **6.** $F(-5, -5)$

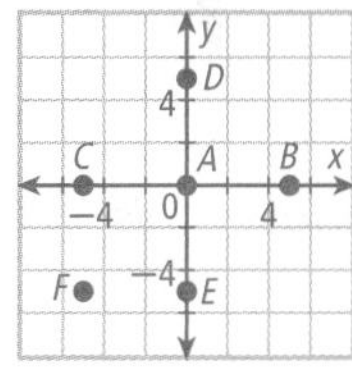

Also available on transparency

Math Humor

Student: I had French class today; I've done enough algebra!
Parent: How?
Student: All we did was translate!

State Resources

1 Introduce

1-8 Exploring Transformations

You can explore transformations by using the graph of a line on a graphing calculator.

Graph y = x on a graphing calculator by pressing [Y=] and entering **Y1 = X** as shown. Then press [GRAPH] to see the graph.

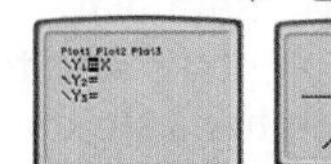

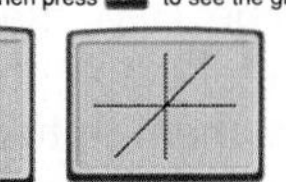

1. Enter and graph **Y2 = X + 5**. Describe the graph of **Y2** as compared to the graph of **Y1**.
2. Enter and graph **Y3 = X − 5**. Describe the graph of **Y3** as compared to the graph of **Y1**.
3. Make a conjecture about how a change in the value of k in the equation y = x + k affects the equation's graph.

THINK AND DISCUSS

4. **Explain** what equation you would use to move the graph of y = x down 3 units.

Motivate

Have students consider their seating arrangement in class. Choose two seats and have the students brainstorm methods for describing how a student might move from one to the other. Introduce the use of aisles and rows as coordinates, and explain that this makes it easier to describe the student's move.

Explorations and answers are provided in the *Explorations* binder.

Power Presentations with PowerPoint®

Additional Examples

Example 1

Perform the given translation on the point (−3, 4). Give the coordinates of the translated point.

A. 5 units right (2, 4)

B. 2 units left and 2 units down (−5, 2)

Example 2

Use a table to perform each transformation of $y = f(x)$. Use the same coordinate plane as the original function.

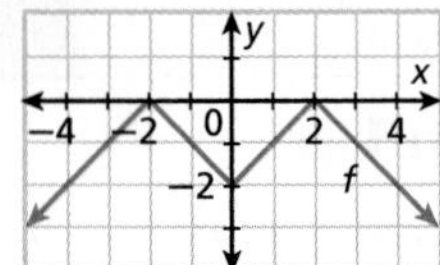

A. translation 2 units up

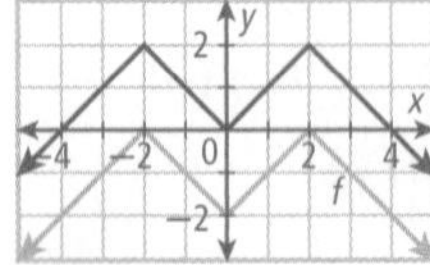

B. reflection across x-axis

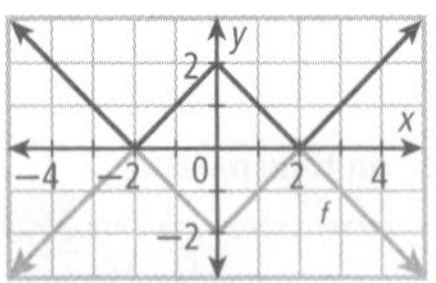

Also available on transparency

INTERVENTION

Questioning Strategies

EXAMPLE 1

- To which direction does an x-coordinate change correspond? a y-coordinate change?
- In **Example 1B,** does it matter if you go up/down or left/right first?

EXAMPLE 2

- What are the important points?
- Which coordinates change under a reflection across the y-axis? the x-axis?

A **reflection** is a transformation that flips a figure across a line called the line of reflection. Each reflected point is the same distance from the line of reflection, but on the opposite side of the line.

Reflections	
Reflection Across y-axis	**Reflection Across x-axis**
Each point flips across the y-axis.	Each point flips across the x-axis.
(−1, 2) (1, 2) 1 unit 1 unit — The x-coordinate changes. $(1, 2) \rightarrow (-1, 2)$ $(x, y) \rightarrow (-x, y)$	(1, 2) 2 units 2 units (1, −2) — The y-coordinate changes. $(1, 2) \rightarrow (1, -2)$ $(x, y) \rightarrow (x, -y)$

You can transform a function by transforming its ordered pairs. When a function is translated or reflected, the original graph and the graph of the transformation are *congruent* because the size and shape of the graphs are the same.

EXAMPLE 2 Translating and Reflecting Functions

Use a table to perform each transformation of $y = f(x)$. Use the same coordinate plane as the original function.

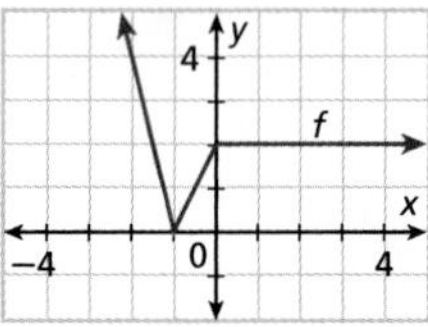

A translation 2 units down

Identify important points from the graph and make a table.

x	y	$y - 2$
−2	4	$4 - 2 = 2$
−1	0	$0 - 2 = -2$
0	2	$2 - 2 = 0$
2	2	$2 - 2 = 0$

The entire graph shifts 2 units down. Subtract 2 from each y-coordinate.

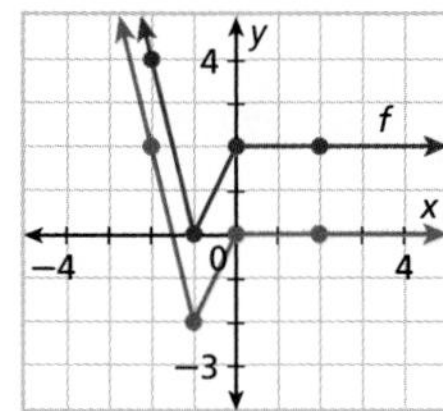

Helpful Hint

Transform x by adding a table column on the left side; transform y by adding a column on the right side.

B reflection across y-axis

Identify important points from the graph and make a table.

$-x$	x	y
$-1(-2) = 2$	−2	4
$-1(-1) = 1$	−1	0
$-1(0) = 0$	0	2
$-1(2) = -2$	2	2

Multiply each x-coordinate by −1. The entire graph flips across the y-axis.

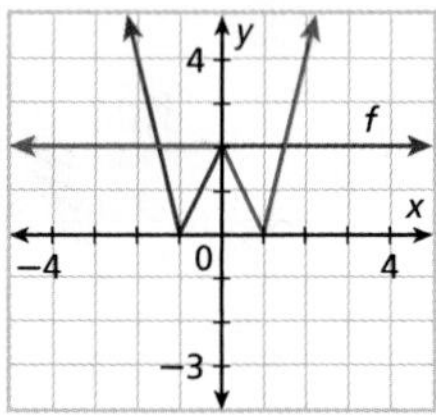

CHECK IT OUT! **For the function from Example 2, use a table to perform each transformation of $y = f(x)$. Use the same coordinate plane as the original function.**

2a. translation 3 units right **2b.** reflection across x-axis

2 Teach

Guided Instruction

In this lesson students will translate points and transform functions. Demonstrate how students can transform functions by choosing important points on the function's graph and then transforming them. As you lead students through the examples, help them identify which types of transformations are congruent to the graph of the original function and which are not.

Reaching All Learners

Through Modeling

Give each student or small group a twist tie or a small piece of wire that can be bent into a shape. Have them place the wire on a piece of graph paper and trace it. Then instruct them to translate the function 2 units up and trace again. Repeat this with several different transformations.

Imagine grasping two points on the graph of a function that lie on opposite sides of the y-axis. If you pull the points away from the y-axis, you would create a horizontal **stretch** of the graph. If you push the points towards the y-axis, you would create a horizontal **compression**.

Stretches and compressions are not congruent to the original graph.

Stretches and Compressions

	Horizontal	Vertical
Stretch	Each point is *pulled away* from the y-axis. The x-coordinate changes. $(4, 0) \rightarrow (2(4), 0)$ $(x, y) \rightarrow (bx, y)$ $\lvert b \rvert > 1$	Each point is *pulled away* from the x-axis. The y-coordinate changes. $(0, 4) \rightarrow (0, 2(4))$ $(x, y) \rightarrow (x, ay)$ $\lvert a \rvert > 1$
Compression	Each point is *pushed toward* the y-axis. The x-coordinate changes. $(4, 0) \rightarrow \left(\frac{1}{2}(4), 0\right)$ $(x, y) \rightarrow (bx, y)$ $0 < \lvert b \rvert < 1$	Each point is *pushed toward* the x-axis. The y-coordinate changes. $(0, 4) \rightarrow \left(0, \frac{1}{2}(4)\right)$ $(x, y) \rightarrow (x, ay)$ $0 < \lvert a \rvert < 1$

EXAMPLE 3 Stretching and Compressing Functions

Use a table to perform a horizontal compression of $y = f(x)$ by a factor of $\frac{1}{2}$. Use the same coordinate plane as the original function.

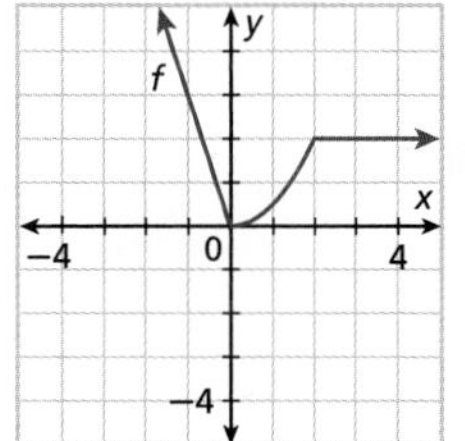

Identify important points from the graph and make a table.

$\frac{1}{2}x$	x	y
$\frac{1}{2}(-1) = -\frac{1}{2}$	−1	3
$\frac{1}{2}(0) = 0$	0	0
$\frac{1}{2}(2) = 1$	2	2
$\frac{1}{2}(4) = 2$	4	2

Multiply each x-coordinate by $\frac{1}{2}$.

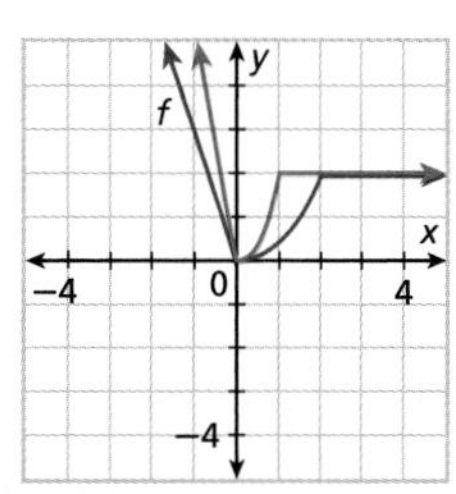

3. For the function from Example 3, use a table to perform a vertical stretch of $y = f(x)$ by a factor of 2. Graph the transformed function on the same coordinate plane as the original function.

COMMON ERROR ALERT

Students may have difficulty choosing the important points to consider when transforming a function. Emphasize that the important points are the ones that provide the most information about the shape of a function's graph and usually are the ones where the graph "turns."

Power Presentations with PowerPoint®

Additional Examples

Example 3

Use a table to perform a horizontal stretch of the function $y = f(x)$ (graphed on p. 61) by a factor of 3. Graph the function and the transformation on the same coordinate plane.

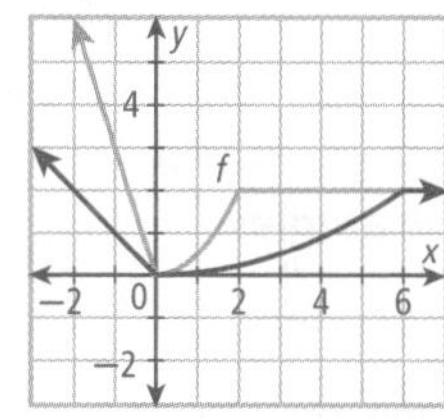

Also available on transparency

INTERVENTION

Questioning Strategies

EXAMPLE 3

- Which coordinate changes under a horizontal stretch or compression? under a vertical stretch or compression?
- How does a horizontal stretch differ from a vertical stretch?

Answers to *Check It Out!*

2a.

$x + 3$	x	y
1	−2	4
2	−1	0
3	0	2
5	2	2

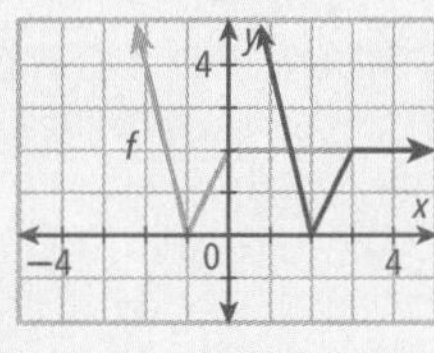

2b.

x	y	$-y$
−2	4	−4
−1	0	0
0	2	−2
2	2	−2

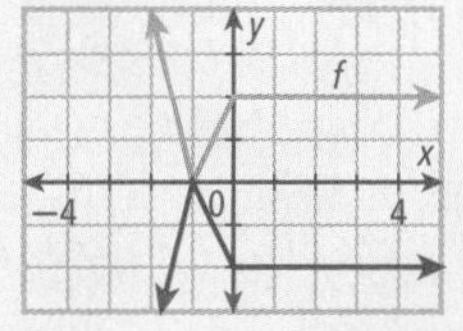

3.

x	y	$2y$
−1	3	6
0	0	0
2	2	4
4	2	4

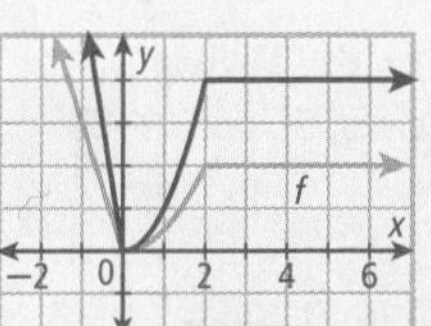

Power Presentations with PowerPoint®

Additional Examples

Example 4

The graph shows the cost of painting based on the number of cans of paint used. Sketch a graph to represent the cost of a can of paint doubling, and identify the transformation of the original graph that it represents.

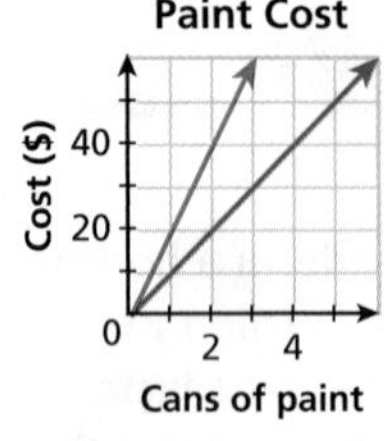

vertical stretch by a factor of 2

Also available on transparency

INTERVENTION

Questioning Strategies

EXAMPLE 4

- How can you use the original graph to perform a vertical stretch?

Answers to *Check It Out!*

4. vertical compression by a factor of $\frac{3}{4}$

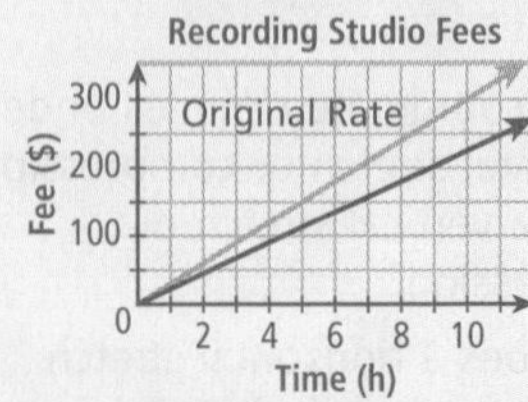

EXAMPLE 4 ***Business Application***

Recording studio fees are usually based on an hourly rate, but the rate can be modified due to various options. The graph shows a basic hourly studio rate. Sketch a graph to represent each situation below and identify the transformation of the original graph that it represents.

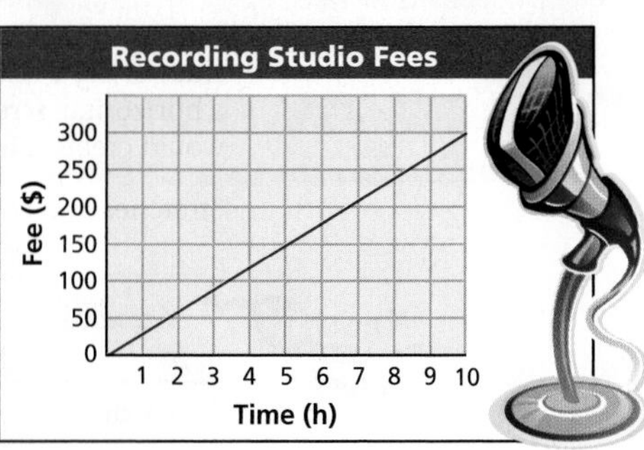

A **The engineer's time is needed, so the hourly rate is 1.5 times the original rate.**

If the fees are 1.5 times the basic hourly rate, the value of each *y*-coordinate would be multiplied by 1.5. This represents a vertical stretch by a factor of 1.5.

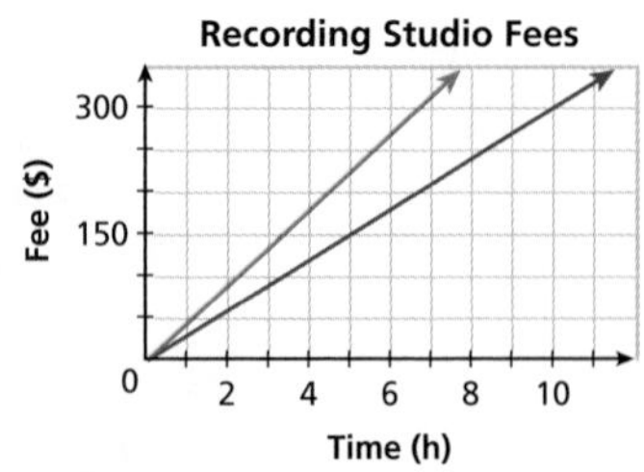

B **A $20 setup fee is added to the basic hourly rate.**

If the prices are $20 more than the original estimate, the value of each *y*-coordinate would increase by 20. This represents a vertical translation up 20 units.

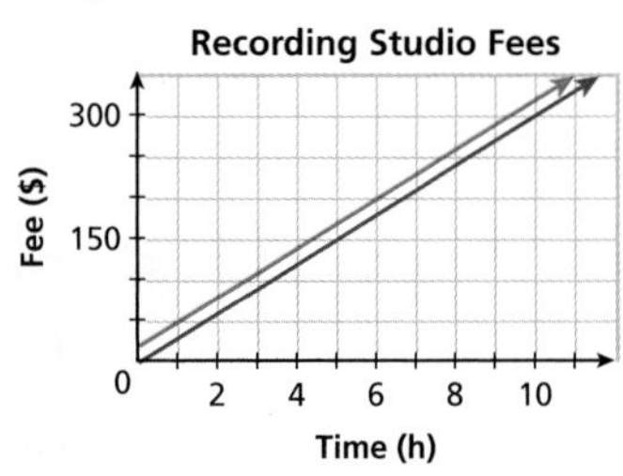

4. **What if...?** Suppose that a discounted rate is $\frac{3}{4}$ of the original rate. Sketch a graph to represent the situation and identify the transformation of the original graph that it represents.

THINK AND DISCUSS

1. Describe two ways to transform (4, 2) to (2, 2).
2. Compare a vertical stretch with a horizontal compression.
3. **GET ORGANIZED** Copy and complete the graphic organizer. In each box, describe the transformations indicated by the given rule.

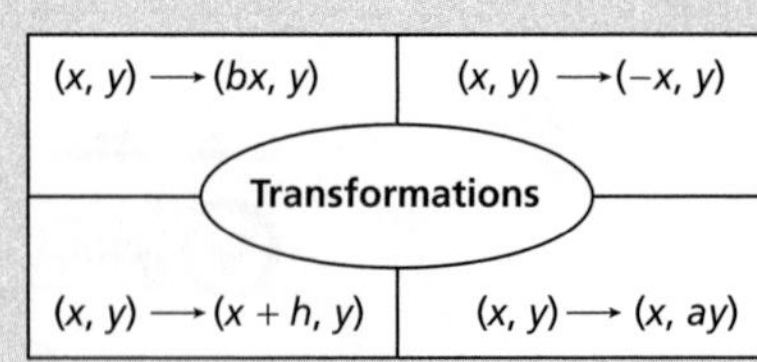

ONGOING ASSESSMENT

and INTERVENTION

***Diagnose Before* the Lesson**
1-8 Warm Up, TE p. 59

***Monitor During* the Lesson**
Check It Out! Exercises, SE pp. 59–62
Questioning Strategies, TE pp. 60–62

***Assess After* the Lesson**
1-8 Lesson Quiz, TE p. 65
Alternative Assessment, TE p. 65

3 Close

Summarize

Sketch the graph of a function. Draw sketches of the same function after it has been translated, reflected, stretched, and compressed.

Answers to *Think and Discuss*

Possible answers:

1. translation 2 units left or horizontal compression by a factor of $\frac{1}{2}$
2. Both squeeze the graph toward the *y*-axis. In a vertical stretch, the *y*-coordinates change. In a horizontal compression, the *x*-coordinates change.
3. See p. A2.

1-8 Exercises

go.hrw.com
Homework Help Online
KEYWORD: MB7 1-8
Parent Resources Online
KEYWORD: MB7 Parent

GUIDED PRACTICE

1. **Vocabulary** A transformation that pushes a graph toward the x-axis is a __?__. (*reflection* or *compression*) compression

SEE EXAMPLE 1 p. 59

Perform the given translation on the point $(4, 2)$ and give the coordinates of the translated point.

2. 5 units left $(-1, 2)$
3. 3 units down $(4, -1)$
4. 1 unit right, 6 units up $(5, 8)$

SEE EXAMPLE 2 p. 60

Use a table to perform each transformation of $y = f(x)$. Use the same coordinate plane as the original function.

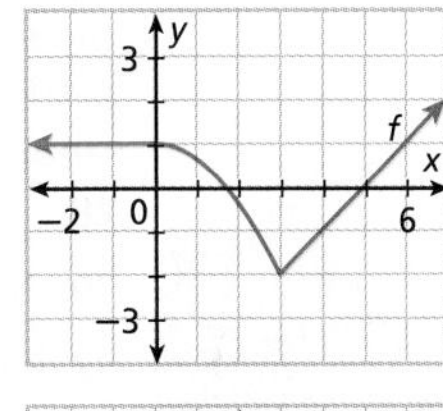

5. translation 2 units up
6. reflection across the y-axis
7. reflection across the x-axis

SEE EXAMPLE 3 p. 61

Use a table to perform each transformation of $y = f(x)$. Use the same coordinate plane as the original function.

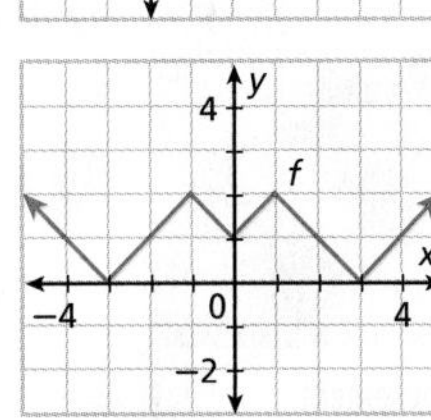

8. horizontal stretch by a factor of 3
9. vertical stretch by a factor of 3
10. vertical compression by a factor of $\frac{1}{3}$

SEE EXAMPLE 4 p. 62

Recreation **The graph shows the price for admission by age at a local zoo. Sketch a graph to represent each situation and identify the transformation of the original graph that it represents.**

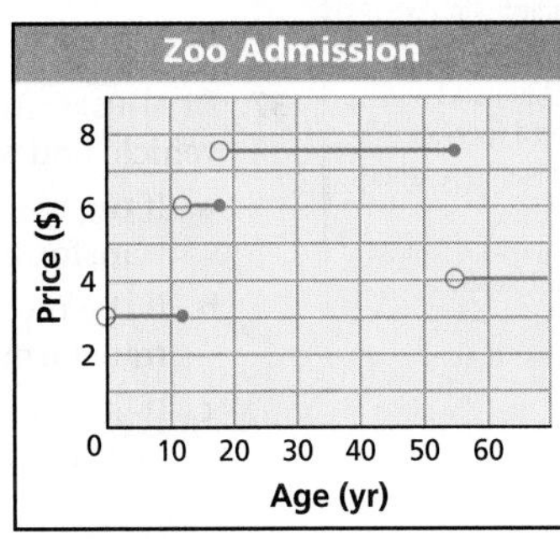

11. Admission is half price on Wednesdays.
12. To raise funds for endangered species, the zoo charges \$1.50 extra per ticket.
13. The maximum age for each ticket price is increased by 5 years.

PRACTICE AND PROBLEM SOLVING

Independent Practice	
For Exercises	See Example
14–16	1
17–20	2
21–24	3
25–27	4

Extra Practice
Skills Practice p. S5
Application Practice p. S32

Perform the given translation on $(3, 1)$. Give the coordinates of the translated point.

14. 2 units right $(5, 1)$
15. 4 units up $(3, 5)$
16. 5 units left, 4 units down $(-2, -3)$

Use a table to perform each transformation of $y = f(x)$. Use the same coordinate plane as the original function.

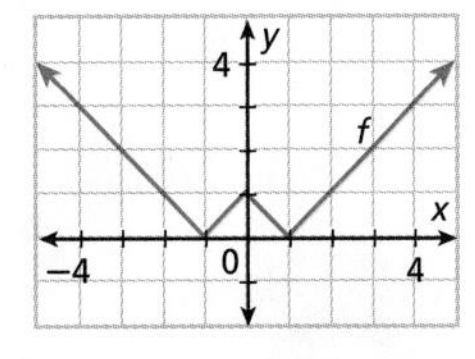

17. translation 2 units down
18. reflection across the x-axis
19. translation 3 units right
20. reflection across the y-axis
21. vertical compression by a factor of $\frac{2}{3}$
22. horizontal compression by a factor of $\frac{1}{2}$
23. horizontal stretch by a factor of $\frac{3}{2}$
24. vertical stretch by a factor of 2

Answers

7.

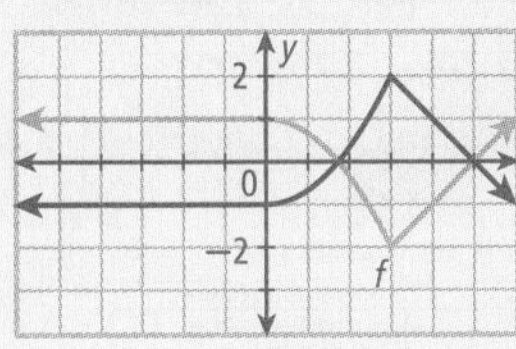

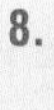

8.

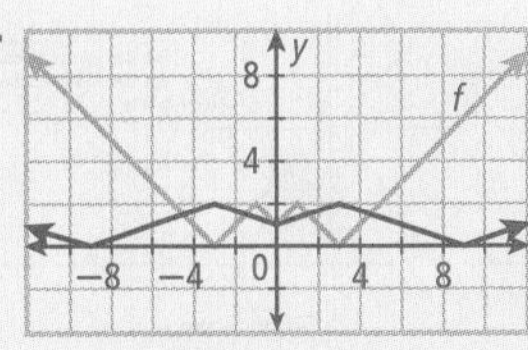

9.

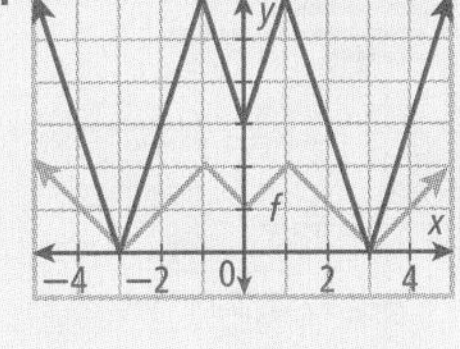

10.

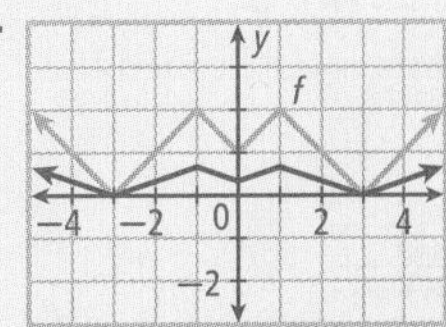

11–13. See p. A15
17–24. See p. A15

1-8 Exercises

Assignment Guide

Assign *Guided Practice* exercises as necessary.

If you finished Examples **1–2**
Basic 14–20, 28–29
Average 14–20, 28–29, 52
Advanced 14–20, 28–29, 52, 54

If you finished Examples **1–4**
Basic 14–31, 37–41, 45–51, 55–61
Average 14–41, 44–52, 54–61
Advanced 14–61

Homework Quick Check
Quickly check key concepts.
Exercises: 16, 18, 20, 24, 26, 40, 42

Answers

5–10. Table values will vary.

5.

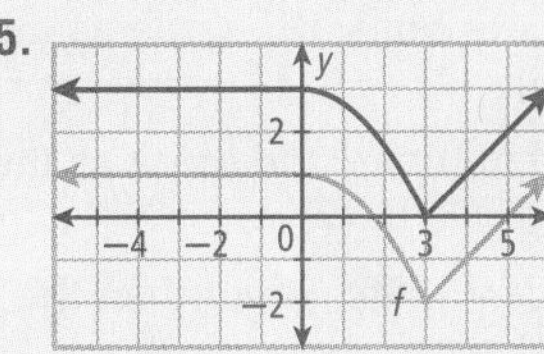

6.

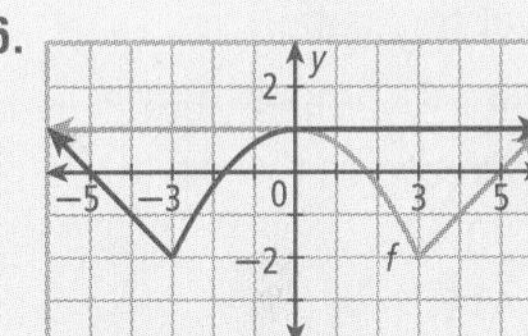

State Resources

go.hrw.com
State Resources Online
KEYWORD: MB7 Resources

Exercise 38 involves comparing functions by transforming them. This exercise prepares students for the Multi-Step Test Prep on page 74.

Reading Math Clues about the answers to **Exercises 31, 32,** and **35** are provided by the language used. A *compression* will reduce the size of an object, while a *stretch* will increase its size.

ENGLISH LANGUAGE LEARNERS

Answers

25–27. See p. A15.

28. 10 square units; the same as the original
29. 10 square units; the same as the original
30. 20 square units; larger than the original
31. 7 square units; smaller than the original
32. 7 square units; smaller than the original
33. 10 square units; the same as the original
34. 10 square units; the same as the original
35. 30 square units; larger than the original

37a. vertical translation

b. horizontal compression

c. the increase in the per-hour labor rate

38. See p. A15.

Technology The graph shows the cost of Web page hosting depending on the Web space used. Sketch a graph to represent each situation and identify the transformation of the original graph that it represents.

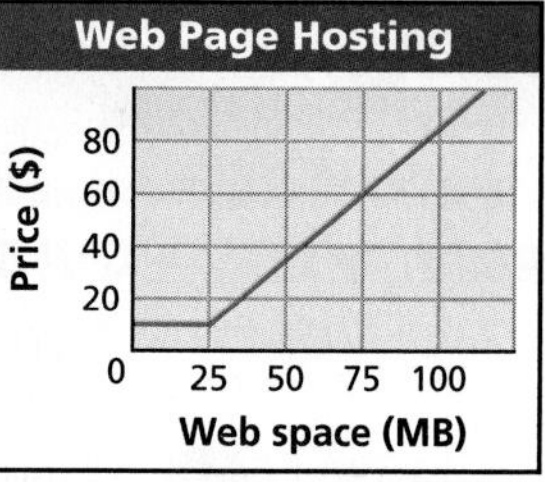

25. The prices are reduced by \$5.
26. The prices are discounted by 25%.
27. A special is offered for double the amount of Web space for the same price.

Estimation The table gives the coordinates for the vertices of a triangle. Estimate the area of each transformed triangle by graphing it and counting the number of squares it covers on the coordinate plane. How does the area of each transformed triangle compare with the area of the original triangle?

x	y
−2	2
2	−4
4	−2

28. reflection across the y-axis
29. 5 units left, 3 units up
30. horizontal stretch by a factor of 2
31. horizontal compression by a factor of $\frac{2}{3}$
32. vertical compression by a factor of $\frac{2}{3}$
33. reflection across the x-axis
34. 1 unit left, 6 units down
35. vertical stretch by a factor of 3

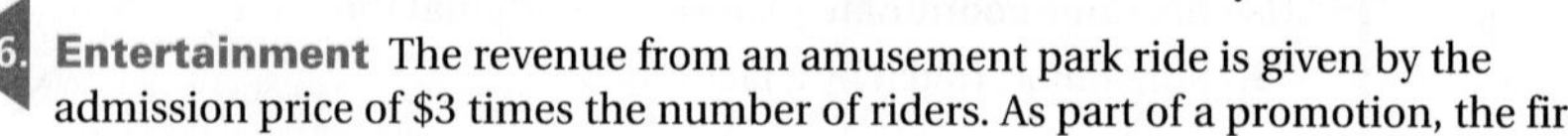

LINK Entertainment

The amusement park industry in the United States includes about 700 parks and accounted for over \$8.5 billion in revenues in 2001.
Source: Statistical Abstract of the United States

36. **Entertainment** The revenue from an amusement park ride is given by the admission price of \$3 times the number of riders. As part of a promotion, the first 10 riders ride for free.
    a. What kind of transformation describes the change in the revenue based on the promotion? **a horizontal shift 10 units right or a vertical shift 30 units down**
    b. Write a function rule for this transformation. **possible answer: $f(x) = 3(x - 10)$**

37. **Business** An automotive mechanic charges \$50 to diagnose the problem in a vehicle and \$65 per hour for labor to fix it.
    a. If the mechanic increases his diagnostic fee to \$60, what kind of transformation is this to the graph of the total repair bill?
    b. If the mechanic increases his labor rate to \$75 per hour, what kind of transformation is this to the graph of the total repair bill?
    c. If it took 3 hours to repair your car, which of the two rate increases would have a greater effect on your total bill?

MULTI-STEP TEST PREP

38. This problem will prepare you for the Multi-Step Test Prep on page 74.
    The student council wants to buy vases for the flowers for the school prom. A florist charges a \$20 delivery fee plus \$1.25 per vase. A home-decorating store charges a \$10 delivery fee plus \$1.25 per vase.
    a. The function $f(x) = 20 + 1.25x$ models the cost of ordering x vases from the florist, and the function $g(x) = 10 + 1.25x$ models the cost of ordering x vases from the home-decorating store. What do the graphs of these functions look like?
    b. How are the graphs related to each other?
    c. How could you modify these functions so that their graphs are identical?
    d. If the florist decided to waive the \$20 delivery fee as long as the number of vases ordered was more than 150, how would the graph of f change? How would it compare with the graph of the other function?

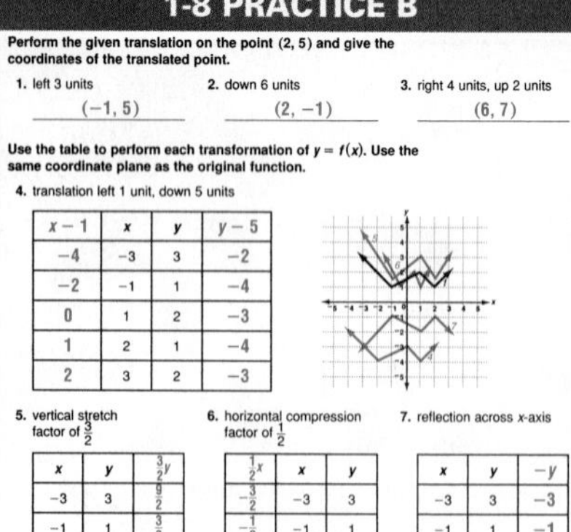

1-8 PRACTICE A

1-8 PRACTICE C

1-8 PRACTICE B

Perform the given translation on the point (2, 5) and give the coordinates of the translated point.

1. left 3 units (−1, 5)
2. down 6 units (2, −1)
3. right 4 units, up 2 units (6, 7)

Use the table to perform each transformation of $y = f(x)$. Use the same coordinate plane as the original function.

4. translation left 1 unit, down 5 units

$x - 1$	x	y	$y - 5$
−4	−3	3	−2
−2	−1	1	−4
0	1	2	−3
1	2	1	−4
2	3	2	−3

5. vertical stretch factor of $\frac{3}{2}$

x	y	$\frac{3}{2}y$
−3	3	$\frac{9}{2}$
−1	1	$\frac{3}{2}$
1	2	3
2	1	$\frac{3}{2}$
3	2	3

6. horizontal compression factor of $\frac{1}{2}$

$\frac{1}{2}x$	x	y
$-\frac{3}{2}$	−3	3
$-\frac{1}{2}$	−1	1
$\frac{1}{2}$	1	2
1	2	1
$\frac{3}{2}$	3	2

7. reflection across x-axis

x	y	$-y$
−3	3	−3
−1	1	−1
1	2	−2
2	1	−1
3	2	−2

Solve.

8. George has a goal for the number of computers he wants to sell each month for the next 6 months at his computer store. He draws a graph to show his projected profits for that period. Then he decides to discount the prices by 10%. How will this affect his profits? Identify the transformation to his graph and describe how to find the ordered pairs for the transformation.
Profits are reduced by 10%; vertical compression; $(x, 0.9y)$.

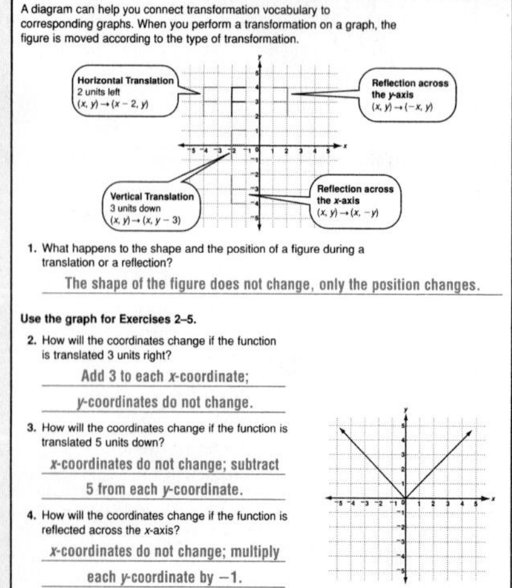

1-8 READING STRATEGIES

A diagram can help you connect transformation vocabulary to corresponding graphs. When you perform a transformation on a graph, the figure is moved according to the type of transformation.

1. What happens to the shape and the position of a figure during a translation or a reflection?
The shape of the figure does not change, only the position changes.

Use the graph for Exercises 2–5.

2. How will the coordinates change if the function is translated 3 units right?
Add 3 to each x-coordinate; y-coordinates do not change.
3. How will the coordinates change if the function is translated 5 units down?
x-coordinates do not change; subtract 5 from each y-coordinate.
4. How will the coordinates change if the function is reflected across the x-axis?
x-coordinates do not change; multiply each y-coordinate by −1.
5. How will the coordinates change if the function is translated 4 units left and 2 units up?
Subtract 4 from each x-coordinate and add 2 to each y-coordinate.

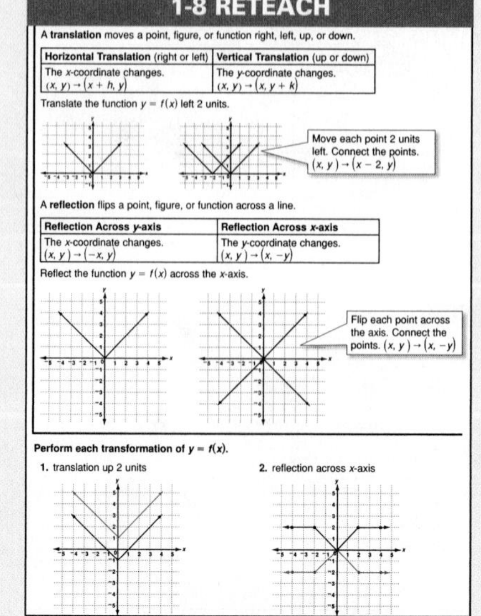

1-8 RETEACH

A **translation** moves a point, figure, or function right, left, up, or down.

Horizontal Translation (right or left)	**Vertical Translation** (up or down)
The x-coordinate changes. $(x, y) \to (x + h, y)$	The y-coordinate changes. $(x, y) \to (x, y + k)$

Translate the function $y = f(x)$ left 2 units.

A **reflection** flips a point, figure, or function across a line.

Reflection Across y-axis	**Reflection Across x-axis**
The x-coordinate changes. $(x, y) \to (-x, y)$	The y-coordinate changes. $(x, y) \to (x, -y)$

Reflect the function $y = f(x)$ across the x-axis.

Perform each transformation of $y = f(x)$.

1. translation up 2 units
2. reflection across x-axis

Transportation Use the graph and the following information for Exercises 39–43.

Roberta left her house at 10:00 A.M. and drove to the library. She was at the library studying until 11:30 A.M. Then she drove to the grocery store. At 12:15 P.M. Roberta left the grocery store and drove home. The graph shows Roberta's position with respect to time.

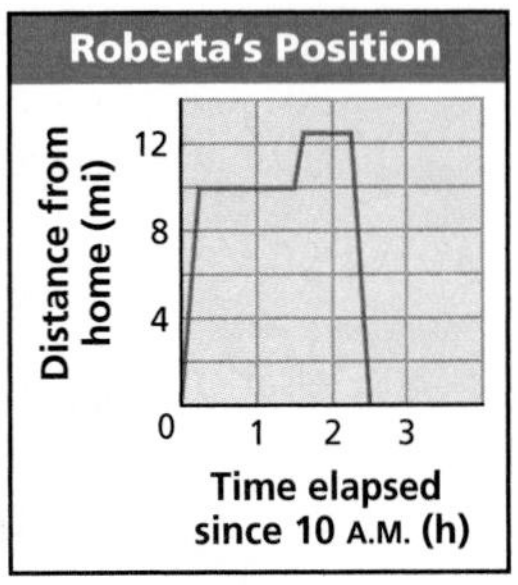

Roberta's Position

Distance from home (mi): 0, 4, 8, 12

Time elapsed since 10 A.M. (h): 1, 2, 3

Sketch a graph to reflect each change to the original story. Assume the time Roberta spends inside each building remains the same.

39. Roberta drove at half the speed from her house to the library.

40. The grocery store she went to is twice as far from the library.

41. The grocery store is 2.5 miles closer to the house than the library is.

Change the original story about Roberta to match each graph.

42.

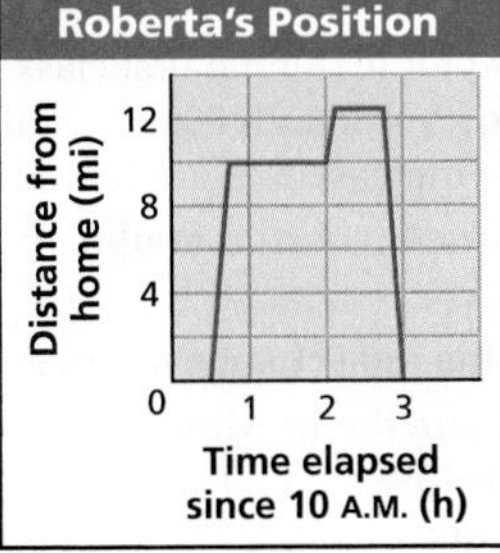

43.

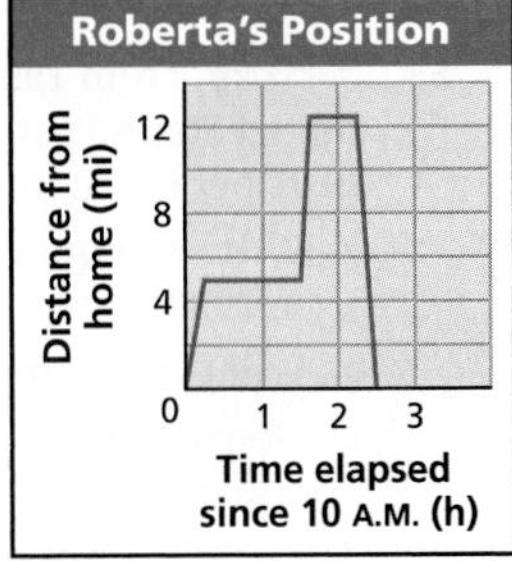

44. Critical Thinking Suppose two transformations are performed on a single point: a translation and a reflection. Does the order in which the transformations are performed make a difference? Does the type of translation or reflection matter? Explain your reasoning.

45. Write About It Describe how transformations might make graphing easier.

46. The function $c(p) = 0.99p$ represents the cost in dollars of p pounds of peaches. If the cost per pound increases by 10%, how will the graph of the function change?

- (A) Translation 0.1 unit up
- (B) Translation 0.1 unit right
- (C) Horizontal stretch by a factor of 1.1
- ((D)) Vertical stretch by a factor of 1.1

47. Which transformation would change the point $(5, 3)$ into $(-5, 3)$?

- (F) Reflection across the x-axis
- (G) Translation 5 units down
- ((H)) Reflection across the y-axis
- (J) Translation 5 units left

48. The graph of the function f is a line that intersects the y-axis at the point $(0, 3)$ and the x-axis at the point $(3, 0)$. Which transformation of f does NOT intersect the y-axis at the point $(0, 6)$?

- (A) Translation 3 units up
- (B) Translation 3 units right
- (C) Vertical stretch by a factor of 2
- ((D)) Horizontal compression by a factor of $\frac{1}{2}$

1-8 PROBLEM SOLVING

Harry is working on a budget for a concert. The graph shows the total cost of renting the hall. A cleaning fee of $40 for each rental is included in the graph. Use the graph for Exercises 1–6.

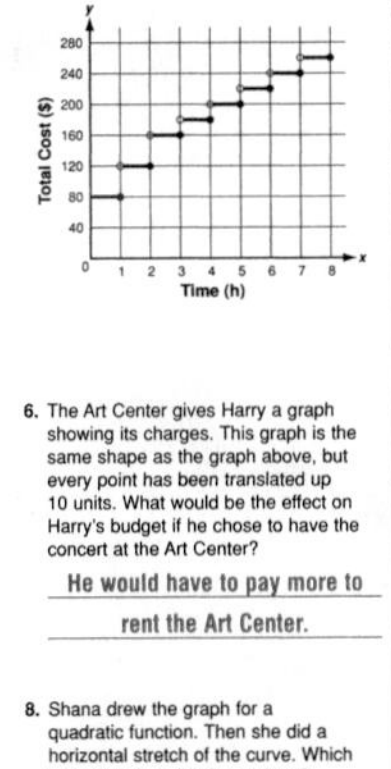

1. What is the cost of renting the hall for 2 hours? for 3 hours? for 6 hours? for 7 hours?

   $120; $160; $220; $240

2. What is the rate per hour not including the cleaning fee if Harry rents the hall for up to 3 hours?

   $40 per hour

3. What is the rate per hour after the first 3 hours?

   $20 per hour

4. Describe the effect on the graph if the cleaning fee were changed to $25.

   Translated down 15 units

5. The managers decide that the minimum time for which the hall can be rented is 3 hours. Describe the effect this change would have on the graph above. How would the range change?

   Possible answers: A line would go from $(0, 160)$ to $(3, 160)$ with no open circle; the range would not include any numbers less than 160.

6. The Art Center gives Harry a graph showing its charges. This graph is the same shape as the graph above, but every point has been translated up 10 units. What would be the effect on Harry's budget if he chose to have the concert at the Art Center?

   He would have to pay more to rent the Art Center.

Choose the letter for the best answer.

7. Martha's profits from her bagel store last year were $0.35 per dozen bagels sold. This year her profits decreased 10%. What kind of transformation does this represent?

   (A) vertical compression
   B vertical stretch
   C horizontal compression
   D horizontal stretch

8. Shana drew the graph for a quadratic function. Then she did a horizontal stretch of the curve. Which transformation did she perform?

   F $(x, y) \to (x, ay); |a| > 1$
   G $(x, y) \to (bx, y); 0 < |b| < 1$
   H $(x, y) \to (x, ay); 0 < |a| < 1$
   (J) $(x, y) \to (bx, y); |b| > 1$

1-8 CHALLENGE

Translations and reflections are transformations in the position of a figure. A third transformation that preserves congruence is called a **rotation**. Point A is at $(4, 0)$. Move point A along the semicircle 90° in a counterclockwise direction. The rotated point has coordinates $(0, 4)$. This is called a rotation of 90° counterclockwise centered at the origin.

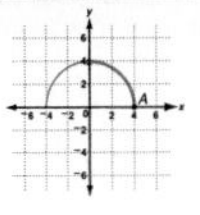

Use the graph at right for Exercises 1–6.

Rotate figure $EFGH$ 90° clockwise through the origin.

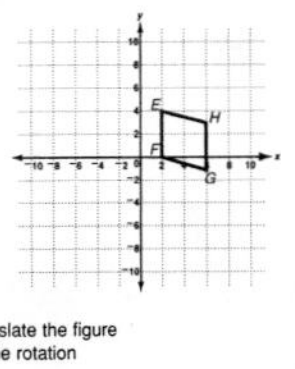

1. What are the coordinates of the vertices of the rotated figure?

   $(4, -2), (0, -2), (-1, -6), (3, -6)$

2. Write a general rule to show the result of rotating a point 90° clockwise through the origin.

   $(x, y) \to (y, -x)$

3. Write a general rule to show the result of rotating a point 90° counterclockwise through the origin.

   $(x, y) \to (-y, x)$

To rotate a figure through a point other than the origin, translate the figure so that the point of rotation is at the origin. Then perform the rotation through the origin. Finally, reverse the translation.

Rotate quadrilateral $EFGH$ counterclockwise 90° through the point $(2, 0)$. First translate the quadrilateral 2 units left to move the point of rotation, $(2, 0)$, to the origin.

4. What are the coordinates of the vertices of the translated quadrilateral?

   $(0, 4), (0, 0), (4, -1), (4, 3)$

Now, rotate the translated quadrilateral 90° counterclockwise through the origin.

5. What are the coordinates of the vertices of the rotated quadrilateral?

   $(-4, 0), (0, 0), (1, 4), (-3, 4)$

Finally, reverse the translation by moving the quadrilateral 2 units right.

6. What are the coordinates of the vertices of the final quadrilateral?

   $(-2, 0), (2, 0), (3, 4), (-1, 4)$

In **Exercise 47,** students having difficulty solving the problem algebraically can plot the points. A graph will help many students find the correct choice.

Exercise 50 requires careful reading. Choices **A** and **B** are translations 4 units *left,* and **C** is a translation 2 units *up.*

Answers

39.

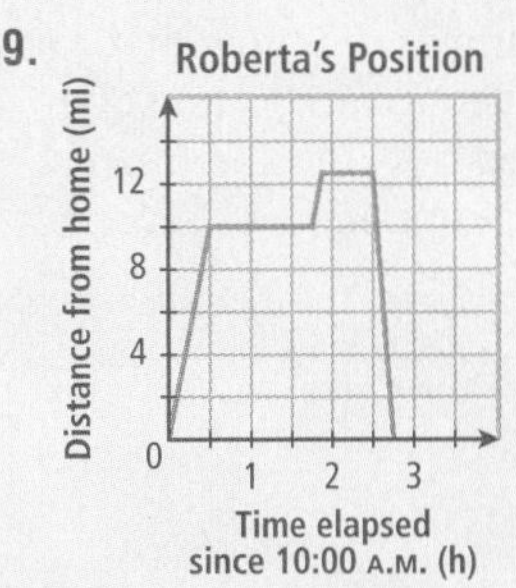

40.

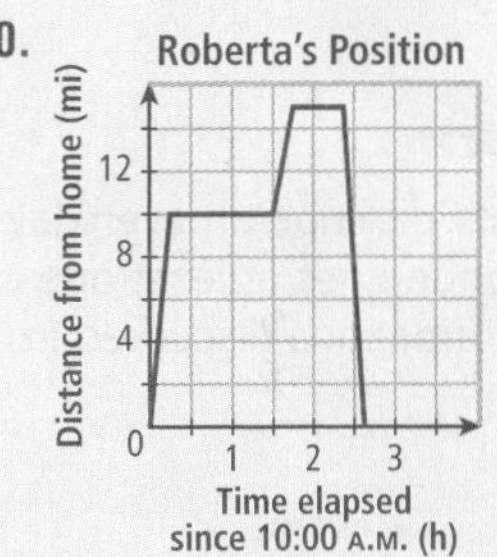

41.

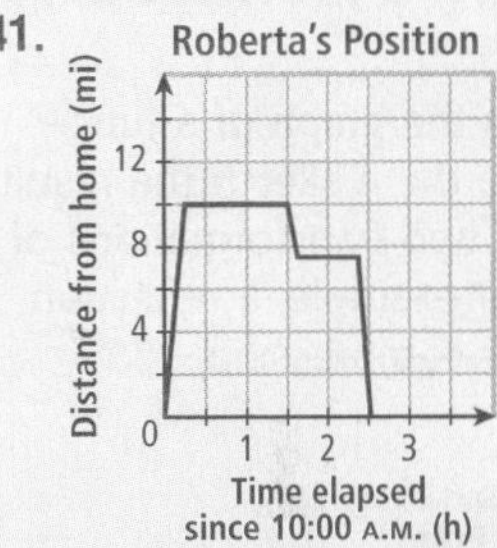

42. Roberta started half an hour later.

43. The library is half as far from Roberta's house.

44. Possible answer: Order is important in these transformations: horizontal translation and reflection across the y-axis; vertical translation and reflection across the x-axis. Order is not important in these transformations: horizontal translation and reflection across the x-axis; vertical translation and reflection across the y-axis.

45. Possible answer: You might not need to make a table of values to graph a transformation of a function. For example, if the graph of a function is translated 2 units right, you can graph the transformation by shifting each point on the graph of the original function 2 units right.

Answers

53a. $c(n) = 0.37n$

b. vertical stretch

c.

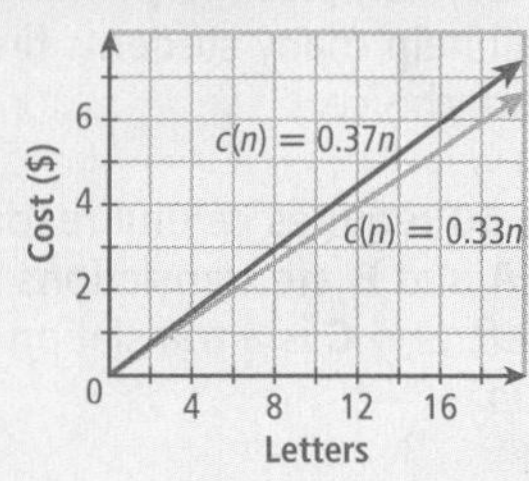

15 in 1999 and 13 in 2002

d. The number of letters that can be mailed for $5.00 must be rounded down to the nearest whole number.

Journal

Have students describe an everyday object that undergoes at least one of the transformations discussed in the lesson.

Alternative Assessment

Give students the graph of a function and have them sketch the result of a series of two transformations of this graph, for example, a reflection followed by a compression.

Power Presentations with PowerPoint®

1-8 Lesson Quiz

1. Translate the point (4, −6) 6 units right and 7 units up. Give the coordinates of the translated point. (10, 1)

Use a table to perform the transformation of $y = f(x)$. Graph the function and the transformation on the same coordinate plane.

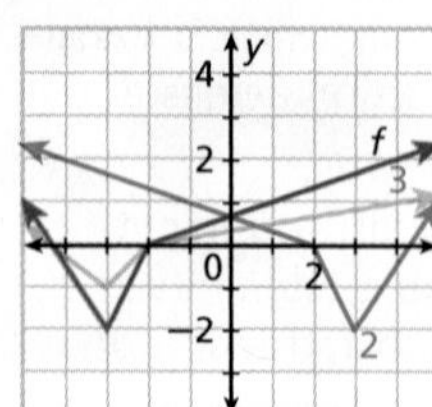

2. reflection across y-axis

3. vertical compression by a factor of $\frac{1}{2}$

Also available on transparency

49. Which transformation is displayed in the graph?

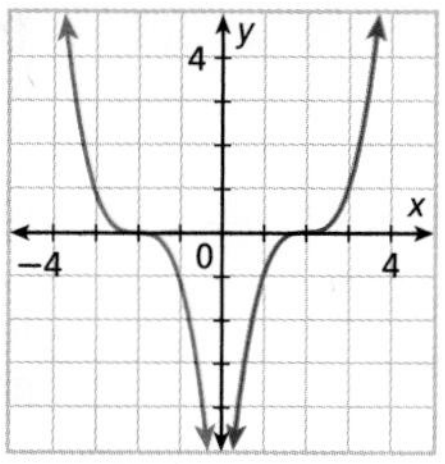

Ⓕ Reflection across the x-axis

Ⓖ Translation 5 units down

Ⓗ Reflection across the y-axis (circled)

Ⓙ Translation 5 units left

50. Which represents a translation 4 units right and 2 units down?

Ⓐ From (4, 2) to (0, 0)

Ⓑ From (4, −2) to (0, 0)

Ⓒ From (−4, −2) to (0, 0)

Ⓓ From (−4, 2) to (0, 0) (circled)

51. Short Response Graph the points (−1, 3) and (−1, −3). Describe two different transformations that would transform (−1, 3) to (−1, −3).
Check students' graphs. Possible answer: Translate down 6 units, or reflect across the x-axis.

CHALLENGE AND EXTEND

52. Suppose the rule $(x, y) \rightarrow (2x, y - 3)$ is used to translate a point. If the coordinates of the translated point are (22, 7), what was the original point? **(11, 10)**

53. History From 1999 to 2001 the cost for mailing n first class letters through the United States Postal Service was $c(n) = 0.33n$. In 2001 the rate was increased by $0.01 per letter. In 2002 the rate was increased an additional $0.03 per letter.

a. Write an equation that represents the cost of mailing n first class letters in 2002.

b. What transformation describes the total change in price?

c. Graph both functions and estimate the maximum number of first class letters you could mail for $5.00 in both 1999 and 2002.

d. Explain the effect of the reasonable domain and range for these functions on your answer for part **c**.

54. Name a point that when reflected across the x-axis has the same coordinates as if it were reflected across the y-axis. How many points are there that satisfy this condition? **(0, 0) is the only point that satisfies this condition.**

SPIRAL REVIEW

55. Sports Katrina's mean bowling score for three games was 144. If the score of her first game was 172 and the score of her second game was 150, what was the score of her third game? *(Previous course)* **110**

Use the vertical-line test to determine whether each relation is a function. *(Lesson 1-6)*

56. 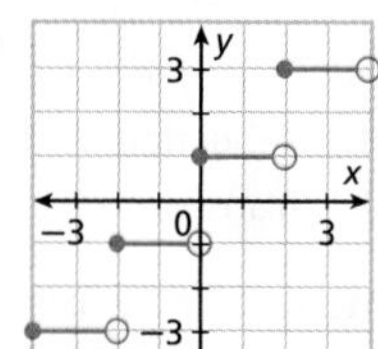 **yes**

57. 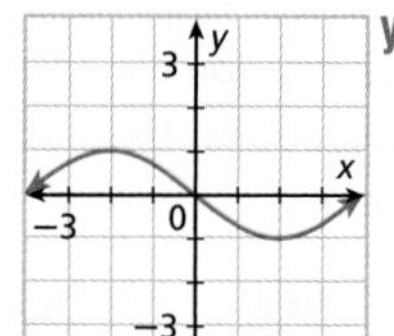 **yes**

58. 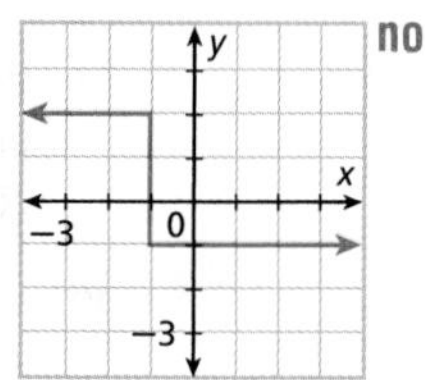 **no**

For each function evaluate $f(1)$, $f(-3)$, and $f\left(\frac{1}{4}\right)$. *(Lesson 1-7)*

59. $f(x) = \frac{4x - 5}{2}$ $-\frac{1}{2}$; $-\frac{17}{2}$; -2

60. $f(x) = 2x^3$ 2; −54; $\frac{1}{32}$

61. $f(x) = (1 - x^2)^2$ 0; 64; $\frac{225}{256}$

1-9 Introduction to Parent Functions

 **A2.1.2** Use and interpret function notation, including evaluation of functions represented by tables, graphs, words, equations or a set of ordered pairs.

Objectives
Identify parent functions from graphs and equations.

Use parent functions to model real-world data and make estimates for unknown values.

Vocabulary
parent function

Who uses this?
Oceanographers use transformations of parent functions to approximate data sets such as wave height versus wind speed. (See Example 3.)

Similar to the way that numbers are classified into sets based on common characteristics, functions can be classified into *families of functions*. The **parent function** is the simplest function with the defining characteristics of the family. Functions in the same family are transformations of their parent function.

Parent Functions

Family	Constant	Linear	Quadratic	Cubic	Square root
Rule	$f(x) = c$	$f(x) = x$	$f(x) = x^2$	$f(x) = x^3$	$f(x) = \sqrt{x}$
Graph					
Domain	$\mathbb{R}$	$\mathbb{R}$	$\mathbb{R}$	$\mathbb{R}$	$x \geq 0$
Range	$y = c$	$\mathbb{R}$	$y \geq 0$	$\mathbb{R}$	$y \geq 0$
Intersects y-axis	$(0, c)$	$(0, 0)$	$(0, 0)$	$(0, 0)$	$(0, 0)$

EXAMPLE 1 Identifying Transformations of Parent Functions

Identify the parent function for g from its function rule. Then graph g on your calculator and describe what transformation of the parent function it represents.

 $g(x) = x + 5$

$g(x) = x + 5$ is linear. *x has a power of 1.*

The linear parent function $f(x) = x$ intersects the y-axis at the point $(0, 0)$.

Graph $\mathbf{Y_1 = X + 5}$ on a graphing calculator. The function $g(x) = x + 5$ intersects the y-axis at the point $(0, 5)$.

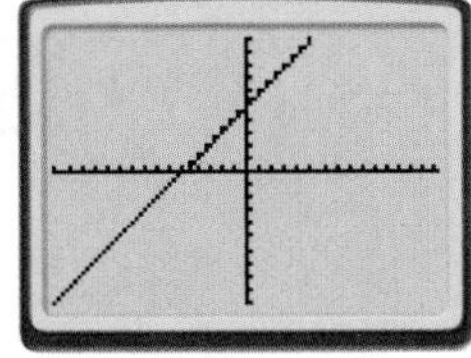

So $g(x) = x + 5$ represents a vertical translation of the linear parent function 5 units up.

Helpful Hint

To make graphs appear accurate on a graphing calculator, use the standard square window. Press ZOOM, choose **6:ZStandard**, press ZOOM again, and choose **5:ZSquare**.

1-9 Organizer

Pacing: Traditional 1 day
Block $\frac{1}{2}$ day

Objectives: Identify parent functions from graphs and equations.

Use parent functions to model real-world data and make estimates for unknown values.

Technology Lab
In Technology Lab Activities

Online Edition
Tutorial Videos, Graphing Calculator, Interactivity

Countdown to Testing Week 2

Power Presentations with PowerPoint®

Warm Up

1. For the power 3^5, identify the exponent and the base.
exponent: 5; base: 3

Evaluate.

2. $\left(\frac{2}{3}\right)^{-2}$ $\frac{9}{4}$

3. $f(9)$ when $f(x) = 2x + \sqrt{x}$ 21

Also available on transparency

Math Humor

Teacher: Why did your mother and father do your algebra homework?
Student: They really understand parent functions.

1 Introduce

EXPLORATION

Introduction to Parent Functions

Although there are an infinite number of functions, many functions can be grouped into families that have similar characteristics.

1. Use your calculator to graph y = x² by pressing [Y=], entering **Y1 = X²**, and pressing [GRAPH]. Describe the graph.
2. Enter and graph **Y2 = X² + 2**. Describe the graph of **Y2** as compared to the graph of **Y1**.
3. Enter and graph **Y3 = 2X²**. Compare this graph to the graphs from Problems 1 and 2.
4. Enter and graph **Y4 = 2X² − 6**. Compare this graph to the graphs above.
5. Make a conjecture about the shape of the graphs of functions of the form y = ax² + b.

THINK AND DISCUSS

6. **Explain** what the graphs of functions of the form y = mx + b look like.

Motivate

Draw the graph of the line $y = x$ on the board. Perform various transformations on the graph; for example, graph $y = -x$, $y = x + 3$, and $y = 3x$. Ask students to describe each new graph. They should begin to see that a line remains a line after each transformation. Explain that the set of lines can be thought of as a family, and the simplest line, $y = x$, is the parent function for the family.

Explorations and answers are provided in the *Explorations* binder.

State Resources

Power Presentations with PowerPoint®

Additional Examples

Example 1

Identify the parent function for g from its function rule. Then graph g on your calculator and describe what transformation of the parent function it represents.

A. $g(x) = x - 3$ linear; translation 3 units down

B. $g(x) = x^2 + 5$ quadratic; translation 5 units up

Example 2

Graph the data from this set of ordered pairs. Describe the parent function and the transformation that best approximates the data set.

$\{(-2, 12), (-1, 3), (0, 0), (1, 3), (2, 12)\}$

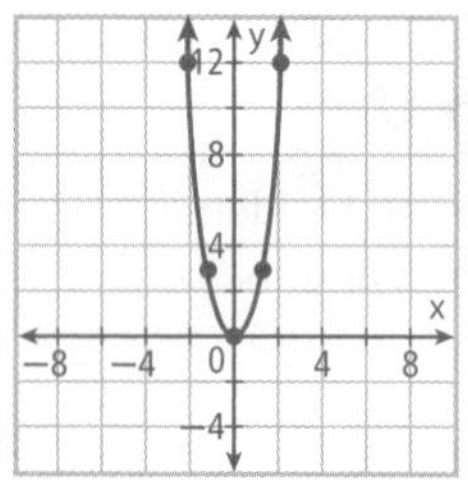

vertical stretch of the quadratic parent function by a factor of 3

Also available on transparency 

INTERVENTION
Questioning Strategies

EXAMPLE 1

- What part of the function rule tells you what the parent function is?

EXAMPLE 2

- What is the shape of the quadratic parent function?

Technology Unless otherwise noted, tick marks on the axes of graphing calculator screens shown in this course are 1 unit apart.

Answers to *Check It Out!*

2\.

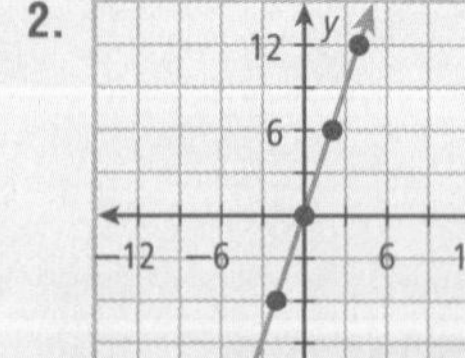

linear; vertical stretch by a factor of 3

Identify the parent function for g from its function rule. Then graph g on your calculator and describe what transformation of the parent function it represents.

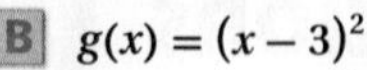

B $g(x) = (x - 3)^2$

$g(x) = (x - 3)^2$ is quadratic. *$x - 3$ has a power of 2.*

The quadratic parent function $f(x) = x^2$ intersects the x-axis at the point $(0, 0)$.

Graph $Y_1 = (X - 3)^2$ on a graphing calculator. The function $g(x) = (x - 3)^2$ intersects the x-axis at the point $(3, 0)$.

So $g(x) = (x - 3)^2$ represents a horizontal translation of the quadratic parent function 3 units right.

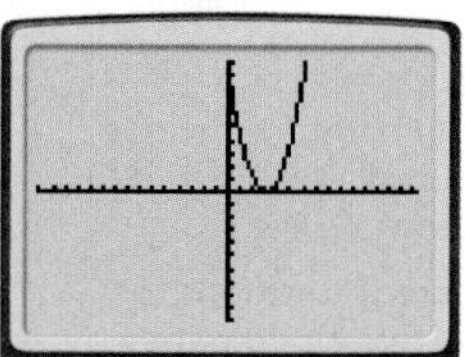

Identify the parent function for g from its function rule. Then graph g on your calculator and describe what transformation of the parent function it represents.

1a. $g(x) = x^3 + 2$ **cubic; translation 2 units up**

1b. $g(x) = (-x)^2$ **quadratic; reflection across the y-axis**

It is often necessary to work with a set of data points like the ones represented by the table at right.

x	−4	−2	0	2	4
y	8	2	0	2	8

With only the information in the table, it is impossible to know the exact behavior of the data between and beyond the given points. However, a working knowledge of the parent functions can allow you to sketch a curve to approximate those values not found in the table.

EXAMPLE 2 Identifying Parent Functions to Model Data Sets

Graph the data from the table. Describe the parent function and the transformation that best approximates the data set.

x	−4	−2	0	2	4
y	8	2	0	2	8

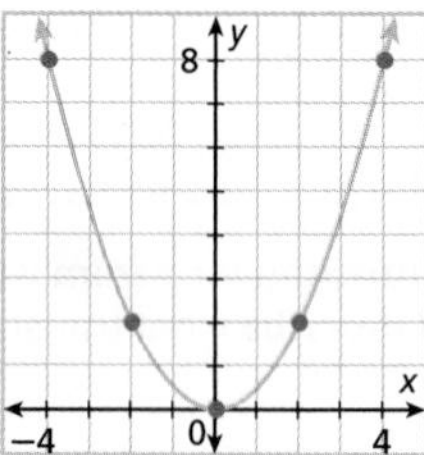

The graph of the data points resembles the shape of the quadratic parent function $f(x) = x^2$.

The quadratic parent function passes through the points $(2, 4)$ and $(4, 16)$. The data set contains the points

$(2, 2) = \left(2, \frac{1}{2}(4)\right)$ and $(4, 8) = \left(2, \frac{1}{2}(16)\right)$.

The data set seems to represent a vertical compression of the quadratic parent function by a factor of $\frac{1}{2}$.

2. Graph the data from the table. Describe the parent function and the transformation that best approximates the data set.

x	−4	−2	0	2	4
y	−12	−6	0	6	12

---

2 Teach

Guided Instruction

In this lesson, students apply their knowledge of transformations to investigate parent functions. Discuss how students can "group" functions that can be transformed into each other. Point out that it can be difficult to determine a parent function from a table of values. Emphasize that students should use a different representation, such as a graph, in order to determine the parent function more easily.

Reaching All Learners
Through Cooperative Learning

Have students work in pairs. One student in each pair should choose a function belonging to a family described in this lesson. This student should give his or her partner the coordinates of points that lie on the function's graph. The partner should plot these points one at a time until he or she can determine the parent function. As a class, discuss how many points had to be plotted before the parent functions could be determined.

Consider the two data points $(0, 0)$ and $(1, 1)$. If you plot them on a coordinate plane you might very well think that they are part of a linear function. In fact they belong to each of the parent functions below.

Linear	Quadratic	Cubic	Square Root
$f(x) = x$	$f(x) = x^2$	$f(x) = x^3$	$f(x) = \sqrt{x}$

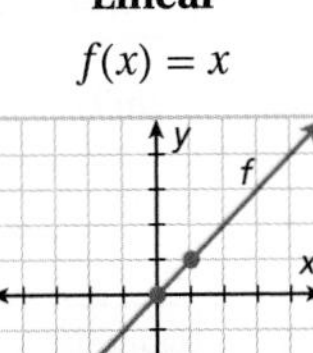

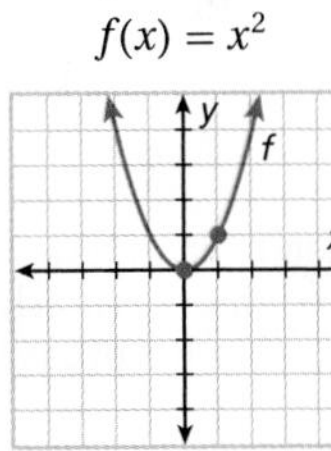

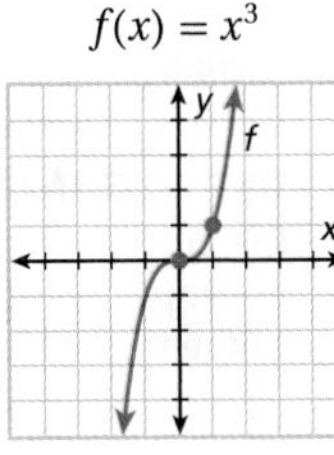

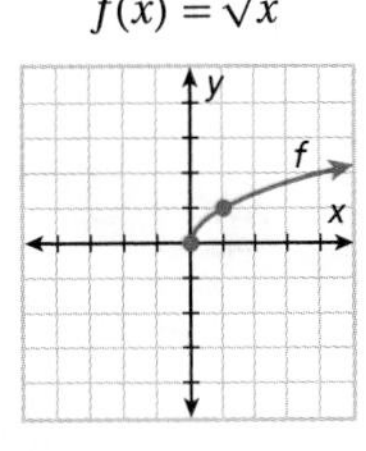

Helpful Hint

A greater number of data points increases your chances of correctly identifying the parent function that best describes the data.

Remember that any parent function you use to approximate a set of data should never be considered exact. However, these function approximations are often useful for estimating unknown values.

EXAMPLE 3 ***Oceanography Application***

An oceanographer wants to determine a model that can be used to estimate wind speed based upon wave height. Graph the relationship from wave height to wind speed and identify which parent function best describes it. Then use the graph to estimate the wave height when the wind speed is 10 knots.

Ocean Waves	
Wave Height (ft)	Wind Speed (knots)
2	8.8
4	12.4
6	15.2
8	17.5
10	19.6

Step 1 Graph the relation.

Graph the points given in the table. Draw a smooth curve through them to help you see the shape.

Step 2 Identify the parent function.

The graph of the data set resembles the shape of the square-root parent function $f(x) = \sqrt{x}$.

Step 3 Estimate the wave height when the wind speed is 10 knots.

The curve indicates that a wind speed of 10 knots would create a wave that is approximately 2.5 feet high.

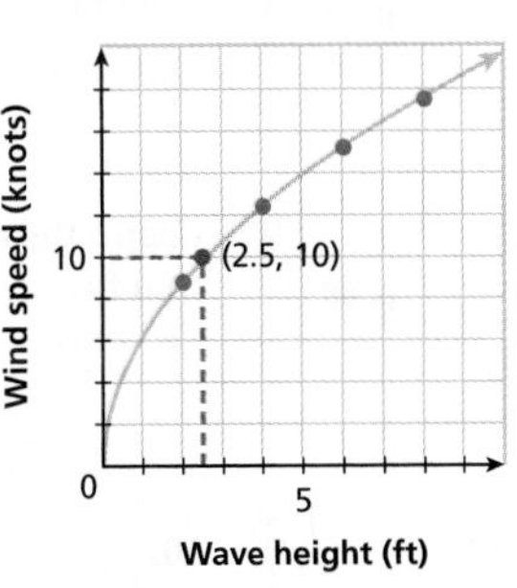

3. The cost of playing an online video game depends on the number of months for which the online service is used. Graph the relationship from number of months to cost, and identify which parent function best describes the data. Then use the graph to estimate the cost for 5 months of online service.

Cost of Online Video Game					
Time (mo)	1	3	6	9	12
Cost ($)	40	56	80	104	128

Power Presentations with PowerPoint®

Additional Examples

Example 3

Graph the relationship from year to sales in millions of dollars and identify which parent function best describes it. Then use the graph to estimate when cumulative sales reached $10 million.

Cumulative Sales	
Year	Sales (million $)
1	0.6
2	1.8
3	4.2
4	7.8
5	12.6

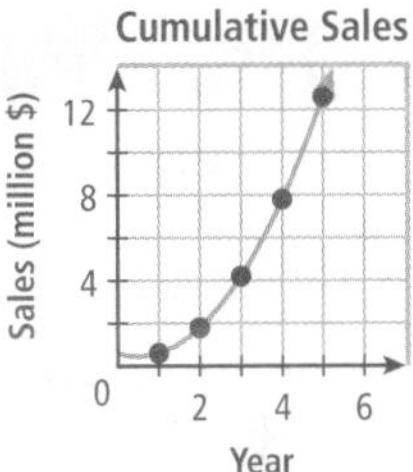

quadratic; after about 4.5 years

Also available on transparency

INTERVENTION

Questioning Strategies

EXAMPLE 3

- How do you find the x-coordinate of a point on the graph of a function when you know the y-coordinate?

Visual Have students sketch the graphs of the parent functions on notecards. They can refer to these cards as they work through the exercises in this lesson and throughout the entire course.

ONGOING ASSESSMENT and INTERVENTION

Diagnose Before **the Lesson**
1-9 Warm Up, TE p. 67

Monitor During **the Lesson**
Check It Out! Exercises, SE pp. 67–69
Questioning Strategies, TE pp. 68–69

Assess After **the Lesson**
1-9 Lesson Quiz, TE p. 73
Alternative Assessment, TE p. 73

3 Close

Summarize

Review the parent functions presented in the lesson. Have students explain how they might recognize each parent function.

Answers to *Check It Out!*

3.

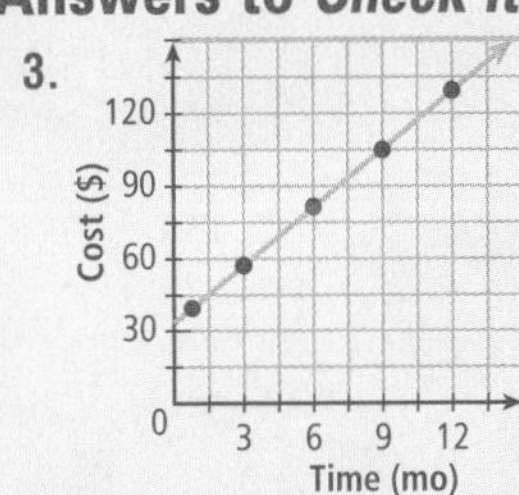

linear; about $72

Answers to *Think and Discuss*

Possible answers:

1. Look at its function rule or sketch the graph of the function to see the shape.
2. Recognizing the parent function can help you predict what the graph will look like and help you fill in missing parts.
3. See p. A2.

1-9 Exercises

Assignment Guide

Assign *Guided Practice* exercises as necessary.

If you finished Examples **1–3**
Basic 11–16, 28–39, 41–46, 51–58
Average 11–22, 28–49, 51–58
Advanced 11–58

Homework Quick Check
Quickly check key concepts.
Exercises: 9, 11, 14, 16, 30, 36

Answers

1. Possible answer: Within a family of functions, each function is a transformation of the parent function.
2. cubic; translation 1 unit right
3. quadratic; translation 1 unit left
4. linear; reflection
5. square root; translation 3 units left
6. quadratic; translation 4 units up
7. linear; translation $\sqrt{2}$ units down
8.

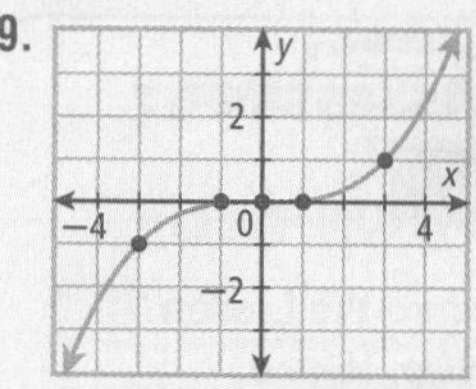

linear; vertical stretch or horizontal compression

9. cubic; vertical compression or horizontal stretch

State Resources

go.hrw.com
State Resources Online
KEYWORD: MB7 Resources

THINK AND DISCUSS

1. Explain how to determine the parent function for a given equation.
2. Explain why recognizing parent functions is useful for graphing.
3. **GET ORGANIZED** Copy and complete the graphic organizer. In each box, give the appropriate information for a translation of the parent function 3 units up.

Know it! Note

Transformed Parent Functions			
Family	Linear	Quadratic	Square root
Rule			
Graph			
Domain			
Range			
Intersects y-axis			

1-9 Exercises

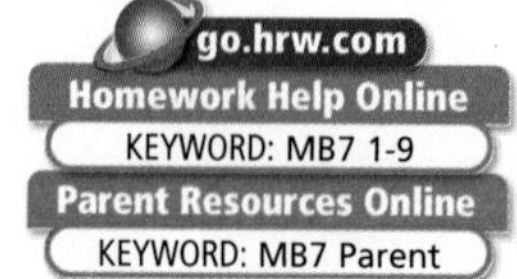

GUIDED PRACTICE

1. **Vocabulary** Explain how transformations, families of functions, and *parent functions* are related.

SEE EXAMPLE 1 p. 67

Identify the parent function for g from its function rule. Then graph g on your calculator and describe what transformation of the parent function it represents.

2. $g(x) = (x - 1)^3$
3. $g(x) = (x + 1)^2$
4. $g(x) = -x$
5. $g(x) = \sqrt{x + 3}$
6. $g(x) = x^2 + 4$
7. $g(x) = x - \sqrt{2}$

SEE EXAMPLE 2 p. 68

Graph the data from the table. Describe the parent function and the transformation that best approximates the data set.

8.

x	−3	−1	0	1	3
y	−15	−5	0	5	15

9.

x	−3	−1	0	1	3
y	−1	$-\frac{1}{27}$	0	$\frac{1}{27}$	1

SEE EXAMPLE 3 p. 69

10. **Physics** The time it takes a pendulum to make one complete swing back and forth depends on its string length.
    a. Graph the relationship from string length to time.
    b. Identify which parent function best describes the data. **square root**
    c. Use your graph to estimate the string length of a pendulum that takes 4.5 seconds to make one complete swing. **about 5 m**
    d. Use your graph to estimate the time it takes to make a complete swing for a string of length 14 meters. **about 7.5 s**

Pendulum Swing	
String Length (m)	**Time (s)**
2	2.8
4	4.0
6	4.9
8	5.7
10	6.3

PRACTICE AND PROBLEM SOLVING

Independent Practice	
For Exercises	See Example
11–13	1
14–15	2
16	3

Extra Practice
Skills Practice p. S5
Application Practice p. S32

Identify the parent function for g from its function rule. Then graph g on your calculator and describe what transformation of the parent function it represents.

11. $g(x) = x^2 - 1$
12. $g(x) = \sqrt{x - 2}$
13. $g(x) = x^3 + 3$

Graph the data from the table. Describe the parent function and the transformation that best approximates the data set.

14.

x	−3	−1	0	1	3
y	3	$\frac{1}{3}$	0	$\frac{1}{3}$	3

15.

x	0	1	4	9	16
y	0	2	4	6	8

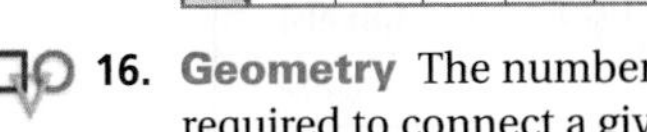

16. **Geometry** The number of segments required to connect a given number of points is shown in the table.
 a. Graph the relationship from the number of points to the number of segments.
 b. Identify which parent function best describes the data. **quadratic**
 c. Use your graph to estimate the number of points if there are 45 segments. **10 points**
 d. Use your graph to estimate the number of segments if there are 7 points. **21 segments**

Connecting Points

Number of Points	2	5	8	11
Number of Segments	1	10	28	55

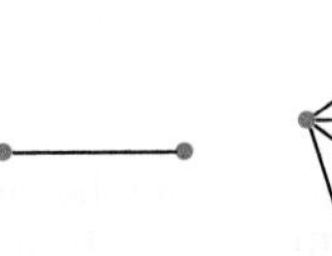

2 points
1 segment

5 points
10 segments

Graphing Calculator **Graph each function with a graphing calculator. Identify the domain and range of the function, and describe the transformation from its parent function.**

17. $g(x) = 3\sqrt{x}$
18. $g(x) = \frac{2}{3}x$
19. $g(x) = -\sqrt{x}$
20. $g(x) = -(x - 2)^2$
21. $g(x) = -x^2 + 1$
22. $g(x) = -\frac{1}{2}x^3$

23. **Sports** Based on the information in the table, what is the total cost of 15 tickets to the hockey game? Explain how you determined your answer.

Hockey Tickets

Number of Tickets	1	5	8	12
Total Cost ($)	13	65	104	156

Graph each function. Identify the parent function that best describes the set of points, and describe the transformation from the parent function.

24. $\{(-2, 8), (-1, 1), (0, 0), (1, -1), (2, -8)\}$
25. $\{(5, 4), (7, 0), (9, 4), (10, 9), (11, 16)\}$
26. $\{(0, 0), (-1, 1), (-4, 2), (-9, 3), (-16, 4)\}$
27. $\{(-4, 3), (-2, 1), (0, -1), (2, -3), (4, -5)\}$

MULTI-STEP TEST PREP

28. This problem will prepare you for the Multi-Step Test Prep on page 74.
 a. One function used in the Multi-Step Test Prep in Lesson 1-8 was $f(x) = 20 + 1.25x$. What is its parent function? **linear**
 b. The graph for a given function has a U shape. What could be the parent function? **quadratic**
 c. Plot the data set $\{(0, 0), (1, 2), (4, 4), (9, 6), (16, 8), (25, 10)\}$. Which parent function best models the data set? **square root**

Teaching Tip **Geometry** For **Exercise 16,** remind students that a segment is a part of a line between two points.

MULTI-STEP TEST PREP **Exercise 28** involves identifying parent functions. This exercise prepares students for the Multi-Step Test Prep on page 74.

Answers

10a.

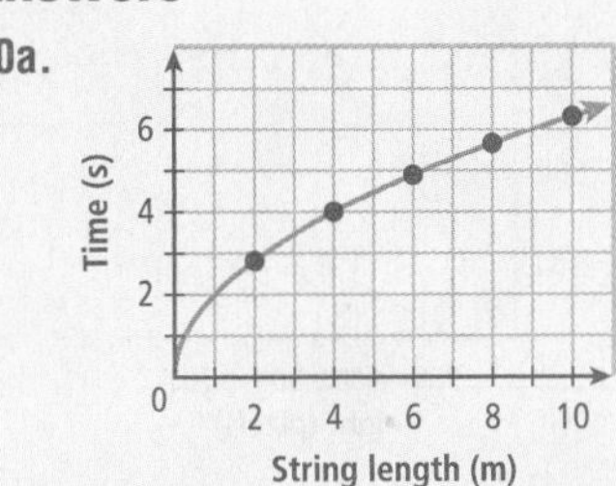

11. quadratic; translation 1 unit down
12. square root; translation 2 units right
13. cubic; translation 3 units up
14.

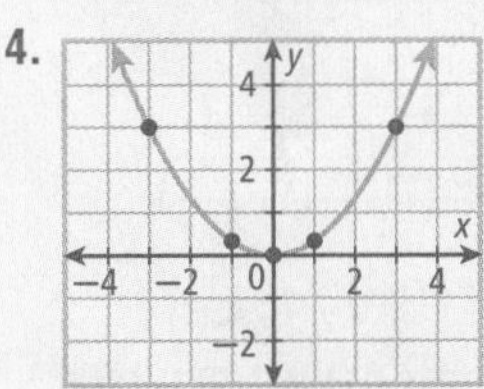

quadratic; vertical compression or horizontal stretch

15.

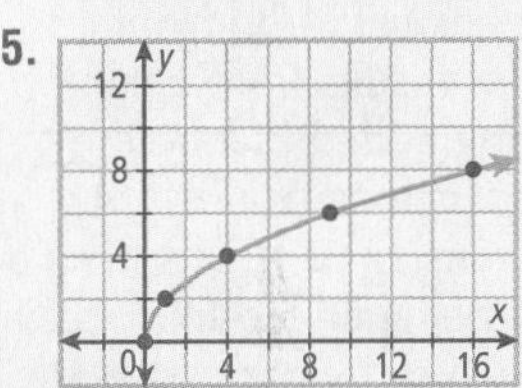

square root; vertical stretch or horizontal compression

16a.

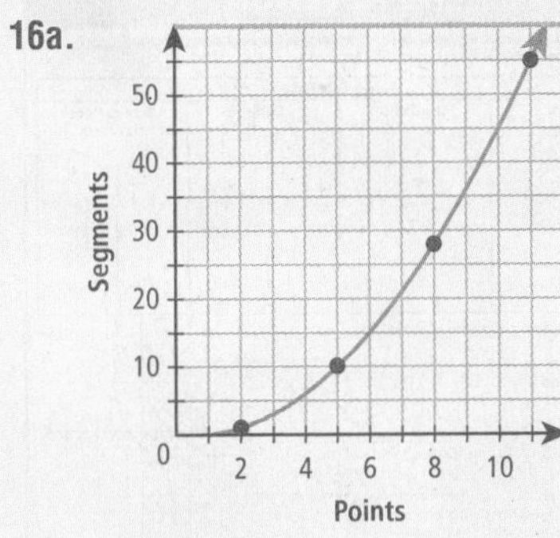

17. D: $\{x \mid x \geq 0\}$; R: $\{y \mid y \geq 0\}$; vertical stretch by a factor of 3

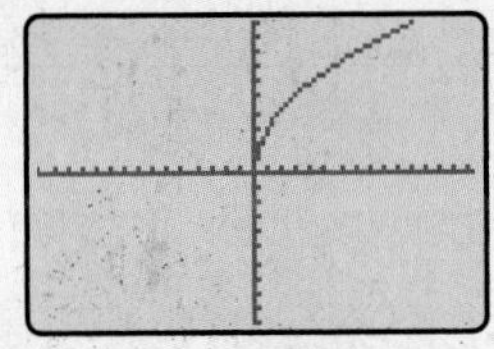

18–22. See p. A16.
23. $195; possible answer: by estimating from a graph of the data in the table
24–27. See p. A16.

1-9 PRACTICE A
1-9 PRACTICE C
1-9 PRACTICE B

Identify the parent function for h from its function rule. Then graph h on your calculator and describe what transformation of the parent function it represents.

1. $h(x) = \sqrt{x + 4}$ Square root; translation 4 units left
2. $h(x) = (x - 4)^3$ Cubic; translation 4 units right
3. $h(x) = 4x^2$ Quadratic; horizontal compression

Graph the data from the table. Describe the parent function and the transformation that best approximates the data set.

4.

x	−2	−1	0	1	2
y	−9	−2	−1	0	7

5.

x	0	2	8	18	32
y	0	1	2	3	4

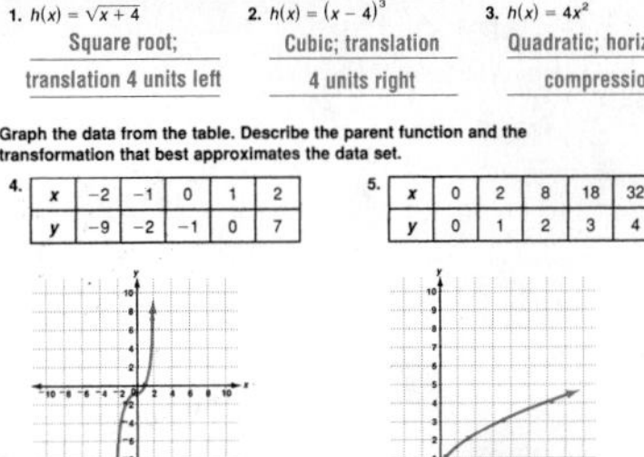

Cubic; translation 1 unit down

Square root; vertical compression

6. Compare the domain and the range for the parent quadratic function to the domain and the range for the parent linear function.
The domain is the same for both functions, all real numbers. The range for the linear function is all real numbers, but the range for the quadratic function is all real numbers greater than or equal to 0.

7. Compare the domain and the range for the parent square-root function to the domain and the range for the parent cubic function.
The domain and the range for the cubic function are all real numbers. The domain and the range for the square-root function are all real numbers greater than or equal to 0.

Answers

29.

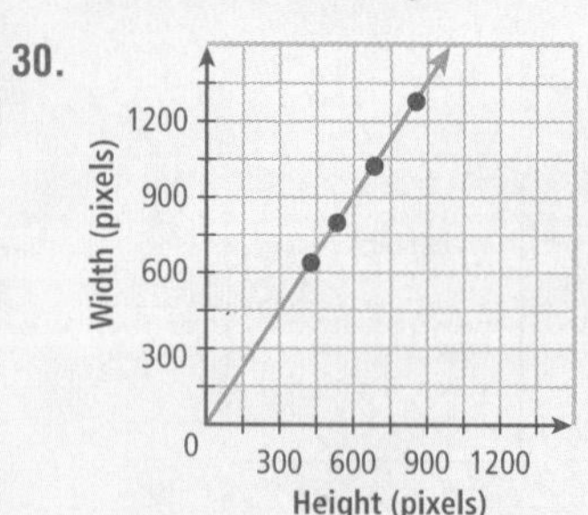

30.

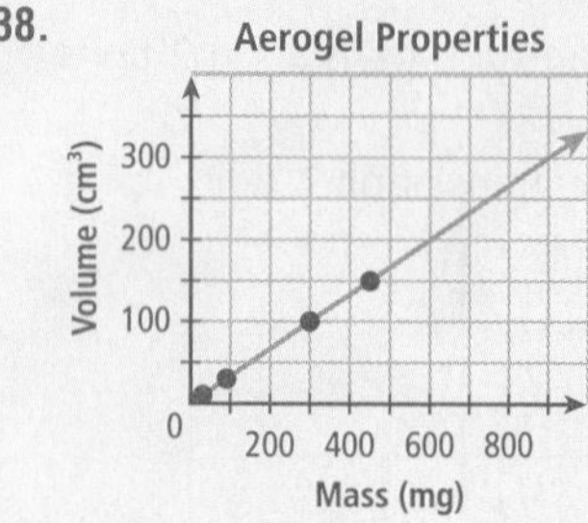

31. For graph, see p. A16.

32–37. See p. A16.

38. Aerogel Properties

Volume (cm^3): 300, 200, 100, 0; Mass (mg): 200 400 600 800

39e. linear; horizontal stretch by a factor of 2 and a vertical shift up 3 units

40. Possible answer: A horizontal translation results from a constant being added to x before squaring, such as $(x + a)^2$. A vertical translation results from a constant being added to x^2, such as $x^2 + a$. A reflection across the x-axis results from negating x^2, such as $-x^2$.

41. Constant, square root, linear, quadratic, cubic; the constant function does not increase at all; the square-root function increases slowly; the linear function increases 1 to 1 as x increases; the quadratic and cubic functions increase quickly, with cubic being the faster of the 2.

50a.

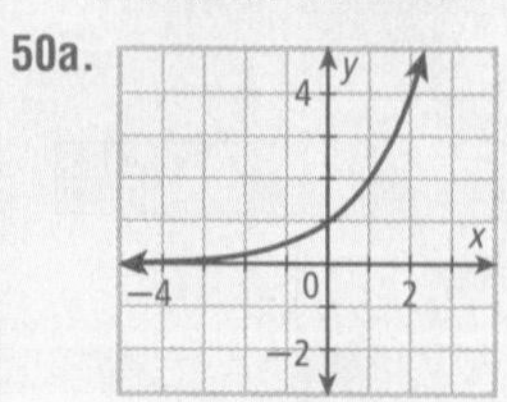

b. D: $\{x \mid x \in \mathbb{R}\}$; R: $\{y \mid y > 0\}$

c. (0, 1)

d. (0, 1); possible answer: $3^0 = 1$, so $f(x) = 3^x$ will have the same y-intercept as $f(x) = 2^x$.

Photography When resizing a digital photo, it is often important to preserve its *aspect ratio*, the ratio of its width to its height. Use the table for Exercises 29–31.

Digital Photos with Aspect Ratio 3:2

Width (pixels)	Height (pixels)	File Size (KB)
640	427	220
800	533	254
1024	683	413
1280	853	750

29. Graph the relationship from width to height and identify which parent function best describes the data. Use the graph to estimate the width of a photo with a height of 1000 pixels. **linear; ≈ 1500 pixels**

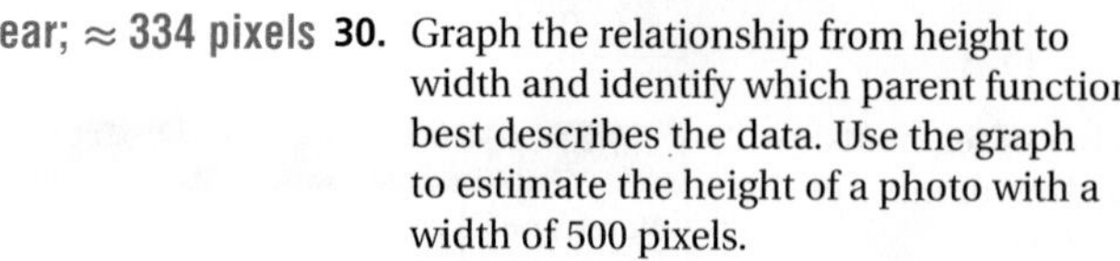

30. Graph the relationship from height to width and identify which parent function best describes the data. Use the graph to estimate the height of a photo with a width of 500 pixels. **linear; ≈ 334 pixels**

31. Resizing a photo changes the file size. Graph the relationship from width to file size and identify which parent function best describes the data. Use the graph to estimate the width of a photo with a file size of 1000 KB. **quadratic; ≈ 1417 pixels**

Sketch a graph for each situation and identify the related parent function. Then explain what the reasonable domain and range for the function is and compare it with the domain and range of the parent function.

32. distance traveled after h hours at a speed of 55 mi/h
33. volume of a cube with side length ℓ
34. area of a room with width w and a length of 15 feet
35. cost to wash n loads of laundry at $1.00 per load
36. cost of an item with original price p after a 15% discount
37. side length of a square with area A

LINK Chemistry

Aerogel has been called the world's lowest density solid. It is 99.8% air and is an excellent heat insulator. As shown above, a layer of aerogel can prevent a flame from melting crayons.

38. **Chemistry** The table shows properties of aerogel. Graph the relationship from mass to volume, and then estimate the volume of 1 gram of aerogel. **≈ 333 cm^3**

Aerogel Properties

Mass (mg)	30	90	300	450
Volume (cm^3)	10	30	100	150

39. **What if...?** Use the set of points $\{(-1, -1), (0, 0), (1, 1)\}$ to answer each question.
   a. What parent function best describes the set of points? **linear**
   b. If the points $(-2, 8)$ and $(2, 8)$ were added, what parent function would best describe the set? **cubic**
   c. If the point $(1, 1)$ were replaced with $(1, -1)$, what parent function would best describe the set? **quadratic**
   d. If the point $(-1, -1)$ were replaced with $(4, 2)$, what parent function would best describe the set? **square root**
   e. **Multi-Step** If the x-coordinate of each point were doubled and 3 were added to each y-coordinate, what parent function would best describe the set? What transformation of the parent function would the set represent?

40. **Critical Thinking** Explain any relationship you have noticed between the quadratic parent function and a function rule that represents a horizontal translation, a vertical translation, or a reflection across the x-axis.

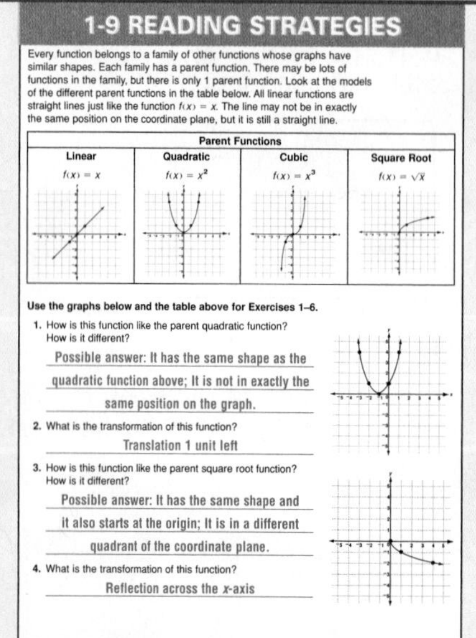

1-9 READING STRATEGIES

Every function belongs to a family of other functions whose graphs have similar shapes. Each family has a parent function. There may be lots of functions in the family, but there is only 1 parent function. Look at the models of the different parent functions in the table below. All linear functions are straight lines just like the function $f(x) = x$. The line may not be in exactly the same position on the coordinate plane, but it is still a straight line.

Parent Functions			
Linear $f(x) = x$	Quadratic $f(x) = x^2$	Cubic $f(x) = x^3$	Square Root $f(x) = \sqrt{x}$

Use the graphs below and the table above for Exercises 1–6.

1. How is this function like the parent quadratic function? How is it different?
   Possible answer: It has the same shape as the quadratic function above; It is not in exactly the same position on the graph.
2. What is the transformation of this function?
   Translation 1 unit left
3. How is this function like the parent square root function? How is it different?
   Possible answer: It has the same shape and it also starts at the origin; It is in a different quadrant of the coordinate plane.
4. What is the transformation of this function?
   Reflection across the x-axis

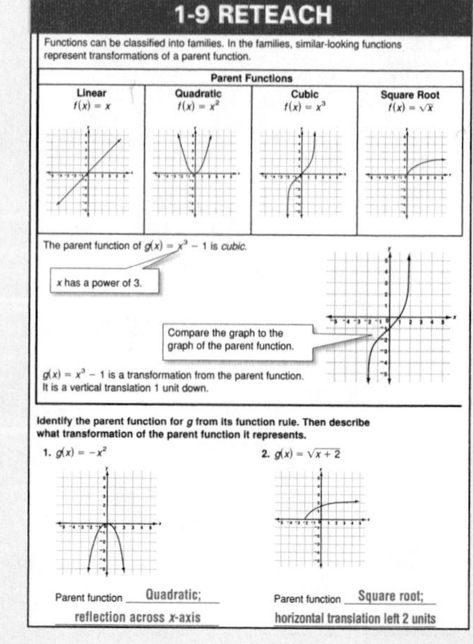

1-9 RETEACH

Functions can be classified into families. In the families, similar-looking functions represent transformations of a parent function.

Parent Functions			
Linear $f(x) = x$	Quadratic $f(x) = x^2$	Cubic $f(x) = x^3$	Square Root $f(x) = \sqrt{x}$

The parent function of $g(x) = x^3 - 1$ is *cubic*.

x has a power of 3.

Compare the graph to the graph of the parent function.

$g(x) = x^3 - 1$ is a transformation from the parent function. It is a vertical translation 1 unit down.

Identify the parent function for g from its function rule. Then describe what transformation of the parent function it represents.

1. $g(x) = -x^2$
   Parent function Quadratic; reflection across x-axis
2. $g(x) = \sqrt{x + 2}$
   Parent function Square root; horizontal translation left 2 units

41. **Write About It** Order the parent functions covered in this lesson from least to greatest by the rate at which $f(x)$ increases as x increases for $x > 1$. Explain your answer.

TEST PREP

42. Which situation could be represented by the graph?

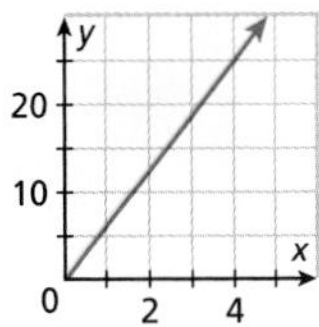

Ⓐ The area of a circle based on its radius
Ⓑ The volume of a sphere based on its radius
Ⓒ The surface area of a sphere based on its radius
Ⓓ The circumference of a circle based on its radius

43. Which graph best represents the function $f(x) = 2x^2 - 2$?

Ⓕ 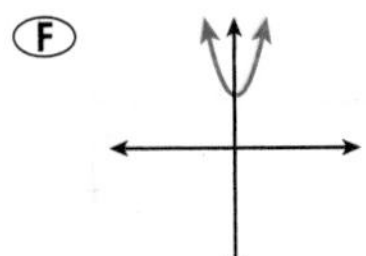 Ⓖ 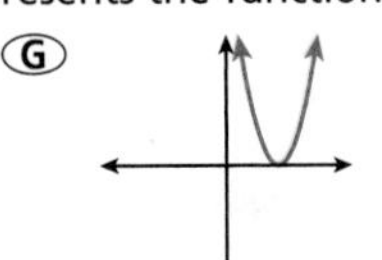 Ⓗ 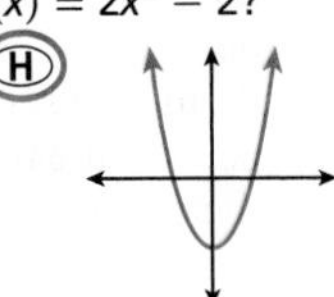 Ⓙ 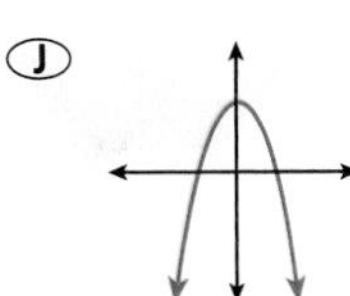

44. Which equation describes a relationship in which every nonzero real number x corresponds to a negative real number y?

Ⓐ $y = -x^3$ Ⓑ $y = -x^2$ Ⓒ $y = (-x)^2$ Ⓓ $y = -x$

45. For which function is -1 NOT an element of the range?

Ⓕ $y = -1$ Ⓖ $y = (-x)^2$ Ⓗ $y = -x$ Ⓙ $y = x^3$

46. What type of function can be used to determine the side length of a square if the independent variable is the square's area?

 Ⓐ Cubic Ⓑ Linear Ⓒ Quadratic  Ⓓ Square root

CHALLENGE AND EXTEND

Identify the parent function for each function.

47. $g(x) = 3(x-1)^2 - 6$ quadratic 48. $h(x) = (4x^3)^0 + 2$ constant 49. $g(x) = 5(3x-2) - 11x$ linear

50. Another parent function is an exponential function of the form $f(x) = a^x$.
   a. Graph $f(x) = 2^x$.
   b. Find the domain and range of the function.
   c. Identify the point where the function crosses the y-axis.
   d. Predict where $f(x) = 3^x$ crosses the y-axis and explain your answer.

SPIRAL REVIEW

Simplify each expression. Write each answer in scientific notation. *(Lesson 1-5)*

51. $(1.5 \times 10^{-4})(5.0 \times 10^{13})$ 7.5×10^9 52. $(8.1 \times 10^3)^2$ 6.561×10^7 53. $\dfrac{1.9 \times 10^{-6}}{9.5 \times 10^{18}}$ 2.0×10^{-25}

Evaluate each function for the given set of input values. *(Lesson 1-7)*

54. $f(x) = \frac{1}{2}x + 3; \left\{-3, 0, \frac{1}{3}, 6\right\}$ $\frac{3}{2}$; 3; $\frac{19}{6}$; 6 55. $f(x) = x(x+2); \left\{-5, -\frac{2}{3}, 1.6, 4\right\}$ 15; $-\frac{8}{9}$; 5.76; 24

Perform each transformation on the point $(3, -5)$. Give the coordinates of the translated point. *(Lesson 1-8)*

56. left 2, up 6 $(1, 1)$ 57. right 1, down 5 $(4, -10)$ 58. reflected across the y-axis $(-3, -5)$

TEST PREP DOCTOR

In **Exercise 42,** encourage students to recall and write out geometric formulas (such as $A = \pi r^2$) to help them identify which one might be linear.

In **Exercise 43,** encourage students to evaluate the function at a couple of key points, noting that $f(0) = -2$ eliminates all choices except the correct choice, **H.**

Journal

Have students describe each parent function in their own words. This will help students visualize and identify the functions.

ALTERNATIVE ASSESSMENT

Have students consider the data set $\{(-1, -1), (0, 0), (1, 1)\}$. Have the students list which parent functions could and which parent functions could not represent the data and explain why.

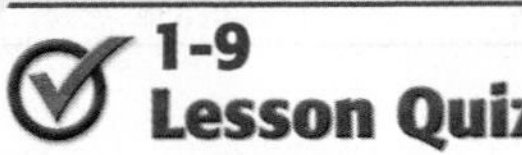

Power Presentations with PowerPoint®

1-9 Lesson Quiz

Identify the parent function for g from its function rule. Then graph g on your calculator and describe what transformation of the parent function it represents.

1. $g(x) = x + 7$ linear; translation up 7 units
2. $g(x) = x^2 - 6$ quadratic; translation down 6 units
3. Stacy earns $7.50 per hour. Graph the relationship from hours to amount earned and identify which parent function best describes it. Then use the graph to estimate how many hours it would take Stacy to earn $60.

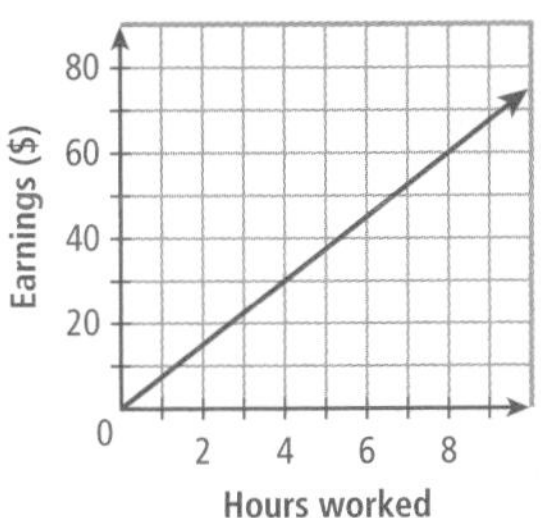

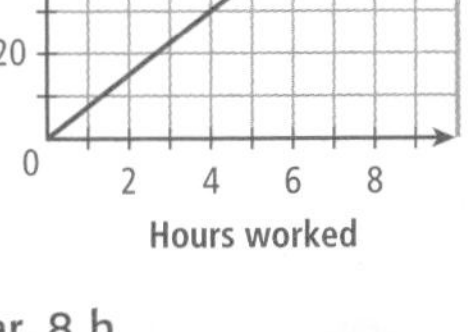

linear, 8 h

Also available on transparency

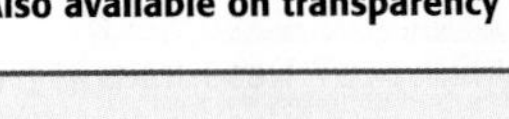

1-9 PROBLEM SOLVING

Katy and Peter are writing a paper about the history and use of cell phones. They make a graph of the data in the table. They want to determine the parent function for the graph.

Cell Phone Subscribers in the United States (estimated in millions)			
1991	7.6	1997	55.3
1992	11.0	1998	69.2
1993	16.0	1999	86.0
1994	24.1	2000	109.5
1995	33.8	2001	128.4
1996	44.0	2002	140.8

1. Peter wants to compare the graph to the function $f(x) = 7x + 2$. How would the graph of $f(x) = 7x + 2$ compare to its parent function $f(x) = x$?
   The graph of $f(x) = 7x + 2$ is translated up 2 units and the line is steeper by a factor of 7.
2. What is the value $f(x) = 7x + 2$ for 1996, when $x = 6$? Does that point fit the graph? Try some other values of x for the function $f(x) = 7x + 2$. How well do the results fit the range of the graph?
   44; yes; Possible answer: I tried points (3, 23), (4, 30), (5, 37), (7, 51), (8, 58); when x has a value greater than 6, the points do not match well.
3. Katy wants to compare the graph to the function $f(x) = x^2 + 5$. How would the graph of $f(x) = x^2 + 5$ compare to its parent function $f(x) = x^2$?
   The graph of $f(x) = x^2 + 5$ is translated up 5 units.
4. Find the value of $f(x) = x^2 + 5$ for 1996, when $x = 6$? Does that point fit the graph? Try some other values of x for the function $f(x) = x^2 + 5$. How well do the results fit the range of the graph?
   41; not exactly; Possible answer: I tried points (2, 9), (4, 21), (5, 30), (8, 69), (10, 105), and (12, 149), and they match reasonably well.
5. Which parent function and transformation best models these data?
   Possible answer: The quadratic parent function translated up 5 units best models these data.

1-9 CHALLENGE

Sometimes it is necessary to identify parent functions from data points obtained through experiments or trials. Look at the data below for the quadratic function $y = x^2 + 2x + 4$. Notice that the second differences have a constant value of 2. Since the second differences are constant, the parent function is a quadratic function.

x	1	2	3	4	5	6
y	7	12	19	28	39	52
First Difference	5	7	9	11	13	
Second Difference	2	2	2	2		

A linear function is indicated by constant first differences.

Find the differences in each set of data.

1.

x	1	2	3	4	5	6
y	5	9	25	59	117	205

a. Which differences have a constant value? third differences
b. Identify the parent function. 3rd degree or cubic

2.

x	−1	0	1	2	3	4	5
y	11	4	11	44	139	356	779

a. Which differences have a constant value? fourth differences
b. Identify the parent function. 4th degree

3. Make a table of data for the function $y = 2^x$ for $1 \le x \le 6$. Find the first, second, and third differences in the y values. What do you notice about the sets of differences?
   Every set of differences is the same (i.e., 2, 4, 8, 16, 32, 64, ...).
4. Make a table using the following data: (1, 10), (2, 13), (3, 18), (4, 27), (5, 44), (6, 77). Find the differences until you observe a pattern. What does this pattern tell you about the parent function?
   The second difference is the same pattern as the differences for $y = 2^x$, so this must be an exponential function.

Organizer

Objective: Assess students' ability to apply concepts and skills in Lessons 1-6 through 1-9 in a real-world format.

 Online Edition

Resources

 ***Algebra II Assessments***
www.mathtekstoolkit.org

Problems	Text Reference
1–2	Lesson 1-6
3–4	Lessons 1-6, 1-7
5	Lesson 1-9
6–8	Lesson 1-8

Answers

1. {−39.4, −37.6, −34.6, −30.6, −30.0, −28.2, −26.0, −25.7, −23.0, −20.0, −19.3, −15.3, −13.7, −10.3, −6.9, 0}
2. {−29.7, −28.7, −27.1, −24.9, −22.1, −15.5, −11.8, −4.2, 3.0, 8.9, 15.0, 15.3, 16.2, 17.5, 20.0, 21.7, 23.2, 24.3, 24.6, 25.5}
3. See page A16.

State Resources

go.hrw.com
State Resources Online
KEYWORD: MB7 Resources

SECTION 1B

Introduction to Functions

Native American Art Much of Native American art, in particular Navajo and Cherokee, displays symmetrical designs.

To reproduce these designs, artists can determine the points that make up the designs and transform them. The set of ordered pairs in the table defines the outline of the left side of a handmade Navajo vase. The graph shows the plotted points.

Vase Outline	
x	*y*
0	25.5
−10.3	24.6
−15.3	24.3
−23.0	23.2
−28.2	21.7
−30.0	20.0
−26.0	17.5
−19.3	16.2
−10.3	15.3
0	15.0
−25.7	8.9
−34.6	3.0
−39.4	−4.2
−39.4	−11.8
−37.6	−15.5
−30.6	−22.1
−25.7	−24.9
−20.0	−27.1
−13.7	−28.7
−6.9	−29.7

1. What is the domain of this relation?
2. What is the range of this relation?
3. Is this relation also a function? Explain why or why not.
4. If the coordinates were plotted such that the vase appears to be on its side (that is, the *x*- and *y*-coordinates switched places), would the relation be a function? Explain why or why not. Yes; no *y*-value is paired with more than one *x*-value.
5. If the vase appears to be on its side, which parent function would best represent the bottom of the vase? quadratic function
6. What transformation would create the right side of the upright vase? reflection across the *y*-axis
7. What kind of transformation could be done on the relation in the table to make the vase shorter? vertical compression
8. What kind of transformation could be done on the relation in the table to make the vase narrower? horizontal compression

74

INTERVENTION

Scaffolding Questions

1. Which values make up the domain? *x*-values
2. Which values make up the range? *y*-values
3. How can you tell whether the relation is a function? No *x*-values repeat.
4. How does switching the *x*- and *y*-values affect the domain and range of the relation? They are switched.
5. Describe the shape of the bottom of the vase when it is on its side. curve that goes up and to the left
6. What kinds of coordinates do you think the points representing the right side of the vase would have? positive *x*-values and the same *y*-values

7–8. What type of transformation pushes points toward the *x*-axis? the *y*-axis? vertical compression; horiz. compression

Extension

Suppose you wanted the vase to be twice as tall. Write the relation for the new vase. All *y*-values should be twice the original values.

CHAPTER 1

SECTION 1B

Quiz for Lessons 1-6 Through 1-9

1-6 Relations and Functions

Give the domain and range for each relation. Then tell whether the relation is a function.

1. 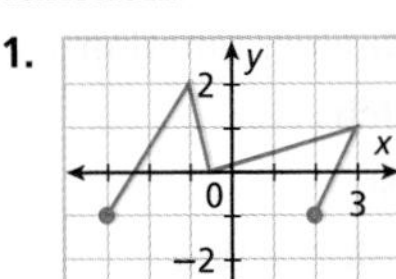

2. 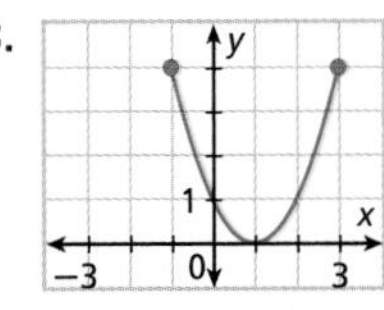

x	0	2	4	6	2
y	5	8	10	20	12

3.

1-7 Function Notation

For each function, evaluate $f(0)$, $f(1)$, and $f(-2)$.

4. $f(x) = 12 - 3x$ 12; 9; 18
5. $f(x) = 3x^3 + 1$ 1; 4; −23
6. $f(x) = 4 - x^2$ 4; 3; 0
7. In a certain city, taxi fares are regulated at \$1.75 per ride plus \$0.25 for each $\frac{1}{4}$ mile.
   a. Write a function to represent the taxi fare per mile.
   b. Graph your function.
   c. What is the value of the function for an input of 5.5, and what does it represent?

1-8 Exploring Transformations

The graph shows some credit card fees for cash advances. Sketch a graph to represent each situation and identify the transformation of the original graph that it represents.

8. Each fee is increased by \$15.
9. Each fee is decreased by 40%.

Credit Card Cash Advance Fees

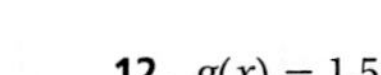

1-9 Introduction to Parent Functions

Identify the parent function for g from its equation. Then graph g on your calculator and describe what transformation of the parent function it represents.

10. $g(x) = -x^2$
11. $g(x) = \sqrt{x-3}$
12. $g(x) = 1.5x$
13. The table lists the maximum load of a three-strand nylon rope based on its diameter. Graph the relationship from diameter to maximum load and identify which parent function best describes the data. Then use your graph to estimate the diameter of a three-strand nylon rope that has a maximum load of 7920 kilograms.

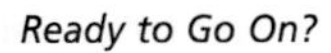

Nylon Rope Maximum Load					
Diameter (mm)	8	10	12	14	16
Maximum Load (kg)	1920	2720	3750	5100	6640

READY TO GO ON? SECTION 1B

Organizer

Objective: Assess students' mastery of concepts and skills in Lessons 1-6 through 1-9.

Resources

 ***Assessment Resources***

Section 1B Quiz

 **Test & Practice Generator One-Stop Planner®**

INTERVENTION

Resources

 ***Ready to Go On? Intervention and Enrichment*** **Worksheets**

 ***Ready to Go On?*** **CD-ROM**

 ***Ready to Go On?*** **Online**

my.hrw.com

Answers

1–3, 7–13. See p. A16.

READY TO GO ON? Diagnose and Prescribe

NO INTERVENE

Ready to Go On? Intervention	Worksheets	CD-ROM	Online
	Ready to Go On? Intervention, Section 1B		
Lesson 1-6	1-6 Intervention	Activity 1-6	Diagnose and Prescribe Online
Lesson 1-7	1-7 Intervention	Activity 1-7	
Lesson 1-8	1-8 Intervention	Activity 1-8	
Lesson 1-9	1-9 Intervention	Activity 1-9	

YES ENRICH

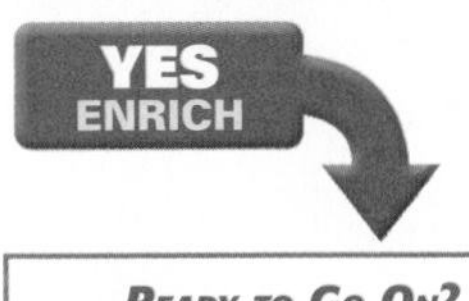

Ready to Go On? Enrichment, Section 1B

Worksheets

CD-ROM

Online

Organizer

Objective: Help students organize and review key concepts and skills presented in Chapter 1.

Online Edition
Multilingual Glossary

Resources

Puzzle Pro
One-Stop Planner®

***Multilingual Glossary* Online**

go.hrw.com
KEYWORD: MB7 Glossary

Lesson Tutorial Videos
CD-ROM

Test & Practice Generator
One-Stop Planner®

Answers

1. domain; range
2. $\{x \mid x \geq -5\}$
3. $(1, 5]$
4. $\{4, 5, 6, 7, \ldots\}$
5. $\{x \mid x < -2 \text{ or } x > 5\}$
6. integers greater than -4 and less than or equal to 5
7. $[5.5, 5.6]$
8. Comm. Prop. of Mult.
9. Distributive Property
10. $-0.55; \frac{1}{0.55}$
11. $\frac{7}{8}; -\frac{8}{7}$
12. $-1.\overline{2}; \frac{1}{1.\overline{2}}$ or $\frac{9}{11}$

CHAPTER 1

Study Guide: Review

Vocabulary

Complete the sentence below with vocabulary words from the list above.

1. For a function, the ___?___ is the set of input values, and the ___?___ is the set of output values.

1-1 Sets of Numbers *(pp. 6–13)*

EXAMPLES

Rewrite each set in the indicated notation.

- [number line from −4 to 3, closed point at −2, arrow to the right]; interval notation

  The interval is the real numbers greater than or equal to -2.

  $[-2, \infty)$ *−2 included, but infinity is not.*

- $(-1, 6)$; set builder notation

  $\{x \mid -1 < x < 6\}$ *Neither endpoint is included.*

EXERCISES

Rewrite each set in the indicated notation.

2. $[-5, \infty)$; set-builder notation
3.  [number line from −1 to 6, open point at 1, closed point at 5]; interval notation
4. $\{x \mid x > 3 \text{ and } x \in \mathbb{N}\}$; roster notation
5. $(-\infty, -2)$ or $(5, \infty)$; set-builder notation
6. $\{x \mid -4 < x \leq 5 \text{ and } x \in \mathbb{Z}\}$; words
7. $5.5 \leq x \leq 5.6$; interval notation

1-2 Properties of Real Numbers *(pp. 14–19)*

EXAMPLE

- **Identify the property demonstrated by the equation $3(8x) = (3 \cdot 8)x$.**

  In the equation, the factors have been regrouped. The property of multiplication that allows regrouping is the Associative Property.

EXERCISES

Identify the property demonstrated by each equation.

8. $2x\sqrt{3} = \sqrt{3} \cdot (2x)$
9. $9.9x - 2x = (9.9 - 2)x$

Find the additive and multiplicative inverse of each number.

10. 0.55
11. $-\frac{7}{8}$
12. $1.\overline{2}$

1-3 Square Roots *(pp. 21–26)*

EXAMPLE

- **Simplify the expression $\frac{3\sqrt{2}}{\sqrt{6}}$.**

$\frac{3\sqrt{2}}{\sqrt{6}} \cdot \frac{\sqrt{6}}{\sqrt{6}}$ *Rationalize the denominator.*

$\frac{3\sqrt{12}}{6}$ *Product Property of Square Roots*

$\frac{3\sqrt{4 \cdot 3}}{6}$ *Product Property of Square Roots*

$\frac{6\sqrt{3}}{6} = \sqrt{3}$

EXERCISES

Estimate to the nearest tenth.

13. $\sqrt{12}$ **14.** $\sqrt{55}$

15. $\sqrt{74}$ **16.** $\sqrt{29}$

Simplify each expression.

17. $\sqrt{32}$ **18.** $\frac{\sqrt{64}}{\sqrt{4}}$

19. $2\sqrt{2} - \sqrt{72}$ **20.** $\sqrt{3} \cdot \sqrt{21}$

21. $\frac{7}{\sqrt{2}}$ **22.** $\frac{2\sqrt{20}}{5\sqrt{8}}$

1-4 Simplifying Algebraic Expressions *(pp. 27–32)*

EXAMPLES

- **Evaluate $6c - 3c^2 + d^3$ for $c = -1$ and $d = 3$.**

$6(-1) - 3(-1)^2 + (3)^3$ *Substitute −1 for c and 3 for d.*

$-6 - 3(1) + 27 = 18$

- **Simplify the expression $3m + (m - 5n)2$.**

$3m + (2m - 10n)$ *Distribute the 2.*

$3m + 2m - 10n$ *Identify like terms.*

$5m - 10n$ *Combine like terms.*

EXERCISES

Evaluate each expression for the given values of the variables.

23. $x^2y - xy^2$ for $x = 6$ and $y = -2$

24. $-\frac{x^2}{2} + 5xy - 9y$ for $x = 4$ and $y = 2$

25. $\frac{n^2 + mn - 1}{4m^2n}$ for $m = 2$ and $n = -1$

Simplify each expression.

26. $-x - 2y + 9x - y + 3x$ **27.** $7 - (5a - b) + 11$

28. $-4(2x + 3y) + 5x$ **29.** $c(a^2 - b) + 3bc$

1-5 Properties of Exponents *(pp. 34–41)*

EXAMPLE

- **Simplify the expression $\frac{6m^4n^{-3}}{18m^3n}$. Assume all variables are nonzero.**

$\frac{6}{18}(m^{4-3}n^{-3-1})$ *Quotient of Powers Property*

$\frac{1}{3}(mn^{-4})$ *Simplify.*

$\frac{m}{3n^4}$ *Negative Exponent Property*

EXERCISES

Simplify each expression. Assume all variables are nonzero.

30. $(-2x^5y^{-3})^3$ **31.** $\frac{-24x^4y^{-6}}{14x^{-3}y^3}$

32. $\left(\frac{r^2s}{s^3}\right)^2$ **33.** $4mn(m^5n^{-5})$

Simplify each expression. Write each answer in scientific notation.

34. $\frac{7.7 \times 10^5}{1.1 \times 10^{-2}}$ **35.** $(4.5 \times 10^{-2})(1.2 \times 10^3)$

Answers

13. 3.5
14. 7.4
15. 8.6
16. 5.4
17. $4\sqrt{2}$
18. 4
19. $-4\sqrt{2}$
20. $3\sqrt{7}$
21. $\frac{7\sqrt{2}}{2}$
22. $\frac{\sqrt{10}}{5}$
23. −96
24. 14
25. $\frac{1}{8}$
26. $11x - 3y$
27. $18 - 5a + b$
28. $-3x - 12y$
29. $a^2c + 2bc$
30. $\frac{-8x^{15}}{y^9}$
31. $\frac{-12x^7}{7y^9}$
32. $\frac{r^4}{s^4}$
33. $\frac{4m^6}{n^4}$
34. 7×10^7
35. 5.4×10^1

Study Guide: Review 77

Answers

36. D: {3, 5, 7}; R: {−1, 0, 9}; not a function
37. D: [−2, ∞); R: [−4, ∞); not a function
38. D: {−2, 0, 3, 4}; R: {3, 4}; function
39. D: {5, 10, 15, 20, 25}; R: {−5, −4, −3, −2, −1}; function
40. D: {a, b, c}; R: {Alabama, Alaska, Arizona, Arkansas, California, Colorado, Connecticut}; not a function
41. $-2; \frac{7}{4}; -2$
42. $-16; -\frac{17}{2}; 4$
43. $-1; 1; 2$
44. $\frac{1}{2}; 2; -\frac{1}{2}$
45.

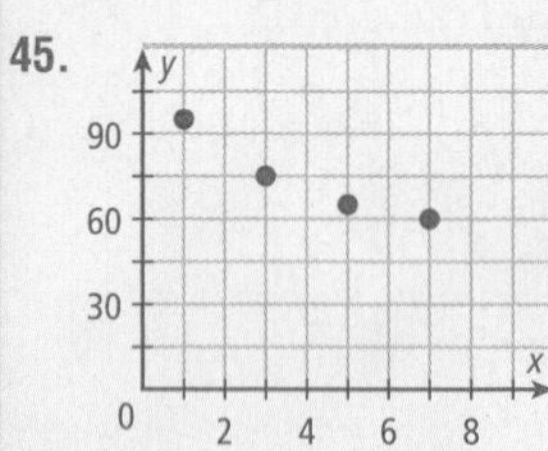

46.

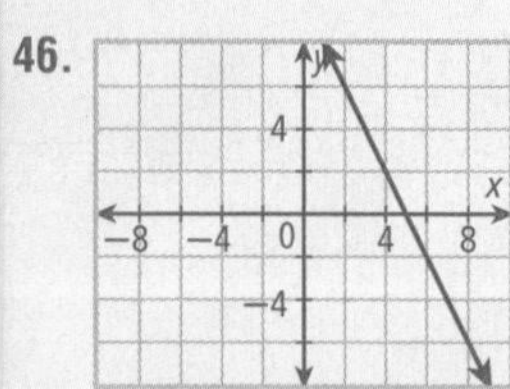

47. $A(s) = 6s^2$, where A is the surface area in square units and s is the side length in linear units; $A(10) = 600$; the surface area for a cube of side length 10 cm is 600 cm^2.

1-6 Relations and Functions *(pp. 44–50)*

EXAMPLE

■ **Give the domain and range for the relation. Then determine whether the relation is a function.**

Arcade Game Costs				
Games	1	2	3	4
Cost ($)	0.50	1.00	1.50	2.00

Domain: $\{1, 2, 3, 4\}$ *Independent variable*

Range: $\{0.50, 1.00, 1.50, 2.00\}$ *Dependent variable*

Each number of games has only one cost associated with it.

The relation from number of games to cost is a function.

EXERCISES

Give the domain and range for each relation. Then determine whether the relation is a function.

36. 3 5 7 → −1 0 9

37.

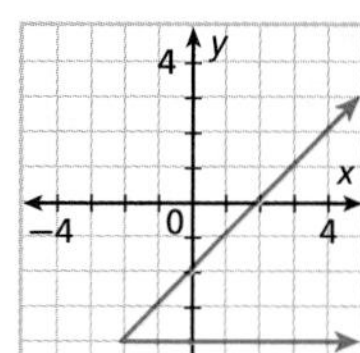

38. $\{(3, 4), (4, 3), (0, 3), (-2, 4)\}$

39.

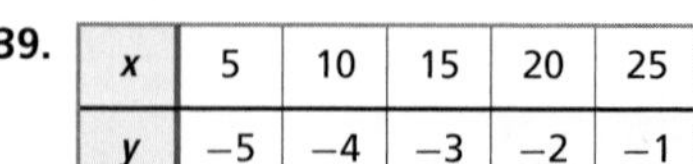

x	5	10	15	20	25
y	−5	−4	−3	−2	−1

40. from the first three letters of the alphabet to the U.S. states that begin with that letter

1-7 Function Notation *(pp. 51–57)*

EXAMPLE

■ **A cell phone company charges $40 per month for the first 500 minutes plus $0.75 for each additional minute used. Write a function to represent the total monthly cost based on the number of minutes used. What is the value of the function for an input of 30, and what does it represent?**

Let c be the total monthly cost and m be the number of additional minutes used.

cost	=	monthly fee	+	rate	·	additional minutes
$c(m)$	=	40	+	0.75	·	m

$$c(30) = 40 + 0.75(30)$$
$$= 40 + 22.5$$
$$= 62.5$$

The value of $c(m)$ for an input of 30 is $c(30) = 62.5$. This means that the monthly cost when 30 additional minutes are used is $62.50.

EXERCISES

For each function, find $f(2)$, $f\left(\frac{1}{2}\right)$, and $f(-2)$.

41. $f(x) = -x^2 + 2$

42. $f(x) = -5x - 6$

43.

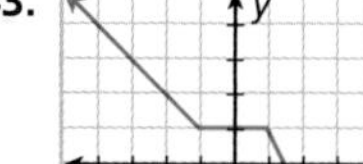

44.

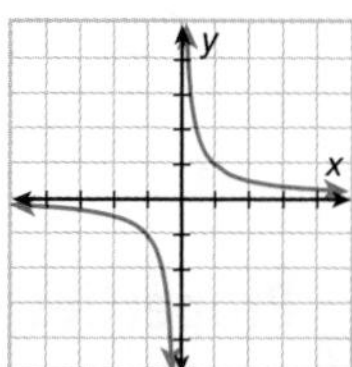

Graph each function.

45.

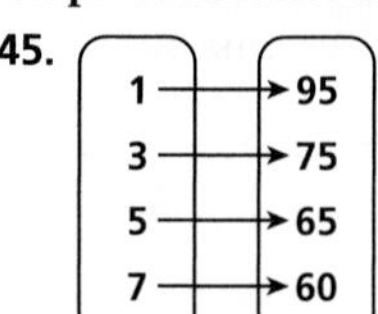

46.

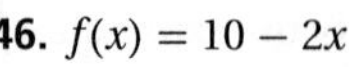

$f(x) = 10 - 2x$

47. **Geometry** The surface area of a cube is 6 times the square of its side length. Write a function to represent the surface area of a cube. What is the value of the function for an input of 10 centimeters, and what does it represent?

1-8 Exploring Transformations *(pp. 59–66)*

EXAMPLE

- **The graph shows household alarm monitoring fees. Sketch a graph to represent a $\frac{1}{5}$ fee reduction on long-term contracts. Then identify the transformation of the original graph that the new graph represents.**

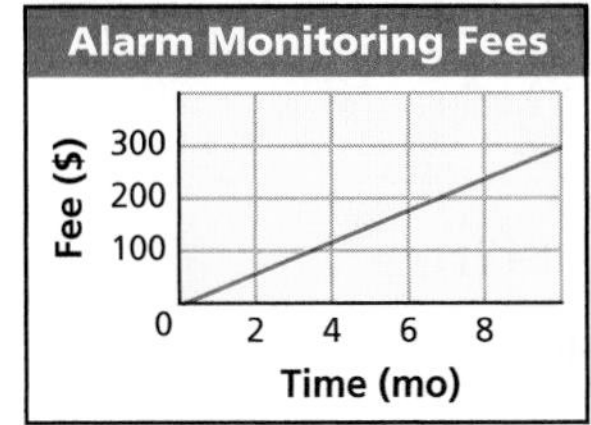

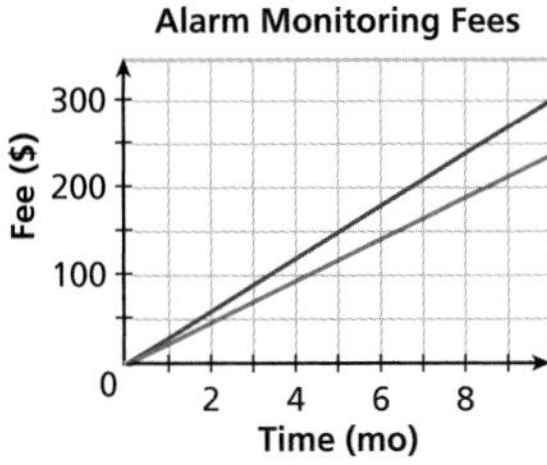

Each price is $\frac{4}{5}$ of the original price. This represents a vertical compression of the graph by a factor of $\frac{4}{5}$.

EXERCISES

Perform the given transformation to the point $(5, -1)$. Give the coordinates of the new point.

48. 5 units left, 4 units down

49. reflection across the x-axis

The graph shows parking garage fees. Sketch a graph to represent each situation and identify the transformation of the original graph that it represents.

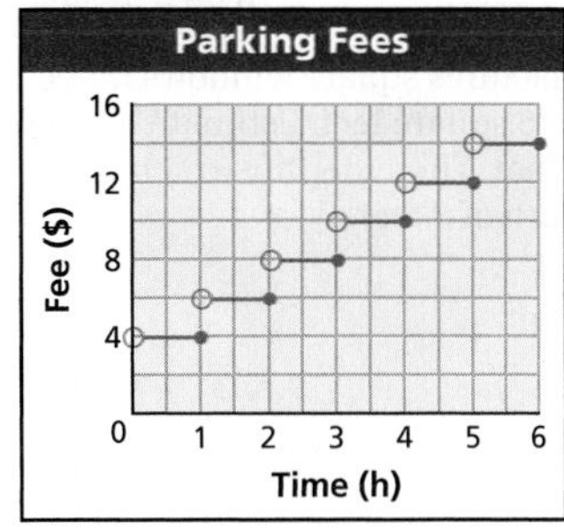

50. The fees are half price on weekends.

51. The fees are increased by 10%.

52. All fees are increased by \$1.00.

1-9 Introduction to Parent Functions *(pp. 67–73)*

EXAMPLE

- **Identify the parent function for $g(x) = \sqrt{x-4}$ from its equation. Then graph g on your calculator and describe what transformation of the parent function it represents.**

$g(x) = \sqrt{x-4}$ is a square-root function.

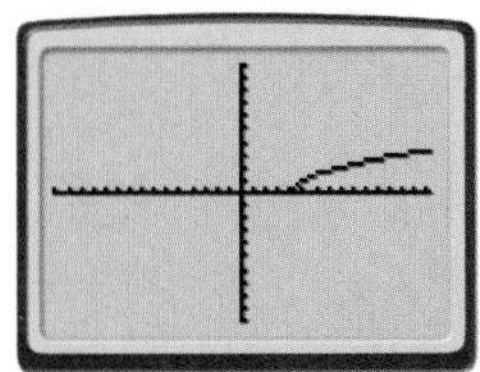

The graph of the square-root parent function intersects the x-axis at the point $(0, 0)$.

The graph of the function $g(x) = \sqrt{x-4}$ intersects the x-axis at the point $(4, 0)$.

So $g(x) = \sqrt{x-4}$ represents a translation of the square-root parent function 4 units right.

EXERCISES

Identify the parent function for g from its equation. Then graph g on your calculator and describe what transformation of the parent function it represents.

53. $g(x) = x^2 - 1$

54. $g(x) = -\sqrt{x}$

55. Graph the data from the table. Describe the parent function that would best approximate the data set. Then use the graph to estimate the tire pressure for a 95-pound rider.

Bicycle Road-Tire Pressures					
Weight of Rider (lb)	110	140	170	200	230
Pressure (psi)	95	105	115	125	135

Answers

48. (0, –5)

49. (5, 1)

50.
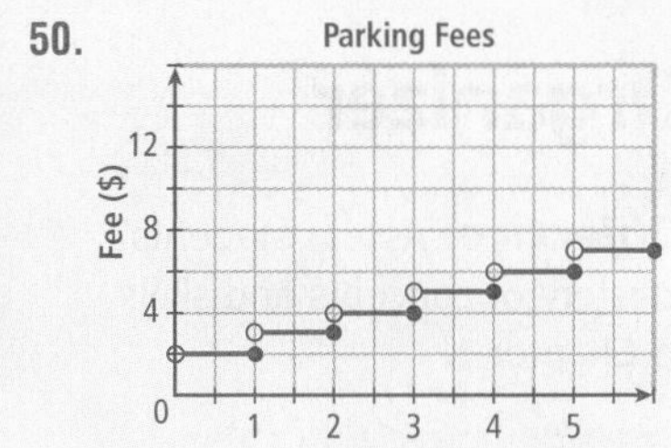

vertical compression by a factor of $\frac{1}{2}$

51.
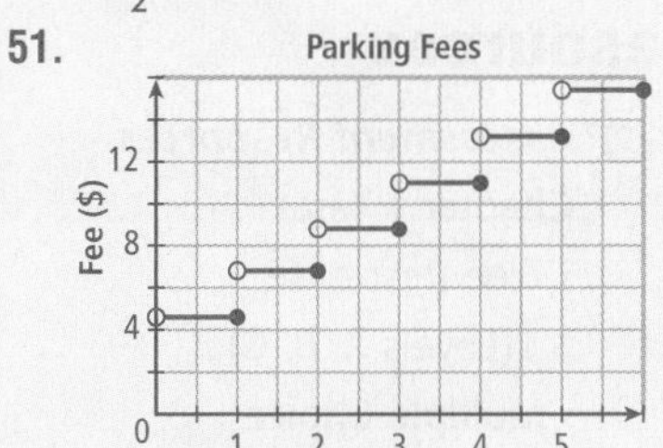

vertical stretch by a factor of 1.1

52.
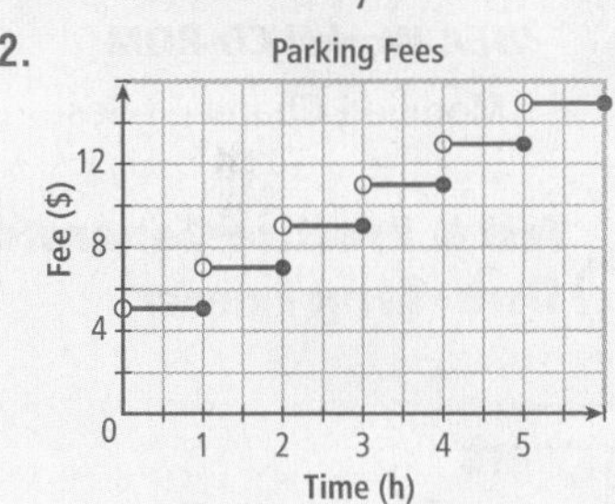

translation 1 unit up

53. quadratic function

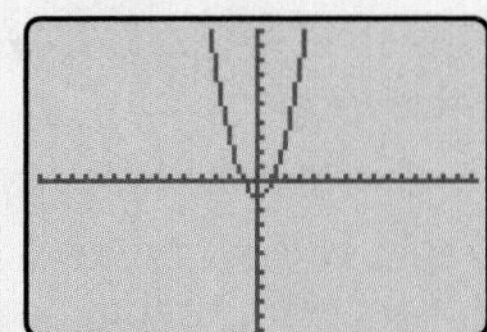

translation 1 unit down

54. square-root function

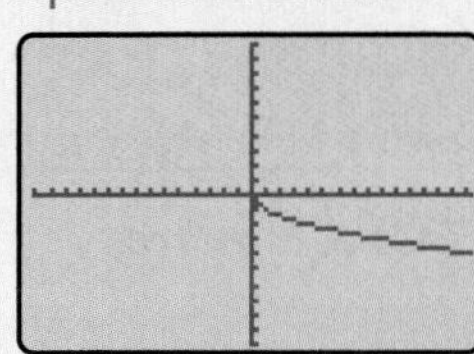

reflection across the x-axis

55.
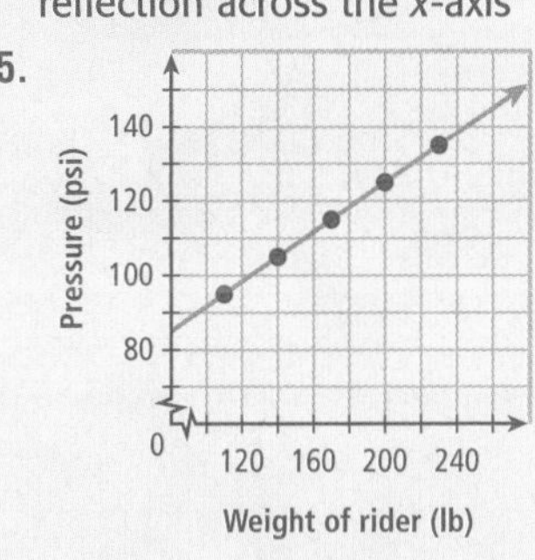

linear function; about 90 psi

Organizer

Objective: Assess students' mastery of concepts and skills in Chapter 1.

Online Edition

Resources

Assessment Resources

Chapter 1 Tests
- Free Response (Levels A, B, C)
- Multiple Choice (Levels A, B, C)
- Performance Assessment

***IDEA Works!* CD-ROM**

Modified Chapter 1 Test

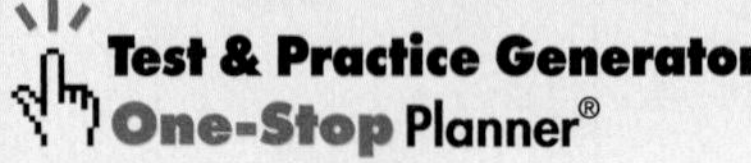

Test & Practice Generator One-Stop Planner®

Answers

1. $-2, -\sqrt{3}, 0.95, 1, 1.\overline{5}$; -2: $\mathbb{R}, \mathbb{Q}, \mathbb{Z}$; $-\sqrt{3}$: $\mathbb{R}$, irrational; 0.95: $\mathbb{R}, \mathbb{Q}$; 1: $\mathbb{R}, \mathbb{Q}, \mathbb{Z}, \mathbb{W}, \mathbb{N}$; $1.\overline{5}$: $\mathbb{R}, \mathbb{Q}$
4. Comm. Prop. of Add.
5. Distributive Property
6. Multiplicative Identity Property
7. 2.4 ft, 2.8 ft, and 3.9 ft; the 8 ft^2 window is the largest that could fit in the wall.
12. $-2x - 4y$
14. $-16a^5b^7$
15. $\frac{7v}{u^4}$
16. $\frac{y^6}{25x^8}$
17. $\frac{y}{3x}$
21. 8; -2; 0
22. -14; $-\frac{1}{4}$; 0
23. 1; ≈ 1.87; ≈ 1.73
24.

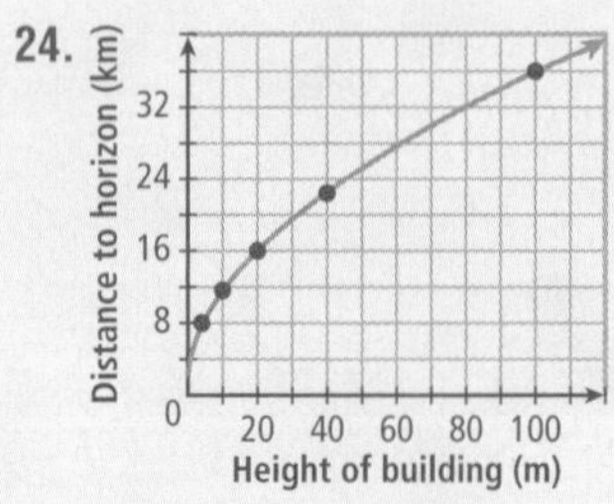

square-root function; $\approx$ 32 km

State Resources

CHAPTER 1 CHAPTER TEST

1. Order $1.\overline{5}$, -2, 0.95, $-\sqrt{3}$, and 1 from least to greatest. Then classify each number by the subsets of the real numbers to which it belongs.

Rewrite each set in the indicated notation.

2. 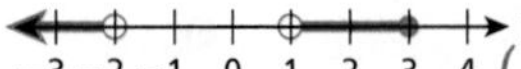 (number line from -3 to 4) interval notation $(-\infty, -2)$ and $(1, 3]$
3. $(-\infty, 12]$; set-builder notation $\{x \mid x \leq 12\}$

Identify the property demonstrated by each equation.

4. $x + y = y + x$
5. $9 \cdot 2 + 9 \cdot 7 = 9 \cdot (2 + 7)$
6. $x = (1)x$
7. A company manufactures square windows that come in three sizes: 6 square feet, 8 square feet, and 15 square feet. Estimate the side length of each window to the nearest tenth of a foot. Then identify which window is the largest one that could fit in a wall with a width of 3 feet.

Simplify each expression.

8. $-2\sqrt{3} + \sqrt{75}$ $3\sqrt{3}$
9. $\sqrt{24} - \sqrt{54}$ $-\sqrt{6}$
10. $\sqrt{22} \cdot \sqrt{55}$ $11\sqrt{10}$
11. $2(x + 1) + 9x$ $11x + 2$
12. $5x - 5y - 7x + y$
13. $12x + 4(x + y) - 6y$ $16x - 2y$

Simplify each expression. Assume all variables are nonzero.

14. $8a^2b^5(-2a^3b^2)$
15. $\frac{28u^{-2}v^3}{4u^2v^2}$
16. $(5x^4y^{-3})^{-2}$
17. $\left(\frac{3x^2y}{xy^2}\right)^{-1}$
18. German shepherds are often used as police dogs because they have 2.25×10^8 smell receptors in their nose. Humans average only 5×10^6 smell receptors in their nose. How many times as great is the number of smell receptors in a German shepherd's nose as that in a human's nose? 45

Give the domain and range for each relation. Then tell whether each relation is a function.

19.

x	10	9	8	9	10
y	2	4	6	8	10

D: $\{8, 9, 10\}$; R: $\{2, 4, 6, 8, 10\}$; not a function

20.

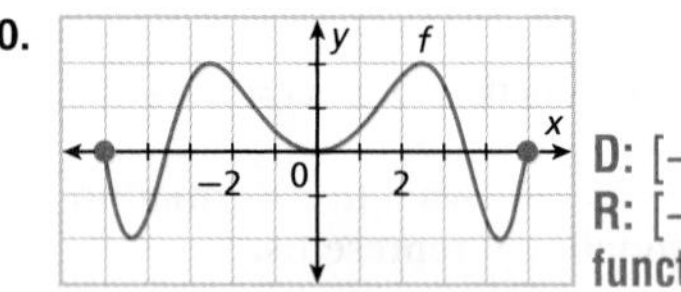

D: $[-5, 5]$; R: $[-2, 2]$; function

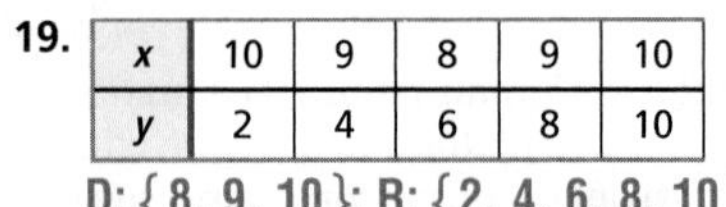

For each function, evaluate $f(-2), f\left(\frac{1}{2}\right)$, and $f(0)$.

21. $f(x) = -4x$
22. $f(x) = -3x^2 + x$
23. $f(x) = \sqrt{x + 3}$
24. The table shows how the distance from the top of a building to the horizon depends on the building's height. Graph the relationship from building height to horizon distance, and identify which parent function best describes the data. Then use your graph to estimate the distance to the horizon from the top of a building with a height of 80 m.

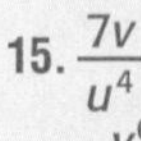

Horizon Distances					
Height of Building (m)	5	10	20	40	100
Distance to Horizon (km)	8.0	11.3	15.9	22.5	35.6

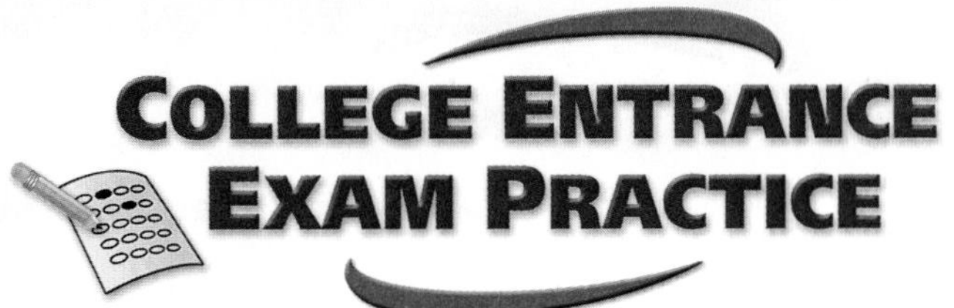

FOCUS ON SAT

The SAT* measures the math and verbal reasoning skills needed for academic success. Your SAT scores show you how you compare with other students taking the test and can be used by colleges to determine admission and to award merit-based financial aid.

On SAT multiple-choice questions, you receive one point for each correct answer, but you lose a fraction of a point for each incorrect response. Guess only when you can eliminate at least one of the answer choices.

You may want to time yourself as you take this practice test. It should take you about 6 minutes to complete.

1. Which element is in the range of the function $\{(-9, -2), (2, 4), (3, -7), (8, 1), (10, 0), (5, 6)\}$?

(A) -9

(B) -1

(C) 2

(D) 3

(E) 6

2. What is the value of $7z^2 + 4 \cdot 3w$ when $w = 8$ and $z = -3$?

(A) 1608

(B) 537

(C) 412

(D) 159

(E) -4068

3. Which of the following is NOT equivalent to $\frac{(mn^3)^4}{m^2n}$?

(A) m^2n^{11}

(B) $\frac{m^4n^{12}}{m^2n}$

(C) $m^{-1}n^{11}$

(D) $(mn^3)^4m^{-2}n^{-1}$

(E) $m^2\frac{(n^3)^4}{n}$

4. If $2 \le x \le 6$, which of the following has the greatest value?

(A) $\sqrt{x}$

(B) $\sqrt{x+1}$

(C) $\sqrt{x+2}$

(D) $\sqrt{x-1}$

(E) $\sqrt{x-2}$

5. Which function is graphed below?

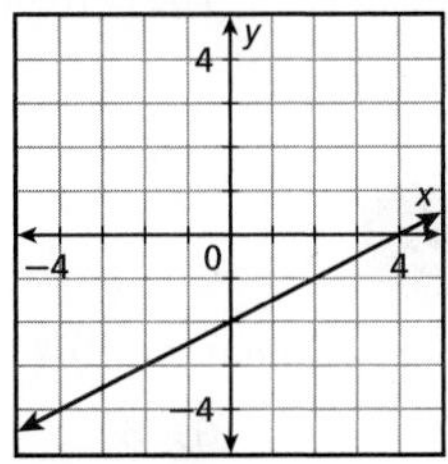

(A) $y = \frac{1}{2}x - 2$

(B) $y = 2x - 2$

(C) $y = \frac{1}{2}(x - 2)$

(D) $y = 2(x - 2)$

(E) $y = \frac{1}{2}x + 2$

Organizer

Objective: Provide practice for college entrance exams such as the SAT.

Resources

College Entrance Exam Practice

Questions on the SAT represent the following math strands:

Number and Operation, 30–32%

Algebra and Functions, 28–32%

Geometry and Measurement, 27–30%

Data Analysis, Statistics, and Probability, 10–12%

Items on this page focus on:

- Algebra and Functions
- Number and Operation

Text References:

Item	1	2	3	4	5
Lesson	1-6	1-4	1-5	1-3	1-9

TEST PREP DOCTOR

1. Remind students of the definitions of the domain and range of a function. Students who did not choose **E** may think that any element listed is in the range.

2. Students who chose **A** or **C** may not have followed the order of operations. Remind students that in this case the power is evaluated first, then multiplication is carried out from left to right, and finally the terms are added.

3. Students who chose **D** may not recognize that negative exponents can be used to express powers in the denominator of a fraction.

4. Explain to students that because $2 \le x \le 6$, each expression is a positive real number. Therefore, the square root of the greatest number will be the greatest.

5. Students who chose **B** may have incorrectly identified the slope of the line. Students who chose **C** may have mistaken a vertical translation by 2 for a horizontal translation by 2.

Organizer

Objective: Provide opportunities to learn and practice common test-taking strategies.

Online Edition

Resources

State Test Prep Workbook

State Test Prep CD-ROM

State Test Practice Online

go.hrw.com
KEYWORD: MB7 TestPrep

This Test Tackler focuses on using multiple methods. Students can use multiple methods to check their answers or to solve a problem in a nontraditional way.

Standardized Test Strategies

Multiple Choice: Use Multiple Methods

Many mathematical problems can be solved by more than one method. After solving a multiple-choice test item, you can use another method to check your answer. If your answers are not the same, you may have made a typical error for that type of question—likely mistakes are generally answer choices!

EXAMPLE 1

Evaluate the expression $\frac{1}{2}(nm - m^2 + n)$ for $n = 10$ and $m = -2$.

Ⓐ 13 Ⓑ −3 Ⓒ −7 Ⓓ −59

Select a method to evaluate.

$\frac{1}{2}(nm - m^2 + n)$

$\frac{1}{2}[10(-2) - (-2)^2 + 10]$ *Substitute.*

$\frac{1}{2}(-20 - 4 + 10)$ *Simplify.*

$\frac{1}{2}(-14) = -7$

Use an alternative method to check.

$\frac{1}{2}(nm - m^2 + n)$

$\frac{1}{2}nm - \frac{1}{2}m^2 + \frac{1}{2}n$ *Distribute.*

$\frac{1}{2}(10)(-2) - \frac{1}{2}(-2)^2 + \frac{1}{2}(10)$ *Substitute.*

$-10 - 2 + 5 = -7$

The answers are the same, −7. The correct choice is C.

EXAMPLE 2

Which expression is equivalent to $(6^3)^4$?

Ⓕ 6^{12} Ⓖ 6^7 Ⓗ 18^4 Ⓙ 72

Select a method. Suppose you add the exponents.

$(6^3)^4 = 6^{(3+4)}$

$= 6^7$ *6^7 is choice G.*

Check using an alternative method.

$(6^3)^4 = 6^3 \cdot 6^3 \cdot 6^3 \cdot 6^3$ *Rewrite in expanded form.*

$= 6^{(3+3+3+3)}$ *Product of Powers Property*

$= 6^{12}$ *6^{12} is choice F.*

Notice that the answers are different! Both answers are given as choices, so a common error was made in one of the methods. Look closely at the first method; the Power of a Power Property was incorrectly used. The exponents should have been *multiplied, not added.* The correct choice is F.

When a multiple-choice test item is created, incorrect answer choices known as *distracters* are created by solving the problem and intentionally making typical mistakes. Even if your answer choice is given, it is not a guarantee that it is the correct answer. Check your work!

Read each test item and answer the questions that follow.

Item A
A pet store has a dog pen discounted 20%. If the original cost of the dog pen is $82.80, what is the amount of the discount?

Ⓐ $1.66 Ⓒ $16.56
Ⓑ $8.28 Ⓓ $66.24

1. Explain how to use mental math to solve this problem.
2. Describe another method you can use to solve this problem. Then explain how you can use this method to check your answer.

Item B
The area of the rectangle is $\sqrt{8} \cdot \sqrt{24}$. This product simplifies to which of the following expressions?

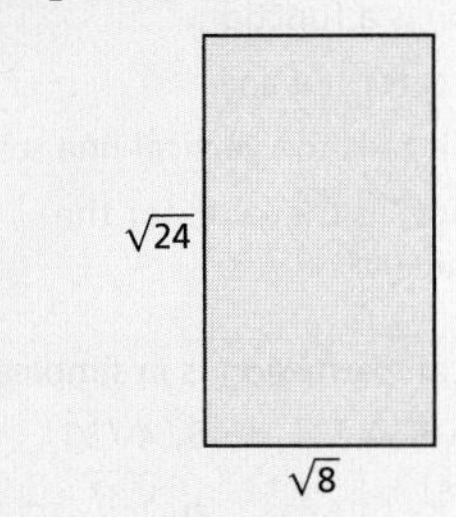

Ⓕ $8\sqrt{3}$ Ⓗ $2\sqrt{8}$
Ⓖ $4\sqrt{8}$ Ⓙ $2\sqrt{12}$

3. Explain two different ways you can simplify the product.
4. Explain how you can use these two methods to check whether your answer is correct.

Item C
The volume of the cube can be simplified to which of the following expressions?

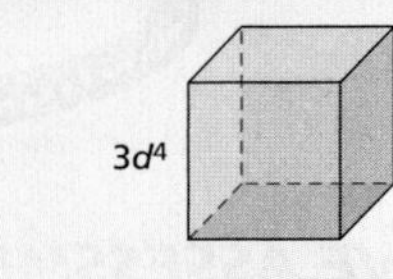

Ⓐ $27d^{12}$ Ⓒ $9d^{12}$
Ⓑ $27d^7$ Ⓓ $9d^7$

5. Describe the method you would use to solve this problem.
6. Explain an alternative method you can use to solve this problem. Then explain how you can use this method to check your answer.
7. Choices B, C, and D are distracters. What common errors were made to generate these expressions?

Item D
Consider the function $f(x) = 6x - 12$. What is $f(-3)$?

Ⓕ -216 Ⓗ -18
Ⓖ -30 Ⓙ -6

8. Explain how you would evaluate this function.
9. How could you use graphing to check your answer?

Item E
The expression $-8(-9 + 12 - 6)$ simplifies to which value?

Ⓐ -216 Ⓒ 11
Ⓑ -72 Ⓓ 24

10. Describe two different methods you can use to simplify the expression.
11. If your answers to each method are not the same, explain what you would do next.

Answers

Possible answers:

1. Find 10% of $82.80 and double the answer.
2. Multiply $82.80 by 0.2. I can compare this value to the value I found using the mental math method to see if the answers are the same.
3. Simplify each radicand and then multiply, or multiply the radicands first and then simplify.
4. Compare both solutions to make sure they give the same result.
5. Substitute the expression $3d^4$ into the volume formula. Then simplify the expression by using the properties of exponents.
6. Write out the product in expanded form and then simplify. If both methods result in the same simplified expression, then the answer is probably correct.
7. Choice **B** is the result of adding the exponents rather than multiplying them based on the Power of a Power Property. Choice **C** is the result of squaring the exponent instead of cubing. Choice **D** is the result of making both of the mistakes described in choices **B** and **C.**
8. Substitute the value -3 for x and simplify.
9. Plot the function on a graph and then find the y-value when $x = -3$. If this value is the same as the value that I found when I simplified the expression, then the answer is probably correct.
10. Evaluate the operations within the parentheses first and then multiply, or apply the Distributive Property and then combine like terms.
11. If the answers to each method are not the same, I will look closely at each step of both methods until I discover the error.

Answers to Test Items

A. C
B. F
C. A
D. G
E. D

State Resources

go.hrw.com
State Resources Online
KEYWORD: MB7 Resources

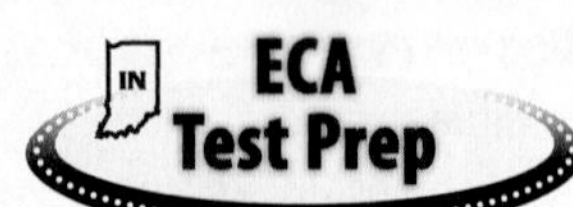

Organizer

Objective: Provide review and practice for Chapter 1 and standardized tests.

Online Edition

Resources

Assessment Resources

Chapter 1 Cumulative Test

State Test Prep Workbook

State Test Prep CD-ROM

State Test Practice Online

go.hrw.com
KEYWORD: MB7 TestPrep

Answers

1. C
2. D
3. B
4. A
5. D
6. A
7. C
8. B
9. D
10. D
11. C
12. B
13. B

Core Standard	Items
3	1, 2, 14
4	5

CUMULATIVE ASSESSMENT, CHAPTER 1

Multiple Choice

1. Which function translates $f(x) = x^2$ left 7 units?
   - A. $g(x) = x^2 - 7$
   - B. $g(x) = x^2 + 7$
   - C. $g(x) = (x + 7)^2$
   - D. $g(x) = (x - 7)^2$

2. For which function does $f(-8) = -6$?
   - A. $f(x) = 2x^2 - 6$
   - B. $f(x) = 10x - 6$
   - C. $f(x) = x^2 - 10$
   - D. $f(x) = 2x + 10$

3. The circumference of Jena's hula hoop is 32π in. Which subset of the real numbers best describes 32π?
   - A. Natural numbers
   - B. Irrational numbers
   - C. Whole numbers
   - D. Rational numbers

4. The following procedure was used to design a logo. The letter *A* was positioned upright in the first quadrant of a coordinate plane and then reflected across the *x*-axis. Then both figures were reflected across the *y*-axis. Which is the correct logo?
   - A. 
   - B.
   - C. 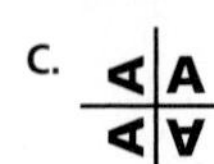
   - D.

5. Which expression simplifies to $x^2 - 3x$?
   - A. $2(x^2 + x) - 3x^2 + 5x$
   - B. $2(x^2 - x) + 3x^2 - 5x$
   - C. $-2(x^2 + x) - 3x^2 + 5x$
   - D. $-2(x^2 - x) + 3x^2 - 5x$

6. The quotient of 7.84×10^{-3} and which divisor is 5.6×10^{-4}?
   - A. 1.4×10^1
   - B. 2.24×10^{-7}
   - C. 1.4×10^{-7}
   - D. 2.24×10^1

7. If milk price is the dependent variable and number of ounces is the independent variable, which statement is true for the graph of the data in the table?

Milk Prices		
Package Size	**Number of Ounces**	**Milk Price**
1 pint	16	\$0.90
1 quart	32	\$1.29
1 half gallon	64	\$1.95
2 quarts	64	\$2.58
1 gallon	128	\$3.90

   - A. The graph is a function.
   - B. The points form a line.
   - C. The graph fails the vertical-line test.
   - D. "Milk price" is the label for the horizontal axis.

8. Which radical expression is in simplest form?
   - A. $\sqrt{45} + 3\sqrt{5}$
   - B. $4\sqrt{30}$
   - C. $\sqrt{2} \cdot \sqrt{10}$
   - D. $\frac{\sqrt{27}}{9}$

9. Simplify $-(5x^2y^{-1}z^{-3})^2$.
   - A. $-\frac{5x^4}{y^2z^6}$
   - B. $25x^4y^{-2}z^{-6}$
   - C. $-25x^4y^{-2}z^{-6}$
   - D. $-\frac{25x^4}{y^2z^6}$

TEST PREP DOCTOR

For **Item 9,** students who chose **A** may not remember that the 5 must be squared also. Students who chose **C** may have applied the properties of exponents correctly, but did not rewrite their answer so that all exponents were positive.

Answers

14. **Part A:** 5.48 m; check students' work.
    Part B: Possible answer: $\sqrt{50}$ simplifies to $5\sqrt{2}$, which is approximately $5(1.41) \approx 7.05$. Therefore, the side length of the plot is about 7.05 m.

15. **Part A:** Seoul, Istanbul, Hong Kong, Cairo, Chicago, Houston
    Part B: Los Angeles would be between Cairo and Chicago. New York would be between Istanbul and Hong Kong.

10. Which does NOT represent the set shown on this number line?

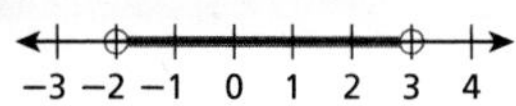

A. All numbers between −2 and 3

B. $-2 < x < 3$

C. $(-2, 3)$

D. All numbers −2 through 3, inclusive

11. The lengths of the legs of a right triangle are 2 and $4\sqrt{3}$. What is the perimeter of the triangle?

A. $\sqrt{52}$

B. $6\sqrt{3} + 2\sqrt{13}$

C. $2 + 4\sqrt{3} + 2\sqrt{13}$

D. $9\sqrt{39}$

Use mental math to calculate 10% of an amount by moving the decimal point left one place. Then you can use that amount to find 5% by taking half of the amount or find 20% by doubling the amount.

12. Which expression can be used to determine 7.5% of a $210 purchase?

A. $0.1(210) - \frac{1}{2}(0.1)(210)$

B. $\frac{1}{2}(0.1)(210) + \frac{1}{4}(0.1)(210)$

C. $0.1(210) + \frac{1}{4}(0.1)(210)$

D. $\frac{1}{2}(0.1)(210) - \frac{1}{4}(0.1)(210)$

13. Craig is mowing lawns and trimming hedges as a community service project. It takes 35 minutes to mow one lawn and 45 minutes to trim the hedges on a property. He plans to work for 4 hours on Saturday. If he mows 3 lawns, how many hedges can he trim?

A. 2

B. 3

C. 4

D. 5

Short Answer

14. A city worker is dividing a community garden into square plots.

Part A One plot will have an area of 30 square meters. Find an approximate value for the side length of the plot without using a calculator or a square-root table. Explain each step and show your work. Give your answer to the nearest hundredth of a meter.

Part B How can you use the fact that $\sqrt{2} \approx 1.41$ to approximate the side length of a plot with an area of 50 square meters?

15. Shown in the table are some of the world's largest cities, ranked according to population statistics.

Selected Cities		
City	Country	Population
Houston, TX	United States	1.953×10^6
Seoul	South Korea	1.023×10^7
Hong Kong	China	6.843×10^6
Chicago, IL	United States	2.896×10^6
Cairo	Egypt	6.800×10^6
Istanbul	Turkey	8.260×10^6

Source: **Citymayors.com**

Part A Order the cities from greatest population to least population.

Part B Two other U.S. cities are in a list of the largest 100 cities in the world. Los Angeles, California, has a population of 3,694,000. New York, New York, has a population of about 8 million. Where would these cities rank if they were included in the table?

Extended Response

16. Change machines charge a fee of $0.089 for every dollar of change turned into cash. The fee is taken from the cash amount returned to the user.

Part A Write a function that represents the amount returned in cash.

Part B Sketch and label the function graph.

Part C Identify the parent function for this function.

Part D What amount is returned from $21.91 of change converted to cash?

Short Answer Rubric

Items 14–15

Score 2 = Thorough understanding of mathematical concepts and processes.

Score 1 = Partial understanding of mathematical concepts and/or processes.

Score 0 = Limited or no understanding of the problem-solving concepts.

Blank = No written response.

Extended Response Rubric

Item 16

Score 4 = Thorough understanding of mathematical concepts and processes.

Score 3 = Demonstrated understanding of mathematical concepts and processes, but an error in computation or explanation.

Score 2 = Partial understanding of mathematical concepts and/or processes.

Score 1 = Limited understanding and execution of the problem-solving concepts.

Score 0 = No understanding of the problem-solving concepts.

Blank = No written response.

16. Part A: $f(c) = c - 0.089c$, where c is the amount of change in dollars

Part B:

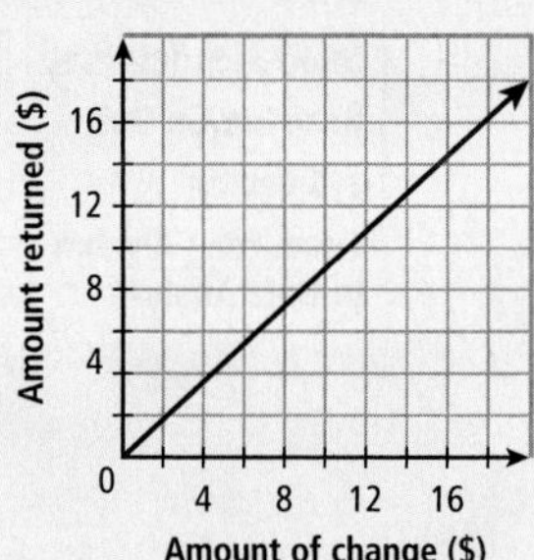

Part C: linear function

Part D: $19.96

CHAPTER 2 Linear Functions

Section 2A

Linear Equations and Inequalities

2-1 Solving Linear Equations and Inequalities
2-2 Proportional Reasoning
Connecting Algebra to Geometry Percent Increase and Decrease
2-3 Graphing Linear Functions
2-3 Technology Lab Explore Graphs and Windows
2-4 Writing Linear Functions
2-5 Linear Equations in Two Variables

Section 2B

Applying Linear Functions

2-6 Transforming Linear Functions
Connecting Algebra to Data Analysis Statistical Graphs
2-7 Curve Fitting with Linear Models
2-8 Solving Absolute-Value Equations and Inequalities
2-9 Technology Lab Solve Absolute-Value Equations
2-9 Absolute-Value Functions

Pacing Guide for 45-Minute Classes

Chapter 2

Countdown to Testing Weeks 3, 4, 5

DAY 1	DAY 2	DAY 3	DAY 4	DAY 5
2-1 Lesson	2-1 Lesson	2-2 Lesson	Connecting Algebra to Geometry 2-3 Lesson	2-3 Lesson 2-3 Technology Lab
DAY 6	**DAY 7**	**DAY 8**	**DAY 9**	**DAY 10**
2-4 Lesson	2-4 Lesson	2-5 Lesson	Multi-Step Test Prep Ready to Go On? 2-6 Lesson	2-6 Lesson Connecting Algebra to Data Analysis
DAY 11	**DAY 12**	**DAY 13**	**DAY 14**	**DAY 15**
2-7 Lesson	2-8 Lesson	2-8 Lesson	2-9 Technology Lab 2-9 Lesson	2-9 Lesson Multi-Step Test Prep Ready to Go On?
DAY 16				
Chapter 2 Test				

Pacing Guide for 90-Minute Classes

Chapter 2

DAY 1	DAY 2	DAY 3	DAY 4	DAY 5
2-1 Lesson	2-2 Lesson Connecting Algebra to Geometry 2-3 Lesson	2-3 Lesson 2-3 Technology Lab 2-4 Lesson	2-4 Lesson 2-5 Lesson	Multi-Step Test Prep Ready to Go On? 2-6 Lesson Connecting Algebra to Data Analysis
DAY 6	**DAY 7**	**DAY 8**		
2-7 Lesson 2-8 Lesson	2-8 Lesson 2-9 Technology Lab 2-9 Lesson	2-9 Lesson Multi-Step Test Prep Ready to Go On? Chapter 2 Test		

ONGOING ASSESSMENT and INTERVENTION

	DIAGNOSE	PRESCRIBE
Assess Prior Knowledge	**Before Chapter 2**	
	Diagnose readiness for the chapter.	Prescribe intervention.
	Are You Ready? SE p. 87	***Are You Ready? Intervention*** Skills 21, 49, 54, 58, 68
Formative Assessment	**Before Every Lesson**	
	Diagnose readiness for the lesson.	Prescribe intervention.
	Warm Up TE, every lesson	**Skills Bank** SE, pp. S46–S73
		Reteach CRB, Ch. 1–2
	During Every Lesson	
	Diagnose understanding of lesson concepts.	Prescribe intervention.
	Check It Out! SE, every example	**Questioning Strategies** TE, every example
	Think and Discuss SE, every lesson	**Reading Strategies** CRB, every lesson
	Write About It SE, every lesson	***Success for ELL*** pp. 19–36
	Journal TE, every lesson	
	After Every Lesson	
	Diagnose mastery of lesson concepts.	Prescribe intervention.
	Lesson Quiz TE, every lesson	**Reteach** CRB, every lesson
	Alternative Assessment TE, every lesson	**Problem Solving** CRB, every lesson
	Test Prep SE, every lesson	**Test Prep Doctor** TE, every lesson
	Test and Practice Generator	***Homework Help Online***
	Before Chapter 2 Testing	
	Diagnose mastery of concepts in the chapter.	Prescribe intervention.
	Ready to Go On? SE pp. 133, 165	***Ready to Go On? Intervention*** pp. 23–42
	Multi-Step Test Prep SE pp. 132, 164	**Scaffolding Questions** TE pp. 132, 164
	Section Quizzes AR pp. 25–26	
	Test and Practice Generator	
	 **Before High Stakes Testing**	
	Diagnose mastery of benchmark concepts.	Prescribe intervention.
	College Entrance Exam Practice SE p. 171	***College Entrance Exam Practice***
	Standardized Test Prep SE pp. 174–175	***State Test Prep Workbook***
	State Test Prep CD-ROM	
Summative Assessment	**After Chapter 2**	
	Check mastery of chapter concepts.	Prescribe intervention.
	Multiple-Choice Tests (Forms A, B, C)	**Reteach** CRB, every lesson
	Free-Response Tests (Forms A, B, C)	***Lesson Tutorial Videos*** Chapter 2
	Performance Assessment AR pp. 27–40	
	Test and Practice Generator	
	Check mastery of benchmark concepts.	Prescribe intervention.
	AYP State Tests	***State Test Prep Workbook***
	College Entrance Exams	***College Entrance Exam Practice***

KEY: **SE** = *Student Edition* **TE** = *Teacher's Edition* **CRB** = *Chapter Resource Book* **AR** = *Assessment Resources*  Available on CD-ROM Available online

Supporting the Teacher

Chapter 2 Resource Book

Practice A, B, C
pp. 3–5, 11–13, 19–21, 27–29, 35–37, 43–45, 51–53, 54–61, 67–69

Reading Strategies ELL
pp. 10, 18, 26, 34, 42, 50, 58, 66, 74

Reteach
pp. 6–7, 14–15, 22–23, 30–31, 38–39, 46–47, 54–55, 62–63, 70–71

Problem Solving
pp. 9, 17, 25, 33, 41, 49, 57, 65, 73

Challenge
pp. 8, 16, 24, 32, 40, 48, 56, 64, 72

Parent Letter pp. 1–2

Transparencies

Lesson Transparencies, Volume 1 .... Chapter 2
- Teaching Tools
- Warm Ups
- Teaching Transparencies
- Additional Examples
- Lesson Quizzes

Alternate Openers: Explorations 10–18

Countdown to Testing 5–10

Know-It Notebook .... Chapter 2
- Graphic Organizers

Teacher Tools

Power Presentations®
Complete PowerPoint® presentations for Chapter 2 lessons

Lesson Tutorial Videos®
Holt authors Ed Burger and Freddie Renfro present tutorials to support the Chapter 2 lessons.

One-Stop Planner®
Easy access to all Chapter 2 resources and assessments, as well as software for lesson planning, test generation, and puzzle creation

IDEA Works!®
Key Chapter 2 resources and assessments modified to address special learning needs

Lesson Plans...pp. 10–18

Solutions Key .... Chapter 2

Algebra Posters

TechKeys **Lab Resources**

Project Teacher Support **Parent Resources**

Workbooks

Homework and Practice Workbook
Teacher's Guide ....pp. 10–18

Know-It Notebook
Teacher's Guide .... Chapter 2

Problem Solving Workbook
Teacher's Guide ....pp. 10–18

State Test Prep Workbook
Teacher's Guide

Technology Highlights for the Teacher

Power Presentations

Dynamic presentations to engage students. Complete PowerPoint® presentations for every lesson in Chapter 2.

2-1 Solving One-Step Equations

Isolate a variable by using inverse operations which "undo" operations on the variable.

An equation is like a balanced scale. To keep the balance, perform the same operation on both sides.

Inverse Operations	
Operation	**Inverse Operation**
Addition	Subtraction
Subtraction	Addition

One-Stop Planner

Easy access to Chapter 2 resources and assessments. Includes lesson-planning, test-generation, and puzzle-creation software.

Premier Online Edition

Chapter 2 includes Tutorial Videos, Lesson Activities, Lesson Quizzes, Homework Help, and Chapter Project.

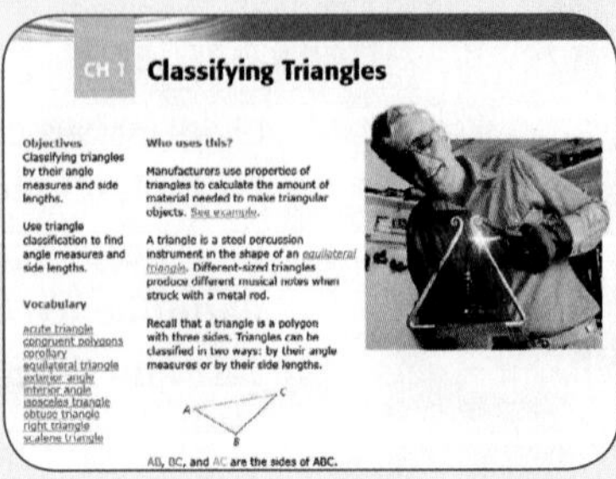

KEY: **SE** = *Student Edition* **TE** = *Teacher's Edition*  English Language Learners  Available on CD-ROM  Available online

Reaching All Learners

Resources for All Learners

Algebra Lab Activities .... Chapter 2
Technology Lab Activities .... Chapter 2
Homework and Practice Workbook .... pp. 10–18
Know-It Notebook .... Chapter 2
Problem Solving Workbook .... pp. 10–18

DEVELOPING LEARNERS

Practice A .... CRB, every lesson
Reteach .... CRB, every lesson
Inclusion .... TE pp. 117, 136, 152
Questioning Strategies .... TE, every example
Modified Chapter 2 Resources .... *IDEA Works!*
Homework Help Online

ON-LEVEL LEARNERS

Practice B .... CRB, every lesson
Multiple Representations .... TE pp. 93, 104, 117, 135
Cooperative Learning .... TE pp. 118, 159

ADVANCED LEARNERS

Practice C .... CRB, every lesson
Challenge .... CRB, every lesson
Reading and Writing Math EXTENSION .... TE p. 89
Multi-Step Test Prep EXTENSION .... TE pp. 132, 164
Critical Thinking .... TE pp. 101, 111, 116, 125, 144, 147

English Language Learners

ENGLISH LANGUAGE LEARNERS

Are You Ready? Vocabulary .... SE p. 87
Vocabulary Connections .... SE p. 88
Lesson Vocabulary .... SE pp. 90, 97, 105, 115, 124, 142, 150, 158
Vocabulary Exercises .... SE pp. 94, 100, 109, 128, 146, 154, 161
Vocabulary Review .... SE p. 166
English Language Learners .... TE pp. 89, 129
Reading Strategies .... CRB, every lesson
Success for English Language Learners .... pp. 19–36
Multilingual Glossary

Reaching All Learners Through...

Concrete Manipulatives .... TE p. 91
Multiple Representations .... TE pp. 93, 104, 117, 135
Kinesthetic Experience .... TE pp. 98, 135, 143
Critical Thinking .... TE pp. 101, 111, 116, 125, 144, 147
Graphic Organizers .... TE p. 106
Auditory Cues .... TE p. 107
Visual Cues .... TE pp. 116, 129, 141, 162
Inclusion .... TE pp. 117, 136, 152
Cooperative Learning .... TE pp. 118, 159
Cognitive Strategies .... TE p. 151
Test Prep Doctor .... TE pp. 96, 103, 112, 123, 131, 140, 148, 156, 163, 171–174
Common Error Alerts .... TE pp. 93, 95, 99, 101, 107, 117, 121, 127, 129, 137, 139, 143, 147, 153
Scaffolding Questions .... TE pp. 132, 164

Technology Highlights for Reaching All Learners

Lesson Tutorial Videos

Starring Holt authors Ed Burger and Freddie Renfro! Live tutorials to support every lesson in Chapter 2.

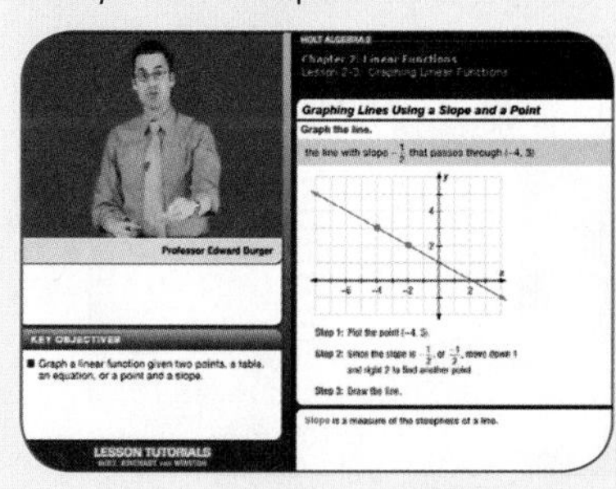

Multilingual Glossary

Searchable glossary includes definitions in English, Spanish, Vietnamese, Chinese, Hmong, Korean, and 4 other languages.

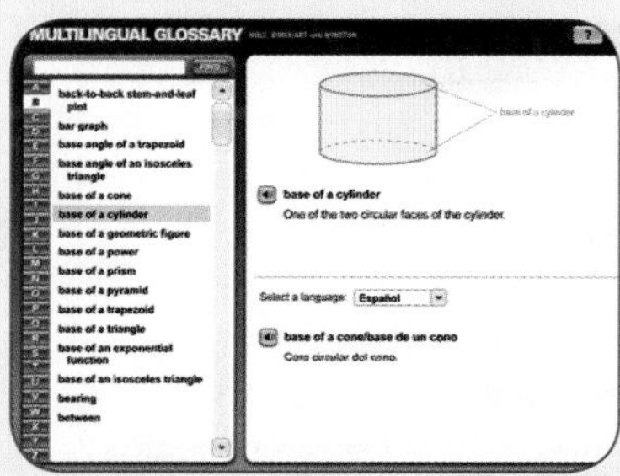

Online Interactivities

Interactive tutorials provide visually engaging alternative opportunities to learn concepts and master skills.

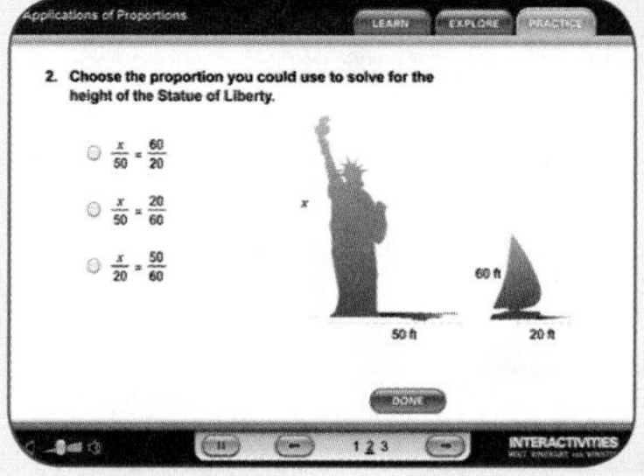

KEY: **SE** = *Student Edition* **TE** = *Teacher's Edition* **CRB** = *Chapter Resource Book* Available on CD-ROM Available online

Ongoing Assessment

Assessing Prior Knowledge

Determine whether students have the required prerequisite concepts and skills for success in Chapter 2.

Are You Ready? SPANISH .... SE p. 87
Warm Up .... TE, every lesson

Test Preparation

Provide review and practice for Chapter 2 and standardized tests.

Multi-Step Test Prep .... SE pp. 132, 164
Study Guide: Review .... SE pp. 166–169
Test Tackler .... SE pp. 172–173
Standardized Test Prep .... SE pp. 174–175
College Entrance Exam Practice .... SE p. 171
***Countdown to Testing* Transparencies** 5–10
State Test Prep Workbook
***State Test Prep* CD-ROM**
IDEA Works!

Alternative Assessment

Assess students' understanding of Chapter 2 concepts and combined problem-solving skills.

Chapter 2 Project .... SE p. 86
Alternative Assessment .... TE, every lesson
Performance Assessment .... AR pp. 39–40
Portfolio Assessment .... AR p. xxxiv

Daily Assessment

Provide formative assessment for each day of Chapter 2.

Questioning Strategies .... TE, every example
Think and Discuss .... SE, every lesson
Check It Out! Exercises .... SE, every example
Write About It .... SE, every lesson
Journal .... TE, every lesson
Lesson Quiz .... TE, every lesson
Alternative Assessment .... TE, every lesson
Modified Lesson Quizzes .... *IDEA Works!*

Weekly Assessment

Provide formative assessment for each week of Chapter 2.

Multi-Step Test Prep .... SE pp. 132, 164
Ready to Go On? .... SE pp. 133, 165
Cumulative Assessment .... SE pp. 174–175
Test and Practice Generator .... *One-Stop Planner*

Formal Assessment

Provide summative assessment of Chapter 2 mastery.

Section Quizzes .... AR pp. 25–26
Chapter 2 Test .... SE p. 170
Chapter Test (Levels A, B, C) .... AR pp. 27–38
• Multiple Choice • Free Response
Cumulative Test .... AR pp. 41–44
Test and Practice Generator .... *One-Stop Planner*
Modified Chapter 2 Test .... *IDEA Works!*

Technology Highlights for Ongoing Assessment

Are You Ready? SPANISH

Automatically assess readiness and prescribe intervention for Chapter 2 prerequisite skills.

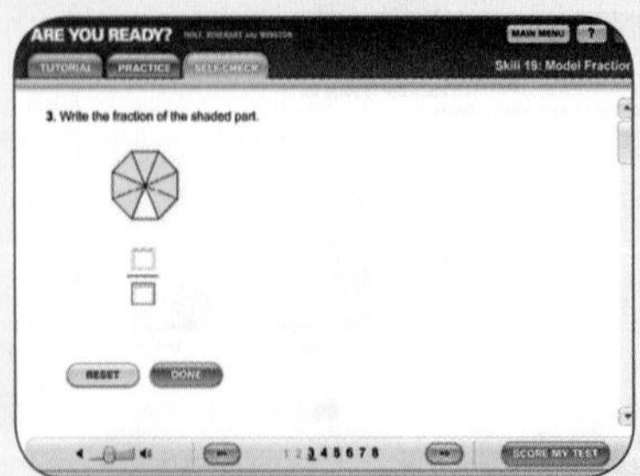

Ready to Go On?

Automatically assess understanding and prescribe intervention for Sections 2A and 2B.

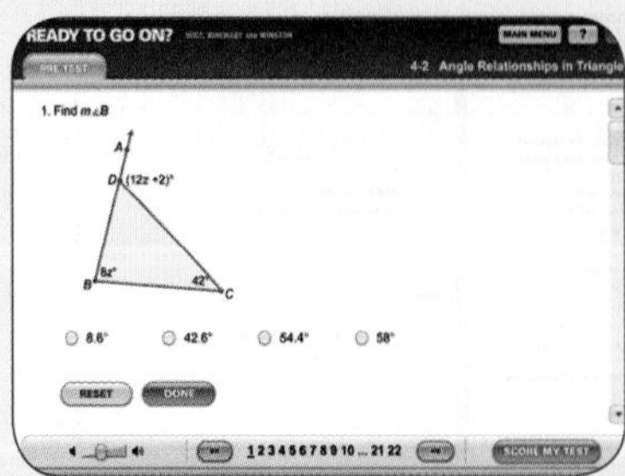

Test and Practice Generator

Use Chapter 2 problem banks to create assessments and worksheets to print out or deliver online. Includes dynamic problems.

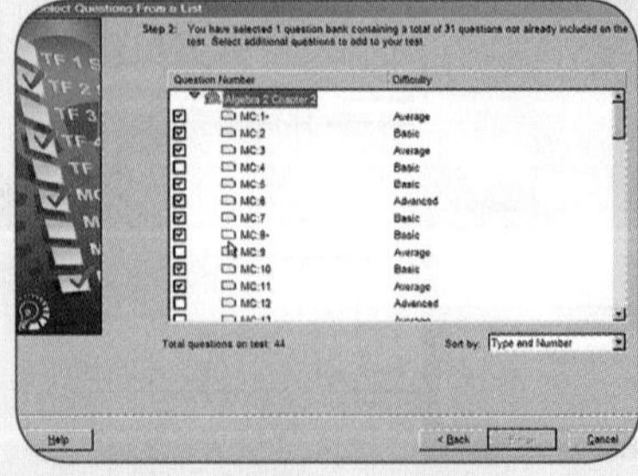

KEY: **SE** = *Student Edition* **TE** = *Teacher's Edition* **AR** = *Assessment Resources* SPANISH Spanish version available  Available on CD-ROM 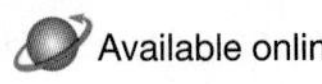 Available online

CHAPTER 2

Formal Assessment

Three levels (A, B, C) of multiple-choice and free-response chapter tests are available in the *Assessment Resources*.

A Chapter 2 Test

C Chapter 2 Test

MULTIPLE CHOICE

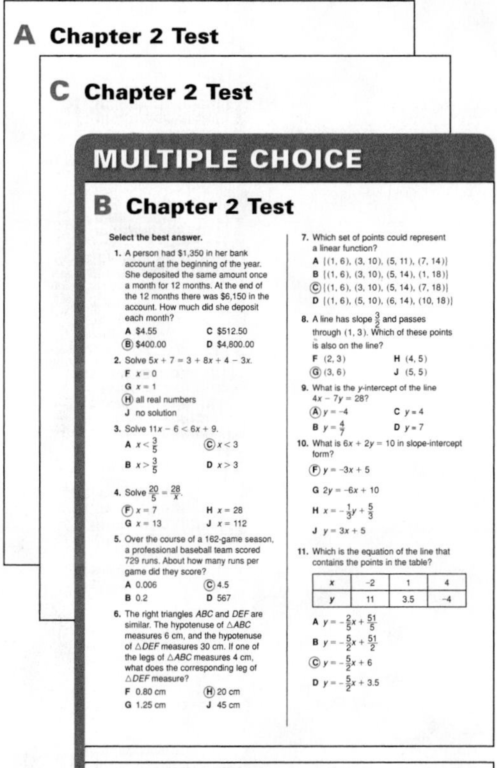

B Chapter 2 Test

Select the best answer.

1. A person had \$1,350 in her bank account at the beginning of the year. She deposited the same amount once a month for 12 months. At the end of the 12 months there was \$6,150 in the account. How much did she deposit each month?
   A \$4.55 C \$512.50
   (B) \$400.00 D \$4,800.00
2. Solve $5x + 7 = 3 + 8x + 4 - 3x$.
   F $x = 0$
   G $x = 1$
   (H) all real numbers
   J no solution
3. Solve $11x - 6 < 6x + 9$.
   A $x < \frac{3}{5}$ (C) $x < 3$
   B $x > \frac{3}{5}$ D $x > 3$
4. Solve $\frac{20}{5} = \frac{28}{x}$.
   (F) $x = 7$ H $x = 28$
   G $x = 13$ J $x = 112$
5. Over the course of a 162-game season, a professional baseball team scored 729 runs. About how many runs per game did they score?
   A 0.006 (C) 4.5
   B 0.2 D 567
6. The right triangles ABC and DEF are similar. The hypotenuse of $\triangle ABC$ measures 6 cm, and the hypotenuse of $\triangle DEF$ measures 30 cm. If one of the legs of $\triangle ABC$ measures 4 cm, what does the corresponding leg of $\triangle DEF$ measure?
   F 0.80 cm (H) 20 cm
   G 1.25 cm J 45 cm
7. Which set of points could represent a linear function?
   A {(1, 6), (3, 10), (5, 11), (7, 14)}
   B {(1, 6), (3, 10), (5, 14), (1, 18)}
   (C) {(1, 6), (3, 10), (5, 14), (7, 18)}
   D {(1, 6), (5, 10), (6, 14), (10, 18)}
8. A line has slope $\frac{3}{2}$ and passes through (1, 3). Which of these points is also on the line?
   F (2, 3) H (4, 5)
   (G) (3, 6) J (5, 5)
9. What is the y-intercept of the line $4x - 7y = 28$?
   (A) $y = -4$ C $y = 4$
   B $y = \frac{4}{7}$ D $y = 7$
10. What is $6x + 2y = 10$ in slope-intercept form?
    (F) $y = -3x + 5$
    G $2y = -6x + 10$
    H $x = -\frac{1}{3}y + \frac{5}{3}$
    J $y = 3x + 5$
11. Which is the equation of the line that contains the points in the table?

x	−2	1	4
y	11	3.5	−4

    A $y = -\frac{2}{5}x + \frac{51}{5}$
    B $y = -\frac{5}{2}x + \frac{51}{2}$
    (C) $y = -\frac{5}{2}x + 6$
    D $y = -\frac{5}{2}x + 3.5$

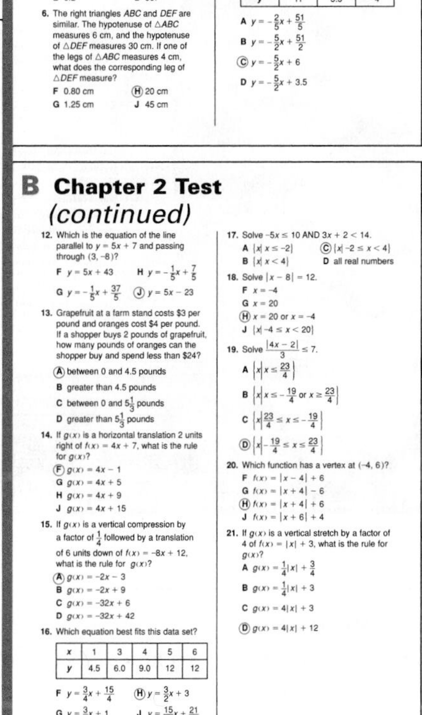

B Chapter 2 Test *(continued)*

12. Which is the equation of the line parallel to $y = 5x + 7$ and passing through (3, −8)?
    F $y = 5x + 43$ H $y = -\frac{1}{5}x + \frac{7}{5}$
    G $y = -\frac{1}{5}x + \frac{37}{5}$ (J) $y = 5x - 23$
13. Grapefruit at a farm stand costs \$3 per pound and oranges cost \$4 per pound. If a shopper buys 2 pounds of grapefruit, how many pounds of oranges can the shopper buy and spend less than \$24?
    (A) between 0 and 4.5 pounds
    B greater than 4.5 pounds
    C between 0 and $5\frac{1}{3}$ pounds
    D greater than $5\frac{1}{3}$ pounds
14. If $g(x)$ is a horizontal translation 2 units right of $f(x) = 4x + 7$, what is the rule for $g(x)$?
    (F) $g(x) = 4x - 1$
    G $g(x) = 4x + 5$
    H $g(x) = 4x + 9$
    J $g(x) = 4x + 15$
15. If $g(x)$ is a vertical compression by a factor of $\frac{1}{4}$ followed by a translation of 6 units down of $f(x) = -8x + 12$, what is the rule for $g(x)$?
    (A) $g(x) = -2x - 3$
    B $g(x) = -2x + 9$
    C $g(x) = -32x + 6$
    D $g(x) = -32x + 42$
16. Which equation best fits this data set?

x	1	3	4	5	6
y	4.5	6.0	9.0	12	12

    F $y = \frac{3}{4}x + \frac{15}{4}$ (H) $y = \frac{3}{2}x + 3$
    G $y = \frac{3}{2}x + 1$ J $y = \frac{15}{8}x + \frac{21}{8}$
17. Solve $-5x \le 10$ AND $3x + 2 < 14$.
    A $\{x \mid x \le -2\}$ (C) $\{x \mid -2 \le x < 4\}$
    B $\{x \mid x < 4\}$ D all real numbers
18. Solve $|x - 8| = 12$.
    F $x = -4$
    G $x = 20$
    (H) $x = 20$ or $x = -4$
    J $\{x \mid -4 \le x \le 20\}$
19. Solve $\frac{|4x - 2|}{3} \le 7$.
    A $\{x \mid x \le \frac{23}{4}\}$
    B $\{x \mid x \le -\frac{19}{4}$ or $x \ge \frac{23}{4}\}$
    C $\{x \mid \frac{23}{4} \le x \le -\frac{19}{4}\}$
    (D) $\{x \mid -\frac{19}{4} \le x \le \frac{23}{4}\}$
20. Which function has a vertex at (−4, 6)?
    F $f(x) = |x - 4| + 6$
    G $f(x) = |x + 4| - 6$
    (H) $f(x) = |x + 4| + 6$
    J $f(x) = |x + 6| + 4$
21. If $g(x)$ is a vertical stretch by a factor of 4 of $f(x) = |x| + 3$, what is the rule for $g(x)$?
    A $g(x) = \frac{1}{4}|x| + \frac{3}{4}$
    B $g(x) = \frac{1}{4}|x| + 3$
    C $g(x) = 4|x| + 3$
    (D) $g(x) = 4|x| + 12$

A Chapter 2 Test

C Chapter 2 Test

FREE RESPONSE

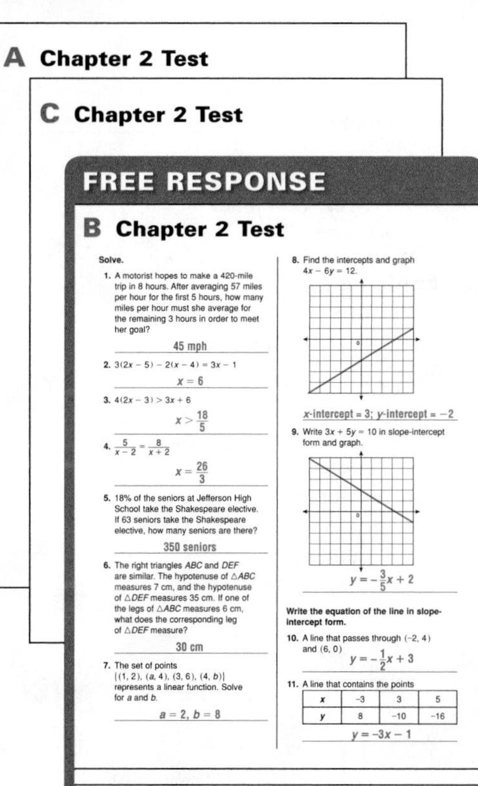

B Chapter 2 Test

Solve.

1. A motorist hopes to make a 420-mile trip in 8 hours. After averaging 57 miles per hour for the first 5 hours, how many miles per hour must she average for the remaining 3 hours in order to meet her goal?
   45 mph
2. $3(2x - 5) - 2(x - 4) = 3x - 1$
   $x = 6$
3. $4(2x - 3) > 3x + 6$
   $x > \frac{18}{5}$
4. $\frac{5}{x - 2} = \frac{8}{x + 2}$
   $x = \frac{26}{3}$
5. 18% of the seniors at Jefferson High School take the Shakespeare elective. If 63 seniors take the Shakespeare elective, how many seniors are there?
   350 seniors
6. The right triangles ABC and DEF are similar. The hypotenuse of $\triangle ABC$ measures 7 cm, and the hypotenuse of $\triangle DEF$ measures 35 cm. If one of the legs of $\triangle ABC$ measures 6 cm, what does the corresponding leg of $\triangle DEF$ measure?
   30 cm
7. The set of points {(1, 2), (a, 4), (3, 6), (4, b)} represents a linear function. Solve for a and b.
   $a = 2, b = 8$
8. Find the intercepts and graph $4x - 6y = 12$.
   x-intercept = 3; y-intercept = −2
9. Write $3x + 5y = 10$ in slope-intercept form and graph.
   $y = -\frac{3}{5}x + 2$

Write the equation of the line in slope-intercept form.

10. A line that passes through (−2, 4) and (6, 0)
    $y = -\frac{1}{2}x + 3$
11. A line that contains the points

x	−3	3	5
y	8	−10	−16

    $y = -3x - 1$

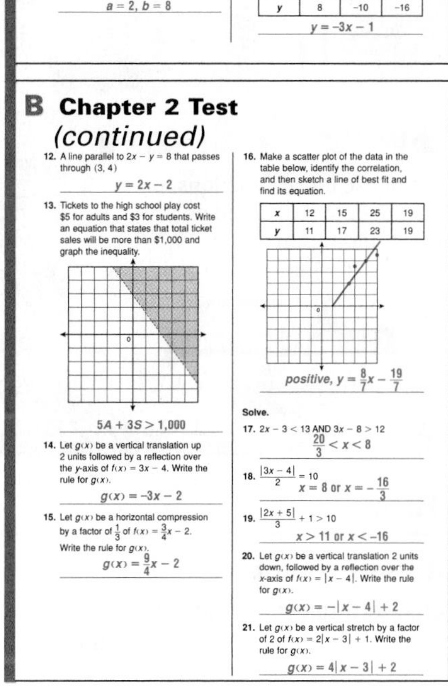

B Chapter 2 Test *(continued)*

12. A line parallel to $2x - y = 8$ that passes through (3, 4)
    $y = 2x - 2$
13. Tickets to the high school play cost \$5 for adults and \$3 for students. Write an equation that states that total ticket sales will be more than \$1,000 and graph the inequality.
    $5A + 3S > 1{,}000$
14. Let $g(x)$ be a vertical translation up 2 units followed by a reflection over the y-axis of $f(x) = 3x - 4$. Write the rule for $g(x)$.
    $g(x) = -3x - 2$
15. Let $g(x)$ be a horizontal compression by a factor of $\frac{1}{3}$ of $f(x) = \frac{3}{4}x - 2$. Write the rule for $g(x)$.
    $g(x) = \frac{9}{4}x - 2$
16. Make a scatter plot of the data in the table below, identify the correlation, and then sketch a line of best fit and find its equation.

x	12	15	25	19
y	11	17	23	19

    positive, $y = \frac{8}{7}x - \frac{19}{7}$

Solve.

17. $2x - 3 < 13$ AND $3x - 8 > 12$
    $\frac{20}{3} < x < 8$
18. $\frac{|3x - 4|}{2} = 10$
    $x = 8$ or $x = -\frac{16}{3}$
19. $\frac{|2x + 5|}{3} + 1 > 10$
    $x > 11$ or $x < -16$
20. Let $g(x)$ be a vertical translation 2 units down, followed by a reflection over the x-axis of $f(x) = |x - 4|$. Write the rule for $g(x)$.
    $g(x) = -|x - 4| + 2$
21. Let $g(x)$ be a vertical stretch by a factor of 2 of $f(x) = 2|x - 3| + 1$. Write the rule for $g(x)$.
    $g(x) = 4|x - 3| + 2$

MODIFIED FOR IDEA

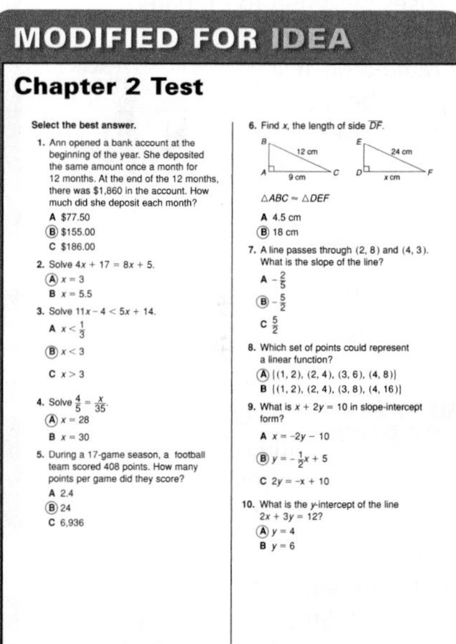

Chapter 2 Test

Select the best answer.

1. Ann opened a bank account at the beginning of the year. She deposited the same amount once a month for 12 months. At the end of the 12 months, there was \$1,860 in the account. How much did she deposit each month?
   A \$77.50
   (B) \$155.00
   C \$186.00
2. Solve $4x + 17 = 8x + 5$.
   (A) $x = 3$
   B $x = 5.5$
3. Solve $11x - 4 < 5x + 14$.
   A $x < \frac{1}{3}$
   (B) $x < 3$
   C $x > 3$
4. Solve $\frac{4}{5} = \frac{x}{35}$.
   (A) $x = 28$
   B $x = 30$
5. During a 17-game season, a football team scored 408 points. How many points per game did they score?
   A 2.4
   (B) 24
   C 6,936
6. Find x, the length of side $\overline{DF}$.
   $\triangle ABC \sim \triangle DEF$
   A 4.5 cm
   (B) 18 cm
7. A line passes through (2, 8) and (4, 3). What is the slope of the line?
   A $-\frac{2}{5}$
   (B) $-\frac{5}{2}$
   C $\frac{5}{2}$
8. Which set of points could represent a linear function?
   (A) {(1, 2), (2, 4), (3, 6), (4, 8)}
   B {(1, 2), (2, 4), (3, 8), (4, 16)}
9. What is $x + 2y = 10$ in slope-intercept form?
   A $x = -2y - 10$
   (B) $y = -\frac{1}{2}x + 5$
   C $2y = -x + 10$
10. What is the y-intercept of the line $2x + 3y = 12$?
    (A) $y = 4$
    B $y = 6$

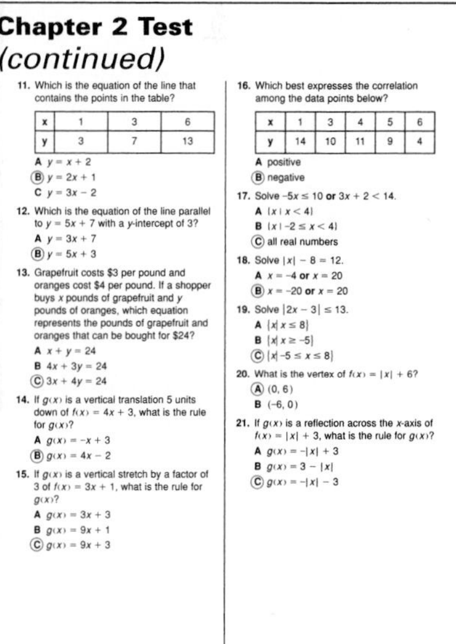

Chapter 2 Test *(continued)*

11. Which is the equation of the line that contains the points in the table?

x	1	3	6
y	3	7	13

    A $y = x + 2$
    (B) $y = 2x + 1$
    C $y = 3x - 2$
12. Which is the equation of the line parallel to $y = 5x + 7$ with a y-intercept of 3?
    A $y = 3x + 7$
    (B) $y = 5x + 3$
13. Grapefruit costs \$3 per pound and oranges cost \$4 per pound. If a shopper buys x pounds of grapefruit and y pounds of oranges, which equation represents the pounds of grapefruit and oranges that can be bought for \$24?
    A $x + y = 24$
    B $4x + 3y = 24$
    (C) $3x + 4y = 24$
14. If $g(x)$ is a vertical translation 5 units down of $f(x) = 4x + 3$, what is the rule for $g(x)$?
    A $g(x) = -x + 3$
    (B) $g(x) = 4x - 2$
15. If $g(x)$ is a vertical stretch by a factor of 3 of $f(x) = 3x + 1$, what is the rule for $g(x)$?
    A $g(x) = 3x + 3$
    B $g(x) = 9x + 1$
    (C) $g(x) = 9x + 3$
16. Which best expresses the correlation among the data points below?

x	1	3	4	5	6
y	14	10	11	9	4

    A positive
    (B) negative
17. Solve $-5x \le 10$ or $3x + 2 < 14$.
    A $\{x \mid x < 4\}$
    B $\{x \mid -2 \le x < 4\}$
    (C) all real numbers
18. Solve $|x| - 8 = 12$.
    A $x = -4$ or $x = 20$
    (B) $x = -20$ or $x = 20$
19. Solve $|2x - 3| \le 13$.
    A $\{x \mid x \le 8\}$
    B $\{x \mid x \ge -5\}$
    (C) $\{x \mid -5 \le x \le 8\}$
20. What is the vertex of $f(x) = |x| + 6$?
    (A) (0, 6)
    B (−6, 0)
21. If $g(x)$ is a reflection across the x-axis of $f(x) = |x| + 3$, what is the rule for $g(x)$?
    A $g(x) = -|x| + 3$
    B $g(x) = 3 - |x|$
    (C) $g(x) = -|x| - 3$

Test & Practice Generator
One-Stop Planner®

Create and customize Chapter 2 Tests. Instantly generate multiple test versions, answer keys, and practice versions of test items.

CHAPTER 2

SECTION **2A**

Linear Equations and Inequalities

On page 132, students write, solve, and graph equations and inequalities to model real-world sailing situations.

Exercises designed to prepare students for success on the Multi-Step Test Prep can be found on pages 95, 102, 111, 122, and 129.

SECTION **2B**

Applying Linear Functions

On page 164, students apply linear functions to model a real-world art situation.

Exercises designed to prepare students for success on the Multi-Step Test Prep can be found on pages 139, 148, 155, and 162.

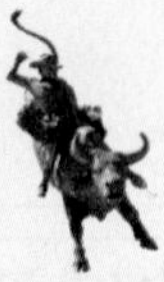

CHAPTER 2

Linear Functions

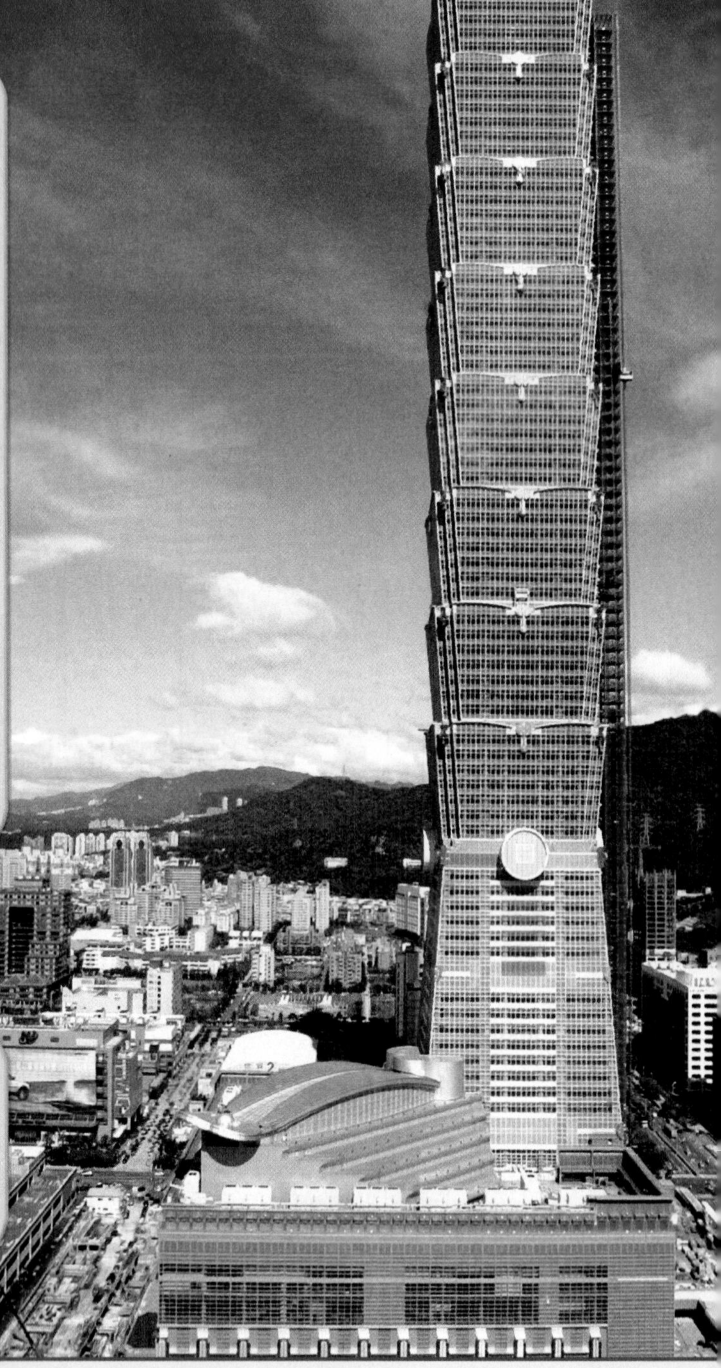

SKY HIGH

You can use linear functions to compare data sets based on the tallest buildings in the world, including the Taipei 101 tower.

go.hrw.com
Chapter Project Online
KEYWORD: MB7 ChProj

Sky High

About the Project

In the Chapter Project, students research heights and other dimensions of buildings and use the data to explore linear relationships.

Project Resources

All project resources for teachers and students are provided online.

Materials:

- computer with Internet access
- graphing calculator

ARE YOU READY?

Vocabulary

Match each term on the left with a definition on the right.

1. absolute value C
2. function A
3. transformation B
4. scatter plot E

A. a relation in which each first coordinate is paired with exactly one second coordinate
B. a change in the position, size, or shape of a figure
C. the distance from a number to zero on the number line
D. a symbol used to represent a quantity that can change
E. a graph on a coordinate plane with points plotted to represent relationships between data sets

Connect Words and Algebra

Write an equation for each phrase.

5. The sum of a number and 4 times another number is 25. $x + 4y = 25$
6. The difference of 3 times a number and 20 is greater than 10. $3x - 20 > 10$
7. A number divided by 12 is less than 15 divided by the same number. $\frac{x}{12} < \frac{15}{x}$

Solve One-Step Equations

Solve each equation for x.

8. $-8 + x = -20$ -12
9. $-12 = -3x$ 4
10. $x - 19 = -12$ 7
11. $0.75 = \frac{x}{5}$ 3.75

Percent Problems

Solve each percent problem.

12. Fifteen is 30% of what number? 50
13. What number is 40% of 140? 56
14. What percent of 140 is 105? 75%
15. What number is 150% of 90? 135

Convert Units of Measure

Convert the units of measure.

16. 12 quarts to gallons 3 gal
17. 15 feet to yards 5 yd
18. 1.5 hours to minutes 90 min
19. 3.5 gallons to quarts 14 qt
20. 17 yards to feet 51 ft
21. 200 minutes to hours $3\frac{1}{3}$ h
22. 107 centimeters to meters 1.07 m
23. 2.5 kilometers to meters 2500 m
24. 50 milliliters to liters 0.05 L

Absolute Value

Find the absolute value of each expression.

25. $|16 - 22|$ 6
26. $|32 - 20|$ 12
27. $|8 - 17 + 9|$ 0
28. $|-0.75 + 0.625|$ 0.125

ARE YOU READY?

Organizer

Objective: Assess students' understanding of prerequisite skills.

Prerequisite Skills

- Connect Words and Algebra
- Solve One-Step Equations
- Percent Problems
- Convert Units of Measure
- Absolute Value

Assessing Prior Knowledge

INTERVENTION

Diagnose and Prescribe

Use this page to determine whether intervention is necessary or whether enrichment is appropriate.

Resources

Are You Ready? Intervention and Enrichment **Worksheets**

Are You Ready? **CD-ROM**

Are You Ready? **Online**

my.hrw.com

ARE YOU READY?

Diagnose and Prescribe

NO INTERVENE

YES ENRICH

	Are You Ready? Intervention, Chapter 2		
Prerequisite Skill	Worksheets	CD-ROM	Online
Connect Words and Algebra	Skill 58	Activity 58	Diagnose and Prescribe Online
Solve One-Step Equations	Skill 68	Activity 68	
Percent Problems	Skill 49	Activity 49	
Convert Units of Measure	Skill 21	Activity 21	
Absolute Value	Skill 54	Activity 54	

Are You Ready? Enrichment, Chapter 2
- Worksheets
- CD-ROM
- Online

CHAPTER 2

Study Guide: Preview

Organizer

Objective: Help students organize the new concepts they will learn in Chapter 2.

Online Edition
Multilingual Glossary

Resources

Puzzle Pro
One-Stop Planner®

***Multilingual Glossary* Online**

go.hrw.com
KEYWORD: MB7 Glossary

Answers to *Vocabulary Connections*

1. *Identical* means "exactly the same"; when an equation says that two things are exactly the same.
2. A rate is a ratio involving different units. Slope is the rate at which something is rising (or falling).
3. To intercept a message is to catch it as it is on its way elsewhere. The line is "caught" by an axis at a specific location.
4. Regression is "going back" to the line or curve that fits the data.

CHAPTER 2

Study Guide: Preview

Where You've Been

Previously, you

- used the properties of real numbers and properties of exponents.
- studied relations and functions.
- graphed parent functions.
- explored transformations.

In This Chapter

You will study

- using properties of equality to write and solve linear equations.
- writing and graphing linear functions.
- solving problems involving transformations of the linear parent function.
- transformations of the absolute-value parent function.

Where You're Going

You can use the skills learned in this chapter

- to model data and make predictions in sports, travel, and financial affairs.
- in fields such as health, chemistry, physics, and economics.
- in your future math classes, including Calculus and Statistics.

Key Vocabulary/Vocabulario

absolute-value function	función de valor absoluto
correlation	correlacíon
identity	identidad
indirect measurement	medición indirecta
line of best fit	línea de mejor ajuste
linear function	función lineal
proportion	proporción
rate	tasa
regression	regresión
scale factor	factor de escala
slope	pendiente
y-intercept	intersección con el eje y

Vocabulary Connections

To become familiar with some of the vocabulary terms in the chapter, consider the following. You may refer to the chapter, the glossary, or a dictionary if you like.

1. What does the word *identical* mean? When do you think an equation might be called an **identity**?
2. How is the word **rate** related to the word **ratio**?
3. What does it mean to *intercept* a message? Why would the value at the crossing location for a line and an axis be called an **intercept**?
4. The word *regress* means "to go back." How can you use the definition of *regress* to understand **regression** in mathematics?

Reading Strategy: Read a Lesson for Understanding

As you read a lesson, read with a purpose. Lessons are centered on one or two specific objectives given at the top of the first page. Reading with the objectives in mind will help guide you through the lesson. You can use some of the following tips to help you follow the math as you read.

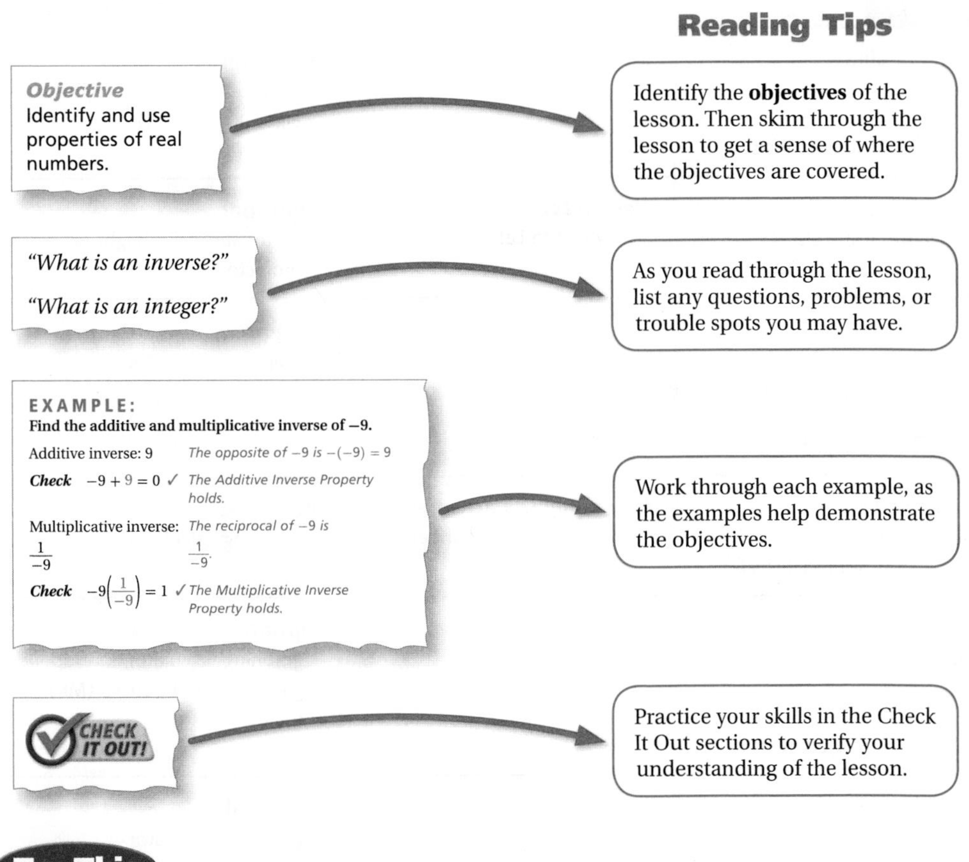

Reading Tips
Objective
Identify and use properties of real numbers.
Identify the objectives of the lesson. Then skim through the lesson to get a sense of where the objectives are covered.
"What is an inverse?"
"What is an integer?"
As you read through the lesson, list any questions, problems, or trouble spots you may have.
EXAMPLE:
Find the additive and multiplicative inverse of –9.
Additive inverse: 9 The opposite of –9 is –(–9) = 9
Check –9 + 9 = 0 ✓ The Additive Inverse Property holds.
Multiplicative inverse: 1/–9 The reciprocal of –9 is 1/–9.
Check –9(1/–9) = 1 ✓ The Multiplicative Inverse Property holds.
Work through each example, as the examples help demonstrate the objectives.
CHECK IT OUT!
Practice your skills in the Check It Out sections to verify your understanding of the lesson.

Try This

Use Lesson 1-4 in your textbook to answer each question.

1. What is the objective of the lesson? simplifying and evaluating algebraic expressions
2. What new terms are defined in the lesson? order of operations
3. Fraction bars, square root symbols, and absolute value symbols are all forms of what type of symbol? grouping symbols
4. What skill is being practiced in the first Check It Out problem in the lesson? simplifying numerical expressions

Organizer

Objective: Help students apply strategies to understand and retain key concepts.

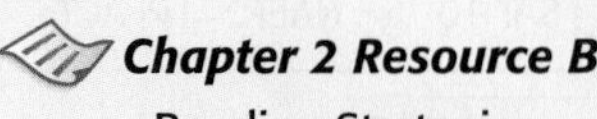

Resources

Chapter 2 Resource Book
Reading Strategies

Reading Strategy: Read a Lesson for Understanding

ENGLISH LANGUAGE LEARNERS

Discuss Students benefit by becoming familiar with the technique of using lesson objectives and terminology to focus their reading. Help students see that reading with a purpose enables them to recognize the important parts of a lesson and gain a better understanding of what the lesson is all about.

Extend Assign the lessons as a reading assignment the night before each lesson is to be presented in class. Encourage students to use the reading tips described in this feature as they read the assigned lesson. When the lesson is presented in class, have students talk about how they applied the reading tips and how the reading tips helped them focus on the important concepts of the lesson.

SECTION

2A Linear Functions

One-Minute Section Planner

Lesson	Lab Resources	Materials
Lesson 2-1 Solving Linear Equations and Inequalities • Solve linear equations using a variety of methods. • Solve linear inequalities. ☐ SAT-10 ☑ NAEP ☑ ACT ☑ SAT ☑ SAT Subject Tests		**Optional** balance scale with weights, algebra tiles (MK)
Lesson 2-2 Proportional Reasoning • Apply proportional relationships to rates, similarity, and scale. ☑ SAT-10 ☑ NAEP ☑ ACT ☑ SAT ☑ SAT Subject Tests	***Algebra Lab Activities*** 2-2 Algebra Lab	**Optional** meter sticks, flashlight or projector
Lesson 2-3 Graphing Linear Functions • Determine whether a function is linear. • Graph a linear function given two points, a table, an equation, or a point and a slope. ☑ SAT-10 ☑ NAEP ☐ ACT ☑ SAT ☐ SAT Subject Tests		**Required** graphing calculator
2-3 Technology Lab Explore Graphs and Windows • Use a graphing calculator to explore graphs and windows. ☐ SAT-10 ☐ NAEP ☐ ACT ☐ SAT ☐ SAT Subject Tests	***Technology Lab Activities*** 2-3 Lab Recording Sheet	**Required** graphing calculator
Lesson 2-4 Writing Linear Functions • Use slope-intercept form and point-slope form to write linear functions. • Write linear functions to solve problems. ☐ SAT-10 ☑ NAEP ☑ ACT ☐ SAT ☐ SAT Subject Tests		**Optional** graphing calculator, Monopoly game, colored pencils (MK), markers
Lesson 2-5 Linear Inequalities in Two Variables • Graph linear inequalities on the coordinate plane. • Solve problems using linear inequalities ☑ SAT-10 ☑ NAEP ☑ ACT ☑ SAT ☑ SAT Subject Tests		**Optional** graphing calculator

MK = *Manipulatives Kit*

Section Overview

Solving Linear Equations, Inequalities, and Proportions

Lesson 2-1, 2-2

Solving linear equations and inequalities is a foundational skill needed for a variety of real-world problem solving.

To solve some linear equations, use properties of real numbers and properties of equality.

$$2(y+3)-8=4y+2$$
$$2y+6-8=4y+2$$
$$2y-2=4y+2$$
$$-2y-2=2$$
$$-2y=4$$
$$y=-2$$

To solve a linear inequality, follow the same steps used to solve a linear equation.

$$2(y+3)-8\le 4y+2$$
$$2y+6-8\le 4y+2$$
$$2y-2\le 4y+2$$
$$-2y-2\le 2$$
$$\frac{-2y}{-2}\ge\frac{4}{-2}$$
$$y\ge -2$$

When multiplying or dividing both sides of an inequality by a negative, reverse the inequality symbol.

Use cross products to solve proportions.

To solve $\frac{12}{5}=\frac{x}{22.5}$:

$$\frac{12}{5}=\frac{x}{22.5}$$
$$(12)(22.5)=5x$$
$$270=5x$$
$$54=x$$

Graphing and Writing Linear Functions

Lessons 2-3, 2-4

Working comfortably with linear functions is a fundamental prerequisite skill for future math courses and is used in a variety of occupations.

To graph $y = mx + b$, first plot the y-intercept, b. Then use the slope m to find a second point.

You can also graph $y = 3x - 6$ by finding the intercepts.

To find the y-intercept, set $x = 0$ and solve for y.

To find the x-intercept, set $y = 0$ and solve for x.

Graph of $y = 3x - 6$

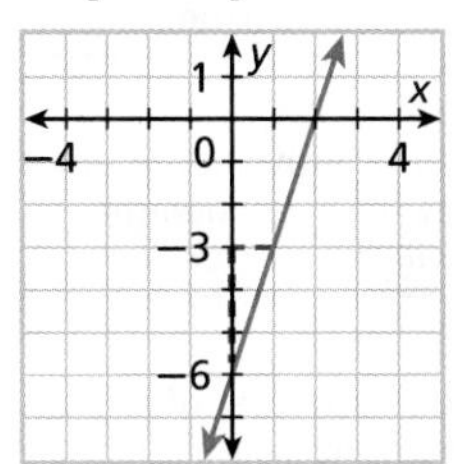

-6 is the y-intercept, and 2 is the x-intercept.

Find the equation of a line passing through (1, 7) and (–1, 11).

Step 1: Find the slope.

$$m=\frac{y_2-y_1}{x_2-x_1}=\frac{11-7}{-1-1}=\frac{4}{-2}=-2$$

Step 2: Use either point and the slope to find b.

$$y=mx+b$$
$$7=-2(1)+b$$
$$9=b$$

Step 3: Write the equation in slope-intercept form.

$$y=mx+b$$
$$y=-2x+9$$

Graphing Linear Inequalities in Two Variables

Lessons 2-5

Graphing an inequality in two variables allows one to view solutions to a problem with more than one solution.

To graph a linear inequality:

1. Graph the boundary line—dashed if points on the boundary are not included (< or >), and solid if points on the boundary are included (≤ or ≥).
2. Shade the half-plane containing the solutions of the inequality.

Graph of $y < \frac{2}{3}x - 1$

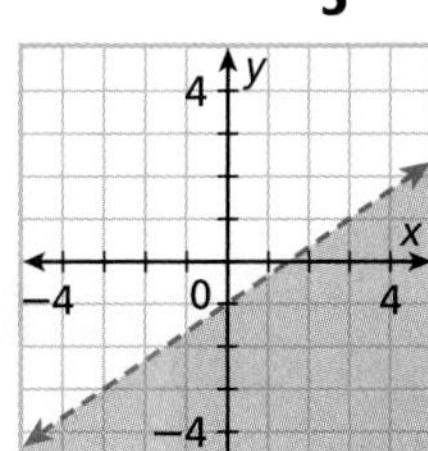

2-1 Organizer

Pacing: Traditional 2 days
Block 1 day

Objectives: Solve linear equations using a variety of methods.
Solve linear inequalities.

Online Edition
Tutorial Videos

Countdown to Testing Week 3

Power Presentations with PowerPoint®

Warm Up

Simplify each expression.

1. $2x + 5 - 3x$ $-x + 5$

2. $-(w - 2)$ $-w + 2$

3. $6(2 - 3g)$ $12 - 18g$

Graph on a number line.

4. $t > -2$

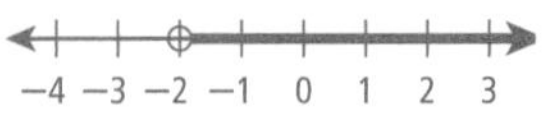

5. Is 2 a solution of the inequality $-2x < -6$? Explain. No; when 2 is substituted for x, the inequality is false: $-4 \not< -6$.

Also available on transparency

Math Fact !!!

The cruise ship *Queen Elizabeth 2* travels 40 feet on 1 gallon of fuel.

2-1 Solving Linear Equations and Inequalities

Objectives
Solve linear equations using a variety of methods.

Solve linear inequalities.

Vocabulary
equation
solution set of an equation
linear equation in one variable
identity
contradiction
inequality

Who uses this?
A hot-air balloonist can use linear equations to calculate the average speed needed to set a world record. (See Example 1.)

An **equation** is a mathematical statement that two expressions are equivalent. The **solution set of an equation** is the value or values of the variable that make the equation true. A **linear equation in one variable** can be written in the form $ax = b$, where a and b are constants and $a \neq 0$.

Linear Equations in One Variable	Nonlinear Equations
$4x = 8$	$3\sqrt{x} + 1 = 32$
$3x - \frac{2}{3}x = -9$	$\frac{2}{x^2} = 41$
$2x - 5 = 0.1x + 2$	$3 - 2^x = -5$

Notice that the variable in a linear equation is not under a radical sign and is not raised to a power other than 1. The variable is also not an exponent and is not in a denominator.

Solving a linear equation requires isolating the variable on one side of the equation by using the properties of equality.

Know it! Note

Properties of Equality

For all real numbers *a*, *b* and *c*,

WORDS	NUMBERS	ALGEBRA
Addition If you add the same quantity to both sides of an equation, the equation will still be true.	$3 = 3$ $3 + 2 = 3 + 2$	$a = b$ $a + c = b + c$
Subtraction If you subtract the same quantity from both sides of an equation, the equation will still be true.	$3 = 3$ $3 - 2 = 3 - 2$	$a = b$ $a - c = b - c$
Multiplication If you multiply both sides of an equation by the same quantity, the equation will still be true.	$3 = 3$ $3(2) = 3(2)$	$a = b$ $ac = bc$
Division If you divide both sides of an equation by the same nonzero quantity, the equation will still be true.	$3 = 3$ $\frac{3}{2} = \frac{3}{2}$	$a = b$ If $c \neq 0$, $\frac{a}{c} = \frac{b}{c}$

State Resources

1 Introduce

EXPLORATION

2-1 Solving Linear Equations and Inequalities

A group of ten friends are on vacation in Canada. They decide to rent an ice-skating rink so they can play hockey.

Rink Rental
$50 plus $25 per hour
Equipment (per person)
$5 + $1.50 per hour

1. Everyone in the group needs to rent equipment. Write an expression for the total cost of the equipment for x hours.
2. Write an expression for the total cost of the rink and the equipment for x hours.
3. Use your expression to help you complete the table.

Time (h)	1	2	3	4	5	6	7	8
Total Cost ($)								

4. The rink and equipment can be rented only in whole-hour increments. The friends want to spend less than $350. For how many hours can they rent the rink and equipment?

THINK AND DISCUSS

5. **Describe** another method you could use to solve Problem 4, other than making a table.
6. **Explain** how the solution to Problem 4 would change if a 10% tax were added to the bill.

Motivate

Use algebra manipulatives (balance scale, weights, etc.) or a drawing of a scale to discuss the concept of isolating a variable in an equation. Emphasize the importance of making the same changes to both sides of the scale in order to keep the scale balanced.

Explorations and answers are provided in the *Explorations* binder.

To isolate the variable, perform the inverse, or opposite, of every operation in the equation on both sides of the equation. Do inverse operations in the reverse order of the order of operations.

EXAMPLE 1 *Travel Application*

Steve Fossett set a 24-hour hot-air balloon record of 3186.8 miles on July 1, 2002. Suppose a balloonist has traveled 1239 miles in 10.5 hours. What speed would the balloonist need to average during the remaining 13.5 hours to tie the record?

Let v represent the speed in miles per hour the balloonist will need to average.

Model

distance already traveled	plus	average speed	times	time remaining hours	=	total distance
1239	+	v	·	13.5	=	3186.8

Solve

$$\begin{aligned} 1239 + 13.5v &= 3186.8 \\ -1239 \quad &\quad -1239 \end{aligned}$$ *Subtract 1239 from both sides.*

$$\frac{13.5v}{13.5} = \frac{1947.8}{13.5}$$ *Divide both sides by 13.5.*

$$v \approx 144.3$$

The balloonist must average about 144.3 mi/h for the remaining 13.5 hours.

1. Stacked cups are to be placed in a pantry. One cup is 3.25 in. high and each additional cup raises the stack 0.25 in. How many cups fit between two shelves 14 in. apart? 44

EXAMPLE 2 Solving Equations with the Distributive Property

Solve $5(y-7)=25$.

Method 1

The quantity $(y-7)$ is multiplied by 5, so divide by 5 first.

$$\frac{5(y-7)}{5} = \frac{25}{5}$$ *Divide both sides by 5.*

$$y - 7 = 5$$

$$+7 \quad +7$$ *Add 7 to both sides.*

$$y = 12$$

Method 2

Distribute before solving.

$$5y - 35 = 25$$ *Distribute 5.*

$$+35 \quad +35$$ *Add 35 to both sides.*

$$5y = 60$$

$$\frac{5y}{5} = \frac{60}{5}$$ *Divide both sides by 5.*

$$y = 12$$

Check

$5(y-7)$	25
$5(12-7)$	25
$5(5)$	25
25	25 ✓

Solve.

2a. $3(2-3p)=42$ -4

2b. $-3(5-4r)=-9\frac{1}{2}$

Teaching Tip **Communicating Math** As students work through the solution process, have them explain *why* they've chosen the particular operation they are using for each step. You may also want to encourage students to show checks for all equations.

Power Presentations with PowerPoint®

Additional Examples

Example 1

The local phone company charges \$12.95 a month for the first 200 minutes of air time, plus \$0.07 for each additional minute. If Nina's bill for the month was \$14.56, how many additional minutes did she use? 23 min

Example 2

Solve $4(m+12)=-36$. -21

Also available on transparency

INTERVENTION

Questioning Strategies

EXAMPLE 1

- How do you translate from the words in the problem to the equation that you solve?
- How do you know which operations to use in order to isolate the variable?
- In what order should you perform these operations?

EXAMPLE 2

- What is the Distributive Property?
- How can you check your answers? Is the check the same for both methods?

2 Teach

Guided Instruction

Review with students how to translate a verbal description into an algebraic statement. For example, for the verbal description "10 minus a number is equal to 2 times that number," students might write the equation $10 - x = 2x$. Discuss what it means for a number to be a solution of an equation or an inequality. In this context, emphasize the meaning of identities and contradictions. Point out that most equations in this course will be neither identities nor contradictions.

Reaching All Learners

Through Concrete Manipulatives

Have students use manipulatives such as algebra tiles to solve several equations, recording each step of the solution process with algebraic notation. Algebra tiles can be found in the Manipulatives Kit (MK).

Through Number Sense

Have students write equations in *calculator-ready form* by rewriting expressions using inverse operations but without simplifying, thus letting the calculator do the work. For example, rewrite $ax + b = c$ in calculator-ready form as $x = (c - b)/a$. Then have students use the calculator to solve. Students can rewrite $2x + 4 = 10$ and $\frac{1}{2}(x + 8) = 16$. $x = (10 - 4)/2$; $x = 16/(1/2) - 8$

Power Presentations with PowerPoint®

Additional Examples

Example 3

Solve.

$3k - 14k + 25 = 2 - 6k - 12$

$k = 7$

Example 4

Solve.

A. $3v - 9 - 4v = -(5 + v)$
no solution, or $\varnothing$

B. $2(x - 6) = -5x - 12 + 7x$
all real numbers, or $\mathbb{R}$

Example 5

Solve and graph
$8a - 2 \geq 13a + 8$. $a \leq -2$

Also available on transparency

INTERVENTION

Questioning Strategies

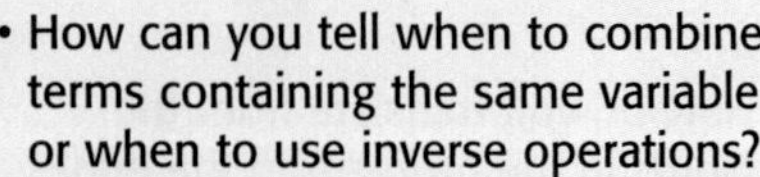

EXAMPLE 3

- How can you tell when to combine terms containing the same variable or when to use inverse operations?

EXAMPLE 4

- What are some examples of equations that are identities?
- What are some examples of equations that are contradictions?

EXAMPLE 5

- Why is it necessary to reverse the inequality symbol when you multiply or divide both sides of an inequality by a negative number?
- How do you know whether to use an open circle or a closed circle when you graph an inequality?

If there are variables on both sides of the equation, (1) simplify each side. (2) collect all variable terms on one side and all constant terms on the other side. (3) isolate the variable as you did in the previous problems.

EXAMPLE 3 **Solving Equations with Variables on Both Sides**

Solve $6y + 21 + 7 = 4y - 20 + 5y$.

$6y + 28 =$	$9y - 20$	*Simplify each side by combining like terms.*
$-6y$	$-6y$	*Collect variables on the right side.*
$28 =$	$3y - 20$	*Subtract.*
$+20$	$+20$	*Collect constants on the left side.*
$\frac{48}{3} =$	$\frac{3y}{3}$	*Isolate the variable.*
$16 = y$		

Check Substitute 16 for y on both sides of the original equation. You can use a calculator to make sure they are equal.

```
6(16)+21+7
             124
4(16)-20+5(16)
             124
```

3. Solve $3(w + 7) - 5w = w + 12$ **3**

You have solved equations that have a single solution. Equations may also have infinitely many solutions or no solution.

An equation that is true for all values of the variable, such as $x = x$, is an **identity**. An equation that has no solution, such as $3 = 5$, is a **contradiction** because there are no values that make it true.

EXAMPLE 4 **Identifying Identities and Contradictions**

Solve.

A $3x + 4x + 5 = 7x + 5$

$7x + 5 = 7x + 5$		*Simplify.*
$-7x$	$= -7x$	
$5 = 5$ ✔		*Identity*

The solution set is all real numbers, or $\mathbb{R}$.

B $8(y + 7) = 6y - 8 + 2y$

$8y + 56 = 8y - 8$		*Simplify.*
$-8y$	$= -8y$	
$56 = -8$ ✘		*Contradiction*

The equation has no solution. The solution set is the *empty set*, which is represented by the symbol $\varnothing$.

Solve.

4a. $5(x - 6) = 3x - 18 + 2x$ $\varnothing$

4b. $3(2 - 3x) = -7x - 2(x - 3)$ $\mathbb{R}$

An **inequality** is a statement that compares two expressions by using the symbols $<$, $>$, $\leq$, $\geq$, or $\neq$. The graph of an inequality is the solution set, the set of all points on the number line that satisfy the inequality.

The properties of equality are true for inequalities, with one important difference. If you multiply or divide both sides by a negative number, you must *reverse* the inequality symbol.

Inequalities — Multiplying or Dividing by a Negative Number

For all real numbers *a*, *b*, and *c*,

WORDS	NUMBERS	ALGEBRA
If you multiply both sides of an inequality by the same negative quantity and reverse the inequality symbol, the inequality will still be true.	$4 < 6$ $4(-2) > 6(-2)$ $-8 > -12$	$a < b$ If $c < 0$, $ac > bc$
If you divide both sides of an inequality by the same negative quantity and reverse the inequality symbol, the inequality will still be true.	$4 < 6$ $\frac{4}{-2} > \frac{6}{-2}$ $-2 > -3$	$a < b$ If $c < 0$, $\frac{a}{c} > \frac{b}{c}$

These properties also apply to inequalities expressed with $>$, $\geq$, and $\leq$.

EXAMPLE 5 Solving Inequalities

Solve and graph $9x + 4 < 12x - 11$.

$$9x + 4 < 12x - 11$$
$$\underline{-12x} \quad \underline{-12x} \qquad \textit{Subtract 12x from both sides.}$$
$$-3x + 4 < -11$$
$$\underline{-4} \quad \underline{-4} \qquad \textit{Subtract 4 from both sides.}$$
$$-3x < -15$$
$$\frac{-3x}{-3} > \frac{-15}{-3} \qquad \textit{Divide both sides by –3 and reverse the inequality.}$$
$$x > 5$$

Check Test values in the original inequality:

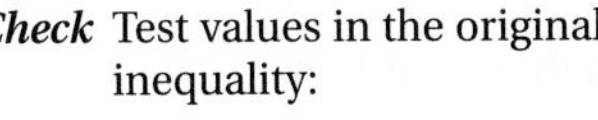

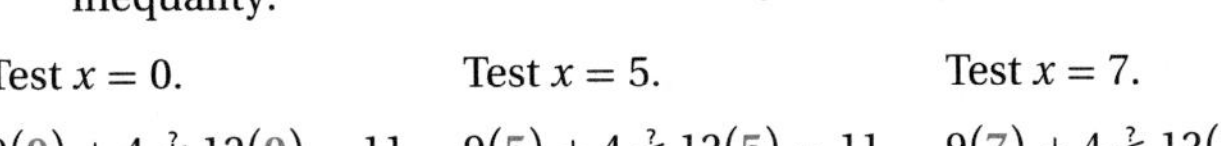

Test $x = 0$.	Test $x = 5$.	Test $x = 7$.
$9(0) + 4 \overset{?}{<} 12(0) - 11$	$9(5) + 4 \overset{?}{<} 12(5) - 11$	$9(7) + 4 \overset{?}{<} 12(7) - 11$
$4 < -11$ ✗	$49 < 49$ ✗	$67 < 73$ ✓
So 0 is not a solution.	So 5 is not a solution.	So 7 is a solution.

Helpful Hint

To check an inequality, test
- the value being compared with *x* (5 in Example 5),
- a value less than that, and
- a value greater than that.

5. Solve and graph $x + 8 \geq 4x + 17$. $x \leq -3$

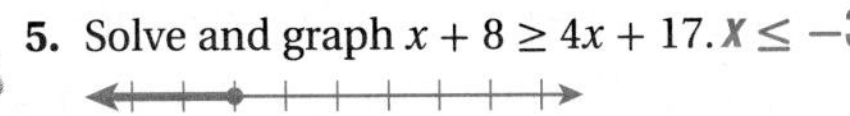

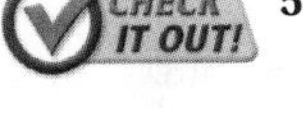

THINK AND DISCUSS

1. Give an example of an equation containing $3x$ that has no solution and another containing $3x$ with all real numbers as solutions.

2. Explain why you must reverse the inequality symbol in an expression when you multiply by a negative number. Use the inequality $-3 < 3$ as an example.

3. GET ORGANIZED Copy and complete the graphic organizer. Note the similarities and differences in the properties and methods you use.

Similarities — **Solving Equations and Inequalities** — Differences

COMMON ERROR ALERT

Students sometimes mistakenly reverse an inequality symbol whenever they encounter a negative number in a step or in an answer. Remind students that they need to reverse the inequality symbol *only* when the number they are multiplying or dividing both sides by is *itself* negative.

Teaching Tip **Multiple Representations** Show students that solving the inequality in **Example 5** by subtracting $9x$ from both sides as the first step results in the equivalent solution $5 < x$.

3 Close

Summarize

Review with students the properties of equality and the properties of inequality used to solve equations and inequalities. Remind students that some equations are identities and some are contradictions.

ONGOING ASSESSMENT and INTERVENTION

***Diagnose Before* the Lesson**
2-1 Warm Up, TE p. 90

***Monitor During* the Lesson**
Check It Out! Exercises, SE pp. 91–93
Questioning Strategies, TE pp. 91, 92

***Assess After* the Lesson**
2-1 Lesson Quiz, TE p. 96
Alternative Assessment, TE p. 96

Answers to *Think and Discuss*

1. $3x - 3x = 1$; $3x - 3x = 0$
2. Multiplying by a negative number reflects the numbers across 0 on the number line, thus reversing their positions from left to right. $-3 < 3$ is true because -3 is left of 3. Unless the inequality symbol is reversed, the resulting statement is false.
3. See p. A3.

2-1 Exercises

Assignment Guide

Assign *Guided Practice* exercises as necessary.

If you finished Examples **1–3**
- **Basic** 21–31, 40, 43–48
- **Average** 21–31, 40–48
- **Advanced** 21–31, 40–48

If you finished Examples **1–5**
- **Basic** 21–39, 40, 43–48, 51–57, 61–68
- **Average** 21–42, 44–58, 61–68
- **Advanced** 21, 24–28, 35–38, 40–43, 46–68

Homework Quick Check
Quickly check key concepts.
Exercises: 21, 24, 30, 32, 38, 40, 44

Answers

18.
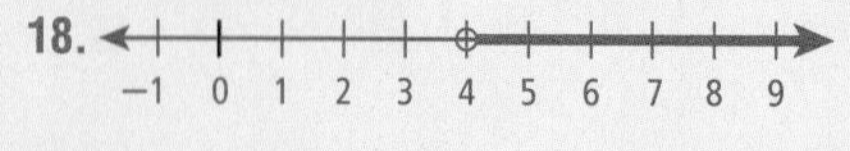

19.
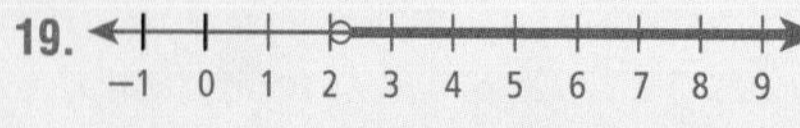

20.
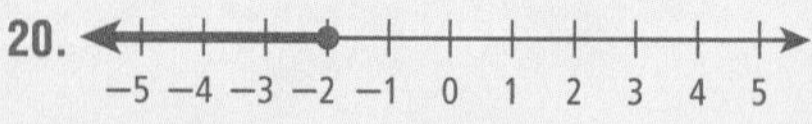

37.
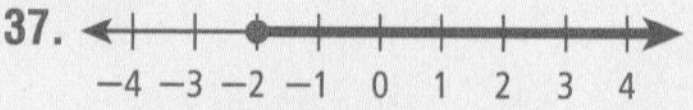

38.
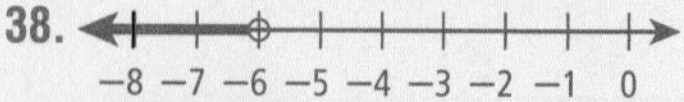

39.
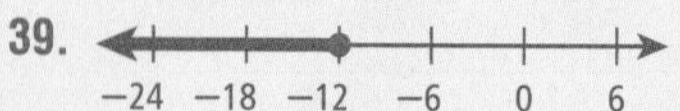

State Resources

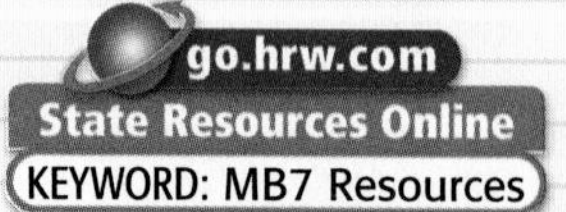

2-1 Exercises

go.hrw.com
Homework Help Online
KEYWORD: MB7 2-1
Parent Resources Online
KEYWORD: MB7 Parent

GUIDED PRACTICE

1. **Vocabulary** The statement $4 = 4$ is a(n) __?__ . (*identity* or *contradiction*) **identity**

SEE EXAMPLE 1 p. 91

2. **Consumer Economics** Shanti has just joined a DVD rental club. She pays a monthly membership fee of \$4.95, and each DVD rental is \$1.95. If Shanti's budget for DVD rentals in a month is \$42, how many DVDs can Shanti rent in her first month if she doesn't want to go over her budget? **19 DVDs**

SEE EXAMPLE 2 p. 91

Solve.

3. $8(x - 5) = 72$ **14**
4. $1.5(x - 4) = 9.6$ **10.4**
5. $-27 = 3(x - 3)$ **−6**

SEE EXAMPLE 3 p. 92

6. $5 - 4c = c + 20$ **−3**
7. $24 + 7x = -4x - 9$ **−3**
8. $3(x - 5) = 5x + 9$ **−12**
9. $x = -2(x - 3)$ **2**
10. $(t - 3)7 = 6t + 21$ **42**
11. $-0.5(r - 2) = -r - 2$ **−6**

SEE EXAMPLE 4 p. 92

12. $-4t + 1 = 3t + 1 - 7t$ **ℝ**
13. $2(3x + 1) = 3(2x + 1)$ **∅**
14. $2(3n + 3) - 9 = 6n$ **∅**
15. $2h + 4 - 5h = -3h + 4$ **ℝ**
16. $4(2 - 6m) = 6(2 - 4m)$ **∅**
17. $0.5(-8p + 1) = -4p + 1$ **∅**

SEE EXAMPLE 5 p. 93

Solve and graph.

18. $5x - 12 > 8$ **$x > 4$**
19. $62 - 18x < 20$ **$x > \frac{7}{3}$**
20. $23 + 3x \le 15 - x$ **$x \le -2$**

PRACTICE AND PROBLEM SOLVING

Independent Practice

For Exercises	See Example
21	1
22–26	2
27–31	3
32–36	4
37–39	5

Extra Practice
Skills Practice p. S6
Application Practice p. S33

21. **Aerospace** A pen floating in the weightlessness of space is 30 inches above the floor of the space capsule and is rising at 1.5 inches per second. In how many seconds will it reach the 6-foot-high ceiling? **28 s**

Solve.

22. $-30 = 6(x - 3)$ **−2**
23. $5(x - 8) - (x + 6) = 18$ **16**
24. $2(x + 4) - 5(x - 3) = 32$ **−3**
25. $\frac{1}{3}(2x - 7) = 4$ **$\frac{19}{2}$**
26. $3x - 8(3 - x) = 53$ **7**
27. $6n - 7 = 2n + 17$ **6**
28. $3n - 40 = \frac{1}{2}n + 35$ **30**
29. $5(x - 4) - 1 = -7x + 3$ **2**
30. $12x + 20 = 6(x + 4)$ **$\frac{2}{3}$**
31. $8t + 11 - 6t = 5t + 35$ **−8**
32. $2x + 4(x + 1) = 6\left(x + \frac{2}{3}\right)$ **ℝ**
33. $8 = -8x + 4(4 + 2x)$ **∅**
34. $-4(2n - 5) = -8n - 20$ **∅**
35. $9(3 - 2x) = -6(3x - 5)$ **∅**
36. $4x - 2(3 + 2x) = -6$ **ℝ**

Solve and graph.

37. $-3x + 8 \le 14$ **$x \ge -2$**
38. $3(x - 1) > 7(x + 3)$ **$x < -6$**
39. $5(x - 2) \ge 4(2x + 6) + 2$ **$x \le -12$**

40. **Business** Pat is paid a salary of \$500 a month plus a commission of 15% of the value of the jewelry she sells. Find the value of the jewelry Pat must sell in a month to earn at least \$2000. **at least \$10,000**

41. **Economics** In 1902, 44 loaves of bread cost the same amount as 1 loaf of bread in 2006. If a loaf of bread in 2006 costs \$1.72 more than in 1902, find the cost of a loaf of bread in 1902. **\$0.04**

42. **Football** In 2004, three wide receivers for the Indianapolis Colts caught a total of 37 touchdown passes. Reggie Wayne caught 2 more than Brandon Stokely, and Marvin Harrison caught 3 more than Reggie Wayne. How many touchdown passes did each receiver catch? **Stokely: 10; Wayne:12; Harrison:15**

2-1 READING STRATEGIES

A **linear equation** has one solution.	A **linear inequality** has many solutions.
$x - 3 = 8$ $x - 3 + 3 = 8 + 3$ $x = 11$	$x - 3 < 8$ $x - 3 + 3 < 8 + 3$ $x < 11$
The solution is 11.	The solution set is $x < 11$.

Answer each question.

1. Circle the linear equations. Cross out the linear inequalities.
   $c + 7 = 13$ (circled) $3 + 5 = 8$ (circled) $4 \cdot m \ge 36$ (crossed out) $7 - 2r = 23$ (circled) $22 \le 9g - 2$ (crossed out) $48 = \frac{w}{6}$ (circled)
2. How is solving an equation like solving an inequality?
   Possible answer: The process is similar because you use the same operations on both sides.
3. What is the solution of an equation?
   The number that makes the equation true
4. How can you check that 11 is the solution of the equation $x - 3 = 8$?
   Substitute 11 for x. $11 - 3 = 8$, so 11 is the solution.
5. What is the solution set of an inequality?
   The numbers that make the inequality true
6. How can you check that $x < 11$ is the solution set for the inequality $x - 3 < 8$?
   Possible answer: Choose some numbers that are less than 11 and substitute them for x to see if the results are true.
7. How are the solution of an equation and the solution set of an inequality different?
   Possible answer: The solution of the equation is one number, 11, but the solution set of the inequality is all the numbers less than 11.

2-1 RETEACH

Use the Distributive Property to solve equations.

$8(y - 6) = 64$ — Distribute the 8 to both terms. Think:
$8y - 48 = 64$
$+48 \quad +48$ — Add 48 to both sides.
$8y = 112$
$\frac{8y}{8} = \frac{112}{8}$ — Divide both sides by 8.
$y = 14$

Combine like terms to solve equations.

$4x + 18 - 3 = 3x - 45 + 5x$ — $3x$ and $5x$ are like terms.
$4x + 15 = 8x - 45$
$-4x \quad -4x$ — Subtract $4x$ from both sides.
$15 = 4x - 45$
$+45 \quad +45$ — Add 45 to both sides.
$60 = 4x$
$\frac{60}{4} = \frac{4x}{4}$ — Divide both sides by 4.
$15 = x$

Solve.

1. $3(x + 9) = 63$; $3x +$ **27** $= 63$; $3x =$ **36**; $x =$ **12**
2. $7(y - 4) = 98$; $7y -$ **28** $= 98$; $7y =$ **126**; $y =$ **18**
3. $8(w - 6) = 168$; **$8w - 48$** $= 168$; **$8w$** $=$ **216**; $w =$ **27**
4. $5a + 3 = 2a + 9$; $-2a \quad -2a$; $3a + 3 =$ **9**; $3a =$ **6**; $a =$ **2**
5. $8y + y = 3y + 30$; **$9y$** $= 3y + 30$; **$6y$** $= 30$; $y =$ **5**
6. $x + 5 = 29 - 3x$; $+3x \quad +3x$; **$4x$** $+$ **5** $= 29$; **$4x$** $=$ **24**; $x =$ **6**

43. **Technology** A digital answering machine has a total capacity of 32 min for the personal announcement and incoming messages. Incoming messages are limited to 3 min each, and the announcement is 30 s long.

43a. $m \le 10.5$; no more than 10 messages

a. Find the possible number of 3 min messages the machine can record.

b. The average length of an incoming message is 1.5 min. How many messages of average length can the machine record? $m \le 21$; no more than 21 messages

c. **What If...?** A friend has left 2 maximum length messages on your machine. In addition you have 5 minutes worth of saved messages. How many more average length messages can your machine record? $m \le 13.67$; no more than 13 messages

Geometry **Find the measure of each angle in the triangles below. (*Hint:* The sum of angle measures in a triangle is 180°.)**

44. Triangle ABC with angles $x°$ at A, $2x°$ at B, $(x - 20)°$ at C.

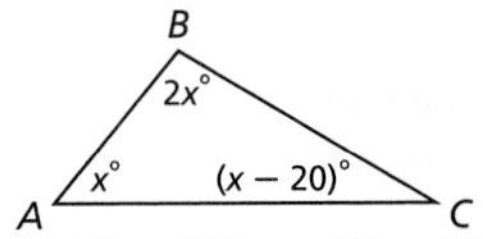

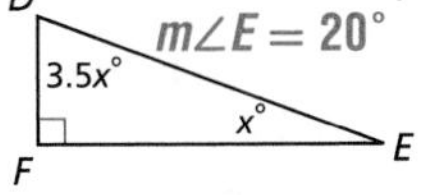

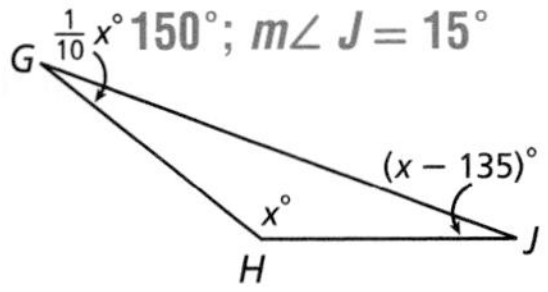

45. Right triangle DEF with angles $3.5x°$ at D, $x°$ at E.

46. Triangle GHJ with angles $\frac{1}{10}x°$ at G, $x°$ at H, $(x - 135)°$ at J.

44. $m\angle A = 50°$; $m\angle B = 100°$; $m\angle C = 30°$

45. $m\angle D = 70°$; $m\angle E = 20°$

46. $m\angle G = 15°$; $m\angle H = 150°$; $m\angle J = 15°$

LINK

Literature

Shakespeare's plays have been made into more than 500 movies and television shows.

Source: IMDB.com

47. **Literature** William Shakespeare wrote 37 plays, including tragedies, comedies, and histories. He wrote the same number of tragedies and histories, but the number of comedies he wrote is 3 less than twice the number of tragedies. How many of each type of play did Shakespeare write? 10 tragedies; 17 comedies; 10 histories

48. **Chemistry** As an experiment, a student filled a water glass with 5 in. of water. The chart shows the height of the water after each day.

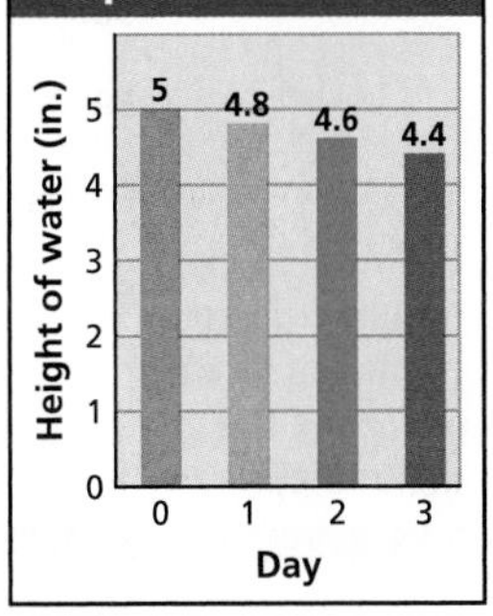

a. How much water evaporates each day? 0.2 in.

b. When will the height of the water drop below 2.5 in.? day 13

c. If the pattern continued, what would the height of the water be after 30 days? Is this reasonable in the context of the problem? −1 in.; no, the height of water cannot be negative.

Evaporation of Water

49. **Critical Thinking** What values of k make the equation $2(x - k) = 2x + 20$ an identity? What values of k make the equation a contradiction? $k = -10$; $k \ne -10$

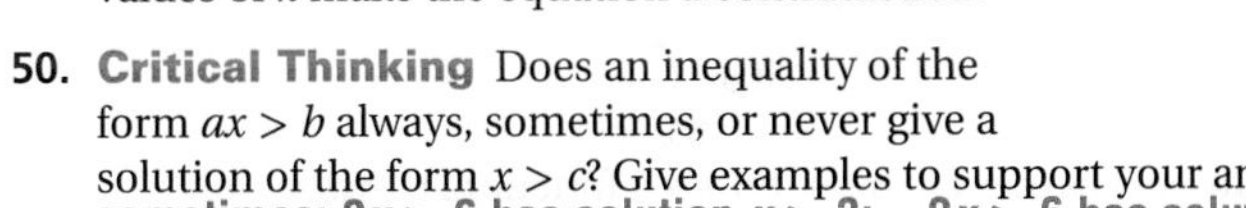

50. **Critical Thinking** Does an inequality of the form $ax > b$ always, sometimes, or never give a solution of the form $x > c$? Give examples to support your answer. sometimes; $2x > 6$ has solution $x > 3$; $-2x > 6$ has solution $x < -3$.

51. **Write About It** How do you recognize when an equation has no real solution or an infinite number of solutions?

MULTI-STEP TEST PREP

52. This problem will prepare you for the Multi-Step Test Prep on page 132.

There are 360° of longitude at the equator.

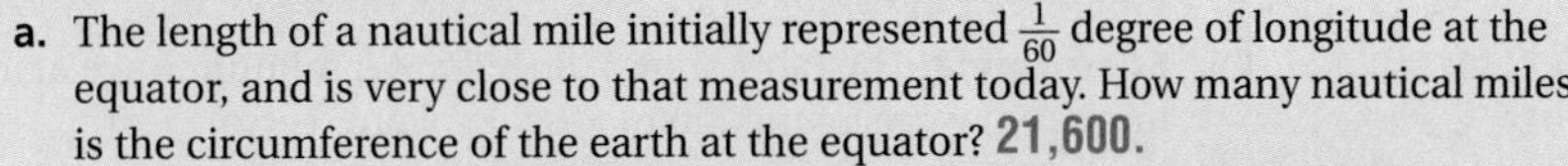

a. The length of a nautical mile initially represented $\frac{1}{60}$ degree of longitude at the equator, and is very close to that measurement today. How many nautical miles is the circumference of the earth at the equator? 21,600.

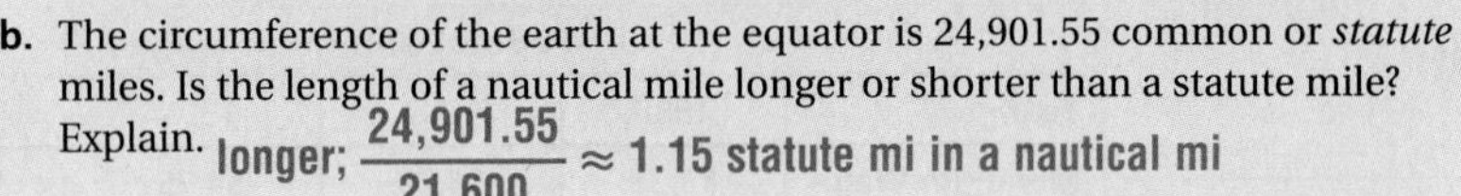

b. The circumference of the earth at the equator is 24,901.55 common or *statute* miles. Is the length of a nautical mile longer or shorter than a statute mile? Explain. longer; $\frac{24{,}901.55}{21{,}600} \approx 1.15$ statute mi in a nautical mi

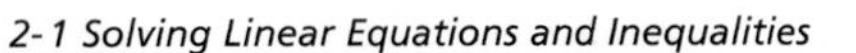

After students solve the equations in **Exercises 44–46,** they may forget to substitute the value of x into the expressions to find the angle measures. Remind students that each of these exercises has three answers.

Teaching Tip **Geometry** For **Exercises 44–46,** have students use the results of their work to classify the triangles as acute, right, or obtuse.

Exercise 52 involves converting units of measurement. This exercise prepares students for the Multi-Step Test Prep on page 132.

Answers

51. When solving, if you get a false equation (e.g., 1 = 2), the equation has no real solution. If you get an identity (e.g., 1 = 1), there are an infinite number of solutions.

2-1 PROBLEM SOLVING

Trish keeps track of a leak in her outside water faucet by measuring the depth of the water that collects in a barrel under the faucet. Her results (rounded to the nearest 0.5 centimeter) are shown in the table. Use the data in the table for Exercises 1–3.

Water Leak						
Day	1	2	3	4	5	6
Water in Barrel (cm)	3.5	8	12.5	17	21.5	26

1. After the first day, what is the depth of the water that leaks each day? 4.5 cm

2. Write an equation for the total depth of the water in the barrel, y, in terms of the number of days that the faucet leaks, x. $y = 4.5(x - 1) + 3.5$

3. If this pattern continues, and assuming no evaporation of the water in the barrel, when will the depth of the water be greater than 45 centimeters? 11 days

Choose the letter for the best answer.

4. A ream of computer paper is 2.1 in. high. Which inequality can be used to find the maximum number of reams that will fit in one stack between two shelves that are 1.5 ft apart?

A $2.1x \le 1.5$
(C) $2.1x \le 18$
B $\frac{2.1}{x} \le 1.5$
D $\frac{2.1}{x} \le 18$

5. Kevin is 5 years older than Keith, but 3 years younger than Kara. The total of their ages is 49. Which equation can be used to find Keith's age?

A $x + (x + 5) + (x + 3) = 49$
B $x + (x - 3) + (x + 8) = 49$
C $x + (x + 5) + (x - 3) = 49$
(D) $x + (x + 5) + (x + 8) = 49$

Tell whether each problem is solved correctly. If not, explain why and find the correct solution.

6. Ana wants to find a solution to a problem by solving this inequality: $-3x < 42$. She multiplies both sides by $-\frac{1}{3}$ and found the solution $x < -14$.

No; she forgot to reverse the inequality sign when multiplying by a negative number.

7. Tyler writes this equation to solve a problem: $3(b - 4) = 9 + 6b$. He divides both sides of the equation by 3 to get $b - 4 = 3 + 2b$ so he concludes that $b = -7$.

Yes

2-1 CHALLENGE

How many points are in the interval $0 \le x \le 10$? Of course there are the 10 points whose coordinates are integers: 1, 2, 3, ..., 10. There are also points like $\frac{1}{2}$, $4\frac{1}{8}$, $7\frac{3}{4}$, and 9.9999. How many other points are in this interval?

1. Consider the interval $0 \le x \le 10$.

a. Write a fraction using the endpoints to find the midpoint. $\frac{10 - 0}{2} = 5$

b. Use the left endpoint and the midpoint to find the midpoint of this half-interval. 2.5

c. Use the pattern from parts *a* and *b* to generate three more points that lie in the original interval.

1.25, 0.625, 0.3125

d. For the original interval, begin with the midpoint and the right endpoint and generate three more points that lie in the original interval.

7.5, 6.25, 5.625

e. How many points are in the original interval?

Infinitely many points

Find three points that lie in the left half of each interval and three points that lie in the right half of each interval.

2. $0.01 \le x \le 0.02$

Possible answer: midpoint: 0.015; three points in the left half of the interval: 0.0125, 0.01125, 0.011125; three points in the right half of the interval: 0.0175, 0.01625, 0.015625

3. $\frac{1}{3} \le x \le \frac{1}{2}$

Possible answer: midpoint: $\frac{5}{12}$; three points in the left half of the interval: $\frac{3}{8}$, $\frac{17}{48}$, and $\frac{11}{32}$; three points in the right half of the interval: $\frac{11}{24}$, $\frac{7}{16}$, and $\frac{41}{96}$

Let n be a positive real number.

4. a. How many points are in the interval $0 \le x \le n$? Infinitely many points

b. How do you think the number of points in the interval $-n \le x \le n$ compares to the number of points in the interval $0 \le x \le n$?

Both contain infinitely many points.

2-1 PRACTICE A

2-1 PRACTICE C

2-1 PRACTICE B

Solve.

1. $2(x - 3) = -4$ — $x = 1$

2. $12 - 3(w + 7) = 15$ — $w = -8$

3. $4(8 - p) - (7 - p) = 22$ — $p = 1$

4. $18 - 4y = -2(6 + 2y)$ — $y = \varnothing$

5. $7t + 6 - 2\left(5 + \frac{3t}{2}\right) = 5t - 11$ — $t = 7$

6. $32 + 4(c - 1) = -(4c + 5)$ — $c = -4\frac{1}{8}$

Solve and graph.

7. $-5x + 7 \ge -3$ — $x \le 2$

8. $4 - (-7 - k) > 2(k + 3)$ — $k < 5$

9. $-18d + 5(8 + 3d) \le 7(3d - 8)$ — $d \ge 4$

Solve.

10. Yvonne's cell phone plan gives her a maximum of 200 minutes each month.

a. Suppose Yvonne's calls average 7 minutes. What is the maximum number of calls she can make each month? 28

b. Yvonne knows she has used 61 minutes during the first week of this month. If she limits her calls to 15 per week for the remaining 3 weeks this month, what is the maximum length of time rounded to the nearest minute that she can use for each call? 3 minutes

11. Blair wants to spend less than $50 at the grocery store. He already has $37 worth of groceries in his shopping cart and is going to buy some fresh vegetables for $0.75 each. What numbers of vegetables v can he buy and stay under his spending limit? $v \le 17$

TEST PREP DOCTOR For **Exercise 56,** encourage students to consider the meaning of *at most* and determine which inequality symbol has the same meaning. Then point out that choices **H** and **J** can be eliminated because they are equal to or greater than 100. Choice **F** is the sum of two sides, not all four.

Journal

Have students write a paragraph explaining how to isolate the variable in a linear equation containing variables on both sides. Then have students write and solve an equation to illustrate their explanations.

ALTERNATIVE ASSESSMENT

Have students create their own equations and inequalities and demonstrate how to solve them using the properties of equality and the properties of inequality. Have students include an identity and a contradiction.

Power Presentations with PowerPoint®

2-1 Lesson Quiz

1. Alex pays \$19.99 for cable service each month. He also pays \$2.50 for each movie he orders through the cable company's pay-per-view service. If his bill last month was \$32.49, how many movies did Alex order? 5 movies

Solve.

2. $2(3x - 1) = 34$ $x = 6$
3. $4y - 9 - 6y = 2(y + 5) - 3$ $y = -4$
4. $r + 8 - 5r = 2(4 - 2r)$ all real numbers, or $\mathbb{R}$
5. $-4(2m + 7) = \frac{1}{2}(6 - 16m)$ no solution, or $\varnothing$
6. Solve and graph $12 + 3q > 9q - 18.$ $q < 5$

−1 0 1 2 3 4 5 6

Also available on transparency

TEST PREP

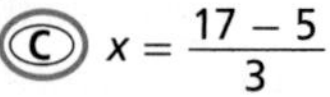

53. If $5 + 3x = 17$, then which equation is true?
Ⓐ $x = \frac{5 - 17}{3}$ Ⓑ $x = \frac{17 - 3}{5}$ Ⓒ $x = \frac{17 - 5}{3}$ Ⓓ $x = \frac{3 - 17}{5}$

54. Which expression does NOT simplify to a? (for $a \neq 0$, for $b \neq 0$)
Ⓕ $(a \div b) \cdot b$ Ⓖ $(a - b) + a + b$ Ⓗ $(a \cdot b) \div b$ Ⓙ $(a + b) - b$

55. Bob has 3 times as much money as Amy has, and Sam has \$5 more than Bob has. Bob, Amy, and Sam have a total of \$75. Which equation can be used to find out how much money Amy has?
Ⓐ $x + 3x + (x - 5) = 75$ Ⓒ $x + 3x + (3x - 5) = 75$
Ⓑ $x + 3x + (x + 5) = 75$ Ⓓ $x + 3x + (3x + 5) = 75$

56. If the perimeter of the rectangle can be at most 100 feet, which inequality can be used to find the width?
Ⓕ $w + (w + 5) \leq 100$ Ⓗ $w + (w + 5) \geq 100$
Ⓖ $2w + 2(w + 5) \leq 100$ Ⓙ $2w + 2(w + 5) \geq 100$

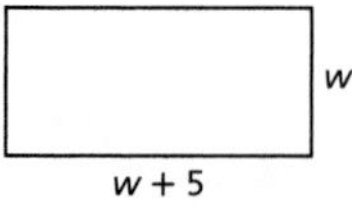

57. **Gridded Response** If $12 = 15 - 2x$, find the value of $8x$. 12

CHALLENGE AND EXTEND

Solve and graph.

58. $\frac{3x - 5}{8} - \frac{4 - 5x}{5} > \frac{3 - 2x}{4}$ $x > \frac{29}{25}$ −4 −3 −2 −1 0 1 2 3 4

59. $8(x - 1) \leq 4(2 + 2x)$ $\mathbb{R}$ −4 −3 −2 −1 0 1 2 3 4

60. Is the statement $4(x - 2) \neq 2(-4 + 2x)$ an identity or a contradiction? Explain.
60. $4(x - 2) = 2(-4 + 2x)$ is an identity, so replacing = with ≠ makes it a contradiction.

61. **Estimation** There are 90 people in line at a theme park ride. Every 5 minutes, 40 people get on the ride and 63 join the line. Estimate how long it would take for 600 people to be in line. About how long will the 600th person have to wait? ≈ 111 min; ≈ 75 min

SPIRAL REVIEW

Simplify each expression. *(Lesson 1-3)*

62. $\sqrt{75}$ $5\sqrt{3}$
63. $\sqrt{90} + \sqrt{250}$ $8\sqrt{10}$
64. $\frac{\sqrt{68}}{22}$ $\frac{\sqrt{17}}{11}$
65. $\frac{5\sqrt{12}}{\sqrt{5}}$ $2\sqrt{15}$

Determine whether each relation is a function. *(Lesson 1-6)*

66. not a function

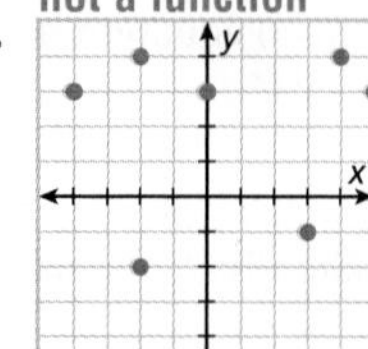

67. function

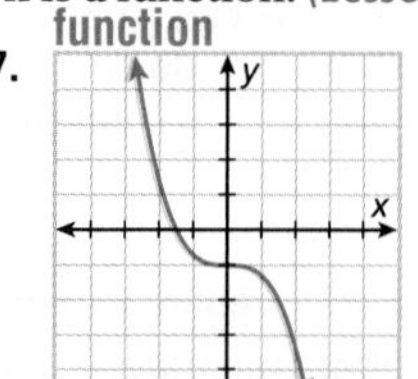

68. function

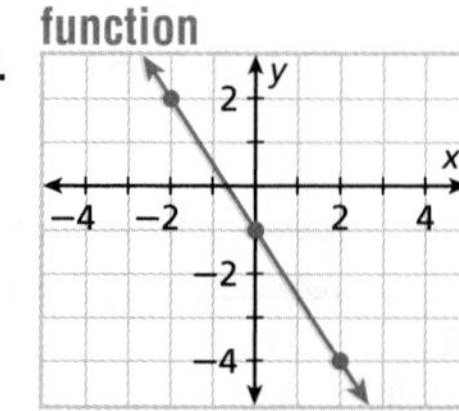

69. **Economics** The table shows the federal minimum wage at four-year intervals. Is minimum wage a function of year? Explain. *(Lesson 1-6)*
69. Yes; for any year, there is only 1 minimum wage.

Federal Minimum Wage					
Year	1988	1992	1996	2000	2004
Minimum Wage	\$3.35	\$4.25	\$4.75	\$5.15	\$5.15

2-2 Proportional Reasoning

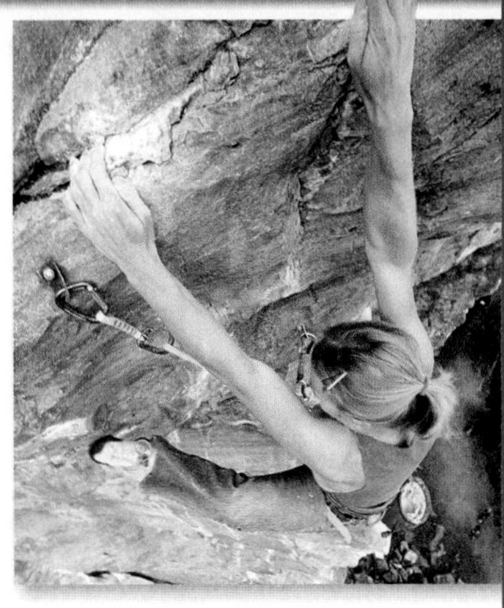

Objective
Apply proportional relationships to rates, similarity, and scale.

Vocabulary
ratio
proportion
rate
similar
indirect measurement

Who uses this?
Rock climbers can use proportions to indirectly measure the height of cliffs. (See Example 5.)

Recall that a **ratio** is a comparison of two numbers by division and a **proportion** is an equation stating that two ratios are equal. In a proportion, the cross products are equal.

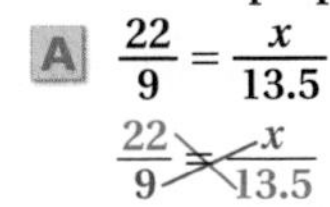

Cross Products Property

WORDS	NUMBERS	ALGEBRA
The cross products of a proportion are equal.	$\frac{3}{5} = \frac{9}{15}$ $3(15) = 5(9)$ $45 = 45$	For real numbers *a*, *b*, *c*, and *d*, where $b \neq 0$ and $d \neq 0$: If $\frac{a}{b} = \frac{c}{d}$, then $ad = bc$.

If a proportion contains a variable, you can cross multiply to solve for the variable. When you set the cross products equal, you create a linear equation that you can solve by using the skills that you learned in Lesson 2-1.

Reading Math

In $a \div b = c \div d$, *b* and *c* are the *means,* and *a* and *d* are the *extremes.* In a proportion, the product of the means is equal to the product of the extremes.

EXAMPLE 1 Solving Proportions

Solve each proportion.

A $\frac{22}{9} = \frac{x}{13.5}$

$\frac{22}{9} \times \frac{x}{13.5}$

$297 = 9x$ *Set cross products equal.*

$\frac{297}{9} = \frac{9x}{9}$ *Divide both sides.*

$33 = x$

B $\frac{512}{16} = \frac{64}{w}$

$\frac{512}{16} \times \frac{64}{w}$

$512w = 1024$

$\frac{512w}{512} = \frac{1024}{512}$

$w = 2$

CHECK IT OUT! Solve each proportion.

1a. $\frac{y}{12} = \frac{77}{84}$ $y = 11$ **1b.** $\frac{15}{x} = \frac{2.5}{7}$ $x = 42$

Because percents can be expressed as ratios, you can use the proportion $\frac{\text{percent}}{100} = \frac{\text{part}}{\text{whole}}$ to solve percent problems.

2-2 Organizer

Pacing: Traditional 1 day
Block $\frac{1}{2}$ day

Objective: Apply proportional relationships to rates, similarity, and scale.

Algebra Lab
In *Algebra Lab Activities*

Online Edition
Tutorial Videos

Countdown to Testing Week 3

Power Presentations with PowerPoint®

Warm Up

Write as a decimal and a percent.

1. $\frac{2}{5}$ 0.4; 40% **2.** $\frac{15}{8}$ 1.875; 187.5%

Graph on a coordinate plane.

3. $A(-1, 2)$ **4.** $B(0, -3)$

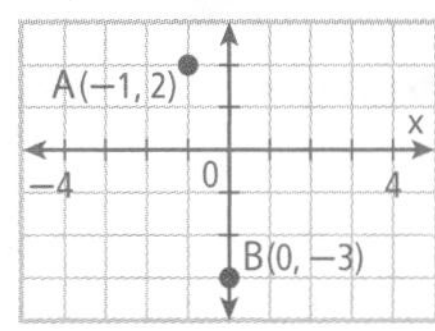

5. The distance from Max's house to the park is 3.5 mi. What is the distance in feet? (1 mi = 5280 ft) 18,480 ft

Also available on transparency

Math Humor

Q: Why were the similar triangles weighing themselves?

A: They were finding their scale.

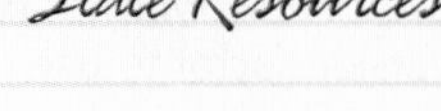

State Resources

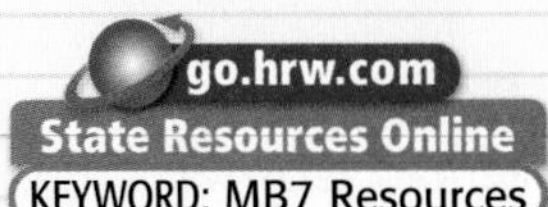

1 Introduce

EXPLORATION

2-2 Proportional Reasoning

Sara is a graphic artist. She has designed this rectangular logo for a chain of supermarkets.

1. The logo will be available in different sizes, as shown in the table. Describe any patterns formed by the numbers in the table.

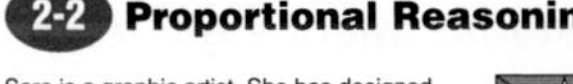

Length (in.)	4	5	6	7	8
Height (in.)	3	3.75	4.5	5.25	6

2. What should the height of the logo be if the length is 9 inches?
3. What should the length of the logo be if the height is 15 inches?
4. Sara sees the logo on a brochure. She wants to check that it is the correct shape, so she measures the length and height. How can she use the measurements to check the shape?

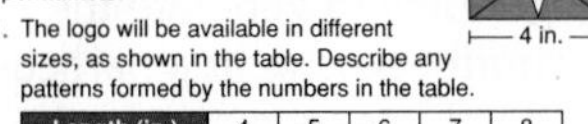

THINK AND DISCUSS

5. **Discuss** how you solved Problems 2 and 3. Describe as many different solution methods as you can.
6. **Give** an equation that relates the length and height of the logo.

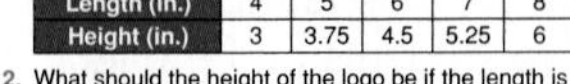

Motivate

Ask students to estimate the length, width, and area of the classroom. Then ask how they "measured." Discuss with students how it is possible to use proportional reasoning by relating the measurements to known lengths. For example, the windows may be about 6 feet wide, and five of them would fit across the room.

Explorations and answers are provided in the *Explorations* binder.

Power Presentations with PowerPoint®

Additional Examples

Example 1

Solve each proportion.

A. $\frac{16}{p} = \frac{24}{12.9}$ $p = 8.6$

B. $\frac{14}{88} = \frac{c}{132}$ $c = 21$

Example 2

A poll taken one day before an election showed that 22.5% of voters planned to vote for a certain candidate. If 1800 voters participated in the poll, how many indicated that they planned to vote for that candidate? 405

Example 3

Ryan ran 600 meters and counted 482 strides. How long is Ryan's stride in inches? (*Hint:* 1 m ≈ 39.37 in.) 49 in.

Also available on transparency

INTERVENTION

Questioning Strategies

EXAMPLE 1

- How can you solve proportions using only the Multiplication and Division Properties of Equality?
- How could you use the concept of equivalent fractions to check the answer?

EXAMPLE 2

- What steps do you use to solve the proportion if you use Method 1?
- Why does the percent need to be changed to a decimal in Method 2 but not in Method 1?

EXAMPLE 3

- How is the concept of *rate* used to solve this problem?
- How do you know which form of the conversion factor to use, $\frac{39.37 \text{ in.}}{1 \text{ m}}$ or its reciprocal?

EXAMPLE 2 Solving Percent Problems

A college brochure states that 11.5% of the students attending the college are majoring in engineering. If 2400 students are attending the college, how many are majoring in engineering?

You know the percent and the total number of students, so you are trying to find the part of the whole (the number of students who are majoring in engineering).

Remember!

Percent is a ratio that means *per hundred*. For example:

$30\% = 0.30 = \frac{30}{100}$

Method 1 Use a proportion.

$\frac{\text{percent}}{100} = \frac{\text{part}}{\text{whole}}$

$\frac{11.5}{100} = \frac{x}{2400}$

$11.5(2400) = 100x$ *Cross multiply.*

$\frac{27600}{100} = x$ *Solve for x.*

$x = 276$

Method 2 Use a percent equation

$11.5\% = 0.115$ *Divide the percent by 100.*

Percent (as decimal) · whole = part

$0.115 \cdot 2400 = x$

$276 = x$

So 276 students at the college are majoring in engineering.

2. At Clay High School, 434 students, or 35% of the students, play a sport. How many students does Clay High School have? **1240 students**

A **rate** is a ratio that involves two different units. You are familiar with many rates, such as miles per hour (mi/h), words per minute (wpm), or dollars per gallon of gasoline. Rates can be helpful in solving many problems.

EXAMPLE 3 *Fitness Application*

A pedometer measures how far a jogger has run. To set her pedometer, Rita must know her stride length. Rita counts 328 strides as she runs once around a 400 m track. A meter is about 39.37 in. How long is her stride in inches?

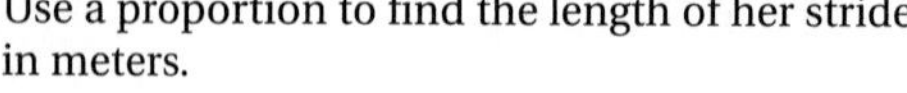

Use a proportion to find the length of her stride in meters.

$\frac{400 \text{ m}}{328 \text{ strides}} = \frac{x \text{ m}}{1 \text{ stride}}$ *Write both ratios in the form* $\frac{\text{meters}}{\text{strides}}$.

$400 = 328x$ *Find the cross products.*

$x \approx 1.22 \text{ m}$

Convert the stride length to inches.

$\frac{1.22 \cancel{\text{m}}}{1 \text{ stride length}} \cdot \frac{39.37 \text{ in.}}{1 \cancel{\text{m}}} \approx \frac{48 \text{ in.}}{1 \text{ stride length}}$ *$\frac{39.37 \text{ in.}}{1 \text{ m}}$ is the conversion factor.*

Rita's stride length is approximately 48 inches.

3. Luis ran the same 400 m track in 297 strides. Find his stride length in inches. ≈ **53 in.**

2 Teach

Guided Instruction

Before students solve proportions, be sure they understand the relationship between ratios and proportions. Throughout the lesson, reinforce the usefulness of proportions for solving a wide variety of real-world problems. Point out that an equation created by setting cross products equal is a linear equation.

Reaching All Learners

Through Kinesthetic Experience

Choose two students—one shorter, one taller. Use a light source to generate the shadow of the shorter person at a particular location. Have volunteers measure the heights of the two students and the length of the shadow. Then have students use a proportion to predict the length of the taller person's shadow. Students can check their prediction by measuring the length of the taller person's shadow at the same location as they measured the shorter person's shadow.

Similar figures have the same shape but not necessarily the same size. Two figures are **similar** if their corresponding angles are congruent and corresponding sides are proportional.

EXAMPLE 4 

Scaling Geometric Figures in the Coordinate Plane

$\triangle ABC$ has vertices $A(0, 0)$, $B(8, 4)$, and $C(8, 0)$. $\triangle ADE$ is similar to $\triangle ABC$ with a vertex at $E(2, 0)$. Graph $\triangle ABC$ and $\triangle ADE$ on the same grid.

Step 1 Graph $\triangle ABC$. Then draw $\overline{AE}$.

Step 2 To find the height of $\triangle ADE$, use a proportion.

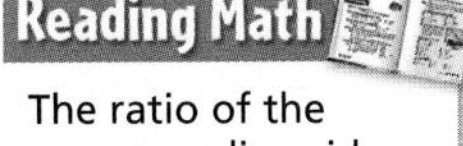

The ratio of the corresponding side lengths of similar figures is often called the *scale factor*.

$$\frac{\text{width of } \triangle ADE}{\text{width of } \triangle ABC} = \frac{\text{height of } \triangle ADE}{\text{height of } \triangle ABC}$$

$$\frac{2}{8} = \frac{x}{4}$$

$$8x = 8, \text{ so } x = 1$$

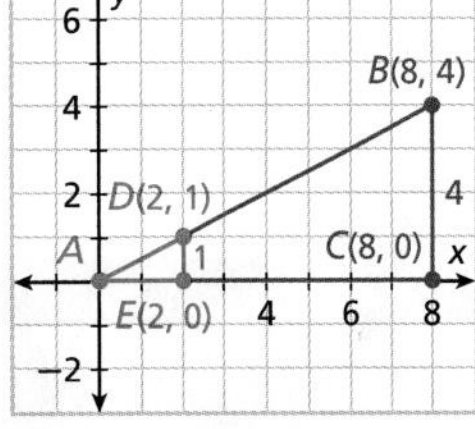

Step 3 To graph $\triangle ADE$, first find the coordinates of D.

The height is 1 unit, and the width is 2 units, so the coordinates of D are $(2, 1)$.

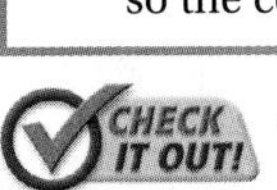

4. $\triangle DEF$ has vertices $D(0, 0)$, $E(-6, 0)$, and $F(0, -4)$. $\triangle DGH$ is similar to $\triangle DEF$ with a vertex at $G(-3, 0)$. Graph $\triangle DEF$ and $\triangle DGH$ on the same grid.

Indirect measurement uses known lengths, similar figures, and proportions to measure objects that cannot easily be measured.

EXAMPLE 5

Recreation Application

A rock climber wants to know the height of a cliff. The climber measures the shadow of her friend, who is 5 feet tall and standing beside the cliff, and measures the shadow of the cliff. If the friend's shadow is 4 feet long and the cliff's shadow is 60 feet long, how tall is the cliff?

Sketch the situation. The triangles formed by using the shadows are similar, so the rock climber can use a proportion to find h the height of the cliff.

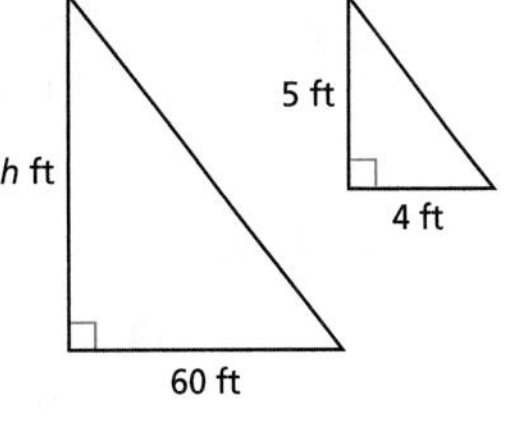

$$\frac{4}{5} = \frac{60}{h} \qquad \frac{\textit{shadow of friend}}{\textit{height of friend}} = \frac{\textit{shadow of cliff}}{\textit{height of cliff}}$$

$$4h = 300$$

$$h = 75$$

The cliff is 75 feet high.

5. A 6-foot-tall climber casts a 20-foot-long shadow at the same time that a tree casts a 90-foot-long shadow. How tall is the tree? **27 ft**

3 Close

Summarize

Propose the following problem to students:

The planet Venus takes 224.7 Earth days to orbit the Sun. If you had spent your life on Venus rather than on Earth, how old would you be in Venusian years?

Have students explain how to set up and solve a proportion to solve this problem, justifying why the proportion models the problem. At age 16, you would be 26 in Venusian years; $\frac{x}{16} = \frac{365}{224.7}$

and INTERVENTION

***Diagnose Before* the Lesson**
2-2 Warm Up, TE p. 97

***Monitor During* the Lesson**
Check It Out! Exercises, SE pp. 97–99
Questioning Strategies, TE pp. 98, 99

***Assess After* the Lesson**
2-2 Lesson Quiz, TE p. 103
Alternative Assessment, TE p. 103

COMMON ERROR ALERT

Before finding cross products, students might try to divide the numerator of one fraction and the denominator of the other by a common factor (as when multiplying fractions). Help students to see that this would create an equation that is not equivalent to the original proportion.

Power Presentations with PowerPoint®

Additional Examples

Example 4

$\triangle XYZ$ has vertices $X(0, 0)$, $Y(-6, 9)$, and $Z(0, 9)$. $\triangle XAB$ is similar to $\triangle XYZ$ with a vertex at $B(0, 3)$. Graph $\triangle XYZ$ and $\triangle XAB$ on the same grid.

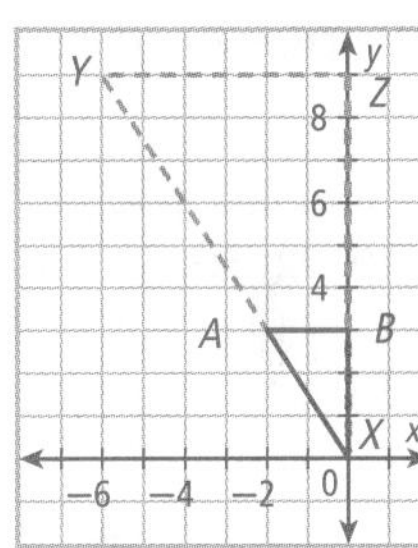

Example 5

The tree in front of Luka's house casts a 6-foot shadow at the same time as the house casts a 22-foot shadow. If the tree is 9 feet tall, how tall is the house? 33 ft

Also available on transparency 

INTERVENTION

Questioning Strategies

EXAMPLE 

- How are the corresponding sides of the original triangle and its image related? How are the corresponding angles related?

EXAMPLE 5

- What kind of triangles can you use to model the heights of objects and their shadows?
- How does a diagram help you solve this type of problem?

Inclusion Point out that a scale factor greater than 1 enlarges and a scale factor less than 1 shrinks.

Answers to *Think and Discuss*

1. Find a common denominator for $\frac{a}{b}$ and $\frac{c}{d}$; $\frac{a}{b} = \frac{a}{b} \cdot \frac{d}{d} = \frac{ad}{bd}$ and $\frac{c}{d} = \frac{b}{b} \cdot \frac{c}{d} = \frac{bc}{bd}$. The numerators must be equal for the fractions to be equal, and the numerators are the cross products, *ac* and *bd*.
2. Indirect measurement lets you use proportions and known lengths to find unknown lengths.
3. See p. A3.

THINK AND DISCUSS

1. Use algebra to explain why equal cross products imply that two ratios are equal.
2. How is it possible to find a length or distance without physically measuring it?

3. **GET ORGANIZED** Copy and complete the graphic organizer. In each box, write examples of each item that relate to the concept of proportion.

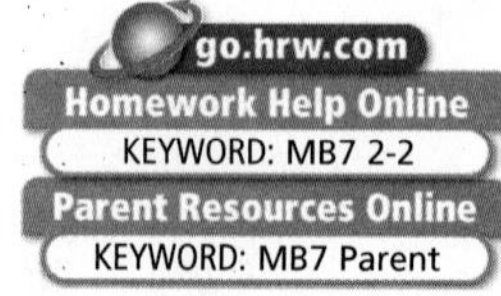

2-2 Exercises

Assignment Guide

Assign *Guided Practice* exercises as necessary.

If you finished Examples **1–3**
- **Basic** 14–19, 22–30, 38–39
- **Average** 14–19, 24–27, 31, 36–39
- **Advanced** 14–19, 36–40, 46

If you finished Examples **1–5**
- **Basic** 14–30, 35, 38–45, 47–51, 58–71
- **Average** 14–21, 30–51, 57–71
- **Advanced** 14–21, 30–71

Homework Quick Check

Quickly check key concepts.
Exercises: 14, 18–21, 30, 38, 40

2-2 Exercises

go.hrw.com
Homework Help Online
KEYWORD: MB7 2-2
Parent Resources Online
KEYWORD: MB7 Parent

GUIDED PRACTICE

1. **Vocabulary** *Miles per hour* is a(n) __?__. (*rate, ratio,* or *indirect measurement*) **rate**

SEE EXAMPLE 1 p. 97

Solve each proportion.

2. $\frac{6.4}{x} = \frac{2}{3}$ **9.6**
3. $\frac{2}{13} = \frac{n}{52}$ **8**
4. $\frac{4}{14} = \frac{24}{x}$ **84**
5. $\frac{\frac{1}{3}}{3} = \frac{6}{t}$ **54**
6. $\frac{8}{x} = \frac{5}{12}$ **19.2**
7. $\frac{4}{9} = \frac{x}{45}$ **20**
8. $\frac{-2}{5} = \frac{18}{x}$ **−45**
9. $\frac{x}{-15} = \frac{63}{45}$ **−21**

SEE EXAMPLE 2 p. 98

10. **School** A college brochure claims that 24% of the students attending the college are majoring in business. If there are 420 students at the college who are majoring in business, how many students are attending the college? **1750 students**

SEE EXAMPLE 3 p. 98

11. **Travel** Jesse drove from Los Angeles to Las Vegas, a distance of 463 km. He used 12 gal of gas on the trip. Find the gas mileage in miles per gallon of Jesse's car. (*Hint*: 1 km ≈ 0.62 mi) **≈ 24 mi/gal**

SEE EXAMPLE 4 p. 98

12. **Geometry** $\triangle ABC$ has vertices $A(0, 0)$, $B(0, 8)$, and $C(-6, 8)$. $\triangle ADE$ is similar to $\triangle ABC$ with a vertex at $D(0, 4)$. Graph $\triangle ABC$ and $\triangle ADE$ on the same grid.

SEE EXAMPLE 5 p. 99

13. **Surveying** A surveyor uses similar triangles to measure the distance across a canyon. What is the distance across the canyon, according to the diagram? **52.5 ft**

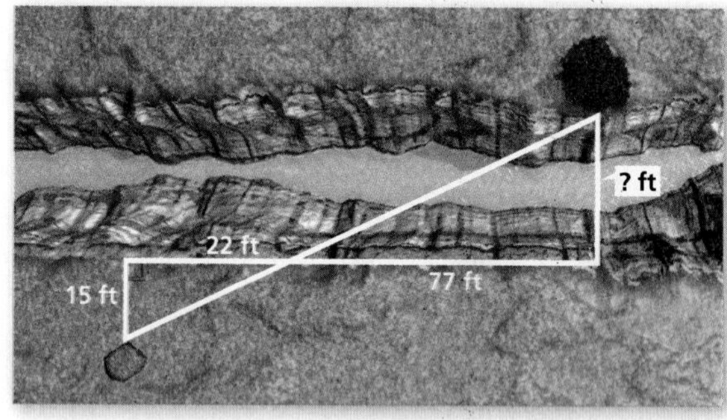

State Resources

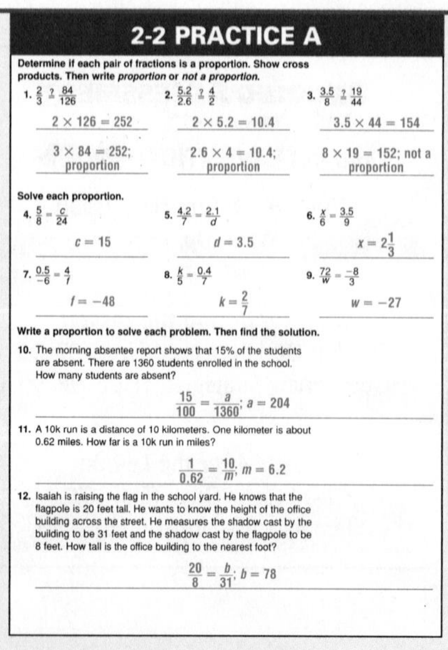

2-2 PRACTICE A

Determine if each pair of fractions is a proportion. Show cross products. Then write *proportion* or *not a proportion*.

1. $\frac{2}{3} \stackrel{?}{=} \frac{84}{126}$ — $2 \times 126 = 252$; $3 \times 84 = 252$; proportion
2. $\frac{5.2}{2.6} \stackrel{?}{=} \frac{4}{2}$ — $2 \times 5.2 = 10.4$; $2.6 \times 4 = 10.4$; proportion
3. $\frac{3.5}{8} \stackrel{?}{=} \frac{19}{44}$ — $3.5 \times 44 = 154$; $8 \times 19 = 152$; not a proportion

Solve each proportion.

4. $\frac{5}{8} = \frac{c}{24}$ — $c = 15$
5. $\frac{4.2}{7} = \frac{2.1}{d}$ — $d = 3.5$
6. $\frac{x}{6} = \frac{3.5}{9}$ — $x = 2\frac{1}{3}$
7. $\frac{0.5}{-6} = \frac{4}{f}$ — $f = -48$
8. $\frac{k}{5} = \frac{0.4}{7}$ — $k = \frac{2}{7}$
9. $\frac{72}{w} = \frac{-8}{3}$ — $w = -27$

Write a proportion to solve each problem. Then find the solution.

10. The morning absentee report shows that 15% of the students are absent. There are 1360 students enrolled in the school. How many students are absent?
$\frac{15}{100} = \frac{a}{1360}$; $a = 204$
11. A 10k run is a distance of 10 kilometers. One kilometer is about 0.62 miles. How far is a 10k run in miles?
$\frac{1}{0.62} = \frac{10}{m}$; $m = 6.2$
12. Isaiah is raising the flag in the school yard. He knows that the flagpole is 20 feet tall. He wants to know the height of the office building across the street. He measures the shadow cast by the building to be 31 feet and the shadow cast by the flagpole to be 8 feet. How tall is the office building to the nearest foot?
$\frac{20}{8} = \frac{b}{31}$; $b = 78$

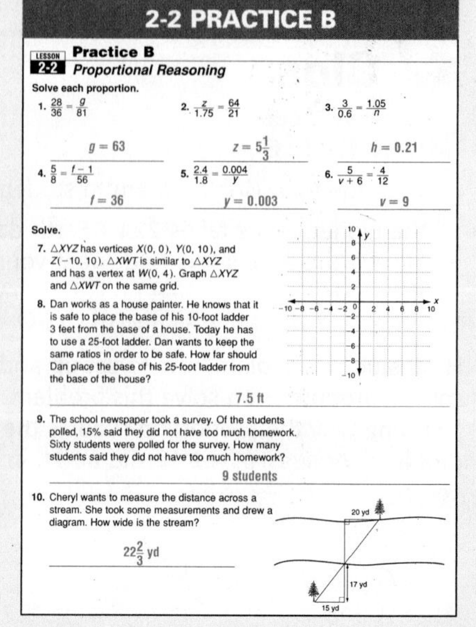

2-2 PRACTICE B

LESSON 2-2 **Practice B**
Proportional Reasoning

Solve each proportion.

1. $\frac{28}{36} = \frac{g}{81}$ — $g = 63$
2. $\frac{z}{1.75} = \frac{64}{21}$ — $z = 5\frac{1}{3}$
3. $\frac{3}{0.6} = \frac{1.05}{n}$ — $h = 0.21$
4. $\frac{5}{8} = \frac{f-1}{56}$ — $f = 36$
5. $\frac{2.4}{1.8} = \frac{0.004}{y}$ — $y = 0.003$
6. $\frac{5}{v+6} = \frac{4}{12}$ — $v = 9$

Solve.

7. $\triangle XYZ$ has vertices $X(0, 0)$, $Y(0, 10)$, and $Z(-10, 10)$. $\triangle XWT$ is similar to $\triangle XYZ$ and has a vertex at $W(0, 4)$. Graph $\triangle XYZ$ and $\triangle XWT$ on the same grid.
8. Dan works as a house painter. He knows that it is safe to place the base of his 10-foot ladder 3 feet from the base of a house. Today he has to use a 25-foot ladder. Dan wants to keep the same ratios in order to be safe. How far should Dan place the base of his 25-foot ladder from the base of the house?
7.5 ft
9. The school newspaper took a survey. Of the students polled, 15% said they did not have too much homework. Sixty students were polled for the survey. How many students said they did not have too much homework?
9 students
10. Cheryl wants to measure the distance across a stream. She took some measurements and drew a diagram. How wide is the stream?
$22\frac{2}{3}$ yd

20 yd
17 yd
15 yd

PRACTICE AND PROBLEM SOLVING

Independent Practice	
For Exercises	See Example
14–17	1
18	2
19	3
20	4
21	5

Extra Practice
Skills Practice p. S6
Application Practice p. S33

Solve each proportion.

14. $\frac{55}{200} = \frac{143}{n}$ 520
15. $\frac{1.24}{3} = \frac{y}{15}$ 6.2
16. $\frac{22}{11} = \frac{7}{x}$ 3.5
17. $\frac{0.1}{x} = \frac{1.1}{110}$ 10

18. **Business** A quality control inspector has found that 3.2% of the garments produced at Standard Garments contain a defect. If Standard Garments produces 4117 garments in one day, how many of those garments are expected to have a defect? ≈ 132

19. **Communication** Latanya made a 17-minute phone call from her hotel in France and was charged 17 euro. At the time, $1 was worth 0.82 euro. Find the cost per minute of the call in dollars. $1.22

20. **Geometry** $\triangle ABC$ has vertices $A(0, 0)$, $B(6, 0)$, and $C(6, -4.5)$. $\triangle ADE$ is similar to $\triangle ABC$ with a vertex at $D(8, 0)$. Graph $\triangle ABC$ and $\triangle ADE$ on the same grid.

21. **Measurement** A basketball rim 10 ft high casts a shadow 15 ft long. At the same time, a nearby building casts a shadow that is 54 ft long. How tall is the building? 36 ft

Solve.

22. $\frac{4}{9} = \frac{r+3}{45}$ 17
23. $\frac{2.8}{1.5} = \frac{t}{0.09}$ 0.168
24. $\frac{9+m}{5} = \frac{15}{4}$ 9.75
25. $\frac{2}{u-5} = \frac{6}{9}$ 8
26. $\frac{12}{27} = \frac{3r}{3}$ $\frac{4}{9}$
27. $\frac{-11}{0.11h} = \frac{10}{3}$ −30
28. $\frac{25}{75} = \frac{80}{5x}$ 48
29. $\frac{0}{17} = \frac{0.5x}{170}$ 0

30. **Food** A sample of students was asked what type of restaurant they visit most often. Their answers are shown in the circle graph. If 126 students chose Chinese restaurants, how many students were polled? 600

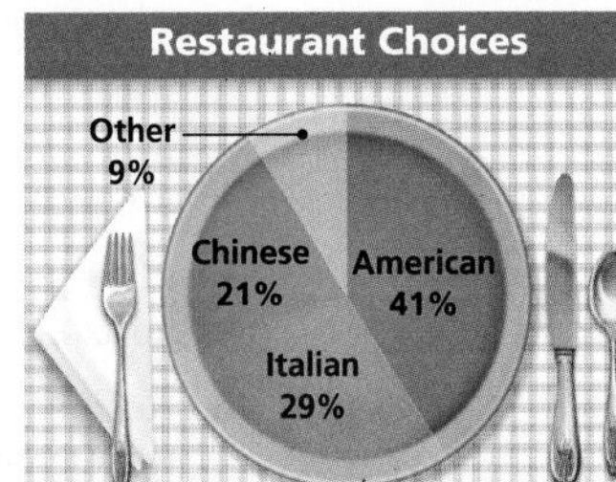

31. **Critical Thinking** If $a \neq 0$, $b \neq 0$, $c \neq 0$, $d \neq 0$, and $\frac{a}{b} = \frac{c}{d}$, explain why $\frac{d}{c} = \frac{b}{a}$ is also true.

32. **What if...?** Suppose you double the lengths of the sides of a rectangle.
    a. What is the relationship between the perimeter of the new rectangle and the perimeter of the original rectangle?
    b. What is the relationship between the area of the image and the area of the preimage? The area of the image is 4 times the area of the preimage.

33. **Critical Thinking** In a film, the 555-feet-tall Washington Monument casts a 100-feet-long shadow, whereas the main character in the film casts a 4 feet-long shadow nearby. Why is this considered a film "goof"? The person would be 22 ft tall.

34. **Estimation** The distance from La Paz to Cabo San Lucas on Mexico's Baja Peninsula is 92 miles, or 148 kilometers.
    a. The red bar representing the scale of the map represents approximately how many miles? ≈ 45 mi
    b. About how many kilometers is El Pescadero from Los Barilles? ≈ 50 km

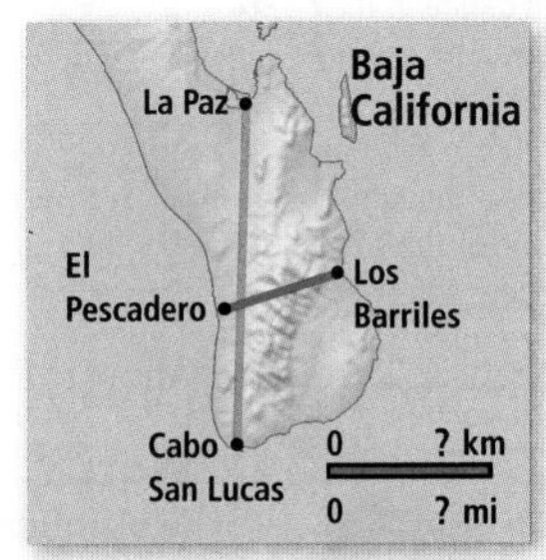

COMMON ERROR ALERT

When finding cross products in proportions such as those in **Exercises 22, 24,** and **25,** students might forget to apply the Distributive Property to a product involving a binomial. Remind students to use parentheses around the binomial when writing the cross product. The parentheses indicate the correct order of operations.

Transformations Point out that the image of $\triangle ABC$ in **Exercise 20** is a *dilation,* or *enlargement,* of $\triangle ABC$.

Critical Thinking For **Exercise 31,** you may want to tell students that $\frac{a}{c} = \frac{b}{d}$ and $\frac{c}{a} = \frac{d}{b}$ are also true by showing them that setting the cross products for these proportions equal to each other also results in $ad = cb$.

Answers

12.

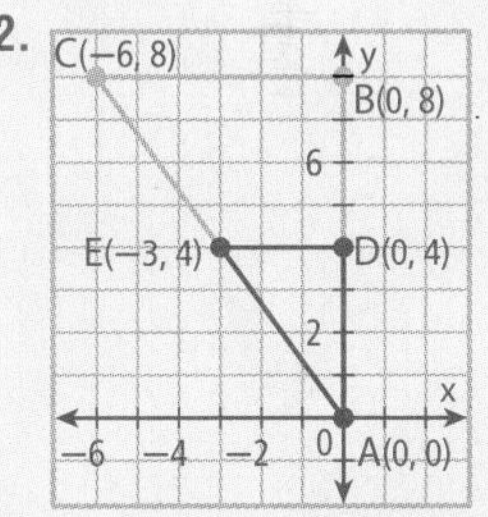

20.

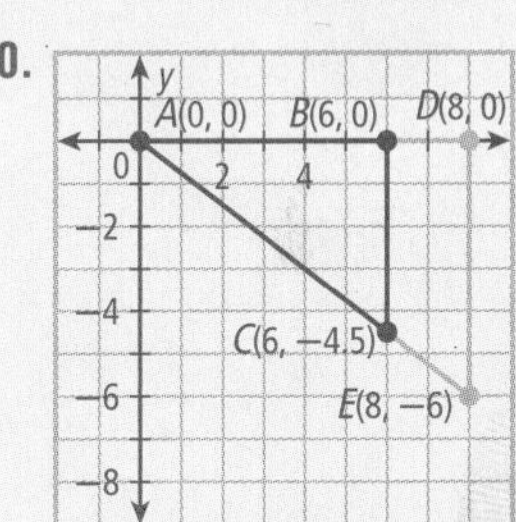

31. Possible answer:
If $\frac{a}{b} = \frac{c}{d}$, then $ad = bc$.
Divide both sides by ac: $\frac{ad}{ac} = \frac{bc}{ac}$.
Simplify:
$\frac{d}{c} = \frac{b}{a}$.

32a. The perimeter of the image is 2 times the perimeter of the preimage.

2-2 PRACTICE C

Solve.

1. $\frac{6n}{16} = \frac{112.5}{40}$ $n = 7.5$
2. $\frac{-3}{0.5} = \frac{-9}{w-5}$ $w = 6.5$
3. $\frac{1+a}{2.5} = \frac{144}{45}$ $a = 7$
4. $\frac{30}{105} = \frac{d+18}{35}$ $d = -8$
5. $\frac{36}{24m} = \frac{3.3}{8.8}$ $m = 4$
6. $\frac{2.55}{0.9} = \frac{1.7}{0.3c}$ $c = 2$

The circle graph shows the annual revenue sources for a local baseball team. Use the graph for Exercises 7 and 8.

Baseball Team Revenue
Ticket Sales 26%
Parking 18%
TV/Radio 33%
Food Sales 23%

7. If the revenue from ticket sales is $386,152, what is the total revenue for the year? $1,485,200
8. If the total revenue for the year is $1,742,800, what is the revenue from parking fees and food sales together? $714,548
9. If the combined revenue from parking and the TV/Radio license is $629,629.17, what is the total revenue for the year? $1,234,567

Solve.

10. Last year, 22% of the students at the high school had perfect attendance. If 165 students had perfect attendance, how many students are enrolled at the high school? 750 students
11. Sammy is 5 feet 3 inches tall. He casts a shadow that is 31 feet 6 inches long. He is standing next to a stop sign that casts a shadow that is 40 feet 6 inches long. How tall is the stop sign in feet and inches? 6 ft 9 in.
12. Each day the exchange rate between U.S. dollars and foreign currency changes. One day, 4 dollars were equivalent to approximately 3 euro. On the same day 3 euro were equivalent to approximately 168.37 Indian rupees. To the nearest rupee, how many Indian rupees are equivalent to 1 dollar? 42 rupees

MULTI-STEP TEST PREP **Exercise 35** involves proportions related to the measurement of nautical speed. This exercise prepares students for the Multi-Step Test Prep on page 132.

Answers

46. $\frac{a}{b} = \frac{c}{d}$

$\frac{a}{b} + 1 = \frac{c}{d} + 1$

$\frac{a}{b} + \frac{b}{b} = \frac{c}{d} + \frac{d}{d}$

$\frac{a+b}{b} = \frac{c+d}{d}$

47. If $\frac{a}{b} = \frac{c}{d}$, then $\frac{ad}{bd} = \frac{bc}{bd}$.
$bd \cdot \frac{ad}{bd} = bd \cdot \frac{bc}{bd}$, so $ad = bc$.

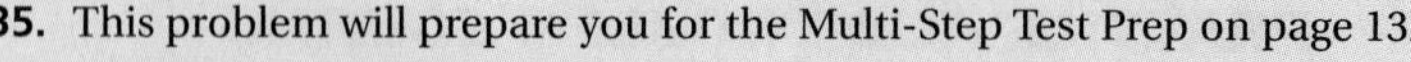

MULTI-STEP TEST PREP

35. This problem will prepare you for the Multi-Step Test Prep on page 132.

Nautical speed was once measured by throwing a rope into the water from the ship. The rope had knots every 47 ft 3 in., and its wedge-shaped end would "grab" the water. The speed was the number of rope knots that went into the water while a 28 s hourglass ran down.

a. What is the ratio of 1 hour to 28 seconds? (*Hint:* Use the same units). ≈ **128.57**

b. A nautical mile is about 6076.1 ft. What is the ratio of this to the length of the rope between knots? ≈ **128.59 times as long**

c. What proportion might have been set up to determine the correct length of rope between knots? **Possible answer:** $\frac{\text{rope knots}}{28 \text{ s}} = \frac{\text{nautical mi}}{\text{h}}$

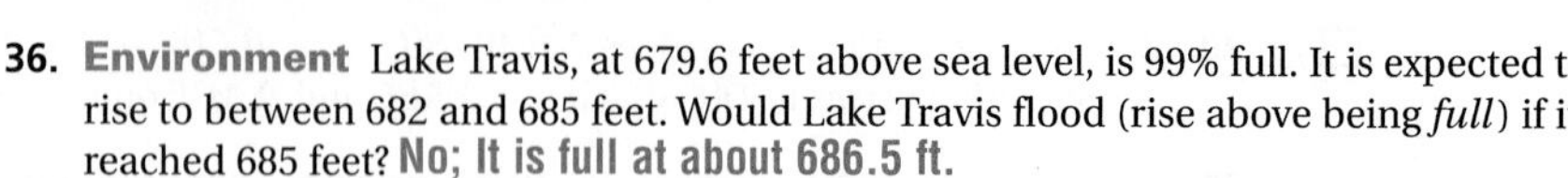

36. Environment Lake Travis, at 679.6 feet above sea level, is 99% full. It is expected to rise to between 682 and 685 feet. Would Lake Travis flood (rise above being *full*) if it reached 685 feet? **No; It is full at about 686.5 ft.**

37. Chemistry There are about 1,400,000 drops in 25 gallons of a liquid. What percent of a gallon is a single drop? ≈ **0.0018%**

Use the following for Exercises 38–40.

Grade is a measure of the steepness of surfaces, such as roads and ramps. Grade is expressed as a percent based on the ratio $\frac{\text{vertical rise}}{\text{horizontal run}}$. For example, a ramp that is 5 feet long and rises 1 foot has a grade of $\frac{1}{5}$, or 20%.

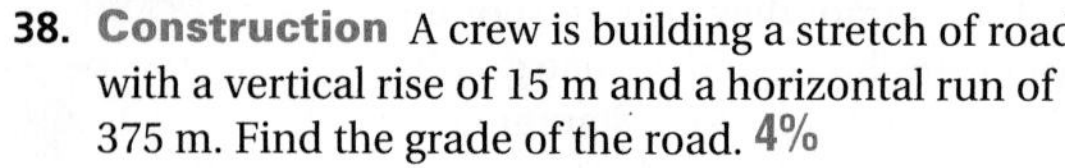

38. Construction A crew is building a stretch of road with a vertical rise of 15 m and a horizontal run of 375 m. Find the grade of the road. **4%**

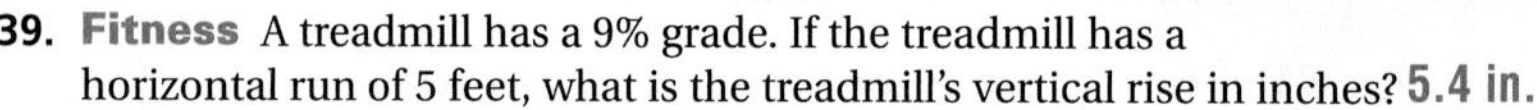

39. Fitness A treadmill has a 9% grade. If the treadmill has a horizontal run of 5 feet, what is the treadmill's vertical rise in inches? **5.4 in.**

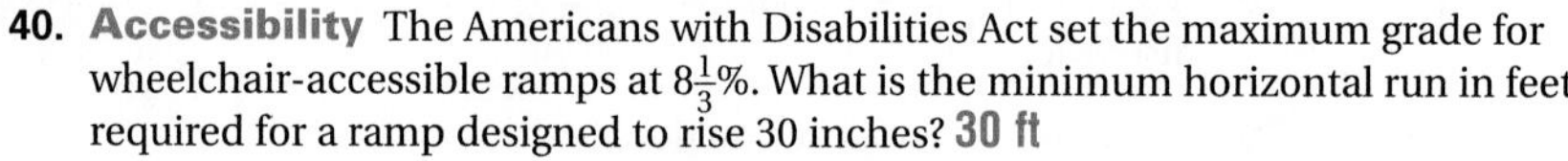

40. Accessibility The Americans with Disabilities Act set the maximum grade for wheelchair-accessible ramps at $8\frac{1}{3}$%. What is the minimum horizontal run in feet required for a ramp designed to rise 30 inches? **30 ft**

LINK

Hobbies

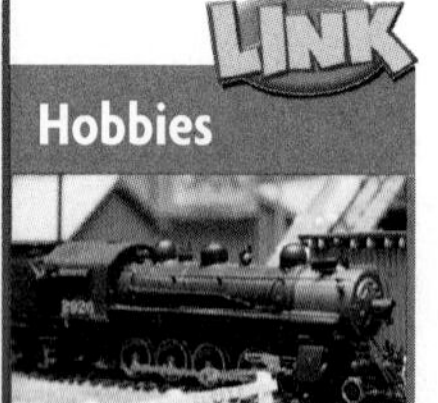

HO is the most popular model train gauge in the United States. The name may have originally meant "Half-O," because it was thought to be about half the size of an O gauge, another model train gauge.

41. Geometry In the diagram shown, $\triangle ABC$ is similar to $\triangle DEF$. Find the lengths of sides $\overline{AB}$ and $\overline{EF}$. $AB = 16\frac{2}{3}$; $EF = 22\frac{1}{2}$

Hobbies Use the information about model trains to complete the table.

	Railroad Gauge	Scale Length (in.)	Actual Length (ft)
42.	O	96	**384**
43.	**HO**	36	261
44.	S	**15**	80
45.	HO	20	**145**

Model Trains

Railroad Gauge	HO	O	S
Model Scale	$\frac{1}{87}$	$\frac{1}{48}$	$\frac{1}{64}$

46. Show that if $b \neq 0$, $d \neq 0$, and $\frac{a}{b} = \frac{c}{d}$, then $\frac{a+b}{b} = \frac{c+d}{d}$.

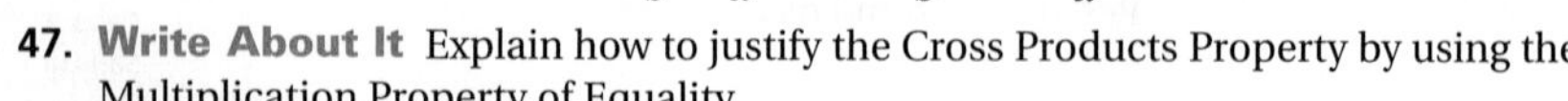

47. Write About It Explain how to justify the Cross Products Property by using the Multiplication Property of Equality.

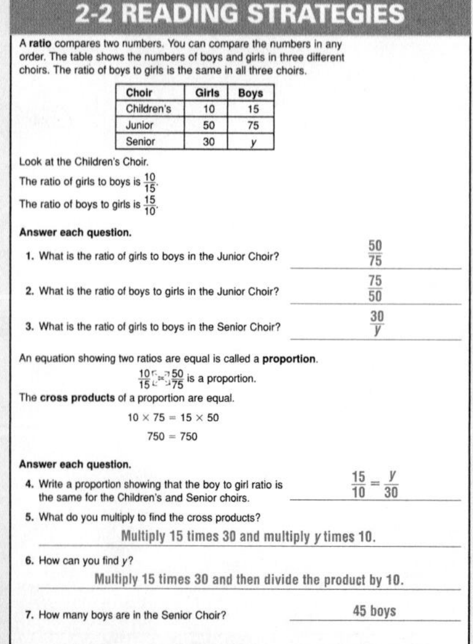

2-2 READING STRATEGIES

A **ratio** compares two numbers. You can compare the numbers in any order. The table shows the numbers of boys and girls in three different choirs. The ratio of boys to girls is the same in all three choirs.

Choir	Girls	Boys
Children's	10	15
Junior	50	75
Senior	30	y

Look at the Children's Choir.

The ratio of girls to boys is $\frac{10}{15}$.

The ratio of boys to girls is $\frac{15}{10}$.

Answer each question.

1. What is the ratio of girls to boys in the Junior Choir? $\frac{50}{75}$
2. What is the ratio of boys to girls in the Junior Choir? $\frac{75}{50}$
3. What is the ratio of girls to boys in the Senior Choir? $\frac{30}{y}$

An equation showing two ratios are equal is called a **proportion**.

$\frac{10}{15} = \frac{50}{75}$ is a proportion.

The **cross products** of a proportion are equal.

$10 \times 75 = 15 \times 50$

$750 = 750$

Answer each question.

4. Write a proportion showing that the boy to girl ratio is the same for the Children's and Senior choirs. $\frac{15}{10} = \frac{y}{30}$
5. What do you multiply to find the cross products? Multiply 15 times 30 and multiply y times 10.
6. How can you find y? Multiply 15 times 30 and then divide the product by 10.
7. How many boys are in the Senior Choir? 45 boys

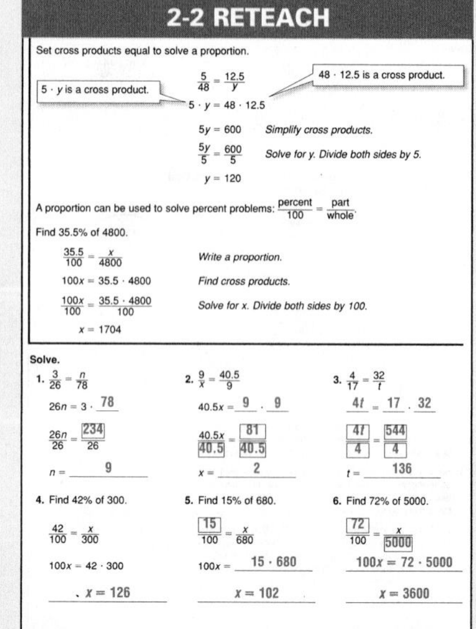

2-2 RETEACH

Set cross products equal to solve a proportion.

$\frac{5}{48} = \frac{12.5}{y}$

5 · y is a cross product. 48 · 12.5 is a cross product.

$5 \cdot y = 48 \cdot 12.5$

$5y = 600$ *Simplify cross products.*

$\frac{5y}{5} = \frac{600}{5}$ *Solve for y. Divide both sides by 5.*

$y = 120$

A proportion can be used to solve percent problems: $\frac{\text{percent}}{100} = \frac{\text{part}}{\text{whole}}$

Find 35.5% of 4800.

$\frac{35.5}{100} = \frac{x}{4800}$ *Write a proportion.*

$100x = 35.5 \cdot 4800$ *Find cross products.*

$\frac{100x}{100} = \frac{35.5 \cdot 4800}{100}$ *Solve for x. Divide both sides by 100.*

$x = 1704$

Solve.

1. $\frac{3}{26} = \frac{n}{78}$; $26n = 3 \cdot 78$; $\frac{26n}{26} = \frac{234}{26}$; $n = 9$
2. $\frac{9}{x} = \frac{40.5}{9}$; $40.5x = 9 \cdot 9$; $\frac{40.5x}{40.5} = \frac{81}{40.5}$; $x = 2$
3. $\frac{4}{17} = \frac{32}{t}$; $4t = 17 \cdot 32$; $\frac{4t}{4} = \frac{544}{4}$; $t = 136$
4. Find 42% of 300. $\frac{42}{100} = \frac{x}{300}$; $100x = 42 \cdot 300$; $x = 126$
5. Find 15% of 680. $\frac{15}{100} = \frac{x}{680}$; $100x = 15 \cdot 680$; $x = 102$
6. Find 72% of 5000. $\frac{72}{100} = \frac{x}{5000}$; $100x = 72 \cdot 5000$; $x = 3600$

TEST PREP

48. **Chemistry** The energy output from a chemical reaction depends on the amount of chemicals used. The table shows this relationship. What is a reasonable amount of energy from the reaction of 40 moles of the chemical?

Energy Output of a Chemical Reaction				
Amount of Chemical (moles)	5	8	12	15
Energy Output (joules)	29.89	48.01	71.96	90.12

(A) 120 joules (B) 160 joules **(C) 240 joules** (D) 300 joules

49. **Technology** A 38 MB file is downloading from the Internet at a constant rate. After 1 min, 18% of the file has downloaded. About how much more time should the download take?

(F) 5.6 min **(G) 4.6 min** (H) 6.75 min (J) 2.1 min

50. A blueprint uses a scale of $\frac{1}{4}$ inch equals 1 foot. A wall on the drawing measures $4\frac{1}{2}$ inches long. How long will the wall be in the actual building?

(A) $\frac{11}{8}$ feet (B) 9 feet (C) 16 feet **(D) 18 feet**

51. **Geometry** In a circle graph, how many degrees does 1% represent?

(F) 1° **(G) 3.6°** (H) 6° (J) 10°

CHALLENGE AND EXTEND

Solve.

52. $\frac{-2}{x+5} = \frac{8}{x-3}$ $x = -3.4$

53. $\frac{h+4}{9} = \frac{h-3}{4}$ $h = 8.6$

54. $\frac{n-2}{4} = \frac{3n+3}{18}$ $n = 8$

55. $\frac{z}{12.8} = \frac{5}{z}$ $z = 8$ or $z = -8$

56. **Construction** A concrete mix has the ratio 1 part cement, 2 parts water, and 3 parts sand. How much water can be used if 78 kg of sand and 21 kg of cement are available? How much concrete can be made? **42 kg; 126 kg**

57. **Critical Thinking** The graph intends to show the increase in the number of dogs registered. Do the icons accurately represent the data? Justify your answer. **No; both the heights and widths of the dogs are proportional, giving areas disproportionate to the data.**

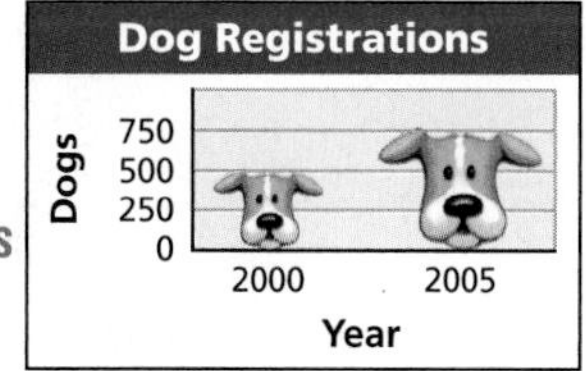

SPIRAL REVIEW

Convert each measure using the given units. *(Previous course)*

58. $\frac{1}{5}$ h = ■ min **12**

59. 108 in. = ■ yd **3**

60. 4.5 lb = ■ oz **72**

61. 3.5 m = ■ cm **350**

62. 12 mm = ■ cm **1.2**

63. 25 mL = ■ L **0.025**

Name the three-dimensional figure that each real-world object models. *(Previous course)*

64. tennis ball **sphere**

65. megaphone **cone**

66. pad of paper **rectangular prism**

67. unsharpened pencil **hexagonal prism or cylinder**

Identify the parent function for h from its function rule. Describe what transformation of the parent function it represents. *(Lesson 1-9)*

68. $h(x) = x^2 - 10$

69. $h(x) = 3x + 4$

70. $h(x) = 2x^3$

71. $h(x) = -\sqrt{x+1}$

68. $f(x) = x^2$; **vertical translation, down 10**

69. $f(x) = x$; **vertical translation, up 4, then stretch by a scale factor of 3.**

70. $f(x) = x^3$; **reflection and then stretch by a scale factor of 2.**

71. $f(x) = \sqrt{x}$; **horizontal translation, left 1, then reflection.**

TEST PREP DOCTOR For **Exercise 50,** students who chose **A** might have forgotten to multiply by the reciprocal of the divisor when dividing the fractions. Also, encourage students to determine if their answers are reasonable. Answer choice **A** is not a reasonable answer.

Journal

Have students describe how proportions and similarity can be used to find the length of a distance or the height of an object without actually measuring it.

ALTERNATIVE ASSESSMENT

Have students create three problems that can be solved using proportions. Require that one involve percents, one involve similar triangles, and one involve rates. Have students demonstrate how proportions are used to model and solve their problems.

Power Presentations with PowerPoint®

2-2 Lesson Quiz

Solve each proportion.

1. $\frac{37.5}{12} = \frac{25}{k}$ $k = 8$

2. $\frac{1.2}{g} = \frac{3.8}{133}$ $g = 42$

3. The results of a recent survey showed that 61.5% of those surveyed had a pet. If 738 people had pets, how many were surveyed? 1200

4. Gina earned $68.75 for 5 hours of tutoring. Approximately how much did she earn per minute? $0.23

5. $\triangle XYZ$ has vertices $X(0, 0)$, $Y(3, -6)$, and $Z(0, -6)$. $\triangle XAB$ is similar to $\triangle XYZ$, with a vertex at $B(0, -4)$. Graph $\triangle XYZ$ and $\triangle XAB$ on the same grid.

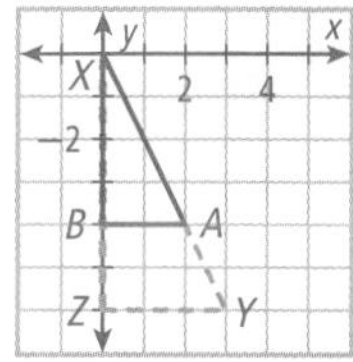

6. A 12-foot flagpole casts a 10-foot shadow. At the same time, a nearby building casts a 48-foot shadow. How tall is the building? 57.6 ft

Also available on transparency

2-2 PROBLEM SOLVING

Leon likes to build model sets of his favorite movies. Solve.

1. In *The Incredible Shrinking Man* (1957), the hero shrinks from about 5 feet 10 inches to about 1 inch tall. If Leon starts with a model character that is $8\frac{3}{4}$ inches tall and shrinks by the same proportion, what is the character's final height?

   0.125 inch or $\frac{1}{8}$ inch

2. In a scene in *King Kong* (1933), the giant gorilla is about 22 feet tall. An ordinary gorilla is about 5 feet tall. In his model, Leon made the giant gorilla 9 inches tall. How tall would an ordinary gorilla be in his model set?

   0.17 feet or about 2 inches

3. In *The Amazing Colossal Man* (1957), a man of about 6 feet becomes 100 feet tall. How tall will Leon's character become if he starts with a model $\frac{1}{2}$ inch tall?

   $8\frac{1}{3}$ inches

4. Leon wants to build a model in a shoe box of the movie *Mothra* (1962), in which a caterpillar with a radius of about $\frac{1}{2}$ inch grew to have a radius of about 30 feet. He starts with a model of an ordinary caterpillar with a radius of $\frac{1}{8}$ inch. Will his final model fit in the shoe box? Why or why not?

   No; possible answer: the caterpillar would have a radius of about 7.5 ft so it wouldn't fit in a shoe box.

Choose the letter for the best answer.

5. There are 372 students, or 30% of the student enrollment, in the 10th grade at Highland School. What is the total student enrollment at the school?
   (A) 1240
   B 1116
   C 744
   D 37.2

6. In this year's city election, 23.6% of the 13,457 registered voters went to the polls. About how many people voted this year?
   A 236
   (B) 3176
   C 9877
   D 317,585

7. Elijah is 5 feet 6 inches tall. He casts a shadow that is 20 feet long. He is standing next to a palm tree that casts a shadow that is 76 feet 6 inches long. How tall is the pine tree to the nearest foot?
   A 19 ft
   (B) 21 ft
   C 25 ft
   D 278 ft

8. How many inches are there in 100 miles?
   A 6.336×10^3 in.
   B 6.336×10^4 in.
   C 6.336×10^5 in.
   (D) 6.336×10^6 in.

2-2 CHALLENGE

Alfred Lord Tennyson (1809–1892) was an English poet of the Victorian Age. One of his more famous poems, "The Vision of Sin," includes the following verses.

Every minute dies a man,
Every minute one is born.

Charles Babbage (1791–1871), an English mathematician and engineer, noted that if these lines were indeed true, the population of England would remain stable, neither growing nor decaying. He wrote to Tennyson and suggested the following lines in his next edition.

Every minute dies a man,
Every minute $1\frac{1}{16}$ is born.

1. a. If Babbage were correct in his revised lines of verse, what would be the ratio of the number of people born to the number who die? 17 to 16

   b. How many births would there be in England during a week in which 592 people died? 629

   c. How many births would there be in England during a week in which the population grew by 23 people? 391

In a more recent era with the growth of new medical techniques, there is now a birth approximately every 9 seconds and a death approximately every 15 seconds.

2. At these revised rates, what would be the ratio of births to deaths in England today? $\frac{5}{3}$

3. If 1215 new babies were born in England in a week, how many deaths would there be for the same week? 729

4. If in one week the population of England increased by 438 people including only births and deaths, determine how many people were born and how many died. 1095 born, 657 died

5. Using Tennyson's lines of verse:

   Every minute dies a man,
   Every minute x is born.

   What value would Babbage replace today for x in these lines of verse?

   $1\frac{2}{3}$

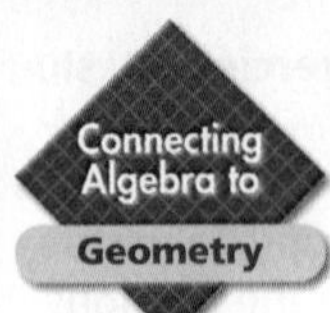

Organizer

See Skills Bank page S56

Pacing:

Traditional $\frac{1}{2}$ day

Block $\frac{1}{4}$ day

Objective: Apply the proportional reasoning skills learned in **Lesson 2-2** to finding percent increase and decrease in the dimensions of similar figures.

Teach

Remember

Students review and apply percent increase and decrease for similar figures.

INTERVENTION For additional review and practice finding percent increase and decrease, see Skills Bank page S56.

Multiple Representations Help students interpret the diagram given in the example. Explain that the length represents the side length of figure A and that 342 mm represents the corresponding side length of figure B.

Close

Assess

Have students show algebraically that figure A is not a 5% decrease of figure B in the Example.

State Resources

go.hrw.com
State Resources Online
KEYWORD: MB7 Resources

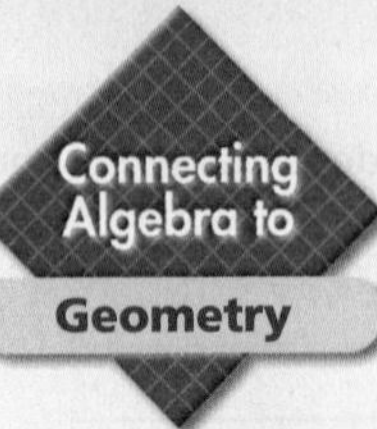

Percent Increase and Decrease

See Skills Bank page S56

Recall that a percent is a ratio that compares a number to 100. A proportion is a statement of two equal ratios. Review the percent change formulas below.

Percent Increase

$$\frac{\text{new measure}}{\text{original measure}} = \frac{100 + \text{percent increase}}{100}$$

Percent Decrease

$$\frac{\text{new measure}}{\text{original measure}} = \frac{100 - \text{percent increase}}{100}$$

When solving problems involving percent change, first check to see if the change is an increase or a decrease. Then write the proportion and solve.

Example

The side lengths of Figure A are decreased by 5% to form figure B. What is the corresponding side length of figure A?

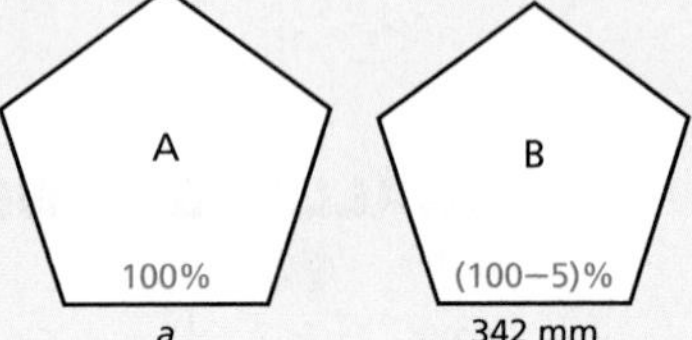

Let a represent the side length of figure A. Then 342 represents the corresponding side length of figure B. Use this information to write a proportion for percent decrease:

$$\begin{matrix}\text{new measure} \rightarrow \\ \text{original measure} \rightarrow\end{matrix} \frac{342}{a} = \frac{100-5}{100} \begin{matrix}\leftarrow 100 - \text{\% decrease} \\ \leftarrow 100\end{matrix}$$

$342 \cdot 100 = a \cdot (100 - 5)$ *Cross multiply.*

$34{,}200 = 95a$ *Multiply and simplify.*

$\frac{34{,}200}{95} = \frac{95a}{95}$ *Divide both sides by 95.*

$360 = a$ *Simplify.*

The corresponding length of figure A is 360 mm.

Try This

The side lengths of figure A are changed as indicated to form a similar figure B. Find the missing measure.

1. A side length of A is decreased by 30%. A side length of B is 91 in. What is the corresponding side length of A? **130 in.**
2. A side length of A is increased by 10%. The perimeter of B is 4200 mm. What is the perimeter of A? $\approx$ **3818.2 mm**
3. A side length of A is increased by 75%. The area of A is 28 cm^2. What is the area of B? Is the area of B 75% greater than the area of A? (*Hint*: Consider a rectangle and look at more than one side.) **85.75 cm^2; no**

2-3 Graphing Linear Functions

Objectives
Determine whether a function is linear.

Graph a linear function given two points, a table, an equation, or a point and a slope.

Vocabulary
linear function
slope
y-intercept
x-intercept
slope-intercept form

Who uses this?
Meteorologists can use linear functions to predict when a hurricane will reach land.

Meteorologists begin tracking a hurricane's distance from land when it is 350 miles off the coast of Florida and moving steadily inland.

The meteorologists are interested in the rate at which the hurricane is approaching land.

Reading Math
The differences in the *y*-values for equally-spaced *x*-values are called *first differences.*

Time (h)	0	1	2	3	4
Distance from Land (mi)	350	325	300	275	250

(Differences in time: +1, +1, +1, +1; differences in distance: −25, −25, −25, −25)

This rate can be expressed as $\frac{\text{change in distance}}{\text{change in time}} = \frac{-25 \text{ miles}}{1 \text{ hour}}$. Notice that the rate of change is constant. The hurricane moves 25 miles closer each hour.

Functions with a constant rate of change are called *linear functions.* A **linear function** can be written in the form $f(x) = mx + b$, where x is the independent variable and m and b are constants. The graph of a linear function is a straight line made up of the set of all points that satisfy $y = f(x)$.

EXAMPLE 1 Recognizing Linear Functions

Determine whether each data set could represent a linear function.

A

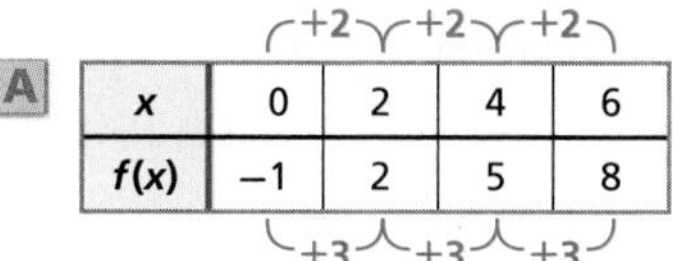

x	0	2	4	6
$f(x)$	−1	2	5	8

(Differences in x: +2, +2, +2; differences in $f(x)$: +3, +3, +3)

The rate of change, $\frac{\text{change in } f(x)}{\text{change in } x}$, is constant $\frac{3}{2}$. So the data set is linear.

B

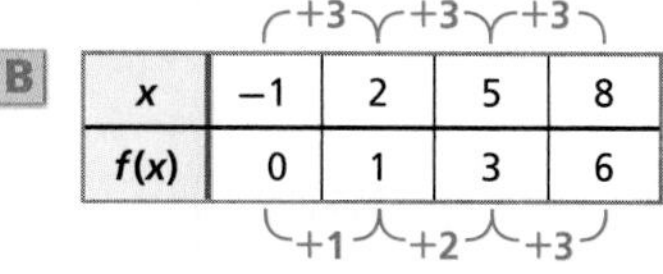

x	−1	2	5	8
$f(x)$	0	1	3	6

(Differences in x: +3, +3, +3; differences in $f(x)$: +1, +2, +3)

The rate of change, $\frac{\text{change in } f(x)}{\text{change in } x}$, is not constant. $\frac{1}{3} \neq \frac{2}{3} \neq \frac{3}{3}$. The data set is not linear.

CHECK IT OUT! **Determine whether each data set could represent a linear function.**

1a. yes

x	4	11	18	25
$f(x)$	−6	−15	−24	−33

1b. no

x	10	8	6	4
$f(x)$	7	5	1	−7

2-3 Organizer

Pacing: Traditional 1 day
Block $\frac{1}{2}$ day

Objectives: Determine whether a function is linear.

Graph a linear function given two points, a table, an equation, or a point and a slope.

Online Edition
Tutorial Videos, Interactivity, TechKeys

Countdown to Testing Week 3

Power Presentations with PowerPoint®

Warm Up

Solve each equation for *y*.

1. $7x + 2y = 6$ $y = -\frac{7}{2}x + 3$

2. $\frac{1}{2}y + x = -4$ $y = -2x - 8$

3. If $3x = 4y + 12$, find y when $x = 0$. $y = -3$

4. If a line passes through (−5, 0) and (0, 2), then it passes through all but which quadrant? IV

Also available on transparency

Math Humor

Q: Why was the student afraid of the *y*-intercept?

A: She thought she'd be stung by the *b*.

1 Introduce

EXPLORATION

2-3 Graphing Linear Functions

Jorge is filling the stock tank at his ranch. He starts when the water in the tank is 5 feet deep. The water rises 1.5 inches per minute.

1. Write an equation that gives the depth of the water in inches y after x minutes.
2. Complete the table.

Time (min)	0	6	12	18	24	30
Water Depth (in.)	60					

3. Find the successive differences in the water depths, as indicated here. What do you notice?

Time (min)	0	6	12	18	24	30
Water Depth (in.)	60					

4. Use your graphing calculator to graph the equation. What is the shape of the graph?

THINK AND DISCUSS

5. **Describe** several different methods you could use to find the depth of the water after 36 minutes.
6. **Explain** how you can find out how long it will take to fill the

Motivate

Draw 3 staircases on the board: 1 uniform and steep; 1 uniform and not steep; 1 with varying degrees of each. Have students compare them using words such as *rise* and *run.*

Connect the upper corners of the stairs of each staircase. Point out the linearity of the first two lines (the steps have a constant rate of change) and non-linearity of the third (the change is not constant).

Explorations and answers are provided in the *Explorations* binder.

State Resources

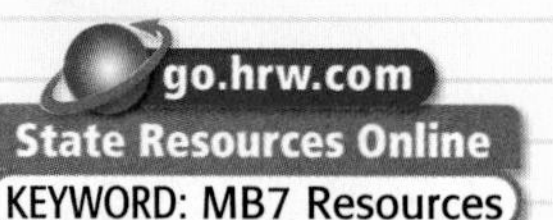

The constant rate of change for a linear function is its *slope*. The **slope** of a linear function is the ratio $\frac{\text{change in } f(x)}{\text{change in } x}$, or $\frac{\text{rise}}{\text{run}}$. The slope of a line is the same between any two points on the line. You can graph lines by using the slope and a point.

EXAMPLE 2 Graphing Lines Using Slope and a Point

Graph each line.

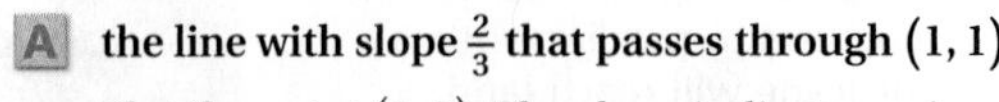

A **the line with slope $\frac{2}{3}$ that passes through $(1, 1)$**

Plot the point $(1, 1)$. The slope indicates a rise of 2 and a run of 3. Move up 2 and right 3 to find another point. Repeat. Then draw a line through the points.

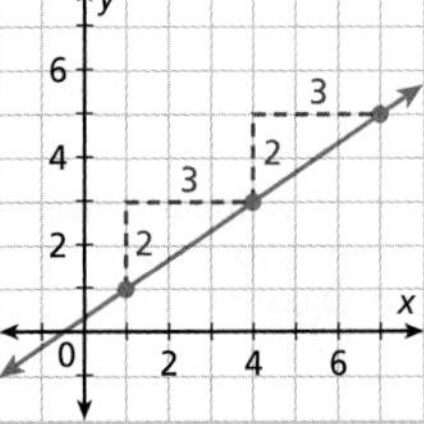

B **the line with slope $-\frac{1}{3}$ that passes through $(-2, 3)$**

Plot the point $(-2, 3)$. The negative slope can be viewed as $\frac{-1}{3}$ or $\frac{1}{-3}$.

You can move down 1 unit and right 3 units, or move up 1 unit and left 3 units. Notice that all three points are on the same line.

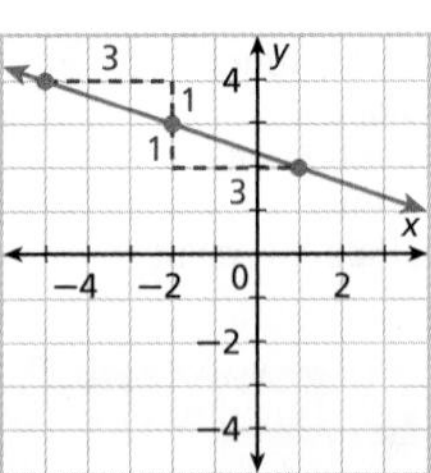

CHECK IT OUT! **2.** Graph the line with slope $\frac{4}{3}$ that passes through $(3, 1)$.

Recall from geometry that two points determine a line. Often the easiest points to find are the points where a line crosses the axes. The **y-intercept** is the y-coordinate of a point where the line crosses the y-axis. The **x-intercept** is the x-coordinate of a point where the line crosses the x-axis.

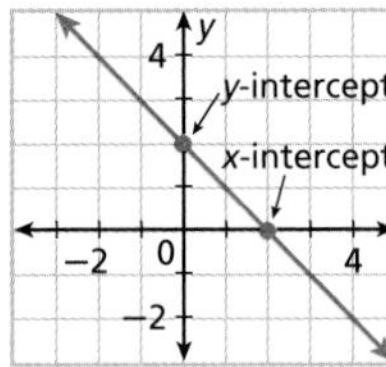

EXAMPLE 3 Graphing Lines Using the Intercepts

Find the intercepts of $2x - 3y = 12$, and graph the line.

Find the x-intercept: $2x - 3y = 12$

$2x - 3(0) = 12$ *Substitute 0 for y.*

$2x = 12$

$x = 6$ *The x-intercept is 6.*

Find the y-intercept: $2x - 3y = 12$

$2(0) - 3y = 12$ *Substitute 0 for x.*

$-3y = 12$

$y = -4$ *The y-intercept is –4.*

Draw the line through $(6, 0)$ and $(0, -4)$.

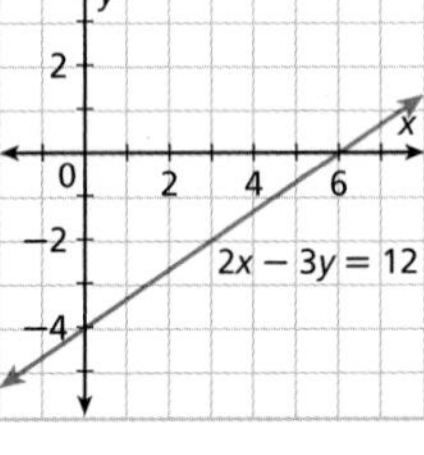

Caution!

The intercept is a single value, not an ordered pair or a point.

CHECK IT OUT! **3.** Find the intercepts of $6x - 2y = -24$, and graph the line.

$x = -4$; $y = 12$

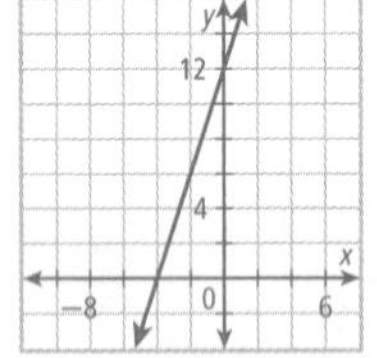

Power Presentations with PowerPoint®

Additional Examples

Example 1

Determine whether each data set could represent a linear function.

A.

x	−2	0	2	4
$f(x)$	2	1	0	−1

linear

B.

x	2	3	4	5
$f(x)$	2	4	8	16

not linear

Example 2

Graph each line.

A. the line with slope $\frac{5}{2}$ that passes through $(-1, -3)$

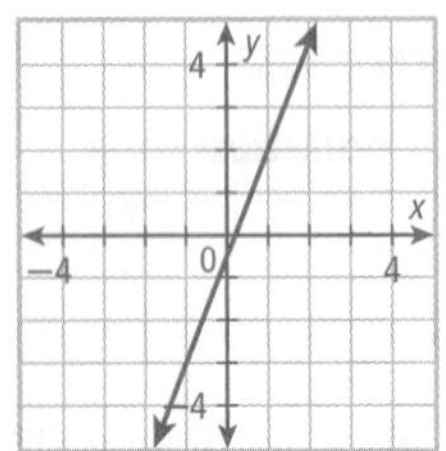

B. the line with slope $-\frac{3}{4}$ that passes through $(0, 2)$

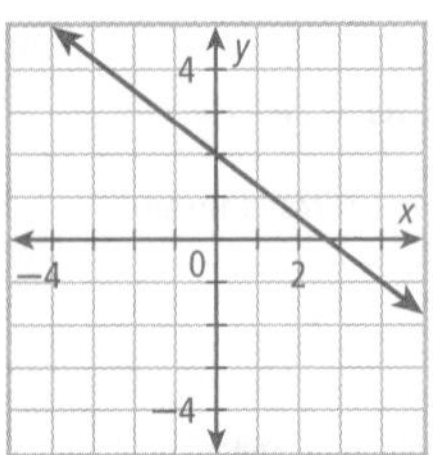

Also available on transparency

INTERVENTION

Questioning Strategies

EXAMPLE 1

- How do you find the rate of change? What does the rate of change tell you?

EXAMPLE 2

- If you know one point on a line, how can you use the slope to find other points on the line?
- How can you use similar triangles and points on a line to show that the slope of a line is constant?

2 Teach

Guided Instruction

Be sure students understand the concept *constant rate of change.* Use the initial hurricane data to show that the rate is constant no matter which two data pairs are used. For example, have students calculate the rate using the second and fifth data pairs to see that the rate remains the same. The constancy of the rate of change is the key concept involved in slope and linearity.

Reaching All Learners

Through Graphic Organizers

To help students make the connection between vertical and horizontal lines and their equations, have them create tables of ordered pairs that satisfy the condition of an equation. For example, for the equation $x = -3$, the x-value in each ordered pair must be -3, whereas the y-values can be any real number. Have students graph their ordered pairs to see that the points all lie on the same vertical line or, in the case of $y = 1$, on the same horizontal line.

Linear functions can also be expressed as linear equations of the form $y = mx + b$. When a linear function is written in the form $y = mx + b$, the function is said to be in **slope-intercept form** because m is the slope of the graph and b is the y-intercept. Notice that slope-intercept form is the equation solved for y.

EXAMPLE 4 Graphing Functions in Slope-Intercept Form

Write each function in slope-intercept form. Then graph the function.

A $3x + y = 5$

Solve for y first.

$$3x + y = 5$$
$$\underline{-3x \quad\quad -3x} \quad \textit{Add } -3x \textit{ to both sides.}$$
$$y = -3x + 5$$

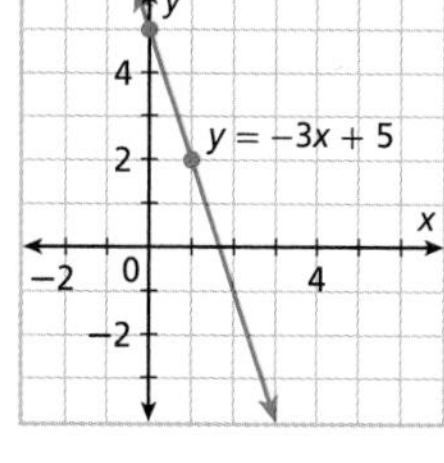

The line has y-intercept 5 and slope -3, which is $\frac{-3}{1}$. Plot the point $(0, 5)$. Then move down 3 and right 1 to find other points.

Helpful Hint

Most graphing calculators require equations to be solved for y, so slope-intercept form is the easiest to enter.

You can also use a graphing calculator to graph. Choose the standard square window to make your graph look like it would on a regular grid. Press  ZOOM, choose **6:ZStandard**, press ZOOM again, and then choose **5:ZSquare**.

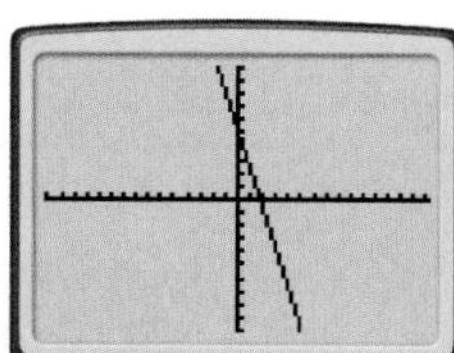

B $\frac{3}{2}y = x - 3$

Solve for y first.

$$\frac{2}{3}\left(\frac{3}{2}y\right) = \frac{2}{3}(x - 3) \quad \textit{Multiply both sides by } \frac{2}{3}.$$

$$y = \frac{2}{3}(x) - \frac{2}{3}(3) \quad \textit{Distribute.}$$

$$y = \frac{2}{3}x - 2$$

The graph of the line has y-intercept -2 and slope $\frac{2}{3}$. Plot the point $(0, -2)$. Then move up 2 and right 3 to find other points.

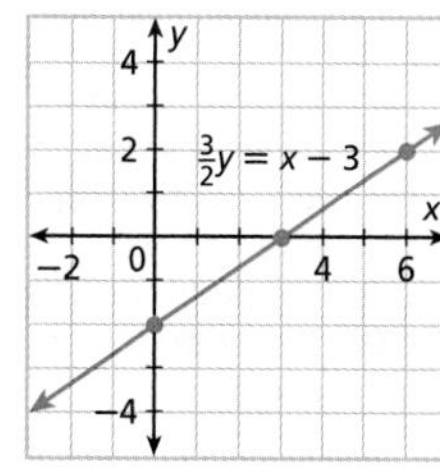

CHECK IT OUT! Write each equation in slope-intercept form. Then graph the function.

4a. $2x - y = 9$ $y = 2x - 9$ **4b.** $5x = 15y + 30$ $y = \frac{1}{3}x - 2$

4a.

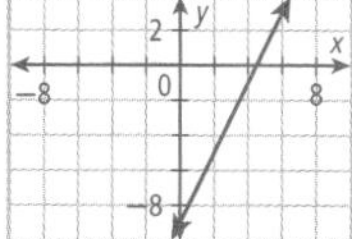

4b.

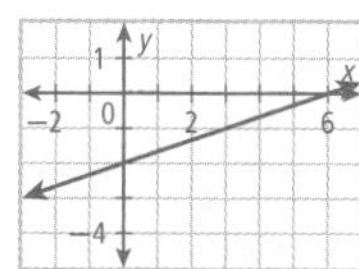

An equation with only one variable can be represented by either a vertical or a horizontal line.

COMMON ERROR ALERT

Students may incorrectly plot points of a line with a negative slope by counting down and left. Help students see that this is equivalent to counting up and right, producing a line with a positive slope.

Power Presentations with PowerPoint®

Additional Examples

Example 3

Find the intercepts of $4x - 2y = 16$ and graph the line.

x-intercept: 4; y-intercept: -8

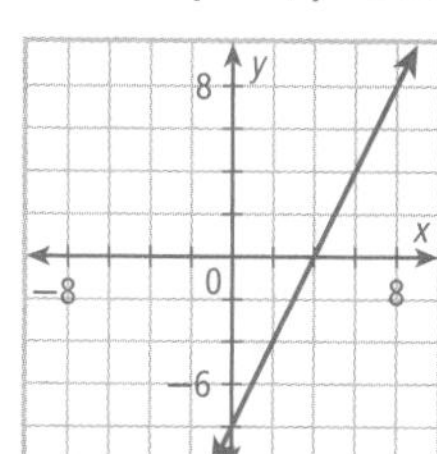

Example 4

Write each function in slope-intercept form. Then graph the function.

A. $-4x + y = -1$ $y = 4x - 1$

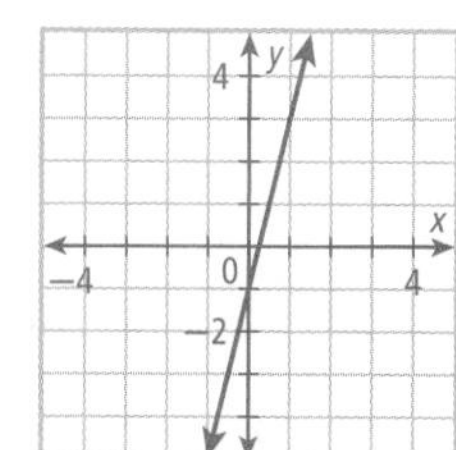

B. $x + \frac{3}{4}y = 6$ $y = -\frac{4}{3}x + 8$

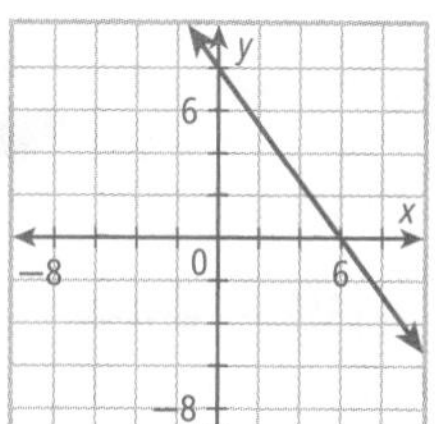

Also available on transparency

Reaching All Learners

Through Auditory Cues

Students sometimes reverse the numerator and denominator in the fraction that represents slope. To help students associate the fraction with $\frac{\text{rise}}{\text{run}}$, point out that *rise* rhymes with *y*'s as a clue to remembering that the numerator is the change in y.

Through Number Sense

The table below may help students find intercepts. Point out that when $x = 0$, the y-value is the y-intercept and when $y = 0$ the x-value is the x-intercept.

x	y
0	y-intercept
x-intercept	0

INTERVENTION

Questioning Strategies

EXAMPLE 3

- How can you use the intercepts of a line to graph it?

EXAMPLE 4

- If all coefficients are positive, do you know the sign of the slope?

Power Presentations with PowerPoint®

Additional Examples

Example 5

Determine if each line is vertical or horizontal. Then graph.

A. $x = 2$ vertical

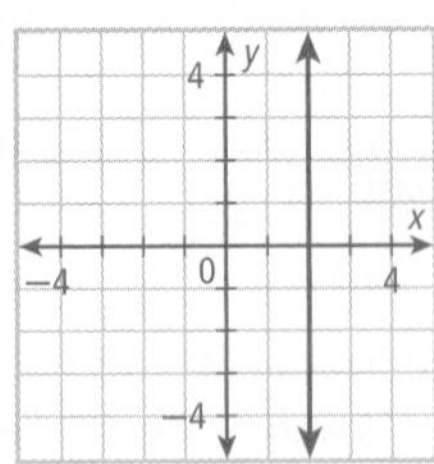

B. $y = -4$ horizontal

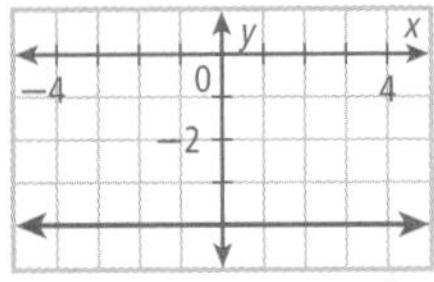

Example 6

A ski lift carries skiers from an altitude of 1800 feet to an altitude of 3000 feet over a horizontal distance of 2000 feet. Find the average slope of this part of the mountain. Graph the elevation against the distance. slope: $\frac{3}{5}$

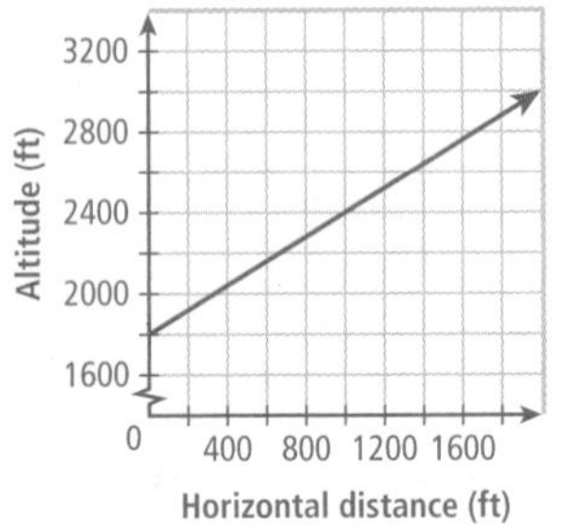

Also available on transparency

INTERVENTION 

Questioning Strategies

EXAMPLE 5

- Why are equations of the form $x = a$ vertical and equations of the form $y = b$ horizontal?
- What are the rise and the run of each of the lines graphed in this example? What does this indicate about their slopes?

EXAMPLE 6

- What does the value of the slope tell you about the steepness of the road?

Vertical and Horizontal Lines	
Vertical Lines	**Horizontal Lines**
The line $x = a$ is a vertical line at a.	The line $y = b$ is a horizontal line at b.

The slope of a vertical line is undefined. The slope of a horizontal line is 0.

EXAMPLE 5 **Graphing Vertical and Horizontal Lines**

Determine if each line is vertical or horizontal. Then graph.

A $x = -3$

This is a vertical line located at the x-value -3. (Note that it is not a function.)

B $y = 1$

This is a horizontal line located at the y-value 1.

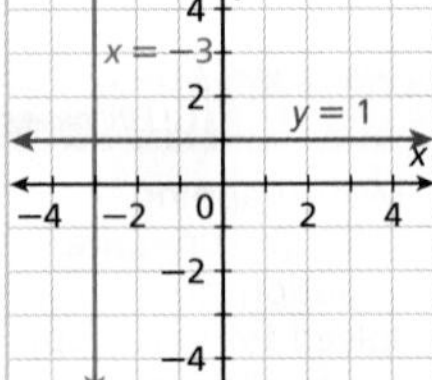

CHECK IT OUT! **Determine if each line is vertical or horizontal. Then graph.**

5a. $y = -5$ **horizontal** **5b.** $x = 0.5$ **vertical**

5a.

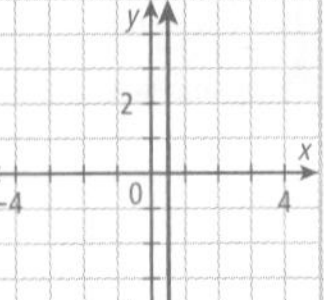

5b.

EXAMPLE 6 ***Travel Application***

Suppose a road rises from 2500 ft above sea level to 7000 ft in 10 mi. Find the average slope of the road. Graph the elevation against distance.

Step 1 Find the slope.

The rise is $7000 - 2500$, or 4500 ft.
The run is 10 mi.

Convert miles to feet:

$10 \text{ mi} = 10(5280) = 52{,}800 \text{ ft}.$

The slope is $\frac{4500}{52{,}800} \approx 0.085$.

Step 2 Graph the line.

The y-intercept is the original altitude, 2500 ft. Use $(0, 2500)$ and $(52{,}800, 7000)$ as two points on the line. Select a scale for each axis that will fit the data, and graph the function.

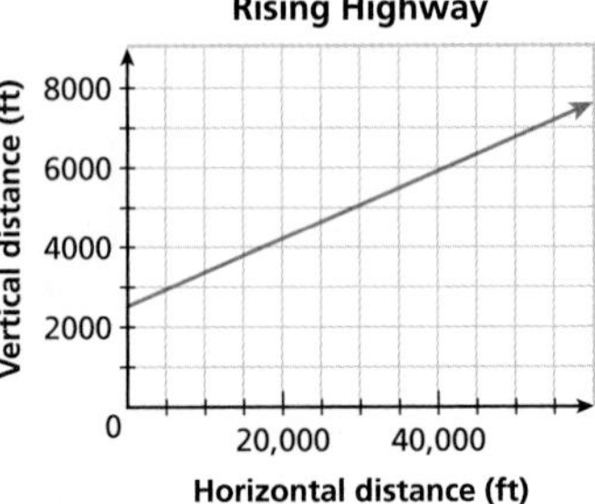

Helpful Hint

Because the graph has different scales for the x- and y-axis, the slope of the graph appears steeper than the slope of the actual road.

CHECK IT OUT! **6.** A truck driver is at mile marker 624 on Interstate 10. After 3 hours, the driver reaches mile marker 432. Find his average speed. Graph his location on I-10 in terms of mile markers.

64 mi/h

3 Close

Summarize

Present the following equations and ask students to consider the equations' graphs. Have students tell all they can about the slopes and intercepts of these graphs. Review procedures for graphing the lines.

$y = 4x - 3$ slope: 4; x-int.: 0.75; y-int.: -3

$2x + y = 18$ slope: -2; x-int.: 9; y-int.: 18

$y = -1$ slope: 0; x-int.: none; y-int.: -1

ONGOING ASSESSMENT and INTERVENTION 

***Diagnose Before* the Lesson**
2-3 Warm Up, TE p. 105

***Monitor During* the Lesson**
Check It Out! Exercises, SE pp. 105–108
Questioning Strategies, TE pp. 106–108

***Assess After* the Lesson**
2-3 Lesson Quiz, TE p. 112
Alternative Assessment, TE p. 112

THINK AND DISCUSS

1. Explain two different ways to graph the equation $4x = 2y - 12$.
2. Can a line have more than one slope? Explain.
3. What are the slope and y-intercept for the line that models the hurricane data at the beginning of this lesson? Explain.

4. **GET ORGANIZED** Copy and complete the graphic organizer for linear functions.

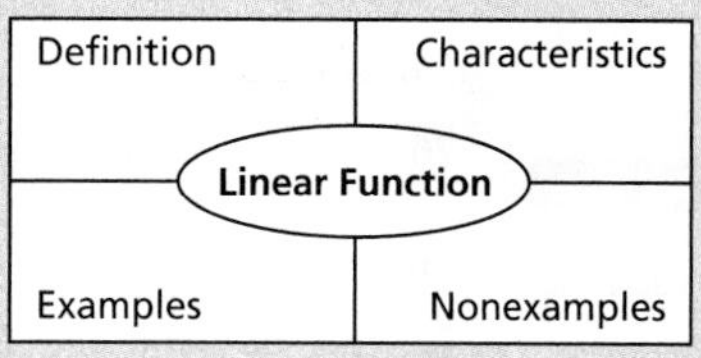

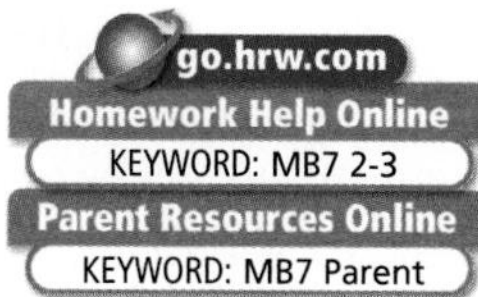

Answers to *Think and Discuss*

1. Possible answer: Set each variable equal to 0 to find the 2 intercept points. Draw the line that passes through them; solve for y, plot the y-intercept point, use the slope to find another point and draw the line through the point.
2. No; slope is a constant ratio of rise to run.
3. y-intercept: 350; distance from land of the hurricane when the time is 0; slope: −25; change in distance during each increase in time of 1 hour
4. See p. A3.

2-3 Exercises

go.hrw.com
Homework Help Online KEYWORD: MB7 2-3
Parent Resources Online KEYWORD: MB7 Parent

GUIDED PRACTICE

Apply the vocabulary from this lesson to answer each question.

1. **Vocabulary** How does the *y-intercept* differ from the *x-intercept*?
2. **Vocabulary** The rate of change of a linear function is its __?__. (*intercept* or *slope*) slope

SEE EXAMPLE 1 p. 105

Determine whether each data set could represent a linear function.

3.

x	2	5	8	11
$f(x)$	9	17	25	33

yes

4.

x	3	9	15	21
$f(x)$	1	4	10	19

no

SEE EXAMPLE 2 p. 106

Graph each line.

5. slope $\frac{5}{2}$; passes through $(0, 2)$
6. slope 2; passes through $(4, -5)$
7. slope $-\frac{4}{3}$; passes through $(-2, -1)$
8. slope $-\frac{2}{5}$; passes through $(3, 0)$

SEE EXAMPLE 3 p. 106

Find the intercepts of each line, and graph the line.

9. $5x + 6y = 30$ $x = 6$; $y = 5$
10. $2x - 3y = 24$ $x = 12$; $y = -8$
11. $5x - 2y = -30$ $x = -6$; $y = 15$
12. $-4x + 5y = 10$ $x = -\frac{5}{2}$; $y = 2$

SEE EXAMPLE 4 p. 107

Write each function in slope-intercept form. Then graph the function.

13. $5x + y = 4$ $y = -5x + 4$
14. $-y = -8x$ $y = 8x$
15. $3y = 15 - 6x$ $y = -2x + 5$
16. $2x - 5y = -6$ $y = \frac{2}{5}x + \frac{6}{5}$

SEE EXAMPLE 5 p. 108

Determine if each line is vertical or horizontal. Then graph the line.

17. $x = 7$ vertical
18. $y = \frac{5}{4}$ horizontal
19. $x = 0$ vertical
20. $y = -4$ horizontal

SEE EXAMPLE 6 p. 108

21. **Business** Art's cash register contained \$150 when he opened the store. After 8 hours, the register contained \$738. Find the average sales per hour, and graph the hourly amount of cash in the register. **\$73.50/h**

2-3 Exercises

Assignment Guide

Assign *Guided Practice* exercises as necessary.

If you finished Examples **1–3**
Basic 22–31, 42, 46, 55–56
Average 22–31, 42, 46, 50–52
Advanced 21–30, 46, 55–56

If you finished Examples **1–6**
Basic 22–47, 51, 54–55, 57–63, 66–79
Average 22–40, 42, 44–63, 66–79
Advanced 22–40, 46–53, 55–79

Homework Quick Check
Quickly check key concepts.
Exercises: 22, 24, 28, 34, 38, 40, 58

11–21. For graphs, see p. A17.

State Resources

go.hrw.com
State Resources Online
KEYWORD: MB7 Resources

Answers

1. See p. A17.

5.

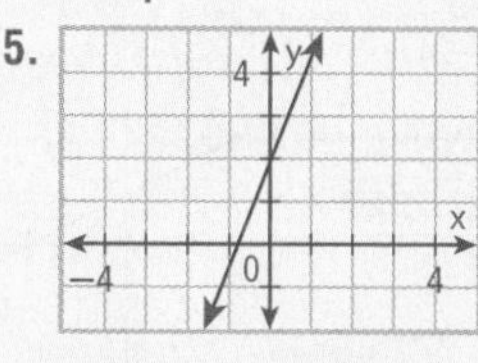

6.

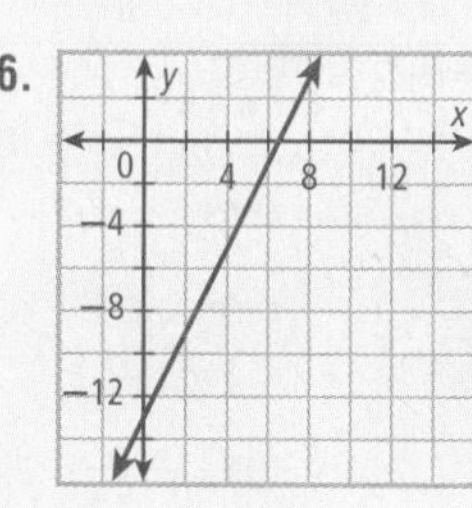

7.

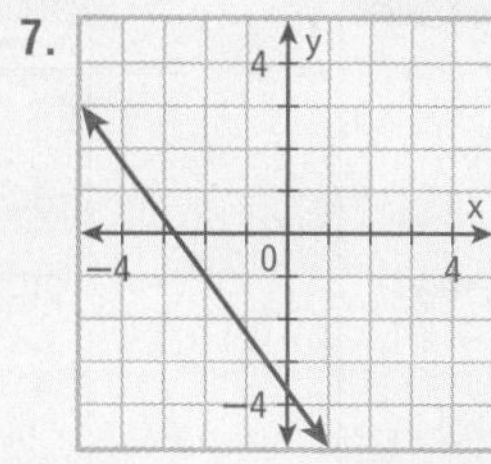

8.

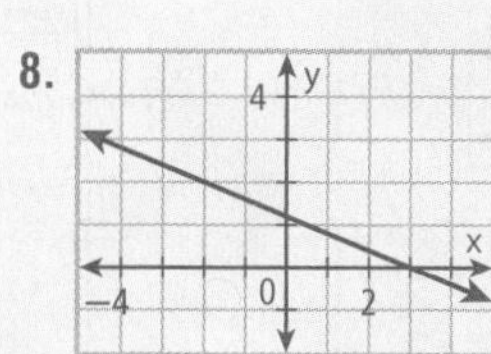

9.

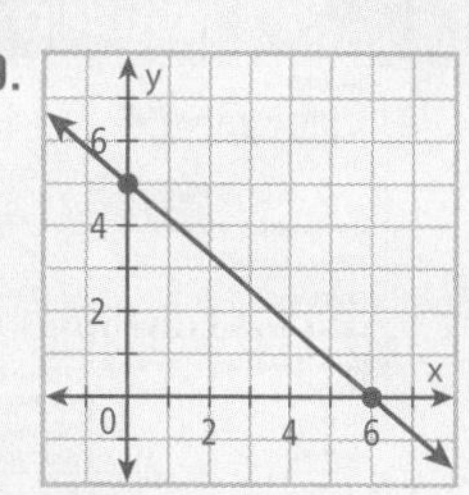

10.

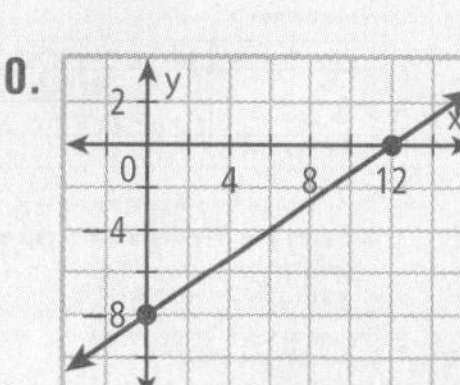

Number Sense For **Exercise 46,** remind students that they might choose to multiply both sides of the equation by 10 to create an equivalent equation that does not contain decimals.

Answers

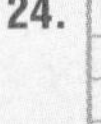

24.
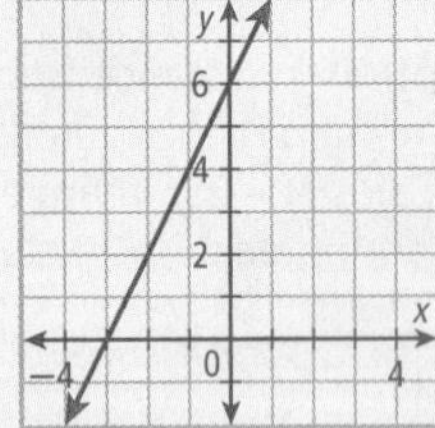

25.
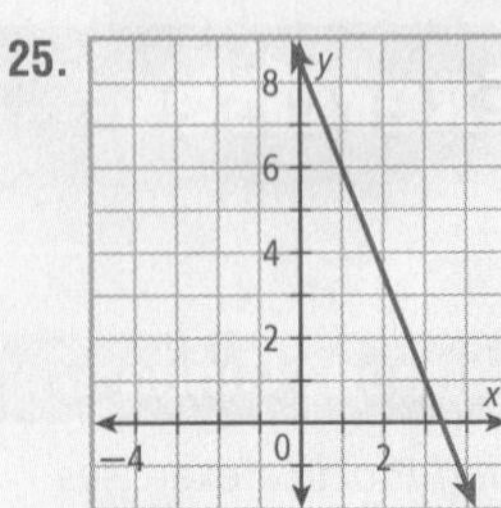

26.
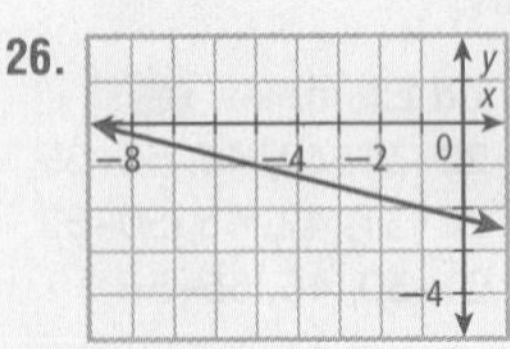

27.
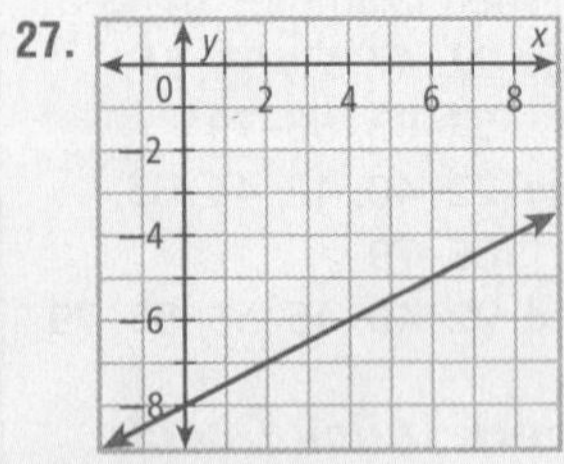

28.
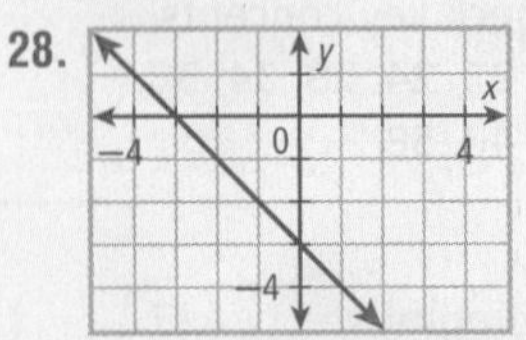

29.
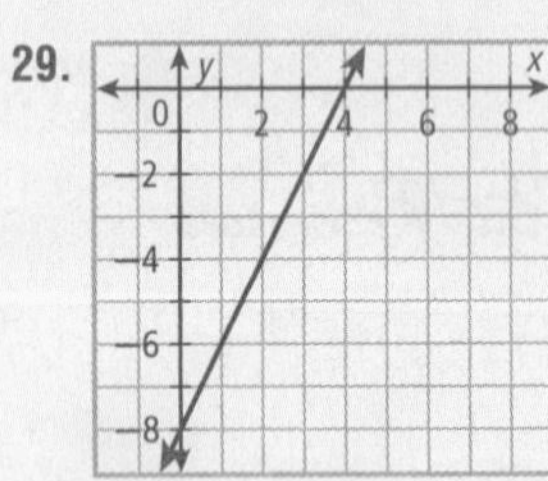

30.
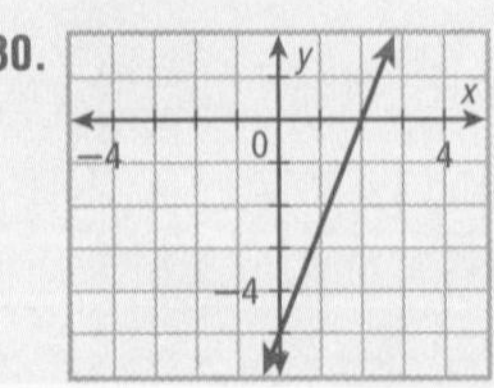

31–46. For graphs, see p. A17–18.

PRACTICE AND PROBLEM SOLVING

Independent Practice

For Exercises	See Example
22–23	1
24–27	2
28–31	3
32–35	4
36–39	5
40	6

Extra Practice
Skills Practice p. S6
Application Practice p. S33

Determine whether each data set could represent a linear function.

22.

x	2	3	4	5
$f(x)$	0	1	2	1

no

23.

x	−3	−1	1	3
$f(x)$	1	1.5	2	2.5

yes

Graph each line.

24. slope 2; passes through $(-3, 0)$
25. slope -2.5; passes through $(1, 6)$
26. slope $-\frac{1}{4}$; passes through $(-1, -2)$
27. slope $\frac{1}{2}$; passes through $(0, -8)$

Find the intercepts of each line, and graph the line.

28. $x + y = -3$ $x = -3$; $y = -3$
29. $2x - y = 8$ $x = 4$; $y = -8$
30. $5x - 2y = 10$ $x = 2$; $y = -5$
31. $-3x + 2y = 6$ $x = -2$; $y = 3$

Write each function in slope-intercept form. Then graph the function.

32. $2x + y = 6$ $y = -2x + 6$
33. $-y = -3x + 2$ $y = 3x - 2$
34. $3y = -6 + x$ $y = \frac{1}{3}x - 2$
35. $8x - 6y = -12$ $y = \frac{4}{3}x + 2$

Determine if each line is vertical or horizontal. Then graph the line.

36. $x = -1$ vertical
37. $y = 0$ horizontal
38. $x = 3.7$ vertical
39. $y = -\frac{4}{5}$ horizontal

40. **Architecture** The fastest elevator in the world is in the Taipei 101 tower in Taiwan. Descending from the observation deck, the elevator travels between the two heights shown in about 7 seconds.
   a. Find the average speed of the elevator, and graph the height against the time. 32 ft/s
   b. Use your graph to estimate when the elevator will reach ground level. ≈ 40 s

Graph each function.

41. $y = -\frac{1}{3}x + 2$
42. $x + y = 8$
43. $y = \frac{4}{7}x - 6$
44. $2y = 3x - 1$
45. $y = 4 - \frac{1}{8}x$
46. $0.2x + 0.6y = 1.8$

47. The beverage prices for a diner are shown.
   a. Are the beverage prices a linear function of the number of ounces? yes
   b. How much should a 32 oz drink cost? $1.99
   c. What is the y-intercept? What does it represent?
   d. **What if...?** Suppose the prices are all decreased by $0.20. How do your answers to parts **a**, **b**, and **c** change? What answers remain the same?

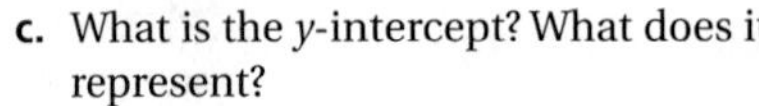

47c. 1.19; possible answer: the fixed cost of providing a beverage is $1.19.
d. changes: $1.79 for a 32-oz cup, 0.99 is the y-intercept; same: beverage prices are a function of the number of ounces

Tell whether each statement is sometimes, always, or never true.

48. If the slope of a linear function is 0, then the line is parallel to the y-axis. never
49. If the y-intercept and the x-intercept of a linear function are equal, then the slope is 1. sometimes
50. If the y-intercept of a linear function is positive and the slope is negative, then the x-intercept is positive. always

2-3 READING STRATEGIES

Definition	Facts
A function with a constant rate of change is called a **linear function**. $f(x) = mx + b$; m is the slope. b is the y-intercept.	The graph of a linear function is always a straight line. You can use the equation of a linear function to find its slope and intercepts: $y = mx + b$.
Example	**Useful Hints**
Linear function: $2x + y = 4$; Slope-intercept form of the linear function: $y = -2x + 4$; Slope = −2; y-intercept = 4	You can use any two points on a line to draw its graph. The intercepts give you two points on the line. You can also graph a line using its slope and one point on the line.

Complete the table

	Linear Function	Slope-Intercept Form	Slope	y-intercept
1.	$4x + y = 7$	$y = -4x + 7$	−4	7
2.	$3y - 3x = -9$	$y = x - 3$	1	−3
3.	$-6x + 2y = 12$	$y = 3x + 6$	3	6

Use the function $x - 2y = 4$ for Exercises 4–6.

4. What do the terms x-intercept and y-intercept mean?
Possible answer: The x-intercept is the point where the line crosses the x-axis. The y-intercept is the point where the line crosses the y-axis.

5. The function passes through the point $(2, -1)$. Describe how to use the slope to find another point on the line.
Possible answer: Plot $(2, -1)$. The slope of the line is $\frac{1}{2}$, so move 1 unit up and 2 units to the right, to $(4, 0)$.

6. Describe how to graph the function using its intercepts.
Possible answer: Plot the points $(4, 0)$ and $(0, -2)$. Draw a line through both points.

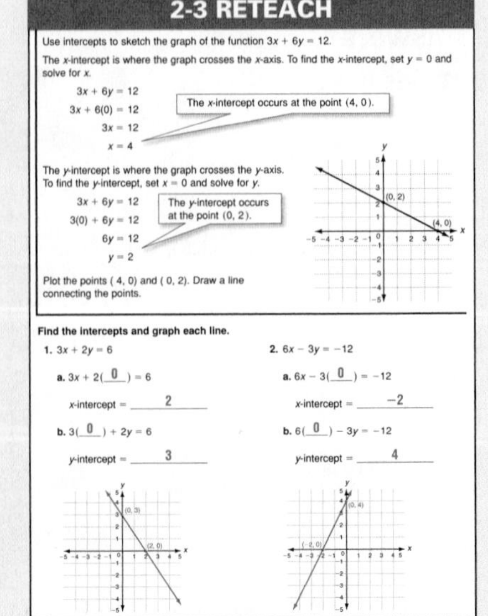

2-3 RETEACH

Use intercepts to sketch the graph of the function $3x + 6y = 12$.

The x-intercept is where the graph crosses the x-axis. To find the x-intercept, set $y = 0$ and solve for x.

$3x + 6y = 12$
$3x + 6(0) = 12$
$3x = 12$
$x = 4$

The x-intercept occurs at the point $(4, 0)$.

The y-intercept is where the graph crosses the y-axis. To find the y-intercept, set $x = 0$ and solve for y.

$3x + 6y = 12$
$3(0) + 6y = 12$
$6y = 12$
$y = 2$

The y-intercept occurs at the point $(0, 2)$.

Plot the points $(4, 0)$ and $(0, 2)$. Draw a line connecting the points.

Find the intercepts and graph each line.

1. $3x + 2y = 6$
a. $3x + 2(\underline{0}) = 6$
x-intercept = 2
b. $3(\underline{0}) + 2y = 6$
y-intercept = 3

2. $6x - 3y = -12$
a. $6x - 3(\underline{0}) = -12$
x-intercept = −2
b. $6(\underline{0}) - 3y = -12$
y-intercept = 4

51c. the number of leagues per foot

51. This problem will prepare you for the Multi-Step Test Prep on page 132.

The deepest point in the world's oceans, in the Marianas Trench, is 35,840 ft deep. A nautical mile is about 6,076.1 ft. **≈ 1.97**

a. A league is 3 nautical miles. How many leagues deep is the Marianas Trench?

b. Graph the relationship between leagues and feet, using feet as the independent variable. Show a point representing the Marianas Trench point on your graph.

c. What does the slope of the line represent?

d. The novel *20,000 Leagues Under the Sea* was written by Jules Verne in 1870. How many feet are in 20,000 leagues? Using this answer, find out how many times the depth of the Marianas Trench 20,000 leagues is.

≈ 364.6 million ft; 10,172

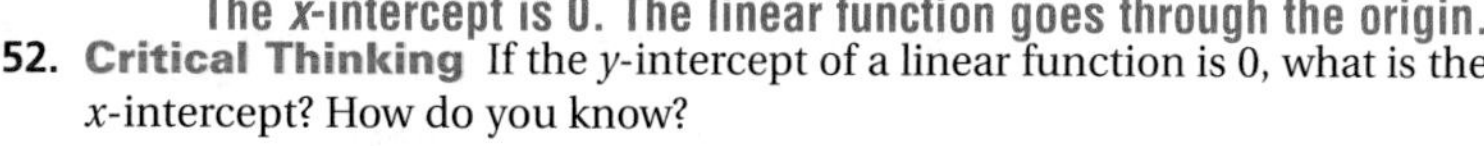

The x-intercept is 0. The linear function goes through the origin.

52. Critical Thinking If the y-intercept of a linear function is 0, what is the x-intercept? How do you know?

LINK Meteorology

Swedish astronomer Anders Celsius (1701–1744), for whom the Celsius temperature scale is named, published numerous observations of the aurora borealis.

53. Critical Thinking The *standard form of a linear equation* is $Ax + By = C$.

a. Find the slope and the y-intercept of a line with this equation. $-\frac{A}{B}$; $\frac{C}{B}$

b. Use your answer to part **a** to quickly find the slope and the y-intercept for the line $12x - 4y = 18$. **53b.** 3; $-\frac{9}{2}$

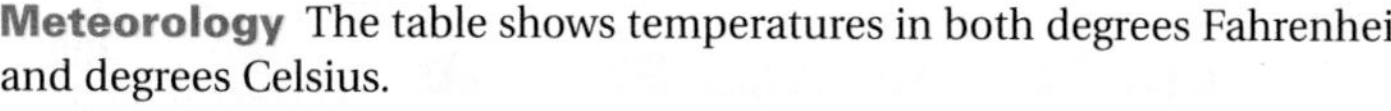

54. Meteorology The table shows temperatures in both degrees Fahrenheit and degrees Celsius.

Temperature Equivalents

Temperature (°C)	−5	0	5	10	15	20
Temperature (°F)	23	32	41	50	59	68

a. Explain why this data set is linear. **54b.** slope: $\frac{9}{5}$; y-intercept: 32

b. Use Celsius temperature as the independent variable. Find the slope and the y-intercept of the line that passes through the points.

c. Graph these data. Use your graph to estimate the Celsius equivalent of 55°F. **≈ 13°C**

54a. For each constant increase of 5°C, the temperature in Fahrenheit increases by a constant 9°

55. School The revenue in dollars from a school play is given by the expression $5x + 2y$, where x is the number of adult tickets sold and y is the number of student tickets sold.

a. How much does each type of ticket cost if the revenue is $220? **adult $5, student $2**

b. Find the x- and y-intercepts. What do the intercepts represent?

c. **What if...?** Suppose that after the equation is modified and graphed, the y-intercept decreases and the x-intercept remains the same. What could this indicate in the context of the problem?

55c. Possible answer: the price of the student tickets was decreased.

56. Determine whether the data in the table are linear. Explain. **No; rates of change differ between pairs of points.**

Time (s)	5	18	20	26	40
Distance (ft)	19.5	32.5	37.5	72	107

57. Write About It Explain how to find the slope of a line from a table of data.

58. Building A roof is 12 feet high at its edge and rises to a height of 20 feet at a point 10 feet horizontally from the edge. What is the slope of the roof? **0.8**

Exercise 51 involves converting and comparing measurements given in feet, nautical miles, and leagues. This exercise prepares students for the Multi-Step Test Prep on page 132.

Teaching Tip

Critical Thinking For **Exercise 52,** encourage students to draw sketches of lines whose y-intercepts are 0. Prompt students to consider different possible orientations for the lines and the resulting x-intercepts. (*Note:* One possible line that students might overlook is the horizontal line that passes through the origin. This line has infinitely many x-intercepts.)

Answers

51b.

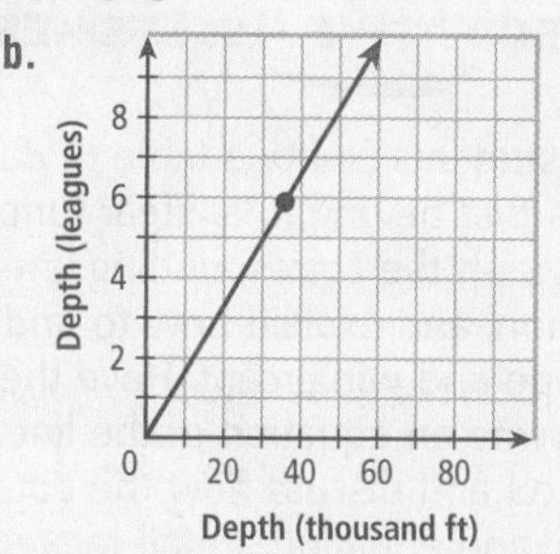

54c.

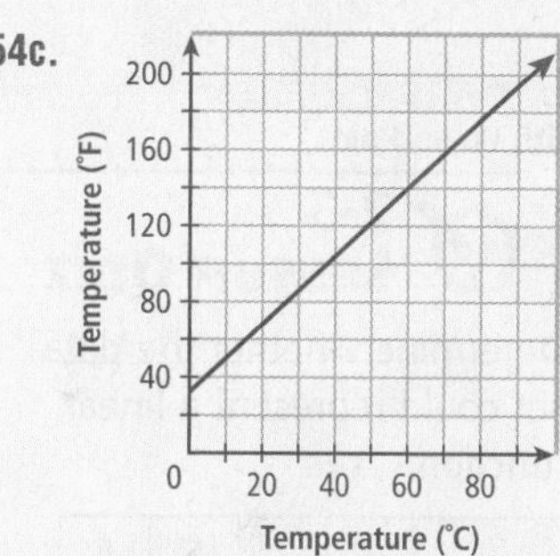

55b, 57 See p. 112

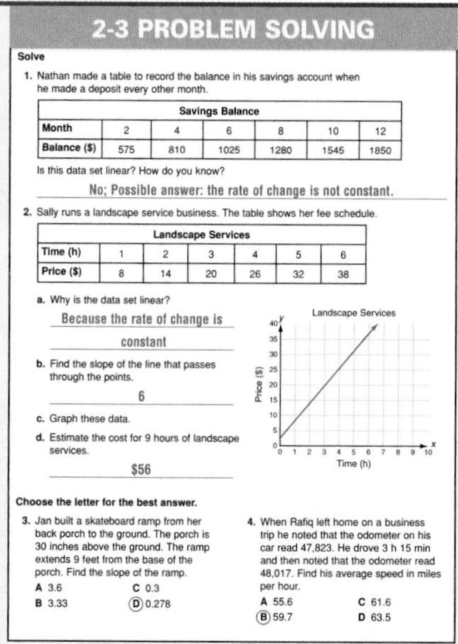

2-3 PROBLEM SOLVING

Solve

1. Nathan made a table to record the balance in his savings account when he made a deposit every other month.

Savings Balance

Month	2	4	6	8	10	12
Balance ($)	575	810	1025	1280	1545	1850

Is this data set linear? How do you know?

No; Possible answer: the rate of change is not constant.

2. Sally runs a landscape service business. The table shows her fee schedule.

Landscape Services

Time (h)	1	2	3	4	5	6
Price ($)	8	14	20	26	32	38

a. Why is the data set linear?

Because the rate of change is constant

b. Find the slope of the line that passes through the points.

6

c. Graph these data.

d. Estimate the cost for 9 hours of landscape services.

$56

Choose the letter for the best answer.

3. Jan built a skateboard ramp from her back porch to the ground. The porch is 30 inches above the ground. The ramp extends 9 feet from the base of the porch. Find the slope of the ramp.

A 3.6 C 0.3
B 3.33 (D) 0.278

4. When Rafiq left home on a business trip he noted that the odometer on his car read 47,823. He drove 3 h 15 min and then noted that the odometer read 48,017. Find his average speed in miles per hour.

A 55.6 C 61.6
(B) 59.7 D 63.5

2-3 CHALLENGE

Every linear equation in x and y can be written in the form $ax + by = c$, where a and b cannot both be 0. If a, b, and c are not zero, then the graph is a line that crosses both the x-axis and the y-axis at points other than the origin, such as in the diagram at right.

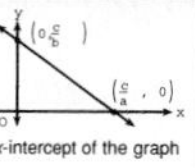

You can use the equation of a line to find the area of a triangle.

1. a, b, and c are nonzero constants and $ax + by = c$. Show that the x-intercept of the graph is $\frac{c}{a}$ and that the equation y-intercept is $\frac{c}{b}$.

To find the x-intercept, let $y = 0$.
$ax + by = c$
$ax + b(0) = c$
$ax = c$
$x = \frac{c}{a}$

To find the y-intercept, let $x = 0$.
$ax + by = c$
$a(0) + by = c$
$by = c$
$y = \frac{c}{b}$

2. Explain why a, b, and c must be nonzero in order to form a triangle whose sides are the line represented by the equation $ax + by = c$ and the coordinate axes.

Possible answer: If any of a, b, or c are 0, then there is no triangle since the lengths of two of the sides are $\frac{c}{b}$ and $\frac{c}{a}$.

3. a. a, b, and c are positive numbers. Write a formula for the area of the triangle formed by the graph of $ax + by = c$ and the coordinate axes. $A = \frac{c^2}{2ab}$

b. Find the area of the right triangle formed by the graph of $4x + 5y = 20$ and the coordinate axes. 10 square units

4. A triangle whose sides are the graph of a line and the coordinate axes has an area of 100 square units. Write an equation of the form $ax + by = c$ for the hypotenuse of the triangle. Possible answer: $2x + y = 20$

Solve.

5. a. Draw the graph of a line with x-intercept 5 and y-intercept 8.

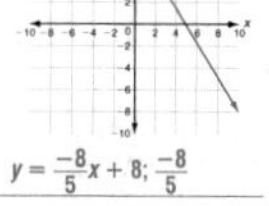

b. Find the constants a, b, and c for the line.

$a = 8$, $b = 5$, $c = 40$

c. Write the equation for the line.

$8x + 5y = 40$

d. Write the equation in slope-intercept form. What is the slope of the line? $y = \frac{-8}{5}x + 8$; $\frac{-8}{5}$

e. What is the area of the right triangle formed by the line and the coordinate axes? 20 square units

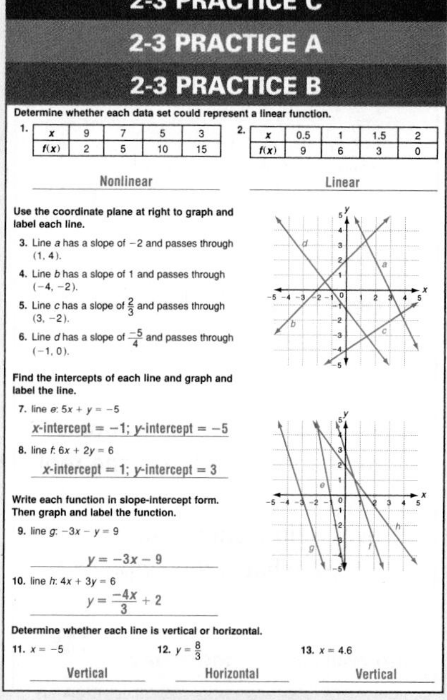

2-3 PRACTICE C
2-3 PRACTICE A
2-3 PRACTICE B

Determine whether each data set could represent a linear function.

1.

x	9	7	5	3
$f(x)$	2	5	10	15

Nonlinear

2.

x	0.5	1	1.5	2
$f(x)$	9	6	3	0

Linear

Use the coordinate plane at right to graph and label each line.

3. Line a has a slope of −2 and passes through (1, 4).
4. Line b has a slope of 1 and passes through (−4, −2).
5. Line c has a slope of $\frac{2}{3}$ and passes through (3, −2).
6. Line d has a slope of $\frac{-5}{4}$ and passes through (−1, 0).

Find the intercepts of each line and graph and label the line.

7. line e: $5x + y = -5$

x-intercept = −1; y-intercept = −5

8. line f: $6x + 2y = 6$

x-intercept = 1; y-intercept = 3

Write each function in slope-intercept form. Then graph and label the function.

9. line g: $-3x - y = 9$

$y = -3x - 9$

10. line h: $4x + 3y = 6$

$y = \frac{-4x}{3} + 2$

Determine whether each line is vertical or horizontal.

11. $x = -5$ Vertical
12. $y = \frac{8}{3}$ Horizontal
13. $x = 4.6$ Vertical

TEST PREP DOCTOR For **Exercise 60,** students who answered **J** might have interchanged the rise and the run.

For **Exercise 61,** encourage students to rewrite the equations in slope-intercept form before choosing the answer.

Journal

Have students describe the relationships among linear functions and equations and their graphs. Ask students to incorporate the following terms in their writing: *rate, constant, linear, slope,* and *intercepts.*

ALTERNATIVE ASSESSMENT

Have students create a table of data points that belong to a linear function, graph the corresponding linear equation, and explain how to find its slope and *y*-intercept. Have them then write an equation of the line graphed and discuss how the data, graph, and equation are all related.

Power Presentations with PowerPoint®

2-3 Lesson Quiz

1. Determine whether the data set could represent a linear function. yes

x	−1	2	5	8
f(x)	−3	1	5	9

2. For $3x - 4y = 24$, find the intercepts, write in slope-intercept form, and graph.
x-int: 8; y-int: −6;
$y = 0.75x - 6$

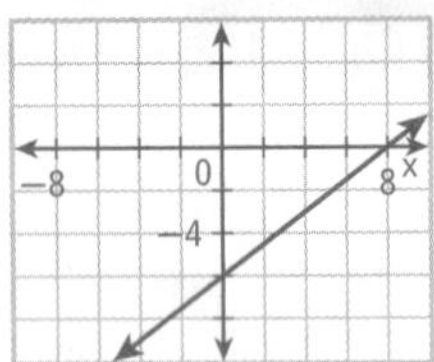

3. Determine if the line $y = -3$ is vertical or horizontal. horizontal

4. The bottom edge of a roof is 62 ft above ground. If the roof rises to 125 ft above ground over a horizontal distance of 7.5 yd, what is the slope of the roof? 2.8

Also available on transparency

TEST PREP

59. At what point does the x-intercept of the line $5x - 4y = 40$ occur?
Ⓐ (5, 0) Ⓑ (0, −10) Ⓒ (0, −4) **Ⓓ (8, 0)**

60. The graph shown could be which of these functions?
Ⓕ $y = \frac{1}{2}x + 3$
Ⓖ $y = 2x + 3$
Ⓗ $y = -\frac{1}{2}x + 3$
Ⓙ $y = -2x + 3$

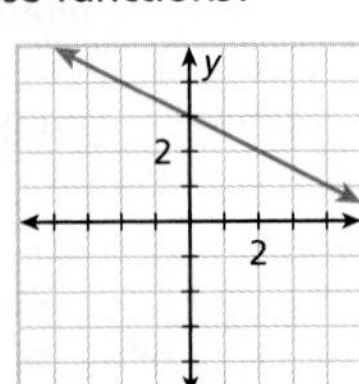

61. If the slope of the line $y = 7 - 3x$ were changed to 5, what would the new equation be?
Ⓐ $y = 7 - 5x$ **Ⓑ $y = 7 + 5x$** Ⓒ $y = 5 - 3x$ Ⓓ $y = -5 - 3x$

62. What is the slope of the line $5(y - 4) = -8x$?
Ⓕ $-\frac{5}{8}$ Ⓖ $\frac{5}{4}$ **Ⓗ $-\frac{8}{5}$** Ⓙ $\frac{4}{5}$

63. **Gridded Response** If the rise and run are reversed for the linear equation $y = 8x + 4$, what is the slope of the new line? 0.125

CHALLENGE AND EXTEND

64. Find the slope and the y-intercept of the line $y = -4$. Does the line have an x-intercept? Explain. **Slope: 0; y-intercept: −4; no; the line is horizontal and parallel to the x-axis, so it does not intersect it.**

65. The *double-intercept form* of a linear equation is $\frac{x}{a} + \frac{y}{b} = 1$.
a. Find the slope, the y-intercept, and the x-intercept of the line $\frac{x}{4} - \frac{y}{9} = 1$. $\frac{9}{4}$; −9; 4
b. Using your answer to part **a,** explain the meaning of the values a and b in the double-intercept form of a line.
c. Write the equation of the line $5x + 2y = 30$ in double-intercept form. $\frac{x}{6} + \frac{y}{15} = 1$

65b. The intercepts are the denominators of $\frac{x}{a} + \frac{y}{b} = 1$; y-intercept $= b$; x-intercept $= a$

66. What happens when you try to find the slope and y-intercept for the equation $3(y + 2) + 6x = 3(4 + 2x + y)$? **The resulting equation is a contradiction.**

SPIRAL REVIEW

Multiply and simplify. *(Previous course)*

67. $\frac{3}{4}\left(\frac{2}{3}\right)$ $\frac{1}{2}$
68. $\frac{4}{6}\left(\frac{8}{3}\right)$ $\frac{16}{9}$
69. $-\frac{9}{12}\left(\frac{9}{8}\right)$ $-\frac{27}{32}$

Use the set of test scores for Exercises 70–72. Find each measure.
{68, 72, 98, 80, 92, 76, 85, 90, 72, 86} *(Previous course)*

70. mode 72
71. mean 81.9
72. median 82.5

For each function, evaluate $f(0)$ and $f(-3)$. *(Lesson 1-7)*

73. $f(x) = \frac{1}{3}x + 7$ $f(0) = 7$; $f(-3) = 6$
74. $f(x) = -4x^2 - 1$ $f(0) = -1$; $f(-3) = -37$
75. $f(x) = \frac{x^3}{3}$ $f(0) = 0$; $f(-3) = -9$

Solve. *(Lesson 2-1)*

76. $7(x + 9) = 8(x - 3)$ $x = 87$
77. $\frac{3}{4}(x + 12) + \frac{1}{2}(x + 6) = -18$ $x = -24$
78. $7n + 4(n - 1) = 3(n + 4)$ $n = 2$
79. $9t - 3(t - 5) = 51$ $t = 6$

Answers

55b. y-intercept: 110; revenue if all tickets sold were student's tickets.
x-intercept: 44; revenue if all tickets sold were adult tickets

57. Possible answer: Divide the constant difference in y by the constant difference in x.

Explore Graphs and Windows

Use with Lesson 2-3

When using a graphing calculator to explore graphs, it is important to understand how the WINDOW settings affect the *visual* behavior of the graph. The standard window is usually not the best window and does not usually show the more accurate graph.

Activity 1

Graph $y = 19 - x$ in a window that shows both x- and y-intercepts.

1. Enter $19 - x$ in **Y1**, and press ZOOM **6:ZStandard** to obtain the standard window, $[-10, 10]$ by $[-10, 10]$. You see only a small piece of the graph.

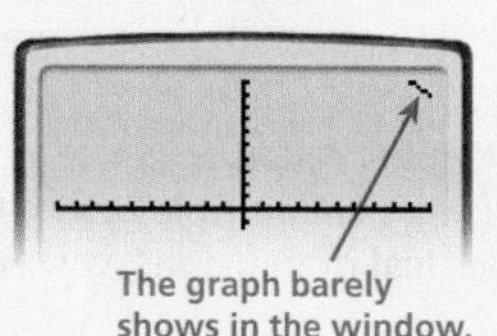

The graph barely shows in the window.

2. Press WINDOW and change the window settings as shown and graph again. By increasing the window dimensions, you can now see both intercepts, but the line looks flatter than the same line graphed on grid paper.

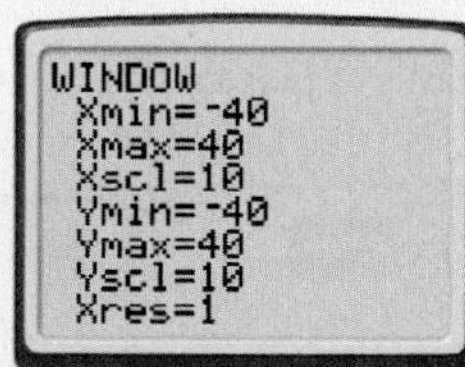

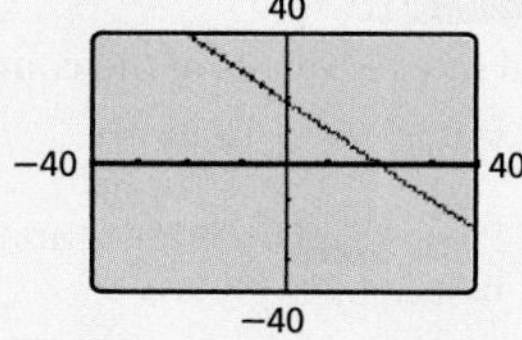

The graphing calculator screen is about 1.5 times as wide (95 pixels) as it is high (63 pixels), so it distorts graphs when the horizontal and vertical dimensions are the same. To correct for this, use a square viewing window.

3. Press ZOOM **5:ZSquare**. **Xmin** and **Xmax** will change to show an accurate graph that displays both intercepts. Notice the change in the window settings.

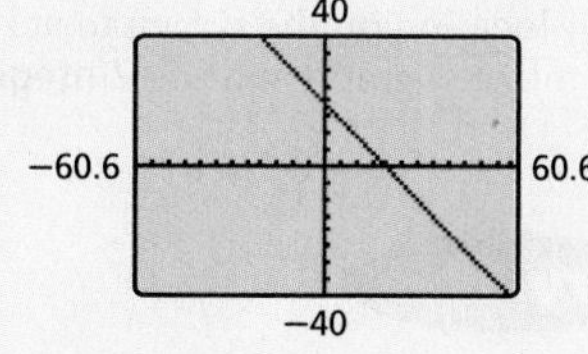

Try This

Graph each function in a window that shows both the x- and y-intercepts.

1. $y = 2x - 25$
2. $y = -3x - 50$
3. $y = 20 + 0.8x$
4. When you enter and graph a function and only a piece of the graph is visible in the lower left, what adjustments can you make to see the key features of the graph?
5. How can you see the graph of $y = 0.01x$?
6. **What if...?** Suppose that you wanted to make $y = 0.5x$ look very steep or $y = 10x$ look flat in the calculator window. How would you change the window settings?

Technology LAB Organizer

Use with Lesson 2-3

Pacing:
Traditional $\frac{1}{2}$ day
Block $\frac{1}{4}$ day

Objective: Use a graphing calculator to explore graphs and windows

Materials: graphing calculator

PREMIER Online Edition
Graphing Calculator, TechKeys

Resources

2-3 Lab Recording Sheet

Teach

Discuss

Encourage students to compare calculator graphs to those they've created by hand.

Close

Key Concept

The accuracy and usefulness of a graph on a calculator screen is affected by the chosen window.

Assessment

Journal Have students explain how to view an accurate graph.

Answers to *Try This*

1–6. See p. 114.

State Resources

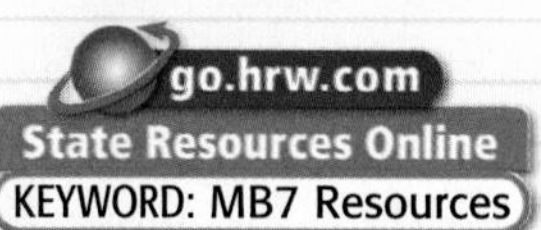

Teacher to Teacher

One of the biggest problems when students begin to graph equations with a calculator is not finding the graph in the window. Students might think they entered it incorrectly. To help students find a window that shows the graph, I tell students to use TRACE and look at the coordinates.

For example, if you graph $y = x + 50$ in the standard window (**ZOOM 6:Standard**), you cannot see the graph at all! Press TRACE, and the calculator gives you $x = 0$, $y = 50$. Trace right and left to get an idea for an appropriate window.

Marilyn Gutman
Las Cruces, NM

When you use the TRACE function, x-values are often long decimals. A *friendly* window allows you to trace along simpler x-values. There are several built-in ZOOM windows that give friendly trace values, such as **ZInteger**, and **ZDecimal**.

Activity 2

Find decimal values of the coordinates of points on $y = 2x - 1$.

1. Enter $2x - 1$ in **Y1**. Press ZOOM **4:ZDecimal**.

2. TRACE right or left to find the decimal values.

3.1

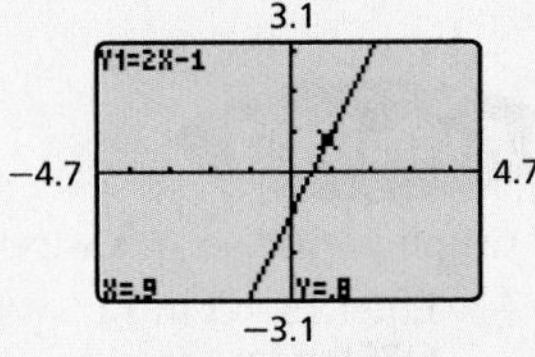

−4.7 4.7

−3.1

Note the following in the decimal window:

Horizontal dimensions: **Xmax** − **Xmin** = 4.7 − (−4.7) = 9.4 and

Vertical dimensions: **Ymax** − **Ymin** = 3.1 − (−3.1) = 6.2

If you use multiples of 9.4 for the horizontal dimensions and multiples of 6.2 for the vertical dimensions, you will always have simple x-values and an undistorted graph.

Activity 3

Find integer values of the coordinates of points on $y = -4x + 15$.

1. Enter $-4x + 15$ in **Y1**.

2. Press ZOOM **8:ZInteger** and press ENTER twice.

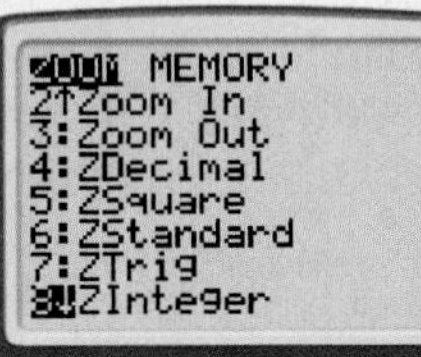

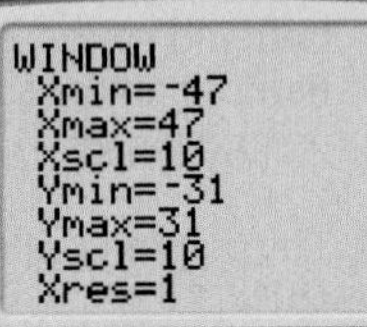

The window changes so that the x-values are integers and tracing to the right increases x-values by 1. The window is also square since **Xmax** − **Xmin** = 94 and **Ymax** − **Ymin** = 62.

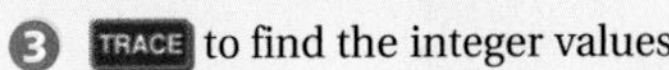

3. TRACE to find the integer values.

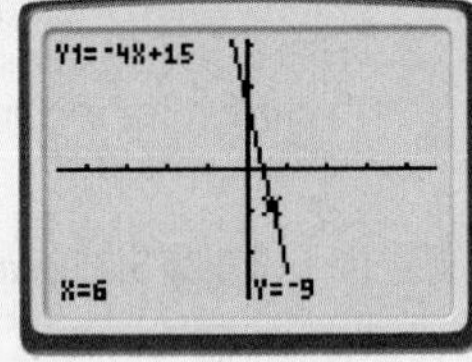

After graphing the function, you can move to any location on the screen to act as the center of the next graph and use **ZInteger** again.

Try This

7. If you ZOOM out on the point (0.9, 0.8) shown in the graph in Activity 3, the window changes to [−8.5, 10.3] by [−5.4, 7]. Find **Xmax** − **Xmin** and **Ymax** − **Ymin**. Use TRACE and the arrow keys to view the coordinates of points on the line. Why is the window friendly?
8. Explain how to graph $y = 3x - 50$ so that the line "looks like" a line with a slope of 3 and allows you to trace to friendly x-values.
9. Graph $y = x + 0.5$ in the standard window.
   a. How can you make the slope of the graph appear to be 1?
   b. Which ZOOM window would create a space between the y-intercept and the origin while keeping an accurate representation of the slope?

Answers to *Try This*

Possible answers are given.

1. 10

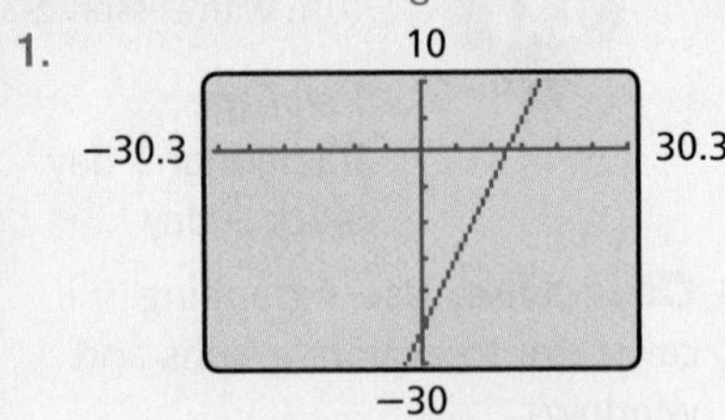

−30.3 30.3

−30

2. 20

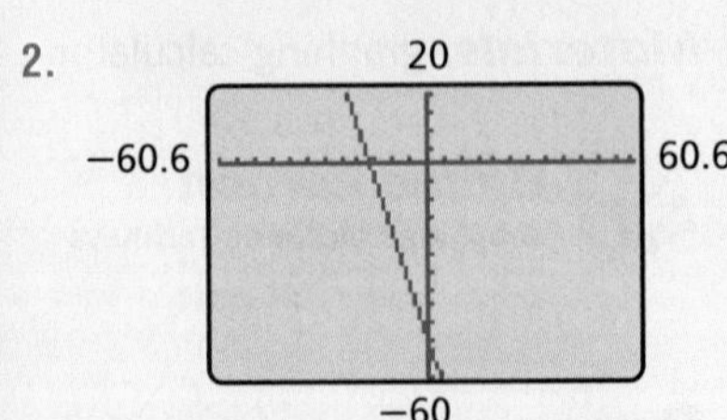

−60.6 60.6

−60

3. 25

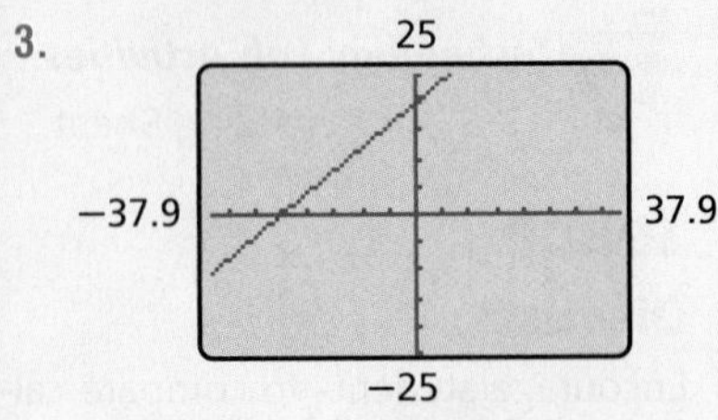

−37.9 37.9

−25

4. Zoom out, use the **ZInteger** window, or decrease **Xmin** and **Ymin**.
5. Change **Ymin** to −0.1 and **Ymax** to 0.1.
6. For a steep $y = 0.5x$, change the window so that $\frac{\text{Ymin} - \text{Ymax}}{\text{Xmin} - \text{Xmax}}$ is small, e.g., [−20, 20] by [−1, 1]; For a flat $y = 10x$, change the window so that $\frac{\text{Ymin} - \text{Ymax}}{\text{Xmin} - \text{Xmax}}$ is large, e.g., [−1, 1] by [−50, 50].

Possible answers are given.

7. **Xmax** − **Xmin** = 18.8; **Ymax** − **Ymin** = 12.4; The window is friendly because $\frac{18.8}{12.4} \approx 1.52$, which is close to $\frac{95}{63}$, and tracing results in simple decimal values for x, such as 1.1, 1.3, and so on.
8. Graph in the window [−47, 47] by [−55, 6].

9a. Use a square window.

b. **ZDecimal**

2-4 Writing Linear Functions

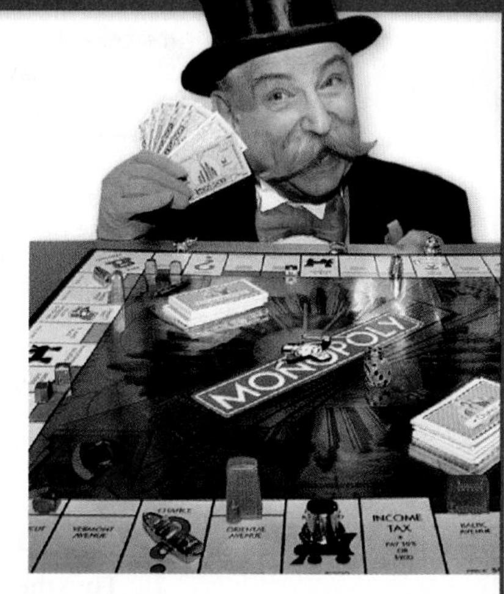

Objectives
Use slope-intercept form and point-slope form to write linear functions.

Write linear functions to solve problems.

Vocabulary
Point-slope form

Why learn this?
When you play Monopoly, it's easy to calculate the rent of most properties by looking at the selling price. (See Example 4.)

Recall from Lesson 2-3 that the slope-intercept form of a linear equation is $y = mx + b$, where m is the slope of the line and b is its y-intercept.

In Lesson 2-3, you graphed lines when you were given the slope and y-intercept. In this lesson you will write linear functions when you are given graphs of lines or problems that can be modeled with a linear function.

EXAMPLE 1 Writing the Slope-Intercept Form of the Equation of a Line

Write the equation of the graphed line in slope-intercept form.

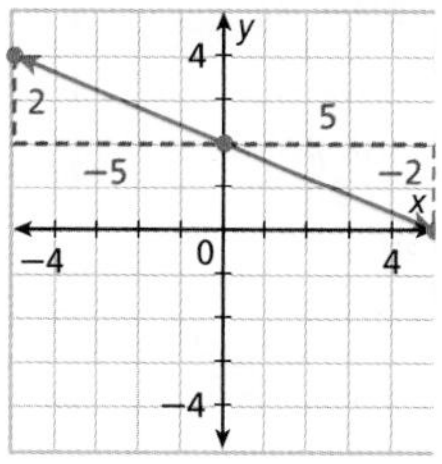

Step 1 Identify the y-intercept.
The y-intercept b is 2.

Step 2 Find the slope.

Choose any two convenient points on the line, such as $(0, 2)$ and $(5, 0)$. Count from $(0, 2)$ to $(5, 0)$ to find the rise and the run. The rise is –2 units and the run is 5 units.

Slope is $\frac{\text{rise}}{\text{run}} = \frac{-2}{5} = -\frac{2}{5}$.

Step 3 Write the equation in slope-intercept form.

$y = mx + b$

$y = -\frac{2}{5}x + 2$ *$m = -\frac{2}{5}$ and $b = 2$*

The equation of the line is $y = -\frac{2}{5}x + 2$.

Remember!
To express a line as a linear function, replace y with $f(x)$.

$y = -\frac{2}{5}x + 2$

$f(x) = -\frac{2}{5}x + 2$

1. Write the equation of the graphed line in slope-intercept form. $y = \frac{3}{4}x + 3$

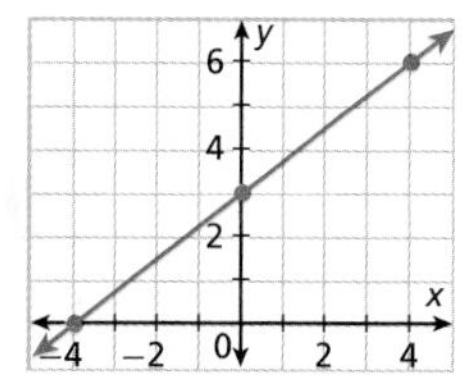

Notice that for two points on a line, the rise is the difference in the y-coordinates, and the run is the difference in the x-coordinates. Using this information, we can define the slope of a line by using a formula.

2-4 Organizer

Pacing: Traditional 2 days
Block 1 day

Objectives: Use slope-intercept form and point-slope form to write linear functions.

Write linear functions to solve problems.

Online Edition
Tutorial Videos

Countdown to Testing Week 4

Power Presentations with PowerPoint®

Warm Up

Write each function in slope-intercept form.

1. $4x + y = 8$ $y = -4x + 8$
2. $-y = 3x$ $y = -3x$
3. $2y = 10 - 6x$ $y = -3x + 5$

Determine whether each line is vertical or horizontal.

4. $x = \frac{3}{4}$ vertical
5. $y = 0$ horizontal

Also available on transparency

Math Humor

Student: I'll just draw a quick line by hand and guess the slope.

Teacher: No, no. It's point-*slope* form, not point-*sloppy* form.

1 Introduce

EXPLORATION

2-4 Writing Linear Functions

Use a graphing calculator for this Exploration.

1. Press Y= and enter the following functions as **Y1** and **Y2**.
$y = \frac{3}{4}x - 2$ (Enter **3/4X–2**).
$y = -\frac{4}{3}x + 1$ (Enter **–4/3X+1**).
2. Press ZOOM and choose **ZStandard**. Then press ZOOM and **ZSquare** to graph the functions in a square window.
3. What appears to be true about the graphs?
4. Examine the two equations. What do you notice about their slopes?
5. Repeat Problems 1–4 but instead use the two linear equations below.
$y = -4x + 3$
$y = \frac{1}{4}x - 1$

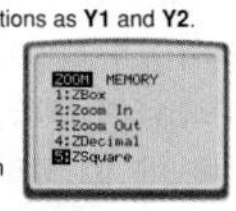

THINK AND DISCUSS

6. **Make** a generalization based on your findings.
7. **Explain** why you needed to set the shape of the viewing window using **ZSquare** for this Exploration.

Motivate

Explain that knowing how to determine the equations of lines can be useful in everyday situations. Give students the following scenario: Suppose you have a linear graph that shows a trend in an item's price over time, and you want to use the graph to predict the price of the item 10 years from now. If you had the equation of the line, you could use it to make a prediction by substituting 10 for the independent variable.

Explorations and answers are provided in the *Explorations* binder.

State Resources

go.hrw.com
State Resources Online
KEYWORD: MB7 Resources

Teaching Tip **Visual** Remind students that when a line falls from left to right, the slope is negative. When the line rises from left to right, the slope is positive.

Power Presentations with PowerPoint®

Additional Examples

Example 1

Write the equation of the line in slope-intercept form.

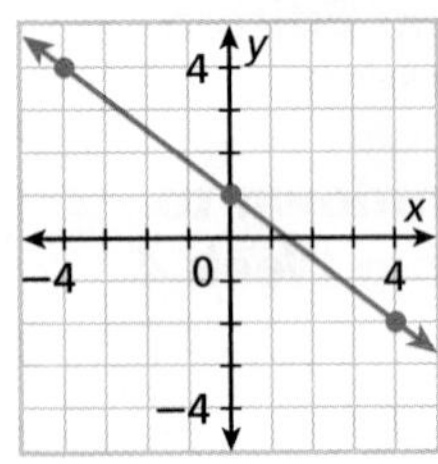

$y = -\frac{3}{4}x + 1$

Example 2

Find the slope of each line.

A. the line through (−1, 1) and (2, −5) −2

B.

x	4	8	12	16
y	2	5	8	11

$\frac{3}{4}$

C.

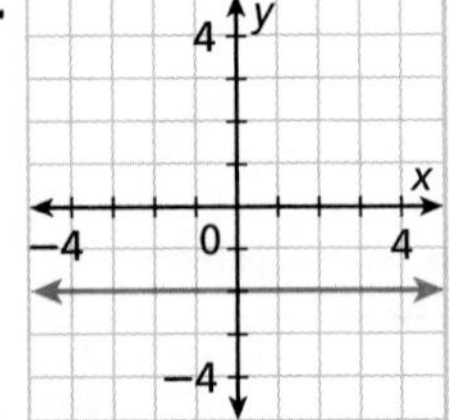

0

Also available on transparency

INTERVENTION

Questioning Strategies

EXAMPLE 1

- How can you find the slope of a line from its graph?
- How can you find the y-intercept of a line from its graph?

EXAMPLE 2

- How do you know what values from a table to use in the slope formula when you are finding the slope?
- How could you check your answer when you determine the slope of a line from a table of values?

Slope Formula

WORDS	ALGEBRA	GRAPH
Given two points on a line, the slope is the ratio of the difference in the y-values to the difference in the corresponding x-values, or rise over run.	The slope of the line containing (x_1, y_1) and (x_2, y_2) is $m = \frac{y_2 - y_1}{x_2 - x_1}$.	(x_2, y_2); rise $= y_2 - y_1$; (x_1, y_1); run $= x_2 - x_1$

EXAMPLE 2 Finding the Slope of a Line Given Two or More Points

Find the slope of each line.

A the line through (3, −2) and (−1, 2)

Let be (x_1, y_1) be $(3, -2)$ and (x_2, y_2) be $(-1, 2)$.

$m = \frac{y_2 - y_1}{x_2 - x_1} = \frac{2-(-2)}{-1-3} = \frac{4}{-4} = -1$ *Use the slope formula.*

The slope of the line is −1.

Helpful Hint

If you reverse the order of the points in Example 2B, the slope is still the same.

$m = \frac{6-16}{5-11} = \frac{-10}{-6}$

$= \frac{5}{3}$

B

x	2	5	8	11
y	1	6	11	16

Let (x_1, y_1) be $(5, 6)$, and (x_2, y_2) be $(11, 16)$. *Choose any two points.*

$m = \frac{y_2 - y_1}{x_2 - x_1} = \frac{16-6}{11-5} = \frac{10}{6} = \frac{5}{3}$ *Use the slope formula.*

The slope of the line is $\frac{5}{3}$.

C **The line shown.**

Either point may be chosen as (x_1, y_1).

Let (x_1, y_1) be $(2, -1)$ and (x_2, y_2) be $(2, 3)$.

$m = \frac{y_2 - y_1}{x_2 - x_1} = \frac{3-(-1)}{2-2} = \frac{4}{0}$

Because division by zero is undefined, the slope of the line is undefined.

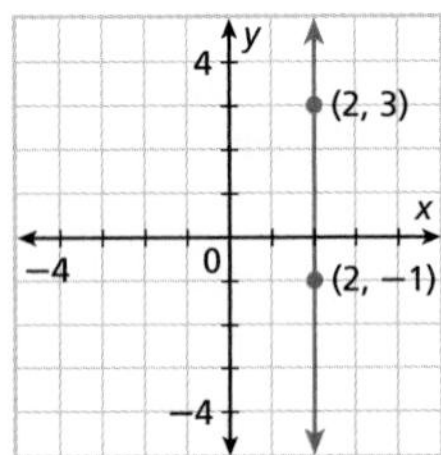

CHECK IT OUT! Find the slope of each line.

2a.

x	−6	−4	−2
y	−3	−1	1

1

2b. the line through (2, −5) and (−3, −5) **0**

Because the slope of a line is constant, it is possible to use any point on a line and the slope of the line to write an equation of the line in **point-slope form**.

2 Teach

Guided Instruction

In this lesson, students continue to practice translating among multiple representations of linear functions. Point out how the point-slope form is derived from the slope formula. Discuss with students when to use each form of a line.

Reaching All Learners

Through Critical Thinking

Have students identify the domain and range of a horizontal line, such as $y = 2$, and of a vertical line, such as $x = 3$. Writing each equation in standard form ($0x + y = 2$ and $x + 0y = 3$) may make the identification easier.

$y = 2$; D: ℝ; R: {2}

$x = 3$; D: {3}; R: ℝ

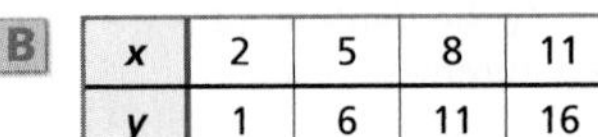

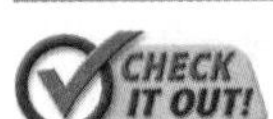

Point-Slope Form

The equation of a line with a slope of m and the point (x_1, y_1) is

$$y - y_1 = m(x - x_1).$$

EXAMPLE 3 **Writing Equations of Lines**

In slope-intercept form, write the equation of the line that contains the points in the table.

x	−3	−1	1	3
y	1.5	1	0.5	0

First, find the slope. Let (x_1, y_1) be $(-1, 1)$ and (x_2, y_2) be $(3, 0)$.

$$m = \frac{y_2 - y_1}{x_2 - x_1} = \frac{0 - 1}{3 - (-1)} = \frac{-1}{3 + 1} = -\frac{1}{4}$$

Next, choose a point and use either form of the equation of a line.

Method A Point-Slope Form

Using (3, 0):

$y - y_1 = m(x - x_1)$

$y - (0) = -\frac{1}{4}(x - 3)$ *Substitute.*

$y = -\frac{1}{4}(x - 3)$ *Simplify.*

Rewrite in slope-intercept form.

$y = -\frac{1}{4}(x - 3)$

$y = -\frac{1}{4}x + \frac{3}{4}$ *Distribute.*

Method B Slope-Intercept Form

Using (3, 0), solve for b.

$y = mx + b$

$0 = \left(-\frac{1}{4}\right)3 + b$ *Substitute.*

$0 = -\frac{3}{4} + b$ *Simplify.*

$b = \frac{3}{4}$ *Solve for b.*

Rewrite the equation using m and b.

$y = -\frac{1}{4}x + \frac{3}{4}$ $y = mx + b$

The equation of the line is $y = -\frac{1}{4}x + \frac{3}{4}$.

Write the equation of each line in slope-intercept form.

3a. with slope −5 through (1, 3) $y = -5x + 8$

3b. through (−2, −3) and (2, 5) $y = 2x + 1$

Student to Student

Slope and Point-Slope Form

Jennifer Chang
Jefferson High School

I learned the point-slope form by relating it to the formula for slope. The formula for slope and point-slope form are basically the same equation in different forms.

Begin with the slope formula:	$m = \frac{y_2 - y_1}{x_2 - x_1}$
Substitute (x, y) for (x_2, y_2):	$m = \frac{y - y_1}{x - x_1}$
Multiply both sides by $(x - x_1)$:	$m(x - x_1) = y - y_1$
Reverse the equation:	$y - y_1 = m(x - x_1)$

COMMON ERROR ALERT

Students may select x_1 and x_2 in one order and incorrectly choose y_1 and y_2 in the opposite order when using the formula to compute slope. Remind students that the variables represent ordered pairs and that x-variables and y-variables must be subtracted in the same order.

Power Presentations with PowerPoint®

Additional Examples

Example 3

In slope-intercept form, write the equation of the line that contains the points in the table.

x	−8	−4	4	8
y	−5	−3.5	−0.5	1

$y = \frac{3}{8}x - 2$

Also available on transparency

INTERVENTION 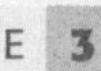

Questioning Strategies

EXAMPLE 3

- Does it matter which points you choose from the table to find the slope? Explain.

Teaching Tip **Multiple Representations** In **Example 3,** graphing could also be used to solve the problem. However, the algebraic methods work better in this case because the slope and the y-intercept are not integers.

Teaching Tip **Inclusion** Help students understand that the slope-intercept form and the point-slope form of the equation of a line are equivalent. They are different ways of writing the same equation. An equation in one form can be rewritten as an equation in the other form.

Teaching Tip **Reading Math** In **Example 4,** make sure students recognize that the selling price corresponds to the independent variable, *x,* and the rent corresponds to the dependent variable, *y.*

Power Presentations with PowerPoint®

Additional Examples

Example 4

The table shows the rents and selling prices of properties from a different game.

Selling Price ($)	Rent ($)
75	9
90	12
160	26
250	44

a. Express the rent as a function of the selling price.

$y = \frac{1}{5}x - 6$

b. Graph the relationship between the selling price and the rent. How much is the rent for a property with a selling price of $230? $40

Also available on transparency

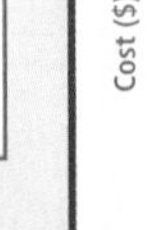

INTERVENTION

Questioning Strategies

EXAMPLE 4

- Why are different scales used in the graph? How do you think they were selected?

EXAMPLE 4 ***Entertainment Application***

In the game of Monopoly, a player who lands on a property that is owned by another player must pay rent to the owner of the property. For most color properties, the rent can be modeled by a linear function of the selling price.

A **Express the rent as a function of the selling price.**

Let x = selling price and y = rent.

Find the slope by choosing two points. Let (x_1, y_1) be $(60, 2)$ and (x_2, y_2) be $(100, 6)$.

$$m = \frac{y_2 - y_1}{x_2 - x_1} = \frac{6 - 2}{100 - 60} = \frac{4}{40} = \frac{1}{10}$$

Monopoly Prices and Rents

Property Name	Selling Price ($)	Rent ($)
Mediterranean Ave.	60	2
Vermont Ave.	100	6
Tennessee Ave.	180	14
Marvin Gardens	280	24
Pennsylvania Ave.	320	28

To find the equation for the rent function, use point-slope form.

$y - y_1 = m(x - x_1)$

$y - 2 = \frac{1}{10}(x - 60)$ *Use the data for Mediterranean Ave.*

$y = \frac{1}{10}x - 4$ *Simplify.*

B **Graph the relationship between the selling price and the rent. How much is the rent for Illinois Ave., which has a selling price of $240?**

Graph the function using a scale that fits the data.

To find the rent for Illinois Avenue, use the graph or substitute its selling price of $240 into the function.

$y = \frac{1}{10}(240) - 4$ *Substitute.*

$y = 24 - 4$

$y = 20$

The rent for Illinois Avenue is $20.

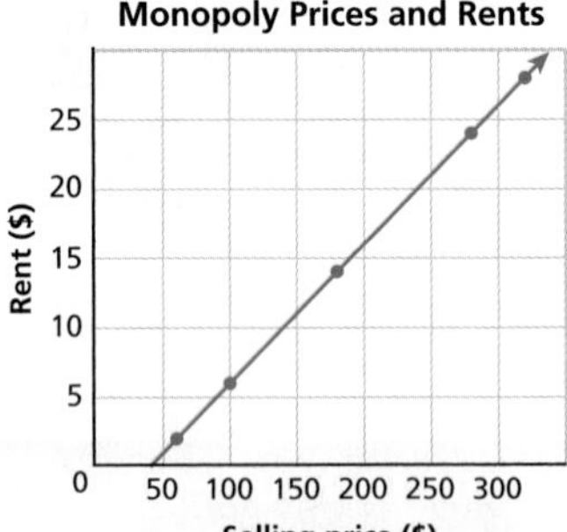

CHECK IT OUT!

4a. Express the cost as a linear function of the number of items.

4b. Graph the relationship between the number of items and the cost. Find the cost of 18 items. $c = 2.5n + 4$; $49

Items	Cost ($)
4	14.00
7	21.50
18	■

Reaching All Learners

Through Cooperative Learning

Display a Monopoly board. Have small groups graph all color property prices and rents. Elicit that there are two *y* points for $60. The graph is linear except for Baltic Avenue, Broadway, and Park Place. Ask: "Is rent a function of selling price?" no; Baltic and Mediterranean each sell for $60 but have different rents "What could be changed to make it so?" Baltic should rent for $2 or sell for $80." Excluding Baltic Avenue, Broadway, and Park Place, does dropping each selling price's last digit and subtracting 4 result in the actual rent?" yes

Through Home Connection

Have students create their own "fifth" side of a Monopoly board, where they use a theme that is important or interesting to them in their daily lives at home. Encourage them to be creative. Students should follow the same linear patterns of rents and selling prices as they found in **Example 4.**

By comparing slopes, you can determine if lines are parallel or perpendicular. You can also write equations of lines that meet certain criteria.

Parallel and Perpendicular Lines

WORDS	GRAPH	ALGEBRA
Parallel Lines If both slopes are defined, the slopes of parallel lines are equal. The slopes of parallel vertical lines are undefined.	$y = 2x + 1$; $y = 2x - 3$	$y_1 = 2x + 1$, so $m_1 = 2$ $y_2 = 2x - 3$ so $m_2 = 2$ $m_1 = m_2$ $2 = 2$
Perpendicular Lines If both slopes are defined, the slopes of perpendicular lines are opposite reciprocals. Their product is −1. A vertical line and a horizontal line are perpendicular.	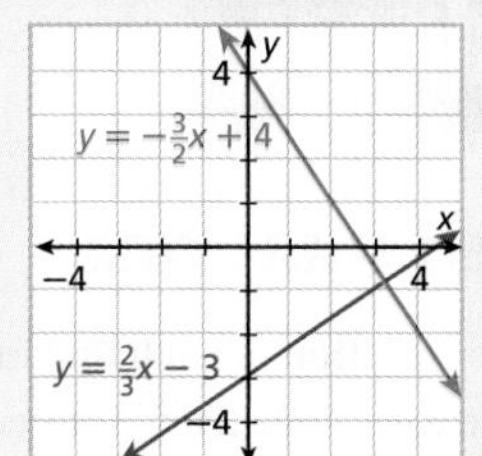	$y_1 = -\frac{3}{2}x + 4$, so $m_1 = -\frac{3}{2}$ $y_2 = \frac{2}{3}x - 3$, so $m_2 = \frac{2}{3}$ $(m_1)(m_2) = -1$ $\left(-\frac{3}{2}\right)\left(\frac{2}{3}\right) = -1$

Remember!

A vertical line has an undefined slope.

EXAMPLE 5 Writing Equations of Parallel and Perpendicular Lines

Write the equation of each line in slope-intercept form.

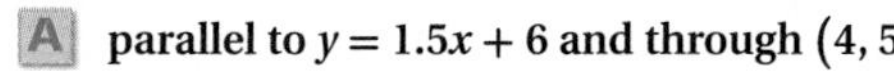

A **parallel to $y = 1.5x + 6$ and through $(4, 5)$**

$m = 1.5$	*Parallel lines have equal slopes.*
$y - 5 = 1.5(x - 4)$	*Use $y - y_1 = m(x - x_1)$ with $(x_1, y_1) = (4, 5)$.*
$y - 5 = 1.5x - 6$	*Distributive property.*
$y = 1.5x - 1$	*Simplify.*

B **perpendicular to $y = -\frac{3}{4}x + 2$ and through $(6, -4)$**

The slope of the given line is $-\frac{3}{4}$, so the slope of the perpendicular line is the opposite reciprocal, $\frac{4}{3}$.

$y + 4 = \frac{4}{3}(x - 6)$	*Use $y - y_1 = m(x - x_1)$. $y + 4$ is equivalent to $y - (-4)$.*
$y + 4 = \frac{4}{3}x - 8$	*Distributive property.*
$y = \frac{4}{3}x - 12$	*Simplify.*

CHECK IT OUT! **Write the equation of each line in slope-intercept form.**

5a. parallel to $y = 5x - 3$ and through $(1, 4)$ $y = 5x - 1$

5b. perpendicular to $y = \frac{5}{6}x - 7$ and through $(0, -2)$ $y = -\frac{6}{5}x - 2$

Power Presentations with PowerPoint®

Additional Examples

Example 5

Write the equation of each line in slope-intercept form.

A. parallel to $y = 1.8x + 3$ and through $(5, 2)$ $y = 1.8x - 7$

B. perpendicular to $y = -\frac{3}{2}x - 1$ and through $(9, -2)$
$y = \frac{2}{3}x - 8$

Also available on transparency

INTERVENTION

Questioning Strategies

EXAMPLE 5

- If you know the equation of a line, how can you determine the slope of a line parallel to it? perpendicular to it?
- After you determine the slope of the line described, how do you write the equation?

Teaching Tip **Technology** In **Example 5,** if the standard window on a graphing calculator is used to view perpendicular lines, the lines will not look perpendicular.

Teaching Tip **Math Background** Slope can also be written as $\frac{\Delta y}{\Delta x}$, where Δy represents the change in y between points on the line and Δx represents the change in x. Reading the change from left to right or right to left will give the same slope as long as the x- and y-values are read in the same direction.

3 Close

Summarize

Ask students:

- What are the two forms for writing the equation of a line? Possible answer: slope-intercept and point-slope, $y = mx + b$ and $y - y_1 = m(x - x_1)$
- Given two points on a line, how do you find the slope of the line? Divide the diff. in y-values by the diff. in x-values.
- How are the slopes of parallel lines related? How are the slopes of perpendicular lines related? parallel: equal; perpendicular: have product of −1

ONGOING ASSESSMENT and INTERVENTION

***Diagnose Before* the Lesson**
2-4 Warm Up, TE p. 115

***Monitor During* the Lesson**
Check It Out! Exercises, SE pp. 115–119
Questioning Strategies, TE pp. 116–119

***Assess After* the Lesson**
2-4 Lesson Quiz, TE p. 123
Alternative Assessment, TE p. 123

Answers to *Think and Discuss*

Possible answers:

1. Slope is $\frac{\text{change in } y}{\text{change in } x}$, but $x = 2$ has 0 change in x, and division by 0 is undefined.
2. a point and slope, 2 points, or slope and intercept
3. See p. A3.

THINK AND DISCUSS

1. Explain why the slope of a vertical line such as $x = 2$ is undefined.
2. Describe the information that you need in order to write the equation of a line.

3. **GET ORGANIZED** Copy and complete the graphic organizer. In each box, write any appropriate formulas and examples of equations.

Slope-intercept form	Point-slope form
Parallel	Perpendicular

(center: Lines)

2-4 Exercises

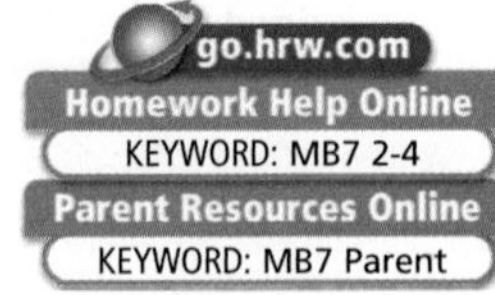

go.hrw.com
Homework Help Online
KEYWORD: MB7 2-4
Parent Resources Online
KEYWORD: MB7 Parent

Assignment Guide

Assign *Guided Practice* exercises as necessary.

If you finished Examples **1–3**
Basic 12–18, 29, 31, 35
Average 12–18, 30–38 even
Advanced 12–18, 26, 27, 30–36 even, 37

If you finished Examples **1–5**
Basic 12–25, 28–35, 38–39 42–46, 52–58
Average 12–28, 30, 32, 34–46, 52–58
Advanced 12–30, 33–34, 38–41, 43–58

Homework Quick Check
Quickly check key concepts.
Exercises: 14, 16, 18–20, 30, 36

GUIDED PRACTICE

SEE EXAMPLE 1 p. 114

Write the equation of each line in slope-intercept form.

1. a line with slope 2 and intercept 1 $1.\ y = 2x + 1$
2. a line with slope $-\frac{1}{7}$ and y-intercept -2 $2.\ y = -\frac{1}{7}x - 2$
3. 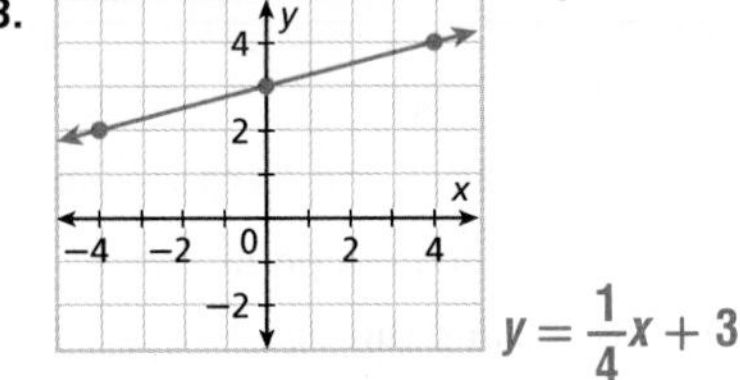 $y = \frac{1}{4}x + 3$
4. 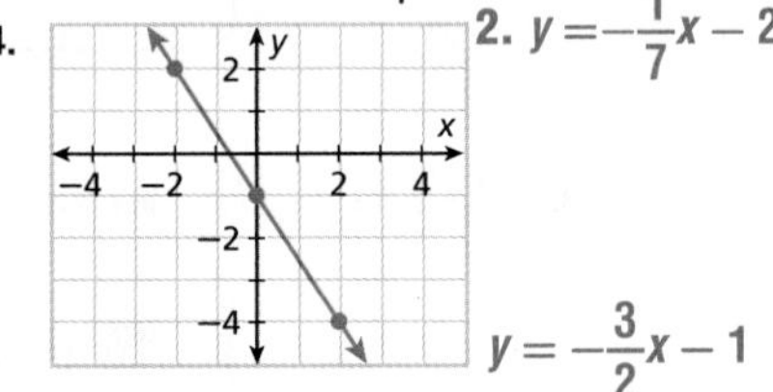 $y = -\frac{3}{2}x - 1$

SEE EXAMPLE 2 p. 115

Find the slope of each line.

5. $\frac{7}{5}$

x	2	7	12	17
y	3	10	17	24

6. a line through $(12, 3)$ and $(3, -4)$ $\frac{7}{9}$

SEE EXAMPLE 3 p. 116

Write the equation of each line in slope-intercept form.

7. a line with slope $-\frac{4}{3}$ passing through $(4, -8)$ $y = -\frac{4}{3}x - \frac{8}{3}$
8. $y = \frac{3}{4}x - \frac{17}{2}$

x	−2	2	6	10
y	−10	−7	−4	−1

SEE EXAMPLE 4 p. 117

9. **Physics** The boiling point of water can be modeled as a linear function of altitude. The boiling point of water at sea level is 212°F, and the boiling point of water at 1100 ft above sea level is 210°F.
   a. Express the boiling point as a function of altitude. $t = -\frac{1}{550}x + 212$
   b. Graph the relationship between boiling point and altitude. See p. 121.
   c. Find the boiling point of water at an altitude of 11,000 ft. 192°

SEE EXAMPLE 5 p. 118

Write the equation of each line in slope-intercept form.

10. parallel to $y = 3x + 4$ passing through $(0, 9)$ $y = 3x + 9$
11. perpendicular to $y = \frac{5}{9}x + 4$ passing through $(0, -4)$ $y = -\frac{9}{5}x - 4$

State Resources

go.hrw.com
State Resources Online
KEYWORD: MB7 Resources

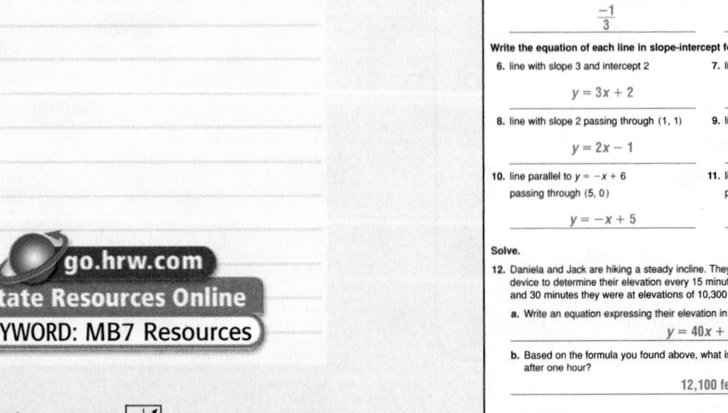

2-4 PRACTICE A

Identify the slope and y-intercept for each equation.

1. $y = 3x + 2$ — Slope = 3; y-intercept = 2
2. $y = \frac{x}{2} - 7$ — Slope = $\frac{1}{2}$; y-intercept = −7
3. $2y = 5x - 4$ — Slope = $\frac{5}{2}$; y-intercept = −2

Find the slope of each line.

4. line through $(2, 4)$ and $(5, 3)$ — $\frac{-1}{3}$
5. line through $(0, 0)$ and $(-1, -3)$ — 3

Write the equation of each line in slope-intercept form, $y = mx + b$.

6. line with slope 3 and intercept 2 — $y = 3x + 2$
7. line with slope $\frac{-1}{2}$ and intercept −1 — $y = \frac{-x}{2} - 1$
8. line with slope 2 passing through $(1, 1)$ — $y = 2x - 1$
9. line with slope $\frac{2}{3}$ passing through $(4, -1)$ — $y = \frac{2}{3}x - \frac{11}{3}$
10. line parallel to $y = -x + 6$ passing through $(5, 0)$ — $y = -x + 5$
11. line perpendicular to $y = \frac{x}{3} - 4$ passing through $(-3, 1)$ — $y = -3x - 8$

Solve.

12. Daniela and Jack are hiking a steady incline. They use their GPS device to determine their elevation every 15 minutes. At 15 minutes and 30 minutes they were at elevations of 10,300 feet and 10,900 feet, respectively.
   a. Write an equation expressing their elevation in relation to time. $y = 40x + 9700$
   b. Based on the formula you found above, what is their elevation after one hour? 12,100 feet

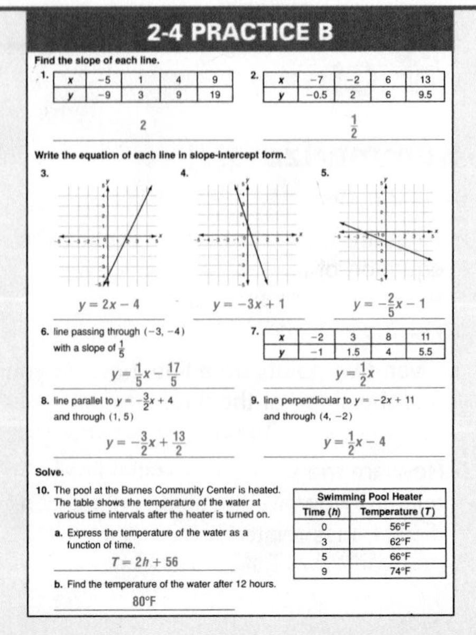

2-4 PRACTICE B

Find the slope of each line.

1. 2

x	−5	1	4	9
y	−9	3	9	19

2. $\frac{1}{2}$

x	−7	−2	6	13
y	−0.5	2	6	9.5

Write the equation of each line in slope-intercept form.

3. $y = 2x - 4$
4. $y = -3x + 1$
5. $y = -\frac{2}{5}x - 1$
6. line passing through $(-3, -4)$ with a slope of $\frac{1}{5}$ — $y = \frac{1}{5}x - \frac{17}{5}$
7. $y = \frac{1}{2}x$

x	−2	3	8	11
y	−1	1.5	4	5.5

8. line parallel to $y = -\frac{3}{2}x + 4$ and through $(1, 5)$ — $y = -\frac{3}{2}x + \frac{13}{2}$
9. line perpendicular to $y = -2x + 11$ and through $(4, -2)$ — $y = \frac{1}{2}x - 4$

Solve.

10. The pool at the Barnes Community Center is heated. The table shows the temperature of the water at various time intervals after the heater is turned on.

Swimming Pool Heater	
Time (h)	Temperature (T)
0	56°F
3	62°F
5	66°F
9	74°F

   a. Express the temperature of the water as a function of time. $T = 2h + 56$
   b. Find the temperature of the water after 12 hours. 80°F

PRACTICE AND PROBLEM SOLVING

Independent Practice

For Exercises	See Example
12–14	1
15–16	2
17–18	3
19	4
20–21	5

Extra Practice
Skills Practice: S6
Application Practice: S33

Write the equation of each line in slope-intercept form.

12.

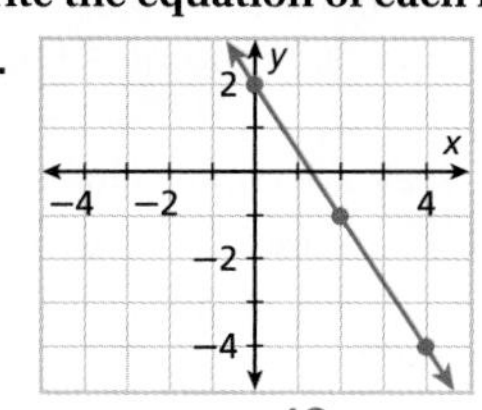

13.

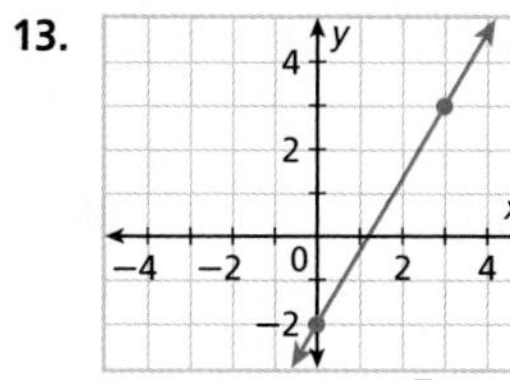

14.

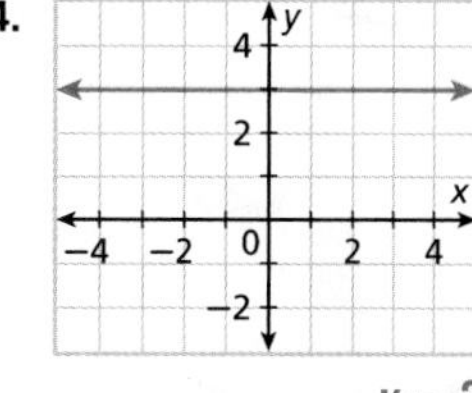

12. $y = -\frac{3}{2}x + 2$ $y = \frac{5}{3}x - 2$ $y = 3$

Find the slope of each line.

15.

x	0	1	2	3
y	$-\frac{1}{3}$	$\frac{1}{3}$	1	$\frac{5}{3}$

$\frac{2}{3}$

16. line $\overleftrightarrow{AB}$ through $A(-1, 3)$ and $B(1, -4)$ $-\frac{7}{2}$

Write the equation of each line in slope-intercept form.

17. passing through $(3, 11)$ with slope $\frac{7}{3}$ $y = \frac{7}{3}x + 4$

18. 18. $y = -x + 8$

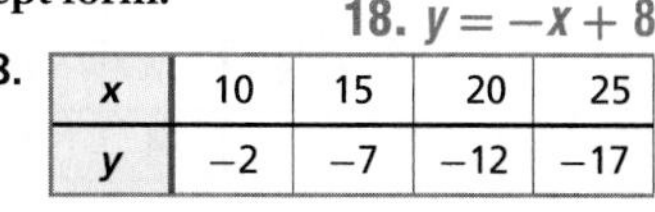

x	10	15	20	25
y	−2	−7	−12	−17

19. Biology The table shows the number of times a firefly flashes per minute at various temperatures.

Firefly Flashing Rate	
Temperature (°F)	**Flashes per Minute**
84	16
93	20
66	8

a. Express the flashing rate $f(T)$ as a function of temperature T. $f = \frac{4}{9}T - \frac{64}{3}$

b. Graph the relationship between temperature and the number of flashes per minute.

c. At what temperature would a firefly flash 25 times per minute? **104.25°F**

d. How many times per minute would a firefly flash at 35°F. Is this reasonable? **−5.8 times; no**

Write the equation of each line in slope-intercept form.

20. parallel to $y = -\frac{1}{5}x - 7$ and through $(2, 3)$ $y = -\frac{1}{5}x + \frac{17}{5}$

21. perpendicular to $y = 3x$ and through $(0, 3)$ $y = -\frac{1}{3}x + 3$

22. Clothing Men's shoe sizes are a linear function of foot length.

a. Write an equation for a man's shoe size as a function of foot length. What men's size shoe is needed for a foot that measures 9.5 in.?

b. Women's shoe sizes are marked $1\frac{1}{2}$ sizes larger than men's sizes for the same foot length. What size shoe is needed for a women's foot that measures 8.5 in.? **3**

Men's Shoe Sizes	
Foot Length (in.)	**Shoe Size**
10	$7\frac{1}{2}$
11	$11\frac{1}{2}$

22a. $s = 4\ell - 32\frac{1}{2}$; $5\frac{1}{2}$

Math History

It is unknown why the letter *m* is used to represent slope. Some have claimed that French mathematician René Descartes used it to represent the French word *monter* (to climb). However, this theory has proven to be false.

Determine if each pair of lines is parallel, perpendicular, or neither.

23. $y = \frac{1}{4}x + 9$
$y = 4x - 9$
neither

24. $y = 5 - \frac{1}{8}x$
$y = 8x + 2$
perpendicular

25. $-3x + 4y = 15$
$9x - 12y = 24$
parallel

Write each linear function.

26. $f(x)$, where $f(3) = 3$ and $f(-1) = 4$ $f(x) = -\frac{1}{4}x + \frac{15}{4}$

27. $f(x)$, where $f(-2) = -5$ and $f(1) = 1$ $f(x) = 2x - 1$

COMMON ERROR ALERT

Students might reverse the numerator and the denominator in the slope formula when finding the slope from a table of values in **Exercises 15, 18, 33,** and **34.** Have students write out the formula for the slope as the first step in finding the slope.

Answers

9b.

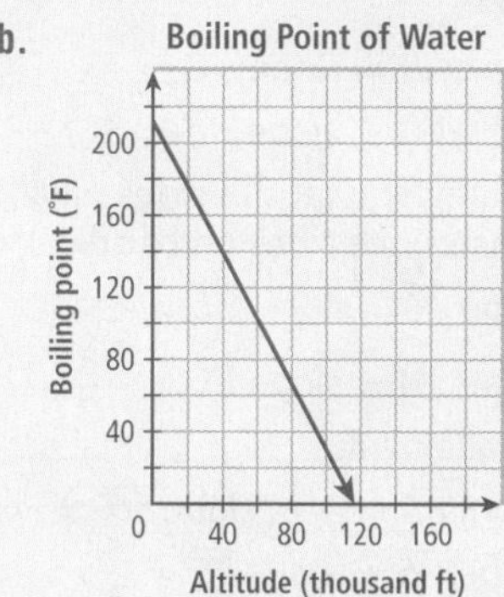

19b.

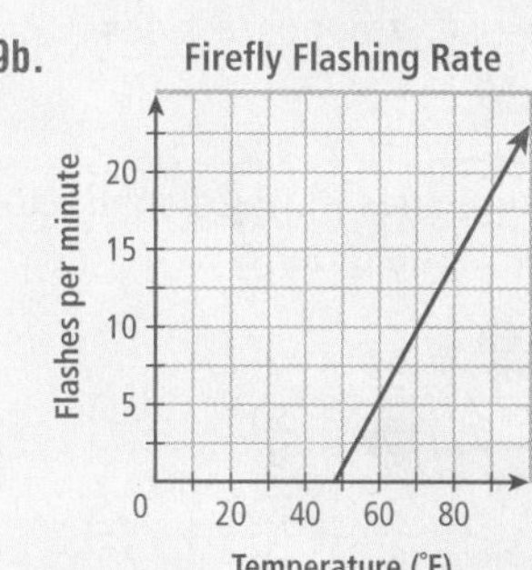

2-4 PRACTICE C

Tell whether each pair of lines is parallel, perpendicular, or neither.

1. $y = \frac{2}{5}x - 7$
$y = \frac{5}{2}x - 7$
Neither

2. $y = 10 - 3x$
$y = \frac{1}{3}x + 7$
Perpendicular

3. $12 + 2y = 8x$
$-12x + 3y = 24$
Parallel

Write the equation of the line with the given properties.

4. slope −4, passing through (5, 4)
$y = -4x + 24$

5. passing through (−4, 2) and (2, 6)
$y = \frac{2}{3}x + \frac{14}{3}$

6.

x	−12	−2	8	21
y	8	3	−2	−8.5

$y = -\frac{1}{2}x + 2$

7.

x	−2.4	−0.3	5.7	8.7
y	0.2	0.9	2.9	3.9

$y = \frac{1}{3}x + 1$

Write each linear function.

8. $f(x)$, where $f(4) = 1$ and $f(1) = 4$
$f(x) = -x + 5$

9. $f(x)$, where $f(-1) = -10$ and $f(-5) = 0$
$f(x) = -\frac{5}{2}x - \frac{25}{2}$

Solve.

10. Each week, Michelle records the average length of her standing long jump.

Long Jump Record	
Week	**Jump Distance (cm)**
1	175
2	178
3	181
4	184

a. Write an equation for the length of Michelle's jumps as a function of the number of weeks she has been practicing.
$y = 3x + 172$

b. If Michelle continues to improve at the same rate, what will be the average length of her jumps by the 8th week?
196 cm

c. Will this function continue to be linear? Explain your reasoning.
Possible answer: No, Michelle will not continue to improve at this rate forever. She will reach a point where she will improve only slightly each week.

Exercise 28 involves using linear equations in a real-world setting. This exercise prepares students for the Multi-Step Test Prep on page 132.

Geometry Review the different types of quadrilaterals for **Exercises 39–41.**

Answers

39. slope $\overline{AB}$ = slope $\overline{DC} = -\frac{1}{3}$; slope $\overline{AD}$ = slope $\overline{BC} = 3$; rectangle; opposite sides parallel, consecutive sides perpendicular.
40. slope $\overline{JK}$ = slope $\overline{ML} = \frac{1}{6}$; slope $\overline{JM}$ = slope $\overline{KL} = -\frac{3}{2}$; parallelogram
41. slope $\overline{RS} = -\frac{1}{4}$; slope $\overline{UT} = -5$; slope $\overline{UR}$ = slope $\overline{TS} = \frac{4}{3}$; trapezoid; 2 opposite sides parallel
42. B is incorrect; x- and y-coordinates must be subtracted in the same order
47. $y - \frac{25}{4} = \frac{2}{5}(x - 15)$

$$y = \frac{2}{5}x - \frac{30}{5} + \frac{25}{4}$$
$$= \frac{2}{5}x - \frac{120}{20} + \frac{125}{20}$$
$$= \frac{2}{5}x + \frac{5}{20}$$
$$= \frac{2}{5}x + \frac{1}{4}$$

50. $y - y_1 = m(x - x_1)$

$$y - b = m(x - 0)$$
$$y = mx - m(0) + b$$
$$y = mx + b$$

28. This problem will prepare you for the Multi-Step Test Prep on page 132.

Steve Fossett, the balloonist in Lesson 2-1, holds the world sailing record for the fastest transatlantic crossing: 4 days, 17 hours, 28 minutes, 6 seconds, at an average speed of 25.78 knots (nautical mi/h).

a. What was his crossing time, in hours, as a decimal value to the nearest tenth? **113.5**

b. How many nautical miles did he travel, to the nearest tenth? **2925.2**

c. Recall that a nautical mile is about 1.15 statute miles. What was Fossett's average speed in statute mi/h, to the nearest tenth? **29.6 mi/h**

Answers:

29. $y = 4x + 3$
30. $y = -\frac{1}{2}x + \frac{1}{2}$
31. $y = -\frac{11}{8}x + \frac{1}{8}$

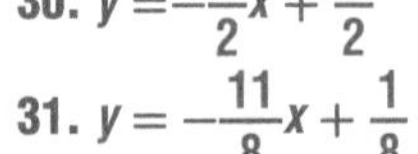

32. $y = -x$

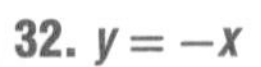

33. $y = 21x - 40$
34. $y = \frac{9}{5}x + 32$
35. $y = \frac{1}{6}x + \frac{4}{3}$
36. $y = -2$
37. $y = -3x - 8$
38. Park Place; it should rent for $\frac{1}{10}(350) - 4 = \$31$.

For Exercises 29–37, write the equation of the line with the given properties.

29. a slope of 4 passing through $(1, 7)$

30. a slope of $-\frac{1}{2}$ passing through $(7, -3)$

31. passing through $(-5, 7)$ and $(3, -4)$

32. passing through $(-3, 3)$ and $(1, -1)$

33.

x	4	7.5	8
y	44	117.5	128

34.

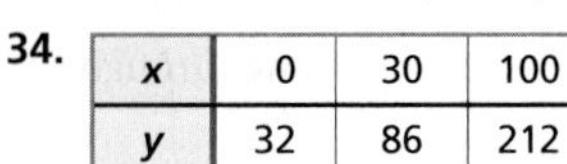

x	0	30	100
y	32	86	212

35. 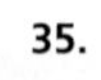

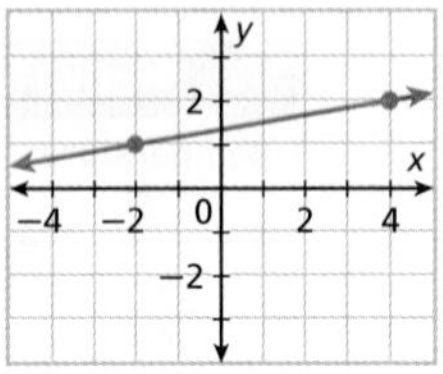

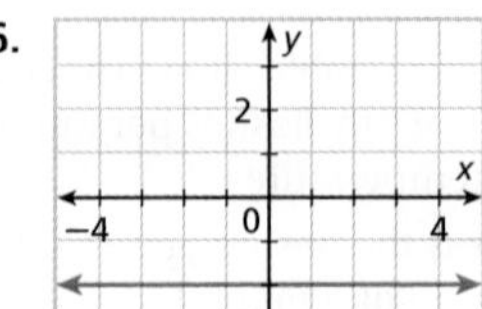

36. 

37.

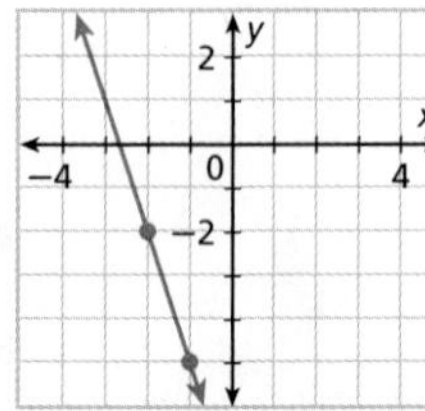

38. **Critical Thinking** Which of the Monopoly properties in the table does not conform to the rent function, $y = \frac{1}{10}x - 4$? Explain.

Monopoly Prices and Rents

Property Name	Selling Price ($)	Rent ($)
Connecticut Ave.	120	8
Kentucky Ave.	220	18
Park Place	350	35

Geometry Find the slope of each segment, and then classify each quadrilateral.

39.

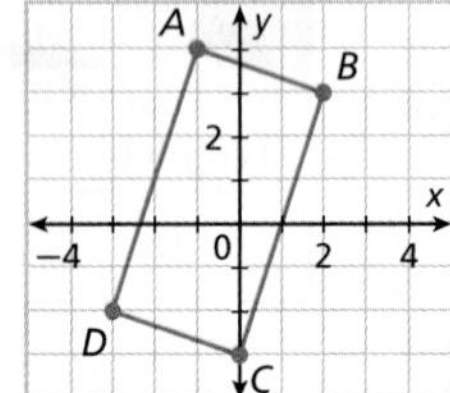

40.

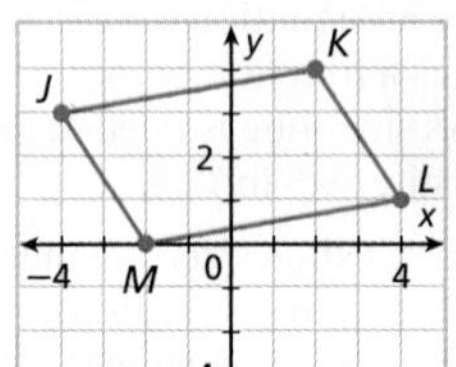

41.

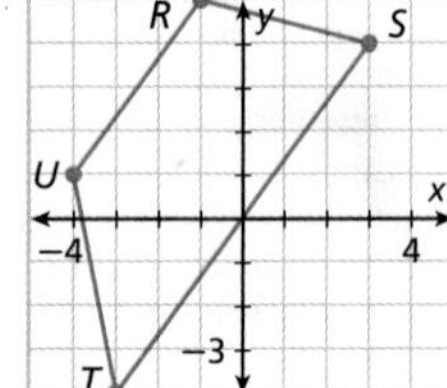

42. **ERROR ANALYSIS** Two attempts to find the slope of the line containing $(5, 8)$ and $(12, 7)$ are shown. Identify which calculation is incorrect. Explain the error.

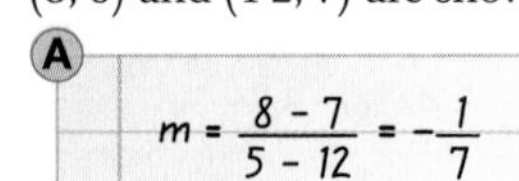

A: $m = \frac{8 - 7}{5 - 12} = -\frac{1}{7}$

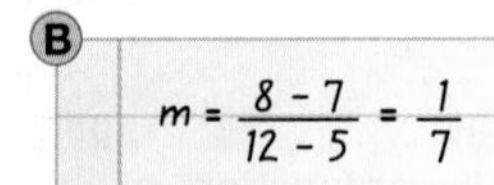

B: $m = \frac{8 - 7}{12 - 5} = \frac{1}{7}$

43. **Write About It** Explain how to write the equation of a line from its graph.

43. Possible answer: Find two points on the line. Subtract y- and x-coordinates. Divide to find the slope. Substitute a point in the point-slope or slope-intercept form to find the intercept and complete the equation.

2-4 READING STRATEGIES

The slopes of parallel or perpendicular lines are related.

Lines are **parallel** if their slopes are equal.	Lines are **perpendicular** if the product of their slopes is −1.
$y = -x + 3$ and $y = -x - 4$ have the same slope.	The product of the slopes of $y = 3x + 7$ and $y = -\frac{1}{3}x + 1$ is −1.

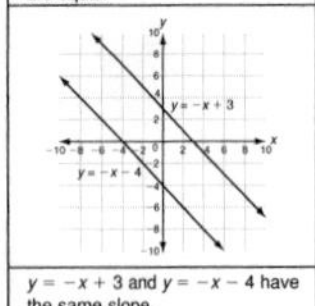

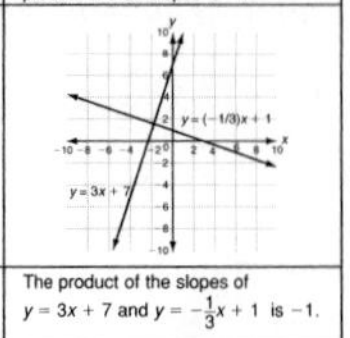

Answer each question.

1. What conclusions can you draw about the lines represented by $12x + 8y = 8$ and $2x = 3y + 15$? Are they parallel, perpendicular or neither? Why?
Perpendicular; because the slopes are $\frac{2}{3}$ and $-\frac{3}{2}$ and their product is −1.

2. a. Write the equation of a line that is parallel to $x + y = 3$. Possible answer: $y = -x + 5$

b. The line $x + y = 3$ is parallel to $y = -x - 4$. Is the line for the equation you just wrote also parallel to $y = -x - 4$? Explain why or why not.
Yes; possible answer: because all three lines have the same slope (−1)

3. Why are the lines $y = 3x + 7$ and $2y - 6x = 2$ parallel?
Because they both have a slope of 3

4. What conclusion can you draw about the slope of a line that is perpendicular to $2y = -4x - 1$? It's slope must be $\frac{1}{2}$.

5. Line *A* is perpendicular to line *B*. Line *C* is also perpendicular to line *B*. What conclusion can you draw about the slopes of lines *A* and *C*?
Lines *A* and *C* are parallel, so their slopes are equal.

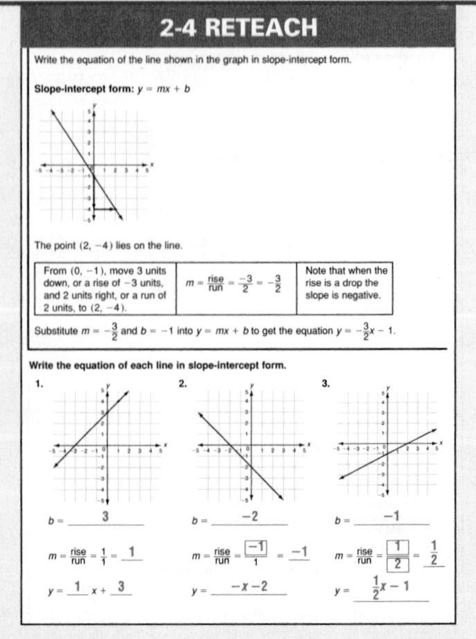

2-4 RETEACH

Write the equation of the line shown in the graph in slope-intercept form.

Slope-intercept form: $y = mx + b$

The point (2, −4) lies on the line.

From (0, −1), move 3 units down, or a rise of −3 units, and 2 units right, or a run of 2 units, to (2, −4).	$m = \frac{rise}{run} = \frac{-3}{2} = -\frac{3}{2}$	Note that when the rise is a drop the slope is negative.

Substitute $m = -\frac{3}{2}$ and $b = -1$ into $y = mx + b$ to get the equation $y = -\frac{3}{2}x - 1$.

Write the equation of each line in slope-intercept form.

1. $b = 3$; $m = \frac{rise}{run} = \frac{1}{1} = 1$; $y = 1x + 3$

2. $b = -2$; $m = \frac{rise}{run} = \frac{-1}{1} = -1$; $y = -x - 2$

3. $b = -1$; $m = \frac{rise}{run} = \frac{1}{2} = \frac{1}{2}$; $y = \frac{1}{2}x - 1$

TEST PREP

44. A carpenter determines the cost of a job by using the formula $C = 25 + 25h$, where h is the number of hours he works. He has decided to increase the amount he charges per hour to $30. Which formula will he use now?

Ⓐ $C = 30 + 25h$ Ⓑ $C = 30 + 30h$  $C = 25 + 30h$ Ⓓ $C = 25h + 30$

45. Which graph best shows a line perpendicular to $y = 3x - 2$?

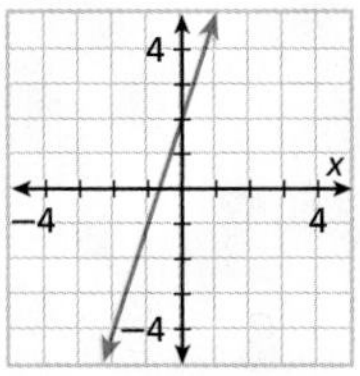

Ⓕ Ⓖ Ⓗ Ⓙ

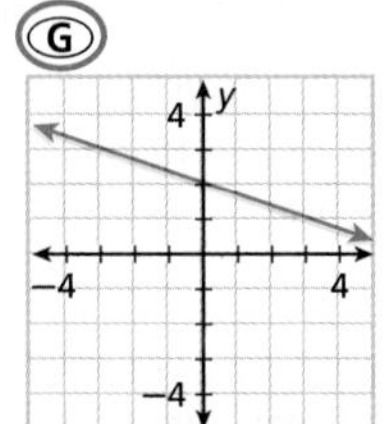
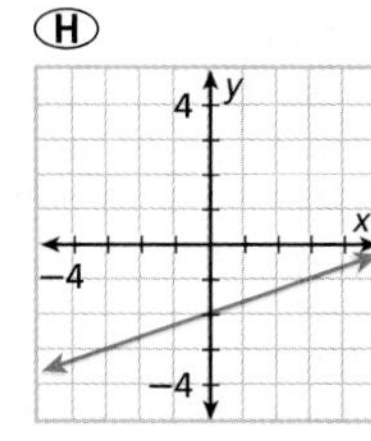
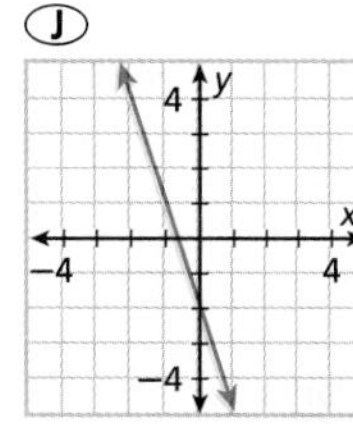

46. An equation can be used to relate the cost c of carpeting a room to the area a of the room in square feet. Which equation accurately reflects the data in the table?

Ⓐ $c = 2a - 125$ Ⓒ $c = a + 275$

Ⓑ $c = 1.5a + 75$ Ⓓ $c = 2a - 1500$

Carpeting Costs	
Area (ft²)	Cost ($)
400	675
550	900
900	1425

CHALLENGE AND EXTEND

47. Show that $y = \frac{2}{5}x + \frac{1}{4}$ and $y - \frac{25}{4} = \frac{2}{5}(x - 15)$ represent the same line.

48. Find the value of k so that the line containing $(4, -3k)$ and $(2k, 5)$ has a slope of $m = \frac{5}{2}$. $k = \frac{15}{2}$

49. No; the slopes between each pair of points are $\frac{4}{3}$, $\frac{5}{4}$, and $\frac{9}{7}$.

49. Are the points $(2, 6)$, $(5, 10)$, and $(9, 15)$ on the same line? Explain.

50. The slope-intercept form of a linear equation can be derived from the point-slope form. Illustrate this statement by substituting the point $(0, b)$ for (x_1, y_1) into the point-slope equation and solving for y.

51. **Aeronautics** A rule that airline pilots use to estimate outside temperature in degrees Fahrenheit at an altitude of h thousand feet is to double h, subtract 15, and multiply the result by –1. State a rule for the altitude in feet based upon the outside temperature. At what altitude is outside temperature about –51°F?

51. Possible answer: Subtract the temperature from 15, divide the result by 2, and multiply by 1000; 33,000 ft.

SPIRAL REVIEW

Use interval notation to represent each set of numbers. *(Lesson 1-1)*

52. $-4 \le x \le 8$ or $x > 12$ $[-4, 8] \cup (12, \infty)$

53. (number line: –10 –8 –6 –4 –2 0 2 4 6 8 10) $(-\infty, -4)$

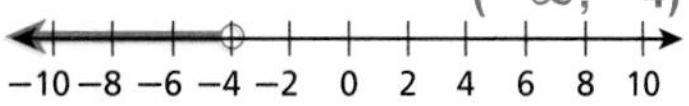

Determine whether the ordered pair is a solution of both $2x + y = 5$ and $\frac{3}{4}x < -5y$. *(Lesson 2-1)*

54. $(0, 0)$ no 55. $(-1, 6)$ no 56. $(2, 1)$ no 57. $(3, -1)$ yes

58. **Entertainment** A scaled replica of the Eiffel Tower at Kings Island Amusement Park is 331 ft 6 in. tall. The Eiffel Tower in Paris is 994 ft 6 in. tall. What percent of the height of the Eiffel Tower is the replica's height? *(Lesson 2-2)* $33\frac{1}{3}\%$

TEST PREP DOCTOR In **Exercise 44,** students who chose **A** or **D** changed the constant in the equation but not the coefficient of the independent variable. Students who chose **B** changed both the constant and the coefficient in the original equation.

In **Exercise 45,** if students chose either **F** or **H,** they did not recognize that the slope of the graph must be negative. If students chose **J,** they did not use the negative reciprocal of 3.

Journal

Have students explain how the point-slope form of a line is different from the slope-intercept form of a line.

ALTERNATIVE ASSESSMENT

Have students draw a line through 2 points they plot on a coordinate plane and find the equation of the line. Then have students draw a third point off the line and find the equations of lines parallel and perpendicular to the original line through the point.

Power Presentations with PowerPoint®

2-4 Lesson Quiz

Write the equation of each line in slope-intercept form.

1.

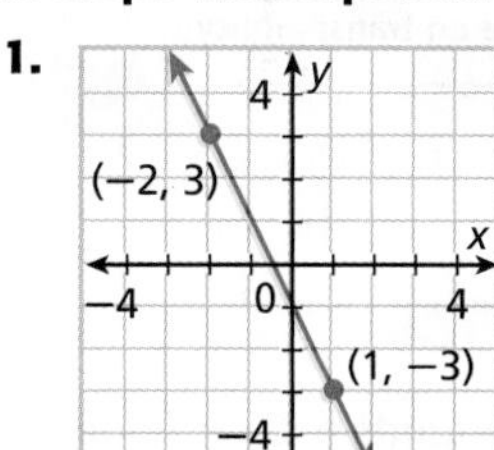

$y = -2x - 1$

2. parallel to $y = 0.5x + 2$ and through $(6, 1)$ $y = 0.5x - 2$

3. perpendicular to $y = -\frac{2}{3}x + 1$ and through $(4, 4)$ $y = \frac{3}{2}x - 2$

4. Express the catering cost as a function of the number of people. Find the cost of catering a meal for 24 people.

Number in Group	Cost ($)
4	98
7	134
15	230

$f(x) = 12x + 50$; $338

Also available on transparency

2-4 PROBLEM SOLVING

Solve.

1. As an image consultant, Antonio is well paid by his celebrity clients. For 20 hours of work, his fee is $1625. He charges $3500 for 45 hours of his time.

a. Express his fee as a function of his hourly rate. $y = 75x + 125$

b. What does the y-intercept represent? A flat fee of $125 charged in addition to the hourly rate.

c. What is the fee for 40 hours of his time? $3125

2. A child's cough medicine has a dosage table on the package.

Medicine Dosage	
Child's Weight (kg)	Dosage (mL)
10	6.0
16	7.5
28	10.5
30	11.0

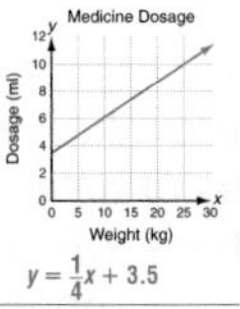

Medicine Dosage (graph: Dosage (ml) vs. Weight (kg))

a. Express the dosage in milliliters as a function of the child's weight in kilograms. $y = \frac{1}{4}x + 3.5$

b. Graph the function.

c. Find the dosage for a child who weighs 22 kg. 9 ml

Choose the letter for the best answer.

3. Kayla's cell phone plan charges a fee of $25 per month and $0.25 per minute. She just received a notice that the fee is being increased to $35 per month. Which equation models her new cell phone plan?

A $y = 0.25x + 25$
B $y = 0.35x + 35$
C $y = 0.25x + 35$
Ⓓ $y = 0.35x + 25$

4. Henry drew 2 lines on a coordinate grid. The red line passes through points $(-2, -4)$ and $(2, -2)$. The blue line is perpendicular to the red line and includes point $(-2, 8)$. What is the equation of the blue line?

A $y = \frac{1}{2}x - 3$ C $y = -\frac{1}{2}x - 3$
Ⓑ $y = -2x + 4$ D $y = 2x + 4$

2-4 CHALLENGE

How can you find the shortest distance from a point to a line? Point $P(-4, 8)$ lies outside of line ℓ. Line ℓ can be represented by the equation $y = 2x - 4$. The distance from point P to line ℓ is the length of the line segment from point P to line ℓ that is perpendicular to line ℓ.

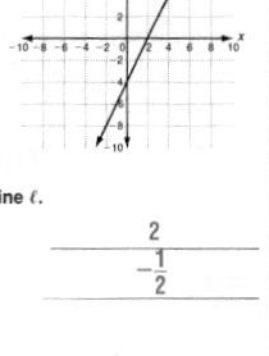

The distance formula $d = \sqrt{(x_2 - x_1)^2 + (y_2 - y_1)^2}$ can be used to find this distance if both endpoints of the perpendicular line segment are known. Since point P is given, the problem is to find the coordinates of point Q on line ℓ such that line segment PQ is perpendicular to line ℓ.

Answer the questions to find the distance from point P to line ℓ.

1. a. What is the slope of line ℓ? 2

b. What is the slope of a line perpendicular to line ℓ? $-\frac{1}{2}$

2. The endpoint Q of line segment PQ must lie on line ℓ and line segment PQ must be perpendicular to line ℓ. Let the coordinates of point Q be (x_Q, y_Q). Use the equation of line ℓ to write y_Q as a function of x_Q. $y_Q = 2x_Q - 4$

3. Use the point-slope form to write an expression for the slope of line segment PQ as a function of x_Q. $m = \frac{2x_Q - 12}{x_Q + 4}$

4. Use the numerical slope from Exercise 1b and the slope expression from Exercise 3 to solve for the values of x_Q and y_Q. $x_Q = 4$, $y_Q = 4$

5. Finally, use the distance formula to find the distance from point P to line ℓ. $4\sqrt{5}$

Find the distance from each point to the line represented by the given equation.

6. $(7, 4)$, $3x + 4y = 12$ 5

7. $(2, -14)$, $6x - 8y = 24$ 10

8. $(-7, 8)$, $15x - 8y = 120$ 17

9. $(7, -17)$, $-7x + 24y = 168$ 25

2-5 Organizer

Pacing: Traditional 1 day
Block $\frac{1}{2}$ day

Objectives: Graph linear inequalities on the coordinate plane.

Solve problems using linear inequalities.

Online Edition
Tutorial Videos, TechKeys

Countdown to Testing Week 4

Power Presentations with PowerPoint®

Warm Up

Find the intercepts of each line.

1. $3x + 2y = 18$ (0, 9), (6, 0)
2. $4x - y = 8$ (0, −8), (2, 0)
3. $5x + 10 = 2y$ (0, 5), (−2, 0)

Write the function in slope-intercept form. Then graph.

4. $2x + 3y = -3$ $y = -\frac{2}{3}x - 1$

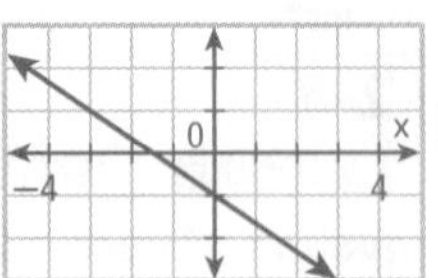

Also available on transparency

Math Fact !!

A solid line bounds a *closed half-plane,* a dashed line bounds an *open half-plane.*

2-5 Linear Inequalities in Two Variables

Objectives
Graph linear inequalities on the coordinate plane.
Solve problems using linear inequalities.

Vocabulary
linear inequality
boundary line

Who uses this?
A movie theater manager may use linear inequalities to find the numbers of different-priced tickets that must be sold to make a profit. (See Example 3.)

Linear functions form the basis of *linear inequalities.* A **linear inequality** in two variables relates two variables using an inequality symbol, such as $y > 2x - 4$. Its graph is a region of the coordinate plane bounded by a line. The line is a **boundary line**, which divides the coordinate plane into two regions.

For example, the line $y = 2x - 4$, shown at right, divides the coordinate plane into two parts: one where $y > 2x - 4$ and one where $y < 2x - 4$. In the coordinate plane higher points have larger y values, so the region where $y > 2x - 4$ is above the boundary line where $y = 2x - 4$.

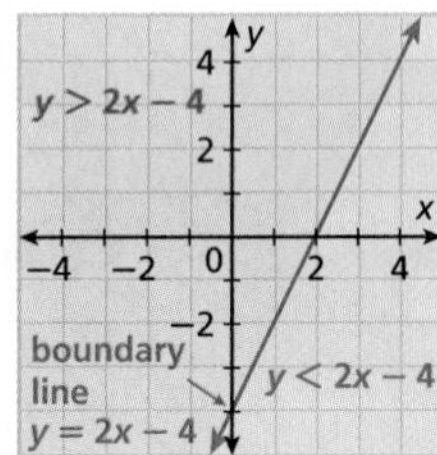

Helpful Hint
Think of the underlines in the symbols ≤ and ≥ as representing solid lines on the graph.

To graph $y \ge 2x - 4$, make the boundary line solid, and shade the region above the line. To graph $y > 2x - 4$, make the boundary line dashed because y-values equal to $2x - 4$ are not included.

EXAMPLE 1 **Graphing Linear Inequalities**

Graph each inequality.

A $y < \frac{1}{2}x + 1$

The boundary line is $y = \frac{1}{2}x + 1$, which has a y-intercept of 1 and a slope of $\frac{1}{2}$.

Draw the boundary line dashed because it is not part of the solution. Then shade the region below the boundary line to show $y < \frac{1}{2}x + 1$.

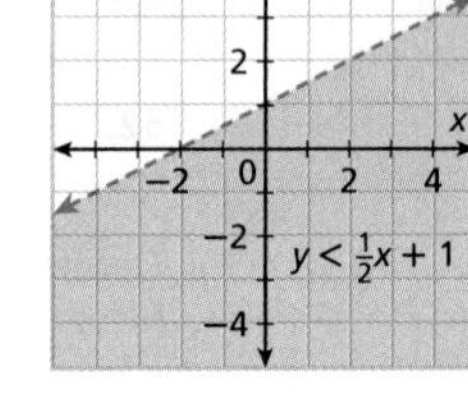

Check Choose a point in the solution region, such as (0, 0) and test it in the inequality.

$$y < \frac{1}{2}x + 1$$
$$0 \overset{?}{<} \frac{1}{2}(0) + 1$$
$$0 \overset{?}{<} 1 \checkmark$$

The test point satisfies the inequality, so the solution region appears to be correct.

State Resources

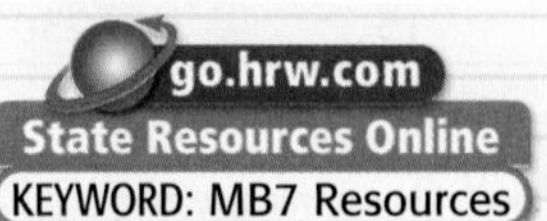

1 Introduce

EXPLORATION

2-5 Linear Inequalities in Two Variables

You can use a graphing calculator to explore inequalities.

1. Press [Y=] and enter the function $y = 2x - 1$ as **Y1**.
2. You can graph the inequality $y \ge 2x - 1$ in the following way: Use the arrow keys to move the cursor to the extreme left of the line on which you entered **Y1**. Press [ENTER] until you see the shaded triangle shown on the graph at right. Press [GRAPH].
3. What points along the y-axis are in the shaded region?
4. What points along the vertical line $x = 2.5$ are in the shaded region?
5. You can enter $y \le 2x - 1$ by moving the cursor to the extreme left of the line on which you entered the function. Press [ENTER] until you see the shaded triangle shown on the graph at right. Press [GRAPH].

Plot1 Plot2 Plot3
Y1■2X−1
Y2=
Y3=

THINK AND DISCUSS

6. Describe what would happen if you graphed $y \ge 2x - 1$ and

Motivate

Discuss boundaries on different playing fields. For example, in baseball the border is "in bounds," but in basketball or football, the border is "out of bounds." Discuss other types of boundary lines, such as borders of national and state parks and borders of nations. Discuss characteristics of borders, such as when borders might be open or closed. Then tell students that they are going to explore boundary lines in the coordinate plane.

Explorations and answers are provided in the *Explorations* binder.

Graph each inequality.

B $y \geq 2$

Recall that $y = 2$ is a horizontal line.

Step 1 Draw a solid line for $y = 2$ because the boundary line is part of the graph.

Step 2 Shade the region above the boundary line to show where $y > 2$.

Check The point $(0, 4)$ is a solution because $4 \geq 2$. Note that any point on or above $y = 2$ is a solution, regardless of the value of x.

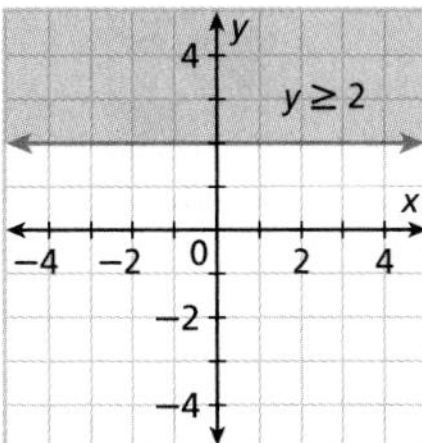

1a. 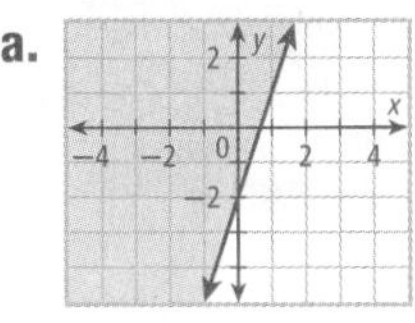

1b. 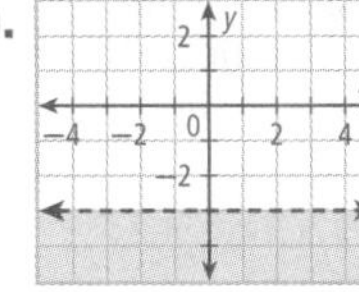

Graph each inequality.

1a. $y \geq 3x - 2$ **1b.** $y < -3$

If the equation of the boundary line is not in slope-intercept form, you can choose a test point that is not on the line to determine which region to shade. If the point satisfies the inequality, then shade the region containing that point. Otherwise, shade the other region.

EXAMPLE 2 Graphing Linear Inequalities Using Intercepts

Graph $2x + 3y \geq 6$ using intercepts.

Step 1 Find the intercepts.

Substitute $x = 0$ and then $y = 0$ into $2x + 3y = 6$ to find the intercepts of the boundary line.

***y*-intercept**	***x*-intercept**
$2x + 3y = 6$	$2x + 3y = 6$
$2(0) + 3y = 6$	$2x + 3(0) = 6$
$3y = 6$	$2x = 6$
$y = 2$	$x = 3$

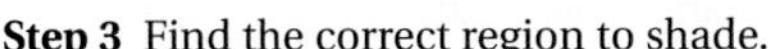

Step 2 Draw the boundary line.

The line goes through $(0, 2)$ and $(3, 0)$. Draw a solid line for the boundary because it is part of the graph.

Step 3 Find the correct region to shade.

Substitute $(0, 0)$ into the inequality. Because $0 + 0 \geq 6$ is false, shade the region that does *not* contain $(0, 0)$.

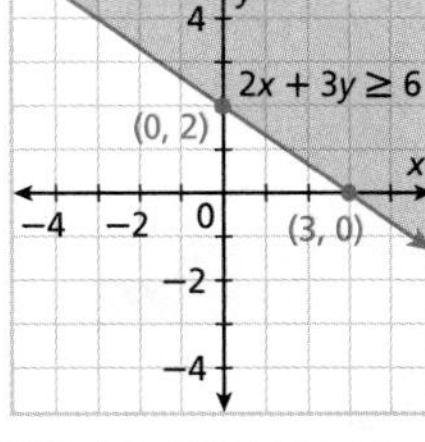

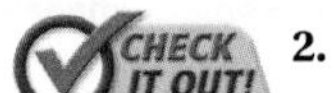

Helpful Hint

The point $(0, 0)$ is the easiest point to test if it is not on the boundary line.

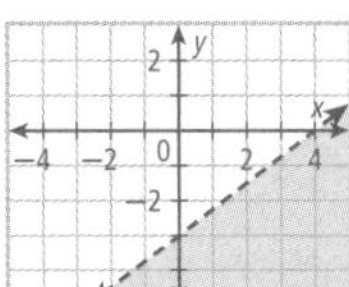

2. Graph $3x - 4y > 12$ using intercepts.

Many applications of inequalities in two variables use only nonnegative values for the variables. Graph only the part of the plane that includes realistic solutions.

Power Presentations with PowerPoint®

Additional Examples

Example 1

Graph each inequality.

A. $y > -\frac{1}{3}x + 2$

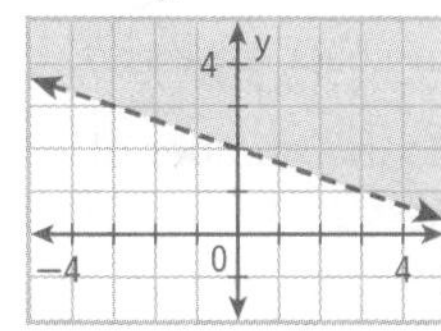

B. $y \leq -1$

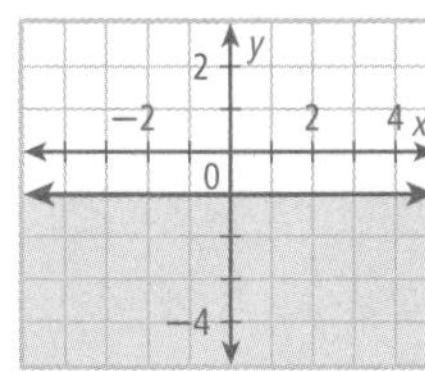

Example 2

Graph $3x + 4y \leq 12$ using intercepts. *y*-int.: 3; *x*-int.: 4

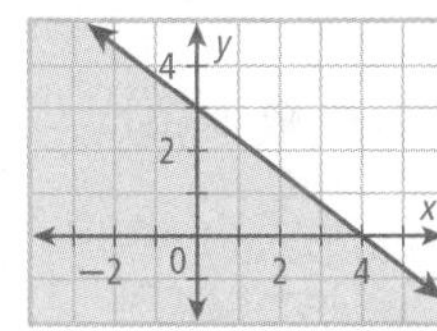

Also available on transparency

INTERVENTION

Questioning Strategies

EXAMPLES 1 and 2

- Why is (0, 0) often a good point to use to determine shading?
- What happens if you choose to test a point on the boundary?
- When might it be easier to use the intercepts to sketch the graph of a linear inequality?

Teaching Tip

Technology To graph an inequality using the TI graphing calculator, use Y= to define the equation that corresponds to the boundary line. Press the left arrow key to move to the far left of the equation. Press ENTER until the *shaded above* or *shaded below* icon appears, as in **Example 4,** and press GRAPH.

2 Teach

Guided Instruction

In this lesson, students graph linear inequalities in the coordinate plane. Remind students that the graph of a linear function divides the coordinate plane into three parts: the points above the line, the points below the line, and the points on the line itself. Point out that the graph of a linear inequality includes either the points above or below a boundary line and may include the boundary line itself. Only if the inequality includes "equal to" is the boundary line included in the solution set.

Reaching All Learners

Through Critical Thinking

Discuss how to sketch the graphs of inequalities such as $x < 2$ and $x \geq -1$. Note that the shaded half-plane lies to the left or the right of the boundary line. Then have students consider how they could use inequalities to describe a square on the coordinate plane. Challenge students to write a set of linear inequalities that describe an area bounded by a rectangle with vertices at (4, 2), (4, −2), (−4, 2), and (−4, −2).

Power Presentations with PowerPoint®

Additional Examples

Example 3

A school carnival charges \$4.50 for adults and \$3.00 for children. The school needs to make at least \$135 to cover expenses.

a. Using x as the number of adult tickets sold and y as the number of child tickets sold, write and graph an inequality for the amount the school makes on ticket sales.
$4.5x + 3y \geq 135$

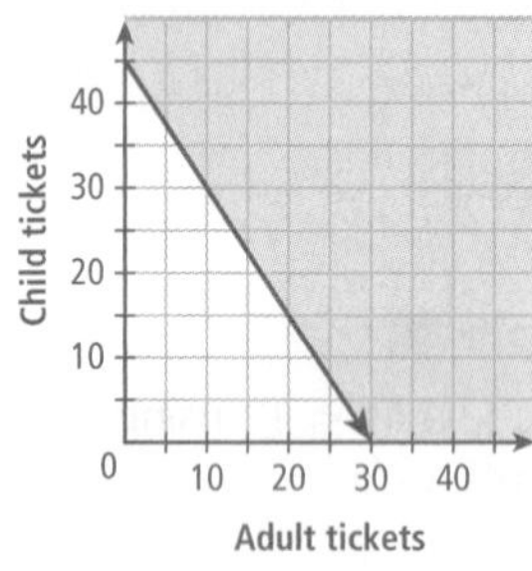

b. If 25 child tickets are sold, how many adult tickets must be sold to cover expenses? at least 14

Also available on transparency

INTERVENTION

Questioning Strategies

EXAMPLE 3

- Can you explain how to set up the inequality using the words in the problem?
- How do you know which variable to substitute for to solve the problem?

EXAMPLE 3 ***Problem-Solving Application***

A local theater charges \$7.50 for adult tickets and \$5.00 for discount tickets. The theater needs to make at least \$240 to cover the rent of the building. How many of each type of ticket must be sold to make a profit? If 20 discount tickets are sold, how many adult tickets must be sold?

1 Understand the Problem

The **answer** will be in two parts: (1) an inequality graph showing the number of each type of ticket that must be sold to make a profit (2) the number of adult tickets that must be sold to make at least \$240 if 20 discount tickets are sold.

List the important information:

- The theater sells tickets for \$7.50 and \$5.00.
- The theater needs to make at least \$240.

2 Make a Plan

Let x represent the number of adult tickets and y represent the number of discount tickets that must be sold. Write an inequality to represent the situation.

Adult price	times	number of adult tickets	plus	discount price	times	number of discount tickets	is at least	total.
7.50	·	x	+	5.00	·	y	$\geq$	240

An inequality that models the problem is $7.5x + 5y \geq 240$.

3 Solve

Find the intercepts of the boundary line.

$7.5(0) + 5y = 240$ $\qquad$ $7.5x + 5(0) = 240$

$y = 48$ $\qquad$ $x = 32$

Graph the boundary line through (0, 48) and (32, 0) as a solid line. Shade the region above the line that is in the first quadrant, as ticket sales cannot be negative.

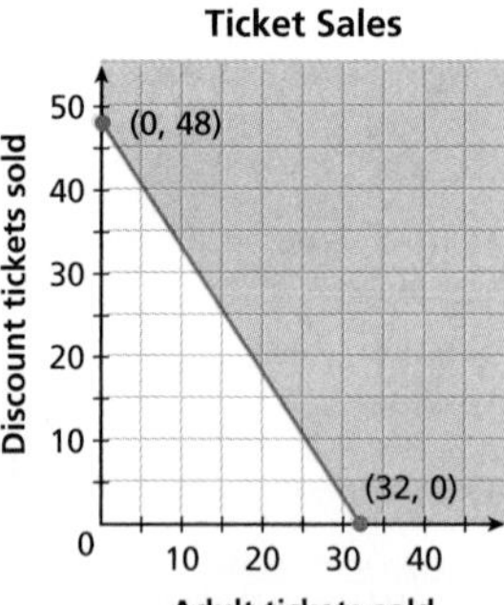

If 20 discount tickets are sold,

$7.5x + 5(20) \geq 240$ *Substitute 20 for y in $7.5x + 5y \geq 240$.*

$7.5x + 100 \geq 240$ *Multiply 5 by 20.*

$7.5x \geq 140$, so $x \geq 18.\overline{6}$ *A whole number of tickets must be sold.*

At least 19 adult tickets must be sold.

4 Look Back

$19(\$7.50) + 20(\$5.00) = \$242.50$, so the answer is reasonable.

Caution!

Don't forget which variable represents which quantity.

$40x + 125y \leq 1500$; no more than 25

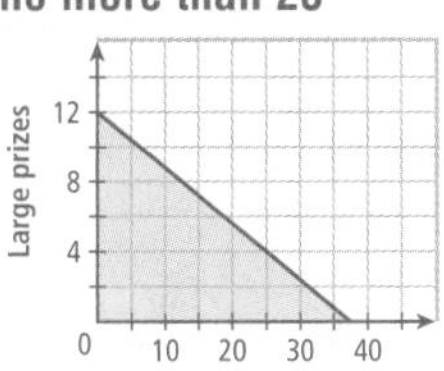

CHECK IT OUT! 3. A café gives away prizes. A large prize costs the café \$125, and the small prize costs \$40. The café will not spend more than \$1500. How many of each prize can be awarded? How many small prizes can be awarded if 4 large prizes are given away?

You can graph a linear inequality that is solved for y with a graphing calculator.

Press **Y=** and use the left arrow key to move to the left side.

Each time you press **ENTER** you will see one of the graph styles shown here. You are already familiar with the line style.

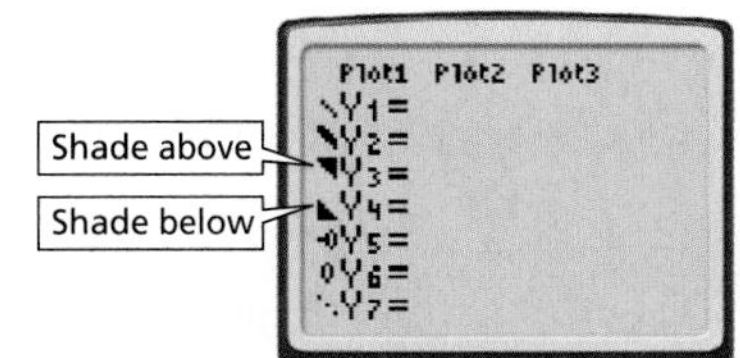

EXAMPLE 4 Solving and Graphing Linear Inequalities

Solve $\frac{2}{3}(2x - y) < 2$ for y. Graph the solution.

$\frac{3}{2} \cdot \frac{2}{3}(2x - y) < \frac{3}{2} \cdot 2$ *Multiply both sides by $\frac{3}{2}$.*

$2x - y < 3$

$-y < -2x + 3$ *Subtract 2x from both sides.*

$y > 2x - 3$ *Multiply by −1, and reverse the inequality symbol.*

Use the calculator option to shade above the line $y = 2x - 3$.

Note that the graph is shown in the standard square window (**ZOOM** **6:ZStandard** followed by **ZOOM** **5:ZSquare**).

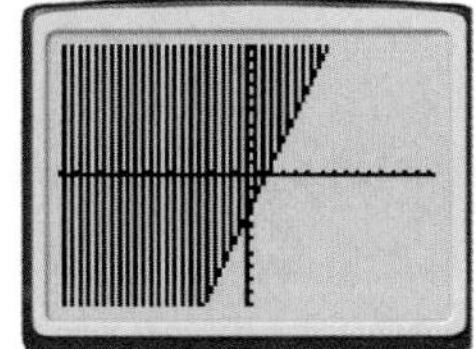

Remember!

When multiplying or dividing an inequality by a negative number, reverse the inequality symbol.

CHECK IT OUT! 4. Solve $2(3x - 4y) > 24$ for y. Graph the solution. $y < \frac{3}{4}x - 3$

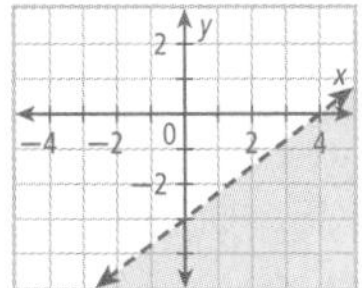

THINK AND DISCUSS

1. Compare the open and closed circles in graphs of inequalities with the dashed and solid lines in graphs of linear inequalities.
2. Describe what the graph of $x \geq 4$ would look like on a coordinate plane.
3. Explain whether you can use $(0, 0)$ to determine which side of the graph of $3x + 5y \leq 0$ to shade.
4. **GET ORGANIZED** Copy and complete the graphic organizer. For each graph description, give examples of corresponding inequalities solved for y and inequalities in other forms.

Dashed Line, Shaded Above	Dashed Line, Shaded Below	Solid Line, Shaded Above	Solid Line, Shaded Below

COMMON ERROR ALERT

Students might shade the wrong half-plane, especially when the equation is not in slope-intercept form. Emphasize the importance of selecting a test point on either side of the boundary to see which half-plane should be shaded.

Power Presentations with PowerPoint®

Additional Examples

Example 4

Solve $\frac{3}{4}(8x - 2y) > 6$ for y.

Graph the solution. $y < 4x - 4$

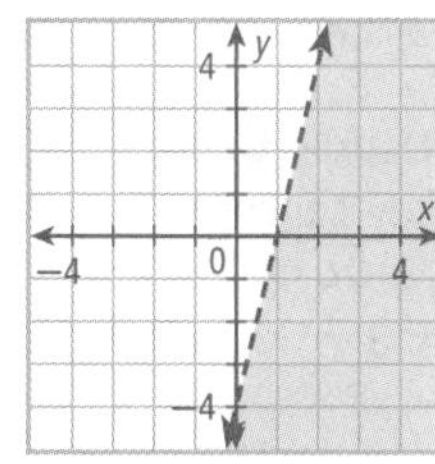

Also available on transparency

INTERVENTION
Questioning Strategies

EXAMPLE 4

- How is solving a linear inequality different from solving a linear equation?
- Once you've solved for y, how does the inequality symbol tell you whether to shade above or below the boundary line?

Answers to *Think and Discuss*

1. The open circle corresponds to the dashed line; the boundary is not part of the solution. The closed circle corresponds to the solid line; the boundary is part of the solution.
2. a solid vertical line at $x = 4$ with everything to the right shaded
3. No; it is a solution to the related equation and only determines whether the boundary line is solid or dashed.
4. See p. A3.

3 Close

Summarize

Ask students to compare and contrast graphing a linear inequality and a linear equation. Then have them explain how to decide which half-plane should be shaded when graphing a linear inequality. Similarity: Boundary line of inequality is graph of equation. Difference: Graph of inequality includes shaded half-plane and possibly boundary line. If inequality is true for a given point, shade half-plane that contains point. Otherwise shade half-plane that does not contain point.

ONGOING ASSESSMENT and INTERVENTION

Diagnose Before the Lesson
2-5 Warm Up, TE p. 124

Monitor During the Lesson
Check It Out! Exercises, SE pp. 125–127
Questioning Strategies, TE pp. 125–127

Assess After the Lesson
2-5 Lesson Quiz, TE p. 131
Alternative Assessment, TE p. 131

2-5 Exercises

Assignment Guide

Assign *Guided Practice* exercises as necessary.

If you finished Examples **1–2**
Basic 14–18, 26, 37
Average 14–18, 25, 28, 37–40
Advanced 14–18, 25, 28, 31, 37–40

If you finished Examples **1–4**
Basic 14–24, 26, 37, 40–41, 54–64
Average 14–33, 36–49, 53–64
Advanced 14–24, 26–36 even, 37–38, 41–64

Homework Quick Check
Quickly check key concepts.
Exercises: 16, 18, 20, 22, 34

Answers

2. 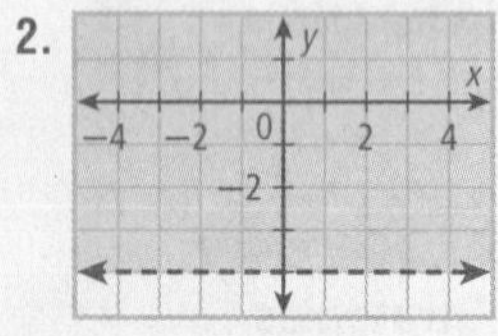

3. 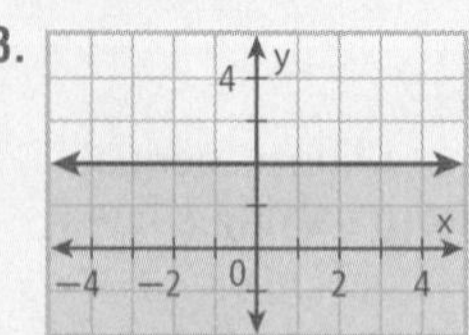

4. 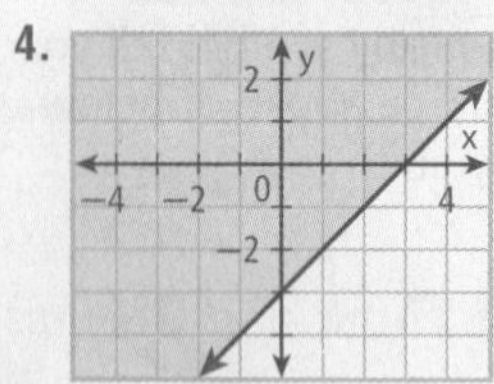

State Resources

2-5 Exercises

go.hrw.com
Homework Help Online
KEYWORD: MB7 2-5
Parent Resources Online
KEYWORD: MB7 Parent

GUIDED PRACTICE

1. **Vocabulary** Explain how the graph of $y = 3x - 4$ can be a *boundary line.* **The line $y = 3x - 4$ splits the coordinate plane into 2 regions, one where $y > 3x - 4$ and one where $y < 3x - 4$**

SEE EXAMPLE 1 p. 124

Graph each inequality.

2. $y > -4$ 3. $y \le 2$ 4. $y \ge x - 3$ 5. $y < -\frac{1}{3}x + 2$

SEE EXAMPLE 2 p. 125

Graph each inequality using intercepts.

6. $3x + 2y > 12$ 7. $5x - 2y \le 20$ 8. $-4x + 5y < -20$

SEE EXAMPLE 3 p. 126

9. **Consumer** Charisse is buying two different types of cereals from the bulk bins at the store. Granola costs $2.29 per pound, and muesli costs $3.75 per pound. She has $7.00. Use x as the amount of granola and y as the amount of muesli.
   a. Write and graph an inequality for the amounts of each cereal she can buy.
   b. How many pounds of granola can she buy if she buys 1.5 pounds of muesli?

10. **School** The senior class sells hamburgers and hot dogs at a football game and makes a profit of $1.75 on each hamburger and $1.25 on each hot dog. The class would like a profit of at least $280. Let x represent the number of hamburgers and y represent the number of hot dogs sold. **10a. $1.75x + 1.25y \ge 280$**
   a. Write and graph an inequality for the profit the senior class wants to make.
   b. If the senior class sells 100 hot dogs and 50 hamburgers, will the class make its goal? **no; $1.25(100) + $1.75(50) = $212.50**

SEE EXAMPLE 4 p. 127

Solve each inequality for y. Graph the solution.

11. $\frac{1}{2}(6x - 2y) \ge 4$ **$y \le 3x - 4$** 12. $-\frac{3}{5}x + y \ge 2$ **$y \ge \frac{3}{5}x + 2$** 13. $3(3x - y) > -12$ **$y < 3x + 4$**

PRACTICE AND PROBLEM SOLVING

Independent Practice

For Exercises	See Example
14–16	1
17–18	2
19–21	3
22–24	4

Extra Practice
Skills Practice p. S6
Application Practice p. S33

Graph each inequality.

14. $y \ge 6$ 15. $y < x + 4$ 16. $y > -\frac{2}{5}x - 3$

Graph each inequality using intercepts.

17. $4x + 2y \ge 8$ 18. $3x - 6y < 12$

19. **Marketing** Quarter page ads in the local papers cost $200 per day, and one minute ads on the local radio stations cost $500. Sheena's Lawn Care has an advertising budget of $10,000. Let x be the number of quarter page ads in newspapers and y be the number of one minute radio ads. Write and graph an inequality for the advertising that Sheena's Lawn Care can afford.

20. **Astronomy** The rockets of a Mars probe require oxygen to lift off from the surface and return to Earth. Suppose the probe can produce 0.78 L of oxygen for every kg of water and 0.32 L of oxygen for every kg of carbon dioxide. At least 56 L of oxygen are needed. Let x represent the kg of water available and y represent the kg of carbon dioxide.
   a. Write and graph an inequality for the liters of oxygen that will be sufficient for liftoff. **$0.78x + 0.32y \ge 56$**
   b. If the probe collects 36 kg of water and 88 kg of carbon dioxide, will it be enough for liftoff? **yes**

5. 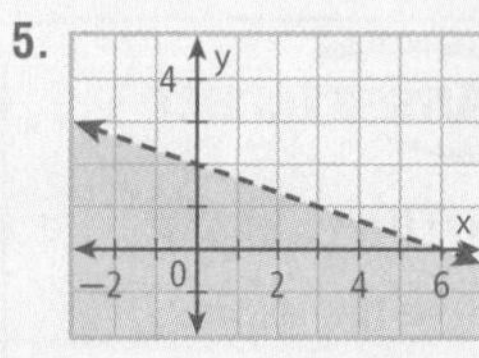

6. 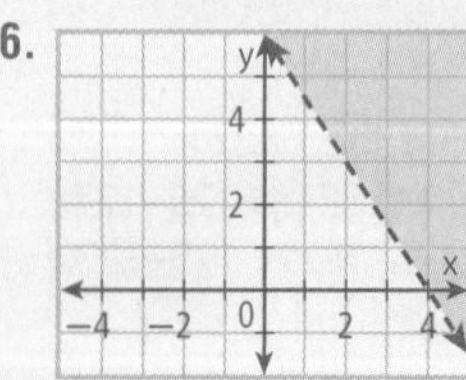

7. 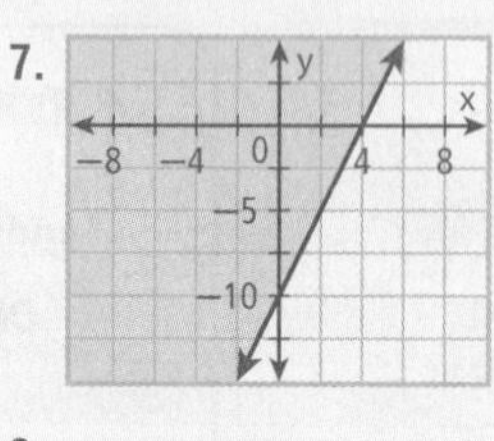

8. 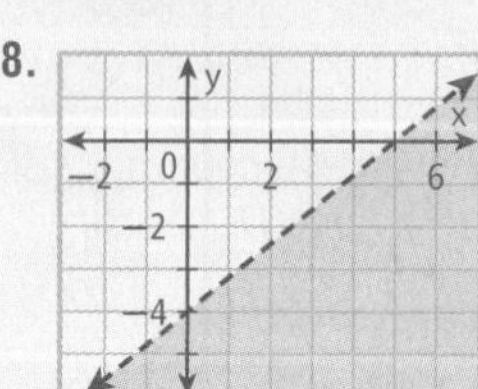

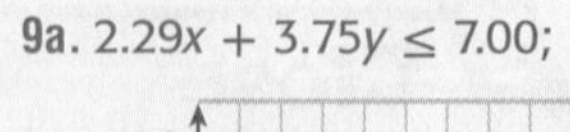
9a. $2.29x + 3.75y \le 7.00$;

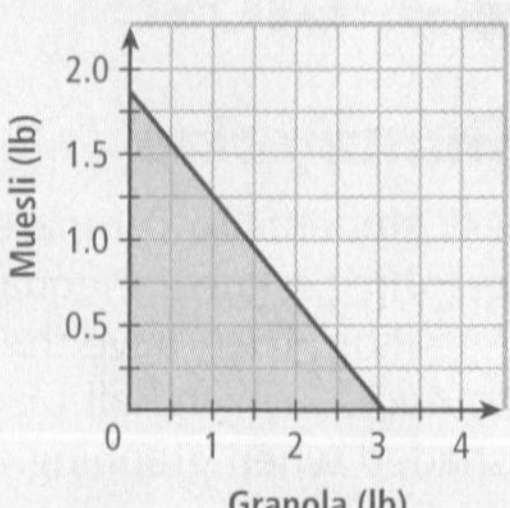

b. no more than 0.6 lb

21. **Recreation** Amber has a \$200 gift card for boat rentals. She rents kayaks at \$8 and canoes at \$12 per hour. Let x be the number of hours of kayak rentals and y be the number of hours of canoe rentals.
   a. Write and graph an inequality for the possible number of hours of each that she can rent.
   b. If Amber rents kayaks for 10 hours, how many hours can she rent canoes for?
   no more than 10 h

21a. $8x + 12y \leq 200$

Solve each inequality for y. Graph the solution.

22. $-4y < 4(3x - 5)$
23. $-3(-10x + 2y) \geq 24$
24. $-\frac{1}{3}x + \frac{1}{5}y \leq -1$

Graph each inequality.

25. $-4y > 10x - 20$
26. $y - 5 \geq 4(x - 2)$
27. $6x + 3y < 0$
28. $y + \frac{3}{4} \leq \frac{5}{2}\left(x - \frac{1}{2}\right)$
29. $\frac{9 - 3y}{2} \geq 6x$
30. $x \leq 4$
31. $4x - 5y < 7x - 3y$
32. $2x - 5y \leq -4x + 15$
33. $x > -2$

34. **School** Tickets to the math club dance cost \$5 if bought in advance and \$6 at the door. The math club needs to make a total of at least \$600 from ticket sales for the dance.
   a. Let x be the number of tickets sold in advance and y be the number of tickets sold at the door. Write and graph an inequality for the total amount in ticket sales that the math club needs. $5x + 6y \geq 600$
   b. If the math club sells 30 tickets in advance, how many tickets must be sold at the door for the math club to reach its goal? at least 75

35. **Fund-raising** The junior class is selling pizza and beverages at a basketball game. The class makes a profit of \$1.25 on each slice of pizza and \$0.50 on each beverage. Let x be the number of pizza slices and y be the number of beverages.
   a. Write and graph an inequality that shows the number of pizza slices and number of beverages the class must sell to make a profit of at least \$150.
   b. If the junior class sells 75 slices of pizza and 150 beverages, will the class make its goal? yes

35a. $1.25x + 0.50y \geq 150$

36. **Critical Thinking** Tickets to an event cost \$5 for adults and \$2 for students. Total ticket sales were more than \$300. Jane and Erin graphed the situation as an inequality. Jane let x be the number of adult tickets sold, and Erin let x be the number of student tickets sold. How did their graphs differ? Which graph, if either, was incorrect? Possible answer: The first graph would be of $5x + 2y > 300$, and the second would be of $2x + 5y > 300$. Neither would be incorrect.

MULTI-STEP TEST PREP

37. This problem will prepare you for the Multi-Step Test Prep on page 132.
   A ship starting 500 nautical miles from port can travel at a speed of 27 knots or less.
   a. How long does the trip to port take? $> \approx 18.5$ h
   b. Graph the ship's distance over the trip. What do the points above the boundary line represent? possible distances from port
   c. **What if...?** Suppose the minimum speed at any point during the trip is 10 knots. How far from port is the ship after 12 hours? between 176 and 380 mi.

10a.

Hot dogs sold (0, 50, 100, 150, 200) vs. Hamburgers sold (0, 50, 100, 150, 200)

b. no; \$1.25(100) + \$1.75(50) = \$212.50

11.

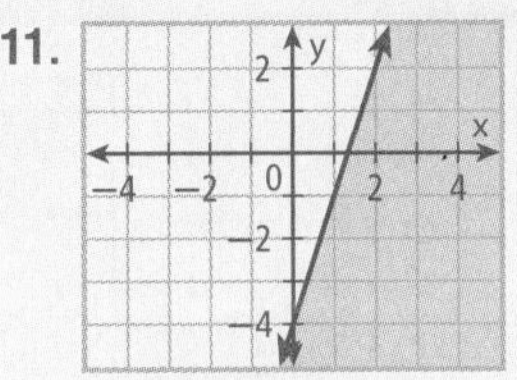

12.

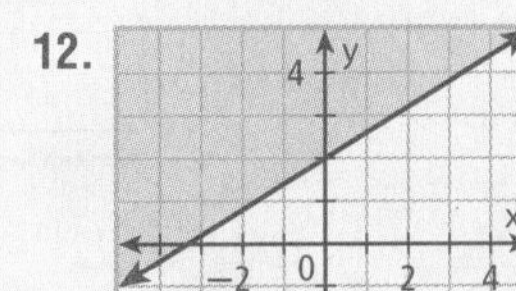

13.

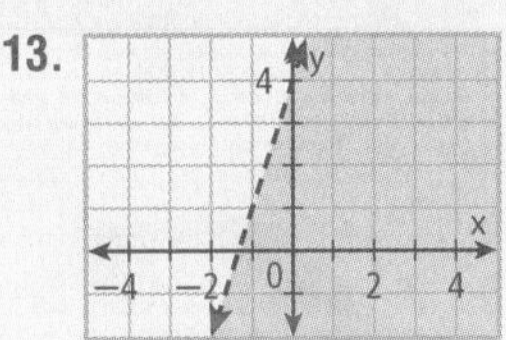

14.

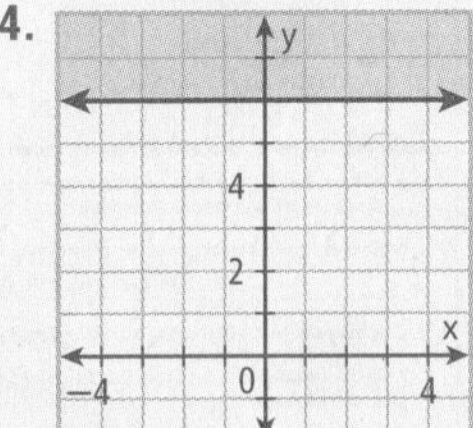

COMMON ERROR ALERT

Students might forget to draw the graphs in only the first quadrant in **Exercises 19–21, 34–36, 42,** and **43.** Stress the importance of graphing *only* the part of the plane that includes reasonable solutions. Neither x nor y can be negative in the exercises.

Visual Suggest that students put the point of the pencil on the y-intercept of the boundary when shading the inequalities in **Exercises 14–16.** If y is greater than the intercept value, they shade up. If y is less than the intercept value, they shade down.

Reading Math In **Exercise 19,** the common inequality word clues (e.g., *at most, at least, more than, less than*) are not used. Discuss what it means for the advertisement to be *affordable.*

ENGLISH LANGUAGE LEARNERS

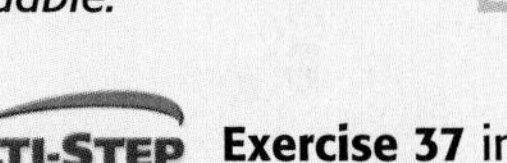

Exercise 37 involves linear inequalities and nautical speeds. This exercise prepares students for the Multi-Step Test Prep on page 132.

Answers

15–20. See p. A18.
21a. For graph, see p. A18.
22–33. See p. A18.
34a, 35a, 37b. For graphs, see p. A18.

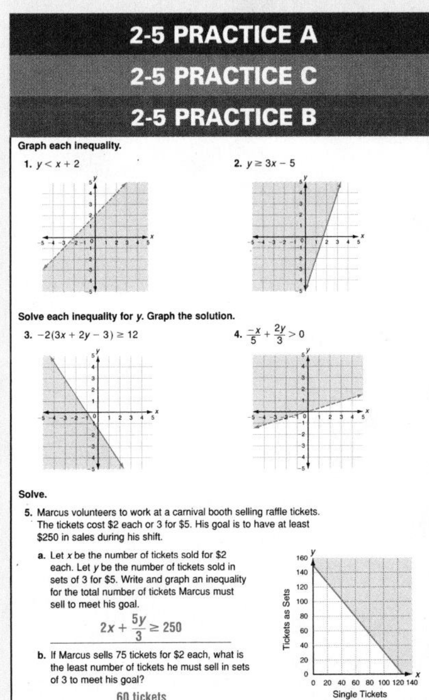

2-5 PRACTICE A
2-5 PRACTICE C
2-5 PRACTICE B

Graph each inequality.

1. $y < x + 2$
2. $y \geq 3x - 5$

Solve each inequality for y. Graph the solution.

3. $-2(3x + 2y - 3) \geq 12$
4. $\frac{-x}{5} + \frac{2y}{3} > 0$

Solve.

5. Marcus volunteers to work at a carnival booth selling raffle tickets. The tickets cost \$2 each or 3 for \$5. His goal is to have at least \$250 in sales during his shift.
   a. Let x be the number of tickets sold for \$2 each. Let y be the number of tickets sold in sets of 3 for \$5. Write and graph an inequality for the total number of tickets Marcus must sell to meet his goal.
   $2x + \frac{5y}{3} \geq 250$
   b. If Marcus sells 75 tickets for \$2 each, what is the least number of tickets he must sell in sets of 3 to meet his goal?
   60 tickets

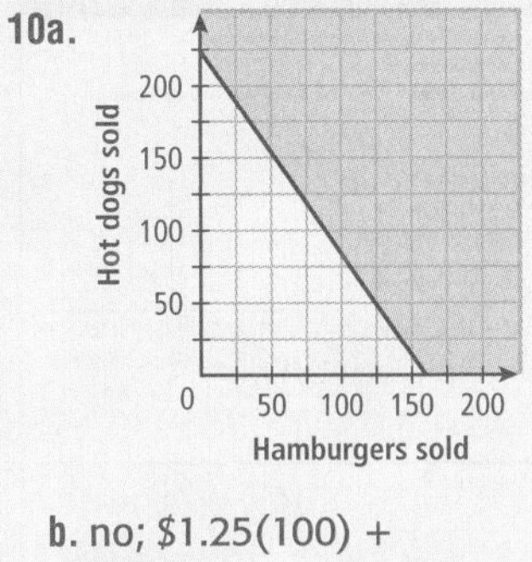

Tickets as Sets (0–160) vs. Single Tickets (0–140)

Answers

42a.

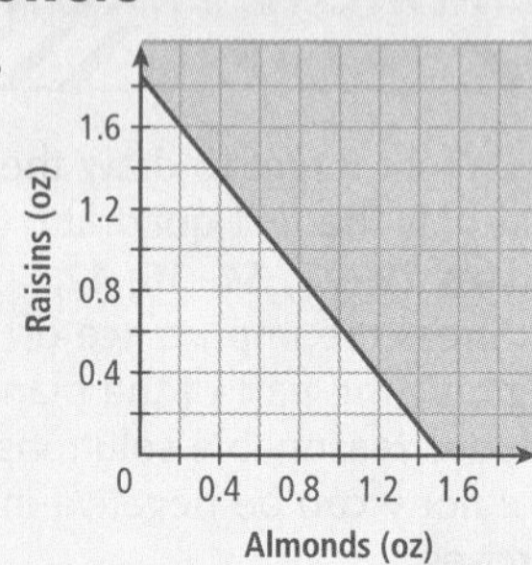

43a. $8x + 6y \geq 220$

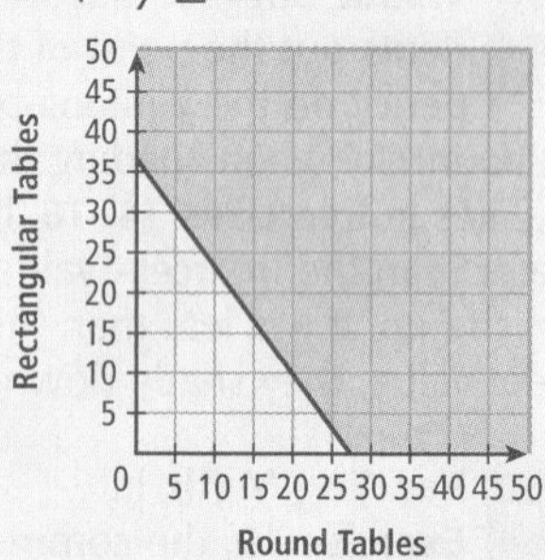

b. $8x + 6y \leq 300$

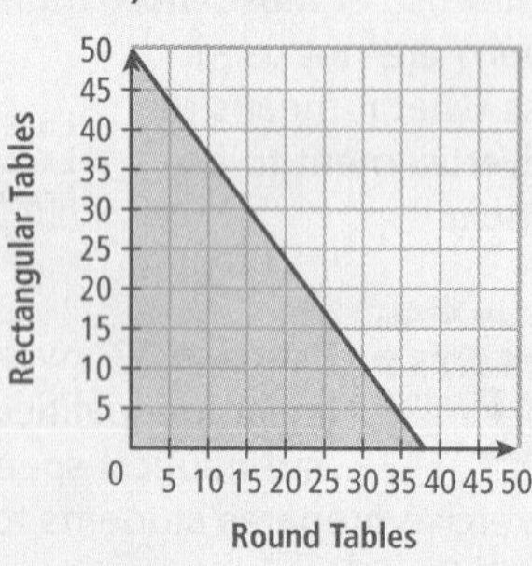

c. Possible answer: the first graph is shaded above $y = 36.\overline{6} - 1.\overline{3}x$, the second is shaded below $y = 50 - 1.\overline{3}x$.

50.

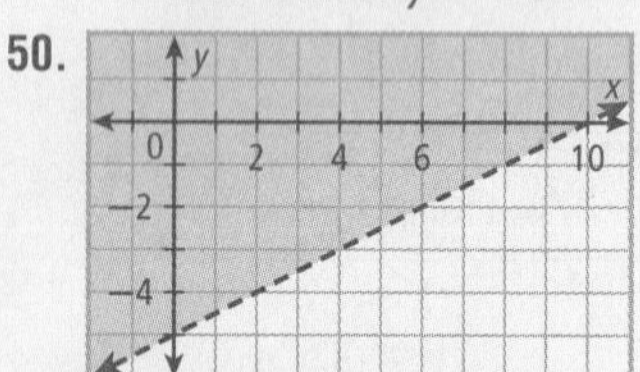

51.

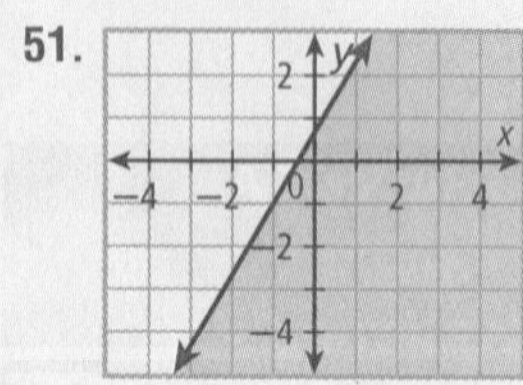

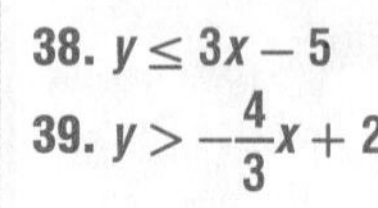

38. $y \leq 3x - 5$

39. $y > -\frac{4}{3}x + 2$

40. $y \leq -3$

41. Both are the areas below dashed lines through (0, 3). $30y = 90 + x$ has slope $\frac{1}{30}$ and x-intercept -90. $30y + x = 90$ has slope $-\frac{1}{30}$ and x-intercept 90.

Write an inequality for each graph.

38.

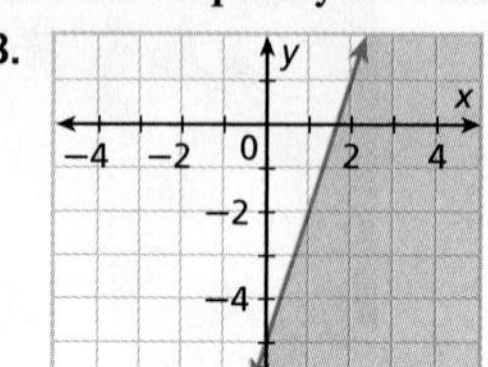

39.

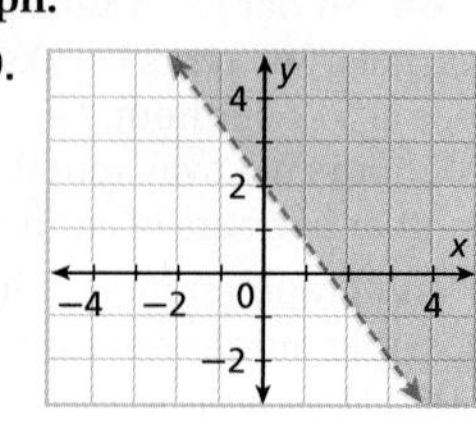

40.

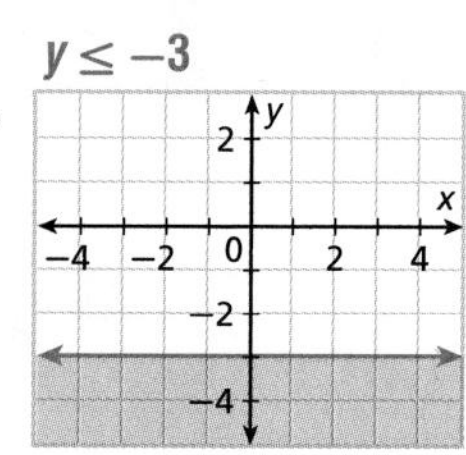

41. **Critical Thinking** Compare the graphs of $30y < 90 + x$ and $30y + x < 90$. How are they alike? How are they different?

42. **Home Economics** Omar uses almonds and raisins in a high-fiber recipe. Almonds have 3.3 g of fiber per ounce and raisins have 2.7 grams of fiber per ounce. He wants at least 5 grams of fiber from these ingredients in a recipe.

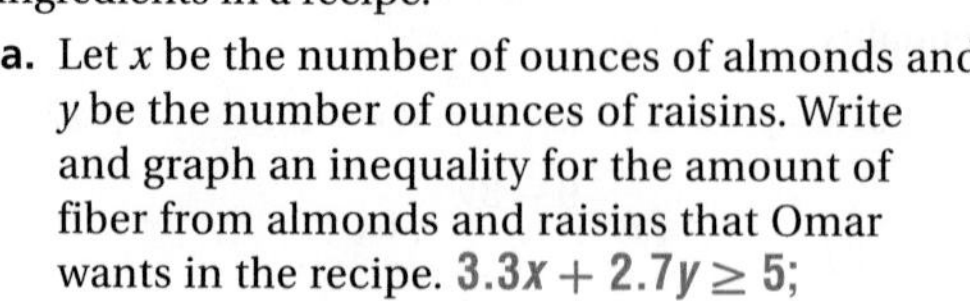

a. Let x be the number of ounces of almonds and y be the number of ounces of raisins. Write and graph an inequality for the amount of fiber from almonds and raisins that Omar wants in the recipe. $3.3x + 2.7y \geq 5$;

b. If Omar uses 0.5 ounce of almonds, how many ounces of raisins can he use? $\approx$ 1.24 oz or more

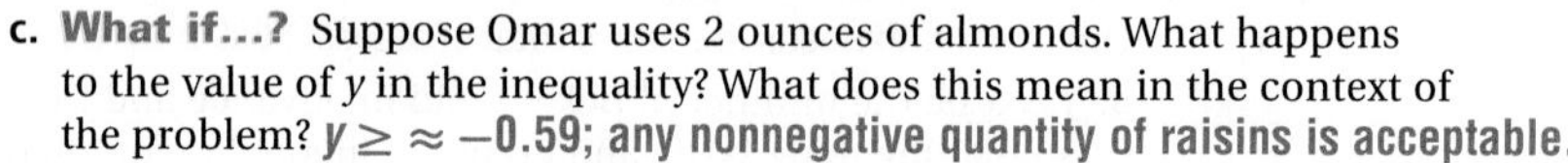

c. **What if...?** Suppose Omar uses 2 ounces of almonds. What happens to the value of y in the inequality? What does this mean in the context of the problem? $y \geq \approx -0.59$; any nonnegative quantity of raisins is acceptable.

43. A banquet room is to be filled with round tables and rectangular tables. The round tables have 8 chairs each, and the rectangular tables have 6 chairs each. Let x be the number of round tables and y be the number of rectangular tables.

a. Write and graph an inequality for the number of each type of table needed to have at least 220 chairs.

b. Due to fire regulations, there can be no more than 300 chairs. Write and graph an inequality to reflect this.

c. Compare your graphs. How do they differ?

TEST PREP

44. Which inequality best represents the set of points graphed here?

Ⓐ $y < 2x + 3$ Ⓑ $4x - 2y < -6$ Ⓒ $y \geq 2x + 3$ Ⓓ $4x + 2y > 6$

45. Which point is NOT a solution of $5x - 3y < 30$?

Ⓕ (0, 0) Ⓖ (3, −5) Ⓗ (−5, 3) Ⓙ (−3, 5)

46. Which inequality is equivalent to $7x - 3y \geq 4$?

Ⓐ $y \leq \frac{7}{3}x - \frac{4}{3}$ Ⓑ $y \leq -\frac{7}{3}x + \frac{4}{3}$ Ⓒ $y \geq -\frac{7}{3}x - \frac{4}{3}$ Ⓓ $y \geq \frac{7}{3}x + \frac{4}{3}$

2-5 READING STRATEGIES

The solution set of a linear inequality is a region in the plane. The linear equation $y = x + 1$ is shown on the graph. The line is the boundary between the two shaded portions. You can describe each shaded portion with or without the boundary by using one of the four inequality symbols: $\leq$, $<$, $\geq$, or $>$. The resulting inequalities are:

$y \leq x + 1$ $y < x + 1$ $y \geq x + 1$ $y > x + 1$

Answer each question. Use the inequalities shown above.

1. a. Which inequality describes both the shaded area above the line and the boundary line? $y \geq x + 1$

b. Give two points that are solutions of that inequality. Possible answer: (0, 6) and (−4, 4)

c. Is the point (−4, −3) a solution of that inequality? Yes

2. Write the inequality that describes just the shaded area above the line. $y > x + 1$

3. How would you change the graph to show that the boundary line is not included in the solution region? Change the solid boundary line to a dashed line.

4. Describe the region represented by $y \leq x + 1$. The boundary line and the shaded area below it

5. Write the inequality that describes just the shaded area below the line? $y < x + 1$

6. The points (0, −3) and (1, 2) are in the solution region of which inequality? $y \leq x + 1$

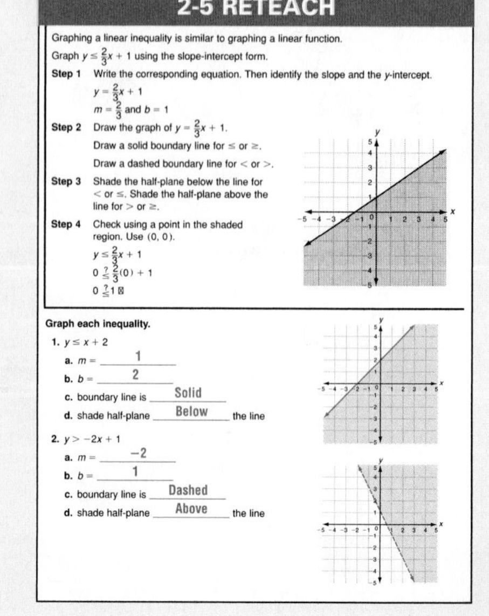

2-5 RETEACH

Graphing a linear inequality is similar to graphing a linear function.

Graph $y \leq \frac{2}{3}x + 1$ using the slope-intercept form.

Step 1 Write the corresponding equation. Then identify the slope and the y-intercept.
$y = \frac{2}{3}x + 1$
$m = \frac{2}{3}$ and $b = 1$

Step 2 Draw the graph of $y = \frac{2}{3}x + 1$.
Draw a solid boundary line for $\leq$ or $\geq$.
Draw a dashed boundary line for $<$ or $>$.

Step 3 Shade the half-plane below the line for $<$ or $\leq$. Shade the half-plane above the line for $>$ or $\geq$.

Step 4 Check using a point in the shaded region. Use (0, 0).
$y \leq \frac{2}{3}x + 1$
$0 \overset{?}{\leq} \frac{2}{3}(0) + 1$
$0 \overset{?}{\leq} 1$ ✓

Graph each inequality.

1. $y \leq x + 2$
a. $m =$ 1
b. $b =$ 2
c. boundary line is Solid
d. shade half-plane Below the line

2. $y > -2x + 1$
a. $m =$ −2
b. $b =$ 1
c. boundary line is Dashed
d. shade half-plane Above the line

47. What points represent the intercepts of the boundary line of the graph of $y \leq 3x - 9$?

Ⓕ (0, 9) and (3, 0) Ⓗ (0, 9) and (−3, 0)
Ⓖ (0, 3) and (−9, 0) Ⓙ (0, −9) and (3, 0)

48. Each dime adds 8 minutes to the time on a parking meter, and each quarter adds 20 minutes. The maximum time is 3 hours. The previous driver left 37 minutes of time. Adding which coins would NOT result in getting the maximum time?

Ⓐ 3 dimes and 6 quarters Ⓒ 8 dimes and 4 quarters
Ⓑ 13 dimes and 2 quarters Ⓓ 5 dimes and 5 quarters

49. **Short Response** Describe a problem situation using inequalities in which it would make sense to have negative *x*- or *y*-values.
Possible answer: a temperature problem

CHALLENGE AND EXTEND

Graph each inequality.

50. $4(4x - 3y) < 5(2 + 3x) - 10y$

51. $\dfrac{4 + 3y - 2x}{6} \geq \dfrac{3x - 2 - 3y}{-4}$

52. The boundary line is below the window. Lower the viewing window or zoom out to view the boundary line.

53a. no; the line has a slope of 500. A vertical line has only an *x*-variable.

52. **What if...?** Suppose when you graph a $y >$ inequality on a graphing calculator, you find that the entire screen is shaded. What does this indicate about the inequality? What might you do to show the graph of the inequality more accurately?

53. The graph of $y = 500(x - 1)$ is shown in the **ZDecimal** window.

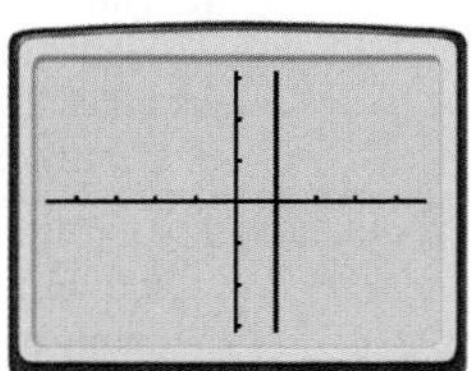

a. Is the line really vertical? Explain.
b. For the graph of $y \leq 500(x - 1)$, which side of the line should be shaded? Justify your answer. The right side; the line has a positive slope, so the shading should be below and to the right of the line, as it would be for $y \leq 2x$.

SPIRAL REVIEW

Use the vertical line test to determine whether each graph represents a function. *(Lesson 1-6)*

54.

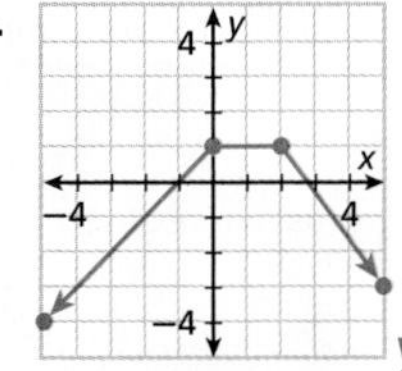

yes

55.

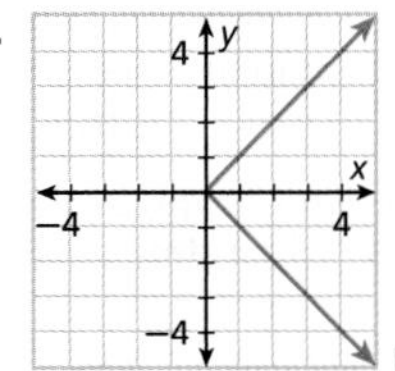

no

56.

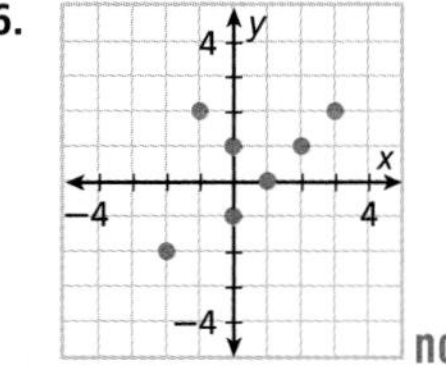

no

Give the coordinates of the translated point when the original point is (−4, 3). *(Lesson 1-8)*

57. horizontal translation of −1 (−5, 3)
58. reflection across the *y*-axis (4, 3)
59. vertical translation of 3 (−4, 6)
60. $(x + 7, y - 5)$ (3, −2)

Write an equation of each line in slope-intercept form. Each line passes through the point (1, −7). *(Lesson 2-4)*

61. passing through (1, 3) $x = 1$
62. parallel to $y = \frac{1}{2}x - 5$ $y = \frac{1}{2}x - \frac{15}{2}$
63. with a slope of 0.25 $y = 0.25x - 7.25$
64. perpendicular to $3x - y = -4$ $y = -\frac{1}{3}x - \frac{20}{3}$

TEST PREP DOCTOR For **Exercise 47,** students who chose **F, G,** or **H** might not understand what it means for a point to be an intercept of a linear equation. Choice **G** might indicate that students are confusing the intercepts.

Journal

Have students list the steps they would follow to sketch the graph of a linear inequality in two variables.

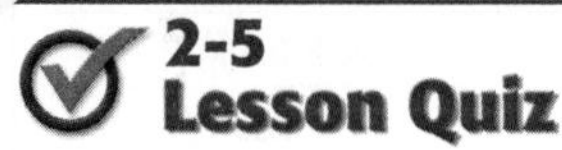

ALTERNATIVE ASSESSMENT

Have students write a linear equation in the slope-intercept form. Then have them write and graph the four different inequalities for which the equation is a boundary line.

Power Presentations with PowerPoint®

2-5 Lesson Quiz

1. Graph $2x - 5y \geq 10$ using intercepts.

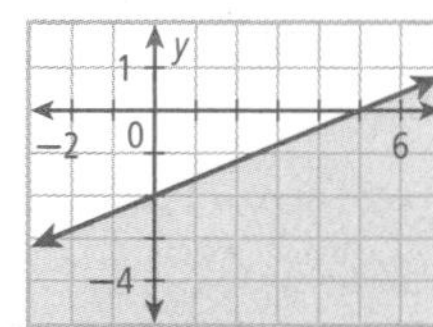

2. Solve $-6y < 18x - 12$ for *y*. Graph the solution.
$y > -3x + 2$

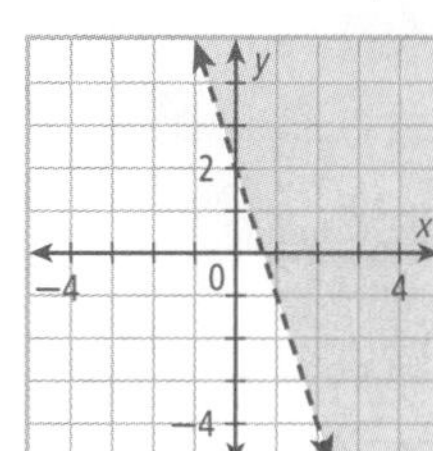

3. Potatoes cost a chef $18 a box, and carrots cost $12 a box. The chef wants to spend no more than $144. Use *x* as the number of boxes of potatoes and *y* as the number of boxes of carrots.
   a. Write an inequality for the number of boxes the chef can buy. $18x + 12y \leq 144$
   b. How many boxes of potatoes can the chef order if she orders 4 boxes of carrots? no more than 5

Also available on transparency

2-5 PROBLEM SOLVING

Mr. and Mrs. Zaragosa are planning a landscape garden for their new house. They have set a budget of $200 for native grasses, at $12 each, and flowering plants, at $8.50 each.

1. Let *n* be the number of native grasses and *p* be the number of flowering plants. Write an inequality for the number of each that they can buy.
$12n + 8.5p \leq 200$
2. Find the intercepts of the boundary line.
n-intercept 16.7
p-intercept 23.5
3. Graph the inequality on the coordinate plane.
4. Define the domain for variables *n* and *p*. $0 < n < 16;\ 0 < p < 23$
5. Should the boundary line be dashed or solid? Why?
Solid, because the total cost could be equal to $200
6. What is the solution region on the graph? How do you know?
The solution region is the area below the line, because they cannot spend any more than $200.
7. Use your graph to determine if they can buy 10 flowering plants and 15 native grasses. How do you know?
No; Possible answer: because the point (10, 15) is not in the shaded region of the graph, so it is not a solution.
8. What is the greatest number of grasses they can they buy if they want to buy at least 5 flowering plants? 13
9. Use your graph to estimate the number of each they could buy if they want the same number of each type of plant. 9 of each type.

Choose the letter for the best answer.

10. What is the greatest number of grasses they can buy if they have already bought 8 flowering plants?
A 8
B 9
C 10
Ⓓ 11

11. What is the greatest number of flowering plants they can buy if they decide to buy a dozen native grasses?
Ⓐ 6
B 7
C 8
D 9

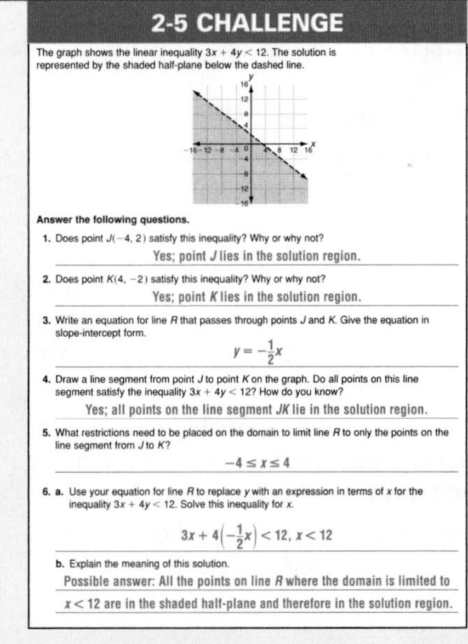

2-5 CHALLENGE

The graph shows the linear inequality $3x + 4y < 12$. The solution is represented by the shaded half-plane below the dashed line.

Answer the following questions.

1. Does point $J(-4, 2)$ satisfy this inequality? Why or why not?
Yes; point *J* lies in the solution region.
2. Does point $K(4, -2)$ satisfy this inequality? Why or why not?
Yes; point *K* lies in the solution region.
3. Write an equation for line *R* that passes through points *J* and *K*. Give the equation in slope-intercept form.
$y = -\frac{1}{2}x$
4. Draw a line segment from point *J* to point *K* on the graph. Do all points on this line segment satisfy the inequality $3x + 4y < 12$? How do you know?
Yes; all points on the line segment *JK* lie in the solution region.
5. What restrictions need to be placed on the domain to limit line *R* to only the points on the line segment from *J* to *K*?
$-4 \leq x \leq 4$
6. a. Use your equation for line *R* to replace *y* with an expression in terms of *x* for the inequality $3x + 4y < 12$. Solve this inequality for *x*.
$3x + 4\left(-\frac{1}{2}x\right) < 12,\ x < 12$
   b. Explain the meaning of this solution.
Possible answer: All the points on line *R* where the domain is limited to $x < 12$ are in the shaded half-plane and therefore in the solution region.

Organizer

Objective: Assess students' ability to apply concepts and skills in Lessons 2-1 through 2-5 in a real-world format.

 Online Edition

Resources

 ***Algebra 2 Assessments***
www.mathtekstoolkit.org

Problem	Text Reference
1	Skills Bank, p. S57
2	Lesson 2-2
3	Lesson 2-3
4	Lesson 2-2, 2-4
5	Lesson 2-5

Answer

5.

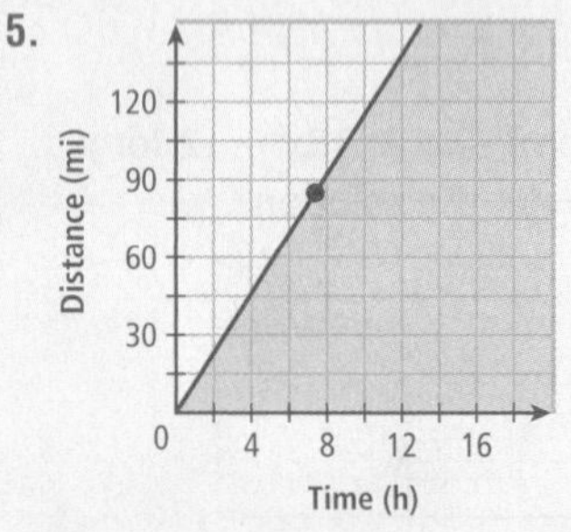

State Resources

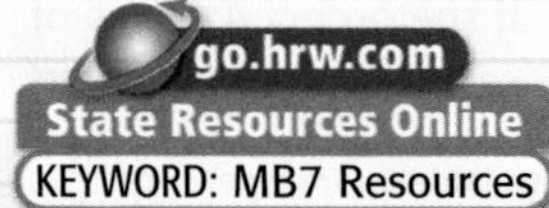

SECTION 2A

Linear Equations and Inequalities

Sailing Away Crossing the Atlantic Ocean in a sailboat is a prestigious feat that many sailors attempt. Some of the speed records for the west-to-east trip from New York to England are shown in the table.

Transatlantic Sailing Records (New York to England)

Yacht	Year	Country	Average Speed (knots)
Atlantic	1905	USA	10.02
Royale II	1986	France	15.47
Jet Services V	1990	France	18.62
PlayStation	2001	USA	25.78

1. The length of the course that each yacht sailed, from the Ambrose Light Tower in New York to Lizard Point in England, is 3364 statute miles. How much longer did the *Atlantic* take to complete the trip than the *PlayStation*? **≈ 178.5 h, or 7.4 days**

3rd (≈ 17.4 knots) 2. Dolphins can swim about 20 statute miles per hour. If a dolphin were racing against each of the yachts in the table, in which place would the dolphin finish?

about 36.7 h 3. Graph the distance in nautical miles that the *PlayStation* could cover over a period from 0 to 48 hours. The sailing distance from New York to Florida is 947 nautical miles. Use your graph to estimate how long it would take the *PlayStation* to make this trip.

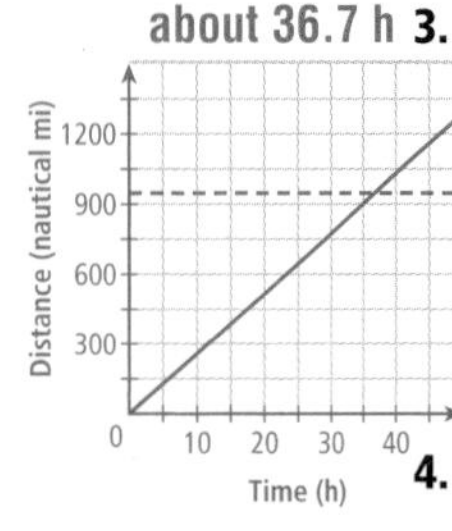

4. In 1980, the *Paul Ricard* broke the *Atlantic's* record for time crossing the Atlantic Ocean. The *Paul Ricard* finished the crossing in 10 days, 5 hours, and 14 minutes. Write a linear equation that describes the distance in nautical miles that the *Paul Ricard* covered as a function of time in hours. **$d \approx 11.9t$**

5. Write and graph an inequality to show the possible distance d in statute miles that the *Atlantic* could cover in t hours. Is the point (7.5, 85) a solution to the inequality? Explain the meaning of this point in the context of the problem. **$d \leq 11.523t$**

yes, $11.523(7.5) \approx 86.4$; (7.5, 85) represents 85 statute mi in 7.5 h.

Unit Conversions

$1 \text{ knot} = \frac{1 \text{ nautical mi}}{1 \text{ h}}$

1 nautical mi = 1.15 statute mi

1 statute mi = 5280 ft

INTERVENTION

Scaffolding Questions

1. If you know a distance in statute miles, would the distance in nautical miles be more or less? Less; 1 nautical mile is about 1.15 statute miles.
2. How do knots differ from miles per hour? Possible answer: Knots is nautical miles per hour while miles per hour is statute miles per hour.
3. In the graph of the possible distances a boat can travel, what does the boundary line represent? the boat's top speed
4. How do you convert days, hours, and minutes to hours? $24(\text{days}) + \text{hours} + \frac{\text{minutes}}{60}$
5. If you missed the fact that the problem uses statute miles and you used nautical miles to solve, would you get the correct answer? no; $10.02(7.5) = 75.15$ nautical miles

Extension

A nautical mile is exactly 6,076.11549 feet. What is the percent error when using 1.15 statute miles for a measurement? At what distance would there be an error of 1 statute mile?

$6076.11549 - 1.15(5280) = 4.11549$ ft

$\frac{4.11549}{6076.11549} \approx 0.000677 \approx 0.0677\%$ error

$\frac{5280}{4.11549} \approx 1282.96$ mi

CHAPTER 2

SECTION 2A

Quiz for Lessons 2-1 Through 2-5

2-1 Solving Linear Equations and Inequalities

Solve.

1. $15 + 8x = 3x$ $x = -3$
2. $\frac{3}{2}(5x + 7) = 16$ $x = \frac{11}{15}$
3. $12 - 15x = 25 - 5x$ $x = -1.3$
4. $3(x + 5) - 8(x - 3) = 20$ $x = 3.8$

Solve and graph.

5. $45 \geq -25 + 10x$ $x \leq 7$
6. $12 - 4x < 24$ $x > -3$
7. $4(9 - 2x) \leq 3(4x + 2)$ $x \geq \frac{3}{2}$
8. $5x - 4(2x + 6) \geq 15$ $x \leq -13$
9. Marie has \$55 in her bank account, and she would like to buy a video game system that costs \$395. Marie saves \$6 for each hour she works. How many hours must Marie work to have enough money to buy the video game system? **57 h**

2-2 Proportional Reasoning

Solve each proportion.

10. $\frac{x}{12} = \frac{8}{3}$ $x = 32$
11. $\frac{3}{5} = \frac{4x}{9}$ $x = \frac{27}{20}$
12. $\frac{5}{-x} = \frac{2.5}{8}$ $x = -16$
13. $\frac{5}{9} = \frac{4}{2x - 3}$ $x = 5.1$
14. A building casts a 24-foot shadow at the same time that a 6-foot-tall person casts an 8-foot shadow. How tall is the building? **18 ft**

2-3 Graphing Linear Functions

Find the intercepts and graph each line.

15. $2x + 3y = 18$ $(9, 0); (0, 6)$
16. $5x - 3y = -15$ $(-3, 0); (0, 5)$
17. $\frac{1}{2}x + 2y = 6$ $(12, 0); (0, 3)$
18. $-x - y = \frac{7}{2}$ $\left(-\frac{7}{2}, 0\right); \left(0, -\frac{7}{2}\right)$

Write each function in slope-intercept form. Then graph the function.

19. $y - 3x = 1$ $y = 3x + 1$
20. $4x + 2y = 8$ $y = -2x + 4$
21. $3x - 10 - 5y = 0$ $y = \frac{3}{5}x - 2$
22. $5 - x = \frac{y}{3}$ $y = -3x + 15$

2-4 Writing Linear Functions

Write an equation in slope-intercept form for each line.

23. through $(3, 12)$ and $(6, 27)$ $y = 5x - 3$
24. slope $\frac{3}{4}$ and through $(4, -6)$ $y = \frac{3}{4}x - 9$
25. parallel to $y = \frac{3}{2}x - 6$ and through $(-6, 2)$ $y = \frac{3}{2}x + 11$
26. perpendicular to $5x + 2y = 8$ and through $(5, 3)$ $y = \frac{2}{5}x + 1$

2-5 Linear Inequalities in Two Variables

Solve for y in each inequality. Then graph.

27. $y - 1 \leq 5$ $y \leq 6$
28. $2x + 5y > 10$ $y > -\frac{2}{5}x + 2$
29. $3x - 4y > 5x + 12$ $y < -\frac{1}{2}x - 3$
30. $3(2x - 1) + y > 6x - 4$ $y > -1$
31. Dorothy has \$30 to spend on holiday cards. Large cards cost \$2.50 each, and small cards cost \$1.50 each. Write and graph an inequality for the number of cards Dorothy can purchase. $2.50L + 1.50S \leq 30$

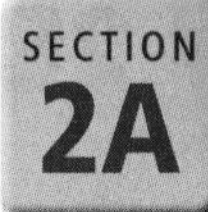

READY TO GO ON? SECTION 2A

Organizer

Objective: Assess students' mastery of concepts and skills in Lessons 2-1 through 2-5.

Resources

 ***Assessment Resources***
Section 2A Quiz

Test & Practice Generator
One-Stop Planner®

INTERVENTION

Resources

 ***Ready to Go On? Intervention and Enrichment* Worksheets**

 ***Ready to Go On?* CD-ROM**

 ***Ready to Go On?* Online**

my.hrw.com

Answers

15–22, 27–31. For graphs, see p. A18.

READY TO GO ON?
Diagnose and Prescribe

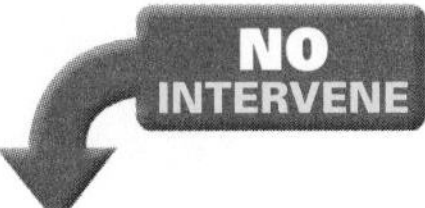

NO INTERVENE

Ready to Go On? Intervention	*Ready to Go On? Intervention,* Section 2A: Worksheets	CD-ROM	Online
Lesson 2-1	2-1 Intervention	Activity 2-1	Diagnose and Prescribe Online
Lesson 2-2	2-2 Intervention	Activity 2-2	
Lesson 2-3	2-3 Intervention	Activity 2-3	
Lesson 2-4	2-4 Intervention	Activity 2-4	
Lesson 2-5	2-5 Intervention	Activity 2-5	

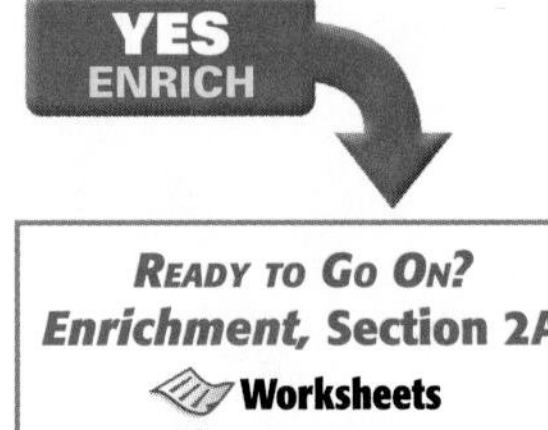

YES ENRICH

Ready to Go On? Enrichment, Section 2A
Worksheets
CD-ROM
Online

SECTION
2B Applying Linear Functions

One-Minute Section Planner

Lesson	Lab Resources	Materials
Lesson 2-6 Transforming Linear Functions • Transform linear functions. • Solve problems involving linear transformations. ☑ SAT-10 ☑ NAEP ☑ ACT ☑ SAT ☑ SAT Subject Tests		**Required** graphing calculator **Optional** copy of Gettysburg address
Lesson 2-7 Curve Fitting with Linear Models • Fit scatter plot data using linear models with and without technology. • Use linear models to make predictions. ☑ SAT-10 ☑ NAEP ☑ ACT ☑ SAT ☑ SAT Subject Tests	***Algebra Lab Activities*** 2-7 Algebra Lab ***Technology Lab Activities*** 2-7 Technology Lab	**Required** graphing calculator **Optional** dry spaghetti CBL or CBR with motion detector
Lesson 2-8 Solving Absolute-Value Equations and Inequalities • Solve compound inequalities • Write and solve absolute-value equations and inequalities. ☑ SAT-10 ☐ NAEP ☑ ACT ☑ SAT ☑ SAT Subject Tests		**Optional** number cubes (MK)
2-9 Technology Lab Solving Absolute Value Equations • Use a graphing calculator to solve absolute-value equations. ☑ SAT-10 ☐ NAEP ☐ ACT ☑ SAT ☑ SAT Subject Tests	***Technology Lab Activities*** 2-9 Lab Recording Sheet	**Required** graphing calculator
Lesson 2-9 Absolute-Value Functions • Graph and transform absolute-value functions. ☑ SAT-10 ☐ NAEP ☑ ACT ☑ SAT ☐ SAT Subject Tests		**Optional** graphing calculator

MK = *Manipulatives Kit*

Section Overview

Transformations of Linear Functions

Lesson 2-6

Transforming linear functions allows students to compare different but related functions at once on the same coordinate plane.

Let $g(x)$ be a vertical shift of $f(x) = x$ 4 units up followed by a horizontal stretch by a factor of 3.

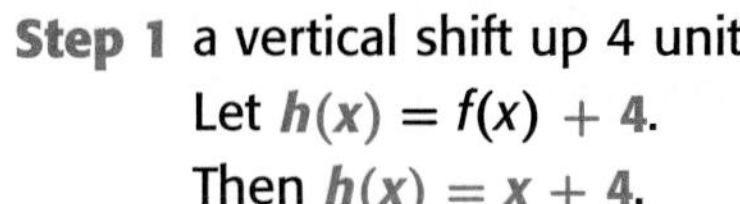

Step 1 a vertical shift up 4 units
Let $h(x) = f(x) + 4$.
Then $h(x) = x + 4$.

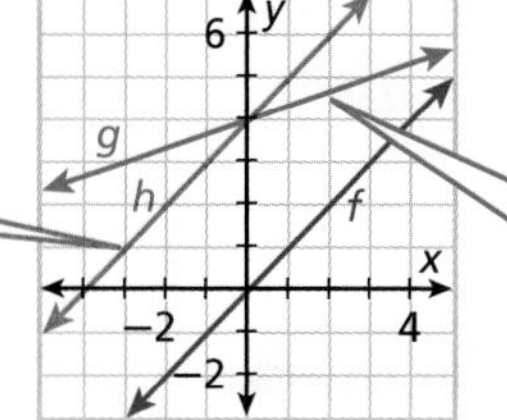

Step 2 a horizontal stretch by a factor of 3
Let $g(x) = h\left(\frac{1}{3}\right)x$.
Then $g(x) = \frac{1}{3}x + 4$.

Curve Fitting with Linear Models

Lesson 2-7

Linear regression is used to find a linear model that describes a general trend in real-world data.

Age (yr)	0	1	4	8	12	16	18
Height (cm)	70	79	101	127	149	170	176

The points show a strong linear relationship.

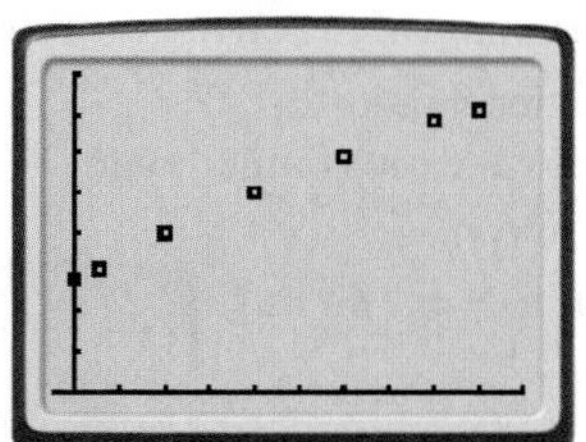

Perform a linear regression.

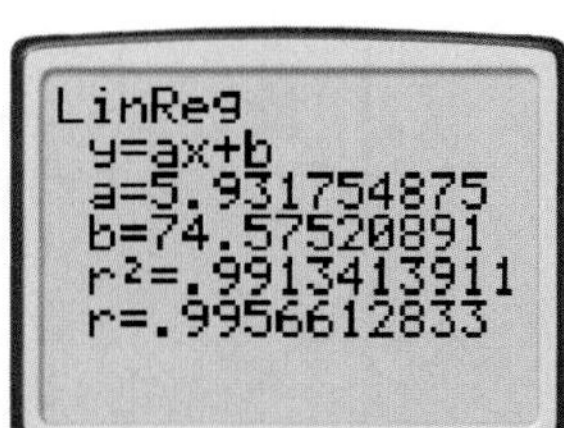

The linear regression function is $y \approx 5.932x + 74.575$.

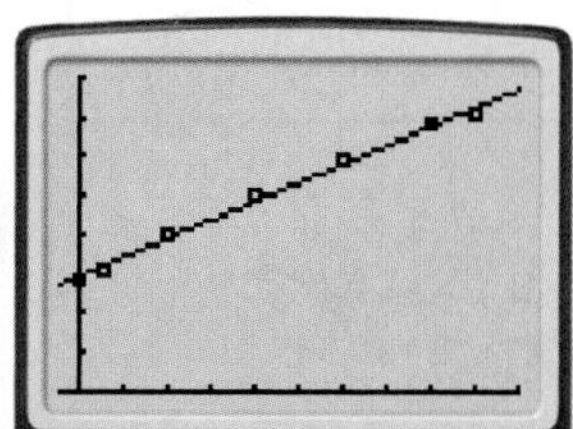

Absolute-Value Functions, Equations, and Inequalities

Lessons 2-8, 2-9

Absolute-value equations and inequalities are often used to model real-world situations involving distance or tolerance levels.

To solve an absolute-value inequality, use the definition of *absolute value* to consider the two possible cases.

Absolute Value $|x| = \begin{cases} x & \text{if } x \geq 0 \\ -x & \text{if } x < 0 \end{cases}$

Solve $|3x + 2| > 8$.

Case 1: if $3x + 2 \geq 0$

$$3x + 2 > 8$$
$$3x > 6$$
$$x > 2$$

Case 2: if $3x + 2 < 0$

$$3x + 2 < -8$$
$$3x < -10$$
$$x < -\frac{10}{3}$$

Solution: $x < -\frac{10}{3}$ or $x > 2$

To translate $f(x) = |x|$ 4 units right, let $g(x) = f(x - 4)$, so $g(x) = |x - 4|$.

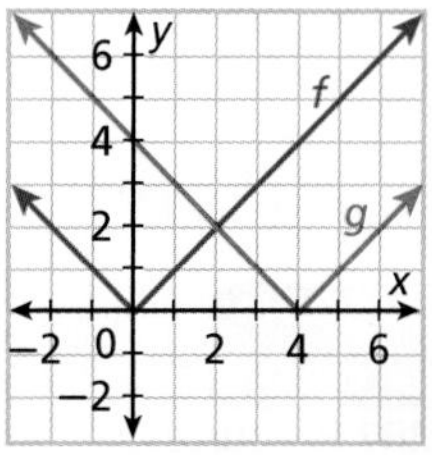

2-6 Organizer

Pacing: Traditional 1 day
Block $\frac{1}{2}$ day

Objectives: Transform linear functions.

Solve problems involving linear transformations.

Online Edition
Tutorial Videos, TechKeys

Countdown to Testing Week 4

Power Presentations with PowerPoint®

Warm Up

Give the coordinates of each transformation of (2, −3).

1. horizontal translation of 5
2. vertical translation of −1
3. reflection across the *x*-axis
4. reflection across the *y*-axis

1. (7, −3) **2.** (2, −4)
3. (2, 3) **4.** (−2, −3)

Evaluate *f*(−2) and *f*(1.5).

5. $f(x) = 3(x + 5) - 1$ 8; 18.5
6. $f(x) = x^2 + 4x$ −4; 8.25

Also available on transparency

Teacher: Why are all your transformations in French?

Student: They're translations.

State Resources

State Resources Online
KEYWORD: MB7 Resources

2-6 Transforming Linear Functions

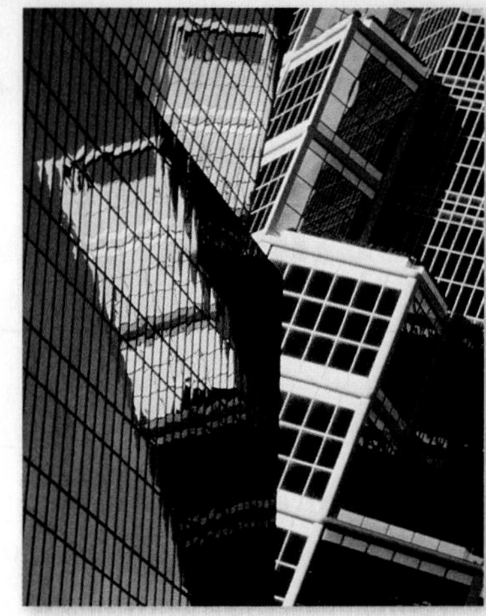

IN **A2.1.2** Use and interpret function notation, including evaluation of functions represented by tables, graphs, words, equations or a set of ordered pairs.

Objectives
Transform linear functions.

Solve problems involving linear transformations.

Why learn this?
Transformations allow you to visualize and compare many different functions at once.

In Lesson 1-8, you learned to transform functions by transforming each point. Transformations can also be expressed by using function notation.

Know it! Note

Helpful Hint

To remember the difference between vertical and horizontal translations, think: "Add to *y*, go high." "Add to *x*, go left."

Translations and Reflections

Translations

Horizontal Shift of $\|h\|$ Units	**Vertical Shift of $\|k\|$ Units**
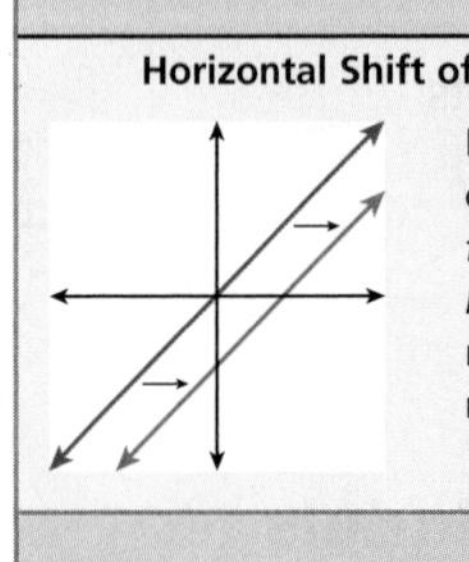 Input value changes. $f(x) \to f(x - h)$ $h > 0$ moves right $h < 0$ moves left	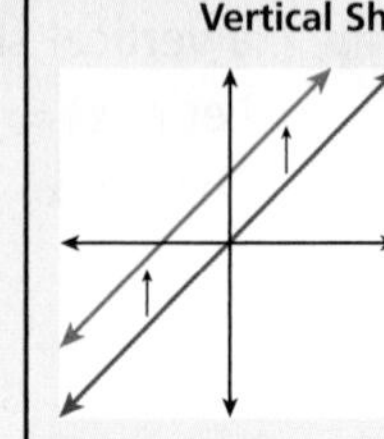 Output value changes. $f(x) \to f(x) + k$ $k > 0$ moves up $k < 0$ moves down

Reflections

Reflection Across *y*-axis	**Reflection Across *x*-axis**
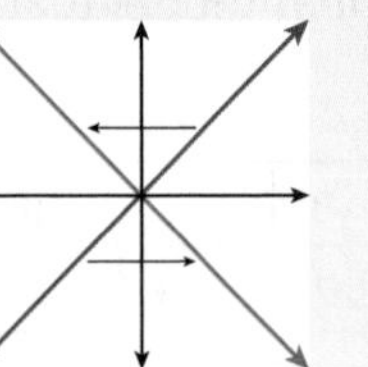 Input value changes. $f(x) \to f(-x)$ The lines are symmetric about the *y*-axis.	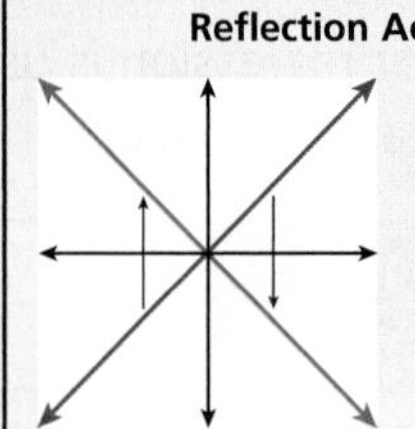 Output value changes. $f(x) \to -f(x)$ The lines are symmetric about the *x*-axis.

EXAMPLE 1 Translating and Reflecting Linear Functions

Let $g(x)$ be the indicated transformation of $f(x)$. Write the rule for $g(x)$.

A $f(x) = 2x + 3$; vertical translation 4 units up

Translating $f(x)$ 4 units up adds 4 to each output value.

$g(x) = f(x) + 4$ *Add 4 to f(x).*

$g(x) = (2x + 3) + 4$ *Substitute 2x + 3 for f(x).*

$g(x) = 2x + 7$ *Simplify.*

Check Graph $f(x)$ and $g(x)$ on a graphing calculator. The slopes are the same, but the *y*-intercept has moved 4 units up from 3 to 7. ✔

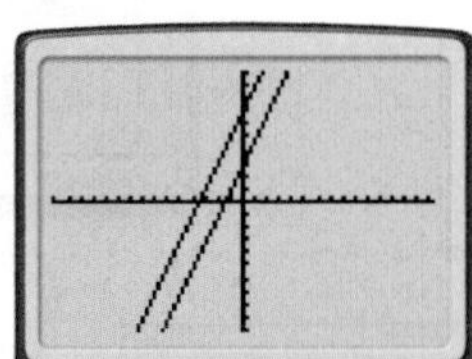

1 Introduce

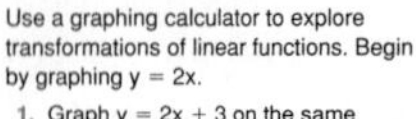

EXPLORATION

2-6 Transforming Linear Functions

Use a graphing calculator to explore transformations of linear functions. Begin by graphing y = 2x.

1. Graph y = 2x + 3 on the same coordinate plane as y = 2x. How does the graph of this function compare to that of y = 2x?
2. Graph y = 2x − 2 on the same coordinate plane as y = 2x. How does the graph of this function compare to that of y = 2x?
3. Graph y = 2(x − 3) on the same coordinate plane as y = 2x. How does the graph of this function compare to that of y = 2x?
4. Graph y = 2(x + 2) on the same coordinate plane as y = 2x. How does the graph of this function compare to that of y = 2x?

THINK AND DISCUSS

5. **Describe** how the graph of y = −4x + k is related to the graph of y = −4x.
6. **Explain** how you can use what you discovered to quickly graph y = 3(x − 5).

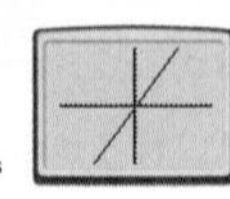

Motivate

Review transformations. Draw a plane figure, such as a triangle. Translate the figure horizontally and vertically. Have students describe the transformation. Then describe a translation and have a volunteer draw the transformation. Repeat with reflections across the *x*-axis and the *y*-axis. Encourage students to discover or recall how the coordinates of an ordered pair change with a given transformation.

Explorations and answers are provided in the *Explorations* binder.

Let $g(x)$ be the indicated transformation of $f(x)$. Write the rule for $g(x)$.

B linear function defined in the table; reflection across y-axis

x	$f(x)$
−1	0
0	2
1	4

Step 1 Write the rule for $f(x)$ in slope-intercept form.

The y-intercept is 2. *The table contains (0, 2).*

Find the slope:

$m = \frac{2-0}{0-(-1)} = \frac{2}{1} = 2$ *Use (−1, 0) and (0, 2).*

$y = mx + b$ *Slope-intercept form*

$y = 2x + 2$ *Substitute 2 for m and 2 for b.*

$f(x) = 2x + 2$ *Replace y with f(x).*

Step 2 Write the rule for $g(x)$. Reflecting $f(x)$ across the y-axis replaces each x with $-x$.

$g(x) = 2(-x) + 2$ *$g(x) = f(-x)$*

$g(x) = -2x + 2$

Check Graph $f(x)$ and $g(x)$ on a graphing calculator. The graphs are symmetric about the y-axis. ✔

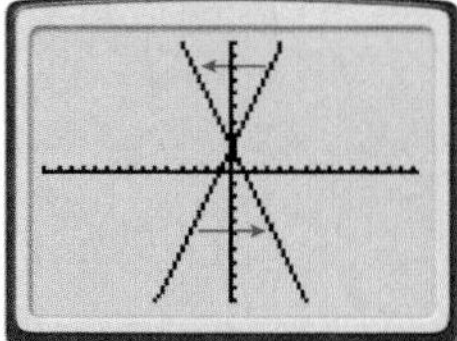

Let $g(x)$ be the indicated transformation of $f(x)$. Write the rule for $g(x)$.

1a. $f(x) = 3x + 1$; translation 2 units right $g(x) = 3(x - 2) + 1$

1b. linear function defined in the table; a reflection across the x-axis

x	−1	0	1
y	1	2	3

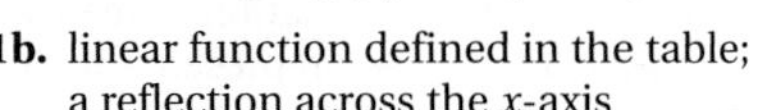

$g(x) = -(x + 2)$

Stretches and compressions change the slope of a linear function. If the line becomes steeper, the function has been stretched vertically or compressed horizontally. If the line becomes flatter, the function has been compressed vertically or stretched horizontally.

Stretches and Compressions

Horizontal	Vertical
Horizontal Stretch/Compression by a Factor of b	**Vertical Stretch/Compression by a Factor of a**
Input value changes. $f(x) \to f\left(\frac{1}{b}x\right)$	Output value changes. $f(x) \to a \cdot f(x)$
$b > 1$ stretches away from the y-axis. $0 < \lvert b \rvert < 1$ compresses toward the y-axis.	$a > 1$ stretches away from the x-axis. $0 < \lvert a \rvert < 1$ compresses toward the x-axis.

Power Presentations with PowerPoint®

Additional Examples

Example 1

Let $g(x)$ be the indicated transformation of $f(x)$. Write the rule for $g(x)$.

A. $f(x) = x - 2$, horizontal translation right 3 units

$g(x) = x - 5$

B. linear function defined in the table; reflection across x-axis

x	−2	0	2
$f(x)$	0	1	2

$g(x) = -\frac{1}{2}x - 1$

Also available on transparency

INTERVENTION

Questioning Strategies

EXAMPLE 1

- Does the slope change when a linear function is translated?
- How does a reflection change the function rule?

Teaching Tip **Multiple Representations** Introduce students to *function notation* to record the transformed function. For a horizontal shift, $g(x) = f(x - h)$. For a vertical shift, $g(x) = f(x) + k$. For a reflection across the y-axis, $g(x) = f(-x)$, and for a reflection across the x-axis, $g(x) = -f(x)$. For a horizontal stretch or compression, $g(x) = f\left(\frac{1}{b}x\right)$, and for a vertical stretch or compression, $g(x) = a \cdot f(x)$.

2 Teach

Guided Instruction

Encourage students to compare and contrast horizontal and vertical shifts in translations of linear functions. Repeat with reflections across the axes and with transformations that stretch and compress. Have students note both the similarities and the differences. Elicit that each transformation is a rule that tells how the parent linear function is changed.

Reaching All Learners

Through Kinesthetic Experience

Have students model the translations and reflections using a pencil to represent a linear function on a coordinate plane. Have students move the pencil up and down, right and left to see how the y-intercept changes in vertical and horizontal shifts while the slope remains the same. Students can use a pair of pencils to model reflections.

Inclusion In **Example 3,** students might simplify complex fractions, such as $\frac{1}{\frac{1}{a}}$, incorrectly. Remind students to use the definition of the fraction bar as division to help simplify the fraction: $\frac{1}{\frac{1}{a}} = 1 \div \frac{1}{a} = 1 \times a = a$.

Power Presentations with PowerPoint®

Additional Examples

Example 2

Let $g(x)$ be a horizontal compression of $f(x) = -x + 4$ by a factor of $\frac{1}{2}$. Write the rule for $g(x)$ and graph the function.

$g(x) = -2x + 4$

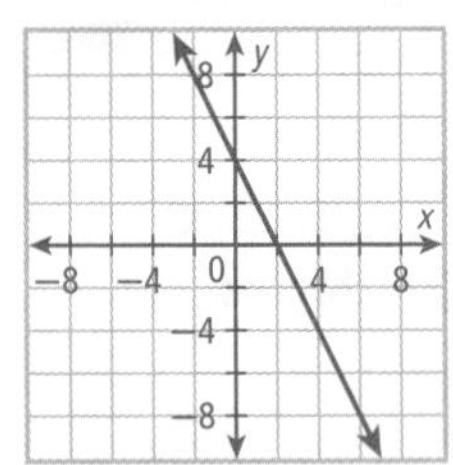

Example 3

Let $g(x)$ be a horizontal shift of $f(x) = 3x$ left 6 units followed by a horizontal stretch by a factor of 4. Write the rule for $g(x)$.

$g(x) = \frac{3}{4}x + 18$

Also available on transparency

INTERVENTION
Questioning Strategies

EXAMPLE 2

- How does a stretch or compression affect the function? How does it affect the graph?

EXAMPLE 3

- Why is another function, $h(x)$, introduced in **Example 3**?

EXAMPLE 2 Stretching and Compressing Linear Functions

Let $g(x)$ be a horizontal compression of $f(x) = 2x - 1$ by a factor of $\frac{1}{3}$. Write the rule for $g(x)$, and graph the function.

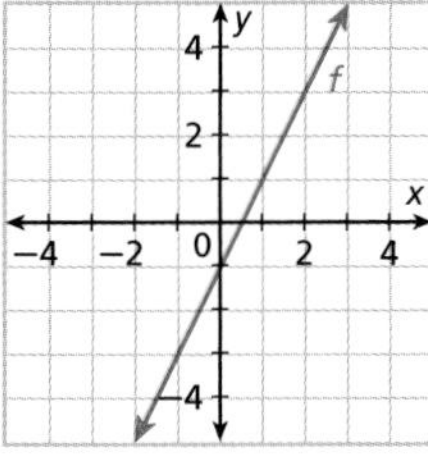

Horizontally compressing $f(x)$ by a factor of $\frac{1}{3}$ replaces each x with $\frac{1}{b}x$ where $b = \frac{1}{3}$.

$g(x) = 2\left(\frac{1}{b}\right)x - 1$ — *For horizontal compression, use $\frac{1}{b}$.*

$= 2\left(\frac{1}{\frac{1}{3}}\right)x - 1$ — *Substitute $\frac{1}{3}$ for b.*

$= 2(3x) - 1$ — *Replace x with 3x.*

$g(x) = 6x - 1$ — *Simplify.*

Check Graph both functions on the same coordinate plane. The graph of $g(x)$ is steeper than $f(x)$, which indicates that $g(x)$ has been horizontally compressed from $f(x)$, or pushed toward the y-axis.

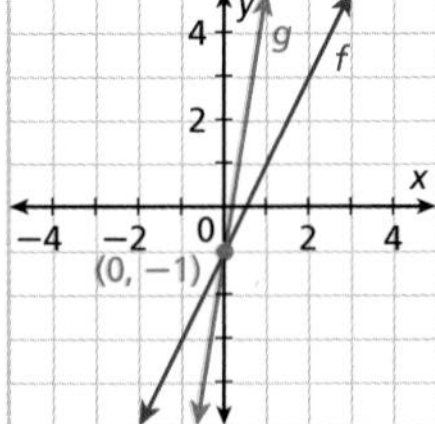

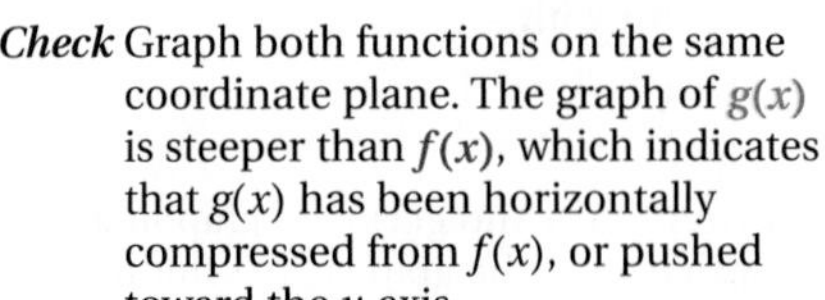

Helpful Hint

These don't change!
- y-intercepts in a horizontal stretch or compression
- x-intercepts in a vertical stretch or compression

CHECK IT OUT! **2.** Let $g(x)$ be a vertical compression of $f(x) = 3x + 2$ by a factor of $\frac{1}{4}$. Write the rule for $g(x)$. $g(x) = \frac{1}{4}(3x + 2)$

Some linear functions involve more than one transformation. Combine transformations by applying individual transformations one at a time in the order in which they are given.

For multiple transformations, create a temporary function—such as $h(x)$ in Example 3 below—to represent the first transformation, and then transform it to find the combined transformation.

EXAMPLE 3 Combining Transformations of Linear Functions

Let $g(x)$ be a vertical shift of $f(x) = x$ down 2 units followed by a vertical stretch by a factor of 5. Write the rule for $g(x)$.

Step 1 First perform the translation.

Translating $f(x) = x$ down 2 units subtracts 2 from the function. You can use $h(x)$ to represent the translated function.

$h(x) = f(x) - 2$ — *Subtract 2 from the function.*

$h(x) = x - 2$ — *Substitute x for f(x).*

Step 2 Then perform the stretch.

Stretching $h(x)$ vertically by a factor of 5 multiplies the function by 5.

$g(x) = 5 \cdot h(x)$ — *Multiply the function by 5.*

$g(x) = 5(x - 2)$ — *Because h(x) = x − 2, substitute x − 2 for h(x).*

$g(x) = 5x - 10$ — *Simplify.*

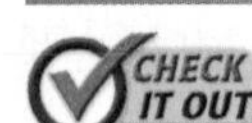

CHECK IT OUT! **3.** Let $g(x)$ be a vertical compression of $f(x) = x$ by a factor of $\frac{1}{2}$ followed by a horizontal shift 8 units left. Write the rule for $g(x)$.

$g(x) = \frac{1}{2}(x + 8)$

EXAMPLE 4 Fund-raising Application

The Dance Club is selling beaded purses as a fund-raiser. The function $R(n) = 12.5n$ represents the club's revenue in dollars where n is the number of purses sold.

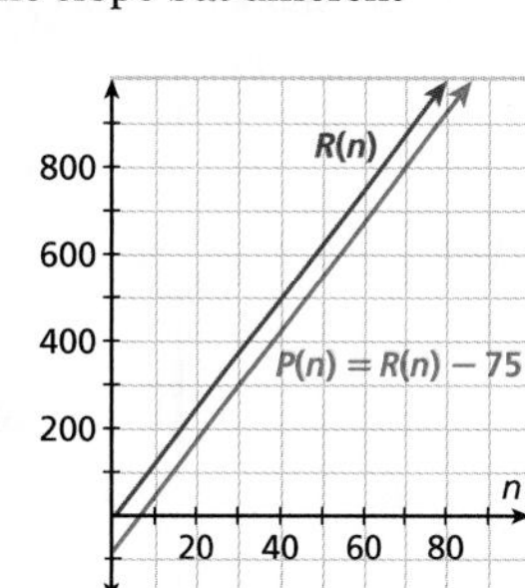

a. The club paid \$75 for the materials needed to make the purses. Write a new function $P(n)$ for the club's profit.

The initial costs must be subtracted from the revenue.

$R(n) = 12.5n$ *Original function*

$P(n) = 12.5n - 75$ *Subtract the expenses.*

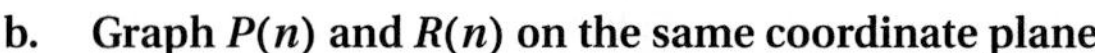

b. Graph $P(n)$ and $R(n)$ on the same coordinate plane.

Graph both functions. The lines have the same slope but different y-intercepts.

Note that the profit can be negative but the number of purses sold cannot be less than 0.

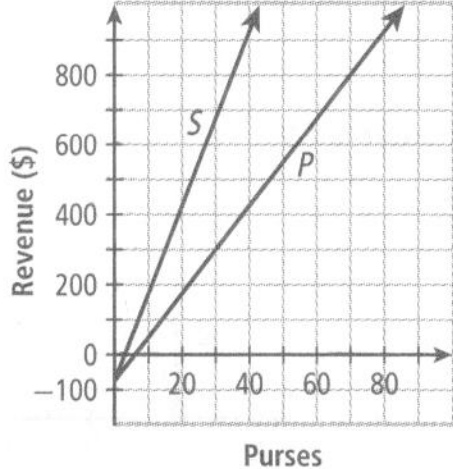

c. Describe the transformation(s) that have been applied.

The graphs indicate that $P(n)$ is a translation of $R(n)$. Because 75 was subtracted, $P(n) = R(n) - 75$. This indicates a vertical shift 75 units down.

CHECK IT OUT! **4. What if...?** The club members decided to double the price of each purse.

a. Write a new profit function $S(n)$ for the club. $S(n) = 25n - 75$

b. Graph $S(n)$ and $P(n)$ on the same coordinate plane.

c. Describe the transformation(s) that have been applied.

horizontal compression by a factor of $\frac{1}{2}$

THINK AND DISCUSS

1. Identify the horizontal translation that would have the same effect on the graph of $f(x) = x$ as a vertical translation of 6 units.
2. Give an example of two different transformations of $f(x) = 2x$ that would result in $g(x) = 2x - 6$.
3. Describe the transformation that would cause all of the function values to double.
4. **GET ORGANIZED** Copy and complete the graphic organizer. In each box, give an example of the indicated transformation of the parent function $f(x) = x$. Include an equation and a graph.

Know it! Note

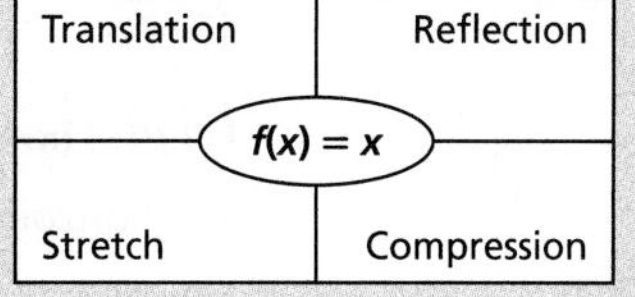

COMMON ERROR ALERT

Students might confuse directions in horizontal translations. Remind them that $f(x-3)$ is in the form $f(x-h)$, the value of h is positive, and the shift is to the right.

Power Presentations with PowerPoint®

Additional Examples

Example 4

The golf team is selling T-shirts as a fund-raiser. The function $R(n) = 7.5n$ represents the team's revenue in dollars, and n is the number of T-shirts sold.

a. The team paid \$60 for the T-shirts. Write a new function $P(n)$ for the team's profit.

$P(n) = 7.5n - 60$

b. Graph both $P(n)$ and $R(n)$ on the same coordinate plane.

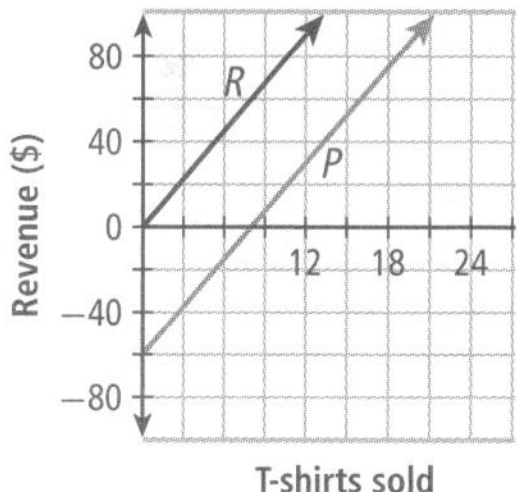

c. Describe the transformation(s) that have been applied.

translation 60 units down

Also available on transparency

INTERVENTION

Questioning Strategies

EXAMPLE 4

- How does graphing the parent function and its transformation help identify the transformation?

3 Close

Summarize

Ask students to explain when input and output values change in translations, reflections, and transformations that stretch and compress. input values: horizontal translations, reflections across the y-axis, stretches/compressions; output values: vertical translations, reflections across the x-axis, stretches/compressions

ONGOING ASSESSMENT and INTERVENTION

***Diagnose Before* the Lesson**
2-6 Warm Up, TE p. 134

***Monitor During* the Lesson**
Check It Out! Exercises, SE pp. 135–137
Questioning Strategies, TE pp. 135–137

***Assess After* the Lesson**
2-6 Lesson Quiz, TE p. 140
Alternative Assessment, TE p. 140

Answers to *Think and Discuss*

1. translation 6 units left
2. vertical translation 6 units down or horizontal translation 3 units right
3. vertical stretch by a factor of 2
4. See p. A3.

2-6 Exercises

Assignment Guide

Assign *Guided Practice* exercises as necessary.

If you finished Examples **1–2**
Basic 8–12, 17
Average 8–12, 16–17
Advanced 8–12, 16–18

If you finished Examples **1–4**
Basic 8–17, 22–27, 31–39
Average 8–19, 21–28, 31–39
Advanced 8–15, 18–39

Homework Quick Check
Quickly check key concepts.
Exercises: 8, 12, 14, 15, 22

Answers

5. $g(x) = \frac{2}{3}x - 6$

6. $g(x) = \frac{2}{3}x - 4$

7b.

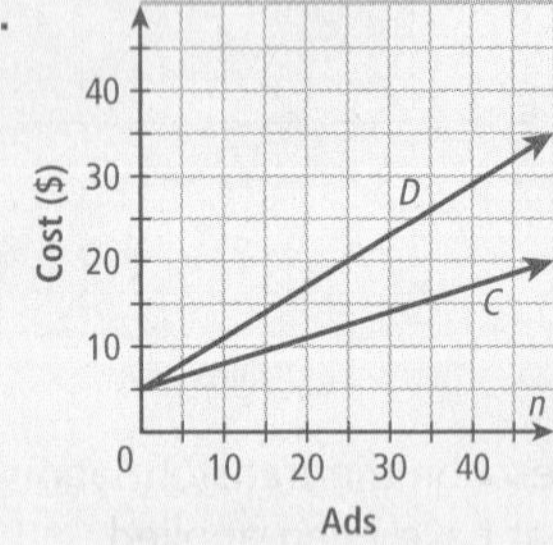

15b.

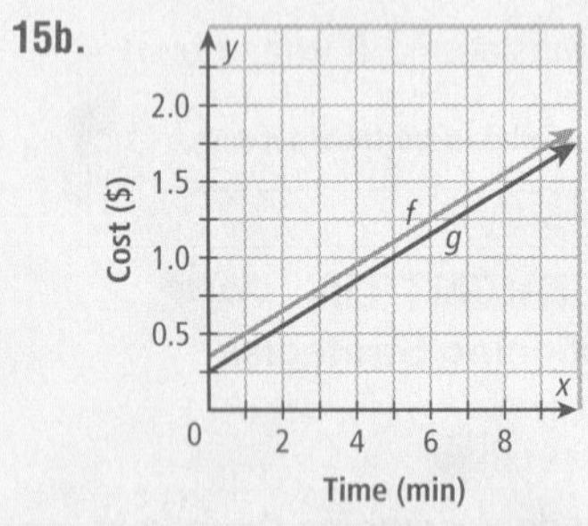

State Resources

2-6 Exercises

go.hrw.com
Homework Help Online
KEYWORD: MB7 2-6
Parent Resources Online
KEYWORD: MB7 Parent

GUIDED PRACTICE

1. $g(x) = -\frac{3}{2}x + 2$

SEE EXAMPLE 1 p. 134

Let $g(x)$ be the indicated transformation of $f(x)$. Write the rule for $g(x)$.

1. linear function defined by the table; vertical translation 1.5 units up

x	−2	−1	0
$f(x)$	3.5	2	0.5

SEE EXAMPLE 2 p. 136

2. $f(x) = -x + 5$; horizontal translation 2 units left $g(x) = -(x + 2) + 5 = -x + 3$
3. $f(x) = \frac{1}{3}x - 2$; vertical stretch by a factor of 3 $g(x) = 3\left(\frac{1}{3}x - 2\right) = x - 6$
4. $f(x) = -2x + 0.5$; horizontal stretch by a factor of $\frac{4}{3}$. $g(x) = -2\left(\frac{3}{4}x\right) + 0.5$

SEE EXAMPLE 3 p. 136

Let $g(x)$ be the indicated combined transformation of $f(x) = x$. Write the rule for $g(x)$.

5. vertical compression by a factor of $\frac{2}{3}$ followed by a vertical shift 6 units down
6. horizontal shift right 4 units followed by a horizontal stretch by a factor of $\frac{3}{2}$

SEE EXAMPLE 4 p. 137

7. **Advertising** An electronics company is changing its Internet ad from a banner ad to a pop-up ad. The cost of the banner ad in dollars is represented by $C(n) = 0.30n + 5.00$ where n is the average number of hits per hour. The cost of the pop-up ad will double the cost per hit. $D(n) = 0.60n + 5.00$
   a. Write a new cost function $D(n)$ for the ads.
   b. Graph $C(n)$ and $D(n)$ on the same coordinate plane.
   c. Describe the transformation(s) that have been applied.
   horizontal compression by a factor of $\frac{1}{2}$

PRACTICE AND PROBLEM SOLVING

Independent Practice	
For Exercises	See Example
8–9	1
10–12	2
13–14	3
15	4

Extra Practice
Skills Practice p. S7
Application Practice p. S33

Let $g(x)$ be the indicated transformation of $f(x)$. Write the rule for $g(x)$.

8.

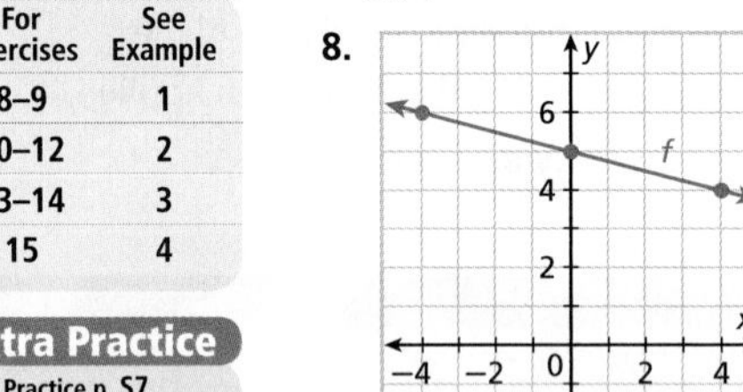

Reflection across the x-axis $g(x) = \frac{1}{4}x - 5$

9.

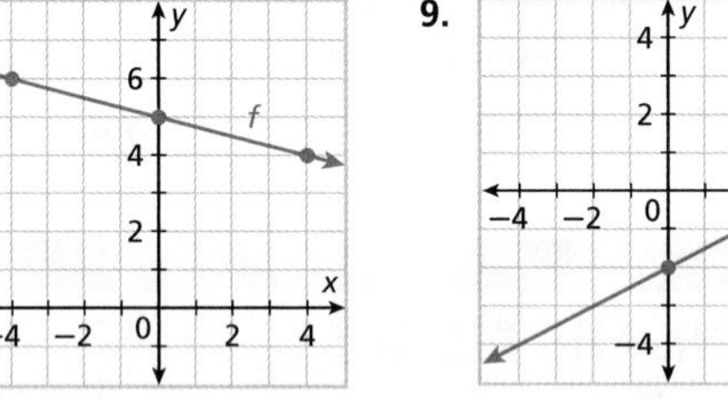

Vertical translation 2 units down $g(x) = \frac{1}{2}x - 4$

10.

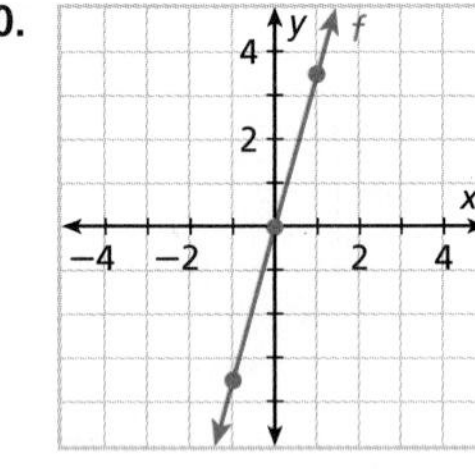

Horizontal compression by a factor of 0.5 $g(x) = 7x$

11. linear function defined by the table; vertical stretch by a factor of 1.2 units $g(x) = 1.2(-0.5x + 0.5)$

x	1	5	9
$f(x)$	0	−2	−4

12. $f(x) = -3x + 7$; vertical compression by a factor of $\frac{3}{4}$ $g(x) = \frac{3}{4}(-3x + 7)$

Let $g(x)$ be the indicated combined transformation of $f(x) = x$. Write the rule for $g(x)$.

13. horizontal stretch by a factor of 2.75 followed by a horizontal shift 1 unit left
14. vertical shift 6 units down followed by a vertical compression by a factor of $\frac{2}{3}$

13. $g(x) = \frac{1}{2.75}(x + 1)$

14. $g(x) = \frac{2}{3}(x - 6)$

2-6 READING STRATEGIES

You can shift the graph of a linear function up or down and right or left. These transformations are called translations.

Transformation	Example	Result
To translate the function **up**, add a constant >0 to the function.	$f(x) = 3x$ $f(x) = 3x + 2$	When $x = 0$ point (0, 0) becomes (0, 2).
To translate the function **down**, subtract a constant >0 from the function.	$f(x) = 3x$ $f(x) = 3x - 1$	When $x = 0$ point (0, 0) becomes (0, −1).

1. How does the graph of $f(x) = 3x$ change when you add 2 to the function?
   The line is shifted up 2 units.
2. How does the graph of $f(x) = 3x$ change when you subtract 1 from the function?
   The line is shifted down 1 unit.
3. Do the graphs of $f(x) = 3x + 2$ and $f(x) = 3x - 1$ intersect? Explain why or why not.
   No; the two lines are parallel because their slopes are the same.

Transformation	Example	Result
To translate the function **to the left**, add a constant >0 to the variable x.	$f(x) = 3x$ $f(x) = 3(x + 2)$ $f(x) = 3x + 6$	When $y = 0$ point (0, 0) becomes (−2, 0).
To translate the function **to the right**, subtract a constant >0 from the variable x.	$f(x) = 3x$ $f(x) = 3(x - 1)$ $f(x) = 3x - 3$	When $y = 0$ point (0, 0) becomes (1, 0).

4. How does the graph of $f(x) = 3x$ change when you add 2 to the variable?
   The line is shifted 6 units to the left.
5. How does the graph of $f(x) = 3x$ change when you subtract 1 from the variable?
   The line is shifted 3 units to the right.

2-6 RETEACH

Translating linear functions vertically or horizontally changes the intercepts of the function. It does NOT change the slope.

Let $f(x) = 3x + 1$. Read the rule for each translation.

Horizontal Translation ⇔ Think: Add to x, go west. Use $f(x) \to f(x - h)$.	Vertical Translation ⇕ Think: Add to y, go high. Use $f(x) \to f(x) + k$.
Translation 2 units right ⇒ $g(x) = f(x - 2)$ $g(x) = 3(x - 2) + 1$ Rule: $g(x) = 3x - 5$	Translation 2 units up ⇑ $g(x) = f(x) + 2$ $g(x) = 3x + 1 + 2$ Rule: $g(x) = 3x + 3$
Translation 2 units left ⇐ $h(x) = f(x - (-2)) = f(x + 2)$ $h(x) = 3(x + 2) + 1$ Rule: $h(x) = 3x + 7$	Translation 2 units down ⇓ $h(x) = f(x) + (-2) = f(x) - 2$ $h(x) = 3x + 1 - 2$ Rule: $h(x) = 3x - 1$

Let $f(x) = 2x - 1$. Write the rule for $g(x)$.

1. horizontal translation 5 units right
   $g(x) = f(x - \underline{5})$
   $g(x) = 2(x - \underline{5}) - 1$
   $g(x) = \underline{2x - 11}$
2. vertical translation 4 units down
   $g(x) = f(x) - \underline{4}$
   $g(x) = \underline{2x - 1} - \underline{4}$
   $g(x) = \underline{2x - 5}$
3. vertical translation 3 units up
   $g(x) = f(x) + \underline{3}$
   $g(x) = \underline{2x - 1} + \underline{3}$
   $g(x) = \underline{2x + 2}$
4. horizontal translation 1 unit left
   $g(x) = f(x + \underline{1})$
   $g(x) = 2(\underline{x + 1}) - 1$
   $g(x) = \underline{2x + 1}$
5. vertical translation 7 units down
   $g(x) = 2x - 8$
6. horizontal translation 9 units right
   $g(x) = 2x - 19$
7. vertical translation 1 unit up
   $g(x) = 2x$
8. horizontal translation $\frac{1}{2}$ unit to the left
   $g(x) = 2x$

15. **Consumer Economics** In 1997, Southwestern Bell increased the price for local pay-phone calls. Before then, the price of a call could be determined by $f(x) = 0.15x + 0.25$, where x was the number of minutes after the *first* minute. The company increased the cost of the first minute by 10 cents.
   a. Write a new price function $g(x)$ for a phone call. **$g(x) = 0.15x + 0.35$**
   b. Graph $f(x)$ and $g(x)$ on the same coordinate plane.
   c. Describe the transformation(s) that have been applied. **vertical shift up 0.1 unit**

Write the rule for the transformed function $g(x)$ and graph.

18. $g(x) = \frac{1}{3}x + 1$

16.

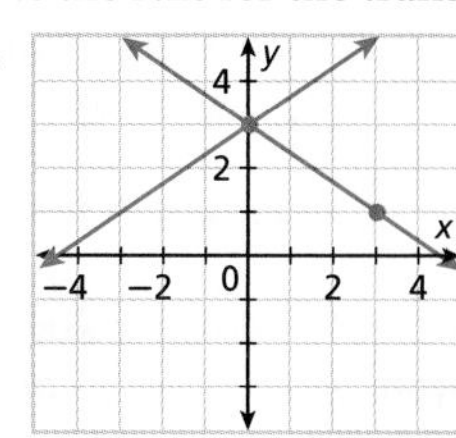

Reflection across the y-axis **$g(x) = \frac{2}{3}x + 3$**

17.

Vertical stretch by a factor of 8 **$g(x) = 2x$**

18.

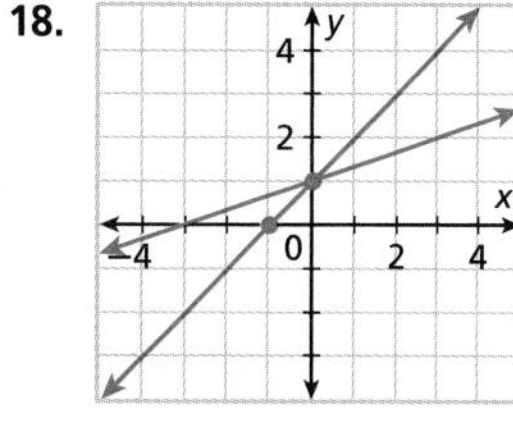

Horizontal stretch by a factor of 3

History

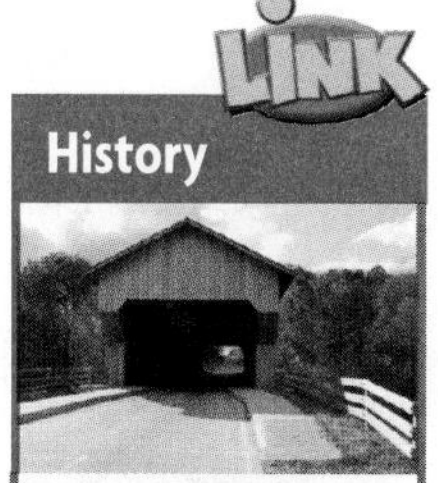

The Cumberland Road, built in the early 1800s from Cumberland, Maryland to St. Louis, Missouri, was the most ambitious road project of its time.

History **Historic tolls for traveling on the Cumberland Road in Pennsylvania are shown on the sign. Toll was paid every 15 miles.**

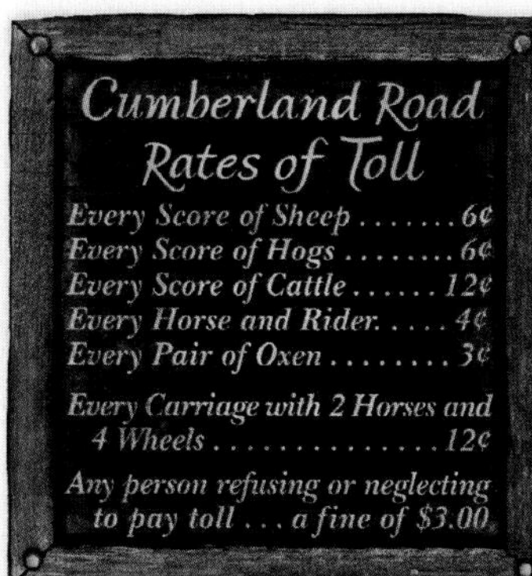

Cumberland Road
Rates of Toll
Every Score of Sheep . . . . 6¢
Every Score of Hogs . . . . 6¢
Every Score of Cattle . . . . . . 12¢
Every Horse and Rider. . . . . . 4¢
Every Pair of Oxen . . . . 3¢
Every Carriage with 2 Horses and 4 Wheels . . . . 12¢
Any person refusing or neglecting to pay toll . . . a fine of $3.00

19. Write a function to represent the cost for 1 horse and rider to travel n miles with a score of sheep. What transformation describes the change in cost if the sheep were replaced by cattle?
20. Write a function to represent the cost for a carriage with 2 horses and 4 wheels to travel n miles. Name two different transformations that would represent a 6¢ increase in the toll rate.
21. **Critical Thinking** Consider the linear function $f(x) = x$.
   a. Shift $f(x)$ 2 units up and then reflect it over the x-axis.
   b. Perform the same transformations on $f(x)$ again but in reverse order.
   c. Make a conjecture about the order in which transformations are performed.

22. **Write About It** Which transformations affect the slope of a linear function, and which transformations affect the y-intercept? Support your answers.

23b. Mean, median, and mode are increased by 7. Range stays the same.

MULTI-STEP TEST PREP

23. This problem will prepare you for the Multi-Step Test Prep on page 164. Use the data set $\{1, 5, 10, 17, 23, 23, 38, 60\}$.
   a. Find the mean, median, mode, and range. **22.125; 20; 23; 59**
   b. How does adding 7 to each number affect the mean, median, mode, and range?
   c. How does multiplying each number by 4 affect the mean, median, mode, and range? **All are multiplied by 4.**
   d. How does multiplying each number by 2 and then adding 5 affect the mean, median, mode, and range? **Mean, median, and mode are multiplied by 2, and 5 is added. Range is multiplied by 2.**

COMMON ERROR ALERT

Students might perform the combined transformations in **Exercises 13** and **14** in the wrong order. Emphasize that the order in which the transformations are performed may affect the resulting function rule.

Teaching Tip **Language Arts** In **Exercises 19** and **20,** students might not know the definition of score. Rather than telling them, explain that in 1863 in his Gettysburg Address, Abraham Lincoln used the phrase "four score and seven years ago" to refer to the year 1776. Have students solve to find that a score is equal to 20.

MULTI-STEP TEST PREP **Exercise 23** involves linear transformations. This exercise prepares students for the Multi-Step Test Prep on page 164.

Answers

19. $T(n) = 0.10\left(\frac{n}{15}\right) = \frac{n}{150}$; vertical stretch by a factor of 1.6
20. $T(n) = 0.12\left(\frac{n}{15}\right) = \frac{n}{125}$; vertical stretch by a factor of $\frac{3}{2}$ or horizontal compression by a factor of $\frac{2}{3}$
21a. $g(x) = -x - 2$
b. $g(x) = -x + 2$
c. Transformations performed in a different order may result in a different function.
22. See p. A19.

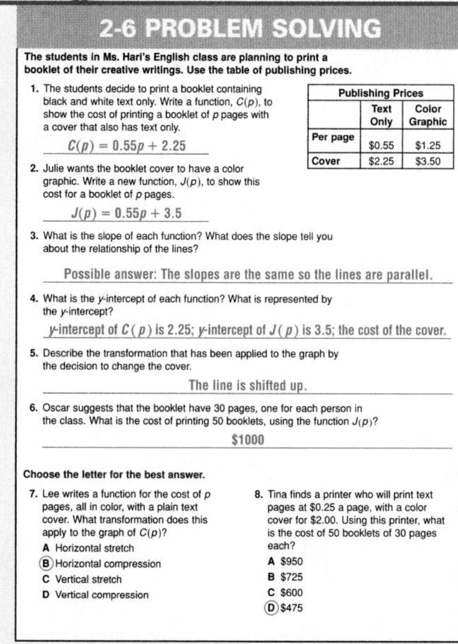

2-6 PROBLEM SOLVING

The students in Ms. Hari's English class are planning to print a booklet of their creative writings. Use the table of publishing prices.

Publishing Prices		
	Text Only	Color Graphic
Per page	$0.55	$1.25
Cover	$2.25	$3.50

1. The students decide to print a booklet containing black and white text only. Write a function, $C(p)$, to show the cost of printing a booklet of p pages with a cover that also has text only. **$C(p) = 0.55p + 2.25$**
2. Julie wants the booklet cover to have a color graphic. Write a new function, $J(p)$, to show this cost for a booklet of p pages. **$J(p) = 0.55p + 3.5$**
3. What is the slope of each function? What does the slope tell you about the relationship of the lines? **Possible answer: The slopes are the same so the lines are parallel.**
4. What is the y-intercept of each function? What is represented by the y-intercept? **y-intercept of $C(p)$ is 2.25; y-intercept of $J(p)$ is 3.5; the cost of the cover.**
5. Describe the transformation that has been applied to the graph by the decision to change the cover. **The line is shifted up.**
6. Oscar suggests that the booklet have 30 pages, one for each person in the class. What is the cost of printing 50 booklets, using the function $J(p)$? **$1000**

Choose the letter for the best answer.

7. Lee writes a function for the cost of p pages, all in color, with a plain text cover. What transformation does this apply to the graph of $C(p)$?
   A Horizontal stretch
   (B) Horizontal compression
   C Vertical stretch
   D Vertical compression
8. Tina finds a printer who will print text pages at $0.25 a page, with a color cover for $2.00. Using this printer, what is the cost of 50 booklets of 30 pages each?
   A $950
   B $725
   C $600
   (D) $475

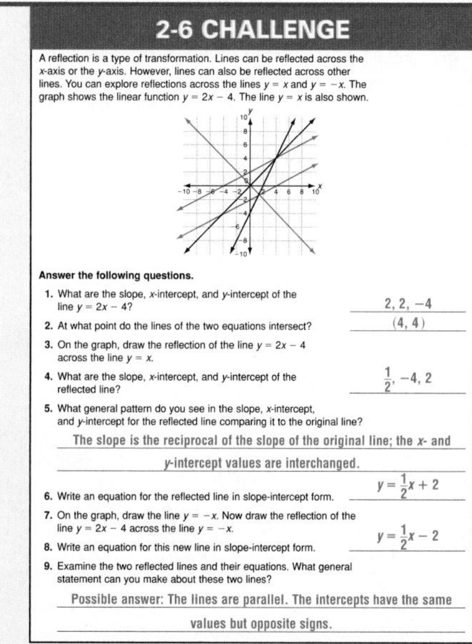

2-6 CHALLENGE

A reflection is a type of transformation. Lines can be reflected across the x-axis or the y-axis. However, lines can also be reflected across other lines. You can explore reflections across the lines $y = x$ and $y = -x$. The graph shows the linear function $y = 2x - 4$. The line $y = x$ is also shown.

Answer the following questions.

1. What are the slope, x-intercept, and y-intercept of the line $y = 2x - 4$? **2, 2, −4**
2. At what point do the lines of the two equations intersect? **(4, 4)**
3. On the graph, draw the reflection of the line $y = 2x - 4$ across the line $y = x$.
4. What are the slope, x-intercept, and y-intercept of the reflected line? **$\frac{1}{2}$, −4, 2**
5. What general pattern do you see in the slope, x-intercept, and y-intercept for the reflected line comparing it to the original line? **The slope is the reciprocal of the slope of the original line; the x- and y-intercept values are interchanged.**
6. Write an equation for the reflected line in slope-intercept form. **$y = \frac{1}{2}x + 2$**
7. On the graph, draw the line $y = -x$. Now draw the reflection of the line $y = 2x - 4$ across the line $y = -x$.
8. Write an equation for this new line in slope-intercept form. **$y = \frac{1}{2}x - 2$**
9. Examine the two reflected lines and their equations. What general statement can you make about these two lines? **Possible answer: The lines are parallel. The intercepts have the same values but opposite signs.**

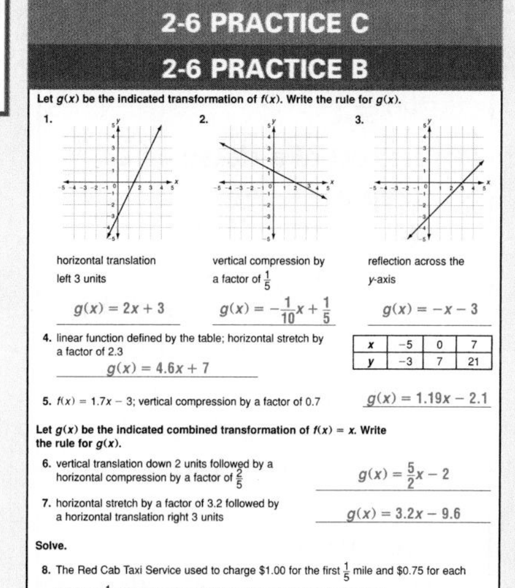

2-6 PRACTICE A
2-6 PRACTICE C
2-6 PRACTICE B

Let $g(x)$ be the indicated transformation of $f(x)$. Write the rule for $g(x)$.

1. horizontal translation left 3 units **$g(x) = 2x + 3$**
2. vertical compression by a factor of $\frac{1}{5}$ **$g(x) = -\frac{1}{10}x + \frac{1}{5}$**
3. reflection across the y-axis **$g(x) = -x - 3$**
4. linear function defined by the table; horizontal stretch by a factor of 2.3 **$g(x) = 4.6x + 7$**

x	−5	0	7
y	−3	7	21

5. $f(x) = 1.7x - 3$; vertical compression by a factor of 0.7 **$g(x) = 1.19x - 2.1$**

Let $g(x)$ be the indicated combined transformation of $f(x) = x$. Write the rule for $g(x)$.

6. vertical translation down 2 units followed by a horizontal compression by a factor of $\frac{2}{5}$ **$g(x) = \frac{5}{2}x - 2$**
7. horizontal stretch by a factor of 3.2 followed by a horizontal translation right 3 units **$g(x) = 3.2x - 9.6$**

Solve.

8. The Red Cab Taxi Service used to charge $1.00 for the first $\frac{1}{5}$ mile and $0.75 for each additional $\frac{1}{5}$ mile. The company just raised its rates by a factor of 1.5.
   a. Write a new price function $g(x)$ for a taxi ride. **$g(x) = 1.5[1 + 0.75(5x - 1)] = 5.625x + 0.375$**
   b. Describe the transformation(s) that have been applied. **Vertical stretch by a factor of 1.5**

TEST PREP DOCTOR In **Exercise 25,** students who chose **F** or **G** might be confusing the slope with the y-intercept. In **Exercise 26,** you may wish to point out that all of the transformations except for choice **C** involve multiplication. For **Exercise 27,** suggest that students sketch the graph of $f(x) = \frac{1}{2}x - 1$ on the same coordinate plane as the graph shown so that they can better visualize and determine the transformation.

Journal

Have students use their own words to explain how a linear function is changed by each transformation described in the lesson.

ALTERNATIVE ASSESSMENT

Have students use the parent function $f(x) = x$. Have them describe a translation, a reflection, and a stretch or compression. Then have students write a rule for each transformation.

Power Presentations with PowerPoint®

2-6 Lesson Quiz

Let $g(x)$ be the indicated transformation of $f(x) = 3x + 1$. Write the rule for $g(x)$.

1. horizontal translation 3 units right $g(x) = 3x - 8$
2. reflection across the x-axis $g(x) = -3x - 1$
3. vertical stretch by a factor of 2 $g(x) = 6x + 2$
4. vertical shift up 4 units followed by a horizontal compression of $\frac{1}{3}$ $g(x) = 9x + 5$
5. **The cost of a classified ad is represented by $C(\ell) = 1.50\ell + 4.00$ where ℓ is the number of lines in the ad. The cost is increased by \$3.00 when color is used.**

   Write a new function $H(\ell)$ for the cost of a classified ad in color, and describe the transformation(s) that have been applied.

   $H(\ell) = 1.50\ell + 7.00$; shift 3 units up

Also available on transparency

TEST PREP

24. The cost function C of rent at an apartment complex increased \$50 last year and another \$60 this year. Which function accurately reflects these changes?

    (A) $60(C + 50)$ (B) $60(50C)$ **(C)** $(C + 50) + 60$ (D) $50C + 60$

25. Given $f(x) = 28.5x + 45.6$, which function decreases the y-intercept by 20.3?

    (F) $g(x) = 8.2x + 45.6$ **(H)** $g(x) = 28.5x + 25.3$
    (G) $g(x) = 8.2x + 66.1$ (J) $g(x) = 28.5x + 66.1$

26. Which transformation describes a line that is parallel to $f(x)$?

    (A) $f(3x)$ (B) $f\left(\frac{x}{2}\right)$ **(C)** $f(x - 4)$ (D) $f(-2x)$

27. Which transformation of $f(x) = \frac{1}{2}x - 1$ could result in the graph shown?

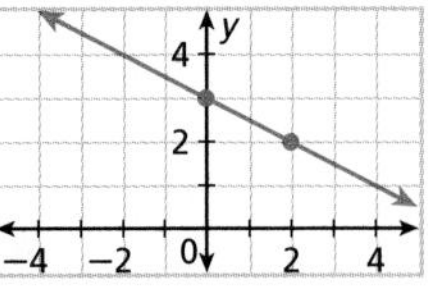

    (F) vertical shift 2 units down and reflection across x-axis
    (G) horizontal shift 2 units left and reflection across x-axis
    (H) vertical shift 2 units up and reflection across x-axis
    (J) horizontal shift 2 units right and reflection across x-axis

CHALLENGE AND EXTEND

28. Give two different combinations of transformations that would transform $f(x) = 3x + 4$ into $g(x) = 15x - 10$.
29. Give an example of two transformations of $f(x) = x$ that can be performed in any order and result in the same transformed function.
30. **Education** The graph shows the tuition at a university based on the number of credit hours taken. The rate per credit hour varies according to the number of hours taken: less than 12 hours, 12 to 18 hours, and greater than 18 hours.

    a. Write the linear function that represents each segment of the graph.

    b. Write the linear functions that would reflect a 12% increase in all tuition costs.

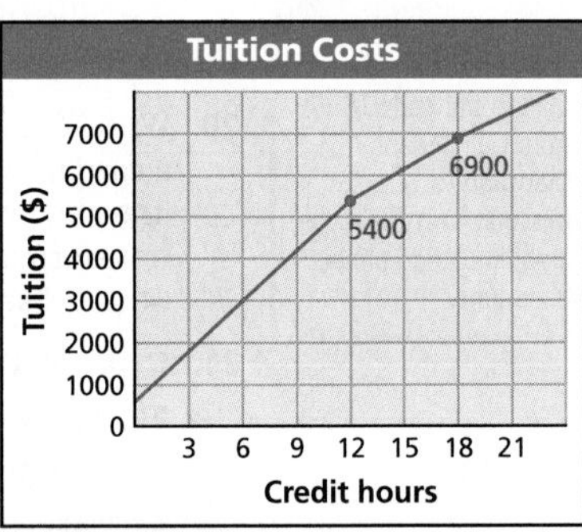

SPIRAL REVIEW

Write each expression in expanded form. *(Lesson 1-5)*

31. $\left(\frac{3}{5}d^2\right)^3$ 32. 2^{-3} $\left(\frac{1}{2}\right)\left(\frac{1}{2}\right)\left(\frac{1}{2}\right)$ 33. $-(2n)^4$ $-(2n)(2n)(2n)(2n)$ 34. $-a^5(6a)^{-1}$ 34. $-a \cdot a \cdot a \cdot a \cdot a \cdot \frac{1}{6a}$

Determine if each line is vertical, horizontal, or neither, and graph the line. *(Lesson 2-3)*

35. $y = -6$ 36. $x = \frac{3}{7}$
37. $y = -x$ 38. $5.1 = y$

39. **Money** Express Henry's bonus as a function of the ads that Henry sells. How many ad spots must Henry sell to earn \$520 as a bonus? *(Lesson 2-4)*

Henry's Bonus

Ads Sold	Bonus (\$)
12	65
16	195
21	357.50

$B(a) = 32.5(a - 10)$; 26 ads

Answers

28. vertical translation 14 units down and horizontal compression by a factor of $\frac{1}{5}$ or vertical stretch by a factor of 5 and a vertical translation 30 units down
29. Possible answer: a translation 2 units up and a translation 2 units right

30a. $T(h) = \begin{cases} 400h + 600 \text{ if } h < 12 \\ 250h + 2400 \text{ if } 12 \le h \le 18 \\ 200h + 3300 \text{ if } h > 18 \end{cases}$

b. $T(h) = \begin{cases} 448h + 672 \text{ if } h < 12 \\ 280h + 2688 \text{ if } 12 \le h \le 18 \\ 224h + 3696 \text{ if } h > 18 \end{cases}$

31. $\left(\frac{3}{5}d \cdot d\right)\left(\frac{3}{5}d \cdot d\right)\left(\frac{3}{5}d \cdot d\right)$

35. horizontal

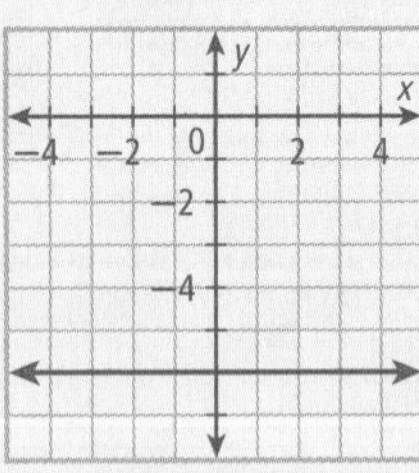

36–38. For graphs, see p. A19.

36. vertical
37. neither
38. horizontal

Statistical Graphs

See Skills Bank page S69

Statistical data may be displayed in bar graphs or circle graphs. Use a bar graph to compare numerical amounts. Use a circle graph to compare parts of a whole.

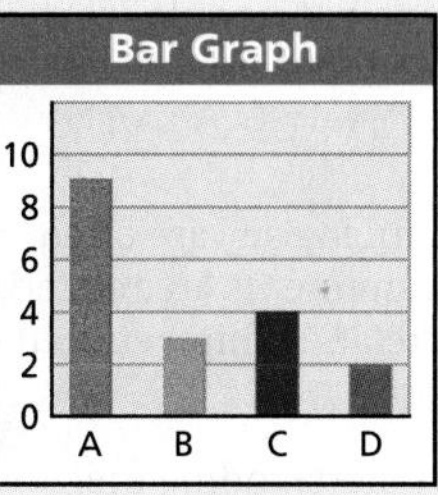

A bar graph compares numerical amounts.

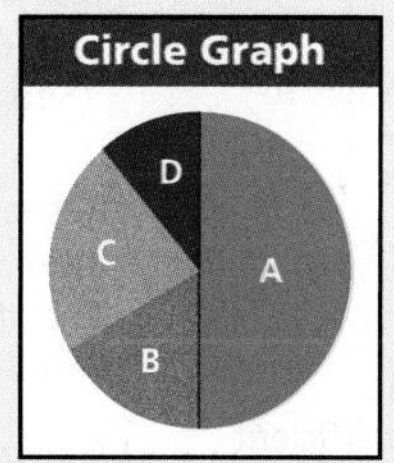

A circle graph compares parts of a whole.

The bar graph shows the numbers of pets owned by a group of students in a pet owners club.

Example

Use the bar graph. Find the central angle measure for the named category in a related circle graph, to the nearest degree.

Pet Ownership

Type of pet	Pets owned
Dogs	
Cats	
Fish	
Birds	
Reptiles	

Pets owned: 0, 10, 20, 30, 40, 50, 60

Category: birds

1. Compute the total number of pets.
   Add the number of dogs, cats, fish, reptiles, and birds.
   $6 + 11 + 43 + 35 + 13 = 108$
2. Find the number of pets in the category.
   11 birds
3. A circle consists of 360°. **Write and solve a proportion.**

$$\text{Part} \rightarrow \frac{11}{108} = \frac{n}{360} \leftarrow \text{Circle part}$$
$$\text{Whole} \rightarrow \qquad\qquad \leftarrow \text{Circle whole}$$

4. Solve for the central angle.
   $11 \cdot 360 = 108n$
   $37° \approx n$

Try This

Find the central angle measure for each category, to the nearest degree.

1. fish **43°**
2. reptiles **20°**
3. dogs **143°**
4. cats **117°**
5. fish, birds, and reptiles combined **100°**
6. What categories combined give a central angle of approximately 207°? **reptiles, dogs, and fish**

Organizer

See Skills Bank page S69

Pacing:
Traditional $\frac{1}{2}$ day
Block $\frac{1}{4}$ day

Objective: Find central angles in circle graphs.

Online Edition

Teach

Remember

Students review graphical representations and apply proportional reasoning.

INTERVENTION For additional review and practice on finding central angles in circle graphs, see Skills Bank page S69.

Visual You may want to have students use a protractor or a spreadsheet program to create the circle graph.

Close

Assess

Ask students how the bar graph and circle graph would change if fish were not included as pets.
Each sector would increase in size proportionally to fill the circle.

State Resources

2-7 Organizer

Pacing: Traditional 1 day
Block $\frac{1}{2}$ day

Objectives: Fit scatter plot data using linear models with and without technology.

Use linear models to make predictions.

Algebra Lab
In *Algebra Lab Activities*

Technology Lab
In *Technology Lab Activities*

Online Edition
Tutorial Videos, Interactivity, TechKeys

Countdown to Testing Week 5

Power Presentations with PowerPoint®

Warm Up

Write the equation of the line passing through each pair of points in slope-intercept form.

1. (5, −1), (0, −3) $y = \frac{2}{5}x - 3$

2. (8, 5), (−8, 7) $y = -\frac{1}{8}x + 6$

Use the equation $y = -0.2x + 4$. Find x for each given value of y.

3. $y = 7$ −15 **4.** $y = 3.5$ 2.5

Also available on transparency

Math Humor

Q: Why did all the apples in the fruit bowl know each other?

A: They were *core-relations.*

State Resources

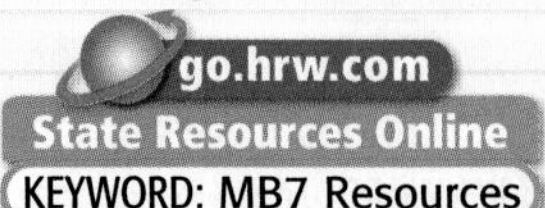

2-7 Curve Fitting with Linear Models

Objectives
Fit scatter plot data using linear models with and without technology.

Use linear models to make predictions.

Vocabulary
regression
correlation
line of best fit
correlation coefficient

Who uses this?
Anthropologists can use linear models to estimate the heights of ancient people from bones that the anthropologists find. (See Example 2.)

Researchers, such as anthropologists, are often interested in how two measurements are related. The statistical study of the relationship between variables is called **regression**.

A *scatter plot* is helpful in understanding the form, direction, and strength of the relationship between two variables. **Correlation** is the strength and direction of the linear relationship between the two variables.

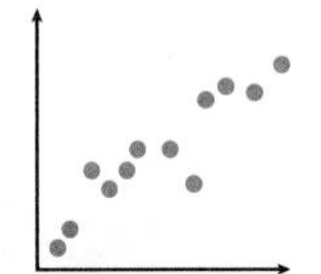
Positive correlation, positive slope

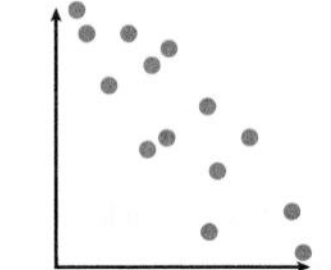
Negative correlation, negative slope

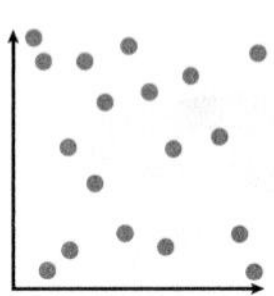
Relatively no correlation

If there is a strong linear relationship between two variables, a **line of best fit**, or a line that best fits the data, can be used to make predictions.

EXAMPLE 1 *Meteorology Application*

Akron, Ohio, and Wellington, New Zealand, are about the same distance from the equator. Make a scatter plot for the temperature data, identify the correlation, and then sketch a line of best fit and find its equation.

Helpful Hint
Try to have about the same number of points above and below the line of best fit.

Average High Temperatures (°F)

	Jan	Feb	Mar	Apr	May	Jun	Jul	Aug	Sep	Oct	Nov	Dec
Akron	33	37	48	59	70	78	82	80	73	61	49	38
Wellington	67	67	65	61	56	53	51	52	55	57	60	64

Step 1 Plot the data points.

Step 2 Identify the correlation.

Notice that the data set is negatively correlated—as the temperature rises in Akron, it falls in Wellington.

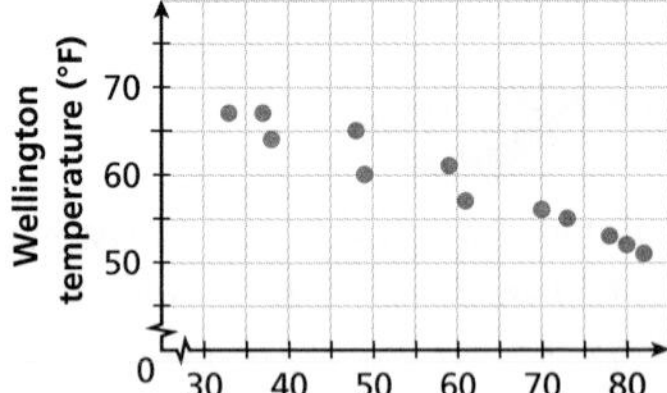

1 Introduce

EXPLORATION

2-7 Curve Fitting with Linear Models

The table shows the dates and winning times for record holders in the men's 100-meter sprint. You can use a graphing calculator to help you see trends in the data.

Date	Record Holder	Time (s)
1983	Calvin Smith	9.93
1988	Carl Lewis	9.92
1991	Leroy Burrell	9.90
1991	Carl Lewis	9.86
1994	Leroy Burrell	9.85
1996	Donovan Bailey	9.84
1999	Maurice Green	9.79
2002	Tim Montgomery	9.78
2005	Asafa Powell	9.77

1. Enter the years in list **L1** by pressing STAT and then 1. Let 1983 be year 0 and 2005 be year 22. Then enter the times in list **L2**.

2. Make a scatter plot in the following way: Press 2nd Y=. Then select **Plot1** and set up the plot as shown. When you are done, press GRAPH. Adjust the viewing window as needed.

THINK AND DISCUSS

Motivate

Make a table that shows shoe size, x, and height, y. Ask about 10 student volunteers to supply values for the table. Make a scatter plot of the points. Ask students to describe any relationships they see in the data. Discuss whether it seems that the data are related and why students think so.

Explorations and answers are provided in the *Explorations* binder.

Step 3 Sketch a line of best fit.

Draw a line that splits the data evenly above and below.

Step 4 Identify two points on the line.

For this data, you might select (30, 70) and (80, 52).

Step 5 Find the slope of the line that models the data.

$$m = \frac{70 - 52}{30 - 80} = \frac{18}{-50} = -0.36$$

Use the point-slope form.

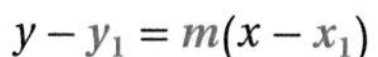

$y - y_1 = m(x - x_1)$	*Point-slope form*
$y - 70 = -0.36(x - 30)$	*Substitute.*
$y = -0.36x + 80.8$	*Simplify.*

An equation that models the data is $y = -0.36x + 80.8$.

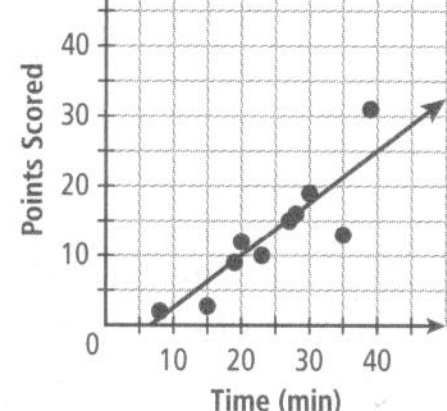

1. Basketball Make a scatter plot for this set of data. Identify the correlation, sketch a line of best fit, and find its equation.

Possible answer: $p = 0.75m - 5$

Points Scored in Ten Games										
Minutes Played	28	35	8	20	39	23	19	27	15	30
Points Scored	16	13	2	12	31	10	9	15	4	19

The **correlation coefficient** r is a measure of how well the data set is fit by a model.

Properties of the Correlation Coefficient r

r is a value in the range $-1 \le r \le 1$.

If $r = 1$, the data set forms a straight line with a positive slope.

If $r = 0$, the data set has no correlation.

If $r = -1$, the data set forms a straight line with a negative slope.

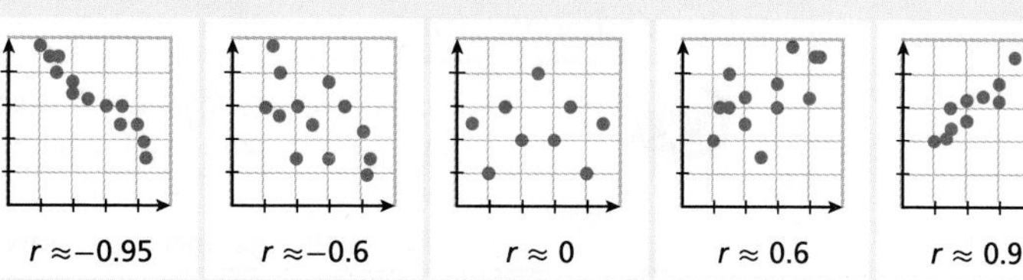

Caution!

Don't confuse slope with the *value* of r. Whether a line has a slope of 10 or a slope of $\frac{1}{10}$, it can have an r-value of 1. The r-value and the slope have the same sign.

You can use a graphing calculator to perform a linear regression and find the correlation coefficient r. To display the correlation coefficient, you may have to turn on the diagnostic mode. To do this, press 2nd 0 (CATALOG), and choose the **DiagnosticOn** mode.

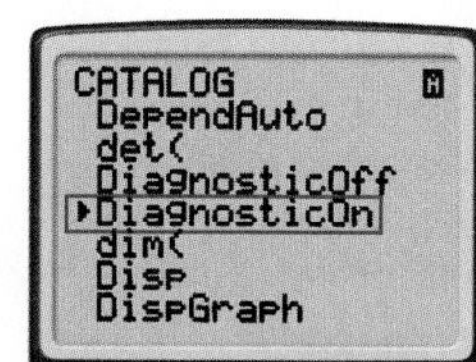

COMMON ERROR ALERT

Students might try to draw a line of best fit through as many points as possible. However, this may not balance points above and below the line. Encourage students to think of the data clustering around the line.

Power Presentations with PowerPoint®

Additional Examples

Example 1

Albany and Sydney are about the same distance from the equator. Make a scatter plot with Albany's temperature as the independent variable. Name the type of correlation. Then sketch a line of best fit and find its equation.

Average Minimum Temperature (°F)		
Month	**Albany**	**Sydney**
Jan	31	65
Feb	34	66
Mar	41	63
Apr	50	58
May	59	53
Jun	67	49
Jul	70	46
Aug	70	48
Sep	62	52
Oct	51	56
Nov	40	60
Dec	33	63

negative;

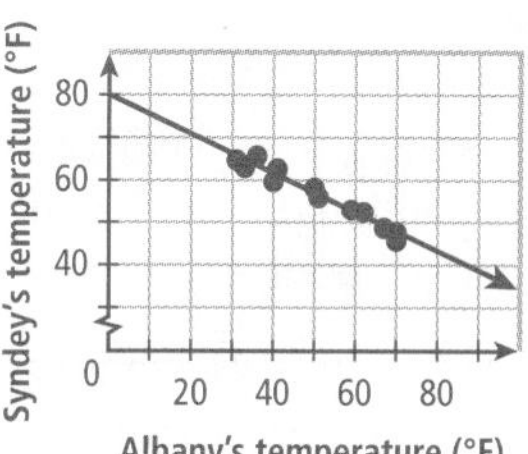

$y = -0.46x + 80.1$

Also available on transparency

2 Teach

Guided Instruction

After completing **Example 1,** show students how to use a graphing calculator to work through each part of **Example 2.** Point out that another name for the line of best fit is the *regression line.* Be sure students understand how to use the line of best fit to make predictions. Discuss how reasonable the predictions are for each example.

Reaching All Learners

Through Kinesthetic Experience

Have students use an uncooked piece of thin spaghetti to estimate a line of best fit. Students can slide and rotate the piece of spaghetti until there are about the same number of data points above the spaghetti as below it. The line may pass through two or more of data points that may be used to find the best-fit equation.

INTERVENTION

Questioning Strategies

EXAMPLE 1

- Why is the line called a line of best fit if there are other ways to draw a line through the data?
- Could you select another pair of points to find the slope of the line? How would this affect the equation?

Power Presentations with PowerPoint®

Additional Examples

Example 2

Anthropologists can use the femur, or thighbone, to estimate the height of a human being. The table shows the results of a randomly selected sample.

Femur Length and Height (cm)	
Length	**Height**
36	160
32	143
46	187
29	142
35	161
38	164
30	140
27	131

a. Make a scatter plot of the data with femur length as the independent variable.

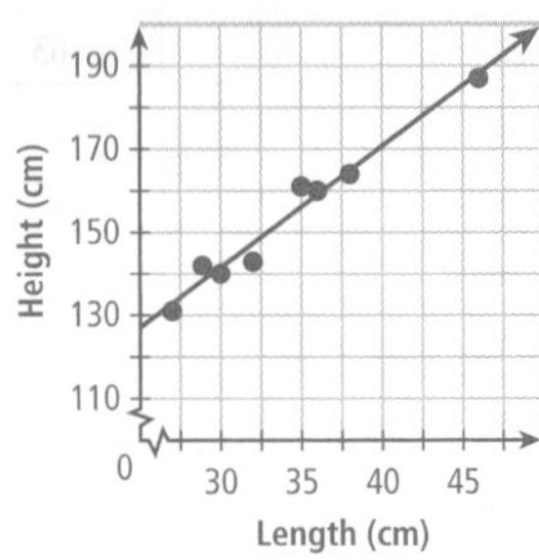

b. Find the correlation coefficient *r* and the line of best fit. Interpret the slope of the line of best fit in the context of the problem. $r \approx 0.986$; $y = 2.91x + 54.04$; slope ≈ 2.91; for each 1 cm increase in length, the height increase is about 2.91 cm.

c. A man's femur is 41 cm long. Predict the man's height. ≈ 173 cm

Also available on transparency

EXAMPLE 2 Anthropology Application

Anthropologists use known relationships between the height and length of a woman's humerus bone, the bone between the elbow and the shoulder, to estimate a woman's height. Some samples are shown in the table.

Bone Length and Height in Women								
Humerus Length (cm)	35	27	30	33	25	39	27	31
Height (cm)	167	146	154	165	140	180	149	155

a. Make a scatter plot of the data with humerus length as the independent variable.

The scatter plot is shown at right.

$h \approx 2.75l + 71.97$

200, 180, 160, 140, 120 — Height (cm); 0, 22, 26, 30, 34, 38 — Humerus length (cm)

b. Find the correlation coefficient *r* and the line of best fit. Interpret the slope of the line of best fit in the context of the problem.

Enter the data into lists **L1** and **L2** on a graphing calculator. Use the linear regression feature by pressing STAT, choosing **CALC**, and selecting **4:LinReg**. The equation of the line of best fit is $h \approx 2.75\ell + 71.97$.

The slope is about 2.75, so for each 1 cm increase in humerus length, the predicted increase in a woman's height is 2.75 cm.

The correlation coefficient is $r \approx 0.991$, which indicates a strong positive correlation.

```
LinReg
y=ax+b
a=2.753883892
b=71.97383483
r²=.9825297615
r=.9912263927
```

Helpful Hint

To enter data into lists on a graphing calculator, press STAT and select **1:Edit**. Enter the *x*-values in the **L1** column and the *y*-values in the **L2** column.

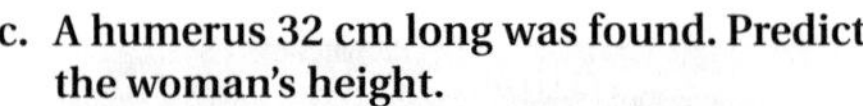

c. A humerus 32 cm long was found. Predict the woman's height.

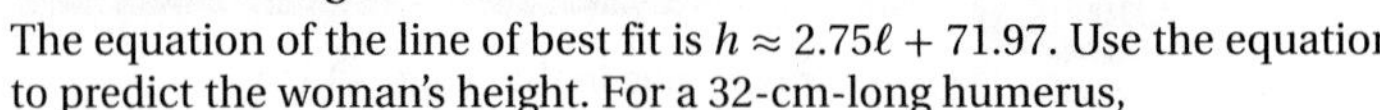

The equation of the line of best fit is $h \approx 2.75\ell + 71.97$. Use the equation to predict the woman's height. For a 32-cm-long humerus,

$h \approx 2.75(32) + 71.97$ *Substitute 32 for ℓ.*

$h \approx 159.97$

The height of a woman with a 32-cm-long humerus would be about 160 cm.

CHECK IT OUT!

2. The gas mileage for randomly selected cars based upon engine horsepower is given in the table.

Gas Mileage and Horsepower of Cars										
Horsepower	175	255	140	165	115	120	190	180	110	125
Mileage (mi/gal)	22	13	25	18	32	28	15	21	35	30

a. Make a scatter plot of the data with horsepower as the independent variable.

b. Find the correlation coefficient *r* and the line of best fit. Interpret the slope of the line in the context of the problem.

c. Predict the gas mileage for a 210-horsepower engine.

b. $r \approx -0.916$; $y \approx -0.15x + 47.5$; for a 1 unit increase in hp, gas mileage drops ≈ 0.15 mi/gal

c. ≈ 16.0 mi/gal.

INTERVENTION

Questioning Strategies

EXAMPLE 2

- Would you be surprised if the correlation coefficient for this data were 0.09? Explain.

EXAMPLE 3

- Are there any restrictions on the domain of the line of best fit?

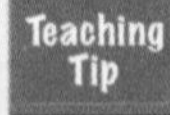

Teaching Tip **Critical Thinking** Discuss with students the value of *r* for the following strictly linear relationships: angle measures of a linear pair ($r = -1$) and proportional relationships ($r = 1$).

Answers to Check It Out!

2a.

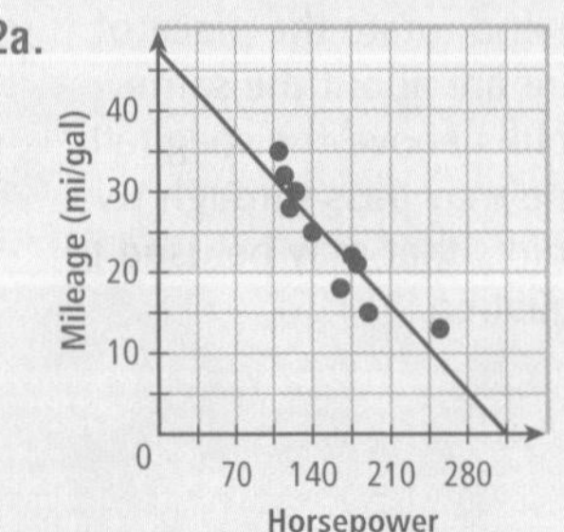

Teaching Tip **Technology** After students enter independent and dependent variables in lists, they can use the **4:LinReg(ax+b)** feature from the STAT **CALC** menu to find the linear regression model. To enter the regression equation for graphing, they can press Y=, press VARS, choose **5:Statistics**, scroll right to **EQ**, and select **1:RegEQ**.

EXAMPLE 3 Nutrition Application

Find the following information for this data set on the number of grams of fat and the number of calories in sandwiches served at Dave's Deli.

Dave's Deli Sandwiches Nutritional Information								
Fat (g)	5	9	12	15	12	10	21	14
Calories	360	455	460	420	530	375	580	390

a. **Make a scatter plot of the data with fat as the independent variable.**
The scatter plot is shown below.

b. **Find the correlation coefficient and the equation of the line of best fit. Draw the line of best fit on your scatter plot.**
The correlation coefficient is $r = 0.682$.
The equation of the line of best fit is
$y \approx 11.1x + 309.8$.

c. **Predict the amount of fat in a sandwich with 500 Calories. How accurate do you think your prediction is?**

$500 \approx 11.1x + 309.8$ *Calories is the dependent variable.*

$190.2 \approx 11.1x$

$17.1 \approx x$

The line predicts 17.1 grams of fat, but the scatter plot and the value of r show that fat content by itself is *not* a good predictor of the number of calories in a sandwich at Dave's.

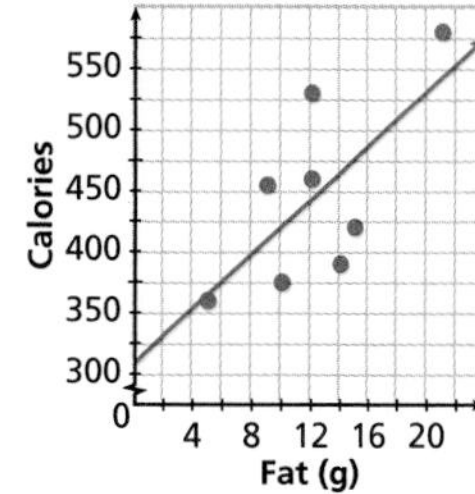

Reading Math
A line of best fit may also be referred to as a *trend line*.

CHECK IT OUT! 3. **What If...?** Use the equation of the line of best fit to predict the number of grams of fat in a sandwich with 420 Calories. How close is your answer to the value given in the table?
≈10 g; not close to the 15 g in the table.

THINK AND DISCUSS

1. **Explain** whether the r-value is positive or negative if the line of best fit for data from two variables is $y = 3.2x - 12.5$.
2. **Tell** which correlation coefficient, $r = 0.65$ or $r = -0.75$, indicates a stronger linear relationship between two variables. Justify your answer.
3. **GET ORGANIZED** Copy and complete the graphic organizer. Make a scatter plot for each type of correlation and estimate the r-value.

Correlation	Scatter Plot	Estimated r-value
Strong positive		
Weak positive		
No correlation		
Weak negative		
Strong negative		

Power Presentations with PowerPoint®

Additional Examples

Example 3

Find the following for this data on average temperature and rainfall for eight months in Boston, MA.

Average Temperature and Rainfall in Boston	
Temp. (°F)	Rainfall (mm)
29	95
30	91
39	100
48	93
58	84
68	79
73	73
72	92

a. Make a scatter plot of the data with temperature as the independent variable.

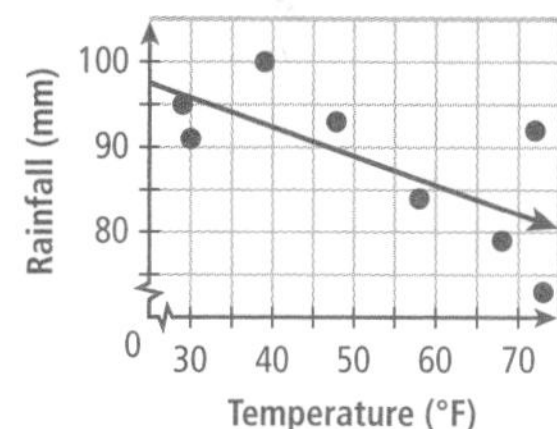

b. Find the correlation coefficient and the equation of the line of best fit. Draw the line of best fit on your scatter plot.
$r \approx -0.70$;
$y = -0.35x + 106.4$

c. Predict the temperature when the rainfall is 86 mm. How accurate do you think your prediction is? ≈58.3°F; scatter plot and value of r show that temperature is not an accurate predictor of rainfall.

Also available on transparency

3 Close

Summarize

Review the following concepts with students:

- Positive/negative slope indicates positive/negative correlation.
- A strong correlation has a correlation coefficient close to 1 or −1.
- A strong correlation allows for more accurate predictions.

ONGOING ASSESSMENT and INTERVENTION

Diagnose **Before** the Lesson
2-7 Warm Up, TE p. 142

Monitor **During** the Lesson
Check It Out! Exercises, SE pp. 143–145
Questioning Strategies, TE pp. 143–145

Assess **After** the Lesson
2-7 Lesson Quiz, TE p. 149
Alternative Assessment, TE p. 149

Answers to *Think and Discuss*

1. Positive; the correlation coefficient has the same sign as the slope of the line of best fit.
2. $r = -0.75$; the strength of the correlation is the absolute value, and $|-0.75| > |0.65|$.
3. See p. A4.

2-7 Exercises

2-7 Exercises

go.hrw.com
Homework Help Online
KEYWORD: MB7 2-7
Parent Resources Online
KEYWORD: MB7 Parent

GUIDED PRACTICE

1. **Vocabulary** Explain what the following *correlation coefficients* tell you about two sets of data.
   a. $r = 0.4$ b. $r = -0.96$ c. $r = -0.02$

SEE EXAMPLE 1 p. 142

2. **Driving** Make a scatter plot for this data set using gallons as the independent variable. Identify the correlation, sketch a line of best fit, and find its equation.

Distance Traveled							
Gallons	11.2	9.8	10.6	10.1	12.3	8.7	10.1
Distance (mi)	338	296	332	324	368	263	305

SEE EXAMPLE 2 p. 144

3. **Home Economics** Use the data relating the average temperature in a month to the heating bill at Claire's house that month.

Claire's Heating Bills							
Mean Temperature (°F)	38	42	44	36	42	49	38
Heating Bill ($)	93	79	75	83	74	67	86

   a. Make a scatter plot using mean temperature as the independent variable.
   b. Find the correlation coefficient and the equation of the line of best fit. Draw the line of best fit on your scatter plot. $r \approx -0.864$; $h \approx -1.68t + 148.88$
   c. Predict the heating bill for a month in which the average temperature is 40° F. How accurate do you think your prediction is?

SEE EXAMPLE 3 p. 145

4. **School** Here are the number of teachers and the number of students at a randomly selected sample of high schools in a city.

Teachers and Students at Selected Schools								
Teachers	92	52	114	49	110	62	76	84
Students	1050	653	753	381	1312	813	496	910

   a. Make a scatter plot of the data using teachers as the independent variable.
   b. Find the correlation coefficient and the equation of the line of best fit. Draw the line of best fit on your scatter plot. $r \approx 0.679$; $y \approx 8.2x + 140.7$
   c. Predict the number of teachers in a high school that has 600 students. How accurate do you think your prediction is? 56 teachers; the correlation coefficient is not very close to 1, so the number of teachers by itself is not a good predictor of the number of students in a school.

PRACTICE AND PROBLEM SOLVING

5. **Chemistry** Make a scatter plot for this data set using the atomic number as the independent variable. Identify the correlation, sketch a line of best fit, and find its equation. Possible answer: $w \approx 2.5n - 5.5$

Selected Chemical Elements														
Atomic Number	89	13	95	51	18	33	85	56	97	4	83	107	5	35
Atomic Mass	227	27	243	122	40	75	210	137	247	9	209	264	11	80

Assignment Guide

Assign *Guided Practice* exercises as necessary.

If you finished Examples **1–3**
Basic 5–14, 17–20, 25–33
Average 5–14, 16–23, 25–33
Advanced 5–13, 15–17, 19–33

Homework Quick Check
Quickly check key concepts.
Exercises: 5–7, 10, 12

Answers

1a. a weak positive linear correlation between data sets
b. a strong negative linear correlation between data sets
c. virtually no correlation between the data sets

2.

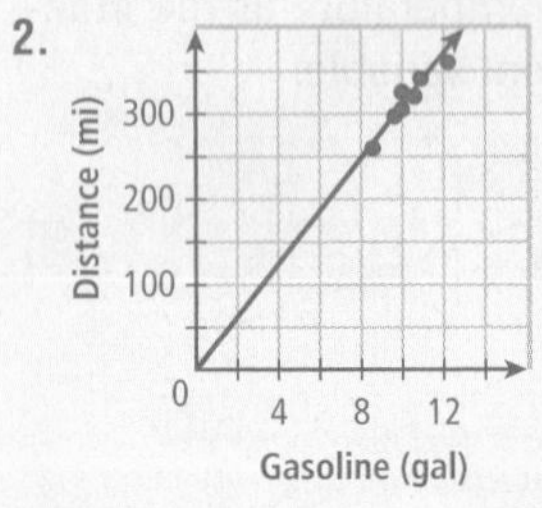

positive; possible answer: $d \approx 30g$

3a.

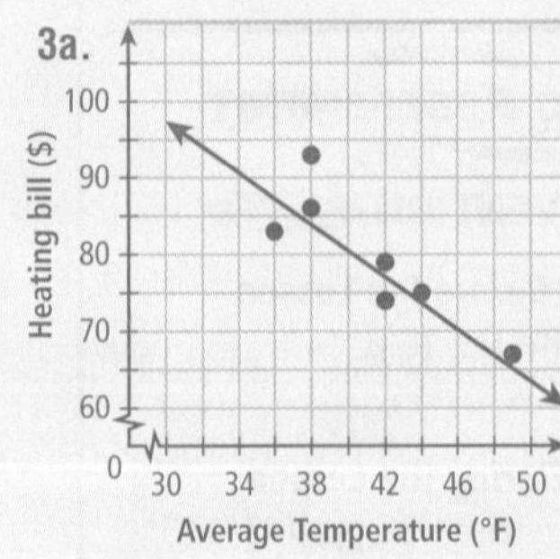

c. $81.68; the correlation coefficient is fairly close to −1, so the prediction is somewhat close to the actual value.

4a. See graph.

b.

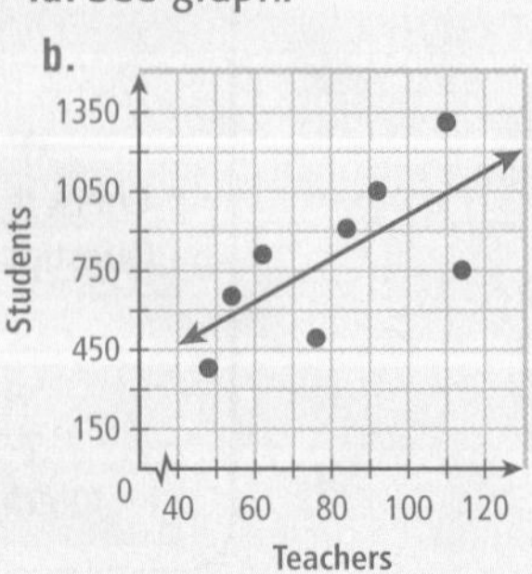

5.

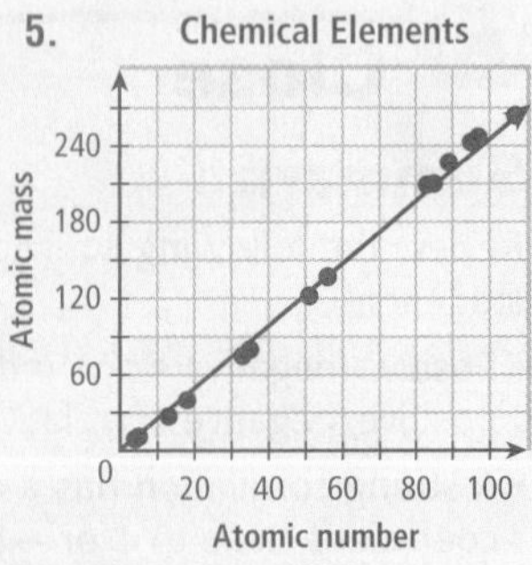

Positive; possible answer: $w = 2.5n - 5.5$

State Resources

Independent Practice	
For Exercises	See Example
5	1
6	2
7	3

Extra Practice
Skills Practice p. S7
Application Practice p. S33

6. **Biology** Hummingbird wing beat rates are much higher than those in other birds. Estimates for various species are given in the table.

Hummingbird Wing Beats							
Mass (g)	3.1	2.0	3.2	4.0	3.7	1.9	4.5
Wing Beats (per *s*)	60	85	50	45	55	90	40

a. Make a scatter plot of the data using mass as the independent variable.
b. Find the correlation coefficient and the equation of the line of best fit. Draw the line of best fit on your scatter plot. $r \approx 0.961$; $w \approx 121.97 - 19.14\,m$
c. Predict the wing beats rate for a Giant Hummingbird with a mass of 19 g. How accurate do you think your prediction is? -241.75 beats/s; not possible

7. **Ticket Pricing** The manager of a band has kept track of the price of tickets and the attendance at the band's recent concerts.

Concert Attendance by Ticket Price									
Price ($)	6	5	8.5	8	10	5.50	7	7.5	8
Attendance	213	256	155	194	160	267	258	210	235

a. Make a scatter plot of the data using price as the independent variable.
b. Find the correlation coefficient and the equation of the line of best fit. Draw the line of best fit on your scatter plot.
c. Predict the attendance at a concert where the price of tickets is $9. How accurate do you think your prediction is? 180 people; fairly accurate.

7b. $r \approx -0.801$; $a \approx -20.95p + 368.89$

8. Make a scatter plot for this data set. Estimate to find the equation of the line of best fit.

x	2	8	15	21	24	30	33	37
y	71	63	64	194	160	267	258	210

Possible answer: $y = \frac{20}{3}x + 20$

Estimation Estimate the value of r for each scatter plot.

9. 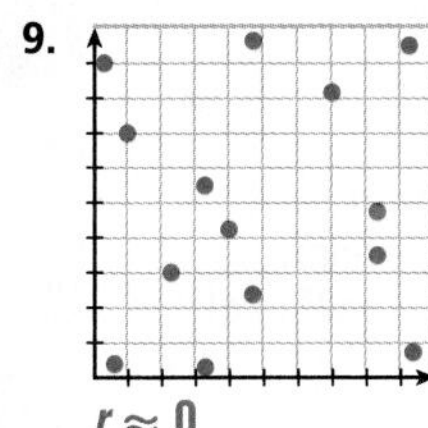
$r \approx 0$

10. 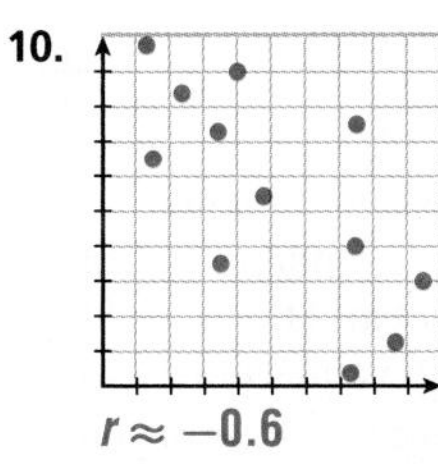
$r \approx -0.6$

11. 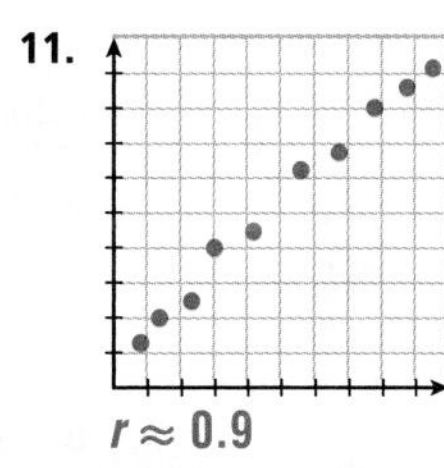
$r \approx 0.9$

12. **Aviation** Make a scatter plot for the lengths and wingspans of planes in the American Airlines fleet. Sketch a line of best fit with length as the independent variable, and find its equation. Possible answer: $w \approx 1.2\ell - 60$

737	Super 80	757	767	A300	777
113 ft	108 ft	124 ft	147 ft	156 ft	200 ft
130 ft	148 ft	155 ft	178 ft	180 ft	209 ft

COMMON ERROR ALERT

For **Exercises 6** and **7,** students might get error messages on their graphing calculators if the lists for the independent variable and the dependent variable do not have the same number of entries. Students should check that each list has the same number of entries and that all numbers were entered correctly.

Teaching Tip **Critical Thinking** In **Exercise 5,** students' lines of best fit might be different. Discuss why their equations should be close but might be different because they chose different points when computing the slope and the *y*-intercept. Compare different equations.

Answers

6a, b.

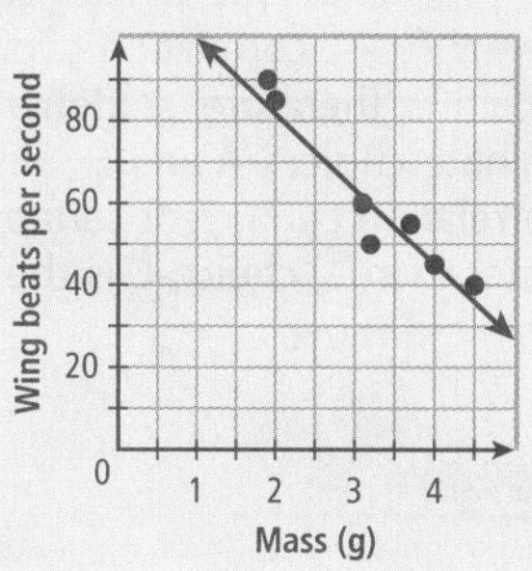

7a.

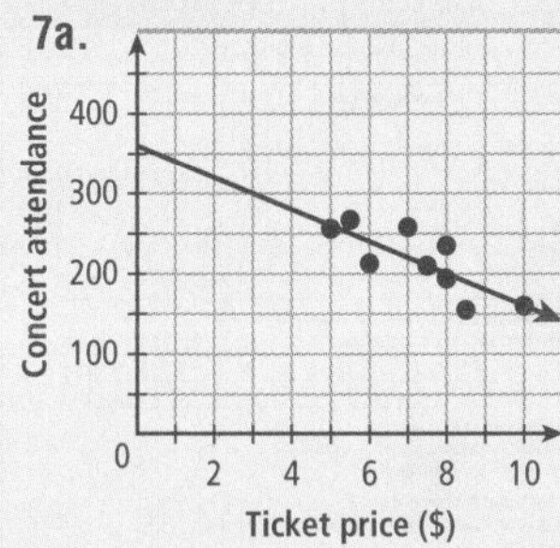

8.

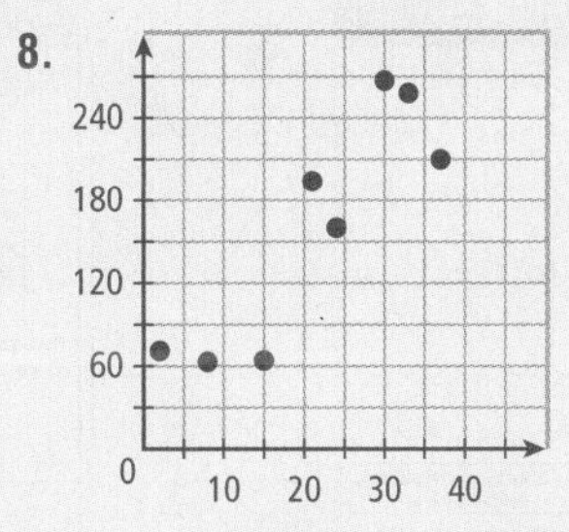

12.

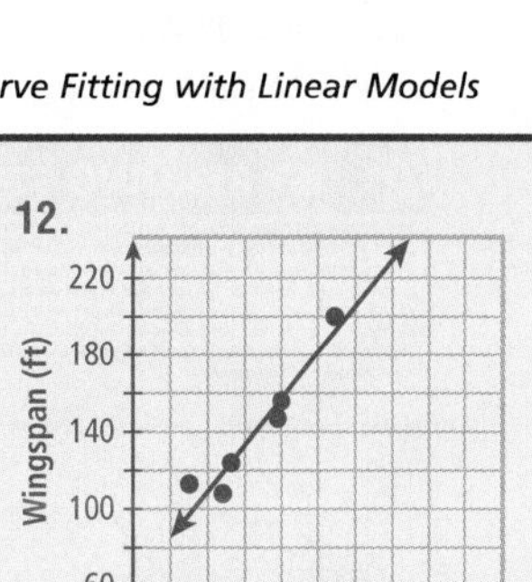

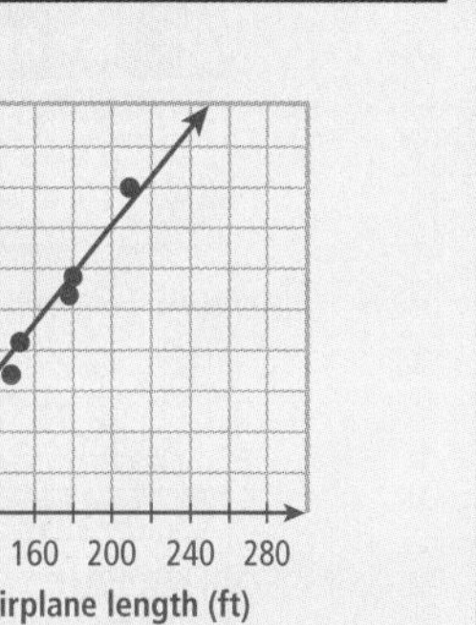

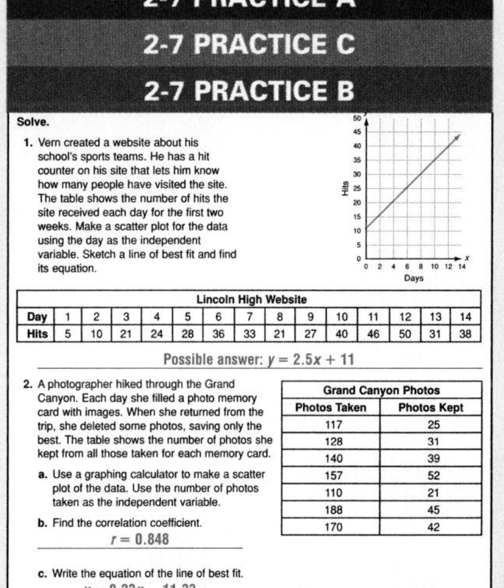

2-7 PRACTICE A
2-7 PRACTICE C
2-7 PRACTICE B

Solve.

1. Vern created a website about his school's sports teams. He has a hit counter on his site that lets him know how many people have visited the site. The table shows the number of hits the site received each day for the first two weeks. Make a scatter plot for the data using the day as the independent variable. Sketch a line of best fit and find its equation.

Lincoln High Website														
Day	1	2	3	4	5	6	7	8	9	10	11	12	13	14
Hits	5	10	21	24	28	36	33	21	27	40	46	50	31	38

Possible answer: $y = 2.5x + 11$

2. A photographer hiked through the Grand Canyon. Each day she filled a photo memory card with images. When she returned from the trip, she deleted some photos, saving only the best. The table shows the number of photos she kept from all those taken for each memory card.

Grand Canyon Photos	
Photos Taken	Photos Kept
117	25
128	31
140	39
157	52
110	21
188	45
170	42

a. Use a graphing calculator to make a scatter plot of the data. Use the number of photos taken as the independent variable.
b. Find the correlation coefficient. $r = 0.848$
c. Write the equation of the line of best fit. $y = 0.33x - 11.33$
d. Predict the number of photos this photographer will keep if she takes 200 photos. Possible answer: about 50 photos

3. What is the relationship between the slope of a line and its correlation coefficient? Possible answer: If the slope is negative, the correlation coefficient is negative. If the slope is positive, the correlation coefficient is positive.

Exercise 13 involves a line of best fit and lines parallel to the line of best fit. This exercise prepares students for the Multi-Step Test Prep on page 164.

Communicating Math After students complete **Exercise 16,** discuss why it is important to recognize that a strong correlation does not imply causality. The correlation coefficient is used to decide whether there is a linear relationship between two variables. It does not say what the relationship is.

Data Collection To help students complete **Exercise 17,** see *Technology Lab Activities.*

In **Exercise 19,** the slope is 1.05 and the correlation coefficient is positive; therefore, students can eliminate choices **A** and **B.** Since a correlation coefficient cannot be greater than 1, choice **C** is the only possible answer.

Answers

13a.

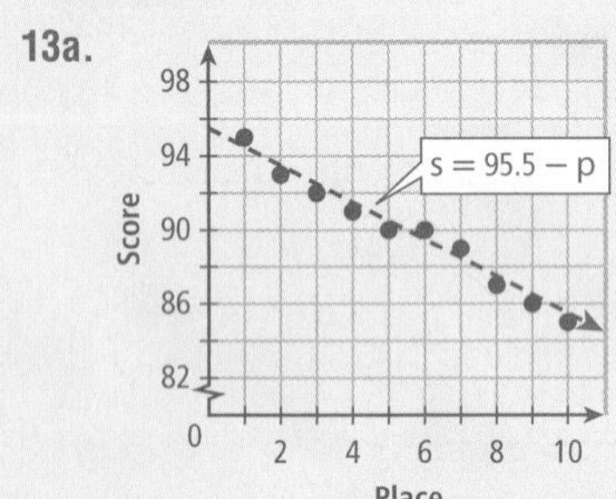

14.

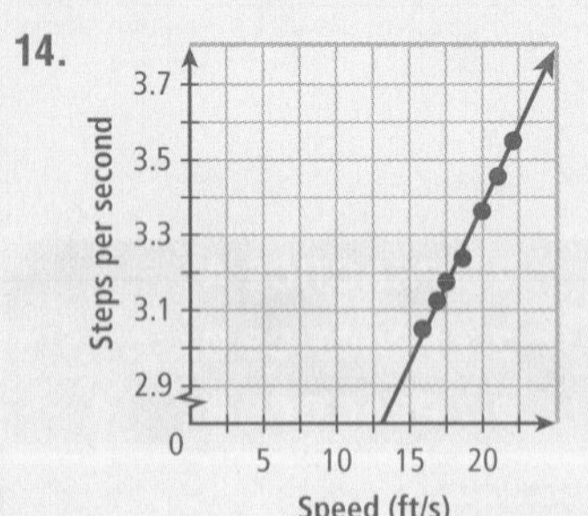

15a.

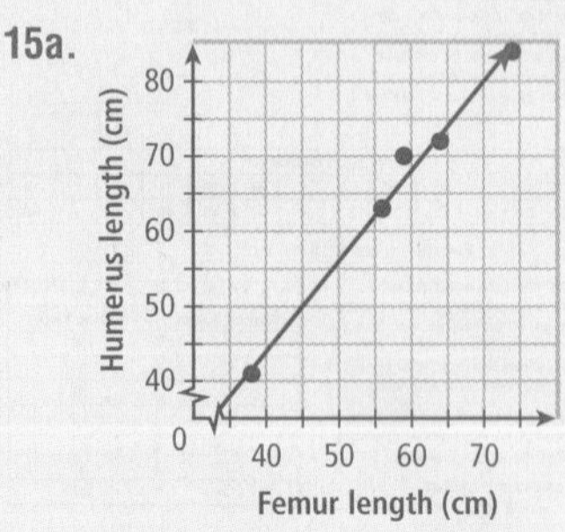

17, 22–24, 32–33. See p. A19.

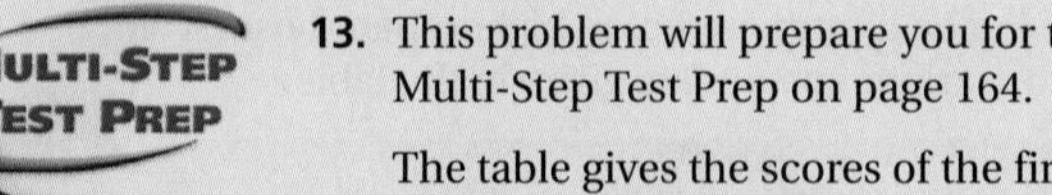

13. This problem will prepare you for the Multi-Step Test Prep on page 164.

The table gives the scores of the first 10 entries in a livestock show competition.

a. What equation could you use to estimate the score from the place? Graph the equation. $s = 95.5 - p$

b. Suppose each score is increased by 5. How would this affect the equation and graph of the line? $s = 100.5 - p$

Competition Results

Place	Score	Place	Score
1	95	6	90
2	93	7	89
3	92	8	87
4	91	9	86
5	90	10	85

14. **Athletics** Use the data set relating the number of steps per second to speed for a group of top female runners at different speeds.

Steps Taken by Distance Runners

Speed (ft/s)	15.86	16.88	17.5	18.62	19.97	21.06	22.11
Steps per second	3.05	3.12	3.17	3.25	3.36	3.46	3.55

Make a scatter plot of the data using speed as the independent variable. Find the correlation coefficient and the line of best fit, and draw it on your scatter plot. Use your equation to predict the number of steps per second taken by a runner going 18 feet per second. How accurate is your prediction? Explain.

14. $r \approx 0.999$; $y = 0.08x + 1.77$; 3.21 steps/s; $r = 0.999$, the data are virtually linear, so the prediction is probably accurate.

15. **Paleontology** The table below shows the lengths of the femur, a leg bone, and the humerus, an arm bone, for five fossil specimens of the archaeopteryx, an extinct animal that had feathers and characteristics of a reptile.

Archaeopteryx Bone Lengths

Femur Length (cm)	38	56	59	64	74
Humerus Length (cm)	41	63	70	72	84

a. Make a scatter plot of the data using femur length as the independent variable. Find the correlation coefficient and the line of best fit. Draw the line of best fit on your scatter plot.

b. What does the slope of your line mean for the archaeopteryx?

c. Use your equation to predict the length of the femur of an archaeopteryx whose humerus is 50 cm long. How accurate do you think your prediction is?

15a. $r = 0.994$; $y \approx 1.20x - 3.66$

b. A 1 cm increase in femur length corresponds to a 1.2 cm increase in humerus length.

c. 44.7 cm; the data are nearly linear, so the prediction is probably accurate.

16. **Critical Thinking** Does a strong linear relationship between two variables mean that one causes the other (for example, if higher daily bee stings correspond to higher ice cream sales)? Explain.

16. No; e.g., there may be a third variable, such as temperature, that causes both variables to change.

17. **Data Collection** Use a graphing calculator and a motion detector. Stand in a doorway and measure the distance to a person as the person walks from the opposite side of the room toward the motion detector. Is a linear model a good model for distance versus time? Explain.

18. **Write About It** Describe the process of finding a line of best fit.
Possible answer: Plot the data, use a calculator to find the r-value and linear regression function $y = mx + b$ that fits the data, and graph the line on the scatter plot.

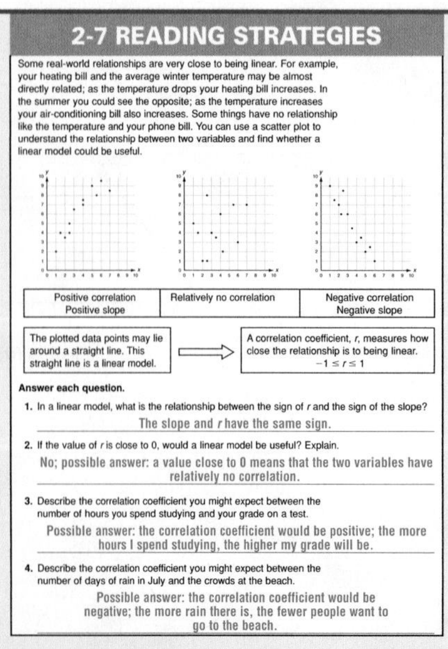

2-7 READING STRATEGIES

Some real-world relationships are very close to being linear. For example, your heating bill and the average winter temperature may be almost directly related; as the temperature drops your heating bill increases. In the summer you could see the opposite; as the temperature increases your air-conditioning bill also increases. Some things have no relationship like the temperature and your phone bill. You can use a scatter plot to understand the relationship between two variables and find whether a linear model could be useful.

Positive correlation Positive slope	Relatively no correlation	Negative correlation Negative slope

The plotted data points may lie around a straight line. This straight line is a linear model. ⟹ A correlation coefficient, r, measures how close the relationship is to being linear. $-1 \le r \le 1$

Answer each question.

1. In a linear model, what is the relationship between the sign of r and the sign of the slope? The slope and r have the same sign.
2. If the value of r is close to 0, would a linear model be useful? Explain. No; possible answer: a value close to 0 means that the two variables have relatively no correlation.
3. Describe the correlation coefficient you might expect between the number of hours you spend studying and your grade on a test. Possible answer: the correlation coefficient would be positive; the more hours I spend studying, the higher my grade will be.
4. Describe the correlation coefficient you might expect between the number of days of rain in July and the crowds at the beach. Possible answer: the correlation coefficient would be negative; the more rain there is, the fewer people want to go to the beach.

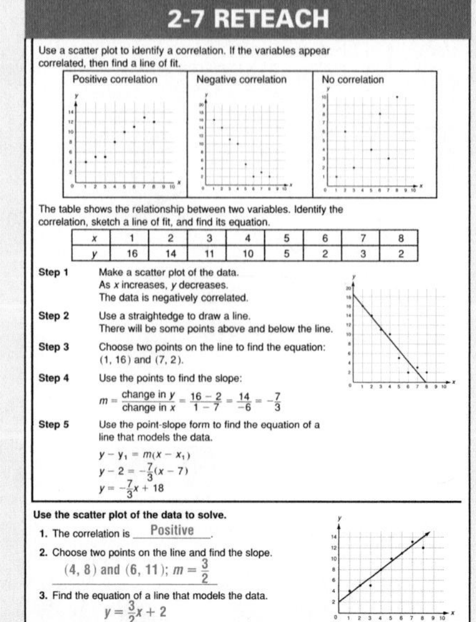

2-7 RETEACH

Use a scatter plot to identify a correlation. If the variables appear correlated, then find a line of fit.

Positive correlation	Negative correlation	No correlation

The table shows the relationship between two variables. Identify the correlation, sketch a line of fit, and find its equation.

x	1	2	3	4	5	6	7	8
y	16	14	11	10	5	2	3	2

Step 1 Make a scatter plot of the data. As x increases, y decreases. The data is negatively correlated.

Step 2 Use a straightedge to draw a line. There will be some points above and below the line.

Step 3 Choose two points on the line to find the equation: (1, 16) and (7, 2).

Step 4 Use the points to find the slope: $m = \frac{\text{change in } y}{\text{change in } x} = \frac{16-2}{1-7} = \frac{14}{-6} = -\frac{7}{3}$

Step 5 Use the point-slope form to find the equation of a line that models the data. $y - y_1 = m(x - x_1)$; $y - 2 = -\frac{7}{3}(x - 7)$; $y = -\frac{7}{3}x + 18$

Use the scatter plot of the data to solve.

1. The correlation is Positive.
2. Choose two points on the line and find the slope. (4, 8) and (6, 11); $m = \frac{3}{2}$
3. Find the equation of a line that models the data. $y = \frac{3}{2}x + 2$

TEST PREP

19. The equation of the line of best fit for a set of data is $y = 1.05x - 1.3$. Which of the following could be the correlation coefficient for the set of data?

   (A) $r = -1.3$ (B) $r = -0.7$ **(C) $r = 0.8$** (D) $r = 1.05$

20. Which of the following best describes the correlation shown?

   (F) Strong positive **(H) Strong negative**
   (G) Weak positive (J) Weak negative

21. Which of the following relationships would likely have a negative correlation coefficient for an automobile?

   (A) Age and total miles (C) Length and width
   (B) Age and resale value (D) Highway mileage and city mileage

CHALLENGE AND EXTEND

Are the data linear? Are the data related? Explain.

22.

x	2	7	13	15	22
y	4	4	4	4	4

23.

x	35	45	55	65	75
y	30	34	36	34	30

24. The following data sets were developed by statistician Frank Anscombe. Make a scatter plot of each set of data, and find r and a line of best fit. Why is it important to plot the data before using a linear model to make predictions?

x	10	8	13	9	11	14	6	4	12	7	5
y	9.14	8.14	8.74	8.77	9.29	8.1	6.13	3.1	9.13	7.26	4.74

x	10	8	13	9	11	14	6	4	12	7	5
y	7.46	6.77	12.74	7.11	7.81	8.84	6.08	5.39	8.15	6.42	5.73

SPIRAL REVIEW

Simplify each expression. *(Lesson 1-4)*

25. $3(x^2 - 2) + 4xy - 10x^2y + 5x^2$

   25. $8x^2 - 10x^2y + 4xy - 6$

26. $-a^4 + 3ab + (2a^2)^2$ $3a^4 + 3ab$

27. $-3g^2 + 3(g - 4) - 2(g - g^2)$ $-g^2 + g - 12$

28. $n(4t^2 - t) - 10nt^2 + nt$ $-6nt^2$

Solve and graph. *(Lesson 2-1)*

29. $3x < x - 12$ $x < -6$

30. $44 + 6x > -5x$ $x > -4$

31. $-2(q - 4) + 3q \le 1 + q$ $\emptyset$; contradiction

Write the equation for each function graphed. Describe $g(x)$ as a transformation of $f(x)$. *(Lesson 2-6)*

32.

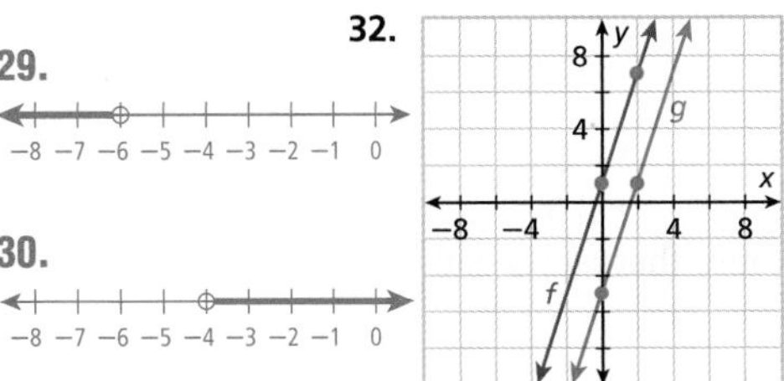

33.

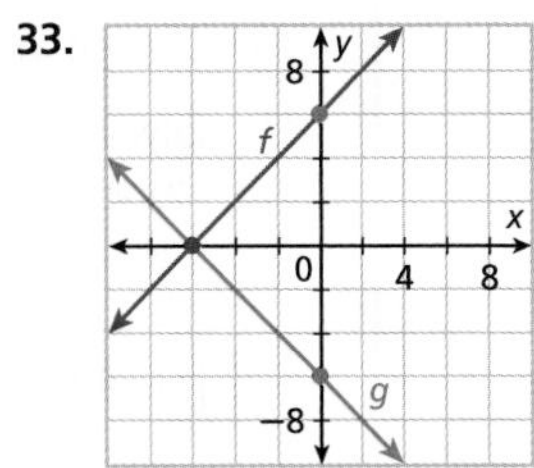

2-7 PROBLEM SOLVING

As a science project, Shelley is studying the relationship of car mileage (miles per gallon) and speed (miles per hour). The table shows the data Shelley gathered using her family's hybrid vehicle.

Speed (miles per hour)	30	40	50	60	70
Mileage (miles per gallon)	34.0	33.5	31.5	29.0	27.5

1. Make a scatter plot of the data. Identify the correlation.
   Negative correlation
2. Sketch a line of best fit on the graph.
3. Use two points on the line to find the slope.
   Slope ≈ -0.15
4. Use the point-slope form to write an equation that models the data.
   Possible answer: $y \approx -0.15x + 38$
5. Use a graphing calculator to plot the data. Find the value of the correlation coefficient r.
   $r \approx -0.98$
6. What does the value of r tell you about the data?
   Possible answer: There is a strong negative correlation.
7. What equation do you find with the calculator for the line of best fit?
   $y \approx -0.175x + 39.85$

Use the equation you wrote in Exercise 3. Choose the letter for the best answer.

8. Predict the mileage for a speed of 55 miles per hour.
   (A) 30
   B 34
   C 39
   D 46
9. Predict the speed if the mileage is 28 miles per gallon.
   A 32
   B 35
   (C) 67
   D 75

2-7 CHALLENGE

The correlation coefficient, r, measures the strength and direction of the linear relationship for a set of data. What happens to r as transformations are applied to the graphs of the data?

x	2	6	9	14	16	21	25	28
y	3	7	15	33	38	35	40	41

1. Make a scatter plot using the data in the table.
2. Use a graphing calculator to find the slope and y-intercept for the line of best fit and the correlation coefficient, r.
   Slope: 1.568; y-intercept: 2.787; $r = 0.925$

Apply each transformation to the original data.

3. horizontal translation 10 units to the right
   a. Describe how the graph would change. Each point would shift 10 units to the right.
   b. How would the relationship between data points change? The relationship between points would not change.
   c. Would you expect a change in the slope or the y-intercept of the line of best fit? The slope would not change; the y-intercept would change.
   d. Would you expect a change in r? Why or why not? No; Possible answer: because the relationship between points has not changed, the correlation is the same.
4. vertical compression by a factor of 0.5
   a. Describe how the graph would change. Each y-value is reduced by half, so the points are closer to the x-axis.
   b. How would the relationship between data points change? The relationship between points would not change.
   c. Would you expect a change in the slope or the y-intercept of the line of best fit? I would expect a change in the slope and the y-intercept
   d. Would you expect a change in r? Why or why not? No; Possible answer: because the relationship between points has not changed, the correlation is the same.
5. reflection across the x-axis
   a. Describe how the graph would change. The x-coordinates are the same, but the y-coordinates are multiplied by −1.
   b. How would the relationship between data points change? The relationship between points would not change.
   c. Would you expect a change in the slope or the y-intercept of the line of best fit? The slope and the y-intercept of the line of best fit are numerically the same, but both are now negative.
   d. Would you expect a change in r? Why or why not? The value of r should be the same, but it is now negative since the data now shows a negative correlation.

Journal

Have students explain in their own words the relationship between the points in a scatter plot and the correlation coefficient that relates the data.

ALTERNATIVE ASSESSMENT

Have students complete a table with 8 to 10 data pairs that show the time it takes one student to get to school and the time the same student stays after school each day. Name the type of correlation and find the equation of the line of best fit. Discuss how accurate the equation would be in making predictions.

Power Presentations with PowerPoint®

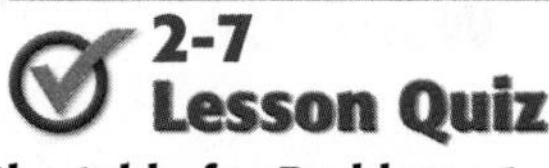

Use the table for Problems 1–3.

Bicycle Tires	
Mass (g)	Price ($)
530	35
520	35
585	30
580	29
540	42
540	35
595	39
730	52

1. Make a scatter plot with mass as the independent variable.

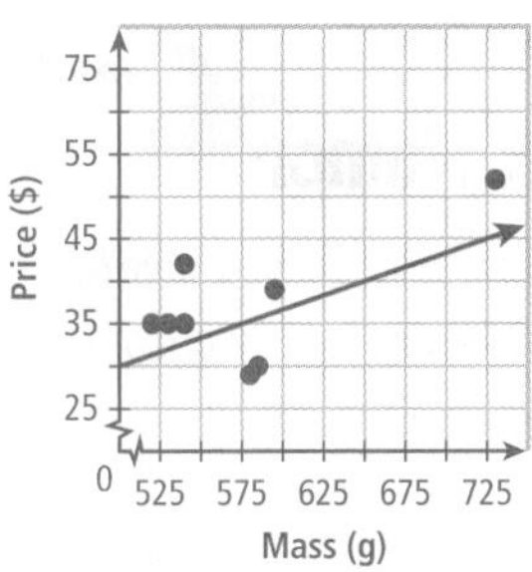

2. Find the correlation coefficient and the equation of the line of best fit. Draw the line of best fit on your scatter plot.
   $r \approx 0.67$; $y = 0.07x - 5.24$; See graph above for line of best fit.
3. Predict the weight of a $40 tire. How accurate do you think your prediction is?
   $\approx$646 g; the scatter plot and value of r show that price is not a good predictor of weight.

Also available on transparency

2-8 Organizer

Pacing: Traditional 2 days
Block 1 day

Objectives: Solve compound inequalities.

Write and solve absolute-value equations and inequalities.

Online Edition
Tutorial Videos, Graphing Calculator

Countdown to Testing Week 5

Power Presentations with PowerPoint®

Warm Up

Solve.

1. $y + 7 < -11$ $y < -18$

2. $4m \geq -12$ $m \geq -3$

3. $5 - 2x \leq 17$ $x \geq -6$

Use interval notation to indicate the graphed numbers.

4.

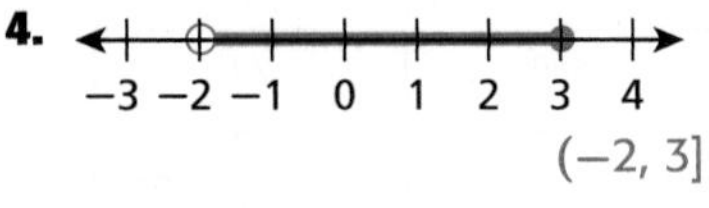

$(-2, 3]$

5.

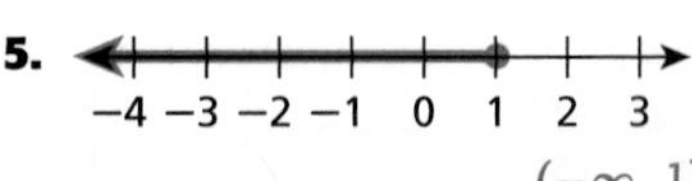

$(-\infty, 1]$

Also available on transparency

Math Humor

Q: Why are you so negative?
A: Just take me for my absolute value!

State Resources

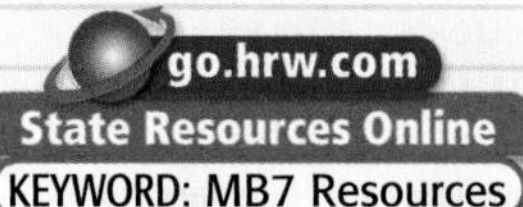

2-8 Solving Absolute-Value Equations and Inequalities

IN **A2.2.4** Solve equations and inequalities involving absolute value of a linear function.

Objectives
Solve compound inequalities.

Write and solve absolute-value equations and inequalities.

Vocabulary
disjunction
conjunction
absolute value

Who uses this?
Absolute value can be used to represent the acceptable ranges for the dimensions of baseball bats classified by length or weight. (See Exercise 43.)

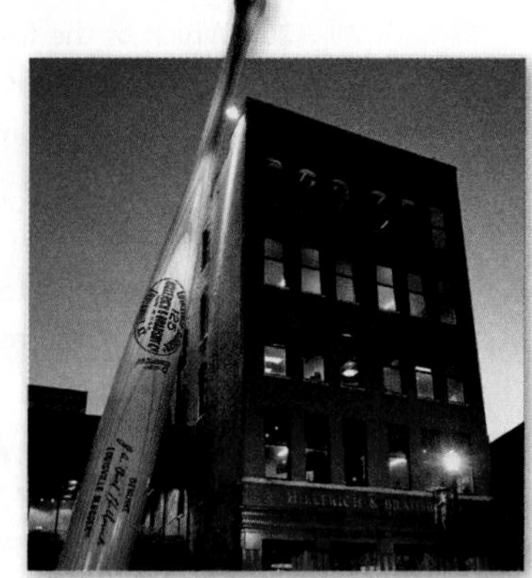

A compound statement is made up of more than one equation or inequality.

A **disjunction** is a compound statement that uses the word *or.*

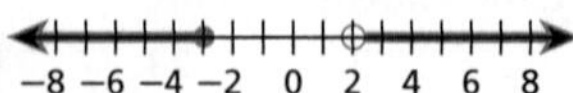

Disjunction: $x \leq -3$ OR $x > 2$ Set builder notation: $\{x|x \leq -3 \cup x > 2\}$

A disjunction is true if and only if at least one of its parts is true.

Reading Math
Dis- means "apart." Disjunctions have two separate pieces. *Con-* means "together." Conjunctions represent one piece.

A **conjunction** is a compound statement that uses the word *and.*

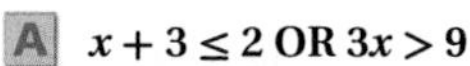

Conjunction: $x \geq -3$ AND $x < 2$ Set builder notation: $\{x|x \geq -3 \cap x < 2\}$
A conjunction is true if and only if all of its parts are true. Conjunctions can be written as a single statement as shown.

$$x \geq -3 \text{ and } x < 2 \rightarrow -3 \leq x < 2$$

EXAMPLE 1 Solving Compound Inequalities

Solve each compound inequality. Then graph the solution set.

A $x + 3 \leq 2$ OR $3x > 9$

Solve both inequalities for x.

$x + 3 \leq 2$	*or*	$3x > 9$
$x \leq -1$		$x > 3$

The solution set is all points that satisfy $\{x|x \leq -1 \text{ or } x > 3\}$.

−8 −6 −4 −2 0 2 4 6 8 $(-\infty, -1] \cup (3, \infty)$

B $-2x < 8$ AND $x - 3 \leq 2$

Solve both inequalities for x.

$-2x < 8$	*and*	$x - 3 \leq 2$
$x > -4$		$x \leq 5$

The solution set is the set of points that satisfy both $x > -4$ and $x \leq 5$, $\{x|-4 < x \leq 5\}$

−8 −6 −4 −2 0 2 4 6 8 $(-4, 5]$

1 Introduce

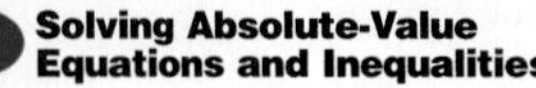

EXPLORATION

2-8 Solving Absolute-Value Equations and Inequalities

A carpenter prepares several wooden dowels whose lengths are 27 cm ± 0.3 cm.

1. What is the range of possible lengths for the dowels?
2. Use the number line to show the range of possible lengths.

26 27 28

3. The carpenter writes the following to show the range of possible lengths.

$-0.3 \leq x - 27 \leq 0.3$

This is equivalent to the two inequalities $-0.3 \leq x - 27$ and $x - 27 \leq 0.3$. Solve the inequalities to show that they represent the same range of lengths.

THINK AND DISCUSS

4. **Describe** different ways to write the range of values shown on this number line.

60 70 80

5. **Demonstrate** how to write an inequality like the one in Problem 3 for the following situation: The weight of a Great Dane is within 5 pounds of 111 pounds.

Motivate

Have students consider a game using a standard number cube. A player wins if the number rolled is even *or* prime. Ask which numbers are winners. 2, 3, 4, 5, 6 Then have students consider a game in which a player wins if the number rolled is even *and* prime. Again, ask which numbers are winners. 2 Discuss the difference between *or* and *and* in this game. Explain that the same distinction exists in the mathematical use of the words.

Explorations and answers are provided in the *Explorations* binder.

Solve each compound inequality. Then graph the solution set.

C $x + 3 > 7$ OR $3x \geq 18$

Solve both inequalities for x.

$x + 3 > 7$ *or* $3x \geq 18$

$x > 4$ $x \geq 6$

Because every point that satisfies $x \geq 6$ also satisfies $x > 4$, the solution set is $\{x \mid x > 4\}$.

−4 −2 0 2 4 6 8

$(4, \infty)$

1a. $\{x \mid x < 3 \cup x \geq 6\}$
b. $\{x \mid x \geq -3 \cap x < 4\}$
c. $\{x \mid x < 17\}$
d. $\{x \mid 4 < x \leq 8\}$

Solve each compound inequality. Then graph the solution set.

1a. $x - 2 < 1$ or $5x \geq 30$ **1b.** $2x \geq -6$ and $-x > -4$

1c. $x - 5 < 12$ or $6x \leq 12$ **1d.** $-3x < -12$ and $x + 4 \leq 12$

Recall that the **absolute value** of a number x, written $|x|$, is the distance from x to zero on the number line. Because absolute value represents distance without regard to direction, the absolute value of any real number is nonnegative.

Absolute Value

WORDS	NUMBERS	ALGEBRA
The absolute value of a real number x, $\lvert x\rvert$, is equal to its distance from zero on a number line.	$\lvert 5\rvert = 5$ $\lvert -5\rvert = 5$	$\lvert x\rvert = \begin{cases} x \text{ if } x \geq 0 \\ -x \text{ if } x < 0 \end{cases}$

Absolute-value equations and inequalities can be represented by compound statements. Consider the equation $|x| = 3$.

Helpful Hint

Think: Greator inequalities involving $>$ or $\geq$ symbols are disjunctions.
Think: Less thand inequalities involving $<$ or $\leq$ symbols are conjunctions.

The solutions of $|x| = 3$ are the two points that are 3 units from zero. The solution is a disjunction: $x = -3$ or $x = 3$.

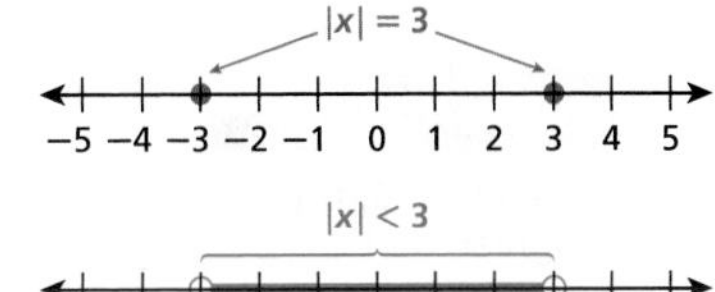

The solutions of $|x| < 3$ are the points that are less than 3 units from zero. The solution is a conjunction: $-3 < x < 3$.

|x| < 3

−5 −4 −3 −2 −1 0 1 2 3 4 5

The solutions of $|x| > 3$ are the points that are more than 3 units from zero. The solution is a disjunction: $x < -3$ or $x > 3$.

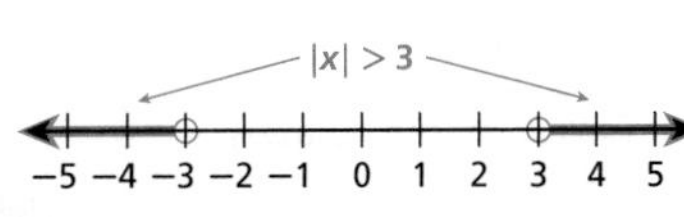

Absolute-Value Equations and Inequalities

For all real numbers x and all positive real numbers a:

$\lvert x\rvert = a$	$\lvert x\rvert < a$	$\lvert x\rvert > a$
$x = -a$ OR $x = a$	$x > -a$ AND $x < a$ $-a < x < a$	$x < -a$ OR $x > a$

Note: The symbol $\leq$ can replace $<$, and the rules still apply. The symbol $\geq$ can replace $>$, and the rules still apply.

Power Presentations with PowerPoint®

Additional Examples

Example 1

Solve each compound inequality. Then graph the solution set.

A. $6y < -24$ or $y + 5 \geq 3$

$\{y \mid y < -4 \text{ or } y \geq -2\}$
$(-\infty, -4) \cup [-2, \infty)$

−6 −5 −4 −3 −2 −1 0 1 2

B. $\frac{1}{2}c \geq -2$ and $2c + 1 < 1$

$\{c \mid -4 \leq c < 0\}$
$[-4, 0)$

−5 −4 −3 −2 −1 0 1 2 3

C. $x - 5 < -2$ or $-2x \leq -10$

$\{x \mid x < 3 \text{ or } x \geq 5\}$
$(-\infty, 3) \cup [5, \infty)$

Also available on transparency

INTERVENTION

Questioning Strategies

EXAMPLE 1

- How do you combine the solutions to the two inequalities to find the solution when the compound inequality is a disjunction? a conjunction?

Answers to Check It Out!

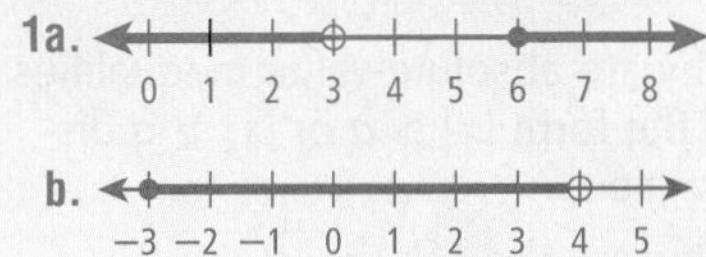

c.

4 6 8 10 12 14 16 18 20

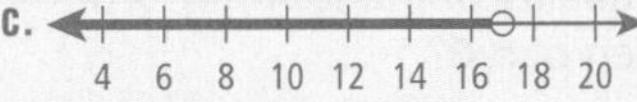

2 Teach

Guided Instruction

Review techniques for graphing inequalities on a number line and review set-builder notation and interval notation. Discuss the definition of *absolute value.* Be sure students can check if a given number is a solution of an absolute-value equation or inequality. Throughout the lesson, emphasize that absolute-value equations are two equations combined into one. Review interval notation and logical connectors for intersection, union, logical OR, and logical AND.

Reaching All Learners

Through Cognitive Strategies

Have students examine $|x|$ by drawing the graphs of $y = |x|$ for $x \geq 0$ and $x < 0$ on the same grid. Discuss the relationship of the two graphs. Point out that for $x \geq 0$, the graph of $y = |x|$ is equivalent to the graph of $y = x$ and that for $x < 0$, the graph of $y = |x|$ is equivalent to the graph of $y = -x$.

Power Presentations with PowerPoint®

Additional Examples

Example 2

Solve each equation.

A. $|-3 + k| = 10$

$k = 13$ or $k = -7$

B. $\left|\frac{x}{4}\right| - 6 = -2$

$x = 16$ or $x = -16$

Example 3

Solve each inequality. Then graph the solution.

A. $|-4q + 2| \geq 10$

$\{q \mid q \leq -2 \text{ or } q \geq 3\}$

$(-\infty, -2] \cup [3, \infty)$

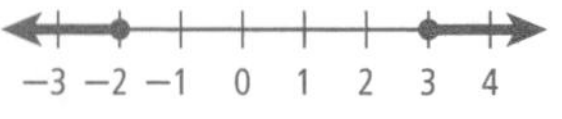

B. $|0.5r| - 3 \geq -3$

{all real numbers}

$(-\infty, \infty)$

−4 −3 −2 −1 0 1 2 3 4

Also available on transparency

INTERVENTION

Questioning Strategies

EXAMPLE 2

- Why is an absolute-value equation really a compound statement?
- How do you know when to write the equation as a disjunction?

EXAMPLE 3

- Why are absolute-value inequalities of the form $|x| > a$ or $|x| \geq a$ disjunctions?
- Why is $\mathbb{R}$ the solution to an inequality of the form $|x| > a$ when $a < 0$?

Answers to *Check It Out!*

3a.

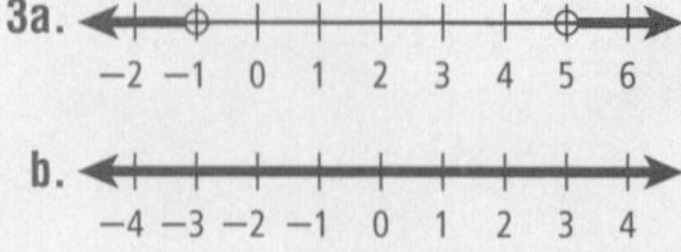

b. −4 −3 −2 −1 0 1 2 3 4

EXAMPLE 2 Solving Absolute-Value Equations

Solve each equation.

A $|x - 7| = 5$ — *This can be read as "the distance from x to 7 is 5."*

$x - 7 = 5$ or $x - 7 = -5$ — *Rewrite the absolute value as a disjunction.*

$x = 12$ or $x = 2$ — *Add 7 to both sides of each equation.*

B $|3x| + 5 = 14$

$|3x| = 9$ — *Isolate the absolute-value expression.*

$3x = 9$ or $3x = -9$ — *Rewrite the absolute value as a disjunction.*

$x = 3$ or $x = -3$ — *Divide both sides of each equation by 3.*

CHECK IT OUT! Solve each equation.

2a. $|x + 9| = 13$ **−22, 4** **2b.** $|6x| - 8 = 22$ **−5, 5**

You can solve absolute-value inequalities using the same methods that are used to solve an absolute-value equation.

Solving an Absolute-value Inequality
1. Isolate the absolute-value expression, if necessary.
2. Rewrite the absolute-value expression as a compound inequality.
3. Solve each part of the compound inequality for x.

EXAMPLE 3 Solving Absolute-Value Inequalities with Disjunctions

Solve each inequality. Then graph the solution set.

A $|2x + 1| > 5$

$2x + 1 > 5$ or $2x + 1 < -5$ — *Rewrite the absolute value as a disjunction.*

$2x > 4$ or $2x < -6$ — *Subtract 1 from both sides of each inequality.*

$x > 2$ or $x < -3$ — *Divide both sides of each inequality by 2.*

$\{x \mid x > 2 \cup x < -3\}$

−8 −6 −4 −2 0 2 4 6 8 $(-\infty, -3) \cup (2, \infty)$

To check, you can test a point in each of the three regions.

$|2(-4) + 1| > 5$ $|-7| > 5$ ✔

$|2(0) + 1| > 5$ $|1| > 5$ ✘

$|2(5) + 1| > 5$ $|11| > 5$ ✔

Helpful Hint

In Example 3B, if you recognize that

$|\text{expression}| > -8$

is always true, you will know the solution immediately.

B $|4x| + 16 > 8$

$|4x| > -8$ — *Isolate the absolute-value expression.*

$4x > -8$ or $4x < 8$ — *Rewrite the absolute value as a disjunction.*

$x > -2$ or $x < 2$ — *Divide both sides of each inequality by 4.*

−4 −2 0 2 4 6 8 $(-\infty, \infty)$

The solution set is *all real numbers*, $\mathbb{R}$.

CHECK IT OUT! Solve each inequality. Then graph the solution set.

3a. $|4x - 8| > 12$ **3b.** $|3x| + 36 > 12$ $\mathbb{R}$

3a. $\{x \mid x < -1 \cup x > 5\}$

Inclusion Demonstrate how to check the solution by substituting numbers from the intervals contained in the solution into the original equation or inequality.

Reading Math Ask students to discuss the meanings of *or* and *and* in everyday usage. Note that the mathematical *or* is not exclusive—a coat *or* a sweater can mean one or both mathematically.

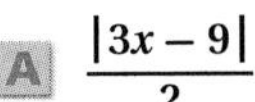

EXAMPLE 4 Solving Absolute-Value Inequalities with Conjunctions

Solve each inequality. Then graph the solution set.

A $\frac{|3x-9|}{2} \leq 12$

$|3x-9| \leq 24$ — *Multiply both sides by 2.*

$3x - 9 \leq 24$ and $3x - 9 \geq -24$ — *Rewrite the absolute value as a conjunction.*

$3x \leq 33$ and $3x \geq -15$ — *Add 9 to both sides of each inequality.*

$x \leq 11$ and $x \geq -5$ — *Divide both sides of each inequality by 3.*

The solution set is $\{x \mid -5 \leq x \leq 11\}$.

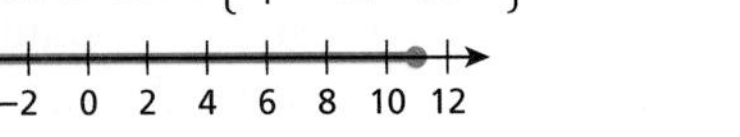

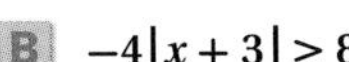

B $-4|x+3| \geq 8$

$|x+3| \leq -2$ — *Divide both sides by −4, and reverse the inequality symbol.*

$x + 3 \leq -2$ and $x + 3 \geq 2$ — *Rewrite the absolute value as a conjunction.*

$x \leq -5$ and $x \geq -1$ — *Subtract 3 from both sides of each inequality.*

Because no real number satisfies both $x \leq -5$ and $x \geq -1$, there is *no solution*. The solution set is ∅.

Helpful Hint

In Example 4B, if you recognize that

|expression| ≤ −2

is never true, you will know the solution immediately.

CHECK IT OUT! Solve each inequality. Then graph the solution set.

4a. $\frac{|x-5|}{2} \leq 4$ $\{x \mid -3 \leq x \leq 13\}$

4b. $-2|x+5| > 10$ ∅

THINK AND DISCUSS

1. Explain why the solution set to $|7x| > -1$ is all real numbers.
2. Explain why there is no solution to $|x+3| \leq -2$. Give another example of an absolute-value equation that has no solution.
3. Write an absolute-value inequality to model "the distance between x and 5 is greater than 10."
4. **GET ORGANIZED** Copy and complete the graphic organizer. Use the flowchart to explain the decisions and steps needed to solve an absolute-value equation or inequality.

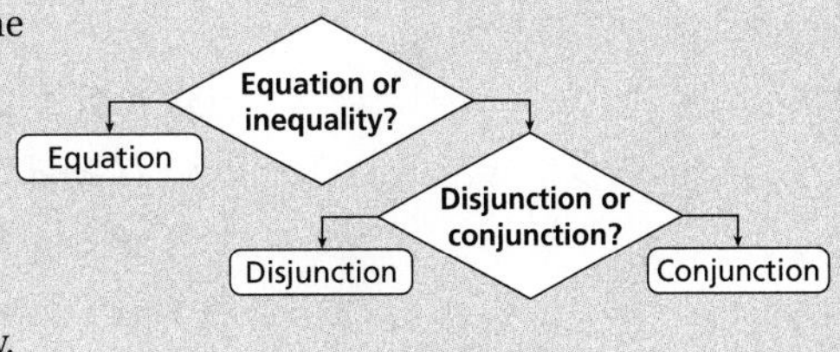

COMMON ERROR ALERT

Students might forget to isolate the absolute-value expression before rewriting an equation or inequality as a compound statement. Remind students that they must first isolate the absolute-value expression and then consider whether the resulting equation or inequality represents a conjunction or a disjunction.

Power Presentations with PowerPoint®

Additional Examples

Example 4

Solve each inequality. Then graph the solution.

A. $\frac{|2x+7|}{3} \leq 1$

$\{x \mid -5 \leq x \leq -2\}$

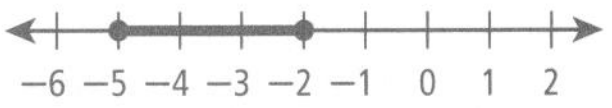

(Number line: −6 −5 −4 −3 −2 −1 0 1 2)

B. $-\frac{1}{2}|p-2| \geq 3$

no solution, ∅

Also available on transparency

INTERVENTION

Questioning Strategies

EXAMPLE 4

- Why are absolute-value inequalities of the form $|x| < a$ or $|x| \leq a$ conjunctions?
- Why is there no solution to an inequality of the form $|x| < a$ when $a \leq 0$?

Answers to *Check It Out!*

4a. (Number line: −10 −5 0 5 10 15 20)

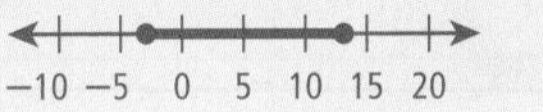

3 Close

Summarize

Review disjunctions as *or* situations and conjunctions as *and* situations.

or

$|x| = a$, $|x| > a$, $|x| \geq a$ are disjunctions

and

$|x| < a$, $|x| \leq a$ are conjunctions

ONGOING ASSESSMENT and INTERVENTION

Diagnose **Before** the Lesson
2-8 Warm Up, TE p. 150

Monitor **During** the Lesson
Check It Out! Exercises, SE pp. 154–156
Questioning Strategies, TE pp. 151–153

Assess **After** the Lesson
2-8 Lesson Quiz, TE p. 156
Alternative Assessment, TE p. 156

Answers to *Think and Discuss*

Possible answers:

1. The left side of the inequality is an absolute value that must be ≥ 0.
2. The left side of the inequality is an absolute value that must be ≥ 0; $|2x-4| + 1 < 0$
3. $|x-5| > 10$
4. See p. A4.

2-8 Exercises

Assignment Guide

Assign *Guided Practice* exercises as necessary.

If you finished Examples **1–2**
- **Basic** 14–19
- **Average** 14–19, 28
- **Advanced** 14–19, 28–31

If you finished Examples **1–4**
- **Basic** 14–33, 36, 43, 53–58, 65–71
- **Average** 14–39, 43–45, 47–60, 65–71
- **Advanced** 14–27, 32, 34, 37–71

Homework Quick Check
Quickly check key concepts.
Exercises: 14, 18, 22, 26, 43

Answers

2.
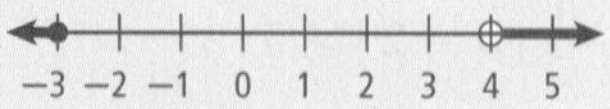

3.
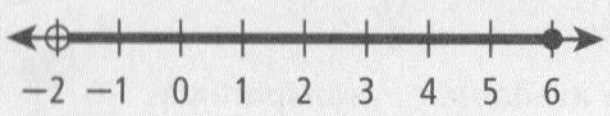

4.
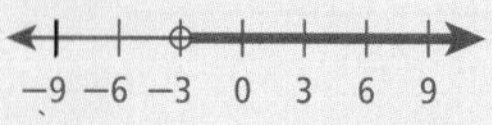

8.
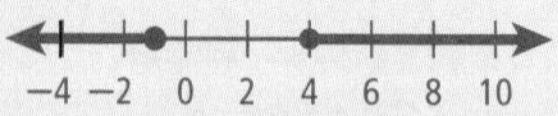

9.
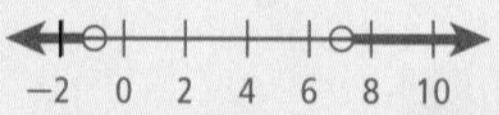

10.
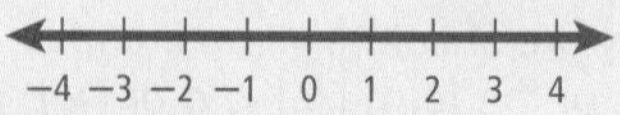

11.
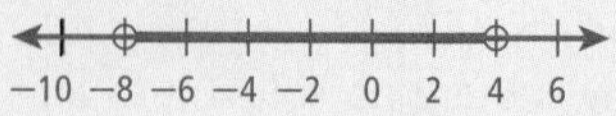

12.
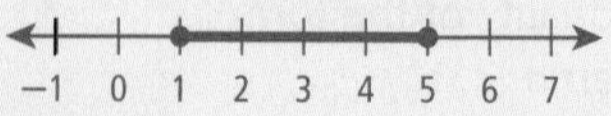

14–15, 20–25, 27, 32–35. For graphs, see p. A19.

State Resources

go.hrw.com
State Resources Online
KEYWORD: MB7 Resources

2-8 Exercises

go.hrw.com
Homework Help Online
KEYWORD: MB7 2-8
Parent Resources Online
KEYWORD: MB7 Parent

GUIDED PRACTICE

1. **Vocabulary** A graph of an inequality on a number line with two parts is a __?__. (*conjunction, disjunction*) **disjunction**

SEE EXAMPLE 1 p. 150

Solve each compound inequality. Then graph the solution set.

2. $x - 7 > -3$ OR $5x \le -15$ **$x \le -3$ or $x > 4$**
3. $3x \le 18$ AND $x + 4 > 2$ **$-2 < x \le 6$**
4. $x - 2 > -5$ OR $5x \ge 25$ **$x > -3$**

SEE EXAMPLE 2 p. 152

Solve each equation.

5. $|x + 5| = 2$ **$-3, -7$**
6. $|2x| - 6 = 4$ **$5, -5$**
7. $|-x| + 4 = 7$ **$3, -3$**

SEE EXAMPLE 3 p. 152

Solve each inequality. Then graph the solution set.

8. $|2x - 3| \ge 5$ **$x \le -1$ or $x \ge 4$**
9. $2|x - 3| > 8$ **$x < -1$ or $x > 7$**
10. $|3x| + 8 > 5$ **$\mathbb{R}$**

SEE EXAMPLE 4 p. 153

11. $\frac{|4x + 8|}{3} < 8$ **$-8 < x < 4$**
12. $|9 - 3x| \le 6$ **$1 \le x \le 5$**
13. $-5|x - 3| \ge 15$ **$\varnothing$**

PRACTICE AND PROBLEM SOLVING

Independent Practice	
For Exercises	See Example
14–15	1
16–19	2
20–23	3
24–27	4

Extra Practice
Skills Practice p. S7
Application Practice p. S33

Solve each compound inequality. Then graph the solution set.

14. $2x - 3 \ge 7$ OR $x + 5 < 2$ **$x < -3$ or $x \ge 5$**
15. $3x + 6 \le 21$ AND $4x - 2 \ge -6$ **$-1 \le x \le 5$**

Solve each equation.

16. $|-3x| = 9$ **$-3, 3$**
17. $|x + 7| = 2$ **$-5, -9$**
18. $|3x - 9| = 6$ **$5, 1$**
19. $5|2x| - 6 = 24$ **$3, -3$**

Solve each inequality. Then graph the solution set.

20. $|-2x| < 2$
21. $|x + 5| \ge 2$
22. $|8x| + 56 \ge 40$
23. $|7x + 14| \ge 35$
24. $|-0.5x| > 1$ **$x < -2$ or $x > 2$**
25. $6|2x + 5| > 66$ **$x < -8$ or $x > 3$**
26. $-8|x + 4| > 48$ **$\varnothing$**
27. $\frac{|8x + 4|}{6} < 10$ **$-8 < x < 7$**

Write a compound inequality for each graph.

28.
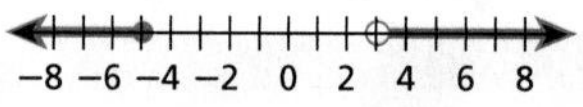

29.
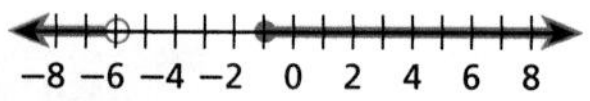

30.
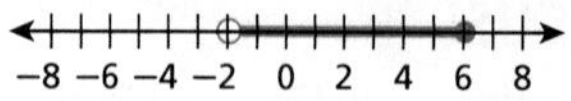

31.
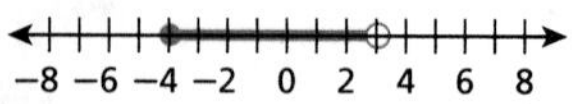

Solve and graph.

32. $5x - 9 > 11$ AND $7x + 12 \le 61$
33. $7x + 4 \le 3x - 12$ OR $\frac{9x - 15}{5} > 6$
34. $4(3 - 2x) < -20$ AND $\frac{3}{2}x - 4 < 5$
35. $5x + 12 > 2x - 3$ OR $3 - 5x < -17$

36. **/// ERROR ANALYSIS ///** Find and explain the error in one solution below.

A

$|3x - 6| < 12$
$3x - 6 < -12$ and $3x - 6 > 12$
$3x < -6$ and $3x > 18$
$x < -2$ and $x > 6$

B

$|3x - 6| < 12$
$3x - 6 > -12$ and $3x - 6 < 12$
$3x > -6$ and $3x < 18$
$x > -2$ and $x < 6$

The second step in A has the inequality symbols reversed.

20. $-1 < x < 1$
21. $x \le -7$ or $x \ge -3$
22. $\mathbb{R}$
23. $x \le -7$ or $x \ge 3$
28. $x \le -5$ or $x > 3$
29. $x < -6$ or $x \ge -1$
30. $-2 < x \le 6$
31. $-4 \le x < 3$
32. $4 < x \le 7$
33. $x \le -4$ or $x > 5$
34. $4 < x < 6$
35. $x > -5$

2-8 READING STRATEGIES

Equations and inequalities can be combined to make compound statements. **Disjunctions** and **conjunctions** are two types of compound statements.

Compound Statement	Definition and Symbol	Example
Disjunction	Two statements joined by the word *or*	$x > 1$ or $x \le -2$
	Symbol: ∪	
Conjunction	Two statements joined by the word *and*	$x > 0$ and $x \le 6$
	Symbol: ∩	

Answer each question.

1. $x > 1$ or $x \le -2$
   a. Is the compound statement true for $x = 6$? Explain.
   Yes; since $x = 6$ makes the first inequality in the disjunction true, the compound statement is also true.
   b. Is the compound statement true for $x = 0$? Explain.
   No; $x = 0$ makes both inequalities false, so the compound statement is also false.
   c. For which values of x is the disjunction false?
   $-2 < x \le 1$; all x-values within this range make both inequalities false.
2. $x > 0$ and $x \le 6$
   a. Describe the values of x for which the conjunction is true.
   The conjunction is true for all numbers greater than 0 and less than or equal to 6.
   b. Describe the values of x for which the conjunction is false?
   The conjunction is false for all numbers less than or equal to 0 and all numbers greater than 6.
3. $|x| > 5$
   a. Describe in words the values of x for which the inequality is true. Then write a compound statement for those values of x.
   All number greater than 5 or all numbers less than -5; $x > 5$ or $x < -5$
   b. Write a compound statement to show all the values of x for which the inequality is false.
   $x \ge -5$ and $x \le 5$

2-8 RETEACH

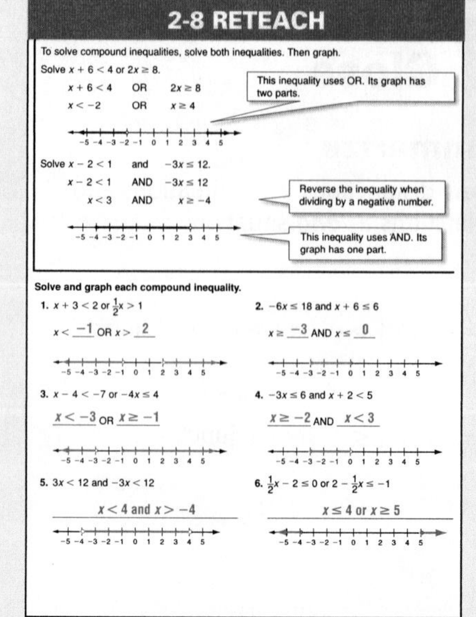

To solve compound inequalities, solve both inequalities. Then graph.

Solve $x + 6 < 4$ or $2x \ge 8$.

$x + 6 < 4$ OR $2x \ge 8$
$x < -2$ OR $x \ge 4$

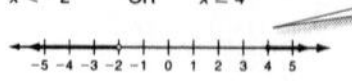

This inequality uses OR. Its graph has two parts.

Solve $x - 2 < 1$ and $-3x \le 12$.

$x - 2 < 1$ AND $-3x \le 12$
$x < 3$ AND $x \ge -4$

Reverse the inequality when dividing by a negative number.

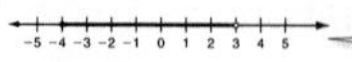

This inequality uses AND. Its graph has one part.

Solve and graph each compound inequality.

1. $x + 3 < 2$ or $\frac{1}{2}x > 1$
   $x <$ **-1** OR $x >$ **2**
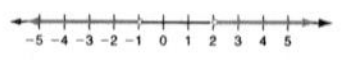

2. $-6x \le 18$ and $x + 6 \le 6$
   $x \ge$ **-3** AND $x \le$ **0**
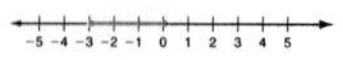

3. $x - 4 < -7$ or $-4x \le 4$
   $x < -3$ OR **$x \ge -1$**
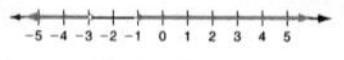

4. $-3x \le 6$ and $x + 2 < 5$
   $x \ge -2$ AND **$x < 3$**
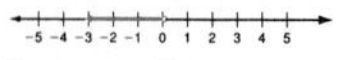

5. $3x < 12$ and $-3x < 12$
   $x < 4$ and $x > -4$
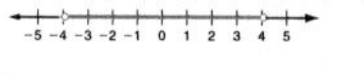

6. $\frac{1}{2}x - 2 \le 0$ or $2 - \frac{1}{2}x \le -1$
   $x \le 4$ or $x \ge 5$
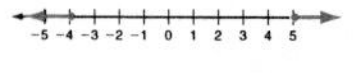

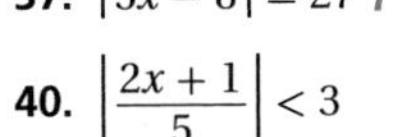

Solve and graph.

37. $|5x - 8| = 27$ $7, -\frac{19}{5}$

38. $8|3x - 10| - 12 = 20$

39. $|4(2x - 5)| \geq 4$

40. $\left|\frac{2x + 1}{5}\right| < 3$

41. $\frac{|4x + 5|}{3} + 9 > 15$

42. $|5 - 6x| - 10 \leq 8$

38. $2, \frac{14}{3}$

39. $x \leq 2$ or $x \geq 3$

40. $-8 < x < 7$

41. $x < -\frac{23}{4}$ or $x > \frac{13}{4}$

42. $-\frac{13}{6} \leq x \leq \frac{23}{6}$

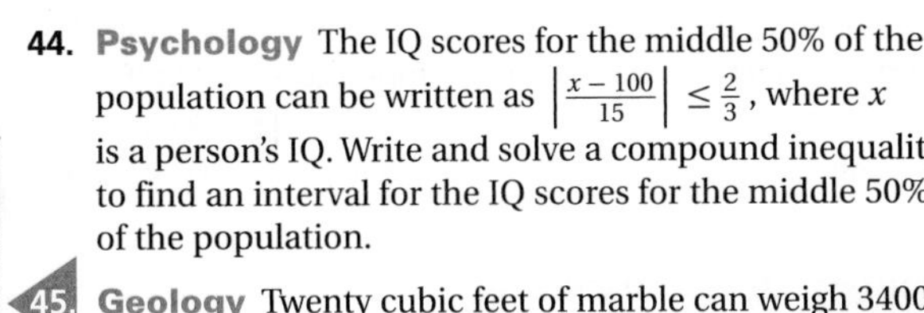

43. Estimation The table shows a sample of baseball bats considered to be within and outside the 32.5-inch-length class by the National Collegiate Athletics Association (NCAA). Write a possible absolute-value inequality to represent the bat lengths considered within the 32.5 inch class of bats.

Bat Lengths (in.)	
32.5-Inch Class	Outside 32.5-Inch Class
32.60	32.18
32.48	32.90
32.36	32.77
32.74	32.24

43. Possible answer: $|\ell - 32.5| < 0.25$

44. Psychology The IQ scores for the middle 50% of the population can be written as $\left|\frac{x - 100}{15}\right| \leq \frac{2}{3}$, where x is a person's IQ. Write and solve a compound inequality to find an interval for the IQ scores for the middle 50% of the population.

LINK

Sculpture

Michelangelo's *David* was sculpted from a single block of Carrara marble. It is nearly 18 feet tall and weighs well over 9 tons.

45. Geology Twenty cubic feet of marble can weigh 3400 pounds, plus or minus 100 pounds. Write and solve an absolute-value inequality for the possible weights of a cubic foot of marble.

46. Business A grocery scale is accurate to within 1 ounce. Write the error in the price when weighing an item that costs \$9 per pound as an absolute value expression.

47. Critical Thinking Is $c|a + b| = |ca + cb|$ always, sometimes, or never true? Justify your answer.

48. Manufacturing The acceptable tolerance of a machine part is 1 foot $\pm \frac{3}{64}$ in. Write the tolerance as an absolute-value equation in feet.

51. Possible answer: $|x - b| = 2a$

The solutions of an absolute-value equation are given. What is the equation?

49. $x = 2 \pm 3$

50. $x = -\frac{5}{2} \pm \frac{9}{2}$

51. $x = b \pm 2a$

49. Possible answer: $|x - 2| = 3$

50. Possible answer: $\left|x + \frac{5}{2}\right| = \frac{9}{2}$

52. Astronomy During 2007, Earth will travel around the Sun along a path that is not a perfect circle. Earth will be closest to the Sun on January 20, at a distance of 91.4 million miles, and farthest on July 7, at a distance of 94.5 million miles. Write and solve an absolute-value inequality for the distance between Earth and the Sun throughout the year.

53. Write About It When is $|x| = |-x|$? When is $|x| = -|x|$? Explain.

MULTI-STEP TEST PREP

54. This problem will help prepare you for the Multi-Step Test Prep on page 164.

For a livestock competition, the weight classes for goats are shown in this table.

a. What is the center of each weight class?

b. How would you express each weight class as an absolute-value expression?

c. Is there exactly one class for any goat in the weight range shown in the table? Explain.

d. **What if...?** Suppose just the upper range of the heavy class were increased by 1 lb. How would the absolute-value expression change to reflect the increase?

Goat Weight Classes	
Class	Weight Range (lb)
Light	40–50
Medium	50–60
Heavy	60–73

MULTI-STEP TEST PREP Exercise 54 involves defining and applying absolute-value equations and inequalities. This exercise prepares students for the Multi-Step Test Prep on page 164.

Answers

37. 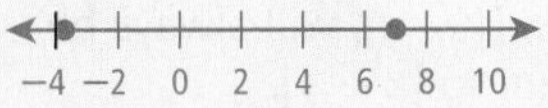 [number line: −4 −2 0 2 4 6 8 10]

38.  [number line: 0 1 2 3 4 5 6 7 8 9]

39. 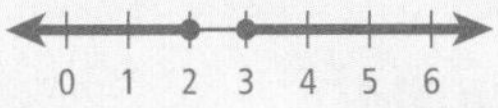 [number line: 0 1 2 3 4 5 6]

40. 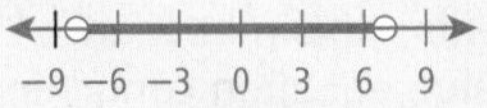 [number line: −9 −6 −3 0 3 6 9]

41. 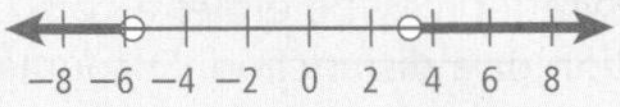 [number line: −8 −6 −4 −2 0 2 4 6 8]

42. 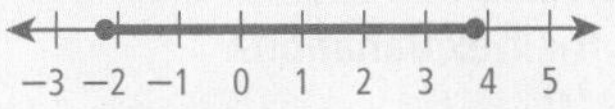 [number line: −3 −2 −1 0 1 2 3 4 5]

44. $\frac{x - 100}{15} \leq \frac{2}{3}$ or $\frac{x - 100}{15} \geq -\frac{2}{3}$; $|x - 100| \leq 10$; $90 \leq x \leq 110$

45. $|20x - 3400| \leq 100$; $165 \leq x \leq 175$

46. $|e| \leq \frac{1}{16}(9)$ or $|e| \leq \$0.5625$

47. Sometimes; if $c \geq 0$, it is true, but if $c < 0$, it is false.

48. $|x - 1| \leq \frac{3}{768}$

52. $|x - 92.95| \leq 1.55$, where x is in millions of mi.

53. Possible answer: Because a number and its opposite are the same distance from 0, $|x| = |-x|$ is always true. Because absolute value is never negative, $|x| = -|x|$ is only true if $x = 0$.

54. See p. A19.

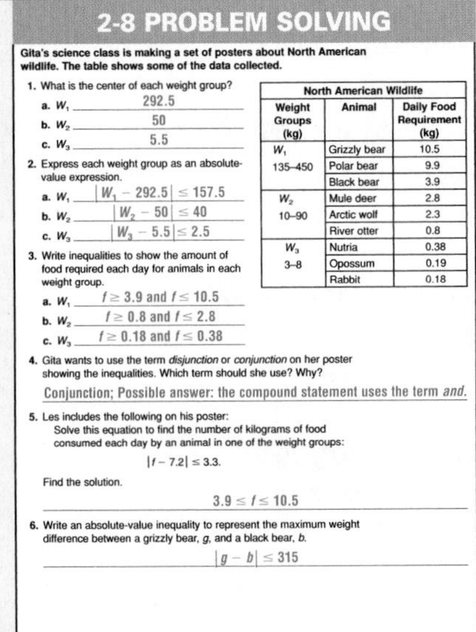

2-8 PROBLEM SOLVING

Gita's science class is making a set of posters about North American wildlife. The table shows some of the data collected.

North American Wildlife		
Weight Groups (kg)	Animal	Daily Food Requirement (kg)
W_1 135–450	Grizzly bear	10.5
	Polar bear	9.9
	Black bear	3.9
W_2 10–90	Mule deer	2.8
	Arctic wolf	2.3
	River otter	0.8
W_3 3–8	Nutria	0.38
	Opossum	0.19
	Rabbit	0.18

1. What is the center of each weight group?
   a. W_1 292.5
   b. W_2 50
   c. W_3 5.5
2. Express each weight group as an absolute-value expression.
   a. W_1 $|W_1 - 292.5| \leq 157.5$
   b. W_2 $|W_2 - 50| \leq 40$
   c. W_3 $|W_3 - 5.5| \leq 2.5$
3. Write inequalities to show the amount of food required each day for animals in each weight group.
   a. W_1 $f \geq 3.9$ and $f \leq 10.5$
   b. W_2 $f \geq 0.8$ and $f \leq 2.8$
   c. W_3 $f \geq 0.18$ and $f \leq 0.38$
4. Gita wants to use the term *disjunction* or *conjunction* on her poster showing the inequalities. Which term should she use? Why?
   Conjunction; Possible answer: the compound statement uses the term *and*.
5. Les includes the following on his poster:
   Solve this equation to find the number of kilograms of food consumed each day by an animal in one of the weight groups:
   $|f - 7.2| \leq 3.3.$
   Find the solution.
   $3.9 \leq f \leq 10.5$
6. Write an absolute-value inequality to represent the maximum weight difference between a grizzly bear, g, and a black bear, b.
   $|g - b| \leq 315$

2-8 CHALLENGE

Changing the value of a coefficient in an absolute-value linear inequality results in a change in the solution interval.

Solve.

1. $|ax + b| \leq c$, where $a > 0$ and $c > 0$.
   a. Solve the inequality for x in terms of a, b, and c. $\frac{-c - b}{a} \leq x \leq \frac{c - b}{a}$
   b. Verify that your solution is equivalent to $\frac{-(b + c)}{a} \leq x \leq \frac{c - b}{a}$.
   Possible answer: The solution of the absolute-value inequality gives $x \leq \frac{c - b}{a}$ and $x \geq \frac{-c - b}{a}$. Read the second inequality from right to left and combine the two inequalities into a single inequality.

Apply the general solution to solve each inequality.

2. $|2x + 3| \leq 5$ $-4 \leq x \leq 1$
3. $|4x + 3| \leq 5$ $-2 \leq x \leq \frac{1}{2}$

Refer to the inequalities in Exercises 2 and 3.

4. a. Compare the values of a, b, and c in the two inequalities.
   The values of b and c are the same in both inequalities. The value of a has increased from the first inequality to the second.
   b. How does the value of a affect the length of the solution interval?
   As a increases, the length of the solution interval decreases.
   c. Predict the solution interval for the inequality $|8x + 3| \leq 5$. $-1 \leq x \leq \frac{1}{4}$
   d. Use the general solution to determine if your prediction was correct.
   $\frac{-5 - 3}{8} \leq x \leq \frac{5 - 3}{8} = \frac{-8}{8} \leq x \leq \frac{2}{8} = -1 \leq x \leq \frac{1}{4}$
   e. What is the relationship between the solution interval and the coefficient of x in this absolute-value inequality?
   Possible answer: When the coefficient of x is doubled, the solution interval is reduced by $\frac{1}{2}$ of the units.

Solve.

5. a. Use the general solution to solve $|3x - 6| \leq 21$. $\frac{-21 + 6}{3} = -5 \leq x \leq \frac{21 + 6}{3} = 9$
   b. Predict the solution interval of $|6x - 6| \leq 21$. $-2.5 \leq x \leq 4.5$
   c. Predict the solution interval of $|12x - 6| \leq 21$. $-1.25 \leq x \leq 2.25$

2-8 PRACTICE A

2-8 PRACTICE C

2-8 PRACTICE B

Solve each equation.

1. $|2x + 1| = 7$ $x = 3$ or $x = -4$
2. $|-7x| = 28$ $x = \pm 4$
3. $3|3x| - 7 = 2$ $x = \pm 1$
4. $|2x - 5| = 5$ $x = 0$ or $x = 5$
5. $2|x + 1| = 14$ $x = 6$ or $x = -8$
6. $|4 - x| + 2 = 9$ $x = -3$ or $x = 11$

Solve each inequality or compound inequality. Then graph the solution.

7. $-4x + 2 > -10$ and $5x - 12 < 8$ $x < 4$
8. $3x - 4 \geq 8$ or $-x + 12 > 16$ $x \geq 4$ or $x < -4$
9. $|9x| \geq 18$ $x \leq -2$ or $x \geq 2$
10. $|3x - 7| > 8$ $x < -\frac{1}{3}$ or $x > 5$
11. $|0.3x| > 1$ $x < -\frac{10}{3}$ or $x > \frac{10}{3}$
12. $|7x| - 12 \leq 9$ $x \geq -3$ and $x \leq 3$

Solve.

13. Any measurement is accurate within ± 0.5 of the measurement unit. For example, if you measure your pencil to the nearest inch, your measurement could be 0.5 inch too long or 0.5 inch too short. Write an absolute-value inequality that shows the maximum and minimum actual measure of a nail measured to be 4.4 centimeters to the nearest 0.1 centimeter.
    $|m - 4.4| \leq 0.05$

For Exercise 55, students should recognize that absolute value can never be negative. Choices **C** and **D** cannot be correct because, depending on the values chosen for x and y, either could be negative. By substituting values into choices **A** and **B,** students should see that choice **B,** $|y - x|$, will always be equivalent to $|x - y|$.

Journal

Have students explain how an absolute-value equation containing a > symbol may be either a conjunction or a disjunction. Encourage students to use examples to illustrate their explanations.

ALTERNATIVE ASSESSMENT

Have students write two absolute-value inequalities, one to illustrate a disjunction and one to illustrate a conjunction. Let students describe how they would use their examples to demonstrate the differences between the meanings of the two inequalities and how they are solved.

2-8 Lesson Quiz

Solve. Then graph the solution.

1. $y - 4 \leq -6$ or $2y > 8$ $\{y \mid y \leq -2 \text{ or } y > 4\}$

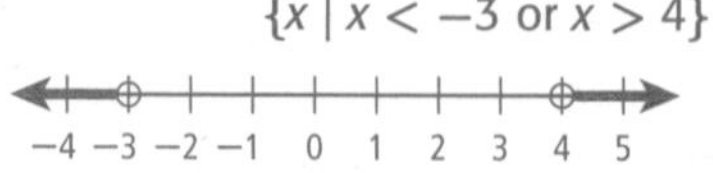

2. $-7x < 21$ and $x + 7 \leq 6$ $\{x \mid -3 < x \leq -1\}$

Solve each equation.

3. $|2v + 5| = 9$ 2 or −7

4. $|5b| - 7 = 13$ ±4

Solve. Then graph the solution.

5. $|1 - 2x| > 7$ $\{x \mid x < -3 \text{ or } x > 4\}$

6. $|3k| + 11 > 8$ $\mathbb{R}$

7. $-2|u + 7| \geq 16$ ∅

Also available on transparency

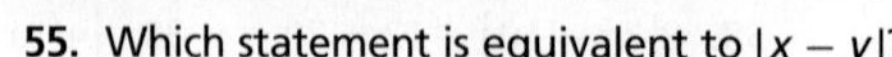

TEST PREP

55. Which statement is equivalent to $|x - y|$?
Ⓐ $|x + y|$ Ⓑ $|y - x|$ Ⓒ $x + y$ Ⓓ $y - x$

56. Which of the following is NOT a solution of $|x - 8| \leq 12$?
Ⓕ $x = 20$ Ⓖ $x = 3$ Ⓗ $x = -2$ Ⓙ $x = -10$

57. How many solutions does $-5|3x + 5| - 6 = 4$ have?
Ⓐ An infinite number Ⓑ 2 Ⓒ 1 Ⓓ 0

58. A thermometer measures 5 body temperatures accurately to within ±0.15°F. Which of the following is an expression for the actual temperature t of a person if this thermometer measures the person's temperature as 98.5°F?
Ⓕ $|t - 98.5| \leq 0.15$ Ⓗ $|t - 98.5| \geq 0.15$
Ⓖ $|t + 98.5| \leq 0.15$ Ⓙ $|t + 98.5| \geq 0.15$

CHALLENGE AND EXTEND

59. Solve $|3x - 8| = 5x$. $x = 1$ or -4

60. Solve $|5x + 2| + 3x \leq 8$. $-5 \leq x \leq \frac{3}{4}$

61. If x is an integer, which statement is equivalent to $|x - 3| < 16$? Explain.
a. $|x - 3| \leq 16$ **b.** $|x - 3| \leq 15$ **c.** $|x - 3| \leq 17$ **d.** $|x - 2| \leq 16$

62. Are the solution sets of $|x + a| = b$ and $|x| + a = b$ the same? Explain.

63. Consider the equation $(a + b) + c = a + (b + c)$.
a. What property of real numbers does this demonstrate?
b. Is $|a + b| + c = a + |b + c|$ a true statement? Support your answer.
c. What can you conclude about this property with respect to absolute value?

64. Technology A binary search repeatedly divides records of a sorted file in half until the correct record is found. For example, to find data in record 6 of an 8-record file, the binary search will examine records 1–8, then it would narrow the search to records 5–8, then 5–6, then locate the data in record 6. Write absolute-value statements for the records searched in the first three search intervals.

SPIRAL REVIEW

65. Travel Pamela filled her 15 gal gas tank before a trip. She added 13 gal after driving 385 mi and 14 gal after another 412 mi. Estimate the number of mi/gal her car got on this trip. *(Previous course)* ≈ 30 mi/gal

Determine the value of n. Identify the property demonstrated. *(Lesson 1-2)*

66. $7 \cdot n = 1$ **67.** $24 + 16 = (n + 4)4$ **68.** $(2 + 3) + n = 0$

Geometry Find the measure of each angle in the quadrilaterals below. (Hint: The sum of the angle measures in a quadrilateral is 360°.) *(Lesson 2-1)*

69.

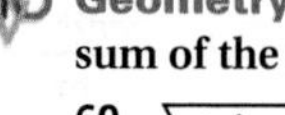

70.

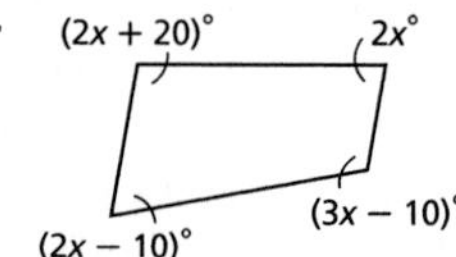

71.

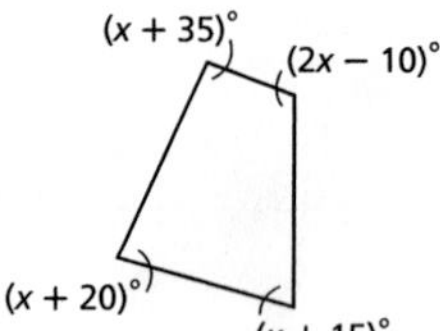

Answers

61. the solutions $-13 < x < 19$ and $-12 \leq x \leq 18$ contain the same integers.

62. No; one solution to each is the same, $x = b - a$, but the second solutions are different. One is $x = a - b$, the other is $x = -a - b$.

63a. Associative Property

b. No, e.g., $|1 + 2| + (-3) = 0$ but $1 + |2 + (-3)| = 2$.

c. The Associative Property does not hold for absolute-value expressions.

64. $|x - 512.5| \leq 511.5$; $|x - 265.5| \leq 255.5$; $|x - 128.5| \leq 127.5$

66. $n = \frac{1}{7}$; Multiplicative Inverse Property

67. $n = 6$; Distributive Property

68. $n = -5$; Additive Inverse Property

69. 60°; 80°; 100°; 120°

70. 100°; 80°; 110°; 70°

71. 95°; 110°; 75°; 80°

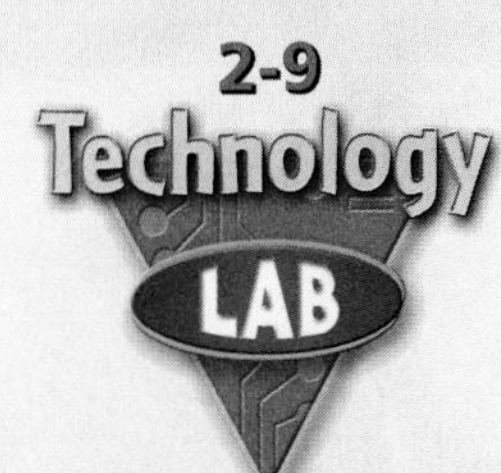

Solving Absolute-Value Equations

A graphing calculator is helpful for visualizing solutions of absolute value equations.

Use with Lesson 2-9

Activity

1 Use a table to solve $2|x-3|=4$.

Enter the left side of expression in the Y= editor. Press MATH and use the **NUM** menu for **ABS(**.

Use the defaults for 2nd WINDOW (TBLSET), and then select 2nd GRAPH (TABLE) to see values for $2|x-3|$ when $x = 0, 1, 2, 3, \ldots$

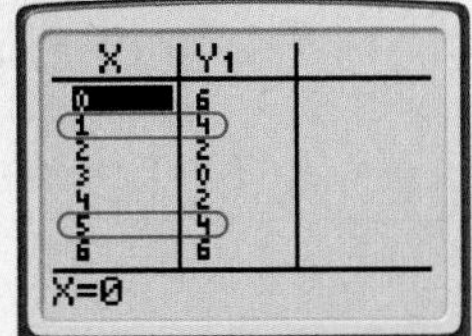

Notice that **Y1** = 4 when $x = 1$ and when $x = 5$. If you scroll up and down the table, you will see that the values of **Y1** get farther and farther from 4. The solution set is $\{1, 5\}$.

2 Use a graph to solve $2|x-3|=4$.

First get 0 on one side by adding -4 to both sides of the equation, obtaining the equation $2|x-3|-4=0$

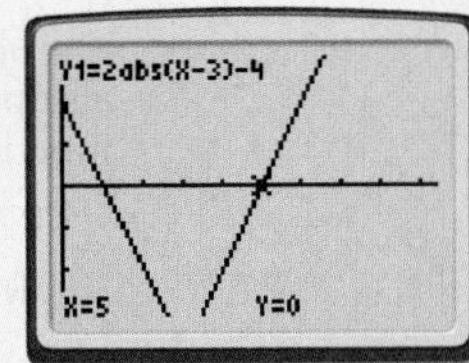

Enter the left side of the equation as **Y1**, and graph in the friendly window $[0, 9.4]$ by $[-3.2, 3.2]$. TRACE to the solutions $x = 1$ and $x = 5$.

You can test $x = 1$ and $x = 5$ back in the original equation on the home screen.

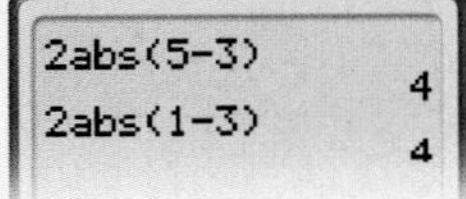

You should check algebraically.

$$\begin{array}{r|l} 2|x-3| & = 4 \\ \hline 2|1-3| & 4 \\ 2(2) & 4 \\ 4 & 4\ \checkmark \end{array} \qquad \begin{array}{r|l} 2|x-3| & = 4 \\ \hline 2|5-3| & 4 \\ 2(2) & 4 \\ 4 & 4\ \checkmark \end{array}$$

Try This

1. Solve $3|x-1|=6$ by using a table of values. Then solve by graphing. $\{-1, 3\}$
2. Solve $5|x+3|=0$ by using a table of values. Then solve by graphing. $\{-3\}$
3. What happens when you solve $2|x+1|=-4$ by using a table of values? What happens when you solve by graphing?
   The left side is never negative; there is no intersection point.

Technology Lab Organizer

Use with Lesson 2-9

Pacing:
Traditional $\frac{1}{2}$ day
Block $\frac{1}{4}$ day

Objective: Use a graphing calculator to solve absolute-value equations.

Materials: graphing calculator

Online Edition
Graphing Calculator, TechKeys

Resources

Technology Lab Activities
Lesson 2-9

Teach

Discuss

Remind students that the solution of an equation is the value or values that make the expressions on both sides equal.

Ask "If an absolute-value equation has exactly one solution, where is the solution on the graph?" It is the value of x at the vertex of the absolute-value function.

Close

Key Concept

The TABLE and GRAPH features of a graphing calculator can be used to solve absolute-value equations.

Assessment

Journal Have students explain how they would use the GRAPH feature to solve an absolute-value equation.

State Resources

go.hrw.com
State Resources Online
KEYWORD: MB7 Resources

2-9 Organizer

Pacing: Traditional 1 day
Block $\frac{1}{2}$ day

Objective: Graph and transform absolute value-functions.

Online Edition
Graphing Calculator, Tutorial Videos, TechKeys

Countdown to Testing Week 5

Power Presentations with PowerPoint®

Warm Up

Evaluate each expression for $f(4)$ and $f(-3)$.

1. $f(x) = -|x + 1|$ $-5; -2$
2. $f(x) = 2|x| - 1$ $7; 5$
3. $f(x) = |x + 1| + 2$ $7; 4$

Let $g(x)$ be the indicated transformation of $f(x)$. Write the rule for $g(x)$.

4. $f(x) = -2x + 5$; vertical translation 6 units down
$g(x) = -2x - 1$
5. $f(x) = \frac{1}{2}x + 2$; vertical stretch by a factor of 4
$g(x) = 2x + 8$

Also available on transparency

Math Humor

Q: Why was the parent function upset with its child?
A: It was stretched to its limit.

2-9 Absolute-Value Functions

A2.1.2 Use and interpret function notation, including evaluation of functions represented by tables, graphs, words, equations or a set of ordered pairs.

Objective
Graph and transform absolute-value functions.

Vocabulary
absolute-value function

Who uses this?
Park rangers can use absolute value to monitor the movement of an animal as it passes a specific location. (See Exercise 30.)

An **absolute-value function** is a function whose rule contains an absolute-value expression. The graph of the parent absolute-value function $f(x) = |x|$ has a V shape with a minimum point or vertex at $(0, 0)$.

Know it! Note

The Absolute-Value Parent Function $f(x) = |x|$

Domain: all real numbers

Range: nonnegative real numbers

Vertex: (0,0)

x	$y = \|x\|$
−10	10
−5	5
0	0
5	5
10	10

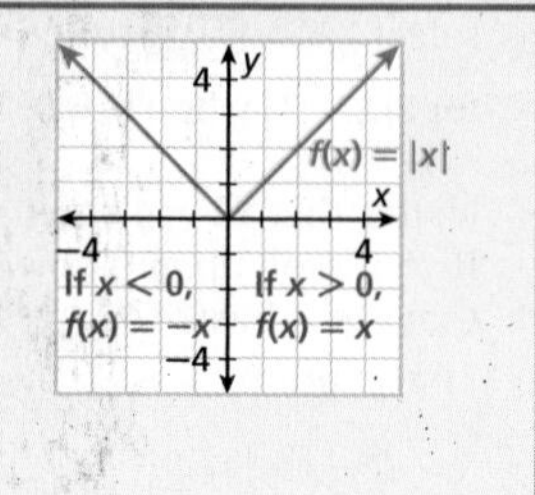

The absolute-value parent function is composed of two linear pieces, one with a slope of −1 and one with a slope of 1. In Lesson 2-6, you transformed linear functions. You can also transform absolute-value functions.

EXAMPLE 1 Translating Absolute-Value Functions

Let $g(x)$ be the indicated transformation of $f(x) = |x|$. Write the rule for $g(x)$ and graph the function.

A 2 units up

$f(x) = x$

$g(x) = f(x) + k$

$g(x) = x + 2$ *Substitute.*

The graph of $g(x) = |x| + 2$ is the graph of $f(x) = |x|$ after a vertical shift of 2 units up. The vertex of $g(x)$ is $(0, 2)$.

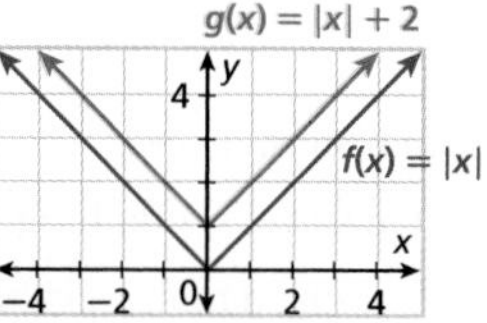

B 3 units left

$f(x) = |x|$

$g(x) = f(x - h)$

$g(x) = \left|x - (-3)\right| = |x + 3|$ *Substitute.*

The graph of $g(x) = |x + 3|$ is the graph of $f(x) = |x|$ after a horizontal shift of 3 units left. The vertex of $g(x)$ is $(-3, 0)$.

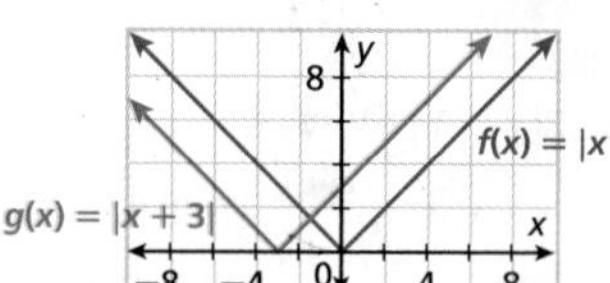

Remember!
The general forms for translations are
Vertical:
$g(x) = f(x) + k$

Horizontal:
$g(x) = f(x - h)$

State Resources

go.hrw.com
State Resources Online
KEYWORD: MB7 Resources

1 Introduce

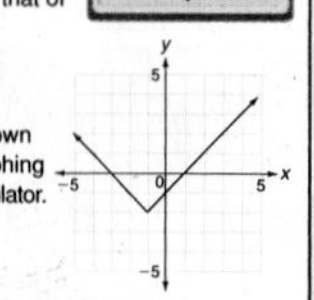

EXPLORATION

2-9 Absolute-Value Functions

You can use a graphing calculator to explore transformations of the function $y = |x|$.

1. Press Y=. To enter the function $y = |x|$ press MATH and then select **NUM** from the menu at the top of the screen. Then press ENTER. You can then complete **Y1** as **Y1=abs(X)**.
2. Graph the function in a square window.
3. Graph $y = |x| + 3$ on the same coordinate plane as $y = |x|$. How does the graph of $y = |x| + 3$ compare to that of $y = |x|$?
4. Graph $y = |x - 4|$. Describe the graph.
5. Write a function for the graph shown here. Check your answer by graphing the function on your graphing calculator.

THINK AND DISCUSS

6. Describe how you would sketch a graph of $y = |x - 1| + 5$.
7. Explain how you know whether a graph of an absolute value

Motivate

Sketch the graph of $f(x) = x$ for $x \geq 0$. Repeat for $f(x) = -x$ for $x \leq 0$ using the same coordinate plane. Have students discuss shapes and properties of the graphs. For example, the graph is symmetric about the y-axis, and it has a minimum point at $(0, 0)$. Remind students of the definition of *absolute value.* Connect the graph on the board to the absolute-value function.

Explorations and answers are provided in the *Explorations* binder.

1a. 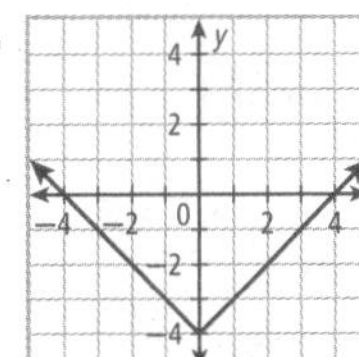

CHECK IT OUT! Let $g(x)$ be the indicated transformation of $f(x) = |x|$. Write the rule for $g(x)$ and graph the function.

1a. 4 units down $g(x) = |x| - 4$

1b. 2 units right $g(x) = |x - 2|$

Because the entire graph moves when shifted, the shift from $f(x) = |x|$ determines the vertex of an absolute-value graph.

Vertex of an Absolute-Value Function

The graph of $g(x) = |x - h| + k$ is the image of $f(x) = |x|$ after a horizontal shift of h units and a vertical shift of k units so that the vertex is at (h, k).

EXAMPLE 2 Translations of an Absolute-Value Function

1b. 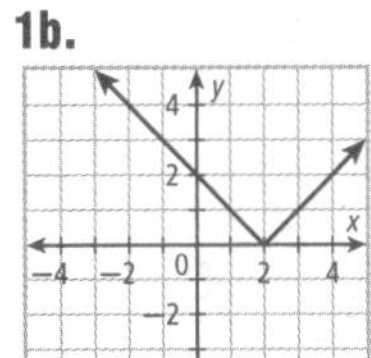

Translate $f(x) = |x|$ so that the vertex is at $(-5, 3)$. Then graph.

$g(x) = |x - h| + k$

$g(x) = |x - (-5)| + 3$ *Substitute.*

$g(x) = |x + 5| + 3$

The graph of $g(x) = |x + 5| + 3$ is the graph of $f(x) = |x|$ after a vertical shift up 3 units and a horizontal shift left 5 units.

The graph confirms that the vertex is $(-5, 3)$

2. 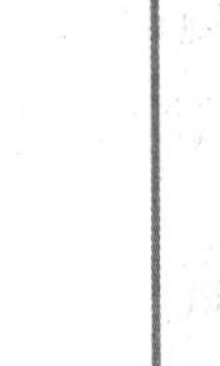

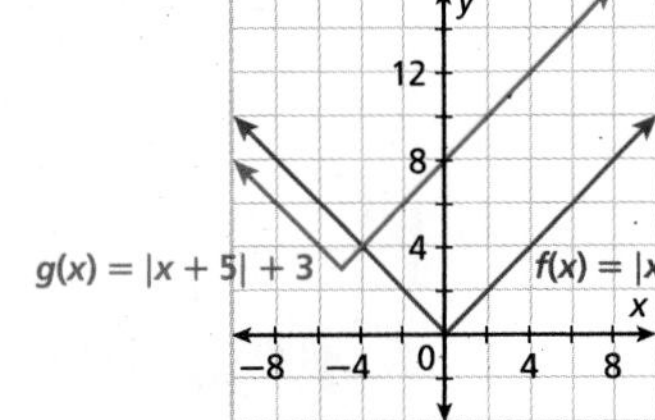

CHECK IT OUT! 2. Translate $f(x) = |x|$ so that the vertex is at $(4, -2)$. Then graph.

$g(x) = |x - 4| - 2$

Absolute-value functions can also be stretched, compressed, and reflected.

EXAMPLE 3 Transforming Absolute-Value Functions

Perform each transformation. Then graph.

A **Reflect the graph of $f(x) = |x + 2| + 1$ across the x-axis.**

$g(x) = -f(x)$ *Take the opposite of the entire function.*

$g(x) = -(|x + 2| + 1)$ *Distribute the negative sign.*

The vertex of the graph of $g(x) = -|x + 2| - 1$ is $(-2, -1)$. The graph is reflected across the x-axis.

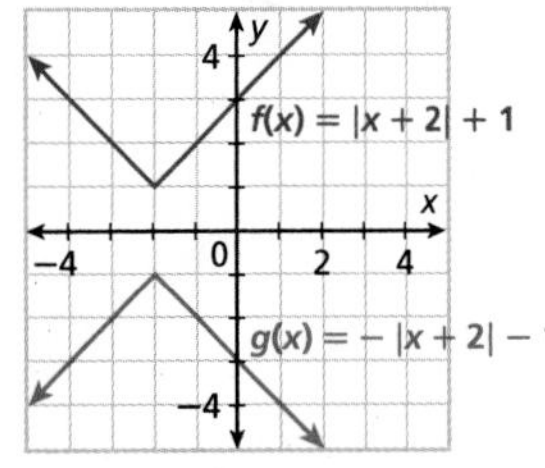

Remember!

Reflection across x-axis: $g(x) = -f(x)$

Reflection across y-axis: $g(x) = f(-x)$

2 Teach

Guided Instruction

Discuss why the absolute-value function is not a linear function and how it is similar to a linear function. The general forms for the transformations of linear functions can also be applied to the absolute-value function. Review the form of each transformation and how it is applied in **Examples 1–3.** You may also wish to review the values of a and b for stretches and compressions (e.g., stretch if $a > 1$; $b > 1$, and compression if $0 < a < 1$; $0 < b < 1$).

Reaching All Learners

Through Cooperative Learning

Have students work in pairs. One student can graph the ray representing either half of an unnamed absolute-value function. Then the other student can use properties of symmetry to complete the graph. Together they can determine the function rule represented by the graph.

Power Presentations with PowerPoint®

Additional Examples

Example 1

Perform each transformation on $f(x) = |x|$. Then graph the transformed function $g(x)$.

A. 5 units down $g(x) = |x| - 5$

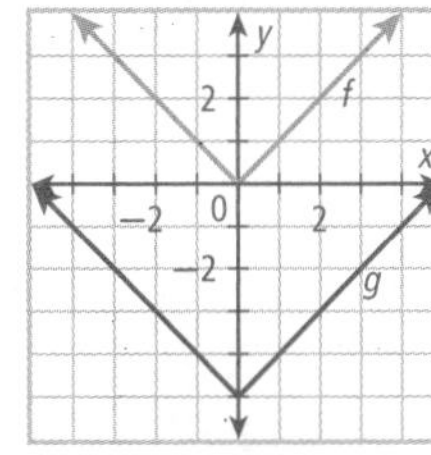

B. 1 unit left $g(x) = |x + 1|$

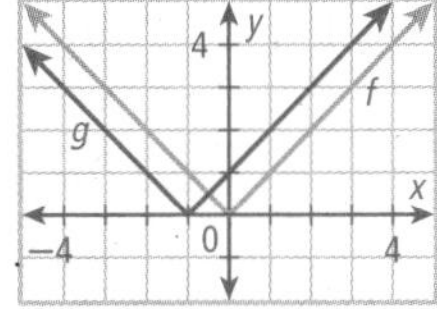

Example 2

Translate $f(x) = |x|$ so that the vertex is at $(-1, -3)$. Then graph.

$g(x) = |x + 1| - 3$

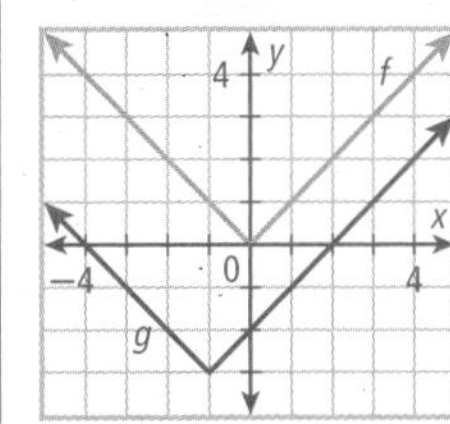

Also available on transparency

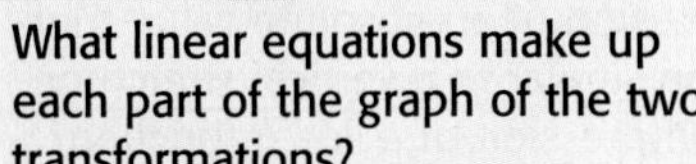

INTERVENTION

Questioning Strategies

EXAMPLE 1

- What linear equations make up each part of the graph of the two transformations?
- How will the graphs of an absolute-value function and its translation look on the same coordinate plane?

EXAMPLE 2

- How can you sketch the graph of the transformation without making a table of values?
- Is the vertex of an absolute-value function always a minimum point? Explain.

Power Presentations with PowerPoint®

Additional Examples

Example 3

Perform each transformation. Then graph.

A. Reflect the graph of $f(x) = |x - 2| + 3$ across the y-axis. $g(x) = |-x - 2| + 3$

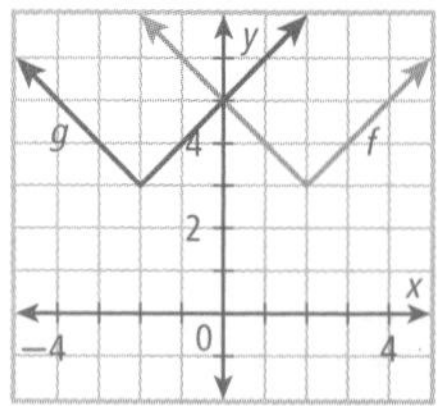

B. Stretch the graph of $f(x) = |x| - 1$ vertically by a factor of 2. $g(x) = 2|x| - 2$

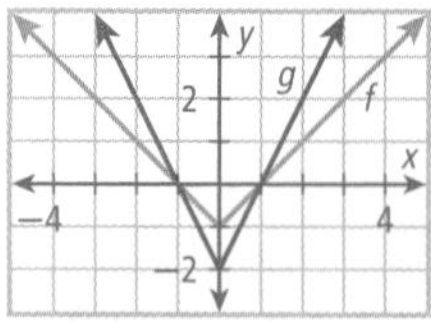

C. Compress the graph of $f(x) = |x + 2| - 1$ horizontally by a factor of $\frac{1}{2}$. $g(x) = |2x + 2| - 1$

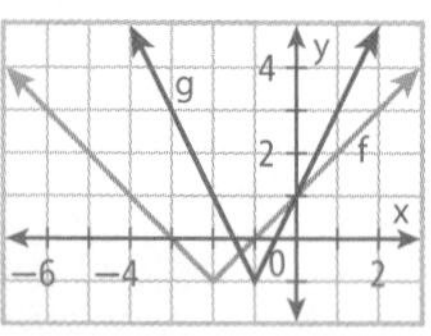

Also available on transparency

INTERVENTION
Questioning Strategies

EXAMPLE 3

- How is a vertical stretch and compression of an absolute-value function similar to a vertical stretch or compression of a linear function? How is it different?

3a.

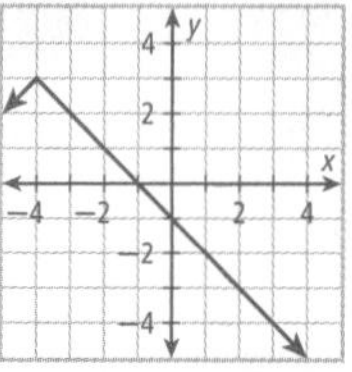

Remember!

Vertical stretch and compression:
$g(x) = af(x)$

Horizontal stretch and compression:
$g(x) = f\left(\frac{1}{b}x\right)$

3b.

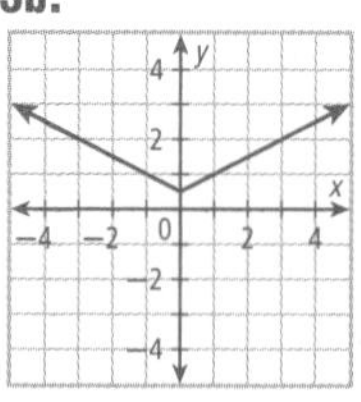

3c.

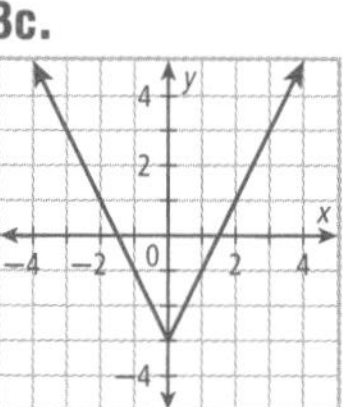

Perform each transformation. Then graph.

B Stretch the graph of $f(x) = |x| - 2$ vertically by a factor of 3.

$g(x) = af(x)$

$g(x) = 3(|x| - 2)$ *Multiply the entire function by 3.*

$g(x) = 3|x| - 6$

The graph of $g(x) = 3|x| - 6$ is the graph of $f(x) = |x| - 2$ after a vertical stretch by a factor of 3. The vertex of g is at $(0, -6)$.

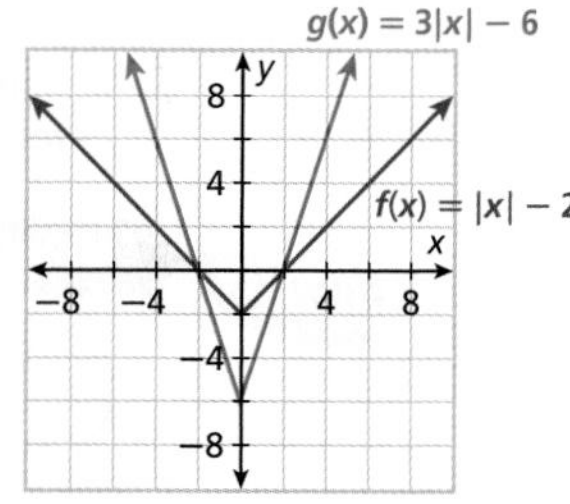

C Compress the graph of $f(x) = |x - 1| - 3$ horizontally by a factor of 0.5.

$g(x) = f\left(\frac{1}{b}x\right)$

$g(x) = \left|\frac{1}{0.5}x - 1\right| - 3$ *Substitute 0.5 for b.*

$g(x) = |2x - 1| - 3$ *Simplify.*

The graph of $g(x) = |2x - 1| - 3$ is the graph of $f(x) = |x - 1| - 3$ after a horizontal compression by a factor of 0.5. The vertex of g is $\left(\frac{1}{2}, -3\right)$.

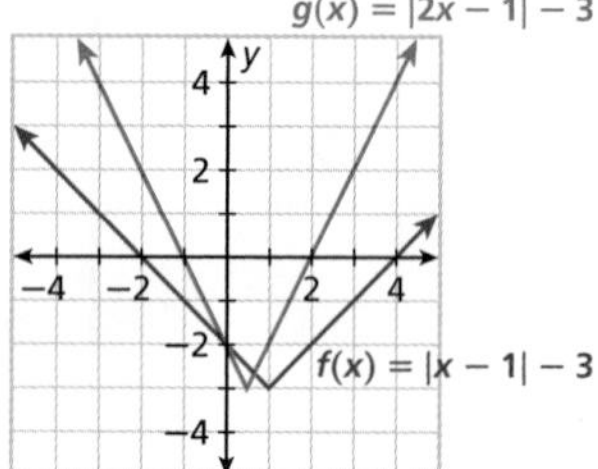

CHECK IT OUT! Perform each transformation. Then graph.

3a. Reflect the graph of $f(x) = -|x - 4| + 3$ across the y-axis.

3b. Compress the graph of $f(x) = |x| + 1$ vertically by a factor of $\frac{1}{2}$.

3c. Stretch the graph of $f(x) = |4x| - 3$ horizontally by a factor of 2.

3a. $g(x) = -|-x - 4| + 3$ **3b.** $g(x) = \frac{1}{2}(|x| + 1)$ **3c.** $g(x) = |2x| - 3$

THINK AND DISCUSS

1. Explain why the vertex of $f(x) = |x|$ stays the same when the graph is stretched but not when the graph is shifted.
2. Tell what the graph of $y = |-x|$ looks like.
3. **GET ORGANIZED** Copy and complete the graphic organizer. Fill in the table with examples of absolute-value transformations.

Transformation	Absolute-Value Function	Transformed Function	Graph
Vertical translation			
Horizontal translation			
(h, k) translation			
Stretch			
Compression			
Reflection			

3 Close

Summarize

Ask students:

- How does a vertical translation affect the graph of an absolute-value function? How does a horizontal translation affect it? Vertex moves up or down in vertical translation; vertex moves right or left in horizontal translation.
- How does the process of stretching an absolute-value function compare to that of other functions you've seen? The process is the same.

ONGOING ASSESSMENT

and INTERVENTION

***Diagnose Before* the Lesson**
2-9 Warm Up, TE p. 158

***Monitor During* the Lesson**
Check It Out! Exercises, SE pp. 159–160
Questioning Strategies, TE p. 159

***Assess After* the Lesson**
2-9 Lesson Quiz, TE p. 163
Alternative Assessment, TE p. 163

Answers to *Think and Discuss*

1. When the vertex is (0, 0), multiplying either coordinate by any real number still results in 0, but adding a nonzero value changes the coordinate and moves the vertex.
2. The graph is the same as $y = |x|$ because it is a reflection across the y-axis and the graph is symmetric about the y-axis.
3. See p. A4.

go.hrw.com
Homework Help Online
KEYWORD: MB7 2-9
Parent Resources Online
KEYWORD: MB7 Parent

GUIDED PRACTICE

1. **Vocabulary** Explain the reason for the shape of the graph of an *absolute-value function.* The graph is the line $y = x$ where negative x-values are reflected over the x-axis, creating a V.

SEE EXAMPLE 1 p. 158

Let $g(x)$ be the indicated transformation of $f(x) = |x|$. Write the rule for $g(x)$ and graph the function.

2. 5 units down $g(x) = |x| - 5$
3. 4 units left $g(x) = |x + 4|$

SEE EXAMPLE 2 p. 159

Translate $f(x) = |x|$ so that the vertex is at the given point. Then graph.

4. $(-4, -5)$ $g(x) = |x + 4| - 5$
5. $(1, 6)$ $g(x) = |x - 1| + 6$

SEE EXAMPLE 3 p. 159

Perform each transformation. Then graph.

6. Reflect the graph of $f(x) = |2x + 3| - 4$ across the y-axis. $g(x) = |2(-x) + 3| - 4$
7. Stretch $f(x) = |x + 3|$ vertically by a factor of 2. $g(x) = 2|x + 3|$
8. Compress $f(x) = |x + 3|$ horizontally by a factor of $\frac{2}{3}$. $g(x) = \left|\frac{3}{2}x + 3\right|$

PRACTICE AND PROBLEM SOLVING

Independent Practice

For Exercises	See Example
9–11	1
12–14	2
15–17	3

Extra Practice
Skills Practice p. S7
Application Practice p. S33

Let $g(x)$ be the indicated transformation of $f(x) = |x|$. Write the rule for $g(x)$ and graph the function.

9. 2 units right $g(x) = |x - 2|$
10. 1 unit down $g(x) = |x| - 1$
11. 4 units left $g(x) = |x + 4|$

Translate $f(x) = |x|$ so that the vertex is at the given point. Then graph.

12. $(8, 0.5)$ $g(x) = |x - 8| + 0.5$
13. $(1.5, 4.5)$ $g(x) = |x - 1.5| + 4.5$
14. $(-2.5, 3)$ $g(x) = |x + 2.5| + 3$

Perform each transformation. Then graph.

15. Reflect $f(x) = |x - 5| + 2$ across the x-axis. $g(x) = -|x - 5| - 2$
16. Compress $f(x) = |2x| - 3$ vertically by a factor of $\frac{1}{4}$. $f(x) = \frac{1}{4}(|2x| - 3)$
17. Stretch $f(x) = |2x| - 3$ horizontally by a factor of $\frac{3}{2}$. $f(x) = \left|2\left(\frac{2}{3}x\right)\right| - 3$ 
18. **Football** Yard lines of a football field have the relationship shown in the table below (0 yard lines are the goal lines).

Football Field Yard Lines

Distance from One End Zone (yd)	0	10	20	30	40	50	60	70	80	90	100
Marked Yard Line	0	10	20	30	40	50	40	30	20	10	0

a. Write an absolute-value function to find the marked yard line for a given distance from the end zone. (*Hint:* Graph the ordered pairs to find the transformation from $f(x) = |x|$.) $g(x) = -|x - 50| + 50$

b. What yard line is 195 feet from the end zone? 35 yard line

c. **What if...?** Suppose the absolute-value function is based on the distance from the end zone *in feet.* How would this relationship affect the function?

18c. The function is horizontally stretched by a factor of 3; $h(x) = -\left|\frac{1}{3}x - 150\right| + 150$

Assignment Guide

Assign *Guided Practice* exercises as necessary.

Basic 9–17, 19–29 odd, 32–37, 43–56
Average 9–25, 27–31 odd, 32–37, 40, 42–56
Advanced 10–17, 19–20, 22–27, 29–56

Homework Quick Check
Quickly check key concepts.
Exercises: 10, 14, 16, 20

Answers

2.
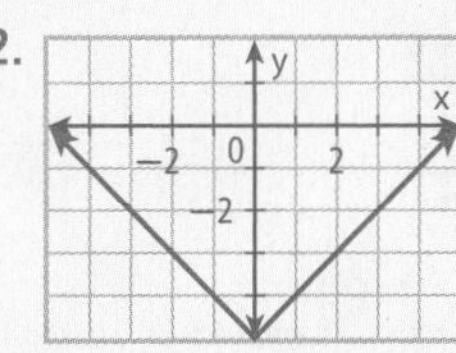

3.
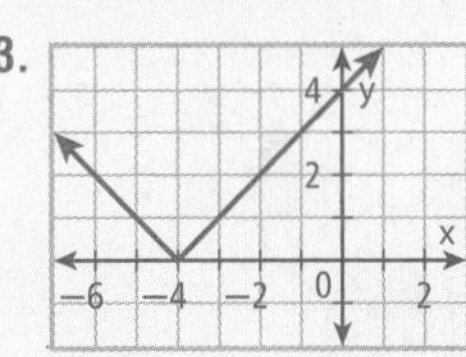

4.
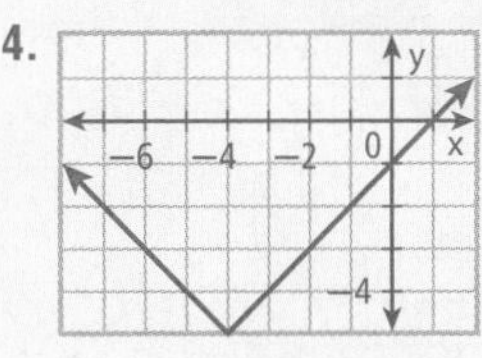

5.
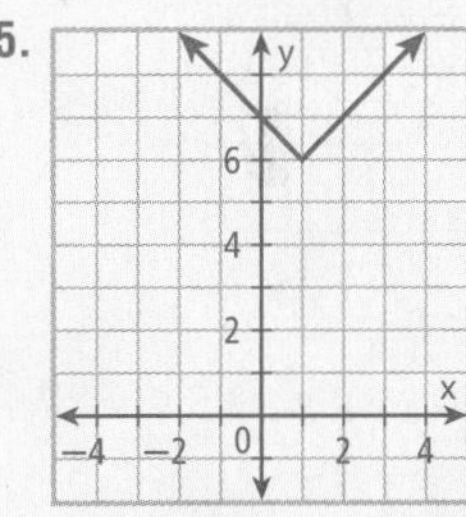

6.
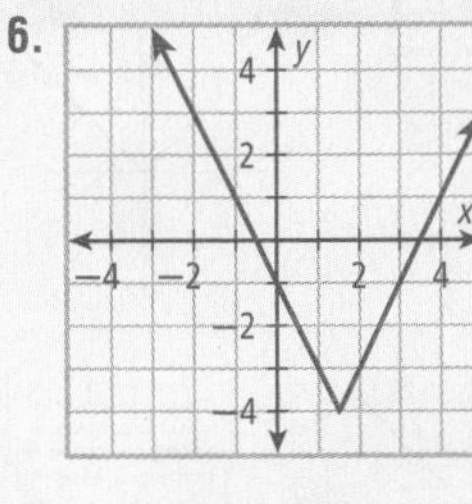

7.
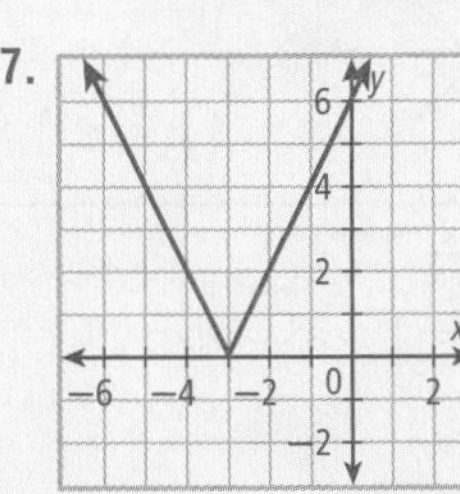

8.
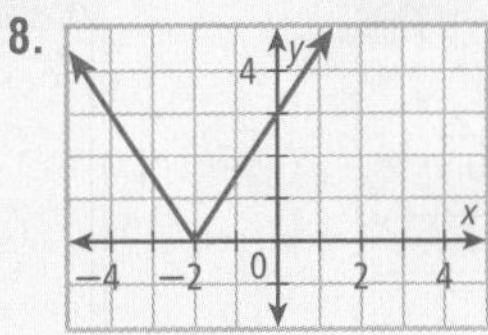

9.
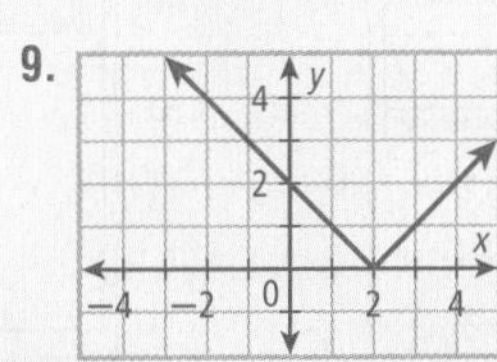

10.
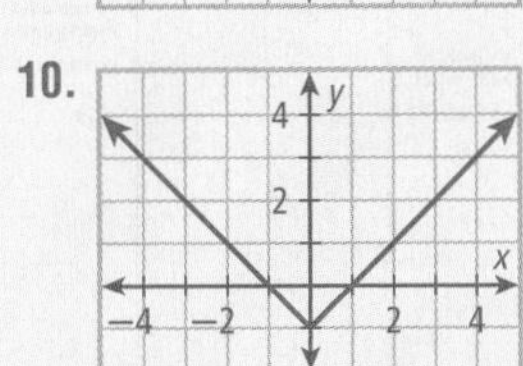

11.
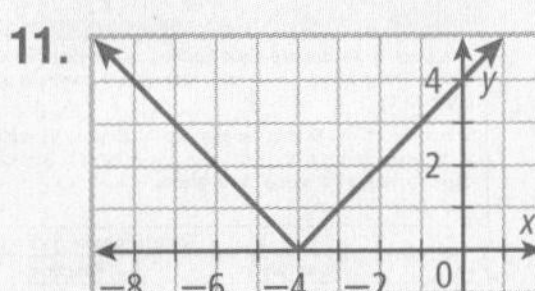

12.
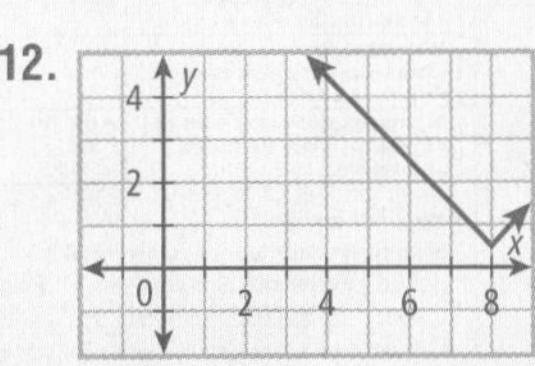

13–17. For graphs, see p. A20.

State Resources

go.hrw.com
State Resources Online
KEYWORD: MB7 Resources

Visual In **Exercises 19–21,** students may need to graph to see the transformation. Encourage them to predict the transformation and to use the graph to check it.

MULTI-STEP TEST PREP **Exercise 32** involves defining and graphing an absolute-value function. This prepares students for the Multi-Step Test Prep on page 164.

Answers

19.

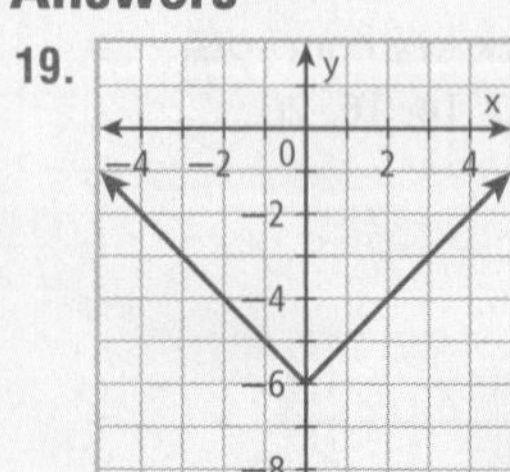

20.

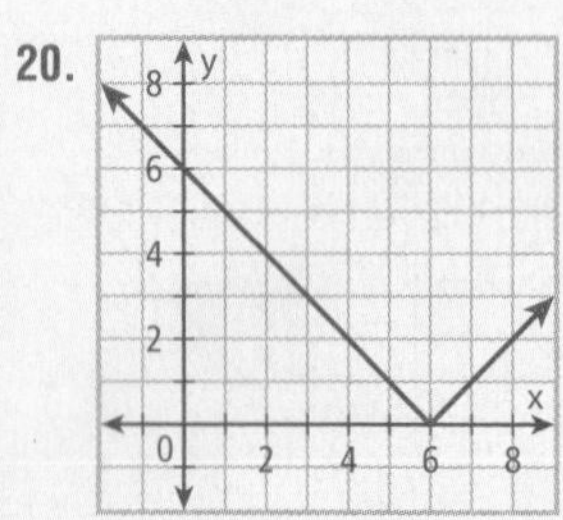

21.

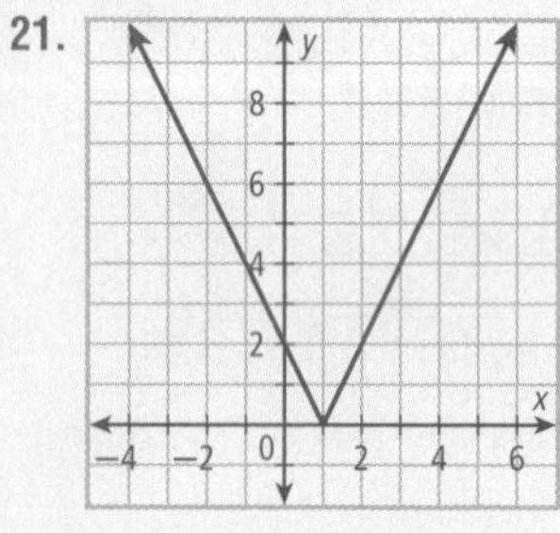

25, 30a–c. See p. A20.

32c, 38–42. For graphs, see p. A20.

19. translated 6 units down

20. translated 6 units right

21. translated 1 unit right and vertically stretched by a factor of 2

22. (12, 8)

23. (−5, 9)

24. (7, 6)

27. $f(x) = |x - 2| - 4$

28. $f(x) = |x + 6| + 4$

29. $f(x) = -|x - 4|$

31. Possible answer: They both make the graph narrower, but a vertical stretch may move the vertex vertically, while a horizontal compression may move the vertex horizontally.

State the transformation from the graph of $f(x) = |x|$. Then graph the transformed function.

19. $g(x) = |x| - 6$ **20.** $g(x) = |x - 6|$ **21.** $g(x) = 2|x - 1|$

Find the vertex of the graph of each function.

22. $g(x) = |x - 12| + 8$ **23.** $g(x) = |x + 5| + 9$ **24.** $g(x) = 6 + |x - 7|$

25. Write About It How do the slopes of the two parts of an absolute-value function compare? Justify your answer and give examples.

26. Critical Thinking Name two different transformations that move $f(x) = |x|$ 4 units up. translation 4 units up; translation 4 units down and reflection across x-axis

Find an absolute-value function for each graph.

27.

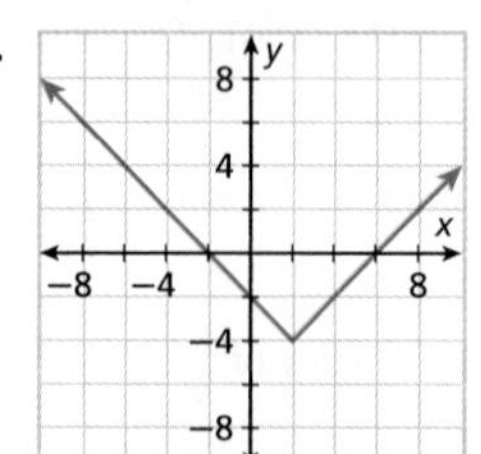

28.

29.

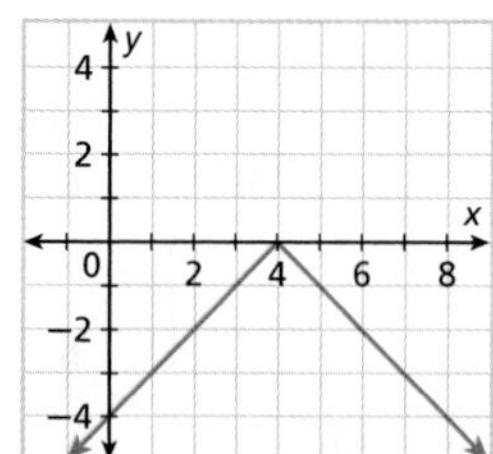

30. Zoology Park rangers track a panther by using a radio transmitter. The panther's distance from the ranger station can be modeled by the function $d = \left|760 - \frac{4}{3}t\right| + 10$, where d is distance in meters and t is the time in seconds since the rangers started timing.

a. How fast is the panther walking along the path? $\frac{4}{3}$ m/s

b. Find the vertex of the function. How long will it take the panther to reach its closest point to the ranger station? (570, 10); 570 s, or 9.5 min

c. How long will the panther be within 200 meters of the ranger station? c. 285 s, or 4.75 min

d. How far from the ranger station will the panther be after 15 minutes? 450 m

31. Critical Thinking Compare vertical stretch to horizontal compression. How are they different? How are they the same?

MULTI-STEP TEST PREP

32. This problem will prepare you for the Multi-Step Test Prep on page 164.

For a livestock competition, the weight classes for hogs are shown in this table.

Hog Weight Classes	
Class	Weight Range (lb)
Light	200–230
Heavy	230–250

a. What is the center of each weight class? 215; 240

b. Write functions in terms of y for the range of each weight class. Specify the domain for each.

c. Graph the functions on the same coordinate plane for the relevant domain.

d. Where would the functions overlap without the domain restrictions? at (227.5, 12.5)

32b. $y = |w - 215|$ D: [200, 230]; $y = |w - 240|$ D: [230, 250]

2-9 PRACTICE A

2-9 PRACTICE C

2-9 PRACTICE B

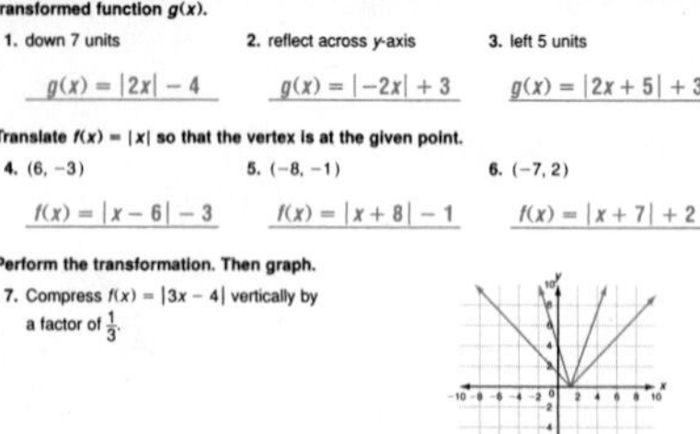

Perform each transformation on $f(x) = |2x| + 3$. Write the transformed function $g(x)$.

1. down 7 units $g(x) = |2x| - 4$
2. reflect across y-axis $g(x) = |-2x| + 3$
3. left 5 units $g(x) = |2x + 5| + 3$

Translate $f(x) = |x|$ so that the vertex is at the given point.

4. (6, −3) $f(x) = |x - 6| - 3$
5. (−8, −1) $f(x) = |x + 8| - 1$
6. (−7, 2) $f(x) = |x + 7| + 2$

Perform the transformation. Then graph.

7. Compress $f(x) = |3x - 4|$ vertically by a factor of $\frac{1}{3}$. $f(x) = \frac{|3x - 4|}{3}$

Solve.

8. At a sugar plantation processing plant, a machine fills a bag with 5 pounds of white sugar. For quality control, another machine weighs each bag in ounces and rejects bags that differ from 5 pounds by more than y ounces.

a. Write an absolute-value function to show the minimum and maximum weight of sugar that could be in each bag. $y = |x - 5|$

b. Graph the function.

c. Describe the transformation from $f(x) = |x|$. Translation 5 units to the right

2-9 READING STRATEGIES

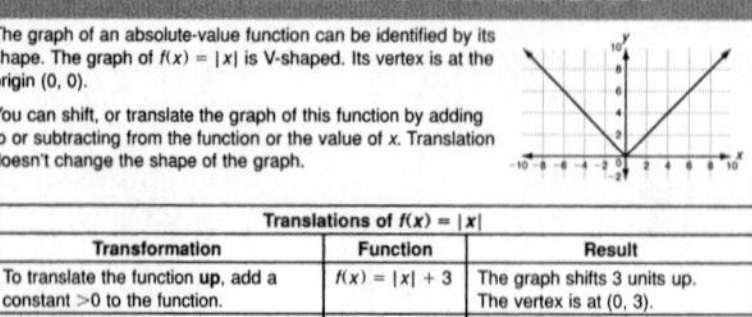

The graph of an absolute-value function can be identified by its shape. The graph of $f(x) = |x|$ is V-shaped. Its vertex is at the origin (0, 0).

You can shift, or translate the graph of this function by adding to or subtracting from the function or the value of x. Translation doesn't change the shape of the graph.

Translations of $f(x) = \|x\|$		
Transformation	Function	Result
To translate the function up, add a constant >0 to the function.	$f(x) = \|x\| + 3$	The graph shifts 3 units up. The vertex is at (0, 3).
To translate the function down, subtract a constant >0 to the function.	$f(x) = \|x\| - 2$	The graph shifts 2 units down. The vertex is at (0, −2).
To translate a function to the right, subtract a constant >0 inside the absolute value function.	$f(x) = \|x - 1\|$	The graph shifts 1 unit to the right. The vertex is at (1, 0).
To translate a function to the left, add a constant >0 inside the absolute value function.	$f(x) = \|x + 3\|$	The graph shifts 3 units to the left. The vertex is at (−3, 0).

Answer each question.

1. What is the domain and range of the function $f(x) = |x|$? Explain why the range is limited.
Domain: {all real numbers}; range: $\{0 \le y\}$; the range must be positive because the absolute value of any number is positive.

2. What is the difference in the function between shifting $f(x) = |x|$ 3 units down or 3 units to the right?
Possible answer: Shifting the function down means changing the y-coordinates so I would subtract 3 from the function value; shifting to the right means changing the x-coordinates, so I would subtract 3 from the x-value.

4. The graph of $f(x) = |x|$ is shifted 2 units left and 1 unit up.
a. Write the equation of the resulting figure. $f(x) = |x + 2| + 1$
b. Give the coordinates of the vertex. (−2, 1)

5. Except at 0, all the values of the function $f(x) = |x|$ are positive. Is this also true for $f(x) = |x| - 2$? Explain.
No; the values of $f(x) = |x| - 2$ are positive only for x greater than 2 or x less than −2.

2-9 RETEACH

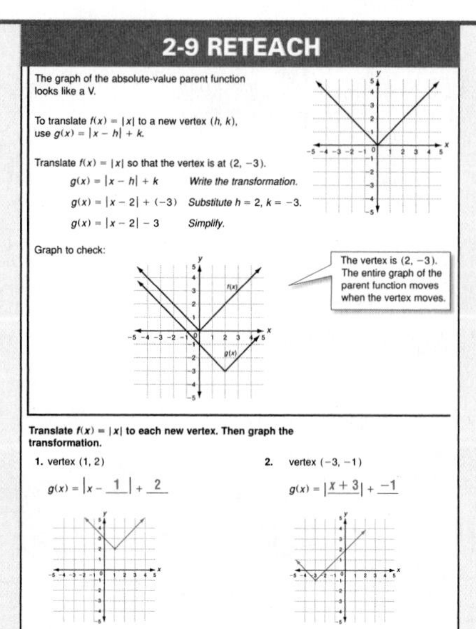

The graph of the absolute-value parent function looks like a V.

To translate $f(x) = |x|$ to a new vertex (h, k), use $g(x) = |x - h| + k$.

Translate $f(x) = |x|$ so that the vertex is at (2, −3).

$g(x) = |x - h| + k$ Write the transformation.
$g(x) = |x - 2| + (-3)$ Substitute h = 2, k = −3.
$g(x) = |x - 2| - 3$ Simplify.

Graph to check:

The vertex is (2, −3). The entire graph of the parent function moves when the vertex moves.

Translate $f(x) = |x|$ to each new vertex. Then graph the transformation.

1. vertex (1, 2) $g(x) = |x - 1| + 2$
2. vertex (−3, −1) $g(x) = |x + 3| + -1$

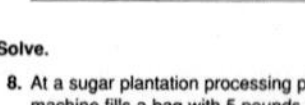

TEST PREP

33. Which function best describes the graph shown?
   (A) $y = |x - 2|$ (C) $y = -|x| - 2$
   (B) $y = |-x| + 2$ (D) $y = -|x + 2|$

34. The graph of which function is the same as the graph of $f(x) = |x|$?
   (F) $g(x) = \left|\frac{1}{x}\right|$ (H) $g(x) = |-x|$
   (G) $g(x) = -\left|\frac{1}{x}\right|$ (J) $g(x) = -|x|$

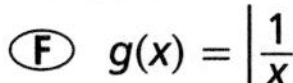

35. At which of the following points are the x-intercepts found for the graph of $f(x) = |3x| - 9$?
   (A) $(9, 0)$ and $(-9, 0)$ (C) $(0, 9)$ and $(0, -9)$
   (B) $(3, 0)$ and $(-3, 0)$ (D) $(0, 3)$ and $(0, -3)$

36. For which function does y correspond to a nonnegative real number?
   (F) $y = |x| - 3$ (G) $y = |x - 3|$ (H) $y = -|3 - x|$ (J) $y + 3 = |x + 3|$

37. If $g(x)$ is the reflection of $f(x) = |x + 1| - 2$ across the y-axis, at which of the following points does the graph of $g(x)$ cross the x-axis?
   (A) $(-3, 0)$ and $(-1, 0)$ (C) $(-3, 0)$ and $(1, 0)$
   (B) $(3, 0)$ and $(-1, 0)$ (D) $(3, 0)$ and $(1, 0)$

CHALLENGE AND EXTEND

38. Graph $y < |x + 2|$.
39. Graph $|y| \le 4$ on a coordinate plane.

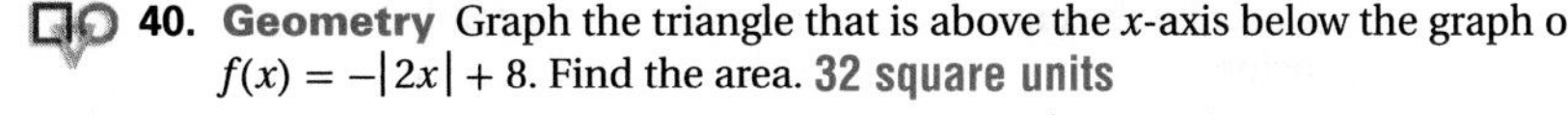

40. **Geometry** Graph the triangle that is above the x-axis below the graph of $f(x) = -|2x| + 8$. Find the area. **32 square units**

$f(x) = 2|x + 3|$ 41. Write an absolute-value equation for $f(x) = \begin{cases} 2x + 6 \text{ if } x \ge -3 \\ -2x - 6 \text{ if } x < -3 \end{cases}$. Then graph.

42. Graph $x = |y|$. Is the graph a function? Explain.
42. No, there are 2 y-values for each nonzero x-value.

SPIRAL REVIEW

Perform the indicated operation. Write each answer in scientific notation. *(Lesson 1-5)*

43. $(1.5 \times 10^{-4})(5.0 \times 10^{13})$ 44. $(9.8 \times 10^{7})(8.9 \times 10^{-7})$ 45. $(8.1 \times 10^{3})^2$

43. 7.5×10^9
44. 8.722×10^1
45. 6.561×10^7

46. $\frac{6.2 \times 10^7}{3.1 \times 10^{-4}}$ **2.0×10^{11}** 47. $\frac{1.9 \times 10^{-6}}{9.5 \times 10^{18}}$ **2.0×10^{-25}** 48. $\frac{2 \times 10^{-3}}{5 \times 10^{-3}}$ **4.0×10^{-1}**

Perform the given transformation on the point $(3, -5)$, and give the coordinates of the translated point. *(Lesson 1-8)*

49. 2 units left, 6 units up **$(1, 1)$**
50. 10 units down **$(3, -15)$**
51. 3 units right **$(6, -5)$**
52. reflected across the x-axis **$(3, 5)$**
53. 1 unit right, 5 units down **$(4, -10)$**
54. reflected across the y-axis **$(-3, -5)$**

Solve. *(Lesson 2-1)*

55. $-2x + 3(1 - x) = -\frac{10x}{2}$ **$\varnothing$**
56. $0.75(-4x - 12) = -3(3 + x)$ **$\mathbb{R}$**

2-9 PROBLEM SOLVING

Linette and Dylan are observing people passing by an outdoor art exhibit in the park. The graph shows the average path of a person walking past the exhibit at a rate of 1 block per minute.

Blocks from the Exhibit
Minutes Before Passing Exhibit
Minutes After Passing Exhibit

1. Write an absolute-value equation that represents the graph. Express the distance in blocks from the exhibit, $D(t)$, as a function of minutes (t) before and after arriving at the exhibit.
   $D(t) = |t|$
2. Find the value of $D(t)$ for $t = 3$ and for $t = -3$. What do these values mean about the position of a person walking past the exhibit?
   3, 3; Possible answer: a person who is 3 minutes away from the exhibit is 3 blocks from the exhibit.
3. What is the domain of the function? **All real numbers**
4. What is the range of the function? **All positive real numbers**
5. A person rides past the exhibit on a bicycle at a rate of 5 blocks per minute.
   a. Write an absolute-value function, $C(t)$, to represent the distance the bicycle is from the exhibit at any time, t.
   $C(t) = 5|t|$
   b. Sketch $C(t)$ on the graph. Describe the transformation.
   Vertical stretch
   c. Compare the vertex of $C(t)$ to the vertex of $D(t)$.
   The vertex stays the same.

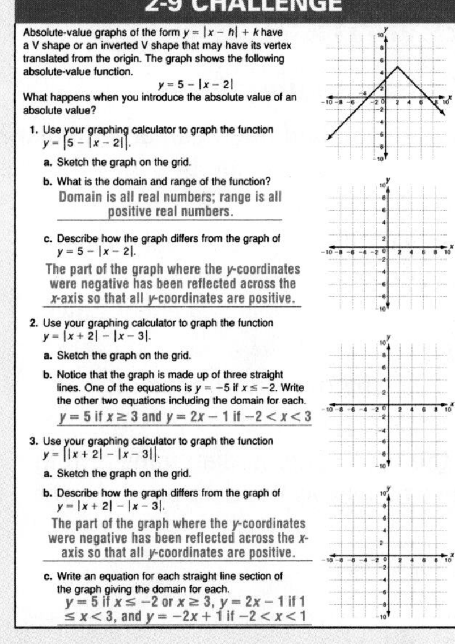

2-9 CHALLENGE

Absolute-value graphs of the form $y = |x - h| + k$ have a V shape or an inverted V shape that may have its vertex translated from the origin. The graph shows the following absolute-value function.

$$y = 5 - |x - 2|$$

What happens when you introduce the absolute value of an absolute value?

1. Use your graphing calculator to graph the function $y = |5 - |x - 2||$.
   a. Sketch the graph on the grid.
   b. What is the domain and range of the function?
   Domain is all real numbers; range is all positive real numbers.
   c. Describe how the graph differs from the graph of $y = 5 - |x - 2|$.
   The part of the graph where the y-coordinates were negative has been reflected across the x-axis so that all y-coordinates are positive.
2. Use your graphing calculator to graph the function $y = |x + 2| - |x - 3|$.
   a. Sketch the graph on the grid.
   b. Notice that the graph is made up of three straight lines. One of the equations is $y = -5$ if $x \le -2$. Write the other two equations including the domain for each.
   $y = 5$ if $x \ge 3$ and $y = 2x - 1$ if $-2 < x < 3$
3. Use your graphing calculator to graph the function $y = ||x + 2| - |x - 3||$.
   a. Sketch the graph on the grid.
   b. Describe how the graph differs from the graph of $y = |x + 2| - |x - 3|$.
   The part of the graph where the y-coordinates were negative has been reflected across the x-axis so that all y-coordinates are positive.
   c. Write an equation for each straight line section of the graph giving the domain for each.
   $y = 5$ if $x \le -2$ or $x \ge 3$, $y = 2x - 1$ if $1 \le x < 3$, and $y = -2x + 1$ if $-2 < x < 1$

TEST PREP DOCTOR Because the graph in **Exercise 33**, turns down, the sign in front of the absolute value must be negative, eliminating **A**. The vertex $(-2, 0)$, satisfies the equation only in **D** in the other choices. Remind students that to find the x-intercept, they should set $y = 0$ or $f(x) = 0$.

Journal

Have students use their own words and drawings to explain how vertical and horizontal translations affect the graph of $f(x) = |x|$.

ALTERNATIVE ASSESSMENT

Have students use the parent function $f(x) = |x|$ and describe a translation, a reflection, and a stretch or compression. Then have students write the rule for each transformation.

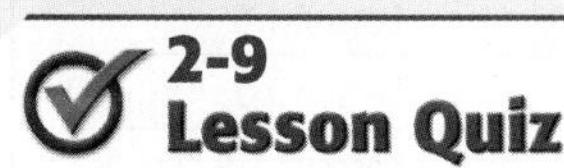

Power Presentations with PowerPoint®

2-9 Lesson Quiz

Perform each transformation. Then graph.

1. Translate $f(x) = |x|$ 3 units right. $g(x) = |x - 3|$

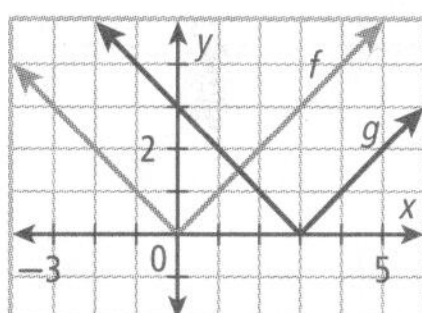

2. Translate $f(x) = |x|$ so that the vertex is at $(2, -1)$. Then graph. $g(x) = |x - 2| - 1$

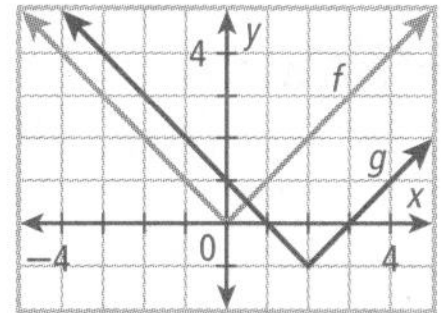

3. Stretch the graph of $f(x) = |2x| - 1$ vertically by a factor of 3 and reflect it across the x-axis.
$g(x) = -3|2x| + 3$

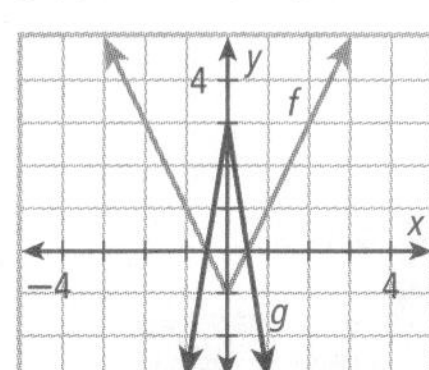

Also available on transparency

Organizer

Objective: Assess students' ability to apply concepts and skills in Lesson 2-6 through Lesson 2-9 in a real-world format.

Online Edition

Resources

Algebra 2 Assessments
www.mathtekstoolkit.org

For additional assessment activities, see www.utdanacenter.org.

Problem	Text Reference
1	Skills Bank, p. S68
2	Lesson 1-9
3	Lesson 2-7
4	Lessons 1-8, 2-6, 2-7
5	Lessons 1-8, 2-6
6	Skills Bank, p. S68
7	Lessons 1-8, 2-6
8	Lesson 2-7

Answers

1–3. See p. A20.
6. For table, see p. A20.
7–8. See p. A20.

State Resources

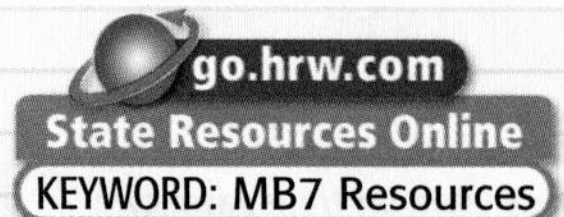

CHAPTER 2

SECTION 2B

Applying Linear Functions

Data Dilemma The Livestock Show and Rodeo School Art Program is an annual competition for students. Participants in grades ranging from kindergarten through 12 must submit an original art project based on Western culture, history, or heritage. Projects are judged by the show's School Art Committee. Each school district selects the top 20 students to compete in this annual citywide competition. The scores for the top entries in the East District are shown in the table.

The Art Committee guidelines state that the top score awarded in district competitions should be 100. The East District judges have decided to add 5 points to each score in order to comply with the competition guidelines.

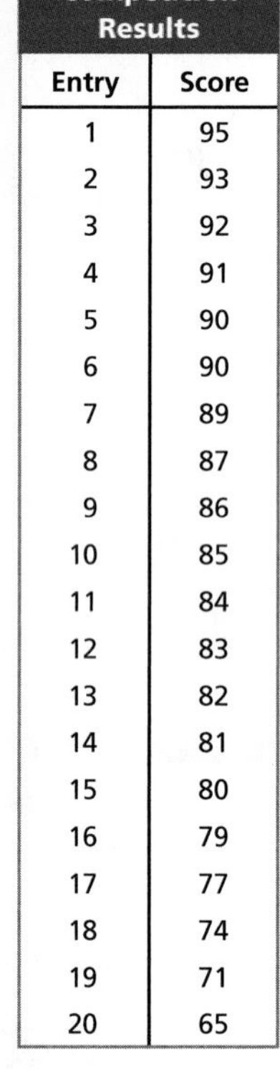

Competition Results

Entry	Score
1	95
2	93
3	92
4	91
5	90
6	90
7	89
8	87
9	86
10	85
11	84
12	83
13	82
14	81
15	80
16	79
17	77
18	74
19	71
20	65

1. Create a table to show the new scores. Compare the mean and median of the original scores with those of the modified scores.
2. Graph the original scores using the entry number as the x-coordinate and the score as the y-coordinate. Describe the parent function to which this graph belongs.
3. Predict how the graph of the modified scores will compare with the graph of the original scores. Graph the modified scores on the same graph as the original scores to check your prediction.
4. If $y = f(x)$ represents the function rule for the original scores, determine a function rule for the modified scores. Explain.
5. One judge suggested that the original scores should be multiplied by a factor that would make the highest score 100 points. What factor should be used?
6. Make a table showing the new scores. Compare the mean and median of the original scores with those of these new scores.
7. Graph the newest set of scores on the same graph as the original scores, and describe the transformation.
8. Which method do you think the judges should use to adjust the scores? Explain your answer.

4. $y = f(x) + 5$; the graph is translated up 5 units.

5. $\frac{100}{95}$, or ≈ 1.053

6. Both are multiplied by $\frac{100}{95}$; original mean: 83.7; new mean: 88.1; original median: 84.5; new median: 88.9.

INTERVENTION 

Scaffolding Questions

1. How can you find the mean and median? Find the sum and divide by 20; find the mean of the 10th and 11th scores.

2–3. How do the last 3 data points affect your choice of a parent function? Without those points, a linear function is a good model.

4–5. What type of transformation is this? a translation; a stretch

6. Do the mean and median transform in the same way as the data points? yes
7. Which scores are affected less by a stretch than by a translation? lower scores
8. Does the type of transformation affect your choice? probably

Extension

What value of r, the correlation coefficient, would you expect for the data? How would it change if the scores were not sorted by entry number? close to −1; it would be close to 0.

CHAPTER 2

SECTION 2B

Quiz for Lessons 2-6 Through 2-9

2-6 Transforming Linear Functions

Let $g(x)$ be the indicated transformation(s) of $f(x)$. Write the rule for $g(x)$.

1. $f(x) = x$; horizontal translation 5 units right $g(x) = x - 5$
2. $f(x) = 2x$; vertical stretch by a factor of 5 $g(x) = 10x$
3. $f(x) = x + 6$; vertical compression by a factor of $\frac{1}{3}$ followed by a horizontal translation left 4 units $g(x) = \frac{1}{3}x + \frac{10}{3}$
4. $f(x) = 3x - 5$; vertical translation 6 units up followed by a horizontal stretch by a factor of $\frac{3}{2}$ $g(x) = 2x + 1$

2-7 Curve Fitting with Linear Models

5. Lea keeps track of the number of hours she works in a week and her income for the week. Here are the results from a randomly selected sample of weeks.

Hours	8	23	18	30	12	28
Income ($)	152	465	315	530	240	525

5b. $r = 0.989$; $I = 17.91t + 15.96$; the increase in income for each additional hour worked.

   a. Draw a scatter plot of the data using hours as the independent variable.
   b. Use your graphing calculator to find the correlation coefficient and the equation of the line of best fit for the data. What does the slope of the line of best fit mean for Lea?
   c. Use your equation to predict how much Lea would make in a 40-hour week. $732.36

2-8 Solving Absolute-Value Equations and Inequalities

Solve each equation.

6. $|9 - 2x| = 15$ $x = -3$ or $x = 12$
7. $2|x| - 12 = 16$ $x = \pm 14$
8. $\frac{|3x - 4|}{-5} = 6$ $\varnothing$
9. $|2x - 5| = x + 3$ $x = 8$ or $x = \frac{2}{3}$

Solve each inequality. Then graph the solution.

10. $|5x + 15| > 20$ $\{x \mid x < -7 \text{ or } x > 1\}$
11. $\left|\frac{x - 2}{4}\right| \le 5$ $\{x \mid -18 \le x \le 22\}$
12. $-3|5x - 8| - 5 \ge 6$ $\varnothing$
13. $|12 - 4x| - 4 > 20$ $\{x \mid x < -3 \text{ or } x > 9\}$

2-9 Absolute-Value Functions

Translate $f(x) = |x|$ so that the vertex is at the given point. Then graph.

14. $(0, -4)$ $g(x) = |x| - 4$
15. $(2, 7)$ $g(x) = |x - 2| + 7$
16. $(-2, 0)$ $g(x) = |x + 2|$
17. A food order at a restaurant is paid for with a $10 bill.
   a. What function represents the difference between the cost of the food and the change returned? Assume that this difference is nonnegative.
   b. Graph the function.

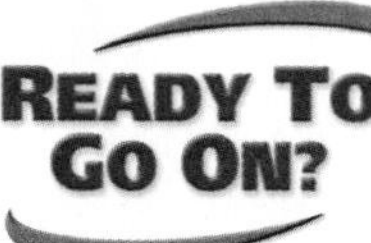

SECTION 2B

Objective: Assess students' mastery of concepts and skills in Lessons 2-6 through 2-9

Resources

Assessment Resources

Section 2B Quiz

Test & Practice Generator
One-Stop Planner®

INTERVENTION

Resources

Ready to Go On? Intervention and Enrichment **Worksheets**

Ready to Go On? **CD-ROM**

Ready to Go On? **Online**

my.hrw.com

Answers

5a, 10–11, 13–16. For graphs, see p. A20.

17. See p. A20.

READY TO GO ON?

Diagnose and Prescribe

NO INTERVENE

Ready to Go On? Intervention	Ready to Go On? Intervention, Section 2B — Worksheets	CD-ROM	Online
Lesson 2-6	2-6 Intervention	Activity 2-6	Diagnose and Prescribe Online
Lesson 2-7	2-7 Intervention	Activity 2-7	
Lesson 2-8	2-8 Intervention	Activity 2-8	
Lesson 2-9	2-9 Intervention	Activity 2-9	

YES ENRICH

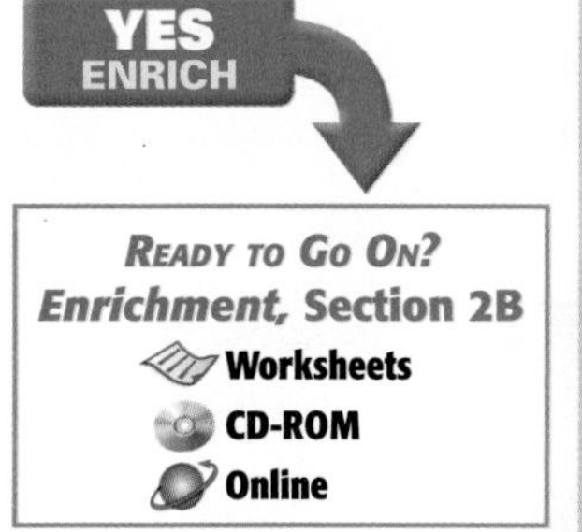

CHAPTER 2 **Study Guide: Review**

Organizer

Objective: Help students organize and review key concepts and skills presented in Chapter 2.

Online Edition
Multilingual Glossary

Resources

Puzzle Pro
One-Stop Planner®

***Multilingual Glossary* Online**
go.hrw.com
KEYWORD: MB7 Glossary

Lesson Tutorial Videos
CD-ROM

Test & Practice Generator
One-Stop Planner®

Answers

1. contradiction
2. point-slope form
3. correlation
4. $x = \frac{13}{2}$
5. identity; $\mathbb{R}$
6. $x = -\frac{4}{7}$
7. $x = \frac{31}{2}$
8. $x = \frac{51}{41}$
9. 140
10. $x \le 7$
11. $x < -\frac{32}{3}$
12. $x \le 9$
13. $19.95 + 2.75x < 50$; fewer than 11 times
14. $x = 33$
15. $x = -15$
16. $x = -\frac{11}{3}$
17. $x = \frac{19}{18}$
18. 4.5 ft
19. yes
20. (5, 0); (0, 2)

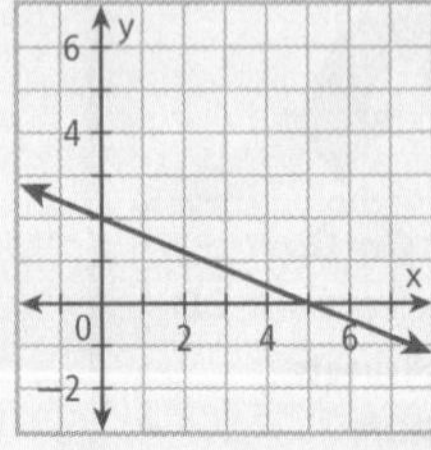

CHAPTER 2

Study Guide: Review

Vocabulary

Complete the sentences below with vocabulary words from the list above.

1. If there are no values that make an equation true, then the equation is a(n) ___?___ .
2. The equation $y - 5 = 2(x - 1)$ is in ___?___ .
3. ___?___ is the strength and direction of the linear relationship between two variables.

2-1 Solving Linear Equations and Inequalities *(pp. 90–96)*

EXAMPLES

Solve.

■ $5(x + 4) = 3x - 2$

$5x + 20 = 3x - 2$ *Use the Distributive Property.*

$2x + 20 = -2$ *Subtract 3x from both sides.*

$2x = -22$ *Subtract 20 from both sides.*

$x = -11$ *Divide both sides by 2.*

■ $\frac{15 - 3x}{2} < 12$

$15 - 3x < 24$ *Multiply both sides by 2.*

$-3x < 9$ *Subtract 15 from both sides.*

$x > -3$ *Divide both sides by –3x, and reverse the inequality.*

EXERCISES

Solve.

4. $35 = 7(2x - 8)$
5. $3x + 12 - 9x = 12 - 6x$
6. $4(3x + 5) = 12 - 2x$
7. $3x - 5(x + 3) = 16 - 4x$
8. $\frac{5}{2}\left(3x - \frac{3}{2}\right) - \frac{3}{4} = \frac{2}{3}x + 4$
9. Magnets cost \$10 plus \$1.25 each to produce. You sell them for \$1.75. How many magnets were sold if you made a profit of \$60?
10. $24 \ge 6x - 18$
11. $8x + 12 < 5x - 20$
12. $\frac{13 - 5x}{8} \ge -4$

Write an equation or inequality, and solve.

13. Ali's health club membership costs \$19.95 per month. Ali pays \$2.75 each time he works out. If Ali wants to spend less than \$50 per month at the health club, how often can he visit?

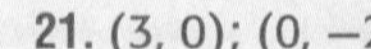
21. (3, 0); (0, –2)

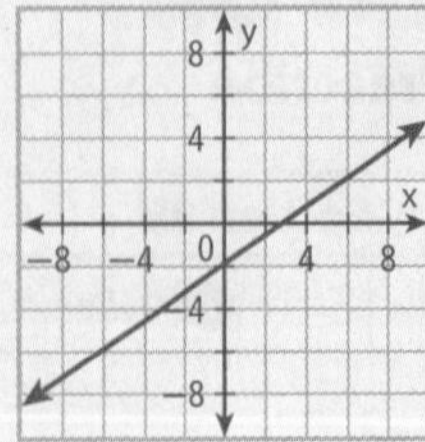

22. (–2.25, 0); (0, 1.5)

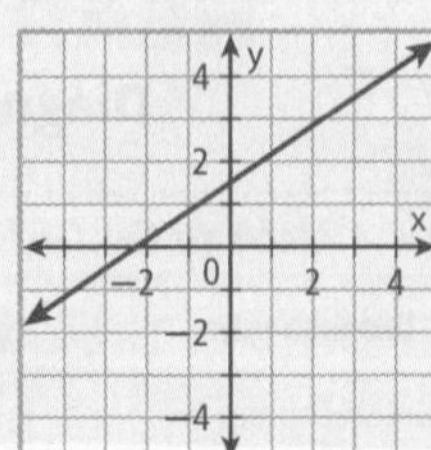

23. (1.5, 0); (0, 6)

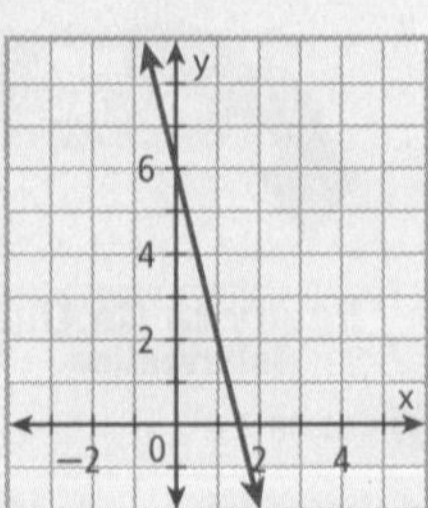

2-2 Proportional Reasoning *(pp. 97–103)*

EXAMPLE

Solve the proportion.

- $\frac{x+2}{12} = \frac{15}{20}$

$20(x+2) = (12)(15)$ *Set cross products equal.*

$20x + 40 = 180$

$20x = 140$

$x = 7$

EXERCISES

Solve each proportion.

14. $\frac{12}{x} = \frac{4}{11}$
15. $\frac{-9}{4} = \frac{3x}{20}$
16. $\frac{x-3}{4} = -\frac{5}{3}$
17. $\frac{4}{5-2x} = \frac{3}{3x-1}$
18. If a flagpole that is 20 feet tall casts a 6 foot shadow, how long a shadow would a building that is 15 feet tall cast at the same time of day?

2-3 Graphing Linear Functions *(pp. 105–112)*

EXAMPLES

Find the intercepts. Then graph.

- $2x - 3y = 12$

$2x = 12$ *Set y equal to 0 to find the x-intercept.*

$x = 6$

$-3y = 12$ *Set x equal to 0 to find the y-intercept.*

$y = -4$

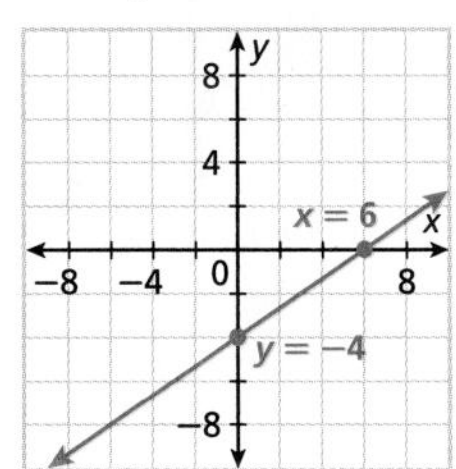

Write each function in slope-intercept form. Then graph.

- $4x + 3y = 24$

$3y = -4x + 24$ *Isolate the y-term.*

$y = -\frac{4}{3}x + 8$ *Divide both sides by 3.*

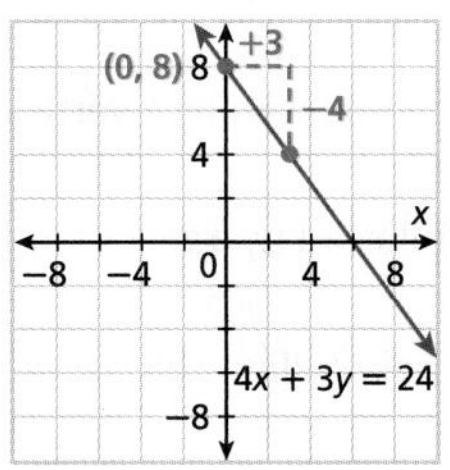

EXERCISES

Determine whether the data set could represent a linear function.

19.

x	1	4	7	10
f(x)	3	−2	−7	−12

Find the intercepts. Then graph.

20. $2x + 5y = 10$
21. $-6x + 9y = -18$
22. $8x = 12y - 18$
23. $y = 6 - 4x$

Write each function in slope-intercept form. Then graph.

24. $6x + 3y = 15$
25. $5x - 3y = -9$
26. $9x = 12 - 6y$
27. $\frac{8}{9}x + \frac{4}{3}y = 12$

Determine whether each line is vertical or horizontal. Then graph.

28. $-3 = x$
29. $y = \frac{5}{2}$
30. A rock climber is descending down a 500-ft-tall cliff. After 8 min, the rock climber has descended to a height of 280 ft. Find the height as a linear function of the time, and graph the function.

Answers

26. $y = -\frac{3}{2}x + 2$

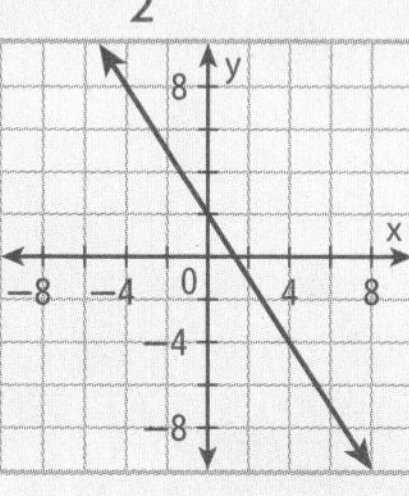

27. $y = -\frac{2}{3}x + 9$

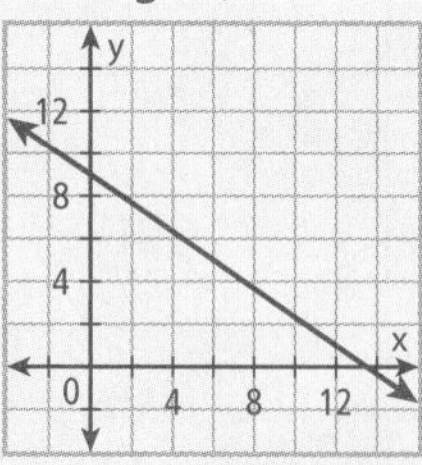

28. vertical

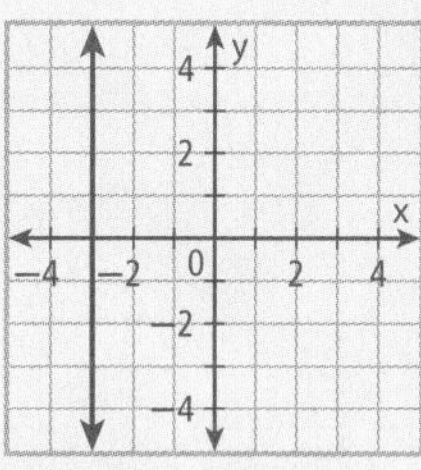

29. horizontal

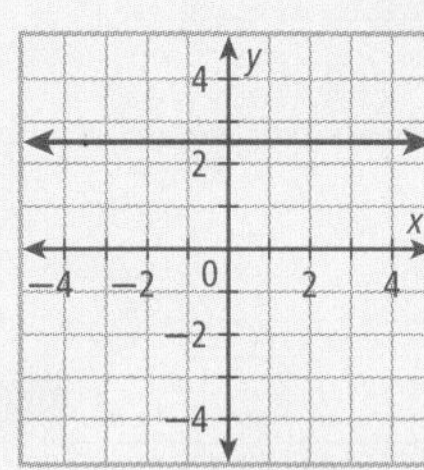

30. $h(t) = -27.5t + 500$

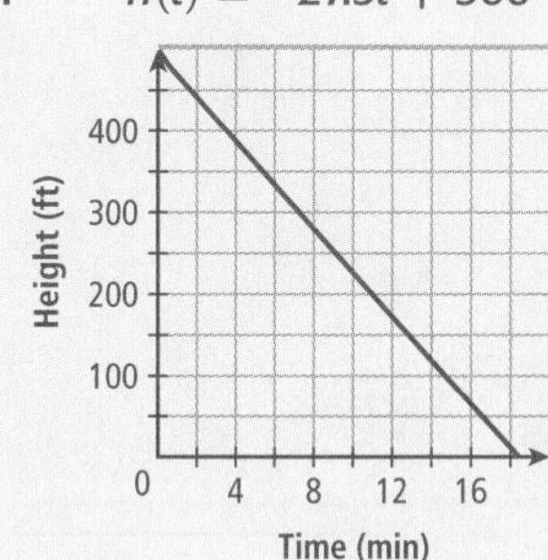

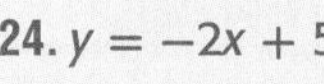

24. $y = -2x + 5$

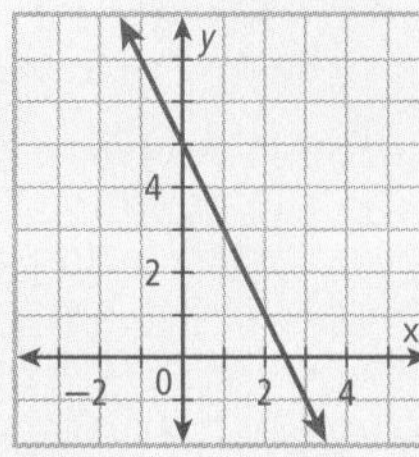

25. $y = \frac{5}{3}x + 3$

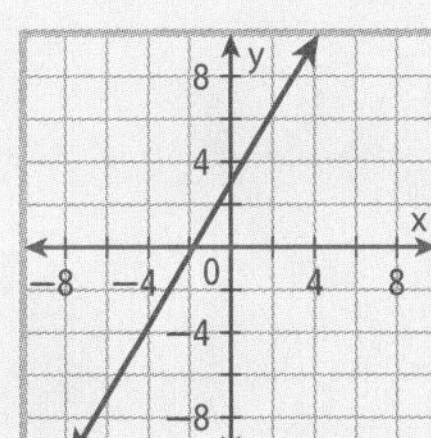

Answers

31. $y = \frac{1}{2}x + 4$

32. $y = 3x$

33. $y = \frac{3}{2}x - 8$

34. $y = -\frac{2}{3}x + 2$

35. $y > -3$

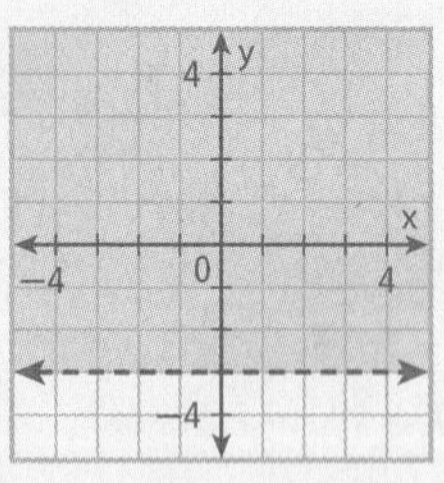

36. $y \leq x + 3$

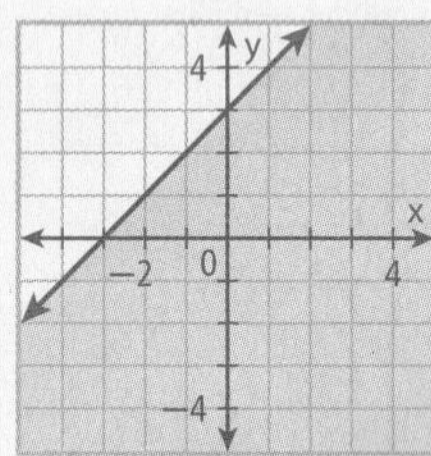

37. $y > -\frac{1}{2}x - 3$

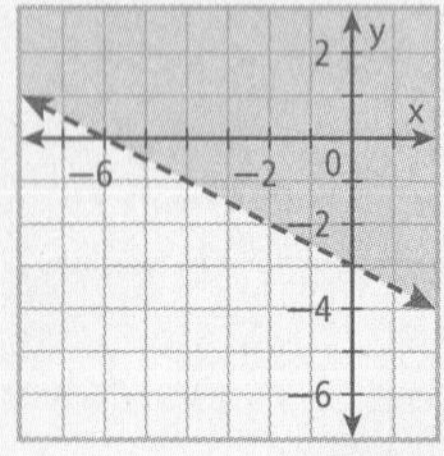

38. $y < 3x - 4$

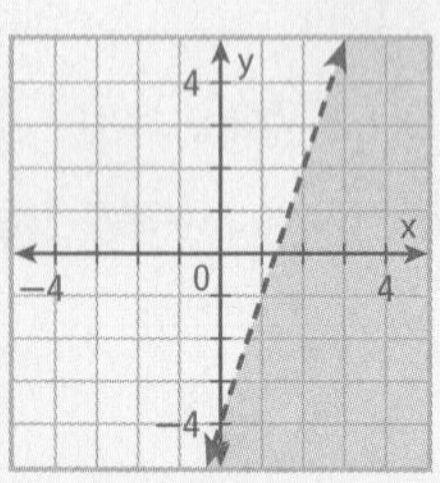

39. $y < -2x + 3$

2-4 Writing Linear Functions *(pp. 115–123)*

EXAMPLE

- Write the equation of the line through (3, 4) and (5, 10) in slope-intercept form.

  Find the slope $m = \frac{10 - 4}{5 - 3} = 3$

  Write an equation:

Method 1	Method 2	
$y - y_1 = m(x - x_1)$	$y = mx + b$	
$y - 4 = 3(x - 3)$	$y = 3x + b$	
$y - 4 = 3x - 9$	$4 = 3(3) + b$	
$y = 3x - 9 + 4$	$-5 = b$	*−5 is the*
$y = 3x - 5$	$y = 3x - 5$	*y-intercept*

EXERCISES

Write the equation of each line in slope-intercept form.

31. passing through (4, 6) with slope $\frac{1}{2}$
32. passing through (2, 6) and (3, 9)
33. through (4, −2) and parallel to $y = \frac{3}{2}x + 9$
34. through (−3, 4) and perpendicular to $y = \frac{3}{2}x + 9$

2-5 Linear Inequalities in Two Variables *(pp. 124–131)*

EXAMPLE

Solve for *y*. Graph the solution.

- $3x - 5y \leq 10$

  $-5y \leq -3x + 10$

  $y \geq \frac{3}{5}x - 2$

  Use a solid boundary line and shade the region above the boundary.

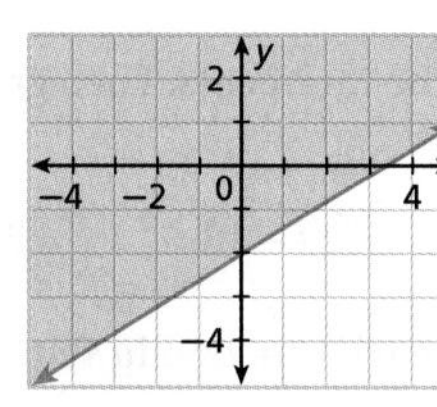

EXERCISES

Solve for *y*. Graph the solution.

35. $y > -3$
36. $y \leq x + 3$
37. $2x + 4y > -12$
38. $6x - 2y > 8$
39. Write an inequality for the graph.

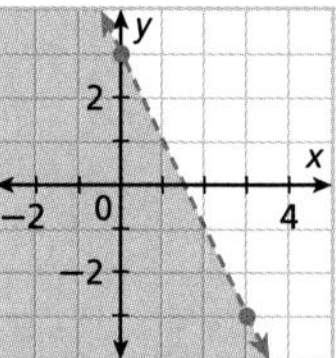

40. A gallery offers a limited-access ticket for $12 and a standard ticket for $21. More than $2520 in tickets were sold. Write and graph an inequality for the numbers of each type of ticket sold.

2-6 Transforming Linear Functions *(pp. 134–140)*

EXAMPLE

Let $g(x)$ be the indicated transformation of $f(x) = x$. Write the rule for $g(x)$.

- horizontal shift 5 units left followed by a horizontal stretch by a factor of 3

  Translating $f(x)$ 5 units left replaces each x with $(x + 5)$.

  Let $h(x) = f(x + 5)$

  Replace each x with $\left(\frac{x}{3}\right)$.

  $g(x) = h\left(\frac{x}{3}\right) = \frac{x}{3} + 5$

EXERCISES

Let $g(x)$ be the indicated transformation of $f(x) = x$. Write the rule for $g(x)$.

41. horizontal shift 8 units right
42. vertical shift 5 units up followed by a vertical stretch by a factor of 3
43. horizontal shift 3 units left followed by a vertical shift down 7 units
44. vertical shift 5 units up followed by a reflection across the x-axis
45. horizontal shift 12 units right followed by a reflection across the y-axis

40. $12x + 21y \geq 2520$

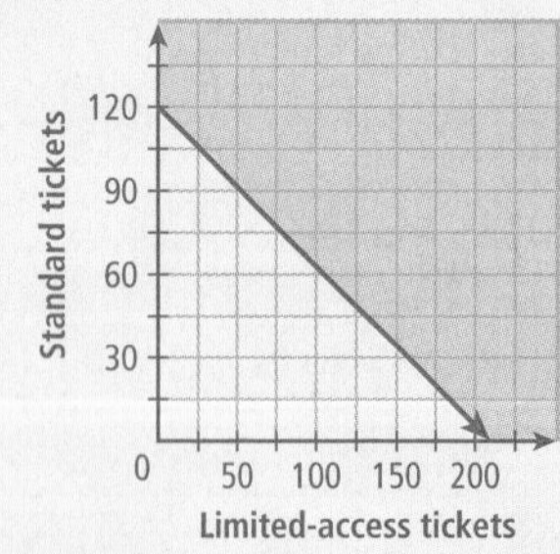

41. $g(x) = x - 8$

42. $g(x) = 3x + 15$

43. $g(x) = x - 4$

44. $g(x) = -x - 5$

45. $g(x) = -x - 12$

2-7 Curve Fitting with Linear Models (pp.142–149)

EXAMPLE

- **Make a scatter plot of the data. Find the correlation coefficient r and the equation of the line of best fit.**

x	2	5	9	13	16
y	8	10	24	16	29

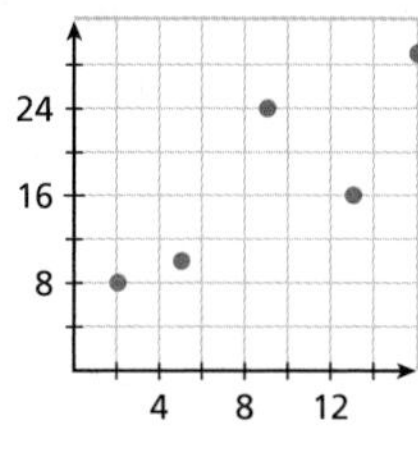

The scatter plot is shown at right

Use **LinReg** on your graphing calculator.

$r \approx 0.834$. The equation of the line of best fit is $y \approx 1.32x + 5.56$.

EXERCISES

46. Find the following for this set of data on median income and median home price.
    a. Make a scatter plot of the data using median income as the independent variable.
    b. Find the correlation coefficient r and the line of best fit for these data.

Median Income (thousands)	Median Home Price (thousands)
69.5	130.2
46.3	94.5
56.7	115.5
65.2	106.4
54.7	98.6
59.6	115.5

2-8 Solving Absolute-Value Equations and Inequalities (pp.150–156)

EXAMPLE

Solve the inequality. Then graph the solution set.

- $|2x + 8| - 10 \le 2$

$|2x + 8| \le 12$

$2x + 8 \le 12$ and $2x + 8 \ge -12$ *Conjunction*

$2x \le 4$ and $2x \ge -20$

$x \le 2$ and $x \ge -10$

The solution set is $\{x \mid -10 \le x \le 2\}$

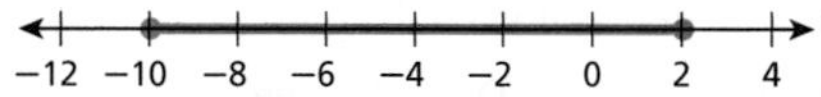

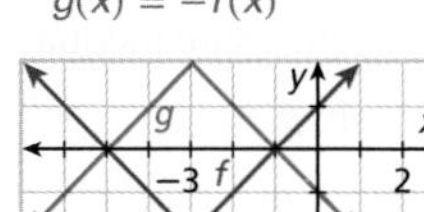

EXERCISES

Solve.

47. $|x - 8| = 20$

48. $\left|\frac{x-6}{5}\right| = 12$

49. $4|3x - 8| + 16 = 2$

Solve each inequality. Then graph the solution.

50. $3x + 6 > 15$ or $5x + 13 < -12$

51. $2(3x + 6) \le 32 + 2x$ AND $5x + 15 \ge 2x + 9$

52. $|4x - 8| < 4$

53. $|5x + 10| \ge 30$

2-9 Absolute Value Functions (pp.158–163)

EXAMPLE

- Reflect the graph of $f(x) = |x + 3| - 2$ across the x-axis, and graph the function.

$g(x) = -(|x + 3| - 2)$ *$g(x) = -f(x)$*

$g(x) = -|x + 3| + 2$

EXERCISES

Translate $f(x) = |x|$ so the vertex is at the given point.

54. $(-5, 7)$

55. $(6, -9)$

Perform each transformation. Then graph.

56. $f(x) = |x - 4| + 1$ reflected across the y-axis

57. $f(x) = |3x + 1|$ compressed vertically by $\frac{1}{3}$

58. $f(x) = |x - 3| + 5$ reflected across the x-axis

Answers

46a.

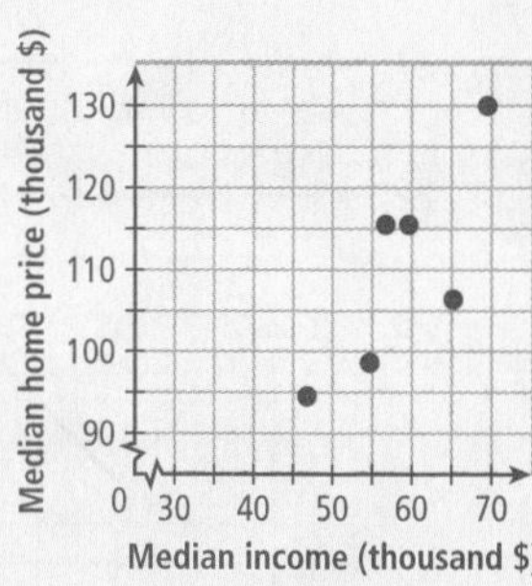

b. $r = 0.800$; $P = 1.279I + 35.074$

47. $x = 28$ or $x = -12$

48. $x = 66$ or $x = -54$

49. $\varnothing$

50. $\{x \mid x < -5 \cup x > 3\}$

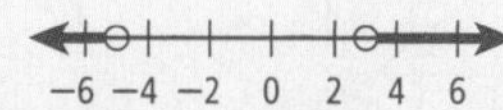

51. $\{x \mid -2 \le x \le 5\}$

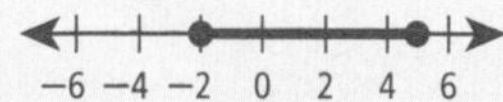

52. $\{x \mid 1 < x < 3\}$

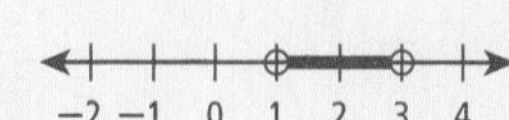

Answers

53. $\{x \mid x \le -8 \cup x \ge 4\}$

−12 −8 −4 0 4 8 12

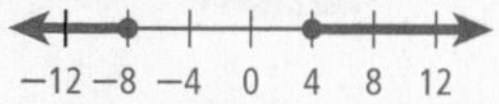

54. $g(x) = |x + 5| + 7$

55. $g(x) = |x - 6| - 9$

56. $g(x) = |-x - 4| + 1$

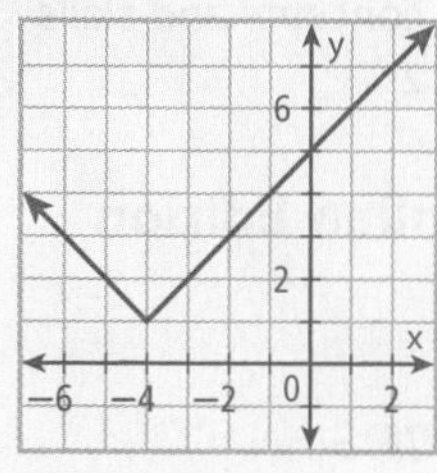

57. $g(x) = \frac{|3x + 1|}{3}$

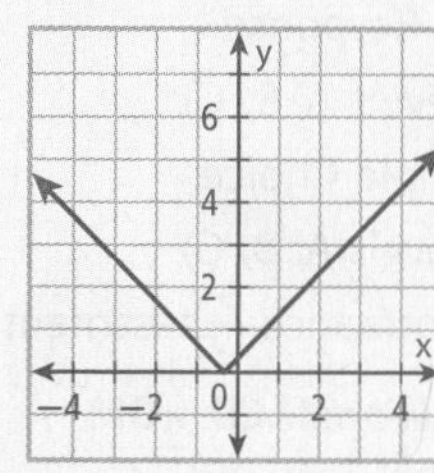

58. $g(x) = -|x - 3| - 5$

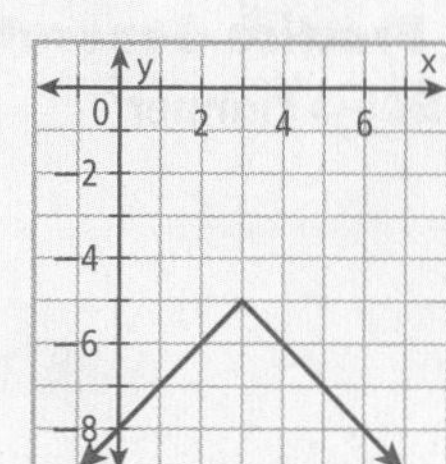

Organizer

Objective: Assess students' mastery of concepts and skills in Chapter 2.

 **Online Edition**

Resources

 ***Assessment Resources***

Chapter 2 Tests
- Free Response (Levels A, B, C)
- Multiple Choice (Levels A, B, C)
- Performance Assessment

 ***IDEA Works!* CD-ROM**

Modified Chapter 2 Test

Test & Practice Generator One-Stop Planner®

Answers

8.

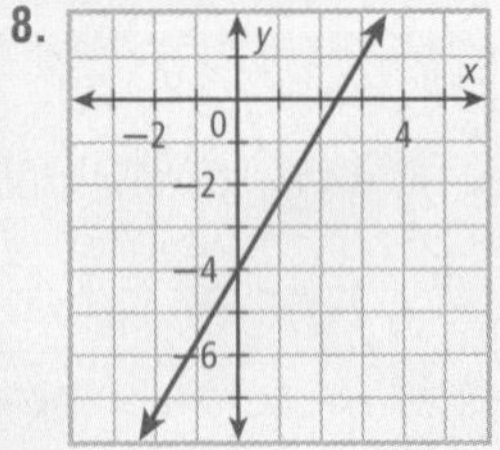

State Resources

go.hrw.com State Resources Online KEYWORD: MB7 Resources

CHAPTER 2 CHAPTER TEST

Solve.

1. $5(3x - 4) - 12 = 73$ $x = 7$
2. $2x + 12 - 8x = 9 - x - 5x$ contradiction; $\varnothing$
3. $4(3 - 3x) - 8x = 15 - 2(5x + 8)$ $x = 1.3$
4. $\frac{-5}{4} = \frac{12}{x}$ $x = -9.6$
5. $\frac{3x - 9}{15} = \frac{18}{12}$ $x = 10.5$
6. $\frac{2}{2x - 5} = \frac{3}{x + 1}$ $x = 4.25$
7. Tim and Kim took 4.6 hours to complete a 25.3 mile kayaking trip. If they want to paddle for 3 hours on their next trip, how far should they plan to go? ≈ 16.5 mi

Graph.

8. $y = \frac{5}{3}x - 4$
9. $6x + 8y = 24$
10. $6x + 2y < 10$

Write the equation of each line in slope-intercept form.

11. passing through $(9, 12)$ and $(7, 2)$ $y = 5x - 33$
12. parallel to $9x - 5y = 8$ and through $(-10, 2)$ $y = \frac{9}{5}x + 20$
13. perpendicular to $y = -\frac{2}{7}x + 3$ and through $(6, 4)$ $y = \frac{7}{2}x - 17$
14. The Spanish Club is selling T-shirts and hats and would like to raise at least \$2400. It sells T-shirts for \$15 and hats for \$8. Write and graph an inequality representing the number of T-shirts and hats the club must sell to meet its goal. $15Ts + 8h \geq 2400$

Let $g(x)$ be the indicated transformation(s) of $f(x) = x$. Write the rule for $g(x)$.

15. vertical stretch by a factor of 4 $g(x) = 4x$
16. horizontal translation 6 units right $g(x) = x - 6$
17. horizontal compression by a factor of $\frac{1}{6}$ followed by a vertical shift 4 units down $g(x) = 6x - 4$
18. A consumer group is studying how hospitals are staffed. Here are the results from eight randomly selected hospitals in a state.

Full-Time Hospital Employees								
Hospital Beds	23	29	35	42	46	54	64	76
Full-Time Employees	69	95	118	126	123	178	156	176

   a. Make a scatter plot of the data with hospital beds as the independent variable.

   b. Find the correlation coefficient and the equation of the line of best fit. Draw the line of best fit on your scatter plot. $r \approx 0.913$; $e \approx 1.95b + 40.1$

   c. Predict the number of beds in a hospital with 80 full-time employees. 20 or 21

19. Solve $|12 + 4x| - 6 = 26$. $x = 5$ or $x = -11$

Solve and graph.

20. $16 \leq \frac{24 - 8x}{5}$ $x \leq -7$
21. $|3x - 9| > 12$ $\{x \mid x < -1 \cup x > 7\}$
22. $3|12 - 4x| + 4 \leq 28$ $\{x \mid 1 \leq x \leq 5\}$
23. A pollster predicts the actual percent p of a population that favors a political candidate by using a sample percent s plus or minus 3%. Write an absolute-value inequality for p. $|p - s| < 3$
24. Translate $f(x) = |x|$ so that its vertex is at $(4, -2)$. Then graph. $g(x) = |x - 4| - 2$
25. Find $g(x)$ if $f(x) = |2x| - 3$ is stretched horizontally by a factor of 3 and reflected across the x-axis. $g(x) = -\left|\frac{2x}{3}\right| + 3$

9.

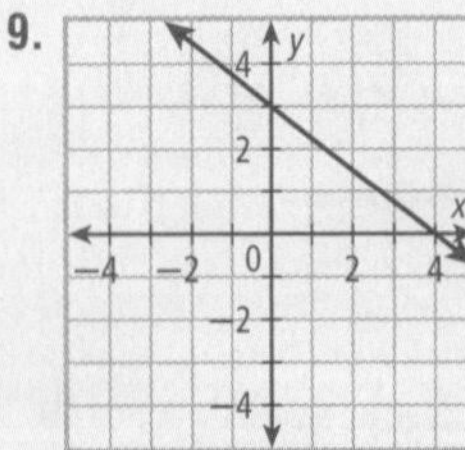

10.

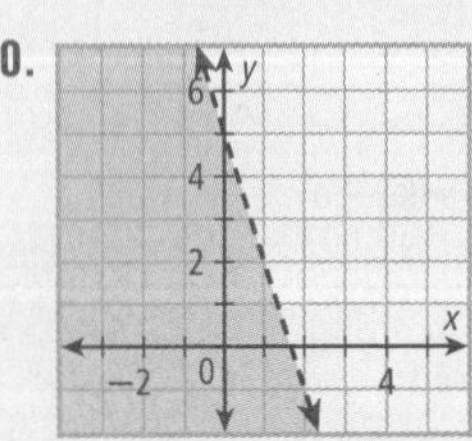

14.

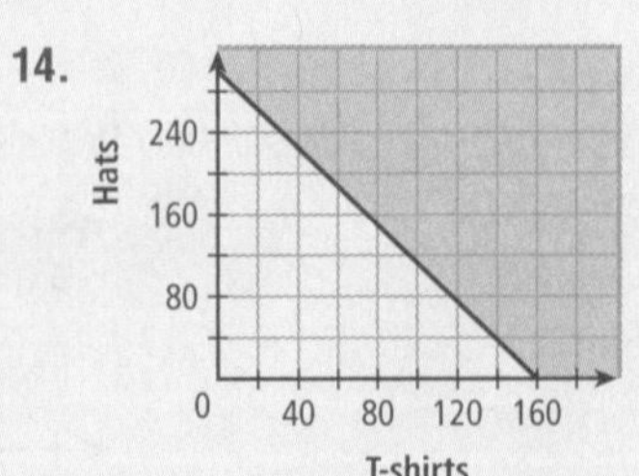

18a.

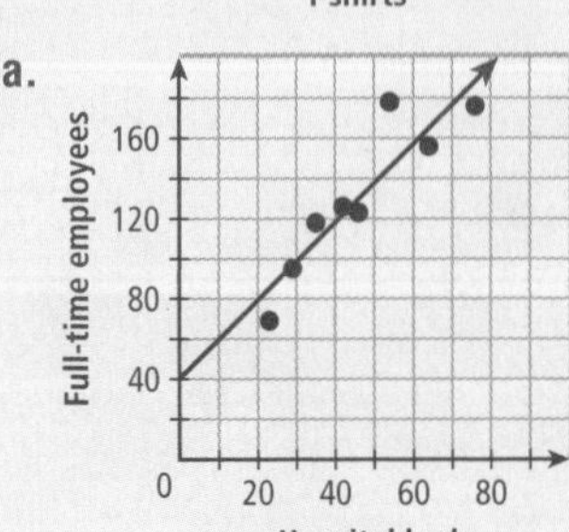

20.–22.

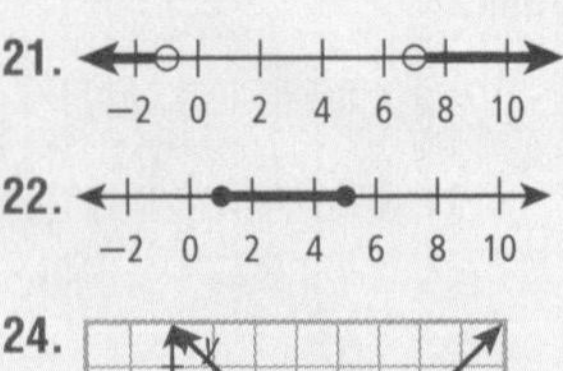

24.

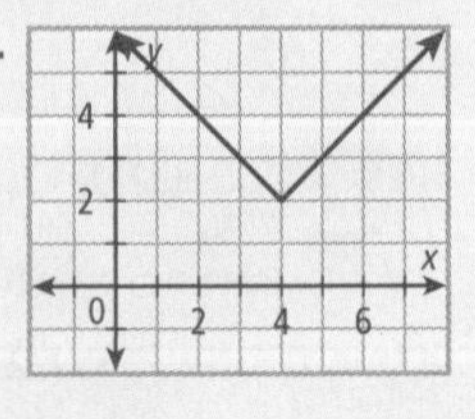

COLLEGE ENTRANCE EXAM PRACTICE

FOCUS ON ACT

The ACT measures college-preparedness by testing skills in English, mathematics, reading, and science. The Mathematics Test is a 60-minute test with 60 multiple-choice questions. There is no penalty for incorrect answers.

You may want to time yourself as you take this practice test. It should take you about 5 minutes to complete.

All questions on the ACT Mathematics Test can be answered without using a calculator, but you are allowed to use one. If you bring a calculator to the test center, make sure it is one of the types of calculators approved for the test, as many types are prohibited.

1. In a school choir, the ratio of boys to girls is 3:5. If there are a total of 24 singers in the choir, how many girls are in the choir?

   (A) 6
   (B) 9
   (C) 14
   (D) 15
   (E) 40

2. If $12 - 3(x + 2) = x + 8$, then what is the value of x?

   (A) $-\frac{5}{2}$
   (B) $-\frac{1}{2}$
   (C) $\frac{1}{2}$
   (D) $\frac{3}{2}$
   (E) $\frac{5}{2}$

3. What are the values of x where $2|x + 4| < 6$?

   (A) $x < -1$ and $x < -7$
   (B) $x > -1$ or $x < -7$
   (C) $x < -1$ or $x > -7$
   (D) $x > -1$ and $x < -7$
   (E) $x < -1$ and $x > -7$

4. Line ℓ passes through $(1,-3)$ and is perpendicular to $y = \frac{1}{5}x - 7$. What is the equation of line ℓ?

   (A) $y = -5x + 2$
   (B) $y = -5x-2$
   (C) $y = \frac{1}{5}x - \frac{14}{5}$
   (D) $y = -\frac{1}{5}x - \frac{14}{5}$
   (E) $y = 5x + 2$

5. Which of the following inequalities is equivalent to $-3y - 5x \leq 15$?

   (A) $y \geq \frac{5}{3}x + 5$
   (B) $y \leq -\frac{5}{3}x-5$
   (C) $y \geq -\frac{5}{3}x-5$
   (D) $y \geq \frac{5}{3}x-5$
   (E) $y \leq -\frac{5}{3}x + 5$

6. In a state park, any trout caught that weighs less than 10 oz or greater than 30 oz must be returned to the water. Which of the following represents the weights of trout that may be kept?

   (A) $|x - 20| \leq 10$
   (B) $|x - 10| \leq 10$
   (C) $|x - 10| \geq 20$
   (D) $|x - 30| \geq 10$
   (E) $|x - 20| \leq 30$

COLLEGE ENTRANCE EXAM PRACTICE CHAPTER 2

Organizer

Objective: Provide practice for college entrance exams such as the ACT.

Online Edition

Resources

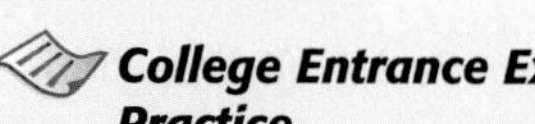

College Entrance Exam Practice

Questions on the ACT represent the following math strands:

Pre-Algebra, 23%
Elementary Algebra, 17%
Intermediate Algebra, 15%
Coordinate Geometry, 15%
Plane Geometry, 23%
Trigonometry, 7%

Items on this page focus on:
- Pre-Algebra
- Elementary Algebra
- Intermediate Algebra
- Coordinate Geometry

Text References:

Item	1	2	3	4	5	6
Lesson	2-2	2-1	2-1	2-4	2-5	2-8

TEST PREP DOCTOR

1. Students who chose **B** found the number of boys in the choir. Remind students to read each test item carefully to determine what question is being asked.
2. Students who chose **D** may have made an error when applying the Distributive Property on the left side of the equation, where they rewrote $12 - 3(x + 2)$ as $12 - 3x + 6$. Remind students to distribute the signs of the factors.
3. Students who chose **C** used a disjunction instead of a conjunction in the final answer. Remind students that inequalities involving *less than* are conjunctions and inequalities involving *greater than* are disjunctions.
4. Students who chose **C** found the equation of a line through the given point but parallel to the given line instead of perpendicular. Remind students that perpendicular lines have slopes that are opposite reciprocals of each other.
5. Students who chose **B** did not reverse the inequality symbol when multiplying or dividing both sides by a negative number. Remind students of the rules for solving inequalities.
6. Students who chose **C** may have reversed the midpoint of the range (20) and the distance from the midpoint to the limits of the range (10). Remind them that the midpoint belongs inside the absolute-value bars and the distance on the other side of the inequality.

Organizer

Objective: Provide opportunities to learn and practice common test-taking strategies.

Resources

 ***State Test Prep Workbook***

 ***State Test Prep* CD-ROM**

 ***State Test Practice Online***

KEYWORD: MB7 TestPrep

This test tackler focuses on how to correctly fill in answers to gridded-response items and how to avoid common gridding errors. Students often solve a test item correctly, but improper completion of the answer grid results in an incorrect response.

In this strategy, students review the rules for filling in a grid and then examine filled-in grids to identify why a correct answer might be scored as incorrect.

Standardized Test Strategies

Gridded Response: Write Gridded Responses

To answer a gridded-response test item, you must write your answer correctly in the top of the provided grid and fill in the bubbles accurately, or the item will be marked as incorrect. Answers may be gridded using several correct formats.

The answer to a gridded-response item is always a *whole number,* a *fraction,* or a *decimal.* Non-numerical signs and symbols, such as units of measure, the percent sign, the degree sign, the negative sign, variables, and commas, cannot be gridded.

EXAMPLE 1

Gridded Response: Solve the equation. $25 - 3(5x - 4) = 32$

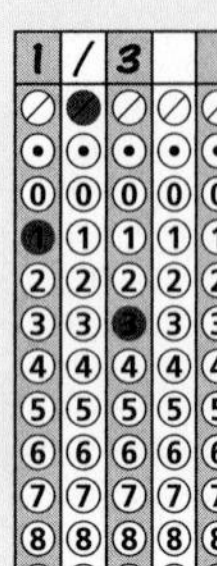
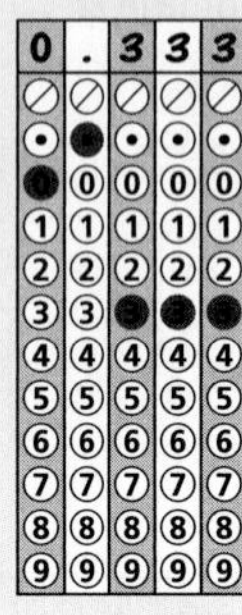

$$25 - 3(5x - 4) = 32$$
$$25 - 15x + 12 = 32$$
$$-15x = -5$$
$$x = \frac{5}{15} = \frac{1}{3}$$

Grid $\frac{1}{3}$ or its rounded decimal equivalent 0.333 or .3333:

Write your answer in the boxes at the top of the grid.
Put only a digit, the fraction bar, or the decimal point in each box.

Put the first digit of your answer in the box on the left OR put the last digit of your answer in the box on the right. Do not leave a blank box in the middle of an answer.

Shade the bubble of each digit or symbol in its corresponding column.

EXAMPLE 2

Gridded Response: Find the slope of the line that passes through $(-2, -5)$ and $(8, 10)$.

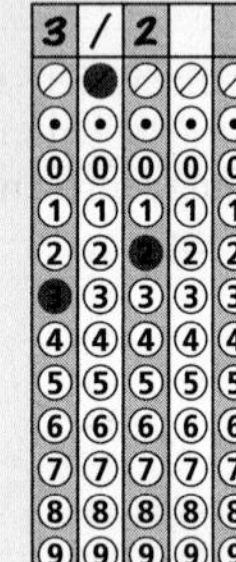

$$m = \frac{y_2 - y_1}{x_2 - x_1} = \frac{10-(-5)}{8-(-2)} = \frac{15}{10} = 1\frac{1}{2}$$

The slope of the line is $1\frac{1}{2}$, but a mixed number must be converted to either a decimal or an improper fraction before the answer can be written on the grid.

Grid the answer 1.5 or $\frac{3}{2}$ following the instructions in Example 1.

Read each statement, and then answer the questions that follow.

Sample A

A student solved a proportion for x and got $\frac{4}{5}$ as a result. He then gridded his answer as shown.

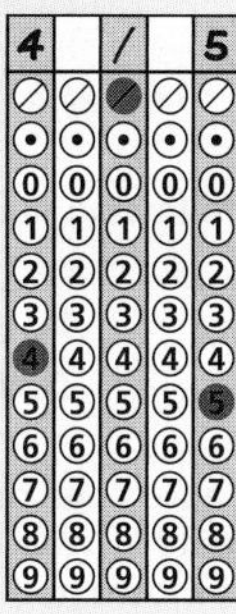

1. Is it possible to grid fractional answers? Explain.
2. If the student solved the proportion correctly, why was the answer marked as incorrect?
3. Describe one way to correctly grid the response $\frac{4}{5}$.

Sample B

What is the x-intercept of the linear function $6x + 9y = 18$?
Wyatt found that the x-intercept point occurs at $(3, 0)$, and then he filled out the grid.

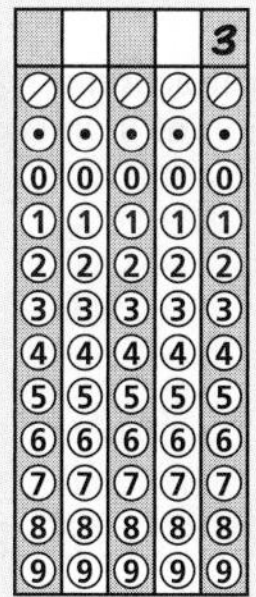

4. Will Wyatt's answer be marked as correct? Explain.
5. Anita got the same answer as Wyatt, but her answer was marked as correct. She did not place the 3 in the last column. Describe Anita's grid.

When filling out a grid, be sure to completely fill in the bubbles, and be careful not to rip the paper.

Sample C

For a gridded-response test item, Jill had to determine the slope of a linear function. She correctly determined the slope to be $2\frac{1}{2}$ and then gridded her answer as shown.

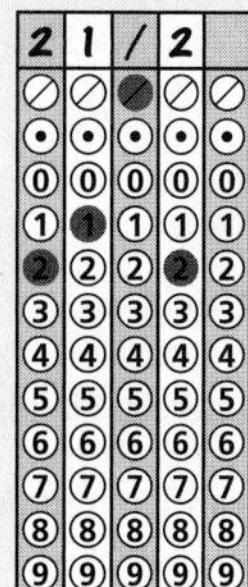

6. Read the number in the answer box grid. What number is recorded in the grid?
7. Why does gridding a mixed number result in an incorrect response?
8. Write a decimal equivalent for $2\frac{1}{2}$, and then write $2\frac{1}{2}$ as an improper fraction. Explain how to correctly grid these values.

Sample D

Daniel is taking an exam where he has to determine the y-intercept of the function shown below.

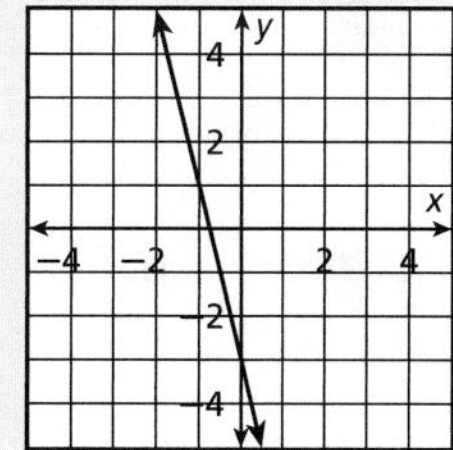

9. Is the y-intercept a positive or negative value?
10. Explain why the answer to this test item cannot be recorded on an answer grid.

Remind students that they can also write an answer in the grid by placing the last digit of the answer in the rightmost box. Reassure students that it is okay for the first box to be blank, as long as the last box is filled and there are no blanks between numbers.

Answers

1. Yes; there is a slash mark in the top row of the grid to represent the fraction bar. When this bubble is shaded, it represents a fraction.
2. The student placed a blank before and after the fraction bar.
3. Place a 4 in the first box, the slash mark in the second box, and a 5 in the third box. Then shade the corresponding digit/symbol bubbles.
4. No; He did not shade the 3 bubble in the last column.
5. Anita placed a 3 in the first box and then shaded the 3 bubble in the same column.
6. $\frac{21}{2}$
7. You cannot use a blank to separate the whole number and fraction. Without a blank, the answer is read as a fraction.
8. 2.5; $\frac{5}{2}$; place a 2 in the first box, a decimal point in the second box, and a 5 in the third box. Then shade the corresponding bubbles. Or place a 5 in the third box, a slash in the fourth box, and a 2 in the last box. Then shade the corresponding bubbles.
9. The y-intercept is negative.
10. There is no symbol to represent a negative sign.

Answers to *Test Samples*

A. | 4 | / | 5 | | | or | | | 4 | / | 5 |

B. | 3 | | | | |

C. | | | 2 | . | 5 |, | 2 | . | 5 | | |,

| | | 5 | / | 2 |, or | 5 | / | 2 | | |

D. −3

State Resources

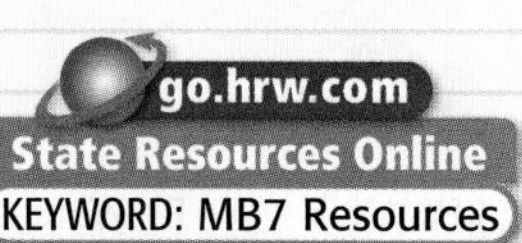

Organizer

Objective: Provide review and practice for Chapters 1–2 and standardized tests.

Resources

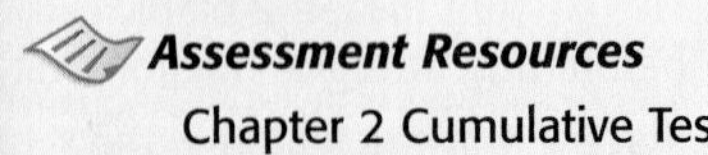

Chapter 2 Cumulative Test

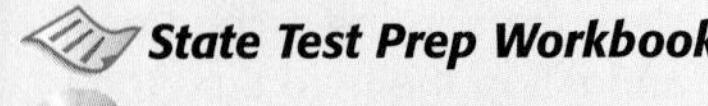

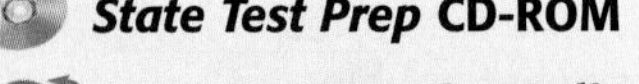

go.hrw.com
KEYWORD: MB7 TestPrep

Answers

1. D
2. C
3. B
4. B
5. D
6. C
7. C
8. D
9. B
10. A
11. C
12. C
13. A

State Resources

Core Standard	Items
1	7, 14
5	2, 10

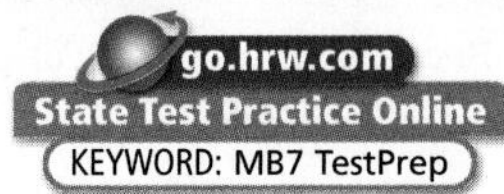

CUMULATIVE ASSESSMENT, CHAPTERS 1–2

Multiple Choice

1. For which function is $g(-3) > g(5)$?

A. $g(x) = 5x - 9$

B. $g(x) = x^2 - 12$

C. $g(x) = (x + 5)^2$

D. $g(x) = (x - 9)^2$

2. A television commercial claims that 4 out of every 5 dentists surveyed preferred Freshen toothpaste to the leading brand. If 120 dentists in the survey preferred Freshen, how many dentists participated in the survey?

A. 30 **B.** 96

C. 150 **D.** 180

3. Which is an equation of a line with a slope of -3 that passes through $(-2, 7)$?

A. $y = -3x - 1$

B. $y = -3x + 1$

C. $y = -3x + 13$

D. $y = -\frac{1}{3}x + 1$

4. Which of the following shows the graph of $y + \frac{3}{4}x \geq 2$?

A.
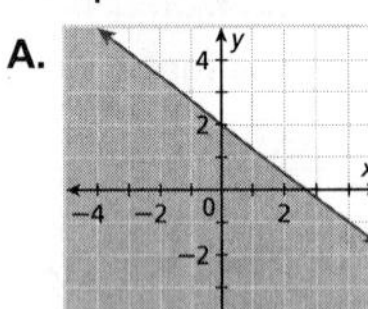

B.
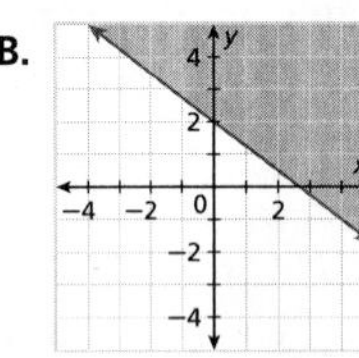

C.
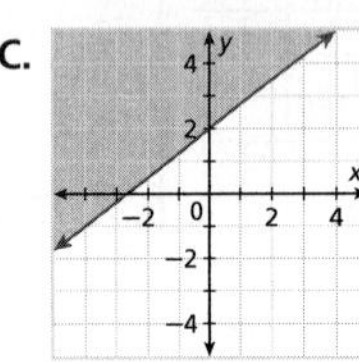

D.
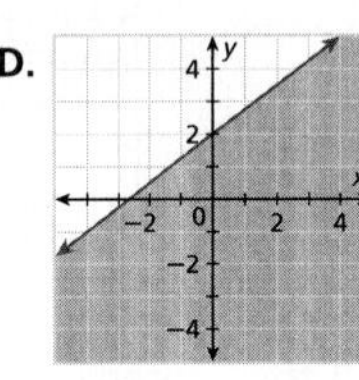

5. In which of the following number sets does -3 NOT belong?

A. Integers **B.** Rational numbers

C. Real numbers **D.** Whole numbers

6. What is a reasonable slope of the line of best fit of the salary data for teachers in a New York school district, as shown in the table below?

Salaries of Teachers	
Years of Experience	Salary
0	$33,407
2	$34,273
5	$37,882
8	$40,185
10	$42,977
12	$45,864
15	$53,811

A. 450 **B.** 750

C. 1275 **D.** 2650

7. Which shows a reflection across the x-axis and a vertical translation of 3 units down of the parent function $y = |x|$?

A. $y = -|x - 3|$ **B.** $y = |x| - 3$

C. $y = -|x| - 3$ **D.** $y = |x - 3|$

8. Simplify the expression $4\sqrt{50} + 3\sqrt{72}$.

A. $4\sqrt{7}$ **B.** $7\sqrt{112}$

C. $12\sqrt{5}$ **D.** $38\sqrt{2}$

9. Find the slope of the line $-3y = 6x + 12$.

A. -4 **B.** -2

C. $-\frac{1}{2}$ **D.** $-\frac{1}{4}$

TEST PREP DOCTOR

For **Item 6,** students should use a graphing calculator. If a graphing calculator is not available, students may create a scatter plot and use a straightedge to estimate a line of best fit.

Calculating slope between only two ordered pairs of data may result in an incorrect answer.

Answers

14. Part A: $x \leq \{x | x \leq -\frac{17}{5} \cup x \geq 1\}$

Part B: number line: −8 −6 −4 −2 0 2 4

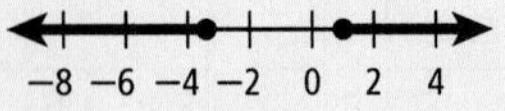

15. Part A: Answers will vary. Possible answer: $25(12 + 5x) = 2000$

Part B: 13

Part C: 1804 ft

When a word problem contains information about dimensions used to solve a problem, you might find it useful to draw a diagram. The diagram should be clearly labeled and sketched close to scale.

10. A lamppost casts a shadow that is 24 feet long. Tad, who is 6 feet tall, is standing directly next to the lamppost. His shadow is 15 feet long. About how tall is the lamppost?

A. 10 feet

B. 15 feet

C. 33 feet

D. 60 feet

11. What is the effect on the graph of $y = 2x + 2$ when it is changed to $y = 2x - 2$?

A. The slope of the line becomes steeper.

B. The line slants down and right instead of up and right.

C. The y-intercept is translated 4 units down.

D. The line is reflected across the y-axis.

12. The cost of renting a moving van is \$39.95 plus \$0.40 per mile. Which equation best represents the relationship between cost c and the number of miles driven m?

A. $c = 39.95 + 0.40$

B. $c = 39.95m + 0.40$

C. $c = 39.95 + 0.40m$

D. $c = 39.95m + 0.40m$

13. The baseball statistic "total bases" is calculated by adding the number of singles, twice the number of doubles, three times the number of triples, and four times the number of home runs. In 2001, a player collected 411 total bases, including 49 singles, 32 doubles and 2 triples. How many home runs did the player hit that year?

A. 73

B. 76

C. 80

D. 81

Short Answer

14. Consider the inequality $|5x + 6| \geq 11$.

Part A Solve the inequality.

Part B Graph your solution on a number line.

15. The city would like to construct a community amphitheater in the park. The stage of the amphitheater should be 25 feet across and 12 feet deep. The production group that uses the facility has anticipated that at least 5 feet of space should be a sufficient amount for each row. The area allotted for placement of the amphitheater's stage and seating is 2000 ft^2.

Part A Write an equation that can be used to determine the maximum number of rows that can be constructed.

Part B Determine the maximum number of rows that can be constructed.

Part C Suppose the city would like to construct a fence at least 200 feet away from the stage and all of the seats. Find the perimeter of fencing needed.

Extended Response

16. A container is filled with water at a constant rate. The water level over time is shown in the graph.

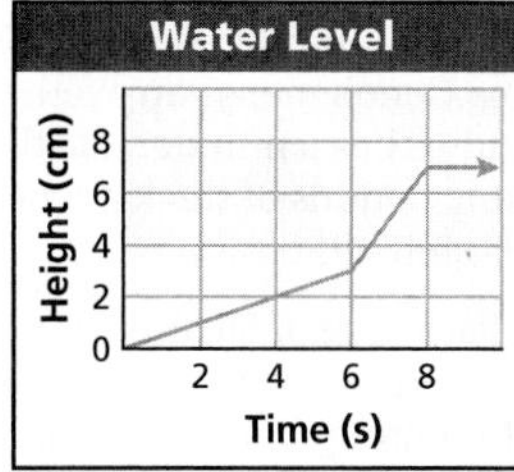

Part A What does the flat portion of the graph represent?

Part B Sketch a possible shape for the container.

Part C Suppose the container is filled twice as fast. Sketch a graph to represent the situation, and identify the transformation of the original graph that it represents.

Part D Suppose the container initially contains 2 cm of water. Would the new graph be a vertical translation of the original graph? Show or explain your work.

Short Answer Rubric

Items 14 and 15

Score 2 = Thorough understanding of mathematical concepts and processes.

Score 1 = Partial understanding of mathematical concepts and/or processes.

Score 0 = Limited or no understanding of the problem-solving concepts.

Blank = No written response.

Extended Response Rubric

Item 16

Score 4 = Thorough understanding of mathematical concepts and processes.

Score 3 = Demonstrated understanding of mathematical concepts and processes, but an error in computation or explanation.

Score 2 = Partial understanding of mathematical concepts and/or processes.

Score 1 = Limited understanding and execution of the problem-solving concepts.

Score 0 = No understanding of the problem-solving concepts.

Blank = No written response.

16. Part A: The container is full.

Part B:

Part C:

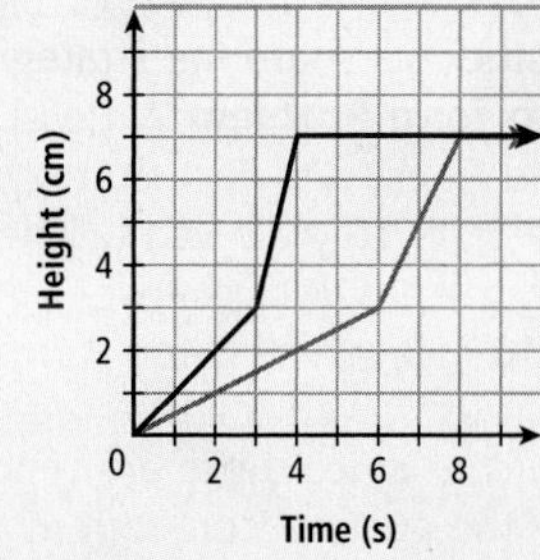

Part D: No; The maximum height of the water would still be 7 cm. The graph is translated 4 units left.

Problem Solving on Location

Organizer

Objective: Choose appropriate problem-solving strategies and use them with skills from Chapters 1 and 2 to solve real-world problems.

Online Edition

The Philly Cheese Steak Sandwich

Reading Strategies

Have students restate **Problem 1** in their own words. Then pose questions to be sure that students understand the given information. How long is the shift? 8 hours How many sandwiches are prepared each hour? 90

Using Data Encourage students to pay close attention to units in the recipe and in the problems. They will need to convert between ounces and pounds, minutes and hours, and dollars and cents.

State Resources

go.hrw.com
State Resources Online
KEYWORD: MB7 Resources

Problem Solving on Location

PENNSYLVANIA

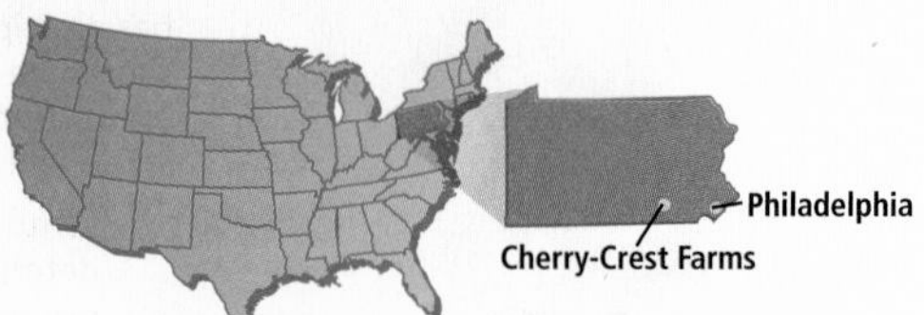

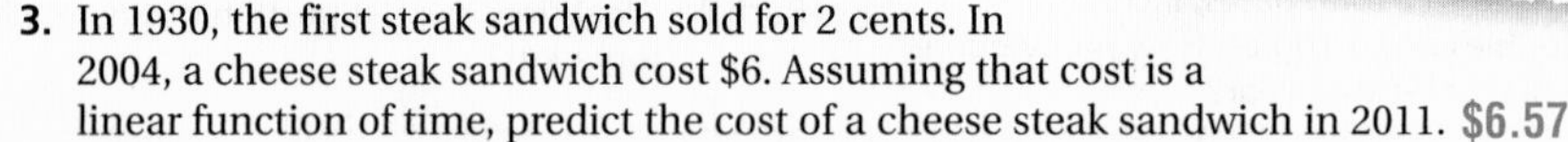

The Philly Cheese Steak Sandwich

Philadelphia's best-known sandwich was created in 1930 when a hot dog vendor tossed some steak and onions onto the grill and then served them on a hot dog bun. Cheese was soon added to the recipe, and the Philly cheese steak sandwich has been a local specialty ever since.

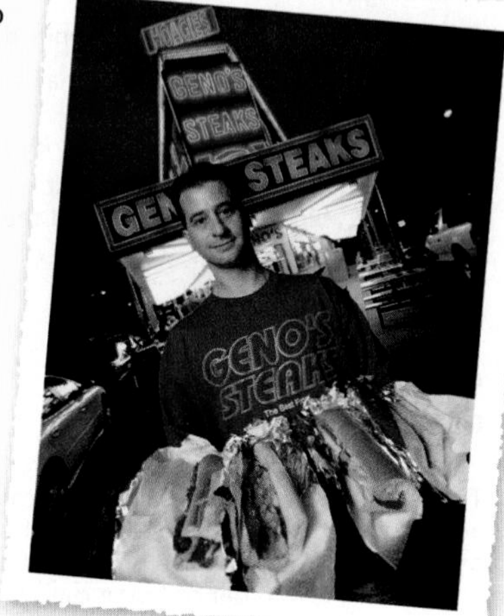

Choose one or more strategies to solve each problem.

1. At Geno's Steaks, the busiest shift of the week is on Saturday from 11:00 A.M. to 7:00 P.M. During that time Geno's makes an average of 1.5 cheese steak sandwiches a minute. Use the recipe below. How many pounds of steak are needed to get through this shift? 225 lb
2. At Pat's King of Steaks, a plain steak sandwich costs \$5.75 and a cheese steak sandwich costs \$6.00. A tour group bought 32 sandwiches for a total of \$189.00. How many of each type did they buy? 12 plain, 20 with cheese
3. In 1930, the first steak sandwich sold for 2 cents. In 2004, a cheese steak sandwich cost \$6. Assuming that cost is a linear function of time, predict the cost of a cheese steak sandwich in 2011. \$6.57
4. You can expect to find a line at many cheese steak stands, but service is quick. Once an order is placed, the sandwich is made and served in 1 minute and 15 seconds. Suppose it takes 18 seconds for each person in line to place an order. What is the maximum number of people who can be in line ahead of you if you want to have your sandwich in less than 10 minutes from the time you get in line? 28

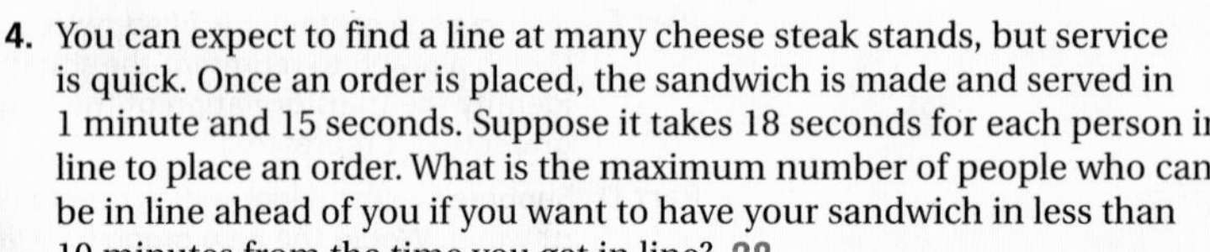

Philly Cheese Steak Recipe

5 oz steak
2 1/2 oz. American cheese
Fried onions
9 1/2 in. roll

Thinly slice steak and fry on grill. Just before it's done, cover with cheese and cook until melted. Serve on roll, topped with onions.

Problem Solving Focus

Have students share the strategies they used to solve **Problem 2.** Possible answer: Use the Guess and Test strategy. For example, try 10 plain sandwiches and 22 sandwiches with cheese. This would cost \$189.50, which is too much, so the group must have bought more of the plain sandwiches since those are less expensive. Revise the guess accordingly, check the total cost, and continue in this way to find that 12 plain sandwiches and 20 with cheese gives the correct total cost.

Problem Solving Strategies

- Draw a Diagram
- Make a Model
- Guess and Test
- Work Backward
- Find a Pattern
- Make a Table
- Solve a Simpler Problem
- Use Logical Reasoning
- Use a Venn Diagram
- Make an Organized List

The Amazing Maize Maze

Cherry-Crest Farm, located in the heart of Pennsylvania Dutch Country, welcomes visitors by telling them to get lost—in an enormous cornfield maze! The design of the maze changes from year to year, but it always includes bridges and tunnels. There are also clues to discover along the way.

Choose one or more strategies to solve each problem.

1. Corn is usually planted at 30,000 plants per acre. The Amazing Maize Maze measures 360 feet by 660 feet. Assuming that 60% of that area is covered with corn plants, about how many plants form the maze? (*Hint:* 1 acre = 43,560 ft^2) **98,000**
2. Admission to Cherry-Crest Farm is $11 for adults and $9 for children. One group of visitors paid $213 for admission, and there were more adults than children in the group. How many of each were in the group? **12 adults, 9 children**

For 3, use the table.

3. Getting through the maze depends on two things: the speed at which you walk and your luck in choosing the right path. The table shows the average walking speeds of eight visitors and the time it took them to exit the maze. Predict the time it would take you to exit the maze if you walked at an average speed of 3.5 mi/h. **55 min**

Average Walking Speed (mi/h)	2.5	3.0	4.0	3.1	2.8	3.9	4.0	2.7
Time to Exit Maze (min)	72	61	45	58	66	50	51	69

4. For most visitors, the time in minutes that it takes to exit the maze satisfies the inequality $|t - 60| \leq 15$.

   However, people who have already been through the maze usually improve their time by about 7 minutes. What are the minimum and maximum times it takes to exit the maze for repeat visitors? **38 min, 68 min**

Problem Solving on Location 177

The Amazing Maize Maze

Reading Strategies

Have students read **Problem 1** all the way through so that they can get an overall sense of the problem. Then ask them to reread the problem carefully, writing down the important information as they read.

Using Data Ask students for the distance-rate-time formula. $d = rt$ Ask whether all of the 8 people represented by the table data walked about the same distance. no Which person walked the farthest? the person walking 4 mi/h About how far did that person walk? 3.4 mi

Problem Solving Focus

For **Problem 2,** focus on the second and third steps of the Problem Solving Process: Make a Plan and Solve. Ask students which strategy might help them approach the problem in an organized way. Possible answer: Use the strategy Make a Table. Students might start by assuming that there was one adult in the group and calculating the number of children that would be necessary to bring the total cost to $213. Making a table that lists the various numbers of adults and children will show that there are only two combinations in which the number of adults and the number of children are both whole numbers. In only one of these is the number of adults greater than the number of children.

Discuss with students any alternate strategies that might be useful in solving **Problem 2.** For example, students might try a Guess-and-Test approach.

Linear Systems

Section 3A Linear Systems in Two Dimensions	Section 3B Linear Systems in Three Dimensions
3-1 Using Graphs and Tables to Solve Linear Systems	**3-5 Linear Equations in Three Dimensions**
3-2 Using Algebraic Methods to Solve Linear Systems	**Connecting Algebra to Geometry** Views of Solid Figures
Connecting Algebra to Geometry Properties of Polygons	**3-6 Solving Linear Systems in Three Variables**
3-3 Solving Systems of Linear Inequalities	**3-6 Technology Lab** Explore Parametric Equations
3-4 Linear Programming	**EXTENSION Parametric Equations**

Pacing Guide for 45-Minute Classes

Chapter 3 — Countdown to Testing Weeks 6, 7

DAY 1	DAY 2	DAY 3	DAY 4	DAY 5
3-1 Lesson	3-2 Lesson	Connecting Algebra to Geometry 3-3 Lesson	3-3 Lesson	3-4 Lesson
DAY 6	**DAY 7**	**DAY 8**	**DAY 9**	**DAY 10**
3-4 Lesson	Multi-Step Test Prep Ready to Go On? 3-5 Lesson	3-5 Lesson Connecting Algebra to Geometry	3-6 Lesson	3-6 Technology Lab Multi-Step Test Prep Ready to Go On?
DAY 11	**DAY 12**			
EXTENSION	Chapter 3 Test			

Pacing Guide for 90-Minute Classes

Chapter 3

DAY 1	DAY 2	DAY 3	DAY 4	DAY 5
3-1 Lesson 3-2 Lesson	Connecting Algebra to Geometry 3-3 Lesson	3-4 Lesson	Multi-Step Test Prep Ready to Go On? 3-5 Lesson Connecting Algebra to Geometry	3-6 Lesson 3-6 Technology Lab Multi-Step Test Prep Ready to Go On?
DAY 6				
EXTENSION Chapter 3 Test				

ONGOING ASSESSMENT and INTERVENTION

Assess Prior Knowledge

Before Chapter 3

DIAGNOSE	PRESCRIBE
Diagnose readiness for the chapter.	Prescribe intervention.
Are You Ready? SE p. 179	***Are You Ready? Intervention*** Skills 2, 60, 69, 71, 76

Formative Assessment

Before Every Lesson

DIAGNOSE	PRESCRIBE
Diagnose readiness for the lesson.	Prescribe intervention.
Warm Up TE, every lesson	**Skills Bank** SE pp. S46–S73
	Reteach CRB, Ch. 1–3

During Every Lesson

DIAGNOSE	PRESCRIBE
Diagnose understanding of lesson concepts.	Prescribe intervention.
Check It Out! SE, every example	**Questioning Strategies** TE, every example
Think and Discuss SE, every lesson	**Reading Strategies** CRB, every lesson
Write About It SE, every lesson	***Success for ELL*** pp. 37–48
Journal TE, every lesson	

After Every Lesson

DIAGNOSE	PRESCRIBE
Diagnose mastery of lesson concepts.	Prescribe intervention.
Lesson Quiz TE, every lesson	**Reteach** CRB, every lesson
Alternative Assessment TE, every lesson	**Problem Solving** CRB, every lesson
Test Prep SE, every lesson	**Test Prep Doctor** TE, every lesson
Test and Practice Generator	***Homework Help Online***

Before Chapter 3 Testing

DIAGNOSE	PRESCRIBE
Diagnose mastery of concepts in the chapter.	Prescribe intervention.
Ready to Go On? SE pp. 213, 229	***Ready to Go On? Intervention*** pp. 43–58
Multi-Step Test Prep SE pp. 212, 228	**Scaffolding Questions** TE pp. 212, 228
Section Quizzes AR pp. 45–46	
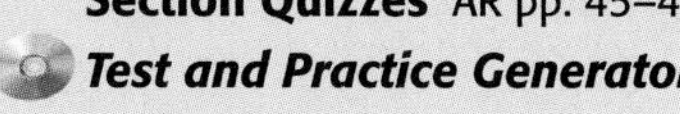	

Before High Stakes Testing

DIAGNOSE	PRESCRIBE
Diagnose mastery of benchmark concepts.	Prescribe intervention.
College Entrance Exam Practice SE p. 237	***College Entrance Exam Practice***
Standardized Test Prep SE pp. 240–241	***State Test Prep Workbook***
State Test Prep CD-ROM	

Summative Assessment

After Chapter 3

DIAGNOSE	PRESCRIBE
Check mastery of chapter concepts.	Prescribe intervention.
Multiple-Choice Tests (Forms A, B, C)	**Reteach** CRB, every lesson
Free-Response Tests (Forms A, B, C)	***Lesson Tutorial Videos*** Chapter 3
Performance Assessment AR pp. 47–60	
Test and Practice Generator	
Check mastery of benchmark concepts.	Prescribe intervention.
AYP State Tests	***State Test Prep Workbook***
College Entrance Exams	***College Entrance Exam Practice***

KEY: **SE** = *Student Edition* **TE** = *Teacher's Edition* **CRB** = *Chapter Resource Book* **AR** = *Assessment Resources* Available on CD-ROM Available online

Supporting the Teacher

Chapter 3 Resource Book

Practice A, B, C
pp. 3–5, 11–13, 19–21, 27–29, 35–37, 43–45

Reading Strategies ELL
pp. 10, 18, 26, 34, 42, 50

Reteach
pp. 6–7, 14–15, 22–23, 30–31, 38–39, 46–47

Problem Solving
pp. 9, 17, 25, 33, 41, 49

Challenge
pp. 8, 16, 24, 32, 40, 48

Parent Letter pp. 1–2

Transparencies

Lesson Transparencies, Volume 1 .... Chapter 3
- Teaching Tools
- Warm Ups
- Teaching Transparencies
- Additional Examples
- Lesson Quizzes

Alternate Openers: Explorations 19–24

Countdown to Testing 11–14

Know-It Notebook .... Chapter 3
- Graphic Organizers

Teacher Tools

Power Presentations® 
Complete PowerPoint® presentations for Chapter 3 lessons

Lesson Tutorial Videos® 
Holt authors Ed Burger and Freddie Renfro present tutorials to support the Chapter 3 lessons.

One-Stop Planner®
Easy access to all Chapter 3 resources and assessments, as well as software for lesson planning, test generation, and puzzle creation

IDEA Works!®
Key Chapter 3 resources and assessments modified to address special learning needs

Lesson Plans .... pp. 19–24

Solutions Key .... Chapter 3

Algebra Posters

TechKeys

Lab Resources

Project Teacher Support

Parent Resources

Workbooks

Homework and Practice Workbook
Teacher's Guide .... pp. 19–24

Know-It Notebook
Teacher's Guide .... Chapter 3

Problem Solving Workbook
Teacher's Guide .... pp. 19–24

State Test Prep Workbook
Teacher's Guide

Technology Highlights for the Teacher

 **Power Presentations**
Dynamic presentations to engage students. Complete PowerPoint® presentations for every lesson in Chapter 3.

2-1 Solving One-Step Equations

Isolate a variable by using inverse operations which "undo" operations on the variable.

An equation is like a balanced scale. To keep the balance, perform the same operation on both sides.

Inverse Operations	
Operation	**Inverse Operation**
Addition	Subtraction
Subtraction	Addition

 **One-Stop Planner**
Easy access to Chapter 3 resources and assessments. Includes lesson-planning, test-generation, and puzzle-creation software.

 **Premier Online Edition**
Chapter 3 includes Tutorial Videos, Lesson Activities, Lesson Quizzes, Homework Help, and Chapter Project.

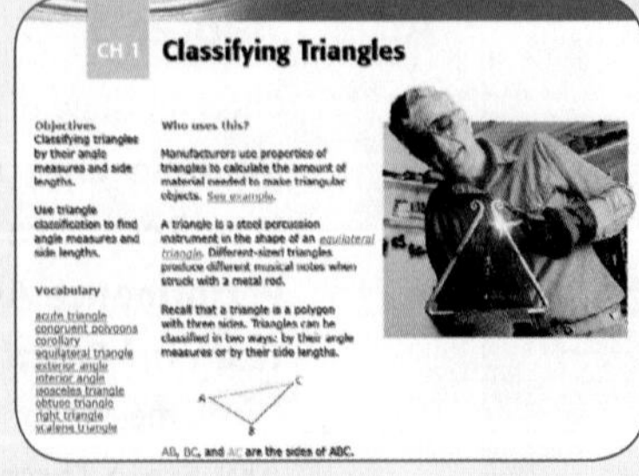

KEY: **SE** = *Student Edition* **TE** = *Teacher's Edition* ELL English Language Learners  Available on CD-ROM Available online

CHAPTER 3

Reaching All Learners

Resources for All Learners

Algebra Lab Activities	Chapter 3
Technology Lab Activities	Chapter 3
Homework and Practice Workbook	pp. 19–24
Know-It Notebook	Chapter 3
Problem Solving Workbook	pp. 19–24

DEVELOPING LEARNERS

Practice A	CRB, every lesson
Reteach	CRB, every lesson
Inclusion	TE pp. 184, 208, 221
Questioning Strategies	TE, every example
Modified Chapter 3 Resources (CD-ROM)	*IDEA Works!*
Homework Help Online (online)	

ON-LEVEL LEARNERS

Practice B	CRB, every lesson
Multiple Representations	TE pp. 191–192, 223
Graphic Organizers	TE p. 206

ADVANCED LEARNERS

Practice C	CRB, every lesson
Challenge	CRB, every lesson
Reading and Writing Math EXTENSION	TE p. 181
Multi-Step Test Prep EXTENSION	TE pp. 212, 228
Critical Thinking	TE pp. 185, 191

English Language Learners

ENGLISH LANGUAGE LEARNERS

Are You Ready? Vocabulary	SE p. 179
Vocabulary Connections	SE p. 180
Lesson Vocabulary	SE pp. 182, 190, 199, 205, 214
Vocabulary Exercises	SE pp. 186, 194, 202, 209, 216
Vocabulary Review	SE p. 232
English Language Learners	TE pp. 181, 207
Reading Strategies	CRB, every lesson
Success for English Language Learners	pp. 37–48
Multilingual Glossary (online)	

Reaching All Learners Through...

Kinesthetic Experience	TE pp. 183, 219, 230
Inclusion	TE pp. 184, 208, 221
Critical Thinking	TE pp. 185, 191
Cooperative Learning	TE p. 187
Multiple Representations	TE pp. 191–192, 223
Auditory Cues	TE p. 198
Visual Cues	TE pp. 200–201, 221
Graphic Organizers	TE p. 206
Concrete Manipulatives	TE p. 217
Test Prep Doctor	TE pp. 188, 196, 203, 211, 218, 226, 237
Common Error Alerts	TE pp. 185, 187, 191, 193, 195, 203, 207, 217, 223
Scaffolding Questions	TE pp. 212, 228

Technology Highlights for Reaching All Learners

Lesson Tutorial Videos

Starring Holt authors Ed Burger and Freddie Renfro! Live tutorials to support every lesson in Chapter 3.

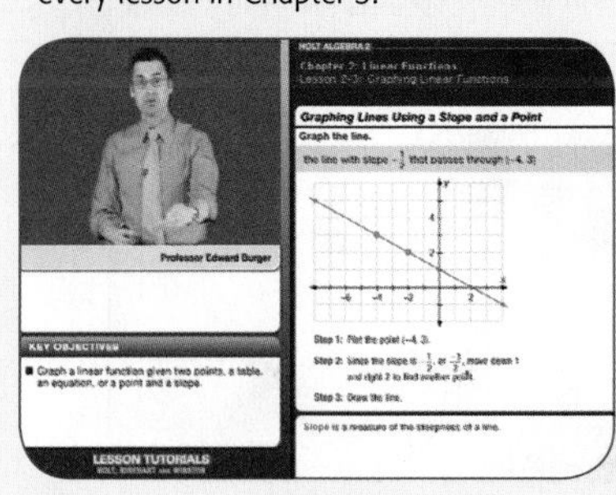

Multilingual Glossary

Searchable glossary includes definitions in English, Spanish, Vietnamese, Chinese, Hmong, Korean, and 4 other languages.

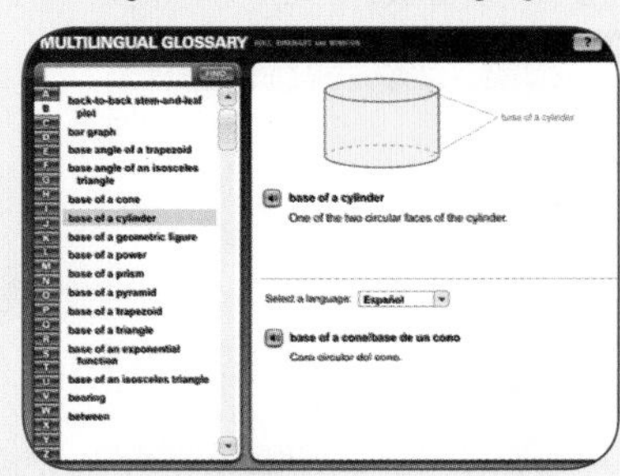

Online Interactivities

Interactive tutorials provide visually engaging alternative opportunities to learn concepts and master skills.

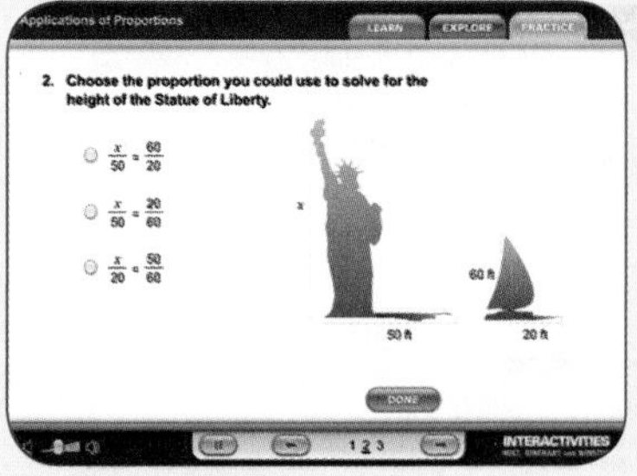

KEY: **SE** = *Student Edition* **TE** = *Teacher's Edition* **CRB** = *Chapter Resource Book*  Available on CD-ROM  Available online

CHAPTER 3

Ongoing Assessment

Assessing Prior Knowledge

Determine whether students have the required prerequisite concepts and skills for success in Chapter 3.

Are You Ready? SPANISH	SE p. 179
Warm Up	TE, every lesson

Test Preparation

Provide review and practice for Chapter 3 and standardized tests.

Multi-Step Test Prep	SE pp. 212, 228
Study Guide: Review	SE pp. 232–235
Test Tackler	SE pp. 238–239
Standardized Test Prep	SE pp. 240–241
College Entrance Exam Practice	SE p. 237
***Countdown to Testing* Transparencies**	11–14
State Test Prep Workbook	
***State Test Prep* CD-ROM**	
IDEA Works!	

Alternative Assessment

Assess students' understanding of Chapter 3 concepts and combined problem-solving skills.

Chapter 3 Project	SE p. 178
Alternative Assessment	TE, every lesson
Performance Assessment	AR pp. 59–60
Portfolio Assessment	AR p. xxxiv

Daily Assessment

Provide formative assessment for each day of Chapter 3.

Questioning Strategies	TE, every example
Think and Discuss	SE, every lesson
Check It Out! Exercises	SE, every example
Write About It	SE, every lesson
Journal	TE, every lesson
Lesson Quiz	TE, every lesson
Alternative Assessment	TE, every lesson
Modified Lesson Quizzes	*IDEA Works!*

Weekly Assessment

Provide formative assessment for each week of Chapter 3.

Multi-Step Test Prep	SE pp. 212, 228
Ready to Go On?	SE pp. 213, 229
Cumulative Assessment	SE pp. 240–241
Test and Practice Generator	*One-Stop Planner*

Formal Assessment

Provide summative assessment of Chapter 3 mastery.

Section Quizzes	AR pp. 45–46
Chapter 3 Test	SE p. 236
Chapter Test (Levels A, B, C) • Multiple Choice • Free Response	AR pp. 47–58
Cumulative Test	AR pp. 61–64
Test and Practice Generator	*One-Stop Planner*
Modified Chapter 3 Test	*IDEA Works!*

Technology Highlights for Ongoing Assessment

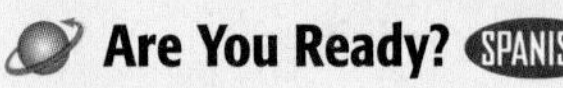
Are You Ready? SPANISH

Automatically assess readiness and prescribe intervention for Chapter 3 prerequisite skills.

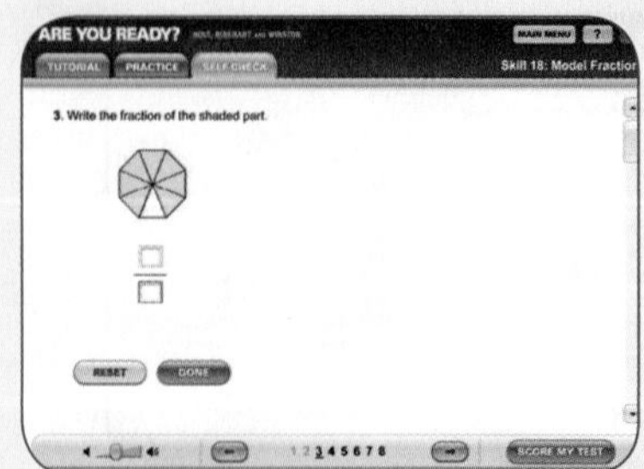

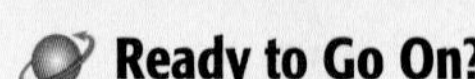
Ready to Go On?

Automatically assess understanding and prescribe intervention for Sections 3A and 3B.

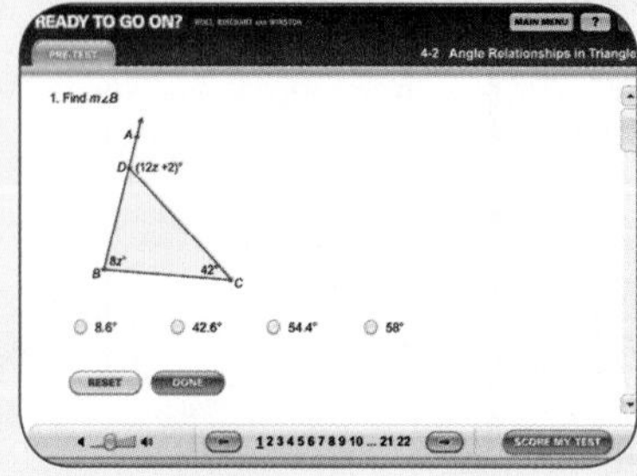

Test and Practice Generator

Use Chapter 3 problem banks to create assessments and worksheets to print out or deliver online. Includes dynamic problems.

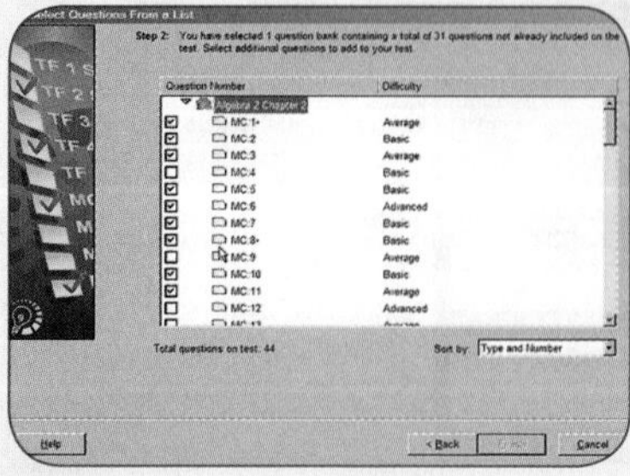

KEY: **SE** = *Student Edition* **TE** = *Teacher's Edition* **AR** = *Assessment Resources*  Spanish version available · Available on CD-ROM · Available online

CHAPTER 3

Formal Assessment

Three levels (A, B, C) of multiple-choice and free-response chapter tests are available in the *Assessment Resources.*

A Chapter 3 Test

C Chapter 3 Test

MULTIPLE CHOICE

B Chapter 3 Test

B Chapter 3 Test *(continued)*

A Chapter 3 Test

C Chapter 3 Test

FREE RESPONSE

B Chapter 3 Test

B Chapter 3 Test *(continued)*

MODIFIED FOR IDEA

Chapter 3 Test

Chapter 3 Test *(continued)*

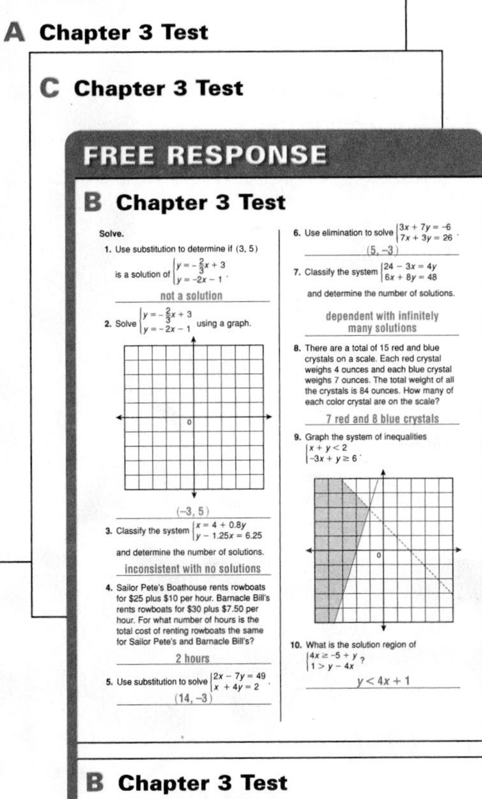

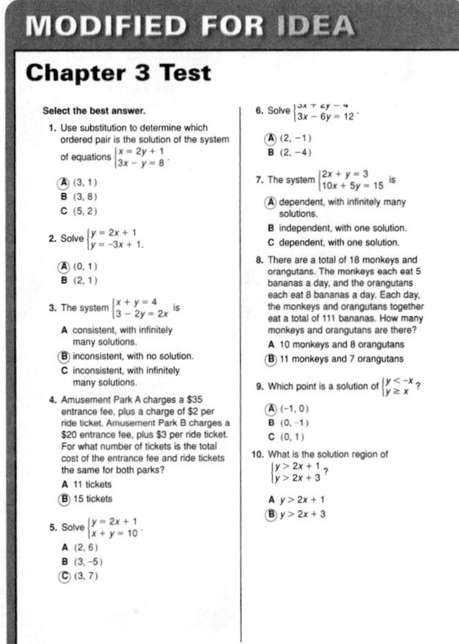

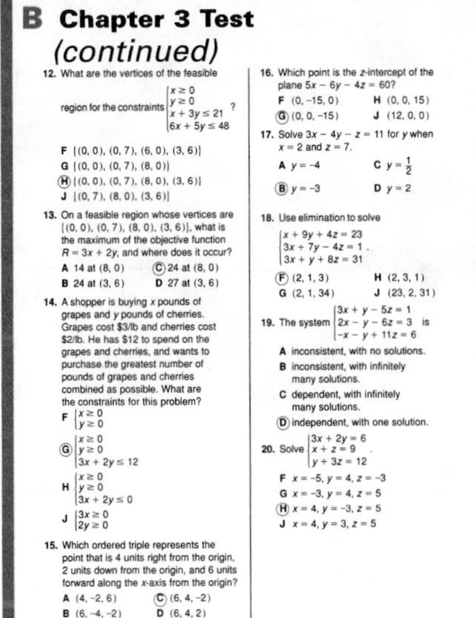

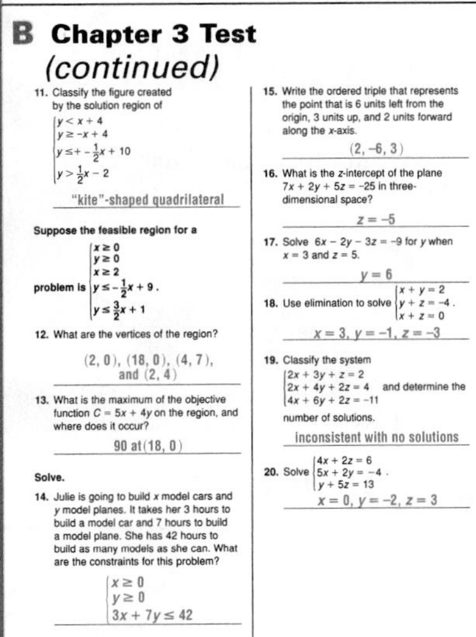

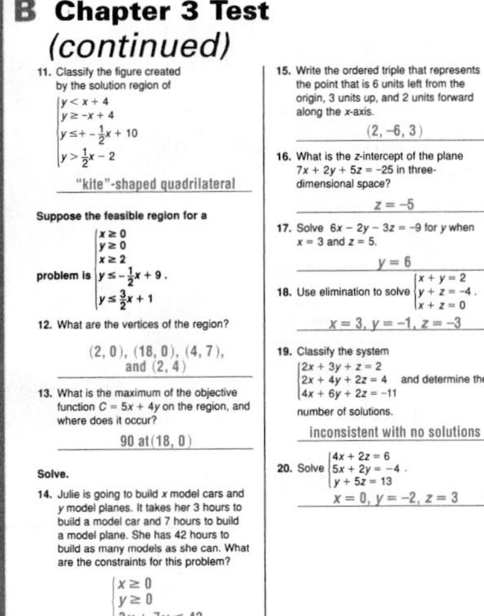

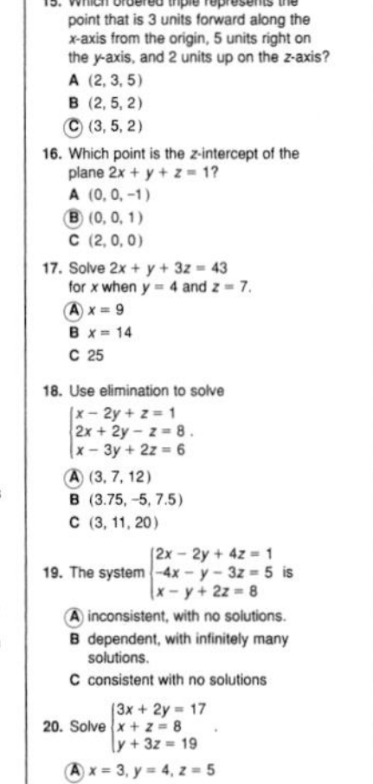

Test & Practice Generator

One-Stop Planner®

Create and customize Chapter 3 Tests. Instantly generate multiple test versions, answer keys, and practice versions of test items.

CHAPTER 3

SECTION 3A
Linear Systems in Two Dimensions

On page 212, students use linear systems to evaluate the speeds and fuel consumption of race cars.

Exercises designed to prepare students for success on the Multi-Step Test Prep can be found on pages 188, 196, 203, and 210.

SECTION 3B
Linear Systems in Three Dimensions

On page 228, students use three-dimensional coordinates to describe architectural designs.

Exercises designed to prepare students for success on the Multi-Step Test Prep can be found on pages 217 and 225.

CHAPTER 3 Linear Systems

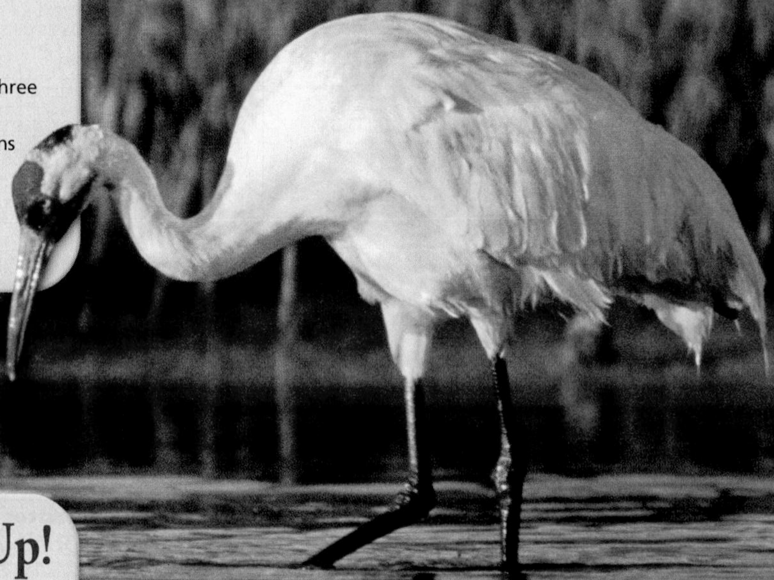

Whooping It Up!

You can use linear systems to plan a fund-raiser in which calendars featuring endangered whooping cranes are sold.

go.hrw.com
Chapter Project Online
KEYWORD: MB7 ChProj

Whooping It Up!

About the Project

In the Chapter Project, students investigate the revenue from the sale of calendars featuring endangered whooping cranes. Students then compare the revenue to the costs of printing the calendars and use linear programming to maximize profit.

Project Resources

All project resources for teachers and students are provided online.

Materials:

- data on the numbers of students and teachers at your school
- graphing calculator
- computers with Internet access

ARE YOU READY?

Vocabulary

Match each term on the left with a definition on the right.

1. equation D
2. inequality C
3. solution set E
4. slope B

A. an equation whose solutions form a line on a coordinate plane
B. steepness of a line given as a ratio of rise over run
C. a mathematical statement using >, <, ≥, or ≤
D. a mathematical statement that says two expressions are equal
E. the set of values that make a statement true

Least Common Multiple

Find the least common multiple, or LCM, for each pair of numbers.

5. 3, 18 **18**
6. 28, 8 **56**
7. 8, 36 **72**
8. 15, 27 **135**

Slopes of Parallel and Perpendicular Lines

State whether the linear equations in each pair are parallel, perpendicular, or neither.

9. $\begin{cases} y = 5x - 4 \\ y = -\frac{1}{5}x - 4 \end{cases}$ **perpendicular**
10. $\begin{cases} 5x - 10y = 3 \\ y = \frac{1}{2}x - 6 \end{cases}$ **parallel**
11. $\begin{cases} x - y = 3 \\ x + y = -4 \end{cases}$ **perpendicular**
12. $\begin{cases} 2x - 3y = -4 \\ 3y - x = 5 \end{cases}$ **neither**

Evaluate Expressions

Evaluate each expression for the given values of the variables.

13. $1.5x + 3y$ for $x = 8, y = 14$ **54**
14. $5x - \frac{3}{4}y$ for $x = 6, y = -4$ **33**
15. $4x - \sqrt{2}y$ for $x = 0.25, y = \sqrt{2}$ **−1**
16. $-\frac{75x}{3y}$ for $x = 1, y = \frac{1}{3}$ **−75**

Solve Multi-Step Equations

Solve each equation.

17. $8x + 19 = -5$ **−3**
18. $5x + 4 = 25 - 2x$ **3**
19. $9x - (x + 12) = -13$ $-\frac{1}{8}$
20. $-3(4x - 5) - 1 = 20$ $-\frac{1}{2}$

Solve Equations with Fractions

Solve each equation.

21. $\frac{1}{4}x + \frac{2}{3}x = 8$ $\frac{96}{11}$
22. $\frac{2}{5}x + \frac{1}{6} = -4$ $-\frac{125}{12}$
23. $x + \frac{1}{2} = -\frac{1}{5}$ $-\frac{7}{10}$
24. $-\frac{1}{2} = 3x - \frac{1}{3}x$ $-\frac{3}{16}$

CHAPTER 3

ARE YOU READY?

Organizer

Objective: Assess students' understanding of prerequisite skills.

Prerequisite Skills

- Least Common Multiple
- Slopes of Parallel and Perpendicular Lines
- Evaluate Expressions
- Solve Multi-Step Equations
- Solve Equations with Fractions

Assessing Prior Knowledge

INTERVENTION

Diagnose and Prescribe

Use this page to determine whether intervention is necessary or whether enrichment is appropriate.

Resources

Are You Ready? Intervention and Enrichment **Worksheets**

Are You Ready? **CD-ROM**

Are You Ready? **Online**

my.hrw.com

ARE YOU READY? Diagnose and Prescribe

NO INTERVENE

Prerequisite Skill	*Are You Ready? Intervention*, Chapter 3: Worksheets	CD-ROM	Online
Least Common Multiple	Skill 2	Activity 2	Diagnose and Prescribe Online
Slopes of Parallel and Perpendicular Lines	Skill 76	Activity 76	
Evaluate Expressions	Skill 60	Activity 60	
Solve Multi-Step Equations	Skill 69	Activity 69	
Solve Equations with Fractions	Skill 71	Activity 71	

YES ENRICH

Are You Ready? Enrichment, Chapter 3
- Worksheets
- CD-ROM
- Online

CHAPTER 3 Study Guide: Preview

Objective: Help students organize the new concepts they will learn in Chapter 3.

Online Edition
Multilingual Glossary

Resources

Puzzle Pro
One-Stop Planner®

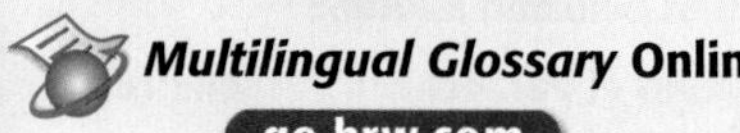

***Multilingual Glossary* Online**
go.hrw.com
KEYWORD: MB7 Glossary

Answers to *Vocabulary Connections*

Possible answers:

1. To eliminate means to get rid of. When solving equations, you can sometimes eliminate a variable to solve for the remaining variable.
2. a restriction that narrows the possible numbers or solutions
3. The plan appears feasible. Due to the late time, it is no longer feasible to go to the store. A feasible region is a region that is suitable or workable.
4. A three-dimensional coordinate system has three dimensions. Since a coordinate plane has two dimensions indicated by x and y, the logical letter for the third dimension is z.

CHAPTER 3 Study Guide: Preview

Where You've Been

Previously, you

- graphed linear equations.
- graphed linear inequalities.
- solved linear equations.
- studied three-dimensional figures such as cubes and prisms.

In This Chapter

You will study

- graphing systems of linear equations.
- graphing systems of linear inequalities.
- solving systems of linear equations.
- the three-dimensional coordinate system.

Where You're Going

You can use the skills in this chapter

- to solve more complicated systems of equations.
- to understand linear systems in other classes, such as Chemistry, Physics, and Economics.
- outside of school to organize fund-raisers, plan a trip, or spend money wisely.

Key Vocabulary/Vocabulario

constraint	restricción
elimination	eliminación
feasible region	región factible
linear programming	programación lineal
linear system	sistema lineal
substitution	sustitución
system of equations	sistema de ecuaciones
system of linear inequalities	sistema de desigualdades lineales
three-dimensional coordinate system	sistema de coordenadas tridimensional

Vocabulary Connections

To become familiar with some of the vocabulary terms in the chapter, consider the following. You may refer to the chapter, the glossary, or a dictionary if you like.

1. What does the word **eliminate** mean? What might the *elimination* method refer to when solving mathematical equations?
2. **Constraint** refers to a restriction or limitation. What might a mathematical *constraint* refer to?
3. The word **feasible** means "capable of being done or used." Give examples of sentences that use the word *feasible*. Then discuss what a *feasible region* might refer to.
4. What can you say about a **three-dimensional coordinate system** from its name? If x and y are used for the first two, which letter would be a logical choice for the third coordinate?

180 Chapter 3

Writing Strategy: Keep a Math Journal

Keeping a math journal will help you improve your writing and reasoning skills. By expressing yourself in a journal, you can make sense of confusing or frustrating math situations.

You can use your journal to reflect on what you learned in class, write out any troubles you are having, summarize important concepts and vocabulary, or express your thoughts about a particular topic. Most importantly, though, a math journal helps you see your progress as you continue through Algebra 2.

Journal Entry: Read the entry a student made in his journal.

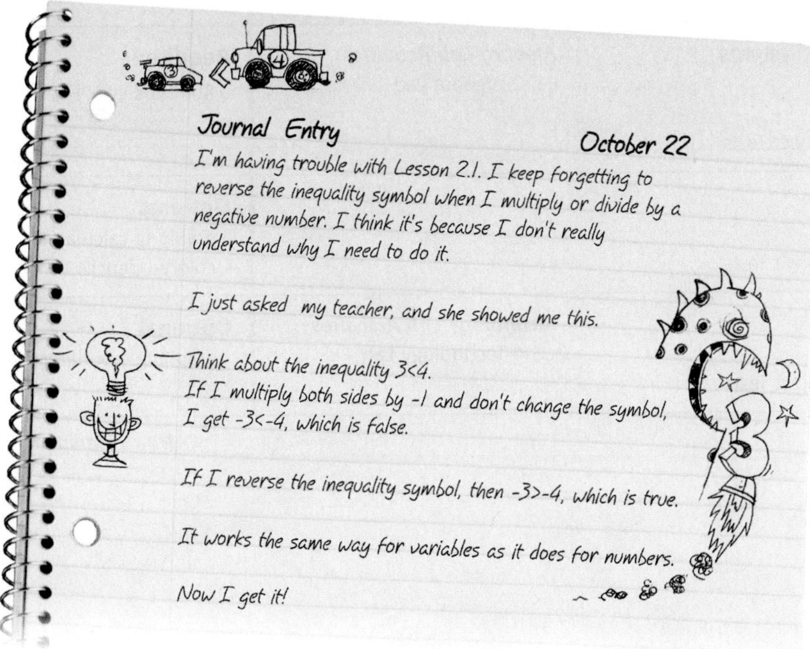

Journal Entry
October 22
I'm having trouble with Lesson 2.1. I keep forgetting to reverse the inequality symbol when I multiply or divide by a negative number. I think it's because I don't really understand why I need to do it.
I just asked my teacher, and she showed me this.
Think about the inequality 3<4.
If I multiply both sides by -1 and don't change the symbol, I get -3<-4, which is false.
If I reverse the inequality symbol, then -3>-4, which is true.
It works the same way for variables as it does for numbers.
Now I get it!

Try This

Begin a math journal. Use these ideas to begin your journal entry each day for this week. Be sure to date and number each page.

- What I already know about this lesson is . . .
- What I am unsure about in this lesson is . . .
- The skills I need in order to finish this lesson are . . .
- What trouble spots did I find? How did I handle these difficulties?
- What I enjoyed/did not enjoy about this lesson was . . .

Organizer

Objective: Help students apply strategies to understand and retain key concepts.

Resources

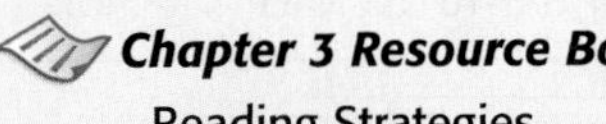

Reading Strategies

ENGLISH LANGUAGE LEARNERS

Writing Strategy: Keep a Math Journal

Discuss Students benefit from writing about mathematics because the process encourages vocabulary use by explaining concepts and questioning what is unclear.

Encourage students to write precisely and frankly in their math journals.

Extend As students work through Chapter 3, have them use new vocabulary when making regular entries in their math journals. Encourage students to include diagrams as visual explanations or examples along with their word descriptions. Remind students to include both successes and difficulties they encounter throughout the chapter. Suggest that students describe any insights, examples, or explanations that help clarify new (or old) topics.

Answers

Check students' work.

SECTION 3A

Linear Systems in Two Dimensions

One-Minute Section Planner

Lesson	Lab Resources	Materials
Lesson 3-1 Using Graphs and Tables to Solve Linear Systems • Solve systems of equations by using graphs and tables. • Classify systems of equations, and determine the number of solutions. ☑ SAT-10 ☑ NAEP ☑ ACT ☑ SAT ☑ SAT Subject Tests		**Required** graphing calculator
Lesson 3-2 Using Algebraic Methods to Solve Linear Systems • Solve systems of equations by substitution. • Solve systems of equations by elimination. ☑ SAT-10 ☑ NAEP ☑ ACT ☑ SAT ☐ SAT Subject Tests	***Algebra Lab Activities*** 3-2 Algebra Lab	**Required** graphing calculator
Lesson 3-3 Solving Systems of Linear Inequalities • Solve systems of linear inequalities. ☐ SAT-10 ☑ NAEP ☐ ACT ☑ SAT ☐ SAT Subject Tests		**Optional** graphing calculator, colored pencils (MK)
Lesson 3-4 Linear Programming • Solve linear programming problems. ☐ SAT-10 ☑ NAEP ☐ ACT ☑ SAT ☐ SAT Subject Tests	***Technology Lab Activities*** 3-4 Technology Lab	**Optional** graphing calculator

MK = *Manipulatives Kit*

Section Overview

Systems of Linear Equations and Inequalities

Lessons 3-1, 3-2, 3-3

Systems of linear equations can be used to represent linear relationships involving different constant rates. Solving systems of linear equations is a foundational skill for working with systems of linear inequalities.

Consider the following system of linear equations: $\begin{cases} x - 3y = -10 \\ 2x + y = 1 \end{cases}$

Solving by Graphing

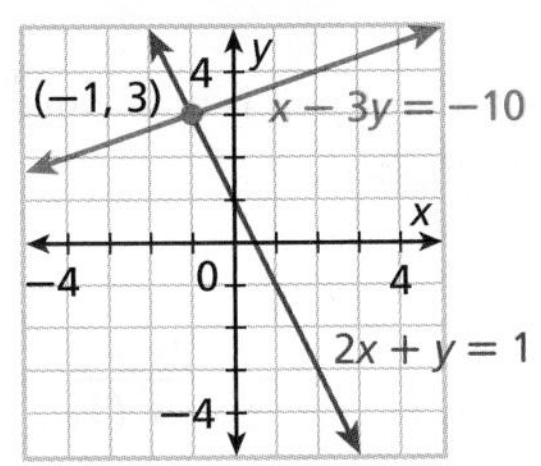

The solution of the system is (−1, 3).

Solving by Using Algebra

$$\begin{aligned} -2(x - 3y &= -10) \\ 2x + y &= 1 \end{aligned} \quad \rightarrow \quad \begin{aligned} -2x + 6y &= 20 \\ 2x + y &= 1 \\ \hline 7y &= 21 \\ y &= 3 \end{aligned}$$

$$\begin{aligned} x - 3y &= -10 \\ x - 3(3) &= -10 \\ x &= -1 \end{aligned}$$

Check

$$\begin{aligned} 2x + y &= 1 \\ 2(-1) + 3 &= 1 \\ 1 &= 1 \checkmark \end{aligned}$$

The solution of the system is (−1, 3).

Consider the following system of linear inequalities:

$$\begin{cases} y \le x + 1 \\ y > 2 - x \end{cases}$$

The solution of a system of inequalities is given by the overlapping region.

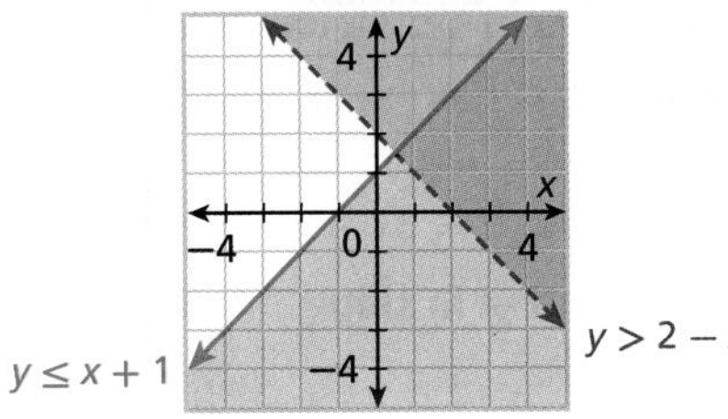

Linear Programming

Lesson 3-4

Linear programming is commonly used in business to find ways to maximize profit, given budget and other constraints.

Vertex Principle
If the objective function has a maximum or minimum value, it occurs at one or more of the vertices of the feasible region.

Graph the feasible region defined by the constraints.

$$\begin{cases} y \ge 0 \\ y \le x - 3 \\ y \le -x + 7 \end{cases}$$

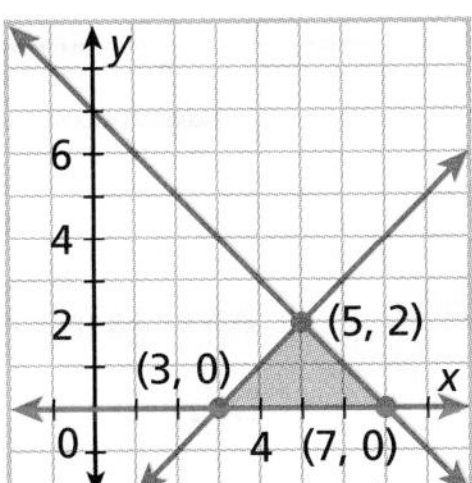

The vertices of the feasible region are (3, 0), (5, 2), and (7, 0).

The objective function is $F = 10x + 4y$.

Vertex	Objective Function
(3, 0)	$F = 10(3) + 4(0) = 30$
(5, 2)	$F = 10(5) + 4(2) = 58$
(7, 0)	$F = 10(7) + 4(0) = 70$

The objective function is maximized at the vertex (7, 0). The maximum value is 70.

3-1 Organizer

Pacing: Traditional 1 day
Block $\frac{1}{2}$ day

Objectives: Solve systems of equations by using graphs and tables.

Classify systems of equations and determine the number of solutions.

Online Edition
Graphing Calculator, Tutorial Videos, TechKeys

Countdown to Testing Week 6

Power Presentations with PowerPoint®

Warm Up

Use substitution to determine if (1, −2) is an element of the solution set of the linear equation.

1. $y = 2x + 1$ no
2. $y = 3x - 5$ yes

Write each equation in slope-intercept form.

3. $2y + 8x = 6$ $y = -4x + 3$

4. $4y - 3x = 8$ $y = \frac{3}{4}x + 2$

Also available on transparency

Math Fact !!!

The term *pencil* can be used to describe the set of all lines that pass through a given point. A pencil may be composed of many consistent, independent linear systems.

3-1 Using Graphs and Tables to Solve Linear Systems

Objectives
Solve systems of equations by using graphs and tables.
Classify systems of equations, and determine the number of solutions.

Vocabulary
system of equations
linear system
consistent system
inconsistent system
independent system
dependent system

Who uses this?
Winter sports enthusiasts can use systems of equations to compare the costs of renting snowboards. (See Example 4.)

A **system of equations** is a set of two or more equations containing two or more variables. A **linear system** is a system of equations containing only linear equations.

Recall that a line is an infinite set of points that are solutions to a linear equation. The solution of a system of equations is the set of all points that satisfy each equation.

On the graph of the system of two equations, the solution is the set of points where the lines intersect. A point is a solution to a system of equations if the *x*- and *y*-values of the point satisfy both equations.

EXAMPLE 1 Verifying Solutions of Linear Systems

Use substitution to determine if the given ordered pair is an element of the solution set for the system of equations.

A $(2, 4); \begin{cases} x - 2y = 6 \\ 2x + y = 8 \end{cases}$

$x - 2y = -6$			$2x + y = 8$	
$(2) - 2(4)$	-6	*Substitute 2 for x and 4 for y in each equation.*	$2(2) + (4)$	8
-6	-6 ✓		8	8 ✓

Because the point is a solution of both equations, it is a solution of the system.

B $(3, 2); \begin{cases} 2x + 3y = 12 \\ 8x - 6y = 24 \end{cases}$

$2x + 3y = 12$			$8x - 6y = 24$	
$2(3) + 3(2)$	12	*Substitute 3 for x and 2 for y in each equation.*	$8(3) + 6(2)$	24
12	12 ✓		36	24 ✗

Because the point is not a solution of both equations, it is not a solution of the system.

Use substitution to determine if the given ordered pair is an element of the solution set for the system of equations.

1a. $(4, 3); \begin{cases} x + 2y = 10 \\ 3x - y = 9 \end{cases}$ solution

1b. $(5, 3); \begin{cases} 6x - 7y = 1 \\ 3x + 7y = 5 \end{cases}$ not a solution

State Resources

State Resources Online
KEYWORD: MB7 Resources

1 Introduce

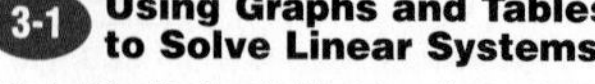

EXPLORATION

3-1 Using Graphs and Tables to Solve Linear Systems

Felipe is driving 55 mi/h on the interstate and is currently at mile marker 125. Gina is driving in the same direction at 65 mi/h and is currently at mile marker 85.

1. Complete the table.

Time (h)	Felipe's Location	Gina's Location
0	125	85
1		
2		
3		
4		
5		

2. Write an equation for Felipe's location. Let y represent the mile marker number, and let x represent the number of hours.
3. Write an equation for Gina's location. Let y represent the mile marker number, and let x represent the number of hours.
4. How long does it take for Gina to catch Felipe? At what location does she catch him?

THINK AND DISCUSS

5. Explain how you could write a system of equations to represent this problem.

Motivate

Draw a pair of intersecting lines. Discuss how each line is described by its slope and *y*-intercept. Ask students to describe how they might find the point of intersection. Explain that the pair of lines corresponds to a system of linear equations and that there are several ways to identify the point of intersection.

Explorations and answers are provided in the *Explorations* binder.

Recall that you can use graphs or tables to find some of the solutions to a linear equation. You can do the same to find solutions to linear systems.

EXAMPLE 2 Solving Linear Systems by Using Graphs and Tables

Use a graph and a table to solve each system. Check your answer.

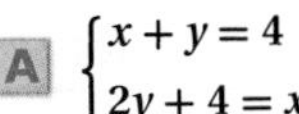

A $\begin{cases} x + y = 4 \\ 2y + 4 = x \end{cases}$

Solve each equation for y. $\begin{cases} y = -x + 4 \\ y = \frac{1}{2}x - 2 \end{cases}$

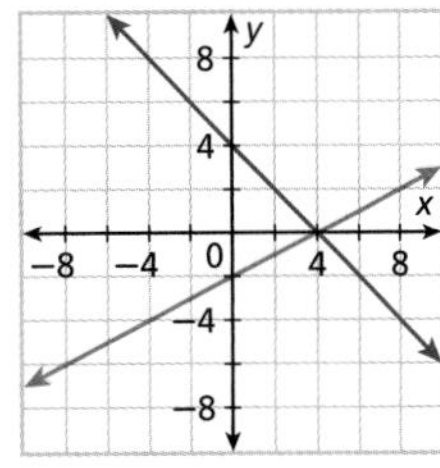

On the graph, the lines appear to intersect at the ordered pair $(4, 0)$.

Make a table of values for each equation. Notice that when $x = 4$, the y-value for both equations is 0.

The solution to the system is $(4, 0)$.

$y = -x + 4$

x	y
1	3
2	2
3	1
4	0

$y = \frac{1}{2}x - 2$

x	y
1	$-\frac{3}{2}$
2	−1
3	$-\frac{1}{2}$
4	0

B $\begin{cases} 3x - y = -2 \\ x - y = -4 \end{cases}$

Solve each equation for y. $\begin{cases} y = 3x + 2 \\ y = x + 4 \end{cases}$

Use your graphing calculator to graph the equations and make a table of values. The lines appear to intersect at $(1, 5)$. This is confirmed by the table of values.

The solution to the system is $(1, 5)$.

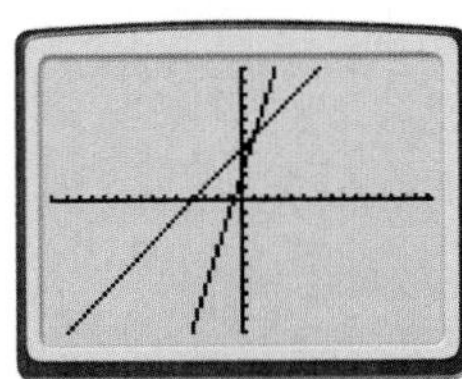

X	Y_1	Y_2
-2	-4	2
-1	-1	3
0	2	4
1	5	5
2	8	6
3	11	7
4	14	8

X=1

Check Substitute $(1, 5)$ in the original equations to verify the solution.

$$\begin{array}{r|l} 3x - y & = -2 \\ \hline 3(1) - (5) & -2 \\ -2 & -2 \checkmark \end{array} \qquad \begin{array}{r|l} x - y & = -4 \\ \hline (1) - (5) & -4 \\ -4 & -4 \checkmark \end{array}$$

Helpful Hint

To enter the equations into your calculator, let Y_1 represent $y = 3x + 2$ and let Y_2 represent $y = x + 4$.

CHECK IT OUT! **Use a graph and a table to solve each system. Check your answer.**

2a. $\begin{cases} 2y + 6 = x \\ 4x = 3 + y \end{cases}$ $(0, -3)$

2b. $\begin{cases} x + y = 8 \\ 2x - y = 4 \end{cases}$ $(4, 4)$

2c. $\begin{cases} y - x = 5 \\ 3x + y = 1 \end{cases}$ $(-1, 4)$

The systems of equations in Example 2 have exactly one solution. However, linear systems may also have infinitely many or no solutions. A **consistent system** is a set of equations or inequalities that has at least one solution, and an **inconsistent system** will have no solutions.

Power Presentations with PowerPoint®

Additional Examples

Example 1

Use substitution to determine if the given ordered pair is an element of the solution set of the system of equations.

A. $(1, 3)$ $\begin{cases} x - 3y = -8 \\ 3x + 2y = 9 \end{cases}$ yes

B. $(-4, \frac{1}{2})$ $\begin{cases} x + 6 = 4y \\ 2x + 8y = 1 \end{cases}$ no

Example 2

Use a graph and a table to solve each system. Check your answer.

A. $\begin{cases} 2x - 3y = 3 \\ y + 2 = x \end{cases}$ $(3, 1)$

B. $\begin{cases} x - y = 2 \\ 2y - 3x = -1 \end{cases}$ $(-3, -5)$

Also available on transparency

INTERVENTION

Questioning Strategies

EXAMPLE 1

- Does it help to put the equations in slope-intercept form? Explain.

EXAMPLE 2

- Why should you solve for y to make a table of values to solve a linear system? Is this necessary?

Technology Work through **Example 2B** to show students how to use a graphing calculator to find the point of intersection. Press 2nd CALC TRACE to enter the **CALCULATE** menu and choose option **5:intersect**. Follow the calculator's prompts to find the point of intersection.

2 Teach

Guided Instruction

Before discussing systems, review parallel, perpendicular, and skew pairs of lines. Point out that in this lesson, students will investigate the variety of relationships between pairs of lines.

Reaching All Learners

Through Kinesthetic Experience

Have students use a pair of pencils to model the lines of a linear system. Have them demonstrate what happens when the pencils representing the lines cross or intersect, when the "lines" overlap, and when the "lines" do not overlap but are parallel. As students model each system, have them classify it.

Inclusion Have students discuss why it is important to consider the slopes when classifying a system. Students should recognize that if two lines have different slopes, then they form an independent system.

Power Presentations with PowerPoint®

Additional Examples

Example 3

Classify each system and determine the number of solutions.

A. $\begin{cases} x = 2y + 6 \\ 3x - 6y = 18 \end{cases}$

consistent, dependent; infinite

B. $\begin{cases} 4x + y = 1 \\ y + 1 = -4x \end{cases}$

inconsistent; none

Example 4

City Park Golf Course charges \$20 to rent golf clubs plus \$55 per hour for golf cart rental. Sea Vista Golf Course charges \$35 to rent clubs plus \$45 per hour to rent a cart. For what number of hours is the cost of renting clubs and a cart the same for each course? $1\frac{1}{2}$ h

Also available on transparency

INTERVENTION

Questioning Strategies

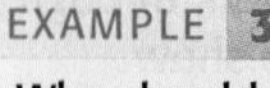

EXAMPLE 3

- Why should you write equations in slope-intercept form to classify linear systems?
- When might a graph be misleading in classifying a linear system?

EXAMPLE 4

- How should you choose the values of x to make the table of values?
- Why do you think the table includes values beyond the solution point?

You can classify linear systems by comparing the slopes and y-intercepts of the equations. An **independent system** has equations with different slopes. A **dependent system** has equations with equal slopes and equal y-intercepts.

Know it! Note

Classifying Linear Systems

EXACTLY ONE SOLUTION	INFINITELY MANY SOLUTIONS	NO SOLUTION
Consistent, independent The graphs are intersecting lines with different slopes.	Consistent, dependent The graphs are coinciding lines; they have the same slope and same y-intercept.	Inconsistent The graphs are parallel lines; they have the same slope but different y-intercepts.

EXAMPLE 3 Classifying Linear Systems

Classify each system and determine the number of solutions.

A $\begin{cases} 2x + y = 3 \\ 6x = 9 - 3y \end{cases}$

Solve each equation for y. $\begin{cases} y = -2x + 3 \\ y = -2x + 3 \end{cases}$ *The equations have the same slope and y-intercept and are graphed as the same line.*

The system is dependent with infinitely many solutions.

Remember!

The slope-intercept form of a linear equation makes comparing slopes and y-intercepts easy.

$y = mx + b$ (Slope: m; y-intercept: b)

B $\begin{cases} 3x + y = 3 \\ 2 + y = -3x \end{cases}$

Solve each equation for y. $\begin{cases} y = -3x + 3 \\ y = -3x - 2 \end{cases}$ *The equations have the same slope but different y-intercepts and are graphed as parallel lines.*

The system is inconsistent and has no solution.

Check A graph shows parallel lines.

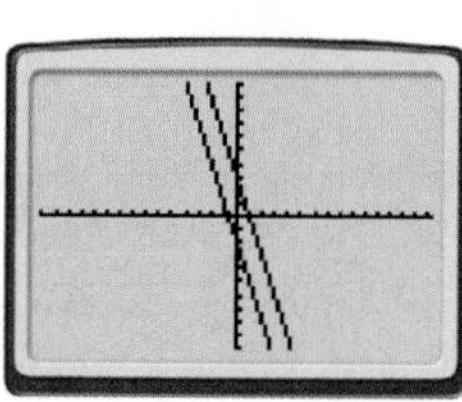

CHECK IT OUT! **Classify each system and determine the number of solutions.**

3a. $\begin{cases} 7x - y = -11 \\ 3y = 21x + 33 \end{cases}$

consistent, dependent; infinite number of solutions

3b. $\begin{cases} x + 4 = y \\ 5y = 5x + 35 \end{cases}$

inconsistent, no solution

EXAMPLE 4 Winter Sports Application

Big Dog Snowboard Co. charges $15 for equipment rental plus $35 per hour for snowboarding lessons. Half-Pipe Snowboards, Inc. charges $40 for equipment rental plus $25 per hour for lessons. For what number of hours is the cost of equipment and lessons the same for each company?

Step 1 Write an equation for the cost of equipment rental and lessons at each company.

Let x represent the number of hours and y represent the total cost in dollars.

Big Dog Snowboard Co.: $y = 35x + 15$

Half-Pipe Snowboards, Inc.: $y = 25x + 40$

Because the slopes are different, the system is independent and has exactly one solution.

Step 2 Solve the system by using a table of values.

Use increments of $\frac{1}{2}$ to represent 30 min.

When $x = 2\frac{1}{2}$, the y-values are both 102.5. The cost of equipment rental and a $2\frac{1}{2}$-hour snowboard lesson is $102.50 at either company. So the cost is the same at each company for $2\frac{1}{2}$ hours.

$y = 35x + 15$

x	y
1	50
$1\frac{1}{2}$	67.5
2	85
$2\frac{1}{2}$	102.5
3	120

$y = 25x + 40$

x	y
1	65
$1\frac{1}{2}$	77.5
2	90
$2\frac{1}{2}$	102.5
3	115

4. Ravi is comparing the costs of long distance calling cards. To use card A, it costs $0.50 to connect and then $0.05 per minute. To use card B, it costs $0.20 to connect and then $0.08 per minute. For what number of minutes does it cost the same amount to use each card for a single call? **10 min**

THINK AND DISCUSS

1. Explain how to find the number of solutions of a system of equations using only a graph.
2. Explain why a system of equations whose graphs are distinct parallel lines has no solution.

3. **GET ORGANIZED** Copy and complete the graphic organizer. In each box, give information about or examples of each solution type.

	Exactly One Solution	Infinitely Many Solutions	No Solution
Example			
Graph			
Slopes			
y-intercepts			

COMMON ERROR ALERT

Students might have difficulty identifying linear systems with infinitely many solutions. Discuss how to identify those types of systems. Encourage students to look for common multiples in equations written in slope-intercept form. It is easiest to start with both equations in this form. Then students can use properties of equality to write other equations that form a dependent system.

Critical Thinking In **Example 4,** discuss how the table of values might look if the correct x-value were not included.

Close

Summarize

Ask students the following questions:

- What solutions are possible when classifying linear systems? none, exactly one, infinitely many
- How does comparing slopes help you classify linear systems? different slopes: exactly 1 solution; same slopes: lines either dependent or parallel
- When does comparing y-intercepts help classify linear systems? same y-intercepts, same slopes: lines are dependent; different y-intercepts, same slopes: lines are parallel

and INTERVENTION

Diagnose **Before** the Lesson
3-1 Warm Up, TE p. 180

Monitor **During** the Lesson
Check It Out! Exercises, SE pp. 180–183
Questioning Strategies, TE pp. 181–182

Assess **After** the Lesson
3-1 Lesson Quiz, TE p. 187
Alternative Assessment, TE p. 187

Answers to *Think and Discuss*

Possible answers:

1. If the lines intersect once, there is 1 solution; if they are parallel, there is no solution; if they coincide, there are infinitely many solutions.
2. A solution to a system is represented on a graph by a point of intersection, and parallel lines never intersect.
3. See p. A4.

3-1 Exercises

Assignment Guide

Assign *Guided Practice* exercises as necessary.

If you finished Examples **1–2**
- **Basic** 15–22, 28, 29
- **Average** 15–22, 28–30
- **Advanced** 15–22, 28–31

If you finished Examples **1–4**
- **Basic** 15–31, 34, 38–42, 44, 46–50, 57–63
- **Average** 15–27, 32–42, 44–50, 56–63
- **Advanced** 17–20, 25–27, 33–63

Homework Quick Check
Quickly check key concepts.
Exercises: 18, 20, 26, 27, 34, 38

Answers

10. inconsistent; no solution
11. consistent, dependent; infinite number of solutions
12. consistent, independent; one solution
13. inconsistent; no solution
23. consistent, dependent; infinite number of solutions
24. consistent, dependent; infinite number of solutions
25. consistent, independent; one solution
26. inconsistent; no solution

State Resources

3-1 Exercises

go.hrw.com
Homework Help Online
KEYWORD: MB7 3-1
Parent Resources Online
KEYWORD: MB7 Parent

GUIDED PRACTICE

1. **Vocabulary** A system of equations with no solution is ___?___. (*consistent* or *inconsistent*) inconsistent

SEE EXAMPLE 1 p. 182

Use substitution to determine if the given ordered pair is an element of the solution set for the system of equations.

2. $(3, 3)$ $\begin{cases} 2x - y = 3 \\ y + x = 6 \end{cases}$ solution
3. $(1, -3)$ $\begin{cases} y - 4x = -7 \\ 5x + y = -6 \end{cases}$ not a solution
4. $(-2, 2)$ $\begin{cases} 5y - 5x = 10 \\ 3x + 10 = 2y \end{cases}$ not a solution
5. $(-1, 4)$ $\begin{cases} y = 3 - x \\ 6x + 2y = 2 \end{cases}$ solution

SEE EXAMPLE 2 p. 183

Use a graph and a table to solve each system. Check your answer.

6. $\begin{cases} y + x = 5 \\ 3x - 5y = -1 \end{cases}$ (3, 2)
7. $\begin{cases} 3y + 6x = 3 \\ x - y = -7 \end{cases}$ (−2, 5)
8. $\begin{cases} y - x = 0 \\ 8x + 4y = -24 \end{cases}$ (−2, −2)
9. $\begin{cases} x - y = -1 \\ 4x - 2y = 2 \end{cases}$ (2, 3)

SEE EXAMPLE 3 p. 184

Classify each system and determine the number of solutions.

10. $\begin{cases} 7x + y = 13 \\ 28x + 4y = -12 \end{cases}$
11. $\begin{cases} 2x - 3y = -15 \\ 3y - 2x = 15 \end{cases}$
12. $\begin{cases} 8y - 24x = 64 \\ 9y + 45x = 72 \end{cases}$
13. $\begin{cases} 2x + 2y = -10 \\ 4x + 4y = -16 \end{cases}$

SEE EXAMPLE 4 p. 185

14. **Aquariums** Marco is draining his two aquariums. The tanks are the same size. One tank has 7 in. of water in it. It is being drained at a rate of 1 in./min. The other tank has 5 in. of water in it. It is being drained at a rate of 0.5 in./min. After how many minutes will the tanks contain the same amount of water? 4 min

PRACTICE AND PROBLEM SOLVING

Independent Practice

For Exercises	See Example
15–18	1
19–22	2
23–26	3
27	4

Extra Practice
Skills Practice p. S8
Application Practice p. S34

Use substitution to determine if the given ordered pair is an element of the solution set for the system of equations.

15. $(-2, 2)$ $\begin{cases} x + y = 0 \\ 7y - 14x = 42 \end{cases}$ solution
16. $(-3, -5)$ $\begin{cases} 2y - 6x = 8 \\ 4y = 8x + 4 \end{cases}$ solution
17. $(3, 2)$ $\begin{cases} y = 2 \\ y + 8 = 6x \end{cases}$ not a solution
18. $(6, 1)$ $\begin{cases} y = 8x + 2 \\ x - 3y = 3 \end{cases}$ not a solution

Use a graph and a table to solve each system. Check your answer.

19. $\begin{cases} 2 + y = x \\ x + y = 4 \end{cases}$ (3, 1)
20. $\begin{cases} 4y - 2x = 4 \\ 10x - 5y = 10 \end{cases}$ (2, 2)
21. $\begin{cases} 12x + 4y = -4 \\ 2x - y = 6 \end{cases}$ (1, −4)
22. $\begin{cases} y = 10 - x \\ 3x - 3y = 0 \end{cases}$ (5, 5)

Classify each system and determine the number of solutions.

23. $\begin{cases} 24x - 27y = 42 \\ -9y + 8x = 14 \end{cases}$
24. $\begin{cases} \frac{3}{2}x + 9 = y \\ 4y - 6x = 36 \end{cases}$
25. $\begin{cases} 7y + 42x = 56 \\ 25x - 5y = 100 \end{cases}$
26. $\begin{cases} 3y = 2x \\ -4x + 6y = 3 \end{cases}$

27. **Business** Jamail and Wanda sell home theater systems. Jamail earns a base salary of $2400 per month, plus $100 for each system he sells. Wanda earns a base salary of $2200 per month, plus $120 for each system she sells. How many systems do Jamail and Wanda have to sell before they earn the same amount of money? 10 system sales

3-1 PRACTICE A

Does the given ordered pair solve the system of equations? Substitute each value for *x* and *y* into the equations. Write *yes* or *no*.

1. $(2, -1)$ $\begin{cases} 3x + y = 3 \\ x - y = 5 \end{cases}$
   $3(2) + (-1) \stackrel{?}{=} 3$
   $(2) - (-1) \stackrel{?}{=} 5$
   No
2. $(4, 5)$ $\begin{cases} x - 6y = -26 \\ 2x + y = 13 \end{cases}$ Yes
3. $(-3, -7)$ $\begin{cases} -x + 2y = 1 \\ 4x - 3y = 19 \end{cases}$ No

Use a table and a graph to solve the system.

4. $\begin{cases} y = x + 1 \\ x = 2y + 2 \end{cases}$

   a. Make a table of values for each equation.

$y = x + 1$

x	y
−2	−1
−1	0
0	1
1	2
2	3

$x = 2y + 2$

x	y
−2	−2
−1	$-\frac{3}{2}$
0	−1
1	$-\frac{1}{2}$
2	0

   b. Use the values in the tables to graph each equation.

   c. Which ordered pair solves both equations? (−4, −3)

Use a graph to solve each system.

5. $\begin{cases} x + y = 2 \\ x - y = 4 \end{cases}$ (3, −1)
6. $\begin{cases} y = 3x - 2 \\ x + y = 6 \end{cases}$ (2, 4)

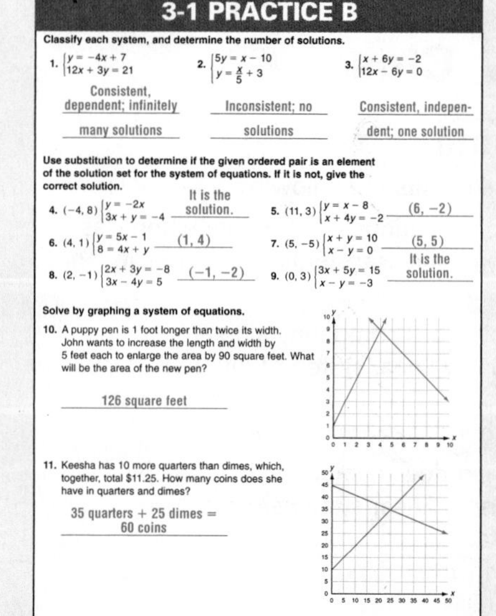

3-1 PRACTICE B

Classify each system, and determine the number of solutions.

1. $\begin{cases} y = -4x + 7 \\ 12x + 3y = 21 \end{cases}$ Consistent, dependent; infinitely many solutions
2. $\begin{cases} 5y = x - 10 \\ y = \frac{x}{5} + 3 \end{cases}$ Inconsistent; no solutions
3. $\begin{cases} x + 6y = -2 \\ 12x - 6y = 0 \end{cases}$ Consistent, independent; one solution

Use substitution to determine if the given ordered pair is an element of the solution set for the system of equations. If it is not, give the correct solution.

4. $(-4, 8)$ $\begin{cases} y = -2x \\ 3x + y = -4 \end{cases}$ It is the solution.
5. $(11, 3)$ $\begin{cases} y = x - 8 \\ x + 4y = -2 \end{cases}$ (6, −2)
6. $(4, 1)$ $\begin{cases} y = 5x - 1 \\ 8 = 4x + y \end{cases}$ (1, 4)
7. $(5, -5)$ $\begin{cases} x + y = 10 \\ x - y = 0 \end{cases}$ (5, 5)
8. $(2, -1)$ $\begin{cases} 2x + 3y = -8 \\ 3x - 4y = 5 \end{cases}$ (−1, −2)
9. $(0, 3)$ $\begin{cases} 3x + 5y = 15 \\ x - y = -3 \end{cases}$ It is the solution.

Solve by graphing a system of equations.

10. A puppy pen is 1 foot longer than twice its width. John wants to increase the length and width by 5 feet each to enlarge the area by 90 square feet. What will be the area of the new pen? 126 square feet
11. Keesha has 10 more quarters than dimes, which, together, total $11.25. How many coins does she have in quarters and dimes? 35 quarters + 25 dimes = 60 coins

28. not a solution; (2, 4)
30. not a solution; (8,1)
31. not a solution; (−3, 0)

Determine if the given ordered pair is a solution of the system of equations. If it is not, give the correct solution.

28. (4, 2)
$\begin{cases} y - x = 2 \\ 2x + y = 8 \end{cases}$

29. (−1, 2) solution
$\begin{cases} 3x + y = -1 \\ 8x + 6 = -y \end{cases}$

30. (7, 2)
$\begin{cases} x + y = 9 \\ 4y + 4 = x \end{cases}$

31. (0, 6)
$\begin{cases} 3x + 4y = -9 \\ y = 2x + 6 \end{cases}$

32. **Bicycling** Roberto is competing in a bicycle race. He has traveled 12 mi and is maintaining a steady speed of 15 mi/h. Alexandra is competing in the same race but got a flat tire. She has traveled 8 mi and is maintaining a steady speed of 18 mi/h.
   a. Write and graph a system of equations that could be used to model the situation.
   b. How long will it take Alexandra to catch Roberto? $\frac{4}{3}$ h
   c. How many miles into the race will they be when they meet? 32 mi

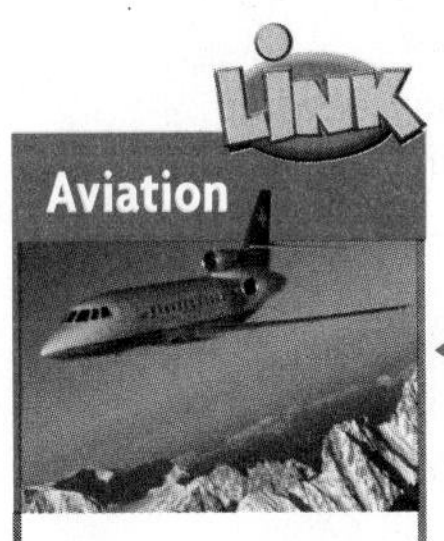

Aviation

When in the air, pilots must follow certain flight-path restrictions to avoid collisions. The direction the airplane travels determines its required altitude. For example, airplanes traveling west fly at even-numbered thousands of feet.

33. **Aviation** Lynn is piloting a plane at an altitude of 10,000 feet. She begins to descend at a rate of 200 feet per minute. Miguel is flying a different plane at an altitude of 5000 feet. At the same time that Lynn begins to descend, Miguel begins to climb at a rate of 50 feet per minute.
   a. Write and graph a system of equations that could be used to model the situation. 33a. $\ell = 10{,}000 - 200x$, $m = 5{,}000 + 50x$
   b. In how many minutes will the planes be at the same altitude? 20 min
   c. What will that altitude be? 6000 ft

34. **Multi-Step** Juan is comparing the cell phone plans shown in the advertisement.
   a. Write and graph a system of equations that could be used to model the situation.
   b. For what number of minutes of use do the plans cost the same? 100 min
   c. If Juan expects to use the phone for about 2 hours a month, which plan should he choose? Explain. plan B, because \$60 (the cost of plan B) is less than \$63 (the cost of plan A)

34a. $y = 15 + 0.4x$
$y = 30 + 0.25x$

Write equations for each system graphed below. Then classify the system and find the solution set.

35. 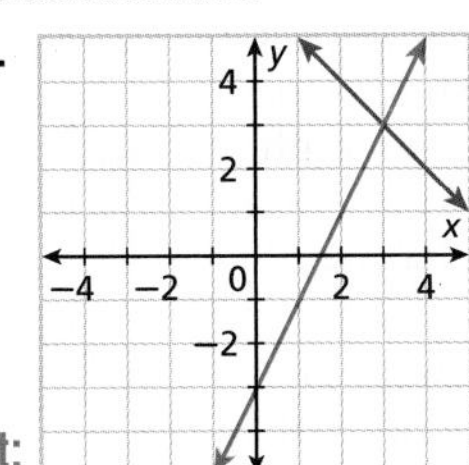

36. 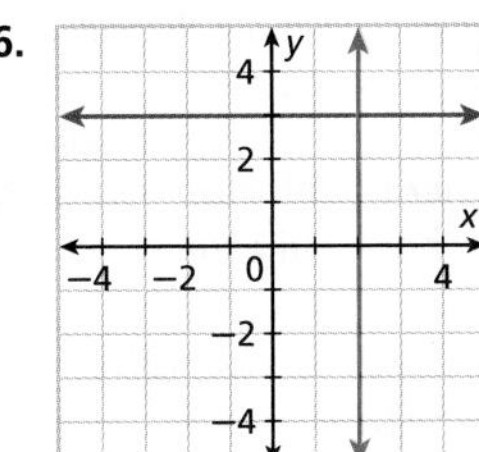

37. 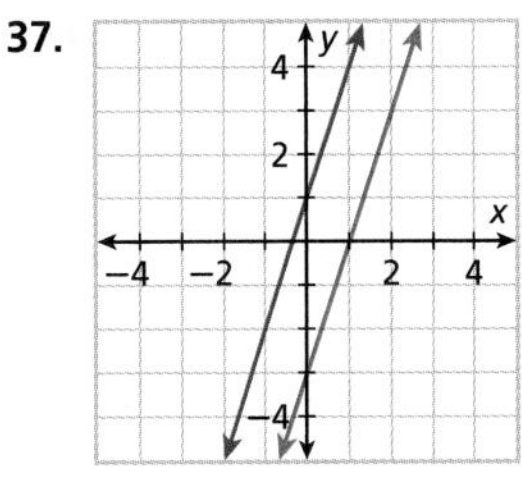

35. $\begin{cases} y = 2x - 3 \\ y = -x + 6 \end{cases}$ consistent, independent; (3, 3)

36. $\begin{cases} y = 3 \\ x = 2 \end{cases}$ consistent, independent; (2, 3)

37. $\begin{cases} y = 3x - 3 \\ y = 3x + 1 \end{cases}$ inconsistent; no solution

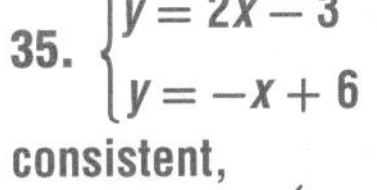
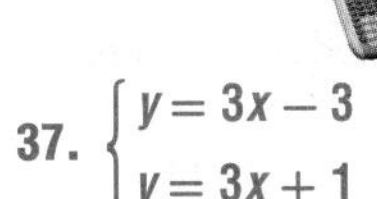

Graphing Calculator The graphing calculator can find points of intersection. Use the intersect feature of a graphing calculator by pressing 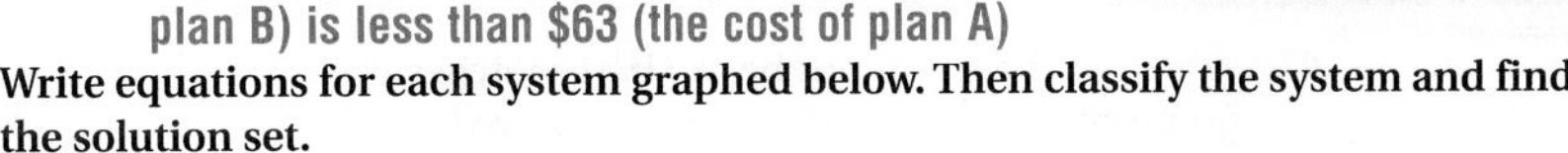 2nd CALC TRACE, then select 5: Intersect to find the solution to each system of equations. Round each solution to the nearest thousandth.

38. $\begin{cases} y = -7x + 11 \\ y = 5x - 13 \end{cases}$ (2, −3)

39. $\begin{cases} y = 4x + 5 \\ y = 12x + 7 \end{cases}$ (−0.25, 4)

40. $\begin{cases} 43 + y = 27x \\ 18x - y = -15 \end{cases}$ (6.444, 131)

41. $\begin{cases} 32x = 121 + y \\ 45x + y = 97 \end{cases}$ (2.831, −30.403)

COMMON ERROR ALERT

For **Exercises 19–22,** students might substitute x- and y-values incorrectly into equations when determining if an ordered pair is a solution to a system of equations. Remind students to examine the form of the equation before substituting so that they substitute the correct value for each variable.

Teaching Tip **Cooperative Learning** After students complete problem solving in **Exercises 32–34,** have students work in pairs to discuss how to interpret the point of intersection.

Answers

32a. $r = 12 + 15x$
$a = 8 + 18x$

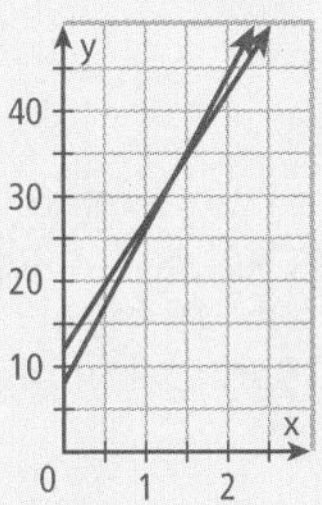

33a.

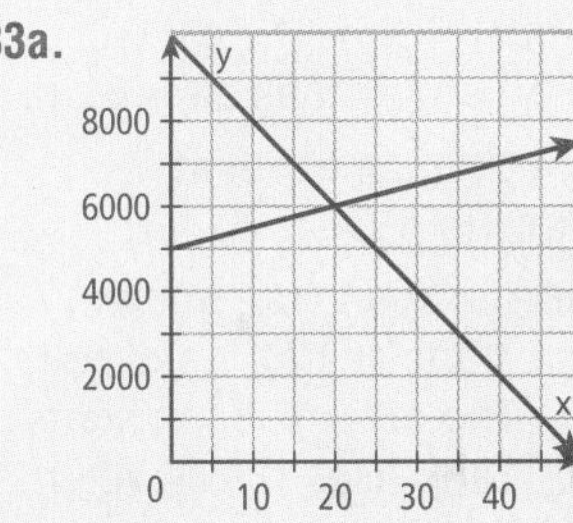

34a.

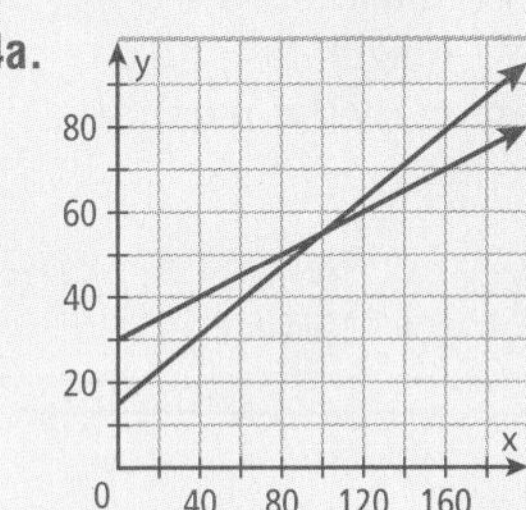
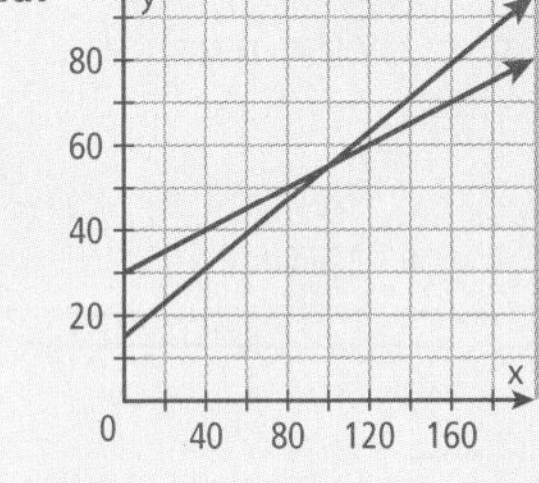

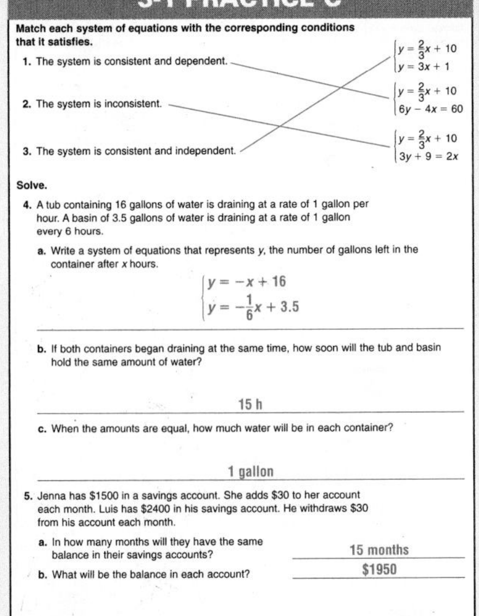

3-1 PRACTICE C

Match each system of equations with the corresponding conditions that it satisfies.

1. The system is consistent and dependent. — $\begin{cases} y = \frac{2}{3}x + 10 \\ 6y - 4x = 60 \end{cases}$
2. The system is inconsistent. — $\begin{cases} y = \frac{2}{3}x + 10 \\ 3y + 9 = 2x \end{cases}$
3. The system is consistent and independent. — $\begin{cases} y = \frac{2}{3}x + 10 \\ y = 3x + 1 \end{cases}$

Solve.

4. A tub containing 16 gallons of water is draining at a rate of 1 gallon per hour. A basin of 3.5 gallons of water is draining at a rate of 1 gallon every 6 hours.
   a. Write a system of equations that represents y, the number of gallons left in the container after x hours. $\begin{cases} y = -x + 16 \\ y = -\frac{1}{6}x + 3.5 \end{cases}$
   b. If both containers began draining at the same time, how soon will the tub and basin hold the same amount of water? 15 h
   c. When the amounts are equal, how much water will be in each container? 1 gallon

5. Jenna has \$1500 in a savings account. She adds \$30 to her account each month. Luis has \$2400 in his savings account. He withdraws \$30 from his account each month.
   a. In how many months will they have the same balance in their savings accounts? 15 months
   b. What will be the balance in each account? \$1950

Exercise 42 involves solving a linear system and interpreting the results. This exercise prepares students for the applications of linear systems in two dimensions in the Multi-Step Test Prep on page 212.

Encourage students to use what they know about slopes and intercepts to eliminate choices in **Exercise 48.** Inspection eliminates choice **J.** Finding the slopes eliminates choice **H.** Since the line with the positive slope has a positive y-intercept and the line with the negative slope has a negative y-intercept, the only possible solution is choice **G.** Similarly, students can eliminate choice **D** in **Exercise 49** since the lines must decrease, or fall, over time.

Answers

42a. The truck gets 24 mi/gal in the city and 28 mi/gal on the highway. The car gets 26 mi/gal in the city and 35 mi/gal on the highway.

b. The truck will have an empty tank after $7\frac{14}{15}$ h. The car will have an empty tank after $8\frac{1}{6}$ h.

c. The truck must travel at $58\frac{2}{7}$ mi/h.

46. Possible answer: One hot-air balloon starts at 120 ft and rises quickly. The other balloon starts at 200 ft and rises slowly. After 4 min, the balloons are at the same height, 280 ft, as represented by the point of intersection.

42. This problem will prepare you for the Multi-Step Test Prep on page 212.

The fuel tank of a compact truck holds 17 gallons. On a full tank, the truck can travel about 408 miles in the city or 476 miles on the highway. The fuel tank of a compact car holds 14 gallons. On a full tank, the car can travel about 364 miles in the city or 490 miles on the highway.

a. Compare the fuel use of the car and the truck in miles per gallon.

b. How many hours of highway driving are required for each to empty its tank? Assume an average speed of 60 miles per hour.

c. If the car travels at a constant 60 miles per hour on the highway, at what speed must the truck travel if it is to empty its tank at the same time as the car?

43. Critical Thinking One equation in a linear system is $x + 2y = 4$. What is an equation that would cause the system to have an infinite number of solutions? no solutions? one solution? **Possible answers: $x + 2y = 4$; $x + 2y = 6$; $2x + y = 6$**

44. Estimation Use a graph to estimate the solution of the following system.

$$\begin{cases} y = 1.25x - 4 \\ y = -1.4x + 5 \end{cases}$$

Possible answer: (3, 0.5)

45. Critical Thinking How would you classify a system of equations that is composed of two lines with different slopes and the same y-intercepts? What is the solution to the system?

45. Consistent, independent; the solution is the point of the y-intercept.

46. Write About It Describe a situation involving two hot-air balloons that could be modeled by the graph shown.

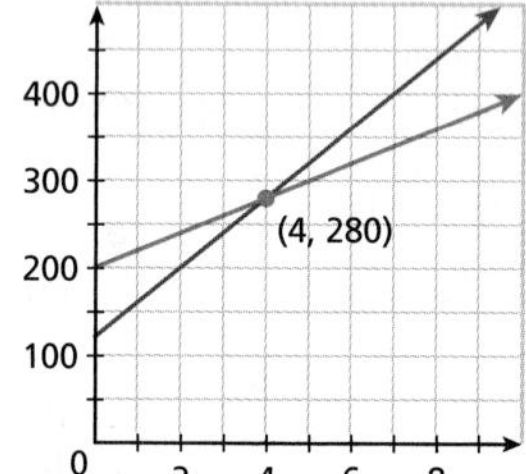

47. Which of the situations below best matches the graph of the system of equations shown?

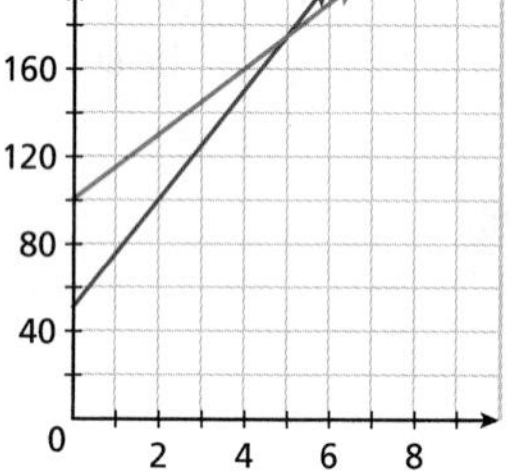

Ⓐ Kameko paid a \$25 sign-up fee plus \$50 per month for a health club membership. Maria paid a \$15 sign-up fee plus \$100 per month for her health club membership. At 5 months, they have paid the same amount for their memberships.

Ⓑ Ruby and Yuri use different companies to host their Web sites. Although the prices they pay are different, if each has 5 gigabytes of traffic per month, Ruby and Yuri pay the same amount, \$200.

Ⓒ James and Renee paid \$100 plus \$15 per day to rent a small sailboat. They kept the boat for 5 days and paid \$175.

Ⓓ Esteban and Ted belong to different country clubs, and they pay different monthly dues and different amounts to play golf. However, they've found that if they play 5 rounds of golf in a month, they each pay the same amount, \$175, in dues and golf fees.

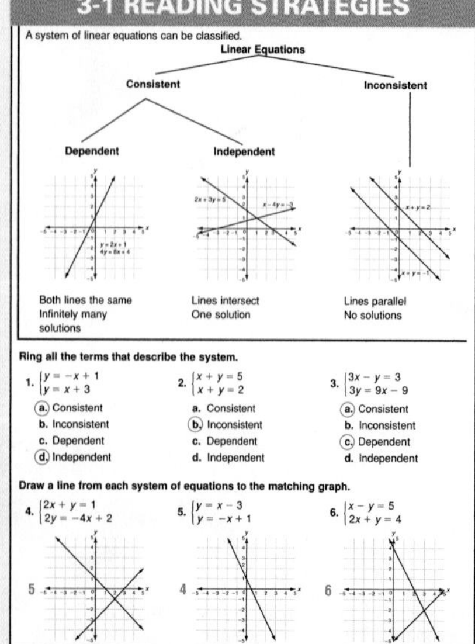

3-1 READING STRATEGIES

A system of linear equations can be classified.

Linear Equations → Consistent (Dependent, Independent); Inconsistent

Both lines the same. Infinitely many solutions | Lines intersect. One solution | Lines parallel. No solutions

Ring all the terms that describe the system.

1. $\begin{cases} y = -x + 1 \\ y = x + 3 \end{cases}$ a. Consistent b. Inconsistent c. Dependent d. Independent

2. $\begin{cases} x + y = 5 \\ x + y = 2 \end{cases}$ a. Consistent b. Inconsistent c. Dependent d. Independent

3. $\begin{cases} 3x - y = 3 \\ 3y = 9x - 9 \end{cases}$ a. Consistent b. Inconsistent c. Dependent d. Independent

Draw a line from each system of equations to the matching graph.

4. $\begin{cases} 2x + y = 1 \\ 2y = -4x + 2 \end{cases}$ 5. $\begin{cases} y = x - 3 \\ y = -x + 1 \end{cases}$ 6. $\begin{cases} x - y = 5 \\ 2x + y = 4 \end{cases}$

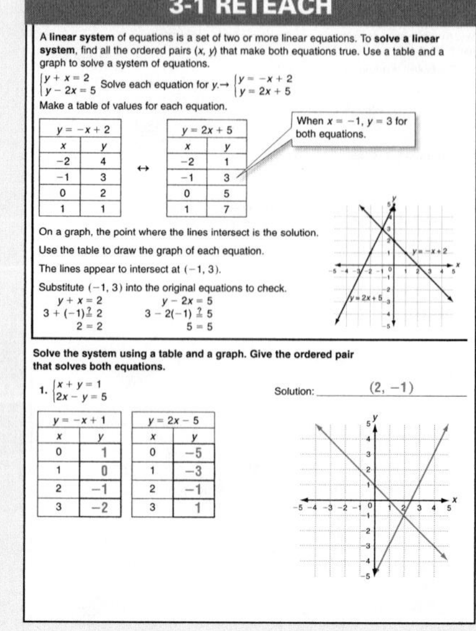

3-1 RETEACH

A **linear system** of equations is a set of two or more linear equations. To **solve a linear system**, find all the ordered pairs (x, y) that make both equations true. Use a table and a graph to solve a system of equations.

$\begin{cases} y + x = 2 \\ y - 2x = 5 \end{cases}$ Solve each equation for y. → $\begin{cases} y = -x + 2 \\ y = 2x + 5 \end{cases}$

Make a table of values for each equation.

$y = -x + 2$	
x	y
−2	4
−1	3
0	2
1	1

$y = 2x + 5$	
x	y
−2	1
−1	3
0	5
1	7

When $x = -1$, $y = 3$ for both equations.

On a graph, the point where the lines intersect is the solution.

Use the table to draw the graph of each equation.

The lines appear to intersect at $(-1, 3)$.

Substitute $(-1, 3)$ into the original equations to check.

$y + x = 2$; $3 + (-1) \stackrel{?}{=} 2$; $2 = 2$ | $y - 2x = 5$; $3 - 2(-1) \stackrel{?}{=} 5$; $5 = 5$

Solve the system using a table and a graph. Give the ordered pair that solves both equations.

1. $\begin{cases} x + y = 1 \\ 2x - y = 5 \end{cases}$ Solution: (2, −1)

$y = -x + 1$	
x	y
0	1
1	0
2	−1
3	−2

$y = 2x - 5$	
x	y
0	−5
1	−3
2	−1
3	1

48. Which system of equations is accurately represented on the graph?

(F) $\begin{cases} y = 3x - 6 \\ y = -3x + 6 \end{cases}$ (H) $\begin{cases} y = 6x - 3 \\ y = -6x + 3 \end{cases}$

(G) $\begin{cases} y = 3x + 6 \\ y = -3x - 6 \end{cases}$ (J) $\begin{cases} y = 6x + 3 \\ y = 6x - 3 \end{cases}$

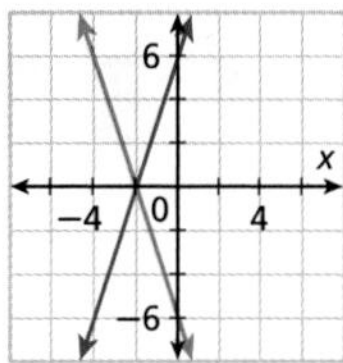

49. Adam's truck has 5 gal of fuel left in the tank and uses 0.1 gal/mi. Zoe's truck has 6 gal of fuel left in the tank and uses 0.15 gal/mi. Which of the following graphs best represents the system of equations that can be used to find the distance driven at which the trucks will have the same amount of fuel?

(A)

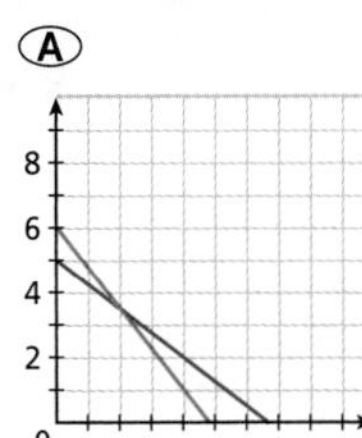

(B)

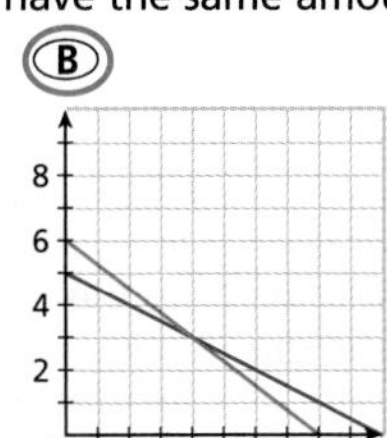

(C)

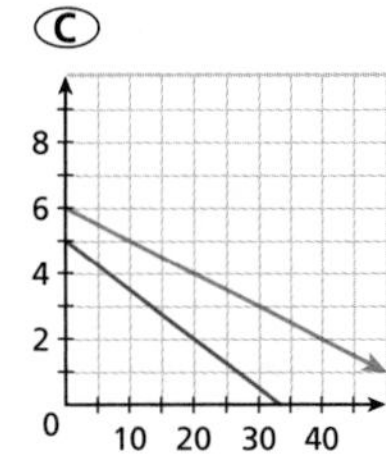

(D)

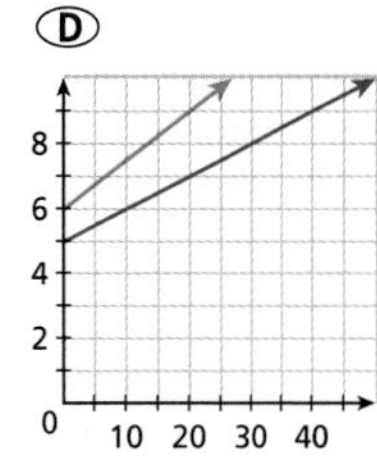

50. **Gridded Response** What is 3 times the y-coordinate of the solution to the following system? $\begin{cases} -x + y = 8 \\ y = 4x \end{cases}$ 32

CHALLENGE AND EXTEND

Solve each system. Round your answer to the nearest thousandth.

51. $\begin{cases} y = 55x + 100 \\ y = 20x + 600 \end{cases}$ 52. $\begin{cases} 20x + 5y = 135 \\ y = -50x + 32 \end{cases}$ 53. $\begin{cases} 9x + 18y = 126 \\ 14y = -7x + 98 \end{cases}$ 54. $\begin{cases} 0.25x - y = 2.25 \\ y = 0.75x + 3.75 \end{cases}$ $(-12, -5.25)$

55. **Business** An economist is studying a system of linear equations representing cost functions for two different products over time. She finds that the solution to the system is $(-6, -200)$. What does the solution tell her about the cost functions?

56. **Multi-Step** Brad is a farmer. He feeds his hogs 12 pounds of feed per day and has 70 pounds of feed in his barn. Cliff is also a farmer. He feeds his hogs 15 pounds of feed per day and has 100 pounds of feed in his barn.
   a. In how many days will Brad and Cliff have the same amount of feed left? Use a system of equations to find your answer. 10 days
   b. Does your answer to part **a** make sense? No; they will both run out of food before that time.
   c. How would your answer change if both Brad and Cliff receive a shipment of 100 pounds of feed on day 4? The answer would make sense. Each farmer would have 50 lb of food on day 10.

51. $\left(\frac{100}{7}, \frac{6200}{7}\right)$

52. $\left(\frac{5}{46}, \frac{611}{23}\right)$

53. infinite number of solutions

55. The solution has no meaning in the real world. Time cannot be negative, and neither can cost. The costs for the two products will never be equal.

SPIRAL REVIEW

Simplify by rationalizing each denominator. *(Lesson 1-3)*

57. $\frac{4}{\sqrt{12}}$ $\frac{2\sqrt{3}}{3}$ 58. $\frac{1}{2\sqrt{5}}$ $\frac{\sqrt{5}}{10}$ 59. $\frac{\sqrt{6}}{\sqrt{12}}$ $\frac{\sqrt{2}}{2}$ 60. $\frac{7\sqrt{14}}{\sqrt{5}}$ $\frac{7\sqrt{70}}{5}$

Solve each equation and check your answer. *(Lesson 2-1)*

61. $\frac{5}{2}x - 1 = \frac{1}{2} + 3x$ -3 62. $6(7n + 2) = (34 + 11n)3$ 10

63. **Manufacturing** On one assembly line, 45 pounds of cheese are sliced and packaged every two hours. How many hours are needed for 900 pounds of cheese to be sliced and packaged on that assembly line? *(Lesson 2-2)* 40 h

Journal

Have students explain how to classify a system of linear equations. Have them draw diagrams to support each classification.

ALTERNATIVE ASSESSMENT

Have students write an equation for a line of the form $y = mx + b$. Have them use the line to create and solve three different systems of equations: one with exactly one solution, one with infinitely many solutions, and one with no solutions.

Power Presentations with PowerPoint®

3-1 Lesson Quiz

Use substitution to determine if the given ordered pair is an element of the solution set of the system of equations.

1. $(4, -2)$ $\begin{cases} x + y = 2 \\ y + 2x = 5 \end{cases}$ no

2. $(-3, -2)$ $\begin{cases} x + 3y = -9 \\ y - 2x = 4 \end{cases}$ yes

Solve the system using a table and a graph. Check your answer.

3. $\begin{cases} x + y = 1 \\ 3x - 2y = 8 \end{cases}$ $(2, -1)$

Classify each system and determine the number of solutions.

4. $\begin{cases} -4x = 2y - 10 \\ y + 2x = -10 \end{cases}$
inconsistent; none

5. $\begin{cases} 3y - 4x = -3 \\ 12x - 9y = 9 \end{cases}$
consistent, dependent; infinite

6. Kayak Kottage charges \$26 to rent a kayak plus \$24 per hour for lessons. Power Paddles charges \$12 for rental plus \$32 per hour for lessons. For what number of hours is the cost of equipment and lessons the same for each company? $1\frac{3}{4}$

Also available on transparency

3-1 PROBLEM SOLVING

Solve.

1. After the lesson, Carl takes the wakeboarding class to the *Glass Cafe*. He pays \$26 for 8 large and 4 small juice drinks. A large glass costs \$1 more than a small glass.
   a. Write a linear system of equations to find the cost of each size drink. $\begin{cases} 4x + 8y = 26 \\ x + 1 = y \end{cases}$
   b. Write one equation at the top of each table and complete the table.
   c. What is the cost of each size drink? Small: \$1.50; large: \$2.50

$4x + 8y = 26$	
x	y
1	2.75
1.5	2.50
2	2.25
2.5	2
3	1.75

$x + 1 = y$	
x	y
1	2
1.5	2.5
2	3
2.5	3.5
3	4

2. Sandy rented a jet ski for \$95 plus \$15 per hour. Pauline rented a jet ski for \$80 plus \$20 per hour.
   a. Write a linear system of equations to find the number of hours for which the rental cost is the same. $\begin{cases} y = 95 + 15x \\ y = 80 + 20x \end{cases}$
   b. Graph the system.
   c. For what number of hours would Sandy and Pauline pay the same to rent a jet ski? 3 h
   d. How much would it cost to rent the jet ski for this amount of time? \$140

Rental Cost (\$) 0 20 40 60 80 100 120 140 160 180 200 y; Time (h) 0 1 2 3 4 5 6 7 8 9 10 x

Choose the letter for the best answer.

3. Juan started with 50 gallons of water in his pool, and he is filling it at a rate of 10 gallons per minute. His next-door neighbor Sam started with 20 gallons of water in his pool, and he is filling it at a rate of 15 gallons per minute. Which system of equations could you use to find when the pools will contain the same amount of water?

A $\begin{cases} y = 50 + 15x \\ y = 20 + 10x \end{cases}$ C $\begin{cases} y = 50 - 15x \\ y = 20 - 10x \end{cases}$

(B) $\begin{cases} y = 50 + 10x \\ y = 20 + 15x \end{cases}$ D $\begin{cases} y = 50 - 10x \\ y = 20 - 15x \end{cases}$

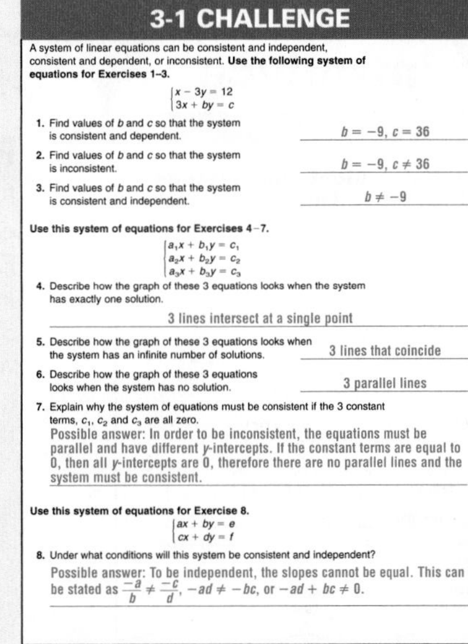

3-1 CHALLENGE

A system of linear equations can be consistent and independent, consistent and dependent, or inconsistent. **Use the following system of equations for Exercises 1–3.**

$\begin{cases} x - 3y = 12 \\ 3x + by = c \end{cases}$

1. Find values of b and c so that the system is consistent and dependent. $b = -9, c = 36$
2. Find values of b and c so that the system is inconsistent. $b = -9, c \neq 36$
3. Find values of b and c so that the system is consistent and independent. $b \neq -9$

Use this system of equations for Exercises 4–7.

$\begin{cases} a_1x + b_1y = c_1 \\ a_2x + b_2y = c_2 \\ a_3x + b_3y = c_3 \end{cases}$

4. Describe how the graph of these 3 equations looks when the system has exactly one solution. 3 lines intersect at a single point
5. Describe how the graph of these 3 equations looks when the system has an infinite number of solutions. 3 lines that coincide
6. Describe how the graph of these 3 equations looks when the system has no solution. 3 parallel lines
7. Explain why the system of equations must be consistent if the 3 constant terms, c_1, c_2 and c_3 are all zero.
   Possible answer: In order to be inconsistent, the equations must be parallel and have different y-intercepts. If the constant terms are equal to 0, then all y-intercepts are 0, therefore there are no parallel lines and the system must be consistent.

Use this system of equations for Exercise 8.

$\begin{cases} ax + by = e \\ cx + dy = f \end{cases}$

8. Under what conditions will this system be consistent and independent?
   Possible answer: To be independent, the slopes cannot be equal. This can be stated as $\frac{-a}{b} \neq \frac{-c}{d}$, $-ad \neq -bc$, or $-ad + bc \neq 0$.

3-2 Organizer

Pacing: Traditional 1 day
Block $\frac{1}{2}$ day

Objectives: Solve systems of equations by substitution.

Solve systems of equations by elimination.

Algebra Lab
In *Algebra Lab Activities*

Online Edition
Graphing Calculator, Tutorial Videos

Countdown to Testing Week 6

Power Presentations with PowerPoint®

Warm Up

Determine if the given ordered pair is an element of the solution set of $\begin{cases} 2x - y = 5 \\ 3y + x = 6 \end{cases}$.

1. (3, 1) yes **2.** (−1, 1) no

Solve each equation for *y*.

3. $x + 3y = 2x + 4y - 4$
$y = -x + 4$

4. $6x + 5 + y = 3y + 2x - 1$
$y = 2x + 3$

Also available on transparency

3-2 Using Algebraic Methods to Solve Linear Systems

Objectives
Solve systems of equations by substitution.
Solve systems of equations by elimination.

Vocabulary
substitution
elimination

Who uses this?
Zookeepers use algebraic methods to solve systems of linear equations that model mixtures of animal foods. (See Example 4.)

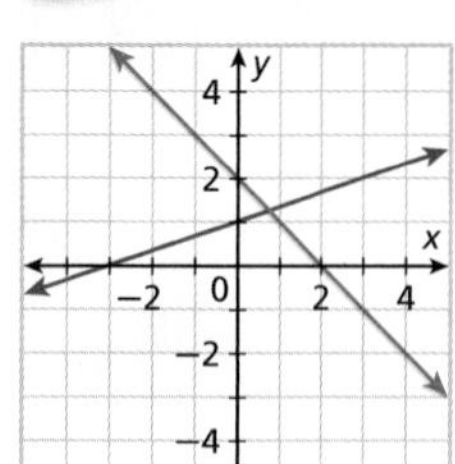

The graph shows a system of linear equations. As you can see, without the use of technology, determining the solution from the graph is not easy. You can use the *substitution* method to find an exact solution. In **substitution**, you solve one equation for one variable and then substitute this expression into the other equation.

EXAMPLE 1 Solving Linear Systems by Substitution

Use substitution to solve each system of equations.

A $\begin{cases} y = x + 2 \\ x + y = 8 \end{cases}$

Step 1 Solve one equation for one variable.
The first equation is already solved for *y*: $y = x + 2$.

Step 2 Substitute the expression into the other equation.

$x + y = 8$
$x + (x + 2) = 8$ *Substitute (x + 2) for y in the other equation.*
$2x + 2 = 8$ *Combine like terms.*
$2x = 6$
$x = 3$

Step 3 Substitute the *x*-value into one of the original equations to solve for *y*.

$y = x + 2$
$y = (3) + 2$ *Substitute x = 3.*
$y = 5$

The solution is the ordered pair (3, 5).

Check A graph or table supports your answer.

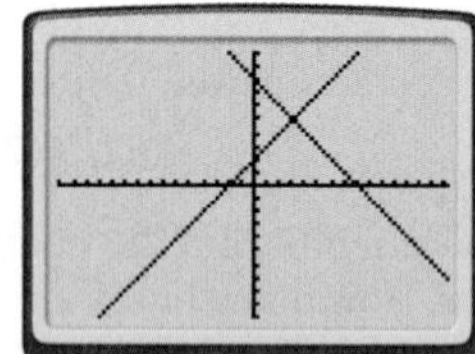

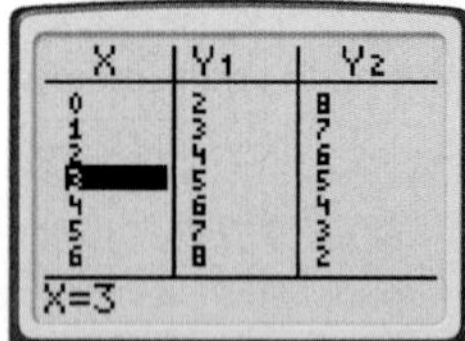

Caution!
The solution to an independent system of equations is an ordered pair. Do not stop working when you have found only one value.

State Resources

go.hrw.com
State Resources Online
KEYWORD: MB7 Resources

1 Introduce

EXPLORATION

3-2 Using Algebraic Methods to Solve Linear Systems

The monthly cost y for a factory to manufacture stereo headphones is $12,600 plus $17.50 per headphone. The headphones are then sold for $25 each.

1. Write an equation for the cost of manufacturing headphones. Let y represent the total cost, and let x represent the number of headphones manufactured.
2. Write an equation for the revenue from the headphones. Let y represent the revenue and let x represent the number of headphones manufactured.
3. Set the expressions for cost and revenue equal to each other and then solve the equation for x.
4. Interpret your solution. What is the result when the factory manufactures this number of headphones?

THINK AND DISCUSS

5. **Determine** the number of headphones the factory should manufacture to make a profit.
6. **Discuss** the advantages of solving this problem algebraically rather than by using a table or graph.

Motivate

Review how to combine like terms to simplify an expression such as $x + 5 - 4x + 6x - 1$. $3x + 4$
Extend to include combining like terms to solve an equation. For example, solve the equation $3y + 2 - 4y = 5$. $y = -3$ Explain that students will use these skills to solve systems algebraically.

Explorations and answers are provided in the *Explorations* binder.

Use substitution to solve each system of equations.

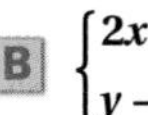

B $\begin{cases} 2x+y=6 \\ y-8x=1 \end{cases}$

Method 1 Isolate y.

$2x+y=6$	*First equation*
$y=6-2x$	*Isolate one variable.*
$y-8x=1$	*Second equation*
$(6-2x)-8x=1$	*Substitute the expression into the second equation.*
$6-10x=1$	*Combine like terms.*
$-10x=-5$	
$x=\frac{1}{2}$	*First part of the solution*

Method 2 Isolate x.

$2x+y=6$

$x=\frac{6-y}{2}=3-\frac{y}{2}$

$y-8x=1$

$y-8\left(3-\frac{y}{2}\right)=1$

$y-24+4y=1$

$5y=25$

$y=5$

Substitute the value into one of the original equations to solve for the other variable.

Method 1		Method 2
$y-8\left(\frac{1}{2}\right)=1$	*Substitute the value to solve for the other variable.*	$2x+(5)=6$
$y-4=1$		$2x=1$
$y=5$	*Second part of the solution*	$x=\frac{1}{2}$

By either method, the solution is $\left(\frac{1}{2}, 5\right)$.

Use substitution to solve each system of equations.

1a. $\begin{cases} y=2x-1 \\ 3x+2y=26 \end{cases}$ $(4, 7)$

1b. $\begin{cases} 5x+6y=-9 \\ 2x-2=-y \end{cases}$ $(3, -4)$

You can also solve systems of equations with the *elimination* method. With **elimination**, you get rid of one of the variables by adding or subtracting equations. You may have to multiply one or both equations by a number to create variable terms that can be eliminated.

EXAMPLE 2 Solving Linear Systems by Elimination

Use elimination to solve each system of equations.

A $\begin{cases} 2x+3y=34 \\ 4x-3y=-4 \end{cases}$

Step 1 Find the value of one variable.

$2x+3y=34$	*The y-terms have opposite coefficients.*
$+\ 4x-3y=-4$	
$6x\quad\quad=30$	*Add the equations to eliminate y.*
$x=5$	*First part of the solution*

Step 2 Substitute the x-value into one of the original equations to solve for y.

$2(5)+3y=34$

$3y=24$

$y=8$ *Second part of the solution*

The solution to the system is $(5, 8)$.

Reading Math

The elimination method is sometimes called the *addition method* or *linear combination.*

COMMON ERROR ALERT

Students might forget to solve for the second variable after finding the first value. Remind them that the solution is an ordered pair and that both values must be found.

Power Presentations with PowerPoint®

Additional Examples

Example 1

Use substitution to solve each system of equations.

A. $\begin{cases} y=x-1 \\ x+y=7 \end{cases}$ $(4, 3)$

B. $\begin{cases} 2y+x=4 \\ 3x-4y=7 \end{cases}$ $\left(3, \frac{1}{2}\right)$

Example 2

Use elimination to solve each system of equations.

A. $\begin{cases} 3x+2y=4 \\ 4x-2y=-18 \end{cases}$ $(-2, 5)$

B. $\begin{cases} 3x+5y=-16 \\ 2x+3y=-9 \end{cases}$ $(3, -5)$

Also available on transparency

INTERVENTION

Questioning Strategies

EXAMPLE 1

- Will solving for x first rather than for y give the same solution? Explain.
- After solving for one variable, how will you choose an equation to solve for the second value?

EXAMPLE 2

- In general, how do you eliminate a variable?
- How would you solve the system in **Example 2B** if you chose to eliminate y rather than x?

Teaching Tip **Critical Thinking** Ask students to consider whether they can use substitution after they have multiplied an equation to change the constants and coefficients.

2 Teach

Guided Instruction

Review how to evaluate an equation for a given value of a variable. For example, find y if $x=3$ in the equation $y=2x-1$. $y=5$ Point out that it is also possible to solve an equation by substituting an expression for one of the variables. This is the concept used in the substitution method.

Reaching All Learners

Through Multiple Representations

Have students work in small groups to compare solving a system of linear equations by using a graph or table, substitution, or elimination. Then, assign each group a method and ask them to present to the class an example of a linear system that is best solved by the given method.

Communicating Math Discuss choosing which variable to solve for in the substitution method and choosing factors in the elimination method. You may wish to have students sort systems of equations by the method they would most likely choose and then justify their selections.

Power Presentations with PowerPoint®

Additional Examples

Example 3

Classify the system and determine the number of solutions.

$$\begin{cases} 3x + y = 1 \\ 2y + 6x = -18 \end{cases}$$

inconsistent; none

Example 4

A veterinarian needs 60 pounds of dog food that is 15% protein. He will combine a beef mix that is 18% protein with a bacon mix that is 9% protein. How many pounds of each does he need to make the 15% protein mix?

40 lb beef, 20 lb bacon

Also available on transparency

INTERVENTION

Questioning Strategies

EXAMPLE 3

- How do you decide which method to use to classify the system?
- What kind of system will result in an identity? a contradiction?

EXAMPLE 4

- What do the variables represent?
- How do the equations translate to words?

Teaching Tip **Multiple Representations** Encourage students to check their solutions. Inspect a graph of the system to support an algebraic solution. Point out that this method of checking is usually quick and easy.

Use elimination to solve each system of equations.

B $\begin{cases} 2x + 4y = -10 \\ 3x + 3y = -3 \end{cases}$

Step 1 To eliminate x, multiply both sides of the first equation by 3 and both sides of the second equation by −2.

$$\begin{aligned} 3(2x + 4y) &= 3(-10) \\ -2(3x + 3y) &= -2(-3) \end{aligned} \quad \rightarrow \quad \begin{aligned} 6x + 12y &= -30 \\ -6x - 6y &= 6 \\ \hline 6y &= -24 \end{aligned} \quad \textit{Add the equations.}$$

$y = -4$ *First part of the solution*

Step 2 Substitute the y-value into one of the original equations to solve for x.

$$\begin{aligned} 3x + 3(-4) &= -3 \\ 3x - 12 &= -3 \\ 3x &= 9 \\ x &= 3 \end{aligned}$$ *Second part of the solution*

The solution to the system is $(3, -4)$.

Check Substitute 3 for x and −4 for y in each equation.

$2x + 4y = -10$	
$2(3) + 4(-4)$	-10
-10	-10 ✔

$3x + 3y = -3$	
$3(3) + 3(-4)$	-3
-3	-3 ✔

Use elimination to solve each system of equations.

2a. $\begin{cases} 4x + 7y = -25 \\ -12x - 7y = 19 \end{cases}$ $\left(\frac{3}{4}, -4\right)$ **2b.** $\begin{cases} 5x - 3y = 42 \\ 8x + 5y = 28 \end{cases}$ $(6, -4)$

In Lesson 3-1, you learned that systems may have infinitely many or no solutions. When you try to solve these systems algebraically, the result will be an identity or a contradiction.

EXAMPLE 3 Classifying Systems with Infinitely Many or No Solutions

Classify the system and determine the number of solutions.

$$\begin{cases} 2x + y = 8 \\ 6x + 3y = -15 \end{cases}$$

Because isolating y is straightforward, use substitution.

$2x + y = 8$

$y = 8 - 2x$ *Solve the first equation for y.*

$6x + 3(8 - 2x) = -15$ *Substitute 8 − 2x for y in the second equation.*

$6x + 24 - 6x = -15$ *Distribute.*

$24 = -15$ ✗ *Simplify.*

Because 24 is never equal to −15, the equation is a contradiction. Therefore, the system is inconsistent and has no solution.

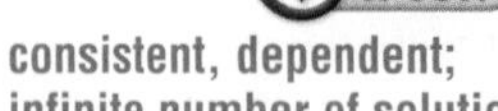

Remember!

An *identity*, such as $0 = 0$, is always true and indicates infinitely many solutions.
A *contradiction*, such as $1 = 3$, is never true and indicates no solution.

Classify the system and determine the number of solutions.

3a. $\begin{cases} 56x + 8y = -32 \\ 7x + y = -4 \end{cases}$ consistent, dependent; infinite number of solutions

3b. $\begin{cases} 6x + 3y = -12 \\ 2x + y = -6 \end{cases}$ inconsistent; no solution

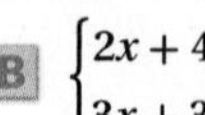

EXAMPLE 4 Zoology Application

A zookeeper needs to mix feed for the prairie dogs so that the feed has the right amount of protein. Feed A has 12% protein. Feed B has 5% protein. How many pounds of each does he need to mix to get 100 lb of feed that is 8% protein?

Let a represent the amount of feed A in the mixture.

Let b represent the amount of feed B in the mixture.

Write one equation based on the amount of feed:

Amount of feed A	plus	amount of feed B	equals	100.
a	$+$	b	$=$	100

Write another equation based on the amount of protein:

Protein of feed A	plus	protein of feed B	equals	protein in mixture.
$0.12a$	$+$	$0.05b$	$=$	$0.08(100)$

Solve the system. $\begin{cases} a + b = 100 \\ 0.12a + 0.05b = 8 \end{cases}$

$a + b = 100$ *First equation*

$b = 100 - a$ *Solve the first equation for b.*

$0.12a + 0.05(100 - a) = 8$ *Substitute (100 − a) for b.*

$0.12a + 5 - 0.05a = 8$ *Distribute.*

$0.07a = 3$ *Simplify.*

$a \approx 42.9$ *Round to the nearest tenth.*

Substitute a into one of the original equations to solve for b.

$(42.9) + b \approx 100$ *Substitute the value of a into one equation.*

$b \approx 57.1$ *Solve for b.*

The mixture will contain about 42.9 lb of feed A and 57.1 lb of feed B.

4. A coffee blend contains Sumatra beans, which cost \$5/lb, and Kona beans, which cost \$13/lb. If the blend costs \$10/lb, how much of each type of coffee is in 50 lb of the blend?
18.75 lb of Sumatra beans and 31.25 lb of Kona beans

Student to Student — *Solving Systems*

Victor Cisneros
Reagan High School

Choosing a method to solve a system of linear equations can be confusing. Here is how I decide which method to use:

Graphing and tables— *when I'm interested in a rough solution or other values around the solution*

Substitution— *when it's simple to solve one of the equations for one variable (for example, solving 3x + y = 7 for y)*

Elimination— *when variables have opposite coefficients, like 5x and −5x, or when I can easily multiply the equations to get opposite coefficients*

COMMON ERROR ALERT

Students might forget to distribute the negative sign when using subtraction or when subtracting to eliminate. Remind them to use the Distributive Property in an expression such as $-(x - 2)$.

Teaching Tip **Communicating Math** Discuss when the substitution and elimination methods are more useful than the graphing method for solving a linear system, such as when the point of intersection is difficult to read or has a coordinate that is not an integer value.

3 Close

Summarize

Review the steps for using the substitution method and the elimination method. Review the two types of equations in a system used to solve mixture problems.

ONGOING ASSESSMENT and INTERVENTION

Diagnose ***Before*** **the Lesson**
3-2 Warm Up, TE p. 188

Monitor ***During*** **the Lesson**
Check It Out! Exercises, SE pp. 189–191
Questioning Strategies, TE pp. 189–190

Assess ***After*** **the Lesson**
3-2 Lesson Quiz, TE p. 195
Alternative Assessment, TE p. 195

Answers to *Think and Discuss*

Possible answers:

1. Elimination, because the *y*-terms have opposite coefficients.
2. See p. A5.

THINK AND DISCUSS

1. Explain which method you would use to solve the system $\begin{cases} 3x + y = 8 \\ 7x - y = 5 \end{cases}$.

2. **GET ORGANIZED** Copy and complete the graphic organizer. In each box, show an example of the given method of solving a linear system.

Graphing

Substitution — Solving Linear Systems — Elimination

3-2 Exercises

3-2 Exercises

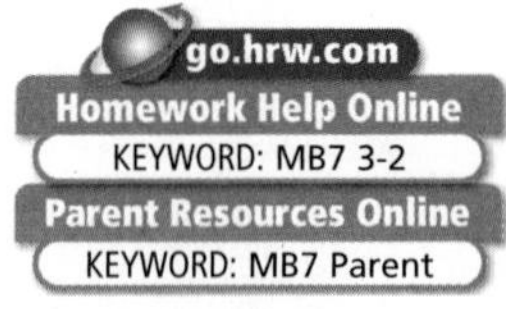

Assignment Guide

Assign *Guided Practice* exercises as necessary.

If you finished Examples **1–2**
- **Basic** 15–22, 29
- **Average** 15–22, 28–29
- **Advanced** 15–22, 28–31

If you finished Examples **1–4**
- **Basic** 15–29, 33, 34, 36, 39–44, 48–56
- **Average** 15–38, 40–45, 48–56
- **Advanced** 17–20, 25–27, 30–32, 34–56

Homework Quick Check
Quickly check key concepts.
Exercises: 18, 20, 26, 27, 28, 36

GUIDED PRACTICE

1. **Vocabulary** The __?__ method solves a system of linear equations by adding or subtracting equations. (*substitution* or *elimination*) **elimination**

SEE EXAMPLE 1 p. 190

Use substitution to solve each system of equations.

2. $\begin{cases} x + y = 17 \\ y = x + 7 \end{cases}$ (5, 12)
3. $\begin{cases} y = x - 19 \\ 2x - y = 27 \end{cases}$ (8, −11)
4. $\begin{cases} 2x - y = 2 \\ 3x - 2y = 11 \end{cases}$ (−7, −16)
5. $\begin{cases} y = 3x + 5 \\ x = -3y - 5 \end{cases}$ (−2, −1)

SEE EXAMPLE 2 p. 191

Use elimination to solve each system of equations.

6. $\begin{cases} 2x + y = 12 \\ -5x - y = -33 \end{cases}$ (7, −2)
7. $\begin{cases} 2x - 5y = -5 \\ -2x + 8y = -58 \end{cases}$ (−55, −21)
8. $\begin{cases} 2x + 6y = -8 \\ 5x - 3y = 88 \end{cases}$ (14, −6)
9. $\begin{cases} \frac{1}{2}x + y = 4 \\ -2x - 2y = -6 \end{cases}$ (−2, 5)

SEE EXAMPLE 3 p. 192

Classify each system and determine the number of solutions.

10. $\begin{cases} 5x - y = -3 \\ 15x - 3y = -9 \end{cases}$
11. $\begin{cases} x - 2y = -8 \\ 4x = 8y - 56 \end{cases}$
12. $\begin{cases} 8x + 12y = 60 \\ 2x + 3y = -24 \end{cases}$
13. $\begin{cases} x - \frac{1}{3}y = -2 \\ 6x - 2y = -12 \end{cases}$

SEE EXAMPLE 4 p. 193

14. **Alternative Fuels** Denise owns a car that runs on a mixture of gasoline and ethanol. She can buy fuels that have 85% ethanol or 25% ethanol. How much of each type of fuel should she buy if she wants to fill her 20 gal tank with a mixture of fuel that contains 50% ethanol? **She should buy $8\frac{1}{3}$ gal of the 85% ethanol fuel and $11\frac{2}{3}$ gal of the 25% ethanol fuel.**

PRACTICE AND PROBLEM SOLVING

Use substitution to solve each system of equations.

15. $\begin{cases} -4y = x \\ 2x + 6y = -3 \end{cases}$ $\left(-6, \frac{3}{2}\right)$
16. $\begin{cases} 12x + y = 21 \\ 18x - 3y = -36 \end{cases}$ $\left(\frac{1}{2}, 15\right)$
17. $\begin{cases} y = 4x \\ 32x + 21y = 29 \end{cases}$ $\left(\frac{1}{4}, 1\right)$
18. $\begin{cases} y + 1 = x \\ -2x + 3y = 2 \end{cases}$ (5, 4)

Use elimination to solve each system of equations.

19. $\begin{cases} 4x - 9y = 26 \\ 4x - 5y = 2 \end{cases}$ (−7, −6)
20. $\begin{cases} 6x - 3y = -6 \\ -5x + 7y = 41 \end{cases}$ (3, 8)
21. $\begin{cases} 12x - 3y = -15 \\ 8x + 8y = -58 \end{cases}$ (−2.45, −4.8)
22. $\begin{cases} 3x + y = 7 \\ -3x + 2y = 11 \end{cases}$ $\left(\frac{1}{3}, 6\right)$

Answers

10. consistent, dependent; infinite number of solutions
11. inconsistent; no solution
12. inconsistent; no solution
13. consistent, dependent; infinite number of solutions

State Resources

go.hrw.com
State Resources Online
KEYWORD: MB7 Resources

3-2 PRACTICE A

Use substitution to solve each system of equations.

1. $\begin{cases} y = x - 3 \\ x + 2y = 6 \end{cases}$
   a. Substitute $x - 3$ for y in $x + 2y = 6$. Then solve the equation for x. $x = 4$
   b. Substitute your value for x in $y = x - 3$ and solve for y. $y = 1$
   c. Write the solution as an ordered pair. (4, 1)
2. $\begin{cases} x = 5 - y \\ 2x + 5y = 16 \end{cases}$ (3, 2)
3. $\begin{cases} y = 3x + 2 \\ 2x + 3y = 17 \end{cases}$ (1, 5)
4. $\begin{cases} x - y = 2 \\ y = 4x + 1 \end{cases}$ (−1, −3)

Use elimination to solve each system of equations.

5. $\begin{cases} 4x - 5y = 7 \\ 3x - 4y = 6 \end{cases}$
   a. Multiply the first equation by −3 and the second equation by 4. $\begin{cases} -12x + 15y = -21 \\ 12x - 16y = 24 \end{cases}$
   b. Add the two equations, which eliminates x. Solve for y. $y = -3$
   c. Substitute your value for y into the first equation. Solve for x. Write the solution as an ordered pair. (−2, −3)
6. $\begin{cases} 5x + y = 19 \\ -2x - y = -7 \end{cases}$ (4, −1)
7. $\begin{cases} -x + 3y = 12 \\ 6x - y = -21 \end{cases}$ (−3, 3)
8. $\begin{cases} 2x + 3y = 4 \\ 4x - 2y = -8 \end{cases}$ (−1, 2)

3-2 PRACTICE B

Use substitution to solve each system of equations.

1. $\begin{cases} x = 7y - 4 \\ 2x - 3y = 14 \end{cases}$ (10, 2)
2. $\begin{cases} y - 3x = 5 \\ 2x = 3y + 6 \end{cases}$ (−3, −4)
3. $\begin{cases} 3x - 4y = 20 \\ y - 2x = 0 \end{cases}$ (−4, −8)

Use elimination to solve each system of equations.

4. $\begin{cases} x + 6y = 1 \\ 3x + 5y = -10 \end{cases}$ (−5, 1)
5. $\begin{cases} 3x + 4y = 6 \\ 2x + 3y = 3 \end{cases}$ (6, −3)
6. $\begin{cases} 3x - 5y = 1 \\ 2x + 3y = -12 \end{cases}$ (−3, −2)

Use substitution or elimination to solve each system of equations.

7. $\begin{cases} x + y = 13 \\ 2x - 3y = 1 \end{cases}$ (8, 5)
8. $\begin{cases} 9x + 2y = 5 \\ 3x - y = -10 \end{cases}$ (−1, 7)
9. $\begin{cases} 2x + y = 1 \\ x = 5 + y \end{cases}$ (2, −3)
10. $\begin{cases} x = -8y \\ x + y = 14 \end{cases}$ (16, −2)
11. $\begin{cases} 2x + 4y = 12 \\ -3x + 3y = 63 \end{cases}$ (−12, 9)
12. $\begin{cases} 5x - 2y = -1 \\ 3x - y = -2 \end{cases}$ (−3, −7)

Solve.

13. Bill leaves his house for Makayla's house riding his bicycle at 8 miles per hour. At the same time, Makayla leaves her house heading toward Bill's house walking at 3 miles per hour.
    a. Write a system of equations to represent the distance, d, each is from Makayla's house in h hours. They live 8.25 miles apart. $\begin{cases} d = 8.25 - 8h \\ d = 3h \end{cases}$
    b. Solve the system to determine how long they travel before meeting. 0.75 h or 45 min

Independent Practice	
For Exercises	See Example
15–18	1
19–22	2
23–26	3
27	4

Extra Practice

Skills Practice p. S8

Application Practice p. S34

23. consistent, dependent; infinite number of solutions

24. inconsistent; no solution

25. consistent, dependent; infinite number of solutions

26. inconsistent; no solution

30. $\left(2\frac{9}{11}, 10\frac{9}{11}\right)$

32a. $\begin{cases} x + y = 3 \\ 325x + 275y = 885 \end{cases}$

33b. The total number of coins increases because every dime must be replaced by 2 nickels.

Classify each system and determine the number of solutions.

23. $\begin{cases} 4y - x = -24 \\ 3x = 12y + 72 \end{cases}$ 24. $\begin{cases} 10x - 2y = 22 \\ 5y - 25x = 65 \end{cases}$ 25. $\begin{cases} 4y - 3x = 32 \\ 8y - 6x = 64 \end{cases}$ 26. $\begin{cases} -x + \frac{3}{4}y = 4 \\ 8x - 6y = -8 \end{cases}$

27. **Business** An office is printing 1200 copies of a document using two printers. During the process, printer A gets a paper jam and prints only half as many copies as printer B. Write and solve a system of equations to determine the number of copies each printer will produce. $x + y = 1200$; $x = \frac{1}{2}y$; $(400, 800)$

Use substitution or elimination to solve each system of equations.

28. $\begin{cases} y + 3x = -21 \\ x = 3y + 3 \end{cases}$ $(-6, -3)$ 29. $\begin{cases} y = -2x + 14 \\ 1.5x - 3.5y = 2 \end{cases}$ $(6, 2)$ 30. $\begin{cases} \frac{4}{5}y - 3x = \frac{1}{5} \\ y - x = 8 \end{cases}$ 31. $\begin{cases} x + 5y = 5 \\ \frac{1}{5}x + 2y = -2 \end{cases}$ $(20, -3)$

32. **Exercise** Ahmit gets exercise on the weekend by working around the house. On Saturday, he worked for 3 hours mowing the lawn and raking leaves. He burned 885 Calories.

a. Write a system of equations that can be used to describe the amount of time Ahmit worked and the number of Calories he burned by mowing and raking.

b. Determine how much time Ahmit spent on mowing and on raking. 1.2 h mowing and 1.8 h raking

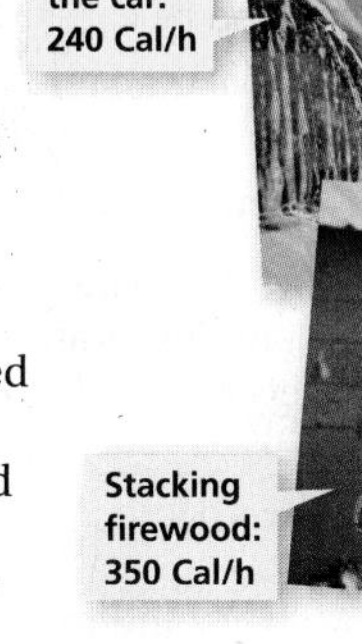

Washing the car: 240 Cal/h

Raking leaves: 275 Cal/h

Stacking firewood: 350 Cal/h

Mowing the lawn: 325 Cal/h

33. Vanessa has collected \$2.10 in dimes and nickels.

a. **Critical Thinking** In how many different ways might Vanessa have combined dimes and nickels to total \$2.10? 22

b. **Critical Thinking** How does the total number of coins change as the number of dimes decreases? Explain. 33c. 12 dimes and 18 nickels

c. If Vanessa has exactly 30 coins, how many of each type of coin does she have?

34. **ERROR ANALYSIS** Two students attempted to solve the system of equations $\begin{cases} 2x + 4y = 38 \\ 2x - 2y = -4 \end{cases}$ and found different answers. Which solution is incorrect? Explain the error. The error is in solution A. $2 + x$ is substituted back into the equation for which it is the value of y.

(A)

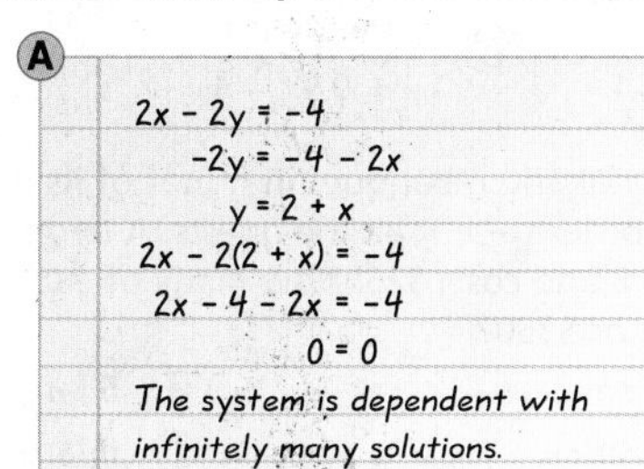

$2x - 2y = -4$
$-2y = -4 - 2x$
$y = 2 + x$
$2x - 2(2 + x) = -4$
$2x - 4 - 2x = -4$
$0 = 0$
The system is dependent with infinitely many solutions.

(B)

$2x - 2y = -4$
$-2y = -4 - 2x$
$y = 2 + x$
$2x + 4(2 + x) = 38$
$2x + 8 + 4x = 38$ $y = 2 + x$
$6x = 30$ $y = 2 + 5$
$x = 5$ $y = 7$
The solution is $(5, 7)$.

COMMON ERROR ALERT

Students might have difficulty in **Exercise 32** organizing the information needed to write the system of equations. Help students first identify the two variables, the time spent mowing and the time spent raking. Then lead them to write an equation for the total time and an equation for the total calories.

Teaching Tip **Number Sense** Remind students that they can use multiplication to clear the fractions to solve each system in **Exercises 30** and **31.**

Teaching Tip **Science Link** After students complete **Exercise 32,** discuss why different numbers of Calories are burned for each activity.

3-2 PRACTICE C

Use substitution or elimination to solve each system of equations.

1. $\begin{cases} x = y - 5.2 \\ 2x + 3y = 9.6 \end{cases}$ $(-1.2, 4)$

2. $\begin{cases} 3x - 4y = 5 \\ x = y + \frac{1}{2} \end{cases}$ $\left(-3, -3\frac{1}{2}\right)$

3. $\begin{cases} x + 4y = \frac{1}{4} \\ 4x - 3y = 39 \end{cases}$ $\left(8\frac{1}{4}, -2\right)$

4. $\begin{cases} 2x + 20y = 3 \\ 2x = -7y - 10 \end{cases}$ $\left(-8\frac{1}{2}, 1\right)$

5. $\begin{cases} x + y = 5 \\ 3x + 2y = 4 \end{cases}$ $(-6, 11)$

6. $\begin{cases} 3x + 4y = 35 \\ 4x - 2y = 21 \end{cases}$ $\left(7, 3\frac{1}{2}\right)$

7. $\begin{cases} 3\frac{1}{4}x + 3y = 42 \\ 5x = 4y \end{cases}$ $\left(6, 7\frac{1}{2}\right)$

8. $\begin{cases} 5x - 5y = 6 \\ 4x + 7y = -4 \end{cases}$ $\left(\frac{2}{5}, -\frac{4}{5}\right)$

9. $\begin{cases} 2x - 8y = 24 \\ x - 21 = 16y \end{cases}$ $\left(9, -\frac{3}{4}\right)$

Solve.

10. Cora bought 4 pounds of nuts and 2 pounds of raisins for \$23.50. Mark bought 2 pounds of nuts and 4 pounds of raisins for \$18.50.

a. Write a system of equations that represents the price of the nuts, n, and the price of the raisins, r. $\begin{cases} 4n + 2r = 23.5 \\ 2n + 4r = 18.5 \end{cases}$

b. Solve the system. How much should a pound of nuts and a pound of raisins cost together? \$7.00

11. Kate and Riley are reading the same book. Kate reads $\frac{1}{3}$ page per minute, and Riley reads $\frac{3}{4}$ page per minute. Kate has already read 70 pages, while Riley has read 30 pages. If they both resume reading together, eventually Riley will catch up to Kate.

a. On what page will that occur? 102

b. How many minutes have they read when Riley catches up? 96

Exercise 34 involves solving a linear system and interpreting the results. This exercise prepares students for the applications of linear systems in two dimensions in the Multi-Step Test Prep on page 212.

Students should immediately be able to eliminate choices **A** and **C** in **Exercise 39** since the slopes of the two lines must have different signs. Then students need to find the equation of only one of the lines to choose the correct answer.

You may wish to suggest that students work backward from the choices in **Exercise 40,** testing each one in turn.

Answers

38b. Solving by graphing is best for equations that intersect at whole-number values or values that are clear on a graph. Solving algebraically is best for solutions that are not easy to read on a graph.

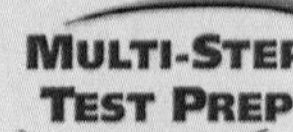

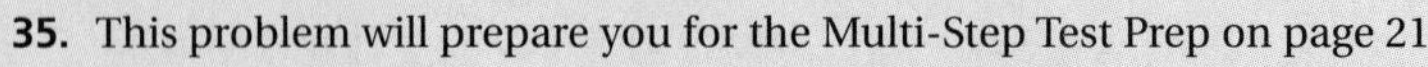

35. This problem will prepare you for the Multi-Step Test Prep on page 212.

A car race is made up of 500 laps around a 0.533-mile track.

a. How many miles long is the race? **266.5 mi**

b. The course record for one lap is 14.94 seconds. Write an equation that could be used to model the distance in miles traveled by the record-setting car if it continues at the same pace. $y = 128.43x$

c. If a second car travels at 125 miles per hour, use your answer to part **b** to determine the distance between the two cars when the lead car finishes the race. ≈ 7.12 **mi**

36a. $\begin{cases} y = 300 + 45x \\ y = 325 + 60x \end{cases}$ $x = -1\frac{2}{3}$

b. Possible answer: The solution isn't reasonable. A negative fraction doesn't make sense as the number of customers.

36. Multi-Step Malcolm and Owen work for a bottled water distributor. Malcolm makes \$300 per week plus \$45 for each new customer who signs a contract. Owen has more sales experience, so he earns \$325 per week plus \$60 for each new customer.

a. Write and solve a system of equations to determine the number of new customers for which Malcolm and Owen will have the same income.

b. Critical Thinking Is the solution reasonable? Explain.

37. Entertainment The band and the orchestra are attending a concert. The band bought 16 student tickets and 3 adult tickets for \$110.50. The orchestra bought 12 student tickets and 4 adult tickets for \$96. Find the cost of each type of ticket. **student = \$5.50 and adult = \$7.50**

38. The graph of the system $\begin{cases} 3x - 6y = -13 \\ 6x + 3y = 24 \end{cases}$ is shown.

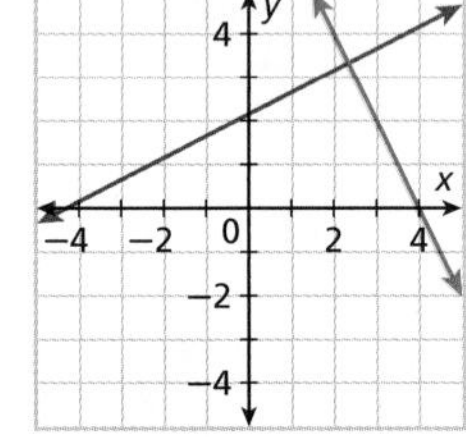

A student says the solution is $\left(2\frac{1}{2}, 3\frac{1}{2}\right)$.

38a. The correct solution is $\left(2\frac{1}{3}, 3\frac{1}{3}\right)$.

a. Find the solution algebraically to see if the student is correct.

b. Write About It Discuss how you can choose the most appropriate method to solve a system of equations.

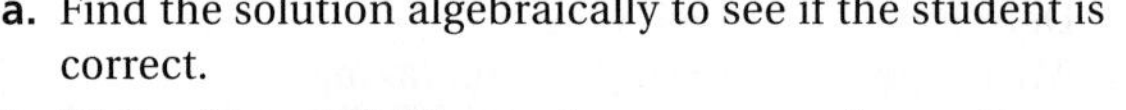

39. Write About It How can you recognize a dependent system of equations by analyzing the equations?

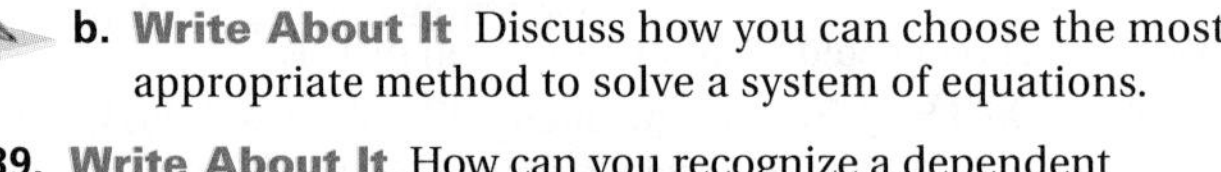

Possible answer: When you simplify the equations, they should have the same slope and y-intercept.

40. Which of the following systems of equations represents the graph at right?

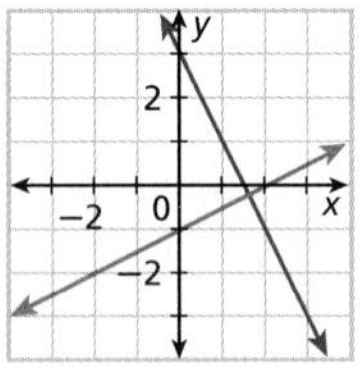

Ⓐ $\begin{cases} y = 2x + 3 \\ y = 0.5x - 1 \end{cases}$ Ⓒ $\begin{cases} y = -2x + 3 \\ y = -0.5x - 1 \end{cases}$

Ⓑ $\begin{cases} y = 2x + 3 \\ y = -0.5x - 1 \end{cases}$ **Ⓓ** $\begin{cases} y = -2x + 3 \\ y = 0.5x - 1 \end{cases}$

41. An organization is holding a banquet in honor of its member of the year. Tables must be rented in order to seat all the guests. A large table seats 12 and costs \$50. A small table seats 8 and costs \$25. How many of each type of table must be rented to seat 100 guests for \$350?

Ⓕ 8 large and 3 small Ⓗ 5 large and 5 small

Ⓖ 3 large and 8 small Ⓙ 6 large and 2 small

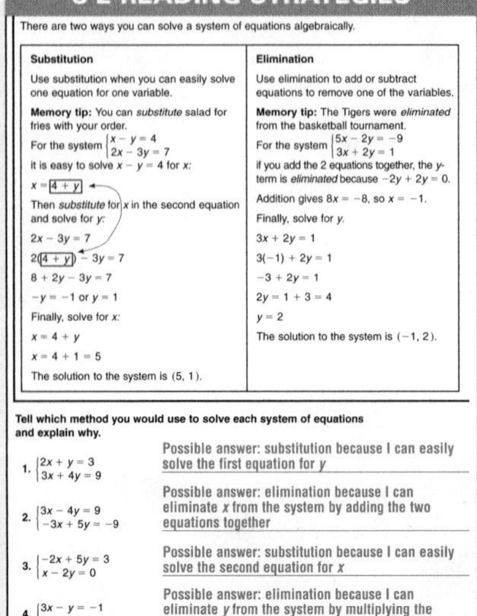

3-2 READING STRATEGIES

There are two ways you can solve a system of equations algebraically.

Substitution	Elimination
Use substitution when you can easily solve one equation for one variable.	Use elimination to add or subtract equations to remove one of the variables.
Memory tip: You can *substitute* salad for fries with your order.	**Memory tip:** The Tigers were *eliminated* from the basketball tournament.
For the system $\begin{cases} x - y = 4 \\ 2x - 3y = 7 \end{cases}$ it is easy to solve $x - y = 4$ for x:	For the system $\begin{cases} 5x - 2y = -9 \\ 3x + 2y = 1 \end{cases}$ if you add the 2 equations together, the y-term is *eliminated* because $-2y + 2y = 0$.
$x = \boxed{4 + y}$	Addition gives $8x = -8$, so $x = -1$.
Then *substitute* for x in the second equation and solve for y:	Finally, solve for y.
$2x - 3y = 7$	$3x + 2y = 1$
$2(\boxed{4 + y}) - 3y = 7$	$3(-1) + 2y = 1$
$8 + 2y - 3y = 7$	$-3 + 2y = 1$
$-y = -1$ or $y = 1$	$2y = 1 + 3 = 4$
Finally, solve for x:	$y = 2$
$x = 4 + y$	The solution to the system is $(-1, 2)$.
$x = 4 + 1 = 5$	
The solution to the system is $(5, 1)$.	

Tell which method you would use to solve each system of equations and explain why.

1. $\begin{cases} 2x + y = 3 \\ 3x + 4y = 9 \end{cases}$ Possible answer: substitution because I can easily solve the first equation for y

2. $\begin{cases} 3x - 4y = 9 \\ -3x + 5y = -9 \end{cases}$ Possible answer: elimination because I can eliminate x from the system by adding the two equations together

3. $\begin{cases} -2x + 5y = 3 \\ x - 2y = 0 \end{cases}$ Possible answer: substitution because I can easily solve the second equation for x

4. $\begin{cases} 3x - y = -1 \\ 4x + \frac{1}{2}y = 1 \end{cases}$ Possible answer: elimination because I can eliminate y from the system by multiplying the second equation by 2, then adding the equations

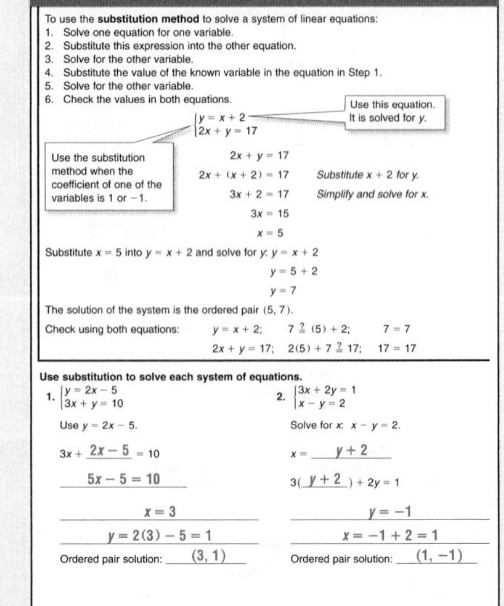

3-2 RETEACH

To use the **substitution method** to solve a system of linear equations:

1. Solve one equation for one variable.
2. Substitute this expression into the other equation.
3. Solve for the other variable.
4. Substitute the value of the known variable in the equation in Step 1.
5. Solve for the other variable.
6. Check the values in both equations.

$\begin{cases} y = x + 2 \\ 2x + y = 17 \end{cases}$

Use this equation. It is solved for y.

Use the substitution method when the coefficient of one of the variables is 1 or −1.

$2x + y = 17$

$2x + (x + 2) = 17$ *Substitute $x + 2$ for y.*

$3x + 2 = 17$ *Simplify and solve for x.*

$3x = 15$

$x = 5$

Substitute $x = 5$ into $y = x + 2$ and solve for y: $y = x + 2$

$y = 5 + 2$

$y = 7$

The solution of the system is the ordered pair $(5, 7)$.

Check using both equations: $y = x + 2$; $7 \stackrel{?}{=} (5) + 2$; $7 = 7$

$2x + y = 17$; $2(5) + 7 \stackrel{?}{=} 17$; $17 = 17$

Use substitution to solve each system of equations.

1. $\begin{cases} y = 2x - 5 \\ 3x + y = 10 \end{cases}$

Use $y = 2x - 5$.

$3x + \underline{2x - 5} = 10$

$5x - 5 = 10$

$x = 3$

$y = 2(3) - 5 = 1$

Ordered pair solution: $(3, 1)$

2. $\begin{cases} 3x + 2y = 1 \\ x - y = 2 \end{cases}$

Solve for x: $x - y = 2$.

$x = \underline{y + 2}$

$3(\underline{y + 2}) + 2y = 1$

$y = -1$

$x = -1 + 2 = 1$

Ordered pair solution: $(1, -1)$

42. Solve the system. $\begin{cases} x + y = 7 \\ x - y = -3 \end{cases}$

(A) (2, 5) (B) (5, 2) (C) (−2, 5) (D) (−5, 2)

43. **Short Response** What is the solution to the system of equations $\begin{cases} x - 4y = 6 \\ y = -4x + 7 \end{cases}$? Classify the system. **(2, −1); independent, consistent**

44. Two cyclists are competing in a 10 mi time trial. The older cyclist, who rides at a speed of 22 mi/h, is given a 1 mi head start. The younger cyclist rides at a speed of 25 mi/h. Let x represent time in hours and let y represent distance in miles. Which of the following systems of equations represents the situation?

(F) $\begin{cases} y = 25 \\ y = 22 + 1 \end{cases}$ (G) $\begin{cases} y = 25x + 1 \\ y = 22x \end{cases}$ **(H)** $\begin{cases} y = 25x \\ y = 22x + 1 \end{cases}$ (J) $\begin{cases} y = 25x \\ y = 22 + x \end{cases}$

CHALLENGE AND EXTEND

45. One equation in a linear system is $x + 2y = 4$. Write another equation so that the system has the unique solution $(-2, 3)$. **Possible answer: $y = -\frac{3}{2}x$**

46. The following system has a solution. Find the solution and explain your method. How do you know you are correct? **(−1, 3); possible answer: Use the elimination method on the first and third equations to solve for y and then substitute that value back into another equation to find x.**

$$\begin{cases} y - x = 4 \\ y - 1 = -2x \\ y + x - 2 = 0 \end{cases}$$

47. **Economics** A software company is considering the release of a new product. The research department has modeled the current market with a set of equations in terms of price p and quantity q.

Supply: $p = 5 + 2q$ **Demand:** $q = 100 - 4p$

a. The equilibrium price and quantity occur when supply meets demand. Find the equilibrium price and quantity for the current market. **$p = 22\frac{7}{9}$; $q = 8\frac{8}{9}$**

b. **What if...?** After the release of the new product, the supply function changes to $p = 3 + 0.5q$. How will the equilibrium price and quantity change? **$p = 17\frac{2}{3}$; $q = 29\frac{1}{3}$**

SPIRAL REVIEW

Simplify each expression. Then evaluate the expression for the given value of the variable. *(Lesson 1-4)*

48. $-b^2(2b + 4) + b^5$, $b = -1$ **$-2b^3 - 4b^2 + b^5$; −3**

49. $3c^2 + 1 + (5c)^2$, $c = 3$ **$28c^2 + 1$; 253**

50. $\frac{20 - 2x^2}{x}$, $x = -2$ **$\frac{20}{x} - 2x$; −6**

51. $y^{-3}\left(\frac{2y}{9}\right)$, $y = -3$ **$\frac{2}{9y^2}$; $\frac{2}{81}$**

Write the equation of the line in slope-intercept form that includes the points in the table. *(Lesson 2-4)*

52. **$f(x) = \frac{1}{2}x + 1$**

x	2	6	10	14	20	26
$f(x)$	2	4	6	8	11	14

53.

x	1	2	3	4	5	6
$f(x)$	−2	−3.5	−5	−6.5	−8	−9.5

$f(x) = -1.5x - 0.5$

Graph each inequality. *(Lesson 2-5)*

54. $y > -5$ 55. $3x - y \le 2(x - 2)$ 56. $5x + 4y > 18$

54.

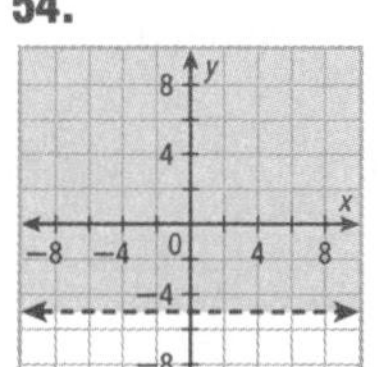

Answers

55.

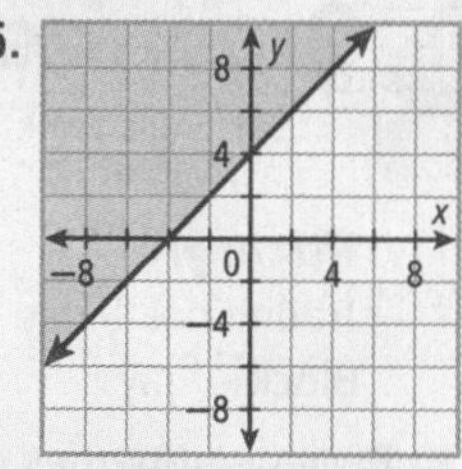

56.

Journal

Have students explain how they would decide whether to use substitution or elimination to solve a system of equations and how to check the solution by using a table.

ALTERNATIVE ASSESSMENT

Have students create two systems of equations that can be solved by substitution and two systems that can be solved by elimination. Ask students to explain how they would determine the number of solutions for each system.

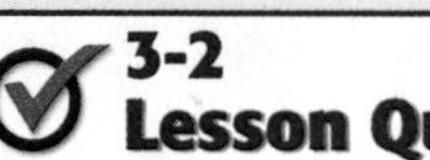

Power Presentations with PowerPoint®

3-2 Lesson Quiz

Use substitution or elimination to solve each system of equations.

1. $\begin{cases} 3x + y = 1 \\ y = x + 9 \end{cases}$ (−2, 7)

2. $\begin{cases} 5x - 4y = 10 \\ 3x - 4y = -2 \end{cases}$ (6, 5)

3. The Miller and Benson families went to a theme park. The Millers bought 6 adult and 15 child tickets for \$423. The Bensons bought 5 adult and 9 child tickets for \$293. Find the cost of each type of ticket. adult: \$28; children's: \$17

Also available on transparency

3-2 PROBLEM SOLVING

Use substitution to solve each system of equations.

1. $\begin{cases} y = x - 3 \\ x + 2y = 6 \end{cases}$

a. Substitute $x - 3$ for y in $x + 2y = 6$. Then solve the equation for x. **$x = 4$**

b. Substitute your value for x in $y = x - 3$ and solve for y. **$y = 1$**

c. Write the solution as an ordered pair. **(4, 1)**

2. $\begin{cases} x = 5 - y \\ 2x + 5y = 16 \end{cases}$ **(3, 2)**

3. $\begin{cases} y = 3x + 2 \\ 2x + 3y = 17 \end{cases}$ **(1, 5)**

4. $\begin{cases} x - y = 2 \\ y = 4x + 1 \end{cases}$ **(−1, −3)**

Use elimination to solve each system of equations.

5. $\begin{cases} 4x - 5y = 7 \\ 3x - 4y = 6 \end{cases}$

a. Multiply the first equation by −3 and the second equation by 4. **$\begin{cases} -12x + 15y = -21 \\ 12x - 16y = 24 \end{cases}$**

b. Add the two equations, which eliminates x. Solve for y. **$y = -3$**

c. Substitute your value for y into the first equation. Solve for x.

Write the solution as an ordered pair. **(−2, −3)**

6. $\begin{cases} 5x + y = 19 \\ -2x - y = -7 \end{cases}$ **(4, −1)**

7. $\begin{cases} -x + 3y = 12 \\ 6x - y = -21 \end{cases}$ **(−3, 3)**

8. $\begin{cases} 2x + 3y = 4 \\ 4x - 2y = -8 \end{cases}$ **(−1, 2)**

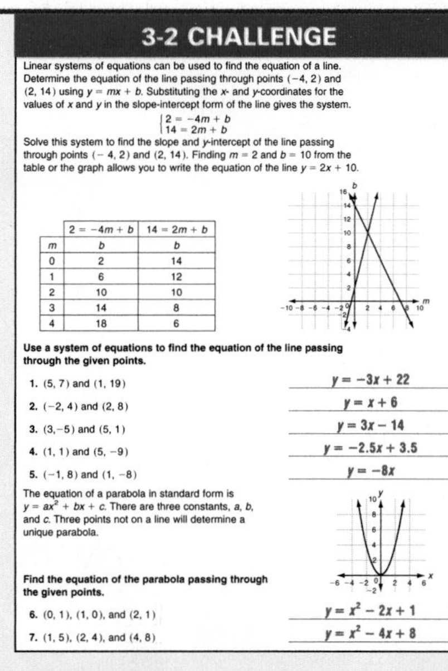

3-2 CHALLENGE

Linear systems of equations can be used to find the equation of a line. Determine the equation of the line passing through points (−4, 2) and (2, 14) using $y = mx + b$. Substituting the x- and y-coordinates for the values of x and y in the slope-intercept form of the line gives the system.

$$\begin{cases} 2 = -4m + b \\ 14 = 2m + b \end{cases}$$

Solve this system to find the slope and y-intercept of the line passing through points (− 4, 2) and (2, 14). Finding $m = 2$ and $b = 10$ from the table or the graph allows you to write the equation of the line $y = 2x + 10$.

	$2 = -4m + b$	$14 = 2m + b$
m	b	b
0	2	14
1	6	12
2	10	10
3	14	8
4	18	6

Use a system of equations to find the equation of the line passing through the given points.

1. (5, 7) and (1, 19) **$y = -3x + 22$**
2. (−2, 4) and (2, 8) **$y = x + 6$**
3. (3, −5) and (5, 1) **$y = 3x - 14$**
4. (1, 1) and (5, −9) **$y = -2.5x + 3.5$**
5. (−1, 8) and (1, −8) **$y = -8x$**

The equation of a parabola in standard form is $y = ax^2 + bx + c$. There are three constants, a, b, and c. Three points not on a line will determine a unique parabola.

Find the equation of the parabola passing through the given points.

6. (0, 1), (1, 0), and (2, 1) **$y = x^2 - 2x + 1$**
7. (1, 5), (2, 4), and (4, 8) **$y = x^2 - 4x + 8$**

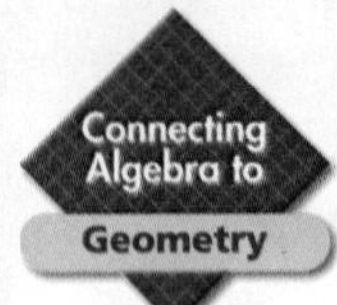

Organizer

See Skills Bank page S61

Pacing:
Traditional $\frac{1}{2}$ day
Block $\frac{1}{4}$ day

Objective: Review properties of polygons.

Online Edition

Countdown to Testing Week 6

Teach

Remember

Students review and apply the definitions of *acute, obtuse, right, congruent,* and *parallel.*

INTERVENTION For additional review and practice on identifying polygons, see Skills Bank page S61.

Auditory Have students take turns choosing two types of triangles or two types of quadrilaterals and describing to a partner how their choices are alike and different.

Close

Assess

Have students sketch an example of each of the six types of triangles and each of the five types of quadrilaterals.

State Resources

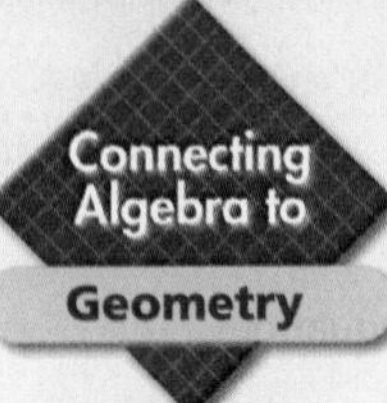

Properties of Polygons

See Skills Bank page S61

A *polygon* is a closed plane figure formed by three or more line segments. Polygons are classified by the properties of their sides and angles.

Polygons can be named by the number of sides they have.

Two angles with the same measure or segments with the same length are *congruent.* If all the sides and angles of a polygon are congruent, the polygon is *regular.* The first four regular polygons are shown.

Number of Sides	3	4	5	6
Name	Triangle	Quadrilateral	Pentagon	Hexagon

Here are some other ways of classifying polygons.

Classifying Triangles	
By Angles	
Acute	Three acute angles (greater than 0° and less than 90°)
Obtuse	One obtuse angle (greater than 90° and less than 180°)
Right	One right angle (90°)
By Sides	
Scalene	No congruent sides
Isosceles	At least two congruent sides
Equilateral	Three congruent sides

Classifying Quadrilaterals	
Types of Quadrilaterals	
Parallelogram	Two pairs of opposite parallel and congruent sides
Trapezoid	Exactly one pair of opposite parallel sides
Types of Parallelograms	
Rectangle	Four right angles
Square	Four congruent sides, 4 right angles
Rhombus	Four congruent sides

Example

Identify each polygon.

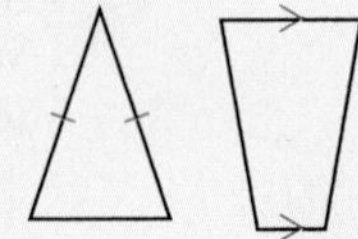

Start by counting the number of sides. Then look at the types of angles and pairs of parallel sides. Compare angles to the corner of a square: acute angles measure less than 90°; obtuse angles measure greater than 90°.

a. Two sides of the triangle are equal, so it is isosceles.

b. This quadrilateral has one pair of parallel sides. It is a trapezoid.

Try This

Identify each polygon.

1. 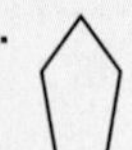 **2.** **3.** **4.** **5.** **6.**

1. pentagon
2. right triangle
3. parallelogram
4. rhombus
5. hexagon
6. rectangle

3-3 Solving Systems of Linear Inequalities

Objective
Solve systems of linear inequalities.

Vocabulary
system of linear inequalities

Who uses this?
Explorers can use systems of inequalities to determine the rates at which they must travel to avoid bad weather. (See Example 2.)

When a problem uses phrases like "greater than" or "no more than," you can model the situation using a system of linear inequalities.

A **system of linear inequalities** is a set of two or more linear inequalities with the same variables. The solution to a system of inequalities is often an infinite set of points that can be represented graphically by shading. When you graph multiple inequalities on the same graph, the region where the shadings overlap is the solution region.

EXAMPLE 1 Graphing Systems of Inequalities

Graph each system of inequalities.

A $\begin{cases} y \le -2x + 4 \\ y > x - 3 \end{cases}$

For $y \le -2x + 4$, graph the solid boundary line $y = -2x + 4$, and shade below it. For $y > x - 3$, graph the dashed boundary line $y = x - 3$, and shade above it.

The overlapping region is the solution region.

Check Test a point from each region on the graph.

Region	Point	$y \le -2x + 4$	$y > x - 3$
Left	(0, 0)	$0 \overset{?}{\le} -2(0) + 4$ $0 \overset{?}{\le} 4$ ✔	$0 \overset{?}{>} 0 - 3$ $0 \overset{?}{>} -3$ ✔
Right	(4, 0)	$0 \overset{?}{\le} -2(4) + 4$ $0 \overset{?}{\le} -4$ ✘	$0 \overset{?}{>} 4 - 3$ $0 \overset{?}{>} 1$ ✘
Top	(2, 2)	$2 \overset{?}{\le} -2(2) + 4$ $2 \overset{?}{\le} 0$ ✘	$2 \overset{?}{>} 2 - 3$ $2 \overset{?}{>} -1$ ✔
Bottom	(2, −2)	$-2 \overset{?}{\le} -2(2) + 4$ $-2 \overset{?}{\le} 0$ ✔	$-2 \overset{?}{>} 2 - 3$ $-2 \overset{?}{>} -1$ ✘

Only the point from the overlapping (left) region satisfies both inequalities.

Helpful Hint

If you are unsure which direction to shade, use the origin as a test point.

3-3 Organizer

Pacing: Traditional $1\frac{1}{2}$ days
Block $\frac{3}{4}$ day

Objective: Solve systems of linear inequalities.

Online Edition
Graphing Calculator, Tutorial Videos

Countdown to Testing Week 6

Power Presentations with PowerPoint®

Warm Up

1. Graph $2x - y > 4$.

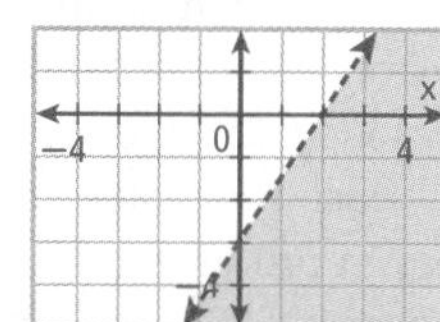

Determine if the given ordered pair is a solution of the system of equations.

2. $(2, -2)$ $\begin{cases} 2x + y = 2 \\ 2y - x = -6 \end{cases}$ yes

3. $(-4, 3)$ $\begin{cases} x - y = -1 \\ x + 2y = 2 \end{cases}$ no

Also available on transparency

Math Humor

Q: Why didn't the chicken cross to the other side of the inequality?

A: It couldn't get past the boundary line.

1 Introduce

EXPLORATION

3-3 Solving Systems of Linear Inequalities

You can use a graphing calculator to graph a system of inequalities.

The Y= menu shows the inequalities $y \ge 2x - 3$ and $y \le -x + 1$. Note that the symbol to the left of **Y** indicate shading.

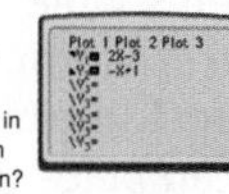

1. Graph only $y \ge 2x - 3$. Name a point in the shaded region. What does it mean for this point to lie in the shaded region?
2. Graph only $y \le -x + 1$. Name a point in the shaded region. What does it mean for this point to lie in the shaded region?
3. The graph shows the two shaded regions on the same coordinate plane. Name a point in the overlapping region. What does it mean for this point to lie in the overlapping region?

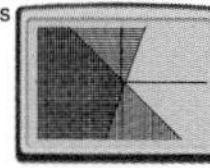

THINK AND DISCUSS

4. **Describe** the steps you must take to find the solution region of a system of inequalities on a graphing calculator.
5. **Explain** how the solution region would change if the

Motivate

Ask students to compare the systems $\begin{cases} -x + y = 0 \\ -2x + y = -2 \end{cases}$ and $\begin{cases} -x + y > 0 \\ -2x + y < -2 \end{cases}$. Remind students that they know how to sketch the graphs of systems of linear equations and graphs of linear inequalities. Explain that they will use these skills together for systems of linear inequalities.

Explorations and answers are provided in the *Explorations* binder.

State Resources

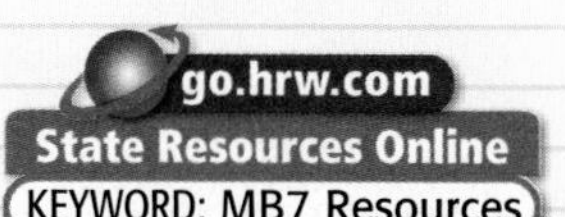

go.hrw.com
State Resources Online
KEYWORD: MB7 Resources

Power Presentations with PowerPoint®

Additional Examples

Example 1

Graph each system of inequalities.

A. $\begin{cases} y < \frac{1}{2}x - 3 \\ y \geq -x + 2 \end{cases}$

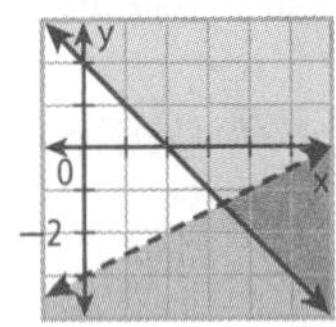

B. $\begin{cases} y < -3x + 2 \\ y \geq -1 \end{cases}$

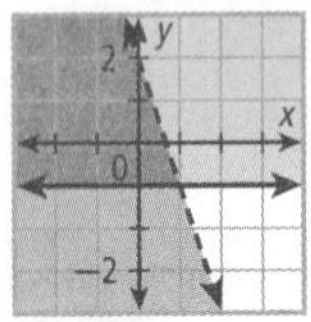

Example 2

Lauren wants to paint no more than 70 plates for the art show. It costs her at least \$50 plus \$2 per item to produce red plates and \$3 per item to produce gold plates. She wants to spend no more than \$215. Write and graph a system of inequalities that can be used to determine the number of each plate that Lauren can make.

$\begin{cases} x + y \leq 70 \\ 50 + 2x + 3y \leq 215 \end{cases}$

Also available on transparency

INTERVENTION

Questioning Strategies

EXAMPLE 1

- Why must you use both inequalities to check a point in the solution region?

EXAMPLE 2

- What are reasonable values for the variables in the problem?

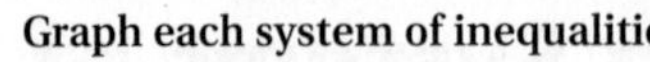

Graph each system of inequalities.

B $\begin{cases} y \geq \frac{3}{2}x + 2 \\ x < 3 \end{cases}$

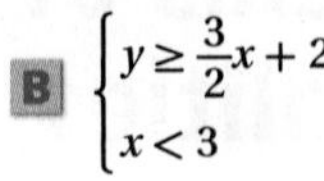

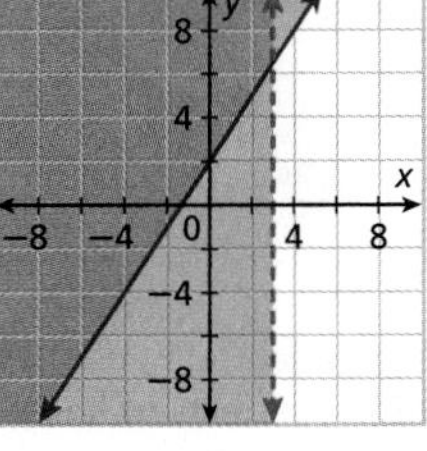

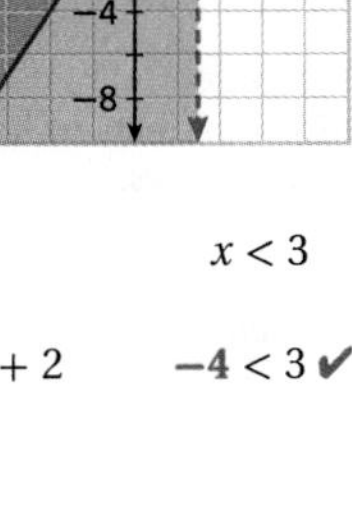

For $y \geq \frac{3}{2}x + 2$, graph the solid boundary line $y = \frac{3}{2}x + 2$, and shade above it. For $x < 3$, graph the dashed boundary line $x = 3$, and shade to the left. The overlapping region is the solution region.

Check Choose a point in the solution region, such as $(-4, 0)$, and test it in both inequalities.

$y \geq \frac{3}{2}x + 2$ $x < 3$

$0 \geq \frac{3}{2}(-4) + 2$ $-4 < 3$ ✔

$0 \geq -4$ ✔

The test point satisfies both inequalities, and suggests that the solution region is correct.

1a.

b.

CHECK IT OUT! Graph each system of inequalities.

1a. $\begin{cases} x - 3y < 6 \\ 2x + y > 1.5 \end{cases}$ **1b.** $\begin{cases} y \leq 4 \\ 2x + y < 1 \end{cases}$

EXAMPLE 2 *Expedition Application*

A polar expedition is 240 miles away from base camp, and a snowstorm is predicted to reach the area in 48 hours. The expedition will travel as far as possible by boat and then walk the remaining distance to camp before the storm hits. The explorers can navigate the boat through the ice at a rate of 12 miles per hour or walk with the equipment at a rate of 3 miles per hour. Write and graph a system of inequalities that can be used to determine how long the explorers may travel by foot or by boat to reach base camp before the storm.

Let x represent the number of hours traveled on foot, and let y represent the number of hours traveled by boat.

The total number of hours can be modeled by the inequality $x + y \leq 48$. The number of miles covered by the explorers can be modeled by $3x + 12y \geq 240$.

The system of inequalities is $\begin{cases} x + y \leq 48 \\ 3x + 12y \geq 240 \end{cases}$.

Graph the solid boundary line $x + y = 48$, and shade below it. Graph the solid boundary line $3x + 12y = 240$, and shade above it. The overlapping region is the solution region.

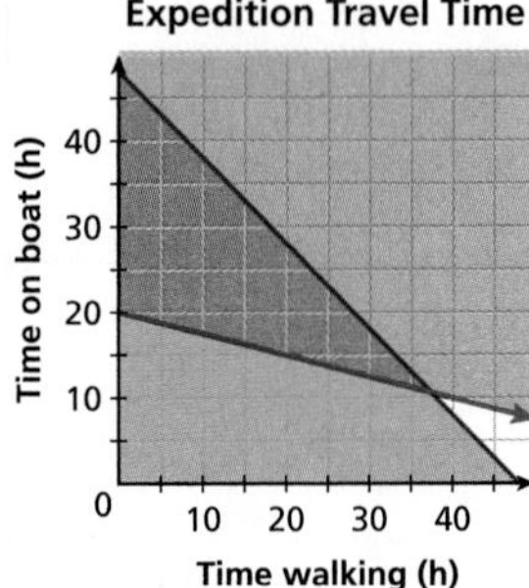

Check Test the point $(15, 25)$ in both inequalities. This point represents traveling 15 hours by foot and 25 hours by boat.

$x + y \leq 48$ $3x + 12y \geq 240$

$(15) + (25) \leq 48$ $3(15) + 12(25) \geq 240$

$40 \leq 48$ ✔ $345 \geq 240$ ✔

2 Teach

Guided Instruction

Introduce graphing a system of linear inequalities by graphing $y \leq x$ and $y > x$. Use colored pencils, found in the Manipulatives Kit (MK), to graph each inequality. Review graphing the boundary line and how to decide which half-plane to shade. Encourage students to guide you through the steps.

Be sure to discuss reasonable values for variables in application problems.

Reaching All Learners

Through Visual Cues

Have students write the inequalities in slope-intercept form, if appropriate, to graph. After students sketch the boundary line, they can place their pencil on the y-axis at the intercept. They can shade down when the inequality is *less than* and up when it is *greater than*.

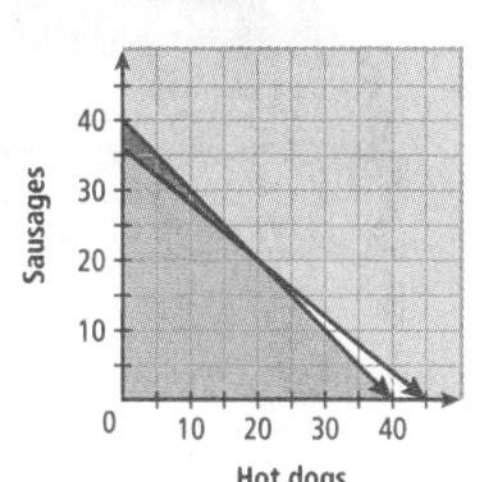

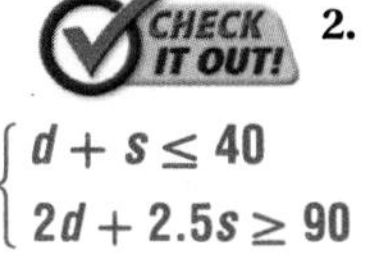

2. Leyla is selling hot dogs and spicy sausages at the fair. She has only 40 buns, so she can sell no more than a total of 40 hot dogs and spicy sausages. Each hot dog sells for \$2, and each sausage sells for \$2.50. Leyla needs at least \$90 in sales to meet her goal. Write and graph a system of inequalities that models this situation.

$$\begin{cases} d + s \le 40 \\ 2d + 2.5s \ge 90 \end{cases}$$

Systems of inequalities may contain more than two inequalities.

EXAMPLE 3 Geometry Application

Geometry

Graph the system of inequalities, and classify the figure created by the solution region.

$$\begin{cases} y \le 5 \\ y \ge 2 \\ y \le 3x + 1 \\ y \ge 3x - 4 \end{cases}$$

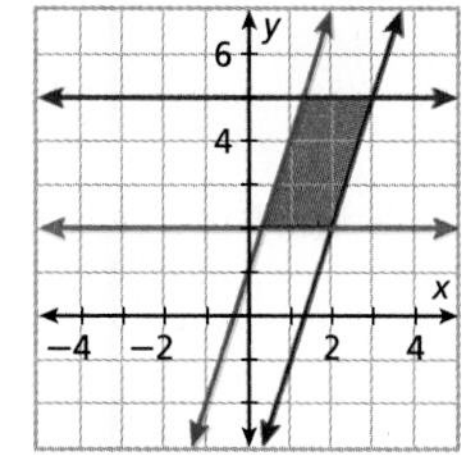

Graph the solid boundary lines $y = 5$ and $y = 3x + 1$, and shade below them. Graph the solid boundary lines $y = 2$ and $y = 3x - 4$, and shade above them. The overlapping region is the solution region.

The solution region is a four-sided figure, or quadrilateral. Notice that the boundary lines $y = 5$ and $y = 2$ are parallel, horizontal lines. The boundary lines $y = 3x + 1$ and $y = 3x - 4$ have the same slope and are also parallel. A quadrilateral with two sets of parallel sides is a parallelogram. The solution region is a parallelogram.

Remember!
Parallel lines have the same slope.

CHECK IT OUT! **Graph the system of inequalities, and classify the figure created by the solution region.**

3a. $\begin{cases} x \le 6 \\ y \le \frac{1}{2}x + 1 \\ y \ge -2x + 4 \end{cases}$ triangle

3b. $\begin{cases} y \le 4 \\ y \ge -1 \\ y \le -x + 8 \\ y \le 2x + 2 \end{cases}$ trapezoid

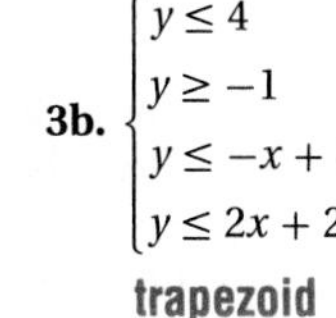

3a. (graph)

b. (graph)

THINK AND DISCUSS

1. Explain how you know which region of the graph of a system of linear inequalities contains the solutions.
2. Find the minimum number of inequalities necessary for a triangular solution region and for a square solution region. Give examples that support your answer.
3. **GET ORGANIZED** Copy and complete the graphic organizer. For each region, write the system of inequalities whose solution it represents.

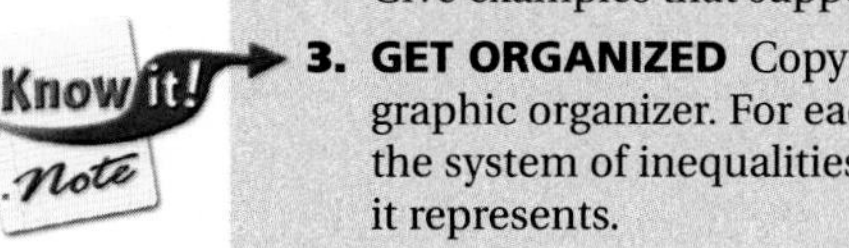

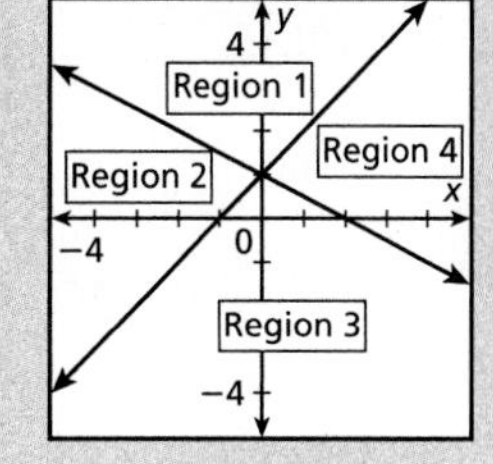

Power Presentations with PowerPoint®

Additional Examples

Example 3

Graph the system of inequalities and classify the figure created by the solution region. trapezoid

$$\begin{cases} x \ge -2 \\ x \le 3 \\ y \ge -x + 1 \\ y \le 4 \end{cases}$$

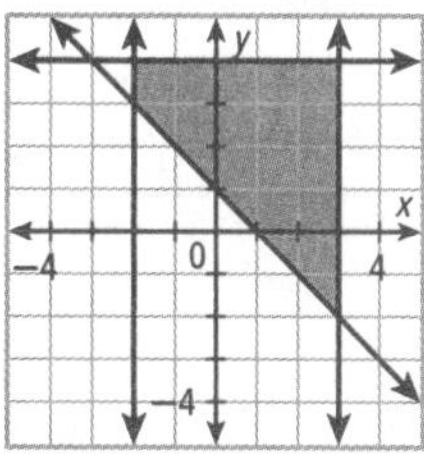

Also available on transparency

INTERVENTION

Questioning Strategies

EXAMPLE 3

- Why is the solution region a quadrilateral?
- How do you know which lines are parallel?

Visual Discuss shading each half-plane in a different way so that the overlap can be distinguished. Ask students for suggestions of different ways to shade the half-planes, e.g., using vertical, horizontal, oblique, or wavy lines, or colored pencils.

3 Close

Summarize

Have students compare and contrast the steps involved in graphing a system of linear inequalities and a system of linear equations.

Review how to choose points to test when determining where to shade the graph.

ONGOING ASSESSMENT and INTERVENTION

***Diagnose Before* the Lesson**
3-3 Warm Up, TE p. 197

***Monitor During* the Lesson**
Check It Out! Exercises, SE pp. 198–199
Questioning Strategies, TE pp. 198–199

***Assess After* the Lesson**
3-3 Lesson Quiz, TE p. 202
Alternative Assessment, TE p. 202

Answers to *Think and Discuss*

Possible answers:

1. The region containing the solutions is the region where the shadings overlap.
2. The minimum number of inequalities is equal to the number of sides. So 3 inequalities can form a triangle, and 4 can form a square. Examples:

$\begin{cases} y \ge 0 \\ x \ge 0 \\ x + y \le 4 \end{cases}$ $\begin{cases} y \ge x \\ y \ge -x \\ y \le x + 4 \\ y \le -x + 4 \end{cases}$

3. See p. A5.

3-3 Exercises

Assignment Guide

Assign *Guided Practice* exercises as necessary.

If you finished Examples **1–3**

Basic 11–25, 28–31, 34–36, 40–50

Average 11–25, 27–36, 39–50

Advanced 13–15, 18–27, 30–50

Homework Quick Check

Quickly check key concepts.

Exercises: 14, 18, 20, 22, 30

Answers

1. Possible answer: The graphs of both systems are created using straight lines. The solutions to the system of equations are the points where the lines intersect. The solutions to the system of inequalities are the points in the region bounded by the lines.

6. $\begin{cases} a + s \le 250 \\ 15a + 10s \ge 3000 \end{cases}$

15. $\begin{cases} x + y \le 10{,}000 \\ y \le 0.2x \\ x \ge 0 \\ y \ge 0 \end{cases}$

2–20. For graphs, see p. A21.

21–24. See p. A21.

20. $\begin{cases} x + y < 2370 \\ y > 1645 \end{cases}$

State Resources

3-3 Exercises

go.hrw.com
Homework Help Online
KEYWORD: MB7 3-3
Parent Resources Online
KEYWORD: MB7 Parent

GUIDED PRACTICE

1. **Vocabulary** Compare a *system of linear inequalities* with a system of linear equations.

SEE EXAMPLE 1 p. 199

Graph each system of inequalities.

2. $\begin{cases} y \ge 4x - 4 \\ y \ge 3x - 3 \end{cases}$
3. $\begin{cases} x + y > 5 \\ x - y < -3 \end{cases}$
4. $\begin{cases} 7x < y - 16 \\ y \le -5x - 2 \end{cases}$
5. $\begin{cases} 2x + 2y \le 4 \\ 3x - y > 1 \end{cases}$

SEE EXAMPLE 2 p. 200

6. **Fund-raising** A charity is selling T-shirts in order to raise money. The cost of a T-shirt is \$15 for adults and \$10 for students. The charity needs to raise at least \$3000 and has only 250 T-shirts. Write and graph a system of inequalities that can be used to determine the number of adult and student T-shirts the charity must sell.

SEE EXAMPLE 3 p. 201

Graph the system of inequalities and classify the figure created by the solution region.

7. $\begin{cases} x \ge 9 \\ y \ge -18 \\ x \le 13 \\ y \le -4 \end{cases}$ rectangle
8. $\begin{cases} y \le 7 \\ 2x - y \le 3 \\ x + 2y \ge -6 \end{cases}$ triangle
9. $\begin{cases} x \le -1 \\ y \le 3x + 2 \\ y \ge -3x - 10 \end{cases}$ isosceles triangle
10. $\begin{cases} y \ge x \\ y \le x + 6 \\ x \le 6 \\ x \ge -2 \end{cases}$ parallelogram

PRACTICE AND PROBLEM SOLVING

Independent Practice	
For Exercises	See Example
11–14	1
15	2
16–19	3

Extra Practice
Skills Practice p. S8
Application Practice p. S34

Graph each system of inequalities.

11. $\begin{cases} 5x - y > 0 \\ y < x \end{cases}$
12. $\begin{cases} 3y \ge 2x - 3 \\ y \ge 3x + 8 \end{cases}$
13. $\begin{cases} x + y > 5 \\ -2x + y \le 2 \end{cases}$
14. $\begin{cases} y > 4 \\ x + 4y \ge 8 \end{cases}$

15. **Music** A musician is releasing a new CD. The record company will manufacture the basic CD plus a special promotional version to distribute to radio stations. No more than 10,000 CDs will be made, and the number of promotional CDs will be at most 20% of the number of basic CDs. Write and graph a system of inequalities that describes the possible number of each type of CD.

Graph the system of inequalities and classify the figure created by the solution region.

16. $\begin{cases} x \ge 0 \\ -\frac{1}{3}x + y \ge -4 \\ \frac{1}{3}x + y \le -1 \end{cases}$ isosceles triangle
17. $\begin{cases} y \le 2.5 \\ y \ge -0.5 \\ y \le -x + 8 \\ y \le 2x + 4 \end{cases}$ trapezoid
18. $\begin{cases} y \le x + 6 \\ y \ge x + 1 \\ y \le -x + 6 \\ y \ge -x - 1 \end{cases}$ rectangle
19. $\begin{cases} y \le x \\ y \le -x + 2 \\ y \ge 0 \end{cases}$ isosceles right triangle

20. **Sports** In 2003, LaDainian Tomlinson led the National Football League in yards from scrimmage, a combination of rushing yards and receiving yards. He had a total of 2370 yards from scrimmage, including 1645 rushing yards. The runner-up, Jamal Lewis, had fewer yards from scrimmage but more rushing yards. Write and graph a system of inequalities that models the possible rushing and receiving yardage for Jamal Lewis.

Geometry Write a system of linear inequalities whose solution region forms the given shape.

21. a rectangle
22. a square
23. a right triangle
24. a trapezoid

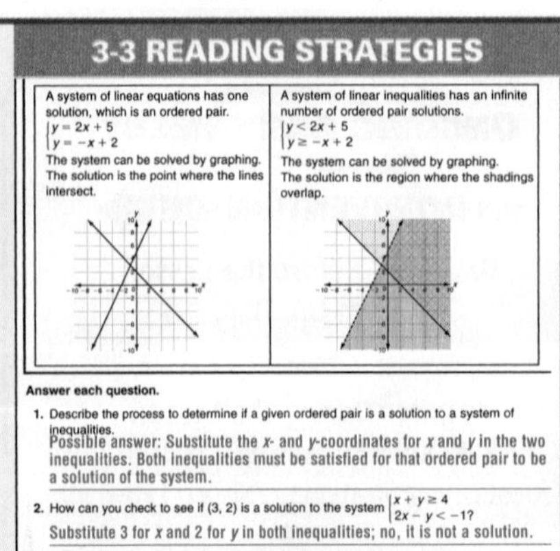
3-3 READING STRATEGIES

A system of linear equations has one solution, which is an ordered pair. The system can be solved by graphing. The solution is the point where the lines intersect.

A system of linear inequalities has an infinite number of ordered pair solutions. The system can be solved by graphing. The solution is the region where the shadings overlap.

Answer each question.

1. Describe the process to determine if a given ordered pair is a solution to a system of inequalities.
Possible answer: Substitute the x- and y-coordinates for x and y in the two inequalities. Both inequalities must be satisfied for that ordered pair to be a solution of the system.
2. How can you check to see if (3, 2) is a solution to the system $\begin{cases} x + y \ge 4 \\ 2x - y < -1 \end{cases}$?
Substitute 3 for x and 2 for y in both inequalities; no, it is not a solution.
3. How is solving a system of inequalities like solving a system of equations?
Possible answer: In both cases, you are finding the ordered pair or pairs that satisfy the equations or inequalities by graphing.
4. How is solving a system of inequalities different from solving a system of equations?
Possible answer: The lines in a system of inequalities can be solid or dashed, and it is also necessary to shade areas above or below the lines.
5. Describe the solution set of a system of inequalities.
Possible answer: It is the region of intersection of two shaded areas on the graph.
6. When would you use a dashed line in graphing an inequality? When would you use a solid line? What is the difference?
Possible answer: You use a dashed line when the symbol is < or > but a solid line when the symbol is ≤ or ≥. The solid line has points included in the solution, but the points on a dashed line are not included in the solution.

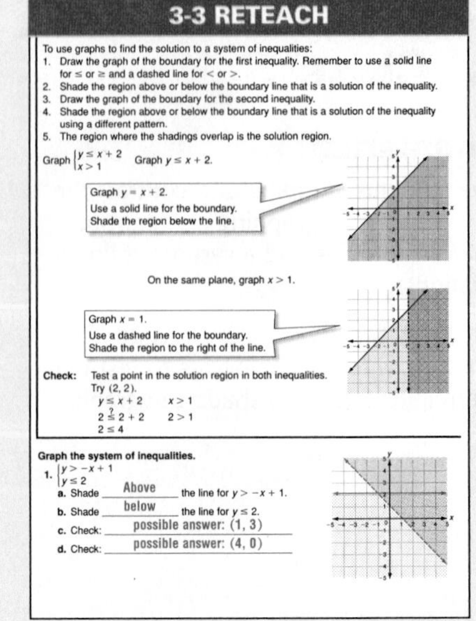
3-3 RETEACH

To use graphs to find the solution to a system of inequalities:
1. Draw the graph of the boundary for the first inequality. Remember to use a solid line for ≤ or ≥ and a dashed line for < or >.
2. Shade the region above or below the boundary line that is a solution of the inequality.
3. Draw the graph of the boundary for the second inequality.
4. Shade the region above or below the boundary line that is a solution of the inequality using a different pattern.
5. The region where the shadings overlap is the solution region.

Graph $\begin{cases} y \le x + 2 \\ x > 1 \end{cases}$ Graph $y \le x + 2$.

Graph $y = x + 2$. Use a solid line for the boundary. Shade the region below the line.

On the same plane, graph $x > 1$.

Graph $x = 1$. Use a dashed line for the boundary. Shade the region to the right of the line.

Check: Test a point in the solution region in both inequalities. Try (2, 2).
$y \le x + 2$ $x > 1$
$2 \le 2 + 2$ $2 > 1$
$2 \le 4$

Graph the system of inequalities.
1. $\begin{cases} y > -x + 1 \\ y \le 2 \end{cases}$
a. Shade Above the line for $y > -x + 1$.
b. Shade below the line for $y \le 2$.
c. Check: possible answer: (1, 3)
d. Check: possible answer: (4, 0)

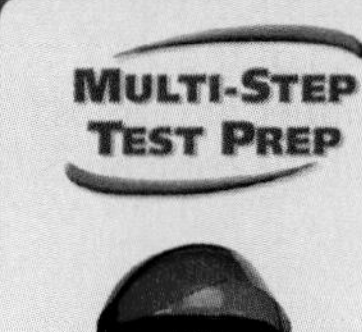

25. This problem will prepare you for the Multi-Step Test Prep on page 212.

Most race cars are subject to various size and weight restrictions, depending on their classification. Champ cars must weigh a minimum of 1565 pounds without the driver. Formula One cars must weigh at least 1322.77 pounds with the driver.

a. Write a system of linear inequalities that could be used to compare the possible weights of Champ cars and Formula One cars without drivers.

b. Identify a reasonable domain and range for the system.

c. Graph the system.

26. Multi-Step Frostbite is a dangerous condition where skin freezes because of exposure to cold temperatures and wind. People can develop frostbite in 10 to 30 minutes under conditions modeled by the system $\begin{cases} w \geq 2.4t + 23 \\ w \leq 1.4t + 43 \end{cases}$, where t represents temperature (°F) and w represents wind speed (mi/h).

a. Identify a reasonable domain and range for the system.

b. Graph the solution region for the system of inequalities.

c. If the temperature is 15°F and the wind speed is 55 mi/h, can a person develop frostbite in 10 to 30 minutes? Explain.

26a. Possible answer:

D: $-40 \leq t \leq 40$
R: $w \geq 0$

b.

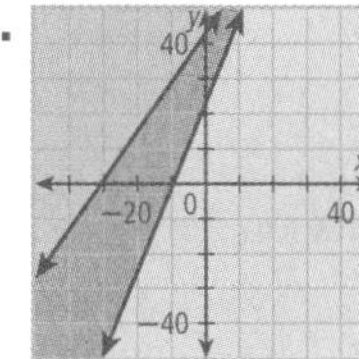

c. No; possible answer: for a temperature of 15°, the wind speed must be between 59 and 64 mi/h for a person to develop frostbite in 10 to 30 min.

27. Income Tax Brian and Maria are married and file their taxes jointly. Currently, they have a combined income within the 25% tax bracket, and Maria earns at least $2000 more per year than Brian. Use the data in the table to write and graph a system of inequalities that models their possible incomes.

2003 Tax Rate Schedule (Married Filing Jointly)

Income	Tax Rate
$14,000 to $56,800	15%
$56,801 to $114,650	25%
$114,651 to $174,700	28%

Graph the solution region for the system of inequalities shown. Then identify three points in the solution region.

28. $\begin{cases} -5y < 2x \\ 5y \geq 2x - 20 \end{cases}$ **29.** $\begin{cases} y + 7 > 0 \\ y < 2x + 5 \\ y < -3x + 4 \end{cases}$ **30.** $\begin{cases} y \geq -8 \\ x + 2y < 4 \\ x > -6 \end{cases}$ **31.** $\begin{cases} \frac{1}{2}x + 3y \leq 2 \\ x - y > 3 \end{cases}$

32. Critical Thinking If the boundary lines in a system of inequalities are parallel, what are the possible solution regions?

33. Write About It Is it possible for a system of two inequalities to have no solution? Explain. **Possible answer: yes, if the lines are parallel and the directions of the inequalities are such that the regions do not overlap; for example, $\begin{cases} y > 6 \\ y < 3 \end{cases}$**

34. Which of the following systems of inequalities describes the graph shown?

Ⓐ $\begin{cases} y > x + 4 \\ y < -2x - 1 \end{cases}$ Ⓒ $\begin{cases} y \leq x + 4 \\ y \geq -2x - 1 \end{cases}$

Ⓑ $\begin{cases} y > x + 4 \\ y > -2x - 1 \end{cases}$ Ⓓ $\begin{cases} y \geq x + 4 \\ y \geq -2x - 1 \end{cases}$

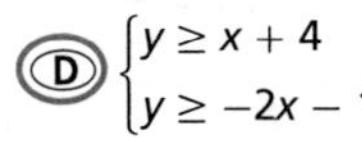

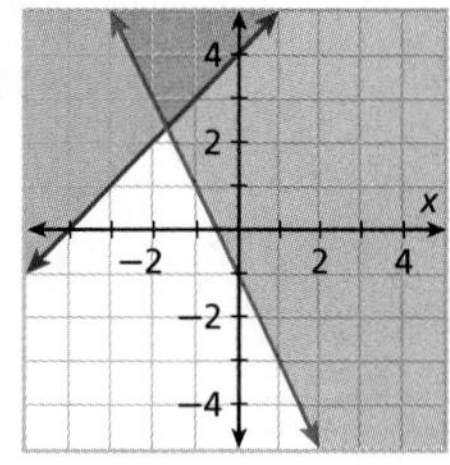

COMMON ERROR ALERT

Students might forget to restrict the solution region to the first quadrant in **Exercises 15, 20, 26,** and **27.** Remind students to consider the reasonable values for each variable when graphing.

MULTI-STEP TEST PREP Exercise 25 involves solving a system of linear inequalities and interpreting the results. This exercise prepares students for the applications of linear systems in two dimensions in the Multi-Step Test Prep on page 212.

TEST PREP DOCTOR Students can check a point from the solution region to solve **Exercise 34.** If they confuse choices **B** and **D,** suggest that they check the boundary lines. Remind them that solid boundary lines are also part of a solution region.

Answers

25a. Possible answer:
$\begin{cases} y \geq 1565 \\ y \geq 1322.77 - x \end{cases}$ where x represents the weight of the driver

b. Possible answer: D: $\{x: 100 \leq x \leq 250\}$;
R: $\{y: 1000 \leq y \leq 2000\}$

c.

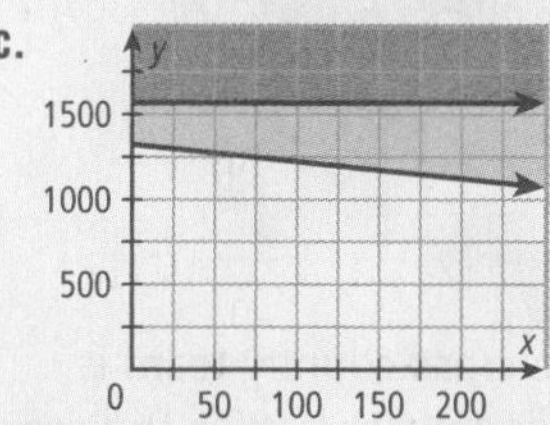

27–32. See p. A21.

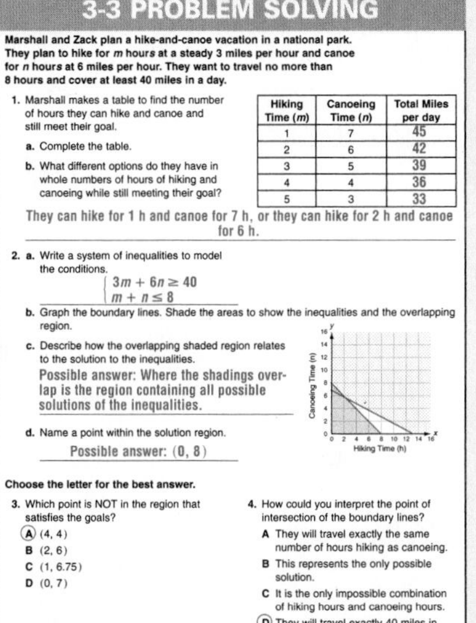

3-3 PROBLEM SOLVING

Marshall and Zack plan a hike-and-canoe vacation in a national park. They plan to hike for m hours at a steady 3 miles per hour and canoe for n hours at 6 miles per hour. They want to travel no more than 8 hours and cover at least 40 miles in a day.

1. Marshall makes a table to find the number of hours they can hike and canoe and still meet their goal.

a. Complete the table.

b. What different options do they have in whole numbers of hours of hiking and canoeing while still meeting their goal?

Hiking Time (m)	Canoeing Time (n)	Total Miles per day
1	7	45
2	6	42
3	5	39
4	4	36
5	3	33

They can hike for 1 h and canoe for 7 h, or they can hike for 2 h and canoe for 6 h.

2. a. Write a system of inequalities to model the conditions.
$\begin{cases} 3m + 6n \geq 40 \\ m + n \leq 8 \end{cases}$

b. Graph the boundary lines. Shade the areas to show the inequalities and the overlapping region.

c. Describe how the overlapping shaded region relates to the solution to the inequalities.
Possible answer: Where the shadings overlap is the region containing all possible solutions of the inequalities.

d. Name a point within the solution region.
Possible answer: (0, 8)

Choose the letter for the best answer.

3. Which point is NOT in the region that satisfies the goals?
Ⓐ (4, 4)
B (2, 6)
C (1, 6.75)
D (0, 7)

4. How could you interpret the point of intersection of the boundary lines?
A They will travel exactly the same number of hours hiking as canoeing.
B This represents the only possible solution.
C It is the only impossible combination of hiking hours and canoeing hours.
Ⓓ They will travel exactly 40 miles in exactly 8 hours.

3-3 CHALLENGE

The absolute value function is known for the V-shape of its graph. Some systems of absolute value inequalities have graphs that form geometric figures.

Use the system $\begin{cases} |x| \leq 2 \\ |y| \leq 2 \end{cases}$ for Exercises 1-5.

1. Graph the system on the grid at right.

2. What geometric figure is formed by the system? square

3. a. Make a conjecture about how the graph of $|x| + |y| \leq 2$ compares to the graph of the given system.
Possible answer: The original square is rotated 45°.

b. Verify your conjecture by graphing $|x| + |y| \leq 2$ on the same grid.

4. What geometric figure would be formed if the constant terms of the system were not equal? rectangle

5. What transformation(s) will change the original figure into the figure formed by each of the following systems?

a. $\begin{cases} |x - 3| \leq 2 \\ |y| \leq 2 \end{cases}$ horizontal translation 3 units to the right

b. $\begin{cases} |x| \leq 2 \\ |y + 3| \leq 2 \end{cases}$ vertical translation 3 units down

c. $\begin{cases} |2x| \leq 2 \\ |y| \leq 2 \end{cases}$ horizontal compression by a factor of $\frac{1}{2}$

Write the coordinates of the vertices of the figure determined by the given system.

6. $\begin{cases} |x - 3| \leq 4 \\ |y + 2| \leq 2 \end{cases}$ (−1, 0), (−1, −4), (7, −4), (7, 0)

7. $\begin{cases} |x + 3| \leq 2 \\ |y - 2| \leq 4 \end{cases}$ (−5, −2), (−5, 6), (−1, 6), (−1, −2)

8. $\begin{cases} |2x| \leq 4 \\ |y| \leq 4 \end{cases}$ (−2, ±4), (2, ±4)

Write a system of inequalities to represent the specified geometric figure.

9. $x = \pm 5$ when $y = \pm 5$ $\begin{cases} |x| \leq 5 \\ |y| \leq 5 \end{cases}$

10. $x = 2$ or -8 when $y = 4$ or 6 $\begin{cases} |x + 3| \leq 5 \\ |y - 5| \leq 1 \end{cases}$

11. $x = \pm 0.5$ when $y = 0$ or 2 $\begin{cases} |2x| \leq 1 \\ |y - 1| \leq 1 \end{cases}$

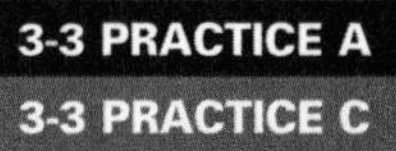

3-3 PRACTICE A

3-3 PRACTICE C

3-3 PRACTICE B

Graph each system of inequalities.

1. $\begin{cases} y \leq 3x - 5 \\ y < -\frac{1}{2}x + 4 \end{cases}$ 2. $\begin{cases} y < x + 5 \\ y \geq 4x - 2 \end{cases}$

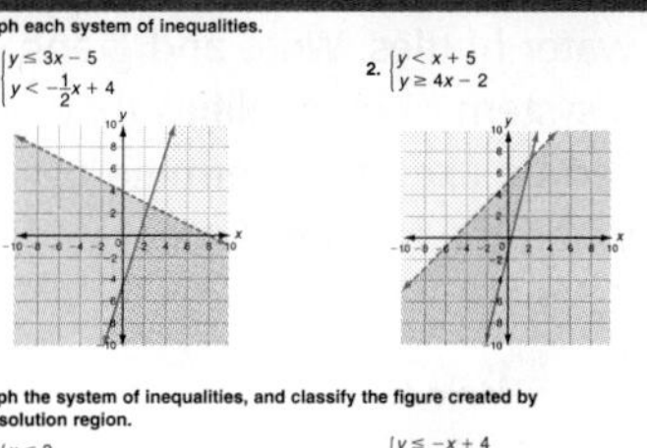

Graph the system of inequalities, and classify the figure created by the solution region.

3. $\begin{cases} x \leq 2 \\ x \geq -3 \\ y \leq 2x + 2 \\ y \geq 2x - 1 \end{cases}$ Parallelogram

4. $\begin{cases} y \leq -x + 4 \\ y \leq 3 \\ y \geq 0 \\ y \geq -2x - 1 \end{cases}$ Trapezoid

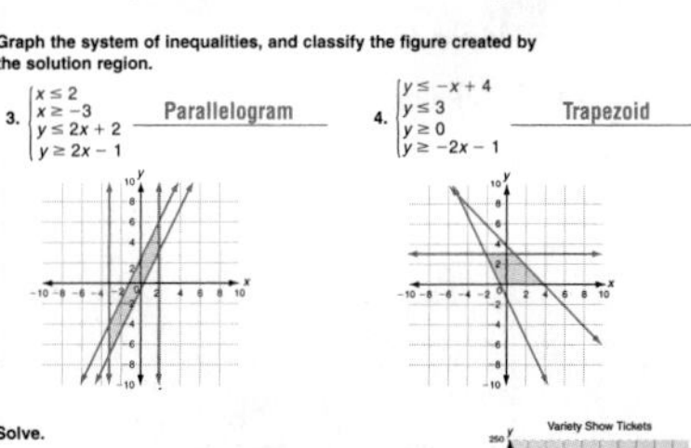

Solve.

5. The Thespian Club is selling tickets to its annual variety show. Prices are $8 for an adult ticket and $4 for a student ticket. The club needs to raise $1000 to pay for costumes and stage sets. The auditorium has a seating capacity of 240. Write and graph a system of inequalities that can be used to determine how many tickets have to be sold for the club to meet its goal.
$\begin{cases} 8x + 4y \geq 1000 \\ x + y \leq 240 \end{cases}$

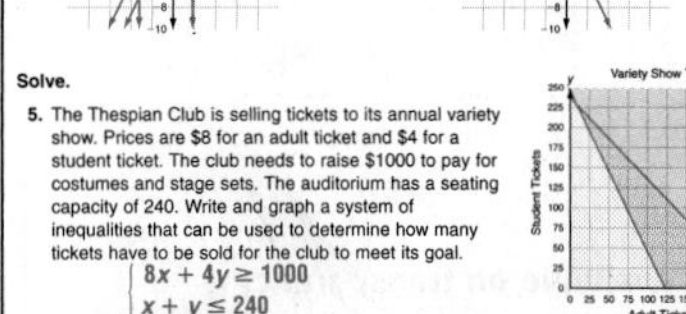

Have students summarize the steps involved in solving a system of linear inequalities.

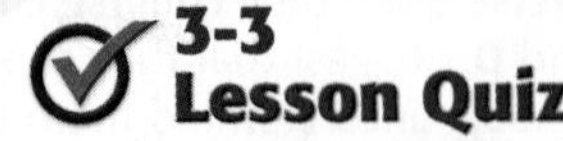

Have students draw and shade a right triangle on the coordinate plane. Then have them write a system of inequalities whose solution region is the shaded triangular region they have created.

Power Presentations with PowerPoint®

3-3 Lesson Quiz

1. Graph the system of inequalities and classify the figure created by the solution region. trapezoid

$$\begin{cases} y \le \frac{2}{3}x - 2 \\ y \ge -2x - 2 \\ x \le 4 \\ x \ge 1 \end{cases}$$

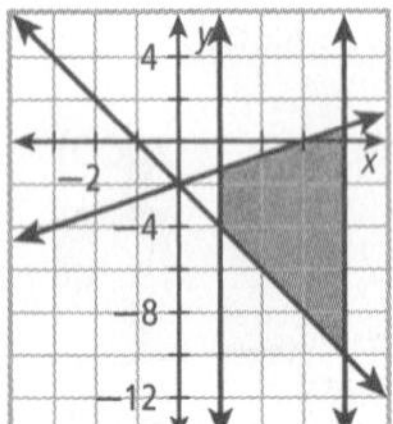

2. The cross-country team is selling water bottles to raise money for the team. The price of a water bottle is $3 for students and $5 for everyone else. The team needs to raise at least $400 and has 100 water bottles. Write and graph a system of inequalities that can be used to determine when the team will meet its goal.

$$\begin{cases} x + y \le 100 \\ 3x + 5y \ge 400 \end{cases}$$

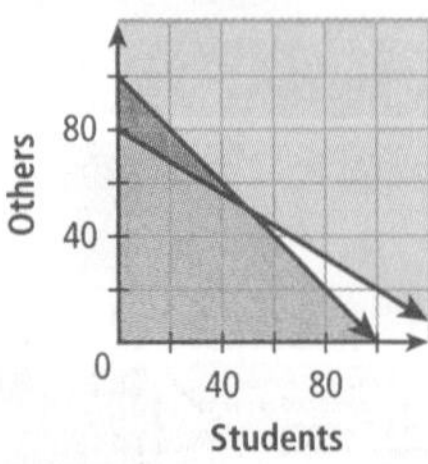

Also available on transparency

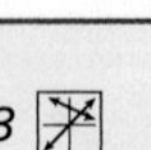

35. A manufacturing company produces gizmos. It costs at least \$300 plus \$1.25 per gizmo to produce the items. Each gizmo sells for \$2.50 at most. Which of the following systems of inequalities, where c is the cost and n is the number of gizmos produced or sold, has a solution region that can be used to represent the company's possible profit?

Ⓕ $\begin{cases} c \le 2.5n \\ c \le 300 + 1.25n \end{cases}$ Ⓗ $\begin{cases} c \ge 2.5n \\ c \le 300 + 1.25n \end{cases}$

Ⓖ $\begin{cases} c \le 2.5n \\ c \ge 300 + 1.25n \end{cases}$ Ⓙ $\begin{cases} c \ge 2.5n \\ c \ge 300 + 1.25n \end{cases}$

36. Which of the tables below contains possible solutions to the following system of inequalities? $\begin{cases} 3x - 12y > 8 \\ x + 5y > -5 \end{cases}$

Ⓐ

x	y
1	−2
2	0
3	0
4	−2

Ⓑ

x	y
1	−2
2	1
3	1
4	−2

Ⓒ

x	y
1	−1
2	−1
3	0
4	0

Ⓓ

x	y
1	−2
2	−2
3	−1
4	−1

CHALLENGE AND EXTEND

37. Write a system of linear inequalities whose solution region is a pentagon.

37. Possible answer:
$$\begin{cases} x \ge 0 \\ y \ge 0 \\ y \le x + 1 \\ y \ge x - 1 \\ y \le -x + 4 \end{cases}$$

38. In the following system of inequalities, is there a value of m that will cause the system to have no solution? If so, find the value. If not, explain. $\begin{cases} y > -3x + 2 \\ y < mx - 3 \end{cases}$ **Yes; for $m = -3$ the system has no solution.**

39. Kira is investing \$30,000 divided between two separate simple interest accounts. One pays 5% and has very low risk, and the other pays 7% and has slightly higher risk. What is the least she can invest in the riskier account and still earn at least \$1900 after one year? **\$20,000**

SPIRAL REVIEW

Find the additive and multiplicative inverse for each number. *(Lesson 1-2)*

40. 7 **$-7; \frac{1}{7}$** **41.** $-\frac{3}{4}$ **$\frac{3}{4}; -\frac{4}{3}$** **42.** 2.48 **$-2.48; \frac{1}{2.48}$** **43.** −1 **1; −1**

Write the equation of each line. *(Lesson 2-4)*

44. through (2, −7) and (1, 1) **$y = -8x + 9$**

45. with slope 0 through (3, −3) **$y = -3$**

46. through (1, −1) and (0, 0) **$y = -x$**

47. with slope $-\frac{1}{3}$ through (9, 6) **$y = -\frac{1}{3}x + 9$**

48. perpendicular to $y = 4x - 1$ and through (−2, 4.5) **$y = -\frac{1}{4}x + 4$**

49. parallel to $y = -x - 7$ and through (3, 2) **$y = -x + 5$**

50. The youth baseball league charted the number of players and coaches in each age bracket. Find the correlation coefficient to the nearest thousandth and the equation of the line of best fit. *(Lesson 2-7)* **$y = 0.118x - 0.117$; $r = 0.985$**

Players	32	18	55	37	50	86
Coaches	3	2	6	5	6	10

3-4 Linear Programming

Objective
Solve linear programming problems.

Vocabulary
linear programming
constraint
feasible region
objective function

Who uses this?
Landscape architects can use linear programming to determine which plants to plant on a green roof.

Green roofs are roofs covered with plants instead of traditional materials like concrete or shingles to help lower heat and improve air quality.

The plants landscape architects choose might depend on the price, the amount of water they require, and the amount of carbon dioxide they absorb.

Linear programming is a method of finding a maximum or minimum value of a function that satisfies a given set of conditions called *constraints*. A **constraint** is one of the inequalities in a linear programming problem. The solution to the set of constraints can be graphed as a **feasible region**.

EXAMPLE 1 Graphing a Feasible Region

Gillian is planning a green roof that will cover up to 600 square feet. She will use two types of plants: blue lagoon sedum and raspberry red sedum. Each blue lagoon sedum will cover 1.2 square feet. Each raspberry red sedum will cover 2 square feet. Each plant costs \$2.50, and Gillian must spend less than \$1000. Write the constraints, and graph the feasible region.

Let $b =$ the number of blue lagoon sedums, and
$r =$ the number of raspberry red sedums.

Write the constraints:

$$\begin{cases} b \geq 0 \\ r \geq 0 \\ 1.2b + 2r \leq 600 \\ 2.50b + 2.50r \leq 1000 \end{cases}$$

The number of plants cannot be negative.

The combined area is less than or equal to 600 ft².

The combined cost is less than or equal to \$1000.

Graph the feasible region. The feasible region is a quadrilateral with vertices at $(0, 0)$, $(400, 0)$, $(250, 150)$, and $(0, 300)$.

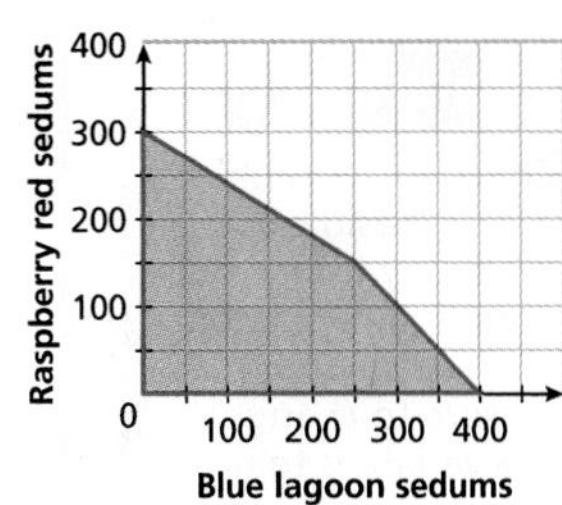

Check A point in the feasible region, such as $(100, 100)$, satisfies all of the constraints. ✔

1. Graph the feasible region for the following constraints.

$$\begin{cases} x \geq 0 \\ y \geq 1.5 \\ 2.5x + 5y \leq 20 \\ 3x + 2y \leq 12 \end{cases}$$

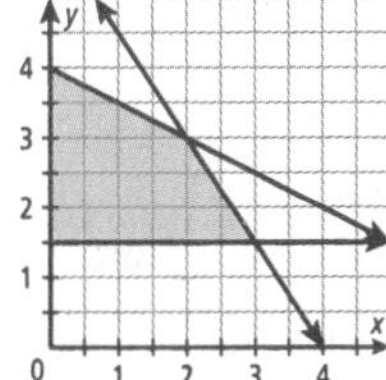

3-4 Organizer

Pacing: Traditional 2 days
Block 1 day

Objective: Solve linear programming problems.

Technology Lab
In *Technology Lab Activities*

Online Edition
Graphing Calculator, Tutorial Videos, Interactivity

Countdown to Testing Week 6

Power Presentations with PowerPoint®

Warm Up

Determine if the given ordered pair is a solution of $\begin{cases} x + y \geq 6 \\ x - 2y > 10 \end{cases}$.

1. (3, 3) no **2.** (10, 1) no

3. (12, 0) yes **4.** (15, 2) yes

5. Graph $\begin{cases} y + 4x \geq 3 \\ y \geq -\frac{1}{3}x + 2 \end{cases}$.

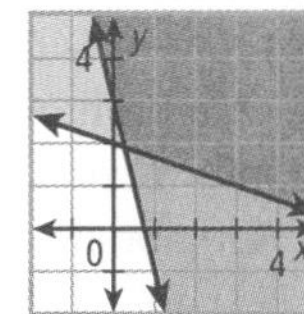

Also available on transparency

Math Humor

Q: What do you get when you cross a linebacker with a computer geek?

A: A linear programmer.

1 Introduce

EXPLORATION

3-4 Linear Programming

Fred has two summer jobs. He can earn \$15 per hour doing yard work and \$10 per hour working at the mall. Each week, he must work less than 40 hours but earn at least \$475.

1. Complete the table to determine if each combination satisfies Fred's criteria.

Plan	Hours of Yard Work	Hours at the Mall	Wages from Yard Work	Wages from the Mall	Total Wages
A	10	25			
B	30	9			
C	20	15			
D	25	10			
E	30	7			

2. Find another combination of work hours that meets Fred's criteria.
3. Let x represent the number of hours Fred does yard work and let y represent the number of hours Fred works at the mall. Write an inequality that describes Fred's goal for his weekly income.

THINK AND DISCUSS

4. **Describe** another inequality you can write to represent one of Fred's criteria.
5. **Discuss** whether Fred could work only at the mall and still

Motivate

A system of linear inequalities has many solutions. Tell students that linear programming is the method for determining which of the many solutions is best.

Explorations and answers are provided in the *Explorations* binder.

State Resources

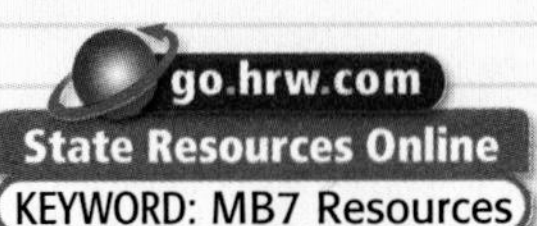

Power Presentations with PowerPoint®

Additional Examples

Example 1

Yum's Bakery bakes two breads, *A* and *B*. One batch of *A* uses 5 pounds of oats and 3 pounds of flour. One batch of *B* uses 2 pounds of oats and 3 pounds of flour. The company has 180 pounds of oats and 135 pounds of flour available. Write the constraints for the problem and graph the feasible region.

$$\begin{cases} A \geq 0 \\ B \geq 0 \\ 5A + 2B \leq 180 \\ 3A + 3B \leq 135 \end{cases}$$

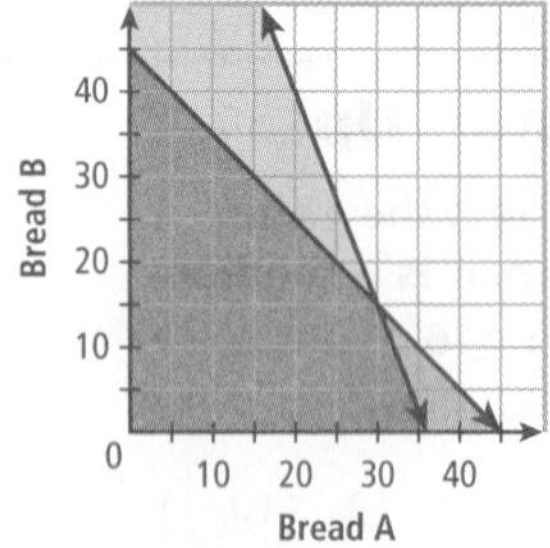

Example 2

Yum's Bakery wants to maximize its profit from bread sales. One batch of *A* yields a profit of $40. One batch of *B* yields a profit of $30. Use the profit information and the data from Additional Example 1 to find how many batches of each bread the bakery should bake. *A*: 30; *B*: 15

Also available on transparency

INTERVENTION

Questioning Strategies

EXAMPLE 1

- What do the four inequalities represent? Explain.

EXAMPLE 2

- Why do you need the feasible region from **Example 1** to solve the problem?
- Why do you think the vertices as well as points inside the feasible region can be used to evaluate the objective function?

In most linear programming problems, you want to do more than identify the feasible region. Often you want to find the best combination of values in order to minimize or maximize a certain function. This function is the **objective function**.

The objective function may have a minimum, a maximum, neither, or both depending on the feasible region.

Bounded and Unbounded Regions	
Bounded Feasible Region	**Unbounded Feasible Regions**
Objective function has both a minimum and a maximum value.	Objective function has either a maximum value or a minimum value but not both.

More advanced mathematics can prove that the maximum or minimum value of the objective function will always occur at a vertex of the feasible region.

Know it! Note

The Vertex Principle of Linear Programming

If an objective function has a maximum or minimum value, it must occur at one or more of the vertices of the feasible region.

EXAMPLE 2 Solving Linear Programming Problems

One of Gillian's priorities for the green roof is to help control air pollution. To do this, she wants to maximize the amount of carbon dioxide the plants on the roof absorb. Use the carbon dioxide absorption rates and the data from Example 1 to find the number of each plant Gillian should plant.

Blue Lagoon Sedum
1.4 lb of CO_2 per year

Raspberry Red Sedum
2.1 lb of CO_2 per year

Helpful Hint

Check your graph of the feasible region by using your graphing calculator.

Be sure to change the variables to *x* and *y*.

Step 1 Let C = the number of pounds of carbon dioxide absorbed.

Write the objective function:

$C = 1.4b + 2.1r$

Step 2 Recall the constraints and the graph from Example 1.

$$\begin{cases} b \geq 0 \\ r \geq 0 \\ 1.2b + 2r \leq 600 \\ 2.50b + 2.50r \leq 1000 \end{cases}$$

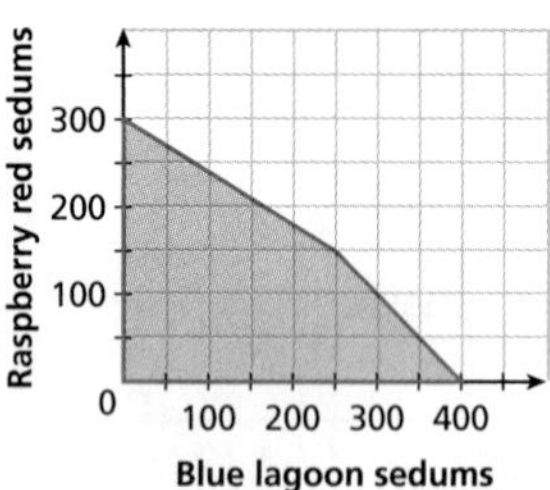

2 Teach

Guided Instruction

Work through **Example 1.** Point out the connection between the definitions of the variables and the constraints. Remind students that they can use the intercepts to graph the boundary lines of each inequality. Then they need to find only the point where the boundary lines intersect.

Point out that constraints are usually inequalities while an objective function is a linear equation.

Reaching All Learners

Through Graphic Organizers

A table is often used to organize the information in linear programming problems. This method is especially useful when matrices and linear algebra are used to solve. You may wish to present the information in **Example 1** using the following table:

	Blue Lagoon	Raspberry Red
Area	1.2	2
Cost	2.50	2.50

Step 3 Evaluate the objective function at the vertices of the feasible region.

(b, r)	**1.4*b* + 2.1*r***	**C(lb)**
(0, 0)	1.4(0) + 2.1(0)	0
(0, 300)	1.4(0) + 2.1(300)	630
(250, 150)	1.4(250) + 2.1(150)	665
(400, 0)	1.4(400) + 2.1(0)	560

The maximum value occurs at the vertex (250, 150).

Gillian should plant 250 blue lagoon sedums and 150 raspberry red sedums to maximize the amount of carbon dioxide absorbed.

2. Maximize the objective function $P = 25x + 30y$ under the following constraints. $\begin{cases} x \geq 0 \\ y \geq 1.5 \\ 2.5x + 5y \leq 20 \\ 3x + 2y \leq 12 \end{cases}$ $P = 140$

EXAMPLE 3 ***Problem-Solving Application***

Brad is an organizer of the Bolder Boulder 10K race and must hire workers for one day to prepare the race packets. Skilled workers cost \$60 a day, and students cost \$40 a day. Brad can spend no more than \$1440. He needs at least 1 skilled worker for every 3 students, but only 16 skilled workers are available. Skilled workers can prepare 25 packets per hour, and students can prepare 18 packets per hour. Find the number of each type of worker that Brad should hire to maximize the number of packets produced.

1 Understand the Problem

The **answer** will have two parts—the number of skilled workers and the number of students that will be hired.

List the important information:

- Skilled workers cost \$60 per day. Students cost \$40 per day.
- Brad can spend no more than \$1440.
- Skilled workers can prepare 25 packets per hour. Students can prepare 18 packets per hour.
- Brad needs at least 1 skilled worker for every 3 students.
- Only 16 skilled workers are available.

2 Make a Plan

Let x = the number of students and y = the number of skilled workers. Write the constraints and objective function based on the important information.

$$\begin{cases} x \geq 0 \\ y \geq 0 \\ 40x + 60y \leq 1440 \\ y \geq \frac{1}{3}x \\ y \leq 16 \end{cases}$$

The number of workers cannot be negative.

Cost of labor must be no more than \$1440.

At least 1 skilled worker for every 3 students

Only 16 experienced workers are available.

Let P represent the number of packets prepared each hour. The objective function is $P = 18x + 25y$.

COMMON ERROR ALERT

Some students have difficulty identifying the information that pertains to the objective function. Remind students that the objective function is what will be minimized or maximized, so they should look for these words.

Power Presentations with PowerPoint®

Additional Examples

Example 3

Sue manages a soccer club and must decide how many members to send to soccer camp. It costs \$75 for each advanced player and \$50 for each intermediate player. Sue can spend no more than \$13,250. Sue must send at least 60 more advanced than intermediate players and a minimum of 80 advanced players. Find the number of each type of player Sue can send to camp to maximize the number of players at camp. 130 advanced, 70 intermediate

Also available on transparency

INTERVENTION

Questioning Strategies

EXAMPLE 3

- How can you distinguish the constraints from the objective function?
- Why should you graph the feasible region?

Reading Math Discuss the meaning of the words *constrain* and *constraint.* Point out real-world constraints that could be represented by inequalities. For example, $d \geq 16$ can be used to represent the constraint that you must be 16 or older to get a driver's license.

ENGLISH LANGUAGE LEARNERS

Math Background In many real-world applications, there are often more than two variables. To use graphing to solve those types of problems would require visualizing more than two dimensions, which can be very difficult. Instead, there is an algorithm called the *simplex method* that is used to solve such large-scale linear programming problems.

Inclusion In **Exercise 15,** students may evaluate the objective function at vertices outside the feasible region. Remind them that they should use only the vertices of the feasible region.

Solve

Graph the feasible region, and identify the vertices. Evaluate the objective function at each vertex.

$P(\mathbf{0,0}) = 18(0) + 25(0) = 0$

$P(\mathbf{0,16}) = 18(0) + 25(16) = 400$

$P(\mathbf{12,16}) = 18(12) + 25(16) = 616$

$P(\mathbf{24,8}) = 18(24) + 25(8) = \mathbf{632}$

The objective function is maximized at $(24, 8)$, so Brad should hire 24 students and 8 skilled workers.

Look Back

Check the values $(24, 8)$ in the constraints.

$x \geq 0$	$y \geq 0$	$y \leq 16$
$24 \geq 0$ ✔	$8 \geq 0$ ✔	$8 \leq 16$ ✔
	$y \geq \frac{1}{3}x$	$40x + 60y \leq 1440$
	$8 \geq \frac{1}{3}(24)$	$40(24) + 60(8) \leq 1440$
	$8 \geq 8$ ✔	$1440 \leq 1440$ ✔

3. A book store manager is purchasing new bookcases. The store needs 320 feet of shelf space. Bookcase A provides 32 ft of shelf space and costs \$200. Bookcase B provides 16 ft of shelf space and costs \$125. Because of space restrictions, the store has room for at most 8 of bookcase A and 12 of bookcase B. How many of each type of bookcase should the manager purchase to minimize the cost?

8 of bookcase A and 4 of bookcase B

THINK AND DISCUSS

1. Explain why linear programming problems often have $x \geq 0$ and $y \geq 0$ as constraints.
2. Explain why an objective function based on the constraints $\begin{cases} x + y > 0 \\ y \leq 4 \end{cases}$ will have a maximum or a minimum, but not both.
3. How can you tell whether a piece of information relates to the constraints or to the objective function?

4. **GET ORGANIZED** Copy and complete the graphic organizer. In each box, write an example of the given characteristic, using data from Examples 1 and 2.

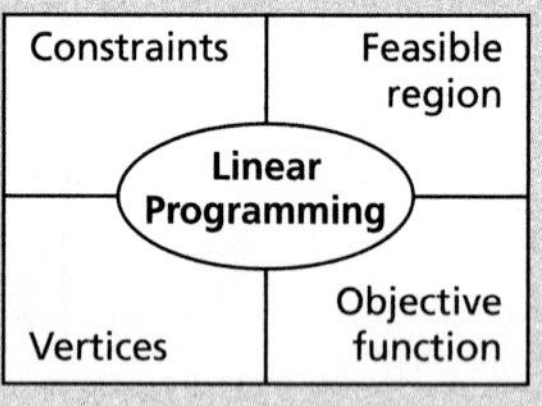

3 Close

Summarize

Review the steps of linear programming.

1) Write the constraints and graph the feasible region.
2) Write the objective function.
3) Evaluate the objective function for the coordinates of the vertices of the feasible region.
4) Identify the coordinates that optimize the function.

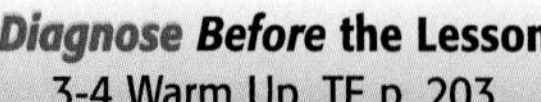

ONGOING ASSESSMENT and INTERVENTION

***Diagnose Before* the Lesson**
3-4 Warm Up, TE p. 203

***Monitor During* the Lesson**
Check It Out! Exercises, SE pp. 203, 205, 206
Questioning Strategies, TE pp. 204–205

***Assess After* the Lesson**
3-4 Lesson Quiz, TE p. 209
Alternative Assessment, TE p. 209

Answers to *Think and Discuss*

Possible answers:

1. Linear-programming problems are often real-world situations in which negative values for x and y do not make sense.
2. The region is unbounded.
3. Possible answer: Look for the units of the numbers in the problem. For example, if the problem asks for a maximum profit, look back to see which values are in dollars.
4. See p. A5.

3-4 Exercises

go.hrw.com
Homework Help Online
KEYWORD: MB7 3-4
Parent Resources Online
KEYWORD: MB7 Parent

GUIDED PRACTICE

1. **Vocabulary** The inequalities in a linear programming problem are called __?__. (*constraints* or *objective functions*) **constraints**

SEE EXAMPLE 1 p. 205

Graph each feasible region.

2. $\begin{cases} x \geq 0 \\ y \geq 0 \\ y \leq 3x + 3 \\ y \leq -x + 7 \end{cases}$

3. $\begin{cases} x \geq 0 \\ y \geq -1 \\ y \leq x + 1 \\ y \leq -\frac{1}{4}x + 6 \end{cases}$

4. $\begin{cases} x \geq -2 \\ y \leq 1 \\ y \geq 0.5x - 2 \\ y \leq -2x + 3 \end{cases}$

SEE EXAMPLE 2 p. 206

Maximize or minimize each objective function.

5. Maximize $P = 10x + 16y$ for the constraints from Exercise 2. **$P = 106$**
6. Minimize $P = 3x + 5y$ for the constraints from Exercise 3. **$P = -5$**
7. Maximize $P = 2.4x + 1.5y$ for the constraints from Exercise 4. **$P = 3.9$**

SEE EXAMPLE 3 p. 207

8. **Dentistry** Dr. Lee's dentist practice is open for 7 hours each day. His receptionist schedules appointments, allowing $\frac{1}{2}$ hour for a cleaning and 1 hour to fill a cavity. He charges $40 for a cleaning and $95 for a filling. Dr. Lee cannot do more than 4 fillings per day. Find the number of each type of appointment that maximizes Dr. Lee's income for the day. **4 fillings; 6 cleanings**

PRACTICE AND PROBLEM SOLVING

Independent Practice

For Exercises	See Example
9–11	1
12–14	2
15	3

Extra Practice
Skills Practice p. S9
Application Practice p. S34

Graph each feasible region.

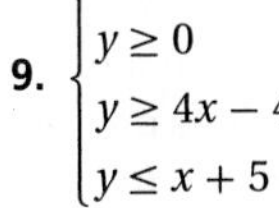

9. $\begin{cases} x \geq 0 \\ y \geq 0 \\ y \geq 4x - 4 \\ y \leq x + 5 \end{cases}$

10. $\begin{cases} x \leq 0 \\ y \geq 0 \\ y \leq 9 \\ y \geq -2x - 7 \end{cases}$

11. $\begin{cases} x \geq 0 \\ x \leq 5 \\ y \geq \frac{1}{5}x - 3 \\ y \leq -x + 4 \end{cases}$

Maximize or minimize each objective function.

12. Maximize $P = -21x + 11y$ for the constraints from Exercise 9. **$P = 55$**
13. Minimize $P = -2x - 4y$ for the constraints from Exercise 10. **$P = -36$**
14. Maximize $P = x + 3y$ for the constraints from Exercise 11. **$P = 12$**

15. **Advertising** A concert tour plans to advertise upcoming tour dates. The advertising budget is $60,000, and the tour manager will focus on prime-time television and radio commercials. She would like to have between 30 and 60 radio commercials. Use the table to find the number of prime-time television and radio commercials that will maximize the on-air time of the advertisements but will stay within the budget.

60 radio and 24 prime-time television commercials

Type	Time(s)	Cost ($)
Radio	20	400
Television (prime time)	30	1500
Television (late night)	30	1200
Newspaper	■	300

3-4 Exercises

Assignment Guide

Assign *Guided Practice* exercises as necessary.

If you finished Examples **1–3**
Basic 9–17, 19, 25–29, 31–38
Average 9–19, 22–29, 31–38
Advanced 10, 11, 13–16, 18–38

Homework Quick Check
Quickly check key concepts.
Exercises: 10, 12, 15, 18

Answers

2.
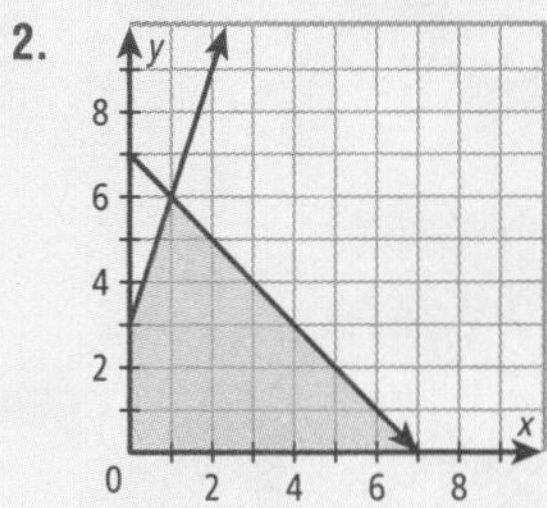

3.
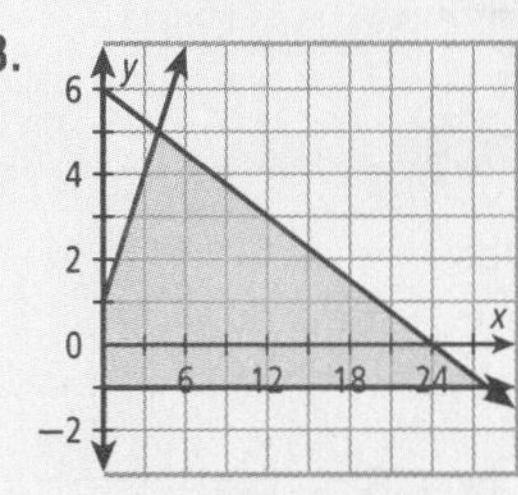

4.
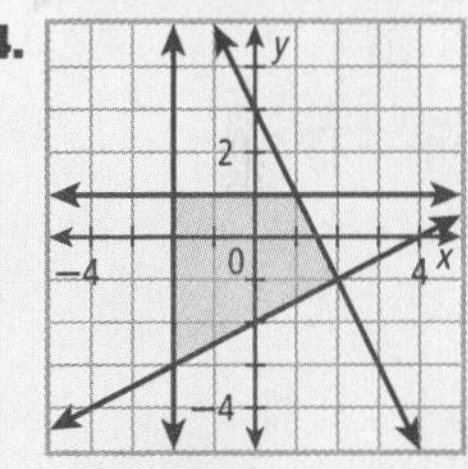

9.
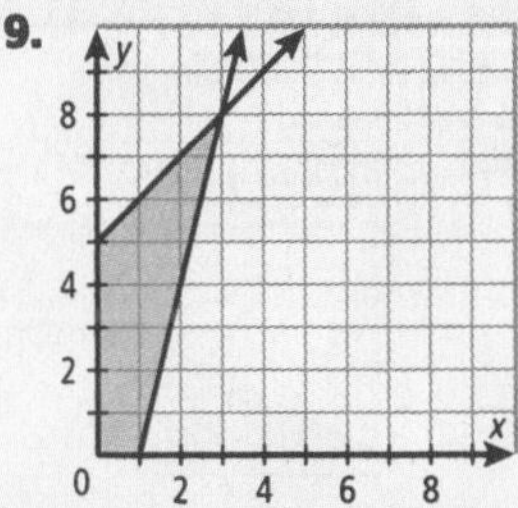

11.
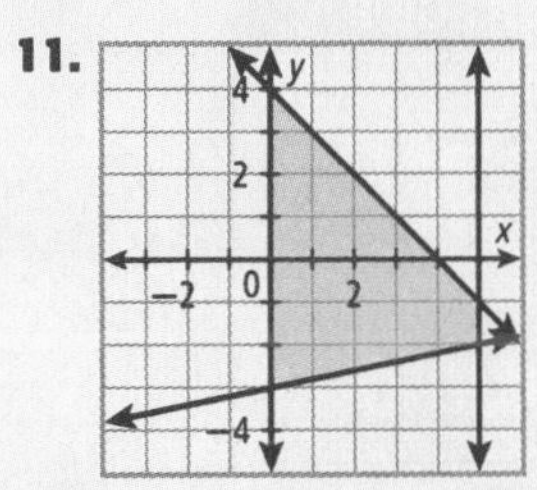

10.
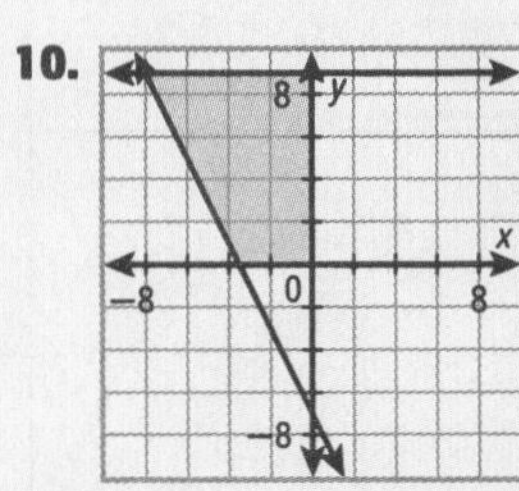

State Resources

 Exercise 16 involves using linear programming to maximize profit. This exercise prepares students for using the formula in the Multi-Step Test Prep on page 212.

 **Science** In **Exercise 23,** linear programming can be used in nutritional analysis to maximize intake of such nutrients as vitamins, minerals, or protein while trying to minimize cost.

Answers

16b. Possible answer: The system of inequalities does not change. Only the objective function changes. The new solution is 120,000 upper deck tickets and 40,000 lower deck tickets.

18. parallelogram;
$$\begin{cases} x \geq -1 \\ x \leq 2 \\ y \leq x + 2 \\ y \geq x - 4 \end{cases}$$

19. right triangle;
$$\begin{cases} y \leq x + 2 \\ y \geq 2x \\ y \geq -\frac{1}{2}x \end{cases}$$

20. trapezoid;
$$\begin{cases} y \geq 1 \\ y \leq 6 \\ y \leq -2x + 8 \\ y \leq 2x + 10 \end{cases}$$

22, 24–26. See p. A22.

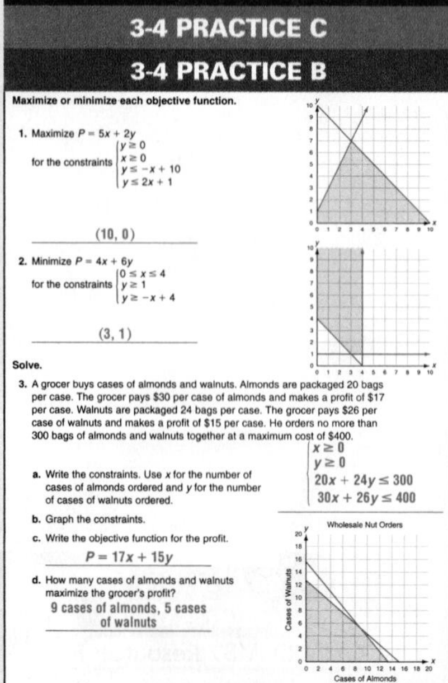

16. This problem will prepare you for the Multi-Step Test Prep on page 212.

Tickets to a car race cost \$25 for the upper deck and \$45 for the lower deck. The track may admit no more than 160,000 spectators by order of the fire marshal.

a. If the lower deck can seat no more than 60,000 fans and the upper deck can seat no more than 120,000 fans, how many of each ticket type should be sold to maximize profit? **100,000 upper deck tickets and 60,000 lower deck tickets**

b. How do the system and solution change if race officials expect to make an additional \$60 per person in the upper deck and \$30 per person in the lower deck from the sale of food and merchandise?

17. Manufacturing A camping supply company produces backpacks in two models, journey and trek. The journey model requires 4 hours of labor, and the company makes a profit of \$40. The trek model requires 6 hours of labor, and the company makes a profit of \$80. The distributor will accept no more than 4 trek models and 15 journey models per week. What is the minimum number of hours of labor that are required for the company to make a profit of at least \$400 per week? **32 h**

Geometry **Given the graph of the feasible region, identify the figure and write the inequalities that represent the constraints.**

18.

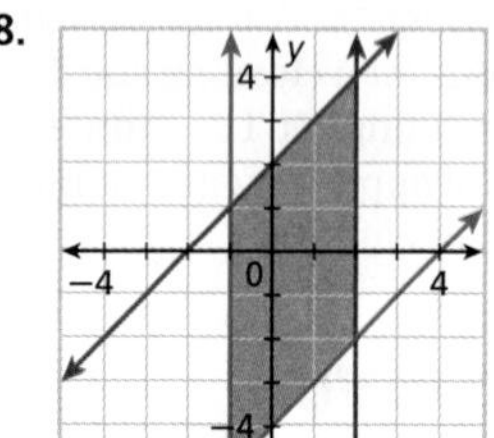

19.

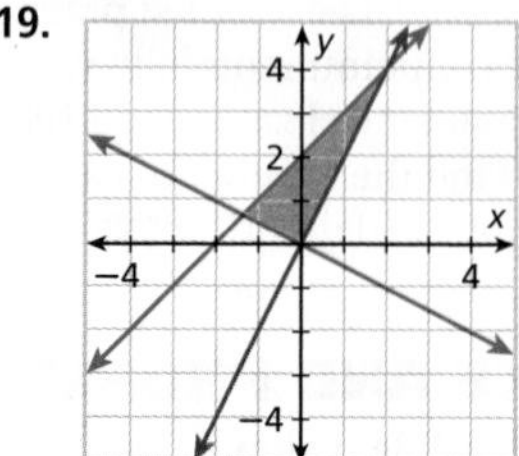

20.

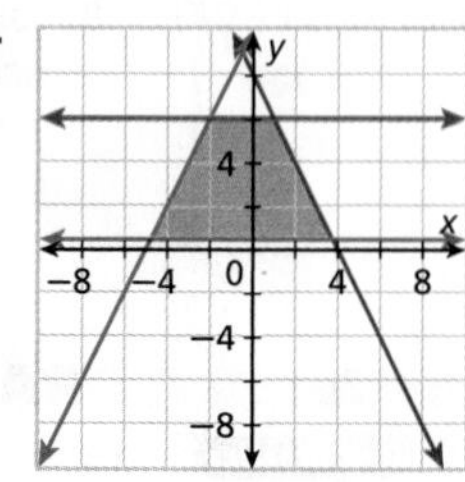

Math History

Linear programming was developed during World War II. Also known as Operations Research (OR), the process played an important part in World War II by helping the military effectively allocate its resources.

21. Highway Traffic To prevent traffic jams, a city funds a courtesy patrol to aid stranded drivers on local roads. The patrol can repair a flat tire, provide the motorist with 2 gallons of gas, or call a tow truck for more serious problems. It takes 15 minutes to help a driver who is out of gas and 45 minutes to help a driver with a flat tire. The courtesy patrol driver carries 28 gallons of gas. What is the maximum number of stops for flat tires or empty gas tanks that the courtesy patrol can make in an 8-hour shift? **20 stops**

22. Critical Thinking Is it possible for a linear programming problem to have no solution? Give an example to support your answer.

23. 40 Soy Joy and 20 Vitamin Boost

23. Nutrition A health food store is creating smoothies with soy protein and vitamin supplements. A Soy Joy smoothie costs \$2.75 and uses 2 ounces of soy and 1 ounce of vitamin supplement. A Vitamin Boost smoothie costs \$3.25 and uses 3 ounces of vitamin supplement and 1 ounce of soy protein. The store has 100 ounces each of vitamin supplement and soy protein in stock. How many of each type of smoothie should the store make in order to maximize revenue?

24. Critical Thinking Give an example of a problem situation where the feasible region might include negative values.

25. Write About It Describe how to recognize when you have found the maximum or minimum value of an objective function for a given set of constraints.

26. Write About It Describe how to find the coordinates of the vertices of the feasible region.

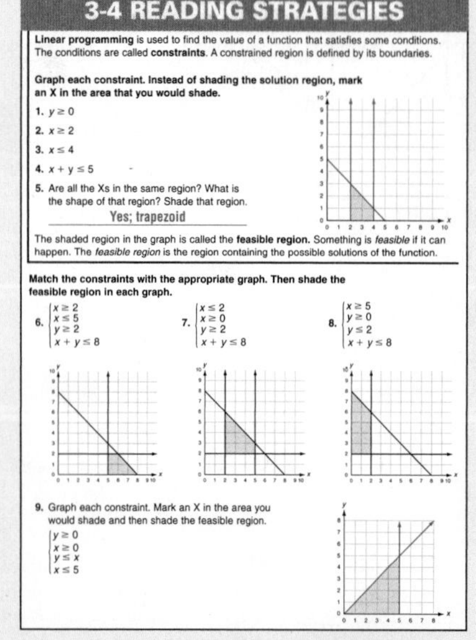

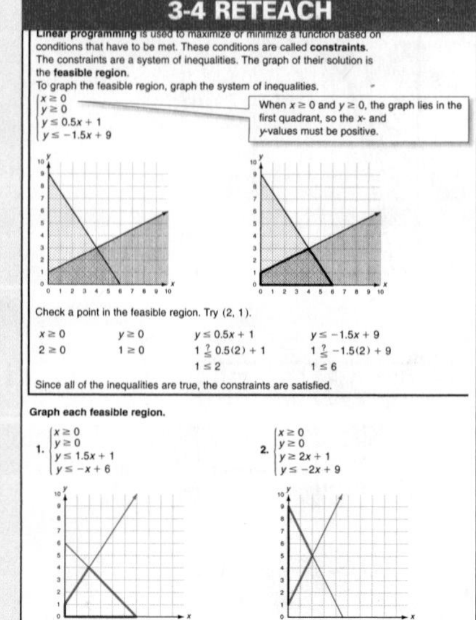

TEST PREP

27. Which point gives the minimum value of $P = -x + y$ in the feasible region shown at right?

Ⓐ P Ⓒ R
Ⓑ Q **Ⓓ S**

$Q(2, 3)$, $P(0, 2)$, $R(4, 2)$, $S(3, 0)$

28. A feasible region has vertices $(0, 0)$, $(-1, 2)$, and $(-2, 6)$. Which of the following objective functions has a minimum value less than zero over this region?

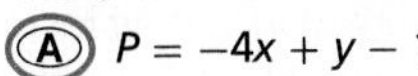

Ⓐ $P = -4x + y - 1$ Ⓒ $P = 12x + 7y$
Ⓑ $P = -x + 3y + 2$ Ⓓ $P = -5x - y$

29. A real estate developer plans to divide a 300,000-square-foot piece of land into commercial and residential properties. Each residential property requires 2500 square feet, and each commercial property requires 30,000 square feet. The developer makes a profit of $1000 for each residential site and $20,000 for each commercial site but is limited to no more than six commercial sites because of zoning ordinances. Which of the following gives the objective function for the maximum profit of the developer?

Ⓕ $P = 2500x + 30{,}000y$ Ⓗ $P = 2500x + 1000y$
Ⓖ $P = 1000x + 20{,}000y$ Ⓙ $P = 300{,}000 - x - 6y$

30a.

CHALLENGE AND EXTEND

30. **Medicine** A pharmaceutical company is testing a new antibiotic on two sample strains of bacteria. To properly assess the effectiveness of the antibiotic, more than 700 viable bacteria samples must be tested, at least 400 of which must be type B. The company would like to minimize the amount of money spent on bacteria.

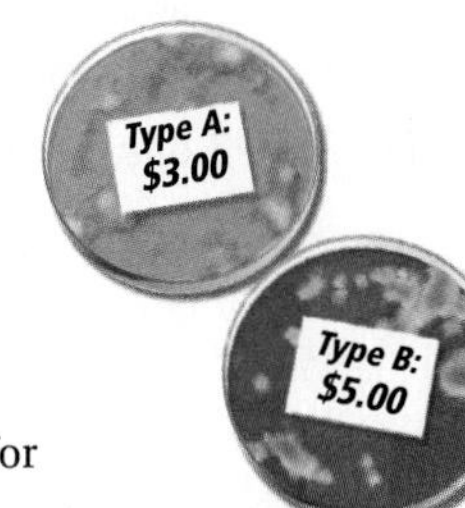

a. Graph the feasible region.

b. What do the points $(350, 400)$ and $(400, 350)$ represent for this problem situation?

30b. $(350, 400)$ represents 350 of bacteria type A and 400 of bacteria type B. $(400, 350)$ represents 400 of bacteria type A and 350 of bacteria type B.

c. Do the points satisfy the constraints? Why or why not?
$(350, 400)$ does, but $(400, 350)$ does not. One constraint specifies that there must be at least 400 of type B.

SPIRAL REVIEW

For each function, evaluate $f(7)$ and $f\left(-\frac{1}{2}\right)$. *(Lesson 1-7)*

31. $f(x) = \dfrac{1}{2x - 3}$ 32. $f(x) = 0.5x$ 33. $f(x) = \dfrac{x^2 - 1}{x - 1}$

Translate $f(x) = |x|$ so that the vertex is at the given point. Then graph. *(Lesson 2-9)*

34. $(6, -3)$ $y = |x - 6| - 3$
35. $\left(\frac{1}{3}, \frac{4}{3}\right)$ $y = \left|x - \frac{1}{3}\right| + \frac{4}{3}$
36. $(-2.5, 0.75)$ $y = |x + 2.5| + 0.75$

Geometry **Graph the system of inequalities and classify the figure created by the solution region.** *(Lesson 3-3)*

37. $\begin{cases} y \le 6 \\ y - 2x \ge 0 \\ x \ge 0 \end{cases}$ right triangle

38. $\begin{cases} y \ge 0 \\ y \le 2 \\ y \le x \\ x + y \le 6 \end{cases}$ isosceles trapezoid

3-4 PROBLEM SOLVING

At the local fair, Tamara wants to demonstrate her "build-it-yourself" products. She decides to hire some skilled technicians and some students to build her garden chairs. Technicians can build 2 chairs in 8 hours; students can build only 1 chair in 8 hours. She wants at least 1 technician to work with every 3 students, but can find only 6 technicians. She will pay $12 per hour for technicians and $7 per hour for students, and can spend up to $800. What combination of technicians and students can build the greatest number of chairs in an 8-hour day?

1. Write the constraints needed to graph the feasible region.
$x \ge 0,\ y \ge 0,\ y \le 6,\ y \ge \frac{1}{3}x,\ y \le \frac{100 - 7x}{12}$

2. Graph the feasible region.

3. List the vertices of the feasible region.
$(0, 0), (0, 6), (4, 6), (9, 3)$

4. Write the objective function, C, to show the total number of chairs that can be built.
$C = x + 2y$

5. At which vertex is the objective function maximized?
$(4, 6)$

6. How many technicians and students should Tamara hire to achieve her goal?
6 technicians and 4 students

Choose the letter for the best answer.

7. Tamara decides that at least 1 technician should work with every 2 students. How does this change her hiring plan?
A She should hire only the 6 technicians.
B She should hire 4 technicians and 7 students.
C She should hire 6 technicians and 12 students.
(D) Her hiring plan will not change.

8. Tamara finds 1 more technician. How does this change her hiring plan?
A She should hire only the 7 technicians.
B She should hire 3 technicians and 9 students.
(C) She should hire 7 technicians and 2 students.
D Her hiring plan will not change.

3-4 CHALLENGE

For a linear programming problem with three variables, the feasible region is defined by a polyhedron, and the maximum or minimum value of the objective function occurs at one of the vertices. There is a method for solving a three-variable problem that does not require drawing the polyhedron.

A polyhedron is a three-dimensional figure bounded by polygons.

A crafter has a budget of $6300 and wants to produce a maximum 100 ornate boxes, some of wood, others with jeweled inlays, and others of stained glass. The table at right shows the cost and profit data per box, in dollars. The crafter wants to maximize profit.

	Wood	Inlay	Glass
Cost	35	80	70
Profit	60	75	90

Let w, i, and g represent the number of boxes of each type. There will be 5 constraints: A, B, C, D, E.

1. Three of the constraints are A: $w \ge 0$, B: $i \ge 0$, C: $g \ge 0$. Write an inequality for constraint
a. D, the number of boxes. D: $w + i + g \le 100$
b. E, the budget. E: $35w + 80i + 70g \le 6300$

2. Write the objective function, P. $P = 60w + 75i + 90g$

3. In the table below, write all 10 possible systems of 3 inequalities. Solve each system to find the intersection. Check whether the intersection is a feasible vertex by testing the coordinates in the constraints A–E. Then evaluate the objective function for all feasible vertices.

System of inequalities	Intersection	Feasible	Dollar value of P
A, B, C	(0, 0, 0)	Yes	0
A, B, D	(0, 0, 100)	No	—
A, B, E	(0, 0, 90)	Yes	8100
A, C, D	(0, 100, 0)	No	—
A, C, E	(0, 78.75, 0)	Yes	5906.25
A, D, E	(0, −70, 170)	No	—
B, C, D	(100, 0, 0)	Yes	6000
B, C, E	(180, 0, 0)	No	—
B, D, E	(20, 0, 80)	Yes	8400
C, D, E	(37.78, 62.22, 0)	Yes	6933.33

4. How can the crafter maximize profit? Produce 20 boxes of wood and 80 boxes of stained glass

5. What is the maximum profit? $8400

TEST PREP DOCTOR In **Exercise 28,** students can eliminate choices **F** and **H** because the inequality that represents the constraint "no more than six commercial sites" is missing. The students can rule out choice **J** because the coefficients 2500 and 30,000 should be present.

30a. For graph, see p. A22.
31–33. See p. A22.
34–38. For graphs, see p. A22.

Journal

Have students use their own words to define the Vertex Principle of Linear Programming.

ALTERNATIVE ASSESSMENT

Have students use the functions $y = x + 2$ and $y = 5x - 2$ to write constraints and an objective function. Then have students graph the feasible region for their constraints and identify the maximum of the objective function for the region.

Power Presentations with PowerPoint®

3-4 Lesson Quiz

1. Ace Guitars produces acoustic and electric guitars. Each acoustic guitar yields a profit of $30, and requires 2 work hours in factory A and 4 work hours in factory B. Each electric guitar yields a profit of $50 and requires 4 work hours in factory A and 3 work hours in factory B. Each factory operates for at most 10 hours each day. Graph the feasible region. Then, find the number of each type of guitar that should be produced each day to maximize the company's profits. 1 acoustic, 2 electric

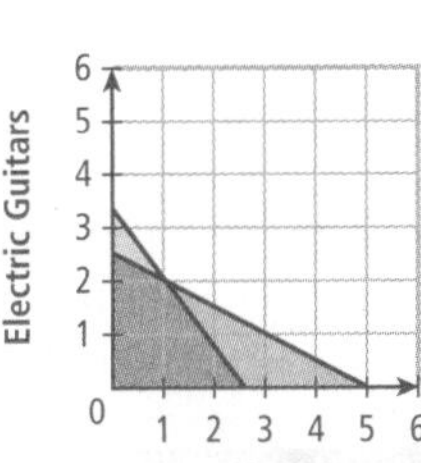

Also available on transparency

SECTION 3A MULTI-STEP TEST PREP

Organizer

Objective: Assess students' ability to apply concepts and skills in Lesson 3-1 through Lesson 3-4 in a real-world format.

 **Online Edition**

Resources

 ***Algebra 2 Assessments***

www.mathtekstoolkit.org

Problems	Text Reference
1	Skills Bank p. S57
2	Lesson 3-1
3–4	Lesson 3-2
5	Lesson 3-3
6	Lesson 3-4

Answers

5. See p. A22.

State Resources

go.hrw.com
State Resources Online
KEYWORD: MB7 Resources

CHAPTER 3

MULTI-STEP TEST PREP

SECTION 3A

Linear Systems in Two Dimensions

What a Drag! Drag racers measure fuel efficiency differently than most drivers. Instead of using miles per gallon, a drag racing team is more likely to consider gallons per second or gallons per mile to gauge a dragster's fuel consumption and performance. Suppose a drag-racing team is trying to choose a car from four possible entrants. The results of a $\frac{1}{4}$-mile test run are shown in the table.

Dragsters' Results

Dragster	Top Speed (mi/h)	Fuel Used (gal)	Time (s)
Black Dragon	288	14.2	6.1
Lucky Lady	302	15.8	5.9
Red Rocket	274	13.7	6.4
Wild Thing	318	16.5	5.4

1. Using gallons per second as a measure, which car was the most fuel efficient? Which car was the least fuel efficient? **Red Rocket; Wild Thing**
2. Black Dragon and Red Rocket each have 18-gallon fuel tanks, and Wild Thing and Lucky Lady have 20-gallon fuel tanks. Write and graph a system of four linear equations that could be used to model the fuel remaining in these cars after *t* seconds.
3. After how many seconds would Black Dragon and Wild Thing have the same amount of fuel left in their tanks? **≈2.74 s**
4. After how many seconds would Red Rocket and Lucky Lady have the same amount of fuel left in their tanks? **≈3.7 s**
5. Suppose that Black Dragon is located at the team garage and Lucky Lady is located 1000 miles away. Use the maximum speeds of the cars to write and graph a system of linear inequalities that can be used to determine when and where the cars would meet if they travel directly toward one another.
6. Is the point $(1.5, 500)$ a possible solution to the system of linear inequalities? Explain.

2.

$$\begin{cases} f = 18 - 2.33s \\ f = 20 - 2.68s \\ f = 18 - 2.14s \\ f = 20 - 3.06s \end{cases}$$

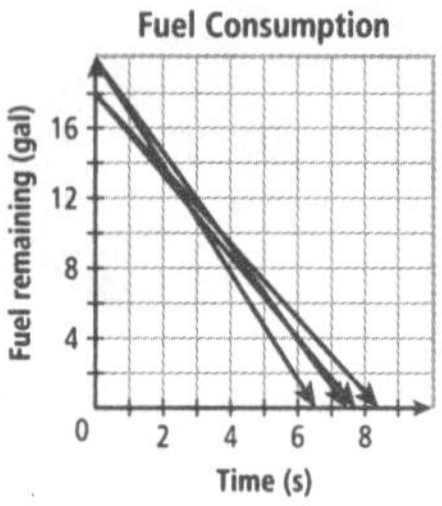

Fuel Consumption (graph: Fuel remaining (gal) 0–16 vs. Time (s) 0–8)

6. No; possible answer: Black Dragon and Lucky Lady do not have maximum speeds great enough to have reached 500 mi after 1.5 h.

INTERVENTION

Scaffolding Questions

1. What quantities from the table should you use to find gallons per second? fuel used and time
2. How will you determine the slope of each linear equation? The slope is the rate of fuel used, or $\frac{\text{fuel used (gal)}}{\text{time (s)}}$.

3–4. Can you solve the system of equations by looking at the graph only? no What is an appropriate solution method? substitution or elimination

5–6. How many constraint equations are necessary? 4; one for Black Dragon, one for Lucky Lady, and 2 to restrict the feasible region to reasonable values

Extension

The distance from Los Angeles to New York is 3961 km. Estimate how long it would take a dragster to make the trip at top speed. 7.5 to 9 h

SECTION 3A

Quiz for Lesson 3-1 Through 3-4

3-1 Solving Linear Systems by Using Graphs and Tables

Solve each system by using a graph and a table. Check your answer.

1. $\begin{cases} 2x + y = -5 \\ x + 2y = 2 \end{cases}$ **(−4, 3)**
2. $\begin{cases} x + y = -1 \\ x - 2y = -4 \end{cases}$ **(−2, 1)**
3. $\begin{cases} x = y - 2 \\ 3x - y = 2 \end{cases}$ **(2, 4)**

Classify each system and determine the number of solutions.

4. $\begin{cases} 8x - 12y = 48 \\ 3y = 2x - 4 \end{cases}$ **inconsistent; no solution**
5. $\begin{cases} 5x - 6y = 14 \\ x + 3y = 15 \end{cases}$ **independent; one solution**
6. $\begin{cases} x = 2y - 10 \\ y = 5 + \frac{1}{2}x \end{cases}$ **dependent; infinitely many solutions**

3-2 Solving Linear Systems by Using Algebraic Methods

Use substitution or elimination to solve each system of equations.

7. $\begin{cases} y = x + 3 \\ 2x + 4y = 24 \end{cases}$ **(2, 5)**
8. $\begin{cases} x = 5 \\ 2x + 3y = 19 \end{cases}$ **(5, 3)**
9. $\begin{cases} x - y = 5 \\ 3x - 2y = 14 \end{cases}$ **(4, −1)**
10. $\begin{cases} x + 2y = 15 \\ x - 2y = -9 \end{cases}$ **(3, 6)**
11. $\begin{cases} 5x - 4y = 0 \\ 8x - 4y = 12 \end{cases}$ **(4, 5)**
12. $\begin{cases} 4x + 2y = 12 \\ 2x + 6y = -4 \end{cases}$ **(4, −2)**

3-3 Solving Systems of Linear Inequalities

Graph each system of inequalities.

13. $\begin{cases} y - x < 3 \\ y + x < 3 \end{cases}$
14. $\begin{cases} y + x \le 0 \\ y \le 4 - x \end{cases}$
15. $\begin{cases} y \ge 2x + 3 \\ y > -x \end{cases}$

16. **Travel** Karen traveled almost 350 mi in under 7 h of highway driving. She stopped for a brief rest that was not included in her driving time. Karen averaged 60 mi/h for the first part of her trip and 50 mi/h for the second part of the trip. Write and graph a system of inequalities that can be used to determine how many hours Karen spent driving in each part of her trip. $\begin{cases} x + y < 7 \\ 60x + 50y < 350 \end{cases}$

3-4 Linear Programming

Graph each feasible region, and maximize or minimize the objective function $P = 4x + 5y$.

17. minimize; $\begin{cases} x \ge 0 \\ y \ge 0 \\ y \le x - 1 \\ y \le -\frac{1}{2}x + 4 \end{cases}$ **$P = 4$**
18. maximize; $\begin{cases} x \le 2 \\ y \ge 0 \\ y \le 2x + 4 \\ y \le -3x + 9 \end{cases}$ **$P = 34$**

19. **Finance** A beauty salon schedules appointments for haircuts for 30 minutes and for special services, such as tinting or curling, for 1 hour. Each haircut costs $20, and special services cost $45. The beauty salon wants to schedule no more than 4 special services each day per beautician. Find the number of each type of appointment that produces the maximum income per beautician in a workday of 8 hours at most. **4 special services and 8 haircuts; $340**

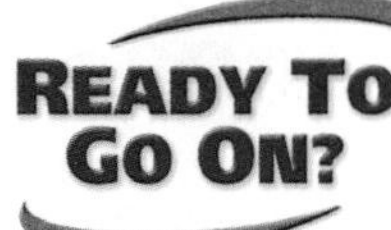

Organizer

Objective: Assess students' mastery of concepts and skills in Lessons 3-1 through 3-4.

Resources

Assessment Resources
Section 3A Quiz

Test & Practice Generator One-Stop Planner®

INTERVENTION

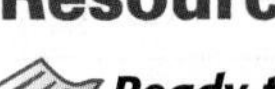

***Ready to Go On? Intervention and Enrichment* Worksheets**

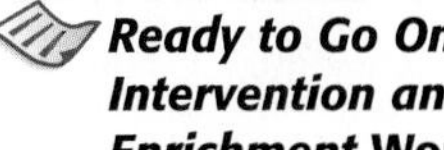

***Ready to Go On?* CD-ROM**

***Ready to Go On?* Online**

my.hrw.com

Answers

13–18. For graphs, see p. A22.

READY TO GO ON? Diagnose and Prescribe

NO INTERVENE

Ready to Go On? Intervention	*Ready to Go On? Intervention*, Section 3A: Worksheets	CD-ROM	Online
Lesson 3-1	3-1 Intervention	Activity 3-1	Diagnose and Prescribe Online
Lesson 3-2	3-2 Intervention	Activity 3-2	
Lesson 3-3	3-3 Intervention	Activity 3-3	
Lesson 3-4	3-4 Intervention	Activity 3-4	

YES ENRICH

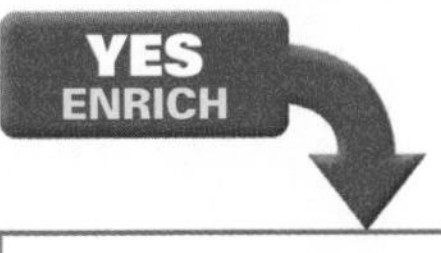

Are You Ready? Enrichment, Chapter 3A
Worksheets
CD-ROM
Online

SECTION
3B Linear Systems in Three Dimensions

One-Minute Section Planner

Lesson	Lab Resources	Materials
Lesson 3-5 Linear Equations in Three Dimensions • Graph points and linear equations in three dimensions. ☐ SAT-10 ☐ NAEP ☐ ACT ☑ SAT ☑ SAT Subject Tests	***Algebra Lab Activities*** 3-5 Algebra Lab	**Optional** unit cubes
Lesson 3-6 Solving Linear Systems in Three Variables • Represent solutions to systems of equations in three dimensions graphically. • Solve systems of equations in three dimensions algebraically. ☐ SAT-10 ☐ NAEP ☐ ACT ☐ SAT ☐ SAT Subject Tests		**Optional** colored pencils (MK)
3-6 Technology Lab Explore Parametric Equations • Use a graphing calculator to explore parametric equations. ☐ SAT-10 ☐ NAEP ☐ ACT ☐ SAT ☑ SAT Subject Tests	***Technology Lab Activities*** 3-6 Lab Recording Sheet	**Required** graphing calculator
Extension Parametric Equations • Graph parametric equations, and use them to model real-world applications. • Write the function represented by a pair of parametric equations. ☐ SAT-10 ☐ NAEP ☐ ACT ☐ SAT ☑ SAT Subject Tests		

MK = *Manipulatives Kit*

Section Overview

Linear Equations in Three Dimensions — Lesson 3-5

Three dimensional representations are important in many fields, including architecture, engineering, and art.

> A coordinate system in three variables is called **coordinate space.**
> A point in coordinate space is represented by an ordered triple (x, y, z).

The graph of a linear equation in three variables is a plane. It can be graphed by plotting the x-, y-, and z-intercepts and drawing the plane determined by them.

$$2x - 6y + 3z = 12$$

x-intercept	y-intercept	z-intercept
$2x - 6(0) + 3(0) = 12$ $x = 6$	$2(0) - 6y + 3(0) = 12$ $y = -2$	$2(0) - 6(0) + 3z = 12$ $z = 4$

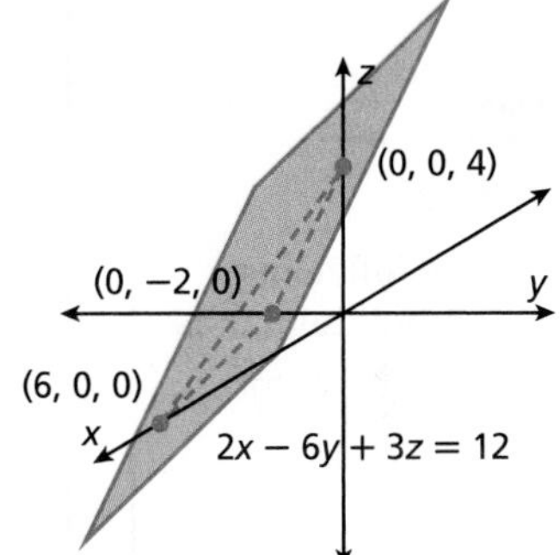

Solving Linear Systems in Three Variables — Lesson 3-6

Systems of equations in three variables can be used to model real-world problems.

Graphing

Graphing a system of linear equations in three variables may result in one, infinitely many, or no solutions.

No Solutions

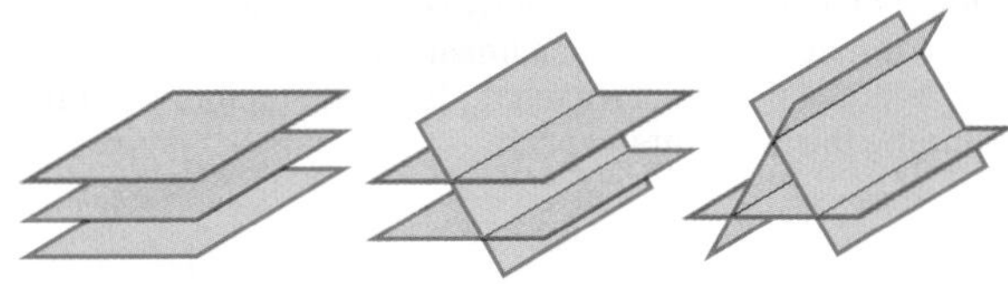

One Solution

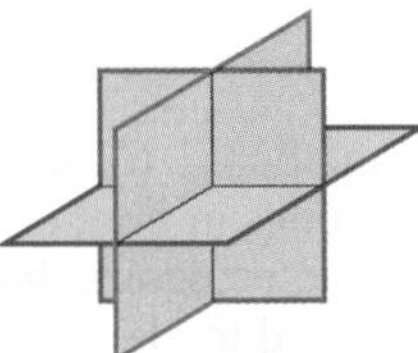

Infinitely Many Solutions

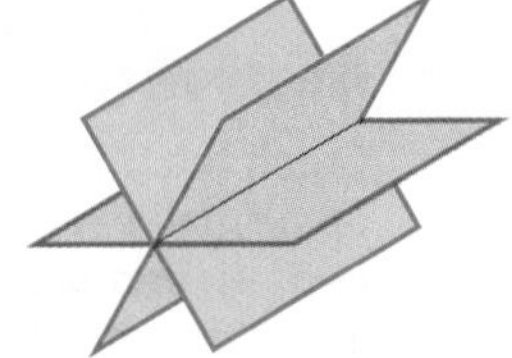

Algebraically

To solve algebraically, first reduce the 3-by-3 system to a 2-by-2 system, and then solve the resulting 2-by-2 system.

Consider the following system:
$$\begin{cases} x + y - 2z = -11 \\ 2x - y + 4z = 15 \\ 3x + y - 6z = -35 \end{cases}$$

$$\begin{array}{r} x + y - 2z = -11 \\ 2x - y + 4z = 15 \\ \hline 3x \quad + 2z = 4 \end{array} \qquad \begin{array}{r} 2x - y + 4z = 15 \\ 3x + y - 6z = -35 \\ \hline 5x \quad - 2z = -20 \end{array}$$

$$\begin{array}{r} 3x + 2z = 4 \\ 5x - 2z = -20 \\ \hline 8x \quad = -16 \\ x = -2 \end{array}$$

$$\begin{array}{r} 3x + 2z = 4 \\ 3(-2) + 2z = 4 \\ z = 5 \end{array} \longrightarrow \begin{array}{r} x + y - 2z = -11 \\ -2 + y - 2(5) = -11 \\ y = 1 \end{array}$$

The solution of the system is $(-2, 5, 1)$.

3-5 Organizer

Pacing: Traditional 1 day
Block $\frac{1}{2}$ day

Objective: Graph points and linear equations in three dimensions.

Algebra Lab
In *Algebra Lab Activities*

Online Edition
Tutorial Videos, Interactivity

Countdown to Testing Week 7

Power Presentations with PowerPoint®

Warm Up

Graph each of the following points in the coordinate plane.

1. $A(2, -1)$ **2.** $B(-4, 2)$

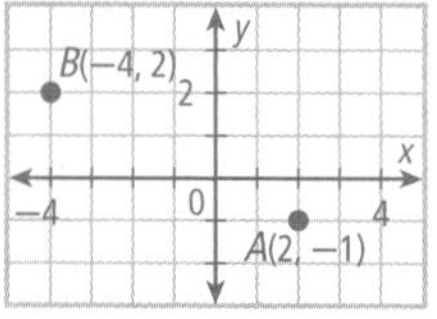

3. Find the intercepts of the line $\frac{2}{3}x - 2y + 6 = 0$.

x: -9; y: 3

Also available on transparency

Math Humor

Q: What did the cranky coordinate system say to the linear equation?

A: Get out of my space!

State Resources

3-5 Linear Equations in Three Dimensions

Objective
Graph points and linear equations in three dimensions.

Vocabulary
three-dimensional coordinate system
ordered triple
z-axis

Why learn this?
You can participate in Geocaching, an outdoor treasure-hunting game, by using three-dimensional coordinates to pinpoint locations on Earth.

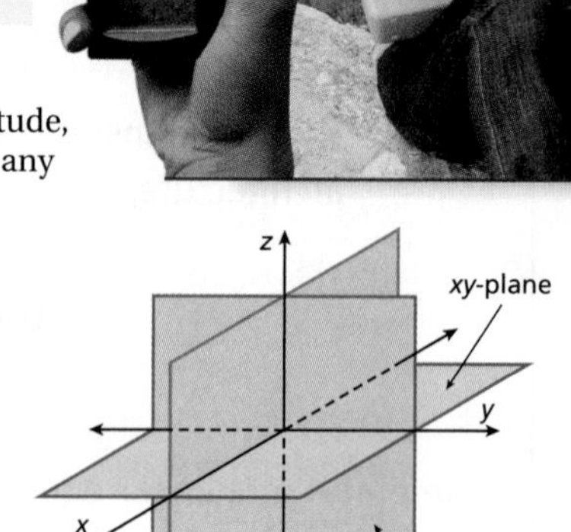

A Global Positioning System (GPS) gives locations using the three coordinates of latitude, longitude, and elevation. You can represent any location in three-dimensional space using a **three-dimensional coordinate system**, sometimes called *coordinate space.*

Each point in coordinate space can be represented by an **ordered triple** of the form (x, y, z). The system is similar to the coordinate plane but has an additional coordinate based on the z**-axis**. Notice that the axes form three planes that intersect at the origin.

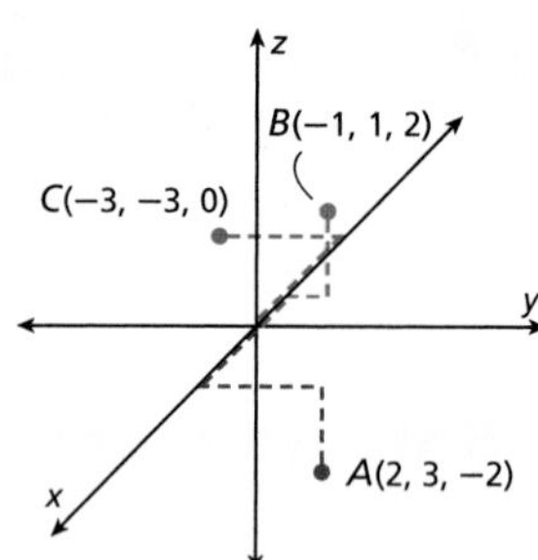

EXAMPLE 1 Graphing Points in Three Dimensions

Graph each point in three-dimensional space.

A $A(2, 3, -2)$
From the origin, move 2 units forward along the x-axis, 3 units right, and 2 units down.

B $B(-1, 1, 2)$
From the origin, move 1 unit back along the x-axis, 1 unit right, and 2 units up.

C $C(-3, -3, 0)$
From the origin, move 3 units back along the x-axis and 3 units left. Notice that this point lies in the xy-plane because the z-coordinate is 0.

z
B(−1, 1, 2)
C(−3, −3, 0)
y
A(2, 3, −2)
x

CHECK IT OUT! **Graph each point in three-dimensional space.**

1a. $D(1, 3, -1)$ **1b.** $E(1, -3, 1)$ **1c.** $F(0, 0, 3)$

1a-c.

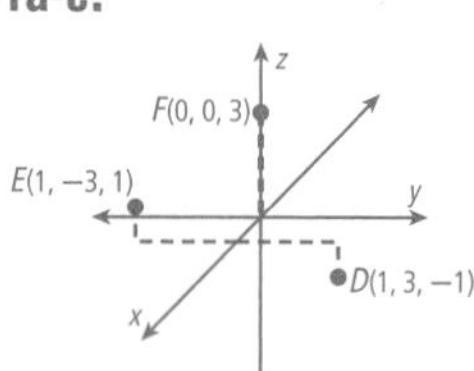

Recall that the graph of a linear equation in two dimensions is a straight line. In three-dimensional space, the graph of a linear equation is a plane. Because a plane is defined by three points, you can graph linear equations in three dimensions by finding the three intercepts.

1 Introduce

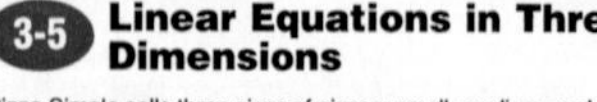

EXPLORATION

3-5 Linear Equations in Three Dimensions

Pizza Simple sells three sizes of pizzas: small, medium, and large. It sells the small for \$8, the medium for \$10, and the large for \$12.

1. The table shows the sales for the weekend, Friday through Sunday. Complete the table to find the total revenue for each day.

	Small Pizzas Sold	Medium Pizzas Sold	Large Pizzas Sold	Total Daily Revenue
Fri	37	103	195	
Sat	60	195	235	
Sun	52	131	210	

2. Write an expression for the total daily revenue R. Let x represent the number of small pizzas sold. Let y represent the number of medium pizzas sold. Let z represent the number of large pizzas sold.
3. Write an equation for the total daily revenue R if the restaurant sells exactly 40 small pizzas.

THINK AND DISCUSS

4. Explain how you can use your equation to find the number of small pizzas sold if you know that 212 medium pizzas and 213 large pizzas were sold and that the total revenue was \$5476.
5. Determine two combinations of pizza sales that would result

Motivate

Graph the point $(-3, 4)$ on the board. Next, hold up a small paper dot about 5 units in front of $(-3, 4)$, and prompt students to recognize that a third coordinate could be added to identify the point suggested by the dot in space. Discuss how the ordered triple $(-3, 4, 5)$ identifies distance in a third dimension and names this point.

Explorations and answers are provided in the *Explorations* binder.

EXAMPLE 2 Graphing Linear Equations in Three Dimensions

Graph the linear equation $3x + 4y + 2z = 12$ in three-dimensional space.

Step 1 Find the intercepts:

x-intercept: $3x + 4(0) + 6(0) = 12$
$x = 4$

y-intercept: $3(0) + 4y + 2(0) = 12$
$y = 3$

z-intercept: $3(0) + 4(0) + 2z = 12$
$z = 6$

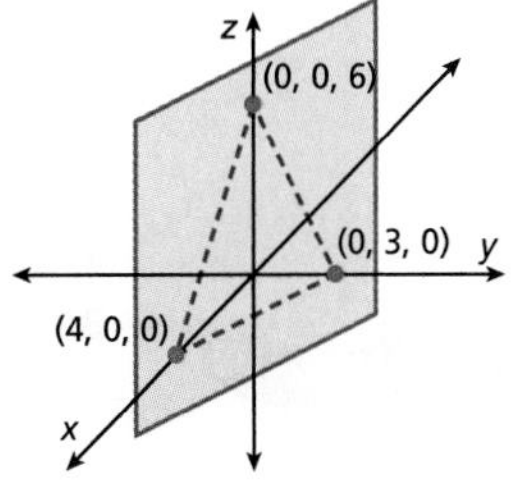

Step 2 Plot the points $(4, 0, 0)$, $(0, 3, 0)$, and $(0, 0, 6)$. Sketch a plane through the three points.

> **Helpful Hint**
>
> To find an intercept in coordinate space, set the other two coordinates equal to 0.

2. Graph the linear equation $x - 4y + 2z = 4$ in three-dimensional space.

2.

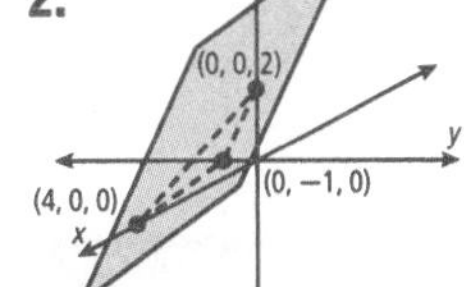

EXAMPLE 3 *Technology Application*

A computer game uses a role-playing scenario in which players build civilizations. Each player begins with 100 gold coins to buy resources. The players then compete for the survival of their civilizations. Each unit of food costs 2 gold coins, wood costs 4 gold coins, and stone costs 5 gold coins.

A **Write a linear equation in three variables to represent this situation.**

Let f = units of food, w = units of wood, and s = units of stone.
Write an equation:

cost of food	+	cost of wood	+	cost of stone	+	100 gold pieces
$2f$	+	$4w$	+	$5s$	+	100

B **Use the table to find the number of units of stone each player can buy.**

Bonnie: $2(20) + 3(10) + 5s = 100$
$s = 6$

Chad: $2(15) + 3(15) + 5s = 100$
$s = 5$

Frederico: $2(40) + 3(5) + 5s = 100$
$s = 1$

LaToya: $2(25) + 3(10) + 5s = 100$
$s = 4$

Player	Units of Food	Units of Wood	Units of Stone
Bonnie	20	10	
Chad	15	15	
Frederico	40	5	
LaToya	25	10	

Bonnie can purchase 6 units of stone, Chad can purchase 5 units, Frederico can purchase 1 unit, and LaToya can purchase 4 units.

CHECK IT OUT! Steve purchased \$61.50 worth of supplies for a hiking trip. The supplies included flashlights for \$3.50 each, compasses for \$1.50 each, and water bottles for \$0.75 each.

3a. Write a linear equation in three variables to represent this situation. $3.5x + 1.5y + 0.75z = 61.5$

3b. Steve purchased 6 flashlights and 24 water bottles. How many compasses did he purchase? **15**

Power Presentations with PowerPoint®

Additional Examples

Example 1

Graph each point in three-dimensional space.

A. $A(3, -2, 1)$

B. $B(2, -1, -3)$

C. $C(-1, 0, 2)$

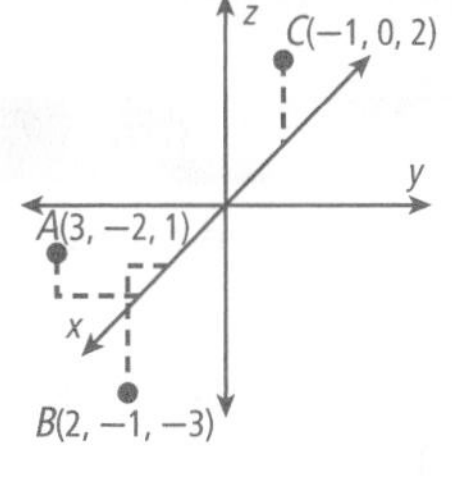

Example 2

Graph the linear equation $2x - 3y + z = -6$ in three-dimensional space.

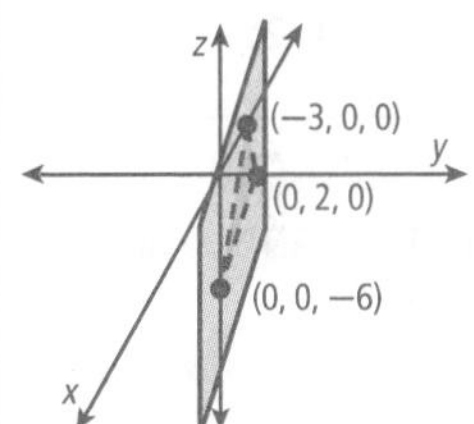

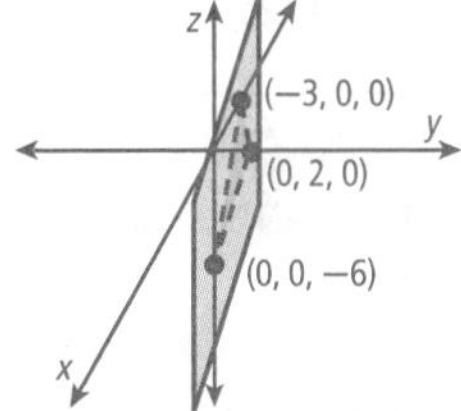

Example 3

Track relay teams score 5 points for finishing first, 3 for second, and 1 for third. Lin's team scored a total of 30 points.

A. Write a linear equation in three variables to represent this situation.
$5f + 3s + t = 30$

B. If Lin's team finished second in six events and third in two events, in how many events did it finish first? 2

Also available on transparency

2 Teach

Guided Instruction

Before plotting points in coordinate space, show students how adding a third axis perpendicular to the x- and y-axes in the coordinate plane creates a three-dimensional coordinate system. Help them see that the three axes define three planes that intersect at the origin.

3 Close

Summarize

Review the three-dimensional coordinate system. Discuss how to graph a linear equation in three variables by finding intercepts.

INTERVENTION

Questioning Strategies

EXAMPLES 1-3

Compare graphing in a three-dimensional system with graphing in a two-dimensional system.

- How are they similar?
- How are they different?

Answers to *Think and Discuss*

Possible answers:

1. (10, 4, 3)
2. passes through (0, 0, 1) and (0, 1, 0) and contains lines parallel to the *x*-axis
3. See p. A5.

3-5 Exercises

Assignment Guide

Assign *Guided Practice* exercises as necessary.

If you finished Examples 1–3

Basic 10–27, 30–36, 43–49
Average 10–31, 33–36, 41–49
Advanced 14–20, 24–30, 33–49

Homework Quick Check

Quickly check key concepts.
Exercises: 14, 18, 24, 25

ONGOING ASSESSMENT and INTERVENTION

***Diagnose Before* the Lesson**
3-5 Warm Up, TE p. 212

***Monitor During* the Lesson**
Check It Out! Exercises, SE pp. 212–213
Questioning Strategies, TE p. 213

***Assess After* the Lesson**
3-5 Lesson Quiz, TE p. 216
Alternative Assessment, TE p. 216

Answers

2–8. See p. A22.
10–23. See p. A23.

State Resources

go.hrw.com
State Resources Online
KEYWORD: MB7 Resources

THINK AND DISCUSS

1. Estimate your current coordinates in three-dimensional space using the front left bottom corner of your classroom as the origin. Let 1 foot represent 1 unit.
2. Describe a plane that has only two intercepts
3. **GET ORGANIZED** Copy and complete the graphic organizer. Label each axis, plane, and line shown.

Know it! Note

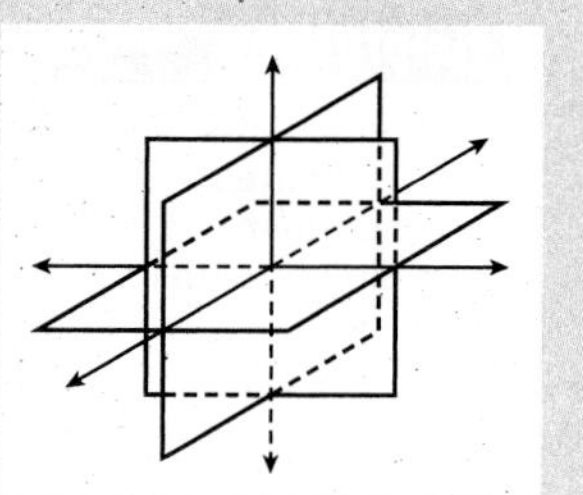

3-5 Exercises

go.hrw.com
Homework Help Online
KEYWORD: MB7 3-5
Parent Resources Online
KEYWORD: MB7 Parent

GUIDED PRACTICE

1. **Vocabulary** Explain the difference between the two- and three-dimensional coordinate systems. Possible answer: The 3-dimensional coordinate system has 3 axes instead of 2 and uses 3 coordinates instead of 2 to describe points.

SEE EXAMPLE 1 p. 214

Graph each point in three-dimensional space.

2. $(-3, -2, 1)$ 3. $(0, 2, 2)$ 4. $(1, 4, 5)$ 5. $(-1, 2, 4)$

SEE EXAMPLE 2 p. 215

Graph each linear equation in three-dimensional space.

6. $x + y + z = 3$ 7. $5x - 2y - 4z = 10$ 8. $1.5x + 3y - 2z = -6$

SEE EXAMPLE 3 p. 215

9a. $225x + 150y + 300z = 3000$

9. **Multi-Step** Whitney's delivery truck has a weight limit of 1.5 tons. She delivers refrigerators that weigh 225 lb, dishwashers that weigh 150 lb, and ovens that weigh 300 lb. (*Hint:* 1 ton = 2000 lb)
   a. Write a linear equation in three variables to represent this situation.
   b. Complete the table for the possible numbers of appliances the truck can hold.
   c. **Estimation** Estimate the maximum number of appliances the truck can hold. 20

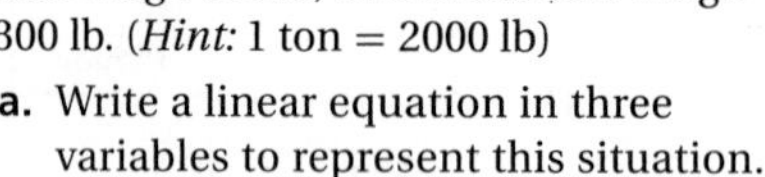

Refrigerators	8	6	4	10
Dishwashers	6	1	6	5
Ovens	1	5	4	0

PRACTICE AND PROBLEM SOLVING

Independent Practice	
For Exercises	See Example
10–17	1
18–23	2
24	3

Extra Practice
Skills Practice p. S9
Application Practice p. S34

Graph each point in three-dimensional space.

10. $(2, -4, 3)$ 11. $(-1, 1, 4)$ 12. $(3, 0, 0)$ 13. $(1, -2, 0)$
14. $(-3, -3, -3)$ 15. $(5, 0, 2)$ 16. $(0, -3, 2)$ 17. $(-4, -1, 1)$

Graph each linear equation in three-dimensional space.

18. $x + y - z = -1$ 19. $2x - y + 2z = 4$ 20. $2x + \frac{1}{2}y + z = -2$
21. $5x + y - z = -5$ 22. $8x + 6y + 4z = 24$ 23. $3x - 3y + 2.5z = 7.5$

3-5 READING STRATEGIES

In a two-dimensional coordinate system there are 2 axes: the *x-axis* and the *y*-axis. Each point is represented by an ordered pair. (3, 2) x y. The graph of a linear equation such as $x + y = 4$ is a line. The *x*-intercept is the point where the line crosses the *x*-axis, (4, 0). The *y*-intercept is the point where the line crosses the *y*-axis, (0, 4).	In a three-dimensional coordinate system there are 3 axes, the *x*-axis, the *y*-axis, and the **z-axis**. Each point is represented by an **ordered triple.** (3, 4, 2) x y z. Tip: *Tri* means 3-as in *tricycle* or *triangle.* The graph of a linear equation such as $x + y + z = 4$ is a plane. The *x*-intercept is the point where the plane crosses the *x*-axis, (4, 0, 0). The *y*-intercept is the point where the plane crosses the *y*-axis, (0, 4, 0). The *z*-intercept is the point where the plane crosses the *z*-axis, (0, 0, 4).

Answer each question.

1. Give an example of a two-dimensional space in your home. Then give an example of a three-dimensional space.
   Possible answer: the surface of a table; a room
2. State one way in which a two-dimensional graph of a linear equation is similar to a three-dimensional graph of a linear equation.
   Possible answer: Both graphs can be determined by finding the intercepts of the linear equations.
3. State one way in which a two-dimensional graph of a linear equation is different from a three-dimensional graph of a linear equation.
   Possible answer: The graph of a two-dimensional linear equation is a line, whereas that of a three-dimensional equation is a plane.
4. Explain how a line is different from a plane.
   Possible answer: A plane has length and width, but a line has just length.

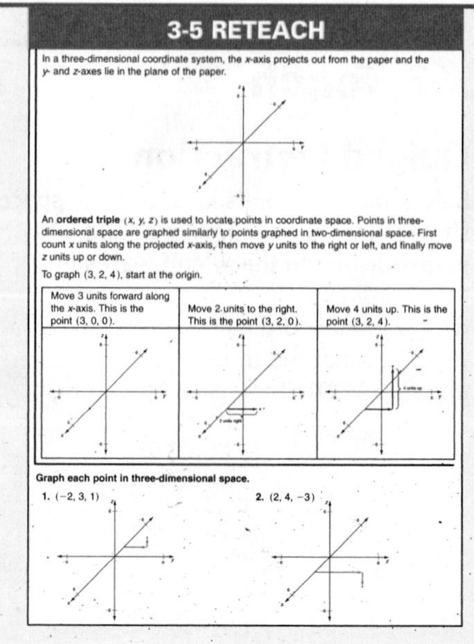

3-5 RETEACH

In a three-dimensional coordinate system, the *x*-axis projects out from the paper and the *y*- and *z*-axes lie in the plane of the paper.

An **ordered triple** (x, y, z) is used to locate points in coordinate space. Points in three-dimensional space are graphed similarly to points graphed in two-dimensional space. First count *x* units along the projected *x*-axis, then move *y* units to the right or left, and finally move *z* units up or down.

To graph (3, 2, 4), start at the origin.

Move 3 units forward along the *x*-axis. This is the point (3, 0, 0).	Move 2 units to the right. This is the point (3, 2, 0).	Move 4 units up. This is the point (3, 2, 4).

Graph each point in three-dimensional space.

1. $(-2, 3, 1)$ 2. $(2, 4, -3)$

24. **Aquariums** Gordon has \$80 to purchase a combination of cinnamon clownfish, anemones, and hermit crabs for his aquarium. Clownfish cost \$10 each, anemones cost \$15 each, and hermit crabs cost \$2.50 each.

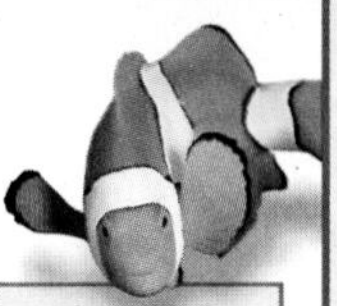

a. Write a linear equation in three variables to represent this situation. $10x + 15y + 2.5z = 80$

b. Complete the table for the possible numbers of sea creatures Gordon may purchase.

Hermit Crabs	Anemones	Clownfish
12	2	2
10	1	4
2	3	3
6	1	5

25. **Sports** Basketball players can score in three different ways: one-point free throws, two-point field goals, or three-point field goals. Cindy Brown of Long Beach State holds the Division 1 NCAA women's record for the most points in a single game, 60, including 20 free throws. Identify five possible combinations of two-point field goals and three-pointers that she may have had in the game.

Geometry Identify the unlabeled vertices of each cube.

26.

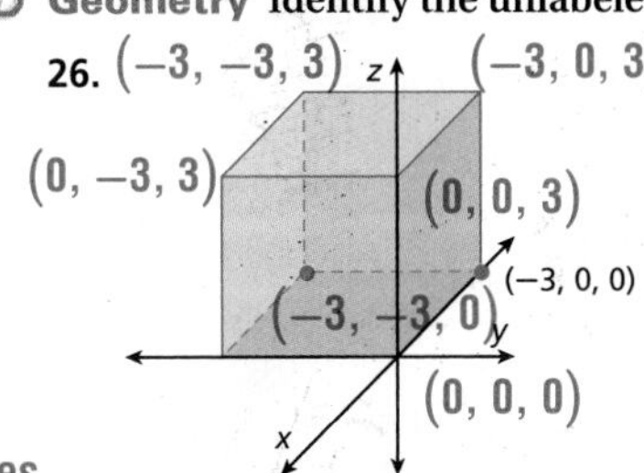

27.

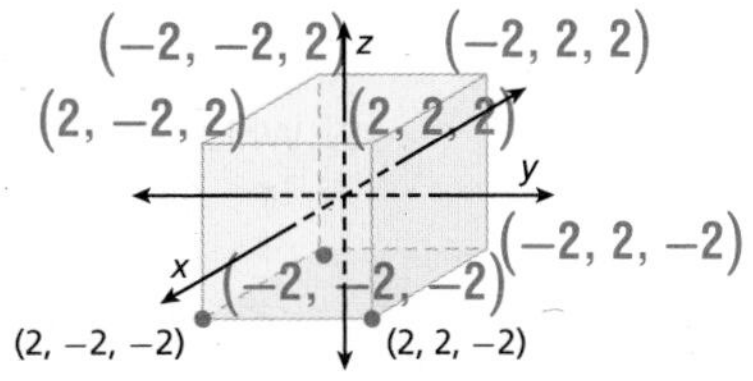

(−2, −2, 2)
z
(−2, 2, 2)
(2, −2, 2)
(2, 2, 2)
y
x
(−2, 2, −2)
(−2, −2, −2)
(2, −2, −2)
(2, 2, −2)

28. **Architecture** An architect is planning the flooring for a 2000 ft^2 home. There will be three types of flooring: hardwood, tile, and carpet. The architect has budgeted \$8000 for the floors and has decided to buy 400 ft^2 of tile. Is it possible for the rest of the flooring to be half wood and half carpet? Explain.

Flooring Sale!
Laminate: \$1.50/ft^2
Carpet: \$2/ft^2
Ceramic Tile: \$4/ft^2
Hardwood Flooring: \$6/ft^2

29. **Critical Thinking** Does moving forward and backward along a line represent two dimensions? Explain.

30. **Write About It** A friend calls you on the phone and asks you how to draw a three-dimensional coordinate system. What would you tell your friend?

30. Possible answer: Draw 2 perpendicular lines the same as for 2 dimensions. Label the horizontal y and the vertical z. Next draw a line that would look like $y = x$ in 2 dimensions. Label it x.

31. This problem will prepare you for the Multi-Step Test Prep on page 228.

Engineers use three-dimensional coordinates to design construction projects. An overhead light is anchored at the point (7, 12, 10) in a design where the floor of a building is represented by the xy-plane and increments on the plane are in feet.

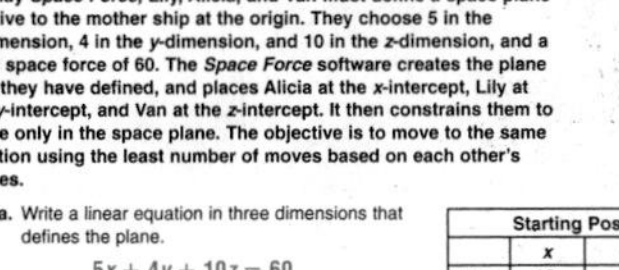

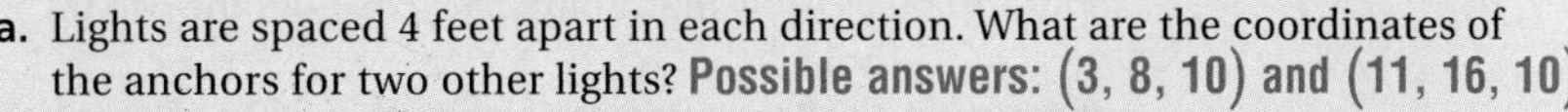

a. Lights are spaced 4 feet apart in each direction. What are the coordinates of the anchors for two other lights? Possible answers: (3, 8, 10) and (11, 16, 10)

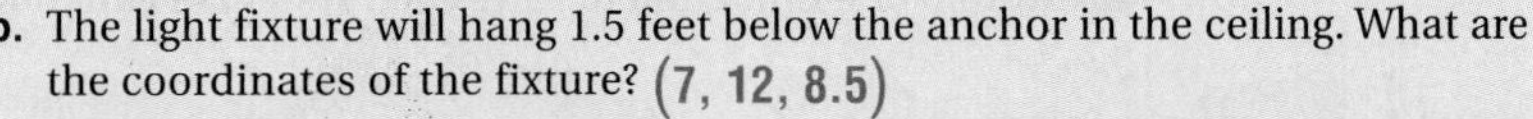

b. The light fixture will hang 1.5 feet below the anchor in the ceiling. What are the coordinates of the fixture? (7, 12, 8.5)

c. What would the new coordinates of the light be if the engineers want to raise the ceiling 4 feet? (7, 12, 12.5)

COMMON ERROR ALERT

Students may often forget about the vertex that is not visible in drawings of cubes, such as those in **Exercises 26** and **27.** You may want to encourage students to use dashed lines to draw the edges of the cube that are not visible, which, in turn, reveal the eighth vertex.

Teaching Tip **Concrete Manipulatives** For **Exercises 26–27,** you may want to show a model of a cube and have students discuss its attributes: 6 square faces, 12 congruent edges, and 8 vertices.

Exercise 30 involves using ordered triples. This exercise prepares students for the Multi-Step Test Prep on page 228.

Answers

25. Possible answer:

Three-pointers	2	4	6	8	10
Two-pointers	17	14	11	8	5

28. Possible answer: Yes; after the tile is purchased, 1600 ft^2 of additional flooring material must be purchased for \$6400. 800 ft^2 of carpet costs \$1600, and 800 ft^2 of wood costs \$4800, for a total of exactly \$6400.

29. Possible answer: No; it represents only 1 dimension. For 2 dimensions, you would need to move up and down in addition to backward and forward.

3-5 PROBLEM SOLVING

To play *Space Force*, Lily, Alicia, and Van must define a space plane relative to the mother ship at the origin. They choose 5 in the x-dimension, 4 in the y-dimension, and 10 in the z-dimension, and a total space force of 60. The *Space Force* software creates the plane that they have defined, and places Alicia at the x-intercept, Lily at the y-intercept, and Van at the z-intercept. It then constrains them to move only in the space plane. The objective is to move to the same location using the least number of moves based on each other's moves.

1. a. Write a linear equation in three dimensions that defines the plane. $5x + 4y + 10z = 60$

b. Complete the table to show the x-, y-, and z-intercept starting positions for each player.

Starting Positions			
	x	y	z
Alicia	12	0	0
Lily	0	15	0
Van	0	0	6

2. Plot the starting locations for each player on the grid and draw the space plane.

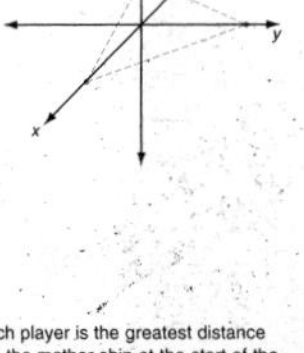

3. To play the game, each player moves by defining a change in two dimensions. The *Space Force* software then uses the linear equation to find the third dimension and relocates the player in the space plane. Find the new location for each player.

a. Alicia changes her location by $(-2, 1, z)$. (10, 1, 0.6)

b. Lily changes her location by $(x, -10, 2)$. (4, 5, 2)

c. Van changes his location by $(1, y, -2)$. (1, 3.75, 4)

Choose the letter for the best answer.

4. Which point is NOT in the space plane?
A (0, 6, 3.6)
B (1, 1.25, 5)
Ⓒ (4, 3.4, 2)
D (8, 2.5, 1)

5. Which player is the greatest distance from the mother ship at the start of the game?
A Alicia
Ⓑ Lily
C Van
D They are all the same distance from the mother ship.

3-5 CHALLENGE

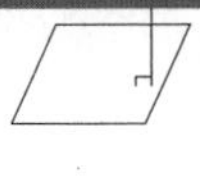

A line, $y = mx + b$, is uniquely determined by a point and a direction, commonly called the slope. A plane, $ax + by + cz = d$, can also be uniquely determined by a point and a direction. However, for a plane, it is not the direction of the plane. It is the direction of a line that is perpendicular to the plane as shown at the right.
This line perpendicular to the plane has the parametric equations

$$x = x_0 + at, \quad y = y_0 + bt, \quad z = z_0 + ct$$

where the point (x_0, y_0, z_0) can be any arbitrary point in the plane and the coefficients a, b, and c describe the direction of that perpendicular line. The coefficients a, b, and c are the same as in the equation of the plane. Consider two lines that lie in the plane given by the following equations.

$$x = x_1 + a_1t \quad\quad x = x_2 + b_1t$$
$$y = y_1 + a_2t \quad \text{and} \quad y = y_2 + b_2t$$
$$z = z_1 + a_3t \quad\quad z = z_2 + b_3t$$

The direction coefficients of these lines can be used to find the direction coefficients of the perpendicular line, a, b, and c, as follows.

$$a = a_2 \times b_3 - a_3 \times b_2$$
$$b = a_3 \times b_1 - a_1 \times b_3$$
$$c = a_1 \times b_2 - a_2 \times b_1$$

To find the value of d in the equation of the plane, substitute the coordinates of one point (x, y, z) with the direction coefficients a, b, and c and solve for the value of d.

Find the equation of each plane as described.

1. determined by the two lines $x = t$, $y = 1 - t$, $z = 1 + t$ and $x = 1 + 2t$, $y = 2 - 3t$, $z = 5 + t$ passing through the point (0, 1, 1)
$2x + y - z = 0$

2. determined by the two lines $x = 2 + 4t$, $y = 5 - 3t$, $z = 3 + t$ and $x = -3 - 4t$, $y = 10 + t$, $z = 8 + 7t$ passing through the point (2, 5, 3)
$22x + 32y + 8z = 228$

3. determined by the two lines $x = 4 + 2t$, $y = -3 - t$, $z = 1 + 6t$ and $x = 1 + 3t$, $y = 2 - 5t$, $z = 2 - t$ passing through the point (6, −4, 7)
$31x + 20y - 7z = 57$

3-5 PRACTICE A
3-5 PRACTICE C
3-5 PRACTICE B

Graph each linear equation in three-dimensional space.

1. $8x + 16y + 4z = 16$ 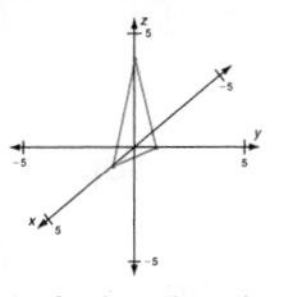
2. $-6x + 8y - 12z = 24$ 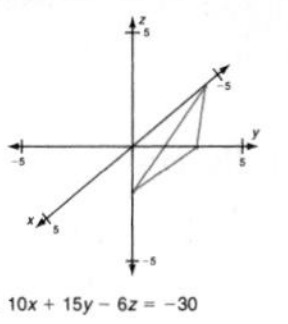
3. $4x + 3y + 6z = -12$ 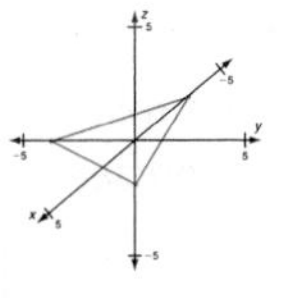
4. $10x + 15y - 6z = -30$

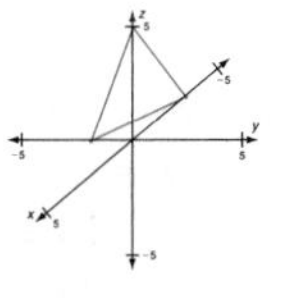

Solve.

5. Bill is buying bulbs for his flower garden. Bags of iris bulbs are \$4 each, bags of tulip bulbs are \$3 each, and bags of daffodil bulbs are \$2 each. He spends \$24 in all.

a. Write an equation to represent the situation. $4x + 3y + 2z = 24$

b. Bill wants to buy 3 bags of iris bulbs and at least 2 bags of daffodil bulbs. What is the maximum number of bags of tulip bulbs he can buy? 2 bags

c. Bill buys 5 bags of daffodil bulbs and the same number of bags of tulip bulbs as iris bulbs. How many bags of each does he buy? 2 bags of each

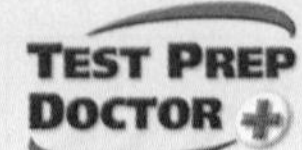

TEST PREP DOCTOR For **Exercise 33,** students who chose **D** or **B** might not realize that they need to count 5 units away in only *one* direction. The correct answer, **A,** shows 5 units subtracted from *only* the *x*-coordinate.

Journal

Have students compare and contrast graphing lines in the coordinate plane and planes in coordinate space.

ALTERNATIVE ASSESSMENT

Let students construct three-dimensional models of coordinate space using materials of their own choosing. Have them use their models to demonstrate how to graph points represented by ordered triples and linear equations.

Power Presentations with PowerPoint®

3-5 Lesson Quiz

Graph each point in three-dimensional space.

1. $A(-2, 3, 1)$ **2.** $B(0, -2, 3)$

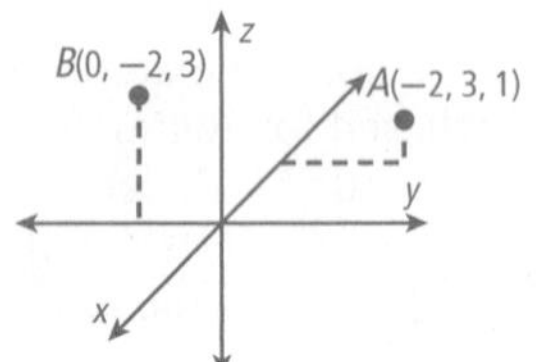

3. Graph the linear equation $6x + 3y - 2z = -12$ in three-dimensional space.

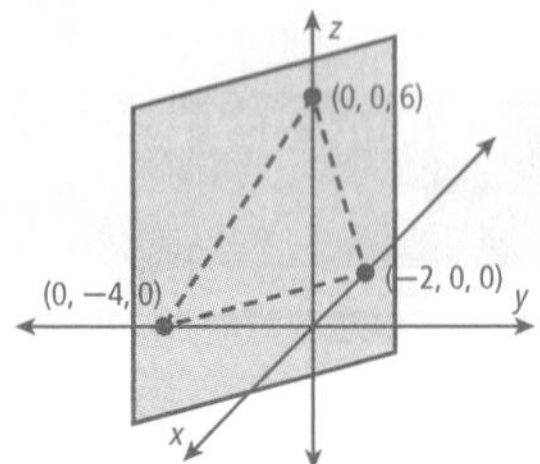

4. Lilly has \$6.00 for school supplies. Pencils cost \$0.20 each, pens cost \$0.30 each, and erasers cost \$0.25 each.

a. Write a linear equation in three variables to represent this situation.
$0.2x + 0.3y + 0.25z = 6$

b. If Lilly buys 6 pencils and 6 erasers, how many pens can she buy? 11

Also available on transparency

32. ERROR ANALYSIS Below are two methods of finding the *x*-intercept of $-5x + 3z = 15$. Which is incorrect? Explain the error.

A

$-5x + 3z = 15$
$-5x + 3(0) = 15$
$-5x = 15$
$x = -3$

B

$-5x + 3z = 15$
$-5(0) + 3z = 15$
$3z = 15$
$z = 5$

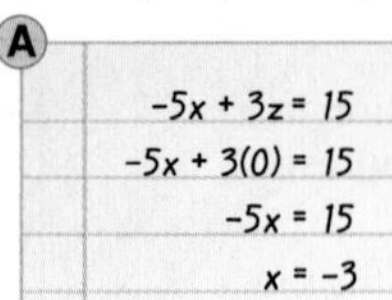

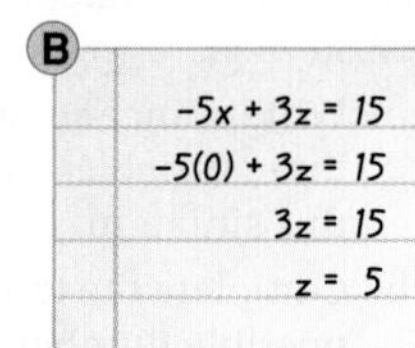

The second solution is incorrect. For you to find the *x*-intercept, the *z*-value must equal 0.

TEST PREP

33. Which point is 5 units away from $(1, 1, 4)$?
Ⓐ $(-4, 1, 4)$ Ⓑ $(1, -4, 9)$ Ⓒ $(2, 3, 6)$ Ⓓ $(6, 6, 9)$

34. The graph of which equation is shown?
Ⓐ $x + 2y + 3z = 6$ Ⓒ $3x + 6y + 2z = 6$
Ⓑ $2x + y + 3z = 6$ Ⓓ $6x + 3y + 2z = 6$

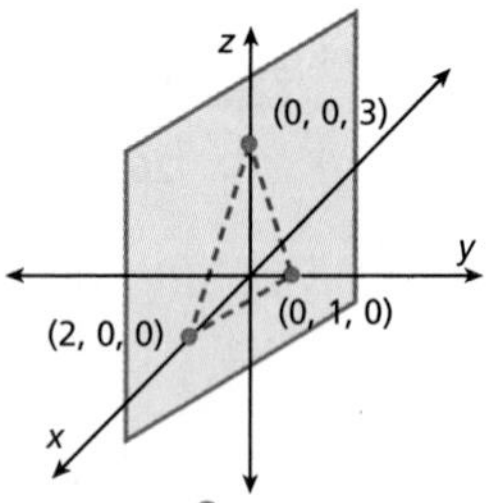

35. Which point is located at the *y*-intercept of $2x - 4y + 3z = -12$?
Ⓕ $(0, -3, 0)$ Ⓗ $(0, 3, 0)$
Ⓖ $(0, 0, -3)$ Ⓙ $(3, 0, 0)$

36. Gridded Response Find the *z*-intercept of $5x - 2y - 4z = -3$. $\frac{3}{4}$

CHALLENGE AND EXTEND

When a linear equation involves only two variables, its graph in three-dimensional space is a plane parallel to one of the axes. Graph each linear equation in three-dimensional space.

37. $x + y = 2$ **38.** $y - 2z = 4$ **39.** $x + z = 3$ **40.** $\frac{1}{2}x + \frac{1}{4}y = 1$

Write a linear equation in three dimensions with the indicated intercepts.

41. *x*-intercept = 4; *y*-intercept = 2; *z*-intercept = −1 $x + 2y - 4z = 4$

42. *x*-intercept = 25; *y*-intercept = 50; *z*-intercept = 10 $2x + y + 5z = 50$

SPIRAL REVIEW

Name the three-dimensional solid with the given number of edges and vertices. *(Previous course)*

43. 5 vertices, 8 edges **square pyramid** **44.** 6 vertices, 9 edges **triangular prism** **45.** 0 vertices, 0 edges **sphere**

46. Fund-raising The Wheels for Charity cycling club rode 1920 miles from Maryland to Montana to raise money for homeless shelters. Each day, the cyclists traveled about 120 miles. How many days of cycling did the trip take? *(Lesson 2-2)* **16 days**

Use substitution or elimination to solve each system of equations. *(Lesson 3-2)*

47. $\begin{cases} 5y = x \\ \frac{2}{5}x + 7y = 18 \end{cases}$ $x = 10;\ y = 2$

48. $\begin{cases} 6x - y = 5 \\ 4y - 3x = 1 \end{cases}$ $x = 1;\ y = 1$

49. $\begin{cases} x + 3y = 6 \\ 2x - 3y = 9 \end{cases}$ $x = 5;\ y = \frac{1}{3}$

Answers

37.

38.

39.

40.

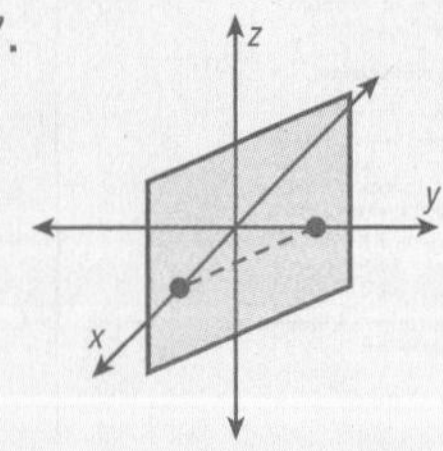

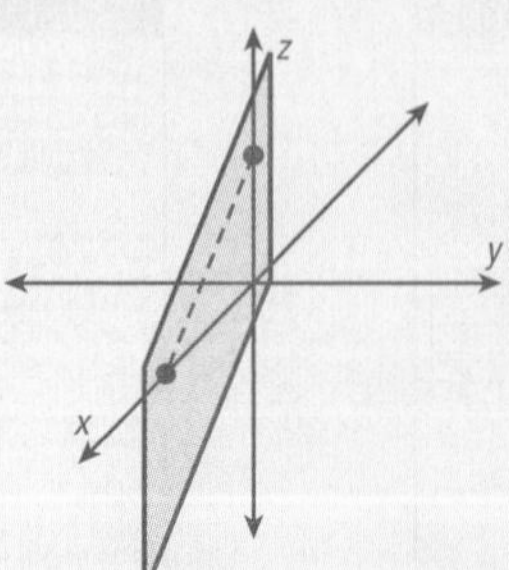

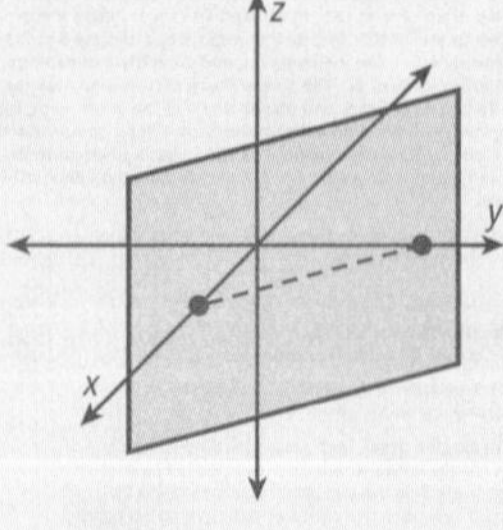

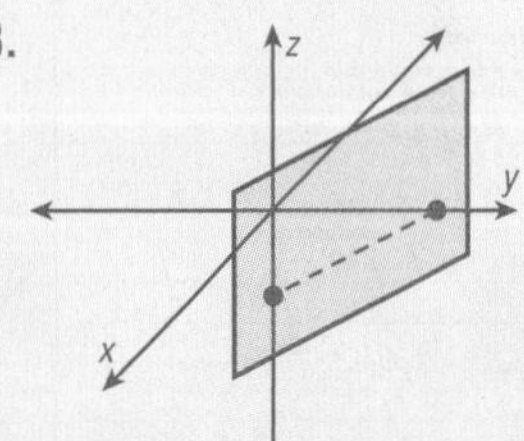

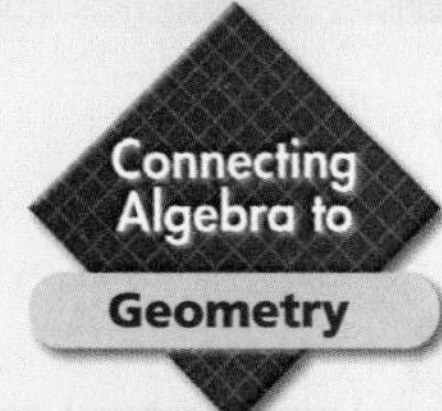

Views of Solid Figures

Here are four different ways to represent the same three-dimensional object.

See Skills Bank page S65

Oblique Grid

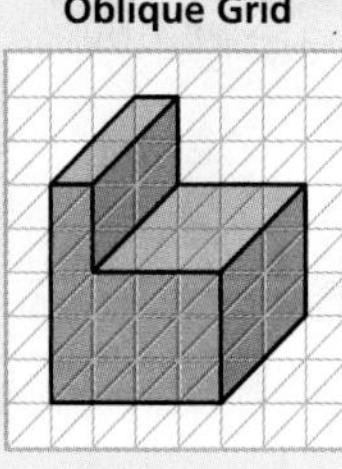

3-D Axes

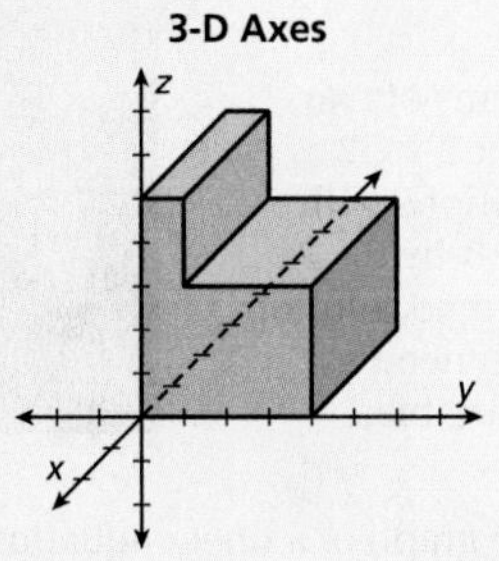

Isometric Grid

Orthographic Views

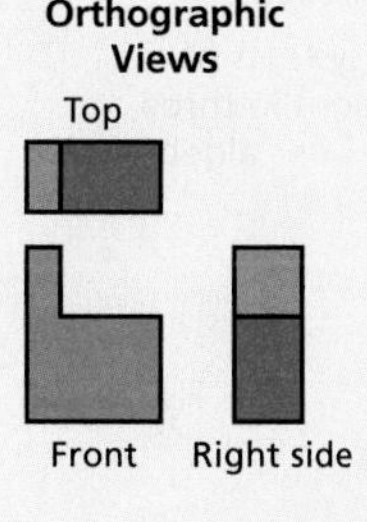

Example

Use graph paper. Show what this figure looks like from the back.

1. Draw the front of the figure. The answer is shown in figure 1.
2. The back view is the mirror image of the front view. Flip the front view to get the back view. The answer is shown in figure 2.

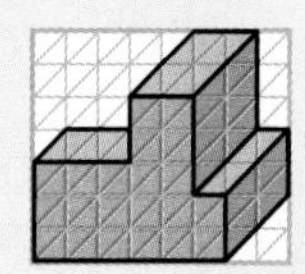

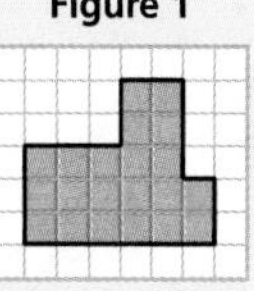

Figure 1

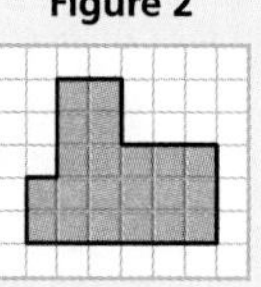

Figure 2

Try This

Use figures 3–6 for Problems 1–5.

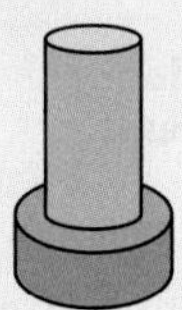

Figure 3

Figure 4

Figure 5

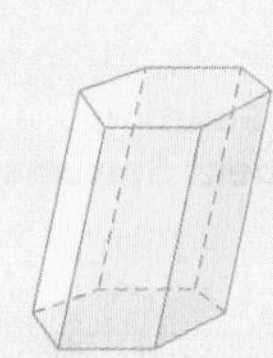

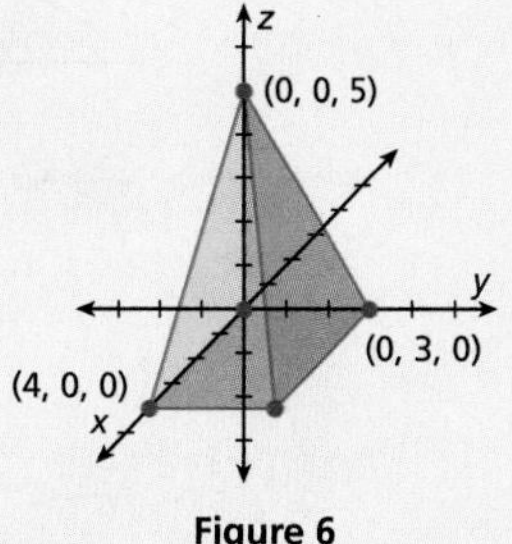

Figure 6

1. Figure 3 is made from two cylinders, one centered on top of the other. Draw front, top, and right-side views of figure 3.
2. In figure 4, the blue cube represents 1 cubic unit. How many of the blue cubes are needed to build the figure? **34 cubes**
3. Draw front, top, and right-side views of figure 4.
4. Figure 5 shows an oblique prism. The sides do not make right angles with the bases. Describe the bases and lateral faces of this prism. **bases: 2 congruent hexagons; lateral faces: 6 congruent parallelograms**
5. In figure 6, three of the vertices are labeled. What are the coordinates of the other two vertices? What is the name of this solid figure? **(0, 0, 0) and (4, 3, 0); rectangular oblique pyramid**

Answers

1. Front, Top, Right side

3. Front, Top, Right side

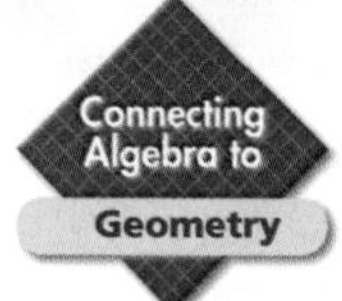

Organizer

See Skills Bank page S65

Pacing:
Traditional $\frac{1}{2}$ day
Block $\frac{1}{4}$ day

Objective: Review ways to represent three-dimensional figures.

Online Edition

Countdown to Testing Week 7

Teach

Remember

Students review the definitions of *prism, pyramid, base,* and *lateral face.*

INTERVENTION For additional review and practice on views of solid figures, see Skills Bank page S65.

Kinesthetic Have students build the example figure from small cubes on a sheet of paper. The paper can be rotated to facilitate viewing from different angles.

Close

Assess

A paper drinking cup is made by gluing 2 squares together along 3 sides. The cup looks like a circle from the top. What is the shape of the cup when viewed from the side?

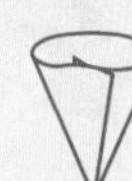

triangle

State Resources

go.hrw.com
State Resources Online
KEYWORD: MB7 Resources

3-6 Organizer

Pacing: Traditional 1 day
Block $\frac{1}{2}$ day

Objectives: Represent solutions to systems of equations in three dimensions graphically.

Solve systems of equations in three dimensions algebraically.

Online Edition
Tutorial Videos

Countdown to Testing Week 7

Power Presentations with PowerPoint®

Warm Up

Solve each system of equations algebraically.

1. $\begin{cases} x = 4y + 10 \\ 4x + 2y = 4 \end{cases}$ $(2, -2)$

2. $\begin{cases} 6x - 5y = 9 \\ 2x - y = 1 \end{cases}$ $(-1, -3)$

Classify each system and determine the number of solutions.

3. $\begin{cases} 3x - y = 8 \\ 6x - 2y = 2 \end{cases}$
inconsistent; none

4. $\begin{cases} x = 3y - 1 \\ 6x - 12y = -4 \end{cases}$
consistent, independent; one

Also available on transparency

Teacher: Why is your homework paper blank?
Student: I solved all the systems by eliminating them.

State Resources

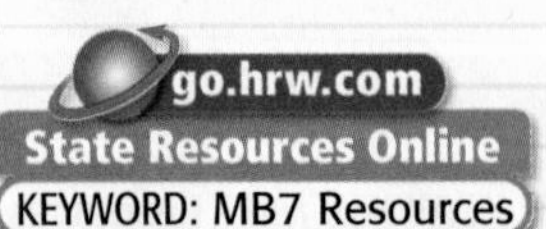

State Resources Online
KEYWORD: MB7 Resources

3-6 Solving Linear Systems in Three Variables

A2.2.1 Solve systems of equations and inequalities in three variables by substitution and elimination.

Objectives
Represent solutions to systems of equations in three dimensions graphically.

Solve systems of equations in three dimensions algebraically.

Why learn this?
You can use systems of equations in three variables to find out the scoring systems for sports awards. (See Example 2.)

You have learned to solve systems of two equations with two variables, or 2-by-2 systems. Systems of three equations with three variables are often called 3-by-3 systems. In general, to find a single solution to *any* system of equations, you need as many equations as you have variables.

Recall from Lesson 3-5 that the graph of a linear equation in three variables is a plane. When you graph a system of three linear equations in three dimensions, the result is three planes that may or may not intersect. The solution to the system is the set of points where all three planes intersect. These systems may have one, infinitely many, or no solution.

No Solutions
Inconsistent Systems

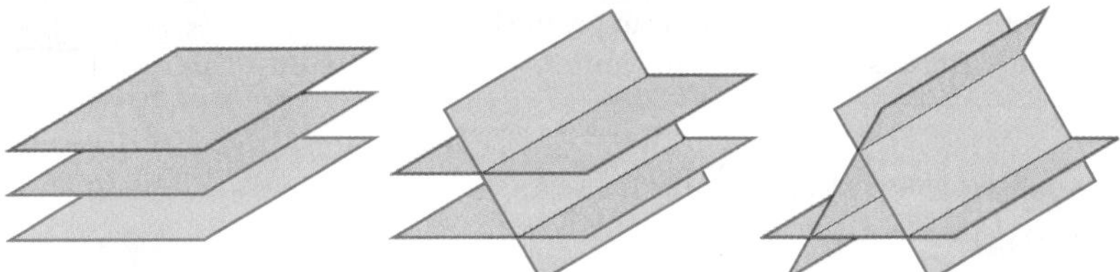

One Solution
Independent Systems

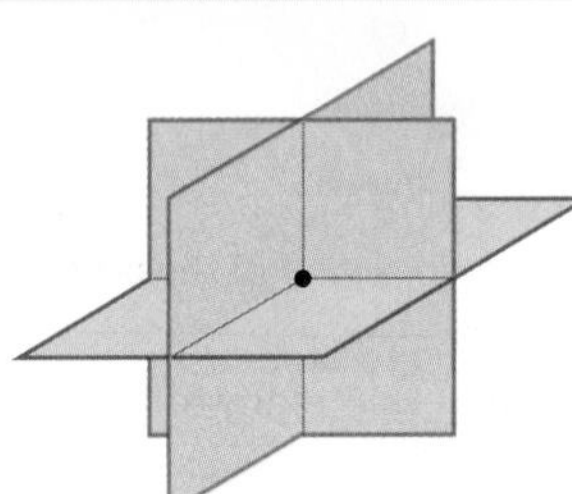

Infinitely Many Solutions
Dependent Systems

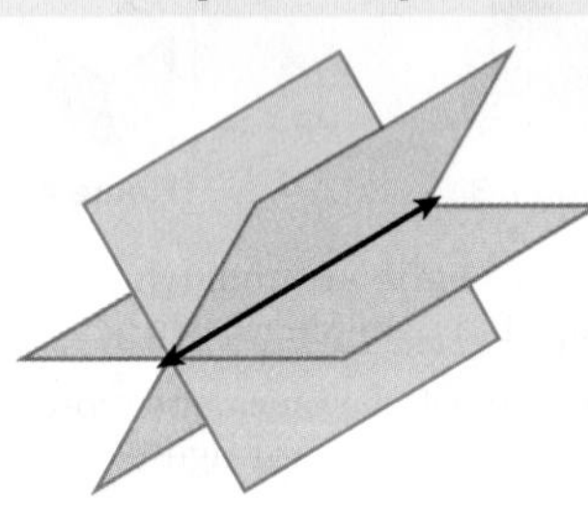

Identifying the exact solution from a graph of a 3-by-3 system can be very difficult. However, you can use the methods of elimination and substitution to reduce a 3-by-3 system to a 2-by-2 system and then use the methods that you learned in Lesson 3-2.

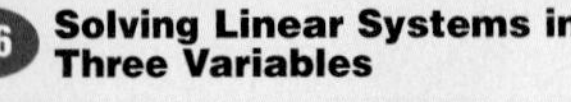

1 Introduce

EXPLORATION

3-6 Solving Linear Systems in Three Variables

JetCo builds planes for major airlines. All of its planes have three sections: first class, business class, and coach.

Plane	Rows in First Class	Rows in Business Class	Rows in Coach	Total Seats
J101	3	4	12	168
J200	5	5	20	270
J444	5	7	25	337

1. All JetCo planes have x seats per row in first class, y seats per row in business class, and z seats per row in coach. For each plane, write an equation that represents the relationship between x, y, and z.
2. What system of equations would you need to solve in order to find the number of seats per row in each section?

THINK AND DISCUSS

3. **Discuss** whether the following advertisement is true: "All JetCo planes have 4 seats per row in first class, 9 seats per row in business class, and 10 seats per row in coach."
4. **Determine** the number of seats per row in coach, given that the planes have 4 seats per row in first class and 6 seats per row in business class.

Motivate

Remind students that the graph of a linear equation in three variables is a plane. Explain that a system of three linear equations in three variables represents three planes in the same three-dimensional space. Use index cards to model and explore the possible ways that planes may or may not intersect.

Explorations and answers are provided in the *Explorations* binder.

EXAMPLE 1 Solving a Linear System in Three Variables

Use elimination to solve the following system of equations.

$$\begin{cases} x + 2y - 3z = -2 & ❶ \\ 2x - 2y + z = 7 & ❷ \\ x + y + 2z = -4 & ❸ \end{cases}$$

Step 1 Eliminate one variable.

In this system, y is a reasonable choice to eliminate first because the coefficients of y are opposites in the equations ❶ and ❷.

$$\begin{aligned} ❶ \quad x + 2y - 3z &= -2 \\ ❷ \quad 2x - 2y + z &= 7 \\ \hline 3x \qquad - 2z &= 5 \; ❹ \end{aligned}$$

Add equations ❶ and ❷.

Use equations ❶ and ❸ to create a second equation in x and z.

❶ $x + 2y - 3z = -2$ → $x + 2y - 3z = -2$

❸ $-2(x + y + 2z = -4)$ → $-2x - 2y - 4z = 8$

$-x \qquad - 7z = 6$ ❺

Multiply equation ❸ by −2, and add to equation ❶.

You now have a 2-by-2 system. $\begin{cases} 3x - 2z = 5 & ❹ \\ -x - 7z = 6 & ❺ \end{cases}$

Step 2 Eliminate another variable. Then solve for the remaining variable.

You can eliminate x by using methods from Lesson 3-2.

❹ $3x - 2z = 5$ → $3x - 2z = 5$

❺ $3(-x - 7z = 6)$ → $-3x - 21z = 18$

Multiply equation ❺ by 3, and add to equation ❹.

$-23z = 23$

$z = -1$ *Solve for z.*

Step 3 Use one of the equations in your 2-by-2 system to solve for x.

❺ $-x - 7z = 6$

$-x - 7(-1) = 6$ *Substitute −1 for z.*

$x = 1$ *Solve for x.*

Step 4 Substitute for x and z in one of the original equations to solve for y.

❸ $x + y + 2z = -4$

$(1) + y + 2(-1) = -4$ *Substitute 1 for x and −1 for z.*

$y = -3$ *Solve for y.*

The solution is $(1, -3, -1)$.

1. Use elimination to solve the following system of equations.

$$\begin{cases} -x + y + 2z = 7 \\ 2x + 3y + z = 1 \\ -3x - 4y + z = 4 \end{cases}$$

$x = -2, y = 1, z = 2$

You can also use substitution to solve a 3-by-3 system. Again, the first step is to reduce the 3-by-3 system to a 2-by-2 system.

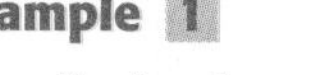

Power Presentations with PowerPoint®

Additional Examples

Example 1

Use elimination to solve the system of equations.

$$\begin{cases} 5x - 2y - 3z = -7 \\ 2x - 3y + z = -16 \\ 3x + 4y - 2z = 7 \end{cases}$$

$(-3, 2, -4)$

Also available on transparency

INTERVENTION

Questioning Strategies

EXAMPLE 1

- Why is it important to eliminate the same variable in each part of **Step 1**?
- Do you think substitution would have been a good strategy to solve the 2-by-2 system in **Step 2**? Why or why not?
- How can you check your answer?

Inclusion Some students may benefit from labeling the equations with numbers to keep track of the solution process. Suggest using 1, 2, and 3 for the original three equations and adding 4 and 5 for the two equations in two variables. Use these labels in step-by-step instructions in your presentation, and encourage students to use them in their work as well.

2 Teach

Guided Instruction

Before they solve 3-by-3 systems, make sure students are proficient in both the elimination and substitution methods for solving 2-by-2 systems. As you demonstrate solving 3-by-3 systems, stress the fact that the objective of the first step is to reduce the system to a 2-by-2 system. This reduced system can then be solved using the methods students learned earlier in the chapter.

Reaching All Learners

Through Visual Cues

Have students use colored pencils (MK) to write each equation in a different color. As they solve the system, students should continue to write each equation in its designated color, enabling them to follow the steps of the solution process more clearly.

Power Presentations with PowerPoint®

Additional Examples

Example 2

The table shows the number of each type of ticket sold and the total sales amount for each night of the school play. Find the price of each type of ticket.

	Orchestra	Mezzanine	Balcony	Total Sales
Fri	200	30	40	$1470
Sat	250	60	50	$1950
Sun	150	30	0	$1050

orchestra: $6; mezzanine: $5; balcony: $3

Example 3

Classify the system as consistent or inconsistent and determine the number of solutions.

$$\begin{cases} 2x - 6y + 4z = 2 \\ -3x + 9y - 6z = -3 \\ 5x - 15y + 10z = 5 \end{cases}$$

consistent, dependent; infinite

Also available on transparency

INTERVENTION
Questioning Strategies

EXAMPLE 2

- What is an alternative way to use substitution to solve this system?
- How might you check the solution?

EXAMPLE 3

- What does the solution tell you about the graph of this system?

EXAMPLE 2 *Sports Application*

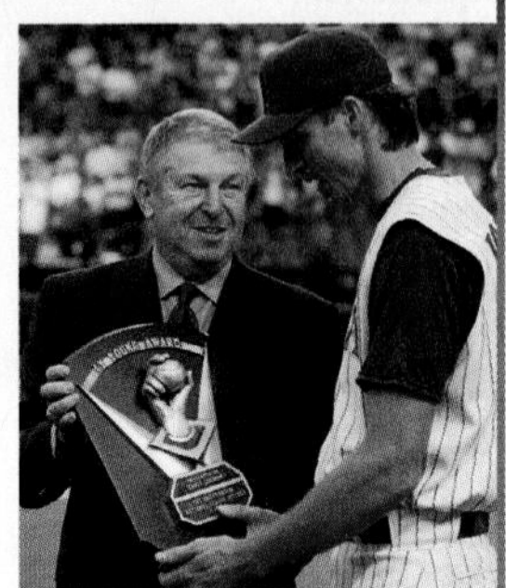

In 2001, Randy Johnson of the Arizona Diamondbacks won Major League Baseball's Cy Young Award as the best pitcher in the National League. The winner is the pitcher who receives the most points, and a different number of points are given for each first-, second-, and third-place vote. The table shows the votes for the top three finishers. Find the number of points awarded for each vote.

Player	1st Place	2nd Place	3rd Place	Total Points
Randy Johnson	30	2	0	156
Curt Schilling	2	29	1	98
Matt Morris	0	1	28	31

Step 1 Let x represent the number of points for a first-place vote, y for a second-place vote, and z for a third-place vote.

Write a system of equations to represent the data in the table.

$$\begin{cases} 30x + 2y = 156 & ❶ \\ 2x + 29y + z = 98 & ❷ \\ y + 28z = 31 & ❸ \end{cases}$$

Randy Johnson's votes
Curt Schilling's votes
Matt Morris's votes

Some variables are "missing" in the equations; however, the same solution methods apply. Substitution is a good choice because solving for y is straightforward.

Step 2 Solve for y in equation ❶.

❶ $30x + 2y = 156$

$\mathbf{y = -15x + 78}$ *Solve for y.*

Step 3 Substitute for y in equations ❷ and ❸.

$$\begin{cases} 2x + 29(\mathbf{-15x + 78}) + z = 98 & ❷ \\ (\mathbf{-15x + 78}) + 28z = 31 & ❸ \end{cases}$$ *Substitute −15x + 78 for y.*

$$\begin{cases} -433x + z = -2164 & ❹ \\ -15x + 28z = -47 & ❺ \end{cases}$$ *Simplify to find a 2-by-2 system.*

Step 4 Solve equation ❹ for z.

❹ $-433x + z = -2164$

$\mathbf{z = 433x - 2164}$ *Solve for z.*

Step 5 Substitute for z in equation ❺.

❺ $-15x + 28(\mathbf{433x - 2164}) = -47$ *Substitute 433x − 2164 for z.*

$12{,}109x = 60{,}545$

$x = 5$ *Solve for x.*

Step 6 Substitute for x to solve for z and then for y.

❹ $z = 433x - 2164$
$z = 433(\mathbf{5}) - 2164$
$z = 1$

❸ $y + 28z = 31$
$y + 28(\mathbf{1}) = 31$
$y = 3$

The solution to the system is $(5, 3, 1)$. So, a first-place vote is worth 5 points, a second-place vote is worth 3 points, and a third-place vote is worth 1 point.

2. Jada's chili won first prize at the winter fair. The table shows the results of the voting.

How many points are first-, second-, and third-place votes worth?

Winter Fair Chili Cook-off				
Name	1st Place	2nd Place	3rd Place	Total Points
Jada	3	1	4	15
Maria	2	4	0	14
Al	2	2	3	13

first place—3 points; second place—2 points; third place—1 point

The systems in Examples 1 and 2 have unique solutions. However, 3-by-3 systems may have no solution or an infinite number of solutions.

EXAMPLE 3 Classifying Systems with Infinitely Many Solutions or No Solution

Classify the system as consistent or inconsistent, and determine the number of solutions.

$$\begin{cases} 4x - 2y + 4z = 8 & (1) \\ -3x + y - z = -4 & (2) \\ -2x + 2y - 6z = 4 & (3) \end{cases}$$

The elimination method is convenient because the numbers you need to multiply the equations by are small. First, eliminate y.

$$\begin{aligned} (1)\quad & 4x - 2y + 4z = 8 \\ (3)\quad & \underline{-2x + 2y - 6z = 4} \\ & 2x \quad\quad - 2z = 12 \quad (4) \end{aligned}$$

Add equations (1) and (3).

$$\begin{aligned} 4x - 2y + 4z = 8 &\qquad 4x - 2y + 4z = 8 \\ 2(-3x + y - z = -4) &\rightarrow \underline{-6x + 2y - 2z = -8} \\ & \qquad -2x \quad\quad + 2z = 0 \quad (5) \end{aligned}$$

Multiply equation (2) by 2, and add to equation (1).

You now have a 2-by-2 system: $\begin{cases} 2x - 2z = 12 & (4) \\ -2x + 2z = 0 & (5) \end{cases}$

Eliminate x.

$$\begin{aligned} (4)\quad & 2x - 2z = 12 \\ (5)\quad & \underline{-2x + 2z = 12} \\ & 0 = 12 \ ✗ \end{aligned}$$

Add equations (4) and (5).

Because 0 is never equal to 12, the equation is a contradiction. Therefore, the system is inconsistent and has no solution.

Remember!

Consistent means that the system of equations has at least one solution.

Classify the system, and determine the number of solutions.

3a. $\begin{cases} 3x - y + 2z = 4 \\ 2x - y + 3z = 7 \\ -9x + 3y - 6z = -12 \end{cases}$

consistent; infinite number of solutions

3b. $\begin{cases} 2x - y + 3z = 6 \\ 2x - 4y + 6z = 10 \\ y - z = -2 \end{cases}$

inconsistent; no solution

COMMON ERROR ALERT

When using elimination to reduce a 3-by-3 system to a 2-by-2 system, students sometimes eliminate one variable from one pair of equations and a different variable from another pair, resulting in a system that still contains three variables. Help students see that a 2-by-2 system cannot be solved unless the resulting equations have only two variables.

Teaching Tip **Multiple Representations** After solving the system in **Example 3** algebraically, use three-dimensional graphing software to solve the system graphically, providing students with a visual representation of the inconsistent system.

3 Close

Summarize

Present the following system of equations, and have students discuss different ways they could go about finding its solution.

$$\begin{cases} 2x - y + z = 7 \\ x + 2y - 5z = -1 \\ x - y = 6 \end{cases}$$

$x = 2, y = -4, z = -1$

ONGOING ASSESSMENT and INTERVENTION

Diagnose **Before** the Lesson
3-6 Warm Up, TE p. 218

Monitor **During** the Lesson
Check It Out! Exercises, SE pp. 219–221
Questioning Strategies, TE pp. 219–221

Assess **After** the Lesson
3-6 Lesson Quiz, TE p. 224
Alternative Assessment, TE p. 224

Answers to *Think and Discuss*

Possible answers:

1. 2 vertical, nonintersecting planes, each cut by a third vertical plane; 2 identical planes cut by a third plane
2. See p. A5.

THINK AND DISCUSS

1. Look at the inconsistent and dependent systems shown on page 220. Describe one other arrangement of three planes that results in an inconsistent system. Describe one other arrangement that results in a dependent system.

2. **GET ORGANIZED** Copy and complete the graphic organizer. In each box, describe the similarities and differences between 2-by-2 and 3-by-3 systems.

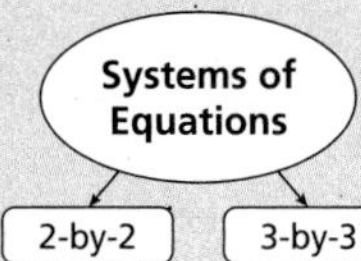

3-6 Exercises

Assignment Guide

Assign *Guided Practice* exercises as necessary.

If you finished Examples 1–3

Basic 8–16, 19–22, 25–30

Average 8–22, 24–30

Advanced 8–30

Homework Quick Check

Quickly check key concepts.

Exercises: 8, 11, 14, 16, 20

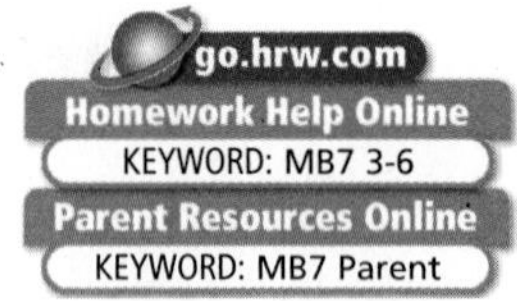

GUIDED PRACTICE

SEE EXAMPLE 1 p. 221

Use elimination to solve each system of equations.

1. $\begin{cases} -2x + y + 3z = 20 \\ -3x + 2y + z = 21 \\ 3x - 2y + 3z = -9 \end{cases}$ $x = -4,\ y = 3,\ z = 3$

2. $\begin{cases} x + 2y + 3z = 9 \\ x + 3y + 2z = 5 \\ x + 4y - z = -5 \end{cases}$ $x = 2,\ y = -1,\ z = 3$

3. $\begin{cases} x + 2y + z = 8 \\ 2x + y - z = 4 \\ x + y + 3z = 7 \end{cases}$ $x = 1,\ y = 3,\ z = 1$

SEE EXAMPLE 2 p. 222

4. **Business** Mabel's Mini-Golf has different prices for seniors, adults, and children. The table shows the total revenue for three hours on a particular night. How much does each type of ticket cost? senior—$8; adult—$15; child—$10

Mabel's Mini-Golf Prices

Time	Senior	Adult	Child	Revenue
6:00 P.M.–7:00 P.M.	5	10	12	$310
7:00 P.M.–8:00 P.M.	5	5	4	$155
8:00 P.M.–9:00 P.M.	4	2	3	$92

SEE EXAMPLE 3 p. 223

Classify each system as consistent or inconsistent, and determine the number of solutions.

5. $\begin{cases} 2x + 4y - 2z = 4 \\ -x - 2y + z = 4 \\ 3x + 6y - 3z = 10 \end{cases}$ inconsistent; no solution

6. $\begin{cases} 2x + 4y - 5z = -10 \\ -x - 2y + 8z = 16 \\ -2x + 4y + 2z = 4 \end{cases}$ consistent; one solution

7. $\begin{cases} -2x + 3y + z = 15 \\ x + 3y - z = -1 \\ -5x - 6y + 4z = -16 \end{cases}$ inconsistent; no solution

PRACTICE AND PROBLEM SOLVING

Use elimination to solve each system of equations.

8. $\begin{cases} 2x - y - 3z = 1 \\ 4x + 3y + 2z = -4 \\ -3x + 2y + 5z = -3 \end{cases}$ $x = 2,\ y = -6,\ z = 3$

9. $\begin{cases} 5x - 6y + 2z = 21 \\ 2x + 3y - 3z = -9 \\ -3x + 9y - 4z = -24 \end{cases}$ $x = 3,\ y = 1,\ z = 6$

10. $\begin{cases} 4x + 7y - z = 42 \\ -2x + 2y + 3z = -26 \\ 2x - 3y + 5z = 10 \end{cases}$ $x = 10,\ y = 0,\ z = -2$

State Resources

go.hrw.com
State Resources Online
KEYWORD: MB7 Resources

3-6 READING STRATEGIES

A system of three equations in three variables can be solved using the methods you used to solve systems of two equations with two variables.

Elimination	Substitution
$\begin{cases} 2x + y - z = -3 \\ 5x - y - z = -8 \\ -x + 3y + z = 6 \end{cases}$	$\begin{cases} 2x - y = 5 \\ x - 3y - z = 1 \\ 2y - 2z = -10 \end{cases}$
Tip: Remember to *eliminate* means to remove, the plan is to *eliminate* one of the variables.	Tip: Remember you can solve an equation for one of the three variables, then *substitute* that expression in the other equations.
In this system, you can *eliminate* z by adding equations 1 and 3 together and then by adding equations 2 and 3 together $(-z + z = 0)$. This gives the system $\begin{cases} x + 4y = 3 \\ 4x + 2y = -2 \end{cases}$	In this system, you can solve the first equation to find y in terms of x. Then, *substitute* that value into the other two equations. This gives the system $\begin{cases} -5x - z = -14 \\ 4x - 2z = 0 \end{cases}$
Eliminate y from this system by multiplying the second equation by -2 and then adding to find $x = -1$. Substitution yields $y = 1$ and $z = 2$.	Solve for z and substitute to find $x = 2$. Substituting gives $y = -1$ and $z = 4$.
The solution to the system is $(-1, 1, 2)$	The solution to the system is $(2, -1, 4)$

Answer these questions.

1. Explain why a system of three equations with three variables requires a three-dimensional coordinate system to graph.
   Possible answer: You need three different axes to graph three variables. A plane contains only two axes.
2. $x + 2y - z = 3$ is one equation in a dependent system of equations. Write two other equations in that system.
   Possible answer: $2x + 4y - 2z = 6$ and $5x + 10y - 5z = 15$
3. What does it mean if a system of three equations with three variables is independent?
   The planes intersect in one point, so there is one solution.
4. If you solve one of the equations in a system for x, why can you substitute that value for x in the other equations?
   Possible answer: The value of x is the same in all three equations, so you can substitute a value of x from one equation into any other equation in the system.

3-6 RETEACH

You know how to solve a system of two linear equations in two variables using the **elimination method**. The same method can be used to solve a system of three linear equations in three variables.

$$\begin{cases} x - y + 2z = 8 \\ 2x + y - z = -2 \\ x + 2y + z = 2 \end{cases}$$

The first and second equations have opposite coefficients of y. So adding these two equations will eliminate y.

$$\begin{array}{r} x - y + 2z = 8 \\ +2x + y - z = -2 \\ \hline 3x + z = 6 \end{array}$$

Multiply the first equation by 2 and add to the third equation to eliminate y.

$$\begin{array}{r} 2x - 2y + 4z = 16 \\ + x + 2y + z = 2 \\ \hline 3x + 5z = 18 \end{array}$$

Now you have two equations in two variables. Solve using the elimination method for a system of two equations.

$$\begin{cases} 3x + z = 6 \\ 3x + 5z = 18 \end{cases}$$

Solving this system gives $x = 1$ and $z = 3$. Substituting these values in any of the original equations gives $y = -1$.

So the solution is the ordered triple $(1, -1, 3)$

Show the steps you would use to eliminate the variable z.

1. $\begin{cases} 2x - y + z = -3 \\ x + 2y - z = 2 \\ x + 3y - 2z = 3 \end{cases}$

a. $\begin{array}{r} 2x - y + z = -3 \\ + \quad x + 2y - z = 2 \\ \hline 3x + y = -1 \end{array}$

b. $2(2x - y + z = -3) = \begin{array}{r} 4x - 2y + 2z = -6 \\ + x + 3y - 2z = 3 \\ \hline 5x + y = -3 \end{array}$

c. Give the resulting system of two equations. $\begin{cases} 3x + y = -1 \\ 5x + y = -3 \end{cases}$

Independent Practice

For Exercises	See Example
8–10	1
11	2
12–14	3

Extra Practice

Skills Practice p. S9

Application Practice p. S34

11. **Entertainment** On the *Star Quality* show, judges score contestants in three categories: Talent, Presentation, and Star Quality. Each category is worth a percent of the final score. Based on the scores in the table below, what percent of the final score is each category worth? Talent—30%; Presentation—20%; Star Quality—50%

Star Quality Scores

Contestant	Talent	Presentation	Star Quality	Final Score
Wanda Wynn	8	9	10	9.2
Amiya Starr	9	7	8	8.1
Kenny Singh	6	10	8	7.8

Classify each system as consistent or inconsistent, and determine the number of solutions.

12. consistent; infinite number of solutions

13. inconsistent; no solution

14. consistent; infinite number of solutions

12. $\begin{cases} 4x - 3y + z = -9 \\ -3x + 2y - z = 6 \\ -x + 3y + 2z = 9 \end{cases}$

13. $\begin{cases} 3x + 3y + 3z = 4 \\ 2x - y - 5z = 2 \\ 5x + 2y - 2z = 8 \end{cases}$

14. $\begin{cases} -x + y + z = 8 \\ 2x - 2y - 2z = -16 \\ 2x - y + 4z = -6 \end{cases}$

15. **Geometry** In triangle ABC, the measure of angle A is twice the sum of the measures of angles B and C. The measure of angle B is three times the measure of angle C. What are the measures of the angles? $m\angle A = 120°$; $m\angle B = 45°$; $m\angle C = 15°$

16. **Sports** Louie Dampier was the leading scorer in the history of the American Basketball Association (ABA). His 13,726 points were scored on three-point baskets, two-point baskets, and one-point free throws. In his ABA career, Dampier made 2144 more two-point baskets than free throws and 1558 more free throws than three-point baskets. How many three-point baskets, two-point baskets, and free throws did Dampier make?

794 3-point baskets, 4496 2-point baskets, and 2352 free throws

17. **Critical Thinking** The following system of equations has three variables and two equations. $\begin{cases} x + 2y + 4z = 4 \\ 2x + 3y + z = 12 \end{cases}$
    a. Describe what happens when you attempt to solve this system.
    b. Explain why a system of equations must have at least as many equations as there are variables to have a single solution.

18. **Write About It** The graphs of two equations in a 3-by-3 system intersect in a line. What types of solutions could the system have? Explain.

19. This problem will prepare you for the Multi-Step Test Prep on page 228.

The roof lines of a building can be described by the system of equations

$\begin{cases} x + y + z = 53 \\ 3x - 2y + z = 69 \\ -x + 2y - z = -59 \end{cases}$, where the floor is represented by the xy-plane and measurements are in feet.

a. Find the point of intersection of the roof lines. (5, −2, 50)

b. A support column will be placed under the intersection point. How tall must the column be to reach from the floor to the intersection point? 50 ft

c. What are the coordinates of the center of the base of the column? (5, −2, 0)

Teaching Tip **Geometry** For **Exercise 15,** prompt students to realize that a third equation is needed to solve the problem. Ask students to recall the equation that applies to the angle measure of any triangle.

MULTI-STEP TEST PREP **Exercise 19** involves intersecting roof lines that can be modeled using a system of three equations. This exercise prepares students for working with three-dimensional coordinates in the design of an architectural model in the Multi-Step Test Prep on page 228.

Answers

17a. Possible answer: You find an infinite number of solutions.

b. Possible answer: A single solution in 3 dimensions is a point with 3 coordinates, so you need 3 pieces of information to identify the point. Each equation represents a piece of information, so you must have 3.

18. Possible answer: The type of solution will depend on the third equation. The third equation could represent a place that contains the line, intersects the line in a single point, or does not intersect the line at all. There could be 1, 0, or infinitely many solutions.

3-6 PROBLEM SOLVING

For an annual violin competition, judges score the musicians in three categories: technique, creativity, and presentation. Each category is worth a percent of the final score. Use the table for Exercises 1–3.

Musician	Technique	Creativity	Presentation	Final Score
Jonathan	7	8	8	7.6
Miguel	9	4	8	7.4
Travis	6	10	6	7.0

1. Find the value of each category in the judging.
   a. Write a system of equations to represent the data in the table. $\begin{cases} 7t + 8c + 8p = 7.6 \\ 9t + 4c + 8p = 7.4 \\ 6t + 10c + 6p = 7.0 \end{cases}$
   b. What percent of the final score is based on technique? 40%
   c. What percent of the final score is based on creativity? 25%
   d. What percent of the final score is based on presentation? 35%
2. How many more points would Miguel have needed to score for creativity to win the competition? 1 more point
3. Leesa scored 8 points for technique and 9 points for creativity. Her final score was 7.2. How many points did she score for presentation? 5 points

A student-written performance is playing at a local high school. Rachelle paid $52 for two adult, two student, and one child tickets; RJ paid $56 for one adult, two student, and three child tickets; and Hong-An paid $44 for one adult and four child tickets. Choose the letter for the best answer.

4. Austin wants to know the cost of each type of ticket, a, s, and c. RJ says she can write a system of equations using the data. Which equation is not part of this system?
   A $2a + 2s + c = 52$
   B $a + 2s + 3c = 56$
   C $a + 4c = 44$
   (D) $2a + s + 2c = 54$
5. Austin solves the correct system of equations. What is the price for each type of ticket?
   A Adult: $13; student: $9; child: $7
   (B) Adult: $12; student: $10; child: $8
   C Adult: $11; student: $10; child: $10
   D Adult: $11; student: $9; child: $8

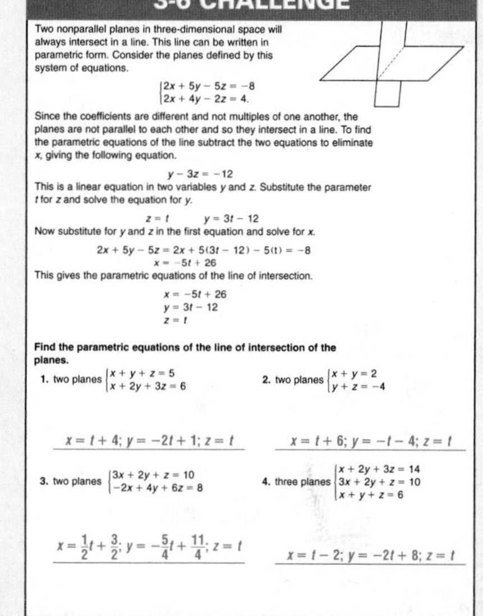

3-6 CHALLENGE

Two nonparallel planes in three-dimensional space will always intersect in a line. This line can be written in parametric form. Consider the planes defined by this system of equations.

$$\begin{cases} 2x + 5y - 5z = -8 \\ 2x + 4y - 2z = 4. \end{cases}$$

Since the coefficients are different and not multiples of one another, the planes are not parallel to each other and so they intersect in a line. To find the parametric equations of the line subtract the two equations to eliminate x, giving the following equation.

$$y - 3z = -12$$

This is a linear equation in two variables y and z. Substitute the parameter t for z and solve the equation for y.

$$z = t \qquad y = 3t - 12$$

Now substitute for y and z in the first equation and solve for x.

$$2x + 5y - 5z = 2x + 5(3t - 12) - 5(t) = -8$$
$$x = -5t + 26$$

This gives the parametric equations of the line of intersection.

$$x = -5t + 26$$
$$y = 3t - 12$$
$$z = t$$

Find the parametric equations of the line of intersection of the planes.

1. two planes $\begin{cases} x + y + z = 5 \\ x + 2y + 3z = 6 \end{cases}$ $x = t + 4;\ y = -2t + 1;\ z = t$
2. two planes $\begin{cases} x + y = 2 \\ y + z = -4 \end{cases}$ $x = t + 6;\ y = -t - 4;\ z = t$
3. two planes $\begin{cases} 3x + 2y + z = 10 \\ -2x + 4y + 6z = 8 \end{cases}$ $x = \frac{1}{2}t + \frac{3}{2};\ y = -\frac{5}{4}t + \frac{11}{4};\ z = t$
4. three planes $\begin{cases} x + 2y + 3z = 14 \\ 3x + 2y + z = 10 \\ x + y + z = 6 \end{cases}$ $x = t - 2;\ y = -2t + 8;\ z = t$

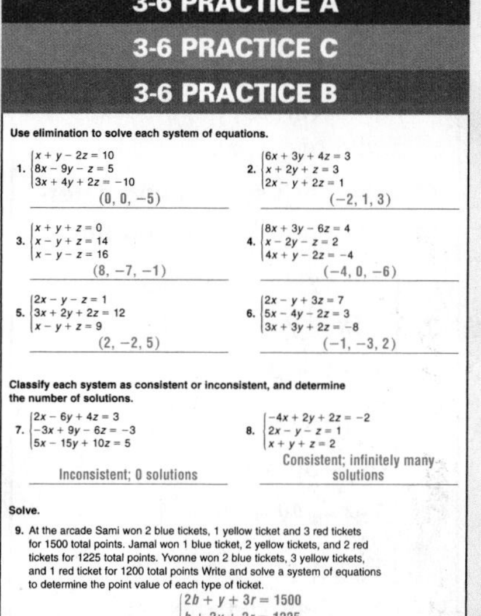

3-6 PRACTICE A

3-6 PRACTICE C

3-6 PRACTICE B

Use elimination to solve each system of equations.

1. $\begin{cases} x + y - 2z = 10 \\ 8x - 9y - z = 5 \\ 3x + 4y + 2z = -10 \end{cases}$ (0, 0, −5)
2. $\begin{cases} 6x + 3y + 4z = 3 \\ x + 2y + z = 3 \\ 2x - y + 2z = 1 \end{cases}$ (−2, 1, 3)
3. $\begin{cases} x + y + z = 0 \\ x - y + z = 14 \\ x - y - z = 16 \end{cases}$ (8, −7, −1)
4. $\begin{cases} 8x + 3y - 6z = 4 \\ x - 2y - z = 2 \\ 4x + y - 2z = -4 \end{cases}$ (−4, 0, −6)
5. $\begin{cases} 2x - y - z = 1 \\ 3x + 2y + 2z = 12 \\ x - y + z = 9 \end{cases}$ (2, −2, 5)
6. $\begin{cases} 2x - y + 3z = 7 \\ 5x - 4y - 2z = 3 \\ 3x + 3y + 2z = -8 \end{cases}$ (−1, −3, 2)

Classify each system as consistent or inconsistent, and determine the number of solutions.

7. $\begin{cases} 2x - 6y + 4z = 3 \\ -3x + 9y - 6z = -3 \\ 5x - 15y + 10z = 5 \end{cases}$ Inconsistent; 0 solutions
8. $\begin{cases} -4x + 2y + 2z = -2 \\ 2x - y - z = 1 \\ x + y + z = 2 \end{cases}$ Consistent; infinitely many solutions

Solve.

9. At the arcade Sami won 2 blue tickets, 1 yellow ticket and 3 red tickets for 1500 total points. Jamal won 1 blue ticket, 2 yellow tickets, and 2 red tickets for 1225 total points. Yvonne won 2 blue tickets, 3 yellow tickets, and 1 red ticket for 1200 total points Write and solve a system of equations to determine the point value of each type of ticket.
$\begin{cases} 2b + y + 3r = 1500 \\ b + 2y + 2r = 1225 \\ 2b + 3y + r = 1200 \end{cases}$
blue tickets: 125 points; yellow tickets: 200 points; red tickets: 350 points

TEST PREP DOCTOR For Exercise 22, you may wish to remind students that a valuable test-taking skill is to work backward from the solution. Students who chose **F** or **G** did not use all the data. Students who chose **H** misread the relationships.

Journal

Have students use their own words to describe how to use elimination to solve a 3-by-3 system.

ALTERNATIVE ASSESSMENT

Have students create a real-world problem that can be modeled using a 3-by-3 system. Have them solve the problem using methods presented in the lesson, and interpret the solution.

Power Presentations with PowerPoint®

3-6 Lesson Quiz

1. At the library book sale, each type of book is priced differently. The table shows the number of books Joy and her friends each bought, and the amount each person spent. Find the price of each type of book.

	Hard-cover	Paper-back	Audio Books	Total Spent
Hal	3	4	1	\$17
Ina	2	5	1	\$15
Joy	3	3	2	\$20

hardcover: \$3; paperback: \$1; audio books: \$4

Classify each system and determine the number of solutions.

2. $\begin{cases} 2x - y + 2z = 5 \\ -3x + y - z = -1 \\ x - y + 3z = 2 \end{cases}$

inconsistent; none

3. $\begin{cases} 9x - 3y + 6z = 3 \\ 12x - 4y + 8z = 4 \\ -6x + 2y - 4z = -2 \end{cases}$

consistent, dependent; infinite

Also available on transparency

TEST PREP

20. Which point is the solution to this system of equations? $\begin{cases} 2x + y + 3z = -1 \\ 4x + 2y + 3z = 1 \\ x - y + 4z = -6 \end{cases}$

Ⓐ (2, −2, −1) Ⓑ (0, 2, −1) Ⓒ (2, 1, −1) Ⓓ (3, −2, 2)

21. Ann, Betty, and Charlotte are sisters. Ann is twice as old as Betty, and Betty is 12 years younger than Charlotte. In 5 years, Charlotte will be twice as old as Betty. What are the sisters' ages?

Ⓕ Ann is 6, Betty is 3, and Charlotte is 15.
Ⓗ Ann is 5, Betty is 10, and Charlotte is 22.
Ⓖ Ann is 34, Betty is 17, and Charlotte is 29.
Ⓙ Ann is 14, Betty is 7, and Charlotte is 19.

22. **Short Response** What is the value of the x-coordinate of the solution to the following system of equations? $\begin{cases} x + 4y = 6 \\ 2x + 3z = 12 \\ 4y + z = 10 \end{cases}$ **x = 0**

CHALLENGE AND EXTEND

23. Use any method to solve the following 4-by-4 system. $\begin{cases} w + 2x + 2y + z = -2 \\ w + 3x - 2y - z = -6 \\ -2w - x + 3y + 3z = 6 \\ w + 4x + y - 2z = -14 \end{cases}$

w = 1, x = −2, y = −1, z = 3

24. **Economics** Three investors each put \$1000 into their retirement accounts. They had three funds to choose from—fund A, fund B, and fund C. Each investor divided the money differently, as shown in the table below. The table also shows the gain for each investor for the year. Find the yield in percents for each fund.

Investor	Fund A	Fund B	Fund C	Gain
M. Nguyen	\$300	\$300	\$400	\$56
A. O'Sullivan	\$600	\$200	\$200	\$76
T. Lane	\$100	\$300	\$600	\$30

Fund A yields 9%. Fund B yields 15%. Fund C yields −4%.

SPIRAL REVIEW

Perform the given translation of the point (−3, 2), and give the coordinates of the translated point. *(Lesson 1-8)*

25. 6 units right and 1 unit up **(3, 3)**
26. 4 units left and 2 units down **(−7, 0)**
27. **Construction** The blueprint for a house showed the kitchen as 11 cm by 8 cm. If the blueprint is drawn to a 1 cm : 0.65 m scale, what are the dimensions of the kitchen in the house? *(Lesson 2-2)* **7.15 m by 5.2 m**

Write each equation in slope-intercept form, and then graph. *(Lesson 2-3)*

28. $4x - 3y = -6$
29. $3y - 2x = -12$
30. $2x + 5y = 15$

Answers

28. $y = \frac{4}{3}x + 2$

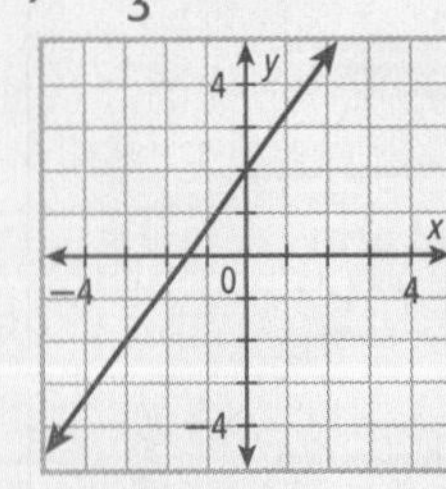

29. $y = \frac{2}{3}x - 4$

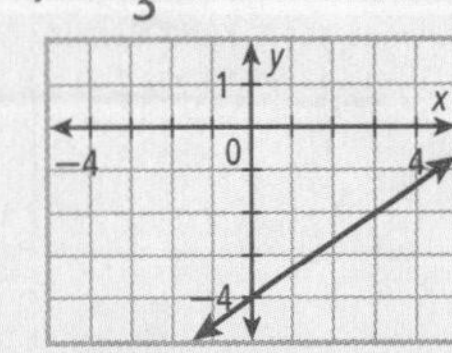

30. $y = -\frac{2}{5}x + 3$

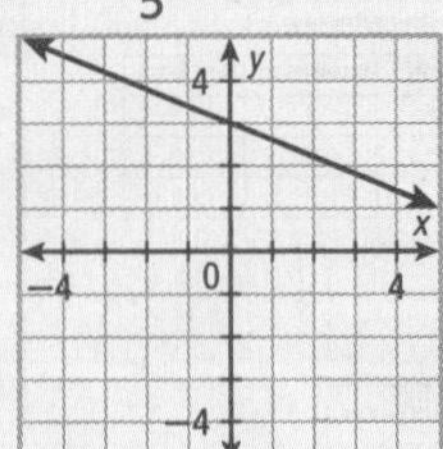

Explore Parametric Equations

A set of *parametric equations* is a system of two equations with the same independent variable, usually *t*. The independent variable *t* is called the *parameter*.

Use with Lesson 3-6

go.hrw.com
Lab Resources Online
KEYWORD: MB7 Lab3

Activity

Follow the steps to graph the following parametric equations. $\begin{cases} x = 2t \\ y = 5t \end{cases}$

Press MODE, and change the graphing mode to **PAR** (for parametric). Press Y=. Enter $2t$ for the first equation (X_{1T}) and $5t$ for the second equation (Y_{1T}). To enter the variable *t*, use the X,T,θ,n key. Graph the equations.

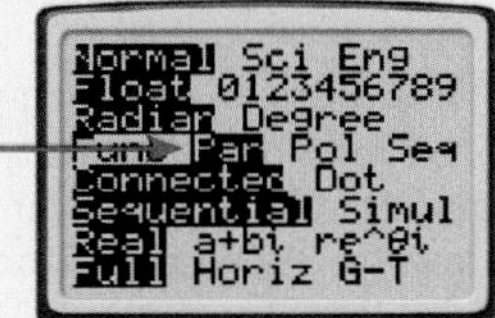

You can use the TRACE key to view values of both equations and *t*. You can change the look of the graph and the values by adjusting the WINDOW settings.

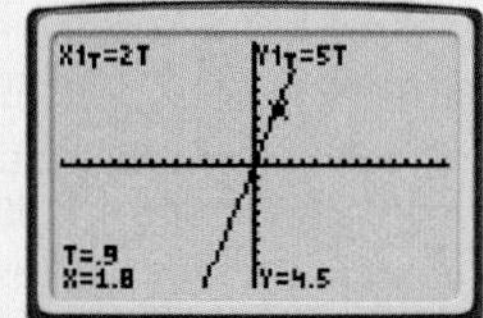

Try This

1. Consider $\begin{cases} x = 2t \\ y = \frac{1}{2}t \end{cases}$.
   a. Graph the relation and estimate the slope of the line created by the graph. Use the following window settings: **Tmin = −10**, **Tmax = 10**, and **Tstep = 0.1**, and use the square viewing window.
   b. **Critical Thinking** How does the slope of the line relate to the slope of the two parametric equations?
   Possible answer: The slope is the quotient of the y1 coefficient and the x1 coefficient.
2. An airplane is traveling at a constant horizontal speed of 500 ft/s and is ascending at a constant rate of 50 ft/s. A model of the path of the airplane is given parametrically by $\begin{cases} x = 500t \\ y = 50t \end{cases}$ for *t* s.
   a. Graph the path of the airplane for $t = 20$ to $t = 180$ s and identify the location of the plane after 50 s.
   b. When will the plane reach an altitude of 5000 ft? (*Hint:* You may have to adjust your viewing window.) **100 s**
3. **Critical Thinking** Create a graph of the line $y = x$ by using parametric equations.
4. **Extension** Consider $\begin{cases} x = t^2 \\ y = t \end{cases}$.
   a. Graph the relation. Use the following window settings: **Tmin = −10**, **Tmax = 10**, and **Tstep = 0.1**, and use the square viewing window.
   b. Describe the relation and write the formula in terms of *x* and *y* only. Is the relation a function?

Teacher to Teacher

Have students graph the path of a golf ball given by the following parametric equations.

$$\begin{cases} x(t) = 64t & t \text{ is in seconds.} \\ y(t) = -16t^2 + 32t & x \text{ and } y \text{ are in yards.} \end{cases}$$

As students experiment to find a viewing window, they learn about the parameters including increments of *t* (0.1 works nicely). Have students use TRACE to estimate the maximum height along its path (16 yd), the distance of the drive (128 yd), and the amount of time that the ball is in the air (2 s). Students discover that they are given the horizontal and vertical distances with the time for every point traced.

Jere Hassberger
Saline, MI

Organizer

Use with Lesson 3-6

Pacing:
Traditional $\frac{1}{2}$ day
Block $\frac{1}{4}$ day

Objective: Use a graphing calculator to explore parametric equations.

Materials: graphing calculator

Online Edition
Graphing Calculator, TechKeys

Countdown to Testing Week 7

Resources

Technology Lab Activities
3-6 Lab Recording Sheet

Teach

Discuss

To help students understand the relationship between the independent and dependent variables, have them calculate (algebraically) the values of *x* and *y* for several values of *t* and then use the TRACE feature to locate and verify the corresponding points on the graph.

Close

Key Concept

In parametric equations, *x* and *y* both depend on the variable *t*.

Assessment

Journal Have students explain how to graph—by hand or with a calculator—a pair of parametric equations.

Answers

1a, 2a, 3–4. See p. A23.

State Resources

go.hrw.com
State Resources Online
KEYWORD: MB7 Resources

Organizer

Objective: Assess students' ability to apply concepts and skills in Lessons 3-5 through 3-6 in a real-world format.

Online Edition

Resources

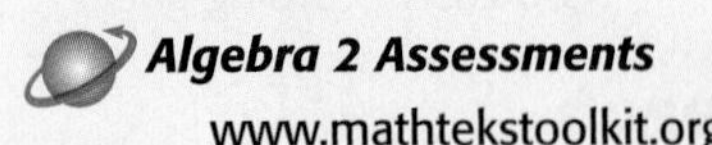

Algebra 2 Assessments
www.mathtekstoolkit.org

Problems	Text Reference
1-3	Lesson 3-5
4	Skills Bank page S61
5	Lesson 3-5

Answers

1. $A'(-30, 0, 0)$, $B'(-30, 16, 0)$, $C'(-30, 16, 11)$, and $D'(-30, 0, 11)$
2. $A''(-60, 0, 0)$, $B''(-60, 16, 0)$, $C''(-60, 16, 11)$, and $D''(-60, 0, 11)$
3. See p. A23.

State Resources

go.hrw.com
State Resources Online
KEYWORD: MB7 Resources

MULTI-STEP TEST PREP

SECTION 3B

Linear Equations in Three Dimensions

Building Bridges A bridge is to be constructed between two buildings. The cross sections of the bridge are 12 steel rectangles 16 feet wide by 11 feet high. The bridge will be represented by a three-dimensional model.

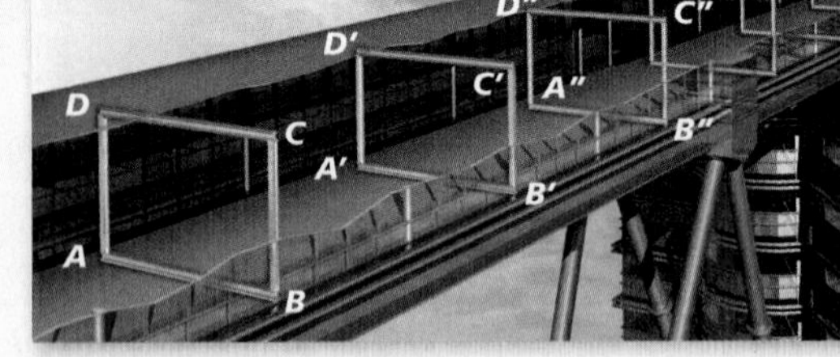

1. The coordinates of the vertices defining the first cross section are $A(0, 0, 0)$, $B(0, 16, 0)$, $C(0, 16, 11)$, and $D(0, 0, 11)$. What are the coordinates of the points A', B', C', and D' if the rectangular cross sections are 30 feet away from each other?
2. What are the coordinates of the points A'', B'', C'', and D''?
3. A supervisor changes the sketch so that point A has coordinates $(150, 0, -16)$. What are the new coordinates for points B, C, and D? What are the new coordinates for points A', B' C', and D'? What about A'', B'', C'', and D''?
4. The steel cross sections will be rigged with sliding metal fire doors that will close in case of emergency. What is the area covered by one of these doors? **176 ft²**
5. Due to some budget restrictions, the bridge has to be reduced to a width of 14 feet and a height of 9 feet. What will be the coordinates of points A, B, and D if point C is defined as the origin $(0, 0, 0)$?

$A(0, -14, -9)$, $B(0, 0, -9)$, and $D(0, -14, 0)$

INTERVENTION

Scaffolding Questions

1. Imagine pushing the first rectangle into the second. Which axis would you slide along? *x*-axis
2. Which coordinate(s) will be different in point A' and point A''? *x*-coordinate
3. How is point A transformed under the change? It is translated 150 units forward along the *x*-axis and 16 units down along the *z*-axis.
4. How can you use the coordinates to find the dimensions of each cross-section? Subtract the *y*-coordinates. Subtract the *z*-coordinates.
5. What is the new distance from C to B? 9 ft From C to D? 14 ft

Extension

Write equations in 3 variables for the planes that contain the walls, floor, and ceiling of the bridge using the coordinates from **Problem 1.** $y = 0, y = 16, z = 0, z = 11$

CHAPTER 3

SECTION 3B

Quiz for Lessons 3-5 Through 3-6

 **3-5 Linear Equations in Three Dimensions**

Graph each point in three-dimensional space.

1. $(-3, 2, 1)$ **2.** $(2, -3, -2)$ **3.** $(3, 1, -3)$

Graph each linear equation in three-dimensional space.

4. $2x - 2y + 4z = 8$ **5.** $2x + y - 2z = -4$ **6.** $x + 5y + 3z = 15$

Finance Use the following information and the table for Problems 7 and 8. A dental office charges $50 for teeth cleanings, $100 for performing a one-surface filling, and $75 for an initial visit with X rays. The dental office's total income was exactly $3500 for each of the days shown in the table.

Day	Cleaning	Filling	Initial Visit
Monday	20	22	■ 4
Tuesday	■ 25	18	6
Wednesday	16	■ 24	4
Thursday	25	21	■ 2

$50x + 100y + 75z = 3500$

7. Write a linear equation in three variables to represent this situation.

8. Complete the table for the possible numbers of appointments each day.

 **3-6 Solving Linear Systems in Three Variables**

Use elimination to solve each system of equations.

9. $\begin{cases} x + y + z = 0 \\ 2x + y - 2z = -8 \\ -x + 4z = 10 \end{cases}$ $(-2, 0, 2)$

10. $\begin{cases} x + 2y + z = 7 \\ x - 2y - 4z = 0 \\ 2x - y + 4z = -3 \end{cases}$ $(2, 3, -1)$

11. $\begin{cases} 2x + 2y + z = 10 \\ x - 2y + 3z = 13 \\ x - y + 3z = 12 \end{cases}$ $(5, -1, 2)$

Business Use the following information and the table for Problems 12 and 13. JoJo's Pretzel Stand has three different types of pretzels, indicated by type A, type B, and type C. The table shows the total revenue for three hours on a particular afternoon.

Time	Type A	Type B	Type C	Revenue
2:00 P.M.–3:00 P.M.	6	8	14	$65
3:00 P.M.–4:00 P.M.	10	10	15	$80
4:00 P.M.–5:00 P.M.	12	6	9	$60

12. Write a system in three variables to represent the data in the table.

13. How much does each type of pretzel cost? A: $2; B: $2.25; C: $2.50

Classify each system as consistent or inconsistent, and determine the number of solutions.

14. $\begin{cases} 2x - 2y + 3z = -2 \\ 4y + 6z = 1 \\ 4x - 4y + 6z = 5 \end{cases}$

15. $\begin{cases} 4x - y + z = 5 \\ 3x + y + 2z = 5 \\ 2x - 5z = -8 \end{cases}$

16. $\begin{cases} 2x + y - 3z = 4 \\ x - 3y + z = -8 \\ -x + 3y - z = 8 \end{cases}$

READY TO GO ON? SECTION 3B

Organizer

Objective: Assess students' mastery of concepts and skills in Lessons 3-5 through 3-6.

Resources

 ***Assessment Resources***

Section 3B Quiz

 **Test & Practice Generator**

One-Stop Planner®

INTERVENTION 

Resources

 ***Ready to Go On? Intervention and Enrichment*** **Worksheets**

 ***Ready to Go On?*** **CD-ROM**

 ***Ready to Go On?*** **Online**

my.hrw.com

Answers

1–6, 12, 14–16. See p. A23.

READY TO GO ON? Diagnose and Prescribe

NO INTERVENE

Ready to Go On? Intervention	Worksheets	CD-ROM	Online
	Ready to Go On? Intervention, Section 3B		
Lesson 3-5	3-5 Intervention	Activity 3-5	Diagnose and Prescribe Online
Lesson 3-6	3-6 Intervention	Activity 3-6	

YES ENRICH

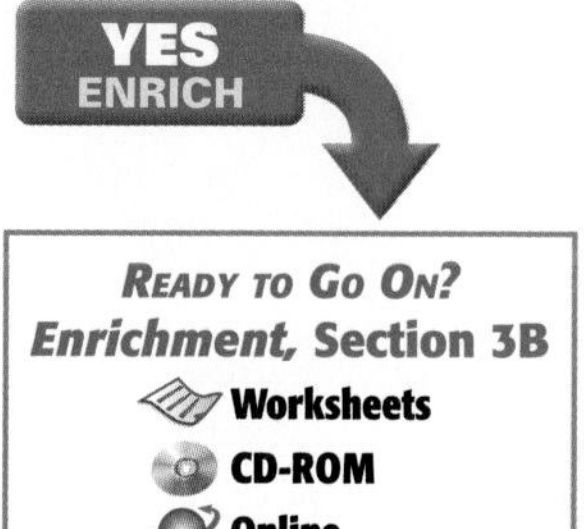

Ready to Go On? Enrichment, **Section 3B**

Worksheets

CD-ROM

Online

CHAPTER 3

Organizer

Pacing: Traditional 1 day
Block $\frac{1}{2}$ day

Objective: Graph parametric equations, and use them to model real-world applications.

Write the function represented by a pair of parametric equations

Using the Extension

In Chapter 3, students learned about systems of equations, their graphs, and their solutions. In this extension, students use what they have learned to work with pairs of parametric equations, which are, essentially, systems of equations in three variables. In this extension, students use parametric equations to model real-world applications.

Teaching Tip **Kinesthetic** Use a toy or paper airplane to solidify students' understanding of the graph in **Example 1.** Trace along the graph as you "tick off" seconds of time. Prompt students to relate the movement of the model to the table of values that was developed to plot points on the graph. Make sure students understand that each column of the table relates three variables, although only two are visible on the graph.

State Resources

EXTENSION

Parametric Equations

Objectives
Graph parametric equations, and use them to model real-world applications.
Write the function represented by a pair of parametric equations.

Vocabulary
parameter
parametric equations

As an airplane ascends after takeoff, its altitude increases at a rate of 45 ft/s while its distance on the ground from the airport increases at 210 ft/s.

Both of these rates can be expressed in terms of time. When two variables, such as x and y, are expressed in terms of a third variable, such as t, the third variable is called a **parameter**. The equations that define this relationship are **parametric equations**.

EXAMPLE 1 **Writing and Graphing Parametric Equations**

As an airplane ascends after takeoff, its altitude increases at a rate of 45 ft/s while its distance on the ground from the airport increases at 210 ft/s.

A **Write parametric equations to model the location of the plane described above. Then graph the equations on a coordinate grid.**

Using the horizontal and vertical speeds given above, write equations for the ground distance x and altitude y in terms of t.

$$\begin{cases} x = 210t \\ y = 45t \end{cases}$$ *Use the distance formula $d = rt$*

Make a table to help you draw the graph. Use different t-values to find x- and y-values. The x and y rows give the points to plot.

t	0	2	4	6	8
x	0	420	840	1260	1680
y	0	90	180	270	360

Plot and connect $(0, 0)$, $(420, 90)$, $(840, 180)$, $(1260, 270)$, and $(1680, 360)$.
The graph is shown at right.

B **Find the location of the airplane 15 seconds after takeoff.**

$x = 210t = 210(15) = 3150$
$y = 45t = 45(15) = 675$ *Substitute $t = 15$*

At $t = 15$, the airplane has a ground distance of 3150 feet from the airport and an altitude of 675 feet.

A helicopter takes off with a horizontal speed of 5 ft/s and a vertical speed of 20 ft/s

1a. Write equations for and draw a graph of the motion of the helicopter.

1b. Describe the location of the helicopter at $t = 10$ seconds.

1a. $\begin{cases} x = 5t \\ y = 20t \end{cases}$

1b. At $t = 10$, the helicopter has a ground distance of 50 ft from its takeoff point and an altitude of 200 ft.

1 Introduce

Motivate

Use the context of the plane's ascent to review the concepts of dependent and independent variables. Help students understand how the value of one independent variable (in this case, time) can influence the values of two dependent variables (in this case, altitude and horizontal distance).

2 Teach

Guided Instruction

Explain that the location of the plane is defined by two distances, one vertical and one horizontal. Remind students of the formula *distance* = *rate* × *time* and show them how the equations model both distances. Have students calculate the values and plot them by hand, as this will help provide them with a better understanding of how x and y are related to the parameter t, and how the graph models the situation.

You can use parametric equations to write a function that relates the two variables by using the substitution method.

EXAMPLE 2 Writing Functions Based on Parametric Equations

Use the data from Example 1 to write an equation for the airplane's altitude y in terms of ground distance x.

Solve one of the two parametric equations for t. Then substitute to get one equation whose variables are x and y.

$x = 210t$, so $\frac{x}{210} = t$	*Solve for t in the first equation.*
$y = 45t$	*Second equation*
$y = 45\left(\frac{x}{210}\right) = \frac{3}{14}x$	*Substitute and simplify.*
$y = \frac{3}{14}x$	

The equation for the airplane's altitude in terms of ground distance is $y = \frac{3}{14}x$.

Recall that the helicopter in Check It Out Problem 1 takes off with a horizontal speed of 5 ft/s and a vertical speed of 20 ft/s.

2. Write an equation for the helicopter's motion in terms of only x and y. $y = 4x$

EXTENSION Exercises

Draw a graph to represent each set of parametric equations.

1. $\begin{cases} x = 4t \\ y = 2t \end{cases}$
2. $\begin{cases} x = t - 2 \\ y = 4t \end{cases}$
3. $\begin{cases} x = \frac{t}{4} \\ y = -3t \end{cases}$
4. $\begin{cases} x = 20t \\ y = 10t + 10 \end{cases}$

Write one equation for each set of parametric equations in terms of only x and y.

5. $\begin{cases} x = 3t \\ y = 2t \end{cases}$ $y = \frac{2}{3}x$
6. $\begin{cases} x = 2t + 4 \\ y = 5t \end{cases}$ $y = \frac{5}{2}(x - 4)$
7. $\begin{cases} x = \frac{3}{5}t \\ y = 6t \end{cases}$ $y = 10x$
8. $\begin{cases} x = 7.5t \\ y = 20t + 2 \end{cases}$ $y = \frac{8}{3}x + 2$

9. **Oceanography** Suppose a research submarine descends from the surface with a horizontal speed of 1.8 m/s and a vertical speed of 0.9 m/s.
   a. Write equations for and draw a graph of the motion of the submarine.
   b. Find the depth of the submarine after 50 s.
   c. Find the submarine's depth after 1 day. Does this answer make sense? Explain.

10. **Hiking** From her starting point, a hiker walks along a straight path. Her north-south speed is 3 mi/h (to the north), and her east-west speed is 0.4 mi/h (to the east). Let x represent how far east of her starting point the hiker is, and let y represent how far north she is. Write an equation for her motion in terms of only x and y. Find the location of the hiker when $x = 2$.
$y = \frac{15}{2}x$; 2 mi east and 15 mi north of the starting point

Power Presentations with PowerPoint®

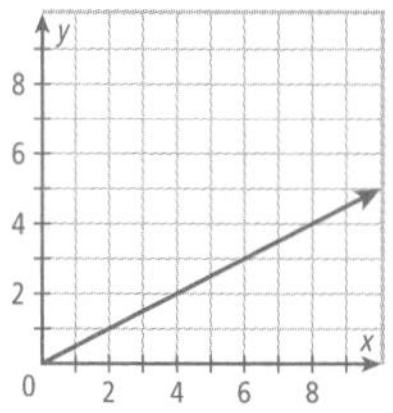

Additional Examples

Example 1

As a cargo plane ascends after takeoff, its altitude increases at a rate of 40 ft/s. Its ground distance from the airport increases at a rate of 240 ft/s.

A. Write equations for and draw a graph of the motion of the cargo plane.

$\begin{cases} x = 240t \\ y = 40t \end{cases}$

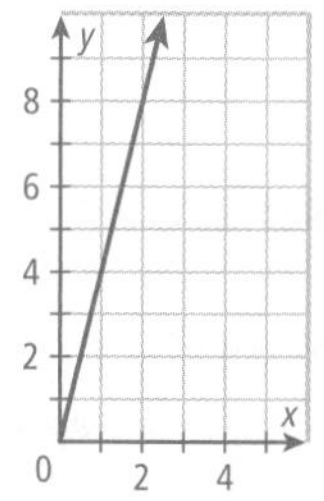

B. Find the location of the cargo plane 20 seconds after takeoff.

ground distance: 4800 ft from airport; altitude: 800 ft

Example 2

Use the data from Additional Example 1 to write an equation for the cargo plane's altitude y in terms of ground distance x.

$y = \frac{1}{6}x$

Also available on transparency

INTERVENTION
Questioning Strategies

EXAMPLE 1

- How are x and y related to t?
- How are the values of t reflected in the graph?

EXAMPLE 2

- What does this solution tell you about the path of the plane?

Answers

3.

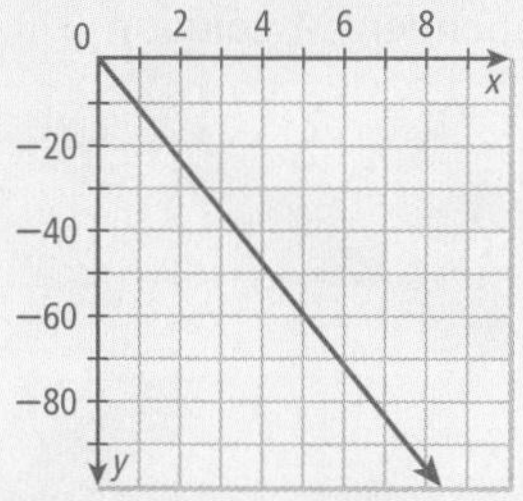

4.

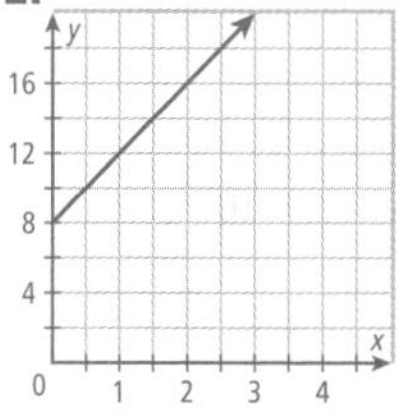

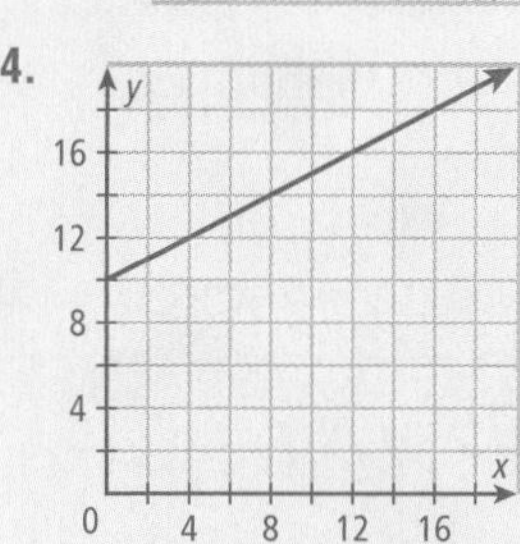

3 Close

Summarize

Ask students to describe parametric equations and how they can be used to model real-world situations. Have students discuss the relationships that exist among the variables in a pair of parametric equations.

Answers

9a. $\begin{cases} x = 1.8t \\ y = -0.9t \end{cases}$

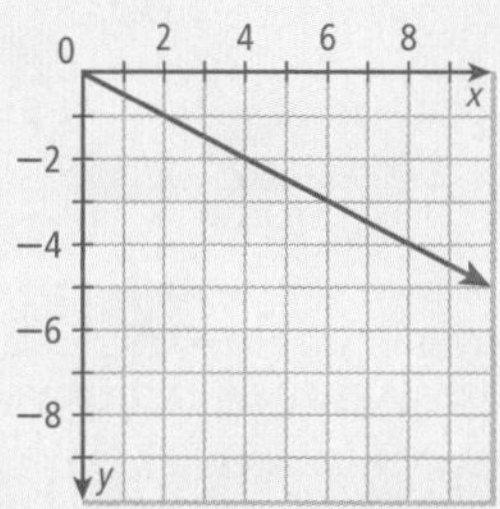

b. −45 m

c. −77,760 m; possible answer: it doesn't make sense, because the ocean is less than 77,760 m deep and the submarine would hit the ocean floor in less than 1 day.

CHAPTER 3 **Study Guide: Review**

Objective: Help students organize and review key concepts and skills presented in Chapter 3.

Online Edition
Multilingual Glossary

Countdown to Testing Week 7

Resources

Puzzle Pro
One-Stop Planner®

Multilingual Glossary Online
go.hrw.com
KEYWORD: MB7 Glossary

Tutorial Videos CD-ROM

Test & Practice Generator
One-Stop Planner®

Answers

1. dependent
2. elimination
3. system of linear inequalities; feasible region
4. three-dimensional coordinate system; ordered triple
5. consistent
6. (5, 10)
7. (4, 2)
8. (−4, −1)
9. (0, −2)
10. independent; one solution
11. dependent; infinitely many solutions
12. inconsistent; no solution
13. independent; 1 solution
14. 3 locks

CHAPTER 3

Study Guide: Review

Vocabulary

Complete the sentences below with vocabulary words from the list above.

1. A consistent and ___?___ system has infinitely many solutions.
2. ___?___ involves adding or subtracting equations to get rid of one of the variables in a system.
3. In a linear programming problem, the solution to the ___?___ can be graphed as a(n) ___?___.
4. Each point in a(n) ___?___ can be represented by a(n) ___?___.
5. A(n) ___?___ system is a set of equations or inequalities that has at least one solution.

3-1 Using Graphs and Tables to Solve Linear Systems *(pp. 182–189)*

EXAMPLES

■ Solve $\begin{cases} x + y = 3 \\ 3x - 6y = -9 \end{cases}$ by using a graph and a table.

Solve each equation for *y*.

$$\begin{cases} y = -x + 3 \\ y = \frac{1}{2}x + \frac{3}{2} \end{cases}$$

Make a table of values.

$y = -x + 3$

x	y
0	3
1	2
4	1

$y = \frac{1}{2}x + \frac{3}{2}$

x	y
0	1.5
1	2
4	2.5

Graph the lines.

The solution is (1, 2).

EXERCISES

Solve each system by using a graph and a table.

6. $\begin{cases} y = 2x \\ 3x - y = 5 \end{cases}$
7. $\begin{cases} x + y = 6 \\ x - y = 2 \end{cases}$
8. $\begin{cases} x - 6y = 2 \\ 2x - 5y = -3 \end{cases}$
9. $\begin{cases} x - 3y = 6 \\ 3x - y = 2 \end{cases}$

Classify each system and determine the number of solutions.

10. $\begin{cases} y = x - 7 \\ x + 9y = 16 \end{cases}$
11. $\begin{cases} \frac{1}{2}x + 2y = 3 \\ x + 4y = 6 \end{cases}$
12. $\begin{cases} 5x - 10y = 8 \\ x - 2y = 4 \end{cases}$
13. $\begin{cases} 4x - 3y = 21 \\ 2x - 2y = 10 \end{cases}$
14. **Security** A locksmith charges $25 to make a house call and $15 for each lock that is re-keyed. Another locksmith charges $10 to make a house call and $20 for each lock that is re-keyed. For how many locks will the total costs be the same?

3-2 Using Algebraic Methods to Solve Linear Systems *(pp. 190–197)*

EXAMPLES

- **Use substitution to solve** $\begin{cases} y = x + 6 \\ 4x - 5y = -18 \end{cases}$.

$4x - 5(x + 6) = -18$ *Substitute for y.*
$4x - 5x - 30 = -18 \rightarrow x = -12$

Substitute the x-value into either equation.

$y = x + 6 \rightarrow y = (-12) + 6 \rightarrow y = -6$

The solution to the system is $(-12, -6)$.

- **Use elimination to solve** $\begin{cases} 7x - 2y = 2 \\ 3x + 4y = 30 \end{cases}$.

Multiply the first equation by 2 to eliminate y.

$\begin{cases} 7x - 2y = 2 \\ 3x + 4y = 30 \end{cases} \rightarrow \begin{matrix} 2(7x - 2y = 2) \\ 3x + 4y = 30 \end{matrix} \rightarrow \begin{matrix} 14x - 4y = 4 \\ 3x + 4y = 30 \end{matrix}$

Add the equations. $17x = 34$
First part of the solution $x = 2$

Substitute the x-value into either equation.

$3x + 4y = 30 \rightarrow 3(2) + 4y = 30$

$\rightarrow y = 6$ *Second part of the solution*

The solution to the system is $(2, 6)$.

EXERCISES

Use substitution to solve each system of equations.

15. $\begin{cases} y = 3x \\ 2x - 3y = -7 \end{cases}$

16. $\begin{cases} y = x - 1 \\ 4x - y = 19 \end{cases}$

17. $\begin{cases} 4x - y = 0 \\ 6x - 3y = 12 \end{cases}$

18. $\begin{cases} 5x = -10y \\ 8x - 4y = 40 \end{cases}$

Use elimination to solve each system of equations.

19. $\begin{cases} 4x + 5y = 41 \\ 7x + 5y = 53 \end{cases}$

20. $\begin{cases} -4x - y = -16 \\ -4x - 5y = -32 \end{cases}$

21. $\begin{cases} 2x - y = 8 \\ x + 2y = 9 \end{cases}$

22. $\begin{cases} 9x - 5y = 13 \\ 4x - 6y = 2 \end{cases}$

23. **Mixtures** A popular mixture of potpourri includes pine needles and lavender. If pine needles cost $1.50 per ounce and lavender costs $4.00 per ounce, how much of each ingredient should be mixed to make 80 oz of the potpourri that is worth $200?

3-3 Solving Systems of Linear Inequalities *(pp. 199–204)*

EXAMPLE

- **The combined annual sales for a company's two divisions was almost $12 million. One of the divisions accounted for at least 75% of the total sales. Write and graph a system of inequalities that can be used to determine the possible combinations of sales for both divisions of the company.**

Let x be one division, and let y be the other division with 75% of the sales.

Write the system of inequalities.

$\begin{cases} x + y < 12 \\ y \geq 0.75(x + y) \end{cases} \rightarrow \begin{cases} x + y < 12 & \text{dashed line} \\ y \geq 3x & \text{solid line} \end{cases}$

Graph the boundary lines, and shade accordingly. Notice also that $x > 0$ and $y > 0$.

The overlapping region is the solution for the system.

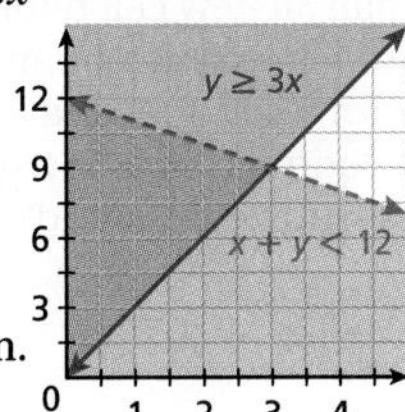

EXERCISES

Graph each system of inequalities.

24. $\begin{cases} y + 1 > 4x \\ y \leq x + 1 \end{cases}$

25. $\begin{cases} y - 3x < 3 \\ 3y \geq x + 3 \end{cases}$

Graph the system of inequalities and classify the figure created by the solution region.

26. $\begin{cases} y \leq -x + 2 \\ x > -1 \\ y > -1 \end{cases}$

27. $\begin{cases} y \geq 2x \\ y < 4 \\ y > 2 \\ y \leq \frac{1}{2}x + 4 \end{cases}$

28. **Business** A coffee shop wants to make a maximum of 120 lb of a coffee mixture that costs less than $10/lb. The shop will mix coffee that is sold at $8/lb with coffee sold at $11.50/lb. Write and graph a system of inequalities that shows the possible mixtures of the two coffee types.

Answers

15. (1, 3)
16. (6, 5)
17. (−2, −8)
18. (4, −2)
19. (4, 5)
20. (3, 4)
21. (5, 2)
22. (2, 1)
23. 48 oz pine; 32 oz lavender
24.

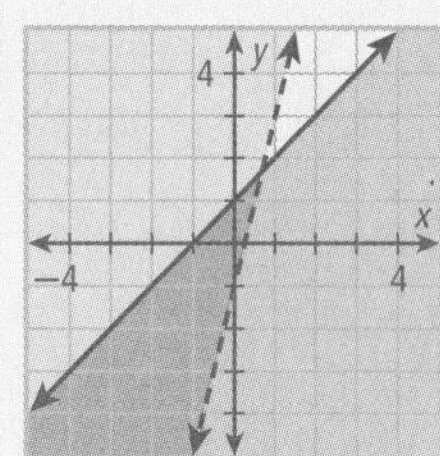

25.

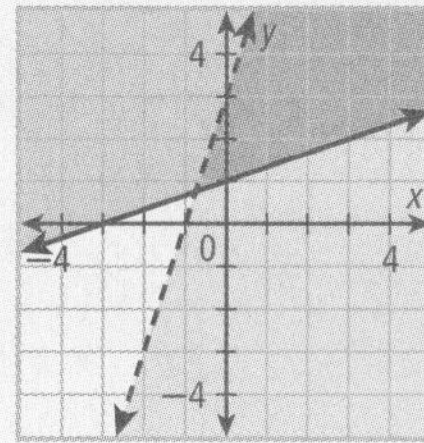

26. right triangle

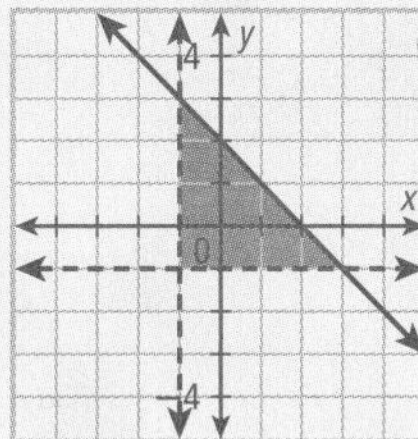

27 trapezoid

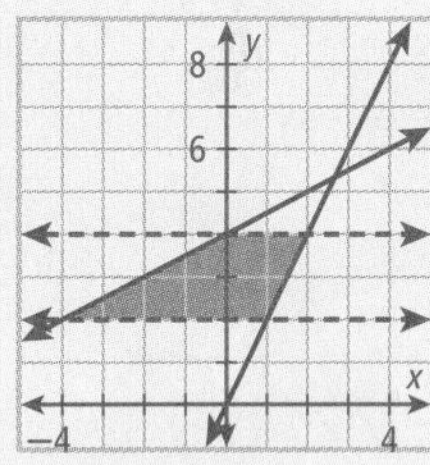

28. $\begin{cases} x + y \leq 120 \\ 8x + 11.5y < 1200 \end{cases}$

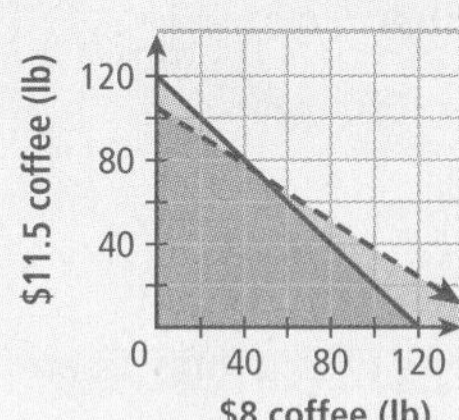

Answers

29. 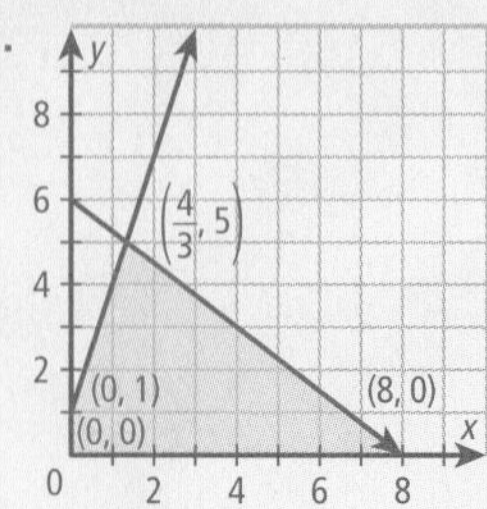

30. 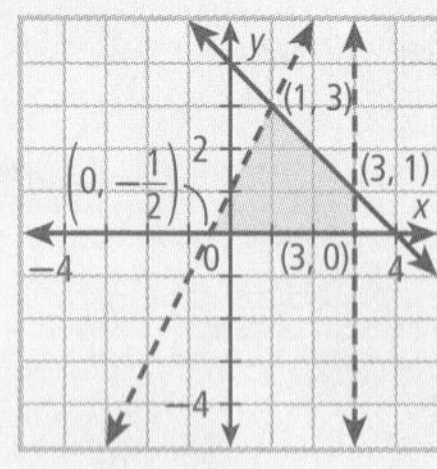

31. 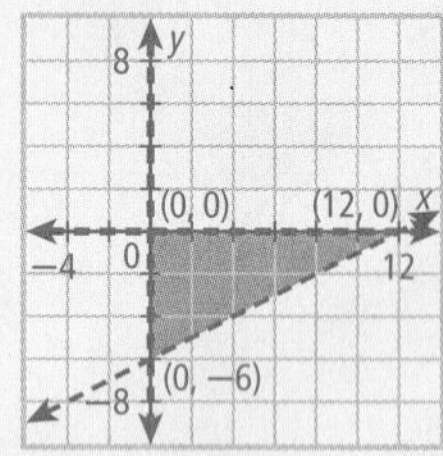

32. 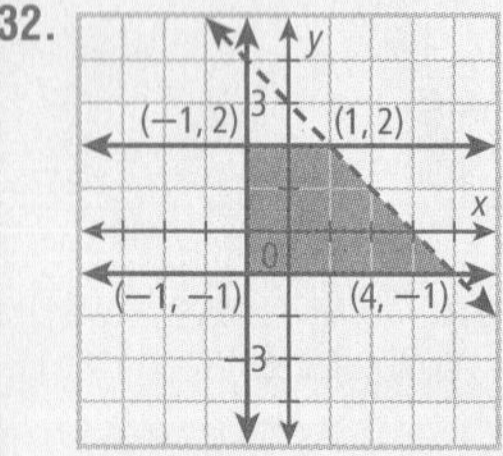

33. 58

34. −4.5

35. $\begin{cases} x \geq 0 \\ y \geq 0 \\ 6x + 4y \leq 720 \\ x \geq 2y \end{cases}$

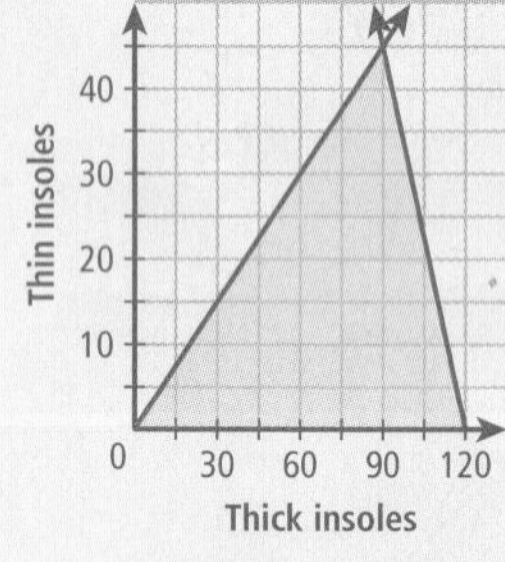

36. $P = 8x + 9y$

37. \$1125

38. 25 phones with contracts and 5 without contracts

3-4 Linear Programming *(pp. 205–211)*

EXAMPLE

■ **A café sells cold sandwiches and hot entrées. The range of items sold is shown in the table. The café has never sold more than a total of 125 sandwiches and entrées in one day. If the café makes a profit of \$0.75 on each sandwich and \$1 on each hot entrée, how many of each item would maximize the café profit?**

Menu Item	Minimum Sold	Maximum Sold
Cold sandwiches	60	80
Hot entrées	40	60

Let x be the number of cold sandwiches, and let y be the number of hot entrées.

Write the constraints.

$$\begin{cases} 60 \leq x \leq 80 & \textit{Number of sandwiches} \\ 40 \leq y \leq 60 & \textit{Number of hot entrées} \\ x + y < 125 & \textit{Number of items sold} \end{cases}$$

Graph the feasible region and identify vertices.

The feasible region has five vertices at (60, 40), (60, 60), (65, 60), (80, 45), and (80, 40).

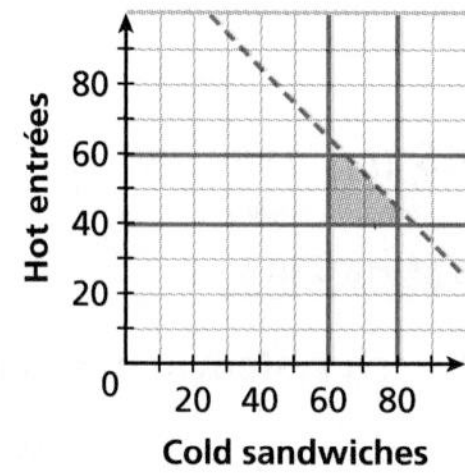

Write the objective function.

The objective function is $P = 0.75x + y$.
$P(0, 0) = 18(0) + 25(0) = 0$

Evaluate the objective function at each vertex.

$P(60, 40) = 0.75(60) + 40 = 85$
$P(60, 60) = 0.75(60) + 60 = 105$
$P(65, 60) = 0.75(65) + 60 = 108.75$
$P(80, 45) = 0.75(80) + 45 = 105$
$P(80, 40) = 0.75(80) + 40 = 100$

The objective function is maximized at (65, 60). The maximum profit of \$108.75 is obtained when 65 cold sandwiches and 60 hot entrées are sold.

EXERCISES

Graph each feasible region.

29. $\begin{cases} x \geq 0 \\ y \geq 0 \\ y \leq 3x + 1 \\ y \leq -\frac{3}{4}x + 6 \end{cases}$

30. $\begin{cases} x < 3 \\ y \geq 0 \\ y < 2x + 1 \\ y \leq -x + 4 \end{cases}$

31. $\begin{cases} x > 0 \\ y < 0 \\ y > \frac{1}{2}x - 6 \end{cases}$

32. $\begin{cases} x \leq 2 \\ y \geq -1 \\ x \geq -1 \\ y \leq -x + 3 \end{cases}$

Maximize or minimize each objective function.

33. Maximize $P = 6x + 10y$ for the constraints from Exercise 29.

34. Minimize $P = 14x + 9y$ for the constraints from Exercise 30.

Manufacturing A shoe insole company produces two models of insoles: an extra thick insole for sports shoes and a thinner insole for dress shoes. The thick insole requires 6 min of manufacturing time and generates a profit of \$8. The thin insole requires 4 min of manufacturing time and generates a profit of \$9. The manufacturing line runs at most 12 h a day, or 720 min. Because of demand, the company manufactures at least twice as many thick insoles as thin insoles.

35. Write the constraints, and graph the feasible region.

36. Write the objective function for the company's profit.

37. What is the maximum profit that can be generated in one day?

38. **Sales** Each day, a cell phone stand sells between 10 and 25 cell phones with new service contracts, and between 5 and 10 cell phones without contracts. The stand never sells more than 30 new cell phones per day. The cell phone stand makes a commission of \$35 for each phone with a contract and \$5 for each phone without a contract. How many of each option would maximize the stand's profit?

3-5 Linear Equations in Three Dimensions (pp. 214–218)

EXAMPLES

- **Graph (2, −1, 3) in three-dimensional space.**

From the origin, move 2 units forward along the x-axis, 1 unit left, and 3 units up.

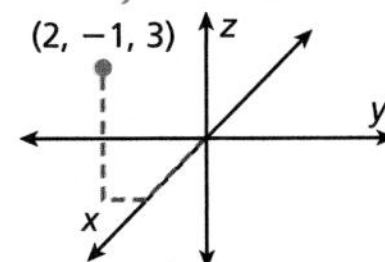

- **Graph the linear equation $3x + 6y - z = -6$ in three-dimensional space.**

Find the intercepts.

x-intercept: $3x = -6 \rightarrow x = -2$

y-intercept: $6y = -6 \rightarrow y = -1$

z-intercept: $-z = -6 \rightarrow z = 6$

Plot the points (−2, 0, 0), (0, −1, 0), and (0, 0, 6). Sketch a plane through the three points.

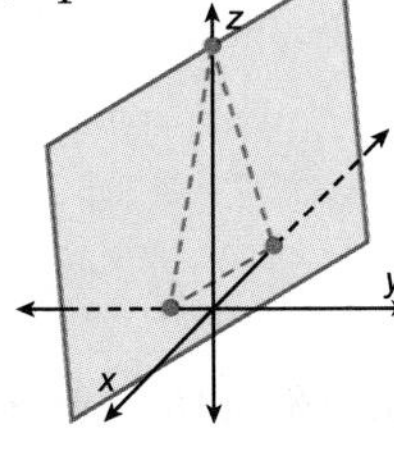

EXERCISES

Graph each point in three-dimensional space.

39. (−1, 0, 3)
40. (2, −2, 1)
41. (0, −1, 1)
42. (3, 1, 0)

Graph each linear equation in three-dimensional space.

43. $x - 3y + 2z = 6$
44. $2x - 4y - 2z = 4$
45. $-x + y - 5z = 5$
46. $3x + 2y + z = -6$

47. Consumer Economics Lee has \$35 to purchase a combination of drinks, pizza, and ice cream for a party. Each drink costs \$2, each pizza costs \$9, and each quart of ice cream costs \$4. Write a linear equation in three variables to represent this situation.

3-6 Solving Linear Systems in Three Variables (pp. 220–226)

EXAMPLES

- **Use elimination to solve** $\begin{cases} 3x + 2y - z = -1 \\ x + 3y - z = -10 \\ 2x - y - 3z = -3 \end{cases}$.

First, eliminate z to obtain a 2-by-2 system.

$$\begin{array}{r} 3x + 2y - z = -1 \\ x + 3y - z = -10 \\ \hline 2x - y \quad = 9 \end{array} \qquad \begin{array}{r} 3(x + 3y - z = -10) \\ 2x - y - 3z = -3 \\ \hline x + 10y \quad = -27 \end{array}$$

The resulting 2-by-2 system is $\begin{cases} 2x - y = 9 \\ x + 10y = -27 \end{cases}$.

Eliminate x.

$$\begin{array}{r} 2x - \quad y = 9 \\ -2(x + 10y = -27) \\ \hline -21y = 63 \rightarrow y = -3 \end{array}$$

Substitute to solve for x and then z.

$2x - y = 9 \rightarrow 2x - (-3) = 9 \rightarrow x = 3$

$3x + 2y - z = -1 \rightarrow 3(3) + 2(-3) - z = -1 \rightarrow z = 4$

The solution to the system is (3, −3, 4).

EXERCISES

Use elimination to solve each system of equations.

48. $\begin{cases} x + 3y + 2z = 13 \\ 2x + 2y - z = 3 \\ x - 2y + 3z = 6 \end{cases}$

49. $\begin{cases} x + y + z = 2 \\ 3x + 2y - z = -1 \\ 3x - y = 4 \end{cases}$

Classify each system as consistent or inconsistent, and determine the number of solutions.

50. $\begin{cases} x + y + z = -2 \\ -x + 2y - 5z = 4 \\ 3x + 3y + 3z = 5 \end{cases}$

51. $\begin{cases} -x - y + 2z = -3 \\ 4x + 4y - 8z = 12 \\ 2x + y - 3z = -2 \end{cases}$

Answers

39–42.

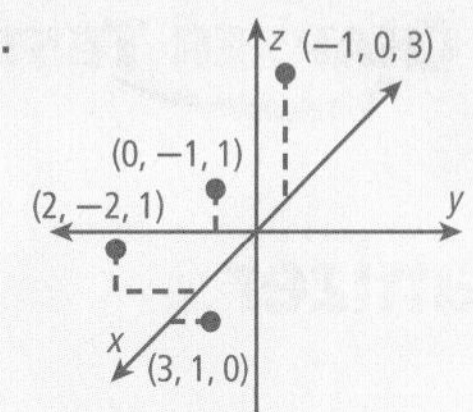

43.

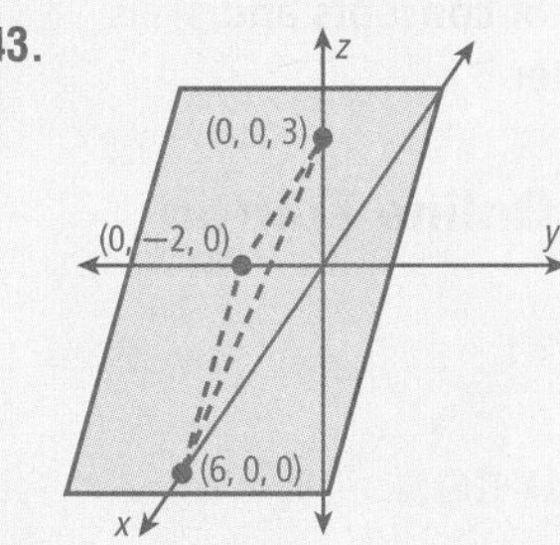

44.

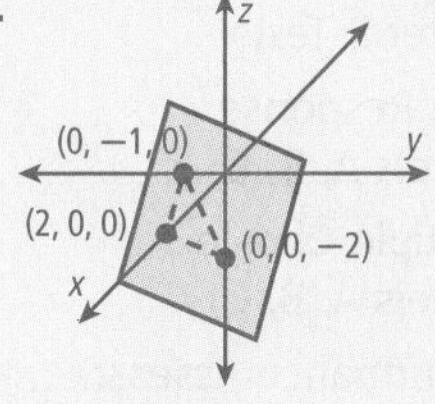

45.

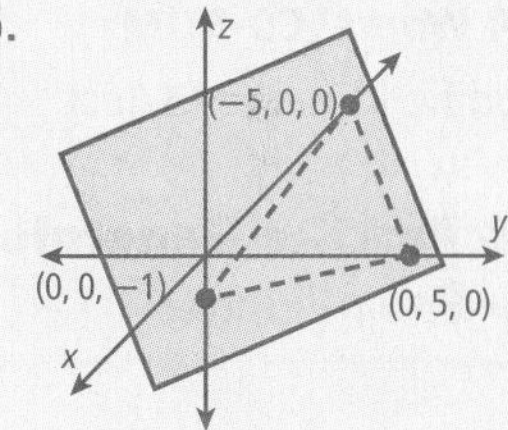

46.

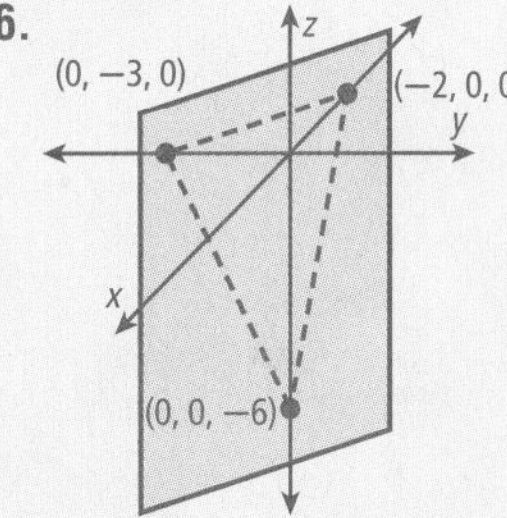

47. $2d + 9p + 4c = 35$, where d = drinks, p = pizza, c = ice cream

48. (1, 2, 3)

49. (1, −1, 2)

50. inconsistent, no solution

51. dependent, infinitely many solutions

Organizer

Objective: Assess students' mastery of concepts and skills in Chapter 3.

Online Edition

Resources

Assessment Resources

Chapter 3 Tests

- Free Response (Levels A, B, C)
- Multiple Choice (Levels A, B, C)
- Performance Assessment

***IDEA Works!* CD-ROM**

Modified Chapter 3 Test

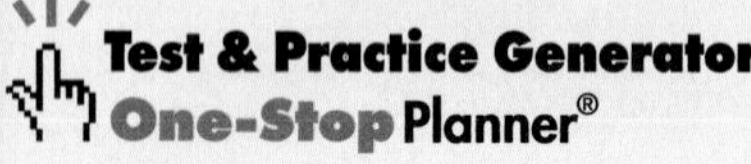

State Resources

Solve each system by using a graph and a table.

1. $\begin{cases} x - y = -4 \\ 3x - 6y = -12 \end{cases}$ $(-4, 0)$
2. $\begin{cases} y = x - 1 \\ x + 4y = 6 \end{cases}$ $(2, 1)$
3. $\begin{cases} x - y = 3 \\ 2x + 3y = 6 \end{cases}$ $(3, 0)$

Classify each system and determine the number of solutions.

4. $\begin{cases} 6y = 9x \\ 8x + 4y = 20 \end{cases}$ independent; one solution
5. $\begin{cases} 12x + 3y = -9 \\ -y - 4x = 3 \end{cases}$ dependent; infinitely many solutions
6. $\begin{cases} 3x - 9y = 21 \\ 6 = x - 3y \end{cases}$ inconsistent; no solution

Use substitution or elimination to solve each system of equations.

7. $\begin{cases} y = x - 2 \\ x + 5y = 20 \end{cases}$ $(5, 3)$
8. $\begin{cases} 5x - y = 33 \\ 7x + y = 51 \end{cases}$ $(7, 2)$
9. $\begin{cases} x + y = 5 \\ 2x + 5y = 16 \end{cases}$ $(3, 2)$

Graph each system of inequalities.

10. $\begin{cases} 2y - 4x \ge 4 \\ y - x \ge 1 \end{cases}$
11. $\begin{cases} x + y \ge 3 \\ y - 4 \le 0 \end{cases}$

12. **Chemistry** A chemist wants to mix a new solution with at least 18% pure salt. The chemist has two solutions with 9% pure salt and 24% pure salt and wants to make at most 250 mL of the new solution. Write and graph a system of inequalities that can be used to find the amounts of each salt solution needed.

13. Minimize the objective function $P = 5x + 9y$ under the following constraints. $\begin{cases} x \ge 0 \\ y \ge 0 \\ y \le 2x + 1 \\ y \le -3x + 6 \end{cases}$
$P = 0$

Graph each point in three-dimensional space.

14. $(2, -1, 3)$
15. $(0, -1, 3)$
16. $(-2, 1, -1)$

Business **Use the following information and the table for Problems 17 and 18.**
A plumber charges \$50 for repairing a leaking faucet, \$150 for installing a sink, and \$200 for an emergency situation. The plumber's total income was exactly \$1000 for each day shown in the table.

Day	Repair Faucet	Install Sink	Emergency
Monday	2	2	■ 3
Tuesday	■ 3	3	2
Wednesday	1	■ 1	4
Thursday	4	4	■ 1

17. Write a linear equation in three variables to represent this situation. $50x + 150y + 200z = 1000$
18. Complete the table for the possible numbers of tasks each day.

Solve each system of equations using elimination, or state that the system is inconsistent or dependent.

19. $\begin{cases} x - y + z = -2 \\ 4x - y + 2z = -3 \\ 2x - 3y + 2z = -7 \end{cases}$ $(-1, 3, 2)$
20. $\begin{cases} 3x - y - z = -1 \\ x + y + 2z = 8 \\ 6x - 2y - 2z = 5 \end{cases}$ inconsistent

Answers

10.

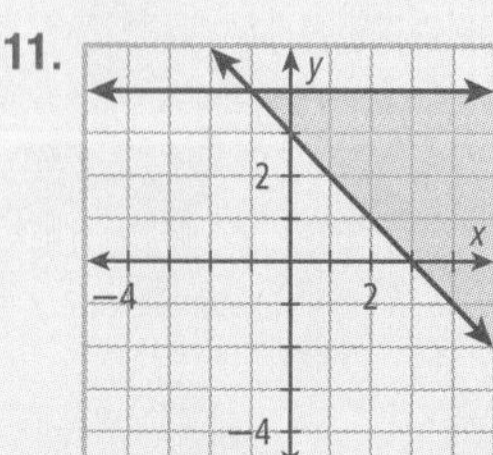

11.

12. $\begin{cases} x + y \le 250 \\ 0.09x + 0.24y < 45 \end{cases}$

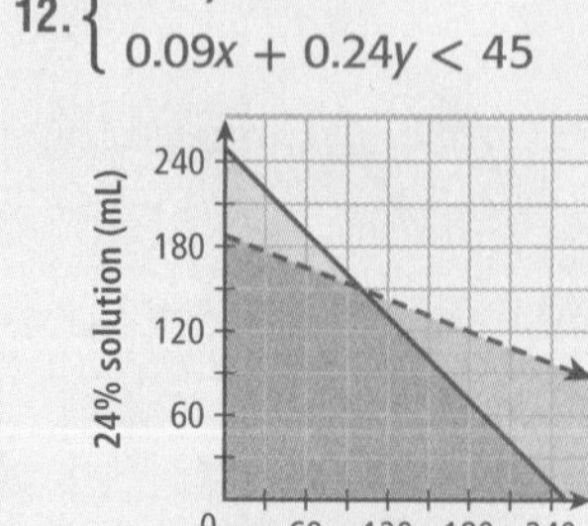

14–16.

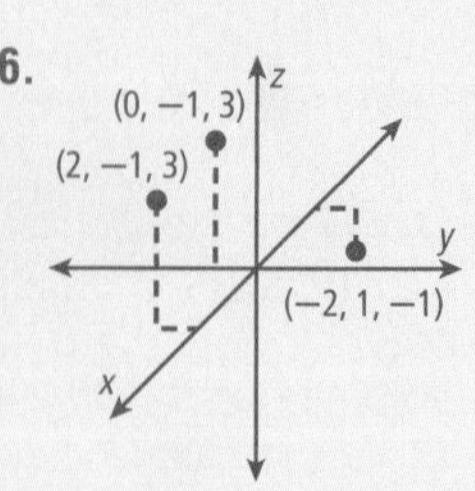

COLLEGE ENTRANCE EXAM PRACTICE

CHAPTER 3

FOCUS ON SAT MATHEMATICS SUBJECT TESTS

In addition to the SAT, the SAT Mathematics Subject Tests are required by some colleges for admission. Colleges that don't require the SAT Mathematics Subject Tests may still use the scores to learn about your academic background and possibly place you in the appropriate college math class.

Take the SAT Mathematics Subject Tests while the subject matter is fresh in your mind. You are not expected to be familiar with all the content covered on the tests, but you should have completed at least three years of college-prep math.

You may want to time yourself as you take this practice test. It should take you about 6 minutes to complete.

1. Which of the following systems of equations is represented by the graph?

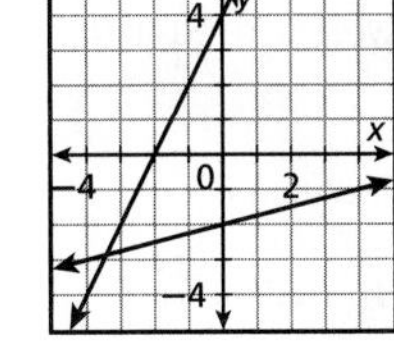

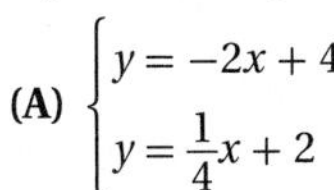

(A) $\begin{cases} y = -2x + 4 \\ y = \frac{1}{4}x + 2 \end{cases}$

(B) $\begin{cases} y = 2x - 4 \\ y = -\frac{1}{4}x - 2 \end{cases}$

(C) $\begin{cases} y = 2x + 4 \\ y = \frac{1}{4}x - 2 \end{cases}$

(D) $\begin{cases} y = \frac{1}{2}x + 4 \\ y = 4x - 2 \end{cases}$

(E) $\begin{cases} y = \frac{1}{2}x - 4 \\ y = 4x + 2 \end{cases}$

2. If $x - 2y = 1$ and $2x - y = -4$, then $x + y = ?$

(A) -9

(B) -7

(C) -5

(D) -3

(E) -1

3. In a fruit salad, there are two more bananas than apples and eight times as many cherries as apples. If a total of 22 pieces of fruit are used, how many of each type are in the salad?

(A) 2 apples, 4 bananas, 18 cherries

(B) 2 apples, 4 bananas, 16 cherries

(C) 2 apples, 0 bananas, 20 cherries

(D) 4 apples, 2 bananas, 12 cherries

(E) 4 apples, 8 bananas, 32 cherries

4. Which of the following inequalities is NOT graphed in the figure?

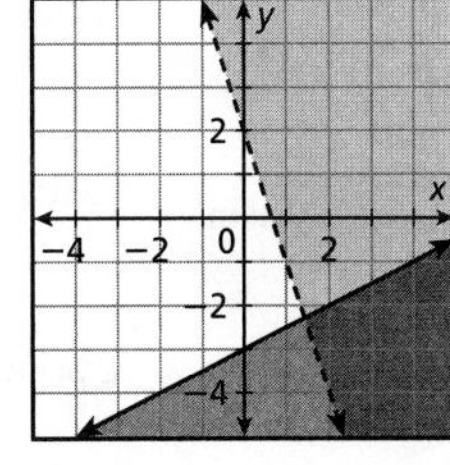

(A) $y > -3x + 2$

(B) $2y \leq x - 6$

(C) $0.5x \geq y + 3$

(D) $3x + y \geq 2$

(E) $6x + 2y > 4$

5. If $r = 3s + 1$ and $t = s - 4$, then what is r in terms of t?

(A) $3t + 13$

(B) $t + 4$

(C) -2.5

(D) $3t + 5$

(E) $3t + 1$

COLLEGE ENTRANCE EXAM PRACTICE CHAPTER 3

Objective: Provide practice for college entrance exams such as the SAT Mathematics Subject Tests.

PREMIER **Online Edition**

Resources

College Entrance Exam Practice

Questions on the SAT Mathematics Subject Tests Levels I and II represent the following math content areas:

	Level	
	I	**II**
Algebra	30%	18%
Plane Euclidean Geometry	20%	0%
Coordinate Geometry	12%	12%
Three-dimensional Geometry	6%	8%
Trigonometry	8%	20%
Functions	12%	24%
Statistics/Probability	6%	6%
Miscellaneous	6%	12%

Items on this page focus on:

- Algebra
- Coordinate Geometry
- Three-dimensional Geometry

Text References:

Item	1	2	3	4	5
Lesson	3-1	3-2	3-6	3-3	3-6

TEST PREP DOCTOR

1. Students who chose **D** incorrectly found the slopes of the given lines. Remind students that slope is rise over run, and show students how to check their answers by substituting test points into the equations.
2. Students who chose **C** or **D** found values for x and y, respectively, but the question asked for the value of $x + y$. Remind students to read the entire question and determine what question is being asked.
3. Students who chose **A**, **B**, or **E** satisfied part of the requirements of the problem but not all of them. Remind students to check their work, not only for accuracy but also to make sure their answers make sense.
4. Students who did not choose **D** either did not recognize an equivalent form of a basic inequality graphed, or did not realize that the inequality symbol in **D** was incorrect for the given graph. Remind students that a dashed line indicates a strict inequality.
5. Students who chose **B** found s in terms of t. Remind students to read each test item carefully.

Objective: Provide opportunities to learn and practice common test-taking strategies.

Online Edition

Resources

 *State Test Prep Workbook*

 *State Test Prep* CD-ROM

 *State Test Practice* Online

go.hrw.com
KEYWORD: MB7 TestPrep

TEST PREP DOCTOR This Test Tackler explains how short-response test items are scored and demonstrates how to write a response to earn full credit. It may help for students to understand that the scoring guides, or rubrics, are designed so that different graders will arrive at the same score for a given student response.

TEST PREP DOCTOR Encourage students to read short-response test items carefully. Have students underline or highlight the key words of the items they should include in their responses. Often, a correct solution consists of more than one part. Look for key words or phrases such as "describe," "give an example of," and "list."

Standardized Test Strategies

Short Response: Write Short Responses

Short-response test items are designed to measure understanding and reasoning skills. Typically, you must show how you solved the problem and explain your answer. Short-response questions are scored using a scoring rubric.

EXAMPLE 

Short Response Kathie earns \$20 per day plus \$0.15 for each newspaper she delivers. Kevin earns \$25 per day plus \$0.10 for each newspaper he delivers. After how many deliveries do they each earn the same amount of money for that day? Write and solve a system of linear equations that models this situation.

Here are examples of how three different responses were scored using the scoring rubric shown.

2-point response:

Let x= the number of newspapers delivered.
Let y= the total amount of money earned.

$\begin{cases} y = 20 + 0.15x \\ y = 25 + 0.10x \end{cases}$ Set up a system of equations.

$20 + 0.15x = 25 + 0.10x$ Use substitution to solve.
$0.05x = 5$
$x = 100$

Check:
$\begin{cases} y = 20 + 0.15x = 20 + 0.15(100) = 35 \checkmark \\ y = 25 + 0.10x = 25 + 0.10(100) = 35 \end{cases}$

Kathie and Kevin will make the same amount of money, \$35, if they both deliver exactly 100 newspapers on any given day.

1-point response:

$\begin{cases} y = 20 + 0.15x \\ y = 25 + 0.10x \end{cases}$ Set up a system of equations.

I solved the system using my graphing calculator and determined that x = 100 newspapers.

Notice that the variables are not defined, and there is no sketch of the graph. Although the answer is correct, no explanation is provided.

0-point response:

Kathie and Kevin will never make the same amount of money on the same day.

Notice that the student provided an incorrect response without showing any work or explanation.

Scoring Rubric

2 points: The student writes and correctly solves a system of equations, showing all work. The student defines the variables, answers the question in a complete sentence, and provides an explanation.

1 point: The student writes and correctly solves a system of equations but does not show all work, does not define the variables, or does not provide an explanation.

1 point: The student writes and solves a system of equations but gives an incorrect answer. The student shows all work and provides an explanation for the answer.

0 points: The student gives no response or provides a solution without showing any work or explanation.

Never leave a short response test item blank. Showing your work and providing a reasonable explanation will result in at least partial credit.

Read each test item, and answer the questions that follow using this scoring rubric.

Scoring Rubric

- **2 points:** The student demonstrates a thorough understanding of the concept, correctly answers the question, and provides a complete explanation.
- **1 point:** The student shows all work and provides an explanation but answers the question incorrectly.
- **1 point:** The student correctly answers the question but does not show all work or does not provide an explanation.
- **0 points:** The student gives a response showing no work or explanation or gives no response.

Item A

Write a real-world situation that can be modeled by this system of equations.

$$\begin{cases} 12x + 15y = 69 \\ 40x + 30y = 170 \end{cases}$$

Solve for x, and make sure that its value makes sense to your situation.

Let x equal the cost of one bag of soil, and let y equal the cost of one potted plant. A landscaper purchased 12 bags of soil and 15 potted plants for $69. He returned to the same store later that week and purchased 40 bags of soil and 30 potted plants for $170. Each bag of soil cost $2, and each potted plant cost $3.

1. How would you score the student's response? Explain.
2. Rewrite the response so that it receives full credit.

Item B

Describe the graph of an independent linear system. Give an example of this type of system, and list the number of solutions it has.

The graph of an independent system is hard to describe because the graph of each equation is independent of the other, and therefore has many solutions.

3. Score the response, and provide your reasoning for the score.
4. Give a response that would receive full credit.

Item C

Explain how to use the intercepts to graph this linear equation in three dimensions. Then graph the equation.

$4x + 3y + 4z = 24$

By finding the x-, y-, and z-intercepts of the linear equation, you can plot three solutions. The plane defined by these points represents the solution set.

x-intercept: $4x+3(0)+4(0)=24$; $x=6$

y-intercept: $4(0)+3y+4(0)=24$; $y=8$

z-intercept: $4(0)+3(0)+4z=24$; $z=6$

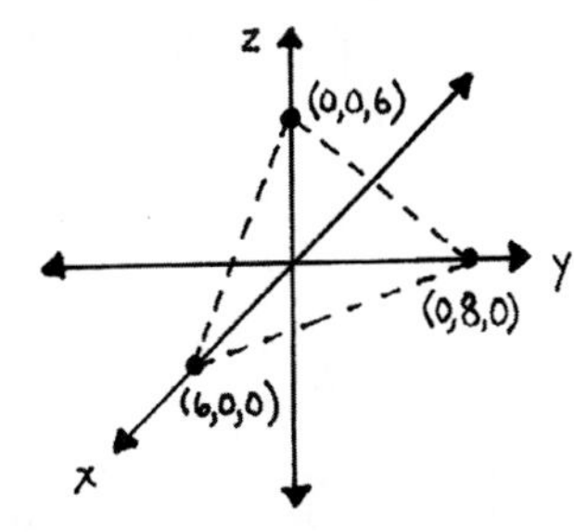

5. Should this response receive full credit? Explain your reasoning.

Answers

Possible answers:

1. The response is worth 1 point. Although the student defines the variables, provides a model, and correctly answers the question, he or she does not show work or provide an explanation for the answer.
2. Let x equal the cost of 1 bag of soil, and let y equal the cost of 1 potted plant. A landscaper purchased 12 bags of soil and 15 potted plants for \$69. He returned to the same store later that week and purchased 40 bags of soil and 30 potted plants for \$170.

   Use the elimination method to solve.

   $-2(12x + 15y) = (69)(-2) \rightarrow -24x - 30y = -138$

   $-24x - 30y = -138$

   $40x + 30y = 170$

   $16x = 32$; so $x = 2$.

   Substitute $x = 2$ into $40x + 30y = 170$ and solve.

   $40(2) + 30y = 170 \rightarrow y = 3$

   Each bag of soil cost \$2, and each potted plant cost \$3. These values make sense for the model, because cost is always positive, and these costs seem reasonable.
3. The response is worth 0 points. The student has failed to demonstrate an understanding of the concept, and the response is completely incorrect.

Answers to *Test Items*

See above.

Answers

4. The graph of an independent system contains lines with different slopes that must intersect exactly 1 time, so the system has 1 solution. An example of this is

$$\begin{cases} 5x + y = 12 \\ x + 2y = 15 \end{cases}$$

5. Yes; the response should receive full credit. The response demonstrates an understanding of the concept and correctly and completely answers the question. All necessary information is provided.

State Resources

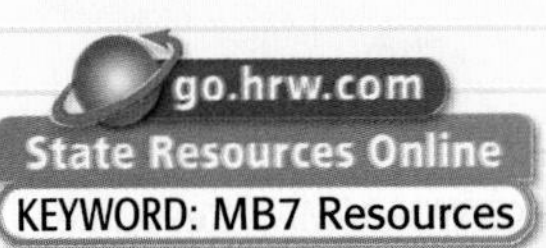

Organizer

Objective: Provide review and practice for Chapters 1–3 and standardized tests.

 **Online Edition**

Resources

 ***Assessment Resources***

Chapter 3 Cumulative Test

 ***State Test Prep Workbook***

 ***State Test Prep* CD-ROM**

State Test Practice Online

KEYWORD: MB7 TestPrep

Answers

1. C
2. A
3. B
4. C
5. A
6. C
7. D
8. C
9. D
10. B
11. D

State Resources

Core Standard	Items
1	3, 6, 9, 10, 11, 12, 15

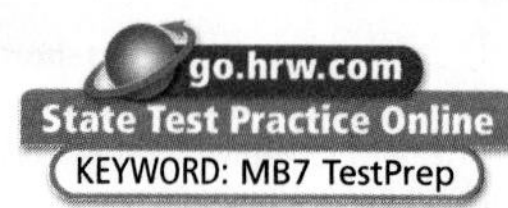

CUMULATIVE ASSESSMENT, CHAPTERS 1–3

Multiple Choice

1. What are the intercepts of the linear equation $2x + y - 5z = 20$?

A. $x = 0, y = 0, z = 0$

B. $x = 2, y = 1, z = -5$

C. $x = 10, y = 20, z = -4$

D. $x = 10, y = 20, z = 4$

2. Sam attends college 440 miles from home. He figures he can make the trip home in about 8 hours driving an average highway speed of 60 miles per hour. Which function represents how many miles Sam is from home after he has been driving for x hours at 60 miles per hour?

A. $f(x) = 440 - 60x$

B. $f(x) = 440 + 60x$

C. $f(x) = 440 - 8x$

D. $f(x) = 60x$

3. Which system of inequalities corresponds to the graph?

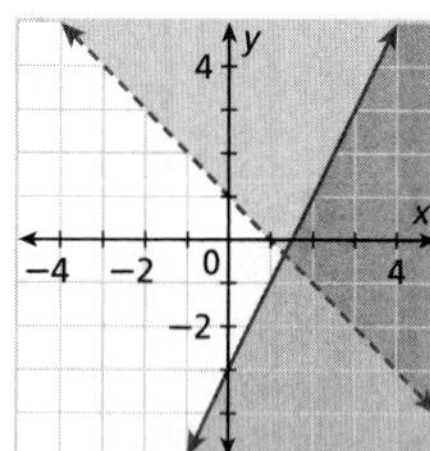

A. $\begin{cases} y \le 2x - 3 \\ y \ge -x + 1 \end{cases}$

B. $\begin{cases} y \le 2x - 3 \\ y > -x + 1 \end{cases}$

C. $\begin{cases} y < 2x - 3 \\ y > -x + 1 \end{cases}$

D. $\begin{cases} y \ge 2x - 3 \\ y < -x + 1 \end{cases}$

4. Kylie read the first 87 pages of a book in 3 hours 40 minutes. At this pace, how long will it take her to finish the book if it has a total of 214 pages?

A. 1 hour 25 minutes

B. 5 hours 5 minutes

C. 9 hours 1 minutes

D. 12 hours 41 minutes

5. What is the equation of a line with a slope of $-\frac{2}{5}$ passing through (1, 4)?

A. $y = -\frac{2}{5}x + 4\frac{2}{5}$

B. $y = -\frac{2}{5}x + 2\frac{3}{5}$

C. $y = -\frac{1}{4}x - \frac{1}{10}$

D. $y = \frac{2}{5}x + 3\frac{3}{5}$

6. Which system of equations is an independent system?

A. $\begin{cases} 2y + 3x = -8 \\ 9x = -24 - 6y \end{cases}$

B. $\begin{cases} y = -x + 4 \\ 3y + 3x = -21 \end{cases}$

C. $\begin{cases} 2y + 7x = 24 \\ 5y - 6 = -4x \end{cases}$

D. $\begin{cases} 2y = 3x - 6 \\ 8y - 12x = 80 \end{cases}$

7. Which relation is a function?

A. $\{(1, 4), (4, 1), (1, 0), (0, 4)\}$

B.

x	3	5	8	8	12
y	5	6	7	8	9

C.

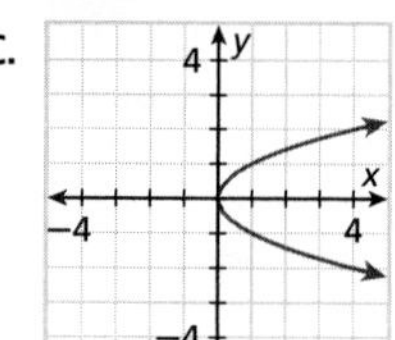

D.

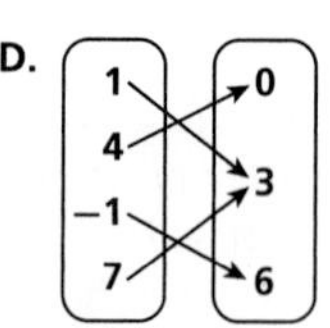

8. A feasible region has vertices (0, 0), (−2, 6), (3, −1), (−1, 1), and (−5, −5). What is the maximum value of the objective function $P = 4x - y$ over this region?

A. 0

B. 7

C. 13

D. 25

TEST PREP DOCTOR

For **Item 3,** encourage students to examine the graph and look for immediate visual characteristics that help eliminate choices. One inequality is graphed using a solid line, and one inequality is graphed using a dashed line. Therefore, choices **A** and **C** can be eliminated as possible answers because neither of their inequalities use a symbol that is represented by a solid line on the graph.

Answers

12. Part A: $\begin{cases} 5c + 4a = 68 \\ 17c + 12a = 216 \end{cases}$

Part B:

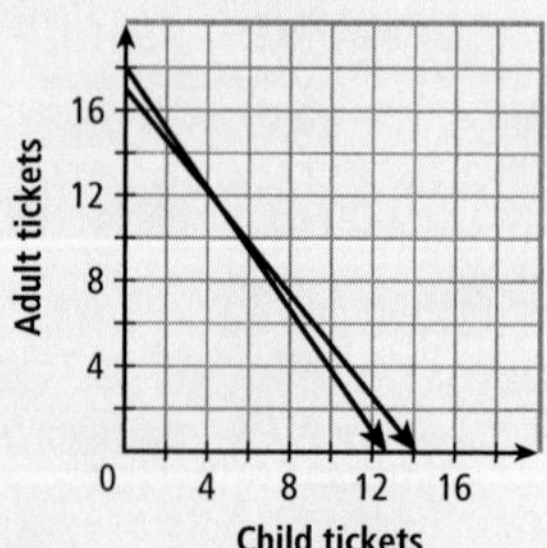

9. Mark has two bowls of cookie dough. One has 30% raisins, and the other has 5% raisins. How much of each dough should he mix to get 18 ounces of cookie dough that has 15% raisins?

A. 14.4 ounces of the dough with 30% raisins and 3.6 ounces of the dough with 5% raisins

B. 5.4 ounces of the dough with 30% raisins and 0.9 ounces of the dough with 5% raisins

C. 8.8 ounces of the dough with 30% raisins and 9.2 ounces of the dough with 5% raisins

D. 7.2 ounces of the dough with 30% raisins and 10.8 ounces of the dough with 5% raisins

In Exercise 10, to solve for the final exam percent, it is not necessary to find the percent for homework or quizzes first.

10. A final grade is based on a student's performance on homework, quizzes, and the final exam. All homework, quizzes, and the final exam are worth 100 points. Each category is worth a different percentage of the final grade. Given the scores of three students in the table below, what percent of the final grade is the final exam worth?

	Homework	Quizzes	Final Exam	Final Grade
Andy	100	82	73	82
Mia	66	94	88	82
Nick	82	46	98	88

A. 50% B. 60%

C. 75% D. 86%

11. Find the lowest positive whole number that is a solution of $\frac{|438 - 3x|}{3} > 816$.

A. −962

B. −670

C. 670

D. 962

Short Answer

12. One group of people going to the zoo bought 5 child tickets and 4 adult tickets for a total of \$68. Another group bought 17 child tickets and 12 adult tickets for a total of \$216.

Part A Write a system of equations that models this problem.

Part B Solve the system using a graph.

Part C Solve the system using another method. Explain why the method you used may be better than using the graphing method. What is the price of each kind of ticket?

13. Point *A* has coordinates (3, 4). Point *B* is a reflection of point *A* across the *x*-axis.

Part A Give the coordinates of point *B*.

Part B Point *C* is a translation of point *B* 3 units left and 2 units down. Give the coordinates of point *C*.

14. The function $g(x)$ is a vertical translation of $f(x) = 4x - 3$ 5 units down.

Part A Write the rule for $g(x)$.

Part B The function $h(x)$ is a reflection of $g(x)$ across the x-axis. Write the rule for $h(x)$.

Extended Response

15. A curtain manufacturer has 820 lots of cotton fiber and 1250 lots of synthetic fiber. A discount curtain uses 18 lots of cotton fiber and 32 lots of synthetic fiber. A premium curtain uses 36 lots of cotton fiber and 28 lots of synthetic fiber.

Part A Write the constraints.

Part B Graph the feasible region. Give the vertices of the polygon that defines the feasible region.

Part C The manufacturer makes a profit of \$170 on each discount curtain sold and a profit of \$190 on each premium curtain sold. Write the objective function.

Part D How many of each kind of curtain should be manufactured to maximize profit?

Short Answer Rubric

Items 12–14

Score 2 = Thorough understanding of mathematical concepts and processes.

Score 1 = Partial understanding of mathematical concepts and/or processes.

Score 0 = Limited or no understanding of the problem-solving concepts.

Blank = No written response.

Extended Response Rubric

Item 15

Score 4 = Thorough understanding of mathematical concepts and processes.

Score 3 = Demonstrated understanding of mathematical concepts and processes, but an error in computation or explanation.

Score 2 = Partial understanding of mathematical concepts and/or processes.

Score 1 = Limited understanding and execution of the problem-solving concepts.

Score 0 = No understanding of the problem-solving concepts.

Blank = No written response.

Part C: In the graphing method, it is difficult to tell the precise coordinates of the point of intersection. Adult tickets are \$9.50 each. Child tickets are \$6.00 each.

13. Part A: (3, −4)

Part B: (0, −6)

14. Part A: $g(x) = 4x - 8$

Part B: $h(x) = -4x + 8$

15. Part A: $\begin{cases} 18d + 36p \leq 820 \\ 32d + 28p \leq 1250 \\ d \geq 0 \\ p \geq 0 \end{cases}$

Part B:

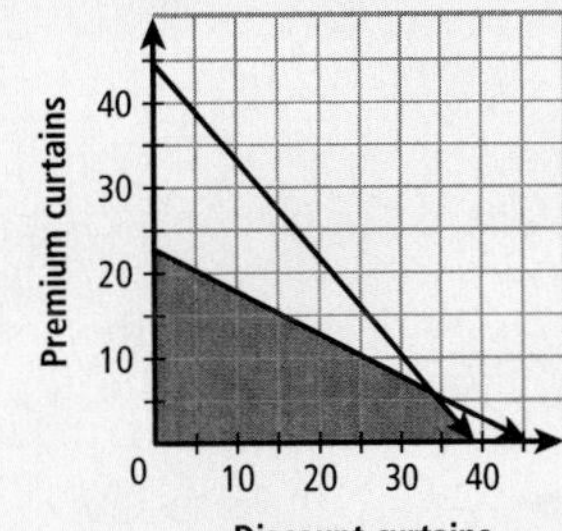

(0, 0), (0, 22.78), (34.01, 5.77), (39.06, 0)

Part C: $P = 170d + 190p$

Part D: 34 discount curtains and 5 premium curtains

Matrices

Section 4A	Section 4B
Matrix Operations	**Using Matrices to Solve Systems**
4-1 Representing Data and Adding Matrices	**4-4 Determinants and Cramer's Rule**
4-2 Multiplying Matrices	**4-5 Matrix Inverses and Solving Systems**
Connecting Algebra to Geometry Transformations	**4-5 Technology Lab** Use Spreadsheets with Matrices
4-3 Using Matrices to Transform Geometric Figures	**4-6 Row Operations and Augmented Matrices**
	EXTENSION Networks and Matrices

Pacing Guide for 45-Minute Classes

Chapter 4

Countdown to Testing Weeks 8, 9

DAY 1	DAY 2	DAY 3	DAY 4	DAY 5
4-1 Lesson	4-2 Lesson	Connecting Algebra to Geometry 4-3 Lesson	4-3 Lesson Multi-Step Test Prep Ready to Go On?	4-4 Lesson
DAY 6	**DAY 7**	**DAY 8**	**DAY 9**	**DAY 10**
4-5 Lesson	4-5 Lesson	4-5 Technology Lab	4-6 Lesson	4-6 Lesson Multi-Step Test Prep Ready to Go On?
DAY 11	**DAY 12**			
EXTENSION	Chapter 4 Test			

Pacing Guide for 90-Minute Classes

Chapter 4

DAY 1	DAY 2	DAY 3	DAY 4	DAY 5
4-1 Lesson 4-2 Lesson	Connecting Algebra to Geometry 4-3 Lesson Multi-Step Test Prep Ready to Go On?	4-4 Lesson 4-5 Lesson	4-5 Lesson 4-5 Technology Lab	4-6 Lesson Multi-Step Test Prep Ready to Go On?
DAY 6				
EXTENSION Chapter 4 Test				

ONGOING ASSESSMENT and INTERVENTION

Assess Prior Knowledge

Before Chapter 4

DIAGNOSE	PRESCRIBE
Diagnose readiness for the chapter.	Prescribe intervention.
Are You Ready? SE p. 243	***Are You Ready? Intervention*** Skills 34, 35, 51, 52, 55

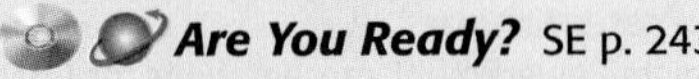

Formative Assessment

Before Every Lesson

DIAGNOSE	PRESCRIBE
Diagnose readiness for the lesson.	Prescribe intervention.
Warm Up TE, every lesson	**Skills Bank** SE pp. S46–S73
	Reteach CRB, Ch. 1–4

During Every Lesson

DIAGNOSE	PRESCRIBE
Diagnose understanding of lesson concepts.	Prescribe intervention.
Check It Out! SE, every example	**Questioning Strategies** TE, every example
Think and Discuss SE, every lesson	**Reading Strategies** CRB, every lesson
Write About It SE, every lesson	***Success for ELL*** pp. 49–60
Journal TE, every lesson	

After Every Lesson

DIAGNOSE	PRESCRIBE
Diagnose mastery of lesson concepts.	Prescribe intervention.
Lesson Quiz TE, every lesson	**Reteach** CRB, every lesson
Alternative Assessment TE, every lesson	**Problem Solving** CRB, every lesson
Test Prep SE, every lesson	**Test Prep Doctor** TE, every lesson
Test and Practice Generator	***Homework Help* Online**

Before Chapter 4 Testing

DIAGNOSE	PRESCRIBE
Diagnose mastery of concepts in the chapter.	Prescribe intervention.
Ready to Go On? SE pp. 269, 295	***Ready to Go On? Intervention*** pp. 59–72
Multi-Step Test Prep SE pp. 268, 294	**Scaffolding Questions** TE pp. 268, 294
Section Quizzes AR pp. 65–66	
Test and Practice Generator	

Before High Stakes Testing

DIAGNOSE	PRESCRIBE
Diagnose mastery of benchmark concepts.	Prescribe intervention.
College Entrance Exam Practice SE p. 303	***College Entrance Exam Practice***
Standardized Test Prep SE pp. 306–307	***State Test Prep Workbook***
***State Test Prep* CD-ROM**	

Summative Assessment

After Chapter 4

DIAGNOSE	PRESCRIBE
Check mastery of chapter concepts.	Prescribe intervention.
Multiple-Choice Tests (Forms A, B, C)	**Reteach** CRB, every lesson
Free-Response Tests (Forms A, B, C)	***Lesson Tutorial Videos*** Chapter 4
Performance Assessment AR pp. 67–80	
Test and Practice Generator	
Check mastery of benchmark concepts.	Prescribe intervention.
AYP State Tests	***State Test Prep Workbook***
College Entrance Exams	***College Entrance Exam Practice***

KEY: **SE** = *Student Edition* **TE** = *Teacher's Edition* **CRB** = *Chapter Resource Book* **AR** = *Assessment Resources* Available on CD-ROM Available online

CHAPTER 4

Supporting the Teacher

Chapter 4 Resource Book

Practice A, B, C
pp. 3–5, 11–13, 19–21, 27–29, 35–37, 43–45

Reading Strategies ELL
pp. 10, 18, 26, 34, 42, 50

Reteach
pp. 6–7, 14–15, 22–23, 30–31, 38–39, 46–47

Problem Solving
pp. 9, 17, 25, 33, 41, 49

Challenge
pp. 8, 16, 24, 32, 40, 48

Parent Letter pp. 1–2

Transparencies

Lesson Transparencies, Volume 1 .... Chapter 4
- Warm Ups
- Teaching Transparencies
- Additional Examples
- Lesson Quizzes

Alternate Openers: Explorations 25–30

Countdown to Testing 15–18

Know-It Notebook .... Chapter 4
- Graphic Organizers

Teacher Tools

Power Presentations®
Complete PowerPoint® presentations for Chapter 4 lessons

Lesson Tutorial Videos®
Holt authors Ed Burger and Freddie Renfro present tutorials to support the Chapter 4 lessons.

One-Stop Planner®
Easy access to all Chapter 4 resources and assessments, as well as software for lesson planning, test generation, and puzzle creation

IDEA Works!®
Key Chapter 4 resources and assessments modified to address special learning needs

Lesson Plans .... pp. 25–30

Solutions Key .... Chapter 4

Algebra Posters

TechKeys

Project Teacher Support

Lab Resources 

Parent Resources

Workbooks

Homework and Practice Workbook
Teacher's Guide .... pp. 25–30

Know-It Notebook
Teacher's Guide .... Chapter 4

Problem Solving Workbook
Teacher's Guide .... pp. 25–30

State Test Prep Workbook
Teacher's Guide

Technology Highlights for the Teacher

Power Presentations

Dynamic presentations to engage students. Complete PowerPoint® presentations for every lesson in Chapter 4.

2-1 Solving One-Step Equations

Isolate a variable by using inverse operations which "undo" operations on the variable.

An equation is like a balanced scale. To keep the balance, perform the same operation on both sides.

Inverse Operations	
Operation	**Inverse Operation**
Addition	Subtraction
Subtraction	Addition

One-Stop Planner

Easy access to Chapter 4 resources and assessments. Includes lesson-planning, test-generation, and puzzle-creation software.

Premier Online Edition

Chapter 4 includes Tutorial Videos, Lesson Activities, Lesson Quizzes, Homework Help, and Chapter Project.

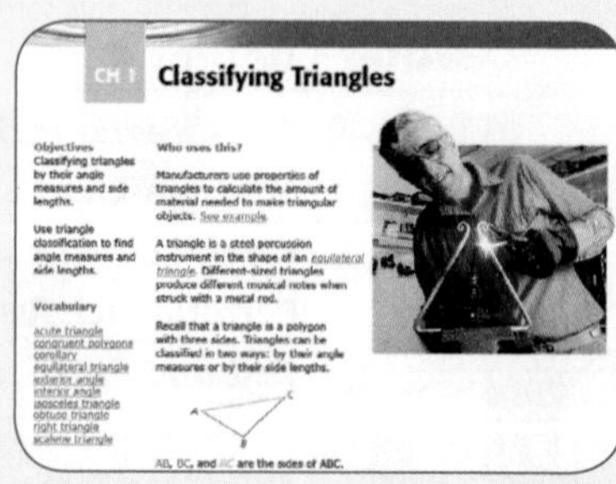

KEY: **SE** = *Student Edition* **TE** = *Teacher's Edition*  English Language Learners  Available on CD-ROM  Available online

Reaching All Learners

Resources for All Learners

Algebra Lab Activities .... Chapter 4
Technology Lab Activities .... Chapter 4
Homework and Practice Workbook .... pp. 25–30
Know-It Notebook .... Chapter 4
Problem Solving Workbook .... pp. 25–30

DEVELOPING LEARNERS

Practice A .... CRB, every lesson
Reteach .... CRB, every lesson
Inclusion .... TE p. 263
Questioning Strategies .... TE, every example
Modified Chapter 4 Resources .... *IDEA Works!*
***Homework Help* Online**

ON-LEVEL LEARNERS

Practice B .... CRB, every lesson
Multiple Representations .... TE p. 255
Number Sense .... TE pp. 271, 272, 279, 290

ADVANCED LEARNERS

Practice C .... CRB, every lesson
Challenge .... CRB, every lesson
Reading and Writing Math EXTENSION .... TE p. 245
Multi-Step Test Prep EXTENSION .... TE pp. 268, 294
Critical Thinking .... TE p. 284

English Language Learners

ENGLISH LANGUAGE LEARNERS

Are You Ready? Vocabulary .... SE p. 243
Vocabulary Connections .... SE p. 244
Lesson Vocabulary .... SE, every lesson
Vocabulary Exercises .... SE, every exercise set
Vocabulary Review .... SE p. 298
English Language Learners .... TE pp. 245, 261, 281, 288, 308–309
Reading Strategies .... CRB, every lesson
Success for English Language Learners .... pp. 49–60
Multilingual Glossary

Reaching All Learners Through...

Multiple Representations .... TE p. 255
Auditory Cues .... TE p. 247
Visual Cues .... TE pp. 249, 261, 263, 288
Kinesthetic Experience .... TE p. 254
Inclusion .... TE p. 263
Critical Thinking .... TE p. 284
Math Background .... TE p. 265
Curriculum Integration .... TE p. 266
Test Prep Doctor .... TE pp. 252, 260, 267, 276, 284, 293, 303, 304, 306
Common Error Alerts .. TE pp. 259, 273, 275, 281, 283, 289
Scaffolding Questions .... TE pp. 268, 294

Technology Highlights for Reaching All Learners

Lesson Tutorial Videos

Starring Holt authors Ed Burger and Freddie Renfro! Live tutorials to support every lesson in Chapter 4.

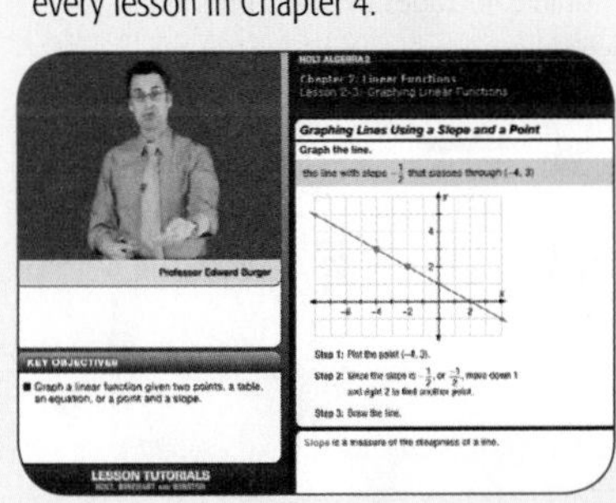

Multilingual Glossary

Searchable glossary includes definitions in English, Spanish, Vietnamese, Chinese, Hmong, Korean, and 4 other languages.

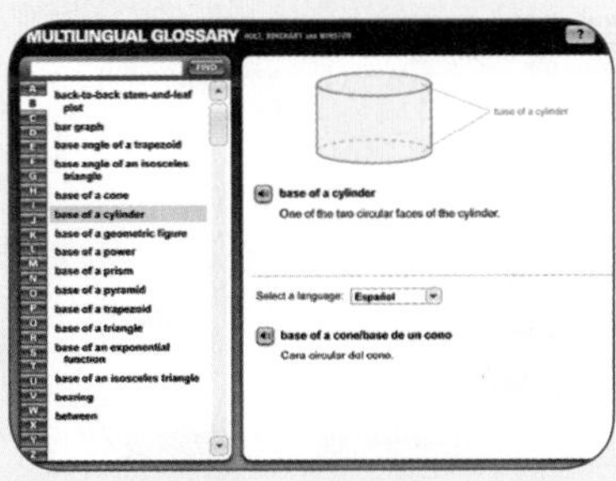

Online Interactivities

Interactive tutorials provide visually engaging alternative opportunities to learn concepts and master skills.

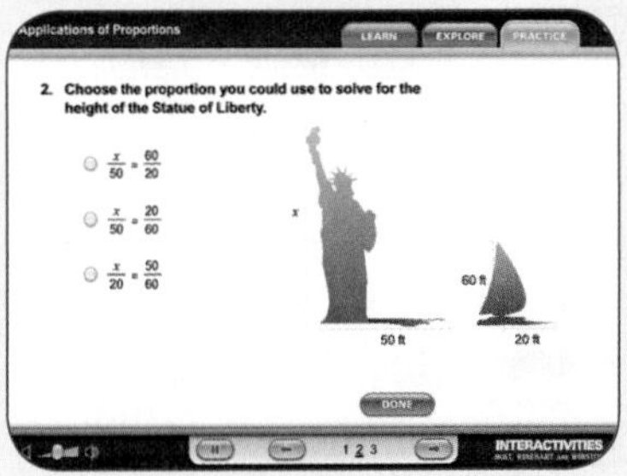

KEY: **SE** = *Student Edition* **TE** = *Teacher's Edition* **CRB** = *Chapter Resource Book*  Available on CD-ROM  Available online

CHAPTER 4

Ongoing Assessment

Assessing Prior Knowledge

Determine whether students have the required prerequisite concepts and skills for success in Chapter 4.

Are You Ready? SPANISH .... SE p. 243
Warm Up .... TE, every lesson

Test Preparation

Provide review and practice for Chapter 4 and standardized tests.

Multi-Step Test Prep .... SE pp. 268, 294
Study Guide: Review .... SE pp. 298–301
Test Tackler .... SE pp. 304–305
Standardized Test Prep .... SE pp. 306–307
College Entrance Exam Practice .... SE p. 303
***Countdown to Testing* Transparencies** 15–18
State Test Prep Workbook
***State Test Prep* CD-ROM**
IDEA Works!

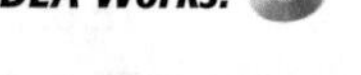

Alternative Assessment

Assess students' understanding of Chapter 4 concepts and combined problem-solving skills.

Chapter 4 Project .... SE p. 242
Alternative Assessment .... TE, every lesson
Performance Assessment .... AR pp. 79–80
Portfolio Assessment .... AR p. xxxiv

Daily Assessment

Provide formative assessment for each day of Chapter 4.

Questioning Strategies .... TE, every example
Think and Discuss .... SE, every lesson
Check It Out! Exercises .... SE, every example
Write About It .... SE, every lesson
Journal .... TE, every lesson
Lesson Quiz .... TE, every lesson
Alternative Assessment .... TE, every lesson
Modified Lesson Quizzes .... *IDEA Works!*

Weekly Assessment

Provide formative assessment for each week of Chapter 4.

Multi-Step Test Prep .... SE pp. 268, 294
Ready to Go On? .... SE pp. 269, 295
Cumulative Assessment .... SE pp. 306–307
Test and Practice Generator .... *One-Stop Planner*

Formal Assessment

Provide summative assessment of Chapter 4 mastery.

Section Quizzes .... AR pp. 65–66
Chapter 4 Test .... SE p. 302
Chapter Test (Levels A, B, C) .... AR pp. 67–78
• Multiple Choice • Free Response
Cumulative Test .... AR pp. 81–84
Test and Practice Generator .... *One-Stop Planner*
Modified Chapter 4 Test .... *IDEA Works!*

Technology Highlights for Ongoing Assessment

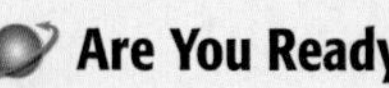

Are You Ready? SPANISH

Automatically assess readiness and prescribe intervention for Chapter 4 prerequisite skills.

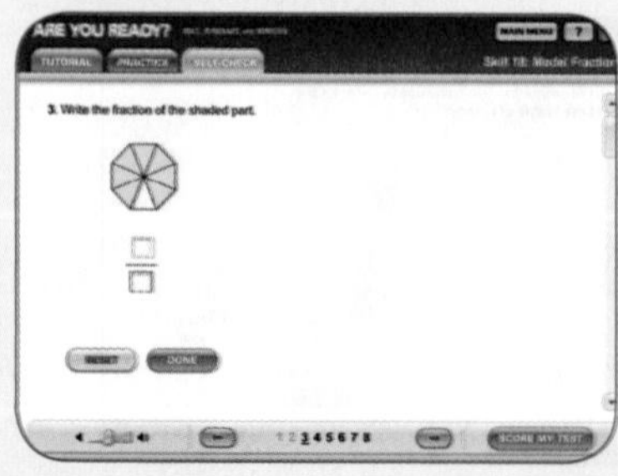

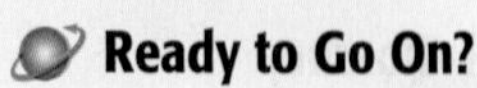

Ready to Go On?

Automatically assess understanding and prescribe intervention for Sections 4A and 4B.

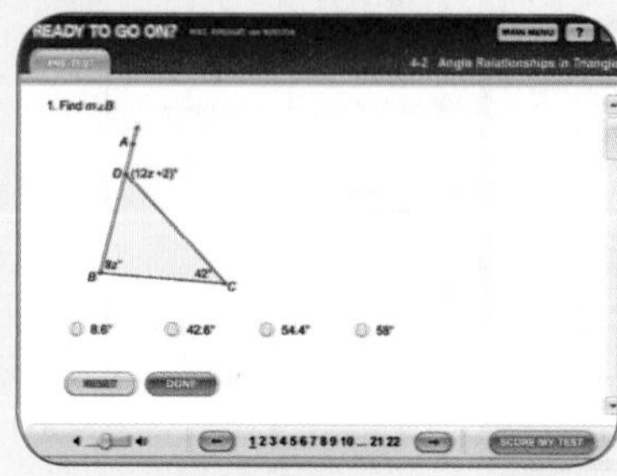

Test and Practice Generator

Use Chapter 4 problem banks to create assessments and worksheets to print out or deliver online. Includes dynamic problems.

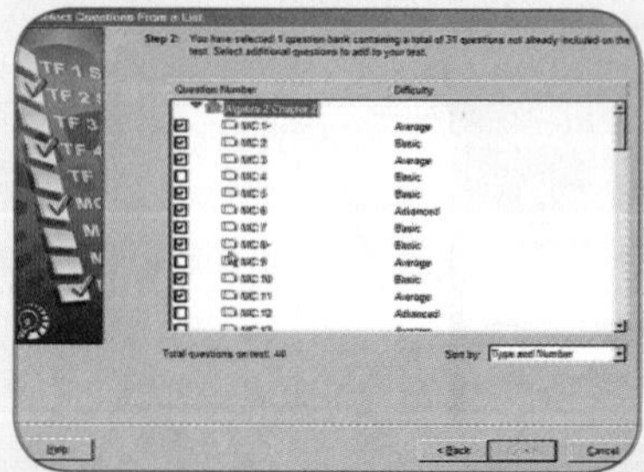

KEY: **SE** = *Student Edition* **TE** = *Teacher's Edition* **AR** = *Assessment Resources*  Spanish version available  Available on CD-ROM Available online

Formal Assessment

Three levels (A, B, C) of multiple-choice and free-response chapter tests are available in the *Assessment Resources.*

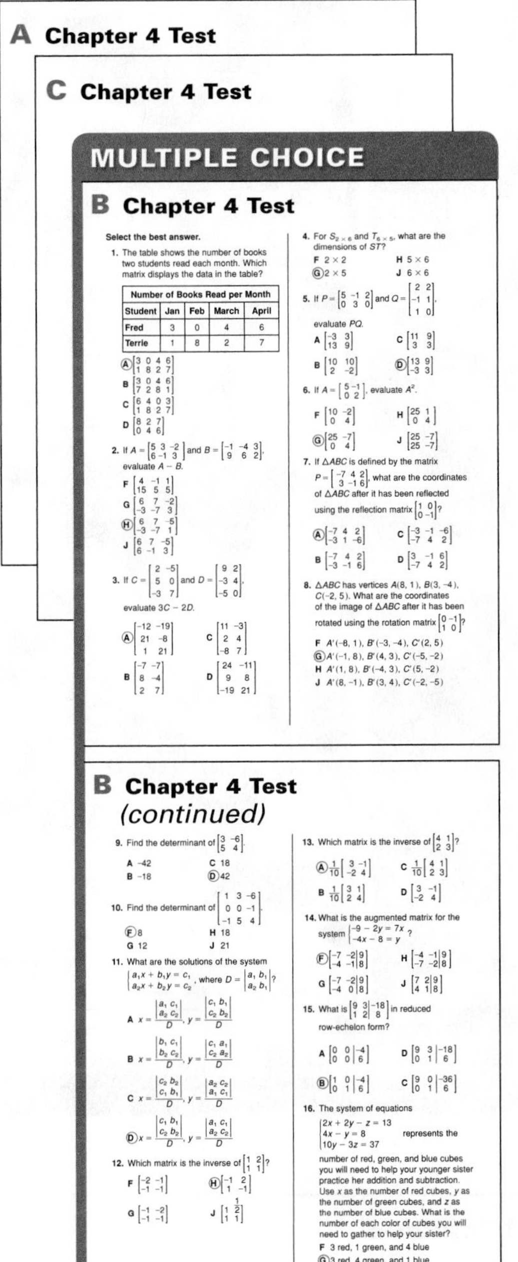

A Chapter 4 Test

C Chapter 4 Test

MULTIPLE CHOICE

B Chapter 4 Test

Select the best answer.

1. The table shows the number of books two students read each month. Which matrix displays the data in the table?

Number of Books Read per Month				
Student	Jan	Feb	March	April
Fred	3	0	4	6
Terrie	1	8	2	7

Ⓐ $\begin{bmatrix} 3 & 0 & 4 & 6 \\ 1 & 8 & 2 & 7 \end{bmatrix}$
B $\begin{bmatrix} 3 & 0 & 4 & 6 \\ 7 & 2 & 8 & 1 \end{bmatrix}$
C $\begin{bmatrix} 6 & 4 & 0 & 3 \\ 1 & 8 & 2 & 7 \end{bmatrix}$
D $\begin{bmatrix} 8 & 2 & 7 \\ 0 & 4 & 6 \end{bmatrix}$

2. If $A = \begin{bmatrix} 5 & 3 & -2 \\ 6 & -1 & 3 \end{bmatrix}$ and $B = \begin{bmatrix} -1 & -4 & 3 \\ 9 & 6 & 2 \end{bmatrix}$, evaluate $A - B$.

F $\begin{bmatrix} 4 & -1 & 1 \\ 15 & 5 & 5 \end{bmatrix}$
G $\begin{bmatrix} 6 & 7 & -2 \\ -3 & -7 & 3 \end{bmatrix}$
Ⓗ $\begin{bmatrix} 6 & 7 & -5 \\ -3 & -7 & 1 \end{bmatrix}$
J $\begin{bmatrix} 6 & 7 & -5 \\ 6 & -1 & 3 \end{bmatrix}$

3. If $C = \begin{bmatrix} 2 & -5 \\ 5 & 0 \\ -3 & 7 \end{bmatrix}$ and $D = \begin{bmatrix} 9 & 2 \\ -3 & 4 \\ -5 & 0 \end{bmatrix}$, evaluate $3C - 2D$.

Ⓐ $\begin{bmatrix} -12 & -19 \\ 21 & -8 \\ 1 & 21 \end{bmatrix}$ C $\begin{bmatrix} 11 & -3 \\ 2 & 4 \\ -8 & 7 \end{bmatrix}$
B $\begin{bmatrix} -7 & -7 \\ 8 & -4 \\ 2 & 7 \end{bmatrix}$ D $\begin{bmatrix} 24 & -11 \\ 9 & 8 \\ -19 & 21 \end{bmatrix}$

4. For $S_{2 \times 6}$ and $T_{6 \times 5}$, what are the dimensions of ST?

F 2×2 H 5×6
Ⓖ 2×5 J 6×6

5. If $P = \begin{bmatrix} 5 & -1 & 2 \\ 0 & 3 & 0 \end{bmatrix}$ and $Q = \begin{bmatrix} 2 & 2 \\ -1 & 1 \\ 1 & 0 \end{bmatrix}$, evaluate PQ.

A $\begin{bmatrix} -3 & 3 \\ 13 & 9 \end{bmatrix}$ C $\begin{bmatrix} 11 & 9 \\ 3 & 3 \end{bmatrix}$
B $\begin{bmatrix} 10 & 10 \\ 2 & -2 \end{bmatrix}$ Ⓓ $\begin{bmatrix} 13 & 9 \\ -3 & 3 \end{bmatrix}$

6. If $A = \begin{bmatrix} 5 & -1 \\ 0 & 2 \end{bmatrix}$, evaluate A^2.

F $\begin{bmatrix} 10 & -2 \\ 0 & 4 \end{bmatrix}$ H $\begin{bmatrix} 25 & 1 \\ 0 & 4 \end{bmatrix}$
Ⓖ $\begin{bmatrix} 25 & -7 \\ 0 & 4 \end{bmatrix}$ J $\begin{bmatrix} 25 & -7 \\ 25 & -7 \end{bmatrix}$

7. If $\triangle ABC$ is defined by the matrix $P = \begin{bmatrix} -7 & 4 & 2 \\ 3 & -1 & 6 \end{bmatrix}$, what are the coordinates of $\triangle ABC$ after it has been reflected using the reflection matrix $\begin{bmatrix} 1 & 0 \\ 0 & -1 \end{bmatrix}$?

Ⓐ $\begin{bmatrix} -7 & 4 & 2 \\ -3 & 1 & -6 \end{bmatrix}$ C $\begin{bmatrix} -3 & -1 & -6 \\ -7 & 4 & 2 \end{bmatrix}$
B $\begin{bmatrix} -7 & 4 & 2 \\ -3 & -1 & 6 \end{bmatrix}$ D $\begin{bmatrix} 3 & -1 & 6 \\ -7 & 4 & 2 \end{bmatrix}$

8. $\triangle ABC$ has vertices $A(8, 1)$, $B(3, -4)$, $C(-2, 5)$. What are the coordinates of the image of $\triangle ABC$ after it has been rotated using the rotation matrix $\begin{bmatrix} 0 & -1 \\ 1 & 0 \end{bmatrix}$?

F $A'(-8, 1)$, $B'(-3, -4)$, $C'(2, 5)$
Ⓖ $A'(-1, 8)$, $B'(4, 3)$, $C'(-5, -2)$
H $A'(1, 8)$, $B'(-4, 3)$, $C'(5, -2)$
J $A'(8, -1)$, $B'(3, 4)$, $C'(-2, -5)$

B Chapter 4 Test (continued)

9. Find the determinant of $\begin{bmatrix} 3 & -6 \\ 5 & 4 \end{bmatrix}$.

A −42 C 18
B −18 Ⓓ 42

10. Find the determinant of $\begin{bmatrix} 1 & 3 & -6 \\ 0 & 0 & -1 \\ -1 & 5 & 4 \end{bmatrix}$.

Ⓕ 8 H 18
G 12 J 21

11. What are the solutions of the system $\begin{cases} a_1x + b_1y = c_1 \\ a_2x + b_2y = c_2 \end{cases}$, where $D = \begin{vmatrix} a_1 & b_1 \\ a_2 & b_1 \end{vmatrix}$?

A $x = \frac{\begin{vmatrix} a_1 & c_1 \\ a_2 & c_2 \end{vmatrix}}{D}, y = \frac{\begin{vmatrix} c_1 & b_1 \\ c_2 & b_2 \end{vmatrix}}{D}$

B $x = \frac{\begin{vmatrix} b_1 & c_1 \\ b_2 & c_2 \end{vmatrix}}{D}, y = \frac{\begin{vmatrix} c_1 & a_1 \\ c_2 & a_2 \end{vmatrix}}{D}$

C $x = \frac{\begin{vmatrix} c_2 & b_2 \\ c_1 & b_1 \end{vmatrix}}{D}, y = \frac{\begin{vmatrix} a_2 & c_2 \\ a_1 & c_1 \end{vmatrix}}{D}$

Ⓓ $x = \frac{\begin{vmatrix} c_1 & b_1 \\ c_2 & b_2 \end{vmatrix}}{D}, y = \frac{\begin{vmatrix} a_1 & c_1 \\ a_2 & c_2 \end{vmatrix}}{D}$

12. Which matrix is the inverse of $\begin{bmatrix} 1 & 2 \\ 1 & 1 \end{bmatrix}$?

F $\begin{bmatrix} -2 & -1 \\ -1 & -1 \end{bmatrix}$ Ⓗ $\begin{bmatrix} -1 & 2 \\ 1 & -1 \end{bmatrix}$
G $\begin{bmatrix} -1 & -2 \\ -1 & -1 \end{bmatrix}$ J $\begin{bmatrix} 1 & \frac{1}{2} \\ 1 & 1 \end{bmatrix}$

13. Which matrix is the inverse of $\begin{bmatrix} 4 & 1 \\ 2 & 3 \end{bmatrix}$?

Ⓐ $\frac{1}{10}\begin{bmatrix} 3 & -1 \\ -2 & 4 \end{bmatrix}$ C $\frac{1}{10}\begin{bmatrix} 4 & 1 \\ 2 & 3 \end{bmatrix}$
B $\frac{1}{10}\begin{bmatrix} 3 & 1 \\ 2 & 4 \end{bmatrix}$ D $\begin{bmatrix} 3 & -1 \\ -2 & 4 \end{bmatrix}$

14. What is the augmented matrix for the system $\begin{cases} -9 - 2y = 7x \\ -4x - 8 = y \end{cases}$?

Ⓕ $\left[\begin{array}{cc|c} -7 & -2 & 9 \\ -4 & -1 & 8 \end{array}\right]$ H $\left[\begin{array}{cc|c} -4 & -1 & 9 \\ -7 & -2 & 8 \end{array}\right]$
G $\left[\begin{array}{cc|c} -7 & -2 & 9 \\ -4 & 0 & 8 \end{array}\right]$ J $\left[\begin{array}{cc|c} 7 & 2 & 9 \\ 4 & 1 & 8 \end{array}\right]$

15. What is $\left[\begin{array}{cc|c} 9 & 3 & -18 \\ 1 & 2 & 8 \end{array}\right]$ in reduced row-echelon form?

A $\left[\begin{array}{cc|c} 0 & 0 & -4 \\ 0 & 0 & 6 \end{array}\right]$ D $\left[\begin{array}{cc|c} 9 & 3 & -18 \\ 0 & 1 & 6 \end{array}\right]$
Ⓑ $\left[\begin{array}{cc|c} 1 & 0 & -4 \\ 0 & 1 & 6 \end{array}\right]$ C $\left[\begin{array}{cc|c} 9 & 0 & -36 \\ 0 & 1 & 6 \end{array}\right]$

16. The system of equations $\begin{cases} 2x + 2y - z = 13 \\ 4x - y = 8 \\ 10y - 3z = 37 \end{cases}$ represents the number of red, green, and blue cubes you will need to help your younger sister practice her addition and subtraction. Use x as the number of red cubes, y as the number of green cubes, and z as the number of blue cubes. What is the number of each color of cubes you will need to gather to help your sister?

F 3 red, 1 green, and 4 blue
Ⓖ 3 red, 4 green, and 1 blue
H 4 red, 1 green, and 3 blue
J 4 red, 3 green, and 1 blue

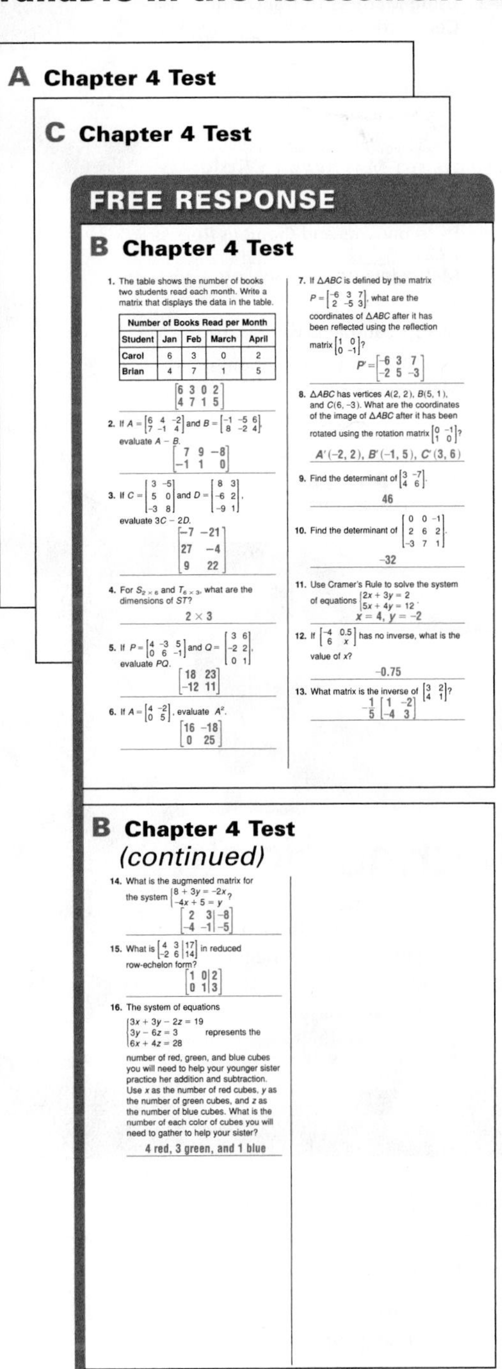

A Chapter 4 Test

C Chapter 4 Test

FREE RESPONSE

B Chapter 4 Test

1. The table shows the number of books two students read each month. Write a matrix that displays the data in the table.

Number of Books Read per Month				
Student	Jan	Feb	March	April
Carol	6	3	0	2
Brian	4	7	1	5

$\begin{bmatrix} 6 & 3 & 0 & 2 \\ 4 & 7 & 1 & 5 \end{bmatrix}$

2. If $A = \begin{bmatrix} 6 & 4 & -2 \\ 7 & -1 & 4 \end{bmatrix}$ and $B = \begin{bmatrix} -1 & -5 & 6 \\ 8 & -2 & 4 \end{bmatrix}$, evaluate $A - B$.

$\begin{bmatrix} 7 & 9 & -8 \\ -1 & 1 & 0 \end{bmatrix}$

3. If $C = \begin{bmatrix} 3 & -5 \\ 5 & 0 \\ -3 & 8 \end{bmatrix}$ and $D = \begin{bmatrix} 8 & 3 \\ -6 & 2 \\ -9 & 1 \end{bmatrix}$, evaluate $3C - 2D$.

$\begin{bmatrix} -7 & -21 \\ 27 & -4 \\ 9 & 22 \end{bmatrix}$

4. For $S_{2 \times 6}$ and $T_{6 \times 3}$, what are the dimensions of ST?

2×3

5. If $P = \begin{bmatrix} 4 & -3 & 5 \\ 0 & 6 & -1 \end{bmatrix}$ and $Q = \begin{bmatrix} 3 & 6 \\ -2 & 2 \\ 0 & 1 \end{bmatrix}$, evaluate PQ.

$\begin{bmatrix} 18 & 23 \\ -12 & 11 \end{bmatrix}$

6. If $A = \begin{bmatrix} 4 & -2 \\ 0 & 5 \end{bmatrix}$, evaluate A^2.

$\begin{bmatrix} 16 & -18 \\ 0 & 25 \end{bmatrix}$

7. If $\triangle ABC$ is defined by the matrix $P = \begin{bmatrix} -6 & 3 & 7 \\ 2 & -5 & 3 \end{bmatrix}$, what are the coordinates of $\triangle ABC$ after it has been reflected using the reflection matrix $\begin{bmatrix} 1 & 0 \\ 0 & -1 \end{bmatrix}$?

$P' = \begin{bmatrix} -6 & 3 & 7 \\ -2 & 5 & -3 \end{bmatrix}$

8. $\triangle ABC$ has vertices $A(2, 2)$, $B(5, 1)$, and $C(6, -3)$. What are the coordinates of the image of $\triangle ABC$ after it has been rotated using the rotation matrix $\begin{bmatrix} 0 & -1 \\ 1 & 0 \end{bmatrix}$?

$A'(-2, 2)$, $B'(-1, 5)$, $C'(3, 6)$

9. Find the determinant of $\begin{bmatrix} 3 & -7 \\ 4 & 6 \end{bmatrix}$.

46

10. Find the determinant of $\begin{bmatrix} 0 & 0 & -1 \\ 2 & 6 & 2 \\ -3 & 7 & 1 \end{bmatrix}$.

−32

11. Use Cramer's Rule to solve the system of equations $\begin{cases} 2x + 3y = 2 \\ 5x + 4y = 12 \end{cases}$.

$x = 4, y = -2$

12. If $\begin{bmatrix} -4 & 0.5 \\ 6 & x \end{bmatrix}$ has no inverse, what is the value of x?

−0.75

13. What matrix is the inverse of $\begin{bmatrix} 3 & 2 \\ 4 & 1 \end{bmatrix}$?

$-\frac{1}{5}\begin{bmatrix} 1 & -2 \\ -4 & 3 \end{bmatrix}$

B Chapter 4 Test (continued)

14. What is the augmented matrix for the system $\begin{cases} 8 + 3y = -2x \\ -4x + 5 = y \end{cases}$?

$\left[\begin{array}{cc|c} 2 & 3 & -8 \\ -4 & -1 & -5 \end{array}\right]$

15. What is $\left[\begin{array}{cc|c} 4 & 3 & 17 \\ -2 & 6 & 14 \end{array}\right]$ in reduced row-echelon form?

$\left[\begin{array}{cc|c} 1 & 0 & 2 \\ 0 & 1 & 3 \end{array}\right]$

16. The system of equations $\begin{cases} 3x + 3y - 2z = 19 \\ 3y - 6z = 3 \\ 6x + 4z = 28 \end{cases}$ represents the number of red, green, and blue cubes you will need to help your younger sister practice her addition and subtraction. Use x as the number of red cubes, y as the number of green cubes, and z as the number of blue cubes. What is the number of each color of cubes you will need to gather to help your sister?

4 red, 3 green, and 1 blue

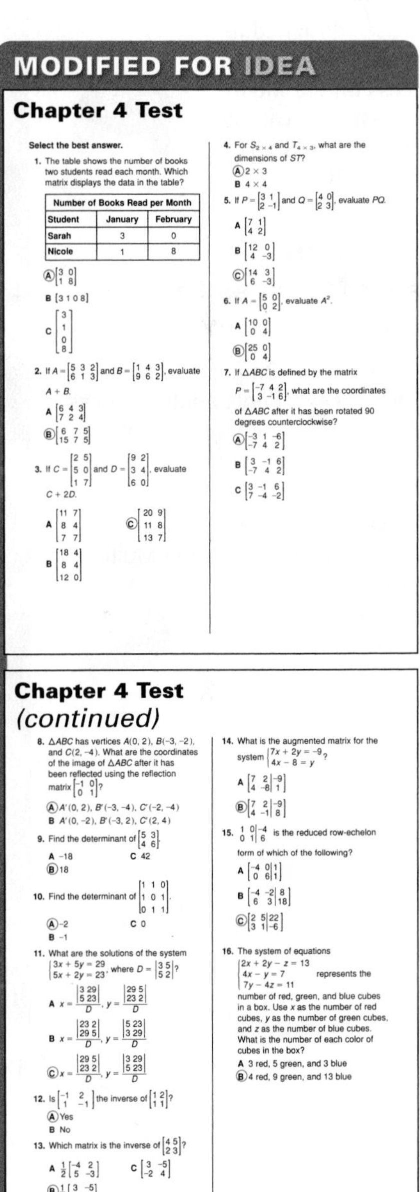

MODIFIED FOR IDEA

Chapter 4 Test

Select the best answer.

1. The table shows the number of books two students read each month. Which matrix displays the data in the table?

Number of Books Read per Month		
Student	January	February
Sarah	3	0
Nicole	1	8

Ⓐ $\begin{bmatrix} 3 & 0 \\ 1 & 8 \end{bmatrix}$
B $\begin{bmatrix} 3 & 1 & 0 & 8 \end{bmatrix}$
C $\begin{bmatrix} 3 \\ 1 \\ 0 \\ 8 \end{bmatrix}$

2. If $A = \begin{bmatrix} 5 & 3 & 2 \\ 6 & 1 & 3 \end{bmatrix}$ and $B = \begin{bmatrix} 1 & 4 & 3 \\ 9 & 6 & 2 \end{bmatrix}$, evaluate $A + B$.

A $\begin{bmatrix} 6 & 4 & 3 \\ 7 & 2 & 4 \end{bmatrix}$
Ⓑ $\begin{bmatrix} 6 & 7 & 5 \\ 15 & 7 & 5 \end{bmatrix}$

3. If $C = \begin{bmatrix} 2 & 5 \\ 5 & 0 \\ 1 & 7 \end{bmatrix}$ and $D = \begin{bmatrix} 9 & 2 \\ 3 & 4 \\ 6 & 0 \end{bmatrix}$, evaluate $C + 2D$.

A $\begin{bmatrix} 11 & 7 \\ 8 & 4 \\ 7 & 7 \end{bmatrix}$ Ⓒ $\begin{bmatrix} 20 & 9 \\ 11 & 8 \\ 13 & 7 \end{bmatrix}$
B $\begin{bmatrix} 18 & 4 \\ 8 & 4 \\ 12 & 0 \end{bmatrix}$

4. For $S_{2 \times 4}$ and $T_{4 \times 3}$, what are the dimensions of ST?

Ⓐ 2×3
B 4×4

5. If $P = \begin{bmatrix} 3 & 1 \\ 2 & -1 \end{bmatrix}$ and $Q = \begin{bmatrix} 4 & 0 \\ 2 & 3 \end{bmatrix}$, evaluate PQ.

A $\begin{bmatrix} 7 & 1 \\ 4 & 2 \end{bmatrix}$
B $\begin{bmatrix} 12 & 0 \\ 4 & -3 \end{bmatrix}$
Ⓒ $\begin{bmatrix} 14 & 3 \\ 6 & -3 \end{bmatrix}$

6. If $A = \begin{bmatrix} 5 & 0 \\ 0 & 2 \end{bmatrix}$, evaluate A^2.

A $\begin{bmatrix} 10 & 0 \\ 0 & 4 \end{bmatrix}$
Ⓑ $\begin{bmatrix} 25 & 0 \\ 0 & 4 \end{bmatrix}$

7. If $\triangle ABC$ is defined by the matrix $P = \begin{bmatrix} -7 & 4 & 2 \\ 3 & -1 & 6 \end{bmatrix}$, what are the coordinates of $\triangle ABC$ after it has been rotated 90 degrees counterclockwise?

Ⓐ $\begin{bmatrix} -3 & 1 & -6 \\ -7 & 4 & 2 \end{bmatrix}$
B $\begin{bmatrix} 3 & -1 & 6 \\ -7 & 4 & 2 \end{bmatrix}$
C $\begin{bmatrix} 3 & -1 & 6 \\ 7 & -4 & -2 \end{bmatrix}$

Chapter 4 Test (continued)

8. $\triangle ABC$ has vertices $A(0, 2)$, $B(-3, -2)$, and $C(2, -4)$. What are the coordinates of the image of $\triangle ABC$ after it has been reflected using the reflection matrix $\begin{bmatrix} -1 & 0 \\ 0 & 1 \end{bmatrix}$?

Ⓐ $A'(0, 2)$, $B'(-3, -4)$, $C'(-2, -4)$
B $A'(0, -2)$, $B'(-3, 2)$, $C'(2, 4)$

9. Find the determinant of $\begin{bmatrix} 5 & 3 \\ 4 & 6 \end{bmatrix}$.

A −18 C 42
Ⓑ 18

10. Find the determinant of $\begin{bmatrix} 1 & 1 & 0 \\ 1 & 0 & 1 \\ 0 & 1 & 1 \end{bmatrix}$.

Ⓐ −2 C 0
B −1

11. What are the solutions of the system $\begin{cases} 3x + 5y = 29 \\ 5x + 2y = 23 \end{cases}$, where $D = \begin{vmatrix} 3 & 5 \\ 5 & 2 \end{vmatrix}$?

A $x = \frac{\begin{vmatrix} 3 & 29 \\ 5 & 23 \end{vmatrix}}{D}, y = \frac{\begin{vmatrix} 29 & 5 \\ 23 & 2 \end{vmatrix}}{D}$

B $x = \frac{\begin{vmatrix} 23 & 2 \\ 29 & 5 \end{vmatrix}}{D}, y = \frac{\begin{vmatrix} 5 & 23 \\ 3 & 29 \end{vmatrix}}{D}$

Ⓒ $x = \frac{\begin{vmatrix} 29 & 5 \\ 23 & 2 \end{vmatrix}}{D}, y = \frac{\begin{vmatrix} 3 & 29 \\ 5 & 23 \end{vmatrix}}{D}$

12. Is $\begin{bmatrix} -1 & 2 \\ 1 & -1 \end{bmatrix}$ the inverse of $\begin{bmatrix} 1 & 2 \\ 1 & 1 \end{bmatrix}$?

Ⓐ Yes
B No

13. Which matrix is the inverse of $\begin{bmatrix} 4 & 5 \\ 2 & 3 \end{bmatrix}$?

A $\frac{1}{2}\begin{bmatrix} -4 & 2 \\ 5 & -3 \end{bmatrix}$ C $\begin{bmatrix} 3 & -5 \\ -2 & 4 \end{bmatrix}$
Ⓑ $\frac{1}{2}\begin{bmatrix} 3 & -5 \\ -2 & 4 \end{bmatrix}$

14. What is the augmented matrix for the system $\begin{cases} 7x + 2y = -9 \\ 4x - 8 = y \end{cases}$?

A $\left[\begin{array}{cc|c} 7 & 2 & -9 \\ 4 & -8 & 1 \end{array}\right]$
Ⓑ $\left[\begin{array}{cc|c} 7 & 2 & -9 \\ 4 & -1 & 8 \end{array}\right]$

15. $\begin{array}{cc|c} 1 & 0 & -4 \\ 0 & 1 & 6 \end{array}$ is the reduced row-echelon form of which of the following?

A $\left[\begin{array}{cc|c} -4 & 0 & 1 \\ 0 & 6 & 1 \end{array}\right]$
B $\left[\begin{array}{cc|c} -4 & -2 & 8 \\ 6 & 3 & 18 \end{array}\right]$
Ⓒ $\left[\begin{array}{cc|c} 2 & 5 & 22 \\ 3 & 1 & -6 \end{array}\right]$

16. The system of equations $\begin{cases} 2x + 2y - z = 13 \\ 4x - y = 7 \\ 7y - 4z = 11 \end{cases}$ represents the number of red, green, and blue cubes in a box. Use x as the number of red cubes, y as the number of green cubes, and z as the number of blue cubes. What is the number of each color of cubes in the box?

A 3 red, 5 green, and 3 blue
Ⓑ 4 red, 9 green, and 13 blue

Create and customize Chapter 4 Tests. Instantly generate multiple test versions, answer keys, and practice versions of test items.

CHAPTER 4

SECTION 4A
Matrix Operations

On page 268, students use matrices to represent and transform a polygon in a real-world computer graphics situation.

Exercises designed to prepare students for success on the Multi-Step Test Prep can be found on pages 251, 258, and 266.

SECTION 4B
Using Matrices to Solve Systems

On page 294, students apply matrices with systems of equations to model a real-world ticketing situation.

Exercises designed to prepare students for success on the Multi-Step Test Prep can be found on pages 276, 284, and 292.

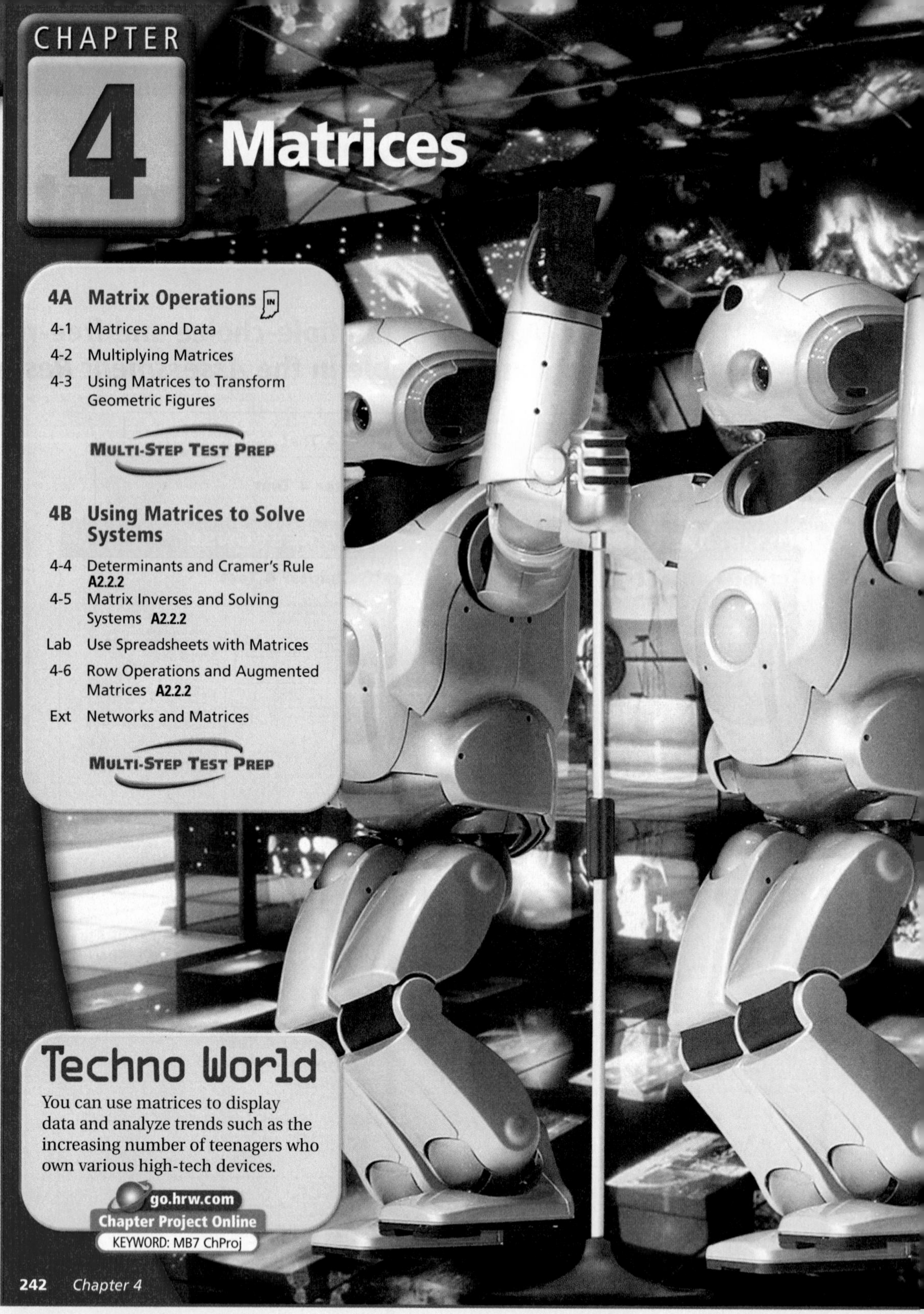

CHAPTER 4

Matrices

Techno World

You can use matrices to display data and analyze trends such as the increasing number of teenagers who own various high-tech devices.

go.hrw.com
Chapter Project Online
KEYWORD: MB7 ChProj

Techno World

About the Project

In the Chapter Project, students gather data; represent it by using different methods, including a matrix; and interpret the results. Students then compare their results with those of a larger survey.

Project Resources

All project resources for teachers and students are provided online.

Materials:

- graphing calculator

ARE YOU READY?

Vocabulary

Match each term on the left with a definition on the right.

1. radius B
2. dependent system E
3. inconsistent system C
4. transformation D

A. an operation that can be performed in either order, as in $a + b = b + a$ and $ab = ba$
B. the distance from the center of a circle to the circle
C. A system of equations or inequalities that has no solution
D. A change in the position, size, or shape of a figure or graph
E. A system of equations that has infinitely many solutions

Add and Subtract Integers

Simplify each expression.

5. $2 + 7 + (-10)$ -1
6. $-8 + 14 + (-3)$ 3
7. $-2 + (-3) + (-5)$ -10
8. $-9 + 15 - 7 + 1$ 0
9. $20 - (-5) + (-3) - 2$ 20
10. $9 + 8 - 7 + 5 - (-3) + 2$ 20

Multiply and Divide Integers

Multiply or divide.

11. $-18 \div 9$ -2
12. $-6(-1)$ 6
13. $16(-2)$ -32
14. $-15 \div (-3)$ 5

Order of Operations

Simplify each expression.

15. $2(0.5) + 2(0.6)$ 2.2
16. $0(6.7) + 1(0.3) - 5(2) - 3(8)$ -33.7
17. $3(2 + 7 + 0) - 5(3 + 6 + 4)$ -38
18. $4(3 - 6 + 2) - 5(2 + 0 - 1)$ -9

Identify Similar Figures

19. Identify which figures are similar. $\triangle JLK$ and $\triangle MNP$

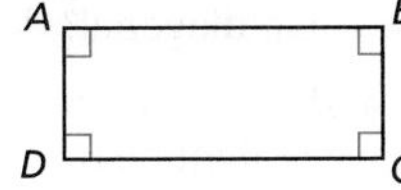

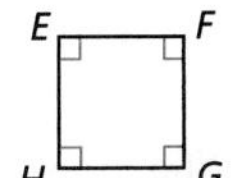

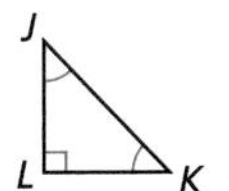

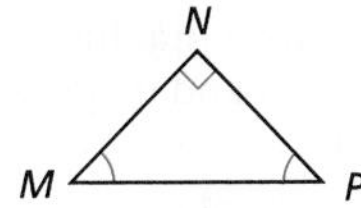

Find Missing Measures in Similar Figures

20. $\triangle ABC$ is similar to $\triangle DEF$. $m\angle FDE = 35°$. What other angle has a measure of 35°? $\angle CAB$
21. $\triangle FGH$ is similar to $\triangle JKL$. $JL = 12$, $GH = 12$, and $FH = 8$. Find KL. 18

CHAPTER 4

ARE YOU READY?

Organizer

Objective: Assess students' understanding of prerequisite skills.

Prerequisite Skills

Add and Subtract Integers
Multiply and Divide Integers
Order of Operations
Identify Similar Figures
Find Missing Measures in Similar Figures

Assessing Prior Knowledge

Diagnose and Prescribe

Use this page to determine whether intervention is necessary or whether enrichment is appropriate.

Resources

 ***Are You Ready? Intervention and Enrichment*** **Worksheets**

 ***Are You Ready?*** **CD-ROM**

 ***Are You Ready?*** **Online**

my.hrw.com

ARE YOU READY?

Diagnose and Prescribe

NO INTERVENE

Prerequisite Skill	*Are You Ready? Intervention*, Chapter 4 Worksheets	CD-ROM	Online
Add and Subtract Integers	Skill 51	Activity 51	Diagnose and Prescribe Online
Multiply and Divide Integers	Skill 52	Activity 52	
Order of Operations	Skill 55	Activity 55	
Identify Similar Figures	Skill 34	Activity 34	
Find Missing Measures in Similar Figures	Skill 35	Activity 35	

YES ENRICH

Are You Ready? Enrichment, Chapter 4

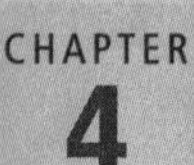

Study Guide: Preview

Organizer

Objective: Help students organize the new concepts they will learn in Chapter 4.

Online Edition
Multilingual Glossary

Resources

Puzzle Pro
One-Stop Planner®

***Multilingual Glossary* Online**

go.hrw.com
KEYWORD: MB7 Glossary

Answers to *Vocabulary Connections*

Possible answers:

1. the name of the street and the number of the house
2. the width and length of the card
3. No; it is in the bottom left corner.
4. The number of rows is the same as the number of columns.
5. the number two

CHAPTER 4

Study Guide: Preview

Where You've Been

Previously, you

- organized data into tables.
- performed operations with real numbers.
- solved systems of linear equations.

In This Chapter

You will study

- organizing data into matrices.
- operating with matrices.
- solving systems of equations several ways by using matrices.

Where You're Going

You can use the skills in this chapter

- as you study other fields of mathematics, such as geometry, statistics, and business math.
- in competitions that have various scores and degrees of difficulty.
- outside of school to set up and manipulate data as you analyze the possible effects of changes.

Key Vocabulary/Vocabulario

address	dirección
dimensions	dimensiónes
entry	entrada
main diagonal	diagonal principal
matrix	matriz
row operation	operación por filas
scalar	escalar
square matrix	matriz cuadrada

Vocabulary Connections

To become familiar with some of the vocabulary terms in the chapter, consider the following. You may refer to the chapter, the glossary, or a dictionary if you like.

1. The **address** for a number in a matrix tells you the row and column of that number. To locate a specific house in a neighborhood, what two pieces of information do you need in the address?
2. The **dimensions** of a matrix tell how many rows and how many columns the matrix has. What do the dimensions of a 3 in. by 5 in. index card tell you?
3. The **main diagonal** of a matrix goes from the upper left corner to the lower right. On this page, would the page number be on the main diagonal?
4. A square's length and width are the same. What do you suppose might be true of a **square matrix**?
5. A **scalar** scales the numbers in a matrix by using multiplication. What number used as a scalar would double a group of numbers?

244 *Chapter 4*

Reading Strategy: Read and Interpret Math Symbols

Interpreting math symbols is a necessary skill that you need in order to comprehend new material. As you study each lesson in this textbook, read aloud the expressions involving symbols and notations. This practice will help you become proficient at translating symbols into words.

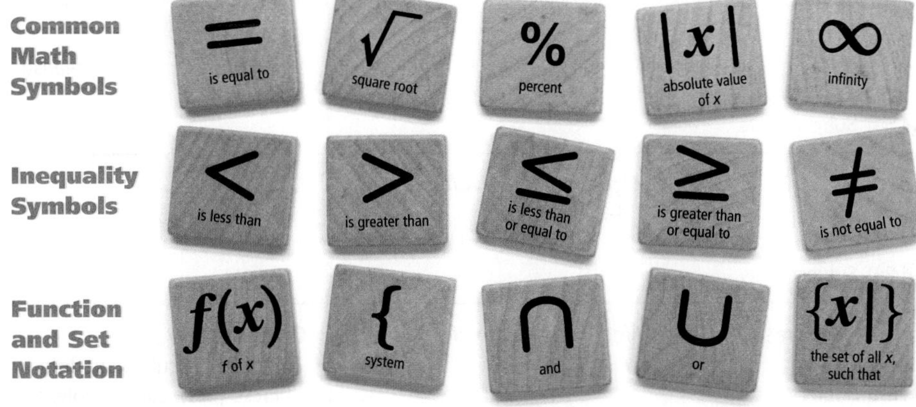

In Algebra, symbols are used to communicate information. As you study each lesson, read aloud expressions involving symbols and expressions. This can help you translate symbols into words.

Expressions	Words
$f(x) = \sqrt{16x} - 4$	*f* of *x* is equal to the square root of 16 times *x*, minus 4.
$\frac{\lvert x - 15 \rvert}{6} \leq 12$	The absolute value of the quantity *x* minus 15, divided by 6, is less than or equal to 12.
$\{x \mid x \leq -19 \cup x > 8\}$	The set of all numbers *x* such that *x* is less than or equal to negative 19 OR *x* is greater than 8
$\begin{cases} y \leq -4x + 8 \\ y > x - 6 \end{cases}$	The system of inequalities containing "*y* is less than or equal to negative 4*x* plus 8" and "*y* is greater than *x* minus 6"

Try This

Translate these mathematical expressions into words.

1. $\{x \mid x \geq -7 \cup x \leq -1\}$ **2.** $f(y) = \lvert 15y \rvert + \frac{y}{2}$ **3.** $\begin{cases} y = 2x + 3 \\ y = x \end{cases}$ **4.** $[-5, \infty)$

Rewrite the statement as an algebraic expression.

5. The set of all numbers *x* such that *x* is between negative 8 and 10.

Reading and Writing Math CHAPTER 4

Organizer

Objective: Help students apply strategies to understand and retain key concepts.

Resources

Chapter 4 Resource Book
Reading Strategies

Reading Strategy: Read and Interpret Math Symbols

Discuss As students progress through and beyond Algebra 2, it will become increasingly important that they be able to correctly interpret and read the language of mathematics. Emphasize the importance of being able to string these symbols together into coherent statements, as in the examples.

Extend Matrix notation will be new to most students and can be confusing. As students work through Chapter 4, have them pay attention to and be careful with the notation and terminology.

Answers to *Try This*

1. the set of all numbers *x* such that *x* is greater than or equal to negative 7 OR *x* is less than or equal to negative 1
2. The function *f* of *y* equals the absolute value of 15*y*, plus *y* divided by 2.
3. the system of equations containing *y* equals 2*x* plus 3 and *y* equals *x*
4. the set containing all real numbers greater than or equal to negative 5
5. $\{x \mid -8 < x < 10\}$

SECTION

4A Matrix Operations

One-Minute Section Planner

Lesson	Lab Resources	Materials
Lesson 4-1 Matrices and Data • Use matrices to display mathematical and real-world data. • Find sums, differences, and scalar products of matrices. ☐ SAT-10 ☐ NAEP ☑ ACT ☑ SAT ☑ SAT Subject Tests		**Optional** graphing calculator, spreadsheet software
Lesson 4-2 Multiplying Matrices • Understand the properties of matrices with respect to multiplication. • Multiply two matrices. ☐ SAT-10 ☐ NAEP ☑ ACT ☑ SAT ☑ SAT Subject Tests	***Algebra Lab Activities*** 4-2 Algebra Lab	**Required** graphing calculator
Lesson 4-3 Using Matrices to Transform Geometric Figures • Use matrices to transform a plane figure. ☐ SAT-10 ☐ NAEP ☑ ACT ☑ SAT ☑ SAT Subject Tests	***Algebra Lab Activities*** 4-3 Algebra Lab	**Optional** graphing calculator, pattern blocks (MK), cut-out polygons, tranparency grid (MK)

MK = *Manipulatives Kit*

Section Overview

Professional Development

Introduction to Matrices — Lessons 4-1, 4-2

Data from a table can be represented efficiently in a matrix. Conclusions about the data can be drawn after using matrix operations.

	1st	2nd	3rd
Bears	5	2	3
Lions	3	6	7

$$\rightarrow \begin{bmatrix} 5 & 2 & 3 \\ 3 & 6 & 7 \end{bmatrix}$$

Scalar Multiplication

$$3\begin{bmatrix} 1 & 2 \\ 3 & 4 \end{bmatrix} = \begin{bmatrix} 3 & 6 \\ 9 & 12 \end{bmatrix}$$

Matrix Addition

$$\begin{bmatrix} -2 & 0 \\ 4 & -5 \end{bmatrix} + \begin{bmatrix} 1 & 7 \\ -6 & -1 \end{bmatrix} = \begin{bmatrix} -2+1 & 0+7 \\ 4+-6 & -5+-1 \end{bmatrix} = \begin{bmatrix} -1 & 7 \\ -2 & -6 \end{bmatrix}$$

Matrix Multiplication

$$\begin{bmatrix} 1 & 3 \\ 3 & 4 \end{bmatrix}\begin{bmatrix} 5 & 6 \\ 7 & 8 \end{bmatrix} = \begin{bmatrix} 1(5)+3(7) & 1(6)+3(8) \\ 3(5)+4(7) & 3(6)+4(8) \end{bmatrix} = \begin{bmatrix} 26 & 30 \\ 43 & 50 \end{bmatrix}$$

$$\begin{bmatrix} 1 & 0 \\ 0 & 1 \end{bmatrix}\begin{bmatrix} a & b \\ c & d \end{bmatrix} = \begin{bmatrix} a & b \\ c & d \end{bmatrix}\begin{bmatrix} 1 & 0 \\ 0 & 1 \end{bmatrix} = \begin{bmatrix} a & b \\ c & d \end{bmatrix}$$

$\begin{bmatrix} 1 & 0 \\ 0 & 1 \end{bmatrix}$ is the 2×2 multiplicative **identity matrix *I*.**

Geometric Transformations with Matrices — Lesson 4-3

Why? Geometric transformations can be performed using matrix operations.

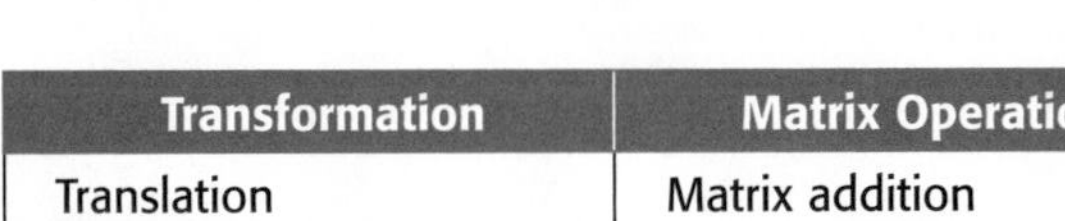

Transformation	Matrix Operations
Translation	Matrix addition
Dilation	Scalar multiplication
Reflection, rotation	Matrix multiplication

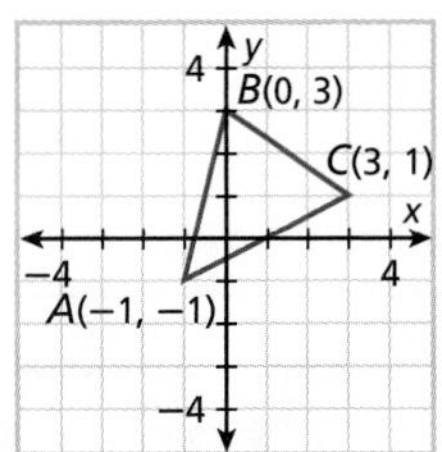

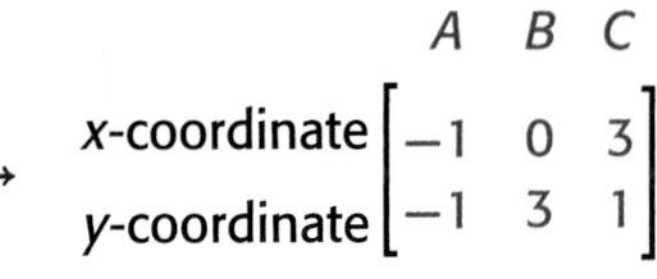

$$\begin{array}{r} \\ x\text{-coordinate} \\ y\text{-coordinate} \end{array} \begin{array}{c} \;\;A \;\;\; B \;\;\; C \\ \begin{bmatrix} -1 & 0 & 3 \\ -1 & 3 & 1 \end{bmatrix} \end{array}$$

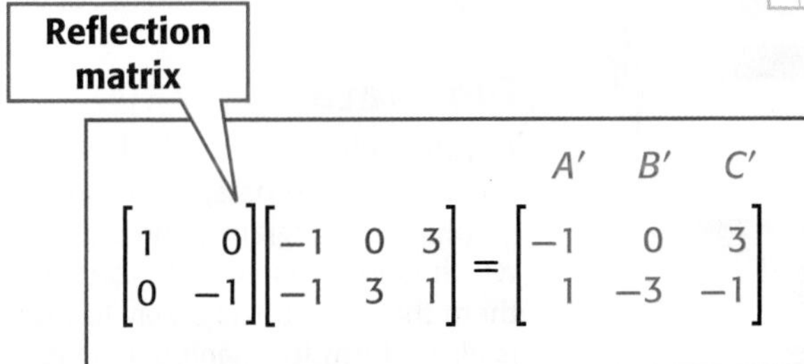

Reflection matrix

$$\begin{bmatrix} 1 & 0 \\ 0 & -1 \end{bmatrix}\begin{bmatrix} -1 & 0 & 3 \\ -1 & 3 & 1 \end{bmatrix} = \begin{array}{c} \;A' \;\;\; B' \;\;\; C' \\ \begin{bmatrix} -1 & 0 & 3 \\ 1 & -3 & -1 \end{bmatrix} \end{array}$$

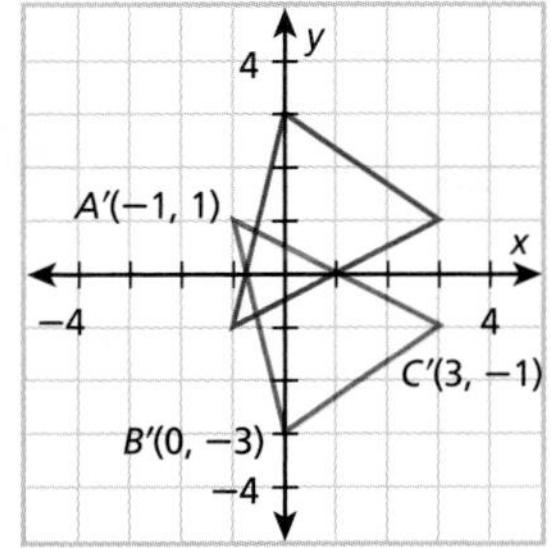

$\triangle A'B'C'$ is a reflection of $\triangle ABC$ across the x-axis.

4-1 Organizer

Pacing: Traditional 1 day
Block $\frac{1}{2}$ day

Objectives: Use matrices to display mathematical and real-world data.

Find sums, differences, and scalar products of matrices.

Online Edition
Tutorial Videos

Countdown to Testing Week 8

Power Presentations with PowerPoint®

Warm Up

Distribute.

1. $3(2x + y + 3z)$ $6x + 3y + 9z$

2. $-1(x - y + 2)$ $-x + y - 2$

State the property illustrated.

3. $(a + b) + c = a + (b + c)$

Associative Property of Addition

4. $p + q = q + p$

Commutative Property of Addition

Also available on transparency

Math Humor

Q: Why did the matrix entry get lost?

A: It couldn't remember its address.

4-1 Matrices and Data

Objectives
Use matrices to display mathematical and real-world data.

Find sums, differences, and scalar products of matrices.

Vocabulary
matrix
dimensions
entry
address
scalar

Who uses this?
Rodeo scorekeepers may use matrices to determine scores of participants for events such as barrel racing.

The table shows the top scores for girls in barrel racing at the 2004 National High School Rodeo finals. The data can be presented in a table or a spreadsheet as rows and columns of numbers. You can also use a *matrix* to show table data. A **matrix** is a rectangular array of numbers enclosed in brackets.

2004 National High School Rodeo Finals—Barrel Racing Scores

Participant	First Ride	Second Ride	Third Ride
Sierra Thomas (UT)	16.781	16.29	17.318
Kelly Allen (TX)	16.206	16.606	17.668

Matrix A has two rows and three columns. A matrix with m rows and n columns has **dimensions** $m \times n$, read "m by n," and is called an $m \times n$ matrix. A has dimensions 2×3. Each value in a matrix is called an **entry** of the matrix.

$$A = \begin{bmatrix} 16.781 & 16.29 & 17.318 \\ 16.206 & 16.606 & 17.668 \end{bmatrix} \begin{matrix} \leftarrow \text{Row 1} \\ \leftarrow \text{Row 2} \end{matrix}$$

Column 1 Column 2 Column 3

The **address** of an entry is its location in a matrix, expressed by using the lowercase matrix letter with the row and column number as subscripts. The score 16.206 is located in row 2 column 1, so a_{21} is 16.206.

$$A = \begin{bmatrix} 16.781 & 16.29 & 17.318 \\ 16.206 & 16.606 & 17.668 \end{bmatrix}$$

a_{21} (points to 16.206)

EXAMPLE  1 **Displaying Data in Matrix Form**

Use the packaging data for the costs of the packages given.

Cost of 4-Inch Cubic Box ($)

	Plastic	Paper
Total Cost	0.48	0.72
Cost per in^2	0.005	0.0075
Cost per in^3	0.0075	0.01125

a. Display the data in matrix form.

$$C = \begin{bmatrix} 0.48 & 0.72 \\ 0.005 & 0.0075 \\ 0.0075 & 0.01125 \end{bmatrix}$$

b. What are the dimensions of C?
C has three rows and two columns, so it is a 3×2 matrix.

State Resources

go.hrw.com
State Resources Online
KEYWORD: MB7 Resources

1 Introduce

EXPLORATION

4-1 Matrices and Data

A car company has three plants: A, B, and C. The company produces three cars: the Zip, the Tip, and the Pip.

The table shows the production numbers for each model at each plant during the first half of the year.

	Zip	Tip	Pip
A	2000	4200	7000
B	1900	4400	6200
C	450	1200	2500

1. Which plant produced the most cars?
2. For which model were the most cars produced?
3. The production numbers for the second half of the year are shown in the table.

	Zip	Tip	Pip
A	2100	3900	6700
B	2000	1200	6000
C	430	1050	2500

Make a new table that gives the production numbers for the entire year.

	Zip	Tip	Pip
A			
B			
C			

THINK AND DISCUSS

4. **Explain** how you found the entries in the table that gives the production numbers for the entire year.
5. **Describe** the dimensions of the table you would use to display data about a car company with four plants and six different models.

Motivate

Ask students for methods they have used to organize and display data, such as tables, lists, bar graphs, tree diagrams, line plots, and so on. Ask which types organize into rows and columns. Tell them that a matrix is a way to display data, and it is also a form for manipulating it.

Explorations and answers are provided in the *Explorations* binder.

c. What is the entry at c_{12}? What does it represent?

The entry at c_{12}, in row 1 column 2, is 0.72. It is the total cost of a 4 in. paper box.

d. What is the address of the entry 0.005?

The entry 0.005 is at c_{21}.

1a. 3 × 4
1b. 11
1c. m_{14} and m_{23}

Use matrix M to answer the questions below.

$$M = \begin{bmatrix} 2 & 1 & 5 & 0 \\ 1 & 5 & 0 & 9 \\ 2 & 11 & 4 & 12 \end{bmatrix}$$

1a. What are the dimensions of M?

1b. What is the entry at m_{32}?

1c. The entry 0 appears at what two addresses?

Corresponding entries in two or more matrices are entries with the same address, such as a_{32} and b_{32} in matrices A and B.

Adding and Subtracting Matrices

WORDS	NUMBERS	ALGEBRA
To add or subtract two matrices, add or subtract the corresponding entries.	$\begin{bmatrix}1 & 2\end{bmatrix} + \begin{bmatrix}5 & 10\end{bmatrix} = \begin{bmatrix}6 & 12\end{bmatrix}$	$\begin{bmatrix}a_{11} & a_{12}\end{bmatrix} + \begin{bmatrix}b_{11} & b_{12}\end{bmatrix} = \begin{bmatrix}a_{11}+b_{11} & a_{12}+b_{12}\end{bmatrix}$

You can add or subtract two matrices only if they have the same dimensions.

✔ **Same Dimensions**

$$\begin{bmatrix}1 & 2\\6 & 7\end{bmatrix} + \begin{bmatrix}2 & 1\\7 & 6\end{bmatrix} \qquad \begin{bmatrix}5\\6\\7\end{bmatrix} + \begin{bmatrix}2\\8\\1\end{bmatrix}$$

✘ **Different Dimensions**

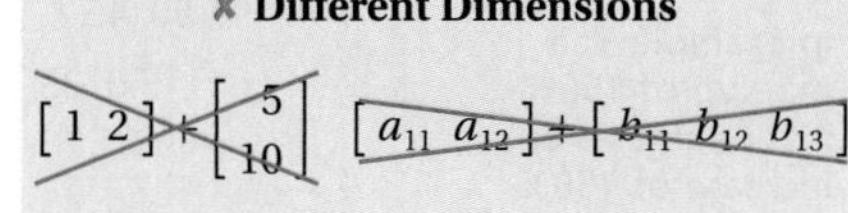

$$\begin{bmatrix}1 & 2\end{bmatrix} + \begin{bmatrix}5\\10\end{bmatrix} \qquad \begin{bmatrix}a_{11} & a_{12}\end{bmatrix} + \begin{bmatrix}b_{11} & b_{12} & b_{13}\end{bmatrix}$$

EXAMPLE 2 Finding Matrix Sums and Differences

$$A = \begin{bmatrix}4 & -2\\-3 & 10\\2 & 6\end{bmatrix} \quad B = \begin{bmatrix}4 & -1 & -5\\3 & 2 & 8\end{bmatrix} \quad C = \begin{bmatrix}3 & 2\\0 & -9\\-5 & 14\end{bmatrix} \quad D = \begin{bmatrix}0 & 1 & -3\\3 & 0 & 10\end{bmatrix}$$

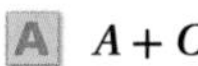

Add or subtract, if possible.

A $A + C$

Add each corresponding entry.

$$A + C = \begin{bmatrix}4 & -2\\-3 & 10\\2 & 6\end{bmatrix} + \begin{bmatrix}3 & 2\\0 & -9\\-5 & 14\end{bmatrix} = \begin{bmatrix}4+3 & -2+2\\-3+0 & 10+(-9)\\2+(-5) & 6+14\end{bmatrix} = \begin{bmatrix}7 & 0\\-3 & 1\\-3 & 20\end{bmatrix}$$

B $C - A$

Subtract each corresponding entry.

$$C - A = \begin{bmatrix}3 & 2\\0 & -9\\-5 & 14\end{bmatrix} - \begin{bmatrix}4 & -2\\-3 & 10\\2 & 6\end{bmatrix} = \begin{bmatrix}3-4 & 2-(-2)\\0-(-3) & -9-10\\-5-2 & 14-6\end{bmatrix} = \begin{bmatrix}-1 & 4\\3 & -19\\-7 & 8\end{bmatrix}$$

C $C + B$

C is a 3 × 2 matrix, and B is a 2 × 3 matrix. Because C and B do not have the same dimensions, they cannot be added.

Power Presentations with PowerPoint®

Additional Examples

Example 1

The prices for different sandwiches are presented below.

	6 in.	9 in.
Roast beef	$3.95	$5.95
Turkey	$3.75	$5.60
Tuna	$3.50	$5.25

a. Display the data in matrix form.

$$P = \begin{bmatrix}3.95 & 5.95\\3.75 & 5.60\\3.50 & 5.25\end{bmatrix}$$

b. What are the dimensions of P? 3 × 2

c. What is entry p_{32}? What does it represent? 5.25; price of a 9 in. tuna sandwich.

d. What is the address of the entry 5.95? p_{12}

Example 2

$$W = \begin{bmatrix}3 & -2\\1 & 0\end{bmatrix}, X = \begin{bmatrix}4 & 7 & 2\\5 & 1 & -1\end{bmatrix}$$

$$Y = \begin{bmatrix}1 & 4\\-2 & 3\end{bmatrix}, Z = \begin{bmatrix}2 & -2 & 3\\1 & 0 & 4\end{bmatrix}$$

Add or subtract if possible.

A. $W + Y$ $\begin{bmatrix}4 & 2\\-1 & 3\end{bmatrix}$

B. $X - Z$ $\begin{bmatrix}2 & 9 & -1\\4 & 1 & -5\end{bmatrix}$

C. $X + Y$ not possible

Also available on transparency

2 Teach

Guided Instruction

When presenting **Example 1,** discuss the vocabulary words to allow students to become familiar with matrix terminology. In **Example 2,** be sure that students understand *corresponding entries* and that the commutative property does not hold for *dimensions* of a matrix. Compare *scalar multiplication* with applying the distributive property.

ENGLISH LANGUAGE LEARNERS

Reaching All Learners

Through Auditory Cues

Have students work in pairs. One student creates a matrix with 12 entries and describes it to the other without showing the matrix. The second student recreates the matrix based on only the description. Then students switch roles. Encourage students to use vocabulary such as *dimensions, entry, address, row,* and *column.*

INTERVENTION

Questioning Strategies

EXAMPLE 1

- Do you always know the address of the upper left entry of any matrix M?
- Suppose A is a 5 × 5 matrix. What would be an address in the next-to-last row?

EXAMPLE 2

- Can any matrix be added to or subtracted from itself?
- If two matrices are added, does the order matter?

Power Presentations with PowerPoint®

Additional Examples

Example 3

Shirt Prices		
	T-shirt	Sweatshirt
Small	$7.50	$15.00
Medium	$8.00	$17.50
Large	$9.00	$20.00
X-Large	$10.00	$22.50

Use a scalar product to find the prices if a 10% discount is applied to the prices above.

$6.75, $13.50;
$7.20, $15.75;
$8.10, $18.00;
$9.00, $20.25

Also available on transparency

INTERVENTION

Questioning Strategies

EXAMPLE 3

- Can scalar multiplication be represented as the addition of matrices?
- How do you know the dimensions of the scalar product matrix?

Teaching Tip **Technology** Graphing calculators and spreadsheets are good at handling matrices. Students may practice using these, as calculations involving matrices could otherwise be time-consuming and lead to errors.

CHECK IT OUT! Add or subtract, if possible.

2a. $B + D$ $\begin{bmatrix} 4 & 0 & -8 \\ 6 & 2 & 18 \end{bmatrix}$ **2b.** $B - A$ not possible **2c.** $D - B$ $\begin{bmatrix} -4 & 2 & 2 \\ 0 & -2 & 2 \end{bmatrix}$

You know that multiplication is repeated addition. The same is true for matrices.

For example, let $E = \begin{bmatrix} 2 & 0 \\ 1 & 5 \end{bmatrix}$.

$$E + E = \begin{bmatrix} 2 & 0 \\ 1 & 5 \end{bmatrix} + \begin{bmatrix} 2 & 0 \\ 1 & 5 \end{bmatrix} = \begin{bmatrix} 2+2 & 0+0 \\ 1+1 & 5+5 \end{bmatrix} = \begin{bmatrix} 2(2) & 2(0) \\ 2(1) & 2(5) \end{bmatrix} = \begin{bmatrix} 4 & 0 \\ 2 & 10 \end{bmatrix}$$

$E + E$ can be written as $2E$. You can multiply a matrix by a number, called a **scalar**. To find the product of a scalar and a matrix, or the *scalar product,* multiply each entry by the scalar.

$$2\begin{bmatrix} 2 & 0 \\ 1 & 5 \end{bmatrix} = \begin{bmatrix} 2(2) & 2(0) \\ 2(1) & 2(5) \end{bmatrix}$$

EXAMPLE 3 *Business Application*

A ticket service marks up prices on tickets to rodeos and other events by 150%. Use a scalar product to find the marked-up prices.

Rodeo Ticket Prices		
Days	Plaza	Balcony
1–2	$60	$35
3–8	$50	$28
9–10	$80	$45

You can multiply by 1.5 and add to the original numbers.

$$\begin{bmatrix} 60 & 35 \\ 50 & 28 \\ 80 & 45 \end{bmatrix} + 1.5\begin{bmatrix} 60 & 35 \\ 50 & 28 \\ 80 & 45 \end{bmatrix}$$

$$= \begin{bmatrix} 60 & 35 \\ 50 & 28 \\ 80 & 45 \end{bmatrix} + \begin{bmatrix} 90 & 52.5 \\ 75 & 42 \\ 120 & 67.5 \end{bmatrix} = \begin{bmatrix} 150 & 87.5 \\ 125 & 70 \\ 200 & 112.5 \end{bmatrix}$$

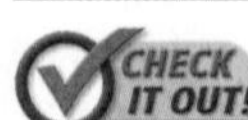

Helpful Hint

In Example 3, a markup of 150% is the same as an increase of 150%.

The marked-up prices are shown below.

Ticket Service Prices		
Days	Plaza	Balcony
1–2	$150	$87.50
3–8	$125	$70.00
9–10	$200	$112.50

CHECK IT OUT! **3.** Use a scalar product to find the prices if a 20% discount is applied to the ticket service prices.
$120, $70; $100, $56; $160, $90;

EXAMPLE 4 Simplifying Matrix Expressions

$A = \begin{bmatrix} 4 & -2 \\ -3 & 10 \end{bmatrix}$ $B = \begin{bmatrix} 4 & -1 & -5 \\ 3 & 2 & 8 \end{bmatrix}$ $C = \begin{bmatrix} 3 & 2 \\ 0 & -9 \end{bmatrix}$ $D = \begin{bmatrix} -6 & 3 & 8 \end{bmatrix}$

A **Evaluate $2A - 3B$, if possible.**

$$2\begin{bmatrix} 4 & -2 \\ -3 & 10 \end{bmatrix} - 3\begin{bmatrix} 4 & -1 & -5 \\ 3 & 2 & 8 \end{bmatrix}$$

A and B do not have the same dimensions; they cannot be subtracted after the scalar products are found.

Helpful Hint

A matrix bracket is a grouping symbol. So in an expression like $C - 2A$, you distribute -2 to all of the entries in A before adding, just as you do with numbers.

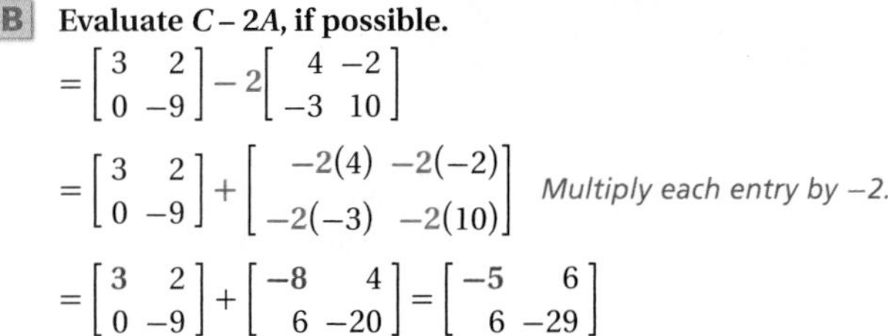

B **Evaluate $C - 2A$, if possible.**

$$= \begin{bmatrix} 3 & 2 \\ 0 & -9 \end{bmatrix} - 2\begin{bmatrix} 4 & -2 \\ -3 & 10 \end{bmatrix}$$

$$= \begin{bmatrix} 3 & 2 \\ 0 & -9 \end{bmatrix} + \begin{bmatrix} -2(4) & -2(-2) \\ -2(-3) & -2(10) \end{bmatrix} \quad \textit{Multiply each entry by } -2.$$

$$= \begin{bmatrix} 3 & 2 \\ 0 & -9 \end{bmatrix} + \begin{bmatrix} -8 & 4 \\ 6 & -20 \end{bmatrix} = \begin{bmatrix} -5 & 6 \\ 6 & -29 \end{bmatrix}$$

CHECK IT OUT! **Evaluate, if possible.**

4a. $3B + 2C$ **4b.** $2A - 3C$ **4c.** $D + 0.5D$

4a. not possible

4b. $\begin{bmatrix} -1 & -10 \\ -6 & 47 \end{bmatrix}$

4c. $\begin{bmatrix} -9 & 4.5 & 12 \end{bmatrix}$

Some properties of equality also apply to matrices.

Properties of Equality for Matrices

WORDS	NUMBERS	ALGEBRA
Commutative Property Matrix addition is commutative.	$\begin{bmatrix} 7 & 2 \\ 3 & 4 \end{bmatrix} + \begin{bmatrix} 1 & 2 \\ 4 & 1 \end{bmatrix} = \begin{bmatrix} 1 & 2 \\ 4 & 1 \end{bmatrix} + \begin{bmatrix} 7 & 2 \\ 3 & 4 \end{bmatrix}$	$A + B = B + A$
Associative Property Matrix addition is associative.	$\left(\begin{bmatrix} 2 \\ 3 \end{bmatrix} + \begin{bmatrix} 0 \\ 1 \end{bmatrix}\right) + \begin{bmatrix} 5 \\ 4 \end{bmatrix} = \begin{bmatrix} 2 \\ 3 \end{bmatrix} + \left(\begin{bmatrix} 0 \\ 1 \end{bmatrix} + \begin{bmatrix} 5 \\ 4 \end{bmatrix}\right)$	$A + B + C = (A + B) + C = A + (B + C)$
Additive Identity The *zero matrix* is the *additive identity matrix O*.	$\begin{bmatrix} 7 & 2 \\ 3 & 4 \end{bmatrix} + \begin{bmatrix} 0 & 0 \\ 0 & 0 \end{bmatrix} = \begin{bmatrix} 7 & 2 \\ 3 & 4 \end{bmatrix}$	$A + O = A$
Additive Inverse The *additive inverse* of matrix A contains the opposite of each entry in matrix A.	$\begin{bmatrix} 5 & -2 \\ -6 & 9 \end{bmatrix} + \begin{bmatrix} -5 & 2 \\ 6 & -9 \end{bmatrix} = \begin{bmatrix} 0 & 0 \\ 0 & 0 \end{bmatrix}$	If $A + B = O$, then A and B are additive inverses.

THINK AND DISCUSS

1. Find the possible dimensions of a matrix that contains eight entries.
2. Describe a matrix operation that reverses the signs of every entry.
3. **GET ORGANIZED** Copy and complete the graphic organizer. Give examples for matrices and real numbers.

Property or Operation	Real Numbers	Matrices
Addition		
Subtraction		
Multiplication by a number		

Power Presentations with PowerPoint®

Additional Examples

Example 4

$$P = \begin{bmatrix} 3 & -2 \\ 1 & 0 \\ 2 & -1 \end{bmatrix} \quad Q = \begin{bmatrix} 4 & 7 & 2 \\ 5 & 1 & -1 \end{bmatrix}$$

$$R = \begin{bmatrix} 1 & 4 \\ -2 & 3 \\ 0 & 4 \end{bmatrix}$$

Evaluate if possible.

A. $3P - Q$ not possible

B. $3R - P$ $\begin{bmatrix} 0 & 14 \\ -7 & 9 \\ -2 & 13 \end{bmatrix}$

Also available on transparency

INTERVENTION

Questioning Strategies

EXAMPLE 4

- Why is it necessary for matrices to have the same dimensions in order to add or subtract them?

Teaching Tip **Visual** Have students create a poster of a mid-sized matrix, such as a 4×5, with the address of each cell as the entry.

3 Close

Summarize

Ask students for the conditions required for matrix addition in the same dimension. Then, for matrices where that is true, ask whether the matrices can be added in any order and which property this represents. yes; Commutative Property Ask whether you can add the sum of A and B to C and get the same result as adding A to the sum of B and C, and which property this represents. yes; Associative Property

ONGOING ASSESSMENT and INTERVENTION

***Diagnose Before* the Lesson**
4-1 Warm Up, TE p. 246

***Monitor During* the Lesson**
Check It Out! Exercises, SE pp. 247–249
Questioning Strategies, TE pp. 247–249

***Assess After* the Lesson**
4-1 Lesson Quiz, TE p. 252
Alternative Assessment, TE p. 252

Answers to *Think and Discuss*

Possible answers:

1. 1×8, 2×4, 4×2, 8×1
2. multiplying by the scalar -1
3. See p. A6.

4-1 Exercises

Assignment Guide

Assign *Guided Practice* exercises as necessary.

If you finished Examples **1–2**
Basic 12–16, 29
Average 12–16, 29, 36
Advanced 12–16, 29, 36

If you finished Examples **1–4**
Basic 12–21, 23, 28, 32–35, 40–44
Average 12–36, 40–44
Advanced 12–28 even, 29–44

Homework Quick Check
Quickly check key concepts.
Exercises: 12, 14, 17, 20, 23

Answers

3. $\begin{bmatrix} 1.5 & 7.8 & 4 \\ -1.2 & 0.4 & 1 \end{bmatrix}$

4. not possible

5. $\begin{bmatrix} -1.5 & 0.2 & -2 \\ 1.2 & -4.4 & 1 \end{bmatrix}$

6. $\begin{bmatrix} 1.5 & 7.8 & 4 \\ -1.2 & 0.4 & 1 \end{bmatrix}$

7. $P_T = \begin{bmatrix} 9.74 & 14.07 & 15.16 \\ 6.50 & 10.28 & 11.91 \\ 16.24 & 22.73 & 24.90 \end{bmatrix}$

8. $\begin{bmatrix} 0 & 12 & 3 \\ 0 & -6 & 3 \end{bmatrix}$

9. $\begin{bmatrix} -\frac{1}{2} & \frac{1}{2} & 3 \\ 2 & 0 & \frac{1}{2} \\ \frac{1}{2} & 1 & \frac{1}{2} \end{bmatrix}$

10. $\begin{bmatrix} 1 & -5 & 1 \\ -1 & 6 & -2 \end{bmatrix}$

12a. $P = \begin{bmatrix} 425.50 & 398.00 & 65.99 \\ 385.98 & 245.50 & 45.90 \\ 275.12 & 103.25 & 29.50 \end{bmatrix}$

b. 3×3

c. 103.25; the cost in dollars of a hotel in economy travel

d. P_{21}

State Resources

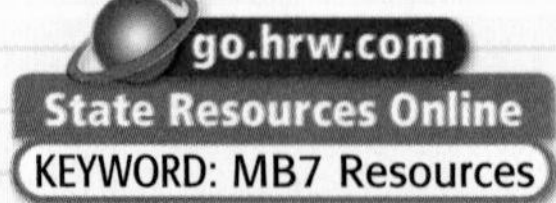

4-1 Exercises

go.hrw.com
Homework Help Online
KEYWORD: MB7 4-1
Parent Resources Online
KEYWORD: MB7 Parent

GUIDED PRACTICE

1. **Vocabulary** The value at a particular place in a matrix is an __?__ . (*address* or *entry*) **entry**

SEE EXAMPLE 1 p. 246

2. Kade, Bo, and Tanner record their ticket-selling activities for a fund-raising carnival.

Carnival Ticket Prices			
Student	**Single Tickets**	**Ticket Packages**	**Total Collected**
Kade	39	15	\$114
Bo	103	8	\$143
Tanner	13	25	\$138

   a. Display the data in the form of a matrix T. **a.** $T = \begin{bmatrix} 39 & 15 & 114 \\ 103 & 8 & 143 \\ 13 & 25 & 138 \end{bmatrix}$
   b. What are the dimensions of T? **3×3**
   c. What is the entry at t_{13}? What does it represent? **c. 114; the total amount in dollars that Kade collected**
   d. What is the address of the entry 143? **t_{23}**

SEE EXAMPLE 2 p. 247

Use the following matrices for Exercises 3–6. Add or subtract, if possible.

$$A = \begin{bmatrix} 1.5 & 3.8 & 3 \\ -1.2 & 2.4 & 0 \end{bmatrix} \quad B = \begin{bmatrix} 0 & 4 & 1 \\ 0 & -2 & 1 \end{bmatrix} \quad C = \begin{bmatrix} -1 & 1.1 & 6 \\ 4 & 0 & 1 \\ 1 & 2.3 & 1 \end{bmatrix}$$

3. $A + B$
4. $B - C$
5. $B - A$
6. $B + A$

SEE EXAMPLE 3 p. 248

7. **Consumer** The table shows prices for three types of clothing. Use a scalar product to find the price with 8.25% sales tax on each item.

Cost of Athletic Clothing (\$)			
	Plain	**Team Logo**	**Individualized**
T-shirt	9.00	13.00	14.00
Shorts	6.00	9.50	11.00
Jogging Pants	15.00	21.00	23.00

SEE EXAMPLE 4 p. 248

Use the following matrices for Exercises 8–11. Evaluate, if possible.

$$A = \begin{bmatrix} 1 & 3 & 3 \\ -1 & 2 & 0 \end{bmatrix} \quad B = \begin{bmatrix} 0 & 4 & 1 \\ 0 & -2 & 1 \end{bmatrix} \quad C = \begin{bmatrix} -1 & 1 & 6 \\ 4 & 0 & 1 \\ 1 & 2 & 1 \end{bmatrix}$$

8. $3B$
9. $\frac{1}{2}C$
10. $A - 2B$
11. $2C - A$ **not possible**

PRACTICE AND PROBLEM SOLVING

12. Use the data to answer the questions.
   a. Display the data as a matrix, P.
   b. What are the dimensions of P?
   c. What is the entry at p_{32}? What does it represent?
   d. What is the address of the entry 385.98?

Travel Options			
	Airfare	**Hotel**	**Car Rental**
Deluxe	425.50	398.00	65.99
Business	385.98	245.50	45.90
Economy	275.12	103.25	29.50

4-1 READING STRATEGIES

In a **matrix**, numbers are arranged in rows and columns. The plural of matrix is **matrices**. You can use a matrix to store and show data. The table below shows some results of a high school long jump competition.

Long Jump Competition			
Contestant	**Trial 1 (m)**	**Trial 2 (m)**	**Trial 3 (m)**
Rafael	6.7	5.8	6.1
Kirk	6.6	5.9	6.1
Morgan	6.8	6.0	6.0

This data from the table can be organized in a matrix. A matrix is a model of the information. It is like a table without lines or labels. The **dimensions** of a matrix tell you the number of rows and columns. A 4×3 matrix has 4 rows and 3 columns. You can add or subtract matrices only if they have the same dimensions. The matrices below use the data from the table.

$$A = \begin{bmatrix} 6.7 & 5.8 & 6.1 \\ 6.6 & 5.9 & 6.1 \\ 6.8 & 6.0 & 6.0 \end{bmatrix} \quad B = \begin{bmatrix} 6.7 & 5.8 & 6.1 \end{bmatrix} \quad C = \begin{bmatrix} 6.8 & 6.0 & 6.0 \end{bmatrix} \quad D = \begin{bmatrix} 5.8 \\ 5.9 \\ 6.0 \end{bmatrix}$$

Use the matrices to answer each question.

1. What information is shown in matrix A?
   The matrix shows the same data as the table. Each row shows the length of each jump by each contestant. The columns show the length of each jump by each trial.
2. What information is shown in matrices B and C?
   Matrix B shows the length of all three of Rafael's jumps, and matrix C shows the length of all three of Morgan's jumps.
3. What information is shown in matrix D?
   Matrix D shows the length of all three jumps in trial 2.
4. Give the dimensions of each matrix.
   A is 3×3, B and C are 1×3, D is 3×1.
5. Can you add matrices A and B? Explain why or why not.
   No; because they have different dimensions
6. Can you subtract matrix B from matrix C? Explain why or why not.
   Yes; because they have the same dimensions

4-1 RETEACH

A **matrix** is a rectangular array of numbers. A matrix can be named by a capital letter. Some examples are shown below.

$$A = \begin{bmatrix} 2 & 4 \end{bmatrix}, B = \begin{bmatrix} -1 \\ 3 \end{bmatrix}, C = \begin{bmatrix} -1 & 2 \\ 3 & -2 \end{bmatrix}, D = \begin{bmatrix} 3 & 5 & 1 \\ -2 & 0 & -1 \end{bmatrix}$$

Row 1
Row 2
Column 1
Column 2

The **dimensions** of a matrix are determined by the number of rows and columns in the matrix. A matrix of dimensions $m \times n$ (read "m by n") has m rows and n columns. Note that the row comes before the column in matrix notation. So, matrix A has dimensions 1×2 and matrix D has dimensions 2×3.

Each value in a matrix is called an **entry**. The **address** of an entry is its location in a matrix. A lowercase letter refers to the entry with the row and column number as subscripts.

$$D = \begin{bmatrix} 3 & 5 & 1 \\ -2 & 0 & -1 \end{bmatrix}$$

$d_{21} = -2$
$d_{13} = 1$
0 is entry d_{22}

Use matrix M to answer the questions. $M = \begin{bmatrix} 2 & 4 & 5 & 8 & 0 \\ -1 & 3 & -2 & 1 & 6 \\ -3 & 0 & 4 & -5 & 7 \end{bmatrix}$

1. a. How many rows does matrix M have? 3
   b. How many columns does matrix M have? 5
   c. What are the dimensions of matrix M? 3×5
2. What is entry m_{11}? 2
3. What is entry m_{35}? 7
4. What is entry m_{23}? -2
5. What is entry m_{32}? 0
6. At which two addresses is the entry 4? m_{12} and m_{33}

Independent Practice	
For Exercises	See Example
12	1
13–16	2
17	3
18–21	4

Extra Practice
Skills Practice p. S10
Application Practice p. S35

Use the following matrices for Exercises 13–16. Add or subtract, if possible.

$$D=\begin{bmatrix}5.1 & 2.5\\ -2 & 0\\ 0 & 1.5\end{bmatrix}\quad E=\begin{bmatrix}3.2 & -1\\ -1.5 & 2.4\end{bmatrix}\quad F=\begin{bmatrix}-4.2 & -1\\ 2.2 & 0\end{bmatrix}$$

13. $F-E$ **14.** $D+E$ **not possible** **15.** $D+F$ **not possible** **16.** $E+F$

16. $\begin{bmatrix}-1 & -2\\ 0.7 & 2.4\end{bmatrix}$

17. College The following table shows estimated college costs in 2004.

Estimated College Costs (per Year) in 2004			
	Private School	In-State Public School	Out-of-State Public School
Cost ($)	27,677	12,841	19,188

Costs are expected to increase 5% per year. Use a scalar product to find the estimated costs for each type of college in 2005. $\begin{bmatrix}29{,}061 & 13{,}483 & 20{,}147\end{bmatrix}$

Use the following matrices for Exercises 18–21. Evaluate, if possible.

$$G=\begin{bmatrix}5 & 2\\ -2 & 0\\ 0 & 1\end{bmatrix}\quad H=\begin{bmatrix}0 & -1\\ -1 & 2\\ 0 & 2\end{bmatrix}\quad J=\begin{bmatrix}4\\ 1\\ -2\end{bmatrix}\quad K=\begin{bmatrix}2 & 3\\ 3 & -1\\ 5 & 0\end{bmatrix}$$

18. $2G$ **19.** $\frac{1}{2}(H+J)$ **not possible** **20.** $2K-G$ **21.** $J-0.3G$ **not possible**

18. $\begin{bmatrix}10 & 4\\ -4 & 0\\ 0 & 2\end{bmatrix}$

20. $\begin{bmatrix}-1 & 4\\ 8 & -2\\ 10 & -1\end{bmatrix}$

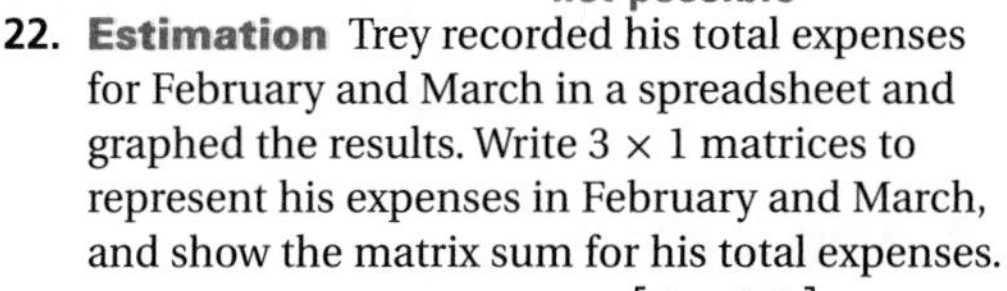

22. Estimation Trey recorded his total expenses for February and March in a spreadsheet and graphed the results. Write 3 × 1 matrices to represent his expenses in February and March, and show the matrix sum for his total expenses.

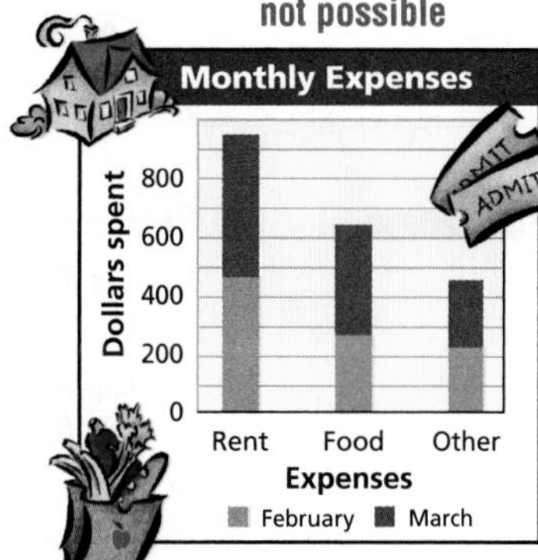

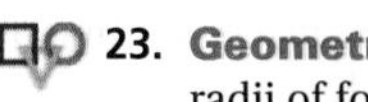

23. Geometry The matrix $R=\begin{bmatrix}2 & 2.5\\ 3 & 3.5\end{bmatrix}$ shows the radii of four circles.

a. Write the matrix operation that gives the related circumferences.

b. Is there an addition or scalar-multiplication matrix operation that could show the related areas of the circles? Explain.

Critical Thinking **Tell whether each statement is sometimes, always, or never true.**

24. If matrices A and B have an equal number of entries, then $A+B$ is defined. **sometimes true**

25. If matrices A and B have a different number of entries, then $A+B$ is defined. **never true**

26. If matrices A and B each have four rows and three columns, then $A+B$ is defined. **always true**

27. If $A+B$ is defined, then $A-B$ is defined. **always true**

MULTI-STEP TEST PREP

28. This problem will prepare you for the Multi-Step Test Prep on page 268.

a. Place the vertices of the triangle in a matrix so that the x-coordinates are in row 1 and the y-coordinates are in row 2.

b. Use a matrix operation to add 3 to each x-coordinate and 1 to each y-coordinate.

c. Draw a new triangle using the new coordinates. Describe the new triangle.

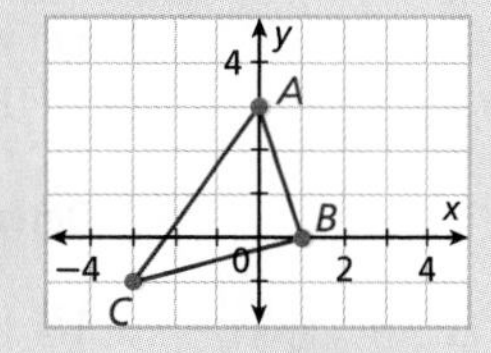

Teaching Tip **Geometry** For **Exercise 23,** remind students that the circumference can be expressed in terms of the radius as $2\pi r$ and in terms of the area as πr^2.

MULTI-STEP TEST PREP **Exercise 28** involves translating the coordinates of the vertices of a triangle. This exercise prepares students for the Multi-Step Test Prep on page 268.

Answers

13. $F-E=\begin{bmatrix}-7.4 & 0\\ 3.7 & -2.4\end{bmatrix}$

22. Possible answer:
$\begin{bmatrix}480\\ 280\\ 220\end{bmatrix};\begin{bmatrix}480\\ 370\\ 250\end{bmatrix};\begin{bmatrix}960\\ 650\\ 470\end{bmatrix}$

23a. $C=2\pi\begin{bmatrix}2 & 2.5\\ 3 & 3.5\end{bmatrix}$

b. No; possible answer: To find the area, you must square the radii of the circles and then multiply by π. You cannot square the radii by using an addition or scalar-multiplication matrix operation.

28a. $\begin{bmatrix}0 & 1 & -3\\ 3 & 0 & -1\end{bmatrix}$

b. $\begin{bmatrix}0 & 1 & -3\\ 3 & 0 & -1\end{bmatrix}+\begin{bmatrix}3 & 3 & 3\\ 1 & 1 & 1\end{bmatrix}=\begin{bmatrix}3 & 4 & 0\\ 4 & 1 & 0\end{bmatrix}$

c.

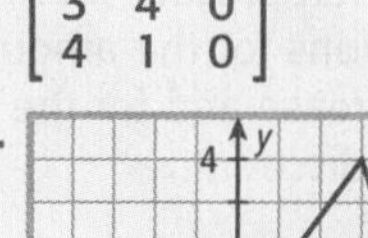

The new triangle is a translation 3 units right and 1 unit up.

4-1 PROBLEM SOLVING

According to the United States Census Bureau, Americans are more educated than ever: about 84% of adults over 25 have at least completed high school and about 26% have at least a bachelor's degree. Olivia is researching whether completing higher levels of education has a payoff in higher lifetime earnings. Use the information in the table to answer the questions.

Average Annual Earnings of Workers in 1999 Dollars (×$1,000)		
Highest Level of Education	Full-Time Workers	All Workers
Bachelor's degree	52.2	45.4
Associate degree	38.2	33.0
High school graduate	30.4	25.9
Not high school graduate	23.4	18.9

1. Display the data in the form of a matrix. Write matrix P.
$P=\begin{bmatrix}52.2 & 45.4\\ 38.2 & 33.0\\ 30.4 & 25.9\\ 23.4 & 18.9\end{bmatrix}$

2. What are the dimensions of matrix P? **4 × 2**

3. Olivia wants to show the earnings per month, rather than annual earnings. Write an equation with a scalar product that she can use to change matrix P into matrix M. $M=\frac{1}{12}P$

4. Write matrix M. Round each entry to the nearest tenth.
$M=\begin{bmatrix}4.4 & 3.8\\ 3.2 & 2.8\\ 2.5 & 2.2\\ 2.0 & 1.6\end{bmatrix}$

Choose the letter for the best answer.

5. Olivia's uncle is represented in matrix P by the entry p_{21}. What are the average annual earnings for this entry?
A $38.20
B $45.40
(C) $38,200
D $45,400

6. Olivia's cousin graduated from high school and works in the summer only. What is the address for the entry that represents her?
A p_{13}
B p_{23}
C p_{31}
(D) p_{32}

4-1 CHALLENGE

An operation exhibits the *Closure Property* if performing this operation on two elements of a set always gives another element of that set. We say the set is *closed* under the operation.

Matrix F has dimensions $m \times n$.

1. In order to find the sum of matrix F and a second matrix G, what must be true about the dimensions of matrix G? **Matrix G must have dimensions $m \times n$.**

2. If matrix H represents $F+G$, what must be true about the dimensions of matrix H? **Matrix H must have dimensions $m \times n$.**

3. Is the set of $m \times n$ matrices closed under the operation of addition? **Yes**

Matrices A and B are shown below. None of the elements a–f is 0.

$A=\begin{bmatrix}a & 0 & 0\\ 0 & b & 0\\ 0 & 0 & c\end{bmatrix}\quad B=\begin{bmatrix}d & 0 & 0\\ 0 & e & 0\\ 0 & 0 & f\end{bmatrix}$

4. How are A and B alike? **They have the same dimensions. There are nonzero entries along the main diagonal.**

5. Let $S=A+B$. Write S in the space at right. $S=\begin{bmatrix}a+d & 0 & 0\\ 0 & b+e & 0\\ 0 & 0 & c+f\end{bmatrix}$

6. Compare the dimensions of S with the dimensions of A and B. **Matrix S has the same dimensions as matrices A and B.**

7. Matrices such as A and B above are called *diagonal matrices.* Is the set of diagonal matrices closed under addition? Explain.
Yes; the sum of A and B is S, which is another diagonal matrix.

Matrices C and D are called 3 × 3 upper triangular matrices. None of the elements a–f or r–w is 0.

$C=\begin{bmatrix}a & b & c\\ 0 & d & e\\ 0 & 0 & f\end{bmatrix}\quad D=\begin{bmatrix}r & s & t\\ 0 & u & v\\ 0 & 0 & w\end{bmatrix}$

8. Is the set of 3 × 3 upper triangular matrices closed under addition? Justify your response.
Yes; $C+D=\begin{bmatrix}a+r & b+s & c+t\\ 0 & d+u & e+v\\ 0 & 0 & f+w\end{bmatrix}$, which is another upper triangular matrix.

9. Modify C and D so that they can be called 3 × 3 *lower triangular matrices.* Show that the sum of two 3 × 3 lower triangular matrices is another lower triangular matrix.
$C=\begin{bmatrix}a & 0 & 0\\ b & c & 0\\ d & e & f\end{bmatrix}, D=\begin{bmatrix}r & 0 & 0\\ s & t & 0\\ u & v & w\end{bmatrix}; C+D=\begin{bmatrix}a+r & 0 & 0\\ b+s & c+t & 0\\ d+u & e+v & f+w\end{bmatrix}$, **which is another lower triangular matrix.**

4-1 PRACTICE A
4-1 PRACTICE C
4-1 PRACTICE B

The table shows the prices for various passes to a theme park.

Theme Park Pass Price List				
Type of Pass	1-Day	2-Day	3-Day	5-Day
Basic	$40	$75	$100	$125
Super	$70	$95	$120	$140
Deluxe	$80	$105	$130	$150

1. Display the data in the form of a matrix, P. $P=\begin{bmatrix}40 & 75 & 100 & 120\\ 70 & 95 & 120 & 140\\ 80 & 105 & 130 & 150\end{bmatrix}$

2. What are the dimensions of P? **3 × 4**

3. What is the entry at p_{31} and what does it represent? **$80; the cost of a 1-day deluxe pass**

4. What is the address of the entry $120? p_{23}

5. Write an expression that represents a matrix that shows the cost of buying theme park tickets for a family of four. **4P**

Use the following matrices for Exercises 6–8. Add or subtract, if possible.

$R=\begin{bmatrix}4 & 12\\ 0 & -6\\ 9 & 15\end{bmatrix}\quad S=\begin{bmatrix}-3 & 9 & 2\\ 10 & -5 & 4\\ 1 & 2 & 3\end{bmatrix}\quad T=\begin{bmatrix}-5 & 9\\ -3 & 6\\ 10 & 5\end{bmatrix}$

6. $S-R$ **Not possible**

7. $T+R$ $\begin{bmatrix}-1 & 21\\ -3 & 0\\ 19 & 20\end{bmatrix}$

8. $R-T$ $\begin{bmatrix}9 & 3\\ 3 & -12\\ -1 & 10\end{bmatrix}$

Use the following matrices for Exercises 9–11. Evaluate, if possible.

$X=\begin{bmatrix}5 & -2 & 0 & 9\\ 4 & 16 & -5 & 6\end{bmatrix}\quad Y=\begin{bmatrix}-6 & 4 & 10 & 8\\ 13 & 6 & 0 & -2\end{bmatrix}$

9. $3X$ $\begin{bmatrix}15 & -6 & 0 & 27\\ 12 & 48 & -15 & 18\end{bmatrix}$

10. $3Y+4X$ $\begin{bmatrix}2 & 4 & 30 & 60\\ 55 & 82 & -20 & 18\end{bmatrix}$

11. $3X-2Y$ $\begin{bmatrix}27 & -14 & -20 & 11\\ -14 & 36 & -15 & 22\end{bmatrix}$

Solve.

12. If $E=\begin{bmatrix}2 & -3\\ 5 & 4\end{bmatrix}$ and $E+F=\begin{bmatrix}0 & 0\\ 0 & 0\end{bmatrix}$, find F. $F=\begin{bmatrix}-2 & 3\\ -5 & -4\end{bmatrix}$

TEST PREP DOCTOR In Exercise 33, have students substitute simple values for m and n, such as $m = 2$ and $n = 3$, and draw an actual matrix before answering the question.

Journal

Have students describe a real situation in which it is necessary to add or subtract matrices or scalar multiples of matrices.

ALTERNATIVE ASSESSMENT

Have students create a price list along the lines of some of the examples in the text that can be converted into a matrix. Then have them produce two related matrices from the first, one that shows a price increase, and one that shows a discount. Students might show scalar products and then present them as matrix additions for the amount of the price increase and for the amount of the discount.

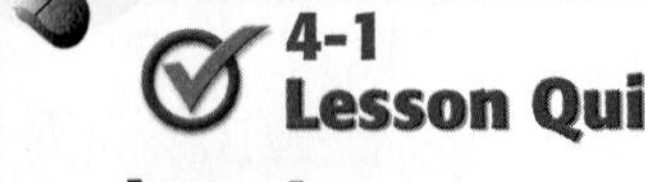

Power Presentations with PowerPoint®

4-1 Lesson Quiz

$A = \begin{bmatrix} 2 & -2 \\ 3 & 0 \\ 2 & 1 \end{bmatrix}$ $B = \begin{bmatrix} 4 & 0.5 & 3 \\ 2 & 1 & -1 \end{bmatrix}$

$C = \begin{bmatrix} 1 & -2 \\ -2 & 5 \\ 0 & -4 \end{bmatrix}$ $D = \begin{bmatrix} 0 & -2 & 3 \\ 1 & -5 & 2 \end{bmatrix}$

1. What are the dimensions of A? 3×2

2. What is entry d_{12}? -2

Evaluate if possible.

3. $2A - C$ $\begin{bmatrix} 3 & -2 \\ 8 & -5 \\ 4 & 6 \end{bmatrix}$

4. $C + 2D$ not possible

5. $10(2B + D)$ $\begin{bmatrix} 80 & -10 & 90 \\ 50 & -30 & 0 \end{bmatrix}$

Also available on transparency

29. Solve for a, b, and c in the matrix equation. $\begin{bmatrix} 3 & a \\ -2 & -8 \end{bmatrix} + \begin{bmatrix} 11 & -4 \\ b & 12 \end{bmatrix} = \begin{bmatrix} 14 & -10 \\ 9 & c \end{bmatrix}$
$a = -6$; $b = 11$; $c = 4$

30. **ERROR ANALYSIS** Explain the error. $\begin{bmatrix} 2 & 8 \\ 4 & 7 \end{bmatrix} + \begin{bmatrix} 6 & 3 & 0 \\ 4 & 1 & 9 \end{bmatrix} = \begin{bmatrix} 8 & 11 & 0 \\ 8 & 8 & 9 \end{bmatrix}$

31. **Write About It** Is subtraction of matrices commutative? Give an example to support your answer.

TEST PREP

32. $P = \begin{bmatrix} 1 & 0.1 & 2 \\ 1.5 & 2.1 & 0 \end{bmatrix}$ $Q = \begin{bmatrix} 2 & 0.4 & 6 \\ 6 & 6.4 & 0 \end{bmatrix}$. Which expression results in $\begin{bmatrix} 1 & 0 & 1 \\ 0 & 1 & 0 \end{bmatrix}$?

Ⓐ $2Q - \frac{1}{2}P$ Ⓑ $Q - 2P$ Ⓒ $P - 2Q$ Ⓓ $2P - \frac{1}{2}Q$

33. For an $m \times n$ matrix E, which statement is always true?

Ⓕ It has $m \cdot n$ entries. Ⓗ It has $m + n$ entries.

Ⓖ It has an entry e_{nm}. Ⓙ It has m columns and n rows.

34. Solve for w: $8\begin{bmatrix} 12 & 8 \\ 2 & 7 \end{bmatrix} = w\begin{bmatrix} 48 & 32 \\ 8 & 28 \end{bmatrix}$.

Ⓐ 0.25 Ⓑ 0.5 Ⓒ 2 Ⓓ 4

35. **Gridded Response** Solve for x: $\begin{bmatrix} 2 & -2 \end{bmatrix} - 2\begin{bmatrix} 5 & -x \end{bmatrix} = \begin{bmatrix} -8 & -1 \end{bmatrix}$. $\frac{1}{2}$

CHALLENGE AND EXTEND

36. **Critical Thinking** If the number of entries in a matrix is a prime number, what must be true about the dimensions of the matrix? Explain.

37. Explain why, for any two $m \times n$ matrices A and B, $A - B$ is equivlent to $A + (-B)$. $A + (-B) = A + (-1B) = A - 1B = A - B$

38. In *magic squares* like those shown, the rows, columns, and diagonals all have the same sum. Is the sum of the two magic squares also a magic square? Explain.

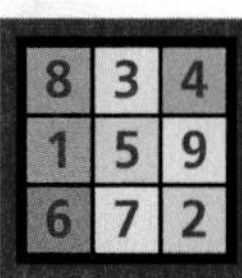

39. $3\begin{bmatrix} 2 & -1 \\ 0 & -4 \end{bmatrix} - 2B = \begin{bmatrix} 1 & 5 \\ -2 & 2 \end{bmatrix}$. Find B.

39. $\begin{bmatrix} 2.5 & -4 \\ 1 & -7 \end{bmatrix}$

SPIRAL REVIEW

Write an algebraic expression to represent each situation. *(Lesson 1-4)*

40. the perimeter of a triangle with side lengths that are consecutive even integers $3s + 6$

41. the total number of raffle tickets sold if 20 people each sold n tickets $20n$

42. **Money** Nyla has 36 nickels and dimes. She has twice as many dimes as nickels. How much money does Nyla have? *(Lesson 2-1)* $3.00

Determine if the given point is a solution of the system of equations. *(Lesson 3-1)*

43. $(2, -2)$ $\begin{cases} x - y = 4 \\ 5x + 6y = 2 \end{cases}$ no

44. $(4.5, 2)$ $\begin{cases} y = 2 \\ 2x - 4y = 1 \end{cases}$ yes

30. The matrices cannot be added because they have different dimensions. The addition shows the sum $\begin{bmatrix} 2 & 8 & 0 \\ 4 & 7 & 0 \end{bmatrix} + \begin{bmatrix} 6 & 3 & 0 \\ 4 & 1 & 9 \end{bmatrix}$, which is incorrect.

31. no; possible answer: $A = \begin{bmatrix} 3 & 4 \\ 5 & 2 \end{bmatrix}$ and $B = \begin{bmatrix} 2 & 0 \\ 9 & 6 \end{bmatrix}$; $A - B = \begin{bmatrix} 1 & 4 \\ -4 & -4 \end{bmatrix}$ and $B - A = \begin{bmatrix} -1 & -4 \\ 4 & 4 \end{bmatrix}$, so $A - B \neq B - A$

36. Possible answer: The number of entries in a matrix is equal to the product of the number of rows and the number of columns. A prime number has only two factors, 1 and itself. So if the number of entries in a matrix is a prime number, then either the number of rows is 1 and the number of columns is the prime number, or the number of columns is 1 and the number of rows is the prime number.

38. Yes; possible answer: the sum of each row, column, and diagonal in the matrix sum is equal to the corresponding sum of the values from the two magic squares.

4-2 Multiplying Matrices

Objectives
Understand the properties of matrices with respect to multiplication.

Multiply two matrices.

Vocabulary
matrix product
square matrix
main diagonal
multiplicative identity matrix

Who uses this?
Skateboard shop owners can use matrices to find the value of their inventory. (See Example 3.)

In Lesson 4-1, you multiplied matrices by a number called a *scalar*. You can also multiply matrices together. The product of two or more matrices is the **matrix product**. The following rules apply when multiplying matrices.

- Matrices A and B can be multiplied only if the number of columns in A equals the number of rows in B.
- The product of an $m \times n$ and an $n \times p$ matrix is an $m \times p$ matrix.

Helpful Hint

The CAR key:
Columns (of A)
As
Rows (of B)
or matrix product AB won't even start

$$A = \begin{bmatrix} 3 & 5 & 7 \\ 4 & 1 & 2 \end{bmatrix} \quad B = \begin{bmatrix} 2 & 3 & 3 & 8 \\ 9 & 5 & 2 & 0 \\ 0 & 1 & 6 & 7 \end{bmatrix}$$

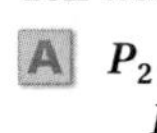

A B AB
$2 \times 3 \quad 3 \times 4 = 2 \times 4$ matrix
columns = rows

$$C = \begin{bmatrix} 3 & 5 \\ 4 & 1 \\ 5 & 8 \end{bmatrix} \quad D = \begin{bmatrix} 2 & 3 & 3 & 8 & 4 \\ 9 & 5 & 2 & 0 & 6 \\ 0 & 1 & 6 & 7 & 2 \end{bmatrix}$$

C D ✗ CD is not defined
$3 \times 2 \quad 3 \times 5$ $(2 \neq 3)$
columns ≠ rows

An $m \times n$ matrix A can be identified by using the notation $A_{m \times n}$.

EXAMPLE 1 Identifying Matrix Products

Tell whether each product is defined. If so, give its dimensions.

A $P_{2 \times 5}$ and $Q_{5 \times 3}$; PQ

P Q PQ
$2 \times 5 \quad 5 \times 3 = 2 \times 3$ matrix

The inner dimensions are equal ($5 = 5$), so the matrix product is defined. The dimensions of the product are the outer numbers, 2×3.

B $R_{4 \times 3}$ and $S_{4 \times 5}$; RS

R S
$4 \times 3 \quad 4 \times 5$

The inner dimensions are not equal ($3 \neq 4$), so the matrix product is not defined. ✗

CHECK IT OUT! **Use the matrices in Example 1. Tell whether each product is defined. If so, give its dimensions.**

1a. QP no **1b.** SR no **1c.** SQ 4×3

Just as you look across the columns of A and down the rows of B to see if a product AB exists, you do the same to find the entries in a matrix product.

4-2 Organizer

Pacing: Traditional 1 day
Block $\frac{1}{2}$ day

Objectives: Understand the properties of matrices with respect to multiplication.

Multiply two matrices.

Algebra Lab
In *Algebra Lab Activities*

Online Edition
Tutorial Videos, Tech Keys

Countdown to Testing Week 8

Power Presentations with PowerPoint®

Warm Up

State the dimensions of each matrix.

1. $[3 \quad 1 \quad 4 \quad 6]$ 1×4

2. $\begin{bmatrix} -1 & 4 \\ 0 & 1 \\ 2 & -1 \end{bmatrix}$ 3×2

Calculate.

3. $3(-4) + (-2)(5) + 4(7)$ 6

4. $(-3)(3) + 2(5) + (-1)(12)$ -11

Also available on transparency

Math Humor

Q: Why was the matrix arrested?
A: Illegal entry.

1 Introduce

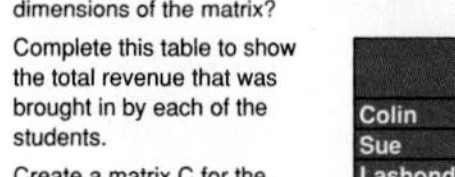

EXPLORATION

4-2 Multiplying Matrices

Three students sold T-shirts for a school fund-raiser. Short-sleeve and long-sleeve shirts were available. The table shows the quantities sold by each student.

	Short Sleeve	Long Sleeve
Colin	20	15
Sue	8	6
Lashonda	32	14

1. Create a matrix A for the quantity data. What are the dimensions of the matrix?
2. The table shows the prices for the two types of T-shirts. Create a matrix B for the pricing data. What are the dimensions of the matrix?

	Price ($)
Short Sleeve	10
Long Sleeve	15

3. Complete this table to show the total revenue that was brought in by each of the students.

	Total Revenue ($)
Colin	
Sue	
Lashonda	

4. Create a matrix C for the revenue data. What are the dimensions of the matrix?

THINK AND DISCUSS

5. Explain how you completed the revenue table.

Motivate

Discuss with students how a team's final basketball score is calculated: 3(number of 3-point goals) + 2(number of 2-point goals) + 1(number of free throws). Explain that matrices can be used to organize the data and that multiplying them can provide the totals.

Explorations and answers are provided in the *Explorations* binder.

State Resources

go.hrw.com
State Resources Online
KEYWORD: MB7 Resources

Power Presentations with PowerPoint®

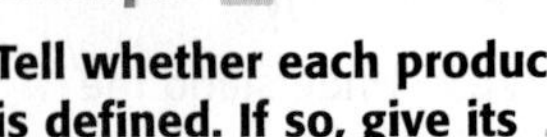

Additional Examples

Example 1

Tell whether each product is defined. If so, give its dimensions.

A. $A_{3 \times 4}$ and $B_{4 \times 2}$; AB
Yes: 3×2

B. $C_{1 \times 4}$ and $D_{3 \times 4}$; CD No

Example 2

$W = \begin{bmatrix} 3 & -2 \\ 1 & 0 \\ 2 & -1 \end{bmatrix}$ $X = \begin{bmatrix} 4 & 7 & -2 \\ 5 & 1 & -1 \end{bmatrix}$

$Y = \begin{bmatrix} 1 & 4 \\ -2 & 3 \end{bmatrix}$

Find each product, if possible.

A. WX $\begin{bmatrix} 2 & 19 & -4 \\ 4 & 7 & -2 \\ 3 & 13 & -3 \end{bmatrix}$

B. XW $\begin{bmatrix} 15 & -6 \\ 14 & -9 \end{bmatrix}$

C. XY not possible

Also available on transparency

INTERVENTION

Questioning Strategies

EXAMPLE 1

- How can you tell whether a matrix product is defined?

EXAMPLE 2

- How would you describe what you do to find a matrix product?

Know it! Note **Multiplying Matrices**

WORDS	NUMBERS	ALGEBRA
In a matrix product $P = AB$, each element p_{ij} is the sum of the products of consecutive entries in row i in matrix A and column j in matrix B.	$P = \begin{bmatrix} 1 & 2 \\ 3 & 4 \end{bmatrix}\begin{bmatrix} 5 & 6 \\ 7 & 8 \end{bmatrix} =$ $\begin{bmatrix} 1 \cdot 5 + 2 \cdot 7 & 1 \cdot 6 + 2 \cdot 8 \\ 3 \cdot 5 + 4 \cdot 7 & 3 \cdot 6 + 4 \cdot 8 \end{bmatrix}$	$P = \begin{bmatrix} a_1 & a_2 \\ b_1 & b_2 \end{bmatrix}\begin{bmatrix} c_1 & c_2 \\ d_1 & d_2 \end{bmatrix} =$ $\begin{bmatrix} a_1c_1 + a_2d_1 & a_1c_2 + a_2d_2 \\ b_1c_1 + b_2d_1 & b_1c_2 + b_2d_2 \end{bmatrix}$

EXAMPLE 2 **Finding the Matrix Product**

Find each product, if possible. $A = \begin{bmatrix} 0 & 4 & 9 \\ -3 & 3 & 2 \end{bmatrix}$ $B = \begin{bmatrix} 5 & 1 \\ -2 & 7 \\ 6 & 0 \end{bmatrix}$ $C = \begin{bmatrix} 11 & -1 \\ 12 & 10 \end{bmatrix}$

A AB

Check the dimensions. A is 2×3, B is 3×2. AB is defined and is 2×2.
Multiply row 1 of A and column 1 of B as shown. Place the result in ab_{11}.

$$AB = \begin{bmatrix} 0 & 4 & 9 \\ -3 & 3 & 2 \end{bmatrix}\begin{bmatrix} 5 & 1 \\ -2 & 7 \\ 6 & 0 \end{bmatrix} = \begin{bmatrix} 46 & ? \\ ? & ? \end{bmatrix} \leftarrow 0(5) + 4(-2) + 9(6)$$

Multiply row 1 of A and column 2 of B. Place the result in ab_{12}.

$$\begin{bmatrix} 0 & 4 & 9 \\ -3 & 3 & 2 \end{bmatrix}\begin{bmatrix} 5 & 1 \\ -2 & 7 \\ 6 & 0 \end{bmatrix} = \begin{bmatrix} 46 & 28 \\ ? & ? \end{bmatrix} \leftarrow 0(1) + 4(7) + 9(0)$$

Multiply row 2 of A and column 1 of B. Place the result in ab_{21}.

$$\begin{bmatrix} 0 & 4 & 9 \\ -3 & 3 & 2 \end{bmatrix}\begin{bmatrix} 5 & 1 \\ -2 & 7 \\ 6 & 0 \end{bmatrix} = \begin{bmatrix} 46 & 28 \\ -9 & ? \end{bmatrix} \leftarrow -3(5) + 3(-2) + 2(6)$$

Multiply row 2 of A and column 2 of B. Place the result in ab_{22}.

$$\begin{bmatrix} 0 & 4 & 9 \\ -3 & 3 & 2 \end{bmatrix}\begin{bmatrix} 5 & 1 \\ -2 & 7 \\ 6 & 0 \end{bmatrix} = \begin{bmatrix} 46 & 28 \\ -9 & 18 \end{bmatrix} \quad AB = \begin{bmatrix} 46 & 28 \\ -9 & 18 \end{bmatrix}$$

$$-3(1) + 3(7) + 2(0)$$

Caution!

Notice that AB and BA are different products.

The Commutative Property does not hold for multiplication of matrices!

B BA

Check the dimensions. B is 3×2, and A is 2×3, so the product is defined and is 3×3.

$$BA = \begin{bmatrix} 5(0) + 1(-3) & 5(4) + 1(3) & 5(9) + 1(2) \\ -2(0) + 7(-3) & -2(4) + 7(3) & -2(9) + 7(2) \\ 6(0) + 0(-3) & 6(4) + 0(3) & 6(9) + 0(2) \end{bmatrix} = \begin{bmatrix} -3 & 23 & 47 \\ -21 & 13 & -4 \\ 0 & 24 & 54 \end{bmatrix}$$

C AC

Check the dimensions: $2 \times 3 \quad 2 \times 2$. The product is not defined. The matrices cannot be multiplied in this order.

Find the product, if possible.

2a. BC $\begin{bmatrix} 67 & 5 \\ 62 & 72 \\ 66 & -6 \end{bmatrix}$ **2b.** CA $\begin{bmatrix} 3 & 41 & 97 \\ -30 & 78 & 128 \end{bmatrix}$

2 Teach

Guided Instruction

Take time to make sure that students understand what matrix multiplications are possible and what result should occur.

$a \times b$ by $c \times d$ yields $a \times d$, but only if $b = c$.

The inner values, b and c, must be equal. The outer values, a and d, are the dimensions of the matrix product. Emphasize that matrix multiplication and multiplication of a matrix by a scalar are two different things.

Reaching All Learners

Through Kinesthetic Experience

Have students place their right index finger over a row in the first matrix with the fingertip over the leftmost element and move the finger right. Then have them move to the second matrix with the fingertip over the top element in the column and move the finger down.

$$\begin{bmatrix} 1 & 2 & 3 \\ 4 & 5 & 6 \\ 7 & 8 & 9 \end{bmatrix} \begin{bmatrix} 10 & 11 & 12 \\ 13 & 14 & 15 \\ 16 & 17 & 18 \end{bmatrix}$$

This can provide a kinesthetic representation of which elements correspond to which when multiplying.

Businesses can use matrix multiplication to find total revenues, costs, and profits.

EXAMPLE 3 Inventory Application

A skateboard kit comes in two styles. Two stores have inventories as shown in the first table. Find the total cost of the skateboards for each store.

Skateboard Kit Inventory

	Complete	Super Complete
Store 1	14	10
Store 2	7	8

Skateboard Kit Profits

	Revenue ($)	Store Cost ($)	Profit ($)
Complete	89	44	45
Super Complete	119	58	61

Use a product matrix to find the revenue, cost, and profit for each store.

$$\begin{bmatrix} 14 & 10 \\ 7 & 8 \end{bmatrix}\begin{bmatrix} 89 & 44 & 45 \\ 119 & 58 & 61 \end{bmatrix} =$$

$$\begin{bmatrix} 14(89) + 10(119) & 14(44) + 10(58) & 14(45) + 10(61) \\ 7(89) + 8(119) & 7(44) + 8(58) & 7(45) + 8(61) \end{bmatrix}$$

Revenue Cost Profit

$$= \begin{bmatrix} 2436 & \mathbf{1196} & 1240 \\ 1575 & \mathbf{772} & 803 \end{bmatrix} \begin{matrix} \textit{Store 1} \\ \textit{Store 2} \end{matrix}$$

The total cost for skateboards for store 1 is $1196 and for store 2 is $772.

CHECK IT OUT! **3.** Change store 2's inventory to 6 complete and 9 super complete. Update the product matrix, and find the profit for store 2.

3. $\begin{bmatrix} 2436 & 1196 & 1240 \\ 1605 & 786 & 819 \end{bmatrix}$; 819

A **square matrix** is any matrix that has the same number of rows as columns; it is an $n \times n$ matrix. The **main diagonal** of a square matrix is the diagonal from the upper left corner to the lower right corner.

The **multiplicative identity matrix** is any square matrix, named with the letter I, that has all of the entries along the main diagonal equal to 1 and all of the other entries equal to 0.

$$I_{2\times 2} = \begin{bmatrix} 1 & 0 \\ 0 & 1 \end{bmatrix} \qquad I_{3\times 3} = \begin{bmatrix} 1 & 0 & 0 \\ 0 & 1 & 0 \\ 0 & 0 & 1 \end{bmatrix}$$

Matrix I is the multiplicative identity when A is any square matrix and $AI = IA = A$.

For $A = \begin{bmatrix} 5 & 7 \\ -1 & 4 \end{bmatrix}$, $I = \begin{bmatrix} 1 & 0 \\ 0 & 1 \end{bmatrix}$ and

$$AI = \begin{bmatrix} 5 & 7 \\ -1 & 4 \end{bmatrix}\begin{bmatrix} 1 & 0 \\ 0 & 1 \end{bmatrix} = \begin{bmatrix} 5(1) + 7(0) & 5(0) + 7(1) \\ -1(1) + 4(0) & -1(0) + 4(1) \end{bmatrix} = \begin{bmatrix} 5 & 7 \\ -1 & 4 \end{bmatrix} = A$$

$$IA = \begin{bmatrix} 1 & 0 \\ 0 & 1 \end{bmatrix}\begin{bmatrix} 5 & 7 \\ -1 & 4 \end{bmatrix} = \begin{bmatrix} 1(5) + 0(-1) & 1(7) + 0(4) \\ 0(5) + 1(-1) & 0(7) + 1(4) \end{bmatrix} = \begin{bmatrix} 5 & 7 \\ -1 & 4 \end{bmatrix} = A$$

Power Presentations with PowerPoint®

Additional Examples

Example 3

Two stores held sales on their videos and DVDs, with prices as shown. Use the sales data to determine how much money each store brought in from the sale on Saturday.

Sale Prices

	Videos	DVDs
Video World	$8.95	$11.95
Star Movies	$7.50	$12.50

Total Sales

	Fri	Sat	Sun
Videos	23	31	25
DVDs	40	48	42

$$\begin{bmatrix} 683.85 & \mathbf{851.05} & 725.65 \\ 672.50 & \mathbf{832.50} & 712.50 \end{bmatrix}$$

Saturday sales appear in the second column.

Also available on transparency

INTERVENTION
Questioning Strategies

EXAMPLE 3

- If the matrix you get for an answer is turned back into a table, what will it look like?

Teaching Tip **Multiple Representations** Have students look at the two tables in **Example 3.** Point out that just as the inner *dimensions* must be the same in order to have a product, the inner *table headings* must also be the same (Complete, Super). And just as the outer dimensions are also the outer dimensions of the product matrix, the outer table headings are also the table headings of the product matrix.

	Complete	Super
Store 1		
Store 2		

×

	Price	Cost	Profit
Complete			
Super			

=

	Price	Cost	Profit
Store 1			
Store 2			

Power Presentations with PowerPoint®

Additional Examples

Example 4

$P = \begin{bmatrix} 4 & 0 \\ 2 & 3 \end{bmatrix} \quad Q = \begin{bmatrix} 1 & 2 & 0 \\ -1 & 0 & 3 \\ 2 & 1 & 2 \end{bmatrix}$

Evaluate, if possible.

A. P^3 $\begin{bmatrix} 64 & 0 \\ 74 & 27 \end{bmatrix}$

B. Q^2 $\begin{bmatrix} -1 & 2 & 6 \\ 5 & 1 & 6 \\ 5 & 6 & 7 \end{bmatrix}$

Also available on transparency

INTERVENTION

Questioning Strategies

EXAMPLE 4

- What do the dimensions of a matrix tell you about the square of the matrix?
- What does it mean to cube a matrix?

Because square matrices can be multiplied by themselves any number of times, you can find powers of square matrices.

EXAMPLE 4 **Finding Powers of Square Matrices**

$A = \begin{bmatrix} 7 & 3 \\ -2 & 0 \end{bmatrix} \quad B = \begin{bmatrix} 2 & 4 & 1 \\ 5 & 0 & -2 \\ 1 & -1 & 3 \end{bmatrix} \quad C = \begin{bmatrix} 1 & 0 & 1 \\ 2 & 0 & -2 \end{bmatrix} \quad I = \begin{bmatrix} 1 & 0 \\ 0 & 1 \end{bmatrix}$

Evaluate, if possible.

A A^2

$$A^2 = \begin{bmatrix} 7 & 3 \\ -2 & 0 \end{bmatrix}\begin{bmatrix} 7 & 3 \\ -2 & 0 \end{bmatrix}$$

$$= \begin{bmatrix} 7(7)+3(-2) & 7(3)+3(0) \\ -2(7)+0(-2) & -2(3)+0(0) \end{bmatrix}$$

$$= \begin{bmatrix} 43 & 21 \\ -14 & -6 \end{bmatrix}$$

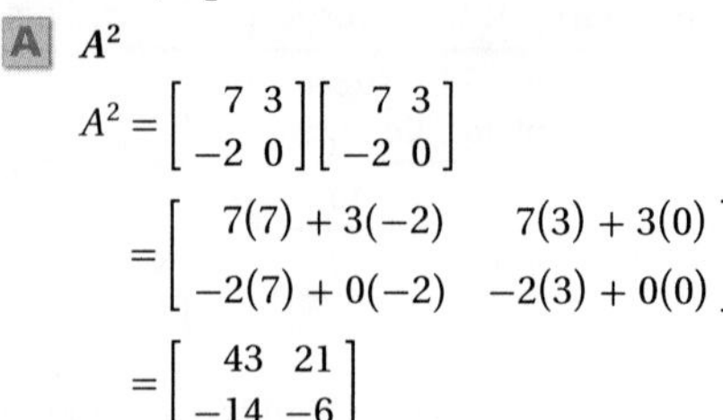

Check Use a calculator.

B B^2

For large matrices, use a graphing calculator.

[B]
[[2 4 1]
[5 0 -2]
[1 -1 3]]

[B]²
[[25 7 -3]
[8 22 -1]
[0 1 12]]

CHECK IT OUT! Evaluate, if possible.

4a. C^2 not possible **4b.** A^3 $\begin{bmatrix} 259 & 129 \\ -86 & -42 \end{bmatrix}$ **4c.** B^3 **4d.** I^4 $\begin{bmatrix} 1 & 0 \\ 0 & 1 \end{bmatrix}$

4c. $\begin{bmatrix} 82 & 103 & 2 \\ 125 & 33 & -39 \\ 17 & -12 & 34 \end{bmatrix}$

THINK AND DISCUSS

1. Describe what happens when you try to find the first element of AB if both A and B have dimensions 2×3.
2. Tell whether matrix multiplication is commutative.
3. A is a 4×2 matrix. Can you find A^2? Why or why not?

4. **GET ORGANIZED** Copy and complete the graphic organizer. In the decision diamond, enter a question to determine whether AB is defined. Then give the general procedure for finding AB, if it is defined.

For $A = [m \times n]$, $B = [p \times q]$...

Yes — ? — No

Dimensions of AB:

To find AB . . .

AB . . .

3 Close

Summarize

In order to multiply matrices A and B to get AB, the number of columns of A must equal the number of rows of B. When performing the multiplication, be sure each product ends up in the correct place.

$$\begin{bmatrix} R_1 \\ R_2 \end{bmatrix} \times [C_1 \ C_2] = \begin{bmatrix} R_1 \times C_1 & R_1 \times C_2 \\ R_2 \times C_1 & R_2 \times C_2 \end{bmatrix}$$

Note that the number of entries in a row of A must equal the number of entries in a column of B, or there will be a mismatch when you multiply.

ONGOING ASSESSMENT and INTERVENTION

Diagnose ***Before*** **the Lesson**
4-2 Warm Up, TE p. 253

Monitor ***During*** **the Lesson**
Check It Out! Exercises, SE pp. 253–256
Questioning Strategies, TE pp. 254–256

Assess ***After*** **the Lesson**
4-2 Lesson Quiz, TE p. 260
Alternative Assessment, TE p. 260

Answers to *Think and Discuss*

Possible answers:

1. Because the third element in the first row of matrix A does not have a corresponding element in the first column of matrix B, you cannot determine the first element of AB. Therefore, the matrix product is not defined.
2. Matrix multiplication is not commutative even if both AB and BA are defined.
3. No, powers of matrices are only defined for square matrices. Because A is not a square matrix, A^2 is not defined.
4. See p. A6.

4-2 Exercises

go.hrw.com
Homework Help Online
KEYWORD: MB7 4-2
Parent Resources Online
KEYWORD: MB7 Parent

GUIDED PRACTICE

1. **Vocabulary** A 2×2 matrix with every entry equal to 1 is a __?__. (*square matrix* or *multiplicative identity matrix*) **multiplicative identity matrix**

SEE EXAMPLE 1 p. 253

Tell whether each product is defined. If so, give its dimensions.

2. $A_{4 \times 5}$ and $B_{5 \times 3}$; AB **yes; 4×3**
3. $A_{4 \times 5}$ and $B_{5 \times 3}$; BA **no**
4. $C_{9 \times 5}$ and $D_{5 \times 9}$; CD **yes; 9×9**
5. $C_{9 \times 5}$ and $D_{5 \times 9}$; DC **yes; 5×5**
6. $E_{6 \times 2}$ and $F_{2 \times 6}$; EF **yes; 6×6**
7. $E_{6 \times 2}$ and $F_{2 \times 6}$; FE **yes; 2×2**

SEE EXAMPLE 2 p. 254

Use the following matrices for Exercises 8–13. Find each product, if possible.

$$A = \begin{bmatrix} 0 & 7 & 3 \\ -2 & 3 & 0 \end{bmatrix} \quad B = \begin{bmatrix} 4 & 2 \\ 1 & -3 \end{bmatrix} \quad C = \begin{bmatrix} -3 & 1 \\ 5 & -2 \\ 0 & 1 \end{bmatrix} \quad D = \begin{bmatrix} 3 & -1 & 7 & 10 \\ 1 & -1 & 3 & 5 \end{bmatrix} \quad I = \begin{bmatrix} 1 & 0 \\ 0 & 1 \end{bmatrix}$$

8. BA
9. CA
10. CB
11. DC
12. BI
13. IB

SEE EXAMPLE 3 p. 255

14. **Recycling** Students collected recyclables for fund-raising over a three-week period. Use matrix multiplication to find the total amount of money collected for each type of item. **glass: $1.24; cans: $14.17; newspaper: $8.65; office paper: $249.70**

Recyclables Collected (lb)			
Item	Week 1	Week 2	Week 3
Glass	29	25	16
Cans	8	11	6
Newspaper	163	127	206
Office paper	53	107	84

Price Per Pound ($)				
Week	Glass	Cans	News-paper	Office Paper
1	0.02	0.70	0.02	1.06
2	0.02	0.55	0.01	1.00
3	0.01	0.42	0.02	1.03

SEE EXAMPLE 4 p. 256

Use the following matrices for Exercises 15–18. Evaluate, if possible.

$$A = \begin{bmatrix} -1 & -2 \\ 1 & 0 \end{bmatrix} \quad B = \begin{bmatrix} 3 & 4 & 2 \\ -1 & 0 & 0 \\ 3 & 0 & 1 \end{bmatrix} \quad C = \begin{bmatrix} 3 & 1 \\ 0 & -2 \\ 1 & 1 \end{bmatrix}$$

15. A^2 $\begin{bmatrix} -1 & 2 \\ -1 & -2 \end{bmatrix}$
16. A^3 $\begin{bmatrix} 3 & 2 \\ -1 & 2 \end{bmatrix}$
17. C^2 **not possible**
18. B^2 $\begin{bmatrix} 11 & 12 & 8 \\ -3 & -4 & -2 \\ 12 & 12 & 7 \end{bmatrix}$

PRACTICE AND PROBLEM SOLVING

Independent Practice

For Exercises	See Example
19–24	1
25–29	2
30	3
31–40	4

Extra Practice
Skills Practice p. S10
Application Practice p. S35

Tell whether each product is defined. If so, give its dimensions.

19. $A_{2 \times 1}$ and $B_{2 \times 3}$; AB **no**
20. $A_{2 \times 1}$ and $B_{2 \times 3}$; BA **no**
21. $C_{3 \times 5}$ and $D_{5 \times 1}$; CD **21. yes; 3×1**
22. $C_{3 \times 5}$ and $D_{5 \times 1}$; DC **no**
23. $E_{7 \times 7}$ and $F_{6 \times 7}$; EF **no**
24. $E_{7 \times 7}$ and $F_{6 \times 7}$; FE **24. yes; 6×7**

Use the following matrices for Exercises 25–29. Find each product, if possible.

$$A = \begin{bmatrix} 4 \\ -1 \\ 2 \end{bmatrix} \quad B = \begin{bmatrix} -3 & 0 \\ 7 & -2 \\ 0 & 1 \end{bmatrix} \quad C = \begin{bmatrix} -2 & 3 & -4 \\ 1 & -1 & 1 \\ 4 & 1 & 3 \end{bmatrix} \quad I = \begin{bmatrix} 1 & 0 & 0 \\ 0 & 1 & 0 \\ 0 & 0 & 1 \end{bmatrix}$$

28, 29. $\begin{bmatrix} -2 & 3 & -4 \\ 1 & -1 & 1 \\ 4 & 1 & 3 \end{bmatrix}$

25. AB **not possible**
26. CA
27. CB
28. IC
29. CI

26. $\begin{bmatrix} -19 \\ 7 \\ 21 \end{bmatrix}$

27. $\begin{bmatrix} 27 & -10 \\ -10 & 3 \\ -5 & 1 \end{bmatrix}$

4-2 Exercises

Assignment Guide

Assign *Guided Practice* exercises as necessary.

If you finished Examples **1–2**
Basic 19–29, 36–39
Average 19–29, 36–39
Advanced 19–29, 36–39

If you finished Examples **1–4**
Basic 19–40, 46–52, 54–57, 61–73
Average 19–49, 51–58, 61–73
Advanced 19–47, 50–51, 54–73

Homework Quick Check
Quickly check key concepts.
Exercises: 20, 26, 30, 38, 50

Answers

8. $\begin{bmatrix} -4 & 34 & 12 \\ 6 & -2 & 3 \end{bmatrix}$

9. $\begin{bmatrix} -2 & -18 & -9 \\ 4 & 29 & 15 \\ -2 & 3 & 0 \end{bmatrix}$

10. $\begin{bmatrix} -11 & -9 \\ 18 & 16 \\ 1 & -3 \end{bmatrix}$

11. not possible

12. $\begin{bmatrix} 4 & 2 \\ 1 & -3 \end{bmatrix}$

13. $\begin{bmatrix} 4 & 2 \\ 1 & -3 \end{bmatrix}$

State Resources

go.hrw.com
State Resources Online
KEYWORD: MB7 Resources

Answers

41a. continued

$$D = \begin{bmatrix} 1.2 & 1.6 & 2.0 & 1.8 \\ 2.3 & 2.0 & 2.8 & 2.5 \\ 2.7 & 2.6 & 3.2 & 3.1 \end{bmatrix};$$

$$SD = \begin{bmatrix} 122.8 & 124.5 & 160.2 & 148.1 \\ 161.85 & 160.4 & 207.8 & 191.95 \\ 131.45 & 130.3 & 168.4 & 155.85 \\ 168.95 & 169.0 & 217.8 & 201.65 \end{bmatrix}$$

c. Only the entries on the main diagonal represent the sum of the products of the scores of one diver and the corresponding difficulty multipliers of that same diver. The other entries represent the sum of the products of the scores of one diver and the corresponding difficulty multipliers of a different diver.

46a. $\begin{bmatrix} 1 & -2 & 1 \\ -2 & 0 & 1 \end{bmatrix}$

b. $\begin{bmatrix} 2 & 0 \\ 0 & 2 \end{bmatrix}\begin{bmatrix} 1 & -2 & 1 \\ -2 & 0 & 1 \end{bmatrix} =$

$\begin{bmatrix} 2 & -4 & 2 \\ -4 & 0 & 2 \end{bmatrix}$

c.

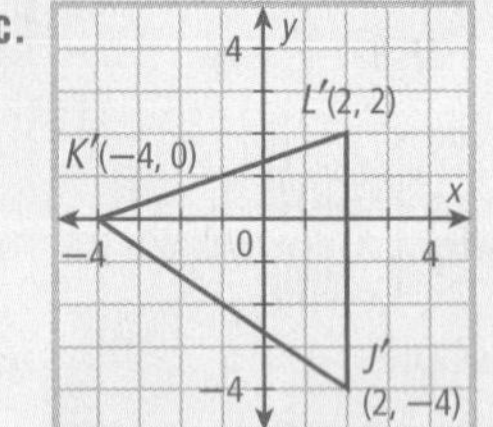

The new triangle is enlarged by a factor of 2.

33. $\begin{bmatrix} 6 & 2 & 1 \\ 5 & 4 & 1 \\ 7 & 3 & 3 \end{bmatrix}$

36. $\begin{bmatrix} 0 & -3 & -5 \\ -2 & 11 & 17 \\ 4 & 11 & 21 \end{bmatrix}$

38. $\begin{bmatrix} 11 & 21 \\ 13 & 55 \end{bmatrix}$

39. $\begin{bmatrix} -2 & 8 & 12 \\ 6 & 0 & 4 \end{bmatrix}$

40. $\begin{bmatrix} 102 & 352 \\ 224 & 806 \end{bmatrix}$

30. Inventory A pet stroller comes in two sizes. Two stores have inventories as shown in the first table. Find the total cost of the pet strollers for each store. **store 1: \$1595; store 2: \$1260**

Pet Stroller Inventory		
	Standard	Large
Store 1	11	7
Store 2	8	6

Pet Stroller Profits			
	Revenue (\$)	Store Cost (\$)	Profit (\$)
Standard	130	75	55
Large	190	110	80

Use the following matrices for Exercises 31–40. Simplify, if possible.

$$Q = \begin{bmatrix} 4 & 13 & -9 \end{bmatrix} \quad S = \begin{bmatrix} 1 & 2 \\ -1 & 0 \end{bmatrix} \quad T = \begin{bmatrix} 2 & 1 & 0 \\ 2 & 0 & 1 \\ 1 & 2 & 1 \end{bmatrix} \quad A = \begin{bmatrix} 0 & -1 \\ -1 & 4 \\ 2 & 3 \end{bmatrix} \quad B = \begin{bmatrix} 2 & 1 & 3 \\ 0 & 3 & 5 \end{bmatrix} \quad C = \begin{bmatrix} -1 & 1 \\ 1 & -1 \end{bmatrix}$$

31. S^2 $\begin{bmatrix} -1 & 2 \\ -1 & -2 \end{bmatrix}$
32. B^2 not possible
33. T^2
34. S^3 $\begin{bmatrix} -3 & -2 \\ 1 & -2 \end{bmatrix}$
35. Q^3 not possible
36. AB
37. BA $\begin{bmatrix} 5 & 11 \\ 7 & 27 \end{bmatrix}$
38. $2BA - C$
39. $3CB + 2B$
40. $(BA)^2$

Diving

Chinese diver Guo Jingjing won two gold medals at the 2004 Summer Olympic Games in Athens, Greece.

41. Diving In a diving competition, the point total for each dive is multiplied by an assigned degree of difficulty to determine the diver's score.

Points for Each Dive			
Diver	Dive 1	Dive 2	Dive 3
Ted	23.0	18.5	19.5
Chloe	24.0	28.5	25.0
Biko	19.0	22.0	21.5
Hana	27.0	26.5	28.0

Degree of Difficulty Multiplier				
Dive	Ted	Chloe	Biko	Hana
1	1.2	1.6	2.0	1.8
2	2.3	2.0	2.8	2.5
3	2.7	2.6	3.2	3.1

41a. $S = \begin{bmatrix} 23.0 & 18.5 & 19.5 \\ 24.0 & 28.5 & 25.0 \\ 19.0 & 22.0 & 21.5 \\ 27.0 & 26.5 & 28.0 \end{bmatrix};$

a. Organize the tables as matrices, and multiply.

b. Use the product matrix to find the scores for each of the four divers.

41b. Ted: 122.8; Chloe: 160.4; Biko: 168.4; Hana: 201.65

c. Explain why only the numbers on the main diagonal of the product matrix are meaningful in the context of the problem.

Critical Thinking For Exercises 42–45, tell whether each statement is always, sometimes, or never true for matrices A and B. Explain your answer.

42. If A is 2×3 and B has three rows, then AB is defined. **always true**
43. If A is 2×3 and B has three columns, then AB is defined. **sometimes true**
44. If AB is defined, then BA is defined. **sometimes true**
45. If both AB and BA are defined, both are square matrices. **sometimes true**

MULTI-STEP TEST PREP

46. This problem will prepare you for the Multi-Step Test Prep on page 268.

a. Place the vertices of the triangle in a matrix so that the x-coordinates are in row 1 and the y-coordinates are in row 2.

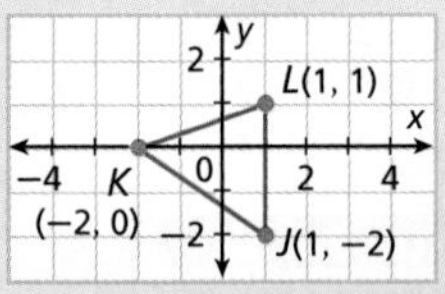

b. Use the matrix $\begin{bmatrix} 2 & 0 \\ 0 & 2 \end{bmatrix}$ to multiply each x- and y-coordinate by 2.

c. Draw a new triangle using the new coordinates. Describe the new triangle.

(Graph: y; 2; L(1, 1); x; −4; K (−2, 0); 0; 2; 4; −2; J(1, −2))

4-2 PRACTICE A
4-2 PRACTICE C
4-2 PRACTICE B

Tell whether each product is defined. If so, give its dimensions.

1. $P_{3 \times 3}$ and $Q_{3 \times 4}$; PQ — 3×4
2. $R_{3 \times 8}$ and $S_{4 \times 3}$; SR — 4×8
3. $W_{2 \times 5}$ and $X_{2 \times 5}$; WX — No

Use the following matrices for Exercises 4–7. Evaluate, if possible.

$$E = \begin{bmatrix} -4 & 1 \\ -2 & 2 \end{bmatrix} \quad F = \begin{bmatrix} 1 & 0 \\ 4 & -3 \\ -2 & 6 \\ -1 & 5 \end{bmatrix} \quad G = \begin{bmatrix} -4 & 0 & 3 & 5 \\ 1 & -2 & 0 & 0 \end{bmatrix} \quad H = \begin{bmatrix} 1 & -2 & -1 & 3 \\ 2 & 0 & 4 & -1 \\ 3 & 5 & -2 & 2 \\ 1 & -1 & 0 & 0 \end{bmatrix}$$

4. EG $\begin{bmatrix} 17 & -2 & -12 & -20 \\ 10 & -4 & -6 & -10 \end{bmatrix}$

5. HF $\begin{bmatrix} -8 & 15 \\ -5 & 19 \\ 25 & -17 \\ -3 & 3 \end{bmatrix}$

6. FG $\begin{bmatrix} -4 & 0 & 3 & 5 \\ -19 & 6 & 12 & 20 \\ 14 & -12 & -6 & -10 \\ 9 & -10 & -3 & -5 \end{bmatrix}$

7. E^2 $\begin{bmatrix} 14 & -2 \\ 4 & 2 \end{bmatrix}$

Solve.

8. Jamal, Ken, and Barry are playing a baseball video game. The first table shows the number of singles, doubles, triples, and home runs each scored. Find the total number of points they each scored.

Hits				
Player	S	D	T	HR
Jamal	3	2	0	1
Ken	2	4	0	0
Barry	0	1	3	1

Points Scored for Hits	
Hit	Points
Single (S)	1
Double (D)	2
Triple (T)	3
Home run (HR)	4

a. Write a matrix that represents the data in each table.

$\begin{bmatrix} 3 & 2 & 0 & 1 \\ 2 & 4 & 0 & 0 \\ 0 & 1 & 3 & 1 \end{bmatrix}, \begin{bmatrix} 1 \\ 2 \\ 3 \\ 4 \end{bmatrix}$

b. Find the product matrix. $\begin{bmatrix} 11 \\ 10 \\ 15 \end{bmatrix}$

c. How many points did each player score? Jamal 11, Ken 10, Barry 15

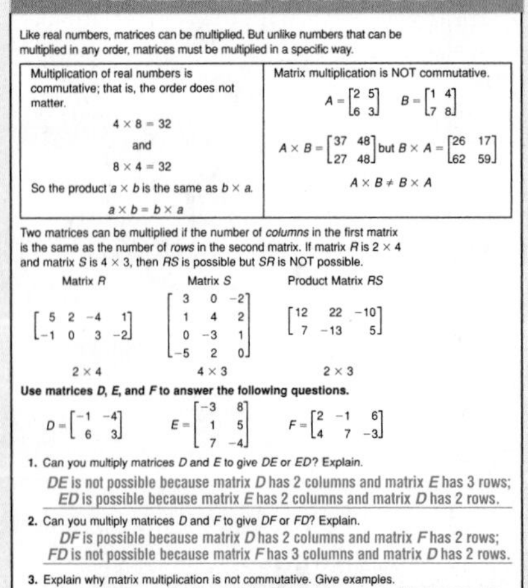

4-2 READING STRATEGIES

Like real numbers, matrices can be multiplied. But unlike numbers that can be multiplied in any order, matrices must be multiplied in a specific way.

Multiplication of real numbers is commutative; that is, the order does not matter.	Matrix multiplication is NOT commutative.
$4 \times 8 = 32$ and $8 \times 4 = 32$	$A = \begin{bmatrix} 2 & 5 \\ 6 & 3 \end{bmatrix}$ $B = \begin{bmatrix} 1 & 4 \\ 7 & 8 \end{bmatrix}$
So the product $a \times b$ is the same as $b \times a$. $a \times b = b \times a$	$A \times B = \begin{bmatrix} 37 & 48 \\ 27 & 48 \end{bmatrix}$ but $B \times A = \begin{bmatrix} 26 & 17 \\ 62 & 59 \end{bmatrix}$ $A \times B \neq B \times A$

Two matrices can be multiplied if the number of *columns* in the first matrix is the same as the number of *rows* in the second matrix. If matrix R is 2×4 and matrix S is 4×3, then RS is possible but SR is NOT possible.

Matrix R: $\begin{bmatrix} 5 & 2 & -4 & 1 \\ -1 & 0 & 3 & -2 \end{bmatrix}$ 2×4

Matrix S: $\begin{bmatrix} 3 & 0 & -2 \\ 1 & 4 & 2 \\ 0 & -3 & 1 \\ -5 & 2 & 0 \end{bmatrix}$ 4×3

Product Matrix RS: $\begin{bmatrix} 12 & 22 & -10 \\ 7 & -13 & 5 \end{bmatrix}$ 2×3

Use matrices D, E, and F to answer the following questions.

$$D = \begin{bmatrix} -1 & -4 \\ 6 & 3 \end{bmatrix} \quad E = \begin{bmatrix} -3 & 8 \\ 1 & 5 \\ 7 & -4 \end{bmatrix} \quad F = \begin{bmatrix} 2 & -1 & 6 \\ 4 & 7 & -3 \end{bmatrix}$$

1. Can you multiply matrices D and E to give DE or ED? Explain.
   DE is not possible because matrix D has 2 columns and matrix E has 3 rows; ED is possible because matrix E has 2 columns and matrix D has 2 rows.
2. Can you multiply matrices D and F to give DF or FD? Explain.
   DF is possible because matrix D has 2 columns and matrix F has 2 rows; FD is not possible because matrix F has 3 columns and matrix D has 2 rows.
3. Explain why matrix multiplication is not commutative. Give examples.
   Possible answer: Matrix multiplication is not commutative because the products are not the same when the order of multiplication is reversed. Matrix DF is not the same as matrix FD.
4. Can you multiply matrices E and F? Describe all possibilities. Give the dimensions of any resulting matrices.
   Yes; both EF and FE are possible. Matrix EF is 3×3 and matrix FE is 2×2.

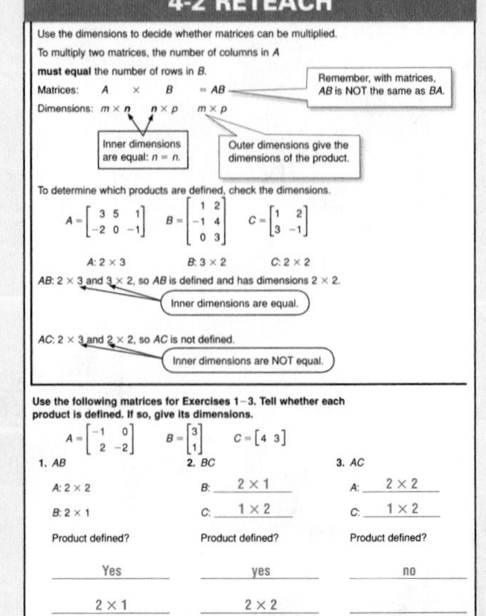

4-2 RETEACH

Use the dimensions to decide whether matrices can be multiplied.

To multiply two matrices, the number of columns in A **must equal** the number of rows in B.

Matrices: $A \times B = AB$

Dimensions: $m \times n$ $\quad n \times p$ $\quad m \times p$

To determine which products are defined, check the dimensions.

$$A = \begin{bmatrix} 3 & 5 & 1 \\ -2 & 0 & -1 \end{bmatrix} \quad B = \begin{bmatrix} 1 & 2 \\ -1 & 4 \\ 0 & 3 \end{bmatrix} \quad C = \begin{bmatrix} 1 & 2 \\ 3 & -1 \end{bmatrix}$$

A: 2×3 $\quad B$: 3×2 $\quad C$: 2×2

AB: 2×3 and 3×2, so AB is defined and has dimensions 2×2.

AC: 2×3 and 2×2, so AC is not defined.

Use the following matrices for Exercises 1–3. Tell whether each product is defined. If so, give its dimensions.

$$A = \begin{bmatrix} -1 & 0 \\ 2 & -2 \end{bmatrix} \quad B = \begin{bmatrix} 3 \\ 1 \end{bmatrix} \quad C = \begin{bmatrix} 4 & 3 \end{bmatrix}$$

1. AB
   A: 2×2
   B: 2×1
   Product defined? Yes
   2×1
2. BC
   B: 2×1
   C: 1×2
   Product defined? yes
   2×2
3. AC
   A: 2×2
   C: 1×2
   Product defined? no

47. Solve for x: $\begin{bmatrix} 4 & 3 \\ 5 & 6 \end{bmatrix}\begin{bmatrix} 6 & \frac{x}{2} \\ -1 & -1 \end{bmatrix} = \begin{bmatrix} 21 & -19 \\ 24 & -26 \end{bmatrix}$ −8

48. Write About It Explain why $\begin{bmatrix} 1 & 0 \\ 0 & 1 \end{bmatrix}\begin{bmatrix} a & b \\ c & d \end{bmatrix} = \begin{bmatrix} a & b \\ c & d \end{bmatrix}$.

49. Fiber Arts The first table shows points awarded by the judges at the New England Sheep & Wool Fair for each competition. The second table shows the multiplier used for the degree of difficulty of each piece. Find the total score for each contestant.
Madison: 122; Devyn: 113.5; Ali: 69.5

Points Awarded			
Contestant	Wall Hanging	Clothing	Rug
Madison	16.5	18.0	17.5
Devyn	12.5	14.0	17.0
Ali	16.0	19.5	18.0

Degree of Difficulty Multiplier			
Category	Madison	Devyn	Ali
Wall Hanging	2	3	2
Clothing	3	3	1
Rug	2	2	1

50. Sales Old and new commission rates for shoe sales are given.
a. Find the product matrix. How much did each person make under each rate?
b. Which salesperson benefited the most from the change in rates? Explain.

Total Sales ($)			
Salesperson	Men's	Women's	Children's
Leigh	5200	4200	2300
Khalid	8100	8400	3100
Ari	2700	7400	630

Commission Rates		
Shoe	Old Rate	New Rate
Men's	9%	9.5%
Women's	9%	10%
Children's	13%	12%

51. Puzzle Contestants in a reality TV show need to get to a location given by entries in the following matrix product:

$$P = \begin{bmatrix} 5 & 1 \\ -11 & 2 \end{bmatrix}\begin{bmatrix} 5 & -2 \\ 9 & -3 \end{bmatrix}$$

latitude: p_{21} (north if positive, south if negative)

longitude: p_{12} (east if positive, west if negative)

What is the location that the contestants must make their way to? **Tristan Island**

Casablanca 34° N, 8° W
0° Longitude
Addis Ababa 9° N, 39° E
0° Latitude
Kalahari Desert 23° S, 26° E
Tristan Island 37° S, 13° W
N
W
E
S

52. Football Find the total number of points scored by each team.

Team	Touchdowns	Extra Points	Field Goals
Redcliffe	11	9	4
Mayson	15	12	6
Rye Harbor	6	5	9

Type of Score	Points
Touchdown	6
Extra point	1
Field goal	3

Redcliffe: 87 points; Mayson: 120 points; Rye Harbor: 68 points

53. Critical Thinking Write A as a scalar product where each entry is a whole number.

$$A = \begin{bmatrix} \frac{1}{2} & \frac{1}{3} \\ \frac{3}{4} & \frac{5}{6} \end{bmatrix}$$

Possible answer: $\frac{1}{12}\begin{bmatrix} 6 & 4 \\ 9 & 10 \end{bmatrix}$

50a. $\begin{bmatrix} 1145.00 & 1190.00 \\ 1888.00 & 1981.50 \\ 990.90 & 1072.10 \end{bmatrix}$;
Leigh old: $1145.00;
Leigh new: $1190.00;
Khalid old: $1888.00;
Khalid new: $1981.50;
Ari old: $990.90;
Ari new: $1072.10

b. Khalid benefited most. Leigh's commission increased by $45.00, Khalid's increased by $93.50, and Ari's increased by $81.20.

COMMON ERROR ALERT

In **Exercises 34–35,** students may just cube each entry. Remind them that taking a square or a cube is multiplication of matrices, and each entry in the resulting matrix is still a sum of products, not a power.

MULTI-STEP TEST PREP **Exercise 46** involves transforming the coordinates of the vertices of a triangle. This exercise prepares students for the Multi-Step Test Prep on page 268.

Answers

48. The matrix $\begin{bmatrix} 1 & 0 \\ 0 & 1 \end{bmatrix}$ is the multiplicative identity of a 2 × 2 matrix. The product of any 2 × 2 matrix and this multiplicative identity is equal to the original 2 × 2 matrix. Therefore, the product of $\begin{bmatrix} 1 & 0 \\ 0 & 1 \end{bmatrix}$ and $\begin{bmatrix} a & b \\ c & d \end{bmatrix}$ is equal to $\begin{bmatrix} a & b \\ c & d \end{bmatrix}$.

4-2 PROBLEM SOLVING

Members of the Cooking Club entered the Culinary Challenge. In this contest, the score for each entry is multiplied by an assigned degree of difficulty.

Cooking Club Members Scores			
	Appetizer	Main Course	Dessert
Beth	25	38	28
Jon	35	29	37
Lupe	20	31	39
Amy	40	32	36

Culinary Challenge Degrees of Difficulty				
	Beth	Jon	Lupe	Amy
Appetizer	3.1	2.0	3.5	1.5
Main Course	2.1	1.8	3.7	2.8
Dessert	2.3	2.4	3.0	3.5

1. Display each table as a matrix. Matrix S should show the scores and matrix D should show the degrees of difficulty.

$$S = \begin{bmatrix} 25 & 38 & 28 \\ 35 & 29 & 37 \\ 20 & 31 & 39 \\ 40 & 32 & 36 \end{bmatrix}; \quad D = \begin{bmatrix} 3.1 & 2.0 & 3.5 & 1.5 \\ 2.1 & 1.8 & 3.7 & 2.8 \\ 2.3 & 2.4 & 3.0 & 3.5 \end{bmatrix}$$

2. Write an equation using S, D, and product matrix P you could use to evaluate the final scores. $S \times D = P$

3. Explain how you know that matrix S can be multiplied by matrix D.
Possible answer: because matrix S has the same number of columns (3) as matrix D has rows (3); the result will be a 4 × 4 matrix.

4. Write the product matrix P.

$$P = \begin{bmatrix} 221.7 & 185.6 & 312.1 & 241.9 \\ 254.5 & 211.0 & 340.8 & 263.2 \\ 216.8 & 189.4 & 301.7 & 253.3 \\ 274.0 & 224.0 & 366.4 & 275.6 \end{bmatrix}$$

5. Roger is writing a story for the school newspaper about the Culinary Challenge. Explain how he can use P to find the final scores for his story.
The numbers along the main diagonal of the product matrix give the final scores.

6. List the contestants and their final scores, in descending order.
Lupe: 301.7; Amy: 275.6; Beth: 221.7; Jon: 211

4-2 CHALLENGE

Matrices can be used to send messages in coded form, and then another matrix can be used to decode the message. Use the code shown in the table for letters and characters.

Code	
A–Z	1–26
Comma	27
Period	28
Space	29

Take a message such as "Math is fun." Code it into numbers and the message becomes:

13 1 20 8 29 9 19 29 6 21 14 28

The message in code can be represented by matrix M. $\begin{bmatrix} 13 & 1 & 20 & 8 \\ 29 & 9 & 19 & 29 \\ 6 & 21 & 14 & 28 \end{bmatrix}$

Notice how the numbers in the message read from left to right. Multiply matrix M by the coding matrix C.

$$C = \begin{bmatrix} 2 & 0 & 1 \\ 3 & 1 & 2 \\ 1 & 0 & 1 \end{bmatrix}, CM = \begin{bmatrix} 2 & 0 & 1 \\ 3 & 1 & 2 \\ 1 & 0 & 1 \end{bmatrix} \times \begin{bmatrix} 13 & 1 & 20 & 8 \\ 29 & 9 & 19 & 29 \\ 6 & 21 & 14 & 28 \end{bmatrix} = \begin{bmatrix} 32 & 23 & 54 & 44 \\ 80 & 54 & 107 & 109 \\ 19 & 22 & 34 & 36 \end{bmatrix}$$

Since many of the numbers are greater than 29, the greatest number in the code, divide each number by 29 and record only the remainder. This is called arithmetic modulo 29.

$$CM \text{ modulo } 29 = \begin{bmatrix} 32 & 23 & 54 & 44 \\ 80 & 54 & 107 & 109 \\ 19 & 22 & 34 & 36 \end{bmatrix} \text{ modulo } 29 = \begin{bmatrix} 3 & 23 & 25 & 15 \\ 22 & 25 & 20 & 22 \\ 19 & 22 & 5 & 7 \end{bmatrix}$$

This gives the coded message CWYOVYTVSVEG. To decode, multiply by the decoding matrix D, $\begin{bmatrix} 1 & 0 & 28 \\ 28 & 1 & 28 \\ 28 & 0 & 2 \end{bmatrix}$. This gives

$$D \times CM = \begin{bmatrix} 1 & 0 & 28 \\ 28 & 1 & 28 \\ 28 & 0 & 2 \end{bmatrix} \times \begin{bmatrix} 3 & 23 & 25 & 15 \\ 22 & 25 & 20 & 22 \\ 19 & 22 & 5 & 7 \end{bmatrix} = \begin{bmatrix} 535 & 639 & 165 & 211 \\ 638 & 1285 & 860 & 638 \\ 122 & 688 & 710 & 434 \end{bmatrix},$$

which in arithmetic modulo 29 is $\begin{bmatrix} 13 & 1 & 20 & 8 \\ 0 & 9 & 19 & 0 \\ 6 & 21 & 14 & 28 \end{bmatrix}$ and translates back to "Math is fun."

Note that in the matrix for the decoded message, 0 corresponds to 29.

When you code a message, be sure to use a matrix with 3 rows. Add spaces at the end of the message, if necessary.

1. Code the message "NOT NOW." V KA.QHNT
2. Decode the message "FE RRIQP CCDORI". CAN I HAVE CAR

In **Exercise 54,** have students make a visual representation, such as:

$\begin{bmatrix} \rightarrow \end{bmatrix}[\downarrow 5 \times 12]$

In **Exercise 55,** students who do not choose **B** might think that multiplying by a matrix where each element is 2 is equivalent to multiplying by 2 as a scalar product. Encourage them to multiply this product out, as well as the product in **A.**

Journal

Discuss why the commutative property does not apply to matrix multiplication. Show an example where $AB \neq BA$.

ALTERNATIVE ASSESSMENT

Have students develop an example that involves matrix multiplication, such as from **Exercises 49** or **50.** Make sure that they show how the multiplication is done, and that they explain what the answer matrix means in the context of the example.

Power Presentations with PowerPoint®

4-2 Lesson Quiz

$A = \begin{bmatrix} 2 & -2 \\ 3 & 0 \\ 2 & 1 \end{bmatrix}$ $B = \begin{bmatrix} 4 & 2 & 3 \\ 2 & 1 & -1 \end{bmatrix}$

$C = \begin{bmatrix} 1 & 1 & 1 \\ 1 & 1 & 0 \\ 1 & 0 & 0 \end{bmatrix}$ $D = \begin{bmatrix} 2 & 0 \\ 0 & 2 \end{bmatrix}$

Evaluate, if possible.

1. AB $\begin{bmatrix} 4 & 2 & 8 \\ 12 & 6 & 9 \\ 10 & 5 & 5 \end{bmatrix}$

2. BA $\begin{bmatrix} 20 & -5 \\ 5 & -5 \end{bmatrix}$

3. A^2 not possible

4. BD not possible

5. C^3 $\begin{bmatrix} 6 & 5 & 3 \\ 5 & 4 & 2 \\ 3 & 2 & 1 \end{bmatrix}$

Also available on transparency

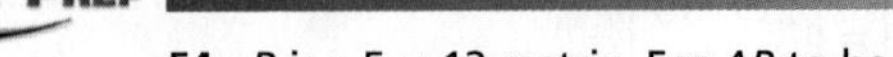

TEST PREP

54. B is a 5×12 matrix. For AB to be defined, what characteristic must A have?

(A) 5 columns (B) 12 columns (C) 5 rows (D) 12 rows

55. Which result is NOT equal to the other three?

(F) $2\begin{bmatrix} a & b \\ c & d \end{bmatrix}$ (G) $\begin{bmatrix} 2 & 2 \\ 2 & 2 \end{bmatrix}\begin{bmatrix} a & b \\ c & d \end{bmatrix}$ (H) $\begin{bmatrix} a & b \\ c & d \end{bmatrix} + \begin{bmatrix} a & b \\ c & d \end{bmatrix}$ (J) $\begin{bmatrix} a & b \\ c & d \end{bmatrix}\begin{bmatrix} 2 & 0 \\ 0 & 2 \end{bmatrix}$

56. For the matrix product $P = \begin{bmatrix} 7 & -1 \\ 4 & 2 \end{bmatrix}\begin{bmatrix} -2 & 5 \\ 3 & 8 \end{bmatrix}$, which expression gives the value of p_{22}?

(A) $4(-2) + 2(3)$ (B) $7(5) + (-1)8$ (C) $4(5) + 2(8)$ (D) $(-1)3 + 2(8)$

57. Short Response For $A = \begin{bmatrix} 3 & 4 \\ -4 & 5 \end{bmatrix}$ and $B = \begin{bmatrix} 3 & -6 \\ 6 & 8 \end{bmatrix}$, tell whether AB, BA, or neither equals $\begin{bmatrix} 33 & -18 \\ -14 & 64 \end{bmatrix}$. *BA*

CHALLENGE AND EXTEND

58. Is matrix multiplication associative? That is, does $ABC = (AB)C = A(BC)$ if the products are defined? Give an example to support your answer.

59. To write the *transpose* A^T of a matrix A for $A = \begin{bmatrix} 2 & 0 & 1 \\ 3 & 1 & 4 \end{bmatrix}$, $A^T = \begin{bmatrix} 2 & 3 \\ 0 & 1 \\ 1 & 4 \end{bmatrix}$, reverse its rows and columns.

a. Can a matrix always be multiplied by its transpose? Explain.

b. Find $P = AA^T$ for $\begin{bmatrix} a & b \\ c & d \end{bmatrix}$. Which entries of the product are equal?

60. On a calculator, enter matrix $A = \begin{bmatrix} 1 & 1 \\ 1 & 0 \end{bmatrix}$. Multiply A by itself, and record the value of the entry in row 2 column 2 of the product matrix. Continue to multiply by A and record the entry in this location. What is the relationship between successive recorded values? 1, 1, 2, 3, 5, 8, 13, . . . ; beginning with the third value, each value is the sum of the previous two values, forming the Fibonacci sequence.

SPIRAL REVIEW

Graphic Design The outer shape of this design is a regular hexagon. The green triangle is an equilateral triangle. *(Previous course)*

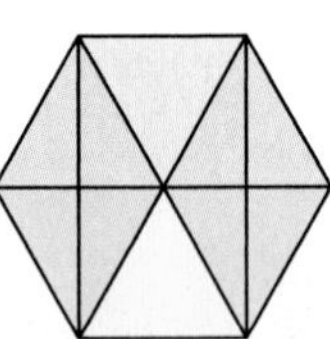

61. How many pairs of vertical angles are in the design? 10

62. How many triangles are congruent to the green triangle? 5

63. How many line segments are congruent to one side of the hexagon? 11

Graph each point in three-dimensional space. *(Lesson 3-5)*

64. $(0, 4, -5)$ **65.** $(2, 2, 6)$ **66.** $(-3, -3, 3)$ **67.** $(1, -1, -1)$

Evaluate, if possible. *(Lesson 4-1)*

$S = \begin{bmatrix} 2 & 4 \\ -1 & 0 \end{bmatrix}$ $T = \begin{bmatrix} 0.5 & 0.83 \\ 5 & 0 \end{bmatrix}$ $V = \begin{bmatrix} 2 & 3 & 0 \\ -4 & 1 & -1 \end{bmatrix}$

68. $S + T$ $\begin{bmatrix} 2.5 & 4.83 \\ 4 & 0 \end{bmatrix}$ **69.** $V - T$ not possible **70.** $4T$ $\begin{bmatrix} 2 & 3.32 \\ 20 & 0 \end{bmatrix}$

58. yes; possible answer:

$A = \begin{bmatrix} 3 & 4 & 5 \\ 2 & 6 & 9 \end{bmatrix}$,

$B = \begin{bmatrix} -5 & 9 \\ 2 & 3 \\ 8 & 7 \end{bmatrix}$, and

$C = \begin{bmatrix} 3 & 5 & 6 & 8 \\ 1 & -1 & 0 & 0 \end{bmatrix}$;

$(AB)C = \begin{bmatrix} 173 & 91 & 198 & 264 \\ 321 & 271 & 444 & 592 \end{bmatrix}$

and

$A(BC) = \begin{bmatrix} 173 & 91 & 198 & 264 \\ 321 & 271 & 444 & 592 \end{bmatrix}$,

so $(AB)C = A(BC)$

64–67.

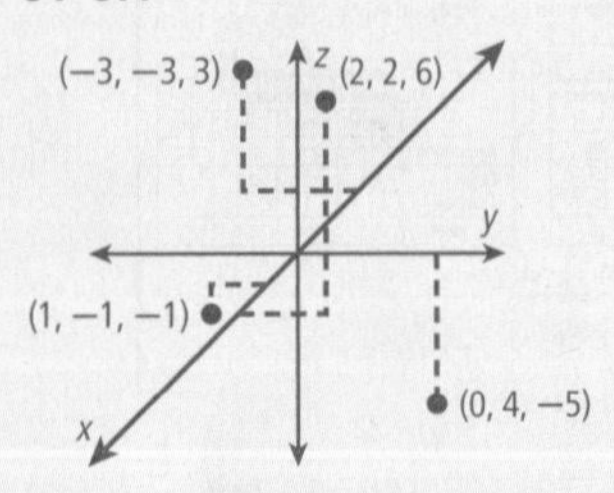

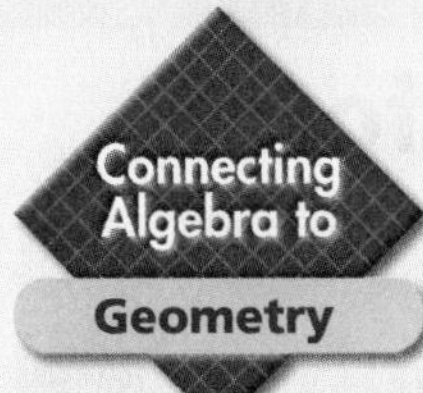

Transformations

See Skills Bank page S63

A *transformation* describes a way of moving or resizing a geometric figure. *Rigid transformations*, or *isometries*, do not change the size and shape of figures. However, not all transformations are rigid.

Transformations are described by distances, angle measures, and lines of reflection, depending on the type of transformation. The properties of a transformation tell you what attributes of the figure remain unchanged.

	Translation	Reflection	Rotation	Dilation
What You Need to Describe It	Horizontal and vertical distance	Line of reflection	Center angle of rotation	Center scale factor
What Does Not Change	Size and shape, area, orientation	Size and shape, area	Size and shape, area, orientation	Orientation

Example

Reflect $\triangle DEF$ across the line $y = x$.

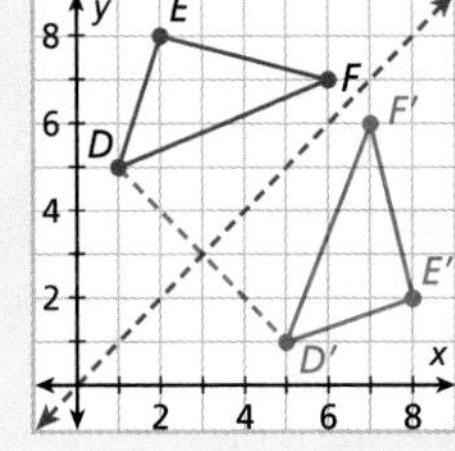

Step 1 Draw a line through D perpendicular to the line of reflection. Mark point D' as the image of point D. Point D and point D' must be the same distance from the line of reflection.

Step 2 Repeat Step 1 for points E and F. Connect the points to make $\triangle D'E'F'$.

Try This

Use graph paper to show each transformation.

1. Plot rectangle $PQRS$ with vertices $P(3, 1)$, $Q(3, -2)$, $R(-2, -2)$, and $S(-2, 1)$. Rotate the rectangle 90° clockwise. Use vertex P as the center of rotation.
2. Plot $\triangle ABC$ with vertices $A(1, 4)$, $B(6, 4)$, and $C(4, 6)$. Enlarge the triangle using the origin as the center of dilation with a scale factor of 1.5.
3. The identity transformation I maps each point of the plane onto itself. Describe consecutive reflections that are equivalent to the identity transformation.
4. Draw the horizontal line $y = 4$. Use $\triangle DEF$ from the example. Translate the triangle 3 units to the right, and then reflect it across the line. Repeat twice. This is an example of a *glide reflection*, the product of a reflection in a line and a translation along the same line.

Answers

1.

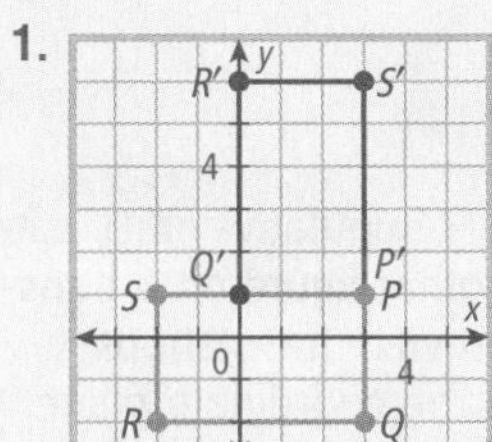

2.

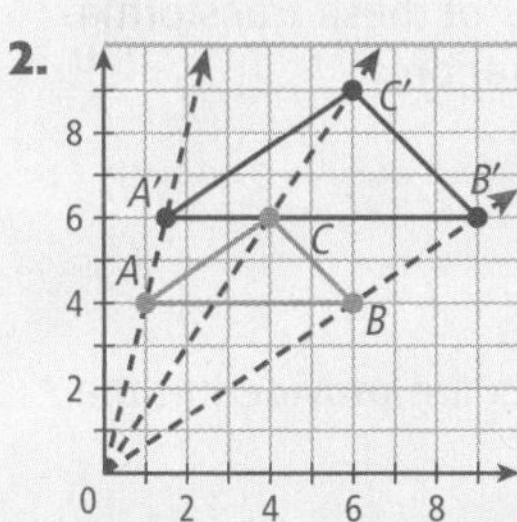

3. Possible answer: Reflect a figure across a line, and then reflect it back across the same line.

4.

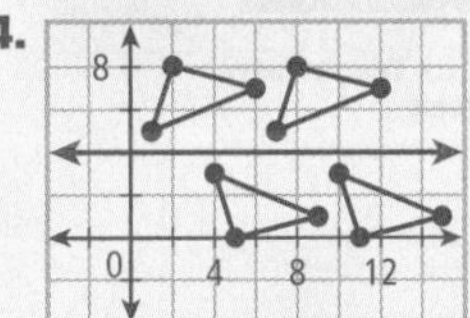

Organizer

See Skills Bank page S59

Pacing:

Traditional $\frac{1}{2}$ day
Block $\frac{1}{4}$ day

Objective: Review geometry concepts related to translations, rotations, reflections, and dilations.

Online Edition

Countdown to Testing Week 8

Teach

Remember

Students apply drawing geometric figures on coordinate grids by plotting the coordinates of their points.

INTERVENTION For additional review and practice on transforming geometric figures, see Skills Bank page S63.

Visual Translation is illustrated with a hexagon. Have students use this same hexagon and create a rotation and a reflection.

Close

Assess

Four types of transformations are shown at the top of the page. Which of these are rigid transformations? translation, rotation, and reflection

State Resources

4-3 Organizer

Pacing: Traditional 1 day
Block $\frac{1}{2}$ day

Objective: Use matrices to transform a plane figure.

Algebra Lab
In *Algebra Lab Activities*

Online Edition
Tutorial Videos, Interactivity

Countdown to Testing Week 8

Warm Up

Perform the indicated operation.

1. $\begin{bmatrix} 1 & 3 & 4 \\ 2 & 5 & 8 \end{bmatrix} + \begin{bmatrix} 1 & 1 & 1 \\ -3 & -3 & -3 \end{bmatrix}$

   $\begin{bmatrix} 2 & 4 & 5 \\ -1 & 2 & 5 \end{bmatrix}$

2. $2\begin{bmatrix} 5 & 2 & 0 \\ 1 & 6 & 1 \end{bmatrix}$ $\begin{bmatrix} 10 & 4 & 0 \\ 2 & 12 & 2 \end{bmatrix}$

3. $\begin{bmatrix} 1 & 0 \\ 0 & -1 \end{bmatrix}\begin{bmatrix} 1 & 3 & 4 \\ 2 & 5 & 8 \end{bmatrix}$

   $\begin{bmatrix} 1 & 3 & 4 \\ -2 & -5 & -8 \end{bmatrix}$

Also available on transparency

Math Humor

Fred: These reflections are tough. I keep getting them reversed.

Fran: My trouble is with rotations. They make my head spin.

4-3 Using Matrices to Transform Geometric Figures

Objective
Use matrices to transform a plane figure.

Vocabulary
translation matrix
reflection matrix
rotation matrix

Who uses this?
Artists, such as M. C. Escher, may use repeated transformed patterns to create their work. (See Exercise 16.)

The Granger Collection, New York

You can describe the position, shape, and size of a polygon on a coordinate plane by naming the ordered pairs that define its vertices.

The coordinates of $\triangle ABC$ below are $A(-2, -1)$, $B(0, 3)$, and $C(1, -2)$.

You can also define $\triangle ABC$ by a matrix:

$$P = \begin{bmatrix} -2 & 0 & 1 \\ -1 & 3 & -2 \end{bmatrix} \begin{matrix} \leftarrow x\text{-coordinates} \\ \leftarrow y\text{-coordinates} \end{matrix}$$

A **translation matrix** is a matrix used to translate coordinates on the coordinate plane. The matrix sum of a *preimage* and a translation matrix gives the coordinates of the translated *image*.

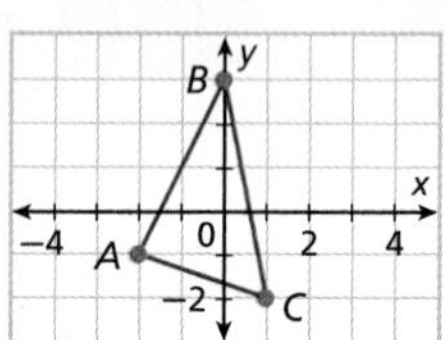

EXAMPLE 1 Using Matrices to Translate a Figure

Translate $\triangle ABC$ with coordinates $A(-2, -1)$, $B(0, 3)$, and $C(1, -2)$ 2 units right and 3 units down. Find the coordinates of the vertices of the image, and graph.

The translation matrix will have 2 in all entries in row 1 and −3 in all entries in row 2.

$$\begin{bmatrix} 2 & 2 & 2 \\ -3 & -3 & -3 \end{bmatrix} \begin{matrix} \leftarrow x\text{-translation} \\ \leftarrow y\text{-translation} \end{matrix}$$

Coordinate matrix + *Translation matrix*

$$\begin{bmatrix} -2 & 0 & 1 \\ -1 & 3 & -2 \end{bmatrix} + \begin{bmatrix} 2 & 2 & 2 \\ -3 & -3 & -3 \end{bmatrix} = \begin{bmatrix} -2+2 & 0+2 & 1+2 \\ -1-3 & 3-3 & -2-3 \end{bmatrix}$$

$$= \begin{bmatrix} 0 & 2 & 3 \\ -4 & 0 & -5 \end{bmatrix}$$

$A'B'C'$, the image of $\triangle ABC$, has coordinates $A'(0, -4)$, $B'(2, 0)$, and $C'(3, -5)$.

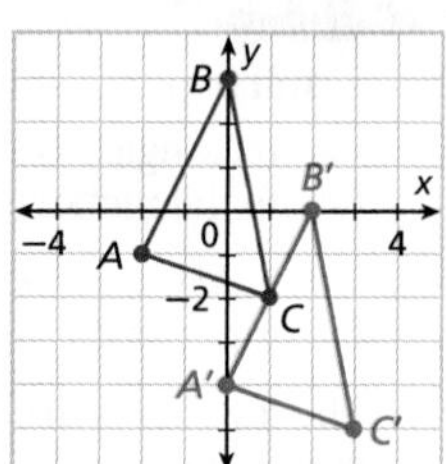

The prefix *pre-* means "before," so the *preimage* is the original figure before any transformations are applied. The *image* is the resulting figure after a transformation.

CHECK IT OUT! **1.** Translate $\triangle GHJ$ with coordinates $G(2, 4)$, $H(3, 1)$, and $J(1, -1)$ 3 units right and 1 unit down. Find the coordinates of the vertices of the image and graph. **$G'(5, 3)$, $H'(6, 0)$, $J'(4, -2)$**

State Resources

1 Introduce

EXPLORATION

4-3 Using Matrices to Transform Geometric Figures

You can use matrices to describe figures in the coordinate plane.

1. Complete the table by finding the coordinates of the vertices of $\triangle ABC$.

	Point A	Point B	Point C
x-coordinate			
y-coordinate			

2. Create a matrix P based on the data in the table.
3. Find the sum P + R when $R = \begin{bmatrix} 3 & 3 & 3 \\ 2 & 2 & 2 \end{bmatrix}$
4. Use the columns of the matrix you found in Problem 3 as the coordinates of the vertices of a triangle $\triangle A'B'C'$. Plot the vertices of $\triangle A'B'C'$ to graph the triangle.

THINK AND DISCUSS

5. **Describe** how $\triangle A'B'C'$ is related to $\triangle ABC$.

Motivate

Use a pattern block (in the Manipulatives Kit), cut-out shape of a polygon, or other figure on a transparency grid. Illustrate and review translations, reflections, and rotations in the coordinate plane. Tell students that they will learn how to find exact coordinates of the vertices of these transformations by using matrix operations.

Explorations and answers are provided in the *Explorations* binder.

A *dilation* is a transformation that scales—enlarges or reduces—the preimage, resulting in similar figures. Remember that for similar figures, the shape is the same but the size may be different. Angles are congruent, and side lengths are proportional.

When the *center of dilation* is the origin, multiplying the coordinate matrix by a scalar gives the coordinates of the dilated image. In this lesson, all dilations assume that the origin is the center of dilation.

EXAMPLE 2 Using Matrices to Dilate a Figure

Reduce triangle $\triangle ABC$ with coordinates $A(-4, 0)$, $B(2, 4)$, and $C(4, -2)$ by a factor of $\frac{1}{2}$. Find the coordinates of the vertices of the image, and graph.

Multiply each coordinate by $\frac{1}{2}$ by multiplying each entry by $\frac{1}{2}$.

$$\frac{1}{2}\begin{bmatrix} -4 & 2 & 4 \\ 0 & 4 & -2 \end{bmatrix} = \begin{bmatrix} \frac{1}{2}(-4) & \frac{1}{2}(2) & \frac{1}{2}(4) \\ \frac{1}{2}(0) & \frac{1}{2}(4) & \frac{1}{2}(-2) \end{bmatrix} = \begin{bmatrix} -2 & 1 & 2 \\ 0 & 2 & -1 \end{bmatrix} \begin{matrix} \leftarrow x\text{-coordinates} \\ \leftarrow y\text{-coordinates} \end{matrix}$$

$A'B'C'$, the image of $\triangle ABC$, has coordinates $A'(-2, 0)$, $B'(1, 2)$, and $C'(2, -1)$.

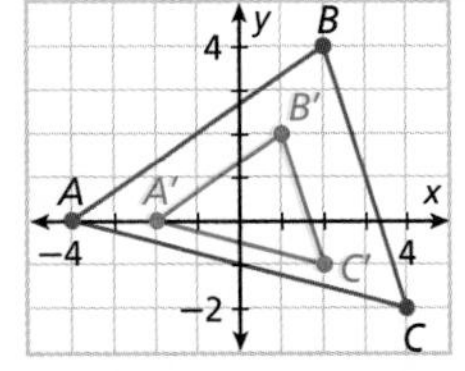

2. Enlarge $\triangle DEF$ with coordinates $D(2, 3)$, $E(5, 1)$, and $F(-2, -7)$ a factor of $\frac{4}{3}$. Find the coordinates of the vertices of the image, and graph.

$D'\left(2\frac{2}{3}, 4\right)$, $E'\left(6\frac{2}{3}, 1\frac{1}{3}\right)$, $F'\left(-2\frac{2}{3}, -9\frac{1}{3}\right)$

A **reflection matrix** is a matrix that creates a mirror image by reflecting each vertex over a specified line of symmetry. To reflect a figure across the y-axis, multiply $\begin{bmatrix} -1 & 0 \\ 0 & 1 \end{bmatrix}$ by the coordinate matrix. This reverses the x-coordinates and keeps the y-coordinates unchanged.

EXAMPLE 3 Using Matrices to Reflect a Figure

Reflect $\triangle JKL$ with coordinates $J(3, 4)$, $K(4, 2)$, and $L(1, -2)$ across the y-axis. Find the coordinates of the vertices of the image, and graph.

$$\begin{bmatrix} -1 & 0 \\ 0 & 1 \end{bmatrix}\begin{bmatrix} 3 & 4 & 1 \\ 4 & 2 & -2 \end{bmatrix} = \begin{bmatrix} -3 & -4 & -1 \\ 4 & 2 & -2 \end{bmatrix}$$

Each x-coordinate is multiplied by -1.

Each y-coordinate is multiplied by 1.

The coordinates of the vertices of the image are $J'(-3, 4)$, $K'(-4, 2)$, and $L'(-1, -2)$.

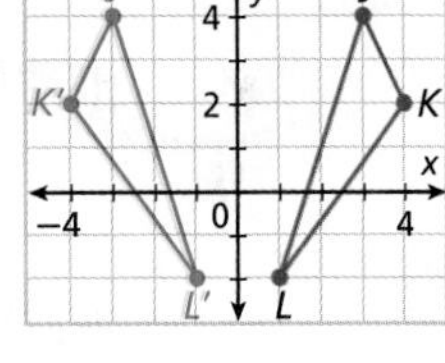

Caution!

Matrix multiplication is not commutative. So be sure to keep the transformation matrix on the left!

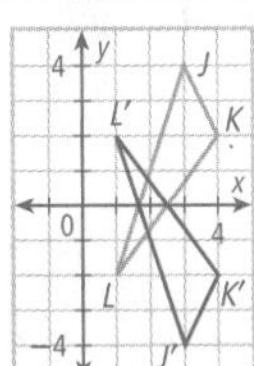

3. To reflect a figure across the x-axis, multiply by $\begin{bmatrix} 1 & 0 \\ 0 & -1 \end{bmatrix}$.

Reflect $\triangle JKL$ across the x-axis. Find the coordinates of the vertices of the image and graph.

$J'(3, -4)$, $K'(4, -2)$, $L'(1, 2)$

Power Presentations with PowerPoint®

Additional Examples

Example 1

Translate ABC with coordinates $A(-2, 1)$, $B(3, 2)$, and $C(0, -3)$, 3 units left and 4 units up. Find the coordinates of the vertices of the image, and graph.

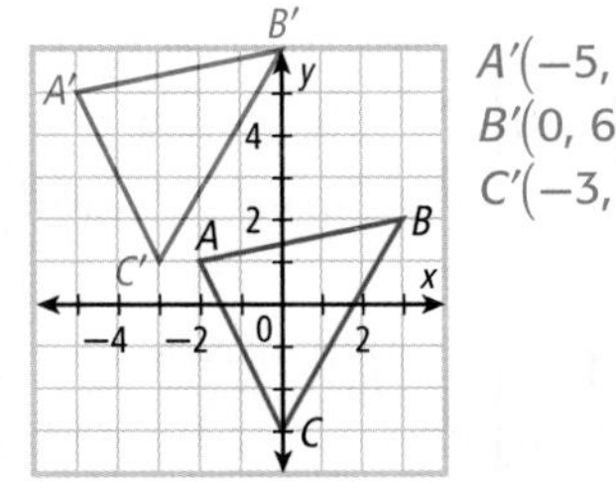

$A'(-5, 5)$, $B'(0, 6)$, $C'(-3, 1)$

Example 2

Enlarge ABC with coordinates $A(2, 3)$, $B(1, -2)$, and $C(-3, 1)$, by a factor of 2. Find the coordinates of the vertices of the image, and graph.

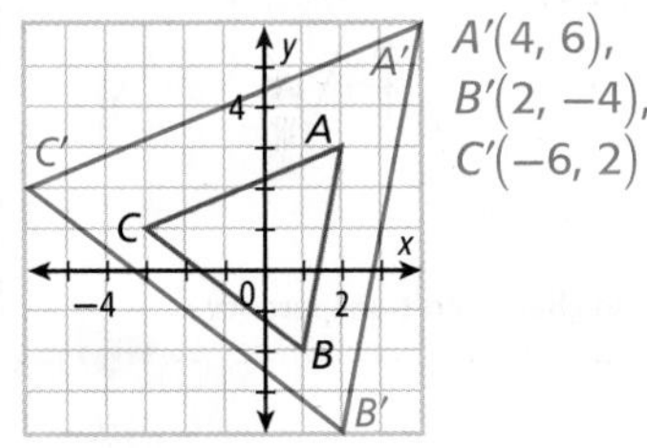

$A'(4, 6)$, $B'(2, -4)$, $C'(-6, 2)$

Example 3

Reflect triangle PQR with coordinates $P(2, 2)$, $Q(2, -1)$, and $R(4, 3)$, across the y-axis. Find the coordinates of the vertices of the image and graph.

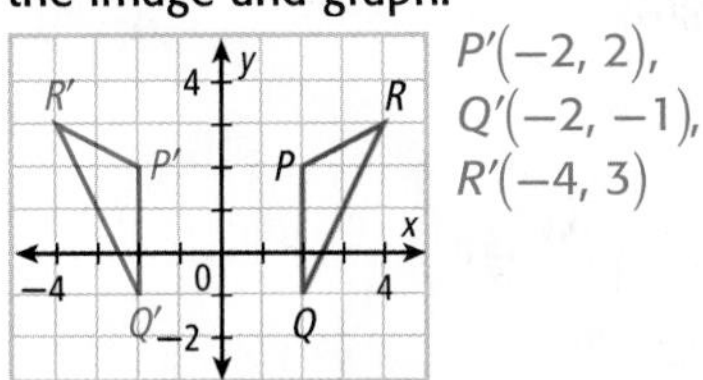

$P'(-2, 2)$, $Q'(-2, -1)$, $R'(-4, 3)$

Also available on transparency

2 Teach

Guided Instruction

Make sure students understand how the coordinates of the polygons become a matrix. For rotations, students need to understand that the 2 × 2 rotation matrix comes before the preimage matrix.

Inclusion Some students will have an easier time with informal vocabulary: translations are "glides," reflections are "flips," and rotations are "turns."

Reaching All Learners

Through Visual Cues

Some students will confuse clockwise and counterclockwise. Have students who experience this difficulty refer to a sketch that reminds them, such as the one below.

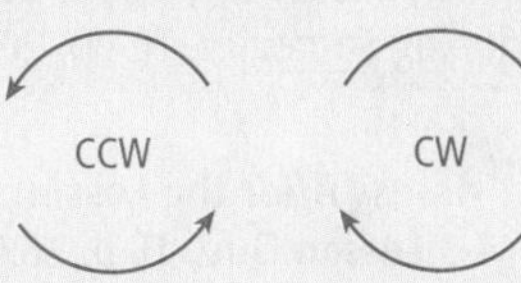

INTERVENTION

Questioning Strategies

EXAMPLE 1

- How do you create a translation matrix?

EXAMPLE 2

- How does a dilation matrix affect each vertex?

EXAMPLE 3

- What does −1 indicate in a reflection matrix?

Power Presentations with PowerPoint®

Additional Examples

Example 4

Use each matrix to rotate polygon *ABCD* with coordinates *A*(0, 1), *B*(2, −4), *C*(5, 1), and *D*(2, 3) about the origin. Graph and describe the image.

A. $\begin{bmatrix} 0 & -1 \\ 1 & 0 \end{bmatrix}$ $A'(-1, 0), B'(4, 2)$ $C'(-1, 5), D'(-3, 2)$

rotated 90° counterclockwise

B. $\begin{bmatrix} 0 & 1 \\ -1 & 0 \end{bmatrix}$ $A''(1, 0), B''(-4, -2)$ $C''(1, -5), D''(3, -2)$

rotated 90° clockwise

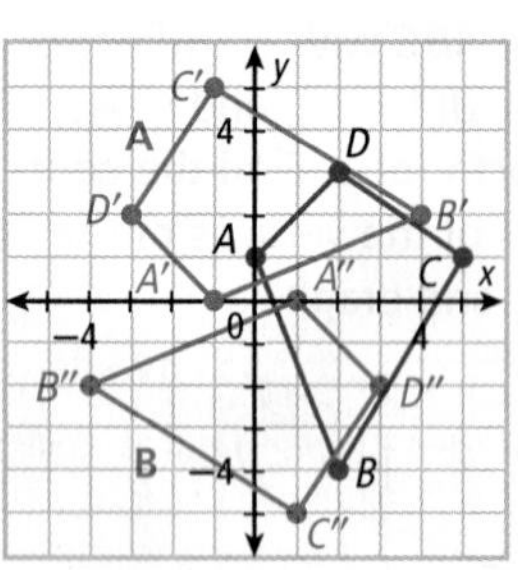

Also available on transparency

INTERVENTION

Questioning Strategies

EXAMPLE 4

- Why does a reflection matrix have 0's in the upper left and lower right?

A **rotation matrix** is a matrix used to rotate a figure. Example 4 gives several types of rotation matrices.

EXAMPLE 4 Using Matrices to Rotate a Figure

Use each matrix to rotate polygon *JKLM* with coordinates *J*(0, 0), *K*(4, 2), *L*(2, −5), and *M*(−1, −3) about the origin. Graph and describe the image.

A $\begin{bmatrix} 0 & -1 \\ 1 & 0 \end{bmatrix}$

$$\begin{bmatrix} 0 & -1 \\ 1 & 0 \end{bmatrix}\begin{bmatrix} 0 & 4 & 2 & -1 \\ 0 & 2 & -5 & -3 \end{bmatrix} = \begin{bmatrix} 0 & -2 & 5 & 3 \\ 0 & 4 & 2 & -1 \end{bmatrix}$$

The image is rotated 90° counterclockwise.

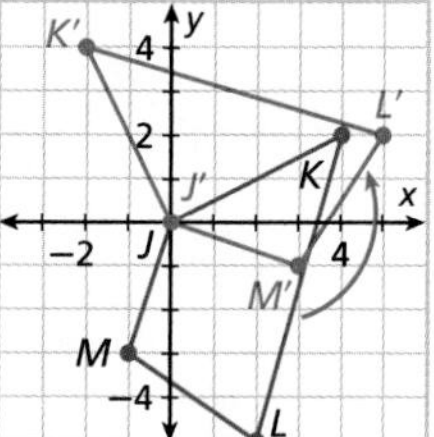

Helpful Hint

Multiplying a coordinate by −1 results in the opposite of the coordinate.

B $\begin{bmatrix} 0 & 1 \\ -1 & 0 \end{bmatrix}$

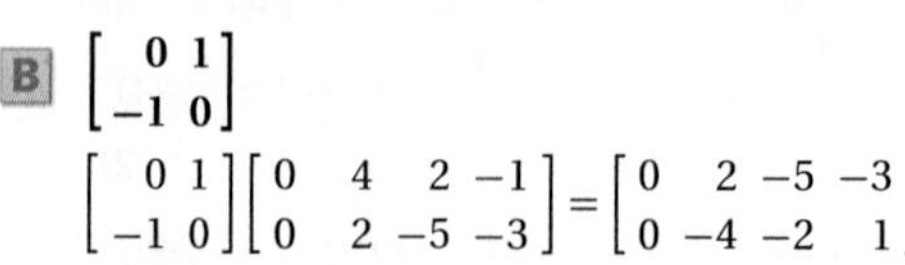

$$\begin{bmatrix} 0 & 1 \\ -1 & 0 \end{bmatrix}\begin{bmatrix} 0 & 4 & 2 & -1 \\ 0 & 2 & -5 & -3 \end{bmatrix} = \begin{bmatrix} 0 & 2 & -5 & -3 \\ 0 & -4 & -2 & 1 \end{bmatrix}$$

The image is rotated 90° clockwise.

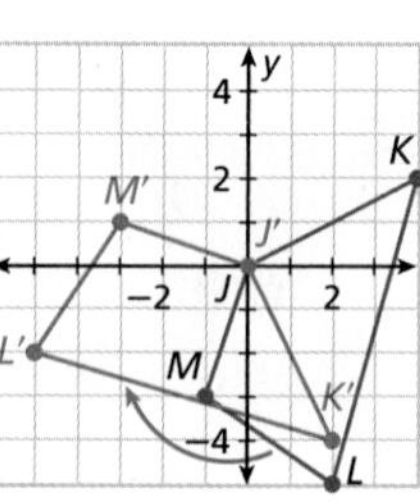

CHECK IT OUT! 4. Use $\begin{bmatrix} -1 & 0 \\ 0 & -1 \end{bmatrix}$. Rotate △*ABC* with coordinates *A*(0, 0), *B*(4, 0), and *C*(0, −3) about the origin. Graph and describe the image.

***A*′(0, 0), *B*′(−4, 0), *C*′(0, 3); the image is rotated 180°.**

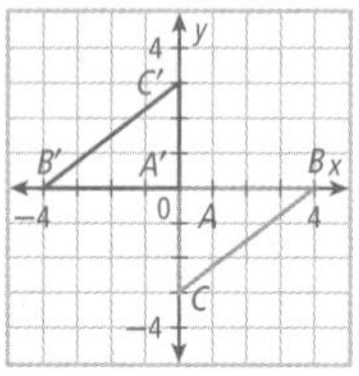

THINK AND DISCUSS

1. Describe the transformation resulting from multiplying a coordinate matrix by $\begin{bmatrix} 1 & 0 \\ 0 & 1 \end{bmatrix}$.
2. Describe what happens to an *x*-coordinate in a matrix when multiplied by this row of a transformation matrix.
   a. $[1 \ 0]$ **b.** $[0 \ 1]$ **c.** $[0.5 \ 0]$ **d.** $[1 \ 1]$
3. **GET ORGANIZED** Copy and complete the graphic organizer. *Q* is a triangle represented by its 2 × 3 coordinate matrix. Complete the summary by filling in a matrix expression.

Know it! Note

Transformation	Matrix Operation
Translate *Q* vertically	
Translate *Q* horizontally	
Enlarge or reduce *Q*.	
Reflect *Q* across the *x*-axis or *y*-axis	
Rotate *Q* 90° clockwise or counterclockwise.	

3 Close

Summarize

Matrices can represent geometric transformations.

It is important to be able to recognize the type of transformation. In particular, students need to be able to distinguish between a reflection and a rotation.

It will help to note where the "0" entries occur.

ONGOING ASSESSMENT and INTERVENTION

***Diagnose Before* the Lesson**
4-3 Warm Up, TE p. 262

***Monitor During* the Lesson**
Check It Out! Exercises, SE pp. 262–264
Questioning Strategies, TE pp. 263–264

***Assess After* the Lesson**
4-3 Lesson Quiz, TE p. 267
Alternative Assessment, TE p. 267

Answers to *Think and Discuss*

1. Possible answer: The image is identical to the original figure.
2a. The coordinate is unchanged.
b. The coordinate changes to the value of *y*.
c. The coordinate is multiplied by 0.5.
d. The coordinate changes to the sum of the coordinates of the original ordered pair.
3. See p. A6.

4-3 Exercises

GUIDED PRACTICE

1. **Vocabulary** A __?__ creates a mirror image of a set of points. (*reflection matrix* or *translation matrix*) reflection matrix

SEE EXAMPLE 1 p. 262

Translate the polygon with coordinates $P(-2, 4)$, $Q(3, 1)$, $R(1, -4)$, and $S(-2, -2)$ as indicated. Find the coordinates of the vertices of the image, and graph.

2. 2 units left and 1 unit up $P'(-4, 5)$, $Q'(1, 2)$, $R'(-1, -3)$, $S'(-4, -1)$
3. 1 unit right and 0 units down $P'(-1, 4)$, $Q'(4, 1)$, $R'(2, -4)$, $S'(-1, -2)$

SEE EXAMPLE 2 p. 263

Use a matrix to reduce or enlarge the polygon with coordinates $P(-2, 4)$, $Q(3, 1)$, $R(1, -4)$, and $S(-2, -2)$ by the given factor. Find the coordinates of the vertices of the image, and graph.

4. Reduce polygon $PQRS$ by a factor of 0.5.
5. Enlarge polygon $PQRS$ by a factor of 2.

SEE EXAMPLE 3 p. 263

Reflect the figure with coordinates $A(-2, 3)$, $B(0, 4)$, $C(2, 3)$, $D(2, 1)$, and $E(-1, -1)$ across the given line. Find the coordinates of the vertices of the image, and graph.

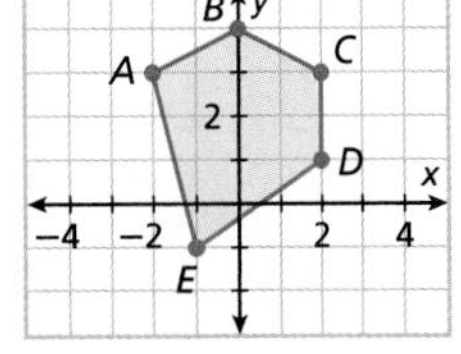

6. Reflect $ABCDE$ across the y-axis.
7. Use $\begin{bmatrix} 0 & 1 \\ 1 & 0 \end{bmatrix}$ to reflect $ABCDE$ across the line $y = x$.

SEE EXAMPLE 4 p. 264

Use each matrix to rotate the figure with coordinates $L(1, 3)$, $M(4, 2)$, $N(1, 1)$, and $O(1, -1)$ about the origin. Graph and describe the image.

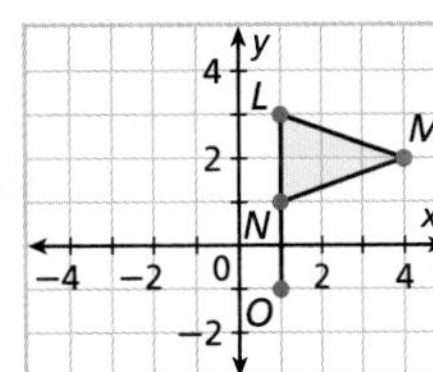

8. $\begin{bmatrix} 0 & 1 \\ -1 & 0 \end{bmatrix}$
9. $\begin{bmatrix} -1 & 0 \\ 0 & -1 \end{bmatrix}$

PRACTICE AND PROBLEM SOLVING

Independent Practice

For Exercises	See Example
10	1
11	2
12	3
13–14	4

Extra Practice
Skills Practice p. S10
Application Practice p. S35

10. Translate the polygon with coordinates $D(0, 4)$, $E(-3, -1)$, $F(1, -5)$, and $G(1, 0)$ 3 units right and 3 units up. Find the coordinates of the vertices of the image, and graph.
11. Dilate the polygon with coordinates $W(1, 2)$, $X(-2, 3)$, $Y(-3, 4)$, and $Z(-4, 1)$ by a factor of $\frac{3}{2}$. Find the coordinates of the vertices of the image, and graph.
12. Reflect the figure with coordinates $A(-2, 3)$, $B(0, 4)$, $C(2, 3)$, $D(2, 1)$, and $E(-1, -1)$ across the x-axis. Graph and describe the image.

Use each matrix to rotate the figure $PQRST$ with coordinates $P(-3, 2)$, $Q(0, 0)$, $R(-4, 1)$, $S(-4, 4)$, and $T(-1, 4)$. Graph and describe the image.

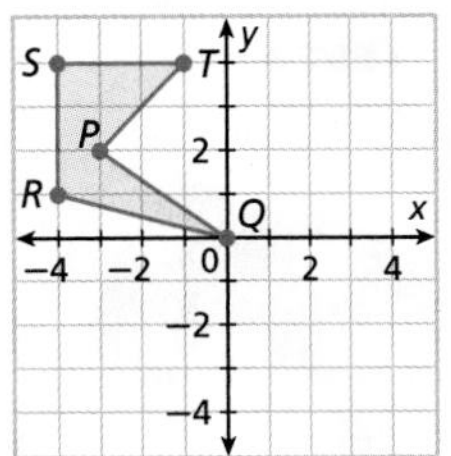

13. $\begin{bmatrix} 0 & -1 \\ 1 & 0 \end{bmatrix}$
14. $\begin{bmatrix} 0 & 1 \\ -1 & 0 \end{bmatrix}$

Teacher to Teacher

My students seem to grasp material for only a short while if they are only given explanations and practice problems, but they seem to retain more concepts longer if they have to use what they have learned in the scope of a project.

The scenario in "Games Away" on page 268 is really motivating for students. The concept of gaming and programming is one that they can relate to and allows them to be creative.

Gerri Chambers
Jackson, MS

4-3 Exercises

Assignment Guide

Assign *Guided Practice* exercises as necessary.

If you finished Examples **1–2**
Basic 10–11, 18–20, 33–38
Average 10–11, 18–20, 33–38
Advanced 10–11, 18–20, 33–38

If you finished Examples **1–4**
Basic 10–16, 18–24, 26–29, 33–38
Average 10–30, 33–38
Advanced 10–38

Homework Quick Check
Quickly check key concepts.
Exercises: 10, 11, 12, 14

Teaching Tip

Math Background
In **Exercise 7,** point out to students that a matrix transformation is actually just a function (performed on a matrix). The transformation matrix is placed *before* the preimage matrix in the same way that we write $f(x)$ to represent a function of x.

Answers

2–14. See p. A24.

State Resources

go.hrw.com
State Resources Online
KEYWORD: MB7 Resources

Language Arts In **Exercise 16,** *tessellations* are discussed. The word *tessellation* is derived from the Latin word *tessera,* meaning a small four-cornered tablet used as a tally item or for mosaic work. A *tessera,* since it is a quadrilateral, would tile the plane, or make a *tessellation*.

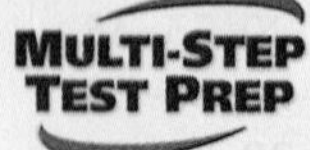

Exercise 26 involves transforming the coordinates of the vertices of a triangle. This exercise prepares students for the Multi-Step Test Prep on page 268.

Answers

15a. $\begin{bmatrix} -2.5 & 2.5 & 4.5 & 0.5 & -4 \\ 3 & 3 & -2 & -4.5 & -1.5 \end{bmatrix}$

b. Counterclockwise; each vertex in the image has been rotated counterclockwise from the preimage.

16a. $\begin{bmatrix} -1 & 0 \\ 0 & -1 \end{bmatrix}$

b. $(-1, -1), (-1, -3), (-4, -1), (-4, -3)$

c. $\begin{bmatrix} 2 & 2 & 2 & 2 \\ 4 & 4 & 4 & 4 \end{bmatrix}$

d. $(1, 3), (1, 1), (-2, 3), (-2, 1)$

e.

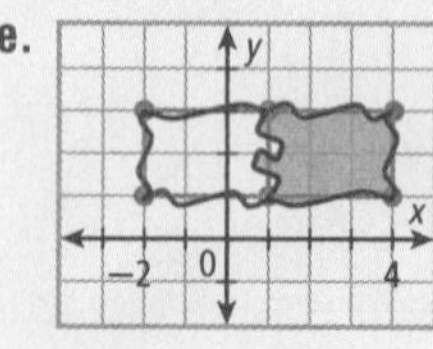

17. The operation rotates the figure 180° about the origin.

18–26. See p. A24.

15. **Design** Skye creates a design based on a starfish as a background for her school ecology club Web page. On a coordinate plane, the ends of the arms of the first image are $S(0, 4)$, $T(4, 1)$, $R(2.5, -4)$, $F(-2.5, -4)$, and $H(-4, 1)$.

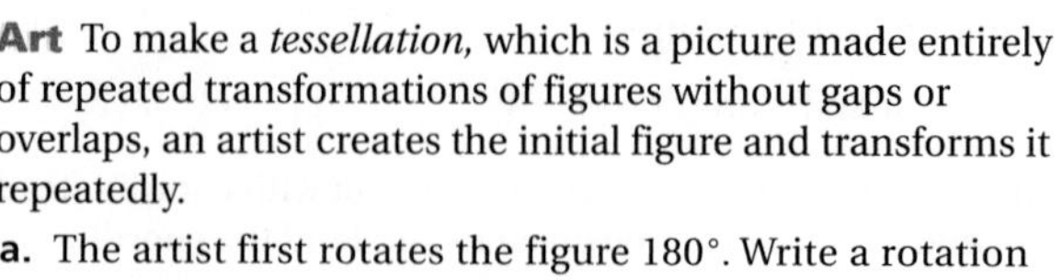

a. Use the matrix $\begin{bmatrix} 0.81 & -0.59 \\ 0.59 & 0.81 \end{bmatrix}$ to rotate the star through $\frac{1}{10}$ of a circle. Round the coordinates of the new image to the nearest half-unit.

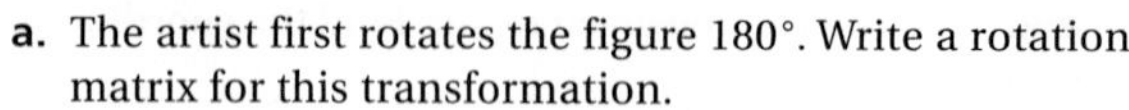

b. Does the star rotate clockwise or counterclockwise? Explain.

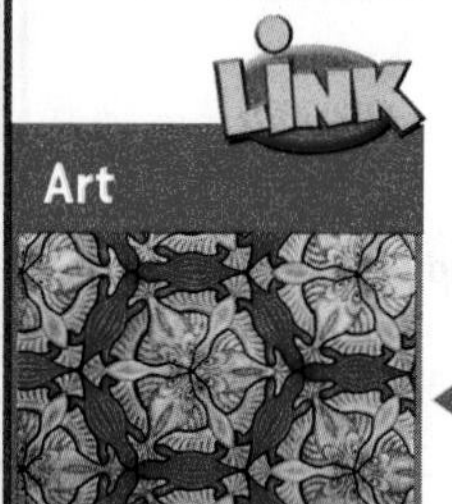

Art

Artist M. C. Escher (1898–1972) transformed symmetric geometric shapes into birds, reptiles, and other figures.

16. **Art** To make a *tessellation,* which is a picture made entirely of repeated transformations of figures without gaps or overlaps, an artist creates the initial figure and transforms it repeatedly.

a. The artist first rotates the figure 180°. Write a rotation matrix for this transformation.

b. Find the vertices of the figure after the rotation matrix is applied.

c. Next, the artist translates the figure 4 units up and 2 units right. Write a translation matrix for this transformation.

d. Find the vertices of the figure after this second transformation is applied.

e. Sketch the original figure and the transformed figure on the same coordinate grid.

17. **Critical Thinking** $T = \begin{bmatrix} 0 & 1 \\ -1 & 0 \end{bmatrix}$. Explain what happens if you multiply T by the coordinate matrix of a figure and then multiply T by the result.

Use a matrix to perform each transformation on the graph representing the constellation the Big Dipper. Find the coordinates of the image.

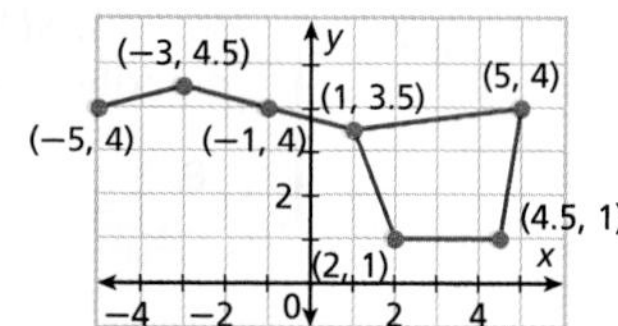

18. translation 2 units up

19. translation 1 unit down and 3 units left

20. enlargement by a factor of 2

21. reflection across the x-axis

22. rotation 90° clockwise

23. rotation 90° counterclockwise

24. **Write About It** What does multiplying $\begin{bmatrix} 0 & 1 \\ 1 & 0 \end{bmatrix}$ by a coordinate matrix do to the figure on the coordinate plane?

25. What transformation matrix represents $g(x) = -f(x)$? What transformation represents $g(x) = f(-x)$?

MULTI-STEP TEST PREP

26. This problem will prepare you for the Multi-Step Test Prep on page 268.

a. Place the vertices of the triangle in a coordinate matrix.

b. Multiply the matrix $\begin{bmatrix} -1 & 0 \\ 0 & -1 \end{bmatrix}$ by the coordinate matrix.

c. Draw a new triangle using the new coordinates. Describe the image.

d. Repeat parts **b** and **c** using the new triangle as the preimage. Describe the final triangle.

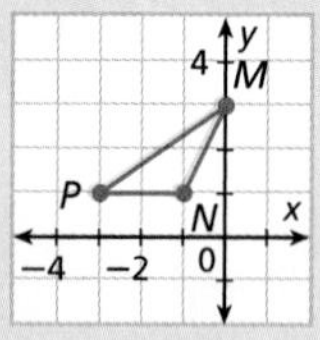

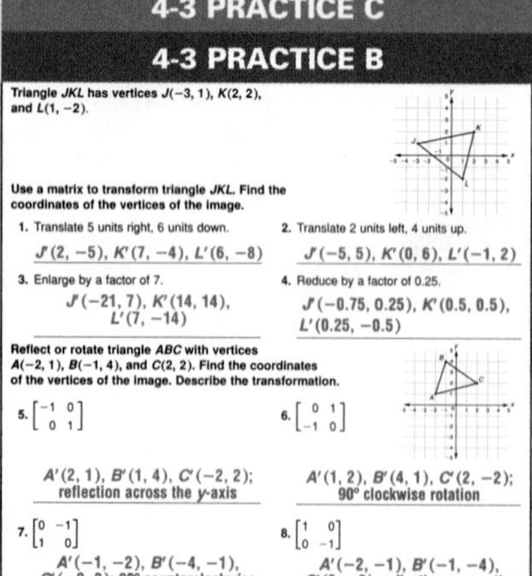

4-3 PRACTICE A

4-3 PRACTICE C

4-3 PRACTICE B

Triangle JKL has vertices $J(-3, 1)$, $K(2, 2)$, and $L(1, -2)$.

Use a matrix to transform triangle JKL. Find the coordinates of the vertices of the image.

1. Translate 5 units right, 6 units down. $J'(2, -5)$, $K'(7, -4)$, $L'(6, -8)$

2. Translate 2 units left, 4 units up. $J'(-5, 5)$, $K'(0, 6)$, $L'(-1, 2)$

3. Enlarge by a factor of 7. $J'(-21, 7)$, $K'(14, 14)$, $L'(7, -14)$

4. Reduce by a factor of 0.25. $J'(-0.75, 0.25)$, $K'(0.5, 0.5)$, $L'(0.25, -0.5)$

Reflect or rotate triangle ABC with vertices $A(-2, 1)$, $B(-1, 4)$, and $C(2, 2)$. Find the coordinates of the vertices of the image. Describe the transformation.

5. $\begin{bmatrix} -1 & 0 \\ 0 & 1 \end{bmatrix}$ $A'(2, 1)$, $B'(1, 4)$, $C'(-2, 2)$; reflection across the y-axis

6. $\begin{bmatrix} 0 & 1 \\ -1 & 0 \end{bmatrix}$ $A'(1, 2)$, $B'(4, 1)$, $C'(2, -2)$; 90° clockwise rotation

7. $\begin{bmatrix} 0 & -1 \\ 1 & 0 \end{bmatrix}$ $A'(-1, -2)$, $B'(-4, -1)$, $C'(-2, 2)$; 90° counterclockwise rotation

8. $\begin{bmatrix} 1 & 0 \\ 0 & -1 \end{bmatrix}$ $A'(-2, -1)$, $B'(-1, -4)$, $C'(2, -2)$; reflection across the x-axis

Solve.

9. a. Natalie drew a figure with vertices $H(-3, -2)$, $O(-3, 3)$, $U(0, 5)$, $S(3, 3)$, $E(3, -2)$ to use as a pattern on a sweatshirt. Write a matrix that defines the figure. $\begin{bmatrix} -3 & -3 & 0 & 3 & 3 \\ -2 & 3 & 5 & 3 & -2 \end{bmatrix}$

b. Natalie wants to enlarge the figure by a factor of 5. Describe a method she can use. Multiply each entry in the matrix by 5.

c. What are the coordinates of Natalie's enlarged figure? $H'(-15, -10)$ $O'(-15, 15)$ $U'(0, 25)$ $S'(15, 15)$ $E'(15, -10)$

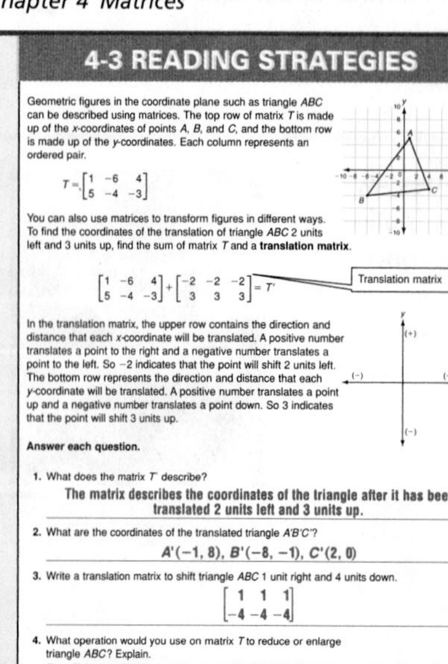

4-3 READING STRATEGIES

Geometric figures in the coordinate plane such as triangle ABC can be described using matrices. The top row of matrix T is made up of the x-coordinates of points A, B, and C, and the bottom row is made up of the y-coordinates. Each column represents an ordered pair.

$T = \begin{bmatrix} 1 & -6 & 4 \\ 5 & -4 & -3 \end{bmatrix}$

You can also use matrices to transform figures in different ways. To find the coordinates of the translation of triangle ABC 2 units left and 3 units up, find the sum of matrix T and a **translation matrix**.

$\begin{bmatrix} 1 & -6 & 4 \\ 5 & -4 & -3 \end{bmatrix} + \begin{bmatrix} -2 & -2 & -2 \\ 3 & 3 & 3 \end{bmatrix} = T'$ Translation matrix

In the translation matrix, the upper row contains the direction and distance that each x-coordinate will be translated. A positive number translates a point to the right and a negative number translates a point to the left. So −2 indicates that the point will shift 2 units left. The bottom row represents the direction and distance that each y-coordinate will be translated. A positive number translates a point up and a negative number translates a point down. So 3 indicates that the point will shift 3 units up.

Answer each question.

1. What does the matrix T' describe? The matrix describes the coordinates of the triangle after it has been translated 2 units left and 3 units up.

2. What are the coordinates of the translated triangle $A'B'C'$? $A'(-1, 8)$, $B'(-8, -1)$, $C'(2, 0)$

3. Write a translation matrix to shift triangle ABC 1 unit right and 4 units down. $\begin{bmatrix} 1 & 1 & 1 \\ -4 & -4 & -4 \end{bmatrix}$

4. What operation would you use on matrix T to reduce or enlarge triangle ABC? Explain. Possible answer: I would use multiplication because you need to reduce or enlarge the position of each vertex by the same factor.

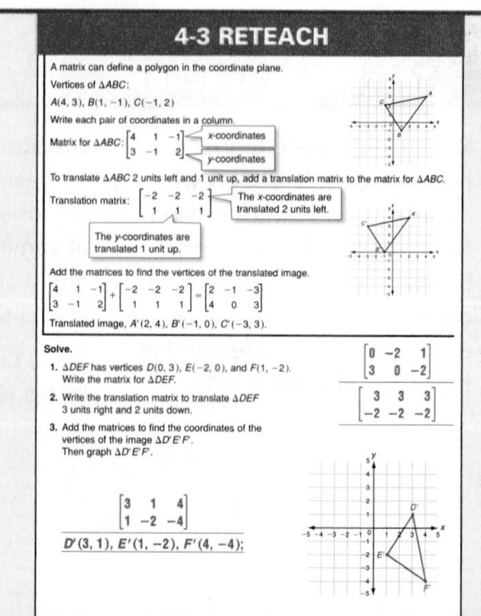

4-3 RETEACH

A matrix can define a polygon in the coordinate plane.

Vertices of $\triangle ABC$: $A(4, 3)$, $B(1, -1)$, $C(-1, 2)$

Write each pair of coordinates in a column.

Matrix for $\triangle ABC$: $\begin{bmatrix} 4 & 1 & -1 \\ 3 & -1 & 2 \end{bmatrix}$ ← x-coordinates ← y-coordinates

To translate $\triangle ABC$ 2 units left and 1 unit up, add a translation matrix to the matrix for $\triangle ABC$.

Translation matrix: $\begin{bmatrix} -2 & -2 & -2 \\ 1 & 1 & 1 \end{bmatrix}$ The x-coordinates are translated 2 units left. The y-coordinates are translated 1 unit up.

Add the matrices to find the vertices of the translated image.

$\begin{bmatrix} 4 & 1 & -1 \\ 3 & -1 & 2 \end{bmatrix} + \begin{bmatrix} -2 & -2 & -2 \\ 1 & 1 & 1 \end{bmatrix} = \begin{bmatrix} 2 & -1 & -3 \\ 4 & 0 & 3 \end{bmatrix}$

Translated image, $A'(2, 4)$, $B'(-1, 0)$, $C'(-3, 3)$.

Solve.

1. $\triangle DEF$ has vertices $D(0, 3)$, $E(-2, 0)$, and $F(1, -2)$. Write the matrix for $\triangle DEF$. $\begin{bmatrix} 0 & -2 & 1 \\ 3 & 0 & -2 \end{bmatrix}$

2. Write the translation matrix to translate $\triangle DEF$ 3 units right and 2 units down. $\begin{bmatrix} 3 & 3 & 3 \\ -2 & -2 & -2 \end{bmatrix}$

3. Add the matrices to find the coordinates of the vertices of the image $\triangle D'E'F'$. Then graph $\triangle D'E'F'$. $\begin{bmatrix} 3 & 1 & 4 \\ 1 & -2 & -4 \end{bmatrix}$ $D'(3, 1)$, $E'(1, -2)$, $F'(4, -4)$;

TEST PREP

27. To create a quilt pattern, Morgan dilates a figure, rotates it 90° clockwise, and reflects it across the y-axis. Which sequence results in the image?
   - (A) scalar multiplication; matrix addition; matrix multiplication
   - **(B)** scalar multiplication; matrix multiplication; matrix multiplication
   - (C) matrix addition; matrix multiplication; matrix addition
   - (D) matrix multiplication; matrix addition; scalar multiplication

28. What effect does multiplying the coordinates of a figure by $\begin{bmatrix} 0 & 2 \\ -2 & 0 \end{bmatrix}$ have?
   - **(F)** The figure is enlarged and rotated 90° clockwise.
   - (G) The figure is reduced and rotated 90° counterclockwise.
   - (H) The figure is reduced and reflected across the x-axis.
   - (J) The figure is enlarged and reflected across the y-axis.

29. Which matrix can be used to rotate a figure 180° about the origin?
   - (A) $\begin{bmatrix} 0 & -1 \\ -1 & 0 \end{bmatrix}$ (B) $\begin{bmatrix} 1 & -1 \\ -1 & 1 \end{bmatrix}$ **(C)** $\begin{bmatrix} -1 & 0 \\ 0 & -1 \end{bmatrix}$ (D) $\begin{bmatrix} -1 & 1 \\ 1 & -1 \end{bmatrix}$

CHALLENGE AND EXTEND

30. $\begin{bmatrix} 0 & -1 \\ -1 & 0 \end{bmatrix}$

30. What matrix could you use to reflect a figure across the line $y = -x$?

31. Position $\triangle JKL$ on a coordinate plane, and assign coordinates to the vertices.
   a. How can you transform $\triangle JKL$ to create a symmetrical compass with four points N, E, S, and W?
   b. Use matrices to transform $\triangle JKL$, and give the coordinates of the four points N, E, S, and W.

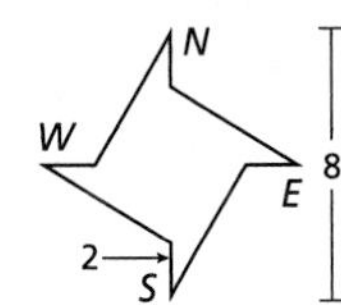

32. Transform a figure using $\begin{bmatrix} -\frac{2}{3} & 0 \\ 0 & \frac{3}{2} \end{bmatrix}$. Describe the transformation.
What would happen if this transformation were performed repeatedly?

SPIRAL REVIEW

33. Determine whether the data set could represent a linear function. *(Lesson 2-3)* **yes**

Tickets	2	5	8	11
Cost ($)	35.00	87.50	140.00	192.50

Determine if the given point is a solution of the system of inequalities. *(Lesson 3-3)*

34. $(2, -4)\begin{cases} y > 2x - 8 \\ y \le \frac{1}{4}x + 2 \end{cases}$ **no**

35. $(0, 5)\begin{cases} y > 0 \\ y \ge 2x - 11 \\ 5x + y < 5.5 \end{cases}$ **yes**

Evaluate, if possible. *(Lesson 4-2)*

36. $\begin{bmatrix} 5 & -5 \\ 2 & 1 \end{bmatrix}\begin{bmatrix} 10 & 1 \\ -2 & 0 \end{bmatrix}$ **$\begin{bmatrix} 60 & 5 \\ 18 & 2 \end{bmatrix}$**

37. $\begin{bmatrix} 3 & 1 & -1 \\ 0 & 2 & 1 \end{bmatrix}\begin{bmatrix} 1 & 1 \\ -2 & 1 \end{bmatrix}$ **not possible**

38. $\begin{bmatrix} 3 & 1 & -1 \end{bmatrix}\begin{bmatrix} 4 \\ 5 \\ 6 \end{bmatrix}$ **[11]**

TEST PREP DOCTOR To get the answer to **Exercise 29,** try the matrices with an actual point, such as (1, 0), which moves to (−1, 0) in a 180° rotation.

Journal

Have students explain how they can tell from looking at a transformation matrix whether it is a reflection matrix or a rotation matrix.

ALTERNATIVE ASSESSMENT

Have students draw a triangle or quadrilateral on a coordinate plane. Then have them perform a translation, dilation, reflection, and rotation of the original figure. Have them give the matrices that produce each transformation that they drew.

Power Presentations with PowerPoint®

4-3 Lesson Quiz

Transform triangle PQR with vertices $P(-1, -1)$, $Q(3, 1)$, and $R(0, 3)$. For each, show the matrix transformation and state the vertices of the image.

1. Translation 3 units to the left and 2 units up.
$\begin{bmatrix} -3 & -3 & -3 \\ 2 & 2 & 2 \end{bmatrix} + \begin{bmatrix} -1 & 3 & 0 \\ -1 & 1 & 3 \end{bmatrix}$
$P'(-4, 1)$, $Q'(0, 3)$, $R'(-3, 5)$

2. Dilation by a factor of 1.5.
$1.5\begin{bmatrix} -1 & 3 & 0 \\ -1 & 1 & 3 \end{bmatrix}$
$P'(-1.5, -1.5)$, $Q'(4.5, 1.5)$, $R'(0, 4.5)$

3. Refection across the x-axis.
$\begin{bmatrix} 1 & 0 \\ 0 & -1 \end{bmatrix}\begin{bmatrix} -1 & 3 & 0 \\ -1 & 1 & 3 \end{bmatrix}$
$P'(-1, 1)$, $Q'(3, -1)$, $R'(0, -3)$

4. 90° rotation, clockwise.
$\begin{bmatrix} 0 & 1 \\ -1 & 0 \end{bmatrix}\begin{bmatrix} -1 & 3 & 0 \\ -1 & 1 & 3 \end{bmatrix}$
$P'(-1, 1)$, $Q'(1, -3)$, $R'(3, 0)$

Also available on transparency

31–32. See pp. A24–A25.

4-3 PROBLEM SOLVING

Sherrill is trying to re-create the pattern of a vintage quilt she saw at an antique store. The shaded parts of the figure show the pattern of the quilt.

1. What directions would you give Sherrill to help her draw triangle A on a grid?
Draw a triangle with vertices at (0, 0), (−3, 0), and (−3, 3).

2. a. What transformation can Sherrill use on triangle A to create triangle B?
Rotate 90° clockwise
b. What transformation matrix should she use to create triangle B?
$\begin{bmatrix} 0 & 1 \\ -1 & 0 \end{bmatrix}$

3. a. What transformation can Sherrill use on triangle A to create triangle C?
Rotate 180°
b. What transformation matrix should she use to create triangle C?
$\begin{bmatrix} -1 & 0 \\ 0 & -1 \end{bmatrix}$

4. a. What transformation can Sherrill use on triangle A to create triangle D?
Rotate 90° counterclockwise
b. What transformation matrix should she use to create triangle D?
$\begin{bmatrix} 0 & -1 \\ 1 & 0 \end{bmatrix}$

Choose the letter for the best answer.

5. Jesse drew a rectangle represented by $R = \begin{bmatrix} 2 & 5 & 5 & 2 \\ -3 & -3 & -5 & -5 \end{bmatrix}$. He added the transformation matrix $\begin{bmatrix} 0 & 0 & 0 & 0 \\ 2 & 2 & 2 & 2 \end{bmatrix}$ to R and drew a second rectangle. Then he added the transformation matrix $\begin{bmatrix} -3 & -3 & -3 & -3 \\ 2 & 2 & 2 & 2 \end{bmatrix}$ to R and drew a third rectangle. Which describes the resulting figure?
   - A Rectangle
   - **(B)** Irregular hexagon
   - C Square
   - D Irregular octagon

6. Tina drew rectangle F with vertices at (0, 0), (0, 5), (3, 5), and (3, 0). She wants to transform F into a rectangle that is 6 units wide and 10 units long with the center of the rectangle located at the origin. Which list of transformations will accomplish that?
   - A Rotate F 90° clockwise, rotate F 90° counterclockwise, translate F 5 units left and 3 units down
   - B Reflect F over the x-axis, translate F 5 units down, rotate F 90° counterclockwise
   - C Translate F 3 units left, translate F 3 units down, rotate F 90° clockwise
   - **(D)** Reflect F over the y-axis, reflect F over the x-axis, rotate F by 180°

4-3 CHALLENGE

Just as functions can be combined to create a new function in a process called composition, transformations can also be composed to form a new transformation. Triangle QRS is shown at right. This triangle can be represented in matrix form by

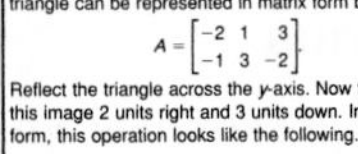

$$A = \begin{bmatrix} -2 & 1 & 3 \\ -1 & 3 & -2 \end{bmatrix}$$

Reflect the triangle across the y-axis. Now translate this image 2 units right and 3 units down. In matrix form, this operation looks like the following.

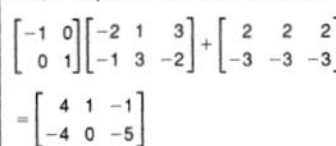

$$\begin{bmatrix} -1 & 0 \\ 0 & 1 \end{bmatrix}\begin{bmatrix} -2 & 1 & 3 \\ -1 & 3 & -2 \end{bmatrix} + \begin{bmatrix} 2 & 2 & 2 \\ -3 & -3 & -3 \end{bmatrix} = \begin{bmatrix} 4 & 1 & -1 \\ -4 & 0 & -5 \end{bmatrix}$$

The result is triangle $Q'R'S'$ with vertices (4, −4), (1, 0), and (−1, 5)

Be careful with the order of transformations. Transformations may or may not be commutative.

Use matrices to transform triangle A with vertices at (−2, −2), (1, 2), and (3, −1). Find the coordinates of the vertices of the final image.

1. Reflect triangle A across the x-axis and translate 4 units left and 3 units up. (−6, 5), (−3, 1), (−1, 4)
2. Enlarge triangle A by a factor of 2, then reflect across the y-axis. (4, −4), (−2, 4), (−6, −2)
3. Reflect triangle A across the line $y = x$, then translate 1 unit right and 4 units up. (−1, 2), (3, 5), (0, 7)
4. Reduce triangle A by a factor of $\frac{1}{2}$, reflect across the line $y = -x$, and finally translate 5 units down. $(1, -4)$, $\left(-1, -5\frac{1}{2}\right)$, $\left(\frac{1}{2}, -6\frac{1}{2}\right)$
5. Rotate triangle A 90° clockwise, then translate 3 units left and 2 units up. (−5, 4), (−1, 1), (−4, −1)
6. Rotate triangle A 90° counterclockwise, enlarge the triangle by a factor of 3, and reflect across the y-axis. Finally translate 8 units right and 5 units down. (2, −11), (14, −2), (5, 4)

Organizer

Objective: Assess students' ability to apply concepts and skills in Lessons 4-1 through 4-3 in a real-world format.

 **Online Edition**

Resources

 ***Algebra II Assessments***
www.mathtekstoolkit.org

Problem	Text Reference
1–2	Lessons 4-1, 4-3
3–6	Lessons 4-2, 4-3
7	Skills Bank page S63, Lessons 4-1, 4-3

Answers

1–7. See p. A25.

CHAPTER 4

MULTI-STEP TEST PREP

SECTION 4A

Games Away

You are making a video game using the space shuttle figure shown on the grid. By applying different transformations to the shuttle, you can simulate different moves.

1. Find the coordinates of the vertices of the shuttle. Write the coordinates in matrix form.
2. The *hyperjump* button causes the shuttle to immediately rise 4 units. What transformation represents the shuttle after hyperjump? Write the transformation matrix, and show the matrix operation.
3. What transformation will make the shuttle reverse direction? Write the transformation matrix, and show the matrix operation.
4. What transformation will make the shuttle fly upside down? Write the transformation matrix, and show the matrix operation.
5. What matrix will rotate the shuttle 180° about the origin? Show the matrix operation.
6. Suppose you reflect the shuttle over one axis and then the other. Compare the result to the rotation in Problem 5.
7. If the shuttle is hit by an asteroid, it is reduced by a factor of $\frac{1}{2}$. What matrix operation will show the reduction? What is the ratio of the area of the preimage to that of the image?

INTERVENTION 

Scaffolding Questions

1. How many columns are in your matrix in **Problem 1**? Why? 5; the number of vertices
2. What matrix operations do you use for **Problems 2–5** and **Problem 7**? 2: matrix addition; 3–5: matrix multiplication; 7: scalar multiplication
3. How are the transformation matrices in **Problems 3–5** the same? They have 0's away from the main diagonal and either 1 or −1 on each entry of the main diagonal.
4. What does an entry of −1 in the top left entry of the rotation matrix in **Problem 6** indicate? multiplying the *x*-coordinate by −1

Extension

Multiply the transformation matrices in **Problem 6**. Then reverse them and multiply again. How do these products support the answer to the problem? The product of the matrices in either order is the rotation matrix.

$$\begin{bmatrix} -1 & 0 \\ 0 & 1 \end{bmatrix}\begin{bmatrix} 1 & 0 \\ 0 & -1 \end{bmatrix} = \begin{bmatrix} -1 & 0 \\ 0 & -1 \end{bmatrix}$$

Quiz for Lessons 4-1 Through 4-3

4-1 Matrices and Data

Use the table for Problems 1–4.

Olympic Medal Specifications			
	Gold	Silver	Bronze
Weight (lb)	1.25	1.25	1
% copper	7.5	7.5	90
Hours of handicrafting	19.65	18.30	18.45

1. Display the data in the form of a matrix M.
2. What are the dimensions of M? 3×3
3. What is the value of the matrix entry with the address m_{32}? What does it represent?
4. What is the address of the entry that has the value 90? m_{23}

Use the matrices below for Problems 5–8. Evaluate, if possible.

$A = \begin{bmatrix} 3 & 4 \\ 1 & -2 \\ 0 & -1 \end{bmatrix}$ $\quad B = \begin{bmatrix} 4 & 0 \\ 0 & 4 \end{bmatrix}$ $\quad C = \begin{bmatrix} 1 & -1 \\ 3 & 2 \\ 5 & -1 \end{bmatrix}$ $\quad D = \begin{bmatrix} 5 & 1 & -1 \\ -1.5 & 2 & -2 \end{bmatrix}$

5. $\begin{bmatrix} 4 & 3 \\ 4 & 0 \\ 5 & -2 \end{bmatrix}$

5. $A + C$
6. $2B$ $\begin{bmatrix} 8 & 0 \\ 0 & 8 \end{bmatrix}$
7. $C - D$ not possible
8. $C - 3A$ $\begin{bmatrix} -8 & -13 \\ 0 & 8 \\ 5 & 2 \end{bmatrix}$

4-2 Multiplying Matrices

Use the matrices named below for Problems 9–12. Tell whether each product is defined. If so, give its dimensions.

$P_{5\times2}$, $Q_{2\times5}$, $R_{1\times5}$, and $S_{5\times2}$

9. PQ yes; 5×5
10. QR no
11. RS yes; 1×2
12. SP no

Use the matrices below for Problems 13–16. Evaluate, if possible.

$E = \begin{bmatrix} 1 & -2 & -1 \\ 5 & 3 & 0 \\ -1 & -1 & 2 \end{bmatrix}$ $\quad F = \begin{bmatrix} 0.5 & 0.75 & -1 \end{bmatrix}$ $\quad G = \begin{bmatrix} 1 & 2 \\ 2 & -1 \end{bmatrix}$ $\quad H = \begin{bmatrix} -1 & 4 \\ 2 & 0 \\ 0 & -1 \end{bmatrix}$

15. $\begin{bmatrix} 7 & -6 \\ 2 & 4 \\ -2 & 1 \end{bmatrix}$

13. EF not possible
14. FH $\begin{bmatrix} 1 & 3 \end{bmatrix}$
15. HG
16. G^2 $\begin{bmatrix} 5 & 0 \\ 0 & 5 \end{bmatrix}$

4-3 Using Matrices to Transform Geometric Figures

For Problems 17–20, use polygon $WXYZ$ with coordinates $W(0, 0)$, $X(1, 4)$, $Y(3, 5)$, and $Z(4, 2)$. Give the coordinates of the image and graph.

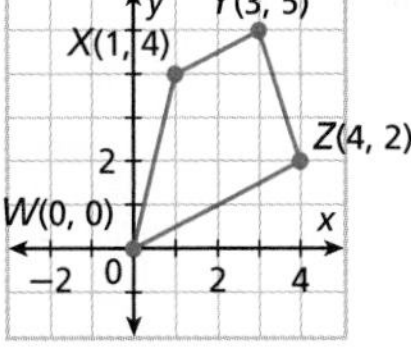

17. Translate polygon $WXYZ$ 1 unit to the left and 2 units down.
18. Reduce polygon $WXYZ$ by a factor of $\frac{2}{3}$.
19. Use $\begin{bmatrix} 1 & 0 \\ 0 & -1 \end{bmatrix}$ to transform polygon $WXYZ$. Describe the image.
20. Use $\begin{bmatrix} 0 & 1 \\ -1 & 0 \end{bmatrix}$ to transform polygon $WXYZ$. Describe the image.
21. How does multiplying by $\begin{bmatrix} 0 & 2 \\ 2 & 0 \end{bmatrix}$ transform polygon $WXYZ$?

The polygon is reflected across the line $y = x$ and enlarged by a factor of 2.

READY TO GO ON?

Organizer

Objective: Assess students' mastery of concepts and skills in Lessons 4-1 through 4-3.

Online Edition

Resources

Assessment Resources

Section 4A Quiz

Test & Practice Generator One-Stop Planner®

INTERVENTION

Resources

***Ready to Go On? Intervention and Enrichment* Worksheets**

***Ready to Go On?* CD-ROM**

***Ready to Go On?* Online**

my.hrw.com

Answers

1, 3, 17–20. See p. A25.

READY TO GO ON? Diagnose and Prescribe

NO INTERVENE

Ready to Go On? Intervention	*Ready to Go On? Intervention*, Section 4A: Worksheets	CD-ROM	Online
Lesson 4-1	4-1 Intervention	Activity 4-1	Diagnose and Prescribe Online
Lesson 4-2	4-2 Intervention	Activity 4-2	
Lesson 4-3	4-3 Intervention	Activity 4-3	

YES ENRICH

SECTION **4B**

Using Matrices to Solve Systems

One-Minute Section Planner

Lesson	Lab Resources	Materials
Lesson 4-4 Determinants and Cramer's Rule • Find the determinants of 2 × 2 and 3 × 3 matrices. • Use Cramer's rule to solve systems of linear equations. ☐ SAT-10 ☐ NAEP ☑ ACT ☑ SAT ☐ SAT Subject Tests		**Optional** graphing calculator
Lesson 4-5 Matrix Inverses and Solving Systems • Determine whether a matrix has an inverse. • Solve systems of equations using inverse matrices. ☐ SAT-10 ☐ NAEP ☑ ACT ☑ SAT ☑ SAT Subject Tests		**Required** graphing calculator
4-5 Technology Lab Use Spreadsheets with Matrices to Solve Systems • Use a spreadsheet to solve systems of equations. ☐ SAT-10 ☐ NAEP ☑ ACT ☐ SAT ☐ SAT Subject Tests	***Technology Lab Activities*** 4-5 Lab Recording Sheet	**Required** spreadsheet software
Lesson 4-6 Row Operations and Augmented Matrices • Use elementary row operations to solve systems of equations. ☑ SAT-10 ☐ NAEP ☑ ACT ☑ SAT ☑ SAT Subject Tests	***Technology Lab Activities*** 4-6 Technology Lab	**Required** graphing calculator
Extension Networks and Matrices • Convert between finite graphs and their matrix representations, and calculate the number of trips via two vertices. ☐ SAT-10 ☐ NAEP ☑ ACT ☑ SAT ☑ SAT Subject Tests		**Optional** graphing calculator

MK = *Manipulatives Kit*

Section Overview

Determinants and Cramer's Rule — Lesson 4-4

Determinants are used in solving systems with matrices in many ways, including in Cramer's rule.

The **determinant** of $A = \begin{bmatrix} a & b \\ c & d \end{bmatrix}$ is $\det A = \begin{vmatrix} a & b \\ c & d \end{vmatrix} = ad - cb$.

Cramer's Rule

c_1, c_2 replaces the x-coefficients.

c_1, c_2 replaces the y-coefficients.

The solution of $\begin{cases} a_1x + b_1y = c_1 \\ a_2x + b_2y = c_2 \end{cases}$ is $x = \dfrac{\begin{vmatrix} c_1 & b_1 \\ c_2 & b_2 \end{vmatrix}}{\begin{vmatrix} a_1 & b_1 \\ a_2 & b_2 \end{vmatrix}}$, $y = \dfrac{\begin{vmatrix} a_1 & c_1 \\ a_2 & c_2 \end{vmatrix}}{\begin{vmatrix} a_1 & b_1 \\ a_2 & b_2 \end{vmatrix}}$.

Cramer's rule can be extended for use in solving larger systems of equations.

Solving Systems with Matrix Equations — Lesson 4-5

A system of equations can be represented using a matrix equation and solved by finding the solution of the corresponding matrix equation.

The **inverse** of $A = \begin{bmatrix} a & b \\ c & d \end{bmatrix}$ is $A^{-1} = \dfrac{1}{\det A}\begin{bmatrix} d & -b \\ -c & a \end{bmatrix}$.

If $\det A = 0$, then $\dfrac{1}{\det A}$ is undefined, so A has no inverse.

The product of inverse matricies is the identity matrix, I.

$$A^{-1} \bullet A = A \bullet A^{-1} = I$$

$$\begin{cases} a_1x + b_1y = c_1 \\ a_2x + b_2y = c_2 \end{cases} \rightarrow \underset{A}{\begin{bmatrix} a_1 & b_1 \\ a_2 & b_2 \end{bmatrix}} \underset{X}{\begin{bmatrix} x \\ y \end{bmatrix}} = \underset{B}{\begin{bmatrix} c_1 \\ c_2 \end{bmatrix}}$$

$$AX = B$$
$$A^{-1}AX = A^{-1}B$$
$$IX = A^{-1}B \rightarrow \underset{X}{\begin{bmatrix} x \\ y \end{bmatrix}} = \underset{A^{-1}}{\begin{bmatrix} a_1 & b_1 \\ a_2 & b_2 \end{bmatrix}^{-1}} \underset{B}{\begin{bmatrix} c_1 \\ c_2 \end{bmatrix}}$$

Row Operations and Augmented Matrices — Lesson 4-6

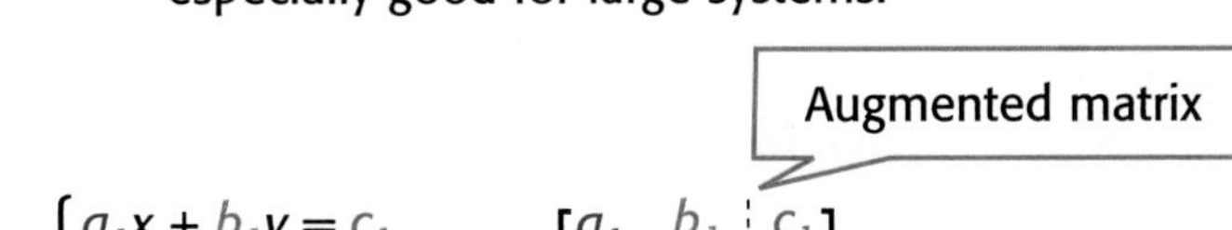

Row operations can also be used for solving systems of equations, and are especially good for large systems.

$$\begin{cases} a_1x + b_1y = c_1 \\ a_2x + b_2y = c_2 \end{cases} \rightarrow \left[\begin{array}{cc|c} a_1 & b_1 & c_1 \\ a_2 & b_2 & c_2 \end{array}\right]$$

Augmented matrix

Elementary Row Operations

- Exchange any two rows.
- Multiply a row by a nonzero constant.
- Add a row or a multiple of it to another row.

When the coefficients form the identity matrix, the augmented matix is in reduced **row-echelon form**, and the solution is given by the right side.

$$\left[\begin{array}{cc|c} 1 & 0 & x \\ 0 & 1 & y \end{array}\right] \rightarrow \text{The solution is } (x, y).$$

Row-echelon

4-4 Organizer

Pacing: Traditional 1 day
Block $\frac{1}{2}$ day

Objectives: Find the determinants of 2 × 2 and 3 × 3 matrices.

Use Cramer's rule to solve systems of linear equations.

Online Edition
Tutorial Videos

Countdown to Testing Week 9

Power Presentations with PowerPoint®

Warm Up

Determine whether each system has zero, one, or infinitely many solutions.

1. $\begin{cases} 3x + y = 15 \\ 3x - 2y = 6 \end{cases}$ one

2. $\begin{cases} x + 2y = 18 \\ -2x - 4y = -36 \end{cases}$ inf. many

3. $\begin{cases} 2x + 3y = 35 \\ 4x + 6y = 75 \end{cases}$ zero

Also available on transparency

Math Humor

Q: Why are you watching *Seinfeld*?

A: I need to find out Kramer's rule.

4-4 Determinants and Cramer's Rule

A2.2.2 Solve problems that can be modeled using systems of linear equations up to three variables, interpret the solutions, and determine whether the solutions . . . are reasonable.

Objectives
Find the determinants of 2 × 2 and 3 × 3 matrices.

Use Cramer's rule to solve systems of linear equations.

Vocabulary
determinant
coefficient matrix
Cramer's rule

Who uses this?
Sports nutritionists planning menus need to solve systems of equations for Calories and grams of protein, fat, and carbohydrates. (See Example 4.)

Every square matrix (n by n) has an associated value called its *determinant,* shown by straight vertical brackets, such as $\begin{vmatrix} 1 & 2 \\ 3 & 4 \end{vmatrix}$. The determinant is a useful measure, as you will see later in this lesson.

Determinant of a 2 × 2 Matrix

WORDS	NUMBERS	ALGEBRA
The **determinant** of a 2 by 2 matrix is the difference of the products of the diagonals	$\det\begin{bmatrix} 1 & 2 \\ 3 & 4 \end{bmatrix} =$ $\begin{vmatrix} 1 & 2 \\ 3 & 4 \end{vmatrix} = (1)(4) - (3)(2) = -2$	$\det\begin{bmatrix} a & b \\ c & d \end{bmatrix} =$ $\begin{vmatrix} a & b \\ c & d \end{vmatrix} = ad - cb$

EXAMPLE 1 **Finding the Determinant of a 2 × 2 Matrix**

Find the determinant of each matrix.

A $\begin{bmatrix} 6 & 5 \\ 8 & 3 \end{bmatrix}$

$\begin{vmatrix} 6 & 5 \\ 8 & 3 \end{vmatrix} = 6(3) - 8(5)$ *Find the difference of the cross products.*

$= 18 - 40 = -22$

The determinant is −22.

B $\begin{bmatrix} \frac{1}{3} & \frac{2}{3} \\ -6 & 3 \end{bmatrix}$

$\begin{vmatrix} \frac{1}{3} & \frac{2}{3} \\ -6 & 3 \end{vmatrix} = \frac{1}{3}(3) - (-6)\left(\frac{2}{3}\right) = 1 + 4 = 5$

The determinant is 5.

Reading Math
The determinant of matrix A may be denoted as det A or $|A|$. Don't confuse the $|A|$ notation with absolute value notation.

Find the determinant of each matrix.

1a. $\begin{bmatrix} 0.2 & 30 \\ -0.3 & 5 \end{bmatrix}$ 10 **1b.** $\begin{bmatrix} \frac{1}{3} & 3 \\ \frac{5}{6} & \frac{3}{4} \end{bmatrix}$ $-2\frac{1}{4}$ **1c.** $\begin{bmatrix} \frac{1}{2} & \frac{1}{8} \\ 4 & 2\pi \end{bmatrix}$ $\pi - \frac{1}{2}$

State Resources

go.hrw.com
State Resources Online
KEYWORD: MB7 Resources

1 Introduce

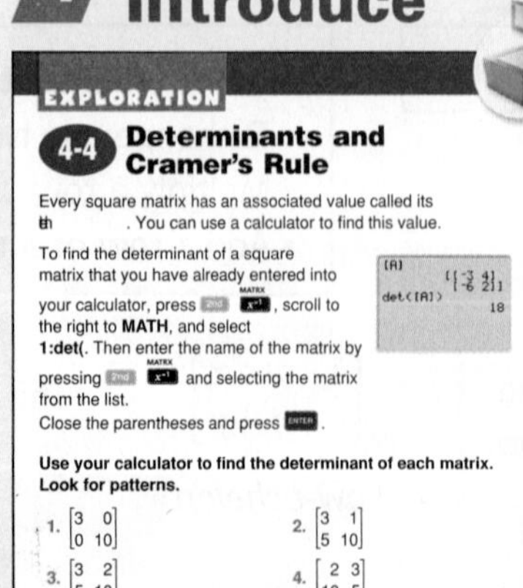
EXPLORATION
4-4 Determinants and Cramer's Rule
Every square matrix has an associated value called its th . You can use a calculator to find this value.
To find the determinant of a square matrix that you have already entered into your calculator, press , scroll to the right to MATH, and select 1:det(. Then enter the name of the matrix by pressing and selecting the matrix from the list.
Close the parentheses and press .
Use your calculator to find the determinant of each matrix. Look for patterns.
1. $\begin{bmatrix} 3 & 0 \\ 0 & 10 \end{bmatrix}$ 2. $\begin{bmatrix} 3 & 1 \\ 5 & 10 \end{bmatrix}$
3. $\begin{bmatrix} 3 & 2 \\ 5 & 10 \end{bmatrix}$ 4. $\begin{bmatrix} 2 & 3 \\ 10 & 5 \end{bmatrix}$
5. $\begin{bmatrix} 2 & 1 \\ 10 & 5 \end{bmatrix}$ 6. $\begin{bmatrix} 1 & 3 \\ -2 & 10 \end{bmatrix}$
THINK AND DISCUSS
7. Describe how the determinant is related to the entries of

Motivate

Ask students for ways they have learned to solve systems of equations (e.g., substitution, elimination, graphing). Ask what they need to do to see if a system has exactly one solution.

Tell them that a number calculated using the entries of a matrix, the *determinant,* can be helpful in *determining* this.

Explorations and answers are provided in the *Explorations* binder.

You can use the determinant of a matrix to help you solve a system of equations. For two equations with two variables written in $ax + by = c$ form, you can construct a matrix of the coefficients of the variables.

For the system $\begin{cases} a_1x + b_1y = c_1 \\ a_2x + b_2y = c_2 \end{cases}$, the coefficient matrix is $\begin{bmatrix} a_1 & b_1 \\ a_2 & b_2 \end{bmatrix}$.

The **coefficient matrix** for a system of linear equations in standard form is the matrix formed by the coefficients for the variables in the equations.

The determinant D of the coefficient matrix is $\begin{vmatrix} a_1 & b_1 \\ a_2 & b_2 \end{vmatrix}$.

Cramer's Rule for Two Equations

$\begin{cases} a_1x + b_1y = c_1 \\ a_2x + b_2y = c_2 \end{cases}$ has solutions $x = \dfrac{\begin{vmatrix} c_1 & b_1 \\ c_2 & b_2 \end{vmatrix}}{D}$, $y = \dfrac{\begin{vmatrix} a_1 & c_1 \\ a_2 & c_2 \end{vmatrix}}{D}$, where $D = \begin{vmatrix} a_1 & b_1 \\ a_2 & b_2 \end{vmatrix}$.

You can use Cramer's rule to tell whether the system represented by the matrix has one solution, no solution, or infinitely many solutions.

Solutions of Systems		
If $D \neq 0$, the system is consistent and has one unique solution.	If $D = 0$ and *at least one* numerator determinant is 0, the system is dependent and has infinitely many solutions.	If $D = 0$ and *neither* numerator determinant is 0, the system is inconsistent and has no solution.
	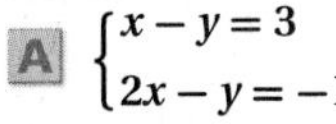	

EXAMPLE 2 Using Cramer's Rule for Two Equations

Use Cramer's rule to solve each system of equations.

A $\begin{cases} x - y = 3 \\ 2x - y = -1 \end{cases}$

Step 1 Find D, the determinant of the coefficient matrix. $\begin{bmatrix} 1 & -1 \\ 2 & -1 \end{bmatrix}$

$D = \begin{vmatrix} 1 & -1 \\ 2 & -1 \end{vmatrix} = 1(-1) - 2(-1) = 1$ *$D \neq 0$, so the system is consistent.*

Step 2 Solve for each variable by replacing the coefficients of that variable with the constants as shown below.

$$x = \frac{\begin{vmatrix} c_1 & b_1 \\ c_2 & b_2 \end{vmatrix}}{D} = \frac{\begin{vmatrix} 3 & -1 \\ -1 & -1 \end{vmatrix}}{1} = -4$$

$$y = \frac{\begin{vmatrix} a_1 & c_1 \\ a_2 & c_2 \end{vmatrix}}{D} = \frac{\begin{vmatrix} 1 & 3 \\ 2 & -1 \end{vmatrix}}{1} = -7$$

The solution is $(-4, -7)$.

2 Teach

Guided Instruction

Students must first be comfortable finding determinants of 2×2 and 3×3 matrices.

Then they need to be able to set up the fractions for solving a system using Cramer's rule. (**Examples 2** and **4**)

Reaching All Learners

Through Number Sense

Emphasize that the question of whether the determinant is zero is directly related to whether a system has a unique solution.

If $D \neq 0$, then $x = \frac{\text{real}}{\text{real}}$, $y = \frac{\text{real}}{\text{real}}$: consistent, independent, 1 unique solution.

If $D = 0$, then $x = \frac{\text{real}}{0}$, $y = \frac{\text{real}}{0}$: inconsistent, no solution.

If $D = 0$, then $x = \frac{0}{0}$, $y = \frac{0}{0}$: consistent, dependent, infinitely many solutions.

Power Presentations with PowerPoint®

Additional Examples

Example 1

Find the determinant of each matrix.

A. $\begin{bmatrix} 1 & 5 \\ 4 & 8 \end{bmatrix}$ -12

B. $\begin{bmatrix} \frac{1}{2} & -1 \\ -\frac{1}{2} & 2 \end{bmatrix}$ $\frac{1}{2}$

Example 2

Use Cramer's rule to solve each system of equations.

A. $\begin{cases} 2x + y = 10 \\ 3x - 2y = 8 \end{cases}$ $(4, 2)$

B. $\begin{cases} 3x + 5 = 2y \\ 15 - 6y = -9x \end{cases}$ inf. many

Also available on transparency

INTERVENTION

Questioning Strategies

EXAMPLE 1

- How can you tell by the brackets whether you are looking at a matrix or a determinant?

EXAMPLE 2

- What does the determinant tell you about the system?
- How do the constant substitutions move as you solve using Cramer's rule?

Math Background Students may want to know why Cramer's rule works. If they solve the following system,

$\begin{cases} a_1x + b_1y = c_1 \\ a_2x + b_2y = c_2 \end{cases}$,

they will get the solution

$$x = \frac{c_1b_2 - c_2b_1}{a_1b_2 - a_2b_1},$$

$$y = \frac{a_1c_2 - a_2c_1}{a_1b_2 - a_2b_1}.$$

This is the expanded form of the solutions presented in the *Know it! Note:* Cramer's Rule for Two Equations.

Power Presentations with PowerPoint®

Additional Examples

Example 3

Find the determinant of M.

$$M = \begin{bmatrix} 2 & 4 & 1 \\ 5 & 2 & 3 \\ 1 & 4 & 8 \end{bmatrix} \quad -122$$

Also available on transparency

INTERVENTION

Questioning Strategies

EXAMPLE 3

- Which column does *not* get rewritten on the right side?
- How do you remember which diagonals are added and which are subtracted?

Teaching Tip **Number Sense** Ask students if they see the patterns in the six terms generated when finding a 3 × 3 determinant. They may notice that there is one *a*, one *b*, and one *c* in each term; each has *sub 1*, *sub 2*, and *sub 3* in the added terms and in reverse order in the subtracted terms.

$$D = \begin{vmatrix} 6 & -2 \\ 3 & -1 \end{vmatrix} = 0$$

$$\begin{vmatrix} c_1 & b_1 \\ c_2 & b_2 \end{vmatrix} = \begin{vmatrix} 14 & -2 \\ 7 & -1 \end{vmatrix} = 0$$

Because $D = 0$ and one of the numerator determinants is equal to 0, the system is dependent and has infinitely many solutions.

Use Cramer's rule to solve each system of equations.

B $\begin{cases} y - 2 = 3x \\ 3x - y = 7 \end{cases}$

Step 1 Write the equations in standard form. $\begin{cases} 3x - y = -2 \\ 3x - y = 7 \end{cases}$

Step 2 Find the determinant of the coefficient matrix.

$$D = \begin{vmatrix} 3 & -1 \\ 3 & -1 \end{vmatrix} = -3 - (-3) = 0$$

$D = 0$, so the system is either inconsistent or dependent. Check the numerators for x and y to see if either is 0.

$$x = \frac{\begin{vmatrix} c_1 & b_1 \\ c_2 & b_2 \end{vmatrix} \to \begin{vmatrix} -2 & -1 \\ 7 & -1 \end{vmatrix} = 9}{0} \qquad y = \frac{\begin{vmatrix} a_1 & c_1 \\ a_2 & c_2 \end{vmatrix} \to \begin{vmatrix} 3 & -2 \\ 3 & 7 \end{vmatrix} = 27}{0}$$

Neither numerator is 0. The system is inconsistent with no solutions.

CHECK IT OUT! **2.** Use Cramer's rule to solve. $\begin{cases} 6x - 2y = 14 \\ 3x = y + 7 \end{cases}$

To apply Cramer's rule to 3 × 3 systems, you need to find the determinant of a 3 × 3 matrix. One method is shown below.

Rewrite the first two columns at the right side of the determinant.

Add the sum of the products of the red diagonals. Then **subtract** the sum of the blue diagonals.

$$\det \begin{bmatrix} a_1 & b_1 & c_1 \\ a_2 & b_2 & c_2 \\ a_3 & b_3 & c_3 \end{bmatrix} = \left| \begin{matrix} a_1 & b_1 & c_1 \\ a_2 & b_2 & c_2 \\ a_3 & b_3 & c_3 \end{matrix} \right| \begin{matrix} a_1 & b_1 \\ a_2 & b_2 \\ a_3 & b_3 \end{matrix} \quad a_1b_2c_3 + b_1c_2a_3 + c_1a_2b_3 - (a_3b_2c_1 + b_3c_2a_1 + c_3a_2b_1)$$

EXAMPLE 3 Finding the Determinant of a 3 × 3 Matrix

Find the determinant of A.

$$A = \begin{bmatrix} 4 & -2 & 0 \\ -3 & 10 & 1 \\ 2 & 6 & -1 \end{bmatrix} \quad \det A = \begin{vmatrix} 4 & -2 & 0 \\ -3 & 10 & 1 \\ 2 & 6 & -1 \end{vmatrix}, \text{ so write } \left| \begin{matrix} 4 & -2 & 0 \\ -3 & 10 & 1 \\ 2 & 6 & -1 \end{matrix} \right| \begin{matrix} 4 & -2 \\ -3 & 10 \\ 2 & 6 \end{matrix}$$

Step 1 Multiply each "down" diagonal and add.
$4(10)(-1) + (-2)(1)(2) + 0(-3)(6) = -44$

Step 2 Multiply each "up" diagonal and add.
$(2)(10)(0) + (6)(1)(4) + (-1)(-3)(-2) = 18$

Step 3 Find the difference of the sums.
$-44 - 18 = -62.$

The determinant is -62.

Check Use a calculator.

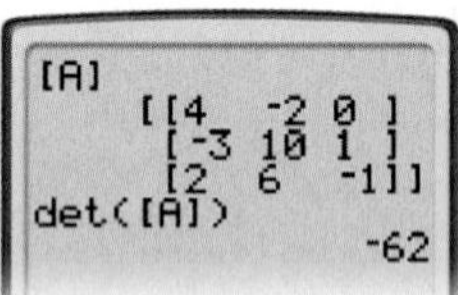

Helpful Hint

Lightly draw the diagonals to help you locate the six products needed to find the determinant.

Teaching Tip **Math Background** Another visual technique for finding determinants of 3 × 3 (and larger) matrices is called *expansion by minors*.

Find a minor of a matrix by covering its row and column and calculating the determinant of the remaining 2 × 2 matrix.

Then multiply each element in the first row by its minor and add these, alternating signs to find the 3 × 3 determinant.

$$\begin{vmatrix} a_1 & b_1 & c_1 \\ a_2 & b_2 & c_2 \\ a_3 & b_3 & c_3 \end{vmatrix} = a_1\begin{vmatrix} b_2 & c_2 \\ b_3 & c_3 \end{vmatrix} - b_1\begin{vmatrix} a_2 & c_2 \\ a_3 & c_3 \end{vmatrix} + c_1\begin{vmatrix} a_2 & b_2 \\ a_3 & b_3 \end{vmatrix}$$

3. Find the determinant of $\begin{bmatrix} 2 & -3 & 4 \\ 5 & 1 & -2 \\ 10 & 3 & -1 \end{bmatrix}$. 75

Cramer's rule can be expanded to cover 3 × 3 systems.

Cramer's Rule for Three Equations

The system $\begin{cases} a_1x + b_1y + c_1z = d_1 \\ a_2x + b_2y + c_2z = d_2 \\ a_3x + b_3y + c_3z = d_3 \end{cases}$ has solutions given by

$$x = \frac{\begin{vmatrix} d_1 & b_1 & c_1 \\ d_2 & b_2 & c_2 \\ d_3 & b_3 & c_3 \end{vmatrix}}{D},\ y = \frac{\begin{vmatrix} a_1 & d_1 & c_1 \\ a_2 & d_2 & c_2 \\ a_3 & d_3 & c_3 \end{vmatrix}}{D},\ z = \frac{\begin{vmatrix} a_1 & b_1 & d_1 \\ a_2 & b_2 & d_2 \\ a_3 & b_3 & d_3 \end{vmatrix}}{D}$$ where $D = \begin{vmatrix} a_1 & b_1 & c_1 \\ a_2 & b_2 & c_2 \\ a_3 & b_3 & c_3 \end{vmatrix}$ and $D \neq 0$.

If $D \neq 0$, then the system has a unique solution.

If $D = 0$ and no numerator is 0, then the system is inconsistent. If $D = 0$ and at least one numerator is 0, then the system may be inconsistent or dependent.

EXAMPLE 4 Nutrition Application

A nutritionist planning a diet for a football player wants him to consume 3600 Calories and 750 grams of food daily. Calories from protein and from fat will be 60% of the total Calories. How many grams of protein, carbohydrates, and fat will this diet include?

Calories per Gram	
Food	Calories
Protein	4
Carbohydrates	4
Fat	9

The diet will include p grams of protein, c grams of carbohydrates, and f grams of fat.

$4p + 4c + 9f = 3600$ *Equation for total Calories*

$p + c + f = 750$ *Total grams of food*

$4p + 0c + 9f = 2160$ *Calories from protein and fat, 60%(3600) = 2160*

Use a calculator.

$$D = \begin{vmatrix} 4 & 4 & 9 \\ 1 & 1 & 1 \\ 4 & 0 & 9 \end{vmatrix} = -20 \quad p = \frac{\begin{vmatrix} 3600 & 4 & 9 \\ 750 & 1 & 1 \\ 2160 & 0 & 9 \end{vmatrix}}{D} \quad c = \frac{\begin{vmatrix} 4 & 3600 & 9 \\ 1 & 750 & 1 \\ 4 & 2160 & 9 \end{vmatrix}}{D} \quad f = \frac{\begin{vmatrix} 4 & 4 & 3600 \\ 1 & 1 & 750 \\ 4 & 0 & 2160 \end{vmatrix}}{D}$$

$$p = \frac{-5400}{-20} \quad c = \frac{-7200}{-20} \quad f = \frac{-2400}{-20}$$

$$p = 270 \quad c = 360 \quad f = 120$$

The diet includes 270 grams protein, 360 grams carbohydrates, and 120 grams fat.

Caution!

When an equation is missing one variable, be sure to write the missing term with a coefficient of zero.

$4p + 0c + 9f = 2160$

4. **What if...?** A diet requires 3200 calories, 700 grams of food, and 70% of the Calories from carbohydrates and fat. How many grams of protein, carbohydrates, and fat does the diet include?

COMMON ERROR ALERT

When forming the numerators for the fractions in **Examples 2** and **4**, students may put the $\begin{vmatrix} c_1 \\ c_2 \end{vmatrix}$ in the wrong place. Remind them that when solving for x, they should replace the coefficients of x; when solving for y, they should replace the coefficients of y.

Power Presentations with PowerPoint®

Additional Examples

Example 4

A nutritionist creates a diet for a long-distance runner that includes 3400 Calories from 680 grams of food, with half the Calories coming from carbohydrates. Use the table on page 273 to write and solve a system using Cramer's rule.

$\begin{cases} 4p + 4c + 9f = 3400 \\ p + c + f = 680 \\ 4c = 1700 \end{cases}$ $p = 119$, $c = 425$, $f = 136$

Also available on transparency

INTERVENTION

Questioning Strategies

EXAMPLE 4

- Why is it sometimes necessary to rewrite a system of equations with terms with 0 coefficients, like 0x?
- How do you determine what three equations need to be created to solve this problem?

Answers to *Check It Out!*

4. 240 g protein, 380 g carbohydrates, and 80 g fat

3 Close

Summarize

Review how to find determinants for 2 × 2 and 3 × 3 matrices. Be sure that students understand how determinants can be used to find the number of solutions.

Review Cramer's rule for solving systems of 2 and 3 equations.

ONGOING ASSESSMENT and INTERVENTION

***Diagnose Before* the Lesson**
4-4 Warm Up, TE p. 270

***Monitor During* the Lesson**
Check It Out! Exercises, SE pp. 270–273
Questioning Strategies, TE pp. 271–273

***Assess After* the Lesson**
4-4 Lesson Quiz, TE p. 277
Alternative Assessment, TE p. 277

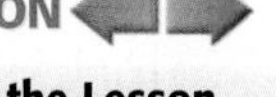

Answers to *Think and Discuss*

Possible answers:

1. Matrix S is not a square matrix.
2. The system is dependent, so the determinant of the coefficient matrix is zero, and at least one numerator determinant is zero.
3. See p. A6.

4-4 Exercises

Assignment Guide

Assign *Guided Practice* exercises as necessary.

If you finished Examples **1–2**
- **Basic** 14–21
- **Average** 14–21, 30, 32
- **Advanced** 14–21, 30–32

If you finished Examples **1–4**
- **Basic** 14–27, 29, 32–35, 37–39, 44–51
- **Average** 14–30, 32–41, 44–51
- **Advanced** 14–28, 30–32, 34–51

Homework Quick Check

Quickly check key concepts.
Exercises: 14, 18, 24, 25, 28

Answers

6. $\left(\frac{1}{5}, \frac{4}{5}\right)$

9. $\left(2\frac{1}{2}, -\frac{1}{4}\right)$

State Resources

go.hrw.com
State Resources Online
KEYWORD: MB7 Resources

THINK AND DISCUSS

1. Describe a matrix S that has no determinant.
2. Explain how you know what the three determinants will be when you apply Cramer's rule to a two-equation system in which one equation is a multiple of the other.

3. **GET ORGANIZED** Copy and complete the graphic organizer. In each box, write the appropriate formula.

	2 × 2 Matrix	3 × 3 Matrix
Determinant		
Cramer's Rule		

4-4 Exercises

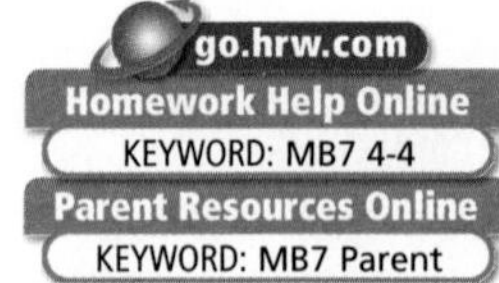

GUIDED PRACTICE

1. **Vocabulary** Explain the meaning of a 0 entry in a *coefficient matrix.* **A 0 entry in a coefficient matrix corresponds to a coefficient of 0 for one variable in one equation.**

SEE EXAMPLE 1 p. 270

Find the determinant of each matrix.

2. $\begin{bmatrix} 7 & 5 \\ 9 & 2 \end{bmatrix}$ **−31**
3. $\begin{bmatrix} 1.5 & 0.25 \\ 6 & 2.5 \end{bmatrix}$ **2.25**
4. $\begin{bmatrix} \frac{1}{2} & \frac{2}{3} \\ \frac{3}{4} & -4 \end{bmatrix}$ $\mathbf{-2\frac{1}{2}}$
5. $\begin{bmatrix} -3 & 40 \\ -5 & 66\frac{2}{3} \end{bmatrix}$ **0**

SEE EXAMPLE 2 p. 271

Use Cramer's rule to solve each system of equations.

6. $\begin{cases} 6x = 2 - y \\ 3x + 1 = 2y \end{cases}$
7. $\begin{cases} 4x + y + 6 = 0 \\ 8x + 2y = 9 \end{cases}$ **no solution**
8. $\begin{cases} 5x - 2y = 3 \\ 2.5x - y = 1.5 \end{cases}$ **infinitely many solutions**
9. $\begin{cases} 2y = 2 - x \\ -3x + 6y = -9 \end{cases}$

SEE EXAMPLE 3 p. 272

Find the determinant of each matrix.

10. $P = \begin{bmatrix} 1 & 2 & -1 \\ 4 & 0 & 1 \\ 1 & -2 & 3 \end{bmatrix}$ **−12**
11. $S = \begin{bmatrix} 0 & -5 & -1 \\ 4 & 1 & 6 \\ 2 & 0.5 & 3 \end{bmatrix}$ **0**
12. $E = \begin{bmatrix} 1 & -1 & 1 \\ -1 & 1 & -1 \\ 1 & -1 & 1 \end{bmatrix}$ **0**

SEE EXAMPLE 4 p. 273

13. **Consumer** Naomi buys 2 pounds of trail mix, 1.5 pounds of mixed nuts, and 3 pounds of dried fruit for a total of $28.42. Briana buys 4.5 pounds of mixed nuts and 2 pounds of dried fruit for a total of $39.39. The price per pound of trail mix plus the price per pound of dried fruit is the same as the price per pound of mixed nuts. What is the price per pound of each product?
trail mix $2.99; mixed nuts $6.98; dried fruit $3.99

PRACTICE AND PROBLEM SOLVING

Find the determinant of each matrix.

14. $\begin{bmatrix} 3 & -0.4 \\ 5 & 0.3 \end{bmatrix}$ **2.9**
15. $\begin{bmatrix} -1 & 0 \\ 0 & 1 \end{bmatrix}$ **−1**
16. $\begin{bmatrix} -\frac{2}{5} & 8 \\ -\frac{1}{2} & 10 \end{bmatrix}$ **0**
17. $\begin{bmatrix} r & -1 \\ -2r^2 & \pi r \end{bmatrix}$ $\pi r^2 - 2r^2$

4-4 PRACTICE A

Find the determinant of each matrix.

1. $\begin{bmatrix} 6 & -2 \\ 1 & 10 \end{bmatrix}$ $= 6(\underline{10}) - (\underline{1})(\underline{-2})$ $= 60 - (-2) = 62$
2. $\begin{bmatrix} 3 & -1 \\ -7 & 2 \end{bmatrix}$ −1
3. $\begin{bmatrix} 2 & 9 \\ 1 & -3 \end{bmatrix}$ −15
4. $\begin{bmatrix} 5 & 6 & -1 \\ -3 & 2 & 0 \\ 2 & -3 & 4 \end{bmatrix} \rightarrow \left[\begin{array}{ccc|cc} 5 & 6 & -1 & 5 & 6 \\ -3 & 2 & 0 & -3 & 2 \\ 2 & -3 & 4 & 2 & -3 \end{array}\right] \rightarrow \left[\begin{array}{ccc|cc} 5 & 6 & -1 & 5 & 6 \\ -3 & 2 & 0 & -3 & 2 \\ 2 & -3 & 4 & 2 & -3 \end{array}\right]$ 107

Use Cramer's rule to solve each system of equations.

5. $\begin{cases} x - 2y = -9 \\ 3x + y = 1 \end{cases}$
   a. Write the coefficient matrix. $\begin{bmatrix} 1 & -2 \\ 3 & 1 \end{bmatrix}$
   b. Find D, the determinant of the coefficient matrix. 7
   c. Use Cramer's rule to write the solutions for x and y.
   $x = \frac{\begin{vmatrix} c_1 & b_1 \\ c_2 & b_2 \end{vmatrix}}{D} = \frac{\begin{vmatrix} -9 & -2 \\ 1 & 1 \end{vmatrix}}{7}$ $y = \frac{\begin{vmatrix} a_1 & c_1 \\ a_2 & c_2 \end{vmatrix}}{D} = \frac{\begin{vmatrix} 1 & -9 \\ 3 & 1 \end{vmatrix}}{7}$
   d. Evaluate the determinants in the numerators and solve for x and y. $x = -1; y = 4$
6. $\begin{cases} 2x + 3y = 4 \\ x - 2y = 9 \end{cases}$ $x = 5; y = -2$
7. $\begin{cases} 3x + y = 5 \\ 2x - 3y = 18 \end{cases}$ $x = 3; y = -4$
8. $\begin{cases} x + 5y = 11 \\ 2x - 3y = 9 \end{cases}$ $x = 6; y = 1$

4-4 PRACTICE B

Find the determinant of each matrix.

1. $\begin{bmatrix} 8 & 2 \\ 4 & -1 \end{bmatrix}$ −16
2. $\begin{bmatrix} -6 & 3 \\ 9 & -5 \end{bmatrix}$ 3
3. $\begin{bmatrix} -2 & 8 \\ -3 & 7 \end{bmatrix}$ 10
4. $\begin{bmatrix} 1 & 0 & -1 \\ 5 & -2 & 0 \\ 1 & 6 & 2 \end{bmatrix}$ −36
5. $\begin{bmatrix} 0 & -4 & 5 \\ 2 & 4 & 3 \\ 1 & 1 & -1 \end{bmatrix}$ −30
6. $\begin{bmatrix} -4 & 3 & 1 \\ 7 & -2 & 0 \\ 1 & -1 & 2 \end{bmatrix}$ −31

Use Cramer's rule to solve each system of equations.

7. $\begin{cases} 2x + 3y = -1 \\ 3x + 2y = 16 \end{cases}$ (10, −7)
8. $\begin{cases} 4x - 3y = 9 \\ 3x + 2y = 28 \end{cases}$ (6, 5)
9. $\begin{cases} 8x - 3y = 20 \\ 3x - 2y = 11 \end{cases}$ (1, −4)
10. $\begin{cases} 4y = -5x + 33 \\ 2y = 3x - 11 \end{cases}$ (5, 2)
11. $\begin{cases} 27 + 4y = 3x \\ y = \frac{1}{3}x - 8 \end{cases}$ (−3, −9)
12. $\begin{cases} 7 - 5y + 4x = 0 \\ 16 - 2y - 5x = 0 \end{cases}$ (2, 3)

Solve.

13. On Monday, Marla babysat for 4 hours, did yard work for 2 hours, and earned a total of $41. On Friday, she babysat for 5 hours, did yard work for 3 hours, and earned a total of $55.
   a. Write a system of equations. Let x = Marla's hourly rate for babysitting, and y = her hourly rate for yard work. $\begin{cases} 4x + 2y = 41 \\ 5x + 3y = 55 \end{cases}$
   b. Write the coefficient matrix. Evaluate its determinant. $\begin{bmatrix} 4 & 2 \\ 5 & 3 \end{bmatrix}$; det $= \begin{vmatrix} 4 & 2 \\ 5 & 3 \end{vmatrix} = 2$
   c. Use Cramer's rule to find x and y. $x = 6.5; y = 7.5$
   d. What is Marla's hourly rate for each activity? Babysitting: $6.50, yard work: $7.50

Independent Practice	
For Exercises	See Example
14–17	1
18–21	2
22–24	3
25	4

Extra Practice
Skills Practice p. S11
Application Practice p. S35

Use Cramer's rule to solve each system of equations.

18. $\begin{cases} 0.5x + 6y = 2 \\ 0.25x + 3y = 0.5 \end{cases}$ no solution

19. $\begin{cases} x + 2y = 3.5 \\ 3x - y = 2.7 \end{cases}$ $(\approx 1.27, \approx 1.11)$

20. $\begin{cases} 2x + y = 3 \\ x + \frac{y}{2} = 2 \end{cases}$ no solution

21. $\begin{cases} 3y - x = 7 \\ 2x + 3y = -7 \end{cases}$ $\left(-4\frac{2}{3}, \frac{7}{9}\right)$

Find the determinant of each matrix.

22. $A = \begin{bmatrix} 2.5 & 1.5 & 0 \\ 3.2 & 1 & -4 \\ 6.4 & -5 & 2.1 \end{bmatrix}$ −93.23

23. $L = \begin{bmatrix} -2.4 & 1 & 0 \\ 3 & 0 & 0.5 \\ 0 & 3.5 & 1 \end{bmatrix}$ 1.2

24. $W = \begin{bmatrix} 1 & 0 & 2 \\ 0 & -5 & 0 \\ 3 & 0 & 4 \end{bmatrix}$ 10

25. **Fitness** Cameron records the hours he exercises and the total Calories he burns each day. How many Calories are burned per hour for each of the three activities? Use Cramer's rule to solve.

Cameron's Activity Log

	Bicycling	Racquetball	Swimming	Calories Burned
Monday	1.5 h	1 h	0.75 h	1620
Wednesday	0.75 h		1 h	915
Friday	1 h	1.5 h		1230

LINK

Geography

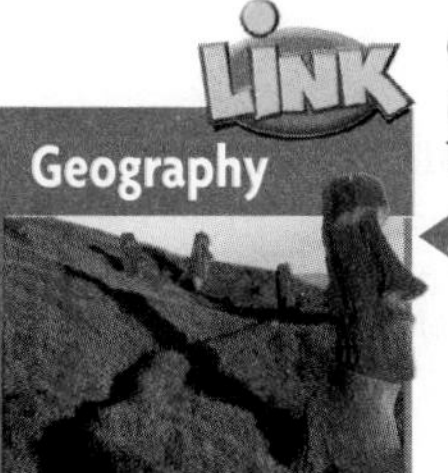

Easter Island, a South Pacific island of Chile, contains more than 600 stone statues. The statues were carved between 1600 and 1730. Most of the heads actually have torsos that have become buried over time.

Geometry **The area of a triangle with vertices (x_1, y_1), (x_2, y_2), and (x_3, y_3) is equal to the absolute value of A. Use this information for Exercises 26 and 27.**

$$A = \frac{1}{2}\begin{vmatrix} x_1 & x_2 & x_3 \\ y_1 & y_2 & y_3 \\ 1 & 1 & 1 \end{vmatrix}$$

26. **Geography** Find the area of Easter Island. 63.75 mi^2

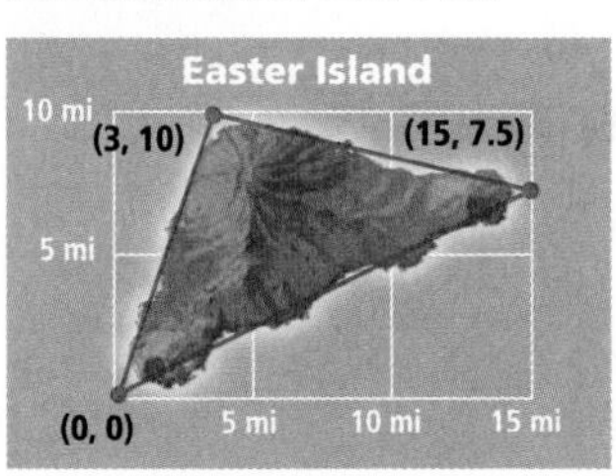

27. Find the area of $\triangle FGH$. 17 square units

F (−1, 4)
y
2
x
−4
−2
0
4
−2
H (3, −2)
G (−2, −3)
−4

28. **Critical Thinking** For the system of equations $2x + y = 6$ and $cy = 3 - x$, for what value of c is the determinant zero? Explain your reasoning.

29. **Internet** John's site asks readers to rate his articles with 1, 2, or 3 points. There were 38 votes, twice as many 3's as 1's, and the point total was 85. How many people gave each rating? 1 point: 9 voters; 2 points: 11 voters; 3 points: 18 voters

Find the determinant of each matrix.

30. $A = \begin{bmatrix} x & x - 1 \\ x + 1 & x \end{bmatrix}$ 1

31. $B = \begin{bmatrix} x - 2 & x + 2 \\ x + 2 & x + 6 \end{bmatrix}$ −16

32. $C = \begin{bmatrix} 6x^2 & -6x + 2x^2 \\ 3x & x - 3 \end{bmatrix}$ 0

33. **Currency** The United States Code specifies that dimes weigh 2.268 grams each and nickels weigh 5 grams each. The approximate weight of 425 dimes and nickels is 1483 grams.
    a. How many of each coin are there? 235 dimes; 190 nickels
    b. What is the total value of the coins? $33

COMMON ERROR ALERT

In **Exercises 26** and **27,** some students may confuse the determinant bars with absolute-value bars. Emphasize that they need to find the product of $\frac{1}{2}$ and the determinant.

Answers

25. bicycling: 420 Cal/h; racquetball: 540 Cal/h; swimming: 600 Cal/h

28. The determinant is zero for $c = \frac{1}{2}$. Possible answer: Write the equations in standard form: $\begin{cases} 2x + y = 6 \\ x + cy = 3 \end{cases}$. Set the determinant of the coefficient matrix equal to 0, and then solve for c.
$2c - 1(1) = 0$
$2c = 1$
$c = \frac{1}{2}$

4-4 PRACTICE C

Find the determinant of each matrix.

1. $\begin{bmatrix} 12 & 5 \\ -14 & -3 \end{bmatrix}$ 34
2. $\begin{bmatrix} -6 & -1 & -2 \\ 2 & 5 & 0 \\ 4 & 3 & 1 \end{bmatrix}$ 0
3. $\begin{bmatrix} 2 & 4 & -1 \\ 0 & 3 & -3 \\ 1 & 0 & 6 \end{bmatrix}$ 27

Use Cramer's rule to solve each system of equations.

4. $\begin{cases} 4x - 3y = 3 \\ -3x + 2y = -1 \end{cases}$ $(-3, -5)$
5. $\begin{cases} 5x - 4y = 22 \\ 4x + 3y = -1 \end{cases}$ $(2, -3)$
6. $\begin{cases} 6x - 7y = -11 \\ 5x + 4y = 40 \end{cases}$ $(4, 5)$
7. $\begin{cases} 8x - 5y = 61 \\ 3x + 4y = 17 \end{cases}$ $(7, -1)$
8. $\begin{cases} x - 6y = 21 \\ 3x + 5y = 17 \end{cases}$ $(9, -2)$
9. $\begin{cases} 5x - 6y = -2 \\ 4x - 5y = -3 \end{cases}$ $(8, 7)$
10. $\begin{cases} 3x - 2y + 4z = 0 \\ 6x + 5y - 3z = 7 \\ 5x + 3y + 5z = 11 \end{cases}$ $(0, 2, 1)$
11. $\begin{cases} 4x - 2y + z = -6 \\ 3x + 3y + 5z = -8 \\ 2x - 4y - 3z = 2 \end{cases}$ $(1, 3, -4)$
12. $\begin{cases} -2x + 6y + 3z = -10 \\ 5x - 5y - 4z = 9 \\ 3x + 2y = 0 \end{cases}$ $(2, -3, 4)$

Solve.

13. Travis invested $20,000 in two simple interest accounts. He invested part at 4.5% interest and the rest at 3.5% interest. He earned $785 in total interest per year.
    a. Write the problem as a system of equations. $\begin{cases} x + y = 20{,}000 \\ 0.045x + 0.035y = 785 \end{cases}$
    b. Find the value of the determinant of the coefficient matrix. −0.01
    c. Use Cramer's rule to write the solution for the amount Travis invested at 4.5%. $\dfrac{\begin{vmatrix} 20{,}000 & 1 \\ 785 & .035 \end{vmatrix}}{-.01}$
    d. How much did Travis invest at 4.5% interest? $8500

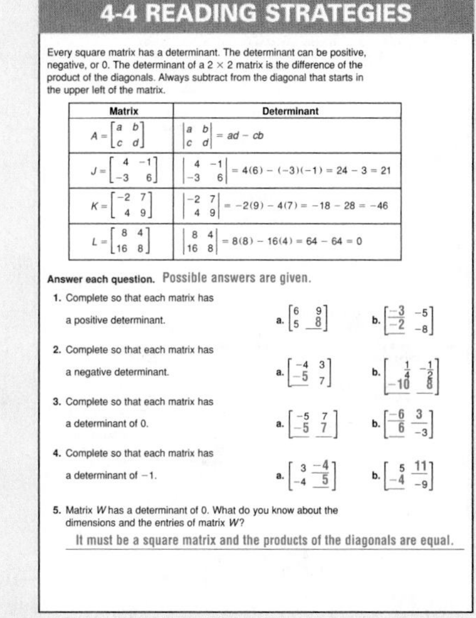

4-4 READING STRATEGIES

Every square matrix has a determinant. The determinant can be positive, negative, or 0. The determinant of a 2 × 2 matrix is the difference of the product of the diagonals. Always subtract from the diagonal that starts in the upper left of the matrix.

Matrix	Determinant
$A = \begin{bmatrix} a & b \\ c & d \end{bmatrix}$	$\begin{vmatrix} a & b \\ c & d \end{vmatrix} = ad - cb$
$J = \begin{bmatrix} 4 & -1 \\ -3 & 6 \end{bmatrix}$	$\begin{vmatrix} 4 & -1 \\ -3 & 6 \end{vmatrix} = 4(6) - (-3)(-1) = 24 - 3 = 21$
$K = \begin{bmatrix} -2 & 7 \\ 4 & 9 \end{bmatrix}$	$\begin{vmatrix} -2 & 7 \\ 4 & 9 \end{vmatrix} = -2(9) - 4(7) = -18 - 28 = -46$
$L = \begin{bmatrix} 8 & 4 \\ 16 & 8 \end{bmatrix}$	$\begin{vmatrix} 8 & 4 \\ 16 & 8 \end{vmatrix} = 8(8) - 16(4) = 64 - 64 = 0$

Answer each question. Possible answers are given.

1. Complete so that each matrix has a positive determinant. a. $\begin{bmatrix} 6 & 9 \\ 5 & 8 \end{bmatrix}$ b. $\begin{bmatrix} -3 & -5 \\ -2 & -8 \end{bmatrix}$
2. Complete so that each matrix has a negative determinant. a. $\begin{bmatrix} -4 & 3 \\ -5 & 7 \end{bmatrix}$ b. $\begin{bmatrix} \frac{1}{4} & -\frac{1}{2} \\ -10 & 8 \end{bmatrix}$
3. Complete so that each matrix has a determinant of 0. a. $\begin{bmatrix} -5 & 7 \\ -5 & 7 \end{bmatrix}$ b. $\begin{bmatrix} -6 & 3 \\ 6 & -3 \end{bmatrix}$
4. Complete so that each matrix has a determinant of −1. a. $\begin{bmatrix} 3 & -4 \\ -4 & 5 \end{bmatrix}$ b. $\begin{bmatrix} 5 & 11 \\ -4 & -9 \end{bmatrix}$
5. Matrix W has a determinant of 0. What do you know about the dimensions and the entries of matrix W?
   It must be a square matrix and the products of the diagonals are equal.

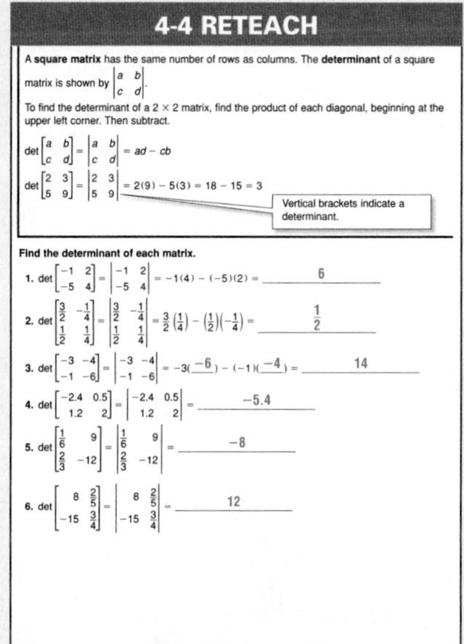

4-4 RETEACH

A **square matrix** has the same number of rows as columns. The **determinant** of a square matrix is shown by $\begin{vmatrix} a & b \\ c & d \end{vmatrix}$.

To find the determinant of a 2 × 2 matrix, find the product of each diagonal, beginning at the upper left corner. Then subtract.

$\det\begin{bmatrix} a & b \\ c & d \end{bmatrix} = \begin{vmatrix} a & b \\ c & d \end{vmatrix} = ad - cb$

$\det\begin{bmatrix} 2 & 3 \\ 5 & 9 \end{bmatrix} = \begin{vmatrix} 2 & 3 \\ 5 & 9 \end{vmatrix} = 2(9) - 5(3) = 18 - 15 = 3$

Vertical brackets indicate a determinant.

Find the determinant of each matrix.

1. $\det\begin{bmatrix} -1 & 2 \\ -5 & 4 \end{bmatrix} = \begin{vmatrix} -1 & 2 \\ -5 & 4 \end{vmatrix} = -1(4) - (-5)(2) =$ 6
2. $\det\begin{bmatrix} \frac{3}{2} & -\frac{1}{4} \\ \frac{1}{2} & \frac{1}{4} \end{bmatrix} = \begin{vmatrix} \frac{3}{2} & -\frac{1}{4} \\ \frac{1}{2} & \frac{1}{4} \end{vmatrix} = \frac{3}{2}\left(\frac{1}{4}\right) - \left(\frac{1}{2}\right)\left(-\frac{1}{4}\right) =$ $\frac{1}{2}$
3. $\det\begin{bmatrix} -3 & -4 \\ -1 & -6 \end{bmatrix} = \begin{vmatrix} -3 & -4 \\ -1 & -6 \end{vmatrix} = -3(-6) - (-1)(-4) =$ 14
4. $\det\begin{bmatrix} -2.4 & 0.5 \\ 1.2 & 2 \end{bmatrix} = \begin{vmatrix} -2.4 & 0.5 \\ 1.2 & 2 \end{vmatrix} =$ −5.4
5. $\det\begin{bmatrix} \frac{1}{6} & 9 \\ \frac{2}{3} & -12 \end{bmatrix} = \begin{vmatrix} \frac{1}{6} & 9 \\ \frac{2}{3} & -12 \end{vmatrix} =$ −8
6. $\det\begin{bmatrix} 8 & \frac{2}{5} \\ -15 & \frac{3}{4} \end{bmatrix} = \begin{vmatrix} 8 & \frac{2}{5} \\ -15 & \frac{3}{4} \end{vmatrix} =$ 12

Multi-Step Test Prep **Exercise 34** involves creating and solving a system of equations by using Cramer's rule. This exercise prepares students for the Multi-Step Test Prep on page 294.

Test Prep Doctor In **Exercise 38,** students who chose **G** or **J** made a mistake in subtracting a negative. The determinants of both **G** and **J** are 23.

Answers

34a. $\begin{cases} 6x + 3y = 48 \\ 2x + 10y = 52 \end{cases}$

b. $\begin{bmatrix} 6 & 3 \\ 2 & 10 \end{bmatrix}$; $D = 54$

c. There is one solution.

d. $(6, 4)$

e. 6 tickets for a Wild ride and 4 tickets for a Mild ride

35. If the cross products of a proportion are equal, then the proportion is true. If the difference of the cross products is equal to 0 for a 2×2 matrix, then $D = 0$.

36a. 15 square units

b. $\begin{vmatrix} 5 & 1 \\ 0 & 3 \end{vmatrix} = 15$; the determinant is equal to the area in square units.

c. Possible answer: Change the width to 6 and the height to 4; area = 24 square units; $\begin{vmatrix} 6 & 1 \\ 0 & 4 \end{vmatrix} = 24$; yes, the relationship still holds.

d. $\begin{vmatrix} 1 & 5 \\ 3 & 0 \end{vmatrix} = -15$; changing the order of the points changes the sign of the determinant.

40. The value of the determinant will be 0 because each product of the diagonals will contain at least one factor of 0.

Multi-Step Test Prep

34. This problem will prepare you for the Multi-Step Test Prep on page 294.

At an amusement park, 6 Wild rides and 3 Mild rides require 48 tickets, while 2 Wild rides and 10 Mild rides require 52 tickets. Let x be the number of tickets for a Wild ride and y be the number of tickets for a Mild ride.

a. Write the problem as a system of equations.
b. Write the coefficient matrix, and find its determinant.
c. How many solutions are there?
d. Use Cramer's rule to find x and y. ⟶
e. How many tickets are required for each ride?

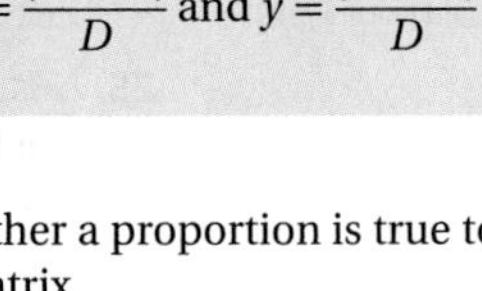

$x = \dfrac{\begin{vmatrix} c_1 & b_1 \\ c_2 & b_2 \end{vmatrix}}{D}$ and $y = \dfrac{\begin{vmatrix} a_1 & c_1 \\ a_2 & c_2 \end{vmatrix}}{D}$

35. **Write About It** Compare the process of deciding whether a proportion is true to the process of determining whether $D = 0$ for a 2×2 matrix.

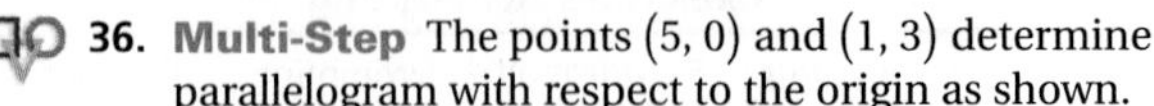

36. **Multi-Step** The points $(5, 0)$ and $(1, 3)$ determine a parallelogram with respect to the origin as shown.

a. Find the area of the parallelogram.
b. Enter the two points in order into $\begin{vmatrix} x_1 & x_2 \\ y_1 & y_2 \end{vmatrix}$, and evaluate. How does this value relate to the area of the parallelogram?
c. Change the width and height of the parallelogram, and find the area and the determinant. Does the relationship between the area and the determinant still hold?
d. Reverse the points in part **b** so that (x_1, y_1) is $(1, 3)$. Do the same for the parallelogram in part **c.** How does the order affect the determinant?

Test Prep

37. Which of the following statements describes the system of equations $\begin{cases} 3x = y - 1 \\ x + 2y = 16 \end{cases}$?

Ⓐ Dependent; many solutions
Ⓑ Inconsistent; no solution
Ⓒ Inconsistent; many solutions
Ⓓ Consistent; one solution

38. Which matrix has a determinant of 1?

Ⓕ $\begin{bmatrix} 3 & 11 \\ 1 & 4 \end{bmatrix}$
Ⓖ $\begin{bmatrix} 3 & -11 \\ 1 & 4 \end{bmatrix}$
Ⓗ $\begin{bmatrix} -3 & 11 \\ 1 & 4 \end{bmatrix}$
Ⓙ $\begin{bmatrix} 3 & 11 \\ -1 & 4 \end{bmatrix}$

39. **Gridded Response** The determinant of $\begin{bmatrix} 4 & -5 \\ 1 & 2x \end{bmatrix}$ is 25. Find x. 2.5, or $\frac{5}{2}$

CHALLENGE AND EXTEND

40. Suppose a 3×3 matrix has a row or column of zeros. Explain the effect on the determinant.

41. Write $x^2 + y^2$ as a determinant. Possible answer: $\begin{vmatrix} x & y \\ -y & x \end{vmatrix}$

42. If $x = \dfrac{\begin{vmatrix} 1 & 2 \\ 3 & 4 \end{vmatrix}}{5}$ and $y = \dfrac{\begin{vmatrix} 7 & a \\ b & c \end{vmatrix}}{5}$, find the values of a, b, and c. $a = 1$, $b = 11.5$, $c = 3$

4-4 PROBLEM SOLVING

As Kristin prepares for a triathlon, she makes a chart of her exercise time, along with the calories burned each day. Part of her chart is shown in the table below. How many calories per hour does she burn for each activity?

Triathlon Training Record

Day	Swimming (h)	Cycling (h)	Running (h)	Calories Burned
Friday	1.5	2.0	0.5	2450
Saturday	2.5	3.0	1.5	4310
Sunday	2.0	1.5	1.6	3150

1. Write a system of equations that relates Kristin's exercise time to the number of calories burned each day. Use s, c, and r for the calories burned per hour for the three activities. $\begin{cases} 1.5s + 2c + 0.5r = 2450 \\ 2.5s + 3c + 1.5r = 4310 \\ 2s + 1.5c + 1.6r = 3150 \end{cases}$

2. Write the coefficient matrix for the system of equations. $D = \begin{bmatrix} 1.5 & 2.0 & 0.5 \\ 2.5 & 3.0 & 1.5 \\ 2.0 & 1.5 & 1.6 \end{bmatrix}$

3. What is the value, D, for the determinant of the coefficient matrix? $D = 0.7$

4. Use Cramer's rule to solve this system of equations. Give the values for s, c, and r. $s = 590$; $c = 620$; $r = 650$

Choose the letter for the best answer.

5. Ty has a bag of pennies, nickels, and dimes. He has 10 times as many pennies as dimes. He has a total of 52 coins and twice as many nickels as dimes. Which coefficient matrix could you use to solve this problem?

Ⓐ $\begin{bmatrix} 1 & 1 & 1 \\ 1 & 0 & -10 \\ 0 & 1 & -2 \end{bmatrix}$
B $\begin{bmatrix} 1 & 1 & 1 \\ 10 & 0 & -1 \\ 0 & 2 & -1 \end{bmatrix}$
C $\begin{bmatrix} 1 & 1 & 1 \\ 1 & 0 & -10 \\ 0 & -1 & 2 \end{bmatrix}$
D $\begin{bmatrix} 1 & 1 & 1 \\ 10 & 0 & -1 \\ 0 & -2 & 1 \end{bmatrix}$

6. Phyllis collects silver dollars and Kennedy half-dollars. She has 5 times as many half-dollars as dollar coins. She has a total of 192 coins. Which solution could you use to find the number of silver dollars Phyllis has?

A $\dfrac{\begin{vmatrix} 192 & 1 \\ 0 & -5 \end{vmatrix}}{-6}$
Ⓑ $\dfrac{\begin{vmatrix} 1 & 192 \\ 1 & 0 \end{vmatrix}}{-6}$
C $\dfrac{\begin{vmatrix} 1 & 192 \\ -5 & 0 \end{vmatrix}}{-6}$
D $\dfrac{\begin{vmatrix} 192 & 1 \\ 0 & 1 \end{vmatrix}}{-6}$

4-4 CHALLENGE

What happens to the determinant of a matrix as the entries in the matrix are changed? Certain changes affect the value of the determinant and others do not. Those operations that do not change the determinant are called invariant operations. The determinant of matrix R is -36. Interchange the first and second rows to get matrix S.

$R = \begin{bmatrix} 1 & 0 & 4 \\ -3 & 2 & 5 \\ 0 & 2 & -1 \end{bmatrix}$ $S = \begin{bmatrix} -3 & 2 & 5 \\ 1 & 0 & 4 \\ 0 & 2 & -1 \end{bmatrix}$

1. a. Calculate the determinant of matrix S. 36
b. Interchange the second and third rows of matrix R. Find the determinant of the new matrix. How do they compare? The determinants are opposites of one another.
c. Make a conjecture about how the value of a matrix changes if you interchange two rows of the matrix. Possible answer: If two rows of a matrix are interchanged, the determinant changes sign.

2. a. Multiply the first row of matrix R by 3. Now find the new determinant. How does this value compare to the original determinant? Determinant is -108, which is 3 times the original determinant of R.
b. Try this with another 3×3 matrix. Then make a conjecture about how the determinant changes when a row is multiplied by a constant.
Possible answer: If a row of a matrix is multiplied by a constant, the value of the determinant is multiplied by that same constant.

3. a. Multiply matrix R by 3 to get matrix T. Find the determinant of matrix T. -972
b. Now create a 2×2 matrix and find its determinant. Multiply the matrix by 4 and find the determinant again. Write a conjecture about how the determinant of a matrix changes when the matrix is multiplied by a constant.
The determinant of T is 27 (3^3) times the determinant of R. The determinant of the second matrix will be 16 (4^2) times greater. Possible answer: If an $n \times n$ matrix is multiplied by a constant k, the determinant will be multiplied by k^n.

4. a. Use matrix R and add twice the first row to the second row. This becomes the new second row. Write the new matrix U. Find its determinant. $U = \begin{bmatrix} 1 & 0 & 4 \\ -1 & 2 & 13 \\ 0 & 2 & -1 \end{bmatrix}$; the determinant of U is -36.
b. Try this with another 3×3 matrix. What conjecture can you make about how this operation affects the determinant?
Possible answer: This is an invariant operation. Adding a multiple of one row to another row does not change the determinant.

43. **Civics** A ballot measure received the vote percentages shown in the table. There were a total of 4826 votes. How many of the votes came from Southside? **254**

Ballot Measure Voting		
District	In Favor	Opposed
Northside	47%	53%
Southside	85%	15%
Total	49%	51%

SPIRAL REVIEW

44. **Consumer Economics** Trish has \$125 and a coupon for \$10 off her total at the Toasty Coats Outlet. She finds a coat that is marked 25% off. Write an inequality for the maximum amount that the coat can be priced before the markdown so Trish can afford to buy it. *(Lesson 2-1)*
$180 \geq x$

Use substitution to solve each system of equations. *(Lesson 3-2)*

45. $\begin{cases} x = \frac{1}{3}y \\ 6x - 6y = 16 \end{cases}$ $\left(-\frac{4}{3}, -4\right)$ 46. $\begin{cases} x + y = -5 \\ 2x - y = -7 \end{cases}$ $(-4, -1)$ 47. $\begin{cases} 2x = y \\ 4x + y = -2 \end{cases}$ $\left(-\frac{1}{3}, -\frac{2}{3}\right)$

Use a matrix to transform the polygon with coordinates $D(1, 1)$, $E(4, -2)$, $F(-2, -3)$, and $G(-1, -1)$. *(Lesson 4-3)*

48. Translate 5 units right and 3 units up. $D'(6, 4), E'(9, 1), F'(3, 0), G'(4, 2)$
49. Reflect *DEFG* across the x-axis. $D'(1, -1), E'(4, 2), F'(-2, 3), G'(-1, 1)$
50. Translate *DEFG* 1 unit left and 2 units down. $D'(0, -1), E'(3, -4), F'(-3, -5), G'(-2, -3)$
51. Dilate *DEFG* by a factor of 3.
$D'(3, 3), E'(12, -6), F'(-6, -9), G'(-3, -3)$

Career Path

go.hrw.com
Career Resources Online
KEYWORD: MB7 Career

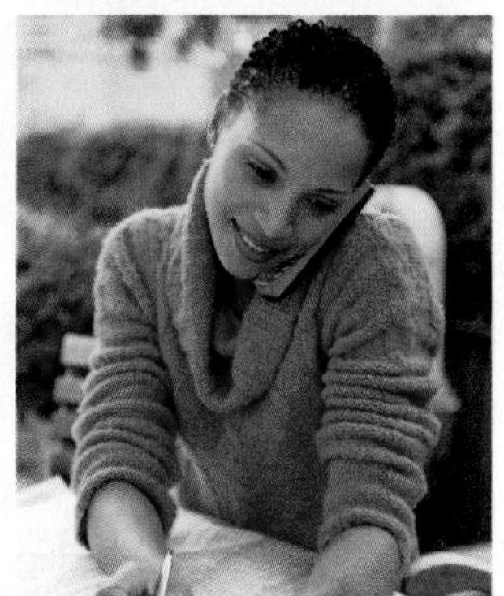

Karen Michaels
Economist

Q: What math classes did you take in high school?
A: I took Algebra 1 and 2, Geometry, and Precalculus.

Q: What math classes did you take in college?
A: Math and economics are closely related, so I took several math classes—Statistics, Calculus, Mathematical Economics.

Q: Any topics you found particularly interesting?
A: Game theory. You wouldn't think it applies, but it has a lot of applications in math, economics, and political science. It's about how people make decisions that affect other people.

Q: How do you use math as an economist?
A: I've conducted research projects on energy costs, interest rates, inflation, and employment levels. I collect, analyze, and summarize data and forecast economic trends.

Journal

Have students explain whether they prefer the methods taught in this lesson or the more traditional techniques taught in Algebra 1 (e.g., linear combination) for solving systems of 2 and 3 equations.

ALTERNATIVE ASSESSMENT

Have students write a system of 2 equations and a system of 3 equations and solve them using Cramer's rule. They should present a solution that includes the proper matrix and the procedure for finding the answers using Cramer's rule.

Power Presentations with PowerPoint®

4-4 Lesson Quiz

Find the determinant of each matrix.

1. $\begin{bmatrix} 6 & 1.5 \\ 10 & 3.5 \end{bmatrix}$ 6

2. $\begin{bmatrix} 3 & 1 & -4 \\ 2 & 0 & -1 \\ 1 & 5 & 4 \end{bmatrix}$ -34

Use Cramer's rule to solve.

3. $\begin{cases} 4x + 3y = 30 \\ 5x - 6y = 31 \end{cases}$ $x = 7, y = \frac{2}{3}$

4. Jeff buys 7 apples and 4 pears for \$7.25. At the same prices, Hayley buys 5 apples and 9 pears for \$10.40. What is the price of one pear? \$0.85

Also available on transparency

Answers

48.

49.

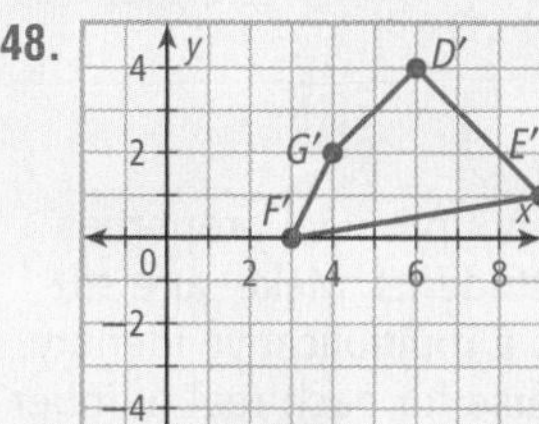

50.

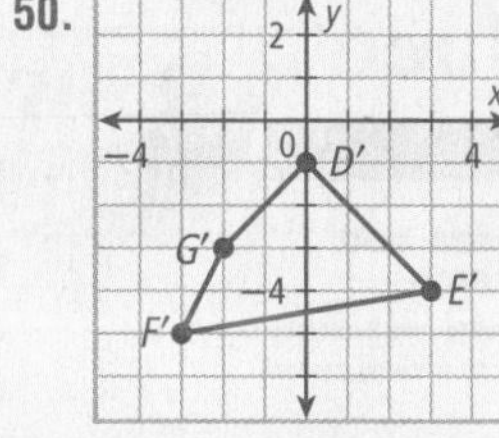

51.

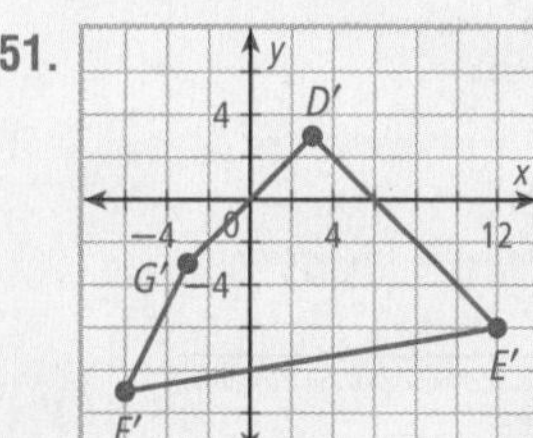

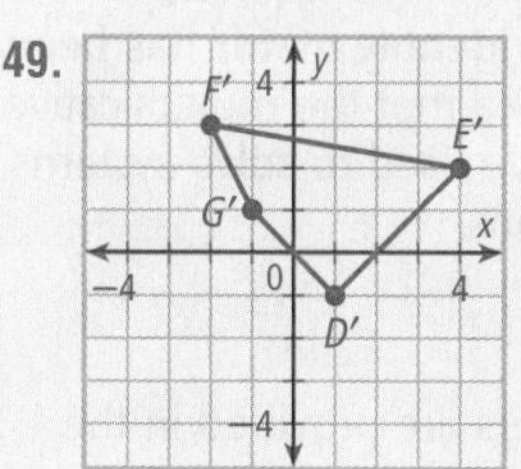

4-5 Organizer

Pacing: Traditional 2 days
Block 1 day

Objectives: Determine whether a matrix has an inverse.

Solve systems of equations using inverse matrices.

Online Edition
Tutorial Videos, Interactivity, TechKeys

Countdown to Testing Week 9

Power Presentations with PowerPoint®

Warm Up

Multiply the matrices.

1. $\begin{bmatrix} 2 & 3 \\ 5 & 7 \end{bmatrix} \begin{bmatrix} 1 & 2 \\ 4 & 8 \end{bmatrix}$ $\begin{bmatrix} 14 & 28 \\ 33 & 66 \end{bmatrix}$

Find the determinant.

2. $\begin{bmatrix} 2 & 3 \\ 5 & 7 \end{bmatrix}$ −1 **3.** $\begin{bmatrix} 1 & 2 & 3 \\ 2 & 3 & 4 \\ 3 & 4 & 5 \end{bmatrix}$ 0

Also available on transparency

Q: Yesterday you were sneezing like crazy. Today you're fine. What happened?

A: I used a decolding matrix.

State Resources

go.hrw.com
State Resources Online
KEYWORD: MP7 Resources

4-5 Matrix Inverses and Solving Systems

A2.2.2 Solve problems that can be modeled using systems of linear equations up to three variables, interpret the solutions, and determine whether the solutions . . . are reasonable.

Objectives
Determine whether a matrix has an inverse.

Solve systems of equations using inverse matrices.

Vocabulary
multiplicative inverse matrix
matrix equation
variable matrix
constant matrix

Who uses this?

Cryptographers, who create and crack codes, may use matrices to protect the privacy of messages. (See Example 4.)

LET'S SEE, NOW..."EXTENSIVE EXPERIENCE WRITING COMPUTER CODE, INCLUDING, BUT NOT LIMITED TO: oic, btw, brb, imho, lol, rofl, ttfn..."
MARK PARISI

Cartoon copyrighted by Mark Parisi, printed with permission

You can encode a message using a matrix. The receiver can use an inverse process to decode your message.

A matrix can have an inverse only if it is a square matrix. But not all square matrices have inverses. If the product of the square matrix A and the square matrix A^{-1} is the identity matrix I, then $AA^{-1} = A^{-1}A = I$, and A^{-1} is the **multiplicative inverse matrix** of A, or just the *inverse* of A.

EXAMPLE 1 **Determining Whether Two Matrices Are Inverses**

Determine whether the two given matrices are inverses.

Remember!
The identity matrix I has 1's on the main diagonal and 0's everywhere else.

$$\begin{bmatrix} 1 & 0 & 0 \\ 0 & 1 & 0 \\ 0 & 0 & 1 \end{bmatrix}$$

A $\begin{bmatrix} 2 & 0 & 1 \\ 4 & 1 & 2 \\ 2 & 0 & 4 \end{bmatrix}$ and $\begin{bmatrix} \frac{2}{3} & 0 & -\frac{1}{6} \\ -2 & 1 & 0 \\ -\frac{1}{3} & 0 & \frac{1}{3} \end{bmatrix}$

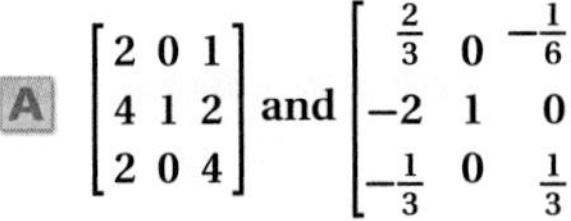

```
[A]*[B]
        [[1 0 0]
         [0 1 0]
         [0 0 1]]
```

```
[B]*[A]
        [[1 0 0]
         [0 1 0]
         [0 0 1]]
```

The product is the identity matrix I, so the matrices are inverses.

B $\begin{bmatrix} 2 & 3 \\ 7 & 10 \end{bmatrix}$ and $\begin{bmatrix} -10 & 6 \\ 7 & -4 \end{bmatrix}$

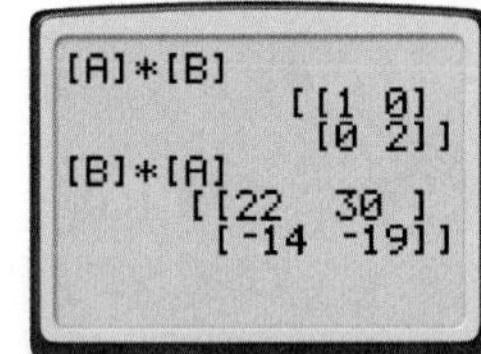

```
[A]*[B]
          [[1 0]
           [0 2]]
[B]*[A]
      [[22  30 ]
       [-14 -19]]
```

Neither product is I, so the matrices are not inverses.

CHECK IT OUT! **1.** Determine whether the given matrices are inverses. yes

$$\begin{bmatrix} -1 & 0 & 2 \\ 4 & 1 & -1 \\ 2 & 0 & 1 \end{bmatrix} \text{ and } \begin{bmatrix} -0.2 & 0 & 0.4 \\ 1.2 & 1 & -1.4 \\ 0.4 & 0 & 0.2 \end{bmatrix}$$

1 Introduce

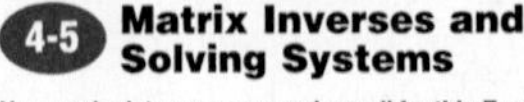

EXPLORATION

4-5 Matrix Inverses and Solving Systems

Use a calculator or paper and pencil for this Exploration.

1. Find the products AB and BA for the following matrices.
   $A = \begin{bmatrix} -2 & 0 \\ 5 & 1 \end{bmatrix}$ $B = \begin{bmatrix} -0.5 & 0 \\ 2.5 & 1 \end{bmatrix}$
2. Find the products PQ and QP for the following matrices.
   $P = \begin{bmatrix} 8 & 5 \\ 6 & 4 \end{bmatrix}$ $Q = \begin{bmatrix} 2 & -2.5 \\ -3 & 4 \end{bmatrix}$
3. Find the products ST and TS for the following matrices.
   $S = \begin{bmatrix} 3 & 1 \\ 11 & 4 \end{bmatrix}$ $T = \begin{bmatrix} 4 & -1 \\ -11 & 3 \end{bmatrix}$
4. What do you notice about the products of the matrices in Problems 1–3?

THINK AND DISCUSS

5. **Explain** what is special about the matrix that you found to be the product in Problems 1–3.
6. **Describe** how the pairs of matrices you multiplied are similar to the numbers $\frac{3}{5}$ and $\frac{5}{3}$.

Motivate

Briefly reintroduce the multiplicative properties of the real numbers to students. Make sure students recall that there is a multiplicative identity and a multiplicative inverse for each real number. Have students recall that, for matrices, they know how to multiply, and the identity matrix has been defined. Introduce the idea that the multiplicative inverse for a matrix will be used to solve systems by solving matrix equations.

Explorations and answers are provided in the *Explorations* binder.

Inverse of a 2 × 2 Matrix

The inverse of a 2 × 2 matrix $A = \begin{bmatrix} a & b \\ c & d \end{bmatrix}$ is $A^{-1} = \dfrac{1}{\det A}\begin{bmatrix} d & -b \\ -c & a \end{bmatrix}$.

If the determinant is 0, $\dfrac{1}{\det A}$ is undefined. So a matrix with a determinant of 0 has no inverse. It is called a *singular* matrix.

EXAMPLE 2 Finding the Inverse of a 2 × 2 Matrix

Find the inverse of the matrix, if it is defined.

A $A = \begin{bmatrix} -2 & 2 \\ 3 & -4 \end{bmatrix}$

First, check that the determinant is nonzero. The determinant is $(-2)(-4) - 3(2) = 8 - 6 = 2$, so the matrix has an inverse.

For $\begin{bmatrix} a & b \\ c & d \end{bmatrix}$, the inverse is $\dfrac{1}{\det A}\begin{bmatrix} d & -b \\ -c & a \end{bmatrix}$.

So the inverse of $A = \begin{bmatrix} -2 & 2 \\ 3 & -4 \end{bmatrix}$ is $A^{-1} = \frac{1}{2}\begin{bmatrix} -4 & -2 \\ -3 & -2 \end{bmatrix} = \begin{bmatrix} -2 & -1 \\ -\frac{3}{2} & -1 \end{bmatrix}$.

Use a calculator to check, as in Example 1.

B $B = \begin{bmatrix} \frac{1}{2} & 2 \\ 3 & 12 \end{bmatrix}$

The determinant is $\frac{1}{2}(12) - 3(2) = 0$, so B has no inverse.

Helpful Hint

To find $\begin{bmatrix} d & -b \\ -c & a \end{bmatrix}$ from $A = \begin{bmatrix} a & b \\ c & d \end{bmatrix}$, think "switch ops" for the cross products. *Switch a* and *d*. Take the *opposites* of *b* and *c*.

$\begin{bmatrix} \frac{1}{6} & \frac{1}{6} \\ \frac{1}{4} & -\frac{1}{4} \end{bmatrix}$ **2.** Find the inverse of $\begin{bmatrix} 3 & 2 \\ 3 & -2 \end{bmatrix}$, if it is defined.

You can use the inverse of a matrix to solve a system of equations. This process is similar to solving an equation such as $5x = 20$ by multiplying each side by $\frac{1}{5}$, the multiplicative inverse of 5.

To solve systems of equations with the inverse, you first write the **matrix equation** $AX = B$, where A is the coefficient matrix, X is the **variable matrix**, and B is the **constant matrix**.

The matrix equation representing $\begin{cases} x + y = 8 \\ 2x + y = 1 \end{cases}$ is shown.

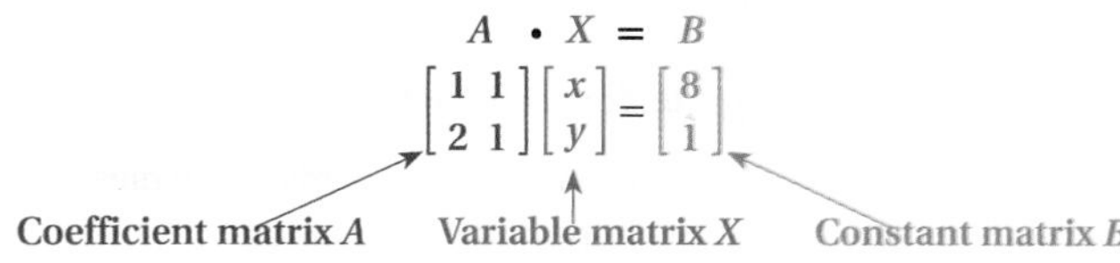

To solve $AX = B$, multiply both sides by the inverse A^{-1}.

$$A^{-1}AX = A^{-1}B$$
$$IX = A^{-1}B \qquad \textit{The product of } A^{-1} \textit{ and } A \textit{ is } I.$$
$$X = A^{-1}B$$

Power Presentations with PowerPoint®

Additional Examples

Example 1

Determine whether the two given matrices are inverses.

A. $\begin{bmatrix} 1 & 5 \\ 4 & 8 \end{bmatrix}$ and $\begin{bmatrix} -\frac{2}{3} & \frac{5}{12} \\ \frac{1}{3} & -\frac{1}{12} \end{bmatrix}$ yes

B. $\begin{bmatrix} 1 & 0 & 1 \\ 1 & 1 & 0 \\ 0 & 1 & 1 \end{bmatrix}$ and $\begin{bmatrix} \frac{1}{2} & \frac{1}{2} & -\frac{1}{2} \\ -\frac{1}{2} & \frac{1}{2} & \frac{1}{2} \\ \frac{1}{2} & -\frac{1}{2} & -\frac{1}{2} \end{bmatrix}$ no

Example 2

Find the inverse of the matrix if it is defined.

A. $\begin{bmatrix} 4 & 3 \\ 2 & 1 \end{bmatrix}$ $\begin{bmatrix} -\frac{1}{2} & \frac{3}{2} \\ 1 & -2 \end{bmatrix}$

B. $\begin{bmatrix} 4 & -3 \\ -\frac{1}{3} & \frac{1}{4} \end{bmatrix}$ not defined

Also available on transparency

INTERVENTION

Questioning Strategies

EXAMPLE 1

- If two matrices, *A* and *B,* are multiplied together, and if *A* × *B* gives the identity matrix, must *B* × *A* also give the identity matrix?

EXAMPLE 2

- How is the determinant used to find the inverse of a matrix?

2 Teach

Guided Instruction

Before **Example 3,** make sure that students understand the relationship between a given system of equations and the corresponding matrix equation. Remind them that matrix multiplication is not commutative, so the inverse matrix always has to be on the left of the coefficient matrix when solving a matrix equation.

Reaching All Learners

Through Number Sense

Help students see the connections between solving an equation with real numbers and solving a matrix equation.

$3x = 18$	$AX = B$
$\frac{1}{3}(3x) = \frac{1}{3}(18)$	$A^{-1}(AX) = A^{-1}B$
Associative property:	
$\left(\frac{1}{3} \cdot 3\right)x = 6$	$(A^{-1}A)X = A^{-1}B$
$1x = 6$	$IX = A^{-1}B$
$x = 6$	$X = A^{-1}B$

Power Presentations with PowerPoint®

Additional Examples

Example 3

Write the matrix equation for the system and solve.

$\begin{cases} 2x + 5y = 0 \\ 5x - 3y = 31 \end{cases}$

$\begin{bmatrix} 2 & 5 \\ 5 & -3 \end{bmatrix}\begin{bmatrix} x \\ y \end{bmatrix} = \begin{bmatrix} 0 \\ 31 \end{bmatrix}$ $\begin{bmatrix} x \\ y \end{bmatrix} = \begin{bmatrix} 5 \\ -2 \end{bmatrix}$

Example 4

Using the encoding matrix $E = \begin{bmatrix} 1 & 7 \\ 7 & 6 \end{bmatrix}$, decode the message

$\begin{bmatrix} 146 & 1 & 34 & 43 & 133 & 149 \\ 205 & 7 & 152 & 86 & 114 & 183 \end{bmatrix}$.

Math is best.

Also available on transparency

INTERVENTION

Questioning Strategies

EXAMPLE 3

- Would it also work to multiply both sides by the inverse, as shown here: $AXA^{-1} = BA^{-1}$?

EXAMPLE 4

- What would happen if you used the identity matrix as the encoding matrix?

Social Studies In **Example 4,** mention that during World War II, a team of British mathematicians led by Alan Turing set out to break the German U-boats' coded messages that had been created by encryption machines called Enigmas. They succeeded by building and using what many people consider the first computer, which they called Colossus.

EXAMPLE 3 Solving Systems Using Inverse Matrices

Write the matrix equation for the system, and solve.

$$\begin{cases} x + y = 8 \\ 2x + y = 1 \end{cases}$$

Matrix multiplication is not commutative, so it is important to multiply by the inverse *in the same order* on both sides of the equation. A^{-1} comes *first* on each side.

Step 1 Set up the matrix equation.

$$\begin{matrix} A & X & = & B \end{matrix}$$

$$\begin{bmatrix} 1 & 1 \\ 2 & 1 \end{bmatrix}\begin{bmatrix} x \\ y \end{bmatrix} = \begin{bmatrix} 8 \\ 1 \end{bmatrix}$$ *Write: coefficient matrix • variable matrix = constant matrix.*

Step 2 Find the determinant.

The determinant of A is $1 - 2 = -1$.

Step 3 Find A^{-1}.

$$A = \begin{bmatrix} 1 & 1 \\ 2 & 1 \end{bmatrix}, \text{ so } A^{-1} = \frac{1}{-1}\begin{bmatrix} 1 & -1 \\ -2 & 1 \end{bmatrix} = \begin{bmatrix} -1 & 1 \\ 2 & -1 \end{bmatrix}$$

$$X = A^{-1} B$$

$$\begin{bmatrix} x \\ y \end{bmatrix} = \begin{bmatrix} -1 & 1 \\ 2 & -1 \end{bmatrix}\begin{bmatrix} 8 \\ 1 \end{bmatrix}$$ *Multiply.*

$$= \begin{bmatrix} -7 \\ 15 \end{bmatrix}$$

The solution is $(-7, 15)$.

CHECK IT OUT! **3.** Write the matrix equation for $\begin{cases} x + y = 4 \\ 2x + 3y = 9 \end{cases}$ and solve.

$\begin{bmatrix} 1 & 1 \\ 2 & 3 \end{bmatrix}\begin{bmatrix} x \\ y \end{bmatrix} = \begin{bmatrix} 4 \\ 9 \end{bmatrix}$; (3,1)

EXAMPLE 4 *Problem-Solving Application: Cryptography*

You receive a coded instant message from Lupe.

Both you and Lupe use the same encoding matrix $E = \begin{bmatrix} 6 & 5 \\ 7 & 6 \end{bmatrix}$.

Upon decoding the message, you will get a matrix where letters are represented by numbers (A is 1, B is 2, ... Z is 26, and 0 is a space). Decode the message.

1 Understand the Problem

The **answer** will be the words of the message, uncoded.

List the important information:

- The encoding matrix is E.
- Lupe used M as the message matrix, with letters written as the integers 0 to 26, and then used EM to create the two-row code matrix C.

$$C = \begin{bmatrix} 240 & 48 & 70 & 5 & 173 & 6 & 245 & 183 & 159 \\ 284 & 56 & 83 & 6 & 205 & 7 & 290 & 216 & 189 \end{bmatrix}$$

Make a Plan

Because $EM = C$, you can use $M = E^{-1}C$ to decode the message into numbers and then convert the numbers to letters.

- Multiply E^{-1} by C to get M, the message written as numbers.
- Use the letter equivalents for the numbers in order to write the message as words so that you can read it.

Solve

Use a calculator to find E^{-1}.

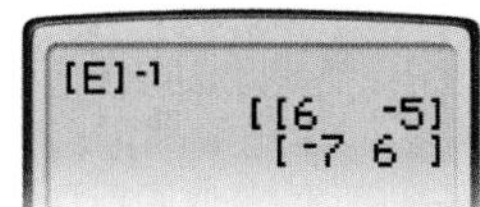

$$E^{-1} = \begin{bmatrix} 6 & -5 \\ -7 & 6 \end{bmatrix}$$

Multiply E^{-1} by C.

20 = T, and so on

$$M = E^{-1}C = \begin{bmatrix} 20 & 8 & 5 & 0 & 13 & 1 & 20 & 18 & 9 \\ 24 & 0 & 8 & 1 & 19 & 0 & 25 & 15 & 21 \end{bmatrix}$$

T H E _ M A T R I
X _ H A S _ Y O U

The message in words is "The matrix has you."

Look Back

You can verify by multiplying E by M to see that the decoding was correct. If the math had been done incorrectly, getting a different message that made sense would have been very unlikely.

4. Use the encoding matrix $E = \begin{bmatrix} 3 & 1 \\ 5 & 2 \end{bmatrix}$ to decode this message.

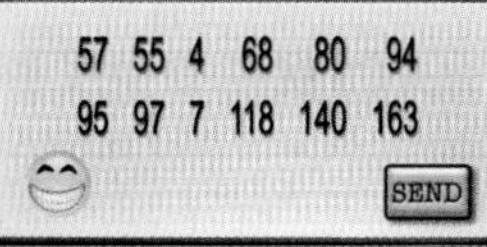

Helpful Hint

To reduce rounding errors, enter fractions when appropriate. The calculator will convert your entries to decimal representations.

THINK AND DISCUSS

1. Explain what the existence of the inverse of matrix S, S^{-1}, tells you about matrix S.
2. Describe the inverse of an identity matrix.
3. **GET ORGANIZED** Copy and complete the graphic organizer. Compare multiplicative inverses of real numbers and matrices.

Multiplicative Inverses		
	Real Numbers	**Matrices**
Notation and Example		
How to Show That It Is the Multiplicative Inverse		
Commutative Property		

COMMON ERROR ALERT

After learning that the commutative property does not hold for matrix multiplication, students may think that $AA^{-1} \neq A^{-1}A$. Assure them that in this special case, they are equal, $AA^{-1} = A^{-1}A = I$.

Teaching Tip

Reading Math The idea of using an inverse to "undo" a function is important throughout mathematics. Students should understand that the use of -1 as an exponent means *inverse*. Some students will have seen inverse functions in the trigonometry section of standard geometry courses, where $\tan^{-1}(x)$ means "inverse tangent of x."

ENGLISH LANGUAGE LEARNERS

3 Close

Summarize

Review how to solve a system of equations by representing it as a matrix equation and then using the inverse of the coefficient matrix to solve for the variable matrix.

ONGOING ASSESSMENT and INTERVENTION

***Diagnose Before* the Lesson**
4-5 Warm Up, TE p. 278

***Monitor During* the Lesson**
Check It Out! Exercises, SE pp. 278–281
Questioning Strategies, TE pp. 279–280

***Assess After* the Lesson**
4-5 Lesson Quiz, TE p. 285
Alternative Assessment, TE p. 285

Answers to *Think and Discuss*

Possible answers:

1. The matrix is a square matrix, and its determinant is not equal to 0.
2. The inverse of an identity matrix is equal to the identity matrix.
3. See p. A6.

4-5 Exercises

Assignment Guide

Assign *Guided Practice* exercises as necessary.

If you finished Examples **1–2**
- **Basic** 14–21, 32, 36, 41
- **Average** 14–21, 32, 36, 41–42
- **Advanced** 14–21, 32, 36, 41–42

If you finished Examples **1–4**
- **Basic** 14–30, 34, 39–44, 48–56
- **Average** 14–28, 30–34, 36–44, 46, 48–56
- **Advanced** 14–29, 32–35, 40–56

Homework Quick Check
Quickly check key concepts.
Exercises: 14, 18, 22, 25, 26

Answers

1. Write the equations in standard form. Then write a coefficient matrix, a variable matrix, and a constant matrix. Set the product of the coefficient matrix and the variable matrix equal to the constant matrix.

6. $\begin{bmatrix} -\frac{3}{4} & \frac{7}{8} \\ \frac{1}{4} & -\frac{1}{8} \end{bmatrix}$

10. $\begin{bmatrix} 3 & -1 \\ -2 & 1 \end{bmatrix}\begin{bmatrix} x \\ y \end{bmatrix} = \begin{bmatrix} 5 \\ -4 \end{bmatrix}$; (1, −2)

11. $\begin{bmatrix} 5 & 9 \\ -4 & -7 \end{bmatrix}\begin{bmatrix} x \\ y \end{bmatrix} = \begin{bmatrix} 1 \\ 2 \end{bmatrix}$; (−25, 14)

12. $\begin{bmatrix} 2 & 4 \\ 2 & 3 \end{bmatrix}\begin{bmatrix} x \\ y \end{bmatrix} = \begin{bmatrix} 3 \\ 1 \end{bmatrix}$; (−2.5, 2)

State Resources

go.hrw.com
State Resources Online
KEYWORD: MB7 Resources

4-5 Exercises

go.hrw.com
Homework Help Online
KEYWORD: MB7 4-5
Parent Resources Online
KEYWORD: MB7 Parent

GUIDED PRACTICE

1. **Vocabulary** Describe how to create a *matrix equation* from a system of equations.

SEE EXAMPLE 1 p. 278

Determine whether the given matrices are inverses.

2. $\begin{bmatrix} 8 & 4 \\ 2 & 1 \end{bmatrix}\begin{bmatrix} -\frac{1}{8} & \frac{3}{2} \\ \frac{1}{2} & -1 \end{bmatrix}$ no

3. $\begin{bmatrix} 1 & 0.4 & 1 \\ 1.2 & 0 & 0.8 \\ -1.6 & 0.2 & -1 \end{bmatrix}\begin{bmatrix} 3 & 12.5 & 2 \\ -1.6 & 2 & -1 \\ 5 & 1 & -10 \end{bmatrix}$ no

4. $\begin{bmatrix} 1 & 1 \\ 0 & 1 \end{bmatrix}\begin{bmatrix} 1 & -1 \\ 0 & 1 \end{bmatrix}$ yes

SEE EXAMPLE 2 p. 279

Find the inverse of the matrix, if it is defined.

5. $\begin{bmatrix} \frac{1}{2} & 0 \\ -\frac{1}{6} & \frac{1}{3} \end{bmatrix}$ $\begin{bmatrix} 2 & 0 \\ 1 & 3 \end{bmatrix}$

6. $\begin{bmatrix} 1 & 7 \\ 2 & 6 \end{bmatrix}$

7. $\begin{bmatrix} \frac{1}{3} & 2 \\ \frac{3}{2} & 9 \end{bmatrix}$ no inverse

8. $\begin{bmatrix} -1 & -1 \\ -1 & -1 \end{bmatrix}$ no inverse

9. $\begin{bmatrix} 8 & 7 \\ 9 & 8 \end{bmatrix}$ $\begin{bmatrix} 8 & -7 \\ -9 & 8 \end{bmatrix}$

SEE EXAMPLE 3 p. 280

Write the matrix equation for the system, and solve.

10. $\begin{cases} 3x - y = 5 \\ y = 2x - 4 \end{cases}$

11. $\begin{cases} 5x + 9y = 1 \\ 2 - 4x - 7y = 4 \end{cases}$

12. $\begin{cases} 2x + 4y = 3 \\ 2x + 3y = 1 \end{cases}$

SEE EXAMPLE 4 p. 280

13. **Cryptography** Rayanne receives the message shown, giving Sara's current location somewhere in Asia. The message was encoded using $\begin{bmatrix} 3 & 4 \\ 5 & 7 \end{bmatrix}$. Write the decoding matrix, and decode the message.
$\begin{bmatrix} 7 & -4 \\ -5 & 3 \end{bmatrix}$; in New Delhi

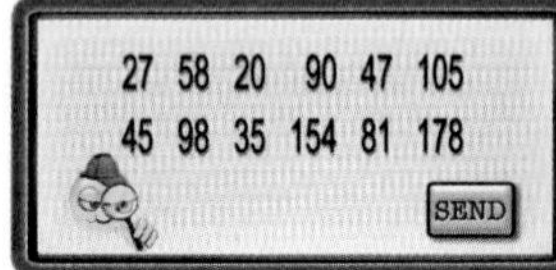

PRACTICE AND PROBLEM SOLVING

Independent Practice	
For Exercises	See Example
14–16	1
17–21	2
22–24	3
25	4

Extra Practice
Skills Practice p. S11
Application Practice p. S35

Determine whether the given matrices are inverses.

14. $\begin{bmatrix} 0 & 1 \\ 1 & 1 \end{bmatrix}\begin{bmatrix} 0 & 1 \\ 1 & -1 \end{bmatrix}$ no

15. $\begin{bmatrix} -1 & \frac{1}{2} \\ \frac{1}{4} & -2 \end{bmatrix}\begin{bmatrix} -\frac{16}{15} & -\frac{4}{15} \\ -\frac{2}{15} & -\frac{8}{15} \end{bmatrix}$ yes

16. $\begin{bmatrix} 1 & 5 & -1 \\ 1 & 0 & -1 \\ 1 & 0 & 0 \end{bmatrix}\begin{bmatrix} 0 & 0 & 1 \\ 0.2 & -0.2 & 0 \\ 0 & -1 & 1 \end{bmatrix}$ yes

Find the inverse of the matrix, if it is defined.

17. $\begin{bmatrix} -0.25 & -0.5 \\ -1.5 & -2 \end{bmatrix}$

18. $\begin{bmatrix} 7 & 14 \\ 3 & 6 \end{bmatrix}$ no inverse

19. $\begin{bmatrix} 2 & 3 \\ 5 & 8 \end{bmatrix}$ 19. $\begin{bmatrix} 8 & -3 \\ -5 & 2 \end{bmatrix}$

20. $\begin{bmatrix} 5 & 4 \\ 4 & 3 \end{bmatrix}$ $\begin{bmatrix} -3 & 4 \\ 4 & -5 \end{bmatrix}$

21. $\begin{bmatrix} -2 & -3 \\ 7 & 11 \end{bmatrix}$ $\begin{bmatrix} -11 & -3 \\ 7 & 2 \end{bmatrix}$

Write the matrix equation for the system, and solve.

22. $\begin{cases} x - y = 5 \\ 2y - x = 6 \end{cases}$

23. $\begin{cases} x + 2y = 6 \\ 2x + y = 9 \end{cases}$

24. $\begin{cases} 4x + 7y = 10 \\ 3x + 5y = 9 \end{cases}$

25. **Cryptography** Quinn receives the coded message shown, which tells him when he needs to report to headquarters. It was encoded using the matrix $\begin{bmatrix} 7 & 3 \\ 9 & 4 \end{bmatrix}$. Write the decoding matrix, and decode the message. When will Quinn need to report?

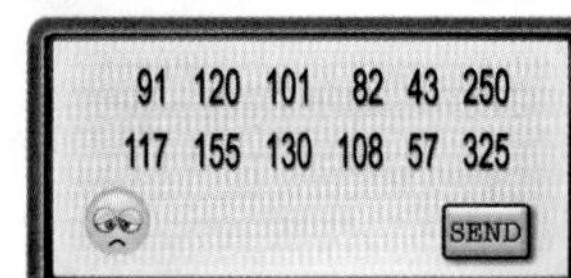

17. $\begin{bmatrix} 8 & -2 \\ -6 & 1 \end{bmatrix}$

25. $\begin{bmatrix} 4 & -3 \\ -9 & 7 \end{bmatrix}$; Monday early

Answers

22. $\begin{bmatrix} 1 & -1 \\ -1 & 2 \end{bmatrix}\begin{bmatrix} x \\ y \end{bmatrix} = \begin{bmatrix} 5 \\ 6 \end{bmatrix}$; (16, 11)

23. $\begin{bmatrix} 1 & 2 \\ 2 & 1 \end{bmatrix}\begin{bmatrix} x \\ y \end{bmatrix} = \begin{bmatrix} 6 \\ 9 \end{bmatrix}$; (4, 1)

24. $\begin{bmatrix} 4 & 7 \\ 3 & 5 \end{bmatrix}\begin{bmatrix} x \\ y \end{bmatrix} = \begin{bmatrix} 10 \\ 9 \end{bmatrix}$; (13, −6)

26. **Packaging** Cara compares three fruit and nut gift packs. Write the matrix equation and solve to find the cost per pound of pears, pecans, and nectarines.

27d. 5 six-person boats and 2 two-person boats

28. A matrix multiplied by its inverse matrix is equal to the identity matrix.

29. M and C must have the same dimensions. The number of rows of M and C must equal the number of columns of E.

27. **Multi-Step** On an outdoor trip, the organizers take seven inflatable boats, 6-person boats and 2-person boats, for 34 people. The system of equations that represents this situation is $\begin{cases} 6x + 2y = 34 \\ x + y = 7 \end{cases}$, where x represents the number of 6-person boats and y the number of 2-person boats.
   a. Write the coefficient matrix. $\begin{bmatrix} 6 & 2 \\ 1 & 1 \end{bmatrix}$
   b. Write the appropriate matrix equation. $\begin{bmatrix} 6 & 2 \\ 1 & 1 \end{bmatrix}\begin{bmatrix} x \\ y \end{bmatrix} = \begin{bmatrix} 34 \\ 7 \end{bmatrix}$
   c. Find the inverse of the coefficient matrix. **c.** $\begin{bmatrix} \frac{1}{4} & -\frac{1}{2} \\ -\frac{1}{4} & \frac{3}{2} \end{bmatrix}$
   d. Solve the matrix equation to find how many of each size boat the group takes.

28. **Critical Thinking** How are the inverse matrix and identity matrix related?

29. E is an encoding matrix for message M that gives a coded message C. What are the dimension restrictions on E, M, and C?

30. **///ERROR ANALYSIS///** Which inverse is incorrect for $\begin{bmatrix} 2 & 3 \\ 4 & 5 \end{bmatrix}$? Explain the error.

B is incorrect. In this matrix, each element is the multiplicative inverse of the corresponding element in the original matrix. However, the inverse of a 2 × 2 matrix should be determined by the formula $A^{-1} = \frac{1}{\det A}\begin{bmatrix} d & -b \\ -c & a \end{bmatrix}$.

A
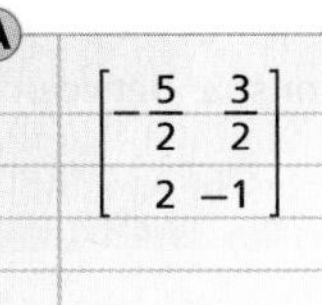
$\begin{bmatrix} -\frac{5}{2} & \frac{3}{2} \\ 2 & -1 \end{bmatrix}$

B
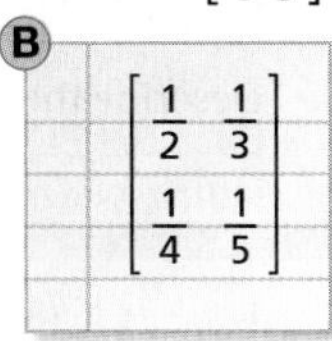
$\begin{bmatrix} \frac{1}{2} & \frac{1}{3} \\ \frac{1}{4} & \frac{1}{5} \end{bmatrix}$

31. **Entertainment** A game show host says that he has $5000 in $50 bills and $100 bills and he will give you the $5000 if you can tell him how many of each type of bill he has. He gives you a hint that he has 73 bills. Use an inverse matrix to find how many of each he has. **46 $50 bills and 27 $100 bills**

32. **Water** A fountain operating 24 hours a day can be set at three different speeds, low, medium, and high. Find the number of kL/h the fountain uses at each speed.

low 5 kL/h; med 12 kL/h; high 20 kL/h

	Time on Low (h)	Time on Med (m)	Time on High (h)	Kiloliters Used
Monday	15	7	2	199
Tuesday	16	4	4	208
Wednesday	12	8	4	236

33. **What if...?** Suppose the entries of $\begin{bmatrix} 3 & 5 \\ 2 & 4 \end{bmatrix}$ are doubled.
   a. What happens to the entries of the inverse matrix? **They are halved.**
   b. Suppose the entries of a square matrix are multiplied by n. Make a conjecture about the entries of the inverse matrix. **They are multiplied by $\frac{1}{n}$.**

**COMMON ERROR /// ALERT **

In **Exercise 22,** students may write an incorrect coefficient matrix because the second equation, $2y - x = 6$, is not in standard form, $-x + 2y = 6$. Remind students to write equations in standard form first.

Answers

26. $\begin{bmatrix} 1.5 & 1.5 & 1.5 \\ 3 & 1.5 & 3 \\ 3 & 3 & 4 \end{bmatrix}\begin{bmatrix} x \\ y \\ z \end{bmatrix} = \begin{bmatrix} 22.5 \\ 39 \\ 51 \end{bmatrix}$; $5.00/lb; $4.00/lb; $6.00/lb

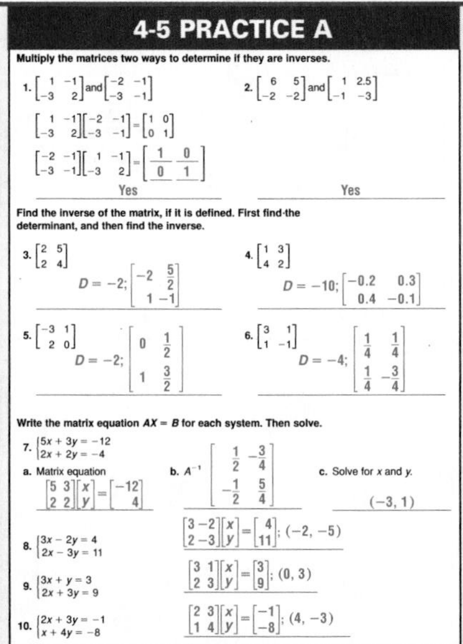

4-5 PRACTICE A

Multiply the matrices two ways to determine if they are inverses.

1. $\begin{bmatrix} 1 & -1 \\ -3 & 2 \end{bmatrix}$ and $\begin{bmatrix} -2 & -1 \\ -3 & -1 \end{bmatrix}$
$\begin{bmatrix} 1 & -1 \\ -3 & 2 \end{bmatrix}\begin{bmatrix} -2 & -1 \\ -3 & -1 \end{bmatrix} = \begin{bmatrix} 1 & 0 \\ 0 & 1 \end{bmatrix}$
$\begin{bmatrix} -2 & -1 \\ -3 & -1 \end{bmatrix}\begin{bmatrix} 1 & -1 \\ -3 & 2 \end{bmatrix} = \begin{bmatrix} 1 & 0 \\ 0 & 1 \end{bmatrix}$
Yes

2. $\begin{bmatrix} 6 & 5 \\ -2 & -2 \end{bmatrix}$ and $\begin{bmatrix} 1 & 2.5 \\ -1 & -3 \end{bmatrix}$
Yes

Find the inverse of the matrix, if it is defined. First find the determinant, and then find the inverse.

3. $\begin{bmatrix} 2 & 5 \\ 2 & 4 \end{bmatrix}$ $D = -2$; $\begin{bmatrix} -2 & \frac{5}{2} \\ 1 & -1 \end{bmatrix}$

4. $\begin{bmatrix} 1 & 3 \\ 4 & 2 \end{bmatrix}$ $D = -10$; $\begin{bmatrix} -0.2 & 0.3 \\ 0.4 & -0.1 \end{bmatrix}$

5. $\begin{bmatrix} -3 & 1 \\ 2 & 0 \end{bmatrix}$ $D = -2$; $\begin{bmatrix} 0 & \frac{1}{2} \\ 1 & \frac{3}{2} \end{bmatrix}$

6. $\begin{bmatrix} 3 & 1 \\ 1 & -1 \end{bmatrix}$ $D = -4$; $\begin{bmatrix} \frac{1}{4} & \frac{1}{4} \\ \frac{1}{4} & -\frac{3}{4} \end{bmatrix}$

Write the matrix equation $AX = B$ for each system. Then solve.

7. $\begin{cases} 5x + 3y = -12 \\ 2x + 2y = -4 \end{cases}$
a. Matrix equation $\begin{bmatrix} 5 & 3 \\ 2 & 2 \end{bmatrix}\begin{bmatrix} x \\ y \end{bmatrix} = \begin{bmatrix} -12 \\ 4 \end{bmatrix}$
b. A^{-1} $\begin{bmatrix} \frac{1}{2} & -\frac{3}{4} \\ -\frac{1}{2} & \frac{5}{4} \end{bmatrix}$
c. Solve for x and y. $(-3, 1)$

8. $\begin{cases} 3x - 2y = 4 \\ 2x - 3y = 11 \end{cases}$ $\begin{bmatrix} 3 & -2 \\ 2 & -3 \end{bmatrix}\begin{bmatrix} x \\ y \end{bmatrix} = \begin{bmatrix} 4 \\ 11 \end{bmatrix}$; $(-2, -5)$

9. $\begin{cases} 3x + y = 3 \\ 2x + 3y = 9 \end{cases}$ $\begin{bmatrix} 3 & 1 \\ 2 & 3 \end{bmatrix}\begin{bmatrix} x \\ y \end{bmatrix} = \begin{bmatrix} 3 \\ 9 \end{bmatrix}$; $(0, 3)$

10. $\begin{cases} 2x + 3y = -1 \\ x + 4y = -8 \end{cases}$ $\begin{bmatrix} 2 & 3 \\ 1 & 4 \end{bmatrix}\begin{bmatrix} x \\ y \end{bmatrix} = \begin{bmatrix} -1 \\ -8 \end{bmatrix}$; $(4, -3)$

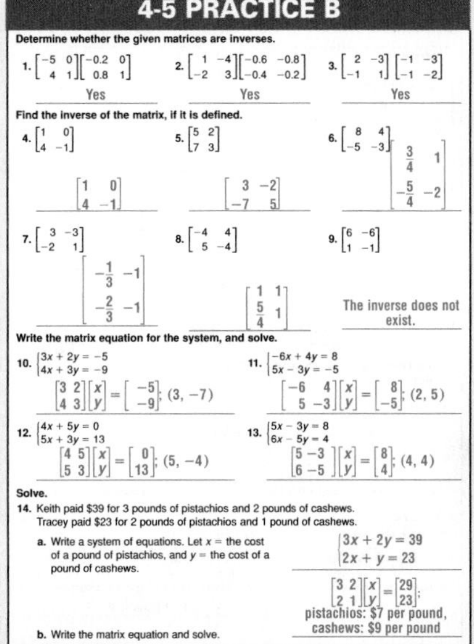

4-5 PRACTICE B

Determine whether the given matrices are inverses.

1. $\begin{bmatrix} -5 & 0 \\ 4 & 1 \end{bmatrix}\begin{bmatrix} -0.2 & 0 \\ 0.8 & 1 \end{bmatrix}$ Yes

2. $\begin{bmatrix} 1 & -4 \\ -2 & 3 \end{bmatrix}\begin{bmatrix} -0.6 & -0.8 \\ -0.4 & -0.2 \end{bmatrix}$ Yes

3. $\begin{bmatrix} 2 & -3 \\ -1 & 1 \end{bmatrix}\begin{bmatrix} -1 & -3 \\ -1 & -2 \end{bmatrix}$ Yes

Find the inverse of the matrix, if it is defined.

4. $\begin{bmatrix} 1 & 0 \\ 4 & -1 \end{bmatrix}$ $\begin{bmatrix} 1 & 0 \\ 4 & -1 \end{bmatrix}$

5. $\begin{bmatrix} 5 & 2 \\ 7 & 3 \end{bmatrix}$ $\begin{bmatrix} 3 & -2 \\ -7 & 5 \end{bmatrix}$

6. $\begin{bmatrix} 8 & 4 \\ -5 & -3 \end{bmatrix}$ $\begin{bmatrix} \frac{3}{4} & 1 \\ -\frac{5}{4} & -2 \end{bmatrix}$

7. $\begin{bmatrix} 3 & -3 \\ -2 & 1 \end{bmatrix}$ $\begin{bmatrix} -\frac{1}{3} & -1 \\ -\frac{2}{3} & -1 \end{bmatrix}$

8. $\begin{bmatrix} -4 & 4 \\ 5 & -4 \end{bmatrix}$ $\begin{bmatrix} 1 & 1 \\ \frac{5}{4} & 1 \end{bmatrix}$

9. $\begin{bmatrix} 6 & -6 \\ 1 & -1 \end{bmatrix}$ The inverse does not exist.

Write the matrix equation for the system, and solve.

10. $\begin{cases} 3x + 2y = -5 \\ 4x + 3y = -9 \end{cases}$ $\begin{bmatrix} 3 & 2 \\ 4 & 3 \end{bmatrix}\begin{bmatrix} x \\ y \end{bmatrix} = \begin{bmatrix} -5 \\ -9 \end{bmatrix}$; $(3, -7)$

11. $\begin{cases} -6x + 4y = 8 \\ 5x - 3y = -5 \end{cases}$ $\begin{bmatrix} -6 & 4 \\ 5 & -3 \end{bmatrix}\begin{bmatrix} x \\ y \end{bmatrix} = \begin{bmatrix} 8 \\ -5 \end{bmatrix}$; $(2, 5)$

12. $\begin{cases} 4x + 5y = 0 \\ 5x + 3y = 13 \end{cases}$ $\begin{bmatrix} 4 & 5 \\ 5 & 3 \end{bmatrix}\begin{bmatrix} x \\ y \end{bmatrix} = \begin{bmatrix} 0 \\ 13 \end{bmatrix}$; $(5, -4)$

13. $\begin{cases} 5x - 3y = 8 \\ 6x - 5y = 4 \end{cases}$ $\begin{bmatrix} 5 & -3 \\ 6 & -5 \end{bmatrix}\begin{bmatrix} x \\ y \end{bmatrix} = \begin{bmatrix} 8 \\ 4 \end{bmatrix}$; $(4, 4)$

Solve.

14. Keith paid $39 for 3 pounds of pistachios and 2 pounds of cashews. Tracey paid $23 for 2 pounds of pistachios and 1 pound of cashews.
a. Write a system of equations. Let x = the cost of a pound of pistachios, and y = the cost of a pound of cashews. $\begin{cases} 3x + 2y = 39 \\ 2x + y = 23 \end{cases}$
b. Write the matrix equation and solve. $\begin{bmatrix} 3 & 2 \\ 2 & 1 \end{bmatrix}\begin{bmatrix} x \\ y \end{bmatrix} = \begin{bmatrix} 29 \\ 23 \end{bmatrix}$; pistachios: $7 per pound, cashews: $9 per pound

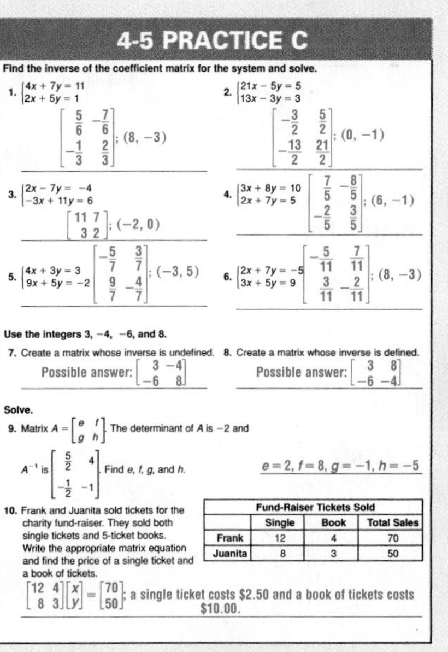

4-5 PRACTICE C

Find the inverse of the coefficient matrix for the system and solve.

1. $\begin{cases} 4x + 7y = 11 \\ 2x + 5y = 1 \end{cases}$ $\begin{bmatrix} \frac{5}{6} & -\frac{7}{6} \\ -\frac{1}{3} & \frac{2}{3} \end{bmatrix}$; $(8, -3)$

2. $\begin{cases} 21x - 5y = 5 \\ 13x - 3y = 3 \end{cases}$ $\begin{bmatrix} -\frac{3}{2} & \frac{5}{2} \\ -\frac{13}{2} & \frac{21}{2} \end{bmatrix}$; $(0, -1)$

3. $\begin{cases} 2x - 7y = -4 \\ -3x + 11y = 6 \end{cases}$ $\begin{bmatrix} 11 & 7 \\ 3 & 2 \end{bmatrix}$; $(-2, 0)$

4. $\begin{cases} 3x + 8y = 10 \\ 2x + 7y = 5 \end{cases}$ $\begin{bmatrix} \frac{7}{5} & -\frac{8}{5} \\ -\frac{2}{5} & \frac{3}{5} \end{bmatrix}$; $(6, -1)$

5. $\begin{cases} 4x + 3y = 3 \\ 9x + 5y = -2 \end{cases}$ $\begin{bmatrix} -\frac{5}{7} & \frac{3}{7} \\ \frac{9}{7} & -\frac{4}{7} \end{bmatrix}$; $(-3, 5)$

6. $\begin{cases} 2x + 7y = -5 \\ 3x + 5y = 9 \end{cases}$ $\begin{bmatrix} -\frac{5}{11} & \frac{7}{11} \\ \frac{3}{11} & -\frac{2}{11} \end{bmatrix}$; $(8, -3)$

Use the integers 3, −4, −6, and 8.

7. Create a matrix whose inverse is undefined. Possible answer: $\begin{bmatrix} 3 & -4 \\ -6 & 8 \end{bmatrix}$

8. Create a matrix whose inverse is defined. Possible answer: $\begin{bmatrix} 3 & 8 \\ -6 & -4 \end{bmatrix}$

Solve.

9. Matrix $A = \begin{bmatrix} e & f \\ g & h \end{bmatrix}$. The determinant of A is −2 and A^{-1} is $\begin{bmatrix} \frac{5}{2} & 4 \\ -\frac{1}{2} & -1 \end{bmatrix}$. Find e, f, g, and h. $e = 2, f = 8, g = -1, h = -5$

10. Frank and Juanita sold tickets for the charity fund-raiser. They sold both single tickets and 5-ticket books. Write the appropriate matrix equation and find the price of a single ticket and a book of tickets.

Fund-Raiser Tickets Sold

	Single	Book	Total Sales
Frank	12	4	70
Juanita	8	3	50

$\begin{bmatrix} 12 & 4 \\ 8 & 3 \end{bmatrix}\begin{bmatrix} x \\ y \end{bmatrix} = \begin{bmatrix} 70 \\ 50 \end{bmatrix}$; a single ticket costs $2.50 and a book of tickets costs $10.00.

MULTI-STEP TEST PREP **Exercise 34** involves creating and solving a system of equations by using an inverse matrix. This exercise prepares students for the Multi-Step Test Prep on page 294.

Teaching Tip **Critical Thinking** In **Exercise 35,** one can show that

$\begin{bmatrix} a & b \\ c & d \end{bmatrix}$ and $\frac{1}{ad-bc}\begin{bmatrix} d & -b \\ -c & a \end{bmatrix}$

are inverses by multiplying them together to get the identity matrix. However, if the inverse was not known, you could find it by solving $\begin{bmatrix} a & b \\ c & d \end{bmatrix}\begin{bmatrix} e & f \\ g & h \end{bmatrix} = \begin{bmatrix} 1 & 0 \\ 0 & 1 \end{bmatrix}$. When multiplied, this becomes two systems of equations that can be solved using standard algebra. This is a good exercise for small groups.

TEST PREP DOCTOR In **Exercise 40,** students who chose **A** or **C** may be unclear about the relationship between a system and its matrix equation form. Students who chose **D** may not have noticed that the second equation had to be altered in order for the matrix to be set up correctly.

Answers

35a. A matrix multiplied by its inverse is equal to the identity matrix. Find the product of

$$\frac{1}{ad-bc}\begin{bmatrix} d & -b \\ -c & a \end{bmatrix} \text{ and } \begin{bmatrix} a & b \\ c & d \end{bmatrix}.$$

$$\frac{1}{ad-bc}\begin{bmatrix} d & -b \\ -c & a \end{bmatrix}\begin{bmatrix} a & b \\ c & d \end{bmatrix} =$$

$$\frac{1}{ad-bc}\begin{bmatrix} ad-bc & bd-bd \\ -ac+ac & -bc+ad \end{bmatrix} =$$

$$\frac{1}{ad-bc}\begin{bmatrix} ad-bc & 0 \\ 0 & ad-bc \end{bmatrix} =$$

$$\begin{bmatrix} \frac{ad-bc}{ad-bc} & 0 \\ 0 & \frac{ad-bc}{ad-bc} \end{bmatrix} = \begin{bmatrix} 1 & 0 \\ 0 & 1 \end{bmatrix}$$

The product is equal to the identity matrix. Therefore, the inverse of $\begin{bmatrix} a & b \\ c & d \end{bmatrix}$ is $\frac{1}{ad-bc}\begin{bmatrix} d & -b \\ -c & a \end{bmatrix}$.

b. $\begin{bmatrix} d & -b \\ -c & a \end{bmatrix}$

c. any integer divided by 1 remains an integer.

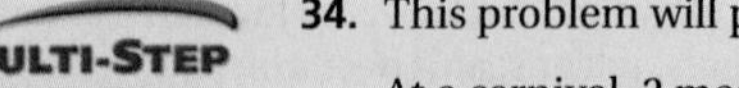

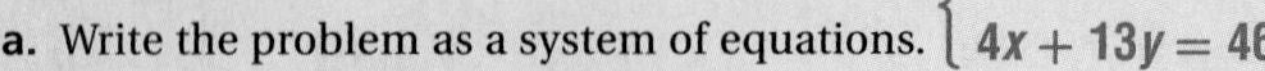

MULTI-STEP TEST PREP

34. This problem will prepare you for the Multi-Step Test Prep on page 294.

At a carnival, 2 meals and 7 rides require 24 tickets, while 4 meals and 13 rides require 46 tickets. Let x be the number of tickets for a meal and y be the number of tickets for a ride.

a. Write the problem as a system of equations. $\begin{cases} 2x + 7y = 24 \\ 4x + 13y = 46 \end{cases}$

b. Is the determinant $D = 0$? How many solutions are there? **no; one solution**

c. Write the coefficient matrix, and find its inverse. $\begin{bmatrix} 2 & 7 \\ 4 & 13 \end{bmatrix}; \begin{bmatrix} -\frac{13}{2} & \frac{7}{2} \\ 2 & -1 \end{bmatrix}$

d. Use $X = A^{-1}B$ to find x and y. **(5, 2)**

e. How many tickets are required for each item?

5 tickets are required for a meal, and 2 tickets are required for a ride.

35. a. **Critical Thinking** Prove that the inverse of matrix $\begin{bmatrix} a & b \\ c & d \end{bmatrix}$ is $\frac{1}{ad-bc}\begin{bmatrix} d & -b \\ -c & a \end{bmatrix}$.

b. If the determinant of matrix $\begin{bmatrix} a & b \\ c & d \end{bmatrix}$ is 1, what is its inverse?

c. If a, b, c, and d are integers, why does the inverse contain only integers?

36. Complete the matrix $\begin{bmatrix} 2 & ? \\ 4 & 3 \end{bmatrix}$ so that it has no inverse. $\begin{bmatrix} 2 & 1.5 \\ 4 & 3 \end{bmatrix}$

37. Suppose A is the 1-entry matrix $[\,a\,]$. What is its inverse? $\left[\frac{1}{a}\right]$

38. **Chemistry** A laboratory has one solution of 15% hydrochloric acid (HCl) and one solution of 40% HCL. A mixture requires 50 liters of 35% HCL. How many liters of each must be used? **10 liters of 15% HCl and 40 liters of 40% HCl**

39. **Write About It** Find the product of $\begin{bmatrix} 6 & 5 \\ 7 & 6 \end{bmatrix}$ and $\begin{bmatrix} 6 & -5 \\ -7 & 6 \end{bmatrix}$.

Describe the relationship between these matrices.

Because the product of the two matrices is an identity matrix, the two matrices are inverses of each other.

TEST PREP

40. Which is the correct matrix equation for the system $\begin{cases} 3x + 2y = 8 \\ x = y + 1 \end{cases}$?

Ⓐ $\begin{bmatrix} 3 & 2 \\ 1 & -1 \end{bmatrix}\begin{bmatrix} 8 \\ 1 \end{bmatrix} = \begin{bmatrix} x \\ y \end{bmatrix}$

Ⓑ $\begin{bmatrix} 3 & 2 \\ 1 & -1 \end{bmatrix}\begin{bmatrix} x \\ y \end{bmatrix} = \begin{bmatrix} 8 \\ 1 \end{bmatrix}$

Ⓒ $\begin{bmatrix} 3 & 2 \\ 1 & 1 \end{bmatrix}\begin{bmatrix} 8 \\ 1 \end{bmatrix} = \begin{bmatrix} x \\ y \end{bmatrix}$

Ⓓ $\begin{bmatrix} 3 & 2 \\ 1 & 1 \end{bmatrix}\begin{bmatrix} x \\ y \end{bmatrix} = \begin{bmatrix} 8 \\ 1 \end{bmatrix}$

41. Which statement is a true statement about matrix $G = \begin{bmatrix} 2 & -3 \\ 6 & -9 \end{bmatrix}$?

Ⓕ G has an inverse because the determinant is NOT 0.

Ⓖ G has an inverse because the determinant is 0.

Ⓗ G has no inverse because the determinant is 0.

Ⓙ G has no inverse because the determinant is NOT 0.

42. B is the inverse of $\begin{bmatrix} -1 & 6 \\ 4 & 3 \end{bmatrix}$. What is entry b_{11}?

Ⓐ 1　Ⓑ $-\frac{1}{9}$　Ⓒ 3　Ⓓ $-\frac{1}{27}$

4-5 READING STRATEGIES

Definition	Facts
The identity matrix, I is $\begin{bmatrix} 1 & 0 \\ 0 & 1 \end{bmatrix}$. If the product of two matrices is the identity matrix, then they are said to be inverses. The inverse of matrix A is written as A^{-1}. $AA^{-1} = A^{-1}A = I$	$A = \begin{bmatrix} a & b \\ c & d \end{bmatrix}$ $A^{-1} = \frac{1}{\det A}\begin{bmatrix} d & -b \\ -c & a \end{bmatrix}$
Example	**Useful Hints**
$G = \begin{bmatrix} 1 & -1 \\ 4 & -6 \end{bmatrix}$ $G^{-1} = -\frac{1}{2}\begin{bmatrix} -6 & 1 \\ -4 & 1 \end{bmatrix} = \begin{bmatrix} 3 & -\frac{1}{2} \\ 2 & -\frac{1}{2} \end{bmatrix}$ $GG^{-1} = \begin{bmatrix} 1 & -1 \\ 4 & -6 \end{bmatrix}\begin{bmatrix} 3 & -\frac{1}{2} \\ 2 & -\frac{1}{2} \end{bmatrix} = \begin{bmatrix} 1 & 0 \\ 0 & 1 \end{bmatrix}$	The identity matrix has 1 in every position on the main diagonal and 0 in every other position. Not all square matrices have inverses. A square matrix can have an inverse only if its determinant is NOT 0.

Use the information in the graphic organizer to answer the following questions.

1. Matrix $H = \begin{bmatrix} -3 & 5 \\ -3 & 4 \end{bmatrix}$

a. Does matrix H have an inverse? How do you know?

Yes; Possible answer: Because matrix H is a square matrix and its determinant is not 0.

b. Describe the resulting matrix if you multiplied matrix H by its inverse.

The identity matrix

2. Explain why a matrix has no inverse if the determinant is 0.

Because the formula involves multiplying by $\frac{1}{\det A}$ and $\frac{1}{0}$ is undefined

3. Matrix F has an inverse, F^{-1}. What characteristics of matrix F can you determine?

F is a square matrix and its determinant is not 0.

4-5 RETEACH

The identity matrix of a 2 × 2 matrix is $\begin{bmatrix} 1 & 0 \\ 0 & 1 \end{bmatrix}$. If a square matrix A has an inverse A^{-1}, then the product of A and A^{-1} is the identity matrix.

Use the following rule to find the **inverse of a 2 × 2 matrix.**

The inverse of $A = \begin{bmatrix} a & b \\ c & d \end{bmatrix}$ is $A^{-1} = \frac{1}{\det A}\begin{bmatrix} d & -b \\ -c & a \end{bmatrix}$.

Think: **"Switch ops."** **Switch** a and d and take the **opposites** of b and c.

If the determinant is 0, the matrix has no inverse.

To find the inverse of $A = \begin{bmatrix} 2 & 1 \\ 4 & 1 \end{bmatrix}$, first find the determinant.

$\det\begin{bmatrix} 2 & 1 \\ 4 & 1 \end{bmatrix} = \begin{vmatrix} 2 & 1 \\ 4 & 1 \end{vmatrix} = 2 - 4 = -2$

The determinant exists, so the matrix has an inverse.

Then **switch ops** and multiply by $-\frac{1}{2}$.

$A^{-1} = -\frac{1}{2}\begin{bmatrix} 1 & -1 \\ -4 & 2 \end{bmatrix} = \begin{bmatrix} -\frac{1}{2}(1) & -\frac{1}{2}(-1) \\ -\frac{1}{2}(-4) & -\frac{1}{2}(2) \end{bmatrix} = \begin{bmatrix} -\frac{1}{2} & \frac{1}{2} \\ 2 & -1 \end{bmatrix}$

Find the inverse of each matrix.

1. $A = \begin{bmatrix} 2 & 7 \\ -1 & -2 \end{bmatrix}$

$\det\begin{bmatrix} 2 & 7 \\ -1 & -2 \end{bmatrix} = \begin{vmatrix} 2 & 7 \\ -1 & -2 \end{vmatrix} =$ **3**

$\frac{1}{\det A} =$ **$\frac{1}{3}$**

$A^{-1} =$ **$\frac{1}{3}$** $\begin{bmatrix} -2 & -7 \\ 1 & 2 \end{bmatrix} =$ **$\begin{bmatrix} -\frac{2}{3} & -\frac{7}{3} \\ \frac{1}{3} & \frac{2}{3} \end{bmatrix}$**

2. $A = \begin{bmatrix} 6 & 1 \\ 8 & 2 \end{bmatrix}$

$\det\begin{bmatrix} 6 & 1 \\ 8 & 2 \end{bmatrix} =$ **4**

$\frac{1}{\det A} =$ **$\frac{1}{4}$**

$A^{-1} =$ **$\begin{bmatrix} \frac{1}{2} & -\frac{1}{4} \\ -2 & \frac{3}{2} \end{bmatrix}$**

3. $A = \begin{bmatrix} -4 & 6 \\ 1 & -2 \end{bmatrix}$ $\det A =$ **2**　$A^{-1} =$ **$\begin{bmatrix} -1 & -3 \\ -\frac{1}{2} & -2 \end{bmatrix}$**

43. In matrix $A = \begin{bmatrix} a & b \\ c & d \end{bmatrix}$, $a > 0$, $b < 0$, $c < 0$, $d > 0$, and $\det A \neq 0$. Which of the following is true?

(F) A^{-1} has no negative entries. (circled)
(G) A^{-1} has one negative entry.
(H) A^{-1} has two negative entries.
(J) A^{-1} has three negative entries.

44. **Extended Response** An art gallery gives away small prints valued at \$25 for donations of \$500, and larger prints valued at \$50 for donations of \$1000 and above. The gallery raises \$24,000 and gives away 35 prints. Find the number of each size print that the gallery gives away. **22 small prints and 13 large prints**

CHALLENGE AND EXTEND

45. **Hobbies** A fantasy league rating system rates NBA point guards by assigning a rating multiplier to each of the following categories: points per game, assists per game, turnovers per game, and steals per game. What multiplier is assigned to each category?
points/game: 2; assists/game: 5; turnovers/game: −4; steals/game: 3

Point Guard Ratings 2004–2005

Point Guard	Points/Game	Assists/Game	Turnovers/Game	Steals/Game	Rating
Nash	15.5	11.5	3.3	1.0	78.3
Marbury	21.7	8.2	2.8	1.5	77.7
B. Davis	19.2	7.9	2.9	1.8	71.7
Kidd	14.4	8.3	2.5	1.9	66.0

46. For what values of e, f, g, and h will matrix $\begin{bmatrix} e & f \\ g & h \end{bmatrix}$ be its own inverse? $\mathbf{e = \pm 1;\ f = 0;\ g = \pm 1;\ h = 0}$

47. Quinn uses a 3 × 3 decoding matrix on the message shown, where each entry on the main diagonal and above it is 1 and each entry below the main diagonal is 0.

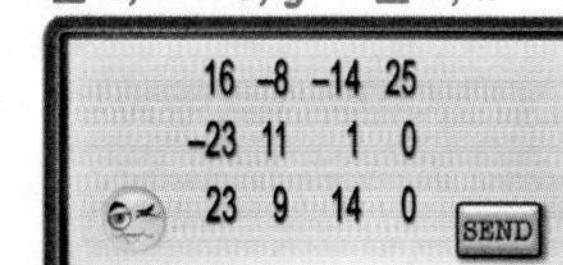

a. What message did he receive? **play to win**
b. What encoding matrix does he use?
c. He sends the reply "I will try" by using the corresponding encoding matrix. What coded message does he send?

$$\begin{bmatrix} -3 & -12 & 23 & -11 \\ -6 & -13 & 0 & 20 \\ 18 & 25 & 0 & 0 \end{bmatrix}$$

47b. $\begin{bmatrix} 1 & -1 & 0 \\ 0 & 1 & -1 \\ 0 & 0 & 1 \end{bmatrix}$

SPIRAL REVIEW

Solve. *(Lesson 2-2)*

48. $\frac{12}{30} = \frac{2x}{10}$ **2**

49. $\frac{100}{7} = \frac{0.5}{0.2x}$ **0.175**

50. 125% of $x = 117$ **93.6**

Use elimination to solve each system of equations. *(Lesson 3-6)*

51. $\begin{cases} x + y - z = 2 \\ 2x + 3y - 6z = 5 \\ -4x - 5y + 0.25z = -9 \end{cases}$ **(1, 1, 0)**

52. $\begin{cases} y - x - 3z = 4 \\ 2x + y - 4z = -3 \\ 0.25x + 8z + 3 = 2y \end{cases}$ $\left(-2\frac{2}{17}, 3\frac{14}{17}, \frac{11}{17}\right)$

Find the determinant of each matrix. *(Lesson 4-4)*

53. $\begin{bmatrix} 5 & -6 \\ 1 & 0.5 \end{bmatrix}$ **8.5**

54. $\begin{bmatrix} \frac{1}{6} & 3 \\ 1 & 12 \end{bmatrix}$ **−1**

55. $\begin{bmatrix} -4 & 1 & 6 \\ 1 & 2 & 1 \\ 3 & -1 & 0 \end{bmatrix}$ **−43**

56. $\begin{bmatrix} \frac{4}{9} & 8 \\ \frac{3}{2} & -81 \end{bmatrix}$ **−48**

Journal

Have students compare solving a real number equation using a multiplicative inverse with solving a matrix equation using an inverse matrix.

ALTERNATIVE ASSESSMENT

Have students write a system of 2 linear equations and solve it using a matrix equation.

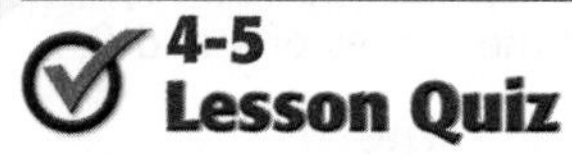

Power Presentations with PowerPoint®

4-5 Lesson Quiz

1. Determine whether $\begin{bmatrix} 1 & 3 \\ -2 & -1 \end{bmatrix}$ and $\begin{bmatrix} -\frac{1}{5} & -\frac{3}{5} \\ \frac{2}{5} & \frac{1}{5} \end{bmatrix}$ are inverses.
Yes

2. Find the inverse of $\begin{bmatrix} 2 & 4 \\ 1 & 3 \end{bmatrix}$, if it exists.
$\begin{bmatrix} \frac{3}{2} & -2 \\ -\frac{1}{2} & 1 \end{bmatrix}$

Write the matrix equation and solve.

3. $\begin{cases} 3x + 2y = 40 \\ 5x - 6y = 34 \end{cases}$
$\begin{bmatrix} 3 & 2 \\ 5 & -6 \end{bmatrix}\begin{bmatrix} x \\ y \end{bmatrix} = \begin{bmatrix} 40 \\ 34 \end{bmatrix}$; (11, 3.5)

4. Decode using $E = \begin{bmatrix} 2 & 1 \\ 1 & -2 \end{bmatrix}$.
$\begin{bmatrix} 12 & 27 & 42 & 30 & 5 & 58 & 35 & 15 \\ 6 & -9 & -14 & -40 & -10 & -16 & -30 & -5 \end{bmatrix}$
"Find the inverse."

Also available on transparency

4-5 PROBLEM SOLVING

For his job at a local restaurant, Alex researches and compares prices. He buys three packaged salad lunches from a competitor. He wants to find the price of one ounce of each kind of salad.

Salad Medley	Tasty Threesome	Sampler Salad Plate
Rainbow pasta: 3 oz	Tender tuna: 2 oz	Fruit cup: 2 oz
Tasty tuna: 3 oz	Mixed pasta: 1 oz	Tuna mix: 2 oz
Fresh fruit: 1 oz	Seasonal fruit: 3 oz	Pasta medley: 2 oz
\$5.52	\$4.59	\$4.68

1. Write a system of equations, using p, t, and f as the cost per ounce of each kind of salad.
$\begin{cases} 3p + 3t + f = 5.52 \\ p + 2t + 3f = 4.59 \\ 2p + 2t + 2f = 4.68 \end{cases}$

2. Set up the matrix equation, $AX = B$.
$\begin{bmatrix} 3 & 3 & 1 \\ 1 & 2 & 3 \\ 2 & 2 & 2 \end{bmatrix}\begin{bmatrix} p \\ t \\ f \end{bmatrix} = \begin{bmatrix} 5.52 \\ 4.59 \\ 4.68 \end{bmatrix}$

3. Find the determinant of matrix A.
4

4. Find A^{-1}.
$A^{-1} = \begin{bmatrix} -0.5 & -1 & 1.75 \\ 1 & 1 & -2 \\ -0.5 & 0 & 0.75 \end{bmatrix}$

5. Solve $X = A^{-1}B$ for X.
$\begin{bmatrix} p \\ t \\ f \end{bmatrix} = \begin{bmatrix} 0.84 \\ 0.75 \\ 0.75 \end{bmatrix}$

6. What is the price per ounce for each kind of salad?
Pasta salad: \$.84 per oz tuna salad: \$.75 per oz fruit salad: \$.75 per oz

A pharmacist is preparing saline solutions. She has a 2% saline solution and a 12% saline solution. How much of each solution should she mix to prepare 10 liters of a 10% solution? Choose the letter for the best answer.

7. Which represents the matrix equation for this problem?
A $\begin{bmatrix} 1 & 1 \\ 0.02 & 0.12 \end{bmatrix}\begin{bmatrix} x \\ y \end{bmatrix} = \begin{bmatrix} 1 \\ 10 \end{bmatrix}$
B $\begin{bmatrix} 1 & 1 \\ 0.2 & 0.12 \end{bmatrix}\begin{bmatrix} x \\ y \end{bmatrix} = \begin{bmatrix} 10 \\ 1 \end{bmatrix}$
C $\begin{bmatrix} 1 & 1 \\ 0.12 & 0.02 \end{bmatrix}\begin{bmatrix} x \\ y \end{bmatrix} = \begin{bmatrix} 1 \\ 10 \end{bmatrix}$
(D) $\begin{bmatrix} 1 & 1 \\ 0.02 & 0.12 \end{bmatrix}\begin{bmatrix} x \\ y \end{bmatrix} = \begin{bmatrix} 10 \\ 1 \end{bmatrix}$ (circled)

8. Which matrix is the inverse of the coefficient matrix for this problem?
A $\begin{bmatrix} 1 & 1.2 \\ 10 & 0.2 \end{bmatrix}$
(B) $\begin{bmatrix} 1.2 & -10 \\ -0.2 & 10 \end{bmatrix}$ (circled)
C $\begin{bmatrix} -1.2 & 1 \\ 0.2 & -1 \end{bmatrix}$
D $\begin{bmatrix} 1.2 & -10 \\ -0.2 & 1 \end{bmatrix}$

4-5 CHALLENGE

You know how to use an inverse matrix to solve a system of equations. You can also use systems of equations to find the inverse of a matrix. So, when the inverse matrix exists, it is possible to solve a system of equations with matrices without using a calculator.

Consider the 2 × 2 matrix shown at right and the general form of its inverse. $A = \begin{bmatrix} 3 & -3 \\ -6 & 7 \end{bmatrix}$ $A^{-1} = \begin{bmatrix} a & b \\ c & d \end{bmatrix}$

1. a. Use the definition of inverse to write an equation involving matrix A and the general form of A^{-1}.
$\begin{bmatrix} 3 & -3 \\ -6 & 7 \end{bmatrix}\begin{bmatrix} a & b \\ c & d \end{bmatrix} = \begin{bmatrix} 1 & 0 \\ 0 & 1 \end{bmatrix}$

b. Use the equation you wrote in part a and matrix multiplication to write four equations, two of which involve a and c and two of which involve b and d.
$3a - 3c = 1, 3b - 3d = 0, -6a + 7c = 0, -6b + 7d = 1$

c. Solve the two systems of equations to determine a, b, c, d. Write A^{-1}.
$A^{-1} = \begin{bmatrix} \frac{7}{3} & 1 \\ 2 & 1 \end{bmatrix}$

d. Verify your result by using matrix multiplication.
$\begin{bmatrix} 3 & -3 \\ -6 & 7 \end{bmatrix}\begin{bmatrix} \frac{7}{3} & 1 \\ 2 & 1 \end{bmatrix} = \begin{bmatrix} 1 & 0 \\ 0 & 1 \end{bmatrix}$ and $\begin{bmatrix} \frac{7}{3} & 1 \\ 2 & 1 \end{bmatrix}\begin{bmatrix} 3 & -3 \\ -6 & 7 \end{bmatrix} = \begin{bmatrix} 1 & 0 \\ 0 & 1 \end{bmatrix}$

Use the above method to find the inverse of the matrix, if it is defined.

2. $\begin{bmatrix} -6 & -2 \\ 11 & -3 \end{bmatrix}$
$\begin{bmatrix} -\frac{3}{40} & \frac{1}{20} \\ -\frac{11}{40} & -\frac{3}{20} \end{bmatrix}$

3. $\begin{bmatrix} -6 & 9 \\ -4 & 6 \end{bmatrix}$
The inverse is not defined.

4. $\begin{bmatrix} 2 & 1 & 3 \\ 1 & 1 & 2 \\ 1 & 4 & 6 \end{bmatrix}$
$\begin{bmatrix} -2 & 6 & -1 \\ -4 & 9 & -1 \\ 3 & -7 & 1 \end{bmatrix}$

Solve the sysem of equations by using matrices. Check your results in the given equations.

5. $\begin{cases} 2x - y = -2 \\ 4x + y = 5 \end{cases}$
$x = \frac{1}{2}, y = 3$

6. $\begin{cases} x + y + z = -2 \\ 3x + 3y + z = -18 \\ 4x + 2y + z = -20 \end{cases}$
$x = -5, y = -3, z = 6$

7. $\begin{cases} x + y + z + w = 6 \\ 2x - y + 3z - w = 2 \\ 3x + 2y - z + w = 5 \\ y - 5z - w = -8 \end{cases}$
$x = 0, y = 3, z = 2, w = 1$

Organizer

Use with Lesson 4-5

Pacing:

Traditional $\frac{1}{2}$ day

Block $\frac{1}{4}$ day

Objective: Use a spreadsheet to solve systems of equations.

Materials: spreadsheet software

Online Edition

Countdown to Testing Week 9

Resources

Technology Lab Activities

4-5 Lab Recording Sheet

Teach

Discuss

Give students a quick review of how a formula like =A1+1 updates when the value in A1 changes.

Close

Key Concept

When you set up a spreadsheet to solve a two-equation system using $A^{-1}B$ and det A, you can solve other two-equation systems by changing just the entries of A and B.

Assessment

Journal Have students explain how to solve a system of equations to set up the spreadsheet.

State Resources

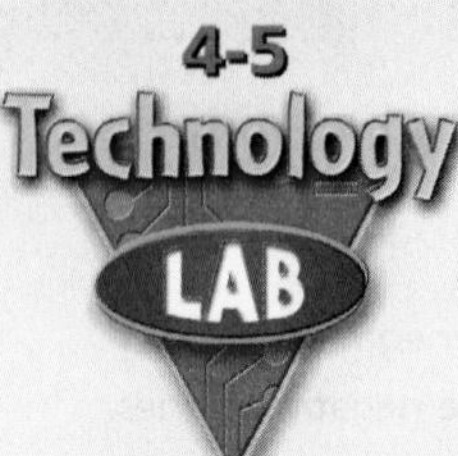

4-5 Use Spreadsheets with Matrices to Solve Systems

You can use matrix inversion on a spreadsheet to solve systems of equations.

Use with Lesson 4-5

Activity

Solve the system $\begin{cases} 7x + 2y = -8 \\ -3x + y = 9 \end{cases}$.

You can find determinants and inverses and solve $X = A^{-1}B$ by using a spreadsheet. To find A^{-1}, first find the determinant of A by using the spreadsheet (subtracting cross products).

Enter the four coefficients of the constant matrix into cells B2, C2, B3, and C3. Calculate its determinant by entering **=B2*C3−B3*C2** in cell C5.

C5 | fx =B2*C3-B3*C2

	A	B	C	D
1				
2	Matrix A	7	2	
3		-3	1	
4				
5	Determinant A		13	

The inverse of a 2 × 2 matrix is $\frac{1}{|A|}\begin{bmatrix} d & -b \\ -c & a \end{bmatrix}$, or $\begin{bmatrix} \frac{d}{|A|} & \frac{-b}{|A|} \\ \frac{-c}{|A|} & \frac{a}{|A|} \end{bmatrix}$.

Begin with cell C7, and enter the formula for the first entry **=C3/C5**. Enter the formulas for the other three entries, D7: =**−C2/C5**, C8: =**−B3/C5**, D8: **=B2/C5**.

The solution is the 2 × 1 matrix $A^{-1}B$. Enter the constant matrix in cells E7 and E8. Multiply A^{-1} by B by entering **=C7*E7+D7*E8** in cell D10 and **=C8*E7+D8*E8** in cell D11.

fx =C7*E7+D7*E8

	A	B	C	D	E
6					Matrix B
7	Inverse A or A^{-1}		0.076923	-0.15385	-8
8			0.230769	0.538462	9
9					
10		Solution A^{-1}B		-2	
11					

The solution is $x = -2$ and $y = 3$. You now have a solving "machine" for any 2 × 2 system. See what happens when you change one or more entries in A or in the constant matrix.

D11 | fx =C8*E7+D8*E8

	A	B	C	D	E
6					Matrix B
7	Inverse A or A^{-1}		0.076923	-0.15385	-8
8			0.230769	0.538462	9
9					
10		Solution A^{-1}B		-2	
11				3	

Try This

1. Change the constants to −5 and 9, and solve the system by using a spreadsheet. **(−1.769, 3.692)**
2. How can you check your answers by using the spreadsheet?
3. **Critical Thinking** Solve a system you know to be inconsistent by using the spreadsheet. Solve a system you know to be dependent. How can you tell from the spreadsheet whether a system is inconsistent or dependent?

Answers to *Try This*

2. Possible answer: Multiply the coefficient matrix by the solution matrix and check whether this product is equal to the constant matrix. For example, enter =B2*D10+C2*D11 in cell 13D and =B3*D10+C3*D11 in cell 13E. Check whether the entries in cells 13D and 13E are equal to the entries in cells 10D and 10E.

3. Possible answer: For both an inconsistent system and a dependent system, $D = 0$, and the entries in the inverse of A and in the solution matrix are undefined. Replace a column of coefficients of A with the constants and calculate the determinant. Then put the original values back and replace the other column with constants. If either determinant is 0, the system is dependent; otherwise, it is inconsistent.

go.hrw.com State Resources Online KEYWORD: MB7 Resources

4-6 Row Operations and Augmented Matrices

A2.2.2 Solve problems that can be modeled using systems of linear equations up to three variables, interpret the solutions, and determine whether the solutions . . .

Objective
Use elementary row operations to solve systems of equations.

Vocabulary
augmented matrix
row operation
row reduction
reduced row-echelon form

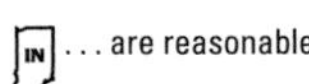
. . . are reasonable.

Who uses this?
Workers at an animal shelter can use augmented matrices to analyze the contents of shipments. (See Example 3.)

In previous lessons, you saw how Cramer's rule and inverses can be used to solve systems of equations. Solving large systems requires a different method using an *augmented matrix*. An **augmented matrix** consists of the coefficients and constant terms of a system of linear equations.

$$\begin{cases} 7x + 3y = 4 \\ 2x - 3y = 10 \end{cases} \qquad \left[\begin{array}{cc|c} 7 & 3 & 4 \\ 2 & -3 & 10 \end{array}\right]$$

A vertical line separates the coefficients from the constants.

EXAMPLE 1 Representing Systems as Matrices

Write the augmented matrix for the system of equations.

A $\begin{cases} -3y = x + 12 \\ -2y = 7 \end{cases}$

Step 1 Write each equation in $ax + by = c$ form.

Step 2 Write the augmented matrix, with coefficients and constants.

$$\begin{array}{l} -x - 3y = 12 \\ 0x - 2y = 7 \end{array} \longrightarrow \left[\begin{array}{cc|c} -1 & -3 & 12 \\ 0 & -2 & 7 \end{array}\right]$$

B $\begin{cases} x - y = 5 \\ z - x = 7 \\ y = z + 6 \end{cases}$

Step 1 Write each equation in $Ax + By + Cz = D$ form.

Step 2 Write the augmented matrix, with coefficients and constants.

$$\begin{array}{l} x - y + 0z = 5 \\ -x + 0y + z = 7 \\ 0x + y - z = 6 \end{array} \longrightarrow \left[\begin{array}{ccc|c} 1 & -1 & 0 & 5 \\ -1 & 0 & 1 & 7 \\ 0 & 1 & -1 & 6 \end{array}\right]$$

CHECK IT OUT! **Write the augmented matrix.**

1a. $\begin{cases} -x = y \\ 2 - y = x \end{cases}$ **1b.** $\begin{cases} -5x - 12 = 4y \\ z = 3 - x \\ 10 = 3z + 4y \end{cases}$

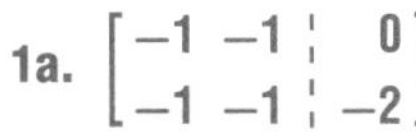

1a. $\left[\begin{array}{cc|c} -1 & -1 & 0 \\ -1 & -1 & -2 \end{array}\right]$

1b. $\left[\begin{array}{ccc|c} -5 & -4 & 0 & 12 \\ 1 & 0 & 1 & 3 \\ 0 & 4 & 3 & 10 \end{array}\right]$

4-6 Organizer

Pacing: Traditional $1\frac{1}{2}$ days
Block $\frac{3}{4}$ day

Objective: Use elementary row operations to solve systems of equations.

Technology Lab
In *Technology Lab Activities*

Online Edition
Tutorial Videos, Tech Keys

Countdown to Testing Week 9

Power Presentations with PowerPoint®

Warm Up

Solve.

1. $\begin{cases} 3x + y = 15 \\ 3x - 2y = 6 \end{cases}$ (4, 3)

2. $\begin{cases} x + 2y = 18 \\ 3x + 4y = 44 \end{cases}$ (8, 5)

3. What are the three types of linear systems? consistent independent, consistent dependent, and inconsistent

Also available on transparency

Math Humor

Watson: Holmes, what kind of row operations did you use to solve that system?

Holmes: Elementary, my dear Watson.

1 Introduce

EXPLORATION

4-6 Row Operations and Augmented Matrices

You can use matrices to keep track of the steps used to solve a system of equations. The *augmented matrix* below contains the coefficients and constant terms of the system of equations.

$$\left[\begin{array}{cc|c} 4 & 1 & 14 \\ 2 & -5 & 18 \end{array}\right] \longrightarrow \begin{cases} 4x + y = 14 \\ 2x - 5y = 18 \end{cases}$$

Write each augmented matrix used to solve the system of equations above. Write the row operation that was used to form it from the previous augmented matrix (Step 1 is done for you).

System	Augmented Matrix	Row Operation
1. $\begin{cases} 4x + y = 14 \\ 4x - 10y = 36 \end{cases}$	→ [ ]	Multiply the second row by 2.
2. $\begin{cases} 4x + y = 14 \\ -11y = 22 \end{cases}$	→ [ ]	
3. $\begin{cases} 4x + y = 14 \\ y = -2 \end{cases}$	→ [ ]	
4. $\begin{cases} 4x = 16 \\ y = -2 \end{cases}$	→ [ ]	
5. $\begin{cases} x = 4 \\ y = -2 \end{cases}$	→ [ ]	

THINK AND DISCUSS

Motivate

Remind students that in the past they have used various techniques to solve systems as large as 3 equations with 3 variables. Introduce that this lesson provides an orderly approach to solving much larger systems that can be performed by hand as well as with a calculator.

Explorations and answers are provided in the *Explorations* binder.

State Resources

go.hrw.com
State Resources Online
KEYWORD: MP7 Resources

Power Presentations with PowerPoint®

Additional Examples

Example 1

Write the augmented matrix for the system of equations.

A. $\begin{cases} 6x - 5y = 14 \\ 2x + 11y = 57 \end{cases}$ $\left[\begin{array}{cc|c} 6 & -5 & 14 \\ 2 & 11 & 57 \end{array}\right]$

B. $\begin{cases} x + 2y = 12 \\ 2x + y + z = 14 \\ y + 3z = 16 \end{cases}$

$\left[\begin{array}{ccc|c} 1 & 2 & 0 & 12 \\ 2 & 1 & 1 & 14 \\ 0 & 1 & 3 & 16 \end{array}\right]$

Example 2

Write the augmented matrix and solve.

A. $\begin{cases} 2x + y = 11 \\ 3x - 2y = 6 \end{cases}$ $\left[\begin{array}{cc|c} 2 & 1 & 11 \\ 3 & -2 & 6 \end{array}\right]$; (4, 3)

B. $\begin{cases} 8x - 5y = 18 \\ 5x + 8y = -11 \end{cases}$

$\left[\begin{array}{cc|c} 8 & -5 & 18 \\ 5 & 8 & -11 \end{array}\right]$; (1, −2)

Also available on transparency

INTERVENTION

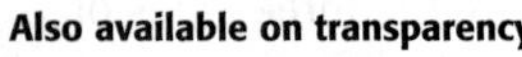

Questioning Strategies

EXAMPLE 1

- Why isn't an augmented matrix a square matrix?

EXAMPLE 2

- How do you decide which operation to do first? which to do next?

Reading Math Students may be unfamiliar with the word *echelon*. It is defined as an arrangement of troops with each unit to the right or left of the one in the rear of it. This is similar to the 1's in the reduced matrix.

ENGLISH LANGUAGE LEARNERS

You can use the augmented matrix of a system to solve the system. First you will do a **row operation** to change the form of the matrix. These row operations create a matrix equivalent to the original matrix. So the new matrix represents a system equivalent to the original system.

For each matrix, the following row operations produce a matrix of an equivalent system.

Elementary Row Operations	
• Switch any two rows.	$\left[\begin{array}{cc|c} 1 & 2 & 3 \\ 4 & 5 & 6 \end{array}\right] \to \left[\begin{array}{cc|c} 4 & 5 & 6 \\ 1 & 2 & 3 \end{array}\right]$
• Multiply a row by a nonzero constant.	$\left[\begin{array}{cc|c} 1 & 2 & 3 \\ 4 & 5 & 6 \end{array}\right] \to \left[\begin{array}{cc|c} 2 & 4 & 6 \\ 4 & 5 & 6 \end{array}\right]$
• Replace a row with the sum or difference of that row and another row. $\left[\begin{array}{cc|c} 1 & 2 & 3 \\ 4 & 5 & 6 \end{array}\right] \to \left[\begin{array}{cc|c} 1 & 2 & 3 \\ 1+4 & 2+5 & 3+6 \end{array}\right]$	
• Combine these operations.	

Row reduction is the process of performing elementary row operations on an augmented matrix to solve a system. The goal is to get the coefficients to reduce to the identity matrix on the left side.

This is called **reduced row-echelon form**. $\left[\begin{array}{cc|c} 1 & 0 & 5 \\ 0 & 1 & 2 \end{array}\right] \begin{array}{l} \to 1x = 5 \\ \to 1y = 2 \end{array}$

EXAMPLE 2 Solving Systems with an Augmented Matrix

Write the augmented matrix, and solve.

A $\begin{cases} 6x + y = 9 \\ 3x + 2y = 0 \end{cases}$

Step 1 Write the augmented matrix. $\left[\begin{array}{cc|c} 6 & 1 & 9 \\ 3 & 2 & 0 \end{array}\right]$

Step 2 Multiply row 2 by 2.

$\left[\begin{array}{cc|c} 6 & 1 & 9 \\ 3 & 2 & 0 \end{array}\right]$ $2❷ \to \left[\begin{array}{cc|c} 6 & 1 & 9 \\ 6 & 4 & 0 \end{array}\right]$

Step 3 Subtract row 1 from row 2. Write the result in row 2.

$❷ - ❶ \to \left[\begin{array}{cc|c} 6 & 1 & 9 \\ 0 & 3 & -9 \end{array}\right]$

Although row 2 is now $3y = -9$, an equation easily solved for y, row operations can be used to solve for both variables.

Step 4 Multiply row 1 by 3.

$3❶ \to \left[\begin{array}{cc|c} 18 & 3 & 27 \\ 0 & 3 & -9 \end{array}\right]$

Step 5 Subtract row 2 from row 1. Write the result in row 1.

$❶ - ❷ \to \left[\begin{array}{cc|c} 18 & 0 & 36 \\ 0 & 3 & -9 \end{array}\right]$

Remember!

2❷ is read as "2 times row 2."
❷ − ❶ is read as "row 2 minus row 1."

2 Teach

Guided Instruction

After students learn how to write an augmented matrix, show them how elementary row operations are related to solving systems by elimination. Remind them that the goal is to get the identity matrix on the left side.

Emphasize the importance of careful arithmetic, since row reduction, particularly of a 3 × 3 matrix, will involve quite a few steps.

Reaching All Learners

Through Visual Cues

To help students remember what the augmented matrix represents throughout the solving process, students can put in the variables' equal signs.

$\left[\begin{array}{ccc|c} 1 & -2 & 3 & = 18 \\ 2 & 1 & -1 & = 14 \\ 4 & 1 & 3 & = 16 \end{array}\right]$

Step 6 Divide row 1 by 18 and row 2 by 3.

$$\begin{array}{l} ❶ \div 18 \rightarrow \\ ❷ \div 3 \rightarrow \end{array} \left[\begin{array}{cc|c} 1 & 0 & 2 \\ 0 & 1 & -3 \end{array}\right] \begin{array}{l} \rightarrow 1x = 2 \\ \rightarrow 1y = -3 \end{array}$$

The solution is $x = 2$, $y = -3$. Check the result in the original equations.

Write the augmented matrix and solve.

B $\begin{cases} x + y = 5 \\ 3x + 3y = 7 \end{cases}$

$\left[\begin{array}{cc|c} 1 & 1 & 5 \\ 3 & 3 & 7 \end{array}\right]$ *Write the augmented matrix.*

$3❶ \rightarrow \left[\begin{array}{cc|c} 3 & 3 & 15 \\ 3 & 3 & 7 \end{array}\right]$ $❷ - ❶ \rightarrow \left[\begin{array}{cc|c} 1 & 1 & 5 \\ 0 & 0 & -8 \end{array}\right]$

The second row means $0 + 0 = -8$, which is always false.
The system is inconsistent.

C $\begin{cases} -4y = 1 - 6x \\ 3x = 2y + \frac{1}{2} \end{cases}$

Write each equation in standard form.

$\begin{cases} 6x - 4y = 1 \\ 3x - 2y = \frac{1}{2} \end{cases}$

$\left[\begin{array}{cc|c} 6 & -4 & 1 \\ 3 & -2 & \frac{1}{2} \end{array}\right]$ *Write the augmented matrix.*

$2❷ - ❶ \rightarrow \left[\begin{array}{cc|c} 6 & -4 & 1 \\ 0 & 0 & 0 \end{array}\right]$

The second row means $0 + 0 = 0$, which is always true.
The system is dependent.

2a. $\left[\begin{array}{cc|c} 4 & 4 & 32 \\ 1 & 3 & 16 \end{array}\right]$; (4, 4)

2b. $\left[\begin{array}{cc|c} 9 & 3 & 15 \\ -6 & -2 & 10 \end{array}\right]$; no solution

CHECK IT OUT! **Write the augmented matrix, and solve.**

2a. $\begin{cases} 4x + 4y = 32 \\ x + 3y = 16 \end{cases}$ **2b.** $\begin{cases} 3y = 15 - 9x \\ -6x = 2y + 10 \end{cases}$

On many calculators, you can add a column to a matrix to create the augmented matrix and can use the row reduction feature. So, the matrices in the Check It Out problem are entered as 2×3 matrices.

Student to Student

Solving Systems of Equations

Marcus Barrett
Memorial High School

I'm glad I learned all of the different methods for solving systems, but if I have a graphing calculator available, I prefer $A^{-1}B$. At first I thought, "Why'd they wait so long to give us this?"

Without a graphing calculator or a spreadsheet, I'd use elimination for most cases.

Another thing I might do—I might use a spreadsheet on my computer, find determinants, and use Cramer's rule. Cramer's rule is good when you just want the value of one variable. Now, if I had to solve a 20 by 20 system...

COMMON ERROR ALERT

When performing the row operation "multiply a row by a nonzero constant," students will sometimes neglect to multiply the rightmost entry by the constant. Remind them to distribute completely across the row.

Power Presentations with PowerPoint®

Additional Examples

Example 3

A shelter receives a shipment of items worth $1040. Bags of cat food are valued at $5 each, flea collars at $6 each, and catnip toys at $2 each. There are 4 times as many bags of food as collars. The number of collars and toys together equals 100. Write the augmented matrix and solve, using row reduction, on a calculator. How many of each item are in the shipment?

$\left[\begin{array}{ccc|c} 5 & 6 & 2 & 1040 \\ 1 & -4 & 0 & 0 \\ 0 & 1 & 1 & 100 \end{array}\right]$; 140 bags, 35 collars, 65 toys

Also available on transparency

INTERVENTION
Questioning Strategies

EXAMPLE 3

- Where does each of the three equations that make up the matrix come from?

Teaching Tip **Language Arts** The word *matrix* comes from the Latin word *mater*, meaning "mother" or "source." The augmented matrix of a system of equations contains all the information in the system and can be considered the system's "source."

Teaching Tip **Number Sense** Rather than completely reducing an augmented matrix to reduced row-echelon form, it may be easier to get a solution to the point where there is a "triangle of zeros." For example, once

$$\left[\begin{array}{ccc|c} 2 & 3 & 1 & 18 \\ 3 & 2 & 4 & 22 \\ 1 & 4 & 2 & 20 \end{array}\right] \text{ is reduced to}$$

$$\left[\begin{array}{ccc|c} 2 & 3 & 1 & 18 \\ 0 & 10 & 2 & 32 \\ 0 & 0 & 4 & 4 \end{array}\right],$$

it is apparent that $z = 1$, and substitution quickly yields $y = 3$ and then $x = 4$.

Teaching Tip **Math Background** Row operations can also be used to find an inverse, using what is known as the Gauss-Jordan method. For example, to find the inverse of $\begin{bmatrix} 2 & 3 & 1 \\ 3 & 2 & 4 \\ 1 & 4 & 2 \end{bmatrix}$, first set up the matrix $\left[\begin{array}{ccc|ccc} 2 & 3 & 1 & 1 & 0 & 0 \\ 3 & 2 & 4 & 0 & 1 & 0 \\ 1 & 4 & 2 & 0 & 0 & 1 \end{array}\right]$ by placing the identity matrix to the right of the matrix for which we are finding the inverse. Now use row operations to transform the left side into the identity matrix.

The right side is the inverse of the original matrix.

$$\left[\begin{array}{ccc|ccc} 1 & 0 & 0 & \frac{3}{5} & \frac{1}{10} & -\frac{1}{2} \\ 0 & 1 & 0 & \frac{1}{10} & -\frac{3}{20} & \frac{1}{4} \\ 0 & 0 & 1 & -\frac{1}{2} & \frac{1}{4} & \frac{1}{4} \end{array}\right]$$

EXAMPLE 3 Charity Application

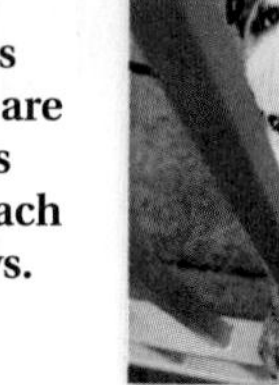

An animal shelter receives a shipment of items worth a total of $1890. Large bags of dog food are $8 each, pet blankets are $5 each, and dog toys are $4 each. There are 5 bags of dog food for each dog toy and twice as many blankets as dog toys. How many of each item are in the shipment? Solve by using row reduction on a calculator.

Use the facts to write three equations.

$5b + 8d + 4t = 1890$ *b = blankets*
$d - 5t = 0$ *d = bags of dog food*
$b - 2t = 0$ *t = toys*

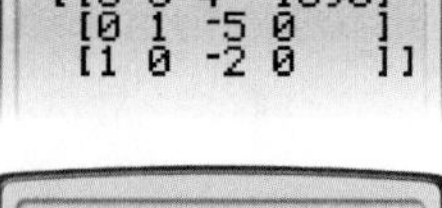

Enter the 3×4 augmented matrix as A.

Press 2nd [MATRX] x^{-1}, select **MATH**, and move down the list to **B:rref(** to find the reduced row-echelon form of the augmented matrix.

rref([A]
[[1 0 0 70]
[0 1 0 175]
[0 0 1 35]]

There are 70 blankets, 175 bags of dog food, and 35 toys.

CHECK IT OUT!

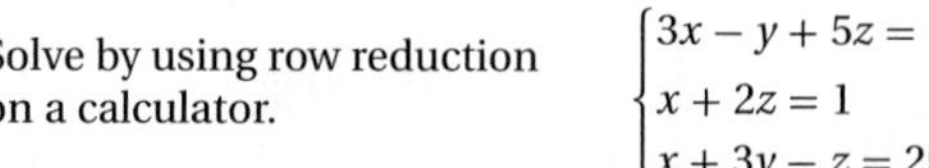

3a. Solve by using row reduction on a calculator. $\begin{cases} 3x - y + 5z = -1 \\ x + 2z = 1 \\ x + 3y - z = 25 \end{cases}$

3b. A new freezer costs $500 plus $0.20 a day to operate. An old freezer costs $20 plus $0.50 a day to operate. After how many days is the cost of operating each freezer equal? Solve by using row reduction on a calculator.

3a. $\left[\begin{array}{ccc|c} 3 & -1 & 5 & -1 \\ 1 & 0 & 2 & 1 \\ 1 & 3 & -1 & 25 \end{array}\right]$; $(5, 6, -2)$

3b. Possible answer: Let t represent the total cost of operating a freezer for d days; $\left[\begin{array}{cc|c} 1 & -0.2 & 500 \\ 1 & -0.5 & 20 \end{array}\right]$; $t = 820$; $d = 1600$; the costs are equal after 1600 days.

THINK AND DISCUSS

1. Explain what the rows $\left[\begin{array}{ccc|c} 0 & 1 & 0 & 3 \end{array}\right]$ and $\left[\begin{array}{ccc|c} 0 & 0 & 0 & 3 \end{array}\right]$ tell you about a system of equations when you solve a system of three equations by using augmented matrices and reduced row-echelon form.
2. Tell how you know when an augmented matrix is in reduced row-echelon form.

3. **GET ORGANIZED** Copy and complete the graphic organizer. Fill in the augmented matrix for a three-equation system. Then write an example of the given operation in each box. Tell whether the operation produces an equivalent system.

	System of Equations	Augmented Matrix
Interchange rows or equations.		
Replace a row or equation with a multiple.		
Replace a row or equation with a sum or difference.		
Combine the above.		

3 Close

Summarize

Summarize that students can solve large systems of equations efficiently by putting the system into an augmented matrix and using elementary row operations or a calculator to reduce it to reduced row-echelon form.

ONGOING ASSESSMENT and INTERVENTION

Diagnose ***Before*** **the Lesson**
4-6 Warm Up, TE p. 287

Monitor ***During*** **the Lesson**
Check It Out! Exercises, SE pp. 287–289
Questioning Strategies, TE pp. 288–289

Assess ***After*** **the Lesson**
4-6 Lesson Quiz, TE p. 293
Alternative Assessment, TE p. 293

Answers to *Think and Discuss*

Possible answers:

1. $\left[\begin{array}{ccc|c} 0 & 1 & 0 & 3 \end{array}\right]$ indicates that $y = 3$. $\left[\begin{array}{ccc|c} 0 & 0 & 0 & 3 \end{array}\right]$ indicates that the system is inconsistent because this row is false.
2. An augmented matrix is in reduced row-echelon form when the coefficient columns form the identity matrix.
3. See p. A6.

4-6 Exercises

go.hrw.com
Homework Help Online
KEYWORD: MB7 4-6
Parent Resources Online
KEYWORD: MB7 Parent

GUIDED PRACTICE

1. **Vocabulary** In an *augmented matrix*, where do you place the coefficients of the variables from the related system of equations? **The coefficients are in columns to the left of the vertical bar that separates them from the constant terms.**

SEE EXAMPLE 1 p. 287

Write the augmented matrix for each system of equations.

2. $\begin{cases} y-3=2x \\ 3x=-y \end{cases}$ $\left[\begin{array}{cc|c} -2 & 1 & 3 \\ 3 & 1 & 0 \end{array}\right]$

3. $\begin{cases} x+y+z=10 \\ 2x+z=12 \\ z-y=3 \end{cases}$

4. $\begin{cases} 2x-9=y \\ 2z=3y+7 \\ z=6-x \end{cases}$

5. $\begin{cases} y+2=3x \\ \frac{1}{4}y=z-1 \\ z-8=\frac{x}{2} \end{cases}$

SEE EXAMPLE 2 p. 288

Write the augmented matrix, and use row reduction to solve.

6. $\begin{cases} 2y=x+1 \\ 3x-2=y \end{cases}$

7. $\begin{cases} 8y=x+7 \\ 3y+\frac{x}{2}=0 \end{cases}$

8. $\begin{cases} x=2y+3 \\ y=\frac{1}{2}(x-3) \end{cases}$

9. $\begin{cases} y=4+x \\ 4y-3=4x \end{cases}$

SEE EXAMPLE 3 p. 290

10. **School** During a game, high school students sell snacks. They sell cold sandwiches for \$2.50, hot dogs for \$1.50, and hamburgers for \$2. By the end of the day, the students have collected \$1060.50 and sold 562 items. Casey estimates that the students sold twice as many hot dogs as cold sandwiches. If his estimate is correct, how many of each item did they sell? Solve by using row reduction on a calculator. **127 cold sandwiches, 254 hot dogs, and 181 hamburgers**

PRACTICE AND PROBLEM SOLVING

Independent Practice	
For Exercises	See Example
11–13	1
14–16	2
17	3

Extra Practice
Skills Practice p. S11
Application Practice p. S35

Write the augmented matrix for each system of equations.

11. $\begin{cases} \frac{1}{2}(x+3y)=z \\ y=2x+4 \\ x+y+z=3 \end{cases}$

12. $\begin{cases} 2y+z=5 \\ y=2z \end{cases}$

13. $\begin{cases} 0.1x+0.2y+0.15z=1.0 \\ x+y=z \\ 2y=1.3x \end{cases}$

13. $\left[\begin{array}{ccc|c} 0.1 & 0.2 & 0.15 & 1.0 \\ 1 & 1 & -1 & 0 \\ 1.3 & -2 & 0 & 0 \end{array}\right]$

Write the augmented matrix, and use row reduction to solve.

14. $\begin{cases} y+2z=9 \\ 2y+4z=13 \end{cases}$

15. $\begin{cases} 5x=y+2 \\ y-x=4 \end{cases}$

16. $\begin{cases} x+y=4 \\ 3x=9-2y \end{cases}$

16. $\left[\begin{array}{cc|c} 1 & 1 & 4 \\ 3 & 2 & 9 \end{array}\right]$; (1, 3)

17. **Math History** The Hundred Fowl problem asks, "A rooster is worth 5 coins, a hen 3 coins, and 3 chicks 1 coin. With 100 coins, we buy 100 of them. How many roosters, hens, and chicks are there?" There are seven times as many chicks as roosters. Write a set of equations and an augmented matrix for this problem. Solve by using row reduction on a calculator.

18. **Geometry** Write an augmented matrix to find the point of intersection of the two lines given by the equations $5y+4x=25$ and $y=3x-14$. Solve by using row reduction.

18. $\left[\begin{array}{cc|c} 4 & 5 & 25 \\ 3 & -1 & 14 \end{array}\right]$; (5, 1)

Write a system of equations for each augmented matrix.

19. $\left[\begin{array}{cc|c} 2 & 5 & -4 \\ 0 & 1 & -2 \end{array}\right]$

20. $\left[\begin{array}{ccc|c} 1 & 0 & -1 & 0 \\ 0 & 1 & -1 & -2 \\ -1 & 9 & 1 & -9 \end{array}\right]$

21. $\left[\begin{array}{ccc|c} 0 & -1 & 0 & 3 \\ -7 & 0 & 2 & 0 \\ 0 & 0 & -10 & 4 \end{array}\right]$

4-6 Exercises

Assignment Guide

Assign *Guided Practice* exercises as necessary.

If you finished Examples **1–3**
Basic 11–23, 27–33, 35–37, 40–45
Average 11–18, 22–37, 40–45
Advanced 11–18, 22–28, 32–45

Homework Quick Check
Quickly check key concepts.
Exercises: 12, 14, 17, 22

Answers

3. $\left[\begin{array}{ccc|c} 1 & 1 & 1 & 10 \\ 2 & 0 & 1 & 12 \\ 0 & -1 & 1 & 3 \end{array}\right]$

4. $\left[\begin{array}{ccc|c} 2 & -1 & 0 & 9 \\ 0 & -3 & 2 & 7 \\ 1 & 0 & 1 & 6 \end{array}\right]$

5. $\left[\begin{array}{ccc|c} -3 & 1 & 0 & -2 \\ 0 & \frac{1}{4} & -1 & -1 \\ -\frac{1}{2} & 0 & 1 & 8 \end{array}\right]$

6. $\left[\begin{array}{cc|c} -1 & 2 & 1 \\ 3 & -1 & 2 \end{array}\right]$; (1, 1)

7. $\left[\begin{array}{cc|c} -1 & 8 & 7 \\ \frac{1}{2} & 3 & 0 \end{array}\right]$; $\left(-3, \frac{1}{2}\right)$

8. $\left[\begin{array}{cc|c} 1 & -2 & 3 \\ \frac{1}{2} & -1 & \frac{3}{2} \end{array}\right]$; the system is dependent.

9. $\left[\begin{array}{cc|c} 1 & -1 & -4 \\ 4 & -4 & -3 \end{array}\right]$; the system is inconsistent.

11. $\left[\begin{array}{ccc|c} \frac{1}{2} & \frac{3}{2} & -1 & 0 \\ 2 & -1 & 0 & -4 \\ 1 & 1 & 1 & 3 \end{array}\right]$

12. $\left[\begin{array}{cc|c} 2 & 1 & 5 \\ 1 & -2 & 0 \end{array}\right]$

14. $\left[\begin{array}{cc|c} 1 & 2 & 9 \\ 2 & 4 & 13 \end{array}\right]$; the system is inconsistent.

15. $\left[\begin{array}{cc|c} 5 & -1 & 2 \\ 1 & -1 & -4 \end{array}\right]$; (1.5, 5.5)

17. Use r for the number of roosters, h for hens, and c for chicks;
$\begin{cases} 5r+3h+\frac{1}{3}c=100 \\ r+h+c=100 \\ 7r=c \end{cases}$;
$\left[\begin{array}{ccc|c} 5 & 3 & \frac{1}{3} & 100 \\ 1 & 1 & 1 & 100 \\ 7 & 0 & -1 & 0 \end{array}\right]$;
$r=12$; $h=4$; $c=84$; there are 12 roosters, 4 hens, and 84 chicks.

19. Possible answer:
$\begin{cases} 2x+5y=-4 \\ y=-2 \end{cases}$

20. Possible answer:
$\begin{cases} x-z=0 \\ y-z=-2 \\ -x+9y+z=-9 \end{cases}$

21. Possible answer:
$\begin{cases} -y=3 \\ -7x+2z=0 \\ -10z=4 \end{cases}$

State Resources

Exercise 33 involves creating and solving a system of equations by using an augmented matrix and row operations. This exercise prepares students for the Multi-Step Test Prep on page 294.

Answers

22. $\left[\begin{array}{cc|c} 2 & 5 & 8 \\ -1 & 1 & 10 \end{array}\right]$; $(-6, 4)$

23. $\left[\begin{array}{cc|c} 3 & -1 & -9 \\ -4 & 7 & 12 \end{array}\right]$; $(-3, 0)$

24. $\left[\begin{array}{cc|c} -1 & 3 & 5 \\ -3 & 9 & 15 \end{array}\right]$; the system is dependent.

25. $\left[\begin{array}{ccc|c} 2 & 5 & -1 & 0 \\ -1 & 3 & 0 & -7 \\ 1 & 0 & 7 & 25 \end{array}\right]$; $(4, -1, 3)$

26. Possible answer: Rewrite the table as an augmented matrix by writing each row of the table as a column. Solve the augmented matrix using row reduction. There are 9.25 measures of type-1 corn in a bundle, 4.25 measures of type-2 corn in a bundle, and 2.75 measures of type-3 corn in a bundle.

27–28, 32. See p. A25.

Math History

The ancient Chinese were fascinated with mathematical puzzles, such as tangrams, which were used to form many shapes.

Write the augmented matrix, and use row reduction to solve.

22. $\begin{cases} 2x + 5y = 8 \\ y - x = 10 \end{cases}$

23. $\begin{cases} 3x - y = -9 \\ 7y - 4x = 12 \end{cases}$

24. $\begin{cases} 3y = x + 5 \\ 9y - 3x = 15 \end{cases}$

25. $\begin{cases} 2x + 5y = z \\ 3y + 7 = x \\ x + 7z = 25 \end{cases}$

26. **Math History** Around the second century B.C.E., a Chinese mathematician posed a problem. He set up a table to show different combinations—A, B, C—of bundles of three types of corn—1, 2, 3—and found the number of measures of corn in each bundle. Use an augmented matrix to solve this problem.

Chinese Math Puzzle

	A	B	C
Type-1 Bundles	3	2	1
Type-2 Bundles	2	3	2
Type-3 Bundles	1	1	3
Total Measures of Corn	39	34	26

27. **Multi-Step** Voting data for the 2003 Heisman Trophy is given in the table.
    a. Write a system of equations to represent the data.
    b. Solve by using an augmented matrix. Show it in reduced row-echelon form. Find the number of points that each vote is worth.

2003 Heisman Trophy Votes

Player	First Place	Second Place	Third Place	Points
Jason White	319	204	116	1481
Larry Fitzgerald	253	233	128	1353
Eli Manning	95	132	161	710

28. **Write About It** Explain the difference between a coefficient matrix and an augmented matrix.

Solve the system by using row reduction on a calculator.

29. $\begin{cases} 3x = 5 - 4z \\ x + y + z = 5 \\ y = 2z \end{cases}$ **$(-1, 4, 2)$**

30. $\begin{cases} x + y = z \\ 5y - 2z = 4 \\ 5y - 2x = 8 \end{cases}$ **$(1, 2, 3)$**

31. $\begin{cases} 2x + y - z = 5 \\ z = -2x - y \\ y = x \end{cases}$ **31. $\left(\frac{5}{6}, \frac{5}{6}, -\frac{5}{2}\right)$**

32. **Critical Thinking** How can you identify a dependent or inconsistent system by looking at an augmented matrix in reduced row-echelon form?

33. This problem will prepare you for the Multi-Step Test Prep on page 294.

    At a carnival, 3 meals and 8 rides require 64 tickets, while 4 meals and 11 rides require 87 tickets. Let x be the number of tickets for a meal and y be the number of tickets for a ride.

    a. Write the problem as a system of equations. **a. $\begin{cases} 3x + 8y = 64 \\ 4x + 11y = 87 \end{cases}$**
    b. Write the augmented matrix. **b. $\left[\begin{array}{cc|c} 3 & 8 & 64 \\ 4 & 11 & 87 \end{array}\right]$**
    c. Use row reduction to solve. **$(8, 5)$**
    d. How many tickets are required for each item? **8 tickets are required for a meal, and 5 tickets are required for a ride.**

4-6 PRACTICE A

4-6 PRACTICE C

4-6 PRACTICE B

Write the augmented matrix for each system of equations.

1. $\begin{cases} 2x + 1 = y \\ x + y + z = 1 \\ 4y + 5z = 3 \end{cases}$ $\left[\begin{array}{ccc|c} 2 & -1 & 0 & -1 \\ 1 & 1 & 1 & 1 \\ 0 & 4 & 5 & 3 \end{array}\right]$

2. $\begin{cases} 3x = 2y + 4 \\ x - y = 3z \\ 2y + 8z = x \end{cases}$ $\left[\begin{array}{ccc|c} 3 & -2 & 0 & 4 \\ 1 & -1 & -3 & 0 \\ -1 & 2 & 8 & 0 \end{array}\right]$

3. $\begin{cases} x + z = 1 \\ 3x - 5y = 12 \\ 2y - 3z = 9 \end{cases}$ $\left[\begin{array}{ccc|c} 1 & 0 & 1 & 1 \\ 3 & -5 & 0 & 12 \\ 0 & 2 & -3 & 9 \end{array}\right]$

Write the augmented matrix, and use row reduction to solve.

4. $\begin{cases} 4x + 3y = -11 \\ 2x - 3y = 17 \end{cases}$ $\left[\begin{array}{cc|c} 4 & 3 & -11 \\ 2 & -3 & 17 \end{array}\right]$; $(1, -5)$

5. $\begin{cases} 3x + 7y = -1 \\ 6x + 11y = 10 \end{cases}$ $\left[\begin{array}{cc|c} 3 & 7 & -1 \\ 6 & 11 & 10 \end{array}\right]$; $(9, -4)$

6. $\begin{cases} 2x = 3y - 1 \\ 5x - 12y = 2 \end{cases}$ $\left[\begin{array}{cc|c} 2 & -3 & -1 \\ 5 & -12 & 2 \end{array}\right]$; $(-2, -1)$

7. $\begin{cases} x + 6y = 0 \\ 2x + 9y = -3 \end{cases}$ $\left[\begin{array}{cc|c} 1 & 6 & 0 \\ 2 & 9 & -3 \end{array}\right]$; $(-6, 1)$

Solve.

8. Dimitri has $4.95 in dimes and quarters. He has 3 fewer dimes than quarters.
   a. Write a system of equations. Let d = the number of dimes and q = the number of quarters. **$\begin{cases} 10d + 25q = 495 \\ d = q - 3 \end{cases}$**
   b. Write the augmented matrix for the system. **$\left[\begin{array}{cc|c} 10 & 25 & 495 \\ 1 & -1 & -3 \end{array}\right]$**
   c. How many of each coin does Dimitri have? **12 dimes and 15 quarters**

9. Clara has a bag of 60 coins with a value of $2.00. The coins are all pennies and nickels. How many of each coin are in the bag? **35 nickels and 25 pennies**

4-6 READING STRATEGIES

Augmented Matrix $\begin{cases} a_1x + b_1y = c_1 \\ a_2x + b_2y = c_2 \end{cases} \rightarrow \left[\begin{array}{cc\|c} a_1 & b_1 & c_1 \\ a_2 & b_2 & c_2 \end{array}\right]$ $\begin{cases} 4x + 3y = 10 \\ x - 2y = -3 \end{cases} \rightarrow \left[\begin{array}{cc\|c} 4 & 3 & 10 \\ 1 & -2 & -3 \end{array}\right]$	A system of linear equations can be represented as an **augmented matrix**. In this form the coefficient terms are to the left of the vertical line, and the constant terms are to the right.
Row Operations For example subtract row 2 from row 1 to create a new row 2. $\left[\begin{array}{cc\|c} a & b & c \\ d & e & f \end{array}\right] = \left[\begin{array}{cc\|c} a & b & c \\ a-d & b-e & c-f \end{array}\right]$ $\left[\begin{array}{cc\|c} 4 & 3 & 10 \\ 1 & -2 & -3 \end{array}\right] = \left[\begin{array}{cc\|c} 4 & 3 & 10 \\ 3 & 5 & 13 \end{array}\right]$	**Row operations** change the form of an augmented matrix in the process of solving a system of equations. The new matrix formed is equivalent to the original matrix.
Row Reduction Use the row reduction feature on your graphing calculator, **rref**, to find the reduced row-echelon form of an augmented matrix. $\left[\begin{array}{cc\|c} 4 & 3 & 10 \\ 1 & -2 & -3 \end{array}\right] = \left[\begin{array}{cc\|c} 1 & 0 & 1 \\ 0 & 1 & 2 \end{array}\right]$ $x = 1$ and $y = 2$	A series of row operations is referred to as **row reduction**. The object is to find an equivalent form of the augmented matrix that solves the system of equations. This form is called the **reduced row-echelon form** $\left[\begin{array}{cc\|c} 1 & 0 & m \\ 0 & 1 & n \end{array}\right]$ where m and n are constants. So $x = m$ and $y = n$.

Use the augmented matrix $\left[\begin{array}{cc|c} -5 & 10 & 3 \\ 2 & -4 & 1 \end{array}\right]$ for Exercises 1–3.

1. Explain how an augmented matrix represents a system of equations.
   Possible answer: An augmented matrix shows the coefficients and the constants of the linear equations in the order they appear in the equations.

2. Write the system of equations represented by the augmented matrix. **$\begin{cases} -5x + 10y = 3 \\ 2x - 4y = 1 \end{cases}$**

3. Compare multiplying the first equation in the system of equations by 3 and the row operation of multiplying the first row of the augmented matrix by 3. What is the effect of each operation?
   Possible answer: Multiplying the equation by 3 gives an equation equivalent to the original equation. In the same way, multiplying one row of the augmented matrix by 3 gives a matrix equivalent to the original matrix.

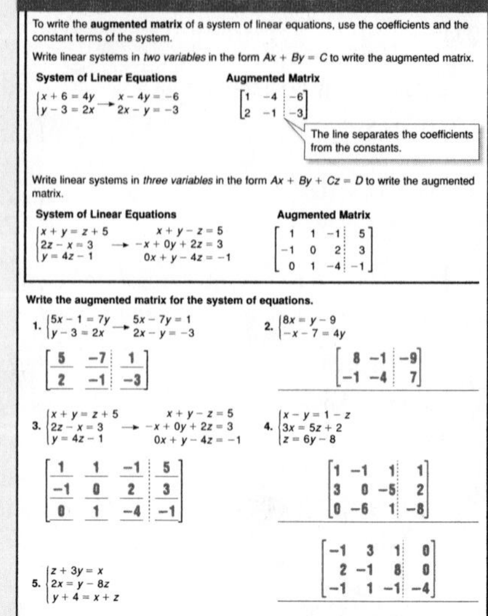

4-6 RETEACH

To write the **augmented matrix** of a system of linear equations, use the coefficients and the constant terms of the system.

Write linear systems in *two variables* in the form $Ax + By = C$ to write the augmented matrix.

System of Linear Equations / **Augmented Matrix**

$\begin{cases} x + 6 = 4y \\ y - 3 = 2x \end{cases} \rightarrow \begin{matrix} x - 4y = -6 \\ 2x - y = -3 \end{matrix}$ $\left[\begin{array}{cc|c} 1 & -4 & -6 \\ 2 & -1 & -3 \end{array}\right]$

The line separates the coefficients from the constants.

Write linear systems in *three variables* in the form $Ax + By + Cz = D$ to write the augmented matrix.

System of Linear Equations / **Augmented Matrix**

$\begin{cases} x + y = z + 5 \\ 2z - x = 3 \\ y = 4z - 1 \end{cases} \rightarrow \begin{matrix} x + y - z = 5 \\ -x + 0y + 2z = 3 \\ 0x + y - 4z = -1 \end{matrix}$ $\left[\begin{array}{ccc|c} 1 & 1 & -1 & 5 \\ -1 & 0 & 2 & 3 \\ 0 & 1 & -4 & -1 \end{array}\right]$

Write the augmented matrix for the system of equations.

1. $\begin{cases} 5x - 1 = 7y \\ y - 3 = 2x \end{cases} \rightarrow \begin{matrix} 5x - 7y = 1 \\ 2x - y = -3 \end{matrix}$ $\left[\begin{array}{cc|c} 5 & -7 & 1 \\ 2 & -1 & -3 \end{array}\right]$

2. $\begin{cases} 8x = y - 9 \\ -x - 7 = 4y \end{cases}$ $\left[\begin{array}{cc|c} 8 & -1 & -9 \\ -1 & -4 & 7 \end{array}\right]$

3. $\begin{cases} x + y = z + 5 \\ 2z - x = 3 \\ y = 4z - 1 \end{cases} \rightarrow \begin{matrix} x + y - z = 5 \\ -x + 0y + 2z = 3 \\ 0x + y - 4z = -1 \end{matrix}$ $\left[\begin{array}{ccc|c} 1 & 1 & -1 & 5 \\ -1 & 0 & 2 & 3 \\ 0 & 1 & -4 & -1 \end{array}\right]$

4. $\begin{cases} x - y = 1 - z \\ 3x = 5z + 2 \\ z = 6y - 8 \end{cases}$ $\left[\begin{array}{ccc|c} 1 & -1 & 1 & 1 \\ 3 & 0 & -5 & 2 \\ 0 & -6 & 1 & -8 \end{array}\right]$

5. $\begin{cases} z + 3y = x \\ 2x = y - 8z \\ y + 4 = x + z \end{cases}$ $\left[\begin{array}{ccc|c} -1 & 3 & 1 & 0 \\ 2 & -1 & 8 & 0 \\ -1 & 1 & -1 & -4 \end{array}\right]$

34. Photography The yearbook photographer sells sets of photos in three sizes. The price of each set includes a base price and the price for each size of print. The base price is twice the price of a large print. Find the base price and the price for each size of print. **base price: \$9.00; small: \$0.50; medium: \$1.25; large: \$4.50**

35. Which operation cannot be used to solve a system of equations by using an augmented matrix and row reduction?

(A) Multiply any two rows together. (C) Switch any two rows.
(B) Subtract one row from another. (D) Multiply a row by a constant.

36. Which row-reduced matrix indicates a dependent system of equations?

(F) $\left[\begin{array}{cc|c} 1 & 0 & 1 \\ 0 & 1 & 1 \end{array}\right]$ (G) $\left[\begin{array}{cc|c} 4 & 5 & 7 \\ 0 & 0 & \frac{2}{3} \end{array}\right]$ (H) $\left[\begin{array}{cc|c} 4 & 5 & 7 \\ 0 & 0 & \frac{0}{5} \end{array}\right]$ (J) $\left[\begin{array}{cc|c} 1 & 0 & 0 \\ 0 & 1 & 0 \end{array}\right]$

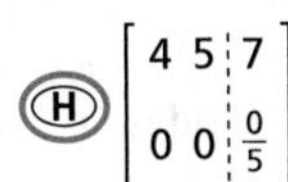

37. Which is the solution to the system represented by $\left[\begin{array}{cc|c} 2 & 0 & 5 \\ 0 & 3 & -3 \end{array}\right]$?

(A) (5, −3) (B) (2.5, −3) (C) (2.5, −1) (D) (5, −1)

CHALLENGE AND EXTEND

38. Write an augmented matrix in which transposing two rows would be the best first step. Justify your reasoning.

39. The system represented by $\left[\begin{array}{cc|c} 1 & -2 & 5 \\ 3 & 1 & 8 \\ -2 & 4 & -10 \end{array}\right]$ has a solution. Explain why. **Possible answer: The equations in this system represent three lines that intersect in a single point, (3, −1).**

SPIRAL REVIEW

Describe each transformation of $f(x) = x^3$. *(Lesson 1-9)*

40. $f(x) = x^3 - 5$ **41.** $f(x) = \frac{3}{8}x^3$ **42.** $f(x) = (x + 3)^3$

40. a translation 5 units down
41. a reduction by a factor of $\frac{3}{8}$
42. a translation 3 units left

43. Maximize $P = 3x + 2y$ given the constraints $x \geq 0$, $y \geq 0$, $x \leq y$ and $-2x + 3 \geq y$, and identify the point where P is maximized. *(Lesson 3-4)* **$P = 6$ at $(0, 3)$**

Write the matrix equation for the system, and solve. *(Lesson 4-5)*

44. $\begin{cases} 5y = x + 12 \\ 2y = 2x + 8 \end{cases}$ **45.** $\begin{cases} 3x - y = 0 \\ x + 2y = 7 \end{cases}$

44. $\begin{bmatrix} -1 & 5 \\ -2 & 2 \end{bmatrix}\begin{bmatrix} x \\ y \end{bmatrix} = \begin{bmatrix} 12 \\ 8 \end{bmatrix}$; (−2, 2)

45. $\begin{bmatrix} 3 & -1 \\ 1 & 2 \end{bmatrix}\begin{bmatrix} x \\ y \end{bmatrix} = \begin{bmatrix} 0 \\ 7 \end{bmatrix}$; (1, 3)

4-6 PROBLEM SOLVING

At the annual craft show, the Ceramics Club members sell mugs for \$6.00, bowls for \$5.50, and plates for \$9.50. They have for sale one more bowl than the number of plates and 3 times as many mugs as plates. They sold everything for a total of \$236.50. How many of each item did they sell?

1. Write a system of equations to represent the problem, using *m*, *b*, and *p* for the variables. $\begin{cases} b = p + 1 \\ m = 3p \\ 6m + 5.5b + 9.5p = 236.5 \end{cases}$

2. Write the augmented matrix for the system of equations. $\left[\begin{array}{ccc|c} 0 & 1 & -1 & 1 \\ 1 & 0 & -3 & 0 \\ 6 & 5.5 & 9.5 & 236.5 \end{array}\right]$

3. Use your calculator to find the reduced row-echelon form of the augmented matrix. $\left[\begin{array}{ccc|c} 1 & 0 & 0 & 21 \\ 0 & 1 & 0 & 8 \\ 0 & 0 & 1 & 7 \end{array}\right]$

4. How many of each item did the Ceramics Club sell? **21 mugs, 8 bowls, 7 plates**

Students earned points for finishing first, second, and third in the field day games. Jake earned a total of 38 points, Wanda earned 33 points, and Jill earned 29 points. How many points were earned for each first-, second-, and third-place finish? Choose the letter for the best answer.

Field Day Tally			
	Jake	Wanda	Jill
First	IIII	I	I
Second		~~IIII~~	III
Third	II		II

5. Which augmented matrix models the problem?

A $\left[\begin{array}{ccc|c} 4 & 1 & 1 & 38 \\ 0 & 5 & 3 & 33 \\ 1 & 0 & 2 & 29 \end{array}\right]$ B $\left[\begin{array}{ccc|c} 4 & 2 & 0 & 38 \\ 1 & 5 & 0 & 33 \\ 0 & 3 & 2 & 29 \end{array}\right]$

(C) $\left[\begin{array}{ccc|c} 4 & 0 & 2 & 38 \\ 1 & 5 & 0 & 33 \\ 1 & 3 & 2 & 29 \end{array}\right]$ D $\left[\begin{array}{ccc|c} 4 & 1 & 2 & 38 \\ 0 & 3 & 5 & 33 \\ 1 & 2 & 3 & 29 \end{array}\right]$

6. Which matrix in reduced row-echelon form is the solution to the problem?

(A) $\left[\begin{array}{ccc|c} 1 & 0 & 0 & 8 \\ 0 & 1 & 0 & 5 \\ 0 & 0 & 1 & 3 \end{array}\right]$ B $\left[\begin{array}{ccc|c} 1 & 0 & 0 & 10 \\ 0 & 1 & 0 & 6 \\ 0 & 0 & 1 & 3 \end{array}\right]$

C $\left[\begin{array}{ccc|c} 0 & 0 & 1 & 8 \\ 0 & 1 & 0 & 5 \\ 1 & 0 & 0 & 3 \end{array}\right]$ D $\left[\begin{array}{ccc|c} 0 & 0 & 1 & 10 \\ 0 & 1 & 0 & 6 \\ 1 & 0 & 0 & 3 \end{array}\right]$

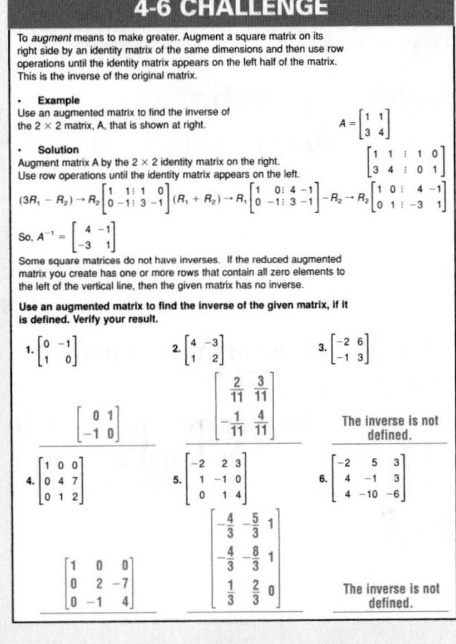

4-6 CHALLENGE

To *augment* means to make greater. Augment a square matrix on its right side by an identity matrix of the same dimensions and then use row operations until the identity matrix appears on the left half of the matrix. This is the inverse of the original matrix.

- **Example**

Use an augmented matrix to find the inverse of the 2 × 2 matrix, A, that is shown at right. $A = \begin{bmatrix} 1 & 1 \\ 3 & 4 \end{bmatrix}$

- **Solution**

Augment matrix A by the 2 × 2 identity matrix on the right. Use row operations until the identity matrix appears on the left. $\left[\begin{array}{cc|cc} 1 & 1 & 1 & 0 \\ 3 & 4 & 0 & 1 \end{array}\right]$

$(3R_1 - R_2) \rightarrow R_2 \left[\begin{array}{cc|cc} 1 & 1 & 1 & 0 \\ 0 & -1 & 3 & -1 \end{array}\right] (R_1 + R_2) \rightarrow R_1 \left[\begin{array}{cc|cc} 1 & 0 & 4 & -1 \\ 0 & -1 & 3 & -1 \end{array}\right] -R_2 \rightarrow R_2 \left[\begin{array}{cc|cc} 1 & 0 & 4 & -1 \\ 0 & 1 & -3 & 1 \end{array}\right]$

So, $A^{-1} = \begin{bmatrix} 4 & -1 \\ -3 & 1 \end{bmatrix}$

Some square matrices do not have inverses. If the reduced augmented matrix you create has one or more rows that contain all zero elements to the left of the vertical line, then the given matrix has no inverse.

Use an augmented matrix to find the inverse of the given matrix, if it is defined. Verify your result.

1. $\begin{bmatrix} 0 & -1 \\ 1 & 0 \end{bmatrix}$ **$\begin{bmatrix} 0 & 1 \\ -1 & 0 \end{bmatrix}$**

2. $\begin{bmatrix} 4 & -3 \\ 1 & 2 \end{bmatrix}$ **$\begin{bmatrix} \frac{2}{11} & \frac{3}{11} \\ -\frac{1}{11} & \frac{4}{11} \end{bmatrix}$**

3. $\begin{bmatrix} -2 & 6 \\ -1 & 3 \end{bmatrix}$ **The inverse is not defined.**

4. $\begin{bmatrix} 1 & 0 & 0 \\ 0 & 4 & 7 \\ 0 & 1 & 2 \end{bmatrix}$ **$\begin{bmatrix} 1 & 0 & 0 \\ 0 & 2 & -7 \\ 0 & -1 & 4 \end{bmatrix}$**

5. $\begin{bmatrix} -2 & 2 & 3 \\ 1 & -1 & 0 \\ 0 & 1 & 4 \end{bmatrix}$ **$\begin{bmatrix} -\frac{4}{3} & -\frac{5}{3} & 1 \\ -\frac{4}{3} & -\frac{8}{3} & 1 \\ \frac{1}{3} & \frac{2}{3} & 0 \end{bmatrix}$**

6. $\begin{bmatrix} -2 & 5 & 3 \\ 4 & -1 & 3 \\ 4 & -10 & -6 \end{bmatrix}$ **The inverse is not defined.**

In **Exercise 36,** it might be helpful to transform the augmented matrix back into the system of equations that it came from.

Journal

Have students compare the process of row reduction with elimination for solving systems of linear equations.

ALTERNATIVE ASSESSMENT

Have students write and solve a system of three equations by row reduction on a calculator. Have them write each step, identify each of the row operations they use, and explain why they chose the row operation.

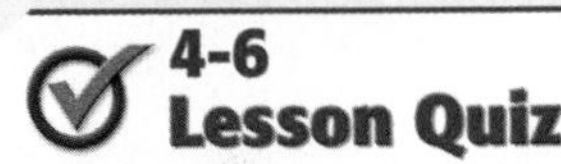

4-6 Lesson Quiz

1. Write an augmented matrix for the system of equations.

$$\begin{cases} 4x - y + 2z = 30 \\ 3x + 5z = 20 \\ 4y - z = 15 \end{cases}$$

$$\left[\begin{array}{ccc|c} 4 & -1 & 2 & 30 \\ 3 & 0 & 5 & 20 \\ 0 & 4 & -1 & 15 \end{array}\right]$$

2. Write an augmented matrix for the system of equations and solve using row operations.

$$\begin{cases} 4x + 7y = 43 \\ 6x - y = 30 \end{cases}$$

$$\left[\begin{array}{cc|c} 4 & 7 & 43 \\ 6 & -1 & 30 \end{array}\right]$$

(5.5, 3)

3. Solve the system using row reduction on a calculator.

$$\begin{cases} 4x + y - 2z = 21 \\ 3x - 5z = 10 \\ 2x - 4y + 3z = 1 \end{cases}$$

(5, 3, 1)

Also available on transparency

Organizer

Objective: Assess students' ability to apply concepts and skills in Lessons 4-4 through 4-6 in a real-world format.

Online Edition

Resources

Algebra II Assessments
www.mathtekstoolkit.org

For additional assessment activities, see www.utdanacenter.org

Problem	Lesson Reference
1–2	Lessons 4-5, 4-6
3	Lessons 4-4, 4-5, 4-6

Answers

1. A Mild ride costs \$1.00, a Wild ride costs \$1.25, and a Super Wild ride costs \$1.50.

2–3. See p. A25.

SECTION 4B

The Mild and Wild Amusement Park

Three friends, Travis, Kaitlyn, and Karsyn, spent the day at Mild and Wild Amusement Park, which features rides classified as Mild, Wild, or Super Wild. The park had two ticket packages as shown in the table.

Mild and Wild Amusement Park Ticket Packages

Package	Admission Fee	Ride Tickets
Pick-ur-Tix	\$5	Your choice at regular price
Mombo Combo	\$5	8 of each type of ride at a 20% discount

The three friends chose the Pick-ur-Tix package. By the end of the day, Travis had ridden on 4 Mild rides, 8 Wild rides, and 8 Super Wild rides for a total ticket cost of \$26. Kaitlyn had ridden on 8 Mild rides, 7 Wild rides, and 5 Super Wild rides for a total ticket cost of \$24.25. Karsyn had ridden on 7 Mild rides, 6 Wild rides, and 4 Super Wild rides for a total ticket cost of \$20.50.

1. Determine the ticket price for each type of ride. Solve an algebraic system for this situation by using matrices and a calculator or spreadsheet.
2. Determine the amount each person would spend if he or she had chosen the Mombo Combo. Explain which method of payment would have been bestfor each person.
3. Suppose that the amusement park had a fourth type of ride, called Colossal Wild. In addition to the other rides, Travis rode 12 Colossal Wild rides and spent \$30. Kaitlyn rode 3 Colossal Wild rides and spent \$30.25. Karsyn rode 1 Colossal Wild ride and spent \$22.50. Would you be able to write and solve a matrix equation for this new situation? Explain.

INTERVENTION

Scaffolding Questions

1. What matrix equation can you write?

$$AX = P$$

$$\begin{bmatrix} 4 & 8 & 8 \\ 8 & 7 & 5 \\ 7 & 6 & 4 \end{bmatrix} \begin{bmatrix} m \\ w \\ s \end{bmatrix} = \begin{bmatrix} 26.00 \\ 24.25 \\ 20.50 \end{bmatrix}$$

m: Mild ride price
w: Wild ride price
s: Super ride price

How do you solve the matrix equation? Find A^{-1} and multiply by P.

2. How does solving a matrix equation help you find the cost of the Mambo Combo? You can substitute the known ride prices.
3. How would you organize the information using matrices? Write a matrix equation. A 3×4 coefficient matrix is the friends (rows) by the number of each type of ride he or she took (columns), and a 3×1 matrix represents the ticket prices.

Extension

Add a fourth person and a fourth type of ride, and find the ticket prices.

READY TO GO ON?

Quiz for Lessons 4-4 Through 4-6

4-4 Determinants and Cramer's Rule

Find the determinant of each matrix.

1. $\begin{bmatrix} 3 & -1 \\ 1 & 3 \end{bmatrix}$ 10

2. $\begin{bmatrix} \frac{1}{2} & 0 \\ 3 & \frac{4}{5} \end{bmatrix}$ $\frac{2}{5}$

3. $\begin{bmatrix} 0.5 & 1.2 \\ -0.2 & 2.0 \end{bmatrix}$ 1.24

4. $\begin{bmatrix} 2 & -1 & 3 \\ 0 & -2 & 1 \\ 4 & 4 & 1 \end{bmatrix}$ 8

Use Cramer's rule to solve.

5. $\begin{cases} 2x + 3y = 5 \\ y = 1 - x \end{cases}$ (−2, 3)

6. $\begin{cases} x - y = 2 \\ y - x + 4 = 0 \end{cases}$ no solution

7. $\begin{cases} 2x - y + z = 3 \\ 3x + 2y = 2z + 1 \\ z = x + 2 \end{cases}$ (1, 2, 3)

4-5 Matrix Inverses and Solving Systems

Find the inverse of each matrix, if it is defined.

8. $\begin{bmatrix} 2 & 4 \\ 3 & 1 \end{bmatrix}$

9. $\begin{bmatrix} -1 & \frac{1}{2} \\ -\frac{2}{3} & \frac{1}{3} \end{bmatrix}$ not defined

10. $\begin{bmatrix} 2 & 1 & -1 \\ 0 & -1 & 3 \\ -1 & 0 & 2 \end{bmatrix}$

Write the matrix equation for the system, and solve, if possible.

11. $\begin{cases} y = 2x - 1.5 \\ y - x = 0.5 \end{cases}$

12. $\begin{cases} 10x + 8y = 13 \\ 15x + 12y = 8 \end{cases}$

13. $\begin{cases} 5x + 7y = 3z + 3 \\ 3x + 4y = 6 - 2z \\ x + 3y = 5z - 7 \end{cases}$

14. You are writing three proposals for playground equipment as a system of equations. Use x as the price of a climbing wall, y as the price of a combination slide, and z as the price of an adventure maze. What is the price of each type of equipment?

$$\begin{cases} 2x + y + 3z = 23{,}650 \\ x + 3y + 2z = 20{,}450 \\ 3x + 2y + z = 24{,}600 \end{cases}$$

4-6 Row Operations and Augmented Matrices

Write the augmented matrix, and use row reduction to solve, if possible.

15. $\begin{cases} 2x + 5y = 5 \\ 50x = 30y + 1 \end{cases}$

16. $\begin{cases} 5x - 4y = 6 \\ 10x = 12 + 8y \end{cases}$

17. $\begin{cases} 6x + 5y + 8 = 0 \\ x - y = \frac{1}{2} \end{cases}$

18. The system of equations represents the costs of three fruit baskets. Use a to represent the cost of a pound of apples, b the cost of a pound of bananas, and g the cost of a pound of grapes. Find the cost of a pound of each type of fruit.

$$\begin{cases} 2a + 2b + g + 1.05 = 6.00 \\ 3a + 2b + 2g + 1.05 = 8.48 \\ 4a + 3b + 2g + 1.05 = 10.46 \end{cases}$$

apples \$1.49/lb; bananas \$0.49/lb; grapes \$0.99/lb

READY TO GO ON?

Organizer

Objective: Assess students' mastery of concepts and skills in Lessons 4-4 through 4-6.

PREMIER Online Edition

Resources

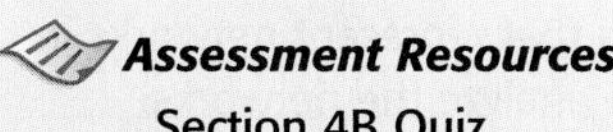
Assessment Resources
Section 4B Quiz

Test & Practice Generator
One-Stop Planner®

INTERVENTION

Resources

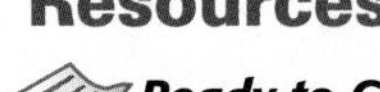

Ready to Go On? Intervention and Enrichment Worksheets

Ready to Go On? CD-ROM

Ready to Go On? Online
my.hrw.com

Answers

8, 10–17. See p. A25.

READY TO GO ON? Diagnose and Prescribe

NO INTERVENE

Ready to Go On? Intervention	*Ready to Go On? Intervention, Section 4B* Worksheets	CD-ROM	Online
Lesson 4-4	4-4 Intervention	Activity 4-4	Diagnose and Prescribe Online
Lesson 4-5	4-5 Intervention	Activity 4-5	
Lesson 4-6	4-6 Intervention	Activity 4-6	

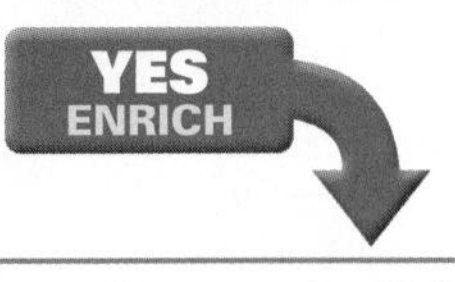
YES ENRICH

Ready to Go On? Enrichment, Section 4B

Worksheets
CD-ROM
Online

CHAPTER 4 Organizer

Pacing: Traditional 1 day
Block $\frac{1}{2}$ day

Objective: Convert between finite graphs and their matrix representations, and calculate the number of trips via two vertices.

Online Edition
Graphing Calculator

Using the Extension

In Chapter 4, students learn to raise square matrices to a power. In this extension, students use powers of matrices that represent networks in order to analyze the networks.

Technology Remind students to be very careful when using their calculators to work with large matrices because the screens may be too small to show the entire matrix.

State Resources

EXTENSION

Networks and Matrices

Objective
Convert between finite graphs and their matrix representations, and calculate the number of trips via two vertices.

Vocabulary
adjacency matrix

A *network* is a finite set of connected points called *vertices*. A *directed network* is a network where arrows show the possible directions of travel between vertices, as in the figure shown. Networks represent connections in areas such as transportation, delivery routes, social interactions, and nature trails.

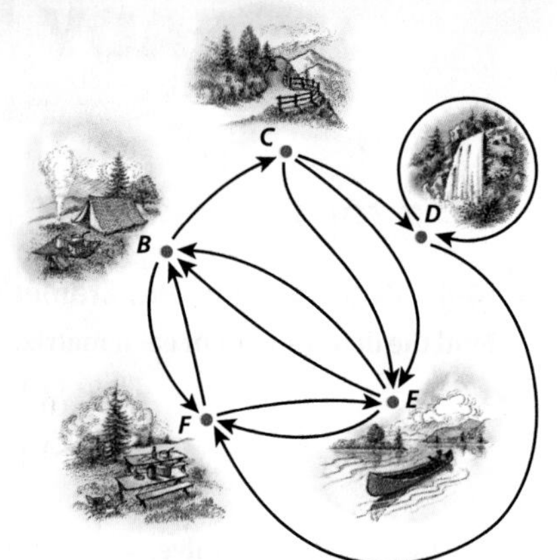

You can represent a network and show how many *1-step* (direct) paths are possible from each vertex to every other vertex by using an **adjacency matrix**.

EXAMPLE **Representing a Network with an Adjacency Matrix**

In the network above, find the number of ways to go from C to F with exactly one stop in between (2-step paths).

First, write the adjacency matrix A that represents the network. This adjacency matrix shows the number of 1-step paths.

From \ To:	B	C	D	E	F
B	0	1	0	0	1
C	0	0	1	2	0
D	0	0	1	0	1
E	2	0	0	0	1
F	1	0	0	1	0

Because there is a 1-step path (an arrow) from B to C, put a 1 in row 1 column 2.

Because there is no 1-step path (an arrow) from C to B, put a 0 in row 2 column 1.

The square of this adjacency matrix shows the number of 2-step paths (with one stop at a vertex in between).

$$A^2 = \begin{bmatrix} 1 & 0 & 1 & 3 & 0 \\ 4 & 0 & 1 & 0 & 3 \\ 1 & 0 & 1 & 1 & 1 \\ 1 & 2 & 0 & 1 & 2 \\ 2 & 1 & 0 & 0 & 2 \end{bmatrix}$$

A^2 shows that there are three 2-step paths from C to F. You can verify on the network that there are two paths from C to E to F and one path from C to D to F.

From \ To:	B	C	D	E	F
B	1	0	1	3	0
C	4	0	1	0	3
D	1	0	1	1	1
E	1	2	0	1	2
F	2	1	0	0	2

As the network gets larger and more complex, this method helps you find the number of paths by calculating instead of by counting the paths on a graph.

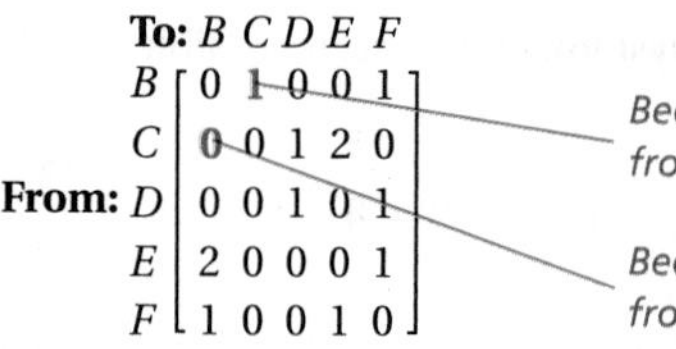

CHECK IT OUT! **1.** Use A^3 to show which vertex pairs in this network have five 3-step paths from one to the other.

$$A^3 = \begin{bmatrix} 6 & 1 & 1 & 0 & 5 \\ 3 & 4 & 1 & 3 & 5 \\ 3 & 1 & 1 & 1 & 3 \\ 4 & 1 & 2 & 6 & 2 \\ 2 & 2 & 1 & 4 & 2 \end{bmatrix};$$
there are five 3-step paths from B to F and from C to F.

1 Introduce

Motivate

Many situations that come up in real life, from transportation to wildlife management, can be represented as networks. Analyzing even mid-sized networks can be quite complex unless the proper tools are used. Matrices can provide simple ways to answer some interesting questions about networks.

2 Teach

Guided Instruction

Review raising a square matrix to a power. Remind students that this can be done with a calculator. Make sure that students understand how the information in the network is represented as a matrix.

EXTENSION Exercises

1. $\begin{bmatrix} 1&0&1&0&0&1 \\ 0&0&1&1&0&0 \\ 1&0&0&1&0&0 \\ 0&0&1&0&0&0 \\ 0&0&0&0&0&1 \\ 0&1&0&0&2&0 \end{bmatrix}$

Ecology **Use the following information for Exercises 1–5.**

Joel draws a habitat map and its network representation. The network vertices represent habitat patches, and the lines connecting them represent boundaries between the patches. The directed network shows wildlife migration patterns that Joel has recorded.

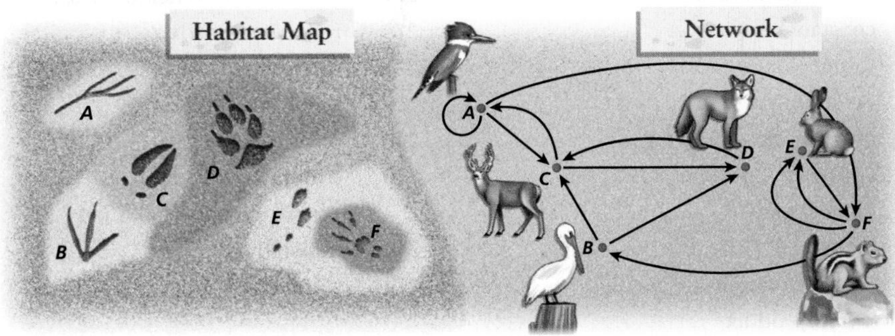

1. Write the adjacency matrix that represents the network shown. Keep the rows and columns in alphabetical order.
2. Find the number of ways to go from A to C.
   a. What is the number of 1-step paths? **1**
   b. Show the matrix, and find the number of 2-step paths.
   c. Show the matrix, and find the number of 3-step paths.
   d. What is the total number of 1-, 2-, and 3-step paths from A to C? **6**
3. Which two vertices are joined by exactly two 3-step paths?
4. Which two vertices are joined by exactly three 2-step paths? **none**
5. For which vertices are 1-, 2-, or 3-step round-trips possible? How can you use the adjacency matrix to find the answer?
6. **Critical Thinking** What does an entry of 1 signify on the main diagonal of an adjacency matrix? **A 1-step path from a vertex to itself exists.**

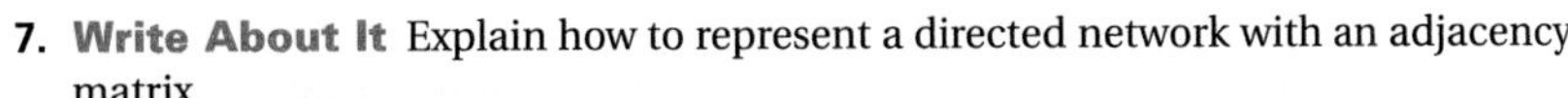

7. **Write About It** Explain how to represent a directed network with an adjacency matrix.
8. **Critical Thinking** What does an entry in the cube of an adjacency matrix tell you? What does a 0 entry in this matrix signify?
9. **ERROR ANALYSIS** A student said that the entry a_{mn} in an $n \times n$ adjacency matrix represents the number of paths from vertex n to vertex m. Explain the error. **The row-column address has been interpreted in reverse order.**

3. *A* to *D*, *A* to *E*, *B* to *A*, *B* to *C*, *C* to *D*, *C* to *E*, *D* to *C*, *E* to *F*, *F* to *B*

Helpful Hint

A *round-trip* path is a path that goes from one network vertex back to itself.

Draw a directed network that can be represented by each adjacency matrix.

10. $\begin{bmatrix} 0&2&1 \\ 1&0&1 \\ 1&1&0 \end{bmatrix}$

11. $\begin{bmatrix} 0&1&0&0 \\ 0&0&1&0 \\ 1&0&0&1 \\ 0&0&2&0 \end{bmatrix}$

12. $\begin{bmatrix} 0&2&0&1 \\ 1&0&0&1 \\ 0&0&1&0 \\ 1&1&0&0 \end{bmatrix}$

COMMON ERROR ALERT

Students may not be consistent when representing directed paths in matrix form. Students must remember that each entry is "the number of ways to get from **row X** to **column Y.**"

Power Presentations with PowerPoint®

Additional Examples

Example 1

In the network shown below, find the number of ways to go from *A* to *F* with exactly three stops in between (4-step paths).

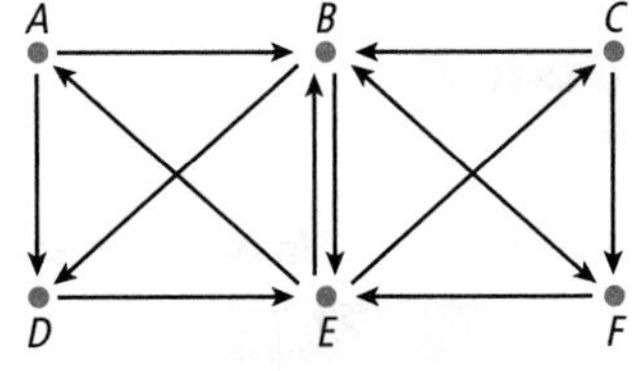

$$\begin{bmatrix} 0&1&0&1&0&0 \\ 0&0&0&1&1&1 \\ 0&1&0&0&0&1 \\ 0&0&0&0&1&0 \\ 1&1&1&0&0&0 \\ 0&1&0&0&1&0 \end{bmatrix}^4 = \begin{bmatrix} 2&6&2&5&3&5 \\ 2&9&2&6&10&6 \\ 3&8&3&5&5&5 \\ 1&3&1&2&6&2 \\ 6&10&6&4&7&4 \\ 3&7&3&5&8&5 \end{bmatrix}$$

5 ways to go from *A* to *F*

Also available on transparency

INTERVENTION

Questioning Strategies

EXAMPLE 1

- How is it possible for there to be 1-step paths from one vertex to another, but no 2-step paths?

Teaching Tip

Kinesthetic To help students visualize the paths in a network, have them trace the paths using their finger, or shade paths using colored pencils.

3 Close

Summarize

Matrices can be used to represent networks. A picture of the network can provide information that is not in the network, such as the spatial relation between elements in the network. The matrix representation can be a powerful tool for analyzing questions about paths from one element to another.

Answers

2b, 2c, 5, 7–8, 10–12. See pp. A25–A26.

Organizer

Objective: Help students organize and review key concepts and skills presented in Chapter 4.

Online Edition
Multilingual Glossary

Countdown to Testing Week 9

Resources

Puzzle Pro
One-Stop Planner®

***Multilingual Glossary* Online**
go.hrw.com
KEYWORD: MB7 Glossary

Lesson Tutorial Videos
CD-ROM

Test & Practice Generator
One-Stop Planner®

Answers

1. scalar
2. constant matrix
3. square matrix
4. not possible
5. $\begin{bmatrix} 0.4 & 0.6 \\ 0.8 & 1 \end{bmatrix}$
6. $\begin{bmatrix} 2 & -\frac{7}{3} & \frac{4}{3} \\ -\frac{11}{3} & \frac{2}{3} & 1 \end{bmatrix}$
7. $\begin{bmatrix} 6 & -9 & 4 \\ -9 & 2 & 5 \end{bmatrix}$
8. Possible answer: $\begin{bmatrix} 125 & 45 \\ 95 & 65 \end{bmatrix}$
9. Possible answer: $\begin{bmatrix} 30 & -20 \end{bmatrix}$
10. Possible answer: $\begin{bmatrix} 250 & 90 \\ 190 & 130 \end{bmatrix}$

CHAPTER 4 Study Guide: Review

Vocabulary

address	246	multiplicative identity matrix	255
augmented matrix	287	multiplicative inverse matrix	278
coefficient matrix	271	reduced row-echelon form	288
constant matrix	279	reflection matrix	263
Cramer's rule	271	rotation matrix	264
determinant	270	row operation	288
dimensions	246	row reduction	288
entry	246	scalar	248
main diagonal	255	square matrix	255
matrix	246	translation matrix	262
matrix equation	279	variable matrix	279
matrix product	253		

Complete the sentences below with vocabulary words from the list above.

1. A(n) ___?___ is a number that is multiplied by all entries of a matrix to form a new matrix.

2. A(n) ___?___ is formed from the constants in a system of equations.

3. Any matrix that has the same number of rows as columns is a(n) ___?___.

4-1 Matrices and Data *(pp. 246–252)*

EXAMPLE

$A = \begin{bmatrix} 0 & 3 \\ -1 & 4 \end{bmatrix}$ $B = \begin{bmatrix} 1 & 9 \\ -7 & 8 \end{bmatrix}$

Evaluate, if possible.

■ $A - 2B$

$$= \begin{bmatrix} 0 & 3 \\ -1 & 4 \end{bmatrix} - 2\begin{bmatrix} 1 & 9 \\ -7 & 8 \end{bmatrix}$$

$$= \begin{bmatrix} 0 & 3 \\ -1 & 4 \end{bmatrix} + \begin{bmatrix} -2(1) & -2(9) \\ -2(-7) & -2(8) \end{bmatrix}$$

$$= \begin{bmatrix} 0 & 3 \\ -1 & 4 \end{bmatrix} + \begin{bmatrix} -2 & -18 \\ 14 & -16 \end{bmatrix} = \begin{bmatrix} -2 & -15 \\ 13 & -12 \end{bmatrix}$$

EXERCISES

$P = \begin{bmatrix} 3 & -5 & 2 \\ -4 & 1 & 3 \end{bmatrix}$ $Q = \begin{bmatrix} 2 & 3 \\ 4 & 5 \end{bmatrix}$ $R = \begin{bmatrix} 6 & -8 & 4 \\ -10 & 2 & 4 \end{bmatrix}$

Evaluate, if possible.

4. $P - 2Q$

5. $(0.2)Q$

6. $\frac{1}{2}R - \frac{1}{3}P$

7. $\frac{1}{2}(2P + R)$

Use the following data for Exercises 8–10.

At a beach cleanup, Ashton's team collected 125 cans and 45 bottles; Mark's team collected 95 cans and 65 bottles.

8. Display the data in the form of a matrix C.

9. Write matrix C_D to show team differences.

10. Each team received double its numbers in party points. Write matrix P to show the party points.

4-2 Multiplying Matrices *(pp. 253–260)*

EXAMPLES

Find the matrix product, if it is defined.

■ $\begin{bmatrix} 1 & 0 \\ -3 & 2 \end{bmatrix}\begin{bmatrix} 2 & 7 & -5 \\ 0 & 1 & 0 \end{bmatrix}$

$(2 \times 2)(2 \times 3)$

$\begin{bmatrix} 2 & 7 & -5 \\ -6 & -19 & 15 \end{bmatrix}$

■ $\begin{bmatrix} 5 & 1 \\ -3 & 7 \end{bmatrix}\begin{bmatrix} 4 & 16 \\ 0 & -2 \\ -12 & 1 \end{bmatrix}$

$(2 \times 2)(3 \times 2)$

undefined

■ **Evaluate A^2, if possible.** $A = \begin{bmatrix} 3 & 4 & -5 \\ 0 & -2 & 7 \\ 9 & -6 & 1 \end{bmatrix}$

$$A^2 = \begin{bmatrix} 3 & 4 & -5 \\ 0 & -2 & 7 \\ 9 & -6 & 1 \end{bmatrix}\begin{bmatrix} 3 & 4 & -5 \\ 0 & -2 & 7 \\ 9 & -6 & 1 \end{bmatrix}$$

$$= \begin{bmatrix} -36 & 34 & 8 \\ 63 & -38 & -7 \\ 36 & 42 & -86 \end{bmatrix}$$

EXERCISES

Find the matrix product, if it is defined.

$D = \begin{bmatrix} -1 & 2 \\ 0 & -2 \\ -3 & 1 \end{bmatrix}$ $E = \begin{bmatrix} 0 & 1 & 3 \\ -2 & -1 & 4 \end{bmatrix}$ $F = \begin{bmatrix} 4 & 0 & 1 \\ 0 & 2 & 1 \\ -1 & 1 & 3 \end{bmatrix}$

11. DE **12.** FD **13.** DF **14.** EF

Evaluate, if possible.

15. D^2 **16.** F^2 **17.** $(ED)^2$

The tables show the prices and number of tickets sold for three theater performances.

	Adult	Student
Thu	$5	$2.50
Fri	$7.50	$4.25
Sat	$9	$5.75

	Thu	Fri	Sat
Adult	67	196	245
Student	104	75	154

18. a. Organize each table as a matrix.

b. Write the matrix product to find the amount of money collected for each performance.

c. Find the total collected for adult tickets and for student tickets for the three performances.

4-3 Using Matrices to Transform Geometric Figures *(pp. 261–267)*

EXAMPLE

Use the matrix $\begin{bmatrix} 1 & 0 \\ 0 & -1 \end{bmatrix}$ to transform triangle *ABC* with $A(-1, -2)$, $B(0, 1)$, and $C(3, -2)$. Graph the figure and its image. Describe the transformation.

■ Multiply $\begin{bmatrix} 1 & 0 \\ 0 & -1 \end{bmatrix}\begin{bmatrix} -1 & 0 & 3 \\ -2 & 1 & -2 \end{bmatrix} = \begin{bmatrix} -1 & 0 & 3 \\ 2 & -1 & 2 \end{bmatrix}$

The coordinates of the image are $A'(-1, 2)$, $B'(0, -1)$, and $C'(3, 2)$.

The triangle is reflected across the x-axis.

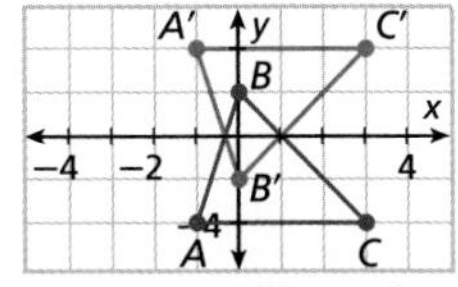

EXERCISES

Use matrices to transform polygon *P* with coordinates $W(-2, -1)$, $X(-1, 3)$, $Y(2, 4)$, and $Z(0, 0)$. Give the coordinates of each image.

19. Translate *P* 2 units right and 1 unit up.

20. Enlarge *P* by a factor of 1.5.

21. Use matrix $\begin{bmatrix} 1 & 0 \\ 0 & -1 \end{bmatrix}$ to transform *P*. Describe the transformation.

22. Use matrix $\begin{bmatrix} 0 & 1 \\ -1 & 0 \end{bmatrix}$ to transform *P*. Describe the transformation.

Answers

11. $\begin{bmatrix} -4 & -3 & 5 \\ 4 & 2 & -8 \\ -2 & -4 & -5 \end{bmatrix}$

12. $\begin{bmatrix} -7 & 9 \\ -3 & -3 \\ -8 & -1 \end{bmatrix}$

13. not defined

14. $\begin{bmatrix} -3 & 5 & 10 \\ -12 & 2 & 9 \end{bmatrix}$

15. not possible

16. $\begin{bmatrix} 15 & 1 & 7 \\ -1 & 5 & 5 \\ -7 & 5 & 9 \end{bmatrix}$

17. $\begin{bmatrix} 71 & -7 \\ 70 & -6 \end{bmatrix}$

18a. Possible answer:

$A = \begin{bmatrix} 5 & 2.5 \\ 7.5 & 4.25 \\ 9 & 5.75 \end{bmatrix}$;

$B = \begin{bmatrix} 67 & 196 & 245 \\ 104 & 75 & 154 \end{bmatrix}$

b. $\begin{bmatrix} 5 & 2.5 \\ 7.5 & 4.25 \\ 9 & 5.75 \end{bmatrix}\begin{bmatrix} 67 & 196 & 245 \\ 104 & 75 & 154 \end{bmatrix}$;

Thursday: $595; Friday: $1788.75; Saturday: $3090.50

c. adults: $4010; students: $1464.25

19. $\begin{bmatrix} -2 & -1 & 2 & 0 \\ -1 & 3 & 4 & 0 \end{bmatrix} + \begin{bmatrix} 2 & 2 & 2 & 2 \\ 1 & 1 & 1 & 1 \end{bmatrix} = \begin{bmatrix} 0 & 1 & 4 & 2 \\ 0 & 4 & 5 & 1 \end{bmatrix}$;

(0, 0), (1, 4), (4, 5), and (2, 1)

20. $1.5\begin{bmatrix} -2 & -1 & 2 & 0 \\ -1 & 3 & 4 & 0 \end{bmatrix} =$

$\begin{bmatrix} -3 & -1.5 & 3 & 0 \\ -1.5 & 4.5 & 6 & 0 \end{bmatrix}$;

(−3, −1.5), (−1.5, 4.5), (3, 6), and (0, 0)

21. $\begin{bmatrix} 1 & 0 \\ 0 & -1 \end{bmatrix}\begin{bmatrix} -2 & -1 & 2 & 0 \\ -1 & 3 & 4 & 0 \end{bmatrix} =$

$\begin{bmatrix} -2 & -1 & 2 & 0 \\ 1 & -3 & -4 & 0 \end{bmatrix}$; (−2, 1),

(−1, −3), (2, −4), and (0, 0); reflected across the *x*-axis

22. $\begin{bmatrix} 0 & 1 \\ -1 & 0 \end{bmatrix}\begin{bmatrix} -2 & -1 & 2 & 0 \\ -1 & 3 & 4 & 0 \end{bmatrix} =$

$\begin{bmatrix} -1 & 3 & 4 & 0 \\ 2 & 1 & -2 & 0 \end{bmatrix}$; (−1, 2),

(3, 1), (4, −2), and (0, 0); rotated 90° clockwise

Answers

23. 2
24. 0
25. $\frac{1}{2}$
26. 22
27. −31
28. 0
29. (5, 4)
30. (2, −5)
31. infinitely many solutions
32. (2, 4, −3)
33. no solution
34. (0.5, 2, 1.5)

35a. $\begin{vmatrix} 2 & 3 \\ -1 & 1 \end{vmatrix} = 5$

b. $x = \frac{\begin{vmatrix} 8 & 3 \\ 1 & 1 \end{vmatrix}}{5} = 1$; $y = \frac{\begin{vmatrix} 2 & 8 \\ -1 & 1 \end{vmatrix}}{5} = 2$

36a. Possible answer:

$$\begin{cases} s + m + \ell = 102 \\ 5s + 8m + 12.50\ell = 654 \\ 6\ell = s \end{cases}$$

b. 72 small, 18 medium, and 12 large

4-4 Determinants and Cramer's Rule *(pp. 270–277)*

EXAMPLES

Find the determinant of each matrix.

■ $\begin{bmatrix} 4 & -5 \\ 1 & 0 \end{bmatrix}$

$\begin{vmatrix} 4 & -5 \\ 1 & 0 \end{vmatrix}$

$= 4(0) - 1(-5)$

$= 0 + 5 = 5$

■ $\begin{bmatrix} -\frac{1}{2} & 9 \\ \frac{2}{3} & -6 \end{bmatrix}$

$\begin{vmatrix} -\frac{1}{2} & 9 \\ \frac{2}{3} & -6 \end{vmatrix}$

$= -\frac{1}{2}(-6) - \frac{2}{3}(9)$

$= 3 - 6 = -3$

■ $\begin{bmatrix} 4 & 0 & 1 \\ 3 & 5 & -2 \\ 2 & -1 & 7 \end{bmatrix}$ write $\begin{vmatrix} 4 & 0 & 1 \\ 3 & 5 & -2 \\ 2 & -1 & 7 \end{vmatrix} \begin{matrix} 4 & 0 \\ 3 & 5 \\ 2 & -1 \end{matrix}$

$140 + (0) + (-3) - [10 + 8 + 0] = 137 - 18$

$D = 119$

Use Cramer's rule to solve each system of equations.

■ $\begin{cases} 3 + y = 3x \\ 5 - y = x \end{cases}$

Write in $ax + by = c$ form: $\begin{cases} 3x - y = 3 \\ x + y = 5 \end{cases}$

$D = \det\begin{bmatrix} 3 & -1 \\ 1 & 1 \end{bmatrix} = 3 - (-1) = 4$

$x = \frac{\begin{vmatrix} 3 & -1 \\ 5 & 1 \end{vmatrix}}{4} = \frac{8}{4} = 2 \quad y = \frac{\begin{vmatrix} 3 & 3 \\ 1 & 5 \end{vmatrix}}{4} = \frac{12}{4} = 3$

The solution is (2, 3).

■ $\begin{cases} 2a + 2b + c = 3 \\ -2a - 4b + 5c = 79 \\ a - 3b + 2c = 50 \end{cases} \rightarrow D = \begin{vmatrix} 2 & 2 & 1 \\ -2 & -4 & 5 \\ 1 & -3 & 2 \end{vmatrix} = 42$

$a = \frac{\begin{vmatrix} 3 & 2 & 1 \\ 79 & -4 & 5 \\ 50 & -3 & 2 \end{vmatrix}}{D} \quad b = \frac{\begin{vmatrix} 2 & 3 & 1 \\ -2 & 79 & 5 \\ 1 & 50 & 2 \end{vmatrix}}{D} \quad c = \frac{\begin{vmatrix} 2 & 2 & 3 \\ -2 & -4 & 79 \\ 1 & -3 & 50 \end{vmatrix}}{D}$

$a = \frac{168}{42} = 4 \quad b = \frac{-336}{42} = -8 \quad c = \frac{462}{42} = 11$

The solution is $a = 4$, $b = -8$, $c = 11$.

EXERCISES

Find the determinant of each matrix.

23. $\begin{bmatrix} 1 & -1 \\ 1 & 1 \end{bmatrix}$

24. $\begin{bmatrix} 3 & 2 \\ 6 & 4 \end{bmatrix}$

25. $\begin{bmatrix} -\frac{1}{4} & 3 \\ -\frac{2}{3} & 6 \end{bmatrix}$

26. $\begin{bmatrix} 4 & 0 & 1 \\ 0 & 2 & 1 \\ -1 & 1 & 3 \end{bmatrix}$

27. $\begin{bmatrix} 2 & 3 & -1 \\ -1 & 5 & 3 \\ 3 & -1 & -6 \end{bmatrix}$

28. $\begin{bmatrix} 3 & 2 & -1 \\ 5 & -3 & 2 \\ 9 & -13 & 8 \end{bmatrix}$

Use Cramer's rule to solve each system of equations.

29. $\begin{cases} x + y = 9 \\ x - y = 1 \end{cases}$

30. $\begin{cases} 2x + 5y + 21 = 0 \\ 6x = 47 + 7y \end{cases}$

31. $\begin{cases} 4.5x + 3y = 10.5 \\ 3x + 2y = 7 \end{cases}$

32. $\begin{cases} 5x - 6y = 7 + 7z \\ 6x - 4y + 10z = -34 \\ 2x + 4y = 29 + 3z \end{cases}$

33. $\begin{cases} x - y + z = 5 \\ y - x - z = 2 \\ x - y + z = 7 \end{cases}$

34. $\begin{cases} y - 2.4x = 0.8 \\ 3x + 0.5z = 2.25 \\ 3.5y + z = 8.5 \end{cases}$

35. Find the point of intersection of the lines given by the equations $2x + 3y = 8$ and $y = x + 1$.
    a. Write the coefficient matrix, and find the determinant.
    b. Solve using Cramer's rule.

36. At an end-of-season sale, a souvenir shop gave away small gifts valued at $5 for sales of $25 to $74.99; medium gifts valued at $8 for sales of $75 to $149.99; and large gifts valued at $12.50 for sales above $150. The store gave away 102 gifts worth a total of $654 and six times as many small gifts as large gifts.
    a. Write a system of equations for the situation.
    b. Use Cramer's rule to solve for the number of small, medium, and large gifts.

4-5 Matrix Inverses and Solving Systems *(pp. 278–285)*

EXAMPLES

Find the inverse of the matrix, if it is defined.

■ $A = \begin{bmatrix} 4 & -2 \\ 0 & -\frac{1}{2} \end{bmatrix}$

$|A| = -2$; because $|A| \neq 0$, the matrix has an inverse.

$\frac{1}{|A|}\begin{bmatrix} d & -b \\ -c & a \end{bmatrix}$ gives $\frac{1}{-2}\begin{bmatrix} -\frac{1}{2} & 2 \\ 0 & 4 \end{bmatrix} = \begin{bmatrix} \frac{1}{4} & -1 \\ 0 & -2 \end{bmatrix}$

Check $\begin{bmatrix} 4 & -2 \\ 0 & -\frac{1}{2} \end{bmatrix}\begin{bmatrix} \frac{1}{4} & -1 \\ 0 & -2 \end{bmatrix} = \begin{bmatrix} 1 & 0 \\ 0 & 1 \end{bmatrix}$ ✓

Write the matrix equation for the system. Solve.

■ $\begin{cases} x + y = -6 \\ 2x + 3y = 8 \end{cases}$

$\begin{bmatrix} 1 & 1 \\ 2 & 3 \end{bmatrix}\begin{bmatrix} x \\ y \end{bmatrix} = \begin{bmatrix} -6 \\ 8 \end{bmatrix}$ so $A^{-1} = \begin{bmatrix} 3 & -1 \\ -2 & 1 \end{bmatrix}$

$\begin{bmatrix} x \\ y \end{bmatrix} = \begin{bmatrix} 3 & -1 \\ -2 & 1 \end{bmatrix}\begin{bmatrix} -6 \\ 8 \end{bmatrix}$ or $\begin{bmatrix} x \\ y \end{bmatrix} = \begin{bmatrix} -26 \\ 20 \end{bmatrix}$

The solution is $(-26, 20)$.

EXERCISES

Find the inverse of the matrix, if it exists.

37. $\begin{bmatrix} 6 & 2 \\ -1 & 3 \end{bmatrix}$

38. $\begin{bmatrix} \frac{3}{4} & -\frac{2}{5} \\ 0 & \frac{1}{5} \end{bmatrix}$

39. $\begin{bmatrix} 2 & 5 \\ 1 & 2.5 \end{bmatrix}$

40. $\begin{bmatrix} 2 & 1 & 0 \\ 0 & 3 & 2 \\ 3 & 2 & 1 \end{bmatrix}$

41. $\begin{bmatrix} -1.5 & 1 & 0.5 \\ 0.5 & 1 & 1 \\ -1 & 1 & 0.5 \end{bmatrix}$

42. $\begin{bmatrix} 5 & -3 & 2 \\ 0 & 0 & 0 \\ 2 & 7 & -1 \end{bmatrix}$

Write the matrix equation for the system. Solve.

43. $\begin{cases} \frac{3}{2}x = 20 + y \\ x + 6y = 80 \end{cases}$

44. $\begin{cases} x = 1 + y \\ x + y = 9 \end{cases}$

45. $\begin{cases} 3x + 3y = 19 + z \\ 5x + 4y - 28 = 2z \\ 2(x + y) - 12 = z \end{cases}$

46. $\begin{cases} 2x + 9 = 2z \\ 5x + y + 32 = 7z \\ 2(3x + y) = 8z - 39 \end{cases}$

4-6 Row Operations and Augmented Matrices *(pp. 287–293)*

EXAMPLE

Write the augmented matrix, and solve.

■ $\begin{cases} x - y = 3 \\ x - y = 0 \end{cases}$

$\left[\begin{array}{cc|c} 1 & -1 & 3 \\ 1 & -1 & 0 \end{array}\right]$ ❶ − ❷ → $\left[\begin{array}{cc|c} 1 & -1 & 3 \\ 0 & 0 & 3 \end{array}\right]$

The second row means $0 + 0y = 3$, which is false. The system is inconsistent.

■ $\begin{cases} 2x + y = 6 \\ x - y = 0 \end{cases}$

$\left[\begin{array}{cc|c} 2 & 1 & 6 \\ 1 & -1 & 0 \end{array}\right]$ (❶ + ❷) ÷ 3 → $\left[\begin{array}{cc|c} 1 & 0 & 2 \\ 1 & -1 & 0 \end{array}\right]$

❶ − ❷ → $\left[\begin{array}{cc|c} 1 & 0 & 2 \\ 0 & 1 & 2 \end{array}\right]$, so $x = 2$ and $y = 2$.

EXERCISES

Write the augmented matrix, and solve.

47. $\begin{cases} 7x + 2y = 0.75 \\ 2x - y = 1 \end{cases}$

48. $\begin{cases} p - q = 4 \\ 2p + 3q = -22 \end{cases}$

Solve the system by using row reduction.

49. $\begin{cases} x + 2z = 0.5 \\ -5y = 0.25 \\ 3x + 4z = 1.1 \end{cases}$

50. $\begin{cases} 2.5x + 1.5y = 4 \\ 3.2x + y = 4z - 3.8 \\ 6.4x - 5y + 2.1z = 5.6 \end{cases}$

51. In gymnastics, Team Osho won 27 awards, which gave them 87 points. The team won one more 1st-place award than 3rd-place awards.

Place	Points
First	5
Second	4
Third	1

Use the table to write a system of equations to represent this situation. Use row reduction to find how many of each award the team won.

Answers

37. $\begin{bmatrix} 0.15 & -0.1 \\ 0.05 & 0.3 \end{bmatrix}$

38. $\begin{bmatrix} \frac{4}{3} & \frac{8}{3} \\ 0 & 5 \end{bmatrix}$

39. no inverse

40. $\begin{bmatrix} -0.25 & -0.25 & 0.5 \\ 1.5 & 0.5 & -1 \\ -2.25 & -0.25 & 1.5 \end{bmatrix}$

41. $\begin{bmatrix} -2 & 0 & 2 \\ -5 & -1 & 7 \\ 6 & 2 & -8 \end{bmatrix}$

42. does not exist

43. $\begin{bmatrix} \frac{3}{2} & -1 \\ 1 & 6 \end{bmatrix}\begin{bmatrix} x \\ y \end{bmatrix} = \begin{bmatrix} 20 \\ 80 \end{bmatrix}$; (20, 10)

44. $\begin{bmatrix} 1 & -1 \\ 1 & 1 \end{bmatrix}\begin{bmatrix} x \\ y \end{bmatrix} = \begin{bmatrix} 1 \\ 9 \end{bmatrix}$; (5, 4)

45. $\begin{bmatrix} 3 & 3 & -1 \\ 5 & 4 & -2 \\ 2 & 2 & -1 \end{bmatrix}\begin{bmatrix} x \\ y \\ z \end{bmatrix} = \begin{bmatrix} 19 \\ 28 \\ 12 \end{bmatrix}$; (4, 3, 2)

46. $\begin{bmatrix} 2 & 0 & -2 \\ 5 & 1 & -7 \\ 6 & 2 & -8 \end{bmatrix}\begin{bmatrix} x \\ y \\ z \end{bmatrix} = \begin{bmatrix} -9 \\ -32 \\ -39 \end{bmatrix}$; (−1, −2.5, 3.5)

47. $\left[\begin{array}{cc|c} 7 & 2 & 0.75 \\ 2 & -1 & 1 \end{array}\right]$; (0.25, −0.5)

48. $\left[\begin{array}{cc|c} 1 & -1 & 4 \\ 2 & 3 & -22 \end{array}\right]$; (−2, −6)

49. $\left[\begin{array}{ccc|c} 1 & 0 & 2 & 0.5 \\ 0 & -5 & 0 & 0.25 \\ 3 & 0 & 4 & 1.1 \end{array}\right]$; (0.1, −0.05, 0.2)

50. $\left[\begin{array}{ccc|c} 2.5 & 1.5 & 0 & 4 \\ 3.2 & 1 & -4 & -3.8 \\ 6.4 & -5 & 2.1 & 5.6 \end{array}\right]$; (1, 1, 2)

51. Possible answer:

$\begin{cases} f + s + t = 27 \\ 5f + 4s + t = 87 \\ f - t = 1 \end{cases}$; $f = 12$; $s = 4$; $t = 11$; 12 first-place, 4 second-place, and 11 third-place

CHAPTER 4 CHAPTER TEST

Organizer

Objective: Assess students' mastery of concepts and skills in Chapter 4.

Online Edition

Resources

Assessment Resources

Chapter 4 Tests
- Free Response (Levels A, B, C)
- Multiple Choice (Levels A, B, C)
- Performance Assessment

***IDEA Works!* CD-ROM**

Modified Chapter 4 Test

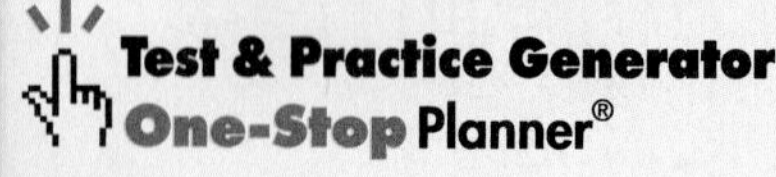
Test & Practice Generator One-Stop Planner®

Answers

1. $A = \begin{bmatrix} 5 & 1 & 2 & 41 \\ 3 & 5 & 1 & 42 \\ 3 & 1 & 4 & 29 \end{bmatrix}$

5. The operation cannot be performed because the matrices do not have the same dimensions.

6. $\begin{bmatrix} 5 & -1 & -6 \\ -4 & 2 & 0 \\ 15 & -7 & -2 \end{bmatrix}$

7. $\begin{bmatrix} 10 & 12 \\ -11 & -5 \end{bmatrix}$

State Resources

CHAPTER 4

CHAPTER TEST

Use the data from the table to answer the questions.

Awards Given				
	First Place	Second Place	Third Place	Total Points
Klete	5	1	2	41
Michael	3	5	1	42
Ryan	3	1	4	29

1. Display the data in the form of matrix A.
2. What are the dimensions of the matrix? **3 x 4**
3. What is the value of the matrix entry with address a_{31}? **3**
4. What is the address of the entry that has a value of 2? a_{13}

Evaluate, if possible.

$$E = \begin{bmatrix} 2 & 3 \\ -1 & 0 \\ 4 & 1 \end{bmatrix} \quad F = \begin{bmatrix} 4 & -2 & 0 \\ -1 & 1 & -2 \end{bmatrix} \quad G = \begin{bmatrix} 2 & -1 \\ 3 & 1 \end{bmatrix} \quad H = \begin{bmatrix} -2 & 1 \\ 3 & 0 \\ 5 & -1 \end{bmatrix} \quad J = \begin{bmatrix} 1 & -5 & 6 \end{bmatrix} \quad K = \begin{bmatrix} 7 \\ 0 \\ -2 \end{bmatrix}$$

5. $E + F$
6. EF
7. FE
8. H^2
9. G^3
10. FK

Use a matrix to transform $\triangle PQR$.

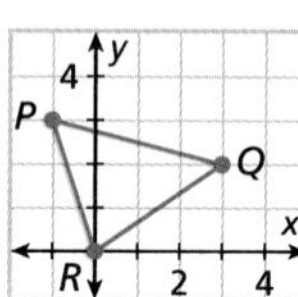

11. Translate $\triangle PQR$ 2 units up and 1 unit right.
12. Enlarge $\triangle PQR$ by a factor of $\frac{3}{2}$.
13. Use $\begin{bmatrix} 0 & 2 \\ 2 & 0 \end{bmatrix}$ to transform $\triangle PQR$. Describe the image.

Find the determinant of each matrix.

14. $\begin{bmatrix} 4 & 0 \\ 0 & -3 \end{bmatrix}$ **−12**
15. $\begin{bmatrix} 0.25 & 1 \\ 2 & 8 \end{bmatrix}$ **0**
16. $\begin{bmatrix} 3 & -1 \\ -2 & -1 \end{bmatrix}$ **−5**
17. $\begin{bmatrix} 1 & -2 & 3 \\ 3 & -1 & -3 \\ 2 & 1 & 5 \end{bmatrix}$ **55**

18. Use Cramer's rule to solve $\begin{cases} x + 2y = 1 \\ 3x - y = 10 \end{cases}$ **(3, −1)**
19. Use Cramer's rule to solve $\begin{cases} x + 3z = 3 + 2y \\ 3x + 22 = y + 3z \\ 2x + y + 5z = 8 \end{cases}$ **(−4, 1, 3)**

Find the inverse, if it exists.

20. $\begin{bmatrix} 2 & 0.7 \\ 4 & 1.4 \end{bmatrix}$ **no inverse**
21. $\begin{bmatrix} 3 & -1 \\ 1 & 3 \end{bmatrix}$
22. $\begin{bmatrix} 3 & 1 \\ 2 & -1 \end{bmatrix}$
23. $\begin{bmatrix} 3 & 2 & -1 \\ 2 & 3 & -5 \\ 1 & 4 & 2 \end{bmatrix}$

24. The cost of 2.5 pounds of figs and 1.5 pounds of dates is \$14.42. The cost of 3.5 pounds of figs and 1 pound of dates is \$16.91. Use a matrix operation to find the price of each per pound. **\$3.98; \$2.98**

Write the matrix equation for each system, and solve, if possible.

25. $\begin{cases} 6x + y = 2 \\ 3x - 2y + 1 = 0 \end{cases}$
26. $\begin{cases} 5x - 2y = 3 \\ 2.5x - y = 1.5 \end{cases}$
27. $\begin{cases} x + 2y = 3.5 \\ 3x = 2.7 + y \end{cases}$
28. $\begin{cases} 2x - z = 3 + y \\ x + 2 = y + 5 \\ 4z + x + y = 1 \end{cases}$

Write the augmented matrix, and use row reduction to solve, if possible.

29. Use the data from Items 1–4 above. Find the number of points assigned for finishing in first, second, and third places.

8. not possible

9. $\begin{bmatrix} -7 & -4 \\ 12 & 11 \end{bmatrix}$

10. $\begin{bmatrix} 28 \\ -3 \end{bmatrix}$

11. $\begin{bmatrix} -1 & 3 & 0 \\ 3 & 2 & 0 \end{bmatrix} + \begin{bmatrix} 1 & 1 & 1 \\ 2 & 2 & 2 \end{bmatrix} = \begin{bmatrix} 0 & 4 & 1 \\ 5 & 4 & 2 \end{bmatrix}$.

The coordinates of the image are $P'(0, 5)$, $Q'(4, 4)$, and $R'(1, 2)$.

12. $\frac{3}{2}\begin{bmatrix} -1 & 3 & 0 \\ 3 & 2 & 0 \end{bmatrix} =$

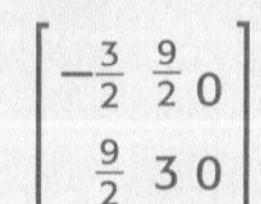

$\begin{bmatrix} -\frac{3}{2} & \frac{9}{2} & 0 \\ \frac{9}{2} & 3 & 0 \end{bmatrix}$

The coordinates of the image are $P'\left(-\frac{3}{2}, \frac{9}{2}\right)$, $Q'\left(\frac{9}{2}, 3\right)$, and $R'(0, 0)$.

13. The coordinates of the image are (6, −2), (4, 6), and (0, 0). The triangle has been enlarged by a factor of 2 and reflected across the line $y = x$.

21. $\begin{bmatrix} 0.3 & 0.1 \\ -0.1 & 0.3 \end{bmatrix}$

22. $\begin{bmatrix} 0.2 & 0.2 \\ 0.4 & -0.6 \end{bmatrix}$

23. $\begin{bmatrix} 0.47 & -0.15 & -0.13 \\ -0.16 & 0.13 & 0.24 \\ 0.09 & -0.18 & 0.09 \end{bmatrix}$

25–29. See p. A26.

COLLEGE ENTRANCE EXAM PRACTICE

CHAPTER 4

FOCUS ON SAT MATHEMATICS SUBJECT TEST

There are two levels of SAT Mathematics Subject Tests: Level 1 and Level 2. Each test has 50 questions, all multiple choice. The content of each test is very different. Getting a high score on one test does not mean you will get a high score on the other test.

You can write all over the test book to sketch figures, do scratch work, or cross out incorrect answers to help you eliminate choices. Remember to mark your final answer on the answer sheet because the test books are not examined for answers.

You may want to time yourself as you take this practice test. It should take you about 6 minutes to complete.

1. If A is a 6×4 matrix and B is a 4×8 matrix, what are the dimensions of matrix AB?

(A) 6×4

(B) 4×8

(C) 10×12

(D) 12×8

(E) 6×8

2. If $D = \begin{bmatrix} 5 & 1 \\ 8 & 3 \\ 6 & 2 \end{bmatrix}$ and $E = \begin{bmatrix} 0 & -5 \\ 1 & 4 \\ -2 & 3 \end{bmatrix}$, which of the following operations gives $\begin{bmatrix} 5 & 11 \\ 6 & -5 \\ 10 & -4 \end{bmatrix}$?

(A) $D + 2E$

(B) $D - 2E$

(C) $2D + E$

(D) $2D - E$

(E) $D + E$

3. Given a matrix representing a system of equations, which of the following row operations is NOT valid for solving the system?

(A) Add the first row to the second row.

(B) Multiply the last row by −1.

(C) Switch the top row and the bottom row.

(D) Subtract the second row from the first row.

(E) Add 1 to each element of the last row.

4. Which of the following matrices has a determinant of 3?

(A) $\begin{bmatrix} 2 & -1 \\ 1 & 2 \end{bmatrix}$

(B) $\begin{bmatrix} 2 & -2 \\ 1 & 2 \end{bmatrix}$

(C) $\begin{bmatrix} 2 & 3 \\ -1 & 0 \end{bmatrix}$

(D) $\begin{bmatrix} 3 & -1 \\ 0 & 2 \end{bmatrix}$

(E) $\begin{bmatrix} 0 & 1 \\ 0 & 3 \end{bmatrix}$

5. What effect does adding the matrix $\begin{bmatrix} 3 & 3 \\ -1 & -1 \end{bmatrix}$ to a matrix representing ordered pairs on a line have?

(A) The line is translated 3 units to the right and 1 unit down.

(B) The line is translated 3 units to the left and 1 unit up.

(C) The line is translated 1 unit to the left and 3 units up.

(D) The line is stretched and rotated 90° clockwise.

(E) The line is stretched and rotated 90° counterclockwise.

COLLEGE ENTRANCE EXAM PRACTICE

CHAPTER 4

Organizer

Objective: Provide practice for college entrance exams such as the SAT Mathematics Subject Tests.

Resources

College Entrance Exam Practice

Questions on the SAT Mathematics Subject Tests represent the following math content areas:

	Level 1	Level 2
Algebra	30%	18%
Plane Euclidean Geometry	20%	0%
Coordinate Geometry	12%	12%
Three-dimentional Geometry	6%	8%
Trigonometry	8%	20%
Functions	12%	24%
Statistics/Probabilty	6%	6%
Miscellaneous	6%	12%

Items on this page focus on:

- Algebra
- Plane Euclidean Geometry
- Miscellaneous

Text References:

Item	1	2	3	4	5
Lesson	4-2	4-1	4-5	4-4	4-3

TEST PREP DOCTOR

1. Students who chose **C** added the number of rows and columns of A and B. Remind students that the product of two matrices has the same number of rows as the first matrix and the same number of columns as the second matrix.
2. Students who did not choose **B** may have checked the results of their answer using only the entry in the first row and column of each matrix. Remind students that the operation must hold for all entries.
3. Students who did not choose **E** should review the types of valid row operations for matrices. Suggest that students create a sample matrix and read the answer choices again.
4. Students who chose **A** may have found the sum of the cross products, or they may have missed the fact that a negative number was to be subtracted.
5. Students who chose **C** may have switched the coordinates. Students who chose **D** or **E** are multiplying when they should be adding. Remind them to read the item carefully before answering.

Objective: Provide opportunities to learn and practice common test-taking strategies.

Online Edition

Resources

State Test Prep Workbook

***State Test Prep* CD-ROM**

***State Test Practice* Online**

go.hrw.com

KEYWORD: MB7 TestPrep

TEST PREP DOCTOR Remind students to include all of their work in a response, even if done on a calculator, and to write down their work systematically, as their thinking process is being evaluated by the grader.

Have students reread an extended-response question after they have answered it, to be sure that they answered all parts of the question.

Standardized Test Strategies

Extended Response: Write Extended Responses

Extended response test items evaluate how well you can apply and explain mathematical concepts. These questions have multiple parts, and you must correctly answer all of the parts to receive full credit. Extended response questions are scored using a 4-point scoring system.

Scoring Rubric

4 points: The student demonstrates a thorough understanding of the concept, correctly answers the question, and provides a complete explanation.

3 points: The student shows most of the work and provides an explanation but has a minor computation error, OR student shows all work and arrives at a correct answer but does not provide an explanation.

2 points: The student makes major errors resulting in an incorrect solution.

1 point: The student shows no work and has an incorrect response, OR student does not follow directions.

0 points: The student gives no response.

EXAMPLE 1

Extended Response An amphitheater has two levels of seating for concerts. Upper-level tickets sell for $25, and lower-level tickets sell for $50. At the last concert, 220 tickets were sold, and $7875 was taken in. How many tickets of each type were sold? Use a system of linear equations to model this situation. Use matrices to solve the system of equations. Interpret your results.

The following shows a response that received **4 points.** Notice that it includes a system of equations that models the situation with variables clearly defined, matrix operations, the final matrix, and a correct solution written in a complete sentence.

Let u = the number of upper-level tickets sold.

Let ℓ = the number of lower-level tickets sold. ← Variables defined

System of Equations

$$\begin{cases} u + \ell = 220 \\ 25u + 50\ell = 7875 \end{cases}$$

Matrix Equation

$$\begin{bmatrix} 1 & 1 \\ 25 & 50 \end{bmatrix} X = \begin{bmatrix} 220 \\ 7875 \end{bmatrix}$$

Inverse

$$\frac{1}{25}\begin{bmatrix} 50 & -1 \\ -25 & 1 \end{bmatrix} = \begin{bmatrix} 2 & -0.04 \\ -1 & 0.04 \end{bmatrix}$$

$X = A^{-1}B$

$$\begin{bmatrix} 2 & -0.04 \\ -1 & 0.04 \end{bmatrix}\begin{bmatrix} 220 \\ 7875 \end{bmatrix} = \begin{bmatrix} 2(220) - 0.04(7875) \\ -1(220) + 0.04(7875) \end{bmatrix} = \begin{bmatrix} 125 \\ 95 \end{bmatrix}$$

Solution: There were 125 upper-level tickets and 95 lower-level tickets sold.

Highlight or underline each part of the test item. Verify that your response addresses each part of the problem before you move on.

Read each test item, and answer the questions that follow.

Item A

Extended Response Explain what row operations were performed to create the new matrix.

$$\left[\begin{array}{cc|c} 4 & 3 & 1 \\ 3 & -2 & 5 \end{array}\right] \Rightarrow \left[\begin{array}{cc|c} -17 & 0 & -17 \\ 7 & 1 & 6 \end{array}\right]$$

1. Tyler wrote this response:

First, add row 1 to row 2 to get a new row 2. This makes a new matrix, $\begin{bmatrix} 4 & 3 & 1 \\ 7 & 1 & 6 \end{bmatrix}$. Then multiply the new row 2 by -3 and add it to row 1. This makes the resulting matrix, $\begin{bmatrix} -17 & 0 & -17 \\ 7 & 1 & 6 \end{bmatrix}$.

Item B

Extended Response Write the matrix that represents the vertices of figure *ABCD*. Then, determine and explain what matrix and which operations you would use to create figure *EFGH*.

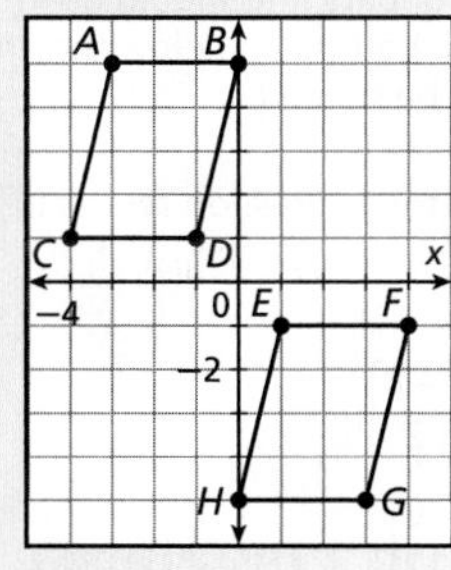

2. Make a list of what needs to be included in a response to this test item so that it receives full credit.

3. Sarah wrote this response:

The matrix for figure ABCD is $\begin{bmatrix} -3 & 0 & -1 & -4 \\ 5 & 5 & 1 & 1 \end{bmatrix}$, where the columns represent points A, B, C, and D and the rows represent the x- and y-coordinates.

Score Sarah's response, and provide your reasoning for the score.

4. Give a response that would receive full credit.

Item C

Extended Response Create a matrix that does not have an inverse. Explain your reasoning.

5. Should the following response receive full credit? Explain your reasoning.

The matrix $\begin{bmatrix} 4 & 3 \\ 12 & 9 \end{bmatrix}$ does not have an inverse because its determinant equals zero.

$\begin{vmatrix} 4 & 3 \\ 12 & 9 \end{vmatrix} = (4 \cdot 9) - (12 \cdot 3) = 36 - 36 = 0$

Item D

Extended Response Consider the system of equations $\begin{cases} x - 4y = 1.5 \\ 2x + y = 8.2 \end{cases}$. Describe which method—row operations, inverse matrices, or Cramer's rule—you would use to solve the system. Explain your reasoning.

6. Score the following response, and explain your score.

$D = \begin{vmatrix} 1 & -4 \\ 2 & 1 \end{vmatrix} = 1 - (-8) = 9$

$x = \dfrac{\begin{vmatrix} 1.5 & -4 \\ 8.2 & 1 \end{vmatrix}}{9} = \dfrac{1.5 - (-32.8)}{9} = \dfrac{34.3}{9} \approx 3.81$

$y = \dfrac{\begin{vmatrix} 1 & 1.5 \\ 2 & 8.2 \end{vmatrix}}{9} = \dfrac{8.2 - 3}{9} = \dfrac{5.2}{9} \approx 0.58$

7. How would you rewrite this response so that it receives full credit?

Answers

Possible answers:

1. The response is worth 4 points. It contains a clear explanation and correct computations. It also demonstrates an understanding of the concept. No additional work or explanation is required.
2. a matrix representing figure *ABCD*; a matrix for figure *EFGH*; an explanation of the transformation from matrix *ABCD* to *EFGH,* including all operations
3. The response is worth 2 points. Sarah did only half of what was expected. Although the matrix she created for figure *ABCD* is correct, she did not determine a matrix or an operation for transforming figure *ABCD* into figure *EFGH*.
4. The matrix for figure *ABCD* is $\begin{bmatrix} -3 & 0 & -1 & -4 \\ 5 & 5 & 1 & 1 \end{bmatrix}$, where the columns represent points *A, B, C,* and *D,* and the row represents the *x*- and *y*-coordinates. The figure is translated 4 units right and 6 units down to obtain figure *EFGH*. So the matrix for *ABCD*, $\begin{bmatrix} -3 & 0 & -1 & -4 \\ 5 & 5 & 1 & 1 \end{bmatrix}$, needs to be added to the transformation matrix $\begin{bmatrix} 4 & 4 & 4 & 4 \\ -6 & -6 & -6 & -6 \end{bmatrix}$ to get the resulting matrix for *EFGH*. This sum, $\begin{bmatrix} -3 & 0 & -1 & -4 \\ 5 & 5 & 1 & 1 \end{bmatrix} + \begin{bmatrix} 4 & 4 & 4 & 4 \\ -6 & -6 & -6 & -6 \end{bmatrix} = \begin{bmatrix} 1 & 4 & 3 & 0 \\ -1 & -1 & -5 & -5 \end{bmatrix}$, represents the coordinates of the figure *EFGH*.

State Resources

go.hrw.com
State Resources Online
KEYWORD: MB7 Resources

Answers to Test Items

See answers to the related problems.

Answers

5. The response should receive a score of 3 points. The answer is correct, but the explanation could include the fact that the formula for the inverse would result in division by 0.
6. The response should receive a score of 2 points. The student chose a method, but solved instead of supplying a reason for using it.
7. Explain that you should use a specific method, such as Cramer's rule, and give a reason for choosing it.

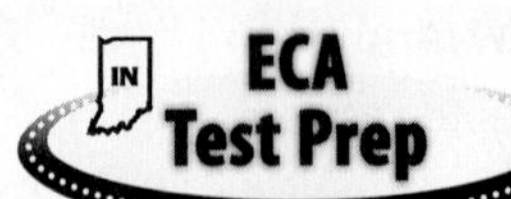

Organizer

Objective: Provide review and practice for Chapters 1–4 and standardized tests.

Resources

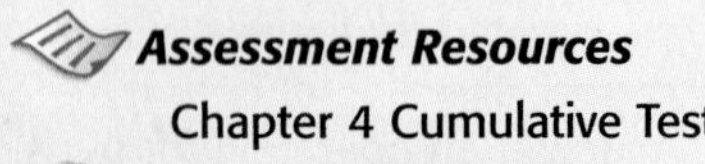

Assessment Resources

Chapter 4 Cumulative Test

***IDEA Works!* CD-ROM**

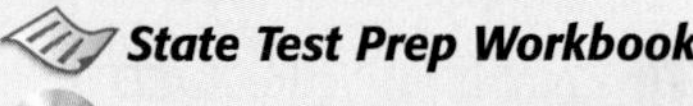

State Test Prep Workbook

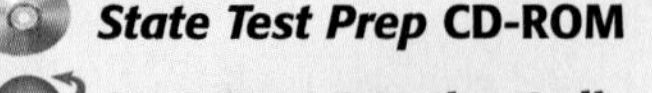

***State Test Prep* CD-ROM**

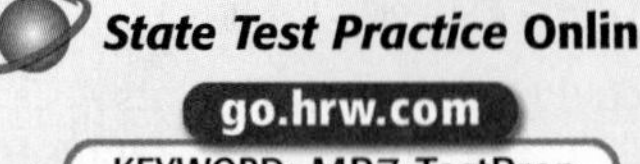

***State Test Practice* Online**

go.hrw.com
KEYWORD: MB7 TestPrep

Answers

1. B
2. D
3. A
4. C
5. C
6. A
7. D
8. B
9. C

State Resources

Core Standard	Items
1	3, 4, 5, 10

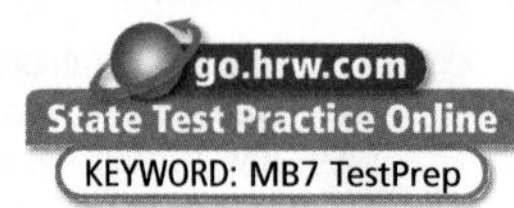

CUMULATIVE ASSESSMENT, CHAPTERS 1–4

Multiple Choice

1. Jack is two less than four times Macy's age. Kirstin is six more than half of Jack's age. If x is Macy's age and y is Jack's age, which expression represents Kirstin's age?

A. $\frac{1}{2}x + 6$ **B.** $2x + 5$

C. $4x + \frac{1}{2}y + 4$ **D.** $\frac{1}{2}(4x + 2) - 6$

2. The matrix below is the augmented matrix for a system of equations. What is the solution of the system of equations?

$$\left[\begin{array}{cc|c} 6 & 8 & 5 \\ 12 & 4 & 16 \end{array}\right]$$

A. $\left(-\frac{3}{2}, \frac{1}{2}\right)$ **B.** $\left(-\frac{1}{2}, \frac{3}{2}\right)$

C. $\left(\frac{2}{3}, -2\right)$ **D.** $\left(\frac{3}{2}, -\frac{1}{2}\right)$

3.

PUTTER'S MINIATURE GOLF
1 putt—HOLE-IN-ONE!
2 putts—BIRDIE
3 putts—PAR
4 putts—BOGEY

Grace played 18 holes of miniature golf. On each hole, she made a birdie, a par, or a bogey. She made four more pars than birdies and bogeys combined. Her total score was 55. How many birdies did Grace get?

A. 3 **B.** 4

C. 7 **D.** 11

4. When stopping a car, a driver takes about 1.5 seconds to react before beginning to brake. A car traveling at 30 miles per hour moves 66 feet before the driver's foot touches the brake pedal. A car traveling at 45 miles per hour moves 99 feet, and a car traveling at 55 miles per hour moves 121 feet. Which set consists of only domain values for the given data?

A. $\{1.5\}$ **B.** $\{30, 66\}$

C. $\{30, 45\}$ **D.** $\{66, 99, 121\}$

5. The graph below shows the graph of an equation that is the boundary line of an inequality. The ordered pairs (21, 83) and (16, 62) are NOT solutions of the inequality. Which of these is true of the graph of the inequality?

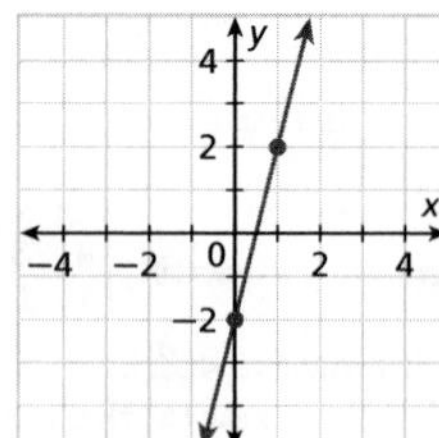

A. The boundary line should be dashed, and the half-plane above the line should be shaded.

B. The boundary line should be solid, and the half-plane above the line should be shaded.

C. The boundary line should be dashed, and the half-plane below the line should be shaded.

D. The boundary line should be solid, and the half-plane below the line should be shaded.

6. Which matrix expression results in the matrix $\begin{bmatrix} 2 & -4 \\ 11 & 14 \end{bmatrix}$?

A. $\frac{1}{2}\begin{bmatrix} 4 & -8 \\ 22 & 28 \end{bmatrix}$

B. $2\begin{bmatrix} 0 & -6 \\ 9 & 12 \end{bmatrix}$

C. $\begin{bmatrix} 2 & -4 \\ 11 & 14 \end{bmatrix} + \begin{bmatrix} 1 & 0 \\ 0 & 1 \end{bmatrix}$

D. $\begin{bmatrix} -6 & 17 \\ 8 & 10 \end{bmatrix} + \begin{bmatrix} 8 & -13 \\ -3 & 4 \end{bmatrix}$

TEST PREP DOCTOR

For **Item 5,** students should use the graph to write the equation of the boundary line. Then use the given coordinates to write the inequality. Encourage students to select other test points to verify that the inequality written is correct. This question fundamentally tests if a student understands when the line is dashed and when it is solid, as well as which half-plane to shade.

In **Item 9,** students may try to answer −6. Remind them that a negative number cannot be entered on the grid.

Answers

10. Part A: $\begin{cases} y > -\frac{1}{5}x - 1 \\ y \leq 2x + 3 \end{cases}$

Part B: $\begin{cases} y > -\frac{1}{5}x - 1 \\ y > 2x + 3 \end{cases}$

Part C: The solution of the system in part **A** includes part of the line $y = 2x + 3$. The common region of this system is above the line $y = -\frac{1}{5}x - 1$ and to the right of, and including, the line $y = 2x + 3$. The solution of the system in part **B** does not include part of either line. The

7. On March 27, 2004, NASA's hypersonic research aircraft X-43A reached a speed of Mach 7. Traveling at seven times the speed of sound, an aircraft moves 16 miles every 12 seconds. Which of these functions represents the number of miles an aircraft traveling at Mach 7 can go in *s* seconds?

A. $f(s) = 16x + 12s$

B. $f(s) = \frac{3}{4}s$

C. $f(s) = 16s$

D. $f(s) = 1\frac{1}{3}s$

In order for the correlation coefficient to be displayed when you calculate the linear regression, your calculator should be set to DiagnosticOn.

8. After a conference, Brent was asked to rate each of the five workshops he attended on a scale from 1 to 10. The table below shows the length and Brent's rating of each workshop.

Minutes	53	93	48	120	32
Rating	7	4	5	9	8

What is the correlation coefficient, rounded to the nearest hundredth, for the relationship between the length and Brent's rating of each workshop?

A. 0.01 B. 0.12

C. 0.88 D. 6.13

9. Examine the graphs of $f(x) = -|x|$ and $g(x) = f(x - h)$. What is the value of *h*?

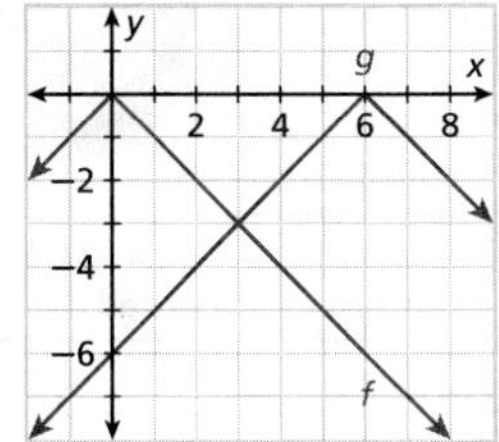

A. 4

B. 5

C. 6

D. 8

Short Answer

10. **Part A** Name the system of inequalities.

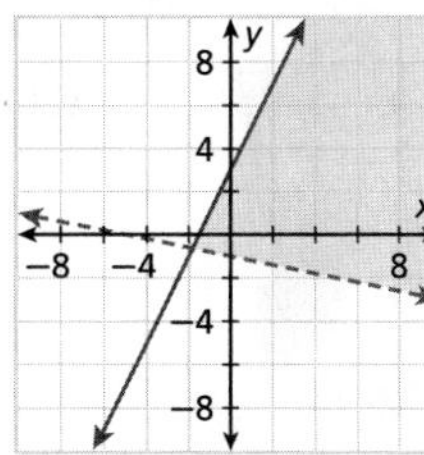

Part B Name the system of inequalities.

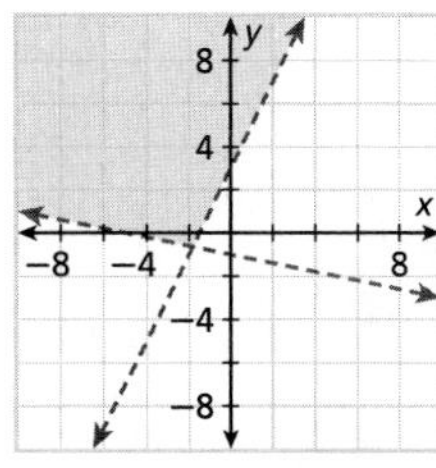

Part C Describe how the system in part **A** differs from the system in part **B**.

11. Use a matrix and $\triangle ABC$ with coordinates $(-1, 0)$, $(4, 3)$, and $(2, -1)$ for the transformations.

Part A Translate $\triangle ABC$ 1 unit to the right and 4 units up. Give the coordinates of $\triangle A'B'C'$.

Part B Reflect $\triangle A'B'C'$ across the *y*-axis. Give the coordinates of $\triangle A''B''C''$.

Extended Response

12. Use the linear function $2x - 3y = -15$.

Part A Explain how to rewrite the equation in slope-intercept form.

Part B Describe why the slope-intercept form is usually the best way to write an equation before you graph it.

Part C Write a step-by-step explanation on how to graph the equation.

Short Answer Rubric

Items 10–11

Score 2 = Thorough understanding of mathematical concepts and processes.

Score 1 = Partial understanding of mathematical concepts and/or processes.

Score 0 = Limited or no understanding of the problem-solving concepts.

Blank = No written response.

Extended Response Rubric

Item 12

Score 4 = Thorough understanding of mathematical concepts and processes.

Score 3 = Demonstrated understanding of mathematical concepts and processes, but an error in computation or explanation.

Score 2 = Partial understanding of mathematical concepts and/or processes.

Score 1 = Limited understanding and execution of the problem-solving concepts.

Score 0 = No understanding of the problem-solving concepts.

Blank = No written response.

common region for this system is above the line $y = -\frac{1}{5}x - 1$ and to the left of the line $y = 2x + 3$.

11. Part A: The coordinates of $\triangle A'B'C'$ are $(0, 4)$, $(5, 7)$, and $(3, 3)$.

Part B: The coordinates of $\triangle A''B''C''$ are $(0, 4)$, $(-5, 7)$, and $(-3, 3)$.

12. Part A: Solve the equation for y. Subtract $2x$ from both sides of the equation. Then divide each term by −3. The slope-intercept form of the equation is $y = \frac{2}{3}x + 5$.

Part B: In slope-intercept form, you know the y-intercept, and the slope of the line. You can plot the y-intercept and use the slope to plot a second point. By connecting these two points, you can draw the graph of the line.

Part C: Possible answer: 1) Plot (0, 5). This is the point where the line intersects the *y*-axis.
2) Move 2 units up and 3 units right and plot a point. This is a second point on the line.
3) Draw a line connecting the two points. 4) To check your line, find the coordinates of a third point on the line. Substitute these coordinates into the equation and check whether they make the equation true.

Problem Solving on Location

Organizer

Objective: Choose appropriate problem-solving strategies and use them with skills from Chapters 3 and 4 to solve real-world problems.

Online Edition

James Island County Park

Reading Strategies

Have students rewrite **Problem 1** in their own words. Ask them to rewrite the question as a statement that tells them what they must find. ENGLISH LANGUAGE LEARNERS

Using Data Encourage students to experiment with different scenarios before formally solving **Problem 1.** For example, ask what it would cost if the group consisted entirely of residents or nonresidents.

State Resources

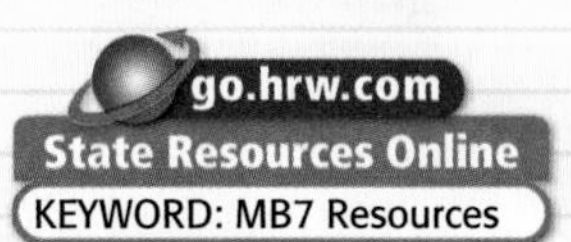

Problem Solving on Location

SOUTH CAROLINA

James Island County Park

James Island County Park in Charleston, South Carolina has something for everyone, but the park may be best known for its climbing wall. Standing 50 feet tall, the structure can accommodate up to 16 climbers at a time, making the park an ideal destination for families and groups of friends.

Choose one or more strategies to solve each problem.

1. County residents pay \$8 to use the climbing wall and nonresidents pay \$10. A group of 11 friends pays a total of \$96 to climb on the wall. How many county residents are in the group?
2. The table shows how many pairs of shoes, harnesses, and chalk bags were rented at the park by three different groups of climbers. The table also shows the total cost of the rentals for each group. What is the cost of renting each item?

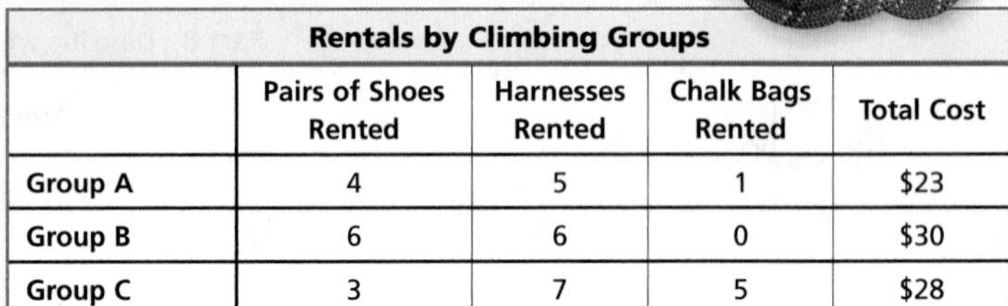

Rentals by Climbing Groups

	Pairs of Shoes Rented	Harnesses Rented	Chalk Bags Rented	Total Cost
Group A	4	5	1	\$23
Group B	6	6	0	\$30
Group C	3	7	5	\$28

3. A climber climbs up the lower part of the wall at a rate of 1.2 ft/min. The upper part of the wall is more difficult, and she climbs at 0.8 ft/min. She reaches the top of the wall in 51.5 min. How long did it take her to climb the lower part of the wall? At what height on the wall did her rate change?

Problem-Solving Focus

Ask students what strategy they would use to solve Problem 1. Possible answer: Some students may choose a Guess and Test method, and others may choose to write a system of equations to solve.

Discuss how to set up the problem as a system of equations. If students did not use this method initially, encourage them to use it as a way to check their answers.

Answers

1. 7
2. shoes: \$3; harness: \$2; chalk bag: \$1
3. 22 min; 26.4 ft

Problem Solving Strategies

- Draw a Diagram
- Make a Model
- Guess and Test
- Work Backward
- Find a Pattern
- Make a Table
- Solve a Simpler Problem
- Use Logical Reasoning
- Use a Venn Diagram
- Make an Organized List

Angel Oak

Many people believe Angel Oak is the oldest living thing in the United States east of the Rockies. This sprawling live oak has stood on John's Island for 1400 years. As is typical of the oldest oaks, its massive limbs touch the ground before curving upward, creating a majestic canopy that covers more than 17,000 square feet.

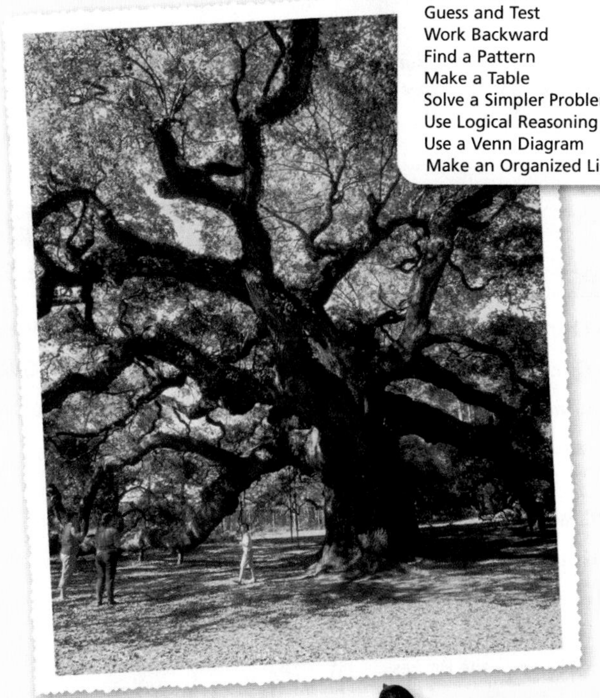

Choose one or more strategies to solve each problem.

1. Tree enthusiasts use a point system to compare trees. They assign a number of points for each inch of circumference, foot of height, and foot of crown spread. The table shows the measurements and point totals for some of South Carolina's champion trees. How many points are assigned to one unit of each measurement?

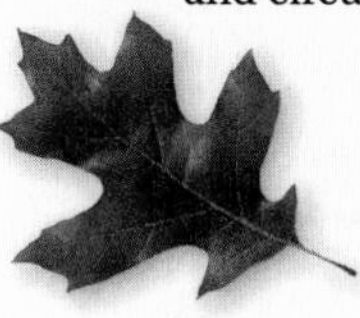

Champion Trees of South Carolina

	Circumference (in.)	Height (ft)	Crown Spread (ft)	Total Points
Angel Oak	306	65	144	407
Green Ash Tree	181	143	96	348
Redwood Tree	168	105	44	284

2. An oak tree produces acorns at two different rates. Until it reaches maturity, it produces an average of 900 acorns a year. Once it reaches full maturity, it produces an average of 2200 acorns a year. Angel Oak has produced about 2.9 million acorns in its lifetime. At what age did it reach maturity?

3. A botanist is studying the growth rates of live oaks. He wants to know the rates at which the height and circumference increase. He knows that the height typically increases 16 times as fast as the circumference. He measures a 10-year-old live oak and finds that

   height + circumference = 255 in.

   Find the growth rates, in inches per year, for the height and circumference.

Answers

1. circumference: 1 pt; height: 1 pt; crown spread: 0.25 pt
2. 138 yr
3. height: 24 in./yr; circumference: 1.5 in./yr

Angel Oak

Reading Strategies

ENGLISH LANGUAGE LEARNERS

As students read **Problem 1,** check that they understand what is meant by the term *crown spread.* You might ask students to use context clues to guess the meaning of the term. Students should understand that a tree's crown is the part consisting of branches and leaves. Its spread is its diameter.

Using Data Have students explore the data in the table before solving **Problem 1.** Ask them how many points each tree would have if one point were assigned to each dimension. Then ask students what they notice and what conclusions they can draw. If one point were assigned to each dimension, the trees would have higher point totals than they actually have. Therefore, less than one point must be assigned to at least one dimension.

Problem-Solving Focus

For **Problem 2,** focus on the second stage of the problem-solving process: **(2) Make a Plan.** Ask students how they can write equations based on the given information. Let y be the number of years of youth, and let m be the number of years of maturity. Then $y + m = 1400$ and $900y + 2200m = 2{,}900{,}000$.

Discuss different ways to solve the system of equations. Some students may wish to multiply the first equation by 900 or 2200 and then subtract it from the second equation. Alternatively, students can use the first equation to solve for m or y and then substitute this expression into the second equation. As a third option, students can solve the system using matrices. Discuss with students the pros and cons of each method.

CHAPTER 5 Quadratic Functions

Section 5A

Quadratic Functions and Complex Numbers

5-1 Technology Lab Explore Parameter Changes
5-1 Using Transformations to Graph Quadratic Functions
5-2 Properties of Quadratic Functions in Standard Form
Connecting Algebra to Previous Courses Factoring Quadratic Expressions
5-3 Technology Lab Explore Graphs and Factors
5-3 Solving Quadratic Equations by Graphing and Factoring
5-4 Completing the Square
Connecting Algebra to Geometry Areas of Composite Figures
5-5 Complex Numbers and Roots
5-6 The Quadratic Formula

Section 5B

Applying Quadratic Functions

5-7 Solving Quadratic Inequalities
5-8 Curve Fitting with Quadratic Models
5-9 Operations with Complex Numbers

Pacing Guide for 45-Minute Classes

Chapter 5 Countdown to Testing Weeks 10, 11, 12

DAY 1	DAY 2	DAY 3	DAY 4	DAY 5
5-1 Technology Lab 5-1 Lesson	5-1 Lesson	5-2 Lesson	Connecting Algebra to Previous Courses 5-3 Technology Lab	5-3 Lesson
DAY 6	**DAY 7**	**DAY 8**	**DAY 9**	**DAY 10**
5-4 Lesson	5-4 Lesson Connecting Algebra to Geometry	5-5 Lesson	5-6 Lesson	Multi-Step Test Prep Ready to Go On?
DAY 11	**DAY 12**	**DAY 13**	**DAY 14**	**DAY 15**
5-7 Lesson	5-8 Lesson	5-9 Lesson	Multi-Step Test Prep Ready to Go On?	Chapter 5 Test

Pacing Guide for 90-Minute Classes

Chapter 5

DAY 1	DAY 2	DAY 3	DAY 4	DAY 5
Chapter 4 Test 5-1 Technology Lab 5-1 Lesson	5-1 Lesson 5-2 Lesson	Connecting Algebra to Previous Courses 5-3 Technology Lab 5-3 Lesson	5-4 Lesson Connecting Algebra to Geometry	5-5 Lesson 5-6 Lesson
DAY 6	**DAY 7**	**DAY 8**		
Multi-Step Test Prep Ready to Go On? 5-7 Lesson	5-8 Lesson 5-9 Lesson	Multi-Step Test Prep Ready to Go On? Chapter 5 Test		

ONGOING ASSESSMENT and INTERVENTION

Assess Prior Knowledge

Before Chapter 5

DIAGNOSE	PRESCRIBE
Diagnose readiness for the chapter.	Prescribe intervention.
Are You Ready? SE p. 311	***Are You Ready? Intervention*** Skills 6, 53, 64, 69, 75

Formative Assessment

Before Every Lesson

DIAGNOSE	PRESCRIBE
Diagnose readiness for the lesson.	Prescribe intervention.
Warm Up TE, every lesson	**Skills Bank** SE pp. S46–S73
	Reteach CRB, Ch. 1–5

During Every Lesson

DIAGNOSE	PRESCRIBE
Diagnose understanding of lesson concepts.	Prescribe intervention.
Check It Out! SE, every example	**Questioning Strategies** TE, every example
Think and Discuss SE, every lesson	**Reading Strategies** CRB, every lesson
Write About It SE, every lesson	***Success for ELL*** pp. 61–78
Journal TE, every lesson	

After Every Lesson

DIAGNOSE	PRESCRIBE
Diagnose mastery of lesson concepts.	Prescribe intervention.
Lesson Quiz TE, every lesson	**Reteach** CRB, every lesson
Alternative Assessment TE, every lesson	**Problem Solving** CRB, every lesson
Test Prep SE, every lesson	**Test Prep Doctor** TE, every lesson
Test and Practice Generator	***Homework Help* Online**

Before Chapter 5 Testing

DIAGNOSE	PRESCRIBE
Diagnose mastery of concepts in the chapter.	Prescribe intervention.
Ready to Go On? SE pp. 365, 391	***Ready to Go On? Intervention*** pp. 73–90
Multi-Step Test Prep SE pp. 364, 390	**Scaffolding Questions** TE pp. 364, 390
Section Quizzes AR pp. 85–86	
Test and Practice Generator	

Before High Stakes Testing

DIAGNOSE	PRESCRIBE
Diagnose mastery of benchmark concepts.	Prescribe intervention.
College Entrance Exam Practice SE p. 397	***College Entrance Exam Practice***
Standardized Test Prep SE pp. 400–401	***State Test Prep Workbook***
***State Test Prep* CD-ROM**	

Summative Assessment

After Chapter 5

DIAGNOSE	PRESCRIBE
Check mastery of chapter concepts.	Prescribe intervention.
Multiple-Choice Tests (Forms A, B, C)	**Reteach** CRB, every lesson
Free-Response Tests (Forms A, B, C)	***Lesson Tutorial Videos*** Chapter 5
Performance Assessment AR pp. 87–100	
Test and Practice Generator	
Check mastery of benchmark concepts.	Prescribe intervention.
AYP State Tests	***State Test Prep Workbook***
College Entrance Exams	***College Entrance Exam Practice***

KEY: **SE** = *Student Edition* **TE** = *Teacher's Edition* **CRB** = *Chapter Resource Book* **AR** = *Assessment Resources*

Supporting the Teacher

Chapter 5 Resource Book

Practice A, B, C
pp. 3–5, 11–13, 19–21, 27–29, 35–37, 43–45, 51–53, 59–61, 67–69

Reading Strategies ELL
pp. 10, 18, 26, 34, 42, 50, 58, 66, 74

Reteach
pp. 6–7, 14–15, 22–23, 30–31, 38–39, 46–47, 54–55, 62–63, 70–71

Problem Solving
pp. 9, 17, 25, 33, 41, 49, 57, 65 ,73

Challenge
pp. 8, 16, 24, 32, 40, 48, 56, 64, 72

Parent Letter pp. 1–2

Transparencies

Lesson Transparencies, Volume 2 .... Chapter 5
- Warm Ups
- Teaching Transparencies
- Additional Examples
- Lesson Quizzes

Alternate Openers: Explorations 31–39

Countdown to Testing 19–24

Know-It Notebook .... Chapter 5
- Graphic Organizers

Teacher Tools

Power Presentations®
Complete PowerPoint® presentations for Chapter 5 lessons

Lesson Tutorial Videos®
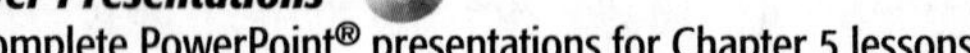
Holt authors Ed Burger and Freddie Renfro present tutorials to support the Chapter 5 lessons.

One-Stop Planner®
Easy access to all Chapter 5 resources and assessments, as well as software for lesson planning, test generation, and puzzle creation

IDEA Works!®
Key Chapter 5 resources and assessments modified to address special learning needs

Lesson Plans..pp. 31–39

Solutions Key .... Chapter 5

Algebra Posters

TechKeys **Lab Resources** 

Project Teacher Support **Parent Resources** 

Workbooks

Homework and Practice Workbook
Teacher's Guide..pp. 31–39

Know-It Notebook
Teacher's Guide .... Chapter 5

Problem Solving Workbook
Teacher's Guide..pp. 31–39

State Test Prep Workbook
Teacher's Guide

Technology Highlights for the Teacher

Power Presentations

Dynamic presentations to engage students. Complete PowerPoint® presentations for every lesson in Chapter 5.

2-1 Solving One-Step Equations

Isolate a variable by using inverse operations which "undo" operations on the variable.

An equation is like a balanced scale. To keep the balance, perform the same operation on both sides.

Inverse Operations	
Operation	**Inverse Operation**
Addition	Subtraction
Subtraction	Addition

One-Stop Planner

Easy access to Chapter 5 resources and assessments. Includes lesson-planning, test-generation, and puzzle-creation software.

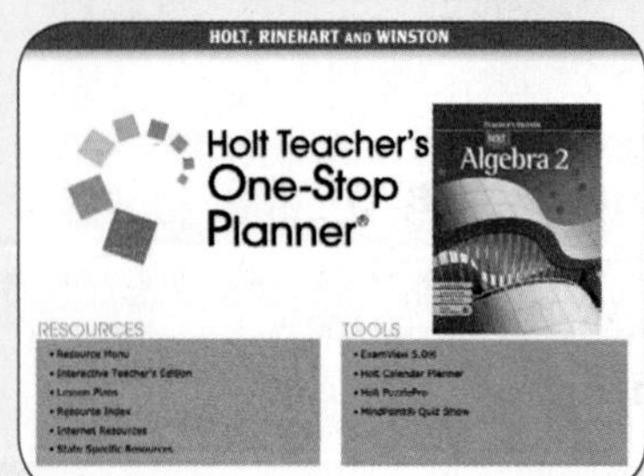

Premier Online Edition

Chapter 5 includes Tutorial Videos, Lesson Activities, Lesson Quizzes, Homework Help, and Chapter Project.

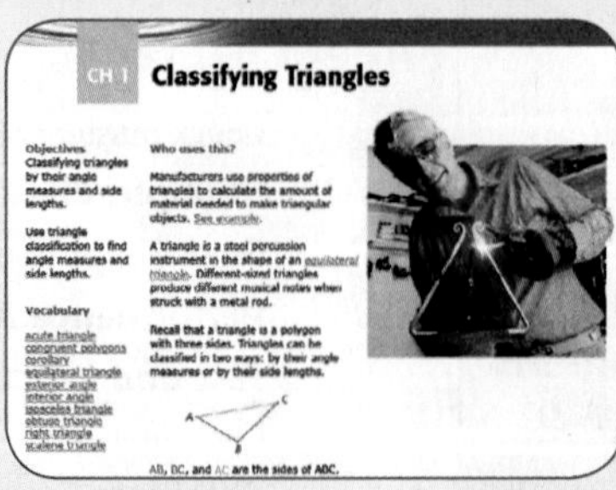

KEY: **SE** = *Student Edition* **TE** = *Teacher's Edition*  English Language Learners  Available on CD-ROM 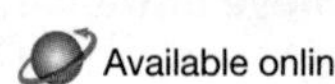 Available online

Reaching All Learners

Resources for All Learners

Algebra Lab Activities	Chapter 5
Technology Lab Activities	Chapter 5
Homework and Practice Workbook	pp. 31–39
Know-It Notebook	Chapter 5
Problem Solving Workbook	pp. 31–39

DEVELOPING LEARNERS

Practice A	CRB, every lesson
Reteach	CRB, every lesson
Inclusion	TE pp. 325, 326, 335, 336, 343, 360, 368
Questioning Strategies	TE, every example
Modified Chapter 5 Resources (CD-ROM)	*IDEA Works!*
***Homework Help* Online** (online)	

ON-LEVEL LEARNERS

Practice B	CRB, every lesson
Multiple Representations	TE pp. 324, 325
Graphic Organizers	TE p. 367

ADVANCED LEARNERS

Practice C	CRB, every lesson
Challenge	CRB, every lesson
Reading and Writing Math EXTENSION	TE p. 313
Multi-Step Test Prep EXTENSION	TE pp. 364, 390
Critical Thinking	TE pp. 325, 334, 349, 369, 378

English Language Learners

ENGLISH LANGUAGE LEARNERS

Are You Ready? Vocabulary	SE p. 311
Vocabulary Connections	SE p. 312
Lesson Vocabulary	SE, every lesson
Vocabulary Exercises	SE, every exercise set
Vocabulary Review	SE p. 392
English Language Learners	TE pp. 318, 323, 331
Reading Strategies	CRB, every lesson
Success for English Language Learners	pp. 61–78
Multilingual Glossary (online)	

Reaching All Learners Through...

Visual Cues	TE pp. 316, 344, 351, 383
Multiple Representations	TE pp. 324, 325
Critical Thinking	TE pp. 325, 334, 349, 369, 378
Inclusion	TE pp. 325, 326, 335, 336, 343, 360, 368
Concrete Manipulatives	TE p. 335
Auditory Cues	TE pp. 353, 357
Graphic Organizers	TE p. 367
Cooperative Learning	TE p. 375
Kinesthetic Experience	TE p. 383
Test Prep Doctor	TE pp. 322, 330, 348, 363, 372, 381, 389, 397, 398, 400
Common Error Alerts	TE pp. 319, 321, 327, 329, 337, 343, 347, 351, 359, 369, 373, 375, 379, 385, 387
Scaffolding Questions	TE pp. 364, 390

Technology Highlights for Reaching All Learners

Lesson Tutorial Videos

Starring Holt authors Ed Burger and Freddie Renfro! Live tutorials to support every lesson in Chapter 5.

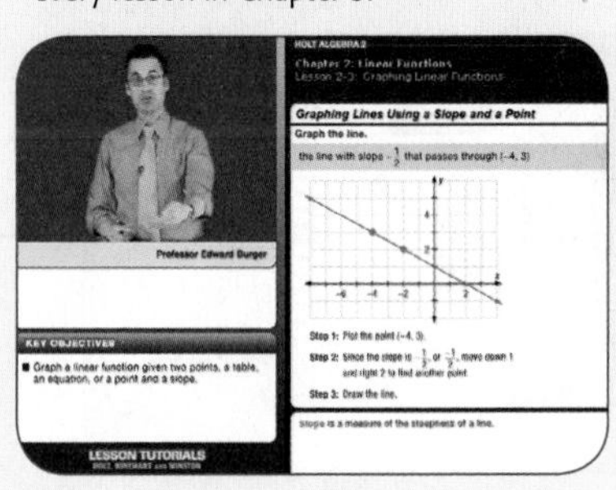

Multilingual Glossary

Searchable glossary includes definitions in English, Spanish, Vietnamese, Chinese, Hmong, Korean, and 4 other languages.

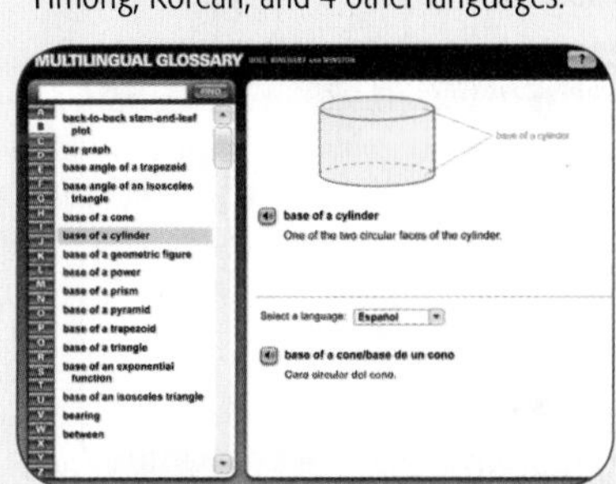

Online Interactivities

Interactive tutorials provide visually engaging alternative opportunities to learn concepts and master skills.

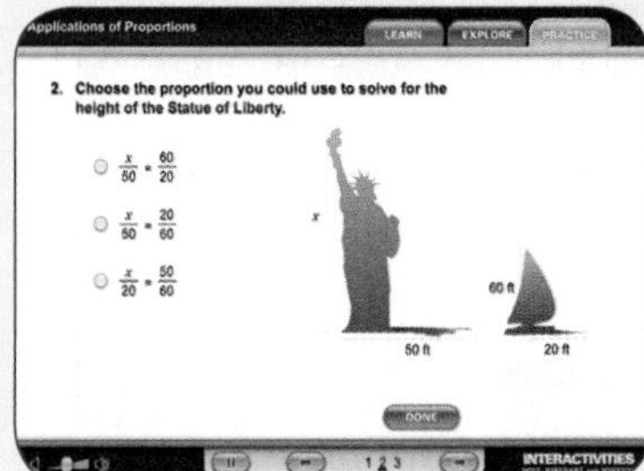

KEY: **SE** = *Student Edition* **TE** = *Teacher's Edition* **CRB** = *Chapter Resource Book* (CD-ROM icon) Available on CD-ROM (globe icon) Available online

Ongoing Assessment

Assessing Prior Knowledge

Determine whether students have the required prerequisite concepts and skills for success in Chapter 5.

Are You Ready? SPANISH .... SE p. 311
Warm Up .... TE, every lesson

Test Preparation

Provide review and practice for Chapter 5 and standardized tests.

Multi-Step Test Prep .... SE pp. 364, 390
Study Guide: Review .... SE pp. 392–395
Test Tackler .... SE pp. 398–399
Standardized Test Prep .... SE pp. 400–401
College Entrance Exam Practice .... SE p. 397
***Countdown to Testing* Transparencies** 19–24
State Test Prep Workbook
***State Test Prep* CD-ROM**
IDEA Works!

Alternative Assessment

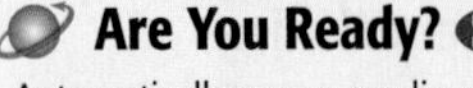

Assess students' understanding of Chapter 5 concepts and combined problem-solving skills.

Chapter 5 Project .... SE p. 310
Alternative Assessment .... TE, every lesson
Performance Assessment .... AR pp. 99–100
Portfolio Assessment .... AR p. xxxiv

Daily Assessment

Provide formative assessment for each day of Chapter 5.

Questioning Strategies .... TE, every example
Think and Discuss .... SE, every lesson
Check It Out! Exercises .... SE, every example
Write About It .... SE, every lesson
Journal .... TE, every lesson
Lesson Quiz .... TE, every lesson
Alternative Assessment .... TE, every lesson
Modified Lesson Quizzes .... *IDEA Works!*

Weekly Assessment

Provide formative assessment for each week of Chapter 5.

Multi-Step Test Prep .... SE pp. 364, 390
Ready to Go On? .... SE pp. 365, 391
Cumulative Assessment .... SE pp. 400–401
Test and Practice Generator .... *One-Stop Planner*

Formal Assessment

Provide summative assessment of Chapter 5 mastery.

Section Quizzes .... AR pp. 85–86
Chapter 5 Test .... SE p. 396
Chapter Test (Levels A, B, C) .... AR pp. 87–98
• Multiple Choice • Free Response
Cumulative Test .... AR pp. 101–104
Test and Practice Generator .... *One-Stop Planner*
Modified Chapter 5 Test .... *IDEA Works!*

Technology Highlights for Ongoing Assessment

Are You Ready? SPANISH

Automatically assess readiness and prescribe intervention for Chapter 5 prerequisite skills.

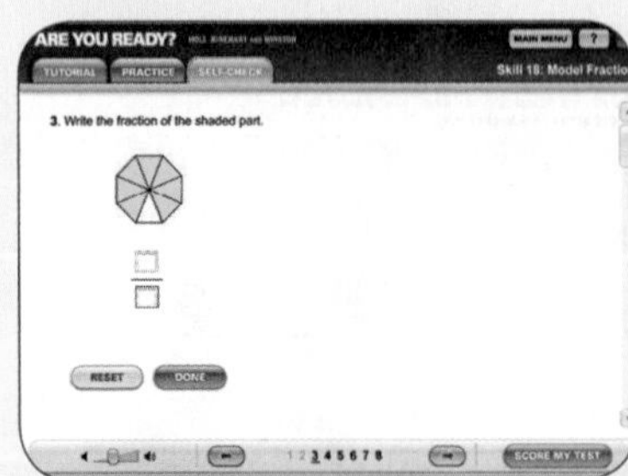

Ready to Go On?

Automatically assess understanding and prescribe intervention for Sections 5A and 5B.

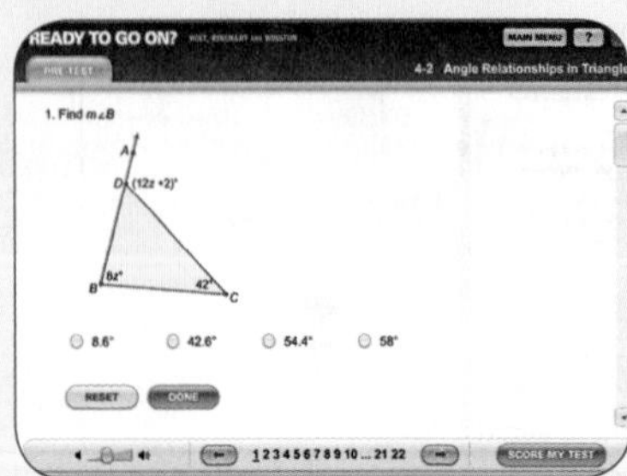

Test and Practice Generator

Use Chapter 5 problem banks to create assessments and worksheets to print out or deliver online. Includes dynamic problems.

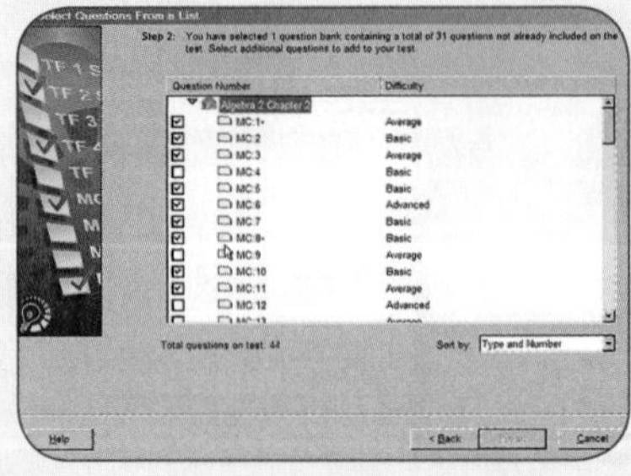

KEY: **SE** = *Student Edition* **TE** = *Teacher's Edition* **AR** = *Assessment Resources* SPANISH Spanish version available  Available on CD-ROM  Available online

Three levels (A, B, C) of multiple-choice and free-response chapter tests are available in the *Assessment Resources.*

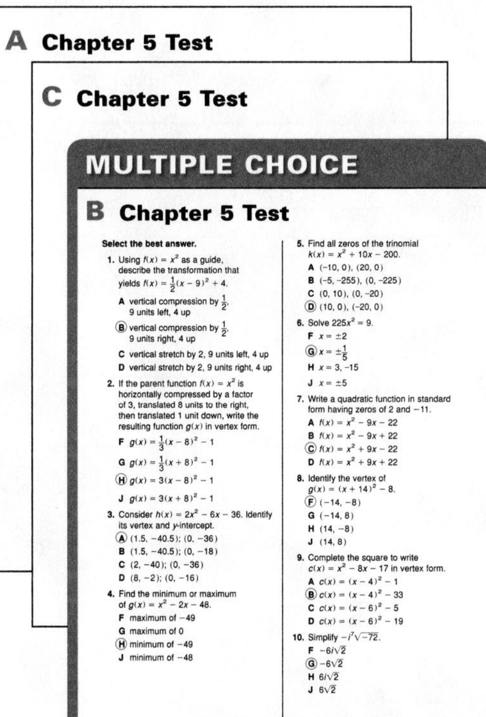

A Chapter 5 Test

C Chapter 5 Test

MULTIPLE CHOICE

B Chapter 5 Test

Select the best answer.

1. Using $f(x) = x^2$ as a guide, describe the transformation that yields $f(x) = \frac{1}{2}(x - 9)^2 + 4$.
   A vertical compression by $\frac{1}{2}$, 9 units left, 4 up
   Ⓑ vertical compression by $\frac{1}{2}$, 9 units right, 4 up
   C vertical stretch by 2, 9 units left, 4 up
   D vertical stretch by 2, 9 units right, 4 up
2. If the parent function $f(x) = x^2$ is horizontally compressed by a factor of 3, translated 8 units to the right, then translated 1 unit down, write the resulting function $g(x)$ in vertex form.
   F $g(x) = \frac{1}{3}(x - 8)^2 - 1$
   G $g(x) = \frac{1}{3}(x + 8)^2 - 1$
   Ⓗ $g(x) = 3(x - 8)^2 - 1$
   J $g(x) = 3(x + 8)^2 - 1$
3. Consider $h(x) = 2x^2 - 6x - 36$. Identify its vertex and y-intercept.
   Ⓐ $(1.5, -40.5)$; $(0, -36)$
   B $(1.5, -40.5)$; $(0, -18)$
   C $(2, -40)$; $(0, -36)$
   D $(8, -2)$; $(0, -16)$
4. Find the minimum or maximum of $g(x) = x^2 - 2x - 48$.
   F maximum of -49
   G maximum of 0
   Ⓗ minimum of -49
   J minimum of -48
5. Find all zeros of the trinomial $k(x) = x^2 + 10x - 200$.
   A $(-10, 0)$, $(20, 0)$
   B $(-5, -255)$, $(0, -225)$
   C $(0, 10)$, $(0, -20)$
   Ⓓ $(10, 0)$, $(-20, 0)$
6. Solve $225x^2 = 9$.
   F $x = \pm 2$
   Ⓖ $x = \pm\frac{1}{5}$
   H $x = 3, -15$
   J $x = \pm 5$
7. Write a quadratic function in standard form having zeros of 2 and -11.
   A $f(x) = x^2 - 9x - 22$
   B $f(x) = x^2 - 9x + 22$
   Ⓒ $f(x) = x^2 + 9x - 22$
   D $f(x) = x^2 + 9x + 22$
8. Identify the vertex of $g(x) = (x + 14)^2 - 8$.
   Ⓕ $(-14, -8)$
   G $(-14, 8)$
   H $(14, -8)$
   J $(14, 8)$
9. Complete the square to write $c(x) = x^2 - 8x - 17$ in vertex form.
   A $c(x) = (x - 4)^2 - 1$
   Ⓑ $c(x) = (x - 4)^2 - 33$
   C $c(x) = (x - 6)^2 - 5$
   D $c(x) = (x - 6)^2 - 19$
10. Simplify $-i^7\sqrt{-72}$.
    F $-6i\sqrt{2}$
    Ⓖ $-6\sqrt{2}$
    H $6i\sqrt{2}$
    J $6\sqrt{2}$

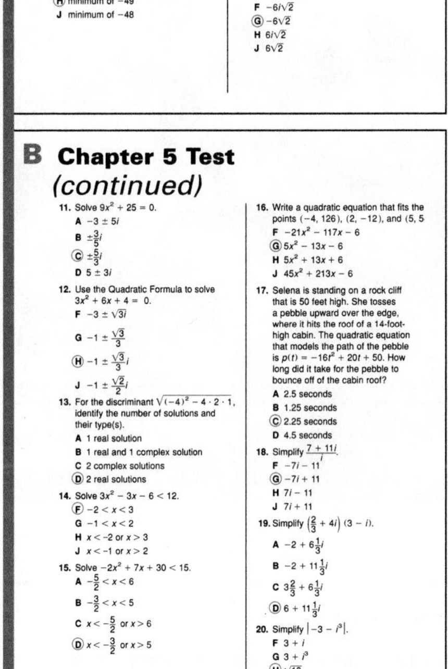

B Chapter 5 Test *(continued)*

11. Solve $9x^2 + 25 = 0$.
    A $-3 \pm 5i$
    B $\pm\frac{3}{5}i$
    Ⓒ $\pm\frac{5}{3}i$
    D $5 \pm 3i$
12. Use the Quadratic Formula to solve $3x^2 + 6x + 4 = 0$.
    F $-3 \pm \sqrt{3}i$
    G $-1 \pm \frac{\sqrt{3}}{3}$
    Ⓗ $-1 \pm \frac{\sqrt{3}}{3}i$
    J $-1 \pm \frac{\sqrt{2}}{2}i$
13. For the discriminant $\sqrt{(-4)^2 - 4 \cdot 2 \cdot 1}$, identify the number of solutions and their type(s).
    A 1 real solution
    B 1 real and 1 complex solution
    C 2 complex solutions
    Ⓓ 2 real solutions
14. Solve $3x^2 - 3x - 6 < 12$.
    Ⓕ $-2 < x < 3$
    G $-1 < x < 2$
    H $x < -2$ or $x > 3$
    J $x < -1$ or $x > 2$
15. Solve $-2x^2 + 7x + 30 < 15$.
    A $-\frac{5}{2} < x < 6$
    B $-\frac{3}{2} < x < 5$
    C $x < -\frac{5}{2}$ or $x > 6$
    Ⓓ $x < -\frac{3}{2}$ or $x > 5$
16. Write a quadratic equation that fits the points $(-4, 126)$, $(2, -12)$, and $(5, 5$
    F $-21x^2 - 117x - 6$
    Ⓖ $5x^2 - 13x - 6$
    H $5x^2 + 13x + 6$
    J $45x^2 + 213x - 6$
17. Selena is standing on a rock cliff that is 50 feet high. She tosses a pebble upward over the edge, where it hits the roof of a 14-foot-high cabin. The quadratic equation that models the path of the pebble is $p(t) = -16t^2 + 20t + 50$. How long did it take for the pebble to bounce off of the cabin roof?
    A 2.5 seconds
    B 1.25 seconds
    Ⓒ 2.25 seconds
    D 4.5 seconds
18. Simplify $\frac{7 + 11i}{i}$.
    F $-7i - 11$
    Ⓖ $-7i + 11$
    H $7i - 11$
    J $7i + 11$
19. Simplify $\left(\frac{2}{3} + 4i\right)(3 - i)$.
    A $-2 + 6\frac{1}{3}i$
    B $-2 + 11\frac{1}{3}i$
    C $3\frac{2}{3} + 6\frac{1}{3}i$
    Ⓓ $6 + 11\frac{1}{3}i$
20. Simplify $|-3 - i^3|$.
    F $3 + i$
    G $3 + i^3$
    Ⓗ $\sqrt{10}$
    J $2\sqrt{2}$

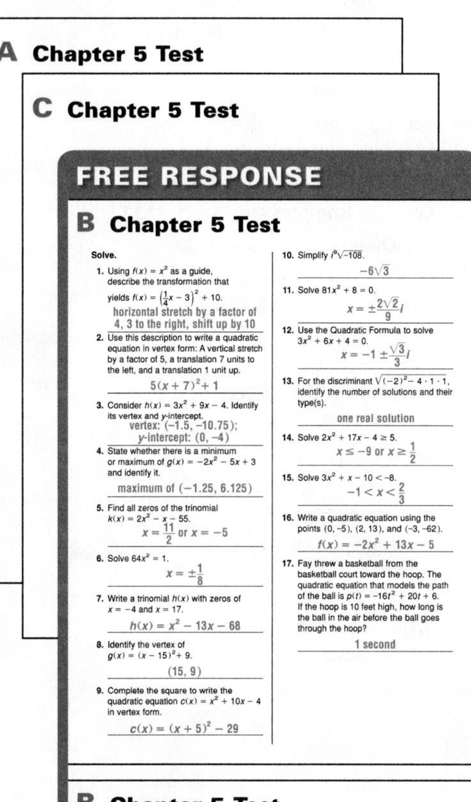

A Chapter 5 Test

C Chapter 5 Test

FREE RESPONSE

B Chapter 5 Test

Solve.

1. Using $f(x) = x^2$ as a guide, describe the transformation that yields $f(x) = \left(\frac{1}{4}x - 3\right)^2 + 10$.
   horizontal stretch by a factor of 4, 3 to the right, shift up by 10
2. Use this description to write a quadratic equation in vertex form: A vertical stretch by a factor of 5, a translation 7 units to the left, and a translation 1 unit up.
   $5(x + 7)^2 + 1$
3. Consider $h(x) = 3x^2 + 9x - 4$. Identify its vertex and y-intercept.
   vertex: $(-1.5, -10.75)$; y-intercept: $(0, -4)$
4. State whether there is a minimum or maximum of $g(x) = -2x^2 - 5x + 3$ and identify it.
   maximum of $(-1.25, 6.125)$
5. Find all zeros of the trinomial $k(x) = 2x^2 - x - 55$.
   $x = \frac{11}{2}$ or $x = -5$
6. Solve $64x^2 = 1$.
   $x = \pm\frac{1}{8}$
7. Write a trinomial $h(x)$ with zeros of $x = -4$ and $x = 17$.
   $h(x) = x^2 - 13x - 68$
8. Identify the vertex of $g(x) = (x - 15)^2 + 9$.
   $(15, 9)$
9. Complete the square to write the quadratic equation $c(x) = x^2 + 10x - 4$ in vertex form.
   $c(x) = (x + 5)^2 - 29$
10. Simplify $i^9\sqrt{-108}$.
    $-6\sqrt{3}$
11. Solve $81x^2 + 8 = 0$.
    $x = \pm\frac{2\sqrt{2}}{9}i$
12. Use the Quadratic Formula to solve $3x^2 + 6x + 4 = 0$.
    $x = -1 \pm \frac{\sqrt{3}}{3}i$
13. For the discriminant $\sqrt{(-2)^2 - 4 \cdot 1 \cdot 1}$, identify the number of solutions and their type(s).
    one real solution
14. Solve $2x^2 + 17x - 4 \geq 5$.
    $x \leq -9$ or $x \geq \frac{1}{2}$
15. Solve $3x^2 + x - 10 < -8$.
    $-1 < x < \frac{2}{3}$
16. Write a quadratic equation using the points $(0, -5)$, $(2, 13)$, and $(-3, -62)$.
    $f(x) = -2x^2 + 13x - 5$
17. Fay threw a basketball from the basketball court toward the hoop. The quadratic equation that models the path of the ball is $p(t) = -16t^2 + 20t + 6$. If the hoop is 10 feet high, how long is the ball in the air before the ball goes through the hoop?
    1 second

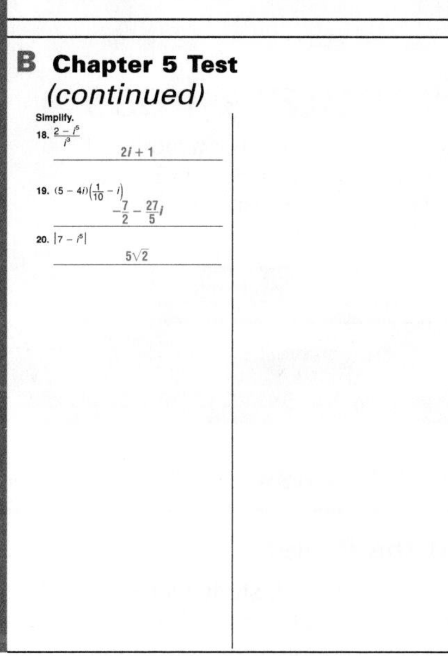

B Chapter 5 Test *(continued)*

Simplify.

18. $\frac{2 - i^5}{i^3}$
    $2i + 1$
19. $(5 - 4i)\left(\frac{1}{10} - i\right)$
    $-\frac{7}{2} - \frac{27}{5}i$
20. $|7 - i^5|$
    $5\sqrt{2}$

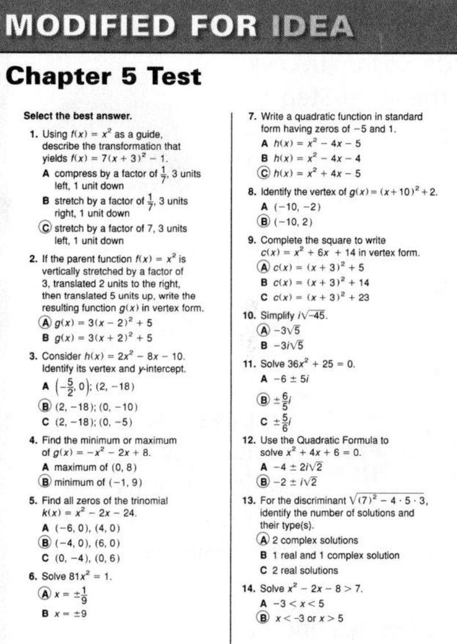

MODIFIED FOR IDEA

Chapter 5 Test

Select the best answer.

1. Using $f(x) = x^2$ as a guide, describe the transformation that yields $f(x) = 7(x + 3)^2 - 1$.
   A compress by a factor of $\frac{1}{7}$, 3 units left, 1 unit down
   B stretch by a factor of $\frac{1}{7}$, 3 units right, 1 unit down
   Ⓒ stretch by a factor of 7, 3 units left, 1 unit down
2. If the parent function $f(x) = x^2$ is vertically stretched by a factor of 3, translated 2 units to the right, then translated 5 units up, write the resulting function $g(x)$ in vertex form.
   Ⓐ $g(x) = 3(x - 2)^2 + 5$
   B $g(x) = 3(x + 2)^2 + 5$
3. Consider $h(x) = 2x^2 - 8x - 10$. Identify its vertex and y-intercept.
   A $\left(-\frac{5}{2}, 0\right)$; $(2, -18)$
   Ⓑ $(2, -18)$; $(0, -10)$
   C $(2, -18)$; $(0, -5)$
4. Find the minimum or maximum of $g(x) = -x^2 - 2x + 8$.
   A maximum of $(0, 8)$
   Ⓑ minimum of $(-1, 9)$
5. Find all zeros of the trinomial $k(x) = x^2 - 2x - 24$.
   A $(-6, 0)$, $(4, 0)$
   Ⓑ $(-4, 0)$, $(6, 0)$
   C $(0, -4)$, $(0, 6)$
6. Solve $81x^2 = 1$.
   Ⓐ $x = \pm\frac{1}{9}$
   B $x = \pm 9$
7. Write a quadratic function in standard form having zeros of -5 and 1.
   A $h(x) = x^2 - 4x - 5$
   B $h(x) = x^2 - 4x - 4$
   Ⓒ $h(x) = x^2 + 4x - 5$
8. Identify the vertex of $g(x) = (x + 10)^2 + 2$.
   A $(-10, -2)$
   Ⓑ $(-10, 2)$
9. Complete the square to write $c(x) = x^2 + 6x + 14$ in vertex form.
   Ⓐ $c(x) = (x + 3)^2 + 5$
   B $c(x) = (x + 3)^2 + 14$
   C $c(x) = (x + 3)^2 + 23$
10. Simplify $i\sqrt{-45}$.
    Ⓐ $-3\sqrt{5}$
    B $-3i\sqrt{5}$
11. Solve $36x^2 + 25 = 0$.
    A $-6 \pm 5i$
    Ⓑ $\pm\frac{6}{5}i$
    C $\pm\frac{5}{6}i$
12. Use the Quadratic Formula to solve $x^2 + 4x + 6 = 0$.
    A $-4 \pm 2i\sqrt{2}$
    Ⓑ $-2 \pm i\sqrt{2}$
13. For the discriminant $\sqrt{(7)^2 - 4 \cdot 5 \cdot 3}$, identify the number of solutions and their type(s).
    Ⓐ 2 complex solutions
    B 1 real and 1 complex solution
    C 2 real solutions
14. Solve $x^2 - 2x - 8 > 7$.
    A $-3 < x < 5$
    Ⓑ $x < -3$ or $x > 5$

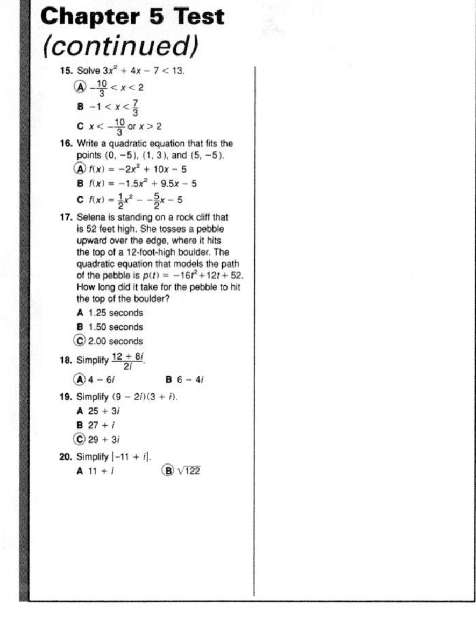

Chapter 5 Test *(continued)*

15. Solve $3x^2 + 4x - 7 < 13$.
    Ⓐ $-\frac{10}{3} < x < 2$
    B $-1 < x < \frac{7}{3}$
    C $x < -\frac{10}{3}$ or $x > 2$
16. Write a quadratic equation that fits the points $(0, -5)$, $(1, 3)$, and $(5, -5)$.
    Ⓐ $f(x) = -2x^2 + 10x - 5$
    B $f(x) = -1.5x^2 + 9.5x - 5$
    C $f(x) = \frac{1}{2}x^2 - -\frac{5}{2}x - 5$
17. Selena is standing on a rock cliff that is 52 feet high. She tosses a pebble upward over the edge, where it hits the top of a 12-foot-high boulder. The quadratic equation that models the path of the pebble is $p(t) = -16t^2 + 12t + 52$. How long did it take for the pebble to hit the top of the boulder?
    A 1.25 seconds
    B 1.50 seconds
    Ⓒ 2.00 seconds
18. Simplify $\frac{12 + 8i}{2i}$.
    Ⓐ $4 - 6i$ B $6 - 4i$
19. Simplify $(9 - 2i)(3 + i)$.
    A $25 + 3i$
    B $27 + i$
    Ⓒ $29 + 3i$
20. Simplify $|-11 + i|$.
    A $11 + i$ Ⓑ $\sqrt{122}$

Create and customize Chapter 5 Tests. Instantly generate multiple test versions, answer keys, and practice versions of test items.

CHAPTER 5

SECTION 5A
Quadratic Functions and Complex Numbers

On page 364, students write and transform quadratic functions and solve quadratic equations in real-world situations involving baseball.

Exercises designed to prepare students for success on the Multi-Step Test Prep can be found on pages 321, 329, 339, 347, 354, and 362.

SECTION 5B
Applying Quadratic Functions

On page 390, students apply quadratic functions and inequalities to model a real-world situation involving mosaic tiles.

Exercises designed to prepare students for success on the Multi-Step Test Prep can be found on pages 372, 378, and 388.

CHAPTER 5 Quadratic Functions

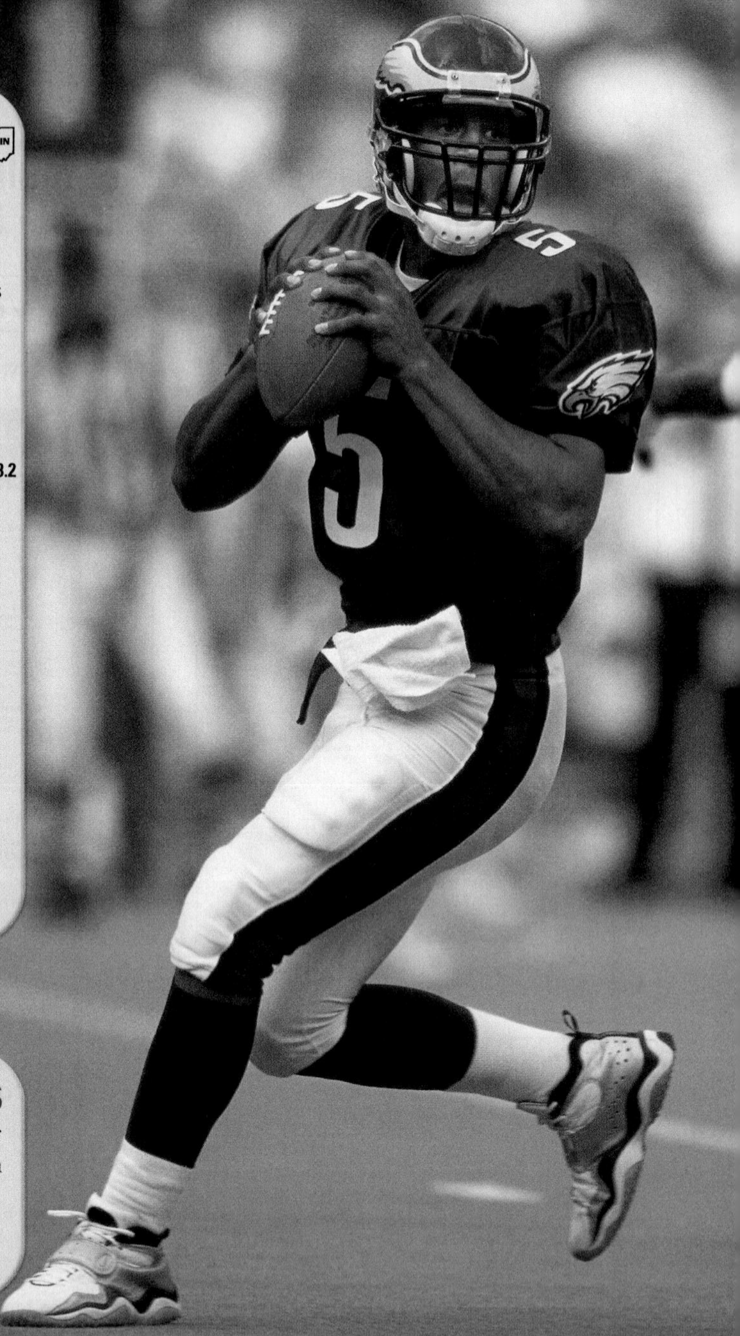

Planetary Pass

How far could you throw a football if you were on Mars or Saturn? You can find the answer by using quadratic functions.

go.hrw.com
Chapter Project Online
KEYWORD: MB7 ChProj

Planetary Pass

About the Project

In the Chapter Project, students use quadratic functions to determine how far an athlete would be able to throw a football on various planets. They will analyze the relationship between the acceleration due to gravity on each planet and the distance the football would travel.

Project Resources

All project resources for teachers and students are provided online.

Materials:

- graphing calculator

ARE YOU READY?

Vocabulary

Match each term on the left with a definition on the right.

1. linear equation **E**
2. solution set **C**
3. transformation **A**
4. x-intercept **B**

A. a change in a function rule and its graph

B. the x-coordinate of the point where a graph crosses the x-axis

C. the group of values that make an equation or inequality true

D. a letter or symbol that represents a number

E. an equation whose graph is a line

Squares and Square Roots

Simplify each expression.

5. 3.2^2 **10.24**
6. $\left(\frac{2}{5}\right)^2$ $\mathbf{\frac{4}{25}}$
7. $\sqrt{121}$ **11**
8. $\sqrt{\frac{1}{16}}$ $\mathbf{\frac{1}{4}}$

Simplify Radical Expressions

Simplify each expression.

9. $\sqrt{72}$ $\mathbf{6\sqrt{2}}$
10. $2\left(\sqrt{144} - 4\right)$ **16**
11. $\sqrt{33} \cdot \sqrt{75}$ $\mathbf{15\sqrt{11}}$
12. $\frac{\sqrt{54}}{\sqrt{3}}$ $\mathbf{3\sqrt{2}}$

Multiply Binomials

Multiply.

13. $(x - 2)(x - 6)$ $\mathbf{x^2 - 8x + 12}$
14. $(x + 9)(x - 9)$ $\mathbf{x^2 - 81}$
15. $(x + 2)(x + 7)$ $\mathbf{x^2 + 9x + 14}$
16. $(2x - 3)(5x + 1)$ $\mathbf{10x^2 - 13x - 3}$

Solve Multi-Step Equations

Solve each equation.

17. $2x + 10 = -32$ **−21**
18. $2x - (1 - x) = 2$ **1**
19. $\frac{2}{3}(x - 1) = 11$ $\mathbf{17\frac{1}{2}}$
20. $2(x + 5) - 5x = 1$ **3**

Graph Linear Functions

Graph each function.

21. $y = -x$
22. $y = 2x - 1$
23. $y = -3x + 6$
24. $y = \frac{1}{3}x + 2$

CHAPTER 5

ARE YOU READY?

Organizer

Objective: Assess students' understanding of prerequisite skills.

Prerequisite Skills

Squares and Square Roots
Simplify Radical Expressions
Multiply Binomials
Solve Multi-Step Equations
Graph Linear Functions

Assessing Prior Knowledge

INTERVENTION

Diagnose and Prescribe

Use this page to determine whether intervention is necessary or whether enrichment is appropriate.

Resources

***Are You Ready? Intervention and Enrichment* Worksheets**

***Are You Ready?* CD-ROM**

***Are You Ready?* Online**

my.hrw.com

Answers

21–24. See p. A26.

ARE YOU READY?
Diagnose and Prescribe

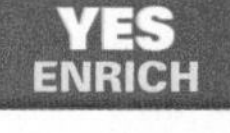

	Are You Ready? Intervention, Chapter 5		
Prerequisite Skill	**Worksheets**	**CD-ROM**	**Online**
Squares and Square Roots	Skill 6	Activity 6	Diagnose and Prescribe Online
Simplify Radical Expressions	Skill 53	Activity 53	
Multiply Binomials	Skill 64	Activity 64	
Solve Multi-Step Equations	Skill 69	Activity 69	
Graph Linear Functions	Skill 75	Activity 75	

***Are You Ready? Enrichment*, Chapter 5**
Worksheets
CD-ROM
Online

Organizer

Objective: Help students organize the new concepts they will learn in Chapter 5.

Resources

go.hrw.com

KEYWORD: MB7 Glossary

Answers to *Vocabulary Connections*

Possible answers:

1. A quadrilateral is a 4-sided polygon, and a square is a type of quadrilateral with 4 right angles and 4 congruent sides; quadrangle–a 4-sided enclosure, quadruplets–4 offspring born at one birth, quadruple–to increase by a factor of 4, quadriceps–large muscle of front thigh that is divided into 4 parts.
2. opposites (3 and −3), square roots (5 and −5 are the square roots of 25), reciprocals (5 and $\frac{1}{5}$)
3. The maximum value of a function is the greatest value that the function can have. Similarly, the minimum value of a function is the least value that a function can have.
4. The vertex form indicates the highest point (or maximum value) of a function.

CHAPTER 5 Study Guide: Preview

Where You've Been

Previously, you

- graphed and transformed linear functions.
- solved linear equations and inequalities.
- fit data using linear models.
- used and performed operations with real numbers.

In This Chapter

You will study

- graphing and transforming quadratic functions.
- solving quadratic equations and inequalities.
- fitting data to quadratic models.
- using and performing operations with imaginary and other complex numbers.

Where You're Going

You can use the skills in this chapter

- in advanced math classes, including Precalculus.
- in other classes, such as Chemistry, Physics, and Economics.
- outside of school to identify patterns and model data.

Key Vocabulary/Vocabulario

absolute value of a complex number	valor absoluto de un número complejo
complex conjugate	conjugado complejo
complex number	número complejo
imaginary number	número imaginario
maximum value	valor máximo
minimum value	valor mínimo
parabola	parábola
quadratic function	función cuadrática
vertex form	forma en vértice
zero of a function	cero de una función

Thinking About Vocabulary

To become familiar with some of the vocabulary terms in the chapter, consider the following. You may refer to the chapter, the glossary, or a dictionary if you like.

1. **Quadratic** is from the Latin *quadrum,* which means "square." A quadratic function always contains a *square* of the variable, such as x^2. What is a quadrilateral, and how does it relate to a square? What are some other words that use the root *quad-*, and what do they mean?
2. The word **conjugate** can mean "joined together, especially in pairs." Name some mathematical relationships that involve pairs.
3. What might the terms **maximum value** or **minimum value** of a function refer to?
4. The word *vertex* can mean "highest point." What might the **vertex form** of a quadratic function indicate about the function's graph?

CHAPTER 5

Study Strategy: Use Multiple Representations

The explanation and example problems used to introduce new math concepts often include various representations of information. Different representations of the same idea help you fully understand the material. As you study, take note of the tables, lists, graphs, diagrams, symbols, and/or words used to clarify a concept.

From Lesson 3-2

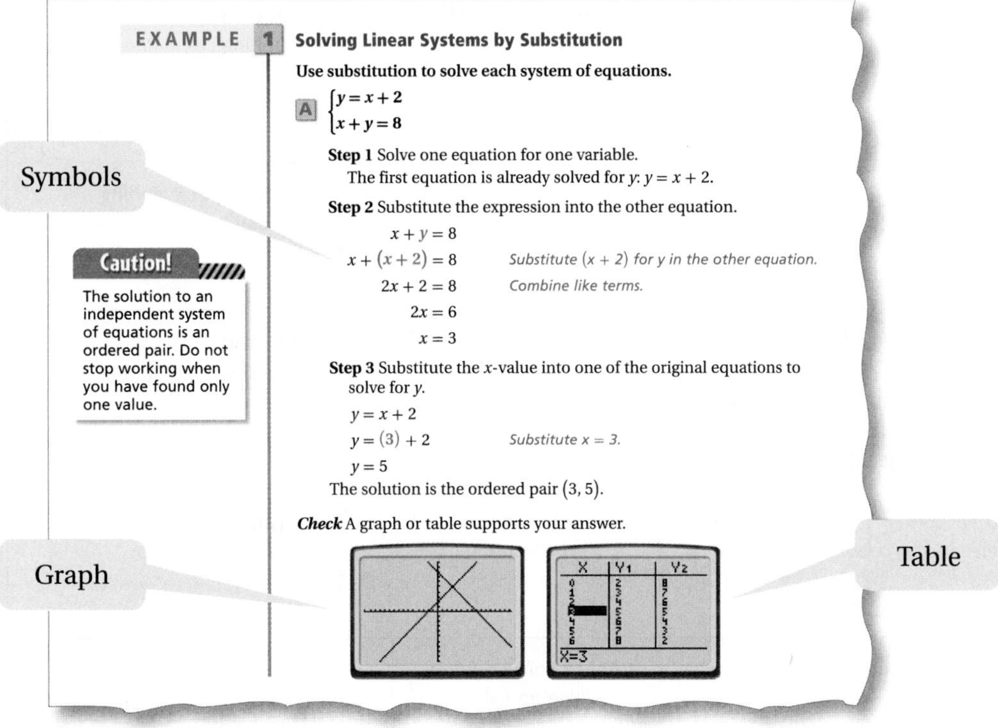

EXAMPLE 1 Solving Linear Systems by Substitution

Use substitution to solve each system of equations.

A $\begin{cases} y = x + 2 \\ x + y = 8 \end{cases}$

Step 1 Solve one equation for one variable.
The first equation is already solved for y: $y = x + 2$.

Step 2 Substitute the expression into the other equation.

$x + y = 8$
$x + (x + 2) = 8$ *Substitute $(x + 2)$ for y in the other equation.*
$2x + 2 = 8$ *Combine like terms.*
$2x = 6$
$x = 3$

Step 3 Substitute the x-value into one of the original equations to solve for y.

$y = x + 2$
$y = (3) + 2$ *Substitute $x = 3$.*
$y = 5$

The solution is the ordered pair $(3, 5)$.

Check A graph or table supports your answer.

Caution! The solution to an independent system of equations is an ordered pair. Do not stop working when you have found only one value.

Try This

Describe two representations you could use to solve each problem.

1. A triangle with coordinates $A(3, 5)$, $B(2, 2)$, and $C(3, -2)$ is translated 3 units left and 2 units up. Give the coordinates of the image.
2. A bottle of juice from a vending machine costs \$1.50. Hiroshi buys a bottle by inserting 8 coins in quarters and dimes. If Hiroshi receives 5 cents in change, how many quarters did he use? how many dimes?
3. What is the slope of the line that passes through the point $(6, 9)$ and has a y-intercept of 3?

Reading and Writing Math CHAPTER 5

Organizer

Objective: Help students apply strategies to understand and retain key concepts.

Online Edition

Resources

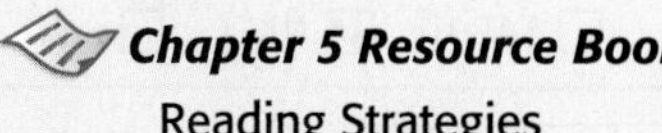

Chapter 5 Resource Book
Reading Strategies

Study Strategy: Use Multiple Representations

Discuss Students may find some representations of information much easier to use and understand than others. Therefore, it is important for them to be aware of the different ways to represent mathematical concepts or information: equations, graphs, tables, and so on.

In Chapter 5, this awareness may be particularly helpful in Lesson 5-3, where zeros of quadratic functions can be found either algebraically or graphically, and in Lesson 5-9, where complex numbers can be added using conventional arithmetic or on the complex plane.

Extend As students work through the exercises in Chapter 5, have them check their work by using a different representation. For example, if they solve a quadratic equation by factoring, they can check their answer by graphing the related function to see if they get the same result.

Answers to *Try This*

Possible answers:

1. using a graph or using a matrix
2. using symbols to write and solve a system of equations algebraically or using a matrix to solve the system
3. determining the slope from a graph or using a formula to find the slope

SECTION **5A**

Quadratic Functions and Complex Numbers

One-Minute Section Planner

Lesson	Lab Resources	Materials
5-1 Technology Lab Explore Parameter Changes • Explore how changes in the parameters of a quadratic function affect its graph. ☐ SAT-10 ☑ NAEP ☐ ACT ☐ SAT ☐ SAT Subject Tests	***Technology Lab Activities*** 5-1 Lab Recording Sheet	**Required** graphing calculator
Lesson 5-1 Using Transformations to Graph Quadratic Functions • Transform quadratic functions. • Describe the effects of changes in the coefficients of $y = a(x - h)^2 + k$. ☐ SAT-10 ☑ NAEP ☐ ACT ☑ SAT ☐ SAT Subject Tests		**Required** graph paper, graphing calculator
Lesson 5-2 Properties of Quadratic Functions in Standard Form • Define, identify, and graph quadratic functions. • Identify and use maximums and minimums of quadratic functions to solve problems. ☐ SAT-10 ☑ NAEP ☐ ACT ☑ SAT ☑ SAT Subject Tests		**Required** graph paper, graphing calculator
5-3 Technology Lab Explore Graphs and Factors • Use a graphing calculator to explore the relationship between the linear factors of a quadratic function and its zeros. ☐ SAT-10 ☑ NAEP ☑ ACT ☐ SAT ☐ SAT Subject Tests	***Technology Lab Activities*** 5-3 Lab Recording Sheet	**Required** graphing calculator
Lesson 5-3 Solving Quadratic Equations by Graphing and Factoring • Solve quadratic equations by graphing or factoring. • Determine a quadratic function from its roots. ☑ SAT-10 ☑ NAEP ☑ ACT ☐ SAT ☑ SAT Subject Tests	***Algebra Lab Activities*** 5-3 Algebra Lab	**Required** graph paper, graphing calculator **Optional** tennis ball or similar object, stopwatch, algebra tiles (MK), note cards
Lesson 5-4 Completing the Square • Solve quadratic equations by completing the square. • Write quadratic equations in vertex form. ☑ SAT-10 ☑ NAEP ☐ ACT ☑ SAT ☐ SAT Subject Tests		**Required** graphing calculator **Optional** algebra tiles (MK)
Lesson 5-5 Complex Numbers and Roots • Define and use imaginary and complex numbers. • Solve quadratic equations with complex roots. ☐ SAT-10 ☐ NAEP ☑ ACT ☐ SAT ☑ SAT Subject Tests		**Required** graph paper **Optional** graphing calculator
Lesson 5-6 The Quadratic Formula • Solve quadratic equations using the Quadratic Formula. • Classify roots using the discriminant. ☑ SAT-10 ☑ NAEP ☑ ACT ☑ SAT ☐ SAT Subject Tests	***Algebra Lab Activities*** 5-6 Algebra Lab	**Required** graph paper **Optional** graphing calculator, poster board

MK = *Manipulatives Kit*

Section Overview

Properties of Quadratic Functions

Lessons 5-1, 5-2

Why? Properties of quadratic functions can be determined from function rules.

Vertex Form

$$f(x) = a(x - h)^2 + k$$

Axis of symmetry: the line $x = h$

Vertex: (h, k)

Standard Form

$$f(x) = ax^2 + bx + c$$

Axis of symmetry: the line $x = -\frac{b}{2a}$

Vertex: $\left(-\frac{b}{2a}, f\left(-\frac{b}{2a}\right)\right)$ **y-intercept:** c

If $a > 0$, then the parabola opens **upward.**

If $a < 0$, then the parabola opens **downward.**

Solving Quadratic Equations

Lessons 5-3, 5-4, 5-6

Why? Students can solve quadratic equations by factoring, by completing the square, or by using the Quadratic Formula.

Factoring	Completing the Square	Quadratic Formula
Zero Product Property: If $ab = 0$ then $a = 0$ or $b = 0$.	Complete the square of $x^2 + bx$ by adding $\left(\frac{b}{2}\right)^2$.	Use the formula $x = \frac{-b \pm \sqrt{b^2 - 4ac}}{2a}$.
$x^2 - 9x + 14 = 0$ $(x - 2)(x - 7) = 0$ $(x - 2) = 0$ or $(x - 7) = 0$ $x = 2$ or $x = 7$	$x^2 + 6x - 11 = 0$ $x^2 + 6x = 11$ $x^2 + 6x + 9 = 11 + 9$ $(x + 3)^2 = 20$ $x + 3 = \pm\sqrt{20}$ $x = -3 \pm 2\sqrt{5}$	$2x^2 + 3x - 4 = 0$ $x = \frac{-3 \pm \sqrt{3^2 - 4(2)(-4)}}{2(2)}$ $x = \frac{-3 \pm \sqrt{41}}{4}$

Introducing Complex Numbers

Lesson 5-5

Why? Quadratic equations can have complex roots.

Imaginary unit

$$i = \sqrt{-1}$$

Complex Number

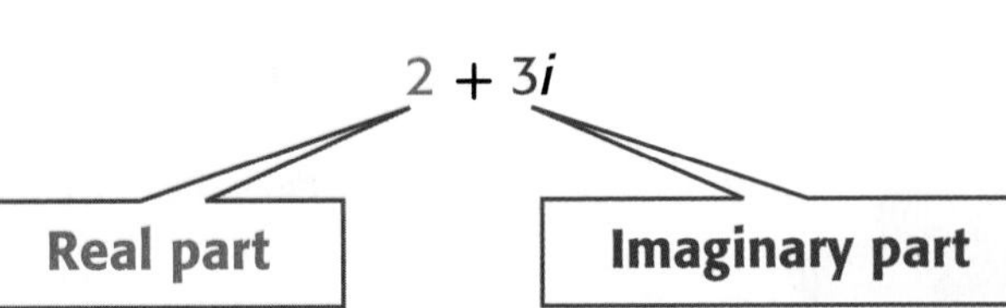

Organizer

Use with Lesson 5-1

Pacing:

Traditional $\frac{1}{2}$ day

Block $\frac{1}{4}$ day

Objective: Explore how changes in the parameters of a quadratic function affect its graph.

Materials: graphing calculator

Online Edition

Graphing Calculator, TechKeys

Countdown to Testing Week 10

Resources

Technology Lab Activities

5-1 Lab Recording Sheet

Teach

Discuss

Have students investigate the effect of changes in the parameter *k* by using the **GRAPH** feature. Discuss with students a general rule that describes their observations.

Close

Key Concept

The graphs of all quadratic functions are transformations of $f(x) = x^2$. The parameters *a*, *h*, and *k* each transform the graph in specific ways.

Assessment

Journal Have students describe the graph of $g(x) = x^2 + 2$ without graphing it.

State Resources

5-1

Explore Parameter Changes

You can use a graphing calculator to explore how changes in the parameters of a quadratic function affect its graph. Recall from Lesson 1-9 that the quadratic parent function is $f(x) = x^2$ and that its graph is a parabola.

Use with Lesson 5-1

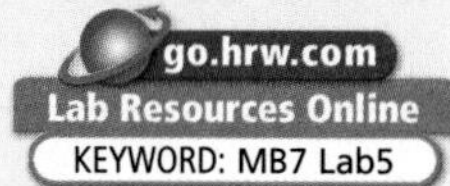

Activity

Describe what happens when you change the value of *k* in the quadratic function $g(x) = x^2 + k$.

1. Choose three values for *k*. Use 0, –5 (a negative value), and 4 (a positive value). Press Y=, and enter **X²** for **Y1**, **X² – 5** for **Y2**, and **X² + 4** for **Y3**.

2. Change the style of the graphs of **Y1** and **Y2** so that you can tell which graph represents which function. To do this, move the cursor to the graph style indicator next to **Y1**. Press ENTER to cycle through the options. For **Y1**, which represents the parent function, choose the thick line.

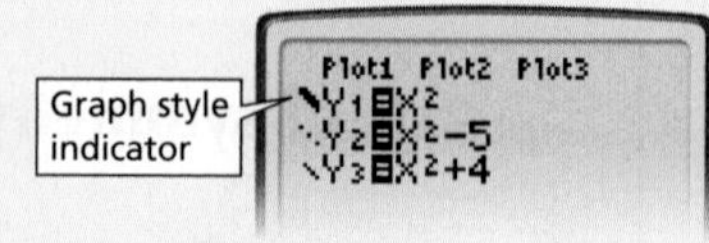

3. Next, change the line style for **Y2** to the dotted line.

4. Graph the functions in the square window by pressing ZOOM and choosing **5 : ZSquare**.

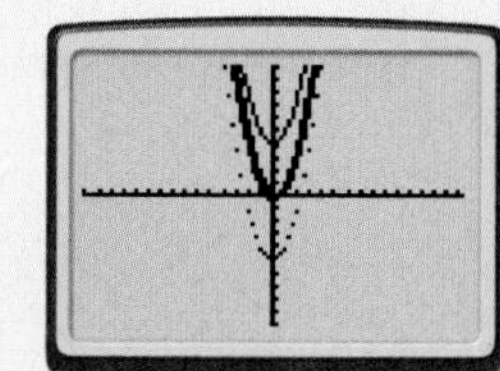

Notice that the graphs are identical except that the graph of **Y2** is shifted 5 units down and the graph of **Y3** has been shifted 4 units up from the graph of **Y1**.

You can conclude that the parameter *k* in the function $g(x) = x^2 + k$ has the effect of translating the parent function $f(x) = x^2$ *k* units up if *k* is positive and $|k|$ units down if *k* is negative.

1. The graph of $g(x) = (x - 4)^2$ is the graph of *f* translated 4 units right.
2. The graph of $g(x) = (x + 3)^2$ is the graph of *f* translated 3 units left.
3. The graph of $g(x) = -x^2$ is the graph of *f* reflected across the *x*-axis.

Try This

Use your graphing calculator to compare the graph of each function to the graph of $f(x) = x^2$. Describe how the graphs differ.

1. $g(x) = (x - 4)^2$ 2. $g(x) = (x + 3)^2$ 3. $g(x) = -x^2$

4. **Make a Conjecture** Use your graphing calculator to determine what happens when you change the value of *h* in the quadratic function $g(x) = (x - h)^2$. Check both positive and negative values of *h*.

5. **Make a Conjecture** Use your graphing calculator to determine what happens when you change the value of *a* in the quadratic function $g(x) = ax^2$. Check values of *a* that are greater than 1 and values of *a* that are between 0 and 1.

Answers to *Try This*

4. The parameter *h* in the function $g(x) = (x - h)^2$ has the effect of translating the parent function $f(x) = x^2$ right *h* units if *h* is positive and left $|h|$ units if *h* is negative.
5. The parameter *a* in the function $g(x) = ax^2$ has the effect of vertically stretching the parent function $f(x) = x^2$ if *a* is greater than 1 and vertically compressing the parent function if *a* is between 0 and 1.

5-1 Using Transformations to Graph Quadratic Functions

A2.3.3 Analyze, describe, and sketch graphs of quadratic functions including the lines of symmetry.

Objectives
Transform quadratic functions.

Describe the effects of changes in the coefficients of $y = a(x - h)^2 + k$.

Vocabulary
quadratic function
parabola
vertex of a parabola
vertex form

Why learn this?
You can use transformations of quadratic functions to analyze changes in braking distance. (See Example 5.)

In Chapters 2 and 3, you studied linear functions of the form $f(x) = mx + b$. A **quadratic function** is a function that can be written in the form $f(x) = a(x - h)^2 + k\ (a \neq 0)$. In a quadratic function, the variable is always squared. The table shows the linear and quadratic parent functions.

Know it! Note

Linear and Quadratic Parent Functions

ALGEBRA	NUMBERS	GRAPH
Linear Parent Function $f(x) = x$	x: −2, −1, 0, 1, 2; $f(x) = x$: −2, −1, 0, 1, 2	
Quadratic Parent Function $f(x) = x^2$	x: −2, −1, 0, 1, 2; $f(x) = x^2$: 4, 1, 0, 1, 4	

x	−2	−1	0	1	2
$f(x) = x$	−2	−1	0	1	2

x	−2	−1	0	1	2
$f(x) = x^2$	4	1	0	1	4

Notice that the graph of the parent function $f(x) = x^2$ is a U-shaped curve called a **parabola**. As with other functions, you can graph a quadratic function by plotting points with coordinates that make the equation true.

EXAMPLE 1 **Graphing Quadratic Functions Using a Table**

Graph $f(x) = x^2 - 6x + 8$ by using a table.

Make a table. Plot enough ordered pairs to see both sides of the curve.

x	$f(x) = x^2 - 6x + 8$	$(x, f(x))$
1	$f(1) = 1^2 - 6(1) + 8 = 3$	(1, 3)
2	$f(2) = 2^2 - 6(2) + 8 = 0$	(2, 0)
3	$f(3) = 3^2 - 6(3) + 8 = -1$	(3, −1)
4	$f(4) = 4^2 - 6(4) + 8 = 0$	(4, 0)
5	$f(5) = 5^2 - 6(5) + 8 = 3$	(5, 3)

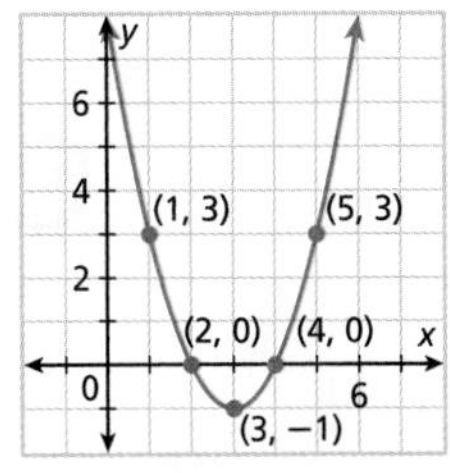

5-1 Organizer

Pacing: Traditional $1\frac{1}{2}$ days
Block $\frac{3}{4}$ day

Objectives: Transform quadratic functions.

Describe the effects of changes in the coefficients of $y = a(x - h)^2 + k$.

PREMIER **Online Edition**
Tutorial Videos, Graphing Calculator, Interactivity

Countdown to Testing Week 10

Power Presentations with PowerPoint®

Warm Up

For each translation of the point (−2, 5), give the coordinates of the translated point.

1. 6 units down (−2, −1)
2. 3 units right (1, 5)

For each function, evaluate $f(-2)$, $f(0)$, and $f(3)$.

3. $f(x) = x^2 + 2x + 6$ 6; 6; 21
4. $f(x) = 2x^2 - 5x + 1$ 19; 1; 4

Also available on transparency

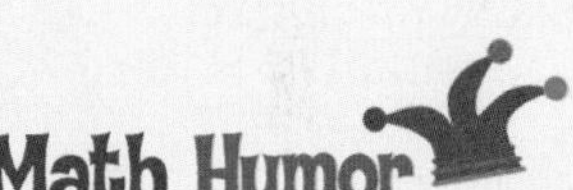

Math Humor

Q: What do you call a rodent with 4 babies?

A: A quad-*rat*-ic parent.

1 Introduce

EXPLORATION

5-1 Using Transformations to Graph Quadratic Functions

The simplest quadratic function is $f(x) = x^2$. You can plot points to explore the graphs of quadratic functions.

1. Complete the table for the function $f(x) = x^2$.

x	−3	−2	−1	0	1	2	3
f(x)							

2. Graph the function f by plotting the ordered pairs on the coordinate plane.
3. Complete the table for the function $g(x) = (x - 1)^2$.

x	−3	−2	−1	0	1	2	3
g(x)							

4. Graph the function g by plotting the ordered pairs on the coordinate plane.

THINK AND DISCUSS

5. **Explain** how the graph of g is related to the graph of f.
6. **Describe** the graph of $h(x) = (x - 2)^2$ as a transformation of the graph of f.

Motivate

Ask students to describe the path of a football that is kicked into the air. Then discuss with them why the football's path cannot be modeled with a linear function. The ball's path is curved; first the ball goes up, and then it goes down. Explain that the ball's path can be modeled by a type of non-linear function called a quadratic function.

Explorations and answers are provided in the *Explorations* binder.

State Resources

go.hrw.com
State Resources Online
KEYWORD: MB7 Resources

Power Presentations with PowerPoint®

Additional Examples

Example 1

Graph $f(x) = x^2 - 4x + 3$ by using a table.

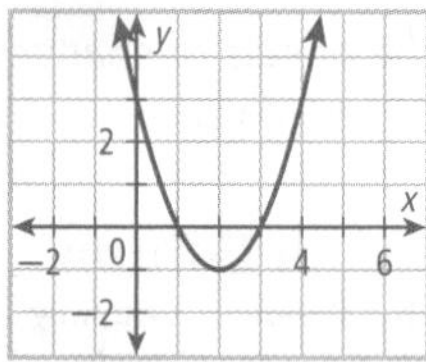

Example 2

Using the graph of $f(x) = x^2$ as a guide, describe the transformations, and then graph each function.

A. $g(x) = (x - 2)^2 + 4$

g is *f* translated 2 units right and 4 units up.

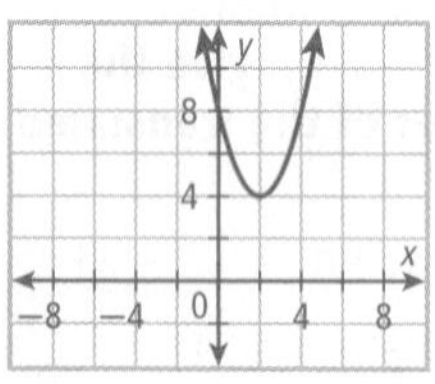

B. $g(x) = (x + 2)^2 - 3$

g is *f* translated 2 units left and 3 units down.

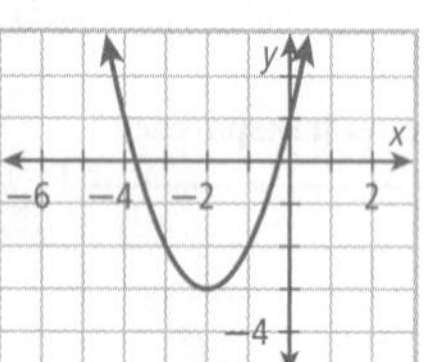

Also available on transparency

INTERVENTION
Questioning Strategies

EXAMPLE 1

- How can you determine the coordinates of points that lie on the function's graph?

EXAMPLE 2

- How does the operation sign inside the parentheses affect the direction of a horizontal translation?
- How does the operation sign outside the parentheses affect the direction of a vertical translation?

1. Graph $g(x) = -x^2 + 6x - 8$ by using a table.

You can also graph quadratic functions by applying transformations to the parent function $f(x) = x^2$. Transforming quadratic functions is similar to transforming linear functions (Lesson 2-6).

Translations of Quadratic Functions	
Horizontal Translations	**Vertical Translations**
Horizontal Shift of $\lvert h \rvert$ Units	Vertical Shift of $\lvert k \rvert$ Units
$f(x) = x^2$ $f(x - h) = (x - h)^2$ Moves left for $h < 0$ Moves right for $h > 0$	$f(x) = x^2$ $f(x) + k = x^2 + k$ Moves down for $k < 0$ Moves up for $k > 0$

EXAMPLE 2 Translating Quadratic Functions

Using the graph of $f(x) = x^2$ as a guide, describe the transformations, and then graph each function.

A $g(x) = (x + 3)^2 + 1$

Identify *h* and *k*.

$g(x) = (x - (-3))^2 + 1$, with $h = -3$ and $k = 1$

Because $h = -3$, the graph is translated 3 units left.

Because $k = 1$, the graph is translated 1 unit up.

Therefore, *g* is *f* translated 3 units left and 1 unit up.

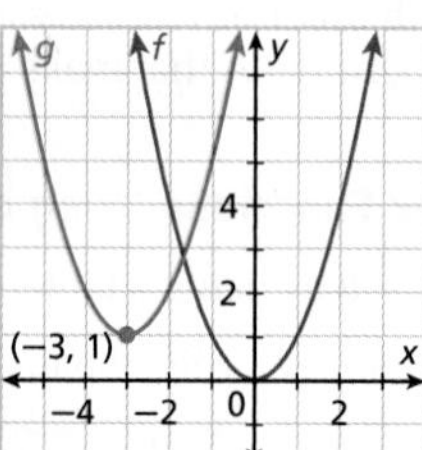

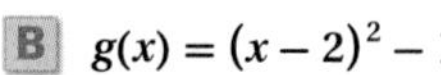

B $g(x) = (x - 2)^2 - 1$

Identify *h* and *k*.

$g(x) = (x - 2)^2 + (-1)$, with $h = 2$ and $k = -1$

Because $h = 2$, the graph is translated 2 units right.

Because $k = -1$, the graph is translated 1 unit down.

Therefore, *g* is *f* translated 2 units right and 1 unit down.

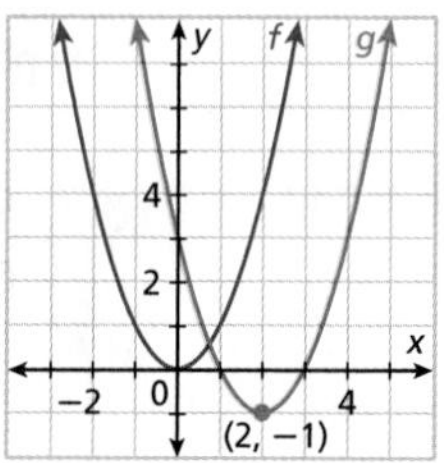

Using the graph of $f(x) = x^2$ as a guide, describe the transformations, and then graph each function.

2a. $g(x) = x^2 - 5$ *g* is *f* translated 5 units down.

2b. $g(x) = (x + 3)^2 - 2$ *g* is *f* translated 3 units left and 2 units down.

2a.

2b.

Recall that functions can also be reflected, stretched, or compressed.

2 Teach

Guided Instruction

In this lesson, students investigate how changes in the values of the parameters *a*, *h*, and *k* affect the graphs of quadratic functions. Help students to understand how changes in each of these parameters result in transformations of the function's graph. Make sure students can perform single transformations before moving on to problems involving multiple transformations.

Reaching All Learners
Through Visual Cues

Suggest that students circle the values of *a*, *h*, and *k* before graphing the vertex form of a quadratic function.

$$f(x) = -2(x - 3)^2 - 4$$

with $a = -2$, $h = 3$, $k = -4$ circled.

Remind students that *h* is the value subtracted from *x* in vertex form. Thus, in the example above, the value of *h* is 3, not −3.

Reflections, Stretches, and Compressions of Quadratic Functions

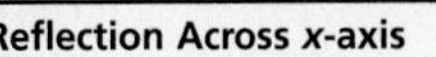

Reflections

Reflection Across y-axis

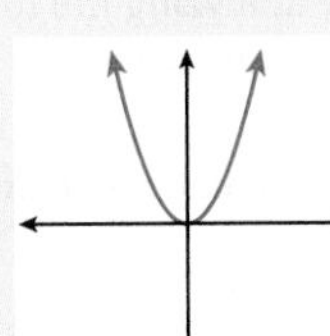

Input values change.

$f(x) = x^2$

$f(-x) = (-x)^2 = x^2$

The function $f(x) = x^2$ is its own reflection across the y-axis.

Reflection Across x-axis

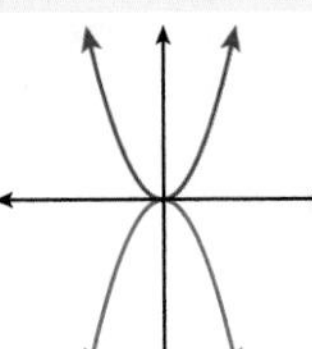

Output values change.

$f(x) = x^2$

$-f(x) = -(x^2)$
$= -x^2$

The function is flipped across the x-axis.

Stretches and Compressions

Horizontal Stretch/Compression by a Factor of $|b|$

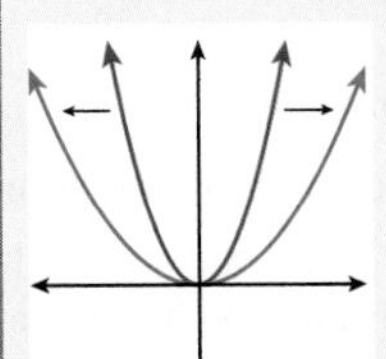

Input values change.

$f(x) = x^2$

$f\left(\frac{1}{b}x\right) = \left(\frac{1}{b}x\right)^2$

$|b| > 1$ stretches away from the y-axis.

$0 < |b| < 1$ compresses toward the y-axis.

Vertical Stretch/Compression by a Factor of $|a|$

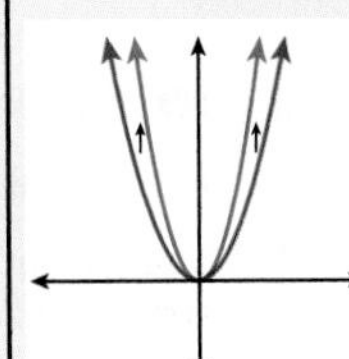

Output values change.

$f(x) = x^2$

$a \cdot f(x) = ax^2$

$|a| > 1$ stretches away from the x-axis.

$0 < |a| < 1$ compresses toward the x-axis.

EXAMPLE 3 Reflecting, Stretching, and Compressing Quadratic Functions

Using the graph of $f(x) = x^2$ as a guide, describe the transformations, and then graph each function.

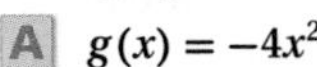

A $g(x) = -4x^2$

Because a is negative, g is a reflection of f across the x-axis. Because $|a| = 4$, g is a vertical stretch of f by a factor of 4.

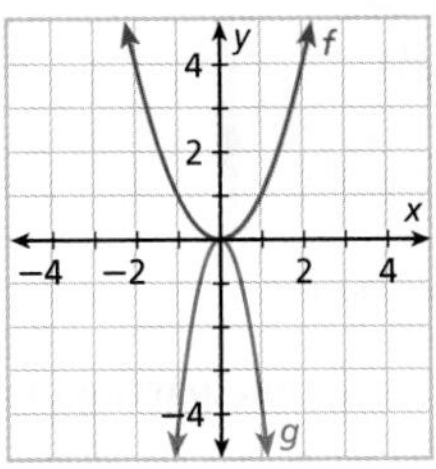

B $g(x) = \left(\frac{1}{2}x\right)^2$

Because $b = 2$, g is a horizontal stretch of f by a factor of 2.

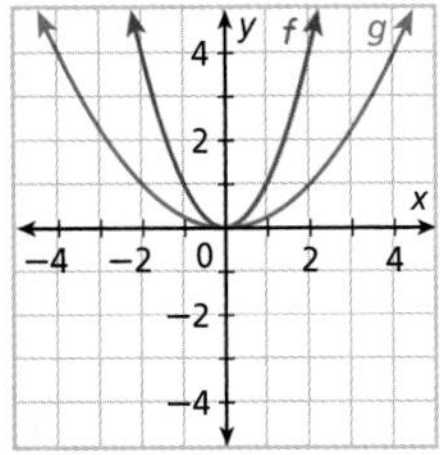

Using the graph of $f(x) = x^2$ as a guide, describe the transformations, and then graph each function.

3a. $g(x) = (2x)^2$ **3b.** $g(x) = -\frac{1}{2}x^2$

Answers to *Check It Out!*

1.

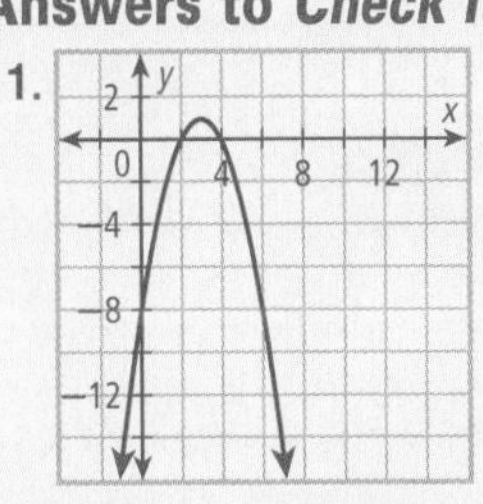

x	−1	1	3	5	7
$g(x)$	−15	−3	1	−3	−15

3a. g is a horizontal compression of f by a factor of $\frac{1}{2}$.

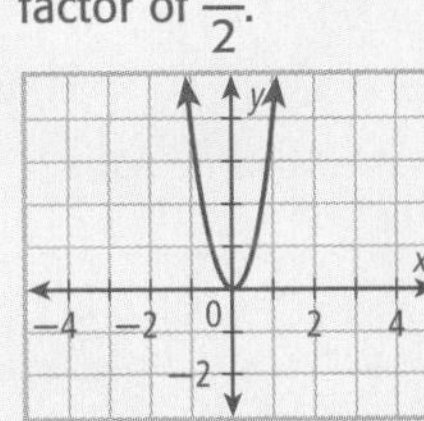

3b. g is f reflected across the x-axis and vertically compressed by a factor of $\frac{1}{2}$.

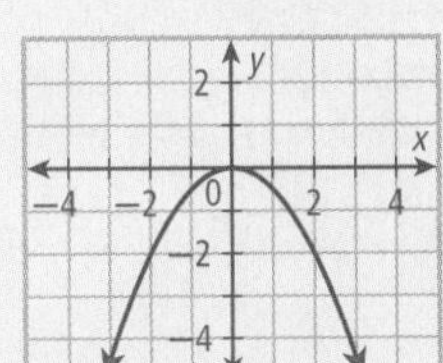

Power Presentations with PowerPoint®

Additional Examples

Example 3

Using the graph of $f(x) = x^2$ as a guide, describe the transformations, and then graph each function.

A. $g(x) = -\frac{1}{4}x^2$

f is g reflected across the x-axis and vertically compressed by a factor of $\frac{1}{4}$.

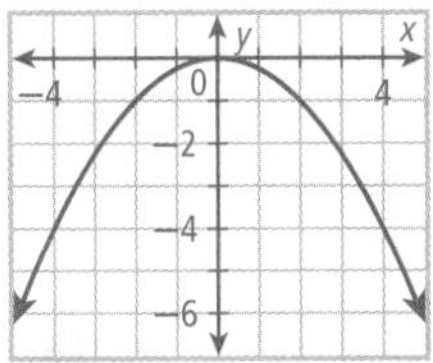

B. $g(x) = (3x)^2$

g is f horizontally compressed by a factor of $\frac{1}{3}$.

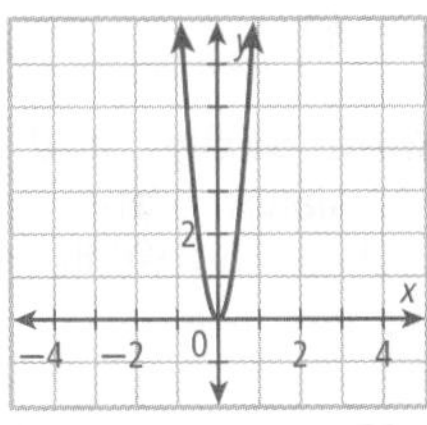

Also available on transparency

INTERVENTION

Questioning Strategies

EXAMPLE 3

- How does the sign of a affect the graph of a quadratic function?
- What is the difference between a stretch and a compression?

Math Background You may want to point out to students that $f(x) = x^2$ is its own reflection across the y-axis. Demonstrate this by using a table to graph $f(x) = x^2$ and its reflection across the y-axis, $g(x) = (-x)^2$, on the same coordinate plane.

Power Presentations with PowerPoint®

Additional Examples

Example 4

Use the description to write the quadratic function in vertex form.

The parent function $f(x) = x^2$ is vertically stretched by a factor of $\frac{4}{3}$ and then translated 2 units left and 5 units down to create g.

$g(x) = \frac{4}{3}(x + 2)^2 - 5$

Also available on transparency

INTERVENTION

Questioning Strategies

EXAMPLE 4

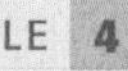

- How do you determine the values of a, h, and k?

Math Background A translation is also called a slide, and a reflection is also called a flip.

Reading Math Students may have seen the word *vertex* in other mathematical contexts. For example, they can probably identify the vertex of an angle. Point out that some mathematical terms may have more than one meaning, just as everyday words such as *bat* and *block* may have multiple meanings.

ENGLISH LANGUAGE LEARNERS

If a parabola opens upward, it has a lowest point. If a parabola opens downward, it has a highest point. This lowest or highest point is the **vertex of a parabola**.

The parent function $f(x) = x^2$ has its vertex at the origin. You can identify the vertex of other quadratic functions by analyzing the function in *vertex form*. The **vertex form** of a quadratic function is $f(x) = a(x - h)^2 + k$, where a, h, and k are constants.

Know it! Note

Vertex Form of a Quadratic Function

$$f(x) = a(x - h)^2 + k$$

a indicates a reflection across the x-axis and/or a vertical stretch or compression.

h indicates a horizontal translation.

k indicates a vertical translation.

Because the vertex is translated h horizontal units and k vertical units from the origin, the vertex of the parabola is at (h, k).

Helpful Hint

When the quadratic parent function $f(x) = x^2$ is written in vertex form, $y = a(x - h)^2 + k$, $a = 1$, $h = 0$, and $k = 0$.

EXAMPLE 4 **Writing Transformed Quadratic Functions**

Use the description to write the quadratic function in vertex form.

The parent function $f(x) = x^2$ is reflected across the x-axis, vertically stretched by a factor of 6, and translated 3 units left to create g.

Step 1 Identify how each transformation affects the constants in vertex form.

reflection across x-axis: a is negative
vertical stretch by 6: $|a| = 6$ } $a = -6$
translation left 3 units: $h = -3$

Step 2 Write the transformed function.

$g(x) = a(x - h)^2 + k$ *Vertex form of a quadratic function*

$= -6(x - (-3))^2 + 0$ *Substitute −6 for a, −3 for h, and 0 for k.*

$= -6(x + 3)^2$ *Simplify.*

Check Graph both functions on a graphing calculator. Enter f as **Y1** and g as **Y2**. The graph indicates the identified transformations.

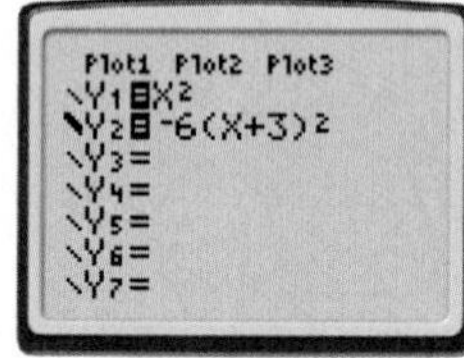

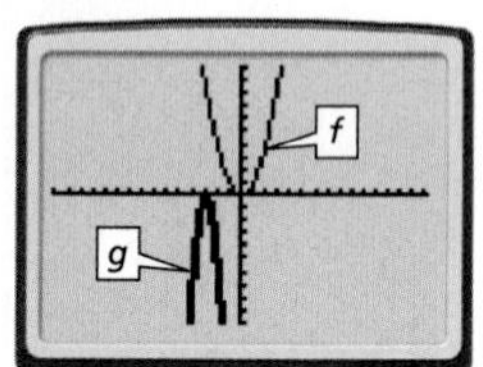

Use the description to write the quadratic function in vertex form.

4a. The parent function $f(x) = x^2$ is vertically compressed by a factor of $\frac{1}{3}$ and translated 2 units right and 4 units down to create g.

4a. $g(x) = \frac{1}{3}(x - 2)^2 - 4$

4b. The parent function $f(x) = x^2$ is reflected across the x-axis and translated 5 units left and 1 unit up to create g.

$g(x) = -(x + 5)^2 + 1$

EXAMPLE 5 ***Automotive Application***

The minimum braking distance d in feet for a vehicle on dry concrete is approximated by the function $d(v) = 0.045v^2$, where v is the vehicle's speed in miles per hour. If the vehicle's tires are in poor condition, the braking-distance function is $d_p(v) = 0.068v^2$. What kind of transformation describes this change, and what does the transformation mean?

Examine both functions in vertex form.

$$d(v) = 0.045(v - 0)^2 + 0 \qquad d_p(v) = 0.068(v - 0)^2 + 0$$

The value of a has increased from 0.045 to 0.068. The increase indicates a vertical stretch.

Find the stretch factor by comparing the new a-value to the old a-value:

$$\frac{a \text{ from } d_p(v)}{a \text{ from } d(v)} = \frac{0.068}{0.045} \approx 1.5$$

The function d_p represents a vertical stretch of d by a factor of approximately 1.5. Because the value of each function approximates braking distance, a vehicle with tires in poor condition takes about 1.5 times as many feet to stop as a vehicle with good tires does.

Check Graph both functions on a graphing calculator. The graph of d_p appears to be vertically stretched compared with the graph of d.

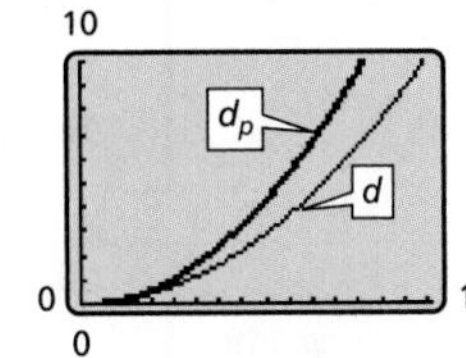

Use the information above to answer the following.

5. The minimum braking distance d_n in feet for a vehicle with new tires at optimal inflation is $d_n(v) = 0.039v^2$, where v is the vehicle's speed in miles per hour. What kind of transformation describes this change from $d(v) = 0.045v^2$, and what does this transformation mean?

Vertical compression by a factor of $\frac{13}{15}$; the braking distance will be less with optimally inflated new tires than with tires having more wear.

THINK AND DISCUSS

1. Explain how the values of a, h, and k in the vertex form of a quadratic function affect the function's graph.
2. Explain how to determine which of two quadratic functions expressed in vertex form has a narrower graph.

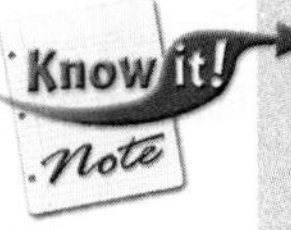

3. **GET ORGANIZED** Copy and complete the graphic organizer. In each row, write an equation that represents the indicated transformation of the quadratic parent function, and show its graph.

Transformation	Equation	Graph
Vertical translation		
Horizontal translation		
Reflection		
Vertical stretch		
Vertical compression		

COMMON ERROR ALERT

Students may have difficulty identifying the direction of a horizontal translation. Emphasize that h is the value *subtracted* from x. If a positive value is subtracted, the graph shifts to the right, in the positive x-direction. If a negative value is subtracted, the graph shifts to the left, in the negative x-direction.

Power Presentations with PowerPoint®

Additional Examples

Example 5

On Earth, the distance d in meters that a dropped object falls in t seconds is approximated by $d(t) = 4.9t^2$. On the moon, the corresponding function is $d_m(t) = 0.8t^2$. What kind of transformation describes this change from $d(t) = 4.9t^2$, and what does the transformation mean? d_m is a vertical compression of d by a factor of about 0.16. An object dropped on the moon falls about 0.16 times as fast as an object dropped on Earth. Therefore, it falls more slowly on the moon.

Also available on transparency

INTERVENTION 
Questioning Strategies

EXAMPLE 5

- How do you know whether a change in the value of a represents a vertical stretch or a vertical compression?

3 Close

Summarize

Ask students to identify how each of the following transformations affects the values of a, h, and k in the function $f(x) = a(x - h)^2 + k$.

translation 3 units left $h = -3$
translation 3 units up $k = 3$
vertical stretch by a factor of 3 $a = 3$
reflection across the x-axis $a = -1$

ONGOING ASSESSMENT and INTERVENTION

***Diagnose Before* the Lesson**
5-1 Warm Up, TE p. 315

***Monitor During* the Lesson**
Check It Out! Exercises, SE pp. 315–319
Questioning Strategies, TE pp. 316–319

***Assess After* the Lesson**
5-1 Lesson Quiz, TE p. 322
Alternative Assessment, TE p. 322

Answers to *Think and Discuss*

Possible answers:

1. a indicates a reflection, vertical stretch, or vertical compression. h indicates a horizontal translation (left or right). k indicates a vertical translation (up or down).
2. The function for which $|a|$ is greater will have a narrower graph.
3. See p. A6.

5-1 Exercises

Assignment Guide

Assign *Guided Practice* exercises as necessary.

If you finished Examples **1–3**
- **Basic** 17–28, 39–41
- **Average** 17–28, 39–41
- **Advanced** 17–28, 36–41

If you finished Examples **1–5**
- **Basic** 17–35, 39–42, 45–50, 53–57
- **Average** 17–35, 39–51, 53–57
- **Advanced** 17–32, 36–57

Homework Quick Check

Quickly check key concepts.
Exercises: 18, 20, 28, 30, 31, 40

Answers

2.

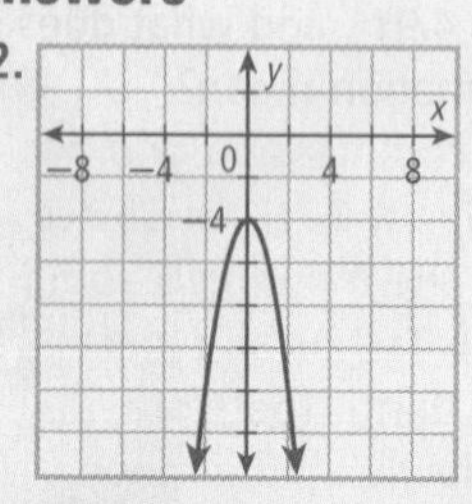

x	−2	−1	0	1	2
$f(x)$	−12	−6	−4	−6	−12

3–13, 17–27. See p. A26.

28. j is a horizontal stretch of f by a factor of 3.

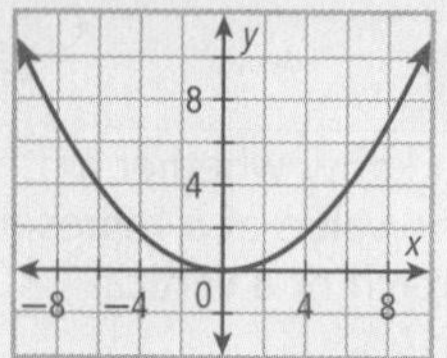

State Resources

5-1 Exercises

go.hrw.com
Homework Help Online
KEYWORD: MB7 5-1
Parent Resources Online
KEYWORD: MB7 Parent

GUIDED PRACTICE

1. **Vocabulary** The highest or lowest point on the graph of a quadratic function is the ___?___. (*vertex* or *parabola*) **vertex**

SEE EXAMPLE 1 p. 315

Graph each function by using a table.

2. $f(x) = -2x^2 - 4$
3. $g(x) = -x^2 + 3x - 2$
4. $h(x) = x^2 + 2x$

SEE EXAMPLE 2 p. 316

Using the graph of $f(x) = x^2$ as a guide, describe the transformations, and then graph each function.

5. $d(x) = (x - 4)^2$
6. $g(x) = (x - 3)^2 + 2$
7. $h(x) = (x + 1)^2 - 3$

SEE EXAMPLE 3 p. 317

8. $g(x) = 3x^2$
9. $h(x) = \left(\frac{1}{8}x\right)^2$
10. $p(x) = 0.25x^2$
11. $h(x) = -(5x)^2$
12. $g(x) = 4.2x^2$
13. $d(x) = -\frac{2}{3}x^2$

SEE EXAMPLE 4 p. 318

Use the description to write each quadratic function in vertex form.

14. The parent function $f(x) = x^2$ is vertically stretched by a factor of 2 and translated 3 units left to create g. $g(x) = 2(x + 3)^2$
15. The parent function $f(x) = x^2$ is reflected across the x-axis and translated 6 units down to create h. $h(x) = -x^2 - 6$

SEE EXAMPLE 5 p. 319

16. **Physics** The safe working load L in pounds for a natural rope can be estimated by $L(r) = 5920r^2$, where r is the radius of the rope in inches. For an old rope, the function $L_o(r) = 4150r^2$ is used to estimate its safe working load. What kind of transformation describes this change, and what does this transformation mean?
Vertical compression by a factor of $\frac{415}{592}$; the safe working load is less for an old rope than for a newer rope of the same radius.

PRACTICE AND PROBLEM SOLVING

Independent Practice

For Exercises	See Example
17–19	1
20–25	2
26–28	3
29–30	4
31	5

Extra Practice
Skills Practice p. S12
Application Practice p. S36

Graph each function by using a table.

17. $f(x) = -x^2 + 4$
18. $g(x) = x^2 - 2x + 1$
19. $h(x) = 2x^2 + 4x - 1$

Using the graph of $f(x) = x^2$ as a guide, describe the transformations, and then graph each function.

20. $g(x) = x^2 - 2$
21. $h(x) = (x + 5)^2$
22. $j(x) = (x - 1)^2$
23. $g(x) = (x + 4)^2 - 3$
24. $h(x) = (x + 2)^2 + 2$
25. $j(x) = (x - 4)^2 - 9$
26. $g(x) = \frac{4}{7}x^2$
27. $h(x) = -20x^2$
28. $j(x) = \left(\frac{1}{3}x\right)^2$

Use the description to write each quadratic function in vertex form.

29. The parent function $f(x) = x^2$ is reflected across the x-axis, vertically compressed by a factor of $\frac{1}{2}$, and translated 1 unit right to create g. $g(x) = -\frac{1}{2}(x - 1)^2$
30. The parent function $f(x) = x^2$ is vertically stretched by a factor of 2.5 and translated 2 units left and 1 unit up to create h. $h(x) = 2.5(x + 2)^2 + 1$
31. **Consumer Economics** The average gas mileage m in miles per gallon for a compact car is modeled by $m(s) = -0.015(s - 47)^2 + 33$, where s is the car's speed in miles per hour. The average gas mileage for an SUV is modeled by $m_u(s) = -0.015(s - 47)^2 + 15$. What kind of transformation describes this change, and what does this transformation mean? **Vertical translation; at any given speed, the gas mileage for an SUV is 18 mi/gal less than for a compact car.**

5-1 READING STRATEGIES

Linear and quadratic functions have some similar properties and some different properties.

Linear Functions	Quadratic Functions
The graph is a straight line.	The graph is a parabola.
The graph has no maximum or minimum.	The graph has a maximum or a minimum at the vertex (h, k).
The domain is the set of all real numbers and the range is the set of all real numbers.	The domain is the set of all real numbers but the range is $[k, \infty)$ when the vertex is a minimum or $(-\infty, k]$ when the vertex is a maximum.
Given the slope and y-intercept, a linear function can be written in slope-intercept form: $f(x) = mx + b$.	Given the vertex (h, k) and the value of a (coefficient of x^2), a quadratic function can be written in vertex form: $f(x) = a(x - h)^2 + k$.
The sign of m determines which direction the line slopes.	The sign of a determines whether the parabola opens upward or downward.

Answer each question.

1. Determine the type of graph for each function.
   a. $f(x) = 3x + 1$ Line
   b. $f(x) = x^2 - 6x + 5$ Parabola
   c. $f(x) = 4x - x^2 + 1$ Parabola
   d. $f(x) = 5 + \frac{2}{3}x$ Line
2. Find the domain and range of the function $f(x) = (x - 4)^2 + 3$.
   Domain = set of all real numbers; range = $[3, \infty)$
3. Find the slope of the line $f(x) = \frac{1}{2}x + 8$. Describe how the line slopes.
   Slope = $\frac{1}{2}$; possible answer: since the slope is positive, the line slopes from the lower left to the upper right.
4. Find the vertex of the function $f(x) = 2(x + 6)^2 - 3$. Does the parabola open upward or downward?
   $(-6, -3)$; since a is positive, the parabola opens upward.

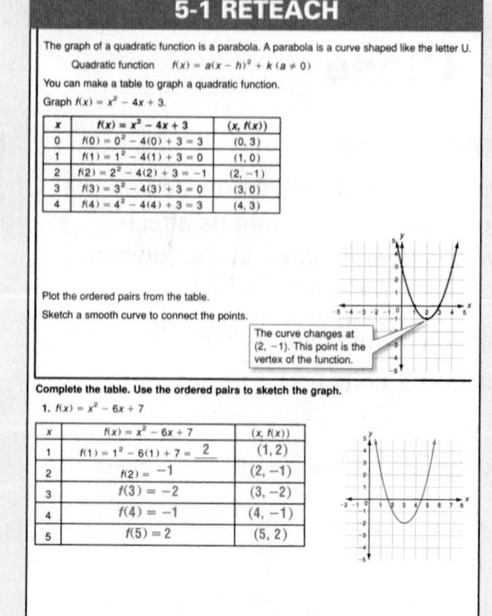

5-1 RETEACH

The graph of a quadratic function is a parabola. A parabola is a curve shaped like the letter U.

Quadratic function $f(x) = a(x - h)^2 + k \ (a \neq 0)$

You can make a table to graph a quadratic function.

Graph $f(x) = x^2 - 4x + 3$.

x	$f(x) = x^2 - 4x + 3$	$(x, f(x))$
0	$f(0) = 0^2 - 4(0) + 3 = 3$	(0, 3)
1	$f(1) = 1^2 - 4(1) + 3 = 0$	(1, 0)
2	$f(2) = 2^2 - 4(2) + 3 = -1$	(2, −1)
3	$f(3) = 3^2 - 4(3) + 3 = 0$	(3, 0)
4	$f(4) = 4^2 - 4(4) + 3 = 3$	(4, 3)

Plot the ordered pairs from the table.

Sketch a smooth curve to connect the points.

The curve changes at (2, −1). This point is the vertex of the function.

Complete the table. Use the ordered pairs to sketch the graph.

1. $f(x) = x^2 - 6x + 7$

x	$f(x) = x^2 - 6x + 7$	$(x, f(x))$
1	$f(1) = 1^2 - 6(1) + 7 =$ 2	(1, 2)
2	$f(2) =$ −1	(2, −1)
3	$f(3) = -2$	(3, −2)
4	$f(4) = -1$	(4, −1)
5	$f(5) = 2$	(5, 2)

32. **Pets** Keille is building a rectangular pen for a pet rabbit. She can buy wire fencing in a roll of 40 ft or a roll of 80 ft. The graph shows the area of pens she can build with each type of roll.

a. Describe the function for an 80 ft roll of fencing as a transformation of the function for a 40 ft roll of fencing.

b. Is the largest pen Keille can build with an 80 ft roll of fencing twice as large as the largest pen she can build with a 40 ft roll of fencing? Explain.

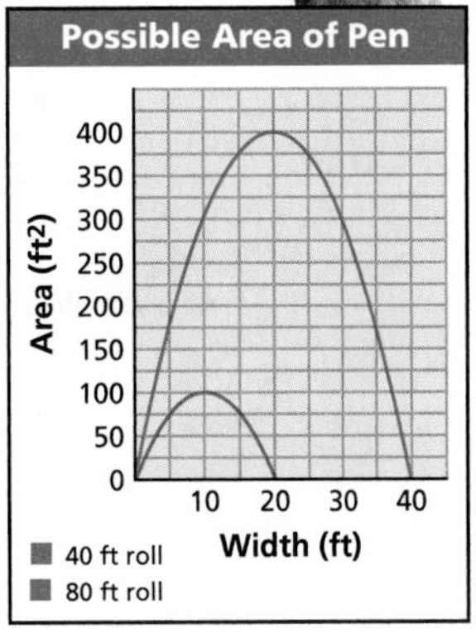

Possible Area of Pen

Area (ft²): 0, 50, 100, 150, 200, 250, 300, 350, 400
Width (ft): 10, 20, 30, 40
■ 40 ft roll
■ 80 ft roll

Using $f(x) = x^2$ as a guide, describe the transformations for each function.

33. $p(x) = -(x - 4)^2$

34. $g(x) = 8(x + 2)^2$

35. $h(x) = 4x^2 - 2$

36. $p(x) = \frac{1}{4}x^2 + 2$

37. $g(x) = (3x)^2 + 1$

38. $h(x) = -\left(\frac{1}{3}x\right)^2$

Match each graph with one of the following functions.

A. $a(x) = 4(x + 8)^2 - 3$

B. $b(x) = -2(x - 8)^2 + 3$

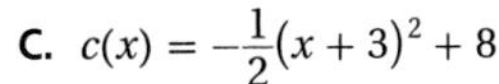
C. $c(x) = -\frac{1}{2}(x + 3)^2 + 8$

39. C

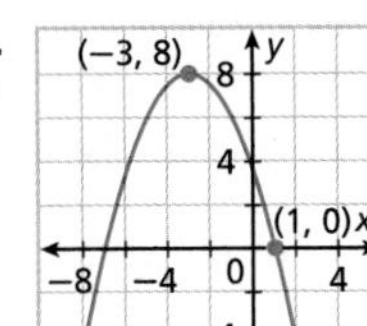

40. B

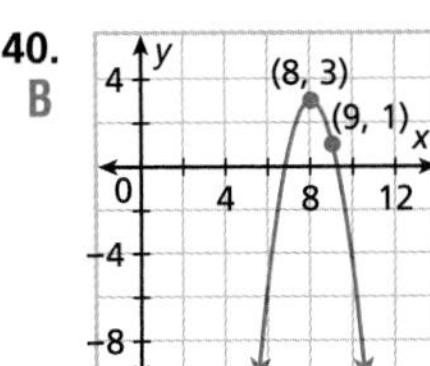

41. A

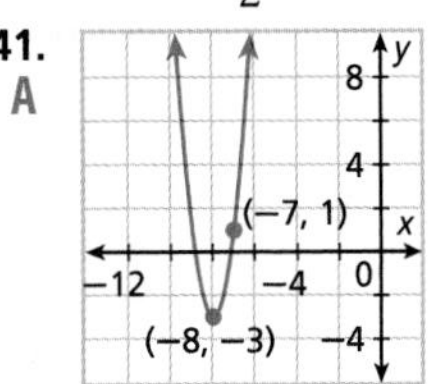

42. **Geometry** The area A of the circle in the figure can be represented by $A(r) = \pi r^2$, where r is the radius.

a. Write a function B in terms of r that represents the area of the shaded portion of the figure.

b. Describe B as a transformation of A.

c. What are the reasonable domain and range for each function? Explain.

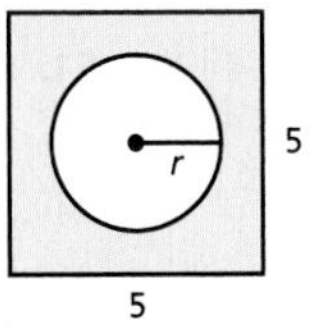

r
5
5

43. **Critical Thinking** What type of graph would a function of the form $f(x) = a(x - h)^2 + k$ have if $a = 0$? What type of function would it be?

44. **Write About It** Describe the graph of $f(x) = 999{,}999(x + 5)^2 + 5$ without graphing it.
very narrow parabola opening upward with its vertex at $(-5, 5)$

45. This problem will prepare you for the Multi-Step Test Prep on page 364.

The height h in feet of a baseball on Earth after t seconds can be modeled by the function $h(t) = -16(t - 1.5)^2 + 36$, where -16 is a constant in ft/s² due to Earth's gravity.

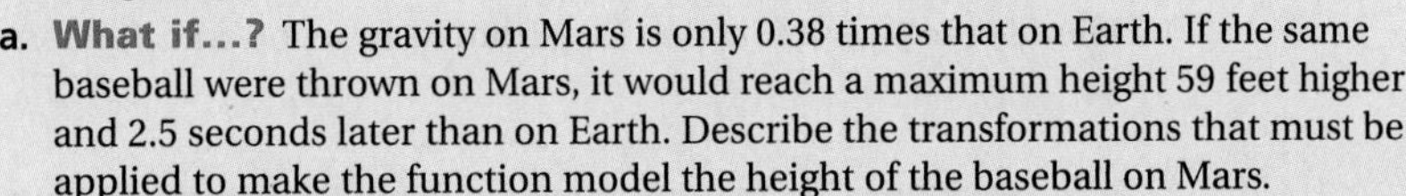

a. **What if...?** The gravity on Mars is only 0.38 times that on Earth. If the same baseball were thrown on Mars, it would reach a maximum height 59 feet higher and 2.5 seconds later than on Earth. Describe the transformations that must be applied to make the function model the height of the baseball on Mars.

b. Write a height function for the baseball thrown on Mars.

COMMON ERROR ALERT

In **Exercise 32,** students may automatically assume that the transformation is a stretch. Suggest that they start by finding the translation that maps the vertex of the function for the 40 ft roll onto the vertex of the function for the 80 ft roll. Then have them check whether this translation works for other points on the functions' graphs.

MULTI-STEP TEST PREP **Exercise 45** involves transformations of quadratic functions representing the height of a baseball. This exercise prepares students for the Multi-Step Test Prep on page 364.

Answers

32a. translation 10 units right and 300 units up

b. No; the largest pen Keille can build with an 80 ft roll has an area of 400 ft², and the largest pen she can build with a 40 ft roll has an area of 100 ft². Therefore, a roll that is twice as long allows her to build a pen with 4 times the area.

33. p is f reflected across the x-axis and translated 4 units right.

34. g is f vertically stretched by a factor of 8 and translated 2 units left.

35. h is f vertically stretched by a factor of 4 and translated 2 units down.

36. p is f vertically compressed by a factor of $\frac{1}{4}$ and translated 2 units up.

37–38, 42–43, 45. See p. A27.

5-1 PROBLEM SOLVING

Christa and Jelani are standing at the top of the Leaning Tower of Pisa in Italy, 185 feet above the ground. Jelani wonders what the path of a dropped object would be as it falls to the ground from the top of the tower. The height of an object after t seconds is given by the function, $f(t) = -16t^2 + 185$.

1. Complete the table to show the height, $f(t)$, of the object for different values of t.

2. Plot the ordered pairs from the table and draw the graph to show the path of the object.

Time (t)	$f(t) = -16t^2 + 185$	$(t, f(t))$
0	$f(0) = -16(0)^2 + 185$	(0, 185)
1	$f(1) = -16(1)^2 + 185$	(1, 169)
2	$f(2) = -16(2)^2 + 185$	(2, 121)
3	$f(3) = -16(3)^2 + 185$	(3, 41)
4	$f(4) = -16(4)^2 + 185$	(4, −71)

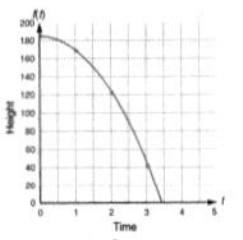

3. What is the parent function for the graph? $f(x) = x^2$

4. What is the name for this U-shaped curve? Parabola

5. Describe the transformations of the parent function into $f(t) = -16t^2 + 185$, which describes the path of an object falling from 185 feet.
The graph is translated up 185 units. Since a is negative, it is reflected across the x-axis. Since $|a| = 16$, it is stretched vertically by a factor of 16.

Choose the letter for the best answer.

6. Mario dropped a wrench from the top of a sailboat mast 58 feet high. Which function describes the path of the falling wrench?
A $f(t) = 16(t - 58)^2 - 185$
B $f(t) = -16(t - 58)^2 + 185$
C $f(t) = 16t^2 - 58$
(D) $f(t) = -16t^2 + 58$

7. Delle wants to transform the parent function $f(t) = t^2$ into $f(t) = -4(t - 0.6)^2 + 6$. Which is NOT a step in that transformation?
A Translation 6 units up
(B) Translation 0.6 unit left
C Reflection across the x-axis
D Vertical stretch by a factor of 4

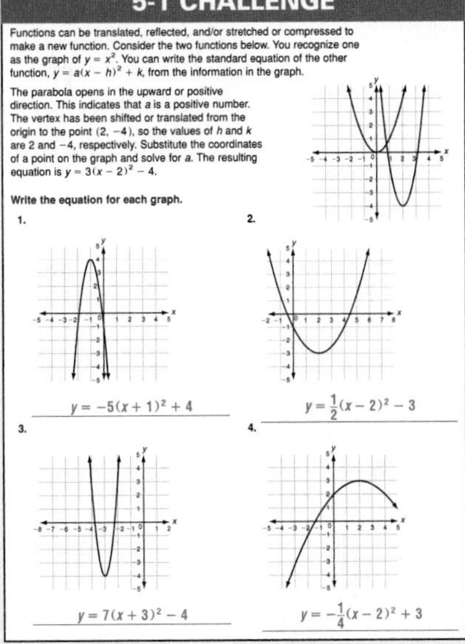

5-1 CHALLENGE

Functions can be translated, reflected, and/or stretched or compressed to make a new function. Consider the two functions below. You recognize one as the graph of $y = x^2$. You can write the standard equation of the other function, $y = a(x - h)^2 + k$, from the information in the graph.

The parabola opens in the upward or positive direction. This indicates that a is a positive number. The vertex has been shifted or translated from the origin to the point $(2, -4)$, so the values of h and k are 2 and -4, respectively. Substitute the coordinates of a point on the graph and solve for a. The resulting equation is $y = 3(x - 2)^2 - 4$.

Write the equation for each graph.

1. $y = -5(x + 1)^2 + 4$

2. $y = \frac{1}{2}(x - 2)^2 - 3$

3. $y = 7(x + 3)^2 - 4$

4. $y = -\frac{1}{4}(x - 2)^2 + 3$

5-1 PRACTICE A

5-1 PRACTICE C

5-1 PRACTICE B

Graph the function by using a table.

1. $f(x) = x^2 + 2x - 1$

x	$f(x) = x^2 + 2x - 1$	$(x, f(x))$
−2	−1	(−2, −1)
−1	−2	(−1, −2)
0	−1	(0, −1)
1	2	(1, 2)
2	7	(2, 7)

Using the graph of $f(x) = x^2$ as a guide, describe the transformations, and then graph each function. Label each function on the graph.

2. $h(x) = (x - 2)^2 + 2$
Translated 2 units right, 2 units up

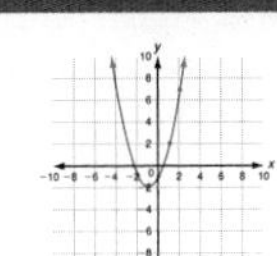

3. $h(x) = -(3x)^2$

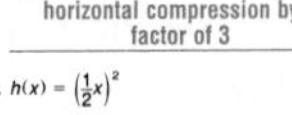
Reflected across the x-axis and horizontal compression by a factor of 3

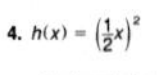
4. $h(x) = \left(\frac{1}{2}x\right)^2$
Horizontal stretch by a factor of 2

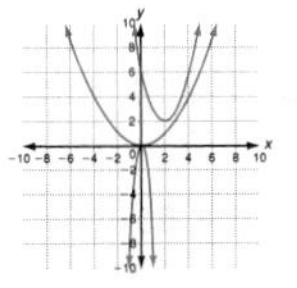

Use the description to write a quadratic function in vertex form.

5. The parent function $f(x) = x^2$ is reflected across the x-axis, horizontally stretched by a factor of 3 and translated 2 units down to create function g.

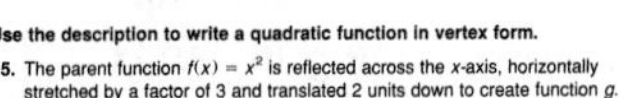
$g(x) = -\frac{1}{3}x^2 - 2$

6. A ball dropped from the top of tower A can be modeled by the function $h(t) = -9.8t^2 + 400$, where t is the time after it is dropped and $h(t)$ is its height at that time. A ball dropped from the top of tower B can be modeled by the function $h(t) = -9.8t^2 + 200$. What transformation describes this change? What does this transformation mean?
Vertical translation; possible answer: at a given time a ball dropped from tower A will be 200 feet higher than a ball dropped from tower B at the same time. Tower A is 200 feet taller than tower B.

TEST PREP DOCTOR Students who answered 1 for **Exercise 50** may have found the *x*-coordinate of the vertex rather than the *y*-coordinate of the vertex.

Journal

Have students explain how they can use the vertex form of a quadratic function to locate the vertex of the function's graph.

ALTERNATIVE ASSESSMENT

Have students perform four different transformations of the function $f(x) = x^2 + 3$: a vertical translation, a horizontal translation, a reflection, and a vertical compression. Have them graph each transformation and write the transformed functions.

Power Presentations with PowerPoint®

5-1 Lesson Quiz

1. Graph $f(x) = x^2 + 3x - 1$ by using a table.

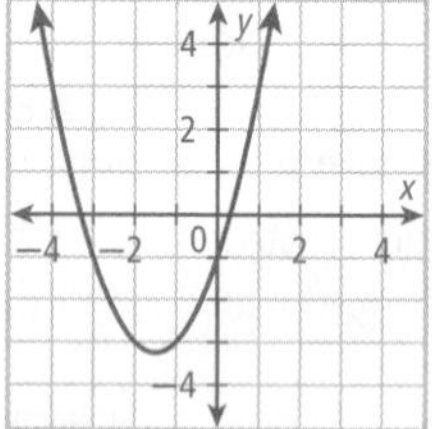

2. Using the graph of $f(x) = x^2$ as a guide, describe the transformations, and then graph $g(x) = -\frac{1}{4}(x + 1)^2$.

   g is *f* reflected across the *x*-axis, vertically compressed by a factor of $\frac{1}{4}$, and translated 1 unit left.

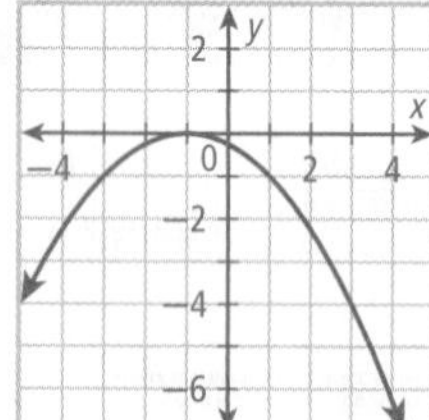

3. The parent function $f(x) = x^2$ is vertically stretched by a factor of 3 and translated 4 units right and 2 units up to create *g*. Write *g* in vertex form.

   $g(x) = 3(x - 4)^2 + 2$

Also available on transparency

TEST PREP

Use the graph for Exercises 46 and 47.

46. Which best describes how the graph of the function $y = -x^2$ was transformed to produce the graph shown?
    - (A) Translation 2 units right and 2 units up
    - (B) Translation 2 units right and 2 units down
    - (C) Translation 2 units left and 2 units up
    - (D) Translation 2 units left and 2 units down

47. Which gives the function rule for the parabola shown?
    - (F) $f(x) = (x + 2)^2 - 2$
    - (G) $f(x) = -(x + 2)^2 - 2$
    - (H) $f(x) = (x - 2)^2 - 2$
    - (J) $f(x) = -(x - 2)^2 - 2$

48. Which shows the functions below in order from widest to narrowest of their corresponding graphs?

    $m(x) = \frac{1}{6}x^2$ $\quad n(x) = 4x^2$ $\quad p(x) = 6x^2$ $\quad q(x) = -\frac{1}{2}x^2$
    - (A) *m*, *n*, *p*, *q*
    - (B) *q*, *m*, *n*, *p*
    - (C) *m*, *q*, *n*, *p*
    - (D) *q*, *p*, *n*, *m*

49. Which of the following functions has its vertex below the *x*-axis?
    - (F) $f(x) = (x - 7)^2$
    - (G) $f(x) = x^2 - 8$
    - (H) $f(x) = -2x^2$
    - (J) $f(x) = -(x + 3)^2$

50. **Gridded Response** What is the *y*-coordinate of the vertex of the graph of $f(x) = -3(x - 1)^2 + 5$? 5

CHALLENGE AND EXTEND

51. Identify the transformations of the graph of $f(x) = -3(x + 3)^2 - 3$ that would cause the graph's image to have a vertex at $(3, 3)$. Then write the transformed function. translation 6 units right and 6 units up: $y = -3(x - 3)^2 + 3$

52. Consider the functions $f(x) = (2x)^2 - 2$ and $g(x) = 4x^2 - 2$.
    a. Describe each function as a transformation of the quadratic parent function.
    b. Graph both functions on the coordinate plane.
    c. Make a conjecture about the relationship between the two functions. The functions are the same.
    d. Write the rule for a horizontal compression of the parent function that would give the same graph as $f(x) = 9x^2$. $g(x) = (3x)^2$

SPIRAL REVIEW

53. **Packaging** Peanuts are packaged in cylindrical containers. A small container is 7 in. tall and has a radius of 2 in. A large container is 5.5 in. tall and has a radius twice that of the small container. The price of the large container is three times the price of the small container. Is this price justified? Explain. *(Previous course)*

Identify the parent function for *g* from its function rule. *(Lesson 1-9)*

54. $g(x) = 4x + \sqrt{3}$ $\quad f(x) = x$
55. $g(x) = 3\sqrt{x + 4}$ $\quad f(x) = \sqrt{x}$

Write each function in slope-intercept form. Then graph the function. *(Lesson 2-3)*

56. $2y + 5x = 14$ $\quad y = -\frac{5}{2}x + 7$
57. $x - \frac{1}{2}y + 4 = -1$ $\quad y = 2x + 10$

Answers

52a. *f*: horizontal compression by a factor of $\frac{1}{2}$ and translation 2 units down; *g*: vertical stretch by a factor of 4 and translation 2 units down

b.

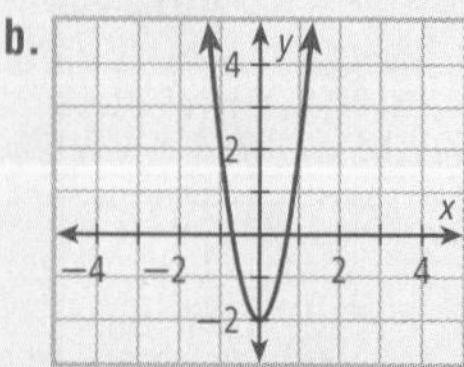

53. Yes; the price is justified because the volume of the large container is more than 3 times the volume of the small container: $V_{small} = 28\pi$; $V_{large} = 88\pi$

56.

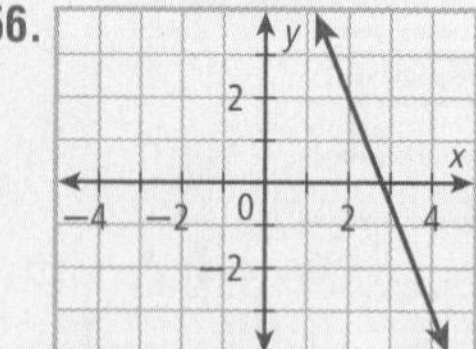

57.

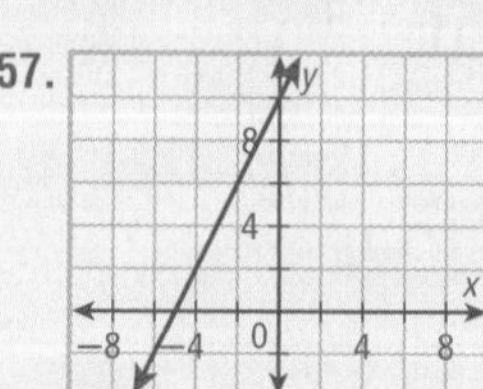

5-2 Properties of Quadratic Functions in Standard Form

A2.3.3 Analyze, describe, and sketch graphs of quadratic functions including the lines of symmetry.

Objectives

Define, identify, and graph quadratic functions.

Identify and use maximums and minimums of quadratic functions to solve problems.

Vocabulary

axis of symmetry
standard form
minimum value
maximum value

Why learn this?

Quadratic functions can be used to find the maximum power generated by the engine of a speedboat. (See Example 4.)

When you transformed quadratic functions in the previous lesson, you saw that reflecting the parent function across the y-axis results in the same function.

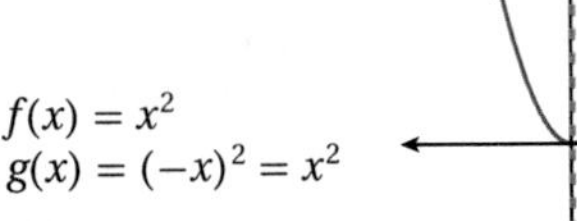

$f(x) = x^2$
$g(x) = (-x)^2 = x^2$

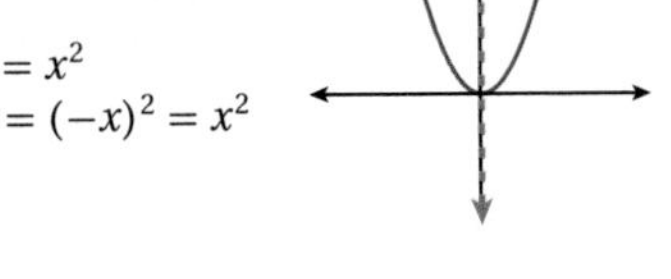

This shows that parabolas are symmetric curves. The **axis of symmetry** is the line through the vertex of a parabola that divides the parabola into two congruent halves.

Axis of Symmetry — Quadratic Functions

WORDS	ALGEBRA	GRAPH
The axis of symmetry is a vertical line through the vertex of the function's graph.	The quadratic function $f(x) = a(x - h)^2 + k$ has the axis of symmetry $x = h$.	(h, k)

EXAMPLE 1 Identifying the Axis of Symmetry

Identify the axis of symmetry for the graph of $f(x) = 2(x + 2)^2 - 3$.

Rewrite the function to find the value of h.

$f(x) = 2[x - (-2)]^2 - 3$

Because $h = -2$, the axis of symmetry is the vertical line $x = -2$.

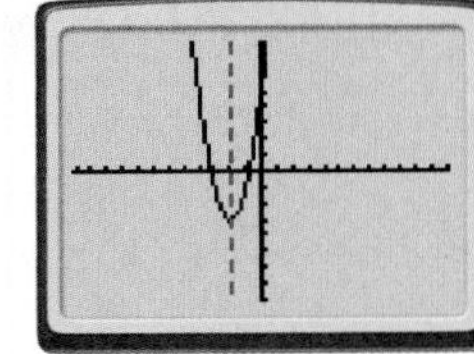

Check Analyze the graph on a graphing calculator. The parabola is symmetric about the vertical line $x = -2$.

1. Identify the axis of symmetry for the graph of $f(x) = (x - 3)^2 + 1$. $x = 3$

5-2 Organizer

Pacing: Traditional 1 day
Block $\frac{1}{2}$ day

Objectives: Define, identify, and graph quadratic functions.

Identify and use maximums and minimums of quadratic functions to solve problems.

Online Edition
Graphing Calculator, Tutorial Videos

Countdown to Testing Week 10

Power Presentations with PowerPoint®

Warm Up

Give the coordinate of the vertex of each function.

1. $f(x) = (x - 2)^2 + 3$ (2, 3)

2. $f(x) = 2(x + 1)^2 - 4$ (−1, −4)

3. Give the domain and range of the following function.

$\{(-2, 4), (0, 6), (2, 8), (4, 10)\}$

D: $\{-2, 0, 2, 4\}$; R: $\{4, 6, 8, 10\}$

Also available on transparency

Math Humor

Q: What is the hidden math term?

BOLA BOLA

A: Parabolas (pair of BOLAs).

1 Introduce

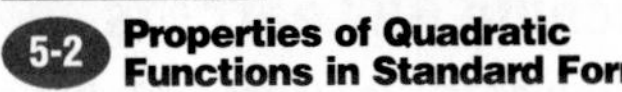

5-2 Properties of Quadratic Functions in Standard Form

You can use a calculator to explore properties of the graphs of quadratic functions. To graph a quadratic function, press [Y=] and enter the function rule. Then press [GRAPH] to see the graph.

1. Use your calculator to graph each function listed below. Then complete the table.

Function	Parabola Opens Upward or Downward?	y-intercept
$f(x) = 2x^2 + 4x + 1$		
$f(x) = -3x^2 - 6x + 2$		
$f(x) = x^2 + 2x - 4$		
$f(x) = -x^2 - 3x - 5$		

2. The quadratic functions in Problem 1 are written in the form $f(x) = ax^2 + bx + c$. For each function, write the values of a and c.

Function	Value of a	Value of c
$f(x) = 2x^2 + 4x + 1$		
$f(x) = -3x^2 - 6x + 2$		
$f(x) = x^2 + 2x - 4$		
$f(x) = -x^2 - 3x - 5$		

THINK AND DISCUSS

3. Explain how the sign of a can help you determine whether the graph of a quadratic function opens upward or downward.

Motivate

ENGLISH LANGUAGE LEARNERS

Ask students to give examples of everyday situations in which the terms *minimum* and *maximum* are used. Possible answers: minimum age requirements for driving, maximum weights on elevators Explain that quadratic functions have a *minimum value* or a *maximum value*. Ask volunteers to offer definitions of these terms based on the class discussion.

Explorations and answers are provided in the *Explorations* binder.

Another useful form of writing quadratic functions is the *standard form.* The **standard form** of a quadratic function is $f(x) = ax^2 + bx + c$, where $a \neq 0$.

The coefficients a, b, and c can show properties of the graph of the function. You can determine these properties by expanding the vertex form.

$$f(x) = a(x-h)^2 + k$$

$$f(x) = a(x^2 - 2xh + h^2) + k \qquad \textit{Multiply to expand } (x-h)^2.$$

$$f(x) = a(x^2) - a(2hx) + a(h^2) + k \qquad \textit{Distribute a.}$$

$$f(x) = ax^2 + (-2ah)x + (ah^2 + k) \qquad \textit{Simplify and group like terms.}$$

$a = a \quad -2ah = b \quad ah^2 + k = c$

$$f(x) = ax^2 + bx + c$$

$a = a$: a in standard form is the same as in vertex form. It indicates whether a reflection and/or vertical stretch or compression has been applied.

$b = -2ah$: Solving for h gives $h = \frac{b}{-2a} = -\frac{b}{2a}$. Therefore, the axis of symmetry, $x = h$, for a quadratic function in standard form is $x = -\frac{b}{2a}$.

$c = ah^2 + k$: Notice that the value of c is the same value given by the vertex form of f when $x = 0$: $f(0) = a(0-h)^2 + k = ah^2 + k$. So c is the y-intercept.

These properties can be generalized to help you graph quadratic functions.

Know it! Note

Properties of a Parabola

For $f(x) = ax^2 + bx + c$, where a, b, and c are real numbers and $a \neq 0$, the parabola has these properties:

The parabola **opens** upward if $a > 0$ and downward if $a < 0$.

The **axis of symmetry** is the vertical line $x = -\frac{b}{2a}$.

The **vertex** is the point $\left(-\frac{b}{2a}, f\left(-\frac{b}{2a}\right)\right)$.

The **y-intercept** is c.

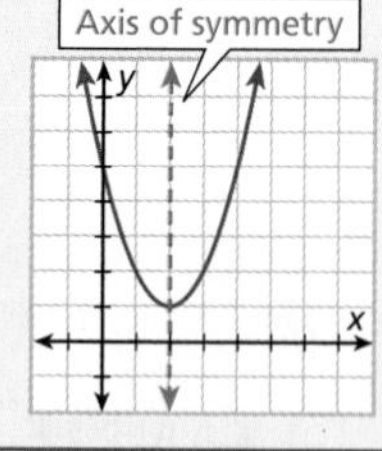

EXAMPLE 2 **Graphing Quadratic Functions in Standard Form**

A Consider the function $f(x) = x^2 - 4x + 6$.

a. Determine whether the graph opens upward or downward.

Because a is positive, the parabola opens upward.

b. Find the axis of symmetry.

The axis of symmetry is given by $x = -\frac{b}{2a}$.

$x = -\frac{(-4)}{2(1)} = 2$ *Substitute −4 for b and 1 for a.*

The axis of symmetry is the line $x = 2$.

Power Presentations with PowerPoint®

Additional Examples

Example 1

Identify the axis of symmetry for the graph of $f(x) = -\frac{1}{2}(x+5)^2 - 8$. $x = -5$

Example 2

A. Consider the function $f(x) = 2x^2 - 4x + 5$.

a. Determine whether the graph opens upward or downward. upward

b. Find the axis of symmetry. $x = 1$

c. Find the vertex. (1, 3)

d. Find the y-intercept. 5

e. Graph the function.

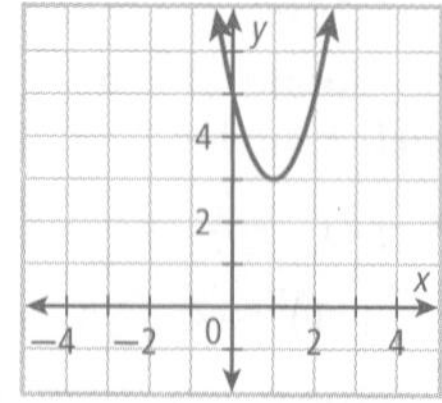

B. Consider the function $f(x) = -x^2 - 2x + 3$.

a. Determine whether the graph opens upward or downward. downward

b. Find the axis of symmetry. $x = -1$

c. Find the vertex. (−1, 4)

d. Find the y-intercept. 3

e. Graph the function.

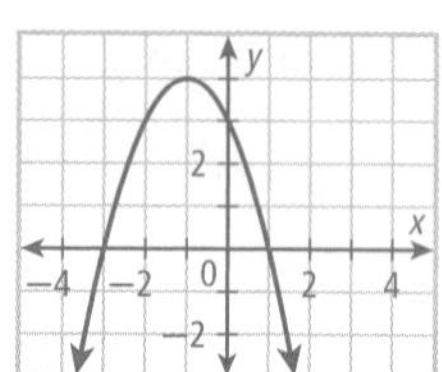

Also available on transparency

2 Teach

Guided Instruction

Focus first on identifying properties of quadratic functions in vertex form. Then introduce the standard form of quadratic functions and explain how to identify properties of the functions using the values of the coefficients. Students may benefit from the explanation on page 324, which connects the parameters a, h, and k from the vertex form to the coefficients a, b, and c from the standard form.

Reaching All Learners

Through Multiple Representations

Have students work in pairs. Give each pair a quadratic function in standard form. Have one student in each pair use a graph to identify the function's axis of symmetry, minimum or maximum value, and y-intercept. Have the other student use algebra to determine these properties. Partners can then compare their results to see if they agree. Ask students to discuss any differences in their answers.

INTERVENTION

Questioning Strategies

EXAMPLE 1

- What is the connection between the value of h and the equation of the axis of symmetry?

EXAMPLE 2

- How do you find the y-coordinate of the vertex of a parabola?

c. **Find the vertex.**

The vertex lies on the axis of symmetry, so the x-coordinate is 2. The y-coordinate is the value of the function at this x-value, or $f(2)$.

$$f(2) = (2)^2 - 4(2) + 6 = 2$$

The vertex is $(2, 2)$.

d. **Find the y-intercept.**

Because $c = 6$, the y-intercept is 6.

e. **Graph the function.**

Graph by sketching the axis of symmetry and then plotting the vertex and the intercept point, $(0, 6)$. Use the axis of symmetry to find another point on the parabola. Notice that $(0, 6)$ is 2 units left of the axis of symmetry. The point on the parabola symmetrical to $(0, 6)$ is 2 units right of the axis at $(4, 6)$.

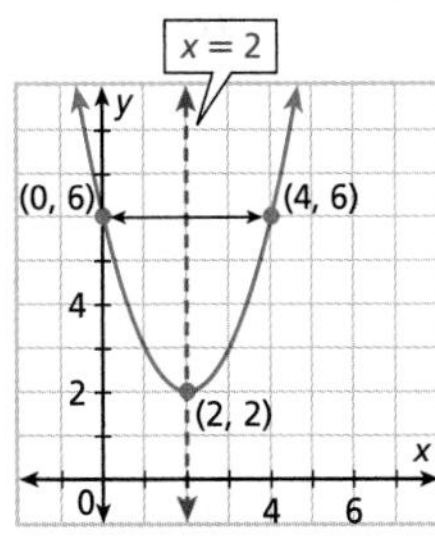

B Consider the function $f(x) = -4x^2 - 12x - 3$.

a. **Determine whether the graph opens upward or downward.**

Because a is negative, the parabola opens downward.

b. **Find the axis of symmetry.**

The axis of symmetry is given by $x = -\frac{b}{2a}$.

$$x = -\frac{(-12)}{2(-4)} = -\frac{3}{2} \quad \textit{Substitute } -12 \textit{ for } b \textit{ and } -4 \textit{ for } a.$$

The axis of symmetry is the line $x = -\frac{3}{2}$, or $x = -1.5$.

c. **Find the vertex.**

The vertex lies on the axis of symmetry, so the x-coordinate is -1.5.

The y-coordinate is the value of the function at this x-value, or $f(-1.5)$.

$$f(-1.5) = -4(-1.5)^2 - 12(-1.5) - 3 = 6$$

The vertex is $(-1.5, 6)$.

d. **Find the y-intercept.**

Because $c = -3$, the y-intercept is -3.

e. **Graph the function.**

Graph by sketching the axis of symmetry and then plotting the vertex and the intercept point, $(0, -3)$. Use the axis of symmetry to find another point on the parabola. Notice that $(0, -3)$ is 1.5 units right of the axis of symmetry. The point on the parabola symmetrical to $(0, -3)$ is 1.5 units left of the axis at $(-3, -3)$.

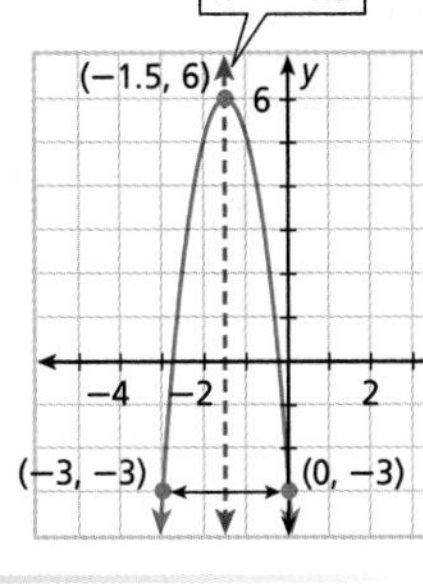

For each function, (a) determine whether the graph opens upward or downward, (b) find the axis of symmetry, (c) find the vertex, (d) find the y-intercept, and (e) graph the function.

2a. $f(x) = -2x^2 - 4x$ **2b.** $g(x) = x^2 + 3x - 1$

Helpful Hint

When a is positive, the parabola is happy (∪). When a is negative, the parabola is sad (∩).

2a(a). downward

2a(b). $x = -1$

2a(c). $(-1, 2)$

2a(d). 0

2a(e).

2b(a). upward

2b(b). $x = -\frac{3}{2}$

2b(c). $\left(-\frac{3}{2}, -\frac{13}{4}\right)$

2b(d). -1

2b(e).

Teaching Tip **Multiple Representations** Emphasize that the vertex form and the standard form of quadratic equations each have their advantages, depending on the situation. Just as it is useful to be able to convert between the slope-intercept form, the point-slope form, and the standard form of a linear equation, students will find it useful to be able to convert between the vertex form and the standard form of a quadratic equation.

Teaching Tip **Critical Thinking** Another way to determine the y-coordinate of the vertex of a quadratic function is to evaluate the expression $-\frac{b^2}{4a} + c$. Students can verify that this expression gives the y-coordinate of the vertex by evaluating $f\left(-\frac{b}{2a}\right)$ for $f(x) = ax^2 + bx + c$.

Teaching Tip **Inclusion** Point out that the y-coordinate of the vertex of a quadratic function represents the maximum value of the function if $a < 0$ and the minimum value of the function if $a > 0$.

Power Presentations with PowerPoint®

Additional Examples

Example 3

Find the minimum or maximum value of $f(x) = -3x^2 + 2x - 4$. Then state the domain and range of the function.

maximum: $-\frac{11}{3}$; D: $\mathbb{R}$;

R: $\left\{y \mid y \leq -\frac{11}{3}\right\}$

Also available on transparency

INTERVENTION 

Questioning Strategies

EXAMPLE 3

- How can you tell from its equation whether a quadratic function has a minimum or a maximum?
- How can you use the minimum or maximum value of a quadratic function to find the range of the function?

Teaching Tip **Inclusion** Remind students how to use set-builder notation to represent the domain and range of functions (Lesson 1-1). For example, $\{x \mid x \in \mathbb{R}\}$ is read, "The set of all numbers x such that x is an element of the real numbers."

Substituting any real value of x into a quadratic equation results in a real number. Therefore, the domain of any quadratic function is all real numbers, $\mathbb{R}$. The range of a quadratic function depends on its vertex and the direction that the parabola opens.

Know it! Note

Minimum and Maximum Values

OPENS UPWARD	OPENS DOWNWARD
When a parabola opens upward, the y-value of the vertex is the **minimum value**.	When a parabola opens downward, the y-value of the vertex is the **maximum value**.
D: $\{x \mid x \in \mathbb{R}\}$ R: $\{y \mid y \geq k\}$ 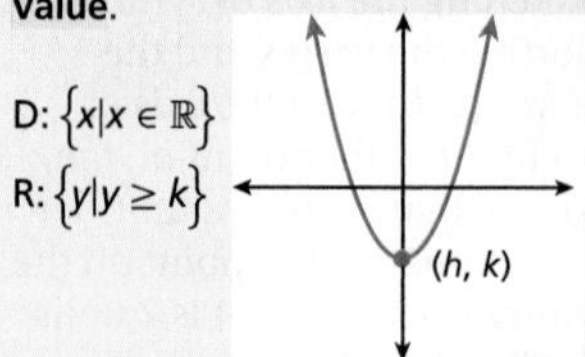	D: $\{x \mid x \in \mathbb{R}\}$ R: $\{y \mid y \leq k\}$ (h, k)
The domain is all real numbers, $\mathbb{R}$. The range is all values greater than or equal to the minimum.	The domain is all real numbers, $\mathbb{R}$. The range is all values less than or equal to the maximum.

EXAMPLE 3 **Finding Minimum or Maximum Values**

Find the minimum or maximum value of $f(x) = 2x^2 - 2x + 5$. Then state the domain and range of the function.

Step 1 Determine whether the function has a minimum or maximum value. Because a is positive, the graph opens upward and has a minimum value.

Step 2 Find the x-value of the vertex.

$$x = -\frac{b}{2a} = -\frac{(-2)}{2(2)} = \frac{2}{4} = \frac{1}{2}$$ *Substitute −2 for b and 2 for a.*

Step 3 Then find the y-value of the vertex, $f\left(-\frac{b}{2a}\right)$.

$$f\left(\frac{1}{2}\right) = 2\left(\frac{1}{2}\right)^2 - 2\left(\frac{1}{2}\right) + 5 = 4\frac{1}{2}$$

The minimum value is $4\frac{1}{2}$, or 4.5. The domain is all real numbers, $\mathbb{R}$. The range is all real numbers greater than or equal to 4.5, or $\{y \mid y \geq 4.5\}$.

Check Graph $f(x) = 2x^2 - 2x + 5$ on a graphing calculator. The graph and table support the answer.

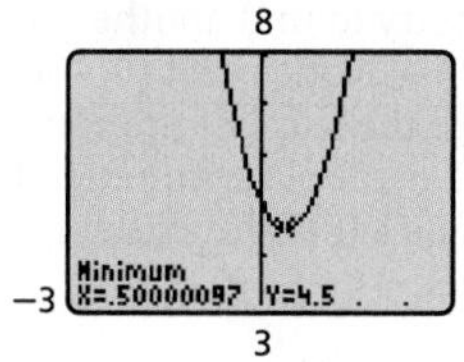

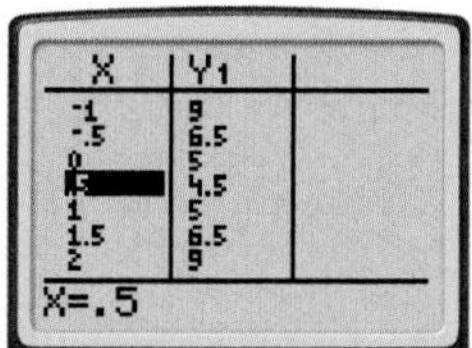

Caution!

The minimum (or maximum) value is the *y-value* of the vertex. It is *not* the ordered pair representing the vertex.

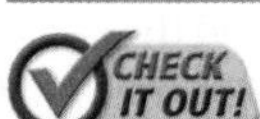

CHECK IT OUT! **Find the minimum or maximum value of each function. Then state the domain and range of the function.**

3a. $f(x) = x^2 - 6x + 3$ min = −6; D: $\mathbb{R}$; R: $\{y \mid y \geq -6\}$

3b. $g(x) = -2x^2 - 4$ max = −4; D: $\mathbb{R}$; R: $\{y \mid y \leq -4\}$

EXAMPLE 4 ***Transportation Application***

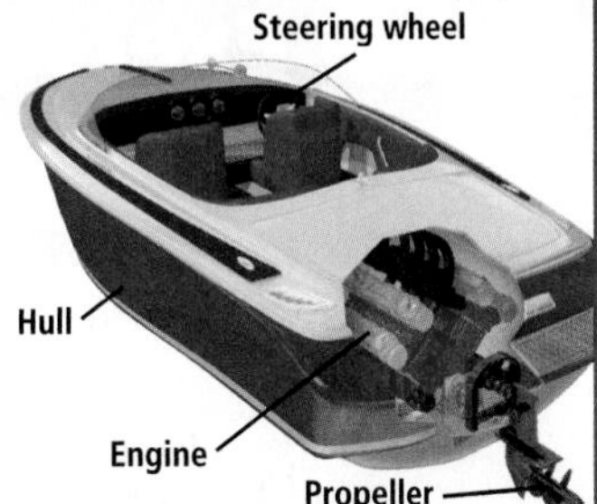

The power p in horsepower (hp) generated by a high-performance speedboat engine operating at r revolutions per minute (rpm) can be modeled by the function $p(r) = -0.0000147r^2 + 0.18r - 251$. What is the maximum power of this engine to the nearest horsepower? At how many revolutions per minute must the engine be operating to achieve this power?

The maximum value will be at the vertex $(r, p(r))$.

Step 1 Find the r-value of the vertex using $a = -0.0000147$ and $b = 0.18$.

$$r = -\frac{b}{2a} = -\frac{0.18}{2(-0.0000147)} \approx 6122$$

Step 2 Substitute this r-value into p to find the corresponding maximum, $p(r)$.

$$p(r) = -0.0000147r^2 + 0.18r - 251$$

$$p(6122) = -0.0000147(6122)^2 + 0.18(6122) - 251 \quad \textit{Substitute 6122 for r.}$$

$$p(6122) \approx 300 \quad \textit{Use a calculator.}$$

The maximum power is about 300 hp at 6122 rpm.

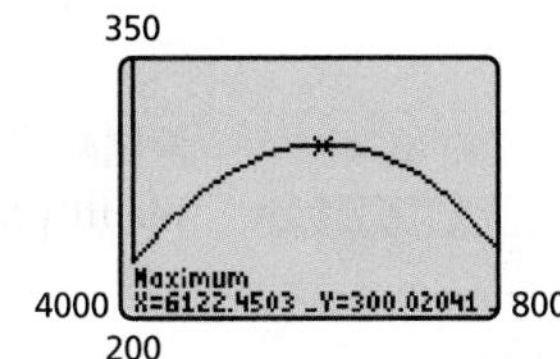

Check Graph the function on a graphing calculator. Use the **maximum** feature under the **CALCULATE** menu to approximate the maximum. The graph supports your answer.

4. The highway mileage m in miles per gallon for a compact car is approximated by $m(s) = -0.025s^2 + 2.45s - 30$, where s is the speed in miles per hour. What is the maximum mileage for this compact car to the nearest tenth of a mile per gallon? What speed results in this mileage? **30.0 mi/gal at 49 mi/h**

THINK AND DISCUSS

1. Explain whether a quadratic function can have both a maximum value and a minimum value.
2. Explain why the value of $f(x) = x^2 + 2x - 1$ increases as the value of x decreases from -1 to -10.

3. **GET ORGANIZED** Copy and complete the graphic organizer. In each box, write the criteria or equation to find each property of the parabola for $f(x) = ax^2 + bx + c$.

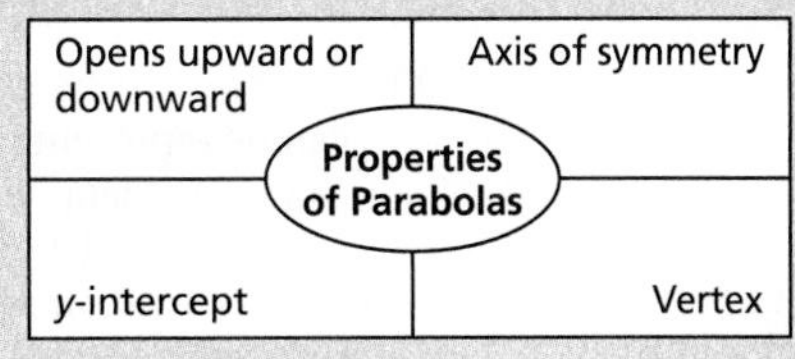

COMMON ERROR ALERT

Because the word *maximum* is often associated with positive amounts, students may incorrectly assume that a quadratic function with a positive leading coefficient should have a maximum. Stress that, in fact, the "positive" parabola has a minimum and the "negative" parabola is the one with the maximum.

Power Presentations with PowerPoint®

Additional Examples

Example 4

The average height h in centimeters of a certain type of grain can be modeled by the function $h(r) = 0.024r^2 - 1.28r + 33.6$, where r is the distance in centimeters between the rows in which the grain is planted. Based on this model, what is the minimum average height of the grain, and what is the row spacing that results in this height?

$\approx$ 16.5 cm; $\approx$ 26.7 cm

Also available on transparency

INTERVENTION
Questioning Strategies

EXAMPLE 4

- How do you use the values of a and b to find the vertex?

3 Close

Summarize

Show students equivalent quadratic functions in both standard form and vertex form, such as $f(x) = 2x^2 - 4x + 6$ and $f(x) = 2(x - 1)^2 + 4$. Review how to use each form to determine the y-intercept (6), axis of symmetry $(x = 1)$, vertex $((1, 4))$, and maximum/minimum value (min: 4). Use a graph to check.

ONGOING ASSESSMENT and INTERVENTION

Diagnose Before **the Lesson**
5-2 Warm Up, TE p. 323

Monitor During **the Lesson**
Check It Out! Exercises, SE pp. 323–327
Questioning Strategies, TE pp. 324, 326–327

Assess After **the Lesson**
5-2 Lesson Quiz, TE p. 330
Alternative Assessment, TE p. 330

Answers to *Think and Discuss*

Possible answers:

1. No; quadratic functions open in 1 direction. If they open upward, they have a minimum value. If they open downward, they have a maximum value.
2. The value of x^2 increases faster than the value of $2x$ decreases.
3. See p. A6.

5-2 Exercises

go.hrw.com
Homework Help Online
KEYWORD: MB7 5-2
Parent Resources Online
KEYWORD: MB7 Parent

GUIDED PRACTICE

1. **Vocabulary** If the graph of a quadratic function opens upward, the y-value of the vertex is a __?__ value. (*maximum* or *minimum*) **minimum**

SEE EXAMPLE 1 p. 323

Identify the axis of symmetry for the graph of each function.

2. $f(x) = -2(x - 2)^2 - 4$ **$x = 2$**
3. $g(x) = 3x^2 + 4$ **$x = 0$**
4. $h(x) = (x + 5)^2$ **$x = -5$**

SEE EXAMPLE 2 p. 324

For each function, (a) determine whether the graph opens upward or downward, (b) find the axis of symmetry, (c) find the vertex, (d) find the y-intercept, and (e) graph the function.

5. $f(x) = -x^2 - 2x - 8$
6. $g(x) = x^2 - 3x + 2$
7. $h(x) = 4x - x^2 - 1$

SEE EXAMPLE 3 p. 326

Find the minimum or maximum value of each function. Then state the domain and range of the function.

8. $f(x) = x^2 - 1$
9. $g(x) = -x^2 + 3x - 2$
10. $h(x) = -16x^2 + 32x + 4$

SEE EXAMPLE 4 p. 327

11. **Sports** The path of a soccer ball is modeled by the function $h(x) = -0.005x^2 + 0.25x$, where h is the height in meters and x is the horizontal distance that the ball travels in meters. What is the maximum height that the ball reaches? **3.125 m**

PRACTICE AND PROBLEM SOLVING

Independent Practice

For Exercises	See Example
12–14	1
15–23	2
24–29	3
30	4

Extra Practice
Skills Practice p. S12
Application Practice p. S36

Identify the axis of symmetry for the graph of each function.

12. $f(x) = -x^2 + 4$ **$x = 0$**
13. $g(x) = (x - 1)^2$ **$x = 1$**
14. $h(x) = 2(x + 1)^2 - 3$ **$x = -1$**

For each function, (a) determine whether the graph opens upward or downward, (b) find the axis of symmetry, (c) find the vertex, (d) find the y-intercept, and (e) graph the function.

15. $f(x) = x^2 + x - 2$
16. $g(x) = -3x^2 + 6x$
17. $h(x) = 0.5x^2 - 2x - 4$
18. $f(x) = -2x^2 + 8x + 5$
19. $g(x) = 3x^2 + 2x - 8$
20. $h(x) = 2x - 1 + x^2$
21. $f(x) = -(2 + x^2)$
22. $g(x) = 0.5x^2 + 3x - 5$
23. $h(x) = \frac{1}{4}x^2 + x + 2$

Find the minimum or maximum value of each function. Then state the domain and range of the function.

24. $f(x) = -2x^2 + 7x - 3$
25. $g(x) = 6x - x^2$
26. $h(x) = x^2 - 4x + 3$
27. $f(x) = -\frac{1}{2}x^2 - 4$
28. $g(x) = -x^2 - 6x + 1$
29. $h(x) = x^2 + 8x + 16$

30. **Weather** The daily high temperature in Death Valley, California, in 2003 can be modeled by $T(d) = -0.0018d^2 + 0.657d + 50.95$, where T is temperature in degrees Fahrenheit and d is the day of the year. What was the maximum temperature in 2003 to the nearest degree? **111°F**

31. **Sports** The height of a golf ball over time can be represented by a quadratic function. Graph the data in the table. What is the maximum height that the ball will reach? Explain your answer in terms of the axis of symmetry and vertex of the graph.

Golf Ball Height

Time (s)	0	0.5	1	2	3
Height (ft)	0	28	48	64	48

Assignment Guide

Assign *Guided Practice* exercises as necessary.

If you finished Examples **1–2**
- **Basic** 12–23
- **Average** 12–23
- **Advanced** 12–23, 47

If you finished Examples **1–4**
- **Basic** 12–38, 40–46, 51–62
- **Average** 12–47, 51–62
- **Advanced** 12–62

Homework Quick Check
Quickly check key concepts.
Exercises: 12, 16, 24, 30, 31

Answers

5–7. For graphs, see p. A27.
5. downward; $x = -1$; $(-1, -7)$; -8
6. upward; $x = \frac{3}{2}$; $\left(\frac{3}{2}, -\frac{1}{4}\right)$; 2
7. downward; $x = 2$; $(2, 3)$; -1
8. min $= -1$; D: $\mathbb{R}$; R: $\{y \mid y \geq -1\}$
9. max $= \frac{1}{4}$; D: $\mathbb{R}$; R: $\left\{y \mid y \leq \frac{1}{4}\right\}$
10. max $= 20$; D: $\mathbb{R}$; R: $\{y \mid y \leq 20\}$

15–18. For graphs, see p. A27.
15. upward; $x = -\frac{1}{2}$; $\left(-\frac{1}{2}, -\frac{9}{4}\right)$; -2
16. downward; $x = 1$; $(1, 3)$; 0
17. upward; $x = 2$; $(2, -6)$; -4
18. downward; $x = 2$; $(2, 13)$; 5

19–29, 31. See p. A27.

State Resources

5-2 READING STRATEGIES

The graph of a quadratic function, $f(x) = ax^2 + bx + c$, is a parabola that can open upward or downward. This tells you whether the function has a **minimum** or a **maximum**.

Minimum	Maximum
$a > 0$, the parabola opens up. The function has a minimum.	$a < 0$, the parabola opens down. The function has a maximum.
The y-value of the vertex is the function's minimum.	The y-value of the vertex is the function's maximum.

The x-value of the vertex is $-\frac{b}{2a}$. Substitute this value of x in the quadratic function to get its maximum or minimum value.

Answer each question.

1. Circle the function(s) whose graph opens upward. Draw a rectangle around those that open downward.
   $f(x) = 2x^2 - 3$ $g(x) = -x^2 + x + 1$ $h(x) = \frac{1}{2}x^2 + x + 3$ $k(x) = -6x^2 - x - 5$
2. For the function $f(x) = 3x^2 + 2x + 4$:
   a. What conclusion can you draw about the graph of the function?
   Possible answer: Since $a > 0$, the parabola opens upward so the vertex is at the lowest point. Therefore, the function has a minimum.
   b. Describe how to find the minimum or maximum of the function.
   Possible answer: Use the formula $x = -\frac{b}{2a}$ to find the x-value of the vertex. Then substitute the x-value in the function to find the y-value, which is the minimum.
3. Can a quadratic function have both a maximum and a minimum? Explain.
   No; a quadratic function opens either upward or downward, not both.
4. The vertex of a function $g(x)$ is at $(3, -5)$. The function opens downward. What is the maximum value of this function?
   Since the function opens downward, the vertex is the highest point. The y-value of the vertex is the maximum of the function. The maximum is -5.

5-2 RETEACH

You can use the properties of a parabola to graph a quadratic function in standard form: $f(x) = ax^2 + bx + c$, $a \neq 0$.

Property	Example: $f(x) = -x^2 - 2x + 2$
$a > 0$: opens upward $a < 0$: opens downward	$a = -1$, $b = -2$, $c = 2$ $a < 0$, so parabola opens downward.
Axis of symmetry: $x = -\frac{b}{2a}$	Axis of symmetry: $x = -\frac{b}{2a} = -\frac{(-2)}{2(-1)} = -1$
Vertex: $\left(-\frac{b}{2a}, f\left(-\frac{b}{2a}\right)\right)$	$f\left(-\frac{b}{2a}\right) = f(-1) = -1(-1)^2 - 2(-1) + 2 = 3$ Vertex: $(-1, 3)$
y-intercept: c	y-intercept is 2, so $(0, 2)$ is a point on the graph.

To graph $f(x) = -x^2 - 2x + 2$:
1. Plot vertex.
2. Sketch axis of symmetry through vertex.
3. Plot y-intercept.
4. Use symmetry to plot $(-2, 2)$.
5. Sketch graph.

Use the properties of a parabola to graph $f(x) = x^2 - 4x + 3$.

1. $a =$ 1, $b =$ −4, $c =$ 3
2. The graph opens Upward.
3. Axis of symmetry: $x = -\frac{b}{2a} =$ $x = 2$
4. $f\left(-\frac{b}{2a}\right) =$ $f(2) = -1$
5. Vertex: $(2, -1)$
6. y-intercept: 3

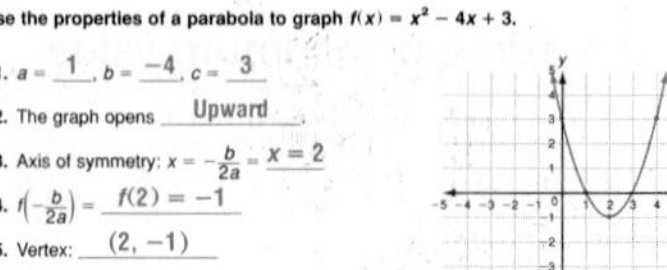

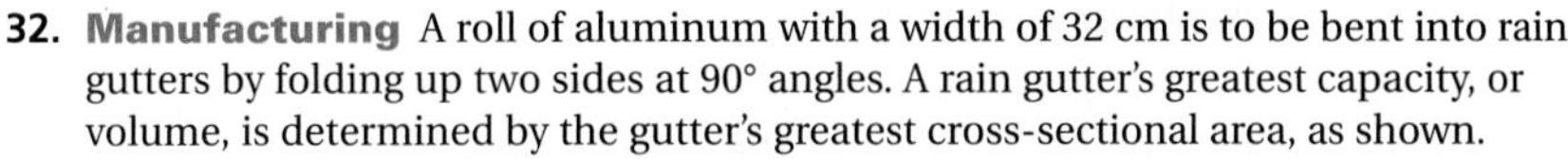

32. **Manufacturing** A roll of aluminum with a width of 32 cm is to be bent into rain gutters by folding up two sides at 90° angles. A rain gutter's greatest capacity, or volume, is determined by the gutter's greatest cross-sectional area, as shown.

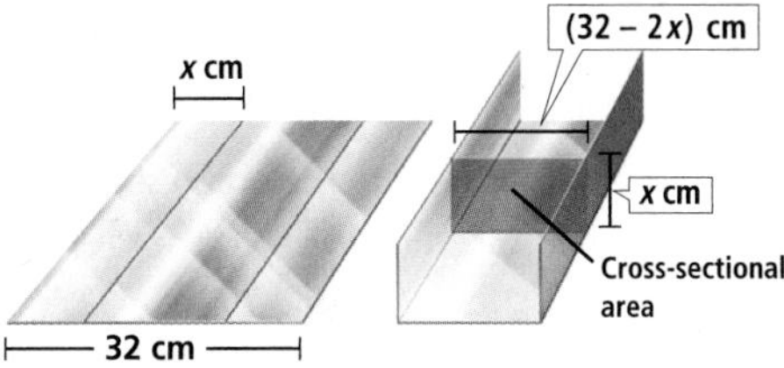

   a. Write a function C to describe the cross-sectional area in terms of the width of the bend x.
   b. Make a table, and graph the function.
   c. Identify the meaningful domain and range of the function.
   d. Find the value of x that maximizes the cross-sectional area. **8 cm**

LINK Biology

Spittlebugs are insects that feed on the sap of plants. Young spittlebug larvae use sap to produce a layer of bubbles around themselves. The bubbles help to keep the larvae from drying out and may protect them from predators.

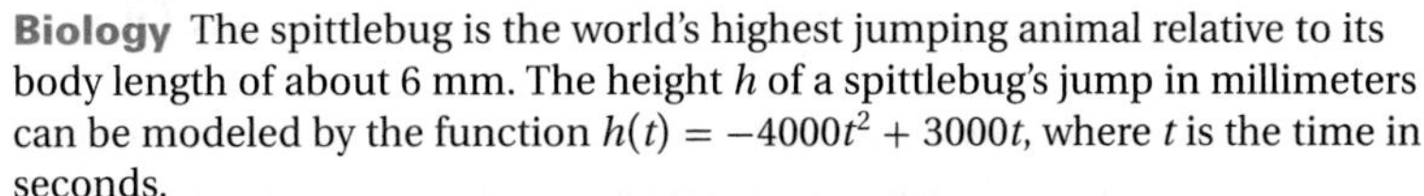

33. **Biology** The spittlebug is the world's highest jumping animal relative to its body length of about 6 mm. The height h of a spittlebug's jump in millimeters can be modeled by the function $h(t) = -4000t^2 + 3000t$, where t is the time in seconds.
   a. What is the maximum height that the spittlebug will reach? **562.5 mm**
   b. What is the ratio of a spittlebug's maximum jumping height to its body length? In the best human jumpers, this ratio is about 1.38. Compare the ratio for spittlebugs with the ratio for the best human jumpers.
   c. **What if...?** Suppose humans had the same ratio of maximum jumping height to body length as spittlebugs. How high would a person with a height of 1.8 m be able to jump? **168.75 m**

34. **Gardening** The function $A(x) = x(10 - x)$ describes the area A of a rectangular flower garden, where x is its width in yards. What is the maximum area of the garden? **25 yd²**

Graphing Calculator Once you have graphed a function, the graphing calculator can automatically find the minimum or maximum value. From the **CALC** menu, choose the **minimum** or **maximum** feature.

Use a graphing calculator to find the approximate minimum or maximum value of each function. **35. min ≈ −3.029771 36. max ≈ 13.178533**

35. $f(x) = 5.23x^2 - 4.84x - 1.91$
36. $g(x) = -12.8x^2 + 8.73x + 11.69$

37. min ≈ −1.253333
38. max ≈ 5.3715

37. $h(x) = \frac{1}{12}x^2 - \frac{4}{5}x + \frac{2}{3}$
38. $j(x) = -\frac{5}{3}x^2 + \frac{9}{10}x + \frac{21}{4}$

39. **Critical Thinking** Suppose you are given a parabola with two points that have the same y-value, such as $(-7, 11)$ and $(3, 11)$. Explain how to find the equation for the axis of symmetry of this parabola, and then determine this equation.

40. **Write About It** Can a maximum value for a quadratic function be negative? Can a minimum value for a quadratic function be positive? Explain by using examples.

MULTI-STEP TEST PREP

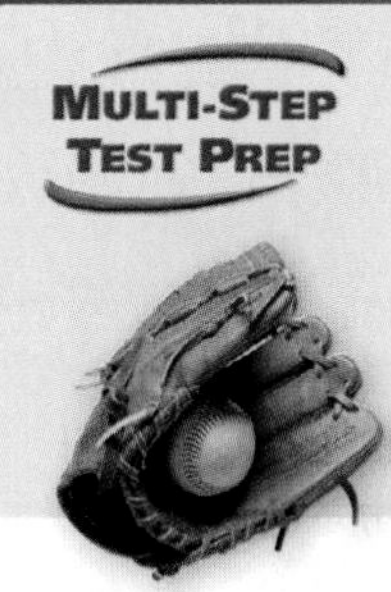

41. This problem will prepare you for the Multi-Step Test Prep on page 364.

   A baseball is thrown with a vertical velocity of 50 ft/s from an initial height of 6 ft. The height h in feet of the baseball can be modeled by $h(t) = -16t^2 + 50t + 6$, where t is the time in seconds since the ball was thrown.
   a. Approximately how many seconds does it take the ball to reach its maximum height? **about 1.6 s**
   b. What is the maximum height that the ball reaches? **about 45 ft**

COMMON ERROR ALERT

In **Exercise 30,** students may give as their answer the value of d at which the maximum temperature occurs rather than the maximum temperature itself. Remind students that once they find the d-value of the vertex, they must substitute this value into the function to find the maximum value of T.

MULTI-STEP TEST PREP **Exercise 41** involves finding the vertex of a quadratic function representing a baseball's height. This exercise prepares students for the Multi-Step Test Prep on page 364.

Answers

32a. $C(x) = x(32 - 2x)$

b.

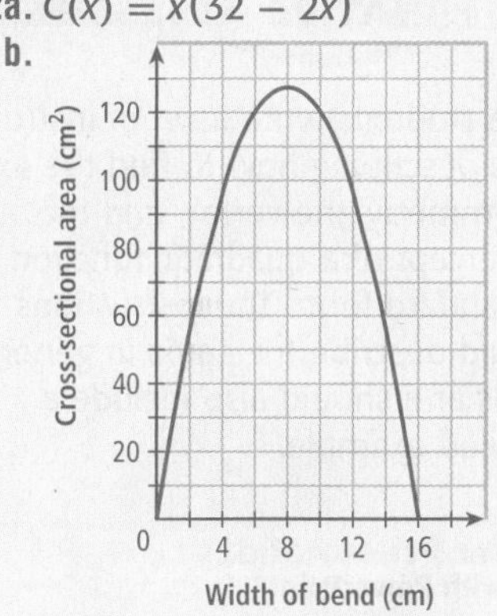

c. The meaningful domain is $0 \le x \le 16$ because neither the width nor the area can be negative. The meaningful range is $0 \le y \le 128$ because the area cannot be negative.

33b. 93.75 to 1; possible answer: the ratio for spittlebugs is more than 67 times as great as the ratio for humans.

39–40. See p. A28.

5-2 PROBLEM SOLVING

Kim wants to buy a used car with good gas mileage. He knows that the miles per gallon, or mileage, varies according to various factors, including the speed. He finds that highway mileage for the make and model he wants can be approximated by the function $f(s) = -0.03s^2 + 2.4s - 30$, where s is the speed in miles per hour. He wants to graph this function to estimate possible gas mileages at various speeds.

1. Determine whether the graph opens upward or downward. $a < 0$, so the graph opens downward.
2. Identify the axis of symmetry for the graph of the function. $x = 40$
3. Find the y-intercept. −30
4. Find the vertex. (40, 18)
5. Graph the function.
6. a. Does the curve have a maximum or a minimum value? Maximum
   b. What is the value of the y-coordinate at the maximum or minimum? 18
   c. Explain what this point means in terms of gas mileage. Possible answer: 18 miles per gallon is the highest gas mileage that this car will achieve. That occurs at a speed of 40 miles per hour.

A ball is hit into the air from a height of 4 feet. The function $g(t) = -16t^2 + 120t + 4$ can be used to model the height of the ball where t is the time in seconds after the ball is hit. Choose the letter for the best answer.

7. About how long is the ball in the air?
   A 3.5 seconds
   B 3.75 seconds
   C 7 seconds
   (D) 7.5 seconds
8. What is the maximum height the ball reaches?
   A 108 feet
   B 124 feet
   (C) 229 feet
   D 394 feet

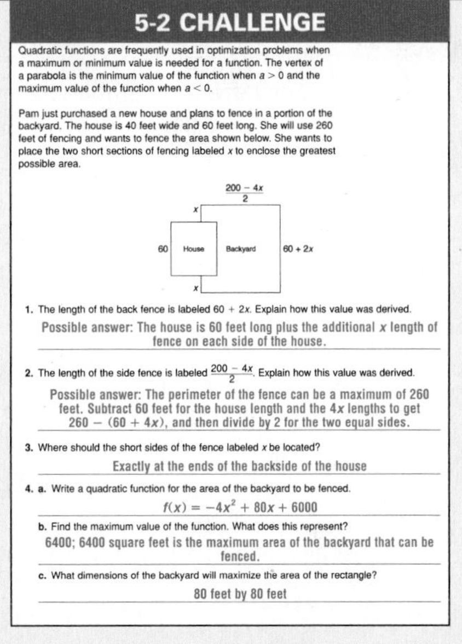

5-2 CHALLENGE

Quadratic functions are frequently used in optimization problems when a maximum or minimum value is needed for a function. The vertex of a parabola is the minimum value of the function when $a > 0$ and the maximum value of the function when $a < 0$.

Pam just purchased a new house and plans to fence in a portion of the backyard. The house is 40 feet wide and 60 feet long. She will use 260 feet of fencing and wants to fence the area shown below. She wants to place the two short sections of fencing labeled x to enclose the greatest possible area.

1. The length of the back fence is labeled $60 + 2x$. Explain how this value was derived. Possible answer: The house is 60 feet long plus the additional x length of fence on each side of the house.
2. The length of the side fence is labeled $\frac{200 - 4x}{2}$. Explain how this value was derived. Possible answer: The perimeter of the fence can be a maximum of 260 feet. Subtract 60 feet for the house length and the $4x$ lengths to get $260 - (60 + 4x)$, and then divide by 2 for the two equal sides.
3. Where should the short sides of the fence labeled x be located? Exactly at the ends of the backside of the house
4. a. Write a quadratic function for the area of the backyard to be fenced. $f(x) = -4x^2 + 80x + 6000$
   b. Find the maximum value of the function. What does this represent? 6400; 6400 square feet is the maximum area of the backyard that can be fenced.
   c. What dimensions of the backyard will maximize the area of the rectangle? 80 feet by 80 feet

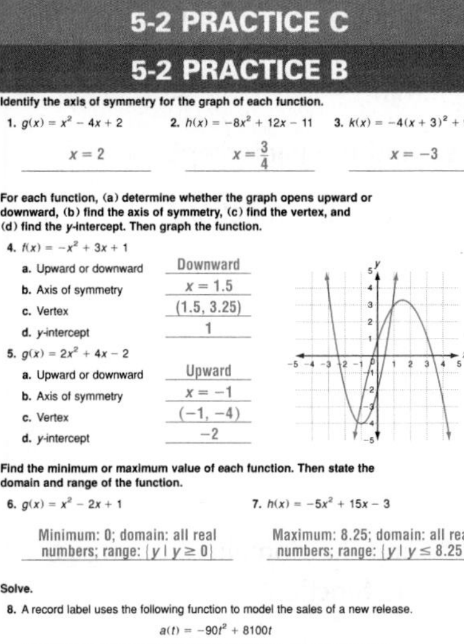

5-2 PRACTICE A
5-2 PRACTICE C
5-2 PRACTICE B

Identify the axis of symmetry for the graph of each function.

1. $g(x) = x^2 - 4x + 2$ $x = 2$
2. $h(x) = -8x^2 + 12x - 11$ $x = \frac{3}{4}$
3. $k(x) = -4(x + 3)^2 + 9$ $x = -3$

For each function, (a) determine whether the graph opens upward or downward, (b) find the axis of symmetry, (c) find the vertex, and (d) find the y-intercept. Then graph the function.

4. $f(x) = -x^2 + 3x + 1$
   a. Upward or downward: Downward
   b. Axis of symmetry: $x = 1.5$
   c. Vertex: (1.5, 3.25)
   d. y-intercept: 1
5. $g(x) = 2x^2 + 4x - 2$
   a. Upward or downward: Upward
   b. Axis of symmetry: $x = -1$
   c. Vertex: (−1, −4)
   d. y-intercept: −2

Find the minimum or maximum value of each function. Then state the domain and range of the function.

6. $g(x) = x^2 - 2x + 1$ Minimum: 0; domain: all real numbers; range: $\{y \mid y \ge 0\}$
7. $h(x) = -5x^2 + 15x - 3$ Maximum: 8.25; domain: all real numbers; range: $\{y \mid y \le 8.25\}$

Solve.

8. A record label uses the following function to model the sales of a new release.

$$a(t) = -90t^2 + 8100t$$

The number of albums sold is a function of time, t, in days. On which day were the most albums sold? What is the maximum number of albums sold on that day? Day 45; 182,250 records

TEST PREP DOCTOR In **Exercise 43,** students who chose **H** may have neglected to consider whether the parabola opens upward or downward. Students who chose **J** may have confused the rules for *vertex form* and *standard form*.

Journal

Have students describe the process they would use to determine the minimum or maximum value of a quadratic function in standard form.

ALTERNATIVE ASSESSMENT

Have students write a set of instructions describing how to find the axis of symmetry, the vertex, and the *y*-intercept of a quadratic function in standard form. The instructions should describe the steps in general terms and should also include a detailed example.

Power Presentations with PowerPoint®

5-2 Lesson Quiz

Consider the function $f(x) = 2x^2 + 6x - 7$.

1. Determine whether the graph opens upward or downward.
   upward
2. Find the axis of symmetry.
   $x = -1.5$
3. Find the vertex.
   $(-1.5, -11.5)$
4. Identify the maximum or minimum value of the function.
   min.: -11.5
5. Find the *y*-intercept. -7
6. Graph the function.

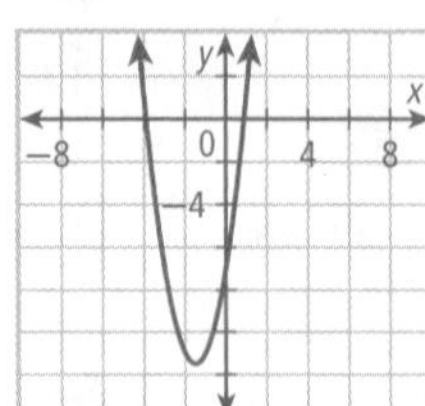

7. Find the domain and range of the function.

   D: $\mathbb{R}$; R: $\{y \mid y \geq -11.5\}$

Also available on transparency

TEST PREP

Use the graph for exercises 42 and 43.

42. What is the range of the function graphed?
    (A) All real numbers (B) $y \geq -2$ (C) $y \leq 2$ (D) $-2 \leq y \leq 2$
43. The graph shown represents which quadratic function?
    (F) $f(x) = x^2 + 2x - 2$
    (G) $f(x) = -x^2 + 4x - 2$
    (H) $f(x) = x^2 - 4x - 2$
    (J) $f(x) = -x^2 - 2x + 2$
44. Which of the following is NOT true of the graph of the function $f(x) = -x^2 - 6x + 5$?
    (A) Its vertex is at $(-3, 14)$.
    (B) Its axis of symmetry is $x = 14$.
    (C) Its maximum value is 14.
    (D) Its *y*-intercept is 5.
45. Which equation represents the axis of symmetry for $f(x) = 2x^2 - 4x + 5$?
    (F) $x = -4$ (G) $x = 1$ (H) $x = 2$ (J) $x = 5$
46. **Short Response** Explain how to find the maximum value or minimum value of a quadratic function such as $f(x) = -x^2 - 8x + 4$.

CHALLENGE AND EXTEND

47. Write the equations in standard form for two quadratic functions that have the same vertex but open in different directions.
48. The graph of a quadratic function passes through the point $(-5, 8)$, and its axis of symmetry is $x = 3$.
    a. What are the coordinates of another point on the graph of the function? Explain how you determined your answer.
    b. Can you determine whether the graph of the function opens upward or downward? Explain.
49. **Critical Thinking** What conclusions can you make about the axis of symmetry and the vertex of a quadratic function of the form $f(x) = ax^2 + c$?
50. **Critical Thinking** Given the quadratic function f and the fact that $f(-1) = f(2)$, how can you find the axis of symmetry of this function?

SPIRAL REVIEW

59. $y + 4 = 3(x - 1)$ **60.** $y - 5 = -6(x + 3)$

Simplify each expression. *(Lesson 1-3)*

51. $\sqrt{40} \cdot \sqrt{180}$ $60\sqrt{2}$
52. $2\sqrt{8} \cdot 4\sqrt{3}$ $16\sqrt{6}$
53. $\sqrt{54} \div \sqrt{30}$ $\frac{3\sqrt{5}}{5}$
54. $\sqrt{304}$ $4\sqrt{19}$

For each function, evaluate $f(0)$, $f\left(\frac{1}{2}\right)$, and $f(-2)$. *(Lesson 1-7)*

55. $f(x) = (x - 3)^2 + 1$ $10; \frac{29}{4}; 26$
56. $g(x) = 2\left(x - \frac{1}{2}\right)^2$ $\frac{1}{2}; 0; \frac{25}{2}$
57. $f(x) = -4(x + 5)$ $-20; -22; -12$
58. $g(x) = x^3 - 4x + 8$ $8; \frac{49}{8}; 8$

Write the equation of each line with the given properties. *(Lesson 2-4)*

59. a slope of 3 passing through $(1, -4)$
60. passing through $(-3, 5)$ and $(-1, -7)$
61. a slope of -2 passing through $(3, 5)$ $y - 5 = -2(x - 3)$
62. passing through $(4, 6)$ and $(-2, 1)$ $y - 6 = \frac{5}{6}(x - 4)$

Answers

46. Because a is negative, the graph will open downward and have a maximum value. To find the maximum value, first find the *x*-value of the vertex: $x = \frac{-b}{2a} = \frac{-(-8)}{2(-1)} = -4$. Then evaluate the function for $x = -4$: $f(-4) = -(-4)^2 - 8(-4) + 4 = 20$. The maximum value is 20.
47. Possible answer: $f(x) = x^2 + 2x + 4$; $g(x) = -x^2 - 2x + 2$
48a. $(11, 8)$; possible answer: the point $(-5, 8)$ is 8 units left of the axis of symmetry. The graph of the quadratic function must also pass through a point that is 8 units right of the axis of symmetry and has the same *y*-value as $(-5, 8)$. This point has coordinates $(11, 8)$.
b. No; possible answer: you would need to know the coordinates of at least one other point on the function's graph to determine whether it opens upward or downward.
49. Possible answer: The function has no *x*-term, so $b = 0$. Therefore, the axis of symmetry is $x = 0$, and the vertex is $(0, c)$.
50. See p. A28.
59. $y + 4 = 3(x - 1)$.
60. $y - 5 = -6(x + 3)$.

Factoring Quadratic Expressions

See Skills Bank page S67

Review the methods of factoring quadratic expressions in the examples below. Recall that the standard form of a quadratic expression is $ax^2 + bx + c$.

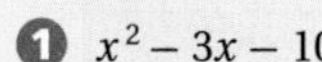

Examples

Factor each expression.

1 $x^2 - 3x - 10$

Because $a = 1$, use a table to find the factors of -10 that have a sum of -3. These factors are 2 and -5.

Factors of -10	Sum
-2 and 5	3 ✗
-1 and 10	9 ✗
1 and -10	-9 ✗
2 and -5	-3 ✓

Rewrite the expression as a product of binomial factors with 2 and -5 as constants.

$$x^2 - 3x - 10 = (x + 2)(x - 5)$$

Check your answer by multiplying.

$$(x + 2)(x - 5) = x^2 - 5x + 2x - 10$$
$$= x^2 - 3x - 10 \checkmark$$

2 $6x^2 - 15x$

Find the greatest common factor (GCF) of the terms.

$$6x^2 = 2 \cdot 3 \cdot x \cdot x$$
$$15x = 3 \cdot 5 \cdot x \quad \textit{The GCF is 3x.}$$

Factor $3x$ from both terms.

$$6x^2 - 15x = 3x(2x - 5)$$

Check your answer by multiplying.

$$3x(2x - 5) = 3x(2x) - 3x(5)$$
$$= 6x^2 - 15x \checkmark$$

3 $-x^2 + 3x + 4$

Because a is negative, factor out -1.

$$-x^2 + 3x + 4 = -1(x^2 - 3x - 4)$$

Use the method from Example 1 to factor the expression in parentheses.

$$-(x^2 - 3x - 4) = -(x + 1)(x - 4)$$

Check your answer by multiplying.

$$-(x + 1)(x - 4) = -(x^2 - 3x - 4)$$
$$= -x^2 + 3x + 4 \checkmark$$

Try This

Factor each expression.

1. $4x^2 + 10x$
2. $16x - 2x^2$
3. $x^2 - 6x + 8$
4. $x^2 + 4x + 3$
5. $x^2 - 8x + 15$
6. $x^2 + 10x - 24$
7. $x^2 - x - 56$
8. $x^2 - 6x + 9$
9. $x^2 + 48x - 100$
10. $-x^2 + 12x - 32$
11. $-x^2 + x + 20$
12. $-x^2 - 14x - 13$
13. $4x^2 + 6x$
14. $x^2 + 14x + 24$
15. $x^2 - 16$
16. $2x^2 - x - 3$
17. $3x^2 + 16x + 5$
18. $2x^2 - 9x + 7$

Answers to *Try This*

1. $2x(2x + 5)$
2. $2x(8 - x)$
3. $(x - 4)(x - 2)$
4. $(x + 3)(x + 1)$
5. $(x - 3)(x - 5)$
6. $(x + 12)(x - 2)$
7. $(x + 7)(x - 8)$
8. $(x - 3)^2$
9. $(x + 50)(x - 2)$
10. $-(x - 8)(x - 4)$
11. $-(x - 5)(x + 4)$
12. $-(x + 13)(x + 1)$
13. $2x(2x + 3)$
14. $(x + 2)(x + 12)$
15. $(x - 4)(x + 4)$
16. $(2x - 3)(x + 1)$
17. $(3x + 1)(x + 5)$
18. $(2x - 7)(x - 1)$

Organizer

See Skills Bank page S67

Pacing:
Traditional $\frac{1}{2}$ day
Block $\frac{1}{4}$ day

Objective: Review the methods of factoring quadratic expressions.

Online Edition

Countdown to Testing Week 10

Teach

Remember

Students review factoring of quadratic expressions for which at least one factor is a binomial.

INTERVENTION For additional review and practice on factoring, see Skills Bank page S67.

Reading Math Make sure students know that a binomial factor is a factor with two terms, such as $3x + 5$. Point out that the prefix *bi-* means *two*.

ENGLISH LANGUAGE LEARNERS

Close

Assess

Have students explain how to factor the expression $x^2 - 2x - 15$ and describe how they can check their answer. $(x + 3)(x - 5)$

State Resources

Organizer

Use with Lesson 5-3

Pacing:

Traditional $\frac{1}{2}$ day

Block $\frac{1}{4}$ day

Objective: Use a graphing calculator to explore the relationship between the linear factors of a quadratic function and its zeros.

Materials: graphing calculator

Online Edition

Graphing Calculator, TechKeys

Countdown to Testing Week 11

Resources

Technology Lab Activities

5-3 Lab Recording Sheet

Teach

Discuss

Have students graph a quadratic function and its linear factors. Discuss what students can learn about the function from its factors.

Close

Key Concept

The *x*-intercepts and axis of symmetry of a quadratic function can be determined from its linear factors.

Assessment

Journal Have students describe a method they could use to determine the *x*-intercepts of a quadratic function without graphing it.

State Resources

go.hrw.com
State Resources Online
KEYWORD: MB7 Resources

5-3

Explore Graphs and Factors

You can use graphs and linear factors to find the *x*-intercepts of a parabola.

Use with Lesson 5-3

go.hrw.com
Lab Resources Online
KEYWORD: MB7 Lab5

Activity

Graph the lines $y = x + 4$ and $y = x - 2$.

1. Press **Y=**, and enter **X + 4** for **Y1** and **X − 2** for **Y2**. Graph the functions in the square window by pressing **ZOOM** and choosing **5 : ZSquare**.
2. Identify the *x*-intercept of each line. The *x*-intercepts are −4 and 2.
3. Find the *x*-value halfway between the two *x*-intercepts. This *x*-value is the average of the *x*-intercepts: $\frac{-4+2}{2} = -1$.

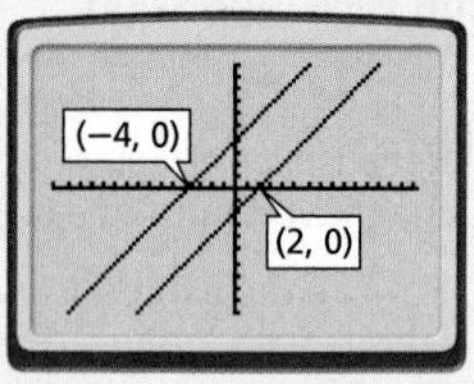

(−4, 0)
(2, 0)

Graph the quadratic function $y = (x + 4)(x - 2)$, which is the product of the two linear factors graphed above.

4. Press **Y=** and enter **(X + 4)(X − 2)** for **Y3**. Press **GRAPH**.
5. Identify the *x*-intercepts of the parabola. The *x*-intercepts are −4 and 2. Notice that they are the same as those of the two linear factors.
6. Examine the parabola at $x = -1$ (the *x*-value that is halfway between the *x*-intercepts). The axis of symmetry and the vertex of the parabola occur at this *x*-value.

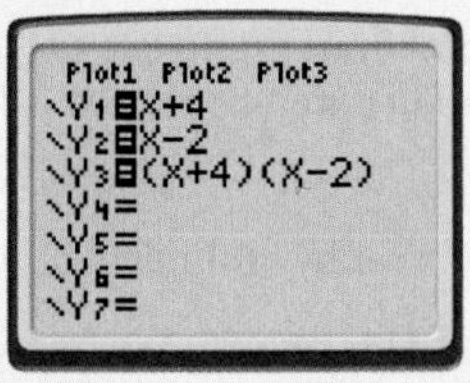

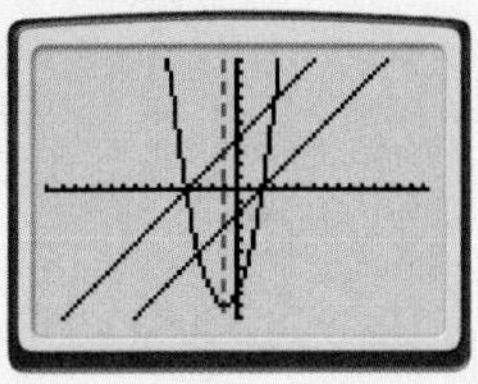

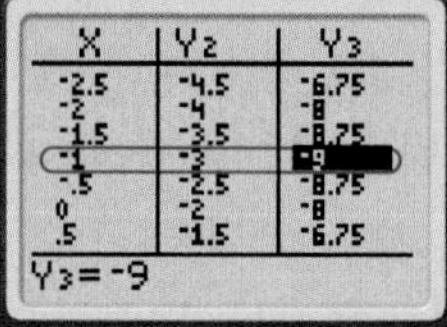

X	Y2	Y3
-2.5	-4.5	-6.75
-2	-4	-8
-1.5	-3.5	-8.75
-1	-3	-9
-.5	-2.5	-8.75
0	-2	-8
.5	-1.5	-6.75

Y3=-9

Try This

Graph each quadratic function and each of its linear factors. Then identify the *x*-intercepts and the axis of symmetry of each parabola.

1. $y = (x - 2)(x - 6)$
2. $y = (x + 3)(x - 1)$
3. $y = (x - 5)(x + 2)$
4. $y = (x + 4)(x - 4)$
5. $y = (x - 5)(x - 5)$
6. $y = (2x - 1)(2x + 3)$
7. **Critical Thinking** Use a graph to determine whether the quadratic function $y = 2x^2 + 5x - 12$ is the product of the linear factors $2x - 3$ and $x + 4$.
8. **Make a Conjecture** Make a conjecture about the linear factors, *x*-intercepts, and axis of symmetry of a quadratic function.

Answers to *Try This*

1.

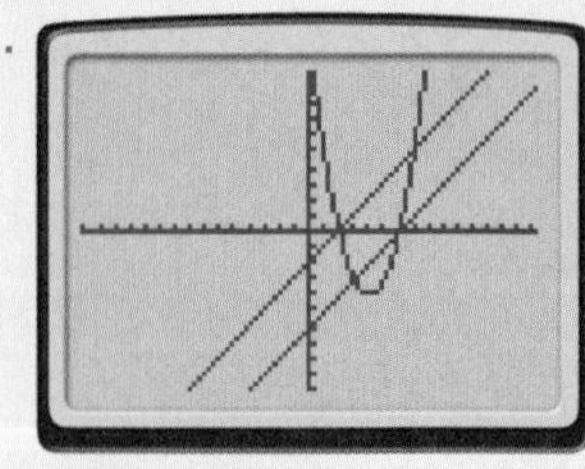

2, 6; $x = 4$

2–7. For calculator screens, see p. A28.

2. −3, 1; $x = -1$
3. 5, −2; $x = \frac{3}{2}$
4. −4, 4; $x = 0$
5. 5; $x = 5$
6. $\frac{1}{2}, -\frac{3}{2}; x = -\frac{1}{2}$
7. yes, because the graphs cross the *x*-axis at the same points.
8. Possible answer: The *x*-intercepts of a quadratic function are the same as the *x*-intercepts of its linear factors. The axis of symmetry is located halfway between the *x*-intercepts.

5-3 Solving Quadratic Equations by Graphing and Factoring

A2.1.1 Find the zeros, domain and range of a function.

Objectives
Solve quadratic equations by graphing or factoring.

Determine a quadratic function from its roots.

Vocabulary
zero of a function
root of an equation
binomial
trinomial

Why learn this?
You can use quadratic functions to model the height of a football, baseball, or soccer ball. (See Example 3.)

When a soccer ball is kicked into the air, how long will the ball take to hit the ground? The height h in feet of the ball after t seconds can be modeled by the quadratic function $h(t) = -16t^2 + 32t$. In this situation, the value of the function represents the height of the soccer ball. When the ball hits the ground, the value of the function is zero.

A **zero of a function** is a value of the input x that makes the output $f(x)$ equal zero. The zeros of a function are the x-intercepts.

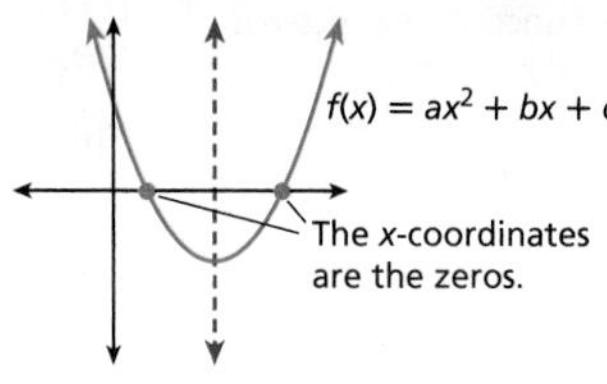

Unlike linear functions, which have no more than one zero, quadratic functions can have two zeros, as shown at right. These zeros are always symmetric about the axis of symmetry.

EXAMPLE 1 **Finding Zeros by Using a Graph or Table**

Find the zeros of $f(x) = x^2 + 2x - 3$ by using a graph and table.

Method 1 Graph the function $f(x) = x^2 + 2x - 3$.

The graph opens upward because $a > 0$. The y-intercept is -3 because $c = -3$.

Find the vertex: $x = -\frac{b}{2a} = -\frac{2}{2(1)} = -1$ *The x-coordinate of the vertex is $-\frac{b}{2a}$.*

Find $f(-1)$: $f(x) = x^2 + 2x - 3$

$f(-1) = (-1)^2 + 2(-1) - 3$ *Substitute −1 for x.*

$f(-1) = -4$

The vertex is $(-1, -4)$.

Plot the vertex and the y-intercept. Use symmetry and a table of values to find additional points.

x	−3	−2	−1	0	1
f(x)	0	−3	−4	−3	0

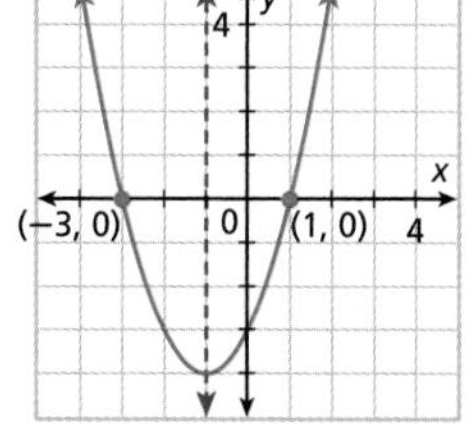

The table and the graph indicate that the zeros are −3 and 1.

Helpful Hint
Recall that for the graph of a quadratic function, *any* pair of points with the same y-value are symmetric about the axis of symmetry.

5-3 Organizer

Pacing: Traditional 1 day
Block $\frac{1}{2}$ day

Objectives: Solve quadratic equations by graphing or factoring.

Determine a quadratic function from its roots.

Algebra Lab
In *Algebra Lab Activities*

Online Edition
Tutorial Videos, Graphing Calculator, TechKeys

Countdown to Testing Week 11

Power Presentations with PowerPoint®

Warm Up

Find the x-intercept of each function.

1. $f(x) = -3x + 9$ 3
2. $f(x) = 6x + 4$ $-\frac{2}{3}$

Factor each expression.

3. $3x^2 - 12x$ $3x(x - 4)$
4. $x^2 - 9x + 18$ $(x - 6)(x - 3)$
5. $x^2 - 49$ $(x - 7)(x + 7)$

Also available on transparency

Math Humor

Q: Why did the algebra students throw bottles of hand cream across the classroom?

A: They were investigating projectile lotion.

1 Introduce

EXPLORATION

5-3 Solving Quadratic Equations by Graphing and Factoring

The zero of a function is a value of the input x that makes the output f(x) equal to zero. The factored form of a quadratic function can help you determine its zeros.

1. Complete the table for the function f(x) = (x − 3)(x + 2).

x	−3	−2	−1	0	1	2	3
f(x)							

2. What are the zeros of the function f?
3. Complete the table for the function g(x) = (x − 2)(x + 1).

x	−3	−2	−1	0	1	2	3
g(x)							

4. What are the zeros of the functiong ?

THINK AND DISCUSS

5. **Explain** the relationship between the zeros of a quadratic function and the factored form of the function's rule.
6. **Describe** how to find the zeros of the function h(x) = (x − 1)(x + 2) without making a table or graph.

Motivate

Toss a tennis ball or other small object into the air. Have students use a stopwatch to attempt to determine how long the ball is in the air before it hits the ground. Explain that by making similar measurements, scientists have developed quadratic models that describe the height of thrown objects over time. Tell students that they will be using quadratic models such as these to make predictions.

Explorations and answers are provided in the *Explorations* binder.

State Resources

Power Presentations with PowerPoint®

Additional Examples

Example 1

Find the zeros of $f(x) = x^2 - 6x + 8$ by using a graph and table. 2, 4

Example 2

Find the zeros of each function by factoring.

A. $f(x) = x^2 - 4x - 12$ −2, 6

B. $g(x) = 3x^2 + 18x$ −6, 0

Also available on transparency

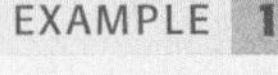

INTERVENTION

Questioning Strategies

EXAMPLE 1

- How can you identify the zeros of a quadratic function from a table? from a graph?

EXAMPLE 2

- How can you use the factored form of a quadratic equation to find the zeros of the related quadratic function?

Technology When the zeros of a function occur at non-integer x-values, using a table to find them can be difficult. Show students that they can also use a graphing calculator to find the zeros by graphing the function and selecting **2:zero** from the **CALCULATE** menu.

Critical Thinking Discuss with students whether there are other product properties similar to the Zero Product Property. Have students demonstrate that there is not a Product Property for 1 by asking them to give examples showing that if $ab = 1$, neither a nor b has to equal 1. Lead students to conclude that the Product Property holds only for 0.

Find the zeros of $f(x) = x^2 + 2x - 3$ by using a graph and table.

Method 2 Use a calculator.

Enter $y = x^2 + 2x - 3$ into a graphing calculator.

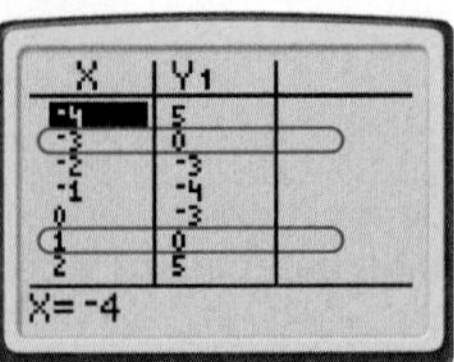

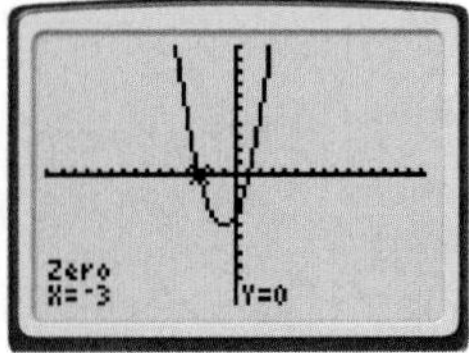

Both the table and the graph show that $y = 0$ at $x = -3$ and $x = 1$. These are the zeros of the function.

1. Find the zeros of $g(x) = -x^2 - 2x + 3$ by using a graph and a table. **−3, 1**

- Functions have *zeros* or *x-intercepts*.
- Equations have *solutions* or *roots*.

You can also find zeros by using algebra. For example, to find the zeros of $f(x) = x^2 + 2x - 3$, you can set the function equal to zero. The solutions to the related equation $x^2 + 2x - 3 = 0$ represent the zeros of the function.

The solutions to a quadratic equation of the form $ax^2 + bx + c = 0$ are *roots*. The **roots of an equation** are the values of the variable that make the equation true.

You can find the roots of some quadratic equations by factoring and applying the Zero Product Property.

Zero Product Property

For all real numbers *a* and *b*,

WORDS	NUMBERS	ALGEBRA
If the product of two quantities equals zero, at least one of the quantities equals zero.	$3(0) = 0$ $0(4) = 0$	If $ab = 0$, then $a = 0$ or $b = 0$.

EXAMPLE 2 **Finding Zeros by Factoring**

Find the zeros of each function by factoring.

A $f(x) = x^2 - 8x + 12$

$x^2 - 8x + 12 = 0$ *Set the function equal to 0.*

$(x - 2)(x - 6) = 0$ *Factor: Find factors of 12 that add to −8.*

$x - 2 = 0$ or $x - 6 = 0$ *Apply the Zero Product Property.*

$x = 2$ or $x = 6$ *Solve each equation.*

Check

$x^2 - 8x + 12 = 0$	
$(2)^2 - 8(2) + 12$	0
$4 - 16 + 12$	0
0	0 ✓

$x^2 - 8x + 12 = 0$	
$(6)^2 - 8(6) + 12$	0
$36 - 48 + 12$	0
0	0 ✓

Substitute each value into the original equation.

2 Teach

Guided Instruction

In this lesson, students will be introduced to two methods of solving quadratic equations: graphing and factoring. Being able to factor is the key to success in this lesson, so be sure that students can factor quadratic trinomials, including the special cases $a^2 - b^2$ and $a^2 + 2ab + b^2$. Point out to students that solving a quadratic equation by graphing uses skills they learned in Lesson 5-1.

Find the zeros of each function by factoring.

B $g(x) = 3x^2 + 12x$

$3x^2 + 12x = 0$	*Set the function equal to 0.*
$3x(x + 4) = 0$	*Factor: The GCF is 3x.*
$3x = 0$ or $x + 4 = 0$	*Apply the Zero Product Property.*
$x = 0$ or $x = -4$	*Solve each equation.*

Check Check algebraically and by graphing.

$3x^2 + 12x = 0$		$3x^2 + 12x = 0$	
$3(0)^2 + 12(0)$	0	$3(-4)^2 + 12(-4)$	0
$0 + 0$	0 ✓	$48 - 48$	0 ✓

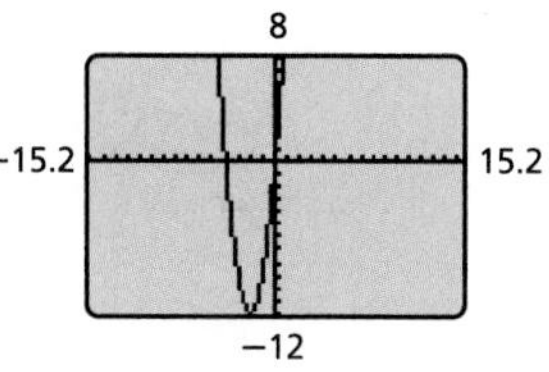

Find the zeros of each function by factoring.

2a. $f(x) = x^2 - 5x - 6$ **−1, 6** **2b.** $g(x) = x^2 - 8x$ **0, 8**

Any object that is thrown or launched into the air, such as a baseball, basketball, or soccer ball, is a *projectile*. The general function that approximates the height h in feet of a projectile on Earth after t seconds is given below.

$$h(t) = -16t^2 + v_0t + h_0$$

Constant due to Earth's gravity in ft/s^2 — Initial vertical velocity in ft/s (at $t = 0$) — Initial height in ft (at $t = 0$)

Note that this model has limitations because it does not account for air resistance, wind, and other real-world factors.

EXAMPLE 3 *Sports Application*

A soccer ball is kicked from ground level with an initial vertical velocity of 32 ft/s. After how many seconds will the ball hit the ground?

$h(t) = -16t^2 + v_0t + h_0$	*Write the general projectile function.*
$h(t) = -16t^2 + 32t + 0$	*Substitute 32 for v_0 and 0 for h_0.*

The ball will hit the ground when its height is zero.

$-16t^2 + 32t = 0$	*Set h(t) equal to 0.*
$-16t(t - 2) = 0$	*Factor: The GCF is −16t.*
$-16t = 0$ or $(t - 2) = 0$	*Apply the Zero Product Property.*
$t = 0$ or $t = 2$	*Solve each equation.*

The ball will hit the ground in 2 seconds. Notice that the height is also zero when $t = 0$, the instant that the ball is kicked.

Check The graph of the function $h(t) = -16t^2 + 32t$ shows its zeros at 0 and 2.

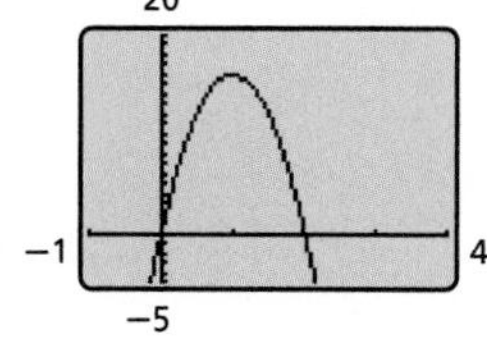

Power Presentations with PowerPoint®

Additional Examples

Example 3

A golf ball is hit from ground level with an initial vertical velocity of 80 ft/s. After how many seconds will the ball hit the ground? after 5 s

Also available on transparency

INTERVENTION

Questioning Strategies

EXAMPLE 3

- How do you know which values to use for v_0 and h_0?
- How do you know which zero of the function to use as your answer?

Inclusion Have students make a note card for each method they have learned for finding the zeros of quadratic functions. Suggest that they describe the steps of the method as well as any advantages or disadvantages that they observe. Students can add to their set of note cards as they learn additional methods later in this chapter.

Reading Math A variable followed by a subscript zero, as in v_0 or h_0, usually indicates an initial value of the variable. The zero indicates the value of the variable when the time t is 0.

Science The projectile function on page 335 is defined in terms of customary units. The corresponding function for metric units is $h(t) = -4.9t^2 + v_0t + h_0$, where t is time in seconds, v_0 is the initial vertical velocity in meters per second, and h_0 is the initial height in meters.

Reaching All Learners

Through Concrete Manipulatives

Students may benefit from using algebra tiles to practice factoring quadratic expressions. For example, show students how to model $x^2 + 6x + 8$ with algebra tiles. Then demonstrate that arranging the tiles in a rectangle models the product $(x + 2)(x + 4)$. Algebra tiles can be found in the Manipulatives Kit (MK).

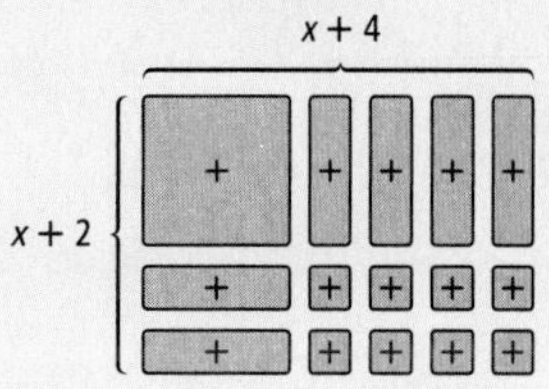

Power Presentations with PowerPoint®

Additional Examples

Example 4

Find the roots of each equation by factoring.

A. $4x^2 = 25$

$-\frac{5}{2}, \frac{5}{2}$

B. $18x^2 = 48x - 32$

$\frac{4}{3}$

Also available on transparency

INTERVENTION

Questioning Strategies

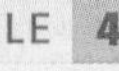

EXAMPLE 4

- What step should you do before you factor the quadratic expressions in these equations?
- How do you factor a difference of squares? a perfect square trinomial?

Teaching Tip **Inclusion** Remind students that they can always check whether they have factored a quadratic expression correctly by multiplying the factors. If the product simplifies to the original quadratic expression, their answer is correct.

CHECK IT OUT! **3.** A football is kicked from ground level with an initial vertical velocity of 48 ft/s. How long is the ball in the air? **3 s**

Quadratic expressions can have one, two, or three terms, such as $-16t^2$, $-16t^2 + 25t$, or $-16t^2 + 25t + 6$. Quadratic expressions with two terms are **binomials**. Quadratic expressions with three terms are **trinomials**. Some quadratic expressions with perfect squares have special factoring rules.

Special Products and Factors	
Difference of Two Squares	**Perfect-Square Trinomial**
$a^2 - b^2 = (a + b)(a - b)$	$a^2 - 2ab + b^2 = (a - b)^2$ $a^2 + 2ab + b^2 = (a + b)^2$

EXAMPLE 4 Finding Roots by Using Special Factors

Find the roots of each equation by factoring.

A $9x^2 = 1$

$9x^2 - 1 = 0$	*Rewrite in standard form.*
$(3x)^2 - (1)^2 = 0$	*Write the left side as $a^2 - b^2$.*
$(3x + 1)(3x - 1) = 0$	*Factor the difference of squares.*
$3x + 1 = 0$ or $3x - 1 = 0$	*Apply the Zero Product Property.*
$x = -\frac{1}{3}$ or $x = \frac{1}{3}$	*Solve each equation.*

Check Graph the related function $f(x) = 9x^2 - 1$ on a graphing calculator. The function appears to have zeros at $-\frac{1}{3}$ and $\frac{1}{3}$.

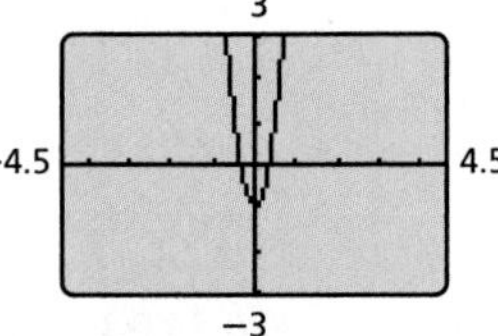

Helpful Hint

A quadratic equation can have two roots that are equal, such as $x = \frac{5}{2}$ and $x = \frac{5}{2}$. Two equal roots are sometimes called a double root.

B $40x = 8x^2 + 50$

$8x^2 - 40x + 50 = 0$	*Rewrite in standard form.*
$2(4x^2 - 20x + 25) = 0$	*Factor. The GCF is 2.*
$4x^2 - 20x + 25 = 0$	*Divide both sides by 2.*
$(2x)^2 - 2(2x)(5) + (5)^2 = 0$	*Write the left side as $a^2 - 2ab + b^2$.*
$(2x - 5)^2 = 0$	*Factor the perfect-square trinomial: $(a - b)^2$.*
$2x - 5 = 0$ or $2x - 5 = 0$	*Apply the Zero Product Property.*
$x = \frac{5}{2}$ or $x = \frac{5}{2}$	*Solve each equation.*

Check Substitute the root $\frac{5}{2}$ into the original equation.

$40x$	$= 8x^2 + 50$
$40\left(\frac{5}{2}\right)$	$8\left(\frac{5}{2}\right)^2 + 50$
100	100 ✓

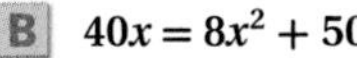

CHECK IT OUT! **Find the roots of each equation by factoring.**

4a. $x^2 - 4x = -4$ **2**

4b. $25x^2 = 9$ $-\frac{3}{5}, \frac{3}{5}$

If you know the zeros of a function, you can work backward to write a rule for the function.

EXAMPLE 5 **Using Zeros to Write Function Rules**

Write a quadratic function in standard form with zeros 2 and −1.

$x = 2$ or $x = -1$	*Write the zeros as solutions for two equations.*
$x - 2 = 0$ or $x + 1 = 0$	*Rewrite each equation so that it equals 0.*
$(x - 2)(x + 1) = 0$	*Apply the converse of the Zero Product Property to write a product that equals 0.*
$x^2 - x - 2 = 0$	*Multiply the binomials.*
$f(x) = x^2 - x - 2$	*Replace 0 with f(x).*

Check Graph the function $f(x) = x^2 - x - 2$ on a calculator. The graph shows the original zeros of 2 and −1.

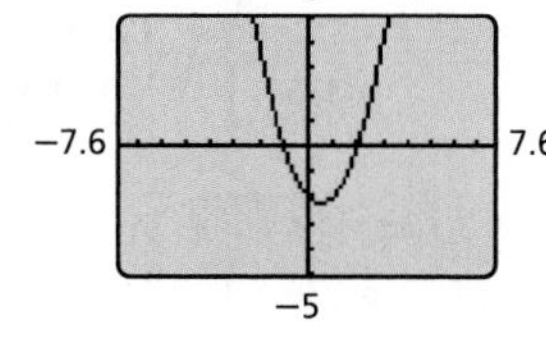

5. Write a quadratic function in standard form with zeros 5 and −5. **Possible answer: $f(x) = x^2 - 25$**

Note that there are many quadratic functions with the same zeros. For example, the functions $f(x) = x^2 - x - 2$, $g(x) = -x^2 + x + 2$, and $h(x) = 2x^2 - 2x - 4$ all have zeros at 2 and −1.

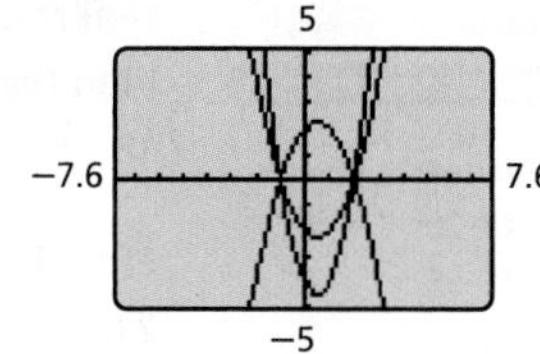

THINK AND DISCUSS

1. Describe the zeros of a function whose terms form a perfect square trinomial.
2. Compare the x- and y-intercepts of a quadratic function with those of a linear function.
3. Explain how a table can be used to find zeros of a function.

4. **GET ORGANIZED** Copy and complete the graphic organizer. In each box, give information about special products and factors.

Name	Rule	Example	Graph
Difference of Two Squares			
Perfect-Square Trinomial			

COMMON ERROR ALERT

In **Example 5,** students may assume that if the zeros of a quadratic function are a and b, the function can be written as $f(x) = (x + a)(x + b)$ rather than $f(x) = (x - a)(x - b)$. Remind students that a zero of a function must make at least one of the factors equal to zero when substituted for x.

Power Presentations with PowerPoint®

Additional Examples

Example 5

Write a quadratic function in standard form with zeros 4 and −7. Possible answer: $f(x) = x^2 + 3x - 28$

Also available on transparency

INTERVENTION
Questioning Strategies

EXAMPLE 5

- What is the converse of the Zero Product Property?

Technology Students can use the TRACE feature of a graphing calculator to view a function rule, the graph of the function, and the coordinates and location of a point on the function's graph, all on the same screen. When a value is entered for x, the corresponding value of y is automatically displayed.

3 Close

Summarize

Review the methods that students have learned for finding the zeros of quadratic functions. On a graph, the zeros of a quadratic function can be determined from the points where the graph crosses the x-axis. To find the zeros by factoring, set the function equal to 0, factor the quadratic expression, and then apply the Zero Product Property to solve the resulting equation. Tell students that they will be learning additional methods of finding zeros of quadratic functions in this chapter.

ONGOING ASSESSMENT and INTERVENTION

***Diagnose* Before the Lesson**
5-3 Warm Up, TE p. 333

***Monitor* During the Lesson**
Check It Out! Exercises, SE pp. 334–337
Questioning Strategies, TE pp. 334–337

***Assess* After the Lesson**
5-3 Lesson Quiz, TE p. 340
Alternative Assessment, TE p. 340

Answers to *Think and Discuss*

Possible answers:

1. The function has only 1 distinct real zero.
2. Both linear and quadratic functions have exactly 1 y-intercept. Linear functions have at most 1 x-intercept, and quadratic functions have at most 2 x-intercepts.
3. A table may show the value or values of x that result in 0 being the value of the function f. These values of x are the zeros of the function.
4. See p. A7.

Assignment Guide

Assign *Guided Practice* exercises as necessary.

If you finished Examples **1–3**
- **Basic** 18–27, 37–46
- **Average** 18–27, 37–46, 73
- **Advanced** 18–27, 37–46, 73

If you finished Examples **1–5**
- **Basic** 18–63, 65–70, 76–85
- **Average** 18–74, 76–85
- **Advanced** 18–85

Homework Quick Check
Quickly check key concepts.
Exercises: 18, 22, 27, 28, 34, 46

Answers

15. Possible answer: $f(x) = x^2 - 7x + 12$

16. Possible answer: $f(x) = x^2 + 8x + 16$

17. Possible answer: $f(x) = x^2 - 3x$

34. Possible answer: $f(x) = x^2 - 4x - 5$

35. Possible answer: $f(x) = x^2 - 8x + 12$

36. Possible answer: $f(x) = x^2 - 6x + 9$

46b. No; possible answer: the relationship between the building height and jump time is quadratic, not linear; therefore, a jump that is half as high will not last half as long.

State Resources

5-3 Exercises

go.hrw.com
Homework Help Online
KEYWORD: MB7 5-3
Parent Resources Online
KEYWORD: MB7 Parent

GUIDED PRACTICE

1. **Vocabulary** The solutions of the equation $3x^2 + 2x + 5 = 0$ are its __?__. (*roots* or *zeros*) **roots**

SEE EXAMPLE 1 p. 333

Find the zeros of each function by using a graph and table.

2. $f(x) = x^2 + 4x - 5$ **−5, 1**
3. $g(x) = -x^2 + 6x - 8$ **2, 4**
4. $f(x) = x^2 - 1$ **−1, 1**

SEE EXAMPLE 2 p. 334

Find the zeros of each function by factoring.

5. $f(x) = x^2 - 7x + 6$ **1, 6**
6. $g(x) = 2x^2 - 5x + 2$ **$\frac{1}{2}$, 2**
7. $h(x) = x^2 + 4x$ **−4, 0**
8. $f(x) = x^2 + 9x + 20$ **−5, −4**
9. $g(x) = x^2 - 6x - 16$ **−2, 8**
10. $h(x) = 3x^2 + 13x + 4$ **−4, $-\frac{1}{3}$**

SEE EXAMPLE 3 p. 335

11. **Archery** The height h of an arrow in feet is modeled by $h(t) = -16t^2 + 63t + 4$, where t is the time in seconds since the arrow was shot. How long is the arrow in the air? **4 s**

SEE EXAMPLE 4 p. 336

Find the roots of each equation by factoring.

12. $x^2 - 6x = -9$ **3**
13. $5x^2 + 20 = 20x$ **2**
14. $x^2 = 49$ **−7, 7**

SEE EXAMPLE 5 p. 337

Write a quadratic function in standard form for each given set of zeros.

15. 3 and 4
16. −4 and −4
17. 3 and 0

PRACTICE AND PROBLEM SOLVING

Independent Practice	
For Exercises	See Example
18–20	1
21–26	2
27	3
28–33	4
34–36	5

Extra Practice
Skills Practice p. S12
Application Practice p. S36

Find the zeros of each function by using a graph and table.

18. $f(x) = -x^2 + 4x - 3$ **1, 3**
19. $g(x) = x^2 + x - 6$ **−3, 2**
20. $f(x) = x^2 - 9$ **−3, 3**

Find the zeros of each function by factoring.

21. $f(x) = x^2 + 11x + 24$ **−8, −3**
22. $g(x) = 2x^2 + x - 10$ **$-\frac{5}{2}$, 2**
23. $h(x) = -x^2 + 9x$ **0, 9**
24. $f(x) = x^2 - 15x + 54$ **6, 9**
25. $g(x) = x^2 + 7x - 8$ **−8, 1**
26. $h(x) = 2x^2 - 12x + 18$ **3**
27. **Biology** A bald eagle snatches a fish from a lake and flies to an altitude of 256 ft. The fish manages to squirm free and falls back down into the lake. Its height h in feet can be modeled by $h(t) = 256 - 16t^2$, where t is the time in seconds. How many seconds will the fish fall before hitting the water? **4 s**

Find the roots of each equation by factoring.

28. $x^2 + 8x = -16$ **−4**
29. $4x^2 = 81$ **$-\frac{9}{2}$, $\frac{9}{2}$**
30. $9x^2 + 12x + 4 = 0$ **$-\frac{2}{3}$**
31. $36x^2 - 9 = 0$ **$-\frac{1}{2}$, $\frac{1}{2}$**
32. $x^2 - 10x + 25 = 0$ **5**
33. $49x^2 = 28x - 4$ **$\frac{2}{7}$**

Write a quadratic function in standard form for each given set of zeros.

34. 5 and −1
35. 6 and 2
36. 3 and 3

Find the zeros of each function.

37. $f(x) = 6x - x^2$ **0, 6**
38. $g(x) = x^2 - 25$ **−5, 5**
39. $h(x) = x^2 - 12x + 36$ **6**
40. $f(x) = 3x^2 - 12$ **−2, 2**
41. $g(x) = x^2 - 22x + 121$ **11**
42. $h(x) = 30 + x - x^2$ **−5, 6**
43. $f(x) = x^2 - 11x + 30$ **5, 6**
44. $g(x) = x^2 - 8x - 20$ **−2, 10**
45. $h(x) = 2x^2 + 18x + 28$ **−7, −2**

5-3 READING STRATEGIES

A **zero** of a function is the value of x that makes $f(x) = 0$. Two different ways of finding the zeros of a function, graphing and factoring, are compared below.

Finding Zeros by Using a Graph	Finding Zeros by Factoring
$f(x) = x^2 + 2x - 3$ The graph opens upward. The vertex is $(-1, -4)$ The y-intercept is -3. The zeros are 1 and −3.	$f(x) = x^2 + 2x - 3$ Set the function equal to zero. $x^2 + 2x - 3 = 0$ Factor. $(x - 1)(x + 3) = 0$ Set each factor equal to 0 and solve. $x - 1 = 0$ $x = 1$ $x + 3 = 0$ $x = -3$ The zeros are 1 and −3

Answer each question.

1. How can you use a graph to find the zeros of a quadratic function?
   Possible answer: The points where the function crosses the x-axis are the zeros of the function.
2. Can a quadratic function have more than two zeros? Explain.
   No; possible answer: a parabola can cross the x-axis at most at two points.
3. Consider the function $f(x) = (x - 1)(x + 1)$.
   a. What are the zeros of the function? 1 and −1
   b. Which method did you use? Why?
   Factoring; possible answer: since the function was already factored, I just set each factor equal to 0 and solved for x.
4. A quadratic function opens down and its vertex is $(0, -3)$. How many zeros does this function have? Explain.
   No zeros exist for this function. Possible answer: Since the parabola opens down and its vertex is below the x-axis, the graph will not cross the x-axis.
5. Compare and contrast the two methods of finding the zeros of a quadratic function. Describe when you would use one or the other method.
   Possible answer: I would check some factors of c to see if I could easily factor the equation. If not, then I would make a graph.

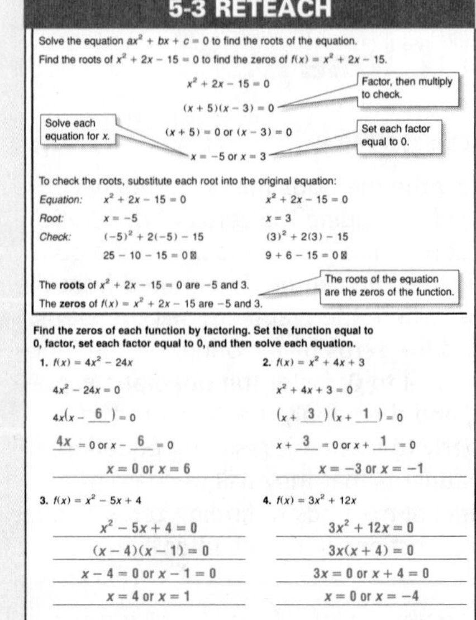
5-3 RETEACH

Solve the equation $ax^2 + bx + c = 0$ to find the roots of the equation.

Find the roots of $x^2 + 2x - 15 = 0$ to find the zeros of $f(x) = x^2 + 2x - 15$.

$x^2 + 2x - 15 = 0$

$(x + 5)(x - 3) = 0$ — Factor, then multiply to check.

$(x + 5) = 0$ or $(x - 3) = 0$ — Set each factor equal to 0.

$x = -5$ or $x = 3$ — Solve each equation for x.

To check the roots, substitute each root into the original equation:

Equation:	$x^2 + 2x - 15 = 0$	$x^2 + 2x - 15 = 0$
Root:	$x = -5$	$x = 3$
Check:	$(-5)^2 + 2(-5) - 15$	$(3)^2 + 2(3) - 15$
	$25 - 10 - 15 = 0$ ✓	$9 + 6 - 15 = 0$ ✓

The **roots** of $x^2 + 2x - 15 = 0$ are −5 and 3.
The **zeros** of $f(x) = x^2 + 2x - 15$ are −5 and 3.
The roots of the equation are the zeros of the function.

Find the zeros of each function by factoring. Set the function equal to 0, factor, set each factor equal to 0, and then solve each equation.

1. $f(x) = 4x^2 - 24x$
   $4x^2 - 24x = 0$
   $4x(x - \underline{6}) = 0$
   $\underline{4x} = 0$ or $x - \underline{6} = 0$
   $x = 0$ or $x = 6$
2. $f(x) = x^2 + 4x + 3$
   $x^2 + 4x + 3 = 0$
   $(x + \underline{3})(x + \underline{1}) = 0$
   $x + \underline{3} = 0$ or $x + \underline{1} = 0$
   $x = -3$ or $x = -1$
3. $f(x) = x^2 - 5x + 4$
   $x^2 - 5x + 4 = 0$
   $(x - 4)(x - 1) = 0$
   $x - 4 = 0$ or $x - 1 = 0$
   $x = 4$ or $x = 1$
4. $f(x) = 3x^2 + 12x$
   $3x^2 + 12x = 0$
   $3x(x + 4) = 0$
   $3x = 0$ or $x + 4 = 0$
   $x = 0$ or $x = -4$

LINK

Entertainment

The Guinness world record for the greatest number of people juggling at one time was set in 1998 by 1508 people, each of whom juggled at least 3 objects for 10 seconds.

46. **Movies** A stuntwoman jumps from a building 73 ft high and lands on an air bag that is 9 ft tall. Her height above ground h in feet can be modeled by $h(t) = 73 - 16t^2$, where t is the time in seconds.
    a. **Multi-Step** How many seconds will the stuntwoman fall before touching the air bag? (*Hint:* Find the time t when the stuntwoman's height above ground is 9 ft.) **2 s**
    b. **What if...?** Suppose the stuntwoman jumps from a building that is half as tall. Will she be in the air for half as long? Explain.

47. **Entertainment** A juggler throws a ball into the air from a height of 5 ft with an initial vertical velocity of 16 ft/s.
    a. Write a function that can be used to model the height h of the ball in feet t seconds after the ball is thrown. $h(t) = -16t^2 + 16t + 5$
    b. How long does the juggler have to catch the ball before it hits the ground? **1.25 s**

Find the roots of each equation.

48. $x^2 - 2x + 1 = 0$ **1**
49. $x^2 + 6x = -5$ **−5, −1**
50. $25x^2 + 40x = -16$ $-\frac{4}{5}$
51. $9x^2 + 6x = -1$ $-\frac{1}{3}$
52. $5x^2 = 45$ **−3, 3**
53. $x^2 - 6 = x$ **−2, 3**

For each function, (a) find its vertex, (b) find its y-intercept, (c) find its zeros, and (d) graph it.

54. $f(x) = x^2 + 2x - 8$
55. $g(x) = x^2 - 16$
56. $h(x) = x^2 - x - 12$
57. $f(x) = -2x^2 + 4x$
58. $g(x) = x^2 - 5x - 6$
59. $h(x) = 3x^2 + x - 4$

60. **Geometry** The hypotenuse of a right triangle is 2 cm longer than one leg and 4 cm longer than the other leg.
    a. Let x represent the length of the hypotenuse. Use the Pythagorean Theorem to write an equation that can be solved for x.
    b. Find the solutions of the equation from part **a.** $x = 10$ or $x = 2$
    c. Are both solutions reasonable in the context of the problem situation? Explain.

Geometry **Find the dimensions of each rectangle.**

61. 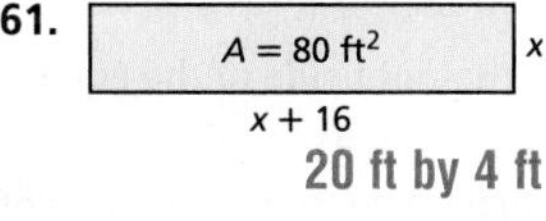

20 ft by 4 ft

62. 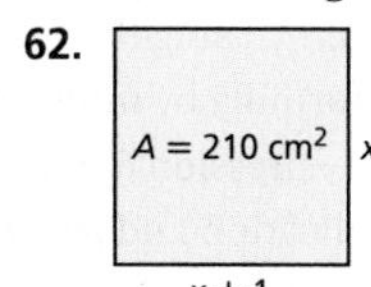

15 cm by 14 cm

63. 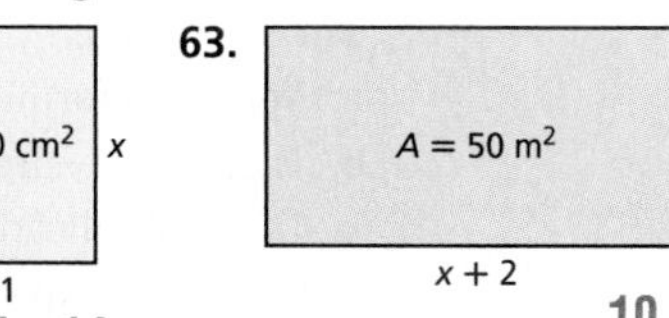

10 m by 5 m

64. **Critical Thinking** Will a function whose rule can be factored as a binomial squared ever have two different zeros? Explain.

65. **Write About It** Explain how the Zero Product Property can be used to help determine the zeros of quadratic functions.

MULTI-STEP TEST PREP

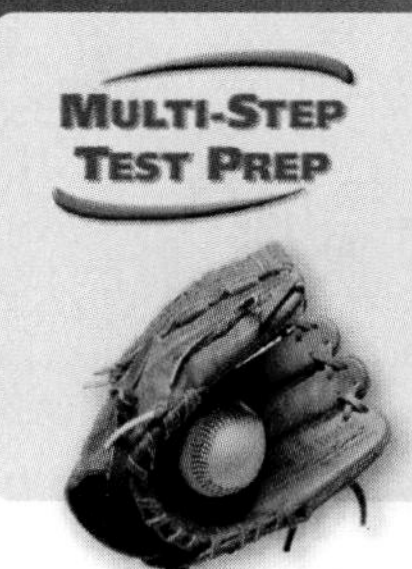

66. This problem will prepare you for the Multi-Step Test Prep on page 364.

    A baseball player hits a ball toward the outfield. The height h of the ball in feet is modeled by $h(t) = -16t^2 + 22t + 3$, where t is the time in seconds. In addition, the function $d(t) = 85t$ models the horizontal distance d traveled by the ball.
    a. If no one catches the ball, how long will it stay in the air? **1.5 s**
    b. What is the horizontal distance that the ball travels before it hits the ground? **127.5 ft**

Teaching Tip **Geometry** For **Exercise 60,** remind students that the Pythagorean Theorem states that $a^2 + b^2 = c^2$, where a and b are the lengths of the legs of a right triangle and c is the length of the hypotenuse.

MULTI-STEP TEST PREP **Exercise 66** involves finding the zeros of a quadratic function representing a baseball's height. This exercise prepares students for the Multi-Step Test Prep on page 364.

Answers

54–59. For graphs, see p. A28.

54. $(-1, -9)$; -8; $-4, 2$
55. $(0, -16)$; -16; $-4, 4$
56. $\left(\frac{1}{2}, -12\frac{1}{4}\right)$; -12; $-3, 4$
57. $(1, 2)$; 0; $0, 2$
58. $\left(2\frac{1}{2}, -12\frac{1}{4}\right)$; -6; $-1, 6$
59. $\left(-\frac{1}{6}, -4\frac{1}{12}\right)$; -4; $-1\frac{1}{3}, 1$

60a. Possible answer: $(x - 2)^2 + (x - 4)^2 = x^2$

60c. Possible answer: The solutions represent possible lengths in centimeters of the hypotenuse. If $x = 10$, the triangle would have side lengths of 10 cm, 8 cm, and 6 cm. If $x = 2$, the triangle would have side lengths of 2 cm, 0 cm, and −2 cm. Because length cannot be negative, only the solution $x = 10$ is reasonable.

64–65. See p. A28.

5-3 PROBLEM SOLVING

Erin and her friends launch a rocket from ground level vertically into the air with an initial velocity of 80 feet per second. The height of the rocket, $h(t)$, after t seconds is given by $h(t) = -16t^2 + 80t$.

1. They want to find out how high they can expect the rocket to go and how long it will be in the air.
   a. Use the standard form $f(x) = ax^2 + bx + c$ to find values for a, b, and c. $a = -16$, $b = 80$, $c = 0$
   b. Use the coordinates for the vertex of the path of the rocket to find t, the number of seconds the rocket will be in the air before it starts its downward path. $t = \frac{-80}{2(-16)} = 2.5$ seconds
   c. Substitute the value for t in the given function to find the maximum height of the rocket. How high can they expect their rocket to go? 100 feet
   d. Megan points out that the rocket will have a height of zero again when it returns to the ground. How long will the rocket stay in the air? 5 seconds
2. Megan gets ready to launch the same rocket from a platform 21 feet above the ground with the same initial velocity. How long will the rocket stay in the air this time?
   a. Write a function that represents the rocket's path for this launch. $h(t) = -16t^2 + 80t + 21$
   b. Factor the corresponding equation to find the values for t when h is zero. $(4t + 1)(-4t + 21) = 0$
   c. Erin says that the roots of the equation are $t = 5.25$ and $t = -20.25$ and that the rocket will stay in the air 5.5 seconds. Megan says she is wrong. Who is correct? How do you know?

   Possible answer: Erin has the roots correct. Set each factor equal to 0 and solve for t. But the rocket will stay in the air 5.25 seconds. (The negative root represents the time before launch since the rocket is starting at 21 feet, not at ground level.)

Choose the letter for the best answer.

3. Which function models the path of a rocket that lands 3 seconds after launch?
   Ⓐ $h(t) = -16t^2 + 32t + 48$
   B $h(t) = -16t^2 + 32t + 10.5$
   C $h(t) = -16t^2 + 40t + 48$
   D $h(t) = -16t^2 + 40t + 10.5$
4. Megan reads about a rocket whose path can be modeled by the function $h(t) = -16t^2 + 100t + 15$. Which could be the initial velocity and launch height?
   A 15 ft/s; 100 ft off the ground
   B 16 ft/s; 100 ft off the ground
   Ⓒ 100 ft/s; 15 ft off the ground
   D 171 ft/s; 15 ft off the ground

5-3 CHALLENGE

Some equations that are not of the second degree can be rewritten in quadratic form. Once in quadratic form, the equation may be solved by factoring. When you solve an equation in quadratic form, you may obtain a value that does not satisfy the original equation. For this reason, it is important to check all solutions in the original equation.

- **Example**

  Solve: $x^4 - 29x^2 + 100 = 0$

- **Solution**

		Check
	$x^4 - 29x^2 + 100 = 0$	$x^4 - 29x^2 + 100 = 0$
		$(\pm5)^4 - 29(\pm5)^2 + 100$
		$= 625 - 725 + 100$
Rewrite the equation in x^2.	$(x^2)^2 - 29(x^2) + 100 = 0$	$= 0$ ✓
Factor.	$(x^2 - 25)(x^2 - 4) = 0$	$x^4 - 29x^2 + 100 = 0$
Zero Product Property	$x^2 - 25 = 0$ or $x^2 - 4 = 0$	$(\pm2)^4 - 29(\pm2)^2 + 100$
Solve for x.	$x = \pm5$ or $x = \pm2$	$= 0$ ✓
	Check all four values in the original equation, as shown at right.	So, there are four solutions: −5, −2, 2, 5

Determine if each equation can be expressed in quadratic form. If so, write the equation in quadratic form. If not, write *no*. Do not solve.

1. $x^4 + 4x^2 - 5 = 0$ $(x^2)^2 + 4(x^2) - 5 = 0$
2. $x^4 - x^3 + 12 = 0$ No
3. $x^8 - 17x^4 + 16 = 0$ $(x^4)^2 - 17(x^4) + 16 = 0$
4. $x^3 - 2x^2 - 5 = 0$ No
5. $x - 2\sqrt{x} - 8 = 0$ $(\sqrt{x})^2 - 2(\sqrt{x}) - 8 = 0$
6. $(x-3)^2 - 4(x-3) - 21 = 0$ It is in quadratic form. Let $y = x - 3$, then $y^2 - 4y - 21 = 0$.

Factor each equation to determine if it contains a quadratic factor. If so, write the factored form of the equation. If not, write *no*. Do not solve.

7. $x^3 - 9x = 0$ $x(x^2 - 9) = 0$
8. $x^5 - 4x^4 - 12x^3 = 0$ $x^3(x^2 - 4x - 12) = 0$
9. $2x^3 - x^2 - 9 = 0$ No

Write each equation in quadratic form and solve. Check your answers.

10. $x^4 - 10x^2 + 9 = 0$ $(x^2)^2 - 10(x^2) + 9 = 0$; $\pm1, \pm3$
11. $9x^4 - 18x^2 + 8 = 0$ $9(x^2)^2 - 18(x^2) + 8 = 0$; $\pm\sqrt{\frac{2}{3}}, \pm\sqrt{\frac{4}{3}}$
12. $x - 3\sqrt{x} - 4 = 0$ $(\sqrt{x})^2 - 3(\sqrt{x}) - 4 = 0$; 16

5-3 PRACTICE A

5-3 PRACTICE C

5-3 PRACTICE B

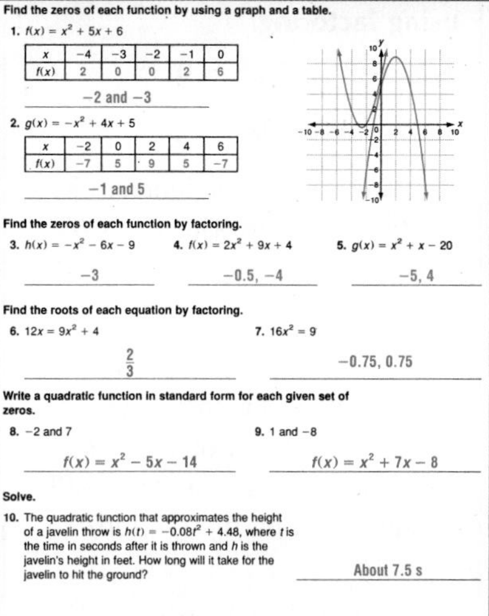

Find the zeros of each function by using a graph and a table.

1. $f(x) = x^2 + 5x + 6$

x	−4	−3	−2	−1	0
$f(x)$	2	0	0	2	6

−2 and −3

2. $g(x) = -x^2 + 4x + 5$

x	−2	0	2	4	6
$f(x)$	−7	5	9	5	−7

−1 and 5

Find the zeros of each function by factoring.

3. $h(x) = -x^2 - 6x - 9$ −3
4. $f(x) = 2x^2 + 9x + 4$ −0.5, −4
5. $g(x) = x^2 + x - 20$ −5, 4

Find the roots of each equation by factoring.

6. $12x = 9x^2 + 4$ $\frac{2}{3}$
7. $16x^2 = 9$ −0.75, 0.75

Write a quadratic function in standard form for each given set of zeros.

8. −2 and 7 $f(x) = x^2 - 5x - 14$
9. 1 and −8 $f(x) = x^2 + 7x - 8$

Solve.

10. The quadratic function that approximates the height of a javelin throw is $h(t) = -0.08t^2 + 4.48$, where t is the time in seconds after it is thrown and h is the javelin's height in feet. How long will it take for the javelin to hit the ground? About 7.5 s

In **Exercise 69,** students who chose **A** may have confused a perfect square trinomial with a difference of squares. Students who chose **B** may think that the middle term of a perfect square trinomial is ab rather than $-2ab$.

Journal

Have students describe the series of steps they would use to write a quadratic function in standard form when given its zeros.

ALTERNATIVE ASSESSMENT

Have students choose two quadratic functions from the exercises and find the zeros of the functions using factoring. Ask them to explain each step of their solution process and to show how they checked their work.

Power Presentations with PowerPoint®

5-3 Lesson Quiz

Find the zeros of each function.

1. $f(x) = x^2 - 7x$ 0, 7
2. $f(x) = x^2 - 9x + 20$ 4, 5

Find the roots of each equation using factoring.

3. $x^2 - 10x + 25 = 0$ 5
4. $7x = 15 - 2x^2$ $-5, \frac{3}{2}$
5. Write a quadratic function in standard form with zeros 6 and −1. Possible answer: $f(x) = x^2 - 5x - 6$
6. A rocket is launched from ground level with an initial vertical velocity of 176 ft/s. After how many seconds will the rocket hit the ground? after 11 s

Also available on transparency

TEST PREP

67. Use the graph provided to choose the best description of what the graph represents.
    - (A) A ball is dropped from a height of 42 feet and lands on the ground after 3 seconds.
    - (B) A ball is dropped from a height of 42 feet and lands on the ground after 1.5 seconds.
    - (C) A ball is shot up in the air and reaches a height of 42 feet after 1 second.
    - (D) A ball is shot up in the air, reaches a height of 42 feet, and lands on the ground after 1.5 seconds.

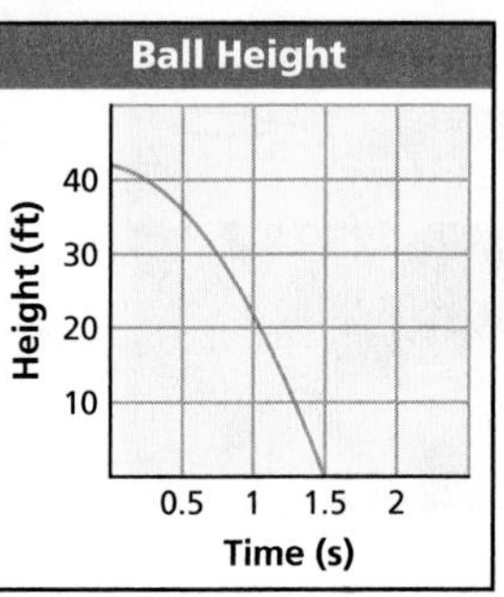

68. Which function has −7 as its only zero?
    - (F) $f(x) = x(x - 7)$
    - (G) $h(x) = (x - 7)^2$
    - (H) $g(x) = (x + 1)(x + 7)$
    - (J) $j(x) = (x + 7)^2$

69. Which expression is a perfect square trinomial?
    - (A) $25y^2 - 16$
    - (B) $25y^2 - 20y + 16$
    - (C) $25y^2 - 40y + 16$
    - (D) $25y^2 - 10y + 16$

70. **Gridded Response** Find the positive root of $x^2 + 4x - 21 = 0$. 3

CHALLENGE AND EXTEND

Find the roots of each equation by factoring.

71. $3(x^2 - x) = x^2$ $0, \frac{3}{2}$
72. $x^2 = \frac{1}{3}x$ $0, \frac{1}{3}$
73. $x^2 - \frac{3}{4}x + \frac{1}{8} = 0$ $\frac{1}{4}, \frac{1}{2}$
74. $x^2 + x + 0.21 = 0$ $-0.7, -0.3$
75. Another special factoring case involves perfect cubes. The sum of two cubes can be factored by using the formula $a^3 + b^3 = (a + b)(a^2 - ab + b^2)$.
    a. Verify the formula by multiplying the right side of the equation.
    b. Factor the expression $8x^3 + 27$. $(2x + 3)(4x^2 - 6x + 9)$
    c. Use multiplication and guess and check to find the factors of $a^3 - b^3$.
    d. Factor the expression $x^3 - 1$. $(x - 1)(x^2 + x + 1)$

    c. $a^3 - b^3 = (a - b)(a^2 + ab + b^2)$

SPIRAL REVIEW

Evaluate each expression. Write the answer in scientific notation. *(Lesson 1-5)*

76. $(1.4 \times 10^8)(6.1 \times 10^{-3})$ 8.54×10^5
77. $(2.7 \times 10^{10})(3.2 \times 10^2)$ 8.64×10^{12}
78. $\frac{(3.5 \times 10^6)}{(1.4 \times 10^{-4})}$ 2.5×10^{10}
79. $\frac{(3.12 \times 10^{-6})}{(4.8 \times 10^3)}$ 6.5×10^{-10}

Solve each proportion. *(Lesson 2-2)*

80. $\frac{12}{7.5} = \frac{n}{5}$ 8
81. $\frac{1.2}{4.8} = \frac{w}{8.8}$ 2.2
82. $\frac{6.8}{4.5} = \frac{r}{90}$ 136

Using the graph of $f(x) = x^2$ as a guide, describe the transformations, and then graph each function. *(Lesson 5-1)*

83. $h(x) = 0.5x^2$
84. $d(x) = x^2 + 2$
85. $g(x) = (x + 1)^2$

Answers

75a. $(a + b)(a^2 - ab + b^2) = a^3 - a^2b + ab^2 + a^2b - ab^2 + b^3 = a^3 + b^3$

83. h is a vertical compression of f by a factor of 0.5.

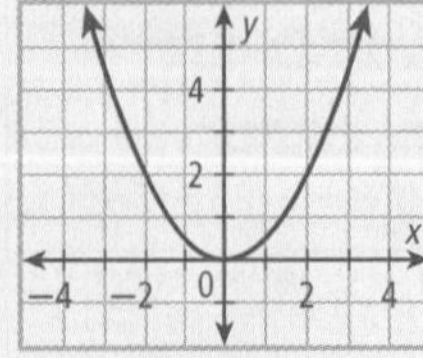

84. d is f translated 2 units up.

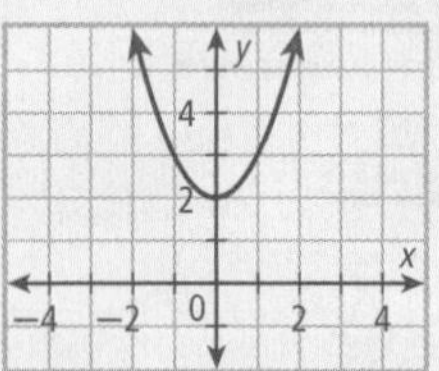

85. g is f translated 1 unit left.

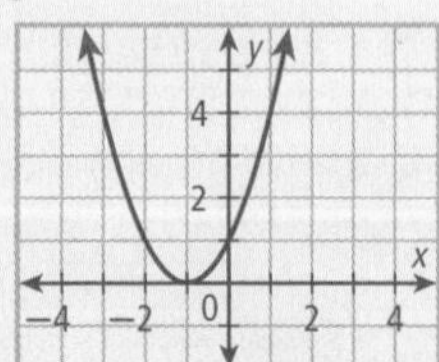

5-4 Completing the Square

A2.3.5 Solve problems that can be modeled using quadratic equations and functions, interpret the solutions, and determine whether the solutions are reasonable.

Objectives

Solve quadratic equations by completing the square.

Write quadratic equations in vertex form.

Vocabulary

completing the square

Why learn this?

You can solve quadratic equations to find how long water takes to fall from the top to the bottom of a waterfall. (See Exercise 39.)

Many quadratic equations contain expressions that cannot be easily factored. For equations containing these types of expressions, you can use square roots to find roots.

Know it! Note

Square-Root Property

WORDS	NUMBERS	ALGEBRA
To solve a quadratic equation, you can take the square root of both sides. Be sure to consider the positive and negative square roots.	$x^2 = 15$ $\|x\| = \sqrt{15}$ $x = \pm\sqrt{15}$	If $x^2 = a$ and a is a nonnegative real number, then $x = \pm\sqrt{a}$.

EXAMPLE 1 Solving Equations by Using the Square Root Property

Solve each equation.

A $3x^2 - 4 = 68$

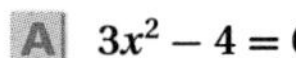

$3x^2 = 72$ *Add 4 to both sides.*

$x^2 = 24$ *Divide both sides by 3 to isolate the squared term.*

$x = \pm\sqrt{24}$ *Take the square root of both sides.*

$x = \pm 2\sqrt{6}$ *Simplify.*

Check Use a graphing calculator.

```
3*(2√(6))²-4
                68
3*(-2√(6))²-4
                68
```

Reading Math

Read $\pm\sqrt{a}$ as "plus or minus square root of *a*."

B $x^2 - 10x + 25 = 27$

$(x - 5)^2 = 27$ *Factor the perfect square trinomial.*

$x - 5 = \pm\sqrt{27}$ *Take the square root of both sides.*

$x = 5 \pm \sqrt{27}$ *Add 5 to both sides.*

$x = 5 \pm 3\sqrt{3}$ *Simplify.*

Check Use a graphing calculator.

```
(5+3√(3))²-10(5+
3√(3))+25
                27
(5-3√(3))²-10(5-
3√(3))+25
                27
```

CHECK IT OUT! Solve each equation.

1a. $4x^2 - 20 = 5$ $\pm\frac{5}{2}$

1b. $x^2 + 8x + 16 = 49$ $-11, 3$

5-4 Organizer

Pacing: Traditional $1\frac{1}{2}$ days
Block $\frac{3}{4}$ day

Objectives: Solve quadratic equations by completing the square.

Write quadratic equations in vertex form.

Online Edition
Graphic Calculator, Tutorial Videos

Countdown to Testing Week 11

Power Presentations with PowerPoint®

Warm Up

Write each expression as a trinomial.

1. $(x - 5)^2$ $x^2 - 10x + 25$

2. $(3x + 5)^2$ $9x^2 + 30x + 25$

Factor each expression.

3. $x^2 - 18x + 81$ $(x - 9)^2$

4. $16x^2 + 24x + 9$ $(4x + 3)^2$

Also available on transparency

Math Humor

Q: How does a ghost solve a quadratic equation?

A: By completing the scare.

1 Introduce

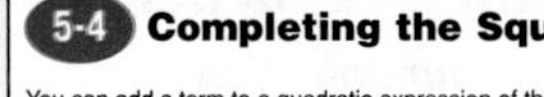

EXPLORATION

5-4 Completing the Square

You can add a term to a quadratic expression of the form $x^2 + bx$ to form a perfect square trinomial. This is called completing the square.

The model shows completing the square for $x^2 + 6x$ by adding 9 unit tiles. The perfect-square trinomial that results is $x^2 + 6x + 9 = (x + 3)^2$.

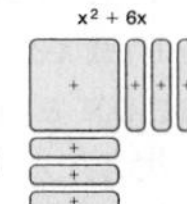

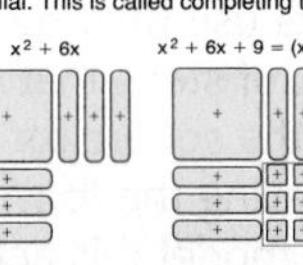

Complete the square for each model by adding unit tiles. Then write the perfect square trinomial that results.

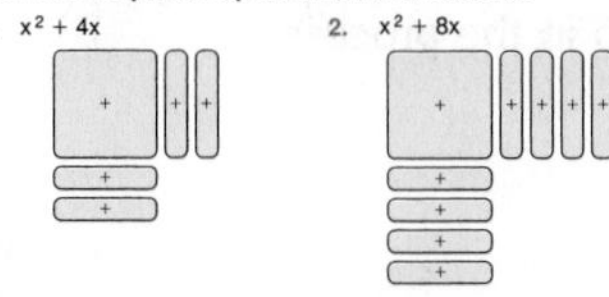

THINK AND DISCUSS

Motivate

Discuss with students the methods learned for solving quadratic equations. Point out that all of the quadratic expressions they have been working with so far have been factorable, but that some quadratic expressions are not easily factorable. Explain that the method of completing the square can be used to solve any quadratic equation, even those that are difficult to solve by factoring.

Explorations and answers are provided in the *Explorations* binder.

State Resources

go.hrw.com
State Resources Online
KEYWORD: MB7 Resources

Power Presentations with PowerPoint®

Additional Examples

Example 1

Solve each equation.

A. $4x^2 + 11 = 59$ $\pm 2\sqrt{3}$

B. $x^2 + 12x + 36 = 28$ $-6 \pm 2\sqrt{7}$

Example 2

Complete the square for each expression. Write the resulting expression as a binomial squared.

A. $x^2 - 14x + \blacksquare$ $x^2 - 14x + 49 = (x - 7)^2$

B. $x^2 + 9x + \blacksquare$ $x^2 + 9x + \frac{81}{4} = \left(x + \frac{9}{2}\right)^2$

Also available on transparency

INTERVENTION

Questioning Strategies

EXAMPLE 1

- Why do you need to consider both positive and negative square roots when you use the Square Root Property to solve a quadratic equation?

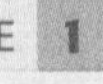

EXAMPLE 2

- How do you determine the value of b?
- How do you find the term needed to complete the square?

Teaching Tip **Math Background** The first recorded solution of a quadratic equation appeared in an Egyptian document known as the Berlin papyrus, which dates from between 2160 and 1700 B.C.E. In this document, the following system of equations is solved:

$$\begin{cases} x^2 + y^2 = 100 \\ y = \frac{3}{4}x \end{cases}$$

Answers to *Check It Out!*

2a. $x^2 + 4x + 4 = (x + 2)^2$

2b. $x^2 - 4x + 4 = (x - 2)^2$

2c. $x^2 + 3x + \frac{9}{4} = \left(x + \frac{3}{2}\right)^2$

The methods in the previous examples can be used only for expressions that are perfect squares. However, you can use algebra to rewrite any quadratic expression as a perfect square.

You can use algebra tiles to model a perfect square trinomial as a perfect square. The area of the square at right is $x^2 + 2x + 1$. Because each side of the square measures $x + 1$ units, the area is also $(x + 1)(x + 1)$, or $(x + 1)^2$. This shows that $(x + 1)^2 = x^2 + 2x + 1$.

If a quadratic expression of the form $x^2 + bx$ *cannot* model a square, you can add a term to form a perfect square trinomial. This is called **completing the square**.

Know it! Note — **Completing the Square**

WORDS	NUMBERS	ALGEBRA
To complete the square of $x^2 + bx$, add $\left(\frac{b}{2}\right)^2$.	$x^2 + 6x + \blacksquare$ $x^2 + 6x + \left(\frac{6}{2}\right)^2$ $x^2 + 6x + 9$ $(x + 3)^2$	$x^2 + bx + \blacksquare$ $x^2 + bx + \left(\frac{b}{2}\right)^2$ $\left(x + \frac{b}{2}\right)^2$

The model shows completing the square for $x^2 + 6x$ by adding 9 unit tiles. The resulting perfect square trinomial is $x^2 + 6x + 9$. Note that completing the square does not produce an equivalent expression.

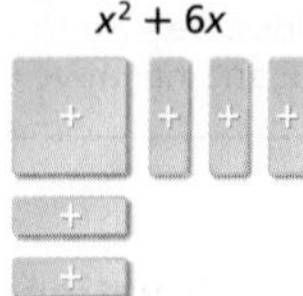

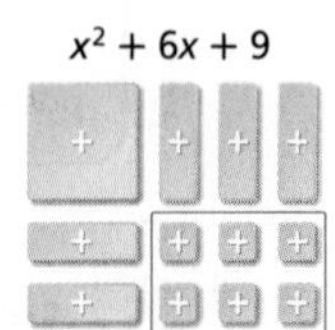

EXAMPLE 2 Completing the Square

Complete the square for each expression. Write the resulting expression as a binomial squared.

A $x^2 - 2x + \blacksquare$

$\left(\frac{-2}{2}\right)^2 = (-1)^2 = 1$ *Find* $\left(\frac{b}{2}\right)^2$.

$x^2 - 2x + 1$ *Add.*

$(x - 1)^2$ *Factor.*

Check Find the square of the binomial.

$(x - 1)^2 = (x - 1)(x - 1)$

$= x^2 - 2x + 1$

B $x^2 + 5x + \blacksquare$

$\left(\frac{5}{2}\right)^2 = \frac{25}{4}$ *Find* $\left(\frac{b}{2}\right)^2$.

$x^2 + 5x + \frac{25}{4}$ *Add.*

$\left(x + \frac{5}{2}\right)^2$ *Factor.*

Check Find the square of the binomial.

$\left(x + \frac{5}{2}\right)^2 = \left(x + \frac{5}{2}\right)\left(x + \frac{5}{2}\right)$

$= x^2 + 5x + \frac{25}{4}$

CHECK IT OUT! **Complete the square for each expression. Write the resulting expression as a binomial squared.**

2a. $x^2 + 4x + \blacksquare$ **2b.** $x^2 - 4x + \blacksquare$ **2c.** $x^2 + 3x + \blacksquare$

2 Teach

Guided Instruction

Make sure students understand the mechanics of completing the square before using this method to solve quadratic equations. Point out the two methods of keeping an equation balanced when completing the square: adding the same amount to both sides, as in **Example 3,** or adding and subtracting the same amount on one side, as in **Example 4.**

Reaching All Learners

Through Communication

Have students use their own words to write a series of steps that can be used to complete the square for a quadratic expression having the form $x^2 + bx$. You may need to model this activity for students by discussing how they could write the first step in the process.

You can complete the square to solve quadratic equations.

Solving Quadratic Equations $ax^2 + bx + c = 0$ by Completing the Square

1. Collect variable terms on one side of the equation and constants on the other.
2. As needed, divide both sides by a to make the coefficient of the x^2-term 1.
3. Complete the square by adding $\left(\frac{b}{2}\right)^2$ to both sides of the equation.
4. Factor the variable expression as a perfect square.
5. Take the square root of both sides of the equation.
6. Solve for the values of the variable.

Caution!

To keep the equation balanced, you must add $\left(\frac{b}{2}\right)^2$ to both sides of the equation.

EXAMPLE 3 Solving a Quadratic Equation by Completing the Square

Solve each equation by completing the square.

A $x^2 = 27 - 6x$

$x^2 + 6x = 27$	*Collect variable terms on one side.*
$x^2 + 6x + \blacksquare = 27 + \blacksquare$	*Set up to complete the square.*
$x^2 + 6x + \left(\frac{6}{2}\right)^2 = 27 + \left(\frac{6}{2}\right)^2$	*Add $\left(\frac{b}{2}\right)^2$ to both sides.*
$x^2 + 6x + 9 = 27 + 9$	*Simplify.*
$(x + 3)^2 = 36$	*Factor.*
$x + 3 = \pm\sqrt{36}$	*Take the square root of both sides.*
$x + 3 = \pm 6$	*Simplify.*
$x + 3 = 6$ or $x + 3 = -6$	*Solve for x.*
$x = 3$ or $x = -9$	

B $2x^2 + 8x = 12$

$x^2 + 4x = 6$	*Divide both sides by 2.*
$x^2 + 4x + \blacksquare = 6 + \blacksquare$	*Set up to complete the square.*
$x^2 + 4x + \left(\frac{4}{2}\right)^2 = 6 + \left(\frac{4}{2}\right)^2$	*Add $\left(\frac{b}{2}\right)^2$ to both sides.*
$x^2 + 4x + 4 = 6 + 4$	*Simplify.*
$(x + 2)^2 = 10$	*Factor.*
$x + 2 = \pm\sqrt{10}$	*Take the square root of both sides.*
$x = -2 \pm \sqrt{10}$	*Solve for x.*

Solve each equation by completing the square.

3a. $x^2 - 2 = 9x$ $\frac{9 \pm \sqrt{89}}{2}$ **3b.** $3x^2 - 24x = 27$ $-1, 9$

Recall the vertex form of a quadratic function from Lesson 5-1: $f(x) = a(x - h)^2 + k$, where the vertex is (h, k).

You can complete the square to rewrite any quadratic function in vertex form.

COMMON ERROR ALERT

Students may have difficulty writing quadratic functions in vertex form when the leading coefficient is not 1, such as in **Example 4B.** They may forget to multiply $\left(\frac{b}{2}\right)^2$ by the leading coefficient when subtracting this term. Emphasize that they must complete this step to keep the equation balanced.

Power Presentations with PowerPoint®

Additional Examples

Example 3

Solve each equation by completing the square.

A. $x^2 = 12x - 20$ 2, 10

B. $18x + 3x^2 = 45$ $-3 \pm 2\sqrt{6}$

Also available on transparency

INTERVENTION

Questioning Strategies

EXAMPLE 3

- How do you keep an equation balanced when completing the square?

Teaching Tip **Inclusion** Help students realize that more than one method may be used to solve a quadratic equation. Make sure they understand that no matter which method they use, their answer should be the same. Have students solve **Example 3A** by using graphing or factoring to confirm that the solution is the same as when they use completing the square.

Power Presentations with PowerPoint®

Additional Examples

Example 4

Write each function in vertex form, and identify its vertex.

A. $f(x) = x^2 + 16x - 12$

$f(x) = (x + 8)^2 - 76$; $(-8, -76)$

B. $g(x) = 3x^2 - 18x + 7$

$g(x) = 3(x - 3)^2 - 20$; $(3, -20)$

Also available on transparency

INTERVENTION

Questioning Strategies

EXAMPLE 4

- Why do you add and subtract the same term on the right side of the equation?
- How do you identify the vertex once the function is written in vertex form?

Teaching Tip **Visual** Suggest that students circle the leading coefficient in each step of the process when changing a quadratic function from standard form to vertex form. This visual cue can help them to remember to take this coefficient into account when completing the square.

Helpful Hint

In Example 3, the equation was balanced by adding $\left(\frac{b}{2}\right)^2$ to *both* sides. Here, the equation is balanced by adding and subtracting $\left(\frac{b}{2}\right)^2$ on *one* side.

EXAMPLE 4 Writing a Quadratic Function in Vertex Form

Write each function in vertex form, and identify its vertex.

A $f(x) = x^2 + 10x - 13$

$f(x) = (x^2 + 10x + \blacksquare) - 13 - \blacksquare$ *Set up to complete the square.*

$f(x) = \left[x^2 + 10x + \left(\frac{10}{2}\right)^2\right] - 13 - \left(\frac{10}{2}\right)^2$ *Add and subtract $\left(\frac{b}{2}\right)^2$.*

$f(x) = (x + 5)^2 - 38$ *Simplify and factor.*

Because $h = -5$ and $k = -38$, the vertex is $(-5, -38)$.

Check Use the axis of symmetry formula to confirm the vertex.

$x = -\frac{b}{2a} = -\frac{10}{2(1)} = -5$ $\quad y = f(-5) = (-5)^2 + 10(-5) - 13 = -38$ ✓

B $g(x) = 2x^2 - 8x + 3$

$g(x) = 2(x^2 - 4x) + 3$ *Factor so the coefficient of x^2 is 1.*

$g(x) = 2(x^2 - 4x + \blacksquare) + 3 - \blacksquare$ *Set up to complete the square.*

$g(x) = 2\left(x^2 - 4x + \left(\frac{-4}{2}\right)^2\right) + 3 - 2\left(\frac{-4}{2}\right)^2$ *Add $\left(\frac{b}{2}\right)^2$. Because $\left(\frac{b}{2}\right)^2$ is multiplied by 2, you must subtract $2\left(\frac{b}{2}\right)^2$.*

$g(x) = 2(x^2 - 4x + 4) - 5$ *Simplify.*

$g(x) = 2(x - 2)^2 - 5$ *Factor.*

Because $h = 2$ and $k = -5$, the vertex is $(2, -5)$.

Check A graph of the function on a graphing calculator supports your answer.

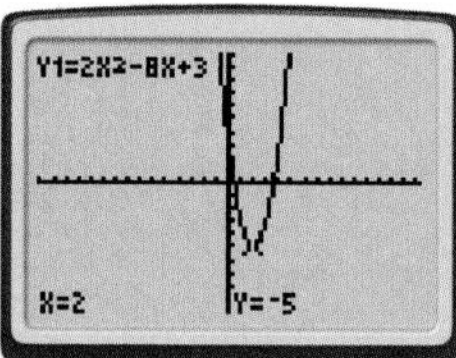

CHECK IT OUT! Write each function in vertex form, and identify its vertex.

4a. $f(x) = x^2 + 24x + 145$ **4b.** $g(x) = 5x^2 - 50x + 128$

$f(x) = (x + 12)^2 + 1$; $(-12, 1)$ $\quad g(x) = 5(x - 5)^2 + 3$; $(5, 3)$

THINK AND DISCUSS

1. Explain two ways to solve $x^2 = 25$.
2. Describe how to change a quadratic function from standard form to vertex form by completing the square.
3. **GET ORGANIZED** Copy and complete the graphic organizer. Compare and contrast two methods of solving quadratic equations.

Using Square-Root Property vs. Completing the Square

Similarities | Differences

3 Close

Summarize

Use the table on page 343 to review the process for solving quadratic equations by completing the square. As you do so, work through an example with students, such as $2x^2 + 4x - 20 = 0$. $x = -1 \pm \sqrt{11}$ Make sure students understand that they must keep the equation balanced by adding $\left(\frac{b}{2}\right)^2$ to both sides of the equation, not just the left side.

ONGOING ASSESSMENT and INTERVENTION

Diagnose Before **the Lesson**
5-4 Warm Up, TE p. 341

Monitor During **the Lesson**
Check It Out! Exercises, SE pp. 341–344
Questioning Strategies, TE pp. 342–344

Assess After **the Lesson**
5-4 Lesson Quiz, TE p. 348
Alternative Assessment, TE p. 348

Answers to *Think and Discuss*

Possible answers:

1. Take the square root of each side by applying the Square Root Property. Rewrite the equation as a difference of squares and factor.
2. Factor the x^2-term and the x-term so that the coefficient of the x^2-term is 1. Complete the square of the x^2-term and the x-term, and factor the perfect square. Multiply the original coefficient of the x^2-term by the number added to complete the square. Subtract this product from the constant term.
3. See p. A7.

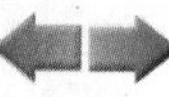

5-4 Exercises

go.hrw.com
Homework Help Online
KEYWORD: MB7 5-4
Parent Resources Online
KEYWORD: MB7 Parent

GUIDED PRACTICE

1. **Vocabulary** What must you add to the expression $x^2 + bx$ to *complete the square*? $\left(\frac{b}{2}\right)^2$

SEE EXAMPLE 1 p. 341

Solve each equation.

2. $(x-2)^2 = 16$ $-2, 6$
3. $x^2 - 10x + 25 = 16$ $1, 9$
4. $x^2 - 2x + 1 = 3$ $1 \pm \sqrt{3}$

SEE EXAMPLE 2 p. 342

Complete the square for each expression. Write the resulting expression as a binomial squared.

5. $x^2 + 14x + \blacksquare$ $x^2 + 14x + 49 = (x+7)^2$
6. $x^2 - 12x + \blacksquare$ $x^2 - 12x + 36 = (x-6)^2$
7. $x^2 - 9x + \blacksquare$ $x^2 - 9x + \frac{81}{4} = \left(x - \frac{9}{2}\right)^2$

SEE EXAMPLE 3 p. 343

Solve each equation by completing the square.

8. $x^2 - 6x = -4$ $3 \pm \sqrt{5}$
9. $x^2 + 8 = 6x$ $2, 4$
10. $2x^2 - 20x = 8$ $5 \pm \sqrt{29}$
11. $x^2 = 24 - 4x$ $-2 \pm 2\sqrt{7}$
12. $10x + x^2 = 42$ $-5 \pm \sqrt{67}$
13. $2x^2 + 8x - 15 = 0$ $-2 \pm \frac{\sqrt{46}}{2}$

SEE EXAMPLE 4 p. 344

Write each function in vertex form, and identify its vertex.

14. $f(x) = x^2 + 6x - 3$
15. $g(x) = x^2 - 10x + 11$
16. $h(x) = 3x^2 - 24x + 53$
17. $f(x) = x^2 + 8x - 10$
18. $g(x) = x^2 - 3x + 16$
19. $h(x) = 3x^2 - 12x - 4$

PRACTICE AND PROBLEM SOLVING

Independent Practice

For Exercises	See Example
20–22	1
23–25	2
26–31	3
32–37	4

Extra Practice
Skills Practice p. S12
Application Practice p. S36

Solve each equation.

20. $(x+2)^2 = 36$ $-8, 4$
21. $x^2 - 6x + 9 = 100$ $-7, 13$
22. $(x-3)^2 = 5$ $3 \pm \sqrt{5}$

Complete the square for each expression. Write the resulting expression as a binomial squared.

23. $x^2 - 18x + \blacksquare$ $x^2 - 18x + 81 = (x-9)^2$
24. $x^2 + 10x + \blacksquare$ $x^2 + 10x + 25 = (x+5)^2$
25. $x^2 - \frac{1}{2}x + \blacksquare$ $x^2 - \frac{1}{2}x + \frac{1}{16} = \left(x - \frac{1}{4}\right)^2$

Solve each equation by completing the square.

26. $x^2 + 2x = 7$ $-1 \pm 2\sqrt{2}$
27. $x^2 - 4x = -1$ $2 \pm \sqrt{3}$
28. $2x^2 - 8x = 22$ $2 \pm \sqrt{15}$
29. $8x = x^2 + 12$ $2, 6$
30. $x^2 + 3x - 5 = 0$
31. $3x^2 + 6x = 1$ $-1 \pm \frac{2\sqrt{3}}{3}$

Write each function in vertex form, and identify its vertex.

32. $f(x) = x^2 - 4x + 13$
33. $g(x) = x^2 + 14x + 71$
34. $h(x) = 9x^2 + 18x - 3$
35. $f(x) = x^2 + 4x - 7$
36. $g(x) = x^2 - 16x + 2$
37. $h(x) = 2x^2 + 6x + 25$

38. **Engineering** The height h above the roadway of the main cable of the Golden Gate Bridge can be modeled by the function $h(x) = \frac{1}{9000}x^2 - \frac{7}{15}x + 500$, where x is the distance in feet from the left tower.

a. Complete the square, and write the function in vertex form.
b. What is the vertex, and what does it represent?
c. **Multi-Step** The left and right towers have the same height. What is the distance in feet between them?

5-4 Exercises

Assignment Guide

Assign *Guided Practice* exercises as necessary.

If you finished Examples **1–2**
Basic 20–25, 41–49
Average 20–25, 41–49, 79
Advanced 20–25, 41–49, 79, 83

If you finished Examples **1–4**
Basic 20–62, 64–70, 72–78, 86–96
Average 20–80, 83–84, 86–96
Advanced 20–49, 51–96

Homework Quick Check
Quickly check key concepts.
Exercises: 20, 24, 26, 32, 40, 64

Transformations As an extension, have students describe each function in **Exercises 14–19** as a transformation of $f(x) = x^2$.

Answers

14. $f(x) = (x+3)^2 - 12$; $(-3, -12)$
15. $g(x) = (x-5)^2 - 14$; $(5, -14)$
16. $h(x) = 3(x-4)^2 + 5$; $(4, 5)$
17. $f(x) = (x+4)^2 - 26$; $(-4, -26)$
18. $g(x) = \left(x - \frac{3}{2}\right)^2 + \frac{55}{4}$; $\left(\frac{3}{2}, \frac{55}{4}\right)$
19. $h(x) = 3(x-2)^2 - 16$; $(2, -16)$
30. $x = -\frac{3}{2} \pm \frac{\sqrt{29}}{2}$
32. $f(x) = (x-2)^2 + 9$; $(2, 9)$
33. $g(x) = (x+7)^2 + 22$; $(-7, 22)$
34. $h(x) = 9(x+1)^2 - 12$; $(-1, -12)$
35. $f(x) = (x+2)^2 - 11$; $(-2, -11)$
36. $g(x) = (x-8)^2 - 62$; $(8, -62)$
37. $h(x) = 2(x+1.5)^2 + 20.5$; $(-1.5, 20.5)$
38a. $h(x) = \frac{1}{9000}(x - 2100)^2 + 10$
b. $(2100, 10)$; the vertex represents the distance from the left tower (2100 ft) at which the height of the main cable reaches its lowest point (10 ft above the roadway).
c. 4200 ft

State Resources

go.hrw.com
State Resources Online
KEYWORD: MB7 Resources

Number Sense For quadratic equations such as the one in **Exercise 55** where b is odd, encourage students to represent the value of $\left(\frac{b}{2}\right)^2$ as a fraction rather than a decimal. Point out that while most people will fail to recognize that 12.25 is the square of 3.5, they can easily see that the equivalent fraction $\frac{49}{4}$ is the square of $\frac{7}{2}$.

Answers

47. $x = \dfrac{-3 \pm 5\sqrt{2}}{2}$

49. $x = \dfrac{-3 \pm \sqrt{5}}{3}$

50. A is incorrect. Possible answer: In the third step, the number 4 is added inside the parentheses. Because the expression in parentheses is multiplied by 2, the total number added to the function rule is 8. Therefore, the number subtracted from the rule should be 8 instead of 4.

55. $x = \dfrac{7 \pm \sqrt{57}}{2}$

58. $x = \dfrac{-5 \pm 2\sqrt{15}}{5}$

60a. 5 m: 1 s; 10 m: ≈ 1.4 s; 20 m: 2 s; 30 m: ≈ 2.4 s

c. 5 m: 18 km/h; 10 m: ≈ 25 km/h; 20 m: 36 km/h; 30 m: ≈ 44 km/h

39. **Waterfalls** Angel Falls in Venezuela is the tallest waterfall in the world. Water falls uninterrupted for 2421 feet before entering the river below. The height h above the river in feet of water going over the edge of the waterfall is modeled by $h(t) = -16t^2 + 2421$, where t is the time in seconds after the initial fall.
    a. Estimate the time it takes for the water to reach the river. **about 12.3 s**
    b. **Multi-Step** Ribbon Falls in California has a height of 1612 ft. Approximately how much longer does it take water to reach the bottom when going over Angel Falls than when going over Ribbon Falls? **about 2.3 s**

40. **Sports** A basketball is shot with an initial vertical velocity of 24 ft/s from 6 ft above the ground. The ball's height h in feet is modeled by $h(t) = -16t^2 + 24t + 6$, where t is the time in seconds after the ball is shot. What is the maximum height of the ball, and when does the ball reach this height?
    The maximum height of 15 ft occurs 0.75 s after the ball is shot.

Solve each equation using square roots.

41. $x^2 - 1 = 2$ $\pm\sqrt{3}$
42. $25x^2 = 0$ 0
43. $8x^2 - 200 = 0$ ± 5
44. $-3x^2 + 6 = -1$ $\pm\dfrac{\sqrt{21}}{3}$
45. $(x + 13)^2 = 7$ $-13 \pm \sqrt{7}$
46. $\left(x + \frac{1}{4}\right)^2 - \frac{9}{16} = 0$ $-1, \dfrac{1}{2}$
47. $\left(x + \frac{3}{2}\right)^2 = \frac{25}{2}$
48. $x^2 + 14x + 49 = 64$ $-15, 1$
49. $9x^2 + 18x + 9 = 5$

50. **ERROR ANALYSIS** Two attempts to write $f(x) = 2x^2 - 8x$ in vertex form are shown. Which is incorrect? Explain the error.

A
$f(x) = 2x^2 - 8x$
$f(x) = 2(x^2 - 4x)$
$f(x) = 2(x^2 - 4x + 4) - 4$
$f(x) = 2(x - 2)^2 - 4$

B
$f(x) = 2x^2 - 8x$
$f(x) = 2(x^2 - 4x)$
$f(x) = 2(x^2 - 4x + 4) - 8$
$f(x) = 2(x - 2)^2 - 8$

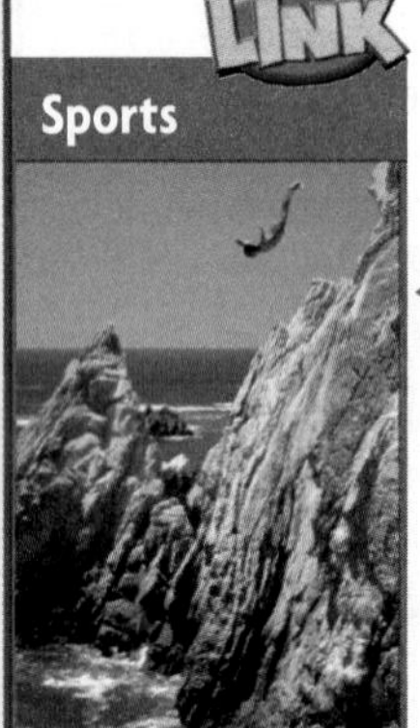

Acapulco, Mexico, is famous for its cliff-diving shows. Divers perform complicated acrobatic dives from heights of up to 80 feet.

Solve each equation by completing the square.

51. $x^2 + 8x = -15$ $-5, -3$
52. $x^2 + 22x = -21$ $-21, -1$
53. $3x^2 + 4x = 1$ $\dfrac{-2 \pm \sqrt{7}}{3}$
54. $2x^2 = 5x + 12$ $-\dfrac{3}{2}, 4$
55. $x^2 - 7x - 2 = 0$
56. $x^2 = 4x + 11$ $2 \pm \sqrt{15}$
57. $x^2 + 6x + 4 = 0$ $-3 \pm \sqrt{5}$
58. $5x^2 + 10x - 7 = 0$
59. $x^2 - 8x = 24$ $4 \pm 2\sqrt{10}$

60. **Sports** A diver's height h in meters above the water is approximated by $h(t) = h_0 - 5t^2$, where h_0 is the initial height in meters, -5 is a constant based on the acceleration due to gravity in m/s^2, and t is the time in seconds that the diver falls through the air.
    a. Find the total time that the diver falls through the air for each type of dive in the table.
    b. How high is a dive that keeps the diver in the air twice as long as a 5-meter dive? **20 m**
    c. The speed of a diver entering the water can be approximated by $s = 18t$, where s is the speed in kilometers per hour and t is the time in seconds. Using your results from part **a**, find the speed of the diver entering the water for each dive height.
    d. How many times as high is a dive that results in a speed that is twice as fast? **4 times as high**

Dive Heights

Type	Height (m)
Platform	5
Platform	10
Cliff	20
Cliff	30

5-4 PRACTICE A
5-4 PRACTICE C
5-4 PRACTICE B

Solve each equation.

1. $2x^2 - 6 = 42$ $x = \pm 2\sqrt{6}$
2. $x^2 - 14x + 49 = 18$ $x = 7 \pm 3\sqrt{2}$

Complete the square for each expression. Write the resulting expression as a binomial squared.

3. $x^2 - 4x +$ 4 $(x-2)^2$
4. $x^2 + 12x +$ 36 $(x+6)^2$

Solve each equation by completing the square.

5. $2d^2 = 8 + 10d$ $d = \frac{5}{2} \pm \frac{\sqrt{41}}{2}$
6. $x^2 + 2x = 3$ $x = -3, 1$
7. $-3x^2 + 18x = -30$ $x = 3 \pm \sqrt{19}$
8. $4x^2 = -12x + 4$ $x = -\frac{3}{2} \pm \frac{\sqrt{13}}{2}$

Write each function in vertex form, and identify its vertex.

9. $f(x) = x^2 - 6x - 2$ $f(x) = (x-3)^2 - 11$; $(3, -11)$
10. $f(x) = x^2 - 4x + 1$ $g(x) = (x-2)^2 - 3$; $(2, -3)$
11. $h(x) = 3x^2 - 6x - 15$ $h(x) = 3(x-1)^2 - 18$; $(1, -18)$
12. $f(x) = -2x^2 - 16x + 4$ $f(x) = -2(x+4)^2 + 36$; $(-4, 36)$

Solve.

13. Nathan made a triangular pennant for the band booster club. The area of the pennant is 80 square feet. The base of the pennant is 12 feet shorter than the height.
    a. What are the lengths of the base and height of the pennant? Base = 8 ft, height = 20 ft
    b. What are the dimensions of the pennant if the base is only 6 feet shorter than the height? Base = 10 ft, height = 16 ft

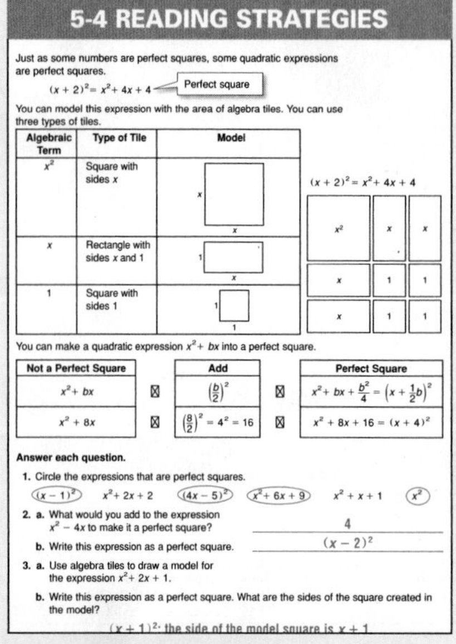

5-4 READING STRATEGIES

Just as some numbers are perfect squares, some quadratic expressions are perfect squares.

$(x + 2)^2 = x^2 + 4x + 4$ — Perfect square

You can model this expression with the area of algebra tiles. You can use three types of tiles.

Algebraic Term	Type of Tile	Model
x^2	Square with sides x	
x	Rectangle with sides x and 1	
1	Square with sides 1	

$(x + 2)^2 = x^2 + 4x + 4$

You can make a quadratic expression $x^2 + bx$ into a perfect square.

Not a Perfect Square		Add		Perfect Square
$x^2 + bx$	⊠	$\left(\frac{b}{2}\right)^2$	⊠	$x^2 + bx + \frac{b^2}{4} = \left(x + \frac{1}{2}b\right)^2$
$x^2 + 8x$	⊠	$\left(\frac{8}{2}\right)^2 = 4^2 = 16$	⊠	$x^2 + 8x + 16 = (x + 4)^2$

Answer each question.

1. Circle the expressions that are perfect squares.
   $(x-1)^2$ $x^2 + 2x + 2$ $(4x-5)^2$ $x^2 + 6x + 9$ $x^2 + x + 1$ x^2
2. a. What would you add to the expression $x^2 - 4x$ to make it a perfect square? 4
   b. Write this expression as a perfect square. $(x-2)^2$
3. a. Use algebra tiles to draw a model for the expression $x^2 + 2x + 1$.
   b. Write this expression as a perfect square. What are the sides of the square created in the model?
   $(x+1)^2$; the side of the model square is $x + 1$

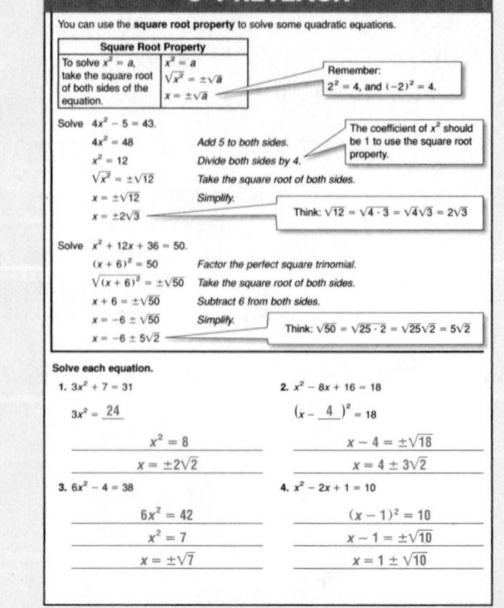

5-4 RETEACH

You can use the **square root property** to solve some quadratic equations.

Square Root Property	
To solve $x^2 = a$, take the square root of both sides of the equation.	$x^2 = a$ $\sqrt{x^2} = \pm\sqrt{a}$ $x = \pm\sqrt{a}$

Remember: $2^2 = 4$, and $(-2)^2 = 4$.

Solve $4x^2 - 5 = 43$.
$4x^2 = 48$ *Add 5 to both sides.*
$x^2 = 12$ *Divide both sides by 4.*
$\sqrt{x^2} = \pm\sqrt{12}$ *Take the square root of both sides.*
$x = \pm\sqrt{12}$ *Simplify.*
$x = \pm 2\sqrt{3}$

The coefficient of x^2 should be 1 to use the square root property.

Think: $\sqrt{12} = \sqrt{4 \cdot 3} = \sqrt{4}\sqrt{3} = 2\sqrt{3}$

Solve $x^2 + 12x + 36 = 50$.
$(x + 6)^2 = 50$ *Factor the perfect square trinomial.*
$\sqrt{(x+6)^2} = \pm\sqrt{50}$ *Take the square root of both sides.*
$x + 6 = \pm\sqrt{50}$ *Subtract 6 from both sides.*
$x = -6 \pm \sqrt{50}$ *Simplify.*
$x = -6 \pm 5\sqrt{2}$

Think: $\sqrt{50} = \sqrt{25 \cdot 2} = \sqrt{25}\sqrt{2} = 5\sqrt{2}$

Solve each equation.

1. $3x^2 + 7 = 31$
   $3x^2 =$ 24
   $x^2 = 8$
   $x = \pm 2\sqrt{2}$
2. $x^2 - 8x + 16 = 18$
   $(x -$ 4 $)^2 = 18$
   $x - 4 = \pm\sqrt{18}$
   $x = 4 \pm 3\sqrt{2}$
3. $6x^2 - 4 = 38$
   $6x^2 = 42$
   $x^2 = 7$
   $x = \pm\sqrt{7}$
4. $x^2 - 2x + 1 = 10$
   $(x - 1)^2 = 10$
   $x - 1 = \pm\sqrt{10}$
   $x = 1 \pm \sqrt{10}$

61. This problem will prepare you for the Multi-Step Test Prep on page 364.

The height h in feet of a baseball hit from home plate can be modeled by the function $h(t) = -16t^2 + 32t + 5.5$, where t is the time in seconds since the ball was hit. The ball is descending when it passes 7.5 ft over the head of a 6 ft player standing on the ground.

a. To the nearest tenth of a second, how long after the ball is hit does it pass over the player's head? **1.7 s**

b. The horizontal distance between the player and home plate is 120 ft. Use your answer from part **a** to determine the horizontal speed of the ball to the nearest foot per second. **71 ft/s**

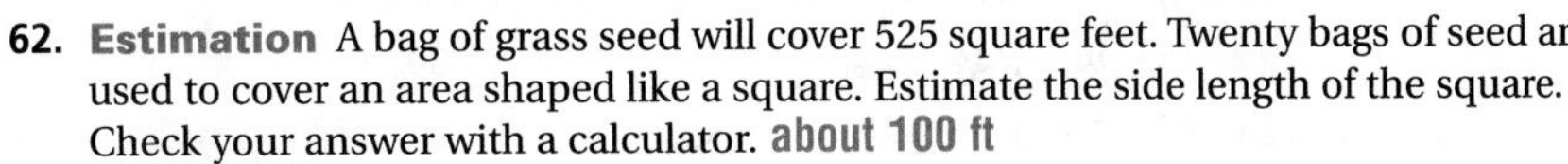

62. **Estimation** A bag of grass seed will cover 525 square feet. Twenty bags of seed are used to cover an area shaped like a square. Estimate the side length of the square. Check your answer with a calculator. **about 100 ft**

63. **Critical Thinking** The functions f and g are defined by $f(x) = x^2 + 2x - 2$ and $g(x) = (x + 1)^2 - 3$. Use algebra to prove that f and g represent the same function.

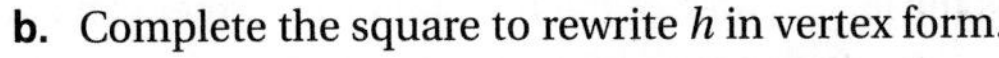

64. **Sports** A player bumps a volleyball with an initial vertical velocity of 20 ft/s.

a. Write a function h in standard form for the ball's height in feet in terms of the time t in seconds after the ball is hit.

b. Complete the square to rewrite h in vertex form.

c. What is the maximum height of the ball?

d. **What if...?** Suppose the volleyball were hit under the same conditions, but with an initial velocity of 32 ft/s. How much higher would the ball go?

Graphing Calculator **Use a graphing calculator to approximate the roots of each equation to the nearest thousandth.**

65. $x^2 - 15 = 40$

66. $x^2 = 2.85$

67. $1.4x^2 = 24.6$

68. $(x + 0.6)^2 = 7.4$

69. $\frac{x^2}{7} = \frac{1}{3}$

70. $\left(x + \frac{1}{4}\right)^2 = \frac{5}{6}$

71. **Critical Thinking** Why do equations of the form $x^2 = k$ have no real solution when $k < 0$? **The square root of a negative number is not a real number.**

72. **Write About It** Compare the methods of factoring and completing the square for solving quadratic equations.

TEST PREP

73. Which gives the solution to $3x^2 = 33$?

Ⓐ $\pm\sqrt{3}$ Ⓑ $\pm\sqrt{11}$ Ⓒ 11 Ⓓ 121

74. Which equation represents the graph at right?

Ⓕ $y = (x - 2)^2 + 1$

Ⓖ $y = (x - 2)^2 - 1$

Ⓗ $y = (x + 2)^2 + 1$

Ⓙ $y = (x + 2)^2 - 1$

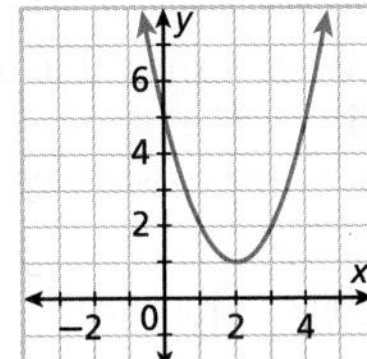

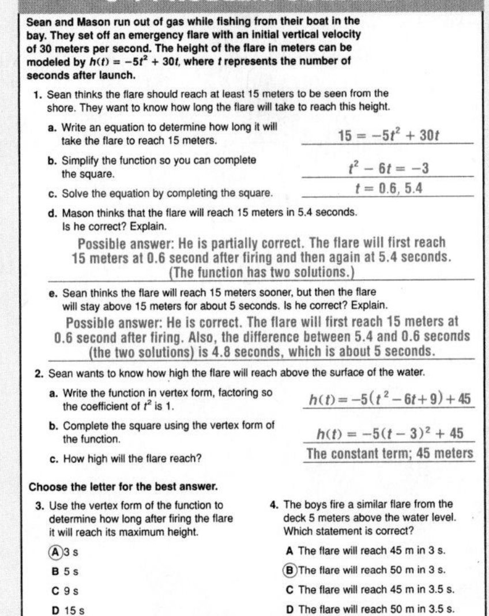

5-4 PROBLEM SOLVING

Sean and Mason run out of gas while fishing from their boat in the bay. They set off an emergency flare with an initial vertical velocity of 30 meters per second. The height of the flare in meters can be modeled by $h(t) = -5t^2 + 30t$, where t represents the number of seconds after launch.

1. Sean thinks the flare should reach at least 15 meters to be seen from the shore. They want to know how long the flare will take to reach this height.

a. Write an equation to determine how long it will take the flare to reach 15 meters. $15 = -5t^2 + 30t$

b. Simplify the function so you can complete the square. $t^2 - 6t = -3$

c. Solve the equation by completing the square. $t = 0.6, 5.4$

d. Mason thinks that the flare will reach 15 meters in 5.4 seconds. Is he correct? Explain.

Possible answer: He is partially correct. The flare will first reach 15 meters at 0.6 second after firing and then again at 5.4 seconds. (The function has two solutions.)

e. Sean thinks the flare will reach 15 meters sooner, but then the flare will stay above 15 meters for about 5 seconds. Is he correct? Explain.

Possible answer: He is correct. The flare will first reach 15 meters at 0.6 second after firing. Also, the difference between 5.4 and 0.6 seconds (the two solutions) is 4.8 seconds, which is about 5 seconds.

2. Sean wants to know how high the flare will reach above the surface of the water.

a. Write the function in vertex form, factoring so the coefficient of t^2 is 1. $h(t) = -5(t^2 - 6t + 9) + 45$

b. Complete the square using the vertex form of the function. $h(t) = -5(t - 3)^2 + 45$

c. How high will the flare reach? The constant term; 45 meters

Choose the letter for the best answer.

3. Use the vertex form of the function to determine how long after firing the flare it will reach its maximum height.

Ⓐ 3 s
B 5 s
C 9 s
D 15 s

4. The boys fire a similar flare from the deck 5 meters above the water level. Which statement is correct?

A The flare will reach 45 m in 3 s.
Ⓑ The flare will reach 50 m in 3 s.
C The flare will reach 45 m in 3.5 s.
D The flare will reach 50 m in 3.5 s.

5-4 CHALLENGE

The ancient Greeks constructed rectangles called golden rectangles because they were thought to be pleasing to the eye. A rectangle is considered golden if the dimensions of the rectangle are in a certain ratio.

$$\frac{l}{w} = \frac{l + w}{l}$$

The ratio $\frac{l}{w}$ is called the golden ratio. A golden rectangle with length l and width w has the property that if it is joined to a square of side length l to form a larger rectangle, the length-to-width ratio of the larger rectangle is the same as that of the original rectangle.

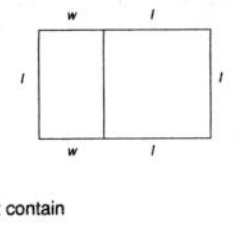

w l
l l
w l

Solve.

1. a. Clear the equation of fractions and collect all the terms that contain variables on the left side of the equation.

$l^2 = wl + w^2$, $l^2 - wl - w^2 = 0$

b. Complete the square and solve for l in terms of w. Ignore the negative solution since l must be a positive number. Use the result to find both the exact value of $\frac{l}{w}$ and a decimal approximation.

$l^2 - wl = w^2$, $l^2 - wl + \left(\frac{w}{2}\right)^2 = w^2 + \left(\frac{w}{2}\right)^2$,

$\left(l - \frac{w}{2}\right)^2 = \frac{5w^2}{4}$, $l - \frac{w}{2} = \frac{\sqrt{5}w}{2}$, $l = \frac{1 + \sqrt{5}}{2}w$, $l \cong 1.618w$

2. Measure the length and width of a credit card and calculate the ratio of the length and width. Does this closely approximate the golden ratio? Possible answer: The ratio of length to width is about 1.588, a little less than the golden ratio.

3. a. In the Fibonacci Sequence, {1, 1, 2, 3, 5, 8, 13, 21, 34, . . .}, each term from the third term on is the sum of the previous two terms. Make a list of values of the ratio of a term and it predecessor.

$1, 2, \frac{3}{2}, \frac{5}{3}, \frac{8}{5}, \frac{13}{8}, \frac{21}{13}, \frac{34}{21}, \frac{55}{34}, \ldots$

b. What decimal value do these ratios approximate as the list is continued? The golden ratio, 1.618

4. Consider the continued fraction $1 + \cfrac{1}{1 + \cfrac{1}{1 + \cfrac{1}{1 + \ldots}}}$.

Make a table of decimal values for this fraction when 1 fraction is used, then 2, then 3, and so on. Round the values to the nearest thousandth. What value do the fractions seem to approach?

2, 1.5, 1.667, 1.6, 1.625, 1.615, 1.619, 1.618; they seem to approach the golden ratio.

COMMON ERROR ALERT

Students may not know where to start when solving **Exercise 38 part c.** Point out that they can find the height of the left tower by finding the value of h when $x = 0$. They can then find the other value of x that gives this value of h.

MULTI-STEP TEST PREP **Exercise 61** involves solving a quadratic equation relating a baseball's height to the time since it was hit. This exercise prepares students for the Multi-Step Test Prep on page 364.

Answers

63. Possible answer: Complete the square to write f in vertex form.

$f(x) = x^2 + 2x - 2$

$f(x) = (x^2 + 2x + 1) - 2 - 1$

$f(x) = (x + 1)^2 - 3$

The vertex forms are identical, so f and g represent the same function.

64a. $h(t) = -16t^2 + 20t + 4$

b. $h(t) = -16\left(t - \frac{5}{8}\right)^2 + 10\frac{1}{4}$

c. $10\frac{1}{4}$ ft

d. $9\frac{3}{4}$ ft higher

65. ± 7.416

66. ± 1.688

67. ± 4.192

68. -3.320, 2.120

69. ± 1.528

70. -1.163, 0.663

72. Possible answer: Factoring is useful for solving quadratic equations with integer roots when the coefficient of the x^2-term is not a large number. Completing the square is useful for solving quadratic equations that cannot be factored easily. It involves rewriting part of an equation so that it can be factored as a perfect-square trinomial.

In **Exercise 76,** students who chose **J** may have forgotten that the value of b must be divided by 2 before it is squared. Students who chose **F** may have forgotten to square the result once they divided the value of b by 2.

Journal

Have students state which method they would use to solve the equation $x^2 - x = 72$ and explain the reasons for their choice.

ALTERNATIVE ASSESSMENT

Have students create a quadratic function in standard form and find its zeros by completing the square. Then have them write the function in vertex form. Instruct students to show each step of their work.

Power Presentations with PowerPoint®

5-4 Lesson Quiz

1. Complete the square for the expression $x^2 - 15x + \blacksquare$. Write the resulting expression as a binomial squared.
$x^2 - 15x + \frac{225}{4} = \left(x - \frac{15}{2}\right)^2$

Solve each equation.

2. $x^2 - 16x + 64 = 20$
$8 \pm 2\sqrt{5}$

3. $x^2 - 27 = 4x$
$2 \pm \sqrt{31}$

Write each function in vertex form and identify its vertex.

4. $f(x) = x^2 + 6x - 7$
$f(x) = (x + 3)^2 - 16$; $(-3, -16)$

5. $f(x) = 2x^2 - 12x - 27$
$f(x) = 2(x - 3)^2 - 45$; $(3, -45)$

Also available on transparency

75. Which gives the vertex of the graph of $y = 3(x - 1)^2 - 22$?
(A) $(1, -22)$ (B) $(-1, -22)$ (C) $(3, -22)$ (D) $(-3, -22)$

76. Which number should be added to $x^2 + 14x$ to make a perfect square trinomial?
(F) 7 (G) 14 (H) 49 (J) 196

77. **Gridded Response** What is the positive root of the equation $2x^2 - x = 10$? 2.5

78. **Extended Response** Solve the quadratic equation $x^2 - 6x = 16$ by completing the square. Explain each step of the solution process, and check your answer.

CHALLENGE AND EXTEND

Find the value of b in each perfect square trinomial.

79. $x^2 - bx + 144$ ± 24

80. $4x^2 - bx + 16$ ± 16

81. $3x^2 + bx + 27$ ± 18

82. $ax^2 + bx + c$ $\pm 2\sqrt{ac}$

Find the zeros of each function.

83. $f(x) = x^2 - 4x\sqrt{5} + 19$ $2\sqrt{5} \pm 1$

84. $f(x) = x^2 + 6x\sqrt{3} + 23$ $-3\sqrt{3} \pm 2$

85. **Farming** To create a temporary grazing area, a farmer is using 1800 feet of electric fencing to enclose a rectangular field and then to subdivide the field into two plots. The fence that divides the field into two plots is parallel to the field's shorter sides.

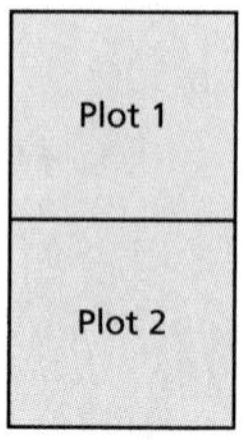

Plot 1
Plot 2

a. What is the largest area of the field that the farmer can enclose?
85a. 135,000 ft²

b. What are the dimensions of the field with the largest area?
85b. 450 ft by 300 ft

c. **What if...?** What would be the largest area of a square field that the farmer could enclose and divide into two plots? 129,600 ft²

SPIRAL REVIEW

Express each set of numbers using set-builder notation. *(Lesson 1-1)*

86. $(72, \infty)$ $\{x \mid x > 72\}$

87. numbers within 10 units of 4 $\{x \mid -6 \le x \le 14\}$

88. positive multiples of 4
$\{x \mid x = 4n \text{ for } n \in N\}$

89. 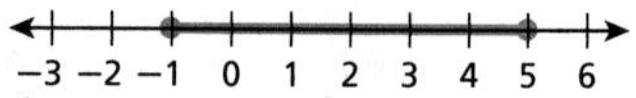 [number line from −3 to 6, shaded from −1 to 5]
$\{x \mid -1 \le x \le 5\}$

Use the table for Exercises 90–93. *(Lesson 4-1)*

Monthly Budget	Food	Housing	Auto
Aboline family	\$352	\$895	\$426
Hernandez family	\$675	\$1368	\$642
Walker family	\$185	\$615	\$295

90. Display the data in the form of a matrix B.
$B = \begin{bmatrix} 352 & 895 & 426 \\ 675 & 1368 & 642 \\ 185 & 615 & 295 \end{bmatrix}$

91. What are the dimensions of the matrix? 3×3

92. What is the address of the entry that has the value 185? b_{31}

93. What is the value of the matrix entry with the address b_{22}? What does it represent?
1368; the amount in dollars the Hernandez family budgeted for housing

Identify the axis of symmetry and the vertex of the graph of each function. *(Lesson 5-2)*

94. $f(x) = 3(x - 2)^2$
$x = 2$; $(2, 0)$

95. $g(x) = \frac{2}{5}x^2 - 1$
$x = 0$; $(0, -1)$

96. $h(x) = 6x^2 + 2.5$
$x = 0$; $(0, 2.5)$

Answers

78. $x = 8$ or $x = -2$; check students' work.

See Skills Bank page S61

Areas of Composite Figures

Quadratic equations can be used to solve problems involving the areas of composite figures. Write an equation that represents the information given in the problem. Then solve the equation.

Example

The diagram shows a rectangular garden surrounded by a walkway. The garden measures 10 m by 34 m. The total area of the garden and walkway is 640 m². What is the width x of the walkway?

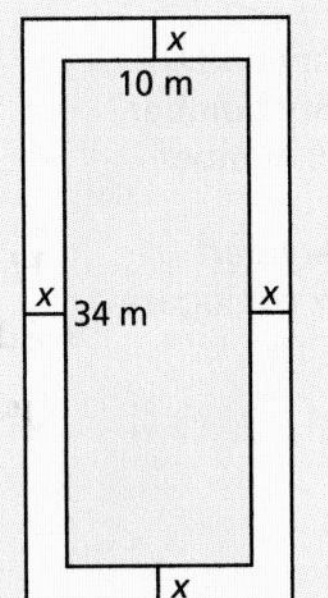

Total area = 640 m²

The total area is equal to the total length multiplied by the total width. The total length is $2x + 34$ m, and the total width is $2x + 10$ m.

$A = \ell \times w$	*Write the formula for total area.*
$640 = (2x + 34)(2x + 10)$	*Substitute.*
$640 = 4x^2 + 88x + 340$	*Multiply the binomials.*
$0 = 4x^2 + 88x - 300$	*Subtract 640 from both sides.*
$0 = x^2 + 22x - 75$	*Divide both sides by 4.*
$0 = (x - 3)(x + 25)$	*Factor.*
$x - 3 = 0$ or $x + 25 = 0$	*Use the Zero Product Property.*
$x = 3$ or $x = -25$	*Solve for x.*

The width cannot be negative. Therefore, the width of the walkway is 3 m.

Try This

Write an equation that represents each problem. Then solve.

1. Use figure 1 below. A ring of grass with an area of 314 yd² surrounds a circular flower bed. Find the width x of the ring of grass.
2. Use figure 2 below. Sid cuts four congruent squares from the corners of a 30-in.-by-50-in. rectangular piece of cardboard so that it can be folded to make a box. Find the side length s of the squares, given that the area of the bottom of the box is 200 in².
3. Use figure 3 below. Harriet has 80 m of fencing materials to enclose three sides of a rectangular garden. She will use the side of her garage as a border for the fourth side. Find the width x of the garden if its area is to be 700 m².

Figure 1

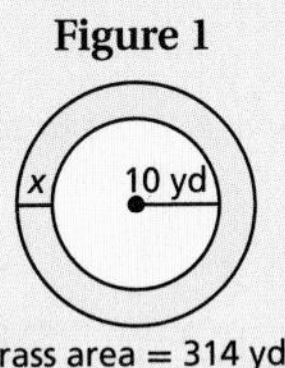

Grass area = 314 yd²

Figure 2

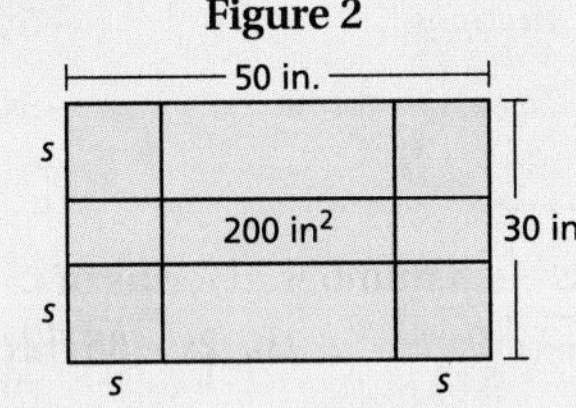

Figure 3

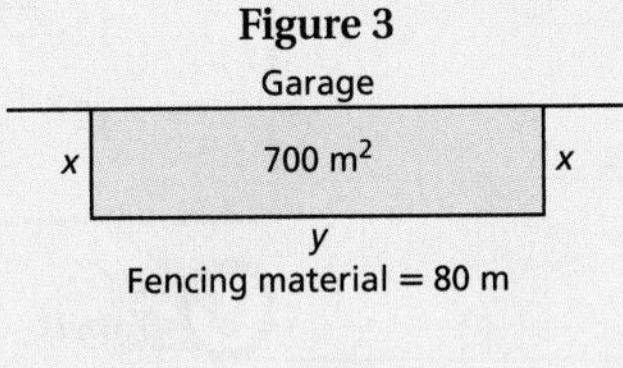

Fencing material = 80 m

Answers to *Try This*

1. Possible answer: $314 = \pi(x + 10)^2 - \pi(10)^2$; about 4.1 yd
2. Possible answer: $200 = (50 - 2s)(30 - 2s)$; about 11.3 in.
3. Possible answer: $700 = x(80 - 2x)$; about 12.9 m (or 27.1 m)

Connecting Algebra to Geometry

Organizer

See Skills Bank page S61

Pacing:

Traditional $\frac{1}{2}$ day
Block $\frac{1}{4}$ day

Objective: Apply algebra skills to solving problems involving areas of geometric figures.

Online Edition

Countdown to Testing Week 11

Teach

Remember

Students review and apply area formulas for geometric figures.

INTERVENTION For additional review and practice on finding the area of geometric figures, see Skills Bank page S61.

Critical Thinking Discuss with students how they can check their answers to the problems on this page.

Close

Assess

Have students write a general set of instructions that can be used to solve area problems like the ones in this activity.

State Resources

go.hrw.com
State Resources Online
KEYWORD: MB7 Resources

5-5 Organizer

Pacing: Traditional 1 day
Block $\frac{1}{2}$ day

Objectives: Define and use imaginary and complex numbers.

Solve quadratic equations with complex roots.

Online Edition
Tutorial Videos

Countdown to Testing Week 11

Power Presentations with PowerPoint®

Warm Up

Simplify each expression.

1. $\sqrt{108}$ $6\sqrt{3}$
2. $\sqrt{6} \cdot \sqrt{24}$ 12
3. $\dfrac{\sqrt{42}}{-\sqrt{3}}$ $-\sqrt{14}$

Find the zeros of each function.

4. $f(x) = x^2 - 18x + 16$
   $9 \pm \sqrt{65}$
5. $f(x) = x^2 + 8x - 24$
   $-4 \pm 2\sqrt{10}$

Also available on transparency

Math Humor

Q: What's a mathematician's favorite dessert?

A: $\sqrt{-1}$ce cream.

5-5 Complex Numbers and Roots

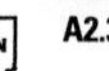

A2.3.2 Solve quadratic equations in the complex number system.

Objectives
Define and use imaginary and complex numbers.

Solve quadratic equations with complex roots.

Vocabulary
imaginary unit
imaginary number
complex number
real part
imaginary part
complex conjugate

Why learn this?
Complex numbers can be used to describe the zeros of quadratic functions that have no real zeros. (See Example 4.)

Andrew Toos/CartoonResource.com

You can see in the graph of $f(x) = x^2 + 1$ below that f has no real zeros. If you solve the corresponding equation $0 = x^2 + 1$, you find that $x = \pm\sqrt{-1}$, which has no *real* solutions.

However, you can find solutions if you define the square root of negative numbers, which is why *imaginary numbers* were invented. The **imaginary unit** i is defined as $\sqrt{-1}$. You can use the imaginary unit to write the square root of any negative number.

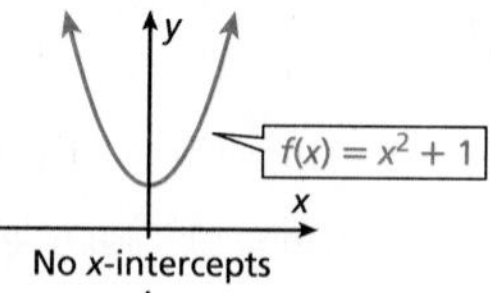

Know it! Note — **Imaginary Numbers**

WORDS	NUMBERS	ALGEBRA
An **imaginary number** is the square root of a negative number.	$\sqrt{-1} = i$	If b is a positive real number,
Imaginary numbers can be written in the form bi, where b is a real number and i is the imaginary unit.	$\sqrt{-2} = \sqrt{-1}\sqrt{2} = i\sqrt{2}$ $\sqrt{-4} = \sqrt{-1}\sqrt{4} = 2i$	then $\sqrt{-b} = i\sqrt{b}$ and $\sqrt{-b^2} = bi$.
The square of an imaginary number is the original negative number.	$\left(\sqrt{-1}\right)^2 = i^2 = -1$	$\left(\sqrt{-b}\right)^2 = -b$

EXAMPLE 1 Simplifying Square Roots of Negative Numbers

Express each number in terms of i.

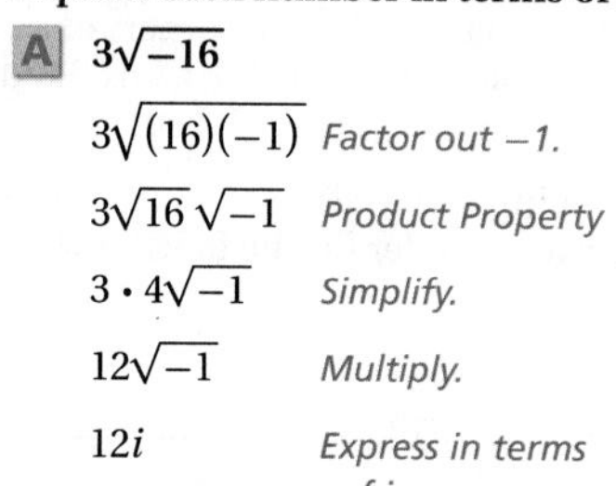

A $3\sqrt{-16}$

$3\sqrt{(16)(-1)}$	*Factor out −1.*
$3\sqrt{16}\sqrt{-1}$	*Product Property*
$3 \cdot 4\sqrt{-1}$	*Simplify.*
$12\sqrt{-1}$	*Multiply.*
$12i$	*Express in terms of i.*

B $-\sqrt{-75}$

$-\sqrt{(75)(-1)}$	*Factor out −1.*
$-\sqrt{75}\sqrt{-1}$	*Product Property*
$-\sqrt{25}\sqrt{3}\sqrt{-1}$	*Product Property*
$-5\sqrt{3}\sqrt{-1}$	*Simplify.*
$-5\sqrt{3}i = -5i\sqrt{3}$	*Express in terms of i.*

CHECK IT OUT! Express each number in terms of i.

1a. $\sqrt{-12}$ $2i\sqrt{3}$ **1b.** $2\sqrt{-36}$ $12i$ **1c.** $-\frac{1}{3}\sqrt{-63}$ $-i\sqrt{7}$

State Resources

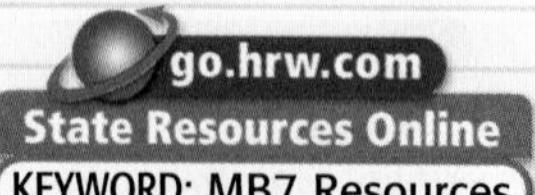

go.hrw.com
State Resources Online
KEYWORD: MB7 Resources

1 Introduce

EXPLORATION

5-5 Complex Numbers and Roots

Recall that the Product Property of Square Roots states that $\sqrt{b} = \sqrt{a} : \sqrt{b}$. Use this property to write each expression as the product of an integer and $\sqrt{-1}$.

1. $\sqrt{-36}$ 2. $-\sqrt{-4}$
3. $\sqrt{-81}$ 4. $-\sqrt{-144}$

The number $\sqrt{-1}$ is often represented by i. For example, $\sqrt{-25}$ can be written as $\sqrt{25} \cdot \sqrt{-1}$, or 5i. Write each expression in terms of i.

5. $\sqrt{-36}$ 6. $-\sqrt{-4}$
7. $\sqrt{-81}$ 8. $-\sqrt{-144}$

THINK AND DISCUSS

9. **Explain** why the square root of any negative number can be written in terms of i.
10. **Discuss** how i can be used to express the solutions of the quadratic equation $x^2 + 4 = 0$.

Motivate

Have students graph the function $f(x) = x^2 + 4x + 8$ on a graphing calculator. Ask them to identify any zeros of the function. Explain that although this function has no real zeros, it does have complex zeros. Tell students that they will be learning about complex numbers and complex zeros in this lesson.

Explorations and answers are provided in the *Explorations* binder.

EXAMPLE 2 Solving a Quadratic Equation with Imaginary Solutions

Solve each equation.

A $x^2 = -81$

$x = \pm\sqrt{-81}$ *Take square roots.*

$x = \pm 9i$ *Express in terms of i.*

Check

$x^2 = -81$	
$(9i)^2$	-81
$81i^2$	-81
$81(-1)$	-81 ✓

$x^2 = -81$	
$(-9i)^2$	-81
$81i^2$	-81
$81(-1)$	-81 ✓

B $3x^2 + 75 = 0$

$3x^2 = -75$ *Add −75 to both sides.*

$x^2 = -25$ *Divide both sides by 3.*

$x = \pm\sqrt{-25}$ *Take square roots.*

$x = \pm 5i$ *Express in terms of i.*

Check

$3x^2 + 75 = 0$	
$3(\pm 5i)^2 + 75$	0
$3(25)i^2 + 75$	0
$75(-1) + 75$	0 ✓

CHECK IT OUT! Solve each equation.

2a. $x^2 = -36$ $\pm 6i$ **2b.** $x^2 + 48 = 0$ $\pm 4i\sqrt{3}$ **2c.** $9x^2 + 25 = 0$ $\pm\frac{5}{3}i$

A **complex number** is a number that can be written in the form $a + bi$, where a and b are real numbers and $i = \sqrt{-1}$. The set of real numbers is a subset of the set of complex numbers $\mathbb{C}$.

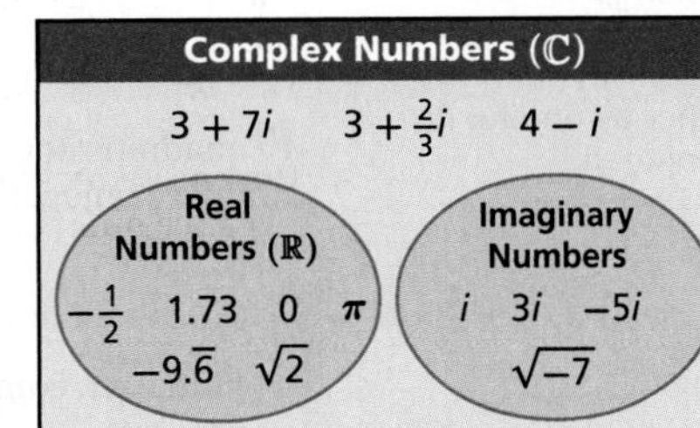

Every complex number has a **real part** a and an **imaginary part** b.

Real numbers are complex numbers where $b = 0$. Imaginary numbers are complex numbers where $a = 0$ and $b \neq 0$. These are sometimes called *pure imaginary numbers*.

Two complex numbers are equal if and only if their real parts are equal and their imaginary parts are equal.

EXAMPLE 3 Equating Two Complex Numbers

Find the values of x and y that make the equation $3x - 5i = 6 - (10y)i$ true.

Real parts

$3x - 5i = 6 - (10y)i$

Imaginary parts

$3x = 6$ *Equate the real parts.* $-5 = -(10y)$ *Equate the imaginary parts.*

$x = 2$ *Solve for x.* $\frac{1}{2} = y$ *Solve for y.*

CHECK IT OUT! Find the values of x and y that make each equation true.

3a. $2x - 6i = -8 + (20y)i$ **3b.** $-8 + (6y)i = 5x - i\sqrt{6}$

3a. $x = -4;\ y = -\frac{3}{10}$

3b. $x = -\frac{8}{5};\ y = -\frac{\sqrt{6}}{6}$

2 Teach

Guided Instruction

The concept of imaginary numbers will be new to most students. Emphasize that the symbol i is simply a shorthand way of writing $\sqrt{-1}$ and that the square root of any negative number can be written as the product of i and the square root of a positive number. Point out that $\sqrt{-1}$ and other imaginary numbers are not on the real number line. Explain that one use of imaginary numbers is to define solutions of quadratic equations that lack real solutions.

Reaching All Learners

Through Visual Cues

Have students make a concept map of the complex number system similar to the one below to help them see the relationship among the different types of numbers. Ask them to include examples in each box.

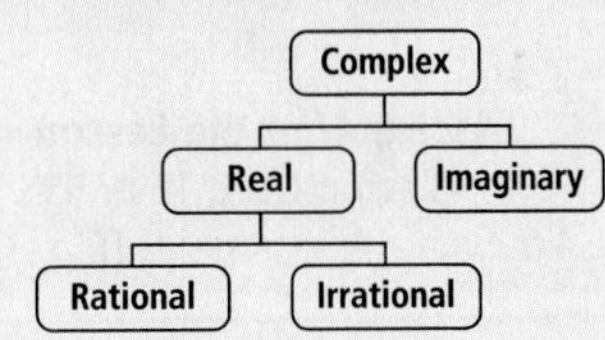

COMMON ERROR ALERT

Some students may try to simplify a complex number by combining the real part and the imaginary part. For example, they may try to write $5 + 6i$ as $11i$. Emphasize that just as unlike terms in an algebraic expression cannot be combined, neither can the real and imaginary parts of a complex number. Therefore, $5i + 6i = 11i$, but $5 + 6i \neq 5i + 6i$.

Power Presentations with PowerPoint®

Additional Examples

Example 1

Express each number in terms of *i*.

A. $5\sqrt{-121}$ $55i$

B. $-\sqrt{-96}$ $-4i\sqrt{6}$

Example 2

Solve each equation.

A. $x^2 = -144$ $\pm 12i$

B. $5x^2 + 90 = 0$ $\pm 3i\sqrt{2}$

Example 3

Find the values of x and y that make the equation $4x + 10i = 2 - (4y)i$ true.

$x = \frac{1}{2};\ y = -\frac{5}{2}$

Also available on transparency

INTERVENTION

Questioning Strategies

EXAMPLES 1–2

- How do you use the imaginary unit to express complex numbers in terms of i?

EXAMPLE 3

- How can you tell which part of a complex number is the real part and which is the imaginary part?

Power Presentations with PowerPoint®

Additional Examples

Example 4

Find the zeros of each function.

A. $f(x) = x^2 + 10x + 26$
$-5 \pm i$

B. $g(x) = x^2 + 4x + 12$
$-2 \pm 2i\sqrt{2}$

Example 5

Find each complex conjugate.

A. $8 + 5i$ $\quad 8 - 5i$

B. $6i$ $\quad -6i$

Also available on transparency

INTERVENTION

Questioning Strategies

EXAMPLE 4

- At which step in the solution process do you know that the function does not have real zeros? How do you know?

EXAMPLE 5

- How do you know the values of a and b?
- How does a complex number differ from its conjugate?

EXAMPLE 4 Finding Complex Zeros of Quadratic Functions

Find the zeros of each function.

A $f(x) = x^2 - 2x + 5$

$x^2 - 2x + 5 = 0$	*Set equal to 0.*
$x^2 - 2x + \square = -5 + \square$	*Rewrite.*
$x^2 - 2x + 1 = -5 + 1$	*Add $\left(\frac{b}{2}\right)^2$.*
$(x-1)^2 = -4$	*Factor.*
$x - 1 = \pm\sqrt{-4}$	*Take square roots.*
$x = 1 \pm 2i$	*Simplify.*

B $g(x) = x^2 + 10x + 35$

$x^2 + 10x + 35 = 0$

$x^2 + 10x + \square = -35 + \square$

$x^2 + 10x + 25 = -35 + 25$

$(x+5)^2 = -10$

$x + 5 = \pm\sqrt{-10}$

$x = -5 \pm i\sqrt{10}$

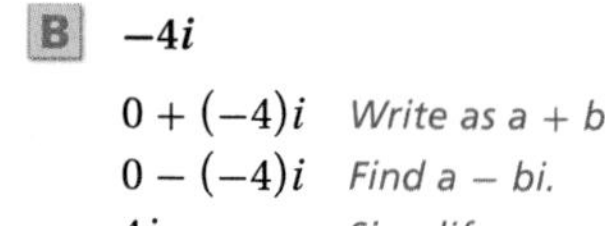

CHECK IT OUT! Find the zeros of each function.

4a. $f(x) = x^2 + 4x + 13$ $\quad -2 \pm 3i$

4b. $g(x) = x^2 - 8x + 18$ $\quad 4 \pm i\sqrt{2}$

Helpful Hint

When given one complex root, you can always find the other by finding its conjugate.

The solutions $-5 + i\sqrt{10}$ and $-5 - i\sqrt{10}$ in Example 4B are related. These solutions are a *complex conjugate* pair. Their real parts are equal and their imaginary parts are opposites. The **complex conjugate** of any complex number $a + bi$ is the complex number $a - bi$.

If a quadratic equation with real coefficients has nonreal roots, those roots are complex conjugates.

EXAMPLE 5 Finding Complex Conjugates

Find each complex conjugate.

A $2i - 15$

$-15 + 2i$	*Write as a + bi.*
$-15 - 2i$	*Find a − bi.*

B $-4i$

$0 + (-4)i$	*Write as a + bi.*
$0 - (-4)i$	*Find a − bi.*
$4i$	*Simplify.*

CHECK IT OUT! Find each complex conjugate.

5a. $9 - i$ $\quad 9 + i$ $\qquad$ **5b.** $i + \sqrt{3}$ $\quad \sqrt{3} - i$ $\qquad$ **5c.** $-8i$ $\quad 8i$

THINK AND DISCUSS

1. Given that one solution of a quadratic equation is $3 + i$, explain how to determine the other solution.
2. Describe a number of the form $a + bi$ in which $a \neq 0$ and $b = 0$. Then describe a number in which $a = 0$ and $b \neq 0$. Are both numbers complex? Explain.
3. **GET ORGANIZED** Copy and complete the graphic organizer. In each box or oval, give a definition and examples of each type of number.

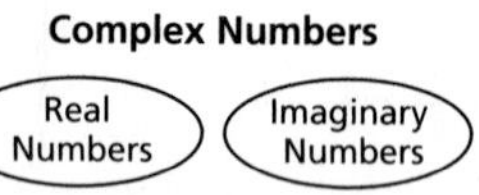

3 Close

Summarize

Have students write the expression $\sqrt{-12} + \sqrt{36}$ as a complex number of the form $a + bi$ and identify its real and imaginary parts. $6 + 2i\sqrt{3}$; real: 6; imaginary: $2\sqrt{3}$ Emphasize that when the solutions of a quadratic equation include the square root of a negative number, the solutions are complex, but not real.

ONGOING ASSESSMENT and INTERVENTION

***Diagnose Before* the Lesson**
5-5 Warm Up, TE p. 350

***Monitor During* the Lesson**
Check It Out! Exercises, SE pp. 350–352
Questioning Strategies, TE pp. 351–352

***Assess After* the Lesson**
5-5 Lesson Quiz, TE p. 355
Alternative Assessment, TE p. 355

Answers to *Think and Discuss*

Possible answers:

1. If a quadratic equation has nonreal roots, the roots are complex conjugates. Because $3 + i$ is nonreal, the other solution is its complex conjugate, $3 - i$.
2. A real number equal to a; an imaginary number equal to bi; yes; both are complex, because real numbers and imaginary numbers are both subsets of complex numbers.
3. See p. A7.

5-5 Exercises

go.hrw.com
Homework Help Online
KEYWORD: MB7 5-5
Parent Resources Online
KEYWORD: MB7 Parent

GUIDED PRACTICE

1. **Vocabulary** The number 7 is the __?__ part of the complex number $\sqrt{5} + 7i$. (*real* or *imaginary*) imaginary

SEE EXAMPLE 1 p. 350

Express each number in terms of i.

2. $5\sqrt{-100}$ $50i$
3. $\frac{1}{2}\sqrt{-16}$ $2i$
4. $-\sqrt{-32}$ $-4i\sqrt{2}$
5. $\sqrt{-144}$ $12i$

SEE EXAMPLE 2 p. 351

Solve each equation.

6. $x^2 = -9$ $\pm 3i$
7. $2x^2 + 72 = 0$ $\pm 6i$
8. $4x^2 = -16$ $\pm 2i$
9. $x^2 + 121 = 0$ $\pm 11i$

SEE EXAMPLE 3 p. 351

Find the values of x and y that make each equation true.

10. $-2x + 6i = (-24y)i - 14$ $x = 7;\ y = -\frac{1}{4}$
11. $-4 + (y)i = -12x - i + 8$ $x = 1;\ y = -1$

SEE EXAMPLE 4 p. 352

Find the zeros of each function.

12. $f(x) = x^2 - 12x + 45$ $6 \pm 3i$
13. $g(x) = x^2 + 6x + 34$ $-3 \pm 5i$

SEE EXAMPLE 5 p. 352

Find each complex conjugate.

14. $-9i$ $9i$
15. $\sqrt{5} + 5i$ $\sqrt{5} - 5i$
16. $8i - 3$ $-3 - 8i$
17. $6 + i\sqrt{2}$ $6 - i\sqrt{2}$

PRACTICE AND PROBLEM SOLVING

Independent Practice

For Exercises	See Example
18–21	1
22–25	2
26–27	3
28–31	4
32–35	5

Extra Practice

Skills Practice p. S13
Application Practice p. S36

Express each number in terms of i.

18. $8\sqrt{-4}$ $16i$
19. $-\frac{1}{3}\sqrt{-90}$ $-i\sqrt{10}$
20. $6\sqrt{-12}$ $12i\sqrt{3}$
21. $\sqrt{-50}$ $5i\sqrt{2}$

Solve each equation.

22. $x^2 + 49 = 0$ $\pm 7i$
23. $5x^2 = -80$ $\pm 4i$
24. $3x^2 + 27 = 0$ $\pm 3i$
25. $\frac{1}{2}x^2 = -32$ $\pm 8i$

Find the values of x and y that make each equation true.

26. $9x + (y)i - 5 = -12i + 4$ $x = 1;\ y = -12$
27. $5(x - 1) + (3y)i = -15i - 20$ $x = -3;\ y = -5$

Find the zeros of each function.

28. $f(x) = x^2 + 2x + 3$ $-1 \pm i\sqrt{2}$
29. $g(x) = 4x^2 - 3x + 1$ $\frac{3 \pm i\sqrt{7}}{8}$
30. $f(x) = x^2 + 4x + 8$ $-2 \pm 2i$
31. $g(x) = 3x^2 - 6x + 10$ $\frac{3 \pm i\sqrt{21}}{3}$

Find each complex conjugate.

32. i $-i$
33. $-\frac{\sqrt{3}}{2} - 2i$ $-\frac{\sqrt{3}}{2} + 2i$
34. $-2.5i + 1$ $1 + 2.5i$
35. $\frac{i}{10} - 1$ $-1 - \frac{i}{10}$

36. **What if...?** A carnival game asks participants to strike a spring with a hammer. The spring shoots a puck upward toward a bell. If the puck strikes the bell, the participant wins a prize. Suppose that a participant strikes the spring and shoots the puck according to the model $d(t) = 16t^2 - 32t + 18$, where d is the distance in feet between the puck and the bell and t is the time in seconds since the puck was struck. Is it possible for the participant to win a prize? Explain your answer.

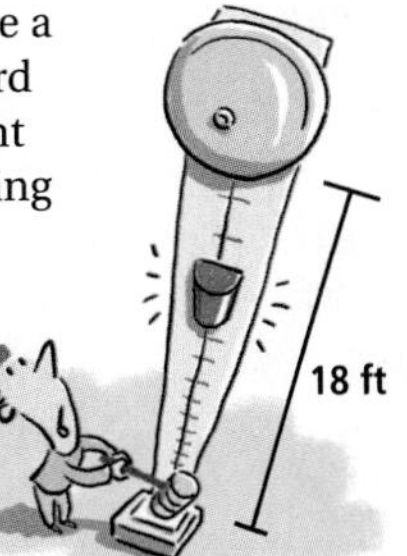

36. No, the participant will not win a prize. Possible answer: The solutions to the equation $16x^2 - 32x + 18 = 0$ are imaginary, so the distance between the puck and the bell never reaches 0.

5-5 Exercises

Assignment Guide

Assign *Guided Practice* exercises as necessary.

If you finished Examples 1–3
Basic 18–27, 43–51
Average 18–27, 43–51
Advanced 18–27, 43–51, 83

If you finished Examples 1–5
Basic 18–71, 75–81, 85–98
Average 18–83, 85–98
Advanced 18–98

Homework Quick Check
Quickly check key concepts.
Exercises: 18, 22, 26, 28, 34, 36

Teaching Tip

Auditory For **Exercises 14–17** and **32–35,** ask volunteers to name the real part and imaginary part of each complex number.

State Resources

go.hrw.com
State Resources Online
KEYWORD: MB7 Resources

Exercise 75 involves solving a quadratic equation representing a baseball's height. This exercise prepares students for the Multi-Step Test Prep on page 364.

Answers

61. Sometimes true; possible answer: $3i$ is a complex number that is imaginary; 3 is a complex number that is not imaginary.

63. Sometimes true; possible answer: the quadratic equation $x^2 = -4$ has no real solutions; the quadratic equation $x^2 = 4$ has 2 real solutions.

64. Sometimes true; possible answer: the quadratic equation $x^2 = 4$ has 2 real, complex roots; the quadratic equation $x^2 = -4$ has 2 complex roots, but these roots are not real.

65. Sometimes true; possible answer: the quadratic equation $x^2 = -4$ has 2 roots that form a conjugate pair; the quadratic equation $x^2 = 4$ has 2 roots that do not form a conjugate pair.

72. No; possible answer: the graph of the function does not cross the x-axis. Therefore, it has nonreal, complex zeros. Algebra must be used to determine these zeros.

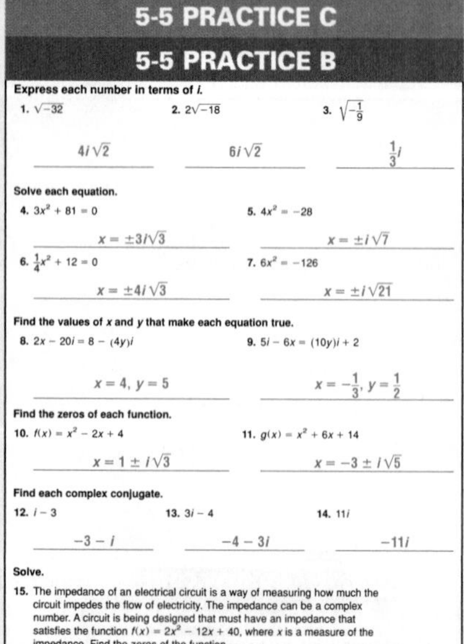

5-5 PRACTICE A

5-5 PRACTICE C

5-5 PRACTICE B

Express each number in terms of i.

1. $\sqrt{-32}$ — $4i\sqrt{2}$
2. $2\sqrt{-18}$ — $6i\sqrt{2}$
3. $\sqrt{-\frac{1}{9}}$ — $\frac{1}{3}i$

Solve each equation.

4. $3x^2 + 81 = 0$ — $x = \pm 3i\sqrt{3}$
5. $4x^2 = -28$ — $x = \pm i\sqrt{7}$
6. $\frac{1}{4}x^2 + 12 = 0$ — $x = \pm 4i\sqrt{3}$
7. $6x^2 = -126$ — $x = \pm i\sqrt{21}$

Find the values of x and y that make each equation true.

8. $2x - 20i = 8 - (4y)i$ — $x = 4,\ y = 5$
9. $5i - 6x = (10y)i + 2$ — $x = -\frac{1}{3},\ y = \frac{1}{2}$

Find the zeros of each function.

10. $f(x) = x^2 - 2x + 4$ — $x = 1 \pm i\sqrt{3}$
11. $g(x) = x^2 + 6x + 14$ — $x = -3 \pm i\sqrt{5}$

Find each complex conjugate.

12. $i - 3$ — $-3 - i$
13. $3i - 4$ — $-4 - 3i$
14. $11i$ — $-11i$

Solve.

15. The impedance of an electrical circuit is a way of measuring how much the circuit impedes the flow of electricity. The impedance can be a complex number. A circuit is being designed that must have an impedance that satisfies the function $f(x) = 2x^2 - 12x + 40$, where x is a measure of the impedance. Find the zeros of the function. — $3 \pm i\sqrt{11}$

Given each solution to a quadratic equation, find the other solution.

37. $1 + 14i$ $1 - 14i$
38. $\frac{5}{7}i$ $-\frac{5}{7}i$
39. $4i - 2\sqrt{5}$ $-2\sqrt{5} - 4i$
40. $-12 - i$ $-12 + i$
41. $9 - i\sqrt{2}$ $9 + i\sqrt{2}$
42. $-\frac{17i}{3}$ $\frac{17i}{3}$

Find the values of c and d that make each equation true.

43. $2ci + 1 = -d + 6 - ci$ $c = 0,\ d = 5$
44. $c + 3ci = 4 + di$ $c = 4,\ d = 12$
45. $c^2 + 4i = d + di$ $c = \pm 2,\ d = 4$

Solve each equation.

46. $8x^2 = -8$ $\pm i$
47. $\frac{1}{3}x^2 = -27$ $\pm 9i$
48. $2x^2 + 12.5 = 0$ $\pm 2.5i$
49. $\frac{1}{2}x^2 + 72 = 0$ $\pm 12i$
50. $x^2 = -30$ $\pm i\sqrt{30}$
51. $2x^2 + 16 = 0$ $\pm 2i\sqrt{2}$
52. $x^2 - 4x + 8 = 0$ $2 \pm 2i$
53. $x^2 + 10x + 29 = 0$ $-5 \pm 2i$
54. $x^2 - 12x + 44 = 0$ $6 \pm 2i\sqrt{2}$
55. $x^2 + 2x = -5$ $-1 \pm 2i$
56. $x^2 + 18 = -6x$ $-3 \pm 3i$
57. $-149 = x^2 - 24x$ $12 \pm i\sqrt{5}$

Math History

The Swiss mathematician Leonhard Euler (1707–1783) was the first to use the notation i to represent $\sqrt{-1}$. He also introduced the notation $f(x)$ to represent the value of a function f at x.

Tell whether each statement is always, sometimes, or never true. If sometimes true, give examples to support your answer.

58. A real number is an imaginary number. **never true**
59. An imaginary number is a complex number. **always true**
60. A rational number is a complex number. **always true**
61. A complex number is an imaginary number.
62. An integer is a complex number. **always true**
63. Quadratic equations have no real solutions.
64. Quadratic equations have roots that are real and complex.
65. Roots of quadratic equations are conjugate pairs.

Find the zeros of each function.

66. $f(x) = x^2 - 10x + 26$ $5 \pm i$
67. $g(x) = x^2 + 2x + 17$ $-1 \pm 4i$
68. $h(x) = x^2 - 10x + 50$ $5 \pm 5i$
69. $f(x) = x^2 + 16x + 73$ $-8 \pm 3i$
70. $g(x) = x^2 - 10x + 37$ $5 \pm 2i\sqrt{3}$
71. $h(x) = x^2 - 16x + 68$ $8 \pm 2i$
72. **Critical Thinking** Can you determine the zeros of $f(x) = x^2 + 64$ by using a graph? Explain why or why not.
73. **Critical Thinking** What is the complex conjugate of a real number? **The complex conjugate of a real number a is the number a.**

74. **Write About It** Explain the procedures you can use to solve for nonreal complex roots. **Possible answer: You can use the Square-Root Property or complete the square to solve for nonreal complex roots.**

75. This problem will prepare you for the Multi-Step Test Prep on page 364.

A player throws a ball straight up toward the roof of an indoor baseball stadium. The height h in feet of the ball after t seconds can be modeled by the function $h(t) = -16t^2 + 112t$.

a. The height of the roof is 208 ft. Solve the equation $208 = -16t^2 + 112t$. $t = \frac{7}{2} \pm \frac{\sqrt{3}}{2}i$

b. Based on your answer to part **a**, does the ball hit the roof? Explain your answer.

c. Based on the function model, what is the maximum height that the ball will reach? **196 ft**

b. Based on the solution to part a, there are no real values of t for which the height of the ball is 208 ft. Therefore, the ball does not hit the roof.

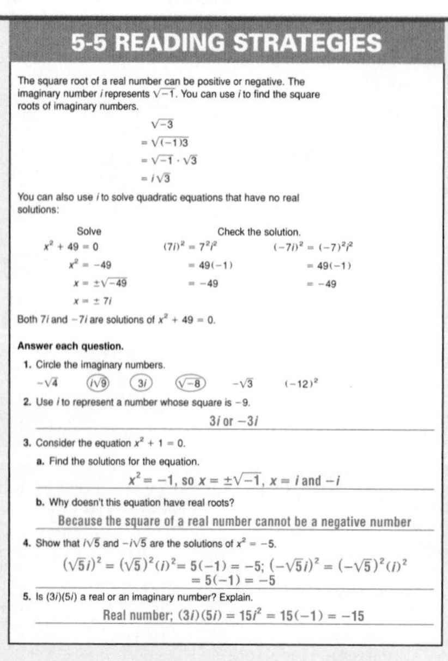

5-5 READING STRATEGIES

The square root of a real number can be positive or negative. The imaginary number i represents $\sqrt{-1}$. You can use i to find the square roots of imaginary numbers.

$$\sqrt{-3} = \sqrt{(-1)3} = \sqrt{-1} \cdot \sqrt{3} = i\sqrt{3}$$

You can also use i to solve quadratic equations that have no real solutions:

Solve: $x^2 + 49 = 0$; $x^2 = -49$; $x = \pm\sqrt{-49}$; $x = \pm 7i$

Check the solution. $(7i)^2 = 7^2i^2 = 49(-1) = -49$; $(-7i)^2 = (-7)^2i^2 = 49(-1) = -49$

Both $7i$ and $-7i$ are solutions of $x^2 + 49 = 0$.

Answer each question.

1. Circle the imaginary numbers. $-\sqrt{4}$ $i\sqrt{9}$ $3i$ $\sqrt{-8}$ $-\sqrt{3}$ $(-12)^2$
2. Use i to represent a number whose square is -9. — $3i$ or $-3i$
3. Consider the equation $x^2 + 1 = 0$.
   a. Find the solutions for the equation. — $x^2 = -1$, so $x = \pm\sqrt{-1}$, $x = i$ and $-i$
   b. Why doesn't this equation have real roots? — Because the square of a real number cannot be a negative number
4. Show that $i\sqrt{5}$ and $-i\sqrt{5}$ are the solutions of $x^2 = -5$. — $(\sqrt{5}i)^2 = (\sqrt{5})^2(i)^2 = 5(-1) = -5$; $(-\sqrt{5}i)^2 = (-\sqrt{5})^2(i)^2 = 5(-1) = -5$
5. Is $(3i)(5i)$ a real or an imaginary number? Explain. — Real number; $(3i)(5i) = 15i^2 = 15(-1) = -15$

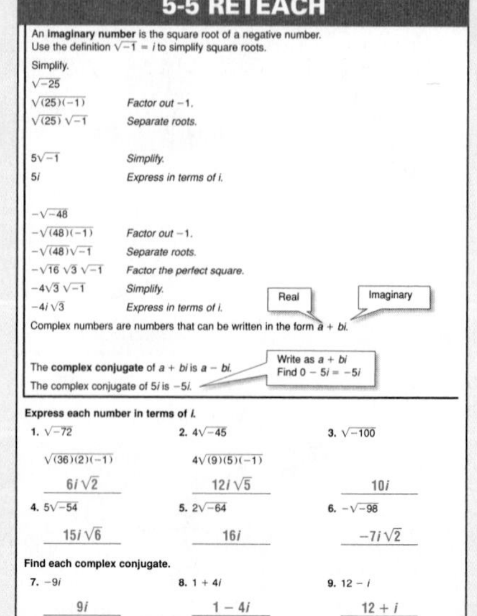

5-5 RETEACH

An **imaginary number** is the square root of a negative number. Use the definition $\sqrt{-1} = i$ to simplify square roots.

Simplify.

$\sqrt{-25}$	
$\sqrt{(25)(-1)}$	*Factor out −1.*
$\sqrt{(25)}\sqrt{-1}$	*Separate roots.*
$5\sqrt{-1}$	*Simplify.*
$5i$	*Express in terms of i.*
$-\sqrt{-48}$	
$-\sqrt{(48)(-1)}$	*Factor out −1.*
$-\sqrt{(48)}\sqrt{-1}$	*Separate roots.*
$-\sqrt{16}\sqrt{3}\sqrt{-1}$	*Factor the perfect square.*
$-4\sqrt{3}\sqrt{-1}$	*Simplify.*
$-4i\sqrt{3}$	*Express in terms of i.*

Complex numbers are numbers that can be written in the form $a + bi$.

The **complex conjugate** of $a + bi$ is $a - bi$.

The complex conjugate of $5i$ is $-5i$.

Express each number in terms of i.

1. $\sqrt{-72}$ — $\sqrt{(36)(2)(-1)}$ — $6i\sqrt{2}$
2. $4\sqrt{-45}$ — $4\sqrt{(9)(5)(-1)}$ — $12i\sqrt{5}$
3. $\sqrt{-100}$ — $10i$
4. $5\sqrt{-54}$ — $15i\sqrt{6}$
5. $2\sqrt{-64}$ — $16i$
6. $-\sqrt{-98}$ — $-7i\sqrt{2}$

Find each complex conjugate.

7. $-9i$ — $9i$
8. $1 + 4i$ — $1 - 4i$
9. $12 - i$ — $12 + i$

TEST PREP

76. What is the complex conjugate of $-2 + i$?

Ⓐ $2 + i$ Ⓑ $2 - i$ Ⓒ $i - 2$ **Ⓓ** $-2 - i$

77. Express $\sqrt{-225}$ in terms of i.

Ⓕ $15i$ Ⓖ $-15i$ Ⓗ $i\sqrt{15}$ Ⓙ $-i\sqrt{15}$

78. Find the zeros of $f(x) = x^2 - 2x + 17$.

Ⓐ $1 \pm 4i$ Ⓑ $4 \pm i$ Ⓒ $-1 \pm 4i$ Ⓓ $-4 \pm i$

79. What value of c makes the equation $3 - 4i - 5 = (9 + ci) - 11$ true?

Ⓕ -2 **Ⓖ** -4 Ⓗ 2 Ⓙ 4

80. Which of the following equations has roots of $-6i$ and $6i$?

Ⓐ $-\frac{1}{6}x^2 = 6$ Ⓒ $\frac{1}{4}x^2 = 9$

Ⓑ $x^2 - 30 = 6$ Ⓓ $20 - x^2 = -16$

81. **Short Response** Explain the types of solutions that equations of the form $x^2 = a$ have when $a < 0$ and when $a > 0$. When $a < 0$, the 2 solutions are imaginary and complex. When $a > 0$, the 2 solutions are real and complex.

CHALLENGE AND EXTEND

82. Find the complex number $a + bi$ such that $5a + 3b = 1$ and $-5b = 7 + 4a$. $2 - 3i$

83. Can a quadratic equation have only one real number root? only one imaginary root? only one complex root? Explain.

84b. If $c \leq 0$, the equation has 2 real solutions.

84. Given the general form of a quadratic $x^2 + bx + c = 0$, determine the effect of each condition on the solutions.

a. $b = 0$ b. $c \leq 0$ c. $c > 0$

d. What is needed for the solutions to have imaginary parts?

The solutions have imaginary parts if $c > \left(\frac{b}{2}\right)^2$.

SPIRAL REVIEW

Use the following matrices for Exercises 85–88. Evaluate, if possible. *(Lesson 4-2)*

$$S = \begin{bmatrix} 1 & -5 \\ -2 & 0 \end{bmatrix} \quad T = \begin{bmatrix} -4 & 1 & -2 \\ 0 & -3 & 1 \\ 2 & -2 & 2 \end{bmatrix} \quad V = \begin{bmatrix} 10 & 1 \\ 0 & -1 \\ -5 & 5 \end{bmatrix}$$

85. T^2 86. TV 87. ST not defined 88. S^2 $\begin{bmatrix} 11 & -5 \\ -2 & 10 \end{bmatrix}$

85. $\begin{bmatrix} 12 & -3 & 5 \\ 2 & 7 & -1 \\ -4 & 4 & -2 \end{bmatrix}$

86. $\begin{bmatrix} -30 & -15 \\ -5 & 8 \\ 10 & 14 \end{bmatrix}$

For each function, (a) determine whether the graph opens upward or downward, (b) find the axis of symmetry, (c) find the vertex, (d) find the y-intercept, and (e) graph the function. *(Lesson 5-2)*

89. $f(x) = \frac{1}{5}x^2 + x - 10$ 90. $f(x) = -x^2 + 3$

91. $f(x) = 2x^2 + 4x - 3$ 92. $f(x) = -\frac{1}{2}x^2 + 3x + 1$

Find the roots of each equation by factoring. *(Lesson 5-3)*

93. $x^2 + 5x = 14$ $-7, 2$ 94. $6x^2 = -x + 2$ $-\frac{2}{3}, \frac{1}{2}$

95. $4x^2 + 9 = 15x$ $\frac{3}{4}, 3$ 96. $4x^2 = 1$ $\pm\frac{1}{2}$

97. $x^2 + 11x = -24$ $-8, -3$ 98. $x^2 = -7x$ $-7, 0$

TEST PREP DOCTOR In **Exercise 76,** students can eliminate **A** and **B** because these choices do not have the same real part as $-2 + i$. They can eliminate **C** because the imaginary part of this choice is not the opposite of the imaginary part of $-2 + i$.

Answers

83. See p. A28.

84a. If $b = 0$ and $c \leq 0$, the equation has 2 real solutions. If $b = 0$ and $c > 0$, the equation has 2 nonreal complex solutions.

84c. If $c > 0$ and $c \leq \left(\frac{b}{2}\right)^2$, the equation has 2 real solutions. If $c > 0$ and $c > \left(\frac{b}{2}\right)^2$, the equation has 2 nonreal complex solutions.

89–92. For graphs, see p. A28.

89. upward; $x = -2.5$; $(-2.5, -11.25)$; -10

90. downward; $x = 0$; $(0, 3)$; 3

91. upward; $x = -1$; $(-1, -5)$; -3

92. downward; $x = 3$; $(3, 5.5)$; 1

Journal

Present students with the following statement: All quadratic equations have complex roots. Ask students to state whether this statement is true or false and to explain their answers.

ALTERNATIVE ASSESSMENT

Have students solve two similar equations, such as $x^2 + 6x + 7 = 0$ and $x^2 + 6x + 12 = 0$, one of which has nonreal solutions, side by side. Ask them to compare the two solution processes and the two solution sets.

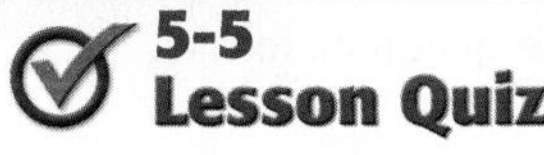

Power Presentations with PowerPoint®

5-5 Lesson Quiz

1. Express $\sqrt{-300}$ in terms of i. $10i\sqrt{3}$

Solve each equation.

2. $3x^2 + 96 = 0$ $\pm 4i\sqrt{2}$

3. $x^2 + 8x + 20 = 0$ $-4 \pm 2i$

4. Find the values of x and y that make the equation $3x + 8i = 12 - (12y)i$ true.

$x = 4, y = -\frac{2}{3}$

5. Find the complex conjugate of $1 - i\sqrt{2}$. $1 + i\sqrt{2}$

Also available on transparency

5-5 PROBLEM SOLVING

At a carnival, a new attraction allows contestants to jump off a springboard onto a platform to be launched vertically into the air. The object is to ring a bell located 20 feet overhead. The distance from the bell in feet is modeled by the function $dt = 16t^2 - bt + 20$, where t is the time in seconds after leaving the platform, and b is the takeoff velocity from the platform.

1. Kate watches some of the contestants. She theorizes that if the platform launches a contestant with a takeoff velocity of at least 32 feet per second, the contestant can ring the bell.

a. Find the zeros for the function using 32 feet per second as the takeoff velocity. $t = 1 \pm \frac{i}{2}$

b. Is Kate's theory valid? Explain.

No; possible answer: the roots are imaginary numbers.

2. Mirko suggests they vary the value of b and determine for which values of b the roots are real.

a. Complete the table to show the roots for different values of b.

b. For which values of b in the table are the roots real?

$b = 40$ and 48

c. What difference does it make if the roots are real?

Possible answer: Real roots mean that ringing the bell is possible.

b	Function	Roots
24	$d(t) = 16t^2 - 24t + 20$	$\frac{1}{4}(3 \pm i\sqrt{11})$
32	$d(t) = 16t^2 - \_t + 20$	$1 \pm \frac{i}{2}$
40	$d(t) = 16t^2 - \_t + 20$	$\frac{1}{4}(5 \pm \sqrt{5})$
48	$d(t) = 16t^2 - \_t + 20$	$\frac{3}{2} \pm \sqrt{1}$

3. Using the results from the table, and the function, estimate the minimum takeoff velocity needed for a contestant to be able to ring the bell. About 36 feet per second

Choose the letter for the best answer.

4. Mirko suggests using four bells at heights of 15, 20, 25, and 30 feet from the platform. How many of the bells can a contestant reach if the takeoff velocity is 32 feet per second?

A 3 **Ⓒ** 1
B 2 D 0

5. At what height must a bell be placed for a contestant to reach it with a takeoff velocity of 48 feet per second?

A 20 feet or less
B 25 feet or less
C 30 feet or less
Ⓓ 36 feet or less

5-5 CHALLENGE

If a quadratic equation with real coefficients has nonreal roots, those roots are complex conjugates. But what if the coefficients of the quadratic equation are also complex or imaginary numbers? Consider the factored equation

$$(x + 3i)(x - i) = 0.$$

The solutions of this equation are i and $-3i$. The expanded polynomial is

$$x^2 + 2ix + 3 = 0.$$

Notice that the coefficients are not all real numbers. That is why the complex solutions are not conjugates of one another. Equations of this type, where the middle term contains an imaginary number, are factored similarly to those with real coefficients except the sign of the constant term will be different due to the presence of the imaginary numbers.

All Real Coefficients	Some Imaginary Coefficients
$x^2 - 11x + 30 = 0$	$x^2 - 11ix - 30 = 0$
$(x - 5)(x - 6) = 0$	$(x - 5i)(x - 6i) = 0$
$x = 5$ or $x = 6$	$x = 5i$ or $x = 6i$

Solve each equation by factoring.

1. $x^2 + 5ix + 14 = 0$ $2i, -7i$
2. $x^2 + 14ix - 48 = 0$ $-6i, -8i$
3. $x^2 + 3ix + 108 = 0$ $9i, -12i$
4. $x^2 - 54ix - 245 = 0$ $5i, 49i$
5. $x^2 + 52ix - 576 = 0$ $-16i, -36i$

Look at equations of the form $2ix^2 + 5x + 12i = 0$. In this case, both the squared term and the constant contain imaginary coefficients. This equation factors into the binomials $(2ix - 3)$ and $(x - 4i)$ and the solutions are $4i$ and $\frac{3}{2i}$. Multiply the numerator and denominator of the fraction by $-2i$ to obtain $-\frac{3}{2}i$.

Solve each equation by factoring. Write the solutions in $a + bi$ form.

6. $3ix^2 - 7x - 4i = 0$ $-\frac{4}{3}i, -i$
7. $5ix^2 + 11x - 2i = 0$ $\frac{1}{5}i, 2i$
8. $2ix^2 - 16x - 30i = 0$ $-3i, -5i$
9. $4ix^2 + 7x + 65i = 0$ $-\frac{13}{4}i, 5i$
10. $12ix^2 + 28x - 15i = 0$ $\frac{5}{6}i, \frac{3}{2}i$

5-6 Organizer

Pacing: Traditional 1 day
Block $\frac{1}{2}$ day

Objectives: Solve quadratic equations using the Quadratic Formula.

Classify roots using the discriminant.

Algebra Lab
In Algebra Lab Activities

Online Edition
Graphing Calculator, Tutorial Videos

Countdown to Testing Week 12

Power Presentations with PowerPoint®

Warm Up

Write each function in standard form

1. $f(x) = (x - 4)^2 + 3$
$f(x) = x^2 - 8x + 19$

2. $g(x) = 2(x + 6)^2 - 11$
$g(x) = 2x^2 + 24x + 61$

Evaluate $b^2 - 4ac$ for the given values of the variables.

3. $a = 2, b = 7, c = 5$ 9

4. $a = 1, b = 3, c = -3$ 21

Also available on transparency

Math Humor

Q: What do you get when you cross an algebra class with the prom?

A: The quadratic formal.

State Resources

go.hrw.com
State Resources Online
KEYWORD: MB7 Resources

5-6 The Quadratic Formula

A2.3.2 Solve quadratic equations in the complex number system.

Objectives
Solve quadratic equations using the Quadratic Formula.

Classify roots using the discriminant.

Vocabulary
discriminant

Who uses this?
Firefighting pilots can use the Quadratic Formula to estimate when to release water on a fire. (See Example 4.)

You have learned several methods for solving quadratic equations: graphing, making tables, factoring, using square roots, and completing the square. Another method is to use the *Quadratic Formula,* which allows you to solve a quadratic equation in standard form.

By completing the square on the standard form of a quadratic equation, you can determine the Quadratic Formula.

Numbers		Algebra
$3x^2 + 5x + 1 = 0$		$ax^2 + bx + c = 0 \; (a \neq 0)$
$x^2 + \frac{5}{3}x + \frac{1}{3} = 0$	*Divide by a.*	$x^2 + \frac{b}{a}x + \frac{c}{a} = 0$
$x^2 + \frac{5}{3}x = -\frac{1}{3}$	*Subtract $\frac{c}{a}$.*	$x^2 + \frac{b}{a}x = -\frac{c}{a}$
$x^2 + \frac{5}{3}x + \left(\frac{5}{2(3)}\right)^2 = -\frac{1}{3} + \left(\frac{5}{2(3)}\right)^2$	*Complete the square.*	$x^2 + \frac{b}{a}x + \left(\frac{b}{2a}\right)^2 = -\frac{c}{a} + \left(\frac{b}{2a}\right)^2$
$\left(x + \frac{5}{6}\right)^2 = \frac{25}{36} - \frac{1}{3}$	*Factor.*	$\left(x + \frac{b}{2a}\right)^2 = \frac{b^2}{4a^2} - \frac{c}{a}$
$x + \frac{5}{6} = \pm\sqrt{\frac{13}{36}}$	*Take square roots.*	$x + \frac{b}{2a} = \pm\sqrt{\frac{b^2 - 4ac}{4a^2}}$
$x = -\frac{5}{6} \pm \frac{\sqrt{13}}{6}$	*Subtract $\frac{b}{2a}$.*	$x = -\frac{b}{2a} \pm \frac{\sqrt{b^2 - 4ac}}{2a}$
$x = \frac{-5 \pm \sqrt{13}}{6}$	*Simplify.*	$x = \frac{-b \pm \sqrt{b^2 - 4ac}}{2a}$

Remember!
To subtract fractions, you need a common denominator.

$$\frac{b^2}{4a^2} - \frac{c}{a}$$
$$\frac{b^2}{4a^2} - \frac{c}{a}\left(\frac{4a}{4a}\right)$$
$$\frac{b^2 - 4ac}{4a^2}$$

The symmetry of a quadratic function is evident in the next to last step, $x = -\frac{b}{2a} \pm \frac{\sqrt{b^2 - 4ac}}{2a}$. These two zeros are the same distance, $\frac{\sqrt{b^2 - 4ac}}{2a}$, away from the axis of symmetry, $x = -\frac{b}{2a}$, with one zero on either side of the vertex.

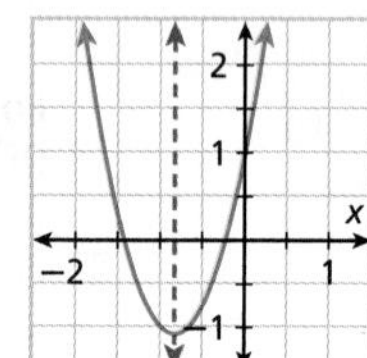

The Quadratic Formula

If $ax^2 + bx + c = 0 \; (a \neq 0)$, then the solutions, or roots, are

$$x = \frac{-b \pm \sqrt{b^2 - 4ac}}{2a}.$$

Introduce

EXPLORATION

5-6 The Quadratic Formula

A quadratic equation may have two real solutions, one real solution, or two nonreal complex solutions. For a quadratic equation of the form $ax^2 + bx + c = 0$, you can use the values of a, b and c to determine the type and number of solutions.

1. Complete the table. Use any method to solve each quadratic equation, and then use its values of a, b and c to evaluate the expression $b^2 - 4ac$.

Equation	Solutions	Value of $b^2 - 4ac$
$x^2 + 5x + 6 = 0$		
$x^2 + 2x + 1 = 0$		
$x^2 + 4 = 0$		
$x^2 - 6x + 9 = 0$		
$x^2 + 10 = 0$		
$x^2 + 3x - 4 = 0$		

2. Based on the table, what type and number of solutions does a quadratic equation have if the value of $b^2 - 4ac$ is 0?
3. What type and number of solutions does a quadratic equation have if the value of $b^2 - 4ac$ is less than 0?
4. What type and number of solutions does a quadratic equation have if the value of $b^2 - 4ac$ is greater than 0?

THINK AND DISCUSS

5. Describe how you can determine the type and number of

Motivate

Ask students to solve the equation $ax + b = 0$ for x. They should be able to determine the answer $x = \frac{-b}{a}$ without much difficulty. Explain that this solution provides a shortcut for solving a linear equation in standard form because it depends only on the coefficients a and b. Tell students that there is also a shortcut for solving quadratic equations in standard form. This shortcut is called the Quadratic Formula.

Explorations and answers are provided in the *Explorations* binder.

You can use the Quadratic Formula to solve any quadratic equation that is written in standard form, including equations with real solutions or complex solutions.

EXAMPLE 1 Quadratic Functions with Real Zeros

Find the zeros of $f(x) = x^2 + 10x + 2$ by using the Quadratic Formula.

$x^2 + 10x + 2 = 0$ *Set f(x) = 0.*

$x = \frac{-b \pm \sqrt{b^2 - 4ac}}{2a}$ *Write the Quadratic Formula.*

$x = \frac{-10 \pm \sqrt{(10)^2 - 4(1)(2)}}{2(1)}$ *Substitute 1 for a, 10 for b, and 2 for c.*

$x = \frac{-10 \pm \sqrt{100 - 8}}{2} = \frac{-10 \pm \sqrt{92}}{2}$ *Simplify.*

$x = \frac{-10 \pm 2\sqrt{23}}{2} = -5 \pm \sqrt{23}$ *Write in simplest form.*

Check Solve by completing the square.

$x^2 + 10x + 2 = 0$

$x^2 + 10x = -2$

$x^2 + 10x + 25 = -2 + 25$

$(x + 5)^2 = 23$

$x = -5 \pm \sqrt{23}$ ✓

CHECK IT OUT! **Find the zeros of each function by using the Quadratic Formula.**

1a. $f(x) = x^2 + 3x - 7$ **1b.** $g(x) = x^2 - 8x + 10$

$\frac{-3 \pm \sqrt{37}}{2}$

$4 \pm \sqrt{6}$

EXAMPLE 2 Quadratic Functions with Complex Zeros

Find the zeros of $f(x) = 2x^2 - x + 2$ by using the Quadratic Formula.

$2x^2 - x + 2 = 0$ *Set f(x) = 0.*

$x = \frac{-b \pm \sqrt{b^2 - 4ac}}{2a}$ *Write the Quadratic Formula.*

$x = \frac{-(-1) \pm \sqrt{(-1)^2 - 4(2)(2)}}{2(2)}$ *Substitute 2 for a, −1 for b, and 2 for c.*

$x = \frac{1 \pm \sqrt{1 - 16}}{4} = \frac{1 \pm \sqrt{-15}}{4}$ *Simplify.*

$x = \frac{1 \pm i\sqrt{15}}{4} = \frac{1}{4} \pm \frac{\sqrt{15}}{4}i$ *Write in terms of i.*

CHECK IT OUT! **2.** Find the zeros of $g(x) = 3x^2 - x + 8$ by using the Quadratic Formula.

$\frac{1}{6} \pm \frac{\sqrt{95}}{6}i$

The **discriminant** is part of the Quadratic Formula that you can use to determine the number of real roots of a quadratic equation.

$x = \frac{-b \pm \sqrt{b^2 - 4ac}}{2a}$ ← Discriminant

Power Presentations with PowerPoint®

Additional Examples

Example 1

Find the zeros of $f(x) = 2x^2 - 16x + 27$ by using the Quadratic Formula.

$4 \pm \frac{\sqrt{10}}{2}$

Example 2

Find the zeros of $f(x) = 4x^2 + 3x + 2$ by using the Quadratic Formula.

$\frac{-3}{8} \pm \frac{\sqrt{23}}{8}i$

Also available on transparency

INTERVENTION

Questioning Strategies

EXAMPLE 1

- How do you identify the values of *a, b,* and *c* when a quadratic equation is in standard form?
- If a quadratic equation is in vertex form, what must you do before you can use the Quadratic Formula?

EXAMPLE 2

- How do you simplify the square root of a negative number?

Teaching Tip **Math Background** The seventh-century Indian mathematician Brahmagupta was among the first to use a general algebraic formula to find roots of quadratic equations.

2 Teach

Guided Instruction

First, have students write a quadratic function in standard form and identify the values of the coefficients *a, b,* and *c.* Then make sure that they are able to simplify the Quadratic Formula once they have substituted values for the coefficients. Finally, ensure that students understand how the discriminant can be used to determine the type of solutions of a quadratic equation.

Reaching All Learners

Through Auditory Cues

Putting the Quadratic Formula to music may help students remember it. Here is one example, sung to the tune of "Pop Goes the Weasel."

x is equal to neg-a-tive b,
Plus or minus the squaaare root,
Of b squared minus fouuur ac
All over twooo a.

Power Presentations with PowerPoint®

Additional Examples

Example 3

Find the type and number of solutions for each equation.

A. $x^2 + 36 = 12x$
1 distinct real

B. $x^2 + 40 = 12x$
2 distinct nonreal complex

C. $x^2 + 30 = 12x$ 2 distinct real

Also available on transparency

INTERVENTION

Questioning Strategies

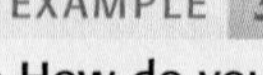

EXAMPLE 3

- How do you find the value of the discriminant?
- Under what conditions does a quadratic equation have 2 distinct real solutions? 1 distinct real solution? 2 distinct nonreal complex solutions?

Teaching Tip **Communicating Math** You may wish to point out that quadratic equations always have two roots. However, when the value of the discriminant is 0, the two roots happen to be the same. In this case, the quadratic equation is said to have a double root. Students will learn more about multiple roots in Chapter 6.

Know it! Note

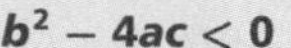

Discriminant

The discriminant of the quadratic equation $ax^2 + bx + c = 0$ $(a \neq 0)$ is $b^2 - 4ac$.

$b^2 - 4ac > 0$	$b^2 - 4ac = 0$	$b^2 - 4ac < 0$
two distinct real solutions	one distinct real solution	two distinct nonreal complex solutions
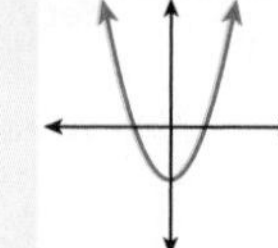	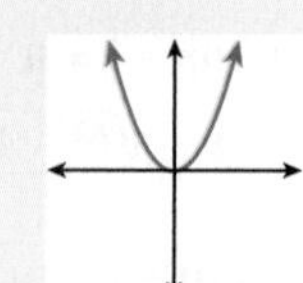	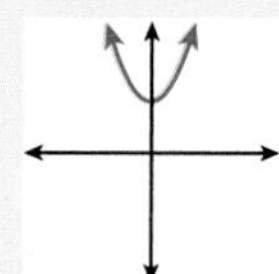

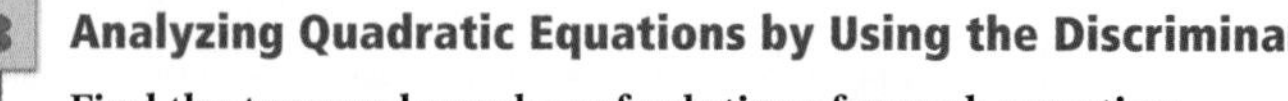

EXAMPLE 3 Analyzing Quadratic Equations by Using the Discriminant

Find the type and number of solutions for each equation.

Caution!

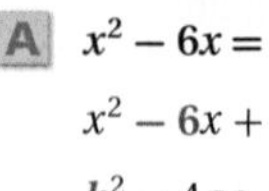

Make sure the equation is in standard form before you evaluate the discriminant, $b^2 - 4ac$.

A $x^2 - 6x = -7$

$x^2 - 6x + 7 = 0$

$b^2 - 4ac$

$(-6)^2 - 4(1)(7)$

$36 - 28 = 8$

$b^2 - 4ac > 0$; the equation has two distinct real solutions.

B $x^2 - 6x = -9$

$x^2 - 6x + 9 = 0$

$b^2 - 4ac$

$(-6)^2 - 4(1)(9)$

$36 - 36 = 0$

$b^2 - 4ac = 0$; the equation has one distinct real solution.

C $x^2 - 6x = -11$

$x^2 - 6x + 11 = 0$

$b^2 - 4ac$

$(-6)^2 - 4(1)(11)$

$36 - 44 = -8$

$b^2 - 4ac < 0$; the equation has two distinct nonreal complex solutions.

CHECK IT OUT! Find the type and number of solutions for each equation.

3a. $x^2 - 4x = -4$ **3b.** $x^2 - 4x = -8$ **3c.** $x^2 - 4x = 2$

3a. 1 distinct real solution

3b. 2 distinct nonreal complex solutions

3c. 2 distinct real solutions

The graph shows the related functions for Example 3. Notice that the number of real solutions for the equation can be changed by changing the value of the constant c.

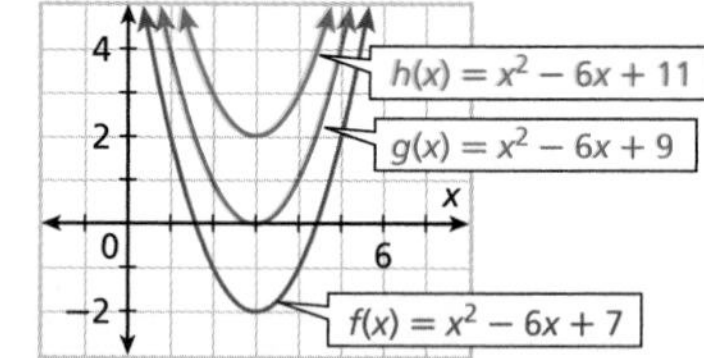

Student to Student

Double-Checking Roots

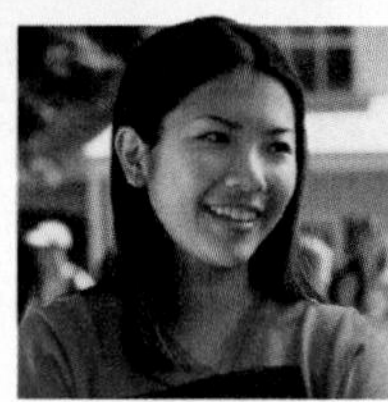

Terry Cannon,
Carver High School

If I get integer roots when I use the Quadratic Formula, I know that I can quickly factor to check the roots. Look at my work for the equation $x^2 - 7x + 10 = 0$.

Quadratic Formula:

$$x = \frac{-(-7) \pm \sqrt{(-7)^2 - 4(1)(10)}}{2(1)}$$

$$= \frac{7 \pm \sqrt{9}}{2} = \frac{10}{2} \text{ or } \frac{4}{2} = 5 \text{ or } 2$$

Factoring:

$x^2 - 7x + 10 = 0$

$(x - 5)(x - 2) = 0$

$x = 5$ or $x = 2$

EXAMPLE 4 Aviation Application

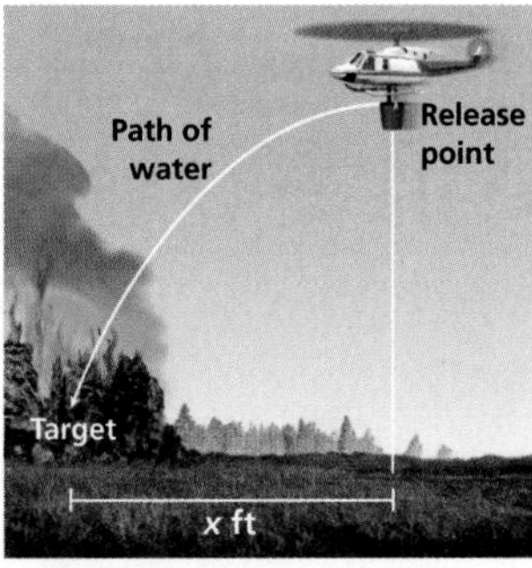

The pilot of a helicopter plans to release a bucket of water on a forest fire. The height y in feet of the water t seconds after its release is modeled by $y = -16t^2 - 2t + 500$. The horizontal distance x in feet between the water and its point of release is modeled by $x = 91t$. At what horizontal distance from the fire should the pilot start releasing the water in order to hit the target?

Step 1 Use the first equation to determine how long it will take the water to hit the ground. Set the height of the water equal to 0 feet, and use the quadratic formula to solve for t.

$$y = -16t^2 - 2t + 500$$

$$0 = -16t^2 - 2t + 500 \quad \textit{Set y equal to 0.}$$

$$t = \frac{-b \pm \sqrt{b^2 - 4ac}}{2a} \quad \textit{Use the Quadratic Formula.}$$

$$t = \frac{-(-2) \pm \sqrt{(-2)^2 - 4(-16)(500)}}{2(-16)} \quad \textit{Substitute for a, b, and c.}$$

$$t = \frac{2 \pm \sqrt{32{,}004}}{-32} \quad \textit{Simplify.}$$

$$t \approx -5.65 \text{ or } t \approx 5.53$$

The time cannot be negative, so the water lands on the target about 5.5 seconds after it is released.

Step 2 Find the horizontal distance that the water will have traveled in this time.

$$x = 91t$$

$$x = 91(5.5) \quad \textit{Substitute 5.5 for t.}$$

$$x = 500.5 \quad \textit{Simplify.}$$

The water will have traveled a horizontal distance of about 500 feet. Therefore, the pilot should start releasing the water when the horizontal distance between the helicopter and the fire is 500 feet.

Check Use substitution to check that the water hits the ground after about 5.53 seconds.

$$y = -16t^2 - 2t + 500$$

$$y = -16(5.53)^2 - 2(5.53) + 500$$

$$y \approx -0.3544 \checkmark \quad \textit{The height is approximately equal to 0 when } t = 5.53.$$

Caution!

Once you have found the value of t, you have solved only part of the problem. You will use this value to find the answer you are looking for.

CHECK IT OUT! **Use the information given above to answer the following.**

4. The pilot's altitude decreases, which changes the function describing the water's height to $y = -16t^2 - 2t + 400$. To the nearest foot, at what horizontal distance from the target should the pilot begin releasing the water? **449 ft**

COMMON ERROR ALERT

Students may sometimes make a mistake in sign when calculating the discriminant, particularly when the quantity $4ac$ is less than 0. Remind them that subtracting a negative number is the same as adding the opposite, or positive, number.

Power Presentations with PowerPoint®

Additional Examples

Example 4

An athlete on a track team throws a shot put. The height y of the shot put in feet t seconds after it is thrown is modeled by $y = -16t^2 + 24.6t + 6.5$. The horizontal distance x in feet between the athlete and the shot put is modeled by $x = 29.3t$. To the nearest foot, how far does the shot put land from the athlete? 52 ft

Also available on transparency

INTERVENTION Questioning Strategies

EXAMPLE 4

- How do you know what value to substitute for y?
- Once you solve the quadratic equation for t, how do you know which value of t to use?

Inclusion Emphasize that choosing which method to use to solve a quadratic equation takes as much skill as being able to use the methods. Have students discuss when each method might be preferred.

Know it! Note

Summary of Solving Quadratic Equations

Method	When to Use	Examples
Graphing	Only approximate solutions or the number of real solutions is needed.	$2x^2 + 5x - 14 = 0$ $x \approx -4.2$ or $x \approx 1.7$
Factoring	$c = 0$ or the expression is easily factorable.	$x^2 + 4x + 3 = 0$ $(x + 3)(x + 1) = 0$ $x = -3$ or $x = -1$
Square roots	The variable side of the equation is a perfect square.	$(x - 5)^2 = 24$ $\sqrt{(x - 5)^2} = \pm\sqrt{24}$ $x - 5 = \pm 2\sqrt{6}$ $x = 5 \pm 2\sqrt{6}$
Completing the square	$a = 1$ and b is an even number.	$x^2 + 6x = 10$ $x^2 + 6x + \blacksquare = 10 + \blacksquare$ $x^2 + 6x + \left(\frac{6}{2}\right)^2 = 10 + \left(\frac{6}{2}\right)^2$ $(x + 3)^2 = 19$ $x = -3 \pm \sqrt{19}$
Quadratic Formula	Numbers are large or complicated, and the expression does not factor easily.	$5x^2 - 7x - 8 = 0$ $x = \frac{-(-7) \pm \sqrt{(-7)^2 - 4(5)(-8)}}{2(5)}$ $x = \frac{7 \pm \sqrt{209}}{10}$

Helpful Hint

No matter which method you use to solve a quadratic equation, you should get the same answer.

THINK AND DISCUSS

1. Describe how the graphs of quadratic functions illustrate the type and number of zeros.
2. Describe the values of c for which the equation $x^2 + 8x + c = 0$ will have zero, one, or two distinct solutions.
3. **GET ORGANIZED** Copy and complete the graphic organizer. Describe the possible solution methods for each value of the discriminant.

Value of Discriminant	Type of Solutions	Possible Solution Methods
Negative		
Zero		
Positive		

3 Close

Summarize

Explain that all methods of solving a quadratic equation give the same answer. Give students a quadratic equation that is easily factorable, such as $x^2 + 7x + 12 = 0$, and have them solve the equation using each of the methods learned in this chapter: graphing, factoring, completing the square, and using the Quadratic Formula. They should get the same result for each method: $x = -3$ or $x = -4$.

ONGOING ASSESSMENT and INTERVENTION

***Diagnose Before* the Lesson**
5-6 Warm Up, TE p. 356

***Monitor During* the Lesson**
Check It Out! Exercises, SE pp. 357–359
Questioning Strategies, TE pp. 357–359

***Assess After* the Lesson**
5-6 Lesson Quiz, TE p. 363
Alternative Assessment, TE p. 363

Answers to *Think and Discuss*

Possible answers:

1. If the function has 2 x-intercepts, there are 2 real zeros. If there is 1 x-intercept, the function has 1 distinct real zero. If there are no x-intercepts, the function has 2 nonreal complex zeros.
2. For $c < 16$, the equation has 2 real solutions. For $c = 16$, the equation has 1 distinct real solution. For $c > 16$, the equation has 2 nonreal complex solutions.
3. See p. A7.

5-6 Exercises

go.hrw.com
Homework Help Online
KEYWORD: MB7 5-6
Parent Resources Online
KEYWORD: MB7 Parent

GUIDED PRACTICE

1. **Vocabulary** What information does the value of the *discriminant* give about a quadratic equation? Possible answer: The value of the discriminant indicates the number and type of roots.

SEE EXAMPLE 1 p. 357

Find the zeros of each function by using the Quadratic Formula.

2. $f(x) = x^2 + 7x + 10$
3. $g(x) = 3x^2 - 4x - 1$
4. $h(x) = 3x^2 - 5x$
5. $g(x) = -x^2 - 5x + 6$
6. $h(x) = 4x^2 - 5x - 6$
7. $f(x) = 2x^2 - 19$

SEE EXAMPLE 2 p. 357

8. $f(x) = 2x^2 - 2x + 3$
9. $r(x) = x^2 + 6x + 12$
10. $h(x) = 3x^2 + 4x + 3$
11. $p(x) = x^2 + 4x + 10$
12. $g(x) = -5x^2 + 7x - 3$
13. $f(x) = 10x^2 + 7x + 4$

SEE EXAMPLE 3 p. 358

Find the type and number of solutions for each equation.

14. $4x^2 + 1 = 4x$
15. $x^2 + 2x = 10$
16. $2x - x^2 = 4$

SEE EXAMPLE 4 p. 359

17. **Geometry** One leg of a right triangle is 6 in. longer than the other leg. The hypotenuse of the triangle is 25 in. What is the length of each leg to the nearest inch? 14 in. and 20 in.

PRACTICE AND PROBLEM SOLVING

Independent Practice	
For Exercises	See Example
18–23	1
24–29	2
30–35	3
36	4

Extra Practice
Skills Practice p. S13
Application Practice p. S36

Find the zeros of each function by using the Quadratic Formula.

18. $f(x) = 3x^2 - 10x + 3$
19. $g(x) = x^2 + 6x$
20. $h(x) = x(x - 3) - 4$
21. $g(x) = -x^2 - 2x + 9$
22. $p(x) = 2x^2 - 7x - 8$
23. $f(x) = 7x^2 - 3$
24. $r(x) = x^2 + x + 1$
25. $h(x) = -x^2 - x - 1$
26. $f(x) = 2x^2 + 8$
27. $f(x) = 2x^2 + 7x - 13$
28. $g(x) = x^2 - x - 5$
29. $h(x) = -3x^2 + 4x - 4$

Find the type and number of solutions for each equation.

30. $2x^2 + 5 = 2x$
31. $2x^2 - 3x = 8$
32. $2x^2 - 16x = -32$
33. $4x^2 - 28x = -49$
34. $3x^2 - 8x + 8 = 0$
35. $3.2x^2 - 8.5x + 1.3 = 0$

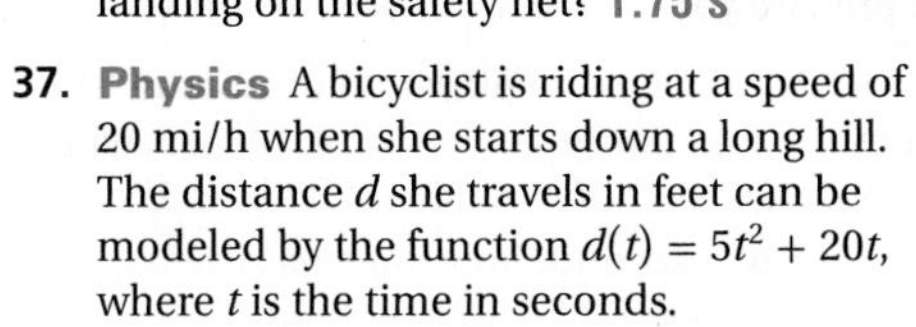

33. 1 distinct real solution
34. 2 distinct nonreal complex solutions
35. 2 distinct real solutions

36. **Safety** If a tightrope walker falls, he will land on a safety net. His height h in feet after a fall can be modeled by $h(t) = 60 - 16t^2$, where t is the time in seconds. How many seconds will the tightrope walker fall before landing on the safety net? 1.75 s

37. **Physics** A bicyclist is riding at a speed of 20 mi/h when she starts down a long hill. The distance d she travels in feet can be modeled by the function $d(t) = 5t^2 + 20t$, where t is the time in seconds.
    a. The hill is 585 ft long. To the nearest second, how long will it take her to reach the bottom? 9 s
    b. **What if...?** Suppose the hill were only half as long. To the nearest second, how long would it take the bicyclist to reach the bottom? 6 s

5-6 Exercises

Assignment Guide

Assign *Guided Practice* exercises as necessary.

If you finished Examples **1–2**
Basic 18–29, 38–43
Average 18–29, 38–43, 65
Advanced 18–29, 38–43, 65, 70

If you finished Examples **1–4**
Basic 18–55, 60–64, 72–78
Average 18–65, 67–69, 72–78
Advanced 18–78

Homework Quick Check
Quickly check key concepts.
Exercises: 18, 24, 30, 36, 44

Answers

2. $-5, -2$
3. $\frac{2 \pm \sqrt{7}}{3}$
4. $0, \frac{5}{3}$
5. $-6, 1$
6. $-\frac{3}{4}, 2$
7. $\pm\frac{\sqrt{38}}{2}$
8. $\frac{1 \pm i\sqrt{5}}{2}$
9. $-3 \pm i\sqrt{3}$
10. $\frac{-2 \pm i\sqrt{5}}{3}$
11. $-2 \pm i\sqrt{6}$
12. $\frac{7 \pm i\sqrt{11}}{10}$
13. $\frac{-7 \pm i\sqrt{111}}{20}$

14–16, 18–32. See p. A28.

State Resources

go.hrw.com
State Resources Online
KEYWORD: MB7 Resources

Teacher to Teacher

Students need to understand that the Quadratic Formula is just another tool of choice for solving quadratic equations. It should *not* be used for every quadratic equation that a student encounters. Many equations are more easily solved using other methods.

Students must be encouraged to select the method that works most efficiently in a problem. They too often pick one method and try to use it for all problems.

James P. Herrington
O'Fallon, IL

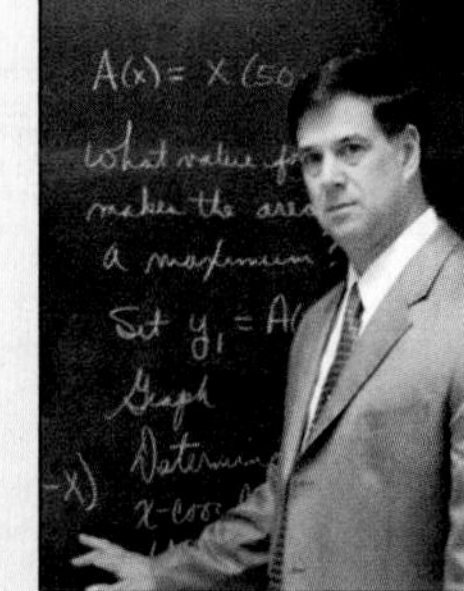

Geometry If students have difficulty setting up an equation for **Exercise 55,** suggest that they start by writing expressions that represent the length and width of the area inside the frame. For example, the inner length is equal to the outer length minus twice the width of the frame, or $25 - 2w$.

Exercise 60 involves solving a quadratic equation representing a baseball's height. This exercise prepares students for the Multi-Step Test Prep on page 364.

Answers

38–43. For graphs, see p. A29.

38. $\frac{2 \pm \sqrt{10}}{3}$

39. $\frac{1 \pm \sqrt{3}}{2}$

40. $\frac{-3 \pm i}{2}$

41. $\frac{-3 \pm \sqrt{17}}{4}$

42. $\frac{5 \pm \sqrt{73}}{6}$

43. $\frac{1 \pm i\sqrt{87}}{2}$

59. Possible answer: the Quadratic Formula; this method would be easier because the absolute value of a is great and the value of c is not an integer. Therefore, it would be difficult to solve the equation by factoring or by completing the square.

60b. See p. A29.

5-6 PRACTICE A

5-6 PRACTICE C

5-6 PRACTICE B

Find the zeros of each function by using the Quadratic Formula.

1. $f(x) = x^2 + 10x + 9$ $x = -9, -1$
2. $g(x) = 2x^2 + 4x - 12$ $x = -1 \pm \sqrt{7}$
3. $h(x) = 3x^2 - 3x + \frac{3}{4}$ $x = 0.5$
4. $f(x) = x^2 + 2x - 3$ $x = -3, 1$
5. $g(x) = 2x^2 + 3x + 1$ $x = -1, -0.5$
6. $g(x) = x^2 + 5x + -3$ $x = \frac{-5 \pm \sqrt{37}}{2}$

Find the type and number of solutions for each equation.

7. $x^2 - 3x = -8$ Two nonreal solutions
8. $x^2 + 4x = -3$ Two real solutions
9. $2x^2 - 12x = -18$ One real solution

Solve.

10. A newspaper delivery person in a car is tossing folded newspapers from the car window to driveways. The speed of the car is 30 feet per second, and the driver does not slow down. The newspapers are tossed horizontally from a height of 4 feet above the ground. The height of the papers as they are thrown can be modeled by $y = -16t^2 + 4$, and the distance they travel to the driveway is $d = 30t$.
    a. How long does it take for a newspaper to land? 0.5 s
    b. From how many feet before the driveway must the papers be thrown? 15 ft
    c. The delivery person starts to throw the newspapers at an angle and the height of the papers as they travel can now be modeled by $y = -16t^2 + 12t + 4$. How long does it take the papers to reach the ground now? 1 s

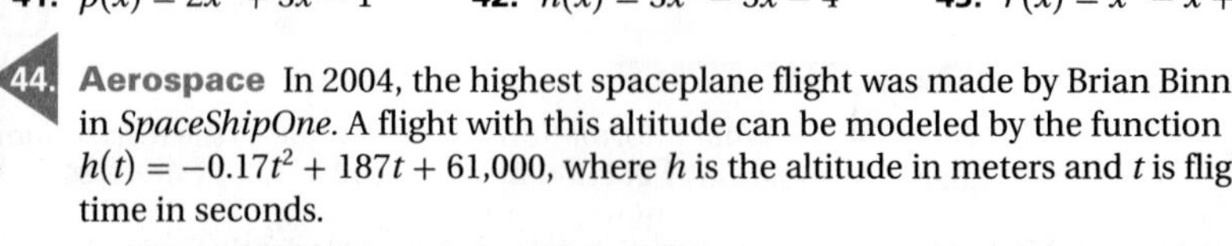

Find the zeros of each function. Then graph the function.

38. $f(x) = 3x^2 - 4x - 2$
39. $g(x) = 2x^2 - 2x - 1$
40. $h(x) = 2x^2 + 6x + 5$
41. $p(x) = 2x^2 + 3x - 1$
42. $h(x) = 3x^2 - 5x - 4$
43. $r(x) = x^2 - x + 22$

LINK Aerospace

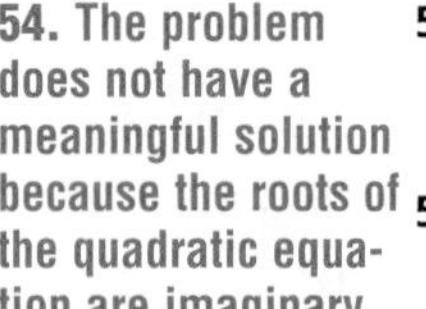

SpaceShipOne was the winner of the Ansari X Prize competition. The X Prize was awarded to the first nongovernmental spacecraft to reach an altitude of at least 100 km twice within a 2 week period.

44. **Aerospace** In 2004, the highest spaceplane flight was made by Brian Binnie in *SpaceShipOne*. A flight with this altitude can be modeled by the function $h(t) = -0.17t^2 + 187t + 61{,}000$, where h is the altitude in meters and t is flight time in seconds.
    a. Approximately how long did the flight last? about 1363 s, or about 23 min
    b. What was the highest altitude to the nearest thousand meters? 112,000 m
    c. The table shows the altitudes of layers of Earth's atmosphere. According to the model, which of these layers did *SpaceShipOne* enter, and at what time(s) did the spaceplane enter them? It entered all 4 layers; thermosphere at $t \approx$ 149 s; mesosphere at $t \approx$ 952 s; stratosphere at $t \approx$ 1156 s; troposphere at $t \approx$ 1326 s.

Earth's Atmosphere

Layer	Altitude (in km)
Troposphere	0 to 10
Stratosphere	10 to 50
Mesosphere	50 to 85
Thermosphere	85 to 600

Solve each equation by any method.

45. $x^2 - 3x = 10$ $-2, 5$
46. $x^2 - 16 = 0$ ± 4
47. $4x^2 + 4x = 15$ $-2.5, 1.5$
48. $x^2 + 2x - 2 = 0$
49. $x^2 - 4x - 21 = 0$ $-3, 7$
50. $4x^2 - 4x - 1 = 0$
51. $6x^2 = 150$ ± 5
52. $x^2 = 7$ $\pm\sqrt{7}$
53. $x^2 - 16x + 64 = 0$ 8

48. $-1 \pm \sqrt{3}$

50. $\frac{1 \pm \sqrt{2}}{2}$

54. The problem does not have a meaningful solution because the roots of the quadratic equation are imaginary.

54. **Critical Thinking** If you are solving a real-world problem involving a quadratic equation, and the discriminant is negative, what can you conclude?

55. **Multi-Step** The outer dimensions of a picture frame are 25 inches by 20 inches. If the area inside the picture frame is 266 square inches, what is the width w of the frame? 3 in.

Critical Thinking **Find the values of c that make each equation have one real solution.**

56. $x^2 + 8x + c = 0$ 16
57. $x^2 + 12x = c$ -36
58. $x^2 + 2cx + 49 = 0$ 7

59. **Write About It** What method would you use to solve the equation $-14x^2 + 6x = 2.7$? Why would this method be easier to use than the other methods?

60. This problem will prepare you for the Multi-Step Test Prep on page 364.

    An outfielder throws a baseball to the player on third base. The height h of the ball in feet is modeled by the function $h(t) = -16t^2 + 19t + 5$, where t is time in seconds. The third baseman catches the ball when it is 4 ft above the ground.
    a. To the nearest tenth of a second, how long was the ball in the air before it was caught?
    b. A player on the opposing team starts running from second base to third base 1.2 s before the outfielder throws the ball. The distance between the bases is 90 ft, and the runner's average speed is 27 ft/s. Will the runner reach third base before the ball does? Explain.

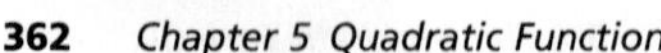

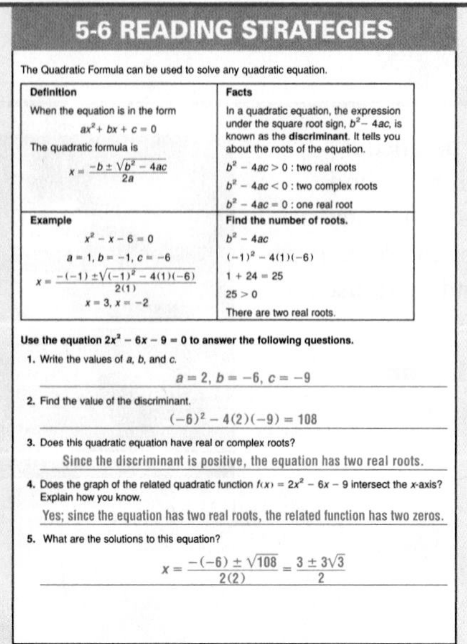

5-6 READING STRATEGIES

The Quadratic Formula can be used to solve any quadratic equation.

Definition	Facts
When the equation is in the form $ax^2 + bx + c = 0$ The quadratic formula is $x = \frac{-b \pm \sqrt{b^2 - 4ac}}{2a}$	In a quadratic equation, the expression under the square root sign, $b^2 - 4ac$, is known as the **discriminant**. It tells you about the roots of the equation. $b^2 - 4ac > 0$: two real roots $b^2 - 4ac < 0$: two complex roots $b^2 - 4ac = 0$: one real root
Example	**Find the number of roots.**
$x^2 - x - 6 = 0$ $a = 1, b = -1, c = -6$ $x = \frac{-(-1) \pm \sqrt{(-1)^2 - 4(1)(-6)}}{2(1)}$ $x = 3, x = -2$	$b^2 - 4ac$ $(-1)^2 - 4(1)(-6)$ $1 + 24 = 25$ $25 > 0$ There are two real roots.

Use the equation $2x^2 - 6x - 9 = 0$ to answer the following questions.

1. Write the values of a, b, and c. $a = 2, b = -6, c = -9$
2. Find the value of the discriminant. $(-6)^2 - 4(2)(-9) = 108$
3. Does this quadratic equation have real or complex roots? Since the discriminant is positive, the equation has two real roots.
4. Does the graph of the related quadratic function $f(x) = 2x^2 - 6x - 9$ intersect the x-axis? Explain how you know. Yes; since the equation has two real roots, the related function has two zeros.
5. What are the solutions to this equation? $x = \frac{-(-6) \pm \sqrt{108}}{2(2)} = \frac{3 \pm 3\sqrt{3}}{2}$

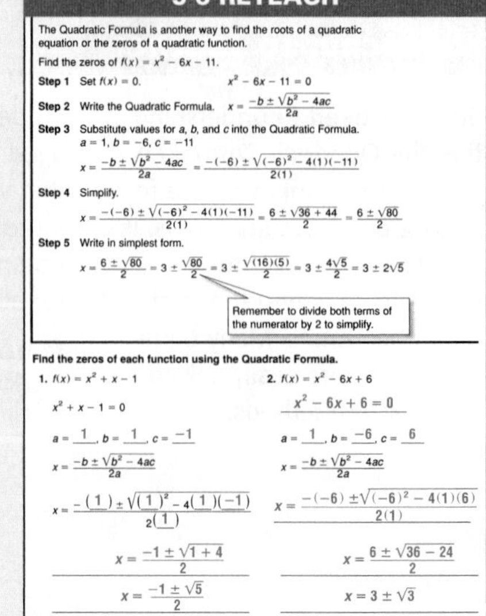

5-6 RETEACH

The Quadratic Formula is another way to find the roots of a quadratic equation or the zeros of a quadratic function.

Find the zeros of $f(x) = x^2 - 6x - 11$.

Step 1 Set $f(x) = 0$. $x^2 - 6x - 11 = 0$

Step 2 Write the Quadratic Formula. $x = \frac{-b \pm \sqrt{b^2 - 4ac}}{2a}$

Step 3 Substitute values for a, b, and c into the Quadratic Formula.
$a = 1, b = -6, c = -11$
$x = \frac{-b \pm \sqrt{b^2 - 4ac}}{2a} = \frac{-(-6) \pm \sqrt{(-6)^2 - 4(1)(-11)}}{2(1)}$

Step 4 Simplify.
$x = \frac{-(-6) \pm \sqrt{(-6)^2 - 4(1)(-11)}}{2(1)} = \frac{6 \pm \sqrt{36 + 44}}{2} = \frac{6 \pm \sqrt{80}}{2}$

Step 5 Write in simplest form.
$x = \frac{6 \pm \sqrt{80}}{2} = 3 \pm \frac{\sqrt{80}}{2} = 3 \pm \frac{\sqrt{(16)(5)}}{2} = 3 \pm \frac{4\sqrt{5}}{2} = 3 \pm 2\sqrt{5}$

Remember to divide both terms of the numerator by 2 to simplify.

Find the zeros of each function using the Quadratic Formula.

1. $f(x) = x^2 + x - 1$
   $x^2 + x - 1 = 0$
   $a = 1$, $b = 1$, $c = -1$
   $x = \frac{-b \pm \sqrt{b^2 - 4ac}}{2a}$
   $x = \frac{-(1) \pm \sqrt{(1)^2 - 4(1)(-1)}}{2(1)}$
   $x = \frac{-1 \pm \sqrt{1 + 4}}{2}$
   $x = \frac{-1 \pm \sqrt{5}}{2}$
2. $f(x) = x^2 - 6x + 6$
   $x^2 - 6x + 6 = 0$
   $a = 1$, $b = -6$, $c = 6$
   $x = \frac{-b \pm \sqrt{b^2 - 4ac}}{2a}$
   $x = \frac{-(-6) \pm \sqrt{(-6)^2 - 4(1)(6)}}{2(1)}$
   $x = \frac{6 \pm \sqrt{36 - 24}}{2}$
   $x = 3 \pm \sqrt{3}$

TEST PREP

61. Which best describes the graph of a quadratic function with a discriminant of −3?
   - (A) Parabola with two x-intercepts
   - **(B)** Parabola with no x-intercepts
   - (C) Parabola that opens upward
   - (D) Parabola that opens downward

62. What is the discriminant of the equation $2x^2 - 8x = 14$?
   - (F) 48
   - **(H)** 176
   - (G) −48
   - (J) −176

63. Which function has zeros of $3 \pm i$?
   - (A) $f(x) = x^2 + 6x + 10$
   - **(C)** $g(x) = x^2 - 6x + 10$
   - (B) $f(x) = x^2 + 6x - 10$
   - (D) $h(x) = x^2 - 6x - 10$

64. Which best describes the discriminant of the function whose graph is shown?
   - **(F)** Positive
   - (H) Negative
   - (G) Zero
   - (J) Undefined

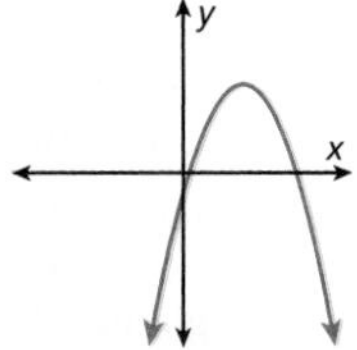

CHALLENGE AND EXTEND

65. **Geometry** The perimeter of a right triangle is 40 cm, and its hypotenuse measures 17 cm. Find the length of each leg. **15 cm and 8 cm**

66. **Geometry** The perimeter of a rectangle is 88 cm.
   a. Find the least possible value of the length of the diagonal. Round to the nearest tenth of a centimeter. **31.1 cm**
   b. What are the dimensions of the rectangle with this diagonal? **22 cm by 22 cm**

Write a quadratic equation whose solutions belong to the indicated sets.

67. integers
68. irrational real numbers
69. complex numbers

70. A quadratic equation has the form $ax^2 + bx + c = 0 \; (a \neq 0)$.
   a. What is the sum of the roots of the equation? the product of the roots? $\frac{-b}{a}$; $\frac{c}{a}$
   b. Determine the standard form of a quadratic equation whose roots have a sum of 2 and a product of −15. $x^2 - 2x - 15 = 0$

71. Describe the solutions to a quadratic equation for which $a = b = c$.
The solutions are nonreal and complex. Regardless of the values of a, b, and c, the roots are $\frac{-1 \pm i\sqrt{3}}{2}$.

SPIRAL REVIEW

72. **Biology** The length of a human hair is a linear function of time. Juan's hair grows 2.1 cm in 60 days. Express the growth in centimeters of Juan's hair as a function of the number of days since his last haircut. *(Lesson 2-4)* $h(x) = 0.035x$

Write the augmented matrix, and use row reduction to solve. *(Lesson 4-6)*

73. $\begin{cases} 3y = 2x + 7 \\ x - 6y = 1 \end{cases}$

74. $\begin{cases} 2x = -3y + 12 \\ x + y = 14 \end{cases}$

75. $\begin{cases} 4x + 5y = -1 \\ 9 + 7y = 2x \end{cases}$

Solve each equation by completing the square. *(Lesson 5-4)*

76. $x^2 - 5x = 1$ $\frac{5 \pm \sqrt{29}}{2}$

77. $2x^2 = 16x - 4$ $4 \pm \sqrt{14}$

78. $3x = 5x^2 - 12$ $\frac{3 \pm \sqrt{249}}{10}$

5-6 PROBLEM SOLVING

In a shot-put event, Jenna tosses her last shot from a position of about 6 feet above the ground with an initial vertical and horizontal velocity of 20 feet per second. The height of the shot is modeled by the function $h(t) = -16t^2 + 20t + 6$, where t is the time in seconds after the toss. The horizontal distance traveled after t seconds is modeled by $d(t) = 20t$.

1. Jenna wants to know the exact distance the shot travels at a velocity of 20 feet per second.
   a. Use the Quadratic Formula $t = \frac{-b \pm \sqrt{b^2 - 4ac}}{2a}$ to solve the height function for t. $t = -0.25, 1.5$
   b. Use the value for t and the distance function to find the distance her shot travels. 30 ft

2. Jenna is working to improve her performance. She makes a table to show how the horizontal distance varies with velocity. Complete the table.

	Velocity (ft/s)	Formula	Time (s)	Distance (ft)
a.	22	$t = \frac{-22 \pm \sqrt{(22)^2 - 4(-16)(6)}}{2(-16)}$	$t = -0.23, 1.61$	35.4 ft
b.	25	$t = \frac{-25 \pm \sqrt{(25)^2 - 4(-16)(6)}}{2(-16)}$	$t = -0.21, 1.77$	44.3 ft
c.	28	$t = \frac{-28 \pm \sqrt{(28)^2 - 4(-16)(6)}}{2(-16)}$	$t = -0.19, 1.94$	54.3 ft

Jenna has not reached her full potential yet. Her goal is to toss the shot from a height of 6 feet 6 inches with a vertical and horizontal velocity of 30 feet per second. Choose the letter for the best answer.

3. If she achieves her goal, how long will her shot stay in the air?
   - A 1.65 s
   - B 1.87 s
   - **(C)** 2.07 s
   - D 2.27 s

4. If she achieves her goal, what horizontal distance will the shot travel?
   - A 41.4 ft
   - B 56.1 ft
   - **(C)** 62.1 ft
   - D 68.1 ft

5-6 CHALLENGE

The general solution of the quadratic equation $ax^2 + bx + c = 0$ can be written in terms of the coefficients a, b, and c, and this solution is known as the Quadratic Formula. You can explore some other relationships between the roots and the coefficients.

1. Complete the table below.

	Equation	Roots	Sum of the Roots	Product of the Roots
a.	$x^2 - 6x + 8 = 0$	4, 2	6	8
b.	$x^2 - 7x + 12 = 0$	4, 3	7	12
c.	$x^2 + 2x - 35 = 0$	5, −7	−2	−35
d.	$4x^2 - 8x + 3 = 0$	$\frac{1}{2}, \frac{3}{2}$	2	$\frac{3}{4}$
e.	$9x^2 + 3x - 2 = 0$	$\frac{1}{3}, -\frac{2}{3}$	$-\frac{1}{3}$	$-\frac{2}{9}$

2. Refer to the table above. Let the roots of the quadratic equation $ax^2 + bx + c = 0$ be represented by r_1 and r_2.
   a. Express the sum of the roots in terms of the coefficients of the equation. $r_1 + r_2 =$ $r_1 + r_2 = -\frac{b}{a}$
   b. Express the product of the roots in terms of the coefficients of the equation. $r_1 r_2 =$ $r_1 r_2 = \frac{c}{a}$

Use the relationships between roots and coefficients that you wrote in Exercise 2. Verify your answer by solving the equation.

3. Write a quadratic equation whose roots are $2 + \sqrt{5}$ and $2 - \sqrt{5}$. $x^2 - 4x - 1 = 0$

4. The sum of the roots of $5x^2 - kx - 3 = 0$ is equal to the product of the roots. Determine the value of k. $k = -3$

5. Without solving, decide which numbers are the roots of $9x^2 - 6x - 1$.
   A. $1 \pm \sqrt{2}$ B. $1 \pm \sqrt{3}$ C. $\frac{1 \pm \sqrt{2}}{3}$ D. $\frac{1 \pm \sqrt{3}}{2}$ C

6. Which of these equations has $\frac{-5 \pm \sqrt{17}}{2}$ as its solutions?
   A. $x^2 + 5x + 2 = 0$ B. $x^2 + 5x - 2 = 0$
   C. $x^2 - 5x - 2 = 0$ D. $x^2 - 5x + 2 = 0$ A

TEST PREP DOCTOR In **Exercise 62,** students who chose **G** may have substituted 14 for c. Remind students that the equation must be in standard form before the Quadratic Formula can be applied.

Answers

67. Possible answer: $x^2 = 4$
68. Possible answer: $x^2 = \frac{1}{2}$
69. Possible answer: $x^2 = -2$

73–75. See p. A29.

Journal

Have students write three different quadratic equations: one that they would solve by factoring, one that they would solve by completing the square, and one that they would solve by using the Quadratic Formula. Students should explain why they would use the chosen method in each case.

ALTERNATIVE ASSESSMENT

Have students explain how to determine the discriminant and how its value indicates the number of real solutions of a quadratic equation.

Power Presentations with PowerPoint®

5-6 Lesson Quiz

Find the zeros of each function by using the Quadratic Formula.

1. $f(x) = 3x^2 - 6x - 5$
   $1 \pm \frac{2\sqrt{6}}{3}$
2. $g(x) = 2x^2 - 6x + 5$
   $\frac{3}{2} \pm \frac{1}{2}i$

Find the type and number of solutions for each equation.

3. $x^2 - 14x + 50 = 0$
   2 distinct nonreal complex
4. $x^2 - 14x + 48 = 0$
   2 distinct real
5. A pebble is tossed from the top of a cliff. The pebble's height in feet is given by $y(t) = -16t^2 + 6t + 200$, where t is the time in seconds. Its horizontal distance in feet from the base of the cliff is given by $d(t) = 5t$. How far will the pebble be from the base of the cliff when it hits the ground? about 19 ft

Also available on transparency

Organizer

Objective: Assess students' ability to apply concepts and skills in Lessons 5-1 through 5-6 in a real-world format.

 **Online Edition**

Resources

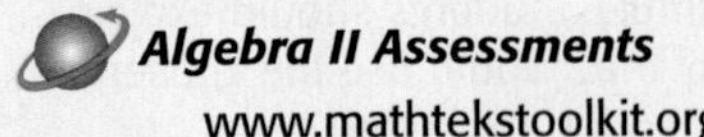

Problem	Text Reference
1	Lesson 5-1
2	Lesson 5-2
3	Lesson 5-6
4	Lesson 5-3
5	Lesson 5-6

Answers

3. Yes; possible answer: based on the ball's horizontal velocity, it will cross home plate in about 0.52 s. The ball's height at this time will be about 4.3 ft. This height is within the batter's strike zone.
5. See p. A29.

State Resources

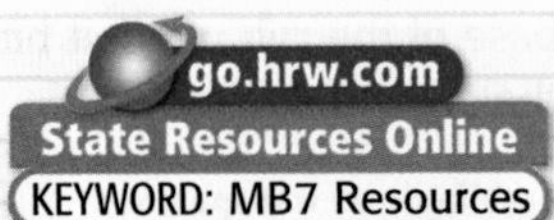

SECTION 5A

Quadratic Functions and Complex Numbers

Ballpark Figures When a baseball is thrown or hit into the air, its height h in feet after t seconds can be modeled by $h(t) = -16t^2 + v_y t + h_0$, where v_y is the initial vertical velocity of the ball in feet per second and h_0 is the ball's initial height. The horizontal distance d in feet that the ball travels in t seconds can be modeled by $d(t) = v_x t$, where v_x is the ball's initial horizontal velocity in feet per second.

1. A short stop makes an error by dropping the ball. As the ball drops, its height h in feet is modeled by $h(t) = -16t^2 + 3$. A slow-motion replay of the error shows the play at half speed. What function describes the height of the ball in the replay? $h(t) = -16(0.5t)^2 + 3$

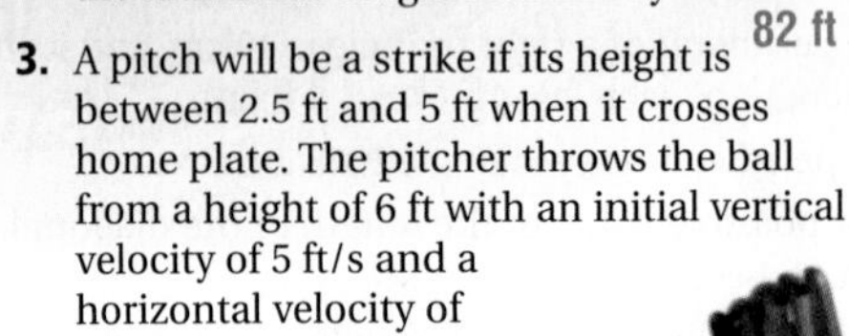

2. A player hits a foul ball with an initial vertical velocity of 70 ft/s and an initial height of 5 ft. To the nearest foot, what is the maximum height reached by the ball? 82 ft
3. A pitch will be a strike if its height is between 2.5 ft and 5 ft when it crosses home plate. The pitcher throws the ball from a height of 6 ft with an initial vertical velocity of 5 ft/s and a horizontal velocity of 116 ft/s. Could this pitch be a strike? Explain.

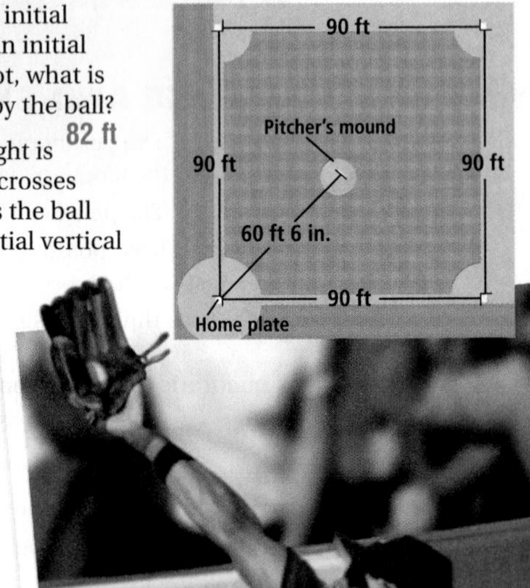

4. The next pitch crosses home plate 1 ft too high to be a strike. The pitch is thrown from a height of 6 ft with an initial vertical velocity of 8 ft/s. What is the initial horizontal velocity of this pitch? 121 ft/s
5. A player throws the ball home from a height of 5.5 ft with an initial vertical velocity of 28 ft/s. The ball is caught at home plate at a height of 5 ft. Three seconds before the ball is thrown, a runner on third base starts toward home plate at an average speed of 25 ft/s. Does the runner reach home plate before the ball does? Explain.

INTERVENTION

Scaffolding Questions

1. What type of transformation is the function that describes the replay? a horizontal stretch
2. How can you determine the value of t when the ball reaches its maximum height? Determine $-\frac{b}{2a}$ from the height function.
3. How can you determine the value of t when the ball crosses home plate? Divide the distance between the pitcher and home plate by the horizontal velocity.

4–5. What equation can you use to find the value of t when the ball reaches home plate? **4.** $6 = -16t^2 + 8t + 6$; **5.** $5 = -16t^2 + 28t + 5.5$

Extension

What if...? Suppose the pitch in Problem 4 crossed home plate 1 ft too low to be a strike. To the nearest foot per second, what would the initial horizontal velocity of this pitch be? 72 ft/s

READY TO GO ON?

CHAPTER 5

SECTION 5A

Quiz for Lessons 5-1 Through 5-6

5-1 Using Transformations to Graph Quadratic Functions

Using the graph of $f(x) = x^2$ as a guide, describe the transformations, and then graph each function.

1. $g(x) = (x + 2)^2 - 4$
2. $g(x) = -4(x - 1)^2$
3. $g(x) = \frac{1}{2}x^2 + 1$

Use the description to write each quadratic function in vertex form.

4. $f(x) = x^2$ is vertically stretched by a factor of 9 and translated 2 units left to create g. $g(x) = 9(x + 2)^2$
5. $f(x) = x^2$ is reflected across the x-axis and translated 4 units up to create g. $g(x) = -x^2 + 4$

5-2 Properties of Quadratic Functions in Standard Form

For each function, (a) determine whether the graph opens upward or downward, (b) find the axis of symmetry, (c) find the vertex, (d) find the y-intercept, and (e) graph the function.

6. $f(x) = x^2 - 4x + 3$
7. $g(x) = -x^2 + 2x - 1$
8. $h(x) = x^2 - 6x$
9. A football kick is modeled by the function $h(x) = -0.0075x^2 + 0.5x + 5$, where h is the height of the ball in feet and x is the horizontal distance in feet that the ball travels. Find the maximum height of the ball to the nearest foot. 13 ft

5-3 Solving Quadratic Equations by Graphing and Factoring

Find the roots of each equation by factoring.

10. $x^2 - 100 = 0$ 10, −10
11. $x^2 + 5x = 24$ 3, −8
12. $4x^2 + 8x = 0$ 0, −2

5-4 Completing the Square

Solve each equation by completing the square.

13. $x^2 - 6x = 40$ −4, 10
14. $x^2 + 18x = 15$ $-9 \pm 4\sqrt{6}$
15. $x^2 + 14x = 8$ $-7 \pm \sqrt{57}$

Write each function in vertex form, and identify its vertex.

16. $f(x) = x^2 + 24x + 138$ $f(x) = (x + 12)^2 - 6$; $(-12, -6)$
17. $g(x) = x^2 - 12x + 39$ $g(x) = (x - 6)^2 + 3$; $(6, 3)$
18. $h(x) = 5x^2 - 20x + 9$ $h(x) = 5(x - 2)^2 - 11$; $(2, -11)$

5-5 Complex Numbers and Roots

Solve each equation.

19. $3x^2 = -48$ $\pm 4i$
20. $x^2 - 20x = -125$ $10 \pm 5i$
21. $x^2 - 8x + 30 = 0$ $4 \pm i\sqrt{14}$

5-6 The Quadratic Formula

Find the zeros of each function by using the Quadratic Formula.

22. $f(x) = (x + 6)^2 + 2$ 22. $-6 \pm i\sqrt{2}$
23. $g(x) = x^2 + 7x + 15$ 23. $-\frac{7}{2} \pm i\frac{\sqrt{11}}{2}$
24. $h(x) = 2x^2 - 5x + 3$ 1, 1.5
25. A bicyclist is riding at a speed of 18 mi/h when she starts down a long hill. The distance d she travels in feet can be modeled by $d(t) = 4t^2 + 18t$, where t is the time in seconds. How long will it take her to reach the bottom of a 400-foot-long hill? 8 s

READY TO GO ON?

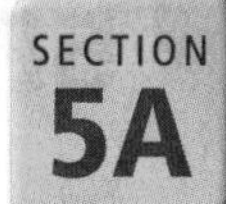

Organizer

Objective: Assess students' mastery of concepts and skills in Lessons 5-1 through 5-6.

Resources

 ***Assessment Resources***

Section 5A Quiz

 **Test & Practice Generator**

One-Stop Planner®

INTERVENTION

Resources

 ***Ready to Go On? Intervention and Enrichment* Worksheets**

 ***Ready to Go On?* CD-ROM**

 ***Ready to Go On?* Online**

my.hrw.com

Answers

1. g is f translated 2 units left and 4 units down.

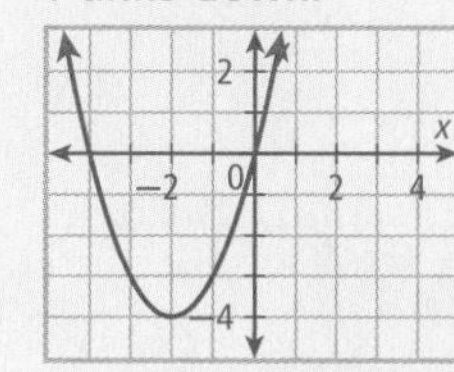

2, 3, 6–8. See p. A29.

READY TO GO ON?

Diagnose and Prescribe

NO INTERVENE

Ready to Go On? Intervention	*Ready to Go On? Intervention,* Section 5A		
	Worksheets	CD-ROM	Online
Lesson 5-1	5-1 Intervention	Activity 5-1	Diagnose and Prescribe Online
Lesson 5-2	5-2 Intervention	Activity 5-2	
Lesson 5-3	5-3 Intervention	Activity 5-3	
Lesson 5-4	5-4 Intervention	Activity 5-4	
Lesson 5-5	5-5 Intervention	Activity 5-5	
Lesson 5-6	5-6 Intervention	Activity 5-6	

YES ENRICH

***Ready to Go On? Enrichment,* Section 5A**

Worksheets

CD-ROM

Online

SECTION 5B

Applying Quadratic Functions

One-Minute Section Planner

Lesson	Lab Resources	Materials
Lesson 5-7 Solving Quadratic Inequalities • Solve quadratic inequalities by using tables and graphs. • Solve quadratic inequalities by using algebra. ☐ SAT-10 ☑ NAEP ☑ ACT ☐ SAT ☐ SAT Subject Tests		**Required** graph paper, graphing calculator
Lesson 5-8 Curve Fitting with Quadratic Models • Use quadratic functions to model data. • Use quadratic models to analyze and predict. ☑ SAT-10 ☑ NAEP ☑ ACT ☑ SAT ☑ SAT Subject Tests	***Technology Lab Activities*** 5-8 Technology Lab	**Required** graph paper, graphing calculator
Lesson 5-9 Operations with Complex Numbers • Perform operations with complex numbers. ☐ SAT-10 ☐ NAEP ☑ ACT ☐ SAT ☑ SAT Subject Tests		**Required** graph paper **Optional** graphing calculator, masking tape

MK = *Manipulatives Kit*

Section Overview

Solving Quadratic Inequalities — Lesson 5-7

Quadratic inequalities can be used to make business decisions such as determining price ranges that will result in a certain level of profit.

$$x^2 + 10x + 21 \leq 0$$

Solve the related equation.

$$x^2 + 10x + 21 = 0$$
$$(x + 7)(x + 3) = 0$$
$$x = -7 \text{ or } x = -3$$

Critical values: $-7, -3$

Test a value in each interval.

$$(-8)^2 + 10(-8) + 21 \leq 0 \quad ✗$$
$$(-6)^2 + 10(-6) + 21 \leq 0 \quad ✓$$
$$(0)^2 + 10(0) + 21 \leq 0 \quad ✗$$

The solution is $-7 \leq x \leq -3$.

Curve Fitting with Quadratic Models — Lesson 5-8

Students can use quadratic models of real-world data to make predictions and estimates.

Write a quadratic model that fits the points $(0, -9)$, $(1, -2)$, and $(2, 9)$.

(x, y)	$f(x) = ax^2 + bx + c$	Linear System in a, b, c
$(0, -9)$	$-9 = a(0)^2 + b(0) + c$	$c = -9$
$(1, -2)$	$-2 = a(1)^2 + b(1) + c$	$a + b + c = -2$
$(2, 9)$	$9 = a(2)^2 + b(2) + c$	$4a + 2b + c = 9$

Solving yields $a = 2$, $b = 5$, and $c = -9$, so the quadratic model is $f(x) = 2x^2 + 5x - 9$.

Operations with Complex Numbers — Lesson 5-9

Why? Operations on complex numbers can be used to create some types of fractals.

Addition

$$(3 + 4i) + (5 + 6i) = 8 + 10i$$

Subtraction

$$(3 + 4i) - (5 + 6i) = -2 - 2i$$

Multiplication

$$\begin{aligned}(3 + 4i)(5 + 6i) &= 3(5 + 6i) + 4i(5 + 6i)\\ &= 15 + 18i + 20i + 24i^2\\ &= 15 + 38i + 24(-1)\\ &= -9 + 38i\end{aligned}$$

Division

$$\begin{aligned}\frac{3 + 4i}{5 + 6i} &= \frac{3 + 4i}{5 + 6i}\left(\frac{5 - 6i}{5 - 6i}\right)\\ &= \frac{39 + 2i}{61}\\ &= \frac{39}{61} + \frac{2}{61}i\end{aligned}$$

5-7 Organizer

Pacing: Traditional 1 day
Block $\frac{1}{2}$ day

Objectives: Solve quadratic inequalities by using tables and graphs.

Solve quadratic inequalities by using algebra.

Online Edition
Graphing Calculator, Tutorial Videos, TechKeys

Countdown to Testing Week 12

Power Presentations with PowerPoint®

Warm Up

1. Graph the inequality $y < 2x + 1$.

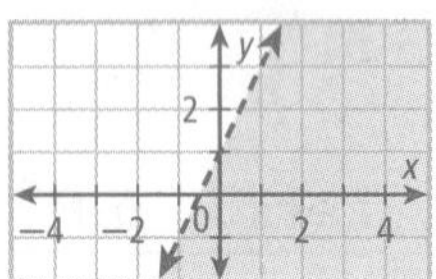

Solve using any method.

2. $x^2 - 16x + 63 = 0$ 7, 9

3. $3x^2 + 8x = 3$ $-3, \frac{1}{3}$

Also available on transparency

Math Humor

Q: How can a fisherman determine how many fish he needs to catch to make a profit?

A: By using a cod-ratic inequality.

5-7 Solving Quadratic Inequalities

Objectives
Solve quadratic inequalities by using tables and graphs.
Solve quadratic inequalities by using algebra.

Vocabulary
quadratic inequality in two variables

Who uses this?
Tour companies and other businesses use quadratic inequalities to make predictions of profits. (See Example 4.)

Many business profits can be modeled by quadratic functions. To ensure that the profit is above a certain level, financial planners may need to graph and solve *quadratic inequalities.*

A **quadratic inequality in two variables** can be written in one of the following forms, where a, b, and c are real numbers and $a \neq 0$. Its solution set is a set of ordered pairs (x, y).

$$y < ax^2 + bx + c \qquad y > ax^2 + bx + c$$
$$y \leq ax^2 + bx + c \qquad y \geq ax^2 + bx + c$$

In Lesson 2-5, you solved linear inequalities in two variables by graphing. You can use a similar procedure to graph quadratic inequalities.

Graphing Quadratic Inequalities	
To graph a quadratic inequality	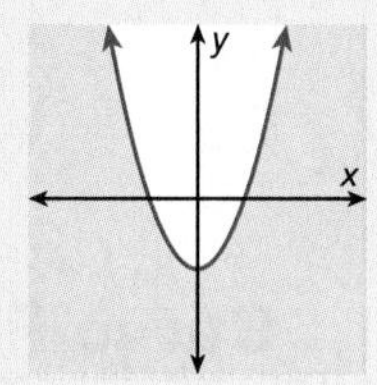
1. Graph the parabola that defines the boundary.	
2. Use a solid parabola for $y \leq$ and $y \geq$ and a dashed parabola for $y <$ and $y >$.	
3. Shade above the parabola for $y >$ or $\geq$ and below the parabola for $y \leq$ or $<$.	

EXAMPLE 1 **Graphing Quadratic Inequalities in Two Variables**

Graph $y < -2x^2 - 4x + 6$.

Step 1 Graph the boundary of the related parabola $y = -2x^2 - 4x + 6$ with a dashed curve.

Its y-intercept is 6, its vertex is $(-1, 8)$, and its x-intercepts are -3 and 1.

Step 2 Shade below the parabola because the solution consists of y-values less than those on the parabola for corresponding x-values.

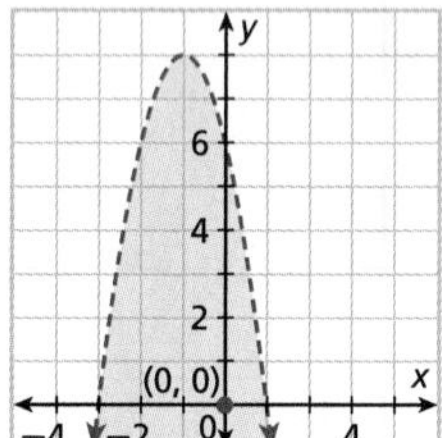

Check Use a test point to verify the solution region.

$y < -2x^2 - 4x + 6$
$0 < -2(0)^2 - 4(0) + 6$ *Try (0, 0).*
$0 < 6$ ✔

State Resources

go.hrw.com
State Resources Online
KEYWORD: MB7 Resources

1 Introduce

EXPLORATION

5-7 Solving Quadratic Inequalities

You can use a graphing calculator to explore quadratic inequalities.

Graph the inequality $y \geq x^2 - 4$ as follows. Press [Y=] and enter $x^2 - 4$ for **Y1**. Then use the arrow keys to move the cursor to the left of **Y1**. Press [ENTER] until the graph style changes to the symbol shown. This symbol indicates that the area above the graph will be shaded. Press [GRAPH] to view the graph.

Graph style symbol

1. Describe the graph of the inequality $y \geq x^2 - 4$.
2. The shaded area of the graph represents the solution set of the inequality. Tell whether each of the following points is in the solution set of $y \geq x^2 - 4$.
 a. (0, 0) b. (3, 0)
 c. (1, 6) d. (−3, −3)
3. What are the possible values of y for x = 0?
4. What is the least possible value of y?

THINK AND DISCUSS

5. Discuss how the graph of $y \leq x^2 - 4$ would differ from the graph of ...

Motivate

Discuss with students what a business's profit is. Explain that profit can sometimes be modeled by a quadratic function of an item's selling price. A procedure for solving quadratic inequalities is needed to determine the range of selling prices that result in a profit.

Explorations and answers are provided in the *Explorations* binder.

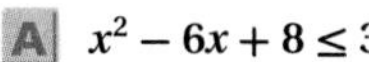

Graph each inequality.

1a. $y \geq 2x^2 - 5x - 2$ **1b.** $y < -3x^2 - 6x - 7$

Quadratic inequalities in one variable, such as $ax^2 + bx + c > 0$ $(a \neq 0)$, have solutions in one variable that are graphed on a number line.

EXAMPLE 2 Solving Quadratic Inequalities by Using Tables and Graphs

Solve each inequality by using tables or graphs.

A $x^2 - 6x + 8 \leq 3$

Use a graphing calculator to graph each side of the inequality. Set **Y1** equal to $x^2 - 6x + 8$ and **Y2** equal to 3. Identify the values of x for which **Y1** ≤ **Y2**.

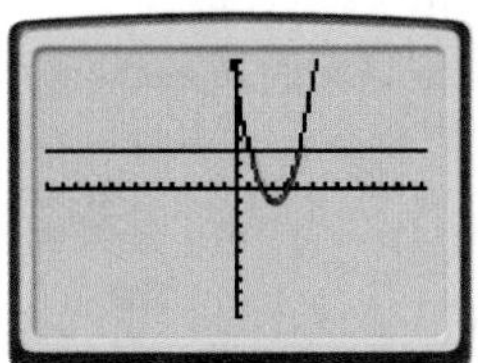

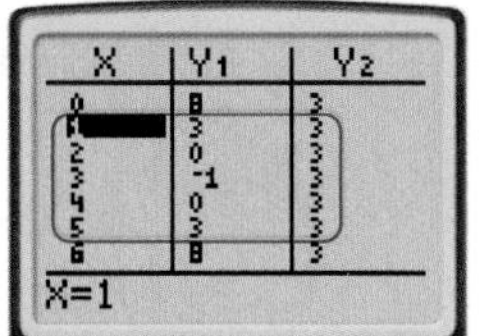

The parabola is at or below the line when x is between 1 and 5 inclusive. So, the solution set is $1 \leq x \leq 5$, or $[1, 5]$. The table supports your answer.

The number line shows the solution set.

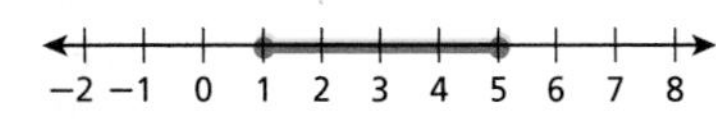

B $x^2 - 6x + 8 > 3$

Use a graphing calculator to graph each side of the inequality. Set **Y1** equal to $x^2 - 6x + 8$ and **Y2** equal to 3. Identify the values of x for which **Y1** > **Y2**.

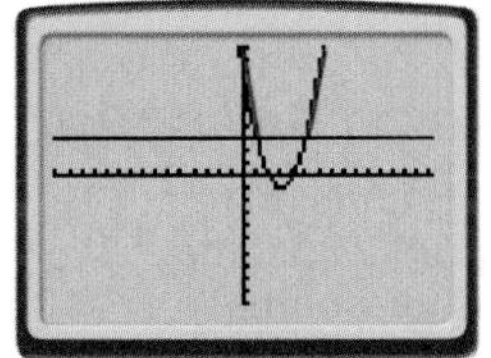

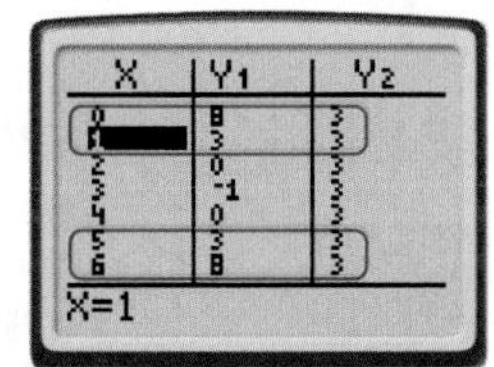

The parabola is above the line $y = 3$ when x is less than 1 or greater than 5. So the solution set is $x < 1$ or $x > 5$, or $(-\infty, 1) \cup (5, \infty)$.

The number line shows the solution set.

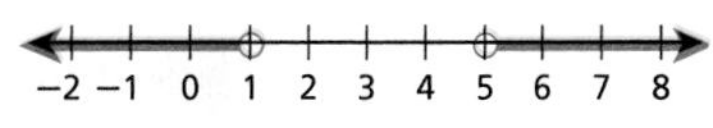

Reading Math

For **and** statements, *both* of the conditions must be true. For **or** statements, *at least one* of the conditions must be true.

Solve each inequality by using tables or graphs.

2a. $x^2 - x + 5 < 7$ **2b.** $2x^2 - 5x + 1 \geq 1$

$-1 < x < 2$ $x \leq 0$ or $x \geq 2.5$

The number lines showing the solution sets in Example 2 are divided into three distinct regions by the points 1 and 5. These points are called *critical values.* By finding the critical values, you can solve quadratic inequalities algebraically.

Power Presentations with PowerPoint®

Additional Examples

Example 1

Graph $y \geq x^2 - 7x + 10$.

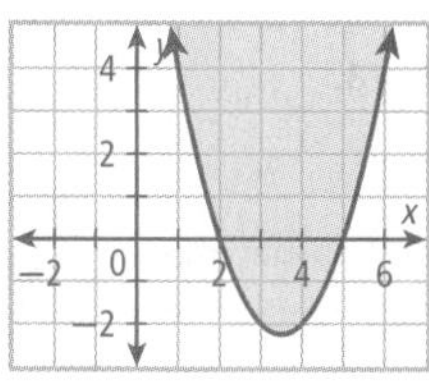

Example 2

Solve each inequality by using tables or graphs.

A. $x^2 + 8x + 20 \geq 5$

$x \leq -5$ or $x \geq -3$

B. $x^2 + 8x + 20 < 5$

$-5 < x < -3$

Also available on transparency

INTERVENTION

Questioning Strategies

EXAMPLE 1

- How do you know whether to graph the boundary with a dashed parabola or a solid parabola?
- How do you choose a test point to verify the solution region?

EXAMPLE 2

- What steps do you use to graph each side of the inequality on a graphing calculator?

Answers to Check It Out!

1a.

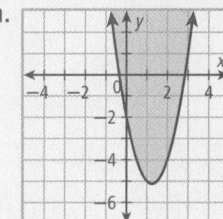

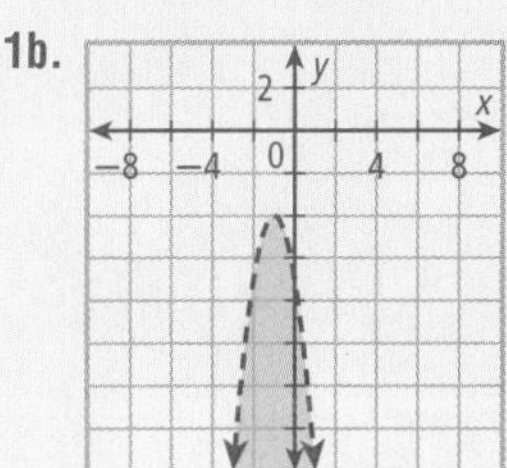

1b.

2 Teach

Guided Instruction

Review the steps of graphing linear inequalities in two variables to help students perform similar steps when graphing quadratic inequalities in two variables. As students solve quadratic inequalities in one variable, emphasize how the solutions of the related equation can help them determine the solutions of the inequality.

Reaching All Learners

Through Graphic Organizers

An alternate approach to **Example 3 Step 3** is to use a chart to determine the sign of the product $(x - 5)(x + 1)$ in each interval. For instance, the following chart could be used to determine that $(x - 5)(x + 1) > 0$ when $x < -1$ or $x > 5$.

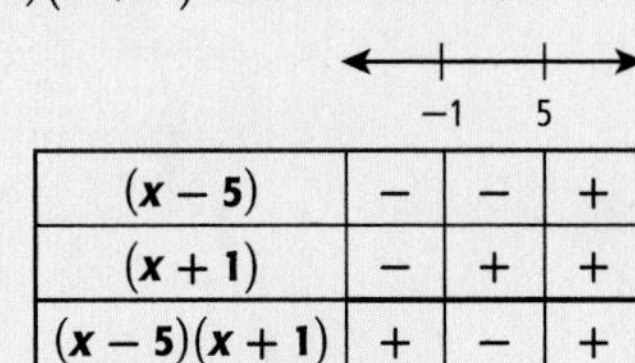

$(x - 5)$	−	−	+
$(x + 1)$	−	+	+
$(x - 5)(x + 1)$	+	−	+

Power Presentations with PowerPoint®

Additional Examples

Example 3

Solve the inequality $x^2 - 10x + 18 \le -3$ by using algebra.

$3 \le x \le 7$

Also available on transparency

INTERVENTION

Questioning Strategies

EXAMPLE 3

- How do you find the critical values?
- How do you know which x-values to test in the original inequality?
- How can you tell which intervals belong to the solution set of the inequality?

Inclusion Remind students to look carefully at the inequality signs in the examples and exercises in this lesson. Whether or not an inequality includes "or equal to" can easily make the difference between a correct or an incorrect response.

EXAMPLE 3 Solving Quadratic Inequalities by Using Algebra

Solve the inequality $x^2 - 4x + 1 > 6$ by using algebra.

Step 1 Write the related equation.

$$x^2 - 4x + 1 = 6$$

Step 2 Solve the equation for x to find the critical values.

$x^2 - 4x - 5 = 0$ *Write in standard form.*

$(x - 5)(x + 1) = 0$ *Factor.*

$x - 5 = 0$ or $x + 1 = 0$ *Zero Product Property*

$x = 5$ or $x = -1$ *Solve for x.*

The critical values are 5 and -1. The critical values divide the number line into three intervals: $x < -1$, $-1 < x < 5$, and $x > 5$.

Step 3 Test an x-value in each interval.

$$x^2 - 4x + 1 > 6$$

$(-2)^2 - 4(-2) + 1 > 6$ ✔ *Try $x = -2$.*

$(0)^2 - 4(0) + 1 > 6$ ✘ *Try $x = 0$.*

$(6)^2 - 4(6) + 1 > 6$ ✔ *Try $x = 6$.*

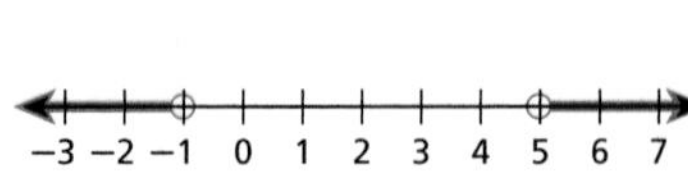

Shade the solution regions on the number line. Use open circles for the critical values because the inequality does not contain *or equal to.*

−3 −2 −1 0 1 2 3 4 5 6 7

The solution is $x < -1$ or $x > 5$, or $(-\infty, -1) \cup (5, \infty)$.

Solve each inequality by using algebra.

3a. $x^2 - 6x + 10 \ge 2$
$x \le 2$ or $x \ge 4$

3b. $-2x^2 + 3x + 7 < 2$
$x < -1$ or $x > 2.5$

EXAMPLE 4 *Problem-Solving Application*

A business offers tours to the Amazon. The profit P that the company earns for x number of tourists can be modeled by $P(x) = -25x^2 + 1000x - 3000$. How many people are needed for a profit of at least \$5000?

1 Understand the Problem

The **answer** will be the number of people required for a profit that is greater than or equal to \$5000.

List the important information:

- The profit must be at least \$5000.
- The function for the profit is $P(x) = -25x^2 + 1000x - 3000$.

2 Make a Plan

Write an inequality showing profit greater than or equal to \$5000. Then solve the inequality by using algebra.

3 Solve

Write the inequality.

$$-25x^2 + 1000x - 3000 \geq 5000$$

Find the critical values by solving the related equation.

$-25x^2 + 1000x - 3000 = 5000$ *Write as an equation.*

$-25x^2 + 1000x - 8000 = 0$ *Write in standard form.*

$-25(x^2 - 40x + 320) = 0$ *Factor out −25 to simplify.*

$$x = \frac{-b \pm \sqrt{b^2 - 4ac}}{2a} = \frac{-(-40) \pm \sqrt{(-40)^2 - 4(1)(320)}}{2(1)}$$ *Use the Quadratic Formula.*

$$= \frac{40 \pm \sqrt{320}}{2}$$ *Simplify.*

$$x \approx 28.94 \text{ or } x \approx 11.06$$

Test an x-value in each of the three regions formed by the critical x-values.

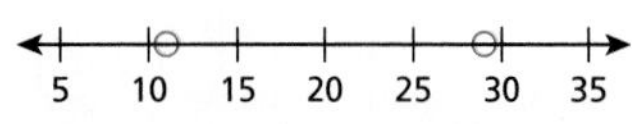

$-25(10)^2 + 1000(10) - 3000 \overset{?}{\geq} 5000$ *Try x = 10.*

$4500 \geq 5000$ ✗

$-25(20)^2 + 1000(20) - 3000 \overset{?}{\geq} 5000$ *Try x = 20.*

$7000 \geq 5000$ ✓

$-25(30)^2 + 1000(30) - 3000 \overset{?}{\geq} 5000$ *Try x = 30.*

$4500 \geq 5000$ ✗

Write the solution as an inequality. The solution is approximately $11.06 \leq x \leq 28.94$. Because you cannot have a fraction of a person, round each critical value to the appropriate whole number.

$$12 \leq x \leq 28$$

For a profit of at least \$5000, from 12 to 28 people are needed.

Remember!

A compound inequality such as $12 \leq x \leq 28$ can be written as $\{x \mid x \geq 12 \cup x \leq 28\}$, or $x \geq 12$ and $x \leq 28$. (See Lesson 2-8.)

4 Look Back

Enter $y = -25x^2 + 1000x - 3000$ into a graphing calculator, and create a table of values. The table shows that integer values of x between 12 and 28 inclusive result in y-values greater than or equal to 5000.

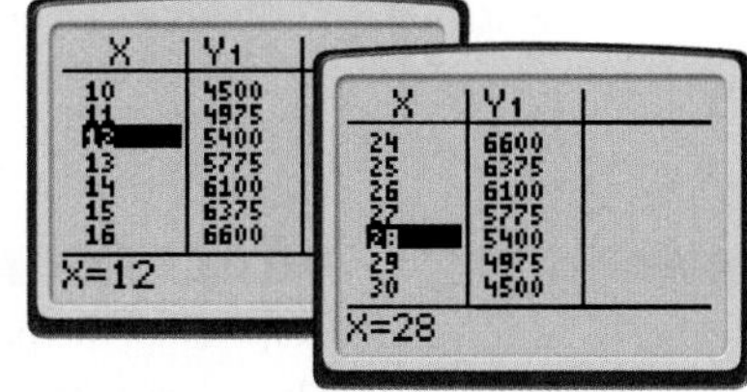

CHECK IT OUT! **4.** The business also offers educational tours to Patagonia, a region of South America that includes parts of Chile and Argentina. The profit P for x number of persons is $P(x) = -25x^2 + 1250x - 5000$. The trip will be rescheduled if the profit is less than \$7500. How many people must have signed up if the trip is rescheduled? **fewer than 14 or more than 36 people**

COMMON ERROR ALERT

When solving quadratic inequalities, some students may stop after finding only one part of the compound inequality that represents the solution. For example, they may answer $x < -1$ when the solution is actually $x < -1$ or $x > 5$. Use a graph to show that the solution to a quadratic equation often includes two intervals.

Power Presentations with PowerPoint®

Additional Examples

Example 4

The monthly profit P of a small business that sells bicycle helmets can be modeled by the function $P(x) = -8x^2 + 600x - 4200$, where x is the average selling price of a helmet. What range of selling prices will generate a monthly profit of at least \$6000?

between \$26.05 and \$48.95, inclusive

Also available on transparency

INTERVENTION

Questioning Strategies

EXAMPLE 4

- How do you know which sign to use in the inequality?
- How do you know how to round the critical values?

Teaching Tip **Critical Thinking** Ask students to explain why they think the critical values in **Example 4** were determined by using the Quadratic Formula rather than by factoring or completing the square. Possible answer: because the values of the coefficients b and c are large

3 Close

Summarize

Review with students the procedures for solving quadratic inequalities. Emphasize the importance of using a graph or solving a quadratic equation to determine the critical values. Remind students that they can check their answers by choosing values from the solution set and using substitution to see whether these values make the inequality true.

ONGOING ASSESSMENT and INTERVENTION

***Diagnose Before* the Lesson**
5-7 Warm Up, TE p. 366

***Monitor During* the Lesson**
Check It Out! Exercises, SE pp. 366–369
Questioning Strategies, TE pp. 367–369

***Assess After* the Lesson**
5-7 Lesson Quiz, TE p. 373
Alternative Assessment, TE p. 373

Answers to *Think and Discuss*

Possible answers:

1. Graphing a quadratic inequality is similar to graphing a linear inequality: graph the boundary with a solid or dashed curve and shade above or below accordingly. For a quadratic inequality, the boundary is a parabola, and for a linear inequality, the boundary is a line.
2. The intersection points are included when the inequality symbol is $\geq$ or $\leq$. The intersection points are not included when the inequality symbol is $>$ or $<$.
3. See p. A7.

5-7 Exercises

Assignment Guide

Assign *Guided Practice* exercises as necessary.

If you finished Examples **1–2**
- **Basic** 12–23, 28–33
- **Average** 12–23, 28–33, 66–68
- **Advanced** 12–23, 28–33, 66–68

If you finished Examples **1–4**
- **Basic** 12–58, 62–65, 71–76
- **Average** 12–68, 71–76
- **Advanced** 12–76

Homework Quick Check
Quickly check key concepts.
Exercises: 12, 20, 24, 27, 34

Answers

2–4, 12–17. See p. A29.

State Resources

go.hrw.com
State Resources Online
KEYWORD: MB7 Resources

THINK AND DISCUSS

1. Compare graphing a quadratic inequality with graphing a linear inequality.
2. Explain how to determine if the intersection point(s) is/are included in the solution set when you solve a quadratic inequality by graphing.
3. **GET ORGANIZED** Copy and complete the graphic organizer. Compare the solutions of quadratic equations and inequalities.

	Equation (=)	"Less Than" Inequality (< or ≤)	"Greater Than" Inequality (> or ≥)
Example			
Graph			
Solution Set			

5-7 Exercises

go.hrw.com
Homework Help Online
KEYWORD: MB7 5-7
Parent Resources Online
KEYWORD: MB7 Parent

GUIDED PRACTICE

1. **Vocabulary** Give an example of a *quadratic inequality in two variables.*
Possible answer: $y < x^2 + 4x + 4$

SEE EXAMPLE 1 p. 366

Graph each inequality.

2. $y > -(x + 1)^2 + 5$
3. $y \leq 2x^2 - 4x - 1$
4. $y \leq -3x^2 + x + 3$

SEE EXAMPLE 2 p. 367

Solve each inequality by using tables or graphs.

5. $x^2 - 5x + 3 \leq 3$ — $0 \leq x \leq 5$
6. $3x^2 - 3x - 1 > -1$ — $x < 0$ or $x > 1$
7. $2x^2 - 9x + 5 \leq -4$ — $1.5 \leq x \leq 3$

SEE EXAMPLE 3 p. 368

Solve each inequality by using algebra.

8. $x^2 + 10x + 1 \geq 12$ — $x \leq -11$ or $x \geq 1$
9. $x^2 + 13x + 45 < 5$ — $-8 < x < -5$
10. $-2x^2 + 3x + 12 > 10$ — $-0.5 < x < 2$

SEE EXAMPLE 4 p. 368

11. **Business** A consultant advises the owners of a beauty salon that their profit p each month can be modeled by $p(x) = -50x^2 + 3500x - 2500$, where x is the average cost that a customer is charged. What range of costs will bring in a profit of at least \$50,000? a range of costs between about \$21.78 and \$48.22

PRACTICE AND PROBLEM SOLVING

Graph each inequality.

12. $y < x^2 + 2x - 5$
13. $y > -\frac{1}{2}x^2 + 3$
14. $y \leq 2(x - 1)^2 - 3$
15. $y \geq x^2 + 6$
16. $y < (x + 1)(x + 4)$
17. $y \leq x^2 - 2x + 6$

Solve each inequality by using tables or graphs.

18. $x^2 - x + 5 < 11$
19. $2x^2 + 3x + 6 \geq 5$
20. $x^2 - 5x + 12 > 6$
21. $x^2 - 2x - 8 > 0$
22. $x^2 + 7x + 6 \leq 6$
23. $x^2 - 12x + 32 < 12$

18. $-2 < x < 3$
19. $x \leq -1$ or $x \geq -0.5$
20. $x < 2$ or $x > 3$
21. $x < -2$ or $x > 4$
22. $-7 \leq x \leq 0$
23. $2 < x < 10$

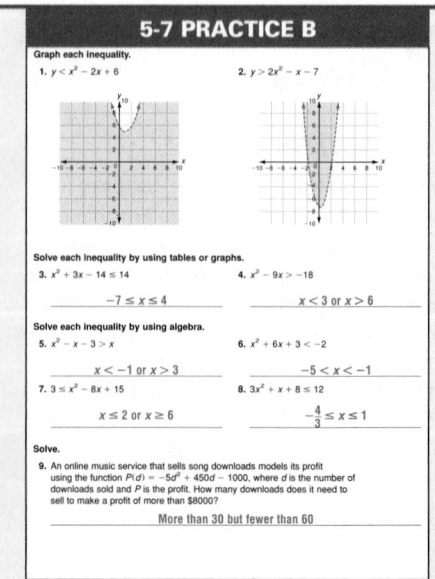

5-7 PRACTICE A

Graph each inequality and shade the solution region. Use a test point to verify the solution region.

1. $y < x^2 - 2x + 3$
   a. y-intercept is 3.
   b. Vertex is (1, 2).
   c. Test point (0, 0)
   $0 < 3$ ☒
2. $y \geq -x^2 + 4x - 5$
   a. y-intercept is -5
   b. Vertex is $(2, -1)$
   c. Test point (0, 0)
   $0 \geq -5$ ☒

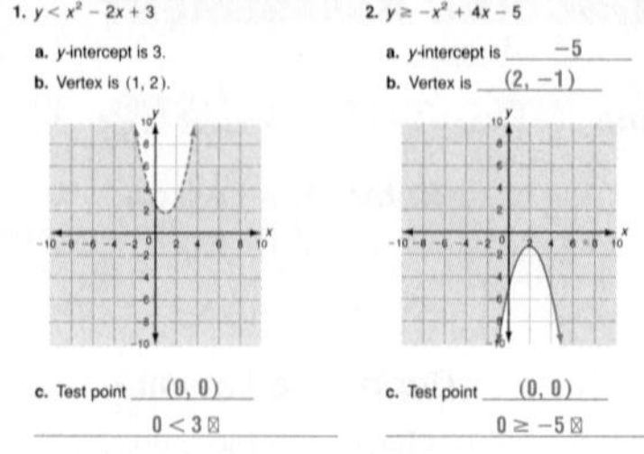

Solve each inequality by using algebra.

3. $x^2 + x - 8 \leq -6$
   a. Write the related equation. $x^2 + x - 8 = -6$
   b. Solve for x to find the critical values. $x = -2, 1$
   c. Test an x-value in each interval. $x = -3, -2 \leq -6$ X; $x = 0, -8 \leq -6$ ☒; $x = 2, -2 \leq -6$ X
   d. Write the solution. $-2 \leq x \leq 1$
4. $x^2 + 10x + 25 > 9$ — $x < -8$ or $x > -2$
5. $x^2 - x < 12$ — $-3 < x < 4$
6. $x^2 + 2x - 10 \geq 14$ — $x \leq -6$ or $x \geq 4$

Solve.

7. The annual profit, $p(x)$, in dollars of a small company varies with the number of employees, x, as $p(x) = -40x^2 + 4400x$. What is the range of the number of employees for which the company's annual profit will be at least \$112,000?
Between 40 and 70 employees

5-7 PRACTICE B

Graph each inequality.

1. $y < x^2 - 2x + 6$
2. $y > 2x^2 - x - 7$

Solve each inequality by using tables or graphs.

3. $x^2 + 3x - 14 \leq 14$ — $-7 \leq x \leq 4$
4. $x^2 - 9x > -18$ — $x < 3$ or $x > 6$

Solve each inequality by using algebra.

5. $x^2 - x - 3 > x$ — $x < -1$ or $x > 3$
6. $x^2 + 6x + 3 < -2$ — $-5 < x < -1$
7. $3 \leq x^2 - 8x + 15$ — $x \leq 2$ or $x \geq 6$
8. $3x^2 + x + 8 \leq 12$ — $-\frac{4}{3} \leq x \leq 1$

Solve.

9. An online music service that sells song downloads models its profit using the function $P(d) = -5d^2 + 450d - 1000$, where d is the number of downloads sold and P is the profit. How many downloads does it need to sell to make a profit of more than \$8000?
More than 30 but fewer than 60

Independent Practice

For Exercises	See Example
12–17	1
18–23	2
24–26	3
27	4

Extra Practice

Skills Practice p. S13

Application Practice p. S36

Solve each inequality by using algebra.

24. $x^2 - 11x + 13 \le 25$ **$-1 \le x \le 12$**

25. $-2x^2 + 3x + 4 \ge -1$ **$-1 \le x \le 2.5$**

26. $x^2 - 5x - 4 < -9$

27. **Sports** A football thrown by a quarterback follows a path given by $h(x) = -0.0095x^2 + x + 7$, where h is the height of the ball in feet and x is the horizontal distance the ball has traveled in feet. If any height less than 10 feet can be caught or knocked down, at what distances from the quarterback can the ball be knocked down? **at distances less than about 3 ft and distances greater than about 102 ft**

Graph each quadratic inequality.

28. $y \le 2x^2 + 4x - 3$

29. $y < 3x^2 - 12x - 4$

30. $y \ge -3x^2 + 4x$

31. $y > -2(x + 3)^2 + 1$

32. $y > -x^2 - 2x - 1$

33. $y \le \frac{1}{3}x^2 + 2x - 1$

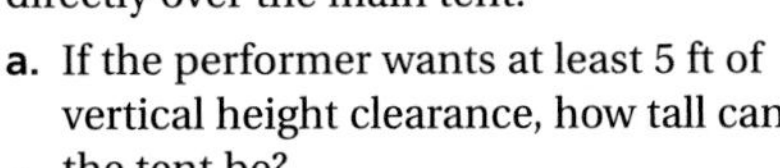

34a. no more than about 51 ft in height

34b. about 71 ft

34. **Circus** The human cannonball is an act where a performer is launched through the air. The height of the performer can be modeled by $h(x) = -0.007x^2 + x + 20$, where h is the height in feet and x is the horizontal distance traveled in feet. The circus act is considering a flight path directly over the main tent.

a. If the performer wants at least 5 ft of vertical height clearance, how tall can the tent be?

b. How far from the central pole should the "cannon" be placed?

Solve each inequality by using any method.

35. $x^2 - 5x - 24 \le 0$

36. $x^2 - 14 \ge 2$

37. $-2x^2 - x + 8 > 6$

38. $x^2 - 4x - 5 \le -9$

39. $3x^2 + 6x + 11 < 10$

40. $4x^2 - 9 > 0$

41. $3x^2 + 5x + 13 \le 16$

42. $-2x^2 + 3x + 17 \ge 11$

43. $5x^2 - 2x - 1 \ge 0$

44. $(x - 2)(x + 11) \ge 2$

45. $x^2 + 27 > 12x$

46. $-2x^2 + 3x + 6 > 0$

47. **Multi-Step** A medical office has a rectangular parking lot that measures 120 ft by 200 ft. The owner wants to expand the size of the parking lot by adding an equal distance to two sides as shown. If zoning restrictions limit the total size of the parking lot to 35,000 ft², what range of distances can be added? **a distance between 0 ft and about 31 ft**

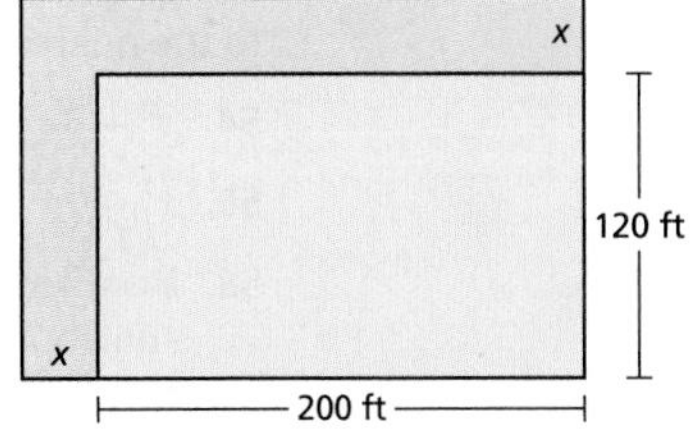

Match each graph with one of the following inequalities.

A. $y < x^2 + 2x - 3$

B. $y > -x^2 - 2x + 3$

C. $y < x^2 - 2x + 3$

48. 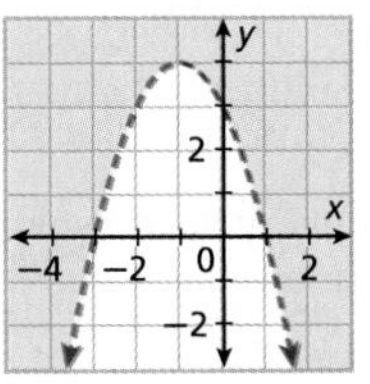 **B**

49. 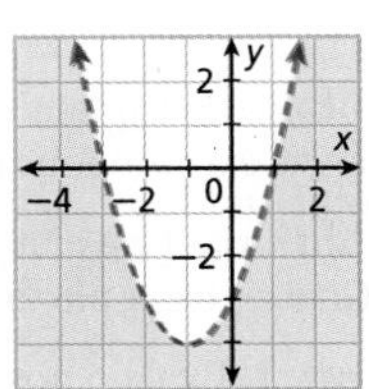 **A**

50. 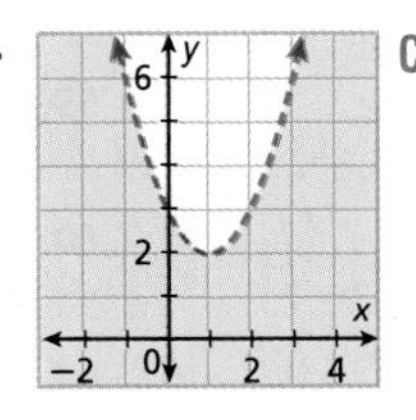 **C**

Teaching Tip **Communicating Math** For **Exercises 48–50,** you may wish to have students explain how they determined which graph represents which inequality.

Answers

26. $\frac{5 - \sqrt{5}}{2} < x < \frac{5 + \sqrt{5}}{2}$

28. 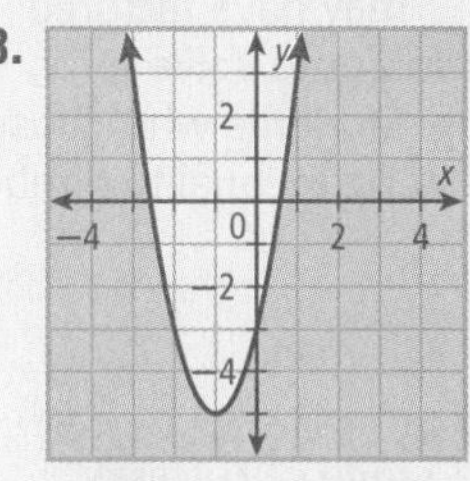

29. 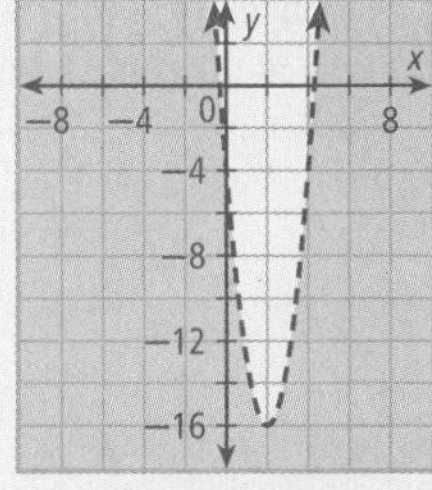

30. 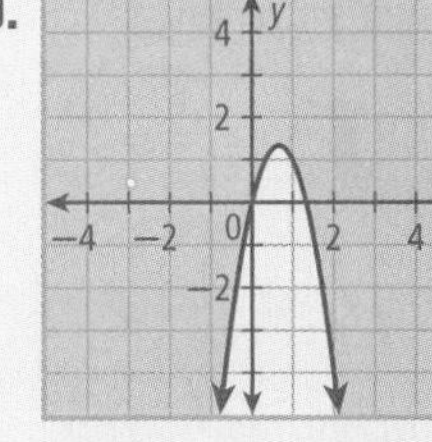

31. 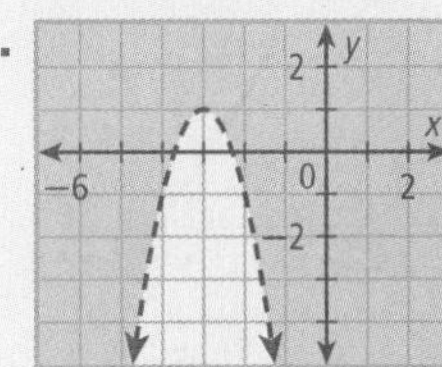

32. 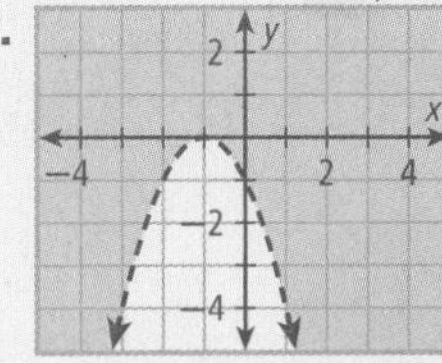

33. 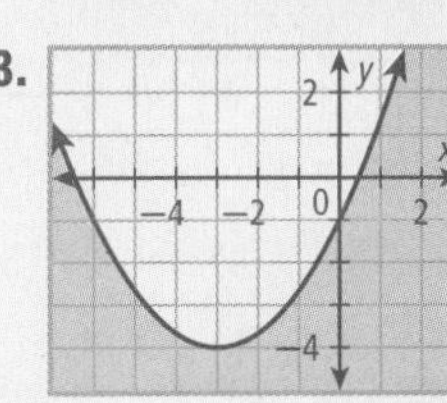

35. $-3 \le x \le 8$

36. $x \le -4$ or $x \ge 4$

37. $\frac{-1 - \sqrt{17}}{4} < x < \frac{-1 + \sqrt{17}}{4}$

38. $x = 2$

39. $-1 - \frac{\sqrt{6}}{3} < x < -1 + \frac{\sqrt{6}}{3}$

40. $x < -1.5$ or $x > 1.5$

41. $\frac{-5 - \sqrt{61}}{6} \le x \le \frac{-5 + \sqrt{61}}{6}$

42. $\frac{3 - \sqrt{57}}{4} \le x \le \frac{3 + \sqrt{57}}{4}$

43. $x \le \frac{1 - \sqrt{6}}{5}$ or $x \ge \frac{1 + \sqrt{6}}{5}$

44. $x \le \frac{-9 - \sqrt{177}}{2}$ or $x \ge \frac{-9 + \sqrt{177}}{2}$

45. $x < 3$ or $x > 9$

46. $\frac{3 - \sqrt{57}}{4} < x < \frac{3 + \sqrt{57}}{4}$

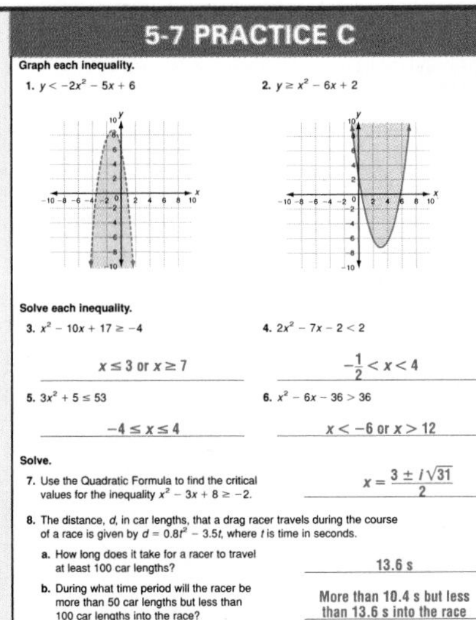

5-7 PRACTICE C

Graph each inequality.

1. $y < -2x^2 - 5x + 6$

2. $y \ge x^2 - 6x + 2$

Solve each inequality.

3. $x^2 - 10x + 17 \ge -4$ $x \le 3$ or $x \ge 7$

4. $2x^2 - 7x - 2 < 2$ $-\frac{1}{2} < x < 4$

5. $3x^2 + 5 \le 53$ $-4 \le x \le 4$

6. $x^2 - 6x - 36 > 36$ $x < -6$ or $x > 12$

Solve.

7. Use the Quadratic Formula to find the critical values for the inequality $x^2 - 3x + 8 \ge -2$. $x = \frac{3 \pm i\sqrt{31}}{2}$

8. The distance, d, in car lengths, that a drag racer travels during the course of a race is given by $d = 0.8t^2 - 3.5t$, where t is time in seconds.

a. How long does it take for a racer to travel at least 100 car lengths? 13.6 s

b. During what time period will the racer be more than 50 car lengths but less than 100 car lengths into the race? More than 10.4 s but less than 13.6 s into the race

c. During what time period will the racer be less than 50 car lengths from the start? Less than 10.4 s into the race

 **Exercise 51** involves writing and solving a quadratic inequality relating to the area of tiles. This exercise prepares students for the Multi-Step Test Prep on page 390.

 In **Exercise 63,** students who chose **H** may have factored correctly but forgot to solve for x after factoring. Students who chose **G** used the wrong inequality symbol.

Answers

61. The solutions of $x^2 - 3x - 4 \leq 6$ include a range of x-values, $-2 \leq x \leq 5$, while the solutions of $x^2 - 3x - 4 = 6$ consist of only two x-values, $x = -2$ and $x = 5$.

72. 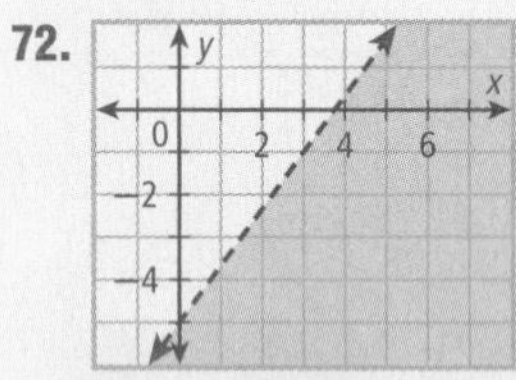

73. 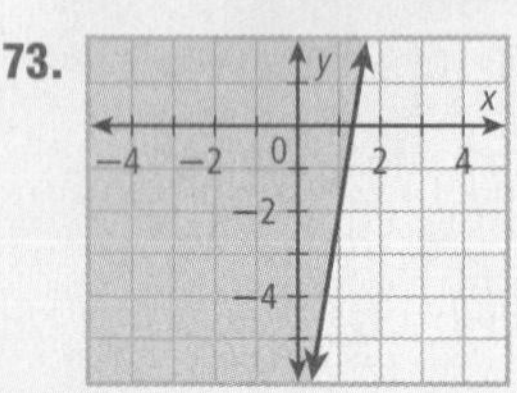

74. 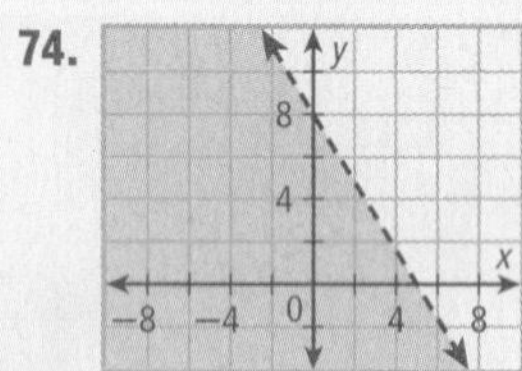

MULTI-STEP TEST PREP

51. This problem will prepare you for the Multi-Step Test Prep on page 390. A small square tile is placed on top of a larger square tile as shown. This creates four congruent triangular regions.

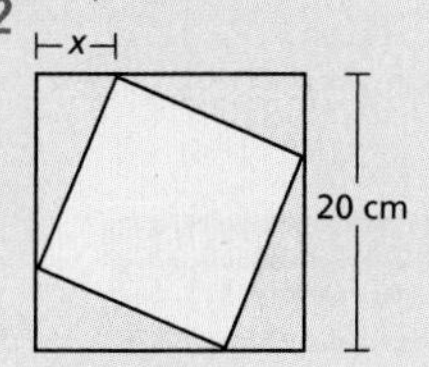

51a. $A(x) = -\frac{1}{2}x^2 + 10x$

a. Write a function for the area A of one of the triangular regions in terms of x.

b. For what values of x, to the nearest tenth, is the area of each triangular region at least 30 cm^2? $3.7 \leq x \leq 16.3$

c. For what values of x, to the nearest tenth, is the area of each triangular region less than 40 cm^2? $0 < x \leq 5.5$ or $14.5 \leq x \leq 20$

52. **Music** A manager estimates a band's profit p for a concert by using the function $p(t) = -200t^2 + 2500t - c$, where t is the price per ticket and c is the band's operating cost. The table shows the band's operating cost at three different concert locations. What range of ticket prices should the band charge at each location in order to make a profit of at least \$1000 at each concert?

Freemont Park: between \$0.82 and \$11.68; Saltillo Plaza: between \$1.10 and \$11.40; Riverside Walk: between \$1.61 and \$10.89

Band's Costs

Location	Operating Cost
Freemont Park	\$900
Saltillo Plaza	\$1500
Riverside Walk	\$2500

53. **Gardening** Lindsey has 40 feet of metal fencing material to fence three sides of a rectangular garden. A tall wooden fence serves as her fourth side.

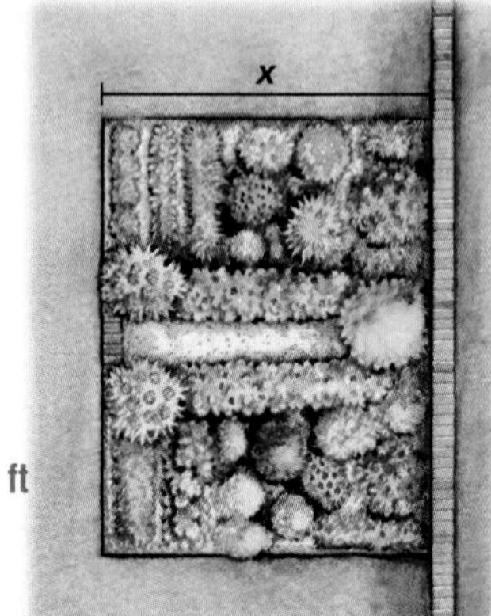

a. Write a function for the area of the garden A in terms of x, the width in feet.

b. What measures for the width will give an area of at least 150 square feet?

c. What measures for the width will give an area of at least 200 square feet? a width of 10 ft

53a. Possible answer: $A(x) = -2x^2 + 40x$

53b. a width between 5 ft and 15 ft

Graphing Calculator **Use the intersect feature of a graphing calculator to solve each inequality to the nearest tenth.**

54. $x^2 + 6x - 13 > 4$ $x < -8.1$ or $x > 2.1$

55. $x^2 - 15x + 20 \leq 7$ $0.9 \leq x \leq 14.1$

56. $x^2 - 24 < 28$ $-7.2 < x < 7.2$

57. $2x^2 + 3x + 5 \geq 8$ $x \leq -2.2$ or $x \geq 0.7$

58. **Business** A wholesaler sells snowboards to sporting-good stores. The price per snowboard varies based on the number purchased in each order. The function $r(x) = -x^2 + 125x$ models the wholesaler's revenue r in dollars for an order of x snowboards.

a. To the nearest dollar, what is the maximum revenue per order? \$3906

b. How many snowboards must the wholesaler sell to make at least \$1500 in revenue in one order? between 14 and 111 inclusive

59. **Critical Thinking** Explain whether the solution to a quadratic inequality in one variable is always a compound inequality. It is not—the solution can be a single value, all real numbers, or the empty set.

60. **Critical Thinking** Can a quadratic inequality have a solution set that is all real numbers? Give an example to support your answer. yes; possible answer: $4x^2 - x + 3 > 0$

61. **Write About It** Explain how the solutions of $x^2 - 3x - 4 \leq 6$ differ from the solutions of $x^2 - 3x - 4 = 6$.

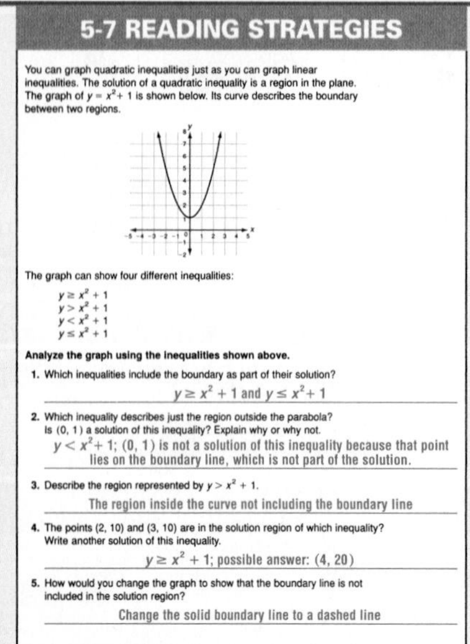

5-7 READING STRATEGIES

You can graph quadratic inequalities just as you can graph linear inequalities. The solution of a quadratic inequality is a region in the plane. The graph of $y = x^2 + 1$ is shown below. Its curve describes the boundary between two regions.

The graph can show four different inequalities:

$y \geq x^2 + 1$
$y > x^2 + 1$
$y < x^2 + 1$
$y \leq x^2 + 1$

Analyze the graph using the inequalities shown above.

1. Which inequalities include the boundary as part of their solution?
$y \geq x^2 + 1$ and $y \leq x^2 + 1$

2. Which inequality describes just the region outside the parabola? Is (0, 1) a solution of this inequality? Explain why or why not.
$y < x^2 + 1$; (0, 1) is not a solution of this inequality because that point lies on the boundary line, which is not part of the solution.

3. Describe the region represented by $y > x^2 + 1$.
The region inside the curve not including the boundary line

4. The points (2, 10) and (3, 10) are in the solution region of which inequality? Write another solution of this inequality.
$y \geq x^2 + 1$; possible answer: (4, 20)

5. How would you change the graph to show that the boundary line is not included in the solution region?
Change the solid boundary line to a dashed line

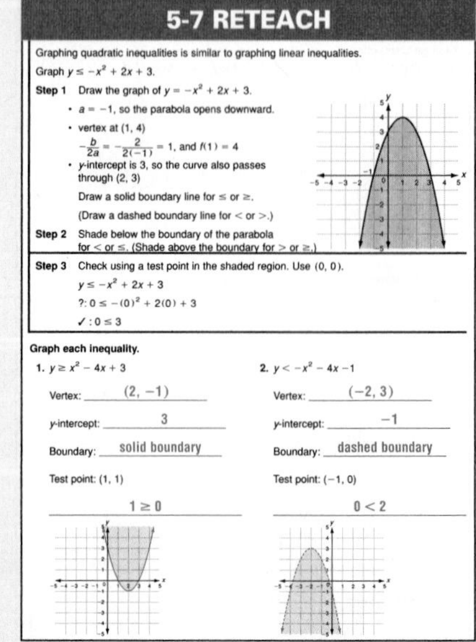

5-7 RETEACH

Graphing quadratic inequalities is similar to graphing linear inequalities.

Graph $y \leq -x^2 + 2x + 3$.

Step 1 Draw the graph of $y = -x^2 + 2x + 3$.
- $a = -1$, so the parabola opens downward.
- vertex at (1, 4)
$-\frac{b}{2a} = -\frac{2}{2(-1)} = 1$, and $f(1) = 4$
- y-intercept is 3, so the curve also passes through (2, 3)

Draw a solid boundary line for $\leq$ or $\geq$.
(Draw a dashed boundary line for $<$ or $>$.)

Step 2 Shade below the boundary of the parabola for $<$ or $\leq$. (Shade above the boundary for $>$ or $\geq$.)

Step 3 Check using a test point in the shaded region. Use (0, 0).
$y \leq -x^2 + 2x + 3$
?: $0 \leq -(0)^2 + 2(0) + 3$
✓: $0 \leq 3$

Graph each inequality.

1. $y \geq x^2 - 4x + 3$
Vertex: (2, −1)
y-intercept: 3
Boundary: solid boundary
Test point: (1, 1)
$1 \geq 0$

2. $y < -x^2 - 4x - 1$
Vertex: (−2, 3)
y-intercept: −1
Boundary: dashed boundary
Test point: (−1, 0)
$0 < 2$

TEST PREP

62. Which is the solution set of $x^2 - 9 < 0$?

   (A) $-3 < x < 3$ (circled)
   (B) $-9 < x < 9$
   (C) $x < -3$ or $x > 3$
   (D) $x < -9$ or $x > 9$

63. Which is the graph of the solution to $x^2 - 7x + 10 \geq 0$?

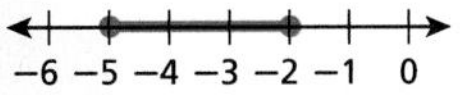

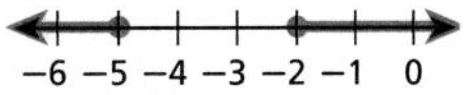

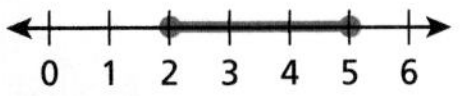

   (F) number line −6 −5 −4 −3 −2 −1 0
   (G) number line 0 1 2 3 4 5 6
   (H) number line −6 −5 −4 −3 −2 −1 0
   (J) number line 0 1 2 3 4 5 6 (circled)

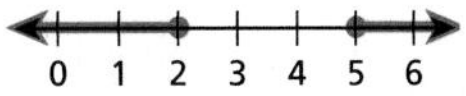

64. Which is the solution set of $x^2 - 7x \leq 0$?

   (A) $0 < x < 7$
   (B) $0 \leq x \leq 7$ (circled)
   (C) $x < 0$ or $x > 7$
   (D) $x \leq 0$ or $x \geq 7$

65. **Short Response** Demonstrate the process for solving $x^2 + 4x + 4 > 1$ algebraically. Justify each step in the solution process.
   $x < -3$ or $x > -1$; check students' work.

CHALLENGE AND EXTEND

Solve each inequality.

$0.5 \leq x \leq 3$ 66. $-2x^2 + 7x - 6 \geq -3$

67. $-2x^2 + 7x - 6 > 2x - 5$ $\frac{5 - \sqrt{17}}{4} < x < \frac{5 + \sqrt{17}}{4}$

68. $2x^2 - 7x + 6 < -2x^2 + x + 3$ $0.5 < x < 1.5$

Geometry The area inside a parabola bounded from above or below by a horizontal line segment is $\frac{2}{3}bh$, where b is the length of the line segment and h is the vertical distance from the vertex of the parabola to the line segment. Find the area bounded by the graphs of each pair of inequalities.

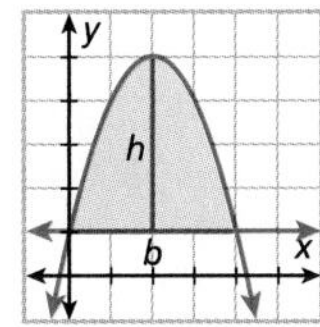

69. $y > x^2 + 5x - 6$; $y < 8$
   121.5 square units

70. $y < -2x^2 + 3x + 9$; $y > -5$
   ≈ 55.46 square units

SPIRAL REVIEW

71. **Community** Once a month, four teams of teens (lawn team, shopping team, cleaning team, and laundry team) spend a day assisting elderly residents of their neighborhood. Lynnette started the assignment chart for June but was interrupted. Complete the chart. Each home has only one team helping during each shift. *(Previous course)*

Shifts	Reed Home	Brown Home	Sondi Home	Clem Home
7:00 A.M.–9:30 A.M.	Lawn	Cleaning	? Shopping	? Laundry
10:00 A.M.–12:30 P.M.	? Laundry	Shopping	? Cleaning	Lawn
1:00 P.M.–3:30 P.M.	? Shopping	? Lawn	Laundry	? Cleaning
4:00 P.M.–6:30 P.M.	Cleaning	? Laundry	? Lawn	? Shopping

Graph each inequality by using intercepts. *(Lesson 2-5)*

72. $4x - 3y > 15$

73. $6x - y \leq 8$

74. $8x + 5y < 40$

Find the values of c that make each equation true. *(Lesson 5-5)*

75. $4 - 2c + 7i = 7i - 14$ 9

76. $4c + 2 - 3i + 2(i - 5) = 4(2i - 6) - 9i$ −4

COMMON ERROR ALERT

In **Exercise 52,** students may be confused about which values to use for p and c. Point out that they should use \$1000 for the profit p and that the value of c for each inequality can be determined from the table.

Journal

Have students describe the steps they would use to solve a quadratic inequality by using algebra.

ALTERNATIVE ASSESSMENT

Have students write and solve a quadratic inequality in one variable, showing each step of the solution process. Ask students to represent the solution to the inequality in more than one way, such as by using both a number line and interval notation.

Power Presentations with PowerPoint®

5-7 Lesson Quiz

1. Graph $y \leq x^2 + 9x + 14$.

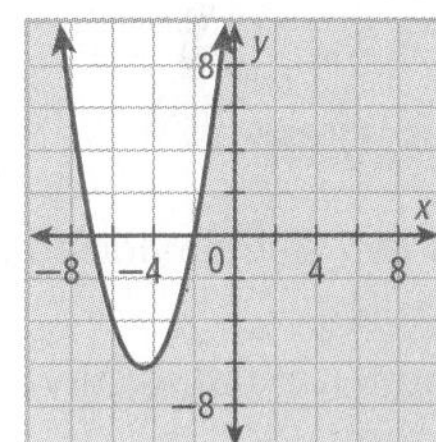

Solve each inequality.

2. $x^2 + 12x + 39 \geq 12$
   $x \leq -9$ or $x \geq -3$

3. $x^2 - 24 \leq 5x$
   $-3 \leq x \leq 8$

4. A boat operator wants to offer tours of San Francisco Bay. His profit P for a trip can be modeled by $P(x) = -2x^2 + 120x - 788$, where x is the cost per ticket. What range of ticket prices will generate a profit of at least \$500?
   between \$14 and \$46, inclusive

Also available on transparency

5-7 PROBLEM SOLVING

The manager at Travel Tours is proposing a fall tour to Australia and New Zealand. He works out the details and finds that the profit P for x persons is $P(x) = -28x^2 + 1400x - 3496$. The owner of Travel Tours has decided that the tour will be canceled if the profit is less than \$10,000.

1. a. Write an inequality that you could use to find the number of people needed to make the tour possible. $-28x^2 + 1400x - 3496 \geq 10{,}000$

   b. Solve the related equation to find the critical values. $x = 13.04, 36.96$

   c. Test an x-value in each interval.

x-value	Evaluate	$P \geq 10{,}000$?
10	$-28(10)^2 + 1400(10) - 3496$	no
30	13,304	yes
40	7704	no

   d. How many people will Travel Tours need to make the tour possible? From 14 to 36 people

2. A year later, the owner of Travel Tours decides that the Australia/New Zealand tour will have to make a profit of at least \$12,000 for the tour to be possible. What effect will this have on the range of people able to take this tour?
   Possible answer: The range is narrower. There must be between 17 and 33 people to take the tour.

The manager plans a tour to the Fiji Islands and determines that the profit P for x persons is $P(x) = -40x^2 + 1920x - 3200$. Choose the letter for the best answer.

3. In order to make \$10,000 profit, how many people will it take for this tour to happen?
   (A) Between 9 and 39 people (circled)
   B Between 14 and 36 people
   C At least 22 people
   D At least 30 people

4. The owner thinks the company should make at least \$15,000 profit on the Fiji Islands tour. How many people will it take for the tour to happen?
   A Between 9 and 39 people
   (B) Between 13 and 35 people (circled)
   C At least 22 people
   D At least 35 people

5-7 CHALLENGE

The area inside a parabola bounded by a horizontal line segment is given by the formula $A = \frac{2}{3}bh$, where b is the length of the line segment and h is the vertical distance from the vertex of the parabola to the line segment.

Consider the region bounded by the curves $y = 5 - x^2$ and $y = x^2 - 3$. This region is shown in the graph at right.

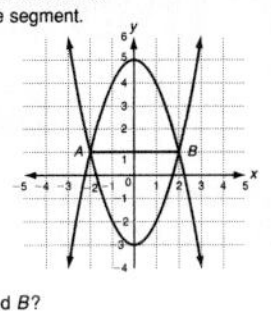

To find the area of the region bounded by the curves, you need to know the length of the horizontal line segment AB.

1. Adapt the substitution method for systems of linear equations to find the coordinates of the intersection points of the parabolas. What are the coordinates of A and B? $(-2, 1), (2, 1)$

2. What is the length of line segment AB? 4 units

3. Find the area enclosed by each parabola and line segment AB. Use this data to find the area bounded between the two curves.
   The area enclosed between the segment and each parabola is $\frac{32}{3}$ square units so the area bounded by both parabolas is $\frac{64}{3}$ square units.

For Exercises 4–6 use this system of inequalities: $\begin{cases} y \geq x^2 - 5 \\ y \leq 2x^2 - 4 \\ y \leq 4 \end{cases}$

4. Graph the system of inequalities and shade the intersection of the three regions.

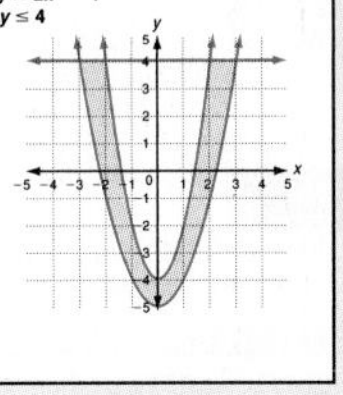

5. Identify the points of intersection of the parabolas and the line $y = 4$.
   $(-3, 4), (-2, 4), (2, 4), (3, 4)$

6. Find the area enclosed by the three inequalities.
   $\text{Area} = \frac{108}{3} - \frac{64}{3} = \frac{44}{3}$ square units

5-8 Organizer

Pacing: Traditional 1 day
Block $\frac{1}{2}$ day

Objectives: Use quadratic functions to model data.

Use quadratic models to analyze and predict.

Technology Lab
In *Technology Lab Activities*

Online Edition
Graphing Calculator, Tutorial Videos, Interactivity, TechKeys

Countdown to Testing Week 12

Power Presentations with PowerPoint®

Warm Up

Solve each system of equations.

1. $\begin{cases} 3a + b = -5 \\ 2a - 6b = 30 \end{cases}$ $a = 0, b = -5$

2. $\begin{cases} 9a + 3b = 24 \\ a + b = 6 \end{cases}$ $a = 1, b = 5$

3. $\begin{cases} 4a - 2b = 8 \\ 2a - 5b = 16 \end{cases}$ $a = \frac{1}{2}, b = -3$

Also available on transparency

Math Humor

Q: Why was the mathematician bad at baseball?

A: He was better at fitting curves than hitting them.

5-8 Curve Fitting with Quadratic Models

A2.3.5 Solve problems that can be modeled using quadratic equations and functions, interpret the solutions and determine whether the solutions are reasonable.

Objectives
Use quadratic functions to model data.
Use quadratic models to analyze and predict.

Vocabulary
quadratic model
quadratic regression

Who uses this?
Film preservationists use quadratic relationships to estimate film run times. (See Example 3.)

The Granger Collection, New York

Recall that you can use differences to analyze patterns in data. For a set of ordered pairs with equally spaced x-values, a quadratic function has constant nonzero second differences, as shown below.

Equally spaced x-values

x	−3	−2	−1	0	1	2	3
$f(x) = x^2$	9	4	1	0	1	4	9

1st differences −5 −3 −1 1 3 5
2nd differences 2 2 2 2 2

Constant 2nd differences

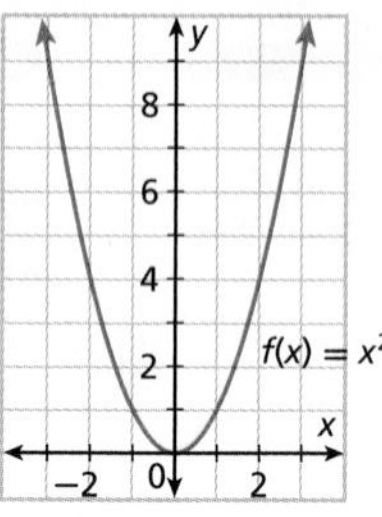

EXAMPLE 1 Identifying Quadratic Data

Determine whether each data set could represent a quadratic function. Explain.

A

x	0	2	4	6	8
y	12	10	9	9	10

Find the first and second differences.

Equally spaced x-values

x	0	2	4	6	8
y	12	10	9	9	10

1st −2 −1 0 1
2nd 1 1 1

Quadratic function; second differences are constant for equally spaced x-values.

B

x	−2	−1	0	1	2
y	1	2	4	8	16

Find the first and second differences.

Equally spaced x-values

x	−2	−1	0	1	2
y	1	2	4	8	16

1st 1 2 4 8
2nd 1 2 4

Not a quadratic function; second differences are not constant for equally spaced x-values.

CHECK IT OUT! **Determine whether each data set could represent a quadratic function. Explain.**

1a.

x	3	4	5	6	7
y	11	21	35	53	75

1b.

x	10	9	8	7	6
y	6	8	10	12	14

1a. Quadratic; second differences are constant for equally spaced x-values.

1b. Not quadratic; first differences are constant so the function is linear.

State Resources

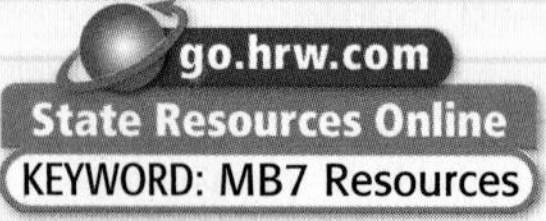

1 Introduce

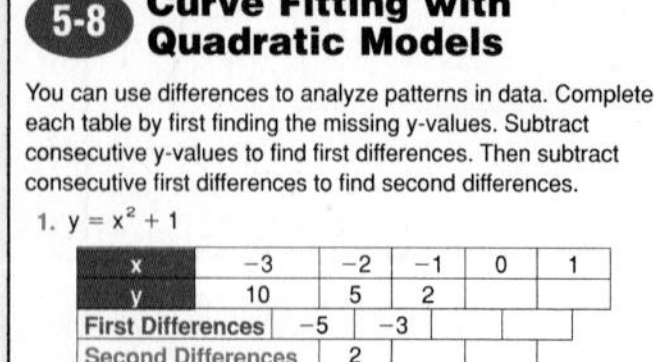

EXPLORATION
5-8 Curve Fitting with Quadratic Models
You can use differences to analyze patterns in data. Complete each table by first finding the missing y-values. Subtract consecutive y-values to find first differences. Then subtract consecutive first differences to find second differences.
1. y = x² + 1
2. y = 3x² + x + 2
3. y = 5x² − 2x
THINK AND DISCUSS

Motivate

Ask students to list objects or situations that could be modeled by a parabola. Examples may include the cables of a suspension bridge, the arc of water in a fountain, or the path of a snowball. Tell students that they will be learning to write quadratic equations that can model these types of objects and situations.

Explorations and answers are provided in the *Explorations* binder.

Just as two points define a linear function, three noncollinear points define a quadratic function. You can find the three coefficients, a, b, and c, of $f(x) = ax^2 + bx + c$ by using a system of three equations, one for each point. The points do not need to have equally spaced x-values.

EXAMPLE 2 Writing a Quadratic Function from Data

Write a quadratic function that fits the points $(0, 5)$, $(2, 1)$, and $(3, 2)$.

Use each point to write a system of equations to find a, b, and c in $f(x) = ax^2 + bx + c$.

(x, y)	$f(x) = ax^2 + bx + c$	System in a, b, c
$(0, 5)$	$5 = a(0)^2 + b(0) + c$	$c = 5$ ❶
$(2, 1)$	$1 = a(2)^2 + b(2) + c$	$4a + 2b + c = 1$ ❷
$(3, 2)$	$2 = a(3)^2 + b(3) + c$	$9a + 3b + c = 2$ ❸

Substitute $c = 5$ from equation ❶ into both equation ❷ and equation ❸.

❷ $4a + 2b + c = 1$ ❸ $9a + 3b + c = 2$

$4a + 2b + 5 = 1$ $9a + 3b + 5 = 2$

$4a + 2b = -4$ ❹ $9a + 3b = -3$ ❺

Solve equation ❹ and equation ❺ for a and b using elimination.

❹ $3(4a + 2b) = 3(-4) \rightarrow 12a + 6b = -12$ *Multiply by 3.*

❺ $-2(9a + 3b) = -2(-3) \rightarrow -18a - 6b = 6$ *Multiply by −2.*

$-6a = -6$ *Add the equations.*

$a = 1$

Substitute 1 for a into equation ❹ or equation ❺ to find b.

❹ $4a + 2b = -4 \rightarrow 4(1) + 2b = -4$

$2b = -8$

$b = -4$

Write the function using $a = 1$, $b = -4$, and $c = 5$.

$$f(x) = ax^2 + bx + c \rightarrow f(x) = 1x^2 - 4x + 5, \text{ or } f(x) = x^2 - 4x + 5$$

Check Substitute or create a table to verify that $(0, 5)$, $(2, 1)$, and $(3, 2)$ satisfy the function rule.

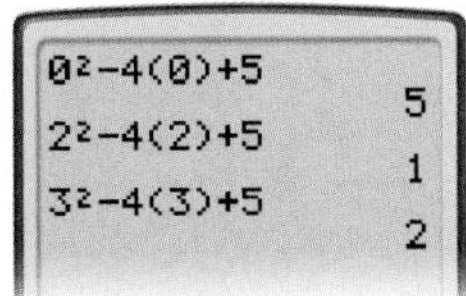

2. Write a quadratic function that fits the points $(0, -3)$, $(1, 0)$, and $(2, 1)$. $f(x) = -x^2 + 4x - 3$

You may use any method that you studied in Chapters 3 or 4 to solve the system of three equations in three variables. For example, you can use a matrix equation as shown.

$$\begin{cases} c = 5 \\ 4a + 2b + c = 1 \\ 9a + 3b + c = 2 \end{cases} \rightarrow \begin{bmatrix} 0 & 0 & 1 \\ 4 & 2 & 1 \\ 9 & 3 & 1 \end{bmatrix}\begin{bmatrix} a \\ b \\ c \end{bmatrix} = \begin{bmatrix} 5 \\ 1 \\ 2 \end{bmatrix} \rightarrow \begin{bmatrix} a \\ b \\ c \end{bmatrix} = \begin{bmatrix} 1 \\ -4 \\ 5 \end{bmatrix}$$

[A]⁻¹[B]
[[1]
[-4]
[5]]

Reading Math

Collinear points lie on the same line. *Noncollinear* points *do not* all lie on the same line.

COMMON ERROR ALERT

Students may make a mistake in signs when determining the first or second differences from a table of values. Remind them to always subtract the previous y-value from the y-value that follows it, even if the result is a negative number. Show how an error in signs when calculating the first differences can affect the values of the second differences.

Power Presentations with PowerPoint®

Additional Examples

Example 1

Determine whether each data set could represent a quadratic function. Explain.

A.

x	1	3	5	7	9
y	−1	1	7	17	31

Quadratic; the second differences are constant for equally spaced x-values.

B.

x	3	4	5	6	7
y	1	3	9	27	81

Not quadratic; the second differences are not constant for equally spaced x-values.

Example 2

Write a quadratic function that fits the points $(1, -5)$, $(3, 5)$, and $(4, 16)$.

$f(x) = 2x^2 - 3x - 4$

Also available on transparency

INTERVENTION

Questioning Strategies

EXAMPLE 1

- How do you find the first differences of a function when the x-values are equally spaced? How do you find the second differences?

EXAMPLE 2

- How do you use the data points to write a system of equations?

2 Teach

Guided Instruction

Before beginning the lesson, make sure that students can solve systems of linear equations, because they will use this skill when writing quadratic functions from data. Demonstrate how quadratic models can be used to make predictions or estimates.

Reaching All Learners

Through Cooperative Learning

Have students work in pairs. Have one student in each pair write a quadratic function and give his or her partner 3 points that lie on the function's graph. Have the partner then determine a quadratic model for the data. Ask students to compare the model with the original function, and have them discuss any discrepancies.

Power Presentations with PowerPoint®

Additional Examples

Example 3

The table shows the cost of circular plastic wading pools based on the pools' diameter. Find a quadratic model for the cost of a pool, given its diameter. Use the model to estimate the cost of a pool with a diameter of 8 ft.

Diameter (ft)	Cost
4	\$19.95
5	\$20.25
6	\$25.00
7	\$34.95

$f(x) \approx 2.4x^2 - 21.6x + 67.6$; $\approx$ \$49.54

Also available on transparency

INTERVENTION

Questioning Strategies

EXAMPLE 

- How do you know which values to enter in List 1 and which to enter in List 2?
- How do you use the values of *a*, *b*, and *c* to write a quadratic model of the data?

Teaching Tip **Math Background** Explain to students that in mathematics, a *regression* is a function that closely models a set of data. A calculator produces a regression by minimizing the vertical distance between each data point and the function's graph.

Teaching Tip **Technology** The coefficient of determination R^2 will only be displayed by the quadratic regression feature if diagnostics are turned on. To do so, press 2nd CATALOG, and scroll down to **DiagnosticOn** and press ENTER.

A **quadratic model** is a quadratic function that represents a real data set. Models are useful for making estimates.

In Chapter 2, you used a graphing calculator to perform a *linear regression* and make predictions. You can apply a similar statistical method to make a quadratic model for a given data set using **quadratic regression.**

EXAMPLE  *Film Application*

The table shows approximate run times for 16 mm films, given the diameter of the film on the reel. Find a quadratic model for the run time given the diameter. Use the model to estimate the run time for a reel of film with a diameter of 15 in.

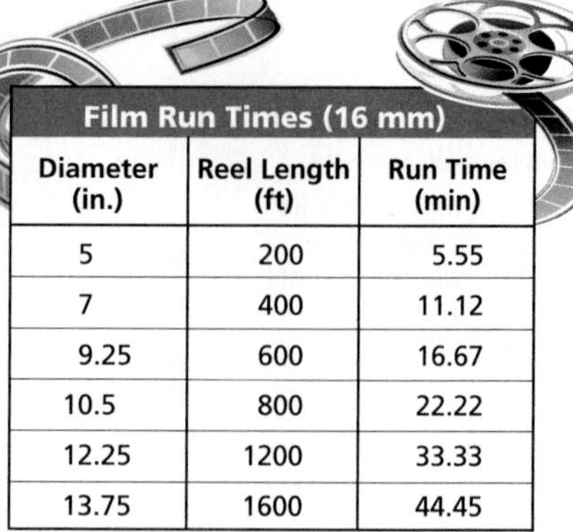

Film Run Times (16 mm)

Diameter (in.)	Reel Length (ft)	Run Time (min)
5	200	5.55
7	400	11.12
9.25	600	16.67
10.5	800	22.22
12.25	1200	33.33
13.75	1600	44.45

Helpful Hint

The coefficient of determination R^2 shows how well a quadratic model fits the data. The closer R^2 is to 1, the better the fit. In this model, $R^2 \approx 0.996$, which is very close to 1, so the quadratic model is a good fit.

Step 1 Enter the data into two lists in a graphing calculator.

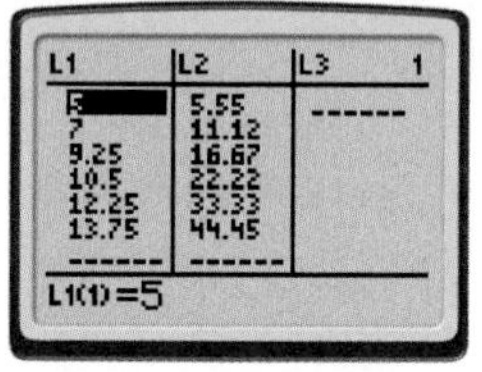

Step 2 Use the quadratic regression feature.

Step 3 Graph the data and function model to verify that the model fits the data.

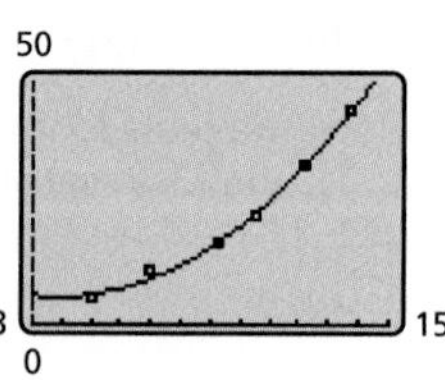

Step 4 Use the table feature to find the function value at $x = 15$.

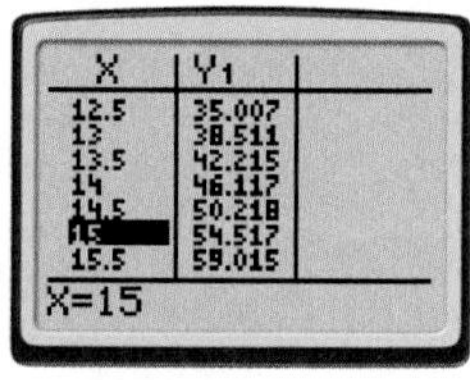

A quadratic model is $T(d) \approx 0.397d^2 - 3.12d + 11.94$, where T is the run time in minutes and d is the film diameter in inches.

For a 15 in. diameter, the model predicts a run time of about 54.5 min, or 54 min 30 s.

CHECK IT OUT! **Use the information given above to answer the following.**

3. Find a quadratic model for the reel length given the diameter of the film. Use the model to estimate the reel length for an 8-inch-diameter film.
$L(d) \approx 14.3d^2 - 112.4d + 430.1$; about 446 ft

 Close

Summarize

Review with students the process for writing quadratic functions from data:

- Use three data points to write a system of equations by substituting the coordinates of the points into the function $f(x) = ax^2 + bx + c$.
- Solve the system for *a*, *b*, and *c*.
- Write a quadratic function in standard form using the values for *a*, *b*, and *c* found in the previous step.

ONGOING ASSESSMENT

and INTERVENTION 

***Diagnose Before* the Lesson**
5-8 Warm Up, TE p. 374

***Monitor During* the Lesson**
Check It Out! Exercises, SE pp. 374–376
Questioning Strategies, TE pp. 375–376

***Assess After* the Lesson**
5-8 Lesson Quiz, TE p. 381
Alternative Assessment, TE p. 381

THINK AND DISCUSS

1. Describe how to determine if a data set is quadratic.
2. Explain whether a quadratic function is a good model for the path of an airplane that ascends, descends, and rises again out of view.
3. **GET ORGANIZED** Copy and complete the graphic organizer. Compare the different quadratic models presented in the lesson.

Quadratic Model	When Appropriate	Procedure
Exact model		
Approximate model		

Answers to *Think and Discuss*

Possible answers:

1. If the data set has equally spaced x-values and the second differences of the corresponding function values are constant and nonzero, then the data set is quadratic.
2. No, a quadratic function would not be a good model, because a quadratic function could only model one of the plane's changes in direction.
3. See p. A7.

5-8 Exercises

go.hrw.com
Homework Help Online
KEYWORD: MB7 5-8
Parent Resources Online
KEYWORD: MB7 Parent

GUIDED PRACTICE

1. **Vocabulary** How does a *quadratic model* differ from a linear model?

SEE EXAMPLE 1 p. 374

Determine whether each data set could represent a quadratic function. Explain.

2.

x	−2	−1	0	1	2
y	16	8	0	−8	−16

3.

x	1	2	3	4	5
y	1	3	9	27	81

4.

x	2	4	6	8	10
y	4	−5	−8	−5	4

SEE EXAMPLE 2 p. 375

Write a quadratic function that fits each set of points.

5. $(-2, 5)$, $(0, -3)$, and $(3, 0)$
6. $(0, 1)$, $(2, -1)$, and $(3, -8)$
7. $(-1, 8)$, $(0, 4)$, and $(2, 2)$
8. $(-4, 9)$, $(0, -7)$, and $(1, -1)$
9. $(2, 3)$, $(6, 3)$, and $(8, -3)$
10. $(-1, -12)$, $(1, 0)$, and $(2, 9)$

SEE EXAMPLE 3 p. 376

11. **Hobbies** The cost of mounting different-sized photos is shown in the table. Find a quadratic model for the cost given the average side length. (For an 8 in. × 10 in. photo, the average side length is $\frac{8+10}{2} = 9$ in.) Estimate the cost of mounting a 24 in. × 36 in. photo.
$C(x) \approx 0.0098x^2 + 0.62x + 3.8$; about \$31.20

Costs of Mounting Photos	
Size (in.)	**Cost (\$)**
8 × 10	10
14 × 18	16
16 × 20	19
24 × 30	27
32 × 40	39

PRACTICE AND PROBLEM SOLVING

Determine whether each data set could represent a quadratic function. Explain.

12.

x	0	2	4	6	8
f(x)	−1	2	11	26	47

13.

x	0	1	2	3	4
f(x)	10	9	6	1	−6

14.

x	1	2	3	4	5
f(x)	−3	0	3	6	9

5-8 Exercises

Assignment Guide

Assign *Guided Practice* exercises as necessary.

If you finished Examples **1–3**
Basic 12–41, 45–49, 52–60
Average 12–50, 52–60
Advanced 12–60

Homework Quick Check
Quickly check key concepts.
Exercises: 12, 16, 19, 22, 26

Answers

1. Possible answer: A linear model is used to fit a set of data whose points lie on or close to a line. A quadratic model is used to fit a set of data whose points lie on or close to a parabola.
2. Not quadratic; first differences are constant so the function is linear.
3. Not quadratic; second differences are not constant for equally spaced x-values.
4. Quadratic; second differences are constant for equally spaced x-values.
5. $y = x^2 - 2x - 3$
6. $y = -2x^2 + 3x + 1$
7. $y = x^2 - 3x + 4$
8. $y = 2x^2 + 4x - 7$
9. $y = -\frac{1}{2}x^2 + 4x - 3$
10. $y = x^2 + 6x - 7$
12. Quadratic; second differences are constant for equally spaced x-values.
13. Quadratic; second differences are constant for equally spaced x-values.
14. Not quadratic; first differences are constant so the function is linear.

State Resources

go.hrw.com
State Resources Online
KEYWORD: MB7 Resources

 **Exercise 28** involves finding a quadratic model based on data related to tiles. This exercise prepares students for the Multi-Step Test Prep on page 390.

 **Critical Thinking** Challenge students to develop a procedure for answering **Exercises 25–27** by using second differences rather than by writing a quadratic function for the data.

Answers

15. $y = \frac{4}{3}x^2 - x - \frac{7}{3}$
16. $y = x^2 - 6x + 7$
17. $y = 0.5x^2 - 3x - 8$
18. $y = 3x^2 + 0.8x + 0.4$

Independent Practice	
For Exercises	See Example
12–14	1
15–18	2
19	3

Extra Practice
Skills Practice p. S13
Application Practice p. S36

Write a quadratic function that fits each set of points.

15. $(-2, 5)$, $(-1, 0)$, and $(1, -2)$
16. $(1, 2)$, $(2, -1)$, and $(5, 2)$
17. $(-4, 12)$, $(-2, 0)$, and $(2, -12)$
18. $(-1, 2.6)$, $(1, 4.2)$, and $(2, 14)$

19. **Gardening** The table shows the amount spent on water gardening in the United States between 1999 and 2003. Find a quadratic model for the annual amount in millions of dollars spent on water gardening based on number of years since 1999. Estimate the amount that people in the United States will spend on water gardening in 2015.
$y \approx -3.7x^2 + 216x + 781$; about \$3290 million, or \$3.29 billion

Water Gardening	
Year	Amount Spent (million \$)
1999	806
2000	943
2001	1205
2002	1441
2003	1565

Write a function rule for each situation, and identify each relationship as linear, quadratic, or neither.

20. the circumference C of a bicycle wheel, given its radius r
The function is $C(r) = 2\pi r$, which is linear.
21. the area of a triangle A with a constant height, given its base length b
22. the population of bacteria P in a petri dish doubling every hour t
23. the area of carpet A needed for square rooms of length s
The function is $A(s) = s^2$, which is quadratic.

21. The function is $A(b) = \left(\frac{1}{2}h\right)b$, which is linear.

22. The function is $P(t) = 2^t$, which is neither linear nor quadratic.

24a. Galileo's rule

24b. Aristotle's rule: linear; da Vinci's rule: quadratic; Galileo's rule: quadratic

24. **Physics** In the past, different mathematical descriptions of falling objects were proposed.
  a. Which rule shows the greatest increase in the distance fallen per second and thus the greatest rate of increase in speed?
  b. Identify each rule as linear, quadratic, or neither.
  c. Describe the differences in da Vinci's rule, and compare it with the differences in Galileo's.
  d. The most accurate rule is sometimes described as the odd-number law. Which rule shows an odd-number pattern of first differences and correctly describes the distance for falling objects? Galileo's rule

Relative Distance Fallen (units)			
Time Interval (s)	Aristotle's Rule	da Vinci's Rule	Galileo's Rule
0	0	0	0
1	1	1	1
2	2	3	4
3	3	6	9
4	4	10	16

Find the missing value for each quadratic function.

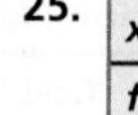
25.

x	-1	0	1	2	3
$f(x)$	0	1	0	■	-8

-3

26.
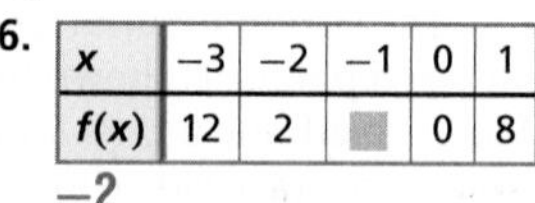

x	-3	-2	-1	0	1
$f(x)$	12	2	■	0	8

-2

27.
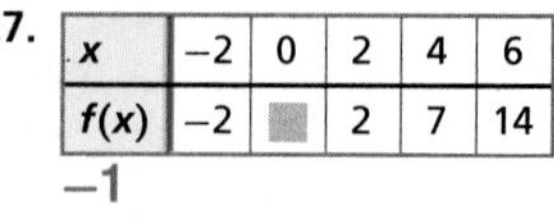

x	-2	0	2	4	6
$f(x)$	-2	■	2	7	14

-1

28. This problem will prepare you for the Multi-Step Test Prep on page 390.
A home-improvement store sells several sizes of rectangular tiles, as shown in the table.
  a. Find a quadratic model for the area of a tile based on its length. $f(x) = x^2 + 3x$
  b. The store begins selling a new size of tile with a length of 9 in. Based on your model, estimate the area of a tile of this size. 108 in^2

Length (in.)	Area (in^2)
4	28
6	54
8	88
10	130

5-8 PRACTICE A

Use each data set to answer the questions.

1.

x	-2	-1	0	1	2
y	24	12	3	-3	-6

a. What are the first differences for this data set? $-12, -9, -6, -3$
b. What are the second differences for this data set? 3, 3, 3
c. Does this data set represent a quadratic function? Why? Yes, because the second differences are a nonzero constant

2.

x	-3	0	3	6	9
y	10	4	-1	-5	-8

a. What are the first differences for this data set? $-6, -5, -4, -3$
b. What are the second differences for this data set? 1, 1, 1
c. Does this data set represent a quadratic function? Why? Yes, because the second differences are a nonzero constant

Write a quadratic function that fits each set of points.

3. $(0, -12)$, $(6, 12)$, $(2, -8)$
  a. Use each ordered pair to write an equation of the form $y = ax^2 + bx + c$.
  $c = -12$ $36a + 6b + c = 12$ $4a + 2b + c = -8$
  b. Solve the system of equations using any method you choose.
  $a = \frac{1}{2}$, $b = 1$, $c = -12$
  c. Use the values of a, b, and c to write the quadratic function.
  $f(x) = \frac{1}{2}x^2 + x - 12$
4. $(1, 11)$, $(2, 2)$, $(3, -5)$ $f(x) = x^2 - 12x + 22$
5. $(1, 18)$, $(2, 12)$, $(3, 2)$ $f(x) = -2x^2 + 20$

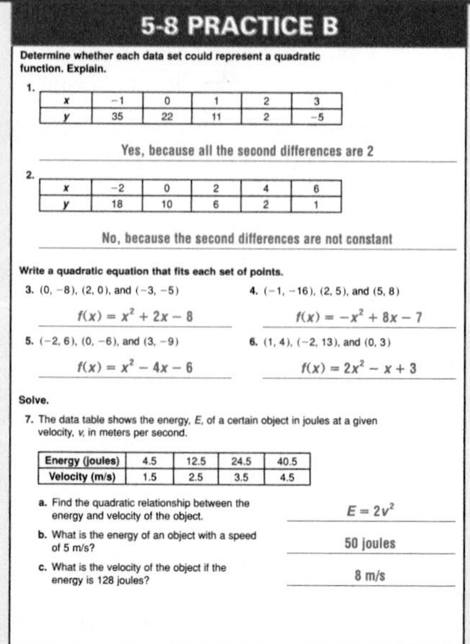

5-8 PRACTICE B

Determine whether each data set could represent a quadratic function. Explain.

1.

x	-1	0	1	2	3
y	35	22	11	2	-5

Yes, because all the second differences are 2

2.

x	-2	0	2	4	6
y	18	10	6	2	1

No, because the second differences are not constant

Write a quadratic equation that fits each set of points.

3. $(0, -8)$, $(2, 0)$, and $(-3, -5)$ $f(x) = x^2 + 2x - 8$
4. $(-1, -16)$, $(2, 5)$, and $(5, 8)$ $f(x) = -x^2 + 8x - 7$
5. $(-2, 6)$, $(0, -6)$, and $(3, -9)$ $f(x) = x^2 - 4x - 6$
6. $(1, 4)$, $(-2, 13)$, and $(0, 3)$ $f(x) = 2x^2 - x + 3$

Solve.

7. The data table shows the energy, E, of a certain object in joules at a given velocity, v, in meters per second.

Energy (joules)	4.5	12.5	24.5	40.5
Velocity (m/s)	1.5	2.5	3.5	4.5

a. Find the quadratic relationship between the energy and velocity of the object. $E = 2v^2$
b. What is the energy of an object with a speed of 5 m/s? 50 joules
c. What is the velocity of the object if the energy is 128 joules? 8 m/s

29. **Food** The pizza prices for DeAngelo's pizza parlor are shown at right.

a. Find a quadratic model for the price of a pizza based upon the size (diameter).

b. Use the quadratic model to find the price of a pizza with an 18 in. diameter. **\$18.95**

c. Graph the quadratic function. Does the function have a minimum or maximum point? What does this point represent?

d. **What if...?** According to the model, how much should a 30 in. pizza cost? How much should an 8 in. pizza cost? **\$9.95; −\$1.05**

e. Is the quadratic function a good model for the price of DeAngelo's pizza? Explain your reasoning.

Determine whether each data set could represent a quadratic function. If so, find a quadratic function rule.

30.

x	0	1	2	3	4
y	−1	0	−1	−4	−9

quadratic; $y = -x^2 + 2x - 1$

31.

x	1	2	3	4	5
y	10	20	40	60	80

not quadratic

32.

x	2	4	6	8	10
y	−1	0	1	3	5

not quadratic

33.

x	−2	−1	0	1	2
y	16	3	0	7	24

quadratic; $y = 5x^2 + 2x$

34.

x	0	1	2	3	4
y	9	5	3	1	0

not quadratic

35.

x	−2	−1	0	1	2
y	0	3	9	27	81

not quadratic

$h(t) \approx -4.95t^2 + 10.44t + 13.2$; about 14.3 m

36. **Winter Sports** The diagram shows the motion of a skier following a jump. Find a quadratic model of the skier's height h in meters based on time t in seconds. Estimate the skier's height after 2 s.

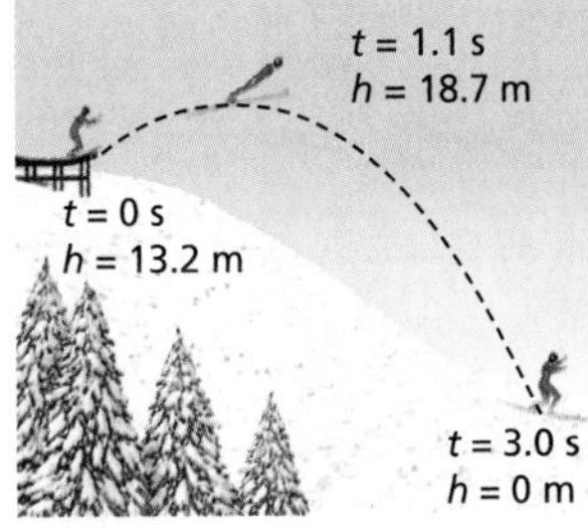

37. **Data Collection** Use a graphing calculator and a motion detector to measure the height of a basketball over time. Drop the ball from a height of 1 m, and let it bounce several times. Position the motion detector 0.5 m above the release point of the ball.

a. What is the greatest height the ball reaches during its first bounce?

b. Find an appropriate model for the height of the ball as a function of time during its first bounce.

37a. Answers will vary. Possible answer: 0.75 m

37b. Answers will vary. Possible answer: $h(t) = -4.7t^2 + 18.1t - 16.8$

38. **Safety** The light produced by high-pressure sodium vapor streetlamps for different energy usages is shown in the table.

High-Pressure Sodium Vapor Streetlamps					
Energy Use (watts)	35	50	70	100	150
Light Output (lumens)	2250	4000	5800	9500	16,000

a. Find a quadratic model for the light output with respect to energy use.

b. Find a linear model for the light output with respect to energy use.

c. Apply each model to estimate the light output in lumens of a 200-watt bulb.

d. Which model gives the better estimate? Explain.

38a. $y \approx 0.187x^2 + 84.3x - 863.6$

38b. $y \approx 119x - 2159$

38c. about 23,476 lumens; about 21,641 lumens

38d. Possible answer: The quadratic model would probably give a better estimate of the light output for higher values of energy usage because the data points lie along a slight curve.

COMMON ERROR ALERT

When solving real-world problems involving quadratic regressions, such as in **Exercises 29, 38,** and **40,** students may not know which variable to use as the independent variable and which to use as the dependent variable. Point out that variables following phrases such as "based upon" and "with respect to" usually represent the independent variable.

Teaching Tip **Data Collection** To help students complete **Exercise 37**, see *Technology Lab Activities.*

Answers

29a. $p(s) = -0.125s^2 + 5.25s - 35.05$

c.

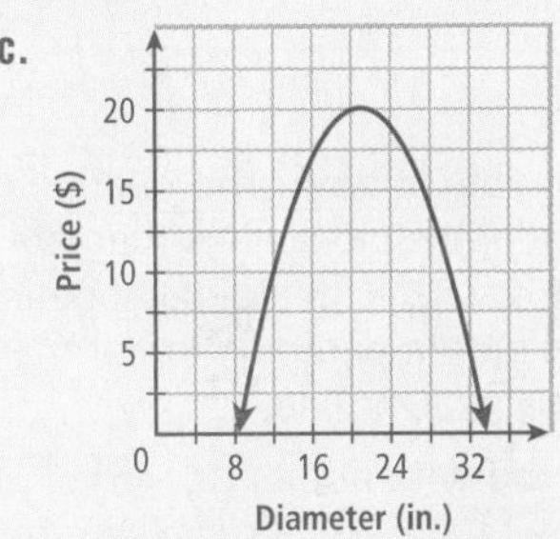

a maximum point; the price and size of the most expensive pizza

e. Possible answer: No, the function is not a good model. It gives negative prices for very small pizzas and low (or negative) prices for very large pizzas.

37a. Answers will vary. Possible answer: 0.75 m

b. Answers will vary. Possible answer: $h(t) = -4.7t^2 + 18.1t - 16.8$

5-8 PRACTICE C

The following data sets represent quadratic functions. Find the missing coordinates.

1.

x	−2	−1	0	1	2	3
y	28	14	3	−5	−10	−12

2.

x	−2	−1	0	1	2	3
y	0	0	2	6	12	20

Write a quadratic function that fits each set of points.

3. (1, 0), (−3, 12), and (0, −3)

$f(x) = 2x^2 + x - 3$

4. (4, 0), (0, −28), and (6, 2)

$f(x) = -x^2 + 11x - 28$

5. (3, 0), (2, 3), and (7, 8)

$f(x) = x^2 - 8x + 15$

6. (5, −6), (−2, 8), and (−1, 0)

$f(x) = x^2 - 5x - 6$

Solve.

7. Do the points (−8, 6), (2, 1), and (6, −1) describe a quadratic function? Explain how you know.

No; possible answer: a quadratic function can be defined by 3 noncollinear points, but these 3 points lie on the same line so the points define a linear function.

8. Teresa is running a chemical reaction that can be modeled by a quadratic function. When she begins the reaction there are 20 grams of sodium chloride present. At 2 minutes there are 48 grams of sodium chloride. At 5 minutes there are 60 grams of sodium chloride, and at 8 minutes there are 36 grams of sodium chloride.

a. Write a quadratic function that models her data.

$f(x) = -2x^2 + 18x + 20$

b. At what point will all of the sodium chloride be used up in the reaction?

10 minutes

Answers

40a. Possible answer: The last 2 columns appear to be quadratic because the successive terms grow faster than a linear function would.

b. Max. length: $y \approx 102x^2 + 114x + 66$; max. weight: $y \approx 1063x^2 + 103x - 16$; yes, the models fit the data well because the coefficient of determination is very close to 1.

41. $t(n) = \frac{1}{2}n^2 + \frac{1}{2}n$

43a.

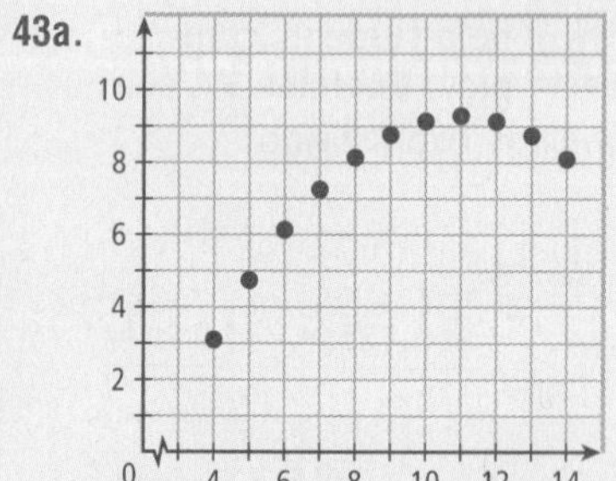

d. Possible answer: The quadratic model best describes the data set because the points appear to lie on a parabola rather than on a straight line.

49. For the data points $(0, -5)$, $(1, -3)$, and $(2, 3)$, the system is

$$\begin{cases} c = -5 \\ a + b + c = -3 \\ 4a + 2b + c = 3 \end{cases}.$$

The coefficients are $a = 2$, $b = 0$, and $c = -5$. The function is $y = 2x^2 - 5$.

50a. $y = -\frac{1}{18}x^2 + \frac{29}{18}x + \frac{4}{9}$; maximum value; $\left(14\frac{1}{2}, 12\frac{1}{8}\right)$

b. $y = \frac{1}{18}x^2 + \frac{19}{18}x + \frac{8}{9}$; minimum value; $\left(-9\frac{1}{2}, -4\frac{1}{8}\right)$

51. Possible answer: Draw a line connecting the point with the least x-value to the point with the greatest x-value. If the third point lies above this line, the parabola opens downward. If the third point lies below this line, the parabola opens upward.

56. $\begin{bmatrix} -\frac{1}{2} & \frac{1}{2} & 0 \\ 1 & -2 & \frac{1}{2} \\ 0 & 1 & 0 \end{bmatrix}$

58. $\frac{2 + \sqrt{2}}{2}$

59. $\pm 3i$

60. $\frac{5 \pm \sqrt{61}}{3}$

39. Sports The table lists the average distance that a normal shot travels for different golf clubs.

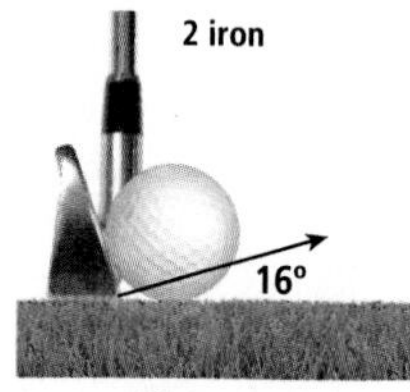

Average Distance for Normal Shot

Club Iron (no.)	2	3	4	5	6	7	8	9
Loft Angle	16°	20°	24°	28°	32°	36°	40°	44°
Distance (yd)	186	176	166	155	143	132	122	112

$y \approx -10.7x + 208.1$

a. Select three data values (club number, distance), and use a system of equations to find a quadratic model. Check your model by using a quadratic regression.

39b. No, the relationship is linear because the coefficient of the x^2-term is 0.

b. Is there a quadratic relationship between club number and average distance of a normal shot? Explain.

c. Is the relationship between club number and loft angle quadratic or linear? Find a model of this relationship. **linear; $y = 4x + 8$**

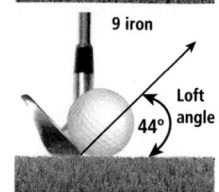

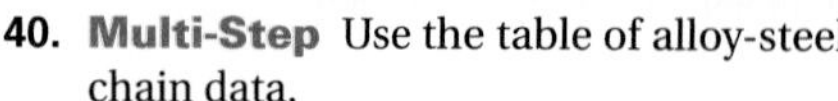

40. Multi-Step Use the table of alloy-steel chain data.

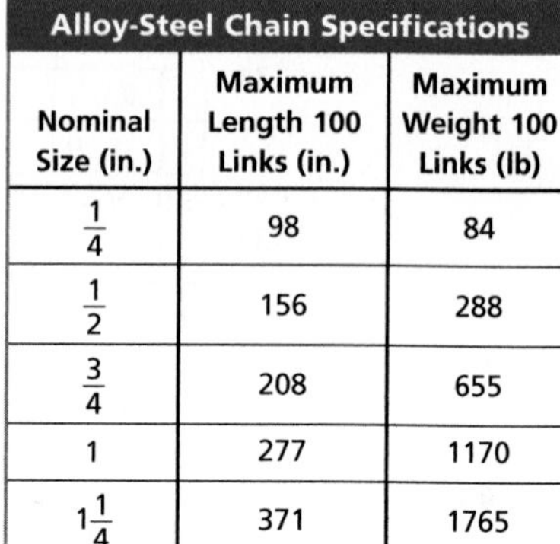

Alloy-Steel Chain Specifications

Nominal Size (in.)	Maximum Length 100 Links (in.)	Maximum Weight 100 Links (lb)
$\frac{1}{4}$	98	84
$\frac{1}{2}$	156	288
$\frac{3}{4}$	208	655
1	277	1170
$1\frac{1}{4}$	371	1765

a. Do each of the last two columns appear to be quadratic functions with respect to the nominal chain size? Explain.

b. Verify your response in part **a** by finding each of the quadratic regression equations. Do the models fit the data well? Explain.

c. Predict the values for the last two columns for a chain with a nominal size of $\frac{5}{8}$ in.

40c. max. length: about 178 in.; max. weight: about 464 lb

LINK

Math History

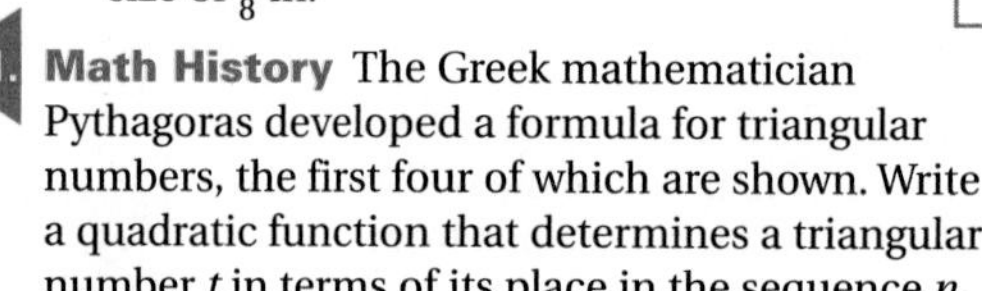

Pythagoras made numerous contributions to mathematics, including the Pythagorean Theorem, which bears his name.

41. Math History The Greek mathematician Pythagoras developed a formula for triangular numbers, the first four of which are shown. Write a quadratic function that determines a triangular number t in terms of its place in the sequence n. (*Hint:* The fourth triangular number has $n = 4$.)

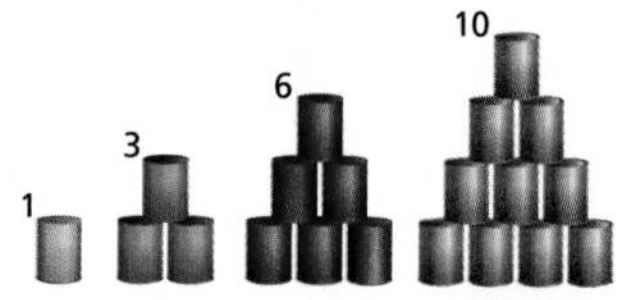

42. Critical Thinking Two points define a unique line. How many points define a unique parabola, and what restriction applies to the points? **Three points define a unique parabola. The 3 points cannot lie on the same line.**

43. Critical Thinking Consider the following data set.

x	10	8	13	9	11	14	6	4	12	7	5
y	9.14	8.14	8.74	8.77	9.29	8.1	6.13	3.1	9.13	7.26	4.74

a. Create a scatter plot of the data.

b. Perform a linear regression on the data. **$y \approx 0.5x + 3$**

c. Perform a quadratic regression on the data. **$y \approx -0.13x^2 + 2.8x - 6$**

d. Which model best describes the data set? Explain your answer.

44. Write About It What does it mean when the coefficient a in a quadratic regression model is zero?

The model is a linear model of the form $y = bx + c$.

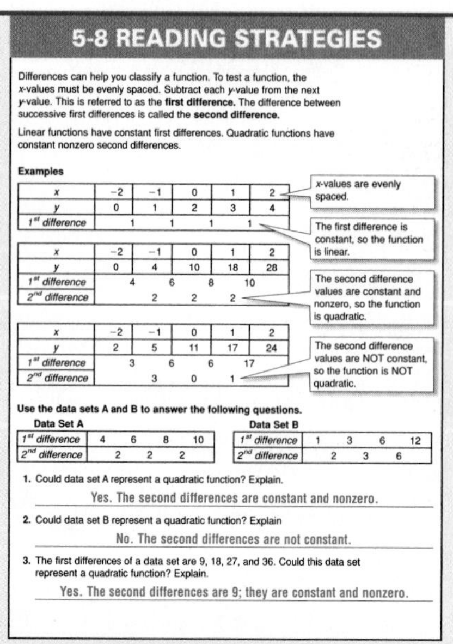

5-8 READING STRATEGIES

Differences can help you classify a function. To test a function, the x-values must be evenly spaced. Subtract each y-value from the next y-value. This is referred to as the **first difference.** The difference between successive first differences is called the **second difference.**

Linear functions have constant first differences. Quadratic functions have constant nonzero second differences.

Examples

x	−2	−1	0	1	2
y	0	1	2	3	4
1st difference	1	1	1	1	

x-values are evenly spaced.

The first difference is constant, so the function is linear.

x	−2	−1	0	1	2
y	0	4	10	18	28
1st difference	4	6	8	10	
2nd difference	2	2	2		

The second difference values are constant and nonzero, so the function is quadratic.

x	−2	−1	0	1	2
y	2	5	11	17	24
1st difference	3	6	6	17	
2nd difference	3	0	1		

The second difference values are NOT constant, so the function is NOT quadratic.

Use the data sets A and B to answer the following questions.

Data Set A

1st difference	4	6	8	10
2nd difference	2	2	2	

Data Set B

1st difference	1	3	6	12
2nd difference	2	3	6	

1. Could data set A represent a quadratic function? Explain.
   Yes. The second differences are constant and nonzero.
2. Could data set B represent a quadratic function? Explain
   No. The second differences are not constant.
3. The first differences of a data set are 9, 18, 27, and 36. Could this data set represent a quadratic function? Explain.
   Yes. The second differences are 9; they are constant and nonzero.

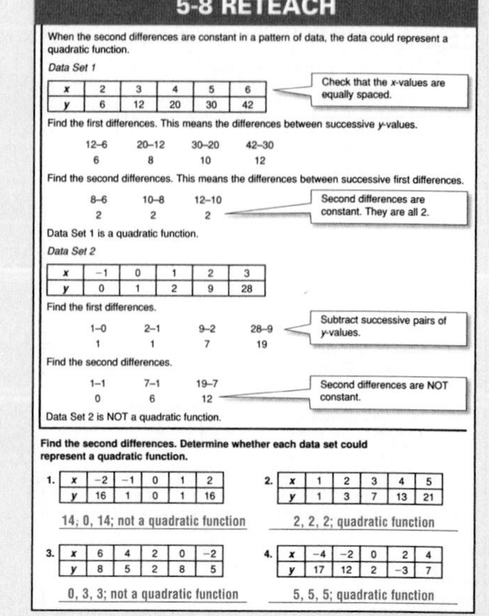

5-8 RETEACH

When the second differences are constant in a pattern of data, the data could represent a quadratic function.

Data Set 1

x	2	3	4	5	6
y	6	12	20	30	42

Check that the x-values are equally spaced.

Find the first differences. This means the differences between successive y-values.

12–6   20–12   30–20   42–30
6   8   10   12

Find the second differences. This means the differences between successive first differences.

8–6   10–8   12–10
2   2   2

Second differences are constant. They are all 2.

Data Set 1 is a quadratic function.

Data Set 2

x	−1	0	1	2	3
y	0	1	2	9	28

Find the first differences.

1–0   2–1   9–2   28–9
1   1   7   19

Subtract successive pairs of y-values.

Find the second differences.

1–1   7–1   19–7
0   6   12

Second differences are NOT constant.

Data Set 2 is NOT a quadratic function.

Find the second differences. Determine whether each data set could represent a quadratic function.

1.

x	−2	−1	0	1	2
y	16	1	0	1	16

14; 0, 14; not a quadratic function

2.

x	1	2	3	4	5
y	1	3	7	13	21

2, 2, 2; quadratic function

3.

x	6	4	2	0	−2
y	8	5	2	8	5

0, 3, 3; not a quadratic function

4.

x	−4	−2	0	2	4
y	17	12	2	−3	7

5, 5, 5; quadratic function

TEST PREP

45. Which of the following would best be modeled by a quadratic function?

Ⓐ Relationship between circumference and diameter
Ⓑ Relationship between area of a square and side length
Ⓒ Relationship between diagonal of a square and side length
Ⓓ Relationship between volume of a cube and side length

46. If (7, 11) and (3, 11) are two points on a parabola, what is the x-value of the vertex of this parabola?

Ⓕ 3 **Ⓖ** 5 Ⓗ 7 Ⓙ 11

47. If y is a quadratic function of x, which value completes the table?

x	−2	0	2	4	6
y	−8	0	12	28	■

Ⓐ 12 Ⓑ 20 Ⓒ 44 **Ⓓ** 48

48. The graph of a quadratic function having the form $f(x) = ax^2 + bx + c$ passes through the points (0, −8), (3, 10), and (6, 34). What is the value of the function when $x = -3$?

Ⓕ −32 Ⓖ −26 **Ⓗ** −20 Ⓙ 10

49. **Extended Response** Write a quadratic function in standard form that fits the data points (0, −5), (1, −3), and (2, 3). Use a system of equations, and show all of your work.

CHALLENGE AND EXTEND

50. Three points defining a quadratic function are (1, 2), (4, 6), and (7, w).

a. If $w = 9$, what is the quadratic function? Does it have a maximum value or a minimum value? What is the vertex?

b. If $w = 11$, what is the quadratic function? Does it have a maximum value or a minimum value? What is the vertex?

c. If $w = 10$, what function best fits the points? $y = \frac{4}{3}x + \frac{2}{3}$

51. Explain how you can determine from three points whether the parabola that fits the points opens upward or downward.

SPIRAL REVIEW

Determine whether each data set could represent a linear function. *(Lesson 2-3)*

52.

x	−2	1	4
$f(x)$	−5	7	1

no

53.

x	−8	−6	0
$f(x)$	−1	0	3

yes

Find the inverse of the matrix, if it is defined. *(Lesson 4-5)*

54. $\begin{bmatrix} \frac{1}{3} & 0 \\ -4 & 1 \end{bmatrix}$ $\begin{bmatrix} 3 & 0 \\ 12 & 1 \end{bmatrix}$

55. $\begin{bmatrix} 2 & -2 \\ 1 & -1 \end{bmatrix}$ The matrix is undefined.

56. $\begin{bmatrix} -2 & 0 & 1 \\ 0 & 0 & 1 \\ 4 & 2 & 2 \end{bmatrix}$

57. $\begin{bmatrix} 3 & -4 \\ 0 & -\frac{1}{2} \end{bmatrix}$ $\begin{bmatrix} \frac{1}{3} & -\frac{8}{3} \\ 0 & -2 \end{bmatrix}$

Find the zeros of each function by using the Quadratic Formula. *(Lesson 5-6)*

58. $f(x) = 2x^2 - 4x + 1$

59. $f(x) = x^2 + 9$

60. $f(x) = -3x^2 + 10x + 12$

TEST PREP DOCTOR Students experiencing difficulty with **Exercise 46** may need to be reminded that two points on the graph of a quadratic function with the same y-value are the same distance from the axis of symmetry.

Journal

Have students describe how they can use a graphing calculator to determine whether a set of ten data points is better modeled by a linear function or a quadratic function.

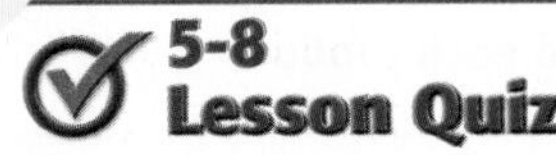

ALTERNATIVE ASSESSMENT

Have students create a set of three noncollinear points and write a quadratic function that fits them. Students should show each step of their work.

Power Presentations with PowerPoint®

5-8 Lesson Quiz

Determine whether each data set could represent a quadratic function.

1.

x	5	6	7	8	9
y	5	8	13	21	34

not quadratic

2.

x	2	3	4	5	6
y	1	11	25	43	65

quadratic

3. Write a quadratic function that fits the points (2, 0), (3, −2), and (5, −12).

$f(x) = -x^2 + 3x - 2$

4. The table shows the prices of an ice cream cake, depending on its size. Find a quadratic model for the cost of an ice cream cake, given the diameter. Then use the model to predict the cost of an ice cream cake with a diameter of 18 in.

Diameter (in.)	Cost
6	$7.50
10	$12.50
15	$18.25

$f(x) \approx -0.011x^2 + 1.43x - 0.67$; $\approx \$21.43$

Also available on transparency

5-8 PROBLEM SOLVING

Ellen and Kelly test Ellen's new car in an empty parking lot. They mark a braking line where Ellen applies the brakes. Kelly then measures the distance from that line to the place where Ellen stops, for speeds from 5 miles per hour to 25 miles per hour.

Brake Test					
Speed (mi/h)	5	10	15	20	25
Stopping Distance (ft)	7	17	30	46	65

1. Ellen wants to know the stopping distance at 60 miles per hour. She cannot drive the car at this speed in the parking lot, so they decide to try curve fitting, using the data they have collected.

a. Can you use a quadratic function to represent the data in the table? Explain how you know.
Yes; possible answer: the first differences of the y-values in the table are not constant. The second differences are constant (3). So this data represents a quadratic function.

b. Use three points to write a system of equations to find a, b, and c in $f(x) = ax^2 + bx + c$.
$\begin{cases} 25a + 5b + c = 7 \\ 100a + 10b + c = 17 \\ 400a + 20b + c = 46 \end{cases}$

c. Use any method to solve 3 equations with 3 variables. Find the values for a, b, and c. $a = 0.06$, $b = 1.1$, $c = 0$

d. Write the quadratic function that models the stopping distance of Ellen's car. $f(x) = 0.06x^2 + 1.1x$

e. What is the stopping distance of Ellen's car at 60 miles per hour? 282 ft

The table shows the sizes and prices of decorative square patio tiles. Choose the letter for the best answer.

Patio Tiles Sale					
Side Length (in.)	6	9	12	15	18
Price Each ($)	1.44	3.24	5.76	9.00	12.96

2. What quadratic function models the price of the patio tiles?

A $P(x) = 0.4x^2$
(B) $P(x) = 0.04x^2$
C $P(x) = 0.04x^2 + 0.4x$
D $P(x) = 0.04x^2 + x + 0.4$

3. What is the second difference constant for the data in the table?

A 1.44
B 1.08
(C) 0.72
D 0.36

5-8 CHALLENGE

The method of finite differences can be used to determine if a polynomial function is an appropriate model of a given data set in two variables.

Consider the data set shown in the table at right.

x	1	2	3	4	5	6
y	6	11	20	33	50	71

1. To construct a *difference table*, begin by listing the y-values in order. The 1st order differences between the y-values are shown. Continue by writing the 2nd order and 3rd order differences.

y-values 6 11 20 33 50 71
1st order differences 5 9 13 17 21
2nd order differences 4 4 4 4
3rd order differences 0 0 0

2. For any set of x-values that increases in constant increments, if the $(n + 1)$ order differences equal zero, a polynomial of degree n can be found to relate the x- and y-values of the data set. Can a polynomial function be used to model the given data set? If so, of what degree and what general form?
Yes; 2nd degree; $y = ax^2 + bx + c$

To find a quadratic function that will model a sequence in which the x-values are consecutive integers beginning with 1, first consider the differences in a general sequence, as shown below.

x-values	1	2	3	4
$y = ax^2 + bx + c$	$a(1)^2 + b(1) + c$	$a(2)^2 + b(2) + c$	$a(3)^2 + b(3) + c$	$a(4)^2 + b(4) + c$
	$a + b + c$	$4a + 2b + c$	$9a + 3b + c$	$16a + 4b + c$

1st order differences $3a + b$ $5a + b$ $7a + b$
2nd order differences $2a$ $2a$

3. You can write a particular quadratic function by using the general differences to determine a, b, and c. Refer to the difference table from Exercise 1 to write a quadratic function for the data set.

a. Use the general 2nd order difference $(2a)$ and your 2nd order difference to determine a. $a = 2$

b. Use the value of a, the first of the general 1st order differences $(3a + b)$, and your first 1st order difference to determine b. $b = -1$

c. In $y = a + b + c$, use the values of a and b and your first y-value to determine c. $c = 5$

d. Write a quadratic function to model the given data set. Check the given data points in your function. $y = 2x^2 - x + 5$;

5-9 Organizer

Pacing: Traditional 1 day
Block $\frac{1}{2}$ day

Objective: Perform operations with complex numbers.

Online Edition
Tutorial Videos

Countdown to Testing Week 12

Power Presentations with PowerPoint®

Warm Up

Express each number in terms of *i*.

1. $\sqrt{-81}$ $9i$
2. $-\sqrt{-18}$ $-3i\sqrt{2}$

Find each complex conjugate.

3. $6 - i\sqrt{3}$ $6 + i\sqrt{3}$
4. $4i + \sqrt{2}$ $\sqrt{2} - 4i$

Find each product.

5. $(2 + \sqrt{2})(3 - \sqrt{2})$ $4 + \sqrt{2}$
6. $(6 + 3\sqrt{3})(1 + \sqrt{3})$ $15 + 9\sqrt{3}$

Also available on transparency

Math Humor

Q: Why did the imaginary number turn red?

A: It ran out of *i*-drops.

5-9 Operations with Complex Numbers

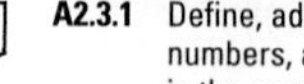

A2.3.1 Define, add, subtract, multiply and divide complex numbers. Represent complex numbers, and the addition, subtraction and absolute value of complex numbers, in the complex plane.

Objective
Perform operations with complex numbers.

Vocabulary
complex plane
absolute value of a complex number

Why learn this?
Complex numbers can be used in formulas to create patterns called fractals. (See Exercise 84.)

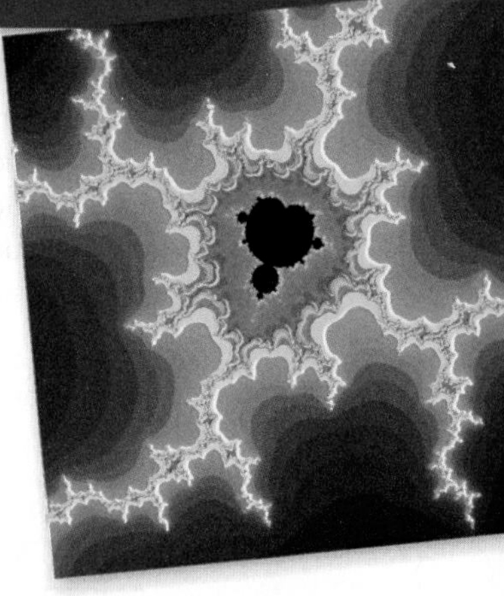

Just as you can represent real numbers graphically as points on a number line, you can represent complex numbers in a special coordinate plane.

The **complex plane** is a set of coordinate axes in which the horizontal axis represents real numbers and the vertical axis represents imaginary numbers.

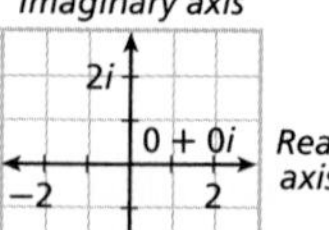

EXAMPLE 1 Graphing Complex Numbers

Helpful Hint
The real axis corresponds to the *x*-axis, and the imaginary axis corresponds to the *y*-axis. Think of $a + bi$ as $x + yi$.

Graph each complex number.

A $-3 + 0i$

B $-3i$

C $4 + 3i$

D $-2 + 4i$

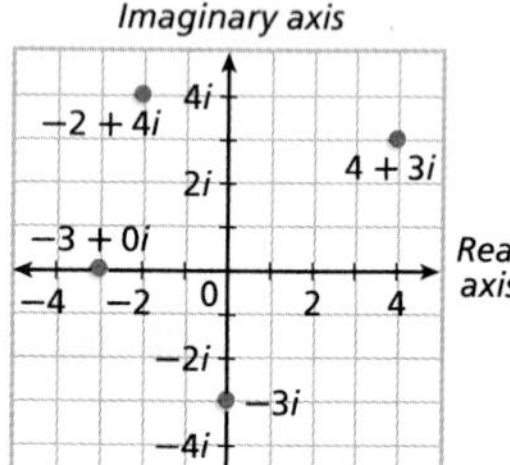

Graph each complex number.

1a. $3 + 0i$ **1b.** $2i$ **1c.** $-2 - i$ **1d.** $3 + 2i$

Recall that the absolute value of a real number is its distance from 0 on the real axis, which is also a number line. Similarly, the absolute value of an imaginary number is its distance from 0 along the imaginary axis.

Know it! Note

Absolute Value of a Complex Number

WORDS	ALGEBRA	EXAMPLE
The **absolute value of a complex number** $a + bi$ is the distance from the origin to the point (a, b) in the complex plane, and is denoted $\lvert a + bi \rvert$.	$\lvert a + bi \rvert = \sqrt{a^2 + b^2}$	Imaginary axis; $4i$; $3 + 4i$; $\lvert 3 + 4i \rvert$; 4; 3; 0; 2; 4; Real axis $\lvert 3 + 4i \rvert = \sqrt{3^2 + 4^2}$ $= \sqrt{9 + 16}$ $= 5$

State Resources

go.hrw.com
State Resources Online
KEYWORD: MB7 Resources

1 Introduce

EXPLORATION

5-9 Operations with Complex Numbers

Recall that $i = \sqrt{-1}$ and that $i^2 = -1$. You can use these facts to simplify other powers of i. For example, $i^3 = i^2 \cdot i = -1 \cdot i = -i$.

1. Complete the table by simplifying the powers of i.

$i^1 =$	$i^2 =$	$i^3 =$	$i^4 =$
$i^5 =$	$i^6 =$	$i^7 =$	$i^8 =$
$i^9 =$	$i^{10} =$	$i^{11} =$	$i^{12} =$
$i^{13} =$	$i^{14} =$	$i^{15} =$	$i^{16} =$

2. What values are possible for the positive integer powers of i?

THINK AND DISCUSS

3. **Discuss** the pattern you notice in the table.
4. **Explain** how you can quickly find the value of i^{64}.

Motivate

Have students search for pictures of fractals on the Internet, or show them some examples. Explain that fractals are geometric figures with unusual properties. One of these properties is self-similarity, which means that a fractal can be divided into smaller parts that are similar to the the fractal itself. Point out that some types of fractals can be generated by performing operations on complex numbers.

Explorations and answers are provided in the *Explorations* binder.

EXAMPLE 2 Determining the Absolute Value of Complex Numbers

Find each absolute value.

A $|-9+i|$

$|-9+1i|$

$\sqrt{(-9)^2+1^2}$

$\sqrt{81+1}$

$\sqrt{82}$

B $|6|$

$|6+0i|$

$\sqrt{6^2+0^2}$

$\sqrt{36}$

6

C $|-4i|$

$|0+(-4)i|$

$\sqrt{0^2+(-4)^2}$

$\sqrt{16}$

4

CHECK IT OUT! Find each absolute value.
2a. $|1-2i|$ $\sqrt{5}$ **2b.** $\left|-\frac{1}{2}\right|$ $\frac{1}{2}$ **2c.** $|23i|$ 23

Adding and subtracting complex numbers is similar to adding and subtracting variable expressions with like terms. Simply combine the real parts, and combine the imaginary parts.

The set of complex numbers has all the properties of the set of real numbers. So you can use the Commutative, Associative, and Distributive Properties to simplify complex number expressions.

EXAMPLE 3 Adding and Subtracting Complex Numbers

Add or subtract. Write the result in the form $a + bi$.

A $(-2+4i)+(3-11i)$

$(-2+3)+(4i-11i)$ *Add real parts and imaginary parts.*

$1-7i$

B $(4-i)-(5+8i)$

$(4-i)-5-8i$ *Distribute.*

$(4-5)+(-i-8i)$ *Add real parts and imaginary parts.*

$-1-9i$

C $(6-2i)+(-6+2i)$

$(6-6)+(-2i+2i)$ *Add real parts and imaginary parts.*

$0+0i$

0

D $(10+3i)-(10-4i)$

$(10+3i)-10-(-4i)$ *Distribute.*

$(10-10)+(3i+4i)$ *Add real parts and imaginary parts.*

$0+7i$

$7i$

Helpful Hint

Complex numbers also have additive inverses. The additive inverse of $a + bi$ is $-(a + bi)$, or $-a - bi$.

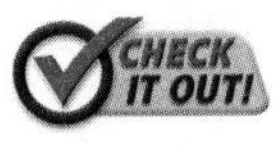

CHECK IT OUT! Add or subtract. Write the result in the form $a + bi$.
3a. $(-3+5i)+(-6i)$ $-3-i$ **3b.** $2i-(3+5i)$ $-3-3i$ **3c.** $(4+3i)+(4-3i)$ 8

You can also add complex numbers by using coordinate geometry.

2 Teach

Guided Instruction

As you focus on graphing and performing operations with complex numbers, stress similarities to performing the analogous operations with real numbers.

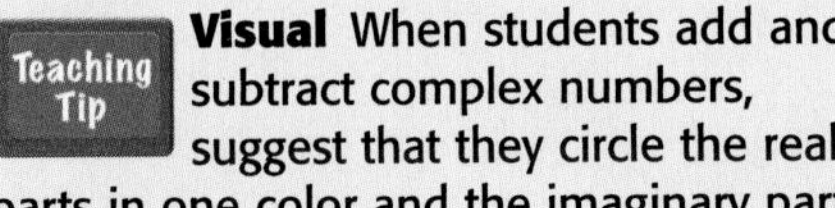

Teaching Tip **Visual** When students add and subtract complex numbers, suggest that they circle the real parts in one color and the imaginary parts in another color.

Reaching All Learners

Through Kinesthetic Experience

If your classroom has a tiled floor, you can use the grid formed by the tiles to model the complex plane. Use masking tape to indicate the real and imaginary axes. Assign a student a complex number such as $3 + i$, and ask the student to move to the point on the floor grid that represents this number. Discuss with the class whether the student moved to the correct position. Repeat this process with several more complex numbers. This activity can also be performed by drawing a complex plane on the board.

Power Presentations with PowerPoint®

Additional Examples

Example 1

Graph each complex number.

A. $2-3i$ **B.** $-1+4i$

C. $4+i$ **D.** $-i$

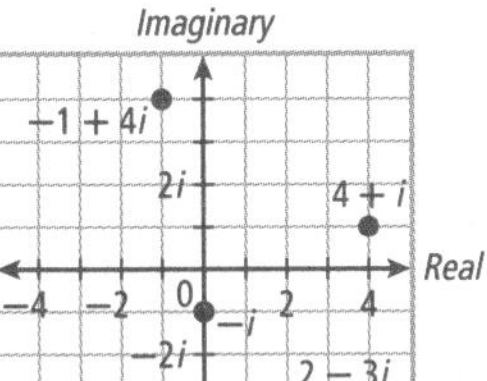

Example 2

Find each absolute value.

A. $|3+5i|$ $\sqrt{34}$

B. $|-13|$ 13

C. $|-7i|$ 7

Example 3

Add or subtract. Write the result in the form $a + bi$.

A. $(4+2i)+(-6-7i)$ $-2-5i$

B. $(5-2i)-(-2-3i)$ $7+i$

C. $(1-3i)+(-1+3i)$ 0

Also available on transparency

INTERVENTION

Questioning Strategies

EXAMPLE 1

- How do you know how many units to move left or right from 0? up or down from 0?

EXAMPLE 2

- What does the absolute value of a complex number represent?

EXAMPLE 3

- How is adding and subtracting complex numbers similar to combining like terms?

Answers to Check It Out!

1a–1d.

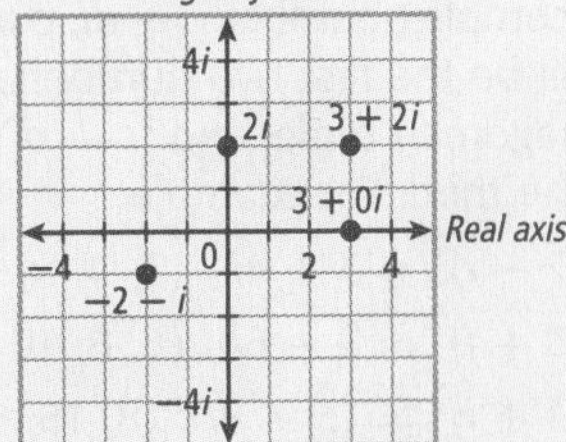

Power Presentations with PowerPoint®

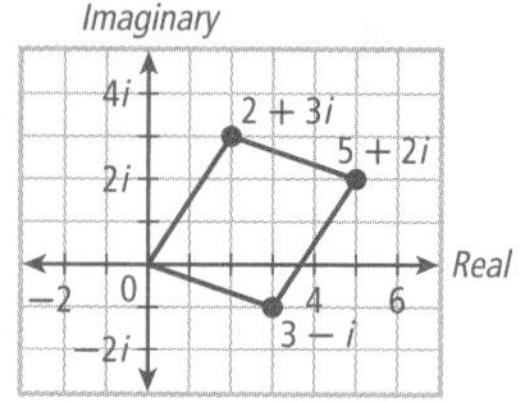

Additional Examples

Example 4

Find $(3 - i) + (2 + 3i)$ by graphing on the complex plane. $5 + 2i$

Imaginary; Real; $2 + 3i$; $5 + 2i$; $3 - i$

Example 5

Multiply. Write the result in the form $a + bi$.

A. $-2i(2 - 4i)$ $-8 - 4i$

B. $(3 + 6i)(4 - i)$ $18 + 21i$

C. $(2 + 9i)(2 - 9i)$ 85

D. $(-5i)(6i)$ 30

Also available on transparency

INTERVENTION

Questioning Strategies

EXAMPLE 4

- How do you know where to put the vertex of the parallelogram that represents the sum of the complex numbers?

EXAMPLE 5

- How do you use the Distributive Property to multiply two complex numbers?

Technology To operate with complex numbers when using a graphing calculator, press MODE and select a+bi. In this mode, the computation in **Example 5A** can be entered as 2 2nd i (3 – 5 2nd i). The result is displayed as **10+6i**.

Math Background Complex numbers provide a way of generating Pythagorean triples. Take any complex number $a + bi$ where $a \neq b$ and square it. In the resulting complex number $c + di$, c and d will be the first two numbers of a Pythagorean triple, and $|c + di|$ will be the third. For example:

$(2 + i)^2 = 3 + 4i$ (3, 4, 5)

$(3 + i)^2 = 8 + 6i$ (6, 8, 10)

$(4 + i)^2 = 15 + 8i$ (8, 15, 17)

EXAMPLE 4 Adding Complex Numbers on the Complex Plane

Find $(4 + 3i) + (-2 + i)$ by graphing on the complex plane.

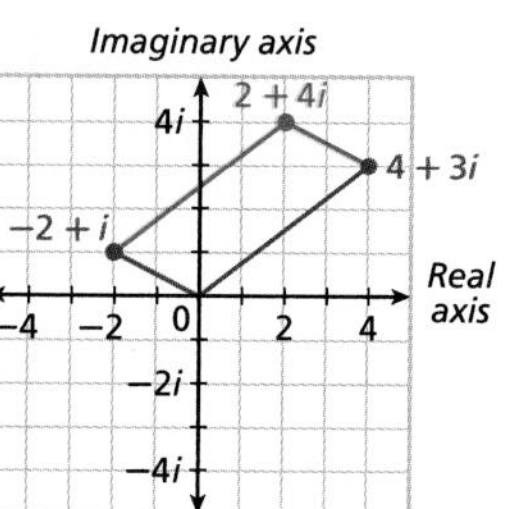

Step 1 Graph $4 + 3i$ and $-2 + i$ on the complex plane. Connect each of these numbers to the origin with a line segment.

Step 2 Draw a parallelogram that has these two line segments as sides. The vertex that is opposite the origin represents the sum of the two complex numbers, $2 + 4i$. Therefore, $(4 + 3i) + (-2 + i) = 2 + 4i$.

Check Add by combining the real parts and combining the imaginary parts.

$$(4 + 3i) + (-2 + i) = [4 + (-2)] + (3i + i) = 2 + 4i$$

Find each sum by graphing on the complex plane.

4a. $(3 + 4i) + (1 - 3i)$ $4 + i$ **4b.** $(-4 - i) + (2 - 2i)$ $-2 - 3i$

You can multiply complex numbers by using the Distributive Property and treating the imaginary parts as like terms. Simplify by using the fact $i^2 = -1$.

EXAMPLE 5 Multiplying Complex Numbers

Multiply. Write the result in the form $a + bi$.

A $2i(3 - 5i)$

$6i - 10i^2$ *Distribute.*

$6i - 10(-1)$ *Use $i^2 = -1$.*

$10 + 6i$ *Write in a + bi form.*

B $(5 - 6i)(4 - 3i)$

$20 - 15i - 24i + 18i^2$ *Multiply.*

$20 - 39i + 18(-1)$ *Use $i^2 = -1$.*

$2 - 39i$

C $(7 + 2i)(7 - 2i)$

$49 - 14i + 14i - 4i^2$ *Multiply.*

$49 - 4(-1)$ *Use $i^2 = -1$.*

53

D $(6i)(6i)$

$36i^2$

$36(-1)$ *Use $i^2 = -1$.*

-36

Multiply. Write the result in the form $a + bi$.

5a. $2i(3 - 5i)$ $10 + 6i$ **5b.** $(4 - 4i)(6 - i)$ $20 - 28i$ **5c.** $(3 + 2i)(3 - 2i)$ 13

Helpful Hint

Notice the repeating pattern in each row of the table. The pattern allows you to express any power of i as one of four possible values: i, -1, $-i$, or 1.

The imaginary unit i can be raised to higher powers as shown below.

Powers of i		
$i^1 = i$	$i^5 = i^4 \cdot i = 1 \cdot i = i$	$i^9 = i$
$i^2 = -1$	$i^6 = i^4 \cdot i^2 = 1 \cdot (-1) = -1$	$i^{10} = -1$
$i^3 = i^2 \cdot i = -1 \cdot i = -i$	$i^7 = i^4 \cdot i^3 = 1 \cdot (-i) = -i$	$i^{11} = -i$
$i^4 = i^2 \cdot i^2 = -1 \cdot (-1) = 1$	$i^8 = i^4 \cdot i^4 = 1 \cdot 1 = 1$	$i^{12} = 1$

Answers to *Check It Out!*

4a.

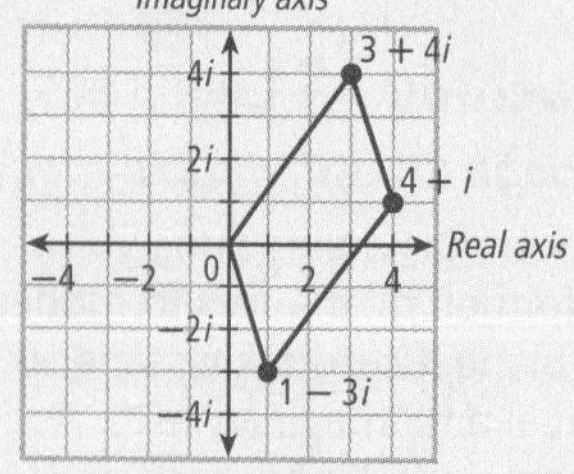

4b.

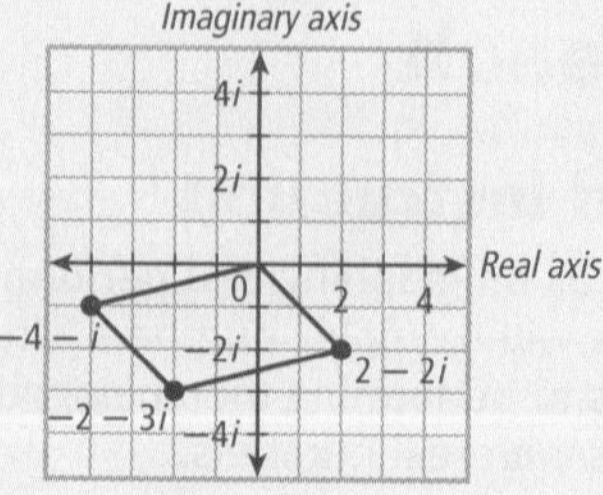

EXAMPLE 6 Evaluating Powers of i

A Simplify $-3i^{12}$.

$-3i^{12} = -3(i^2)^6$ — *Rewrite i^{12} as a power of i^2.*

$= -3(-1)^6 = -3(1) = -3$ — *Simplify.*

B Simplify i^{25}.

$i^{25} = i \cdot i^{24}$ — *Rewrite as a product of i and an even power of i.*

$= i \cdot (i^2)^{12}$ — *Rewrite i^{24} as a power of i^2.*

$= i \cdot (-1)^{12} = i \cdot 1 = i$ — *Simplify.*

6a. Simplify $\frac{1}{2}i^7$. $-\frac{1}{2}i$ **6b.** Simplify i^{42}. -1

Remember!
The complex conjugate of a complex number $a + bi$ is $a - bi$. (Lesson 5-5)

Recall that expressions in simplest form cannot have square roots in the denominator (Lesson 1-3). Because the imaginary unit represents a square root, you must rationalize any denominator that contains an imaginary unit. To do this, multiply the numerator and denominator by the complex conjugate of the denominator.

EXAMPLE 7 Dividing Complex Numbers

A Simplify $\frac{3 + 7i}{8i}$.

$\frac{3 + 7i}{8i}\left(\frac{-8i}{-8i}\right)$ — *Multiply by the conjugate.*

$\frac{-24i - 56i^2}{-64i^2}$ — *Distribute.*

$\frac{-24i + 56}{64}$ — *Use $i^2 = -1$.*

$\frac{-3i + 7}{8} = \frac{7}{8} - \frac{3}{8}i$ — *Simplify.*

B Simplify $\frac{5 + i}{2 - 4i}$.

$\frac{5 + i}{2 - 4i}\left(\frac{2 + 4i}{2 + 4i}\right)$

$\frac{10 + 20i + 2i + 4i^2}{4 + 8i - 8i - 16i^2}$

$\frac{10 + 22i - 4}{4 + 16}$

$\frac{6 + 22i}{20} = \frac{3}{10} + \frac{11}{10}i$

7a. Simplify $\frac{3 + 8i}{-i}$. $-8 + 3i$ **7b.** Simplify $\frac{3 - i}{2 - i}$. $\frac{7}{5} + \frac{1}{5}i$

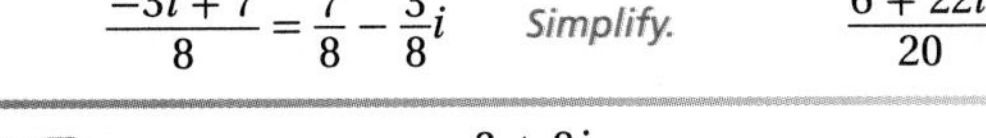

THINK AND DISCUSS

1. Explain when a complex number $a + bi$ and its conjugate are equal.
2. Find the product $(a + bi)(c + di)$, and identify which terms in the product are real and which are imaginary.
3. **GET ORGANIZED** Copy and complete the graphic organizer. In each box, give an example.

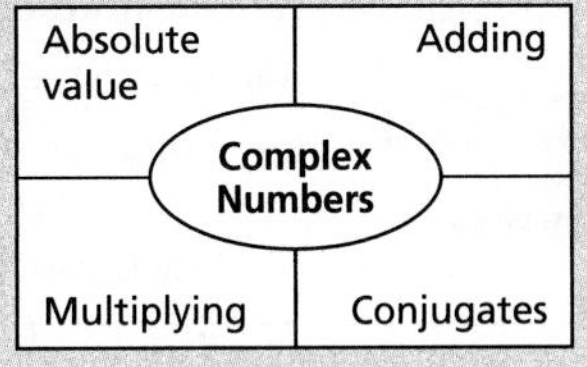

COMMON ERROR ALERT

When working with complex numbers, students may make an error in sign when simplifying a product. For example, students may incorrectly simplify the term $-4i^2$ to -4 instead of 4, especially when using mental math. You may want to suggest that students write out the step in which they replace i^2 with -1, rather than doing this step mentally: $-4i^2 = -4(-1) = 4$.

Power Presentations with PowerPoint®

Additional Examples

Example 6

Simplify.

A. $-6i^{14}$ 6

B. i^{63} $-i$

Example 7

Simplify.

A. $\frac{3 + 10i}{5i}$ $2 - \frac{3}{5}i$

B. $\frac{2 + 8i}{4 - 2i}$ $-\frac{2}{5} + \frac{9}{5}i$

Also available on transparency

INTERVENTION
Questioning Strategies

EXAMPLE 6

- How can you write an even power of i as a power of i^2?
- Why is an even power of -1 equal to 1?

EXAMPLE 7

- How do you find the complex conjugate of the denominator?

3 Close

Summarize

Give students two complex numbers, such as $5 + 6i$ and $3 - i$. Have students graph the numbers on the complex plane and find their sum, difference, product, and quotient.

$(5 + 6i) + (3 - i)$ $8 + 5i$

$(5 + 6i) - (3 - i)$ $2 + 7i$

$(5 + 6i)(3 - i)$ $21 + 13i$

$\frac{(5 + 6i)}{(3 - i)}$ $\frac{9}{10} + \frac{23}{10}i$

ONGOING ASSESSMENT and INTERVENTION

Diagnose ***Before*** **the Lesson**
5-9 Warm Up, TE p. 382

Monitor ***During*** **the Lesson**
Check It Out! Exercises, SE pp. 382–385
Questioning Strategies, TE pp. 383–385

Assess ***After*** **the Lesson**
5-9 Lesson Quiz, TE p. 389
Alternative Assessment, TE p. 389

Answers to *Think and Discuss*

Possible answers:

1. A complex number $a + bi$ and its conjugate $a - bi$ can be equal only when $b = 0$.
2. The real terms are ac and $-bd$. The imaginary terms are adi and bci.
3. See p. A7.

Assignment Guide

Assign *Guided Practice* exercises as necessary.

If you finished Examples **1–4**
Basic 36–54, 70–83, 85–87
Average 36–54, 70–83, 85–87
Advanced 36–54, 70–83, 85–87

If you finished Examples **1–7**
Basic 36–109, 111–116, 120–126
Average 36–117, 120–126
Advanced 36–108, 110–126

Homework Quick Check

Quickly check key concepts.
Exercises: 38, 40, 46, 52, 56, 62, 64, 84

Answers

2–5.

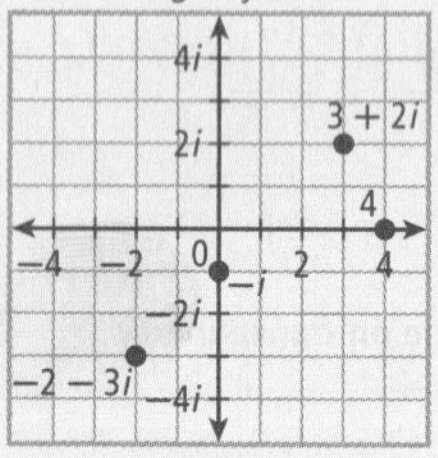

Imaginary axis
Real axis
4i
2i
3 + 2i
4
0
−i
−2i
−2 − 3i
−4i
−4
−2
2
4

18.

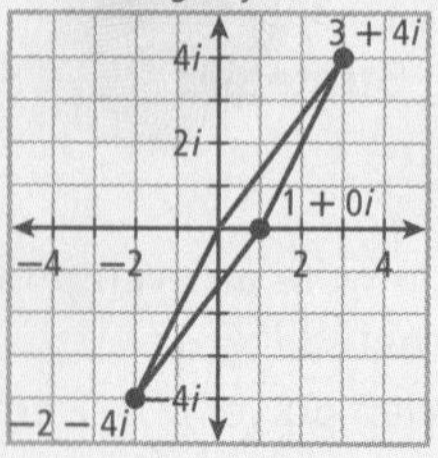

Imaginary axis
Real axis
3 + 4i
4i
2i
1 + 0i
−4
−2
2
4
−2 − 4i
−4i

State Resources

go.hrw.com
State Resources Online
KEYWORD: MB7 Resources

5-9 Exercises

go.hrw.com
Homework Help Online
KEYWORD: MB7 5-9
Parent Resources Online
KEYWORD: MB7 Parent

GUIDED PRACTICE

1. **Vocabulary** In the complex number plane, the horizontal axis represents __?__ numbers, and the vertical axis represents __?__ numbers. (*real, irrational,* or *imaginary*) **real; imaginary**

SEE EXAMPLE 1 p. 382
Graph each complex number.
2. 4 3. $-i$ 4. $3 + 2i$ 5. $-2 - 3i$

SEE EXAMPLE 2 p. 383
Find each absolute value.
6. $|4 - 5i|$ **$\sqrt{41}$** 7. $|-33.3|$ **33.3** 8. $|-9i|$ **9**
9. $|5 + 12i|$ **13** 10. $|-1 + i|$ **$\sqrt{2}$** 11. $|15i|$ **15**

SEE EXAMPLE 3 p. 383
Add or subtract. Write the result in the form $a + bi$.
12. $(2 + 5i) + (-2 + 5i)$ **$10i$** 13. $(-1 - 8i) + (4 + 3i)$ **$3 - 5i$** 14. $(1 - 3i) - (7 + i)$ **$-6 - 4i$**
15. $(4 - 8i) + (-13 + 23i)$ **$-9 + 15i$** 16. $(6 + 17i) - (18 - 9i)$ **$-12 + 26i$** 17. $(-30 + i) - (-2 + 20i)$ **$-28 - 19i$**

SEE EXAMPLE 4 p. 384
Find each sum by graphing on the complex plane.
18. $(3 + 4i) + (-2 - 4i)$ **1** 19. $(-2 - 5i) + (-1 + 4i)$ **$-3 - i$** 20. $(-4 - 4i) + (4 + 2i)$ **$-2i$**

SEE EXAMPLE 5 p. 384
Multiply. Write the result in the form $a + bi$.
21. $(1 - 2i)(1 + 2i)$ **5** 22. $3i(5 + 2i)$ **$-6 + 15i$** 23. $(9 + i)(4 - i)$ **$37 - 5i$**
24. $(6 + 8i)(5 - 4i)$ **$62 + 16i$** 25. $(3 + i)^2$ **$8 + 6i$** 26. $(-4 - 5i)(2 + 10i)$ **$42 - 50i$**

SEE EXAMPLE 6 p. 385
Simplify.
27. $-i^9$ **$-i$** 28. $2i^{15}$ **$-2i$** 29. i^{30} **-1**

SEE EXAMPLE 7 p. 385
30. $\frac{5 - 4i}{i}$ **$-4 - 5i$** 31. $\frac{11 - 5i}{2 - 4i}$ **$\frac{21}{10} + \frac{17}{10}i$** 32. $\frac{8 + 2i}{5 + i}$ **$\frac{21}{13} + \frac{1}{13}i$**
33. $\frac{17}{4 + i}$ **$4 - i$** 34. $\frac{45 - 3i}{7 - 8i}$ **$3 + 3i$** 35. $\frac{-3 - 12i}{6i}$ **$-2 + \frac{1}{2}i$**

PRACTICE AND PROBLEM SOLVING

Independent Practice	
For Exercises	See Example
36–39	1
40–45	2
46–51	3
52–54	4
55–60	5
61–63	6
64–69	7

Extra Practice
Skills Practice p. S13
Application Practice p. S36

Graph each complex number.
36. -3 37. $-2.5i$ 38. $1 + i$ 39. $4 - 3i$

Find each absolute value.
40. $|2 + 3i|$ **$\sqrt{13}$** 41. $|-18|$ **18** 42. $\left|\frac{4}{5}i\right|$ **$\frac{4}{5}$**
43. $|6 - 8i|$ **10** 44. $|-0.5i|$ **0.5** 45. $|10 - 4i|$ **$2\sqrt{29}$**

Add or subtract. Write the result in the form $a + bi$.
46. $(8 - 9i) - (-2 - i)$ **$10 - 8i$** 47. $4i - (11 - 3i)$ **$-11 + 7i$** 48. $(4 - 2i) + (-9 - 5i)$ **$-5 - 7i$**
49. $(13 + 6i) + (15 + 35i)$ **$28 + 41i$** 50. $(3 - i) - (-3 + i)$ **$6 - 2i$** 51. $-16 + (12 + 9i)$ **$-4 + 9i$**

Find each sum by graphing on the complex plane.
52. $(4 + i) + (-3i)$ 53. $(5 + 4i) + (-1 + 2i)$ 54. $(-3 - 3i) + (4 - 3i)$

5-9 PRACTICE A

Graph each complex number.
1. $2i$
2. $-4i$
3. $3 + i$
4. $-3 - 2i$
5. $2 + 3i$
6. $4 - 4i$

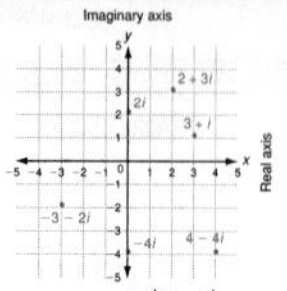

Imaginary axis
Real axis
2 + 3i
2i
3 + i
−3 − 2i
−4i
4 − 4i

Find each absolute value.
7. $|6 + 2i|$ **$2\sqrt{10}$** 8. $|3 + i|$ **$\sqrt{10}$** 9. $|3 - 4i|$ **5**

Add or subtract. Write the result in the form $a + bi$.
10. $6i + 4i$ **$10i$** 11. $-i - 3i$ **$-4i$** 12. $(4i) + (2 + 8i)$ **$2 + 12i$**
13. $(1 + 2i) + (3 + 4i)$ **$4 + 6i$** 14. $(2 - 7i) - (5 - 3i)$ **$-3 - 4i$** 15. $(7 - 4i) + (3 - i)$ **$10 - 5i$**

Multiply. Write the result in the form $a + bi$.
16. $2(3i)$ **$6i$** 17. $-4(5i)$ **$-20i$** 18. $2(6 + 8i)$ **$12 + 16i$**
19. $2i(3 + 5i)$ **$-10 + 6i$** 20. $(3 + i)(1 - 4i)$ **$7 - 11i$** 21. $(1 + 2i)(2 + 5i)$ **$-8 + 9i$**

Simplify.
22. i^7 **$-i$** 23. $\frac{2 + 5i}{3i}$ **$\frac{5}{3} - \frac{2}{3}i$** 24. $\frac{8 + 2i}{1 - 3i}$ **$\frac{1}{5} + \frac{13}{5}i$**

5-9 PRACTICE B

Graph each complex number.
1. -6
2. $4i$
3. $6 + 7i$
4. $-8 - 5i$
5. $-3i$

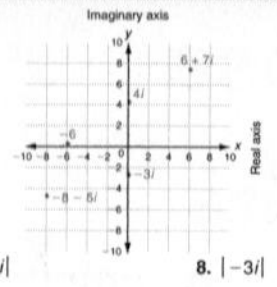

Imaginary axis
Real axis
6 + 7i
4i
−6
−3i
−8 − 5i

Find each absolute value.
6. $|4 + 2i|$ **$2\sqrt{5}$** 7. $|5 - i|$ **$\sqrt{26}$** 8. $|-3i|$ **3**

Add or subtract. Write the result in the form $a + bi$.
9. $(-1 + 2i) + (6 - 9i)$ **$5 - 7i$** 10. $(3 - 3i) - (4 + 7i)$ **$-1 - 10i$** 11. $(-5 + 2i) + (-2 + 8i)$ **$-7 + 10i$**

Multiply. Write the result in the form $a + bi$.
12. $3i(2 - 3i)$ **$9 + 6i$** 13. $(4 + 5i)(2 + i)$ **$3 + 14i$** 14. $(-1 + 6i)(3 - 2i)$ **$9 + 20i$**

Simplify.
15. $\frac{2 + 4i}{3i}$ **$\frac{4}{3} - \frac{2}{3}i$** 16. $\frac{3 + 2i}{4 + i}$ **$\frac{14}{17} + \frac{5}{17}i$** 17. $2i^{11}$ **$-2i$**

Solve.
18. In electronics, the total resistance to the flow of electricity in a circuit is called the impedance, Z. Impedance is represented by a complex number. The total impedance in a series circuit is the sum of individual impedances. The impedance in one part of a circuit is $Z_1 = 3 + 4i$. In another part of a circuit, the impedance is $Z_1 = 5 - 2i$. What is the total impedance of the circuit?
$8 + 2i$

Multiply. Write the result in the form $a + bi$.

55. $-12i(-1 + 4i)$ **$48 + 12i$**
56. $(3 - 5i)(2 + 9i)$ **$51 + 17i$**
57. $(7 + 2i)(7 - 2i)$ **53**
58. $(5 + 6i)^2$ **$-11 + 60i$**
59. $(7 - 5i)(-3 + 9i)$ **$24 + 78i$**
60. $-4(8 + 12i)$ **$-32 - 48i$**

Simplify.

61. i^{27} **$-i$**
62. $-i^{11}$ **i**
63. $5i^{10}$ **-5**
64. $\frac{2 - 3i}{i}$ **$-3 - 2i$**
65. $\frac{5 - 2i}{3 + i}$ **$\frac{13}{10} - \frac{11}{10}i$**
66. $\frac{3}{-1 - 5i}$ **$-\frac{3}{26} + \frac{15}{26}i$**
67. $\frac{19 + 9i}{5 + i}$ **$4 + i$**
68. $\frac{8 + 4i}{7 + i}$ **$\frac{6}{5} + \frac{2}{5}i$**
69. $\frac{6 + 3i}{2 - 2i}$ **$\frac{3}{4} + \frac{9}{4}i$**

Write the complex number represented by each point on the graph.

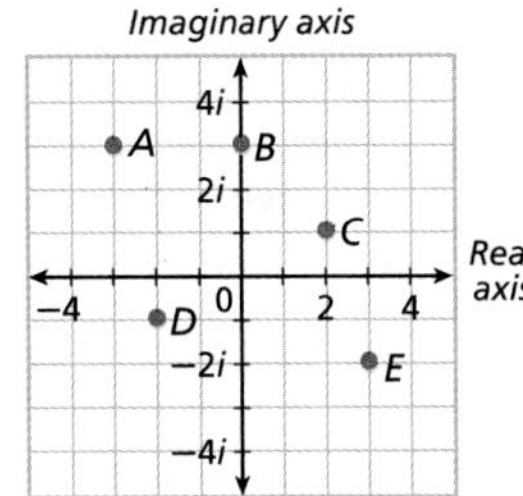

70. A **$-3 + 3i$**
71. B **$3i$**
72. C **$2 + i$**
73. D **$-2 - i$**
74. E **$3 - 2i$**

Find the absolute value of each complex number.

75. $3 - i$ **$\sqrt{10}$**
76. $7i$ **7**
77. $-2 - 6i$ **$2\sqrt{10}$**
78. $-1 - 8i$ **$\sqrt{65}$**
79. 0 **0**
80. $5 + 4i$ **$\sqrt{41}$**
81. $\frac{3}{2} - \frac{1}{2}i$ **$\frac{\sqrt{10}}{2}$**
82. $5 - i\sqrt{3}$ **$2\sqrt{7}$**
83. $2\sqrt{2} - i\sqrt{3}$ **$\sqrt{11}$**

Fractals

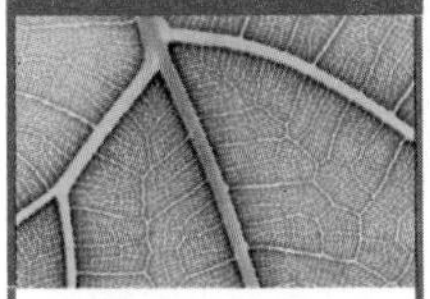

Fractals are self-similar, which means that smaller parts of a fractal are similar to the fractal as a whole. Many objects in nature, such as the veins of leaves and snow crystals, also exhibit self-similarity. As a result, scientists can use fractals to model these objects.

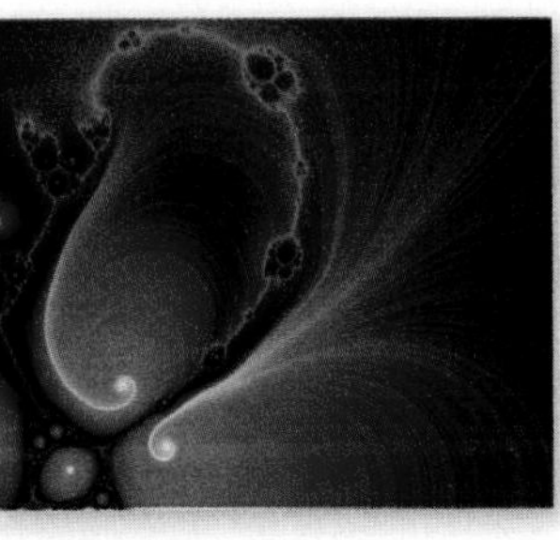

84. **Fractals** Fractals are patterns produced using complex numbers and the repetition of a mathematical formula. Substitute the first number into the formula. Then take the result, put it back into the formula, and so on. Each complex number produced by the formula can be used to assign a color to a pixel on a computer screen. The result is an image such as the one at right. Many common fractals are based on the Julia Set, whose formula is $Z_{n+1} = (Z_n)^2 + c$, where c is a constant.
   a. Find Z_2 using $Z_2 = (Z_1)^2 + 0.25$. Let $Z_1 = 0.5 + 0.6i$. **$Z_2 = 0.14 + 0.6i$**
   b. Find Z_3 using $Z_3 = (Z_2)^2 + 0.25$. Use Z_2 that you obtained in part **a**.
   c. Find Z_4 using $Z_4 = (Z_3)^2 + 0.25$. Use Z_3 that you obtained in part **b**.

84b. $Z_3 = -0.0904 + 0.168i$ **84c. $Z_4 = 0.22994816 - 0.0303744i$**

Simplify. Write the result in the form $a + bi$.

85. $(3.5 + 5.2i) + (6 - 2.3i)$ **$9.5 + 2.9i$**
86. $6i - (4 + 5i)$ **$-4 + i$**
87. $(-2.3 + i) - (7.4 - 0.3i)$ **$-9.7 + 1.3i$**
88. $(-8 - 11i) + (-1 + i)$ **$-9 - 10i$**
89. $i(4 + i)$ **$-1 + 4i$**
90. $(6 - 5i)^2$ **$11 - 60i$**
91. $(-2 - 3i)^2$ **$-5 + 12i$**
92. $(5 + 7i)(5 - 7i)$ **74**
93. $(2 - i)(2 + i)(2 - i)$ **93. $10 - 5i$**
94. $3 - i^{11}$ **$3 + i$**
95. $i^{52} - i^{48}$ **0**
96. $i^{35} - i^{24} + i^{18}$ **$-2 - i$**
97. $\frac{12 + i}{i}$ **$1 - 12i$**
98. $\frac{18 - 3i}{i}$ **$-3 - 18i$**
99. $\frac{4 + 2i}{6 + i}$ **$\frac{26}{37} + \frac{8}{37}i$**
100. $\frac{1 + i}{-2 + 4i}$ **$\frac{1}{10} - \frac{3}{10}i$**
101. $\frac{4}{2 - 3i}$ **$\frac{8}{13} + \frac{12}{13}i$**
102. $\frac{6}{\sqrt{2} - i}$ **$2\sqrt{2} + 2i$**

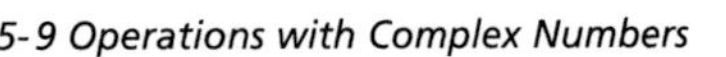

COMMON ERROR ALERT

When subtracting complex numbers as in **Exercises 86** and **87,** students may forget to distribute the negative sign to the number being subtracted. Remind them to subtract both the real part and the imaginary part of the number being subtracted. It may help them to draw arrows from the minus sign, as shown below.

$6i - (4 + 5i)$

Teaching Tip **Math Background** **Exercise 84** uses the variable Z to represent a complex number. Z or z is often used in formulas when the value of the variable is a complex number of the form $a + bi$, where $b \neq 0$.

Answers

19.

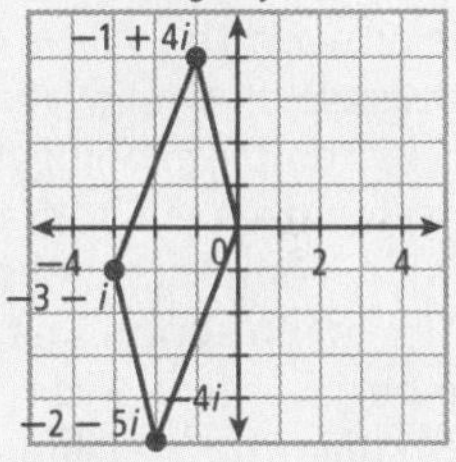

20.

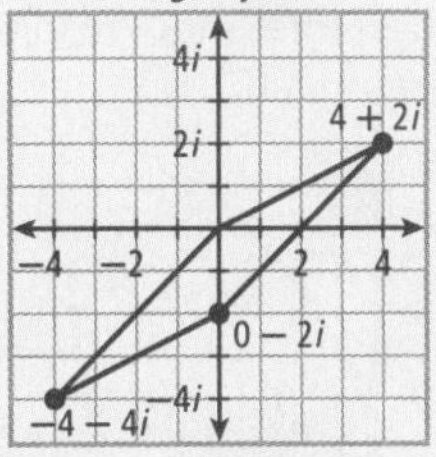

36–39.

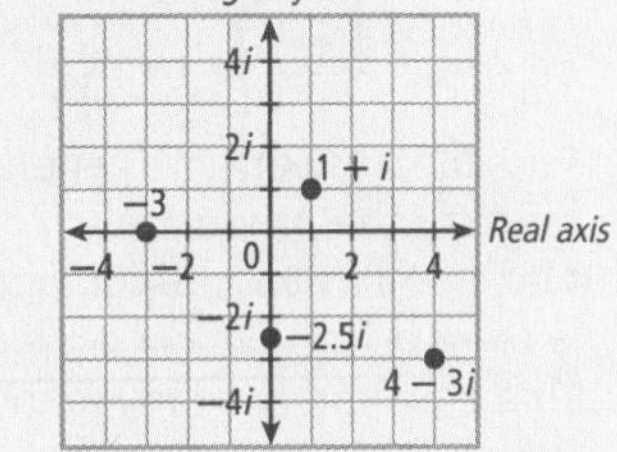

52. $4 - 2i$

54. $1 - 6i$

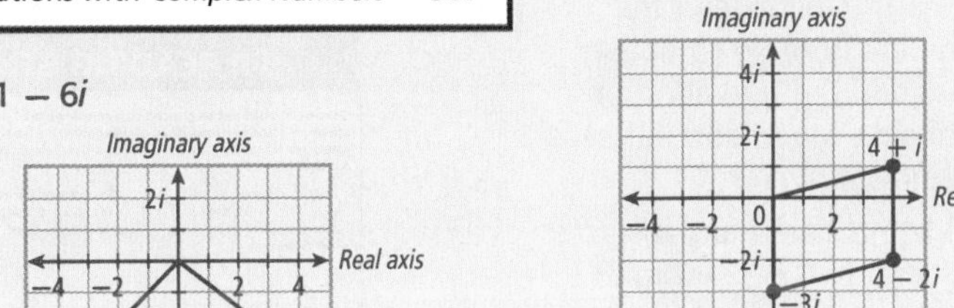

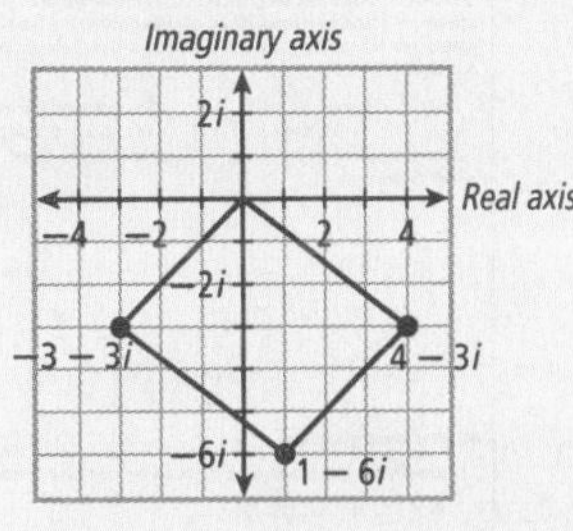

53. $4 + 6i$

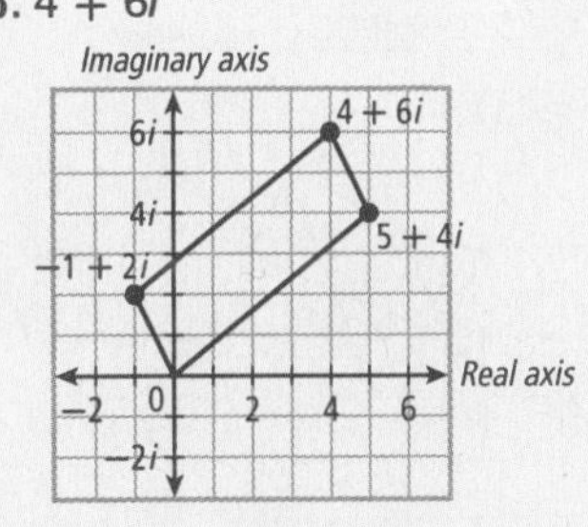

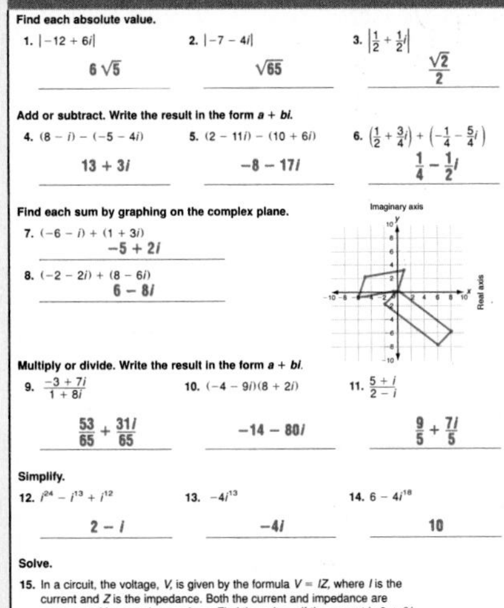

5-9 PRACTICE C

Find each absolute value.

1. $|-12 + 6i|$ **$6\sqrt{5}$**
2. $|-7 - 4i|$ **$\sqrt{65}$**
3. $\left|\frac{1}{2} + \frac{1}{2}i\right|$ **$\frac{\sqrt{2}}{2}$**

Add or subtract. Write the result in the form $a + bi$.

4. $(8 - i) - (-5 - 4i)$ **$13 + 3i$**
5. $(2 - 11i) - (10 + 6i)$ **$-8 - 17i$**
6. $\left(\frac{1}{2} + \frac{3}{4}i\right) + \left(-\frac{1}{4} - \frac{5}{4}i\right)$ **$\frac{1}{4} - \frac{1}{2}i$**

Find each sum by graphing on the complex plane.

7. $(-6 - i) + (1 + 3i)$ **$-5 + 2i$**
8. $(-2 - 2i) + (8 - 6i)$ **$6 - 8i$**

Multiply or divide. Write the result in the form $a + bi$.

9. $\frac{-3 + 7i}{1 + 8i}$ **$\frac{53}{65} + \frac{31i}{65}$**
10. $(-4 - 9i)(8 + 2i)$ **$-14 - 80i$**
11. $\frac{5 + i}{2 - i}$ **$\frac{9}{5} + \frac{7i}{5}$**

Simplify.

12. $i^{24} - i^{13} + i^{12}$ **$2 - i$**
13. $-4i^{13}$ **$-4i$**
14. $6 - 4i^{18}$ **10**

Solve.

15. In a circuit, the voltage, V, is given by the formula $V = IZ$, where I is the current and Z is the impedance. Both the current and impedance are represented by complex numbers. Find the voltage if the current is $3 + 2i$ and the impedance is $4 - i$. **$14 + 5i$**

Exercise 112 involves adding complex numbers. This exercise prepares students for the Multi-Step Test Prep on page 390.

Science Link
Exercises 103 and 104 involve the impedance of an electric circuit. Impedance is determined by two components: resistance and reactance. When impedance is modeled by a complex number, the real part represents the resistance of the circuit and the imaginary part represents the reactance.

Answers

108. Sometimes true; possible answer: true when $b = -2$ and $d = 4$ because $(bi)(di) = (-2i)(4i) = 8$; false when $b = 2$ and $d = 4$ because $(bi)(di) = (2i)(4i) = -8$

110. Possible answer: The values are equal because a complex number and its complex conjugate are the same distance from the origin in the complex number plane. The graph shows that the number $3 + 4i$ and its complex conjugate $3 - 4i$ are the same distance from the origin; therefore, their absolute values are equal.

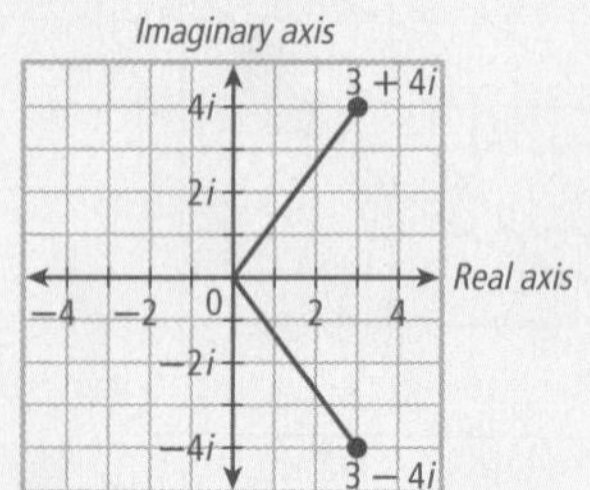

111. Possible answer: The general form for the product of a complex number and its conjugate is $(a + bi)(a - bi) = a^2 + b^2$. This equation is nearly identical to the equation for a difference of squares except that the factors on the left side of the equation are nonreal complex numbers and the operation on the right side is addition rather than subtraction.

112a. Possible answer: 4 and $4i$; $2 + 5i$ and $2 - i$; $5 + 2i$ and $-1 + 2i$

b. Possible answer:

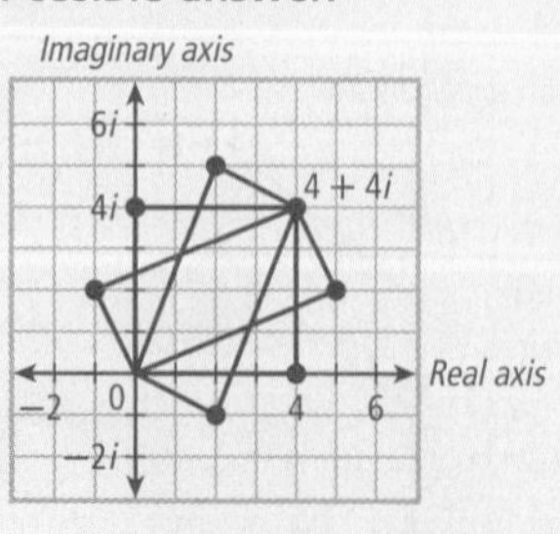

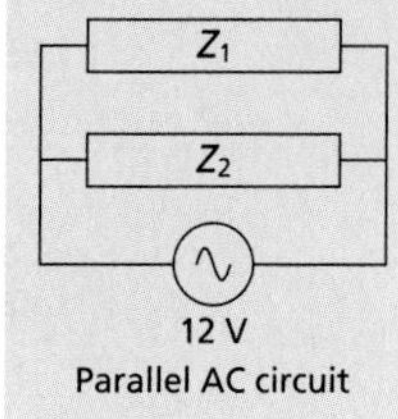

Multi-Step *Impedance* is a measure of the opposition of a circuit to an electric current. Electrical engineers find it convenient to model impedance Z with complex numbers. In a parallel AC circuit with two impedances Z_1 and Z_2, the *equivalent* or total impedance in ohms can be determined by using the formula $Z_{eq} = \frac{Z_1Z_2}{Z_1 + Z_2}$.

103. Find the equivalent impedance Z_{eq} for $Z_1 = 3 + 2i$ and $Z_2 = 1 - 2i$ arranged in a parallel AC circuit. $Z_{eq} = \frac{7}{4} - i$

104. Find the equivalent impedance Z_{eq} for $Z_1 = 2 + 2i$ and $Z_2 = 4 - i$ arranged in a parallel AC circuit. $Z_{eq} = \frac{66}{37} + \frac{26}{37}i$

Tell whether each statement is sometimes, always, or never true. If the statement is sometimes true, give an example and a counterexample. If the statement is never true, give a counterexample.

105. The sum of any complex number $a + bi$ and its conjugate is a real number. always true

106. The difference between any complex number $a + bi$ $(b \neq 0)$ and its conjugate is a real number.

106. Never true; the difference between any complex number $a + bi$ and its complex conjugate is an imaginary number: $(a + bi) - (a - bi) = 2bi$.

107. The product of any complex number $a + bi$ $(a \neq 0)$ and its conjugate is a positive real number. always true

108. The product of any two imaginary numbers bi $(b \neq 0)$ and di $(d \neq 0)$ is a positive real number.

109. **ERROR ANALYSIS** Two attempts to simplify $\frac{3}{2 + i}$ are shown. Which is incorrect? Explain the error.

109. A is incorrect. The product $(2 + i)(2 + i)$ is equal to $4 + 4i + i^2$, not $4 + i^2$. Students may also note that multiplying the numerator and denominator by $2 + i$ will not rationalize the denominator of the original expression.

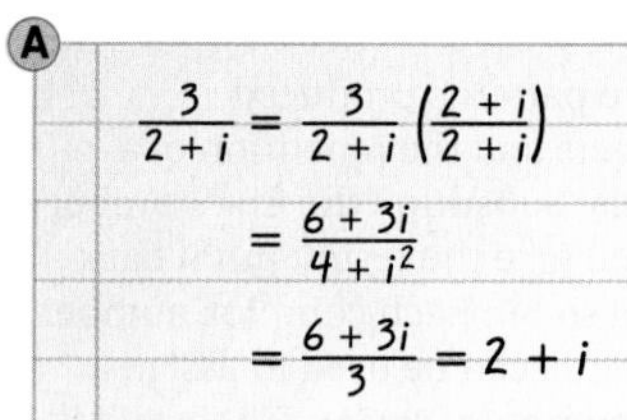

A
$\frac{3}{2+i} = \frac{3}{2+i}\left(\frac{2+i}{2+i}\right)$
$= \frac{6+3i}{4+i^2}$
$= \frac{6+3i}{3} = 2 + i$

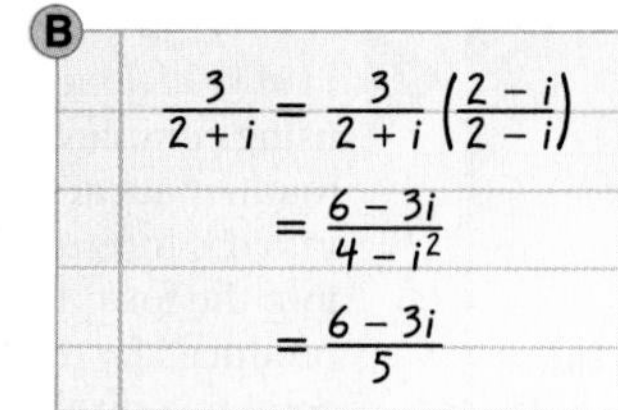

110. **Critical Thinking** Why are the absolute value of a complex number and the absolute value of its conjugate equal? Use a graph to justify your answer.

111. **Write About It** Discuss how the difference of two squares, $a^2 - b^2 = (a + b)(a - b)$, relates to the product of a complex number and its conjugate.

MULTI-STEP TEST PREP

112. This problem will prepare you for the Multi-Step Test Prep on page 390.

You have seen how to graph sums of complex numbers on the complex plane.

a. Find three pairs of complex numbers whose sum is $4 + 4i$.

b. Graph each of the sums on the same complex plane.

c. Describe the results of your graph.

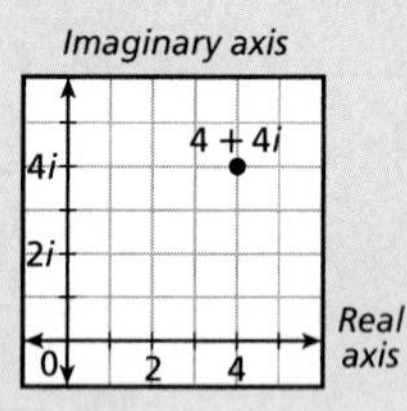

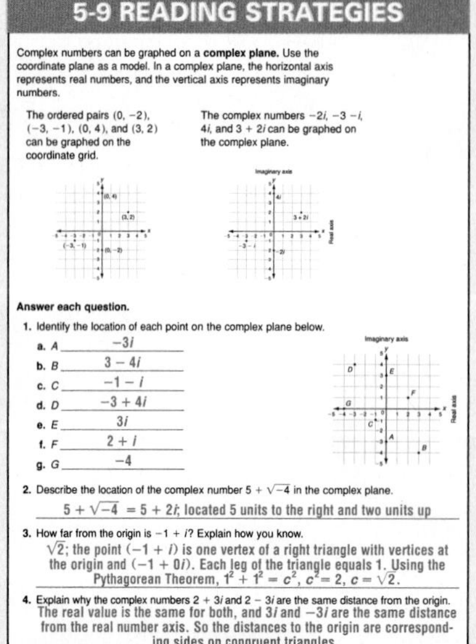

5-9 READING STRATEGIES

Complex numbers can be graphed on a **complex plane.** Use the coordinate plane as a model. In a complex plane, the horizontal axis represents real numbers, and the vertical axis represents imaginary numbers.

The ordered pairs (0, −2), (−3, −1), (0, 4), and (3, 2) can be graphed on the coordinate grid.

The complex numbers $-2i$, $-3 - i$, $4i$, and $3 + 2i$ can be graphed on the complex plane.

Answer each question.

1. Identify the location of each point on the complex plane below.
   a. A $-3i$
   b. B $3 - 4i$
   c. C $-1 - i$
   d. D $-3 + 4i$
   e. E $3i$
   f. F $2 + i$
   g. G -4
2. Describe the location of the complex number $5 + \sqrt{-4}$ in the complex plane.
   $5 + \sqrt{-4} = 5 + 2i$; located 5 units to the right and two units up
3. How far from the origin is $-1 + i$? Explain how you know.
   $\sqrt{2}$; the point $(-1 + i)$ is one vertex of a right triangle with vertices at the origin and $(-1 + 0i)$. Each leg of the triangle equals 1. Using the Pythagorean Theorem, $1^2 + 1^2 = c^2$, $c^2 = 2$, $c = \sqrt{2}$.
4. Explain why the complex numbers $2 + 3i$ and $2 - 3i$ are the same distance from the origin.
   The real value is the same for both, and $3i$ and $-3i$ are the same distance from the real number axis. So the distances to the origin are corresponding sides on congruent triangles.

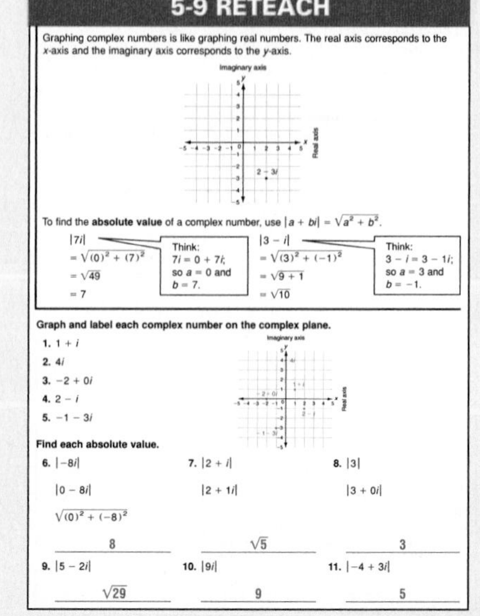

5-9 RETEACH

Graphing complex numbers is like graphing real numbers. The real axis corresponds to the x-axis and the imaginary axis corresponds to the y-axis.

To find the **absolute value** of a complex number, use $|a + bi| = \sqrt{a^2 + b^2}$.

$|7i| = \sqrt{(0)^2 + (7)^2} = \sqrt{49} = 7$ — Think: $7i = 0 + 7i$; so $a = 0$ and $b = 7$.

$|3 - i| = \sqrt{(3)^2 + (-1)^2} = \sqrt{9 + 1} = \sqrt{10}$ — Think: $3 - i = 3 - 1i$; so $a = 3$ and $b = -1$.

Graph and label each complex number on the complex plane.

1. $1 + i$
2. $4i$
3. $-2 + 0i$
4. $2 - i$
5. $-1 - 3i$

Find each absolute value.

6. $|-8i|$ — $|0 - 8i|$ — $\sqrt{(0)^2 + (-8)^2}$ — 8
7. $|2 + i|$ — $|2 + 1i|$ — $\sqrt{5}$
8. $|3|$ — $|3 + 0i|$ — 3
9. $|5 - 2i|$ — $\sqrt{29}$
10. $|9i|$ — 9
11. $|-4 + 3i|$ — 5

Use the graph for Exercises 113–114.

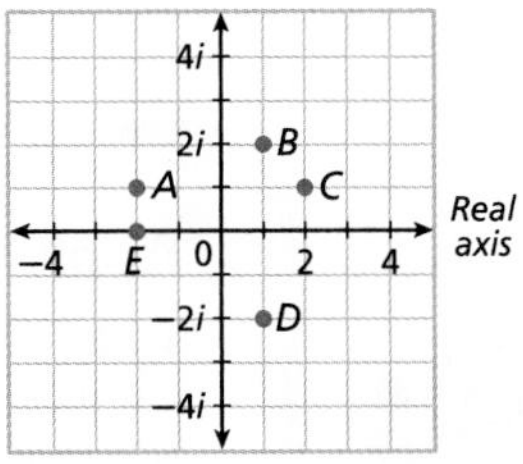

113. Which point on the graph represents $1 - 2i$?

Ⓐ A Ⓑ B Ⓒ C ⓓ D (circled)

114. What is the value of the complex number represented in the graph by E?

Ⓕ -2 (circled) Ⓖ 2 Ⓗ $-2i$ Ⓙ $2i$

Imaginary axis; Real axis; $4i$, $2i$, $-2i$, $-4i$; -4, E, 0, 2, 4; points A, B, C, D

115. Which expression is equivalent to $(2 - 5i) - (2 + 5i)$?

Ⓐ $10i$ Ⓑ $4 + 10i$ Ⓒ $-10i$ (circled) Ⓓ $4 - 10i$

116. Which expression is equivalent to $(-5 + 3i)^2$?

Ⓕ $16 - 15i$ Ⓖ $16 - 30i$ (circled) Ⓗ $34 - 15i$ Ⓙ $34 - 30i$

CHALLENGE AND EXTEND

117b. The resulting pattern is very similar to the pattern for positive powers of i. The only possible values of negative powers of i are 1, -1, i, and $-i$.

117. Consider the powers of i.

a. Complete the table, and look for a pattern.

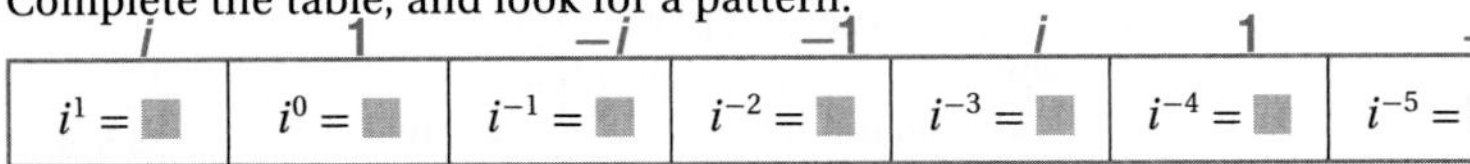

$i^1 = i$	$i^0 = 1$	$i^{-1} = -i$	$i^{-2} = -1$	$i^{-3} = i$	$i^{-4} = 1$	$i^{-5} = -i$

b. Explain the pattern that you observed for i raised to negative powers. What are the only possible values of i raised to a negative integer power?

c. Simplify i^{-12}, i^{-37}, and i^{-90}. $1, -i, -1$

Find the general form of the result for each complex operation.

118. $(a + bi)(c + di)$ $(ac - bd) + (ad + bc)i$

119. $\dfrac{a + bi}{c + di}$ $\dfrac{ac + bd}{c^2 + d^2} + \dfrac{(bc - ad)}{c^2 + d^2}i$

SPIRAL REVIEW

$y \approx 1.16x + 3.88$

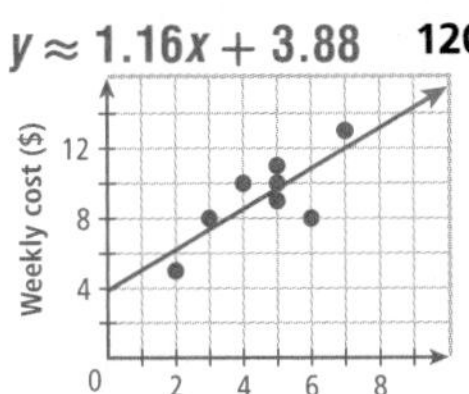

120. Money The table shows the amount that James spent for lunches each week over an eight-week period. Make a scatter plot of the data. Sketch a line of best fit, and find its equation. *(Lesson 2-7)*

Lunches Purchased	5	7	3	5	6	2	4	5
Weekly Cost ($)	10	13	8	9	8	5	10	11

Solve each inequality by using algebra. *(Lesson 5-7)*

121. $0 \geq 3x^2 - 6x$ $0 \leq x \leq 2$

122. $10 < x^2 - 4x - 11$ $x < -3$ or $x > 7$

123. $-6 \geq 2x^2 + 7x - 21$ $-5 \leq x \leq \frac{3}{2}$

124. $3 - x^2 < 7 - 5x$ $x < 1$ or $x > 4$

Determine whether each data set could represent a quadratic function. Explain. *(Lesson 5-8)*

125.

x	-2	-1	0	1
y	5	-1	-3	-1

Yes; the function has constant second differences for equally spaced x-values.

126.

x	0	2	4	6
y	18	10	2	-6

No; the function is linear because it has constant first differences.

TEST PREP DOCTOR + In Exercise 113, students who chose A may have confused the real axis with the imaginary axis.

Answers

112c. Each sum can be represented by a parallelogram with one pair of opposite vertices at $0 + 0i$ and $4 + 4i$ in the complex plane.

Journal

Have students describe the process they would use to simplify i^n, where n is any natural number.

ALTERNATIVE ASSESSMENT

Have students write a guide for working with complex numbers. The guide should include examples of how to graph a complex number and find its absolute value and how to perform each of the four basic arithmetic operations on complex numbers.

5-9 Lesson Quiz

Graph each complex number.

1. $-3 + 2i$ **2.** $4 - 2i$

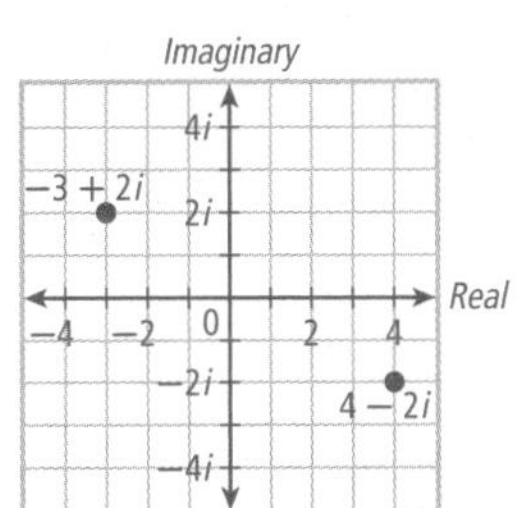

3. Find $|7 + 3i|$. $\sqrt{58}$

Perform the indicated operation. Write the result in the form $a + bi$.

4. $(2 + 4i) + (-6 - 4i)$ -4

5. $(5 - i) - (8 + 2i)$ $-3 - 3i$

6. $(2 + 5i)(3 - 2i)$ $16 + 11i$

7. $\dfrac{4 - 2i}{1 - i}$ $3 + i$

8. Simplify i^{31}. $-i$

Also available on transparency

5-9 PROBLEM SOLVING

Hannah and Aoki are designing fractals. Aoki recalls that many fractals are based on the Julia Set, whose formula is $Z_{n+1} = (Z_n)^2 + c$, where c is a constant. Hannah suggests they make their own fractal pattern using this formula, where $c = 1$ and $Z_1 = 1 + 2i$.

1. Complete the table to show values of n and Z_n.

n	$Z_{n+1} = (Z_n)^2 + c$	Z_n
1	$Z_1 = 1 + 2i$	$Z_1 = 1 + 2i$
2	$Z_2 = (1 + 2i)^2 + 1$	$Z_2 = -2 + 4i$
3	$Z_3 = (-2 + 4i)^2 + 1$	$Z_3 = -11 - 16i$
4	$Z_4 = (-11 - 16i)^2 + 1$	$Z_4 = -134 + 352i$

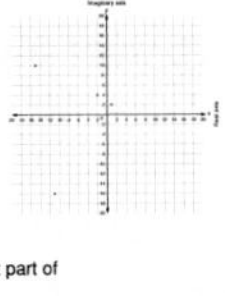

2. Four points are shown on the complex plane. Which point is not part of the fractal pattern they have created? Explain.

$(-13, -35i)$; possible answer: this point cannot be generated using the given formula.

Choose the letter for the best answer.

3. Aoki creates a second pattern by changing the value of c to 3. What happens to Z_n as n increases?

A The imaginary part is always twice the real part.
B The real and imaginary parts become equal.
C The real part becomes zero.
Ⓓ The imaginary part becomes zero.

4. Hannah changes the formula to $Z_{n+1} = \frac{1}{(Z_n)^2} + c$. Leaving $c = 1$ and $Z_1 = 1 + 2i$, what is the value of Z_2?

A $0.48 - 0.16i$
Ⓑ $0.88 - 0.16i$
C $1.2 - 0.4i$
D $2.2 - 0.4i$

5. Aoki takes Hannah's new formula, leaves $c = 1$, and sets $Z_1 = \frac{1}{1 + 2i}$. What is the value of Z_3?

Ⓐ $Z_3 = -11 - 16i$
B $Z_3 = 2 + 2i$
C $Z_3 = 0.48 - 0.16i$
D $Z_3 = 147.4 + i$

6. Hannah reverts to $Z_{n+1} = (Z_n)^2 + c$. She sets $Z_1 = i$ and $c = i$. Which statement is NOT true?

A Z_n flip-flops between $(-1 + i)$ and $(-i)$.
B The coefficient of i never reaches 2.
Ⓒ The imaginary part becomes zero.
D On a graph $Z_1 - Z_3$ create a triangle.

5-9 CHALLENGE

The real number system is a subset of the complex number system and both systems share many properties. However, there are properties of one system that may not apply in the other system.

Exercises 1–3 are performed in the set of real numbers.

1. In the expression $\sqrt{a} \cdot \sqrt{b}$ there are square root operations and multiplication. Which operation should be done first according to the order of operations? Square roots should be simplified first.

2. Evaluate $\sqrt{3} \cdot \sqrt{12}$ and $\sqrt{3 \cdot 12}$. 6; 6

3. What do you notice about the two answers? Will this result always happen? What does that say about the order of operations?

The answers are the same. Yes; this will always be true in the system of real numbers. The order of operations can be reversed in this case.

For nonnegative real numbers a and b, $\sqrt{a} \cdot \sqrt{b} = \sqrt{a \cdot b}$.
Is the equation true when a and b are imaginary numbers?

Answer the following questions about complex numbers.

4. Evaluate $\sqrt{-3} \cdot \sqrt{-12}$ and $\sqrt{(-3) \cdot (-12)}$.

$\sqrt{3}i \cdot \sqrt{12}i = \sqrt{3} \cdot \sqrt{12} \cdot i^2 = \sqrt{36}i^2 = 6 \cdot -1 = -6; \sqrt{36} = 6$

5. What do you notice about your two answers? Is this the same as Exercise 3?

The answers are different. The order of operations cannot be changed in this case.

6. Write a general rule for the product of radicals when using complex numbers.

Possible answer: When multiplying radicals that have negative radicands, first simplify the radical using the imaginary number i, and then find the product.

Evaluate and simplify.

7. $\sqrt{-8} \cdot \sqrt{-128}$ -32

8. $\sqrt{-3} \cdot \sqrt{-2} \cdot \sqrt{-6} \cdot \sqrt{-4}$ 12

9. $(\sqrt{-5})^2$ -5

10. $\sqrt{-2} \cdot \sqrt{-90} \cdot \sqrt{-5}$ $-30i$

11. $\sqrt{-3} \cdot \sqrt{12}$ $6i$

12. $(\sqrt{-2})^5$ $4i\sqrt{2}$

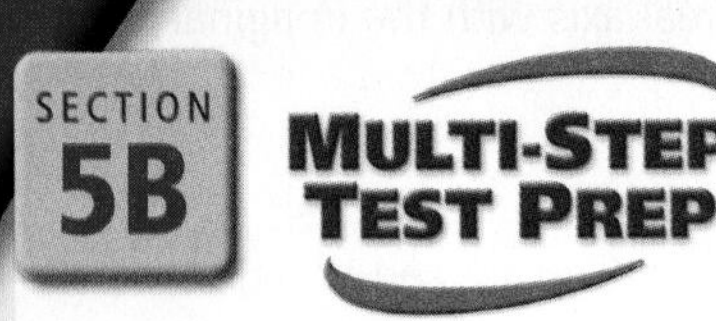

Organizer

Objective: Assess students' ability to apply concepts and skills in Lessons 5-7 through 5-9 in a real-world format.

Online Edition

Resources

Algebra II Assessments

www.mathtekstoolkit.org

For additional assessment activities, see www.utdanacenter.org.

Problem	Text Reference
1	Lesson 5-8
2	Lesson 5-8
3	Lesson 5-8
4	Lesson 5-8
5	Lesson 5-9

Answers

1–3. See p. A29.

4. $y \approx 0.6922$; when the distance from the upper right corner of a grid square to the upper corner of a tile is 3.8 cm, the ratio of the area of the tile to the area of the grid square is about 0.6922.
5. $0 < x \leq 2.9$ or $17.1 \leq x < 20$

State Resources

MULTI-STEP TEST PREP

SECTION 5B

Applying Quadratic Functions

Tilted Tiles Mitch and Jacob are making mosaics in an art class. To make one mosaic, Mitch first divides a wall into a grid made up of squares with a side length of 20 cm. Then Jacob glues a tile on each square, making sure that each corner of the tile touches a side of the grid square.

They measure the side length of each tile as well as the distance x from the upper right corner of the grid square to a corner of the tile. They find that for each tile there are two possible values of x, as shown.

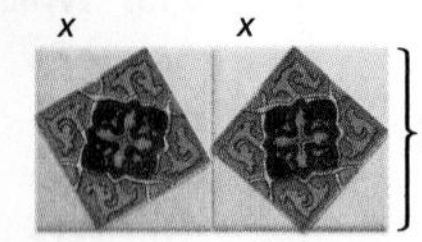

1. Complete the table by finding the area of each tile and the ratio y of the area of each tile to the area of the grid square.
2. Make a scatterplot of the ordered pairs (x, y). Find and graph a quadratic model for the data. Is the model a reasonable representation of the data? Explain.
3. Describe the domain for the problem situation. Explain why the domain of the problem situation is different from the domain of the model.
4. Use your model to determine the value of y when $x = 3.8$. Explain the meaning of your answer in the context of the problem.
5. For what values of x does a tile cover at least 75% of the grid square? Round to the nearest tenth.

Side Length of Tile (cm)	x (cm)	Area of Tile (cm^2)	y
15	6.4		
15	13.6		
15.5	5.5		
15.5	14.5		
16	4.7		
16	15.3		
17	3.3		
17	16.7		
18	2.1		
18	17.9		
19	1.1		
19	18.9		
20	0		

INTERVENTION

Scaffolding Questions

1. How can you determine the area of a tile? by finding the square of its side length
2. How can you use a calculator to find a quadratic model of the data? Enter the data in lists, and use the quadratic regression feature.
3. Can a tile have a negative side length? no What is the greatest side length a tile can have and still fit in a grid square? 20 cm
4. What does y represent? the ratio of a tile's area to the area of a grid square
5. For what values of y does a tile cover at least 75% of a grid square? $0.75 \leq y \leq 1$

Extension

What is the smallest percentage of a grid square that a tile can cover if all four corners of the tile touch the sides of the grid square? Explain how you determined your answer. 50%; the minimum value of y predicted by the quadratic model is 0.5.

CHAPTER 5

SECTION 5B

Quiz for Lessons 5-7 Through 5-9

5-7 Solving Quadratic Inequalities

Graph each inequality.

1. $y > -x^2 + 6x$
2. $y \le -x^2 - x + 2$

Solve each inequality by using tables or graphs.

3. $x^2 - 4x + 1 > 6$ $x < -1$ or $x > 5$
4. $2x^2 + 2x - 10 \le 2$ $-3 \le x \le 2$

Solve each inequality by using algebra.

5. $x^2 + 4x - 7 \ge 5$ $x \le -6$ or $x \ge 2$
6. $x^2 - 8x < 0$ $0 < x < 8$
7. The function $p(r) = -1000r^2 + 6400r - 4400$ models the monthly profit p of a small DVD-rental store, where r is the rental price of a DVD. For what range of rental prices does the store earn a monthly profit of at least $5000? a rental price between $2.29 and $4.11

5-8 Curve Fitting with Quadratic Models

Determine whether each data set could represent a quadratic function. Explain.

8.

x	5	6	7	8	9
y	13	11	7	1	−7

9.

x	−4	−2	0	2	4
y	10	8	4	8	10

Write a quadratic function that fits each set of points.

10. (0, 4), (2, 0), and (3, 1) $y = x^2 - 4x + 4$
11. (1, 3), (2, 5), and (4, 3) $y = -x^2 + 5x - 1$

For Exercises 12–14, use the table of maximum load allowances for various heights of spruce columns.

12. Find a quadratic regression equation to model the maximum load given the height. $y \approx -127.5x^2 + 961.5x + 5474.5$
13. Use your model to predict the maximum load allowed for a 6.5 ft spruce column. about 6337 lb
14. Use your model to predict the maximum load allowed for an 8 ft spruce column. about 5007 lb

Maximum Load Allowance No. 1 Common Spruce

Height of Column (ft)	Maximum Load (lb)
4	7280
5	7100
6	6650
7	5960

5-9 Operations with Complex Numbers

Find each absolute value.

15. $|-6i|$ 6
16. $|3 + 4i|$ 5
17. $|2 - i|$ $\sqrt{5}$

Perform each indicated operation, and write the result in the form $a + bi$.

18. $(3 - 5i) - (6 - i)$ $-3 - 4i$
19. $(-6 + 4i) + (7 - 2i)$ $1 + 2i$
20. $3i(4 + i)$ $-3 + 12i$
21. $(3 + i)(5 - i)$ $16 + 2i$
22. $(1 - 4i)(1 + 4i)$ 17
23. $3i^{15}$ $-3i$
24. $\frac{2 - 7i}{-i}$ $7 + 2i$
25. $\frac{3 - i}{4 - 2i}$ $\frac{7}{10} + \frac{1}{10}i$

READY TO GO ON? SECTION 5B

Organizer

Objective: Assess students' mastery of concepts and skills in Lessons 5-7 through 5-9.

Resources

 *Assessment Resources*
Section 5B Quiz

INTERVENTION

Resources

 *Ready to Go On? Intervention and Enrichment* Worksheets

 *Ready to Go On?* CD-ROM

 *Ready to Go On?* Online

Answers

1.

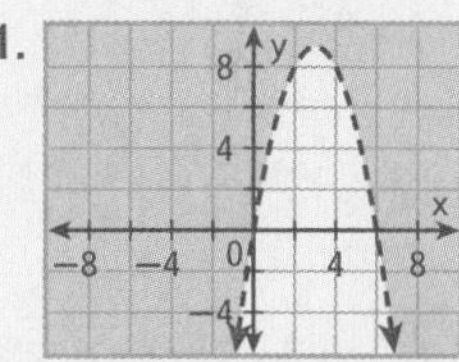

2, 8–9. See p. A30.

READY TO GO ON? Diagnose and Prescribe

Ready to Go On? Intervention	READY TO GO ON? Intervention, Section 5B: Worksheets	CD-ROM	Online
Lesson 5-7	5-7 Intervention	Activity 5-7	Diagnose and Prescribe Online
Lesson 5-8	5-8 Intervention	Activity 5-8	
Lesson 5-9	5-9 Intervention	Activity 5-9	

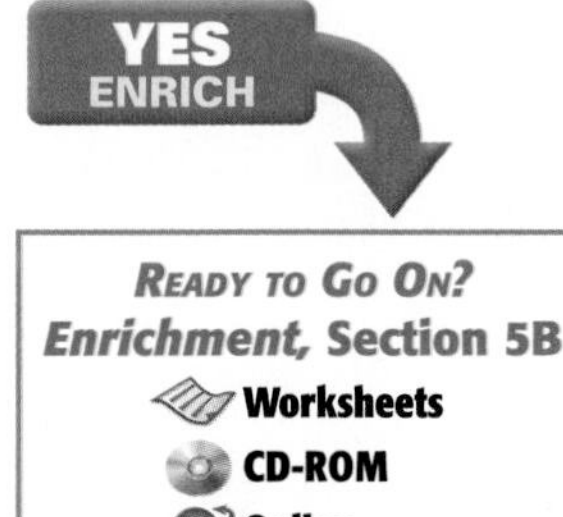

READY TO GO ON? Enrichment, Section 5B
Worksheets
CD-ROM
Online

Organizer

Objective: Help students organize and review key concepts and skills presented in Chapter 5.

Online Edition
Multilingual Glossary

Countdown to Testing Week 12

Resources

Puzzle Pro
One-Stop Planner®

***Multilingual Glossary* Online**

go.hrw.com
KEYWORD: MB7 Glossary

Lesson Tutorial Videos
CD-ROM

Test & Practice Generator
One-Stop Planner®

Answers

1. imaginary number; complex number
2. zero of a function
3. vertex of a parabola
4. discriminant
5. minimum value
6. 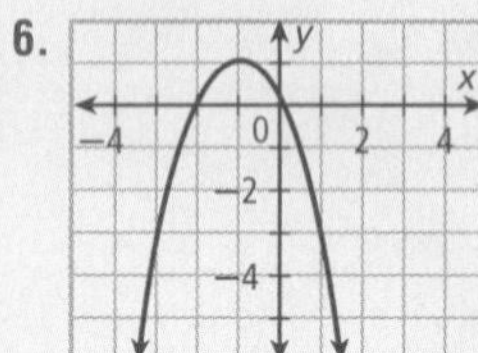
7. 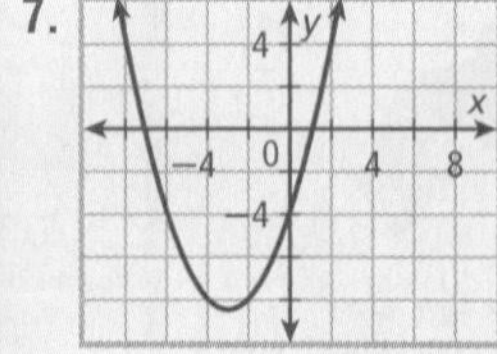
8. g is f vertically stretched by a factor of 4 and translated 2 units right.
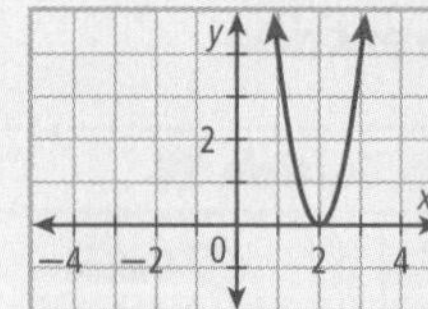
9. g is f reflected across the x-axis, vertically stretched by a factor of 2, and translated 1 unit left.
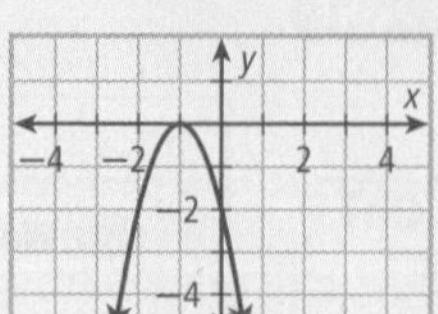

CHAPTER 5 Study Guide: Review

Vocabulary

Complete the sentences below with vocabulary words from the list above.

1. The number $5i$ can be classified as both a(n) ___?___ and a ___?___.
2. The value of the input x that makes the output $f(x)$ equal zero is called the ___?___.
3. The ___?___ is the point at which the parabola intersects the axis of symmetry.
4. The type and number of solutions to a quadratic equation can be determined by finding the ___?___.
5. When a parabola opens upward, the y-value of the vertex is the ___?___ of a quadratic function.

5-1 Using Transformations to Graph Quadratic Functions *(pp. 315–322)*

EXAMPLES

- **Using the graph of $f(x) = x^2$ as a guide, describe the transformations, and then graph $g(x) = \frac{1}{2}x^2 + 3$.**

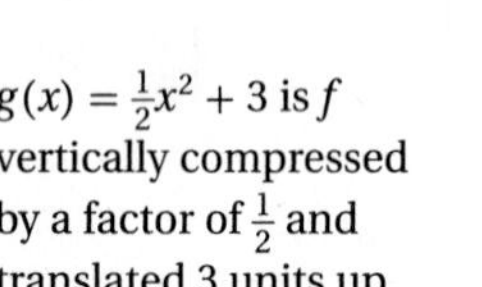

$g(x) = \frac{1}{2}x^2 + 3$ is f vertically compressed by a factor of $\frac{1}{2}$ and translated 3 units up.

- **Use the description to write a quadratic function in vertex form. The function $f(x) = x^2$ is translated 1 unit right to create g.**

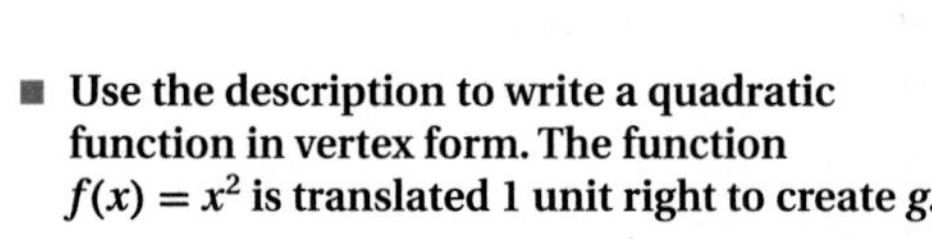

translation 1 unit right: $h = 1$

$g(x) = a(x - h)^2 + k \rightarrow g(x) = (x - 1)^2$

EXERCISES

Graph each function by using a table.

6. $f(x) = -x^2 - 2x$
7. $f(x) = \frac{1}{2}x^2 + 3x - 4$

Using the graph of $f(x) = x^2$ as a guide, describe the transformations, and then graph each function.

8. $g(x) = 4(x - 2)^2$
9. $g(x) = -2(x + 1)^2$
10. $g(x) = \frac{1}{3}x^2 - 3$
11. $g(x) = -(x + 2)^2 + 6$

Use the description to write each quadratic function in vertex form.

12. $f(x) = x^2$ is reflected across the x-axis and translated 3 units down to create g.
13. $f(x) = x^2$ is vertically stretched by a factor of 2 and translated 4 units right to create g.
14. $f(x) = x^2$ is vertically compressed by a factor of $\frac{1}{4}$ and translated 1 unit left to create g.

5-2 Properties of Quadratic Functions in Standard Form *(pp. 323–330)*

EXAMPLE

- **For $f(x) = -x^2 + 2x + 3$, (a) determine whether the graph opens upward or downward, (b) find the axis of symmetry, (c) find the vertex, (d) find the y-intercept, and (e) graph the function.**

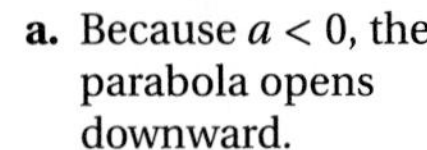

a. Because $a < 0$, the parabola opens downward.

b. axis of symmetry:
$x = -\frac{b}{2a} = -\frac{2}{2(-1)} = 1$

c. $f(1) = -1^2 + 2(1) + 3 = 4$
The vertex is $(1, 4)$.

d. Because $c = 3$, the y-intercept is 3.

e.

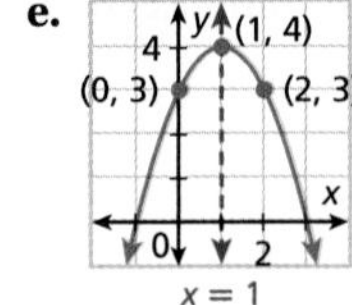

EXERCISES

For each function, (a) determine whether the graph opens upward or downward, (b) find the axis of symmetry, (c) find the vertex, (d) find the y-intercept, and (e) graph the function.

15. $f(x) = x^2 - 4x + 3$ **16.** $g(x) = x^2 + 2x + 3$

17. $h(x) = x^2 - 3x$ **18.** $j(x) = \frac{1}{2}x^2 - 2x + 4$

Find the minimum or maximum value of each function.

19. $f(x) = x^2 + 2x + 6$ **20.** $g(x) = 6x - 2x^2$

21. $f(x) = x^2 - 5x + 1$ **22.** $g(x) = -2x^2 - 8x + 10$

23. $f(x) = -x^2 - 4x + 8$ **24.** $g(x) = 3x^2 + 7$

5-3 Solving Quadratic Equations by Graphing and Factoring *(pp. 333–340)*

EXAMPLES

- **Find the roots of $x^2 + x = 30$ by factoring.**

$x^2 + x - 30 = 0$	*Rewrite in standard form.*
$(x - 5)(x + 6) = 0$	*Factor.*
$x - 5 = 0$ or $x + 6 = 0$	*Zero Product Property.*
$x = 5$ or $x = -6$	*Solve each equation.*

- **Write a quadratic function with zeros 8 and −8.**

$x = 8$ or $x = -8$	*Write zeros as solutions.*
$x - 8 = 0$ or $x + 8 = 0$	*Set equations equal to 0.*
$(x - 8)(x + 8) = 0$	*Converse Zero Product Property*
$f(x) = x^2 - 64$	*Replace 0 with f(x).*

EXERCISES

Find the roots of each equation by factoring.

25. $x^2 - 7x - 8 = 0$ **26.** $x^2 - 5x + 6 = 0$

27. $x^2 = 144$ **28.** $x^2 - 21x = 0$

29. $4x^2 - 16x + 16 = 0$ **30.** $2x^2 + 8x + 6 = 0$

31. $x^2 + 14x = 32$ **32.** $9x^2 + 6x + 1 = 0$

Write a quadratic function in standard form for each given set of zeros.

33. 2 and −3 **34.** 1 and −1

35. 4 and 5 **36.** −2 and −3

37. −5 and −5 **38.** 9 and 0

5-4 Completing the Square *(pp. 342–349)*

EXAMPLE

- **Solve $x^2 - 8x = 12$ by completing the square.**

$x^2 - 8x + \blacksquare = 12 + \blacksquare$	*Set up equation.*
$x^2 - 8x + 16 = 12 + 16$	*Add $\left(\frac{b}{2}\right)^2$.*
$(x - 4)^2 = 28$	*Factor.*
$x - 4 = \pm\sqrt{28}$	*Take square roots.*
$x = 4 \pm 2\sqrt{7}$	*Solve for x.*

EXERCISES

Solve each equation by completing the square.

39. $x^2 - 16x + 48 = 0$ **40.** $x^2 + 20x + 84 = 0$

41. $x^2 - 6x = 16$ **42.** $x^2 - 14x = 13$

Write each function in vertex form, and identify its vertex.

43. $f(x) = x^2 - 4x + 9$ **44.** $g(x) = x^2 + 2x - 7$

Answers

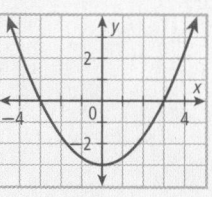

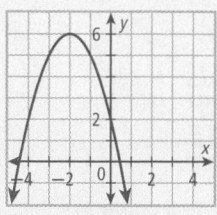

10. g is f vertically compressed by a factor of $\frac{1}{3}$ and translated 3 units down.
11. g is f reflected across the x-axis and translated 2 units left and 6 units up.
12. Possible answer: $g(x) = -x^2 - 3$
13. Possible answer: $g(x) = 2(x - 4)^2$
14. Possible answer: $g(x) = \frac{1}{4}(x + 1)^2$
15. opens upward; $x = 2$; $(2, -1)$; 3
16. opens upward; $x = -1$; $(-1, 2)$; 3
17. opens upward; $x = 1.5$; $(1.5, -2.25)$; 0
18. opens upward; $x = 2$; $(2, 2)$; 4

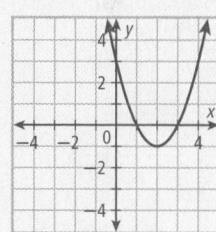

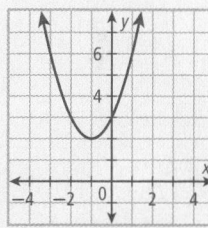

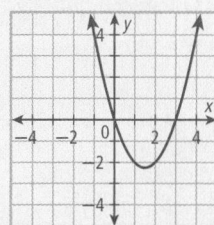

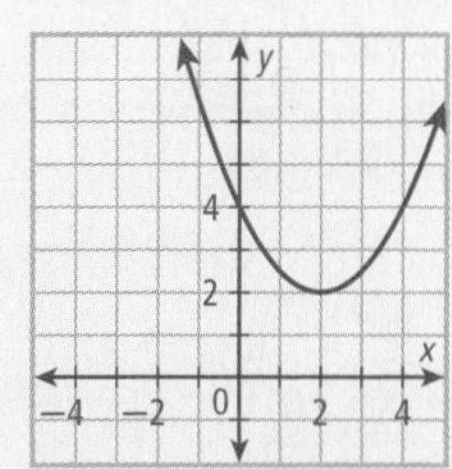

Answers

19. min.: 5
20. max.: 4.5
21. min.: −5.25
22. max.: 18
23. max.: 12
24. min.: 7
25. $x = -1$ or $x = 8$
26. $x = 2$ or $x = 3$
27. $x = -12$ or $x = 12$
28. $x = 0$ or $x = 21$
29. $x = 2$
30. $x = -1$ or $x = -3$
31. $x = 2$ or $x = -16$
32. $x = -\frac{1}{3}$
33. Possible answer: $f(x) = x^2 + x - 6$
34. Possible answer: $f(x) = x^2 - 1$
35. Possible answer: $f(x) = x^2 - 9x + 20$
36. Possible answer: $f(x) = x^2 + 5x + 6$
37. Possible answer: $f(x) = x^2 + 10x + 25$
38. Possible answer: $f(x) = x^2 - 9x$
39. $x = 4$ or $x = 12$
40. $x = -14$ or $x = -6$
41. $x = -2$ or $x = 8$
42. $x = 7 \pm \sqrt{62}$
43. $f(x) = (x - 2)^2 + 5$; $(2, 5)$
44. $g(x) = (x + 1)^2 - 8$; $(-1, -8)$

Answers

45. $x = \pm 9i$
46. $x = \pm 5i$
47. $x = -3 \pm i$
48. $x = -6 \pm 3i$
49. $x = 7 \pm i\sqrt{26}$
50. $x = 11 \pm 2i\sqrt{3}$
51. $-5i - 4$
52. $3 - i\sqrt{5}$
53. $\frac{3 \pm \sqrt{41}}{2}$
54. $5 \pm 2i\sqrt{3}$
55. $\frac{5}{2} \pm \frac{i\sqrt{11}}{2}$
56. $-\frac{3}{2} \pm i\frac{\sqrt{3}}{2}$
57. $\frac{5}{2} \pm i\frac{\sqrt{15}}{2}$
58. 1 distinct real solution
59. 2 real solutions
60. 2 nonreal complex solutions
61. 2 real solutions
62. 2 nonreal complex solutions
63. 2 nonreal complex solutions
64. 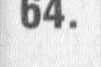

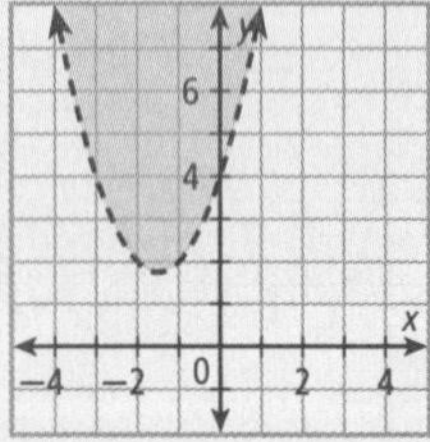

65.

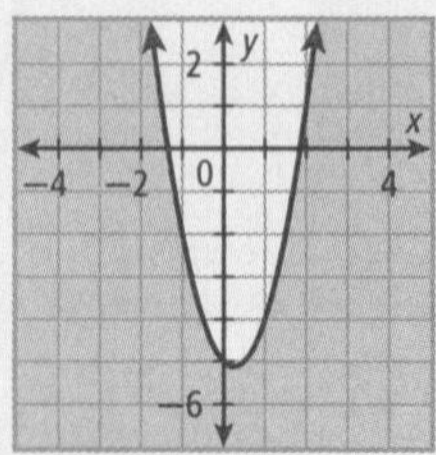

66. $x \le -3$ or $x \ge 1$
67. $-4 < x < -1$
68. $x < 1$ or $x > 5$
69. $-3 \le x \le 3$
70. $-\sqrt{3} < x < \sqrt{3}$
71. $-2 \le x \le \frac{2}{3}$

5-5 Complex Numbers and Roots *(pp. 350–355)*

EXAMPLE

- **Solve $x^2 - 22x + 133 = 0$.**

$x^2 - 22x + \blacksquare = -133 + \blacksquare$	*Rewrite.*
$x^2 - 22x + 121 = -133 + 121$	*Add* $\left(\frac{b}{2}\right)^2$.
$(x - 11)^2 = -12$	*Factor.*
$x - 11 = \pm\sqrt{-12}$	*Take square roots.*
$x = 11 \pm 2i\sqrt{3}$	*Solve.*

EXERCISES

Solve each equation.

45. $x^2 = -81$
46. $6x^2 + 150 = 0$
47. $x^2 + 6x + 10 = 0$
48. $x^2 + 12x + 45 = 0$
49. $x^2 - 14x + 75 = 0$
50. $x^2 - 22x + 133 = 0$

Find each complex conjugate.

51. $5i - 4$
52. $3 + i\sqrt{5}$

5-6 The Quadratic Formula *(pp. 356–363)*

EXAMPLES

- **Find the zeros of $f(x) = 3x^2 - 5x + 3$ by using the Quadratic Formula.**

$x = \dfrac{-b \pm \sqrt{b^2 - 4ac}}{2a}$	*Quadratic Formula*
$x = \dfrac{-(-5) \pm \sqrt{(-5)^2 - 4(3)(3)}}{2(3)}$	*Substitute.*
$= \dfrac{5 \pm \sqrt{-11}}{6} = \dfrac{5}{6} \pm i\dfrac{\sqrt{11}}{6}$	*Simplify.*

- **Find the type and number of solutions for $x^2 + 9x + 20 = 0$.**

$b^2 - 4ac = 9^2 - 4(1)(20)$
$= 81 - 80 = 1$

There are two distinct real roots because the discriminant is positive.

EXERCISES

Find the zeros of each function by using the Quadratic Formula.

53. $f(x) = x^2 - 3x - 8$
54. $h(x) = (x - 5)^2 + 12$
55. $f(x) = 2x^2 - 10x + 18$
56. $g(x) = x^2 + 3x + 3$
57. $h(x) = x^2 - 5x + 10$

Find the type and number of solutions for each equation.

58. $2x^2 - 16x + 32 = 0$
59. $x^2 - 6x = -5$
60. $x^2 + 3x + 8 = 0$
61. $x^2 - 246x = -144$
62. $x^2 + 5x = -12$
63. $3x^2 - 5x + 3 = 0$

5-7 Solving Quadratic Inequalities *(pp. 366–373)*

EXAMPLE

- **Solve $x^2 - 4x - 9 \ge 3$ by using algebra.**

Write and solve the related equation.

$x^2 - 4x - 12 = 0$	*Write in standard form.*
$(x + 2)(x - 6) = 0$	*Factor.*
$x = -2$ or $x = 6$	*Solve.*

The critical values are −2 and 6. These values divide the number line into three intervals: $x \le -2$, $-2 \le x \le 6$, and $x \ge 6$.

Testing an x-value in each interval gives the solution of $x \le -2$ or $x \ge 6$.

EXERCISES

Graph each inequality.

64. $y > x^2 + 3x + 4$
65. $y \le 2x^2 - x - 5$

Solve each inequality by using tables or graphs.

66. $x^2 + 2x - 4 \ge -1$
67. $-x^2 - 5x > 4$

Solve each inequality by using algebra.

68. $-x^2 + 6x < 5$
69. $3x^2 - 25 \le 2$
70. $x^2 - 3 < 0$
71. $3x^2 + 4x - 3 \le 1$

5-8 Curve Fitting with Quadratic Models *(pp. 374–381)*

EXAMPLE

■ **Find a quadratic model for the wattage of fluorescent bulbs *F* given the comparable incandescent bulb wattage *I*. Use the model to estimate the wattage of a fluorescent bulb that produces the same amount of light as a 120-watt incandescent bulb.**

Wattage Comparison					
Incandescent (watts)	40	60	75	90	100
Fluorescent (watts)	11	15	20	23	28

Enter the data into two lists in a graphing calculator. Use the quadratic regression feature.

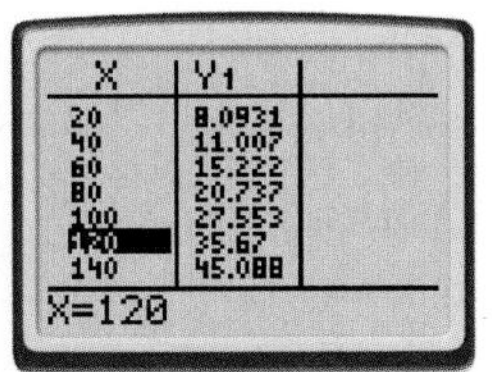

The model is $F(I) \approx 0.0016I^2 + 0.0481I + 6.48$. A 36-watt fluorescent bulb produces about the same amount of light as a 120-watt incandescent bulb.

EXERCISES

Write a quadratic function that fits each set of points.

72. $(-1, 8)$, $(0, 6)$, and $(1, 2)$

73. $(0, 0)$, $(1, -1)$, and $(2, -6)$

Construction **For Exercises 74–77, use the table of copper wire gauges.**

Common U.S. Copper Wire Gauges		
Gauge	Diameter (in.)	Resistance per 1000 ft (ohms)
24	0.0201	25.67
22	0.0254	16.14
20	0.0320	10.15
18	0.0403	6.385

74. Find a quadratic regression equation to model the diameter given the wire gauge.

75. Use your model to predict the diameter for a 12-gauge copper wire.

76. Find a quadratic regression equation to model the resistance given the wire gauge.

77. Use your model to predict the resistance for a 26-gauge copper wire.

5-9 Operations with Complex Numbers *(pp. 382–389)*

EXAMPLES

Perform each indicated operation, and write the result in the form $a + bi$.

■ $|-2 + 4i|$

$\sqrt{(-2)^2 + 4^2} = \sqrt{4 + 16} = \sqrt{20} = 2\sqrt{5}$

■ $(3 + 2i)(4 - 5i)$

$12 - 15i + 8i - 10i^2$

$12 - 7i - 10(-1) = 22 - 7i$

■ $\dfrac{-5 + 3i}{1 - 2i}$

$$\frac{-5 + 3i}{1 - 2i}\left(\frac{1 + 2i}{1 + 2i}\right) = \frac{-5 - 7i + 6i^2}{1 - 4i^2}$$

$$= \frac{-11 - 7i}{1 + 4} = -\frac{11}{5} - \frac{7}{5}i$$

EXERCISES

Perform each indicated operation, and write the result in the form $a + bi$.

78. $|-3i|$

79. $|4 - 2i|$

80. $|12 - 16i|$

81. $|7i|$

82. $(1 + 5i) + (6 - i)$

83. $(9 + 4i) - (3 + 2i)$

84. $(5 - i) - (11 - i)$

85. $-5i(3 - 4i)$

86. $(5 - 2i)(6 + 8i)$

87. $(3 + 2i)(3 - 2i)$

88. $(4 + i)(1 - 5i)$

89. $(-7 + 4i)(3 + 9i)$

90. i^{32}

91. $-5i^{21}$

92. $\dfrac{2 + 9i}{-2i}$

93. $\dfrac{5 + 2i}{3 - 4i}$

94. $\dfrac{8 - 4i}{1 + i}$

95. $\dfrac{-12 + 26i}{2 + 4i}$

Answers

72. $y = -x^2 - 3x + 6$
73. $y = -2x^2 + x$
74. $y \approx 0.000188x^2 - 0.0112x + 0.182$
75. ≈ 0.074 in.
76. $y \approx 0.360x^2 - 11.9x + 105$
77. ≈ 37.8 ohms
78. 3
79. $2\sqrt{5}$
80. 20
81. 7
82. $7 + 4i$
83. $6 + 2i$
84. -6
85. $-20 - 15i$
86. $46 + 28i$
87. 13
88. $9 - 19i$
89. $-57 - 51i$
90. 1
91. $-5i$
92. $-\frac{9}{2} + i$
93. $\frac{7}{25} + \frac{26}{25}i$
94. $2 - 6i$
95. $4 + 5i$

Study Guide: Review 395

Organizer

Objective: Assess students' mastery of concepts and skills in Chapter 5.

Online Edition

Resources

Assessment Resources

Chapter 5 Tests

- Free Response (Levels A, B, C)
- Multiple Choice (Levels A, B, C)
- Performance Assessment

***IDEA Works!* CD-ROM**

Modified Chapter 5 Test

Answers

1.
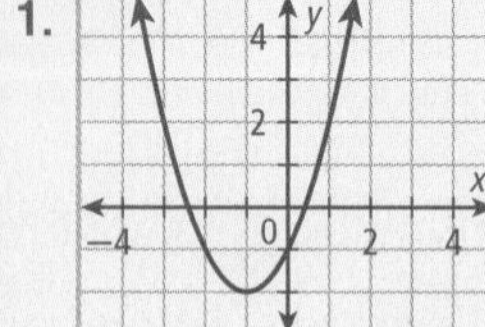

State Resources

CHAPTER TEST

Using the graph of $f(x) = x^2$ as a guide, describe the transformations, and then graph each function.

1. $g(x) = (x + 1)^2 - 2$ **g is f translated 1 unit left and 2 units down.**
2. $h(x) = -\frac{1}{2}x^2 + 2$ **h is f reflected across the x-axis, vertically compressed by a factor of $\frac{1}{2}$, and translated 2 units up.**
3. Use the following description to write a quadratic function in vertex form: $f(x) = x^2$ is vertically compressed by a factor of $\frac{1}{2}$ and translated 6 units right to create g. $g(x) = \frac{1}{2}(x - 6)^2$

For each function, (a) determine whether the graph opens upward or downward, (b) find the axis of symmetry, (c) find the vertex, (d) find the y-intercept, and (e) graph the function.

4. $f(x) = -x^2 + 4x + 1$ **downward; $x = 2$; $(2, 5)$; 1**
5. $g(x) = x^2 - 2x + 3$ **upward; $x = 1$; $(1, 2)$; 3**
6. The area A of a rectangle with a perimeter of 32 cm is modeled by the function $A(x) = -x^2 + 16x$, where x is the width of the rectangle in centimeters. What is the maximum area of the rectangle? **64 cm^2**

Find the roots of each equation by using factoring.

7. $x^2 - 2x + 1 = 0$ **1**
8. $x^2 + 10x = -21$ **$-3, -7$**

Solve each equation.

9. $x^2 + 4x = 12$ **$-6, 2$**
10. $x^2 - 12x = 25$ **$6 \pm \sqrt{61}$**
11. $x^2 + 25 = 0$ **$\pm 5i$**
12. $x^2 + 12x = -40$ **$-6 \pm 2i$**

Write each function in vertex form, and identify its vertex.

13. $f(x) = x^2 - 4x + 9$ **$f(x) = (x - 2)^2 + 5$; $(2, 5)$**
14. $g(x) = x^2 - 18x + 92$ **$g(x) = (x - 9)^2 + 11$; $(9, 11)$**

Find the zeros of each function by using the Quadratic Formula.

15. $f(x) = (x - 1)^2 + 7$ **$1 \pm i\sqrt{7}$**
16. $g(x) = 2x^2 - x + 5$ **$\frac{1}{4} \pm \frac{\sqrt{39}}{4}i$**
17. The height h in feet of a person on a waterslide is modeled by the function $h(t) = -0.025t^2 - 0.5t + 50$, where t is the time in seconds. At the bottom of the slide, the person lands in a swimming pool. To the nearest tenth of a second, how long does the ride last? **≈ 35.8 s**
18. Graph the inequality $y < x^2 - 3x - 4$.

Solve each inequality.

19. $-x^2 + 3x + 5 \geq 7$ **$1 \leq x \leq 2$**
20. $x^2 - 4x + 1 > 1$ **$x < 0$ or $x > 4$**

For Exercises 21 and 22, use the table showing the average cost of LCD televisions at one store.

Costs of LCD Televisions				
Size (in.)	15	17	23	30
Cost ($)	550	700	1500	2500

21. Find a quadratic model for the cost of a television given its size. **$y \approx 1.8x^2 + 52x - 662$**
22. Use the model to estimate the cost of a 42 in. LCD television. **about $4697**

Perform the indicated operation, and write the result in the form $a + bi$.

23. $(12 - i) - (5 + 2i)$ **$7 - 3i$**
24. $(6 - 2i)(2 - 2i)$ **$8 - 16i$**
25. $-2i^{18}$ **2**
26. $\frac{1 - 8i}{4i}$ **$-2 - \frac{1}{4}i$**

2.
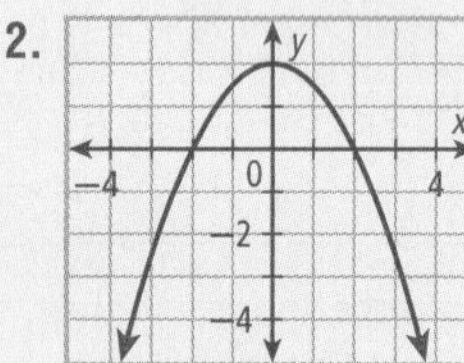

5.
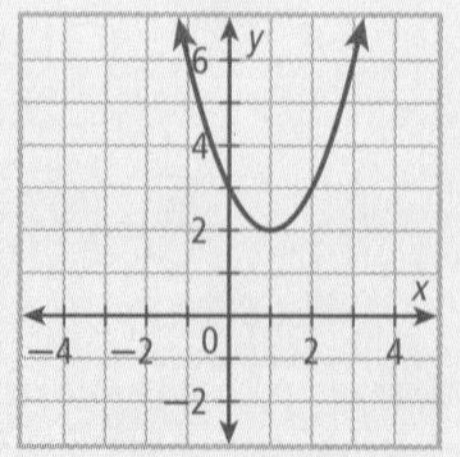

4.
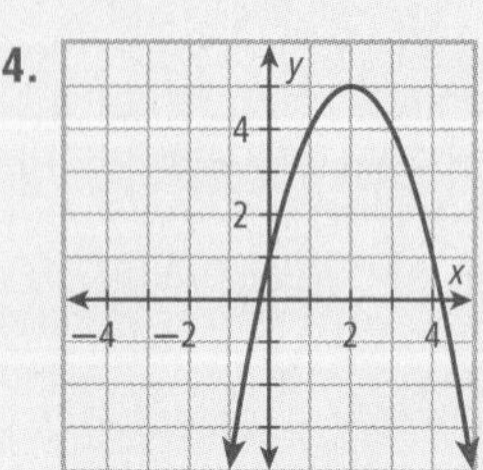

18.
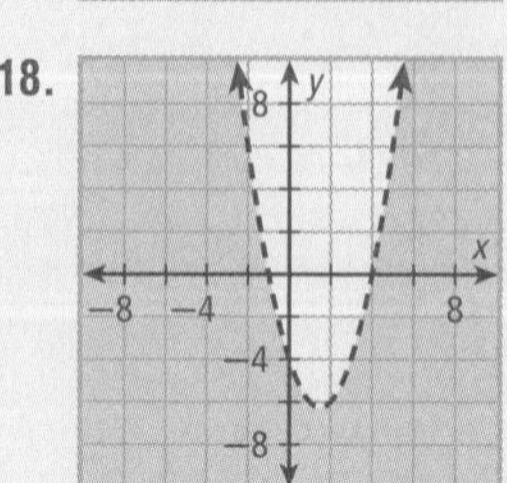

COLLEGE ENTRANCE EXAM PRACTICE

CHAPTER 5

FOCUS ON SAT MATHEMATICS SUBJECT TESTS

The SAT Mathematics Subject Tests assess knowledge from course work rather than ability to learn. The Level 1 test is meant to be taken by students who have completed two years of algebra and one year of geometry, and it tests more elementary topics than the Level 2 test.

HOT TIP! You will need to use a calculator for some of the problems on the SAT Mathematics Subject Tests. Before test day, make sure that you are familiar with the features of the calculator that you will be using.

You may want to time yourself as you take this practice test. It should take you about 8 minutes to complete.

1. For what value of c will $3x^2 - 2x + c = 0$ have exactly one distinct real root?
   (A) $-\frac{2}{3}$
   (B) $-\frac{1}{3}$
   (C) 0
   (D) $\frac{1}{3}$
   (E) $\frac{2}{3}$

2. If m and n are real numbers, $i^2 = -1$, and $(m - n) - 4i = 7 + ni$, what is the value of m?
   (A) -4
   (B) -3
   (C) 1
   (D) 3
   (E) 4

3. If $x^2 - 5x + 6 = (x - h)^2 + k$, what is the value of k?
   (A) $-\frac{25}{4}$
   (B) $-\frac{5}{2}$
   (C) $-\frac{1}{4}$
   (D) 0
   (E) 6

4. What is the solution set of $y^2 - 2y \leq 3y + 14$?
   (A) $y \geq -2$
   (B) $y \leq 7$
   (C) $y \leq -2$ or $y \geq 7$
   (D) $-7 \leq y \leq 2$
   (E) $-2 \leq y \leq 7$

5. Which of the following is a factor of $(a - 1)^2 - b^2$?
   (A) $a + b - 1$
   (B) $a - b$
   (C) $a - 1$
   (D) $a - b + 1$
   (E) $1 - b$

6. If $z = 5 - 4i$ and $i^2 = -1$, what is $|z|$?
   (A) 1
   (B) 3
   (C) 9
   (D) $\sqrt{41}$
   (E) $\sqrt{42}$

COLLEGE ENTRANCE EXAM PRACTICE CHAPTER 5

Organizer

Objective: Provide practice for college entrance exams such as the SAT Mathematics Subject Test Level 1.

PREMIER **Online Edition**

Resources

College Entrance Exam Practice

Questions on the SAT Mathematics Subject Test Level 1 represent the following math content areas:

Algebra, 30%
Plane Euclidean Geometry, 20%
Coordinate Geometry, 12%
Three-dimensional Geometry, 6%
Trigonometry, 8%
Functions, 12%
Statistics/Probability, 6%
Miscellaneous, 6%

Items on this page focus on:
- Algebra
- Functions

Text References:

Item	1	2	3	4	5	6
Lesson	5-6	5-5	5-4	5-7	5-3	5-9

TEST PREP DOCTOR

1. Remind students that the value of the discriminant determines the number of roots of a quadratic equation and that the value of the discriminant is equal to $b^2 - 4ac$.
2. Remind students that complex numbers are equal only if their real parts are equal and their imaginary parts are equal. Suggest that students set up two equations, one for the real parts and one for the imaginary parts of these equivalent complex numbers.
3. Students who chose **E** may have used the value of c for k. Remind them that they must complete the square to change a quadratic equation from standard form to vertex form.
4. Students who chose **D** may have made a mistake in sign when determining the critical values. Students who chose **C** may have found the solution to $y^2 - 2y \geq 3y + 14$ instead of $y^2 - 2y \leq 3y + 14$.
5. Students should recognize the expression as a difference of squares. Remind students of the rule for factoring this type of quadratic expression.
6. Students who chose **C** may have found $|5| + |-4|$ instead of $\sqrt{5^2 + (-4)^2}$. Remind students that the absolute value of a complex number is related to the Pythagorean Theorem.

Organizer

Objective: Provide opportunities to learn and practice common test-taking strategies.

Online Edition

Resources

State Test Prep Workbook

State Test Prep CD-ROM

State Test Practice Online

go.hrw.com
KEYWORD: MB7 TestPrep

This Test Tackler focuses on how to work backward to obtain an answer or to eliminate answers for multiple-choice test items. Although this strategy is not always the most efficient, it can help students more easily solve problems that would otherwise be difficult for them.

Standardized Test Strategies

Multiple Choice: Work Backward

When taking a multiple-choice test, you can sometimes work backward to determine which answer is correct. Because this method can be time consuming, it is best used only when you cannot solve a problem in any other way.

EXAMPLE 1

Which expression is equivalent to $2x^2 - 3x - 14$?

Ⓐ $(2x + 7)(x + 2)$　　Ⓒ $(2x - 7)(x + 2)$

Ⓑ $(2x - 7)(x - 2)$　　Ⓓ $(2x + 7)(x - 2)$

If you have trouble factoring the quadratic expression given in the question, you can multiply the binomials in the answer choices to find the product that is the same as $2x^2 - 3x - 14$.

Try Choice A: $(2x + 7)(x + 2) = 2x^2 + 11x + 14$

Try Choice B: $(2x - 7)(x - 2) = 2x^2 - 11x + 14$

Try Choice C: $(2x - 7)(x + 2) = \mathbf{2x^2 - 3x - 14}$

Choice C is the answer.

Note: *Trying choice D can help you check your work.*

EXAMPLE 2

What is the solution set of $x^2 - 36 < 0$?

Ⓕ $x < -6$ or $x > 6$　　Ⓗ $-36 < x < 36$

Ⓖ $-6 < x < 6$　　Ⓙ $x < -36$ or $x > 36$

If you have trouble determining the solution set, substitute values of x into the inequality. Based on whether the values make the inequality true or false, you may be able to eliminate one or more of the answer choices.

Substitute 0 for x: $x^2 - 36 < 0 \rightarrow (\mathbf{0})^2 - 36 \overset{?}{<} 0 \rightarrow -36 < 0$ ✔

When $x = 0$, the inequality is true. Therefore, the solution set must include $x = 0$. Because choices F and J do not include $x = 0$, they can be eliminated.

Substitute 10 for x: $x^2 - 36 < 0 \rightarrow (\mathbf{10})^2 - 36 \overset{?}{<} 0 \rightarrow 64 \overset{?}{<} 0$ ✘

When $x = 10$, the inequality is false. Therefore, the solution set does not include $x = 10$. Because choice H includes $x = 10$, it can be eliminated.

The only remaining choice is choice G. Therefore, choice G must be correct.

You can also work backward to check whether the answer you found by another method is correct or reasonable.

Read each test item, and answer the questions that follow.

Item A
What are the zeros of the function $g(x) = 6x^2 - 8x - 4$, rounded to the nearest hundredth?

Ⓐ -10.32 and 2.32 Ⓒ 1.72 and -0.39

Ⓑ -1.72 and 0.39 Ⓓ 10.32 and -2.32

1. Rachel cannot remember how to determine the zeros of a quadratic function, so she plans to pick one of the answer choices at random. What could Rachel do to make a more educated guess?
2. Describe how to find the correct answer by working backward.

Item B
A portable television has a screen with a diagonal of 4 inches. The length of the screen is 1 inch greater than its width. What are the dimensions of the screen to the nearest hundredth?

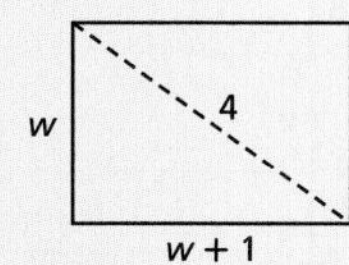

Ⓕ 1.28 inches by 2.28 inches

Ⓖ 1.28 inches by 3.28 inches

Ⓗ 2.28 inches by 2.28 inches

Ⓙ 2.28 inches by 3.28 inches

3. Can any of the answer choices be eliminated immediately? If so, which choices and why?
4. Describe how you can determine the correct answer by using the Pythagorean Theorem and working backward.

Item C
Which of the following is a solution of $(x + 4)^2 = 25$?

Ⓐ $x = -9$ Ⓒ $x = 0$

Ⓑ $x = -1$ Ⓓ $x = 9$

5. Explain how to use substitution to determine the correct answer.
6. Check whether choice A is correct by working backward. Explain your findings. What should you do next?

Item D
The height h of a golf ball in feet t seconds after it is hit into the air is modeled by $h(t) = -16t^2 + 64t$. How long is the ball in the air?

Ⓕ 2 seconds Ⓗ 12 seconds

Ⓖ 4 seconds Ⓙ 16 seconds

7. The measurements given in the answer choices represent possible values of which variable in the function?
8. Describe how you can work backward to determine that choice F is not correct.

Item E
The base of a triangle is 4 in. longer than twice its height. If the triangle has an area of 24 in^2, what is its height?

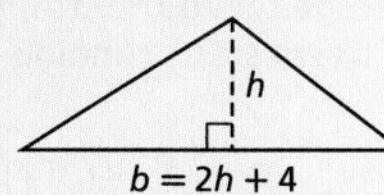

Ⓐ 2 in. Ⓒ 6 in.

Ⓑ 4 in. Ⓓ 8 in.

9. What equation do you need to solve to find the value of h?
10. Try choice A by working backward. Explain your findings. What should you do next?

Answers

Possible answers:

1. Rachel could work backward to find the answer.
2. Substitute the values of x for each answer choice into the function. If both values of x make the function approximately equal to 0, then those values of x are the zeros of the function.
3. Yes; choices G and H can be eliminated because the length must be 1 in. greater than the width.
4. Use the right triangle formed by the length, width, and diagonal of the screen to write an equation using the Pythagorean Theorem. The sum of the squares of the lengths of the legs must equal the square of the hypotenuse.
$\ell^2 + w^2 = 4^2$
Substitute the dimensions from each answer choice into this equation and check to see whether they make the equation true.
5. Substitute each value of x into the equation and simplify. If the left side simplifies to 25, the value substituted for x is a solution of the equation.
6. Substitute -9 for x in the equation.
$(-9 + 4)^2 \stackrel{?}{=} 25$
$25 = 25$
Because the equation is true when $x = -9$, choice A is correct. I can substitute the other answer choices to check my answer.
7. t

Answers to *Test Items*

A. C
B. J
C. A
D. G
E. B

Answers

8. Substitute 2 for t in the function.
$h(2) = -16(2)^2 + 64(2) = 64$
Because the height is not 0 when $t = 2$, choice F is incorrect.
9. $\frac{1}{2}(2h + 4)h = 24$
10. Substitute 2 for h into the equation.
$\frac{1}{2}[2(2) + 4](2) \stackrel{?}{=} 24$
$8 \neq 24$
Because the equation is false when $h = 2$, choice A can be eliminated. Next, I should try one of the other answer choices.

State Resources

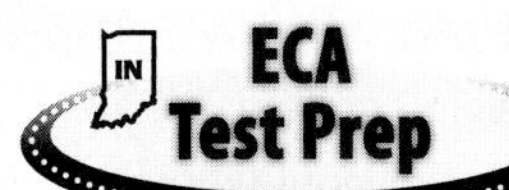

Organizer

Objective: Provide review and practice for Chapters 1–5 and standardized tests.

Resources

 ***Assessment Resources***

Chapter 5 Cumulative Test

 ***State Test Prep Workbook***

 ***State Test Prep* CD-ROM**

 ***State Test Practice* Online**

go.hrw.com
KEYWORD: MB7 TestPrep

Answers

1. B
2. B
3. C
4. D
5. C
6. B
7. C
8. D
9. C
10. B
11. A

State Resources

Core Standard	Items
1	3, 12, 15
2	8
3	2, 6, 7, 11, 14

go.hrw.com
State Resources Online
KEYWORD: MA7 Resources

CUMULATIVE ASSESSMENT, CHAPTERS 1–5

Multiple Choice

1. $M = \begin{bmatrix} 6 & -2 \\ 3 & 7 \end{bmatrix}$ $N = \begin{bmatrix} -1 & 8 & 2 \\ 0 & 1 & 6 \end{bmatrix}$

What is the matrix product $2MN$?

A. $\begin{bmatrix} -24 & 184 & 0 \\ -12 & 124 & 192 \end{bmatrix}$

B. $\begin{bmatrix} -12 & 92 & 0 \\ -6 & 62 & 96 \end{bmatrix}$

C. $\begin{bmatrix} -24 & -12 \\ 184 & 124 \\ 0 & 192 \end{bmatrix}$

D. $\begin{bmatrix} -12 & -6 \\ 92 & 62 \\ 0 & 96 \end{bmatrix}$

2. Which of these functions does NOT have zeros at -1 and 4?

A. $f(x) = x^2 - 3x - 4$

B. $f(x) = 2x^2 + 6x - 8$

C. $f(x) = -x^2 + 3x + 4$

D. $f(x) = 2x^2 - 6x - 8$

3. Dawn and Julia are running on a jogging trail. Dawn starts running 5 minutes after Julia does. If Julia runs at an average speed of 8 ft/s and Dawn runs at an average speed of 9 ft/s, how many minutes after Dawn starts running will she catch up with Julia?

A. 5 minutes **B.** 27 minutes

C. 40 minutes **D.** 45 minutes

4. Which equation has intercepts at (20, 0, 0), (0, 40, 0), and (0, 0, 5)?

A. $20x + 40y + 5z = 0$

B. $20x + 40y + 5z = 1$

C. $4x + 8y + z = 5$

D. $2x + y + 8z = 40$

5. Which graph represents the function $f(x) = -\frac{1}{2}(x - 3) - 4$?

A.
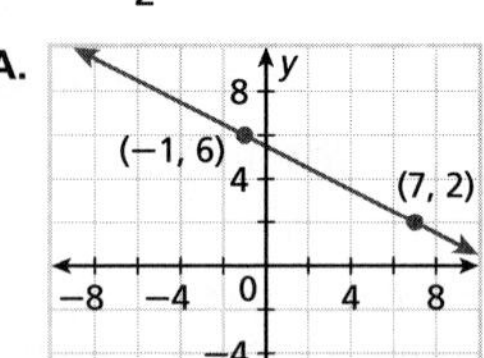

B.
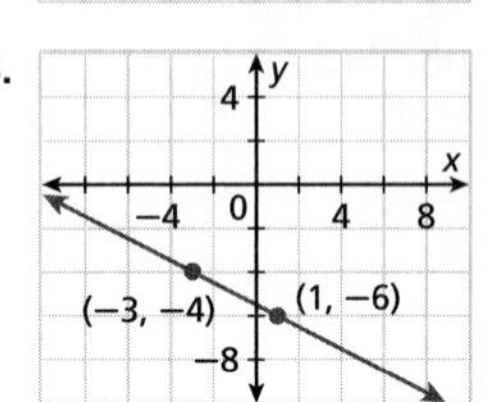

C.
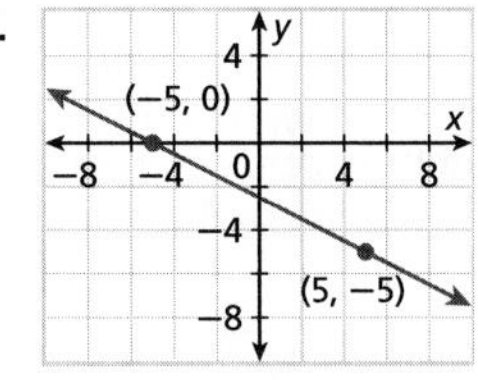

D.
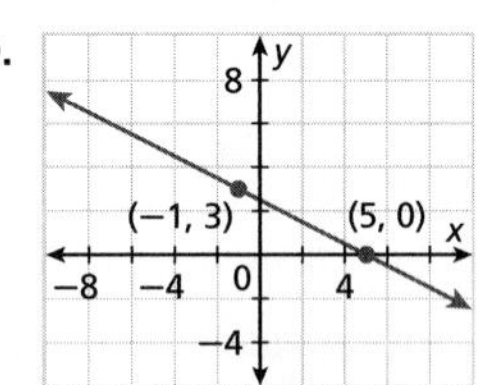

6. What is the equation of the function graphed below?

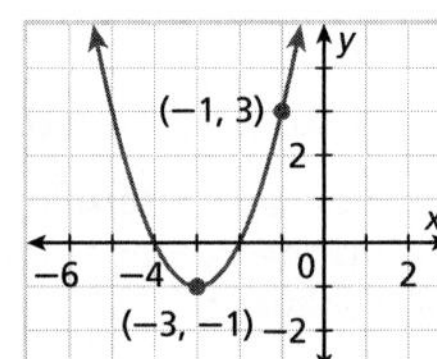

A. $y = (x - 3)^2 - 1$ **B.** $y = (x + 3)^2 - 1$

C. $y = (x - 1)^2 - 3$ **D.** $y = (x + 1)^2 - 3$

TEST PREP DOCTOR

For **Item 6,** students who chose **A** may have forgotten that *h* is the value subtracted from *x* (rather than added to *x*) inside the parentheses. Students who chose **C** or **D** may be confused about which parameter indicates a vertical translation and which indicates a horizontal translation.

For **Item 12,** encourage students to first rewrite each equation in slope-intercept form. If necessary, remind them of the characteristics of a dependent system. Once they realize that both equations in the system represent the same line, they will be able to set up a simple equation to solve for the value of *c*.

7. If the relationship between x and y is quadratic, which value of y completes the table?

x	−3	−1	1	3	5
y	21	7	■	27	61

A. 3 B. 7
C. 9 D. 17

8. Which is equivalent to the expression $\frac{5(6-8i)}{2-i}$?

A. $-20 + 10i$ B. $15 - 8i$
C. $15 - 40i$ D. $20 - 10i$

9. What is the inverse of the following matrix?

$$\begin{bmatrix} -2 & -4 \\ 4 & 2 \end{bmatrix}$$

A. $\begin{bmatrix} -\frac{1}{6} & -\frac{1}{3} \\ \frac{1}{3} & \frac{1}{6} \end{bmatrix}$ B. $\begin{bmatrix} -\frac{1}{2} & -\frac{1}{4} \\ \frac{1}{4} & \frac{1}{2} \end{bmatrix}$

C. $\begin{bmatrix} \frac{1}{6} & \frac{1}{3} \\ -\frac{1}{3} & -\frac{1}{6} \end{bmatrix}$ D. $\begin{bmatrix} 2 & 4 \\ -4 & -2 \end{bmatrix}$

10. What value of x makes the equation $x^2 + 64 = 16x$ true?

A. 4
B. 8
C. 16
D. 32

11. What is the x-value of the vertex of $f(x) = 2x^2 - 15x + 5$?

A. 3.75
B. 4
C. 7.5
D. 8

Short Answer

12. $\begin{cases} -4x + 8y - 2z = 8 \\ 4x - 4y + 2z = -5 \\ x + 4y - 2z = 15 \end{cases}$

Part A Write the augmented matrix that could be used to solve the system of equations given above.

Part B Find the solution of the system, and explain how you determined your answer.

13. The graph below shows a feasible region for a set of constraints.

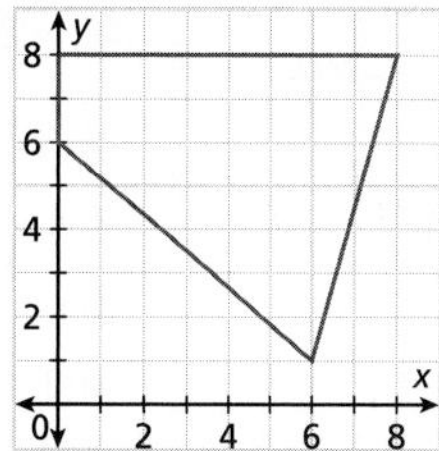

Part A Write the constraints for the feasible region.

Part B Maximize the objective function $P = 3x - 4y$ under these constraints.

14. Consider the function $f(x) = x^2 - 2x - 48$.

Part A Determine the roots of the function. Show or explain your work.

Part B The function f is translated to produce the function g. The vertex of g is the point $(3, 30)$. Write the function rule for g in vertex form, and explain how you determined your answer.

Extended Response

15. A small alteration store charges \$15.00 per hour plus a \$12.50 consulting fee for alterations. A competing store charges \$20.00 per hour but does not charge a consulting fee.

Part A For each store, write a linear function c that can be used to find the total cost of an alteration that takes h hours.

Part B For which values of h is the small alteration store less expensive than the competing store? Show or explain your work.

Part C The small store wants to adjust its pricing so that it is less expensive than the competing store for any alteration job that takes an hour or more. By how much should the small store lower its consulting fee in order to make this adjustment?

Short Answer Rubric

Items 12–14

Score 2 = Thorough understanding of mathematical concepts and processes.

Score 1 = Partial understanding of mathematical concepts and/or processes.

Score 0 = Limited or no understanding of the problem-solving concepts.

Blank = No written response.

Extended Response Rubric

Item 15

Score 4 = Thorough understanding of mathematical concepts and processes.

Score 3 = Demonstrated understanding of mathematical concepts and processes, but an error in computation or explanation.

Score 2 = Partial understanding of mathematical concepts and/or processes.

Score 1 = Limited understanding and execution of the problem-solving concepts.

Score 0 = No understanding of the problem-solving concepts.

Blank = No written response.

Answers

12. Part A: $\left[\begin{array}{ccc|c} -4 & 8 & -2 & 8 \\ 4 & -4 & 2 & -5 \\ 1 & 4 & -2 & 15 \end{array}\right]$

Part B: $(2, 0.75, -5)$; check students' work.

13. Part A: $\begin{cases} x \ge 0 \\ y \le 8 \\ y \ge -\frac{5}{6}x + 6 \\ y \ge \frac{7}{2}x - 20 \end{cases}$

Part B. The maximum value is 14.

14. Part A: −6, 8; check students' work.

Part B: $g(x) = (x-3)^2 + 30$; possible answer: the vertex form of f is $f(x) = (x-1)^2 - 49$. If f is translated so that its vertex is at the point (3, 30), the value of h will change from 1 to 3, and the value of k will change from −49 to 30. Therefore, the function rule for g is $g(x) = (x-3)^2 + 30$.

15. Part A: small store: $c(h) = 15h + 12.50$; competing store: $c(h) = 20h$

Part B: The small store is less expensive for any alteration that takes more than 2.5 h. Possible answer: Set the functions equal to each other, and solve to find the value of h for which the cost is the same at either store. Then substitute a value greater than this value of h and a value less than this value of h into the functions to determine in which interval the small store is less expensive.

Part C: It should lower its consulting fee by at least \$7.51.

CHAPTER 6 Polynomial Functions

Section 6A

Operations with Polynomials

6-1 Polynomials
Connecting Algebra to Number Theory Pascal's Triangle
6-2 Multiplying Polynomials
Connecting Algebra to Geometry Nets
6-3 Dividing Polynomials
6-4 Algebra Lab Explore the Difference of Two Cubes
6-4 Factoring Polynomials

Section 6B

Applying Polynomial Functions

6-5 Finding Real Roots of Polynomial Equations
6-6 Fundamental Theorem of Algebra
6-7 Technology Lab Explore End Behavior
6-7 Investigating Graphs of Polynomial Functions
6-8 Transforming Polynomial Functions
6-9 Curve Fitting with Polynomial Models

Pacing Guide for 45-Minute Classes

Chapter 6

Countdown to Testing Weeks 13, 14

DAY 1	DAY 2	DAY 3	DAY 4	DAY 5
6-1 Lesson	Connecting Algebra to Number Theory 6-2 Lesson	6-2 Lesson Connecting Algebra to Geometry	6-3 Lesson	6-3 Lesson
DAY 6	**DAY 7**	**DAY 8**	**DAY 9**	**DAY 10**
6-4 Algebra Lab 6-4 Lesson	6-4 Lesson Multi-Step Test Prep Ready to Go On?	6-5 Lesson	6-6 Lesson	6-6 Lesson
DAY 11	**DAY 12**	**DAY 13**	**DAY 14**	**DAY 15**
6-7 Technology Lab 6-7 Lesson	6-7 Lesson 6-8 Lesson	6-8 Lesson 6-9 Lesson	6-9 Lesson Multi-Step Test Prep Ready to Go On?	Chapter 6 Test

Pacing Guide for 90-Minute Classes

Chapter 6

DAY 1	DAY 2	DAY 3	DAY 4	DAY 5
6-1 Lesson Connecting Algebra to Number Theory 6-2 Lesson	6-2 Lesson Connecting Algebra to Geometry 6-3 Lesson	6-3 Lesson 6-4 Algebra Lab 6-4 Lesson	6-4 Lesson Multi-Step Test Prep Ready to Go On? 6-5 Lesson	6-6 Lesson
DAY 6	**DAY 7**	**DAY 8**		
6-7 Technology Lab 6-7 Lesson 6-8 Lesson	6-8 Lesson 6-9 Lesson Multi-Step Test Prep Ready to Go On?	Chapter 6 Test 7-1 Lesson		

ONGOING ASSESSMENT and INTERVENTION

Assess Prior Knowledge

Before Chapter 6

DIAGNOSE	PRESCRIBE
Diagnose readiness for the chapter.	Prescribe intervention.
Are You Ready? SE p. 403	***Are You Ready? Intervention*** Skills 8, 41, 42, 60, 61

Formative Assessment

Before Every Lesson

DIAGNOSE	PRESCRIBE
Diagnose readiness for the lesson.	Prescribe intervention.
Warm Up TE, every lesson	**Skills Bank** SE pp. S46–S73
	Reteach CRB, Ch. 1–6

During Every Lesson

DIAGNOSE	PRESCRIBE
Diagnose understanding of lesson concepts.	Prescribe intervention.
Check It Out! SE, every example	**Questioning Strategies** TE, every example
Think and Discuss SE, every lesson	**Reading Strategies** CRB, every lesson
Write About It SE, every lesson	***Success for ELL*** pp. 79–96
Journal TE, every lesson	

After Every Lesson

DIAGNOSE	PRESCRIBE
Diagnose mastery of lesson concepts.	Prescribe intervention.
Lesson Quiz TE, every lesson	**Reteach** CRB, every lesson
Alternative Assessment TE, every lesson	**Problem Solving** CRB, every lesson
Test Prep SE, every lesson	**Test Prep Doctor** TE, every lesson
Test and Practice Generator	***Homework Help Online***

Before Chapter 6 Testing

DIAGNOSE	PRESCRIBE
Diagnose mastery of concepts in the chapter.	Prescribe intervention.
Ready to Go On? SE pp. 437, 473	***Ready to Go On? Intervention*** pp. 91–107
Multi-Step Test Prep SE pp. 436, 472	**Scaffolding Questions** TE pp. 436, 472
Section Quizzes AR pp. 105–106	
Test and Practice Generator	

Before High Stakes Testing

DIAGNOSE	PRESCRIBE
Diagnose mastery of benchmark concepts.	Prescribe intervention.
College Entrance Exam Practice SE p. 479	***College Entrance Exam Practice***
Standardized Test Prep SE pp. 482–483	***State Test Prep Workbook***
***State Test Prep* CD-ROM**	

Summative Assessment

After Chapter 6

DIAGNOSE	PRESCRIBE
Check mastery of chapter concepts.	Prescribe intervention.
Multiple-Choice Tests (Forms A, B, C)	**Reteach** CRB, every lesson
Free-Response Tests (Forms A, B, C)	***Lesson Tutorial Videos*** Chapter 6
Performance Assessment AR pp. 107–120	
Test and Practice Generator	
Check mastery of benchmark concepts.	Prescribe intervention.
AYP State Tests	***State Test Prep Workbook***
College Entrance Exams	***College Entrance Exam Practice***

KEY: **SE** = *Student Edition* **TE** = *Teacher's Edition* **CRB** = *Chapter Resource Book* **AR** = *Assessment Resources* Available on CD-ROM Available online

CHAPTER 6

Supporting the Teacher

Chapter 6 Resource Book

Practice A, B, C
pp. 3–5, 11–13, 19–21, 27–29, 35–37, 43–45, 51–53, 59–61, 67–69

Reading Strategies ELL
pp. 10, 18, 26, 34, 42, 50, 58, 66, 74

Reteach
pp. 6–7, 14–15, 22–23, 30–31, 38–39, 46–47, 54–55, 62–63, 70–71

Problem Solving
pp. 9, 17, 25, 33, 41, 49, 57, 65, 73

Challenge
pp. 8, 16, 24, 32, 40, 48, 56, 64, 72

Parent Letter pp. 1–2

Transparencies

Lesson Transparencies, Volume 2 .... Chapter 6
- Warm Ups
- Teaching Transparencies
- Additional Examples
- Lesson Quizzes

Alternate Openers: Explorations 40–48

Countdown to Testing 25–28

Know-It Notebook .... Chapter 6
- Graphic Organizers

Teacher Tools

Power Presentations®
Complete PowerPoint® presentations for Chapter 6 lessons

Lesson Tutorial Videos®
Holt authors Ed Burger and Freddie Renfro present tutorials to support the Chapter 6 lessons.

One-Stop Planner®
Easy access to all Chapter 6 resources and assessments, as well as software for lesson planning, test generation, and puzzle creation

IDEA Works!®
Key Chapter 6 resources and assessments modified to address special learning needs

Lesson Plans .... pp. 40–48

Solutions Key .... Chapter 6

Algebra Posters

TechKeys

Lab Resources

Project Teacher Support

Parent Resources 

Workbooks

Homework and Practice Workbook
Teacher's Guide .... pp. 40–48

Know-It Notebook
Teacher's Guide .... Chapter 6

Problem Solving Workbook
Teacher's Guide .... pp. 40–48

State Test Prep Workbook
Teacher's Guide

Technology Highlights for the Teacher

Power Presentations

Dynamic presentations to engage students. Complete PowerPoint® presentations for every lesson in Chapter 6.

2-1 Solving One-Step Equations

Isolate a variable by using inverse operations which "undo" operations on the variable.

An equation is like a balanced scale. To keep the balance, perform the same operation on both sides.

Inverse Operations	
Operation	**Inverse Operation**
Addition	Subtraction
Subtraction	Addition

One-Stop Planner

Easy access to Chapter 6 resources and assessments. Includes lesson-planning, test-generation, and puzzle-creation software.

Premier Online Edition

Chapter 6 includes Tutorial Videos, Lesson Activities, Lesson Quizzes, Homework Help, and Chapter Project.

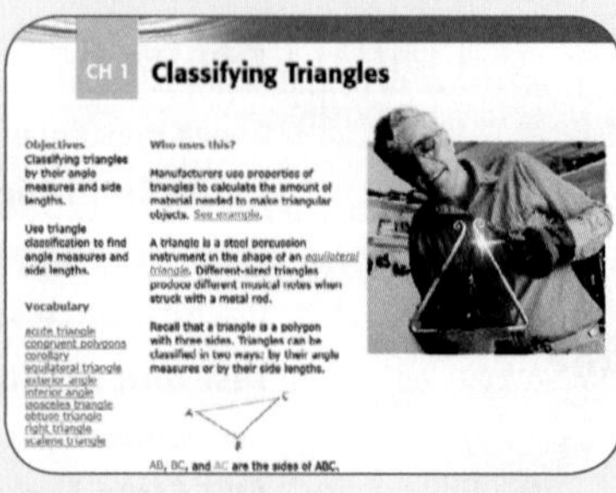

KEY: **SE** = *Student Edition* **TE** = *Teacher's Edition*  English Language Learners  Available on CD-ROM 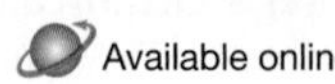 Available online

Reaching All Learners

Resources for All Learners

Algebra Lab Activities .... Chapter 6
Technology Lab Activities .... Chapter 6
Homework and Practice Workbook .... pp. 40–48
Know-It Notebook .... Chapter 6
Problem Solving Workbook .... pp. 40–48

DEVELOPING LEARNERS

Practice A .... CRB, every lesson
Reteach .... CRB, every lesson
Inclusion .... TE pp. 407, 408, 423, 440, 448
Questioning Strategies .... TE, every example
Modified Chapter 6 Resources .... *IDEA Works!*
***Homework Help* Online**

ON-LEVEL LEARNERS

Practice B .... CRB, every lesson
Graphic Organizers .... TE p. 407
Multiple Representations .... TE pp. 423, 432, 446

ADVANCED LEARNERS

Practice C .... CRB, every lesson
Challenge .... CRB, every lesson
Reading and Writing Math EXTENSION .... TE p. 405
Multi-Step Test Prep EXTENSION .... TE pp. 436, 472
Critical Thinking .... TE pp. 419, 439, 458, 470

English Language Learners

ENGLISH LANGUAGE LEARNERS

Are You Ready? Vocabulary .... SE p. 403
Vocabulary Connections .... SE p. 404
Lesson Vocabulary .... SE pp. 406, 422, 438, 453
Vocabulary Exercises .... SE pp. 410, 426, 442, 457
Vocabulary Review .... SE p. 474
English Language Learners .... TE pp. 405, 412, 423, 431, 447
Reading Strategies .... CRB, every lesson
Success for English Language Learners .... pp. 79–96
Multilingual Glossary

Reaching All Learners Through...

Graphic Organizers .... TE p. 407
Inclusion .... TE pp. 407, 408, 423, 440, 448
Visual Cues .... TE pp. 413, 415, 450, 454, 464, 467
Diversity .... TE p. 416
Critical Thinking .... TE pp. 419, 439, 458, 470
Kinesthetic Experience .... TE pp. 421, 432
Multiple Representations .... TE pp. 423, 432, 446
Cognitive Strategies .... TE pp. 431, 454
Cooperative Learning .... TE p. 461
Test Prep Doctor .... TE pp. 412, 420, 428, 434, 444, 451, 459, 465, 471, 479, 480, 482
Common Error Alerts .... TE pp. 411, 417, 425, 427, 441, 443, 447, 455
Scaffolding Questions .... TE pp. 436, 472

Technology Highlights for Reaching All Learners

Lesson Tutorial Videos

Starring Holt authors Ed Burger and Freddie Renfro! Live tutorials to support every lesson in Chapter 6.

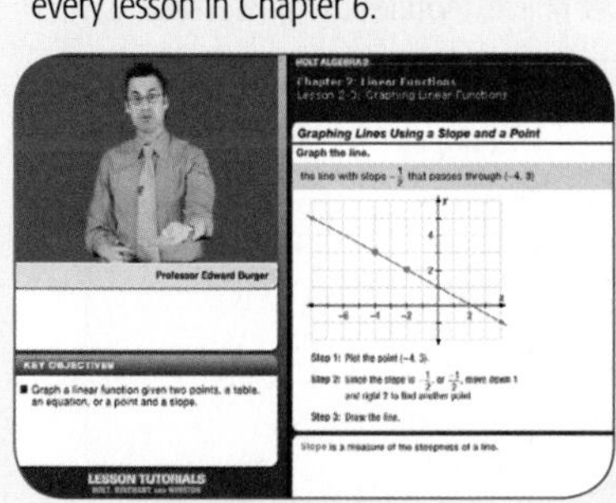

Multilingual Glossary

Searchable glossary includes definitions in English, Spanish, Vietnamese, Chinese, Hmong, Korean, and 4 other languages.

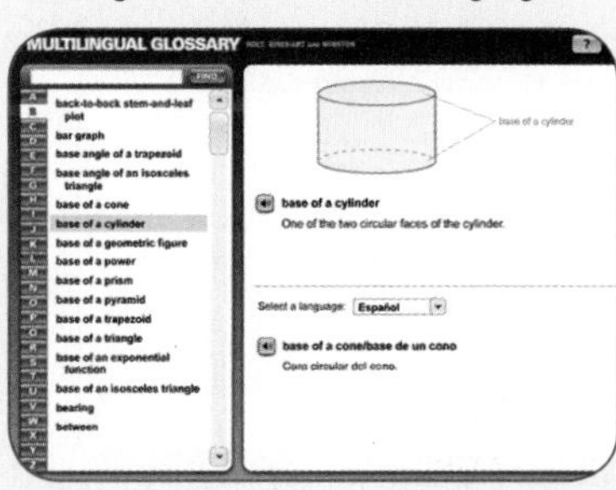

Online Interactivities

Interactive tutorials provide visually engaging alternative opportunities to learn concepts and master skills.

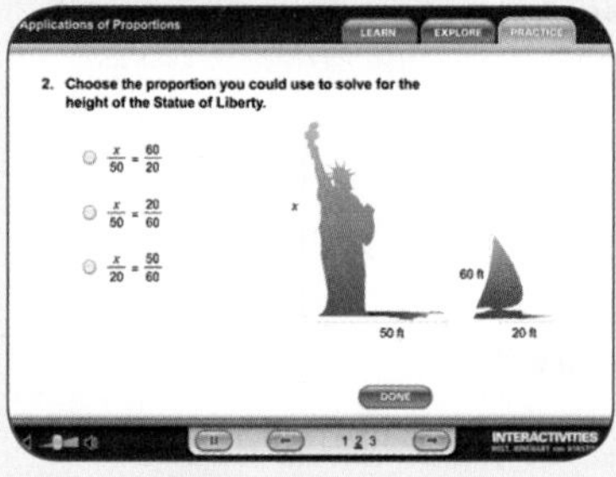

KEY: **SE** = *Student Edition* **TE** = *Teacher's Edition* **CRB** = *Chapter Resource Book* Available on CD-ROM Available online

Ongoing Assessment

Assessing Prior Knowledge

Determine whether students have the required prerequisite concepts and skills for success in Chapter 6.

Are You Ready? SPANISH .... SE p. 403

Warm Up .... TE, every lesson

Test Preparation

Provide review and practice for Chapter 6 and standardized tests.

Multi-Step Test Prep .... SE pp. 436, 472

Study Guide: Review .... SE pp. 474–477

Test Tackler .... SE pp. 480–481

Standardized Test Prep .... SE pp. 482–483

College Entrance Exam Practice .... SE p. 479

***Countdown to Testing* Transparencies** 25–28

State Test Prep Workbook

***State Test Prep* CD-ROM**

IDEA Works!

Alternative Assessment

Assess students' understanding of Chapter 6 concepts and combined problem-solving skills.

Chapter 6 Project .... SE p. 402

Alternative Assessment .... TE, every lesson

Performance Assessment .... AR pp. 119–120

Portfolio Assessment .... AR p. xxxiv

Daily Assessment

Provide formative assessment for each day of Chapter 6.

Questioning Strategies .... TE, every example

Think and Discuss .... SE, every lesson

Check It Out! Exercises .... SE, every example

Write About It .... SE, every lesson

Journal .... TE, every lesson

Lesson Quiz .... TE, every lesson

Alternative Assessment .... TE, every lesson

Modified Lesson Quizzes .... *IDEA Works!*

Weekly Assessment

Provide formative assessment for each week of Chapter 6.

Multi-Step Test Prep .... SE pp. 436, 472

Ready to Go On? .... SE pp. 437, 473

Cumulative Assessment .... SE pp. 482–483

Test and Practice Generator .... *One-Stop Planner*

Formal Assessment

Provide summative assessment of Chapter 6 mastery.

Section Quizzes .... AR pp. 105–106

Chapter 6 Test .... SE p. 478

Chapter Test (Levels A, B, C) .... AR pp. 107–118
- Multiple Choice
- Free Response

Cumulative Test .... AR pp. 121–124

Test and Practice Generator .... *One-Stop Planner*

Modified Chapter 6 Test .... *IDEA Works!*

Technology Highlights for Ongoing Assessment

Are You Ready? SPANISH

Automatically assess readiness and prescribe intervention for Chapter 6 prerequisite skills.

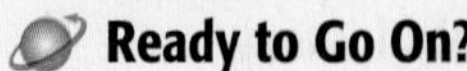

Ready to Go On?

Automatically assess understanding and prescribe intervention for Sections 6A and 6B.

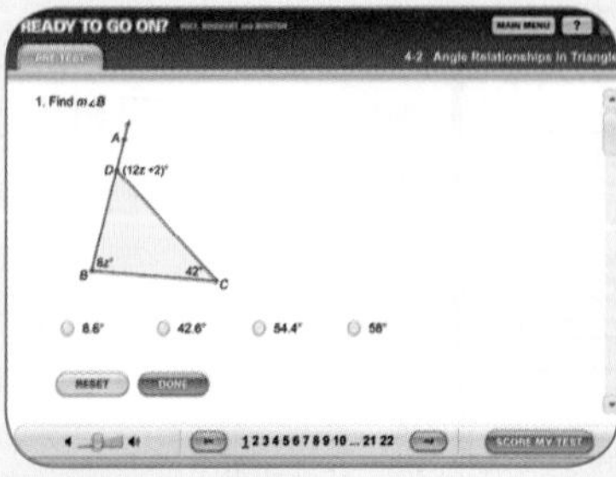

Test and Practice Generator

Use Chapter 6 problem banks to create assessments and worksheets to print out or deliver online. Includes dynamic problems.

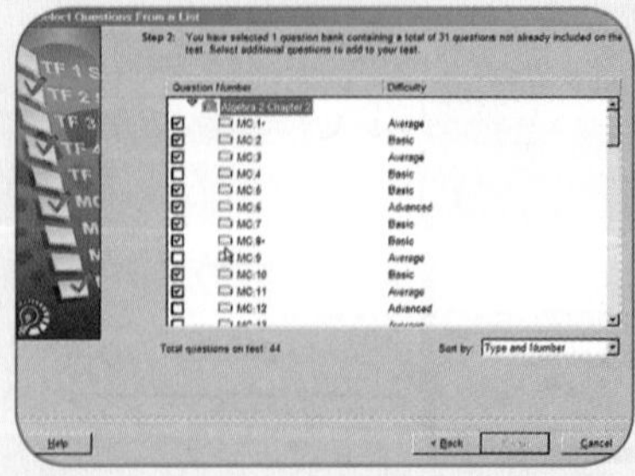

KEY: **SE** = *Student Edition* **TE** = *Teacher's Edition* **AR** = *Assessment Resources*  Spanish version available  Available on CD-ROM 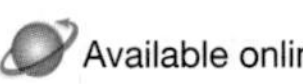 Available online

Three levels (A, B, C) of multiple-choice and free-response chapter tests are available in the *Assessment Resources.*

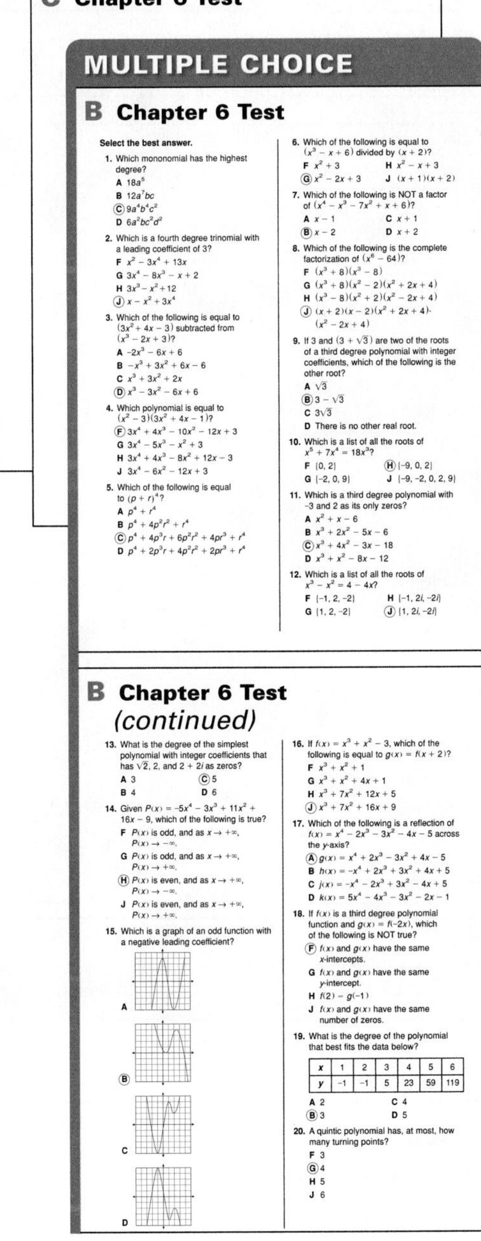

A Chapter 6 Test

C Chapter 6 Test

MULTIPLE CHOICE

B Chapter 6 Test

Select the best answer.

1. Which mononomial has the highest degree?
 A $18a^5$
 B $12a^7bc$
 (C) $9a^4b^4c^2$
 D $6a^2bc^3d^2$
2. Which is a fourth degree trinomial with a leading coefficient of 3?
 F $x^2 - 3x^4 + 13x$
 G $3x^4 - 8x^3 - x + 2$
 H $3x^3 - x^2 + 12$
 (J) $x - x^2 + 3x^4$
3. Which of the following is equal to $(3x^2 + 4x - 3)$ subtracted from $(x^3 - 2x + 3)$?
 A $-2x^3 - 6x + 6$
 B $-x^3 + 3x^2 + 6x - 6$
 C $x^3 + 3x^2 + 2x$
 (D) $x^3 - 3x^2 - 6x + 6$
4. Which polynomial is equal to $(x^2 - 3)(3x^2 + 4x - 1)$?
 (F) $3x^4 + 4x^3 - 10x^2 - 12x + 3$
 G $3x^4 - 5x^3 - x^2 + 3$
 H $3x^4 + 4x^3 - 8x^2 + 12x - 3$
 J $3x^4 - 6x^2 - 12x + 3$
5. Which of the following is equal to $(p + r)^4$?
 A $p^4 + r^4$
 B $p^4 + 4p^2r^2 + r^4$
 (C) $p^4 + 4p^3r + 6p^2r^2 + 4pr^3 + r^4$
 D $p^4 + 2p^3r + 4p^2r^2 + 2pr^3 + r^4$
6. Which of the following is equal to $(x^3 - x + 6)$ divided by $(x + 2)$?
 F $x^2 + 3$
 (G) $x^2 - 2x + 3$
 H $x^2 - x + 3$
 J $(x + 1)(x + 2)$
7. Which of the following is NOT a factor of $(x^4 - x^3 - 7x^2 + x + 6)$?
 A $x - 1$
 (B) $x - 2$
 C $x + 1$
 D $x + 2$
8. Which of the following is the complete factorization of $(x^6 - 64)$?
 F $(x^3 + 8)(x^3 - 8)$
 G $(x^3 + 8)(x^2 - 2)(x^2 + 2x + 4)$
 H $(x^3 - 8)(x^2 + 2)(x^2 - 2x + 4)$
 (J) $(x + 2)(x - 2)(x^2 + 2x + 4)(x^2 - 2x + 4)$
9. If 3 and $(3 + \sqrt{3})$ are two of the roots of a third degree polynomial with integer coefficients, which of the following is the other root?
 A $\sqrt{3}$
 (B) $3 - \sqrt{3}$
 C $3\sqrt{3}$
 D There is no other real root.
10. Which is a list of all the roots of $x^5 + 7x^4 = 18x^3$?
 F {0, 2}
 G {-2, 0, 9}
 (H) {-9, 0, 2}
 J {-9, -2, 0, 2, 9}
11. Which is a third degree polynomial with -3 and 2 as its only zeros?
 A $x^2 + x - 6$
 B $x^3 + 2x^2 - 5x - 6$
 (C) $x^3 + 4x^2 - 3x - 18$
 D $x^3 + x^2 - 8x - 12$
12. Which is a list of all the roots of $x^3 - x^2 = 4 - 4x$?
 F {-1, 2, -2}
 G {1, 2, -2}
 H {-1, 2i, -2i}
 (J) {1, 2i, -2i}

B Chapter 6 Test *(continued)*

13. What is the degree of the simplest polynomial with integer coefficients that has $\sqrt{2}$, 2, and $2 + 2i$ as zeros?
 A 3
 B 4
 (C) 5
 D 6
14. Given $P(x) = -5x^4 - 3x^3 + 11x^2 + 16x - 9$, which of the following is true?
 F $P(x)$ is odd, and as $x \to +\infty$, $P(x) \to -\infty$.
 G $P(x)$ is odd, and as $x \to +\infty$, $P(x) \to +\infty$.
 (H) $P(x)$ is even, and as $x \to +\infty$, $P(x) \to -\infty$.
 J $P(x)$ is even, and as $x \to +\infty$, $P(x) \to +\infty$.
15. Which is a graph of an odd function with a negative leading coefficient?
 A (graph) (B) (graph) C (graph) D (graph)
16. If $f(x) = x^3 + x^2 - 3$, which of the following is equal to $g(x) = f(x + 2)$?
 F $x^3 + x^2 + 1$
 G $x^3 + x^2 + 4x + 1$
 H $x^3 + 7x^2 + 12x + 5$
 (J) $x^3 + 7x^2 + 16x + 9$
17. Which of the following is a reflection of $f(x) = x^4 - 2x^3 - 3x^2 - 4x - 5$ across the y-axis?
 (A) $g(x) = x^4 + 2x^3 - 3x^2 + 4x - 5$
 B $h(x) = -x^4 + 2x^3 + 3x^2 + 4x + 5$
 C $j(x) = -x^4 - 2x^3 + 3x^2 - 4x + 5$
 D $k(x) = 5x^4 - 4x^3 - 3x^2 - 2x - 1$
18. If $f(x)$ is a third degree polynomial function and $g(x) = f(-2x)$, which of the following is NOT true?
 (F) $f(x)$ and $g(x)$ have the same x-intercepts.
 G $f(x)$ and $g(x)$ have the same y-intercept.
 H $f(2) = g(-1)$
 J $f(x)$ and $g(x)$ have the same number of zeros.
19. What is the degree of the polynomial that best fits the data below?

x	1	2	3	4	5	6
y	-1	-1	5	23	59	119

 A 2
 (B) 3
 C 4
 D 5
20. A quintic polynomial has, at most, how many turning points?
 F 3
 (G) 4
 H 5
 J 6

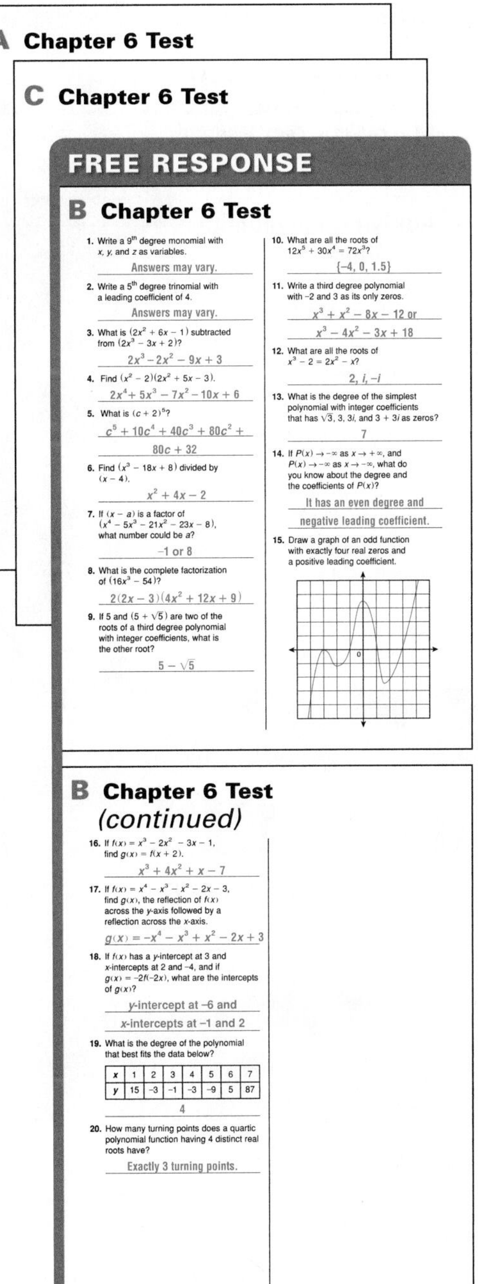

A Chapter 6 Test

C Chapter 6 Test

FREE RESPONSE

B Chapter 6 Test

1. Write a 9th degree monomial with x, y, and z as variables.
 Answers may vary.
2. Write a 5th degree trinomial with a leading coefficient of 4.
 Answers may vary.
3. What is $(2x^2 + 6x - 1)$ subtracted from $(2x^3 - 3x + 2)$?
 $2x^3 - 2x^2 - 9x + 3$
4. Find $(x^2 - 2)(2x^2 + 5x - 3)$.
 $2x^4 + 5x^3 - 7x^2 - 10x + 6$
5. What is $(c + 2)^5$?
 $c^5 + 10c^4 + 40c^3 + 80c^2 + 80c + 32$
6. Find $(x^3 - 18x + 8)$ divided by $(x - 4)$.
 $x^2 + 4x - 2$
7. If $(x - a)$ is a factor of $(x^4 - 5x^3 - 21x^2 - 23x - 8)$, what number could be a?
 -1 or 8
8. What is the complete factorization of $(16x^3 - 54)$?
 $2(2x - 3)(4x^2 + 12x + 9)$
9. If 5 and $(5 + \sqrt{5})$ are two of the roots of a third degree polynomial with integer coefficients, what is the other root?
 $5 - \sqrt{5}$
10. What are all the roots of $12x^5 + 30x^4 = 72x^3$?
 {-4, 0, 1.5}
11. Write a third degree polynomial with -2 and 3 as its only zeros.
 $x^3 + x^2 - 8x - 12$ or $x^3 - 4x^2 - 3x + 18$
12. What are all the roots of $x^3 - 2 = 2x^2 - x$?
 2, i, −i
13. What is the degree of the simplest polynomial with integer coefficients that has $\sqrt{3}$, 3, 3i, and $3 + 3i$ as zeros?
 7
14. If $P(x) \to -\infty$ as $x \to +\infty$, and $P(x) \to -\infty$ as $x \to -\infty$, what do you know about the degree and the coefficients of $P(x)$?
 It has an even degree and negative leading coefficient.
15. Draw a graph of an odd function with exactly four real zeros and a positive leading coefficient.
 (graph)

B Chapter 6 Test *(continued)*

16. If $f(x) = x^3 - 2x^2 - 3x - 1$, find $g(x) = f(x + 2)$.
 $x^3 + 4x^2 + x - 7$
17. If $f(x) = x^4 - x^3 - x^2 - 2x - 3$, find $g(x)$, the reflection of $f(x)$ across the y-axis followed by a reflection across the x-axis.
 $g(x) = -x^4 - x^3 + x^2 - 2x + 3$
18. If $f(x)$ has a y-intercept at 3 and x-intercepts at 2 and -4, and if $g(x) = -2f(-2x)$, what are the intercepts of $g(x)$?
 y-intercept at -6 and x-intercepts at -1 and 2
19. What is the degree of the polynomial that best fits the data below?

x	1	2	3	4	5	6	7
y	15	-3	-1	-3	-9	5	87

 4
20. How many turning points does a quartic polynomial function having 4 distinct real roots have?
 Exactly 3 turning points.

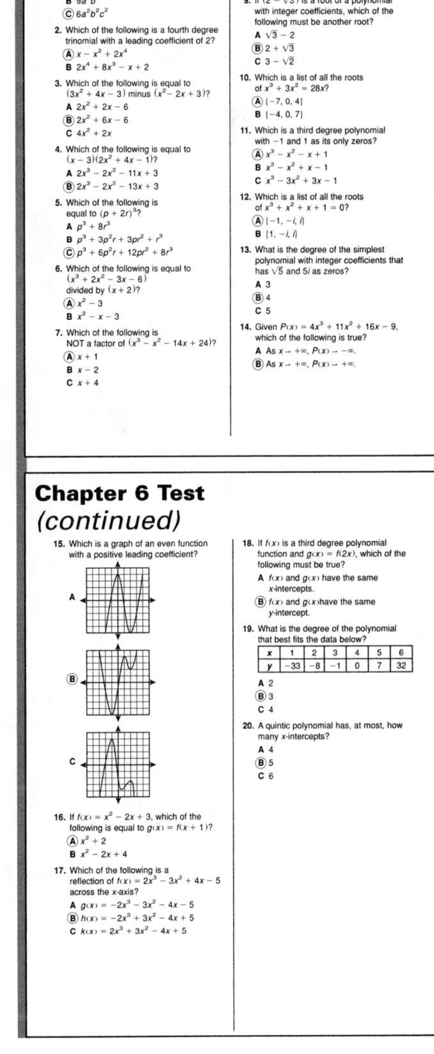

MODIFIED FOR IDEA

Chapter 6 Test

Select the best answer.

1. Which monomial has the highest degree?
 A $12a^6b$
 B $9a^4b^4$
 (C) $6a^2b^5c^2$
2. Which of the following is a fourth degree trinomial with a leading coefficient of 2?
 (A) $x - x^2 + 2x^4$
 B $2x^4 + 8x^3 - x + 2$
3. Which of the following is equal to $(3x^2 + 4x - 3)$ minus $(x^2 - 2x + 3)$?
 A $2x^2 + 2x - 6$
 (B) $2x^2 + 6x - 6$
 C $4x^2 + 2x$
4. Which of the following is equal to $(x - 3)(2x^2 + 4x - 1)$?
 A $2x^3 - 2x^2 - 11x + 3$
 (B) $2x^3 - 2x^2 - 13x + 3$
5. Which of the following is equal to $(p + 2r)^3$?
 A $p^3 + 8r^3$
 B $p^3 + 3p^2r + 3pr^2 + r^3$
 (C) $p^3 + 6p^2r + 12pr^2 + 8r^3$
6. Which of the following is equal to $(x^3 + 2x^2 - 3x - 6)$ divided by $(x + 2)$?
 (A) $x^2 - 3$
 B $x^2 - x - 3$
7. Which of the following is NOT a factor of $(x^3 - x^2 - 14x + 24)$?
 (A) $x + 1$
 B $x - 2$
 C $x + 4$
8. Which of the following is the complete factorization of $(x^4 - 16)$?
 A $(x^2 + 4)(x^2 - 4)$
 (B) $(x^2 + 4)(x + 2)(x - 2)$
9. If $(2 - \sqrt{3})$ is a root of a polynomial with integer coefficients, which of the following must be another root?
 A $\sqrt{3} - 2$
 (B) $2 + \sqrt{3}$
 C $3 - \sqrt{2}$
10. Which is a list of all the roots of $x^3 + 3x^2 = 28x$?
 (A) {-7, 0, 4}
 B {-4, 0, 7}
11. Which is a third degree polynomial with -1 and 1 as its only zeros?
 (A) $x^3 - x^2 - x + 1$
 B $x^3 - x^2 + x - 1$
 C $x^3 - 3x^2 + 3x - 1$
12. Which is a list of all the roots of $x^3 + x^2 + x + 1 = 0$?
 (A) {-1, -i, i}
 B {1, -i, i}
13. What is the degree of the simplest polynomial with integer coefficients that has $\sqrt{5}$ and 5i as zeros?
 A 3
 (B) 4
 C 5
14. Given $P(x) = 4x^3 + 11x^2 + 16x - 9$, which of the following is true?
 A As $x \to +\infty$, $P(x) \to -\infty$.
 (B) As $x \to +\infty$, $P(x) \to +\infty$.

Chapter 6 Test *(continued)*

15. Which is a graph of an even function with a positive leading coefficient?
 A (graph) (B) (graph) C (graph)
16. If $f(x) = x^2 - 2x + 3$, which of the following is equal to $g(x) = f(x + 1)$?
 (A) $x^2 + 2$
 B $x^2 - 2x + 4$
17. Which of the following is a reflection of $f(x) = 2x^3 - 3x^2 + 4x - 5$ across the x-axis?
 A $g(x) = -2x^3 - 3x^2 - 4x - 5$
 (B) $h(x) = -2x^3 + 3x^2 - 4x + 5$
 C $k(x) = 2x^3 + 3x^2 - 4x + 5$
18. If $f(x)$ is a third degree polynomial function and $g(x) = f(2x)$, which of the following must be true?
 A $f(x)$ and $g(x)$ have the same x-intercepts.
 (B) $f(x)$ and $g(x)$ have the same y-intercept.
19. What is the degree of the polynomial that best fits the data below?

x	1	2	3	4	5	6
y	-33	-8	-1	0	7	32

 A 2
 (B) 3
 C 4
20. A quintic polynomial has, at most, how many x-intercepts?
 A 4
 (B) 5
 C 6

Create and customize Chapter 6 Tests. Instantly generate multiple test versions, answer keys, and practice versions of test items.

CHAPTER 6

SECTION 6A
Operations with Polynomials

On page 436, students apply operations with polynomials to model real-world stage lights.

Exercises designed to prepare students for success on the Multi-Step Test Prep can be found on pages 411, 419, 427, and 434.

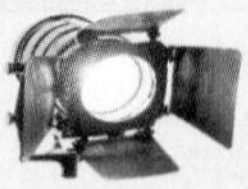

SECTION 6B
Applying Polynomial Functions

On page 472, students apply polynomial functions to model building pyramids.

Exercises designed to prepare students for success on the Multi-Step Test Prep can be found on pages 443, 450, 458, 464, and 470.

CHAPTER 6

Polynomial Functions

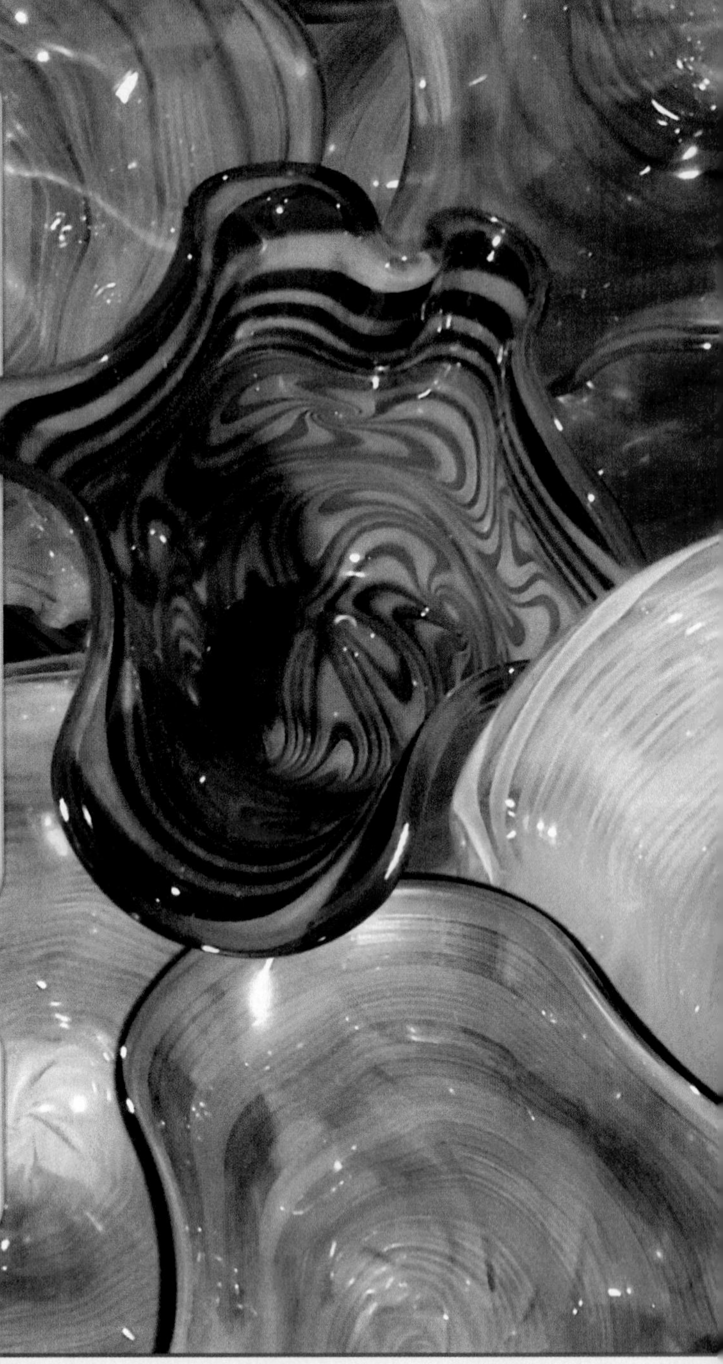

FILL IT UP!

You can use polynomials to predict the shape of containers.

go.hrw.com
Chapter Project Online
KEYWORD: MB7 ChProj

Fill It Up!

About the Project

In the Chapter Project, students collect data on the relationship between the volume of water in a container and the height of the water. Students then use the data to write polynomial functions that model the relationship between volume and height.

Project Resources

All project resources for teachers and students are provided online.

Materials:

- irregularly shaped containers
- beaker
- ruler
- water

ARE YOU READY?

Vocabulary

Match each term on the left with a definition on the right.

1. coefficient C
2. like terms E
3. root of an equation D
4. x-intercept F
5. maximum of a function A

A. the y-value of the highest point on the graph of the function
B. the horizontal number line that divides the coordinate plane
C. the numerical factor in a term
D. a value of the variable that makes the equation true
E. terms that contain the same variables raised to the same powers
F. the x-coordinate of a point where a graph intersects the x-axis

Evaluate Powers

Evaluate each expression.

6. 6^4 1296
7. -5^4 -625
8. $(-1)^5$ -1
9. $\left(-\frac{2}{3}\right)^2$ $\frac{4}{9}$

Evaluate Expressions

Evaluate each expression for the given value of the variable.

10. $x^4 - 5x^2 - 6x - 8$ for $x = 3$ 10
11. $2x^3 - 3x^2 - 29x - 30$ for $x = -2$ 0
12. $2x^3 - x^2 - 8x + 4$ for $x = \frac{1}{2}$ 0
13. $3x^4 + 5x^3 + 6x^2 + 4x - 1$ for $x = -1$ -1

Multiply and Divide Monomials

Multiply or divide.

14. $2x^3y \cdot 4x^2$ $8x^5y$
15. $-5a^2b \cdot ab^4$ $-5a^3b^5$
16. $\frac{-7t^4}{3t^2}$ $-\frac{7}{3}t^2$
17. $\frac{3p^3q^2r}{12pr^4}$ $\frac{p^2q^2}{4r^3}$

Surface Area

Find the surface area of each solid.

18. cube with side length 4 cm 96 cm^2
19. rectangular prism with height 3 ft, width 1.5 ft, and length 8 ft 81 ft^2

Volume

Find the volume of each solid.

20. rectangular prism with height 1 in., width 6 in., and length $\frac{2}{3}$ in. 4 in^3
21. rectangular prism with height 5 cm and a square base with side length 2 cm 20 cm^3

CHAPTER 6

ARE YOU READY?

Organizer

Objective: Assess students' understanding of prerequisite skills.

Prerequisite Skills

Evaluate Powers
Evaluate Expressions
Multiply and Divide Monomials
Surface Area
Volume

Assessing Prior Knowledge

INTERVENTION

Diagnose and Prescribe

Use this page to determine whether intervention is necessary or whether enrichment is appropriate.

Resources

 ***Are You Ready? Intervention and Enrichment* Worksheets**

 ***Are You Ready?* CD-ROM**

 ***Are You Ready?* Online**

my.hrw.com

ARE YOU READY? Diagnose and Prescribe

NO INTERVENE

Prerequisite Skill	*Are You Ready? Intervention,* Chapter 6 Worksheets	CD-ROM	Online
Evaluate Powers	Skill 8	Activity 8	Diagnose and Prescribe Online
Evaluate Expressions	Skill 60	Activity 60	
Multiply and Divide Monomials	Skill 61	Activity 61	
Surface Area	Skill 41	Activity 41	
Volume	Skill 42	Activity 42	

YES ENRICH

Are You Ready? Enrichment, Chapter 6
Worksheets
CD-ROM
Online

CHAPTER 6 Study Guide: Preview

Organizer

Objective: Help students organize the new concepts they will learn in Chapter 6.

Online Edition
Multilingual Glossary

Resources

***Multilingual Glossary* Online**

go.hrw.com
KEYWORD: MB7 Glossary

Answers to *Vocabulary Connections*

1. The leading runner would be first in the race. The leading coefficient would be first in the polynomial.
2. local maximum
3. Possible answer: Monorail, monopoly, monotone; they all have "one" in their definitions.
4. Possible answer: The graph of the polynomial might change direction.

CHAPTER 6

Study Guide: Preview

Where You've Been

Previously, you

- used transformations to graph quadratic functions.
- solved quadratic equations.
- used the Zero Product Property to find the zeros of quadratic functions.
- modeled data with quadratic models.

In This Chapter

You will study

- using transformations to graph polynomial functions.
- solving polynomial equations.
- the zeros of polynomial functions.
- modeling data with polynomial models.

Where You're Going

You can use the skills in this chapter

- to solve problems in future math classes, including College Algebra and Trigonometry.
- to solve real-life problems in physics and graphic arts.
- to predict the value of stocks.
- to maximize or minimize volume and area.

Key Vocabulary/Vocabulario

end behavior	comportamiento extremo
leading coefficient	coeficiente principal
local maximum	máximo local
local minimum	mínimo local
monomial	monomio
multiplicity	multiplicidad
polynomial	polinomio
polynomial function	función polinomial
synthetic division	división sintética
turning point	punto de inflexión

Vocabulary Connections

To become familiar with some of the vocabulary terms in the chapter, consider the following. You may refer to the chapter, the glossary, or a dictionary if you like.

1. In what position would you find the *leading* runner in a race? In what position do you suppose you would find the **leading coefficient** in a polynomial?
2. A **local minimum** of a function is a value less than any other value in the region around it. Which of the vocabulary terms do you think describes the value of a function that is greater than any other value in the region around it?
3. The word **monomial** begins with the root *mono-*. List some other words that begin with *mono-*. What do all of these words have in common?
4. The everyday meaning of **turning point** is "a point at which a change takes place." What might happen at a *turning point* on the graph of a polynomial function?

Reading and Writing Math

CHAPTER 6

Study Strategy: Remember Theorems and Formulas

In math, there are many formulas, properties, theorems, and rules that you must commit to memory. To help you remember an important rule, write it on an index card. Include a diagram or an example, and add notes about the important details. Study your index cards on a regular basis.

From Lesson 5-6

The Quadratic Formula

If $ax^2 + bx + c = 0$ $(a \neq 0)$, then the solutions, or roots, are

$$x = \frac{-b \pm \sqrt{b^2 - 4ac}}{2a}.$$

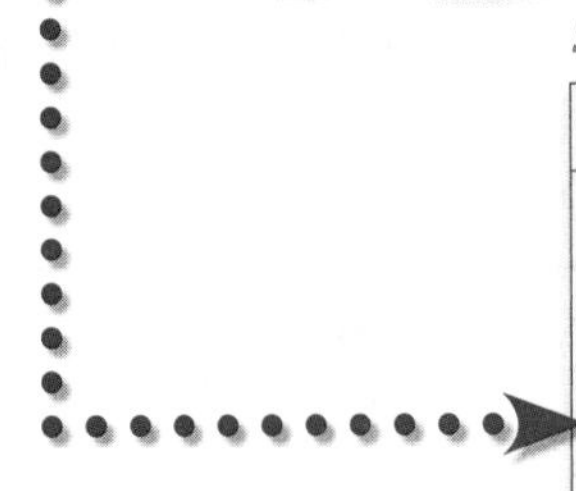

Sample Index Card

Quadratic Formula
If $ax^2 + bx + c = 0$ $(a \neq 0)$, then the roots are

$$x = \frac{-b \pm \sqrt{b^2 - 4ac}}{2a}$$

- *This can be used to solve any quadratic equation.*
- *Before using the formula, make sure the equation is written in standard form.*
- *$f(x) = x^2 + 2x - 24 \rightarrow x = \dfrac{-(2) \pm \sqrt{(2)^2 - 4(1)(-24)}}{2(1)}$*

Try This

1. Create index cards for the discriminant formulas shown in the table below.
2. Explain why you need to understand the principles and concepts of the quadratic formula prior to memorizing the discriminant properties.
3. Describe a plan to help you memorize the quadratic formula and the discriminant formulas.

Discriminant

The discriminant of the quadratic equation $ax^2 + bx + c = 0$ $(a \neq 0)$ is $b^2 - 4ac$.

If $b^2 - 4ac > 0$, the equation has two distinct real solutions.	If $b^2 - 4ac = 0$, the equation has one distinct real solution.	If $b^2 - 4ac < 0$, the equation has two distinct nonreal complex solutions.
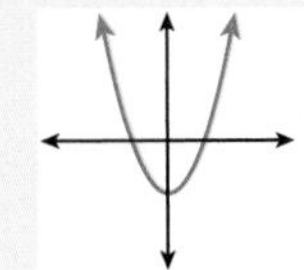	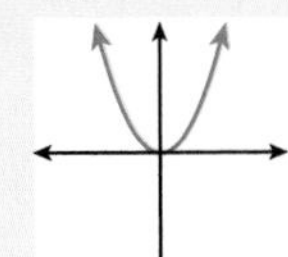	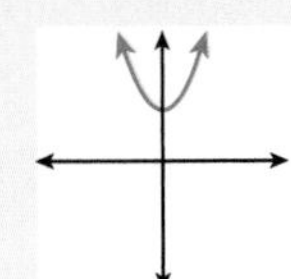

Reading and Writing Math

CHAPTER 6

Organizer

Objective: Help students apply strategies to understand and retain key concepts.

Online Edition

Resources

Chapter 6 Resource Book
Reading Strategies

ENGLISH LANGUAGE LEARNERS

Study Strategy: Remember Theorems and Formulas

Discuss Students benefit from writing rules on index cards because they use their own words to summarize important principles and concepts. This process helps students learn and communicate the ideas. Encourage students to identify ways to make their index cards useful.

Extend As students work through Chapter 6, have them make cards for all the new theorems and concepts. Remind students to include explanations and examples.

The cards do not have to be limited to theorems and formulas. The cards can be a handy reference of steps for finding roots of polynomial equations. The cards can provide a quick check for graphing or transforming polynomial functions.

Answers to *Try This*

Possible answers:

1. Check students' cards. Cards should include a graph.
2. The discriminant is part of the quadratic formula. By knowing the quadratic formula, I can remember the discriminant.
3. Possible answer: I plan to learn the quadratic formula first, and then apply what I know about the quadratic formula to help me learn the properties of the discriminant.

SECTION 6A

Operations with Polynomials

One-Minute Section Planner

Lesson	Lab Resources	Materials
Lesson 6-1 Polynomials • Identify, evaluate, add, and subtract polynomials. • Classify and graph polynomials. ☐ SAT-10 ☑ NAEP ☑ ACT ☐ SAT ☑ SAT Subject Tests	***Algebra Lab Activities*** 6-1 Algebra Lab	**Required** graphing calculator
Lesson 6-2 Multiplying Polynomials • Multiply polynomials. • Use binomial expansion to expand binomial expressions that are raised to positive integer powers. ☐ SAT-10 ☑ NAEP ☐ ACT ☐ SAT ☑ SAT Subject Tests		**Optional** colored pencils (MK)
Lesson 6-3 Dividing Polynomials • Use long division and synthetic division to divide polynomials. ☐ SAT-10 ☑ NAEP ☐ ACT ☐ SAT ☑ SAT Subject Tests		**Optional** graphing calculator
6-4 Algebra Lab Explore the Sum and Difference of Two Cubes • Use models to explore factoring the difference and sum of two cubes. ☐ SAT-10 ☑ NAEP ☐ ACT ☐ SAT ☐ SAT Subject Tests	***Algebra Lab Activities*** 6-4 Lab Recording Sheet	**Optional** unit cubes or blocks
Lesson 6-4 Factoring Polynomials • Use the Factor Theorem to determine factors of a polynomial. • Factor the sum and difference of two cubes. ☐ SAT-10 ☑ NAEP ☑ ACT ☐ SAT ☐ SAT Subject Tests		**Optional** graphing calculator

MK = *Manipulatives Kit*

Section Overview

Polynomials

Lesson 6-1

Knowing the terminology and classifications for polynomials enables students to accurately discuss mathematical ideas and problems.

A **polynomial** is a monomial or a sum or difference of monomials.

Classifying Polynomials by Degree	
Name	**Degree**
Constant	0
Linear	1
Quadratic	2
Cubic	3
Quartic	4

Classifying Polynomials by Number of Terms	
Name	**Terms**
Monomial	1
Binomial	2
Trinomial	3

Example: $7x^4 + 3x^3 + 8$
quartic trinomial

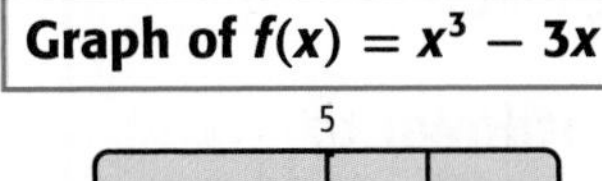
Graph of $f(x) = x^3 - 3x$

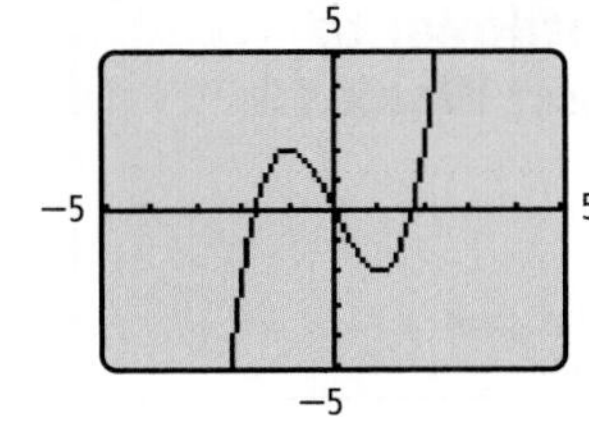

three x-intercepts → three real roots

Multiplying and Dividing Polynomials

Lessons 6-2, 6-3

Students need to know how to multiply and divide polynomials in order to simplify expressions and evaluate formulas.

Binomial Expansion

$n = 0$	1
$n = 1$	1 1
$n = 2$	1 2 1
$n = 3$	1 3 3 1
$n = 4$	1 4 6 4 1

$$(x+1)^4 = 1x^4 + 4x^3 + 6x^2 + 4x + 1x^0$$
$$= x^4 + 4x^3 + 6x^2 + 4x + 1$$

Synthetic Division

$x + 1\overline{)x^4 + 4x^3 + 6x^2 + 4x + 1} \leftrightarrow x - (-1)\overline{)1x^4 + 4x^3 + 6x^2 + 4x + 1}$

$$\begin{array}{r} 1x^3 + 3x^2 + 3x + 1 \text{ R: } 0 \\ x+1 \overline{) \; x^4 + 4x^3 + 6x^2 + 4x + 1} \end{array} \quad \leftrightarrow \quad \begin{array}{r|rrrrr} -1 & 1 & 4 & 6 & 4 & 1 \\ & & -1 & -3 & -3 & -1 \\ \hline & 1 & 3 & 3 & 1 & \boxed{0} \end{array}$$

Factoring Polynomials

Lesson 6-4

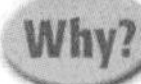

Factoring polynomials is foundational to solving polynomial equations.

The Factor Theorem

For any polynomial $P(x)$: $(x - a)$ is a factor of $P(x) \Leftrightarrow P(a) = 0$

$x - 3$ is a factor of $x^3 - 3x^2 - 4x + 12$. $\Leftrightarrow$ $(3)^3 - 3(3)^2 - 4(3) + 12 = 0$

$$\begin{array}{r|rrrr} 3 & 1 & -3 & -4 & 12 \\ & & 3 & 0 & -12 \\ \hline & 1 & 0 & -4 & \boxed{0} \end{array} \leftarrow x - 3 \text{ is a factor.}$$

$x^2 - 4$ can be factored further.

$$(x-3)(x^2-4) = 0$$
$$(x-3)(x-2)(x+2) = 0$$
$$x = 3 \quad or \quad x = 2 \quad or \quad x = -2$$

6-1 Organizer

Pacing: Traditional 1 day
Block $\frac{1}{2}$ day

Objectives: Identify, evaluate, add, and subtract polynomials.

Classify and graph polynomials.

Algebra Lab
In *Algebra Lab Activities*

Technology Lab
In *Technology Lab Activities*

Online Edition
Graphing Calculator, Tutorial Videos, TechKeys

Countdown to Testing Week 13

Power Presentations with PowerPoint®

Warm Up

Evaluate.

1. -2^4 -16 **2.** $(-2)^4$ 16

Simplify each expression.

3. $x - 2(3x - 1)$ $-5x + 2$

4. $3(y^2 + 6y)$ $3y^2 + 18y$

Also available on transparency

Math Humor

Knock, knock.
Who's there?
Polly.
Polly who?
Polynomial. Why the third degree?

State Resources

State Resources Online
KEYWORD: MB7 Resources

6-1 Polynomials

A2.4.3 Perform arithmetic operations, including long division and division with remainders, on polynomials by others of equal or lower degree.

Objectives
Identify, evaluate, add, and subtract polynomials.
Classify and graph polynomials.

Vocabulary
monomial
polynomial
degree of a monomial
degree of a polynomial
leading coefficient
binomial
trinomial
polynomial function

Who uses this?
Doctors can use polynomials to model blood flow. (See Example 4.)

A **monomial** is a number or a product of numbers and variables with whole number exponents. A **polynomial** is a monomial or a sum or difference of monomials. Each monomial in a polynomial is a term. Because a monomial has only one term, it is the simplest type of polynomial.

Polynomials have no variables in denominators or exponents, no roots or absolute values of variables, and all variables have whole number exponents.

Polynomials:	$3x^4$	$2z^{12} + 9z^3$	$\frac{1}{2}a^7$	$0.15x^{101}$	$3t^2 - t^3$
Not polynomials:	3^x	$\lvert 2b^3 - 6b \rvert$	$\frac{8}{5y^2}$	$\frac{1}{2}\sqrt{x}$	$m^{0.75} - m$

The **degree of a monomial** is the sum of the exponents of the variables.

EXAMPLE 1 Identifying the Degree of a Monomial

Identify the degree of each monomial.

A x^4

x^4 *Identify the exponent.*

The degree is 4.

B 12

$12 = 12x^0$ *Identify the exponent.*

The degree is 0.

C $4a^2b$

$4a^2b^1$ *Add the exponents.*

The degree is 3.

D x^3y^4z

$x^3y^4z^1$ *Add the exponents.*

The degree is 8.

Identify the degree of each monomial.

1a. x^3 3 **1b.** 7 0 **1c.** $5x^3y^2$ 5 **1d.** a^6bc^2 9

The **degree of a polynomial** is given by the term with the greatest degree. A polynomial with one variable is in standard form when its terms are written in descending order by degree. So, in standard form, the degree of the first term indicates the degree of the polynomial, and the **leading coefficient** is the coefficient of the first term.

Standard Form

Leading coefficient → 5; Degree of polynomial → 3

$$5x^3 + 8x^2 + 3x - 17$$

Degree of term:	3	2	1	0

1 Introduce

EXPLORATION

6-1 Polynomials

The table shows examples of expressions that are polynomials and examples of expressions that are not polynomials.

Polynomials	Not Polynomials
$5x^2$	$5x^{-2}$
$3y^7 - 4y^2 + 1$	$3y^{-7} - 4y^2 + 1$
$\frac{1}{3}x^4$	$x^{1/3}$
$\sqrt{7}t$	$7\sqrt{t}$
$0.13a^3 + 5.12a^2$	$0.13a^{0.4}$
$-m + 1$	$\lvert m + 1 \rvert$
$\frac{6}{7}y^8$	$\frac{6}{7y^8}$
$7x - 5$	$7^x - 5$

Use the examples to help you decide whether each of the following is a polynomial.

1. $14x^5 - 4x^2 + x$
2. $-3y^2 + y^{-2}$
3. $m^{0.5} - m^{12}$
4. $3^{1/2} \cdot x - 6$
5. What do you notice about the exponents of the variables in the expressions that are polynomials?

THINK AND DISCUSS

6. **Describe** the characteristics of expressions that are polynomials.

Motivate

Write $3(x^2 - 1) - x^2 + 5x$ and $5x - 3 + 2x^2$ on the board, and ask students to compare the two expressions. After students determine that the expressions are equivalent, discuss the form and appearance of each. Ask for ideas about how to make the two expressions easier to compare as a way of introducing the usefulness of a standard form.

Explorations and answers are provided in the *Explorations* binder.

A polynomial can be classified by its number of terms. A polynomial with two terms is called a **binomial**, and a polynomial with three terms is called a **trinomial**. A polynomial can also be classified by its degree.

Classifying Polynomials by Degree		
Name	Degree	Example
Constant	0	-9
Linear	1	$x-4$
Quadratic	2	x^2+3x-1
Cubic	3	x^3+2x^2+x+1
Quartic	4	$2x^4+x^3+3x^2+4x-1$
Quintic	5	$7x^5+x^4-x^3+3x^2+2x-1$

EXAMPLE 2 Classifying Polynomials

Rewrite each polynomial in standard form. Then identify the leading coefficient, degree, and number of terms. Name the polynomial.

A $2x+4x^3-1$

Write terms in descending order by degree.

$4x^3+2x-1$

Leading coefficient: 4

Degree: 3

Terms: 3

Name: cubic trinomial

B $7x^3-11x+x^5-2$

Write terms in descending order by degree.

$1x^5+7x^3-11x-2$

Leading coefficient: 1

Degree: 5

Terms: 4

Name: quintic polynomial with four terms

CHECK IT OUT! Rewrite each polynomial in standard form. Then identify the leading coefficient, degree, and number of terms. Name the polynomial.

2a. $4x-2x^2+2$
$-2x^2+4x+2$; -2; 2; 3; quadratic trinomial

2b. $-18x^2+x^3-5+2x$
x^3-18x^2+2x-5; 1; 3; 4; cubic polynomial with 4 terms

To add or subtract polynomials, combine like terms. You can add or subtract horizontally or vertically.

EXAMPLE 3 Adding and Subtracting Polynomials

Add or subtract. Write your answer in standard form.

A $(3x^2+7+x)+(14x^3+2+x^2-x)$

Add vertically.

$(3x^2+7+x)+(14x^3+2+x^2-x)$

$3x^2+x+7$	*Write in standard form.*
$+\ 14x^3+x^2-x+2$	*Align like terms.*
$14x^3+4x^2+0x+9$	*Add.*
$14x^3+4x^2+9$	*Combine like terms.*

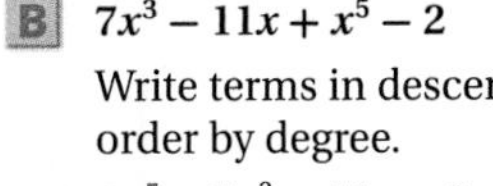

Power Presentations with PowerPoint®

Additional Examples

Example 1

Identify the degree of each monomial.

A. z^6 6 **B.** 5.6 0

C. $8xy^3$ 4 **D.** a^2bc^3 6

Example 2

Rewrite each polynomial in standard form. Then identify the leading coefficient, degree, and number of terms. Name the polynomial.

A. $3-5x^2+4x$

$-5x^2+4x+3$; -5; 2; 3; quadratic trinomial

B. $3x^2-4+8x^4$

$8x^4+3x^2-4$; 8; 4; 3; quartic trinomial

Example 3

Add or subtract. Write your answer in standard form.

A. $(2x^3+9-x)+(5x^2+4+7x+x^3)$

$3x^3+5x^2+6x+13$

B. $(3-2x^2)-(x^2+6-x)$

$-3x^2+x-3$

Also available on transparency

2 Teach

Guided Instruction

Remind students that they have already seen a type of polynomial, quadratic polynomials, in Chapter 5. Give an example of a quadratic and a cubic polynomial. Discuss with students the degree, leading coefficient, and number of terms of each.

ENGLISH LANGUAGE LEARNERS

Reaching All Learners

Through Graphic Organizers

Have students create a table, with examples, to classify polynomials by the number of terms. Ask students to compare their tables with the table on page 407 that classifies polynomials by degree. Example:

Type	Example
monomial	$3x^3$
binomial	$3x^3+5x^2$
trinomial	$3x^3+5x^2+6x$

INTERVENTION

Questioning Strategies

EXAMPLE 1

- How do you find the degree of a term with no exponent?
- How do you find the degree when there is more than one variable?

EXAMPLE 2

- How can you recognize the leading coefficient?

EXAMPLE 3

- Why should you write the polynomials in standard form before you add or subtract?

Teaching Tip **Inclusion** Review with students each of the nonexamples on page 406.

Power Presentations with PowerPoint®

Additional Examples

Example 4

The cost of manufacturing a certain product can be approximated by $f(x) = 3x^3 - 18x + 45$, where x is the number of units of the product in hundreds. Evaluate $f(0)$ and $f(200)$ and describe what the values represent.

$f(0) = 45$ represents the initial cost before manufacturing any products. $f(200) = 23{,}996{,}445$ represents the cost of manufacturing 20,000 units of the product.

Also available on transparency

INTERVENTION 

Questioning Strategies

EXAMPLE 4

- What do the variables stand for?
- How do you use the function to solve the problem?

Technology You can use a graphing calculator to support your answer to **Example 4.** Graph the function and then use the TRACE key to find the value of the function when $t = 3$.

Inclusion In **Example 5,** point out that whether a graph increases or decreases is always determined when moving from left to right on the graph.

Remember!

To subtract a polynomial, distribute the negative to all terms.

Add or subtract. Write your answer in standard form.

B $(1 - x^2) - (3x^2 + 2x - 5)$

Add the opposite horizontally.

$(1 - x^2) - (3x^2 + 2x - 5)$

$(-x^2 + 1) + (-3x^2 - 2x + 5)$ *Write in standard form.*

$(-x^2 - 3x^2) + (-2x) + (1 + 5)$ *Group like terms.*

$-4x^2 - 2x + 6$ *Add.*

Add or subtract. Write your answer in standard form.

3a. $(-36x^2 + 6x - 11) + (6x^2 + 16x^3 - 5)$ $16x^3 - 30x^2 + 6x - 16$

3b. $(5x^3 + 12 + 6x^2) - (15x^2 + 3x - 2)$ $5x^3 - 9x^2 - 3x + 14$

A **polynomial function** is a function whose rule is a polynomial. In this course, you will study only polynomial functions with one variable.

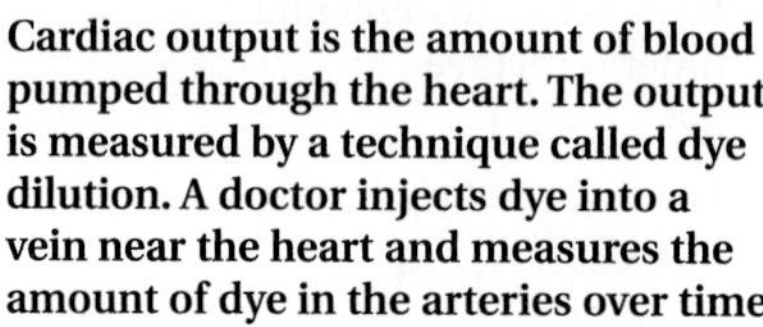

EXAMPLE 4 ***Medical Application***

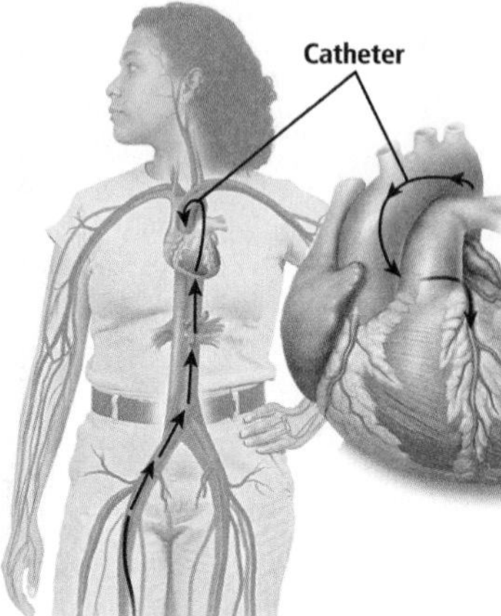

Cardiac output is the amount of blood pumped through the heart. The output is measured by a technique called dye dilution. A doctor injects dye into a vein near the heart and measures the amount of dye in the arteries over time.

The cardiac output of a particular patient can be approximated by the function $f(t) = 0.0056t^3 - 0.22t^2 + 2.33t$, where t represents time (in seconds after injection, $0 \le t \le 23$) and $f(t)$ represents the concentration of dye (in milligrams per liter).

a. Evaluate $f(t)$ for $t = 0$ and $t = 3$.

$f(0) = 0.0056(0)^3 - 0.22(0)^2 + 2.33(0) = 0$

$f(3) = 0.0056(3)^3 - 0.22(3)^2 + 2.33(3) = 5.1612$

b. Describe what the values of the function from part a represent.

$f(0)$ represents the concentration of dye, 0 mg/L, in the artery at the start of the dye dilution process.

$f(3)$ represents the concentration of dye, 5.1612 mg/L, in the artery after 3 seconds.

4. For a different patient, the dye dilution can be modeled by the function $f(t) = 0.000468x^4 - 0.016x^3 + 0.095x^2 + 0.806x$. Evaluate $f(t)$ for $t = 4$ and $t = 17$, and describe what the values of the function represent.

$f(4) = 3.8398$; $f(17) = 1.6368$; the concentration of dye after 4 s; the concentration of dye after 17 s

Graphing polynomial functions can be a challenge. Throughout this chapter, you will learn skills for analyzing, describing, and graphing higher-degree polynomials. Until then, the graphing calculator will be a useful tool.

Answers to *Check It Out*

5c.

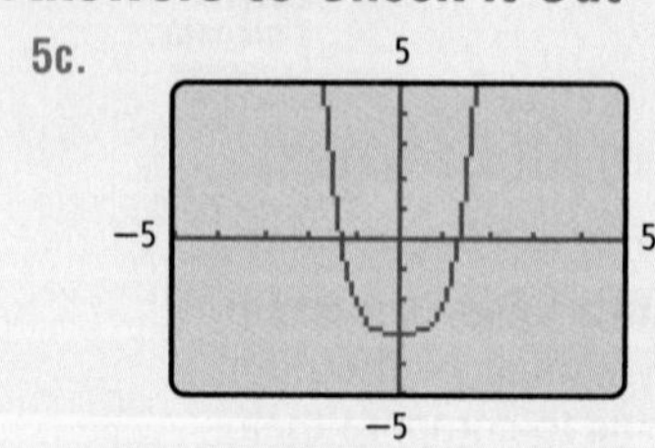

From left to right, the graph decreases and then increases. It crosses the x-axis twice, so there appear to be 2 real zeros.

d.

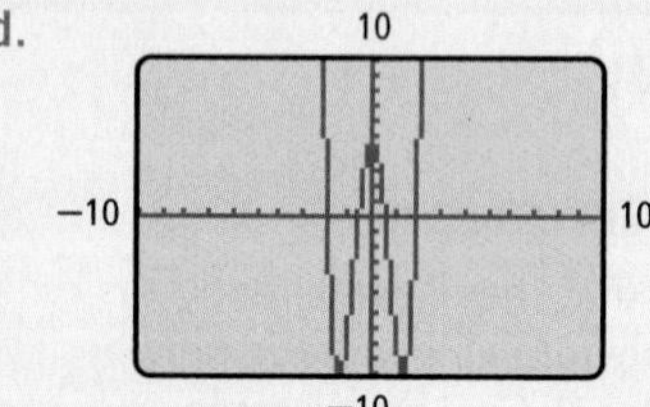

From left to right, the graph alternately decreases and increases, changing direction 3 times. It crosses the x-axis 4 times, so there appear to be 4 real zeros.

EXAMPLE 5 Graphing Higher-Degree Polynomials on a Calculator

Graph each polynomial function on a calculator. Describe the graph, and identify the number of real zeros.

A $f(x) = x^3 - x$

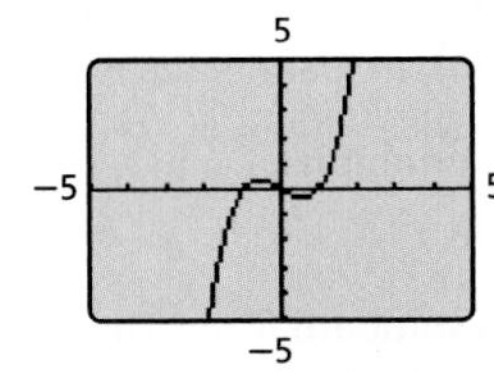

From left to right, the graph increases, decreases slightly, and then increases again. It crosses the x-axis three times, so there appear to be three real zeros.

B $f(x) = 3x^3 + 2x + 1$

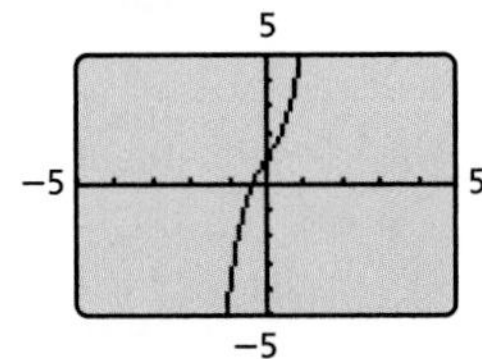

From left to right, the graph increases. It crosses the x-axis once, so there appears to be one real zero.

C $h(x) = x^4 - 8x^2 + 1$

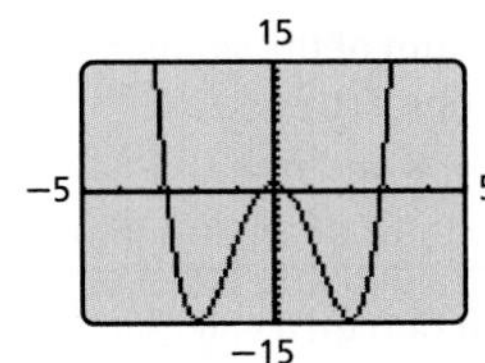

From left to right, the graph alternately decreases and increases, changing direction three times. It crosses the x-axis four times, so there appear to be four real zeros.

D $k(x) = x^4 + x^3 - x^2 + 2x - 3$

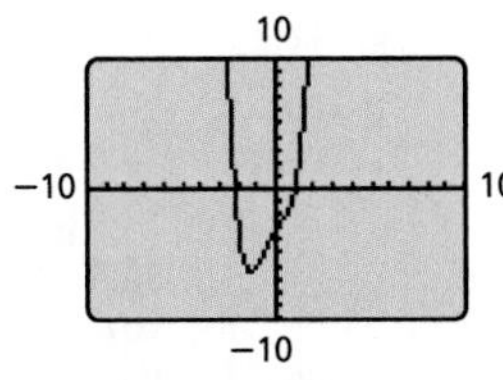

From left to right, the graph decreases and then increases. It crosses the x-axis twice, so there appear to be two real zeros.

Caution!

Depending on your viewing window, a calculator may not show all of the important features of a graph. Watch out for hidden behavior.

a.

From left to right, the graph increases, decreases slightly, and then increases again. It crosses the x-axis 3 times, so there appear to be 3 real zeros.

b.

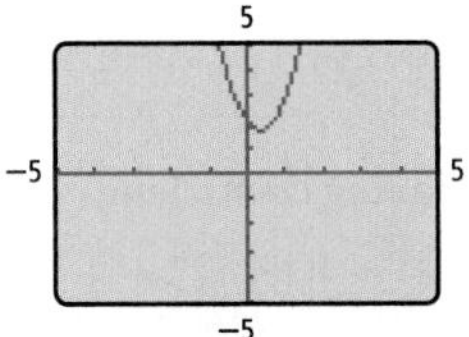

From right to left, the graph decreases and then increases. It does not cross the x-axis, so there are no real zeros.

For 5c, d. See p.408.

CHECK IT OUT! Graph each polynomial on a calculator. Describe the graph, and identify the number of real zeros.

5a. $f(x) = 6x^3 + x^2 - 5x + 1$ **5b.** $f(x) = 3x^2 - 2x + 2$

5c. $g(x) = x^4 - 3$ **5d.** $h(x) = 4x^4 - 16x^2 + 5$

THINK AND DISCUSS

1. Can a polynomial have a leading coefficient of $\sqrt{3}$? Explain.
2. What is the degree of the sum of a quartic polynomial and a cubic polynomial? Explain.
3. Is the sum of two trinomial polynomials always a trinomial? Explain.
4. **GET ORGANIZED** Copy and complete the graphic organizer.

Know it! Note

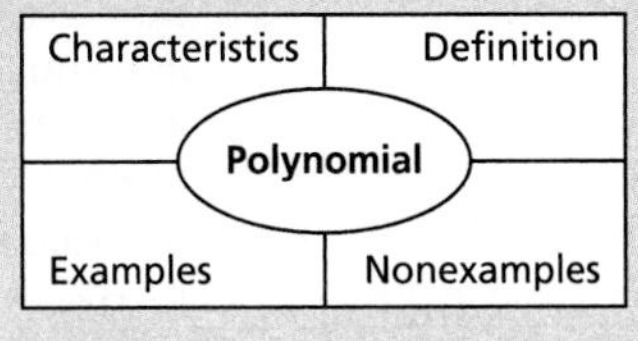

Power Presentations with PowerPoint®

Additional Examples

Example 5

Graph each polynomial function on a calculator. Describe the graph and identify the number of real zeros.

A. $f(x) = 2x^3 - 3x$

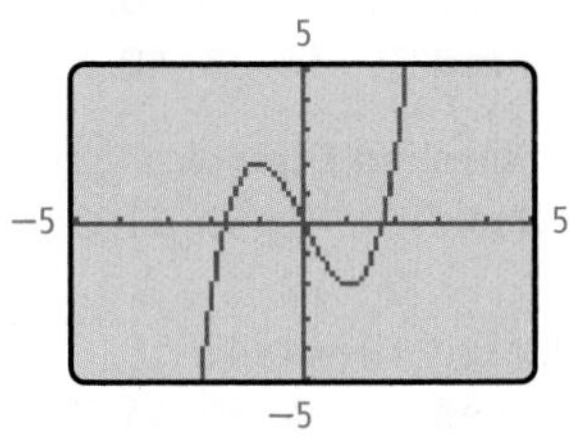

From left to right, the graph increases, then decreases, and increases again, crossing the x-axis 3 times; 3 real zeros.

B. $f(x) = 2x^3 - 2$

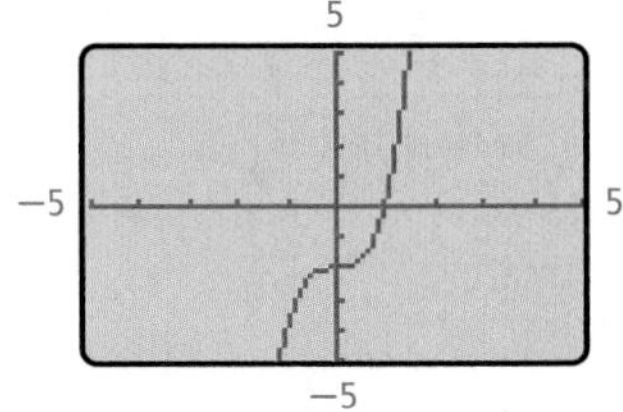

From left to right, the graph increases, crossing the x-axis 1 time; 1 real zero.

Also available on transparency

INTERVENTION Questioning Strategies

EXAMPLE 5

- What are the important features of the graph of a polynomial?

3 Close

Summarize

Ask students to describe different ways to classify or name a polynomial. by number of terms, by its degree

Have them make a list of points to remember when adding or subtracting polynomials. combine like terms, write in standard form, align like terms

Ask students to explain how to recognize a real zero of a function. A real zero is represented by the graph crossing or touching the x-axis.

ONGOING ASSESSMENT and INTERVENTION

Diagnose ***Before*** **the Lesson**
6-1 Warm Up, TE p. 406

Monitor ***During*** **the Lesson**
Check It Out! Exercises, SE pp. 406–409
Questioning Strategies, TE pp. 407–409

Assess ***After*** **the Lesson**
6-1 Lesson Quiz, TE p. 412
Alternative Assessment, TE p. 412

Answers to *Think and Discuss*

Possible answers:

1. Yes; square roots of numbers are allowed. Square roots of variables are not.
2. 4; the sum of polynomials has the degree of the term with the greatest degree.
3. No; it depends on the degrees of the terms and their coefficients.
4. See p. A7.

6-1 Exercises

Assignment Guide

Assign *Guided Practice* exercises as necessary.

If you finished Examples **1–3**
- **Basic** 19–30, 36–39
- **Average** 19–30, 36–40, 53
- **Advanced** 19–30, 36–40, 52, 53

If you finished Examples **1–5**
- **Basic** 19–45, 50, 51, 54–58, 64–72
- **Average** 19–44, 47–58, 62–72
- **Advanced** 21–24, 29–33, 40–72

Homework Quick Check
Quickly check key concepts.
Exercises: 20, 24, 30–32, 41

Answers

6. $x^3 + 2x^2 + 4x - 7$; 1; 3; 4; cubic with 4 terms
7. $3x^2 + 5x - 4$; 3; 2; 3; quadratic trinomial
8. $-4x^3 + 5x^2$; -4; 3; 2; cubic binomial
9. $4x^4 + 8x^2 - 3x + 1$; 4; 4; 4; quartic with 4 terms

15–18. See p. A30.

31b. $d(1)$ represents a bend of 3 cm below the resting position for the stabilized point 1 m from the end of the board. $d(2)$ represents a bend of 28 cm below the resting position for the stabilized point 2 m from the end of the board.

State Resources

6-1 Exercises

go.hrw.com
Homework Help Online
KEYWORD: MB7 6-1
Parent Resources Online
KEYWORD: MB7 Parent

GUIDED PRACTICE

1. **Vocabulary** Explain how to identify the leading coefficient of a polynomial. **The leading coefficient of a polynomial is the number being multiplied by the variable with the greatest degree.**

SEE EXAMPLE 1 p. 406

Identify the degree of each monomial.

2. $-7x$ **1**
3. $4x^2y^3$ **5**
4. 13 **0**
5. m^3n^2p **6**

SEE EXAMPLE 2 p. 407

Rewrite each polynomial in standard form. Then identify the leading coefficient, degree, and number of terms. Name the polynomial.

6. $4x + 2x^2 - 7 + x^3$
7. $3x^2 + 5x - 4$
8. $5x^2 - 4x^3$
9. $4x^4 + 8x^2 + 1 - 3x$

SEE EXAMPLE 3 p. 407

Add or subtract. Write your answer in standard form.

10. $(15x^2 - 3x + 11) + (2x^3 - x^2 + 6x + 1)$ **$2x^3 + 14x^2 + 3x + 12$**
11. $(12x - 1 + 2x^2) + (x^2 + 4)$ **$3x^2 + 12x + 3$**
12. $(3x^2 - 5x) - (-4 + x^2 + x)$ **$2x^2 - 6x + 4$**
13. $(x^2 - 3x + 7) - (6x^2 + 4x + 12)$ **$-5x^2 - 7x - 5$**

SEE EXAMPLE 4 p. 408

14. **Number Theory** The sum of the squares of the first n natural numbers is given by the polynomial function $F(n) = \frac{1}{3}n^3 + \frac{1}{2}n^2 + \frac{1}{6}n$.
    a. Evaluate $F(n)$ for $n = 5$ and $n = 10$. **$F(5) = 55$; $F(10) = 385$**
    b. Describe what the values of the function from part **a** represent. **the sum of squares of the first 5 natural numbers; the sum of squares of the first 10 natural numbers**

SEE EXAMPLE 5 p. 409

Graph each polynomial function on a calculator. Describe the graph, and identify the number of real zeros.

15. $f(x) = 4x^3 + 2x + 1$
16. $g(x) = \frac{1}{4}x^4 - 3x^2$
17. $h(x) = -3x^3 - 6$
18. $p(x) = -4x^4 + 6x^3 - 3x^2$

PRACTICE AND PROBLEM SOLVING

Independent Practice

For Exercises	See Example
19–22	1
23–26	2
27–30	3
31	4
32–35	5

Extra Practice
Skills Practice p. S14
Application Practice p. S37

Identify the degree of each monomial.

19. x^8 **8**
20. $6x^3y$ **4**
21. 8 **0**
22. $a^4b^6c^3$ **13**

Rewrite each polynomial in standard form. Then identify the leading coefficient, degree, and number of terms. Name the polynomial.

23. $3x^3 + 2x^4 - 7x + x^2$ **$2x^4 + 3x^3 + x^2 - 7x$; 2; 4; 4; quartic with 4 terms**
24. $6x - 4x^4 + 5^7$ **$-4x^4 - 6x + 5^7$; -4; 4; 3; quartic trinomial**
25. $2x^3 + 10x - 9$ **$2x^3 + 10x - 9$; 2; 3; 3; cubic trinomial**
26. $3x^2 + 2x^6 - 4x^4 - 1$ **$2x^6 - 4x^4 + 3x^2 - 1$; 2; 6; 4; sixth-degree polynomial with 4 terms**

Add or subtract. Write your answer in standard form.

27. $(x^2 - 3x + 4) + (x^3 + 3x - 4)$ **$x^3 + x^2$**
28. $(x^2 - 3x + 4) - (3x + x^3 - 4)$ **$-x^3 + x^2 - 6x + 8$**
29. $(5y^3 - 2y^2 - 1) - (y^2 - 2y - 3)$ **$5y^3 - 3y^2 + 2y + 2$**
30. $(2y^2 - 5y + 3) + (y^2 - 2y - 5)$ **$3y^2 - 7y - 2$**
31. **Recreation** The distance d, in centimeters, that a diving board bends below its resting position when you stand at its end is dependent on your distance x, in meters, from the stabilized point. This relationship can be modeled by the function $d(x) = -4x^3 + x^2$.
    a. Evaluate $d(x)$ for $x = 1$ and $x = 2$. **$d(1) = -3$; $d(2) = -28$**
    b. Describe what the values of the function from part **a** represent.

6-1 READING STRATEGIES

A **monomial** is a number or a product of a number and a variable, such as $-2x$ or $3x^2$. A monomial cannot have

- variables in denominators or exponents. 6^x or $\frac{3}{x^2}$
- roots of variables. $6\sqrt{x}$
- absolute value signs. $|x^3|$
- exponents that are not whole numbers. $x^{0.3}$

These are NOT monomials.

A **polynomial** is a monomial or the sum or difference of monomials. Each monomial in a polynomial is called a **term**. Here are some ways to describe polynomials.

	Standard Form	Degree	Number of Terms	Leading Coefficient
Definition	Terms arranged in descending order by degree	The greatest exponent in a polynomial	The number of monomials	The coefficient of the first term in standard form
Example	$5x^3 - 2x^2 + x + 3$	3	4	5

Answer each question.

1. What is the difference between a monomial and a polynomial?
   A monomial has only one term, whereas a polynomial has one or more terms.
2. Circle the polynomials below. Cross out the expressions that are not polynomials.
   $4x^2 - x$ $\quad 2n^3 + 1 \quad 3x\sqrt{17} \quad 6z^2 \quad \frac{2}{z^2} + 1$
3. Write the polynomials in standard form. Classify the polynomial based on its degree.
   a. $x - x^5 + 1$ **$-x^5 + x + 1$** Degree **quintic**
   b. $x^2 + 6 + x^3 - 2x$ **$x^3 + x^2 - 2x + 6$** Degree **cubic**

Complete the table.

	Polynomial	Degree	Number of Terms	Leading Coefficient
4.	$2y^4 + 3y^3 + y^2 - 7$	4	4	2
5.	$-6x^5 - x^3 + 2$	5	3	-6

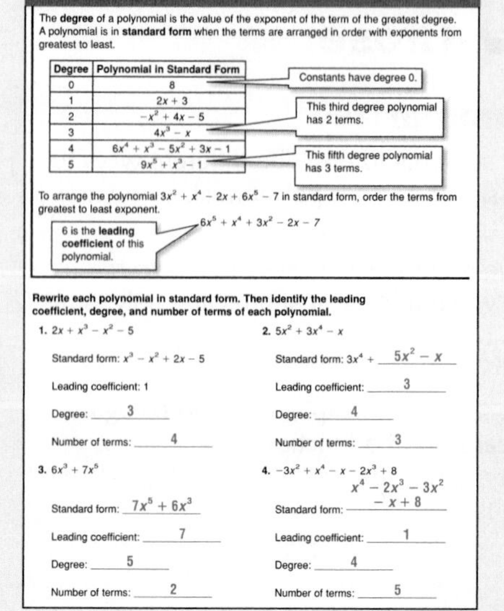

6-1 RETEACH

The **degree** of a polynomial is the value of the exponent of the term of the greatest degree. A polynomial is in **standard form** when the terms are arranged in order with exponents from greatest to least.

Degree	Polynomial in Standard Form
0	8
1	$2x + 3$
2	$-x^2 + 4x - 5$
3	$4x^3 - x$
4	$6x^4 + x^3 - 5x^2 + 3x - 1$
5	$9x^5 + x^3 - 1$

Constants have degree 0.
This third degree polynomial has 2 terms.
This fifth degree polynomial has 3 terms.

To arrange the polynomial $3x^2 + x^4 - 2x + 6x^5 - 7$ in standard form, order the terms from greatest to least exponent.

$6x^5 + x^4 + 3x^2 - 2x - 7$

6 is the **leading coefficient** of this polynomial.

Rewrite each polynomial in standard form. Then identify the leading coefficient, degree, and number of terms of each polynomial.

1. $2x + x^3 - x^2 - 5$
   Standard form: $x^3 - x^2 + 2x - 5$
   Leading coefficient: 1
   Degree: **3**
   Number of terms: **4**
2. $5x^2 + 3x^4 - x$
   Standard form: $3x^4 +$ **$5x^2 - x$**
   Leading coefficient: **3**
   Degree: **4**
   Number of terms: **3**
3. $6x^3 + 7x^5$
   Standard form: **$7x^5 + 6x^3$**
   Leading coefficient: **7**
   Degree: **5**
   Number of terms: **2**
4. $-3x^2 + x^4 - x - 2x^3 + 8$
   Standard form: **$x^4 - 2x^3 - 3x^2 - x + 8$**
   Leading coefficient: **1**
   Degree: **4**
   Number of terms: **5**

Graph each polynomial function on a calculator. Describe the graph, and identify the number of real zeros.

32. $f(x) = -2x^2 + x - 1$

33. $g(x) = x^3 + 1$

34. $h(x) = x^4 - 6x^2 + 10$

35. $p(x) = -x^5 + x - 1$

Complete the table.

	Polynomial	Standard Form	Leading Coefficient	Degree
36.	$8x + 3x^2 - 5$	$3x^2 + 8x - 5$	3	2
37.	$3x^2 + x^4 - 2$	$x^4 + 3x^2 - 2$	1	4
38.	$x^3 - x^4 + x - 1$	$-x^4 + x^3 + x - 1$	−1	4
39.	$64 + x^2$	$x^2 + 64$	1	2

40. Critical Thinking Write a quartic trinomial with a leading coefficient of 2. Possible answer: $2x^4 + x^3 + 2$

Geometry Find a polynomial expression in terms of x for the surface area of each figure.

41.

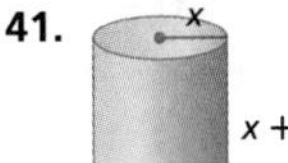

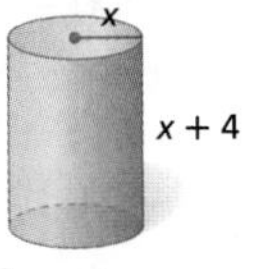

$S(x) = 4\pi x^2 + 8\pi x$

42.

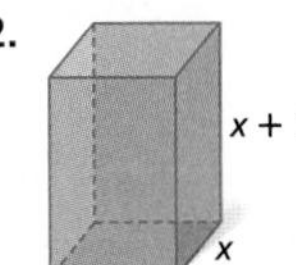

$S(x) = 6x^2 + 4x$

43.

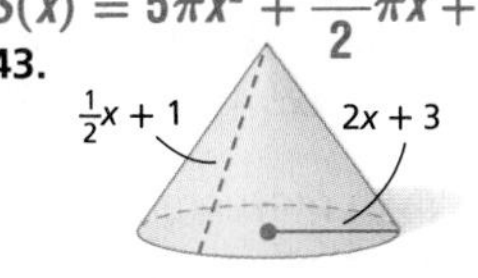

$S(x) = 5\pi x^2 + \frac{31}{2}\pi x + 12\pi$

44.

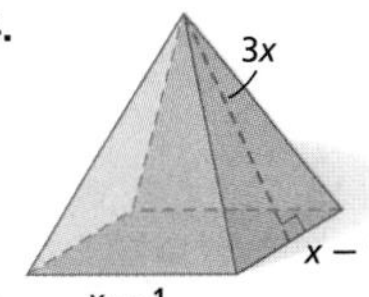

$S(x) = 7x^2 - 8x + 1$

45. Business The manager of a gift-basket business will ship the baskets anywhere in the country. The cost to mail a basket based on its weight x, in pounds, is given by $C(x) = 0.03x^3 - 0.75x^2 + 4.5x + 7$.

a. What is the cost of shipping a 7-pound gift basket? **\$12.04**

b. What is the cost of shipping a 19-pound gift basket? **\$27.52**

46. Estimation Estimate the value of $P(x) = -2.03x^3 + \pi x^2 - x + 5.8$ for $P(-2.78)$. **90**

Tell whether each statement is sometimes, always, or never true. If it is sometimes true, give examples to support your answer.

47. A quadratic polynomial is a trinomial. **Sometimes true**

48. The degree of a polynomial in standard form is equal to the degree of the first term. **always true**

49. The leading coefficient of a polynomial is the greatest coefficient of any term. **Sometimes true**

50. This problem will prepare you for the Multi-Step Test Prep on page 436.

The total number of lights in a triangular lighting rig is related to the triangular numbers, as shown at right. The nth triangular number is given by $T(n) = \frac{1}{2}n^2 + \frac{1}{2}n$.

a. Write a polynomial function that represents the $(n + 1)$th triangular number, $T(n + 1)$.

b. The difference between two consecutive triangular numbers is $T(n + 1) - T(n)$. Subtract these two polynomial functions, and state a conclusion about the difference between consecutive triangular numbers.

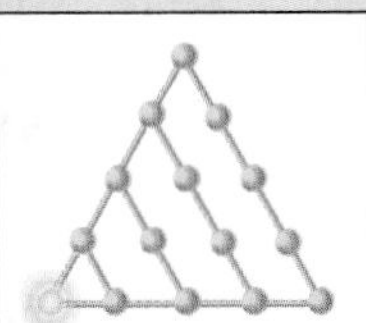

Triangular numbers: 1, 3, 6, 10, 15, . . .

COMMON ERROR ALERT

When students work with exponents, as in **Exercises 1–18,** they might confuse coefficients and exponents. Have students read problems aloud, stating the terms clearly and carefully—for example, either "four x" or "x to the fourth"—as appropriate.

Teaching Tip

Geometry For **Exercises 41–44,** review the surface area formulas.

For a cylinder: $SA = 2\pi r^2 + 2\pi rh$

For a pyramid: $SA = 2\ell s + s^2$ where s is the length of the base edge and ℓ is slant height

For a cone: $SA = \pi r^2 + \pi r\ell$ where ℓ is slant height

Exercise 50 involves writing a polynomial function to represent triangular numbers. This exercise prepares students for the Multi-Step Test Prep on page 436.

Answers

32–35. See p. A30.

47. Possible answer: $x^2 + x + 1$ is a quadratic that is also a trinomial. $x^2 + 1$ is a quadratic that is not a trinomial.

49. Possible answer: $5x^2 + 2x + 1$ is a polynomial in which the leading coefficient is also the greatest. $x^2 + 2x + 5$ is a polynomial in which the leading coefficient is not the greatest.

50a. $T(n + 1) = \frac{1}{2}n^2 + \frac{3}{2}n + 1$

b. $n + 1$; the difference between the $(n + 1)$th triangular number and the nth triangular number is $n + 1$.

6-1 PROBLEM SOLVING

As part of a project to build a model castle, Julian wants to find the surface area of solid towers of various sizes, shaped like the one shown in the figure below. The diameter of the circular base is d inches, the height of the cylinder is $d + 4$ inches, and the slant height of the right circular cone is $d - 0.6$ inch.

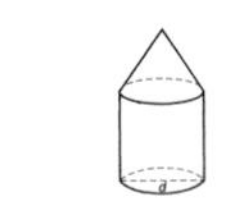

1. The general formula for the surface area of a cone is $SA = \pi r^2 + \pi rs$, where r is the radius of the base, and s is the slant height of the cone.

a. Write the formula in terms of d.

$SA = \pi\left(\frac{d}{2}\right)^2 + \pi\left(\frac{d}{2}\right)s$

b. What part of the formula will you use to find the surface area of the cone part of the model? Why?

Possible answer: πrs because it gives the surface area of the curved part of the cone, not the circular base; the base is against the cylinder so it isn't part of the surface area of the castle.

2. The general formula for the surface area of a cylinder (with radius r and height h) is $SA = 2\pi r^2 + 2\pi rh$.

a. Write the formula in terms of d. $SA = \frac{\pi d^2}{2} + dh\pi$

b. What part of the formula will you use to find the surface area of the cylinder part of the model? Why?

Possible answer: just the curved part and one base; the top of the cylinder is hidden because the cone sits on it.

3. Write a general polynomial expression for the surface area of the model tower.

$SA = \pi\left(\frac{d}{2}\right)(d - 0.6) + \pi d(d + 4) + \pi\left(\frac{d}{2}\right)^2$

Choose the letter for the best answer.

4. What is the approximate surface area in square inches of a tower with a diameter of 5 inches?
A 278
B 196 (circled)
C 44
D 38

5. What is the approximate surface area in square inches of a tower with a diameter of 10 inches?
A 176
B 278
C 666 (circled)
D 1174

6. What is the approximate surface area in square inches of a tower where the height of the cylinder is 12 inches?
A 931
B 716
C 445 (circled)
D 395

7. What is the approximate surface area in square inches of a tower where the slant height of the cone is 3.4 inches?
A 103
B 134 (circled)
C 158
D 268

6-1 CHALLENGE

A polynomial function in x is of the form $a_nx^n + a_{n-1}x^{n-1} + ... + a_1x + a_0$, where a_n is a nonzero real number and n is a nonnegative integer.

Explore polynomial functions whose coefficients are all 1.

Consider $Q_n(x) = x^n + x^{n-1} + ... + x^3 + x^2 + x + 1$.

1. Write the function when $n = 6$. $Q_6(x) = x^6 + x^5 + x^4 + x^3 + x^2 + x + 1$

2. Is $Q_6(x)$ positive or negative

a. when $x > 0$? positive

b. when $x < 0$? positive

c. when $x = 0$? positive

3. Consider $Q_n(x)$ for other even values of n, including 0. When n is even, what can you say

a. about the values of the function $Q_n(x)$? always positive

b. about the graph of the function $Q_n(x)$? The graph is always above the x-axis.

4. Write the function when $n = 3$. $Q_3(x) = x^3 + x^2 + x + 1$

5. State a value of x for which $Q_3(x)$

a. is negative. $x = -10$

b. is positive. $x = 10$

c. is 0. $x = -1$

6. a. Use a graphing calculator to graph the function when $n = 1, 3, 5$, and 7. Sketch these graphs on the grid at right.

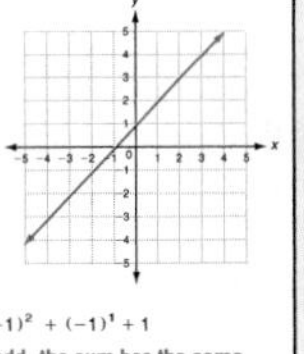

b. Describe what these graphs have in common when $x < -1$, when $x = -1$, and when $x > -1$.

When $x < -1$ the graphs are below the x-axis; when $x = -1$ the graphs cross x-axis; when $x > -1$ the graphs are above the x-axis.

c. Verify that the function $Q_n(x)$ changes its value from negative to positive at $x = -1$ when n is odd. Show that $Q_n(-1) = 0$, for all odd values of n by evaluating the expression below.

$Q_n(-1) = (-1)^n + (-1)^{n-1} + ... + (-1)^3 + (-1)^2 + (-1)^1 + 1$

The sum consists of only 1 and −1. When n is odd, the sum has the same number of (−1)s as it has (1)s, so the sum is 0.

7. When $x = -1$ and n is even, what is the value of $Q_n(-1)$? 1

6-1 PRACTICE A

6-1 PRACTICE C

6-1 PRACTICE B

Identify the degree of each monomial.

1. $6x^2$ — 2

2. $3p^3m^4$ — 7

3. $2x^8y^3$ — 11

Rewrite each polynomial in standard form. Then identify the leading coefficient, degree, and number of terms. Name the polynomial.

4. $6 + 7x - 4x^3 + x^2$

$-4x^3 + x^2 + 7x + 6$; −4; 3; 4; cubic polynomial with 4 terms

5. $x^2 - 3 + 2x^5 + 7x^4 - 12x$

$2x^5 + 7x^4 + x^2 - 12x - 3$; 2; 5; 5; quintic polynomial with 5 terms

Add or subtract. Write your answer in standard form.

6. $(2x^2 - 2x + 6) + (11x^3 - x^2 - 2 + 5x)$

$11x^3 + x^2 + 3x + 4$

7. $(x^2 - 8) - (3x^3 + 6x - 4 + 9x^2)$

$-3x^3 - 8x^2 - 6x - 4$

8. $(5x^4 + x^2) + (7 + 9x^2 - 2x^4 + x^3)$

$3x^4 + x^3 + 10x^2 + 7$

9. $(12x^2 + x) - (6 - 9x^2 + x^7 - 8x)$

$-x^7 + 21x^2 + 9x - 6$

Graph each polynomial function on a calculator. Describe the graph, and identify the number of real zeros.

10. $f(x) = x^3 + 2x^2 - 3$

From left to right, the graph increases, decreases slightly, and then increases again. It crosses the x-axis once, so there is 1 real zero.

11. $f(x) = x^4 - 5x^2 + 1$

From left to right, the graph alternately decreases and increases, changing direction 3 times. It crosses the x-axis 4 times, so there are 4 real zeros.

Solve.

12. The height, h, in feet, of a baseball after being struck by a bat can be approximated by $h(t) = -16t^2 + 100t + 5$, where t is measured in seconds.

a. Evaluate $h(t)$ for $t = 3$ and $t = 5$. 161 ft and 105 ft

b. Describe what the values of the function from part a represent.

The height of the baseball 3 s after being hit by the bat and the height of the baseball 5 s after being hit by the bat

If students chose **B, C,** or **D** in **Exercise 54,** have them rewrite the monomial with powers for x and z ($x^1y^4z^1$).

In **Exercise 55,** students can eliminate both **F** and **H** if they notice that the first step in the subtraction results in $0x^2$. Suggest that they look at the constant term to find the answer.

Journal

Have students relate the prefixes *poly-*, *mono-*, *bi-*, and *tri-* and the roots *quart-* and *quint-* to common words such as *bicycle* or *quintuplets* to help them remember the meaning of the mathematics vocabulary.

ALTERNATIVE ASSESSMENT

Have students write a quartic polynomial function f in standard form and identify the leading coefficient and number of terms. Then have them graph f, describe the graph, identify the number of real zeros, and evaluate $f(3)$.

ENGLISH LANGUAGE LEARNERS

Power Presentations with PowerPoint®

6-1 Lesson Quiz

Rewrite in standard form. Identify the degree of the polynomial and the number of terms.

1. $9 - x^2 + 2x^5 - 7x$
$2x^5 - x^2 - 7x + 9$; 5; 4

2. $23 + 4x^3$ $4x^3 + 23$; 3; 2

3. Subtract $4x^5 - 8x + 2$ from $3x^4 + 10x - 9$. Write your answer in standard form.
$-4x^5 + 3x^4 + 18x - 11$

4. Evaluate $h(x) = 0.4x^2 - 1.2x + 7.5$ for $x = 0$ and $x = 3$. 7.5; 7.5

5. Describe the graph of $j(x) = 3x^2 - 6x + 6$ and identify the number of real zeros.

From left to right, the graph decreases then increases, but it never crosses the x-axis; no real zeros.

Also available on transparency

52. Yes; possible answer: if you switch around the terms of a polynomial, it may no longer be in standard form, but it is still the same polynomial.

51. Graphing Calculator The functions below are polynomials in factored form. Graph each function. Identify the x-intercepts. What can you say about the x-intercepts and the linear binomial factors in the functions?

a. $f(x) = (x + 3)(x - 1)(x - 4)$
b. $g(x) = (x + 1)(x + 2)(x - 3)(x - 1)$
c. $h(x) = x(x + 1)(x - 2)$
d. $k(x) = (x + 2)(x - 3)$
e. $j(x) = x\left(x + \frac{1}{2}\right)\left(x - \frac{1}{2}\right)$

Write About It Recall the properties of real numbers from Lesson 1-2.

52. Is the addition of polynomial functions commutative? Explain.

53. Is the addition of polynomial functions associative? Explain.
Yes; possible answer: if you are adding 3 polynomials, it does not matter which 2 you add first.

54. What is the degree of the monomial $5xy^4z$?
Ⓐ 6 (circled) Ⓑ 1 Ⓒ 4 Ⓓ 5

55. For $f(x) = 2x^2 + 4x - 6$ and $g(x) = 2x^2 + 2x + 8$, find $f(x) - g(x)$.
Ⓕ $-4x^2 - 2x + 2$ Ⓖ $2x + 2$ Ⓗ $4x^2 + 6x + 2$ Ⓙ $2x - 14$ (circled)

56. Which polynomial is written in standard form?
Ⓐ $7 + 2x^4 - x^6$ Ⓑ $3x^3 - x^5$ Ⓒ x^4 (circled) Ⓓ $x^2 + 3 - 2x$

57. What is the degree of the polynomial function $h(x) = 7x^3 - x^6 + x$?
Ⓕ 10 Ⓖ 3 Ⓗ −1 Ⓙ 6 (circled)

58. Short Response Evaluate $P(x) = \frac{1}{2}x^3 - x^2 + 8$ for $x = -2$.
$P(-2) = 0$

CHALLENGE AND EXTEND

$P(x)$ and $R(x)$ are polynomials. $P(x)$ is a trinomial. Give examples of $P(x)$ and $R(x)$ that meet the given conditions.

59. $P(x) - R(x)$ is a binomial. Possible answer: $P(x) = x^2 + x + 1$; $R(x) = x^2$

60. $P(x) - R(x)$ is a trinomial. Possible answer: $P(x) = x^2 + x + 1$; $R(x) = -2x^2 - x - 1$

61. $P(x) - R(x)$ is a polynomial with four terms. Possible answer: $P(x) = x^3 + x^2 + 2$; $R(x) = x + 1$

62. $P(x) - R(x)$ is a quartic.
Possible answer: $P(x) = x^4 + x^2 + 1$; $R(x) = x^3 + 2$

63. $P(x) - R(x)$ is a quintic.
Possible answer: $P(x) = x^5 + x + 2$; $R(x) = -x^5 + 5$

SPIRAL REVIEW

Graph each line. *(Lesson 2-3)*

64. slope $\frac{3}{4}$, point $(0, -1)$ **65.** slope -2, point $(3, 0)$ **66.** slope 1, point $(1, 2)$

Determine if each line is vertical or horizontal. Then graph the line. *(Lesson 2-3)*

67. $x = 4$ vertical **68.** $y = -2$ horizontal **69.** $y = \frac{3}{4}$ horizontal

Using $f(x) = x^2$ as a guide, graph each function and describe the transformations. *(Lesson 5-1)*

70. $g(x) = (x - 5)^2 + 6$
shift 5 units right and 6 units up

71. $g(x) = (x + 3)^2 + 2$
shift 3 units left and 2 units up

72. $h(x) = \frac{1}{5}x^2 + 2$
vertical compression by a factor of $\frac{1}{5}$ and shift up 2 units

Answers

51. Possible answer: The factors give the x-intercepts of the graphs.

a. The x-intercepts are −3, 1, and 4.

b. The x-intercepts are −1, −2, 3, and 1.

c. The x-intercepts are 0, −1, and 2.

d. The x-intercepts are −2 and 3.

e. The x-intercepts are $-\frac{1}{2}$, 0, and $\frac{1}{2}$.

51, 64–72. For graphs, see p. A30.

Pascal's Triangle

See Skills Bank page S70

Each number in Pascal's triangle is the sum of the two numbers diagonally above it. All of the outside numbers are 1.

Many interesting number patterns can be found in Pascal's triangle, such as Fibonnacci's sequence and powers of 2.

Pascal's Triangle is useful for many different mathematical situations, such as expanding binomials and probability.

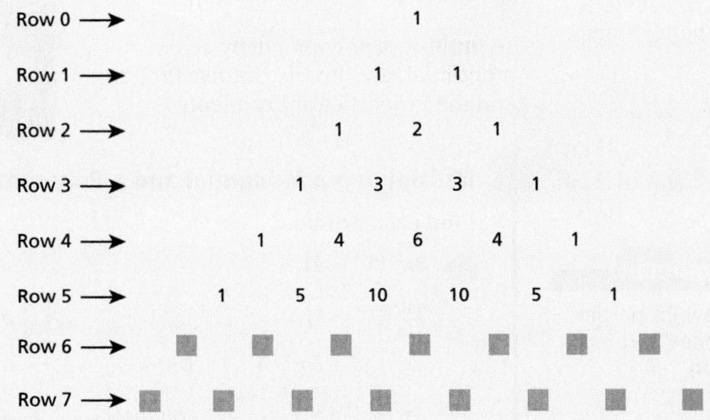

Activity

Find rows 6 and 7 of Pascal's triangle.

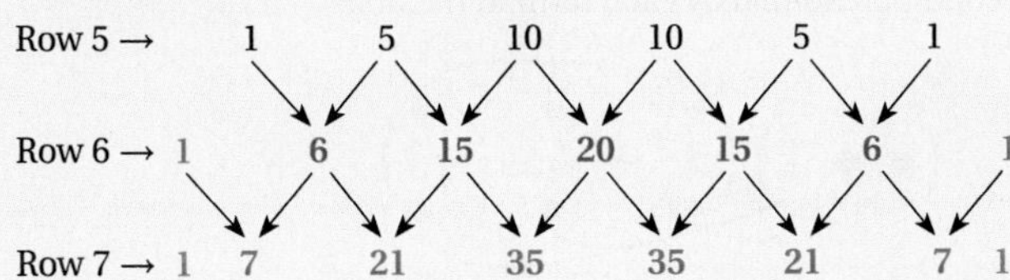

All of the outside numbers are 1. Fill in values by adding the numbers in row 5 that are diagonally above the new values.

Repeat the process for row 7.

Try This

1. Find rows 8, 9, and 10 of Pascal's triangle.
2. **Make a Conjecture** What can you say about the relationship between the row number and the number of terms in a row?
3. **Make a Conjecture** What can you say about the relationship between the row number and the second term in each row?
4. **Make a Conjecture** Expand $(x + 1)(x + 1)$ *and* $(x + 1)(x + 1)(x + 1)$, and use your answers to make a conjecture about the relationship between Pascal's triangle and the multiplication of binomials.
5. Test your conjecture from Problem 4 by expanding $(x + 1)(x + 1)(x + 1)(x + 1)$ with multiplication and by using Pascal's triangle.
   $x^4 + 4x^3 + 6x^2 + 4x + 1$; multiplication and Pascal's triangle give the same coefficients.

Answers to *Try This*

1. row 8: 1 8 28 56 70 56 28 8 1
   row 9: 1 9 36 84 126 126 84 36 9 1
   row 10: 1 10 45 120 210 252 210 120 45 10 1
2. Possible answer: The number of terms is 1 plus the row number.
3. Possible answer: The second term in each row is equal to the row number.
4. $x^2 + 2x + 1$; $x^3 + 3x^2 + 3x + 1$; possible answer: the coefficients are values from the corresponding row of Pascal's triangle.

Organizer

See Skills Bank page S70

Pacing:
Traditional $\frac{1}{2}$ day
Block $\frac{1}{4}$ day

Objective: Review Pascal's triangle.

Teach

Remember

Students review Pascal's triangle and investigate its construction.

INTERVENTION For additional review and practice on Pascal's triangle, see Skills Bank page S70.

Visual Point out patterns in Pascal's triangle, such as the ones at the beginning and end of each row and the relationship between the row number and the second entry in each row.

Close

Assess

Describe how to find subsequent rows in Pascal's triangle.

State Resources

6-2 Organizer

Pacing: Traditional 1 day
Block $\frac{1}{2}$ day

Objectives: Multiply polynomials.

Use binomial expansion to expand binomial expressions that are raised to positive integer powers.

Online Edition
Tutorial Videos, Interactivity

Countdown to Testing Week 13

Power Presentations with PowerPoint®

Warm Up

Multiply.

1. $x(x^3)$ x^4 **2.** $3x^2(x^5)$ $3x^7$

3. $2(5x^3)$ $10x^3$ **4.** $x(6x^2)$ $6x^3$

5. $xy(7x^2)$ $7x^3y$

6. $3y^2(-3y)$ $-9y^3$

Also available on transparency

Math Humor

Q: When is a solution not an answer?

A: When you make it in a chemistry lab.

6-2 Multiplying Polynomials

A2.4.3 Perform arithmetic operations, including long division and division with remainders, on polynomials by others of equal or lower degree.

Objectives
Multiply polynomials.

Use binomial expansion to expand binomial expressions that are raised to positive integer powers.

Who uses this?
Business managers can multiply polynomials when modeling total manufacturing costs. (See Example 3.)

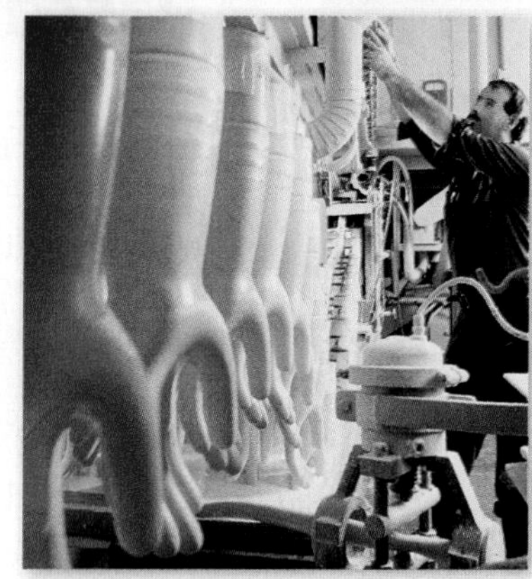

To multiply a polynomial by a monomial, use the Distributive Property and the Properties of Exponents.

Remember!
To review Properties of Exponents, refer to Lesson 1-5.

EXAMPLE 1 Multiplying a Monomial and a Polynomial

Find each product.

A $3x^2(x^3 + 4)$

$3x^2(x^3 + 4)$

$3x^2 \cdot x^3 + 3x^2 \cdot 4$ *Distribute.*

$3x^5 + 12x^2$ *Multiply.*

B $ab(a^3 + 3ab^2 - b^3)$

$ab(a^3 + 3ab^2 - b^3)$

$ab(a^3) + ab(3ab^2) + ab(-b^3)$

$a^4b + 3a^2b^3 - ab^4$

CHECK IT OUT! Find each product.

1a. $3cd^2(4c^2d - 6cd + 14cd^2)$ $12c^3d^3 - 18c^2d^3 + 42c^2d^4$

1b. $x^2y(6y^3 + y^2 - 28y + 30)$ $6x^2y^4 + x^2y^3 - 28x^2y^2 + 30x^2y$

To multiply any two polynomials, use the Distributive Property and multiply each term in the second polynomial by each term in the first.

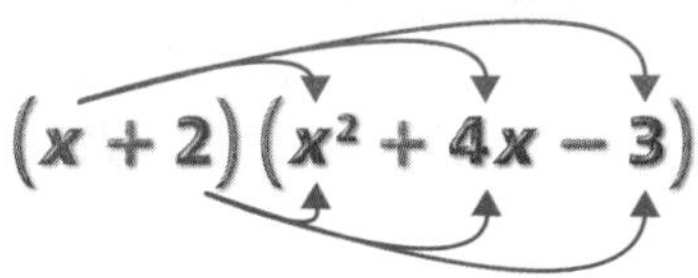

Keep in mind that if one polynomial has m terms and the other has n terms, then the product has mn terms before it is simplified.

EXAMPLE 2 Multiplying Polynomials

Find each product.

A $(x - 2)(1 + 3x - x^2)$

Method 1 Multiply horizontally.

$(x - 2)(-x^2 + 3x + 1)$ *Write polynomials in standard form.*

$x(-x^2) + x(3x) + x(1) - 2(-x^2) - 2(3x) - 2(1)$ *Distribute x and then −2.*

$-x^3 + 3x^2 + x + 2x^2 - 6x - 2$ *Multiply. Add exponents.*

$-x^3 + 5x^2 - 5x - 2$ *Combine like terms.*

State Resources

go.hrw.com
State Resources Online
KEYWORD: MB7 Resources

1 Introduce

EXPLORATION

6-2 Multiplying Polynomials

You can use a calculator to check whether you have correctly multiplied polynomials. For example, to verify that $(x + 1)(x - 1)$ is equal to $x^2 - 1$, enter the expressions as Y1 and Y2. The table shows that the two expressions have the same value for all the listed values of x. In addition, the graphs of the corresponding functions appear to coincide.

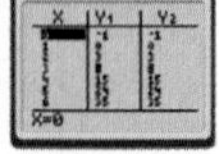
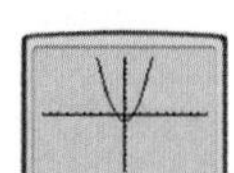

Use a calculator to determine whether each multiplication was performed correctly.

1. $5x^2(2x^2 + 3) = 10x^4 + 3$
2. $(3x^2 - 2)(x - 7) = 3x^3 - 21x^2 - 2x + 14$
3. $-4x^3(2x - 3) = -8x^4 + 12x^3$
4. $(3x + 1)(4x^3 - 3x^2 + 1) = 12x^4 - 9x^3 + 3x$

THINK AND DISCUSS

5. **Explain** how to recognize that certain expressions are not equivalent.

Motivate

Draw a rectangle with sides labeled $x + 3$ and $x + 4$. Ask students to find an expression for the area. $A = x^2 + 7x + 12$ Point out that writing the function in standard form involves multiplying binomials. Extend the process to represent the volume of a cube or a rectangular prism.

Explorations and answers are provided in the *Explorations* binder.

Method 2 Multiply vertically.

$-x^2 + 3x + 1$	*Write each polynomial in standard form.*
$x - 2$	
$2x^2 - 6x - 2$	*Multiply $(-x^2 + 3x + 1)$ by -2.*
$-x^3 + 3x^2 + x$	*Multiply $(-x^2 + 3x + 1)$ by x, and align like terms.*
$-x^3 + 5x^2 - 5x - 2$	*Combine like terms.*

Find each product.

B $(x^2 + 3x - 5)(x^2 - x + 1)$

Multiply each term of one polynomial by each term of the other. Use a table to organize the products.

	x^2	$-x$	$+1$
x^2	x^4	$-x^3$	$+x^2$
$+3x$	$+3x^3$	$-3x^2$	$+3x$
-5	$-5x^2$	$+5x$	-5

The top left corner is the first term in the product. Combine terms along diagonals to get the middle terms. The bottom right corner is the last term in the product.

$x^4 + (3x^3 - x^3) + (-5x^2 - 3x^2 + x^2) + (5x + 3x) + (-5)$

$x^4 + 2x^3 - 7x^2 + 8x - 5$

Helpful Hint

When using a table to multiply, the polynomials must be in standard form. Use a zero for any missing terms.

CHECK IT OUT! **Find each product.**

2a. $(3b - 2c)(3b^2 - bc - 2c^2)$ **$9b^3 - 9b^2c - 4bc^2 + 4c^3$**

2b. $(x^2 - 4x + 1)(x^2 + 5x - 2)$ **$x^4 + x^3 - 21x^2 + 13x - 2$**

EXAMPLE 3 ***Business Application***

Mr. Silva manages a manufacturing plant. From 1990 through 2005, the number of units produced (in thousands) can be modeled by $N(x) = 0.02x^2 + 0.2x + 3$. The average cost per unit (in dollars) can be modeled by $C(x) = -0.002x^2 - 0.1x + 2$, where x is the number of years since 1990. Write a polynomial $T(x)$ that can be used to model Mr. Silva's total manufacturing costs.

Total cost is the product of the number of units and the cost per unit.

$T(x) = N(x) \cdot C(x)$.

Multiply the two polynomials.

$$
\begin{array}{r}
0.02x^2 + 0.2x + 3 \\
\times\ -0.002x^2 - 0.1x + 2 \\
\hline
0.04x^2 + 0.4x + 6 \\
-0.002x^3 - 0.02x^2 - 0.3x \\
-0.00004x^4 - 0.0004x^3 - 0.006x^2 \\
\hline
-0.00004x^4 - 0.0024x^3 + 0.014x^2 + 0.1x + 6
\end{array}
$$

Mr. Silva's total manufacturing costs, in thousands of dollars, can be modeled by $T(x) = -0.00004x^4 - 0.0024x^3 + 0.014x^2 + 0.1x + 6$.

CHECK IT OUT! **3. What if...?** Suppose that in 2005 the cost of raw materials increases and the new average cost per unit is modeled by $C(x) = -0.004x^2 - 0.1x + 3$. Write a polynomial $T(x)$ that can be used to model the total costs.

$T(x) = -0.00008x^4 - 0.0028x^3 + 0.288x^2 + 0.3x + 9$

2 Teach

Guided Instruction

Before multiplying polynomials, review the properties of exponents in Lesson 1-5. Stress that when two polynomials are multiplied, each term of one polynomial must be multiplied by each term of the other polynomial. The process is an extension of the process for finding the product of two binomials.

ENGLISH LANGUAGE LEARNERS

Reaching All Learners

Through Communication

Have students work in small groups to multiply two polynomials, such as $(x^2 + 3x + 1)(x^2 - 5x - 4)$. Each student in the group should choose a different method, such as multiplying horizontally, vertically, or using a table. Have students discuss the ways in which the methods are alike and the ways in which they differ.

Power Presentations with PowerPoint®

Additional Examples

Example 1

Find each product.

A. $4y^2(y^2 + 3)$ $4y^4 + 12y^2$

B. $fg(f^4 + 2f^3g - 3f^2g^2 + fg^3)$ $f^5g + 2f^4g^2 - 3f^3g^3 + f^2g^4$

Example 2

Find each product.

A. $(a - 3)(2 - 5a + a^2)$ $a^3 - 8a^2 + 17a - 6$

B. $(y^2 - 7y + 5)(y^2 - y - 3)$ $y^4 - 8y^3 + 9y^2 + 16y - 15$

Example 3

A standard Burly Box is p ft by 3p ft by 4p ft. A large Burly Box has 1.5 ft added to each dimension. Write a polynomial $V(p)$ in standard form that can be used to find the volume of a large Burly Box.

$V(p) = 12p^3 + 28.5p^2 + 18p + 3.375$

Also available on transparency

INTERVENTION

Questioning Strategies

EXAMPLE 1

- How do you use the Distributive Property in **Example 1A?**
- How do you determine the sign of each term of a product?

EXAMPLE 2

- What properties of exponents are used to multiply polynomials?

EXAMPLE 3

- How do you know what operation is necessary?

Visual Suggest that students use colored pencils to draw arrows like the ones shown on p. 414 as they multiply in **Example 2A** and **Check It Out Problem 2a.** Colored pencils can be found in the Manipulatives Kit (MK).

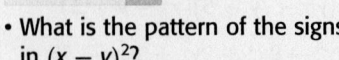

Power Presentations with PowerPoint®

Additional Examples

Example 4

Find the product.

$(a + 2b)^3$

$a^3 + 6a^2b + 12ab^2 + 8b^3$

Also available on transparency

INTERVENTION

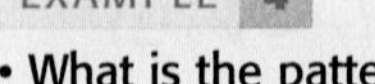

Questioning Strategies

EXAMPLE 4

- What is the pattern of the signs in $(x - y)^2$?
- How is the expansion of $(x - y)^2$ different from that of $(2x - y)^2$?

Teaching Tip **Diversity** Blaise Pascal was not the first to discover the triangle that became named for him. It had already been described by tenth-century Indian mathematicians, by the eleventh-century Persian poet and mathematician Omar Khayyam, and by the fourteenth-century Chinese mathematician Chu Shih Chieh.

You can also raise polynomials to powers.

EXAMPLE 4 Expanding a Power of a Binomial

Find the product.

$(x + y)^3$

$(x+y)(x+y)(x+y)$	*Write in expanded form.*
$(x+y)(x^2+2xy+y^2)$	*Multiply the last two binomial factors.*
$x(x^2)+x(2xy)+x(y^2)+y(x^2)+y(2xy)+y(y^2)$	*Distribute x and then y.*
$x^3+2x^2y+xy^2+x^2y+2xy^2+y^3$	*Multiply.*
$x^3+3x^2y+3xy^2+y^3$	*Combine like terms.*

CHECK IT OUT! Find each product.

4a. $(x + 4)^4$ $x^4 + 16x^3 + 96x^2 + 256x + 256$

4b. $(2x - 1)^3$ $8x^3 - 12x^2 + 6x - 1$

Notice the coefficients of the variables in the final product of $(x + y)^3$. These coefficients are the numbers from the third row of Pascal's triangle.

Binomial Expansion		Pascal's Triangle (Coefficients)
$(a+b)^0 =$	1	1
$(a+b)^1 =$	$a+b$	1 1
$(a+b)^2 =$	$a^2+2ab+b^2$	1 2 1
$(a+b)^3 =$	$a^3+3a^2b+3ab^2+b^3$	1 3 3 1
$(a+b)^4 =$	$a^4+4a^3b+6a^2b^2+4ab^3+b^4$	1 4 6 4 1
$(a+b)^5 =$	$a^5+5a^4b+10a^3b^2+10a^2b^3+5ab^4+b^5$	1 5 10 10 5 1

Each row of Pascal's triangle gives the coefficients of the corresponding binomial expansion. The pattern in the table can be extended to apply to the expansion of any binomial of the form $(a + b)^n$, where n is a whole number.

Know it! Note

Binomial Expansion

For a binomial expansion of the form $(a + b)^n$, the following statements are true.

1. There are $n + 1$ terms.
2. The coefficients are the numbers from the nth row of Pascal's triangle.
3. The exponent of a is n in the first term, and the exponent decreases by 1 in each successive term.
4. The exponent of b is 0 in the first term, and the exponent increases by 1 in each successive term.
5. The sum of the exponents in any term is n.

This information is formalized by the *Binomial Theorem*, which you will study further in Chapter 11.

Student to Student — *Expanding Binomials*

Caitlin Humphrey
Hillcrest High School

I like to use a chart to expand binomials. I will use the binomial $(x + 2)^4$ as an example.

I write the coefficients from Pascal's triangle in the top row. I write the decreasing powers in the second row.

Then I shift one column to the right and write the increasing powers in the third row.

1	4	6	4	1
x^4	x^3	x^2	x	
	2	4	8	16

Finally, I multiply vertically to get $x^4 + 8x^3 + 24x^2 + 32x + 16$.

EXAMPLE 5 Using Pascal's Triangle to Expand Binomial Expressions

Expand each expression.

A $(y-3)^4$

1 4 6 4 1   *Identify the coefficients for n = 4, or row 4.*

$$\left[1y^4(-3)^0\right] + \left[4y^3(-3)^1\right] + \left[6y^2(-3)^2\right] + \left[4y^1(-3)^3\right] + \left[1y^0(-3)^4\right]$$

$$y^4 - 12y^3 + 54y^2 - 108y + 81$$

B $(4z+5)^3$

1 3 3 1   *Identify the coefficients for n = 3, or row 3.*

$$\left[1(4z)^3 5^0\right] + \left[3(4z)^2 5^1\right] + \left[3(4z)^1 5^2\right] + \left[1(4z)^0 5^3\right]$$

$$64z^3 + 240z^2 + 300z + 125$$

CHECK IT OUT! Expand each expression.

5a. $(x+2)^3$ **5b.** $(x-4)^5$ **5c.** $(3x+1)^4$

5a. $x^3 + 6x^2 + 12x + 8$

5b. $x^5 - 20x^4 + 160x^3 - 640x^2 + 1280x - 1024$

5c. $81x^4 + 108x^3 + 54x^2 + 12x + 1$

THINK AND DISCUSS

1. The product of $(3x^4 - 2x^2 - 1)$ and a polynomial $P(x)$ results in a polynomial of degree 9. What is the degree of $P(x)$? Explain.
2. After $(2x+8)^7$ is expanded, what is the degree of the result, and how many terms does the result have? Explain.

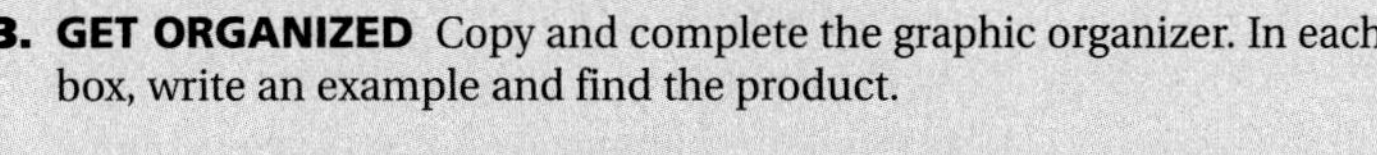

3. **GET ORGANIZED** Copy and complete the graphic organizer. In each box, write an example and find the product.

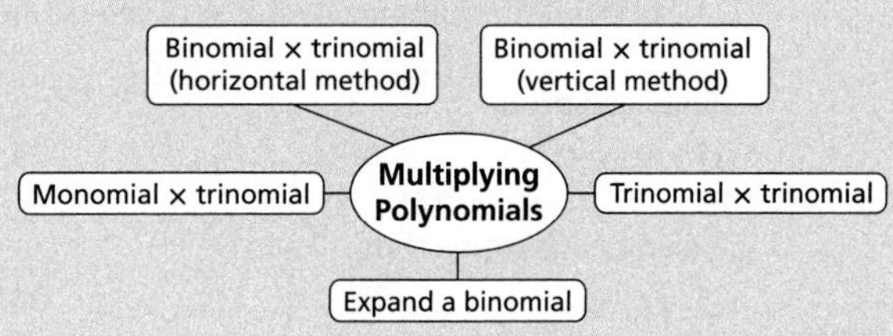

COMMON ERROR ALERT

Students might incorrectly expand binomial expressions by choosing the wrong row of coefficients in Pascal's triangle. Remind students that for an exponent of *n*, choose row *n* of Pascal's triangle. Row *n* will be the row with the value *n* as the second entry.

Power Presentations with PowerPoint®

Additional Examples

Example 5

Expand each expression.

A. $(k-5)^3$

$k^3 - 15k^2 + 75k - 125$

B. $(6m-8)^3$

$216m^3 - 864m^2 + 1152m - 512$

Also available on transparency

INTERVENTION

Questioning Strategies

EXAMPLE 5

- How do you choose which row of Pascal's triangle to use?
- What is the pattern of exponents of a binomial expansion?

3 Close

Summarize

Remind students that every term of a polynomial must be multiplied by every term of the other polynomial. Review with students how to use Pascal's triangle to expand $(x+1)^5$.

ONGOING ASSESSMENT and INTERVENTION

***Diagnose Before* the Lesson**
6-2 Warm Up, TE p. 414

***Monitor During* the Lesson**
Check It Out! Exercises, SE pp. 414–417
Questioning Strategies, TE pp. 415–417

***Assess After* the Lesson**
6-2 Lesson Quiz, TE p. 420
Alternative Assessment, TE p. 420

Answers to *Think and Discuss*

1. 5; the degree of the product is the sum of the degrees of the 2 polynomials.
2. degree 7; 8 terms; the degree is given by the exponent of $(2x)^7$, and there are always $(n+1)$ terms.
3. See p. A8.

6-2 Exercises

Assignment Guide

Assign *Guided Practice* exercises as necessary.

If you finished Examples **1–3**
- **Basic** 18–26, 37
- **Average** 18–26, 35, 37
- **Advanced** 18–26 even, 35–37

If you finished Examples **1–5**
- **Basic** 18–38, 40–45, 54–62, 70–77
- **Average** 18–39, 46–62, 67–77
- **Advanced** 18–50 even, 53, 55–77

Homework Quick Check

Quickly check key concepts.
Exercises: 20, 24, 26, 30, 32

Answers

14. $x^4 - 8x^3 + 24x^2 - 32x + 16$
15. $16x^4 + 32x^3y + 24x^2y^2 + 8xy^3 + y^4$
16. $x^3 + 6x^2y + 12xy^2 + 8y^3$
17. $32x^5 - 80x^4y + 80x^3y^2 - 40x^2y^3 + 10xy^4 - y^5$
21. $12r^5 + 28r^4 - 60r^3 + 28r^2$
22. $x^3 - 2x^2y + 2xy^2 - y^3$
23. $6x^3 + 7x^2y - 16xy^2 + 10y^3$
24. $x^5 - 6x^3 - 4x^2 - x - 5$
25. $12x^4 + 17x^3 + 8x^2 + x - 2$

State Resources

6-2 Exercises

go.hrw.com
Homework Help Online
KEYWORD: MB7 6-2
Parent Resources Online
KEYWORD: MB7 Parent

5. $x^3 + x^2y - 3xy^2 + y^3$
6. $6x^3 + 5x^2 - 9x + 2$
7. $3x^5 + 15x^4 + 16x^3 - 3x^2 + 6x - 2$
8. $3x^4 + 36x^3 + 107x^2 + 108x + 35$

GUIDED PRACTICE

Find each product.

SEE EXAMPLE 1 p. 414

1. $-4c^2d^3(5cd^2 + 3c^2d)$ $-20c^3d^5 - 12c^4d^4$
2. $3x^2(2y + 5x)$ $6x^2y + 15x^3$
3. $xy(5x^2 + 8x - 7)$ $5x^3y + 8x^2y - 7xy$
4. $2xy(3x^2 - xy + 7)$ $6x^3y - 2x^2y^2 + 14xy$

SEE EXAMPLE 2 p. 414

5. $(x - y)(x^2 + 2xy - y^2)$
6. $(3x - 2)(2x^2 + 3x - 1)$
7. $(x^3 + 3x^2 + 1)(3x^2 + 6x - 2)$
8. $(x^2 + 9x + 7)(3x^2 + 9x + 5)$

SEE EXAMPLE 3 p. 415

9. **Business** A businessman models the number of items (in thousands) that his company sold from 1998 through 2004 as $N(x) = -0.1x^3 + x^2 - 3x + 4$ and the average price per item (in dollars) as $P(x) = 0.2x + 5$, where x represents the number of years since 1998. Write a polynomial $R(x)$ that can be used to model the total revenue for this company. $-0.02x^4 - 0.3x^3 + 4.4x^2 - 14.2x + 20$

SEE EXAMPLE 4 p. 416

Find each product.

10. $(x + 2)^3$ $x^3 + 6x^2 + 12x + 8$
11. $(x + y)^4$ $x^4 + 4x^3y + 6x^2y^2 + 4xy^3 + y^4$
12. $(x + 1)^4$ $x^4 + 4x^3 + 6x^2 + 4x + 1$
13. $(x - 3y)^3$ $x^3 - 9x^2y + 27xy^2 - 27y^3$

SEE EXAMPLE 5 p. 417

Expand each expression.

14. $(x - 2)^4$
15. $(2x + y)^4$
16. $(x + 2y)^3$
17. $(2x - y)^5$

PRACTICE AND PROBLEM SOLVING

Independent Practice	
For Exercises	See Example
18–21	1
22–25	2
26	3
27–30	4
31–34	5

Extra Practice
Skills Practice p. S14
Application Practice p. S37

Find each product.

18. $7x^3(2x + 3)$ $14x^4 + 21x^3$
19. $3x^2(2x^2 + 9x - 6)$ $6x^4 + 27x^3 - 18x^2$
20. $xy^2(x^2 + 3xy + 9)$ $x^3y^2 + 3x^2y^3 + 9xy^2$
21. $2r^2(6r^3 + 14r^2 - 30r + 14)$
22. $(x - y)(x^2 - xy + y^2)$
23. $(2x + 5y)(3x^2 - 4xy + 2y^2)$
24. $(x^3 + x^2 + 1)(x^2 - x - 5)$
25. $(4x^2 + 3x + 2)(3x^2 + 2x - 1)$

26. **Measurement** A bottom for a box can be made by cutting congruent squares from each of the four corners of a piece of cardboard. The volume of a box made from an 8.5-by-11-inch piece of cardboard would be represented by $V(x) = x(11 - 2x)(8.5 - 2x)$, where x is the side length of one square.

a. Express the volume as a sum of monomials. **26a.** $4x^3 - 39x^2 + 93.5x$

b. Find the volume when $x = 1$ inch. 58.5 in^3

Find each product.

27. $(2x - 2)^3$ $8x^3 - 24x^2 + 24x - 8$
28. $\left(x + \frac{1}{3}\right)^4$ $x^4 + \frac{4}{3}x^3 + \frac{2}{3}x^2 + \frac{4}{27}x + \frac{1}{81}$
29. $(x - y)^4$ $x^4 - 4x^3y + 6x^2y^2 - 4xy^3 + y^4$
30. $(4 + y)^3$ $64 + 48y + 12y^2 + y^3$

Expand each expression.

31. $(x - 3y)^4$ $x^4 - 12x^3y + 54x^2y^2 - 108xy^3 + 81y^4$
32. $(x - 2)^5$ $x^5 - 10x^4 + 40x^3 - 80x^2 + 80x - 32$
33. $(x + y)^5$ $x^5 + 5x^4y + 10x^3y^2 + 10x^2y^3 + 5xy^4 + y^5$
34. $(2x - 3y)^4$ $16x^4 - 96x^3y + 216x^2y^2 - 216xy^3 + 81y^4$

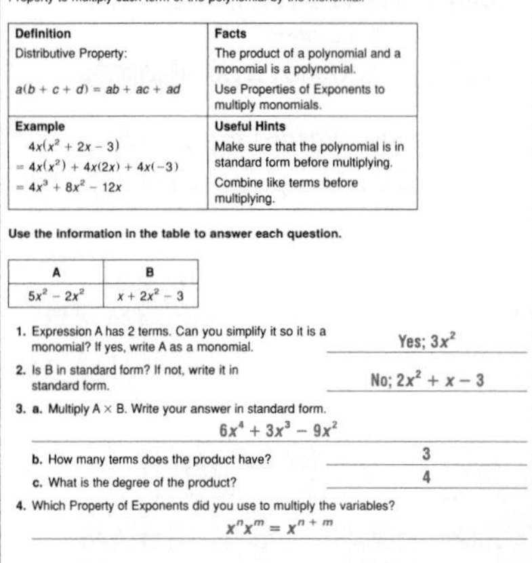

6-2 READING STRATEGIES

You can multiply a polynomial by a monomial. Use the Distributive Property to multiply each term of the polynomial by the monomial.

Definition	Facts
Distributive Property: $a(b + c + d) = ab + ac + ad$	The product of a polynomial and a monomial is a polynomial. Use Properties of Exponents to multiply monomials.
Example	**Useful Hints**
$4x(x^2 + 2x - 3)$ $= 4x(x^2) + 4x(2x) + 4x(-3)$ $= 4x^3 + 8x^2 - 12x$	Make sure that the polynomial is in standard form before multiplying. Combine like terms before multiplying.

Use the information in the table to answer each question.

A	B
$5x^2 - 2x^2$	$x + 2x^2 - 3$

1. Expression A has 2 terms. Can you simplify it so it is a monomial? If yes, write A as a monomial. Yes; $3x^2$
2. Is B in standard form? If not, write it in standard form. No; $2x^2 + x - 3$
3. a. Multiply A × B. Write your answer in standard form. $6x^4 + 3x^3 - 9x^2$
   b. How many terms does the product have? 3
   c. What is the degree of the product? 4
4. Which Property of Exponents did you use to multiply the variables? $x^nx^m = x^{n+m}$

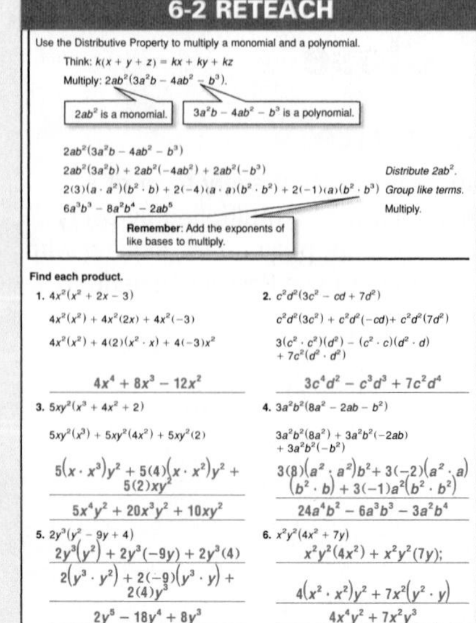

6-2 RETEACH

Use the Distributive Property to multiply a monomial and a polynomial.

Think: $k(x + y + z) = kx + ky + kz$

Multiply: $2ab^2(3a^2b - 4ab^2 - b^3)$.

$2ab^2$ is a monomial. $3a^2b - 4ab^2 - b^3$ is a polynomial.

$2ab^2(3a^2b - 4ab^2 - b^3)$

$2ab^2(3a^2b) + 2ab^2(-4ab^2) + 2ab^2(-b^3)$ Distribute $2ab^2$.

$2(3)(a \cdot a^2)(b^2 \cdot b) + 2(-4)(a \cdot a)(b^2 \cdot b^2) + 2(-1)(a)(b^2 \cdot b^3)$ Group like terms.

$6a^3b^3 - 8a^2b^4 - 2ab^5$ Multiply.

Remember: Add the exponents of like bases to multiply.

Find each product.

1. $4x^2(x^2 + 2x - 3)$
   $4x^2(x^2) + 4x^2(2x) + 4x^2(-3)$
   $4x^2(x^2) + 4(2)(x^2 \cdot x) + 4(-3)x^2$
   $4x^4 + 8x^3 - 12x^2$
2. $c^2d^2(3c^2 - cd + 7d^2)$
   $c^2d^2(3c^2) + c^2d^2(-cd) + c^2d^2(7d^2)$
   $3(c^2 \cdot c^2)(d^2) - (c^2 \cdot c)(d^2 \cdot d) + 7c^2(d^2 \cdot d^2)$
   $3c^4d^2 - c^3d^3 + 7c^2d^4$
3. $5xy^2(x^3 + 4x^2 + 2)$
   $5xy^2(x^3) + 5xy^2(4x^2) + 5xy^2(2)$
   $5(x \cdot x^3)y^2 + 5(4)(x \cdot x^2)y^2 + 5(2)xy^2$
   $5x^4y^2 + 20x^3y^2 + 10xy^2$
4. $3a^2b^2(8a^2 - 2ab - b^2)$
   $3a^2b^2(8a^2) + 3a^2b^2(-2ab) + 3a^2b^2(-b^2)$
   $3(8)(a^2 \cdot a^2)b^2 + 3(-2)(a^2 \cdot a)(b^2 \cdot b) + 3(-1)a^2(b^2 \cdot b^2)$
   $24a^4b^2 - 6a^3b^3 - 3a^2b^4$
5. $2y^3(y^2 - 9y + 4)$
   $2y^3(y^2) + 2y^3(-9y) + 2y^3(4)$
   $2(y^3 \cdot y^2) + 2(-9)(y^3 \cdot y) + 2(4)y^3$
   $2y^5 - 18y^4 + 8y^3$
6. $x^2y^2(4x^2 + 7y)$
   $x^2y^2(4x^2) + x^2y^2(7y);$
   $4(x^2 \cdot x^2)y^2 + 7x^2(y^2 \cdot y)$
   $4x^4y^2 + 7x^2y^3$

Graphing Calculator Compare each pair of expressions with your graphing calculator. Use the table feature to make a conjecture about whether the expressions are equivalent.

35. $(x-6)^3$; $x^3-18x^2+108x-216$ equivalent

36. $(11x+10)(11x+1)$; $121x^2+121x+10$ equivalent

37. $(3x^2+2x)(3x+2)$; $9x^3+12x^2+4$ not equivalent

38. $(2x+1)^4$; $16x^4+32x^3+24x^2+8x+1$ equivalent

39. Business Ms. Liao runs a small dress company. From 1995 through 2005, the number of dresses she made can be modeled by $N(x)=0.3x^2-1.6x+14$ and the average cost to make each dress can be modeled by $C(x)=-0.001x^2-0.06x+8.3$, where x is the number of years since 1995. Write a polynomial that can be used to model Ms. Liao's total dressmaking costs, $T(x)$, for those years. $T(x)=-0.0003x^4-0.0164x^3+2.572x^2-14.12x+116.2$

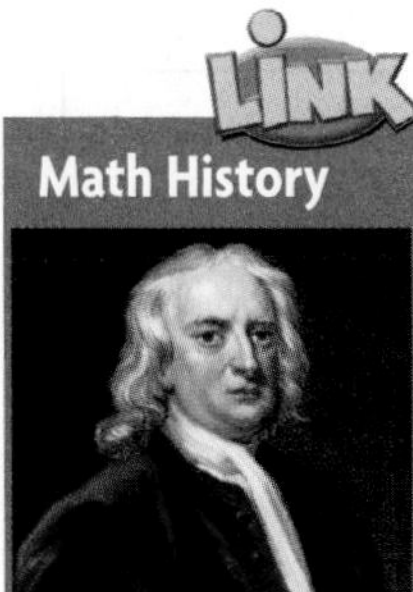

LINK

Math History

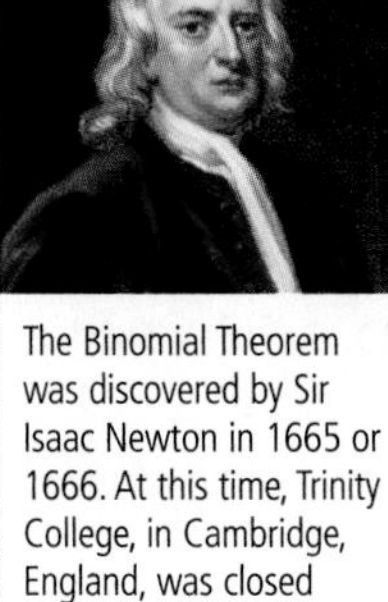

The Binomial Theorem was discovered by Sir Isaac Newton in 1665 or 1666. At this time, Trinity College, in Cambridge, England, was closed because of the plague, and Newton, working in solitude, was able to focus solely on his mathematical studies.

Multiply. **40.** $-90x^3y^4+42x^4y^3-12x^3$ **41.** $p^3-6p^2q+12pq^2-8q^3$

40. $-6x^3(15y^4-7xy^3+2)$	**41.** $(p-2q)^3$	**42.** $(x^2-2yz-y^2)(y^2+x)$
43. $(x^4+xy^3)(x^2+y^3)$	**44.** $(3-3y)^4$	**45.** $(5x^3+x^2-9x)(y+2)$
46. $(3+x-2x^2)(x-1)$	**47.** $3(x-2)^4$	**48.** $(x-6)(x^4-2x^3+x^2+1)$
49. $(30+x^3+x^2)(x-15-x^2)$	**50.** $\left(\frac{1}{2}+z\right)^4$	**51.** $(2x-3)(x^5-4x^3+7)$

52. Generate the coefficients that would be used to expand $(a+b)^7$ by using binomial expansion. 1, 7, 21, 35, 35, 21, 7, 1

53. Physics An object t seconds after it is thrown in the air has a velocity that can be described by $v(t)=-9.8t+24$ (in meters/second) and a height $h(t)=-4.9t^2+24t+60$ (in meters). The object has mass $m=2$ kilograms. The kinetic energy of the object is given by $K=\frac{1}{2}mv^2$, and the potential energy is given by $U=9.8mh$. Can you find a polynomial expression for the total kinetic and potential energy $K+U$ as a function of time, t? Explain.

54. ///ERROR ANALYSIS/// Two students used binomial expansion to expand $(a+b)^2$. Which answer is incorrect? Identify the error.

B; the error is that the powers of b should begin at 0 and increase, not decrease.

A

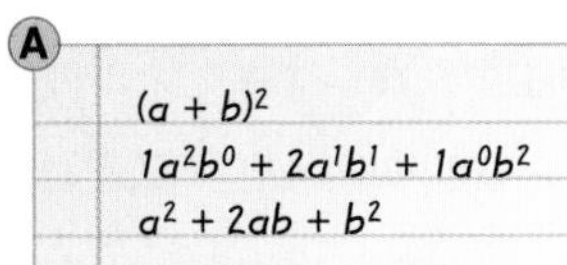

$(a+b)^2$
$1a^2b^0+2a^1b^1+1a^0b^2$
$a^2+2ab+b^2$

B

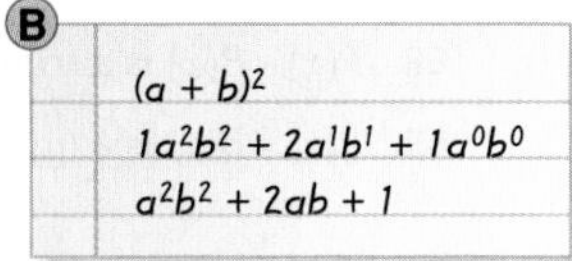

$(a+b)^2$
$1a^2b^2+2a^1b^1+1a^0b^0$
$a^2b^2+2ab+1$

MULTI-STEP TEST PREP

55. This problem will prepare you for the Multi-Step Test Prep on page 436.

The total number of lights in a triangular lighting rig is related to the triangular numbers, as shown at right. The product of the nth triangular number and the $(n+1)$th triangular number is given by $f(n)=\frac{n(n+1)^2(n+2)}{4}$. **55a.** $f(n)=\frac{1}{4}n^4+n^3+\frac{5}{4}n^2+\frac{1}{2}n$

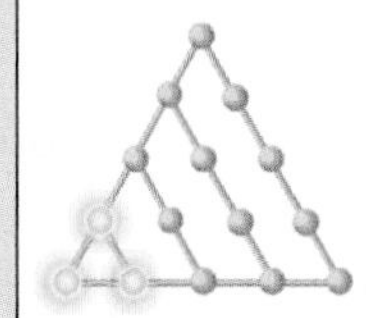

Triangular numbers: 1, 3, 6, 10, 15, . . .

a. Write $f(n)$ as a polynomial function.

b. Find the product of the twelfth and thirteenth triangular numbers. 7098

c. Evaluate $f(n)$ for $n=20$ and describe what this value represents. $f(20)=48510$; the product of the 20th and 21st triangular numbers

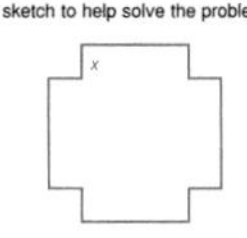

Teaching Tip **Critical Thinking** In **Exercise 53,** students must use all the given information to find a solution. Remind students to read carefully to determine the relationships between the given variables.

MULTI-STEP TEST PREP In **Exercise 55,** students write a polynomial function to represent triangular numbers. This exercise prepares students for the Multi-Step Test Prep on page 436.

Answers

42. $x^2y^2+x^3-2y^3z-2xyz-y^4-xy^2$
43. $x^6+x^4y^3+x^3y^3+xy^6$
44. $81-324y+486y^2-324y^3+81y^4$
45. $5x^3y+x^2y-9xy+10x^3+2x^2-18x$
46. $-2x^3+3x^2+2x-3$
47. $3x^4-24x^3+72x^2-96x+48$
48. $x^5-8x^4+13x^3-6x^2+x-6$
49. $-x^5-14x^3-45x^2+30x-450$
50. $\frac{1}{16}+\frac{1}{2}z+\frac{3}{2}z^2+2z^3+z^4$
51. $2x^6-3x^5-8x^4+12x^3+14x-21$
53. Possible answer: No, you get a constant 1752 joules, which is independent of time t.

6-2 PROBLEM SOLVING

Latesha is making an open wooden toy box to hold the building blocks at her day care center. She has a square panel of cedar with side length of 24 inches. The first step is to cut out congruent squares from each corner. She needs to know what the side length of the cutout square should be in order for the finished toy box to have the greatest volume possible.

1. Draw a sketch to help solve the problem.

x

2. The toy box will be square and x inches deep. Write an expression for the side length of the finished box. $24-2x$
3. Write an equation to represent the volume. $V=(x)(24-2x)(24-2x)$
4. Express the volume as the sum of monomials. $V=4x^3-96x^2+576x$
5. Latesha decides to try some possible values for x. She knows that x must be less than 12. Explain why.
   Possible answer: The side length of the finished box is $24-2x$, and $24-2(12)=0$.
6. Complete the table for each value of x.

x (in.)	2	3	4	5	6
Volume (sq in.)	800	972	1024	980	864

7. Latesha decides that she will use an integer value for x, so that she does not have to cut fractions of an inch.
   a. What value for x should she choose? 4
   b. Explain why this is the best choice.
   Possible answer: The volume increases up to $x=4$ and then decreases after that.
   c. What are the dimensions of her finished toy box?
   4 by 16 by 16 inches

6-2 CHALLENGE

Pascal's triangle can be used to raise a binomial to a power. What if you wanted to raise a trinomial of the form x^2+x+1 to a power, like the fifth power? This can be done with normal expansion techniques using the distributive laws, but it is very tedious.

Consider the products of x^2+x+1 and the triangle of coefficients.

$(x^2+x+1)^0=1$ 1
$(x^2+x+1)^1=x^2+x+1$ 1 1 1
$(x^2+x+1)^2=x^4+2x^3+3x^2+2x+1$ 1 2 3 2 1
$(x^2+x+1)^3=x^6+3x^5+6x^4+7x^3+6x^2+3x+1$ 1 3 6 7 6 3 1

Each row of this triangle, let's call it Pascal[3], starts and ends with 1 and reads the same forward and backward. Each of the numbers is the sum of the 3 numbers above it if we consider the numbers before and after the ones to be zeros. For instance, the second number in the fourth row is $3=0+1+2$. The fourth number in this row is $7=2+3+2$. Subsequent rows follow the same pattern.

1. a. Find the numbers in the fifth row of Pascal[3]. 1, 4, 10, 16, 19, 16, 10, 4, 1
   b. Use these numbers to expand the trinomial x^2+x+1 to the fourth power. $x^8+4x^7+10x^6+16x^5+19x^4+16x^3+10x^2+4x+1$
2. a. Find the numbers in the sixth row of Pascal[3]. 1, 5, 15, 30, 45, 51, 45, 30, 15, 5, 1
   b. Expand the expression $(x^2+x+1)^5$. $x^{10}+5x^9+15x^8+30x^7+45x^6+51x^5+45x^4+30x^3+15x^2+5x+1$
3. What is the eighth term in the expansion of $(x^2+x+1)^6$? $126x^5$

Look for and use an analogous pattern in the triangle Pascal[4].

4. Write the first 5 rows of this triangle.

1
1 1 1 1
1 2 3 4 3 2 1
1 3 6 10 12 12 10 6 3 1
1 4 10 20 31 40 44 40 31 20 10 4 1

5. What is the sixth term in the expansion of $(x^3+x^2+x+1)^3$? $12x^4$
6. What is the fifth term in the expansion of $(x^3+x^2+x+1)^4$? $31x^8$

6-2 PRACTICE A
6-2 PRACTICE C
6-2 PRACTICE B

Find each product.

1. $4x^2(3x^2+1)$ $12x^4+4x^2$
2. $-9x(x^2+2x+4)$ $-9x^3-18x^2-36x$
3. $-6x^2(x^3+7x^2-4x+3)$ $-6x^5-42x^4+24x^3-18x^2$
4. $x^3(-4x^3+10x^2-7x+2)$ $-4x^6+10x^5-7x^4+2x^3$
5. $-5m^3(7n^4-2mn^3+6)$ $-35m^3n^4+10m^4n^3-30m^3$
6. $(x+2)(y^2+2y-12)$ $xy^2+2xy-12x+2y^2+4y-24$
7. $(p+q)(4p^2-p-8q^2-q)$ $4p^3-p^2+4p^2q-2pq-8pq^2-q^2-8q^3$
8. $(2x^2+xy-y)(y^2+3x)$ $2x^2y^2+6x^3+xy^3+3x^2y-y^3-3xy$

Expand each expression.

9. $(3x-1)^3$ $27x^3-27x^2+9x-1$
10. $(x-4)^4$ $x^4-16x^3+96x^2-256x+256$
11. $3(a-4b)^2$ $3a^2-24ab+48b^2$
12. $5(x^2-2y^3)^3$ $5x^6-30x^4y+60x^2y^2-40y^3$

Solve.

13. A biologist has found that the number of branches on a certain rare tree in its first few years of life can be modeled by the polynomial $b(y)=4y^2+y$. The number of leaves on each branch can be modeled by the polynomial $l(y)=2y^3+3y^2+y$, where y is the number of years after the tree reaches a height of 6 feet. Write a polynomial describing the total number of leaves on the tree.
    $8y^5+14y^4+7y^3+y^2$

TEST PREP DOCTOR In **Exercise 59,** suggest that students pay attention to the key words *multiplied* and *perimeter* before calculating. Multiplying the width $2x$ by itself results in a new width of $4x^2$, so the perimeter must have a term that contains x^2. That eliminates choices **F** and **G.** Since **H** and **J** have the same first term, compare the second terms. Since the new length is $2xy$, there must be a term with xy in the perimeter, so choice **H** is eliminated.

Journal

Have students write an explanation for a classmate of what *binomial expansion* means and how it is related to multiplying polynomials.

ALTERNATIVE ASSESSMENT

Give students a simple binomial such as $(x + 4)^3$. Have students both find the product by using polynomial multiplication and expand the expression by using Pascal's triangle. Ask students to compare and contrast the two methods.

Power Presentations with PowerPoint®

6-2 Lesson Quiz

Find each product.

1. $5jk(k - 2j)$ $5jk^2 - 10j^2k$
2. $(2a^3 - a + 3)(a^2 + 3a - 5)$ $2a^5 + 6a^4 - 11a^3 + 14a - 15$
3. The number of items is modeled by $f(x) = 0.3x^2 + 0.1x + 2$, and the cost per item is modeled by $g(x) = -0.1x^2 - 0.3x + 5$. Write a polynomial $c(x)$ that can be used to model the total cost. $-0.03x^4 - 0.1x^3 + 1.27x^2 - 0.1x + 10$
4. Find the product. $(y - 5)^4$ $y^4 - 20y^3 + 150y^2 - 500y + 625$
5. Expand the expression. $(3a - b)^3$ $27a^3 + 27a^2b + 9ab^2 + b^3$

Also available on transparency

56. Critical Thinking Using binomial expansion, explain why every other term of the resulting polynomial for $(x - y)^5$ is negative. Possible answer: The powers of $-y$ alternate between positive and negative.

57. Write About It Explain how to expand a binomial raised to a power by using Pascal's Triangle.

TEST PREP

58. Multiply $(y - 3)(y^2 - 6y - 9)$.

Ⓐ $y^3 + 18y - 9$ Ⓑ $y^3 - 3y^2 + 3y + 27$ Ⓒ $y^3 + 9y^2 + 27y + 27$ Ⓓ $y^3 - 9y^2 + 9y + 27$

59. The rectangle shown is enlarged such that each side is multiplied by the value of the width, $2x$. Which expression represents the perimeter of the enlarged rectangle?

Ⓕ $4x + 2y$ Ⓖ $6x + 4xy$ Ⓗ $8x^2 + 2y$ Ⓙ $8x^2 + 4xy$

60. What is the third term of the binomial expansion of $(x - 4)^6$?

Ⓐ $240x^4$ Ⓑ $15x^4$ Ⓒ $160x^3$ Ⓓ $8x^3$

61. Find the product $a^2b(2a^3b - 5ab^4)$.

Ⓕ $-3a^4b^{-2}$ Ⓖ $2a^6b - 5a^2b^4$ Ⓗ $2a^5b^2 - 5a^3b^5$ Ⓙ $2a^5b^2 - 5ab^4$

62. Short Response Expand $(4 - x)^4$ by using binomial expansion. $256 - 256x + 96x^2 - 16x^3 + x^4$

CHALLENGE AND EXTEND

Find the product.

63. $(x - 1)^{10}$ **64.** $(14 + y)^5$ **65.** $(m - n)^3(m + n)^3$ **66.** $(ab + 2c)^4$

64. $537824 + 192080y + 27440y^2 + 1960y^3 + 70y^4 + y^5$

65. $m^6 - 3m^4n^2 + 3m^2n^4 - n^6$

66. $a^4b^4 + 8a^3b^3c + 24a^2b^2c^2 + 32abc^3 + 16c^4$

Suppose $P(x) = x + 3$. Find a binomial $B(x)$ that satisfies the given condition.

67. $P(x) \cdot B(x)$ is a binomial. $B(x) = x - 3$

68. $P(x) \cdot B(x)$ is a trinomial. $B(x) = x + 1$

69. $P(x) \cdot B(x)$ is a quartic polynomial. $B(x) = x^3 + 1$

SPIRAL REVIEW

70. Athletics A basketball coach makes his players run five sprints for every point they lost by in a game. Write a function to represent the number of sprints the team has to run after losing a game. How many sprints must the players run if they lose a game by a score of 84–73? *(Lesson 1-7)* $f(x) = 5x$; $f(11) = 55$

Use the following matrices for Exercises 71–74. Evaluate, if possible. *(Lesson 4-2)*

$A = \begin{bmatrix} -2 & 1 \\ 4 & 3 \end{bmatrix}$ $B = \begin{bmatrix} 0 & 4 & 2 \\ 2 & -1 & 1 \\ -2 & 1 & 3 \end{bmatrix}$ $C = \begin{bmatrix} 6 & 3 \\ -1 & 5 \\ 0 & 7 \end{bmatrix}$

71. A^2 $\begin{bmatrix} 8 & 1 \\ 4 & 13 \end{bmatrix}$ **72.** CA $\begin{bmatrix} 0 & 15 \\ 22 & 14 \\ 28 & 21 \end{bmatrix}$ **73.** B^2 $\begin{bmatrix} 4 & -2 & 10 \\ -4 & 10 & 6 \\ -4 & -6 & 6 \end{bmatrix}$ **74.** BC $\begin{bmatrix} -4 & 34 \\ 13 & 8 \\ -13 & 20 \end{bmatrix}$

Rewrite each polynomial in standard form. Then identify the leading coefficient, degree, and number of terms. Name the polynomial. *(Lesson 6-1)*

75. $3x + 5x^2 + 4x^4 - 6x^3$ **76.** $10x^2 + 5x^3 - x$ **77.** $9 - 4x^2 + 3x^5 - 2x$

Answers

57. Possible answer: Find the row of Pascal's triangle that corresponds to the power of the binomial. Write the decreasing powers of the first term of the binomial times the increasing powers of the second term, and multiply by the appropriate value from the row of Pascal's triangle.

63. $x^{10} - 10x^9 + 45x^8 - 120x^7 + 210x^6 - 252x^5 + 210x^4 - 120x^3 + 45x^2 - 10x + 1$

75. $4x^4 - 6x^3 + 5x^2 + 3x$; 4; 4; 4; quartic with 4 terms

76. $5x^3 + 10x^2 - x$; 5; 3; 3; cubic trinomial

77. $3x^5 - 4x^2 - 2x + 9$; 3; 5; 4; quintic with 4 terms

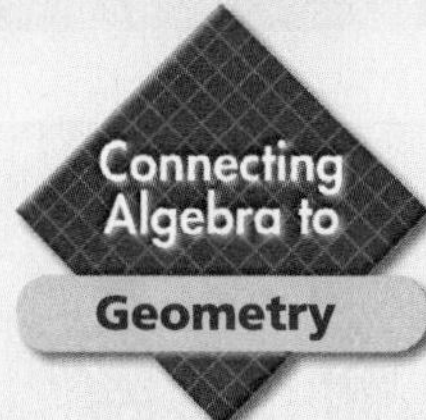

Nets

See Skills Bank page S65

For a prism, volume equals the area of the base times the height. For a pyramid, volume equals $\frac{1}{3}$ the area of the base times the height. To find the surface area of a solid, add the areas of all of the faces.

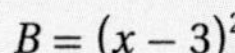

Activity

Find the volume and surface area of the square pyramid shown by this net.

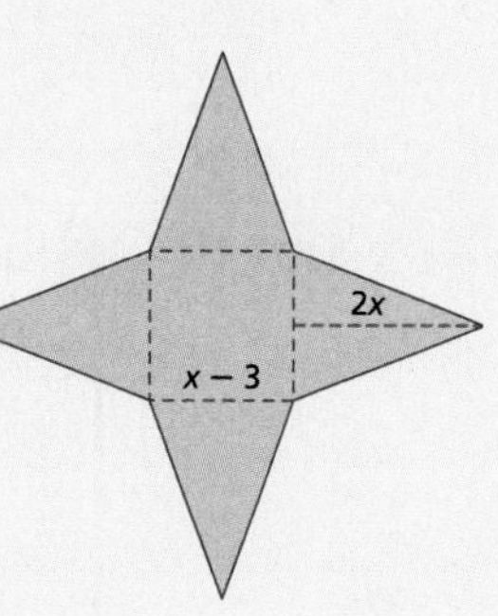

For the volume, multiply the area of the square base by the height and then multiply by $\frac{1}{3}$.

$B = (x-3)^2$ *Find the area of the square base.*

$V = \frac{1}{3}(x-3)^2 x$ *The height of the pyramid is x.*

$V = \frac{x^3}{3} - 2x^2 + 3x$ *Multiply the polynomials, and simplify.*

For the surface area, add the area of the square base to the area of the four triangular faces.

$B = (x-3)^2$ *Find the area of the square base.*

$A = \frac{1}{2}(x-3) \cdot 2x$ *Find the area of 1 triangular face.*

$L = 4A = 4 \cdot \frac{1}{2}(x-3) \cdot 2x$ *Find the area of 4 triangular faces.*

$SA = (x-3)^2 + 4 \cdot \frac{1}{2}(x-3) \cdot 2x$ *Add the area of the base to the area of the four triangular faces.*

$SA = (x^2 - 6x + 9) + (4x^2 - 12x)$ *Multiply.*

$SA = 5x^2 - 18x + 9$ *Add.*

Try This

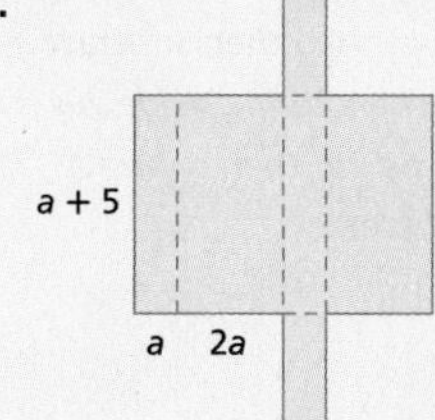

Find the volume and surface area of the solid shown by each net.

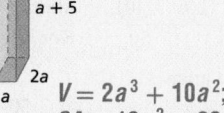

1. $V = 2a^3 + 10a^2$; $SA = 10a^2 + 30a$

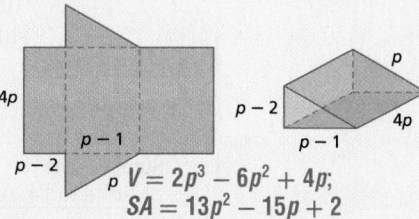

2. $V = 2p^3 - 6p^2 + 4p$; $SA = 13p^2 - 15p + 2$

3. The volume of a rectangular prism is $6c^3 - 22c^2 - 8c$. Find the length and width of this prism if the height is $2c$. $(c-4)$ and $(3c+1)$

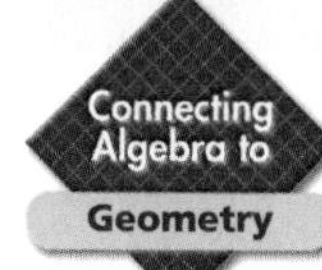

Organizer

See Skills Bank page S65

Pacing:
Traditional $\frac{1}{2}$ day
Block $\frac{1}{4}$ day

Objective: Use nets to find volumes and surface areas of figures.

Online Edition

Teach

Remember

Students review and apply finding the volumes and surface areas of various solids.

INTERVENTION For additional review and practice on finding volumes and surface areas from nets, see Skills Bank page S65.

Kinesthetic Students will benefit from building a few solids from nets similar to those shown on the page. Provide graph paper for this activity.

Close

Assess

Have students compare the square pyramid in the example with its net. Ask them what important dimension is not shown in the net. height

State Resources

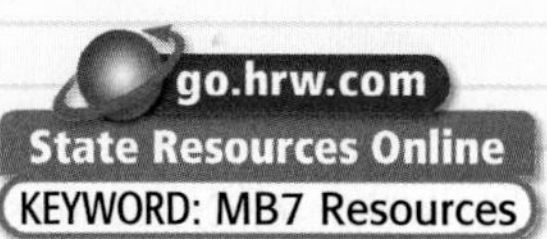

6-3 Organizer

Pacing: Traditional 2 days
Block 1 day

Objective: Use long division and synthetic division to divide polynomials.

PREMIER Online Edition
Tutorial Videos

Countdown to Testing Week 13

Power Presentations with PowerPoint®

Warm Up

Divide using long division.

1. $161 \div 7$ 23
2. $12.18 \div 2.1$ 5.8

Divide.

3. $\dfrac{6x + 15y}{3}$ $2x + 5y$
4. $\dfrac{7a^2 - ab}{a}$ $7a - b$

Also available on transparency

Math Humor

Teacher: Why didn't you do your homework?

Student: The long division took too long, and the synthetic division just wasn't real.

6-3 Dividing Polynomials

A2.4.3 Perform arithmetic operations, including long division and division with remainders, on polynomials by others of equal or lower degree.

Objective
Use long division and synthetic division to divide polynomials.

Vocabulary
synthetic division

Who uses this?
Electricians can divide polynomials in order to find the voltage in an electrical system. (See Example 4.)

"Okay, Copper—what's the charge? Assault and Battery? I have contacts, you know"

© Cartoon Stock

Polynomial long division is a method for dividing a polynomial by another polynomial of a lower degree. It is very similar to dividing numbers.

Arithmetic Long Division

$$\begin{array}{r} 23 \\ 12\overline{)277} \\ \underline{24} \\ 37 \\ \underline{36} \\ 1 \end{array}$$

Divisor: 12; Quotient: 23; Dividend: 277; Remainder: 1

Polynomial Long Division

$$\begin{array}{r} 2x + 3 \\ x + 2\overline{)2x^2 + 7x + 7} \\ \underline{2x^2 + 4x} \\ 3x + 7 \\ \underline{3x + 6} \\ 1 \end{array}$$

Divisor: $x + 2$; Quotient: $2x + 3$; Dividend: $2x^2 + 7x + 7$; Remainder: 1

EXAMPLE 1 Using Long Division to Divide Polynomials

Divide by using long division.

$(4x^2 + 3x^3 + 10) \div (x - 2)$

Step 1 Write the dividend in standard form, including terms with a coefficient of 0.

$3x^3 + 4x^2 + 0x + 10$

Step 2 Write division in the same way as you would when dividing numbers.

$x - 2\overline{)3x^3 + 4x^2 + 0x + 10}$

Step 3 Divide.

$$\begin{array}{r} 3x^2 + 10x + 20 \\ x - 2\overline{)3x^3 + 4x^2 + 0x + 10} \\ \underline{-(3x^3 - 6x^2)} \\ 10x^2 + 0x \\ \underline{-(10x^2 - 20x)} \\ 20x + 10 \\ \underline{-(20x - 40)} \\ 50 \end{array}$$

Notice that x times $3x^2$ is $3x^3$. Write $3x^2$ above $3x^3$.
Multiply $x - 2$ by $3x^2$. Then subtract.
Bring down the next term. Divide $10x^2$ by x.
Multiply $x - 2$ by 10x, then subtract.
Bring down the next term. Divide 20x by x.
Multiply $x - 2$ by 20, then subtract.
Find the remainder.

Step 4 Write the final answer.

$$\frac{4x^2 + 3x^3 + 10}{x - 2} = 3x^2 + 10x + 20 + \frac{50}{x - 2}$$

CHECK IT OUT! **Divide by using long division.**

1a. $(15x^2 + 8x - 12) \div (3x + 1)$ $5x + 1 - \dfrac{13}{3x + 1}$

1b. $(x^2 + 5x - 28) \div (x - 3)$ $x + 8 - \dfrac{4}{x - 3}$

State Resources

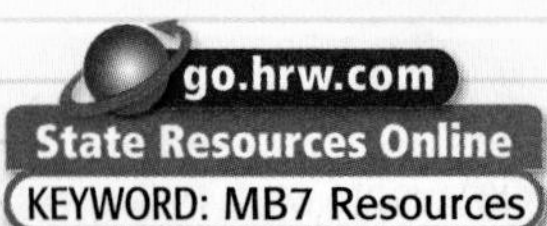

go.hrw.com
State Resources Online
KEYWORD: MB7 Resources

1 Introduce

EXPLORATION

6-3 Dividing Polynomials

To divide polynomials, you can use the same method as that for dividing numbers.

1. Use arithmetic long division to divide $693 \div 21$.
2. Use polynomial long division to divide $(6x^2 + 9x + 3) \div (2x + 1)$.
3. Compare your answers in Problems 1 and 2. What can you say about the coefficients of the quotients for each?
4. Use your answer to Problem 3 to make a conjecture about the quotient of $(x^2 + 6x + 8) \div (x + 4)$ based on the quotient of $168 \div 14$. Verify your conjecture by using polynomial long division.

THINK AND DISCUSS

5. **Explain** how you can find the quotient of $(x^2 + 6x + 5) \div (x + 5)$.
6. **Discuss** whether every polynomial long division problem matches exactly with a numerical long division problem. Give an example to support your response.

Motivate

Ask students to describe the process of long division with numbers, such as $9\overline{)3241}$. Tell them that just as they need to divide numbers, they will also need to divide polynomial expressions. Polynomial long division is an identical process to arithmetic long division except that it uses polynomial expressions instead of numbers.

Explorations and answers are provided in the *Explorations* binder.

Use synthetic substitution to evaluate the polynomial for the given value.

B $P(x) = 4x^4 + 2x^3 + 3x + 5$ for $x = -\frac{1}{2}$

$-\frac{1}{2}$	4	2	0	3	5
		−2	0	0	$-\frac{3}{2}$
	4	0	0	3	$3\frac{1}{2}$

Write the coefficients of the dividend. Use 0 for the coefficient of x^2 and $a = -\frac{1}{2}$.

$P\left(-\frac{1}{2}\right) = 3\frac{1}{2}$

Use synthetic substitution to evaluate the polynomial for the given value.

3a. $P(x) = x^3 + 3x^2 + 4$ for $x = -3$ $P(-3) = 4$

3b. $P(x) = 5x^2 + 9x + 3$ for $x = \frac{1}{5}$ $P\left(\frac{1}{5}\right) = 5$

EXAMPLE 4 *Physics Application*

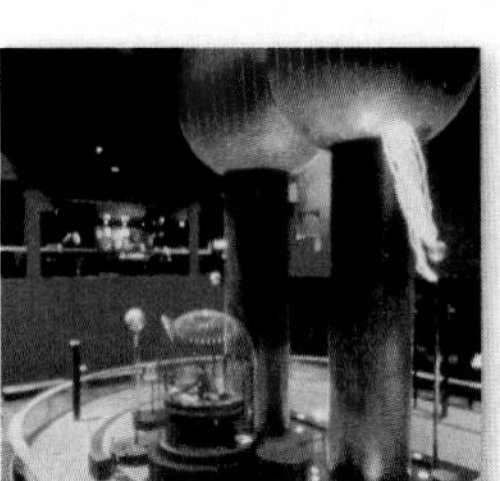

A Van de Graaff generator is a machine that produces very high voltages by using small, safe levels of electric current. One machine has a current that can be modeled by $I(t) = t + 2$, where $t > 0$ represents time in seconds. The power of the system can be modeled by $P(t) = 0.5t^3 + 6t^2 + 10t$. Write an expression that represents the voltage of the system.

The voltage V is related to current I and power P by the equation $V = \frac{P}{I}$.

$V(t) = \frac{0.5t^3 + 6t^2 + 10t}{t + 2}$ *Substitute.*

−2	0.5	6	10	0
		−1	−10	0
	0.5	5	0	0

Use synthetic division.

The voltage can be represented by $V(t) = 0.5t^2 + 5t$.

4. Write an expression for the length of a rectangle with width $y - 9$ and area $y^2 - 14y + 45$. $y - 5$

THINK AND DISCUSS

1. Can you use synthetic division to divide a polynomial by $x^2 + 3$? Explain.

2. Explain how to quickly find $P(6)$ for the function $P(x) = 2x^3 - 11x^2 - 5x + 2$ without using a calculator. Find $P(6)$.

3. GET ORGANIZED Copy and complete the graphic organizer.

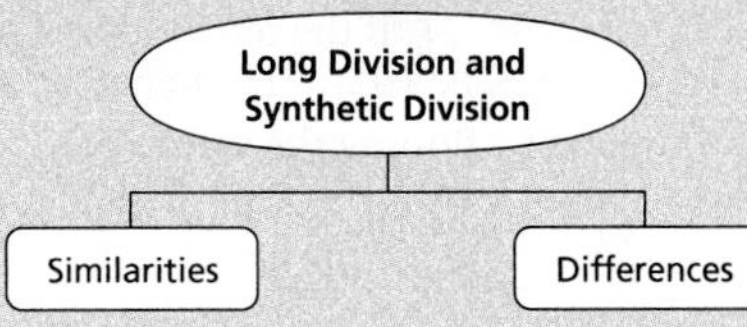

COMMON ERROR ALERT

Students might make errors in signs when doing synthetic division and synthetic substitution because values are added rather than subtracted as in long division. Remind them that terms are always added for synthetic substitution and synthetic division.

Power Presentations with PowerPoint®

Additional Examples

Example 4

Write an expression that represents the area of the top face of a rectangular prism when the height is $x + 2$ and the volume of the prism is $x^3 - x^2 - 6x$.

$x^2 - 3x$

Also available on transparency

INTERVENTION

Questioning Strategies

EXAMPLE 4

- Explain what the variables in the problem represent.

3 Close

Summarize

Ask students to explain the process of synthetic division and when and why it is useful. Discuss possible sources of error in the process. Synthetic division uses only the coefficients. If the last sum is 0, then the binomial is a factor of the polynomial; possible errors: not bringing down the first coefficient, forgetting to add instead of subtract, forgetting to include coefficients that are 0.

ONGOING ASSESSMENT and INTERVENTION

***Diagnose Before* the Lesson**
6-3 Warm Up, TE p. 422

***Monitor During* the Lesson**
Check It Out! Exercises, SE pp. 422–425
Questioning Strategies, TE pp. 423–425

***Assess After* the Lesson**
6-3 Lesson Quiz, TE p. 428
Alternative Assessment, TE p. 428

Answers to *Think and Discuss*

Possible answers:

1. No; the divisor must be a linear binomial in the form $x - a$; $x^2 + 3$ is a quadratic binomial.
2. Use synthetic substitution; $P(6) = 8$.
3. See p. A8.

Assignment Guide

Assign *Guided Practice* exercises as necessary.

If you finished Examples **1–2**
Basic 13–24, 38, 40, 43, 48
Average 13–24, 33, 39, 41, 43, 45, 48
Advanced 13–18, 20, 22, 24, 32, 38–42, 44, 46, 47

If you finished Examples **1–4**
Basic 13–30, 34–36, 38–50 53–56, 64–72
Average 13–33, 37–49, 51–58, 64–72
Advanced 16–21, 27–29, 31–33, 37–44, 50–72

Homework Quick Check
Quickly check key concepts.
Exercises: 16, 20, 22, 28, 29

State Resources

6-3 Exercises

go.hrw.com
Homework Help Online
KEYWORD: MB7 6-3
Parent Resources Online
KEYWORD: MB7 Parent

1. Possible answer: Synthetic division is a method of division that uses only the coefficients for linear binomial divisors.

GUIDED PRACTICE

1. **Vocabulary** Describe *synthetic division* in your own words.

SEE EXAMPLE 1 p. 422

Divide by using long division.

2. $(20x^2 - 13x + 2) \div (4x - 1)$ **$5x - 2$**
3. $(x^2 + x - 1) \div (x - 1)$ **$x + 2 + \frac{1}{x - 1}$**
4. $(x^2 - 2x + 3) \div (x + 5)$ **$x - 7 + \frac{38}{x + 5}$**

SEE EXAMPLE 2 p. 423

Divide by using synthetic division.

5. $(7x^2 - 23x + 6) \div (x - 3)$ **$7x - 2$**
6. $(x^4 - 5x + 10) \div (x + 3)$ **6. $x^3 - 3x^2 + 9x - 32 + \frac{106}{x + 3}$**
7. $(x^2 + x - 42) \div (x + 7)$ **$x - 6$**

SEE EXAMPLE 3 p. 424

Use synthetic substitution to evaluate the polynomial for the given value.

8. $P(x) = 2x^3 - 9x^2 + 27$ for $x = 2$ **$P(2) = 7$**
9. $P(x) = x^2 - x - 30$ for $x = -8$ **$P(-8) = 42$**
10. $P(x) = 3x^3 + 5x^2 + 4x + 2$ for $x = \frac{1}{3}$ **10. $P\left(\frac{1}{3}\right) = 4$**
11. $P(x) = 3x^5 + 4x^2 + x + 6$ for $x = -1$ **$P(-1) = 6$**

SEE EXAMPLE 4 p. 425

12. **Geometry** Find an expression for the width of a rectangle whose length is represented by $x - 2$ and whose area is represented by $2x^3 - 8x^2 + 2x + 12$. **$2x^2 - 4x - 6$**

PRACTICE AND PROBLEM SOLVING

Independent Practice

For Exercises	See Example
13–18	1
19–24	2
25–28	3
29	4

Extra Practice
Skills Practice p. S14
Application Practice p. S37

Divide by using long division.

13. $(2x^2 + 10x + 8) \div (2x + 2)$ **$x + 4$**
14. $(9x^2 - 18x) \div (3x)$ **$3x - 6$**
15. $(x^3 + 2x^2 - x - 2) \div (x + 2)$ **$x^2 - 1$**
16. $(x^4 - 3x^3 - 7x - 14) \div (x - 4)$ **16. $x^3 + x^2 + 4x + 9 + \frac{22}{x - 4}$**
17. $(x^6 - 4x^5 - 7x^3) \div (2x^3)$ **$\frac{1}{2}x^3 - 2x^2 - \frac{7}{2}$**
18. $(6x^2 - 7x - 5) \div (3x - 5)$ **$2x + 1$**

Divide by using synthetic division.

19. $(x^2 + 5x + 6) \div (x + 1)$ **$x + 4 + \frac{2}{x + 1}$**
20. $(x^4 + 6x^3 + 6x^2) \div (x + 5)$ **$x^3 + x^2 + x - 5 + \frac{25}{x + 5}$**
21. $(x^2 + 9x + 6) \div (x + 8)$ **$x + 1 - \frac{2}{x + 8}$**
22. $(2x^2 + 3x - 20) \div (x - 2)$ **22. $2x + 7 - \frac{6}{x - 2}$**
23. $(2x^2 + 13x - 8) \div \left(x - \frac{1}{2}\right)$ **23. $2x + 14 - \frac{1}{x - \frac{1}{2}}$**
24. $(4x^2 + 5x + 1) \div (x + 1)$ **$4x + 1$**

Use synthetic substitution to evaluate the polynomial for the given value.

25. $P(x) = 2x^2 - 5x - 3$ for $x = 4$ **$P(4) = 9$**
26. $P(x) = 4x^3 - 5x^2 + 3$ for $x = -1$ **$P(-1) = -6$**
27. $P(x) = 3x^3 - 5x^2 - x + 2$ for $x = -\frac{1}{3}$ **$P\left(-\frac{1}{3}\right) = \frac{5}{3}$**
28. $P(x) = 25x^2 - 16$ for $x = \frac{4}{5}$ **$P\left(\frac{4}{5}\right) = 0$**
29. **Physics** An experimental electrical system has a voltage that can be modeled by $V(t) = 0.5t^3 + 4.5t^2 + 4t$, where t represents time in seconds. The resistance in the system also varies and can be modeled by $R(t) = t + 1$. The current I is related to voltage and resistance by the equation $I = \frac{V}{R}$. Write an expression that represents the current in the system. **$I(t) = 0.5t^2 + 4t$**
30. **What if...?** If the remainder of polynomial division is 0, what does it mean? **Possible answer: The divisor is a factor of the polynomial.**

Complete by finding the values of a, b, and c.

31. $\begin{array}{r|rrrrr} 2 & 3 & -4 & 0 & 7 & -1 \\ & & 6 & 4 & b & 30 \\ \hline & 3 & a & 4 & 15 & c \end{array}$ **$a = 2;\ b = 8;\ c = 29$**

32. $\begin{array}{r|rrr} -2 & 1 & 5 & 6 \\ & & a & c \\ \hline & 1 & b & 0 \end{array}$ **$a = -2;\ b = 3;\ c = -6$**

33. $\begin{array}{r|rrrr} 3 & a & -2 & 3 & c \\ & & b & 21 & 72 \\ \hline & 3 & 7 & 24 & 68 \end{array}$ **$a = 3;\ b = 9;\ c = -4$**

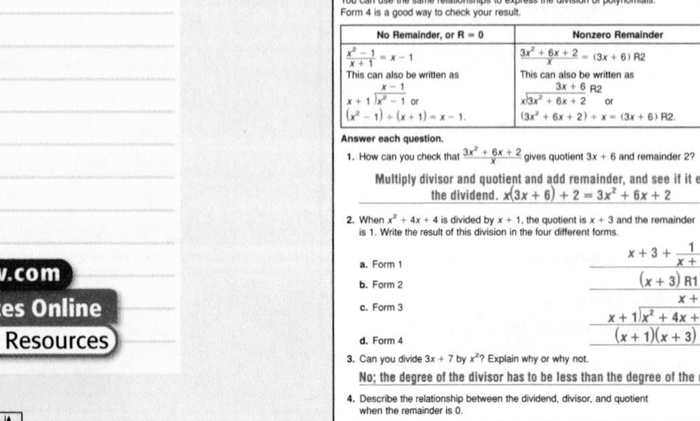

6-3 READING STRATEGIES

Two polynomials can be divided as long as the divisor has a lower degree. Think about division with numbers and the relationships of the dividend, divisor, quotient, and remainder. When 465 (dividend) is divided by 7 (divisor), the quotient is 66 and the remainder is 3. You can write this division in different ways.

Form 1	Form 2	Form 3	Form 4
$\frac{465}{7} = 66 + \frac{3}{7}$	$465 \div 7 = 66$ R3	$7\overline{)465}$ = 66 R3	$465 = 66 \times 7 + 3$

You can use the same relationships to express the division of polynomials. Form 4 is a good way to check your result.

No Remainder, or R = 0	Nonzero Remainder
$\frac{x^2 - 1}{x + 1} = x - 1$ This can also be written as $x + 1\overline{)x^2 - 1}$ = $x - 1$ or $(x^2 - 1) \div (x + 1) = x - 1$.	$\frac{3x^2 + 6x + 2}{x} = (3x + 6)$ R2 This can also be written as $x\overline{)3x^2 + 6x + 2}$ = $3x + 6$ R2 or $(3x^2 + 6x + 2) \div x = (3x + 6)$ R2.

Answer each question.

1. How can you check that $\frac{3x^2 + 6x + 2}{x}$ gives quotient $3x + 6$ and remainder 2?
Multiply divisor and quotient and add remainder, and see if it equals the dividend. $x(3x + 6) + 2 = 3x^2 + 6x + 2$

2. When $x^2 + 4x + 4$ is divided by $x + 1$, the quotient is $x + 3$ and the remainder is 1. Write the result of this division in the four different forms.
a. Form 1 **$x + 3 + \frac{1}{x + 1}$**
b. Form 2 **$(x + 3)$ R1**
c. Form 3 **$x + 1\overline{)x^2 + 4x + 4}$ = $x + 3$ R1**
d. Form 4 **$(x + 1)(x + 3) + 1$**

3. Can you divide $3x + 7$ by x^2? Explain why or why not.
No; the degree of the divisor has to be less than the degree of the dividend.

4. Describe the relationship between the dividend, divisor, and quotient when the remainder is 0.
The product of the divisor and the quotient equals the dividend.

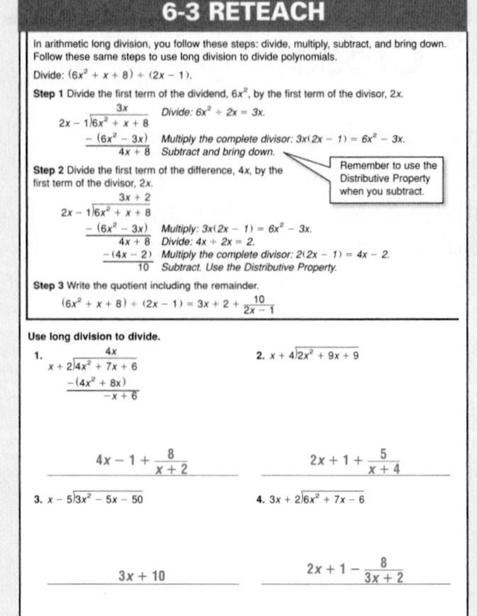

6-3 RETEACH

In arithmetic long division, you follow these steps: divide, multiply, subtract, and bring down. Follow these same steps to use long division to divide polynomials.

Divide: $(6x^2 + x + 8) \div (2x - 1)$.

Step 1 Divide the first term of the dividend, $6x^2$, by the first term of the divisor, $2x$.
Divide: $6x^2 \div 2x = 3x$.
Multiply the complete divisor: $3x(2x - 1) = 6x^2 - 3x$.
Subtract and bring down.

Step 2 Divide the first term of the difference, $4x$, by the first term of the divisor, $2x$.
Remember to use the Distributive Property when you subtract.
Multiply: $3x(2x - 1) = 6x^2 - 3x$.
Divide: $4x \div 2x = 2$.
Multiply the complete divisor: $2(2x - 1) = 4x - 2$.
Subtract. Use the Distributive Property.

Step 3 Write the quotient including the remainder.
$(6x^2 + x + 8) \div (2x - 1) = 3x + 2 + \frac{10}{2x - 1}$

Use long division to divide.

1. $x + 2\overline{)4x^2 + 7x + 6}$ **$4x - 1 + \frac{8}{x + 2}$**
2. $x + 4\overline{)2x^2 + 9x + 9}$ **$2x + 1 + \frac{5}{x + 4}$**
3. $x - 5\overline{)3x^2 - 5x - 50}$ **$3x + 10$**
4. $3x + 2\overline{)6x^2 + 7x - 6}$ **$2x + 1 - \frac{8}{3x + 2}$**

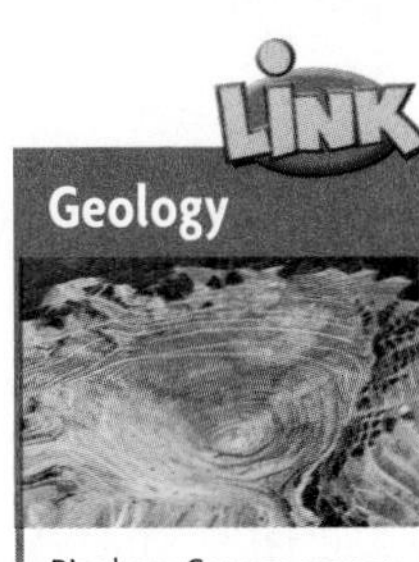

Geology

Bingham Canyon copper mine in Utah is the largest copper mine in the world in terms of both total metal production and size. Nicknamed "the richest hole on Earth," the mine has produced more than 14.5 million tons of copper.

Fill in each box to illustrate the Remainder Theorem for $P(x) = x^2 + 3x - 7$ and divisor $x - 2$.

34. Divide $P(x)$ by $(x - 2)$: $\frac{P(x)}{x-2} = \square$ $x + 5 + \frac{3}{x-2}$

35. Multiply both sides by $\square$: $P(x) = (x + 5)(x - 2) + 3$ $x - 2$

36. Evaluate $P(2)$: $P(2) = \square$ 3

37. **Geology** Geologists have taken a collection of samples of a substance from a proposed mining site and must identify the substance. Each sample is roughly cylindrical, and the volume of each sample as a function of cylinder height (in centimeters) is $V(h) = \frac{1}{4}\pi h^3$. The mass (in grams) of each sample in terms of height can be modeled by $M(h) = \frac{1}{4}h^3 - h^2 + 5h$. Write an expression that represents the density of the samples. (*Hint:* $D = \frac{M}{V}$) $D(h) = \frac{1}{\pi} - \frac{4}{\pi h} + \frac{20}{\pi h^2}$

38. **Geometry** The volume of a hexagonal pyramid is modeled by the function $V(x) = \frac{1}{3}x^3 + \frac{4}{3}x^2 + \frac{2}{3}x - \frac{1}{3}$. Use polynomial division to find an expression for the area of the base. (*Hint:* For a pyramid, $V = \frac{1}{3}Bh$.) $x^2 + 3x - 1$

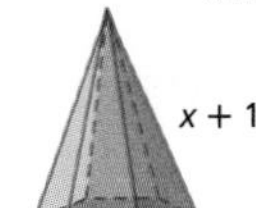

41. $x^2 - 5x - 12$

44. $y - 17 - \frac{3}{y-1}$

Divide.

39. $(y^4 + 9y^2 + 20) \div (y^2 + 4)$ $y^2 + 5$

40. $(2x^2 - 5x + 2) \div \left(x - \frac{1}{2}\right)$ $2x - 4$

41. $(3x^3 - 11x^2 - 56x - 48) \div (3x + 4)$

42. $(60 - 16y^2 + y^4) \div (10 - y^2)$ $-y^2 + 6$

43. $(t^3 - 7t^2 + 12t) \div (t^2 - 3t)$ $t - 4$

44. $(y^2 - 18y + 14) \div (y - 1)$

45. $(x^4 - 3x^3 - 28x^2 + 59x + 6) \div (x - 6)$

46. $(2d^2 + 10d + 8) \div (2d + 2)$ $d + 4$

47. $(x^4 - 7x^3 + 9x^2 - 22x + 25) \div (x - 6)$

48. $(6x^3 - 14x^2 + 10x - 4) \div (x - 1)$

49. **///ERROR ANALYSIS///** Two students used synthetic division to divide $x^3 - 2x - 8$ by $x - 2$. Determine which solution is correct. Find the error in the other solution.

45. $x^3 + 3x^2 - 10x - 1$

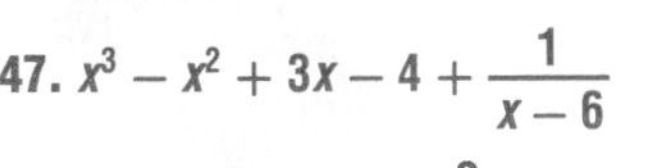

47. $x^3 - x^2 + 3x - 4 + \frac{1}{x-6}$

48. $6x^2 - 8x + 2 - \frac{2}{x-1}$

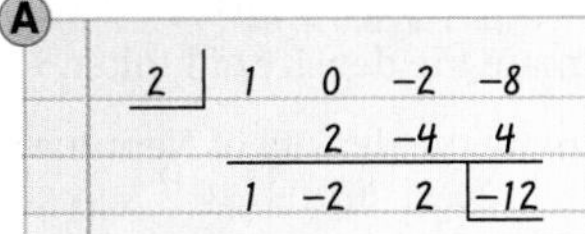

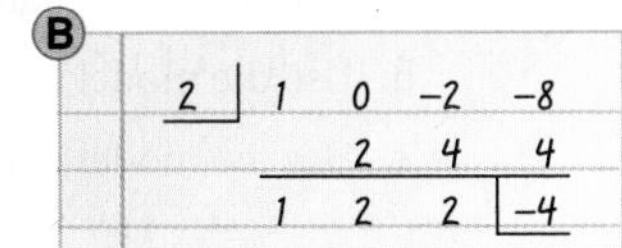

50. **Critical Thinking** Is $x + 3$ a factor of $3x^3 + 5x^2 + 2x - 12$? Explain.

51. **Write About It** What conditions must be met in order to use synthetic division?

MULTI-STEP TEST PREP

52. This problem will prepare you for the Multi-Step Test Prep on page 436.

The total number of lights in a triangular lighting rig is related to the triangular numbers, as shown at right. The sum of the first n triangular numbers is given by the polynomial function $g(n) = \frac{1}{6}n^3 + \frac{1}{2}n^2 + \frac{1}{3}n$.

a. Find the sum of the first five triangular numbers in the figure at right, and verify that the formula works when $n = 5$. 35; $g(5) = 35$

b. Use synthetic substitution to find the sum of the first 24 triangular numbers.

$g(24) = 2600$

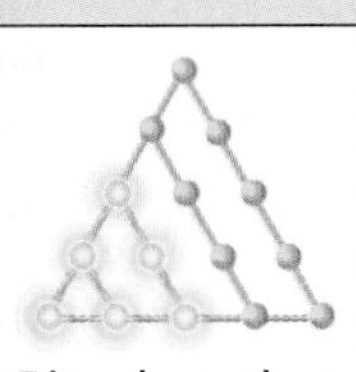

Triangular numbers: 1, 3, 6, 10, 15, . . .

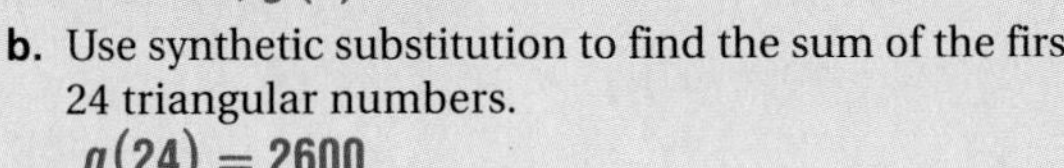

COMMON ERROR ALERT

In **Exercise 39,** the dividend is missing the cubic and linear terms. Students might forget to include the missing terms, written as $0x^3$ and $0x^1$. Remind them that they will need to add the two missing terms to complete the synthetic division.

MULTI-STEP TEST PREP **Exercise 52** involves using synthetic substitution to evaluate a polynomial. This exercise prepares students for the Multi-Step Test Prep on page 436.

Answers

49. Solution B is correct. In solution A, the second row is subtracted from the first row instead of being added.

50. No; possible answer: by synthetic substitution, the remainder is not 0, so $x + 3$ is not a factor of the polynomial.

51. Possible answer: The divisor must be a linear binomial with a leading coefficient of 1. The dividend must be written in standard form with 0 representing any missing terms.

6-3 PROBLEM SOLVING

An art class is making pedestals in the shape of regular prisms to display sculptures in an art show. Blake is in charge of the mirrors for the tops of the pedestals. He needs to estimate the total area of the mirrored surfaces. He will use that total to help determine the amount of mirrored product to purchase.

The figures below show the shape of the bases for each of the three kinds of prisms that will be used for pedestals. Each regular polygon has a side length of x. Recall that, for a prism, $V = Bh$.

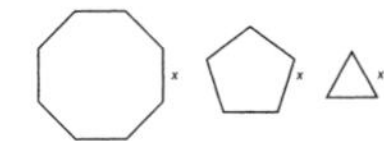

1. The triangular prism has a height of $2x + 1$ and its volume can be modeled by $V(x) = \frac{\sqrt{3}}{2}x^3 + \frac{\sqrt{3}}{4}x^2$. What is the area of the top of the pedestal?

$\frac{\sqrt{3}}{4}x^2$

Choose the letter for the best answer.

2. The volume of the pentagonal prism can be modeled by $V = 6.88x^3 - 1.72x^2$. Which expression represents the area of the top of the prism if the height is $4x - 1$?
A $0.57x^2$
(B) $1.72x^2$
C $2.28x^2$
D $6.88x^2$

3. The volume of the octagonal prism can be modeled by $V = 4.83x^3 - 24.15x^2$. Which expression represents the area of the top of the prism if the height is $x - 5$?
A $48.3x^2$
B $38.64x^2$
(C) $4.83x^2$
D $3.86x^2$

4. Which expression represents the total area that will be mirrored?
(A) $A = x^2\left(\frac{\sqrt{3}}{4} + 6.55\right)$
B $A = 6.98x$
C $A = 12.58x^3 + 22.86x^2$
D $A = \sqrt{6.98x}$

5. If $x = 5$, what is the total mirrored area in square units?
A 6.98
B 34.9
C 69.8
(D) 174.5

6-3 CHALLENGE

Synthetic division is an efficient tool for dividing a polynomial by a binomial and also for evaluating a polynomial for a given constant. However, the process works only when the divisor is a binomial of the form $(x - a)$, where the coefficient of x is 1. How could the process be used to divide the polynomial $3x^2 + 8x - 12$ by $2x - 6$?
Write the division as a fraction and then multiply both the numerator and denominator by $\frac{1}{2}$ to get the divisor in the form for synthetic division.

$$\frac{3x^2 - 8x - 12}{2x - 6} \cdot \frac{\frac{1}{2}}{\frac{1}{2}} = \frac{\frac{3}{2}x^2 - 4x - 6}{x - 3}$$

Now use synthetic division to find the quotient.

3	$\frac{3}{2}$	-4	-6
		$\frac{9}{2}$	$\frac{3}{2}$
	$\frac{3}{2}$	$\frac{1}{2}$	$-\frac{9}{2}$

Read the quotient from the bottom line.

$$\frac{3}{2}x + \frac{1}{2} - \frac{\frac{9}{2}}{2x - 6}, \text{ which simplifies to } \frac{3}{2}x + \frac{1}{2} - \frac{9}{4x - 12}$$

Divide using synthetic division.

1. $(4x^2 + 8x - 10) \div (2x + 6)$ $2x - 2 + \frac{1}{x+3}$

2. $(3x^3 + 12x^2 - 15x + 15) \div (3x - 9)$ $x^2 + 7x + 16 + \frac{53}{x-3}$

3. $(25x^3 + 30x + 40) \div (5x + 10)$ $5x^2 - 10x + 26 - \frac{44}{x+2}$

4. $\left(x^4 - \frac{1}{16}\right) \div (2x - 1)$ $\frac{1}{2}x^3 + \frac{1}{4}x^2 + \frac{1}{8}x + \frac{1}{16}$

5. $(2x^2 - 5x + 7) \div (2x - 1)$ $x - 2 + \frac{5}{2x-1}$

6. $(3x^2 + 7x - 13) \div (3x + 5)$ $x + \frac{2}{3} - \frac{16\frac{1}{3}}{3x+5}$

7. $(4x^5 - 129) \div (4x - 8)$ $x^4 + 2x^3 + 4x^2 + 8x + 16 - \frac{1}{4x-8}$

8. $(x^6 - 729) \div [(x + 3)(x - 3)]$ $x^4 + 9x^2 + 81$

6-3 PRACTICE A

6-3 PRACTICE C

6-3 PRACTICE B

Divide by using long division.

1. $(x^2 - x - 6) \div (x - 3)$ $x + 2$

2. $(2x^3 - 10x^2 + x - 5) \div (x - 5)$ $2x^2 + 1$

3. $(-3x^2 + 20x - 12) \div (x - 6)$ $-3x + 2$

4. $(3x^3 + 9x^2 - 14) \div (x + 3)$ $3x^2 - \frac{14}{x+3}$

Divide by using synthetic division.

5. $(3x^2 - 8x + 4) \div (x - 2)$ $3x - 2$

6. $(5x^2 - 4x + 12) \div (x + 3)$ $5x - 19 + \frac{69}{x+3}$

7. $(9x^2 - 7x + 3) \div (x - 1)$ $9x + 2 + \frac{5}{x-1}$

8. $(-6x^2 + 5x - 10) \div (x + 7)$ $-6x + 47 - \frac{339}{x+7}$

Use synthetic substitution to evaluate the polynomial for the given value.

9. $P(x) = 4x^2 - 9x + 2$ for $x = 3$ $P(3) = 11$

10. $P(x) = -3x^2 + 10x - 4$ for $x = -2$ $P(-2) = -36$

Solve.

11. The total number of dollars donated each year to a small charitable organization has followed the trend $d(t) = 2t^3 + 10t^2 + 2000t + 10{,}000$, where d is dollars and t is the number of years since 1990. The total number of donors each year has followed the trend $p(t) = t^2 + 1000$. Write an expression describing the average number of dollars per donor.

$2t + 10$

In **Exercise 53,** if students chose **A,** they probably used 3 instead of −3 for the divisor. If they chose **C** or **D,** have them carefully review their calculations.

In **Exercise 54, G** is the reciprocal of the expression rather than its equivalent. In the first term of **F,** the variables were correctly divided, but the coefficients were not. In **J,** the numerator has been divided by 3, but the denominator has not.

Journal

Have students describe a mnemonic device that can help them remember the steps in synthetic division.

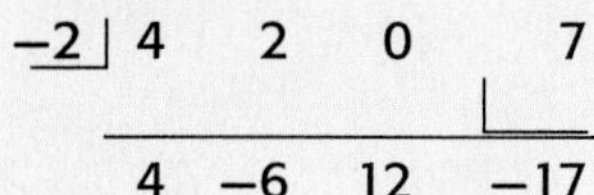

Give students the following synthetic division calculation and have them write the long division expression that it represents. Then have them show the steps of long division to confirm the quotient given by synthetic divison.

$$\begin{array}{r|rrrr} -2 & 4 & 2 & 0 & 7 \\ \hline & 4 & -6 & 12 & -17 \end{array}$$

Possible answer:

$(4x^3 + 2x^2 + 7) \div (x + 2)$

Power Presentations with PowerPoint®

6-3 Lesson Quiz

1. Divide by using long division. $(8x^3 + 6x^2 + 7) \div (x + 2)$
   $8x^2 - 10x + 20 - \dfrac{33}{x+2}$
2. Divide by using synthetic division. $(x^3 - 3x + 5) \div (x + 2)$
   $x^2 - 2x + 1 + \dfrac{3}{x+2}$
3. Use synthetic substitution to evaluate $P(x) = x^3 + 3x^2 - 6$ for $x = 5$ and $x = -1$. 194; −4
4. Find an expression for the height of a parallelogram whose area is represented by $2x^3 - x^2 - 20x + 3$ and whose base is represented by $(x + 3)$.
   $2x^2 - 7x + 1$

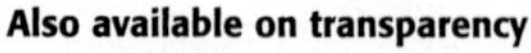

Also available on transparency

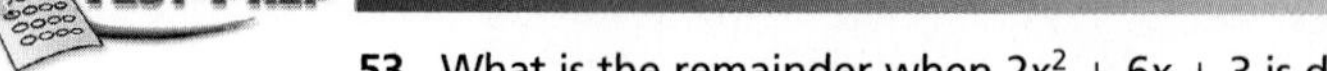

TEST PREP

53. What is the remainder when $2x^2 + 6x + 3$ is divided by $x + 3$?
    (A) 39 (B) 3 (C) 1 (D) 0
54. Which expression is equivalent to $\dfrac{6a^2b + 9b^2}{3a^2}$?
    (F) $6b + \dfrac{9b^2}{a^2}$ (G) $\dfrac{3a^2}{6a^2b + 9b^2}$ (H) $2b + \dfrac{3b^2}{a^2}$ (J) $\dfrac{2a^2b + 3b^2}{3a^2}$
55. Which expression is equivalent to $(x^2 + 3x - 28) \div (x - 4)$?
    (A) $x + 7 + \dfrac{3}{x-4}$ (B) $x - 7$ (C) $28 + \dfrac{4}{x-7}$ (D) $x + 7$
56. **Gridded Response** Use synthetic substitution to evaluate $f(x) = 3x^4 - 6x^2 + 12$ for $x = -2$. $f(-2) = 36$

CHALLENGE AND EXTEND

57. $P(-4) = -1{,}189{,}150$ 58. $P(-1) = -28$ 59. $P(1) = 0$ 60. $P(3) = 89{,}260$

Evaluate $P(x) = 4x^9 + 7x^7 - 6x^6 - 5x^4 - x^2 + 3x - 2$ for the given value of x.

57. $x = -4$ 58. $x = -1$ 59. $x = 1$ 60. $x = 3$
61. If −3 is a zero of $P(x) = 2x^3 + 3x^2 - kx - 27$, find the value of k. $k = 18$
62. Divide $(5a^2b - 3ab^2 - 2b^3)$ by $(ab - b^2)$ $5a + 2b$
63. **Astronomy** The volumes of several planets in cubic kilometers can be modeled by $V(d) = \frac{1}{6}\pi d^3$, where d is the diameter of the planet in kilometers. The mass of each planet in kilograms in terms of diameter d can be modeled by $M(d) = (3.96 \times 10^{12})d^3 - (6.50 \times 10^{17})d^2 + (2.56 \times 10^{22})d - 5.56 \times 10^{25}$.
    a. The density of a planet in kilograms per cubic kilometer can be found by dividing the planet's mass by its volume. Use polynomial division to find a model for the density of a planet in terms of its diameter.
    b. Use the model to estimate the density of Jupiter. $\approx 1.236 \times 10^{12}$ kg/km³
    c. Use the model to estimate the density of Neptune. $\approx 1.556 \times 10^{12}$ kg/km³

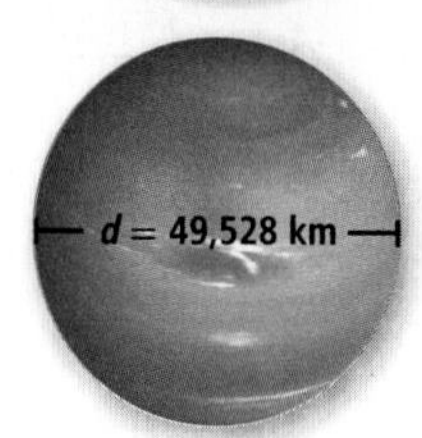

SPIRAL REVIEW

64. A class conducted a survey on eye color. The class found that 70% of students have brown eyes. If 448 students have brown eyes, how many students took the survey? *(Lesson 2-2)* 640

65. max: 1.25; $\{x \mid x \in \mathbb{R}\}$; $\{y \mid y \le 1.25\}$ 66. min: −6.5; $\{x \mid x \in \mathbb{R}\}$; $\{y \mid y \ge -6.5\}$ 67. min: −2; $\{x \mid x \in \mathbb{R}\}$; $\{y \mid y \ge -2\}$ 68. max: 10; $\{x \mid x \in \mathbb{R}\}$; $\{y \mid y \le 10\}$

Find the maximum or minimum value of each function. Then state the domain and range of the function. *(Lesson 5-2)*

65. $f(x) = -4x^2 + 2x + 1$
66. $g(x) = \frac{1}{2}x^2 - 5x + 6$
67. $f(x) = \frac{1}{3}x^2 - 4x + 10$
68. $g(x) = -\frac{1}{4}x^2 - 2x + 6$

Find each product. *(Lesson 6-2)*

69. $4x^2y(3xy^2 + 6x + 5y^3)$ $12x^3y^3 + 24x^3y + 20x^2y^4$
70. $5y^2(3xy + 4x^2y^2 - 8x^3y)$ $15xy^3 + 20x^2y^4 - 40x^3y^3$
71. $(2x - 2y)(2x^2 - 2xy + 2y^2)$ $4x^3 - 8x^2y + 8xy^2 - 4y^3$
72. $2(y - 2)^4$ $2y^4 - 16y^3 + 48y^2 - 64y + 32$

Answers

63a. $D(d) = \dfrac{(2.376 \times 10^{13})}{\pi} + \dfrac{(-3.9 \times 10^{18})d^2 + (1.536 \times 10^{23})d - 3.336 \times 10^{26}}{\pi d^3}$

Explore the Sum and Difference of Two Cubes

You can use a diagram of a cube with a corner removed to discover how to factor the difference of two cubes. You can use a similar diagram to discover how to factor the sum of two cubes.

Use with Lesson 6-4

Activity

The figure shown is a large cube with a small cube removed from one corner.

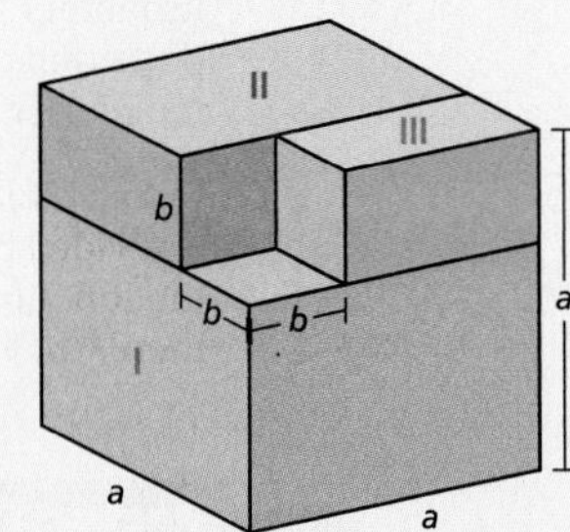

1. Explain why the volume of the figure is $a^3 - b^3$. How is this related to the volumes of the rectangular prisms labeled I, II, and III?

   The volume of the complete cube is a^3, and the volume of the cube removed from the corner is b^3. The volume of the figure with the corner removed is $a^3 - b^3$ and can be expressed as the sum of the volumes of the rectangular prisms I, II, and III: $a^3 - b^3 = V_I + V_{II} + V_{III}$.

2. Use the diagram to write an algebraic expression for the volume of each rectangular prism.

   $V_I = a^2(a - b)$ $\quad$ $V_{II} = ab(a - b)$ $\quad$ $V_{III} = b^2(a - b)$

3. Write the equation for $a^3 - b^3$ by using the expressions for the rectangular prisms labeled I, II, and III from Problem 2. Factor to get the factored form of $a^3 - b^3$.

   $a^3 - b^3 = V_I + V_{II} + V_{III}$

   $a^3 - b^3 = a^2(a - b) + ab(a - b) + b^2(a - b)$

   $a^3 - b^3 = (a - b)(a^2 + ab + b^2)$

Try This

The figure shown is a large cube with a small cube added to one corner.

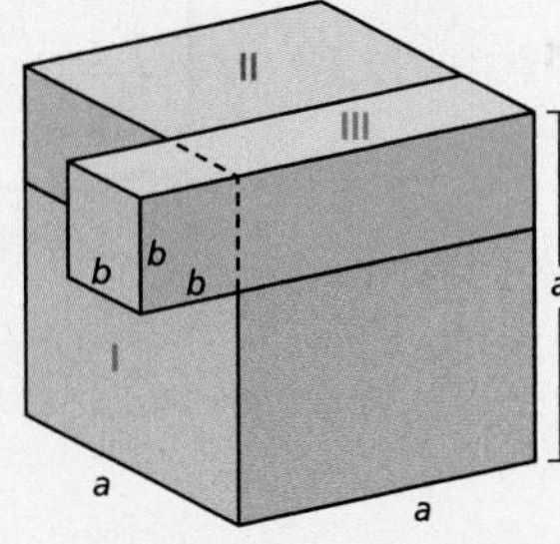

1. Explain why the volume of the figure is $a^3 + b^3$. How is this related to the volumes of the rectangular prisms labeled I, II, and III?
2. Use the diagram to write an algebraic expression for the volume of each rectangular prism.
3. Write the equation for $a^3 + b^3$ by using the expressions for the rectangular prisms labeled I, II, and III from Problem 2. Factor to get the factored form of $a^3 + b^3$. (*Hint:* Factor the expressions for I and II before adding the expression for III.) $a^3 + b^3 = (a + b)(a^2 - ab + b^2)$

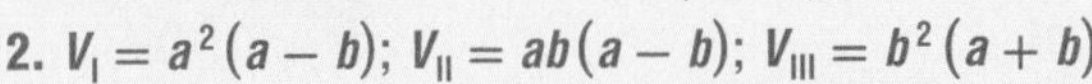

2. $V_I = a^2(a - b)$; $V_{II} = ab(a - b)$; $V_{III} = b^2(a + b)$

Answers to Try This

1. Possible answer: The large cube has side length a, so its volume is a^3. The small cube has side length b, so its volume is b^3. The volume of the figure is the volume of the two cubes, $a^3 + b^3$. It is also the volume of the three rectangular prisms.

Organizer

Use with Lesson 6-4

Pacing:

Traditional $\frac{1}{2}$ day

Block $\frac{1}{4}$ day

Objective: Use models to explore factoring the difference and sum of two cubes.

Online Edition

Resources

Algebra Lab Activities

6-4 Lab Recording Sheet

Teach

Discuss

Review the formula for the volume of a cube, $V = s^3$, as well as the formula for the volume of a rectangular prism, $V = lwh$.

Alternative Approach

Have students build a cube from blocks and label it. Then have them use their labels to illustrate the formulas.

Close

Key Concept

You can use a diagram to factor the sum or difference of two cubes.

Assessment

Journal Have students explain how the cube and its corner helped them understand how to factor the difference of two cubes.

State Resources

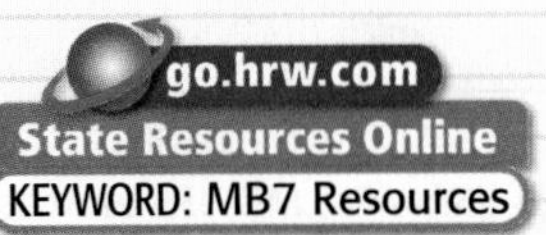

6-4 Organizer

Pacing: Traditional 1 day
Block $\frac{1}{2}$ day

Objectives: Use the Factor Theorem to determine factors of a polynomial.

Factor the sum and difference of two cubes.

Online Edition
Graphing Calculator, Tutorial Videos

Countdown to Testing Week 13

Power Presentations with PowerPoint®

Warm Up

Factor each expression.

1. $3x - 6y$ $3(x - 2y)$
2. $a^2 - b^2$ $(a + b)(a - b)$

Find each product.

3. $(x - 1)(x + 3)$ $x^2 + 2x - 3$
4. $(a + 1)(a^2 + 1)$ $a^3 + a^2 + a + 1$

Also available on transparency

Math Humor

Student: The artist Picasso must have been really good at algebra.
Parent: Why do you say that?
Student: He was a famous cubist, so he probably had to do a lot of factoring.

6-4 Factoring Polynomials

A2.4.4 Factor polynomials completely and solve polynomial equations by factoring.

Objectives
Use the Factor Theorem to determine factors of a polynomial.

Factor the sum and difference of two cubes.

Who uses this?
Ecologists may use factoring polynomials to determine when species might become extinct. (See Example 4.)

Recall that if a number is divided by any of its factors, the remainder is 0. Likewise, if a polynomial is divided by any of its factors, the remainder is 0.

The Remainder Theorem states that if a polynomial is divided by $(x - a)$, the remainder is the value of the function at a. So, if $(x - a)$ is a factor of $P(x)$, then $P(a) = 0$.

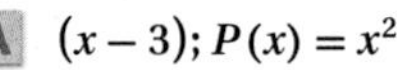

Factor Theorem

THEOREM	EXAMPLE
For any polynomial $P(x)$, $(x - a)$ is a factor of $P(x)$ if and only if $P(a) = 0$.	Because $P(1) = 1^2 - 1 = 0$, $(x - 1)$ is a factor of $P(x) = x^2 - 1$.

EXAMPLE 1 Determining Whether a Linear Binomial is a Factor

Determine whether the given binomial is a factor of the polynomial $P(x)$.

A $(x - 3)$; $P(x) = x^2 + 2x - 3$

Find $P(3)$ by synthetic substitution.

$$\begin{array}{r|rrr} 3 & 1 & 2 & -3 \\ & & 3 & 15 \\ \hline & 1 & 5 & 12 \end{array}$$

$P(3) = 12$

$P(3) \neq 0$, so $(x - 3)$ is not a factor of $P(x) = x^2 + 2x - 3$.

B $(x + 4)$; $P(x) = 2x^4 + 8x^3 + 2x + 8$

Find $P(-4)$ by synthetic substitution.

$$\begin{array}{r|rrrrr} -4 & 2 & 8 & 0 & 2 & 8 \\ & & -8 & 0 & 0 & -8 \\ \hline & 2 & 0 & 0 & 2 & 0 \end{array}$$

$P(-4) = 0$, so $(x + 4)$ is a factor of $P(x) = 2x^4 + 8x^3 + 2x + 8$.

Determine whether the given binomial is a factor of the polynomial $P(x)$.

1a. $(x + 2)$; $P(x) = 4x^2 - 2x + 5$ no

1b. $(3x - 6)$; $P(x) = 3x^4 - 6x^3 + 6x^2 + 3x - 30$ yes

You are already familiar with methods for factoring quadratic expressions. You can factor polynomials of higher degrees using many of the same methods you learned in Lesson 5-3.

State Resources

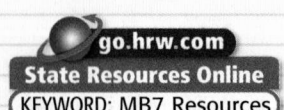

go.hrw.com
State Resources Online
KEYWORD: MB7 Resources

1 Introduce

EXPLORATION

6-4 Factoring Polynomials

Recall from the Remainder Theorem that if a polynomial function $P(x)$ is divided by $x - a$, then the remainder is $P(a)$.

1. Use synthetic division to find the remainder when the polynomial $P(x) = x^3 - 3x^2 + x - 3$ is divided by $x - 3$.
2. What is $P(3)$?
3. Use the results of the synthetic division in Problem 1 to write $P(x)$ as the product of $x - 3$ and another polynomial.
4. Use synthetic division to find the remainder when the polynomial $Q(x) = 2x^4 - 4x^3 + 4x^2 - 7x - 2$ is divided by $x - 2$.
5. What is $Q(2)$?
6. Use the results of the synthetic division in Problem 4 to write $Q(x)$ as the product of $x - 2$ and another polynomial.

THINK AND DISCUSS

7. **Describe** what you can conclude about $x - a$ if you know that $P(a) = 0$.
8. **Explain** why $x - 1$ must be a factor of $x^6 - 1$.

Motivate

Use numbers such as $24 \div 3 = 8$ R 0 to remind students that in the division of numbers, the divisor is a factor of the dividend if the remainder is zero. Ask students how they might factor the expression $x^2 + 3x + 2$. $(x + 2)(x + 1)$ Explain that factoring a general polynomial is the same concept as factoring a quadratic but requires some new techniques.

Explorations and answers are provided in the *Explorations* binder.

EXAMPLE 2 Factoring by Grouping

Factor $x^3 + 3x^2 - 4x - 12$.

$(x^3 + 3x^2) + (-4x - 12)$	*Group terms.*
$x^2(x + 3) - 4(x + 3)$	*Factor common monomials from each group.*
$(x + 3)(x^2 - 4)$	*Factor out the common binomial $(x + 3)$.*
$(x + 3)(x + 2)(x - 2)$	*Factor the difference of squares.*

Check Use the table feature of your calculator to compare the original expression and the factored form.

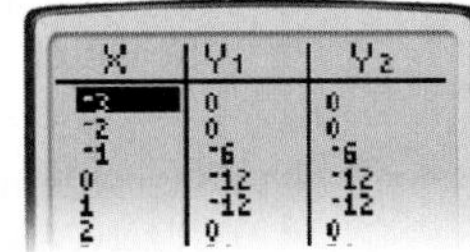

The table shows that the original function and the factored form have the same function values. ✔

CHECK IT OUT! Factor each expression.

2a. $x^3 - 2x^2 - 9x + 18$ $(x + 3)(x - 3)(x - 2)$

2b. $2x^3 + x^2 + 8x + 4$ $(x^2 + 4)(2x + 1)$

Just as there is a special rule for factoring the difference of two squares, there are special rules for factoring the sum or difference of two cubes.

Know it! Note

Factoring the Sum and the Difference of Two Cubes

METHOD	ALGEBRA
Sum of two cubes	$a^3 + b^3 = (a + b)(a^2 - ab + b^2)$
Difference of two cubes	$a^3 - b^3 = (a - b)(a^2 + ab + b^2)$

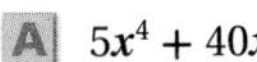

EXAMPLE 3 Factoring the Sum or Difference of Two Cubes

Factor each expression.

A $5x^4 + 40x$

$5x(x^3 + 8)$	*Factor out the GCF, 5x.*
$5x(x^3 + 2^3)$	*Rewrite as the sum of cubes.*
$5x(x + 2)(x^2 - x \cdot 2 + 2^2)$	*Use the rule $a^3 + b^3 = (a + b)(a^2 - ab + b^2)$.*
$5x(x + 2)(x^2 - 2x + 4)$	

B $8y^3 - 27$

$(2y)^3 - 3^3$	*Rewrite as the difference of cubes.*
$(2y - 3)[(2y)^2 + 2y \cdot 3 + 3^2]$	*Use the rule $a^3 - b^3 = (a - b)(a^2 + ab + b^2)$.*
$(2y - 3)(4y^2 + 6y + 9)$	

Remember!

GCF stands for "greatest common factor." Always factor out the GCF before using other methods.

CHECK IT OUT! Factor each expression.

3a. $8 + z^6$ $(2 + z^2)(4 - 2z^2 + z^4)$

3b. $2x^5 - 16x^2$ $2x^2(x - 2)(x^2 + 2x + 4)$

2 Teach

Guided Instruction

Review factoring quadratics from Chapter 5. Remind students that factoring can always be checked by multiplying the factors and comparing the product with the original expression. Then discuss ways to determine whether the factoring is complete.

Reaching All Learners

Through Cognitive Strategies

Ask these questions to help students relate the present lesson to previous learning and to help them develop self-awareness of the mathematics learning strategies they are using.

- In what ways does this lesson relate to the previous lesson? Division can be used to factor a polynomial.
- How are you using the strategy of Solve a Simpler Problem in this lesson? by factoring out common monomials first

Power Presentations with PowerPoint®

Additional Examples

Example 1

Determine whether the given binomial is a factor of the polynomial $P(x)$.

A. $(x + 1)$; $(x^2 - 3x + 1)$ no

B. $(x + 2)$; $(3x^4 + 6x^3 - 5x - 10)$ yes

Example 2

Factor $x^3 - x^2 - 25x + 25$.

$(x - 1)(x - 5)(x + 5)$

Example 3

Factor each expression.

A. $4x^4 + 108x$

$4x(x + 3)(x^2 - 3x + 9)$

B. $125d^3 - 8$

$(5d - 2)(25d^2 + 10d + 4)$

Also available on transparency

INTERVENTION

Questioning Strategies

EXAMPLE 1

- How can you use synthetic substitution to tell whether a given binomial is a factor of a polynomial?

EXAMPLE 2

- How can you tell whether factoring by grouping will work or not?

EXAMPLE 3

- What are the steps for using the sum or difference of cubes formulas?

Teaching Tip **Technology** In **Example 2,** use caution when checking an answer on a graphing calculator. The calculator provides support that the answer is correct, but it cannot be used to prove correctness.

Teaching Tip **Inclusion** To help students remember the formulas for the sum and difference of cubes, you may wish to use the mnemonic device SOPPS for the order of the terms in the second factor: **S**quare **O**pposite sign **P**roduct **P**lus **S**quare.

ENGLISH LANGUAGE LEARNERS

Power Presentations with PowerPoint®

Additional Examples

Example 4

The volume of a plastic storage box is modeled by the function $V(x) = x^3 + 6x^2 + 3x - 10$. Identify the values of x for which $V(x) = 0$, then use the graph to factor $V(x)$.

$x = -5, -2, 1;$
$V(x) = (x + 5)(x + 2)(x - 1)$

Also available on transparency

INTERVENTION

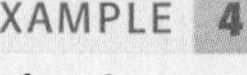

Questioning Strategies

EXAMPLE 4

- What is a reasonable domain and range for this problem situation?

Multiple Representations After students complete **Example 4,** help them understand that the zeros of a polynomial function are the values of x where the graph crosses the x-axis. The zeros of a function $f(x)$ are also equivalent to the solutions of the equation $f(x) = 0$ and are related to the factors of the polynomial.

Kinesthetic Have students practice factoring techniques by using algebra tiles.

You can also use a graph to help you factor a polynomial. Recall that the real zeros of a function appear as x-intercepts on its graph. By the Factor Theorem, if you can determine the zeros of a polynomial function from its graph, you can determine the corresponding factors of the polynomial.

EXAMPLE 4 *Ecology Application*

The population of an endangered species of bird in the years since 1990 can be modeled by the function $P(x) = -x^3 + 32x^2 - 224x + 768$. Identify the year that the bird will become extinct if the model is accurate and no protective measures are taken. Use the graph to factor $P(x)$.

Because $P(x)$ represents the population, the real zero of $P(x)$ represents a population of zero, meaning extinction. $P(x)$ has only one real zero at $x = 24$, which corresponds to the year 2014.

If the model is accurate, the bird will become extinct in 2014.

The corresponding factor is $(x - 24)$.

24	−1	32	−224	768
		−24	192	−768
	−1	8	−32	0

Use synthetic division to factor the polynomial.

$P(x) = (x - 24)(-x^2 + 8x - 32)$ *Write P(x) as a product.*

$P(x) = -(x - 24)(x^2 - 8x + 32)$ *Factor out −1 from the quadratic.*

CHECK IT OUT!

4. The volume of a rectangular prism is modeled by the function $V(x) = x^3 - 8x^2 + 19x - 12$, which is graphed at right. Identify the values of x for which $V(x) = 0$, and use the graph to factor $V(x)$.
$x = 1, 3, 4;\ V(x) = (x - 1)(x - 3)(x - 4)$

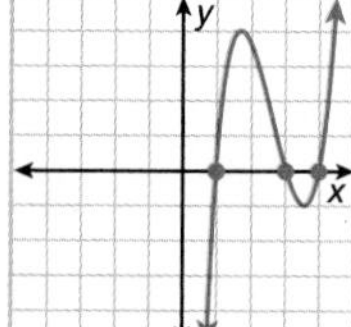

THINK AND DISCUSS

1. Explain how to use the Factor Theorem to determine whether a linear binomial is a factor of a polynomial.
2. Explain how you know when to use the sum or difference of cubes to factor a binomial.

3. **GET ORGANIZED** Copy and complete the graphic organizer. For each method, give an example of a polynomial and its factored form.

Method	Polynomial	Factored Form
Difference of Two Squares		
Difference of Two Cubes		
Sum of Two Cubes		

3 Close

Summarize

Help students develop their own lists of strategies that can be used to factor a polynomial completely. The lists should include factoring out the GCF, synthetic division, the Factor Theorem, and applying rules for factoring the sum and difference of two cubes. They should also include applying previously learned rules such as factoring the difference of two squares.

ONGOING ASSESSMENT and INTERVENTION

***Diagnose Before* the Lesson**
6-4 Warm Up, TE p. 430

***Monitor During* the Lesson**
Check It Out! Exercises, SE pp. 430–432
Questioning Strategies, TE pp. 431–432

***Assess After* the Lesson**
6-4 Lesson Quiz, TE p. 435
Alternative Assessment, TE p. 435

Answers to *Think and Discuss*

Possible answers:

1. For a linear binomial $x - a$, use synthetic substitution to find $P(a)$. If $P(a) = 0$, then the linear binomial is a factor.
2. First, factor out any common monomial. Then if each term of the binomial is a perfect cube, you can use the sum or difference of cubes to factor.
3. See p. A8.

go.hrw.com
Homework Help Online
KEYWORD: MB7 6-4
Parent Resources Online
KEYWORD: MB7 Parent

GUIDED PRACTICE

SEE EXAMPLE 1 p. 430

Determine whether the given binomial is a factor of the polynomial $P(x)$.

1. $(x + 1)$; $P(x) = 2x^4 + 2x^3 - x^2 - 5x - 4$ yes
2. $(x - 2)$; $P(x) = 5x^3 + x^2 - 7$ no
3. $(2x - 4)$; $P(x) = 2x^5 - 4x^4 + 2x^2 - 2x - 4$ yes

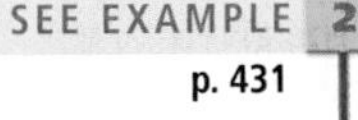

SEE EXAMPLE 2 p. 431

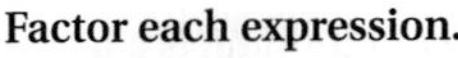

Factor each expression.

4. $x^3 + x^2 - x - 1$ $(x + 1)(x + 1)(x - 1)$
5. $x^3 + 5x^2 - 4x - 20$ 5. $(x + 2)(x - 2)(x + 5)$
6. $8x^3 + 4x^2 - 2x - 1$ 6. $(2x + 1)(2x + 1)(2x - 1)$
7. $2x^3 - 2x^2 - 8x + 8$ $2(x + 2)(x - 2)(x - 1)$
8. $2x^3 - 3x^2 - 2x + 3$ $(x + 1)(x - 1)(2x - 3)$
9. $12x^2 + 3x - 24x - 6$ $3(x - 2)(4x + 1)$

SEE EXAMPLE 3 p. 431

10. $8 - m^6$
11. $2t^7 + 54t^4$
12. $x^3 + 64$ $(x + 4)(x^2 - 4x + 16)$
13. $27 + x^3$ $(3 + x)(9 - 3x + x^2)$
14. $4t^5 - 32t^2$ $4t^2(t - 2)(t^2 + 2t + 4)$
15. $y^3 - 125$ $(y - 5)(y^2 + 5y + 25)$

SEE EXAMPLE 4 p. 432

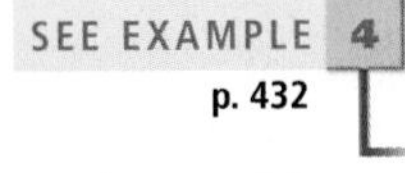

16. The volume of a cargo container is modeled by the function $V(x) = x^3 - 39x - 70$. Identify the values of x for which $V(x) = 0$, and use the graph to factor $V(x)$.

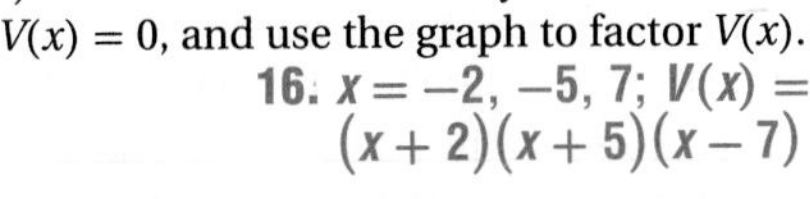

16. $x = -2, -5, 7$; $V(x) = (x + 2)(x + 5)(x - 7)$

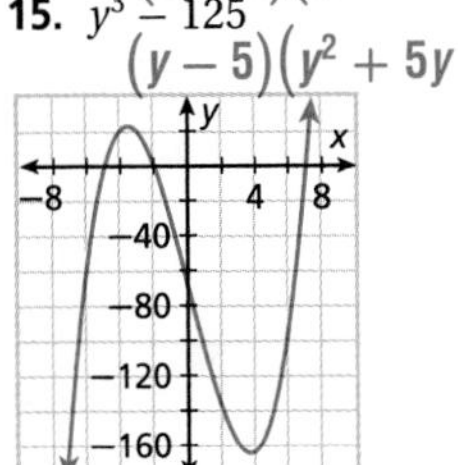

10. $(2 - m^2)(4 + 2m^2 + m^4)$
11. $2t^4(t + 3)(t^2 - 3t + 9)$

PRACTICE AND PROBLEM SOLVING

Independent Practice

For Exercises	See Example
17–19	1
20–25	2
26–31	3
32	4

Extra Practice
Skills Practice p. S14
Application Practice p. S37

Determine whether the given binomial is a factor of the polynomial $P(x)$.

17. $(x - 3)$; $P(x) = 4x^6 - 12x^5 + 2x^3 - 6x^2 - 5x + 10$ no
18. $(x - 8)$; $P(x) = x^5 - 8x^4 + 8x - 64$ yes
19. $(3x + 12)$; $P(x) = 3x^4 + 12x^3 + 6x + 24$ yes

Factor each expression.

20. $8y^3 - 4y^2 - 50y + 25$ 20. $(2y + 5)(2y - 5)(2y - 1)$
21. $4b^3 + 3b^2 - 16b - 12$ 21. $(b + 2)(b - 2)(4b + 3)$
22. $3p^3 - 21p^2 - p + 7$ 22. $(3p^2 - 1)(p - 7)$
23. $3x^3 + x^2 - 27x - 9$
24. $8z^2 - 4z + 10z - 5$
25. $5x^3 - x^2 - 20x + 4$
26. $125 + z^3$
27. $s^6 - 1$
28. $24n^2 + 3n^5$
29. $6x^4 - 162x$ 29. $6x(x - 3)(x^2 + 3x + 9)$
30. $40 - 5t^3$ 30. $5(2 - t)(4 + 2t + t^2)$
31. $y^5 + 27y^2$

32. **Recreation** The volume of a bowling ball can be modeled by the function $V(x) = 168 - 28x - 28x^2$, where x represents the radius of the finger holes in inches. Identify the values of x for which $V(x) = 0$, and use the graph to factor $V(x)$. $x = -3, 2$; $V(x) = -28(x + 3)(x - 2)$

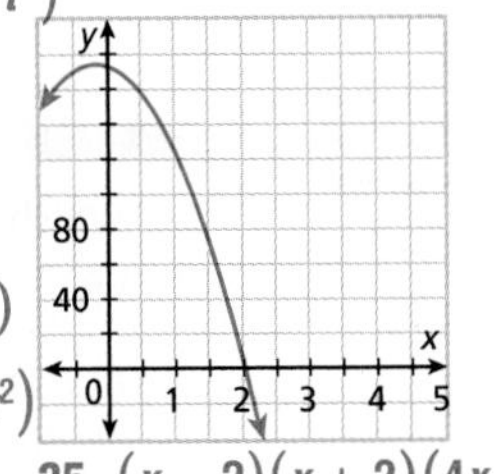

23. $(x + 3)(x - 3)(3x + 1)$
24. $(4z + 5)(2z - 1)$ 25. $(x + 2)(x - 2)(5x - 1)$ 26. $(5 + z)(25 - 5z + z^2)$

Factor completely.

33. $x^6 - 14x^4 + 49x^2$ 33. $x^2(x^2 - 7)(x^2 - 7)$
34. $2x^3 + x^2 - 72x - 36$ 34. $(x - 6)(x + 6)(2x + 1)$
35. $4x^3 + x^2 - 16x - 4$ 35. $(x - 2)(x + 2)(4x + 1)$
36. $9x^9 - 16x^7 + 9x^6 - 16x^4$
37. $8x^7 - 4x^5 - 18x^3 + 9x$
38. $x^{13} - 15x^9 - 16x^5$

39. **Critical Thinking** The polynomial $ax^3 + bx^2 + cx + d$ is factored as $3(x - 2)(x + 3)(x - 4)$. What are the values of a and d? Explain.

39. $a = 3$; $d = 72$; possible answer: the value of a is the leading coefficient, 3; the value of d is the product of the constant terms of each factor and the leading coefficient 3.

Assignment Guide

Assign *Guided Practice* exercises as necessary.

If you finished Examples 1–2
Basic 17–25, 41
Average 17–25, 41, 42
Advanced 18–24 even, 41–45

If you finished Examples 1–4
Basic 17–35, 40–44, 46–48, 50–52, 60–68
Average 17–38, 40–54, 60–68
Advanced 18–38 even, 39, 40, 45–68

Homework Quick Check
Quickly check key concepts.
Exercises: 18, 20, 26, 28, 32

Answers

27. $(s - 1)(s + 1)(s^2 + s + 1)(s^2 - s + 1)$
28. $3n^2(2 + n)(4 - 2n + n^2)$
31. $y^2(y + 3)(y^2 - 3y + 9)$
36. $x^4(x + 1)(x^2 - x + 1)(3x - 4)(3x + 4)$
37. $x(2x^2 - 1)(2x^2 - 3)(2x^2 + 3)$
38. $x^5(x^4 + 1)(x^2 + 4)(x + 2)(x - 2)$

State Resources

go.hrw.com
State Resources Online
KEYWORD: MB7 Resources

MULTI-STEP TEST PREP Exercise **40** involves factoring polynomials related to triangular numbers. This exercise prepares students for the Multi-Step Test Prep on page 436.

TEST PREP DOCTOR In **Exercise 51,** the zeros to test are 4, −2, and −1. Students should notice that the only positive root is 4. In choices **F** and **H,** the value of $P(x)$ for 4 could not be 0 because all the terms are positive and the sum is greater than 0. Both **G** and **J** have 4 as a root. Since calculations are simplest for $x = -1$, students should test that root in **G** and **J.** The test eliminates choice **G.**

Answers

40b. Possible answer: For $n = 7$, $g(7) = 84$. So if $\frac{1}{6}n^3 + \frac{1}{2}n^2 + \frac{1}{3}n = 84$, then $n^3 + 3n^2 + 2n = 504$ and $n^3 + 3n^2 + 2n - 504 = 0$. The equation is true for $n = 7$, so $n - 7$ must be a factor of $n^3 + 3n^2 + 2n - 504$.

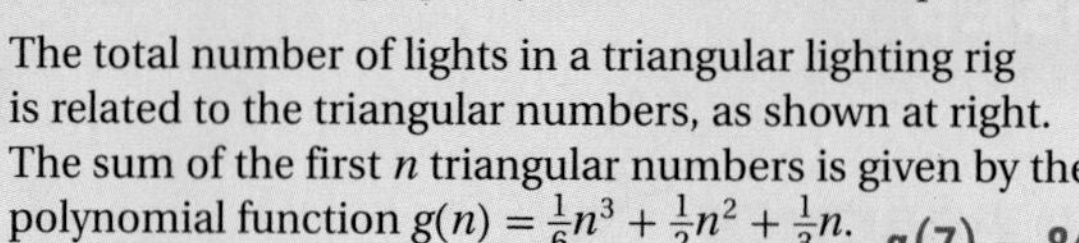

MULTI-STEP TEST PREP

40. This problem will prepare you for the Multi-Step Test Prep on page 436.

The total number of lights in a triangular lighting rig is related to the triangular numbers, as shown at right. The sum of the first n triangular numbers is given by the polynomial function $g(n) = \frac{1}{6}n^3 + \frac{1}{2}n^2 + \frac{1}{3}n$.

a. Find the sum of the first seven triangular numbers. $g(7) = 84$

b. Explain why $n - 7$ must be a factor of $n^3 + 3n^2 + 2n - 504$.

c. Factor $n^3 + 3n^2 + 2n - 504$. $(n - 7)(n^2 + 10n + 72)$

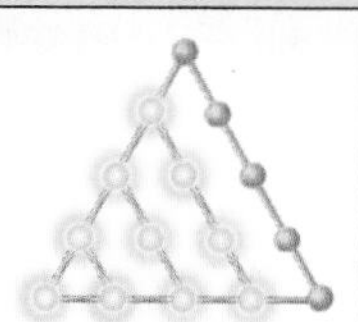

Triangular numbers: 1, 3, 6, 10, 15, . . .

42. $P(x) = (x - 1)(4x^5 - 2x^3 + x^2 - 7)$

Use the Factor Theorem to verify that each linear binomial is a factor of the given polynomial. Then use synthetic division to write the polynomial as a product.

41. $(x - 2)$; $P(x) = x^4 - 2x^3 + 5x^2 - 9x - 2$. $P(x) = (x - 2)(x^3 + 5x + 1)$

42. $(x - 1)$; $P(x) = 4x^6 - 4x^5 - 2x^4 + 3x^3 - x^2 - 7x + 7$.

43. $(x + 2)$; $P(x) = 2x^5 + 4x^4 - 6x^2 - 9x + 6$. $P(x) = (x + 2)(2x^4 - 6x + 3)$

44. $(x - 4)$; $P(x) = 2x^4 - 9x^3 + 7x^2 - 14x + 8$. $P(x) = (x - 4)(2x^3 - x^2 + 3x - 2)$

45. Business The profit of a small business (in thousands of dollars) since it was founded can be modeled by the polynomial $f(t) = -t^4 + 44t^3 - 612t^2 + 2592t$, where t represents the number of years since 1980.

a. Factor $f(t)$ completely. $f(t) = -t(t - 8)(t - 18)(t - 18)$

b. What was the company's profit in 1985? $2,535,000

c. Find and interpret $f(15)$. $f(15) = -945$; the company lost $945,000 in 1995.

d. What can you say about the company's long-term prospects? Possible answer: the company will continue to lose money after breaking even in 1998.

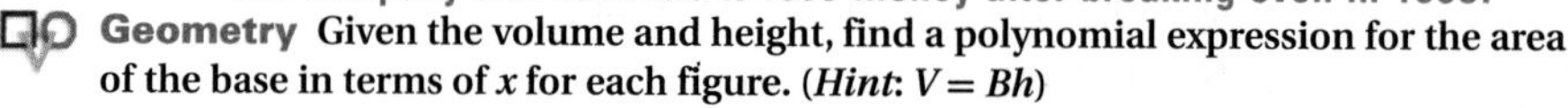

Geometry **Given the volume and height, find a polynomial expression for the area of the base in terms of x for each figure. (*Hint:* $V = Bh$)**

46. $V(x) = 2x^3 - 17x^2 + 27x + 18$ **47.** $V(x) = x^4 - 16$ **48.** $V(x) = 3x^6 + 3x^3$

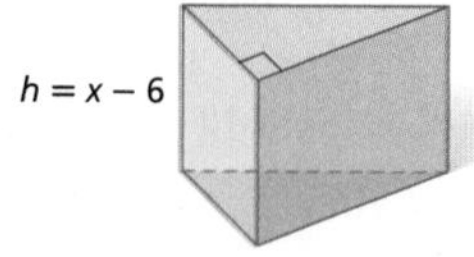

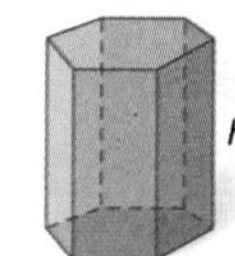

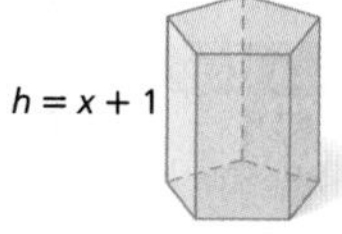

46. $B(x) = 2x^2 - 5x - 3$ **47.** $B(x) = x^3 - 2x^2 + 4x - 8$ **48.** $B(x) = 3x^5 - 3x^4 + 3x^3$

49. Write About It Describe how synthetic division can be used to factor a polynomial. Possible answer: If you know a possible root of the related equation, you can use synthetic division to test the value. If the remainder is 0, the value corresponds to a factor of the polynomial.

TEST PREP

50. Which is a factor of $x^3 + 2x^2 - 9x + 30$?

Ⓐ $x + 2$ Ⓑ $x - 3$ **Ⓒ $x + 5$** Ⓓ $x - 6$

51. $P(x)$ is a polynomial, and $P(4) = P(-2) = P(-1) = 0$. Which of the following could be $P(x)$?

Ⓕ $x^3 + 7x^2 + 14x + 8$ Ⓗ $x^2 + 3x + 2$

Ⓖ $-x^2 + 2x + 8$ **Ⓙ $x^3 - x^2 - 10x - 8$**

52. Short Response Factor $4p^5 - 16p^3 - 20p$ completely. $4p(p^2 - 5)(p^2 + 1)$

6-4 PRACTICE A

6-4 PRACTICE C

6-4 PRACTICE B

Determine whether the given binomial is a factor of the polynomial $P(x)$.

1. $(x - 4)$; $P(x) = x^2 + 8x - 48$ Yes
2. $(x + 5)$; $P(x) = 2x^2 - 6x - 1$ No
3. $(x - 6)$; $P(x) = -2x^2 + 15x - 18$ Yes
4. $(x + 3)$; $P(x) = 2x^2 - x + 7$ No

Factor each expression.

5. $2x^4 + 2x^3 - x^2 - x$ $(2x^3 - x)(x + 1)$
6. $4x^3 + x^2 - 8x - 2$ $(4x + 1)(x^2 - 2)$
7. $5x^6 - 5x^4 + x^3 - x$ $(5x^4 + x)(x^2 - 1)$
8. $2x^4 + 54x$ $2x(x + 3)(x^2 - 3x + 9)$
9. $64x^3 - 1$ $(4x - 1)(16x^2 + 4x + 1)$
10. $3x^4 + 24x$ $3x(x + 2)(x^2 - 2x + 4)$

Solve.

11. Since 2006, the water level in a certain pond has been modeled by the polynomial $d(x) = -x^3 + 16x^2 - 74x + 140$, where the depth d, is measured in feet over x years. Identify the year that the pond will dry up. Use the graph to factor $d(x)$.

2016; $-(x - 10)(x^2 - 6x + 14)$

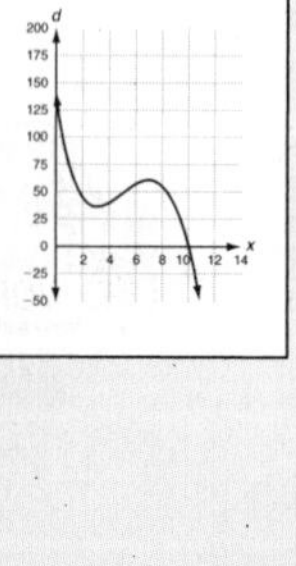

6-4 READING STRATEGIES

You already know how to factor linear and quadratic functions, which are polynomials. Higher-degree polynomials can also be factored. One method is to group the terms in the polynomial and find common factors.

The table shows four steps for factoring $x^3 + 3x^2 + 2x + 6$.

STEP 1: Group the terms. $x^3 + 3x^2 + 2x + 6 = (x^3 + 3x^2) + (2x + 6)$	**STEP 2:** Find the common factors of each group. Common factor of $(x^3 + 3x^2)$ is x^2 Common factor of $(2x + 6)$ is 2
STEP 3: Factor out the common factors in each group. $(x^3 + 3x^2) + (2x + 6)$ $= x^2(x + 3) + 2(x + 3)$ Notice that $x + 3$ is the common factor.	**STEP 4:** Factor out $x + 3$. $x^2(x + 3) + 2(x + 3) = (x + 3)(x^2 + 2)$ The factors of $x^3 + 3x^2 + 2x + 6$ are $(x + 3)$ and $(x^2 + 2)$.

Answer each question.

1. How can you check that $x + 3$ and $x^2 + 2$ are factors of $x^3 + 3x^2 + 2x + 6$?
Multiply $(x + 3)$ and $(x^2 + 2)$.

2. $x^2 + 2$ is a polynomial. Can you factor $x^2 + 2$ into two linear factors? If yes, write the factors. If no, explain.
No; there are no two factors that have $x^2 + 2$ as their product.

3. Suppose you multiply a polynomial of degree 3 by a polynomial of degree 2. What is the degree of the product of the two polynomials? 5

Use $x^3 - 8x^2 - x + 8$ to answer the following questions.

4. a. How would you group this polynomial to factor it? $(x^3 - 8x^2) + (-x + 8)$
b. What is the common factor of the first group? x^2
c. What is the common factor of the second group? -1
d. Find the common binomial factor in both groups and write the factors.
$x^2(x - 8) - 1(x - 8) = (x - 8)(x^2 - 1)$
e. Which of the two factors can also be factored? Write its factors. $x^2 - 1$; $(x + 1)(x - 1)$
f. What are the factors of $x^3 - 8x^2 - x + 8$? $(x - 8)(x + 1)(x - 1)$

6-4 RETEACH

Sometimes you can use grouping to factor a third degree polynomial. To **factor by grouping** means to group terms with common factors. Then factor the common factors. Continue to factor until the expression can no longer be factored.

Factor: $x^3 + 4x^2 - 9x - 36$.

Start by grouping terms to factor out the greatest possible power of x.

$x^3 + 4x^2 - 9x - 36$ — x^2 is a factor of x^3 and $4x^2$.

$(x^3 + 4x^2) + (-9x - 36)$ — -9 is a factor of -9 and -36.

$x^2(x + 4) - 9(x + 4)$ — $(x + 4)$ is a common factor.

$(x + 4)(x^2 - 9)$ — $(x^2 - 9)$ is the difference of squares.

$(x + 4)(x + 3)(x - 3)$ — Recall that $(a^2 - b^2) = (a + b)(a - b)$. So $(x^2 - 9) = (x + 3)(x - 3)$.

Factor each expression.

1. $x^3 - 3x^2 - 4x + 12$
$(x^3 - 3x^2) + (-4x + 12)$
$x^2(x - 3) - 4(x - 3)$
$(x - 3)(x^2 - 4)$
$(x - 3)(x + 2)(x - 2)$

2. $x^3 + 6x^2 - x - 6$
$(x^3 + 6x^2) + (-x - 6)$
$x^2(x + 6) - 1(x + 6)$
$(x + 6)(x^2 - 1)$
$(x + 6)(x + 1)(x - 1)$

3. $x^3 + x^2 - 9x - 9$
$(x^3 + x^2) + (-9x - 9)$
$x^2(x + 1) - 9(x + 1)$
$(x + 1)(x^2 - 9)$
$(x + 1)(x + 3)(x - 3)$

4. $x^3 + 2x^2 - 16x - 32$
$(x^3 + 2x^2) + (-16x - 32)$
$x^2(x + 2) - 16(x + 2)$
$(x + 2)(x^2 - 16)$
$(x + 2)(x + 4)(x - 4)$

CHALLENGE AND EXTEND

53. Factor $(x-3)^3 + 8$ as the sum of two cubes. Then simplify each factor.

53. $[(x-3)+2][(x-3)^2 - 2(x-3) + 4]$; $(x-1)(x^2 - 8x + 19)$

54. Factor $(2a+b)^3 - b^3$ as the difference of two cubes. Then simplify each factor.

54. $((2a+b) - b)((2a+b)^2 + (2a+b)b + b^2)$; $(2a)(4a^2 + 6ab + 3b^2)$

55. Divide (x^2-1), (x^3-1), and (x^4-1) by $(x-1)$ using synthetic division. Use the pattern you observe to find a formula for $(x^n - 1)$ divided by $(x-1)$.

55. $(x-1)(x+1)$; $(x-1)(x^2+x+1)$; $(x-1)(x^3+x^2+x+1)$; $(x^n - 1) = (x-1)(x^{n-1} + x^{n-2} + \ldots + x + 1)$, with all coefficients of the quotient equal to 1.

The polynomial $au^2 + bu + c$ is in quadratic form when u is any function of x. Identify u, and factor each expression, simplifying the factors if possible.

56. $x + 3\sqrt{x} + 2$

56. $u = \sqrt{x}$; $(\sqrt{x}+2)(\sqrt{x}+1)$

57. $(3x-8)^2 + 6(3x-8) + 9$

57. $u = 3x - 8$; $(3x-5)(3x-5)$

58. $2x^{\frac{1}{2}} - 2x^{\frac{1}{4}} - 12$

58. $u = x^{\frac{1}{4}}$; $2\left(x^{\frac{1}{4}}+2\right)\left(x^{\frac{1}{4}}-3\right)$

59. $\frac{1}{2}\left(x-\frac{1}{3}\right)^2 + \frac{5}{2}\left(x-\frac{1}{3}\right) - 42$

59. $u = x - \frac{1}{3}$; $\left(x - \frac{22}{3}\right)\left(\frac{1}{2}x + \frac{35}{6}\right)$

SPIRAL REVIEW

60. **Finance** Amy invests \$100 total in the stock of three companies. She buys 20 shares of Big-Mart stock, 15 shares of Total Telephone, and 25 shares of Zoom Motors. Write a linear equation in three variables to represent this situation. *(Lesson 3-5)* $20b + 15t + 25z = 100$

Simplify. Write the result in the form $a + bi$. *(Lesson 5-9)*

61. $(2+4i)(2-4i)$ 20

62. $4i(6+9i)$ $-36 + 24i$

63. $\frac{3+4i}{5+i}$ $\frac{19}{26} + \frac{17}{26}i$

64. $\frac{8-2i}{i}$ $-2 - 8i$

Use synthetic substitution to evaluate the polynomial for the given value. *(Lesson 6-3)*

65. $P(x) = 3x^2 - 2x - 1$ for $x = 5$ $P(5) = 64$

66. $P(x) = x^3 - 4x^2 + x - 2$ for $x = -2$ $P(-2) = -28$

67. $P(x) = 8x^2 - 5x + 7$ for $x = -1$ $P(-1) = 20$

68. $P(x) = 6x^2 - 3x - 8$ for $x = 3$ $P(3) = 37$

Career Path

go.hrw.com
Career Resources Online
KEYWORD: MB7 Career

Katherine Shields
Nuclear propulsion officer candidate

Q: What math classes did you take in high school?

A: I took Algebra 1 and 2, Geometry, Trigonometry, and Precalculus.

Q: What math classes are you taking now?

A: I've taken two calculus classes. Right now, I'm taking Physics and an engineering class, both of which use a lot of math.

Q: How do you use math in the navy?

A: Nuclear propulsion officers operate aircraft carriers and nuclear-propelled submarines. It's amazing how much math is behind the theory and mechanics of nuclear propulsion.

Q: What are your future plans?

A: There are many options available after my nuclear officer training. While serving as an officer, I'd like to go to graduate school for an advanced degree in nuclear engineering.

Journal

Have students write their own explanations of how to factor the sum and difference of two cubes. Have them include a method to check that an answer is correct.

ALTERNATIVE ASSESSMENT

Have students create a polynomial by multiplying a monomial and the sum or difference of cubes $x^3(a^3 \pm b^3)$. Then have students exchange papers and factor their partner's polynomial.

Power Presentations with PowerPoint®

6-4 Lesson Quiz

Determine whether the given binomial is a factor of $P(x)$.

1. $x - 1$; $P(x) = 3x^2 - 2x + 5$
   $P(1) \neq 0$, so $x - 1$ is not a factor of $P(x)$.
2. $x + 2$; $P(x) = x^3 + 2x^2 - x - 2$
   $P(-2) = 0$, so $x + 2$ is a factor of $P(x)$.

Factor each expression.

3. $x^3 + 3x^2 - 9x - 27$
   $(x+3)(x+3)(x-3)$
4. $x^3 + 3x^2 - 28x - 60$
   $(x+6)(x-5)(x+2)$
5. $64p^3 - 8q^3$
   $8(2p-q)(4p^2 + 2pq + q^2)$

Also available on transparency

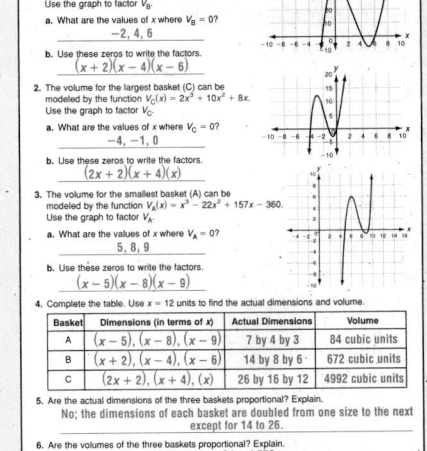

6-4 PROBLEM SOLVING

Paulo is drawing plans for a set of three proportional nesting baskets, in the shape of open rectangular prisms.

1. The volume for the middle-sized basket (B) can be modeled by the function $V_B(x) = x^3 - 8x^2 + 4x + 48$. Use the graph to factor V_B.
   a. What are the values of x where $V_B = 0$? $-2, 4, 6$
   b. Use these zeros to write the factors. $(x+2)(x-4)(x-6)$
2. The volume for the largest basket (C) can be modeled by the function $V_C(x) = 2x^3 + 10x^2 + 8x$. Use the graph to factor V_C.
   a. What are the values of x where $V_C = 0$? $-4, -1, 0$
   b. Use these zeros to write the factors. $(2x+2)(x+4)(x)$
3. The volume for the smallest basket (A) can be modeled by the function $V_A(x) = x^3 - 22x^2 + 157x - 360$. Use the graph to factor V_A.
   a. What are the values of x where $V_A = 0$? $5, 8, 9$
   b. Use these zeros to write the factors. $(x-5)(x-8)(x-9)$
4. Complete the table. Use $x = 12$ units to find the actual dimensions and volume.

Basket	Dimensions (in terms of x)	Actual Dimensions	Volume
A	$(x-5), (x-8), (x-9)$	7 by 4 by 3	84 cubic units
B	$(x+2), (x-4), (x-6)$	14 by 8 by 6	672 cubic units
C	$(2x+2), (x+4), (x)$	26 by 16 by 12	4992 cubic units

5. Are the actual dimensions of the three baskets proportional? Explain.
   No; the dimensions of each basket are doubled from one size to the next except for 14 to 26.
6. Are the volumes of the three baskets proportional? Explain.
   No; $\frac{84}{672} = \frac{672}{4992}$

6-4 CHALLENGE

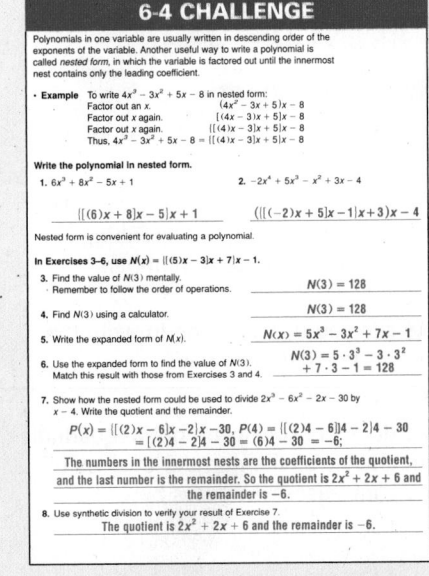

Polynomials in one variable are usually written in descending order of the exponents of the variable. Another useful way to write a polynomial is called *nested form*, in which the variable is factored out until the innermost nest contains only the leading coefficient.

- **Example** To write $4x^3 - 3x^2 + 5x - 8$ in nested form:
  Factor out an x. $(4x^2 - 3x + 5)x - 8$
  Factor out x again. $[(4x-3)x + 5]x - 8$
  Factor out x again. $\{[(4)x - 3]x + 5\}x - 8$
  Thus, $4x^3 - 3x^2 + 5x - 8 = \{[(4)x - 3]x + 5\}x - 8$

Write the polynomial in nested form.

1. $6x^3 + 8x^2 - 5x + 1$ $\{[(6)x + 8]x - 5\}x + 1$
2. $-2x^4 + 5x^3 - x^2 + 3x - 4$ $(\{[(-2)x + 5]x - 1\}x + 3)x - 4$

Nested form is convenient for evaluating a polynomial.

In Exercises 3–6, use $N(x) = \{[(5)x - 3]x + 7\}x - 1$.

3. Find the value of $N(3)$ mentally. Remember to follow the order of operations. $N(3) = 128$
4. Find $N(3)$ using a calculator. $N(3) = 128$
5. Write the expanded form of $N(x)$. $N(x) = 5x^3 - 3x^2 + 7x - 1$
6. Use the expanded form to find the value of $N(3)$. Match this result with those from Exercises 3 and 4. $N(3) = 5 \cdot 3^3 - 3 \cdot 3^2 + 7 \cdot 3 - 1 = 128$
7. Show how the nested form could be used to divide $2x^3 - 6x^2 - 2x - 30$ by $x - 4$. Write the quotient and the remainder.
   $P(x) = \{[(2)x - 6]x - 2\}x - 30$, $P(4) = \{[(2)4 - 6]]4 - 2\}4 - 30 = [(2)4 - 2]4 - 30 = (6)4 - 30 = -6$;
   The numbers in the innermost nests are the coefficients of the quotient, and the last number is the remainder. So the quotient is $2x^2 + 2x + 6$ and the remainder is -6.
8. Use synthetic division to verify your result of Exercise 7.
   The quotient is $2x^2 + 2x + 6$ and the remainder is -6.

SECTION 6A MULTI-STEP TEST PREP

Organizer

Objective: Assess students' ability to apply concepts and skills in Lessons 6-1 through 6-4 in a real-world format.

Online Edition

Resources

Algebra II Assessments
www.mathtekstoolkit.org

Problem	Text Reference
1–5	Lesson 6-1
6	Lesson 6-3

State Resources

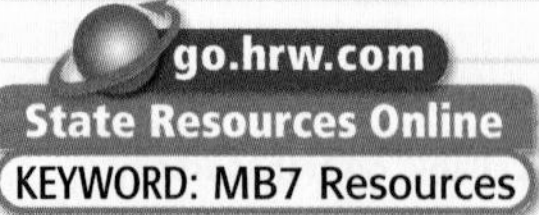

go.hrw.com
State Resources Online
KEYWORD: MB7 Resources

CHAPTER 6 MULTI-STEP TEST PREP

SECTION 6A

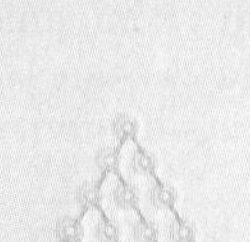

Operations with Polynomials

In the Spotlight A lighting rig is a large bank of lights that is used to create lighting effects at concerts and sporting events. A company makes rigs with lights arranged in polygonal patterns. The number of lights in a rig depends on the shape of the rig and the number of rows of lights. For example, a triangular rig may have 1, 3, 6, 10, or 15 lights, depending on the number of rows. The figures show the number of lights in a variety of rigs.

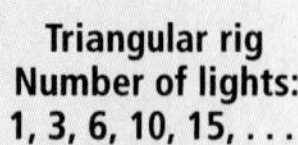

Triangular rig
Number of lights:
1, 3, 6, 10, 15, . . .

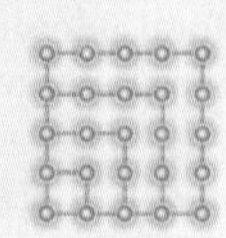

Square rig
Number of lights:
1, 4, 9, 16, 25, . . .

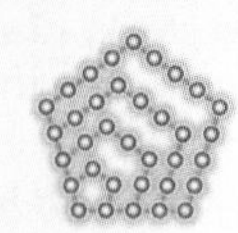

Pentagonal rig
Number of lights
1, 5, 12, 22, 35, . .

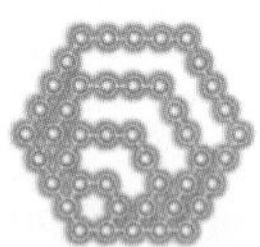

Hexagonal rig
Number of lights:
1, 6, 15, 28, 45, . .

1. 1, 3, 6, 10, 15, 21, 28, 36, 45, 55
2. 1, 4, 9, 16, 25, 36, 49, 64, 81, 100
3. 1, 5, 12, 22, 35, 51, 70, 92, 117, 145
4. $H(n) = 2n^2 - n$
5. $2n^2$; the sum is twice a perfect square.
6. $2 - \frac{1}{n}$; the ratio gets closer and closer to 2.

1. The number of lights in a triangular rig with n rows is given by $T(n) = \frac{1}{2}n^2 + \frac{1}{2}n$. Find the number of lights in triangular rigs with 1 to 10 rows.
2. The number of lights in a square rig with n rows is given by $S(n) = n^2$. Find the number of lights in square rigs with 1 to 10 rows.
3. The number of lights in a pentagonal rig with n rows is given by $P(n) = \frac{3}{2}n^2 - \frac{1}{2}n$. Find the number of lights in pentagonal rigs with 1 to 10 rows.
4. Write a polynomial function, $H(n)$, that gives the number of lights in a hexagonal rig with n rows. (*Hint:* Look for a pattern in the coefficients of the polynomial functions in parts **a–c**.)
5. Find $T(n) + P(n)$. What do you notice about this sum?
6. Find $H(n) \div S(n)$. What can you say about the ratio of the number of lights in a hexagonal rig with n rows to the number of lights in a square rig with n rows as n gets larger and larger?

INTERVENTION

Scaffolding Questions

1. How can you use factoring to write the function in a different way? $T(n) = \frac{1}{2}n(n + 1)$
2. What is a familiar way of describing or naming this sequence of numbers? perfect squares
3. How can you use factoring to write the function in a different way? $P(n) = \frac{1}{2}n(3n - 1)$
4. How does the coefficient of the quadratic term change as the number of sides of the rig increases? increases by $\frac{1}{2}$
5. How do you add polynomials? combine like terms
6. What is the remainder? What happens to the remainder as n becomes very large? $\frac{1}{n}$; the remainder gets very close to 0.

Extension

What can you say about the average of the number of lights in a square rig and in a hexagonal rig, both with n rows? equal to the number of lights in a pentagonal rig with n rows

CHAPTER 6

SECTION 6A

Quiz for Lesson 6-1 Through 6-4

6-1 Polynomials

Rewrite each polynomial in standard form. Then identify the leading coefficient, degree, and number of terms. Name the polynomial.

1. $4x^2 + 3x^5 - 5$
2. $7 + 13x$
3. $1 + 5x^3 + x^2 - 3x$
4. $8x + 2x^4 - 5x^3$

7. $6x^3 + 15x^2 - 2x + 7$

Add or subtract. Write your answer in standard form.

5. $(3x^2 + 1) + (4x^2 + 3)$ $7x^2 + 4$
6. $(9x^3 - 6x^2) - (2x^3 + x^2 + 2)$ $7x^3 - 7x^2 - 2$
7. $(11x^2 + x^3 + 7) + (5x^3 + 4x^2 - 2x)$
8. $(x^5 - 4x^4 + 1) - (-7x^4 + 11)$ $x^5 + 3x^4 - 10$
9. The cost of manufacturing x units of a product can be modeled by $C(x) = x^3 - 15x + 15$. Evaluate $C(x)$ for $x = 100$, and describe what the value represents.
$C(100) = 998{,}515$; the cost of manufacturing 100 units is $998,515.

Graph each polynomial function on a calculator. Describe the graph, and identify the number of real zeros.

10. $f(x) = -\frac{1}{4}x^5 - x^2$
11. $h(x) = \frac{1}{5}x^3 + x^2 - 2$
12. $f(x) = -2x^6 - 1$

6-2 Multiplying Polynomials

Find each product.

13. $2y(4x^2 + 7xy)$ $8x^2y + 14xy^2$
14. $(a + b)(3ab + b^2)$ $3a^2b + 4ab^2 + b^3$
15. $\left(2x + \frac{1}{3}\right)^2$ $4x^2 + \frac{4}{3}x + \frac{1}{9}$
16. $(2x - 3)(x^3 - x^2 + 3x + 5)$ $2x^4 - 5x^3 + 9x^2 + x - 15$

Expand each expression.

17. $(x - 3)^4$
18. $(x + 2y)^3$
19. $(4x - 1)^4$
20. Find a polynomial expression in terms of x for the volume of the rectangular prism shown. $6x^3 - 21x^2 - 12x$

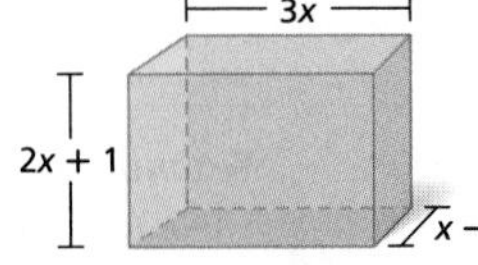

6-3 Dividing Polynomials

Divide.

21. $(6y^2 + 13y - 8) \div (2y - 1)$ $3y + 8$
22. $(3x^3 + 11x^2 + 11x + 15) \div (x + 3)$ $3x^2 + 2x + 5$

Use synthetic substitution to evaluate the polynomial for the given value.

23. $P(x) = x^3 + 2x^2 - 5x + 6$ for $x = -1$ 12
24. $P(x) = x^4 + x^2 + x - 6$ for $x = 2$ 16

6-4 Factoring Polynomials

Factor each expression.

25. $3t^3 - 21t^2 - 12t$ $3t(t^2 - 7t - 4)$
26. $16y^2 - 49$ $(4y - 7)(4y + 7)$
27. $y^3 + 7y^2 + 2y + 14$
28. $a^6 + 125$
29. The volume of a box is modeled by the function $V(x) = x^3 + 2x^2 - 11x - 12$. Identify the values of x for which the volume is 0 and use the graph to factor $V(x)$. $-4, -1, 3$; $(x + 4)(x + 1)(x - 3)$

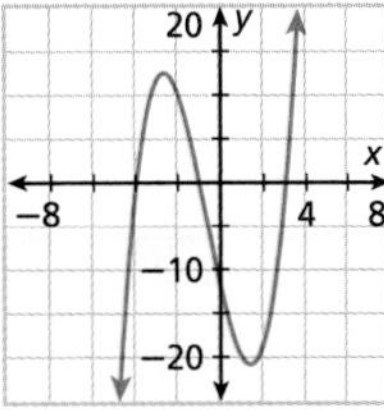

27. $(y + 7)(y^2 + 2)$ 28. $(a^2 + 5)(a^4 - 5a^2 + 25)$

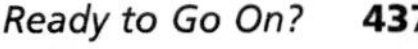

READY TO GO ON? SECTION 6A

Organizer

Objective: Assess students' mastery of concepts and skills in Lessons 6-1 through 6-4.

Resources

 ***Assessment Resources***
Section 6A Quiz

 **Test & Practice Generator One-Stop Planner®**

INTERVENTION

Resources

 ***Ready to Go On? Intervention and Enrichment*** **Worksheets**

 ***Ready to Go On?*** **CD-ROM**

Ready to Go On? **Online**

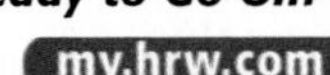

my.hrw.com

Answers

1–4, 10–12, 17–19. See p. A31.

READY TO GO ON? Diagnose and Prescribe

NO INTERVENE

Ready to Go On? Intervention	*Ready to Go On? Intervention,* Section 6A: Worksheets	CD-ROM	Online
Lesson 6-1	6-1 Intervention	Activity 6-1	Diagnose and Prescribe Online
Lesson 6-2	6-2 Intervention	Activity 6-2	
Lesson 6-3	6-3 Intervention	Activity 6-3	
Lesson 6-4	6-4 Intervention	Activity 6-4	

YES ENRICH

***Ready to Go On? Enrichment,* Section 6A**
 Worksheets
 CD-ROM
Online

SECTION

6B Applying Polynomial Functions

One-Minute Section Planner

Lesson	Lab Resources	Materials
Lesson 6-5 Finding Real Roots of Polynomial Equations • Identify the multiplicity of roots. • Use the Rational Root Theorem and the Irrational Root Theorem to solve polynomial equations. ☐ SAT-10 ☐ NAEP ☑ ACT ☐ SAT ☐ SAT Subject Tests		**Required** graphing calculator
Lesson 6-6 Fundamental Theorem of Algebra • Use the Fundamental Theorem of Algebra and its corollary to write a polynomial equation of least degree with given roots. • Identify all the roots of a polynomial equation. ☐ SAT-10 ☐ NAEP ☑ ACT ☐ SAT ☐ SAT Subject Tests		**Required** graphing calculator
6-7 Technology Lab Explore End Behavior • Use a graphing calculator to explore the end behavior of functions from their graphs. ☐ SAT-10 ☐ NAEP ☐ ACT ☐ SAT ☐ SAT Subject Tests	***Technology Lab Activities*** 6-7 Lab Recording Sheet	**Required** graphing calculator
Lesson 6-7 Investigating Graphs of Polynomial Functions • Use properties of end behavior to analyze, describe, and graph polynomial functions. • Identify and use maxima and minima of polynomial functions to solve problems. ☐ SAT-10 ☐ NAEP ☑ ACT ☐ SAT ☑ SAT Subject Tests	***Technology Lab Activities*** 6-7 Technology Lab	**Required** graphing calculator
Lesson 6-8 Transforming Polynomial Functions • Transform polynomial functions. ☐ SAT-10 ☐ NAEP ☑ ACT ☐ SAT ☑ SAT Subject Tests		**Required** graphing calculator
Lesson 6-9 Curve Fitting with Polynomial Functions • Use finite differences to determine the degree of a polynomial that will fit a given set of data. • Use technology to find polynomial models for a given set of data. ☐ SAT-10 ☐ NAEP ☑ ACT ☐ SAT ☑ SAT Subject Tests		**Required** graphing calculator

MK = *Manipulatives Kit*

Section Overview

Roots of Polynomial Equations — *Lessons 6-5, 6-6*

The roots of a polynomial are used to graph the polynomial.

Finding Roots of Polynomial Equations
- Factoring
- Rational Root Theorem
- Irrational Root Theorem
- Fundamental Theorem of Algebra

$x^3 + x^2 - 25x - 25 = 0$
$(x + 1)(x - 5)(x + 5) = 0$
$x = -1$ or $x = 5$ or $x = -5$
The roots are -1, 5, and -5.

$x^4 + 7x^2 - 18 = 0$
$(x^2 - 2)(x^2 + 9) = 0$
$x^2 = 2$ or $x^2 = -9$
$x = \pm\sqrt{2}$ or $x = \pm 3i$
The roots are $\pm\sqrt{2}$ and $\pm 3i$.

Irrational and complex roots come in **conjugate pairs.**

Graphs of Polynomial Functions — *Lessons 6-7, 6-8*

Students understand the behavior of polynomial functions by learning to graph them.

Graph $f(x) = x^3 - 5x^2 - 2x + 24$.
- Identify the zeros and *y*-intercept.

  $f(x) = (x - 3)(x + 2)(x - 4)$
  $\rightarrow$ zeros 3, -2, 4

  $f(0) = 24$
- Determine end behavior.

  $x \rightarrow -\infty, f(x) \rightarrow -\infty$

  $x \rightarrow +\infty, f(x) \rightarrow +\infty$

- Plot other points as guidelines.

  $f(1) = 18 \rightarrow (1, 18)$

  $f(-1) = 20 \rightarrow (-1, 20)$
- Sketch the graph.

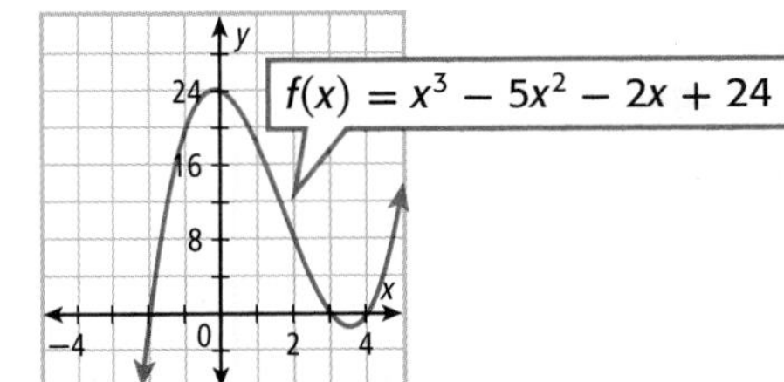

Curve Fitting — *Lesson 6-9*

Some real-world data might be better modeled by cubic or quartic functions.

To find a function model for the data below, identify the degree of the polynomial.

x	40	45	50	55	60
y	350	500	665	880	1180

First differences: 150 165 215 300

Second differences: 15 50 85

Third differences: 35 35

Constant third differences indicate a cubic function.

Enter the data into the lists of a graphing calculator.

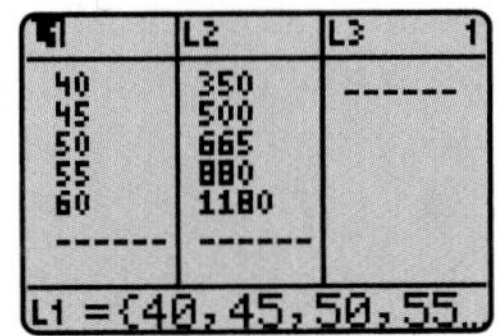

Use the **regression feature** to find the cubic function model.

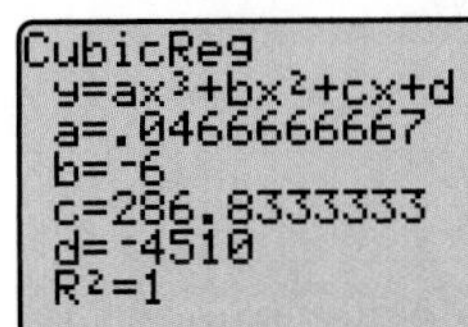

$f(x) \approx 0.05x^3 - 6x^2 + 286.83x - 4510$

Graph the model with the points.

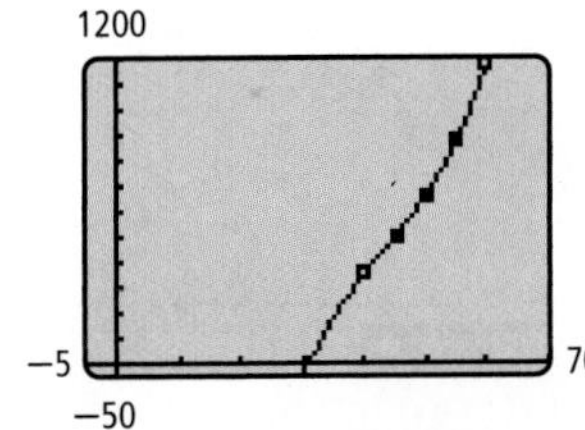

6-5 Organizer

Pacing: Traditional 1 day
Block $\frac{1}{2}$ day

Objectives: Identify the multiplicity of roots.

Use the Rational Root Theorem and the Irrational Root Theorem to solve polynomial equations.

Online Edition
Graphing Calculator, Tutorial Videos, TechKeys

Countdown to Testing Week 13

Power Presentations with PowerPoint®

Warm Up

Factor completely.

1. $2y^3 + 4y^2 - 30y$
   $2y(y-3)(y+5)$
2. $3x^4 - 6x^2 - 24$
   $3(x-2)(x+2)(x^2+2)$

Solve each equation.

3. $x^2 - 9 = 0$ $x = -3, 3$
4. $x^3 + 3x^2 - 4x = 0$
   $x = -4, 0, 1$

Also available on transparency

Math Humor

Q: Why is the Rational Root Theorem so polite?

A: It minds its p's and q's.

6-5 Finding Real Roots of Polynomial Equations

IN **A2.4.4** Factor polynomials completely and solve polynomial equations by factoring.

Objectives
Identify the multiplicity of roots.

Use the Rational Root Theorem and the Irrational Root Theorem to solve polynomial equations.

Vocabulary
multiplicity

Who uses this?
Package designers can use roots of polynomial equations to set production specifications. (See Example 3.)

In Lesson 6-4, you used several methods for factoring polynomials. As with some quadratic equations, factoring a polynomial equation is one way to find its real roots.

Recall the Zero Product Property from Lesson 5-3. You can find the *roots*, or *solutions*, of the polynomial equation $P(x) = 0$ by setting each factor equal to 0 and solving for x.

EXAMPLE 1 Using Factoring to Solve Polynomial Equations

Solve each polynomial equation by factoring.

A $3x^5 + 18x^4 + 27x^3 = 0$

$3x^3(x^2 + 6x + 9) = 0$ *Factor out the GCF, $3x^3$.*

$3x^3(x+3)(x+3) = 0$ *Factor the quadratic.*

$3x^3 = 0,\ x + 3 = 0,\ \text{or } x + 3 = 0$ *Set each factor equal to 0.*

$x = 0,\ x = -3,\ \text{or } x = -3$ *Solve for x.*

The roots are 0 and −3.

Check Use a graph. The roots appear to be located at $x = 0$ and $x = -3$. ✔

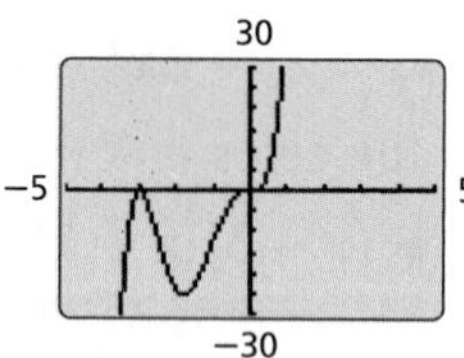

B $x^4 - 13x^2 = -36$

$x^4 - 13x^2 + 36 = 0$ *Set the equation equal to 0.*

$(x^2 - 4)(x^2 - 9) = 0$ *Factor the trinomial in quadratic form.*

$(x+2)(x-2)(x+3)(x-3) = 0$ *Factor the difference of two squares.*

$x + 2 = 0,\ x - 2 = 0,\ x + 3 = 0,\ \text{or } x - 3 = 0$

$x = -2,\ x = 2,\ x = -3,\ \text{or } x = 3$

The roots are −2, 2, −3, and 3.

CHECK IT OUT! **Solve each polynomial equation by factoring.**

1a. $2x^6 - 10x^5 - 12x^4 = 0$ **0, −1, 6**

1b. $x^3 - 2x^2 - 25x = -50$ **−5, 2, 5**

State Resources

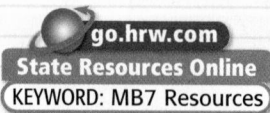

go.hrw.com
State Resources Online
KEYWORD: MB7 Resources

1 Introduce

EXPLORATION

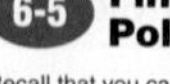

6-5 Finding Real Roots of Polynomial Equations

Recall that you can find the roots of the polynomial equation P(x) = 0 by setting each factor of P(x) equal to zero and solving for x.

1. Complete the table. Write your answers in fraction form.

P(x)	Factored Form of P(x)	Roots of P(x) = 0
$12x^2 - 41x + 35$	$(3x-5)(4x-7)$	
$6x^2 - 5x - 4$	$(2x+1)(3x-4)$	
$10x^3 + 3x^2 - 31x + 6$	$(2x-3)(5x-1)(x+2)$	
$48x^3 - 32x^2 - 27x + 18$	$(3x-2)(4x+3)(4x-3)$	

2. Look for a pattern in the table. The numerators of the roots are factors of the coefficient of which term of the polynomial?
3. The denominators of the roots are factors of the coefficient of which term of the polynomial?

THINK AND DISCUSS

4. **Explain** how you might complete the following statement: If the polynomial P(x) has integer coefficients and if $\frac{a}{b}$ is a root of P(x) = 0, then ______.

Motivate

Draw a *U*, a curvy *N*, and a curvy *W* on the board. Draw a line through them representing the *x*-axis. Ask students how many zeros the functions represented by the graphs have. Repeat the process by moving the *x*-axis up or down to change the number of zeros. Explain that polynomial functions can have many zeros.

Explorations and answers are provided in the *Explorations* binder.

Sometimes a polynomial equation has a factor that appears more than once. This creates a *multiple root*. In Example 1A, $3x^5 + 18x^4 + 27x^3 = 0$ has two multiple roots, 0 and −3. For example, the root 0 is a factor three times because $3x^3 = 0$.

The **multiplicity** of root r is the number of times that $x - r$ is a factor of $P(x)$. When a real root has even multiplicity, the graph of $y = P(x)$ touches the x-axis but does not cross it. When a real root has odd multiplicity greater than 1, the graph "bends" as it crosses the x-axis.

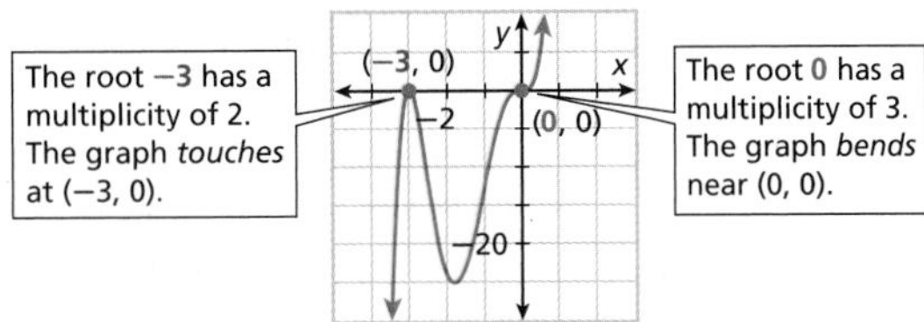

You cannot always determine the multiplicity of a root from a graph. It is easiest to determine multiplicity when the polynomial is in factored form.

EXAMPLE 2 **Identifying Multiplicity**

Identify the roots of each equation. State the multiplicity of each root.

A $x^3 - 9x^2 + 27x - 27 = 0$

$x^3 - 9x^2 + 27x - 27 = (x - 3)(x - 3)(x - 3)$

$x - 3$ is a factor three times.

The root 3 has a multiplicity of 3.

Check Use a graph. A calculator graph shows a bend near (3, 0). ✔

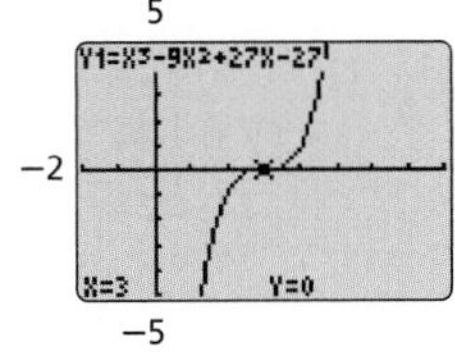

B $-2x^3 - 12x^2 + 30x + 200 = 0$

$-2x^3 - 12x^2 + 30x + 200 = -2(x - 4)(x + 5)(x + 5)$

$x - 4$ is a factor once, and $x + 5$ is a factor twice.

The root 4 has a multiplicity of 1.

The root −5 has a multiplicity of 2.

Check Use a graph. The graph crosses at (4, 0) and touches at (−5, 0). ✔

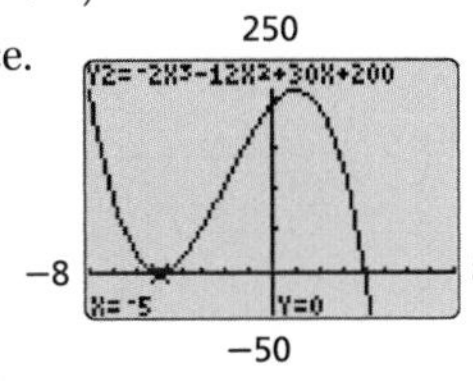

Identify the roots of each equation. State the multiplicity of each root.

2a. $x^4 - 8x^3 + 24x^2 - 32x + 16 = 0$ **2 with multiplicity 4**

2b. $2x^6 - 22x^5 + 48x^4 + 72x^3 = 0$

0 with multiplicity 3; −1 with multiplicity 1; 6 with multiplicity 2

Not all polynomials are factorable, but the Rational Root Theorem can help you find all possible rational roots of a polynomial equation.

Rational Root Theorem

If the polynomial $P(x)$ has integer coefficients, then every rational root of the polynomial equation $P(x) = 0$ can be written in the form $\frac{p}{q}$, where p is a factor of the constant term of $P(x)$ and q is a factor of the leading coefficient of $P(x)$.

Power Presentations with PowerPoint®

Additional Examples

Example 1

Solve each polynomial equation by factoring.

A. $4x^6 + 4x^5 - 24x^4 = 0$
−3, 0, 2

B. $x^4 + 25 = 26x^2$ −5, 5, −1, 1

Example 2

Identify the roots of each equation. State the multiplicity of each root.

A. $x^3 + 6x^2 + 12x + 8 = 0$
−2 with multiplicity 3

B. $x^4 + 8x^3 + 18x^2 - 27 = 0$
−3 with multiplicity 3; 1 with multiplicity 1

Also available on transparency

INTERVENTION

Questioning Strategies

EXAMPLE 1

- Why do you set each factor equal to zero to find the roots?
- How can you use a graph to check your answer?

EXAMPLE 2

- How can you determine the multiplicity of real roots of a polynomial from its graph? Explain.
- How is a real root with odd multiplicity different from a real root with even multiplicity?

Technology In **Example 2A,** the calculator supports the solution, but graphs may often have hidden behavior that can be misleading. For example, the graphs of $f(x) = (x - 3)^3$ and $g(x) = (x - 3)(x - 3.01)(x - 2.99)$ may look exactly alike, but they have different zeros.

2 Teach

Guided Instruction

Discuss how to recognize when a quadratic function has real roots. Have students distinguish between rational and irrational roots of quadratic functions. Extend the discussion to include speculation about the roots of polynomials of a degree greater than 2. Introduce the Rational Root Theorem and the Irrational Root Theorem and have students practice using them.

Reaching All Learners

Through Critical Thinking

Have students sketch the functions with the following characteristics: roots −3, 1, and 4, each with a multiplicity of 1; roots −3, 1 with a multiplicity of 2, and 4; roots −3, 1 with a multiplicity of 2, and 4 with a multiplicity of 2. Ask students to identify the degree of each function.

Inclusion Help students interpret the table in **Example 3.** The numbers in the top row represent the coefficients of the equation. The numbers in the left column are potential divisors. Each row beyond the first column represents the coefficients of the quotient for the given divisor, with the last column representing the remainder.

Power Presentations with PowerPoint®

Additional Examples

Example 3

The design of a box specifies that its length is 4 inches greater than its width. The height is 1 inch less than the width. The volume of the box is 12 cubic inches. What is the width of the box?
2 in.

Also available on transparency

INTERVENTION

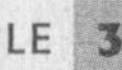

Questioning Strategies

EXAMPLE 3

- Why is it necessary to find only one rational root in the synthetic substitution table?

Reading Math Make sure students can distinguish between roots and multiplicity. Stress that the roots tell where the graph of the equation intercepts the x-axis, while multiplicity refers to how the roots behave near the x-axis and the number of times a factor appears. ENGLISH LANGUAGE LEARNERS

EXAMPLE 3 Marketing Application

A popcorn producer is designing a new box for the popcorn. The marketing department has designed a box with the width 2 inches less than the length and with the height 5 inches greater than the length. The volume of each box must be 24 cubic inches. What is the length of the box?

x + 5
José's Popcorn Pop
x
x − 2

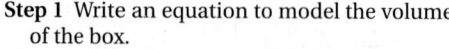

Step 1 Write an equation to model the volume of the box.

Let x represent the length in inches. Then the width is $x - 2$, and the height is $x + 5$.

$x(x-2)(x+5) = 24$ — *$V = \ell wh$.*

$x^3 + 3x^2 - 10x = 24$ — *Multiply the left side.*

$x^3 + 3x^2 - 10x - 24 = 0$ — *Set the equation equal to 0.*

Step 2 Use the Rational Root Theorem to identify all possible rational roots.

Factors of −24: ±1, ±2, ±3, ±4, ±6, ±8, ±12, ±24

Helpful Hint

In Example 3, substitute 3 for x to check your (answer).

$x(x-2)(x+5)$	$=24$
$3(3-2)(3+5)$	24
$3(1)(8)$	24
24	24 ✓

Step 3 Test the possible roots to find one that is actually a root. The length must be positive, so try only positive rational roots.

$\frac{p}{q}$	1	3	−10	−24
1	1	4	−6	−30
2	1	5	0	−24
3	1	6	8	0
4	1	7	18	48

Use a synthetic substitution table to organize your work. The first row represents the coefficients of the polynomial. The first column represents the divisors and the last column represents the remainders. Test divisors to identify at least one root.

Step 4 Factor the polynomial. The synthetic substitution of 3 results in a remainder of 0, so 3 is a root and the polynomial in factored form is $(x-3)(x^2+6x+8)$.

$(x-3)(x^2+6x+8) = 0$ — *Set the equation equal to 0.*

$(x-3)(x+2)(x+4) = 0$ — *Factor $x^2 + 6x + 8$.*

$x = 3, x = -2, \text{ or } x = -4$ — *Set each factor equal to 0, and solve.*

The length must be positive, so the length should be 3 inches.

Check Substitute 3 for x in the formula for volume.

$x(x-2)(x+5) = 24$

$3(3-2)(3+5) = 24$

$24 = 24$ ✓

3. A shipping crate must hold 12 cubic feet. The width should be 1 foot less than the length, and the height should be 4 feet greater than the length. What should the length of the crate be? **2 ft**

Polynomial equations may also have irrational roots.

Irrational Root Theorem

If the polynomial $P(x)$ has rational coefficients and $a + b\sqrt{c}$ is a root of the polynomial equation $P(x) = 0$, where a and b are rational and $\sqrt{c}$ is irrational, then $a - b\sqrt{c}$ is also a root of $P(x) = 0$.

The Irrational Root Theorem says that irrational roots of the form $a + b\sqrt{c}$ come in conjugate pairs. For example, if you know that $1 + \sqrt{2}$ is a root of $x^3 - x^2 - 3x - 1 = 0$, then you know that $1 - \sqrt{2}$ is also a root.

Recall that the real numbers are made up of the rational and the irrational numbers. You can use the Rational Root Theorem and the Irrational Root Theorem together to find *all* of the real roots of $P(x) = 0$.

EXAMPLE 4 **Identifying All of the Real Roots of a Polynomial Equation**

Identify all of the real roots of $4x^4 - 21x^3 + 18x^2 + 19x - 6 = 0$.

Step 1 Use the Rational Root Theorem to identify possible rational roots.

$$\frac{\pm 1, \pm 2, \pm 3, \pm 6}{\pm 1, \pm 2, \pm 4} = \pm 1, \pm 2, \pm 3, \pm 6, \pm \frac{1}{2}, \pm \frac{3}{2}, \pm \frac{1}{4}, \pm \frac{3}{4}$$ *$p = -6$ and $q = 4$*

Step 2 Graph $y = 4x^4 - 21x^3 + 18x^2 + 19x - 6$ to find the x-intercepts.

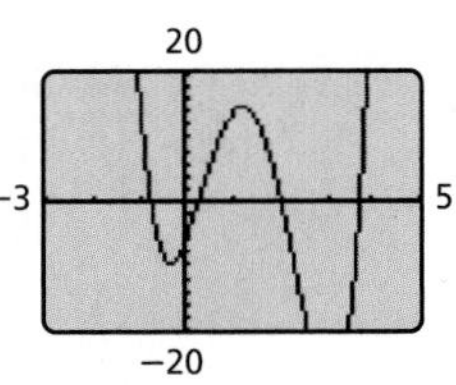

The x-intercepts are located at or near -0.75, 0.27, 2, and 3.73. The x-intercepts 0.27 and 3.73 do not correspond to any of the possible rational roots.

Helpful Hint

In Example 4, the x-intercepts 0.27 and 3.73 correspond to the irrational roots $2 - \sqrt{3}$ and $2 + \sqrt{3}$.

Step 3 Test the possible rational roots 2 and $-\frac{3}{4}$.

2	4	−21	18	19	−6
		8	−26	−16	6
	4	−13	−8	3	0

Test 2. The remainder is 0, so $(x - 2)$ is a factor.

The polynomial factors into $(x - 2)(4x^3 - 13x^2 - 8x + 3)$.

$-\frac{3}{4}$	4	−13	−8	3
		−3	12	−3
	4	−16	4	0

Test $-\frac{3}{4}$ in the cubic polynomial. The remainder is 0, so $\left(x + \frac{3}{4}\right)$ is a factor.

The polynomial factors into $(x - 2)\left(x + \frac{3}{4}\right)(4x^2 - 16x + 4)$.

Step 4 Solve $4x^2 - 16x + 4 = 0$ to find the remaining roots.

$4(x^2 - 4x + 1) = 0$ *Factor out the GCF of 4.*

$x = \frac{4 \pm \sqrt{16 - 4}}{2} = 2 \pm \sqrt{3}$ *Use the quadratic formula to identify the irrational roots.*

The fully factored equation is $4(x-2)\left(x+\frac{3}{4}\right)\left[x-(2+\sqrt{3})\right]\left[x-(2-\sqrt{3})\right]=0$.

The roots are 2, $-\frac{3}{4}$, $2 + \sqrt{3}$, and $2 - \sqrt{3}$.

4. Identify all of the real roots of $2x^3 - 3x^2 - 10x - 4 = 0$.

$x = -\frac{1}{2}, 1 \pm \sqrt{5}$

COMMON ERROR ALERT

Students might stop factoring after finding only one root of a polynomial equation. For example, after using the Rational Root Theorem to factor a polynomial into $(x - 3)(x^2 + 6x + 8)$, students might find only the root 3. Remind students that they must continue using the methods they know to try to completely factor the polynomial.

Power Presentations with PowerPoint®

Additional Examples

Example 4

Identify all the real roots of $2x^3 - 9x^2 + 2 = 0$.

$\frac{1}{2}, 2 + \sqrt{6}, 2 - \sqrt{6}$

Also available on transparency

INTERVENTION

Questioning Strategies

EXAMPLE 4

- How can you use a graph to help you decide which of the possible roots to try?
- How do you test the possible root after choosing it?

3 Close

Summarize

Ask students to list the steps they should follow to identify all the real roots of a polynomial equation. 1. Use the Rational Root Theorem to identify rational roots. 2. Graph the equation to find the x-intercepts. 3. Test the possible rational roots.

ONGOING ASSESSMENT and INTERVENTION

***Diagnose* Before the Lesson**
6-5 Warm Up, TE p. 438

***Monitor* During the Lesson**
Check It Out! Exercises, SE pp. 438–441
Questioning Strategies, TE pp. 439–441

***Assess* After the Lesson**
6-5 Lesson Quiz, TE p. 444
Alternative Assessment, TE p. 444

Answers to *Think and Discuss*

1. Possible answer: The multiplicity of a root is equal to the number of times the factor corresponding to the root appears in the factored form of the equation.
2. See p. A8.

THINK AND DISCUSS

1. Explain how to recognize the multiplicity of a root of a polynomial in factored form.
2. **GET ORGANIZED** Copy and complete the graphic organizer. Give roots that satisfy each theorem and write a polynomial equation that has those roots.

Theorem	Roots	Polynomial
Rational Root Theorem		
Irrational Root Theorem		

6-5 Exercises

Assignment Guide

Assign *Guided Practice* exercises as necessary.

If you finished Examples **1–2**
Basic 14–21
Average 14–21, 27
Advanced 14–21, 27

If you finished Examples **1–4**
Basic 15–28, 36, 40–43, 48–54
Average 15–26, 27, 29–43, 46–54
Advanced 16–26 even, 27, 35–54

Homework Quick Check
Quickly check key concepts.
Exercises: 20, 22–24, 27

6-5 Exercises

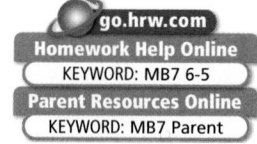

go.hrw.com
Homework Help Online
KEYWORD: MB7 6-5
Parent Resources Online
KEYWORD: MB7 Parent

GUIDED PRACTICE

1. **Vocabulary** Explain how *multiplicity* is related to the word *multiple.* Possible answer: A root with a multiplicity greater than 1 appears as a factor multiple times.

SEE EXAMPLE 1 p. 438

Solve each polynomial equation by factoring.

2. $2x^4 + 16x^3 + 32x^2 = 0$ $0, -4$
3. $x^4 - 37x^2 + 36 = 0$ $6, -6, 1, -1$
4. $4x^7 - 28x^6 = -48x^5$ $0, 3, 4$
5. $3x^4 + 11x^3 = 4x^2$ $0, \frac{1}{3}, -4$
6. $2x^3 - 12x^2 = 32x - 192$ $-4, 4, 6$
7. $x^4 + 100 = 29x^2$ $-5, -2, 2, 5$

SEE EXAMPLE 2 p. 439

Identify the roots of each equation. State the multiplicity of each root.

8. $2x^5 + 12x^4 + 16x^3 - 12x^2 - 18x = 0$ 8. -3 with multiplicity 2; $-1, 0, 1$ with multiplicity 1
9. $x^6 - 12x^4 + 48x^2 - 64 = 0$ $-2, 2$ with multiplicity 3

SEE EXAMPLE 3 p. 440

10. **Storage** A cedar chest has a length that is 3 feet longer than its width and a height that is 1 foot longer than its width. The volume of the chest is 30 cubic feet. What is the width? 2 ft

SEE EXAMPLE 4 p. 440

Identify all of the real roots of each equation.

11. $x^3 + 6x^2 - 5x - 30 = 0$ $-6, \pm\sqrt{5}$
12. $3x^3 - 18x^2 - 9x + 132 = 0$ $4, 1 \pm 2\sqrt{3}$
13. $2x^3 - 42x + 40 = 0$ $-5, 1, 4$
14. $x^4 - 9x^2 + 20 = 0$ $\pm 2, \pm\sqrt{5}$

PRACTICE AND PROBLEM SOLVING

Independent Practice	
For Exercises	See Example
15–20	1
21–22	2
23	3
24–26	4

Extra Practice
Skills Practice p. S14
Application Practice p. S37

Solve each polynomial equation by factoring.

15. $x^3 + 3x^2 - 9x = 27$ $-3, 3$
16. $4x^5 - 8x^3 + 4x = 0$ $-1, 0, 1$
17. $10x^3 - 640x = 0$ $-8, 0, 8$
18. $x^4 - 12x^2 = -36$ $\pm\sqrt{6}$
19. $2x^3 - 5x^2 - 4x + 10 = 0$ 19. $x = \frac{5}{2}, \pm\sqrt{2}$
20. $4x^3 + 7x^2 - 5x = 6$ $-2, -\frac{3}{4}, 1$

Identify the roots of each equation. State the multiplicity of each root.

21. $8x^5 - 192x^4 + 1536x^3 - 4096x^2 = 0$ 0 with multiplicity 2; 8 with multiplicity 3
22. $x^4 + 2x^3 - 11x^2 - 12x + 36 = 0$ $-3, 2$ with multiplicity 2
23. **Measurement** An open box is to be made from a square piece of material with a side length of 10 inches by cutting equal squares from the corners and turning up the sides. What size of square would you cut out if the volume of the box must be 48 cubic inches? 3 in. by 3 in.

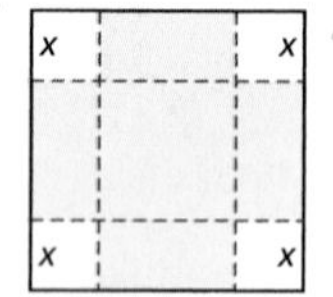

State Resources

6-5 READING STRATEGIES

To find an equation's roots, you must perform two operations: First, factor the expression. Second, set the factors equal to zero. When a linear factor, such as $x - 3$, appears more than once, then 3 is a multiple root of the equation. You can find the multiplicity of any root, r, by counting the number of times the factor $x - r$ appears in the polynomial.

Polynomial Equation	Step 1: Factor.	Step 2: Set factors equal to 0.	Multiplicity
$x^3 + 8x^2 + 16x = 0$	$x(x + 4)(x + 4)$	Root 1: $x + 4 = 0$; $x = -4$ Root 2: $x = 0$	2 1

If -4 and 0 are real roots of the polynomial $P(x) = x^3 + 8x^2 + 16x$, then $P(-4) = 0$ and $P(0) = 0$. From the roots of a polynomial function, you can find its factors.

Answer each question.

1. How can you check if a number is a root of a polynomial function?
Substitute the value of the root in the function and see if it equals 0.
2. In a polynomial function, $P(3) = 0$ and $P(-2) = 0$. Find two factors of the polynomial.
$(x - 3)$ and $(x + 2)$
3. A polynomial equation has a multiple root -4. Its multiplicity is 3.
a. Write the factor that corresponds to this root. $(x + 4)$
b. How many times is this a factor of the polynomial? 3 times

Complete the table.

	Polynomial Equation	Factors	Roots
4.	$4x(x^2 - 9) = 0$	$4x, (x - 3), (x + 3)$	$-3, 0, 3$
5.	$-x(x^2 - 6x + 5) = 0$	$-x, (x - 5), (x - 1)$	$0, 1, 5$
6.	$(x + 2)(x^2 - 4) = 0$	$(x + 2), (x + 2), (x - 2)$	$-2, 2$

6-5 RETEACH

To find the roots of a polynomial equation, set the equation equal to zero. Factor the polynomial expression completely. Then set each factor equal to zero to solve for the variable.

Solve the equation: $2x^5 + 6x^4 = 8x^3$.

Step 1 To set the equation equal to 0, rearrange the equation so that all the terms are on one side.
$2x^5 + 6x^4 = 8x^3$
$2x^5 + 6x^4 - 8x^3 = 0$

Step 2 Look for the greatest number and the greatest power of x that can be factored from each term.
$2x^5 + 6x^4 - 8x^3 = 0$ — The GCF is $2x^3$.
$2x^3(x^2 + 3x - 4) = 0$

Step 3 Factor the quadratic.
$2x^3(x^2 + 3x - 4) = 0$
$2x^3(x + 4)(x - 1) = 0.$

Step 4 Set each factor equal to 0.
$2x^3 = 0$ $x + 4 = 0$ $x - 1 = 0$

Step 5 Solve each equation.
$2x^3 = 0$ $x + 4 = 0$ $x - 1 = 0$
$x = 0$ $x = -4$ $x = 1$

The solutions of the equation are called the roots.
The roots are -4, 0, and 1.

Solve each polynomial equation.

1. $3x^6 - 9x^5 = 30x^4$
$3x^6 - 9x^5 - 30x^4 = 0$
$3x^4(x^2 - 3x - 10) = 0$
$3x^4(x - 5)(x + 2)$
$-2, 0, 5$
2. $x^4 + 6x^2 = 5x^3$
$x^4 - 5x^3 + 6x^2 = 0$
$x^2(x^2 - 5x + 6)$
$x^2(x - 2)(x - 3)$
$0, 2, 3$
3. $2x^3 - 6x^2 - 36x = 0$
$2x(x^2 - 3x - 18)$
$2x(x - 6)(x + 3)$
$-3, 0, 6$
4. $2x^6 - 32x^4 = 0$
$2x^4(x^2 - 16)$
$2x^4(x + 4)(x - 4)$
$-4, 0, 4$

Identify all of the real roots of each equation.

24. $x^4 - 3x^2 - 4 = 0$ $x = -2, 2$ **25.** $3x^3 + 4x^2 - 6x - 8 = 0$ **26.** $x^4 - 2x^3 - 2x^2 = 0$

27. Graphing Calculator Consider the polynomial function $f(x) = x^4 + 3x^3 - 3x^2 - 12x - 4$.

a. Use the Rational Root Theorem to list the possible rational roots of this equation. $\pm 1, \pm 2, \pm 4$

b. Graph the polynomial on a graphing calculator. Which possible rational roots are zeros of $f(x)$? $x = -2, 2$

c. According to the graph, how many other real zeros does the function have? 2

d. Approximate these zeros to the nearest hundredth by using the zero feature.

25. $x = -\frac{4}{3}, \pm\sqrt{2}$

26. $x = 0, 1 \pm \sqrt{3}$

27d. $x = -2.62, -0.38$

28. Multi-Step A manufacturing company must design a box that holds 55 cubic inches. The width must be 4 inches less than the length, and the height must be 10 inches greater than the width.

a. Let the length equal $x + 1$, and write expressions in x for the width and height of the box. Possible answer: width $= x - 3$ and height $= x + 7$

b. Write a polynomial equation to represent the volume of the box.

c. Identify all possible rational roots of the equation $V(x) = 55$.

d. Factor the polynomial. What are the roots of the equation? $x = 4, -\frac{9}{2} \pm \frac{\sqrt{5}}{2}$

e. What are the dimensions of the box? 5 in. × 1 in. × 11 in.

28b. $V(x) = x^3 + 5x^2 - 17x - 21$

28c. $\pm 1, \pm 2, \pm 4, \pm 19, \pm 38, \pm 76$

34. $x = 9, \frac{5}{2} \pm \frac{\sqrt{29}}{2}$

32. $x = -\frac{1}{3}, 2, 3 \pm 2\sqrt{3}$

Identify all of the real roots of each equation.

29. $x^3 - 7x^2 + 14x - 6 = 0$ $x = 3, 2 \pm \sqrt{2}$

30. $\frac{5}{3}x^3 + \frac{8}{3}x^2 - \frac{4}{3}x = 0$ $x = -2, 0, \frac{2}{5}$

31. $x^4 - x^3 - 31x^2 + 25x + 150 = 0$ $x = -5, -2, 3, 5$

32. $3x^4 + 19x^2 + 27x + 6 = 23x^3$

33. $x^5 - 4x^4 - 2x^3 + 4x^2 + x = 0$ $x = -1, 0, 1, 2 \pm \sqrt{5}$

34. $x^3 + 9 - 6x^2 = -4(11x - 2x^2)$

LINK

Entertainment

The SheiKra roller coaster at Busch Gardens in Tampa is Florida's tallest roller coaster and includes a 138 ft dive into an underground tunnel.

35. Entertainment The paths of some roller coasters may be modeled by a polynomial function, where t is the time, in tens of seconds, after the ride has started and $h(t)$ is the height, in feet. Some roller coasters go underground as well as above the ground. In factored form, the beginning part of one roller-coaster ride can be modeled by the function $h(t) = \frac{1}{4}(t - 2)(t - 4)(t - 7)(t - 9)$.

a. What is the starting height of this roller coaster? 126 ft

b. Graph this function on your graphing calculator, and describe the path of the roller coaster for the first 100 seconds.

c. Write an equation of a polynomial function that can be used to model a portion of a roller-coaster ride when the coaster starts 45 feet above the ground, enters an underground tunnel after 30 seconds, and then emerges from underground 20 seconds later. Possible answer: $h(t) = 3(t - 3)(t - 5)$

MULTI-STEP TEST PREP

36. This problem will prepare you for the Multi-Step Test Prep on page 472.

A type of cheese is packaged in a cardboard box shaped like a pyramid. As shown in the figure, the height is 2 cm greater than the length of the base.

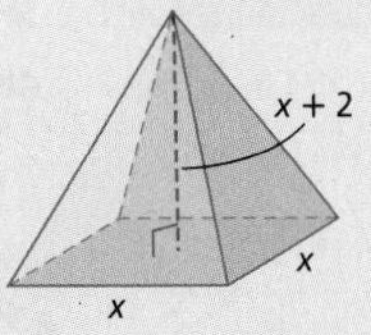

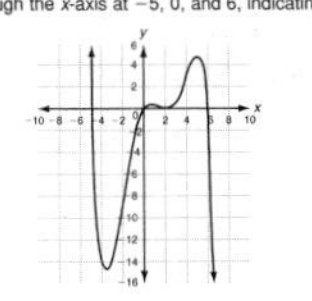

a. Write a polynomial function for the volume of the box.

b. The volume of the box must be 147 cm³. Write a polynomial equation with integer coefficients that you can solve in order to find the length of the base.

c. What are the dimensions of the box? 7 cm × 7 cm × 9 cm

36a. $V(x) = \frac{1}{3}x^3 + \frac{2}{3}x^2$

36b. $x^3 + 2x^2 - 441 = 0$

COMMON ERROR ALERT

In **Exercise 30,** students might encounter difficulties if they attempt to use the Rational Root Theorem to solve before factoring out the GCF, $\frac{1}{3}x$. Remind students to always check for a GCF before they use other methods to factor.

Reading Math Alert students to be careful with units in **Exercise 35.** Time is in 10-second intervals.

Exercise 36 involves using the volume of a square pyramid to find the length of its base. This exercise prepares students for the Multi-Step Test Prep on page 472.

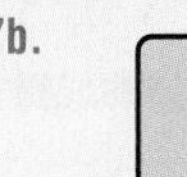

Geometry Students will need the formula for the volume of a square pyramid $\left(V = \frac{1}{3}Bh\right)$ to complete **Exercise 36.**

Answers

27b.

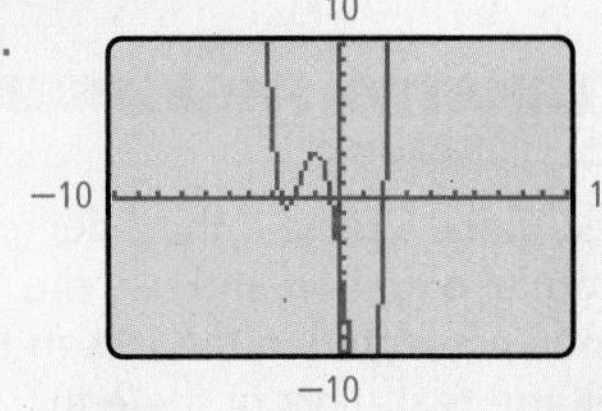

35b. The coaster passes through 2 tunnels within the first 100 s.

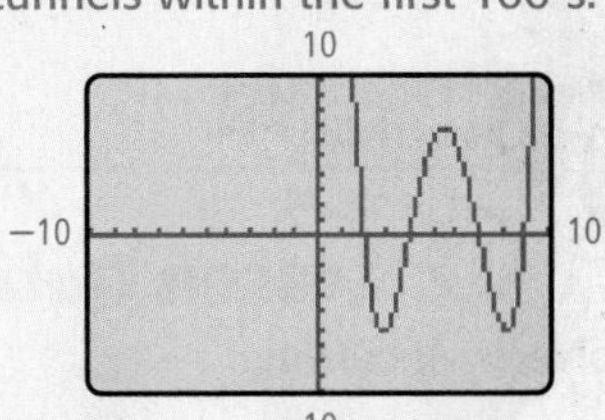

6-5 PROBLEM SOLVING

Most airlines have rules concerning the size of checked baggage. The rules for Budget Airline are such that the dimensions of the largest bag cannot exceed 45 in. by 55 in. by 62 in. A designer is drawing plans for a piece of luggage that athletes can use to carry their equipment. It will have a volume of 76,725 cubic inches. The length is 10 in. greater than the width and the depth is 14 in. less than the width. What are the dimensions of this piece of luggage?

1. Write an equation in factored form to model the volume of the piece of luggage.
$V = w(w + 10)(w - 14)$

2. Multiply and set the equation equal to zero.
$w^3 - 4w^2 - 140w - 76{,}725 = 0$

3. Think about possible roots of the equation. Could a root be a multiple of 4? No a multiple of 5? yes a multiple of 10? no. How do you know?
The constant term is 76,725, which is not a multiple of 4 or 10, but is a multiple of 5.

4. Use synthetic substitution to test possible roots. Choose positive integers that are factors of the constant term and reasonable in the context of the problem. Possible answers

Possible Root	1	−4	−140	−76,725
5	1	1	−135	−77,400
25	1	21	385	−67,100
45	1	41	1705	0

Students should test possible roots that are multiples of 5 but not multiples of 10, such as 35, 45, and 55.

Choose the letter for the best answer.

5. Which equation represents the factored polynomial?
A $(w + 55)(w^2 + 25w + 1550) = 0$
B $(w - 35)(w^2 + 60w + 1405) = 0$
(C) $(w - 45)(w^2 + 41w + 1705) = 0$
D $(w - 4)(w^2 - 140w + 76{,}725) = 0$

6. Which could be the dimensions of this piece of luggage?
(A) 31 in. by 45 in. by 55 in.
B 45 in. by 55 in. by 55 in.
C 45 in. by 45 in. by 55 in.
D 45 in. by 55 in. by 62 in.

6-5 CHALLENGE

Solving a polynomial equation means to find the roots of the equation. The multiplicity of each root determines whether the graph of the equation crosses the x-axis or just touches the x-axis.

The graph at left below shows x-intercepts of −5, 0, 2, and 6. The curve just touches the x-axis at 2, indicating an even multiplicity, and passes through the x-axis at −5, 0, and 6, indicating an odd multiplicity.

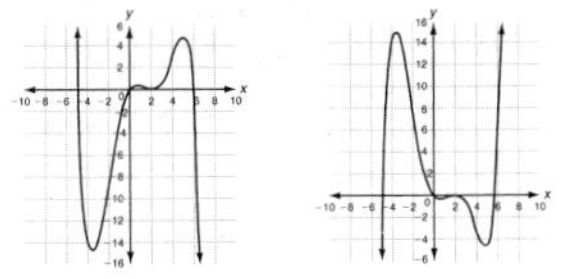

An equation for this polynomial function is
$y = 0.01(x + 5)(x)(x - 2)^2(x - 6)$.
Graphing this function gives the graph at right above. It is the reflection across the x-axis of the graph at left. To reflect a graph across the x-axis, replace each y with $-y$, which gives the polynomial function
$y = -[0.01(x + 5)(x)(x - 2)^2(x - 6)]$.

Write a possible polynomial function whose graph fits the given conditions.

1. Crosses the x-axis at −3, 0, and 4; lies above the x-axis between −3 and 0; and lies below the x-axis between 0 and 4 — $y = (x + 3)(x)(x - 4)$

2. Touches the x-axis at −1, crosses the x-axis at 1 and 3, and lies above the x-axis between 1 and 3 — $y = -(x + 1)^2(x - 1)(x - 3)$

3. Has x-intercepts of −5, −2, $\frac{1}{2}$, and 3; lies above the x-axis between −5 and −2 and also between −2 and $\frac{1}{2}$ but lies below the x-axis between $\frac{1}{2}$ and 3 — $y = (x + 5)(x + 2)^2\left(x - \frac{1}{2}\right)(x - 3)$

4. Has x-intercepts of −6, 0, 1, 3, and 4; lies above the x-axis at all points between the x-intercepts except on the interval from 0 to 1 — $y = (x + 6)^2(x)(x - 1)(x - 3)^2(x - 4)^2$

5. Real coefficients, roots $-3i$, 1, and $1 + \sqrt{3}$; and touches the x-axis at 1 — $y = (x + 3i)(x - 3i)(x - 1)^2(x - (1 + \sqrt{3}))(x + (1 + \sqrt{3}))$

6-5 PRACTICE A
6-5 PRACTICE C
6-5 PRACTICE B

Solve each polynomial equation by factoring.

1. $9x^3 - 3x^2 - 3x + 1 = 0$ — $\frac{1}{3}, \frac{\sqrt{3}}{3}, -\frac{\sqrt{3}}{3}$

2. $x^5 - 2x^4 - 24x^3 = 0$ — $-4, 0, 6$

3. $3x^5 + 18x^4 - 21x^3 = 0$ — $-7, 0, 1$

4. $-x^4 + 2x^3 + 8x^2 = 0$ — $-2, 0, 4$

Identify the roots of each equation. State the multiplicity of each root.

5. $x^3 + 3x^2 + 3x + 1 = 0$ — $x = -1$ with multiplicity 3

6. $x^3 + 5x^2 - 8x - 48 = 0$ — $x = 3$ with multiplicity 1; $x = -4$ with multiplicity 2

Identify all the real roots of each equation.

7. $x^3 + 10x^2 + 17x = 28$ — $-4, 1, -7$

8. $3x^3 + 10x^2 - 27x = 10$ — $-5, -\frac{1}{3}, 2$

Solve.

9. An engineer is designing a storage compartment in a spacecraft. The compartment must be 2 meters longer than it is wide and its depth must be 1 meter less than its width. The volume of the compartment must be 8 cubic meters.

a. Write an equation to model the volume of the compartment. $x^3 + x^2 - 2x - 8 = 0$

b. List all possible rational roots. $\pm 1, \pm 2, \pm 4, \pm 8$

c. Use synthetic division to find the roots of the polynomial equation. Are the roots all rational numbers? $2, \frac{-3 \pm i\sqrt{7}}{2}$; no, 2 of the roots are irrational numbers.

d. What are the dimensions of the storage compartment? 2 m wide, 4 m long, and 1 m deep

TEST PREP DOCTOR In Exercise 39, all answer choices have 2 as a root. Students should factor out $x - 2$ and then examine the quadratic. Students who chose **C** or **D** applied the Rational Root Theorem incorrectly. Students who chose **A** made an error when using the quadratic formula.

Journal

Have students state the Rational Root Theorem and the Irrational Root Theorem in their own words.

ALTERNATIVE ASSESSMENT

Have students create a third-degree polynomial equation and use the methods presented in the lesson to find all the real roots of the equation. Students should also state the multiplicity of each root.

Power Presentations with PowerPoint®

6-5 Lesson Quiz

Solve by factoring.

1. $x^3 + 9 = x^2 + 9x$ $-3, 3, 1$

Identify the roots of each equation. State the multiplicity of each root.

2. $5x^4 - 20x^3 + 20x^2 = 0$
   0 and 2 each with multiplicity 2
3. $x^3 - 12x^2 + 48x - 64 = 0$
   4 with multiplicity 3
4. A box is 2 inches longer than its height. The width is 2 inches less than the height. The volume of the box is 15 cubic inches. How tall is the box? 3 in.
5. Identify all the real roots of $x^3 + 5x^2 - 3x - 3 = 0$.
   $1, -3 + \sqrt{6}, -3 - \sqrt{6}$

Also available on transparency

37. **Critical Thinking** Suppose you are looking at a graph to identify which possible rational roots correspond to zeros. You see an x-intercept near 4. You have 4 as a possible rational root, but $P(4) \neq 0$. What can you say about the zero that you located on the graph?
38. **Write About It** Graph the functions $f(x) = (x - 2)^2(x + 2)^3$, $g(x) = (x - 2)^2$, and $h(x) = (x + 2)^3$ on your graphing calculator. How does the behavior of f compare to the behavior of g near $x = 2$? How does the behavior of f compare to the behavior of h near $x = -2$? Explain.
39. **Write About It** How does the graph of $5x^4 - 20x^3$ behave near $(0, 0)$? How can you determine the behavior by factoring the expression? **Possible answer: The graph bends near (0, 0). Since $5x^4 - 20x^3 = 5x^3(x - 4)$, 0 is a root with multiplicity 3, and roots with odd multiplicities have this behavior when graphed.**

TEST PREP

40. Find the solutions to the equation $8x^3 - 2x^2 - 43x + 30 = 0$.
    (A) 2 and $\frac{-7 \pm \sqrt{42}}{8}$ (B) $2, -\frac{5}{2}$, and $\frac{3}{4}$ (C) 2, 15, and 1 (D) 1, 2, and -3
41. How many real zeros does the polynomial $f(x) = 4x^2 - 3x + 2x^4 - 5x^3 - 7$ have?
    (F) 2 (G) 3 (H) 4 (J) 5
42. Which of the following is NOT a factor of $g(x) = 6x^3 + 13x^2 - 4$?
    (A) $x + 2$ (B) $2x - 1$ (C) $x - 3$ (D) $3x + 2$
43. Use the graph shown at right to identify the multiplicity of the roots of $f(x) = 0$.
    (F) Root 2 with a multiplicity of 1
    (G) Root 2 with a multiplicity of 2
    (H) Root 1 with a multiplicity of 2
    (J) Root 1 with a multiplicity of 3

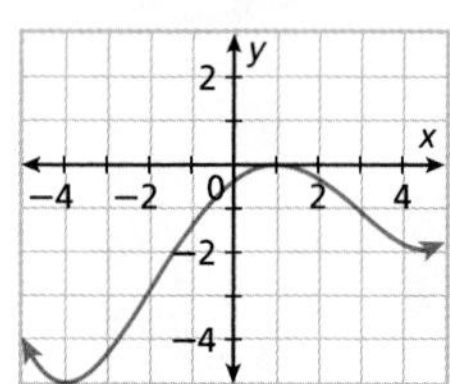

CHALLENGE AND EXTEND

44. Give a polynomial function that has the zeros 0, 1, and $3 - \sqrt{5}$.
    $f(x) = x^4 - 7x^3 + 10x^2 - 4x$

Identify the value of k that makes the x-value a solution to the cubic equation.

45. $x^3 + 3x^2 - x + k = 0; x = 2$ -18
46. $kx^3 - 2x^2 + x - 6 = 0; x = -3$ -1
47. $6x^3 - 23x^2 - kx + 8 = 0; x = 4$ 6

SPIRAL REVIEW

48. **Physics** A water balloon is dropped from the top of an 85-foot-tall building. The height of the water balloon in feet after t seconds is modeled by $h(t) = 85 - 16t^2$. What is the height of the water balloon after 2 seconds? *(Lesson 5-3)* **21 ft**

Solve each inequality by using algebra. *(Lesson 5-7)*

49. $x^2 + x + 5 > 11$ $x < -3$ or $x > 2$
50. $x^2 - 10x + 2 \leq -23$ $x = 5$
51. $x^2 < 1$ $-1 < x < 1$

Factor each expression. *(Lesson 6-4)*

52. $x^3 + 3x^2 - 4x - 12$ $(x + 2)(x - 2)(x + 3)$
53. $8x^3 + 4x^2 - 8x - 4$ $4(2x + 1)(x + 1)(x - 1)$
54. $x^3 + 27$ $(x + 3)(x^2 - 3x + 9)$

Answers

37. Possible answer: The zero on the graph does not represent a rational root of the related equation. $P(4)$ must equal 0 in order for the root to correspond to a zero at $x = 4$.
38. Possible answer: $x = 2$ is a root with a multiplicity of 2 for both f and g. The graphs of f and g each intersect the x-axis at $(2, 0)$ but do not cross it. $x = -2$ is a root with a multiplicity of 3 for both f and h. The graphs of f and h each bend at the intersection with the x-axis at $(-2, 0)$.

6-6 Fundamental Theorem of Algebra

A2.4.7 Find a polynomial function of lowest degree with real coefficients given its roots and use the relationship between solutions of an equation, zeros of a . . . function, x-intercepts of a graph and factors of a polynomial expression to solve problems.

Objectives
Use the Fundamental Theorem of Algebra and its corollary to write a polynomial equation of least degree with given roots.

Identify all of the roots of a polynomial equation.

Who uses this?
Aerospace engineers may find roots of polynomial equations to determine dimensions of rockets. (See Example 4.)

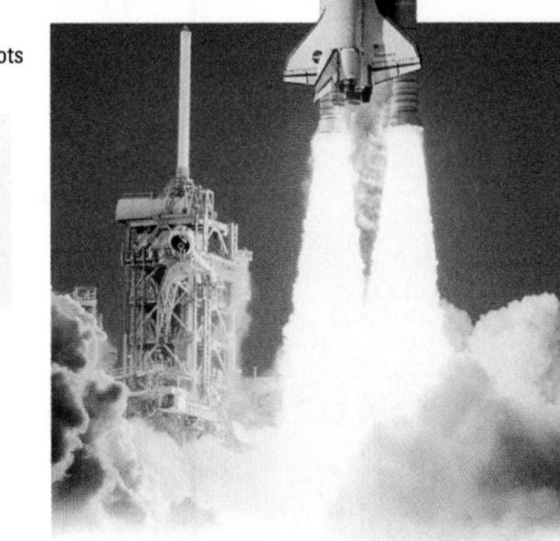

You have learned several important properties about real roots of polynomial equations.

Know it! Note

The following statements are equivalent:
A real number r is a root of the polynomial equation $P(x) = 0$.
$P(r) = 0$
r is an x-intercept of the graph of $P(x)$.
$x - r$ is a factor of $P(x)$.
When you divide the rule for $P(x)$ by $x - r$, the remainder is 0.
r is a zero of $P(x)$.

You can use this information to write a polynomial function when given its zeros.

EXAMPLE 1 Writing Polynomial Functions Given Zeros

Write the simplest polynomial function with zeros $-3, \frac{1}{2}$, and 1.

$P(x) = (x+3)\left(x-\frac{1}{2}\right)(x-1)$ *If r is a zero of $P(x)$, then $x - r$ is a factor of $P(x)$.*

$P(x) = \left(x^2+\frac{5}{2}x-\frac{3}{2}\right)(x-1)$ *Multiply the first two binomials.*

$P(x) = x^3 + \frac{3}{2}x^2 - 4x + \frac{3}{2}$ *Multiply the trinomial by the binomial.*

$P(x) = x^3 + \frac{3}{2}x^2 - 4x + \frac{3}{2}$

Write the simplest polynomial function with the given zeros.

1a. $-2, 2, 4$ $P(x) = x^3 - 4x^2 - 4x + 16$

1b. $0, \frac{2}{3}, 3$ $P(x) = x^3 - \frac{11}{3}x^2 + 2x$

Notice that the degree of the function in Example 1 is the same as the number of zeros. This is true for all polynomial functions. However, all of the zeros are not necessarily real zeros. Polynomial functions, like quadratic functions, may have complex zeros that are not real numbers.

6-6 Organizer

Pacing: Traditional 2 days
Block 1 day

Objectives: Use the Fundamental Theorem of Algebra and its corollary to write a polynomial equation of least degree with given roots.

Identify all the roots of a polynomial equation.

Online Edition
Graphing Calculator, Tutorial Videos, TechKeys

Countdown to Testing Week 14

Power Presentations with PowerPoint®

Warm Up

Identify all the real roots of each equation.

1. $4x^5 - 8x^4 - 32x^3 = 0$ $0, -2, 4$

2. $x^3 - x^2 + 9 = 9x$ $1, -3, 3$

3. $x^4 + 16 = 17x^2$ $-1, 1$ $-4, 4$

4. $3x^3 + 75x = 30x^2$ $0, 5$

Also available on transparency

Math Humor

Q: Why did the polynomial plant wilt?

A: Its roots were imaginary.

1 Introduce

EXPLORATION

6-6 Fundamental Theorem of Algebra

In this Exploration you will make a conjecture about the number of roots of a polynomial function.

1. Complete the table. Include multiplicities when finding the number of roots.

$P(x)$	Factored Form of $P(x)$	Roots of $P(x) = 0$	Number of Roots
$x^2 - 16$			
$x^3 - 5x^2 + 8x - 4$	$(x-1)(x-2)^2$		
$x^5 - x^4 - 2x^3$			
$x^4 - 9x^2$			
$x^6 - x^5 - 16x^4 - 20x^3$	$x^3(x-5)(x+2)^2$		

2. Look for a pattern in your table. How is the number of roots related to $P(x)$?

THINK AND DISCUSS

3. **Discuss** how you can make a generalization based on your findings.
4. **Explain** how you can use your generalization to make a statement about the roots of $x^{10} - 5x^7 + 12x = 0$.

Motivate

Ask students to draw some quadratic functions that have imaginary zeros on the board. Ask them how they can recognize the presence of imaginary zeros. Explain that like quadratic functions, polynomial functions can also have imaginary zeros.

Explorations and answers are provided in the *Explorations* binder.

State Resources

go.hrw.com
State Resources Online
KEYWORD: MB7 Resources

Teaching Tip

Multiple Representations Discuss with students the relationships between roots, x-intercepts, factors, solutions, remainders of zero, and zeros of functions, as summarized in the table of equivalent statements on page 445.

Power Presentations with PowerPoint®

Additional Examples

Example 1

Write the simplest polynomial equation with roots $-1, \frac{2}{3}$, and 4.

$P(x) = x^3 - \frac{11}{3}x^2 - 2x + \frac{8}{3} = 0$

Example 2

Solve
$x^4 - 3x^3 + 5x^2 - 27x - 36 = 0$
by finding all roots.

$-1, 4, 3i, -3i$

Also available on transparency

INTERVENTION

Questioning Strategies

EXAMPLE 1

- Could there be other polynomial equations with the same roots?

EXAMPLE 2

- Explain what types of roots the polynomial has.
- How can you check that the roots are correct?

The Fundamental Theorem of Algebra

Every polynomial function of degree $n \geq 1$ has at least one zero, where a zero may be a complex number.

Corollary: Every polynomial function of degree $n \geq 1$ has exactly n zeros, including multiplicities.

Using this theorem, you can write any polynomial function in factored form.

To find all roots of a polynomial equation, you can use a combination of the Rational Root Theorem, the Irrational Root Theorem, and methods for finding complex roots, such as the quadratic formula.

EXAMPLE 2 **Finding All Roots of a Polynomial Equation**

Solve $x^4 + x^3 + 2x^2 + 4x - 8 = 0$ by finding all roots.

The polynomial is of degree 4, so there are exactly four roots for the equation.

Step 1 Use the Rational Root Theorem to identify possible rational roots.

$\frac{\pm 1, \pm 2, \pm 4, \pm 8}{\pm 1} = \pm 1, \pm 2, \pm 4, \pm 8$ *$p = -8$ and $q = 1$*

Step 2 Graph $y = x^4 + x^3 + 2x^2 + 4x - 8$ to find the real roots.

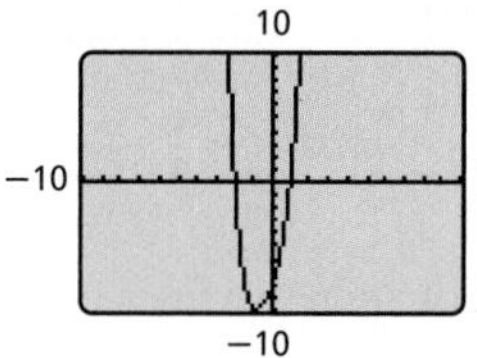

Find the real roots at or near −2 and 1.

Step 3 Test the possible real roots.

1	1	1	2	4	−8
		1	2	4	8
	1	2	4	8	0

Test 1. The remainder is 0, so $(x - 1)$ is a factor.

The polynomial factors into $(x - 1)(x^3 + 2x^2 + 4x + 8) = 0$.

−2	1	2	4	8
		−2	0	−8
	1	0	4	0

Test −2 in the cubic polynomial. The remainder is 0, so $(x + 2)$ is a factor.

The polynomial factors into $(x - 1)(x + 2)(x^2 + 4) = 0$.

Step 4 Solve $x^2 + 4 = 0$ to find the remaining roots.

$x^2 + 4 = 0$

$x^2 = -4$

$x = \pm 2i$

The fully factored form of the equation is $(x - 1)(x + 2)(x + 2i)(x - 2i) = 0$.

The solutions are 1, -2, $2i$, and $-2i$.

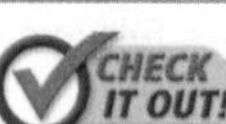

CHECK IT OUT! **2.** Solve $x^4 + 4x^3 - x^2 + 16x - 20 = 0$ by finding all roots.

$-5, 1, \pm 2i$

2 Teach

Guided Instruction

Review the multiple representations summarized in the table on page 445. Explain that the Fundamental Theorem of Algebra states that a polynomial of degree n has n roots. Point out that although the theorem tells how many roots there are, it does not give an easy method for finding the roots. Help students to formulate a systematic method for finding all the roots of a polynomial equation.

Reaching All Learners

Through Multiple Representations

Give students flashcards that have polynomial functions on them. Have them identify the number of possible roots based on the function rule and then graph on a graphing calculator to determine the number of real roots as shown by the x–intercepts.

The real numbers are a subset of the complex numbers, so a real number a can be thought of as the complex number $a + 0i$. But here the term *complex root* will only refer to a root of the form $a + bi$, where $b \neq 0$. Complex roots, like irrational roots, come in conjugate pairs. Recall from Chapter 5 that the complex conjugate of $a + bi$ is $a - bi$.

Complex Conjugate Root Theorem

If $a + bi$ is a root of a polynomial equation with real-number coefficients, then $a - bi$ is also a root.

EXAMPLE 3 **Writing a Polynomial Function with Complex Zeros**

Write the simplest polynomial function with zeros $1 + i$, $\sqrt{2}$, and -3.

Step 1 Identify all roots.

By the Irrational Root Theorem and the Complex Conjugate Root Theorem, the irrational roots and complex roots come in conjugate pairs. There are five roots: $1 + i$, $1 - i$, $\sqrt{2}$, $-\sqrt{2}$, and -3. The polynomial must have degree 5.

Step 2 Write the equation in factored form.

$$P(x) = [x - (1 + i)][x - (1 - i)](x - \sqrt{2})[x - (-\sqrt{2})][x - (-3)]$$

Step 3 Multiply.

$$P(x) = (x^2 - 2x + 2)(x^2 - 2)(x + 3)$$
$$= (x^4 - 2x^3 + 4x - 4)(x + 3)$$
$$P(x) = x^5 + x^4 - 6x^3 + 4x^2 + 8x - 12$$

3. Write the simplest polynomial function with zeros $2i$, $1 + \sqrt{2}$, and 3.
$P(x) = x^5 - 5x^4 + 9x^3 - 17x^2 + 20x + 12$

EXAMPLE 4 ***Problem-Solving Application***

An engineering class is designing model rockets for a competition. The body of the rocket must be cylindrical with a cone-shaped top. The cylinder part must be 60 cm tall, and the height of the cone must be twice the radius. The volume of the payload region must be 558π cm³ in order to hold the cargo. Find the radius of the rocket.

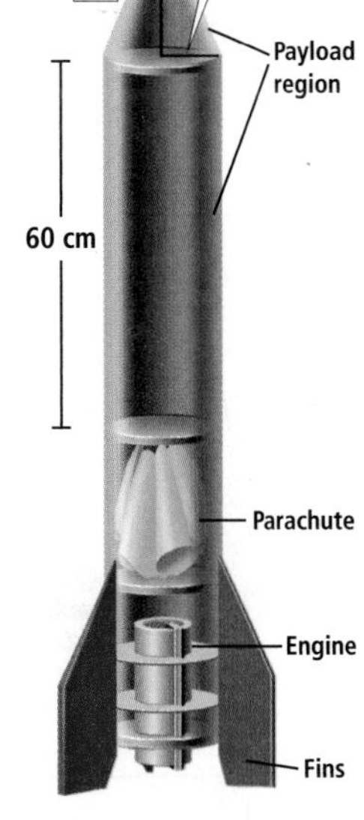

 **Understand the Problem**

The cylinder and the cone have the same radius, x. The answer will be the value of x.

List the important information:

- The cylinder is 60 cm tall.
- The height of the cone part is twice the radius, $2x$.
- The volume of the payload region is 558π cm³.

COMMON ERROR ALERT

Students sometimes have difficulty with the extensive multiplication required in problems such as **Example 4** to change an equation from factored form to standard form. Suggest that students first look for conjugate pairs to multiply. Stress the importance of systematically multiplying all the factors, especially as the degree and the number of terms increase.

Power Presentations with PowerPoint®

Additional Examples

Example 3

Write the simplest polynomial function with zeros $2 + i$, $\sqrt{3}$, and 1.

$P(x) = x^5 - 5x^4 + 6x^3 + 10x^2 - 27x + 15$

Example 4

A silo is in the shape of a cylinder with a cone-shaped top. The cylinder is 20 feet tall. The height of the cone is 1.5 times the radius. The volume of the silo is 828π cubic feet. Find the radius of the silo. 6 ft

Also available on transparency

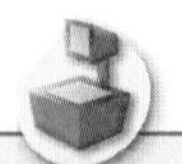

INTERVENTION

Questioning Strategies

EXAMPLE 3

- Do rational roots ever come in pairs? Explain.

EXAMPLE 4

- Why are the volumes of the cone and cylinder added?
- Why are the negative roots not reasonable solutions?

Communicating Math Have students discuss whether it is easier to create a polynomial of degree n from its roots or to find all the roots of a polynomial. Students will practice using the vocabulary and describing processes as they communicate.

ENGLISH LANGUAGE LEARNERS

Inclusion If students have difficulty understanding how to apply the Fundamental Theorem of Algebra, write examples of polynomials of different degree, circle the degree, and then use the degree to tell the number of roots for each polynomial. Discuss different combinations of rational, irrational, and complex roots that will give the appropriate number of roots.

Make a Plan

Write an equation to represent the volume of the body of the rocket.

$V = V_{\text{cone}} + V_{\text{cylinder}}$

$V(x) = \frac{2}{3}\pi x^3 + 60\pi x^2$ $\quad$ *$V_{cone} = \frac{1}{3}\pi x^2 h$ and $V_{cylinder} = \pi x^2 h$*

Set the volume equal to 558π.

$\frac{2}{3}\pi x^3 + 60\pi x^2 = 558\pi$

3 Solve

$\frac{2}{3}\pi x^3 + 60\pi x^2 - 558\pi = 0$ $\quad$ *Write in standard form.*

$\frac{2}{3}x^3 + 60x^2 - 558 = 0$ $\quad$ *Divide both sides by π.*

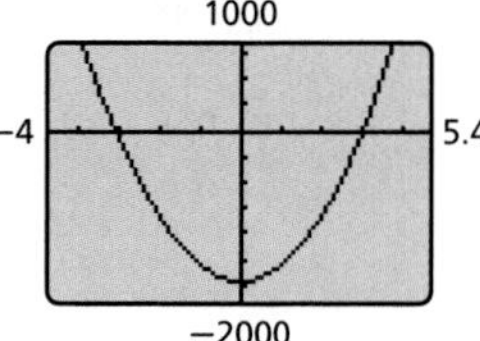

The graph indicates a possible positive root of 3. Use synthetic division to verify that 3 is a root, and write the equation as $(x - 3)\left(\frac{2}{3}x^2 + 62x + 186\right) = 0$. By the quadratic formula, you can find that −3.1 and −89.9 are approximate roots of $\frac{2}{3}x^2 + 62x + 186 = 0$. The radius must be a positive number, so the radius of the rocket is 3 cm.

3	$\frac{2}{3}$	60	0	−558
		2	186	550
	$\frac{2}{3}$	62	186	0

Look Back

Substitute 3 cm into the original equation for the volume of the rocket.

$V(3) = \frac{2}{3}\pi(3)^3 + 60\pi(3)^2$

$V(3) = 558\pi$ ✔

4. A grain silo is in the shape of a cylinder with a hemisphere top. The cylinder is 20 feet tall. The volume of the silo is 2106π cubic feet. Find the radius of the silo. **9 ft**

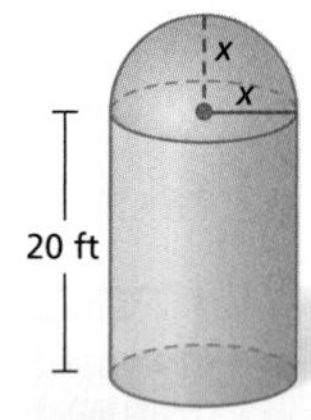

THINK AND DISCUSS

1. Explain why a polynomial equation with real coefficients and root $1 - i$ must be of degree two or greater.
2. If $P(x)$ is the product of a linear polynomial and a cubic polynomial, how many roots does $P(x) = 0$ have? Explain.

3. **GET ORGANIZED** Copy and complete the graphic organizer. Give an example of a polynomial with each type of root.

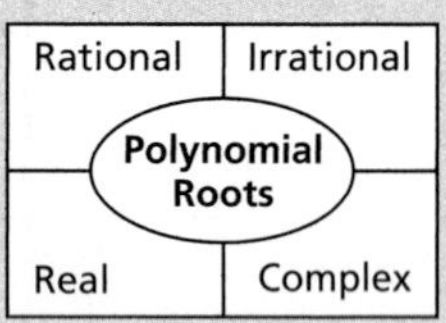

3 Close

Summarize

Ask students how to identify the number of roots of a polynomial equation. number of roots = degree of polynomial Then have them summarize how to find all the roots. 1. Use the Rational Root Theorem to identify rational roots. 2. Graph the equation to find the x-intercepts. 3. Test the possible rational roots. 4. Identify any irrational roots. 5. Identify any complex roots.

ONGOING ASSESSMENT and INTERVENTION

***Diagnose Before* the Lesson**
6-6 Warm Up, TE p. 445

***Monitor During* the Lesson**
Check It Out! Exercises, SE pp. 445–448
Questioning Strategies, TE pp. 446–447

***Assess After* the Lesson**
6-6 Lesson Quiz, TE p. 451
Alternative Assessment, TE p. 451

Answers to *Think and Discuss*

Possible answers:

1. Complex roots come in conjugate pairs for polynomial equations with real coefficients. The second root is $1 + i$, and polynomials that have at least 2 roots must have a degree of at least 2.
2. The linear polynomial has 1 root, and the cubic polynomial has 3 roots. The product will have 4 roots, of which at least 2 roots will be real.
3. See p. A8.

6-6 Exercises

go.hrw.com
Homework Help Online
KEYWORD: MB7 6-6
Parent Resources Online
KEYWORD: MB7 Parent

GUIDED PRACTICE

SEE EXAMPLE 1 p. 445

Write the simplest polynomial function with the given zeros.

1. $\frac{1}{3}, 1, 2$
2. $-2, 2, 3$ $P(x) = x^3 - 3x^2 - 4x + 12$
3. $-2, \frac{1}{2}, 2$ $P(x) = x^3 - \frac{1}{2}x^2 - 4x + 2$

SEE EXAMPLE 2 p. 446

Solve each equation by finding all roots.

4. $x^4 - 81 = 0$ $3, -3, \pm 3i$
5. $3x^3 - 10x^2 + 10x - 4 = 0$
6. $x^3 - 3x^2 + 4x - 12 = 0$ $3, \pm 2i$

SEE EXAMPLE 3 p. 447

Write the simplest polynomial function with the given zeros.

7. $1 - i$ and 2 $P(x) = x^3 - 4x^2 + 6x - 4$
8. $1 + \sqrt{5}$ and 3 $P(x) = x^3 - 5x^2 + 2x + 12$
9. $2i, \sqrt{2}$, and 2

SEE EXAMPLE 4 p. 447

10. **Farming** A grain silo is shaped like a cylinder with a cone-shaped top. The cylinder is 30 feet tall. The volume of the silo is 1152π cubic feet. Find the radius of the silo. $r = 6$

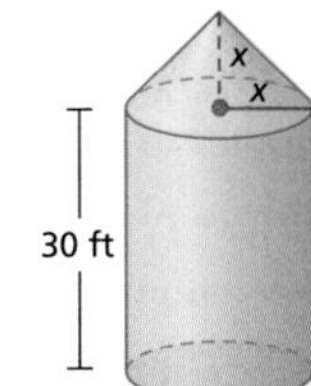

1. $P(x) = x^3 - \frac{10}{3}x^2 + 3x - \frac{2}{3}$

5. $2, \frac{2 \pm i\sqrt{2}}{3}$

PRACTICE AND PROBLEM SOLVING

Independent Practice	
For Exercises	See Example
11–13	1
14–19	2
20–22	3
23	4

Extra Practice
Skills Practice p. S15
Application Practice p. S37

Write the simplest polynomial function with the given zeros.

11. $-1, -1, 2$ $P(x) = x^3 - 3x - 2$
12. $2, 1, \frac{2}{3}$ $P(x) = x^3 - \frac{11}{3}x^2 + 4x - \frac{4}{3}$
13. $-4, -1, 2$ $P(x) = x^3 + 3x^2 - 6x - 8$

Solve each equation by finding all roots.

14. $x^4 - 16 = 0$
15. $x^3 - 7x^2 + 15x - 9 = 0$
16. $x^4 + 5x^2 - 36 = 0$ $2, -2, \pm 3i$
17. $2x^3 - 3x^2 + 8x - 12 = 0$
18. $x^4 - 5x^3 + 3x^2 + x = 0$ $0, 1, 2 \pm \sqrt{5}$
19. $x^4 - 4x^2 + 3 = 0$ $1, -1, \pm\sqrt{3}$

Write the simplest polynomial function with the given zeros.

20. $2 - i, \sqrt{3}$, and 2
21. $2\sqrt{2}, \sqrt{5}$, and -3
22. $-2i$ and $1 + i$

23. **Storage** A storage bin is shaped like a cylinder with a hemisphere-shaped top. The cylinder is 45 inches tall. The volume of the bin is 4131π cubic inches. Find the radius of the bin. 9 ft

21. $P(x) = x^5 + 3x^4 - 13x^3 - 39x^2 + 40x + 120$
22. $P(x) = x^4 - 2x^3 + 6x^2 - 8x + 8$

Solve each equation by finding all roots.

24. $x^4 - 3x^3 + 5x^2 - 27x - 36 = 0$
25. $x^4 + 4x^3 - 3x^2 - 14x - 8 = 0$ $2, -4, -1$
26. $x^3 + 3x^2 + 3x + 1 = 0$ -1
27. $x^4 + 4x^3 + 6x^2 + 4x + 1 = 0$ -1
28. $6x^3 + 11x^2 - 3x - 2 = 0$
29. $x^3 - 2x^2 - 2x - 3 = 0$ $3, \frac{-1 \pm i\sqrt{3}}{2}$
30. $x^3 - 6x^2 + 11x - 6 = 0$ $1, 2, 3$
31. $x^4 - 13x^3 + 55x^2 - 91x = 0$
32. $x^4 + x^2 - 12 = 0$ $\pm 2i, \pm\sqrt{3}$
33. $x^4 + 14x^2 + 45 = 0$ $\pm 3i, \pm i\sqrt{5}$
34. $x^3 + 13x - 85 = 31$ $4, -2 \pm 5i$
35. $x^3 - 4x^2 + x + 14 = 8$ $-1, 2, 3$

36. **Geometry** The volume of the rectangular prism is 105 cubic units. Find the dimensions of the prism. $7 \times 5 \times 3$

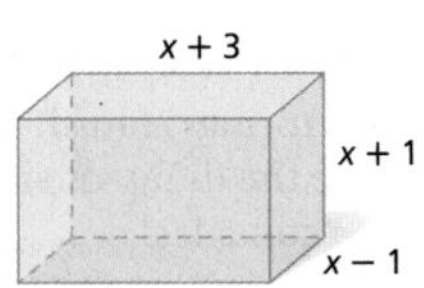

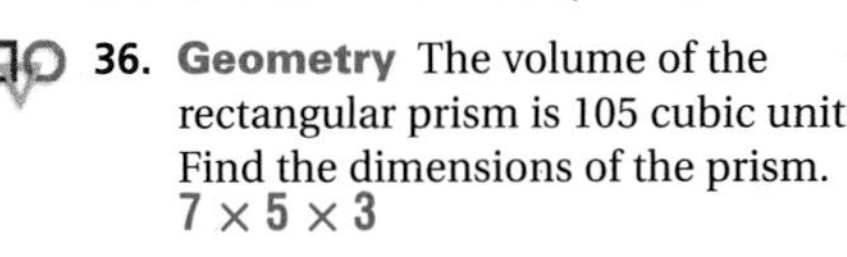

14. $2, -2, \pm 2i$
15. $1, 3$
17. $\frac{3}{2}, \pm 2i$
24. $-1, 4, \pm 3i$
28. $-2, \frac{1}{2}, -\frac{1}{3}$
31. $0, 7, 3 \pm 2i$

6-6 Exercises

Assignment Guide

Assign *Guided Practice* exercises as necessary.

If you finished Examples **1–2**
Basic 11–19, 25–35 odd
Average 11–19, 24–34 even
Advanced 11–19, 24–34 even

If you finished Examples **1–4**
Basic 11–23, 36, 37, 48–51, 53, 57–62, 72–79
Average 11–23, 25–35 odd, 36, 37, 38–40, 44–52, 54–64, 72–79
Advanced 13–16, 21–23, 24–36 even, 37, 41–52, 54, 57–79

Homework Quick Check
Quickly check key concepts.
Exercises: 12, 14, 20, 23, 48

Answers

9. $P(x) = x^5 - 2x^4 + 2x^3 - 4x^2 - 8x + 16$
20. $P(x) = x^5 - 6x^4 + 10x^3 + 8x^2 - 39x + 30$

State Resources

Exercise 37 involves using the volume of a square pyramid to find the length of its base. This exercise prepares students for the Multi-Step Test Prep on page 472.

Teaching Tip **Geography Link** In **Exercise 52,** students find the volume of a tree in Sequoia National Park. Ask students to describe other memorable natural features in national or state parks with which they are familiar. For example, students might be familiar with Yellowstone Lake in Yellowstone National Park. They could speculate on how to estimate the volume of the lake.

Teaching Tip **Visual** In **Exercise 53,** have students draw diagrams to help them understand the shape of the propane tank.

Answers

48. $x \approx -1.748, -0.420, 0.625, 1.542$

49. $x = 0$ or $x \approx \pm 0.537$

50. $x \approx -0.361, -0.500, 1.305$

51. $x \approx -0.782, 0.975, 3.965$

55. Possible answer: $\pm 2.25, \frac{2}{3}$; $x = \pm\sqrt{5}, \frac{2}{3}$

56. Possible answer: Graph the polynomial to find the number of real zeros. Factor out the real zeros of the polynomial by using a graph, the Rational Root Theorem, or synthetic division. Use the quadratic equation to factor the remaining part of the polynomial. There may be 0, 2, or 4 imaginary zeros.

MULTI-STEP TEST PREP

37. This problem will prepare you for the Multi-Step Test Prep on page 472.

The volume of a pyramid-shaped tent with a square base can be represented by the function $V(x) = \frac{1}{3}x^3 - 2x^2$, where x is the length of the base in meters.

a. The volume of the tent is 81 m^3. Write a polynomial equation with integer coefficients that you can solve in order to find the length of the base.

b. Find the length of the base. **9 m** **37a. $x^3 - 6x^2 - 243 = 0$**

c. What can you say about the other roots of the polynomial equation? Why? **They are complex. After $x - 9$ is factored out, the remaining quadratic equation has a negative discriminant.**

38. $P(x) = x^4 - 2x^3 - 5x^2 + 10x$ **40. $P(x) = x^6 + 2x^5 + 9x^4 + 16x^3 - x^2 - 18x - 9$**

Write the simplest polynomial function with the given zeros.

38. 0, $\sqrt{5}$, and 2 39. $4i$, 2, and -2 40. 1, -1 (multiplicity of 3), and $3i$

41. 1, 1, and 2 42. $1 - \sqrt{2}$, and $2i$ 43. 3 (multiplicity of 2), and $3i$

39. $P(x) = x^4 + 12x^2 - 64$

41. $P(x) = x^3 - 4x^2 + 5x - 2$ **$P(x) = x^4 - 2x^3 + 3x^2 - 8x - 4$**

Tell whether each statement is sometimes, always, or never true. If it is sometimes true, give examples to support your answer. **43. $P(x) = x^4 - 6x^3 + 18x^2 - 54x + 81$**

44. A cubic polynomial has no real zeros. **never true**

45. A quartic polynomial has an odd number of real zeros. **never true**

46. There are infinitely many polynomials with zeros a, b, and c. **always true**

47. The multiplicity of a root is equal to the degree of the polynomial.

47. Sometimes true; $(x - 1)^2 = 0$ has root 1 with multiplicity 2 and degree 2. $x(x - 1)^2 = 0$ has root 1 with multiplicity 2 and degree 3.

Use your graphing calculator to approximate the solutions of each equation by finding all roots. Round your answer to the nearest thousandth.

48. $3x^4 - x = 6x^2 + \sqrt{2}$ 49. $2\sqrt{3}x^4 - x^2 = 0$

50. $-6x^3 = -5\sqrt{3}x + \sqrt{2}$ 51. $\sqrt{7}x^3 - 11x^2 + 8 = 0$

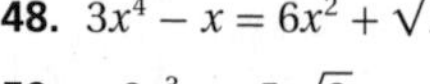

LINK **Forestry**

The sequoias in Sequoia National Park in California are among the largest trees in the world. Many are as tall as a 26-story building and wider than some city streets.

52. **Forestry** The volume of a giant sequoia can be modeled by $V(h) = 0.485h^3 - 362h^2 + 89889h - 7379874$, where h represents the height of a tree in feet and $220 \le h \le 280$.

a. Find the height of a tree with volume 39,186 cubic feet. **220 ft**

b. The Lincoln tree in the Giant Forest in Sequoia National Park has a volume of 44,471 cubic feet. What are its possible heights? **226.9 ft, 258 ft, and 261.4 ft**

c. The actual height of the Lincoln tree is 255.8 feet. What is the difference between the true volume of the tree and the volume given by the model? **177.2 ft^3**

53. The volume of a cylindrical propane tank with a hemispherical top and bottom can be represented by the function $V(r) = 33\pi r^2 + \frac{4}{3}\pi r^3$, where V is the volume in cubic inches and r is the radius in inches. What is the radius if the volume of the tank is 1476π cubic inches? **$r = 6$**

54. **Critical Thinking** What is the least degree of a polynomial equation that has $3i$ as a root with a multiplicity of 3? Explain. **6; since $3i$ is a root 3 times, $-3i$ must also be a root 3 times.**

55. **Estimation** Use the graph to estimate the roots of $y = 3x^3 - 2x^2 - 15x + 10$. Then find the exact roots. (*Hint:* Factor by grouping.)

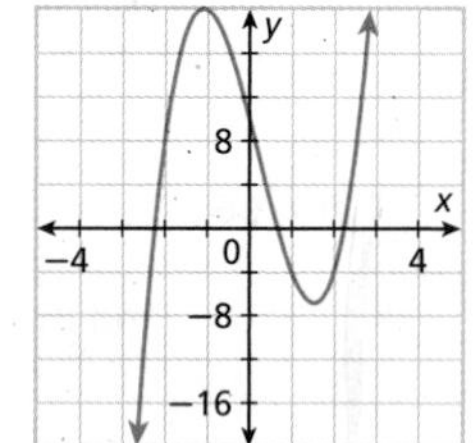

56. **Write About It** Describe your method for factoring a fourth-degree polynomial. What are the different situations that you need to consider?

6-6 PRACTICE A

6-6 PRACTICE C

6-6 PRACTICE B

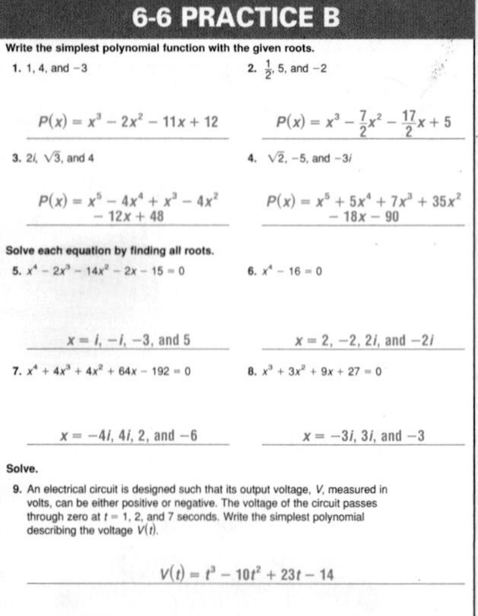

Write the simplest polynomial function with the given roots.

1. 1, 4, and −3 — $P(x) = x^3 - 2x^2 - 11x + 12$

2. $\frac{1}{2}$, 5, and −2 — $P(x) = x^3 - \frac{7}{2}x^2 - \frac{17}{2}x + 5$

3. $2i$, $\sqrt{3}$, and 4 — $P(x) = x^5 - 4x^4 + x^3 - 4x^2 - 12x + 48$

4. $\sqrt{2}$, −5, and $-3i$ — $P(x) = x^5 + 5x^4 + 7x^3 + 35x^2 - 18x - 90$

Solve each equation by finding all roots.

5. $x^4 - 2x^3 - 14x^2 - 2x - 15 = 0$ — $x = i, -i, -3$, and 5

6. $x^4 - 16 = 0$ — $x = 2, -2, 2i$, and $-2i$

7. $x^4 + 4x^3 + 4x^2 + 64x - 192 = 0$ — $x = -4i, 4i, 2$, and -6

8. $x^3 + 3x^2 + 9x + 27 = 0$ — $x = -3i, 3i$, and -3

Solve.

9. An electrical circuit is designed such that its output voltage, V, measured in volts, can be either positive or negative. The voltage of the circuit passes through zero at t = 1, 2, and 7 seconds. Write the simplest polynomial describing the voltage $V(t)$. — $V(t) = t^3 - 10t^2 + 23t - 14$

6-6 READING STRATEGIES

You've learned how to find the roots of a polynomial equation. If you know the roots, then you can find a polynomial function that has those roots. The table below shows the method for a polynomial function that has two roots.

Step 1: Identify factors from the given roots.	**Root** → **Factor** $x = 2$ → $x - 2$ $x = -5$ → $x + 5$
Step 2: Use the factors to write an equation.	$(x - 2)(x + 5) = 0$
Step 3: Multiply the factors to find the polynomial with the given roots.	$x^2 + 5x - 2x - 10 = 0$ $x^2 + 3x - 10 = 0$

$x^2 + 3x - 10 = 0$ is the simplest polynomial with roots 2 and −5. If you multiply this equation by any nonzero number, the new equation will also have the same roots.

Answer each question.

1. How can you use the method described above if you know all three roots of a polynomial equation? **Find the factors corresponding to the roots and multiply the factors.**

2. Suppose one of the roots of a polynomial is 0. What is the simplest factor that corresponds to 0? **x**

3. The number −2 is a multiple root of a polynomial. The multiplicity of −2 is 3. There are no other roots of the equation.

a. Write the simplest polynomial that has the given roots. **$(x + 2)(x + 2)(x + 2) = 0$, or $x^3 + 6x^2 + 12x + 8$.**

b. Explain why this is the simplest polynomial. **because multiplying the equation by a nonzero number will not change its roots**

4. a. Write the simplest polynomial function with roots 0, 0, 0, and 2. **$(x)(x)(x)(x + 2) = x^4 + 2x^3 = 0$**

b. What is the degree of this polynomial? **4**

6-6 RETEACH

If r is a root of a polynomial function, then $(x - r)$ is a factor of the polynomial, $P(x)$. So, you can use the roots to write the simplest form of a polynomial function.

Write the simplest polynomial function with roots −4, −2, and 3.

Step 1 Write the factors of the polynomial, $P(x) = 0$.
$(x + 4)(x + 2)(x - 3) = 0$

Root (a)	−4	−2	3
Factor ($x - a$)	$x + 4$	$x + 2$	$x - 3$

Step 2 Multiply the first two factors, $(x + 4)(x + 2)$.
$(x^2 + 6x + 8)(x - 3) = 0$

Step 3 Multiply $(x^2 + 6x + 8)(x - 3)$. Then simplify.
$x^3 - 3x^2 + 6x^2 - 18x + 8x - 24 = 0$
$x^3 + 3x^2 - 10x - 24 = 0$

The function is $P(x) = x^3 + 3x^2 - 10x - 24 = 0$.

Write the simplest polynomial function with the given roots.

1. −5, 1, and 2
$(x + 5)(x - 1)(x - 2) = 0$
$(x^2 + 4x - 5)(x - 2) = 0$
$x^3 + 4x^2 - 5x - 2x^2 - 8x + 10$
$x^3 + 2x^2 + 13x + 10$

2. −3, −1, and 0
$x(x + 3)(x + 1) = 0$
$(x^2 + 3x)(x + 1)$
$x^3 + 3x^2 + x^2 + 3x$
$x^3 + 4x^2 + 3x$

3. 1, 4, and 5
$(x - 1)(x - 4)(x - 5)$
$(x^2 - 5x + 4)(x - 5)$
$x^3 - 10x^2 + 29x - 20$

4. −2, 3, and 6
$(x + 2)(x - 3)(x - 6)$
$(x^2 - x - 6)(x - 6)$
$x^3 - 7x^2 + 36$

5. 2, 4, and 6
$(x - 2)(x - 4)(x - 6)$
$(x^2 - 6x + 8)(x - 6)$
$x^3 - 12x^2 + 44x - 48$

6. −5, 0, and 5
$(x + 5)(x)(x - 5)$
$x(x^2 - 25)$
$x^3 - 25x$

TEST PREP

57. What is the multiplicity of the root −1 in the equation $y = x^4 - 2x^3 - 3x^2 + 4x + 4$?
   Ⓐ 1 Ⓑ 2 (circled) Ⓒ 3 Ⓓ 4

58. What is the conjugate of $-6 - 5i$?
   Ⓕ $-6 - 5i$ Ⓖ $-6 + 5i$ (circled) Ⓗ $6 - 5i$ Ⓙ $6 + 5i$

59. Which polynomial function has zeros 0, i, and $-i$?
   Ⓐ $P(x) = x^3 + 2x^2 + 1$ Ⓒ $P(x) = x^3 + 2x^2 + x$
   Ⓑ $P(x) = x^3 + x^2$ Ⓓ $P(x) = x^3 + x$ (circled)

60. A polynomial has zeros $3 - \sqrt{2}$, 4, and $6i$. What is the minimum degree of the polynomial?
   Ⓕ 3 Ⓖ 4 Ⓗ 5 (circled) Ⓙ 6

61. Which polynomial function has zeros $1 + \sqrt{3}$ and $1 - \sqrt{3}$?
   Ⓐ $f(x) = x^2 + 8$ Ⓒ $f(x) = x^2 - x + \sqrt{3}$
   Ⓑ $f(x) = x^2 - 3x + 9$ Ⓓ $f(x) = x^2 - 2x - 2$ (circled)

62. **Short Response** Solve the equation $2x^3 - 6x^2 + 8x - 24 = 0$ by finding all roots. $x = 3, \pm 2i$

63. $f(3i) = 0$; $f(-\sqrt{3}) = -6 - 36\sqrt{3}$; yes, $x = 3i$ is a zero.

CHALLENGE AND EXTEND

63. Use synthetic substitution to evaluate $f(x) = x^3 - 3x^2 + 9x - 27$ for $x = 3i$ and $x = -\sqrt{3}$. Is either $x = 3i$ or $x = -\sqrt{3}$ a zero of f?

64. $2i$ is a zero of $P(x) = x^3 - 2ix^2 - 4x + 8i$. Find the other zeros of P. 2, −2

65. One zero of $Q(x) = x^3 - \sqrt{2}x^2 + 9x - 9\sqrt{2}$ is $\sqrt{2}$. Find the other zeros of Q. $\pm 3i$

66. **Critical Thinking** Based on your answers to Exercises 64 and 65, what can you say about a polynomial function with nonreal or irrational coefficients?

66. Possible answer: Polynomials with nonreal or irrational coefficients do not have complex or irrational roots in conjugate pairs.

67. Factor the sum $a^2 + b^2$. $(a + bi)(a - bi)$

68. Factor the sum $a^4 + b^4$. $(a + bi\sqrt{i})(a - bi\sqrt{i})(a + b\sqrt{i})(a - b\sqrt{i})$

69. Factor the sum $a^6 + b^6$. $(a + bi)(a - bi)(a^4 - a^2b^2 + b^4)$

70. **Critical Thinking** Does your answer to Exercise 67 help you answer Exercises 68 or 69? Explain.

70. Possible answer: Yes; $a^2 + b^2$ is a factor of both $a^4 + b^4$ and $a^6 + b^6$ after the first steps.

71. **Critical Thinking** Give an example of a fourth-degree polynomial equation that has no real zeros. What are the roots of your example? $x^4 + 2x^2 + 1 = 0$; $\pm i$

SPIRAL REVIEW

State the transformation that maps the graph of $f(x) = |x|$ onto the graph of each function. Then graph each function. *(Lesson 2-9)*

72. $f(x) = |x + 5| - 7$ shift 5 units left and 7 units down

73. $f(x) = -|x - 2| + 3$ shift 2 units right, reflection across x-axis, and shift 3 units up

72. 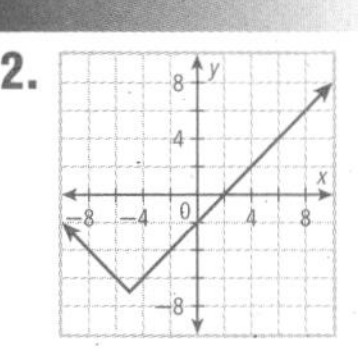

73. 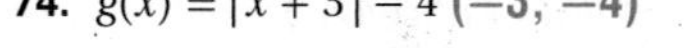

Find the vertex of the graph of each function. *(Lesson 2-9)*

74. $g(x) = |x + 3| - 4$ (−3, −4)

75. $f(x) = |x - 9| - 3$ (9, −3)

Solve each equation by factoring. *(Lesson 6-5)*

76. $4x^4 + 32x^3 + 64x^2 = 0$ $x = 0, -4$

77. $x^3 - 43x^2 + 42x = 0$ $x = 0, 42, 1$

78. $3x^5 + 18x^4 - 81x^3 = 0$ $x = 0, -9, 3$

79. $2x^3 + 12x^2 = 32x$ $x = 0, -8, 2$

TEST PREP DOCTOR Students who chose **H** in **Exercise 58** may have changed the sign of a instead of b to find the conjugate. Students who chose **J** may have changed the sign of both a and b. Remind students that the conjugate of $a + bi$ is $a - bi$.

In **Exercise 60,** students who chose **F** or **G** have not counted the conjugates of either the irrational or the complex roots. Students who chose **J** have counted all roots, including the rational roots, in pairs.

Journal

Have students explain how to use the Fundamental Theorem of Algebra in their own words.

ALTERNATIVE ASSESSMENT

Have students create their own polynomial functions with a complex root and a real root. Students should write the function in simplest form. Then have them trade with a partner and work through the steps to find all the roots of the function.

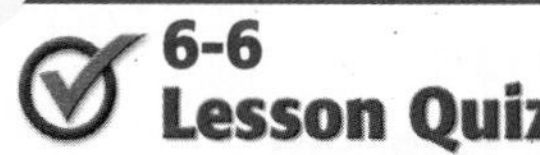

Power Presentations with PowerPoint®

6-6 Lesson Quiz

Write the simplest polynomial function with the given zeros.

1. 2, −1, 1
   $P(x) = x^3 - 2x^2 - x + 2$
2. 0, −2, $\sqrt{3}$
   $P(x) = x^4 + 2x^3 - 3x^2 - 6x$
3. $2i$, 1, −2
   $P(x) = x^4 + x^3 + 2x^2 + 4x - 8$
4. Solve by finding all roots.
   $x^4 - 5x^3 + 7x^2 - 5x + 6 = 0$
   2, 3, i, $-i$
5. The volume of a cylindrical vitamin pill with a hemispherical top and bottom can be modeled by the function $V(x) = 10\pi r^2 + \frac{4}{3}\pi r^3$, where r is the radius in millimeters. For what value of r does the vitamin have a volume of 160 mm³? about 2 mm

Also available on transparency

6-6 PROBLEM SOLVING

A company that makes accessories for cars needs a container like that shown at the right to hold touch-up paint. The hemispherical top will be fitted with a brush applicator. The cylindrical part of the container should be 4 inches tall. The volume of the entire container is $\frac{13}{12}\pi$ cubic inches. Find the value of x, the radius of the hemisphere.

1. a. Write a formula for the volume of the cylindrical part of the container.
   $V = 4\pi r^2$
   b. Write a formula for the volume of the hemispherical part of the container.
   $V = \frac{1}{2}\left(\frac{4}{3}\pi r^3\right)$
2. Write an equation to represent the total volume of the container.
   $\frac{13}{12}\pi = 4\pi r^2 + \frac{2}{3}\pi r^3$
3. Write the equation in standard form.
   $8r^3 + 48r^2 - 13 = 0$
4. Graph the equation with a graphing calculator. Hint: Use a window with x-values from −8 to 5 with a scale of 1, and y-values from −20 to 250 with a scale of 30 to see the general shape of the graph. Sketch the graph. Then focus on the area of the positive root by using a window of −8 to 3 on the x-axis and −20 to 20 on the y-axis. Use Trace to help you find a possible positive root.
5. Verify the root using synthetic substitution. What is the positive root?
   $\frac{1}{2}$
6. Use the Quadratic Formula to find approximate values for the other two roots. Explain why these two roots cannot also be solutions to the problem.
   $x = \frac{-26 \pm 21.6}{8}$; both these roots are negative, so they cannot be the radius.
7. What is the value of x, the radius of the hemisphere, for this paint container? 0.5 inch

6-6 CHALLENGE

A polynomial function may be written in standard form.

$$P(x) = a_nx^n + a_{n-1}x^{n-1} + a_{n-2}x^{n-2} + \ldots + a_2x^2 + a_1x + a_0$$

Dividing by the leading coefficient, a_n, does not change the zeros of the polynomial. This produces a new polynomial that can also be written in descending order.

$$Q(x) = x^n + A_1x^{n-1} + A_2x^{n-2} + A_3x^{n-3} + \ldots + A_{n-1}x + A_n$$

The properties below illustrate some relationships that occur between the coefficients in this form and the zeros of the polynomial.

i) The sum of the zeros (roots) is equal to $-A_1$.
$$z_1 + z_2 + z_3 + \ldots + z_n = -A_1$$
ii) The sum of the products of the zeros taken two at a time is equal to A_2.
$$z_1z_2 + z_1z_3 + z_1z_4 + \ldots + z_{n-2}z_n + z_{n-1}z_n = A_2$$
iii) The sum of the products of the zeros taken three at a time is equal to $-A_3$.
$$z_1z_2z_3 + z_1z_2z_4 + \ldots + z_{n-2}z_{n-1}z_n = -A_3$$
iv) The product of the zeros is equal to A_n or $-A_n$.
$$z_1z_2z_3z_4 - \ldots - z_{n-2}z_{n-1}z_n = (-1)^n A_n$$

Solve.

1. Show that the relationships *i*) and *ii*) hold true for the polynomial function $P(x) = x^2 + 2x - 15$, which has zeros at $z_1 = 3$ and $z_2 = -5$.
   $-5 + 3 = -2$; $(-5)(3) = -15$
2. Show that the relationships *i*), *ii*), and *iii*) hold true for the polynomial function $P(x) = x^3 - 3x^2 - 6x + 8$, which has zeros at $z_1 = 1$, $z_2 = 4$, and $z_3 = -2$.
   $-2 + 1 + 4 = -(-3) = 3$; $(-2)(1) + (-2)(4) + (1)(4) = -6$; $(-2)(1)(4) = -8$
3. Use the relationships to find the final zero of the polynomial $P(x) = x^3 - 8x^2 - 5x + 84$ given that two of the zeros are at $z_1 = 7$ and $z_2 = -3$.
   $z_1z_2z_3 = -84 = (7)(-3)(z_3)$; $z_3 = 4$
4. Use the relationships and solve a system of equations to find the remaining zeros of the polynomial $P(x) = x^4 - x^3 - 19x^2 - 11x + 30$ given that two zeros are at $z_1 = 5$ and $z_2 = -2$.
   $-2 + 5 + z_3 + z_4 = 1$; $(-2)(5) + (-2)(z_3) + (-2)(z_4) + (5)(z_3) + (5)(z_4) + (z_3)(z_4) = -19$; $z_3 = 1$; $z_4 = -3$
5. Prove that the relationships above are true for a polynomial with three zeros by expanding $(x - z_1)(x - z_2)(x - z_3)$.
   $(x - z_1)(x - z_2)(x - z_3) = x^3 - (z_1 + z_2 + z_3)x^2 + (z_1z_2 + z_1z_3 + z_2z_3)x - z_1z_2z_3$

Organizer

Use with Lesson 6-7

Pacing:

Traditional $\frac{1}{2}$ day

Block $\frac{1}{4}$ day

Objective: Use a graphing calculator to explore the end behavior of functions from their graphs.

Materials: Graphing calculator

Online Edition
Graphing Calculator, TechKeys

Countdown to Testing Week 14

Resources

Technology Lab Activities

6-7 Lab Recording Sheet

Teach

Discuss

Have students graph $f(x) = 2x^4 + x$ and $g(x) = -2x^4 + x$. Lead students to discover how the leading coefficient and degree can be used to describe end behavior.

Close

Key Concept

The end behavior of a polynomial function is determined by its degree and leading coefficient.

Assessment

Journal Have students explain how to describe the end behavior of a polynomial function.

Answers

1–4. See p. A31.

State Resources

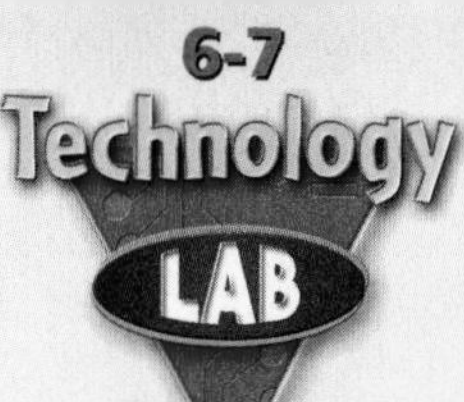

Explore End Behavior

End behavior is a description of the values of the function as x approaches positive infinity ($x \to +\infty$) or negative infinity ($x \to -\infty$).

Use with Lesson 6-7

go.hrw.com
Lab Resources Online
KEYWORD: MB7 Lab6

Activity

Describe the end behavior of $f(x) = 2x^3 - x^2 - 7x + 5$.

Enter $f(x)$ into your graphing calculator. Choose a large window, and graph.

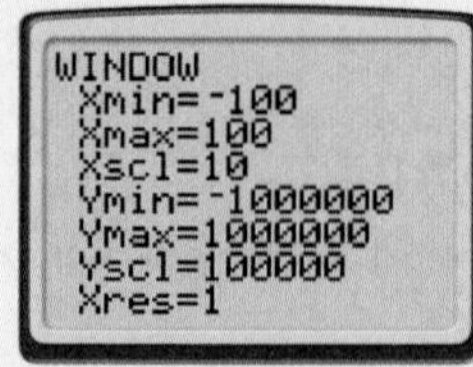

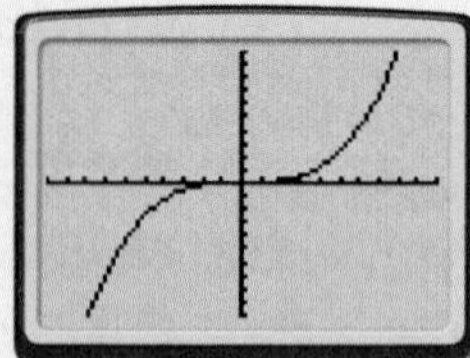

Notice $f(x)$ appears to rise for positive x-values and fall for negative x-values.

Try This

1. Consider the functions $g(x) = 3x^3 - 2x^2 + x + 4$, $h(x) = \frac{1}{2}x^3 + 3x^2 + x - 9$, and $k(x) = 5x^3 - 8x^2 - 2x + 1$.
   a. What do the functions $g(x)$, $h(x)$, and $k(x)$ have in common?
   b. Graph $g(x)$, $h(x)$, and $k(x)$ on your graphing calculator, and describe the end behavior of each.
   c. **Make a Conjecture** What can you say about the end behavior of functions of the same type as $g(x)$, $h(x)$, and $k(x)$?
2. Consider the functions $a(x) = -3x^3 - 2x^2 + x + 4$, $b(x) = -\frac{1}{2}x^3 + 3x^2 + x - 9$, and $c(x) = -5x^3 - 8x^2 - 2x + 1$.
   a. What do the functions $a(x)$, $b(x)$, and $c(x)$ have in common?
   b. Graph $a(x)$, $b(x)$, and $c(x)$ on your graphing calculator, and describe the end behavior of each.
   c. **Make a Conjecture** What can you say about the end behavior of functions of the same type as $a(x)$, $b(x)$, and $c(x)$?
3. Consider the functions $p(x) = 3x^4 - x^2 + x + 4$, $r(x) = \frac{1}{2}x^4 + 3x^3 + x - 9$, and $s(x) = 5x^4 - 8x^3 - 2x^2 + 1$.
   a. What do the functions $p(x)$, $r(x)$, and $s(x)$ have in common?
   b. Graph $p(x)$, $r(x)$, and $s(x)$ on your graphing calculator, and describe the end behavior of each.
   c. **Make a Conjecture** What can you say about the end behavior of functions of the same type as $p(x)$, $r(x)$, and $s(x)$?
4. **Critical Thinking** Compare your conjectures from Problems 1c, 2c, and 3c. What are the characteristics of a function that seem to affect the function's end behavior?

Teacher to Teacher

My students use arrows to indicate end behavior, as shown. Using the arrows is more intuitive for many students. After they are comfortable with identifying polynomial end behavior, students can make the next step to using notation involving $+\infty$ and $-\infty$.

	Odd Degree	Even Degree
$a > 0$	↙ ↗	↖ ↗
$a < 0$	↖ ↘	↙ ↘

Marti Freihofer
Taylor Mill, KY

6-7 Investigating Graphs of Polynomial Functions

A2.4.1 Analyze, describe and sketch graphs of polynomial functions by examining intercepts, zeros, domain and range and end behavior.

Objectives
Use properties of end behavior to analyze, describe, and graph polynomial functions.

Identify and use maxima and minima of polynomial functions to solve problems.

Vocabulary
end behavior
turning point
local maximum
local minimum

Who uses this?
Welders can use graphs of polynomial functions to optimize the use of construction materials. (See Example 5.)

Polynomial functions are classified by their degree. The graphs of polynomial functions are classified by the degree of the polynomial. Each graph, based on the degree, has a distinctive shape and characteristics.

Graphs of Polynomial Functions				
Linear function Degree 1	Quadratic function Degree 2	Cubic function Degree 3	Quartic function Degree 4	Quintic function Degree 5

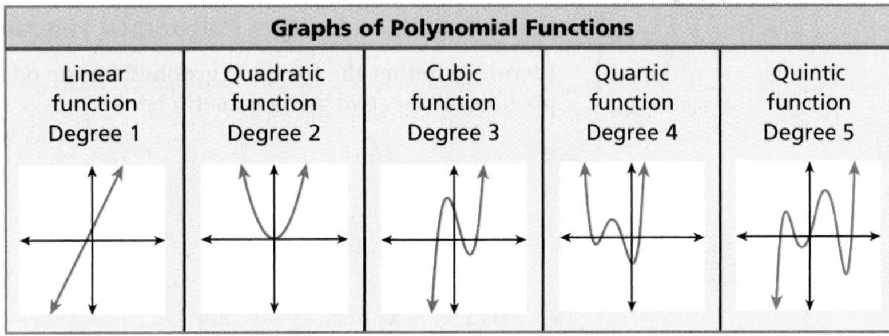

End behavior is a description of the values of the function as x approaches positive infinity ($x \to +\infty$) or negative infinity ($x \to -\infty$). The degree and leading coefficient of a polynomial function determine its end behavior. It is helpful when you are graphing a polynomial function to know about the end behavior of the function.

Polynomial End Behavior

$P(x)$ has...	Odd Degree	Even Degree
Leading coefficient $a > 0$	As $x \to +\infty$, $P(x) \to +\infty$ As $x \to -\infty$, $P(x) \to -\infty$	As $x \to -\infty$, $P(x) \to +\infty$ As $x \to +\infty$, $P(x) \to +\infty$
Leading coefficient $a < 0$	As $x \to -\infty$, $P(x) \to +\infty$ As $x \to +\infty$, $P(x) \to -\infty$	As $x \to -\infty$, $P(x) \to -\infty$ As $x \to +\infty$, $P(x) \to -\infty$

6-7 Organizer

Pacing: Traditional 1 day
Block $\frac{1}{2}$ day

Objectives: Use properties of end behavior to analyze, describe, and graph polynomial functions.

Identify and use maxima and minima of polynomial functions to solve problems.

Technology Lab
In *Technology Lab Activities*

Online Edition
Graphing Calculator, Tutorial Videos, Interactivity, TechKeys

Countdown to Testing Week 14

Power Presentations with PowerPoint®

Warm Up

Identify all the real roots of each equation.

1. $x^3 - 7x^2 + 8x + 16 = 0$
$-1, 4$

2. $2x^3 - 14x - 12 = 0$
$-1, -2, 3$

3. $x^4 + x^3 - 25x^2 - 27x = 0$ 0

4. $x^4 - 26x^2 + 25 = 0$
$1, -1, 5, -5$

Also available on transparency

Math Humor

Q: Why did the function $f(x) = -x^2$ finally get kicked out of class?

A: In the end, its behavior was just too negative.

State Resources

go.hrw.com
State Resources Online
KEYWORD: MB7 Resources

1 Introduce

EXPLORATION

6-7 Investigating Graphs of Polynomial Functions

Use a calculator to explore the connection between the graph of a polynomial function and the degree of the polynomial.

Graph each of the following polynomial functions.

1. $f(x) = x^2 - x - 8$
2. $f(x) = 2x^3 - 3x + 4$
3. $f(x) = x^4 - 8x^2 + 8$
4. $f(x) = x^5 - 6x^3 + 5x - 3$
5. In general, what happens to the graph of a polynomial function as the degree of the polynomial increases?
6. Graph $f(x) = x^8 + 2x^2 + 1$. Does this graph fit the relationship you observed in Problem 2? Why or why not?

THINK AND DISCUSS

7. **Describe** how the graphs of the functions with odd degrees are different from the graphs of the functions with even degrees.
8. **Describe** what you would expect the graph of a 7th-degree polynomial function to look like.

Motivate

Draw a linear, a quadratic, and a cubic function on the board. Ask students to identify what type of function each is based only on the graphs. Have them explain how they know. Explain that all polynomial functions have characteristics that help you identify them.

Explorations and answers are provided in the *Explorations* binder.

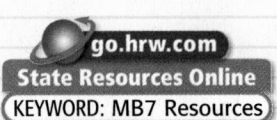

EXAMPLE 1 Determining End Behavior of Polynomial Functions

Identify the leading coefficient, degree, and end behavior.

A $P(x) = -4x^3 - 3x^2 + 5x + 6$

The leading coefficient is -4, which is negative.

The degree is 3, which is odd.

As $x \to -\infty$, $P(x) \to +\infty$, and as $x \to +\infty$, $P(x) \to -\infty$.

B $R(x) = x^6 - 7x^5 + x^3 - 2$

The leading coefficient is 1, which is positive.

The degree is 6, which is even.

As $x \to -\infty$, $P(x) \to +\infty$, and as $x \to +\infty$, $P(x) \to +\infty$.

Helpful Hint

Both the leading coefficient and the degree of the polynomial are contained in the term of greatest degree. When determining end behavior, you can ignore all other terms.

CHECK IT OUT! Identify the leading coefficient, degree, and end behavior.

1a. $P(x) = 2x^5 + 3x^2 - 4x - 1$ **1a. 2; 5; as $x \to -\infty$, $P \to -\infty$, as $x \to +\infty$, $P \to +\infty$**

1b. $S(x) = -3x^2 + x + 1$ **-3; 2; as $x \to \pm\infty$, $P \to -\infty$**

EXAMPLE 2 Using Graphs to Analyze Polynomial Functions

Identify whether the function graphed has an odd or even degree and a positive or negative leading coefficient.

A

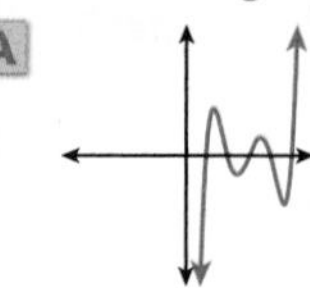

As $x \to -\infty$, $P(x) \to -\infty$, and as $x \to +\infty$, $P(x) \to +\infty$.

$P(x)$ is of odd degree with a positive leading coefficient.

B

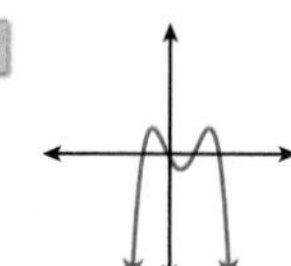

As $x \to -\infty$, $P(x) \to -\infty$, and as $x \to +\infty$, $P(x) \to -\infty$.

$P(x)$ is of even degree with a negative leading coefficient.

CHECK IT OUT! Identify whether the function graphed has an odd or even degree and a positive or negative leading coefficient.

2a. **odd; negative**

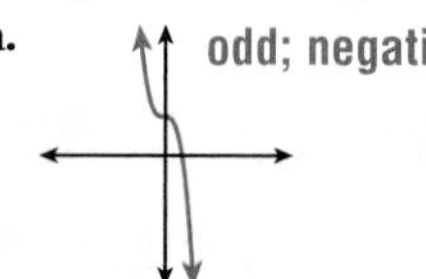

2b. **even; positive**

Now that you have studied factoring, solving polynomial equations, and end behavior, you can graph a polynomial function.

Steps for Graphing a Polynomial Function
1. Find the real zeros and y-intercept of the function.
2. Plot the x- and y-intercepts.
3. Make a table for several x-values that lie between the real zeros.
4. Plot the points from your table.
5. Determine the end behavior of the graph.
6. Sketch the graph.

Power Presentations with PowerPoint®

Additional Examples

Example 1

Identify the leading coefficient, degree, and end behavior.

A. $Q(x) = -x^4 + 6x^3 - x + 9$

-1; 4; as $x \to \pm\infty$, $Q \to -\infty$.

B. $P(x) = 2x^5 + 6x^4 - x + 4$

2; 5; as $x \to -\infty$, $P \to -\infty$, as $x \to +\infty$, $P \to +\infty$.

Example 2

Identify whether the function graphed has an odd or even degree and a positive or negative leading coefficient.

A.

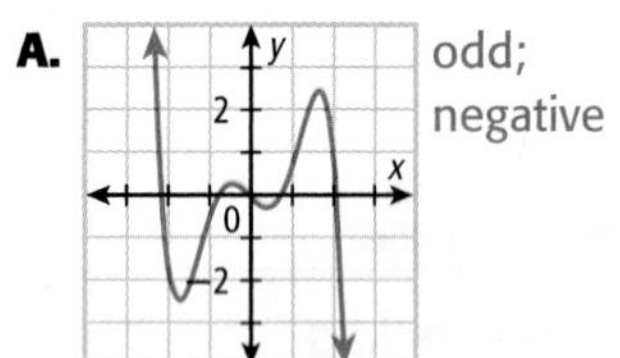

odd; negative

B.

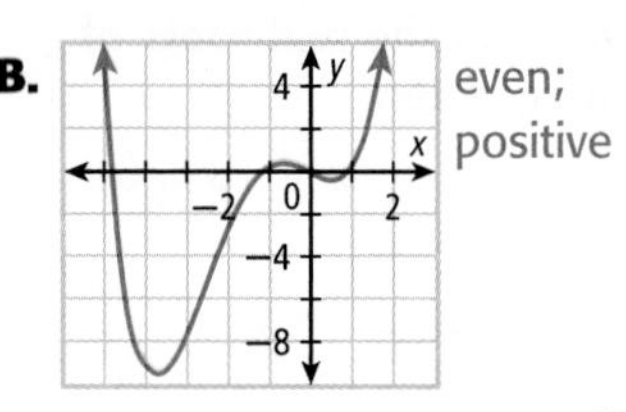

even; positive

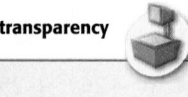

Also available on transparency

INTERVENTION

Questioning Strategies

EXAMPLES 1–2

- Why does the sign of the leading coefficient affect end behavior?
- How does end behavior relate to whether the degree is odd or even?

2 Teach

Guided Instruction

Sketch the graph of $y = x^2$. Ask a student to describe how the graph behaves. It falls and then rises, or decreases and then increases. Repeat for the graph of $y = x^3$. It is always increasing. Then introduce polynomial end behavior and infinity notation.

Reaching All Learners

Through Visual Cues

When discussing local maxima and minima, have students cover irrelevant parts of the graph with a sheet of paper to focus on the local extreme value of interest.

Through Cognitive Strategies

Suggest that students create reference cards that show the general shapes of polynomial functions of degree 2 through 5. Students can think of the cards as a "vocabulary of graphs" and use them when graphing polynomial functions.

EXAMPLE 3 Graphing Polynomial Functions

Graph the function.

$f(x) = x^3 + 3x^2 - 6x - 8$

Step 1 Identify the possible rational roots by using the Rational Root Theorem.

$\pm 1, \pm 2, \pm 4, \pm 8$ *p = −8 and q = 1*

Step 2 Test possible rational zeros until a zero is identified.

Test $x = 1$.

1	1	3	−6	−8
		1	4	−2
	1	4	−2	−10

Test $x = -1$.

−1	1	3	−6	−8
		−1	−2	8
	1	2	−8	0

$x = -1$ is a zero, and $f(x) = (x + 1)(x^2 + 2x - 8)$.

Step 3 Factor: $f(x) = (x + 1)(x - 2)(x + 4)$.
The zeros are −1, 2, and −4.

Step 4 Plot other points as guidelines.
$f(0) = -8$, so the y-intercept is −8.

Plot points between the zeros. Choose $x = -3$ and $x = 1$ for simple calculations.
$f(-3) = 10$ and $f(1) = -10$

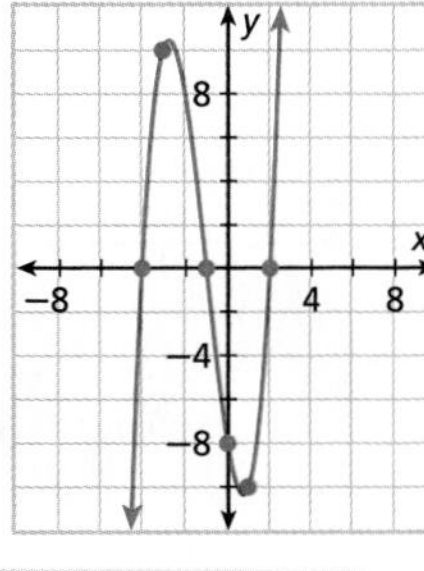

Step 5 Identify end behavior.
The degree is odd and the leading coefficient is positive so as $x \to -\infty$, $P(x) \to -\infty$, and as $x \to +\infty$, $P(x) \to +\infty$.

Step 6 Sketch the graph of $f(x) = x^3 + 3x^2 - 6x - 8$ by using all of the information about $f(x)$.

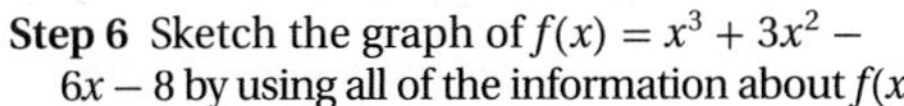

CHECK IT OUT! Graph each function.

3a. $f(x) = x^3 - 2x^2 - 5x + 6$ **3b.** $f(x) = -2x^2 - x + 6$

3a.

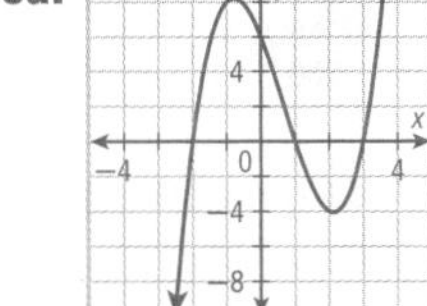

3b.

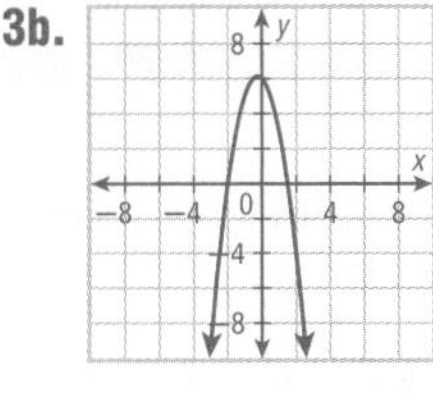

A **turning point** is where a graph changes from increasing to decreasing or from decreasing to increasing. A turning point corresponds to a *local maximum* or *minimum*.

Local Maxima and Minima

For a function $f(x)$, $f(a)$ is a **local maximum** if there is an interval around a such that $f(x) < f(a)$ for every x-value in the interval except a.

For a function $f(x)$, $f(a)$ is a **local minimum** if there is an interval around a such that $f(x) > f(a)$ for every x-value in the interval except a.

A polynomial function of degree n has at most $n - 1$ turning points and at most n x-intercepts. If the function has n distinct real roots, then it has exactly $n - 1$ turning points and exactly n x-intercepts. You can use a graphing calculator to graph and estimate maximum and minimum values.

Technology Students can use a graphing calculator to estimate local maxima and minima.

Press 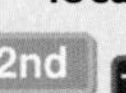 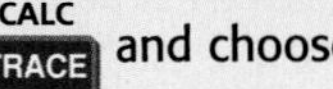 and choose **3: minimum** or **4: maximum.** Enter the lower bound by moving the cursor to a point left of the turning point and pressing ENTER. Repeat for the upper bound.

Inclusion Students need to look at only the first term of a polynomial function to determine end behavior. They can use a graphing calculator with the function as **Y1** and the first term as **Y2** and can zoom out to investigate the curves' similar end behavior.

COMMON ERROR ALERT

Students may not graph enough points between the zeros to accurately represent the function. Suggest that they choose at least two points between zeros to sketch the graph. Remind students to use the original function to evaluate $f(x)$ for the chosen values.

Power Presentations with PowerPoint®

Additional Examples

Example 3

Graph the function.

$f(x) = x^3 + 4x^2 + x - 6$

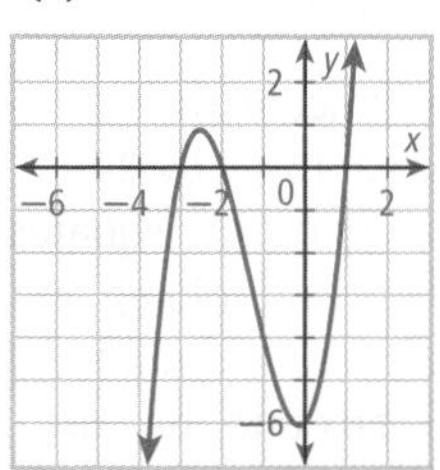

Also available on transparency

INTERVENTION
Questioning Strategies

EXAMPLE 3

- Why is plotting points between the zeros helpful?
- How does determining the end behavior help you sketch the graph?

Math Background *Maxima* and *minima* are together referred to as *extrema*. Point out that there are different types of *extrema:* local and absolute. A graph of a quadratic function will only have an absolute extreme value, but graphs of quartic functions might have both absolute and local extrema. Graphs of cubic and quintic functions will have only local extrema.

Power Presentations with PowerPoint®

Additional Examples

Example 4

Graph $f(x) = 2x^3 - 18x + 1$ on a calculator and estimate the local maxima and minima.

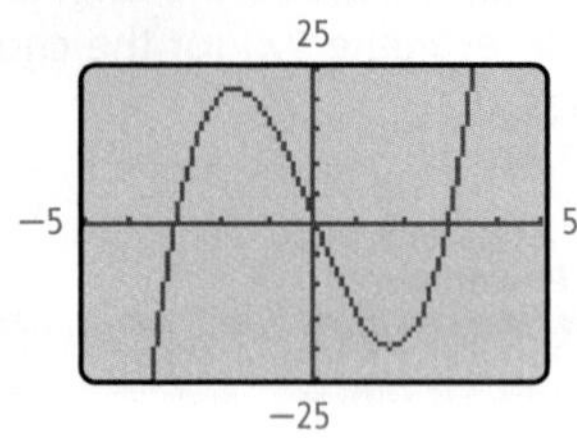

max.: ≈ 21.7846;
min.: ≈ -19.7846

Example 5

An artist plans to construct an open box from a 15 in. by 20 in. sheet of metal by cutting squares from the corners and folding up the sides. Find the maximum volume of the box and the corresponding dimensions.
$x \approx 2.83$; max. vol.: about 379.04 in^3; 2.83 in. × 9.34 in. × 14.34 in.

Also available on transparency

INTERVENTION

Questioning Strategies

EXAMPLE 4

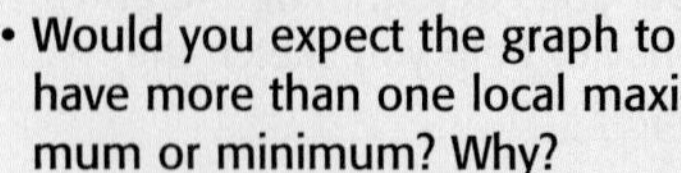

- Would you expect the graph to have more than one local maximum or minimum? Why?
- Can knowing the general shape of a cubic function help you find local maxima or minima?

EXAMPLE 5

- How does this application problem relate to **Example 4**?

EXAMPLE 4 Determine Maxima and Minima with a Calculator

Graph $g(x) = 2x^3 - 12x + 6$ on a calculator, and estimate the local maxima and minima.

Step 1 Graph.

The graph appears to have one local maximum and one local minimum.

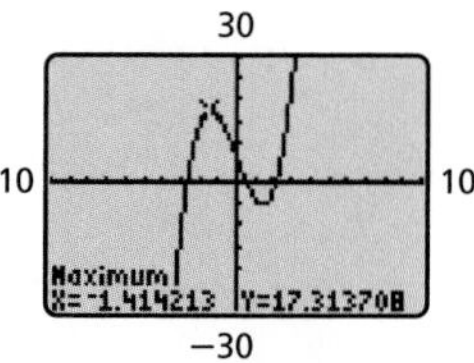

Step 2 Find the maximum.

Press 2nd TRACE (CALC) to access the **CALC** menu. Choose **4:maximum**.

The local maximum is approximately 17.3137.

Step 3 Find the minimum.

Press 2nd TRACE (CALC) to access the **CALC** menu. Choose **3:mininum**.

The local minimum is approximately −5.3137.

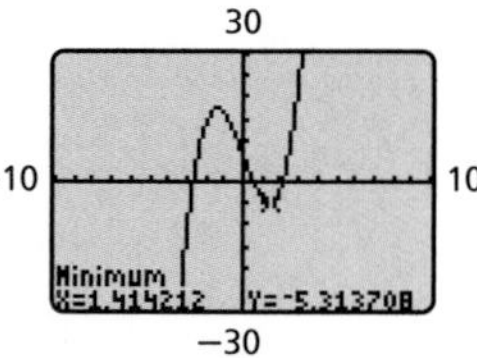

Reading Math

Maxima is the plural form of *maximum*. *Minima* is the plural form of *minimum*.

CHECK IT OUT! Graph each function on a calculator, and estimate the local maxima and minima.

4a. $g(x) = x^3 - 2x - 3$ min.: −4.0887; max.: −1.9113

4b. $h(x) = x^4 + 4x^2 - 6$ min.: −6

4a.

4b.

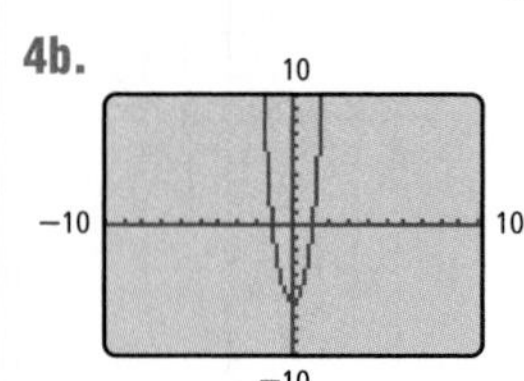

EXAMPLE 5 *Industrial Application*

A welder plans to construct an open box from an 18.5 ft by 24.5 ft sheet of metal by cutting squares from the corners and folding up the sides. Find the maximum volume of the box and the corresponding dimensions.

Find a formula to represent volume.

$V(x) = x(18.5 - 2x)(24.5 - 2x)$ $\quad V = \ell wh$

Graph $V(x)$. Note that values of x greater than 9.25 or less than 0 do not make sense for this problem.

The graph has a local maximum of about 704.4 when $x \approx 3.48$. So, the largest open box will have a volume of 704.4 ft^3.

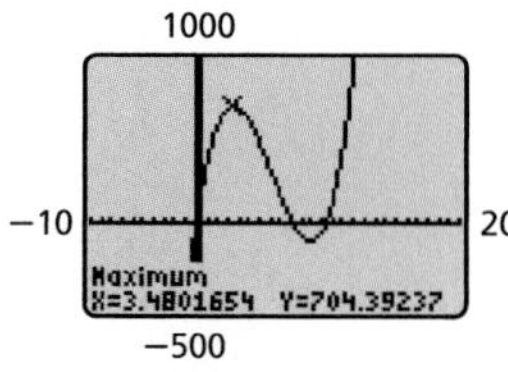

CHECK IT OUT! **5.** What is the maximum volume of a box made from a 16 ft by 20 ft sheet of metal? 420.1 ft^3

THINK AND DISCUSS

1. Explain why a polynomial function that has exactly n distinct real roots must have $n - 1$ turning points.

2. GET ORGANIZED Copy and complete the graphic organizer. In each box, sketch a graph that fits the description.

Leading Coefficient	Odd Degree	Even Degree
Positive		
Negative		

3 Close

Summarize

Ask students to summarize how end behavior and local maxima and minima can be used to sketch the graph of a polynomial function. The end behavior tells whether the graph rises or falls at the ends; the local maxima and minima tell the turning points of the graph.

ONGOING ASSESSMENT and INTERVENTION

Diagnose **Before** the Lesson
6-7 Warm Up, TE p. 453

Monitor **During** the Lesson
Check It Out! Exercises, SE pp. 454–456
Questioning Strategies, TE pp. 454–456

Assess **After** the Lesson
6-7 Lesson Quiz, TE p. 459
Alternative Assessment, TE p. 459

Answers to *Think and Discuss*

1. Possible answer: The graph must turn between each pair of roots in order to cross the x-axis again.
2. See p. A8.

go.hrw.com
Homework Help Online
KEYWORD: MB7 6-7
Parent Resources Online
KEYWORD: MB7 Parent

GUIDED PRACTICE

1. A graph "turns around" at a turning point.

1. **Vocabulary** Explain why a *turning point* is appropriately named.

SEE EXAMPLE 1 p. 454

Identify the leading coefficient, degree, and end behavior.

2. $P(x) = -4x^4 - 3x^3 + x^2 + 4$ — 2. -4; 4; $x \to \pm\infty$, $P \to -\infty$
3. $Q(x) = -2x^7 + 6x^5 + 2x^3$ — 3. -2; 7; $x \to -\infty$ $Q \to +\infty$; $x \to +\infty$ $Q \to -\infty$
4. $R(x) = x^5 - 4x^2 + 3x - 1$ — 4. 1; 5; $x \to -\infty$ $R \to -\infty$; $x \to +\infty$ $R \to +\infty$
5. $S(x) = 3x^2 + 6x - 10$ — 5. 3; 2; $x \to \pm\infty$ $S \to +\infty$

SEE EXAMPLE 2 p. 454

Identify whether the function graphed has an odd or even degree and a positive or negative leading coefficient.

6. 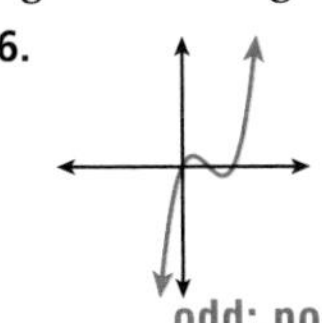 odd; positive
7. 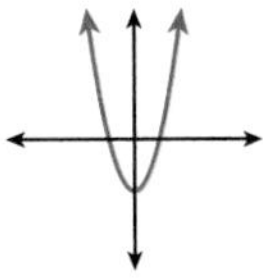 even; positive
8. 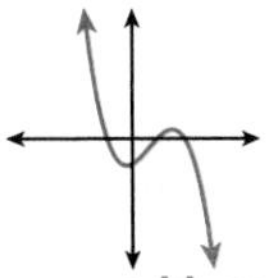 odd; negative
9. 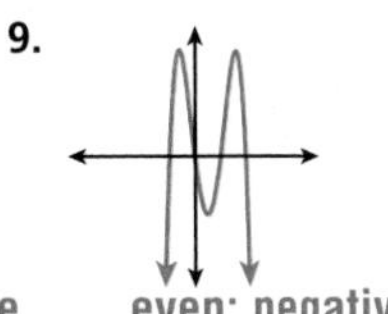 even; negative

SEE EXAMPLE 3 p. 455

Graph each function.

10. $f(x) = x^2 - 5x - 50$
11. $f(x) = -x^3 + \frac{3}{2}x^2 + 25x + 12$

SEE EXAMPLE 4 p. 456

Graph each function on a calculator, and estimate the local maxima and minima.

12. $f(x) = x^4 - 4x^3 + 3x + 5$ — max.: 6.0761; min.: 4.0539 and -13.13
13. $f(x) = 2x^3 - 3x^2 - 6x - 5$ — max.: -2.9098; min $= -14.0902$

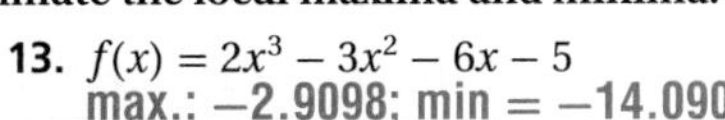

SEE EXAMPLE 5 p. 456

14. **Landscape Design** Vera has 60 ft of fencing and wants to enclose a patio, using an existing wall for one side as shown. The area of the patio can be modeled by $A(x) = 60x - 3x^2$, where x is in feet. Find the maximum area of the patio. 300 ft²

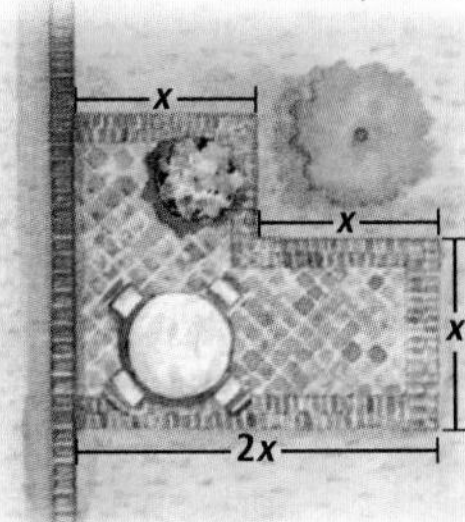

PRACTICE AND PROBLEM SOLVING

Independent Practice	
For Exercises	See Example
15–18	1
19–22	2
23–26	3
27–30	4
31	5

Extra Practice
Skills Practice p. S15
Application Practice p. S37

Identify the leading coefficient, degree, and end behavior.

15. $P(x) = 2x^3 + 3x^2 - 4x$ — 2; 3; $x \to -\infty$ $P \to -\infty$, $x \to +\infty$ $P \to +\infty$
16. $Q(x) = -3x^4 - 8x^2$ — 16. -3; 4; $x \to \pm\infty$ $Q \to -\infty$
17. $R(x) = -x^5 + 5x^4 + 1$ — -1; 5; $x \to -\infty$ $R \to +\infty$; $x \to +\infty$ $R \to -\infty$
18. $S(x) = 5.5x^8 + 7.5x^4$ — 18. 5.5; 8; $x \to \pm\infty$ $S \to +\infty$

Identify whether the function graphed has an odd or even degree and a positive or negative leading coefficient.

19. 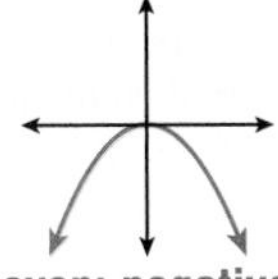 even; negative
20. 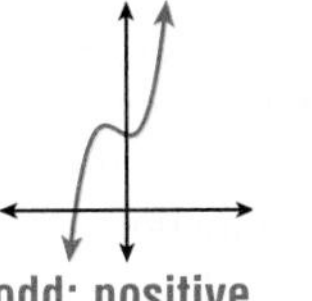 odd; positive
21. 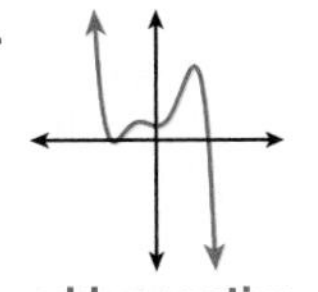 odd; negative
22. 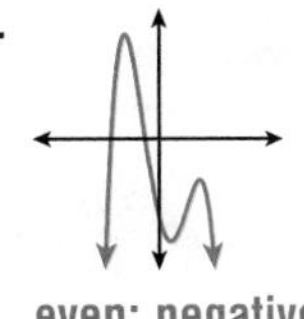 even; negative

Graph each function.

23. $f(x) = x^3 - \frac{7}{3}x^2 - \frac{43}{3}x + 5$
24. $f(x) = 25x^2 - 4$
25. $f(x) = x^4 + x^3 - 28x^2 + 20x + 48$
26. $f(x) = x^3 + \frac{13}{2}x^2 + 11x + 4$

Assignment Guide

Assign *Guided Practice* exercises as necessary.

If you finished Examples 1–2
Basic 15–22, 37, 39
Average 15–22, 32–37
Advanced 15–22, 32–39

If you finished Examples 1–5
Basic 15–38, 45, 47–50, 56–62
Average 15–31, 36–42, 44–50, 56–62
Advanced 17–20, 25–31, 38–62

Homework Quick Check
Quickly check key concepts.
Exercises: 18, 20, 26, 28, 31, 38

Answers

23. 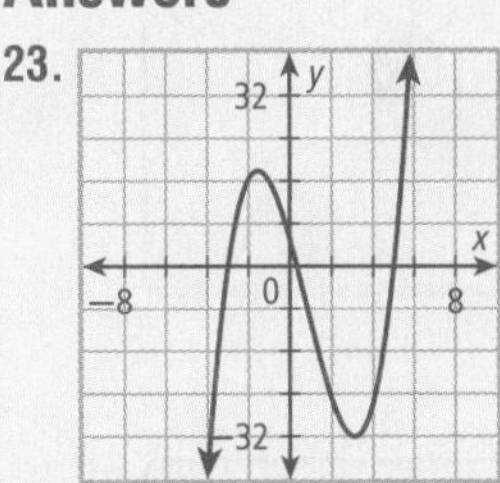

24. 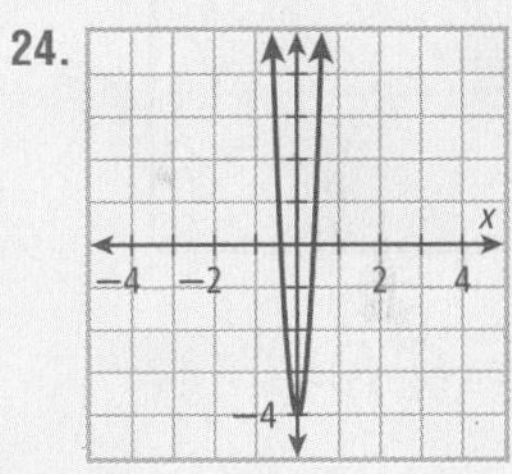

25–26. See p. A31.

Answers

10. 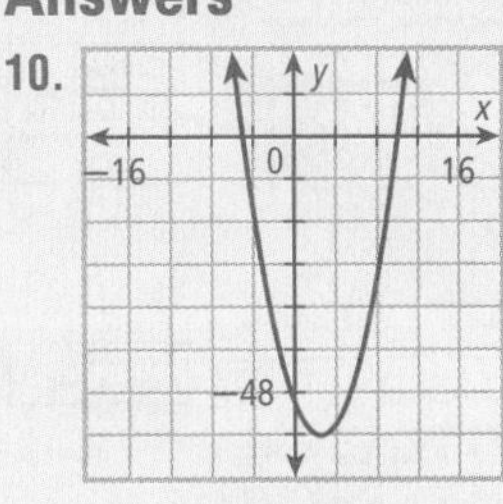

11. 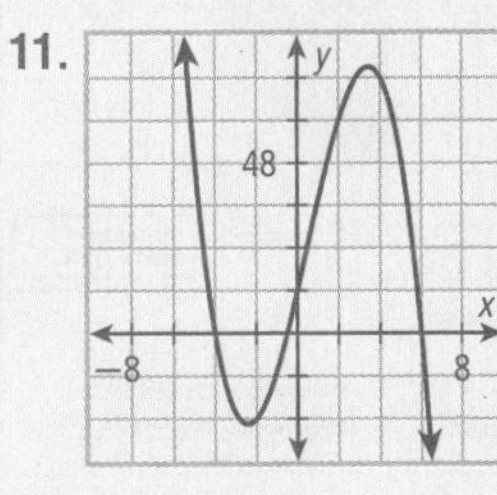

12. 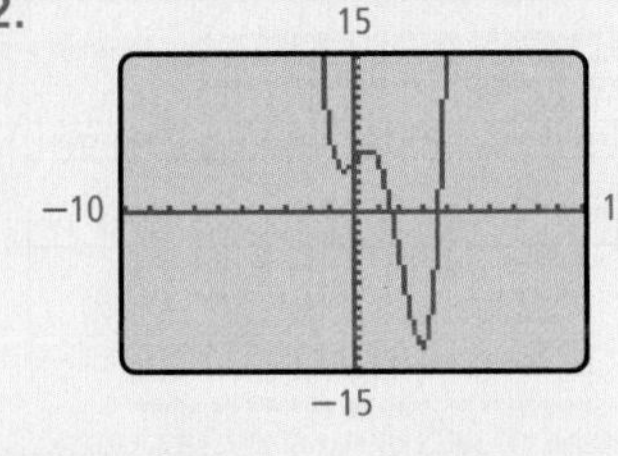

13. 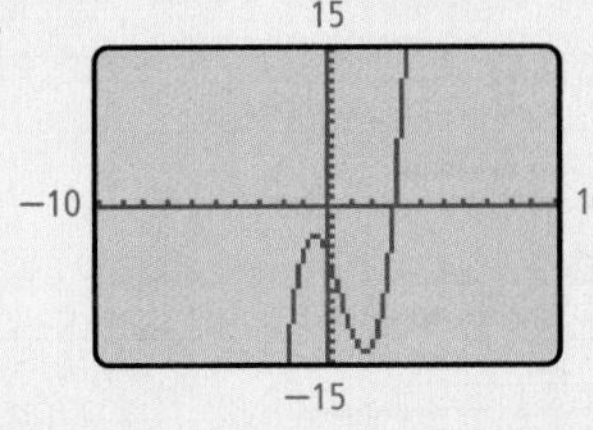

State Resources

Critical Thinking Before students graph the polynomial functions in **Exercises 27–30,** encourage them to predict how the graph should look based on the degree and end behavior.

Teaching Tip

Economics Link Discuss how Hiromi models his revenue in **Exercise 40.** The first factor is an expression for the price, and the second factor is an expression for the quantity. Make sure students understand why price and quantity are used to describe the revenue.

Exercise 43 involves maximizing the volume of a rectangular pyramid. This exercise prepares students for the Multi-Step Test Prep on page 472.

Answers

27.

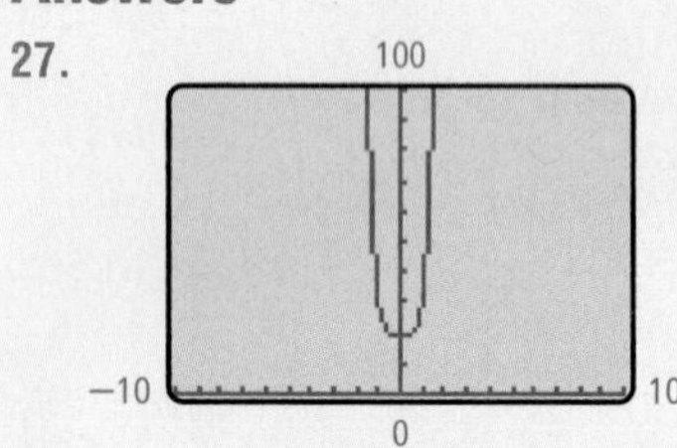

28.

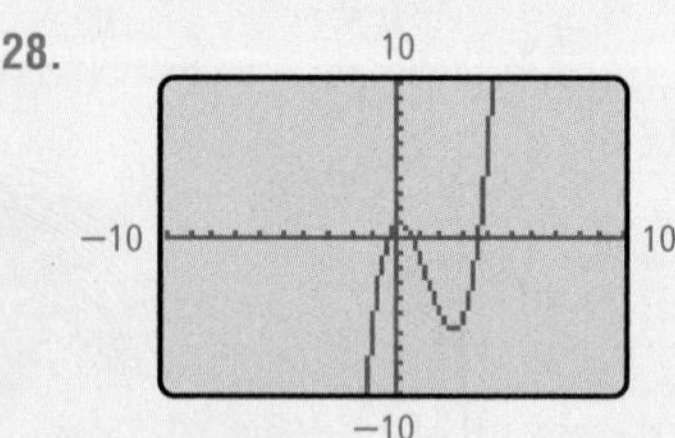

29–30. See p. A31.

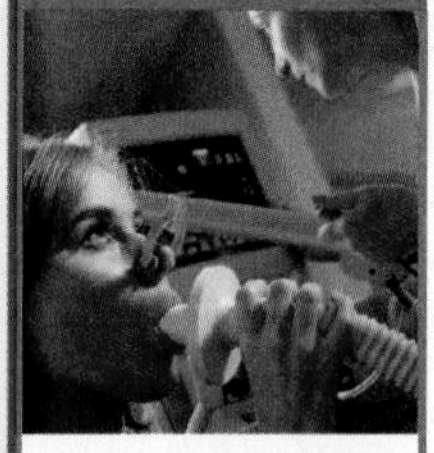

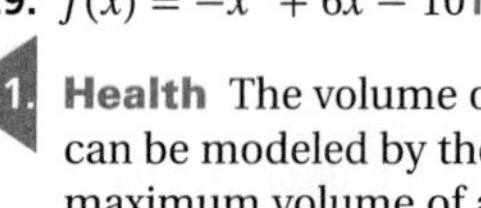

A person's total lung capacity depends on many factors. Typically, age, weight, gender, and physical fitness affect the volume of air that a person's lungs can hold.

Graph each function on a calculator, and estimate the local maxima and minima.

27. $f(x) = 9x^6 + 20$ **min.: 20**

28. $f(x) = x^3 - 4x^2 + x + 1$ **28. max.: 1.06; min.: −5.88**

29. $f(x) = -x^2 + 6x - 10$ **max.: −1**

30. $f(x) = -5x^2 + 7$ **max.: 7**

31. **Health** The volume of air (in liters) in the human lung during one normal breath can be modeled by the function $V(t) = -1.7t^2 + 1.7t + 3$, for $0 \le t \le 1$. What is the maximum volume of air in the lungs during a normal breath, and at what time does it occur? **3.425 L; 0.5 s**

Use the degree and end behavior to match each polynomial to its graph.

A.

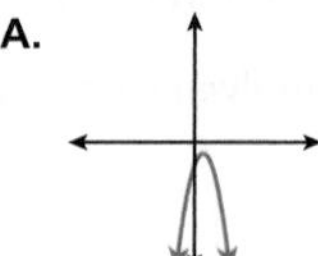

B.

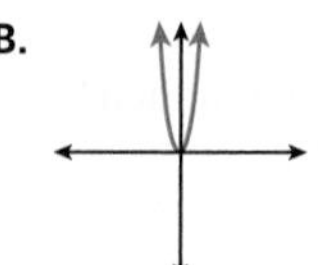

C.

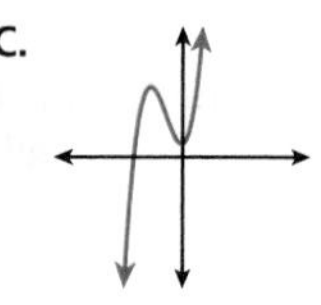

D.

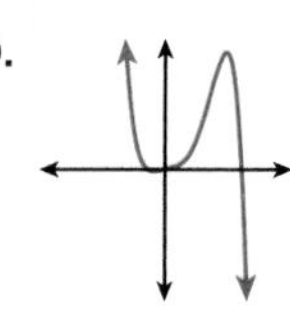

32. $5x^3 + 9x^2 + 1$ **C**

33. $2x^6 + 3x^4 + 5x^2$ **B**

34. $3x^4 - x^5 + x$ **D**

35. $-4x^2 + 3x - 1$ **A**

Describe the end behavior of each function by completing the statements $f(x) \to$ ______ as $x \to -\infty$, and $f(x) \to$ ______ as $x \to +\infty$.

36. $f(x) = 2x^5 - x^2 + 75$ **$-\infty$; $+\infty$**

37. $f(x) = 10x^4 + 9x^2$ **$+\infty$; $+\infty$**

38. $f(x) = -5x^3 + x - 8$ **$+\infty$; $-\infty$**

39. $f(x) = 1000x^4 - 0.0002x^8$ **$+\infty$; $+\infty$**

40. $f(x) = x^{13} - x^7 + 12x$ **$-\infty$; $+\infty$**

41. $f(x) = -331x^{44} + 98$ **$-\infty$; $-\infty$**

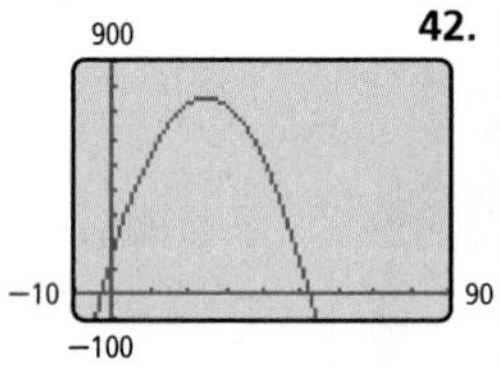

42. **Retail** Hiromi sells 12 T-shirts each week at a price of \$13.00. Past sales have shown that for every \$0.25 decrease in price, 4 more T-shirts are sold. Knowing that revenue is a product of price and quantity, Hiromi models his revenue by $R(x) = (13 - 0.25x)(12 + 4x)$, where x represents the number of times there is a reduction in price.

a. Graph the function on a graphing calculator.

b. What is the maximum revenue Hiromi can generate each week? **\$756.25**

c. How many \$0.25 reductions will maximize Hiromi's revenue? What would be the price per T-shirt, given the price is $13 - 0.25x$? **25; \$6.75**

42a.

43. **Critical Thinking** Why are the leading coefficient and degree of the first term of the polynomial the only characteristics that determine end behavior?

43. Possible answer: For very large values of x, the leading term overpowers the other terms, so its degree and coefficient are all that matter.

44. Which of the following functions has end behavior that is different from the others? Explain.

$f(x) = 2x^7 - 10x^4 + 125$ $\quad g(x) = -x^7 + x^6$ $\quad h(x) = 5x^3 - 1$ $\quad k(x) = -x + 4x^5$

g; The leading coefficient of g is negative.

MULTI-STEP TEST PREP

45. This problem will prepare you for the Multi-Step Test Prep on page 472.

A packaging company wants to manufacture a pyramid-shaped gift box with a rectangular base. The base must have a perimeter of 20 in., and the height of the box must be equal to the length of the base.

a. Write a polynomial function, $V(x)$, for the volume of the box, where x is the length of the base. **45a. $V(x) = -\frac{1}{3}x^3 + \frac{10}{3}x^2$**

b. Find the maximum volume of the box. **49.4 in^3**

c. What dimensions result in a box with the maximum volume? **6.7 in. × 3.3 in. × 6.7 in.**

6-7 PRACTICE A

6-7 PRACTICE C

6-7 PRACTICE B

Identify the leading coefficient, degree, and end behavior.

1. $P(x) = 2x^5 - 6x^3 + x^2 - 2$
   2; 5; as $x \to +\infty$, $P(x) \to +\infty$; and as $x \to -\infty$, $P(x) \to -\infty$

2. $Q(x) = -4x^2 + x - 1$
   −4; 2; as $x \to -\infty$, $Q(x) \to -\infty$; and as $x \to +\infty$, $Q(x) \to -\infty$

Identify whether the function graphed has an odd or even degree and a positive or negative leading coefficient.

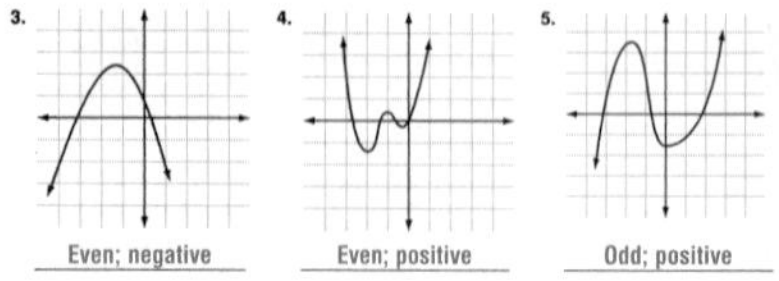

3. Even; negative

4. Even; positive

5. Odd; positive

Graph the function $P(x) = x^3 + 6x^2 + 5x - 12$.

6. Identify the possible rational roots.
   ±1, ±2, ±3, ±4, ±6, ±12

7. Identify the zeros.
   −4, −3, and 1

8. Describe the end behavior of the function.
   As $x \to +\infty$, $P(x) \to +\infty$, and as $x \to -\infty$, $P(x) \to -\infty$

9. Sketch the graph of the function.

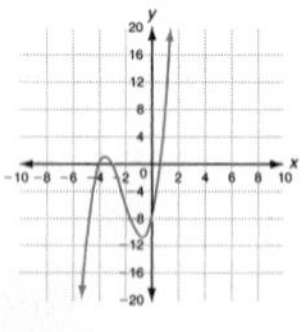

Solve.

10. The number, $N(y)$, of subscribers to a local magazine can be modeled by the function $N(y) = 0.1y^4 - 3y^3 + 10y^2 - 30y + 10{,}000$, where y is the number of years since the magazine was founded. Graph the polynomial on a graphing calculator and find the minimum number of subscribers and the year in which this occurs.
    About 5400 in year 20

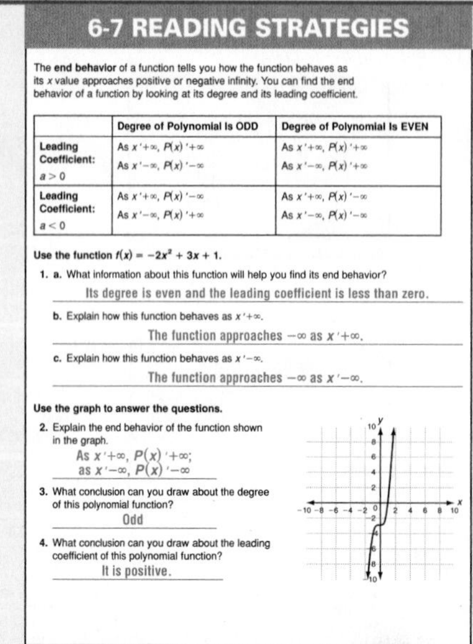

6-7 READING STRATEGIES

The **end behavior** of a function tells you how the function behaves as its x value approaches positive or negative infinity. You can find the end behavior of a function by looking at its degree and its leading coefficient.

	Degree of Polynomial Is ODD	Degree of Polynomial Is EVEN
Leading Coefficient: $a > 0$	As x '+∞, P(x) '+∞ As x '−∞, P(x) '−∞	As x '+∞, P(x) '+∞ As x '−∞, P(x) '+∞
Leading Coefficient: $a < 0$	As x '+∞, P(x) '−∞ As x '−∞, P(x) '+∞	As x '+∞, P(x) '−∞ As x '−∞, P(x) '−∞

Use the function $f(x) = -2x^2 + 3x + 1$.

1. a. What information about this function will help you find its end behavior?
   Its degree is even and the leading coefficient is less than zero.

   b. Explain how this function behaves as x '+∞.
   The function approaches −∞ as x '+∞.

   c. Explain how this function behaves as x '−∞.
   The function approaches −∞ as x '−∞.

Use the graph to answer the questions.

2. Explain the end behavior of the function shown in the graph.
   As x '+∞, P(x) '+∞; as x '−∞, P(x) '−∞

3. What conclusion can you draw about the degree of this polynomial function?
   Odd

4. What conclusion can you draw about the leading coefficient of this polynomial function?
   It is positive.

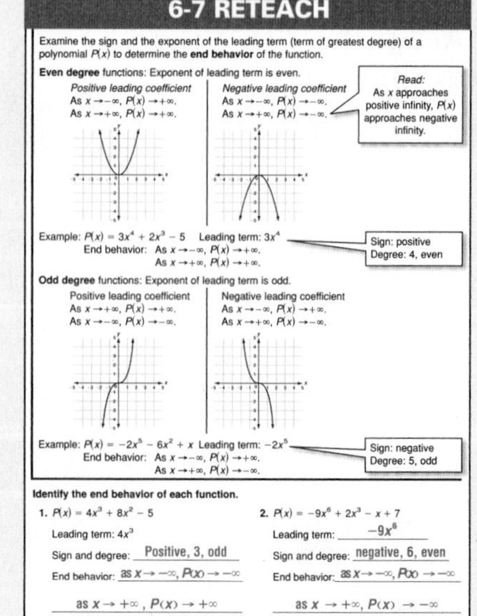

6-7 RETEACH

Examine the sign and the exponent of the leading term (term of greatest degree) of a polynomial $P(x)$ to determine the **end behavior** of the function.

Even degree functions: Exponent of leading term is even.

Positive leading coefficient
As $x \to -\infty$, $P(x) \to +\infty$.
As $x \to +\infty$, $P(x) \to +\infty$.

Negative leading coefficient
As $x \to -\infty$, $P(x) \to -\infty$.
As $x \to +\infty$, $P(x) \to -\infty$.

Read: As x approaches positive infinity, $P(x)$ approaches negative infinity.

Example: $P(x) = 3x^4 + 2x^3 - 5$ Leading term: $3x^4$
End behavior: As $x \to -\infty$, $P(x) \to +\infty$.
As $x \to +\infty$, $P(x) \to +\infty$.

Sign: positive
Degree: 4, even

Odd degree functions: Exponent of leading term is odd.

Positive leading coefficient
As $x \to +\infty$, $P(x) \to +\infty$.
As $x \to -\infty$, $P(x) \to -\infty$.

Negative leading coefficient
As $x \to -\infty$, $P(x) \to +\infty$.
As $x \to +\infty$, $P(x) \to -\infty$.

Example: $P(x) = -2x^5 - 6x^2 + x$ Leading term: $-2x^5$
End behavior: As $x \to -\infty$, $P(x) \to +\infty$.
As $x \to +\infty$, $P(x) \to -\infty$.

Sign: negative
Degree: 5, odd

Identify the end behavior of each function.

1. $P(x) = 4x^3 + 8x^2 - 5$
   Leading term: $4x^3$
   Sign and degree: Positive, 3, odd
   End behavior: as $x \to -\infty$, $P(x) \to -\infty$
   as $x \to +\infty$, $P(x) \to +\infty$

2. $P(x) = -9x^6 + 2x^3 - x + 7$
   Leading term: $-9x^6$
   Sign and degree: negative, 6, even
   End behavior: as $x \to -\infty$, $P(x) \to -\infty$
   as $x \to +\infty$, $P(x) \to -\infty$

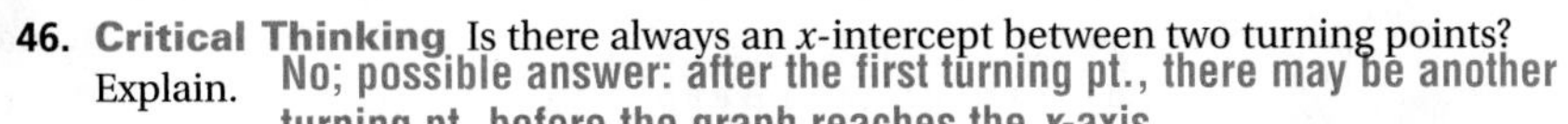

46. **Critical Thinking** Is there always an x-intercept between two turning points? Explain. No; possible answer: after the first turning pt., there may be another turning pt. before the graph reaches the x-axis.

47. **Write About It** Describe the steps for graphing a polynomial by hand.

TEST PREP

48. How many turning points will a quartic function with four real zeros have?

Ⓐ 1 Ⓑ 2 Ⓒ 3 (circled) Ⓓ 4

49. Which function could describe the graph?

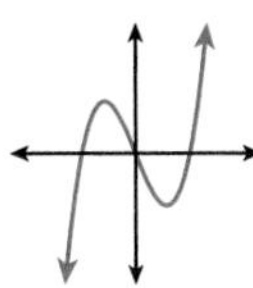

Ⓕ $f(x) = -2x^5 + x - 4$

Ⓗ $f(x) = 3x^3 - 9x$ (circled)

Ⓖ $f(x) = -x^3 + 5x^2 + 4x + 3$

Ⓙ $f(x) = \frac{1}{4}x^2 + \frac{1}{2}x + 1$

50. **Extended Response** Consider the polynomial function $f(x) = 2x^4 + 12x^3 + 24x^2 + 16x$.

a. Find all solutions to the equation $f(x) = 0$. $x = -2, 0$

b. Describe the end behavior of $f(x)$. Explain your reasoning.

c. Sketch a graph of $f(x)$ by using your answers to part **a** and part **b**.

50b. $x \to \pm\infty, f \to +\infty$; positive leading coefficient, even degree

50c.

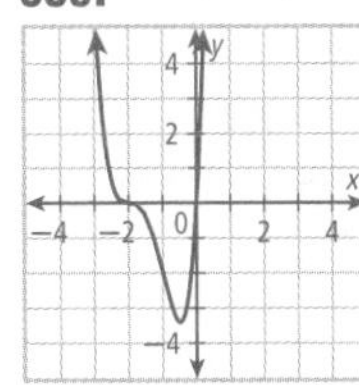

CHALLENGE AND EXTEND

Graph each function without using a graphing calculator.

51. $3x^6 - 57x^4 + 6x^3 + 144x^2 - 96x$

52. $-2x^5 - 14x^4 - 30x^3 - 18x^2$

51.

52.

Examine the behavior of the cubic polynomials $f(x) = x^3$ and $g(x) = x^3 - 6x^2 + 4x - 20$ for the given values of x by using a spreadsheet or graphing calculator.

53. Complete the table.

x	$f(x)$	$g(x)$	$\frac{f(x)}{g(x)}$
5	■	■	■
10	■	■	■
50	■	■	■
100	■	■	■
500	■	■	■
1000	■	■	■
5000	■	■	■

54. Use your answer to Exercise 50 to complete this statement.

As $x \to +\infty$, $\frac{f(x)}{g(x)} \to$ 1.

55. Explain what the statement in Exercise 54 implies about the end behavior of $f(x)$ and $g(x)$. Possible answer: the same end behavior

SPIRAL REVIEW

Use substitution to determine if the given point is a solution to the system of equations. *(Lesson 3-1)*

56. $(2, -2)\begin{cases} 2x + y = 2 \\ 6x - 2y = 16 \end{cases}$ yes

57. $(3, -1)\begin{cases} x + 3y = 0 \\ 8x + 4y = 21 \end{cases}$ no

58. $(5, -5)\begin{cases} x + y = 5 \\ x - y = 10 \end{cases}$ no

59. **Sports** A tennis ball is served with an initial velocity of 64 ft/s^2 from 6 ft above the ground. The tennis ball's height in feet is modeled by $h(t) = -16t^2 + 64t + 6$, where t is the time in seconds after the tennis ball is hit. Write the function in vertex form and identify the vertex. *(Lesson 5-4)* $h(t) = -16(t-2)^2 + 70$; vertex $(2, 70)$

Divide by using long division. *(Lesson 6-3)*

60. $x + 3\overline{)x^2 + 4x + 10}$ $x + 1 + \frac{7}{x+3}$

61. $x + 1\overline{)10x^2 + 8x + 6}$ $10x - 2 + \frac{8}{x+1}$

62. $x + 8\overline{)x^2 + x - 64}$ $x - 7 - \frac{8}{x+8}$

TEST PREP DOCTOR In **Exercise 47,** students who chose **F** or **G** may have confused the leading coefficient. Have them review end behavior. Students who chose **J** may have forgotten that the graph of a quadratic function is a parabola. Have those students review the different shapes of polynomial functions.

Answers

47, 53. See p. A31.

Journal

Have students explain how they can use only the leading term to describe end behavior of a polynomial.

ALTERNATIVE ASSESSMENT

Have students write a cubic polynomial equation and identify the leading coefficient and end behavior of the function. Then have them use the techniques of the lesson to graph the function and estimate local maxima and minima.

Power Presentations with PowerPoint®

6-7 Lesson Quiz

1. Identify whether the function graphed has an odd or even degree and a positive or negative leading coefficient.

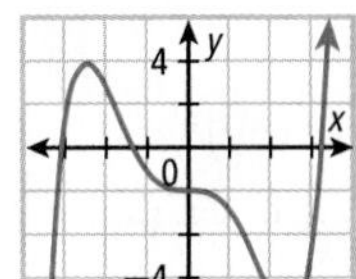

odd; positive

2. Graph the function.
$f(x) = x^3 - 3x^2 - x + 3$

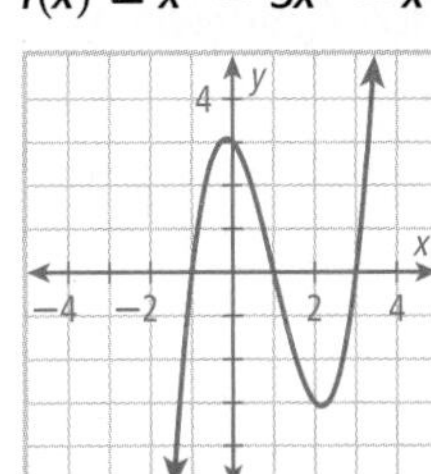

3. Estimate the local maxima and minima of $f(x) = x^3 - 15x - 2$.

20.3607; −24.3607

Also available on transparency

6-7 PROBLEM SOLVING

The Spanish Club members are baking and selling fruit bars to raise money for a trip. They are going to make open boxes to display the bars from sheets of cardboard that are 11 inches by 17 inches. They will cut a square from each corner and fold up the sides and tape them. Find the maximum value for the volume of the box and find its dimensions.

1. Write a formula to represent the volume of the box. $V(x) = x(11 - 2x)(17 - 2x)$
2. a. Write the equation in standard form. $4x^3 - 56x^2 + 187x = 0$
   b. Is the leading coefficient positive or negative? Positive
   c. Is the degree of the polynomial even or odd? Odd
   d. Describe the end behavior of the graph.
   As $x \to +\infty$, $V \to +\infty$, and as $x \to -\infty$, $V \to -\infty$.
3. Use a graphing calculator to graph the equation. Hint: Try a window from −10 to 10 on the x-axis, with a scale of 1, and from −500 to 500 on the y-axis, with a scale of 100.
   a. How many turning points does the graph have? 2
   b. Estimate the local maxima and minima from the graph. About 183 and −64
4. What values of x are excluded as solutions because they do not make sense for this problem? Values of x greater than 5.5 or less than 0
5. Use the CALC menu on your graphing calculator to find the approximate values of x and y at the local maximum for the graph. About 2.3 and 183
6. What is the maximum volume of the box? 183 cubic inches
7. What are the dimensions of the box to the nearest tenth of an inch?
   2.3 in. by 6.4 in. by 12.4 in.

Choose the letter for the best answer.

8. Arturo is going to build a dog run using one side of his house and 100 feet of fencing. His design has an area that can be modeled by $A(x) = 100x - 7x^2$. What is the maximum area he can enclose?
   Ⓐ 357 ft^2 (circled)
   B 204 ft^2
   C 100 ft^2
   D 70 ft^2

9. In order to eliminate some choices on a standardized test, Ruth identifies which of these functions could NOT have a local maximum.
   A $F(x) = -7x^2 + 5x + 2$
   B $F(x) = -7x^3 + 5x - 11$
   C $F(x) = 7x^3 - 5x^2 - 2$
   Ⓓ $F(x) = 7x^2 - 3x - 18$ (circled)

6-7 CHALLENGE

In general, the graph of a polynomial equation of degree n contains $(n - 1)$ or fewer turning points. You can explore the factored form of a polynomial equation to note the effect that different constant values have on the shape of the curve.

$P(x) = (x - a)(x - b)(x - c)(x - d)$ Where a, b, c, and d are real numbers.

1. Suppose that a, b, c, and d are all different nonzero numbers.
   a. Make a conjecture about the number of turning points. 3
   b. Write a particular function that satisfies the conditions.
   $y = (x + 3)(x + 1)(x - 1)(x - 5)$
   c. Use a graphing calculator to obtain a graph of the function you wrote in part **b**. Sketch the graph on the grid at right.

Follow the steps outlined in Exercise 1 to explore different conditions placed on a, b, c, and d. Summarize your results in the table shown below.

	Conditions Placed on a, b, c, and d	Example	Number of Turning Points	Other Observations
2.	All of a, b, c, and d are different and nonzero	$y = (x+3)(x+1)(x-1)(x-5)$	3	4 distinct x- intercepts
3.	All of a, b, c, and d nonzero and exactly two are the same	$y = (x+3)^2(x-1)(x-5)$	3	tangent to the x-axis at $x = -3$
4.	All of a, b, c, and d nonzero and exactly three are the same	$y = (x+3)^3(x-5)$	1	curve "bends" at $x = -3$
5.	All of a, b, c, and d nonzero and all are equal	$y = (x+3)^4$	1	tangent to the x-axis at $x = -3$
6.	All of a, b, c, and d different and exactly one is 0	$y = x(x+3)(x-1)(x-5)$	3	4 distinct x- intercepts
7.	Two of a, b, c, and d are 0 and the other two are different	$y = x^2(x+3)(x-3)$	3	tangent to the x-axis at $x = 0$
8.	Exactly three of a, b, c, and d are 0	$y = x^3(x-3)$	1	curve "bends" at $x = 0$
9.	All of a, b, c, and d are 0	$y = x^4$	1	looks like a parabola

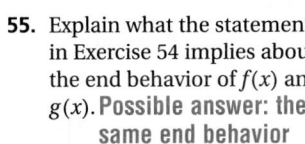

6-8 Organizer

Pacing: Traditional 1 day
Block $\frac{1}{2}$ day

Objective: Transform polynomial functions.

Online Edition
Graphing Calculator, Tutorial Videos

Countdown to Testing Week 14

Power Presentations with PowerPoint®

Warm Up

Let g be the indicated transformation of $f(x) = 3x + 1$. Write the rule for g.

1. horizontal translation 1 unit right $g(x) = 3x - 2$
2. vertical stretch by a factor of 2 $g(x) = 6x + 2$
3. horizontal compression by a factor of 4 $g(x) = 12x + 1$

Also available on transparency

Math Humor

Q: Why didn't the function recognize itself in the mirror?

A: It had been completely transformed.

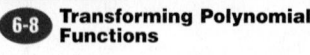

6-8 Transforming Polynomial Functions

A2.1.2 Use and interpret function notation, including evaluation of functions represented by tables, graphs, words, equations or a set of ordered pairs.

Objective
Transform polynomial functions.

Why learn this?
Transformations can be used in business to model sales. (See Example 5.)

You can perform the same transformations on polynomial functions that you performed on quadratic and linear functions.

Transformations of $f(x)$

Transformation	$f(x)$ Notation	Examples	
Vertical translation	$f(x) + k$	$g(x) = x^3 + 3$	3 units up
		$g(x) = x^3 - 4$	4 units down
Horizontal translation	$f(x - h)$	$g(x) = (x - 2)^3$	2 units right
		$g(x) = (x + 1)^3$	1 unit left
Vertical stretch/compression	$af(x)$	$g(x) = 6x^3$	stretch by 6
		$g(x) = \frac{1}{2}x^3$	compression by $\frac{1}{2}$
Horizontal stretch/compression	$f\left(\frac{1}{b}x\right)$	$g(x) = \left(\frac{1}{5}x\right)^3$	stretch by 5
		$g(x) = (3x)^3$	compression by $\frac{1}{3}$
Reflection	$-f(x)$	$g(x) = -x^3$	across x-axis
	$f(-x)$	$g(x) = (-x)^3$	across y-axis

EXAMPLE 1 Translating a Polynomial Function

For $f(x) = x^3 + 4$, write the rule for each function and sketch its graph.

A $g(x) = f(x) + 3$

$g(x) = (x^3 + 4) + 3$

$g(x) = x^3 + 7$

To graph $g(x) = f(x) + 3$, translate the graph of $f(x)$ 3 units up.

This is a vertical translation.

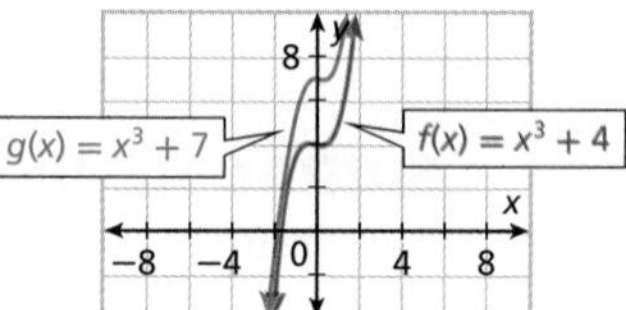

Helpful Hint
You can use a calculator to check your graph.

B $g(x) = f(x - 5)$

$g(x) = (x - 5)^3 + 4$

$g(x) = (x - 5)^3 + 4$

To graph $g(x) = f(x - 5)$, translate the graph of $f(x)$ 5 units right.

This is a horizontal translation.

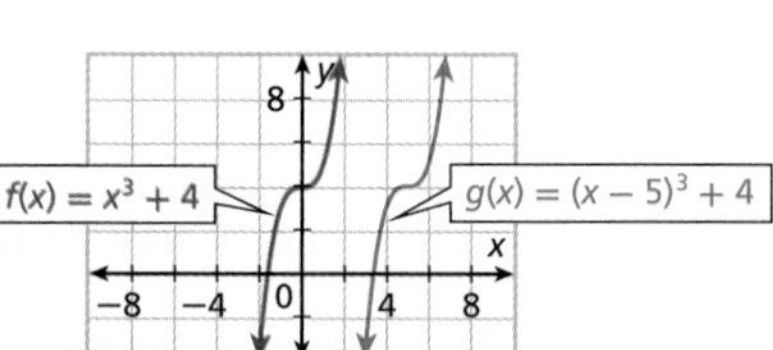

State Resources

go.hrw.com
State Resources Online
KEYWORD: MB7 Resources

1 Introduce

EXPLORATION

6-8 Transforming Polynomial Functions

Use your calculator to investigate transformations of polynomial functions.

1. Graph $f(x) = x^3 - 6x + 2$.

Graph each of the following functions in the same window as $f(x)$. In each case, use the language of transformations to explain how the graph of $g(x)$ is related to the graph of $f(x)$.

2. $g(x) = x^3 - 6x + 5$
3. $g(x) = (x - 3)^3 - 6(x - 3) + 2$
4. $g(x) = \frac{1}{2}x^3 - 3x + 1$
5. $g(x) = \left(\frac{1}{3}x\right)^3 - 2x + 2$
6. $g(x) = -x^3 + 6x - 2$

THINK AND DISCUSS

7. **Explain** how you can write a polynomial function whose graph is the same as that of $f(x)$ but is translated 6 units down.

Motivate

Ask students to identify all the types of transformations with which they are familiar. Explain that the same transformations will also apply to polynomial functions.

Explorations and answers are provided in the *Explorations* binder.

For $f(x) = x^3 + 4$, write the rule for each function and sketch its graph.

1a. $g(x) = f(x) - 5$ $g(x) = x^3 - 1$

1b. $g(x) = f(x + 2)$ $g(x) = x^3 + 6x^2 + 12x + 12$

1a. 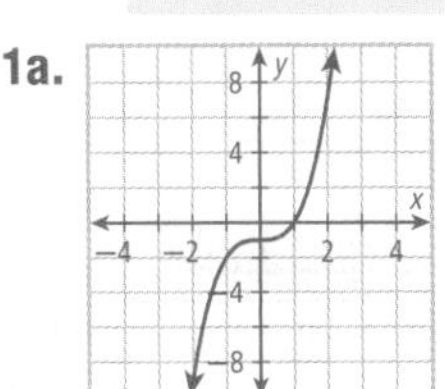

1b. 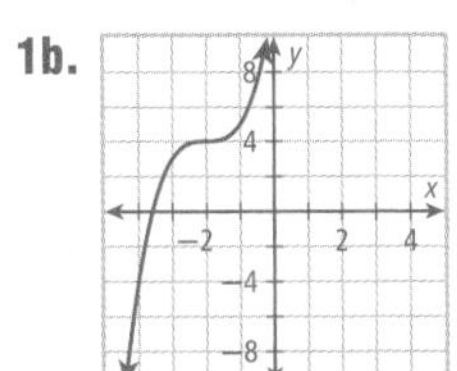

EXAMPLE 2 Reflecting Polynomial Functions

Let $f(x) = x^3 - 7x^2 + 6x - 5$. Write a function g that performs each transformation.

A Reflect $f(x)$ across the x-axis.

$g(x) = -f(x)$

$g(x) = -(x^3 - 7x^2 + 6x - 5)$

$g(x) = -x^3 + 7x^2 - 6x + 5$

Check Graph both functions. The graph appears to be a reflection. ✔

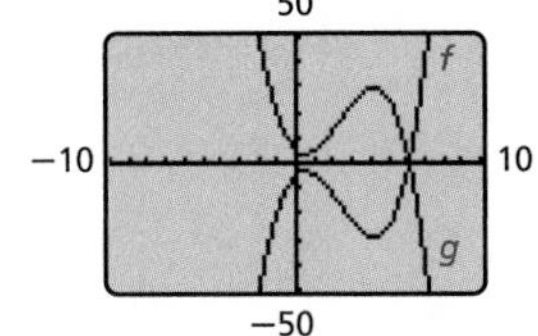

B Reflect $f(x)$ across the y-axis.

$g(x) = f(-x)$

$g(x) = (-x)^3 - 7(-x)^2 + 6(-x) - 5$

$g(x) = -x^3 - 7x^2 - 6x - 5$

Check Graph both functions. The graph appears to be a reflection. ✔

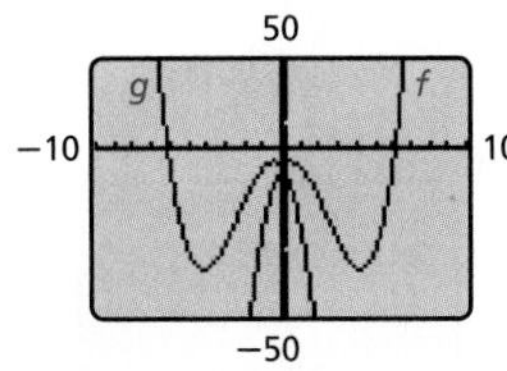

CHECK IT OUT! Let $f(x) = x^3 - 2x^2 - x + 2$. Write a function $g(x)$ that performs each transformation.

2a. Reflect $f(x)$ across the x-axis. $g(x) = -x^3 + 2x^2 + x - 2$

2b. Reflect $f(x)$ across the y-axis. $g(x) = -x^3 - 2x^2 + x + 2$

EXAMPLE 3 Compressing and Stretching Polynomial Functions

Let $f(x) = x^4 - 4x^2 + 2$. Graph f and g on the same coordinate plane. Describe g as a transformation of f.

A $g(x) = 2f(x)$

$g(x) = 2(x^4 - 4x^2 + 2)$

$g(x) = 2x^4 - 8x^2 + 4$

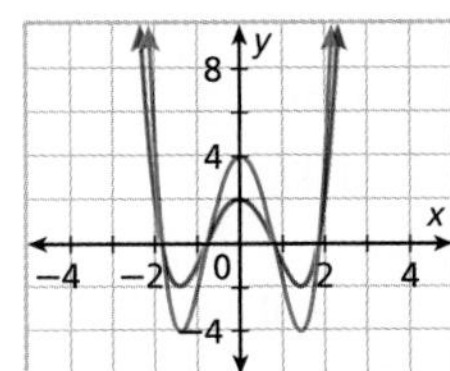

$g(x)$ is a vertical stretch of $f(x)$.

B $g(x) = f(3x)$

$g(x) = (3x)^4 - 4(3x)^2 + 2$

$g(x) = 81x^4 - 36x^2 + 2$

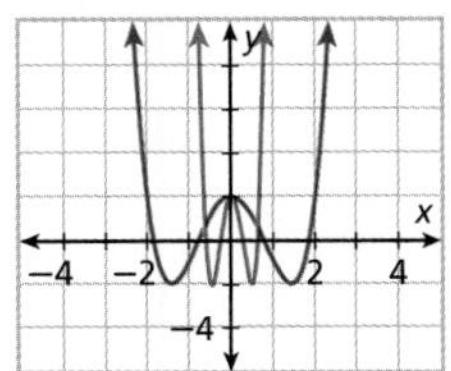

$g(x)$ is a horizontal compression of $f(x)$.

3a. 3b.

Let $f(x) = 16x^4 - 24x^2 + 4$. Graph f and g on the same coordinate plane. Describe g as a transformation of f.

3a. $g(x) = \frac{1}{4}f(x)$ vertical compression

3b. $g(x) = f\left(\frac{1}{2}x\right)$ horizontal stretch

Power Presentations with PowerPoint®

Additional Examples

Example 1

For $f(x) = x^3 - 6$, write the rule for each function and sketch its graph.

A. $g(x) = f(x) - 2$ $g(x) = x^3 - 8$

B. $h(x) = f(x + 3)$

$h(x) = (x + 3)^3 - 6$

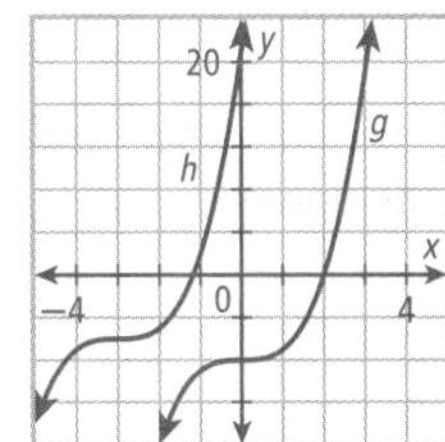

Example 2

Let $f(x) = x^3 + 5x^2 - 8x + 1$. Write a function g that performs each transformation.

A. Reflect f across the x-axis.

$g(x) = -x^3 - 5x^2 + 8x - 1$

B. Reflect f across the y-axis.

$g(x) = -x^3 + 5x^2 + 8x + 1$

Example 3

Let $f(x) = 2x^4 - 6x^2 + 1$. Graph f and g on the same coordinate plane. Describe g as a transformation of f.

A. $g(x) = \frac{1}{2}f(x)$ vertical compression

B. $h(x) = f\left(\frac{1}{3}x\right)$ horizontal stretch

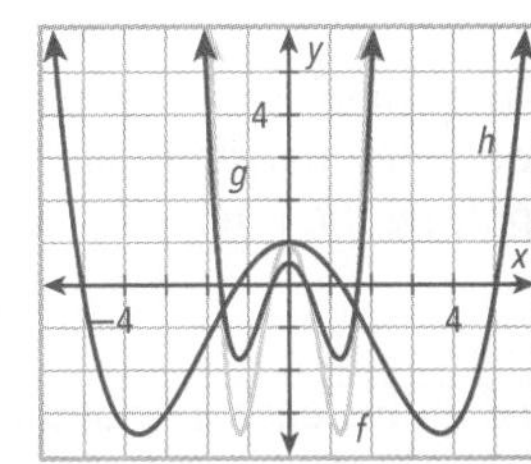

Also available on transparency

2 Teach

Guided Instruction

Give students examples of transformations using $f(x)$ notation and ask them to identify the type of transformation based on what they learned in Chapter 5. Then give students transformations using a simple polynomial such as $g(x) = x^4$.

Reaching All Learners

Through Cooperative Learning

Have students form pairs. Give each pair of students a polynomial function and a graphing calculator. Have them graph the function. Then have both partners predict what the graphs of several transformed functions based on the given function will look like. Include a reflection across the x-axis, a reflection across the y-axis, and a vertical stretch. Have them graph each transformation to verify their predictions.

INTERVENTION

Questioning Strategies

EXAMPLES 1–3

- How is the algebraic representation different for vertical and horizontal transformations?

Power Presentations with PowerPoint®

Additional Examples

Example 4

Write a function that transforms $f(x) = 6x^3 - 3$ in each of the following ways. Support your solution by using a graphing calculator.

A. Compress vertically by $\frac{1}{3}$ and shift 2 units right.

$g(x) = 2(x - 2)^3 - 1$

B. Reflect across the y-axis and shift 2 units down.

$h(x) = -6x^3 - 5$

Example 5

The number of skateboards sold per month can be modeled by $f(x) = 0.1x^3 + 0.2x^2 + 0.3x + 130$, where x represents the number of months since May. Let $g(x) = f(x) + 20$. Find the rule for g and explain the meaning of the transformation in terms of monthly skateboard sales.

$g(x) = 0.1x^3 + 0.2x^2 + 0.3x + 150$; vertical shift 20 units up; increase in sales of 20 units per month

Also available on transparency

INTERVENTION

Questioning Strategies

EXAMPLE 4

- Why is it helpful to write the rule for the combined transformation before applying the rule?

EXAMPLE 5

- How could an increase in monthly sales be represented by a transformation?

EXAMPLE 4 Combining Transformations

Write a function that transforms $f(x) = 3x^3 + 6$ in each of the following ways. Support your solution by using a graphing calculator.

A **Stretch vertically by a factor of 2, and shift 3 units left.**

A vertical stretch is represented by $af(x)$, and a horizontal shift is represented by $f(x - h)$. Combining the two transformations gives $g(x) = af(x - h)$.

Substitute 2 for a and 3 for h.

$g(x) = 2f(x + 3)$

$g(x) = 2\left(3(x + 3)^3 + 6\right)$

$g(x) = 6(x + 3)^3 + 12$

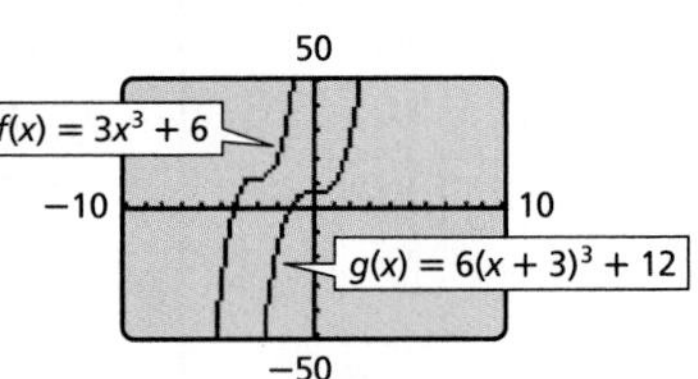

B **Reflect across the x-axis and shift 3 units up.**

A reflection across the x-axis is represented by $-f(x)$, and a vertical shift is represented by $f(x) + k$. Combining the two transformations gives $h(x) = -f(x) + k$.

Substitute 3 for k.

$h(x) = -f(x) + 3$

$h(x) = -(3x^3 + 6) + 3$

$h(x) = -3x^3 - 3$

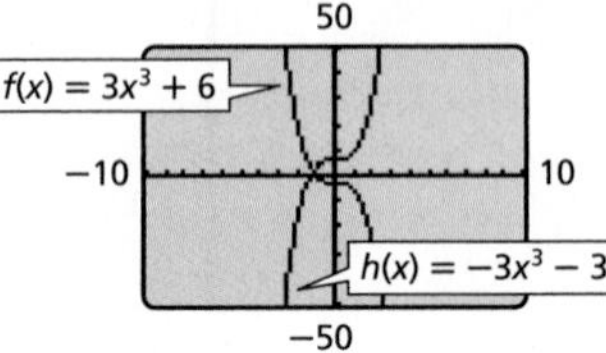

CHECK IT OUT! **Write a function that transforms $f(x) = 8x^3 - 2$ in each of the following ways. Support your solution by using a graphing calculator.**

4a. Compress vertically by a factor of $\frac{1}{2}$, and move the x-intercept 3 units right. $f(x) = 4x^3 - 36x^2 + 108x - 109$

4b. Reflect across the x-axis, and move the x-intercept 4 units left. $f(x) = -8x^3 - 96x^2 - 384x - 510$

4a.

4b.

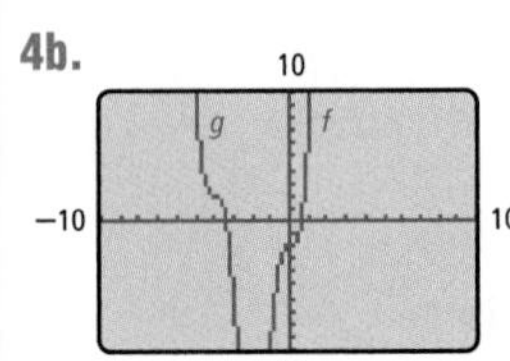

EXAMPLE 5 *Bicycle Sales*

The number of bicycles sold per month by a business can be modeled by $f(x) = 0.01x^3 + 0.7x^2 + 0.4x + 120$, where x represents the number of months since January. Let $g(x) = f(x) - 30$. Find the rule for g, and explain the meaning of the transformation in terms of monthly bicycle sales.

Step 1 Write the new rule.

The new rule is $g(x) = f(x) - 30$.

$g(x) = f(x) - 30$

$g(x) = 0.01x^3 + 0.7x^2 + 0.4x + 120 - 30$

$g(x) = 0.01x^3 + 0.7x^2 + 0.4x + 90$

Step 2 Interpret the transformation.

The transformation represents a vertical shift 30 units down, which corresponds to a decrease in sales of 30 units per month.

CHECK IT OUT! **5.** Let $g(x) = f(x - 5)$. Find the rule for g, and explain the meaning of the transformation in terms of monthly bicycle sales.

$g(x) = 0.01x^3 + 0.55x^2 - 5.85x + 134.25$

Possible answer: The model represents the number of sales since Mar

3 Close

Summarize

Ask students to describe transformations of polynomial functions and the effect of each transformation. translation–graph moves vertically or horizontally; stretch–graph enlarges vertically or horizontally with no change in the other direction; compression–graph is squeezed vertically or horizontally with no change in the other direction; reflection across x-axis/y-axis–graph is mirror image of original graph

ONGOING ASSESSMENT and INTERVENTION

***Diagnose Before* the Lesson**
6-8 Warm Up, TE p. 460

***Monitor During* the Lesson**
Check It Out! Exercises, SE pp. 461–462
Questioning Strategies, TE pp. 461–462

***Assess After* the Lesson**
6-8 Lesson Quiz, TE p. 465
Alternative Assessment, TE p. 465

THINK AND DISCUSS

1. How does shifting $f(x) = x^4 - 4$ up 5 units affect the number of real zeros? What if $f(x)$ is shifted 5 units down?
2. Does a horizontal shift affect the number of real zeros of a function? Explain.

3. **GET ORGANIZED** Copy and complete the graphic organizer.

Transformation	Vertical shift	Horizontal shift	Vertical stretch	Horizontal compression
Example				

Answers to *Think and Discuss*

1. Possible answer: It eliminates all real zeros. It does not change the number of real zeros.
2. No; possible answer: the zeros change location, not quantity.
3. See p. A8.

6-8 Exercises

Parent Resources Online
KEYWORD: MB7 Parent

GUIDED PRACTICE

SEE EXAMPLE 1 p. 460

For $f(x) = x^4 - 8$, write the rule for each function, and sketch its graph.

1. $g(x) = f(x) + 4$ $g(x) = x^4 - 4$
2. $h(x) = f(x - 2)$ $h(x) = x^4 - 8x^3 + 24x^2 - 32x + 8$
3. $j(x) = f(3x)$ $j(x) = 81x^4 - 8$
4. $k(x) = f(x) - \frac{1}{2}$ $k(x) = x^4 - 8.5$

SEE EXAMPLE 2 p. 461

Let $f(x) = -x^3 + 3x^2 - 2x + 1$. Write a function g that performs each transformation.

5. Reflect $f(x)$ across the y-axis. $g(x) = x^3 + 3x^2 + 2x + 1$
6. Reflect $f(x)$ across the x-axis. $g(x) = x^3 - 3x^2 + 2x - 1$

SEE EXAMPLE 3 p. 461

Let $f(x) = x^3 - 4x^2 + 2$. Graph f and g on the same coordinate plane. Describe g as a transformation of f.

7. $g(x) = f\left(\frac{1}{2}x\right)$ 7. horizontal stretch
8. $g(x) = 3f(x)$ 8. vertical stretch
9. $g(x) = f(2x) + 4$ 9. horizontal compression and vertical shift

SEE EXAMPLE 4 p. 462

Write a function that transforms $f(x) = 4x^3 + 2$ in each of the following ways. Support your solution by using a graphing calculator.

10. Compress vertically by a factor of $\frac{1}{2}$, and move the y-intercept 2 units down. 10. $g(x) = 2x^3 - 1$
11. Reflect across the y-axis, and compress horizontally by a factor of $\frac{1}{2}$. 11. $g(x) = -32x^3 + 2$
12. Move 2 units right, move 3 units down, and reflect across the x-axis. $g(x) = -4x^3 + 24x^2 - 48x + 33$

SEE EXAMPLE 5 p. 462

13. **Manufacturing** The cost to manufacture x units of a product can be modeled by the function $C(x) = 2x^3 - 3x + 30$, where the cost is in thousands of dollars. Describe the transformation $2C(x)$ by writing the new rule and explaining the change in the context of the problem.
$c(x) = 4x^3 - 6x + 60$; the cost has doubled.

PRACTICE AND PROBLEM SOLVING

For $f(x) = x^3 - 4$, write the rule for each function and sketch its graph.

14. $g(x) = f(x) - 3$ $g(x) = x^3 - 7$
15. $h(x) = f(x - 3)$ $h(x) = x^3 - 9x^2 + 27x - 31$
16. $j(x) = f(x) + 5$ $j(x) = x^3 + 1$

Let $f(x) = x^3 - 2x^2 + 5x - 3$. Write a function g that performs each transformation.

17. Reflect $f(x)$ across the x-axis. $g(x) = -x^3 + 2x^2 - 5x + 3$
18. Reflect $f(x)$ across the y-axis. $g(x) = -x^3 - 2x^2 - 5x - 3$

6-8 Exercises

Assignment Guide

Assign *Guided Practice* exercises as necessary.

If you finished Examples **1–3**
Basic 14, 15, 17–20
Average 14–20
Advanced 14–21

If you finished Examples **1–5**
Basic 14–26, 30–34, 39–45
Average 14–36, 39–45
Advanced 14–25, 27, 28, 30–45

Homework Quick Check
Quickly check key concepts.
Exercises: 14, 18, 20, 22, 25

Answers

1.

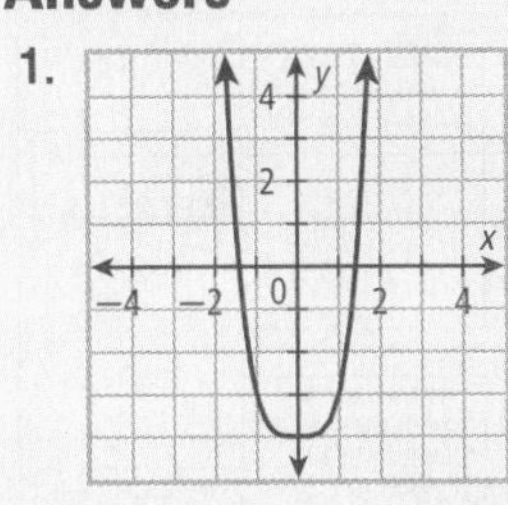

2.

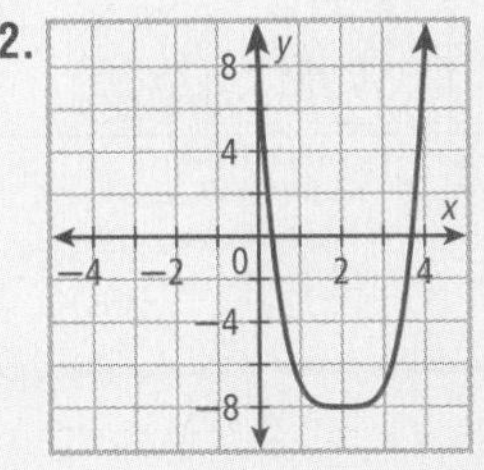

3.

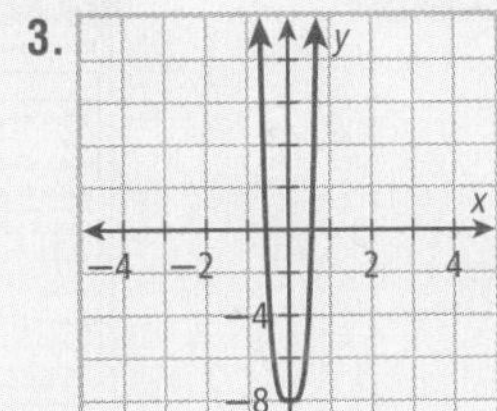

4.

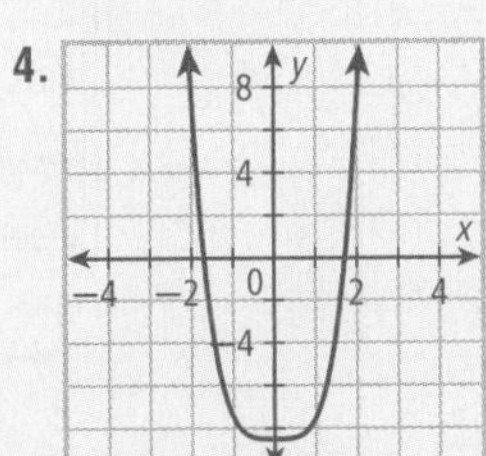

7–12, 14–16. For graphs, see p. A32.

State Resources

Visual In **Exercise 28,** help students visualize the solution by reminding them to think of k as a vertical translation of $g(x) = (x + 5)^4$.

MULTI-STEP TEST PREP **Exercise 30** involves transforming the function for the volume of a square pyramid. This exercise prepares students for the Multi-Step Test Prep on page 472.

Answers

19.

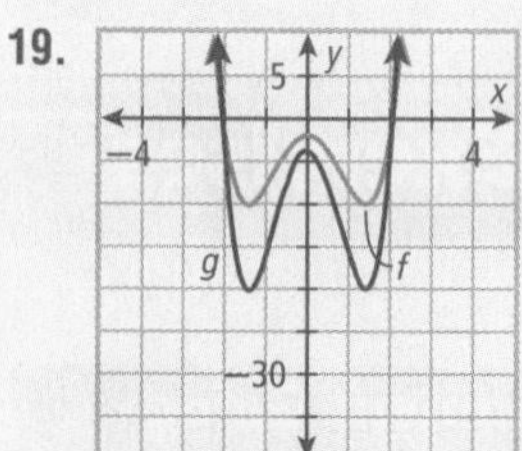

20.

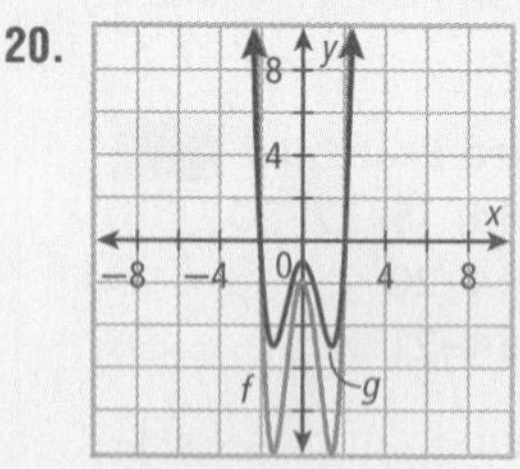

21.

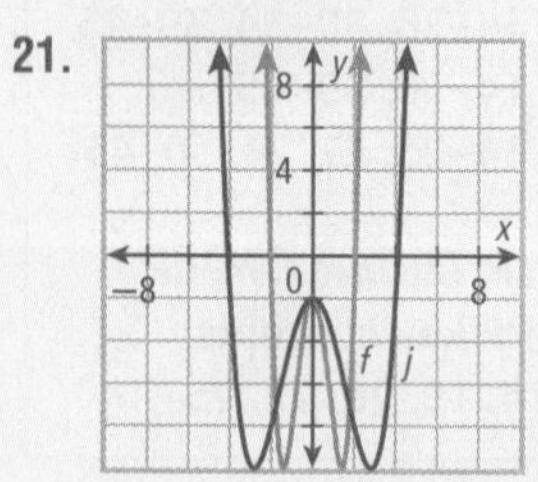

22–24, 27a. For graphs, see p. A32.
25, 28, 29. See p. A32.

Independent Practice	
For Exercises	See Example
14–16	1
17–18	2
19–21	3
22–24	4
25	5

Extra Practice
Skills Practice: S15
Application Practice: S37

Let $f(x) = 2x^4 - 8x^2 - 2$. Graph f and g on the same coordinate plane. Describe g as a transformation of f.

19. $g(x) = 2f(x)$ **vertical stretch**
20. $g(x) = \frac{1}{2}f(x)$ **vertical compression**
21. $g(x) = f\left(\frac{1}{2}x\right)$ **21. horizontal stretch**

22. $g(x) = -x^4 - 12x^3 - 54x^2 - 108x - 75$

Write a function that transforms $f(x) = x^4 - 6$ in each of the following ways. Support your solution by using a graphing calculator.

22. Reflect across the x-axis, and move the x-intercept 3 units left.
23. Compress vertically by a factor of $\frac{1}{3}$, and move 1 unit up. **23.** $g(x) = \frac{1}{3}x^4 - 1$
24. Stretch horizontally by a factor of 2, move 4 units down, and reflect across the y-axis.

24. $g(x) = \frac{1}{16}x^4 - 10$

25. **Geometry** The volume of a rectangular prism can be modeled by the function $V(x) = x^3 + 3x^2 + x + 8$, where V is the volume in cubic meters and x represents length in meters. Describe the transformation $V\left(\frac{2}{3}x\right)$ by writing the new rule and explaining the change in the context of the problem.

26. **///ERROR ANALYSIS///** Students were asked to write a function g that translates f 3 units to the right. Which answer is incorrect? Identify and explain the error.

26. B; possible answer: a shift to the right is represented by $f(x - 3)$, not $f(x + 3)$.

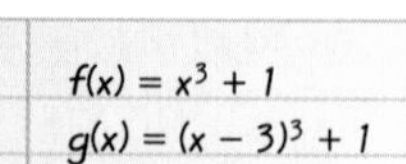

A
$f(x) = x^3 + 1$
$g(x) = (x - 3)^3 + 1$

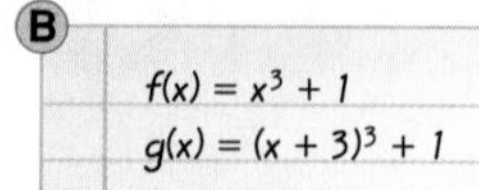

B
$f(x) = x^3 + 1$
$g(x) = (x + 3)^3 + 1$

27. **Fish** Some flying fish travel in the air up to a quarter of a mile by using a lift force F to overcome their weight W while in the air. The lift force is modeled by $F(v) = 0.24v^2$, where $v \geq 0$ is the initial air speed in meters per second.
    a. Graph $F(v) = 0.24v^2$. For $W = 1$, find the values of v such that $F > W$. $v > 2.04$
    b. A flying fish swimming with a current leaps out of the water with a speed that is 5 units greater than normal. Write a function $G(v)$ for the lift force. What transformation does this represent? $G(v) = 0.24v^2 + 2.4x + 6$; **a shift 5 units left**
    c. Find the values of v for which $G > W$. $v \geq 0$
    d. $H(v) = 20v^2$ represents the underwater lift force. What transformation of $F(v)$ does this represent? **a vertical stretch**

28. **Critical Thinking** In the function $f(x) = (x + 5)^4 + k$, for which values of k does the function have two real solutions? no real solutions? Explain.

29. **Write About It** Explain in your own words what happens to the graph of a function when you reflect it across the x-axis.

MULTI-STEP TEST PREP

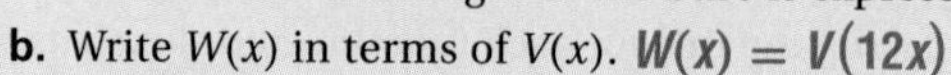

30. This problem will prepare you for the Multi-Step Test Prep on page 472.

    The volume of a pyramid with a square base is modeled by the function $V(x) = \frac{1}{3}x^3 + x^2$, where x is the length of the base in inches.
    a. Write a new function, $W(x)$, that gives the volume of the pyramid in cubic inches when the length of the base is expressed in feet. $W(x) = 576x^3 + 144x^2$
    b. Write $W(x)$ in terms of $V(x)$. $W(x) = V(12x)$
    c. Graph W and V on the same coordinate plane. How is the graph of W related to the graph of V? **horizontal compression by $\frac{1}{12}$**
    d. How would your answer to part c be different if the length of the base were expressed in centimeters?
    Possible answer: Expressing the length of the base in centimeters corresponds to a horizontal stretch rather than a compression.

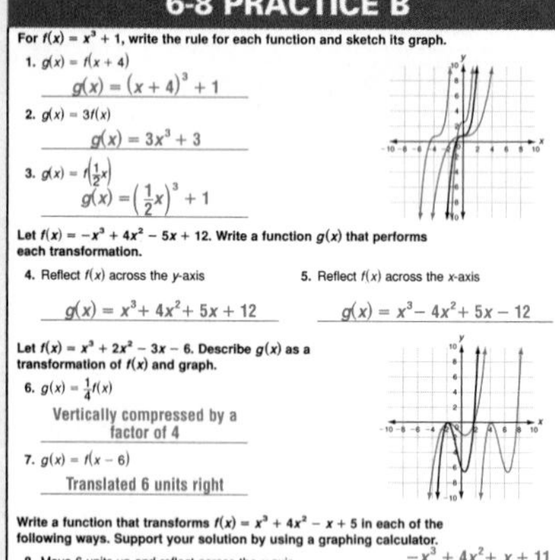

6-8 PRACTICE A
6-8 PRACTICE C
6-8 PRACTICE B

For $f(x) = x^3 + 1$, write the rule for each function and sketch its graph.

1. $g(x) = f(x + 4)$ — $g(x) = (x + 4)^3 + 1$
2. $g(x) = 3f(x)$ — $g(x) = 3x^3 + 3$
3. $g(x) = f\left(\frac{1}{2}x\right)$ — $g(x) = \left(\frac{1}{2}x\right)^3 + 1$

Let $f(x) = -x^3 + 4x^2 - 5x + 12$. Write a function $g(x)$ that performs each transformation.

4. Reflect $f(x)$ across the y-axis — $g(x) = x^3 + 4x^2 + 5x + 12$
5. Reflect $f(x)$ across the x-axis — $g(x) = x^3 - 4x^2 + 5x - 12$

Let $f(x) = x^3 + 2x^2 - 3x - 6$. Describe $g(x)$ as a transformation of $f(x)$ and graph.

6. $g(x) = \frac{1}{4}f(x)$ — Vertically compressed by a factor of 4
7. $g(x) = f(x - 6)$ — Translated 6 units right

Write a function that transforms $f(x) = x^3 + 4x^2 - x + 5$ in each of the following ways. Support your solution by using a graphing calculator.

8. Move 6 units up and reflect across the y-axis. — $-x^3 + 4x^2 + x + 11$
9. Compress vertically by a factor of 0.25 and move 3 units right. — $\frac{1}{4}(x - 3)^3 + (x - 3)^2 - \frac{1}{4}(x - 3) + \frac{5}{4}$

Solve.

10. The number of participants, N, in a new Internet political forum during each month of the first year can be modeled by $N(t) = 4t^2 - t + 2000$, where t is the number of months since January. In the second year, the number of forum participants doubled compared to the same month in the previous year. Write a function that describes the number of forum participants in the second year. — $N(t) = 8t^2 - 2t + 4000$

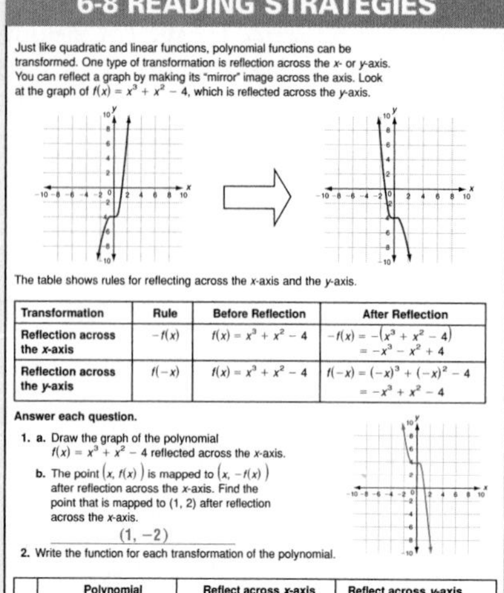

6-8 READING STRATEGIES

Just like quadratic and linear functions, polynomial functions can be transformed. One type of transformation is reflection across the x- or y-axis. You can reflect a graph by making its "mirror" image across the axis. Look at the graph of $f(x) = x^3 + x^2 - 4$, which is reflected across the y-axis.

The table shows rules for reflecting across the x-axis and the y-axis.

Transformation	Rule	Before Reflection	After Reflection
Reflection across the x-axis	$-f(x)$	$f(x) = x^3 + x^2 - 4$	$-f(x) = -(x^3 + x^2 - 4) = -x^3 - x^2 + 4$
Reflection across the y-axis	$f(-x)$	$f(x) = x^3 + x^2 - 4$	$f(-x) = (-x)^3 + (-x)^2 - 4 = -x^3 + x^2 - 4$

Answer each question.

1. a. Draw the graph of the polynomial $f(x) = x^3 + x^2 - 4$ reflected across the x-axis.
   b. The point $(x, f(x))$ is mapped to $(x, -f(x))$ after reflection across the x-axis. Find the point that is mapped to (1, 2) after reflection across the x-axis. — $(1, -2)$
2. Write the function for each transformation of the polynomial.

	Polynomial	Reflect across x-axis	Reflect across y-axis
a.	$f(x) = x^3 + 4$	$f(x) = -x^3 - 4$	$f(x) = -x^3 + 4$
b.	$g(x) = -6x^5 - x^3 + 2$	$g(x) = 6x^5 + x^3 - 2$	$g(x) = 6x^5 + x^3 + 2$
c.	$h(x) = x^2 - 3x + 5$	$h(x) = -x^2 + 3x - 5$	$h(x) = x^2 + 3x + 5$

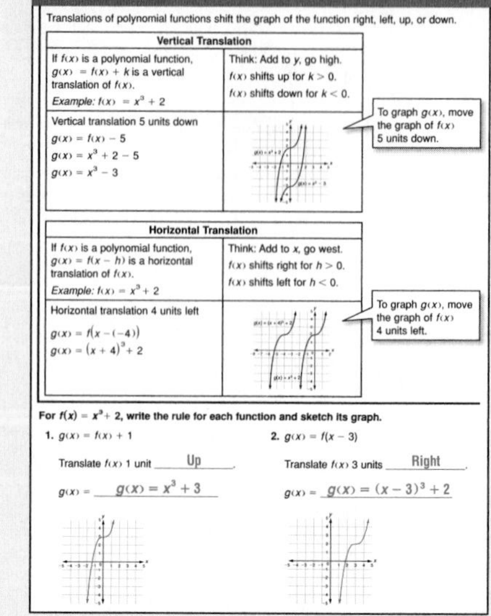

6-8 RETEACH

Translations of polynomial functions shift the graph of the function right, left, up, or down.

Vertical Translation	
If $f(x)$ is a polynomial function, $g(x) = f(x) + k$ is a vertical translation of $f(x)$. *Example:* $f(x) = x^3 + 2$	Think: Add to y, go high. $f(x)$ shifts up for $k > 0$. $f(x)$ shifts down for $k < 0$.
Vertical translation 5 units down $g(x) = f(x) - 5$ $g(x) = x^3 + 2 - 5$ $g(x) = x^3 - 3$	

To graph $g(x)$, move the graph of $f(x)$ 5 units down.

Horizontal Translation	
If $f(x)$ is a polynomial function, $g(x) = f(x - h)$ is a horizontal translation of $f(x)$. *Example:* $f(x) = x^3 + 2$	Think: Add to x, go west. $f(x)$ shifts right for $h > 0$. $f(x)$ shifts left for $h < 0$.
Horizontal translation 4 units left $g(x) = f(x - (-4))$ $g(x) = (x + 4)^3 + 2$	

To graph $g(x)$, move the graph of $f(x)$ 4 units left.

For $f(x) = x^3 + 2$, write the rule for each function and sketch its graph.

1. $g(x) = f(x) + 1$
   Translate $f(x)$ 1 unit Up.
   $g(x) =$ $g(x) = x^3 + 3$
2. $g(x) = f(x - 3)$
   Translate $f(x)$ 3 units Right.
   $g(x) =$ $g(x) = (x - 3)^3 + 2$

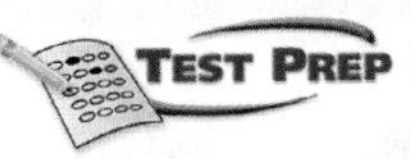

TEST PREP

31. Which graph represents a vertical shift of $f(x) = x^3 - 3x^2 - x + 3$ up 3 units?

Ⓐ Ⓑ (circled) Ⓒ Ⓓ

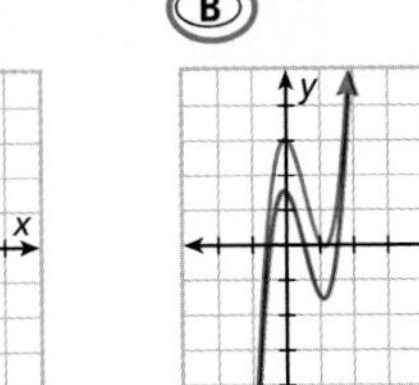

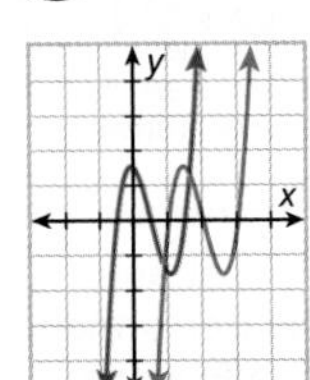

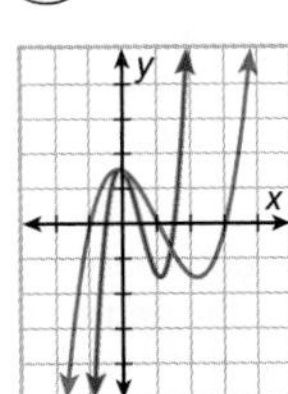

32. Which description matches the transformation from $f(x)$ to $g(x)$ shown?

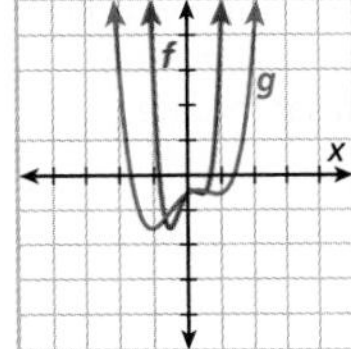

Ⓕ Vertical shift Ⓗ Horizontal shift
Ⓖ Vertical stretch Ⓙ (circled) Horizontal stretch

33. $f(x) = x^3 - 6x^2 + 6x + 1$ has three real zeros. How many real zeros does $f(x) - 6$ have?

Ⓐ 0 Ⓒ 2
Ⓑ (circled) 1 Ⓓ 3

34a. $x \to +\infty, f \to +\infty$; $x \to -\infty, f \to -\infty$

34b. $g(x) = -3x^3 - 9x^2 + 3x + 9$; reflection across the x-axis

34. **Extended Response** Consider the function $f(x) = 3x^3 - 9x^2 - 3x + 9$.

a. Use the leading coefficient and degree of $f(x)$ to describe the end behavior.

b. Write the rule for the function $g(x) = f(-x)$, and describe the transformation.

c. Describe the end behavior of $g(x)$. How does the end behavior of $g(x)$ relate to the transformation of $f(x)$? **Possible answer: A reflection across the y-axis of an odd function changes the end behavior by changing the sign of the leading coefficient.**

CHALLENGE AND EXTEND

37. shift right 3 units and up 8 units

Identify the transformation(s) that would take $f(x) = (x + 2)^3 - 6$ to $g(x)$.

35. $g(x) = x^3 - 6$ **shift right 2 units**
36. $g(x) = (x + 2)^3$ **shift up 6 units**
37. $g(x) = (x - 1)^3 + 2$

38. For $f(x) = x^4 - x^2 - 9x + 9$, describe three different transformations that could be performed to obtain a function with a y-intercept of 3.

Possible answer: shift down 6 units; vertical compression by factor of 3; shift left 2 units

SPIRAL REVIEW

39. **Computers** An administrative assistant recorded the number of words that he typed in one minute. He then recorded the number of words that he typed during different time intervals. His results are in the table below. Write an equation to express this situation. Is this a function? *(Lesson 1-6)* $w(t) = 60t$; **yes**

Minutes	1	3	6	8
Words	60	180	360	480

Add or subtract. Write your answer in standard form. *(Lesson 6-1)*

40. $(6y + 4y^2 - 3) + (9y^2 - 5 + 8y)$ $13y^2 + 14y - 8$

41. $(2x^5 - 4x + 8x^2) - (3x^4 - x^5 + 3x^2)$ $3x^5 - 3x^4 + 5x^2 - 4x$

Find all of the roots of the polynomial equation. *(Lesson 6-6)*

42. $x^4 - 81 = 0$ $\pm 3, \pm 3i$

43. $x^4 + x^3 + 3x^2 + 5x - 10 = 0$ $-2, 1, \pm i\sqrt{5}$

44. $x^3 - 5x^2 - 17x + 21 = 0$ $-3, 7, 1$

45. $x^5 + 3x^4 + 2x^3 + 16x^2 - 48x - 64 = 0$ $-4, -1, 2, \pm 2i\sqrt{2}$

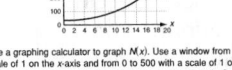

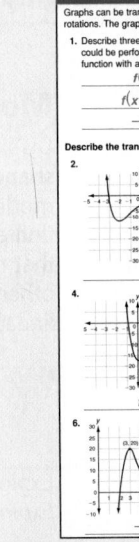

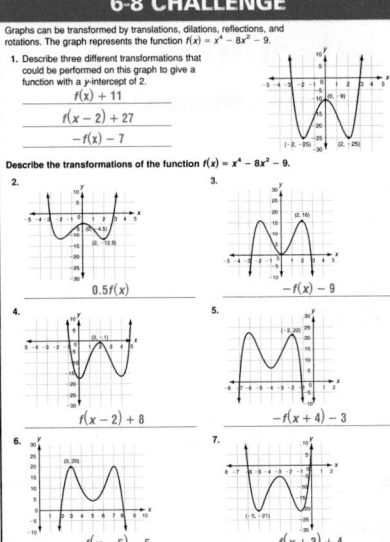

TEST PREP DOCTOR In **Exercise 33,** students who did not choose **B** might not have checked the graph of the transformation. Students should transform the original function and then graph to identify real zeros.

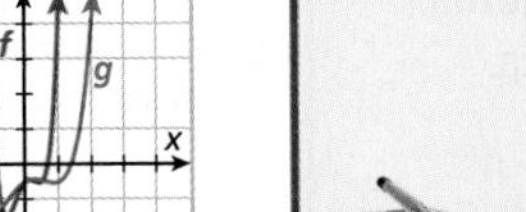

Journal

Have students compare and contrast algebraic representations of vertical and horizontal translations of polynomial functions.

ALTERNATIVE ASSESSMENT

Have students create a cubic function with two terms: third-degree and constant. Then have them choose a translation and a stretch, write the rule, and sketch the graphs. Finally, have students choose an axis to reflect the function across.

Power Presentations with PowerPoint®

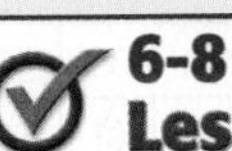

6-8 Lesson Quiz

1. For $f(x) = x^3 + 5$, write the rule for $g(x) = f(x - 1) - 2$ and sketch its graph.
$g(x) = (x - 1)^3 + 3$

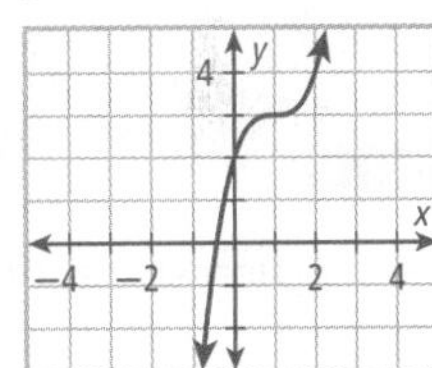

2. Write a function that reflects $f(x) = 2x^3 + 1$ across the x-axis and shifts it 3 units down. $h(x) = -2x^3 - 4$

3. The number of videos sold per month can be modeled by $f(x) = 0.02x^3 + 0.6x^2 + 0.2x + 125$, where x represents the number of months since July. Let $g(x) = f(x) - 15$. Find the rule for g and explain the meaning of the transformation in terms of monthly video sales.
$0.02x^3 + 0.6x^2 + 0.2x + 110$; vertical shift 15 units down; decrease of 15 units per month

Also available on transparency

6-8 PROBLEM SOLVING

A traffic engineer determines that the number of cars passing through a certain intersection each week can be modeled by $C(x) = 0.02x^3 + 0.4x^2 + 0.2x + 35$, where x is the number of weeks since the survey began. A new road has just opened that affects the traffic at that intersection. Let $N(x) = C(x) + 200$.

1. Find the rule for $N(x)$.
$N(x) = 0.02x^3 + 0.4x^2 + 0.2x + 235$

2. What transformation of $C(x)$ is represented by $N(x)$?
Vertical translation of 200 units up

3. On the graph of $C(x)$, sketch the graph for $N(x)$.

4. Use a graphing calculator to graph $N(x)$. Use a window from 0 to 20 with a scale of 1 on the x-axis and from 0 to 500 with a scale of 1 on the y-axis. Compare it to your sketch. Explain why only the values in Quadrant 1 are considered for this problem.
Because only positive values have meaning in the context of the problem

5. Explain the meaning of the transformation of $C(x)$ into $N(x)$ in terms of the weekly number of cars passing through the intersection.
An additional 200 cars are passing through the intersection every week.

6. Emergency roadwork temporarily closes off most of the traffic to this intersection. Write a function $R(x)$ that could model the effect on $C(x)$. Explain how the graph of $C(x)$ might be transformed into $R(x)$.
Possible answer: $R(x) = C(x) - 30$; vertical shift of 30 units down

7. Describe the transformation $2C(x)$ by writing the new rule and explaining the change in the context of the problem.
$2C(x) = 0.04x^3 + 0.8x^2 + 0.4x + 70$; possible answer: a new mall opened at the intersection.

6-8 CHALLENGE

Graphs can be transformed by translations, dilations, reflections, and rotations. The graph represents the function $f(x) = x^4 - 8x^2 - 9$.

1. Describe three different transformations that could be performed on this graph to give a function with a y-intercept of 2.
$f(x) + 11$
$f(x - 2) + 27$
$-f(x) - 7$

Describe the transformations of the function $f(x) = x^4 - 8x^2 - 9$.

2. $0.5f(x)$
3. $-f(x) - 9$

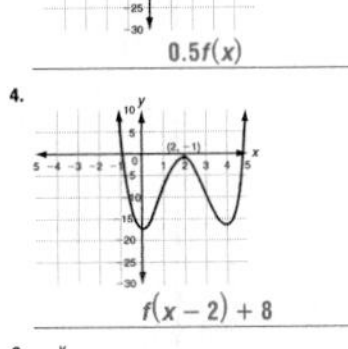

4. $f(x - 2) + 8$

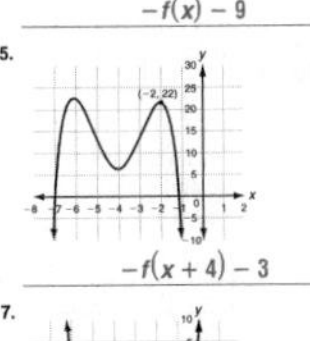

5. $-f(x + 4) - 3$

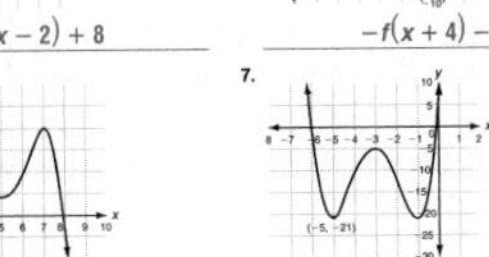

6. $-f(x - 5) - 5$
7. $f(x + 3) + 4$

6-9 Organizer

Pacing: Traditional 1 day
Block $\frac{1}{2}$ day

Objectives: Use finite differences to determine the degree of a polynomial that will fit a given set of data.

Use technology to find polynomial models for a given set of data.

Online Edition
Graphing Calculator, Tutorial Videos, TechKeys

Countdown to Testing Week 14

Power Presentations with PowerPoint®

Warm Up

Find a line of best fit for the data.

1.

x	2	8	15	21	24
y	70	62	80	190	160

$y = 5.45x + 36.12$

2.

x	38	42	44	35	49
y	92	80	75	81	68

$y = -1.28x + 132.66$

Also available on transparency

Math Humor

Q: Why was the function so bent out of shape?

A: Its regression model was too tight a fit.

State Resources

State Resources Online
KEYWORD: MB7 Resources

6-9 Curve Fitting with Polynomial Models

A2.4.6 Solve problems that can be represented or modeled using polynomial equations, interpret the solutions, and determine whether the solutions are reasonable.

Objectives
Use finite differences to determine the degree of a polynomial that will fit a given set of data.

Use technology to find polynomial models for a given set of data.

Who uses this?
Market analysts can use curve fitting to predict the performance of a stock index. (See Example 3.)

The table shows the closing value of a stock index on the first day of trading for various years.

Year	1994	1995	1996	1997	2000	2001	2003	2004
Price ($)	774	751	1053	1293	4186	2474	1347	2011

To create a mathematical model for the data, you will need to determine what type of function is most appropriate. In Lesson 5-8, you learned that a set of data that has constant second differences can be modeled by a quadratic function. Finite differences can be used to identify the degree of any polynomial data.

Finite Differences of Polynomials

Function Type	Degree	Constant Finite Differences
Linear	1	First
Quadratic	2	Second
Cubic	3	Third
Quartic	4	Fourth
Quintic	5	Fifth

EXAMPLE 1 Using Finite Differences to Determine Degree

Use finite differences to determine the degree of the polynomial that best describes the data.

Remember!
To find the differences in the *y*-values, subtract each *y*-value from the *y*-value that follows it. For the first differences,
$-4 - (-10) = 6$
$-1.4 - (-4) = 2.6$
$0 - (-1.4) = 1.4$
and so on.

A

x	−2	−1	0	1	2	3
y	−10	−4	−1.4	0	2.4	8

The *x*-values increase by a constant 1. Find the differences of the *y*-values.

y	−10	−4	−1.4	0	2.4	8

First differences:	6	2.6	1.4	2.4	5.6	Not constant
Second differences:	−3.4	−1.2	1	3.2		Not constant
Third differences:	2.2	2.2	2.2			Constant

The third differences are constant. A cubic polynomial best describes the data.

1 Introduce

EXPLORATION

6-9 Curve Fitting with Polynomial Models

You can discover an interesting property of polynomial functions by investigating finite differences.

1. Complete the table by finding the y-values of the function $y = x^3 + 2x$ and calculating the first, second, and third differences of the y-values.

x	−2	−1	0	1	2	3
y						
First Differences						
Second Differences						
Third Differences						

2. Complete the table by finding the y-values of the function $y = x^4 - 3x$ and calculating the first, second, and third differences of the y-values.

x	−1	0	1	2	3	4	5
y							
First Differences							
Second Differences							
Third Differences							
Fourth Differences							

THINK AND DISCUSS

3. Discuss the relationship between finite differences and the

Motivate

Display a scatter plot that has a cubic shape. Ask students what function best models the data. Ask them how they might find an equation for the model. Explain that regressions can be performed on other polynomial functions in addition to linear and quadratic ones.

Explorations and answers are provided in the *Explorations* binder.

Use finite differences to determine the degree of the polynomial that best describes the data.

x	−6	−4	−2	0	2	4
y	−30	15	30	34	41	60

The x-values increase by a constant, 2. Find the differences of the y-values.

First differences:	45	15	4	7	19	Not constant
Second differences:	−30	−11	3	12		Not constant
Third differences:	19	14	9			Not Constant
Fourth differences:	−5	−5				Constant

The fourth differences are constant. A quartic polynomial best describes the data.

1. Use finite differences to determine the degree of the polynomial that best describes the data.

x	12	15	18	21	24	27
y	3	23	29	29	31	43

cubic

Once you have determined the degree of the polynomial that best describes the data, you can use your calculator to create the function.

EXAMPLE 2

Using Finite Differences to Write a Function

The table below shows the population of a city from 1950 to 2000. Write a polynomial function for the data.

Year	1950	1960	1970	1980	1990	2000
Population (thousands)	2853	4011	5065	6720	9704	14,759

Helpful Hint

Keep the scale of the original data in mind. In Example 2, the population ranges from 2853 to 14,759. The gap between 705 and 728 is small in comparison.

Step 1 Find the finite differences of the y-values.

Let x represent the number of years since 1950. The years increase by a constant amount of 10. The populations are the y-values.

First differences:	1158	1054	1655	2984	5055	
Second differences:	−104	601	1329	2071		
Third differences:	705	728	742			Close

Step 2 Determine the degree of the polynomial.

Because the third differences are relatively close, a cubic function should be a good model.

Step 3 Use the cubic regression feature on your calculator.

$f(x) \approx 0.12x^3 - 4.21x^2 + 146.37x + 2851.64$

2. The table below shows the gas consumption of a compact car driven a constant distance at various speeds. Write a polynomial function for the data.

Speed	25	30	35	40	45	50	55	60
Gas (gal)	23.8	25	25.2	25	25.4	27	30.6	37

$f(x) = 0.001x^3 - 0.113x^2 + 4.134x - 24.867$

Teaching Tip **Technology** For **Example 2,** remind students to use the number of years elapsed, not the numerals in the actual years, when they enter the figures for L1 on their calculators.

Power Presentations with PowerPoint®

Additional Examples

Example 1

Use finite differences to determine the degree of the polynomial that best describes the data.

A.

x	y	x	y
4	−2	10	10.5
6	4.3	12	11.4
8	8.3	14	11.5

cubic

B.

x	y	x	y
−6	−9	3	41
−3	16	6	78
0	26	9	151

quartic

Example 2

The table below shows the population of a city from 1960 to 2000. Write a polynomial function for the data.

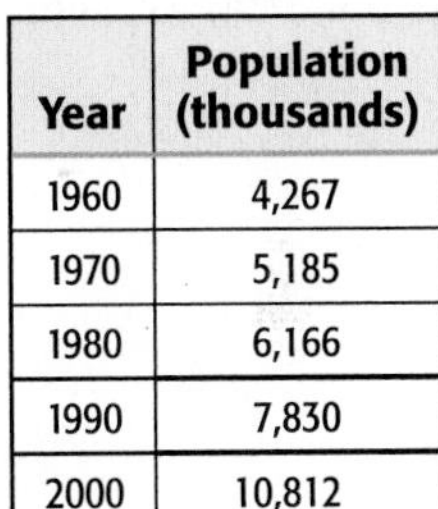

Year	Population (thousands)
1960	4,267
1970	5,185
1980	6,166
1990	7,830
2000	10,812

$f(x) \approx 0.10x^3 - 2.84x^2 + 109.78x + 4266.79$

Also available on transparency

2 Teach

Guided Instruction

Review linear and quadratic regression. Have students explain when each method is useful. Make sure students remember how to use the STAT menu and the regression feature on their calculators. After introducing finite differences in **Example 1,** have students use their calculators to write the functions. Remind students that there may be some variation in the coefficients depending on the calculator.

Reaching All Learners

Through Visual Cues

Have students make scatter plots of the data. Encourage them to imagine how a cubic or quartic equation might model the data.

After students find a regression equation, have them graph it and then compare the equation to the scatter plot of the data.

INTERVENTION

Questioning Strategies

EXAMPLE 1

- How do you know when you have calculated enough differences to identify the degree of the polynomial that best describes the data?

EXAMPLE 2

- What information is given by the R^2-value on the calculator?

Power Presentations with PowerPoint®

Additional Examples

Example 3

The table below shows the opening value of a stock on the first day of trading in various years. Use a polynomial model to estimate the value on the first day of trading in 2000.

Year	Price ($)	Year	Price ($)
1994	683	1997	1306
1995	652	1998	863
1996	948	1999	901

$f(x) \approx 32.23x^4 - 339.13x^3 + 1069.59x^2 - 858.99x + 693.88$; about $2563.18

Also available on transparency

INTERVENTION

Questioning Strategies

EXAMPLE 3

- Do the x-values increase by a constant? Explain.
- Why does the function appear to be cubic or quartic?
- How closely do you think the function actually fits the data? Explain.

Often, real-world data can be too irregular for you to use finite differences or find a polynomial function that fits perfectly. In these situations, you can use the regression feature of your graphing calculator. Remember that the closer the R^2-value is to 1, the better the function fits the data.

EXAMPLE 3 *Finance Application*

The table shows the opening value of a stock index on the first day of trading in various years. Use a polynomial model to estimate the value on the first day of trading in 2002.

Year	Price ($)	Year	Price ($)
1994	774	2000	4186
1995	751	2001	2474
1996	1053	2003	1347
1997	1293	2004	2011

Step 1 Choose the degree of the polynomial model.

Let x represent the number of years since 1994. Make a scatter plot of the data.

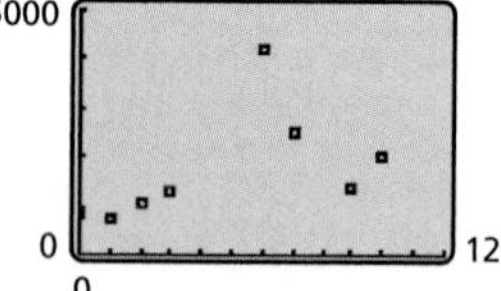

The function appears to be cubic or quartic. Use the regression feature to check the R^2-values.

cubic: $R^2 \approx 0.6279$ quartic: $R^2 \approx 0.8432$

The quartic function is a more appropriate choice.

Step 2 Write the polynomial model.

The data can be modeled by
$f(x) = 9.27x^4 - 191.56x^3 + 1168.22x^2 - 1702.58x + 999.60$

Step 3 Find the value of the model corresponding to 2002.

2002 is 8 years after 1994. Substitute 8 for x in the quartic model.

$f(x) = 9.27(8)^4 - 191.56(8)^3 + 1168.22(8)^2 - 1702.58(8) + 999.60 \approx 2036.24$

Based on the model, the opening value was about $2036.24 in 2002.

3. Use a polynomial model to estimate the value of the index in 1999.

Year	1994	1995	1996	2000	2003	2004
Price ($)	3754	3835	5117	11,497	8342	10,454

$11,482.84

THINK AND DISCUSS

1. Suppose that finite differences are used to determine that a quartic polynomial best describes a particular data set. What is the minimum number of data pairs in the data set? Explain.

2. GET ORGANIZED Copy and complete the graphic organizer. For each type of function, indicate the degree and the constant differences and give an example of a data set.

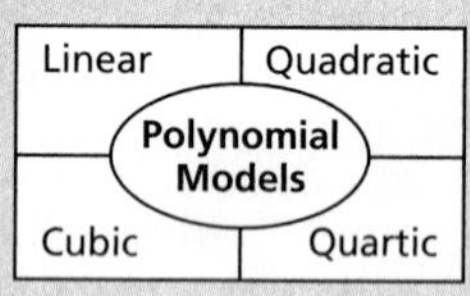

3 Close

Summarize

Ask students to explain how to use finite differences to determine the degree of a polynomial that will fit a given set of data. The degree is equal to the number of finite differences necessary to reach a constant difference. Then have them tell how to model data that are too irregular for finite differences. Use the regression feature of a graphing calculator.

ONGOING ASSESSMENT and INTERVENTION

*Diagnose **Before** the Lesson*
6-9 Warm Up, TE p. 466

*Monitor **During** the Lesson*
Check It Out! Exercises, SE pp. 467–468
Questioning Strategies, TE pp. 467–468

*Assess **After** the Lesson*
6-9 Lesson Quiz, TE p. 471
Alternative Assessment, TE p. 471

Answers to *Think and Discuss*

Possible answers:

1. At each step, there is one fewer value with which to compute. To have values left after 4 finite differences, there must be at least 5 data points.
2. See p. A8.

6-9 Exercises

go.hrw.com
Homework Help Online
KEYWORD: MB7 6-9
Parent Resources Online
KEYWORD: MB7 Parent

GUIDED PRACTICE

SEE EXAMPLE 1 p. 466

Use finite differences to determine the degree of the polynomial that best describes the data.

1.

x	y
−2	22
−1	16
0	10
1	4
2	−2
3	−8

linear

2.

x	y
−2	0
−1	−5
0	−3
1	5
2	18
3	35

cubic

3.

x	y
−2	23
−1	−2
0	1
1	2
2	−5
3	−2

quartic

SEE EXAMPLE 2 p. 467

4. Business The table below shows the number of square feet of retail space available for rent in various years. Write a polynomial function for the data.

Year	1957	1967	1977	1987	1997	2007
Retail Space (billion ft²)	2.8	6.7	14.7	27.3	44.9	67.9

$f(x) = -0.000071x^3 + 0.0186x^2 + 0.196x + 2.804$ where x is the number of years since 1957

SEE EXAMPLE 3 p. 468

5. Health The table below shows the number of infected patients at various stages of a flu outbreak. Use a polynomial model to estimate the number of infected patients after 120 hours. 831 patients

Time (h)	12	24	48	96	144	240
Patients	21	301	679	973	562	320

PRACTICE AND PROBLEM SOLVING

Independent Practice

For Exercises	See Example
6–8	1
9	2
10–11	3

Extra Practice
Skills Practice p. S15
Application Practice p. S37

Use finite differences to determine the degree of the polynomial that best describes the data.

6.

x	y
−5	−20
−4	−19
−3	−9
−2	5.5
−1	20
0	30

cubic

7.

x	y
−2	−2
−1	−6
0	0
1	10
2	20
3	28

quartic

8.

x	y
−2	−3
−1	1
0	4.3
1	6.9
2	8.8
3	10

quadratic

9. Hobbies The table below shows the number of Chess Club members in various years. Write a polynomial function for the data.

Year	2002	2003	2004	2005	2006	2007
Members	23	23	23	25	29	35

$f(x) = 0.821x^2 - 1.821x + 23.357$

6-9 Exercises

Assignment Guide

Assign *Guided Practice* exercises as necessary.

If you finished Examples 1–3
Basic 6–11, 13, 14, 16–19, 24–30
Average 6, 8–21, 24–30
Advanced 6, 8–12, 14–30

Homework Quick Check
Quickly check key concepts.
Exercises: 6, 8, 9, 10

State Resources

go.hrw.com
State Resources Online
KEYWORD: MB7 Resources

Critical Thinking Remind students to refer back to the scale of the original data as they write their answers for **Exercises 10** and **11.**

Geography Link Discuss students' reactions to the relationships between latitude, longitude, and temperature in **Exercise 12.**

Exercise 14 involves writing a polynomial function to describe data for a pyramid. This exercise prepares students for the Multi-Step Test Prep on page 472.

Answers

12a. Latitude and temperature; possible answer: a quartic model fits best. $R^2 \approx 0.9981$, but for longitude and temperature, $R^2 \approx 0.5130$.

b. No; possible answer: the latitude value 30 corresponds to 2 different temperature values, 40 and 42.

c. No; possible answer: the longitude value 83 corresponds to 2 different temperature values, 20 and 52.

13a. $f(x) = 0.019x^3 - 0.185x^2 + 0.95x + 12.056$; $R^2 = 0.9944$

b. $f(x) = 0.0075x^4 - 0.071x^3 + 0.143x^2 + 0.604x + 12.083$; $R^2 = 0.9967$

c. no

d. Possible answer: The cubic and quartic polynomials are almost equally appropriate models.

10. **Tourism** The table below shows the number of Canadian visitors to the United States. Use a polynomial model to predict the number of visitors in 2005.

Year	1996	1998	2000	2001	2002	2003
Visitors (millions)	15.3	13.4	14.6	13.5	13.0	12.7

Possible answer: 24.2 million visitors

Possible answer: 58,745 graduates

11. **Education** The table shows the total high school graduates in the United States. Use a polynomial model to estimate the total graduates in 1999.

Year	1989	1991	1995	1996	1998	2000
Graduates (thousands)	59,336	61,272	56,450	56,559	58,174	58,086

12. **Weather** The figure shows the latitude, longitude, and average January minimum temperature of various locations.

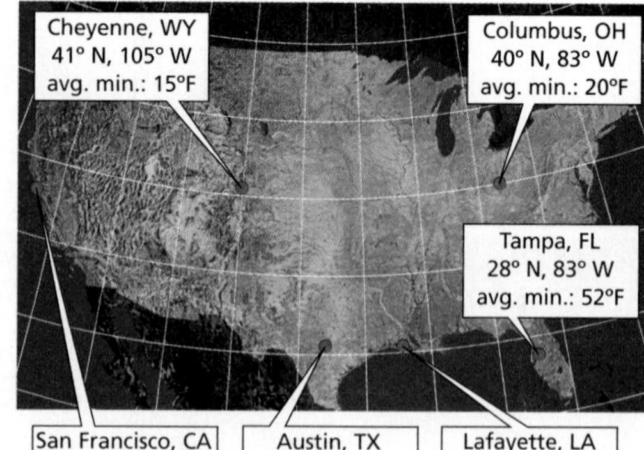

a. Which pair of variables has a closer polynomial relationship: latitude and temperature or longitude and temperature? Give numerical data to support your answer.

b. Is the relationship between latitude and temperature a function? Explain.

c. Is a polynomial model relating longitude and temperature a function? Explain.

13. **Multi-Step** The table shows the total December clothing sales in the United States in billions of dollars.

Year	1997	1998	1999	2001	2002	2003
Sales (billions of $)	12.1	12.7	13.5	14.1	14.6	15.3

a. Write a cubic polynomial to model the data. What is the R^2-value?

b. Write a quartic polynomial to model the data. What is the R^2-value?

c. Is the difference in R^2-values significant?

d. What do the R^2-values say about your answers to part **a** and part **b**?

MULTI-STEP TEST PREP

14. This problem will prepare you for the Multi-Step Test Prep on page 472. You can make a pyramid by stacking balls in triangular layers. For example, three balls can be arranged as a triangle with a fourth ball on top of the other three.

Number of Balls on One Side of the Bottom Layer	1	2	3	4	5
Total Number of Balls in the Pyramid	1	4	10	20	35

a. Use finite differences to determine the degree of the polynomial that best describes the data. cubic

b. Write a polynomial function for the data. $f(x) = \frac{1}{6}x^3 + \frac{1}{2}x^2 + \frac{1}{3}x$

c. How many balls are in a pyramid that has 12 balls on one side of the bottom layer? 364

6-9 PRACTICE A
6-9 PRACTICE C
6-9 PRACTICE B

Use finite differences to determine the degree of the polynomial that best describes the data.

1. Quartic

x	y
0	4
1	14
2	24
3	30
4	30
5	24

2. Cubic

x	y
−2	70
−1	35
0	15
1	7
2	8
3	15

3. Quadratic

x	y
2	1
1	7
0	12
−1	16
−2	19
−3	21

4. Cubic

x	y
−6	−31
−5	0
−4	16
−3	19
−2	11
−1	−6

Solve.

5. The data set shows the average price for a luxury commodity for the years since 1998.

Year	1998	1999	2000	2001	2002	2003	2004	2005
Price ($)	1000	2027	4472	7507	10,472	12,875	14,392	14,867

a. Write a polynomial function for the data.

$f(x) = 7y^4 - 180y^3 + 1200y^2 + 1000$

b. Predict the price of the item in 2008.

$11,000

6-9 READING STRATEGIES

You can find the degree of a polynomial by finding the differences in its data set.

Degree	1	2	3	4
Type	Linear	Quadratic	Cubic	Quartic
Constant Differences	First differences	Second differences	Third differences	Fourth differences

Look at the first and second differences of the following data set.

x	0	1	2	3	4	5
y	1	6	17	34	57	86

First Differences: 6 − 1 = 5, 17 − 6 = 11, 34 − 17 = 17, 57 − 34 = 23, 86 − 57 = 29

Second Differences: 11 − 5 = 6, 17 − 11 = 6, 23 − 17 = 6, 29 − 23 = 6

The first differences are not constant, but the second differences all equal 6. The data set represents a polynomial of degree 2, or a quadratic function.

Answer each question.

1. In a data set, the third differences all equal −2. What type of function is represented by this data set? Cubic function

2. The ordered pairs (1, 3), (2, 5), and (3, 7) represent a linear function. Use the constant finite difference to find the value of the function at $x = 6$. 13

Use the following data set for Exercise 3.

x	−2	−1	0	1	2	3
y	−9	−2	−1	0	7	26

3. a. What are the first differences of this data set? 7, 1, 1, 7, 19

b. What are the second differences? Yes; −6, 0, 6, 12

c. Do you need to find the third differences? If so, what are they? Yes; 6, 6, 6

d. What kind of function does this data set represent? Cubic function

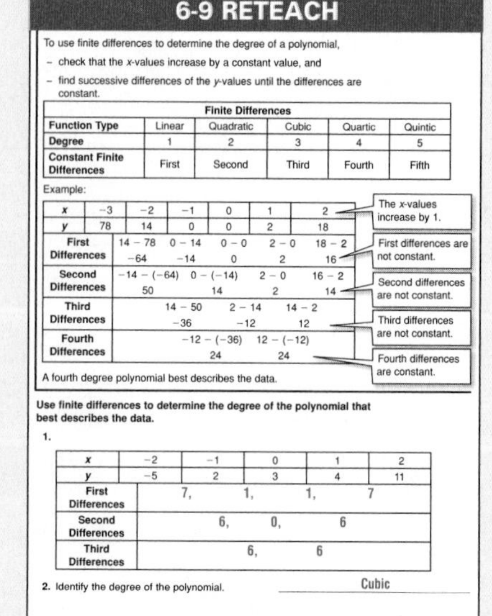

6-9 RETEACH

To use finite differences to determine the degree of a polynomial,

- check that the x-values increase by a constant value, and
- find successive differences of the y-values until the differences are constant.

Finite Differences					
Function Type	Linear	Quadratic	Cubic	Quartic	Quintic
Degree	1	2	3	4	5
Constant Finite Differences	First	Second	Third	Fourth	Fifth

Example:

x	−3	−2	−1	0	1	2
y	78	14	0	0	2	18

First Differences: 14 − 78 = −64, 0 − 14 = −14, 0 − 0 = 0, 2 − 0 = 2, 18 − 2 = 16

Second Differences: −14 − (−64) = 50, 0 − (−14) = 14, 2 − 0 = 2, 16 − 2 = 14

Third Differences: 14 − 50 = −36, 2 − 14 = −12, 14 − 2 = 12

Fourth Differences: −12 − (−36) = 24, 12 − (−12) = 24

The x-values increase by 1.

First differences are not constant.

Second differences are not constant.

Third differences are not constant.

Fourth differences are constant.

A fourth degree polynomial best describes the data.

Use finite differences to determine the degree of the polynomial that best describes the data.

1.

x	−2	−1	0	1	2
y	−5	2	3	4	11

First Differences: 7, 1, 1, 7

Second Differences: 6, 0, 6

Third Differences: 6, 6

2. Identify the degree of the polynomial. Cubic

15. **Critical Thinking** The fourth differences of a given data set are 0.01, 0, 0, and −0.01. Is a cubic polynomial appropriate to model the data? Explain.

16. **Write About It** Describe the process you would use to determine the appropriate type of polynomial for a given data set.

TEST PREP

17. What type of polynomial best models the data below?
$\{(0, 1), (1, 21), (2, 27), (3, 27), (4, 29), (5, 41)\}$
(A) Linear (B) Quadratic  (C) Cubic (D) Quartic

18. Which cubic function represents the graph?
(F) $f(x) = -(x + 2)(x - 1)(x - 3)$
(G) $f(x) = (x + 2)(x - 1)(x - 3)$
(H) $f(x) = -(x - 2)(x + 1)(x + 3)$
(J) $f(x) = (x - 2)(x + 1)(x + 3)$

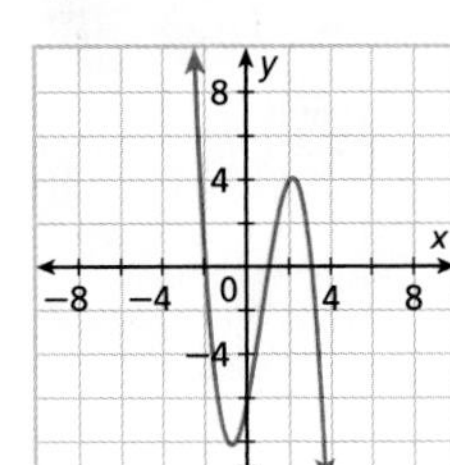

19. **Short Response** Give a cubic polynomial that can be used to model the data below.
$\{(0, 4), (-1, 8), (1, 0), (-2, 6), (2, 2)\}$ $f(x) = x^3 - 5x + 4$

CHALLENGE AND EXTEND

The *average slope* of the graph of $f(x)$ between $x = a$ and $x = b$ is the slope of the line through $(a, f(a))$ and $(b, f(b))$. Use the table to complete Exercises 20–22.

x	$f(x)$
−3	−5.5
−2	−1
−1	1.5
0	2
1	0.5
2	−3

20. What is the average slope between $x = -2$ and $x = 2$? $-\frac{1}{2}$

21. How can you use first differences to find the average slope between each pair of points given in the table?

21. Possible answer: Divide the first differences by the change in the x-values.

22. What happens to the average slope of the graph as the chosen points get closer to the maximum point? It approaches 0.

23. Use finite differences to create a data set that could be modeled by a quartic polynomial. Possible answer:

x	1	2	3	4	5	6
y	60	54	40	28	30	60

SPIRAL REVIEW

Simplify each expression. *(Lesson 1-4)*

24. $-b^2(2b^2 + 5b - 3)$ $-2b^4 - 5b^3 + 3b^2$

25. $a + 3a - 5a^2(6a - a)$ $4a - 25a^3$

26. $\frac{u^2 - v + 3v}{v(v^2 - u)}$ $\frac{u^2 + 2v}{v^3 - uv}$

27. **Multi-Step** The chart below shows the number of copies sold (in thousands) of a new music CD for 5 weeks. Graph the data. Describe the parent function and the transformation that best approximates the data set. *(Lesson 1-9)*

Week	1	2	3	4	5
Copies Sold (thousands)	2	3	10	29	66

cubic parent function; shift 1 unit right and 2 units up

Identify the leading coefficient, degree, and end behavior. *(Lesson 6-7)*

28. $f(x) = x^4 - x^2 + 3x - 1$ 1; 4; $x \to \pm\infty$, $f(x) \to +\infty$

29. $f(x) = 4x^5 - x^3 + 10$ 4; 5; $x \to -\infty$, $f(x) \to -\infty$; $x \to +\infty$, $f(x) \to +\infty$

30. $f(x) = -3x^6 + 5x$ −3; 6; $x \to \pm\infty$, $f(x) \to -\infty$

TEST PREP DOCTOR Students who chose **G** or **J** in **Exercise 18** did not check end behavior. Students who chose **H** or **J** have confused the signs of the roots. Remind them that a factor must equal zero when evaluated for the root value shown on the graph.

Answers

15, 16. See p. A32.

Journal

Explain why it is important to check the value for R^2 when using the regression feature on a calculator to model a data set.

ALTERNATIVE ASSESSMENT

Have students plot five points that might lie on the graph of a cubic or quartic equation. Have them write a polynomial function for the data.

Power Presentations with PowerPoint®

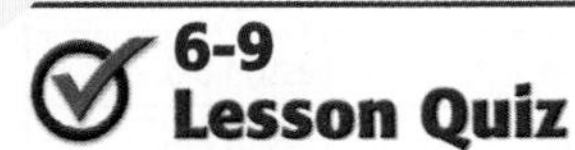

6-9 Lesson Quiz

1. Use finite differences to determine the degree of the polynomial that best describes the data. cubic

x	y
8	7.2
10	1.2
12	−8.3
14	−19.1
16	−29
18	−35.8

2. The table shows the opening value of a stock index on the first day of trading in various years. Write a polynomial model for the data and use the model to estimate the value on the first day of trading in 2002.

Year	Price ($)	Year	Price ($)
1994	2814	2000	3962
1996	3603	2001	4117
1998	5429	2004	3840

$f(x) = 7.08x^4 - 126.92x^3 + 595.95x^2 - 241.81x + 2780.54$; about $3003.50

Also available on transparency

6-9 PROBLEM SOLVING

Carla has been making a "wild scape" in her backyard. The table shows the number of birds visiting her feeder at the same hour on the first day of each month since she began her project. Use a polynomial model to make a reasonable estimate of the number of birds there might be in July.

Birds at Feeder from 7:00 to 8:00 A.M.					
Jan	Feb	Mar	Apr	May	Jun
3	8	18	36	65	108

1. Use finite differences to determine the degree of the polynomial that best fits the data.
   a. First differences 5, 10, 18, 29, 43
   b. Second differences 5, 8, 11, 14
   c. Third differences 3, 3, 3
   d. Fourth differences 0, 0
   e. Which degree polynomial best describes the data? Cubic
2. Use your graphing calculator to find values for R^2.
   a. For LinReg, R^2 = $R^2 \approx 0.8945$.
   b. For QuadReg, R^2 = $R^2 \approx 0.9458$.
   c. For CubicReg, R^2 = 1.
3. Write the polynomial model for this data. $f(x) = 0.5x^3 - 0.5x^2 + 3x$
4. Use your polynomial model to make a reasonable estimate of the number of birds there might be in July. 168

The table below shows the number of travel insurance policies sold by a travel agency over a six-year period. Choose the letter for the best answer.

Year	2001	2002	2003	2004	2005	2006
Policies Sold	73	126	163	185	192	184

5. Which function best models the data?
   A $f(x) \approx -0.926x^2 - 6.88x + 6.3$
   B $f(x) \approx -7.59x^2 + 75.27x + 5.5$
   (C) $f(x) \approx 0.05x^3 + 8.08x^2 + 76.74x + 4.3$
   D $f(x) \approx -0.02x^3 + 0.34x^2 - 9.47x + 2.8$
6. Use the polynomial model to estimate the number of policies that may be sold in 2008.
   A About 150
   B About 140
   (C) About 130
   D About 120

6-9 CHALLENGE

Polynomials can be fit to any finite number of points if no two points lie on the same vertical line. For instance, one form of a linear equation frequently used is the slope-intercept form, $y = mx + b$. Given two points on a line, (3, 12) and (−1, 4), these values may be substituted for x and y in the slope-intercept form to obtain the system of linear equations below.

$$\begin{cases} 12 = 3m + b \\ 4 = -m + b \end{cases}$$

Solving this system by eliminating b yields $m = 2$ and $b = 6$ to give the linear equation $y = 2x + 6$ that passes through the two points given.

This process works equally well for quadratic equations. Every quadratic equation can be written in the form $y = ax^2 + bx + c$. Given three points, you can write a system of three linear equations in the variables a, b, and c. Solving this system yields values for a, b, and c to write a quadratic equation.

Use a polynomial model to represent the data given.

1. Quadratic polynomial $y = ax^2 + bx + c$

x	5	10	15	20	25
y	30	34	36	36	34

$y = -\frac{1}{25}x^2 + \frac{7}{5}x + 24$

2. Quadratic polynomial $y = ax^2 + bx + c$

x	0	1	2	3	4	5	6	7	8
y	45	24	11	1	−2	1	9	26	47

Possible answer: $y = 3x^2 - 24x + 45$

3. Cubic polynomial $y = ax^3 + bx^2 + cx + d$

x	−3	2	5	8
y	0	0	24	264

$y = x^3 - 3x^2 - 10x + 24$

4. Quartic polynomial $y = ax^4 + bx^3 + cx^2 + dx + e$

x	−3	−1	1	3	5
y	0	0	24	−24	−144

$y = \frac{1}{4}x^4 - 2x^3 - \frac{11}{2}x^2 + 14x + \frac{69}{4}$

Organizer

Objective: Assess students' ability to apply concepts and skills in Lessons 6-5 through 6-9 in a real-world format.

 Online Edition

Resources

 ***Algebra II Assessments***
www.mathtekstoolkit.org

Problem	Text Reference
1	Previous course
2–3	Lesson 6-9
4	Lesson 6-3
5–6	Lesson 6-5
7	Lesson 6-6

Answer

6. No; possible answer: if it were possible, there would be a whole-number solution to $\frac{1}{3}x^3 + \frac{1}{2}x^2 + \frac{1}{6}x = 811$ or $2x^3 + 3x^2 + x - 4866 = 0$. The only possible rational roots are $\pm1, \pm2, \pm3, \pm811, \pm\frac{1}{2}, \pm\frac{3}{2}$, and $\pm\frac{811}{2}$, so the only possible whole-number roots are 1, 2, 3, and 811. Synthetic division shows that none of these is a root.

State Resources

CHAPTER 6

MULTI-STEP TEST PREP

SECTION 6B

Applying Polynomial Functions

Pyramid Pile-Up You can build a pyramid by stacking blocks in layers. The blocks in each layer are arranged in a square, and the layers grow successively larger as shown below.

1. The figure shows the relationship between the number of layers and the total number of blocks in the pyramid. Make a table that shows the relationship for the first five layers.

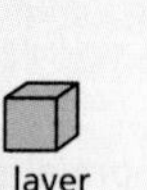
1 layer
1 block

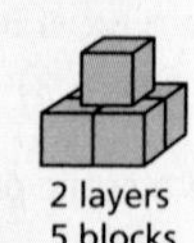
2 layers
5 blocks

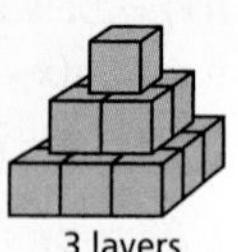
3 layers
14 blocks

1.

Layer	Blocks
1	1
2	5
3	14
4	30
5	55

2. Use finite differences to determine the degree of the polynomial that best describes the data. **cubic**
3. Write a polynomial function for the data. $f(x) = \frac{1}{3}x^3 + \frac{1}{2}x^2 + \frac{1}{6}x$
4. The Great Pyramid in Giza, Egypt, has 201 layers. Use your function to estimate the number of blocks in the pyramid. **2,727,101**
5. A pyramid contains a total of 285 blocks. How many layers are in the pyramid? **9**
6. Is it possible to build a pyramid that uses exactly 811 blocks? Why or why not? Give an explanation in terms of the solutions to a polynomial equation.
7. A pyramid is known to contain at least 10,000 blocks. What is the minimum number of layers in the pyramid? **31**

INTERVENTION 

Scaffolding Questions

1. How can you use a pattern to fill in the table? If you know the number of blocks in row n, add $(n + 1)^2$ to get the number of blocks in row $n + 1$.
2. Do the values of the dependent variable differ by a constant? yes
3. Is a cubic polynomial an exact fit for the data or is it an approximation? exact fit
4. How can you use your function to find the total number of blocks? Evaluate for $x = 201$.
5. What equation do you need to solve? $\frac{1}{3}x^3 + \frac{1}{2}x^2 + \frac{1}{6}x = 285$
6. What equation do you need to solve? What must be true about the equation for such a pyramid? $\frac{1}{3}x^3 + \frac{1}{2}x^2 + \frac{1}{6}x = 811$; it must have a whole-number solution.
7. How can you use a graphing calculator for this problem? Use the table feature.

Extension

The total number of blocks in a pyramid is equal to 200 times the number of layers, plus 100. How many layers are in the pyramid? 24

READY TO GO ON?

Quiz for Lessons 6-5 Through 6-9

6-5 Finding Real Roots of Polynomial Equations

1. The yearly profit of a company in thousands of dollars can be modeled by $P(t) = t^4 - 10t^2 + 9$, where t is the number of years since 2000. Factor to find the years in which the profit was 0. 2001 and 2003

Identify the roots of each equation. State the multiplicity of each root.

2. $x^3 + 6x^2 + 12x + 8 = 0$ —2 with multiplicity 3
3. $2x^3 + 8x^2 - 32x - 128 = 0$ 4 with multiplicity 1; −4 with multiplicity 2
4. $x^4 - 6x^3 + 9x^2 = 0$ 0 with multiplicity 2; 3 with multiplicity 2

6-6 Fundamental Theorem of Algebra

Write the simplest polynomial function with the given roots.

5. 1, 1, 2 $x^3 - 4x^2 + 5x - 2$
6. i, −1, 0 $x^4 + x^3 + x^2 + x$
7. Solve $x^4 - 2x^3 + 6x^2 - 18x - 27 = 0$ by finding all roots. $3, -1, \pm 3i$

6-7 Investigating Graphs of Polynomial Functions

Graph each function.

8. $f(x) = x^4 - 13x^2 + 36$
9. $f(x) = x^3 - 4x^2 - 15x + 18$

Identify whether the function graphed has an odd or even degree and a positive or negative leading coefficient.

10. 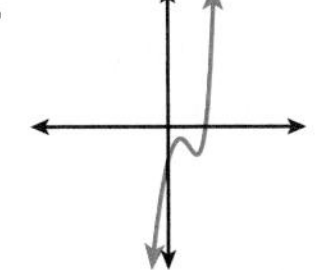
odd; positive

11. 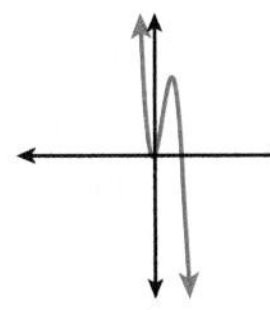
odd; negative

12. 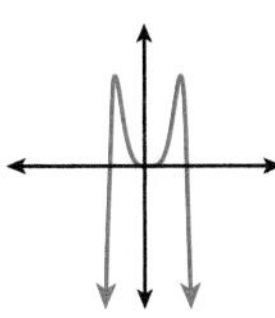
even; negative

6-8 Transforming Polynomial Functions

Let $f(x) = x^4 - 3x^2 + 6$. Write a function $g(x)$ that performs each transformation.

13. Reflect $f(x)$ across the x-axis. $g(x) = -x^4 + 3x^2 - 6$
14. Reflect $f(x)$ across the y-axis. $g(x) = x^4 - 3x^2 + 6$

Let $f(x) = 8x^4 - 12x^2 + 2$. Graph $f(x)$ and $g(x)$ on the same coordinate plane. Describe $g(x)$ as a transformation of $f(x)$.

15. $g(x) = 3f(x)$ vertical stretch
16. $g(x) = f\left(\frac{1}{2}x\right)$ horizontal stretch
17. $g(x) = f(x - 4)$ horizontal shift

6-9 Curve Fitting with Polynomial Models

18. The table shows the population of a bacteria colony over time. Write a polynomial function for the data. $f(x) = 8.25x^3 - 13.18x^2 + 49.58x - 0.6$

Time (h)	1	2	3	4	5
Bacteria	44	112	252	515	949

READY TO GO ON?

Organizer

Objective: Assess students' mastery of concepts and skills in Lessons 6-5 through 6-9.

Resources

 ***Assessment Resources***
Section 6B Quiz

 **Test & Practice Generator**
One-Stop Planner®

INTERVENTION

Resources

 ***Ready to Go On? Intervention and Enrichment*** **Worksheets**

 ***Ready to Go On?*** **CD-ROM**

 ***Ready to Go On?*** **Online**

my.hrw.com

Answers

8, 9, 15–17. For graphs, see p. A32.

READY TO GO ON? Diagnose and Prescribe

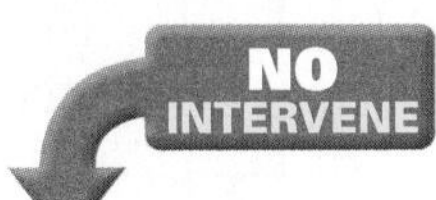
NO INTERVENE

Ready to Go On? Intervention	*Ready to Go On? Intervention,* Section 6B		
	Worksheets	CD-ROM	Online
Lesson 6-5	6-5 Intervention	Activity 6-5	Diagnose and Prescribe Online
Lesson 6-6	6-6 Intervention	Activity 6-6	
Lesson 6-7	6-7 Intervention	Activity 6-7	
Lesson 6-8	6-8 Intervention	Activity 6-8	
Lesson 6-9	6-9 Intervention	Activity 6-9	

YES ENRICH

Ready to Go On? Enrichment, **Section 6B**
 Worksheets
 CD-ROM
Online

Organizer

Objective: Help students organize and review key concepts and skills in Chapter 6.

Online Edition
Multilingual Glossary

Resources

Puzzle Pro
One-Stop Planner®

Multilingual Glossary **Online**
go.hrw.com
KEYWORD: MB7 Glossary

Lesson Tutorial Videos
CD-ROM

Test & Practice Generator
One-Stop Planner®

Answers

1. monomial
2. synthetic division
3. multiplicity
4. end behavior
5. $-3x^3 + 4x^2 + 6x + 7$; -3; 3; 4; cubic polynomial with 4 terms
6. $-x^5 + 2x^4 + 5x^3 + 8x$; -1; 5; 4; quintic polynomial with 4 terms
7. $9x^2 - 11x + 1$; 9; 2; 3; quadratic trinomial
8. $x^4 - 6x^2$; 1; 4; 2; quartic binomial
9. $8x^3 + x^2 - 4x$
10. $-5x^3 + 6x^2 + 10x - 1$
11. $-6x^2 - x + 9$
12. $-4x^4 - x^3 - 3$
13.

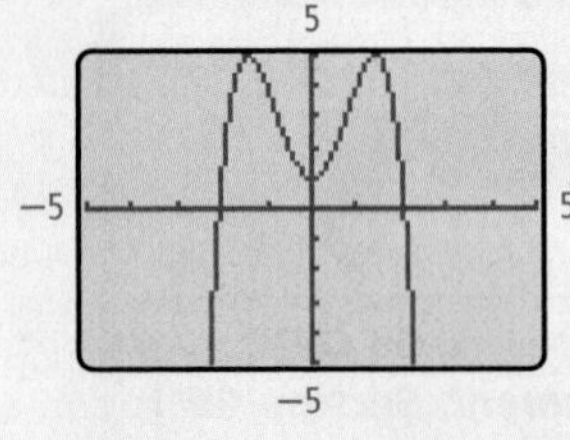

From left to right, it alternately increases and decreases, changing direction 3 times and crossing the x-axis 2 times. There appear to be 2 real zeros.

14.

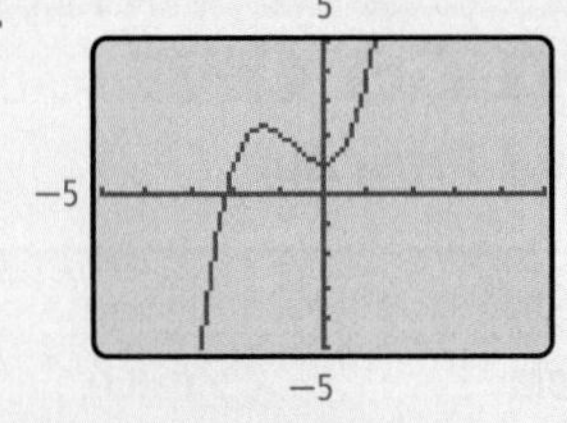

From left to right, it increases, decreases slightly, and then increases again. It crosses the x-axis 1 time. There appears to be 1 real zero.

15.

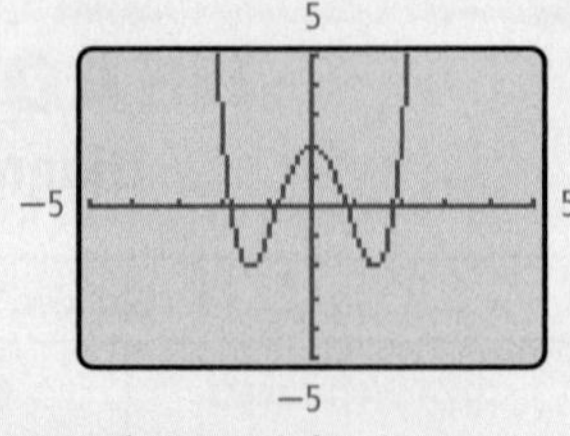

From left to right, it alternately decreases and increases, changing direction 3 times. It crosses the x-axis 4 times. There appear to be 4 real zeros.

16.

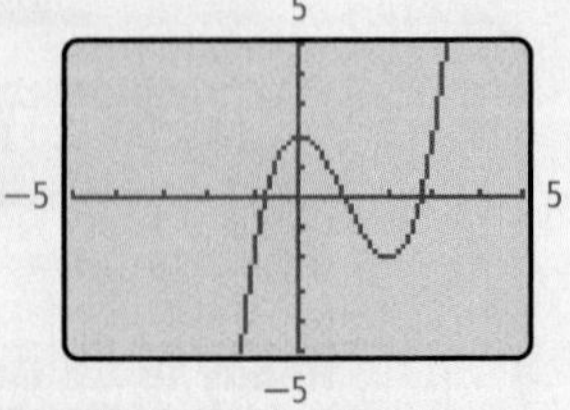

From left to right, it increases, decreases, and then increases again. It crosses the x-axis 3 times. There appear to be 3 real zeros.

CHAPTER 6 Study Guide: Review

Vocabulary

Complete the sentences below with vocabulary words from the list above.

1. A(n) ___?___ is a number or product of numbers and variables with whole number exponents.
2. A method of dividing a polynomial by a linear binomial of the form $x - a$ by using only the coefficients is ___?___.
3. The number of times $x - r$ is a factor of $P(x)$ is the ___?___ of r.
4. The ___?___ of a function is a description of the function values as x approaches positive infinity or negative infinity.

6-1 Polynomials *(pp. 406–412)*

EXAMPLES

■ **Subtract. Write your answer in standard form.**

$(6x - 2x^2 + 1) - (4x - 5x^2)$

$(-2x^2 + 6x + 1) + (5x^2 - 4x)$ *Add the opposite.*

$(-2x^2 + 5x^2) + (6x - 4x) + 1$ *Combine like terms.*

$3x^2 + 2x + 1$

■ **Graph $f(x) = -x^3 + 4x + 1$ on a calculator. Describe the graph, and identify the number of real zeros.**

From left to right, the function decreases, increases, and then decreases again. It crosses the x-axis three times. There appear to be three real zeros.

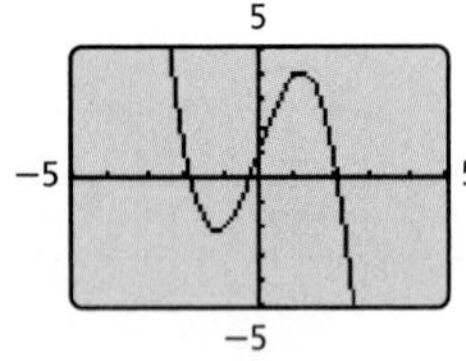

EXERCISES

Rewrite each polynomial in standard form. Then identify the leading coefficient, degree, and number of terms. Name the polynomial.

5. $4x^2 - 3x^3 + 6x + 7$
6. $5x^3 - x^5 + 8x + 2x^4$
7. $1 - 11x + 9x^2$
8. $-6x^2 + x^4$

Add or subtract. Write your answer in standard form.

9. $(8x^3 - 4x^2 - 3x + 1) - (1 - 5x^2 + x)$
10. $(6x^2 + 7x - 2) + (1 - 5x^3 + 3x)$
11. $(5x - 2x^2) - (4x^2 + 6x - 9)$
12. $(x^4 - x^2 + 4) + (x^2 - x^3 - 5x^4 - 7)$

Graph each polynomial function on a calculator. Describe the graph, and identify the number of real zeros.

13. $f(x) = -x^4 + 4x^2 + 1$
14. $f(x) = x^3 + 2x^2 + 1$
15. $f(x) = x^4 - 5x^2 + 2$
16. $f(x) = x^3 - 3x^2 + 2$

6-2 Multiplying Polynomials *(pp. 414–420)*

EXAMPLE

- **Find the product.**

$(x-3)(5-x-2x^2)$

Multiply horizontally.

$(x-3)(-2x^2-x+5)$ *Write in standard form.*

$x(-2x^2)+x(-x)+x(5)-3(-2x^2)-3(-x)-3(5)$

$-2x^3-x^2+5x+6x^2+3x-15$ *Multiply.*

$-2x^3+5x^2+8x-15$ *Combine like terms.*

EXERCISES

Find each product.

17. $5x^2(3x-2)$ **18.** $-3t(2t^2-6t+1)$

19. $ab^2(a^2-a+ab)$ **20.** $(x-2)(x^2-2x-3)$

21. $(2x+5)(x^3-x^2+1)$ **22.** $(x-3)^3$

23. $(x+4)(x^4-3x^2+x)$ **24.** $(2x+1)^4$

25. A cylinder has a height of x^2-x-3 and a radius of $2x$ as shown. Express the volume of the cylinder as a sum of monomials.

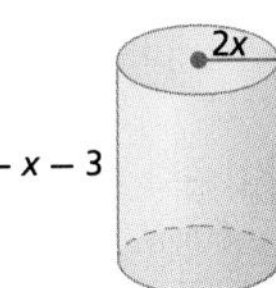

6-3 Dividing Polynomials *(pp. 422–428)*

EXAMPLE

- **Divide by using synthetic division.**

$(x^3-3x^2+8)\div(x+2)$

$a=-2$

x^3-3x^2+0x+8 *Write in standard form.*

−2	1	−3	0	8
		−2	10	−20
	1	−5	10	−12

Write the coefficients of the terms.

$$\frac{x^3-3x^2+8}{x+2}=x^2-5x+10+\frac{-12}{x+2}$$

EXERCISES

Divide by using long division.

26. $(x^3-5x^2+2x-7)\div(x+2)$

27. $(8x^4+6x^2-2x+4)\div(2x-1)$

Divide by using synthetic division.

28. $(x^3-4x^2+3x+2)\div(x-3)$

29. $(x^3+2x-1)\div(x-2)$

30. A spool of ribbon has a length of x^3+x^2 inches. Write an expression that represents the number of strips of ribbon with a length of $x-1$ inches that can be cut from one spool.

6-4 Factoring Polynomials *(pp. 430–435)*

EXAMPLES

Determine whether each binomial is a factor of the polynomial $P(x)=2x^2+x-10$.

- $(x+5)$

−5	2	1	−10
		−10	45
	2	−9	35

$x+5$ is not a factor of $P(x)$.

- $(x-2)$

2	2	1	−10
		4	10
	2	5	0

$x-2$ is a factor of $P(x)$.

EXERCISES

Determine whether the given binomial is a factor of the polynomial $P(x)$.

31. $(x+3)$; $P(x)=x^3+2x^2-5$

32. $(x-1)$; $P(x)=4x^4-5x^2+3x-2$

33. $(x-2)$; $P(x)=2x^3-3x^2+x-6$

Factor each expression.

34. $x^3-x^2-16x+16$ **35.** $4x^3-8x^2-x+2$

36. $3x^3+81$ **37.** $16x^3-2$

Answers

17. $15x^3-10x^2$
18. $-6t^3+18t^2-3t$
19. $a^3b^2-a^2b^2+a^2b^3$
20. x^3-4x^2+x+6
21. $2x^4+3x^3-5x^2+2x+5$
22. $x^3-9x^2+27x-27$
23. $x^5+4x^4-3x^3-11x^2+4x$
24. $16x^4+32x^3+24x^2+8x+1$
25. $4\pi x^4-4\pi x^3-12\pi x^2$
26. $x^2-7x+16-\frac{39}{x+2}$
27. $4x^3+2x^2+4x+1+\frac{5}{2x-1}$
28. $x^2-x+\frac{2}{x-3}$
29. $x^2+2x+6+\frac{11}{x-2}$
30. x^2+2x+2 in., remainder 2 in.
31. no
32. yes
33. yes
34. $(x-1)(x-4)(x+4)$
35. $(x-2)(2x-1)(2x+1)$
36. $3(x+3)(x^2-3x+9)$
37. $2(2x-1)(4x^2+2x+1)$

Answers

38. 1, 2
39. $-2, -2 \pm \sqrt{3}$
40. -1
41. $-3, 3, \pm\sqrt{3}$
42. $-1, \pm\sqrt{2}$
43. $1, 2 \pm 2\sqrt{2}$
44. $2m$
45. $P(x) = x^3 - 3x^2 - 10x + 24$
46. $P(x) = x^3 - \frac{1}{2}x^2 - \frac{13}{2}x - 3$
47. $P(x) = x^3 + x^2 - 2x - 2$
48. $P(x) = x^3 + 3x^2 + x + 3$
49. $P(x) = x^4 - 5x^2 + 6$
50. $P(x) = x^4 - 2x^3 + 2x^2 - 8x - 8$
51. $1, -2i, 2i$
52. $-i, i, -\sqrt{2}, \sqrt{2}$
53. $\pm 4, \pm\frac{1}{2}i$
54. $\pm\sqrt{5}, -3$

6-5 Finding Real Roots of Polynomial Equations *(pp. 438–444)*

EXAMPLE

■ **Identify all of the real roots of $x^4 - 4x^3 + 4x^2 - 1 = 0$.**

By the Rational Root Theorem, possible roots are ± 1.

$$\begin{array}{r|rrrrr} 1 & 1 & -4 & 4 & 0 & -1 \\ & & 1 & -3 & 1 & 1 \\ \hline & 1 & -3 & 1 & 1 & \boxed{0} \end{array}$$ *Try 1.*

$$\begin{array}{r|rrrr} 1 & 1 & -3 & 1 & 1 \\ & & 1 & -2 & -1 \\ \hline & 1 & -2 & -1 & \boxed{0} \end{array}$$ *Try 1 again.*

Factor $x^2 - 2x - 1$ by using the quadratic formula.

$$x = \frac{-(-2) \pm \sqrt{(-2)^2 - 4(1)(-1)}}{2(1)} = 1 \pm \sqrt{2}$$

The roots are 1 with a multiplicity of 2, and $1 \pm \sqrt{2}$.

EXERCISES

Identify all of the real roots of each equation.

38. $x^3 - 5x^2 + 8x - 4 = 0$
39. $x^3 + 6x^2 + 9x + 2 = 0$
40. $x^3 + 3x^2 + 3x + 1 = 0$
41. $x^4 - 12x^2 + 27 = 0$
42. $x^3 + x^2 - 2x - 2 = 0$
43. $x^3 - 5x^2 + 4 = 0$
44. A rectangular prism has length that is twice its width and height that is 4 meters longer than its width. The volume of the rectangular prism is 48 cubic meters. What is the width of the rectangular prism?

6-6 Fundamental Theorem of Algebra *(pp. 445–451)*

EXAMPLES

■ **Write the simplest polynomial function with roots -2, -1, and 4.**

$P(x) = 0$

$a(x + 2)(x + 1)(x - 4) = 0$ *If r is a root of P(x), then x − r is a factor of P(x).*

$a(x^3 - x^2 - 10x - 8) = 0$ *Multiply. For the simplest equation, let a = 1.*

$x^3 - x^2 - 10x - 8 = 0$

■ **Solve $x^3 + 2x^2 + x + 2 = 0$ by finding all roots.**

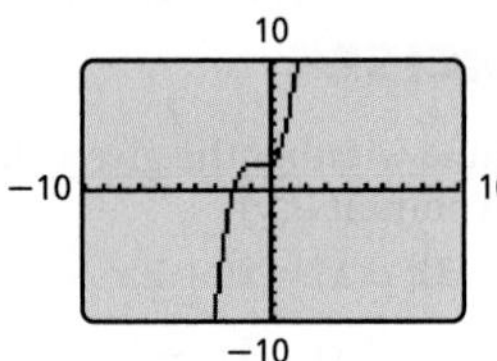

The graphing calculator shows -2 as a root. Use synthetic division to write the equation as $(x + 2)(x^2 + 1) = 0$. Solve $x^2 + 1 = 0$ to find the remaining roots. The solutions are -2, i, and $-i$.

EXERCISES

Write the simplest polynomial function with the given roots.

45. $-3, 2, 4$
46. $-\frac{1}{2}, -2, 3$
47. $-\sqrt{2}, -1$
48. $-3, i$
49. $\sqrt{2}, \sqrt{3}$
50. $1 + \sqrt{3}, 2i$

Solve the equation by finding all roots.

51. $x^3 - x^2 + 4x - 4 = 0$
52. $x^4 - x^2 - 2 = 0$
53. $x^4 - \frac{63}{4}x^2 - 4 = 0$
54. $x^3 + 3x^2 - 5x - 15 = 0$

6-7 Investigating Graphs of Polynomial Functions *(pp. 453–459)*

EXAMPLE

- **Graph the function $f(x) = x^3 + 2x^2 - 5x - 6$.**

Leading coefficient: 1; Degree: 3;
End behavior: $x \to -\infty, f(x) \to -\infty$
$x \to +\infty, f(x) \to +\infty$

The zeros are $-3, -1, 2$. *Factor to find the zeros.*

$f(0) = -6; f(-2) = 4; f(1) = -8$ *Evaluate f(x) at values between the roots. Plot these points.*

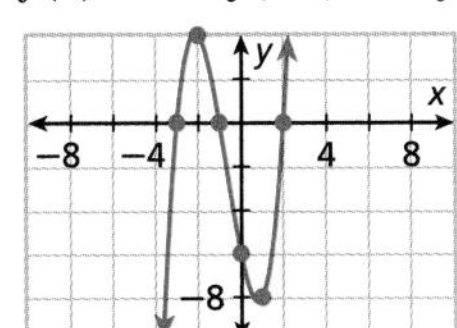

EXERCISES

Identify the leading coefficient, degree, and end behavior.

55. $-2x^3 + 5x^2 + 3$
56. $x^4 + 2x^3 - 3x + 1$
57. $-3x^6 + 9x^3 - 2x - 9$
58. $7x^5 + x^4 - 2x^2 + 5$

Graph each function.

59. $f(x) = x^3 - x^2 - 5x + 6$
60. $f(x) = x^4 - 10x^2 + 9$
61. $f(x) = -x^3 + 5x^2 + x - 5$

6-8 Transforming Polynomial Functions *(pp. 460–465)*

EXAMPLE

- **Write a function that transforms $f(x) = x^3 + 5$ by reflecting it across the x-axis and shifting it 2 units right. Support your solution by using a graphing calculator.**

$g(x) = -f(x - 2)$

$g(x) = -(x - 2)^3 - 5$

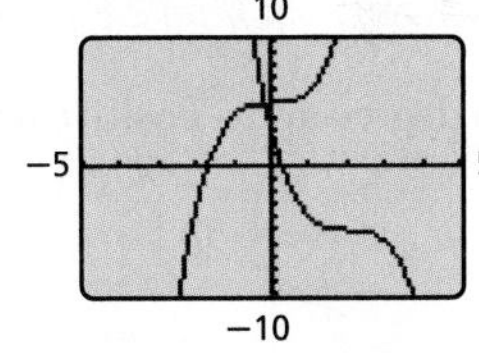

EXERCISES

Write a function that transforms $f(x) = x^4 - 6x^2 - 4$ in each of the following ways. Support your solution by using a graphing calculator.

62. Stretch vertically by a factor of 2, and move 9 units up.
63. Move 2 units down, and reflect across the x-axis.
64. Move 3 units right, and reflect across the y-axis.

6-9 Curve Fitting with Polynomial Models *(pp. 466–471)*

EXAMPLE

- **The table shows the profit for a company in thousands of dollars for the years shown. Write a polynomial function for the data.**

Year	1999	2000	2001	2002	2003
Profits	\$286	\$401	\$507	\$671	\$960

First differences: 115 106 164 289
Second differences: −9 58 125
Third differences: 67 67 *Constant*

A cubic polynomial best describes the data. Use the cubic regression feature on your graphing calculator.

$f(x) = 11.17x^3 - 38x^2 + 141.3x + 286$

EXERCISES

65. The chart shows the attendance for a new movie theater over five days. Write a polynomial function for the data.

Day	1	2	3	4	5
Attendance	248	298	318	388	428

66. The chart shows the population of a city for five years. Write a polynomial function for the data.

Year	1	2	3	4	5
Population (thousands)	1891	2674	3376	4480	6469

Answers

55. -2; 3; as $x \to -\infty$, $f(x) \to +\infty$; as $x \to +\infty$, $f(x) \to -\infty$
56. 1; 4; as $x \to \pm\infty$, $f(x) \to +\infty$
57. -3; 6; as $x \to \pm\infty$, $f(x) \to -\infty$
58. 7; 5; as $x \to -\infty$, $f(x) \to -\infty$; as $x \to +\infty$, $f(x) \to +\infty$
59.

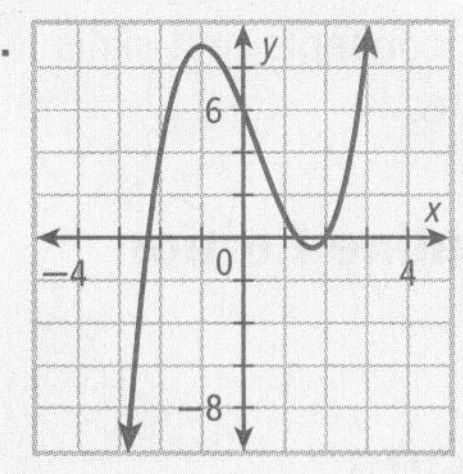

60.

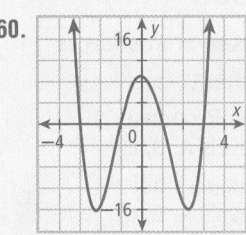

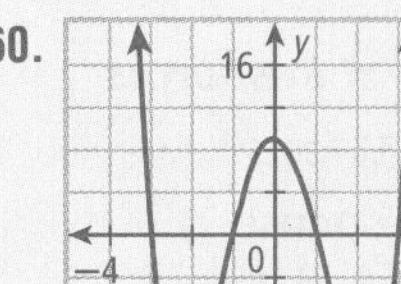

61.

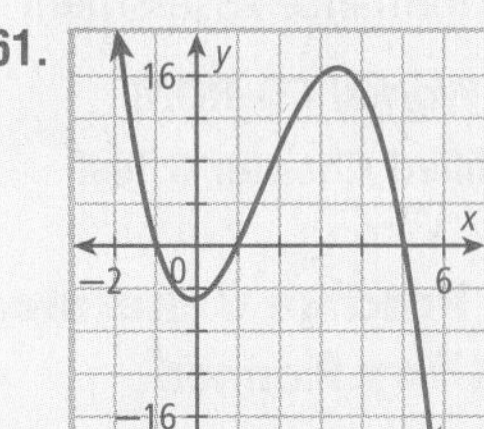

62. $g(x) = 2x^4 - 12x^2 + 1$

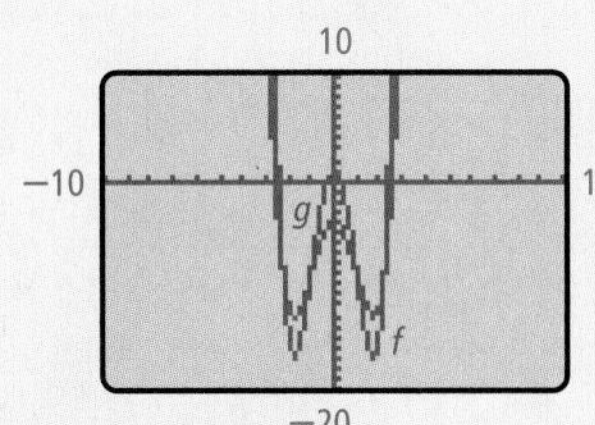

63. $g(x) = -x^4 + 6x^2 + 6$

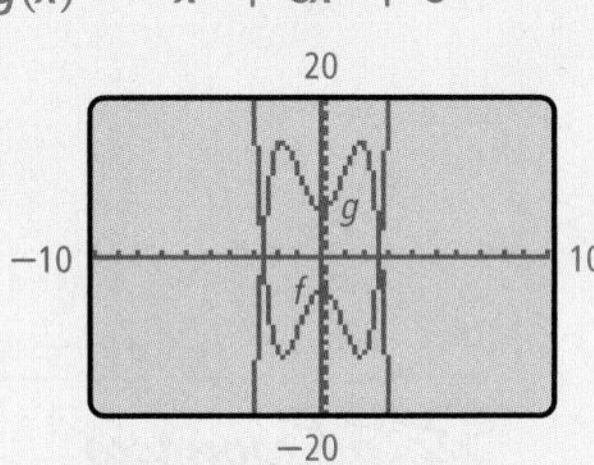

64. $g(x) = (-x - 3)^4 - 6(-x - 3)^2 - 4$

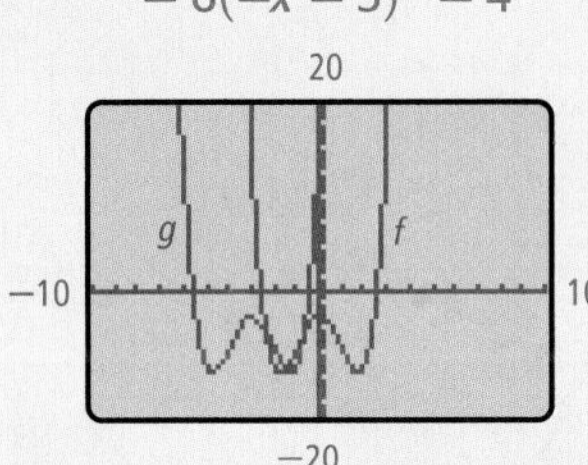

65. $f(x) \approx -6\frac{2}{3}x^4 + 80x^3 - 328\frac{1}{3}x^2 + 575x - 72$
66. $f(x) \approx 80.5x^3 - 523.5x^2 + 1790x + 544$

Organizer

Objective: Assess students' mastery of concepts and skills in Chapter 6.

Online Edition

Resources

Assessment Resources

Chapter 6 Tests

- Free Response (Levels A, B, C)
- Multiple Choice (Levels A, B, C)
- Performance Assessment

 ***IDEA Works!* CD-ROM**

Modified Chapter 6 Test

Test & Practice Generator One-Stop Planner®

State Resources

go.hrw.com
State Resources Online
KEYWORD: MB7 Resources

CHAPTER 6 CHAPTER TEST

Add or subtract. Write your answer in standard form.

1. $(3x^2 - x + 1) + (x)$ $3x^2 + 1$
2. $(6x^3 - 3x + 2) - (7x^3 + 3x + 7)$ $-x^3 - 6x - 5$
3. $(y^2 + 3y^2 + 2) + (y^4 + y^3 - y^2 + 5)$ $y^4 + y^3 + 3y^2 + 7$
4. $(4x^4 + x^2) - (x^3 - x^2 - 1)$ $4x^4 - x^3 + 2x^2 + 1$
5. The cost of producing x units of a product can be modeled by $C(x) = \frac{1}{10}x^3 - x^2 + 25$. Evaluate $C(x)$ for $x = 15$, and describe what the value represents. $C(15) = 137.50$; the cost of manufacturing 15 units is $137.50.

Find each product.

6. $xy(2x^4y + x^2y^2 - 3xy^3)$ $2x^5y^2 + x^3y^3 - 3x^2y^4$
7. $(t + 3)(2t^2 - t + 3)$ $2t^3 + 5t^2 + 9$
8. $(x + 5)^3$ $x^3 + 15x^2 + 75x + 125$
9. $(2y + 3)^4$ $16y^4 + 96y^3 + 216y^2 + 216y + 81$

Divide.

10. $(5x^2 - 6x - 8) \div (x - 2)$ $5x + 4$
11. $(2x^3 - 7x^2 + 9x - 4) \div (2x - 1)$ $x^2 - 3x + 3 + \frac{-1}{2x - 1}$
12. Use synthetic substitution to evaluate $x^4 + 3x^3 - x^2 + 2x - 6$ for $x = 3$. 153

Factor each expression.

13. $-2x^2 - 6x + 56$ $-2(x + 7)(x - 4)$
14. $m^5 + m^4 - 625m - 625$ $(m + 1)(m + 5)(m - 5)(m^2 + 25)$
15. $4x^3 - 32$ $4(x - 2)(x^2 + 2x + 4)$
16. Identify the roots of the equation $2x^4 - 9x^3 + 7x^2 + 2x - 2 = 0$. State the multiplicity of each root. $1, -\frac{1}{2}, 2 + \sqrt{2}, 2 - \sqrt{2}$, all with multiplicity 1
17. Write the simplest polynomial function with roots of 1, 4, and −5. $x^3 - 21x + 20$

Identify whether the function graphed has an odd or even degree and a positive or negative leading coefficient.

18. 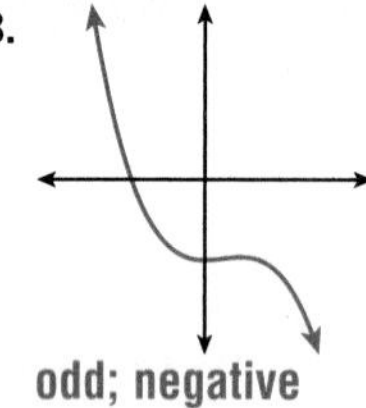
odd; negative

19. 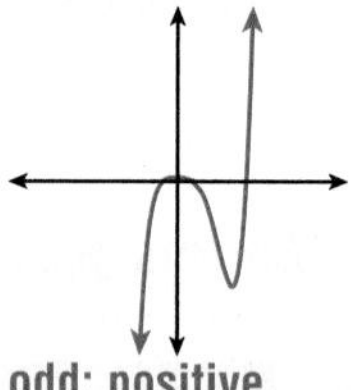
odd; positive

20. 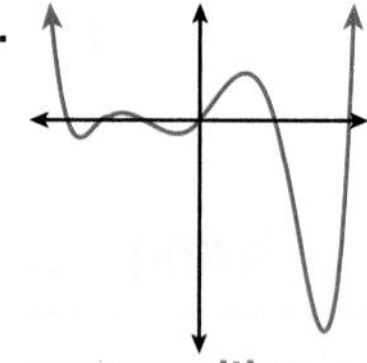
even; positive

Let $f(x) = 12x^3 + 4$. Graph $f(x)$ and $g(x)$ on the same coordinate plane. Describe $g(x)$ as a transformation of $f(x)$.

21. $g(x) = f(-x)$
22. $g(x) = \frac{1}{2}f(x)$
23. $g(x) = -f(x) + 3$
24. The table shows the number of bracelets Carly can make over time. Write a polynomial function for the data. $f(x) = 2x^2 - 4x + 5$

Time (h)	1	2	3	4	5	6
Bracelets	3	5	11	21	35	53

25. The table shows the number of sandwiches sold each day at a deli over 5 days. Write a polynomial function for the data. $f(x) = 3.54x^4 - 44.58x^3 + 185.96x^2 - 283.92x + 196$

Day	1	2	3	4	5
Sandwiches	57	72	101	89	66

Answers

21. 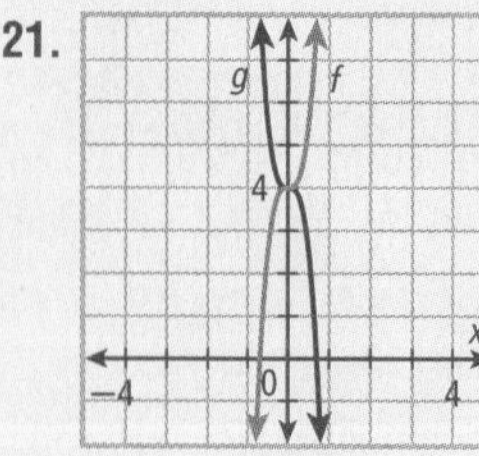

reflection across y-axis

22. 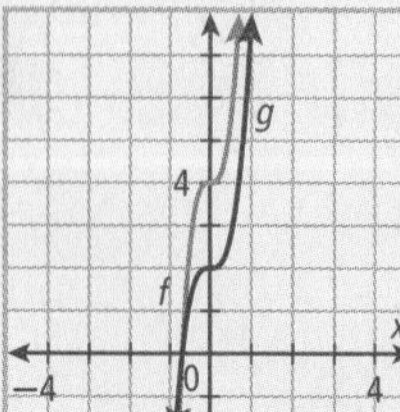

vertical compression by $\frac{1}{2}$

23. 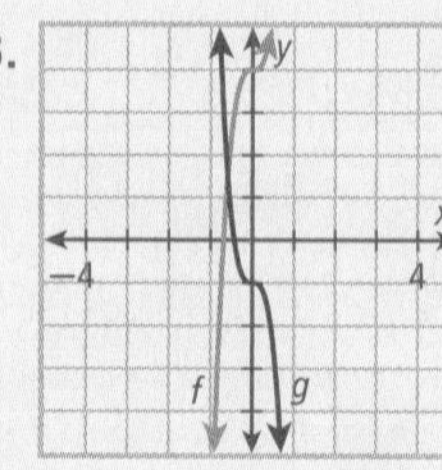

reflection across x-axis and shift 3 units up

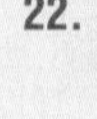

COLLEGE ENTRANCE EXAM PRACTICE

FOCUS ON SAT MATHEMATICS SUBJECT TESTS

SAT Mathematics Subject Test results include scaled scores and percentiles. Your scaled score is a number from 200 to 800, calculated by using a formula that varies. The percentile indicates the percentage of people who took the same test and scored lower than you did.

The questions are written so that you should not need to do any lengthy calculations. If you find yourself getting involved in a long calculation, think again about all of the information in the problem to see if you might have missed something helpful.

You may want to time yourself as you take this practice test. It should take you about 7 minutes to complete.

1. If $x^4 - 7x^3 - 24x^2 + 112x + 128$ has a rational root a. Which could NOT be the value of a?

(A) 0

(B) 16

(C) 24

(D) 32

(E) 64

2. If there is a remainder of 3 when you divide $p(x) = x^3 + 4x^2 - hx + 30$ by $x - 3$, what is the value of h?

(A) -90

(B) 4

(C) 12

(D) 27

(E) 30

3. The graph of $q(x) = ax^4 + bx^3 + cx^2 + dx + f$ is shown below. Which of the following is true?

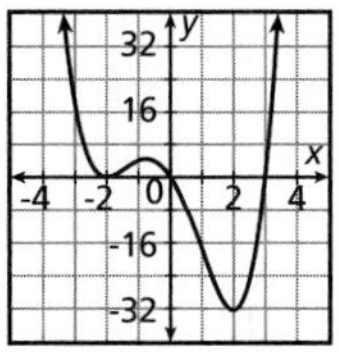

(A) $q(x)$ has an odd degree.

(B) $q(x) = (x + 3)h(x)$ for some polynomial $h(x)$.

(C) $f > 0$

(D) $q(0)$ is a local minimum.

(E) $q(x) \to \infty$ as $x \to \infty$

4. Which of the following is the expanded form of $(3x + 2)^3$?

(A) $9x + 6$

(B) $27x^3 + 8$

(C) $27x^3 + 90x + 8$

(D) $27x^3 + 60x^2 + 30x + 8$

(E) $27x^3 + 54x^2 + 36x + 8$

5. If $f(x)$ is a polynomial, which of the following transformations may affect the number of zeros of $f(x)$?

(A) Reflecting $f(x)$ across the y-axis

(B) Reflecting $f(x)$ across the x-axis

(C) Translating $f(x)$ 2 units to the right

(D) Translating $f(x)$ 6 units down

(E) Vertically stretching by a factor of 2

6. Which of the following is a possible root of the polynomial $16x^4 + 80x^3 - 191x^2 + 8x + 15$?

(A) $\frac{1}{12}$

(B) $\frac{1}{5}$

(C) $\frac{3}{8}$

(D) $\frac{3}{5}$

(E) $\frac{8}{3}$

Organizer

Objective: Provide practice for college entrance exams such as the SAT Mathematics Subject Tests.

PREMIER **Online Edition**

Resources

College Entrance Exam Practice

Questions on the SAT Mathematics Subject Tests Levels 1 and 2 represent the following math content areas:

	Level	
	I	**II**
Algebra	30%	18%
Plane Euclidean Geometry	20%	0%
Coordinate Geometry	12%	12%
Three-dimensional Geometry	6%	8%
Trigonometry	8%	20%
Functions	12%	24%
Statistics/Probability	6%	6%
Miscellaneous	6%	12%

Items on this page focus on:
- Algebra
- Functions

Text References:

Item	1	2	3	4	5	6
Lesson	6-4	6-3	6-7	6-2	6-8	6-5

TEST PREP DOCTOR

1. Students who chose **C, D,** or **E** may have guessed the selected answer because it is a factor of the constant term, 128. Remind students that $(x - a)$ is a factor of $P(x)$ if and only if $P(a) = 0$.

2. Ask students how the Factor Theorem can be used instead of lengthy division to solve this problem.

3. Students who chose **D** may not understand the meaning of a *local* minimum. Students who answered **B** may not understand the connection between zeros of a polynomial function and factors of the polynomial.

4. Students who chose **A, B,** or **C** may not understand that they must expand using multiplication or binomial expansion.

5. Students who chose **E** may have considered only one possible graph when checking the other answer choices. Ask students to consider a polynomial with a zero of multiplicity 2.

6. Students who chose **B, D,** or **E** may have inverted the rules in the Rational Root Theorem. Remind students that the value in the numerator must be a factor of the constant term and the value in the denominator must be a factor of the leading coefficient.

Organizer

Objective: Provide opportunities to learn and practice common test-taking strategies.

Online Edition

Resources

State Test Prep Workbook

State Test Prep CD-ROM

State Test Practice Online

go.hrw.com

KEYWORD: MB7 TestPrep

This Test Tackler describes how to identify key words and context clues and use them to answer a test item correctly. Encourage students to read a problem statement once for understanding and then to reread the statement, underlining the key words or clues. When students complete their response, have them go back and refer to the words they underlined in the problem statement to confirm that their response is appropriate.

Standardized Test Strategies

Any Question Type: Identify Key Words and Context Clues

When reading a test item, you should pay attention to key words and context clues in the problem statement. These clues will help you provide a correct response.

EXAMPLE 1

Short Response

Write a polynomial in standard form for the volume of the rectangular prism. Find the volume when $x = 5$ inches.

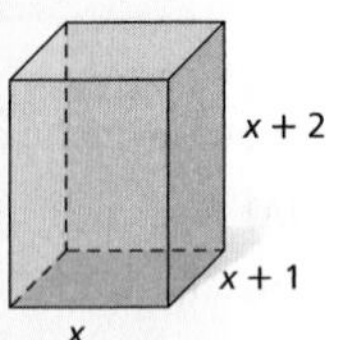

Look *for key words and context clues. Identify what they mean.*

Write a **polynomial** in **standard form** for the **volume** of the rectangular prism.

polynomial → a monomial or a sum or difference of monomials

standard form → a polynomial written with its terms in descending order by degree

volume → volume of a rectangular prism ($V = \ell wh$) in cubic inches

$V(x) = x(x + 1)(x + 2) = x^3 + 3x^2 + 2x$ ← Standard form

$V(5) = 5^3 + 3(5^2) + 2(5) = 125 + 75 + 10 = 210$ cubic inches

The volume of the prism can be represented by $V(x) = x^3 + 3x^2 + 2x$, and when $x = 5$, $V = 210$ cubic inches.

EXAMPLE 2

Multiple Choice

Paige runs a small jewelry business. From 2000 through 2005, the number of items she created can be modeled by $24x + 12$, and the average cost to make each item can be modeled by $-0.05x^2 + 10$, where x is the number of years since 2000. Which polynomial can be used to model Paige's total jewelry-making costs for those years?

Ⓐ $-0.05x^2 + 24x + 22$

Ⓑ $0.05x^2 + 24x + 2$

Ⓒ $-12x^3 - 6x^2 + 240x + 120$

Ⓓ $-1.2x^3 - 0.6x^2 + 240x + 120$

The key words in this test item are **total cost.**

total cost → average cost per unit **times** the number of units

$= -0.05x^2 + 10 \quad \times \quad 24x + 12$

$= -1.2x^3 - 0.6x^2 + 240x + 120$

The correct answer is choice D.

If you do not understand what a word means, reread the sentences around the word and make a logical guess.

Read each test item and answer the questions that follow.

Item A

Short Response **A box can be made by cutting squares from each of the four corners of a piece of cardboard. The volume of a box made from a 27.5-by-40-centimeter piece of cardboard can be modeled by $x(27.5 - 2x)(40 - 2x)$, where x is the length of one side of the square. Write the volume as a sum of monomials, and find the volume when $x = 5$ centimeters.**

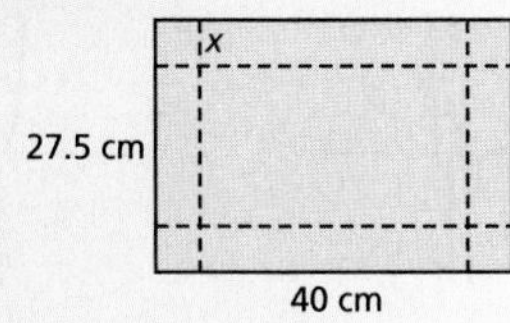

1. What do $(27.5 - 2x)$ and $(40 - 2x)$ represent in the model?
2. Describe what "sum of monomials" means.
3. When you calculate the volume for $x = 5$, in what units should you give your response?

Item B

Short Response **The volume of a cylindrical tank with a hemispherical top and bottom can be represented by the function $V(r) = 24\pi r^2 + \frac{4}{3}\pi r^3$, where V is the volume in cubic meters and r is the radius in meters. What is the radius if the volume of the tank is 5760π cubic meters?**

4. Which word(s) in the problem statement tells you that the volume of a sphere is part of the function?
5. What does the term $24\pi r^2$ in the function represent?
6. Describe how to find the radius given the volume of the tank.

Item C

Multiple Choice **Which description matches the transformation from f to g shown?**

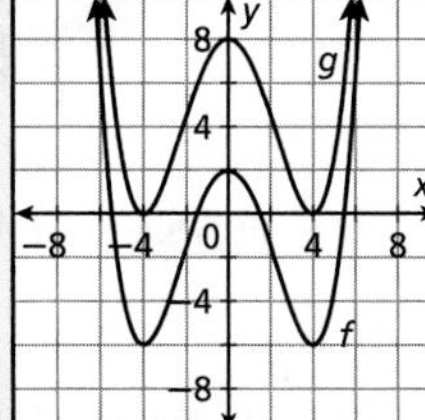

Ⓐ Vertical shift of 3 units

Ⓑ Vertical stretch by a factor of 3

Ⓒ Horizontal shift of 3 units

Ⓓ Horizontal stretch by a factor of 3

7. How do you know which is the original function and which is the image of the function?
8. Because the graphs are shown with an x- and y-scale of 1, how can you use the grid to identify a shift of 3 units?

Item D

Gridded Response **A rectangular storage compartment has a length equal to its width and a height that is 5 feet greater than its width. The volume of the compartment is 72 cubic feet. What is the width?**

9. Make a list of the key words given in the problem statement, and link each word to its mathematical meaning.
10. Write expressions representing the length and height of the compartment in terms of width.
11. Write an expression for the volume of the compartment.

Answers

1. height and width of the box
2. monomials separated by the addition sign
3. cubic centimeters
4. hemispherical top and bottom
5. the volume of the cylinder
6. Set the function equal to 5760π. Write the function in standard form. Divide both sides by π. Use synthetic division to find the roots of the function.
7. Possible answer: The original function is named $f(x)$. Look for that label on the graph. The image is named $g(x)$ and is also a label on the graph.
8. Possible answer: 3 units would be the same as 3 squares on the grid. Find a point on the first function, and count 3 squares left or right to see if you end up on the same point of the other function.
9. "equal to": =; "is": =; "greater than": +
10. length: w; height: $w + 5$
11. $V = w^2 (w + 5)$

Answers to Test Items

A. $4x^3 - 135x^2 + 1100x$; 2625 cm^3

B. 12 m

C. A

D. 3

State Resources

go.hrw.com
State Resources Online
KEYWORD: MB7 Resources

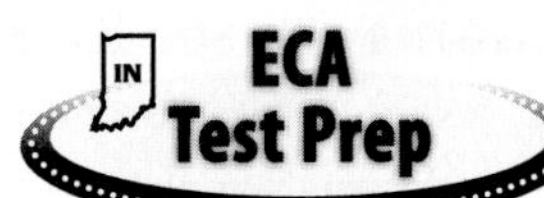

Organizer

Objective: Provide review and practice for Chapters 1–6 and standardized tests.

Resources

 ***Assessment Resources***

Chapter 6 Cumulative Test

 ***Idea Works!* CD-ROMs**

Modified Cumulative Test

 ***State Test Prep Workbook***

 ***State Test Prep* CD-ROM**

***State Test Practice* Online**

go.hrw.com

KEYWORD: MB7 TestPrep

Answers

1. C
2. B
3. A
4. A
5. B
6. A
7. A
8. C
9. B
10. D
11. D

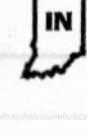 *State Resources*

Core Standard	Items
2	5
3	10
4	2, 6, 12, 13, 14, 15, 16

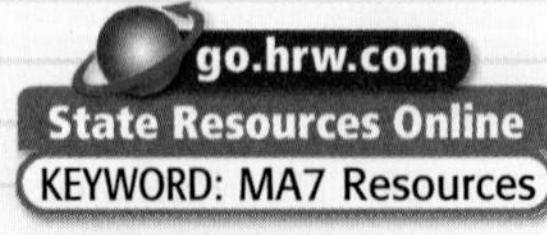

CUMULATIVE ASSESSMENT, CHAPTERS 1–6

Multiple Choice

1. Which row of Pascal's triangle gives the coefficients for the binomial expansion of $(a + b)^4$?

A. 1 2 1

B. 1 3 3 1

C. 1 4 6 4 1

D. 1 5 10 10 5 1

2. Which binomial is a factor of $2x^4 - 11x^3 + 19x^2 - 13x + 3$?

A. $x - 2$ **B.** $x - 3$

C. $x + 1$ **D.** $x + 2$

3. Which graph shows the ordered triple $(-3, 3, -4)$ graphed in a three-dimensional coordinate plane?

A.
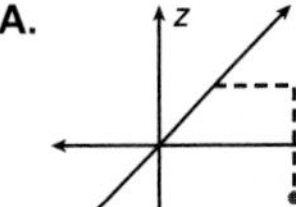

B.
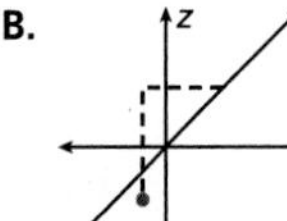

C.
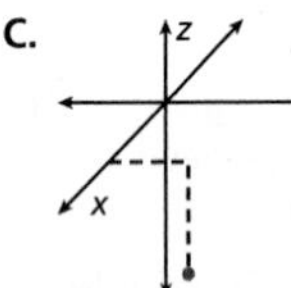

D.
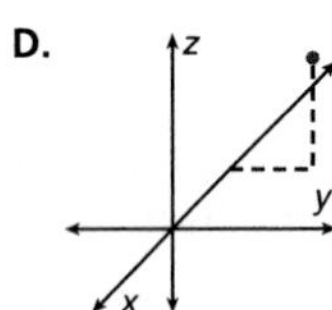

4. What is the value of the y-intercept of $2x + 4y = 1$?

A. $\frac{1}{4}$ **B.** $-\frac{1}{2}$

C. 1 **D.** -2

5. Simplify $\frac{4 - i}{1 + 3i}$.

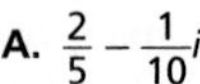

A. $\frac{2}{5} - \frac{1}{10}i$ **B.** $\frac{1}{10} - \frac{13}{10}i$

C. $\frac{7}{10} + \frac{11}{10}i$ **D.** $4 - \frac{1}{3}i$

6. Which graph represents an odd degree polynomial function with a positive leading coefficient?

A.
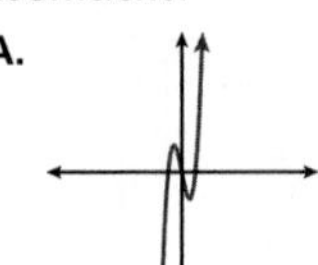

B.
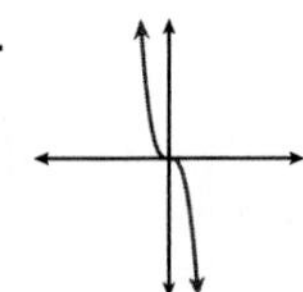

C.
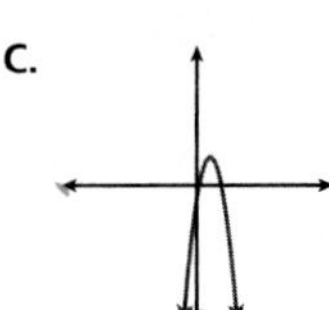

D.
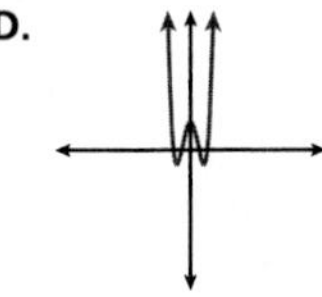

7. Solve the compound inequality $-3x < 12$ and $-8x + 1 < 9 - 12x$. Which of the following is a graph of the solution?

A. −5 −4 −3 −2 −1 0 1 2 3 4 5

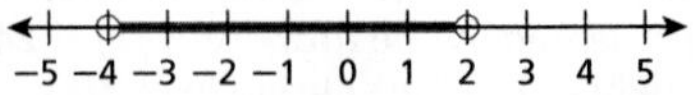

B. −5 −4 −3 −2 −1 0 1 2 3 4 5

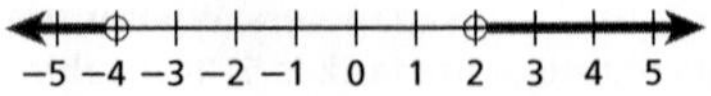

C. −5 −4 −3 −2 −1 0 1 2 3 4 5

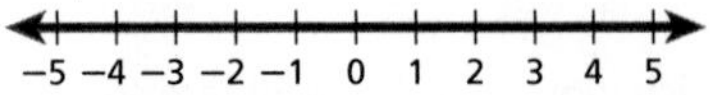

D. −5 −4 −3 −2 −1 0 1 2 3 4 5

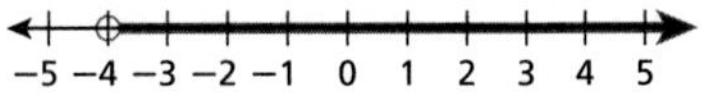

TEST PREP DOCTOR

Item 7 illustrates the importance of graphing an answer. The algebraic solution is a compound inequality. However, when graphed, it becomes easier to see how the two parts of the compound inequality work together. Encourage students to select multiple test values to verify their solutions to the inequality.

Answers

12. Part A: $f(x) = 29x^3 - 343x^2 + 1174x - 7$

Part B: 605

13. Part A: 3, −2

Part B: The root 3 has a multiplicity of 1. The root −2 has a multiplicity of 2. The graph crosses (3, 0) and touches at (−2, 0).

14. $x^3 - 6x^2 + 5x + 12 = 0$

15. $f(-2) = 0$; $f(3) = 40$

Use matrix N for Items 8 and 9.

$$N = \begin{bmatrix} 2 & -1 \\ 4 & -3 \end{bmatrix}$$

8. What is the value of entry n_{21}?

A. 2

B. −3

C. 4

D. −6

9. Find the inverse of matrix N.

A. $\begin{bmatrix} 2 & -1 \\ \frac{3}{2} & -\frac{1}{2} \end{bmatrix}$ **B.** $\begin{bmatrix} \frac{3}{2} & -\frac{1}{2} \\ 2 & -1 \end{bmatrix}$

C. $\begin{bmatrix} \frac{3}{2} & -2 \\ 2 & -1 \end{bmatrix}$ **D.** $\begin{bmatrix} 2 & -1 \\ \frac{3}{2} & -2 \end{bmatrix}$

In Item 10, use the end behavior of the graph to identify the sign of the leading coefficent and eliminate answer choices. Then use the *y*-intercept to choose the correct response.

10. What is the equation of the parabola shown?

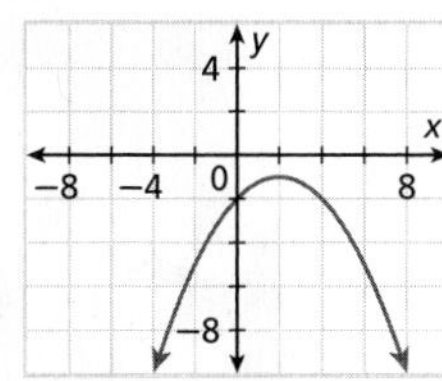

A. $f(x) = 0.25x^2 + x - 2$

B. $f(x) = 0.25x^2 - x - 2$

C. $f(x) = -0.25x^2 + x + 2$

D. $f(x) = -0.25x^2 + x - 2$

11. What is the degree of the polynomial $7x^4 + 3x^2 - x^6 + 4$?

A. 1

B. 2

C. 4

D. 6

Short Answer

12. The table below shows the number of spyware traces detected and removed from Larry's computer from January to June.

Jan	Feb	Mar	Apr	May	Jun
120	395	545	220	145	130

Part A Write a cubic function for the data.

Part B Using your answer to part **A**, about how many traces can Larry expect to find in July?

13. Consider $5x^3 + 5x^2 - 40x - 60 = 0$.

Part A Identify the roots of the equation.

Part B State the multiplicity of each root. Explain what the multiplicity means in terms of the graph.

14. Write the simplest polynomial function with zeros −1, 3, and 4.

15. Use synthetic substitution to evaluate $f(x) = x^3 + 5x^2 - 4x - 20$ for $x = -2$ and $x = 3$.

Extended Response

16. The functions g and h are the result of transformations of the function f.

Part A $f(x) = x^3 - 5x^2 + 8x - 1$ is reflected across the x-axis. Write the equation for $g(x)$.

Part B Use a graphing calculator to graph f and g. Explain how the graph supports your answer to part **A**.

Part C $f(x) = 4(x + 1)^3 + 4$ is translated 1 unit to the right and 3 units down. Write the equation for $h(x)$.

Part D Use a graphing calculator to graph f and h. Explain how the graph supports your answer to part **C**.

Short Answer Rubric

Items 12–15

Score 2 = Thorough understanding of mathematical concepts and processes.

Score 1 = Partial understanding of mathematical concepts and/or processes.

Score 0 = Limited or no understanding of the problem-solving concepts.

Blank = No written response.

Extended Response Rubric

Items 16

Score 4 = Thorough understanding of mathematical concepts and processes.

Score 3 = Demonstrated understanding of mathematical concepts and processes, but an error in computation or explanation.

Score 2 = Partial understanding of mathematical concepts and/or processes.

Score 1 = Limited understanding and execution of the problem-solving concepts.

Score 0 = No understanding of the problem-solving concepts.

Blank = No written response.

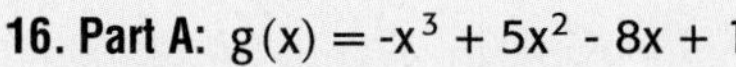

16. Part A: $g(x) = -x^3 + 5x^2 - 8x + 1$

Part B:

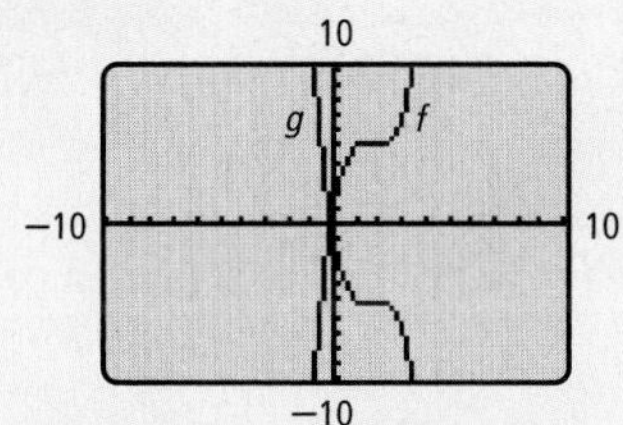

Possible answer: The graphs are mirror images of each other across the *x*-axis.

Part C: $h(x) = 4x^3 + 1$

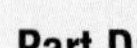

Part D:

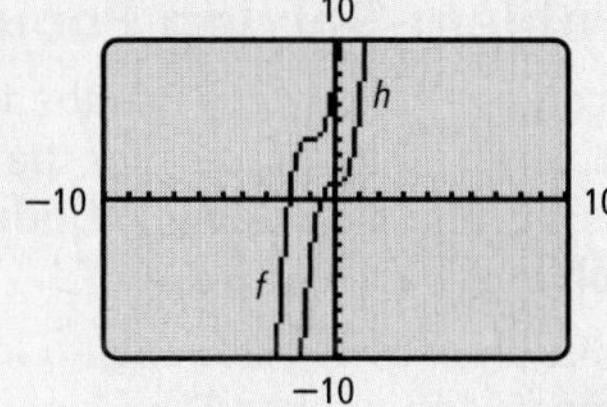

Possible answer: The bend in the graph is 1 unit to the left and 3 units up from the original graph.

Problem Solving on Location

Organizer

Objective: Apply problem-solving strategies to solve problems involving quadratic and polynomial functions.

Online Edition

The Camden Waterfront

Reading Strategies

In **Problem 1,** students must choose which column of the table to use based on the appropriate unit of measurement.

Discuss with students what unit for volume would be appropriate when height is given in meters.

Using Data Have students get familiar with the volumes by comparing a gallon to a cubic meter. Which is greater? cubic meter Ask students to give examples of liquids that are commonly measured in gallons.

State Resources

Problem Solving on Location

NEW JERSEY

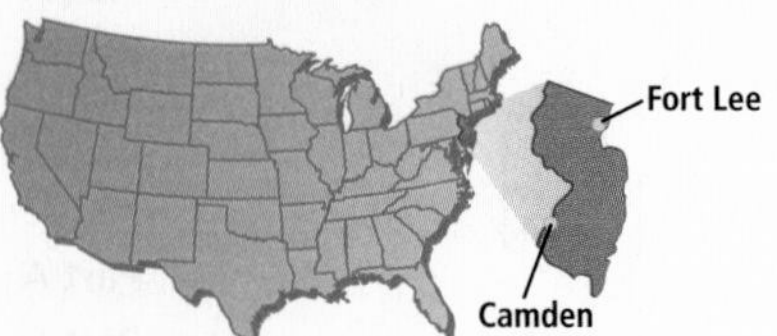

The Camden Waterfront

Located along the Delaware River, the Camden Waterfront offers a variety of attractions, including the Camden Riversharks minor league baseball team and the former home of poet Walt Whitman. The waterfront's most popular destination is the interactive Adventure Aquarium, which features two huge tanks: a 760,000-gallon open tank and a two-story, 550,000-gallon shark tank.

Choose one or more strategies to solve each problem. For 1 and 2, use the table.

Adventure Aquarium		
Tank	Volume (gal)	Volume (m^3)
Open Ocean	760,000	2877
Shark Realm	550,000	2082

1. The volume of a cylindrical tank can be modeled by the function $V(h) = \pi(h^3 + 6h^2 + 9h)$, where h is the tank's height in meters. Use this model to find the height of the Open Ocean tank. 7.82 m
2. The Shark Realm tank has a viewing tunnel along its length. The volume of the tank can be modeled by $V(\ell) = \ell(\ell - 3.2)(\ell + 6.8)$, where ℓ is the tank's length in meters. What is the length of the viewing tunnel? 12.2 m
3. The children's garden at the Camden Waterfront includes a 1200-square-foot room where visitors can walk among hundreds of flying butterflies. During one month of the year, the population of butterflies is modeled by $P(x) = 0.026x^3 - 1.3x^2 + 15.3x + 200$, where x is the number of days since the beginning of the month. What is the maximum population of butterflies during the month? 252

Problem-Solving Focus

Encourage students to use the four-step problem-solving process for the problems. Focus on the first step: **(1) Understand the Problem.**

In **Problem 3,** ask students to identify the given information and to identify the form of the final answer. Is all the necessary information given in the problem? yes Is any unnecessary information present? yes

The George Washington Bridge

When the George Washington Bridge opened to traffic in 1931, it was the world's longest suspension bridge. Since then, it has been eclipsed by longer spans, but it remains one of the world's busiest bridges. On a typical day, more than 300,000 vehicles use the bridge to cross the Hudson River between Upper Manhattan and Fort Lee, New Jersey.

Problem Solving Strategies

- Draw a Diagram
- Make a Model
- Guess and Test
- Work Backward
- Find a Pattern
- Make a Table
- Solve a Simpler Problem
- Use Logical Reasoning
- Use a Venn Diagram
- Make an Organized List

Choose one or more strategies to solve each problem.

1. The height in feet of the main cable above the roadway can be modeled by the equation $h = \frac{2}{15625}(x - 1750)^2$, where x is the distance in feet from the west tower. Find the height of the west tower. **392 ft**

2. The cable touches the roadway at the midpoint between the two towers. What is the length of the span between the towers? **3500 ft**

3. The distance d traveled by a vehicle moving at an initial velocity of v_0 mi/h with a constant acceleration of a mi/h^2 is given by $d = \frac{1}{2}at^2 + v_0t$, where t is the time in hours. Given that the George Washington Bridge is 0.9 mi long, how long does it take a motorist to cross the bridge if she enters the bridge at 50 mi/h and accelerates at 10 mi/h^2? **0.018 h, or 1.08 min**

For 4, use the table.

4. The table shows the average hourly volume of eastbound traffic into Manhattan. Use a quadratic model to predict the hourly volume of traffic during the rush-hour peak from 6:00 A.M. to 7:00 A.M. **11,912**

George Washington Bridge, Eastbound	
Hour	**Average Vehicular Volume**
3:00 A.M. to 4:00 A.M.	1274
4:00 A.M. to 5:00 A.M.	2035
5:00 A.M. to 6:00 A.M.	5581

The George Washington Bridge

Reading Strategies

Students may not be familiar with the phrase "volume of traffic" in **Problem 4.** Help students use context clues to understand the meaning of the problem.

Using Data Discuss what values from the table will be the independent and dependant variables in the quadratic model.

Problem-Solving Focus

For **Problems 1** and **2,** students may need to draw a diagram in which the west tower of the bridge is on the y-axis of a coordinate plane and the bridge's roadway is on the x-axis. In this case, encourage students to mark as much information as possible on their diagrams.

Exponential and Logarithmic Functions

Section 7A

Exponential Functions and Logarithms

- **7-1 Exponential Functions, Growth, and Decay**
- **7-2 Technology Lab** Explore Inverses of Functions
- **7-2 Inverses of Relations and Functions**
- **7-3 Logarithmic Functions**
- **7-4 Properties of Logarithms**

Section 7B

Applying Exponential and Logarithmic Functions

- **7-5 Using Formulas in Geometry**
- **Connecting Algebra to Probability** Exponents in Probability Formulas
- **7-6 Technology Lab** Explore the Rule of 72
- **7-6 The Natural Base, e**
- **7-7 Transforming Exponential and Logarithmic Functions**
- **7-8 Curve Fitting with Exponential and Logarithmic Models**

Pacing Guide for 45-Minute Classes

Chapter 7

Countdown to Testing Weeks 15, 16

DAY 1	DAY 2	DAY 3	DAY 4	DAY 5
7-1 Lesson	7-2 Technology Lab	7-2 Lesson	7-3 Lesson	7-4 Lesson
DAY 6	**DAY 7**	**DAY 8**	**DAY 9**	**DAY 10**
7-4 Lesson	Multi-Step Test Prep Ready to Go On? 7-5 Lesson	7-5 Lesson	7-5 Lesson 7-5 Technology Lab Connecting Algebra to Probability	7-6 Technology Lab 7-6 Lesson
DAY 11	**DAY 12**	**DAY 13**	**DAY 14**	
7-6 Lesson 7-7 Lesson	7-7 Lesson 7-8 Lesson	7-8 Lesson Multi-Step Test Prep Ready to Go On?	Chapter 7 Test	

Pacing Guide for 90-Minute Classes

Chapter 7

DAY 1	DAY 2	DAY 3	DAY 4	DAY 5
Chapter 6 Test 7-1 Lesson	7-2 Technology Lab 7-2 Lesson	7-3 Lesson 7-4 Lesson	7-4 Lesson Multi-Step Test Prep Ready to Go On? 7-5 Lesson	7-5 Lesson Connecting Algebra to Probability
DAY 6	**DAY 7**	**DAY 8**		
7-6 Technology Lab 7-6 Lesson 7-7 Lesson	7-7 Lesson 7-8 Lesson Multi-Step Test Prep Ready to Go On?	Chapter 7 Test 8-1 Algebra Lab		

ONGOING ASSESSMENT and INTERVENTION

	DIAGNOSE	PRESCRIBE
Assess Prior Knowledge	**Before Chapter 7**	
	Diagnose readiness for the chapter.	Prescribe intervention.
	Are You Ready? SE p. 487	***Are You Ready? Intervention*** Skills 15, 40, 50, 59, 72
Formative Assessment	**Before Every Lesson**	
	Diagnose readiness for the lesson.	Prescribe intervention.
	Warm Up TE, every lesson	**Skills Bank** SE pp. S46–S73 **Reteach** CRB, Ch. 1–7
	During Every Lesson	
	Diagnose understanding of lesson concepts.	Prescribe intervention.
	Check It Out! SE, every example **Think and Discuss** SE, every lesson **Write About It** SE, every lesson **Journal** TE, every lesson	**Questioning Strategies** TE, every example **Reading Strategies** CRB, every lesson ***Success for ELL*** pp. 97–112
	After Every Lesson	
	Diagnose mastery of lesson concepts.	Prescribe intervention.
	Lesson Quiz TE, every lesson **Alternative Assessment** TE, every lesson **Test Prep** SE, every lesson ***Test and Practice Generator***	**Reteach** CRB, every lesson **Problem Solving** CRB, every lesson **Test Prep Doctor** TE, every lesson ***Homework Help* Online**
	Before Chapter 7 Testing	
	Diagnose mastery of concepts in the chapter.	Prescribe intervention.
	Ready to Go On? SE pp. 521, 553 **Multi-Step Test Prep** SE pp. 520, 552 **Section Quizzes** AR pp. 125–126 ***Test and Practice Generator***	***Ready to Go On? Intervention*** pp. 108–125 **Scaffolding Questions** TE pp. 520, 552
	Before High Stakes Testing	
	Diagnose mastery of benchmark concepts.	Prescribe intervention.
	College Entrance Exam Practice SE p. 559 **Standardized Test Prep** SE pp. 562–563 ***State Test Prep* CD-ROM**	***College Entrance Exam Practice*** ***State Test Prep Workbook***
Summative Assessment	**After Chapter 7**	
	Check mastery of chapter concepts.	Prescribe intervention.
	Multiple-Choice Tests (Forms A, B, C) **Free-Response Tests (Forms A, B, C)** **Performance Assessment** AR pp. 127–140 ***Test and Practice Generator***	**Reteach** CRB, every lesson ***Lesson Tutorial Videos*** Chapter 7
	Check mastery of benchmark concepts.	Prescribe intervention.
	AYP State Tests **College Entrance Exams**	***State Test Prep Workbook*** ***College Entrance Exam Practice***

KEY: **SE** = *Student Edition* **TE** = *Teacher's Edition* **CRB** = *Chapter Resource Book* **AR** = *Assessment Resources* Available on CD-ROM  Available online

Supporting the Teacher

Chapter 7 Resource Book

Practice A, B, C
pp. 3–5, 11–13, 19–21, 27–29, 35–37, 43–45, 51–53, 59–61

Reading Strategies ELL
pp. 10, 18, 26, 34, 42, 50, 58, 66

Reteach
pp. 6–7, 14–15, 22–23, 30–31, 38–39, 46–47, 54–55, 62–63

Problem Solving
pp. 9, 17, 25, 33, 41, 49, 57, 65

Challenge
pp. 8, 16, 24, 32 ,40, 48, 56, 64

Parent Letter pp. 1–2

Transparencies

Lesson Transparencies, Volume 2 .... Chapter 7
- Warm Ups
- Teaching Transparencies
- Additional Examples
- Lesson Quizzes

Alternate Openers: Explorations 49–56

Countdown to Testing 29–32

Know-It Notebook .... Chapter 7
- Graphic Organizers

Teacher Tools

Power Presentations®
Complete PowerPoint® presentations for Chapter 7 lessons

Lesson Tutorial Videos®
Holt authors Ed Burger and Freddie Renfro present tutorials to support the Chapter 7 lessons.

One-Stop Planner®
Easy access to all Chapter 7 resources and assessments, as well as software for lesson planning, test generation, and puzzle creation

IDEA Works!®
Key Chapter 7 resources and assessments modified to address special learning needs

Lesson Plans .... pp. 49–56

Solutions Key .... Chapter 7

Algebra Posters

TechKeys 

Lab Resources

Project Teacher Support

Parent Resources

Workbooks

Homework and Practice Workbook
Teacher's Guide .... pp. 49–56

Know-It Notebook
Teacher's Guide .... Chapter 7

Problem Solving Workbook
Teacher's Guide .... pp. 49–56

State Test Prep Workbook
Teacher's Guide

Technology Highlights for the Teacher

Power Presentations

Dynamic presentations to engage students. Complete PowerPoint® presentations for every lesson in Chapter 7.

2-1 Solving One-Step Equations

Isolate a variable by using inverse operations which "undo" operations on the variable.

An equation is like a balanced scale. To keep the balance, perform the same operation on both sides.

Inverse Operations	
Operation	**Inverse Operation**
Addition	Subtraction
Subtraction	Addition

One-Stop Planner

Easy access to Chapter 7 resources and assessments. Includes lesson-planning, test-generation, and puzzle-creation software.

Premier Online Edition

Chapter 7 includes Tutorial Videos, Lesson Activities, Lesson Quizzes, Homework Help, and Chapter Project.

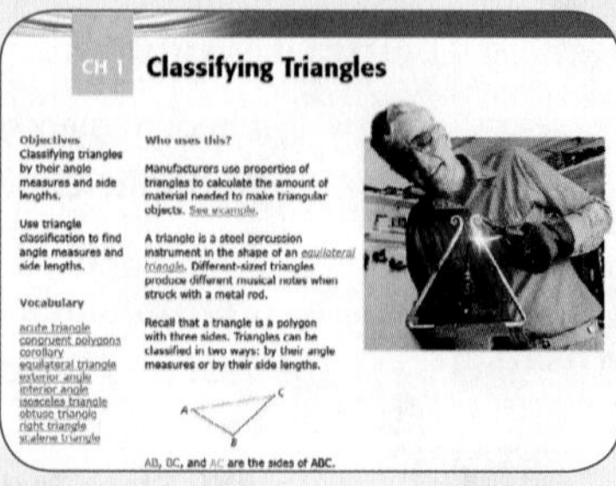

KEY: **SE** = *Student Edition* **TE** = *Teacher's Edition* ELL English Language Learners — Available on CD-ROM — Available online

Reaching All Learners

Resources for All Learners

Algebra Lab Activities .... Chapter 7
Technology Lab Activities .... Chapter 7
Homework and Practice Workbook .... pp. 49–56
Know-It Notebook .... Chapter 7
Problem Solving Workbook .... pp. 49–56

DEVELOPING LEARNERS

Practice A .... CRB, every lesson
Reteach .... CRB, every lesson
Inclusion .... TE pp. 513, 523, 529, 534
Questioning Strategies .... TE, every example
Modified Chapter 7 Resources .... *IDEA Works!*
***Homework Help* Online**

ON-LEVEL LEARNERS

Practice B .... CRB, every lesson
Multiple Representations .... TE pp. 491, 492, 517, 538, 549
Cognitive Strategies .... TE pp. 506, 513, 546

ADVANCED LEARNERS

Practice C .... CRB, every lesson
Challenge .... CRB, every lesson
Reading and Writing Math EXTENSION .... TE p. 489
Multi-Step Test Prep EXTENSION .... TE pp. 520, 552
Critical Thinking .... TE pp. 495, 503, 509, 514, 524, 528, 533, 538, 550

English Language Learners

ENGLISH LANGUAGE LEARNERS

Are You Ready? Vocabulary .... SE p. 487
Vocabulary Connections .... SE p. 488
Lesson Vocabulary .... SE pp. 490, 498, 505, 522, 531, 545
Vocabulary Exercises .... SE pp. 493, 501, 509, 526, 534, 548
Vocabulary Review .... SE p. 554
English Language Learners .... TE pp. 489, 494
Reading Strategies .... CRB, every lesson
Success for English Language Learners .... pp. 97–112
Multilingual Glossary

Reaching All Learners Through...

Critical Thinking .... TE pp. 495, 503, 509, 514, 533, 550
Multiple Representations .... TE pp. 491, 492, 517, 538, 549
Concrete Manipulatives .... TE p. 499
Visual Cues .... TE pp. 500, 502, 540
Auditory Cues .... TE p. 502
Cognitive Strategies .... TE pp. 506, 513, 546
Kinesthetic Experience .... TE pp. 508, 523
Inclusion .... TE pp. 524, 529, 534
Curriculum Integration .... TE p. 491
Test Prep Doctor .... TE pp. 496, 503, 510, 519, 536, 544, 550, 559, 560
Common Error Alerts .... TE pp. 507, 515, 523, 547
Scaffolding Questions .... TE pp. 520, 552

Technology Highlights for Reaching All Learners

Lesson Tutorial Videos

Starring Holt authors Ed Burger and Freddie Renfro! Live tutorials to support every lesson in Chapter 7.

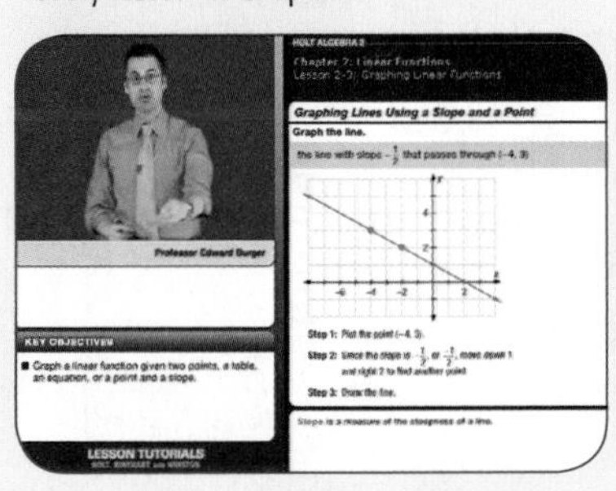

Multilingual Glossary

Searchable glossary includes definitions in English, Spanish, Vietnamese, Chinese, Hmong, Korean, and 4 other languages.

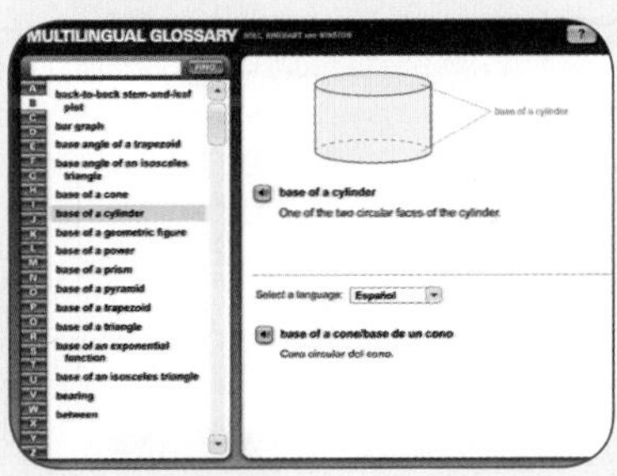

Online Interactivities

Interactive tutorials provide visually engaging alternative opportunities to learn concepts and master skills.

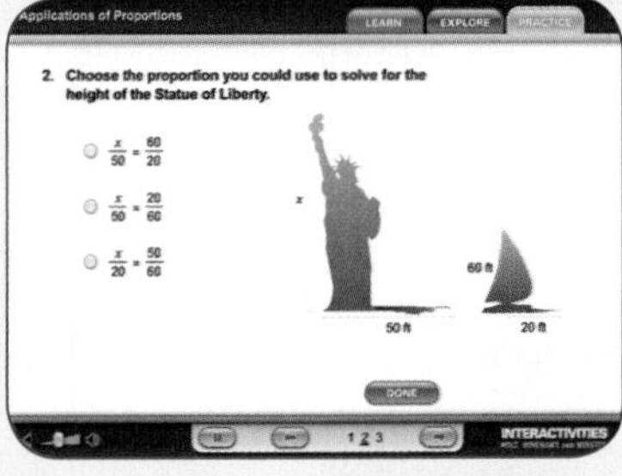

KEY: **SE** = *Student Edition* **TE** = *Teacher's Edition* **CRB** = *Chapter Resource Book*

Available on CD-ROM

Available online

Ongoing Assessment

Assessing Prior Knowledge

Determine whether students have the required prerequisite concepts and skills for success in Chapter 7.

Are You Ready? SPANISH .... SE p. 487
Warm Up .... TE, every lesson

Test Preparation

Provide review and practice for Chapter 7 and standardized tests.

Multi-Step Test Prep .... SE pp. 520, 552
Study Guide: Review .... SE pp. 554–557
Test Tackler .... SE pp. 560–561
Standardized Test Prep .... SE pp. 562–563
College Entrance Exam Practice .... SE p. 559
***Countdown to Testing* Transparencies** 29–32
State Test Prep Workbook
***State Test Prep* CD-ROM**
IDEA Works!

Alternative Assessment

Assess students' understanding of Chapter 7 concepts and combined problem-solving skills.

Chapter 7 Project .... SE p. 486
Alternative Assessment .... TE, every lesson
Performance Assessment .... AR pp. 139–140
Portfolio Assessment .... AR p. xxxiv

Daily Assessment

Provide formative assessment for each day of Chapter 7.

Questioning Strategies .... TE, every example
Think and Discuss .... SE, every lesson
Check It Out! Exercises .... SE, every example
Write About It .... SE, every lesson
Journal .... TE, every lesson
Lesson Quiz .... TE, every lesson
Alternative Assessment .... TE, every lesson
Modified Lesson Quizzes .... *IDEA Works!*

Weekly Assessment

Provide formative assessment for each week of Chapter 7.

Multi-Step Test Prep .... SE pp. 520, 552
Ready to Go On? .... SE pp. 521, 553
Cumulative Assessment .... SE pp. 562–563
Test and Practice Generator SPANISH .. *One-Stop Planner*

Formal Assessment

Provide summative assessment of Chapter 7 mastery.

Section Quizzes .... AR pp. 125–126
Chapter 7 Test .... SE p. 558
Chapter Test (Levels A, B, C) .... AR pp. 127–138
• Multiple Choice • Free Response
Cumulative Test .... AR pp. 141–144
Test and Practice Generator SPANISH .. *One-Stop Planner*
Modified Chapter 7 Test .... *IDEA Works!*

Technology Highlights for Ongoing Assessment

Are You Ready? SPANISH

Automatically assess readiness and prescribe intervention for Chapter 7 prerequisite skills.

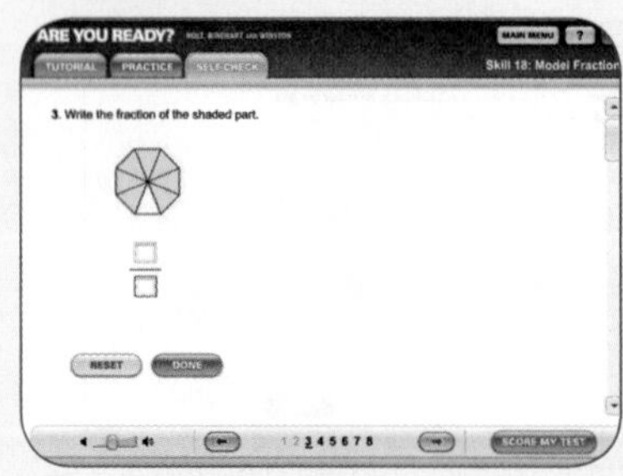

Ready to Go On?

Automatically assess understanding and prescribe intervention for Sections 7A and 7B.

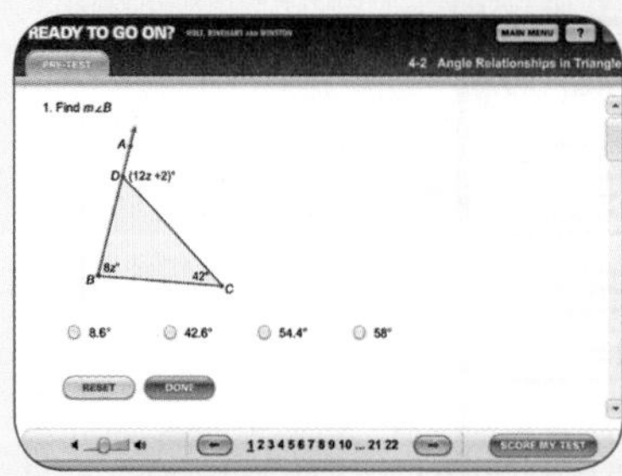

Test and Practice Generator SPANISH

Use Chapter 7 problem banks to create assessments and worksheets to print out or deliver online. Includes dynamic problems.

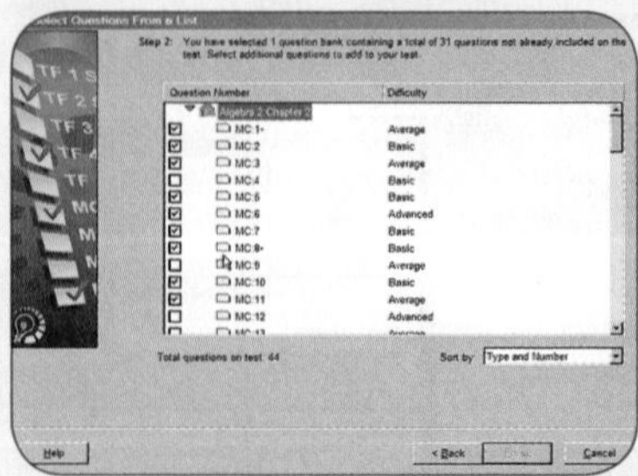

KEY: **SE** = *Student Edition* **TE** = *Teacher's Edition* **AR** = *Assessment Resources* SPANISH Spanish version available; Available on CD-ROM; Available online

CHAPTER 7

Formal Assessment

Three levels (A, B, C) of multiple-choice and free-response chapter tests are available in the *Assessment Resources.*

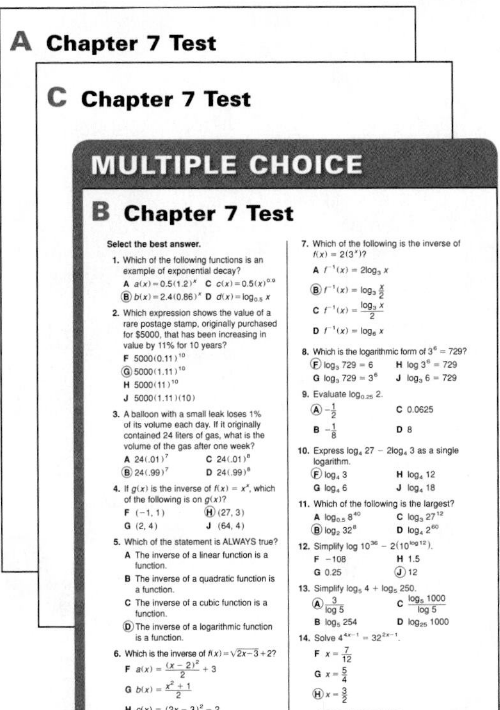

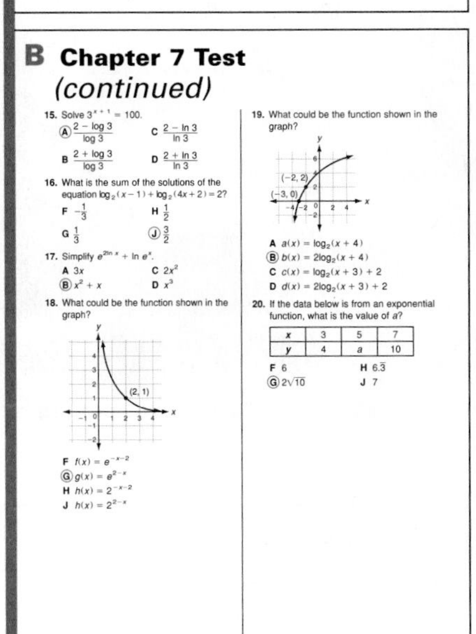

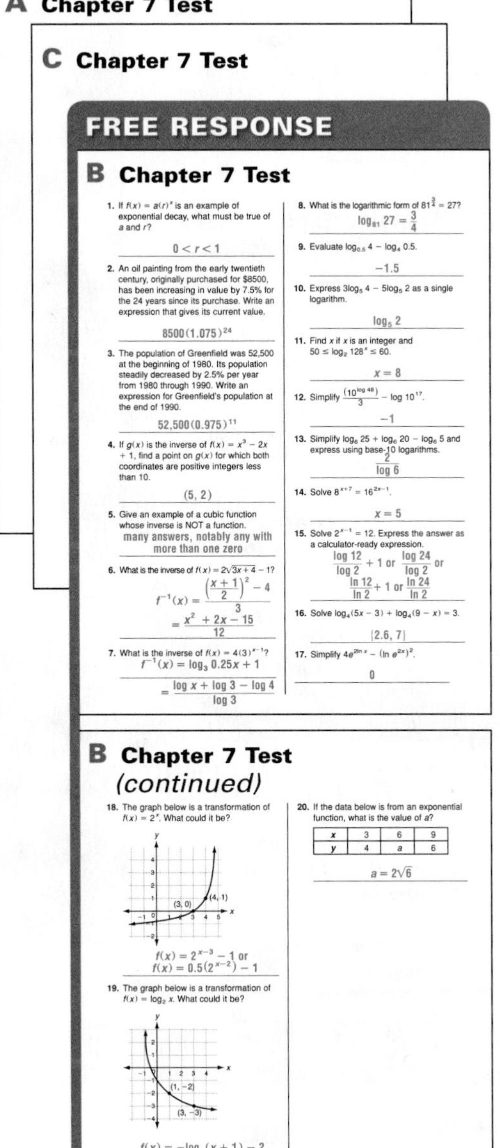

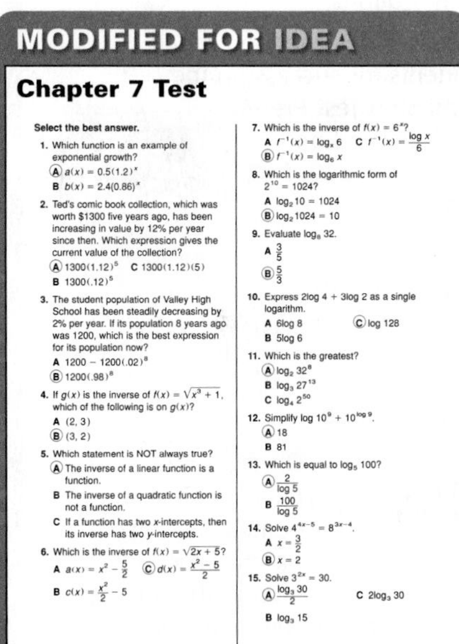

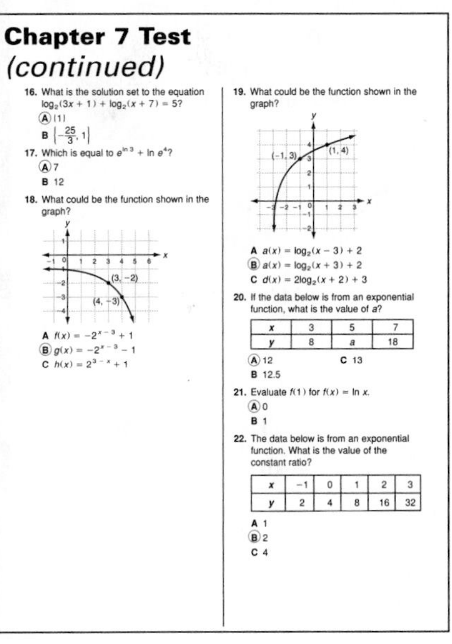

Test & Practice Generator
One-Stop Planner®

Create and customize Chapter 7 Tests. Instantly generate multiple test versions, answer keys, and practice versions of test items.

CHAPTER 7

SECTION 7A
Exponential Functions and Logarithms

On page 520, students use exponential and logarithmic functions to model real-world credit card fees and payment options.

Exercises designed to prepare students for success on the Multi-Step Test Prep can be found on pages 494, 502, 510, and 517.

SECTION 7B
Applying Exponential and Logarithmic Functions

On page 552, students apply exponential and logarithmic functions to model the reduction in the number of farms in the United States.

Exercises designed to prepare students for success on the Multi-Step Test Prep can be found on pages 527, 535, 543, and 550.

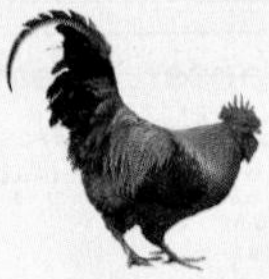

CHAPTER 7

Exponential and Logarithmic Functions

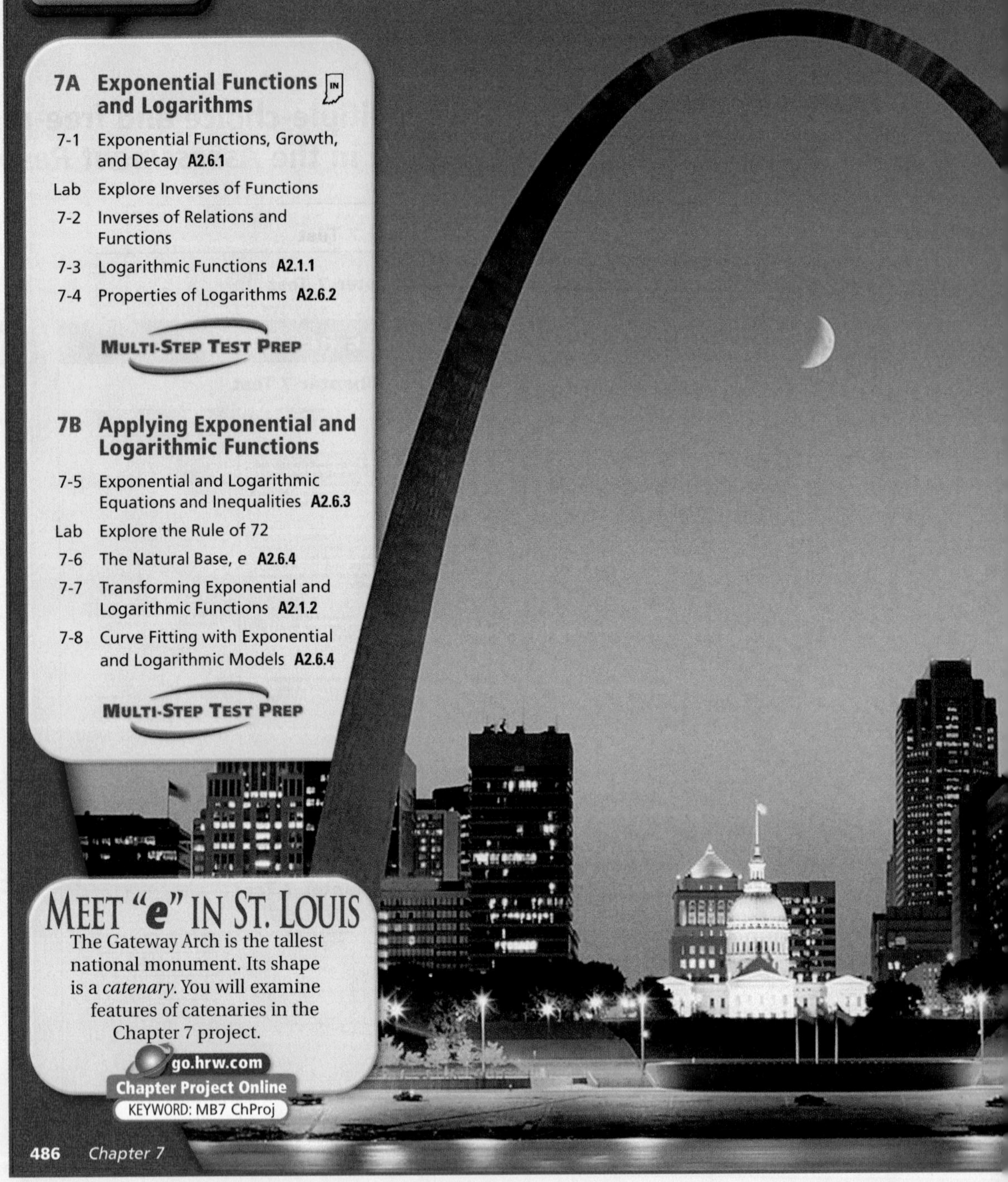

MEET "e" IN ST. LOUIS

The Gateway Arch is the tallest national monument. Its shape is a *catenary*. You will examine features of catenaries in the Chapter 7 project.

go.hrw.com
Chapter Project Online
KEYWORD: MB7 ChProj

Meet "e" in St. Louis

About the Project

In the Chapter Project, students examine the shape of the St. Louis Arch, a *catenary,* and use exponential and logarithmic functions to model it.

Project Resources

All project resources for teachers and students are provided online.

Materials:

- graphing calculator

Are You Ready?

Vocabulary

Match each term on the left with a definition on the right.

1. exponent **D**
2. function **C**
3. relation **E**
4. variable **A**

A. a symbol used to represent one or more numbers
B. the set of counting numbers and their opposites
C. a relation with at most one y-value for each x-value
D. the number of times the base of a power is used as a factor
E. a set of ordered pairs

Properties of Exponents

Simplify each expression.

5. $x^2(x^3)(x)$ x^6
6. $3y^{-1}(5x^2y^2)$ $15x^2y$
7. $\frac{a^8}{a^2}$ a^6
8. $y^{15} \div y^{10}$ y^5
9. $\frac{x^2y^5}{xy^6}$ $\frac{x}{y}$
10. $\left(\frac{x}{3}\right)^{-3}$ $\frac{27}{x^3}$
11. $(3x)^2(4x^3)$ $36x^5$
12. $\frac{a^{-2}b^3}{a^4b^{-1}}$ $\frac{b^4}{a^6}$

Simple Interest

Use the simple interest formula, $I = Prt$, where I is the interest, P is the initial amount (the principal), and r is the interest rate for Problems 13–15.

13. Find the simple interest on an investment of \$3000 at 3% for 2 years. **\$180**
14. A savings account of \$2000 earned \$90 simple interest in 3 years. Find the interest rate. **$1\frac{1}{2}\%$**
15. Jeri got a loan at 6% simple interest for 3 years. She paid back a total of \$5310. How much was the loan? **\$4500**

Solve for a Variable

Solve each equation for x.

16. $3x - y = 4$ $\frac{y+4}{3}$
17. $y = -7x + 3$ $\frac{-y+3}{7}$
18. $\frac{x}{2} = 3y - 4$ $6y - 8$
19. $y = \frac{3}{4}x - \frac{1}{2}$ $\frac{4y+2}{3}$

Symmetry

20. Copy the graph, and use the line of symmetry to complete the figure.

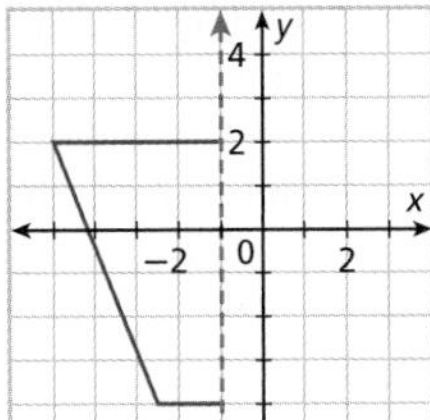

Scientific Notation

Write in scientific notation.

21. 7,000,000,000 7×10^9
22. 0.0000000093 9.3×10^{-9}
23. 16.75 1.675×10^1

Write in standard notation.

24. 9.4×10^{-6} 0.0000094
25. 4.7×10^5 470,000
26. 7.8×10^4 78,000

CHAPTER 7

Are You Ready?

Organizer

Objective: Assess students' understanding of prerequisite skills.

Prerequisite Skills

Properties of Exponents
Simple Interest
Solve for a Variable
Symmetry
Scientific Notation

Assessing Prior Knowledge

INTERVENTION 

Diagnose and Prescribe

Use this page to determine whether intervention is necessary or whether enrichment is appropriate.

Resources

 ***Are You Ready? Intervention and Enrichment*** **Worksheets**

 ***Are You Ready?*** **CD-ROM**

 ***Are You Ready?*** **Online**

my.hrw.com

Are You Ready?

Diagnose and Prescribe

NO INTERVENE

Prerequisite Skill	*Are You Ready?* Intervention, Chapter 7: Worksheets	CD-ROM	Online
Properties of Exponents	Skill 59	Activity 59	Diagnose and Prescribe Online
Simple Interest	Skill 50	Activity 50	
Solve for a Variable	Skill 72	Activity 72	
Symmetry	Skill 40	Activity 40	
Scientific Notation	Skill 15	Activity 15	

***Are You Ready?* Enrichment, Chapter 7**

Worksheets
CD-ROM
Online

Organizer

Objective: Help students organize the new concepts they will learn in Chapter 7.

Online Edition
Multilingual Glossary

Resources

Puzzle Pro
One-Stop Planner®

***Multilingual Glossary* Online**

go.hrw.com
KEYWORD: MB7 Glossary

Answers to *Vocabulary Connections*

1. 10
2. 3
3. in the exponent
4. Undo or reverse the function.
5. Possible answer: π, i

CHAPTER 7

Study Guide: Preview

Where You've Been

Previously, you

- used the properties of exponents to simplify expressions.
- performed inverse operations.
- solved problems involving linear, quadratic, and polynomial functions.

In This Chapter

You will study

- exponential functions.
- logarithms, the inverse of exponents, and logarithmic functions.
- solving problems involving exponents and logarithms.

Where You're Going

You can use the skills in this chapter

- to solve problems involving compound interest.
- in scientific fields such as biology and sociology where you collect, organize, and analyze data.
- in future math classes, including Statistics and Business Calculus.

Key Vocabulary/Vocabulario

asymptote	asíntota
base	base
common logarithm	logaritmo común
exponential equation	ecuación exponencial
inverse function	función inversa
logarithmic equation	ecuación logarítmica
logarithmic function	función logarítmica
natural logarithm	logaritmo natural

Vocabulary Connections

To become familiar with some of the vocabulary terms in the chapter, consider the following. You may refer to the chapter, the glossary, or a dictionary if you like.

1. You can think of the **base** as carrying its exponent. Which number in $10^3 = 1000$ is the base?
2. A logarithm is an exponent. The base for common logarithms is 10. What would you think would be the **common logarithm** of 1000?
3. Where would you expect to find the variable x in an **exponential equation**?
4. Multiplication and division are *inverse functions.* What would you expect an **inverse function** to do to its corresponding function?
5. The base of a **natural logarithm** is the number e. What are other constant values that are often named by a letter or symbol?
6. The Greek word *asymptōtos* means “not meeting.” How do you think a line on a graph called an **asymptote** would relate to a curve on a graph?

Writing Strategy: Use Your Own Words

When studying a difficult mathematical concept, rewrite the concept using your own words so that you can better comprehend the material. You may also find it helpful to provide your own example.

The **degree of a polynomial** is given by the term with the greatest degree. A polynomial with one variable is in standard form when its terms are written in descending order by degree. So, in standard form, the degree of the first term indicates the degree of the polynomial, and the **leading coefficient** is the coefficient of the first term.

REWRITE the above paragraph with short phrases and sentences to clarify important concepts about polynomials.

INCLUDE an example to connect the words and the mathematics.

Polynomials:

1. The term with the highest degree gives the degree of the polynomial.
2. Standard form—terms are in decreasing order of degree.
3. In standard form, the degree of the first term is the degree of the polynomial.
4. The coefficient of the first term is called the leading coefficient.

Example:
Standard form: $2x^4 - 5x^3 + 3x^2 - 9x + 10$

Leading coefficient: 2
Degree of polynomial: 4

Read the following paragraph from Lesson 6-5, and rewrite it using your own words.

The Irrational Root Theorem states that irrational roots come in conjugate pairs. For example, if you know that $1 + \sqrt{2}$ is a root of $x^3 - x^2 - 3x - 1 = 0$, then you know that $1 - \sqrt{2}$ is also a root.

Recall that the real numbers are made up of the rational and the irrational numbers. You can use the Rational Root Theorem and the Irrational Root Theorem together to find *all* of the real roots of $P(x) = 0$.

Organizer

Objective: Help students apply strategies to understand and retain key concepts.

Resources

 ***Chapter 7 Resource Book***

Reading Strategies

ENGLISH LANGUAGE LEARNERS

Writing Strategy: Use Your Own Words

Discuss Students benefit from taking complex ideas and breaking them down into smaller, simpler pieces. Encourage students to use bulleted lists and underlining to emphasize the most important points.

Extend As students work through Chapter 7, have them rewrite some of the explanatory pieces that appear before the examples in each lesson in ways that are most useful to them. Students need not limit themselves to rewriting the text, but may find that using graphic organizers is a better way to express the meaning of the explanatory pieces.

Answers to *Try This*

Possible answer:

Irrational Root Theorem:

- Irrational roots come in conjugate pairs.
- The conjugate of $a + \sqrt{b}$ is $a - \sqrt{b}$.

For example, if $1 + \sqrt{2}$ is a root of $x^3 - x^2 - 3x - 1 = 0$, then $1 - \sqrt{2}$ is also a root.

All real numbers are rational numbers (e.g., 3, $\frac{2}{3}$, 0.5) or irrational numbers (e.g., π, $\sqrt{2}$).

To find all real roots of a polynomial equation $P(x) = 0$,

- use the Rational Root Theorem

AND

- the Irrational Root Theorem.

SECTION 7A

Exponential Functions and Logarithms

One-Minute Section Planner

Lesson	Lab Resources	Materials
Lesson 7-1 Exponential Functions, Growth, and Decay • Write and evaluate exponential expressions to model growth and decay situations. ☑ SAT-10 ☑ NAEP ☑ ACT ☑ SAT ☑ SAT Subject Tests	***Algebra Lab Activities*** 7-1 Algebra Lab	**Required** graphing calculator
7-2 Technology Lab Explore Inverses of Functions • Use a graphing calculator to explore inverse functions and their relationship to the linear parent function. ☐ SAT-10 ☑ NAEP ☐ ACT ☐ SAT ☐ SAT Subject Tests	***Technology Lab Activities*** 7-2 Lab Recording Sheet	**Required** graphing calculator
Lesson 7-2 Inverses of Functions • Graph and recognize inverses of relations and functions. • Find inverses of functions. ☐ SAT-10 ☑ NAEP ☐ ACT ☑ SAT ☐ SAT Subject Tests		**Optional** graphing calculator, tracing paper, Mira
Lesson 7-3 Logarithmic Functions • Write equivalent forms for exponential and logarithmic functions. • Write, evaluate, and graph logarithmic functions. ☐ SAT-10 ☐ NAEP ☐ ACT ☐ SAT ☑ SAT Subject Tests		**Required** scientific calculator **Optional** graphing calculator
Lesson 7-4 Properties of Logarithms • Use properties to simplify logarithmic expressions. • Translate between logarithms in any base. ☐ SAT-10 ☐ NAEP ☐ ACT ☐ SAT ☑ SAT Subject Tests		**Required** scientific calculator **Optional** graphing calculator

MK = *Manipulatives Kit*

Section Overview

Professional Development

Exponential Functions — Lesson 7-1

Many real-world situations, such as credit card debt and bacteria growth, can be modeled by exponential functions.

Parent Exponential Function $f(x) = b^x$, where $b > 0$ and $b \neq 1$

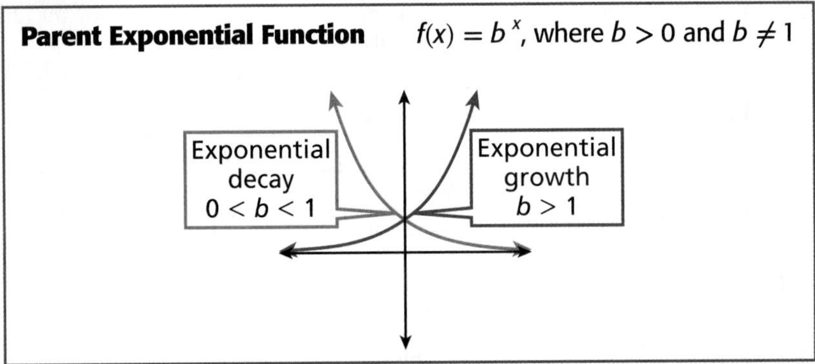

Constant Percent Decrease
$A(t) = a(1 - r)^t$
$1 - r$ is the ***decay factor.***

Constant Percent Increase
$A(t) = a(1 + r)^t$
$1 + r$ is the ***growth factor.***

Inverse Functions — Lesson 7-2

An inverse of a function performs the opposite operations of the function, effectively "undoing" the function.

To find the inverse of a function:
1) Switch x and y in $y = f(x)$.
2) Solve for y.

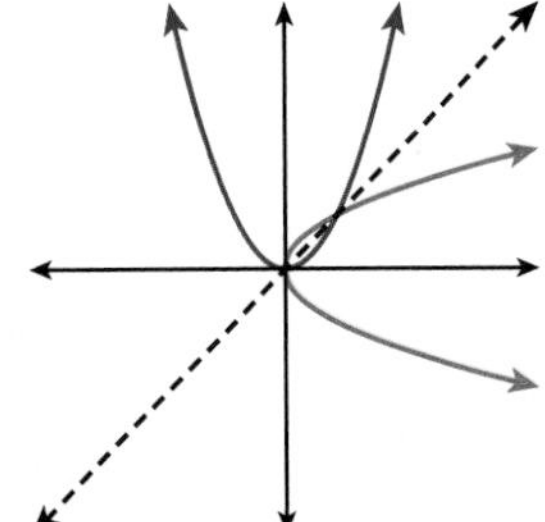

The graphs of inverse relations are reflections across the line $y = x$.

Logarithmic Functions and Properties — Lessons 7-3, 7-4

Logarithms are used to compare quantities on a very large or very small scale because they represent an exponent.

Logarithmic functions and exponential functions are inverse functions.

$\log_b a = x$ if and only if $b^x = a$

Example: $\log_2 8 = 3$ if and only if $2^3 = 8$

Properties

Exponents	Logarithms
$b^m b^n = b^{m+n}$	$\log_b mn = \log_b m + \log_b n$
$\frac{b^m}{b^n} = b^{m-n}$	$\log_b\left(\frac{m}{n}\right) = \log_b m - \log_b n$
$(b^m)^n = b^{mn}$	$\log_b a^p = p\log_b a$

7-1 Organizer

Pacing: Traditional 1 day
Block $\frac{1}{2}$ day

Objective: Write and evaluate exponential expressions to model growth and decay situations.

Algebra Lab
In *Algebra Lab Activities*

Online Edition
Tutorial Videos, Graphing Calculator, TechKeys

Countdown to Testing Week 15

Warm Up

Evaluate.

1. $100(1.08)^{20}$ ≈ 466.1
2. $100(0.95)^{25}$ ≈ 27.74
3. $100(1 - 0.02)^{10}$ ≈ 81.71
4. $100(1 + 0.08)^{-10}$ ≈ 46.32

Also available on transparency

Q: How do you know that your dentist studied algebra?

A: She said all that candy gave me exponential decay.

7-1 Exponential Functions, Growth, and Decay

IN **A2.6.1** Analyze, describe and sketch graphs of exponential functions by examining intercepts, zeros, domain and range, and asymptotic and end behavior.

Objective
Write and evaluate exponential expressions to model growth and decay situations.

Vocabulary
exponential function
base
asymptote
exponential growth
exponential decay

Who uses this?
Collectors can use exponential functions to model the value of rare musical instruments. (See Example 2.)

Moore's law, a rule used in the computer industry, states that the number of transistors per integrated circuit (the processing power) doubles every year. Beginning in the early days of integrated circuits, the growth in capacity may be approximated by this table.

Transistors per Integrated Chip

Year	1965	1966	1967	1968	1969	1970	1971
Transistors	60	120	240	480	960	1920	3840
	×2	×2	×2	×2	×2	×2	

Remember!
In the function $y = b^x$, y is a function of x because the value of y *depends* on the value of x.

Growth that doubles every year can be modeled by using a function with a variable as an exponent. This function is known as an *exponential function.* The parent **exponential function** is $f(x) = b^x$, where the **base** b is a constant and the exponent x is the independent variable.

Base Exponent

$$f(x) = b^x, \text{ where } b > 0, b \neq 1$$

The graph of the parent function $f(x) = 2^x$ is shown. The domain is all real numbers and the range is $\{y \mid y > 0\}$.

x	-2	-1	0	1	2	3
$f(x) = 2^x$	$\frac{1}{4}$	$\frac{1}{2}$	1	2	4	8

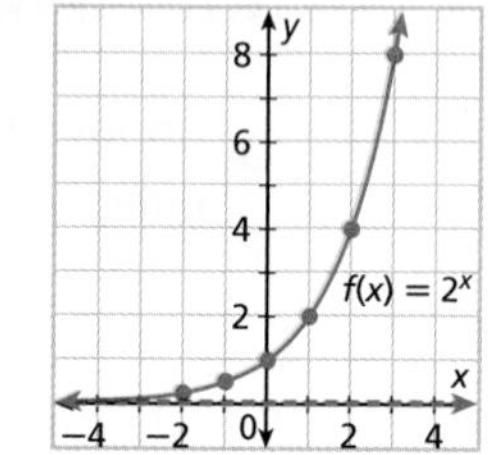

Notice that as the x-values decrease, the graph of the function gets closer and closer to the x-axis. The function never reaches the x-axis because the value of 2^x cannot be zero. In this case, the x-axis is an *asymptote.* An **asymptote** is a line that a graphed function approaches as the value of x gets very large or very small.

A function of the form $f(x) = ab^x$, with $a > 0$ and $b > 1$, is an **exponential growth** function, which increases as x increases. When $0 < b < 1$, the function is called an **exponential decay** function, which decreases as x increases.

State Resources

go.hrw.com
State Resources Online
KEYWORD: MB7 Resources

1 Introduce

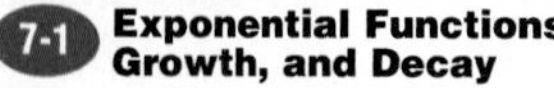

EXPLORATION

7-1 Exponential Functions, Growth, and Decay

A biologist is studying a type of cell that divides in two every hour. The biologist begins the experiment with a single cell. The population doubles every hour.

1. Complete the table.

Time (h)	0	1	2	3	4	5
Cells	1					

2. How many hours will it take until there are more than 500 cells?
3. How many cells will there be after 10 hours?
4. How many cells will there be after n hours?

THINK AND DISCUSS

5. **Explain** how you can write a function that models this situation.
6. **Describe** how your function would be different if the biologist started the experiment with 3 cells

Motivate

Go around the class and have each student *double* the previous number, starting with the number 1. Write each number on the board. Note how quickly the numbers increase. Then start at 1 and have students give the fraction that is *half* the previous number. Write these alongside the doubled numbers. See if students recognize that these are reciprocals of the first set and note how quickly the numbers decrease. Tell them they will study growth and decay patterns in this lesson.

Explorations and answers are provided in the *Explorations* binder.

EXAMPLE 1 Graphing Exponential Functions

Tell whether the function shows growth or decay. Then graph.

A $f(x) = 1.5^x$

Step 1 Find the value of the base.

$f(x) = 1.5^x$ *The base, 1.5, is greater than 1. This is an exponential growth function.*

Step 2 Graph the function by using a table of values.

x	−2	−1	0	1	2	3	4
$f(x)$	0.4	0.7	1	1.5	2.3	3.4	5.1

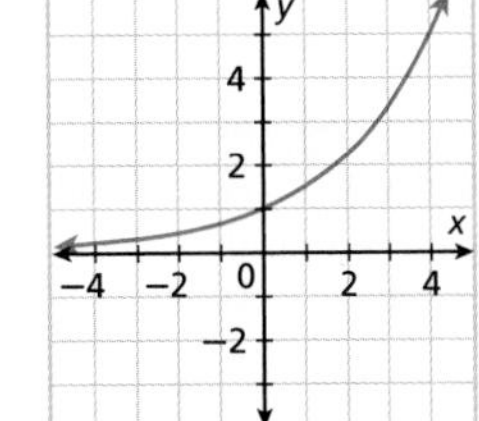

Remember!

Negative exponents indicate a reciprocal. For example:

$$x^{-2} = \frac{1}{x^2}$$

B $g(x) = 30(0.8^x)$

Step 1 Find the value of the base.

$g(x) = 30(0.8^x)$ *The base, 0.8, is less than 1. This is an exponential decay function.*

Step 2 Graph the function by using a graphing calculator.

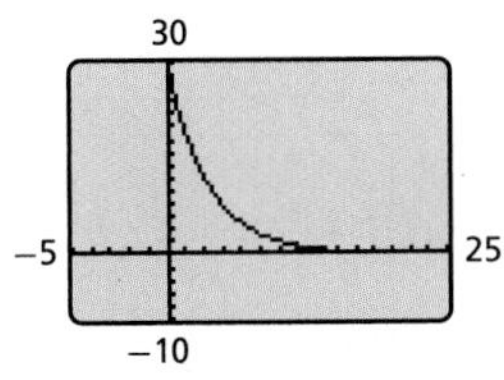

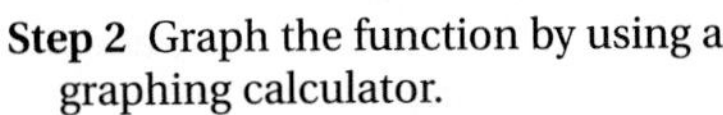

CHECK IT OUT! 1. Tell whether the function $p(x) = 5(1.2^x)$ shows growth or decay. Then graph.

1. growth

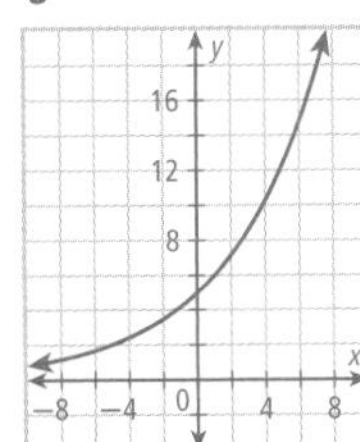

You can model growth or decay by a constant percent increase or decrease with the following formula:

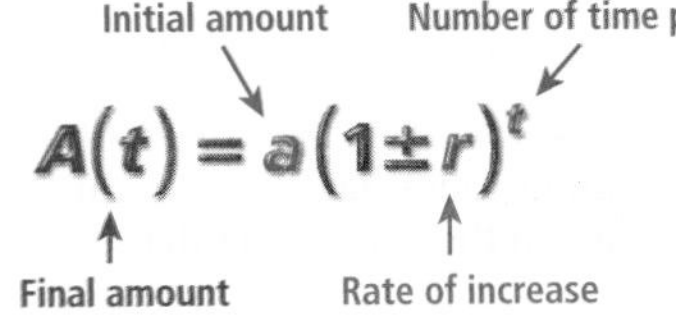

In the formula, the base of the exponential expression, $1 + r$, is called the *growth factor*. Similarly, $1 - r$ is the *decay factor*.

Student to Student — *Growth and Decay*

Angela Jones, Independence High School

When a function increases by a constant rate, such as 7%, this is the same as multiplying by 100% + 7%, or 107%.

In decimal form, I would multiply by 1 + 0.07, or 1.07.

When a function decreases by a constant rate, such as 12%, this is the same as multiplying by 100% − 12%, or 88%.

In decimal form, it's (1 − 0.12), or 0.88.

Teaching Tip **Language Arts** The word *asymptote* comes from the Greek *asymptotos,* meaning "converging but not intersecting."

Power Presentations with PowerPoint®

Additional Examples

Example 1

Tell whether the function shows growth or decay. Then graph.

A. $f(x) = 10\left(\frac{3}{4}\right)^x$ decay

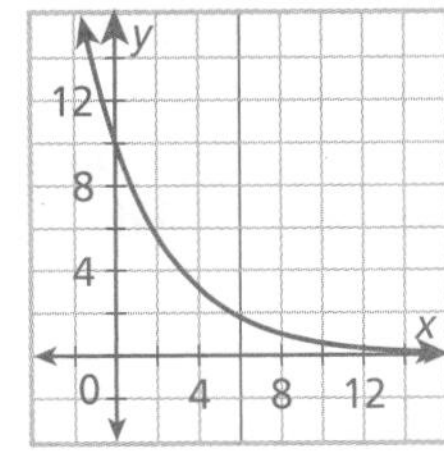

B. $g(x) = 100(1.05)^x$ growth

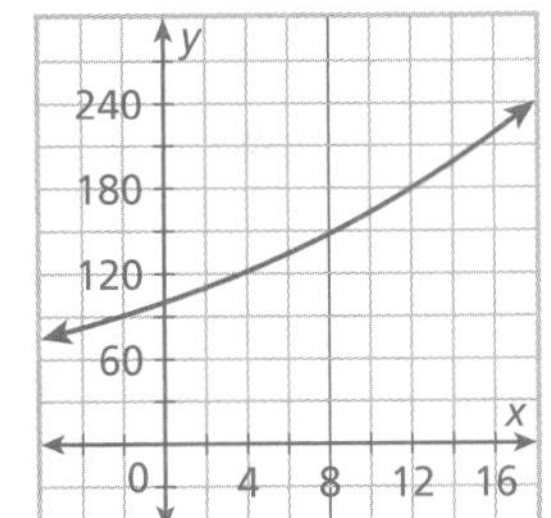

Also available on transparency

2 Teach

Guided Instruction

Introduce students to the parent exponential function. Explain that the base tells whether a function represents exponential growth or decay. For the formula for growth or decay by a constant percent, emphasize that the growth factor is 1 plus or minus the percent change. For example, a 20% decrease is represented by 1 − 0.2, or 0.8.

Reaching All Learners
Through Multiple Representations

To help students understand the growth described by exponential functions, have them complete the table below and compare the function values at each x-value.

Function	$x = 1$	$x = 10$	$x = 20$
$f(x) = 2x$	2	20	40
$f(x) = 2x^2$	2	200	800
$f(x) = 2x^3$	2	2000	16,000
$f(x) = 2^x$	2	1024	1,048,576

INTERVENTION
Questioning Strategies

EXAMPLE 1

- Does a function with an exponent always indicate an exponential function?
- How can you differentiate between exponential growth and exponential decay?

Teaching Tip **Technology** Make sure that students are comfortable using their calculators to graph exponential functions. They may need practice putting in the appropriate domains and ranges.

Power Presentations with PowerPoint®

Additional Examples

Example 2

Clara invests $5000 in an account that pays 6.25% interest per year. After how many years will her investment be worth $10,000? about 11.4 yr

Example 3

A city population, which was initially 15,500, has been dropping by 3% a year. Write an exponential function and graph the function. Use the graph to predict when the population will drop below 8000.
$P(t) = 15,500(0.97)^t$

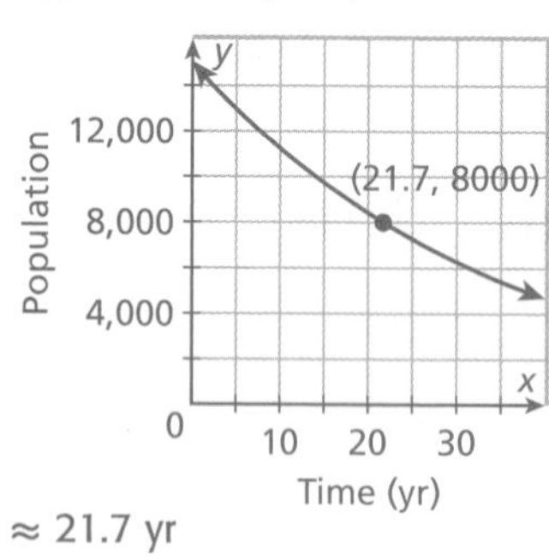

≈ 21.7 yr

Also available on transparency

INTERVENTION
Questioning Strategies

EXAMPLE 2

- What does the value $1 + r$ represent?
- What do you notice about the window settings for the calculator screen?

EXAMPLE 3

- How does the graph of an exponential function change when r is subtracted from 1 rather than added to 1?

Teaching Tip **Multiple Representations** For quick sketches, students should be aware that the graph of $f(x) = ab^x$ always passes through the points $(0, a)$ and $(1, ab)$.

Answers to Check It Out

3. $v(t) = 1000(0.85)^t$

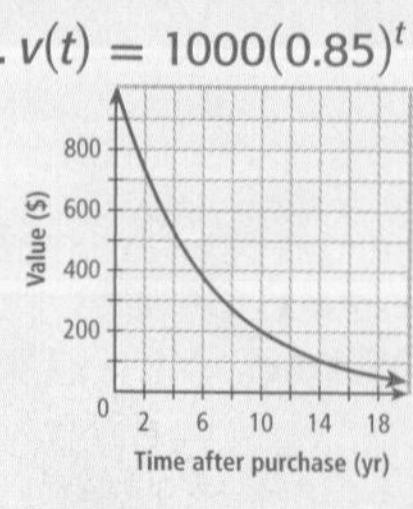

14.2 yr

EXAMPLE 2 Economics Application

Tony purchased a rare 1959 Gibson Les Paul guitar in 2000 for $12,000. Experts estimate that its value will increase by 14% per year. Use a graph to find when the value of the guitar will be $60,000.

Step 1 Write a function to model the growth in value for this guitar.

$f(t) = a(1 + r)^t$ — *Exponential growth function*

$= 12,000(1 + 0.14)^t$ — *Substitute 12,000 for a and 0.14 for r.*

$= 12,000(1.14)^t$

Step 2 Graph the function.

When graphing exponential functions in an appropriate domain, you may need to adjust the range a few times to show the key points.

Step 3 Use the graph to predict when the value of the guitar will reach $60,000.

Use the TRACE feature to find the t-value where $f(t) \approx 60,000$.

The function value is approximately 60,000 when $t \approx 12.29$. The guitar will be worth $60,000 about 12.29 years after it is purchased, or sometime in 2012.

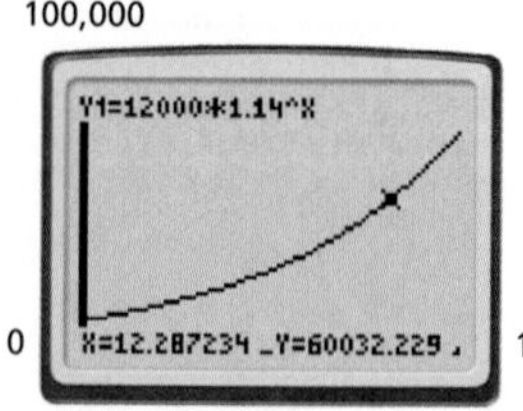

Helpful Hint

X is used on the graphing calculator for the variable t:
Y1=12000*1.14^X

CHECK IT OUT!

2. In 1981, the Australian humpback whale population was 350 and has increased at a rate of about 14% each year since then. Write a function to model population growth. Use a graph to predict when the population will reach 20,000.

2. $P(t) = 350(1.14)^t$

Whale population: 16,000; 12,000; 8,000; 4,000; 0 — Time since 1981 (yr): 10, 20, 30, 40

30.9 yr

EXAMPLE 3 Depreciation Application

The value of a truck bought new for $28,000 decreases 9.5% each year. Write an exponential function, and graph the function. Use the graph to predict when the value will fall to $5000.

Write a function to model the growth in value for this truck.

$f(x) = a(1 - r)^t$ — *Exponential decay function*

$= 28,000(1 - 0.095)^t$ — *Substitute 28,000 for a and 0.095 for r.*

$= 28,000(0.905)^t$ — *Simplify.*

Graph the function. Use TRACE to find when the value of the truck will fall below $5000.

It will take about 17.3 years for the value to drop to $5000.

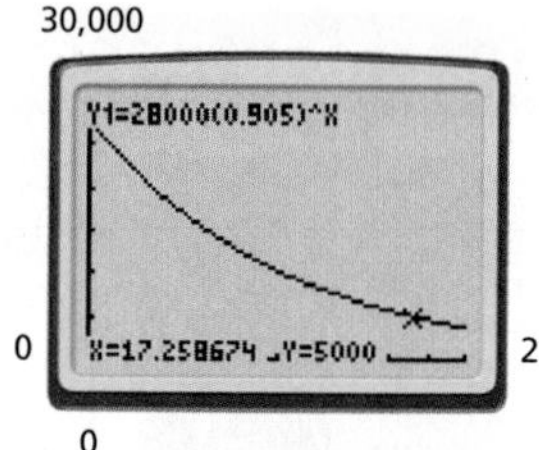

3. A motor scooter purchased for $1000 depreciates at an annual rate of 15%. Write an exponential function, and graph the function. Use the graph to predict when the value will fall below $100.

---

3 Close

Summarize

Review the parent exponential function with students. Emphasize that the exponent is a variable and that the base b is a constant. Explain that the value of b determines whether an exponential function will show growth or decay as x increases.

ONGOING ASSESSMENT and INTERVENTION

Diagnose **Before** the Lesson
7-1 Warm Up, TE p. 490

Monitor **During** the Lesson
Check It Out! Exercises, SE pp. 491–492
Questioning Strategies, TE pp. 491–492

Assess **After** the Lesson
7-1 Lesson Quiz, TE p. 496
Alternative Assessment, TE p. 496

THINK AND DISCUSS

1. Use a calculator to compare the values of 1.01^{500} and 0.99^{500}. Explain the results.
2. Discuss the differences between the graph of $f(x) = 1.1^x$ and the graph of $g(x) = 0.9^x$. What happens in each when $x = 0$?
3. Describe the function $f(t) = a(1 - r)^t$ when $0 < r < 1$ and $t > 0$. Describe the function when $-1 < r < 0$ and $t > 0$.

4. **GET ORGANIZED** Copy and complete the graphic organizer. Compare exponential growth and decay.

$f(x) = ab^x$, where $a > 0$	Growth	Decay
Value of b		
General shape of the graph		
What happens to $f(x)$ as x increases?		
What happens to $f(x)$ as x decreases?		

Answers to Think and Discuss

Possible answers:

1. $1.01^{500} \approx 144$; $0.99^{500} \approx 0.00657$; Possible answer: Although 1.01 and 0.99 are very close to 1, 1.01^{500} gets very large because it is a growth function, and 0.99^{500} gets close to 0 because it is a decay function.
2. $f(x) = 1.1^x$ shows growth, and $f(x) = 0.9^x$ shows decay. The graphs intersect at (0, 1).
3. exponential decay; exponential growth
4. See p. A8.

6b.

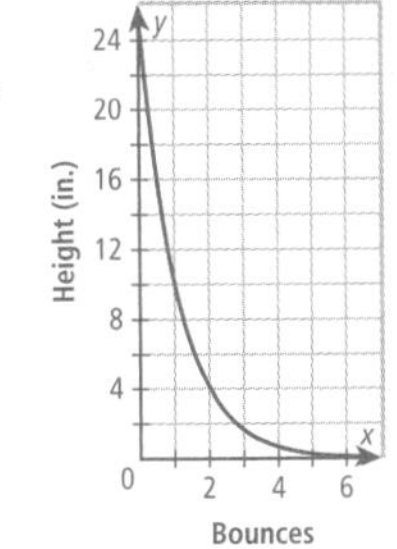

7-1 Exercises

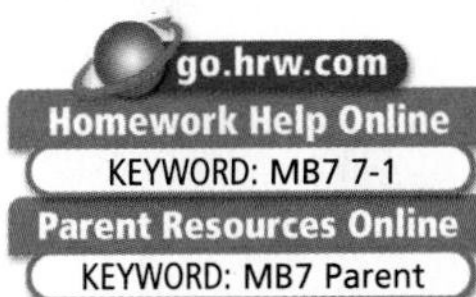

GUIDED PRACTICE

1. **Vocabulary** When the base in an exponential function is between 0 and 1, the function shows __?__. (*exponential growth* or *exponential decay*) **exponential decay**

SEE EXAMPLE 1 p. 491

Tell whether the function shows growth or decay. Then graph.

2. $f(x) = 32(0.5^x)$ **decay**
3. $f(x) = 0.5(1.2^x)$ **growth**
4. $f(x) = 0.4\left(\frac{3}{4}\right)^x$ **decay**

SEE EXAMPLE 2 p. 492

5. **Biology** An acidophilus culture containing 150 bacteria doubles in population every hour. Predict the number of bacteria after 12 hours.
   a. Write a function representing the bacteria population for every hour that passes. $f(x) = 150(2^x)$
   b. Graph the function.
   c. Use the graph to predict the number of bacteria after 12 hours. $\approx$ **600,000**

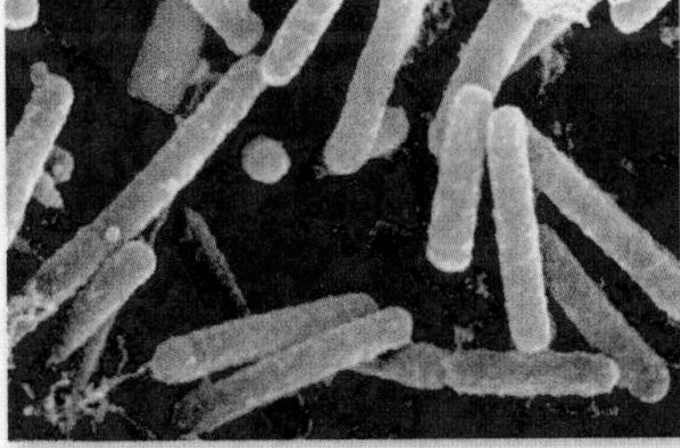

SEE EXAMPLE 3 p. 492

6. **Physics** A new softball dropped onto a hard surface from a height of 25 inches rebounds to about $\frac{2}{5}$ the height on each successive bounce.
   a. Write a function representing the rebound height for each bounce. $f(x) = 25(0.4)^x$
   b. Graph the function.
   c. After how many bounces would a new softball rebound less than 1 inch? **4 bounces**

7-1 Exercises

Assignment Guide

Assign *Guided Practice* exercises as necessary.

If you finished Examples **1–3**

Basic 7–15, 17–21, 27–28, 30–34, 42–49

Average 7–15, 17–36, 39, 42–49

Advanced 7–11, 15–17, 20–49

Homework Quick Check

Quickly check key concepts.
Exercises: 8, 10, 11, 12, 18

Answers

2–6. For graphs, see p. A32.

Math Background Exercise 6 presents a variation of an interesting geometric question known as Zeno's paradox. Based on the mathematics alone, the softball never stops bouncing because the height $y = 0$ is the asymptote.

The "proof" that a dropped softball *actually* lands and stays on the ground is found in the study of physics.

State Resources

Reading Math For **Exercise 17,** remind students that to *depreciate* means to lower in value.

English Language Learners

Exercise 20 involves working with exponential functions. This exercise prepares students for the Multi-Step Test Prep on page 520.

Answers

7–9. For graphs, see p. A33.

10b.

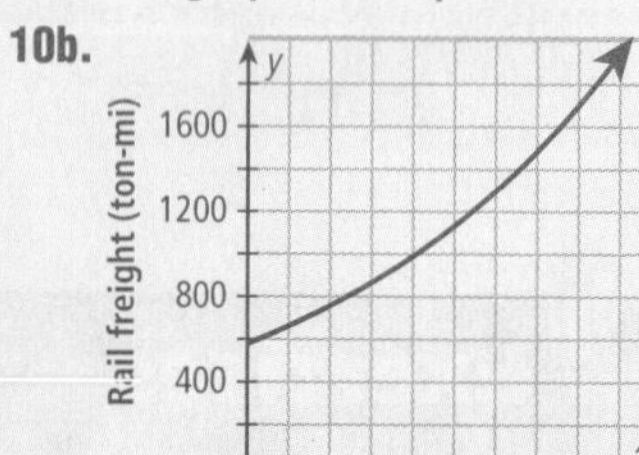

11b.

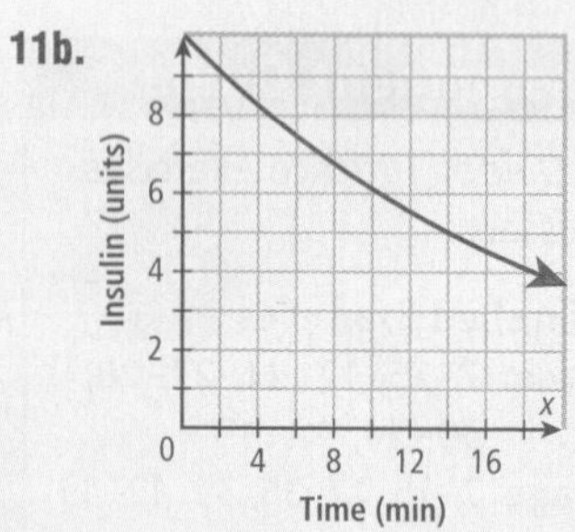

12. No; the variable does not contain an exponent.

13. No; 0^x is 0, a constant function.

14. Yes; the variable is in the exponent.

16, 20a. See p. A33.

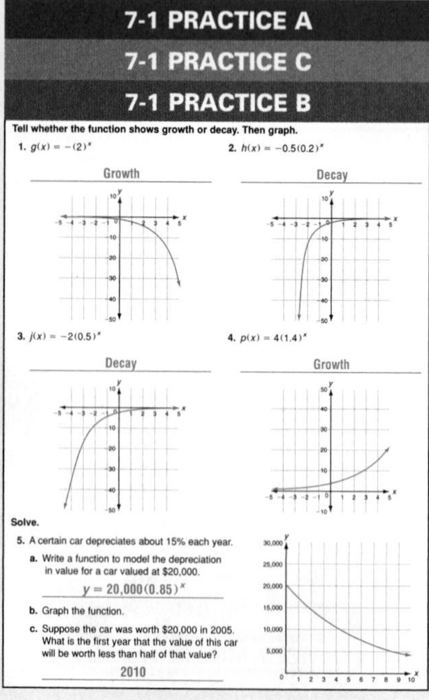

7-1 PRACTICE A

7-1 PRACTICE C

7-1 PRACTICE B

Tell whether the function shows growth or decay. Then graph.

1. $g(x) = -(2)^x$ — Growth

2. $h(x) = -0.5(0.2)^x$ — Decay

3. $j(x) = -2(0.5)^x$ — Decay

4. $p(x) = 4(1.4)^x$ — Growth

Solve.

5. A certain car depreciates about 15% each year.
   a. Write a function to model the depreciation in value for a car valued at \$20,000. $y = 20{,}000(0.85)^x$
   b. Graph the function.
   c. Suppose the car was worth \$20,000 in 2005. What is the first year that the value of this car will be worth less than half of that value? 2010

PRACTICE AND PROBLEM SOLVING

Independent Practice

For Exercises	See Example
7–9	1
10	2
11	3

Extra Practice
Skills Practice p. S16
Application Practice p. S38

Tell whether the function shows growth or decay. Then graph.

7. $f(x) = \left(\frac{1}{3}\right)^x$ decay
8. $f(x) = \left(\frac{1}{3}\right)(1.3)^x$ growth
9. $f(x) = 10(2.7)^x$ growth

10. **Railroads** The amount of freight transported by rail in the United States was about 580 billion *ton-miles* in 1960 and has been increasing at a rate of 2.32% per year since then.
    a. Write a function representing the amount of freight, in billions of ton-miles, transported annually (1960 = year 0). $f(t) = 580(1.0232)^t$
    b. Graph the function.
    c. In what year would you predict that the number of ton-miles would have exceeded or would exceed 1 trillion (1000 billion)? year 24, or 1984

11. **Medicine** A quantity of insulin used to regulate sugar in the bloodstream breaks down by about 5% each minute. A body-weight adjusted dose is generally 10 units.
    a. Write a function representing the amount of the dose that remains. $f(x) = 10(0.95)^x$
    b. Use a calculator to graph the function.
    c. About how much insulin remains after 10 minutes? ≈ 6 units
    d. About how long does it take for half of the dose to remain? 13.6 min.

LINK

History

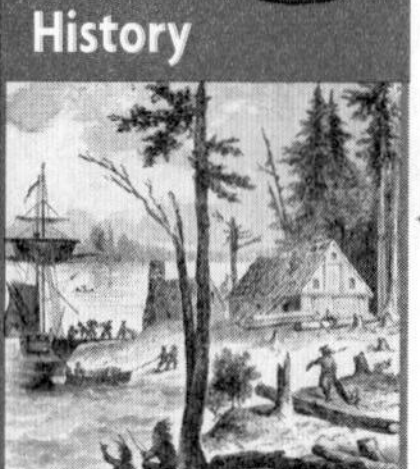

The name *Manhattan* is probably a combination of two Native American words, the Delaware word *mannah,* "island," and the Algonquian word *hatin,* "hills." So the name *Manhattan* means "hilly island."

Explain whether each function is exponential.

12. $f(x) = 2x^{10}$ no
13. $f(x) = 0^x$ no
14. $f(x) = 1 \cdot 0.5^x$ yes

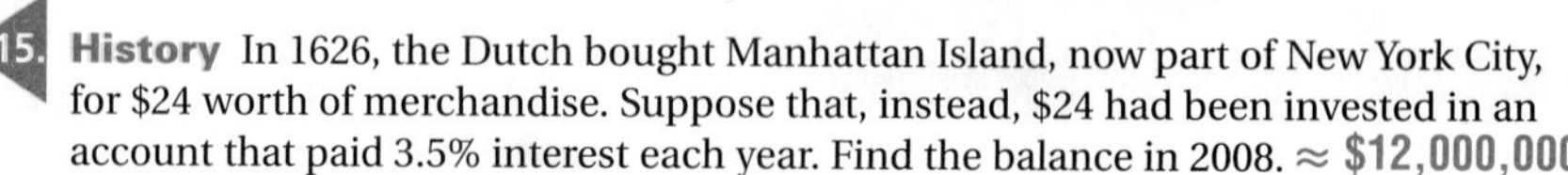

15. **History** In 1626, the Dutch bought Manhattan Island, now part of New York City, for \$24 worth of merchandise. Suppose that, instead, \$24 had been invested in an account that paid 3.5% interest each year. Find the balance in 2008. ≈ \$12,000,000

16. **Technology** The quantity of new information stored electronically in 2002 was about 5 *exabytes,* or 5×10^{18} bytes. Researchers estimate that this is double what was stored in 1999. Suppose this trend continues. Write and graph a function to predict the pattern of growth beginning in 1999.

17. **Business** On federal income tax returns, self-employed people can depreciate the value of business equipment. Suppose a computer valued at \$2765 depreciates at a rate of 30% per year. Estimate the number of years it will take for the computer's value to be less than \$350. 5.8 yr

Complete the table for each function. Round each value to the nearest hundredth.

	x	−3	−2	−1	0	1	2	3	4	5
18.	$f(x) = 2.2^x$	0.09	0.21	0.45	1.00	2.20	4.84	10.65	23.43	51.54
19.	$g(x) = 0.4^x$	15.63	6.25	2.50	1.00	0.40	0.16	0.06	0.03	0.01

Multi-Step Test Prep

20. This problem will prepare you for the Multi-Step Test Prep on page 520.

    For a certain credit card, the total amount A that you owe after n months is given by $A = P(1.015)^n$, where P is the starting balance.
    a. Suppose that you begin with a debt of \$1000. Graph the function for the amount that you owe.
    b. How much will you owe after one year? \$1195.62
    c. How long will it take for the total amount that you owe to reach \$1300? ≈ 18 months

7-1 READING STRATEGIES

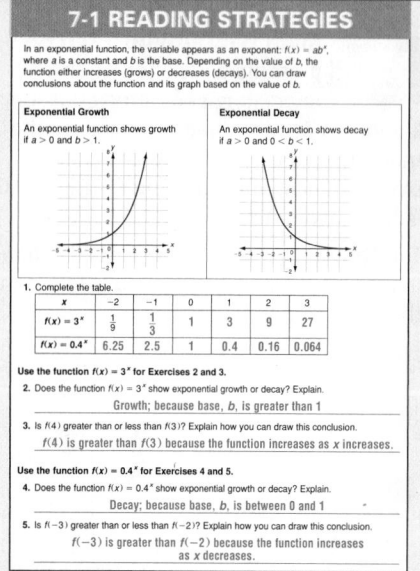

In an exponential function, the variable appears as an exponent: $f(x) = ab^x$, where a is a constant and b is the base. Depending on the value of b, the function either increases (grows) or decreases (decays). You can draw conclusions about the function and its graph based on the value of b.

Exponential Growth	Exponential Decay
An exponential function shows growth if $a > 0$ and $b > 1$.	An exponential function shows decay if $a > 0$ and $0 < b < 1$.

1. Complete the table.

x	−2	−1	0	1	2	3
$f(x) = 3^x$	$\frac{1}{9}$	$\frac{1}{3}$	1	3	9	27
$f(x) = 0.4^x$	6.25	2.5	1	0.4	0.16	0.064

Use the function $f(x) = 3^x$ for Exercises 2 and 3.

2. Does the function $f(x) = 3^x$ show exponential growth or decay? Explain.
   Growth; because base, b, is greater than 1

3. Is $f(4)$ greater than or less than $f(3)$? Explain how you can draw this conclusion.
   $f(4)$ is greater than $f(3)$ because the function increases as x increases.

Use the function $f(x) = 0.4^x$ for Exercises 4 and 5.

4. Does the function $f(x) = 0.4^x$ show exponential growth or decay? Explain.
   Decay; because base, b, is between 0 and 1

5. Is $f(-3)$ greater than or less than $f(-2)$? Explain how you can draw this conclusion.
   $f(-3)$ is greater than $f(-2)$ because the function increases as x decreases.

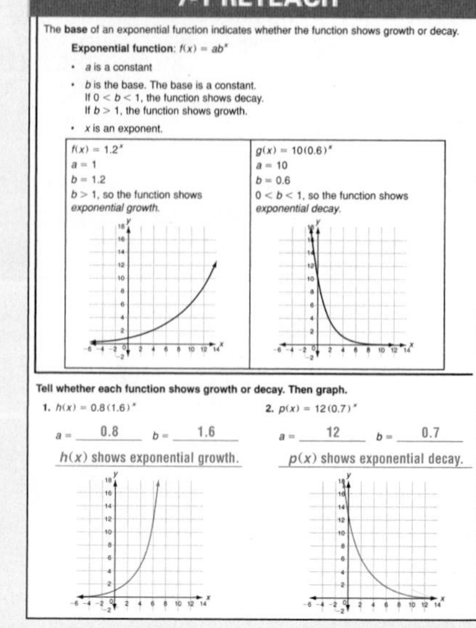

7-1 RETEACH

The **base** of an exponential function indicates whether the function shows growth or decay.

Exponential function: $f(x) = ab^x$

- a is a constant
- b is the base. The base is a constant.
  If $0 < b < 1$, the function shows decay.
  If $b > 1$, the function shows growth.
- x is an exponent.

$f(x) = 1.2^x$ $a = 1$ $b = 1.2$ $b > 1$, so the function shows *exponential growth.*	$g(x) = 10(0.6)^x$ $a = 10$ $b = 0.6$ $0 < b < 1$, so the function shows *exponential decay.*

Tell whether each function shows growth or decay. Then graph.

1. $h(x) = 0.8(1.6)^x$
   $a =$ 0.8 $b =$ 1.6
   $h(x)$ shows exponential growth.

2. $p(x) = 12(0.7)^x$
   $a =$ 12 $b =$ 0.7
   $p(x)$ shows exponential decay.

21. **Collectibles** At the peak of a beanbag animal fad, one sales representative sold 12,000 of the animals in one month. Each month after that, the rep sold about 20% fewer animals.

a. About how many beanbag animals did the rep sell in the 6th month after the peak? $\approx$ **3146**

b. In which month did the rep first sell fewer than 1000 animals? **12th month**

22. **Banking** The compound interest formula is $A = P\left(1 + \frac{r}{n}\right)^{nt}$, where A is the amount earned, P is the principal, r is the annual interest rate, t is the time in years, and n is the number of compounding periods per year. Harry invested \$5000 at 5% interest compounded quarterly (4 times per year).

a. How much will the investment be worth after 5 years? **\$6410.19**

b. When will the investment be worth more than \$10,000? **after 14 yr**

c. **What if...?** Harry could have invested the same amount in an account that paid 5% interest compounded monthly (12 times per year). How much more would his investment have been worth after 5 years? **\$6.60**

23. **Critical Thinking** What are the coordinates of the point that is common to the graph of $f(x) = \left(\frac{2}{3}\right)^x$ and the graph of $f(x) = \left(\frac{3}{2}\right)^x$? **(0, 1)**

Find the range of each function for the domain (0, 10].

24. $f(x) = 3^x - 2^x$ 25. $f(x) = 100(0.9)^x$ 26. $f(x) = \frac{3}{4}(2)^x$

24. (0, 58,025]

25. (34.868, 100]

26. $\left(\frac{3}{4}, 768\right]$

27. **Geology** Radon-222 is a gas that escapes from rocks and soil. It can accumulate in buildings and can be dangerous for people who breathe it. Radon-222 decays to polonium and eventually to lead.

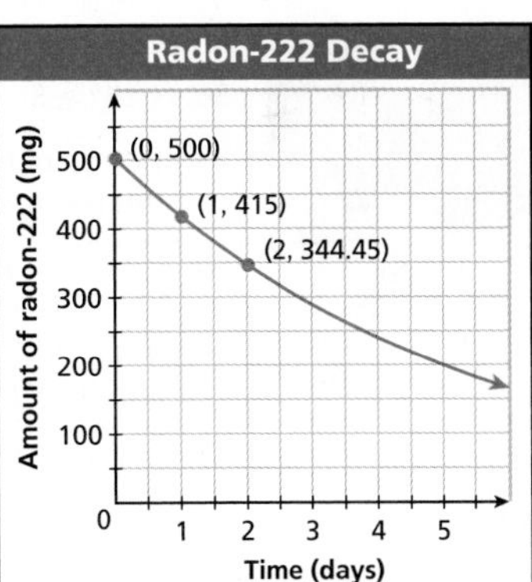

a. Find the percent decrease in the amount of radon-222 each day. **17%**

b. Write an exponential decay function for the amount of a 500 mg sample of radon-222 remaining after t days. **b.** $A(t) = 500(0.83)^t$

c. How much of the radon-222 sample would remain after 14 days? **36.8 mg**

28. **Estimation** According to the Population Reference Bureau, the world population in 2000 was 6.1 billion and increasing at an annual rate of 1.4%. Estimate the world population in 2020. Then write and evaluate an exponential function to predict the actual population, and compare it to your estimate.

28. for $t = 20$ yr, $N(t) = 6.1(1.014)^t$ = 8.1 billion

29. **Critical Thinking** Which grows faster as x increases, x^3 or 3^x? Explain.

29. 3^x; When $x = 3$, they are equal, but 3^x becomes greater quickly as x increases.

30. **Write About It** Describe a situation that could be modeled by an exponential function. Give the function and describe the meanings of several function values. **Possible answer: A company doubles in size each year from an initial size of 12 people; $f(p) = 12(2)^x$; $f(3) = 12(2)^3$ means there are 96 people in 3 yr.**

31. Which function represents exponential decay?

(A) $f(x) = 0.9(1.001^x)$

(B) $f(x) = 1.5\left(\frac{10}{11}\right)^x$ (circled)

(C) $f(x) = 0.5(2^x)$

(D) $f(x) = \left(\frac{1}{0.5}\right)^x$

Teaching Tip **Critical Thinking** To expand on **Example 23,** students may want to see if they can convince themselves that (0, 1) is the only point of intersection of any two functions $f(x) = a^x$, and $g(x) = b^x$ where $a \neq b$.

Teaching Tip **Science Link Exercise 27** deals with the decay of a radioactive element. An important characteristic of such elements is the "half-life," the time it takes for half the substance to decay. Some radioactive elements have long half-lives; thus, they can pose a radioactive danger for a long time. The half-life of plutonium-239 is 24,110 years.

Teaching Tip **Math Background Exercise 29** compares the different growth rates of exponential and power functions. Any exponential growth function will overtake and grow faster than any power function. This can be seen by making a graph and zooming out far enough. Here, for example, are $f(x) = x^3$ and $g(x) = 1.01^x$, which intersect near $(2339, 1.28 \times 10^{10})$.

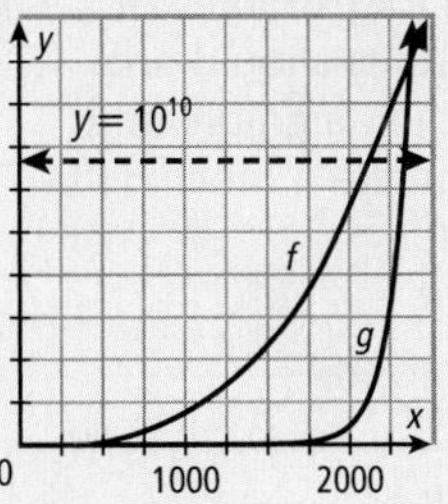

In **Exercise 31,** students who chose **D** need to remember that the reciprocal of a positive number less than 1 is greater than 1.

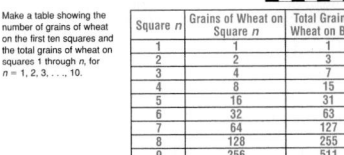

7-1 PROBLEM SOLVING

Justin drove his pickup truck about 22,000 miles in 2004. He read that in 1988 the average residential vehicle traveled about 10,200 miles, which increased by about 2.9% per year through 2004.

1. Write a function for the average mileage, $m(t)$, as a function of t, the time in years since 1988. $m(t) = 10{,}200(1 + 0.029)^t$

2. Assume that the 2.9% increase is valid through 2008 and use your function to complete the table to show the average annual miles driven.

Year	1988	1992	1996	2000	2004	2008
t	0	4	8	12	16	20
$m(t)$	10,200	11,436	12,821	14,374	16,116	18,068

3. Did Justin drive more or fewer miles than the average residential vehicle driver in 2004? by how much (to the nearest 100 miles)?
He drove more miles; about 5,900 miles more.

4. Later Justin read that the annual mileage for light trucks increased by 7.8% per year from 1988 to 2004.

a. Write a function for the average miles driven for a light truck, $n(t)$, as a function of t, the time in years since 1988. He assumes that the average number of miles driven in 1988 was 10,200. $n(t) = 10{,}200(1 + 0.078)^t$

b. Graph the function. Then use your graph to estimate the average number of miles driven (to the nearest 1000) for a light truck in 2004.
About 34,000 miles

c. Did Justin drive more or fewer miles than the average light truck driver in 2004? by how much?
He drove fewer miles than the average light truck driver by about 12,000 miles.

Justin bought his truck new for \$32,000. Its value decreases 9.0% each year. Choose the letter for the best answer.

5. Which function represents the yearly value of Justin's truck?
A $f(t) = 32{,}000(1 + 0.9)^t$
B $f(t) = 32{,}000(1 - 0.9)^t$
C $f(t) = 32{,}000(1 + 0.09)^t$
(D) $f(t) = 32{,}000(1 - 0.09)^t$

6. When will the value of Justin's truck fall below half of what he paid for it?
F In 6 years
(G) In 8 years
H In 10 years
J In 12 years

7-1 CHALLENGE

According to legend, Sissa Ben Dahir, the Vizier of the court of King Shirham of India, worked diligently and invented a new game that was called Chess. The King decided to grant Sissa the reward of his choosing. Sissa pondered carefully and requested the following from the King.

One grain of wheat on the first square of the chessboard, two grains of wheat on the second square, four grains on the third square, eight on the fourth square, and so on.

The King thought this was a very modest request and said that he would grant the Vizier's request.

At right is a chessboard with 64 squares.

1. Make a table showing the number of grains of wheat on the first ten squares and the total grains of wheat on squares 1 through n, for $n = 1, 2, 3, \ldots, 10$.

Square n	Grains of Wheat on Square n	Total Grains of Wheat on Board
1	1	1
2	2	3
3	4	7
4	8	15
5	16	31
6	32	63
7	64	127
8	128	255
9	256	511
10	512	1023

2. Using the information from the table, look for a pattern and write an expression for the number of grains of wheat that would be placed on square n. 2^{n-1}

3. How many grains of wheat would be placed on the last square? $2^{63} = 9{,}223{,}372{,}036{,}854{,}775{,}808$

4. Look for a pattern and write a formula for the total number of grains of wheat on the board after wheat has been placed on square n. $2^n - 1$

5. What is the total number of grains of wheat that Sissa received? $2^{64} - 1 = 18{,}446{,}744{,}073{,}709{,}551{,}615$

6. One grain of wheat weighs approximately 0.000008 kilogram. Find the total weight of wheat the Vizier requested. 147,573,952,589,676 kilograms

7. In 2000 the world's wheat production was approximately 580 million metric tons. At this rate how many years would it take to fill Sissa's request? One metric ton is 1000 kilograms. 254.4 years

TEST PREP DOCTOR In **Exercise 34,** students who chose **C** or **D** may need to review how to convert a percent less than 1% into a decimal.

Journal

Have students write about the two types of exponential models, and how they differ from polynomial models such as quadratic and cubic.

Alternative Assessment

Have students describe two specific situations, one for exponential growth and one for exponential decay. For each, they should produce a function and a graph, and use them to generate a meaningful value.

Power Presentations with PowerPoint®

7-1 Lesson Quiz

In 2000, the world population was 6.08 billion and was increasing at a rate of 1.21% each year.

1. Write a function for world population. Does the function represent growth or decay? $P(t) = 6.08(1.0121)^t$, growth
2. Use a graph to predict the population in 2020. ≈ 7.73 billion

The value of a $3000 computer decreases about 30% each year.

3. Write a function for the computer's value. Does the function represent growth or decay? $V(t) = 3000(0.7)^t$, decay
4. Use a graph to predict the value in 4 years. $\approx \$720.30$

Also available on transparency

32. Which number line represents the values of b in $y = ab^x$ for an exponential decay function?

Ⓕ (number line from −5 to 5, shaded to the left of 0)
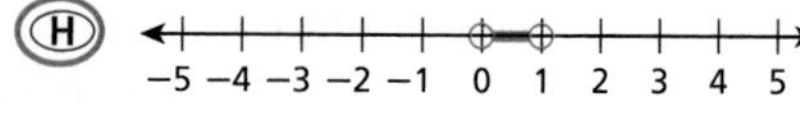
Ⓗ (number line from −5 to 5, open circles at 0 and 1, shaded between)
Ⓖ (number line from −5 to 5, shaded from 0 to 1, closed)
Ⓙ (number line from −5 to 5, shaded to the left of 0, open circle)

33. Short Response What are the values of a and b in $f(x) = ab^x$ for the graph shown?
$a = 1$; $b = 2.5$

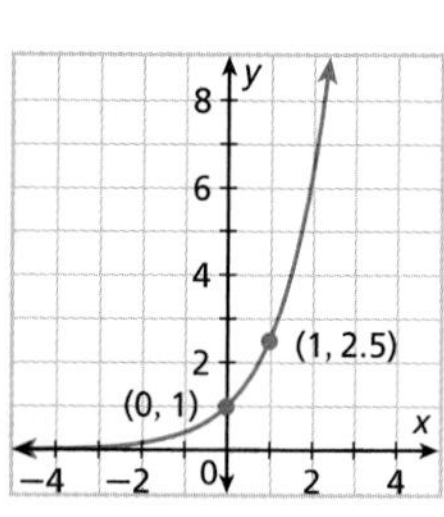

34. The population of a town was 89,443 in 1990 and has increased at a rate of 0.6% per year since then. Which function represents the town's population t years after 1990?

Ⓐ $89{,}443(1.6)^t$ Ⓒ $89{,}443(1.06)^t$
Ⓑ $89{,}443(1.006)^t$ Ⓓ $89{,}443(1.0006)^t$

CHALLENGE AND EXTEND

35. Critical Thinking Recall that polynomials are classified by degree. Why doesn't an exponential function have a degree? The degree of a polynomial is the greatest exponent, but exponential functions have variable exponents that may be infinitely large.

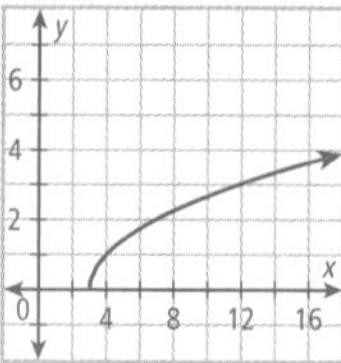

Solve by graphing. Write the answer to the nearest hundredth.

36. $1.15^x \geq 3$ $x \geq 7.86$ **37.** $0.97^x < 0.5$ $x > 22.76$ **38.** $5 < 1.5^x < 6$ $3.97 < x < 4.42$

39. Compare the graphs of $y = 2^x$ and $y = x^2$, where $-10 < x < 10$. How many points of intersection are there? Give the coordinates of these points.

39. 2; $(2, 4)$, $(-0.767, 0.588)$

40. Biology Researchers found that the number of mosquitoes per acre of wetland after a frost is about 10 to the power $\frac{1}{2}d + 2$, where d is the number of days since the frost. How many mosquitoes per acre are there at the time of the frost? How long after the frost does it take for the population to quadruple? 100; ≈ 1.2 days

41. In $f(x) = b^x$, why is the domain of b restricted $(b > 0, b \neq 1)$ for exponential functions? If $b = 0$, $f(x) = 0$; if $b = 1$, $f(x) = 1$. These are constant functions. If $b < 0$, noninteger exponents are not defined.

SPIRAL REVIEW

Graph each function with a graphing calculator. Identify the domain and range of the function, and describe the transformation from its parent function. *(Lesson 1-9)*

42. $f(x) = \sqrt{x - 3}$ **43.** $f(x) = -x^2 + 1$ **44.** $f(x) = 2x^3$ **45.** $f(x) = x - 4$

42. D: $\{x \mid x \geq 3\}$; R: $\{f(x) \mid f(x) \geq 0\}$; $f(x) = \sqrt{x}$ shifted right 3 units

46. Entertainment Fred and Katrina are buying video games. Fred bought 3 new video games and 2 old video games for $235. Katrina bought 1 new video game and 4 old video games for $195. Find the cost of each type of video game. *(Lesson 3-2)*
old $35; new $55

Identify whether the function graphed has an odd or even degree and a positive or negative leading coefficient. *(Lesson 6-7)*

47.
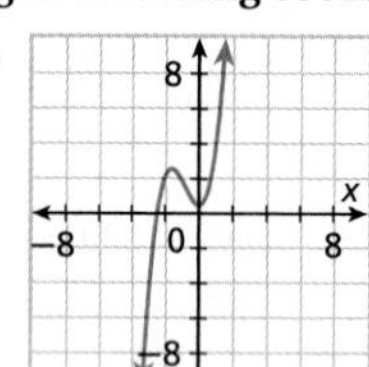

48.
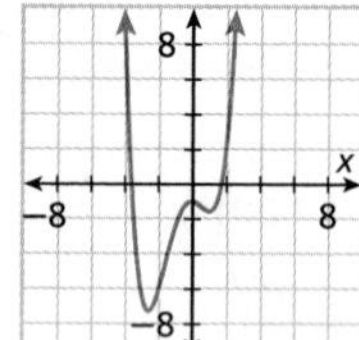

49.
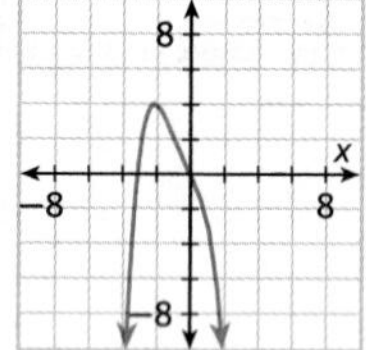

47. odd; positive
48. even; positive
49. even; negative

Answers

35. The degree of a polynomial is the greatest exponent, but exponential functions have variable exponents that may be infinitely large.

36. 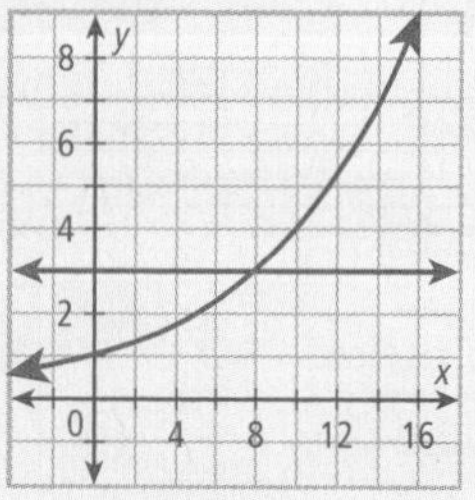 (graph)

37.
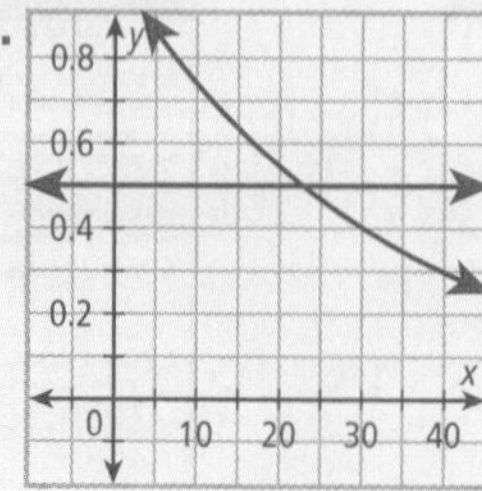

38.
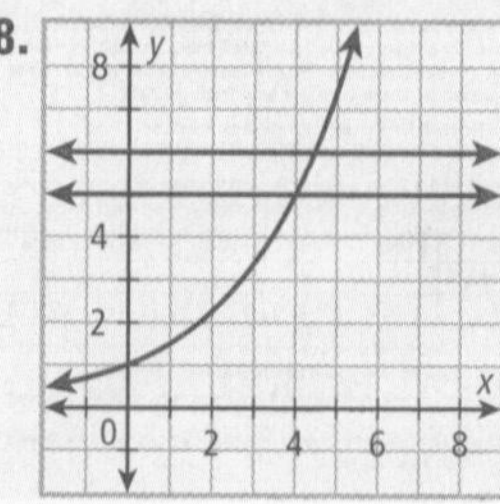

42–45. See p. A33.

7-2 Technology LAB

Explore Inverses of Functions

You can use a graphing calculator to explore inverse functions and their relationship to the linear parent function $f(x) = x$.

Use with Lesson 7-2

Activity

Graph the function $f(x) = 2^x$ and its inverse.

1. Graph the function $f(x) = 2^x$ and the linear parent $f(x) = x$ in the decimal window. Enter the functions, and then press ZOOM and select **4:ZDecimal**.

2. Use the **DrawInv** feature to graph the inverse of **Y1**. Enter the DRAW menu by pressing 2nd DRAW PRGM. Then select **8:DrawInv**.

   To select **Y1**, press VARS. Use the arrow keys to move to the **Y-VARS** submenu. Select **1:Function**, and then select **1:Y1** and press ENTER.

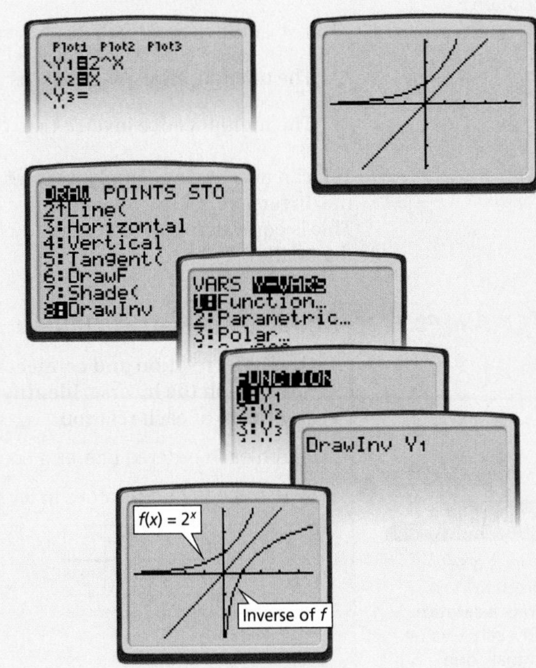
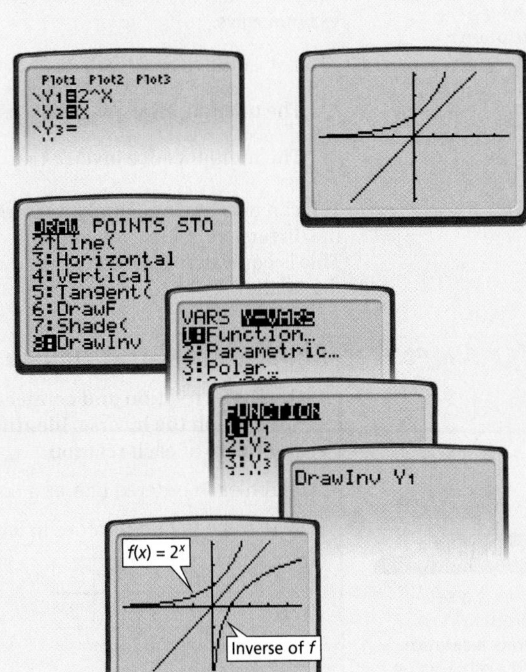

The graph shows the original function $f(x) = 2^x$, its inverse, and the linear parent $f(x) = x$. Notice that the inverse appears to be a function. Its domain is $\{x|x > 0\}$, and its range is $\mathbb{R}$.

Try This

Graph $f(x) = x^2$, its inverse, and $f(x) = x$.

1. Compare the domain and range of $f(x) = x^2$ with the domain and range of its inverse. Is the inverse of $f(x) = x^2$ a function? Explain why or why not.

Graph $f(x) = x^3$, its inverse, and $f(x) = x$.

2. Compare the domain and range of $f(x) = x^3$ with the domain and range of its inverse. Is the inverse of $f(x) = x^3$ a function? Explain why or why not.
3. **Make a Conjecture** Make a conjecture about the relationship between the domain and range of a function and its inverse.
4. **Make a Conjecture** Make a conjecture about the relationship of a function and its inverse to the line $f(x) = x$. They are reflections across $f(x) = x$.

Answers

1. D: $\mathbb{R}$; R: $\{y \mid y \geq 0\}$; inverse: D: $\{x \mid x \geq 0\}$; R: $\mathbb{R}$; No; it fails the vertical line test for $\{x \mid x > 0\}$.
2. D: $\mathbb{R}$; R: $\mathbb{R}$ for both; Yes; for any input, there is at most 1 output.
3. The domain of a function is the range of the inverse, and the range of a function is the domain of the inverse.

Technology LAB Organizer

Use with Lesson 7-2

Pacing:
Traditional 1 day
Block $\frac{1}{2}$ day

Objective: Use a graphing calculator to explore inverse functions and their relationship to the linear parent function.

Materials: graphing calculator

Online Edition
Graphing Calculator, TechKeys

Countdown to Testing Week 15

Resources

Technology Lab Activities
7-2 Lab Recording Sheet

Teach

Discuss

Have students identify the domain and range of the function and its inverse. Discuss whether the inverse is also a function.

Close

Key Concept

The graph of an inverse function will be the reflection of the original function over the line $y = x$.

Assessment

Journal Give students a function and have them sketch what the inverse will look like and tell why.

State Resources

7-2 Organizer

Pacing: Traditional 1 day
Block $\frac{1}{2}$ day

Objectives: Graph and recognize inverses of relations and functions.

Find inverses of functions.

Online Edition
Tutorial Videos, Graphing Calculator

Countdown to Testing Week 15

Power Presentations with PowerPoint®

Warm Up

Solve for *y*.

1. $x = 3y - 7$ $\quad y = \frac{x+7}{3}$
2. $x = \frac{y+5}{8}$ $\quad y = 8x - 5$
3. $x = 4 - y$ $\quad y = 4 - x$
4. $x = y^2$ $\quad y = \pm\sqrt{x}$

Also available on transparency

Math Humor

Q: How did the chicken find the inverse?

A: It reflected the function across y = eggs.

7-2 Inverses of Relations and Functions

Objectives
Graph and recognize inverses of relations and functions.

Find inverses of functions.

Vocabulary
inverse relation
inverse function

Why learn this?
Inverse functions can be used to find prices before taxes, discounts, and extra charges. (See Example 5.)

You have seen the word *inverse* used in various ways.

The additive inverse of 3 is −3.

The multiplicative inverse of 5 is $\frac{1}{5}$.

The multiplicative inverse matrix of $A = \begin{bmatrix} 3 & 1 \\ 4 & 2 \end{bmatrix}$ is $A^{-1} = \begin{bmatrix} 1 & -0.5 \\ -2 & 1.5 \end{bmatrix}$.

You can also find and apply inverses to relations and functions. To graph the **inverse relation**, you can reflect each point across the line $y = x$. This is equivalent to switching the x- and y-values in each ordered pair of the relation.

Remember!
A *relation* is a set of ordered pairs. A *function* is a relation in which each x-value has, at most, one y-value paired with it.

EXAMPLE 1 Graphing Inverse Relations

Graph the relation and connect the points. Then graph the inverse. Identify the domain and range of each relation.

x	0	1	2	4	8
y	2	4	5	6	7

Graph each ordered pair and connect them.

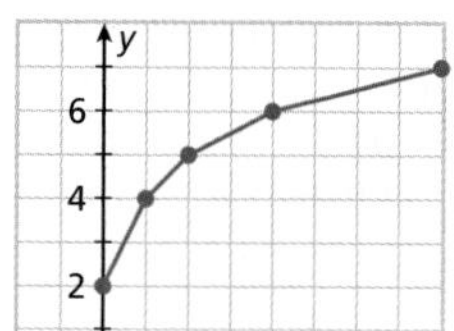

Switch the x- and y-values in each ordered pair.

x	2	4	5	6	7
y	0	1	2	4	8

Reflect each point across $y = x$, and connect them. Make sure the points match those in the table.

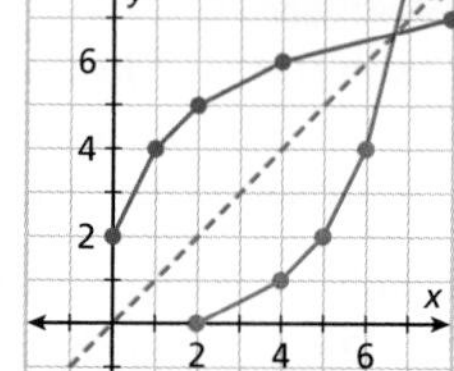

Domain: $\{x \mid 0 \le x \le 8\}$ **Range:** $\{y \mid 2 \le y \le 7\}$

Domain: $\{x \mid 2 \le x \le 7\}$ **Range:** $\{y \mid 0 \le y \le 8\}$

1. Graph the relation and connect the points. Then graph the inverse. Identify the domain and range of each relation.

x	1	3	4	5	6
y	0	1	2	3	5

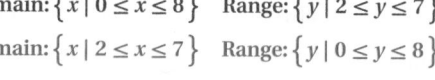

relation: D: $\{1 \le x \le 6\}$; R: $\{0 \le y \le 5\}$

inverse: D: $\{0 \le x \le 5\}$; R: $\{1 \le y \le 6\}$

State Resources

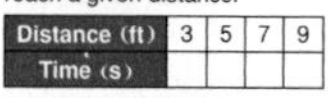

go.hrw.com
State Resources Online
KEYWORD: MB7 Resources

1 Introduce

EXPLORATION

7-2 Inverses of Relations and Functions

The graph shows the distance of a particle from a location over time.

1. Complete the table based on the data in the graph.

Time (s)	0	1	2	3
Distance (ft)				

2. Write an equation that gives the distance of the particle as a function of time.
3. Complete the table showing the time it takes the particle to reach a given distance.

Distance (ft)	3	5	7	9
Time (s)				

4. Plot the ordered pairs on the same coordinate plane as the original set of data.

THINK AND DISCUSS

5. **Discuss** how the two sets of data points in the graph are related to each other. (Hint: Consider the line $y = x$.)
6. **Explain** how you could use your equation to find the time it takes the particle to reach a given distance.

Motivate

Inverses can be very useful for converting between different measures. For example, suppose, while planning a trip to Mexico, you learn that a dollar is worth 12 Mexican pesos. In other words, $P = 12D$. You can figure out the number of dollars equivalent to one peso by solving for D: $D = \frac{P}{12}$. We call the functions $f(x) = 12x$ and $g(x) = \frac{x}{12}$ *inverses* because they "undo" each other.

Explorations and answers are provided in the *Explorations* binder.

When the relation is also a function, you can write the inverse of the function $f(x)$ as $f^{-1}(x)$. This notation does *not* indicate a reciprocal.

Functions that undo each other are **inverse functions**.

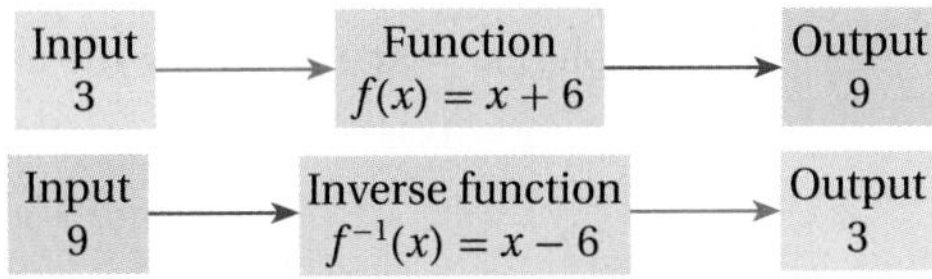

To find the inverse function, use the inverse operation. In the example above, 6 is added to x in $f(x)$, so 6 is subtracted to find $f^{-1}(x)$.

EXAMPLE 2 Writing Inverse Functions by Using Inverse Operations

Use inverse operations to write the inverse of $f(x) = 2x$.

$f(x) = 2x$ *The variable, x, is multiplied by 2.*

$f^{-1}(x) = \frac{x}{2}$ *Divide x by 2 to write the inverse.*

Check Use the input $x = 7$ in $f(x)$.

$f(x) = 2x$

$f(7) = 2(7)$ *Substitute 7 for x.*

$= 14$

Substitute the result into $f^{-1}(x)$.

$f^{-1}(x) = \frac{x}{2}$

$f^{-1}(14) = \frac{14}{2}$ *Substitute 14 for x.*

$= 7$

The inverse function *does* undo the original function. ✔

Use inverse operations to write the inverse of each function.

2a. $f(x) = \frac{x}{3}$ $f^{-1}(x) = 3x$

2b. $f(x) = x + \frac{2}{3}$ $f^{-1}(x) = x - \frac{2}{3}$

Undo operations in the opposite order of the order of operations.

EXAMPLE 3 Writing Inverses of Multi-Step Functions

Use inverse operations to write the inverse of $f(x) = \frac{x}{4} - 5$.

$f(x) = \frac{x}{4} - 5$ *The variable x is divided by 4, then 5 is subtracted.*

$f^{-1}(x) = 4(x + 5)$ *First, undo the subtraction by adding 5 to x. Then, undo the division by multiplying by 4.*

Check Use a sample input.

$f(40) = \frac{40}{4} - 5 = 10 - 5 = 5$ → $f^{-1}(5) = 4(5 + 5) = 4(10) = 40$ ✔

Helpful Hint

The *reverse* order of operations:
Addition or Subtraction
Multiplication or Division
Exponents
Parentheses

3. Use inverse operations to write the inverse of $f(x) = 5x - 7$. $f^{-1}(x) = \frac{x + 7}{5}$

2 Teach

Guided Instruction

Walk students through reversing ordered pairs to find an inverse, graphing the point(s), and noting that each point "mirrors" the original point across the line $y = x$.

Reaching All Learners

Through Concrete Manipulatives

Some students may find it easier to draw an inverse function by using tracing paper. Draw any relation on a piece of tracing paper, and then fold the paper over along the line $y = x$. The original relation will now lie where the inverse relation goes.

A Mira may also be used. Students can place the Mira along the line $y = x$ and draw the reflection they see.

Power Presentations with PowerPoint®

Additional Examples

Example 1

Graph the relation and connect the points. Then graph the inverse. Identify the domain and range of each relation.

x	0	1	5	8
y	2	5	6	9

x	2	5	6	9
y	0	1	5	8

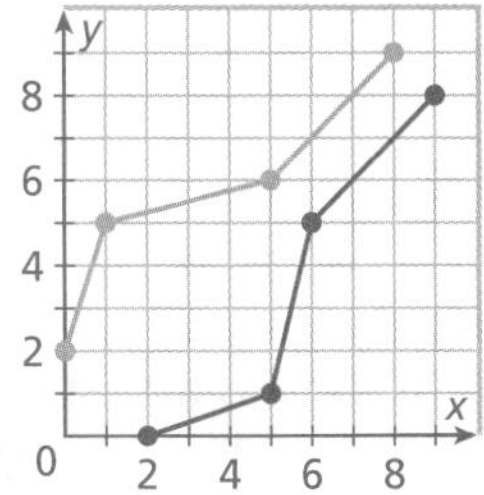

D: $0 \le x \le 8$ $2 \le x \le 9$

R: $2 \le y \le 9$ $0 \le y \le 8$

Example 2

Use inverse operations to write the inverse of $f(x) = x - \frac{1}{2}$.

$f^{-1}(x) = x + \frac{1}{2}$

Example 3

Use inverse operations to write the inverse of $f(x) = 3(x - 7)$.

$f^{-1}(x) = \frac{1}{3}x + 7$

Also available on transparency

INTERVENTION

Questioning Strategies

EXAMPLE 1

- Where is the inverse of a point in Quadrant II located?

EXAMPLE 2

- If $f(10)$ is 20, what do you know about $f^{-1}(20)$?

EXAMPLE 3

- How do you know what operation to undo first?

Power Presentations with PowerPoint®

Additional Examples

Example 4

Graph $f(x) = -\frac{1}{2}x - 5$. Then write and graph the inverse.

$f^{-1}(x) = -2x - 10$

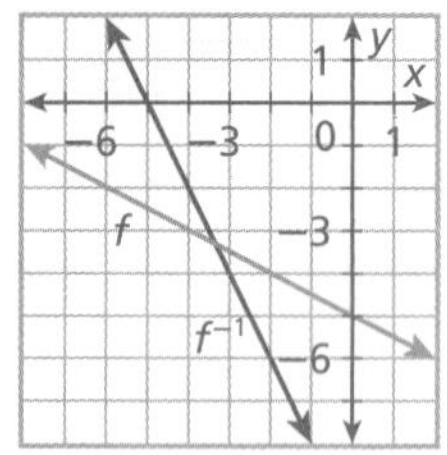

Example 5

Juan buys a CD online for 20% off the list price. He has to pay \$2.50 for shipping. The total charge is \$13.70. What is the list price of the CD?

$L = \frac{c - 2.5}{0.8}$; \$14

Also available on transparency

INTERVENTION

Questioning Strategies

EXAMPLE 4

- How do you know whether the graphs of a function and its inverse cross each other?

EXAMPLE 5

- How do you reverse the process of finding a total after sales tax has been applied? What does this reverse process give you?

Visual Post a copy of a large mapping diagram, including arrows representing a function and its inverse for students to reference while considering the domains and ranges of functions and their inverses.

Communicating Math Another way to think about inverses: They switch the role of the dependent and independent variables. The dependent variable becomes independent, and vice versa.

You can also find the inverse function by writing the original function with x and y switched and then solving for y.

EXAMPLE 4 Writing and Graphing Inverse Functions

Graph $f(x) = 3x + 6$. Then write and graph the inverse.

$y = 3x + 6$	*Set $y = f(x)$ and graph f.*
$x = 3y + 6$	*Switch x and y.*
$x - 6 = 3y$	*Solve for y.*
$\frac{x-6}{3} = y$	
$y = \frac{x-6}{3}$	*Write in $y =$ format.*
$f^{-1}(x) = \frac{x-6}{3}$	*Set $y = f(x)$.*
$= \frac{1}{3}x - 2$	*Simplify. Then graph f^{-1}.*

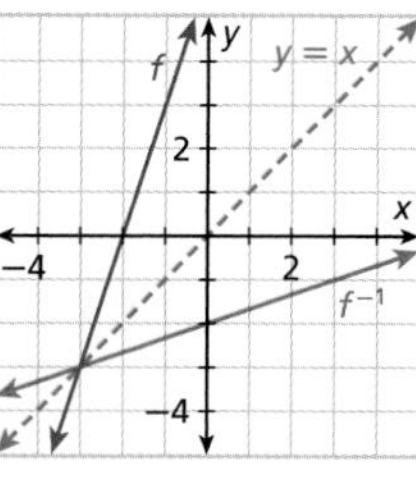

$f^{-1}(x) = \frac{3}{2}x - 3$

CHECK IT OUT! 4. Graph $f(x) = \frac{2}{3}x + 2$. Then write the inverse and graph.

Any time you need to undo an operation or work backward from a result to the original input, you can apply inverse functions.

EXAMPLE 5 *Retailing Application*

A clerk needs to price a digital camera returned by a customer. The customer paid a total of \$103.14, which included a gift-wrapping charge of \$3 and 8% sales tax. What price should the clerk mark on the tag?

Step 1 Write an equation for the total cost as a function of price.

$c = 1.08(p + 3)$ *Cost c is a function of price p.*

Step 2 Find the inverse function that models price as a function of cost.

$c = 1.08(p + 3)$	
$c = 1.08p + 3.24$	*Distribute.*
$c - 3.24 = 1.08p$	*Subtract 3.24 from both sides.*
$\frac{c - 3.24}{1.08} = p$	*Divide to isolate p.*

Step 3 Evaluate the inverse function for $c = \$103.14$.

$p = \frac{103.14 - 3.24}{1.08} = 92.50$

The clerk should mark the tag as \$92.50.

Check $c = 1.08(92.50 + 3)$ *Substitute.*

$= 1.08(95.50)$

$= 103.14$ ✔

Remember!

In a real-world situation, don't switch the variables, because they are named for specific quantities.

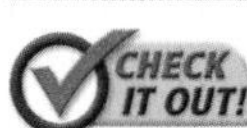

CHECK IT OUT! 5. To make tea, use $\frac{1}{6}$ teaspoon of tea per ounce of water plus a teaspoon for the pot. Use the inverse to find the number of ounces of water needed if 7 teaspoons of tea are used.

inverse: $z = 6t - 6$; 36 oz of water

3 Close

Summarize

Review that the inverse can be used to "undo" a function and that in the real world, inverses are used to switch the role of the dependent and independent variables.

Ask students to answer the following, "How would you undo the following: *Add three, double the result, and then subtract 5?*" Add five, take half the result, and then subtract 3.

ONGOING ASSESSMENT and INTERVENTION

***Diagnose Before* the Lesson**
7-2 Warm Up, TE p. 498

***Monitor During* the Lesson**
Check It Out! Exercises, SE pp. 498–500
Questioning Strategies, TE pp. 499–500

***Assess After* the Lesson**
7-2 Lesson Quiz, TE p. 504
Alternative Assessment, TE p. 504

THINK AND DISCUSS

1. Explain the result of interchanging x and y to find the inverse function of $f(x) = x$. How could you have predicted this from the graph of $f(x)$?
2. Give an example of a function whose inverse is a function. Give an example of a function whose inverse is not a function.
3. Tell what happens when you take the inverse of the inverse of a function. Is the result necessarily a function? Explain.

4. **GET ORGANIZED** Copy and complete the graphic organizer. Show a possible input value, inverse function, and output value for a function $f(x)$.

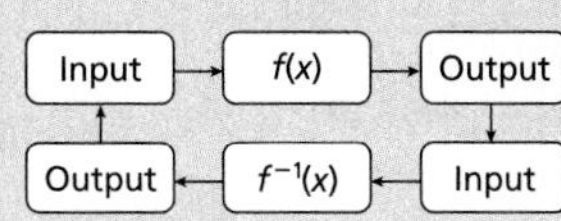

Answers to *Think and Discuss*

Possible answers:

1. When x and y are interchanged, the inverse function is the same as the original function. The graph of an inverse is the reflection across $y = x$, but the original function is $y = x$.
2. Possible answers: $y = x$; $y = x^2$
3. You get the original function; yes, the original is a function.
4. See p. A8.

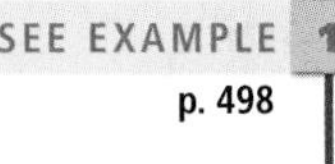

7-2 Exercises

Homework Help Online
KEYWORD: MB7 7-2

Parent Resources Online
KEYWORD: MB7 Parent

Assignment Guide

Assign *Guided Practice* exercises as necessary.

If you finished Examples **1–3**
- **Basic** 18–25
- **Average** 18–25, 50–51
- **Advanced** 18–25, 50–51

If you finished Examples **1–5**
- **Basic** 18–29, 32–33, 36–38, 48–51, 60–68
- **Average** 18–36, 38–43, 47–52, 60–68
- **Advanced** 18–31, 33–35, 38–68

Homework Quick Check
Quickly check key concepts.
Exercises: 20, 22, 24, 28, 30, 32

GUIDED PRACTICE

1. **Vocabulary** When switching x and y, the result is always an *inverse* __?__. (*relation* or *function*) **relation**

SEE EXAMPLE 1 p. 498

Graph the relation and connect the points. Then graph the inverse. Identify the domain and range of each relation.

2.

x	1	2	3	4
y	1	2	4	8

3.

x	3	4	1	−1
y	−1	−2	−4	−4

SEE EXAMPLE 2 p. 499

Use inverse operations to write the inverse of each function.

4. $f(x) = x + 3$
5. $f(x) = 4x$
6. $f(x) = \frac{x}{2}$
7. $f(x) = x - 2\frac{1}{2}$

SEE EXAMPLE 3 p. 499

8. $f(x) = 5x - 1$
9. $f(x) = \frac{x}{2} + 3$
10. $f(x) = 3 - \frac{1}{2}x$
11. $f(x) = \frac{1}{2}(3 - 3x)$
12. $f(x) = 4(x + 1)$
13. $f(x) = \frac{3x - 5}{2}$

SEE EXAMPLE 4 p. 500

Graph each function. Then write and graph its inverse.

14. $f(x) = 5 - 2x$
15. $f(x) = \frac{x}{4} + 2$
16. $f(x) = 10 + 0.6x$

SEE EXAMPLE 5 p. 500

17. **Meteorology** The formula $C = \frac{5}{9}(F - 32)$ gives degrees Celsius as a function of degrees Fahrenheit. Find the inverse of this function to convert degrees Celsius to Fahrenheit and use it to find 16°C in degrees Fahrenheit. $F = \frac{9}{5}C + 32$; **61°F**

PRACTICE AND PROBLEM SOLVING

Graph the relation and connect the points. Then graph the inverse. Identify the domain and range of each relation.

18.

x	−1	2	3	5
y	1	3	5	5

19.

x	−4	−2	0	2	4
y	−2	−1	0	1	2

State Resources

Answers

2.

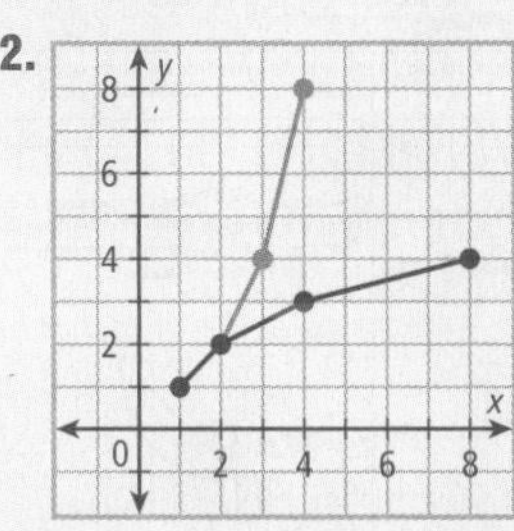

relation: D: $\{1 \le x \le 4\}$; R: $\{1 \le y \le 8\}$;
inverse: D: $\{1 \le x \le 8\}$; R: $\{1 \le y \le 4\}$

3.

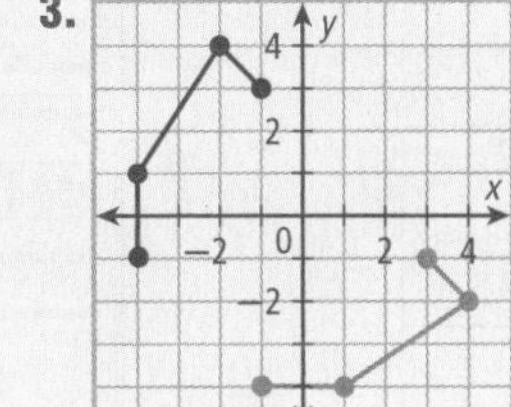

relation: D: $\{-1 \le x \le 4\}$; R: $\{-4 \le y \le -1\}$;
inverse: D: $\{-4 \le x \le -1\}$; R: $\{-1 \le y \le 4\}$

4. $f^{-1}(x) = x - 3$
5. $f^{-1}(x) = \frac{1}{4}x$
6. $f^{-1}(x) = 2x$
7. $f^{-1}(x) = x + 2\frac{1}{2}$
8. $f^{-1}(x) = \frac{1}{5}(x + 1)$
9. $f^{-1}(x) = 2(x - 3)$
10. $f^{-1}(x) = -2x + 6$
11. $f^{-1}(x) = -\frac{2}{3}x + 1$
12. $f^{-1}(x) = \frac{1}{4}x - 1$
13. $f^{-1}(x) = \frac{2}{3}x + \frac{5}{3}$

14–16, 18–19. See p. A33.

go.hrw.com
State Resources Online
KEYWORD: MB7 Resources

Teaching Tip **Auditory** For **Exercises 20–25,** it may help students to identify the operations verbally before writing the inverses algebraically. For example, in **Exercise 24,** "*x* is multiplied by 12.5, then added to 145." Its inverse would "subtract 145 and then divide by 12.5."

Teaching Tip **Visual** For **Exercises 26–28,** it may be useful to note that when you are graphing an inverse, the *y*-intercepts of the original function become the *x*-intercepts of the inverse and vice versa. So if you are graphing a line, it is easy to quickly establish the two points necessary to determine it.

MULTI-STEP TEST PREP **Exercise 36** involves finding and using inverse functions as they relate to credit card charges. This exercise prepares students for the Multi-Step Test Prep on page 520.

Answers

20. $f^{-1}(x) = 1.\overline{21}x$
21. $f^{-1}(x) = x + 1\frac{3}{4}$
22. $f^{-1}(x) = 0.25x$
23. $f^{-1}(x) = -\frac{1}{32}x + \frac{21}{32}$
24. $f^{-1}(x) = 0.08x - 11.6$
25. $f^{-1}(x) = 5x - 60$

Independent Practice

For Exercises	See Example
18–19	1
20–22	2
23–25	3
26–28	4
29	5

Extra Practice
Skills Practice p. S16
Application Practice p. S38

LINK **Physics**

Mountain climbers at very high altitudes can drink tea while it's boiling with bubbles because it's cool enough not to burn them.

Use inverse operations to write the inverse of each function.

20. $f(x) = 0.825x$
21. $f(x) = x - 1\frac{3}{4}$
22. $f(x) = \frac{x}{0.25}$
23. $f(x) = 21 - 32x$
24. $f(x) = 145 + 12.5x$
25. $f(x) = \frac{1}{5}x + 12$

Graph each function. Then write and graph its inverse.

26. $f(x) = \frac{4}{5}(x - 15)$
27. $f(x) = 2 - \frac{x}{3}$
28. $f(x) = 1.21x$

29. **Education** A linear model projects that the number of bachelor's degrees awarded in the United States will increase by 19,500 each year. In 2001, 1.28 million bachelor's degrees were awarded. Use the inverse function to predict the number of years after 2001 that 1.7 million bachelor's degrees will be awarded. *Source: nces.ed.gov* **22**

30. **Critical Thinking** Graph the line that passes through (2, 9) and (3, 4).
    a. What is the slope of this line? **−5**
    b. What is the slope of the line that is the inverse of the original line? $-\frac{1}{5}$

31. **Physics** At sea level, the boiling point of water is 212°F. At *x* thousand feet, the boiling point of water is given by the function $f(x) = 212 - 1.85x$.
    a. Write the inverse function. $f^{-1}(x) = \frac{212 - x}{1.85}$
    b. Above what altitude, to the nearest 500 feet, does the boiling point of water fall below 200°F? **6500 ft**
    c. At the summit of Nepal's Lhotse Mountain, water boils at 160.3°F. What is the mountain peak's altitude? **27,946 ft**

Geometry **Find the coordinates of the vertices of the inverse for each figure.**

32.
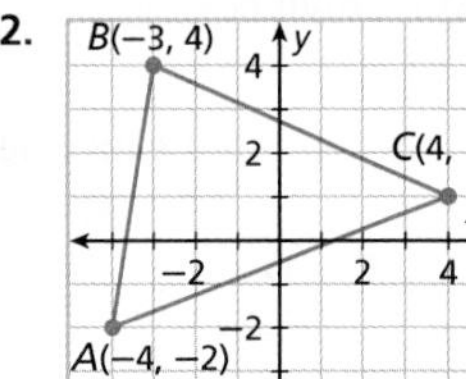

(4, −3), (1, 4), (−2, −4)

33.
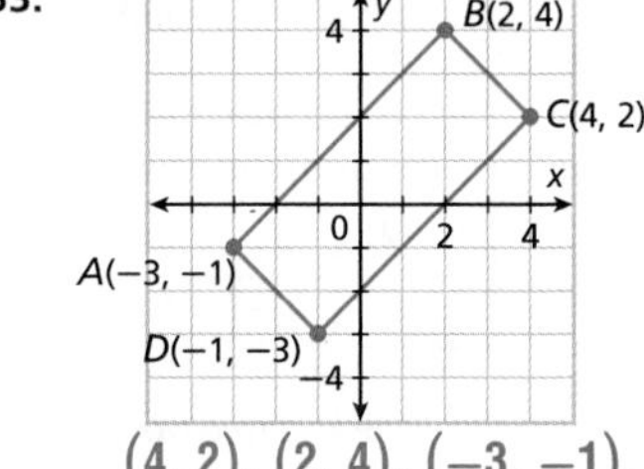

(4, 2), (2, 4), (−3, −1), (−1, −3)

34. **Critical Thinking** What is the inverse of $f(x) = 3$? (Hint: Write this function as $y = 0x + 3$.) Is the inverse a function? Explain.

34. The inverse is $x = 3$, which is a line parallel to the *y*-axis. So it is not a function.

35. **Animals** In 1999, Warhol the albino ferret ran a 10 m tube race in 12.59 s. Assume that he ran at a constant rate. Write a function that gives distance as a function of time. Write and use the inverse function to find the time it would take Warhol to complete a 25 m race at the same speed. $f(x) = \frac{10}{12.59}x$; $f^{-1}(x) = 1.259x$; **31.48 s**

MULTI-STEP TEST PREP

36b. $n = \frac{C - 3.5}{22}$; **7**

36. This problem will prepare you for the Multi-Step Test Prep on page 520.

    A theater sells tickets for $22. If you pay by credit card, the theater adds a service charge of $3.50 to the entire order.
    a. Write a function that gives the amount billed to the credit card as a function of the number of tickets purchased. $C = 22n + 3.5$
    b. Write the inverse function, and use it to find the number of tickets purchased when the credit card bill is $157.50.
    c. Is it possible to have a total of $332.50 billed to your credit card for these tickets? Why or why not? **No; when $C = \$332.50$, n is not an integer.**

7-2 PRACTICE A
7-2 PRACTICE C
7-2 PRACTICE B

Use inverse operations to write the inverse of each function.

1. $f(x) = 15x - 10$ — $f^{-1}(x) = \frac{x + 10}{15}$
2. $f(x) = 10 - 4x$ — $f^{-1}(x) = -\frac{x - 10}{4}$
3. $f(x) = 12 - 9x$ — $f^{-1}(x) = -\frac{x - 12}{9}$
4. $f(x) = 5x + 2$ — $f^{-1}(x) = \frac{x - 2}{5}$
5. $f(x) = x + 6$ — $f^{-1}(x) = x - 6$
6. $f(x) = x + \frac{1}{2}$ — $f^{-1}(x) = x - \frac{1}{2}$
7. $f(x) = -\frac{x}{12}$ — $f^{-1}(x) = -12x$
8. $f(x) = \frac{x - 12}{4}$ — $f^{-1}(x) = 4x + 12$
9. $f(x) = \frac{3x + 1}{6}$ — $f^{-1}(x) = \frac{6x - 1}{3}$, or $f^{-1}(x) = 2x - \frac{1}{3}$

Graph each function. Then write and graph its inverse.

10. $f(x) = 2x - 4$ — $f^{-1}(x) = \frac{1}{2}x + 2$
11. $f(x) = \frac{5}{2}x - 2$ — $f^{-1}(x) = \frac{2}{5}(x + 2)$

Solve.

12. Dan works at a hardware store. The employee discount is determined by the formula $d = 0.15(c - 10)$. Use the inverse of this function to find the cost of the item for which Dan received an $18.00 discount.
    a. Find the inverse function that models cost as a function of the discount. $c = \frac{d + 1.5}{0.15}$
    b. Evaluate the inverse function for $d = 18$. $c = 130$
    c. What was Dan's final cost for this item? $112

7-2 READING STRATEGIES

Every function has an inverse. But the inverse may or may not be a function. Remember that a function is a relation in which each value of *x* has only one value of *y*. You can find the inverse of a function by switching the *x*-values (domain) and *y*-values (range) in each ordered pair.

Function	Domain and Range	Inverse Function
$f(x) = \{(1, 2), (2, 2), (3, 4)\}$	Domain: {1, 2, 3} Range: {2, 4}	Switch the *x*-values and *y*-values. {(2, 1), (2, 2), (4, 3)} The inverse is not a function because the number 2 is mapped to two *y*-values, 1 and 2.
$f(x) = \{(1, 3), (2, 5), (3, 7)\}$	Domain: {1, 2, 3} Range: {3, 5, 7}	Switch the *x* and *y* values. $f^{-1}(x) = \{(3, 1), (5, 2), (7, 3)\}$
$f(x) = 2x - 3$	Domain: all real numbers Range: all real numbers	Use inverse operations to find the inverse. $f^{-1}(x) = \frac{x + 3}{2}$

Answer each question.

1. a. Describe how could you find the inverse of the relation $R = \{(-1, 1), (1, 1), (-2, 4), (2, 4)\}$.
   Possible answer: Reverse each ordered pair.
   b. Write the inverse of *R*.
   $R^{-1} = \{(1, -1), (1, 1), (4, -2), (4, 2)\}$
   c. Is R^{-1} a function? Explain.
   No; possible answer: Both *x*-values 1 and 4 have more than one *y*-value.
2. A function $g(x)$ has an inverse $g^{-1}(x)$. Find the value of the function and its inverse. Use the fact that the inverse can be used to undo the original function.
   a. $g(3) = 4$; $g^{-1}(4) = ?$ 3
   b. $g^{-1}(2) = 1$; $g(1) = ?$ 2
   c. $g^{-1}(8) = 7$; $g(7) = ?$ 8
3. Describe the inverse operations you could use to find the inverse of $f(x) = \frac{x}{2} + 1$.
   Possible answer: Subtract 1 to undo the addition. Then multiply by 2 to undo the division.

7-2 RETEACH

To graph an **inverse** relation, reflect each point across the line $y = x$. Or you can switch the *x*- and *y*-values in each ordered pair of the relation to find the ordered pairs of the inverse.

Remember, a relation is a set of ordered pairs.

x	0	1	4	6	10
y	3	6	9	10	11

The domain is all possible values of *x*: $\{x \mid 0 \le x \le 10\}$.

The range is all possible values of *y*: $\{y \mid 3 \le y \le 11\}$.

To write the **inverse** of the relation, switch the places of *x* and *y* in each ordered pair.

x	3	6	9	10	11
y	0	1	4	6	10

The domain of the inverse corresponds to the range of the original relation: $\{x \mid 3 \le x \le 11\}$. The range of the inverse corresponds to the domain of the original relation: $\{y \mid 0 \le y \le 10\}$.

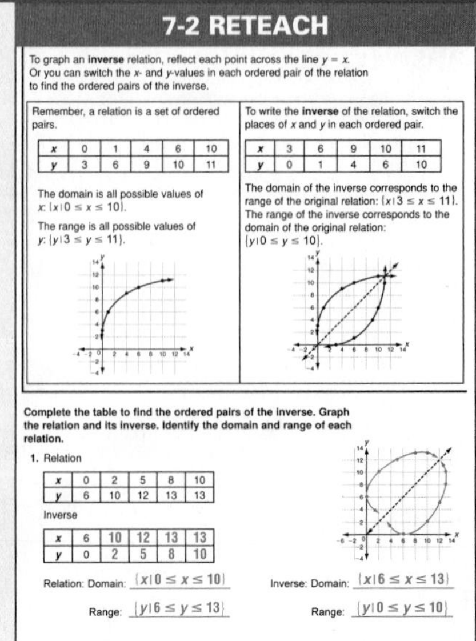

Complete the table to find the ordered pairs of the inverse. Graph the relation and its inverse. Identify the domain and range of each relation.

1. Relation

x	0	2	5	8	10
y	6	10	12	13	13

Inverse

x	6	10	12	13	13
y	0	2	5	8	10

Relation: Domain: $\{x \mid 0 \le x \le 10\}$ Range: $\{y \mid 6 \le y \le 13\}$

Inverse: Domain: $\{x \mid 6 \le x \le 13\}$ Range: $\{y \mid 0 \le y \le 10\}$

37. **ERROR ANALYSIS** Two students found the inverse of $f(x) = \frac{1}{2}x + 1$. Which is incorrect? Explain the error.

B; the student may have found the inverse of each term.

Ⓐ
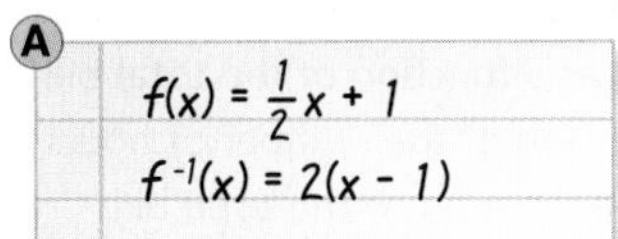

Ⓑ
$f(x) = \frac{1}{2}x + 1$
$f^{-1}(x) = 2x - 1$

38. **Write About It** Explain the effect on a function and its graph when you switch the coordinates of the ordered pairs.

39. **Critical Thinking** Can the inverse of a relation that is not a function be a function itself? Explain your answer by using an example.

40. **Clothing** Hat size is a linear function of head circumference. A person with a head circumference of $21\frac{1}{2}$ in. has a hat size of $6\frac{7}{8}$, while a person with a head circumference of $21\frac{7}{8}$ in. has a hat size of 7.
   a. Find hat size as a function of head circumference. $S(c) = \frac{1}{3}c - \frac{7}{24}$
   b. Find the inverse. Is it a function? What does the inverse represent?
   c. A hat was found with a size of $7\frac{3}{8}$. What is the head circumference of the owner? 23 in.

Tell whether each statement is sometimes, always, or never true.

41. The inverse of an ordered pair on a graph is its reflection across the line $y = x$. always
42. The inverse of a linear function is a linear function. sometimes
43. The inverse of a line with positive slope is a line with negative slope. never
44. The inverse of a line with a slope greater than 1 is a line with slope less than 1. always
45. The inverse of the inverse of a point (x, y) is the original point. always
46. The line $y = k$, where k is a constant, has an inverse. always

47. **Diving** Scuba divers must know that the deeper the dive, the greater the water pressure in pounds per square inch (psi) for fresh water diving, as shown in the diagram.
   a. Write the pressure as a function of depth.
   b. Identify a reasonable domain and range of the pressure function.
   c. Find the inverse of the function from part **a.** What does the inverse function represent?
   d. The point (25.9, 25.9) is an approximate solution to both the function from part **a** and its inverse. What does this point mean in the context of the problem?
   d. At 25.9 ft, the pressure is 25.9 psi.

a. $P = \frac{147}{340}d + 14.7$

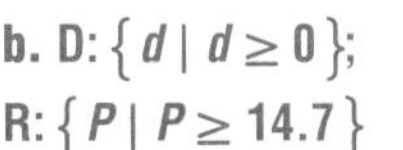
b. D: $\{d \mid d \geq 0\}$; R: $\{P \mid P \geq 14.7\}$

c. $d = \frac{340}{147}P - 34$; depth as a function of pressure

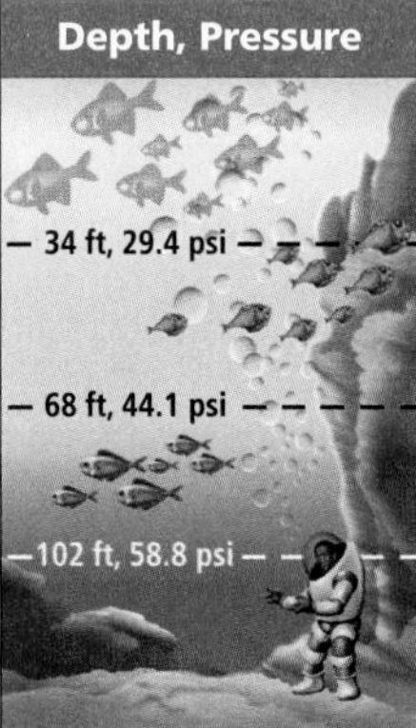

48. Which function is the inverse of $f(x) = 4x - \frac{3}{4}$?

Ⓐ $f^{-1}(x) = \frac{1}{4}x + \frac{3}{16}$

Ⓒ $f^{-1}(x) = \frac{1}{4}x + 3$

Ⓑ $f^{-1}(x) = -\frac{1}{4}x + 3$

Ⓓ $f^{-1}(x) = -\frac{1}{4}x + \frac{3}{16}$

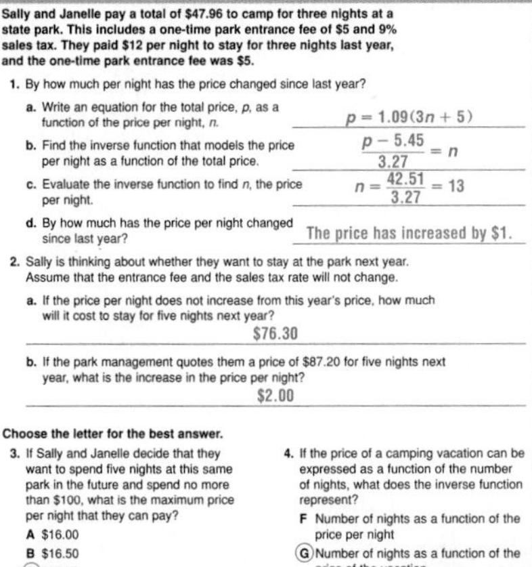

7-2 PROBLEM SOLVING

Sally and Janelle pay a total of \$47.96 to camp for three nights at a state park. This includes a one-time park entrance fee of \$5 and 9% sales tax. They paid \$12 per night to stay for three nights last year, and the one-time park entrance fee was \$5.

1. By how much per night has the price changed since last year?
   a. Write an equation for the total price, p, as a function of the price per night, n. $p = 1.09(3n + 5)$
   b. Find the inverse function that models the price per night as a function of the total price. $\frac{p - 5.45}{3.27} = n$
   c. Evaluate the inverse function to find n, the price per night. $n = \frac{42.51}{3.27} = 13$
   d. By how much has the price per night changed since last year? The price has increased by \$1.
2. Sally is thinking about whether they want to stay at the park next year. Assume that the entrance fee and the sales tax rate will not change.
   a. If the price per night does not increase from this year's price, how much will it cost to stay for five nights next year? \$76.30
   b. If the park management quotes them a price of \$87.20 for five nights next year, what is the increase in the price per night? \$2.00

Choose the letter for the best answer.

3. If Sally and Janelle decide that they want to spend five nights at this same park in the future and spend no more than \$100, what is the maximum price per night that they can pay?
   A \$16.00
   B \$16.50
   Ⓒ \$17.00
   D \$17.50
4. If the price of a camping vacation can be expressed as a function of the number of nights, what does the inverse function represent?
   F Number of nights as a function of the price per night
   Ⓖ Number of nights as a function of the price of the vacation
   H Price of the vacation as a function of the price per night
   J Price of the vacation as a function of the number of nights

7-2 CHALLENGE

Every function $f(x)$ has an inverse, but not every inverse is a function. Consider the function $f(x) = x^2$. You can also write this function as $y = x^2$. One way to find the inverse of a function is to switch y and x in the original function. Switching variables gives the equation $x = y^2$. Notice that the graph of $x = y^2$ does not satisfy the function definition since the x-value of 4 has both 2 and -2 as y-values.

If a function meets the requirement that each element of the range is paired with exactly one element in the domain, then it is called a one-to-one function. In the graph of a one-to-one function, no horizontal line intersects the graph at more than one point.

1. Examine the graph of $y = x^2$ above. Tell why it does not pass the horizontal line test. Possible answer: For every value of y, except 0, there are 2 values of x.
2. Graph the function $f(x) = 3x - 4$. Is this a one-to-one function? Find the inverse. Is the inverse a one-to-one function? Yes; $y = \frac{x + 4}{3}$; yes
3. Graph the function $f(x) = \frac{1}{x}$. Is this a one-to-one function? Find the inverse. Is the inverse a one-to-one function? Yes; $y = \frac{1}{x}$; yes
4. Graph the function $f(x) = x^3$. Is this a one-to-one function? Find the inverse. Is the inverse a one-to-one function? Yes; $y = \sqrt[3]{x}$; yes
5. Graph the function $f(x) = x^2 + 3x + 2$. Is this a one-to-one function? Is the inverse a function and a one-to-one function? No; function is not one-to-one; $y = -3 \pm \frac{\sqrt{1 - 4x}}{2}$; inverse is not a function.

Critical Thinking In **Exercise 39,** students may attempt to create complicated examples. Remind students that an example having only one or two points is often sufficient.

TEST PREP DOCTOR In **Exercise 48,** students who chose **B** or **C** may be having trouble dividing a fraction by a whole number. Remind them that they should be dividing $\frac{3}{4}$ by 4, not multiplying.

Answers

26. $f^{-1}(x) = \frac{5}{4}x + 15$

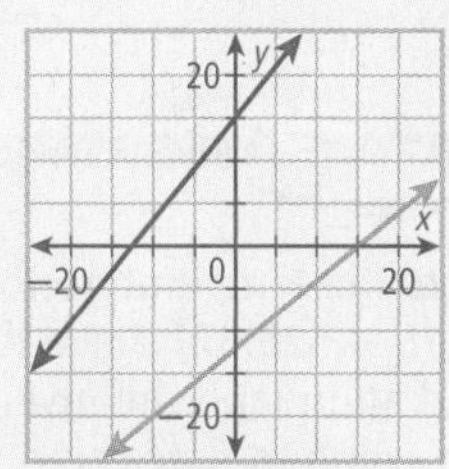

27. $f^{-1}(x) = -3x + 6$

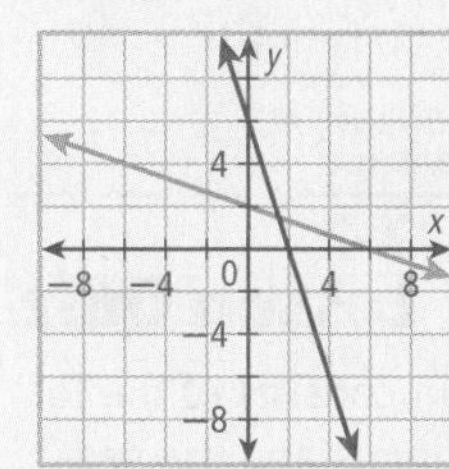

28. $f^{-1}(x) = \frac{x}{1.21}$

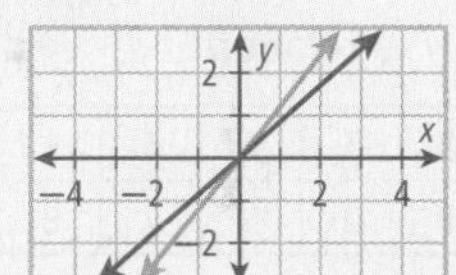

38. The function is inversed, and the graph is reflected over the line $y = x$. The result may or may not be a function.
39. Yes; possible answer: for the ordered pairs (2, 1) and (2, 3), the inverse relation is (1, 2) and (3, 2), which is a function.
40b. $C(s) = 3s + \frac{7}{8}$; yes; head circumference as a function of hat size

Answers

55. 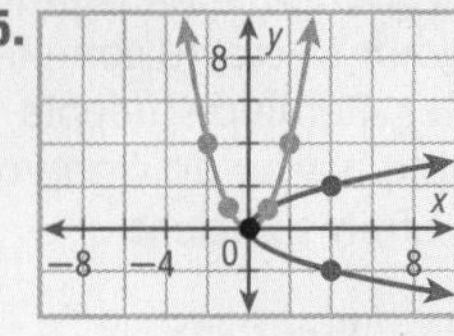

$y = x^2$; switch x and y: $x = y^2$

 **Journal**

Have students describe a real-world situation in which it would be useful to find an inverse in order to answer a question.

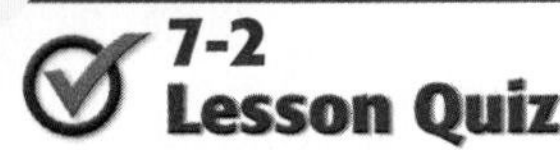

ALTERNATIVE ASSESSMENT

Give students the temperature formula $K = \frac{5}{9}(F - 523.67)$. Have them graph it, find and graph the inverse, and use the graph to determine the temperature that is the same in degrees Fahrenheit as in Kelvin.

Power Presentations with PowerPoint®

7-2 Lesson Quiz

1. A relation consists of the following points and the segments drawn between them. Find the domain and range of the *inverse* relation:

x	0	3	4	6	9
y	1	2	5	7	8

$D: \{x \mid 1 \le x \le 8\}$;
$R: \{y \mid 0 \le y \le 9\}$

2. Graph $f(x) = 3x - 4$. Then write and graph the inverse.

$f^{-1}(x) = \frac{1}{3}x + \frac{4}{3}$

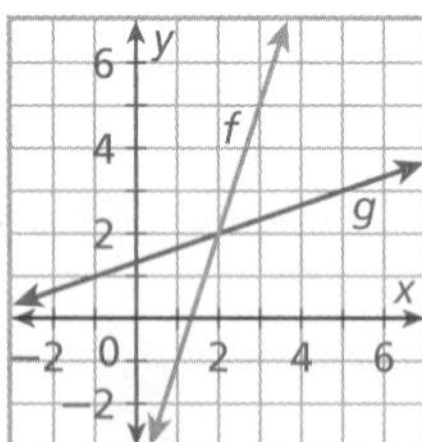

3. A thermometer gives a reading of 25°C. Use the formula $C = \frac{5}{9}(F - 32)$. Write the inverse function and use it to find the equivalent temperature in °F.

$F = \frac{9}{5}C + 32$; 77° F

Also available on transparency

49. Eliza's auto repair bill includes $175 for parts and $35 per hour for labor. The bill can be expressed as a function of hours x with the function $f(x) = 175 + 35x$. Which statement explains the meaning of the inverse of the function?
 Ⓕ Number of hours as a function of the total bill
 Ⓖ Total bill as a function of the number of hours
 Ⓗ Cost per hour as a function of the total bill
 Ⓙ Total bill as a function of the cost per hour

50. The inverse of a point is (5, –2). What point is this the inverse of?
 Ⓐ (–5, 2) Ⓑ (5, 2) Ⓒ (–2, 5) Ⓓ (2, –5)

51. **Short Response** Make a table to show the inverse of the relation shown in the graph.

x	1	2	3	4	5
y	0	1	2	3	4

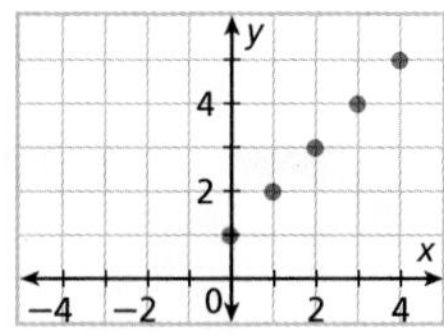

CHALLENGE AND EXTEND

Give the inverse of each linear function, where $y = f(x)$.

52. $y = \frac{x}{m} - \frac{b}{m}$
53. $y = -\frac{b}{a}x + \frac{c}{a}$
54. $y = \frac{x - y_1}{m} + x_1$

52. $y = mx + b$ 53. $ax + by = c$ 54. $y - y_1 = m(x - x_1)$

55. Graph the relation given by the points in the table. Then reflect each point across the line $y = x$ to see the graph of the inverse relation. If the equation of the relation is $f(x) = x^2$, verify algebraically that the equation of the inverse relation is $x = y^2$.

x	y
–3	9
–2	4
–1	1
0	0
1	1
2	4
3	9

56. **Critical Thinking** A linear function and its inverse have the same slope. What must be true of these functions?

Graph each function and its inverse.

57. $y = 3$ 58. $y = x^3$ 59. $y = 2^x$

SPIRAL REVIEW

60a. 44.95, 45.18, 46.04, 46.89, 47.53, 48.16

60. **Business** A stock was purchased for $45.18 per share. The change in value is shown in the table. *(Lesson 1-1)*
 a. Order the stock values from least to greatest. Include the purchase day as day 0.
 b. Use set-builder notation to represent the range of the stock value. $\{v \mid 44.95 \le v \le 48.16\}$

Stock Market Value

Day	Change in Value ($)
1	–0.23
2	+2.58
3	–0.64
4	+1.27
5	–2.12

Write the polynomial equation of least degree with the given roots and leading coefficient of 2. *(Lesson 6-6)*

61. –3, 2, 1 $2x^3 - 14x + 12 = 0$
62. $\sqrt{5}, -\sqrt{5}$ $2x^2 - 10 = 0$
63. $1 - i$, 2 $2x^3 - 8x^2 + 12x - 8 = 0$
64. –3, 8, 9 $2x^3 - 28x^2 + 42x + 432 = 0$

Tell whether the function shows growth or decay. Then graph. *(Lesson 7-1)*

65. $f(x) = 15\left(\frac{89}{100}\right)^x$ decay
66. $f(x) = \frac{1}{25}(0.5^x)$ decay
67. $f(x) = 2(1.1^x)$ growth
68. $f(x) = 0.01(1.9^x)$ growth

Answers

56. Either the function and its inverse are both $f(x) = f^{-1}(x) = x$, or the function and its inverse are both $f(x) = f^{-1}(x) = -x + k$, where k is any real number constant.

57. 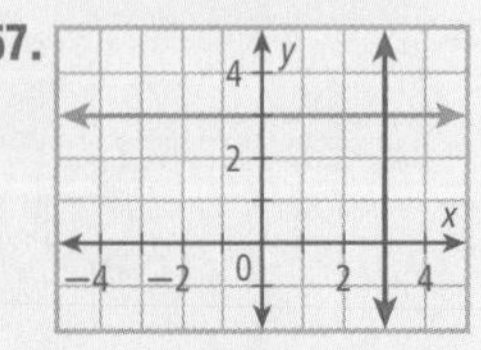

58. 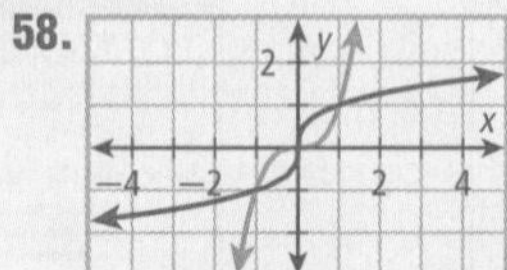

59. 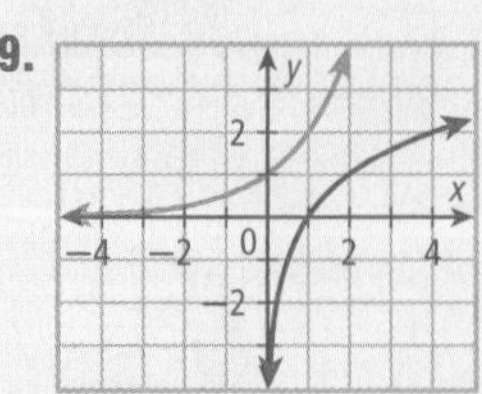

65–68. For graphs, see p. A33.

7-3 Logarithmic Functions

A2.1.1 Find the zeros, domain and range of a function.

Objectives
Write equivalent forms for exponential and logarithmic functions.

Write, evaluate, and graph logarithmic functions.

Vocabulary
logarithm
common logarithm
logarithmic function

Why learn this?

A logarithmic scale is used to measure the acidity, or pH, of water. (See Example 5.)

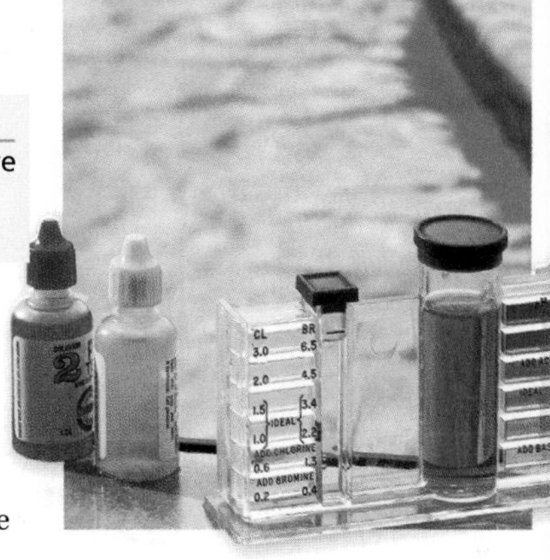

How many times would you have to double \$1 before you had \$8? You could use an exponential equation to model this situation. $1(2^x) = 8$. You may be able to solve this equation by using mental math if you know that $2^3 = 8$. So you would have to double the dollar 3 times to have \$8.

How many times would you have to double \$1 to have \$512? You could solve this problem if you could solve $2^x = 8$ by using an inverse operation that undoes raising a base to an exponent. This operation is called finding the logarithm. A **logarithm** is the exponent to which a specified base is raised to obtain a given value.

Reading Math

Read $\log_b a = x$, as "the log base b of a is x." Notice that the log is the exponent.

You can write an exponential equation as a logarithmic equation and vice versa.

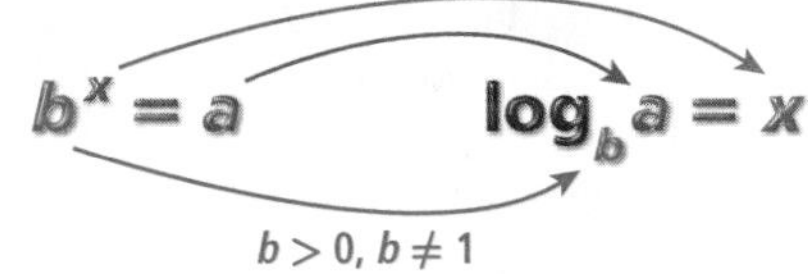

EXAMPLE 1 **Converting from Exponential to Logarithmic Form**

Write each exponential equation in logarithmic form.

	Exponential Equation	Logarithmic Form	
a.	$2^6 = 64$	$\log_2 64 = 6$	*The base of the exponent becomes the base of the logarithm.*
b.	$4^1 = 4$	$\log_4 4 = 1$	*The exponent is the logarithm.*
c.	$5^0 = 1$	$\log_5 1 = 0$	*Any nonzero base to the 0 power is 1.*
d.	$5^{-2} = 0.04$	$\log_5 0.04 = -2$	*An exponent (or log) can be negative.*
e.	$3^x = 81$	$\log_3 81 = x$	*The log (and the exponent) can be a variable.*

CHECK IT OUT! **Write each exponential equation in logarithmic form.**

1a. $9^2 = 81$ $\log_9 81 = 2$ **1b.** $3^3 = 27$ $\log_3 27 = 3$ **1c.** $x^0 = 1 (x \neq 0)$ $\log_x 1 = 0$

7-3 Organizer

Pacing: Traditional 1 day
Block $\frac{1}{2}$ day

Objectives: Write equivalent forms for exponential and logarithmic functions.

Write, evaluate, and graph logarithmic functions.

Online Edition
Graphing Calculator

Countdown to Testing Week 15

Power Presentations with PowerPoint®

Warm Up

Use mental math to evaluate.

1. 4^{-3} $\frac{1}{64}$ **2.** $16^{\frac{1}{4}}$ 2

3. 10^{-5} 0.00001 **4.** $\left(\frac{2}{3}\right)^{-3}$ $\frac{27}{8}$

5. A power has a base of -2 and an exponent of 4. Write and evaluate the power.
$(-2)^4 = 16$

Also available on transparency

Math Humor

Q: Why are you drumming on your algebra book with two big sticks?

A: Because we're studying log rhythms.

1 Introduce

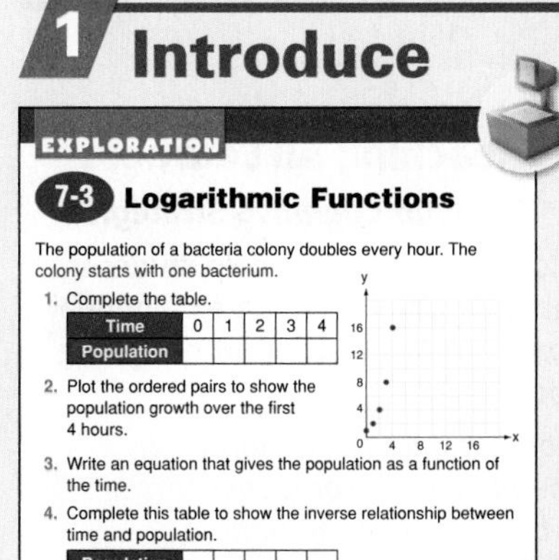

EXPLORATION

7-3 Logarithmic Functions

The population of a bacteria colony doubles every hour. The colony starts with one bacterium.

1. Complete the table.

Time	0	1	2	3	4
Population					

2. Plot the ordered pairs to show the population growth over the first 4 hours.
3. Write an equation that gives the population as a function of the time.
4. Complete this table to show the inverse relationship between time and population.

Population					
Time	0	1	2	3	4

5. Plot the ordered pairs from this table on the same coordinate plane.

THINK AND DISCUSS

6. Discuss the relationship between the graphs of the two sets of data points.

Motivate

Present students with the situation where three celestial objects are 2.4×10^5, 4.5×10^5, and 2.5×10^7 miles away. By focusing on the exponents (5, 5, 7), they can see that the third object is significantly farther away, despite 2.4 being near 2.5. Point out that logarithms, as the inverses of exponents, are useful as a tool for manipulating very large and small numbers.

Explorations and answers are provided in the *Explorations* binder.

State Resources

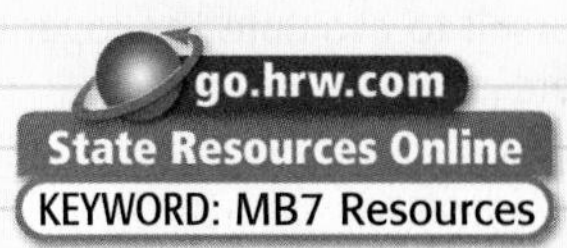

Power Presentations with PowerPoint®

Additional Examples

Example 1

Write each exponential equation in logarithmic form.

Exponential Equation	Logarithmic Form
$3^5 = 243$	$\log_3 243 = 5$
$25^{\frac{1}{2}} = 5$	$\log_{25} 5 = \frac{1}{2}$
$10^4 = 10{,}000$	$\log_{10} 10{,}000 = 4$
$6^{-1} = \frac{1}{6}$	$\log_6 \frac{1}{6} = -1$
$a^b = c$	$\log_a c = b$

Example 2

Write each logarithmic equation in exponential form.

Logarithmic Form	Exponential Form
$\log_9 9 = 1$	$9^1 = 9$
$\log_2 512 = 9$	$2^9 = 512$
$\log_8 2 = \frac{1}{3}$	$8^{\frac{1}{3}} = 2$
$\log_4 \frac{1}{16} = -2$	$4^{-2} = \frac{1}{16}$
$\log_b 1 = 0$	$b^0 = 1$

Example 3

Evaluate by using mental math.

A. $\log 0.01$ -2

B. $\log_5 125$ 3

C. $\log_5 \frac{1}{5}$ -1

Also available on transparency

INTERVENTION

Questioning Strategies

EXAMPLE 1

- Why do some of these equations in logarithmic form have a negative number on the right side of the equation?
- What does a logarithm equal to 0 mean? What does a logarithm equal to 1 mean?

EXAMPLE 2

- How would you change $\log_x x^3 = 3$ into exponential form?

EXAMPLE 3

- What question can you ask yourself to evaluate the logarithmic expression?

EXAMPLE 2 Converting from Logarithmic to Exponential Form

Write each logarithmic equation in exponential form.

	Logarithmic Equation	Exponential Form	
a.	$\log_{10} 100 = 2$	$10^2 = 100$	*The base of the logarithm becomes the base of the power.*
b.	$\log_7 49 = 2$	$7^2 = 49$	*The logarithm is the exponent.*
c.	$\log_8 0.125 = -1$	$8^{-1} = 0.125$	*A logarithm can be a negative number.*
d.	$\log_5 5 = 1$	$5^1 = 5$	
e.	$\log_{12} 1 = 0$	$12^0 = 1$	

CHECK IT OUT! Write each logarithmic equation in exponential form.

2a. $\log_{10} 10 = 1$ $10^1 = 10$ **2b.** $\log_{12} 144 = 2$ $12^2 = 144$ **2c.** $\log_{\frac{1}{2}} 8 = -3$ $\left(\frac{1}{2}\right)^{-3} = 8$

A logarithm is an exponent, so the rules for exponents also apply to logarithms. You may have noticed the following properties in the last example.

Special Properties of Logarithms

For any base b such that $b > 0$ and $b \neq 1$,

LOGARITHMIC FORM	EXPONENTIAL FORM	EXAMPLE
Logarithm of Base b $\log_b b = 1$	$b^1 = b$	$\log_{10} 10 = 1$ $10^1 = 10$
Logarithm of 1 $\log_b 1 = 0$	$b^0 = 1$	$\log_{10} 1 = 0$ $10^0 = 1$

A logarithm with base 10 is called a **common logarithm**. If no base is written for a logarithm, the base is assumed to be 10. For example, $\log 5 = \log_{10} 5$.

You can use mental math to evaluate some logarithms.

EXAMPLE 3 Evaluating Logarithms by Using Mental Math

Evaluate by using mental math.

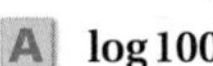

A $\log 1000$

$10^? = 1000$ *The log is the exponent.*

$10^3 = 1000$ *Think: What power of the base is the value?*

$\log 1000 = 3$

B $\log_4 \frac{1}{4}$

$4^? = \frac{1}{4}$

$4^{-1} = \frac{1}{4}$

$\log_4 \frac{1}{4} = -1$

2 Teach

Guided Instruction

Ask students "What are some powers you know by heart?" Write some of these on one side of the board. Explain that for every power they know, they already know the logarithm. Write the logarithmic form alongside each of their exponential equations, with assistance from students. Review the meanings of positive, negative, and fractional exponents. Be sure that students are comfortable moving back and forth between exponential and logarithmic forms.

Reaching All Learners

Through Cognitive Strategies

The following rhyme may help students remember which part of the exponential equation becomes which part of the log equation.

To convert it to the log form,
Remember each component.
The base goes at the bottom,
And the log is the exponent!

Evaluate by using mental math.

3a. $\log 0.00001$ −5   **3b.** $\log_{25} 0.04$ −1

Because logarithms are the inverses of exponents, the inverse of an exponential function, such as $y = 2^x$, is a **logarithmic function**, such as $y = \log_2 x$.

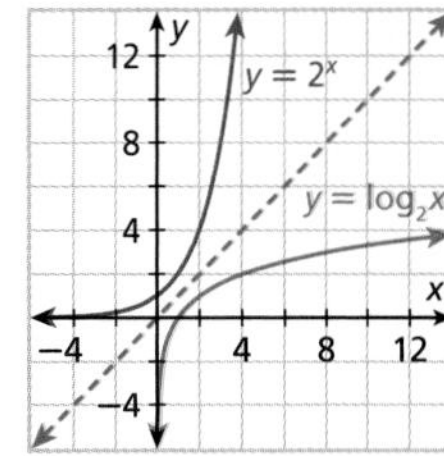

You may notice that the domain and range of each function are switched.

The domain of $y = 2^x$ is all real numbers ($\mathbb{R}$), and the range is $\{y \mid y > 0\}$. The domain of $y = \log_2 x$ is $\{x \mid x > 0\}$, and the range is all real numbers ($\mathbb{R}$).

EXAMPLE 4 Graphing Logarithmic Functions

Use the given x-values to graph each function. Then graph its inverse. Describe the domain and range of the inverse function.

A $f(x) = 3^x$; $x = -2, -1, 0, 1,$ and 2

Graph $f(x) = 3^x$ by using a table of values.

x	−2	−1	0	1	2
$f(x) = 3^x$	$\frac{1}{9}$	$\frac{1}{3}$	1	3	9

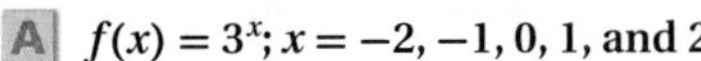

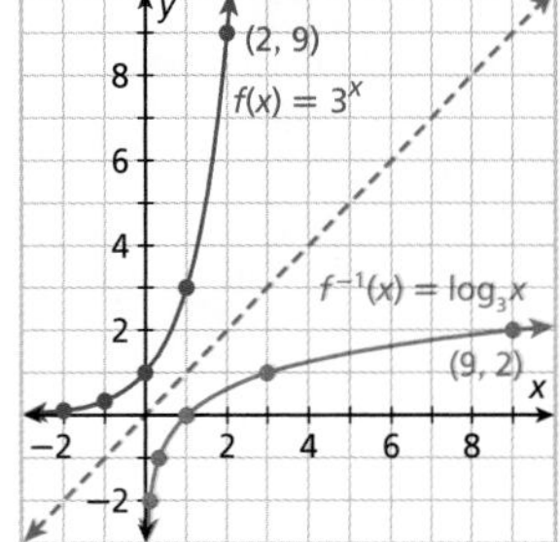

To graph the inverse, $f^{-1}(x) = \log_3 x$, reverse each ordered pair.

x	$\frac{1}{9}$	$\frac{1}{3}$	1	3	9
$f^{-1}(x) = \log_3 x$	−2	−1	0	1	2

The domain of $f^{-1}(x)$ is $\{x \mid x > 0\}$, and the range is $\mathbb{R}$.

B $f(x) = 0.8^x$; $x = -3, 0, 1, 4,$ and 7

Graph $f(x) = 0.8^x$ by using a table of values. Round the output values to the nearest tenth, if necessary.

x	−3	0	1	4	7
$f(x) = 0.8^x$	2	1	0.8	0.4	0.2

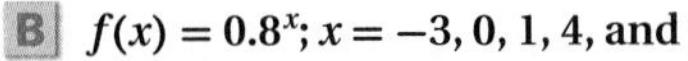

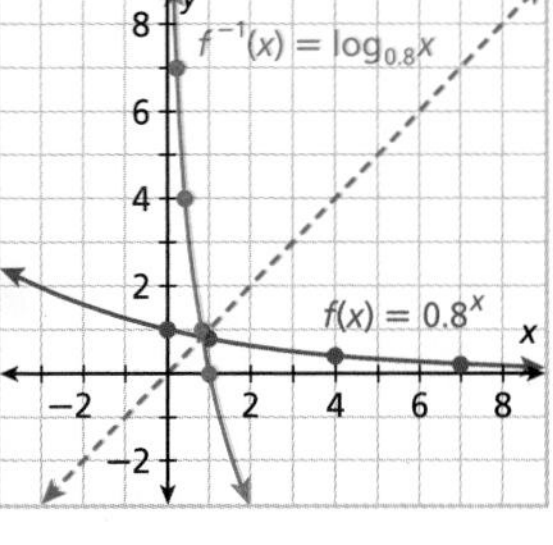

To graph $f^{-1}(x) = \log_{0.8} x$, reverse each ordered pair.

x	2	1	0.8	0.4	0.2
$f^{-1}(x) = \log_{0.8} x$	−3	0	1	4	7

The domain of $f^{-1}(x)$ is $\{x \mid x > 0\}$, and the range is $\mathbb{R}$.

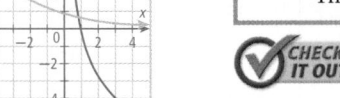

4. Use $x = -2, -1, 1, 2,$ and 3 to graph $f(x) = \left(\frac{3}{4}\right)^x$. Then graph its inverse. Describe the domain and range of the inverse function. D: $\{x \mid x > 0\}$; R: $\mathbb{R}$

COMMON ERROR ALERT

Students may try to use a negative number such as −2 as a base of a logarithm. Remind them that the inverse relationship is defined only for positive bases ≠ 1.

Power Presentations with PowerPoint®

Additional Examples

Example 4

Use the x-values $\{-2, -1, 0, 1, 2\}$. Graph the function and its inverse. Describe the domain and range of the inverse function.

A. $f(x) = 1.25^x$

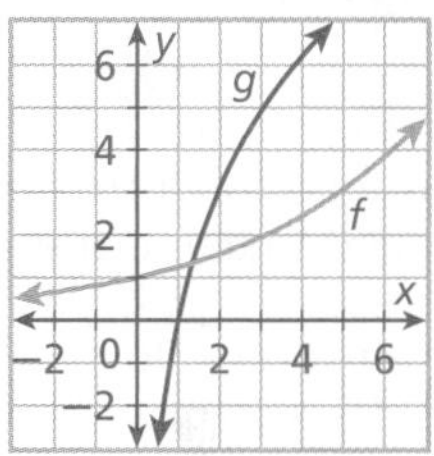

D: $\{x \mid x > 0\}$; R: $\mathbb{R}$

B. $f(x) = \left(\frac{1}{2}\right)^x$.

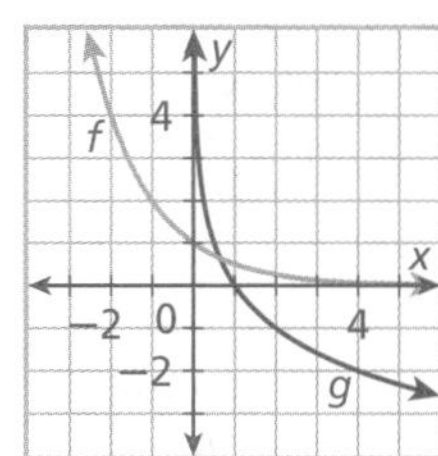

D: $\{x \mid x > 0\}$; R: $\mathbb{R}$

Also available on transparency

INTERVENTION

Questioning Strategies

EXAMPLE 4

- What do inverses of growth functions look like? What do inverses of decay functions look like?

Reaching All Learners

Through Visual Cues

To help students remember how to convert between exponential and logarithmic equations, display this graphic in the classroom.

$\log_b a = x$ (is; to the)

Math Background Logarithms were invented in the early 1700s by John Napier, a Scottish mathematician. His primary interest was to save astronomers time and reduce errors in complex calculations. Napier is also credited with inventing a set of rods with numbers marked on them called "Napier's bones." They were used as an aid for doing multiplication and are an early predecessor of the slide rule.

Power Presentations with PowerPoint®

Additional Examples

Example 5

The table lists the hydrogen ion concentrations for a number of food items. Find the pH of each.

Substance	H^+ conc. (mol/L)	pH
Milk	0.00000025	6.6
Tomatoes	0.0000316	4.5
Lemon juice	0.0063	2.2

Also available on transparency

INTERVENTION

Questioning Strategies

EXAMPLE 5

- As H^+ concentration increases, what happens to the related pH?

Teaching Tip **Kinesthetic** To help students remember how to convert a logarithmic equation into exponential form, have them repeatedly trace a counterclockwise "circle" in the equation using their finger. That is, in the equation $\log_b a = x$, they should trace the path while saying "*b* to the *x* equals *a*."

EXAMPLE 5 ***Environmental Application***

Chemists regularly test rain samples to determine the rain's acidity, or concentration of hydrogen ions (H^+). Acidity is measured in pH, as given by the function $pH = -\log[H^+]$, where $[H^+]$ represents the hydrogen ion concentration in moles per liter.

Find the pH of rainwater from each location.

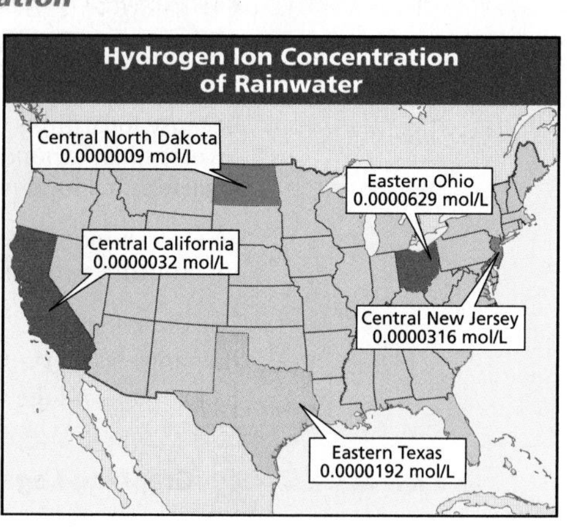

Helpful Hint

The LOG key is used to evaluate logarithms in base 10. 2nd LOG (10^x) is used to find 10^x, the inverse of log.

A **Central New Jersey**

The hydrogen ion concentration is 0.0000316 moles per liter.

$pH = -\log[H^+]$

$pH = -\log(0.0000316)$ *Substitute the known values in the function.*

Use a calculator to find the value of the logarithm in base 10. Press the LOG key.

The rainwater has a pH of about 4.5.

B **Central North Dakota**

The hydrogen ion concentration is 0.0000009 moles per liter.

$pH = -\log[H^+]$

$pH = -\log(0.0000009)$ *Substitute the known values in the function.*

Use a calculator to find the value of the logarithm in base 10. Press the LOG key.

The rainwater has a pH of about 6.0.

CHECK IT OUT! 5. What is the pH of iced tea with a hydrogen ion concentration of 0.000158 moles per liter? **3.8**

THINK AND DISCUSS

1. Explain why $\log_b b$ is always equal to 1 for $b > 0$ and $b \neq 1$.

2. Explain whether $\log_b a$ is the same as $\log_a b$. Support your answer.

3. GET ORGANIZED Copy and complete the graphic organizer. Use your own words to explain a logarithmic function.

Definition	Characteristics
Logarithmic Function	
Examples	Nonexamples

3 Close

Summarize

Review that a logarithm is an exponent and that exponential *equations* can be converted into their logarithmic equivalents, and vice versa, using the definition of a logarithm. Emphasize also that a logarithmic *function* is the inverse of a corresponding exponential function.

ONGOING ASSESSMENT and INTERVENTION

***Diagnose Before* the Lesson**
7-3 Warm Up, TE p. 505

***Monitor During* the Lesson**
Check It Out! Exercises, SE pp. 505–508
Questioning Strategies, TE pp. 506–508

***Assess After* the Lesson**
7-3 Lesson Quiz, TE p. 511
Alternative Assessment, TE p. 511

Answers to *Think and Discuss*

Possible answers:

1. If $x = \log_b b$, then $b^x = b$, or $b^x = b^1$, so $x = 1$.
2. No; $\log_2 16 = 4$, but $\log_{16} 2 = 0.25$.
3. See p. A8.

7-3 Exercises

go.hrw.com
Homework Help Online
KEYWORD: MB7 7-3
Parent Resources Online
KEYWORD: MB7 Parent

GUIDED PRACTICE

1. **Vocabulary** In the exponential equation $a^x = b$, the logarithm is __?__. (a, x, or b) **x**

SEE EXAMPLE 1 p. 505

Write each exponential equation in logarithmic form.

2. $2.4^0 = 1$ $\log_{2.4} 1 = 0$
3. $4^{1.5} = 8$ $\log_4 8 = 1.5$
4. $10^{-2} = 0.01$ $\log 0.01 = -2$
5. $3^x = 243$ $\log_3 243 = x$

SEE EXAMPLE 2 p. 506

Write each logarithmic equation in exponential form.

6. $\log_4 0.0625 = -2$ $4^{-2} = 0.0625$
7. $\log_x(-16) = 3$ $x^3 = -16$
8. $\log_{0.9} 0.81 = 2$ $0.9^2 = 0.81$
9. $\log_6 x = 3$ $6^3 = x$

SEE EXAMPLE 3 p. 506

Evaluate by using mental math.

10. $\log_7 343$ 3
11. $\log_3\left(\frac{1}{9}\right)$ −2
12. $\log_{0.5} 0.25$ 2
13. $\log_{1.2} 1.44$ 2

SEE EXAMPLE 4 p. 507

Use the given x-values to graph each function. Then graph its inverse. Describe the domain and range of each function.

14. $f(x) = 5^x$; $x = -2, -1, 0, 1, 1.5$
15. $f(x) = 0.5^x$; $x = -2, -1, 0, 1, 2$

SEE EXAMPLE 5 p. 508

16. **Chemistry** The acid potential of a solution is given by pOH, where $pOH = -\log[OH^-]$, and OH^- represents the concentration of hydroxide ions in moles per liter. The water in one sample contains a hydroxide ion concentration of 0.000000004. What is the pOH of the water? **8.4**

PRACTICE AND PROBLEM SOLVING

Independent Practice

For Exercises	See Example
17–20	1
21–24	2
25–28	3
29–30	4
31	5

Extra Practice
Skills Practice p. S16
Application Practice p. S38

Write each exponential equation in logarithmic form.

17. $x^{2.5} = 32$ $\log_x 32 = 2.5$
18. $6^x = 216$ $\log_6(216) = x$
19. $1.2^0 = 1$ $\log_{1.2} 1 = 0$
20. $4^{-1} = 0.25$ $\log_4 0.25 = -1$

Write each logarithmic equation in exponential form.

21. $\log_5 625 = 4$ $5^4 = 625$
22. $\log_2 x = 6$ $2^6 = x$
23. $\log_{4.5} 1 = 0$ $4.5^0 = 1$
24. $\log_\pi \pi = 1$ $\pi^1 = \pi$

Evaluate by using mental math.

25. $\log_2 1$ 0
26. $\log 0.001$ −3
27. $\log_4 64$ 3
28. $\log_{0.1} 100$ −2

Use the given x-values to graph each function. Then graph its inverse. Describe the domain and range of each function.

29. $f(x) = \left(\frac{4}{5}\right)^x$; $x = -2, -1, 0, 1, 2, 3$
30. $f(x) = \left(\frac{4}{3}\right)^x$; $x = -2, -1, 0, 1, 2, 3$

31. **Gardening** The flower color of bigleaf hydrangeas is determined by the soil pH. A gardener growing blue hydrangeas believes that lime may be leaching out of a nearby sidewalk and increasing the pH of the soil. The gardener measures the hydrogen ion concentration and finds it to be 0.0000006 moles per liter. Is the soil still good for growing blue flowers? Explain.

No; the pH is 6.2, so the flowers will be pink

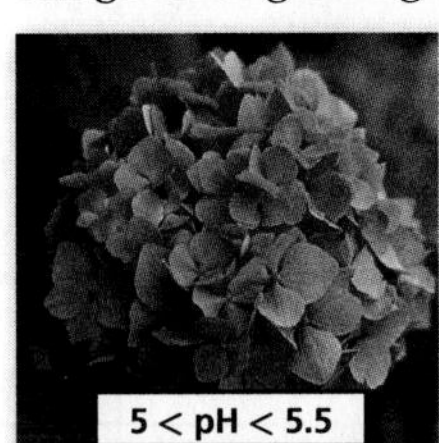
5 < pH < 5.5

5.5 < pH < 6

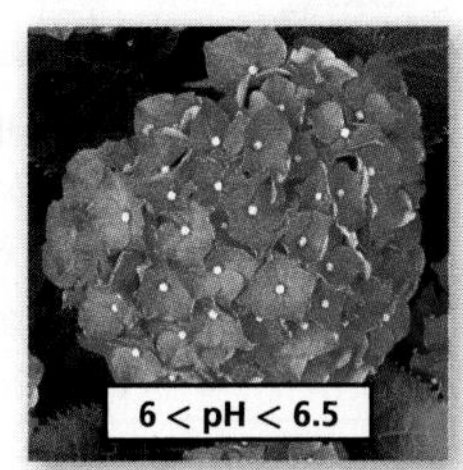
6 < pH < 6.5

7-3 Exercises

Assignment Guide

Assign *Guided Practice* exercises as necessary.

If you finished Examples **1–3**
Basic 17–28
Average 17–28, 44
Advanced 17–28, 44–45

If you finished Examples **1–5**
Basic 17–32, 34, 36–43, 48–55
Average 17–44, 47–55
Advanced 17–35, 38–55

Homework Quick Check
Quickly check key concepts.
Exercises: 18, 24, 28, 30, 31, 34

Teaching Tip **Critical Thinking** Students sometimes have difficulty identifying which problems result in negative logarithms. The key is to look for situations like **Exercises 26** and **28.** If the problem is to find $\log_b a$, and $b > 1$ while $0 < a < 1$, as in **Exercise 26,** the log will be negative. Similarly, if $0 < b < 1$ while $a > 1$, as in **Exercise 28,** the log will also be negative.

Answers

14.
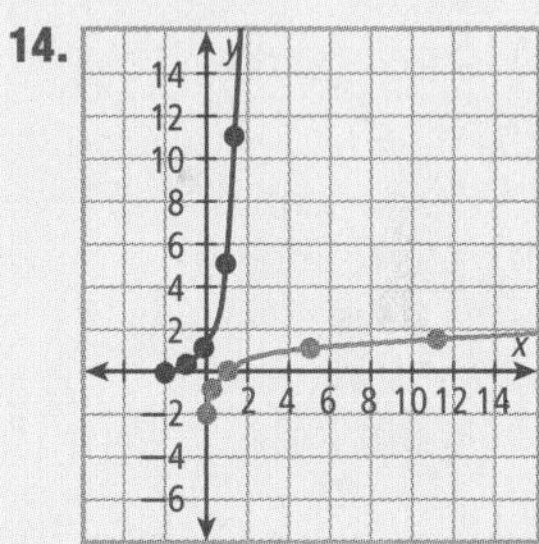

$f(x)$: D: $\mathbb{R}$, R: $\{y \mid y > 0\}$;
$f^{-1}(x)$: D: $\{x \mid x > 0\}$; R: $\mathbb{R}$

State Resources

Answers

15.
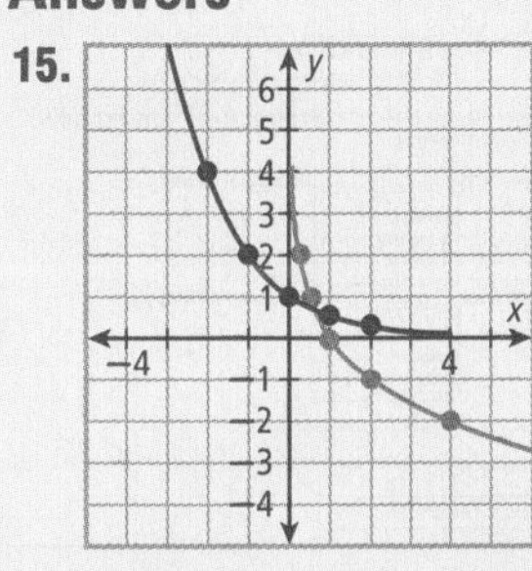

$f(x)$: D: $\mathbb{R}$, R: $\{y \mid y > 0\}$;
$f^{-1}(x)$: D: $\{x \mid x > 0\}$; R: $\mathbb{R}$

29.
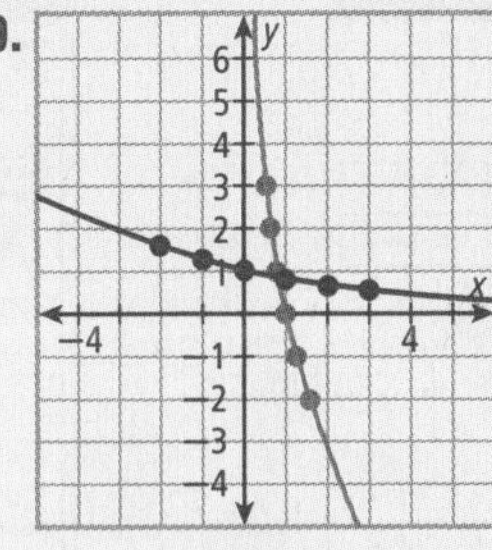

$f(x)$: D: $\mathbb{R}$, R: $\{y \mid y > 0\}$;
$f^{-1}(x)$: D: $\{x \mid x > 0\}$; R: $\mathbb{R}$

30.
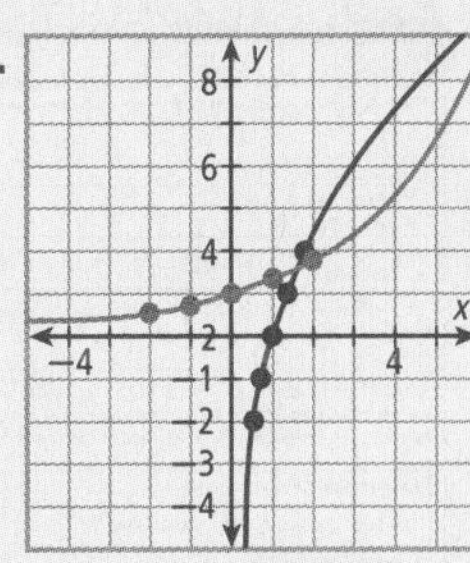

$f(x)$: D: $\mathbb{R}$, R: $\{y \mid y > 0\}$;
$f^{-1}(x)$: D: $\{x \mid x > 0\}$; R: $\mathbb{R}$

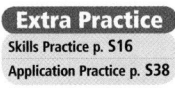

go.hrw.com
State Resources Online
KEYWORD: MB7 Resources

MULTI-STEP TEST PREP **Exercise 32** involves doing calculations with logarithms to solve problems involving credit card debt. This exercise prepares students for the Multi-Step Test Prep on page 520.

TEST PREP DOCTOR Students who chose **A** in **Exercise 39** may be reacting to the shape of the graph alone. Encourage them to substitute a point from the curve, in particular, (4, 1).

In **Exercise 42,** students who chose **H** or **J** should be reminded that (1, 0) lies on any curve of the type $f(x) = \log_a x$.

Answers

44.

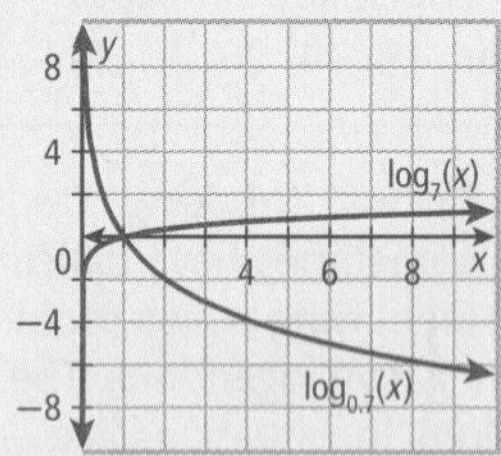

The range of $\log_7 x$ is negative for $0 < x < 1$ and positive for $x > 1$. The range of $\log_{0.7} x$ is positive for $0 < x < 1$ and negative for $x > 1$.

45. 2; 3; 5; $\log_3 9 + \log_3 27 = \log_3 243$; $\log_b(b^x) + \log_b(b^y) = \log_b(b^{x+y})$

46. Let $\log_7 7^{2x+1} = y$. Rewrite in exponential form $7^y = 7^{2x+1}$; Since both expressions have a base of 7, the exponents are equal, $y = 2x + 1$. But $\log_7 7^{2x+1} = y$ so $\log_7 7^{2x+1} = 2x + 1$ by substitution.

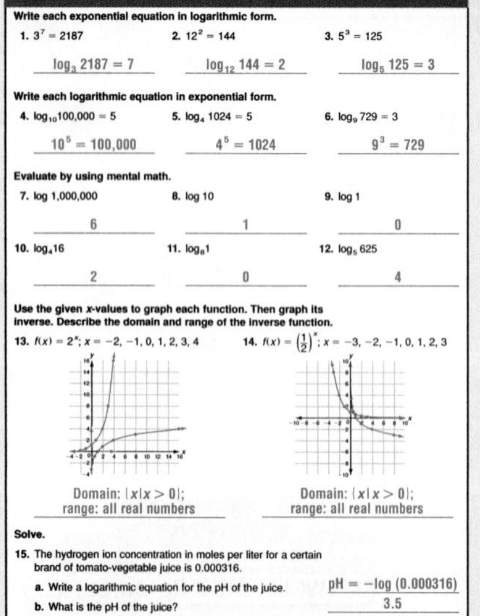

7-3 PRACTICE A
7-3 PRACTICE C
7-3 PRACTICE B

Write each exponential equation in logarithmic form.

1. $3^7 = 2187$ — $\log_3 2187 = 7$
2. $12^2 = 144$ — $\log_{12} 144 = 2$
3. $5^3 = 125$ — $\log_5 125 = 3$

Write each logarithmic equation in exponential form.

4. $\log_{10} 100{,}000 = 5$ — $10^5 = 100{,}000$
5. $\log_4 1024 = 5$ — $4^5 = 1024$
6. $\log_9 729 = 3$ — $9^3 = 729$

Evaluate by using mental math.

7. log 1,000,000 — 6
8. log 10 — 1
9. log 1 — 0
10. $\log_4 16$ — 2
11. $\log_8 1$ — 0
12. $\log_5 625$ — 4

Use the given x-values to graph each function. Then graph its inverse. Describe the domain and range of the inverse function.

13. $f(x) = 2^x$; $x = -2, -1, 0, 1, 2, 3, 4$ — Domain: $\{x \mid x > 0\}$; range: all real numbers
14. $f(x) = \left(\frac{1}{2}\right)^x$; $x = -3, -2, -1, 0, 1, 2, 3$ — Domain: $\{x \mid x > 0\}$; range: all real numbers

Solve.

15. The hydrogen ion concentration in moles per liter for a certain brand of tomato-vegetable juice is 0.000316.
 a. Write a logarithmic equation for the pH of the juice. $\text{pH} = -\log(0.000316)$
 b. What is the pH of the juice? 3.5

MULTI-STEP TEST PREP

32. This problem will prepare you for the Multi-Step Test Prep on page 520.

For a certain credit card, given a starting balance of P and an ending balance of A, the function $n = \frac{\log A - \log P}{\log(1.0175)}$ gives the number of months that have passed, assuming that there were no payments or additional purchases during that time.

a. You started with a debt of \$1000 and now owe \$1210.26. For how many months has the debt been building? Use a calculator. **11**

b. How many additional months will it take until the debt exceeds \$1420? **≈ 9.2**

c. What do you notice from the results of parts **a** and **b**? **As the debt builds, it takes a shorter time for the debt to increase by a relatively constant amount.**

33. **Critical Thinking** If $\log_a b = 0$, what is the value of b? Explain.

33. 1; $\log_a b = 0$ means $a^0 = b$ and a^0 is 1 for any $a \neq 0$.

34. **Sound** The loudness of sound is measured on a logarithmic scale according to the formula $L = 10\log\left(\frac{I}{I_0}\right)$, where L is the loudness of sound in decibels (dB), I is the intensity of sound, and I_0 is the intensity of the softest audible sound.

a. Find the loudness in decibels of each sound listed in the table.

b. The sound at a rock concert is found to have a loudness of 110 decibels. Where should this sound be placed in the table in order to keep the sound intensities in order from least to greatest?

c. **What if...?** A decibel is $\frac{1}{10}$ of a *bel*. Is a jet plane louder than a sound that measures 20 *bels*? Explain. **No; 20 bels is 200 dB.**

Sound	Intensity
Jet takeoff	$10^{15} I_0$
Jackhammer	$10^{12} I_0$
Hair dryer	$10^{7} I_0$
Whisper	$10^{3} I_0$
Leaves rustling	$10^{2} I_0$
Softest audible sound	I_0

34a. jet: 150 dB; jackhammer: 120 dB; hairdryer: 70 dB; whisper: 30 dB; leaves: 20dB; softest audible: 0 dB

34b. $10^{11} I_0$; below jackhammer

35. **Critical Thinking** If n is an integer, and 10^n is written in expanded form, can you find $\log 10^n$ by counting the number of zeros in 10^n? Support your answer with an example or counterexample.

35. Yes; $\log 10^3 = \log 1000 = 3$, and there are 3 zeros after the 1. $\log 10^{-2} = \log 0.01 = -2$, and there are 2 zeros.

36. **Estimation** Given that $\log 100 = 2$ and $\log 1000 = 3$, estimate the values of log 200 and log 500. **$10^{2.3} \approx 199.5$, 2.3; $10^{2.7} \approx 501.2$, 2.7**

37. **Food** The hydrogen ion concentrations of three juice samples are given. Identify the type of juice in each sample.

a. 0.00014 moles per liter **orange**

b. 0.0081 moles per liter **lemon**

c. 0.00074 moles per liter **grapefruit**

Juice	pH Range
Lemon	2.0–2.6
Grapefruit	2.9–3.2
Orange	3.3–4.1
Tomato	4.1–4.6

38. **Write About It** Explain why $\log_0 3$ and $\log_1 3$ do not exist.

38. $\log_0 3$ means $0^x = 3$, and $\log_1 3$ means $1^x = 3$. These have no solution.

TEST PREP

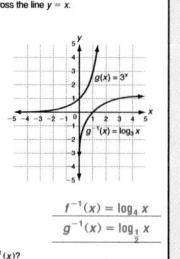

39. The graph of which function is shown?

Ⓐ $f(x) = \log x$

Ⓑ $f(x) = \log_2 x$

Ⓒ $f(x) = \log_4 x$

Ⓓ $f(x) = 2^x$

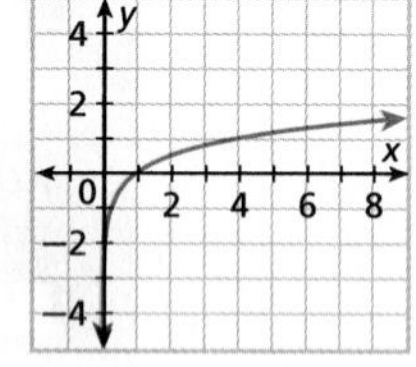

7-3 READING STRATEGIES

Exponential equations can also be written as logarithmic equations. The logarithm is equal to the exponent in the exponential equation.

$b^x = a$ $\log_b a = x$

1. Complete the table.

Exponential Equation	$3^3 = 27$	$5^{-1} = 0.2$	$4^2 = 16$	$8^0 = 1$
Logarithmic Equation	$\log_3 27 = 3$	$\log_5 0.2 = -1$	$\log_4 16 = 2$	$\log_8 1 = 0$

2. Explain why the logarithm of 1 with base b is always 0.
 $\log_b 1 = 0$ is the same as $b^0 = 1$ and any number to the 0 power is 1.

A logarithmic function is the inverse of an exponential function. You can identify an inverse function by comparing its graph to the graph of the original function. The two graphs are a reflection of each other across the line $y = x$.

Exponential function: $f(x) = b^x$
The base b is any number greater than 1.
Example: $g(x) = 3^x$
The domain is all real numbers.
The range is all positive numbers.

Logarithm function: $f^{-1}(x) = \log_b x$
Use the same base to find the inverse function.
The inverse of $g(x)$ is $g^{-1}(x) = \log_3 x$.
In the inverse function, the domain and range are switched.

$g(x) = 3^x$
$g^{-1}(x) = \log_3 x$

3. Find the inverse function of $f(x) = 4^x$. $f^{-1}(x) = \log_4 x$

4. a. Find the inverse function of $g(x) = \left(\frac{1}{2}\right)^x$. $g^{-1}(x) = \log_{\frac{1}{2}} x$
 b. What are the domain and range of $g(x)$ and $g^{-1}(x)$?
 Domain of $g(x)$: Domain of $g(x)$ is all real numbers   Range of $g(x)$: range of $g(x)$ is $y > 0$
 Domain of $g^{-1}(x)$: domain of $g^{-1}(x)$ is $x > 0$ Range of $g^{-1}(x)$: range of $g^{-1}(x)$ is all real numbers.

7-3 RETEACH

A **logarithm** is another way to work with exponents in equations.

If $b^x = a$, then $\log_b a = x$.

If b to the x power equals a, then x is the logarithm of a in base b.

Use the definition of the logarithm to write exponential equations in logarithmic form and to write logarithmic equations in exponential form.

Exponential Form		Logarithmic Form
$3^4 = 81$	base, $b = 3$; exponent, $x = 4$; value, $a = 81$	$\log_3 81 = 4$

Logarithmic Form		Exponential Form
$\log_5 125 = 3$	base, $b = 5$; exponent, $x = 3$; value, $a = 125$	$5^3 = 125$

If no base is written for a logarithm, the base is assumed to be 10.

Example: $\log 100 = 2$ because $10^2 = 100$.

Assume the base is 10.

Write each exponential equation in logarithmic form.

1. $7^2 = 49$ — $b = 7, x = 2, a = 49$ — $\log_7 49 = 2$
2. $6^3 = 216$ — $b = 6, x = 3, a = 216$ — $\log_6 216 = 3$
3. $2^5 = 32$ — $b = 2, x = 5, a = 32$ — $\log_2 32 = 5$

Write each logarithmic equation in exponential form.

4. $\log_9 729 = 3$ — $b = 9, x = 3, a = 729$ — $9^3 = 729$
5. $\log_2 64 = 6$ — $b = 2, x = 6, a = 64$ — $2^6 = 64$
6. $\log 1000 = 3$ — $b = 10, x = 3, a = 1000$ — $10^3 = 1000$

40. Which logarithmic equation is equivalent to $2^7 = 128$?

F $\log_7 2 = 128$ H $\log_2 7 = 128$

(G) $\log_2 128 = 7$ J $\log_7 128 = 2$

41. Which is the best estimate of $\log 50$?

(A) 1.7 B 2.5 C 5 D 10

42. Which graph is the best representation of $f(x) = \log_{0.5} x$?

(F) 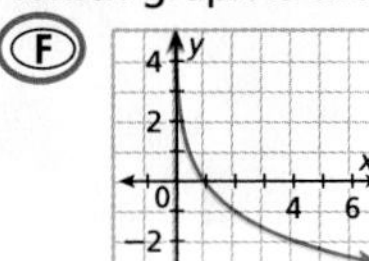

G 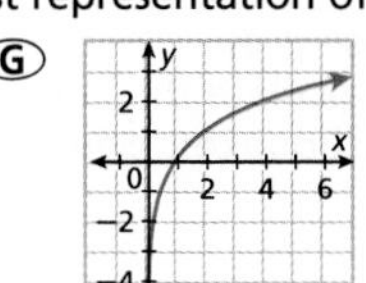

H 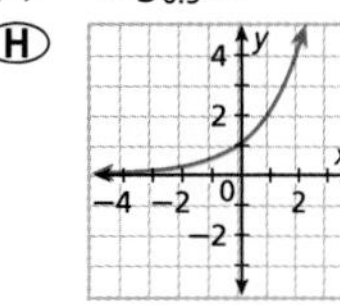

J 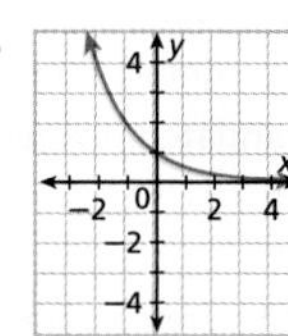

43. Gridded Response Evaluate $\log_2 64$. **6**

CHALLENGE AND EXTEND

44. Graph $\log_7 x$ and $\log_{0.7} x$. Describe the difference between the two functions in terms of their graphs.

45. Evaluate $\log_3 9$, $\log_3 27$, and $\log_3 243$. Make a statement about the relationship between the three logarithms. Generalize the result by using variables.

46. Prove that $\log_7 7^{2x+1} = 2x + 1$, giving a reason for each step.

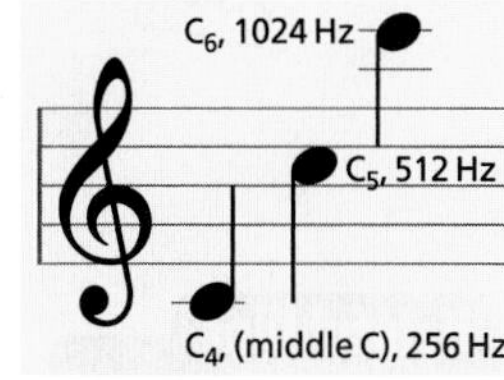

47. Music Musical scales are logarithmic. One scale uses a pitch standard called "scientific pitch." In this scale, the frequency of each C note, in vibrations per second, or Hz, can be expressed as a power of 2, as shown.

a. Express the frequency of the note C_7 in exponential form and in logarithmic form. **$2^{11} = 2048$ Hz, $\log_2 2048 = 11$**

b. If the frequency of one note C is 32 vibrations per second, how many octaves higher or lower than middle C is this note? Explain by using logarithms.
3 octaves lower; $\log_2 256 = 8$, $\log_2 32 = 5$, $8 - 5 = 3$

SPIRAL REVIEW

Simplify each expression. Assume that all variables are nonzero. *(Lesson 1-5)*

48. $\left[(2a^4)(5b^2)\right]^2$ **$100a^8b^4$** **49.** $\dfrac{8s^2t^6}{4st^8}$ **$\dfrac{2s}{t^2}$**

50. $-2t^2(5st^{-1})$ **$-10st$** **51.** $7a^{-2}b^3(3ab + 4a^{-1}b^2)$ **$21a^{-1}b^4 + 28a^{-3}b^5$**

52. Construction A brick fell at a construction site from a height of 25 feet. Use $h(t) = h_0 - 16t^2$, where h is the height in feet and t is the time in seconds, to determine the time that it took for the brick to hit the ground. *(Lesson 5-3)* **1.25 s**

Complete the table of values for each function. Round to the nearest hundredth. *(Lesson 7-1)*

	x	−2	−1	0	1	2
53.	$f(x) = 1.7^x$	0.35	0.59	1	1.7	2.89
54.	$f(x) = 0.6^x$	2.78	1.67	1	0.6	0.36
55.	$f(x) = 0.3^x$	11.11	3.33	1	0.3	0.09

Journal

Have students describe how to write an exponential expression in logarithmic form, and vice versa.

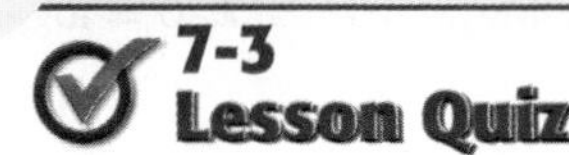

Have students change between exponential and logarithmic form, find logarithms by using mental math, and graph the inverse of an exponential function.

Power Presentations with PowerPoint®

7-3 Lesson Quiz

1. Change $6^4 = 1296$ to logarithmic form. $\log_6 1296 = 4$

2. Change $\log_{27} 9 = \frac{2}{3}$ to exponential form.
$27^{\frac{2}{3}} = 9$

Calculate the following using mental math.

3. $\log 100{,}000$ 5

4. $\log_{64} 8$ 0.5

5. $\log_3 \frac{1}{27}$ −3

6. Use the x-values $\{-2, -1, 0, 1, 2, 3\}$ to graph $f(x) = \left(\frac{3}{2}\right)^x$. Then graph its inverse. Describe the domain and range of the inverse function.

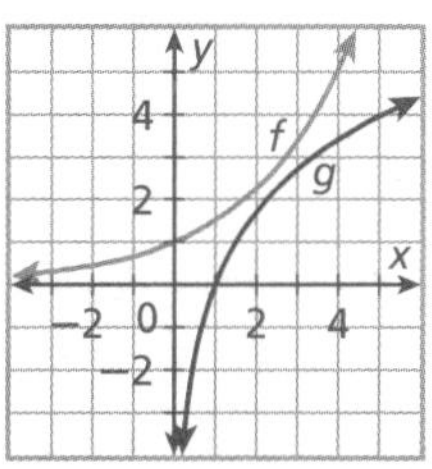

D: $\{x > 0\}$; R: $\mathbb{R}$

Also available on transparency 

7-3 PROBLEM SOLVING

The acidity of rainwater varies from location to location. Acidity is measured in pH and is given by the function $pH = -\log[H^+]$, where $[H^+]$ represents the hydrogen ion concentration in moles per liter. The table gives the $[H^+]$ of rainwater in different locations.

Hydrogen Ion Concentration of Rainwater	
Location	$[H^+]$ (moles per liter)
Central California	0.0000032
Eastern Texas	0.0000192
Eastern Ohio	0.0000629

1. Find the acidity of rainwater in eastern Ohio.
   a. Substitute the hydrogen ion concentration for rainwater in eastern Ohio in the function for pH. **$pH = -\log(0.0000629)$**
   b. Evaluate the function. What is the acidity of rainwater in eastern Ohio to the nearest tenth of a unit? **pH = 4.2**
2. Find how the acidity of rainwater in central California compares to the acidity of rainwater in eastern Ohio.
   a. Write a function for the acidity of rainwater in central California. **$pH = -\log(0.0000032)$**
   b. Evaluate the function. What is the acidity of rainwater in central California to the nearest tenth of a unit? **pH = 5.5**
   c. Compare the pH of rainwater in the two locations. Is the pH of rainwater in eastern Ohio greater than or less than that in central California? By how much? **Rainwater in eastern Ohio has a lower pH than that in central California by 1.3 units.**

Choose the letter for the best answer.

3. What is the pH of rainwater in eastern Texas?
   A pH = 3.7 C pH = 4.4
   B pH = 4.0 (D) pH = 4.7
4. Nick makes his own vegetable juice. It has a hydrogen ion concentration of 5.9×10^{-6} moles per liter. What is the pH of his vegetable juice?
   F pH = 4.9 H pH = 5.1
   G pH = 5.0 (J) pH = 5.2
5. What is the pH of a sample of irrigation water with a hydrogen ion concentration of 8.3×10^{-7} moles per liter?
   (A) pH = 6.1 C pH = 6.3
   B pH = 6.2 D pH = 6.4
6. What is the pH of a shampoo sample with a hydrogen ion concentration of 1.7×10^{-8} moles per liter?
   F pH = 7.4 (H) pH = 7.8
   G pH = 7.6 J pH = 8.0

7-3 CHALLENGE

The logarithmic function $y = \log_b x$, where $b > 0$ and $b \neq 1$, is the inverse of the exponential function $y = b^x$. The inverse relationship of these functions can be seen in their graphs; each is the reflection of the other across the line $y = x$.

The graphs of $y = \log_{10} x$ and $y = 10^x$ are shown at right.

You can explore some variations of the graph of the logarithmic function in base 10.

1. a. Use the definition of logarithm to evaluate the expression $y = \log_{10} 10^x$. **$\log_{10} 10^x = x$**
   b. Based on your answer to part **a**, make a conjecture about the nature of the graph of the function $y = \log_{10} 10^x$. **The graph is the line $y = x$.**
   c. Use a graphing calculator to graph $y = \log_{10} 10^x$. Describe the graph. **The graph is the line $y = x$.**
2. Consider the function $y = 10^{\log_{10} x}$.
   a. Write the domain and the range of the function. **Domain: $x > 0$; range: $y > 0$**
   b. Based on your answer to part **a** and the result of Exercise 1, make a conjecture about the graph of the function. **The graph is the line $y = x$ where $x > 0$.**
   c. Use a graphing calculator to graph. Describe the graph. **The portion of the line $y = x$ that is in the first quadrant, not including the point (0, 0)**

For each function write the domain and the range. Then use a graphing calculator to graph. Draw the graph on the grid provided.

3. $y = \log_{10} x^2$ **Domain: $x \neq 0$; range: all real numbers**
4. $y = (\log_{10} x)^2$ **Domain: $x > 0$; range: $y > 0$**
5. $y = \log_{10} |x|$ **Domain: $x \neq 0$; range: all real numbers**

7-4 Organizer

Pacing: Traditional 2 days
Block 1 day

Objectives: Use properties to simplify logarithmic expressions.

Translate between logarithms in any base.

Online Edition
Graphing Calculator, Interactivity

Countdown to Testing Week 15

Power Presentations with PowerPoint®

Warm Up

Simplify.

1. $(2^6)(2^8)$ 2^{14}
2. $(3^{-2})(3^5)$ 3^3
3. $\frac{3^{12}}{3^4}$ 3^8
4. $\frac{4^3}{4^{-1}}$ 4^4
5. $(7^3)^5$ 7^{15}

Write in exponential form.

6. $\log_x x = 1$ $x^1 = x$
7. $0 = \log_x 1$ $x^0 = 1$

Also available on transparency

Math Humor

Teacher: What are some properties of logs?

Student: They're round, they have bark, and they come from trees.

7-4 Properties of Logarithms

A2.6.2 Know that the inverse of an exponential function is a logarithm, use laws of exponents to derive laws of logarithms, and use the inverse relationships . . .

Objectives
Use properties to simplify logarithmic expressions.

Translate between logarithms in any base.

Who uses this?
Seismologists use properties of logarithms to calculate the energy released by earthquakes. (See Example 6.)

. . . between exponential functions and logarithms, and the laws of logarithms to solve problems.

The logarithmic function for pH that you saw in the previous lesson, $\text{pH} = -\log[\text{H}^+]$, can also be expressed in exponential form, as $10^{-\text{pH}} = [\text{H}^+]$. Because logarithms are exponents, you can derive the properties of logarithms from the properties of exponents.

Remember that to *multiply* powers with the same base, you *add* exponents.

$$b^m b^n = b^{m+n}$$

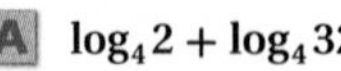

Product Property of Logarithms

For any positive numbers m, n, and b $(b \neq 1)$,

WORDS	NUMBERS	ALGEBRA
The logarithm of a product is equal to the sum of the logarithms of its factors.	$\log_3 1000 = \log_3(10 \cdot 100)$ $= \log_3 10 + \log_3 100$	$\log_b mn = \log_b m + \log_b n$

Helpful Hint

Think:
$\log j + \log a + \log m = \log jam$

The property above can be used in reverse to write a sum of logarithms (exponents) as a single logarithm, which can often be simplified.

EXAMPLE 1 Adding Logarithms

Express as a single logarithm. Simplify, if possible.

A $\log_4 2 + \log_4 32$

$\log_4(2 \cdot 32)$ — *To add the logarithms, multiply the numbers.*

$\log_4 64$ — *Simplify.*

3 — *Think: $4^? = 64$*

CHECK IT OUT! **Express as a single logarithm. Simplify, if possible.**

1a. $\log_5 625 + \log_5 25$ $\log_5(625 \cdot 25) = 6$

1b. $\log_{\frac{1}{3}} 27 + \log_{\frac{1}{3}} \frac{1}{9}$ $\log_{\frac{1}{3}} 3 = -1$

Remember that to *divide* powers with the same base, you *subtract* exponents.

$$\frac{b^m}{b^n} = b^{m-n}$$

Because logarithms are exponents, subtracting logarithms with the same base is the same as finding the logarithm of the quotient with that base.

State Resources

go.hrw.com
State Resources Online
KEYWORD: MB7 Resources

1 Introduce

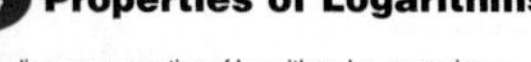

EXPLORATION

7-4 Properties of Logarithms

You can discover properties of logarithms by comparing logarithmic expressions.

1. Evaluate the expressions in the table.

$\log_2(4 \cdot 8) = \log_2 32 =$ ___	$\log_2 4 + \log_2 8 =$ ___
$\log_2(2 \cdot 32) = \log_2 64 =$ ___	$\log_2 2 + \log_2 32 =$ ___
$\log_2(1 \cdot 8) = \log_2 8 =$ ___	$\log_2 1 + \log_2 8 =$ ___

2. What do you notice?
3. Evaluate the expressions in the table.

$\log_2\left(\frac{64}{16}\right) = \log_2 4 =$ ___	$\log_2 64 - \log_2 16 =$ ___
$\log_2\left(\frac{16}{2}\right) = \log_2 8 =$ ___	$\log_2 16 - \log_2 2 =$ ___
$\log_2\left(\frac{256}{8}\right) = \log_2 32 =$ ___	$\log_2 256 - \log_2 8 =$ ___

4. What do you notice?

THINK AND DISCUSS

5. Make a conjecture about the expression $\log_b(m$).

Motivate

Ask students to name some mathematical properties they have used in the past. Possible answers: Associative Property, Distributive Property, properties of equality, and properties of exponents Ask students why these properties are helpful. Possible answer: They make problems easier to solve. Explain that properties of logarithms can work the same way.

Explorations and answers are provided in the *Explorations* binder.

Quotient Property of Logarithms

For any positive numbers m, n, and b $(b \neq 1)$,

WORDS	NUMBERS	ALGEBRA
The logarithm of a quotient is the logarithm of the dividend minus the logarithm of the divisor.	$\log_5\left(\frac{16}{2}\right) = \log_5 16 - \log_5 2$	$\log_b \frac{m}{n} = \log_b m - \log_b n$

Caution!

Just as a^5b^3 cannot be simplified, logarithms must have the *same* base to be simplified.

The property above can also be used in reverse.

EXAMPLE 2 Subtracting Logarithms

Express $\log_2 32 - \log_2 4$ as a single logarithm. Simplify, if possible.

$\log_2 32 - \log_2 4$

$\log_2 (32 \div 4)$ *To subtract the logarithms, divide the numbers.*

$\log_2 8$ *Simplify.*

3 *Think: $2^? = 8$*

CHECK IT OUT! **2.** Express $\log_7 49 - \log_7 7$ as a single logarithm. Simplify, if possible. $\log_7 7 = 1$

Because you can multiply logarithms, you can also take powers of logarithms.

Power Property of Logarithms

For any real number p and positive numbers a and b $(b \neq 1)$,

WORDS	NUMBERS	ALGEBRA
The logarithm of a power is the product of the exponent and the logarithm of the base.	$\log 10^3$ $\log(10 \cdot 10 \cdot 10)$ $\log 10 + \log 10 + \log 10$ $3 \log 10$	$\log_b a^p = p\log_b a$

EXAMPLE 3 Simplifying Logarithms with Exponents

Express as a product. Simplify, if possible.

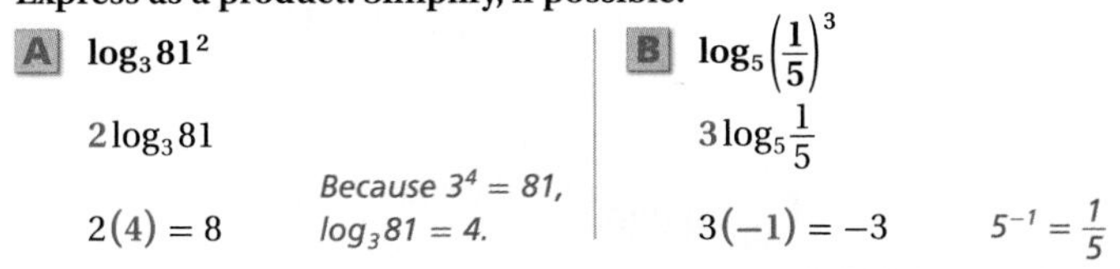

A $\log_3 81^2$

$2\log_3 81$

$2(4) = 8$ *Because $3^4 = 81$, $\log_3 81 = 4$.*

B $\log_5\left(\frac{1}{5}\right)^3$

$3\log_5 \frac{1}{5}$

$3(-1) = -3$ $\quad 5^{-1} = \frac{1}{5}$

CHECK IT OUT! **Express as a product. Simplify, if possible.**

3a. $\log 10^4$ $\quad 4\log 10 = 4$

3b. $\log_5 25^2$ $\quad 2\log_5 25 = 4$

3c. $\log_2\left(\frac{1}{2}\right)^5$ $\quad -5\log_2 2 = -5$

Power Presentations with PowerPoint®

Additional Examples

Example 1

Express $\log_6 4 + \log_6 9$ as a single logarithm. Simplify, if possible. $\log_6 36 = 2$

Example 2

Express $\log_5 100 - \log_5 4$ as a single logarithm. Simplify, if possible. $\log_5 25 = 2$

Example 3

Express as a product. Simplify, if possible.

A. $\log_2 32^6$ $\quad 6\log_2 32 = 30$

B. $\log_8 4^{20}$ $\quad 20\log_8 4 = \frac{40}{3}$

Also available on transparency

INTERVENTION

Questioning Strategies

EXAMPLE 1

- Can you get the same result by adding together the two individual logs?

EXAMPLE 2

- What property of exponents is related to the property of logarithms used in the example?

EXAMPLE 3

- Can you apply the power property when you have a negative exponent?

Teaching Tip **Visual** Post a copy of the properties of exponents on a wall for students to reference while discussing the properties of logarithms.

2 Teach

Guided Instruction

First, review the laws of exponents from Lesson 1-5.

As you introduce each property of logarithms, remind students of the related property of exponents.

Make sure that students can convince themselves that the log laws hold by constructing "mental math" examples for themselves, e.g.
$\log_2 4 + \log_2 8 = \log_2 32$.

Reaching All Learners

Through Cognitive Strategies

To help students understand the property $\log_b b^x = x$ and to reinforce the definition of logarithms,

1) have them rewrite $\log_b b^x = x$ in exponential form, $b^x = b^x$.
2) have them rewrite $b^{\log_b x} = x$ in logarithmic form, $\log_b x = \log_b x$.

Power Presentations with PowerPoint®

Additional Examples

Example 4

Simplify each expression.

A. $\log_3 3^{11}$ 11

B. $\log_3 81$ $\log_3 3^4 = 4$

C. $5^{\log_5 10}$ 10

Example 5

Evaluate $\log_{32} 8$. 0.6

Also available on transparency

INTERVENTION

Questioning Strategies

EXAMPLE 4

- How do you write these expressions in exponential form?

EXAMPLE 5

- Why would you want to change the base of a logarithm?

Technology Have students experiment with the LOG and 10^x functions, which are located on the same calculator key, to see the inverse properties.

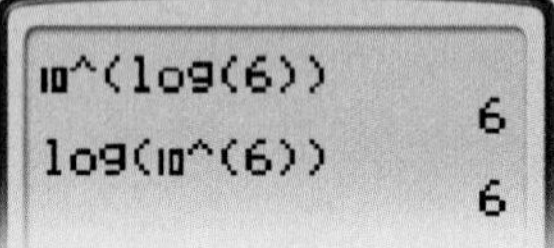

Math Background Before powerful calculators, students had to calculate logs by using tables of values. Logarithms were generally given for numbers from 1 to 10. Students had to use properties to find any other logs. For example, to find log 48,600, you would find $\log 4.86 \approx 0.6866$ in the table and use the properties of logarithms.

$$\begin{aligned}\log 48{,}600 &= \log(4.86 \times 10^4)\\ &= \log 4.86 + \log(10^4)\\ &\approx 0.6866 + 4\\ &\approx 4.6866\end{aligned}$$

Exponential and logarithmic operations undo each other since they are inverse operations.

Inverse Properties of Logarithms and Exponents

For any base b such that $b > 0$ and $b \neq 1$,

ALGEBRA	EXAMPLE
$\log_b b^x = x$	$\log_{10} 10^7 = 7$
$b^{\log_b x} = x$	$10^{\log_{10} 2} = 2$

EXAMPLE 4 Recognizing Inverses

Simplify each expression.

A $\log_8 8^{3x+1}$

$\log_8 8^{3x+1}$

$3x + 1$

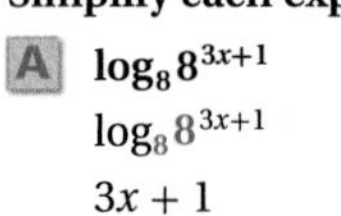

B $\log_5 125$

$\log_5 (5 \cdot 5 \cdot 5)$

$\log_5 5^3$

3

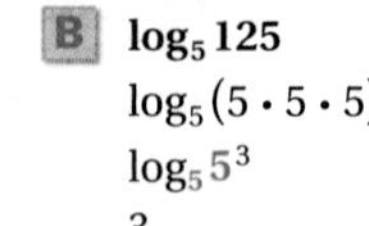

C $2^{\log_2 27}$

$2^{\log_2 27}$

27

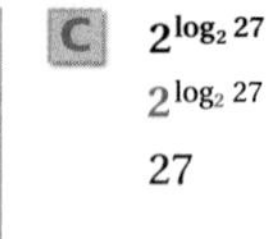

4a. Simplify $\log 10^{0.9}$. **0.9**

4b. Simplify $2^{\log_2 (8x)}$. **8x**

Most calculators calculate logarithms only in base 10 or base e (see Lesson 7-6). You can change a logarithm in one base to a logarithm in another base with the following formula.

Change of Base Formula

For $a > 0$ and $a \neq 1$ and any base b such that $b > 0$ and $b \neq 1$,

ALGEBRA	EXAMPLE
$\log_b x = \frac{\log_a x}{\log_a b}$	$\log_4 8 = \frac{\log_2 8}{\log_2 4}$

EXAMPLE 5 Changing the Base of a Logarithm

Evaluate $\log_4 8$.

Method 1 Change to base 10.

$\log_4 8 = \frac{\log 8}{\log 4}$

$\approx \frac{0.0903}{0.602}$ *Use a calculator.*

$= 1.5$ *Divide.*

Method 2 Change to base 2, because both 4 and 8 are powers of 2.

$\log_4 8 = \frac{\log_2 8}{\log_2 4} = \frac{3}{2}$

$= 1.5$

5a. Evaluate $\log_9 27$. **1.5**

5b. Evaluate $\log_8 16$. $1.\overline{3}$

Logarithmic scales are useful for measuring quantities that have a very wide range of values, such as the intensity (loudness) of a sound or the energy released by an earthquake.

Reaching All Learners

Through Critical Thinking

Students may wish to know how to prove the Product Property:

$\log_b mn = \log_b m + \log_b n$

Proof: Let $x = \log_b m$ and $y = \log_b n$. By def., $b^x = m$ and $b^y = n$. Multiplying, $mn = b^{x+y}$. Taking the logarithm of both sides, $\log_b mn = \log_b b^{x+y}$. By def., $\log_b b^{x+y} = x + y$. Substituting, $\log_b mn = x + y = \log_b m + \log_b n$.

A similar proof to the one at left gives the Quotient Property.

To prove the change-of-base formula:

Proof: By the Inverse Property, $x = b^{\log_b x}$. Taking the logarithm of both sides, $\log_a x = \log_a b^{\log_b x}$. By the Power Property, $\log_a x = (\log_b x)(\log_a b)$.

Dividing, $\log_b x = \frac{\log_a x}{\log_a b}$.

EXAMPLE 6 Geology Application

Seismologists use the Richter scale to express the energy, or magnitude, of an earthquake. The Richter magnitude of an earthquake, M, is related to the energy released in ergs E shown by the formula $M = \frac{2}{3}\log\left(\frac{E}{10^{11.8}}\right)$.

In 1964, an earthquake centered at Prince William Sound, Alaska, registered a magnitude of 9.2 on the Richter scale. Find the energy released by the earthquake.

Helpful Hint

The Richter scale is logarithmic, so an increase of 1 corresponds to a release of 10 times as much energy.

$9.2 = \frac{2}{3}\log\left(\frac{E}{10^{11.8}}\right)$	*Substitute 9.2 for M.*
$\left(\frac{3}{2}\right)9.2 = \log\left(\frac{E}{10^{11.8}}\right)$	*Multiply both sides by $\frac{3}{2}$.*
$13.8 = \log\left(\frac{E}{10^{11.8}}\right)$	*Simplify.*
$13.8 = \log E - \log 10^{11.8}$	*Apply the Quotient Property of Logarithms.*
$13.8 = \log E - 11.8$	*Apply the Inverse Properties of Logarithms and Exponents.*
$25.6 = \log E$	
$10^{25.6} = E$	*Given the definition of a logarithm, the logarithm is the exponent.*
$3.98 \times 10^{25} = E$	*Use a calculator to evaluate.*

The energy released by an earthquake with a magnitude of 9.2 is 3.98×10^{25} ergs.

6. How many times as much energy is released by an earthquake with a magnitude of 9.2 than by an earthquake with a magnitude of 8? **≈ 63**

THINK AND DISCUSS

1. Explain how to graph $y = \log_5 x$ on a calculator.
2. Tell how you could find $10^{25.6}$ in Example 6 by applying a law of exponents.
3. Describe what happens when you use the change-of-base formula, $\log_b x = \frac{\log_a x}{\log_a b}$, when $x = a$.
4. **GET ORGANIZED** Copy and complete the graphic organizer. Use your own words to show related properties of exponents and logarithms.

Property of Exponents	Property of Logarithms

COMMON ERROR ALERT

Students will sometimes try to treat log(*quantity*) as if log could be distributed. Reinforce to students these two facts:

a. $\log(ab) \neq (\log a)(\log b)$

b. $\log\left(\frac{a}{b}\right) \neq \frac{\log a}{\log b}$

Remind them that multiplication is simplified not with multiplication, but with addition.

Power Presentations with PowerPoint®

Additional Examples

Example 6

The tsunami that devastated parts of Asia in December 2004 was spawned by an earthquake with magnitude 9.3. How many times as much energy did this earthquake release compared to the 6.9-magnitude earthquake that struck San Francisco in 1989?

tsunami: $\approx 5.6 \times 10^{25}$ ergs

S.F.: $\approx 1.4 \times 10^{22}$ ergs

≈ 4000 times as much

Also available on transparency

INTERVENTION 

Questioning Strategies

EXAMPLE 6

- How was the fraction in the logarithm simplified?
- Could you solve the equation used in the example for E in terms of M? How do you know?

3 Close

Summarize

Properties of logarithms let us deal with logs effectively. Remind students that the properties are related to those of exponents because logarithmic and exponential functions are inverses. The change of base formula allows you to convert any log to base 10, so that you can use a calculator.

ONGOING ASSESSMENT and INTERVENTION 

***Diagnose Before* the Lesson**
7-4 Warm Up, TE p. 512

***Monitor During* the Lesson**
Check It Out! Exercises, SE pp. 512–515
Questioning Strategies, TE pp. 513–515

***Assess After* the Lesson**
7-4 Lesson Quiz, TE p. 519
Alternative Assessment, TE p. 519

Answers to *Think and Discuss*

1. Change the base and enter Y=log(X)/log(5).
2. $10^{25.6}$ is $10^{0.6} \times 10^{25}$, and $10^{0.6}$ is about 3.98, so $10^{25.6}$ is about 3.98×10^{25}.
3. You get $\log_b a = \frac{1}{\log_a b}$.
4. See p. A9.

7-4 Exercises

Assignment Guide

Assign *Guided Practice* exercises as necessary.

If you finished Examples **1–3**
- **Basic** 20–28, 37–38
- **Average** 20–28, 37–38, 69
- **Advanced** 20–28, 37–39, 69, 76

If you finished Examples **1–6**
- **Basic** 20–35, 37–38, 50–53, 65–68, 81–96
- **Average** 20–35, 37–38, 40–42, 45–48, 50–54, 56–58, 62–72, 78–79, 81–96
- **Advanced** 20–39, 43–46, 48–50, 53, 55–64, 66–96

Homework Quick Check

Quickly check key concepts.
Exercises: 20, 24, 26, 30, 34, 35, 48

7-4 Exercises

go.hrw.com
Homework Help Online
KEYWORD: MB7 7-4
Parent Resources Online
KEYWORD: MB7 Parent

GUIDED PRACTICE

SEE EXAMPLE 1 p. 512

Express as a single logarithm. Simplify, if possible.

1. $\log_5 50 + \log_5 62.5$ **$\log_5 3125 = 5$**
2. $\log 100 + \log 1000$ **$\log 100000 = 5$**
3. $\log_3 3 + \log_3 27$ **$\log_3 81 = 4$**

SEE EXAMPLE 2 p. 513

Express as a single logarithm. Simplify, if possible.

4. $\log_4 320 - \log_4 5$ **$\log_4 64 = 3$**
5. $\log 5.4 - \log 0.054$ **$\log 100 = 2$**
6. $\log_6 496.8 - \log_6 2.3$ **$\log_6 216 = 3$**

SEE EXAMPLE 3 p. 513

Simplify, if possible.

7. $\log_8 8^2$ **2**
8. $\log_3 3^5$ **5**
9. $\log_7 49^3$ **6**
10. $\log_{\frac{1}{2}}(0.25)^4$ **8**

SEE EXAMPLE 4 p. 514

11. $\log_2 2^{\frac{x}{2}+5}$ **$\frac{x}{2} + 5$**
12. $2.5^{\log_{2.5} 19}$ **19**
13. $\log_4 1024$ **5**
14. $\log_2(0.5)^4$ **−4**

SEE EXAMPLE 5 p. 514

Evaluate.

15. $\log_9\left(\frac{1}{27}\right)$ **−1.5**
16. $\log_8 32$ **$1.\overline{6}$**
17. $\log_5 10 \approx$ **1.43**
18. $\log_2 27 \approx$ **4.75**

SEE EXAMPLE 6 p. 515

19. **Geology** The Richter magnitude M of an earthquake is related to the energy released in ergs E shown by the formula $M = \frac{2}{3}\log\left(\frac{E}{10^{11.8}}\right)$. How many times as much energy was released by the 1811 New Madrid, Missouri, earthquake than by the Fort Tejon, California, earthquake?
2 times as much

Largest Earthquakes in Continental U.S.

Location	Year	*M*
New Madrid, MO	1811	8.1
New Madrid, MO	1812	8.0
Fort Tejon, CA	1957	7.9
San Francisco, CA	1906	7.8
Imperial Valley, CA	1892	7.8

PRACTICE AND PROBLEM SOLVING

Independent Practice

For Exercises	See Example
20–22	1
23–25	2
26–28	3
29–31	4
32–34	5
35	6

Extra Practice
Skills Practice p. S16
Application Practice p. S38

Express as a single logarithm. Simplify, if possible.

20. $\log_8 4 + \log_8 16$
21. $\log 2 + \log 5$
22. $\log_{2.5} 3.125 + \log_{2.5} 5$ **$\log_{2.5}(15.625) = 3$**
23. $\log 1000 - \log 100$ **$\log 10 = 1$**
24. $\log_2 16 - \log_2 2$ **$\log_2 8 = 3$**
25. $\log_{1.5} 6.75 - \log_{1.5} 2$ **$\log_{1.5} 3.375 = 3$**

Simplify, if possible.

26. $\log_2 16^3$ **12**
27. $\log(100)^{0.1}$ **0.2**
28. $\log_5 125^{\frac{1}{3}}$ **1**
29. $\log_3 3^{7+x}$ **$7 + x$**
30. $3^{\log_3 4.52}$ **4.52**
31. $\log_9 6561$ **4**

Evaluate.

32. $\log_{\frac{1}{2}} 16$ **−4**
33. $\log_{25} 125$ **1.5**
34. $\log_4 9 \approx$ **1.58**

35. **Sound** After some complaints, it was found that the music from an outdoor concert was 5 decibels louder than the city's allowable level of 100 decibels. The loudness L of sound in decibels is given by $L = 10\log\left(\frac{I}{I_0}\right)$, where I is the intensity of sound and I_0 is the intensity of the softest audible sound. How many times more intense is the concert sound than the allowable level? **≈ 3.16 times as intense**

20. $\log_8 64 = 2$
21. $\log 10 = 1$

State Resources

go.hrw.com
State Resources Online
KEYWORD: MB7 Resources

7-4 PRACTICE A

Express as a single logarithm. Simplify, if possible.

1. $\log_3 9 + \log_3 27$
$\log_3(9 \cdot 27) = \log_3 243$
$3^x = 243$, so $x =$ **4**
2. $\log_2 16 + \log_2 4$
$\log_2(16 \cdot 4) = \log_2$ **64**
$2^x =$ **64**, so $x =$ **6**
3. $\log_5 125 + \log_5 25$
$\log_5(125 \cdot 25) = \log_5$ **3125**
$5^x =$ **3125**, so $x =$ **5**
4. $\log_{10} 250 + \log_{10} 40$ **$\log_{10} 10{,}000 = 4$**
5. $\log_6 3 + \log_6 2$ **$\log_6 6 = 1$**
6. $\log_8 16 + \log_8 4$ **$\log_8 64 = 2$**

Express as a single logarithm. Simplify, if possible.

7. $\log_5 250 - \log_5 10$ **$\log_5 25 = 2$**
8. $\log_3 21 - \log_3 7$ **$\log_3 3 = 1$**
9. $\log_2 160 - \log_2 5$ **$\log_2 32 = 5$**
10. $\log_4 128 - \log_4 8$ **$\log_4 16 = 2$**
11. $\log_6 72 - \log_6 2$ **$\log_6 36 = 2$**
12. $\log_5 1000 - \log_5 8$ **$\log_5 125 = 3$**

Simplify, if possible.

13. $\log_6 36^2$
$2\log_6 36$
$2 \cdot 2 =$ **4**
14. $\log_5 5^4$
$4\log_5 5$
4
15. $\log_2 8^3$
$3\log_2 8$
9
16. $\log_3 3^4$ **4**
17. $\log_4 64^4$ **12**
18. $\log_8 8^2$ **2**

Evaluate. Round to the nearest hundredth.

19. $\log_5 13$ **1.59**
20. $\log_3 7$ **1.77**
21. $\log_8 21$ **1.46**

Solve.

22. The Richter magnitude of an earthquake, M, is related to the energy released in ergs, E, by the formula $M = \frac{2}{3}\log\left(\frac{E}{10^{11.8}}\right)$. Find the energy released by an earthquake of magnitude 6.8. **10^{22} ergs**

7-4 PRACTICE B

Express as a single logarithm. Simplify, if possible.

1. $\log_3 9 + \log_3 27$ **$\log_3 243 = 5$**
2. $\log_2 8 + \log_2 16$ **$\log_2 128 = 7$**
3. $\log_{10} 80 + \log_{10} 125$ **$\log_{10} 10{,}000 = 4$**
4. $\log_6 8 + \log_6 27$ **$\log_6 216 = 3$**
5. $\log_3 6 + \log_3 13.5$ **$\log_3 81 = 4$**
6. $\log_4 32 + \log_4 128$ **$\log_4 4096 = 6$**

Express as a single logarithm. Simplify, if possible.

7. $\log_2 80 - \log_2 10$ **$\log_2 8 = 3$**
8. $\log_{10} 4000 - \log_{10} 40$ **$\log_{10} 100 = 2$**
9. $\log_4 384 - \log_4 6$ **$\log_4 64 = 3$**
10. $\log_2 1920 - \log_2 30$ **$\log_2 64 = 6$**
11. $\log_3 486 - \log_3 2$ **$\log_3 243 = 5$**
12. $\log_6 180 - \log_6 5$ **$\log_6 36 = 2$**

Simplify, if possible.

13. $\log_4 4^6$ **6**
14. $\log_5 5^{x-5}$ **$x - 5$**
15. $7^{\log_7 30}$ **30**
16. $12^{\log_{12} 1}$ **1**
17. $\log_8 8^5$ **5**
18. $\log_3 9^4$ **8**

Evaluate. Round to the nearest hundredth.

19. $\log_{12} 1$ **0**
20. $\log_3 30$ **3.10**
21. $\log_5 10$ **1.43**

Solve.

22. The Richter magnitude of an earthquake, M, is related to the energy released in ergs, E, by the formula $M = \frac{2}{3}\log\left(\frac{E}{10^{11.8}}\right)$. Find the energy released by an earthquake of magnitude 4.2. **$10^{18.1}$ ergs**

36. **Astronomy** The difference between the apparent magnitude (brightness) m of a star, and its absolute magnitude M is given by the formula $m - M = 5\log\frac{d}{10}$, where d is the distance of the star from Earth, measured in parsecs.
    a. Find the distance d of Antares from Earth. **182 parsecs**
    b. Sigma Sco is 225 parsecs from Earth. Find its absolute magnitude. **-3.9**
    c. How many times as great is the distance to Antares as the distance to Rho Oph? **≈ 1.5**

Write the equivalent logarithmic form for each equation.

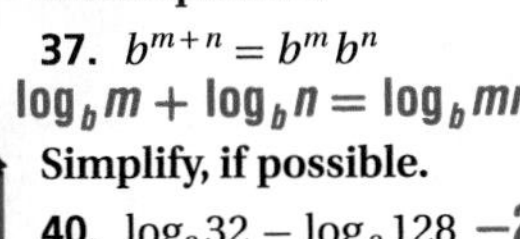

37. $b^{m+n} = b^m b^n$ **$\log_b m + \log_b n = \log_b mn$**

38. $b^{m-n} = \frac{b^m}{b^n}$ **$\log_b m - \log_b n = \log_b \frac{m}{n}$**

39. $(b^m)^n = b^{mn}$ **$n\log_b b^m = mn$**

Simplify, if possible.

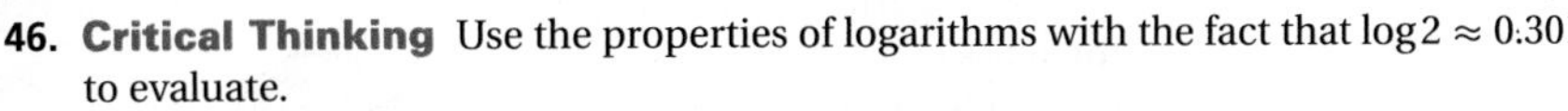

40. $\log_2 32 - \log_2 128$ **-2**

41. $\log 0.1 + \log 1 + \log 10$ **0**

42. $2 - \log_{11} 121$ **0**

43. $\log_{\frac{1}{2}} 2 + \log_{\frac{1}{2}} 2^{\frac{1}{2}}$ **$-\frac{3}{2}$**

44. $7^{\log_7 7} - \log_7 7^7$ **0**

45. $\frac{10^{\log 10}}{\log 10^{10}}$ **1**

Math History

Scottish mathematician John Napier (1550–1617) invented logarithms and named them by joining the Greek words *logos* (ratio) and *arithmos* (number).

46. **Critical Thinking** Use the properties of logarithms with the fact that $\log 2 \approx 0.301$ to evaluate.
    a. $\log 20 \approx$ **1.301** b. $\log 200 \approx$ **2.301** c. $\log 2000 \approx$ **3.301**

47. **Chemistry** Most swimming pool experts recommend a pH of between 7.0 and 7.6 for water in a swimming pool. Use $\text{pH} = -\log[H^+]$, and write an expression for the difference in hydrogen ion concentration over this pH range. **$10^{-7} - 10^{-7.6}$**

48. **Multi-Step** Suppose that the population of one endangered species decreases at a rate of 4% per year. In one habitat, the current population of the species is 143.
    a. Write an exponential function for the population by year. **$P = 143(0.96)^t$**
    b. Write a logarithmic function for the time based upon population.
    c. Write the keystrokes necessary to enter the logarithmic function on a calculator.
    d. After how long will the population drop below 30, to the nearest year? **39**

48b. $t = \log_{0.96}\left(\frac{P}{143}\right)$

c. $\frac{\log\left(\frac{X}{143}\right)}{\log 0.96}$

49. **Finance** A stock priced at \$40 increases at a rate of 8% per year. Write and evaluate a logarithmic expression for the number of years that it will take for the value of the stock to reach \$50. (*Hint:* Write the expression in exponential form first.) **$\log_{1.08}\left(\frac{50}{40}\right)$; 2.9**

50. This problem will prepare you for the Multi-Step Test Prep on page 520.

    For a certain credit card with 19.2% annual interest compounded monthly, the total amount A that you owe after n months is given by $A = P(1.016)^n$, where P is the starting balance. **$\log 2 = n\log(1.016)$; 43.7 mo.**
    a. You start with a balance of \$500. Write and solve a logarithmic expression for the number of months it will take for the debt to double.
    b. How many additional months will it take for the debt to double again? **43.7 mo**
    c. Does the amount of time that it takes the debt to double depend on the starting balance? **no**

COMMON ERROR ALERT

In **Exercise 47,** students may try to simplify $10^{-7} - 10^{-7.6}$. Remind them this is not possible. Point out that this is like trying to simplify $x^3 - x^2$.

Teaching Tip **Multiple Representations** It is possible to do **Exercise 47** by calculating the respective hydrogen ion concentrations and comparing them. However, it is enough to know that pH works on a common log scale. The difference between the two concentrations is a pH of 0.6; the difference between the hydrogen ion concentrations is $10^{0.6} \approx 3.98$.

Exercise 50 involves working with logarithmic equations to solve problems involving credit card debt. This exercise prepares students for the Multi-Step Test Prep on page 520.

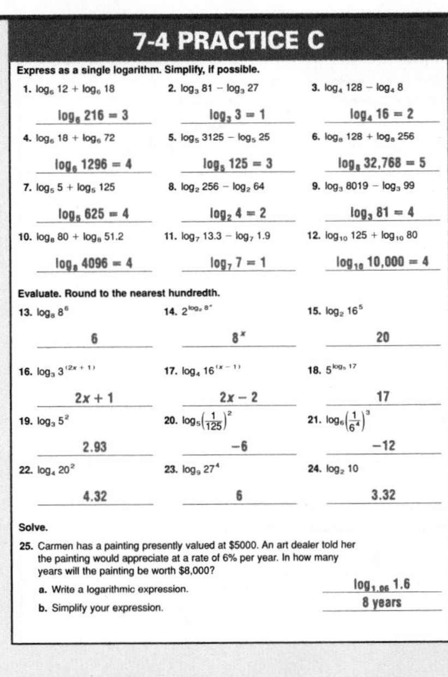

7-4 PRACTICE C

Express as a single logarithm. Simplify, if possible.

1. $\log_6 12 + \log_6 18$ **$\log_6 216 = 3$**
2. $\log_3 81 - \log_3 27$ **$\log_3 3 = 1$**
3. $\log_4 128 - \log_4 8$ **$\log_4 16 = 2$**
4. $\log_6 18 + \log_6 72$ **$\log_6 1296 = 4$**
5. $\log_5 3125 - \log_5 25$ **$\log_5 125 = 3$**
6. $\log_8 128 + \log_8 256$ **$\log_8 32{,}768 = 5$**
7. $\log_5 5 + \log_5 125$ **$\log_5 625 = 4$**
8. $\log_2 256 - \log_2 64$ **$\log_2 4 = 2$**
9. $\log_3 8019 - \log_3 99$ **$\log_3 81 = 4$**
10. $\log_8 80 + \log_8 51.2$ **$\log_8 4096 = 4$**
11. $\log_7 13.3 - \log_7 1.9$ **$\log_7 7 = 1$**
12. $\log_{10} 125 + \log_{10} 80$ **$\log_{10} 10{,}000 = 4$**

Evaluate. Round to the nearest hundredth.

13. $\log_8 8^6$ **6**
14. $2^{\log_2 8^x}$ **8^x**
15. $\log_2 16^5$ **20**
16. $\log_3 3^{(2x+1)}$ **$2x + 1$**
17. $\log_4 16^{(x-1)}$ **$2x - 2$**
18. $5^{\log_5 17}$ **17**
19. $\log_3 5^2$ **2.93**
20. $\log_5\left(\frac{1}{125}\right)^2$ **-6**
21. $\log_6\left(\frac{1}{6^4}\right)^3$ **-12**
22. $\log_4 20^2$ **4.32**
23. $\log_9 27^4$ **6**
24. $\log_2 10$ **3.32**

Solve.

25. Carmen has a painting presently valued at \$5000. An art dealer told her the painting would appreciate at a rate of 6% per year. In how many years will the painting be worth \$8,000?
    a. Write a logarithmic expression. **$\log_{1.06} 1.6$**
    b. Simplify your expression. **8 years**

Answers

51. 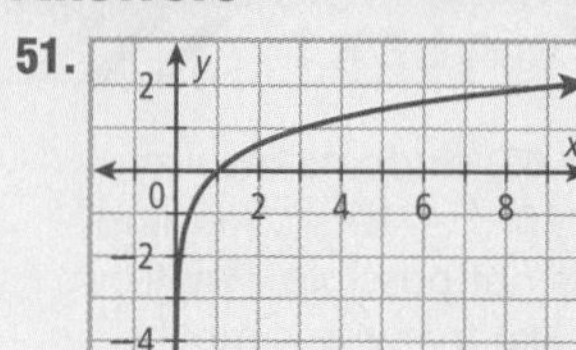

52. 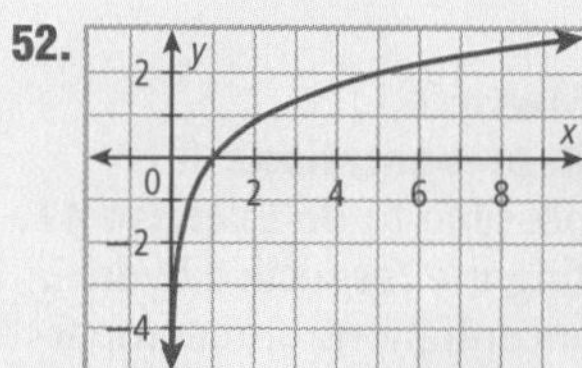

53. 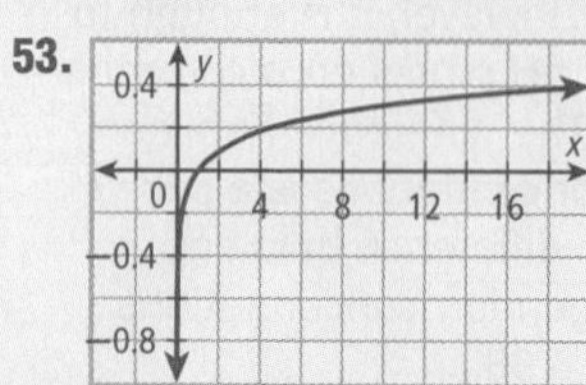

54. Possible answer: Change the base from 16 to 10 by writing $\log_{16}x$ as $\frac{\log x}{\log 16}$. Enter log(X)/log(16), using the calculator's LOG key.

69a. 3 on the top scale is lined up with 1 on the bottom scale. At 2 on the bottom scale, the product, 6, is read on the top scale.

b. The lengths show $\log 3 + \log 2 = \log(3 \cdot 2) = \log 6$.

76. $\log_b a^p = \log_b(\underbrace{a \times a \times a \ldots}_{p \text{ factors}})$
$= \underbrace{\log_b a + \log_b a + \log_b a + \ldots}_{p \text{ factors}} = p\log_b a$

56c. ≈ 2.398; $\log(a \times 10^x) = x + \log a$

d. ≈ -2.602; yes, it is $-3 + 0.398$

Graphing Calculator Use the change of base formula and a graphing calculator to graph.

51. $y = \log_3 x$ 52. $y = 2\log_5 x$ 53. $y = \frac{\log_{12} x}{3}$

54. **Write About It** Explain how to graph a logarithm in a base other than 10 on a calculator.

55. **Critical Thinking** Given $\log_{12} 20 \approx 1.2$ and $\log_{12} 33 \approx 1.4$, find each approximate value.
a. $\log_{12} 1.65 \approx$ **0.2** b. $\log_{12} 660 \approx$ **2.6** c. $\log_{12} 400 \approx$ **2.4**

56. **Critical Thinking** There is an interesting relationship between logarithms and scientific notation.
a. Find the logarithm of 2.5. **0.398**
b. Find the logarithm of the mass of the *Titanic*. Compare it to your answer from part **a.** **7.398**
c. **Make a Conjecture** A lion has a mass of 2.5×10^2 kg. Find the logarithm of this number. Use your answers and the answers to parts **a** and **b,** to explain how to find the base 10 logarithm of a number written in scientific notation.
d. Use your conjecture to find the logarithm of the mass of a dime. Does your conjecture hold for scientific notation with negative exponents?

mass: $\approx 2.5 \times 10^{-3}$ kg

Assume $b > 0$ and $b \neq 1$. **Tell whether each statement is sometimes, always, or never true.**

57. A logarithm with base b can be changed to another rational-number base. **sometimes**
58. The logarithm with base 6 of 6 raised to an expression is equal to the expression. **always**
59. Subtracting log base b of 1 from a number is just the number itself. **always**
60. The base of a logarithm can be a negative number. **never**
61. The logarithm of the square of a number is equal to twice the logarithm of the number. **always**
62. Logarithms with different bases can be added without changing a base. **never**
63. $\frac{\log_b 16}{\log_b 8}$ can be simplified. **sometimes**
64. A logarithm of a logarithm of a number is the number. **never**
65. **ERROR ANALYSIS** Two simplifications of $\log 80 + \log 20$ are shown. Which of these is incorrect? Explain. **B; $\log 80 + \log 20 \neq \log(80 + 20)$**

A 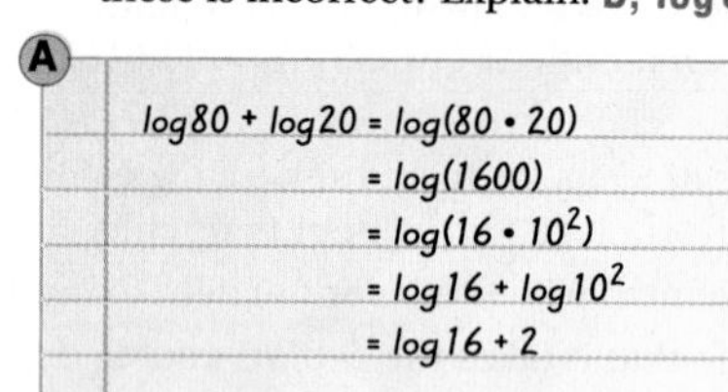

$\log 80 + \log 20 = \log(80 \cdot 20)$
$= \log(1600)$
$= \log(16 \cdot 10^2)$
$= \log 16 + \log 10^2$
$= \log 16 + 2$

B 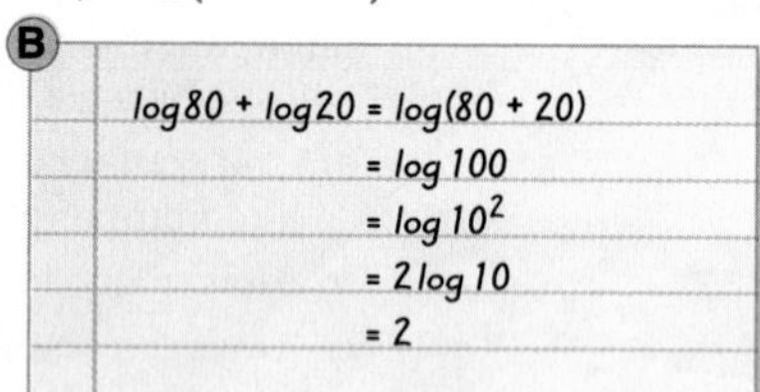

$\log 80 + \log 20 = \log(80 + 20)$
$= \log 100$
$= \log 10^2$
$= 2\log 10$
$= 2$

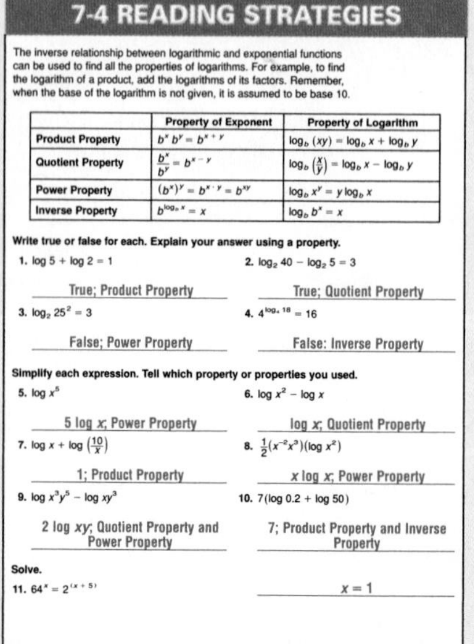

7-4 READING STRATEGIES

The inverse relationship between logarithmic and exponential functions can be used to find all the properties of logarithms. For example, to find the logarithm of a product, add the logarithms of its factors. Remember, when the base of the logarithm is not given, it is assumed to be base 10.

	Property of Exponent	Property of Logarithm
Product Property	$b^x b^y = b^{x+y}$	$\log_b(xy) = \log_b x + \log_b y$
Quotient Property	$\frac{b^x}{b^y} = b^{x-y}$	$\log_b\left(\frac{x}{y}\right) = \log_b x - \log_b y$
Power Property	$(b^x)^y = b^{x \cdot y} = b^{xy}$	$\log_b x^y = y\log_b x$
Inverse Property	$b^{\log_b x} = x$	$\log_b b^x = x$

Write true or false for each. Explain your answer using a property.

1. $\log 5 + \log 2 = 1$ — True; Product Property
2. $\log_2 40 - \log_2 5 = 3$ — True; Quotient Property
3. $\log_2 25^2 = 3$ — False; Power Property
4. $4^{\log_4 16} = 16$ — False: Inverse Property

Simplify each expression. Tell which property or properties you used.

5. $\log x^5$ — 5 log x; Power Property
6. $\log x^2 - \log x$ — log x; Quotient Property
7. $\log x + \log\left(\frac{10}{x}\right)$ — 1; Product Property
8. $\frac{1}{2}(x^{-2}x^3)(\log x^2)$ — x log x; Power Property
9. $\log x^3y^5 - \log xy^3$ — 2 log xy; Quotient Property and Power Property
10. $7(\log 0.2 + \log 50)$ — 7; Product Property and Inverse Property

Solve.

11. $64^x = 2^{(x+5)}$ — $x = 1$

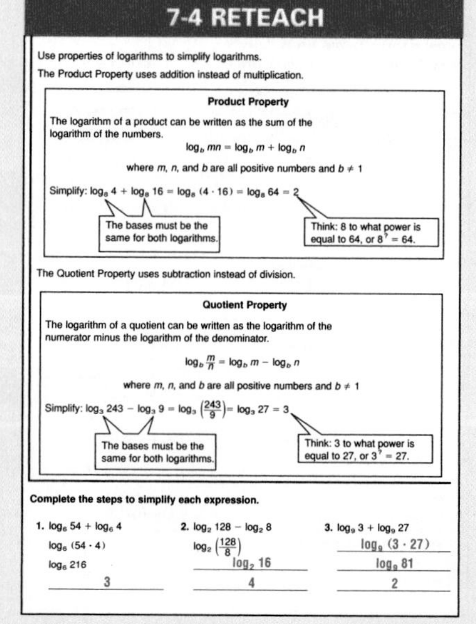

7-4 RETEACH

Use properties of logarithms to simplify logarithms.

The Product Property uses addition instead of multiplication.

Product Property

The logarithm of a product can be written as the sum of the logarithm of the numbers.

$$\log_b mn = \log_b m + \log_b n$$

where m, n, and b are all positive numbers and $b \neq 1$

Simplify: $\log_8 4 + \log_8 16 = \log_8(4 \cdot 16) = \log_8 64 = 2$

The bases must be the same for both logarithms.

Think: 8 to what power is equal to 64, or $8^? = 64$.

The Quotient Property uses subtraction instead of division.

Quotient Property

The logarithm of a quotient can be written as the logarithm of the numerator minus the logarithm of the denominator.

$$\log_b \frac{m}{n} = \log_b m - \log_b n$$

where m, n, and b are all positive numbers and $b \neq 1$

Simplify: $\log_3 243 - \log_3 9 = \log_3\left(\frac{243}{9}\right) = \log_3 27 = 3$

The bases must be the same for both logarithms.

Think: 3 to what power is equal to 27, or $3^? = 27$.

Complete the steps to simplify each expression.

1. $\log_6 54 + \log_6 4$
$\log_6(54 \cdot 4)$
$\log_6 216$
3

2. $\log_2 128 - \log_2 8$
$\log_2\left(\frac{128}{8}\right)$
$\log_2 16$
4

3. $\log_9 3 + \log_9 27$
$\log_9(3 \cdot 27)$
$\log_9 81$
2

TEST PREP

66. Which statement is NOT true?

(A) $\log 140 - \log 35 = \log 4$ (C) $\log 35 + \log 4 = \log 140$

(B) $\dfrac{\log 140}{\log 35} = \log 4$ (D) $\log \dfrac{140}{35} = \log 4$

67. Simplify $\log_9 x^2 + \log_9 x$.

(F) $\log_9(x^2 + x)$ (G) $\log_9 3x$ **(H)** $3\log_9 x$ (J) $3(x^2 + x)$

68. Which logarithmic expression is equal to $\log 6$?

(A) $\log 3 + \log 2$ (B) $\log 3 + \log 3$ (C) $(\log 3)(\log 2)$ (D) $(\log 3)(\log 3)$

CHALLENGE AND EXTEND

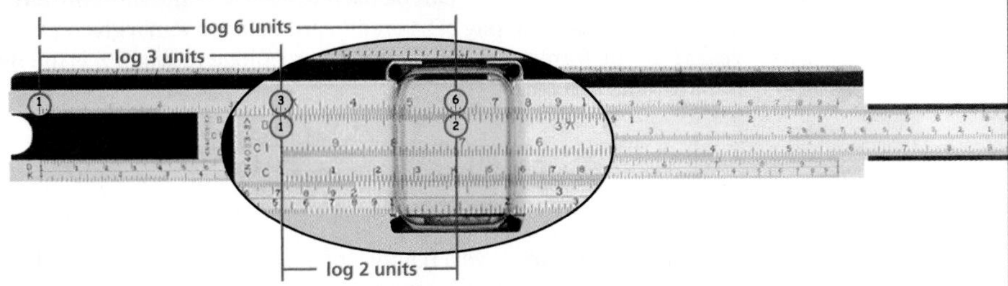

69. **Math History** The slide rule used two number lines that slid against each other. The scale on each was logarithmic, so the properties of logarithms could be applied to multiply and divide numbers.
   a. Explain how the product of 2 and 3 is shown on the slide rule.
   b. How does this show the product property of logarithms?

Find the domain of each function.

70. $f(x) = \log(x^2 - 4)$ $\{x \mid x < -2 \cup x > 2\}$

71. $f(x) = \log x - \log(x - 1)$ $\{x \mid x > 1\}$

72. $f(x) = \log\left(\dfrac{x}{x^2 - 1}\right)$ $\{x \mid -1 < x < 0 \cup x > 1\}$

73. $f(x) = \log\left(\dfrac{1}{x}\right)^2$ $\{x \mid x > 0\}$

74. $f(x) = -\sqrt{\log(x + 1)}$ $\{x \mid x > -1\}$

75. $f(x) = \sqrt{-2\log(-x)}$ $\{x \mid -1 \le x < 0\}$

76. Prove: $\log_b a^p = p\log_b a$.

77. Simplify $\log_9 3^{2x}$. x

Solve.

78. $\log_x 25 = 2$ 5

79. $\log_x(-8) = 3$ ∅

80. $0 = \log_x 1$ $\{x \mid x > 0 \text{ and } x \neq 1\}$

SPIRAL REVIEW

Solve. *(Lesson 2-1)*

81. $9 = 3(x - 14)$ 17

82. $4(x + 1) = 3(2x - 6)$ 11

83. $-20 + 8n = n + 29$ 7

84. $8\left(n + \dfrac{3}{4}\right) = 10n - 4$ 5

Express each number in terms of i. *(Lesson 5-5)*

85. $3\sqrt{-16}$ $12i$

86. $-\dfrac{1}{2}\sqrt{-40}$ $-i\sqrt{10}$

87. $4\sqrt{-8}$ $8i\sqrt{2}$

88. $\sqrt{-125}$ $5i\sqrt{5}$

Write each exponential equation in logarithmic form. *(Lesson 7-3)*

89. $5^3 = 125$ $\log_5 125 = 3$

90. $10^{-1} = 0.1$ $\log 0.1 = -1$

91. $36^{0.5} = 6$ $\log_{36} 6 = 0.5$

92. $4^x = 256$ $\log_4 256 = x$

Evaluate. *(Lesson 7-3)*

93. $\log_{12} 1$ 0

94. $\log_5 25$ 2

95. $\log_{16} 4$ 0.5

96. $\log_{625} 0.04$ -0.5

7-4 PROBLEM SOLVING

Trina and Willow are researching information on earthquakes. One of the largest earthquakes in the United States, centered at San Francisco, occurred in 1906 and registered 7.8 on the Richter scale. The Richter magnitude of an earthquake, M, is related to the energy released in ergs, E, by the formula $M = \frac{2}{3}\log\left(\frac{E}{10^{11.8}}\right)$.

1. Find the amount of energy released by the earthquake in 1906.
   a. Substitute 7.8 for magnitude, M, in the equation. $7.8 = \frac{2}{3}\log\left(\frac{E}{10^{11.8}}\right)$
   b. Solve for the value of log E. $23.5 = \log E$
   c. Willow says that E is equal to 10 to the power of the value of log E. Is she correct? What property or definition can be used to find the value of E? Explain.
   Yes; by the definition of logarithm; $E = 10^{23.5}$
   d. Trina says the energy of the 1906 earthquake was 3.16×10^{23} ergs. Willow says the energy was $10^{23.5}$ ergs. Who is correct? How do you know?
   They are both correct; $10^{23.5} = 3.16 \times 10^{23}$.

Choose the letter for the best answer.

2. An earthquake in 1811 in Missouri measured 8.1 on the Richter scale. About how many times as much energy was released by this earthquake as by the California earthquake of 1906?
   (A) 2.8
   B 3.0
   C 3.6
   D 5.7

3. Another large earthquake in California measured 7.9 on the Richter scale. Which statement is true?
   F 0.1 times as much energy was released by the larger earthquake.
   (G) The difference in energy released is 1.3×10^{23} ergs.
   H The energy released by the second earthquake was 3.26×10^{23} ergs.
   J The total energy released by the two earthquakes is equal to the energy released by an 8.0 earthquake.

4. Larry wrote the following: $\log 10^{0.0038} = 3.8 \times 10^{-3}$. Which property of logarithms did he use?
   A Product Property
   B Quotient Property
   (C) Inverse Property
   D Power Property

5. Vijay wants to change $\log_5 7$ to base 10. Which expression should he use?
   (F) $\dfrac{\log_{10} 7}{\log_{10} 5}$ H $\dfrac{\log_{10} 7}{\log_5 5}$
   G $\dfrac{\log_{10} 5}{\log_{10} 7}$ J $\dfrac{\log_7 5}{\log_{10} 7}$

7-4 CHALLENGE

Logarithmic properties allow simplification of expressions that otherwise would be difficult to compute. One such property is

$$\log_b \sqrt[r]{x} = \frac{\log_b x}{r}$$

which shows that the logarithm of a root is equal to the logarithm of the radicand divided by the index of the radical.

1. Evaluate $\log_{10} \sqrt{1000}$ on your calculator and then evaluate $\frac{\log_{10} 1000}{2}$ without a calculator. How do your answers compare?
   Both expressions equal $\frac{3}{2}$.
2. Evaluate $\log_2 \sqrt[4]{64}$ with your calculator and with the above formula. Which is easier to compute? (Hint: You will need the Change of Base Formula for one of the calculations.)
   Result is $\frac{3}{2}$; formula is easier to compute.
3. Evaluate $\log_3 \sqrt[5]{729}$ with your calculator and with the above formula. Which is easier to compute?
   Result is $\frac{6}{5}$; formula is easier to compute.

Another useful property of logarithms is called the Chain Rule for Logarithms.

$$\log_a b \cdot \log_b c = \log_a c$$

4. Prove this formula by changing all the logarithms to base 10.
   $\log_a b \cdot \log_b c = \log_a c$
   $\log_a b \cdot \log_b c = \dfrac{\log b}{\log a} \cdot \dfrac{\log c}{\log b}$
   $= \dfrac{\log c}{\log a} \cdot \dfrac{\log b}{\log b} = \dfrac{\log c}{\log a} = \log_a c$
5. Evaluate $\log_2 3 \cdot \log_3 5 \cdot \log_5 8 \cdot \log_8 13$ using your calculator and the Change of Base Formula both with and without using the above formula.
   $\log_2 13 = \dfrac{\log 13}{\log 2} \approx 3.7$
6. Evaluate $\log_2 3 \cdot \log_3 4 \cdot \log_4 5 \cdot \log_5 6 \cdot \cdots \cdot \log_{31} 32$ both with and without using the above formula. Which is easier to compute?
   $\log_2 32 = 5$; possible answer: using the Chain Rule is much easier.

TEST PREP DOCTOR In **Exercise 66,** students who chose **D** may not be aware that the division of 140 by 35 is permissible with a log. Tell them to think of the fraction as being within parentheses, and that operations within parentheses are always done first.

Students who have difficulty with **Exercise 67** could try substituting a *friendly* number, like $x = 9$. Now, the expression $\log_9 9^2 + \log_9 9$ is equal to 3. Answer choice **H** is the only choice equal to 3 when $x = 9$, so it must be correct.

Journal

Have students write how they would convince another student in the class that $b^{\log_b x} = x$.

ALTERNATIVE ASSESSMENT

Have students create a poster that states the five logarithm rules from this lesson and give a unique example to illustrate each.

Power Presentations with PowerPoint®

7-4 Lesson Quiz

Express each as a single logarithm and simplify.

1. $\log_6 9 + \log_6 24$ $\log_6 216 = 3$
2. $\log_3 108 - \log_3 4$ $\log_3 27 = 3$

Simplify.

3. $\log_2 8^{10{,}000}$ 30,000
4. $\log_4 4^{x-1}$ $x - 1$
5. $10^{\log 125}$ 125
6. $\log_{64} 128$ $\frac{7}{6}$

Use a calculator to find each logarithm to the nearest thousandth.

7. $\log_3 20$ 2.727
8. $\log_{\frac{1}{2}} 10$ -3.322
9. How many times as much energy is released by a magnitude-8.5 earthquake as a magnitude-6.5 earthquake? 1000

Also available on transparency

Organizer

Objective: Assess students' ability to apply concepts and skills in Lessons 7-1 through 7-4 in a real-world format.

Online Edition

Resources

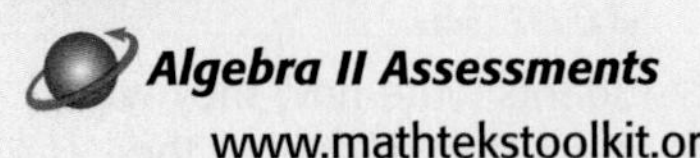

Algebra II Assessments
www.mathtekstoolkit.org

Problem	Text Reference
1	Lesson 7-1
2	Lesson 7-3
3–5	Lesson 7-4

State Resources

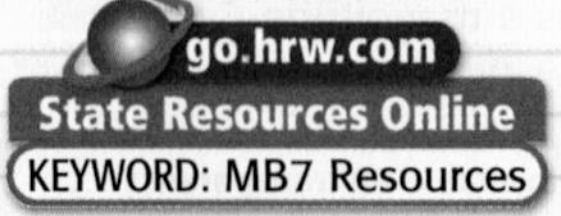

go.hrw.com
State Resources Online
KEYWORD: MB7 Resources

CHAPTER 7

MULTI-STEP TEST PREP

SECTION 7A

Exponential Functions and Logarithms

Charged Up There are more than 1 billion credit cards in circulation in the United States, and the average American carries a credit card debt of approximately $8600. Given that many credit cards charge an annual percentage rate (APR) of 18.3%, it can be difficult to escape the "credit hole."

The formula shown below can be used to compute the monthly payment M that is necessary to pay off a credit card balance P in a given number of years t. In the formula, r is the annual percentage rate and n is the number of payments per year.

$$M = \frac{P\left(\frac{r}{n}\right)}{1 - \left(1 + \frac{r}{n}\right)^{-nt}}$$

1. Suppose that you have a balance of $8600 on a credit card with an APR of 18.3%. What monthly payment should you make in order to pay off the debt in exactly five years? **$219.79**
2. How much money do you end up paying altogether over the five years? **$13,187.40**

   In order to calculate the number of years necessary for a given payment schedule, the formula can be written as shown.

$$t = \frac{\log\left(1 - \frac{Pr}{Mn}\right)}{-n\log\left(1 + \frac{r}{n}\right)}$$

3. If you can afford only a monthly payment of $160, how long will it take to pay off the credit card debt? **9.4 yr**
4. Suppose you can afford a monthly payment of $130. Will you be able to pay off the debt? If so, how long will it take? If not, why not?
5. What is the minimum monthly payment that will work toward paying off the debt? **$131.16**

4. No; the monthly interest alone amounts to $131.15, so the payments do not even keep pace with the interest.

"I didn't have time to mow the lawn, so I used your credit card to have it carpeted."

INTERVENTION

Scaffolding Questions

1. What does $\frac{r}{n}$ represent in the formula? the monthly interest rate
2. How many payments do you make over 5 years? 60 How much is each payment? $219.79 How much is interest? $4587.40
3. What do you notice about the quantity $\left(1 - \frac{Pr}{Mn}\right)$ after substituting? It is < 1. What can you say about its logarithm? It is < 0.
4. What do you notice about the quantity $\left(1 - \frac{Pr}{Mn}\right)$ in this case? It is < 1. What can you say about its logarithm? It is undefined.
5. To find t, what must be true for $\left(1 - \frac{Pr}{Mn}\right)$? $1 - \frac{Pr}{Mn} > 0$ What does this tell you about M? $M > \frac{Pr}{n}$

Extension

A credit card has a 17.5% APR. You make monthly payments to pay off the $8600 in 5 years. How much do you save in interest compared to the original credit card? $224.34

Quiz for Lesson 7-1 Through 7-4

7-1 Exponential Functions, Growth, and Decay

Tell whether the function shows growth or decay. Then graph.

1. $f(x) = \left(\frac{1}{4}\right)^x$ **decay**
2. $f(x) = \frac{1}{5}(0.2)^x$ **decay**
3. $f(x) = 14(1.4^x)$ **growth**
4. $f(x) = 6.4\left(1\frac{3}{8}\right)^x$ **growth**
5. Suppose that the number of bacteria in a culture was 1000 on Monday and the number has been increasing at a rate of 50% per day since then.
   a. Write a function representing the growth of the culture per day. $p = 1000(1.5)^d$
   b. Graph the function, and use the graph to predict the number of bacteria in the culture the following Monday. $\approx$ **17,086 bacteria**

7-2 Inverses of Relations and Functions

Graph each relation. Then graph its inverse.

6.

x	−1	0	1	2	3
y	0	4	8	12	16

7.

x	0	1	2	3	4
y	−1	$-\frac{1}{3}$	$\frac{1}{3}$	1	$1\frac{2}{3}$

Graph each function. Then write and graph the inverse. **10.** $f^{-1}(x) = \frac{1}{5}x - \frac{4}{5}$

8. $f(x) = x + 2.1$ **$f^{-1}(x) = x - 2.1$**
9. $f(x) = \frac{3}{4} - x$
10. $f(x) = 5x + 4$
11. $f(x) = 0.4\left(\frac{x}{2} + 1.5\right)$ **11.** $f^{-1}(x) = 5x - 3$
12. Rebekah's computer repair bill includes \$210 for parts and \$55 per hour for labor. Her bill can be expressed as a function of hours x by $f(x) = 210 + 55x$. Find the inverse function. Use it to find the number of hours of labor if her bill was \$402.50. $f^{-1}(x) = \frac{(x - 210)}{55}$; **3.5 h**

7-3 Logarithmic Functions

Write the exponential equation in logarithmic form.

13. $3^2 = 9$ **$\log_3 9 = 2$**
14. $17.6^0 = 1$ **$\log_{17.6} 1 = 0$**
15. $2^{-2} = 0.25$ **$\log_2 0.25 = -2$**
16. $0.5^x = 0.0625$ **$\log_{0.5} 0.0625 = x$**

Write the logarithmic equation in exponential form.

17. $\log_4 64 = 3$ **$4^3 = 64$**
18. $\log_{\frac{1}{5}} 25 = -2$
19. $\log_{0.99} 1 = 0$ **$0.99^0 = 1$**
20. $\log_e x = 5$ **$e^5 = x$**
21. Use the given x-values to graph $f(x) = \left(\frac{5}{6}\right)^x$; $x = -1, 0, 1, 2, 3$. Then graph the inverse function.

7-4 Properties of Logarithms

Express as a single logarithm. Simplify, if possible.

22. $\log_3 81 + \log_3 9$ **$\log_3 729 = 6$**
23. $\log_{\frac{1}{5}} 25 + \log_{\frac{1}{5}} 5$ **$\log_{\frac{1}{5}} 125 = -3$**
24. $\log_{1.2} 2.16 - \log_{1.2} 1.5$ **$\log_{1.2} 1.44 = 2$**

Simplify each expression.

25. $\log_4 256^2$ **8**
26. $\log_7 343$ **3**
27. $17^{\log_{17} 0.73}$ **0.73**

Evaluate.

28. $\log_{27} 243$ **$\frac{5}{3}$**
29. $\log_{10} 0.01$ **−2**
30. $\log_5 625$ **4**

READY TO GO ON? SECTION 7A

Organizer

Objective: Assess students' mastery of concepts and skills in Lessons 7-1 through 7-4.

Resources

 ***Assessment Resources***
Section 7A Quiz

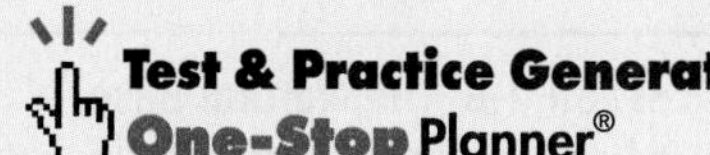
Test & Practice Generator One-Stop Planner®

INTERVENTION

Resources

 ***Ready to Go On? Intervention and Enrichment Worksheets***

 ***Ready to Go On? CD-ROM***

 ***Ready to Go On? Online***

my.hrw.com

Answers

1–11. For graphs, see p. A33–A34.

9. $f^{-1}(x) = \frac{3}{4} + x$

18. $\left(\frac{1}{5}\right)^{-2} = 25$

21. See p. A34.

READY TO GO ON? Diagnose and Prescribe

Ready to Go On? Intervention	Worksheets	CD-ROM	Online
	Ready to Go On? Intervention, Section 7A		
Lesson 7-1	7-1 Intervention	Activity 7-1	Diagnose and Prescribe Online
Lesson 7-2	7-2 Intervention	Activity 7-2	
Lesson 7-3	7-3 Intervention	Activity 7-3	
Lesson 7-4	7-4 Intervention	Activity 7-4	

Ready to Go On? Enrichment, Section 7A

Worksheets
CD-ROM
Online

SECTION 7B

Applying Exponential and Logarithmic Functions

One-Minute Section Planner

Lesson	Lab Resources	Materials
Lesson 7-5 Exponential and Logarithmic Equations and Inequalities • Solve exponential and logarithmic equations and inequalities. • Solve problems involving exponential and logarithmic equations. ☑ SAT-10 ☐ NAEP ☐ ACT ☑ SAT ☑ SAT Subject Tests	***Algebra Lab Activities*** 7-5 Algebra Lab	**Required** graphing calculator
7-6 Technology Lab Explore the Rule 72 • Use a spreadsheet to discover the "rule of 72" ☐ SAT-10 ☐ NAEP ☐ ACT ☐ SAT ☐ SAT Subject Tests	***Technology Lab Activities*** 7-6 Lab Recording Sheet	**Required** spreadsheet
Lesson 7-6 The Natural Base, *e* • Use the number *e* to write and graph exponential functions representing real-world situations. • Solve equations and problems involving e or natural logarithms. ☐ SAT-10 ☐ NAEP ☐ ACT ☐ SAT ☐ SAT Subject Tests		**Required** graphing calculator
Lesson 7-7 Transforming Exponential and Logarithmic Functions • Transform exponential and logarithmic functions by changing parameters. • Describe the effects of changes in the coefficients of exponential and logarithmic functions. ☐ SAT-10 ☐ NAEP ☑ ACT ☑ SAT ☑ SAT Subject Tests		**Required** scientific calculator **Optional** graphing calculator
Lesson 7-8 Curve Fitting by Using Exponential and Logarithmic Models • Model data by using exponential and logarithmic functions. • Use exponential and logarithmic models to analyze and predict. ☐ SAT-10 ☑ NAEP ☑ ACT ☑ SAT ☑ SAT Subject Tests	***Technology Lab Activities*** 7-8 Technology Lab	**Required** graphing calculator **Optional** CBL, temperature probe

MK = *Manipulatives Kit*

Section Overview

Exponential and Logarithmic Equations and Inequalities — Lesson 7-5

Exponential and logarithmic equations and inequalities are used to represent many real-world situations, such as measuring light in photography.

Properties used to solve exponential and logarithmic equations and inequalities:

$x = y \leftrightarrow b^x = b^y$

$x = y \leftrightarrow \log x = \log y$

The Natural Base, *e* — Lesson 7-6

Natural exponential and logarithmic functions, involving base *e*, are used to describe many natural growth and decay patterns.

The **natural logarithmic function** is the logarithmic function with base *e*.

$$\log_e x = \ln x$$

$\log_b x$	$\log x$	$\ln x$
$\log_b 1 = 0$	$\log 1 = 0$	$\ln 1 = 0$
$\log_b b = 1$	$\log 10 = 1$	$\ln e = 1$
$\log_b b^x = x$	$\log 10^x = x$	$\ln e^x = x$
$b^{\log_b x} = x$	$10^{\log x} = x$	$e^{\ln x} = x$

Exponential and Logarithmic Models — Lessons 7-7, 7-8

The exponential and logarithmic parent functions can be transformed into functions that model real-world behavior.

If the *ratio* of function values is constant for equally spaced *x*-values, then the data can be fit by an exponential function of the form $f(x) = ab^x$.

x	-1	0	1	2	3
$f(x)$	$\frac{2}{3}$	2	6	18	54

× 3 × 3 × 3 × 3 → $f(x) = 2(3^x)$

Using data to find an *exponential* model is called an **exponential regression.**

Using data to find a *logarithmic* model is called a **logarithmic regression.**

7-5 Organizer

Pacing: Traditional $1\frac{1}{2}$ days
Block $\frac{3}{4}$ day

Objectives: Solve exponential and logarithmic equations and inequalities.

Solve problems involving exponential and logarithmic equations.

Algebra Lab
In *Algebra Lab Activities*

Online Edition
Graphing Calculator, TechKeys

Countdown to Testing Week 16

Power Presentations with PowerPoint®

Warm Up

Solve.

1. $\log_{16} x = \frac{3}{2}$ 64
2. $\log_x 1.331 = 3$ 1.1
3. $\log 10{,}000 = x$ 4

Also available on transparency

Math Humor

Teacher: Did you get the answer?

Student: Well, I got closer and closer to it, but I guess it was just an asymptote.

7-5 Exponential and Logarithmic Equations and Inequalities

A2.6.3 Solve exponential and logarithmic equations.

Objectives
Solve exponential and logarithmic equations and inequalities.

Solve problems involving exponential and logarithmic equations.

Vocabulary
exponential equation
logarithmic equation

Who uses this?
Exponential scales are used to measure light in photography. (See Exercise 40.)

An **exponential equation** is an equation containing one or more expressions that have a variable as an exponent. To solve exponential equations:

- Try writing them so that the bases are all the same. If $b^x = b^y$, then $x = y$ $(b \neq 0, b \neq 1)$.
- Take the logarithm of both sides. If $a = b$, then $\log a = \log b$ $(a > 0, b > 0)$.

EXAMPLE 1 Solving Exponential Equations

Solve and check.

A $8^x = 2^{x+6}$

$(2^3)^x = 2^{x+6}$	*Rewrite each side with the same base; 8 is a power of 2.*
$2^{3x} = 2^{x+6}$	*To raise a power to a power, multiply exponents.*
$3x = x + 6$	*Bases are the same, so the exponents must be equal.*
$x = 3$	*Solve for x.*

Check

8^x	2^{x+6}
8^3	2^{3+6}
8^3	2^9
512	512 ✓

The solution is $x = 3$.

B $5^{x-2} = 200$

$\log 5^{x-2} = \log 200$	*200 is not a power of 5, so take the log of both sides.*
$(x-2)\log 5 = \log 200$	*Apply the Power Property of Logarithms.*
$x - 2 = \frac{\log 200}{\log 5}$	*Divide both sides by log 5.*
$x = 2 + \frac{\log 200}{\log 5} \approx 5.292$	

Check Use a calculator.

```
5^(5.292-2)
      199.9904485
```

The solution is $x \approx 5.292$.

Helpful Hint
When you use a rounded number in a check, the result will not be exact, but it should be reasonable.

CHECK IT OUT! Solve and check.

1a. $3^{2x} = 27$ **1.5** **1b.** $7^{-x} = 21$ $\approx$ **−1.565** **1c.** $2^{3x} = 15$ $\approx$ **1.302**

State Resources

go.hrw.com
State Resources Online
KEYWORD: MB7 Resources

1 Introduce

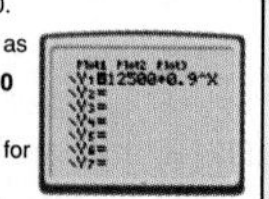

EXPLORATION

7-5 Exponential and Logarithmic Equations and Inequalities

To predict the number of prairie dogs in a region, a scientist uses the equation $P = 12{,}500(0.9)^t$ where P is the population after t years.

1. Based on the equation, is the population of prairie dogs increasing or decreasing? How do you know?
2. Find the initial population at time t = 0.
3. Enter the function into your calculator as Y1. Press [2nd] [WINDOW] to set TblStart=0 and ΔTbl=1. Then press [2nd] [GRAPH] to make a table for the function.
4. After how many years will the population of prairie dogs be 10,125?
5. After how many years will the population of prairie dogs fall below 6000?

THINK AND DISCUSS

6. **Explain** how you could write an equation that represents Problem 4.
7. **Explain** how you could write an inequality that represents Problem 5.

Motivate

Remind students that they have been solving equations using inverse operations to isolate the variable. For example, to solve $2x = 8$, they divided by 2, which is the inverse of multiplying by 2. Present them with a new equation, $2^x = 8$. Ask: Where is the variable? It is an exponent. What is the inverse of an exponential function? a logarithmic function What might be done to isolate the variable? Take logarithms of both sides.

Explorations and answers are provided in the *Explorations* binder.

EXAMPLE 2 Money Application

You can choose a prize of either a \$20,000 car or one penny on the first day, double that (2 cents) on the second day, and so on for a month. On what day would you receive more than the value of the car?

\$20,000 is 2,000,000 cents. On day 1, you would receive 1 cent, or 2^0 cents. On day 2, you would receive 2 cents, or 2^1 cents, and so on. So, on day n you would receive 2^{n-1} cents.

Solve $2^{n-1} > 2 \times 10^6$. *Write 2,000,000 in scientific notation.*

$\log 2^{n-1} > \log(2 \times 10^6)$ *Take the log of both sides.*

$(n-1)\log 2 > \log 2 + \log 10^6$ *Use the Power Property and Product Property.*

$(n-1)\log 2 > \log 2 + 6$ *$\log 10^6$ is 6.*

$n - 1 > \frac{\log 2 + 6}{\log 2}$ *Divide both sides by log 2.*

$n > \approx \frac{0.301 + 6}{0.301} + 1$ *Evaluate by using a calculator.*

$n > \approx 21.93$ *Round this up to the next whole number.*

Beginning on day 22, you would receive more than the value of the car.

Check On day 22, you would receive 2^{22-1} cents.

$2^{22-1} = 2^{21} = 2{,}097{,}152$ cents, or \$20,971.52.

2. In Example 2, suppose that you receive triple the amount each day. On what day would you receive at least a million dollars? **day 18**

A **logarithmic equation** is an equation with a logarithmic expression that contains a variable. You can solve logarithmic equations by using the properties of logarithms.

$$\text{If } \log_b x = \log_b y \text{ then } x = y$$

EXAMPLE 3 Solving Logarithmic Equations

Solve.

A $\log_3(x-5) = 2$

$3^{\log_3(x-5)} = 3^2$ *Use 3 as the base for both sides.*

$x - 5 = 9$ *Use inverse properties to remove 3 to the log base 3.*

$x = 14$ *Simplify.*

B $\log 45x - \log 3 = 1$

$\log\left(\frac{45x}{3}\right) = 1$ *Write as a quotient.*

$\log(15x) = 1$ *Divide.*

$10^{\log 15x} = 10^1$ *Use 10 as a base for both sides.*

$15x = 10$ *Use inverse properties on the left side.*

$x = \frac{2}{3}$

Remember!

Review the properties of logarithms from Lesson 7-4.

COMMON ERROR ALERT

In problems such as **Example 2,** it is very easy to make an "off by 1" error. Some students may read the problem and come up with the incorrect equation $2^n > 2 \times 10^6$. Students should note that the amount is one after the first time interval. In **Additional Example 2,** the starting amount has already doubled once after the first time interval.

Power Presentations with PowerPoint®

Additional Examples

Example 1

Solve and check.

A. $9^{8-x} = 27^{x-3}$ $x = 5$

B. $4^{x-1} = 5$ $x \approx 2.161$

Example 2

Suppose a bacteria culture doubles in size every hour. How many hours will it take for the number of bacteria to exceed 1,000,000? ≈ 19.94 h

Example 3

Solve.

A. $\log_6(2x-1) = -1$ $x = \frac{7}{12}$

B. $\log_4 100 - \log_4(x+1) = 1$ $x = 24$

C. $\log_5 x^4 = 8$ $x = 25$

D. $\log_{12} x + \log_{12}(x+1) = 1$ $x = 3$

Also available on transparency

2 Teach

Guided Instruction

First, review the logarithm properties. As students work through the equations, have them state the properties they are using.

Encourage students to recognize powers in equations, such as in **Example 1A,** where 8 is a power of 2.

Note the extraneous solution in **Example 3D,** and advise students that solutions that are negative numbers may be indicators of extraneous solutions.

Reaching All Learners

Through Kinesthetic Experience

To help students convert between logarithmic and exponential expressions, suggest the following: Lay out an exponential equation with numbers on cards and move them to form the corresponding log equation.

$2^3 = 8 \rightarrow \log_2 8 = 3$

INTERVENTION

Questioning Strategies

EXAMPLE 1

- How can you tell when you can write both sides using the same base?

EXAMPLE 2

- Why does it help to write the number in scientific notation?

EXAMPLE 3

- How do you know what to use as a first step in solving?
- How is it possible to get a solution that doesn't make sense in the original problem?

Inclusion Encourage students to estimate before solving to establish a "ballpark" answer. For example, for $3^x = 30$, the answer should be "a little more than 3," since $3^3 = 27$ and $3^4 = 81$.

Power Presentations with PowerPoint®

Additional Examples

Example 4

Use a table and graph to solve.

A. $2^{x+1} > 8192x$ $x > 16$

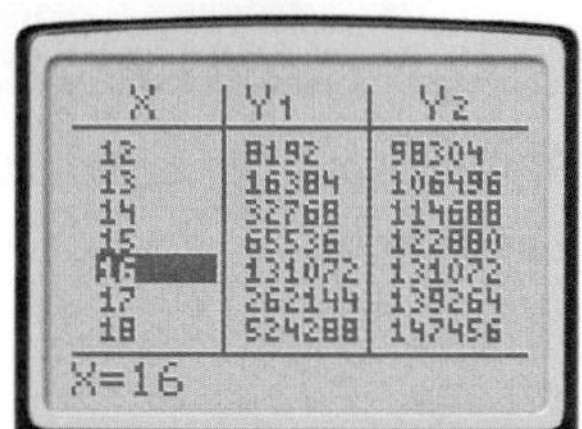

150,000

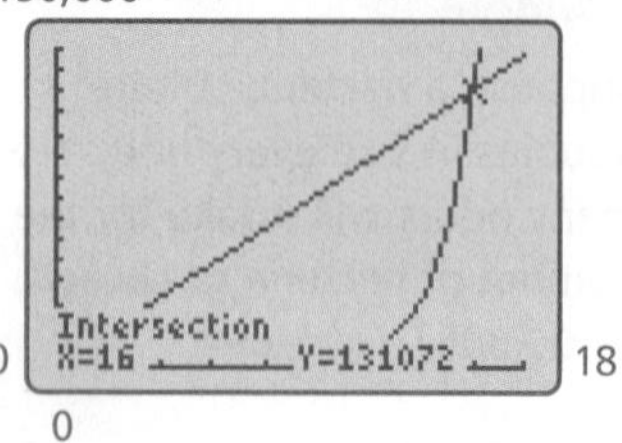

0 18
0

$x > 16$

B. $\log(x + 70) = 2\log\left(\frac{x}{3}\right)$

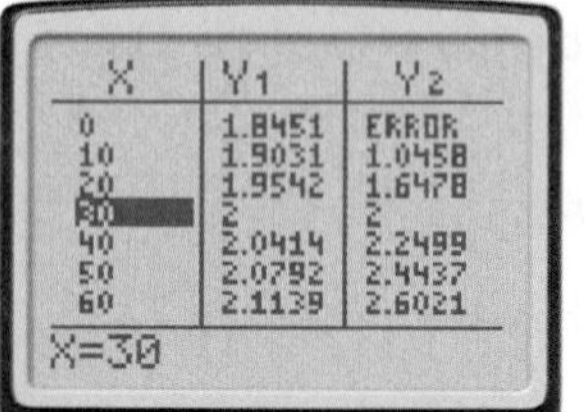

4

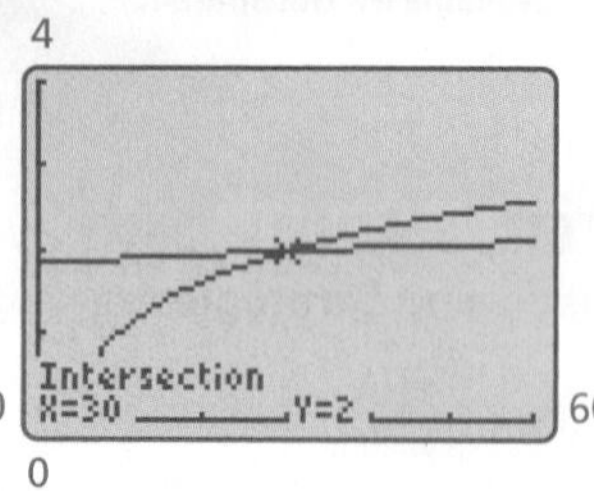

0 60
0

$x = 30$

Also available on transparency

INTERVENTION
Questioning Strategies

EXAMPLE 4

- What do you do if the table skips over the solution?

Solve.

C $\log_4 x^2 = 7$

$2\log_4 x = 7$	*Power Property of Logarithms*
$\log_4 x = \frac{7}{2}$	*Divide both sides by 2 to isolate $\log_4 x$.*
$x = 4^{\frac{7}{2}}$	*Definition of a logarithm*
$x = (2^2)^{\frac{7}{2}}$	*4 is a power of 2.*
$x = 2^7$, or 128	

D $\log x + \log(x + 9) = 1$

$\log x(x + 9) = 1$	*Product Property of Logarithms.*
$10^{\log x(x+9)} = 10^1$	*Exponential form*
$x(x + 9) = 10$	*Use the inverse properties.*
$x^2 + 9x - 10 = 0$	*Multiply and collect terms.*
$(x - 1)(x + 10) = 0$	*Factor.*
$x - 1 = 0$ or $x + 10 = 0$	*Set each of the factors equal to zero.*
$x = 1$ or $x = -10$	*Solve.*

Caution!
Watch out for calculated solutions that are not solutions of the original equation.

Check Check both solutions in the original equation.

$\log x + \log(x + 9)$	1
$\log 1 + \log(1 + 9)$	1
$\log 1 + \log 10$	1
$0 + 1$	1
1	1 ✓

$\log x + \log(x + 9)$	1
$\log(-10) + \log(-10 + 9)$	1 ✗

$\log(-10)$ is undefined.

The solution is $x = 1$.

3a. Solve $3 = \log 8 + 3\log x$. 5 **3b.** Solve $2\log x - \log 4 = 0$. 2

EXAMPLE 4 Using Tables and Graphs to Solve Exponential and Logarithmic Equations and Inequalities

Use a table and graph to solve.

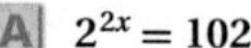

A $2^{2x} = 1024$

Use a graphing calculator. Enter **2^(2X)** as **Y1** and **1024** as **Y2**.

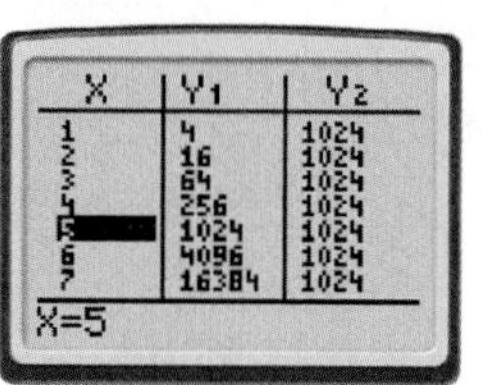

In the table, find the x-value where Y1 and Y2 are equal.

2000

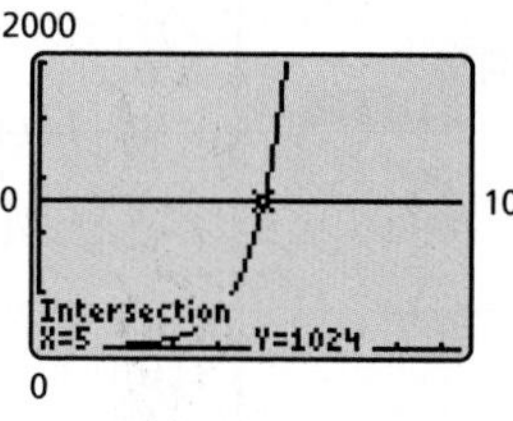

0 10
0

In the graph, find the x-value at the point of intersection.

The solution is $x = 5$.

Teacher to Teacher

When my class begins to solve logarithmic equations, I give them these basic rules for solving them.

1. Make single logs on each side of the equation.
2. When $\log a = \log b$, then equate a to b and solve.

Mohamad Elkhatib
Houston, TX

Use a table and graph to solve.

B $\log x - \log 2 \leq \log 75$

Use a graphing calculator. Enter $\log x - \log 2$ as **Y1** and $\log 75$ as **Y2**.

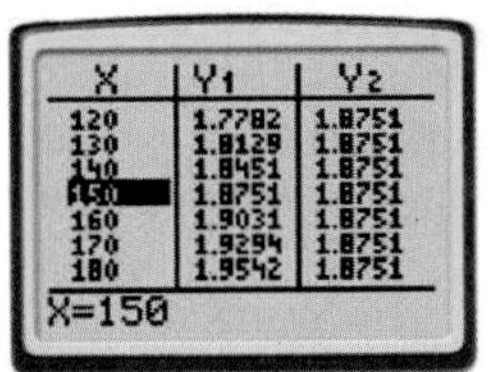

X	Y1	Y2
120	1.7782	1.8751
130	1.8129	1.8751
140	1.8451	1.8751
150	1.8751	1.8751
160	1.9031	1.8751
170	1.9294	1.8751
180	1.9542	1.8751

X=150

In the table, find the x-values where Y1 is less than or equal to Y2.

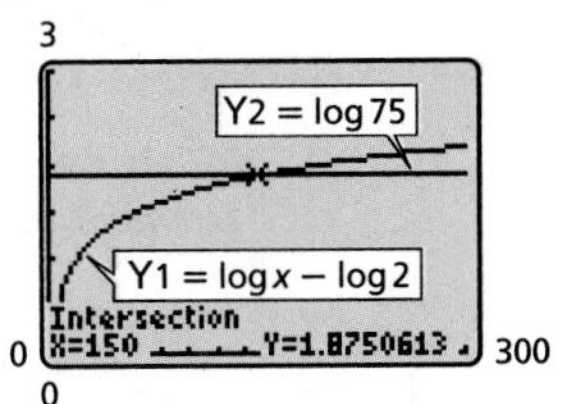

In the graph, find the x-value at the point of intersection.

The solution set is $\{x \mid 0 < x \leq 150\}$.

Check Use algebra.

$$\log x - \log 2 \leq \log 75$$

$$\log\left(\frac{x}{2}\right) \leq \log 75 \qquad \textit{Quotient Property of Logarithms}$$

$$10^{\log\left(\frac{x}{2}\right)} \leq 10^{\log 75} \qquad \textit{Use 10 as a base for both sides.}$$

$$\frac{x}{2} \leq 75 \qquad \textit{Inverse Property}$$

$$x \leq 150 \checkmark \qquad \textit{log x is only defined for } x > 0.$$

Use a table and graph to solve.

4a. $2^x = 4^{x-1}$ $x = 2$ **4b.** $2^x > 4^{x-1}$ $x < 2$ **4c.** $\log x^2 = 6$ $x = 1000$

THINK AND DISCUSS

1. Explain why a and b must be equal if $\log a = \log b$ $(a > 0, b > 0)$.

2. Give only the first step you would use to solve each equation.

a. $\log x^5 = 10$ **b.** $\log 2x + \log 2 = 1$

c. $x^4 = 100$ **d.** $\log(x + 1000) = 2$

e. $\log(x + 4) + \log x = 2$ **f.** $\log_6(x + 6) = 3$

3. Explain whether a logarithmic equation can have a negative number as a solution. Justify your answer. Give an example, if possible.

4. GET ORGANIZED Copy and complete the graphic organizer. Write the strategies and points to remember in your own words for both exponential and logarithmic equations.

Equation
- Exponential
  - Strategies to solve
  - Points to remember
- Logarithmic
  - Strategies to solve
  - Points to remember

Teaching Tip **Communicating Math** **Example 3D** leads to an *extraneous* solution. You may want to use this vocabulary before it is formally defined in Chapter 8 as it relates to radical equations.

Teaching Tip **Number Sense** When you are working with logs, it is often helpful to recognize when a number is a perfect power. In **Example 4A,** if students recognize 1024 as a power of 2, they can rewrite the equation as $2^{2x} = 2^{10}$, which is easily solved by setting the exponents equal.

Answers to *Check It Out*

4a. Intersection X=2 Y=4

b.

X	Y1	Y2
1	2	1
2	4	4
3	8	16
4	16	64
5	32	256
6	64	1024
7	128	4096

X=2

c.

X	Y1	Y2
700	5.6902	6
800	5.8062	6
900	5.9085	6
1000	6	6
1100	6.0828	6
1200	6.1584	6
1300	6.2279	6

X=1000

3 Close

Summarize

Review the key methods for solving exponential and logarithmic equations:

- Rewrite equations so that the bases are the same.
- Take the log of both sides.
- Use a table or graph.

Encourage students to become familiar with all three methods, so they can determine which one is most efficient in different situations.

ONGOING ASSESSMENT and INTERVENTION

***Diagnose Before* the Lesson**
7-5 Warm Up, TE p. 522

***Monitor During* the Lesson**
Check It Out! Exercises, SE pp. 522–525
Questioning Strategies, TE pp. 523–524

***Assess After* the Lesson**
7-5 Lesson Quiz, TE p. 528
Alternative Assessment, TE p. 528

Answers to *Think and Discuss*

1. If $\log a = \log b$, then $10^a = 10^b$. The exponents must be equal for the exponential expressions to be equal.
2. a. Write $\log x^5 = 10$ as $5\log x$.
   b. Write $\log 2x + \log 2$ as $\log 4x$.
   c. Take the log of both sides.
   d. Use 10 as a base for each side.
   e. Rewrite $\log(x + 4) + \log(x)$ as $\log(x^2 + 4x)$.
   f. Use 6 as a base for each side.
3. Yes; possible answer: $\log(-x) = 2$ has -100 as a solution.
4. See p. A9.

7-5 Exercises

Assignment Guide

Assign *Guided Practice* exercises as necessary.

If you finished Examples **1–2**
- **Basic** 21–27, 38
- **Average** 21–27, 38
- **Advanced** 21–27, 38

If you finished Examples **1–4**
- **Basic** 21–36, 39, 41–42, 44–46, 48–50, 54–62
- **Average** 21–36, 39–50, 53–62
- **Advanced** 21–38, 40, 43, 47–62

Homework Quick Check
Quickly check key concepts.
Exercises: 22, 27, 30, 36, 40

State Resources

go.hrw.com
State Resources Online
KEYWORD: MB7 Resources

7-5 Exercises

go.hrw.com
Homework Help Online
KEYWORD: MB7 7-5
Parent Resources Online
KEYWORD: MB7 Parent

GUIDED PRACTICE

1. **Vocabulary** You can solve a(n) __?__ by taking the logarithm of both sides. (*exponential equation* or *logarithmic equation*) **exponential equation**

SEE EXAMPLE 1 p. 522

Solve and check.

2. $4^{2x} = 32^{\frac{1}{2}}$ **$\frac{5}{8}$**
3. $9^x = 3^{x-2}$ **−2**
4. $2^x = 4^{x+1}$ **−2**
5. $4^x = 10$ **≈ 1.661**
6. $\left(\frac{1}{4}\right)^{2x} = \left(\frac{1}{2}\right)^x$ **0**
7. $2.4^{3x+1} = 9$ **≈ 0.503**

SEE EXAMPLE 2 p. 523

8. **Population** The population of a small coastal resort town, currently 3400, grows at a rate of 3% per year. This growth can be expressed by the exponential equation $P = 3400(1 + 0.03)^t$, where P is the population after t years. Find the number of years it will take for the population to exceed 10,000. **37 yr**

SEE EXAMPLE 3 p. 523

Solve.

9. $\log_2(7x + 1) = \log_2(2 - x)$ **$\frac{1}{8}$**
10. $\log_6(2x + 3) = 3$ **106.5**
11. $\log 72 - \log\left(\frac{2x}{3}\right) = 0$ **108**
12. $\log_3 x^9 = 12$ **≈ 4.33**
13. $\log_7(3 - 4x) = \log_7\left(\frac{x}{3}\right)$ **$\frac{9}{13}$**
14. $\log 50 + \log\left(\frac{x}{2}\right) = 2$ **4**
15. $\log x + \log(x + 48) = 2$ **2**
16. $\log\left(x + \frac{3}{10}\right) + \log x + 1 = 0$ **$\frac{1}{5}$**

SEE EXAMPLE 4 p. 524

Use a table and graph to solve.

17. $2^{2x+1} = 256$ **3.5**
18. $2^x 3^x \le 7776$ **$x \le 5$**
19. $2\log x^4 = 16$ **100**
20. $x > 10\log x$ **$0 < x <\approx 1.37$ or $x > 10$**

PRACTICE AND PROBLEM SOLVING

Independent Practice	
For Exercises	See Example
21–26	1
27	2
28–33	3
34–36	4

Extra Practice
Skills Practice p. S17
Application Practice p. S38

Solve and check.

21. $2^{x-1} = \frac{1}{64}$ **−5**
22. $\left(\frac{1}{4}\right)^x = 8^{x-1}$ **0.6**
23. $\left(\frac{1}{5}\right)^{x-2} = 125^{\frac{x}{2}}$ **0.8**
24. $\left(\frac{1}{2}\right)^{-x} = 1.6$ **≈ 0.678**
25. $(1.5)^{x-1} = 14.5$ **≈ 7.595**
26. $3^{\frac{x}{2}+1} = 12.2$ **≈ 2.554**
27. **Pets** A veterinarian has instructed Harrison to give his 75 lb dog one 325 mg aspirin tablet for arthritis. The amount of aspirin A remaining in the dog's body after t minutes can be expressed by $A = 325\left(\frac{1}{2}\right)^{\frac{t}{15}}$. Write and solve a logarithmic inequality to find the time it takes for the amount of aspirin to drop below 50 mg.

27. $\frac{15\log\left(\frac{A}{325}\right)}{\log\left(\frac{1}{2}\right)} < t$; **41 min**

Solve.

28. $\log_3(7x) = \log_3(2x + 0.5)$ **0.1**
29. $\log_2\left(1 + \frac{x}{2}\right) = 4$ **30**
30. $\log 5x - \log(15.5) = 2$ **310**
31. $\log_5 x^4 = 2.5$ **≈ 2.73**
32. $\log x - \log\left(\frac{x}{100}\right) = x$ **2**
33. $2 - \log 3x = \log\left(\frac{x}{12}\right)$ **20**

Use a table and graph to solve.

34. $2 \cdot 3^{x-1} = 162$ **5**
35. $4x < 2^{x+1}$ **$x < 1$**
36. $\log(2x - 17) + \log x \ge 2$ **$x \ge 12.5$**

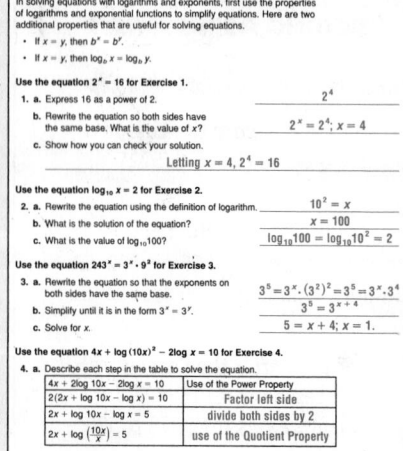

7-5 READING STRATEGIES

In solving equations with logarithms and exponents, first use the properties of logarithms and exponential functions to simplify equations. Here are two additional properties that are useful for solving equations.

- If $x = y$, then $b^x = b^y$.
- If $x = y$, then $\log_b x = \log_b y$.

Use the equation $2^x = 16$ for Exercise 1.

1. a. Express 16 as a power of 2. 2^4
   b. Rewrite the equation so both sides have the same base. What is the value of x? $2^x = 2^4$; $x = 4$
   c. Show how you can check your solution. Letting $x = 4$, $2^4 = 16$

Use the equation $\log_{10} x = 2$ for Exercise 2.

2. a. Rewrite the equation using the definition of logarithm. $10^2 = x$
   b. What is the solution of the equation? $x = 100$
   c. What is the value of $\log_{10}100$? $\log_{10}100 = \log_{10}10^2 = 2$

Use the equation $243^x = 3^x \cdot 9^2$ for Exercise 3.

3. a. Rewrite the equation so that the exponents on both sides have the same base. $3^5 = 3^x \cdot (3^2)^2 = 3^5 = 3^x \cdot 3^4$
   b. Simplify until it is in the form $3^x = 3^y$. $3^5 = 3^{x+4}$
   c. Solve for x. $5 = x + 4$; $x = 1$.

Use the equation $4x + \log(10x)^2 - 2\log x = 10$ for Exercise 4.

4. a. Describe each step in the table to solve the equation.

$4x + 2\log 10x - 2\log x = 10$	Use of the Power Property
$2(2x + \log 10x - \log x) = 10$	Factor left side
$2x + \log 10x - \log x = 5$	divide both sides by 2
$2x + \log\left(\frac{10x}{x}\right) = 5$	use of the Quotient Property

   b. Simplify and solve the resulting equation. $2x + 1 = 5$; $x = 2$

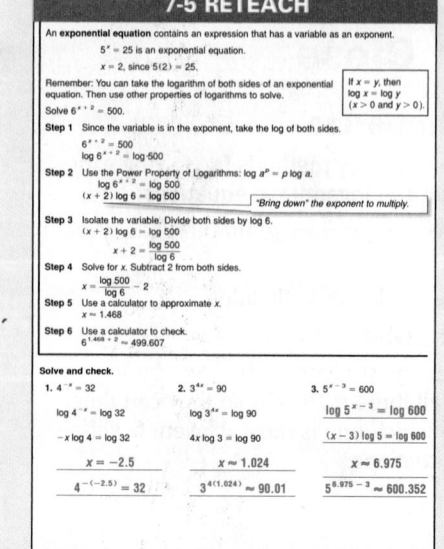

7-5 RETEACH

An **exponential equation** contains an expression that has a variable as an exponent.

$5^x = 25$ is an exponential equation.

$x = 2$, since $5(2) = 25$.

Remember: You can take the logarithm of both sides of an exponential equation. Then use other properties of logarithms to solve.

If $x = y$, then $\log x = \log y$ ($x > 0$ and $y > 0$).

Solve $6^{x+2} = 500$.

Step 1 Since the variable is in the exponent, take the log of both sides.
$6^{x+2} = 500$
$\log 6^{x+2} = \log 500$

Step 2 Use the Power Property of Logarithms: $\log a^p = p\log a$.
$\log 6^{x+2} = \log 500$
$(x + 2)\log 6 = \log 500$
"Bring down" the exponent to multiply.

Step 3 Isolate the variable. Divide both sides by log 6.
$(x + 2)\log 6 = \log 500$
$x + 2 = \frac{\log 500}{\log 6}$

Step 4 Solve for x. Subtract 2 from both sides.
$x = \frac{\log 500}{\log 6} - 2$

Step 5 Use a calculator to approximate x.
$x \approx 1.468$

Step 6 Use a calculator to check.
$6^{1.468+2} \approx 499.607$

Solve and check.

1. $4^{-x} = 32$
   $\log 4^{-x} = \log 32$
   $-x\log 4 = \log 32$
   $x = -2.5$
   $4^{-(-2.5)} = 32$
2. $3^{4x} = 90$
   $\log 3^{4x} = \log 90$
   $4x\log 3 = \log 90$
   $x \approx 1.024$
   $3^{4(1.024)} \approx 90.01$
3. $5^{x-3} = 600$
   $\log 5^{x-3} = \log 600$
   $(x - 3)\log 5 = \log 600$
   $x \approx 6.975$
   $5^{6.975-3} \approx 600.352$

37. Solve $\log x = \log(x^2 - 12)$. Explain your answer. **$\log(-3)$ is undefined, so the only solution is $x = 4$.**

38. Solve $5^{2x} = 100$ to the nearest hundredth. **1.43**

39. Solve $2^{x+2} = 64$ using more than one method. **4**

40. **Photography** On many cameras, the amount of light admitted through the lens can be controlled by changing the size of the opening, or *aperture*. The size of the aperture is measured as an f-stop setting. The relationship between the f-stop and the amount of light admitted can be represented by the equation $n = \log_2 \frac{1}{\ell}$, where n is the change in f-stop setting from the starting value, f/5.6.

F-stop Setting	f/2	f/2.8	f/4	f/5.6	f/8	f/11	f/16
Change in F-stop Setting	−3	−2	−1	0	1	2	3

a. Solve the equation for ℓ when the f-stop setting is increased to f/16. $\frac{1}{8}$

b. Solve the equation for n when the light admitted through the lens is twice the amount at f/5.6. What is the f-stop setting? Use a calculator to verify the solution. **−1; the f-stop setting is f/4.**

41. **Music** The frequency of a note on the piano, in Hz, is related to its position on the keyboard by the function $f(n) = 440 \cdot 2^{\frac{n}{12}}$, where n is the number of keys above or below the note concert A. (A negative value for n means that the key is to the left of, or lower on the keyboard than, concert A.) Find the position n of the key that has a frequency of 110 Hz. **24 keys below concert A.**

42. **Finance** Suppose that $250 is deposited into an account that pays 4.5% compounded quarterly. The equation $A = P\left(1 + \frac{r}{4}\right)^n$ gives the amount A in the account after n quarters for an initial investment P that earns interest at a rate r. Solve for n to find how long it will take for the account to contain at least $500. (*Hint:* Divide both sides by P first.) **$n \approx 61.96$, so at least 62 quarters (15.5 yr)**

43. **Critical Thinking** How many real-number solutions are there for $\log x^2 < 2\log x$? Use a calculator to graph and verify the answer. Explain what the graph indicates about the answer.

44. **ERROR ANALYSIS** When a student solved $\log x + 4 = 8$, he arrived at 99,999,996. Give a possible reason for the error. **The student solved $\log(x + 4) = 8$.**

45. **Write About It** Describe two methods you can use to solve an exponential equation. Give an example of when you would use each method.

MULTI-STEP TEST PREP

46. This problem will prepare you for the Multi-Step Test Prep on page 552.

The number of farms in Iowa (in thousands) can be modeled by $N(t) = 119(0.987)^t$, where t is the number of years since 1980.

a. Has the number of farms in Iowa been increasing or decreasing since 1980? How can you tell? **Decreasing; 0.987 is less than 1.**

b. Find the number of farms in Iowa in 1980 and 2000. **≈ 119,000; ≈ 92,000**

c. According to the model, when will be the number of farms in Iowa be about 80,000? **2010**

43. **0; $\log x^2 = 2\log x$, no value of x satisfies the inequality; the graphs coincide, so there is no region where $\log x^2 < 2\log x$.**

LINK — Music

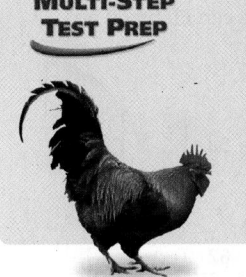

Pianos could be considered both percussion and stringed instruments, with hammers that hit each string. Pianos are usually located near the drums in an orchestra.

COMMON ERROR ALERT

In **Exercise 40,** students may attempt to include f-stop settings, such as f/5.6, when solving parts **a** and **b.** Emphasize that although these are ordered ratios correlated to the lens opening, they are used as labels for the purposes of this exercise.

MULTI-STEP TEST PREP **Exercise 46** involves using logarithms to solve exponential equations. This exercise prepares students for the Multi-Step Test Prep on page 552.

Answers

45. Possible answer: Write them so that the bases are the same, take the logarithm of both sides; for $10^x = 100^{2x}$ write both sides as a power of 10, for $10^x = 350$ take the log of both sides.

7-5 PROBLEM SOLVING

While John and Cody play their favorite video game, John drinks 4 cups of coffee and a cola, and Cody drinks 2 cups of brewed tea and a cup of iced tea. John recalls reading that up to 300 mg of caffeine is considered a moderate level of consumption per day. The rate at which caffeine is eliminated from the bloodstream is about 15% per hour.

Caffeine Content of Some Beverages	
Beverage	Caffeine (mg per serving)
Brewed coffee	103
Brewed tea	36
Iced tea	30
Cola	25

1. John wants to know how long it will take for the caffeine in his bloodstream to drop to a moderate level.
   a. How much caffeine did John consume? **437 mg**
   b. Write an equation showing the amount of caffeine in the bloodstream as a function of time. **$C(t) = C_0(1 - 0.15)^t$**
   c. How long, to the nearest tenth of an hour, will it take for the caffeine in John's system to reach a moderate level? **2.3 h**
2. a. Cody thinks that it will take at least 8 hours for the level of caffeine in John's system to drop to the same level of caffeine that Cody consumed. Explain how he can use his graphing calculator to prove that. **He can graph the equation $102 = 437(0.85)^t$ and find the value of t where $C(t)$ is 102.**
   b. What equations did Cody enter into his calculator? **$y = 102$ and $y = 437(0.85)^t$**
   c. Sketch the resulting graph.

Choose the letter for the best answer.

3. About how long would it take for the level of caffeine in Cody's system to drop by a factor of 2?
   A 0.2 hour
   B 1.6 hours
   C 2.7 hours
   (D) 4.3 hours
4. If John drank 6 cups of coffee and a cola, about how long would it take for the level of caffeine in his system to drop to a moderate level?
   F 0.5 hour
   G 1.6 hours
   (H) 4.7 hours
   J 5 3 hours

7-5 CHALLENGE

Newton's Law of Cooling states that the rate of heat loss of an object is proportional to the difference in temperatures between the object and its surrounding ambient temperature. This phenomenon is modeled with a differential equation and that equation may be solved to give

$$T(t) = T_A + [T_0 - T_A]\, b^t$$

where $T(t)$ is the varying temperature of the object at a given time, t, T_A is the surrounding ambient temperature, T_0 is the initial temperature of the object, and b is a constant that depends on the material the object is composed of and how fast it heats or cools.

Suppose you decided to make a cup of hot chocolate heated to 180°F in the kitchen that is at 72°F.

1. Solve the above equation for the constant b.
   $T(t) - T_A = [T_0 - T_A]\, b^t$; $\frac{T(t) - T_A}{T_0 - T_A} = b^t$; $\log\left(\frac{T(t) - T_A}{T_0 - T_A}\right) = t \log b$; $\frac{\log\left(\frac{T(t) - T_A}{T_0 - T_A}\right)}{t} = \log b$; $10^{\left(\frac{\log\left(\frac{T(t) - T_A}{T_0 - T_A}\right)}{t}\right)} = b$
2. If the cup of hot chocolate cooled to 150°F in 15 minutes, find the value of the constant b in the above equation. Express your answer to five decimal places. **$b \approx 0.97854$**
3. Solve the above equation for t. **First 3 steps same as #1; $\frac{\log\left(\frac{T(t) - T_A}{T_0 - T_A}\right)}{\log b} = t$**
4. Suppose you like your hot chocolate at the tepid temperature of 120°F. How long, to the nearest minute, will you have to wait until it cools to this temperature? **About 37 min**

To go along with your hot chocolate, you take a frozen cherry pie from the freezer and place it in the oven preheated to 350°F. Assume the freezer is at 32°F.

5. If the cherry pie comes to a temperature of 120°F in 20 minutes, find the value of the constant b in the above equation. Express your answer to 5 decimal places. **$b \approx 0.98362$**
6. How long will it take for the pie to reach its final temperature of 220°F? **About 55 min**
7. The pie is taken out of the oven and set on a table in a room at 80°F. In 10 minutes it has cooled to 185°F. However, the pie must cool to 125°F before it is ready to eat. How much longer will you have to wait? **About 30 min**

7-5 PRACTICE A

7-5 PRACTICE C

7-5 PRACTICE B

Solve and check.

1. $5^{2x} = 20$ — **$x \approx 0.9307$**
2. $12^{2x-8} = 15$ — **$x \approx 4.5449$**
3. $2^{x+6} = 4$ — **$x = -4$**
4. $16^{5x} = 64^{x+7}$ — **$x = 3$**
5. $243^{0.2x} = 81^{x+5}$ — **$x \approx -6.67$**
6. $25^x = 125^{x-2}$ — **$x = 6$**
7. $\left(\frac{1}{2}\right)^x = 16^2$ — **$x = -8$**
8. $\left(\frac{1}{32}\right)^{2x} = 64$ — **$x = -0.6$**
9. $\left(\frac{1}{27}\right)^{x-6} = 27$ — **$x = 5$**

Solve.

10. $\log_4 x^5 = 20$ — **$x = 256$**
11. $\log_3 x^6 = 12$ — **$x = 9$**
12. $\log_4 (x - 6)^3 = 6$ — **$x = 22$**
13. $\log x - \log 10 = 14$ — **$x = 10^{15}$**
14. $\log x + \log 5 = 2$ — **$x = 20$**
15. $\log(x+9) = \log(2x-7)$ — **$x = 16$**
16. $\log(x+4) - \log 6 = 1$ — **$x = 56$**
17. $\log x^2 + \log 25 = 2$ — **$x = \pm 2$**
18. $\log(x-1)^2 = \log(-5x-1)$ — **$x = -1, -2$**

Use a table and graph to solve.

19. $2^{x-5} < 64$ — **$x < 11$**
20. $\log x^3 = 12$ — **$x = 10{,}000$**
21. $2^x 3^x = 1296$ — **$x = 4$**

Solve.

22. The population of a small farming community is declining at a rate of 7% per year. The decline can be expressed by the exponential equation $P = C(1 - 0.07)^t$, where P is the population after t years and C is the current population. If the population was 8,500 in 2004, when will the population be less than 6,000? **2009**

 Students who have difficulty with **Exercise 48** could plug in "friendly numbers." For instance, if $b = 10$, $x = 2$, and $y = 100$, the problem is reduced to finding the answer choice that is true for those values, and only choice **B** works.

Students who have difficulty with **Exercise 50** should remember to use the Quotient Property:

$\log_b x - \log_b y = \log_b \frac{x}{y}$

Journal

Have students explain how extraneous solutions occur.

Have students write and solve an equation to demonstrate each of the key methods of solving techniques used in **Examples 1** and **3**:

- Rewrite equations so that the bases are the same.
- Take the log of both sides.
- Use a table or graph.

Power Presentations with PowerPoint®

7-5 Lesson Quiz

Solve.

1. $4^{3x-1} = 8^{x+1}$ $x = \frac{5}{3}$
2. $3^{2x-1} = 20$ $x \approx 1.86$
3. $\log_7(5x + 3) = 3$ $x = 68$
4. $\log(3x + 1) - \log 4 = 2$ $x = 133$
5. $\log_4(x - 1) + \log_4(3x - 1) = 2$ $x = 3$
6. A single cell divides every 5 minutes. How long will it take for one cell to become more than 10,000 cells? 70 min
7. Use a table and graph to solve the equation $2^{3x} = 3^{3x-1}$. $x \approx 0.903$

Also available on transparency

47. **Meteorology** In one part of the atmosphere where the temperature is a constant –70°F, pressure can be expressed as a function of altitude by the equation $P(h) = 128(10)^{-0.0682h}$, where P is the atmospheric pressure in kilopascals (kPa) and h is the altitude in kilometers above sea level. The pressure ranges from 2.55 kPa to 22.9 kPa in this region.
   a. What are the lowest and highest altitudes where this model is appropriate? In what part of the atmosphere is the model useful? 11 km; 25 km; lower stratosphere and upper troposphere
   b. **What if...?** A kilopascal is 0.145 psi. Would the model predict a sea-level pressure less than or greater than the actual sea-level pressure, 14.7 psi? Explain. greater; It predicts a psi of 18.6.

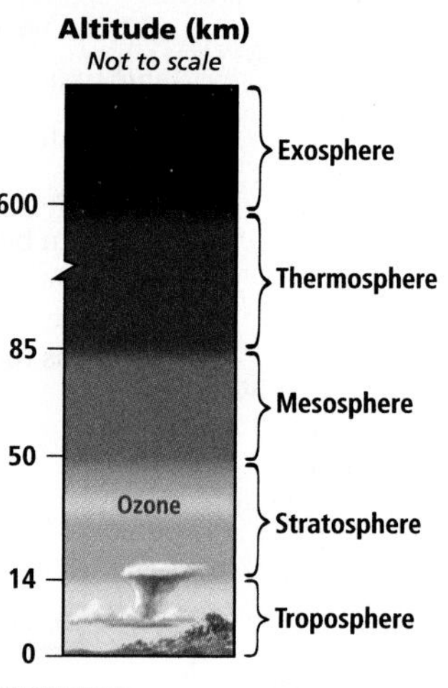

TEST PREP

48. What is the solution of the equation $b^x = c$?
   (A) $x = \frac{\log b}{\log c}$ (B) $x = \frac{\log c}{\log b}$ (C) $x = \frac{\log b}{c}$ (D) $x = \frac{\log c}{b}$

49. What is the solution of $\log(x - 21) = 2 - \log x$?
   (F) $x = 4$ (G) $x = \frac{25}{4}$ (H) $x = \frac{21}{2}$ (J) $x = 25$

50. Which expression has the greatest value when $p = 5$ and $q = 2$?
   (A) $\log 2p - \log 3q$ (C) $2\log q - 3\log p$
   (B) $\log p^2 - \log q^3$ (D) $\log p - \log q$

CHALLENGE AND EXTEND

51. If $\log_x x = x$, can the equation be solved for x? Explain. Possible answer: no; $x = x^x$, and $x^1 = x^x$, so $x = 1$, but $\log_1$ is not defined.
52. Solve $x = 0.125^{\log_2 5}$ algebraically. 0.008
53. For what domain is $\log_3 36 - \log_3 x > 1$? Use a calculator to graph and support your solution. $\{x \mid 0 < x < 12\}$

SPIRAL REVIEW

54. **Photography** It costs $0.75 to develop an 8-by-10-inch photograph and $0.35 to develop a 4-by-6-inch photograph. Eli has $5.25. Use x as the number of 8-by-10-inch photographs and y as the number of 4-by-6-inch photographs. *(Lesson 2-5)*
   a. Write an inequality for the number of each type of photograph Eli can buy. 54a. $0.75x + 0.35y \le 5.25$
   b. Graph the inequality. How many 4-by-6-inch photographs can Eli buy if he buys four 8-by-10-inch photographs? 6 photos

54b.

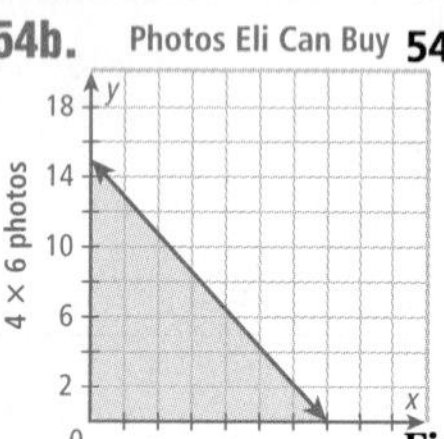

Find the determinant of each matrix. *(Lesson 4-4)*

55. $\begin{bmatrix} 4 & 2 \\ 1 & 7 \end{bmatrix}$ 26
56. $\begin{bmatrix} -1 & -5 \\ 9 & 10 \end{bmatrix}$ 35
57. $\begin{bmatrix} \frac{1}{2} & -1 \\ 0 & 6 \end{bmatrix}$ 3
58. $\begin{bmatrix} \frac{2}{3} & \frac{1}{3} \\ 6 & 9 \end{bmatrix}$ 4

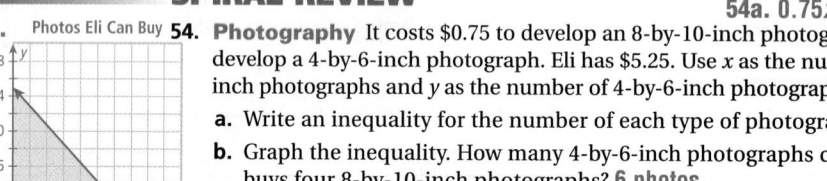

Use inverse operations to find $f^{-1}(x)$. *(Lesson 7-2)*

59. $f(x) = 4x + 3$ $f^{-1}(x) = \frac{1}{4}x - \frac{3}{4}$
60. $f(x) = 6(x - 2)$ $f^{-1}(x) = \frac{1}{6}x + 2$
61. $f(x) = \frac{x}{3} + 9$ $f^{-1}(x) = 3x - 27$
62. $f(x) = \frac{7x - 1}{5}$ $f^{-1}(x) = \frac{5}{7}x + \frac{1}{7}$

Exponents in Probability

You can use exponents to determine a probability when a certain experiment is repeated.

See Skills Bank page S70

Recall that the probability P of an event is $P(\text{Event } E) = \dfrac{\text{number of favorable outcomes}}{\text{total number of outcomes}}$.

For example, when rolling a number cube with six possible outcomes, the probability of rolling an odd prime number, 3 or 5, is $\frac{2}{6}$, or $\frac{1}{3}$. The probability of rolling an odd prime number two rolls in a row is $\frac{1}{3} \cdot \frac{1}{3}$. If the probability of an event is r and the events are independent, then the probability of getting the same result when the event is repeated n times is $P(\text{Event } E \text{ occurring } n \text{ times in succession}) = r^n$

Examples

A machine on an assembly line makes an acceptable product 90% of the time. The machine makes 10 samples of the product.

1 What is the probability that all 10 samples are acceptable, to the nearest percent?

$P(\text{All 10 samples are acceptable}) = 0.9^{10}$ *Substitute 0.9 for r and 10 for n in r^n.*

≈ 0.35 *Use a calculator.*

The probability that all 10 samples are acceptable is about 35%.

2 At what number of samples does the probability fall below 10%?

You can solve an inequality.

$0.9^n < 0.1$

$\log 0.9^n < \log 0.1$ *Take the log of both sides.*

$n \log 0.9 < \log 0.1$ *Use the Power Property of Logarithms.*

$n > \dfrac{\log 0.1}{\log 0.9}$ *← = −1* *← ≈ −0.0458*

$n > \approx 21.85$

For 22 or more samples, the probability that all are acceptable drops below 10%.

Try This

1. You toss a coin 6 times. Find the probability of getting heads every time.
2. You toss a number cube 10 times. Find the probability that no roll is a six.
3. A basketball player has a 70% chance of making each free throw. For what number of free throws does the probability of making them all drop below 10%? 7
4. A test contains multiple-choice questions with 4 choices for each question. For what number of questions does the probability of guessing all of them correctly drop below 0.01%? 7

1. $\frac{1}{64} \approx 0.016$; about 1.6%
2. $\left(\frac{5}{6}\right)^{10} \approx 0.162$; about 16.2%

Organizer

See Skills Bank page S70

Pacing:
Traditional $\frac{1}{2}$ day
Block $\frac{1}{4}$ day

Objective: Students apply exponents and logarithms to probability problems.

Teach

Remember

Students review probability and use exponents to solve probability problems.

INTERVENTION For additional review and practice on basic probability, see Skills Bank page S70.

Inclusion Remind students that the probability range is always from 0 to 1.

Close

Assess

Change the number of samples in part **a** and the 10% value in part **b** and ask students for the new solutions.

A field goal kicker has a 95% chance of making each extra point successfully.

a. What is the probability that the kicker makes the next 20 extra points? ≈ 0.36

b. For how many kicks does the probability of making all successful kicks drop below 25%? 28

State Resources

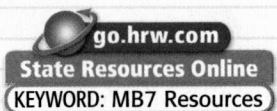

go.hrw.com
State Resources Online
KEYWORD: MB7 Resources

 **Organizer**

Use with Lesson 7-6

Pacing:

Traditional $\frac{1}{2}$ day

Block $\frac{1}{4}$ day

Objective: Use a spreadsheet to discover the "rule of 72."

Materials: spreadsheet software

 **Online Edition**

 **Countdown to Testing Week 16**

Resources

 ***Technology Lab Activities***

7-6 Lab Recording Sheet

Teach

Discuss

Students should understand that percents are actually decimals, and that the rule of 72 is actually the rule of 0.72. Be sure that students know how to copy and paste in a spreadsheet.

Close

Key Concept

The number of years it takes an investment to double can be estimated by the formula $N = \frac{72}{r}$.

Assessment

Journal Have students explain how they might find a rule for tripling time based upon the interest rate.

State Resources

7-6

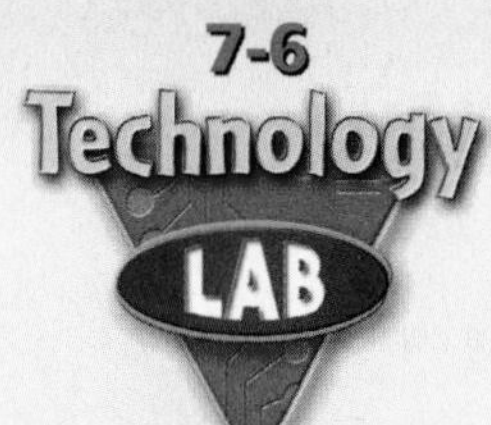

Explore the Rule of 72

You can use a spreadsheet to discover a rule to estimate the time needed to double an investment at different interest rates.

Use with Lesson 7-6

Activity

Use a spreadsheet to find the number of years it will take for an investment to double at 3% annual interest. Find the product of the interest rate and the doubling time.

Find a formula for doubling time as a function of interest rate. Use the compound interest formula.

$A = P\left(1+\frac{r}{n}\right)^{nt}$	*A is the total amount, P is the principal, r is the interest rate, n is the number of compounding periods, and t is the time in years.*
$2 = 1(1+r)^t$	*Substitute 2 for A, 1 for P, and 1 for n. Then solve for t.*
$\log 2 = \log(1+r)^t$	*Take the log of both sides.*
$\log 2 = t\log(1+r)$	*Power Property of Logarithms*
$t = \frac{\log 2}{\log(1+r)}$	*Divide both sides by log(1 + r) to solve for t.*

1. In cells A1 through C1, enter column headings for rate, doubling time, and their product. Enter **3%** in cell A2.

2. In cell B2, enter the formula derived above as shown in the screenshot.

	A	B	C
1	Rate	Doubling Time	Product
2	3%	=LOG(2)/LOG(1+A2)	

3. In cell C2, enter the formula for the product as shown.

	A	B	C
1	Rate	Doubling Time	Product
2	3%	23.44977225	=A2*B2

The spreadsheet shows that at 3% annual interest, an investment will double in about 23.4 years. The product of the interest rate and the doubling time is about 70.

	A	B	C
1	Rate	Doubling Time	Product
2	3%	23.44977225	0.703493168

Try This

1. Complete cells A3 through A20 with interest rates from 3.5% to 12%.
2. Copy and paste the formula from cell B2 into cells B3 through B20.
3. Copy and paste the formula from cell C2 into cells C3 through C20.
4. What is the lowest interest rate that gives you a doubling time less than 9 years? **8.5%**
5. **Make a Conjecture** The rule of 72 is a rule used by investors to estimate the time it will take for an investment to double at a certain rate. Explain why.
6. **Critical Thinking** Write an equation for the rule of 72. $d = \frac{0.72}{r}$

5. The product of the interest rate written as a percent and the doubling time is about 72.

Answers

1.

	Rate
A3	0.035
A4	0.04
A5	0.045
⋮	⋮
A19	0.115
A20	0.12

2.

	Doubling Time
B3	20.14879
B4	17.67299
B5	15.7473
⋮	⋮
B19	6.367654
B20	6.116255

3.

	Product
C3	0.705208
C4	0.70692
C5	0.708629
⋮	⋮
C19	0.733951
C20	0.735619

7-6 The Natural Base, *e*

IN **A2.6.4** Solve problems that can be modeled using exponential and logarithmic equations, interpret the solutions and determine . . . whether the solutions are reasonable using technology as appropriate.

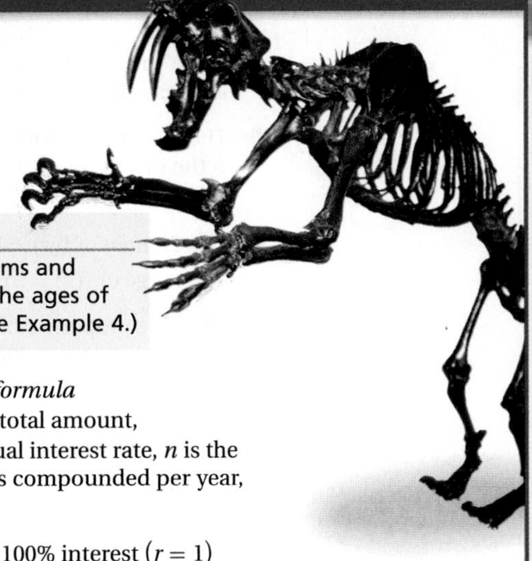

Objectives
Use the number e to write and graph exponential functions representing real-world situations.

Solve equations and problems involving e or natural logarithms.

Vocabulary
natural logarithm
natural logarithmic function

Why learn this?
Scientists use natural logarithms and carbon dating to determine the ages of ancient bones and fossils. (See Example 4.)

Recall the *compound interest formula* $A = P\left(1 + \frac{r}{n}\right)^{nt}$, where A is the total amount, P is the principal, r is the annual interest rate, n is the number of times the interest is compounded per year, and t is the time in years.

Suppose that \$1 is invested at 100% interest $(r = 1)$ compounded n times for one year as represented by the function $f(n) = \left(1 + \frac{1}{n}\right)^n$.

As n gets very large, interest is *continuously compounded*. Examine the graph of $f(n) = \left(1 + \frac{1}{n}\right)^n$. The function has a horizontal asymptote. As n becomes infinitely large, the value of the function approaches approximately 2.7182818.... This number is called *e*. Like π, the constant e is an irrational number.

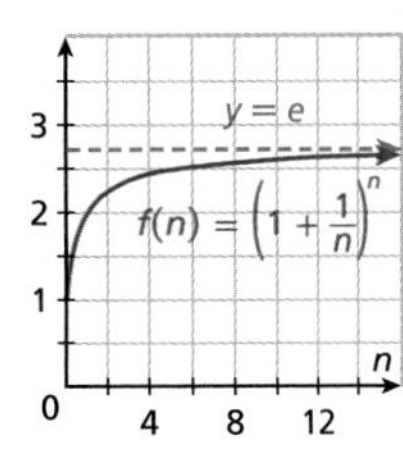

Caution!
The decimal value of e looks like it repeats: 2.718281828.... The value is actually 2.7182818284590.... There is no repeating portion.

Exponential functions with e as a base have the same properties as the functions you have studied. The graph of $f(x) = e^x$ is like other graphs of exponential functions, such as $f(x) = 3^x$.

The domain of $f(x) = e^x$ is all real numbers. The range is $\{y \mid y > 0\}$.

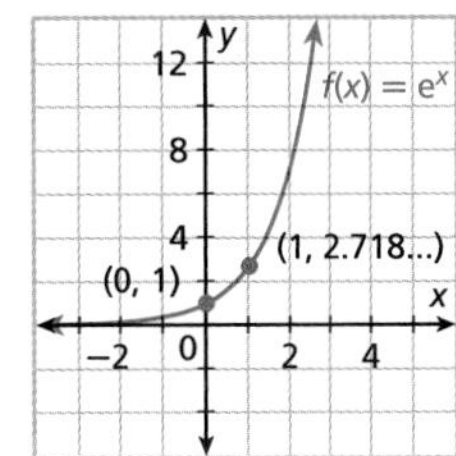

EXAMPLE 1 Graphing Exponential Functions

Graph $f(x) = e^x + 2$.

Make a table. Because e is irrational, the table values are rounded to the nearest tenth.

x	−3	−2	−1	0	1	2	3
$f(x) = e^x + 2$	2.0	2.1	2.4	3	4.7	9.4	22.1

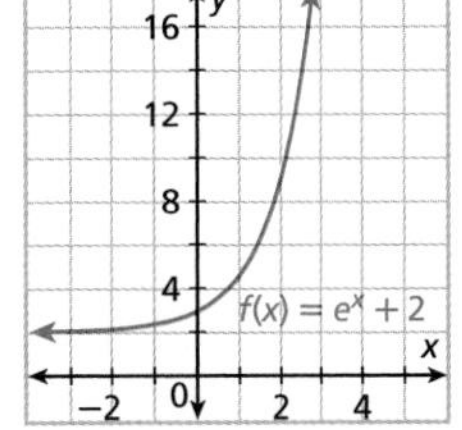

CHECK IT OUT! 1. Graph $f(x) = e^x - 3$.

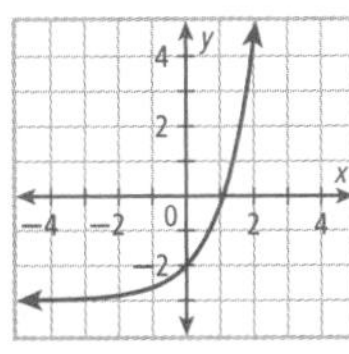

7-6 Organizer

Pacing: Traditional $1\frac{1}{2}$ days
Block $\frac{3}{4}$ day

Objectives: Use the number e to write and graph exponential functions representing real-world situations.

Solve equations and problems involving e or natural logarithms.

Online Edition
Tutorial Videos, Graphing Calculator

Countdown to Testing Week 16

Power Presentations with PowerPoint®

Warm Up

Simplify.

1. $\log 10^x$ x
2. $\log_b b^{3w}$ $3w$
3. $10^{\log z}$ z
4. $b^{\log_b (x-1)}$ $x - 1$
5. $\left(\frac{1}{3}\right)3^{x+1}$ 3^x

Also available on transparency

Math Humor

Kurt: What are you studying?
Amy: e!
Kurt: Natural logarithms?
Amy: No, I mean "eee!" There's a wasp on your leg!

1 Introduce

EXPLORATION

7-6 The Natural Base, e

In this Exploration, you will investigate the expression $\left(1 + \frac{1}{n}\right)^n$.

1. Evaluate $\left(1 + \frac{1}{n}\right)^n$ for n = 1.
2. Evaluate $\left(1 + \frac{1}{n}\right)^n$ for n = 2.
3. You can use your calculator to help you evaluate the expression for larger values of n. First enter the expression as the function Y1. Then press 2nd MODE to return to the home screen. Press VARS, scroll right to Y-VARS, select 1:Function, and choose 1:Y1. Now you can evaluate the function for any input by entering a value in parentheses as shown.
4. Use your calculator to evaluate the expression for n = 10,000, n = 100,000, and n = 1,000,000.

THINK AND DISCUSS

5. **Describe** what happens to the value of the expression as n gets larger.
6. **Explain** what you think the graph of the function $f(n) = \left(1 + \frac{1}{n}\right)^n$ would look like.

Motivate

Discuss with students their previous experience with the irrational number π, which is so important to geometric relationships. Explain that in this lesson they will learn about another irrational constant, e, which is also applicable to many situations.

Explorations and answers are provided in the *Explorations* binder.

State Resources

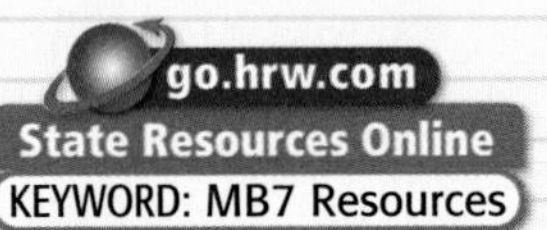

go.hrw.com
State Resources Online
KEYWORD: MB7 Resources

Technology Tell students that most calculators can calculate only logs with two bases, one of which is base 10. Ask students to study their calculators and find any keys that might relate to logs. If necessary, guide them to noticing the similarity of the LOG key and the LN key.

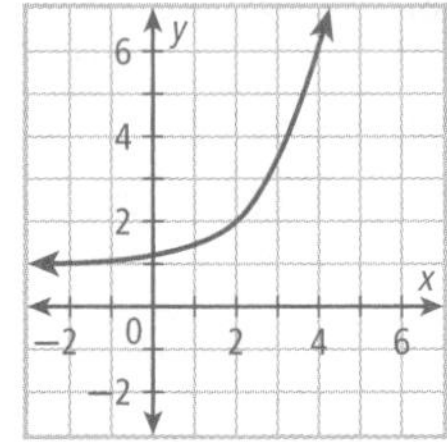

Power Presentations with PowerPoint®

Additional Examples

Example 1

Graph $f(x) = e^{x-2} + 1$.

Example 2

Simplify.

A. $\ln e^{0.15t}$ $0.15t$

B. $e^{3\ln(x+1)}$ $(x+1)^3$

C. $\ln e^{2x} + \ln e^{x}$ $3x$

Example 3

What is the total amount for an investment of \$500 invested at 5.25% for 40 years and compounded continuously? \$4083.08

Also available on transparency

INTERVENTION

Questioning Strategies

EXAMPLE 1

- How does the graph of $f(x) = e^x$ compare to the graphs of $g(x) = 2^x$ and $h(x) = 3^x$?

EXAMPLE 2

- What properties do you use to simplify these expressions?

EXAMPLE 3

- How does compounding continuously differ from compounding daily?

A logarithm with a base of e is called a **natural logarithm** and is abbreviated as "ln" (rather than as $\log_e$). Natural logarithms have the same properties as log base 10 and logarithms with other bases.

The **natural logarithmic function** $f(x) = \ln x$ is the inverse of the natural exponential function $f(x) = e^x$.

The domain of $f(x) = \ln x$ is $\{x \mid x > 0\}$.
The range of $f(x) = \ln x$ is all real numbers.

All of the properties of logarithms from Lesson 7-4 also apply to natural logarithms.

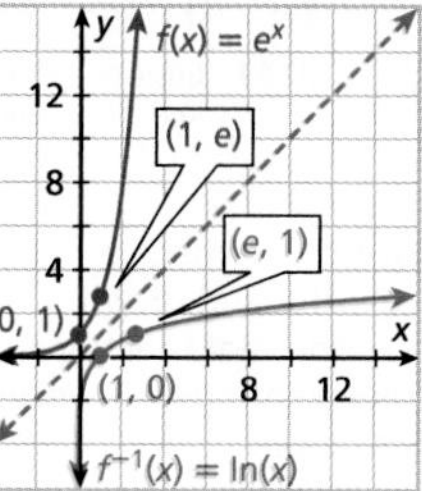

EXAMPLE 2 Simplifying Expressions with e or ln

Simplify.

A $\ln e^{-2t}$

$\ln e^{-2t} = -2t$

B $e^{\ln(t-1)}$

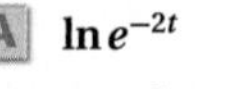

$e^{\ln(t-1)} = t - 1$

C $e^{5\ln x}$

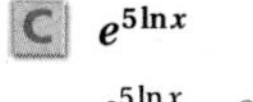

$e^{5\ln x} = e^{\ln x^5} = x^5$

CHECK IT OUT! Simplify.

2a. $\ln e^{3.2}$ 3.2 **2b.** $e^{2\ln x}$ x^2 **2c.** $\ln e^{x+4y}$ $x + 4y$

The formula for continuously compounded interest is $A = Pe^{rt}$, where A is the total amount, P is the principal, r is the annual interest rate, and t is the time in years.

EXAMPLE 3 Economics Application

What is the total amount for an investment of \$1000 invested at 5% for 10 years compounded continuously?

$A = Pe^{rt}$ *Substitute 1000 for P, 0.05 for r, and 10 for t.*

$A = 1000e^{0.05(10)}$

$A \approx 1648.72$ *Use the e^x key on a calculator.*

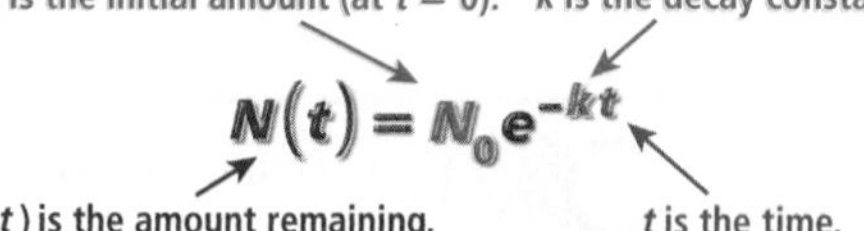

The total amount is \$1648.72.

CHECK IT OUT! **3.** What is the total amount for an investment of \$100 invested at 3.5% for 8 years and compounded continuously? \$132.31

The *half-life* of a substance is the time it takes for half of the substance to breakdown or convert to another substance during the process of decay. Natural decay is modeled by the function below.

N_0 is the initial amount (at $t = 0$). k is the decay constant.

$$N(t) = N_0 e^{-kt}$$

$N(t)$ is the amount remaining. t is the time.

2 Teach

Guided Instruction

Review the rules of exponents and logarithms and emphasize that they all work with e as the base. Remind them that a base only needs to be a positive *real* number $\neq 1$.

Lead students through compounding interest at smaller and smaller intervals and explain that there is a limit for the compounded amount. Then discuss the function $f(x) = e^{-x}$ and ask whether it represents growth or decay. decay Explain that the half-life formula is a transformation of the decay function.

Reaching All Learners

Through Number Sense

Lead students though an activity where they look at the effects of each of the following, using the numbers from **Example 3.**

- doubling the size of an initial investment
- doubling the interest rate
- doubling the time of the investment

Have them compare the results and make some conclusions.

EXAMPLE 4 Paleontology Application

A paleontologist uncovers a fossil of a saber-toothed cat in California. He analyzes the fossil and concludes that the specimen contains 15% of its original carbon-14. Carbon-14 has a half-life of 5730 years. Use carbon-14 dating to determine the age of the fossil.

Step 1 Find the decay constant for carbon-14.

$N(t) = N_0 e^{-kt}$ — *Use the natural decay function.*

$\frac{1}{2} = 1e^{-k(5730)}$ — *Substitute 1 for N_0, 5730 for t, and $\frac{1}{2}$ for N(t), because half of the initial quantity will remain.*

$\ln\frac{1}{2} = \ln e^{-5730k}$ — *Simplify and take the ln of both sides.*

$\ln 2^{-1} = -5730k$ — *Write $\frac{1}{2}$ as 2^{-1}, and simplify the right side.*

$-\ln 2 = -5730k$ — *$\ln 2^{-1} = -1\ln 2 = -\ln 2$*

$k = \frac{\ln 2}{5730} \approx 0.00012$

Step 2 Write the decay function and solve for *t*.

$N(t) = N_0 e^{-0.00012t}$ — *Substitute 0.00012 for k.*

$15 = 100e^{-0.00012t}$ — *Substitute 100 for N_0 and 15 for N(t), since N(t) is 15% of N_0.*

$0.15 = e^{-0.00012t}$ — *Divide both sides by 100.*

$\ln 0.15 = \ln e^{-0.00012t}$ — *Take the ln of both sides.*

$\ln 0.15 = -0.00012t$ — *Simplify.*

$t = -\frac{\ln 0.15}{0.00012} \approx 15{,}809$

The fossil is approximately 15,800 years old.

4. Determine how long it will take for 650 mg of a sample of chromium-51, which has a half-life of about 28 days, to decay to 200 mg. ≈ **47.6 days**

THINK AND DISCUSS

1. Tell how *e* and π are alike. Tell how they are different.
2. Explain how *e* and ln are related.

3. **GET ORGANIZED** Copy and complete the graphic organizer. Fill in each box to compare and contrast the two kinds of logarithms. Give general forms and examples. Simplify, if appropriate.

	Common Logarithms	Natural Logarithms
Base		
Logarithmic Form		
Exponential Form		
$\log_b 1$		
$\log_b b$		
$\log_b b^x$		
$b^{\log_b x}$		

Power Presentations with PowerPoint®

Additional Examples

Example 4

Plutonium-239 (Pu-239) has a half-life of 24,110 years. How long does it take for a 1 g sample of Pu-239 to decay to 0.1 g?

≈ 80,000 yr

Also available on transparency

INTERVENTION
Questioning Strategies

EXAMPLE 4

- What is a decay constant?
- Why don't you need to know the initial amount in a problem involving half-life?

Critical Thinking Have students consider where they could start solving if the half-life were changed to 4000 years in **Example 4.** Note that solving one problem often gives you a head start in solving related problems.

Teaching Tip

Reading Math The notation "ln*x*" dates back only to 1893 and was invented by Irving Stringham, a professor of mathematics at The University of California at Berkeley.

3 Close

Summarize

Reiterate that the number e, which is approximately 2.718, is the base of the natural logarithmic function $f(x) = \ln x$. A natural logarithm behaves, in all ways, like a logarithm in any other base. Its importance is its role in applications in physics, biology, and economics (such as continuously compounded interest). The number e also plays a critical role in calculus.

ONGOING ASSESSMENT and INTERVENTION

***Diagnose Before* the Lesson**
7-6 Warm Up, TE p. 531

***Monitor During* the Lesson**
Check It Out! Exercises, SE pp. 531–533
Questioning Strategies, TE pp. 532–533

***Assess After* the Lesson**
7-6 Lesson Quiz, TE p. 536
Alternative Assessment, TE p. 536

Answers to *Think and Discuss*

1. Possible answer: e and π are irrational constants. π is a ratio of parts of a circle and is greater than e.
2. e^x and $\ln x$ are inverse functions. ln represents the logarithm, or exponent, when e is used as a base.
3. See p. A9.

7-6 Exercises

Assignment Guide

Assign *Guided Practice* exercises as necessary.

If you finished Examples **1–2**
Basic 13–20
Average 13–20
Advanced 13–20, 44

If you finished Examples **1–4**
Basic 13–23, 27–36, 39–44, 48–58
Average 13–25, 27–36, 38–44, 47–58
Advanced 13–26, 31–38, 40–58

Homework Quick Check
Quickly check key concepts.
Exercises: 14, 18, 20–22, 30

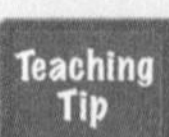

Inclusion For students unsure of how to begin **Exercises 23, 24,** and **26,** remind them to consider the Change of Base Formula from Lesson 7-4.

Answers

2–5, 13–16. See p. A34.

24. $\log x = \frac{\ln x}{\ln 10}$ by change of base, so $\ln 10(\log x) = \ln 10\left(\frac{\ln x}{\ln 10}\right)$ $\ln 10(\log x) = \ln x$

25c. See p. A34.

State Resources

7-6 Exercises

go.hrw.com
Homework Help Online
KEYWORD: MB7 7-6
Parent Resources Online
KEYWORD: MB7 Parent

GUIDED PRACTICE

1. **Vocabulary** Write the logarithm of a number x to the natural base e as a function of x. This function is called the __?__. **$f(x) = \ln x$; natural logarithm**

SEE EXAMPLE 1 p. 531

Graph.

2. $f(x) = e^x - 4$
3. $f(x) = -e^x$
4. $f(x) = 4 - e^x$
5. $f(x) = e^{1-x}$

SEE EXAMPLE 2 p. 532

Simplify.

6. $\ln e^1$ **1**
7. $\ln e^{x-y}$ **$x - y$**
8. $\ln e^{\left(-\frac{x}{3}\right)}$ **$-\frac{x}{3}$**
9. $e^{\ln 2x}$ **$2x$**
10. $e^{3 \ln x}$ **x^3**

SEE EXAMPLE 3 p. 532

11. **Economics** Emma receives $7750 and invests it in an account that earns 4% interest compounded continuously. What is the total amount of her investment after 5 years? **$9465.87**

SEE EXAMPLE 4 p. 533

12. **Physics** Technetium-99m, a radioisotope used to image the skeleton and the heart muscle, has a half-life of about 6 hours. Find the decay constant. Use the decay function $N(t) = N_0 e^{-kt}$ to determine the amount of a 250 mg dose that remains after 24 hours. **$\approx$ 16 mg**

PRACTICE AND PROBLEM SOLVING

Independent Practice

For Exercises	See Example
13–16	1
17–20	2
21	3
22	4

Extra Practice
Skills Practice p. S17
Application Practice p. S38

Graph.

13. $f(x) = e^x + 1$
14. $f(x) = e^x - 1$
15. $f(x) = 1 - e^x$
16. $f(x) = 10 - e^x$

Simplify.

17. $\ln e^0$ **0**
18. $\ln e^{2a}$ **$2a$**
19. $e^{\ln(c+2)}$ **$c + 2$**
20. $e^{4 \ln x}$ **x^4**

21. **Economics** Aidan has $7565 in his checking account. He invests $5000 of it in an account that earns 3.5% interest compounded continuously. What is the total amount of his investment after 3 years? **$\approx$ $5553.55**

22. **Environment** An accident in 1986 at the Chernobyl nuclear plant in the Ukraine released a large amount of plutonium (Pu-239) into the atmosphere. The half-life of Pu-239 is about 24,110 years. Find the decay constant. Use the function $N(t) = N_0 e^{-kt}$ to find what remains of an initial 20 grams of Pu-239 after 5000 years. How long will it take for these 20 grams to decay to 1 gram? **$k \approx 0.000029$; $\approx$ 17 g; $\approx$ 100,000 yr**

23. **Calculator** Find the approximate values of $\ln 10$ and $\log e$.
    a. How are these numbers related?
    b. How can you use the change of base formula to support your answer?

23. $\ln 10 \approx 2.3$; $\log e \approx 0.43$; $\ln 10 = \frac{1}{\log e}$

24. Show that $\ln x = \ln 10 \times \log x$.

25. **Multi-Step** Newton's law of cooling states that the temperature of an object decreases exponentially as a function of time, according to $T = T_s + (T_0 - T_s)e^{-kt}$, where T_0 is the initial temperature of the liquid, T_s is the surrounding temperature, and k is a constant. For a time in minutes, the constant for coffee is approximately 0.283. The corner coffee shop has an air temperature of 70°F and serves coffee at 206°F. Coffee experts say coffee tastes best at 140°F.
    a. How long does it take for the coffee to reach its best temperature? **$t \approx$ 2.4 min**
    b. The air temperature on the patio is 86°F. How long does it take for coffee to reach its best temperature there? **$t \approx$ 2.8 min**
    c. Graph the cooling functions from parts **a** and **b.** Use the graph to find the time it takes for the coffee to cool to 71°F.

7-6 READING STRATEGIES

Definition	Facts
The number e is an irrational constant like π. You can estimate e by using very large values of n in the formula. $f(n) = \left(1 + \frac{1}{n}\right)^n \approx 2.7182818...$ $e \approx 2.7182818...$	A logarithm with base e is called a natural logarithm ($\ln x$). The functions e^x and $\ln x$ have the same properties as the other exponential and logarithmic functions you have studied.
Example (compound interest)	**Useful Hints**
For a **principal** investment of $100 with a growth **rate** of 5% for 10 **years** compounded continuously, the total **amount** will be: $A = Pe^{rt} = 100 \cdot e^{0.05 \times 10} = \$164.87$	You can use the property of inverse functions to solve many problems containing e and ln. For example: $\ln e^3 = 3$ and $e^{\ln 3} = 3$

Answer each question.

1. a. Rewrite $e^{3 \ln x}$ using the Power Property of logarithms. **$e^{3 \ln x} = e^{\ln x^3}$**
   b. Now simplify. **x^3**
2. The graph shows $g(x) = e^x$ and $g^{-1}(x) = \ln x$.
   a. Label each curve with the correct function.
   b. What transformation is represented by the 2 curves?
   Reflection over the line $y = x$
   c. Explain how you can tell that they are inverse functions.
   Possible answer: The x- and y-values of each point in one graph are reversed in the other graph.

$g(x) = e^x$
$g^{-1}(x) = \ln x$

3. $A = Pe^{rt}$ is a formula used for continuously compounded interest.
   a. Which variable represents the principal or starting amount? **P**
   b. Which variable represents the time length of the investment? **t**
   c. Which variable represents the rate of interest paid on the investment? **r**

7-6 RETEACH

The **natural logarithmic function**, $f(x) = \ln x$, is the inverse of the exponential function with the natural base e, $f(x) = e^x$.

The constant e is an irrational number. $e \approx 2.71828....$

Properties of logarithms apply to the natural logarithm.

In particular:

$\ln 1 = 0$ The base is e and $e^0 = 1$.
$\ln e = 1$ Think: $e^1 = e$.
$\ln e^x = x$, $e^{\ln x} = x$ The natural logarithm and the exponential function are inverses, so they undo each other.

Use properties of logarithms to simplify expressions with e or "ln."

Simplify: $\ln e^{x+2}$	Simplify: $e^{4 \ln x}$
Step 1 Use the Power Property. "Bring down" the exponent to multiply. $\ln e^{x+2}$ $(x + 2) \ln e$ **Step 2** Simplify. $(x + 2) \ln e$ $x + 2$ ($\ln e = 1$)	**Step 1** Use the Power Property. Write the exponent. $e^{4 \ln x}$ $e^{\ln x^4}$ **Step 2** Simplify. $e^{\ln x^4}$ x^4 ($e^{\ln x} = x$)

Simplify each expression.

1. $\ln e^{-6x}$ $-6x \ln e$ **$-6x$**
2. $\ln e^{t-3}$ $(t - 3) \ln e$ **$t - 3$**
3. $e^{2 \ln x}$ $e^{\ln x^2}$ **x^2**
4. $\ln e^{1.8}$ **$1.8 \ln e$** **1.8**
5. $\ln e^{x+1}$ **$(x + 1) \ln e$** **$x + 1$**
6. $e^{7 \ln x}$ **$e^{\ln x^7}$** **x^7**

26. Graph the functions $y = \frac{\ln x}{\ln 6}$ and $y = \frac{\log x}{\log 6}$. Explain how the graphs compare with each other and with the graph of $y = \log_6 x$.

Match each transformation of $f(x) = \ln x$ with one of the following graphs.

A. 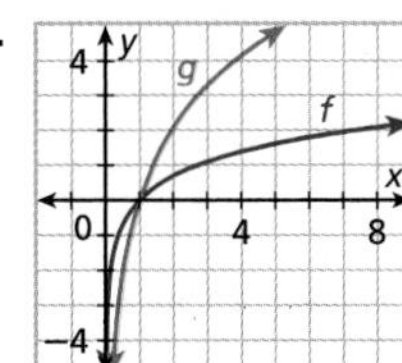

B. 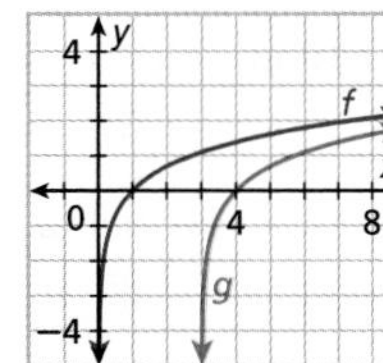

C. 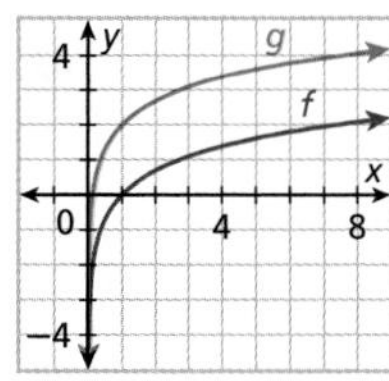

27. $g(x) = \ln(x - 3)$ **B**

28. $g(x) = 3\ln x$ **A**

29. $g(x) = \ln x + 3$ **C**

LINK

Ecology

The George River herd, the largest caribou herd in the world, reached its peak population in 1993 at about 776,000.

30. **Ecology** The George River herd of caribou in Canada was estimated to be about 4700 in 1954 and grew at an exponential rate to about 472,000 in 1984.
   a. Use the exponential growth function $P(t) = P_0e^{kt}$, where P_0 is the initial population and $P(t)$ is the population at time t, to determine the growth factor k. $k \approx 0.154$
   b. **What if...?** If the herd had continued to grow at the same rate, what would its population be in 2010? $\approx$ **25.6 million**

Solve.

31. $\ln 5 + \ln x = 1$

32. $\ln 5 - \ln x = 3$

33. $\ln 10 + \ln x^2 = 10$

34. $2\ln x - 2 = 0$ $x = e$

35. $4\ln x - \ln x^4 = 0$

36. $e^{\ln x^3} = 8$ $x = 2$

35. $\{x \mid x > 0\}$

37. **Logistics** A *logistic function*, such as $f(x) = \frac{1}{(1 + e^{-x})}$, can be used to describe the spread of an epidemic in a population.
   a. Graph the function.
   b. How many asymptotes does the function have?
   c. Describe the function in the context of the real-world situation of an epidemic.

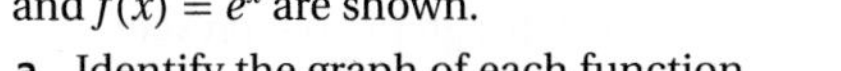

38. **Critical Thinking** The graphs of $f(x) = 2^x$, $f(x) = 10^x$, and $f(x) = e^x$ are shown.
   a. Identify the graph of each function.
   b. Name the coordinates of the point that all three functions have in common.
   c. Explain why this point is common to all three functions.

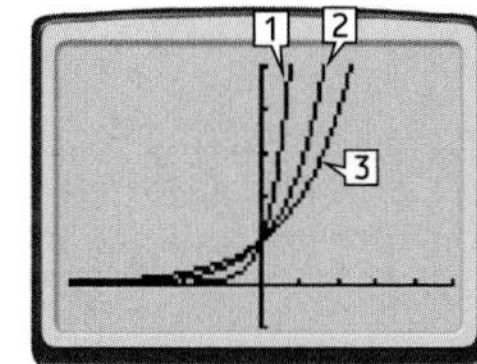

38a. 1: $f(x) = 10^x$; 2: $f(x) = e^x$; 3: $f(x) = 2^x$

b. $(0, 1)$

c. $2^0 = 10^0 = e^0 = 1$

39. **Write About It** Compare compounding interest continuously with compounding daily. How much more is an investment worth when compounding interest continuously? Include an example.

MULTI-STEP TEST PREP

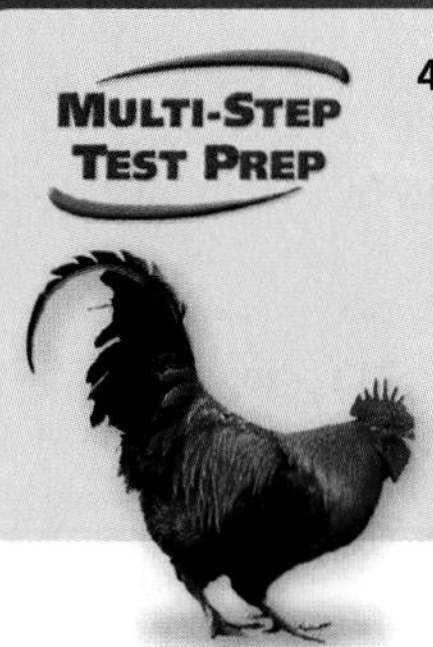

40. This problem will prepare you for the Multi-Step Test Prep on page 552.

In 1990, there were 33,500 farms in North Dakota. In 2000, there were 30,800.
   a. Find the value of k for the exponential function $N(t) = N_0e^{kt}$ to model the number of farms.
   b. Use your model to predict the number of farms in North Dakota in 2010.
   c. From 1990 to 2000, the average farm increased from 1209 acres to 1279 acres. Use an exponential model to predict the average farm size in 2010.

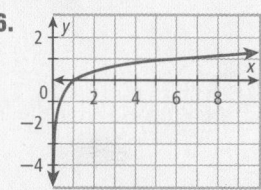

Teaching Tip

Science Link Logistic functions, such as the one in **Exercise 37**, are usually more accurate representations of population growth than simple exponential functions. This is because all populations will eventually be limited by various factors causing them to approach the environment's carrying capacity.

MULTI-STEP TEST PREP **Exercise 40** involves solving exponential equations with the base e. This exercise prepares students for the Multi-Step Test Prep on page 552.

Answers

26. Possible answer: They are the same. $y = \log_6 x$ is changed to base e by $y = \frac{\ln x}{\ln 6}$ and to base 10 by $y = \frac{\log x}{\log 6}$.

31. $x = \frac{e}{5} \approx 0.54$

32. $x = 5e^{-3} \approx 0.25$

33. $x = \pm\frac{e^5}{\sqrt{10}} \approx \pm 47$

37, 39, 40. See p. A34.

7-6 PROBLEM SOLVING

Irene reads that the 2004 census of whooping cranes tallied 213 birds at one wildlife refuge in Texas. This number exceeded the 2003 record by 19. If the population of whooping cranes can be modeled using the exponential growth function $P_t = P_0e^{kt}$, the population, P_t, at time t can be found, where P_0 is the initial population and k is the growth factor. Predict the population of whooping cranes over the next few years.

1. What was the size of the population of whooping cranes in 2003? 194
2. Use the population figures for 2003 and 2004 to find the growth factor, k. $k = 0.0934$
3. Complete the table to predict the population of whooping cranes through 2010.

Year	2006	2007	2008	2009	2010
t	3	4	5	6	7
Population, P_t	257	282	309	340	373

Choose the letter for the best answer.

4. Irene wants to know when the population of whooping cranes will exceed 1000. Using the 2003 population as P_0, which year is the best prediction?
   A 2017
   B 2019
   (C) 2021
   D 2023
5. Irene wonders how the 2010 whooping crane population would change if the growth factor doubled. Which statement is true?
   F The population would increase by a factor of e^2.
   G The population would increase by a factor of $e^{0.0934}$.
   (H) The population would increase by a factor of $e^{(0.0934)(7)}$.
   J The population would increase by a factor of $7e^2$.
6. How long will it take for an investment in an account paying 6% compounded continuously to double?
   A 10.2 years
   B 10.8 years
   (C) 11.6 years
   D 12.4 years
7. Darlene has a sample of a fossil that has 33% of its original carbon-14. Carbon-14 has a half-life of 5730 years. The decay constant for carbon-14 is 1.2×10^{-4}. Find the age of the fossil.
   F About 7820 years
   G About 8450 years
   H About 8980 years
   (J) About 9240 years

7-6 CHALLENGE

John Napier, the inventor of logarithms in 1614, based his work on a number the Swiss mathematician Leonard Euler later called e. The value of e is the irrational number 2.71828 . . .

As you have seen, one way to approximate the value of e is to let the value of n become very large in the sequence of numbers obtained from the expression $1\left(1 + \frac{1}{n}\right)^n$. You can explore some other methods for evaluating e.

Consider the sequence $1, \frac{1}{1}, \frac{1}{2 \cdot 1}, \frac{1}{3 \cdot 2 \cdot 1}, \cdots$

1. Write the 9th term of the sequence. $\frac{1}{8 \cdot 7 \cdot 6 \cdot 5 \cdot 4 \cdot 3 \cdot 2 \cdot 1}$
2. Using a calculator, determine
   a. the sum of the first 5 terms of the sequence. 2.7083
   b. the sum of the first 7 terms of the sequence. 2.718055556
   c. the sum of the first 10 terms of the sequence. 2.718281526
3. Use what you know about the value of e and the results of Exercise 2 to write an expression for e in terms of the given sequence of numbers. $e = 1 + \frac{1}{1} + \frac{1}{2 \cdot 1} + \frac{1}{3 \cdot 2 \cdot 1} + \cdots$

A *continued fraction* is formed by a number added to a fraction whose denominator is a fraction added to a fraction whose denominator is a fraction, and so on, forming a pattern.

• **Example** To evaluate, start with the last denominator.

$$1 + \cfrac{1}{2 + \cfrac{1}{3 + \frac{1}{4}}} = 1 + \cfrac{1}{2 + \cfrac{1}{\frac{13}{4}}} = 1 + \cfrac{1}{2 + \frac{4}{13}} = 1 + \cfrac{1}{\frac{30}{13}} = 1 + \frac{13}{30} = \frac{43}{30}$$

Start.

Complete the continued fraction by finding the missing denominator. Then evaluate.

4. $2 + \cfrac{1}{1 + \cfrac{1}{2 + \cfrac{2}{3 + \cfrac{3}{4 + \frac{4}{\ }}}}}$

$5 + \frac{5}{6}; \frac{5760}{2119} \approx 2.718263332$

5. $1 + \cfrac{2}{1 + \cfrac{1}{6 + \cfrac{1}{10 + \cfrac{1}{14 + \frac{1}{\ }}}}}$

$18 + \frac{1}{22}; \frac{1,084,483}{398,959} \approx 2.718281828$

6. Continue the pattern further in the fractions above and make an observation.
Possible answer: Both of the given continued fractions can be used to determine the value of e.

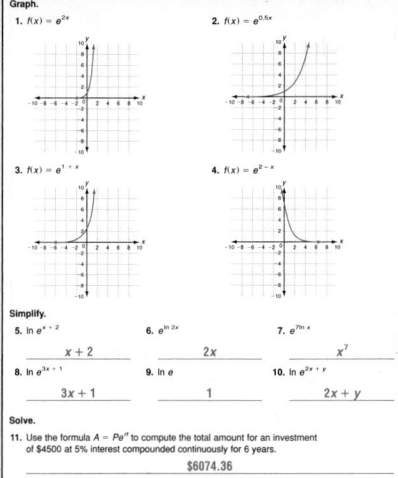

7-6 PRACTICE A

7-6 PRACTICE C

7-6 PRACTICE B

Graph.

1. $f(x) = e^{2x}$
2. $f(x) = e^{0.5x}$
3. $f(x) = e^{1+x}$
4. $f(x) = e^{2-x}$

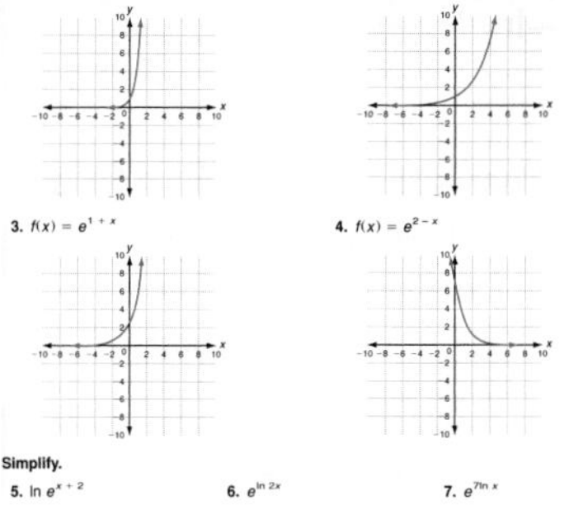

Simplify.

5. $\ln e^{x+2}$ $x + 2$
6. $e^{\ln 2x}$ $2x$
7. $e^{7\ln x}$ x^7
8. $\ln e^{3x+1}$ $3x + 1$
9. $\ln e$ 1
10. $\ln e^{2x+y}$ $2x + y$

Solve.

11. Use the formula $A = Pe^{rt}$ to compute the total amount for an investment of \$4500 at 5% interest compounded continuously for 6 years. \$6074.36
12. Use the natural decay function, $N(t) = N_0e^{-kt}$, to find the decay constant for a substance that has a half-life of 1000 years. 0.000693

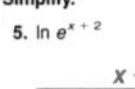

TEST PREP DOCTOR Students who have difficulty with **Exercise 41** could try sketching the two curves. It should be clear from a rough sketch that **C** is correct.

Students who have difficulty with **Exercise 43** should realize that the Change of Base Formula applies here. Estimating is helpful in ruling out choices **C** and **D,** since log 50 is between 1 and 2, and these are clearly greater than 2.

Journal

Have students compare the properties of the natural log function to those of log base 10 and give examples to support them.

ALTERNATIVE ASSESSMENT

Have students write and graph functions involving e and the natural log and demonstrate solving related equations. They may also find the time it takes for a specific amount of a decaying substance to remain, given its half-life.

Power Presentations with PowerPoint®

7-6 Lesson Quiz

Simplify.

1. $\ln e^{-10t}$ $\quad -10t$
2. $e^{0.25 \ln t}$ $\quad t^{0.25}$
3. $-\ln e^x$ $\quad -x$
4. $2 \ln e^{x^2}$ $\quad 2x^2$
5. What is the total amount for an investment of $1000 invested at 7.25% for 15 years and compounded continuously? $\approx$ $2966.85
6. The half-life of carbon-14 is 5730 years. What is the age of a fossil that has only 8% of its original carbon-14? $\approx$ 25,000 yr

Also available on transparency

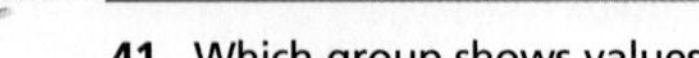

TEST PREP

41. Which group shows values in the order from least to greatest?
    (A) $\log e$, $\ln 10$, $\log 10$, $\ln 1$
    (B) $\ln 1$, $\log e$, $\ln 10$, $\log 10$
    (C) $\ln 1$, $\log e$, $\log 10$, $\ln 10$
    (D) $\ln 1$, $\log 10$, $\ln 10$, $\log e$

42. Which expression is NOT equal to x where $x \neq 0$?
    (F) $e^{\ln x}$ (G) $\ln e^x$ (H) $x \ln e$ **(J)** $x + \ln e$

43. Which expression is equal to log 50?
    (A) $\ln 50 \div \ln 10$ (B) $\ln(50 \div 10)$ (C) $\ln 50 + \ln 10$ (D) $\ln 50(\ln 10)$

44. **Short Response** Write an expression that is equivalent to $-\ln x$ without using a negative sign. **Possible answer:** $\ln\left(\frac{1}{x}\right)$

CHALLENGE AND EXTEND

45. **Finance** For how many compounding periods in a year would the yield of an investment after 1 year at 8% interest be at least 99.9% of the yield if interest were compounded continuously? Does changing the interest rate change the answer? Explain. **4; Possible answer: Yes, at 18% interest it takes 17 periods.**

46. Graph the function $f(x) = \frac{1}{\sqrt{2\pi}} e^{-\left(\frac{x^2}{2}\right)}$. Describe the graph, the domain, and the range.

47. Consider the graph of $f(x) = \ln x$.
    a. What function represents the reflection of f across the y-axis?
    b. What function represents the reflection of f across the x-axis?
    c. What function represents the reflection of f across both axes?
    d. Graph the function and the three reflections. Name any asymptotes that the four graphs have in common.

SPIRAL REVIEW

48. **Entertainment** The graph shows the price of a movie ticket by age of the viewer. Sketch a graph to represent each situation below, and identify the transformation of the original graph that it represents. *(Lesson 1-8)*
    a. Before 5:00 P.M., tickets are half price.
    b. The maximum age of viewer for each ticket price is decreased by 3 years.
    c. The price for each ticket doubles for a newly released movie.

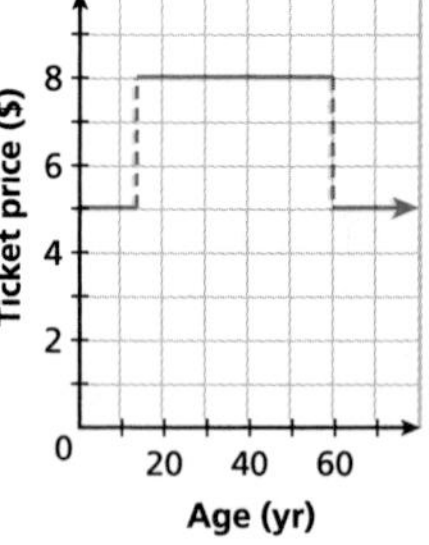

Write a function that transforms $f(x) = -2x^2 + 3x - 4$ in each of the following ways. Support your solution by using a graphing calculator. *(Lesson 6-8)*

49. Translate up 5 units
50. Translate left 2 units
51. Reflect across the x-axis
52. Stretch horizontally by a factor of 2

Express as a single logarithm. Simplify, if possible. *(Lesson 7-4)*

53. $\log_2 8 + \log_2 \frac{1}{2}$
54. $\log_4 64 - \log_4 1$
55. $\log_3 243 - \log_3 2187$
56. $\log_5 25 + \log_5 125$
57. $\log_8 8 + \log_8 \frac{1}{8}$
58. $\log x^2 - \log x$

Answers

46.

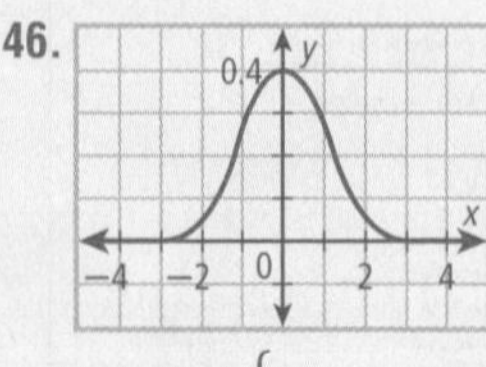

D: $\mathbb{R}$; R: $\left\{0 < y \le \frac{1}{\sqrt{2\pi}}\right\}$

47a. $f(x) = \ln(-x)$
b. $f(x) = -\ln x$
c. $f(x) = -\ln(-x)$

d.

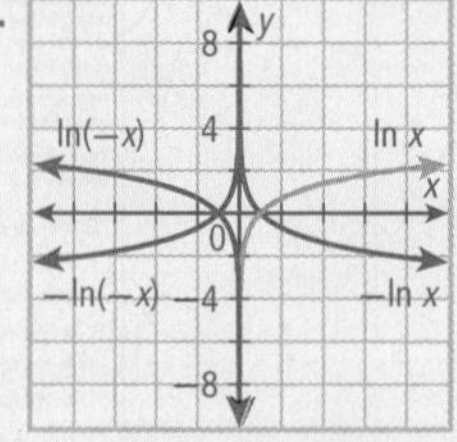

one asymptote: $x = 0$

48. See p. A34.

49. $g(x) = f(x) + 5 = -2x^2 + 3x + 1$

50. $g(x) = f(x + 2) = -2x^2 - 5x - 6$

51. $g(x) = -f(x) = 2x^2 - 3x + 4$

52. $g(x) = f\left(\frac{x}{2}\right) = -\frac{1}{2}x^2 + \frac{3}{2}x - 4$

53. $\log_2 4 = 2$

54. $\log_4 64 = 3$

55. $\log_3\left(\frac{243}{2187}\right) = \log_3\left(\frac{1}{9}\right) = -2$

56. $\log_5(25 \cdot 125) = \log_5(5^5) = 5$

57. $\log_8 1 = 0$

58. $\log x$

7-7 Transforming Exponential and Logarithmic Functions

A2.1.2 Use and interpret function notation, including evaluation of functions represented by tables, graphs, words, equations or a set of ordered pairs.

Objectives

Transform exponential and logarithmic functions by changing parameters.

Describe the effects of changes in the coefficients of exponential and logarithmic functions.

Who uses this?

Psychologists can use transformations of exponential functions to describe knowledge retention rates over time. (See Example 5.)

You can perform the same transformations on exponential functions that you performed on polynomial, quadratic, and linear functions.

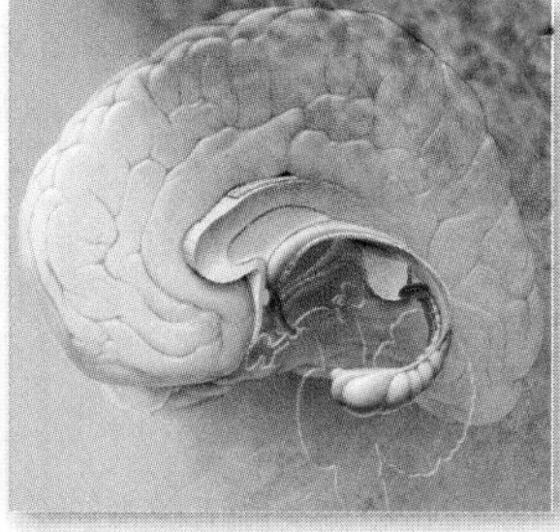

The hippocampus, in blue, directs the storage of memory in the brain.

Helpful Hint

It may help you remember the direction of the shift if you think of "*h* is for **h**orizontal."

Transformations of Exponential Functions

Transformation	f(x) Notation	Examples	
Vertical translation	$f(x) + k$	$y = 2^x + 3$	3 units up
		$y = 2^x - 6$	6 units down
Horizontal translation	$f(x - h)$	$y = 2^{x-2}$	2 units right
		$y = 2^{x+1}$	1 unit left
Vertical stretch or compression	$af(x)$	$y = 6(2^x)$	stretch by 6
		$y = \frac{1}{2}(2^x)$	compression by $\frac{1}{2}$
Horizontal stretch or compression	$f\left(\frac{1}{b}x\right)$	$y = 2^{\left(\frac{1}{5}x\right)}$	stretch by 5
		$y = 2^{3x}$	compression by $\frac{1}{3}$
Reflection	$-f(x)$	$y = -2^x$	across *x*-axis
	$f(-x)$	$y = 2^{-x}$	across *y*-axis

EXAMPLE 1 **Translating Exponential Functions**

Make a table of values, and graph the function $g(x) = 2^x - 4$. Describe the asymptote. Tell how the graph is transformed from the graph of $f(x) = 2^x$.

x	−2	−1	0	1	2	3
g(x)	−3.75	−3.5	−3	−2	0	4

The asymptote is $y = -4$, and the graph approaches this line as the value of x decreases. The transformation moves the graph of $f(x) = 2^x$ down 4 units. The range changes to $\{y \mid y > -4\}$.

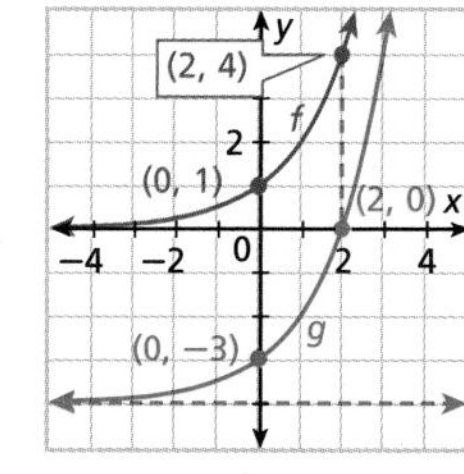

CHECK IT OUT! 1. Make a table of values, and graph $j(x) = 2^{x-2}$. Describe the asymptote. Tell how the graph is transformed from the graph of $f(x) = 2^x$.

1.

x	−2	−1	0	1	2
j (x)	$\frac{1}{16}$	$\frac{1}{8}$	$\frac{1}{4}$	$\frac{1}{2}$	1

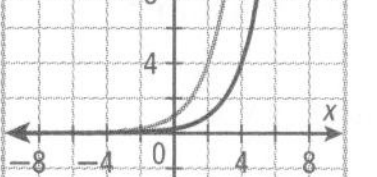

$y = 0$; $j(x) = 2^x$; translation 2 units right

7-7 Organizer

Pacing: Traditional 1 day
Block $\frac{1}{2}$ day

Objectives: Transform exponential and logarithmic functions by changing parameters.

Describe the effects of changes in the coefficients of exponential and logarithmic functions.

Online Edition
Tutorial Videos, Graphing Calculator

Countdown to Testing Week 16

Power Presentations with PowerPoint®

Warm Up

How does each function compare to its parent function?

1. $f(x) = 2(x - 3)^2 - 4$

vertically stretched by a factor of 2, translated 3 units right, translated 4 units down

2. $g(x) = (-x)^3 + 1$

reflected across the *y*-axis, translated 1 unit up

Also available on transparency

Math Humor

Lee: We need to stretch the exponential function.

Sal: It looks stretched enough already!

1 Introduce

EXPLORATION

7-7 Transforming Exponential and Logarithmic Functions

Use a calculator to explore transformations of exponential functions.

1. Enter the parent function $y = e^x$ by pressing [Y=] and then [2ND] [LN] [X,T,θ,n] [)]. Graph the function.

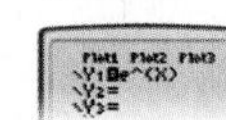

2. Enter each of the following functions as **Y2** and graph them in the same window as the graph of $y = e^x$. In each case, describe how the graph of the function is related to that of $y = e^x$.
   a. $y = e^x - 5$
   b. $y = e^{x-4}$
   c. $y = -e^x$
   d. $y = e^{-x}$

THINK AND DISCUSS

3. **Explain** how the graph of $y = e^{x-1} + 2$ is related to the graph of $y = e^x$.
4. **Describe** how you would change the equation $y = 4^x$ if you wanted to translate the graph of this function 3 units to the left. $y = 4^{x+3}$

Motivate

Populations may grow exponentially and can be modeled by $f(x) = ab^t$, where a is the initial population and b is the growth rate. Have students consider how to model the following: a) The initial population is double what it was thought to be. $g(x) = 2ab^t$ b) The growth rate is doubled. $g(x) = a(2b)^t$ c) Growth occurs twice a year. $g(x) = ab^{t/2}$ Tell students that these represent transformations of the exponential parent function.

Explorations and answers are provided in the *Explorations* binder.

State Resources

Power Presentations with PowerPoint®

Additional Examples

Example 1

Make a table of values, and graph $g(x) = 2^{-x} + 1$. Describe the asymptote. Tell how the graph is transformed from the graph of the function $f(x) = 2^x$.

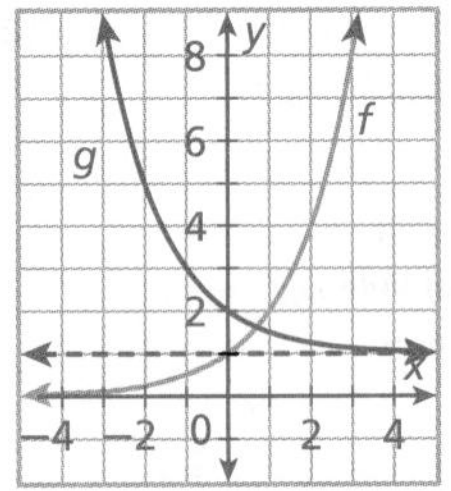

$y = 1$; reflected across y-axis, shifted 1 unit up, R: $\{y \mid y > 1\}$

Example 2

Graph each function. Find the y-intercept and the asymptote. Describe how the graph is transformed from the graph of its parent function.

A. $g(x) = \frac{2}{3}(1.5^x)$

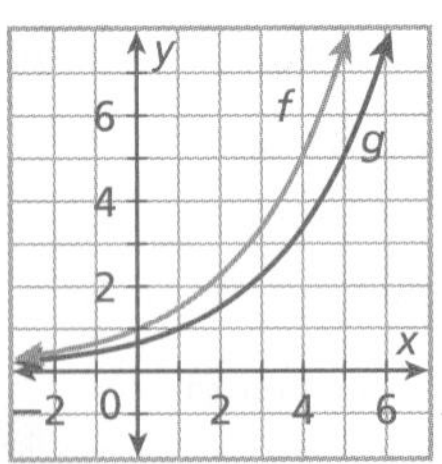

$\frac{2}{3}$; $y = 0$; vertical compression of $f(x) = 1.5^x$ by a factor of $\frac{2}{3}$

B. $h(x) = e^{-x+1}$

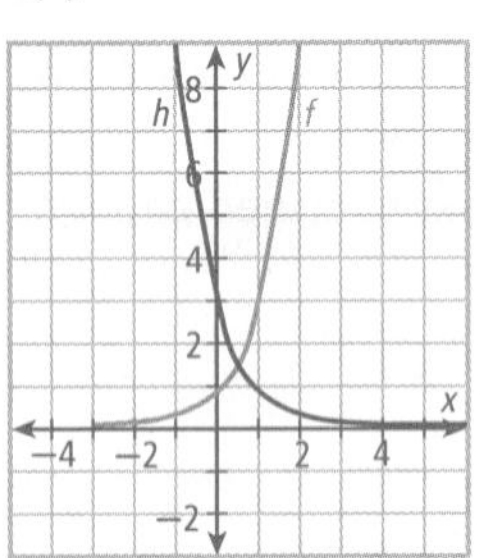

e; $y = 0$; reflection of $f(x) = e^x$ across the y-axis, shifted 1 unit right

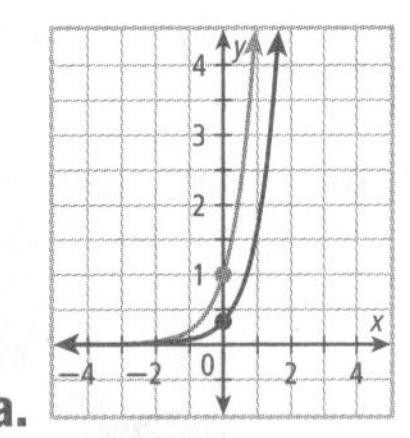

2a. $\frac{1}{3}$; $y = 0$; $f(x) = 5^x$; vertical compression by a factor of $\frac{1}{3}$

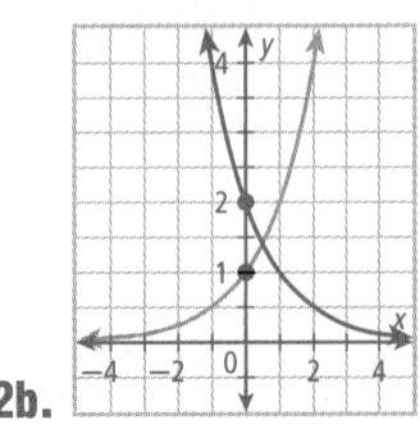

2b. 2; $y = 0$; $j(x) = 2^x$; reflection across y-axis and vertical stretch by a factor of 2

EXAMPLE 2 Stretching, Compressing, and Reflecting Exponential Functions

Graph the exponential function. Find the y-intercept and the asymptote. Describe how the graph is transformed from the graph of its parent function.

A $g(x) = 2(3^x)$

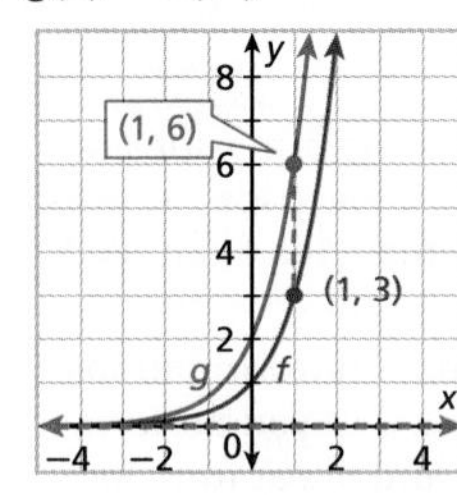

parent function: $f(x) = 3^x$

y-intercept: 2, asymptote: $y = 0$

The graph of $g(x)$ is a vertical stretch of the parent function $f(x) = 3^x$ by a factor of 2.

B $h(x) = -\frac{1}{4}(2^x)$

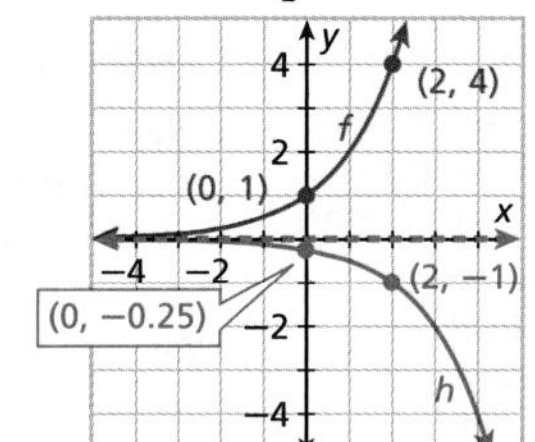

parent function: $f(x) = 2^x$

y-intercept: $-\frac{1}{4}$, asymptote: $y = 0$

The graph of $h(x)$ is a reflection of the parent function $f(x) = 2^x$ across the x-axis and a vertical compression by a factor of $\frac{1}{4}$. The range is $\{y \mid y < 0\}$.

CHECK IT OUT! Graph the exponential function. Find the y-intercept and the asymptote. Describe how the graph is transformed from the graph of its parent function.

2a. $h(x) = \frac{1}{3}(5^x)$ **2b.** $g(x) = 2(2^{-x})$

Remember!

Transformations of $\ln x$ work the same way because $\ln x$ means $\log_e x$.

Because a log is an exponent, transformations of logarithmic functions are similar to transformations of exponential functions. You can stretch, reflect, and translate the graph of the parent logarithmic function $f(x) = \log_b x$.

Examples are given in the table below for $f(x) = \log x$.

Transformations of Logarithmic Functions

Transformation	$f(x)$ Notation	Examples	
Vertical translation	$f(x) + k$	$y = \log x + 3$	3 units up
		$y = \log x - 4$	4 units down
Horizontal translation	$f(x - h)$	$y = \log(x - 2)$	2 units right
		$y = \log(x + 1)$	1 unit left
Vertical stretch or compression	$af(x)$	$y = 6\log x$	stretch by 6
		$y = \frac{1}{2}\log x$	compression by $\frac{1}{2}$
Horizontal stretch or compression	$f\left(\frac{1}{b}x\right)$	$y = \log\left(\frac{1}{5}x\right)$	stretch by 5
		$y = \log(3x)$	compression by $\frac{1}{3}$
Reflection	$-f(x)$	$y = -\log x$	across x-axis
	$f(-x)$	$y = \log(-x)$	across y-axis

2 Teach

Guided Instruction

Before working the examples, review the effects of different transformations on a simpler function, such as $f(x) = x^2$. Then make sure that students are comfortable with the basic features of the basic exponential and logarithmic graphs.

Reaching All Learners

Through Multiple Representations

Have students create a table or chart with different parent functions and the effects of various changes in their parameters. For example, have students graph $f(x) + 1$ for the linear, quadratic, cubic, and exponential parent functions. Have them do the same for horizontal shifts, stretches, compressions, and reflections.

INTERVENTION

Questioning Strategies

EXAMPLES 1-2

- Is there always an asymptote, regardless of the transformation?
- If there is more than one transformation, which do you do first?

EXAMPLE 3 Transforming Logarithmic Functions

Graph each logarithmic function. Find the asymptote. Then describe how the graph is transformed from the graph of its parent function.

A $q(x) = -\ln(x - 4)$

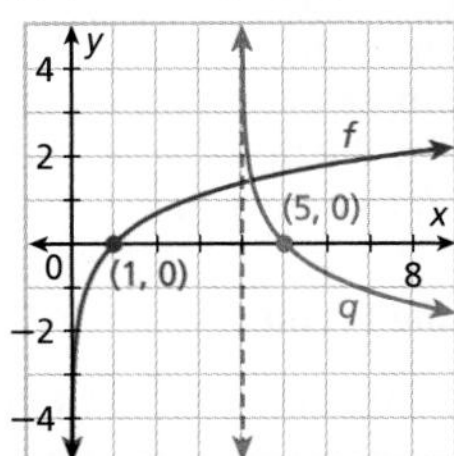

asymptote: $x = 4$

The graph of $q(x)$ is a translation of the parent function $f(x) = \ln x$ 4 units right and a reflection across the x-axis. The domain is $\{x \mid x > 4\}$.

B $p(x) = 3\log x + 5$

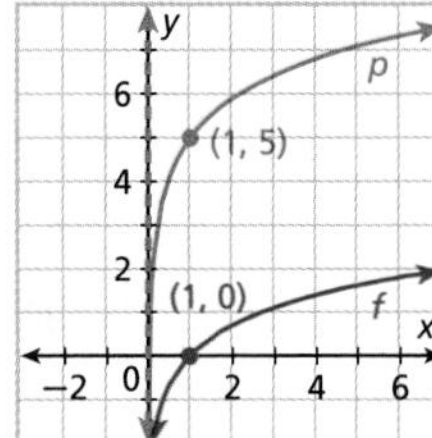

asymptote: $x = 0$

The graph of $p(x)$ is a vertical stretch of the parent function $f(x) = \log x$ by a factor of 3 and a translation 5 units up.

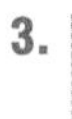

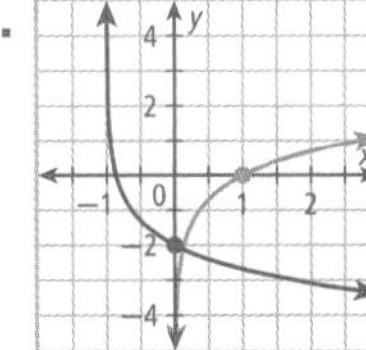

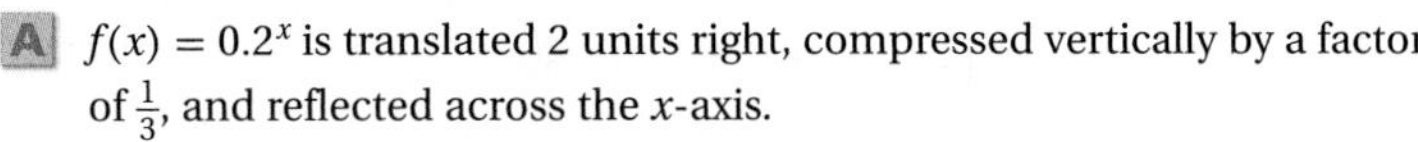

3. Graph the logarithmic function $p(x) = -\ln(x + 1) - 2$. Find the asymptote. Then describe how the graph is transformed from the graph of its parent function.

-2; $x = -1$; $f(x) = \ln x$ translation 1 unit left, reflection across the x-axis, and translation 2 units down; D: $\{x \mid x > -1\}$

EXAMPLE 4 Writing Transformed Functions

Write each transformed function.

A $f(x) = 0.2^x$ is translated 2 units right, compressed vertically by a factor of $\frac{1}{3}$, and reflected across the x-axis.

$f(x) = 0.2^x$ *Begin with the parent function.*

$g(x) = 0.2^{x-2}$ *To translate 2 units right, replace x with x − 2.*

$= \left(-\frac{1}{3}\right)0.2^{x-2}$ *Compress vertically by $\frac{1}{3}$ and reflect across the x-axis.*

B $f(x) = \ln x$ is translated 1 unit left and 3 units up and horizontally stretched by a factor of 5.

$f(x) = \ln\left(\frac{x}{5} + 1\right) + 3$

When you write a transformed function, you many want to graph it as a check.

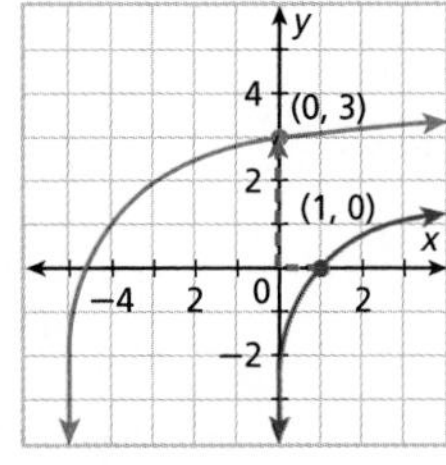

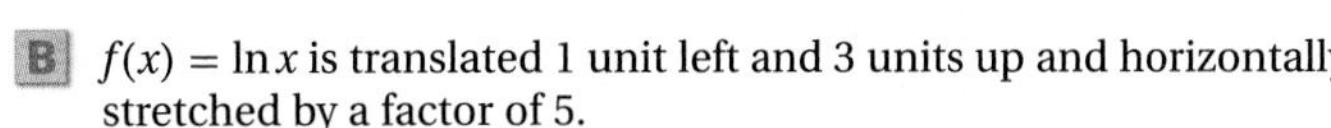

4. Write the transformed function when $f(x) = \log x$ is translated 3 units left and stretched vertically by a factor of 2.

$g(x) = 2\log(x + 3)$

Teaching Tip **Math Background** In Geometry, students may have encountered the *golden rectangle*. Successive points dividing parts of a golden rectangle into squares lie on a *logarithmic spiral*.

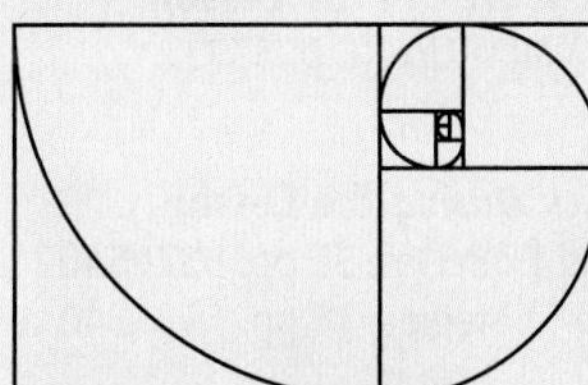

Logarithmic spirals occur frequently in nature (e.g., nautilus shells) and are closely related to Fibonacci numbers, which students may have also encountered.

Power Presentations with PowerPoint®

Additional Examples

Example 3

Graph each logarithmic function. Find the asymptote. Describe how the graph is transformed from the graph of its parent function.

A. $g(x) = 5\log x - 2$

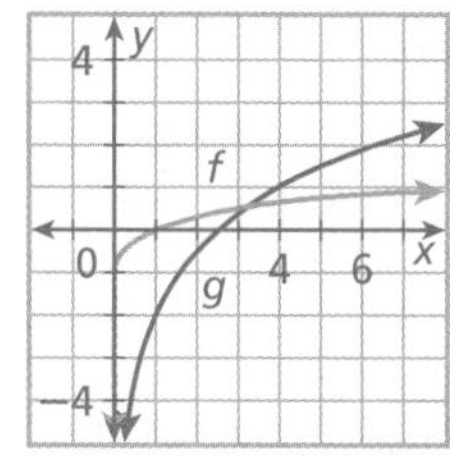

$x = 0$; a vertical stretch by a factor of 5 and a translation 2 units down

B. $h(x) = \ln(-x + 2)$

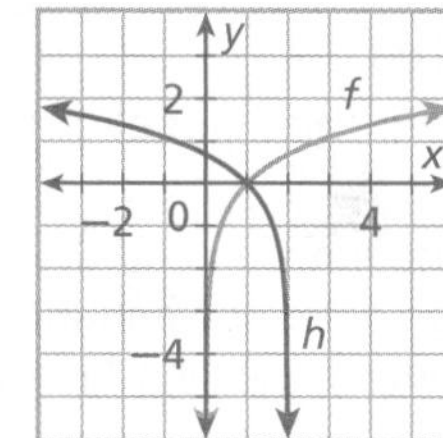

$x = 2$; a reflection of $f(x) = \ln x$ across the y-axis and a shift two units to the right, D: $\{x \mid x < 2\}$

Example 4

Write each transformed function.

A. $f(x) = 4^x$ is reflected across both axes and moved 2 units down. $g(x) = -(4^{-x}) - 2$

B. $f(x) = \ln x$ is compressed horizontally by a factor of $\frac{1}{2}$ and moved 3 units left. $g(x) = \ln 2(x + 3)$

Also available on transparency

INTERVENTION Questioning Strategies

EXAMPLE 3

- How can you determine where the asymptote is just by looking at the function?

EXAMPLE 4

- Which transformation will cause the asymptote to move?

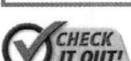

Power Presentations with PowerPoint®

Additional Examples

Example 5

The temperature in °F that milk must be kept at to last n days can be modeled by $T(n) = 75 - 16\ln n$. Describe how the model is transformed from $f(n) = \ln n$. Use the model to predict how long milk will last if kept at 34°F.

It is stretched by a factor of 16, reflected across the x-axis, and translated 75 units up; about 13 days.

Also available on transparency

INTERVENTION 

Questioning Strategies

EXAMPLE 5

- What is the meaning of each of the constants?
- Are both the function and the parent function defined when the independent variable is 0? How do you know?

Visual It may be necessary to remind students that exponential graphs have only horizontal asymptotes, while logarithmic graphs have only vertical asymptotes. They grow so quickly (exponential) or slowly (logarithmic) that it will often appear to students that they are asymptotic where they are not.

EXAMPLE 5 Problem-Solving Application

A group of students retake the written portion of a driver's test after several months without reviewing the material. A model used by psychologists describes retention of the material by the function $a(t) = 85 - 15\log(t + 1)$, where a is the average score at time t (in months). Describe how the model is transformed from its parent function. Then use the model to predict the number of months when the average score falls below 70.

1 Understand the Problem

The **answers** will be the description of the transformations in $a(t) = 85 - 15\log(t + 1)$ and the number of months when the score falls below 70.

List the important information:

- The model is the function $a(t) = 85 - 15\log(t + 1)$.
- The function is a transformation of $f(t) = \log(t)$.
- The problem asks for t when $a < 70$.

2 Make a Plan

Rewrite the function in a more familiar form, and then use what you know about the effect of changing the parent function to describe the transformations. Substitute known values into $a(t) = 85 - 15\log(t + 1)$, and solve for the unknown.

3 Solve

Rewrite the function, and describe the transformations.

$a(t) = 85 - 15\log(t + 1)$

$a(t) = -15\log(t + 1) + 85$ *Commutative Property*

The graph of $f(t) = \log(t)$ is reflected across the x-axis, vertically stretched by a factor of 15, and translated 85 units up and 1 unit left. The domain $\{t \mid t \geq 0\}$ makes sense in the problem.

Find the time when the average score drops below 70.

$70 > -15\log(t + 1) + 85$ *Substitute 70 for a(t) and replace = with >.*

$-15 > -15\log(t + 1)$ *Subtract 85 from both sides.*

$1 < \log(t + 1)$ *Divide by −15, and reverse the inequality symbol.*

$10^1 < t + 1$ *Change to exponential form.*

$9 < t$

The model predicts a score below 70 after 9 months.

4 Look Back

It is reasonable that scores would drop from 85 to below 70 nine months after the students take the test without reviewing the material.

CHECK IT OUT! **5. What if...?** When would the average score drop to 0? Is your answer reasonable? $t \geq \approx 38{,}683$ yr; no

3 Close

Summarize

The transformation of exponential and logarithmic graphs is, in every way, just like the transformation of any other kind of graph. It may help to pay attention to where the intercept point goes and where the asymptote lies.

ONGOING ASSESSMENT and INTERVENTION

***Diagnose Before* the Lesson**
7-7 Warm Up, TE p. 537

***Monitor During* the Lesson**
Check It Out! Exercises, SE pp. 537–540
Questioning Strategies, TE pp. 538–540

***Assess After* the Lesson**
7-7 Lesson Quiz, TE p. 544
Alternative Assessment, TE p. 544

THINK AND DISCUSS

1. Describe the domain of $f(x) = \log_b(-x)$.
2. Explain how the process of transforming exponential and logarithmic functions is similar to transforming quadratic functions.
3. Tell which transformations of $f(x) = a^x$ change the domain or range. Tell which transformations of $f(x) = \log_b x$ change the domain or range. Are these transformations the same?

4. **GET ORGANIZED** Copy and complete the graphic organizer. Give an example of an indicated transformation for both types of exponential and logarithmic functions. Remember, e is a constant.

Transformation	$f(x) = 5^x$ $f(x) = e^x$	$f(x) = \log_b x$ $f(x) = \ln x$
Vertical translation		
Horizontal translation		
Reflection		
Vertical stretch		
Vertical compression		

Answers to *Think and Discuss*

Possible answers:

1. $\{x \mid x < 0\}$
2. Possible answer: The transformations of x and $f(x)$ are the same for the functions $f(x) + k$, $f(x - h)$, $af(x)$, $f\left(\frac{1}{b}x\right)$, $-f(x)$, and $f(-x)$.
3. Possible answer: $f(x) = a^x$: vertical translations and reflections across the x-axis change the range; $f(x) = \log_b x$: horizontal translations and reflections across the y-axis change the domain; no.
4. See p. A9.

7-7 Exercises

GUIDED PRACTICE

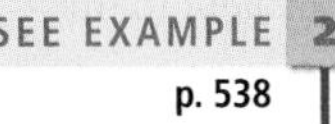

SEE EXAMPLE 1 p. 537

Make a table of values, and graph each function. Describe the asymptote. Tell how the graph is transformed from the graph of $f(x) = 3^x$.

1. $g(x) = 3^x + 2$
2. $h(x) = 3^x - 2$
3. $j(x) = 3^{x+1}$

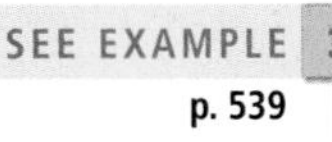

SEE EXAMPLE 2 p. 538

Graph each exponential function. Find the y-intercept and the asymptote. Describe how the graph is transformed from the graph of its parent function.

4. $g(x) = 3(4^x)$
5. $h(x) = \frac{1}{3}(4^x)$
6. $j(x) = -\frac{1}{3}(4^x)$
7. $k(x) = -2(4^x)$
8. $m(x) = -(4^{-x})$
9. $n(x) = e^{2x}$

SEE EXAMPLE 3 p. 539

Graph each logarithmic function. Find the asymptote. Then describe how the graph is transformed from the graph of its parent function.

10. $g(x) = 2.5 \log x$
11. $h(x) = 2.5 \log(x + 3)$
12. $j(x) = -\frac{1}{3} \ln x + 1.5$

SEE EXAMPLE 4 p. 539

Write each transformed function by using the given parent function and the indicated transformations. $g(x) = -0.7^{\left(\frac{x}{3} + 2\right)}$

13. The parent exponential function $f(x) = 0.7^x$ is horizontally stretched by a factor of 3, reflected across the x-axis, and translated 2 units left.
14. The parent logarithmic function $f(x) = \log x$ is translated 12 units right, vertically compressed by a factor of $\frac{1}{2}$, and translated 25 units up. $g(x) = \frac{1}{2}\log(x - 12) + 25$

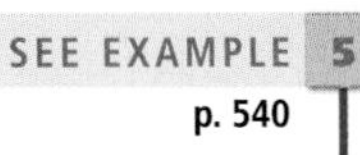

SEE EXAMPLE 5 p. 540

15. **Forestry** The height of a poplar tree in feet, at age t years can be modeled by the function $h(t) = 6 + 3\ln(t + 1)$. Describe how the model is transformed from its parent function. Then use the model to predict the number of years when the height will exceed 17 feet.
translated 1 unit left, stretched vertically by a factor of 3, and translated 6 units up; after about 39 years.

Assignment Guide

Assign *Guided Practice* exercises as necessary.

If you finished Examples 1–3
- **Basic** 16–27
- **Average** 16–27, 44
- **Advanced** 16–27, 44–45

If you finished Examples 1–5
- **Basic** 16–31, 40–42, 45–47, 50–54, 58–65
- **Average** 16–31, 33–45, 49–55, 58–65
- **Advanced** 16–44, 48–49, 51–65

Homework Quick Check
Quickly check key concepts.
Exercises: 18, 22, 26, 28, 30, 31

State Resources

go.hrw.com
State Resources Online
KEYWORD: MB7 Resources

Answers

1.

x	−2	−1	0	1	2
$g(x)$	2.1	2.3	3	5	11

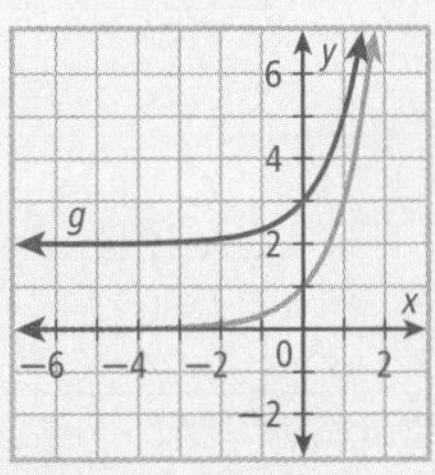

$y = 2$; translation 2 units up; R: $\{y \mid y > 2\}$

2.

x	−2	−1	0	1	2
$h(x)$	−1.9	−1.7	−1	1	7

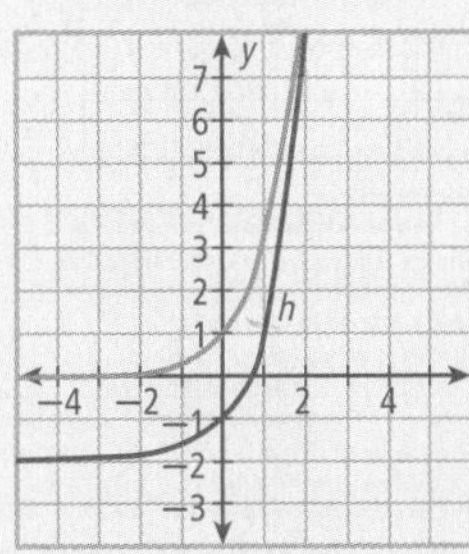

$y = -2$; translation 2 units down; R: $\{y \mid y > -2\}$

3–12. See p. A34–A35.

Science Link **Exercise 31** mentions the *Cassini* spacecraft. Giovanni Domenico Cassini (1625–1712) was a professor of mathematics and astronomy at the University of Bologna. In addition to discovering four of Saturn's moons, he was an expert in hydraulics and engineering and, in 1668, was the first to hypothesize that light travels at a finite speed.

Answers

16–27, 31. For graphs, see p. A35.

16.

x	−2	−1	0	1	2
$g(x)$	−0.96	−0.8	0	4	24

$y = -1$; translation 1 unit down; R: $\{y \mid y > -1\}$

17.

x	−2	−1	0	1	2
$h(x)$	1	5	25	125	625

$y = 0$; translation 2 units left

18.

x	$j(x)$
−2	−1
−1	−1
0	0.8
1	0
2	4

$y = -1$; translation 1 unit left and 1 unit down; R: $\{y \mid y > -1\}$

19. 4; $y = 0$; vertical stretch by a factor of 4

20. 0.25; $y = 0$; vertical compression by a factor of 0.25

PRACTICE AND PROBLEM SOLVING

Independent Practice

For Exercises	See Example
16–18	1
19–24	2
25–27	3
28–30	4
31	5

Extra Practice
Skills Practice p. S17
Application Practice p. S38

Make a table of values, and graph each function. Describe the asymptote. Tell how the graph is transformed from the graph of $f(x) = 5^x$.

16. $g(x) = 5^x - 1$ **17.** $h(x) = 5^{x+2}$ **18.** $j(x) = 5^{x-1} - 1$

Graph each exponential function. Find the y-intercept and the asymptote. Describe how the graph is transformed from the graph of its parent function.

19. $g(x) = 4\left(\frac{1}{2}\right)^x$ **20.** $h(x) = 0.25\left(\frac{1}{2}\right)^x$ **21.** $j(x) = -0.25\left(\frac{1}{2}\right)^x$

22. $k(x) = -\left(\frac{1}{2}\right)^{\frac{x}{2}}$ **23.** $m(x) = 4\left(\frac{1}{2}\right)^{-x}$ **24.** $n(x) = -4\left(\frac{1}{2}\right)^{-x}$

Graph each logarithmic function. Find the asymptote. Describe how the graph is transformed from the graph of its parent function.

25. $g(x) = \ln(x - 5)$ **26.** $h(x) = \frac{4}{5}\log(x + 3) - 2$ **27.** $m(x) = -4\log x$

Write each transformed function.

28. $f(x) = -1.5\left(\frac{1}{2}\right)^{x-4}$

28. The function $f(x) = \left(\frac{1}{2}\right)^x$ is translated 4 units right, reflected across the x-axis, and vertically stretched by a factor of 1.5.

29. The function $f(x) = \ln x$ is translated 3 units left, horizontally compressed by a factor of $\frac{1}{4}$ and translated 0.5 units down. $f(x) = \ln(4x + 3) - 0.5$

30. $f(x) = e^{\left(1 - \frac{x}{3}\right)}$

30. The function $f(x) = e^x$ is horizontally stretched by a factor of 3, reflected across the y-axis, and translated 1 unit right.

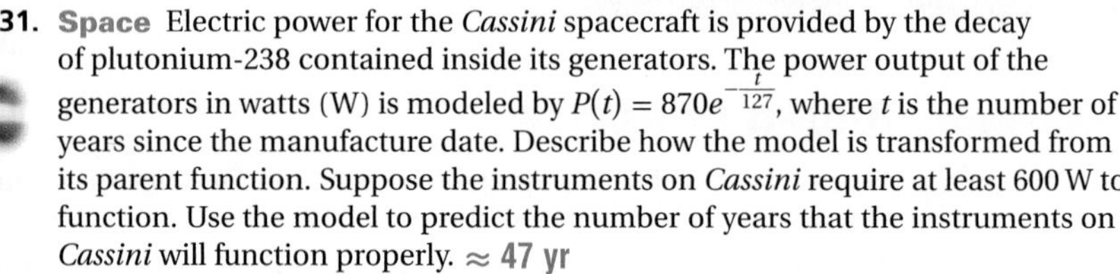

31. **Space** Electric power for the *Cassini* spacecraft is provided by the decay of plutonium-238 contained inside its generators. The power output of the generators in watts (W) is modeled by $P(t) = 870e^{-\frac{t}{127}}$, where t is the number of years since the manufacture date. Describe how the model is transformed from its parent function. Suppose the instruments on *Cassini* require at least 600 W to function. Use the model to predict the number of years that the instruments on *Cassini* will function properly. $\approx$ **47 yr**

32. **Critical Thinking** What vertical transformation of $f(x) = e^x$ is equivalent to the horizontal translation $g(x) = e^{x+2}$? Write the transformed function.
vertical stretch by e^2; $g(x) = e^2 e^x$

For Exercises 33–38, match each order of transformation of $f(x) = e^x$ with its transformed function.

33. stretch by a factor of 2, reflect across the x-axis, and translate 5 units down. **A**

34. stretch by a factor of 2, translate 5 units down, and reflect across the x-axis **E**

35. reflect across the x-axis, stretch by a factor of 2, and translate 5 units down. **D**

36. reflect across the x-axis, translate 5 units down, and stretch by a factor of 2. **C**

37. translate 5 units down, stretch by a factor of 2, and reflect across the x-axis. **F**

38. translate 5 units down, reflect across the x-axis, and stretch by a factor of 2. **B**

A. $g(x) = -2e^x - 5$

B. $g(x) = 2[-(e^x - 5)]$

C. $g(x) = 2(-e^x - 5)$

D. $g(x) = 2(-e^x) - 5$

E. $g(x) = -(2e^x - 5)$

F. $g(x) = -2(e^x - 5)$

39. Which, if any, of the functions in A–F above are equivalent? **B and F**

7-7 PRACTICE A
7-7 PRACTICE C
7-7 PRACTICE B

Graph each function. Find the asymptote. Tell how the graph is transformed from the graph of its parent function.

1. $f(x) = 5(2^x)$
$y = 0$; it is the graph of $f(x) = 2^x$ stretched vertically by a factor of 5.

2. $f(x) = 5^{\frac{x}{4}}$
$y = 0$; it is the graph of $f(x) = 5^x$ stretched horizontally by a factor of 4.

3. $f(x) = \log(x + 5)$
$x = -5$; it is the graph of $f(x) = \log x$ translated 5 units left.

4. $f(x) = 3 + \ln x$
$x = 0$; it is the graph of $f(x) = \ln x$ translated 3 units up.

Write each transformed function.

5. The function $f(x) = \log(x + 1)$ is reflected across the y-axis and translated down 4 units. $g(x) = \log(-x + 1) - 4$

6. The function $f(x) = -8^{x-3}$ is reflected across the x-axis, compressed horizontally by a factor of 0.2, and stretched vertically by a factor of 2. $g(x) = 2 \cdot 8^{5x-3}$

Solve.

7. The function $A(t) = Pe^{rt}$ can be used to calculate the growth of an investment in which the interest is compounded continuously at an annual rate, r, over t years. What annual rate would double an investment in 8 years?
8.7%

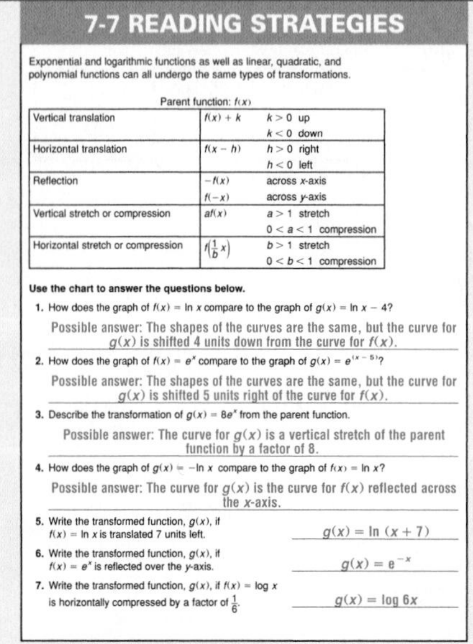

7-7 READING STRATEGIES

Exponential and logarithmic functions as well as linear, quadratic, and polynomial functions can all undergo the same types of transformations.

Parent function: $f(x)$

Vertical translation	$f(x) + k$	$k > 0$ up $k < 0$ down
Horizontal translation	$f(x - h)$	$h > 0$ right $h < 0$ left
Reflection	$-f(x)$ $f(-x)$	across x-axis across y-axis
Vertical stretch or compression	$af(x)$	$a > 1$ stretch $0 < a < 1$ compression
Horizontal stretch or compression	$f\left(\frac{1}{b}x\right)$	$b > 1$ stretch $0 < b < 1$ compression

Use the chart to answer the questions below.

1. How does the graph of $f(x) = \ln x$ compare to the graph of $g(x) = \ln x - 4$?
Possible answer: The shapes of the curves are the same, but the curve for $g(x)$ is shifted 4 units down from the curve for $f(x)$.

2. How does the graph of $f(x) = e^x$ compare to the graph of $g(x) = e^{(x-5)}$?
Possible answer: The shapes of the curves are the same, but the curve for $g(x)$ is shifted 5 units right of the curve for $f(x)$.

3. Describe the transformation of $g(x) = 8e^x$ from the parent function.
Possible answer: The curve for $g(x)$ is a vertical stretch of the parent function by a factor of 8.

4. How does the graph of $g(x) = -\ln x$ compare to the graph of $f(x) = \ln x$?
Possible answer: The curve for $g(x)$ is the curve for $f(x)$ reflected across the x-axis.

5. Write the transformed function, $g(x)$, if $f(x) = \ln x$ is translated 7 units left. $g(x) = \ln(x + 7)$

6. Write the transformed function, $g(x)$, if $f(x) = e^x$ is reflected over the y-axis. $g(x) = e^{-x}$

7. Write the transformed function, $g(x)$, if $f(x) = \log x$ is horizontally compressed by a factor of $\frac{1}{6}$. $g(x) = \log 6x$

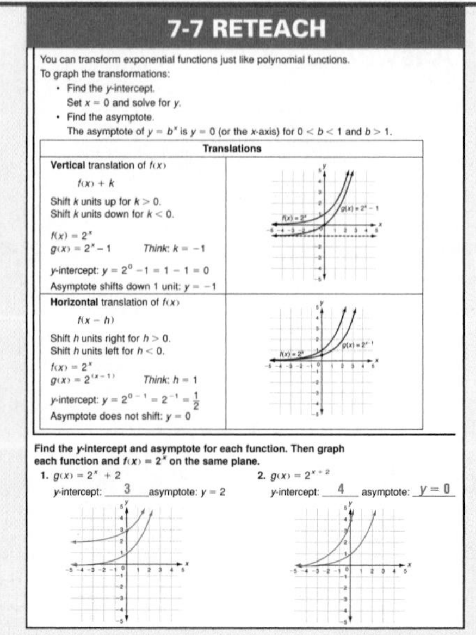

7-7 RETEACH

You can transform exponential functions just like polynomial functions.
To graph the transformations:
- Find the y-intercept.
Set $x = 0$ and solve for y.
- Find the asymptote.
The asymptote of $y = b^x$ is $y = 0$ (or the x-axis) for $0 < b < 1$ and $b > 1$.

Translations	
Vertical translation of $f(x)$ $f(x) + k$ Shift k units up for $k > 0$. Shift k units down for $k < 0$. $f(x) = 2^x$ $g(x) = 2^x - 1$ *Think:* $k = -1$ y-intercept: $y = 2^0 - 1 = 1 - 1 = 0$ Asymptote shifts down 1 unit: $y = -1$	$f(x) = 2^x$ $g(x) = 2^x - 1$
Horizontal translation of $f(x)$ $f(x - h)$ Shift h units right for $h > 0$. Shift h units left for $h < 0$. $f(x) = 2^x$ $g(x) = 2^{(x-1)}$ *Think:* $h = 1$ y-intercept: $y = 2^{0-1} = 2^{-1} = \frac{1}{2}$ Asymptote does not shift: $y = 0$	$f(x) = 2^x$ $g(x) = 2^{x-1}$

Find the y-intercept and asymptote for each function. Then graph each function and $f(x) = 2^x$ on the same plane.

1. $g(x) = 2^x + 2$
y-intercept: 3 asymptote: $y = 2$

2. $g(x) = 2^{x+2}$
y-intercept: 4 asymptote: $y = 0$

Tell whether each statement is sometimes, always, or never true.

40. A vertical translation of $f(x) = \log x$ changes its asymptote. **never**

41. A vertical translation of $f(x) = e^x$ changes its asymptote. **always**

42. A horizontal translation of $f(x) = \log x$ has a range of $\mathbb{R}$. **never**

43. The graph of a transformation of $f(x) = \ln x$ intersects the graph of $f(x)$. **sometimes**

44. **Banking** The function $A(t) = 1000\left(1 + \frac{r}{n}\right)^{nt}$ can be used to calculate the growth of an investment of \$1000 in an account where the interest is compounded n times per year at an annual rate r. Suppose that you invest \$1000 in such an account compounded quarterly (4 times per year).

a. What annual rate would double your investment in 5 years? **≈ 14.1%**

b. At an annual rate of 3.5%, how long (to the nearest year) would it take for your investment to double? **20 yr**

c. What does the model predict for the amount in the account after 10 years if the investment continues to grow at an annual rate of 3.5%? **\$1416.91**

Match each equation with one of the following graphs.

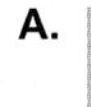

A.

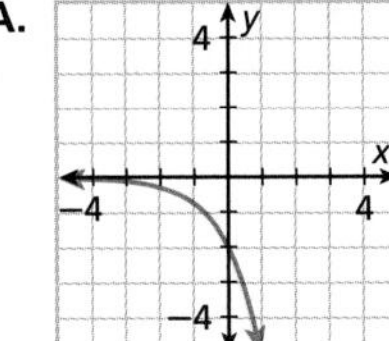

B.

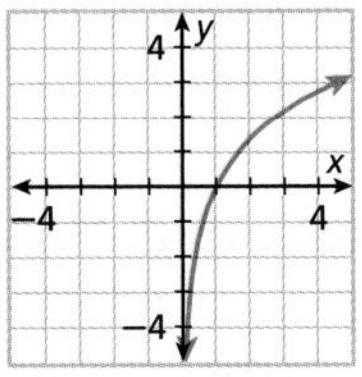

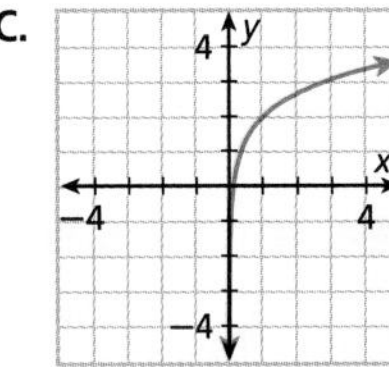

C.

45. $f(x) = \ln x + 2$ **C**

46. $f(x) = -2e^x$ **A**

47. $f(x) = 2\ln x$ **B**

LINK

Medicine

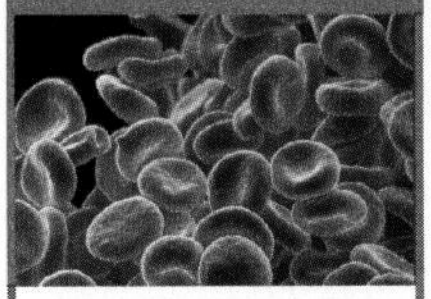

Insulin is a hormone that allows the body's cells, including red blood cells, to absorb glucose. Synthetic insulin can help diabetics maintain a healthy level of blood sugar.

48. **Medicine** A dose of synthetic insulin breaks down in the bloodstream over time. The amount of insulin in the blood with an initial dose of A_0 mg, under some conditions, is given by $A = A_0 0.97^t$, where t is the time in minutes. The standard dose is 10 mg. Describe each transformation.

a. The initial dose is changed from 10 mg to 20 mg.

b. The breakdown of the medicine does not begin for 5 minutes.

c. The breakdown time period is increased from one-minute intervals to two-minute intervals.

d. **What if...?** The breakdown rate of 0.97 is reduced to 0.95. Is this a transformation of A?

49. **Critical Thinking** Describe how changing the value of h and changing the value of k differ in the effect on the graph of $f(x) = a(b^{x-h}) + k$.

50. **Write About It** Explain how to translate, reflect, stretch, and compress the graph of $f(x) = b^x$.

MULTI-STEP TEST PREP

51. This problem will prepare you for the Multi-Step Test Prep on page 552.

The number of farms in a county is modeled by $N(t) = 1257(0.99)^t$, where t is the number of years since 1990.

a. One-third of the farms in the county always produce soybeans. Write a new function that models the number of soybean farms. $N(t) = 419(0.99)^t$

b. Write a new function that gives the number of soybean farms m months after January 1, 1990. $N(t) = 419(0.99)^{\frac{m}{12}}$

c. How many soybean farms were there at the end of May 1991? **413**

Exercise 51 involves transforming exponential functions. This exercise prepares students for the Multi-Step Test Prep on page 552.

Answers

21. −0.25; $y = 0$; vertical compression by a factor of 0.25 and reflection across the x-axis; R: $\{y \mid y < 0\}$

22. −1; $y = 0$; horizontal stretch by a factor of 2 and reflection across the x-axis; R: $\{y \mid y < 0\}$

23. 4; $y = 0$; vertical stretch by a factor of 4 and reflection across the y-axis

24. −4; $y = 0$; vertical compression by a factor of 4 and reflection across both axes; R: $\{y \mid y < 0\}$

25. $x = 5$; translation 5 units right; D: $\{x \mid x > 5\}$

26. $x = -3$; translation 3 units left, vertical compression by a factor of $\frac{4}{5}$, and translation 2 units down; D: $\{x \mid x > -3\}$

27. $x = 0$; vertical stretch by a factor of 4 and reflection across the x-axis

31. horizontal stretch by a factor of 127, reflection across the y-axis, and vertical stretch by a factor of 870

48a. vertical stretch by a factor of 2

b. horizontal translation 5 units right; D: $\{x \mid x > 5\}$

c. horizontal stretch by a factor of 2

d. Possible answer: horizontal compression since $0.95^t = 0.97^{kt}$, where $k =$ the constant $\frac{\log 0.95}{\log 0.97}$, which is > 1

49. Changing h translates the graph right (+) or left (−), and changing k translates the graph up (+) or down (−).

50. Possible answer: Translation left or right: Replace x with $x - h$. Translation up or down: Add k. Reflect across x-axis: Multiply b^x by −1. Reflect across y-axis: Replace x with $-x$. Vertical stretch or compression: Multiply b^x by $a \neq \pm 1$. Horizontal stretch or compression: Divide x by $c \neq \pm 1$.

7-7 PROBLEM SOLVING

Alex is studying a new species of hybrid plant. The average height of the plant can be modeled by the function $h(t) = 2 \ln(t + 1.25)$, where h is the height in feet and t is the number of weeks after planting.

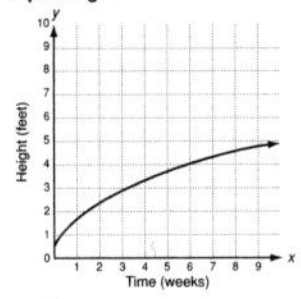

1. Alex graphs the function to see the rate an average plant grows.

a. About how tall can he expect the plant to be after 3 weeks? **About 3 ft tall**

b. What is the y-intercept? What does it tell Alex about the plant? **About 0.45 ft; that is the initial height of the plant.**

2. Alex plants seeds and finds that the height is now modeled by the parent function.

a. Give the parent function $g(t)$. $g(t) = \ln t$

b. Describe how the function $h(t)$ is transformed from the parent function. **The parent function is translated 1.25 units left and stretched vertically by a factor of 2.**

c. Choose the letter of the graph that represents the parent function. **B**

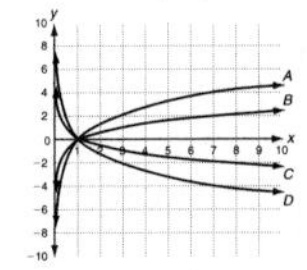

Alex experiments with different fertilizers and finds that he can change the growth curve of the hybrid plant. Choose the letter for the best answer.

3. Alex finds that the height of the plants can now be modeled by the function $f(t) = 1.5 \ln(t + 1) + 0.4$. Which statement describes the transformation from the parent function?

(A) Translation 0.4 unit up and 1 unit left; vertical stretch by 1.5

B Translation 1 unit up and 0.4 unit right; vertical stretch by 1.5

C Translation 0.4 unit down and 1 unit left; horizontal compression by 1.5

D Translation 1 unit down and 0.4 unit right; horizontal compression by 1.5

4. Alex looks at the graph of the growth of his plants after trying a different fertilizer. The graph is transformed from the parent function by a vertical compression by a factor of 0.5 and a translation 1 unit right. Which function describes this transformation?

F $k(t) = 2\ln(t + 1)$

G $k(t) = 2\ln(t - 1)$

(H) $k(t) = 0.5\ln(t - 1)$

J $k(t) = 0.5\ln(t + 1)$

7-7 CHALLENGE

Transformations of exponential and logarithmic functions may appear in several forms due to the properties of exponents and logarithms. In other words, functions that have equations that look different may produce equivalent graphs. Consider the function $f(x) = \log x$ shown at right.

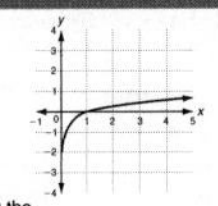

Use your calculator to graph $g(x) = \log \frac{1}{x}$ and $h(x) = -\log x$.

1. Compare the graphs of $g(x)$ and $h(x)$. What do you notice about the two functions? Describe the transformation of $f(x) = \log x$ to $g(x)$ and $h(x)$. **They are identical. The graphs are reflections of $f(x) = \log x$ over the x-axis.**

2. Use the properties of logarithms to show that $g(x)$ and $h(x)$ are equivalent. $\log \frac{1}{x} = \log(x^{-1}) = -1 \cdot \log x = -\log x$

Use your calculator to graph $j(x) = \log(100\sqrt{x})$ and $k(x) = \frac{\log x}{2} + 2$.

3. Compare the graphs of $j(x)$ and $k(x)$. What do you notice about the two functions? Describe the transformation of $f(x) = \log x$ to $j(x)$ and $k(x)$. **They are identical. The function is vertically compressed by a factor of 0.5 and then translated 2 units up.**

4. Use the properties of logarithms to show that $j(x)$ and $k(x)$ are equivalent.
$\log(100\sqrt{x}) = \log 100 + \log\sqrt{x}$
$= \log 10^2 + \log x^{\frac{1}{2}} = 2\log 10 + \frac{1}{2}\log x = 2 + \frac{\log x}{2}$

Look at the graph of the function $f(x) = 2^x$ shown at right. Use your calculator to graph $g(x) = 2^{2x-3}$, $h(x) = 4^{x-1.5}$, and $k(x) = \frac{4^x}{8}$.

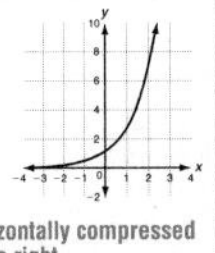

5. Compare the graphs and table of values for $g(x)$, $h(x)$, and $k(x)$. What do you notice about the three functions? Describe the transformation of $f(x) = 2^x$ to each of these three functions. **The three functions are identical. The function is horizontally compressed by a factor of 2 and then shifted 1.5 units right.**

6. Use the properties of exponents to show that $g(x)$, $h(x)$, and $k(x)$ are equivalent. $2^{2x-3} = 2^{2(x-1.5)} = 4^{x-1.5} = \frac{4^x}{4^{1.5}} = \frac{4^x}{8}$

TEST PREP DOCTOR In **Exercise 51,** students may not believe that *every* point must be stretched vertically and shifted. Remind them that they should see how (0, 1) is transformed if exponential, and (1, 0) if logarithmic.

Students having difficulty with **Exercise 54** could try to see which function fits the story: Only **B** gives 4500 for $t = 0$ and 2700 for $t = 1$.

Transformations

Exercise 55 illustrates an interesting point about logarithmic and exponential functions: a horizontal compression can lead to the same graph as a vertical shift.

Journal

Have students describe the steps they would take to graph $f(x) = 2^{-x+1}$ and describe and explain the transformations from the parent function.

ALTERNATIVE ASSESSMENT

Have students transform $f(x) = e^x$ and $g(x) = \ln x$. Then have them choose a translation and a stretch, write the rule, and sketch the graphs. If desired, have students choose an axis to reflect the function across and repeat.

Power Presentations with PowerPoint®

7-7 Lesson Quiz

1. Graph $g(x) = 2^{0.25x} - 1$. Find the asymptote. Describe how the graph is transformed from the graph of its parent function.

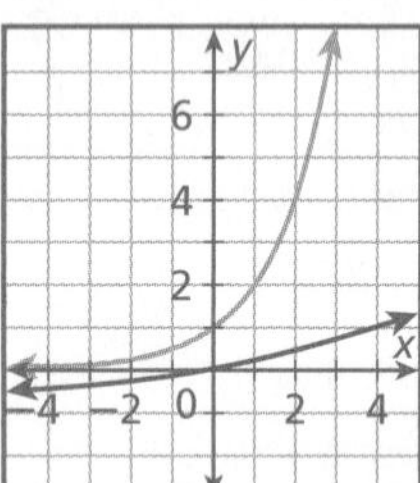

$y = -1$; the graph of $g(x)$ is a horizontal stretch of $f(x) = 2^x$ by a factor of 4 and a shift 1 unit down.

2. Write the transformed function: $f(x) = \ln x$ is stretched vertically by a factor of 3, reflected across the x-axis, and shifted by 2 units left.

$g(x) = -3\ln(x + 2)$

Also available on transparency

TEST PREP

52. Which function is vertically stretched by a factor of 3 and translated 2 units left from its parent function?

(A) $f(x) = 3(2^{x+2})$ (circled)
(B) $f(x) = 2^{3x} - 2$
(C) $f(x) = 3\log(x - 2)$
(D) $f(x) = \log(3x + 2)$

53. Which list shows the functions in order from the most compressed horizontally from $f(x) = \log x$ to the most stretched?

(F) $f(x) = \log(x - 10)$, $f(x) = \log(10x)$, $f(x) = \log\left(\frac{x}{10}\right)$
(G) $f(x) = \log\left(\frac{x}{10}\right)$, $f(x) = \log(x - 10)$, $f(x) = \log(10x)$
(H) $f(x) = \log(10x)$, $f(x) = \log(x - 10)$, $f(x) = \log\left(\frac{x}{10}\right)$ (circled)
(J) $f(x) = \log\left(\frac{x}{10}\right)$, $f(x) = \log(10x)$, $f(x) = \log(x - 10)$

54. The trade-in value of Cindy's car is $4500 and decreases by about 40% per year. Which choice represents the trade-in value as a function of time?

(A) $f(t) = 4500(0.4)^t$
(B) $f(t) = 4500(0.6)^t$ (circled)
(C) $f(t) = 0.6(4500)^t$
(D) $f(t) = 0.4(4500)^t$

CHALLENGE AND EXTEND

55. **Critical Thinking** Consider the function $f(x) = \log x$.

a. Identify the transformation applied to $f(x)$ to create $g(x) = \log x + 1$.
b. Identify the transformation applied to $f(x)$ to create $h(x) = \log(10x)$.
c. Use a graphing calculator to compare the graphs and tables of both functions. What do you notice? They are equivalent.
d. Use the properties of logarithms to explain your answer to part **c.**

a. translation 1 unit up
b. horizontal compression by $\frac{1}{10}$
d. $\log(10x) = \log 10 + \log x = 1 + \log x$

56. **Graphing Calculator** Graph the function $y = -\ln(x + 2)$ in the standard window. Make a conjecture explaining why the calculator screen appears to show that the graph stops abruptly and does not extend infinitely in two directions.

56. The value of y is undefined for $x \leq -2$.

57. What can you say about the value of $f(x)$ as the value of x gets closer and closer to h in the standard equation for a logarithmic function, $f(x) = a\log(x - h) + k$, given that a, h, and $k \geq 0$? For $(x - h) > 1$, $f(x) > 0$. For $(x - h) = 1$, $f(x) = 0$. For $0 < (x - h) < 1$, $f(x) < 0$. For $(x - h) < 0$, $f(x) < 0$ is undefined.

SPIRAL REVIEW

Find the minimum or maximum value. Then state the domain and range of the function. *(Lesson 5-2)*

58. $f(x) = x^2 - 2x + 5$
59. $f(x) = 4x^2 + x - 5$
60. $f(x) = -x^2 - x + 1$

58. min: $(1, 4)$; D: $\mathbb{R}$; R: $\{y \mid y \geq 4\}$
59. min: $\left(-\frac{1}{8}, -\frac{81}{16}\right)$; D: $\mathbb{R}$; R: $\{y \mid y \geq -5\}$
60. max: $\left(-\frac{1}{2}, \frac{5}{4}\right)$; D: $\mathbb{R}$; R: $\left\{y \mid y \leq \frac{5}{4}\right\}$

61. The table shows the volumes of containers of varying heights. Write a cubic function to model the volume. *(Lesson 6-9)* $f(x) \approx 0.032x^3 - 0.0076x^2 + 0.073x + 1.30$

Height (in.)	5	7	10	12	15
Volume (qt)	5.5	12.5	33.5	56.8	109.5

Simplify each expression. *(Lesson 7-6)*

62. $\ln e^{x+2}$ $x + 2$
63. $\ln e^{-5x}$ $-5x$
64. $e^{\ln(x-1)}$ $x - 1$
65. $e^{\ln\left(\frac{x}{4}\right)}$ $\frac{x}{4}$

Answers

56.

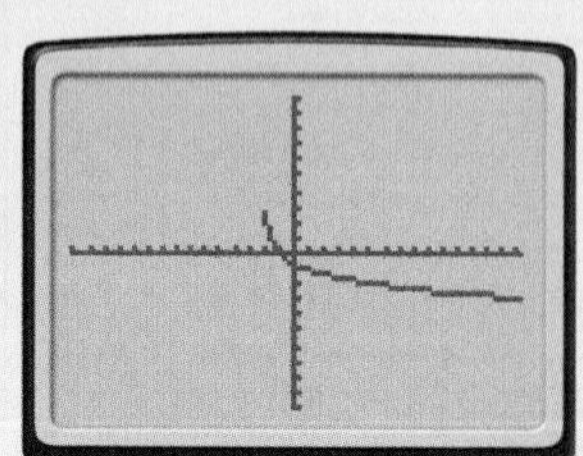

7-8 Curve Fitting with Exponential and Logarithmic Models

A2.6.4 Solve problems that can be modeled using exponential and logarithmic equations, interpret the solutions and determine whether the solutions are reasonable using technology as appropriate.

Objectives
Model data by using exponential and logarithmic functions.
Use exponential and logarithmic models to analyze and predict.

Vocabulary
exponential regression
logarithmic regression

Who uses this?
Gem cutters know that values of precious stones of similar quality are exponentially related to the gems' weights. (See Example 2.)

Analyzing data values can identify a pattern, or repeated relationship, between two quantities.

Look at this table of values for the exponential function $f(x) = 2(3^x)$.

x	−1	0	1	2	3
$f(x)$	$\frac{2}{3}$	2	6	18	54

$\times 3 \quad \times 3 \quad \times 3 \quad \times 3$

Remember!
For linear functions (first degree), first differences are constant. For quadratic functions, second differences are constant, and so on.

Notice that the *ratio* of each y-value and the previous one is constant. Each value is three times the one before it, so the ratio of function values is constant for equally spaced x-values. This data can be fit by an exponential function of the form $f(x) = ab^x$.

EXAMPLE 1 Identifying Exponential Data

Determine whether f is an exponential function of x of the form $f(x) = ab^x$. If so, find the constant ratio.

A

x	−1	0	1	2	3
$f(x)$	−3	−1	1	3	5

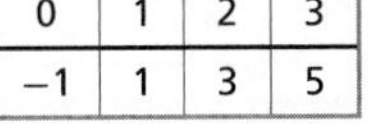

$+2 \quad +2 \quad +2 \quad +2$ *First differences*

y is a linear function of x.

B

x	−1	0	1	2	3
$f(x)$	$\frac{1}{2}$	1	2	4	8

$+\frac{1}{2} \quad +1 \quad +2 \quad +4$

Ratios $\frac{1}{\frac{1}{2}} = \frac{2}{1} = \frac{4}{2} = \frac{8}{4} = 2$

This data set is exponential, with a constant ratio of 2.

CHECK IT OUT! Determine whether y is an exponential function of x of the form $f(x) = ab^x$. If so, find the constant ratio.

1a.

x	−1	0	1	2	3
$f(x)$	$2.\overline{6}$	4	6	9	13.5

yes; 1.5

1b.

x	−1	0	1	2	3
$f(x)$	−3	2	7	12	17

no

7-8 Organizer

Pacing: Traditional 1 day
Block $\frac{1}{2}$ day

Objectives: Model data by using exponential and logarithmic functions.
Use exponential and logarithmic models to analyze and predict.

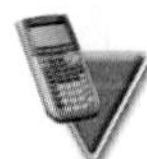

Technology Lab
In *Technology Lab Activities*

Online Edition
Tutorial Videos, Interactivity, TechKeys

Countdown to Testing Week 16

Power Presentations with PowerPoint®

Warm Up

Perform a quadratic regression on the following data:

x	1	2	6	11	13
$f(x)$	3	6	39	120	170

$f(x) \approx 0.98x^2 + 0.1x + 2.1$

Also available on transparency

Math Humor

Gia: We're fitting curves to data again.

Pam: I want to move forward, but we keep regressing!

1 Introduce

EXPLORATION

7-8 Curve Fitting with Exponential and Logarithmic Models

Two scientists use two different models to predict populations of elk in a national forest.

Model 1	
Year t	Population p
0	32,000
1	33,500
2	35,000
3	36,500

Model 2	
Year t	Population p
0	32,000
1	33,600
2	35,280
3	37,044

1. For model 1, is p a linear function of t, a quadratic function of t, or neither? How do you know?
2. For model 2, is p a linear function of t, a quadratic function of t, or neither? How do you know?
3. For model 2, find the ratio of each y-value to the previous one. What do you notice?
4. Describe how the population of elk increases in model 2.

THINK AND DISCUSS

5. **Explain** what type of function is used to model the elk population in model 2.

Motivate

Present students with the following growth scenario and lead the discussion below.

Year	0	3	7	10	15	18
Population	120	143	190	232	331	405

What will the population be after 30 years? Have students recall previous methods for predicting from data sets. Do any finite difference methods apply to the set? What type of function might model the growth?

Explorations and answers are provided in the *Explorations* binder.

State Resources

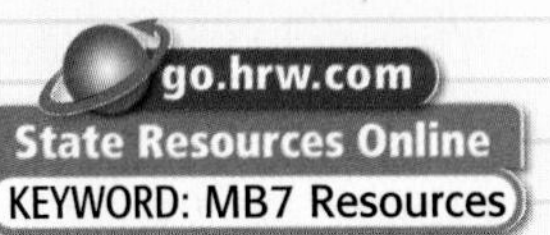

go.hrw.com
State Resources Online
KEYWORD: MB7 Resources

Power Presentations with PowerPoint®

Additional Examples

Example 1

Determine whether f is an exponential function of x. If so, find the constant ratio.

A.

x	−1	0	1	2	3
$f(x)$	2	3	5	8	12

Second differences are constant; f is a quadratic function of x.

B.

x	−1	0	1	2	3
$f(x)$	16	24	36	54	81

The data set is exponential with a constant ratio of 1.5.

Example 2

Find an exponential model for the data. Use the model to predict when the tuition at U.T. Austin will be $6000.

Tuition at The University of Texas	
Year	Tuition
1999–00	$3128
2000–01	$3585
2001–02	$3776
2002–03	$3950
2003–04	$4188

$f(x) \approx 3236(1.07^t)$ where $t = 0$ represents 1999–2000. Tuition will be about $6000 when $t = 9$, or 2008–09.

Also available on transparency

INTERVENTION

Questioning Strategies

EXAMPLE 1

- Can the common ratio be between 0 and 1? Can the common ratio be negative?

EXAMPLE 2

- How could you use the same set of data to find a logarithmic model?

In Chapters 2 and 5, you used a graphing calculator to perform *linear regressions* and *quadratic regressions* to make predictions. You can also use an *exponential model,* which is an exponential function that represents a real data set.

Once you know that data are exponential, you can use **ExpReg** (exponential regression) on your calculator to find a function that fits. This method of using data to find an exponential model is called an **exponential regression**. The calculator fits exponential functions to ab^x, so translations cannot be modeled.

EXAMPLE 2 *Gemology Application*

The table gives the approximate values of diamonds of the same quality. Find an exponential model for the data. Use the model to estimate the weight of a diamond worth $2325.

Diamond Values	
Weight (carats)	Value ($)
0.5	920
1.0	1160
2.0	1580
3.0	2150
4.0	2900

Step 1 Enter the data into two lists in a graphing calculator. Use the exponential regression feature.

```
ExpReg
 y=a*b^x
 a=814.9602955
 b=1.379191229
 r²=.9962061645
 r=.9981012797
```

An exponential model is $V(w) \approx 814.96(1.38)^w$, where V is the diamond value and w is the weight in carats.

Remember!

If you do not see r^2 and **r** when you calculate regression, use **2nd** CATALOG **0** and turn these features on by selecting **DiagnosticOn**.

Step 2 Graph the data and the function model to verify that it fits the data.

To enter the regression equation as **Y1** from the **Y=** screen, press **VARS**, choose **5:Statistics**, press **ENTER**, scroll to the **EQ** menu and select **1:RegEQ**.

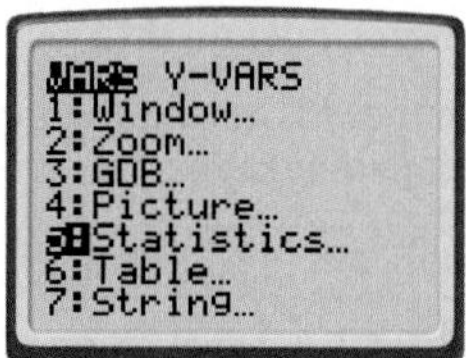

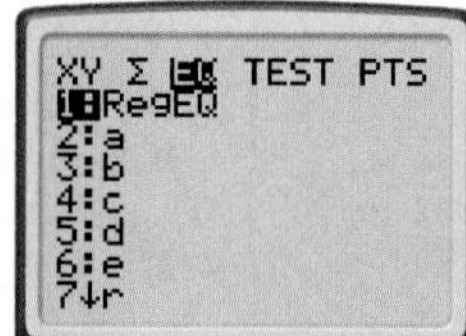

Enter 2325 as **Y2**. Use the intersection feature. You may need to adjust the window dimensions to find the intersection.

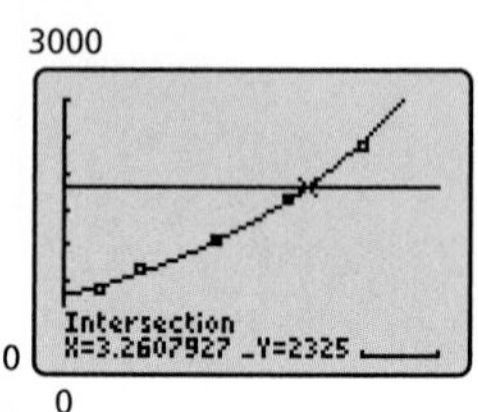

A diamond weighing about 3.26 carats will have a value of $2325.

CHECK IT OUT!

2. Use exponential regression to find a function that models this data. When will the number of bacteria reach 2000?

Time (min)	0	1	2	3	4	5
Bacteria	200	248	312	390	489	610

$B(t) \approx 199(1.25)^t$; $\approx$10.3 min

2 Teach

Guided Instruction

First, review the process of looking at first and second differences. Then, be sure that students recall the process for doing a regression on a graphing calculator.

Remind students that they need to scroll for some calculator features, such as **ExpReg** and **LnReg**.

Reaching All Learners

Through Cognitive Strategies

Have students create a list of words that have been associated with exponential and logarithmic functions, such as growth, decay, interest, etc. This list can be used to eliminate some models when attempting to fit a model to data. For example, a data set that records the growth of bacteria will probably demonstrate exponential growth. This may allow students to avoid the need to first look for common differences.

Many natural phenomena can be modeled by natural log functions. You can use a **logarithmic regression** to find a function.

EXAMPLE 3 ***Physics Application***

The table gives the Richter scale equivalent for an explosion involving a quantity of TNT. Find a natural log model for the data. Use the model to estimate the number of tons of TNT that would be the equivalent of an earthquake measuring 6.5 on the Richter scale.

Richter Scale TNT Equivalence

TNT (tons)	Magnitude
1 TON	2.0
10 TONS	3.0
1000 TONS	4.0
10,000 TONS	5.0

Helpful Hint

Most calculators that perform logarithmic regression use ln rather than log.

Enter the data into two lists in a graphing calculator. Then use the logarithmic regression feature. Press  **CALC 9:LnReg.** A logarithmic model is $R(t) \approx 2 + 0.29 \ln t$, where R is the Richter scale reading and t is the equivalent number of tons of TNT.

The calculated value of r^2 shows that the function fits the data.

Graph the data and function model to verify that it fits the data.

Use the intersection feature to find x when y is 6.5. The TNT equivalent of an earthquake measuring 6.5 on the Richter scale is about 5.3 million tons.

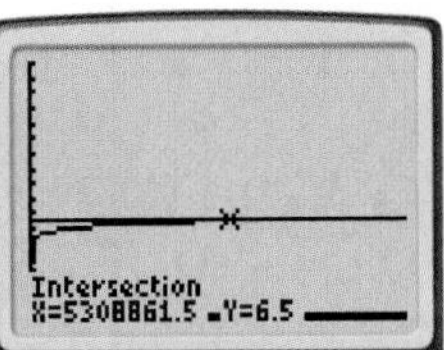

CHECK IT OUT! 3. Use logarithmic regression to find a function that models this data. When will the speed reach 8.0 m/s?

Time (min)	1	2	3	4	5	6	7
Speed (m/s)	0.5	2.5	3.5	4.3	4.9	5.3	5.6

$S(t) \approx 0.59 + 2.64 \ln t$; ≈ 16.6 min

THINK AND DISCUSS

1. Explain how you can determine whether or not a data set can be fit by an exponential function of the form $f(x) = ab^x$.
2. Explain why having only two data points is not enough to tell you whether the data set is exponential or logarithmic.

3. **GET ORGANIZED** Copy and complete the graphic organizer. Show the procedures and tools for finding an exponential or logarithmic model.

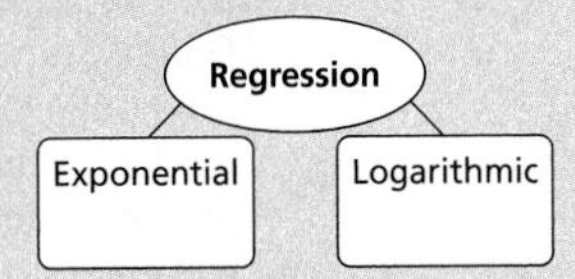

COMMON ERROR ALERT

Students must be careful to select **Lnreg**, rather than **Linreg**, for logarithmic regression. After performing a regression, they should verify that the function displayed is the one they had intended to use, in this case, **y=a+blnx.**

Power Presentations with PowerPoint®

Additional Examples

Example 3

Find a natural log model for the data. According to the model, when will the global population exceed 9,000,000,000?

Global Population Growth

Population (billions)	Year
1	1800
2	1927
3	1960
4	1974
5	1987
6	1999

$f(x) \approx 1824 + 106 \ln x$; 2058

Also available on transparency

INTERVENTION 

Questioning Strategies

EXAMPLE 3

- What characteristics of the data make you think that a logarithmic model is appropriate?

3 Close

Summarize

Remind students that they can do exponential and logarithmic regressions in the same way that they do other regressions. Pure exponential functions can be recognized because there is a constant ratio between either the terms or the first differences.

ONGOING ASSESSMENT and INTERVENTION 

***Diagnose Before* the Lesson**
7-8 Warm Up, TE p. 545

***Monitor During* the Lesson**
Check It Out! Exercises, SE pp. 545–547
Questioning Strategies, TE pp. 546–547

***Assess After* the Lesson**
7-8 Lesson Quiz, TE p. 551
Alternative Assessment, TE p. 551

Answers to *Think and Discuss*

1. if there is a common ratio between the data values
2. Possible answer: There is only 1 ratio between data values, so there is no way to determine if that ratio is constant.
3. See p. A9.

7-8 Exercises

go.hrw.com
Homework Help Online
KEYWORD: MB7 7-8
Parent Resources Online
KEYWORD: MB7 Parent

Assignment Guide

Assign *Guided Practice* exercises as necessary.

If you finished Examples **1–3**

Basic 8–13, 15–17, 19, 21–22, 24, 26–28, 32–43

Average 8–13, 15–19, 21–28, 32–43

Advanced 8–13, 17, 19–23, 26–43

Homework Quick Check

Quickly check key concepts.

Exercises: 10–12, 16

GUIDED PRACTICE

1. **Vocabulary** __?__ is useful when data can be modeled by a function of the form $f(x) = ab^x$. (*Exponential regression* or *Logarithmic regression*) **exponential regression**

SEE EXAMPLE 1 p. 545

Determine whether f is an exponential function of x of the form $f(x) = ab^x$. If so, find the constant ratio.

2.

x	−1	0	1	2	3
$f(x)$	$-2\frac{5}{7}$	−1	11	95	683

no

3.

x	−1	0	1	2	3
$f(x)$	27	18	12	8	$5\frac{1}{3}$

yes; $\frac{2}{3}$

4.

x	−1	0	1	2	3
$f(x)$	5	1	−3	−7	−11

no

5.

x	−1	0	1	2	3
$f(x)$	$2\frac{1}{4}$	3	4	$5\frac{1}{3}$	$7\frac{1}{9}$

yes; $\frac{4}{3}$

SEE EXAMPLE 2 p. 546

6. **Physics** The table gives the approximate number of degrees Fahrenheit above room temperature of a cup of tea as it cools. Find an exponential model for the data. Use the model to estimate how long it will take the tea to reach a temperature that is less than 40 degrees above room temperature. **$T(t) \approx 131(0.92)^t$; ≈ 13.6 min**

Cooling Tea					
Time (min)	0	1	2	3	4
Degrees above room temperature (°F)	132	120	110	101	93

SEE EXAMPLE 3 p. 547

7. **Community** The table shows the population milestones for a small town following its incorporation. Find a natural log model for the data. Use the model to predict how long it will take for the population to reach 8000. **$P(t) \approx 621.6 + 1221 \ln t$; ≈ 421 mo**

Town Population Milestones					
Time (mo)	6	18	42	90	150
Population	3000	4000	5000	6000	7000

PRACTICE AND PROBLEM SOLVING

Independent Practice

For Exercises	See Example
8–11	1
12	2
13	3

Extra Practice

Skills Practice p. S17
Application Practice p. S38

Determine whether f is an exponential function of x of the form $f(x) = ab^x$. If so, find the constant ratio.

8.

x	−1	0	1	2	3
$f(x)$	1.25	1	0.75	0.5	0.25

no

9.

x	−5	−3	1	3	5
$f(x)$	20	6	2	12	30

no

10.

x	−1	0	1	2	3
$f(x)$	0.667	1	1.5	2.25	3.375

yes; 1.5

11.

x	−1	0	1	2	3
$f(x)$	−16	−8	−4	−2	−1

yes; $\frac{1}{2}$

12. **Social Studies** The table gives the United States Hispanic population from 1980 to 2000. Find an exponential model for the data. Use the model to predict when the Hispanic population will exceed 120 million.
$P(t) \approx 9.35(1.045)^t$; ≈ 2027

United States Hispanic Population			
Years After 1970	10	20	30
Population (millions)	14.6	22.5	35.3

Source: Census 2000

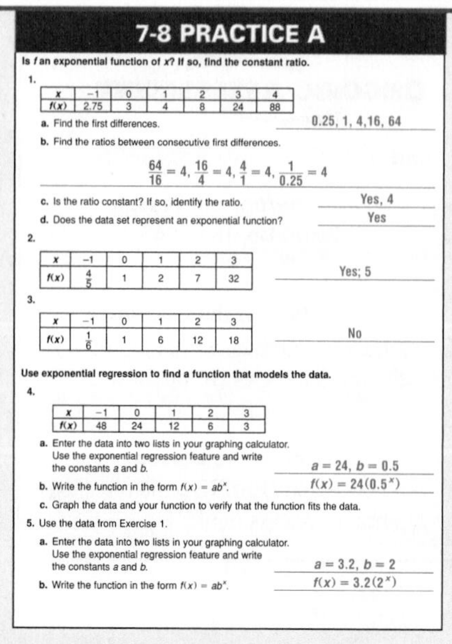

7-8 PRACTICE A

Is f an exponential function of x? If so, find the constant ratio.

1.

x	−1	0	1	2	3	4
$f(x)$	2.75	3	4	8	24	88

a. Find the first differences. **0.25, 1, 4, 16, 64**

b. Find the ratios between consecutive first differences.

$\frac{64}{16} = 4, \frac{16}{4} = 4, \frac{4}{1} = 4, \frac{1}{0.25} = 4$

c. Is the ratio constant? If so, identify the ratio. **Yes, 4**

d. Does the data set represent an exponential function? **Yes**

2.

x	−1	0	1	2	3
$f(x)$	$\frac{4}{5}$	1	2	7	32

Yes; 5

3.

x	−1	0	1	2	3
$f(x)$	$\frac{1}{6}$	1	6	12	18

No

Use exponential regression to find a function that models the data.

4.

x	−1	0	1	2	3
$f(x)$	48	24	12	6	3

a. Enter the data into two lists in your graphing calculator. Use the exponential regression feature and write the constants a and b. **$a = 24$, $b = 0.5$**

b. Write the function in the form $f(x) = ab^x$. **$f(x) = 24(0.5^x)$**

c. Graph the data and your function to verify that the function fits the data.

5. Use the data from Exercise 1.

a. Enter the data into two lists in your graphing calculator. Use the exponential regression feature and write the constants a and b. **$a = 3.2$, $b = 2$**

b. Write the function in the form $f(x) = ab^x$. **$f(x) = 3.2(2^x)$**

7-8 PRACTICE B

Determine whether f is an exponential function of x. If so, find the constant ratio.

1.

x	−1	0	1	2	3
$f(x)$	9	3	1	0.3	0.9

No

2.

x	−1	0	1	2	3
$f(x)$	0.01	0.03	0.15	0.87	5.19

Yes; 6

3.

x	−1	0	1	2	3
$f(x)$	$\frac{5}{6}$	$\frac{5}{2}$	7.5	22.5	67.5

Yes; 3

4.

x	−1	0	1	2	3
$f(x)$	1	0.5	0.33	0.25	0.2

No

Use exponential regression to find a function that models the data.

5.

x	1	2	3	4	5
$f(x)$	14	7.1	3.4	1.8	0.8

$f(x) = 29(0.49)^x$

6.

x	2	12	22	32	42
$f(x)$	5	20	80	320	1280

$f(x) = 3.8(1.15)^x$

Solve.

7. a. Bernice is selling seashells she has found at the beach. The price of each shell depends on its length. Find an exponential model for the data.

Length of Shell (cm)	5	8	12	20	25
Price ($)	2	3.5	5	18	40

$f(x) = 0.97(1.16)^x$

b. What is the length of a shell selling for $9.00? **15 cm**

c. If Bernice found a 40 cm Conch shell. How much could she sell it for? **$367.36**

8. a. Use logarithmic regression to find a function that models this data.

Time (min)	1	2	3	4	5
Speed (m/s)	1.5	6.2	10.6	12.9	14.8

$f(x) = 1.14 + 8.42 \ln x$

b. When will the speed exceed 20 m/s? **9.4 s**

c. What will the speed be after 1 hour? **35.6 m/s**

State Resources

13. **Telecommunication** The table gives the number of telecommuters in the United States from 1990 to 2000. Find an exponential model for the data. Use the model to estimate when the number of telecommuters will exceed 100 million.

U.S. Telecommuters											
Years After 1990	0	1	2	3	4	5	6	7	8	9	10
Telecommuters (millions)	4.4	5.5	6.6	7.3	9.1	8.5	8.7	11.1	15.7	19.6	23.6

Source: Federal Highway Administration

$T(t) \approx 4.45(1.17)^t$; ≈ 2011

14. **Ecology** Data on an endangered crane species indicate that their numbers are increasing. The table shows the population size over the last 55 years. Find a logarithmic model for the data. Predict the year when the population will reach 500.

14. $t(p) \approx -60 + 22.4 \ln p$; 2020

Crane Population					
Population Size	18	40	85	120	185
Years Since 1940	5	22	40	47	57

Decide whether the data set is exponential, and if it is, use exponential regression to find a function that models the data.

15.

x	1	2	3	4
$f(x)$	11	95	683	4799

15. yes; $f(x) = 1.55(7.54)^x$

16.

x	−1	0	2	3
$f(x)$	4	2	0.5	0.25

yes; $f(x) = 2(0.5)^x$

American alligator, Everglades National Park

17. **Critical Thinking** According to one source, the population of nesting wading birds in the wetlands of the Florida Everglades Park System has decreased from more than a half-million in the 1930s to less than 15,000 today. What do you need to know to determine whether this decrease in numbers is exponential? Explain.

18. **Ecology** One research study showed that the rate of calf survival in Yellowstone elk herds depends on spring snow depths. At snow depths of about 5000 mm, the rate of survival is about 0.9 per hundred cows; at 6700 mm it is about 0.3; and at 8250 mm, it is about 0.17. Find an exponential function to model the data. Use the model to predict the calf survival rate per hundred cows at snow depths of 4000 mm. $r(d) \approx 10.99(0.9995)^d$; 1.40 per 100 cows

19. **Technology** Holiday season sales of a portable digital music player are shown in the graph. Assume that growth rate continues in the same way. Write an exponential function to model the data. Use the model to predict sales in three years.

19. $s(t) = 68.24(3.69)^t$; ≈ 46.5 million

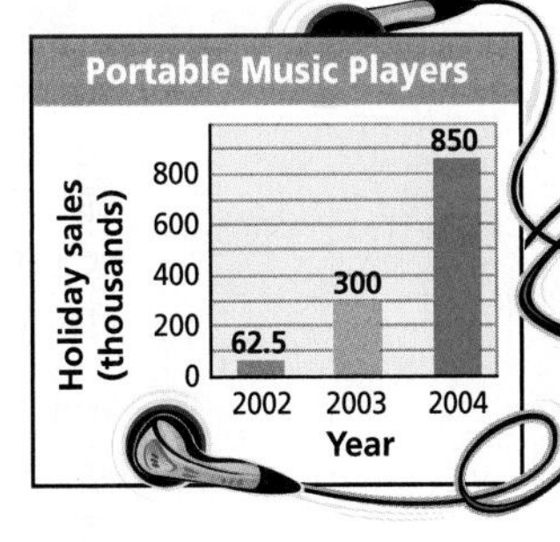

20. **Data Collection** Use a graphing calculator and a temperature probe to measure the temperature of a refrigerated liquid from the time it is taken from refrigeration. Use the list feature to subtract the temperatures from room temperature. Find a model for the difference from room temperature over time. Describe the model and explain why you chose it.

21. **Make a Conjecture** Make a table of values for an exponential function with $x = 1, 2, 3, \ldots 8$. Find the first differences, second differences, and third differences. Make a conjecture about the nth differences, assuming that the domain of the function is all natural numbers.
Possible answer: nth differences have the same common ratio as first differences.

Teaching Tip **Multiple Representations** Because exponential and logarithmic functions are inverses of each other, any set of data that is appropriate for an exponential regression can also be used for a logarithmic regression by switching the role of the variables. For instance, **Exercise 14** yields the logarithmic function $f(x) = -60 + 22.4 \ln x$. We could just as easily describe the population as an exponential function of time, $P(t) = 14.6(1.046)^t$.

Teaching Tip **Data Collection** To help students complete **Exercise 20,** see Technology Lab Activities.

Answers

17. Possible answer: a third data point because 2 points can be fit by many different functions

20. Possible answer: an exponential decay model; the ratios are nearly constant.

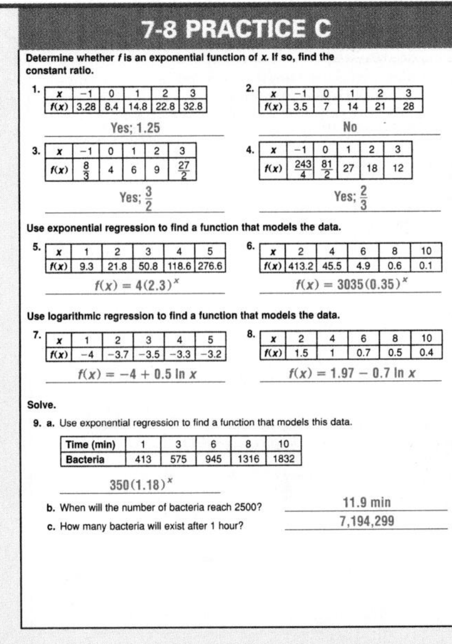

7-8 PRACTICE C

Determine whether f is an exponential function of x. If so, find the constant ratio.

1.

x	−1	0	1	2	3
$f(x)$	3.28	8.4	14.8	22.8	32.8

Yes; 1.25

2.

x	−1	0	1	2	3
$f(x)$	3.5	7	14	21	28

No

3.

x	−1	0	1	2	3
$f(x)$	$\frac{8}{3}$	4	6	9	$\frac{27}{2}$

Yes; $\frac{3}{2}$

4.

x	−1	0	1	2	3
$f(x)$	$\frac{243}{4}$	$\frac{81}{2}$	27	18	12

Yes; $\frac{2}{3}$

Use exponential regression to find a function that models the data.

5.

x	1	2	3	4	5
$f(x)$	9.3	21.8	50.8	118.6	276.6

$f(x) = 4(2.3)^x$

6.

x	2	4	6	8	10
$f(x)$	413.2	45.5	4.9	0.6	0.1

$f(x) = 3035(0.35)^x$

Use logarithmic regression to find a function that models the data.

7.

x	1	2	3	4	5
$f(x)$	−4	−3.7	−3.5	−3.3	−3.2

$f(x) = -4 + 0.5 \ln x$

8.

x	2	4	6	8	10
$f(x)$	1.5	1	0.7	0.5	0.4

$f(x) = 1.97 - 0.7 \ln x$

Solve.

9. a. Use exponential regression to find a function that models this data.

Time (min)	1	3	6	8	10
Bacteria	413	575	945	1316	1832

$350(1.18)^x$

b. When will the number of bacteria reach 2500? 11.9 min

c. How many bacteria will exist after 1 hour? 7,194,299

Exercise 22 involves performing an exponential regression. This exercise prepares students for the Multi-Step Test Prep on page 552.

Reading Math
Exercise 23 uses language that students who take calculus or physics may encounter. The difference in an object's position over time is its *speed.* The difference in an object's *speed* over time is its *acceleration.* Students may even encounter the *jerk,* which is the change in an object's *acceleration* over time.

ENGLISH LANGUAGE LEARNERS

Students who have difficulty with **Exercise 26** could try making a short table for each choice in order to examine the data without being distracted by the wording. Otherwise, one would be tempted by the incorrect choice of **D.**

Critical Thinking
If students are looking for an exponential function in the form $f(x) = ab^x$, they can find it from two points, since for two unknowns you need two equations. See **Exercise 29.**

Answers

24. Possible answer: There will be a constant ratio between consecutive values rather than constant differences.

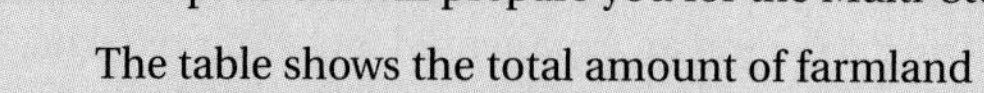

MULTI-STEP TEST PREP

22. This problem will prepare you for the Multi-Step Test Prep on page 552.

The table shows the total amount of farmland in Vermont since 1970.

Farmland in Vermont	
Year	Farmland (thousands of acres)
1970	2010
1980	1740
1990	1440
2000	1270

a. Use exponential regression to find a function that models the data.

b. According to the model, by what percent does the amount of farmland decrease each year? ≈ **1.6%**

c. Predict the amount of farmland in 2010. ≈ **1,075,000 acres**

22a. $F(t) = 2011.6(0.984)^t$

23a. 20.5 mi/h; 36.8 mi/h; 84.0 mi/h.
b. $s = 100(0.8^t)$

23. Recreation At the Autosport Show in Birmingham, England, in January 2001, karting champion Stuart Ziemelis demonstrated an electric race kart with a top speed of over 100 mi/h and acceleration from 0-to-60 mi/h in less than 4 s. The *difference* between the race kart's speed S and its top speed can be modeled by $(100 - S) = 100(0.795)^t$, where t is the time in seconds after the start.

a. Predict the electric race kart's speed at 1, 2, and 8 s.

b. Use your answers to part **a** to verify that the speed is an exponential function of time. Use exponential regression to find the function that models the speed.

24. Write About It Describe how to tell whether data is exponential rather than linear, quadratic, or cubic.

24. Possible answer: There will be a constant ratio between consecutive values rather than constant differences.

25. Biology The number of fronds of duckweed present during an experiment are given in the table.

Day	0	2	3	4	5	6
Fronds	18	32	43	57	76	101

a. Which fits the data better, an exponential function or a linear function? **exponential**

b. Enter the day numbers in L1 and the logarithm of each number of fronds in L2 (use either log or ln). Which fits this data better, an exponential function or a linear function? Why?

Linear; the log of an exponential function of x is linear.

26. Which situation can be modeled by an exponential function?

Ⓐ A cost that increases by $100 each month

Ⓑ The area of a square as the length increases by increments of 10 cm

Ⓒ The radius of a spiral that gets 10% larger with each rotation

Ⓓ A population that doubles as the time doubles

27. Which data set is exponential?

Ⓕ (0, 0.1), (1, 0.5), (2, 2.5), (3, 12.5)

Ⓖ (0, −1), (1, 0), (2, 7), (3, 20)

Ⓗ (0, −1), (1, 0.5), (2, 2), (3, 3.5)

Ⓙ (0, −1), (1, 2), (2, 11), (3, 26)

28. Gridded Response Find the missing value if f is an exponential function. **6.125**

x	0	1	2	3
y	2	3.5	■	10.71875

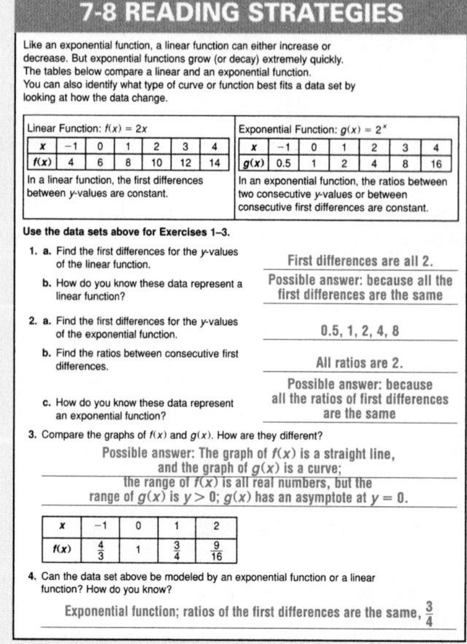

7-8 READING STRATEGIES

Like an exponential function, a linear function can either increase or decrease. But exponential functions grow (or decay) extremely quickly. The tables below compare a linear and an exponential function. You can also identify what type of curve or function best fits a data set by looking at how the data change.

Linear Function: $f(x) = 2x$

x	−1	0	1	2	3	4
$f(x)$	4	6	8	10	12	14

In a linear function, the first differences between y-values are constant.

Exponential Function: $g(x) = 2^x$

x	−1	0	1	2	3	4
$g(x)$	0.5	1	2	4	8	16

In an exponential function, the ratios between two consecutive y-values or between consecutive first differences are constant.

Use the data sets above for Exercises 1–3.

1. a. Find the first differences for the y-values of the linear function. **First differences are all 2.**
   b. How do you know these data represent a linear function? **Possible answer: because all the first differences are the same**
2. a. Find the first differences for the y-values of the exponential function. **0.5, 1, 2, 4, 8**
   b. Find the ratios between consecutive first differences. **All ratios are 2.**
   c. How do you know these data represent an exponential function? **Possible answer: because all the ratios of first differences are the same**
3. Compare the graphs of $f(x)$ and $g(x)$. How are they different?
   Possible answer: The graph of $f(x)$ is a straight line, and the graph of $g(x)$ is a curve; the range of $f(x)$ is all real numbers, but the range of $g(x)$ is $y > 0$; $g(x)$ has an asymptote at $y = 0$.

x	−1	0	1	2
$f(x)$	$\frac{4}{3}$	1	$\frac{3}{4}$	$\frac{9}{16}$

4. Can the data set above be modeled by an exponential function or a linear function? How do you know?
   Exponential function; ratios of the first differences are the same, $\frac{3}{4}$

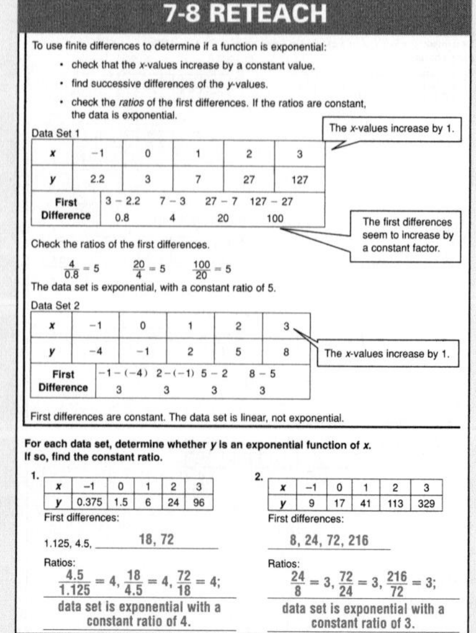

7-8 RETEACH

To use finite differences to determine if a function is exponential:

- check that the x-values increase by a constant value.
- find successive differences of the y-values.
- check the *ratios* of the first differences. If the ratios are constant, the data is exponential.

Data Set 1

x	−1	0	1	2	3
y	2.2	3	7	27	127
First Difference	3 − 2.2 0.8	7 − 3 4	27 − 7 20	127 − 27 100	

Check the ratios of the first differences.

$\frac{4}{0.8} = 5$ $\frac{20}{4} = 5$ $\frac{100}{20} = 5$

The data set is exponential, with a constant ratio of 5.

Data Set 2

x	−1	0	1	2	3
y	−4	−1	2	5	8
First Difference	−1 − (−4) 3	2 − (−1) 3	5 − 2 3	8 − 5 3	

First differences are constant. The data set is linear, not exponential.

For each data set, determine whether y is an exponential function of x. If so, find the constant ratio.

1.

x	−1	0	1	2	3
y	0.375	1.5	6	24	96

First differences:

1.125, 4.5, **18, 72**

Ratios:

$\frac{4.5}{1.125} = 4$, $\frac{18}{4.5} = 4$, $\frac{72}{18} = 4$; data set is exponential with a constant ratio of 4.

2.

x	−1	0	1	2	3
y	9	17	41	113	329

First differences:

8, 24, 72, 216

Ratios:

$\frac{24}{8} = 3$, $\frac{72}{24} = 3$, $\frac{216}{72} = 3$; data set is exponential with a constant ratio of 3.

CHALLENGE AND EXTEND

29. Find an exponential function that goes through the points $(2, 48)$ and $(4, 300)$. Show your work.

30. Environment Helena works in a chemistry laboratory. Due to equipment failure, she may have inhaled toxic fumes. Five hours after the incident, a blood sample shows a toxin concentration of 0.01006 mg/cm^3. Two hours later, another sample detects a concentration of 0.00881 mg/cm^3. Assume that concentration varies exponentially with time.

  a. Write an exponential function to model the data. $f(t) \approx 0.014(0.936)^t$

  b. There is a health risk if the toxin concentration was as high as 0.015 mg/cm^3. Was the initial concentration above this level? 0.014 mg/cm^3; no

  c. Helena can return to work when the concentration drops below 0.00010 mg/cm^3. How many hours (to the nearest hour) after the incident will this be? 75 h

31. The calculator uses logarithms to fit data to exponential and logarithmic functions. Determine what domains or ranges of data cause the calculator to get an error when using the exponential regression and logarithmic regression functions.
Exponential: $\{y \mid y \le 0\}$ causes an error.
Logarithmic: $\{x \mid x \le 0\}$ causes an error.

SPIRAL REVIEW

Solve. *(Lesson 5-3)*

32. $|-5x| = 45$ ± 9 **33.** $|x + 4| = 0$ -4 **34.** $|2x - 4| = 3$ $\frac{1}{2}, \frac{7}{2}$ **35.** $2|2x| + 1 = 10$ $\pm\frac{9}{4}$

Find the zeros of each function by factoring. *(Lesson 5-3)*

36. $f(x) = x^2 + 2x - 3$ 1, -3 **37.** $f(x) = 3x^2 + 24x$ -8, 0

38. $f(x) = 2x^2 + 10x + 12$ -3, -2 **39.** $f(x) = x^2 + 9x - 36$ -12, 3

Solve and check. *(Lesson 7-5)*

40. $\frac{1}{64} = 4^{x+5}$ -8 **41.** $81^x = 3^{x+4}$ $\frac{4}{3}$ **42.** $8^{\frac{x}{3}} = \left(\frac{1}{2}\right)^{x+2}$ -1 **43.** $216^x = 6^{2x}$ 0

Career Path

go.hrw.com
Career Resources Online
KEYWORD: MB7 Career

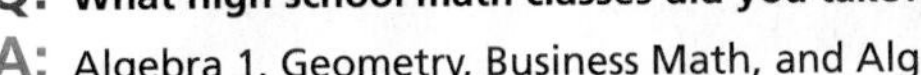

Q: What high school math classes did you take?
A: Algebra 1, Geometry, Business Math, and Algebra 2.

Q: How did you become a real estate agent?
A: After high school, I took an online training course in real estate. Then I had to pass a state license exam.

Q: How is math used in real estate?
A: We calculate house prices, interest rates, payments, taxes, closing costs, commissions, and other fees. I use geometry to calculate areas and formulas to convert between units of measurement, such as square feet to acres.

Q: What are your future plans?
A: I may look into becoming a broker. Then I can supervise other agents and manage my own office.

Colleen Murray
Real estate agent

7-8 PROBLEM SOLVING

Solve.

1. A small group of farmers joined together to grow and sell wheat in 1985. The table shows how their production of wheat increased over 20 years.

Wheat Produced by Growers Co-op						
Years After 1985	3	6	10	13	16	20
Wheat (tons)	70	105	150	210	340	580

  a. Find an exponential model for the data. $W(t) = 47.34(1.13)^t$

  b. Use the model to predict when their wheat production will exceed 2000 tons. 2016

2. The table shows the U.S. production of tobacco from 1997 to 2002.

Tobacco Production						
Years After 1996	1	2	3	4	5	6
Tobacco (× 100,000 pounds)	1787	1480	1293	1053	992	890

  a. Find a logarithmic model for the data. $T(t) = 1809.17 - 510.69 \ln t$

  b. Use the model to predict when tobacco production could fall below 50,000,000 pounds. 2009

Robert recently discovered a forgotten student loan bill. The amount due after 10 years is now \$10,819.33. He found some old statements and determined that after 7 years the bill was \$8831.80 and after 5 years he owed \$7714.03. Choose the letter for the best answer.

3. Which function models the data?
  A $S(x) = 5000(1.07)^x$
  B $S(x) = 1.07(5000)^x$
  (C) $S(x) = 5500(1.07)^x$
  D $S(x) = 1.07(5500)^x$

4. How much did Robert borrow initially?
  F \$5750
  (G) \$5500
  H \$5250
  J \$5000

5. Robert is planning to pay the loan in full next year. How much will he owe then?
  A \$12,092.14
  B \$11,925.07
  C \$11,869.33
  (D) \$11,576.69

6. What is the interest rate on Robert's student loan?
  (F) 7%
  G 6%
  H 5%
  J 4%

7-8 CHALLENGE

According to the CTIA Semi-Annual Wireless Survey, the number of wireless telephone customers has been growing since its founding in 1985.

Estimated Wireless Subscribers								
Years Since 1984	3	5	7	9	11	13	15	17
Subscribers (millions)	1.23	3.51	7.56	16.01	33.76	55.31	86.05	128.37

1. Plot the data in the table. Which is the independent and which is the dependent variable? Which model, exponential or logarithmic, would best fit the data?
Independent variable, years; dependent variable, number of subscribers; exponential model

2. Use your calculator to fit an appropriate regression curve to this set of data. Are the data highly correlated? How do you know?
$y \approx 0.67(1.39)^x$; yes, because $r^2 = 0.9767$

3. Use your model to make a prediction about the number of wireless subscribers in 1998. The estimated number of wireless subscribers in 1998 was 69,209,321. How does your prediction compare?
Predicted value is about 67,341,000, which is close to the estimated number.

4. Use your model to make a prediction about the number of wireless subscribers in 2000. The estimated number of wireless subscribers in 2000 was 109,478,031. How does your prediction compare?
Possible answer: Predicted value is about 130,110,000, which is slightly higher than the estimated number.

A common problem in regression analysis involves using data to make predictions outside the realm of the data. This process is called extrapolation and is not recommended. For instance, to use your regression equation to make predictions far in the future would be questionable. Without supporting evidence, the trend observed may or may not continue into the future.

5. Use your model to make a prediction about the number of wireless subscribers in the year 2004. The estimated number of subscribers was 182,140,362. How does your prediction compare?
Possible answer: Predicted value is 485,703,000, which is more than twice the estimated number.

6. Graph your model equation on top of the scatter plot of the data. Comment on the position of your 2004 prediction.
Looking at the curve, as you move to the right, the graph of the model rises very sharply and grossly overestimates the number of subscribers.

Answers

29. Solve the system $\begin{cases} 48 = ab^2 \\ 300 = ab^4 \end{cases}$ for a and b. Substitute for a: $300 = \left(\frac{48}{b^2}\right)b^4$. Solve for b: $6.25 = b^2$; $b = 2.5$ $(b > 0)$. Solve for a: $a = 7.68$. So $f(x) = 7.68(2.5)^x$.

Journal

Have students describe one or two situations that would be modeled by an exponential function and would be modeled by a logarithmic function.

ALTERNATIVE ASSESSMENT

Have students find an example of a real data set based on exponential growth (e.g., population growth or radioactive decay). They should perform an exponential regression on the data and answer two specific questions (e.g., what will the population be after t years).

Power Presentations with PowerPoint®

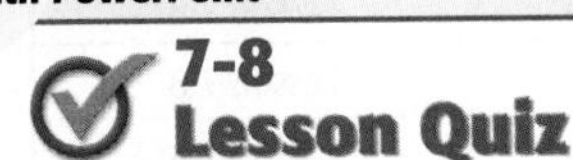

7-8 Lesson Quiz

Determine whether f is an exponential function of x. If so, find the constant ratio.

1.

x	-1	0	1	2
$f(x)$	10	9	8.1	7.29

yes; constant ratio = 0.9

2.

x	-1	0	1	2	3
$f(x)$	3	6	12	21	33

no, second differences are constant; f is quadratic.

3. Find an exponential model for the data. Use the model to estimate when the insurance value will drop below \$2000.

Insurance Value	
Year (1990 = year 0)	Value
0	10,000
2	9,032
5	7,753
9	6,290
11	5,685

$f(x) \approx 10{,}009(0.95)^t$; value will dip below 2000 in year 32, or 2022.

Also available on transparency

Organizer

Objective: Assess students' ability to apply concepts and skills in Lessons 7-5 through 7-8 in a real-world format.

 Online Edition

Resources

 ***Algebra II Assessments***
www.mathtekstoolkit.org

Problem	Text Reference
1	Lesson 7-6
2	Lessons 7-5, 7-6
3	Lesson 7-6
4–5	Lesson 7-8
6–7	Lesson 7-6

State Resources

SECTION 7B

Applying Exponential and Logarithmic Functions

Down on the Farm According to data from the U.S. Department of Agriculture, the number of farms in the United States has been decreasing over the past several decades. During this time, however, the average size of each farm has increased.

Farms in the United States	
Year	**Number of Farms (millions)**
1940	6.35
1950	5.65
1960	3.96
1970	2.95
1980	2.44
1990	2.15
2000	2.17

1. From 1940 to 1980, the average size A of a U.S. farm can be modeled by the function $A(t) = 174e^{0.022t}$, where t is the number of years since 1940. What was the average farm size in 1940? in 1980? **174 acres; 419.5 acres**
2. In what year did the average farm size reach 250 acres? **1956**
3. During the period from 1940 to 1980, how many years did it take for the average farm size to double? **31.5**
4. The table shows the number of farms in the United States since 1940. Find an exponential model for the data. $N(t) = 6.14(0.98)^t$
5. Predict the number of farms in the United States in 2010. **1.49 million**
6. According to your model, how many years does it take for the number of farms to decrease by 50%? **34.3**
7. According to your model, when will the number of farms in the United States fall below 1 million? **2030**

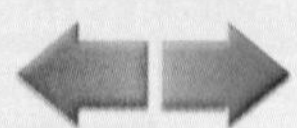

INTERVENTION

Scaffolding Questions

1. What is the value of t in 1940? 0 What is the value of t in 1980? 40
2. What equation do you need to solve? $250 = 174e^{0.022t}$ What process can you use to solve it? Divide both sides by 174. Take the ln of both sides.
3. What equation do you need to solve? $2 = e^{0.022t}$ Does the specific starting date matter? no

4–5. What is the general form of the equation that models this situation? $y = ab^x$ Will the value of b be greater than or less than 1? < 1 Why? The number of farms is decreasing.

6–7. What equation or inequality do you need to solve? $0.5 = (0.98)^t$; $1 > 6.14(0.98)^t$

Extension

If the data for 1990 and 2000 indicate the beginning of an exponential increase in the number of farms, how many farms will there be in 2010? 2.19 million

SECTION 7B

Quiz for Lessons 7-5 Through 7-8

7-5 Exponential and Logarithmic Equations and Inequalities

Solve.

1. $3^x = \frac{1}{27}$ $x = -3$
2. $49^{x+4} < 7^{\frac{x}{2}}$ $x < -\frac{16}{3}$
3. $13^{3x-1} = 91$ $x \approx 0.92$
4. $2^{x+4} = 20$ $x \approx 0.32$
5. $\log_4(x - 1) \geq 3$ 5. $x \geq 65$
6. $\log_2 x^{\frac{1}{3}} = 5$ $x = 2^{15} = 32{,}768$
7. $\log 16x - \log 4 = 2$ $x = 25$
8. $\log x + \log(x + 3) = 1$ $x = 2$
9. Suppose that you deposit $500 into an account that pays 3.5% compounded quarterly. The equation $A = P\left(1 + \frac{r}{4}\right)^n$ gives the amount A in the account after n quarters for an initial investment of P that earns interest at a rate of r. Use logarithms to solve for n to find how long it will take for the account to contain at least $2000. $n \geq 160$ quarters or 40 yr

7-6 The Natural Base, e

Graph.

10. $f(x) = e^x + 3$
11. $f(x) = 3 - e^x$
12. $f(x) = \frac{e^x}{3}$
13. $f(x) = 3(e^x - 1)$

Simplify.

14. $\ln e^2$ 2
15. $\ln e^{\frac{x}{2}}$ $\frac{x}{2}$
16. $e^{\ln(1-3a)}$ $1 - 3a$
17. $\ln e^{b+5}$ $b + 5$
18. Carbon-14 is a useful dating tool for specimens between 500 and 25,000 years old, such as ancient manuscripts and artifacts. Carbon-14's half-life is 5730 years.
   a. Use the formula $\frac{1}{2} = e^{-kt}$ to find the value of the decay constant for carbon-14. $k = \frac{\ln \frac{1}{2}}{-5730} = 1.20 \times 10^{-4}$
   b. Use the decay function $N_t = N_0 e^{-kt}$ to determine how much of 10 grams of carbon-14 will remain after 1000 years. ≈ 8.87 g

7-7 Transforming Exponential and Logarithmic Functions

Graph the function. Find the y-intercept and asymptote. Describe how the graph is transformed from the graph of the parent function.

19. $g(x) = 1.5(3^x)$
20. $k(x) = e^{\frac{x}{2}}$

Graph the function. Find the x-intercept and asymptote. Describe how the graph is transformed from the graph of the parent function.

21. $n(x) = 3.5 \log(x + 1)$
22. $p(x) = -\ln(x + 2)$

Write the transformed function.

23. $f(x) = 0.5^x$ is horizontally compressed by a factor of $\frac{1}{2}$ and reflected across the x-axis. $f(x) = -0.5^{2x}$

7-8 Curve Fitting with Exponential and Logarithmic Models

Determine whether y is an exponential function of x. If so, find the constant ratio. Then use exponential regression to find a function that models the data.

24.

x	0	1	2	3	4	5
y	1.5	3	6	12	24	48

yes; constant ratio: 2; $f(x) = (1.5)2^x$

25.

x	0	1	2	3	4	5
y	1.5	2.4	3.3	4.2	5.1	6.0

no

READY TO GO ON? SECTION 7B

Organizer

Objective: Assess students' mastery of concepts and skills in Lessons 7-5 through 7-8.

Resources

Assessment Resources
Section 7B Quiz

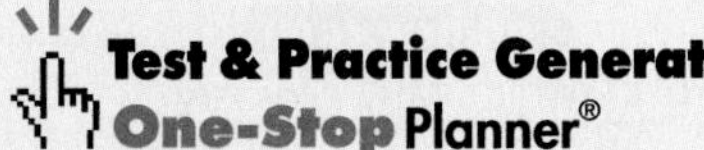
Test & Practice Generator
One-Stop Planner®

INTERVENTION

Resources

Ready to Go On? Intervention and Enrichment **Worksheets**

Ready to Go On? **CD-ROM**

Ready to Go On? **Online**

Answers

10–13, 19–22. See p. A35.

READY TO GO ON? Diagnose and Prescribe

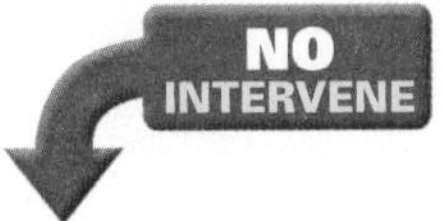

NO INTERVENE

Ready to Go On? Intervention	READY TO GO ON? Intervention, Section 7B: Worksheets	CD-ROM	Online
Lesson 7-5	7-5 Intervention	Activity 7-5	Diagnose and Prescribe Online
Lesson 7-6	7-6 Intervention	Activity 7-6	
Lesson 7-7	7-7 Intervention	Activity 7-7	
Lesson 7-8	7-8 Intervention	Activity 7-8	

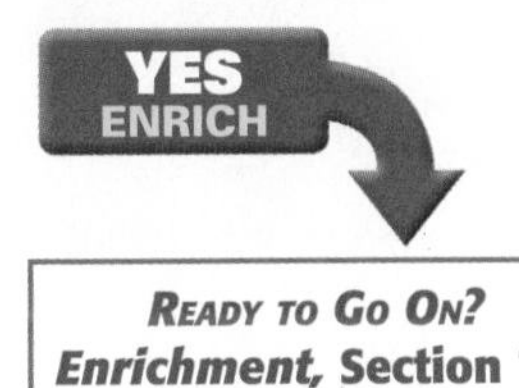

YES ENRICH

READY TO GO ON? Enrichment, Section 7B
Worksheets
CD-ROM
Online

Organizer

Objective: Help students organize and review key concepts and skills presented in Chapter 7.

Online Edition
Multilingual Glossary

Resources

Puzzle Pro
One-Stop Planner®

***Multilingual Glossary* Online**
go.hrw.com
KEYWORD: MB7 Glossary

Lesson Tutorial Videos
CD-ROM

Test & Practice Generator
One-Stop Planner®

Answers

1. natural logarithmic function
2. asymptote
3. inverse relation
4. growth

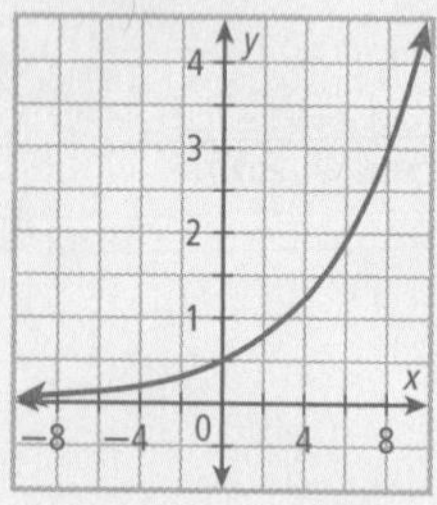

5. growth

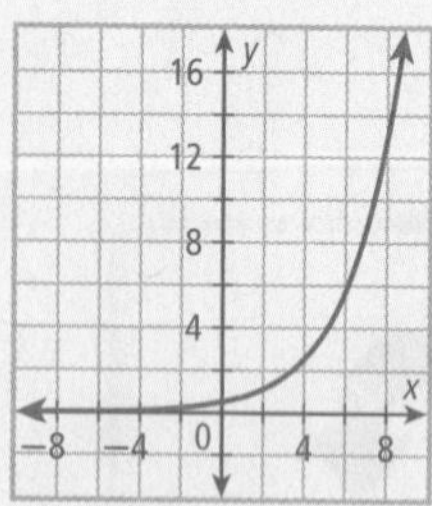

6. decay

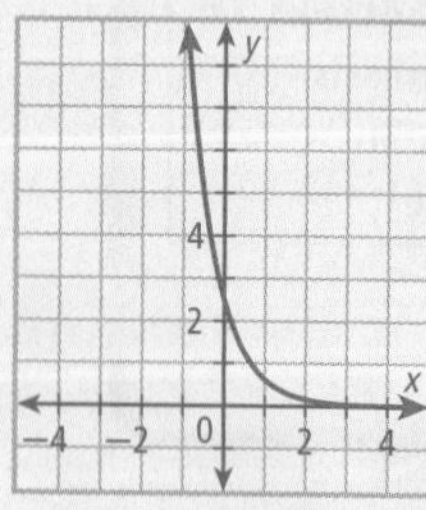

CHAPTER 7

Study Guide: Review

Vocabulary

Complete the sentences below with vocabulary words from the list above.

1. A(n) __?__ has a base of e.
2. A(n) __?__ is a line that a graphed function approaches but does not touch.
3. To graph a(n) __?__, reflect each point in the relation across the line $y = x$.

7-1 Exponential Functions, Growth, and Decay *(pp. 490–496)*

EXAMPLE

A quantity of a certain vitamin is eliminated from the bloodstream at about 15% per hour.

- Will the function that represents this situation show growth or decay?

  It will show decay because the quantity decreases.

- Write a function to show the amount of the vitamin that remains t hours after the peak level of 400 mg.

  $f(x) = 400(0.85)^t$

- Graph the function. Use the graph to predict the amount remaining after 7 hours.

  After 7 hours, about 130 mg are left.

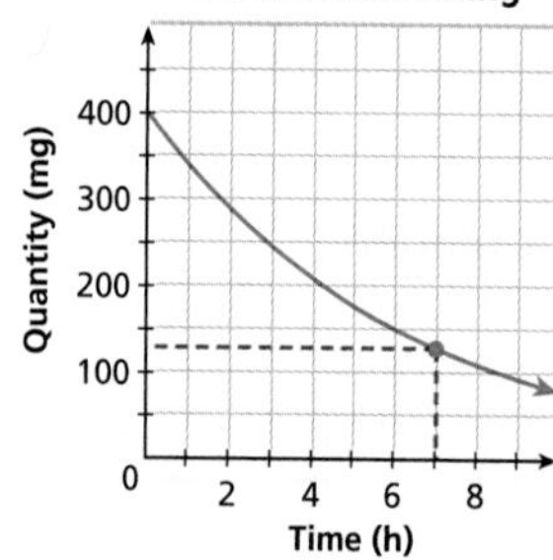

EXERCISES

Tell whether the function shows growth or decay. Then graph.

4. $f(x) = 0.5(1.25)^x$
5. $f(x) = 0.5\left(\frac{3}{2}\right)^x$
6. $f(x) = 2.5(0.25)^x$
7. $f(x) = 2(1 + 0.25)^x$

Use the following data to answer the questions.

The student population in a small resort town has increased by 2% per year for the last 5 years. This year's population is 765 students.

8. Will the function that represents this situation show growth or decay?
9. Suppose that the student population continues to follow the same trend. Write a function to show the number of students as a function of the year, starting with the current year.
10. Graph the function.
11. Use the graph to predict the number of students in 5 years.
12. When will the population exceed 1000 students?

7. growth

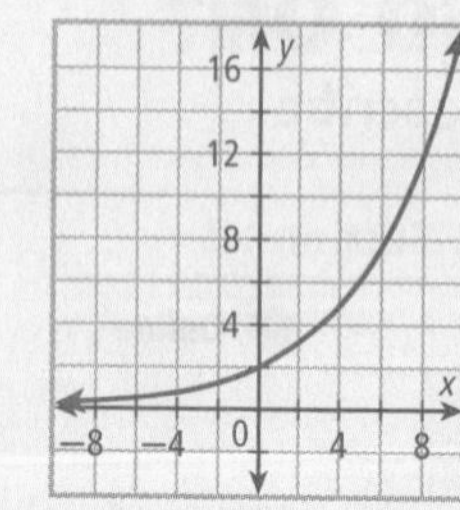

8. growth
9. $P(t) = 765(1.02)^t$

10\.

Student population: 1800, 1400, 1000, 600, 200, 0
Time (yr): 2, 6, 10, 14, 18

11. ≈ 845
12. ≈ 13.5 yr

7-2 Inverses of Relations and Functions *(pp. 498–504)*

EXAMPLE

- **Graph the function $f(x) = \frac{4}{5} - 3x$. Then write its inverse and graph.**

$y = -3x + \frac{4}{5}$ — *Set $y = f(x)$ and graph*

$x = -3y + \frac{4}{5}$ — *Interchange x and y.*

$3y = -x + \frac{4}{5}$ — *Solve for y.*

$y = -\frac{1}{3}x + \frac{4}{15}$

Write the inverse and graph.

$f^{-1}(x) = -\frac{1}{3}x + \frac{4}{15}$

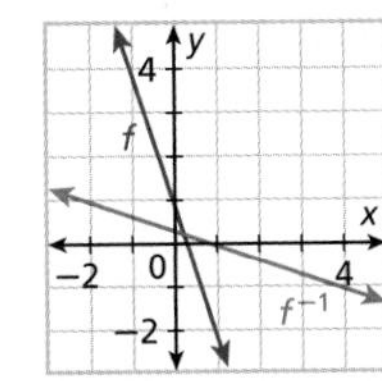

EXERCISES

13. Graph the relation and connect the points. Then graph and write the inverse.

x	−1	0	1	2	3
y	1	0.2	0.04	0.008	0.001

This year the population of a species decreased by 3% from last year.

14. Write an expression for the size of the population this year P_T as a function of last year's population P_L.

15. Write an expression for the year as a function of the size of the population.

16. The formula $M = \frac{5}{8}K$ gives the approximate distance in miles as a function of kilometers. Write and use the inverse of this function to express 25 miles in kilometers.

7-3 Logarithmic Functions *(pp. 505–511)*

EXAMPLES

- **Write the exponential equation $9^{1.5} = 27$ in logarithmic form.**

$9^{1.5} = 27$

$\log_9 27 = 1.5$ — *A logarithm is an exponent.*

- **Evaluate $\log_4 64$.**

Because $4^3 = 64$, $\log_4 64 = 3$.

- **Graph $f(x) = 0.6^x$. Then graph its inverse. Describe the domain and range of the inverse function.**

x	−2	−1	0	1	2
f(x)	2.8	1.7	1	0.6	0.4

To graph the inverse, reverse each ordered pair.

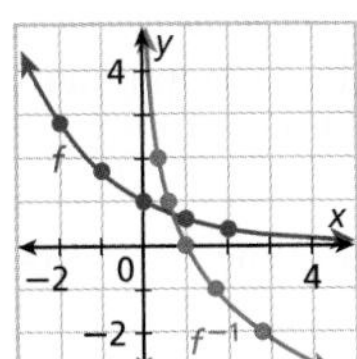

For the inverse function, the domain is $\{x \mid x > 0\}$, and the range is $\mathbb{R}$.

EXERCISES

Write each exponential equation in logarithmic form.

17. $3^5 = 243$ **18.** $1 = 9^0$ **19.** $\left(\frac{1}{3}\right)^{-3} = 27$

Write each logarithmic equation in exponential form.

20. $\log_2 16 = 4$ **21.** $\log 10 = 1$ **22.** $2 = \log_{0.6} 0.36$

Evaluate by using mental math.

23. $\log_7 49$ **24.** $\log_{0.5} 0.25$

25. $\log_{12}\left(\frac{1}{12}\right)$ **26.** $\log 0.01$ **27.** $\log_2 1$

28. Make a table of ordered pairs for $f(x) = \left(\frac{1}{2}\right)^x$. Graph the function and its inverse. Describe the domain and range of the inverse function.

Answers

13.

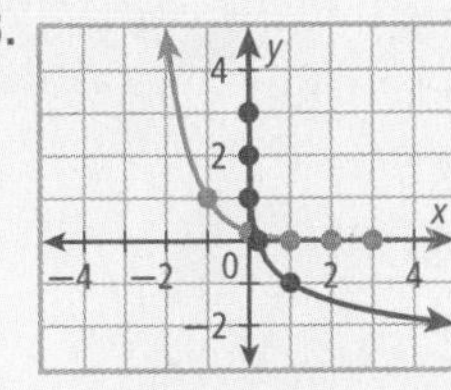

14. $P_T = P_L(1 - 0.03)$

15. $P_L = \frac{P_T}{0.97}$

16. $K = \frac{8}{5}M$; 40 km

17. $\log_3 243 = 5$

18. $\log_9 1 = 0$

19. $\log_{\frac{1}{3}} 27 = -3$

20. $2^4 = 16$

21. $10^1 = 10$

22. $0.6^2 = 0.36$

23. 2

24. 2

25. −1

26. −2

27. 0

28.

x	−2	−1	0	1	2
y	4	2	1	0.5	0.25

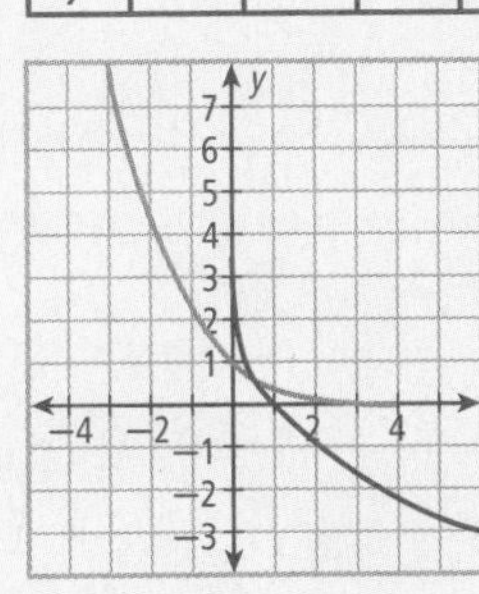

D: $\{x \mid x > 0\}$; R: $\mathbb{R}$

Answers

29. $\log_2 128 = 7$
30. $\log 1{,}000{,}000 = 6$
31. $\log_2 64 = 6$
32. $\log 100 = 2$
33. $\log_5 5^4 = 4$
34. $9 \log 10 = 9$
35. 10
36. -1
37. $x \geq -6$
38. $x > 10$
39. $17\frac{2}{3}$ yr

40a. $k = 0.0346$

b. ≈ 349

7-4 Properties of Logarithms *(pp. 512–519)*

EXAMPLES

Express as a single logarithm and simplify.

- $\log 25 + \log 40$
  $= \log(25 \cdot 40) = \log 1000 = 3$
- $\log_5 125 - \log_5 25$
  $= \log_5\left(\frac{125}{25}\right) = \log_5 5 = 1$
- $\log_3 8^2$
  $= 2\log_3 8 = 2 \cdot 2 = 4$
- **Evaluate $\log_5 16$.**

  $= \frac{\log 16}{\log 5}$ *Use the change of base formula.*

  $\approx \frac{1.2}{0.7} \approx 1.72$ *Use a calculator to evaluate.*

EXERCISES

Express as a single logarithm and simplify.

29. $\log_2 8 + \log_2 16$

30. $\log 100 + \log 10{,}000$

31. $\log_2 128 - \log_2 2$

32. $\log 10 - \log 0.1$

33. $\log_5 25^2$

34. $\log 10^5 + \log 10^4$

35. The apparent loudness of the music today at Sam's Café was 10 decibels greater than the loudness yesterday. Apparent loudness L is given by $L = 10\log\frac{I}{I_0}$, where I is the intensity of sound, in W/m^2 and I_0 is the lowest intensity that the ear can detect. How many times more intense was the sound today than yesterday?

7-5 Exponential and Logarithmic Equations and Inequalities *(pp. 522–528)*

EXAMPLES

Solve.

- $5^x = 50$

  $\log 5^x = \log 50$

  $x \log 5 = \log 50$

  $x = \frac{\log 50}{\log 5} \approx 2.43$

- $\log_9 x^2 = 5$

  $2\log_9 x = 5$

  $\log_9 x = \frac{5}{2}$

  $x = 9^{\frac{5}{2}}$

  $x = (3^2)^{\frac{5}{2}} = 3^5 = 243$

EXERCISES

Solve and check.

36. $3^{x-1} = \frac{1}{9}$

37. $\left(\frac{1}{2}\right)^x \leq 64$

38. $\log x^{\frac{5}{2}} > 2.5$

39. $A = P(1 + r)^n$ gives amount A in an account after n years for an initial investment P that earns interest at an annual rate r. How long will it take for \$250 to increase to \$500 at 4% annual interest?

7-6 The Natural Base, *e* *(pp. 531–536)*

EXAMPLE

- **Simplify $e^{\ln(2s+1)}$.**

  $e^{\ln(2s+1)} = 2s + 1$ *e to the ln of a number is just the number.*

- **What is the total value of an investment of \$5000 that earned 6% interest compounded continuously for 5 years?**

  $A = 5000e^{0.06(5)}$ *Substitute in $A = Pe^{rt}$.*

  $A \approx 6749.29$ *Use a calculator.*

  The value is \$6749.29.

EXERCISES

40. The population of whooping cranes was about 22 in 1940 and grew at an exponential rate to about 194 in 2003.

a. Use the exponential growth function $P(t) = P_0e^{kt}$, where P_0 is the initial population and $P(t)$ is the population at time t, to determine the growth factor k.

b. If the flock continues to grow at the same rate, how large will it be in 2020?

7-7 Transforming Exponential and Logarithmic Functions *(pp. 537–544)*

EXAMPLES

Write each transformed function.

- $f(x) = \left(\frac{1}{3}\right)^x$ is shifted 1 unit left, stretched vertically by a factor of 2, and reflected across the y-axis.

$f(x) = \left(\frac{1}{3}\right)^x$ *Begin with the parent function. To shift 1 unit left, replace x with x + 1.*

$g(x) = \left(\frac{1}{3}\right)^{x+1}$

$g(x) = 2\left(\frac{1}{3}\right)^{x+1}$ *Stretch vertically by 2.*

$g(x) = 2\left(\frac{1}{3}\right)^{-x+1}$ *Reflect across the y-axis.*

- $f(x) = \log x$ is shifted 2 units right and 1 unit down and is compressed vertically by a factor of 0.3.

$g(x) = \log\left(\frac{x}{0.3} - 2\right) - 1$

EXERCISES

Write the transformed function.

41. $f(x) = e^x$ is reflected across the x-axis, stretched vertically by a factor of 3, and shifted 2 units down.

Graph each function. Find the intercept and asymptote. Describe how the graph is transformed from the graph of the parent function.

42. $k(x) = \frac{3}{5}(1.5)^{6x}$ **43.** $m(x) = 2\log\left(x + \frac{1}{2}\right)$

The trade-in value of Marc's truck is \$5300. A truck dealer tells him that the trade-in value of a truck decreases by about 35% each year.

44. Write an equation for the trade-in value as a function of time.

45. Describe how the graph of this function is transformed from the graph of the parent function.

7-8 Curve Fitting with Exponential and Logarithmic Models *(pp. 545–551)*

EXAMPLES

- **Use logarithmic regression to find a function that models the increase in the number of pepper trees in a wilderness preserve over six years. Predict the year when the number of trees will reach 70.**

Year	1	2	3	4	5	6
Trees	14	30	40	46	53	55

$y \approx 14 + 23.4 \ln x$ *Write the model. Substitute 70.*

$\ln x \approx \frac{70 - 14}{23.4} \approx 2.39$ *There will be 70 trees in about 11 years.*

$e^{2.39} \approx 10.9$

EXERCISES

The table gives the population size of a flock of birds in one habitat over the last 55 years.

Years Since Data Was First Collected	Population Size
5	18
22	22
40	85
57	185

46. Use exponential regression, **ExpReg**, to find an exponential function that models the data.

47. Use logarithmic regression, **LnReg**, to find a logarithmic function that models the data.

48. Compare r^2-values of the two functions. Tell which function best models the data and why.

Answers

41. $g(x) = -3e^x - 2$

42. 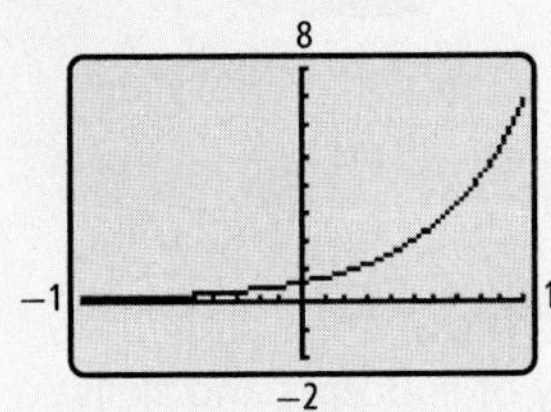

$y = 0.6$; $y = 0$; vertically compressed by a factor of $\frac{3}{5}$ and horizontally compressed by a factor of $\frac{1}{6}$

43. 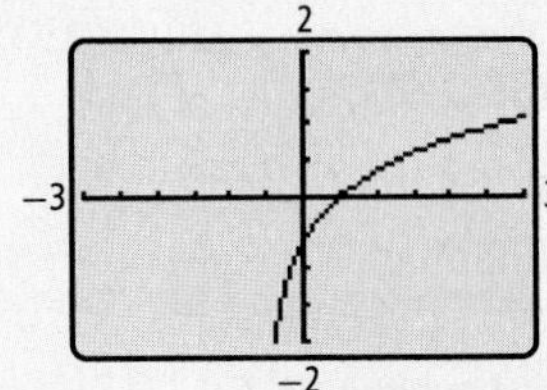

$x = 0.5$; $x = -0.5$; translated $\frac{1}{2}$ unit left and vertically stretched by a factor of 2.

44. $V(t) = 5300(1 - 0.35)^t$

45. vertically stretched by a factor of 5300

46. $f(x) \approx 11.26(1.05)^x$

47. $f(x) \approx -97.8 + 56.4 \ln x$

48. the exponential function; $r^2 \approx 0.94$ versus $r^2 \approx 0.60$ for the logarithmic function

Organizer

Objective: Assess students' mastery of concepts and skills in Chapter 7.

Online Edition

Resources

Assessment Resources

Chapter 7 Tests
- Free Response (Levels A, B, C)
- Multiple Choice (Levels A, B, C)
- Performance Assessment

***IDEA Works!* CD-ROM**

Modified Chapter 7 Test

Answers

1. 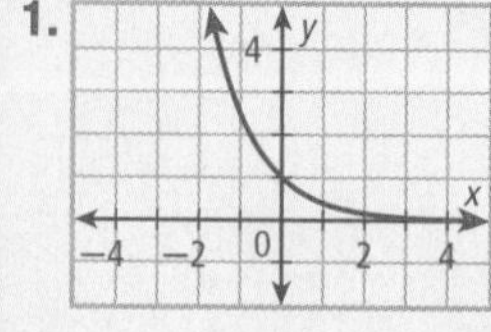

2. 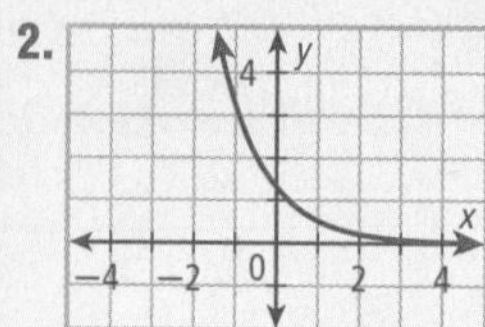

State Resources

Tell whether the function shows growth or decay. Then graph.

1. $f(x) = 0.4^x$ **decay**
2. $f(x) = 1.3\left(\frac{2}{5}\right)^x$ **decay**
3. $f(x) = \frac{7}{8}(1.1)^x$ **growth**
4. $f(x) = 50(1 + 0.04)^x$ **growth**
5. Gina buys a car for $13,500. Assume that its value will decrease by about 15% per year. Write an exponential function to model the value of the car. Graph the function. When will the value fall below $3000? $f(x) = 13500(1 - 0.15)^t$

Graph each function. Then write its inverse and graph.

6. $f(x) = x - 1.06$ $f^{-1}(x) = x + 1.06$
7. $f(x) = \frac{5}{6}x - 1.06$ $f^{-1}(x) = \frac{6}{5}(x + 1.06)$
8. $f(x) = 1.06 - \frac{5}{6}x$ $f^{-1}(x) = \frac{6}{5}(1.06 - x)$
9. $f(x) = \frac{1}{4}\left(1.06 - \frac{5}{6}x\right)$ $f^{-1}(x) = \frac{6}{5}(1.06 - 4x)$

Write in the alternative form (exponential or logarithmic).

10. $16^{\frac{1}{4}} = 2$ $\log_{16} 2 = \frac{1}{4}$
11. $16^{-0.5} = \frac{1}{4}$ $\log_{16}\frac{1}{4} = -0.5$
12. $\log_{\frac{1}{4}} 64 = -3$ $\left(\frac{1}{4}\right)^{-3} = 64$
13. $\log_{81}\frac{1}{3} = -\frac{1}{4}$ $81^{-\frac{1}{4}} = \frac{1}{3}$

Use the given x-values to graph each function. Then write and graph its inverse. Describe the domain and range of the inverse function.

14. $f(x) = \left(\frac{1}{4}\right)^x$; $x = -1, 0, 2, 4$ $f^{-1}(x) = \log_{\frac{1}{4}} x$
15. $f(x) = 2.5^x$; $x = -1, 0, 1, 2, 3$ $f^{-1}(x) = \log_{2.5} x$
16. $f(x) = 5^{-x}$; $x = -1, 0, 1, 2, 3$ $f^{-1}(x) = -\log_5 x$

Simplify.

17. $\log_4 128 - \log_4 8$ $\log_4 16 = 2$
18. $\log_2 12.8 + \log_2 5$ $\log_2 64 = 6$
19. $\log_3 243^2$ $10\log_3 3 = 10$
20. $5^{\log_5 x}$ x

Solve.

21. $3^{x-1} = 729^{\frac{x}{2}}$ $x = -\frac{1}{2}$
22. $5^{1.5-x} \le 25$ $x \ge -0.5$
23. $\log_4(x + 48) = 3$ $x = 16$
24. $\log(6x^2) - \log 2x = 1$ $x = 3\frac{1}{3}$
25. The rate at which a liquid vitamin breaks down in the average human body can be modeled by $y = D(0.95)^x$, where y ml of the original dose D remains after x minutes. How long will it take for an original dose of 15 ml to be reduced to less than 5 ml? $\approx$ **21.4 min**
26. Plutonium Pu-239 has a half-life of about 24,000 years. The formula $\frac{1}{2} = e^{-kt}$ relates the half-life t to the decay constant k for a given substance. How much of a 100-gram quantity of plutonium will remain after 5 years? $\approx$ **99.986 g**
27. $f(x) = \ln x$ is shifted 2 units left and 1 unit up and is vertically stretched by a factor of 3. Write the transformed function. $f(x) = 3\ln(x + 2) + 1$
28. Use logarithmic regression to find the function that models the population data in the table. In what year will the population exceed 100?
$f(x) = 48.64 + 24.61\ln x$; **year 8**

Population	50	62	78
Year	1	2	3

Answers

3. 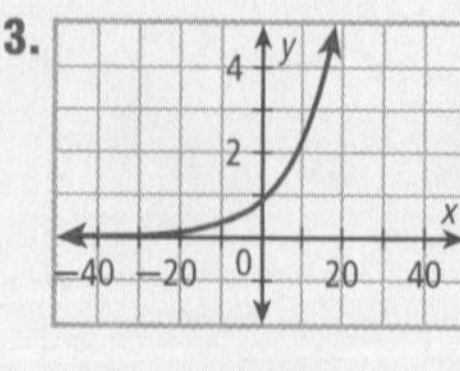

4. 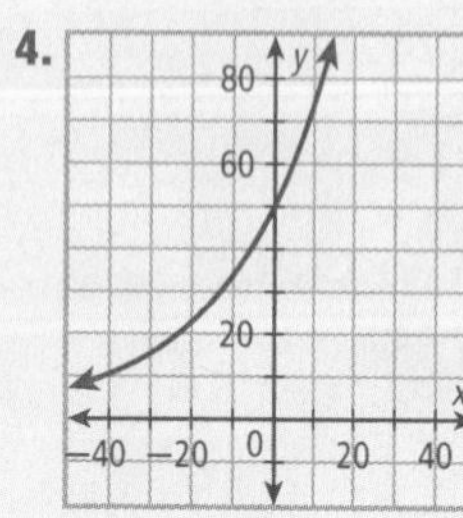

5. 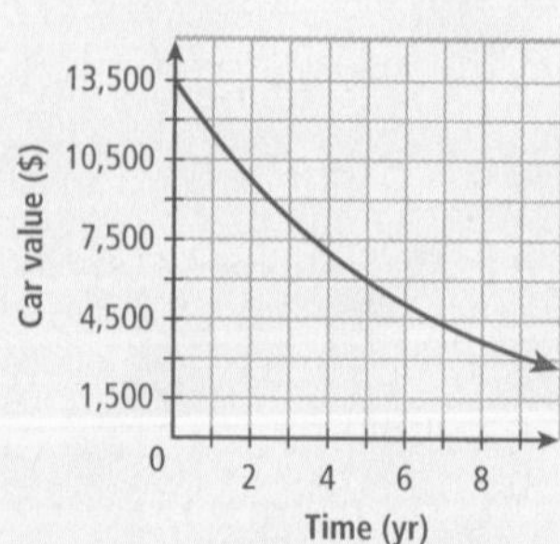
in the 10th year

6. 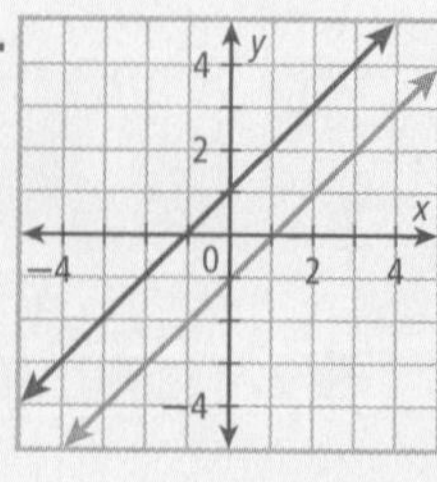

7. 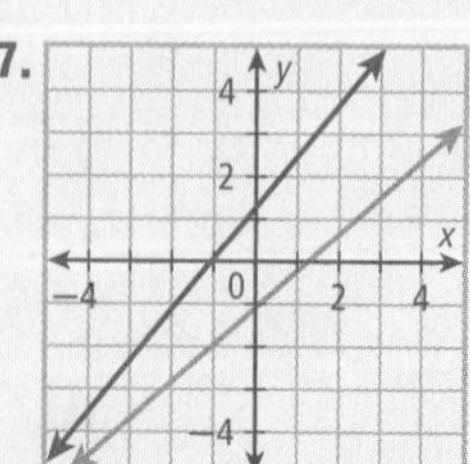

8–9, 14–16. For graphs, see p. A35–A36.

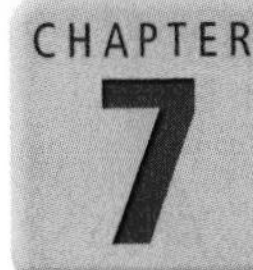

College Entrance Exam Practice

CHAPTER 7

FOCUS ON SAT SUBJECT TESTS

The SAT Mathematics Subject Test Level 2 test is meant to be taken by students who have completed two years of algebra and one year of geometry and have studied elementary functions, trigonometry, and some precalculus topics, such as limits.

HOT TIP! The questions are placed in an order of increasing difficulty. Because each question is worth the same amount of points, answer as many of the less difficult questions as you can before tackling the more difficult ones.

You may want to time yourself as you take this practice test. It should take you about 6 minutes to complete.

1. If $f^{-1}(x) = \frac{4}{3}x + 8$, what is $f(x)$?

(A) $f(x) = \frac{3}{4}(x - 8)$

(B) $f(x) = \frac{3}{4}x - 8$

(C) $f(x) = \frac{3}{4}(x + 6)$

(D) $f(x) = \frac{4}{3}(x - 8)$

(E) $f(x) = \frac{4}{3}x - 6$

2. If $f(x) = e^x$, then which of the following is $f^{-1}(7)$?

(A) e^7

(B) 7

(C) log 7

(D) ln 7

(E) $\ln(e^7)$

3. If $e^x e^{2.5} = e^{2.5x}$, what is the vaue of x?

(A) 0

(B) 1

(C) $\frac{5}{3}$

(D) $\mathbb{R}$

(E) ∅

4. What is $\log_{27} 9$?

(A) $\frac{1}{2}$

(B) $\frac{2}{3}$

(C) $\frac{3}{2}$

(D) 2

(E) 3

5. What is the y-coordinate of the point where the graphs of $y = \log_2\left(\frac{3}{4}x - \frac{23}{4}\right)$ and $y = \log_2\left(-2x + \frac{65}{4}\right)$ intersect?

(A) −2

(B) $\frac{1}{4}$

(C) $\frac{1}{2}$

(D) 2

(E) 8

6. If $\log_9\{\log_2[\log_4(x)]\} = \frac{1}{2}$, then what is x?

(A) 1.73

(B) 8

(C) 81

(D) 6561

(E) 65,536

College Entrance Exam Practice

CHAPTER 7

Organizer

Objective: Provide practice for college entrance exams such as the SAT Mathematics Subject Test Level 2.

PREMIER Online Edition

Resources

College Entrance Exam Practice

Questions on the SAT Mathematics Subject Test Level 2 represent the following math content areas:

Algebra, 18%
Coordinate Geometry, 12%
Three-dimensional Geometry, 8%
Trigonometry, 20%
Functions, 24%
Statistics/Probability, 6%
Miscellaneous, 12%

Items on this page focus on:

- Algebra
- Functions

Text References:

Item	1	2	3	4	5
Lesson	7-2	7-6	7-3	7-4	7-5

Test Prep Doctor

1. Students who chose **D** have the right idea about the order in which the actions must take place, but they multiplied by $\frac{4}{3}$ when they should have divided. Remind students that this type of problem can easily be checked using a sample value or graphing.
2. Students who did not choose **D** may not understand that the natural logarithmic function is the inverse of the natural exponential function.
3. Students who chose **D** multiplied exponents. Remind them that $b^x b^y = b^{x+y}$.
4. Students who chose **C** found $\frac{\log_3 27}{\log_3 9}$ instead of $\frac{\log_3 9}{\log_3 27}$. Students who chose **A** may have incorrectly calculated $(\log_9 3)(\log_9 9)$ instead of $\log_9 3 + \log_9 9$.
5. Students who chose **B** found the value of each expression in parentheses. Remind them that they still have a logarithm to evalute.
6. Students may not know how to approach this problem. Suggest that students work from the outside in, beginning with "log base 9 of something is $\frac{1}{2}$."

Organizer

Objective: Provide opportunities to learn and practice common test-taking strategies.

Online Edition

Resources

State Test Prep Workbook

***State Test Prep* CD-ROM**

***State Test Practice* Online**

go.hrw.com
KEYWORD: MB7 TestPrep

This Test Tackler reinforces the importance of reading a test item slowly and carefully, extracting the important information, and being aware of all parts of the question. Explain to students that if they rush through reading a question, they might make assumptions that are untrue, or they might end up answering the wrong question. Show students how to read a question for understanding by using the process shown in the examples.

Show students some of the common mistakes that they might make if they read too quickly through the question. For instance, in a short- or extended-response test item, students often forget to answer all parts of the question. For instance, in **Item D,** the students should write both the function and its inverse as part of their response. Omitting either function would result in a loss of credit.

CHAPTER 7

TEST TACKLER
Standardized Test Strategies

Any Question Type: Read a Test Item for Understanding

Test items given on a standardized test may vary in type from multiple choice to gridded response to short and extended response. All test items should be read thoroughly so that you recognize important information and have a complete understanding of what is being asked.

EXAMPLE 1

Extended Response The value of a computer purchased new for \$2300 goes down by 15.5% each year. Write and graph an exponential function to estimate the value of the computer after 3 years. When will the value of the computer fall below \$500?

READ the problem again.

RESTATE the important parts of the test item by using your own words:

What information are you given? The cost of the computer: \$2300
The annual percent decrease: 15.5%

What are you asked to do?
1. Write an exponential function.
2. Graph the exponential function.
3. Estimate the computer's value after 3 years.
4. Find when the value will fall below \$500.

What should your response include?
1. An exponential function
2. A graph
3. An estimated value, in dollars
4. The time in years

NOTE: Your response should include four parts.

EXAMPLE 2

Short Response Two samples of water taken Monday from a wastewater treatment holding tank have a pH of 4.2 and 4.9. To record the pH for the day, a technician finds the average pH for the two samples. What is the difference in the average pH for Monday and the sample that is most acidic?

READ the problem again.

RESTATE the important parts of the test item by using your own words:

What information are you given? The pH of two samples: 4.2, 4.9

What are you asked to do? Subtract: $\text{pH}_{\text{average}} - \text{pH}_{\text{most acidic sample}}$

Make a plan for your response. Calculate the average pH.
Identify the most acidic sample.
Find the difference.

NOTE: The question requires an intermediate step.

Break a test item into parts to help you organize your approach to the problem.

Read each test item, and answer the questions that follow.

Item A

Gridded Response What is the total amount, to the nearest whole dollar, for an investment of $800 invested at 3.5% for 15 years and compounded continuously?

1. What information are you given?
2. What are you asked to find?
3. Antonio solved this problem and got an incorrect answer of $1220 after using the formula $I = Prt$. What important word(s) did Antonio overlook that may have led him to the correct formula? Explain.
4. Cleo solved this problem by using the formula $800(1 + 0.035)^{15}$ and got an answer of $1340. Did Cleo solve the problem correctly? Explain.

Item B

Gridded Response A doctor prescribed a daily 15-milligram dose of vitamin D to a 55-year-old man. The man weighs 225 pounds. The half-life of vitamin D is about 25 days. The amount A of vitamin D left after t days can be expressed by the exponential function $A = 15\left(\frac{1}{2}\right)^{\frac{t}{25}}$. Find the number of days (to the nearest day) that it takes for the initial dose of vitamin D to drop below 9 milligrams.

5. What information are you given?
6. Identify any information not necessary for your calculations. Explain.
7. Describe a plan that you can use to solve this problem.
8. A student gridded a decimal answer for his response. What part of the problem statement did he overlook?

Item C

Short Response Martha has $6435 in her home safe. She decides to take two-thirds of this amount and invest it in an account that earns 4.25% interest, compounded continuously. What is the total amount of money that Martha has in 3 years?

9. List the information given and what you are being asked to find.
10. Are there intermediate steps that you need to perform to solve the problem? If so, describe the steps.

Item D

Extended Response A runner ran a 3000 m race in 12 minutes and 48 seconds. Write a function that gives distance as a function of time. Write and use the inverse function to find the time it would take the runner to complete a 10,000 m race at the same speed.

11. How many parts are there to this question? Make a list of what needs to be included in your response.
12. What question are you to answer? What units would be acceptable for your answer?

Item E

Short Response Which data set is best represented by using a logarithmic model? Explain your reasoning, and give the function of the logarithmic model.

A)

x	1	20	40	60	80
y	88	218	341	647	980

B)

x	5	15	25	35	45
y	26	43	52	59	61

13. To determine which data set *best* represents a logarithmic model, what intermediate step must you perform to make a comparison?
14. Make a plan for your response.

Answers

1. investment amount, investment rate, duration of investment
2. Find the total amount of the investment after 15 yr.
3. Continuously compounded; Antonio calculated simple interest, not compound interest.
4. No; she calculated interest compounded annually.
5. half-life, dosage, amount of time, age, weight, and the exponential function
6. Age, weight, and gender are irrelevant.
7. Possible answer: Solve for t and then evaluate the result for $A = 9$. Round the answer to the nearest day.
8. "to the nearest day"
9. The principal, interest rate, and number of years compounded continuously are given in the problem. The problem asks for the total amount of money.
10. Yes; find $\frac{2}{3}$ of $6435; find the investment amount after 3 yr.
11. 3; a function of distance based on time, the inverse function, and calculations to find the time it takes to complete a 10,000 m race at the same speed
12. How long would it take a runner to run a 10,000 m race at the same speed? Time units (h, min, s) are acceptable.
13. Determine the correlation coefficient for each model.
14. For both data sets, use logarithmic regression on a calculator to find a model of the form $y = ab\ln x$. Then use the correlation coefficient R^2 to see how closely the model fits the data.

Answers to Test Items

A. $1352

B. 19 days

C. $7018.38

D. Possible answer: $d = 234.375t$, where t is time in min and d is distance in m; $t = \frac{d}{234.375}$; $42.\overline{6}$ min, or 4 min 40 s

E. Set B; $R^2 \approx 0.996$, while R^2 for set A ≈ 0.59

State Resources

Organizer

Objective: Provide review and practice for Chapters 1–7 and standardized tests.

 Online Edition

Resources

 ***Assessment Resources***

Chapter 7 Cumulative Test

 ***State Test Prep Workbook***

 ***State Test Prep* CD-ROM**

***State Test Practice* Online**

go.hrw.com

KEYWORD: MB7 TestPrep

Answers

1. B
2. D
3. C
4. B
5. A
6. D
7. C
8. C
9. A
10. B
11. B
12. C
13. A

State Resources

Core Standard	Items
3	7, 9, 13
4	6, 10
6	2, 3, 4, 15, 17

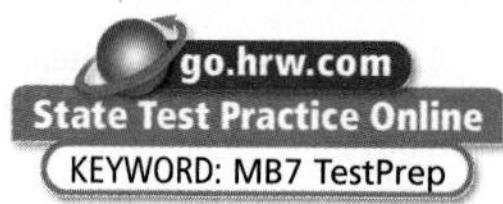

CUMULATIVE ASSESSMENT, CHAPTERS 1–7

Multiple Choice

1. Which graph is the inverse of $f(x) = -3x + 6$?

A. 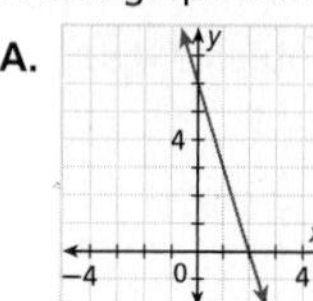

B. 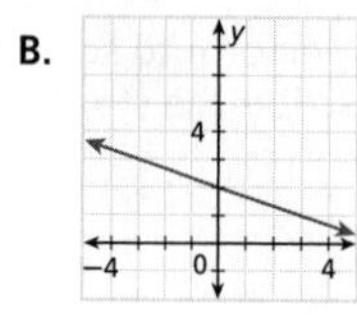

C. 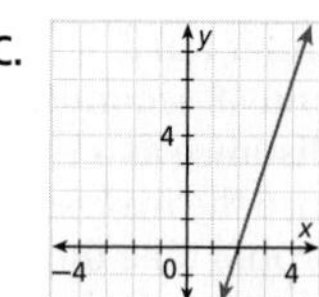

D. 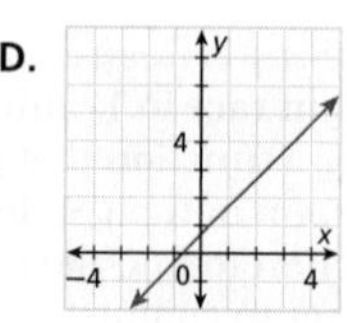

2. Which is equivalent to $log_5 12 - log_5 4$?

A. $log_5 48$

B. $log_5 8$

C. $log_5 16$

D. $log_5 3$

3. What is the value of x in the equation $\log_4(x-1)^3 = 9$?

A. $x = 27$

B. $x = 64$

C. $x = 65$

D. $x = 81$

4. The parent logarithmic function $f(x) = \ln x$ is shifted 2 units to the right and 7 units down and is horizontally stretched by a factor of 6. Which is the transformed function?

A. $f(x) = 6\ln(x-2) - 7$

B. $f(x) = \ln\left(\frac{x}{6} - 2\right) - 7$

C. $f(x) = 6\ln(x+2) + 7$

D. $f(x) = 6\ln\left(\frac{x}{6} + 2\right) + 7$

5. Which equation best fits the data in the scatter plot?

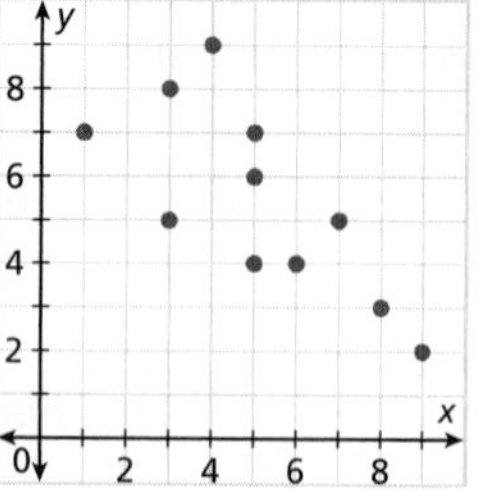

A. $y = -\frac{10}{11}x + 10$

B. $y = \frac{10}{11}x + 10$

C. $y = -\frac{11}{10}x + 1$

D. $y = \frac{11}{10}x + 1$

6. Which is a factor of $P(x) = 8x^3 - 26x^2 + 17x + 6$?

A. $4x - 1$

B. $x + 2$

C. $2x + 3$

D. $2x - 3$

7. Which is a function in standard form with zeros at 0 and −1?

A. $f(x) = x^2 + x - 1$

B. $f(x) = x^2 - x$

C. $f(x) = x^2 + x$

D. $f(x) = -x^2 + x$

8. The linear correlation coefficient r relating two sets of data is found to be −0.24, and the line of best fit has a y-intercept of 10. Which of the following is NOT necessarily true?

A. As the values of one set of data increase, the values of the other set decrease.

B. For positive values of x, the y-value of the line of best fit is less than 10.

C. The line of best fit is a good model for the data.

D. The line of best fit has a negative slope.

TEST PREP DOCTOR

For **Item 1,** students may not remember that the inverse is the graph reflected across $y = x$. Remind them that they can consider what happens to the graph as well as what happens to the function.

For **Item 5,** students who chose **B** or **D** have chosen lines with a positive slope. Remind them that for negative correlations, the value of m in $y = mx + b$ must be negative.

9. Which has a vertex at (–2, –3)?

A. $y = x^2 + 4x + 1$

B. $y = x^2 + 4x - 1$

C. $y = x^2 - 4x + 1$

D. $y = x^2 - 4x - 1$

10. What is the product $3(x + y)^4$?

A. $x^4 + 4x^3y + 6x^2y^2 + 4xy^3 + y^4$

B. $3x^4 + 12x^3y + 18x^2y^2 + 12xy^3 + 3y^4$

C. $81x^4 + y^4$

D. $3x^4 + 3y^4$

11. A line in $y = mx + b$ form has a positive slope and a y-intercept of 5. The slope of the line is decreased. Which of the following must be true?

A. The x-intercept of the new line is less than the x-intercept of the original line.

B. The original line and the new line intersect only at (0, 5).

C. The slope of the nwew line is greater than 0.

D. The new line is parallel to the original line.

In Item 12, you can replace a missing number with a variable, such as *x*. Choose a different variable if there is already an *x* in the problem.

12. What number is missing in the matrix?

$\begin{bmatrix} 5 & 8 \\ 4 & 3 \end{bmatrix} \times \begin{bmatrix} & 2 \\ -6 & 0 \end{bmatrix} = \begin{bmatrix} -28 & 10 \\ -2 & 8 \end{bmatrix}$

A. –5.6

B. 2

C. 4

D. 4.8

13. Use the parent function $f(x) = x^2$. What is the horizontal compression factor of the function $f(x) = \frac{1}{2}(5x)^2 - 4$?

A. $\frac{1}{5}$

B. $\frac{1}{2}$

C. 4

D. 5

Short Answer

14. A school is selling used computers and printers. The school sells the computers for \$500 each and the printers for \$50 each. The goal is for the school to make at least \$5200. The school expects to sell at least five computers for every two printers.

Part A Write a system of inequalities that models this situation, where x is the number of computers sold, and y is the number of printers sold.

Part B Graph the system of inequalities.

15. Radium-226, which has a half-life of 1620 years, is used in medicine for treatment of disease.

Part A Find the value of k for radium-226.

Part B How much of a 100-gram dose of radium-226 will remain after 3240 years? Round to the nearest gram.

16. Twenty equally spaced points along a 6-foot board are marked for drilling. The distance from the first and last point to the ends is equal to the space between points. What is the distance between consecutive points, to the nearest hundredth of an inch?

Extended Response

17. The chart below shows how many hours students in different grades study each night.

Grade (x)	4	6	8	10	12
Hours (y)	$\frac{1}{4}$	$\frac{1}{2}$	1	2	4

Part A Determine if the data set is exponential or logarithmic.

Part B Graph the points.

Part C Find a function to model the data. Round to the nearest ten thousandths.

Part D In which grade do students study 45 minutes each night? Round to the nearest grade.

Part E How long do third graders study each night? Round to the nearest half minute.

Short Answer Rubric

Items 14–16

Score 2 = Thorough understanding of mathematical concepts and processes.

Score 1 = Partial understanding of mathematical concepts and/or processes.

Score 0 = Limited or no understanding of the problem-solving concepts.

Blank = No written response.

Extended Response Rubric

Item 17

Score 4 = Thorough understanding of mathematical concepts and processes.

Score 3 = Demonstrated understanding of mathematical concepts and processes, but an error in computation or explanation.

Score 2 = Partial understanding of mathematical concepts and/or processes.

Score 1 = Limited understanding and execution of the problem-solving concepts.

Score 0 = No understanding of the problem-solving concepts.

Blank = No written response.

Answers

14. Part A: $\begin{cases} 500x + 50y \geq 5200 \\ 5x \geq 2y \end{cases}$

Part B:

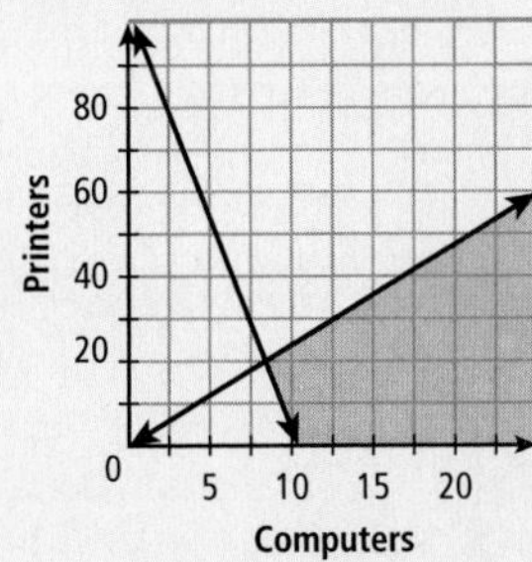

15. Part A: $k = \frac{\ln 2}{1620} \approx 0.0004279$

Part B: 25 g

16. 3.43 in

17. Part A: exponential

Part B:

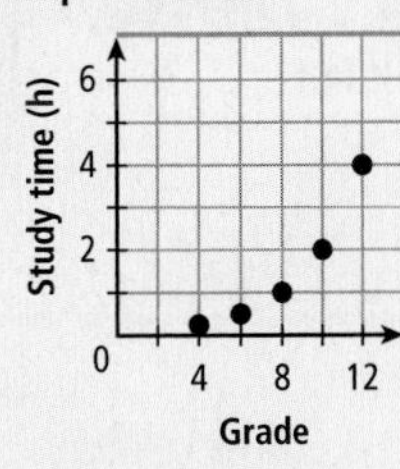

Part C: $y = 0.0625 \times 1.4142^x$

Part D: 7th grade

Part E: 10.5 min

Rational and Radical Functions

Section 8A

Rational Functions

8-1 **Algebra Lab** Model Inverse Variation
8-1 **Variation Functions**
8-2 **Multiplying and Dividing Rational Expressions**
8-3 **Adding and Subtracting Rational Expressions**
8-4 **Technology Lab** Explore Holes in Graphs
8-4 **Rational Functions**
8-5 **Solving Rational Equations and Inequalities**

Section 8B

Radical Functions

8-6 **Radical Expressions and Rational Exponents**
Connecting Algebra to Geometry Area and Volume Relationships
8-7 **Radical Functions**
8-8 **Solving Radical Equations and Inequalities**

Pacing Guide for 45-Minute Classes

Chapter 8 — Countdown to Testing Weeks 17, 18

DAY 1	DAY 2	DAY 3	DAY 4	DAY 5
8-1 Algebra Lab	8-1 Lesson	8-2 Lesson	8-3 Lesson	8-4 Technology Lab 8-4 Lesson
DAY 6	**DAY 7**	**DAY 8**	**DAY 9**	**DAY 10**
8-4 Lesson	8-5 Lesson	Multi-Step Test Prep Ready to Go On?	8-6 Lesson	Connecting Algebra to Geometry 8-7 Lesson
DAY 11	**DAY 12**	**DAY 13**	**DAY 14**	
8-7 Lesson	8-8 Lesson	Multi-Step Test Prep Ready to Go On?	Chapter 8 Test	

Pacing Guide for 90-Minute Classes

Chapter 8

DAY 1	DAY 2	DAY 3	DAY 4	DAY 5
Chapter 7 Test 8-1 Algebra Lab	8-1 Lesson 8-2 Lesson	8-3 Lesson 8-4 Technology Lab 8-4 Lesson	8-4 Lesson 8-5 Lesson	Multi-Step Test Prep Ready to Go On? 8-6 Lesson
DAY 6	**DAY 7**	**DAY 8**		
Connecting Algebra to Geometry 8-7 Lesson	8-8 Lesson Multi-Step Test Prep Ready to Go On?	Chapter 8 Test 9-1 Lesson		

ONGOING ASSESSMENT and INTERVENTION

	DIAGNOSE	PRESCRIBE
Assess Prior Knowledge	**Before Chapter 8**	
	Diagnose readiness for the chapter.	Prescribe intervention.
	Are You Ready? SE p. 565	***Are You Ready? Intervention*** Skills 4, 57, 59, 67, 81
Formative Assessment	**Before Every Lesson**	
	Diagnose readiness for the lesson.	Prescribe intervention.
	Warm Up TE, every lesson	**Skills Bank** SE pp. S46–S73
		Reteach CRB, Ch. 1–8
	During Every Lesson	
	Diagnose understanding of lesson concepts.	Prescribe intervention.
	Check It Out! SE, every example	**Questioning Strategies** TE, every example
	Think and Discuss SE, every lesson	**Reading Strategies** CRB, every lesson
	Write About It SE, every lesson	***Success for ELL*** pp. 113–128
	Journal TE, every lesson	
	After Every Lesson	
	Diagnose mastery of lesson concepts.	Prescribe intervention.
	Lesson Quiz TE, every lesson	**Reteach** CRB, every lesson
	Alternative Assessment TE, every lesson	**Problem Solving** CRB, every lesson
	Test Prep SE, every lesson	**Test Prep Doctor** TE, every lesson
	Test and Practice Generator	***Homework Help* Online**
	Before Chapter 8 Testing	
	Diagnose mastery of concepts in the chapter.	Prescribe intervention.
	Ready to Go On? SE pp. 609, 637	***Ready to Go On? Intervention*** pp. 126–145
	Multi-Step Test Prep SE pp. 608, 636	**Scaffolding Questions** TE pp. 608, 636
	Section Quizzes AR pp. 145–146	
	Test and Practice Generator	
	Before High Stakes Testing	
	Diagnose mastery of benchmark concepts.	Prescribe intervention.
	College Entrance Exam Practice SE p. 643	***College Entrance Exam Practice***
	Standardized Test Prep SE pp. 646–647	***State Test Prep Workbook***
	***State Test Prep* CD-ROM**	
Summative Assessment	**After Chapter 8**	
	Check mastery of chapter concepts.	Prescribe intervention.
	Multiple-Choice Tests (Forms A, B, C)	**Reteach** CRB, every lesson
	Free-Response Tests (Forms A, B, C)	***Lesson Tutorial Videos*** Chapter 8
	Performance Assessment AR pp. 147–160	
	Test and Practice Generator	
	Check mastery of benchmark concepts.	Prescribe intervention.
	AYP State Tests	***State Test Prep Workbook***
	College Entrance Exams	***College Entrance Exam Practice***

KEY: **SE** = *Student Edition* **TE** = *Teacher's Edition* **CRB** = *Chapter Resource Book* **AR** = *Assessment Resources* Available on CD-ROM  Available online

Supporting the Teacher

Chapter 8 Resource Book

Practice A, B, C
pp. 3–5, 11–13, 19–21, 27–29, 35–37, 43–45, 51–53, 59–61

Reading Strategies ELL
pp. 10, 18, 26, 34, 42, 50, 58, 66

Reteach
pp. 6–7, 14–15, 22–23, 30–31, 38–39, 46–47, 54–55, 62–63

Problem Solving
pp. 9, 17, 25, 33, 41, 49, 57, 65

Challenge
pp. 8, 16, 24, 32, 40, 48, 56, 64

Parent Letter pp. 1–2

Transparencies

Lesson Transparencies, Volume 3 .... Chapter 8
- Warm Ups
- Teaching Transparencies
- Additional Examples
- Lesson Quizzes

Alternate Openers: Explorations 57–64

Countdown to Testing 33–36

Know-It Notebook .... Chapter 8
- Graphic Organizers

Teacher Tools

Power Presentations®
Complete PowerPoint® presentations for Chapter 8 lessons

Lesson Tutorial Videos®
Holt authors Ed Burger and Freddie Renfro present tutorials to support the Chapter 8 lessons.

One-Stop Planner®
Easy access to all Chapter 8 resources and assessments, as well as software for lesson planning, test generation, and puzzle creation

IDEA Works!®
Key Chapter 8 resources and assessments modified to address special learning needs

Lesson Plans .... pp. 57–64

Solutions Key .... Chapter 8

Algebra Posters

TechKeys **Lab Resources**

Project Teacher Support **Parent Resources** 

Workbooks

Homework and Practice Workbook
Teacher's Guide .... pp. 57–64

Know-It Notebook
Teacher's Guide .... Chapter 8

Problem Solving Workbook
Teacher's Guide .... pp. 57–64

State Test Prep Workbook
Teacher's Guide

Technology Highlights for the Teacher

Power Presentations

Dynamic presentations to engage students. Complete PowerPoint® presentations for every lesson in Chapter 8.

2-1 Solving One-Step Equations

Isolate a variable by using inverse operations which "undo" operations on the variable.

An equation is like a balanced scale. To keep the balance, perform the same operation on both sides.

Inverse Operations	
Operation	**Inverse Operation**
Addition	Subtraction
Subtraction	Addition

One-Stop Planner

Easy access to Chapter 8 resources and assessments. Includes lesson-planning, test-generation, and puzzle-creation software.

Premier Online Edition

Chapter 8 includes Tutorial Videos, Lesson Activities, Lesson Quizzes, Homework Help, and Chapter Project.

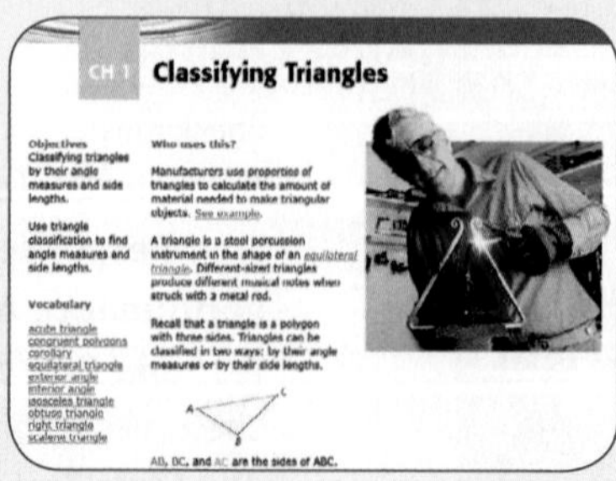

KEY: **SE** = *Student Edition* **TE** = *Teacher's Edition*  English Language Learners  Available on CD-ROM  Available online

Reaching All Learners

Resources for All Learners

Algebra Lab Activities .... Chapter 8
Technology Lab Activities .... Chapter 8
Homework and Practice Workbook .... pp. 57–64
Know-It Notebook .... Chapter 8
Problem Solving Workbook .... pp. 57–64

DEVELOPING LEARNERS

Practice A .... CRB, every lesson
Reteach .... CRB, every lesson
Inclusion .... TE pp. 575, 580, 584, 589, 598, 611, 615, 625
Questioning Strategies .... TE, every example
Modified Chapter 8 Resources .... *IDEA Works!*
***Homework Help* Online**

ON-LEVEL LEARNERS

Practice B .... CRB, every lesson
Cognitive Strategies .... TE p. 570
Graphic Organizers .... TE p. 584

ADVANCED LEARNERS

Practice C .... CRB, every lesson
Challenge .... CRB, every lesson
Reading and Writing Math EXTENSION .... TE p. 567
Multi-Step Test Prep EXTENSION .... TE pp. 608, 636
Critical Thinking .... TE pp. 587, 596, 612, 630

English Language Learners

ENGLISH LANGUAGE LEARNERS

Are You Ready? Vocabulary .... SE p. 565
Vocabulary Connections .... SE p. 566
Lesson Vocabulary .... SE, every lesson
Vocabulary Exercises .... SE, every exercise set
Vocabulary Review .... SE p. 638
English Language Learners .... TE pp. 585, 611, 649
Reading Strategies .... CRB, every lesson
Success for English Language Learners .... pp. 113–128
Multilingual Glossary

Reaching All Learners Through...

Modeling .... TE p. 620
Cognitive Strategies .... TE p. 570
Inclusion .... TE pp. 575, 580, 584, 589, 598, 611, 615, 625
Visual Cues .... TE pp. 578, 629
Graphic Organizers .... TE p. 584
Auditory Cues .... TE pp. 585, 611
Critical Thinking .... TE pp. 587, 596, 612, 630
Cooperative Learning .... TE p. 593
Multiple Representations .... TE pp. 598, 601
Test Prep Doctor .... TE pp. 576, 582, 590, 599, 607, 617, 627, 635, 643, 644, 646
Common Error Alerts .... TE pp. 571, 575, 579, 581, 585, 589, 595, 603, 613, 615, 621, 625, 629, 633
Scaffolding Questions .... TE pp. 608, 636

Technology Highlights for Reaching All Learners

Lesson Tutorial Videos

Starring Holt authors Ed Burger and Freddie Renfro! Live tutorials to support every lesson in Chapter 8.

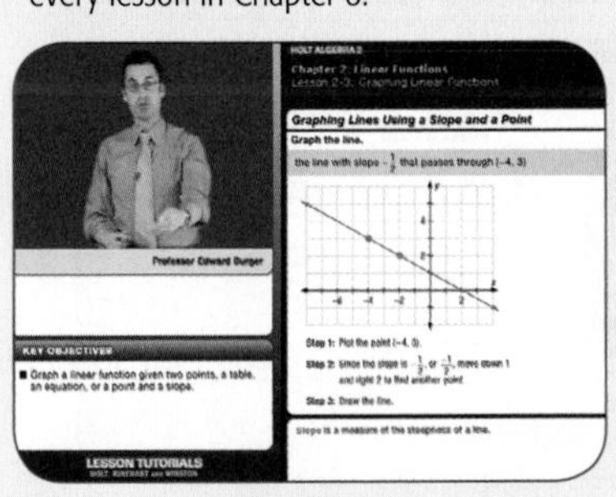

Multilingual Glossary

Searchable glossary includes definitions in English, Spanish, Vietnamese, Chinese, Hmong, Korean, and 4 other languages.

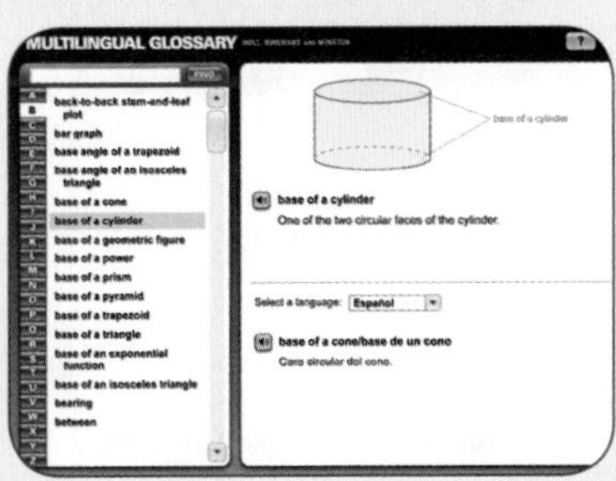

Online Interactivities

Interactive tutorials provide visually engaging alternative opportunities to learn concepts and master skills.

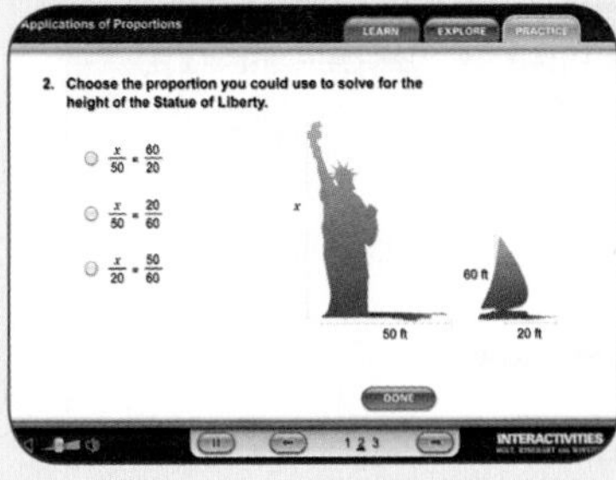

KEY: **SE** = *Student Edition* **TE** = *Teacher's Edition* **CRB** = *Chapter Resource Book*  Available on CD-ROM Available online

CHAPTER 8

Ongoing Assessment

Assessing Prior Knowledge

Determine whether students have the required prerequisite concepts and skills for success in Chapter 8.

Are You Ready? SPANISH .... SE p. 565
Warm Up .... TE, every lesson

Test Preparation

Provide review and practice for Chapter 8 and standardized tests.

Multi-Step Test Prep .... SE pp. 608, 636
Study Guide: Review .... SE pp. 638–641
Test Tackler .... SE pp. 644–645
Standardized Test Prep .... SE pp. 646–647
College Entrance Exam Practice .... SE p. 643
***Countdown to Testing* Transparencies** 33–36
State Test Prep Workbook
***State Test Prep* CD-ROM**
IDEA Works!

Alternative Assessment

Assess students' understanding of Chapter 8 concepts and combined problem-solving skills.

Chapter 8 Project .... SE p. 564
Alternative Assessment .... TE, every lesson
Performance Assessment .... AR pp. 159–160
Portfolio Assessment .... AR p. xxxiv

Daily Assessment

Provide formative assessment for each day of Chapter 8.

Questioning Strategies .... TE, every example
Think and Discuss .... SE, every lesson
Check It Out! Exercises .... SE, every example
Write About It .... SE, every lesson
Journal .... TE, every lesson
Lesson Quiz .... TE, every lesson
Alternative Assessment .... TE, every lesson
Modified Lesson Quizzes .... *IDEA Works!*

Weekly Assessment

Provide formative assessment for each week of Chapter 8.

Multi-Step Test Prep .... SE pp. 608, 636
Ready to Go On? .... SE pp. 609, 637
Cumulative Assessment .... SE pp. 646–647
Test and Practice Generator .... *One-Stop Planner*

Formal Assessment

Provide summative assessment of Chapter 8 mastery.

Section Quizzes .... AR pp. 145–146
Chapter 8 Test .... SE p. 642
Chapter Test (Levels A, B, C) .... AR pp. 147–158
• Multiple Choice • Free Response
Cumulative Test .... AR pp. 161–164
Test and Practice Generator .... *One-Stop Planner*
Modified Chapter 8 Test .... *IDEA Works!*

Technology Highlights for Ongoing Assessment

Are You Ready? SPANISH

Automatically assess readiness and prescribe intervention for Chapter 8 prerequisite skills.

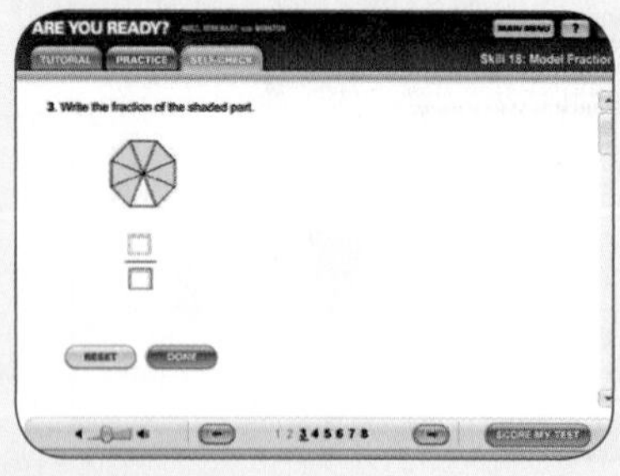

Ready to Go On?

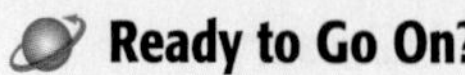

Automatically assess understanding and prescribe intervention for Sections 8A and 8B.

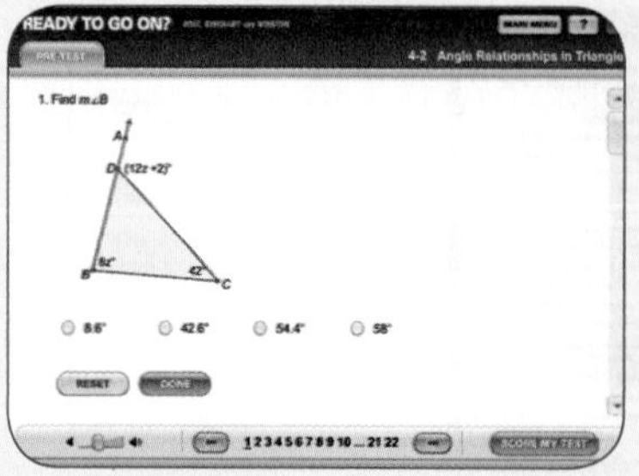

Test and Practice Generator

Use Chapter 8 problem banks to create assessments and worksheets to print out or deliver online. Includes dynamic problems.

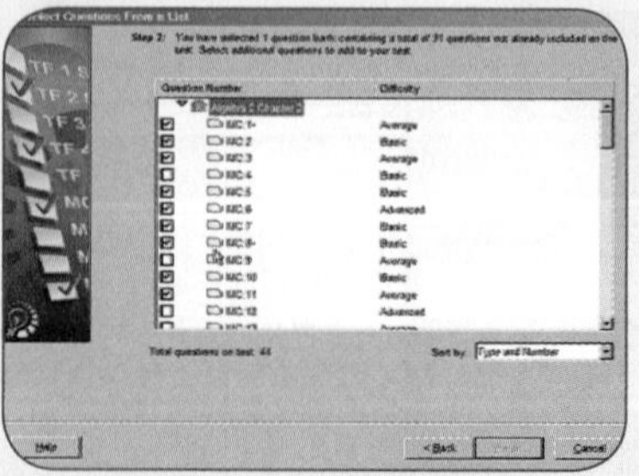

KEY: **SE** = *Student Edition* **TE** = *Teacher's Edition* **AR** = *Assessment Resources*  Spanish version available  Available on CD-ROM 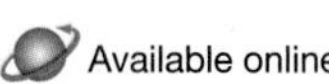 Available online

CHAPTER 8

Formal Assessment

Three levels (A, B, C) of multiple-choice and free-response chapter tests are available in the *Assessment Resources.*

A Chapter 8 Test

C Chapter 8 Test

MULTIPLE CHOICE

B Chapter 8 Test

B Chapter 8 Test (continued)

A Chapter 8 Test

C Chapter 8 Test

FREE RESPONSE

B Chapter 8 Test

B Chapter 8 Test (continued)

MODIFIED FOR IDEA

Chapter 8 Test

Chapter 8 Test (continued)

Test & Practice Generator
One-Stop Planner®

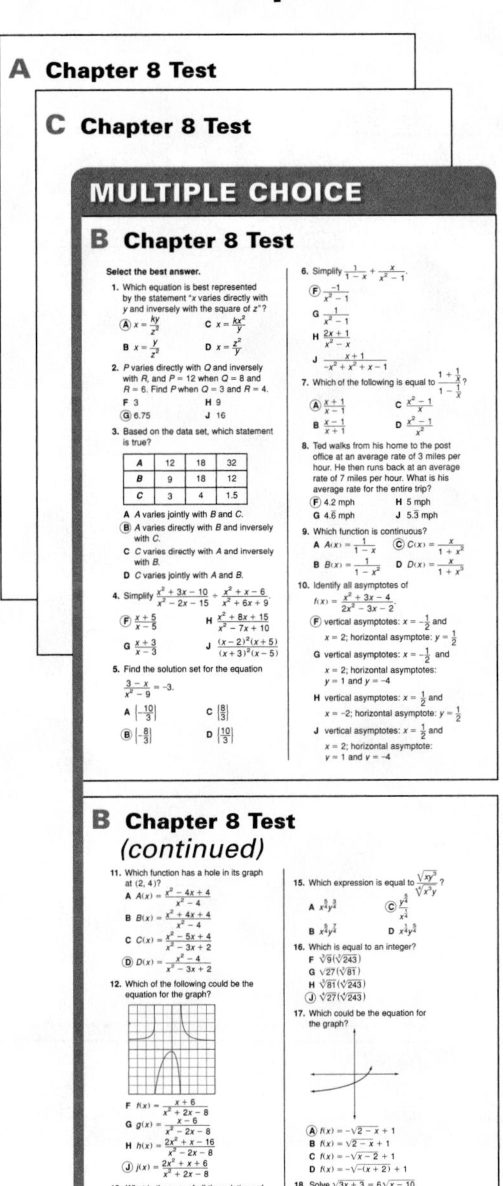

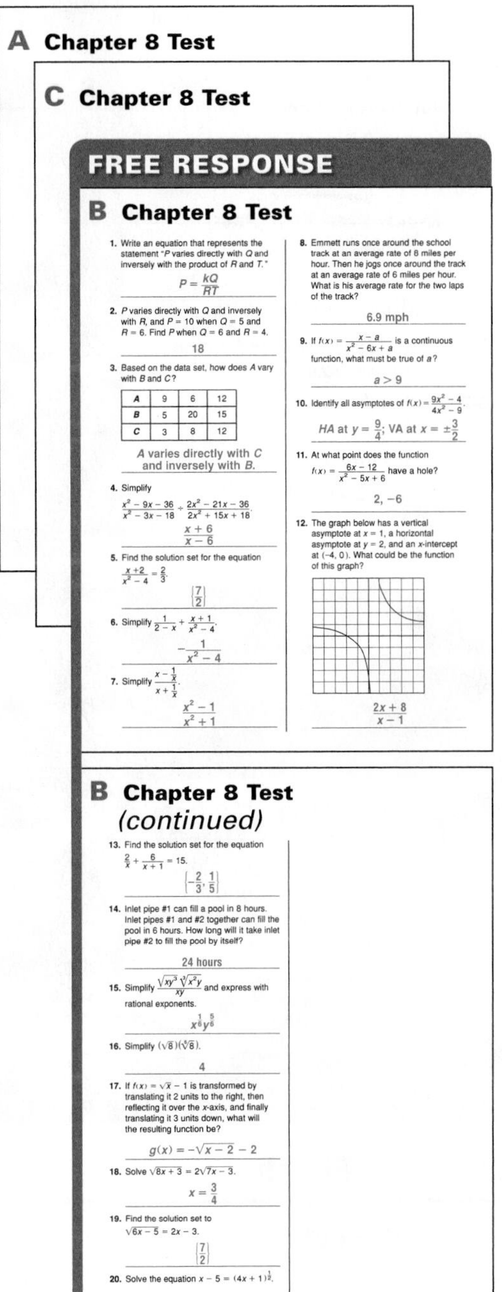

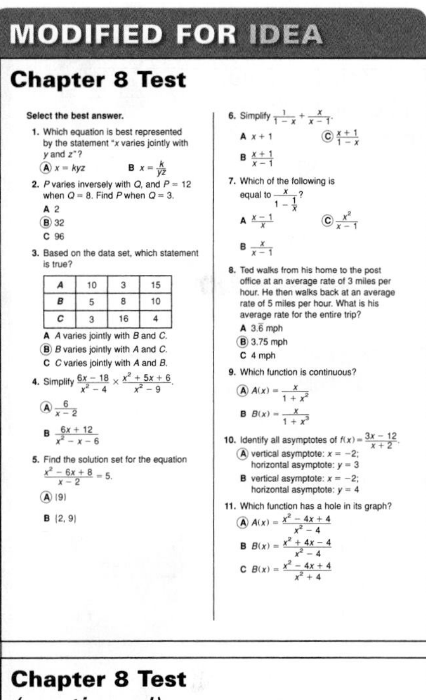

Create and customize Chapter 8 Tests. Instantly generate multiple test versions, answer keys, and practice versions of test items.

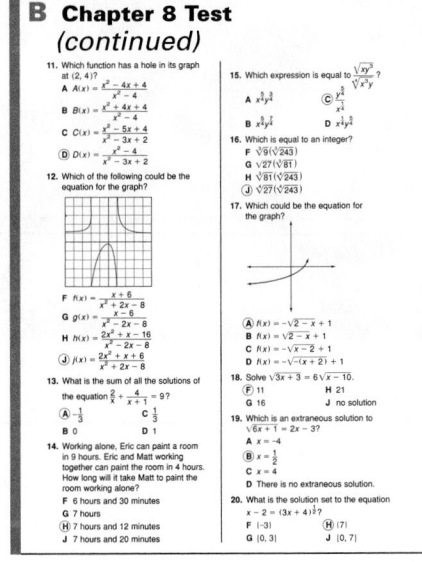

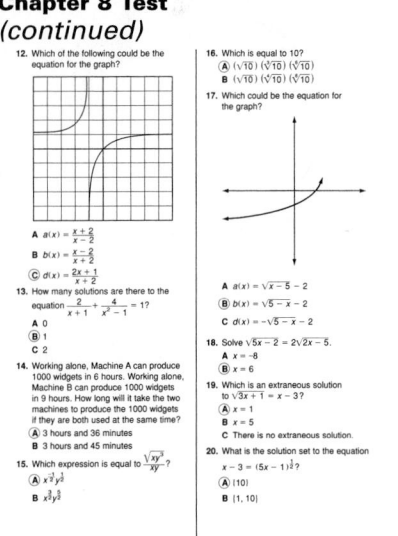

CHAPTER 8

SECTION 8A Rational Functions

On page 608, students write rational functions and solve rational equations to solve problems involving the Indianapolis 500.

Exercises designed to prepare students for success on the Multi-Step Test Prep can be found on pages 575, 581, 589, 598, and 606.

SECTION 8B Radical Functions

On page 636, students apply radical functions and equations to model a real-world situation involving clock pendulums.

Exercises designed to prepare students for success on the Multi-Step Test Prep can be found on pages 616, 626, and 634.

CHAPTER 8

Rational and Radical Functions

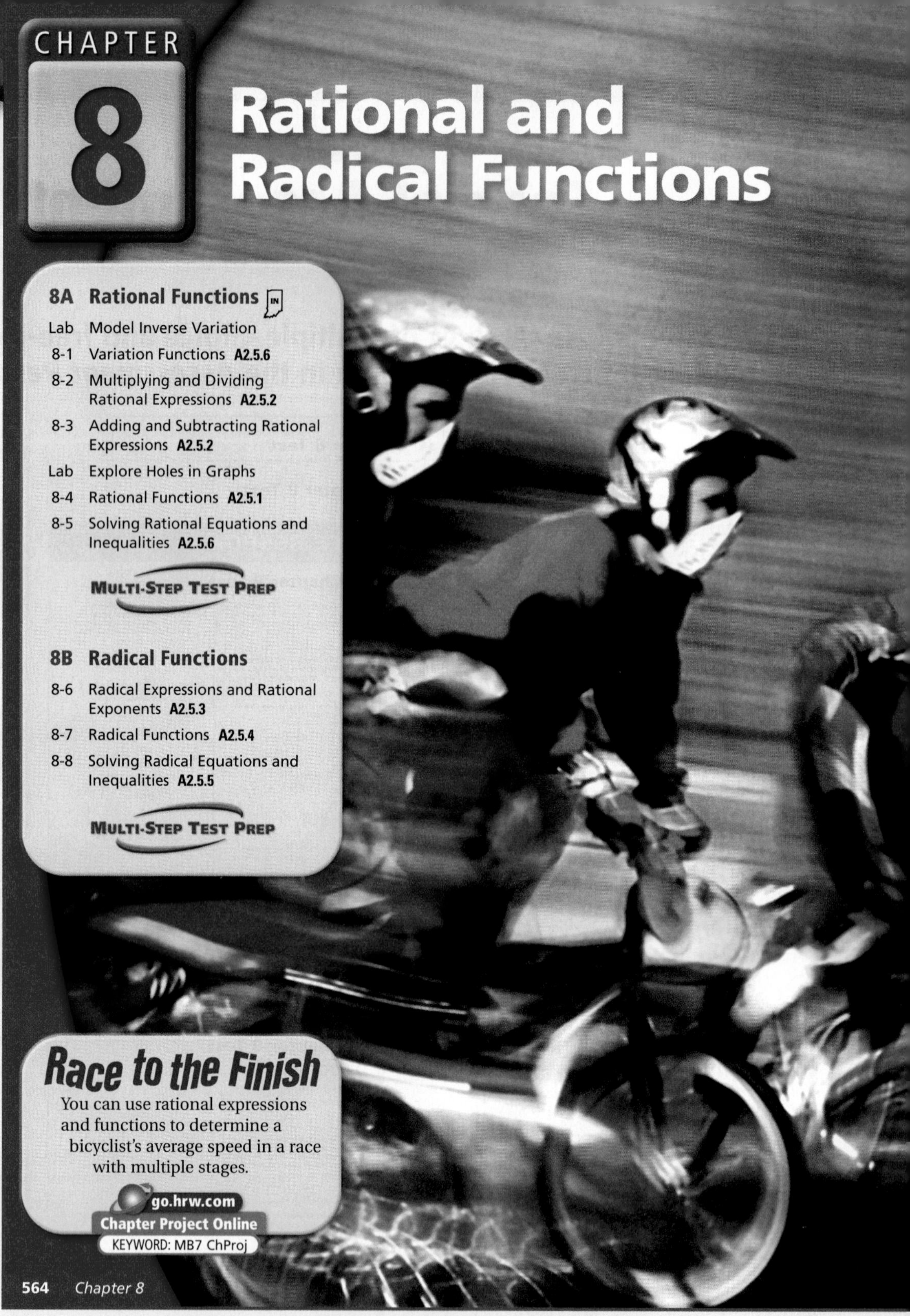

Race to the Finish

You can use rational expressions and functions to determine a bicyclist's average speed in a race with multiple stages.

go.hrw.com
Chapter Project Online
KEYWORD: MB7 ChProj

Race to the Finish

About the Project

In the Chapter Project, students investigate how the speeds of bicyclists change as they ride up and down hills. They use rational functions to calculate bicyclists' average speed during a race with multiple stages by using a weighted harmonic mean.

Project Resources

All project resources for teachers and students are provided online.

Materials:

- graphing calculator

ARE YOU READY?

Vocabulary

Match each term on the left with a definition on the right.

1. asymptote D
2. rational number A
3. reflection B
4. translation F
5. zero of a function C

A. any number that can be expressed as a quotient of two integers, where the denominator is not zero
B. a transformation that flips a figure across a line
C. any number x such that $f(x) = 0$
D. a line that a curve approaches as the value of x or y becomes very large or very small
E. a whole number or its opposite
F. a transformation that moves each point in a figure the same distance in the same direction

Properties of Exponents

Simplify each expression. Assume that all variables are nonzero.

6. $\frac{x^{11}y^5}{x^4y^7}$ $\frac{x^7}{y^2}$
7. $\left(\frac{3x^2y}{z}\right)^4$ $\frac{81x^8y^4}{z^4}$
8. $(x^3)^{-2}$ $\frac{1}{x^6}$
9. $(3x^3y)(6xy^5)$ $18x^4y^6$
10. $(2x^{-4})^3$ $\frac{8}{x^{12}}$
11. $12x^0$ 12

Combine Like Terms

Simplify each expression.

12. $5x^2 + 10x - 4x + 6$ $5x^2 + 6x + 6$
13. $3x + 12 - 10x$ $-7x + 12$
14. $x^2 + x + 3x^2 - 4x$ $4x^2 - 3x$

Greatest Common Factor

Find the greatest common factor of each pair of expressions.

15. $3a^2$ and $12a$ $3a$
16. c^2d and cd^2 cd
17. $16x^4$ and $40x^3$ $8x^3$

Factor Trinomials

Factor each trinomial.

18. $x^2 - 4x - 5$ $(x - 5)(x + 1)$
19. $x^2 + 2x - 24$ $(x - 4)(x + 6)$
20. $x^2 + 12x + 32$ $(x + 4)(x + 8)$
21. $x^2 + 9x + 18$ $(x + 3)(x + 6)$
22. $x^2 - 6x + 9$ $(x - 3)^2$
23. $x^2 - 8x - 20$ $(x - 10)(x + 2)$

Solve Quadratic Equations

Solve.

24. $5x^2 = 45$ ± 3
25. $4x^2 - 7 = 93$ ± 5
26. $2(x - 2)^2 = 32$ $-2, 6$

CHAPTER 8

ARE YOU READY?

Organizer

Objective: Assess students' understanding of prerequisite skills.

Prerequisite Skills

Properties of Exponents
Combine Like Terms
Greatest Common Factor
Factor Trinomials
Solve Quadratic Equations

Assessing Prior Knowledge

INTERVENTION

Diagnose and Prescribe

Use this page to determine whether intervention is necessary or whether enrichment is appropriate.

Resources

 ***Are You Ready? Intervention and Enrichment* Worksheets**

 ***Are You Ready?* CD-ROM**

 ***Are You Ready?* Online**

my.hrw.com

ARE YOU READY? Diagnose and Prescribe

NO INTERVENE

Prerequisite Skill	*Are You Ready? Intervention,* Chapter 8 — Worksheets	CD-ROM	Online
Properties of Exponents	Skill 59	Activity 59	Diagnose and Prescribe Online
Combine Like Terms	Skill 57	Activity 57	
Greatest Common Factor	Skill 4	Activity 4	
Factor Trinomials	Skill 67	Activity 67	
Solve Quadratic Equations	Skill 81	Activity 81	

YES ENRICH

Are You Ready? Enrichment, Chapter 8
Worksheets
CD-ROM
Online

Organizer

Objective: Help students organize the new concepts they will learn in Chapter 8.

Resources

Multilingual Glossary **Online**

go.hrw.com

KEYWORD: MB7 Glossary

Answers to *Vocabulary Connections*

Possible answers:

1. *Extra* means "more than is needed." An extraneous solution might be a solution that is not needed.
2. The graph of a discontinuous function has at least 1 gap or break.
3. Discontinuous; a hole is probably a type of break.
4. an exponent that can be written as a ratio of 2 integers

CHAPTER 8 Study Guide: Preview

Where You've Been

Previously, you

- solved problems with linear functions.
- simplified polynomial expressions.
- graphed functions with asymptotes.
- solved quadratic equations and inequalities.

In This Chapter

You will study

- solving problems with variation functions.
- simplifying rational and radical expressions.
- graphing rational and radical functions.
- solving rational and radical equations and inequalities.

Where You're Going

You can use the skills in this chapter

- in future math classes, including Precalculus.
- to solve problems in other classes, such as Chemistry, Physics, and Biology.
- outside of school to make predictions involving time, money, or speed.

Key Vocabulary/Vocabulario

complex fraction	fracción compleja
constant of variation	constante de variación
continuous function	función continua
direct variation	variación directa
discontinuous function	función discontinua
extraneous solutions	soluciones extrañas
hole (in a graph)	hoyo (en una gráfica)
inverse variation	variación inversa
radical equation	ecuación radical
radical function	función radical
rational equation	ecuación racional
rational exponent	exponente racional
rational function	función racional

Vocabulary Connections

To become familiar with some of the vocabulary terms in the chapter, consider the following. You may refer to the chapter, the glossary, or a dictionary if you like.

1. The word *extraneous* contains the word *extra*. What does *extra* mean? What do you think an **extraneous solution** is?
2. The graph of a **continuous function** has no gaps or breaks. How do you think a **discontinuous function** differs from a continuous function?
3. Do you think a **hole** could occur in the graph of a *continuous function* or a *discontinuous function*? Why?
4. A rational number can be written as a ratio of two integers. What do you think a **rational exponent** is?

Study Strategy: Make Flash Cards

You can use flash cards to help you remember a sequence of steps, the definitions of vocabulary words, or important formulas and properties.

Use these hints to make useful flash cards:

- Write a vocabulary word or the name of a formula or property on one side of a card and the meaning on the other.
- When memorizing a sequence of steps, make a flash card for each step.
- Use examples or diagrams if needed.
- Label each card with a lesson number in case you need to look back at your textbook for more information.

From Lesson 7-4

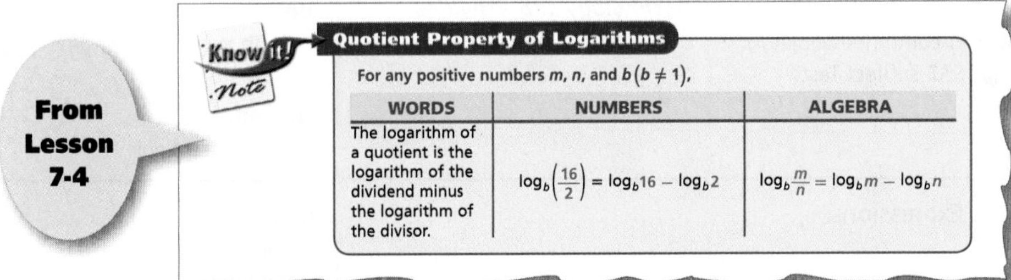

Know it! Note — **Quotient Property of Logarithms**

For any positive numbers m, n, and b $(b \neq 1)$,

WORDS	NUMBERS	ALGEBRA
The logarithm of a quotient is the logarithm of the dividend minus the logarithm of the divisor.	$\log_b\left(\frac{16}{2}\right) = \log_b 16 - \log_b 2$	$\log_b \frac{m}{n} = \log_b m - \log_b n$

Sample Flash Card

Lesson 7-4

Quotient Property of Logarithms

$\log_b \frac{m}{n} = ?$

Front

$\log_b \frac{m}{n} = \log_b m - \log_b n$

example:

$\log_2\left(\frac{16}{2}\right) = \log_2 16 - \log_2 2$

Back

Try This

Make flash cards that can help you remember each piece of information.

1. The Product of Powers Property states that to multiply powers with the same base, add the exponents. (See Lesson 1-5.)
2. The quadratic formula, $x = \frac{-b \pm \sqrt{b^2 - 4ac}}{2a}$, can be used to find the roots of an equation with the form $ax^2 + bx + c = 0$ $(a \neq 0)$. (See Lesson 5-6.)

Reading and Writing Math — CHAPTER 8

Organizer

Objective: Help students apply strategies to understand and retain key concepts.

Online Edition

Resources

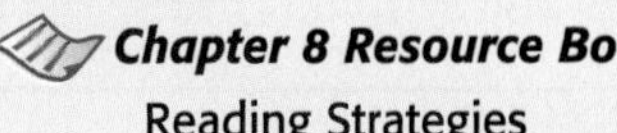

Chapter 8 Resource Book

Reading Strategies

Study Strategy: Make Flash Cards

Discuss Ask students to describe when and how they have used flash cards before. Elicit that flash cards can be a useful study tool because they can provide a quick check or review of what you have learned.

Emphasize that flash cards should summarize information in an easy-to-read format.

Extend As students work through Chapter 8, ask them to identify new concepts that would be appropriate to include on flash cards. Have students work in pairs to create a set of flash cards for the chapter, and ask them to develop a game using the cards that will help them review the chapter content. Encourage volunteers to share their games with the class.

Answers to *Try This*

1. Possible answer:

Lesson 1-5

Product of Powers Property

$a^m \cdot a^n = ?$

Front

$a^m \cdot a^n = a^{m+n}$

example:

$4^3 \cdot 4^2 = 4^{3+2} = 4^5$

Back

2. See p. A36.

SECTION
8A Rational Functions

One-Minute Section Planner

Lesson	Lab Resources	Materials
8-1 Algebra Lab Model Inverse Variation • Explore an inverse variation relationship. ☐ SAT-10 ☑ NAEP ☐ ACT ☑ SAT ☐ SAT Subject Tests	***Algebra Lab Activities*** 8-1 Lab Recording Sheet	**Required** tape, ruler (MK), pennies, graph paper and/or graphing calculator
Lesson 8-1 Variation Functions • Solve problems involving direct, inverse, joint, and combined variation. ☐ SAT-10 ☑ NAEP ☐ ACT ☑ SAT ☑ SAT Subject Tests	***Technology Lab Activities*** 8-1 Technology Lab	**Required** graph paper and/or graphing calculator **Optional** science textbook
Lesson 8-2 Multiplying and Dividing Rational Expressions • Simplify rational expressions. • Multiply and divide rational expressions. ☐ SAT-10 ☑ NAEP ☑ ACT ☑ SAT ☑ SAT Subject Tests		**Required** graph paper and/or graphing calculator **Optional** highlighters or colored pencils (MK), flash cards
Lesson 8-3 Adding and Subtracting Rational Expressions • Add and subtract rational expressions. • Simplify complex fractions. ☐ SAT-10 ☑ NAEP ☑ ACT ☑ SAT ☑ SAT Subject Tests		**Required** graph paper and/or graphing calculator **Optional** poster board
8-4 Technology Lab Explore Holes in Graphs • Identify breaks, or holes, in graphs. ☐ SAT-10 ☐ NAEP ☐ ACT ☐ SAT ☑ SAT Subject Tests	***Technology Lab Activities*** 8-4 Lab Recording Sheet	**Required** graphing calculator
Lesson 8-4 Rational Functions • Graph rational functions. • Transform rational functions by changing parameters. ☐ SAT-10 ☐ NAEP ☑ ACT ☑ SAT ☐ SAT Subject Tests	***Algebra Lab Activities*** 8-4 Algebra Lab	**Required** graph paper and/or graphing calculator
Lesson 8-5 Solving Rational Equations and Inequalities • Solve rational equations and inequalities. ☐ SAT-10 ☑ NAEP ☑ ACT ☑ SAT ☑ SAT Subject Tests		**Required** graphing calculator **Optional** graph paper

MK = *Manipulatives Kit*

Section Overview

Variation Functions — Lesson 8-1

Many real-world situations, from geometry and chemistry to engineering and agriculture, can be modeled by variation functions.

k is constant.

Direct Variation

$y = kx \qquad k = \frac{y}{x}$

As the value of one variable **increases**, the value of the other **increases**.

Inverse Variation

$y = \frac{k}{x} \qquad k = yx$

As the value of one variable **increases**, the value of the other **decreases**.

Operations with Rational Expressions — Lessons 8-2, 8-3

Performing operations with rational expressions is a fundamental skill for solving rational equations and inequalities.

Operations with rational expressions follow the same rules as operations with fractions.

Multiply or Divide

$$\frac{x^2 + x - 2}{x^2 - 6x + 9} \cdot \frac{x^2 - 9}{x^2 - 1}$$

$$\frac{(x+2)\cancel{(x-1)}}{\cancel{(x-3)}(x-3)} \cdot \frac{\cancel{(x-3)}(x+3)}{\cancel{(x-1)}(x+1)}$$

$$\frac{(x+2)(x+3)}{(x-3)(x+1)}$$

Add or Subtract

$$\frac{x+2}{x^2+2x-3} - \frac{x}{x-1} = \frac{x+2}{(x-1)(x+3)} - \frac{x}{x-1}$$

$$= \frac{x+2}{(x-1)(x+3)} - \frac{x(x+3)}{(x-1)(x+3)}$$

$$= \frac{x+2-x^2-3x}{(x-1)(x+3)}$$

$$= \frac{-x^2-2x+2}{(x-1)(x+3)}$$

Rational Functions — Lessons 8-4, 8-5

Graphing rational functions and solving rational equations builds a foundation that students will use as they continue in more-advanced math classes.

Factor the numerator and denominator to find the zeros and asymptotes.

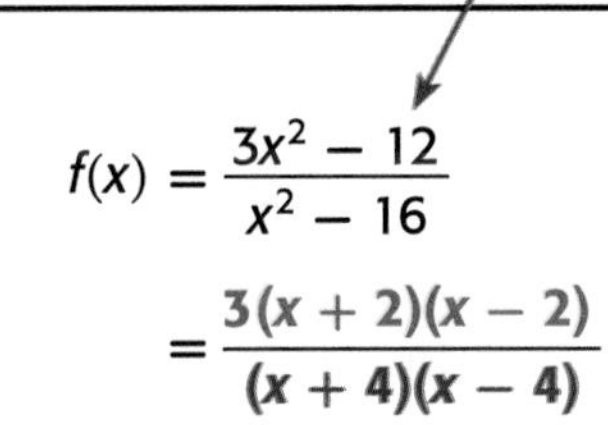

$$f(x) = \frac{3x^2 - 12}{x^2 - 16}$$

$$= \frac{3(x+2)(x-2)}{(x+4)(x-4)}$$

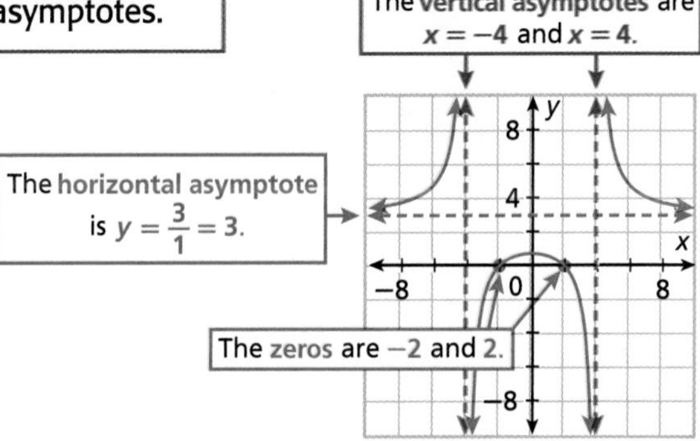

Organizer

Use with Lesson 8-1

Pacing:

Traditional 1 day
Block $\frac{1}{2}$ day

Objective: Explore an inverse variation relationship.

Materials: pencil, tape, ruler, 8 pennies

Online Edition

Countdown to Testing Week 17

Resources

Algebra Lab Activities
8-1 Lab Recording Sheet

Teach

Discuss

Ask students to predict whether they should move the pennies closer to or farther from the fulcrum as they increase the number of pennies.

Close

Key Concept

In an inverse variation, one quantity increases as another decreases, and the product of the quantities is constant.

Assessment

Journal Have students describe the relationship they observe between the number of pennies in the stack and the distance in centimeters from the fulcrum.

Model Inverse Variation

In this activity, you will explore the relationship between the mass of an object and the object's distance from the pivot point, or fulcrum, of a balanced lever.

Use with Lesson 8-1

Activity

1. Secure a pencil to a tabletop with tape. The pencil will be the *fulcrum*.

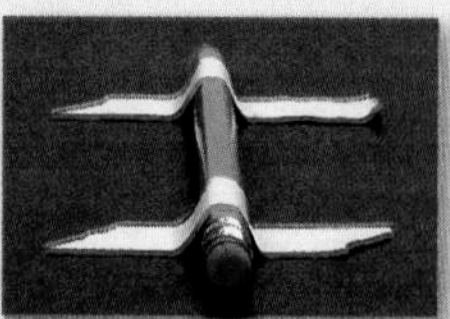

2. Draw an arrow on a piece of tape, and use the arrow to mark the midpoint of a ruler. Then tape a penny to the end of the ruler.

3. Place the midpoint of the ruler on top of the pencil. The ruler is the *lever*.

4. Place one penny on the lever opposite the taped penny. If needed, move the untaped penny to a position that makes the lever balanced. Find the distance from the untaped penny to the fulcrum, and record the distance in a table like the one below. (Measure from the center of the penny.) Repeat this step with stacks of two to seven pennies.

Let x be the number of pennies and y be the distance from the fulcrum. Plot the points from your table on a graph. Then draw a smooth curve through the points.

Number of Pennies	1	2	3	4	5	6	7
Distance from Fulcrum (cm)	■	■	■	■	■	■	■

Possible answers: 15 7.5 5 3.8 3 2.5 2.1

Try This

Possible answer: The products are all approximately equal.

1. Multiply the corresponding x- and y-values together. What do you notice?
2. Use your answer to Problem 1 to write an equation relating distance from the fulcrum to the number of pennies. Possible answer: $xy = 15$
3. Would it be possible to balance a stack of 20 pennies on the lever? Use your equation from Problem 2 to justify your answer.
4. **Make a Conjecture** The relationship between the mass of an object on a balanced lever and the object's distance from the fulcrum can be modeled by an *inverse variation* function. Based on your data and graph, how are the variables in an inverse variation related?

Answer to *Activity*

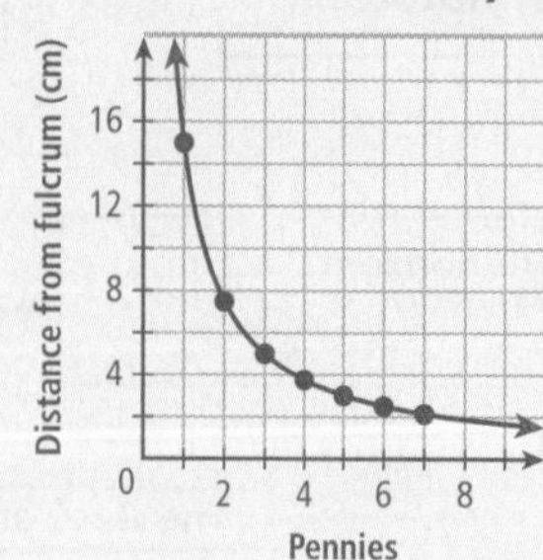

Answers to *Try This*

3. Possible answer: Substituting 20 for x in the equation yields $20y = 15$, or $y = 0.75$. According to the equation, it is possible to balance a stack of 20 pennies by placing them 0.75 cm from the fulcrum. However, this would probably not be possible because of the size of the pennies.
4. Possible answer: An increase in 1 variable causes a decrease in the other variable, and a decrease in 1 variable causes an increase in the other variable.

8-1 Variation Functions

A2.5.6 Solve problems that can be modeled using equations involving rational and radical functions, including problems of direct and inverse variation. Interpret the . . .

Objective
Solve problems involving direct, inverse, joint, and combined variation.

Vocabulary
direct variation
constant of variation
joint variation
inverse variation
combined variation

. . . solutions, and determine whether the solutions are reasonable.

Why learn this?
You can use variation functions to determine how many people are needed to complete a task, such as building a home, in a given time. (See Example 5.)

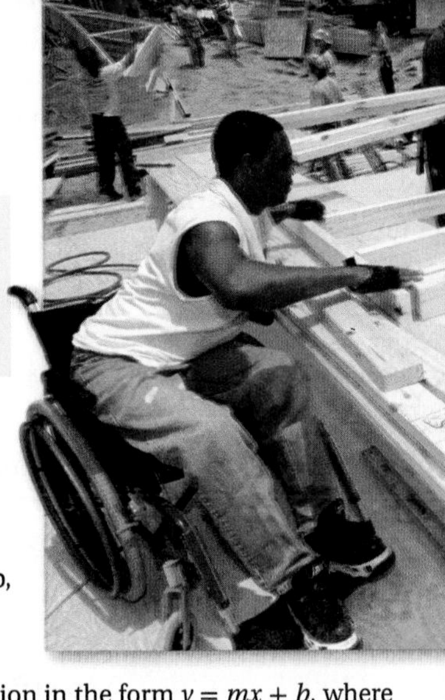

In Chapter 2, you studied many types of linear functions. One special type of linear function is called *direct variation*. A **direct variation** is a relationship between two variables x and y that can be written in the form $y = kx$, where $k \neq 0$. In this relationship, k is the **constant of variation**. For the equation $y = kx$, y varies directly as x.

A direct variation equation is a linear equation in the form $y = mx + b$, where $b = 0$ and the constant of variation k is the slope. Because $b = 0$, the graph of a direct variation always passes through the origin.

EXAMPLE 1 Writing and Graphing Direct Variation

Given: y varies directly as x, and $y = 14$ when $x = 3.5$. Write and graph the direct variation function.

$y = kx$	*y varies directly as x.*
$14 = k(3.5)$	*Substitute 14 for y and 3.5 for x.*
$4 = k$	*Solve for the constant of variation k.*
$y = 4x$	*Write the variation function by using the value of k.*

Graph the direct variation function.

The y-intercept is 0, and the slope is 4.

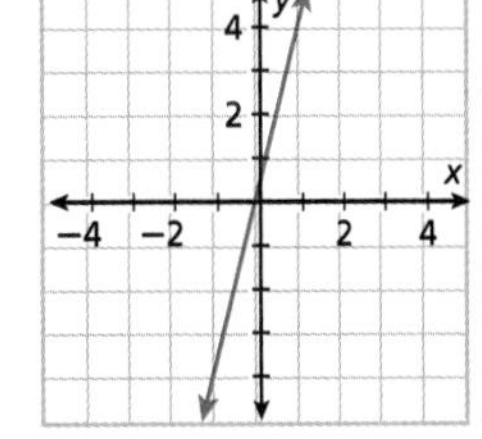

Check Substitute the original values of x and y into the equation.

$y = 4x$	
14	4(3.5)
14	14✔

Helpful Hint

If k is positive in a direct variation, the value of y increases as the value of x increases.

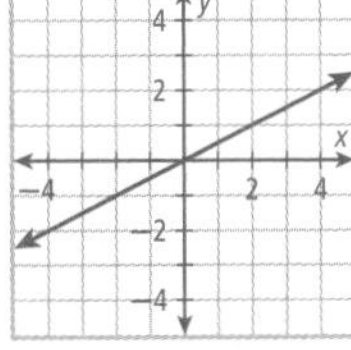

1. Given: y varies directly as x, and $y = 6.5$ when $x = 13$. Write and graph the direct variation function.

$y = 0.5x$

When you want to find specific values in a direct variation problem, you can solve for k and then use substitution or you can use the proportion derived below.

$$y_1 = kx_1 \rightarrow \frac{y_1}{x_1} = k \quad \text{and} \quad y_2 = kx_2 \rightarrow \frac{y_2}{x_2} = k \quad \text{so,} \quad \frac{y_1}{x_1} = \frac{y_2}{x_2}.$$

8-1 Organizer

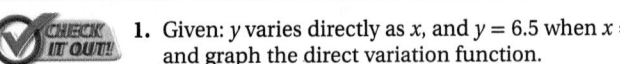

Pacing: Traditional 1 day
Block $\frac{1}{2}$ day

Objective: Solve problems involving direct, inverse, joint, and combined variation.

Technology Lab
In *Technology Lab Activities*

Online Edition
Tutorial Videos

Countdown to Testing Week 17

Power Presentations with PowerPoint®

Warm Up

Solve each equation.

1. $\frac{2.4}{x} = \frac{2}{9}$ 10.8

2. $1.6x = 1.8(24.8)$ 27.9

Determine whether each data set could represent a linear function.

3.

x	2	4	6	8
y	12	6	4	3

no

4.

x	−2	−1	0	1
y	−6	−2	2	6

yes

Also available on transparency

Math Humor

Q: What's reverse variation?

A: The relationship between the length of a driveway and the chance of backing into a mailbox.

1 Introduce

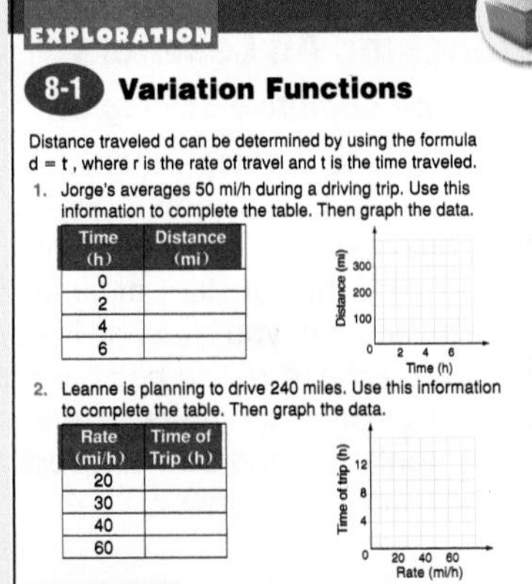

EXPLORATION

8-1 Variation Functions

Distance traveled d can be determined by using the formula d = t , where r is the rate of travel and t is the time traveled.

1. Jorge's averages 50 mi/h during a driving trip. Use this information to complete the table. Then graph the data.

Time (h)	Distance (mi)
0	
2	
4	
6	

2. Leanne is planning to drive 240 miles. Use this information to complete the table. Then graph the data.

Rate (mi/h)	Time of Trip (h)
20	
30	
40	
60	

THINK AND DISCUSS

3. **Tell** how the graphs in Problems 1 and 2 are different.
4. **Describe** how the amount of time Jorge travels affects the distance he travels.

Motivate

Give students a few examples of quantities that vary directly or indirectly, such as number of songs downloaded and total cost of songs, or number of workers and time needed to build a highway. Ask students to describe how an increase in one quantity would affect the other. Explain to students that relationships such as these can be described mathematically by using variation functions.

Explorations and answers are provided in the *Explorations* binder.

State Resources

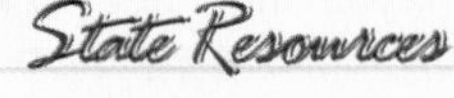

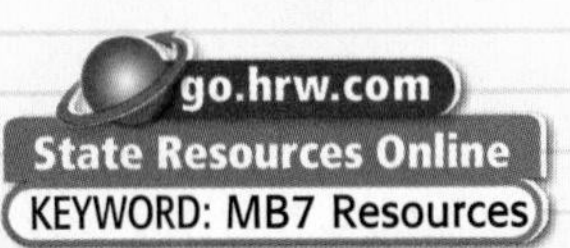

Power Presentations with PowerPoint®

Additional Examples

Example 1

Given: y varies directly as x, and $y = 27$ when $x = 6$. Write and graph the direct variation function. $y = 4.5x$

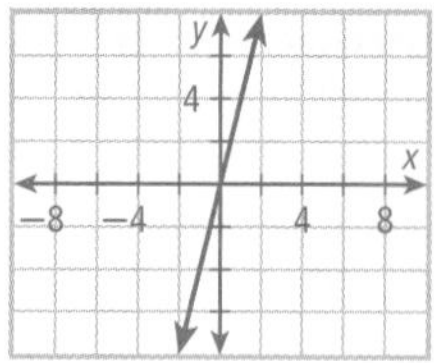

Example 2

The cost of an item in euros e varies directly as the cost of the item in dollars d, and $e = 3.85$ euros when $d = \$5.00$. Find d when $e = 10.00$ euros. $12.99

Example 3

The volume V of a cone varies jointly as the area of the base B and the height h, and $V = 12\pi$ ft^3 when $B = 9\pi$ ft^2 and $h = 4$ ft. Find B when $V = 24\pi$ ft^3 and $h = 9$ ft. 8π ft^2

Also available on transparency

INTERVENTION

Questioning Strategies

EXAMPLE 1

- How do you determine the constant of variation?
- How can you determine the slope and y-intercept of a direct variation function before you graph it?

EXAMPLE 2

- How do you set up a proportion to solve a direct variation problem?

EXAMPLE 3

- How do you know how to write the joint variation equation from the information given in the problem?

Reading Math Emphasize that the phrase "*y* varies jointly as *x* and *z*" indicates that *y* varies directly as the *product* of *x* and *z*, rather than as the *sum* of *x* and *z*. ENGLISH LANGUAGE LEARNERS

EXAMPLE 2 Solving Direct Variation Problems

Geometry

Reading Math

The phrases "*y* varies directly as *x*" and "*y* is directly proportional to *x*" have the same meaning.

The circumference of a circle C varies directly as the radius r, and $C = 7\pi$ ft when $r = 3.5$ ft. Find r when $C = 4.5\pi$ ft.

Method 1 Find k.

$C = kr$

$7\pi = k(3.5)$ *Substitute.*

$2\pi = k$ *Solve for k.*

Write the variation function.

$C = (2\pi)r$ *Use 2π for k.*

$4.5\pi = (2\pi)r$ *Substitute 4.5π for C.*

$2.25 = r$ *Solve for r.*

Method 2 Use a proportion.

$\frac{C_1}{r_1} = \frac{C_2}{r_2}$

$\frac{7\pi}{3.5} = \frac{4.5\pi}{r}$ *Substitute.*

$7\pi r = 15.75\pi$ *Find the cross products.*

$r = 2.25$ *Solve for r.*

The radius r is 2.25 ft.

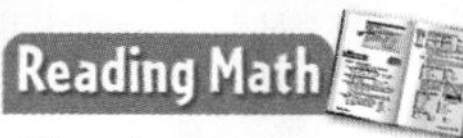

CHECK IT OUT! **2.** The perimeter P of a regular dodecagon varies directly as the side length s, and $P = 18$ in. when $s = 1.5$ in. Find s when $P = 75$ in. 6.25 in.

A **joint variation** is a relationship among three variables that can be written in the form $y = kxz$, where k is the constant of variation. For the equation $y = kxz$, y varies jointly as x and z.

EXAMPLE 3 Solving Joint Variation Problems

Geometry

The area A of a triangle varies jointly as the base b and the height h, and $A = 12$ m^2 when $b = 6$ m and $h = 4$ m. Find b when $A = 36$ m^2 and $h = 8$ m.

Step 1 Find k.

$A = kbh$ *Joint variation*

$12 = k(6)(4)$ *Substitute.*

$\frac{1}{2} = k$ *Solve for k.*

Step 2 Use the variation function.

$A = \frac{1}{2}bh$ *Use $\frac{1}{2}$ for k.*

$36 = \frac{1}{2}b(8)$ *Substitute.*

$9 = b$ *Solve for b.*

The base b is 9 m.

CHECK IT OUT! **3.** The lateral surface area L of a cone varies jointly as the base radius r and the slant height ℓ, and $L = 63\pi$ m^2 when $r = 3.5$ m and $\ell = 18$ m. Find r to the nearest tenth when $L = 8\pi$ m^2 and $\ell = 5$ m. 1.6 m

A third type of variation describes a situation in which one quantity increases and the other decreases. For example, the table shows that the time needed to drive 600 miles decreases as speed increases.

Speed (mi/h)	Time (h)	Distance (mi)
30	20	600
40	15	600
50	12	600

This type of variation is an inverse variation. An **inverse variation** is a relationship between two variables x and y that can be written in the form $y = \frac{k}{x}$, where $k \neq 0$. For the equation $y = \frac{k}{x}$, y varies inversely as x.

2 Teach

Guided Instruction

As you work through the direct-variation examples, point out that one quantity increases as the other increases, but that this alone does not make a direct variation. The relationship is a direct variation only if the ratio of the x- and y-values is constant. Likewise, a relationship in which one quantity increases as the other decreases is only an inverse variation if the product of the x- and y-values is constant. Introduce students to joint and combined variation by using what they have learned about direct and inverse variation.

Reaching All Learners

Through Cognitive Strategies

Work with students to develop mnemonic devices that they can use to remember the properties of direct and inverse variations. For example, to find the constant of variation of a direct variation, you must divide y by x, and both *direct* and *divide* begin with *d*. Likewise, the graph of an indirect variation is always nonlinear, and both *indirect* and *nonlinear* contain the letter *n*.

EXAMPLE 4 Writing and Graphing Inverse Variation

Given: y varies inversely as x, and $y = 3$ when $x = 8$. Write and graph the inverse variation function.

$y = \frac{k}{x}$ *y varies inversely as x.*

$3 = \frac{k}{8}$ *Substitute 3 for y and 8 for x.*

$k = 24$ *Solve for k.*

$y = \frac{24}{x}$ *Write the variation function.*

To graph, make a table of values for both positive and negative values of x. Plot the points, and connect them with two smooth curves. Because division by 0 is undefined, the function is undefined when $x = 0$.

x	y
−3	−8
−4	−6
−8	−3
−12	−2

x	y
3	8
4	6
8	3
12	2

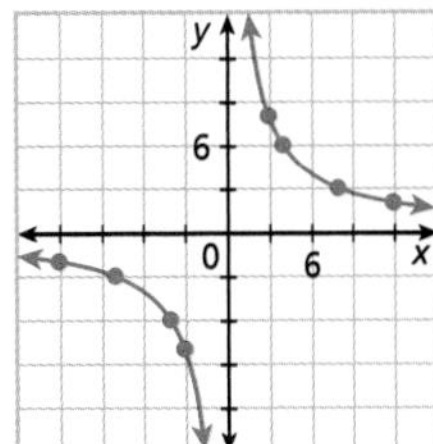

Helpful Hint

When graphing an inverse variation function, use values of x that are factors of k so that the y-values will be integers.

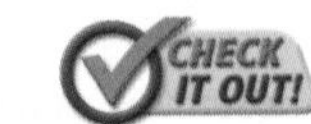

4. Given: y varies inversely as x, and $y = 4$ when $x = 10$. Write and graph the inverse variation function. $y = \frac{40}{x}$

When you want to find specific values in an inverse variation problem, you can solve for k and then use substitution or you can use the equation derived below.

$$y_1 = \frac{k}{x_1} \rightarrow y_1x_1 = k \quad \text{and} \quad y_2 = \frac{k}{x_2} \rightarrow y_2x_2 = k \quad \text{so,} \quad y_1x_1 = y_2x_2.$$

EXAMPLE 5 *Community Service Application*

The time t that it takes for a group of volunteers to construct a house varies inversely as the number of volunteers v. If 20 volunteers can build a house in 62.5 working hours, how many volunteers would be needed to build a house in 50 working hours?

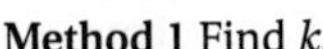

Method 1 Find k.

$t = \frac{k}{v}$

$62.5 = \frac{k}{20}$ *Substitute.*

$1250 = k$ *Solve for k.*

$t = \frac{1250}{v}$ *Use 1250 for k.*

$50 = \frac{1250}{v}$ *Substitute 50 for t.*

$v = 25$ *Solve for v.*

Method 2 Use $t_1v_1 = t_2v_2$.

$t_1v_1 = t_2v_2$

$62.5(20) = 50v$ *Substitute.*

$1250 = 50v$ *Simplify.*

$25 = v$ *Solve for v.*

So 25 volunteers would be needed to build a home in 50 working hours.

5. What if...? How many working hours would it take 15 volunteers to build a house? $83\frac{1}{3}$ working hours

Math Background The constant of variation is also called the *constant of proportionality.*

Geometry Review with students common formulas for perimeter, area, and volume. Discuss with students the types of variation in these formulas. For example, the perimeter P of a square varies directly as its side length s, and the volume V of a rectangular prism varies jointly as its length ℓ, width w, and height h.

COMMON ERROR ALERT

Students might determine the constant of variation and then forget to use it to solve the original problem. Remind students that variation problems usually involve more than one step. Often, the first step is to write the variation function by finding the constant of variation. The second step is to use the variation function to solve the problem.

Power Presentations with PowerPoint®

Additional Examples

Example 4

Given: y varies inversely as x, and $y = 4$ when $x = 5$. Write and graph the inverse variation function. $y = \frac{20}{x}$

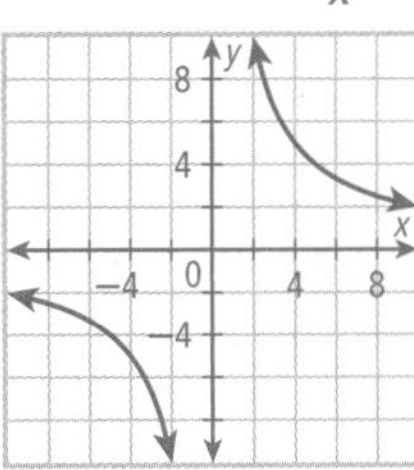

Example 5

The time t needed to complete a certain race varies inversely as the runner's average speed s. If a runner with an average speed of 8.82 mi/h completes the race in 2.97 h, what is the average speed of a runner who completes the race in 3.5 h? ≈ 7.48 mi/h

Also available on transparency

INTERVENTION

Questioning Strategies

EXAMPLE 4

- How do you use the given information to find the value of k?
- Does an inverse variation function have a y-intercept? Explain.

EXAMPLE 5

- How can you solve the problem without finding the value of k?
- How can you check your answer to an inverse variation problem?

Power Presentations with PowerPoint®

Additional Examples

Example 6

Determine whether each data set represents a direct variation, an inverse variation, or neither.

A.

x	6.5	13	104
y	8	4	0.5

inverse variation

B.

x	5	8	12
y	30	48	72

direct variation

C.

x	3	6	8
y	5	14	21

neither

Example 7

The change in temperature T of an aluminum wire varies inversely as its mass m and directly as the amount of heat energy E transferred. The temperature of an aluminum wire with a mass of 0.1 kg rises 5°C when 450 joules (J) of heat energy are transferred to it. How much heat energy must be transferred to an aluminum wire with a mass of 0.2 kg to raise its temperature 20°C? 3600 J

Also available on transparency

INTERVENTION

Questioning Strategies

EXAMPLE 6

- What does a constant ratio $\frac{y}{x}$ indicate about a data set? a constant product xy?

EXAMPLE 7

- How do you know which quantities to write in the numerator and which to write in the denominator?

You can use algebra to rewrite variation functions in terms of k.

Direct Variation

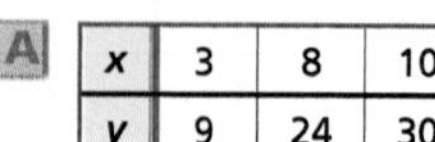

$$y = kx \rightarrow k = \frac{y}{x}$$

Constant ratio

Inverse Variation

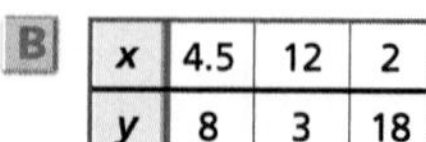

$$y = \frac{k}{x} \rightarrow k = xy$$

Constant product

Notice that in direct variation, the *ratio* of the two quantities is constant. In inverse variation, the *product* of the two quantities is constant.

EXAMPLE 6 Identifying Direct and Inverse Variation

Determine whether each data set represents a direct variation, an inverse variation, or neither.

A

x	3	8	10
y	9	24	30

In each case, $\frac{y}{x} = 3$. The ratio is constant, so this represents a direct variation.

B

x	4.5	12	2
y	8	3	18

In each case, $xy = 36$. The product is constant, so this represents an inverse variation.

CHECK IT OUT! **Determine whether each data set represents a direct variation, an inverse variation, or neither.**

6a.

x	3.75	15	5
y	12	3	9

inverse

6b.

x	1	40	26
y	0.2	8	5.2

direct

A **combined variation** is a relationship that contains both direct and inverse variation. Quantities that vary directly appear in the numerator, and quantities that vary inversely appear in the denominator.

EXAMPLE 7 *Chemistry Application*

The volume V of a gas varies inversely as the pressure P and directly as the temperature T. A certain gas has a volume of 10 liters (L), a temperature of 300 kelvins (K), and a pressure of 1.5 atmospheres (atm). If the gas is compressed to a volume of 7.5 L and is heated to 350 K, what will the new pressure be?

Helpful Hint

A kelvin (K) is a unit of temperature that is often used by chemists.
0°C = 273.15 K
100°C = 373.15 K

Step 1 Find k.

$V = \frac{kT}{P}$	*Combined variation*
$10 = \frac{k(300)}{1.5}$	*Substitute.*
$0.05 = k$	*Solve for k.*

Step 2 Use the variation function.

$V = \frac{0.05T}{P}$	*Use 0.05 for k.*
$7.5 = \frac{0.05(350)}{P}$	*Substitute.*
$P = 2.\overline{3}$	*Solve for P.*

The new pressure will be $2.\overline{3}$, or $2\frac{1}{3}$, atm.

CHECK IT OUT! **7.** If the gas is heated to 400 K and has a pressure of 1 atm, what is its volume? 20 L

3 Close

Summarize

Ask students to describe the type of variation that each function represents, assuming that d is the dependent variable.

$d = \frac{26}{m}$	*d* varies inversely as *m*.
$d = (7.3s)t$	*d* varies jointly as *s* and *t*.
$d = \frac{\pi}{4}p$	*d* varies directly as *p*.
$d = \frac{8g}{3h}$	*d* varies directly as *g* and inversely as *h*.

ONGOING ASSESSMENT and INTERVENTION

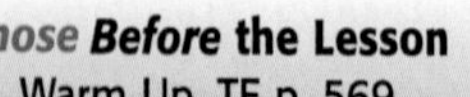

***Diagnose* Before the Lesson**
8-1 Warm Up, TE p. 569

***Monitor* During the Lesson**
Check It Out! Exercises, SE pp. 569–572
Questioning Strategies, TE pp. 570–572

***Assess* After the Lesson**
8-1 Lesson Quiz, TE p. 576
Alternative Assessment, TE p. 576

THINK AND DISCUSS

1. Explain why the graph of a direct variation is a line.
2. Describe the type of variation between the length and the width of a rectangular room with an area of 400 ft^2.

3. **GET ORGANIZED** Copy and complete the graphic organizer. In each box, write the general variation equation, draw a graph, or give an example.

Type of Variation	Equation	Graph	Example
Direct			
Joint			
Inverse			

Answers to *Think and Discuss*

Possible answers:

1. A direct variation equation is in the form $y = mx + b$, with $m = k$ and $b = 0$.
2. The length varies inversely as the width, with a constant of variation of 400.
3. See p. A9.

8-1 Exercises

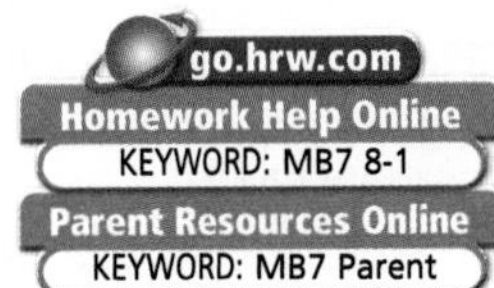

GUIDED PRACTICE

1. **Vocabulary** A variation function in which k is positive and one quantity decreases when the other increases is a(n) __?__. (*direct variation* or *indirect variation*) indirect variation

SEE EXAMPLE 1 p. 569

Given: y varies directly as x. Write and graph each direct variation function.

2. $y = 6$ when $x = 3$ $y = 2x$
3. $y = 45$ when $x = -5$ $y = -9x$
4. $y = 54$ when $x = 4.5$ $y = 12x$

SEE EXAMPLE 2 p. 570

5. **Physics** The wavelength λ of a wave of a certain frequency varies directly as the velocity v of the wave, and $\lambda = 60$ ft when $v = 15$ ft/s. Find λ when $v = 3$ ft/s. 12 ft
6. **Work** The dollar amount d that Julia earns varies directly as the number of hours t that she works, and $d = \$116.25$ when $t = 15$ h. Find t when $d = \$178.25$. 23 h

SEE EXAMPLE 3 p. 570

7. **Geometry** The volume V of a rectangular prism of a particular height varies jointly as the length ℓ and the width w, and $V = 224$ ft^3 when $\ell = 8$ ft and $w = 4$ ft. Find ℓ when $V = 210$ ft^3 and $w = 5$ ft. 6 ft
8. **Economics** The total cost C of electricity for a particular light bulb varies jointly as the time t that the light bulb is used and the cost k per kilowatt-hour, and $C = 12¢$ when $t = 50$ h and $k = 6¢$ per kilowatt-hour. Find C to the nearest cent when $t = 30$ h and $k = 8¢$ per kilowatt-hour. 10¢

SEE EXAMPLE 4 p. 571

Given: y varies inversely as x. Write and graph each inverse variation function.

9. $y = 2$ when $x = 7$ $y = \frac{14}{x}$
10. $y = 8$ when $x = 4$ $y = \frac{32}{x}$
11. $y = \frac{1}{2}$ when $x = -10$ $y = -\frac{5}{x}$

SEE EXAMPLE 5 p. 571

12. **Travel** The time t that it takes for a salesman to drive a certain distance d varies inversely as the average speed r. It takes the salesman 4.75 h to travel between two cities at 60 mi/h. How long would the drive take at 50 mi/h? 5.7 h

SEE EXAMPLE 6 p. 572

Determine whether each data set represents a direct variation, an inverse variation, or neither.

13. neither

x	2	5	9
y	3	6	4

14. inverse

x	6	4	1
y	2	3	12

15. direct

x	24	4	12
y	30	5	15

8-1 Exercises

Assignment Guide

Assign *Guided Practice* exercises as necessary.

If you finished Examples **1–3**
- **Basic** 17–23, 39, 40
- **Average** 17–23, 39, 40, 50
- **Advanced** 17–23, 39, 40, 49–50

If you finished Examples **1–7**
- **Basic** 17–42, 44–48, 52–56
- **Average** 17–48, 50, 52–56
- **Advanced** 17–56

Homework Quick Check
Quickly check key concepts.
Exercises: 18, 20, 22, 24, 27, 28, 31, 39

Teaching Tip

Science Link In **Exercise 5,** the symbol λ is the Greek letter lambda. This symbol is traditionally used by physicists to represent wavelength.

State Resources

Answers

2.

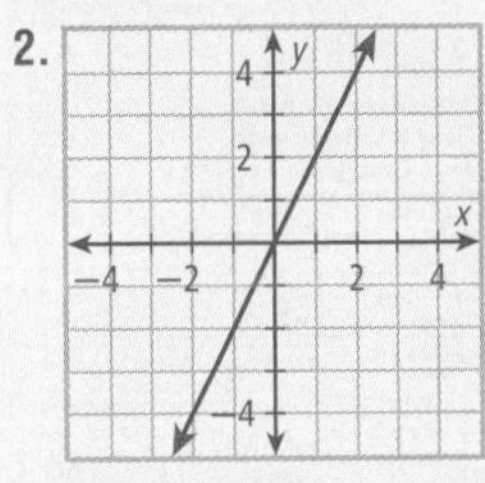

3.

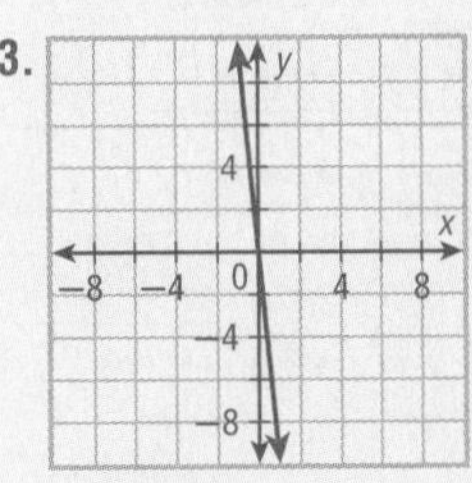

4.

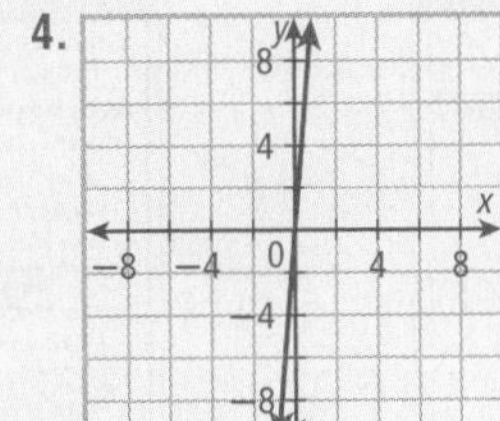

9.

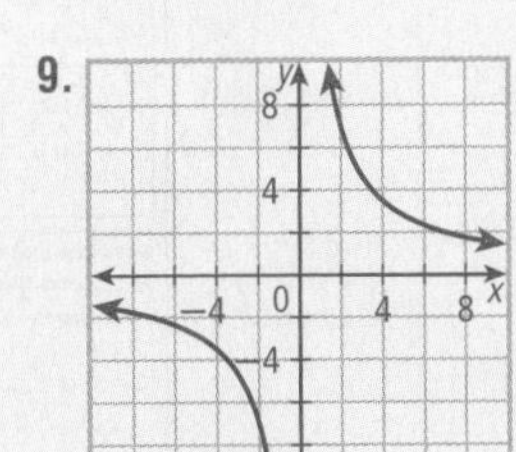

10.

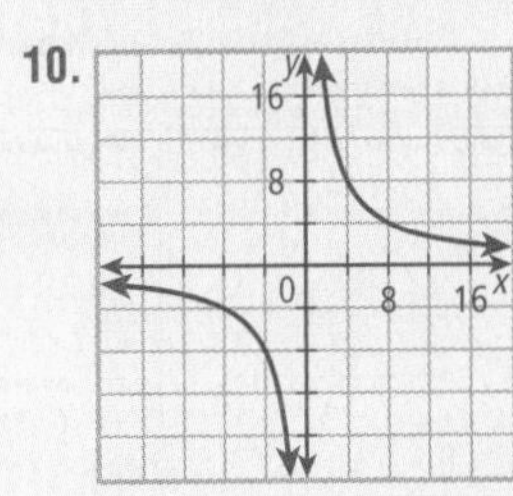

11.

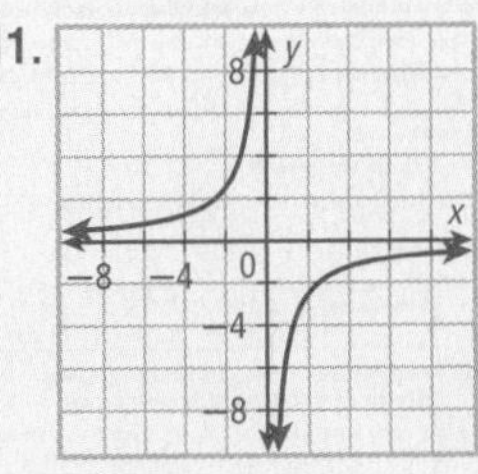

Answers

17. 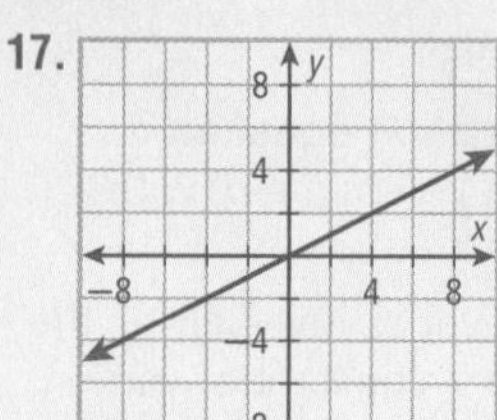

18. 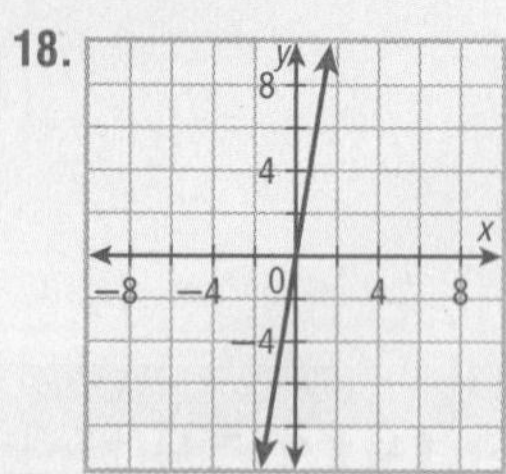

19. 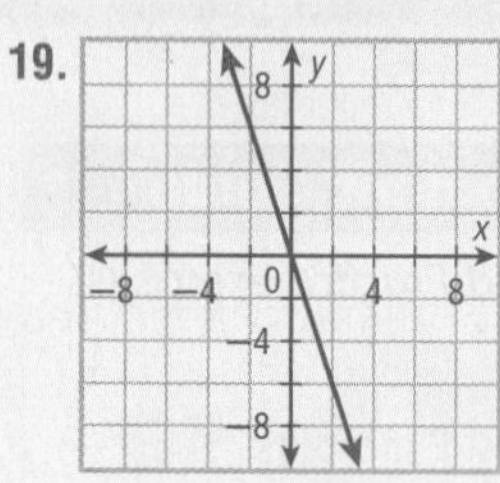

24. $y = \frac{4}{5x}$

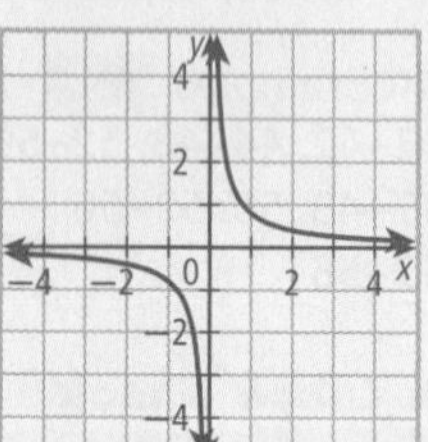

SEE EXAMPLE 7 p. 572

16. **Cars** The power P that must be delivered by a car engine varies directly as the distance d that the car moves and inversely as the time t required to move that distance. To move the car 500 m in 50 s, the engine must deliver 147 kilowatts (kW) of power. How many kilowatts must the engine deliver to move the car 700 m in 30 s? **343 kilowatts**

PRACTICE AND PROBLEM SOLVING

Independent Practice

For Exercises	See Example
17–19	1
20–21	2
22–23	3
24–26	4
27	5
28–30	6
31	7

Extra Practice

Skills Practice p. S18
Application Practice p. S39

Given: y varies directly as x. Write and graph each direct variation function.

17. $y = 4$ when $x = 8$ **$y = \frac{1}{2}x$**
18. $y = 12$ when $x = 2$ **$y = 6x$**
19. $y = -15$ when $x = 5$ **$y = -3x$**

20. **Medicine** The dosage d of a drug that a physician prescribes varies directly as the patient's mass m, and $d = 100$ mg when $m = 55$ kg. Find d to the nearest milligram when $m = 70$ kg. **127 mg**

21. **Nutrition** The number of Calories C in a horned melon varies directly as its weight w, and $C = 25$ Cal when $w = 3.5$ oz. How many Calories are in the horned melon shown on the scale? Round to the nearest Calorie. **88 Cal**

12.35 oz

22. **Agriculture** The number of bags of soybean seeds N that a farmer needs varies jointly as the number of acres a to be planted and the pounds of seed needed per acre p, and $N = 980$ when $a = 700$ acres and $p = 70$ lb/acre. Find N when $a = 1000$ acres and $p = 75$ lb/acre. **1500**

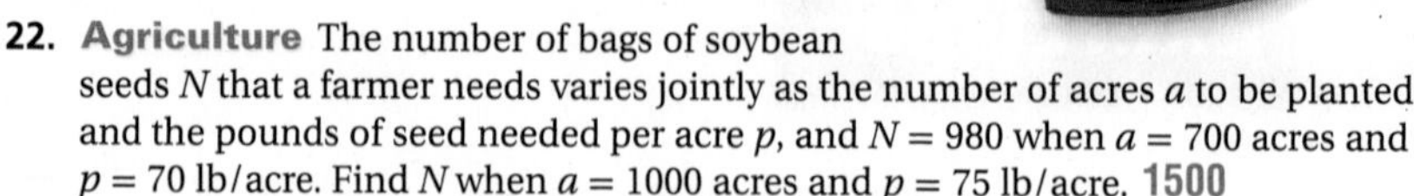

23. **Physics** The heat Q required to raise the temperature of water varies jointly as the mass m of the water and the amount of temperature change T, and $Q = 20{,}930$ joules (J) when $m = 1$ kg and $T = 5°C$. Find m when $Q = 8372$ J and $T = 10°C$. **0.2 kg**

LINK Entertainment

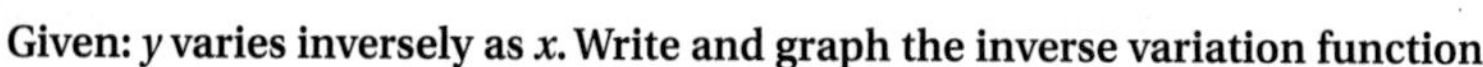

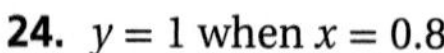

Given: y varies inversely as x. Write and graph the inverse variation function.

24. $y = 1$ when $x = 0.8$
25. $y = 1.75$ when $x = 6$
26. $y = -2$ when $x = 3$

27. **Entertainment** The number of days it takes a theater crew to set up a stage for a muscial varies inversely as the number of workers. If the stage can be set up in 3 days by 20 workers, how many days would it take if only 12 workers were available? **5 days**

Determine whether each data set represents a direct variation, an inverse variation, or neither.

28.

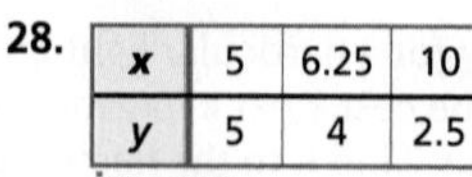

x	5	6.25	10
y	5	4	2.5

inverse

29.

x	5	7	9
y	3	5	7

neither

30.

x	8	14	24
y	12	21	36

direct

Broadway shows are plays or musicals presented in larger theaters near New York City's Times Square. In 2004, 11.3 million tickets were sold to Broadway shows for a total of almost \$750 million.

31. **Chemistry** The volume V of a gas varies inversely as the pressure P and directly as the temperature T. A certain gas has a volume of 20 L, a temperature of 320 K, and a pressure of 1 atm. If the gas is compressed to a volume of 15 L and is heated to 330 K, what will the new pressure be? **1.375 atm**

Tell whether each statement is sometimes, always, or never true.

32. Direct variation is a linear function. **always**
33. A linear function is a direct variation. **sometimes**
34. An inverse variation is a linear function. **never**
35. In a direct variation, $x = 0$ when $y = 0$. **always**
36. The graph of an inverse variation passes through the origin. **never**

8-1 PRACTICE A
8-1 PRACTICE C
8-1 PRACTICE B

Write and graph each function.

1. y varies directly as x, and $y = 30$ when $x = -6$. **$y = -5x$**
2. y varies inversely as x, and $y = 5$ when $x = 3$. **$y = \frac{15}{x}$**

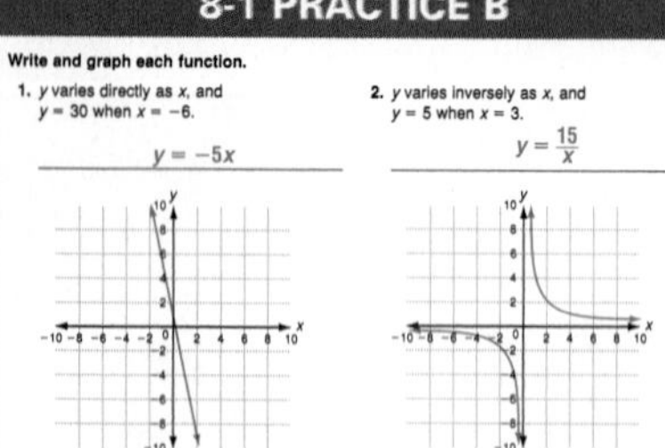

Determine whether each data set represents a direction variation, an inverse variation, or neither.

3.

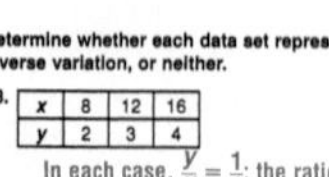

x	8	12	16
y	2	3	4

In each case, $\frac{y}{x} = \frac{1}{4}$; the ratio is constant, so this represents a direct variation.

4.

x	3	1	0.5
y	5	15	30

In each case, $xy = 15$; the product is constant, so this represents an inverse variation.

Solve.

5. The number of chaperones, c, needed for the class trip varies directly as the number of students, s, going on the trip, and $c = 7$ when $s = 56$. How many chaperones are needed if 104 students go on the class trip? **13 chaperones**

6. The owner of a bookstore developed a model for determining the price of rare comic books. The price, P, of each book should vary directly with the number of people, N, that have requested the book and inversely to the number of such books in existence, M. If $N = 10$ people, $M = 10{,}000$ copies and $P = \$5$, then find P for $N = 200$ people and $M = 100$ copies. **\$10,000**

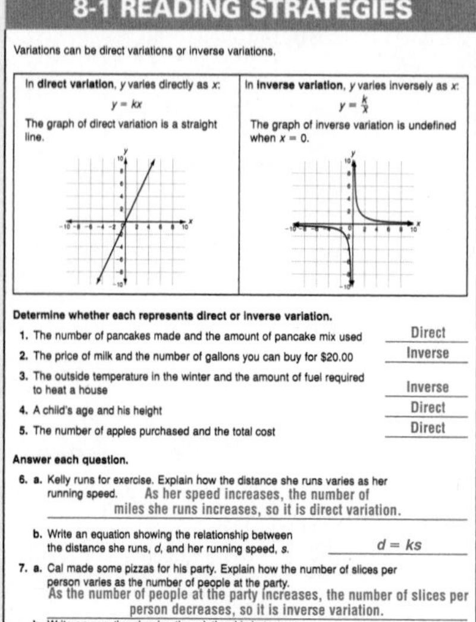

8-1 READING STRATEGIES

Variations can be direct variations or inverse variations.

In **direct variation**, y varies directly as x: $y = kx$ The graph of direct variation is a straight line.	In **inverse variation**, y varies inversely as x: $y = \frac{k}{x}$ The graph of inverse variation is undefined when $x = 0$.

Determine whether each represents direct or inverse variation.

1. The number of pancakes made and the amount of pancake mix used **Direct**
2. The price of milk and the number of gallons you can buy for \$20.00 **Inverse**
3. The outside temperature in the winter and the amount of fuel required to heat a house **Inverse**
4. A child's age and his height **Direct**
5. The number of apples purchased and the total cost **Direct**

Answer each question.

6. a. Kelly runs for exercise. Explain how the distance she runs varies as her running speed. **As her speed increases, the number of miles she runs increases, so it is direct variation.**
   b. Write an equation showing the relationship between the distance she runs, d, and her running speed, s. **$d = ks$**
7. a. Cal made some pizzas for his party. Explain how the number of slices per person varies as the number of people at the party. **As the number of people at the party increases, the number of slices per person decreases, so it is inverse variation.**
   b. Write an equation showing the relationship between the number of slices per person, p, and the number of people at the party, n. **$p = \frac{k}{n}$**

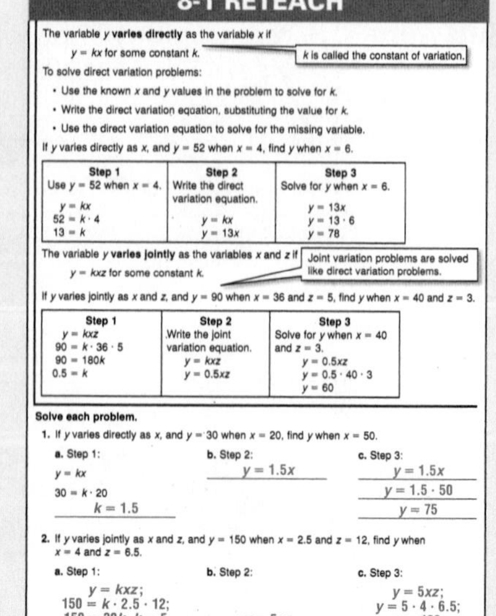

8-1 RETEACH

The variable y **varies directly** as the variable x if

$y = kx$ for some constant k. — k is called the constant of variation.

To solve direct variation problems:

- Use the known x and y values in the problem to solve for k.
- Write the direct variation eqúation, substituting the value for k.
- Use the direct variation equation to solve for the missing variable.

If y varies directly as x, and $y = 52$ when $x = 4$, find y when $x = 6$.

Step 1	Step 2	Step 3
Use $y = 52$ when $x = 4$. $y = kx$ $52 = k \cdot 4$ $13 = k$	Write the direct variation equation. $y = kx$ $y = 13x$	Solve for y when $x = 6$. $y = 13x$ $y = 13 \cdot 6$ $y = 78$

The variable y **varies jointly** as the variables x and z if

$y = kxz$ for some constant k. — Joint variation problems are solved like direct variation problems.

If y varies jointly as x and z, and $y = 90$ when $x = 36$ and $z = 5$, find y when $x = 40$ and $z = 3$.

Step 1	Step 2	Step 3
$y = kxz$ $90 = k \cdot 36 \cdot 5$ $90 = 180k$ $0.5 = k$	Write the joint variation equation. $y = kxz$ $y = 0.5xz$	Solve for y when $x = 40$ and $z = 3$. $y = 0.5xz$ $y = 0.5 \cdot 40 \cdot 3$ $y = 60$

Solve each problem.

1. If y varies directly as x, and $y = 30$ when $x = 20$, find y when $x = 50$.
   a. Step 1: $y = kx$; $30 = k \cdot 20$; **$k = 1.5$**
   b. Step 2: **$y = 1.5x$**
   c. Step 3: **$y = 1.5x$; $y = 1.5 \cdot 50$; $y = 75$**
2. If y varies jointly as x and z, and $y = 150$ when $x = 2.5$ and $z = 12$, find y when $x = 4$ and $z = 6.5$.
   a. Step 1: **$y = kxz$; $150 = k \cdot 2.5 \cdot 12$; $150 = 30k$, $k = 5$**
   b. Step 2: **$y = 5xz$**
   c. Step 3: **$y = 5xz$; $y = 5 \cdot 4 \cdot 6.5$; $y = 130$**

37. This problem will prepare you for the Multi-Step Test Prep on page 608.

In an auto race, a car with an average speed of 200 mi/h takes an average of 31.5 s to complete one lap of the track.

a. Write an inverse variation function that gives the average speed s of a car in miles per hour as a function of the time t in seconds needed to complete one lap. $s = \frac{6300}{t}$

b. How many seconds does it take the car to complete one lap at an average speed of 210 mi/h? 30 s

38. Data Collection Use a graphing calculator, a motion detector, and a light detector to measure the intensity of light as distance from the light source increases. Position the detectors next to each other. Place a flashlight in front of the detectors, and then pull the flashlight away from them. Find an appropriate model for the intensity of the light as a function of the square of the distance from the light source.

38. Answers will vary. Possible answer: $I(d) = \frac{1150}{d^2}$, where I is intensity in milliwatts per square centimeter and d is distance from the light source in centimeters

39. Multi-Step Interest earned on a certificate of deposit (CD) at a certain rate varies jointly as the principal in dollars and the time in years.

a. Diane purchased a CD for \$2500 that earned \$12.50 simple interest in 3 months. Write a variation function for this data. $I = 0.02Pt$

b. At which bank did Diane buy her CD?

c. How much interest would Diane earn in 6 months on a \$3000 CD bought from the same bank? \$30

39b. True Federal Bank

Complete each table.

40. y varies jointly as x and z.

x	y	z	
2	■	4	12
5	52.5	7	
1.5	−36	■	−16
■	1.38	23	0.04

41. y varies directly as x and inversely as z.

x	y	z	
25	13.75	4	
■	1	11	5
17	18.7	■	2
10	■	5	4.4

42. Estimation Shane swims 42 laps in 26 min 19 s. Without using a calculator, estimate how many minutes it would take Shane to swim 15 laps at the same average speed. ≈ 9 min

43. Critical Thinking Explain why only one point (x, y) is needed to write a direct variation function whose graph passes through this point.

43. Possible answer: 2 points are needed to determine a line. Since direct variations always include $(0, 0)$, only 1 other point is needed to write the equation.

44. Write About It Explain how to identify the type of variation from a list of ordered pairs. Possible answer: If the ratios of the coordinates in each ordered pair are the same, the variation is direct. If the products of the coordinates in each ordered pair are the same, the variation is inverse.

45. Which of the following would best be represented by an inverse variation function?

Ⓐ The distance traveled as a function of speed

Ⓑ The total cost as a function of the number of items purchased

Ⓒ The area of a circular swimming pool as a function of its radius

Ⓓ The number of posts in a 20-ft fence as a function of distance between posts

COMMON ERROR ALERT

Students may have difficulty graphing the inverse variation functions in **Exercises 24–26.** Remind them that the graphs will have two unconnected branches and that neither branch will cross the x- or y-axis.

Exercise 37 involves writing and using an inverse variation function that gives the average speed of a car. This exercise prepares students for the Multi-Step Test Prep on page 608.

Data Collection To help students complete **Exercise 38,** see *Technology Lab Activities.*

Inclusion To complete the tables in **Exercises 40–41,** students should start by using the completed row to find the constant of variation. Then they can use the variation functions to complete the rest of the table.

Answers

25. $y = \frac{10.5}{x}$

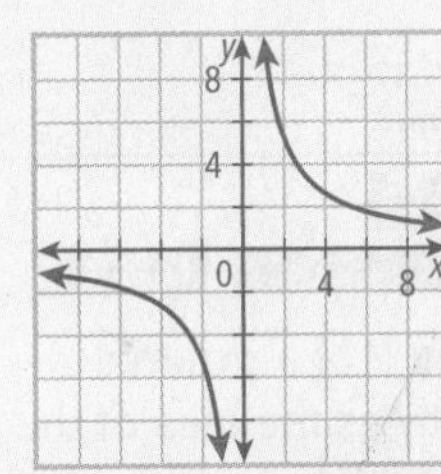

26. $y = -\frac{6}{x}$

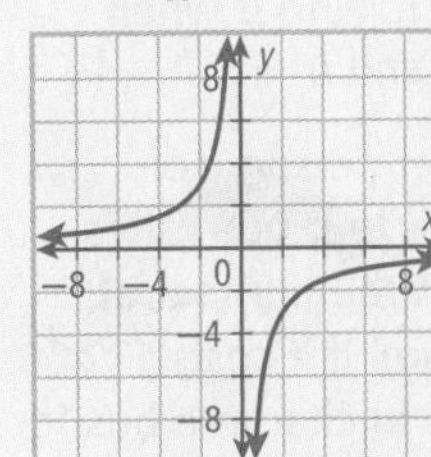

8-1 PROBLEM SOLVING

Last semester 5 of Mr. Dewayne's students built a 7-foot sailboat in 195 working hours. The time, t, that it takes for a group of students to build a sailboat varies inversely as the number of students. Mr. Dewayne uses this data to plan activities for next semester.

1. How many working hours would it take 12 students to build the same kind of sailboat?
   a. Write an equation relating the time required to the number of students working. $t = \frac{k}{s}$
   b. Find the constant k. $k = 975$
   c. Explain the meaning of k in terms of student hours. It is the total number of student hours that it takes to build a 7-foot sailboat.
   d. Solve the equation to answer the question. 81.25 h
2. How many students would be needed to build a 7-foot sailboat in 75 working hours? 13 students

Choose the letter for the best answer.

3. Which equation represents the number of hours it would take 15 students to build a 7-foot sailboat?
   A $\frac{195}{5} = \frac{t}{15}$
   B $\frac{t}{195} = \frac{15}{5}$
   Ⓒ $(195)(5) = 15t$
   D $195t = (5)(15)$
4. How many students must Mr. Dewayne get to participate in order to build a 7-foot sailboat in 65 hours?
   A 14 students
   Ⓑ 15 students
   C 16 students
   D 17 students
5. Penny sells hot dogs from a cart at the beach. Her daily income, s, varies directly as the number of hot dogs, h, that she sells, and s = \$255.50 when $h = 73$. Find h when s = \$304.50.
   A 81
   B 83
   C 85
   Ⓓ 87
6. The cost, c, of hiring a contractor to build a patio varies jointly as the area, A, in square feet, of the patio and the price, p, per square foot of the patio tiles; and c = \$2832 when $A = 80$ ft^2 and p = \$2.95. Find p when c = \$4368 and $A = 112$ ft^2.
   A \$2.95
   Ⓑ \$3.25
   C \$3.45
   D \$3.60

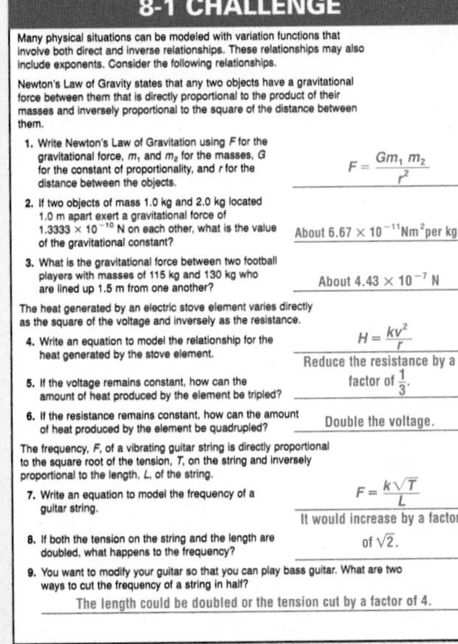

8-1 CHALLENGE

Many physical situations can be modeled with variation functions that involve both direct and inverse relationships. These relationships may also include exponents. Consider the following relationships.

Newton's Law of Gravity states that any two objects have a gravitational force between them that is directly proportional to the product of their masses and inversely proportional to the square of the distance between them.

1. Write Newton's Law of Gravitation using F for the gravitational force, m_1 and m_2 for the masses, G for the constant of proportionality, and r for the distance between the objects. $F = \frac{Gm_1 m_2}{r^2}$
2. If two objects of mass 1.0 kg and 2.0 kg located 1.0 m apart exert a gravitational force of 1.3333×10^{-10} N on each other, what is the value of the gravitational constant? About 6.67×10^{-11} Nm^2 per kg^2
3. What is the gravitational force between two football players with masses of 115 kg and 130 kg who are lined up 1.5 m from one another? About 4.43×10^{-7} N

The heat generated by an electric stove element varies directly as the square of the voltage and inversely as the resistance.

4. Write an equation to model the relationship for the heat generated by the stove element. $H = \frac{kv^2}{r}$
5. If the voltage remains constant, how can the amount of heat produced by the element be tripled? Reduce the resistance by a factor of $\frac{1}{3}$.
6. If the resistance remains constant, how can the amount of heat produced by the element be quadrupled? Double the voltage.

The frequency, F, of a vibrating guitar string is directly proportional to the square root of the tension, T, on the string and inversely proportional to the length, L, of the string.

7. Write an equation to model the frequency of a guitar string. $F = \frac{k\sqrt{T}}{L}$
8. If both the tension on the string and the length are doubled, what happens to the frequency? It would increase by a factor of $\sqrt{2}$.
9. You want to modify your guitar so that you can play bass guitar. What are two ways to cut the frequency of a string in half? The length could be doubled or the tension cut by a factor of 4.

 In **Exercise 48,** students who answered 19 or 20 may have solved the problem using direct variation instead of inverse variation.

Journal

Have students compare and contrast direct and inverse variation functions, including characteristics of the functions' graphs.

ALTERNATIVE ASSESSMENT

Have students choose formulas from a science textbook that exemplify each type of variation function covered in this lesson (direct, joint, inverse, combined). For each formula, ask them to identify the type of variation and the constant of variation and to describe the relationship between the quantities involved.

Power Presentations with PowerPoint®

8-1 Lesson Quiz

1. The volume V of a pyramid varies jointly as the area of the base B and the height h, and $V = 24$ ft^3 when $B = 12$ ft^2 and $h = 6$ ft. Find B when $V = 54$ ft^3 and $h = 9$ ft. 18 ft^2
2. The cost per person c of chartering a tour bus varies inversely as the number of passengers n. If it costs \$22.50 per person to charter a bus for 20 passengers, how much will it cost per person to charter a bus for 36 passengers? \$12.50
3. The pressure P of a gas varies inversely as its volume V and directly as the temperature T. A certain gas has a pressure of 2.7 atm, a volume of 3.6 L, and a temperature of 324 K. If the volume of the gas is kept constant and the temperature is increased to 396 K, what will the new pressure be? 3.3 atm

Also available on transparency

46. Which statement is best represented by the graph?
 Ⓕ y varies directly as x^2.
 Ⓖ y varies inversely as x.
 Ⓗ y varies directly as x.
 Ⓙ x varies inversely as y.

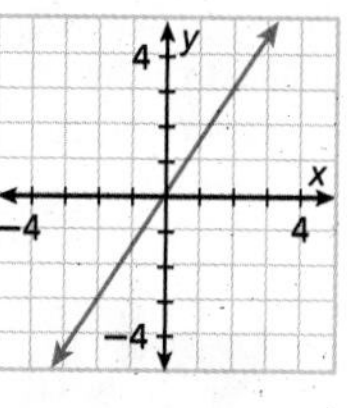

47. Which equation is best represented by the following statement: y varies directly as the square root of x?
 Ⓐ $y = \frac{k}{\sqrt{x}}$ Ⓑ $y = \frac{k}{x^2}$ Ⓒ $k = \sqrt{xy}$ Ⓓ $y = k\sqrt{x}$

48. **Gridded Response** The cost per student of a ski trip varies inversely as the number of students who attend. It will cost each student \$250 if 24 students attend. How many students would have to attend to get the cost down to \$200? **30**

CHALLENGE AND EXTEND

49. Given: y varies jointly as x and the square of z, and $y = 189$ when $x = 7$ and $z = 9$. Find y when $x = 2$ and $z = 6$. **24**

50. **Government** The number of U.S. Representatives that each state receives can be approximated with a direct variation function where the number of representatives (rounded to the nearest whole number) varies directly with the state's population.
 a. Given that Pennsylvania has 19 representatives, find k to eight decimal places and write the direct variation function.
 b. Find the number of representatives for each state shown. **FL: 25; IL: 19; MI: 15**
 c. Given that Texas had 32 U.S. representatives in the year 2000, estimate the state's population in that year. **≈ 21,000,000**

50a. $k \approx 0.00000155$; $r \approx 0.00000155p$

State Populations from the 2000 U.S. Census

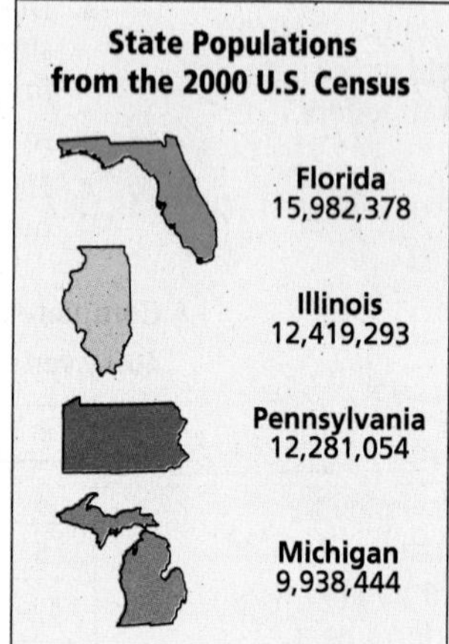

51. **Estimation** Given: y is inversely proportional to x, directly proportional to z^2, and the constant of variation is 7π. Estimate the value of y when $x = 12$ and $z = 2$. $y \approx 7$

SPIRAL REVIEW

52. **Architecture** Brad stands next to the Eiffel Tower. He is 6 ft 8 in. tall and casts a shadow of 9 ft 4 in. The Eiffel Tower is 985 ft tall. How long is the Eiffel Tower's shadow, in feet? *(Lesson 2-2)* **1379 ft**

Write an equation of the line that includes the points in the table. *(Lesson 2-4)*

53.

x	1	3	5	7	9
y	1.5	4	6.5	9	11.5

54.

x	−4	−2	0	2	4
y	10	9	8	7	6

53. $y = \frac{5}{4}x + \frac{1}{4}$
54. $y = -\frac{1}{2}x + 8$

Make a table of values, and graph the exponential function. Describe the asymptote. Tell how the graph is transformed from the graph of $f(x) = 4^x$. *(Lesson 7-7)*

55. $g(x) = \frac{1}{2}(4^x) - 2$

56. $h(x) = (4^{x-1}) + 1$

Answers

55.

x	−2	−1	0	1	2
$g(x)$	$-\frac{63}{32}$	$-\frac{15}{8}$	$-\frac{3}{2}$	0	6

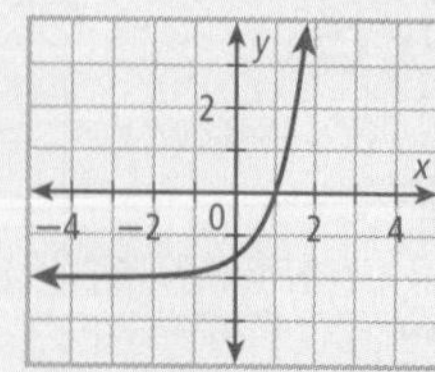

asymptote: $y = -2$; vertically compressed by a factor of $\frac{1}{2}$ and translated 2 units down

56.

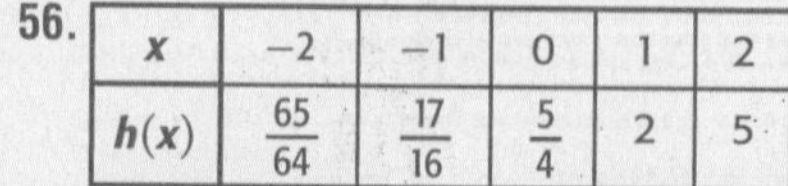

x	−2	−1	0	1	2
$h(x)$	$\frac{65}{64}$	$\frac{17}{16}$	$\frac{5}{4}$	2	5

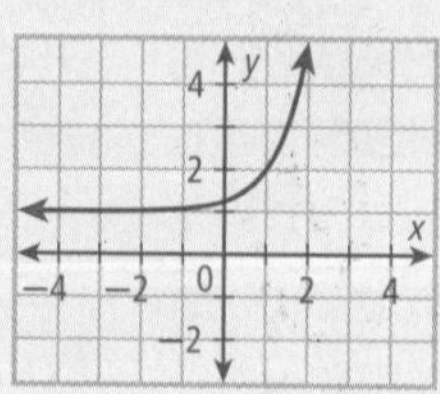

asymptote: $y = 1$; translated 1 unit right and 1 unit up

8-2 Multiplying and Dividing Rational Expressions

A2.5.2 Add, subtract, multiply, divide, reduce and evaluate rational expressions with polynomial denominators. Simplify rational expressions, including expressions...

Objectives
Simplify rational expressions.

Multiply and divide rational expressions.

Vocabulary
rational expression

... with negative exponents in the denominator

Why learn this?
You can simplify rational expressions to determine the probability of hitting an archery target. (See Exercise 35.)

In Lesson 8-1, you worked with inverse variation functions such as $y = \frac{5}{x}$. The expression on the right side of this equation is a *rational expression*. A **rational expression** is a quotient of two polynomials. Other examples of rational expressions include the following:

$$\frac{x^2 - 4}{x + 2} \qquad \frac{10}{x^2 - 6} \qquad \frac{x + 3}{x - 7}$$

Because rational expressions are ratios of polynomials, you can simplify them the same way as you simplify fractions. Recall that to write a fraction in simplest form, you can divide out common factors in the numerator and denominator.

$$\frac{9}{24} = \frac{3 \cdot \cancel{3}}{8 \cdot \cancel{3}} = \frac{3}{8}$$

EXAMPLE 1 Simplifying Rational Expressions

Simplify. Identify any x-values for which the expression is undefined.

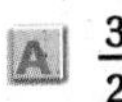

A $\frac{3x^7}{2x^4}$

$\frac{3}{2}x^{7-4} = \frac{3}{2}x^3$ *Quotient of Powers Property*

The expression is undefined at $x = 0$ because this value of x makes $2x^4$ equal 0.

B $\frac{x^2 - 2x - 3}{x^2 + 5x + 4}$

$\frac{(x-3)\cancel{(x+1)}}{\cancel{(x+1)}(x+4)} = \frac{(x-3)}{(x+4)}$ *Factor; then divide out common factors.*

The expression is undefined at $x = -1$ and $x = -4$ because these values of x make the factors $(x + 1)$ and $(x + 4)$ equal 0.

Check Substitute $x = -1$ and $x = -4$ into the original expression.

$$\frac{(-1)^2 - 2(-1) - 3}{(-1)^2 + 5(-1) + 4} = \frac{0}{0} \qquad \frac{(-4)^2 - 2(-4) - 3}{(-4)^2 + 5(-4) + 4} = \frac{21}{0}$$

Both values of x result in division by 0, which is undefined.

Caution!
When identifying values for which a rational expression is undefined, identify the values of the variable that make the original denominator equal to 0.

CHECK IT OUT! **Simplify. Identify any x-values for which the expression is undefined.**

1a. $\frac{16x^{11}}{8x^2}$ **1b.** $\frac{3x + 4}{3x^2 + x - 4}$ **1c.** $\frac{6x^2 + 7x + 2}{6x^2 - 5x - 6}$

1a. $2x^9$; $x \neq 0$

1b. $\frac{1}{x - 1}$; $x \neq -\frac{4}{3}$ and $x \neq 1$

1c. $\frac{(2x + 1)}{(2x - 3)}$; $x \neq -\frac{2}{3}$ and $x \neq \frac{3}{2}$

8-2 Organizer

Pacing: Traditional 1 day
Block $\frac{1}{2}$ day

Objectives: Simplify rational expressions.

Multiply and divide rational expressions.

Online Edition
Tutorial Videos, TechKeys

Countdown to Testing Week 17

Power Presentations with PowerPoint®

Warm Up

Simplify each expression. Assume all variables are nonzero.

1. $x^5 \cdot x^2$ x^7 **2.** $y^3 \cdot y^3$ y^6

3. $\frac{x^6}{x^2}$ x^4 **4.** $\frac{y^2}{y^5}$ $\frac{1}{y^3}$

Factor each expression.

5. $x^2 - 2x - 8$ $(x - 4)(x + 2)$

6. $x^2 - 5x$ $x(x - 5)$

7. $x^5 - 9x^3$ $x^3(x - 3)(x + 3)$

Also available on transparency

Math Humor

Q: Why did the doctor send the expression to a psychiatrist?

A: Because it wasn't rational.

1 Introduce

EXPLORATION

8-2 Multiplying and Dividing Rational Expressions

A is a quotient of two polynomials. You can multiply and divide rational expressions much like you would multiply and divide fractions.

Find each product. Simplify if necessary.

1. $\frac{1}{3} \cdot \frac{2}{3}$ 2. $\frac{3}{10} \cdot \frac{5}{6}$

3. List the steps you used to multiply the fractions.

Find each product by using the steps you listed in Problem 3. Assume that $x \neq 0$.

4. $\frac{2}{5} \cdot \frac{3}{x}$ 5. $\frac{x}{8} \cdot \frac{y}{x}$

Find each quotient. Simplify if necessary.

6. $\frac{7}{10} \div \frac{1}{2}$ 7. $\frac{3}{4} \div \frac{9}{16}$

8. List the steps you used to divide the fractions.

Find each quotient by using the steps you listed in Problem 8. Assume that $x \neq 0$.

9. $\frac{4}{x} \div \frac{2}{3}$ 10. $\frac{y}{x} \div \frac{3}{x}$

THINK AND DISCUSS

11. **Discuss** how to multiply and divide rational expressions.

Motivate

Ask students to explain the steps needed to multiply fractions such as $\frac{5}{8}$ and $\frac{1}{5}$. Then have students discuss how they would multiply the fractions if the number 5 in each fraction were replaced by the expression $x + 5$. Explain that in this lesson students will learn to multiply and divide fractions that have algebraic expressions in the numerator and denominator.

Explorations and answers are provided in the *Explorations* binder.

State Resources

go.hrw.com
State Resources Online
KEYWORD: MB7 Resources

Power Presentations with PowerPoint®

Additional Examples

Example 1

Simplify. Identify any x-values for which the expression is undefined.

A. $\dfrac{10x^8}{6x^4}$ $\quad \dfrac{5}{3}x^4;\ x \neq 0$

B. $\dfrac{x^2+x-2}{x^2+2x-3}$ $\quad \dfrac{x+2}{x+3};\ x \neq -3, 1$

Example 2

Simplify $\frac{4x-x^2}{x^2-2x-8}$. Identify any x-values for which the expression is undefined. $\quad \dfrac{-x}{x+2};\ x \neq -2, 4$

Example 3

Multiply. Assume that all expressions are defined.

A. $\dfrac{3x^5y^3}{2x^3y^7} \cdot \dfrac{10x^3y^4}{9x^2y^5}$ $\quad \dfrac{5x^3}{3y^5}$

B. $\dfrac{x-3}{4x+20} \cdot \dfrac{x+5}{x^2-9}$ $\quad \dfrac{1}{4(x+3)}$

Also available on transparency

INTERVENTION

Questioning Strategies

EXAMPLE 1

- How do you know which values of the variable make the expression undefined?

EXAMPLE 2

- When might you want to factor out -1?

EXAMPLE 3

- Why should you factor the numerators and the denominators before you multiply?

Technology In **Example 2,** remind students that they can access the table feature of their graphing calculators by pressing **2nd** **TABLE.** Point out that the entry **ERROR** appears in the table for values of x that make the functions **Y1** or **Y2** undefined.

EXAMPLE 2 Simplifying by Factoring −1

Simplify $\frac{2x-x^2}{x^2-x-2}$. Identify any x-values for which the expression is undefined.

$\dfrac{-1(x^2-2x)}{x^2-x-2}$ — *Factor out −1 in the numerator so that x^2 is positive, and reorder the terms.*

$\dfrac{-1(x)\cancel{(x-2)}}{\cancel{(x-2)}(x+1)}$ — *Factor the numerator and denominator. Divide out common factors.*

$\dfrac{-x}{x+1}$ — *Simplify.*

The expression is undefined at $x = 2$ and $x = -1$.

Check The calculator screens suggest that $\frac{2x-x^2}{x^2-x-2} = \frac{-x}{x+1}$ except when $x = 2$ or $x = -1$.

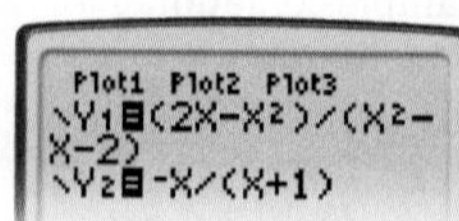

Simplify. Identify any x-values for which the expression is undefined.

2a. $\dfrac{10-2x}{x-5}$ $\quad -2;\ x \neq 5$

2b. $\dfrac{-x^2+3x}{2x^2-7x+3}$ $\quad \dfrac{-x}{2x-1};\ x \neq 3$ and $x \neq \dfrac{1}{2}$

You can multiply rational expressions the same way that you multiply fractions.

Multiplying Rational Expressions
1. Factor all numerators and denominators completely.
2. Divide out common factors of the numerators and denominators.
3. Multiply numerators. Then multiply denominators.
4. Be sure the numerator and denominator have no common factors other than 1.

EXAMPLE 3 Multiplying Rational Expressions

Multiply. Assume that all expressions are defined.

A $\dfrac{2x^4y^5}{3x^2} \cdot \dfrac{15x^2}{8x^3y^2}$

$\dfrac{\cancel{2}x^{\cancel{4}\,1}y^{\cancel{5}\,3}}{\cancel{3}\cancel{x^2}} \cdot \dfrac{{}^5\cancel{15}\cancel{x^2}}{{}_4\cancel{8}\cancel{x^3}\cancel{y^2}}$

$\dfrac{5xy^3}{4}$

B $\dfrac{x+2}{3x+12} \cdot \dfrac{x+4}{x^2-4}$

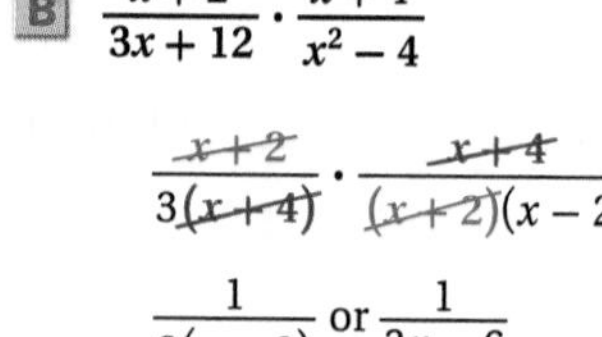

$\dfrac{\cancel{x+2}}{3\cancel{(x+4)}} \cdot \dfrac{\cancel{x+4}}{\cancel{(x+2)}(x-2)}$

$\dfrac{1}{3(x-2)}$ or $\dfrac{1}{3x-6}$

Multiply. Assume that all expressions are defined.

3a. $\dfrac{x}{15} \cdot \dfrac{x^7}{2x} \cdot \dfrac{20}{x^4}$ $\quad \dfrac{2x^3}{3}$

3b. $\dfrac{10x-40}{x^2-6x+8} \cdot \dfrac{x+3}{5x+15}$ $\quad \dfrac{2}{x-2}$

2 Teach

Guided Instruction

Before introducing operations with rational expressions, make sure that students can simplify rational expressions by dividing out common factors. Lead students to make connections between the processes of multiplying and dividing numerical fractions and the processes of multiplying and dividing rational expressions.

Reaching All Learners

Through Visual Cues

When students simplify rational expressions, suggest that they highlight each different factor in the numerator and denominator with a different color by using highlighters or colored pencils. Colored pencils can be found in the Manipulatives Kit (MK). This process can help them keep track of common factors, as shown below.

$$\frac{x^2(x+1)(x-2)^2}{x(x+3)(x+1)} = \frac{x(x-2)^2}{(x+3)}$$

You can also divide rational expressions. Recall that to divide by a fraction, you multiply by its reciprocal. $\frac{1}{2} \div \frac{3}{4} = \frac{1}{2} \cdot \frac{4^2}{3} = \frac{2}{3}$

EXAMPLE 4 Dividing Rational Expressions

Divide. Assume that all expressions are defined.

A $\frac{4x^3}{9x^2y} \div \frac{16}{9y^5}$

$\frac{4x^3}{9x^2y} \cdot \frac{9y^5}{16}$ *Rewrite as multiplication by the reciprocal.*

$\frac{4x^{3\,1}}{9x^2y} \cdot \frac{9y^{5\,4}}{16_4}$

$\frac{xy^4}{4}$

B $\frac{x^5 - 4x^3}{x^2 - x - 2} \div \frac{x^5 - x^4 - 2x^3}{x^2 - 1}$

$\frac{x^5 - 4x^3}{x^2 - x - 2} \cdot \frac{x^2 - 1}{x^5 - x^4 - 2x^3}$

$\frac{x^3(x^2 - 4)}{x^2 - x - 2} \cdot \frac{x^2 - 1}{x^3(x^2 - x - 2)}$

$\frac{x^3(x-2)(x+2)}{(x-2)(x+1)} \cdot \frac{(x-1)(x+1)}{x^3(x-2)(x+1)}$

$\frac{(x+2)(x-1)}{(x+1)(x-2)}$ or $\frac{x^2 + x - 2}{x^2 - x - 2}$

CHECK IT OUT! Divide. Assume that all expressions are defined.

4a. $\frac{x^2}{4} \div \frac{x^4y}{12y^2}$ $\frac{3y}{x^2}$

4b. $\frac{2x^2 - 7x - 4}{x^2 - 9} \div \frac{4x^2 - 1}{8x^2 - 28x + 12}$ $\frac{4(x-4)}{x+3}$

EXAMPLE 5 Solving Simple Rational Equations

Solve. Check your solution.

A $\frac{x^2 - 9}{x + 3} = 7$

$\frac{(x-3)(x+3)}{x+3} = 7$ *Note that $x \neq -3$.*

$x - 3 = 7$

$x = 10$

Check

$\frac{x^2 - 9}{x+3}$	$= 7$
$\frac{(10)^2 - 9}{10 + 3}$	7
$\frac{91}{13}$	7
7	7 ✓

B $\frac{x^2 + 3x - 4}{x - 1} = 5$

$\frac{(x-1)(x+4)}{x-1} = 5$ *Note that $x \neq 1$.*

$x + 4 = 5$

$x = 1$

Because the left side of the original equation is undefined when $x = 1$, there is no solution.

Check A graphing calculator shows that 1 is not a solution.

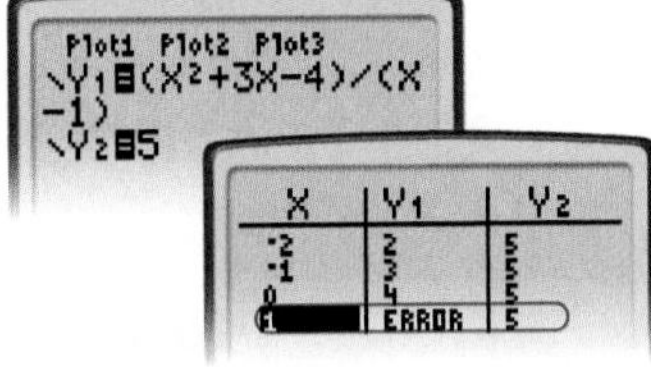

Caution!

As you simplify a rational expression, take note of values that must be excluded. The excluded values are those that make the rational expression undefined.

CHECK IT OUT! Solve. Check your solution.

5a. $\frac{x^2 + x - 12}{x + 4} = -7$ no solution

5b. $\frac{4x^2 - 9}{(2x + 3)} = 5$ 4

3 Close

Summarize

Ask students to list the steps they would use to multiply two rational expressions and the steps they would use to divide two rational expressions. Possible answer: To multiply, factor the expressions, divide out common factors, multiply numerators, and multiply denominators. To divide, multiply by the reciprocal of the divisor. Suggest that students list these steps on flash cards and that they make additional flash cards as they learn new operations.

ONGOING ASSESSMENT and INTERVENTION

Diagnose **Before** the Lesson
8-2 Warm Up, TE p. 577

Monitor **During** the Lesson
Check It Out! Exercises, SE pp. 577–579
Questioning Strategies, TE pp. 578–579

Assess **After** the Lesson
8-2 Lesson Quiz, TE p. 582
Alternative Assessment, TE p. 582

COMMON ERROR ALERT

Students sometimes forget that when all of the factors in the numerator (or denominator) divide out, as in **Example 3B,** the numerator (or denominator) becomes 1, not 0. A numerical example may help them to realize this. For instance, they know that $\frac{6}{12}$ simplifies to $\frac{1}{2}$, not to $\frac{0}{2}$.

Power Presentations with PowerPoint®

Additional Examples

Example 4

Divide. Assume that all expressions are defined.

A. $\frac{5x^4}{8x^2y^2} \div \frac{15}{8y^5}$ $\frac{x^2y^3}{3}$

B. $\frac{x^4 - 9x^2}{x^2 - 4x + 3} \div \frac{x^4 + 2x^3 - 8x^2}{x^2 - 16}$ $\frac{(x+3)(x-4)}{(x-1)(x-2)}$

Example 5

Solve. Check your solution.

A. $\frac{x^2 - 25}{x - 5} = 14$ $x = 9$

B. $\frac{x^2 + 3x - 10}{x - 2} = 7$ no solution

Also available on transparency

INTERVENTION
Questioning Strategies

EXAMPLE 4

- How do you find the reciprocal of a rational expression?

EXAMPLE 5

- Why must you check your solutions when you solve rational equations?

Teaching Tip **Reading Math** In **Examples 3** and **4,** discuss with students the meaning of the statement "Assume that all expressions are defined." Explain that when this direction line is given, students do not need to worry about identifying values of the variables that make the expressions undefined.

Answers to *Think and Discuss*

Possible answers:

1. Set the denominator of the unsimplified expression equal to 0, and solve.
2. Solving a rational equation may produce extraneous solutions.
3. See p. A9.

THINK AND DISCUSS

1. Explain how you find undefined values for a rational expression.
2. Explain why it is important to check solutions to rational equations.

3. **GET ORGANIZED** Copy and complete the graphic organizer. In each box, write a worked-out example.

	Numerical Fractions	Rational Expressions
Simplifying		
Multiplying		
Dividing		

8-2 Exercises

Assignment Guide

Assign *Guided Practice* exercises as necessary.

If you finished Examples **1–3**
- **Basic** 18–27, 36–37
- **Average** 18–27, 36–37
- **Advanced** 18–27, 36–37, 50–51

If you finished Examples **1–5**
- **Basic** 18–41, 43–49, 54–59
- **Average** 18–49, 52, 54–59
- **Advanced** 18–44, 46–59

Homework Quick Check
Quickly check key concepts.
Exercises: 18, 22, 24, 28, 32, 43

Teaching Tip

Inclusion For **Exercises 21–23,** encourage students to check the sign of the leading coefficient in the numerator and denominator. If the leading coefficient is negative, suggest that students factor out −1 before they factor the expression further.

State Resources

8-2 Exercises

go.hrw.com
Homework Help Online
KEYWORD: MB7 8-2
Parent Resources Online
KEYWORD: MB7 Parent

GUIDED PRACTICE

1. **Vocabulary** How can you tell if an algebraic expression is a *rational expression*?
Possible answer: A rational expression is the quotient of 2 polynomials.

SEE EXAMPLE 1 p. 577

Simplify. Identify any x-values for which the expression is undefined.

2. $\dfrac{4x^6}{2x-6}$ $\quad \dfrac{2x^6}{x-3}; x \neq 3$
3. $\dfrac{6x^2+13x-5}{6x^2-23x+7}$
4. $\dfrac{x+4}{3x^2+11x-4}$

SEE EXAMPLE 2 p. 578

5. $\dfrac{-x-4}{x^2-x-20}$
6. $\dfrac{6x^2+7x-3}{-3x^2+x}$
7. $\dfrac{6x^3+6x}{x^2+1}$

SEE EXAMPLE 3 p. 578

Multiply. Assume that all expressions are defined.

8. $\dfrac{x-2}{2x-3} \cdot \dfrac{4x-6}{x^2-4}$ $\quad \dfrac{2}{x+2}$
9. $\dfrac{x-2}{x-3} \cdot \dfrac{2x-6}{x+5}$ $\quad \dfrac{2(x-2)}{(x+5)}$
10. $\dfrac{x^2-16}{x^2-4x+4} \cdot \dfrac{x-2}{x^2+6x+8}$ $\quad$ 10. $\dfrac{x-4}{(x+2)(x-2)}$

SEE EXAMPLE 4 p. 579

Divide. Assume that all expressions are defined.

11. $\dfrac{x^5y^4}{3xy} \div \dfrac{1}{x^3y}$ $\quad \dfrac{x^7y^4}{3}$
12. $\dfrac{x+3}{x^2-2x+1} \div \dfrac{x+3}{x-1}$ $\quad \dfrac{1}{x-1}$
13. $\dfrac{x^2-25}{2x^2+5x-12} \div \dfrac{x^2-3x-10}{x^2+9x+20}$
14. $\dfrac{x^2+2x+1}{x^2-3x-18} \div \dfrac{x^2-1}{x^2-7x+6}$ $\quad \dfrac{x+1}{x+3}$

SEE EXAMPLE 5 p. 579

Solve. Check your solution.

15. $\dfrac{16x^2-9}{4x+3} = -6$ $\quad$ no solution
16. $\dfrac{2x^2+7x-15}{2x-3} = 10$ $\quad 5$
17. $\dfrac{x^2-4}{x-2} = 1$ $\quad -1$

PRACTICE AND PROBLEM SOLVING

Simplify. Identify any x-values for which the expression is undefined.

18. $\dfrac{4x-8}{x^2-2x}$
19. $\dfrac{8x-4}{2x^2+9x-5}$
20. $\dfrac{x^2-36}{x^2-12x+36}$ $\quad$ 20. $\dfrac{x+6}{x-6}; x \neq 6$
21. $\dfrac{3x+18}{24-2x-x^2}$ $\quad \dfrac{-3}{x-4}; x \neq -6$ and $x \neq 4$
22. $\dfrac{-2x^2-9x}{4x^2-81}$ $\quad \dfrac{-x}{2x-9}; x \neq -\dfrac{9}{2}$ and $x \neq \dfrac{9}{2}$
23. $\dfrac{4x+20}{-5-x}$ $\quad -4; x \neq -5$

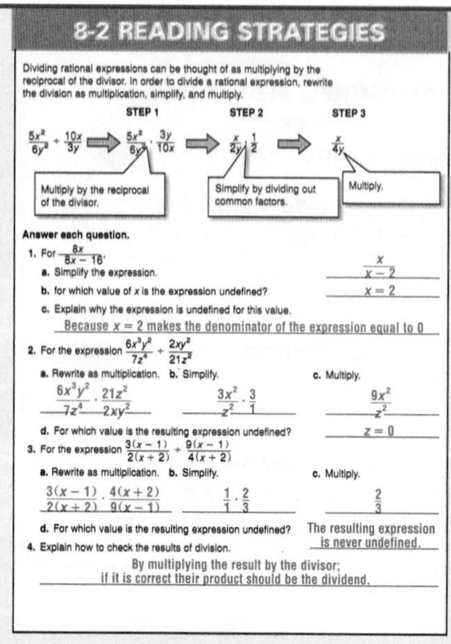

8-2 READING STRATEGIES

Dividing rational expressions can be thought of as multiplying by the reciprocal of the divisor. In order to divide a rational expression, rewrite the division as multiplication, simplify, and multiply.

STEP 1 $\quad$ STEP 2 $\quad$ STEP 3

$\dfrac{5x^2}{6y^2} \div \dfrac{10x}{3y} \Rightarrow \dfrac{5x^2}{6y^2} \cdot \dfrac{3y}{10x} \Rightarrow \dfrac{x}{2y} \cdot \dfrac{1}{2} \Rightarrow \dfrac{x}{4y}$

Multiply by the reciprocal of the divisor.

Simplify by dividing out common factors.

Multiply.

Answer each question.

1. For $\dfrac{8x}{8x-16}$,
   a. Simplify the expression. $\quad \dfrac{x}{x-2}$
   b. for which value of x is the expression undefined? $\quad x = 2$
   c. Explain why the expression is undefined for this value.
   Because $x = 2$ makes the denominator of the expression equal to 0
2. For the expression $\dfrac{6x^3y^2}{7z^4} \div \dfrac{2xy^2}{21z^2}$
   a. Rewrite as multiplication. $\quad \dfrac{6x^3y^2}{7z^4} \cdot \dfrac{21z^2}{2xy^2}$
   b. Simplify. $\quad \dfrac{3x^2}{z^2} \cdot \dfrac{3}{1}$
   c. Multiply. $\quad \dfrac{9x^2}{z^2}$
   d. For which value is the resulting expression undefined? $\quad z = 0$
3. For the expression $\dfrac{3(x-1)}{2(x+2)} \div \dfrac{9(x-1)}{4(x+2)}$
   a. Rewrite as multiplication. $\quad \dfrac{3(x-1)}{2(x+2)} \cdot \dfrac{4(x+2)}{9(x-1)}$
   b. Simplify. $\quad \dfrac{1}{1} \cdot \dfrac{2}{3}$
   c. Multiply. $\quad \dfrac{2}{3}$
   d. For which value is the resulting expression undefined? $\quad$ The resulting expression is never undefined.
4. Explain how to check the results of division.
   By multiplying the result by the divisor; if it is correct their product should be the dividend.

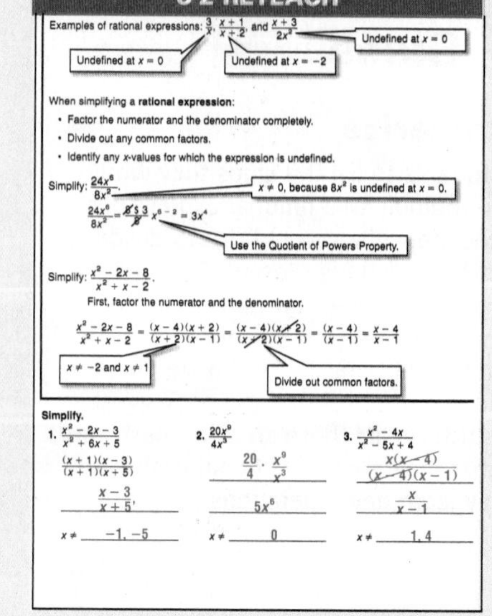

8-2 RETEACH

Examples of rational expressions: $\dfrac{3}{x}$, $\dfrac{x+1}{x+2}$, and $\dfrac{x+3}{2x^2}$

Undefined at $x = 0$ $\quad$ Undefined at $x = -2$ $\quad$ Undefined at $x = 0$

When simplifying a **rational expression**:

- Factor the numerator and the denominator completely.
- Divide out any common factors.
- Identify any x-values for which the expression is undefined.

Simplify: $\dfrac{24x^6}{8x^2}$. $\quad x \neq 0$, because $8x^2$ is undefined at $x = 0$.

$\dfrac{24x^6}{8x^2} = \dfrac{8 \cdot 3}{8} x^{6-2} = 3x^4$ $\quad$ Use the Quotient of Powers Property.

Simplify: $\dfrac{x^2-2x-8}{x^2+x-2}$.

First, factor the numerator and the denominator.

$\dfrac{x^2-2x-8}{x^2+x-2} = \dfrac{(x-4)(x+2)}{(x+2)(x-1)} = \dfrac{(x-4)(x+2)}{(x+2)(x-1)} = \dfrac{(x-4)}{(x-1)} = \dfrac{x-4}{x-1}$

$x \neq -2$ and $x \neq 1$ $\quad$ Divide out common factors.

Simplify.

1. $\dfrac{x^2-2x-3}{x^2+6x+5}$ $\quad \dfrac{(x+1)(x-3)}{(x+1)(x+5)}$ $\quad \dfrac{x-3}{x+5}$, $\quad x \neq -1, -5$
2. $\dfrac{20x^9}{4x^3}$ $\quad \dfrac{20}{4} \cdot \dfrac{x^9}{x^3}$ $\quad 5x^6$ $\quad x \neq 0$
3. $\dfrac{x^2-4x}{x^2-5x+4}$ $\quad \dfrac{x(x-4)}{(x-4)(x-1)}$ $\quad \dfrac{x}{x-1}$ $\quad x \neq 1, 4$

Independent Practice	
For Exercises	See Example
18–20	1
21–23	2
24–27	3
28–31	4
32–34	5

Extra Practice
Skills Practice p. S18
Application Practice p. S39

Multiply. Assume that all expressions are defined.

24. $\frac{x^2y}{4xy} \cdot \frac{x}{6} \cdot \frac{3y^5}{x^4}$ $\frac{y^5}{8x^2}$

25. $\frac{x-4}{x-3} \cdot \frac{2x-1}{x+4}$ $\frac{(x-4)(2x-1)}{(x-3)(x+4)}$

26. $\frac{x^2-2x-8}{9x^2-16} \cdot \frac{3x^2+10x+8}{x^2-16}$

27. $\frac{4x^2-20x+25}{x^2-4x} \cdot \frac{3x-12}{2x-5}$ $\frac{3(2x-5)}{x}$

Divide. Assume that all expressions are defined.

28. $\frac{4x^2+15x+9}{8x^2+10x+3} \div \frac{x^2+4x}{2x+1}$ $\frac{x+3}{x(x+4)}$

29. $\frac{x^2-4x-5}{x^2-3x+2} \div \frac{x^2-3x-10}{x^2-4}$ $\frac{x+1}{x-1}$

30. $\frac{x+2}{x-4} \div \frac{1}{3x-12}$ $3x+6$

31. $\frac{x^2-2x-3}{x^2-x-2} \div \frac{x^2+2x-15}{x^2+x-6}$ $\frac{x+3}{x+5}$

Solve. Check your solution.

32. $\frac{3x^2+10x+8}{-x-2} = -2$ $-\frac{2}{3}$

33. $\frac{x^2-9}{x-3} = 5$ 2

34. $\frac{x^2+3x-28}{(x+7)(x-4)} = -11$ no solution

LINK

Archery

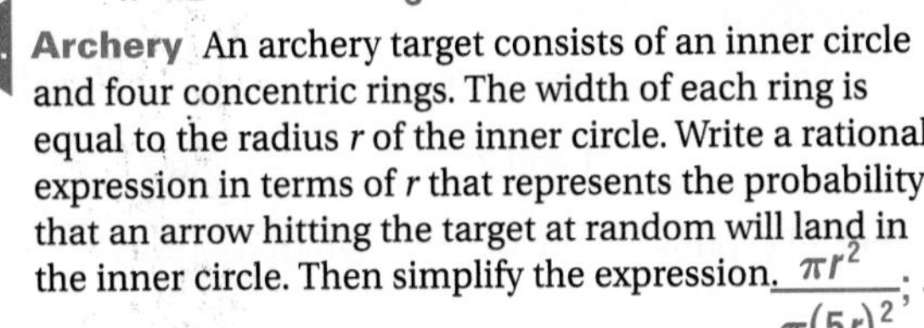

Archery was practiced in ancient times on every inhabited continent except Australia. The painting in the photo above dates from about 1400 B.C.E. and shows archers from ancient Egypt.

35. **Archery** An archery target consists of an inner circle and four concentric rings. The width of each ring is equal to the radius r of the inner circle. Write a rational expression in terms of r that represents the probability that an arrow hitting the target at random will land in the inner circle. Then simplify the expression. $\frac{\pi r^2}{\pi(5r)^2}$; $\frac{1}{25}$

Multiply or divide. Assume that all expressions are defined.

36. $\frac{2x}{3} \cdot \frac{x^3}{6x-8}$ $\frac{x^4}{3(3x-4)}$

37. $\frac{4x^2-3x}{4x^2-1} \cdot \frac{2x+1}{x}$ $\frac{4x-3}{2x-1}$

38. $\frac{1}{25x^2-49} \div \frac{x}{10x-14}$ $\frac{2}{x(5x+7)}$

39. $2xy \cdot \frac{2x^2}{y} \cdot \frac{y^2}{2x}$ $2x^2y^2$

40. $\frac{14x^4}{xy} \cdot \frac{x^3}{6y^3} \div \frac{5x^2}{12y^5}$ $\frac{28x^4y}{5}$

41. $(y+4) \div \frac{4x+4+xy+y}{3}$ $\frac{3}{x+1}$

42. **Critical Thinking** What polynomial completes the equation $\frac{x-5}{x-2} \cdot \frac{■}{x-5} = x+1$?

43. **Geometry** Use the table to determine the following.

a. For each figure, find the ratio of the volume to the area of the base.

b. For each figure, find the ratio of the surface area to the volume.

	Square Prism	Cylinder
Area of Base	s^2	πr^2
Volume	s^2h	πr^2h
Surface Area	$2s^2 + 4sh$	$2\pi r^2 + 2\pi rh$

c. **What if...?** If the radius and the height of a cylinder were doubled, what effect would this have on the ratio of the cylinder's surface area to its volume? The ratio would be reduced by a factor of $\frac{1}{2}$.

43a. square prism: $\frac{h}{1}$; cylinder: $\frac{h}{1}$

43b. square prism: $\frac{2s+4h}{sh}$; cylinder: $\frac{2r+2h}{rh}$

MULTI-STEP TEST PREP

44. This problem will prepare you for the Multi-Step Test Prep on page 608.

For a car moving with initial speed v_0 and acceleration a, the distance d that the car travels in time t is given by $d = v_0t + \frac{1}{2}at^2$.

a. Write a rational expression in terms of t for the average speed of the car during a period of acceleration. Simplify the expression.

b. During a race, a driver accelerates for 3 s at a rate of 10 ft/s² in order to pass another car. The driver's initial speed was 264 ft/s. What was the driver's average speed during the acceleration? 279 ft/s

COMMON ERROR ALERT

Students often list only the values that make the simplest form of a rational expression undefined. In **Exercises 18–23,** stress the importance of recording all of the values for which the *original* expression is undefined.

Teaching Tip

Probability In **Exercise 35,** remind students how to determine probability by using geometric figures. Point out that the probability that the arrow will hit the inner circle is the ratio of the area of the inner circle to the area of the entire target.

MULTI-STEP TEST PREP **Exercise 44** involves simplifying and evaluating a rational expression for the average speed of a car during acceleration. This exercise prepares students for the Multi-Step Test Prep on page 608.

Answers

3–5. See p. A36.

6. $\frac{2x+3}{-x}$; $x \neq 0$ and $x \neq \frac{1}{3}$

7. $6x$; defined for all real values of x

13. $\frac{(x+5)^2}{(2x-3)(x+2)}$

18. $\frac{4}{x}$; $x \neq 0$ and $x \neq 2$

19. $\frac{4}{x+5}$; $x \neq \frac{1}{2}$ and $x \neq -5$

26. $\frac{(x+2)^2}{(3x-4)(x+4)}$

42. $x^2 - x - 2$

44a. $\frac{v_0t + \frac{1}{2}at^2}{t} = v_0 + \frac{1}{2}at$

8-2 PROBLEM SOLVING

Anders designs a running field that consists of three concentric tracks as shown in the diagram.

5 meters; T_1; T_2; T_3; r_1

1. How do the lengths of each track compare?

a. Write an equation for the length of the inner track, T_1, in terms of radius, r_1. $T_1 = 2\pi r_1$

b. Write an equation for the length of the middle track, T_2, in terms of radius r_1. $T_2 = 2\pi(r_1 + 5)$

c. Then write a rational expression for the ratio of the length of track T_2 to the length of track T_1 in terms of radius r_1. $\frac{r_1+5}{r_1}$

2. Mari writes the expression $\frac{(r_1+10)(r_1-5)}{r_1^2-25}$ for the ratio of the length of the outer track, T_3, to that of the middle track, T_2. Anders thinks that is the wrong expression. Simplify Mari's expression to determine if she is correct. Explain.

$\frac{(r_1+10)(r_1-5)}{(r_1^2-25)} = \frac{(r_1+10)(r_1-5)}{(r_1+5)(r_1-5)} = \frac{r_1+10}{r_1+5}$; Mari is correct.

3. Anders sets the radius of the inner track, T_1, at 70 meters.

a. How many times longer is the middle track, T_2, than the inner track, T_1? $\frac{T_2}{T_1} = 1.071$

b. How many times longer is the outer track, T_3, than the middle track, T_2? $\frac{T_3}{T_2} = 1.067$

c. How many times longer is the outer track, T_3, than the inner track, T_1? $\frac{T_3}{T_1} = 1.143$

Choose the letter for the best answer.

4. How many times as large is the area enclosed by the outer track, T_3, than the area enclosed by the inner track, T_1?

A $\left(\frac{10}{r_1}\right)$ B $\left(\frac{10}{r_1}\right)^2$ C $\left(\frac{r_1+10}{r_1}\right)$ (D) $\left(\frac{r_1+10}{r_1}\right)^2$

5. What is the ratio of the area between the inner track and the outer track to the area enclosed by the inner track?

(A) $20\left(\frac{r_1+5}{r_1^2}\right)$ B $\frac{(r_1+10)^2-1}{r_1^2}$ C $\pi\left(\frac{r_1+10}{r_1}\right)^2$ D $\pi\left(\frac{10}{r_1}\right)^2$

8-2 CHALLENGE

The process of multiplying and dividing rational expressions requires an understanding of the process of factoring. The following exercises will challenge some of your factoring skills. Remember to follow all factoring rules. Assume all expressions are defined.

1. Simplify the rational expression. $\frac{x^{3y}+4x^{2y}-3x^y-12}{x^y+4}$ $x^{2y}-3$

2. Simplify the rational expression. $\frac{5x^{3a}+5x^{2a}y^a}{x^{2a}-y^{2a}}$ $\frac{5x^{2a}}{x^a-y^a}$

3. Simplify the rational expression. $\frac{j^3k+j^3-k^4-k^3}{j^2k+j^2+jk^2+jk+k^3+k^2}$ $j-k$

4. Multiply. $\frac{4r^2+2rs+s^2}{2r+s} \cdot \frac{4r^2-s^2}{8r^3-s^3}$ 1

5. Multiply. $\frac{2a^2-2a-12}{a^2-49} \cdot \frac{4a^2-1}{2a^2+5a+2} \cdot \frac{2a^2-13a-7}{2a^2-7a+3}$ $\frac{2(2a+1)}{a+7}$

6. Multiply. $\frac{p^3-4p^2+p-4}{2p^3-8p^2+p-4} \cdot \frac{2p^3+2p^2+p+1}{p^4-p^3+p^2-p}$ $\frac{p+1}{p(p-1)}$

7. Divide. $\frac{\frac{m^3+n^3}{mp-mq-np+nq}}{\frac{mn-m^2-n^2}{mp-mq+np-nq}}$ $\frac{(m+n)^2}{n-m}$

8. Divide. $\frac{\frac{a^{2n}-1}{a^{2n}+3a^n+2}}{\frac{a^{2n}+a^n-12}{a^{2n}-a^n-6}}$ $\frac{a^n-1}{a^n+4}$

9. Divide. $\frac{\left(\frac{x-y}{4z}\right)}{\frac{\left(\frac{y-x}{z}\right)}{\left(\frac{x-y}{z^2}\right)}}$ $\frac{z^2}{4(y-x)}$

10. Solve the following equation for y in terms of x, and write the resulting expression for y in simplest form. Identify any excluded values of x.
$x^2(y+1) = 9(y+1) + 4x + 12$
$y = \frac{7-x}{x-3}$; $x \neq -3$ or 3

8-2 PRACTICE A

8-2 PRACTICE C

8-2 PRACTICE B

Simplify. Identify any x-values for which the expression is undefined.

1. $\frac{x^2+3x+2}{x^2-3x-4}$ $\frac{x+2}{x-4}$; $x \neq -1$, $x \neq 4$

2. $\frac{4x^6}{2x^4}$ $2x^2$; $x \neq 0$

3. $\frac{x^2-x^3}{2x^2-5x+3}$ $\frac{-x^2}{2x-3}$; $x \neq 1$, $x \neq \frac{3}{2}$

4. $\frac{x^3+x^2-20x}{x^2-16}$ $\frac{x^2+5x}{x+4}$; $x \neq 4$, $x \neq -4$

5. $\frac{3x^2-9x-12}{6x^2+9x+3}$ $\frac{x-4}{2x+1}$; $x \neq -1$, $x \neq -\frac{1}{2}$

6. $\frac{9-3x}{15-2x-x^2}$ $\frac{3}{x+5}$; $x \neq 3$, $x \neq -5$

Multiply. Assume all expressions are defined.

7. $\frac{4x+16}{2x+6} \cdot \frac{x^2+2x-3}{x+4}$ $2x-2$

8. $\frac{x+3}{x-1} \cdot \frac{x^2-2x+1}{x^2+5x+6}$ $\frac{x-1}{x+2}$

Divide. Assume all expressions are defined.

9. $\frac{5x^6}{x^2y} \div \frac{10x^2}{y}$ $\frac{x^2}{2}$

10. $\frac{x^2-2x-8}{x^2-2x-15} \div \frac{2x^2-8x}{2x^2-10x}$ $\frac{x+2}{x+3}$

Solve. Check your solution.

11. $\frac{x^2+x-12}{x-3} = 15$ $x = 11$

12. $\frac{2x^2+8x-10}{2x^2+14x+20} = 4$ $x = -3$

Solve.

13. The distance, d, traveled by a car undergoing constant acceleration, a, for a time, t, is given by $d = v_0t + \frac{1}{2}at^2$, where v_0 is the initial velocity of the car. Two cars are side by side with the same initial velocity. One car accelerates, $a = A$, and the other car does not accelerate, $a = 0$. Write an expression for the ratio of the distance traveled by the accelerating car to the distance traveled by the nonaccelerating car as a function of time. $1 + \frac{At}{2v_0}$

TEST PREP DOCTOR Students who chose **B** or **C** in **Exercise 47** may have made a mistake in sign when factoring or may have applied the Zero-Product Property incorrectly.

In **Exercise 48,** choosing **H** indicates that the student may have multiplied by the divisor rather than by the reciprocal of the divisor. Students who chose **G** may be confused about which expression should be written as a reciprocal. Have students review the steps involved in dividing fractions and then extend these steps to include dividing rational expressions.

Journal

Have students explain how they can determine whether a rational expression can be simplified.

ALTERNATIVE ASSESSMENT

Give students a rational expression such as $\frac{x+2}{x^2-5x+6}$, and ask them to write a pair of rational expressions with this product and a pair of rational expressions with this quotient. Have students provide mathematical support for their answers. Tell them to assume that all variable expressions are defined.

Power Presentations with PowerPoint®

8-2 Lesson Quiz

Simplify. Identify any x-values for which the expression is undefined.

1. $\frac{x^2-6x+5}{x^2-3x-10}$ $\frac{x-1}{x+2}$; $x \neq -2, 5$

2. $\frac{6x-x^2}{x^2-7x+6}$ $\frac{-x}{x-1}$; $x \neq 1, 6$

Multiply or divide. Assume that all expressions are defined.

3. $\frac{x+1}{3x+6} \cdot \frac{6x+12}{x^2-1}$ $\frac{2}{x-1}$

4. $\frac{x^2+4x+3}{x^2-4} \div \frac{x^2+2x-3}{x^2-6x+8}$ $\frac{(x+1)(x-4)}{(x+2)(x-1)}$

Solve. Check your solution.

5. $\frac{4x^2-1}{2x-1} = 9$ $x = 4$

Also available on transparency

45. **ERROR ANALYSIS** Two students simplified the same expression. Which is incorrect? Explain the error.
Student A; the student didn't leave a 1 in the numerator.

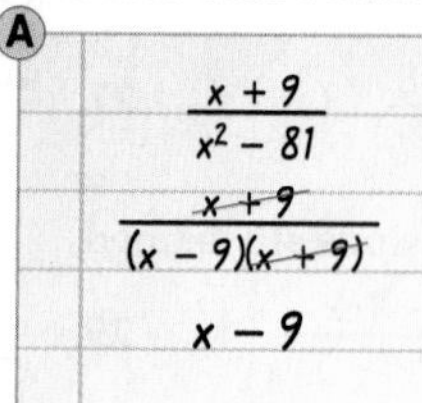

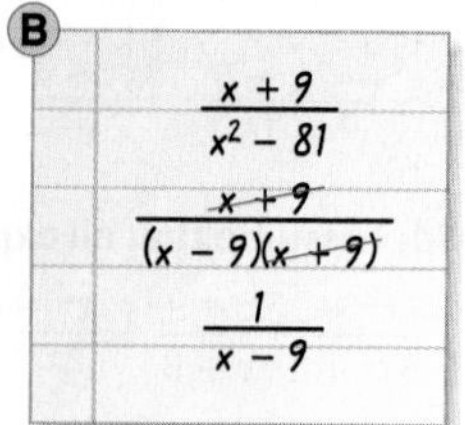

46. **Write About It** You can use polynomial division to find that $\frac{x^3-7x+6}{x-2} = x^2+2x-3$. Is this equation true for all values of x? Explain.

TEST PREP

47. For which values of x is the expression $\frac{x^2-x-12}{x^2+x-2}$ undefined?

Ⓐ 0 and 1 Ⓑ 1 and 2 Ⓒ −1 and 2 **Ⓓ −2 and 1**

48. Assume that all expressions are defined. Which expression is equivalent to $\frac{x^2+7x+10}{x^2-6x} \div \frac{x^3-4x}{x^2-8x+12}$?

Ⓕ $\frac{x+5}{x^2}$ Ⓖ $\frac{x^2}{x+5}$ Ⓗ $\frac{(x+5)(x+2)^2}{(x-6)^2}$ Ⓙ $\frac{(x-6)^2}{(x+5)(x+2)^2}$

49. The area of a rectangle is equal to $x^2+13x+36$ square units. If the length of the rectangle is equal to $x+9$ units, which expression represents its width?

Ⓐ $x+4$ Ⓑ $x+27$ Ⓒ x^2+4 Ⓓ x^2+27

CHALLENGE AND EXTEND

Multiply or divide. Assume that all expressions are defined.

50. $\frac{8x^3-1}{x+2} \cdot \frac{x^2-4}{2x^2-5x+2}$ $4x^2+2x+1$

51. $\frac{2x^2-50}{x^3+125} \cdot \frac{x^3-125}{x^2-10x+25}$ $\frac{2(x^2+5x+25)}{x^2-5x+25}$

52. $\frac{x^2-16}{x-3} \div \left(\frac{x^2-9}{x+4}\right)^{-1}$ $(x-4)(x+3)$

53. $\frac{x^5-4x^3-x^2+4}{x^3-2x^2+x-2} \div \frac{3x^3+3x^2+3x}{x^2-1} \cdot \frac{6x}{x^2-2x+1}$ $\frac{2(x+1)(x+2)}{x^2+1}$

SPIRAL REVIEW

Find each product. *(Lesson 6-2)*

54. $6x^2(x^4-2)$ $6x^6-12x^2$

55. $(x+5)(3x^2-7x-1)$ $3x^3+8x^2-36x-5$

56. $8x^2y^3(xy^2-4x+7y)$ $8x^3y^5-32x^3y^3+56x^2y^4$

57. **Biology** The table shows the number of births in a population of mice over a 5-year period. Find an exponential model for the data. Use the model to estimate the number of births in the 8th year. *(Lesson 7-8)*

Years	1	2	3	4	5
Births	70,000	120,000	170,000	220,400	271,100

$y \approx 56{,}800(1.39)^x$; about 800,000 births

Given: y varies directly as x. Write and graph each direct variation function. *(Lesson 8-1)*

58. $y = 7$ when $x = 14$ $y = \frac{1}{2}x$

59. $y = 8$ when $x = -2$ $y = -4x$

Answers

46. No; it is true for all real numbers except $x = 2$. At this value, the rational expression is undefined.

58.

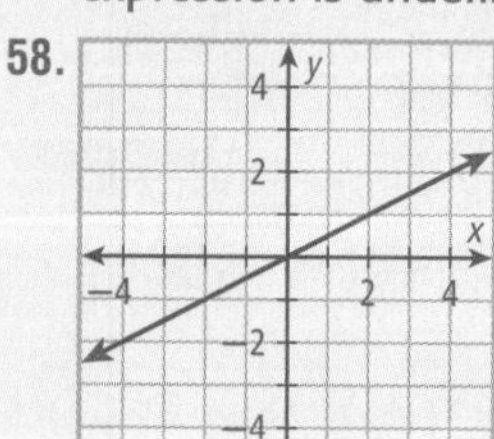

59.

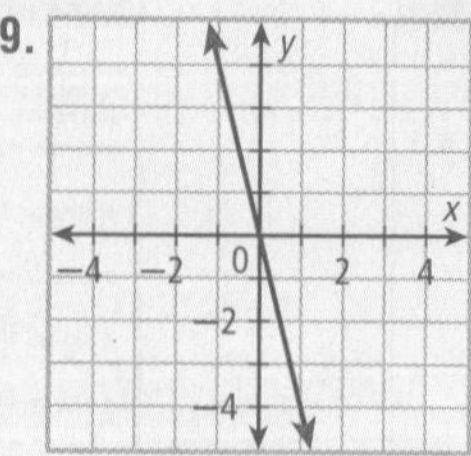

8-3 Adding and Subtracting Rational Expressions

 **A2.5.2** Add, subtract, multiply, divide, reduce and evaluate rational expressions with polynomial denominators. Simplify rational expressions, including expressions . . .

Objectives
Add and subtract rational expressions.
Simplify complex fractions.

Vocabulary
complex fraction

. . . with negative exponents in the denominator.

Why learn this?
You can add and subtract rational expressions to estimate a train's average speed. (See Example 6.)

Adding and subtracting rational expressions is similar to adding and subtracting fractions. To add or subtract rational expressions with like denominators, add or subtract the numerators and use the same denominator.

$$\frac{1}{5}+\frac{3}{5}=\frac{4}{5} \quad \frac{6}{7}-\frac{4}{7}=\frac{2}{7}$$

EXAMPLE 1 Adding and Subtracting Rational Expressions with Like Denominators

Add or subtract. Identify any x-values for which the expression is undefined.

A $\frac{3x-4}{x+3}+\frac{2x+5}{x+3}$

$\frac{3x-4+2x+5}{x+3}$ *Add the numerators.*

$\frac{5x+1}{x+3}$ *Combine like terms.*

The expression is undefined at $x = -3$ because this value makes $x + 3$ equal 0.

B $\frac{2x-1}{x^2+2}-\frac{4x+4}{x^2+2}$

$\frac{2x-1-(4x+4)}{x^2+2}$ *Subtract the numerators.*

$\frac{2x-1-4x-4}{x^2+2}$ *Distribute the negative sign.*

$\frac{-2x-5}{x^2+2}$ *Combine like terms.*

There is no real value of x for which $x^2 + 2 = 0$; the expression is always defined.

CHECK IT OUT! Add or subtract. Identify any x-values for which the expression is undefined.

1a. $\frac{6x+5}{x^2-3}+\frac{3x-1}{x^2-3}$ **1b.** $\frac{3x^2-5}{3x-1}-\frac{2x^2-3x-2}{3x-1}$

1a. $\frac{9x+4}{x^2-3}$; $x \neq \pm\sqrt{3}$

1b. $\frac{x^2+3x-3}{3x-1}$; $x \neq \frac{1}{3}$

To add or subtract rational expressions with unlike denominators, first find the least common denominator (LCD). The LCD is the least common multiple of the polynomials in the denominators.

8-3 Organizer

Pacing: Traditional 1 day
Block $\frac{1}{2}$ day

Objectives: Add and subtract rational expressions.
Simplify complex fractions.

Online Edition
Tutorial Videos

Countdown to Testing Week 17

Power Presentations with PowerPoint®

Warm Up

Add or subtract.

1. $\frac{2}{5}+\frac{7}{15}$ $\frac{13}{15}$

2. $\frac{11}{12}-\frac{3}{8}$ $\frac{13}{24}$

Simplify. Identify any x-values for which the expression is undefined.

3. $\frac{4x^9}{12x^3}$ $\frac{1}{3}x^6; x \neq 0$

4. $\frac{x-1}{x^2-1}$ $\frac{1}{x+1}; x \neq -1, x \neq 1$

Also available on transparency

Math Humor

Teacher: Why didn't you simplify the fraction $\frac{\frac{x}{x+2}}{\frac{x^2}{x-3}}$?

Student: It was too complex.

1 Introduce

EXPLORATION

8-3 Adding and Subtracting Rational Expressions

You can add and subtract rational expressions much like you would add and subtract fractions.

Find each sum. Simplify if necessary.

1. $\frac{3}{5}+\frac{4}{5}$ 2. $\frac{7}{10}+\frac{5}{10}$

3. List the steps you used to add the fractions.

Find each sum by using the steps you listed in Problem 3. Assume that $x \neq 0$.

4. $\frac{2}{x}+\frac{5}{x}$ 5. $\frac{4}{3x}+\frac{8}{3x}$

Find each difference. Simplify if necessary.

6. $\frac{5}{8}-\frac{3}{8}$ 7. $\frac{4}{12}-\frac{8}{12}$

8. List the steps you used to subtract the fractions.

Find each difference by using the steps you listed in Problem 8. Assume that $x \neq 0$.

9. $\frac{6}{4x}-\frac{1}{4x}$ 10. $\frac{12}{5x}-\frac{7}{5x}$

THINK AND DISCUSS

11. Discuss how to add and subtract rational expressions with like denominators.

Motivate

Ask a volunteer to add the fractions $\frac{1}{4}$ and $\frac{1}{3}$ on the board. As the student works, have the class describe each step of the process, including finding a common denominator. Explain that students will follow a similar procedure when adding rational expressions.

Explorations and answers are provided in the *Explorations* binder.

State Resources

go.hrw.com
State Resources Online
KEYWORD: MB7 Resources

Power Presentations with PowerPoint®

Additional Examples

Example 1

Add or subtract. Identify any x-values for which the expression is undefined.

A. $\frac{x-3}{x+4} + \frac{x-2}{x+4}$ $\frac{2x-5}{x+4}$; $x \neq -4$

B. $\frac{3x-4}{x^2+1} - \frac{6x+1}{x^2+1}$ $\frac{-3x-5}{x^2+1}$

Example 2

Find the least common multiple for each pair.

A. $4x^2y^3$ and $6x^4y^5$ $12x^4y^5$

B. $x^2 - 2x - 3$ and $x^2 - x - 6$

$(x-3)(x+1)(x+2)$

Also available on transparency

INTERVENTION

Questioning Strategies

EXAMPLE 1

- What are like denominators?
- When you add or subtract rational expressions with like denominators, how do you find the numerator of the sum or difference? How do you find the denominator?

EXAMPLE 2

- What step should you do first to find the LCM of polynomials?
- If two polynomials have a common factor, which power of the factor do you use in the LCM?

Inclusion Review the Distributive Property. Emphasize the importance of applying this property correctly when subtracting rational expressions.

Least Common Multiple (LCM) of Polynomials
To find the LCM of polynomials:
1. Factor each polynomial completely. Write any repeated factors as powers. For example, $x^3 + 6x^2 + 9x = x(x+3)^2$.
2. List the different factors. If the polynomials have common factors, use the highest power of each common factor.

EXAMPLE 2 **Finding the Least Common Multiple of Polynomials**

Find the least common multiple for each pair.

A $2x^3y^4$ and $3x^5y^3$

$2x^3y^4 = 2 \cdot x^3 \cdot y^4$

$3x^5y^3 = 3 \cdot x^5 \cdot y^3$

The LCM is $2 \cdot 3 \cdot x^5 \cdot y^4$, or $6x^5y^4$.

B $x^2 + 3x - 4$ and $x^2 - 3x + 2$

$x^2 + 3x - 4 = (x+4)(x-1)$

$x^2 - 3x + 2 = (x-2)(x-1)$

The LCM is $(x+4)(x-1)(x-2)$.

Find the least common multiple for each pair.

2a. $4x^3y^7$ and $3x^5y^4$ $12x^5y^7$

2b. $x^2 - 4$ and $x^2 + 5x + 6$ $(x+2)(x-2)(x+3)$

To add rational expressions with unlike denominators, rewrite both expressions with the LCD. This process is similar to adding fractions.

$$\frac{2}{6} + \frac{3}{10} = \frac{2}{2 \cdot 3}\left(\frac{5}{5}\right) + \frac{3}{2 \cdot 5}\left(\frac{3}{3}\right) = \frac{10}{30} + \frac{9}{30} = \frac{19}{30}$$

EXAMPLE 3 **Adding Rational Expressions**

Add. Identify any x-values for which the expression is undefined.

A $\frac{x-1}{x^2+3x+2} + \frac{x}{x+1}$

$\frac{x-1}{(x+2)(x+1)} + \frac{x}{x+1}$ *Factor the denominators.*

$\frac{x-1}{(x+2)(x+1)} + \frac{x}{x+1}\left(\frac{x+2}{x+2}\right)$ *The LCD is $(x+2)(x+1)$, so multiply $\frac{x}{x+1}$ by $\frac{x+2}{x+2}$.*

$\frac{x-1+x(x+2)}{(x+2)(x+1)}$ *Add the numerators.*

$\frac{x^2+3x-1}{(x+2)(x+1)}$ *Simplify the numerator.*

$\frac{x^2+3x-1}{(x+2)(x+1)}$ or $\frac{x^2+3x-1}{x^2+3x+2}$ *Write the sum in factored or expanded form.*

The expression is undefined at $x = -2$ and $x = -1$ because these values of x make the factors $(x+2)$ and $(x+1)$ equal 0.

Remember!

Multiplying by 1 or a form of 1, such as $\frac{x+2}{x+2}$, does not change the value of an expression.

2 Teach

Guided Instruction

Throughout the lesson, remind students of the connections between operations with numerical fractions and operations with rational expressions. Make sure students can add and subtract expressions with like denominators before moving on to expressions with unlike denominators.

Reaching All Learners

Through Graphic Organizers

Have students create a poster that shows the steps for adding and subtracting rational expressions. Suggest that they use a graphic organizer, such as the chart shown, to list these steps. Display students' posters in the classroom.

Adding and Subtracting Rational Expressions	
Step 1	Factor the denominators.
Step 2	Identify x-values for which the expressions are undefined.
Step 3	Write equivalent rational expressions using a common denominator.
Step 4	Add or subtract numerators.
Step 5	Simplify.

Add. Identify any x-values for which the expression is undefined.

B $\frac{x}{x+3} + \frac{-18}{x^2-9}$

$\frac{x}{x+3} + \frac{-18}{(x+3)(x-3)}$ — *Factor the denominators.*

$\frac{x}{x+3}\left(\frac{x-3}{x-3}\right) + \frac{-18}{(x+3)(x-3)}$ — *The LCD is $(x+3)(x-3)$, so multiply $\frac{x}{x+3}$ by $\frac{x-3}{x-3}$.*

$\frac{x(x-3)+(-18)}{(x+3)(x-3)}$ — *Add the numerators.*

$\frac{x^2-3x-18}{(x+3)(x-3)}$ — *Write the numerator in standard form.*

$\frac{\cancel{(x+3)}(x-6)}{\cancel{(x+3)}(x-3)}$ — *Factor the numerator.*

$\frac{x-6}{x-3}$ — *Divide out common factors.*

The expression is undefined at $x = -3$ and $x = 3$ because these values of x make the factors $(x+3)$ and $(x-3)$ equal 0.

Helpful Hint

Always simplify the sum or difference of rational expressions. A rational expression can be simplified if its numerator and denominator contain the same factor.

Add. Identify any x-values for which the expression is undefined.

3a. $\frac{3x}{2x-2} + \frac{3x-2}{3x-3}$ $\frac{15x-4}{6(x-1)}$; $x \neq 1$

3b. $\frac{x}{x+3} + \frac{2x+6}{x^2+6x+9}$ $\frac{x+2}{x+3}$; $x \neq -3$

EXAMPLE 4 Subtracting Rational Expressions

Subtract $\frac{2x^2-16}{x^2-4} - \frac{x+4}{x+2}$. Identify any x-values for which the expression is undefined.

$\frac{2x^2-16}{(x-2)(x+2)} - \frac{x+4}{x+2}$ — *Factor the denominators.*

$\frac{2x^2-16}{(x-2)(x+2)} - \frac{x+4}{x+2}\left(\frac{x-2}{x-2}\right)$ — *The LCD is $(x-2)(x+2)$, so multiply $\frac{x+4}{x+2}$ by $\frac{x-2}{x-2}$.*

$\frac{2x^2-16-(x+4)(x-2)}{(x-2)(x+2)}$ — *Subtract the numerators.*

$\frac{2x^2-16-(x^2+2x-8)}{(x-2)(x+2)}$ — *Multiply the binomials in the numerator.*

$\frac{2x^2-16-x^2-2x+8}{(x-2)(x+2)}$ — *Distribute the negative sign.*

$\frac{x^2-2x-8}{(x-2)(x+2)}$ — *Write the numerator in standard form.*

$\frac{(x-4)\cancel{(x+2)}}{(x-2)\cancel{(x+2)}}$ — *Factor the numerator.*

$\frac{x-4}{x-2}$ — *Divide out common factors.*

The expression is undefined at $x = 2$ and $x = -2$ because these values of x make the factors $(x-2)$ and $(x+2)$ equal 0.

Auditory Encourage students to use the terms *least common denominator* and *least common multiple* instead of the abbreviations LCD and LCM when they speak in class. Doing so can help them remember what the abbreviations mean.

ENGLISH LANGUAGE LEARNERS

COMMON ERROR ALERT

Some students may add or subtract rational expressions by adding the numerators and adding the denominators. Use substitution to demonstrate that this procedure is incorrect by showing students that $\frac{3}{x} + \frac{x^2}{4}$ is not equal to $\frac{3+x^2}{x+4}$.

Power Presentations with PowerPoint®

Additional Examples

Example 3

Add. Identify any x-values for which the expression is undefined.

A. $\frac{x-3}{x^2+3x-4} + \frac{2x}{x+4}$ $\frac{2x^2-x-3}{(x+4)(x-1)}$; $x \neq -4, x \neq 1$

B. $\frac{x}{x+2} + \frac{-8}{x^2-4}$ $\frac{x-4}{x-2}$; $x \neq \pm 2$

Example 4

Subtract $\frac{2x^2-30}{x^2-9} - \frac{x+5}{x+3}$. Identify any x-values for which the expression is undefined. $\frac{x-5}{x-3}$; $x \neq \pm 3$

Also available on transparency

INTERVENTION

Questioning Strategies

EXAMPLE 3

- How do you find the LCD of rational expressions?
- What steps do you use to rewrite the expressions with like denominators?

EXAMPLE 4

- What do you need to do before you can subtract the numerators?
- How can you tell if your answer is written in simplest form?

Power Presentations with PowerPoint®

Additional Examples

Example 5

Simplify. Assume that all expressions are defined.

A. $\dfrac{\frac{x+2}{x-1}}{\frac{x-3}{x+5}}$ $\quad \dfrac{(x+2)(x+5)}{(x-1)(x-3)}$

B. $\dfrac{\frac{3}{x}+\frac{x}{2}}{\frac{x-1}{x}}$ $\quad \dfrac{x^2+6}{2(x-1)}$

Also available on transparency

INTERVENTION

Questioning Strategies

EXAMPLE 5

- How can you write a complex fraction as a division problem?
- How do you find the LCD of the fractions in the numerator and denominator of a complex fraction?

Math Background
Complex fractions are also called *compound fractions.*

Subtract. Identify any x-values for which the expression is undefined.

4a. $\dfrac{3x-2}{2x+5} - \dfrac{2}{5x-2}$ **4b.** $\dfrac{2x^2+64}{x^2-64} - \dfrac{x-4}{x+8}$

4a. $\dfrac{15x^2-20x-6}{(2x+5)(5x-2)}$; $x \neq -\dfrac{5}{2}$ and $x \neq \dfrac{2}{5}$

4b. $\dfrac{x+4}{x-8}$; $x \neq \pm 8$

Some rational expressions are *complex fractions.* A **complex fraction** contains one or more fractions in its numerator, its denominator, or both. Examples of complex fractions are shown below.

$$\frac{x+2}{\frac{3}{x}} \qquad \frac{1+\frac{1}{x}}{4x+5} \qquad \frac{\frac{x+3}{x}}{\frac{x+4}{7x}}$$

Recall that the bar in a fraction represents division. Therefore, you can rewrite a complex fraction as a division problem and then simplify. You can also simplify complex fractions by using the LCD of the fractions in the numerator and denominator.

EXAMPLE 5 Simplifying Complex Fractions

Simplify $\dfrac{\frac{2}{x}+\frac{x}{4}}{\frac{x+1}{x}}$. Assume that all expressions are defined.

Method 1 Write the complex fraction as division.

$\left(\frac{2}{x}+\frac{x}{4}\right) \div \frac{x+1}{x}$	*Write as division.*
$\left(\frac{2}{x}+\frac{x}{4}\right) \cdot \frac{x}{x+1}$	*Multiply by the reciprocal.*
$\left[\frac{2}{x}\left(\frac{4}{4}\right)+\frac{x}{4}\left(\frac{x}{x}\right)\right] \cdot \frac{x}{x+1}$	*The LCD is 4x.*
$\left[\frac{2(4)+x(x)}{4x}\right] \cdot \frac{x}{x+1}$	*Add the numerators.*
$\frac{8+x^2}{4\cancel{x}} \cdot \frac{\cancel{x}}{x+1}$	*Simplify and divide out common factors.*
$\frac{8+x^2}{4(x+1)}$ or $\frac{x^2+8}{4x+4}$	*Multiply.*

Method 2 Multiply the numerator and denominator of the complex fraction by the LCD of the fractions in the numerator and denominator.

$\dfrac{\frac{2}{\cancel{x}}(4\cancel{x})+\frac{x}{\cancel{4}}(\cancel{4}x)}{\frac{x+1}{\cancel{x}}(4\cancel{x})}$	*The LCD is 4x.*
$\dfrac{(2)(4)+(x)(x)}{(x+1)(4)}$	*Divide out common factors.*
$\dfrac{8+x^2}{(x+1)(4)}$ or $\dfrac{x^2+8}{4x+4}$	*Simplify.*

Simplify. Assume that all expressions are defined.

5a. $\dfrac{\frac{x+1}{x^2-1}}{\frac{x}{x-1}}$ $\quad \dfrac{1}{x}$

5b. $\dfrac{\frac{20}{x-1}}{\frac{6}{3x-3}}$ $\quad 10$

5c. $\dfrac{\frac{1}{x}+\frac{1}{2x}}{\frac{x+4}{x-2}}$ $\quad \dfrac{3(x-2)}{2x(x+4)}$

Student to Student

Simplifying Complex Fractions

Brian Carr
Riverside High School

When I simplify complex fractions, I draw arrows connecting the outermost and innermost numbers.

$$\frac{\frac{3}{5}}{\frac{1}{2}} = \frac{6}{5} = 1\frac{1}{5}$$

Then I make a new fraction by writing the product of the outermost numbers as the numerator and the product of the innermost numbers as the denominator.

It also works for rational expressions.

$$\frac{\frac{x^2}{x+1}}{\frac{x}{2}} = \frac{2x^2}{x(x+1)} = \frac{2x}{x+1}$$

EXAMPLE 6 ***Transportation Application***

A freight train averages 30 mi/h traveling to its destination with full cars and 40 mi/h on the return trip with empty cars. What is the train's average speed for the entire trip? Round to the nearest tenth.

Total distance: $2d$	*Let d represent the one-way distance.*
Total time: $\frac{d}{30} + \frac{d}{40}$	*Use the formula $t = \frac{d}{r}$.*
Average speed: $\dfrac{2d}{\frac{d}{30} + \frac{d}{40}}$	*The average speed is $\frac{\text{total distance}}{\text{total time}}$.*
$\dfrac{2d(120)}{\frac{d}{30}(120) + \frac{d}{40}(120)}$	*The LCD of the fractions in the denominator is 120.*
$\dfrac{240d}{4d + 3d}$	*Simplify.*
$\dfrac{240\cancel{d}}{7\cancel{d}} \approx 34.3$	*Combine like terms and divide out common factors.*

The train's average speed is 34.3 mi/h.

6. Justin's average speed on his way to school is 40 mi/h, and his average speed on the way home is 45 mi/h. What is Justin's average speed for the entire trip? Round to the nearest tenth. **42.4 mi/h**

THINK AND DISCUSS

1. Explain how to find the LCD of two rational expressions.

2. **GET ORGANIZED** Copy and complete the graphic organizer. In each box, write an example and show how to simplify it.

Rational Expressions
- Adding (like denominators)
- Subtracting (unlike denominators)
- Simplifying a complex fraction

Power Presentations with PowerPoint®

Additional Examples

Example 6

A hiker averages 1.4 mi/h when walking downhill on a mountain trail and 0.8 mi/h on the return trip when walking uphill. What is the hiker's average speed for the entire trip? Round to the nearest tenth. 1.0 mi/h

Also available on transparency

INTERVENTION
Questioning Strategies

EXAMPLE 6

- What expression should you use for the total distance traveled?
- In terms of *d*, how long does the first part of the trip last? How long does the return trip last?

Teaching Tip **Critical Thinking** In **Example 6,** point out that the average speed for a round-trip is not the average of the one-way average speeds, because more time is spent traveling at the slower speed than at the faster speed.

3 Close

Summarize

Review with students the steps for adding and subtracting rational expressions. Remind students that they can use the steps for adding or subtracting fractions such as $\frac{5}{8}$ and $\frac{3}{5}$ to help them remember the steps for adding and subtracting rational expressions. Then have students explain what a complex fraction is and ask them to describe how complex fractions can be simplified.

ONGOING ASSESSMENT and INTERVENTION

***Diagnose* Before the Lesson**
8-3 Warm Up, TE p. 583

***Monitor* During the Lesson**
Check It Out! Exercises, SE pp. 583–587
Questioning Strategies, TE pp. 584–587

***Assess* After the Lesson**
8-3 Lesson Quiz, TE p. 590
Alternative Assessment, TE p. 590

Answers to *Think and Discuss*

Possible answers:

1. Factor each denominator. Find the product of the different factors. If the same factor is in both denominators, use the highest power of that factor.
2. See p. A10.

8-3 Exercises

Assignment Guide

Assign *Guided Practice* exercises as necessary.

If you finished Examples **1–3**
Basic 17–24, 33–36
Average 17–24, 33–36
Advanced 17–24, 33–36

If you finished Examples **1–6**
Basic 17–46, 48–52, 58–64
Average 17–53, 58–64
Advanced 17–64

Homework Quick Check
Quickly check key concepts.
Exercises: 18, 20, 22, 26, 28, 31, 42

Answers

1. Possible answer: A complex fraction has 1 or more fractions in its numerator, its denominator, or both.
2. $\frac{5x+1}{4x-1}; x \neq \frac{1}{4}$
3. $\frac{-2x-7}{4x+5}; x \neq -\frac{5}{4}$
7. $\frac{2(4x^2+x-8)}{(x+6)(2x-1)}$; $x \neq -6$ and $x \neq \frac{1}{2}$
8. $\frac{16x-9}{4(3x+1)}; x \neq -\frac{1}{3}$
9. $\frac{2x^2-4x-1}{(x+3)(x-3)}; x \neq \pm 3$

10, 17–19, 22–29. See p. A36.

State Resources

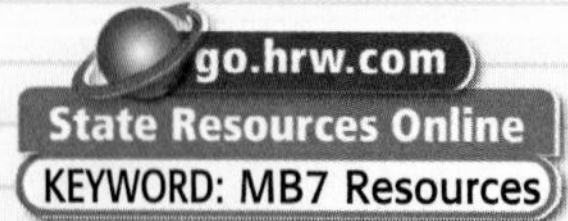

8-3 Exercises

go.hrw.com
Homework Help Online
KEYWORD: MB7 8-3
Parent Resources Online
KEYWORD: MB7 Parent

GUIDED PRACTICE

1. **Vocabulary** How does a *complex fraction* differ from other types of fractions?

SEE EXAMPLE 1 p. 583

Add or subtract. Identify any x-values for which the expression is undefined.

2. $\frac{2x-3}{4x-1} + \frac{3x+4}{4x-1}$
3. $\frac{3x-4}{4x+5} - \frac{5x+3}{4x+5}$
4. $\frac{4x-3}{2x-5} - \frac{4x+3}{2x-5}$ $\frac{-6}{2x-5}; x \neq \frac{5}{2}$

SEE EXAMPLE 2 p. 584

Find the least common multiple for each pair.

5. $4x^2y^3$ and $16x^4y$ $16x^4y^3$
6. x^2-25 and $x^2+10x+25$ $(x-5)(x+5)^2$

SEE EXAMPLE 3 p. 584

Add or subtract. Identify any x-values for which the expression is undefined.

7. $\frac{3x-2}{x+6} + \frac{2x-3}{2x-1}$
8. $\frac{4x-5}{12x+4} + \frac{3x-1}{3x+1}$
9. $\frac{3x-4}{x^2-9} + \frac{2x-1}{x+3}$

SEE EXAMPLE 4 p. 585

10. $\frac{3x-5}{2x-5} - \frac{2x-5}{3x+1}$
11. $\frac{2x+8}{x^2-16} - \frac{3}{x-4}$ $\frac{-1}{x-4}; x \neq \pm 4$
12. $\frac{x+2}{x^2+4x+3} - \frac{x+1}{x+3}$ $\frac{-(x^2+x-1)}{(x+1)(x+3)}; x \neq -3$ and $x \neq -1$

SEE EXAMPLE 5 p. 586

Simplify. Assume that all expressions are defined.

13. $\frac{\frac{2x-3}{x-2}}{\frac{4x-3}{x^2-4}}$ $\frac{(2x-3)(x+2)}{4x-3}$
14. $\frac{\frac{3x-7}{4x+5}}{\frac{6x-1}{5x-6}}$ $\frac{(3x-7)(5x-6)}{(4x+5)(6x-1)}$
15. $\frac{\frac{2}{x}+\frac{1}{x}}{\frac{2x}{x+2}}$ $\frac{3(x+2)}{2x^2}$

SEE EXAMPLE 6 p. 587

16. **Track** Yvette ran at an average speed of 6.20 ft/s during the first two laps of a race and an average speed of 7.75 ft/s during the second two laps of a race. What was Yvette's average speed for the entire race? Round to the nearest tenth. 6.9 ft/s

PRACTICE AND PROBLEM SOLVING

Independent Practice	
For Exercises	See Example
17–19	1
20–21	2
22–24	3
25–27	4
28–30	5
31	6

Extra Practice
Skills Practice p. S18
Application Practice p. S39

Add or subtract. Identify any x-values for which the expression is undefined.

17. $\frac{2x-3}{4x-7} + \frac{2x-3}{4x-7}$
18. $\frac{x-5}{3x+4} - \frac{3x-5}{3x+4}$
19. $\frac{x^2-3}{2x+7} - \frac{2x-5}{2x+7}$

Find the least common multiple for each pair.

20. $12x^2y^3$ and $14x^3y^2$ $84x^3y^3$
21. $16x^2-25$ and $4x^2-x-5$ $(4x-5)(4x+5)(x+1)$

Add or subtract. Identify any x-values for which the expression is undefined.

22. $\frac{3x-2}{x+2} + \frac{2x}{4x-1}$
23. $\frac{2x-7}{x-2} + \frac{8x}{3x-6}$
24. $\frac{5x}{4x^2} + \frac{7}{x+1}$
25. $\frac{4x-3}{x^2-9} - \frac{2x-3}{x-3}$
26. $\frac{x}{2x+3} - \frac{2x+1}{2x-3}$
27. $\frac{1}{x-4} - \frac{2}{x^2-6x+8}$

Simplify. Assume that all expressions are defined.

28. $\frac{\frac{2x-5}{x^2-9}}{\frac{3x-1}{x+3}}$
29. $\frac{\frac{3x-2}{x^2-4}}{\frac{5x+1}{x^2+x-6}}$
30. $\frac{\frac{x}{x+1}}{x+\frac{x}{3}}$ $\frac{3}{4(x+1)}$

31. **Chemistry** A solution is heated from 0°C to 100°C. Between 0°C and 50°C, the rate of temperature increase is 1.5°C/min. Between 50°C and 100°C, the rate of temperature increase is 0.4°C/min. What is the average rate of temperature increase during the entire heating process? Round to the nearest tenth. 0.6°C/min

8-3 READING STRATEGIES

The addition or subtraction of rational expressions can be compared to the addition or subtraction of fractions. As with fractions, in order to add or subtract rational expressions, the denominators must be the same. The least common multiple of the polynomials is the least common denominator (LCD).

	Add Fractions	Add Rational Expressions
	$\frac{3}{4}+\frac{1}{6}$	$\frac{5}{2x}+\frac{x+1}{x^2}$
Find the LCD.	12	$2x^2$
Rename each term using the LCD.	$\frac{9}{12}+\frac{2}{12}$	$\frac{5x}{2x^2}+\frac{2x+2}{2x^2}$
Add the numerators.	$\frac{11}{12}$	$\frac{7x+2}{2x^2}$

Find the least common multiple for each pair.

1. $2x^6$ and $6x$ $6x^6$
2. $10xy$ and $5x^4y^3$ $10x^4y^3$
3. $(x-8)(x+1)$ and $(x+1)$ $(x-8)(x+1)$
4. x^2-5x+6 and $x-3$ $(x-3)(x-2)$

A **complex fraction** is an expression that contains a fraction in the numerator, $\frac{\frac{8x}{x-3}}{x^2}$, the denominator, $\frac{3x+5}{\frac{13}{9x}}$, or both $\frac{\frac{4x}{x^2+1}}{\frac{x-3}{x+2}}$. To simplify, treat it as a division of rational expressions.

$\frac{\frac{4(x-1)}{x^2-1}}{\frac{x-3}{x+1}} = \frac{4(x-1)}{x^2-1} \div \frac{x-3}{x+1} = \frac{4(x-1)}{(x+1)(x-1)} \cdot \frac{x+1}{x-3} = \frac{4}{x-3}$

Write the division expression and the corresponding multiplication expression you could use to simplify the complex fraction.

5. $\frac{\frac{8x}{x-3}}{\frac{x^2}{2}}$ $\frac{8x}{x-3} \div \frac{x^2}{2}$; $\frac{8x}{x-3} \cdot \frac{2}{x^2}$
6. $\frac{\frac{2}{x-1}}{\frac{x+1}{x^3}}$ $\frac{2}{x-1} \div \frac{x+1}{x^3}$; $\frac{2}{x-1} \cdot \frac{x^3}{x+1}$

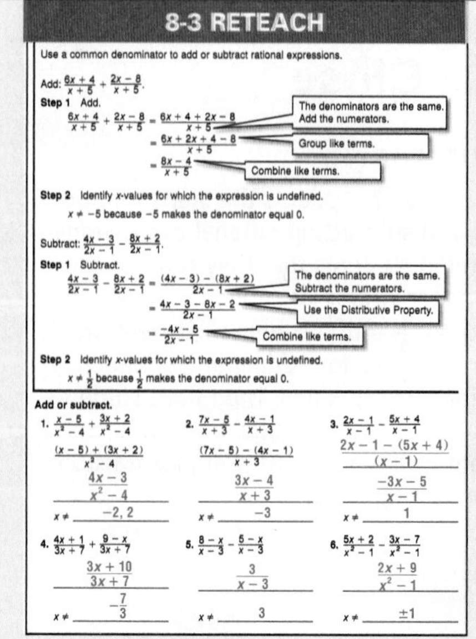
8-3 RETEACH

Use a common denominator to add or subtract rational expressions.

Add: $\frac{6x+4}{x+5} + \frac{2x-8}{x+5}$.

Step 1 Add.

$\frac{6x+4}{x+5} + \frac{2x-8}{x+5} = \frac{6x+4+2x-8}{x+5}$ — The denominators are the same. Add the numerators.

$= \frac{6x+2x+4-8}{x+5}$ — Group like terms.

$= \frac{8x-4}{x+5}$ — Combine like terms.

Step 2 Identify x-values for which the expression is undefined.

$x \neq -5$ because -5 makes the denominator equal 0.

Subtract: $\frac{4x-3}{2x-1} - \frac{8x+2}{2x-1}$.

Step 1 Subtract.

$\frac{4x-3}{2x-1} - \frac{8x+2}{2x-1} = \frac{(4x-3)-(8x+2)}{2x-1}$ — The denominators are the same. Subtract the numerators.

$= \frac{4x-3-8x-2}{2x-1}$ — Use the Distributive Property.

$= \frac{-4x-5}{2x-1}$ — Combine like terms.

Step 2 Identify x-values for which the expression is undefined.

$x \neq \frac{1}{2}$ because $\frac{1}{2}$ makes the denominator equal 0.

Add or subtract.

1. $\frac{x-5}{x^2-4} + \frac{3x+2}{x^2-4}$; $\frac{(x-5)+(3x+2)}{x^2-4}$; $\frac{4x-3}{x^2-4}$; $x \neq -2, 2$
2. $\frac{7x-5}{x+3} - \frac{4x-1}{x+3}$; $\frac{(7x-5)-(4x-1)}{x+3}$; $\frac{3x-4}{x+3}$; $x \neq -3$
3. $\frac{2x-1}{x-1} - \frac{5x+4}{x-1}$; $\frac{2x-1-(5x+4)}{(x-1)}$; $\frac{-3x-5}{x-1}$; $x \neq 1$
4. $\frac{4x+1}{3x+7} + \frac{9-x}{3x+7}$; $\frac{3x+10}{3x+7}$; $x \neq -\frac{7}{3}$
5. $\frac{8-x}{x-3} - \frac{5-x}{x-3}$; $\frac{3}{x-3}$; $x \neq 3$
6. $\frac{5x+2}{x^2-1} - \frac{3x-7}{x^2-1}$; $\frac{2x+9}{x^2-1}$; $x \neq \pm 1$

MULTI-STEP TEST PREP

32. This problem will prepare you for the Multi-Step Test Prep on page 608.

An auto race consists of 8 laps. A driver completes the first 3 laps at an average speed of 185 mi/h and the remaining laps at an average speed of 200 mi/h.

a. Let d represent the length of one lap. Write an expression in terms of d that represents the time in hours that it takes the driver to complete the race.

b. What is the driver's average speed during the race to the nearest mile per hour? **194 mi/h**

32a. $\frac{3d}{185} + \frac{5d}{200}$

Add or subtract. Identify any x-values for which the expression is undefined.

33. $\frac{2}{x+4} + \frac{x}{x-3}$ **34.** $\frac{2x}{x^2-36} + \frac{x+4}{x+6}$ **35.** $\frac{2}{x^2-x-20} + \frac{3}{x^2+7x+12}$

36. $\frac{7x}{x^2-5x} + \frac{x^2}{x-5}$ **37.** $\frac{2x}{x-1} - \frac{9}{x-2}$ **38.** $\frac{2x+3}{3x+4} - \frac{x}{9x+12}$

39. $\frac{4x^2}{3x+4} - \frac{2}{2x-3}$ **40.** $\frac{6}{x^2+4x-32} - \frac{x-5}{x-4}$ **41.** $\frac{x+7}{x^2+13x+42} - \frac{10x}{x^2+8x+7}$

42. Environment The junior and senior classes of a high school are cleaning up a beach. Each class has pledged to clean 1600 m of shoreline. The junior class has 12 more students than the senior class.

a. Let s represent the number of students in the senior class. Write and simplify an expression in terms of s that represents the difference between the number of meters of shoreline each senior must clean and the number each junior must clean.

b. If there are 48 seniors, how many more meters of shoreline must each senior clean than the number each junior must clean? Round to the nearest tenth of a meter.

c. Multi-Step If it takes each student about 10 min to clean 15 m of shoreline, approximately how much sooner will the junior class finish than the senior class?

42a. $\frac{19{,}200}{s(s+12)}$

b. 6.7 m

c. about 4.4 min

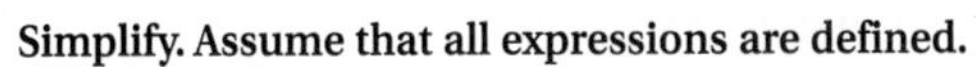

Simplify. Assume that all expressions are defined.

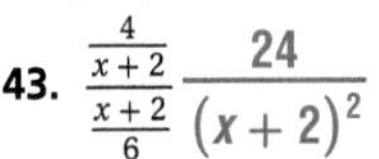

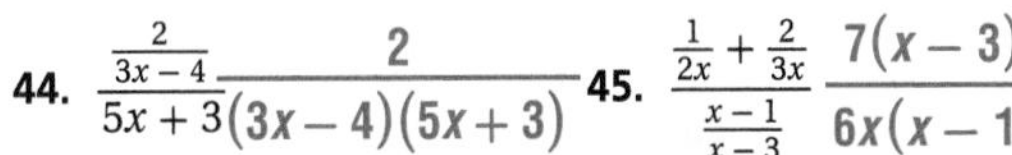

43. $\dfrac{\frac{4}{x+2}}{\frac{x+2}{6}}$ $\frac{24}{(x+2)^2}$ **44.** $\dfrac{\frac{2}{3x-4}}{5x+3}$ $\frac{2}{(3x-4)(5x+3)}$ **45.** $\dfrac{\frac{1}{2x}+\frac{2}{3x}}{\frac{x-1}{x-3}}$ $\frac{7(x-3)}{6x(x-1)}$

LINK Architecture

Andrea Palladio stated that his preferred room shapes were squares, circles, and rectangles with precise length-to-width ratios. Some of these shapes can be seen above in Il Redentore church that Palladio designed.

46. Architecture The Renaissance architect Andrea Palladio preferred that the length and width of rectangular rooms be limited to certain ratios. These ratios are listed in the table. Palladio also believed that the height of a room with vaulted ceilings should be the harmonic mean of the length and width.

a. The harmonic mean of two positive numbers a and b is equal to $\frac{2}{\frac{1}{a}+\frac{1}{b}}$. Simplify this expression. $\frac{2ab}{a+b}$

b. Complete the table for a rectangular room with a width of 30 feet that meets Palladio's requirements for its length and height. If necessary, round to the nearest tenth.

c. What if...? A Palladian room has a length-to-width ratio of 4:3. If the length of this room is doubled, what effect should this change have on the room's width and height, according to Palladio's principles?
Both the width and the height will double.

Rooms with a Width of 30 ft

Length-to-Width Ratio	Length (ft)	Height (ft)
2:1	60	40
3:2	45	36
4:3	40	34.3
5:3	50	37.5
$\sqrt{2}$:1	42.4	35.1

47. Critical Thinking Write two expressions whose sum is $\frac{x-3}{x+2}$.
Possible answer: $\frac{x}{x+2} + \frac{-3}{x+2}$ or $\frac{x^2-6x+8}{x^2-4} + \frac{1}{x+2}$

COMMON ERROR ALERT

In exercises involving complex fractions, such as **Exercises 43–45,** students may become confused by the multiple fraction bars. Suggest that they draw a circle around the bar that separates the numerator of the complex fraction from the denominator. Point out that this bar is slightly longer and wider than the other fraction bars.

MULTI-STEP TEST PREP **Exercise 32** involves writing and simplifying a rational expression for average speed. This exercise prepares students for the Multi-Step Test Prep on page 608.

Teaching Tip **Inclusion** In **Exercises 33–41,** remind students that factoring the denominators will not only make it easier to identify any x-values for which the expression is undefined, but it will also help them identify the LCD of the rational expressions.

Answers

33. $\frac{x^2+6x-6}{(x+4)(x-3)}$; $x \neq -4$ and $x \neq 3$

34. $\frac{x^2-24}{(x+6)(x-6)}$; $x \neq \pm 6$

35. $\frac{5x-9}{(x-5)(x+4)(x+3)}$; $x \neq -4$, $x \neq -3$, and $x \neq 5$

36. $\frac{x^2+7}{x-5}$; $x \neq 0$ and $x \neq 5$

37–41. See p. A36.

8-3 PROBLEM SOLVING

Vicki and Lorena motor downstream at about 6 knots (nautical miles per hour) in their boat. The return trip is against the current, and they can motor at only about 3 knots.

1. Vicki wants to find the average speed for the entire trip.
   a. Write an expression for the time it takes to travel downstream plus the time it takes for the return trip if the distance in each direction is d. $\frac{d}{6}+\frac{d}{3}$
   b. What is the total distance they travel downstream and upstream in terms of d? $2d$
   c. Write an expression for their average speed using the expressions for the total time and the total distance. $\dfrac{2d}{\frac{d}{6}+\frac{d}{3}}$
   d. Vicki says that the average speed is 4 knots. Lorena says that the average speed is 4.5 knots. Explain who is correct and why.
   Vicki is correct. Possible answer: Lorena calculated the average speed as if it took the same amount of time for each leg of the trip. Vicki took into consideration the time for each leg.
2. If they delay the return trip until the current changes direction, they can motor back at 4 knots. What is the average speed for the entire trip under these conditions? 4.8 knots

Zak runs at an average speed of 7.0 miles per hour during the first half of a race and an average speed of 5.5 miles per hour during the second half of the race. Choose the letter for the best answer.

3. Which expression gives Zak's average speed for the entire race?
   A $\frac{(7+5.5)}{2}$ B $\frac{12.5(7+5.5)d}{2}$ C $\frac{(38.5)d}{(7+5.5)}$ (D) $\frac{2(38.5)d}{(7+5.5)d}$
4. If Zak runs the race in 1.25 hours, what is the length of the race in miles?
   A 3.85 B 6.25 (C) 7.7 D 12.5
5. In a later race, Zak increased his average speed during the second half of the race to 6.0 miles per hour. What is his average speed for this race in miles per hour?
   A 6.42 (B) 6.46 C 6.52 D 6.56
6. It took Zak 1.6 hours to run this later race. What is the length of this race in miles?
   A 5.17 B 7.28 C 9.55 (D) 10.34

8-3 CHALLENGE

To add or subtract algebraic fractions, first find a common denominator.

$\frac{3}{x+1}+\frac{2}{x-2}=\frac{3(x-2)+2(x+1)}{(x+1)(x-2)}=\frac{3x-6+2x+2}{(x+1)(x-2)}=\frac{5x-4}{x^2-x-2}$

The decomposition of an algebraic fraction into partial fractions is the reverse of this process. The method shown in the example below can be used for fractions in which the degree of the numerator is less than the degree of the denominator, and in which the denominator can be factored into linear factors.

Example To decompose $\frac{5x-4}{x^2-x-2}$ into partial fractions:

Factor the denominator. $\frac{5x-4}{x^2-x-2}=\frac{5x-4}{(x+1)(x-2)}$

Express the fraction as the sum of two fractions, with the individual factors as denominators and the unknown numerators A and B. $\frac{5x-4}{(x+1)(x-2)}=\frac{A}{x+1}+\frac{B}{x-2}$

To clear fractions, multiply both sides of the rational equation by the LCD, $(x+1)(x-2)$. $5x-4=A(x-2)+B(x+1)$

To determine A and B, first eliminate B by letting $x=-1$. Then eliminate A by letting $x=2$.
$5(-1)-4=A(-1-2)+B(-1+1)$; $-5-4=-3A$; $A=3$
$5(2)-4=A(2-2)+B(2+1)$; $10-4=3B$; $B=2$

Use the values for A and B to express the original fraction as the sum of two partial fractions. $\frac{5x-4}{(x+1)(x-2)}=\frac{3}{x+1}+\frac{2}{x-2}$

Express the given fraction as the sum of partial fractions.

1. $\frac{3x+18}{x^2+5x+4}$ $\frac{5}{x+1}-\frac{2}{x+4}$
2. $\frac{6x^2+2x-4}{x^3-4x}$ $\frac{1}{x}+\frac{2}{x+2}+\frac{3}{x-2}$
3. $\frac{7x^2+18x-19}{x^3+2x^2-5x-6}$ $\frac{5}{x+1}+\frac{3}{x-2}-\frac{1}{x+3}$

The example above showed one way to find the numerators of the partial fractions. Another method can be used. After clearing fractions in the equation, regroup the terms on the right side to get an expression of the form $ax+b$. Then equate coefficients to obtain a system of two equations in A and B. Solve the system.
$5x-4=A(x-2)+B(x+1)$
$5x-4=(A+B)x+(-2A+B)$
$5=A+B$ and $-4=-2A+B$
$A=3$ and $B-2$

4. Consider a rational expression that has a repeated linear factor in its denominator, such as the one at right. Use the method of equating coefficients to find the partial fractions. $\frac{x^2-4x+6}{(x-1)^2(x-2)}=\frac{A}{x-1}+\frac{B}{(x-1)^2}+\frac{C}{x-2}$
   $\frac{-1}{x-1}-\frac{3}{(x-1)^2}+\frac{2}{x-2}$

8-3 PRACTICE A
8-3 PRACTICE C
8-3 PRACTICE B

Find the least common multiple for each pair.

1. $3x^2y^6$ and $5x^3y^2$ $15x^3y^6$
2. x^2+x-2 and x^2-x-6 $(x-1)(x+2)(x-3)$

Add or subtract. Identify any x-values for which the expression is undefined.

3. $\frac{2x-3}{x+4}+\frac{4x-5}{x+4}$ $\frac{6x-8}{x+4}$; $x \neq -4$
4. $\frac{x+12}{2x-5}-\frac{3x-2}{2x-5}$ $\frac{-2x+14}{2x-5}$; $x \neq \frac{5}{2}$
5. $\frac{x+4}{x^2-x-12}+\frac{2x}{x-4}$ $\frac{2x^2+7x+4}{x^2-x-12}$; $x \neq 4$, $x \neq -3$
6. $\frac{3x^2-1}{x^2-3x-18}-\frac{x+2}{x-6}$ $\frac{2x^2-5x-7}{x^2-3x-18}$; $x \neq 6$, $x \neq -3$
7. $\frac{x+2}{x^2-2x-15}+\frac{x}{x+3}$ $\frac{x^2-4x+2}{x^2-2x-15}$; $x \neq -3$, $x \neq 5$
8. $\frac{x+6}{x^2-7x-18}-\frac{2x}{x-9}$ $\frac{-2x^2-3x+6}{x^2-7x-18}$; $x \neq -2$, $x \neq 9$

Simplify. Assume all expressions are defined.

9. $\dfrac{\frac{x-1}{x+5}}{\frac{x+6}{x-3}}$ $\frac{x^2-4x+3}{x^2+11x+30}$
10. $\dfrac{\frac{12}{x+3}}{\frac{x^2+1}{x-2}}$ $\frac{12x-24}{x^3+3x^2+x+3}$

Solve.

11. A messenger is required to deliver 10 packages per day. Each day, the messenger works only for as long as it takes to deliver the daily quota of 10 packages. On average, the messenger is able to deliver 2 packages per hour on Saturday and 4 packages per hour on Sunday. What is the messenger's average delivery rate on the weekend? $2.6\overline{6}$ packages per hour

TEST PREP DOCTOR Students who chose C in **Exercise 49** may have forgotten to multiply the numerator of $\frac{3}{3x}$ by the LCD. Remind students that both the numerator and the denominator must be multiplied by the LCD so that the value of the original expression does not change.

Journal

Refer students to the method of simplifying complex fractions shown in the Student to Student feature on page 587. Have students explain why this method works.

ALTERNATIVE ASSESSMENT

Ask students to write two rational expressions with unlike denominators. Have them find the sum and difference of the expressions. Then have them write and simplify a complex fraction with one expression as the numerator and the other as the denominator.

Power Presentations with PowerPoint®

8-3 Lesson Quiz

Add or subtract. Identify any *x*-values for which the expression is undefined.

1. $\frac{2x+1}{x-2} + \frac{x-3}{x+1}$
   $\frac{3x^2-2x+7}{(x-2)(x+1)}; x \neq -1, x \neq 2$
2. $\frac{x}{x+4} - \frac{x+36}{x^2-16}$ $\frac{x-9}{x-4}$; $x \neq \pm 4$
3. Find the least common multiple of $x^2 - 6x + 5$ and $x^2 + x - 2$. $(x-5)(x-1)(x+2)$
4. Simplify $\frac{\frac{x+2}{x^2-4}}{\frac{x}{x-2}}$. Assume that all expressions are defined. $\frac{1}{x}$
5. Tyra averages 40 mi/h driving to the airport during rush hour and 60 mi/h on the return trip late at night. What is Tyra's average speed for the entire trip? 48 mi/h

Also available on transparency

48. **Write About It** The first step in adding rational expressions is to write them with a common denominator. This denominator does not necessarily need to be the least common denominator (LCD). Why is it often easier to use the LCD than it is to use other common denominators?
Possible answer: Using the LCD reduces the need for simplifying the sum of the rational expressions.

TEST PREP

49. Which best represents $\frac{3}{3x} + \frac{5}{9x}$?
Ⓐ $\frac{2}{3x}$ Ⓑ $\frac{7}{2x}$ Ⓒ $\frac{8}{9x}$ **Ⓓ** $\frac{14}{9x}$

50. Which of the following is equivalent to $\frac{5}{x+2} - \frac{8}{x+4}$?
Ⓕ $\frac{-3x+4}{x^2+8}$ Ⓖ $\frac{-5}{x+4}$ **Ⓗ** $\frac{-3x+4}{x^2+6x+8}$ Ⓙ $\frac{-3x+36}{x^2+6x+8}$

51. Which of the following is equivalent to $\frac{\frac{8}{7x}}{\frac{-4}{x+1}}$?
Ⓐ $-\frac{2x+2}{7x}$ Ⓑ $-\frac{32}{7x^2+7}$ Ⓒ $-\frac{2}{7x^2+7}$ Ⓓ $-\frac{7x}{2x+2}$

52. A three-day bicycle race has 3 stages of equal length. The table shows a rider's average speed in each of the stages. What is the rider's average speed for the entire race, rounded to the nearest tenth of a kilometer per hour?
Ⓕ 29.5 km/h **Ⓗ** 30.2 km/h
Ⓖ 29.7 km/h Ⓙ 30.7 km/h

Race Results

Stage	Speed (km/h)
1	35.5
2	31.1
3	25.6

CHALLENGE AND EXTEND

Simplify. Assume that all expressions are defined.

53. $\frac{x-1}{x+2} + \frac{4}{x^2-4} - \frac{6x}{x-2}$ $\frac{-5x^2-15x+6}{(x+2)(x-2)}$
54. $\frac{x^{-1}+y^{-1}}{x^{-1}-y^{-1}}$ $\frac{y+x}{y-x}$
55. $(x+2)^{-2} - (x^2-4)^{-1}$ $\frac{-4}{(x+2)^2(x-2)}$
56. $(x-y)^{-1} - (x+y)^{-1}$ $\frac{2y}{(x-y)(x+y)}$
57. What polynomial completes the equation $\frac{■}{x^3+4x^2-5x} - \frac{x+4}{x^2-x} = \frac{5}{x+5}$?
$6x^2 + 4x + 20$

SPIRAL REVIEW

Evaluate each expression for the given values of the variables. *(Lesson 1-4)*

58. $\frac{-x^2}{y^2-x^2}$ for $x = -2$ and $y = 3$ $-\frac{4}{5}$
59. $\frac{m^2-mn}{n^2+10}$ for $m = -4$ and $n = 0$ $\frac{8}{5}$

Graph each logarithmic function. Find the asymptote. Then describe how the graph is transformed from the graph of its parent function. *(Lesson 7-7)*

60. $g(x) = 2\log(x-1)$
61. $h(x) = \log(x+4)$

Simplify. Identify any *x*-values for which the expression is undefined. *(Lesson 8-2)*

62. $\frac{2x^2+5x^3}{x}$ $5x^2 + 2x; x \neq 0$
63. $\frac{x^2-2x-48}{x^2+10x+24}$ $\frac{x-8}{x+4}; x \neq -6$ and $x \neq -4$
64. $\frac{x-2}{x^2-3x+2}$ $\frac{1}{x-1}; x \neq 1$ and $x \neq 2$

Answers

60. The asymptote is $x = 1$. The transformation is a vertical stretch by a factor of 2 and a translation 1 unit right.

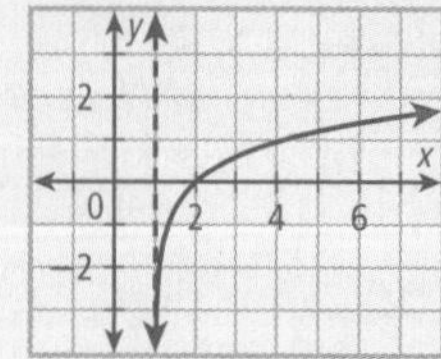

61. The asymptote is $x = -4$. The transformation is a translation 4 units left.

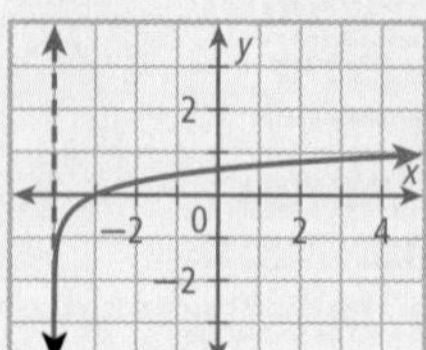

Explore Holes in Graphs

You can use a graphing calculator to explore the relationship between the graphs of rational functions and their simplified forms.

Use with Lesson 8-4

Activity

Use a graph and a table to identify holes in the graph of $f(x) = \dfrac{(x+1)(x-1)}{(x-1)}$.

1. Graph the function $f(x) = \frac{(x+1)(x-1)}{(x-1)}$ in the square window.

   The graph appears to be identical to the graph of the function in simplified form, $f(x) = x + 1$.

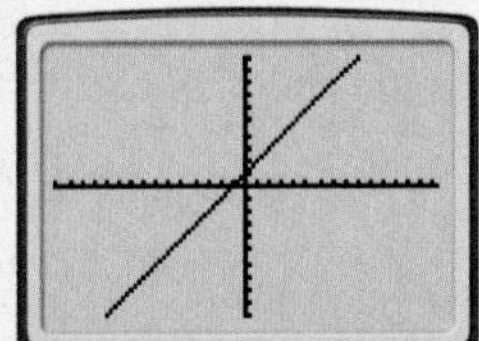

2. Change the window on your graph to the decimal window by pressing ZOOM and selecting **4:ZDecimal**.

   Notice that there is a break, or *hole,* in the graph when $x = 1$ because the function is undefined at that x-value.

   The hole appears only if you are in a friendly window that allows the calculator to evaluate the function exactly at that point.

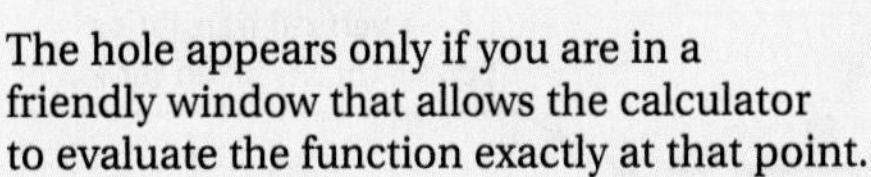

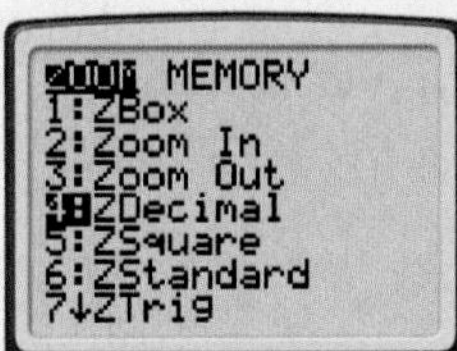

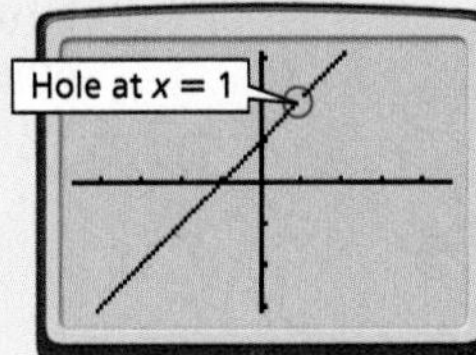

3. Use a table to compare the function $f(x) = \frac{(x+1)(x-1)}{(x-1)}$ to the linear function $f(x) = x + 1$. The table suggests that the graphs are identical except when $x = 1$.

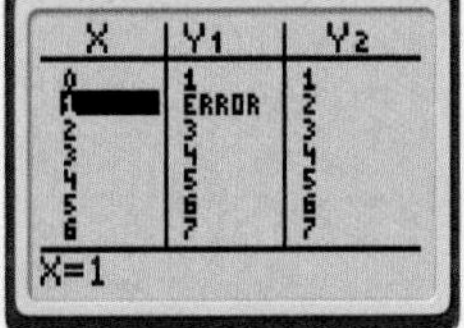

Try This

Use a graph and a table to identify the hole in the graph of each function.

1. $f(x) = \dfrac{(x-2)(x+3)}{x+3}$ hole at $x = -3$
2. $g(x) = \dfrac{(x+1)(x+3)}{x+1}$ hole at $x = -1$
3. $h(x) = \dfrac{x(x+2)}{x+2}$ hole at $x = -2$
4. **Make a Conjecture** Make a conjecture about where the holes in the graph of a rational function appear, based on the factors of the numerator and the denominator. Possible answer: The graph of a rational function has a hole for values of x that make both the numerator and the denominator equal to 0.

Use a graph and a table to identify the hole(s) in the graph of each function. Confirm your answer by factoring.

5. $f(x) = \dfrac{x^2 - 4x + 3}{x - 3}$ hole at $x = 3$
6. $g(x) = \dfrac{x^2 + x - 2}{x - 1}$ hole at $x = 1$
7. $h(x) = \dfrac{x^3 - x}{x^2 - 1}$ hole at $x = \pm 1$

Teaching Tip

Technology The **ZDecimal** feature under the **ZOOM** menu changes the viewing window of the calculator screen so that the distance between adjacent pixels is set equal to 0.1. As a result, holes in the graph of a function that occur at integer values of x show up as gaps in the graph of the function.

Organizer

Use with Lesson 8-4

Pacing:
Traditional $\frac{1}{2}$ day
Block $\frac{1}{4}$ day

Objective: Identify breaks, or holes, in graphs.

Materials: graphing calculator

Online Edition
Graphing Calculator, TechKeys

Countdown to Testing Week 17

Resources

Technology Lab Activities
8-4 Lab Recording Sheet

Teach

Discuss

Have students observe the hole in the graph of $f(x) = \frac{(x+1)(x-1)}{(x-1)}$ by using the decimal viewing window. Discuss why the function is undefined at this point.

Close

Key Concept

The graph of a rational function may have a hole if the numerator and denominator have the same factor.

Assessment

Journal Have students explain how to identify a hole in the graph of a function.

State Resources

go.hrw.com
State Resources Online
KEYWORD: MB7 Resources

8-4 Organizer

Pacing: Traditional $1\frac{1}{2}$ days
Block $\frac{3}{4}$ day

Objectives: Graph rational functions.

Transform rational functions by changing parameters.

Algebra Lab
In *Algebra Lab Activities*

Online Edition
Graphing Calculator, Tutorial Videos

Countdown to Testing Week 18

Power Presentations with PowerPoint®

Warm Up

Find the zeros of each function.

1. $f(x) = x^2 + 2x - 15$ $-5, 3$
2. $f(x) = x^2 - 49$ ± 7

Simplify. Identify any *x*-values for which the expression is undefined.

3. $\dfrac{x^2 + 5x + 4}{x^2 - 1}$ $\dfrac{x+4}{x-1}; x \neq \pm 1$
4. $\dfrac{x^2 - 8x + 12}{x^2 - 12x + 36}$ $\dfrac{x-2}{x-6}; x \neq 6$

Also available on transparency

Q: What's the difference between Tiger Woods and $f(x) = \frac{x^2 - 1}{x - 1}$?
A: One gets a hole in 1, and the other has a hole at 1.

8-4 Rational Functions

A2.5.1 Analyze, describe and sketch graphs of rational functions by examining intercepts, zeros, domain and range, and asymptotic and end behavior.

Objectives
Graph rational functions.
Transform rational functions by changing parameters.

Vocabulary
rational function
discontinuous function
continuous function
hole (in a graph)

Why learn this?
Rational functions can be used to model the cost per person for group events, such as a band trip to a bowl game. (See Exercise 32.)

A **rational function** is a function whose rule can be written as a ratio of two polynomials. The parent rational function is $f(x) = \frac{1}{x}$. Its graph is a *hyperbola*, which has two separate branches. You will learn more about hyperbolas in Chapter 10.

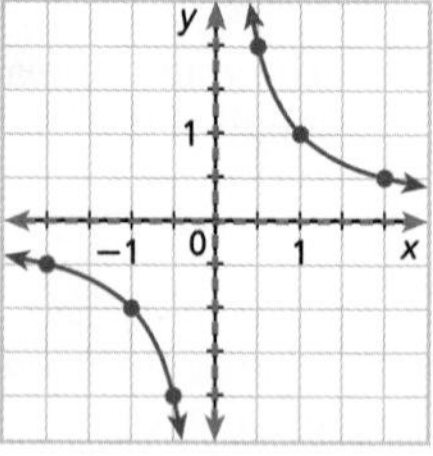

Like logarithmic and exponential functions, rational functions may have asymptotes. The function $f(x) = \frac{1}{x}$ has a vertical asymptote at $x = 0$ and a horizontal asymptote at $y = 0$.

The rational function $f(x) = \frac{1}{x}$ can be transformed by using methods similar to those used to transform other types of functions.

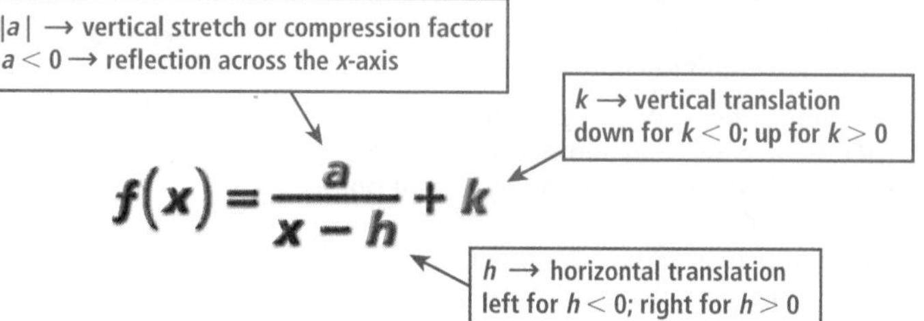

EXAMPLE 1 Transforming Rational Functions

Using the graph of $f(x) = \frac{1}{x}$ as a guide, describe the transformation and graph each function.

A $g(x) = \dfrac{1}{x-3}$

Because $h = 3$, translate f 3 units right.

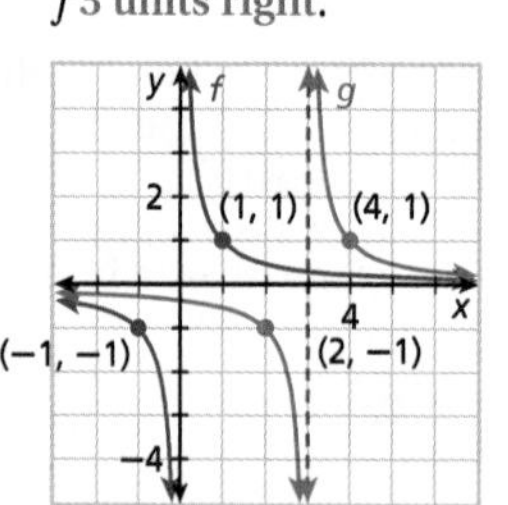

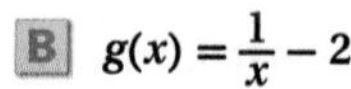

B $g(x) = \frac{1}{x} - 2$

Because $k = -2$, translate f 2 units down.

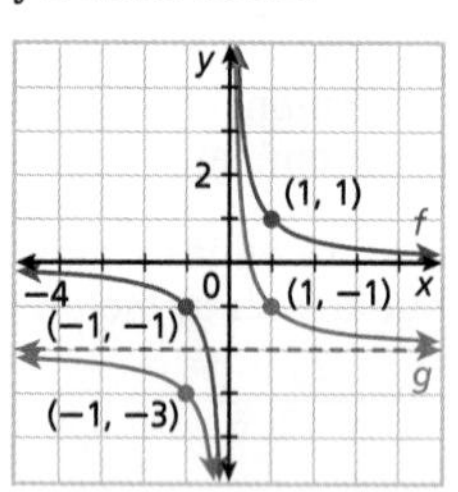

State Resources

1 Introduce

EXPLORATION

8-4 Rational Functions

You can explore the behavior of the rational function $f(x) = \frac{1}{x-2}$ by using a graphing calculator.

1. Enter the function rule by pressing [Y=] and entering **1/(X − 2)**. Graph the function by pressing [ZOOM] and selecting **4:ZDecimal**. Describe the function's graph.

Select the function you entered by pressing [VARS], scrolling right to **Y-VARS**, selecting **1:Function**, and choosing **1:Y1**. You can evaluate the function for any x-value by entering a value in parentheses as shown.

Y1(1.9)   -10

2. Complete the tables for the function $f(x) = \frac{1}{x-2}$.

x	y
1.9	
1.99	
1.999	

x	y
2.1	
2.01	
2.001	

THINK AND DISCUSS

3. Explain what happens to the value of y as the value of x gets closer and closer to 2.
4. Discuss why the function $f(x) = \frac{1}{x-2}$ is undefined at x = 2.

Motivate

Ask students to describe the graph of an indirect variation function, such as $y = \frac{12}{x}$. Lead students to recall that an indirect variation function is undefined when $x = 0$ and that its graph has two separate branches. Tell students that in this lesson they will be learning more about functions whose rules contain rational expressions.

Explorations and answers are provided in the *Explorations* binder.

Using the graph of $f(x) = \frac{1}{x}$ as a guide, describe the transformation and graph each function.

1a. $g(x) = \frac{1}{x+4}$ *g is f translated 4 units left.*

1b. $g(x) = \frac{1}{x} + 1$ *g is f translated 1 unit up.*

The values of h and k affect the locations of the asymptotes, the domain, and the range of rational functions whose graphs are hyperbolas.

Rational Functions

For a rational function of the form $f(x) = \frac{a}{x-h} + k$,
- the graph is a hyperbola.
- there is a vertical asymptote at the line $x = h$, and the domain is $\{x \mid x \neq h\}$.
- there is a horizontal asymptote at the line $y = k$, and the range is $\{y \mid y \neq k\}$.

EXAMPLE 2 Determining Properties of Hyperbolas

Identify the asymptotes, domain, and range of the function $g(x) = \frac{1}{x+2} + 4$.

$g(x) = \frac{1}{x-(-2)} + 4$ *$h = -2$, $k = 4$*

Vertical asymptote: $x = -2$ *The value of h is −2.*

Domain: $\{x \mid x \neq -2\}$

Horizontal asymptote: $y = 4$ *The value of k is 4.*

Range: $\{y \mid y \neq 4\}$

Check Graph the function on a graphing calculator. The graph suggests that the function has asymptotes at $x = -2$ and $y = 4$.

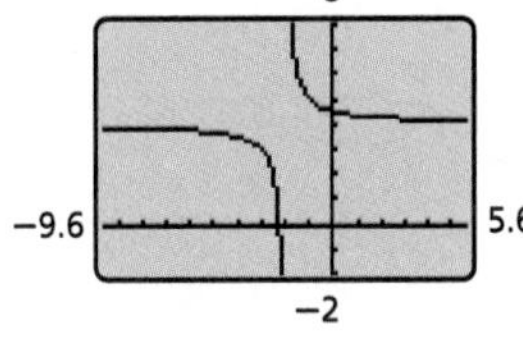

Caution!

Graphing calculators may incorrectly connect two branches of the graph of a rational function with a nearly vertical segment that looks like an asymptote.

2. Identify the asymptotes, domain, and range of the function $g(x) = \frac{1}{x-3} - 5$. **asymptotes: $x = 3$, $y = -5$; D: $\{x \mid x \neq 3\}$; R: $\{y \mid y \neq -5\}$**

A **discontinuous function** is a function whose graph has one or more gaps or breaks. The hyperbola graphed above and many other rational functions are discontinuous functions.

A **continuous function** is a function whose graph has no gaps or breaks. The functions you have studied before this, including linear, quadratic, polynomial, exponential, and logarithmic functions, are continuous functions.

The graphs of some rational functions are not hyperbolas. Consider the rational function $f(x) = \frac{(x-3)(x+2)}{x+1}$ and its graph. The numerator of this function is 0 when $x = 3$ or $x = -2$. Therefore, the function has x-intercepts at -2 and 3. The denominator of this function is 0 when $x = -1$. As a result, the graph of the function has a vertical asymptote at the line $x = -1$.

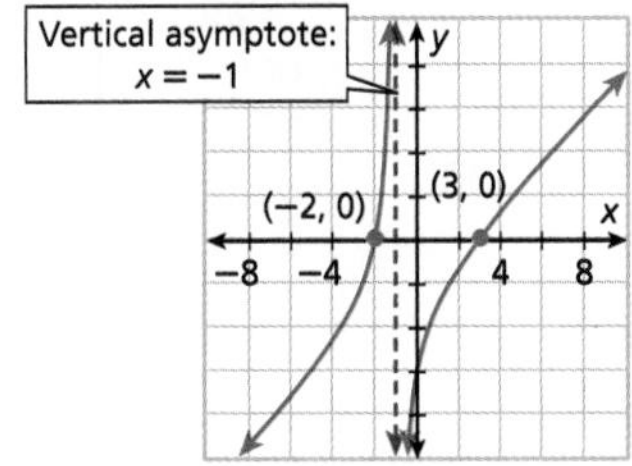

Power Presentations with PowerPoint®

Additional Examples

Example 1

Using the graph of $f(x) = \frac{1}{x}$ as a guide, describe the transformation and graph each function.

A. $g(x) = \frac{1}{x+2}$

g is f translated left 2 units.

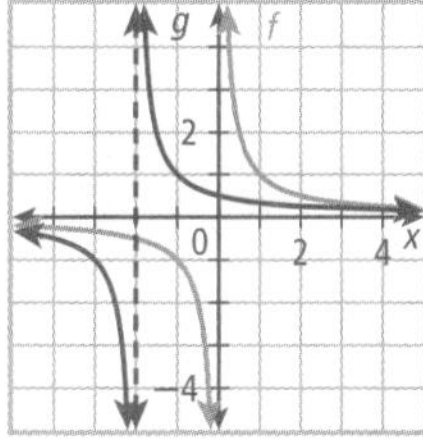

B. $g(x) = \frac{1}{x} - 3$

g is f translated down 3 units.

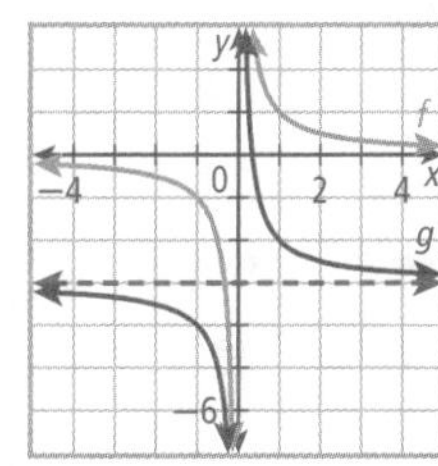

Also available on transparency

INTERVENTION

Questioning Strategies

EXAMPLE 1

- How can you tell if the function is translated left or right compared to $f(x) = \frac{1}{x}$? translated up or down?

Answers to *Check It Out!*

1a.

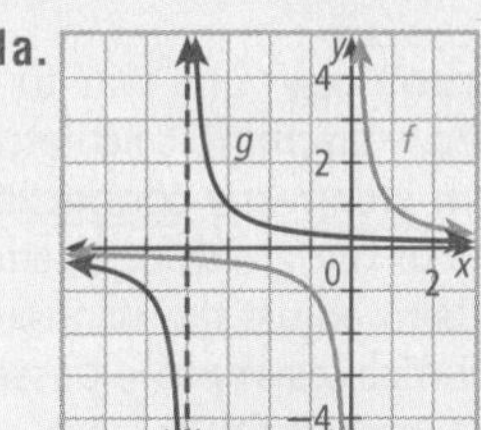

1b.

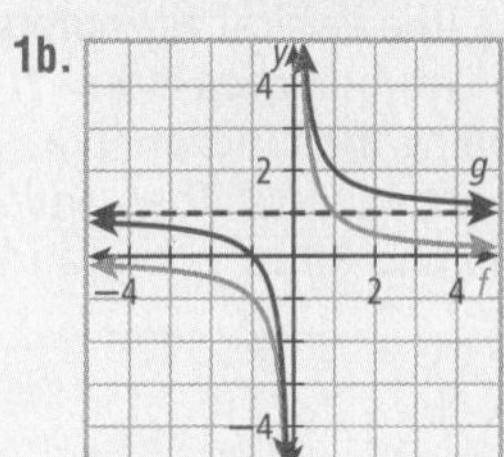

2 Teach

Guided Instruction

Introduce students to rational functions by having them investigate simple transformations of the graph of the parent function $f(x) = \frac{1}{x}$. Then discuss how they can determine properties of more-complicated rational functions by analyzing the polynomials that define them. Explain how students can then use these properties to help them graph the functions.

Reaching All Learners

Through Cooperative Learning

Have students work in pairs. Give one student in each pair a rational function of the form $f(x) = \frac{(x+a)(x+b)}{(x+c)(x+d)}$, where a, b, c, and d are integers. Have that student describe the function solely in terms of its zeros, asymptotes, and holes if any. The partner should attempt to write a rational function that fits this description. Pairs can then discuss their results. Point out that more than one rational function can have the same zeros, asymptotes, and holes.

Power Presentations with PowerPoint®

Additional Examples

Example 2

Identify the asymptotes, domain, and range of the function $g(x) = \frac{1}{x+3} - 2$.

asymptotes: $x = -3$, $y = -2$; D: $\{x \mid x \neq -3\}$; R: $\{y \mid y \neq -2\}$

Example 3

Identify the zeros and vertical asymptotes of $f(x) = \frac{x^2 + 3x - 4}{x + 3}$. Then graph. zeros: -4, 1; vertical asymptote: $x = -3$

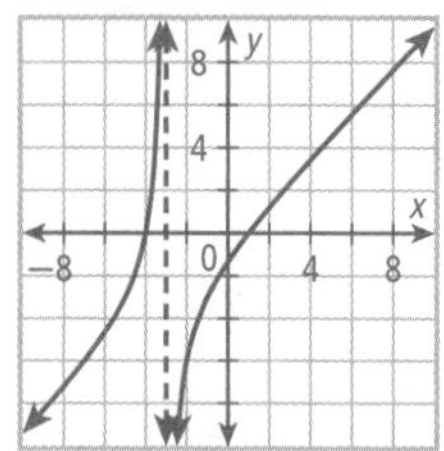

Also available on transparency

INTERVENTION

Questioning Strategies

EXAMPLE 2

- What is the relationship between the vertical asymptote and the domain? between the horizontal asymptote and the range?

EXAMPLE 3

- How do you find the zeros of the function? the vertical asymptotes?
- How can you determine the y-intercept of the function's graph?

Technology One way to keep a graphing calculator from incorrectly connecting two branches of the graph of a rational function is to adjust the window so that the vertical asymptote passes through the center of the screen.

In **Example 3,** the vertical asymptote between the two branches is $x = 2$. Start by graphing the function in a standard square window. Then add 2 to the **Xmin** and **Xmax** values and press GRAPH.

Know it! Note — Zeros and Vertical Asymptotes — Rational Functions

If $f(x) = \frac{p(x)}{q(x)}$, where p and q are polynomial functions in standard form with no common factors other than 1, then the function f has

- zeros at each real value of x for which $p(x) = 0$.
- a vertical asymptote at each real value of x for which $q(x) = 0$.

EXAMPLE 3 Graphing Rational Functions with Vertical Asymptotes

Identify the zeros and vertical asymptotes of $f(x) = \frac{x^2 - 2x - 3}{x - 2}$. Then graph.

Remember! For a review of factoring and finding zeros of polynomial functions, see Lessons 6-4 and 6-5.

Step 1 Find the zeros and vertical asymptotes.

$f(x) = \frac{(x+1)(x-3)}{x-2}$ *Factor the numerator.*

Zeros: -1 and 3 *The numerator is 0 when $x = -1$ or $x = 3$.*

Vertical asymptote: $x = 2$ *The denominator is 0 when $x = 2$.*

Step 2 Graph the function.

Plot the zeros and draw the asymptote. Then make a table of values to fill in missing points.

x	-4	-1	0	1.5	2.5	3	5
y	-3.5	0	1.5	7.5	-3.5	0	4

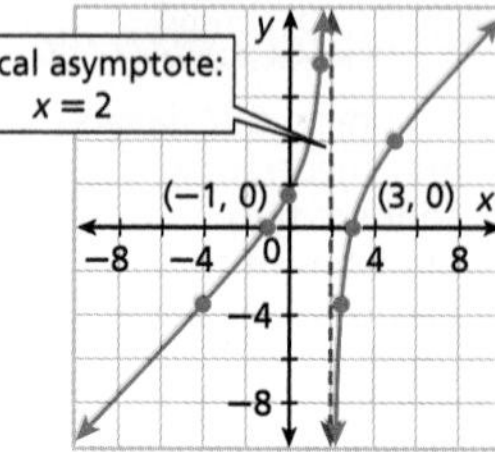

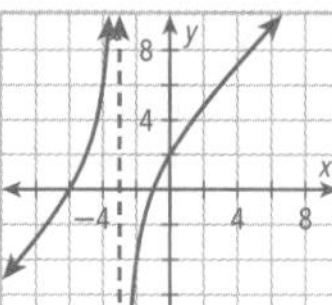

3. Identify the zeros and vertical asymptotes of $f(x) = \frac{x^2 + 7x + 6}{x + 3}$. Then graph. zeros: -6, -1; asymptote: $x = -3$

Some rational functions, including those whose graphs are hyperbolas, have a horizontal asymptote. The existence and location of a horizontal asymptote depends on the degrees of the polynomials that make up the rational function.

Note that the graph of a rational function can sometimes cross a horizontal asymptote. However, the graph will approach the asymptote when $|x|$ is large.

Know it! Note — Horizontal Asymptotes — Rational Functions

Let $f(x) = \frac{p(x)}{q(x)}$, where p and q are polynomial functions in standard form with no common factors other than 1. The graph of f has at most one horizontal asymptote.

- If degree of p > degree of q, there is no horizontal asymptote.
- If degree of p < degree of q, the horizontal asymptote is the line $y = 0$.
- If degree of p = degree of q, the horizontal asymptote is the line $y = \frac{\text{leading coefficient of } p}{\text{leading coefficient of } q}$.

Teacher to Teacher

I like to let students first explore many graphs of rational functions by using a graphing calculator. I ask them to make conjectures about horizontal asymptotes of rational functions. Students can make and test conjectures to see if they hold true for other cases. I ask students to try to explain why their conjectures would be true for all cases.

Given the fact that horizontal asymptotes of rational functions depend on the degrees of the polynomials in the rational function, students can often come up with the rules for horizontal asymptotes on their own or when working together as a group.

Margie Hill
Overland Park, KS

EXAMPLE 4 Graphing Rational Functions with Vertical and Horizontal Asymptotes

Identify the zeros and asymptotes of each function. Then graph.

A $f(x) = \frac{x^2 + x - 6}{x}$

$f(x) = \frac{(x+3)(x-2)}{x}$ *Factor the numerator.*

Zeros: −3 and 2 *The numerator is 0 when x = −3 or x = 2.*

Vertical asymptote: $x = 0$ *The denominator is 0 when x = 0.*

Horizontal asymptote: none *Degree of p > degree of q*

Graph with a graphing calculator or by using a table of values.

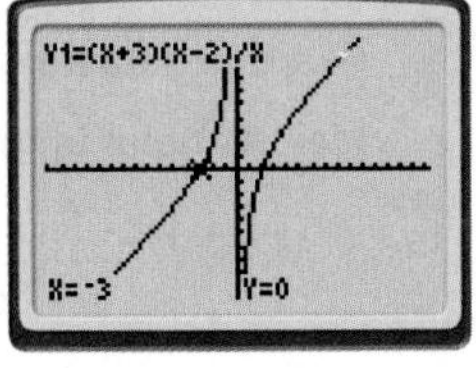

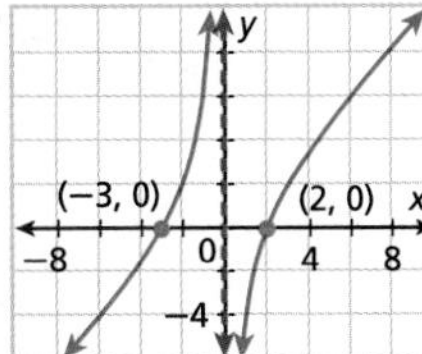

B $f(x) = \frac{x - 1}{x^2}$

Zero: 1 *The numerator is 0 when x = 1.*

Vertical asymptote: $x = 0$ *The denominator is 0 when x = 0.*

Horizontal asymptote: $y = 0$ *Degree of p < degree of q*

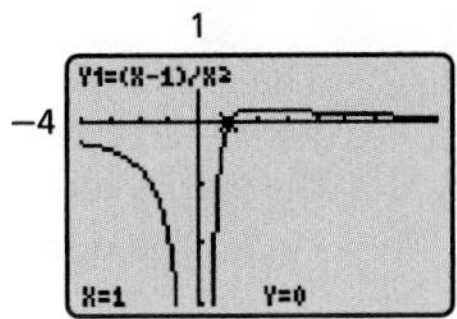

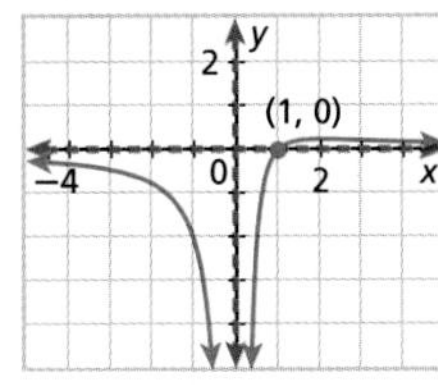

C $f(x) = \frac{2x^2 - 2}{x^2 - 4}$

$f(x) = \frac{2(x+1)(x-1)}{(x+2)(x-2)}$ *Factor the numerator and denominator.*

Zeros: −1 and 1 *The numerator is 0 when x = −1 or x = 1.*

Vertical asymptotes: $x = -2, x = 2$ *The denominator is 0 when x = ±2.*

Horizontal asymptote: $y = 2$ *The horizontal asymptote is* $y = \frac{\text{leading coefficient of } p}{\text{leading coefficient of } q} = \frac{2}{1} = 2.$

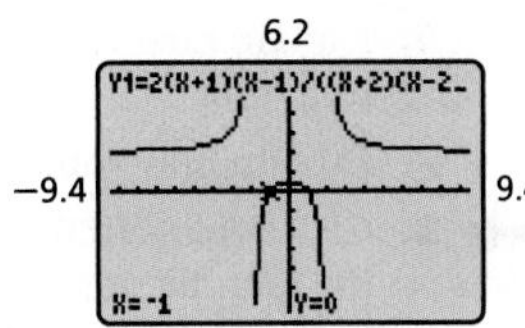

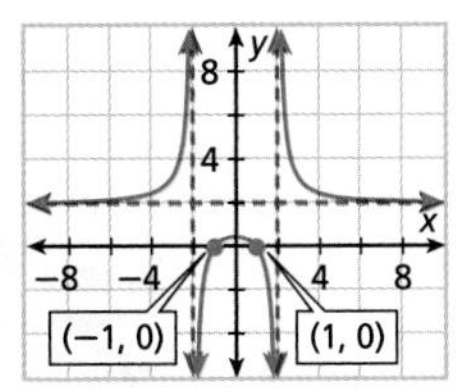

Identify the zeros and asymptotes of each function. Then graph.

4a. $f(x) = \frac{x^2 + 2x - 15}{x - 1}$ **4b.** $f(x) = \frac{x - 2}{x^2 + x}$ **4c.** $f(x) = \frac{3x^2 + x}{x^2 - 9}$

Remember!

Recall from Lesson 6-1 that the leading coefficient of a polynomial is the coefficient of the first term when the polynomial is written in standard form.

Answers to Check It Out!

4a. zeros: −5, 3; asymptote: $x = 1$

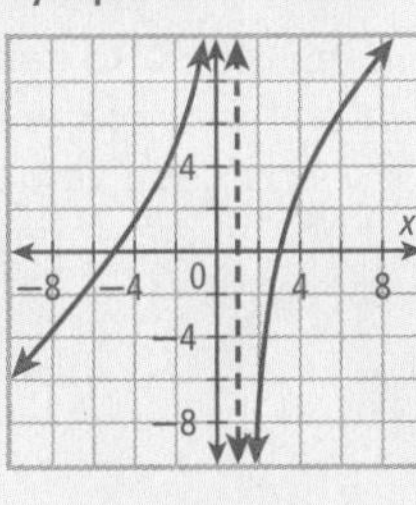

4b. zero: 2; asymptotes: $x = -1, x = 0, y = 0$

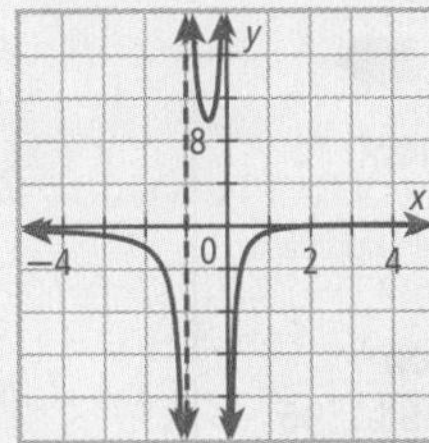

4c. zeros: $-\frac{1}{3}$, 0; asymptotes: $x = -3, x = 3, y = 3$

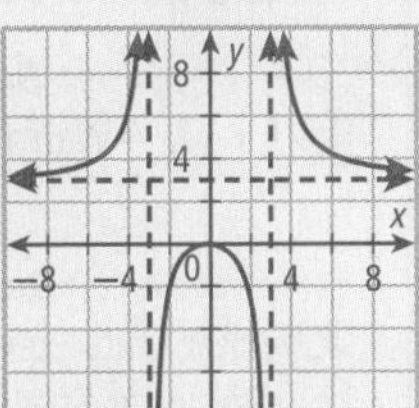

COMMON ERROR ALERT

Students sometimes rely too heavily on their calculators when graphing rational functions. Depending on the window they use, they may miss one or more branches of the graph entirely. Remind students that they should first determine the zeros and asymptotes of a rational function so that they have a general idea of what its graph will look like.

Power Presentations with PowerPoint®

Additional Examples

Example 4

Identify the zeros and asymptotes of each function. Then graph.

A. $f(x) = \frac{x^2 - 3x - 4}{x}$

zeros: −1, 4; asym.: $x = 0$

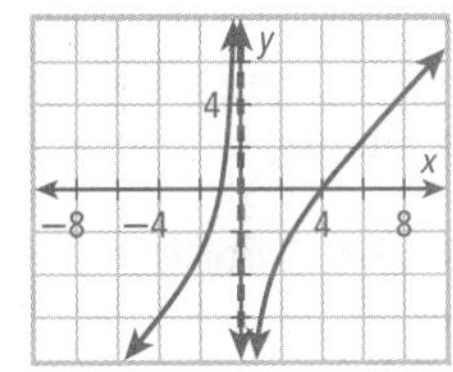

B. $f(x) = \frac{x - 2}{x^2 - 1}$

zero: 2; asym.: $x = -1, x = 1, y = 0$

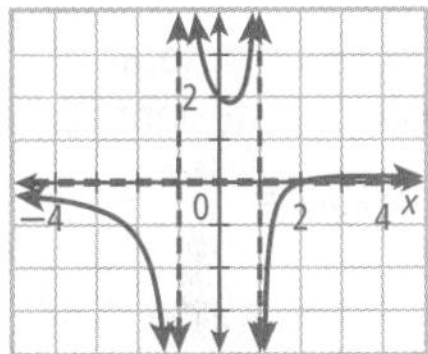

C. $f(x) = \frac{4x - 12}{x - 1}$

zero: 3; asym.: $x = 1, y = 4$

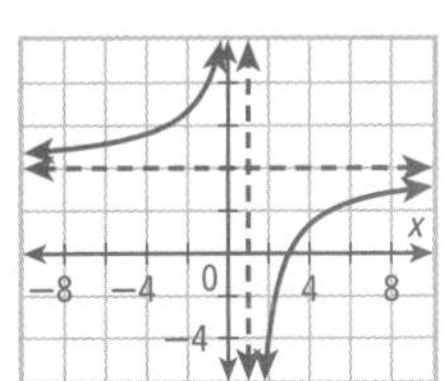

Also available on transparency

INTERVENTION Questioning Strategies

EXAMPLE 4

- How do you use the properties of p and q to find the horizontal asymptote of a rational function having the form $f(x) = \frac{p(x)}{q(x)}$?

Power Presentations with PowerPoint®

Additional Examples

Example 5

Identify holes in the graph of $f(x) = \frac{x^2 - 9}{x - 3}$. Then graph.

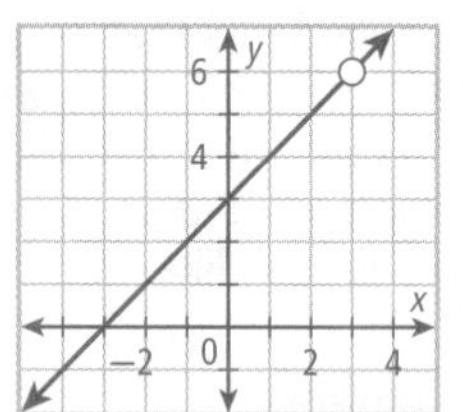

hole at $x = 3$

Also available on transparency

INTERVENTION

Questioning Strategies

EXAMPLE 5

- How can you determine whether the graph of a rational function has a hole?
- How do you indicate a hole in the graph of a rational function?

Critical Thinking A rational function with the same factor $x - b$ in both the numerator and denominator does not necessarily have a hole at $x = b$. If the factor $x - b$ is raised to a higher power in the denominator than in the numerator, the function has a vertical asymptote at $x = b$. As an illustration, ask students to graph and compare $f(x) = \frac{(x+1)^2}{(x+1)^3}$, $f(x) = \frac{(x+1)^2}{x+1}$, and $f(x) = \frac{x+1}{x+1}$.

In some cases, both the numerator and the denominator of a rational function will equal 0 for a particular value of x. As a result, the function will be undefined at this x-value. If this is the case, the graph of the function may have a *hole*. A **hole** is an omitted point in a graph.

Know it! Note

Holes in Graphs — Rational Functions

If a rational function has the same factor $x - b$ in both the numerator and the denominator, then there is a hole in the graph at the point where $x = b$, unless the line $x = b$ is a vertical asymptote.

EXAMPLE 5 Graphing Rational Functions with Holes

Identify holes in the graph of $f(x) = \frac{x^2 - 4}{x + 2}$. Then graph.

$f(x) = \frac{(x-2)(x+2)}{(x+2)}$ — *Factor the numerator.*

There is a hole in the graph at $x = -2$. — *The expression $x + 2$ is a factor of both the numerator and the denominator.*

For $x \neq -2$, $f(x) = \frac{(x-2)\cancel{(x+2)}}{\cancel{(x+2)}} = x - 2$ — *Divide out common factors.*

The graph of f is the same as the graph of $y = x - 2$, except for the hole at $x = -2$. On the graph, indicate the hole with an open circle. The domain of f is $\{x \mid x \neq -2\}$.

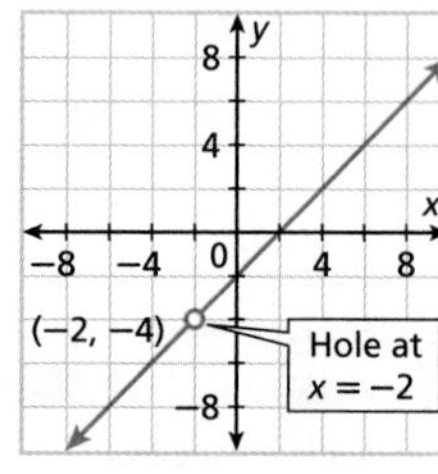

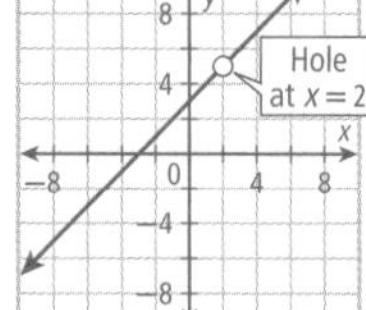

5. Identify holes in the graph of $f(x) = \frac{x^2 + x - 6}{x - 2}$. Then graph.
hole at $x = 2$

THINK AND DISCUSS

1. Explain how vertical asymptotes relate to the domain of a rational function.
2. Explain how you can tell if the graph of a rational function has a hole.

3. **GET ORGANIZED** Copy and complete the graphic organizer. In each box, write the formula or method for identifying the characteristic of graphs of rational functions.

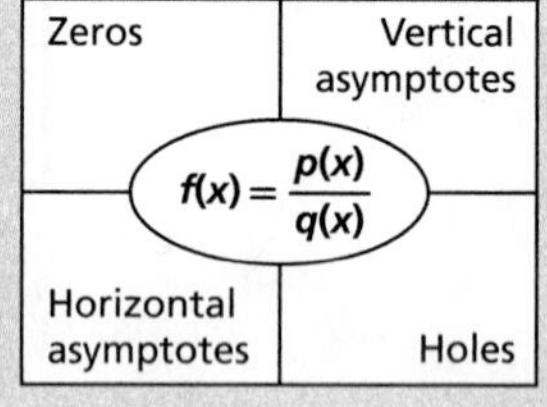

3 Close

Summarize

Review the process for graphing rational functions of the form $f(x) = \frac{p(x)}{q(x)}$.

- Identify the zeros.
- Identify both the vertical and horizontal asymptotes.
- Identify any holes.
- Plot the zeros, asymptotes, and holes.
- Use a table of values to identify additional points on the function's graph.
- Draw each branch with a smooth curve.

ONGOING ASSESSMENT and INTERVENTION

***Diagnose Before* the Lesson**
8-4 Warm Up, TE p. 592

***Monitor During* the Lesson**
Check It Out! Exercises, SE pp. 593–596
Questioning Strategies, TE pp. 593–596

***Assess After* the Lesson**
8-4 Lesson Quiz, TE p. 599
Alternative Assessment, TE p. 599

Answers to *Think and Discuss*

Possible answers:

1. The x-values of the vertical asymptotes are excluded from the domain.
2. If both the numerator and denominator have a common factor of the form $x - a$ and $x = a$ is not a vertical asymptote, then the graph has a hole at $x = a$.
3. See p. A10.

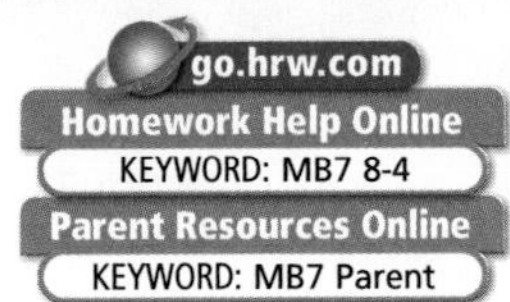

GUIDED PRACTICE

1. **Vocabulary** A function with a hole in its graph is __?__. (*continuous* or *discontinuous*) discontinuous

SEE EXAMPLE 1 p. 592

Using the graph of $f(x) = \frac{1}{x}$ as a guide, describe the transformation and graph each function.

2. $g(x) = \frac{1}{x} - 2$ — g is f translated 2 units down.
3. $g(x) = \frac{1}{x+5}$ — g is f translated 5 units left.
4. $g(x) = \frac{1}{x-1} + 4$ — 4. g is f translated 1 unit right and 4 units up.

SEE EXAMPLE 2 p. 593

Identify the asymptotes, domain, and range of each function.

5. $f(x) = \frac{1}{x} - 1$
6. $f(x) = \frac{1}{x+4} + 3$
7. $f(x) = \frac{2}{x-2} - 8$

SEE EXAMPLE 3 p. 594

Identify the zeros and vertical asymptotes of each function. Then graph.

8. $f(x) = \frac{x^2 - x - 12}{x}$
9. $f(x) = \frac{x^2 - 5x}{x-2}$
10. $f(x) = \frac{x^2}{x-1}$

SEE EXAMPLE 4 p. 595

Identify the zeros and asymptotes of each function. Then graph.

11. $f(x) = \frac{x^2 + 3x + 2}{3 - x}$
12. $f(x) = \frac{x-2}{x^2 + 6x}$
13. $f(x) = \frac{5x+2}{x+1}$

SEE EXAMPLE 5 p. 596

Identify holes in the graph of each function. Then graph.

14. $f(x) = \frac{x^2 - 5x + 6}{x^2 - 4x + 3}$ hole at $x = 3$
15. $f(x) = \frac{x^2 - 4x + 4}{x - 2}$ hole at $x = 2$
16. $f(x) = \frac{4x + 20}{2x + 10}$ hole at $x = -5$

PRACTICE AND PROBLEM SOLVING

Independent Practice	
For Exercises	See Example
17–19	1
20–22	2
23–25	3
26–28	4
29–31	5

Extra Practice
Skills Practice p. S18
Application Practice p. S39

Using the graph of $f(x) = \frac{1}{x}$ as a guide, describe the transformation and graph each function.

17. $g(x) = \frac{1}{x} - 5$ — g is f translated 5 units down.
18. $g(x) = \frac{1}{x+3}$ — g is f translated 3 units left.
19. $g(x) = \frac{2}{x}$ — 19. g is f vertically stretched by a factor of 2

Identify the asymptotes, domain, and range of each function.

20. $f(x) = \frac{1}{x+6}$
21. $f(x) = \frac{4}{x} + 5$
22. $f(x) = \frac{3}{x-4} - 1$

Identify the zeros and vertical asymptotes of each function. Then graph.

23. $f(x) = \frac{(x+2)(x-5)}{(x-2)}$
24. $f(x) = \frac{(2-x)(4+x)}{(x-1)}$
25. $h(x) = \frac{x^2 - 4}{x+3}$

Identify the zeros and asymptotes of each function. Then graph.

26. $f(x) = \frac{x^2 - x - 2}{1 - x}$
27. $f(x) = \frac{x-3}{x^2 - 4}$
28. $f(x) = \frac{2x^2 + x}{1 - x^2}$

Identify holes in the graph of each function. Then graph.

29. $f(x) = \frac{x^4}{x}$ hole at $x = 0$
30. $f(x) = \frac{-x^2 + x}{x - 1}$ hole at $x = 1$
31. $f(x) = \frac{x^2 - 14x + 49}{x - 7}$ hole at $x = 7$

32. **Band** Members of a high school band plan to play at a college bowl game. The trip will cost \$350 per band member plus a \$2000 deposit.
    a. Write a function to represent the total average cost of the trip per band member. 32a. $f(x) = \frac{2000}{x} + 350$
    b. Graph the function.
    c. **What if...?** Find the total average cost per person if 40 band members attend the bowl game. \$400

Assignment Guide

Assign *Guided Practice* exercises as necessary.

If you finished Examples **1–3**
Basic 17–25, 32, 44
Average 17–25, 32, 44
Advanced 17–25, 32, 44, 55

If you finished Examples **1–5**
Basic 17–45, 47, 49–52, 58–64
Average 17–54, 58–64
Advanced 17–44, 46–64

Homework Quick Check
Quickly check key concepts.
Exercises: 18, 20, 24, 26, 30, 44

Answers

2–4. For graphs, see p. A36.

5. asymptotes: $x = 0$, $y = -1$; D: $\{x \mid x \neq 0\}$; R: $\{y \mid y \neq -1\}$
6. asymptotes: $x = -4$, $y = 3$; D: $\{x \mid x \neq -4\}$; R: $\{y \mid y \neq 3\}$
7. asymptotes: $x = 2$, $y = -8$; D: $\{x \mid x \neq 2\}$; R: $\{y \mid y \neq -8\}$

8–13. For graphs, see p. A36.

8. zeros: −3, 4; vertical asymptote: $x = 0$
9. zeros: 0, 5; vertical asymptote: $x = 2$
10. zero: 0; vertical asymptote: $x = 1$
11. zeros: −2, −1; asymptote: $x = 3$

Answers

12. zero: 2; asymptotes: $x = -6$, $x = 0$, $y = 0$
13. zero: $-\frac{2}{5}$; asymptotes: $x = -1$, $y = 5$

14–19. For graphs, see p. A36.

20. asymptotes: $x = -6$, $y = 0$; D: $\{x \mid x \neq -6\}$; R: $\{y \mid y \neq 0\}$
21. asymptotes: $x = 0$, $y = 5$; D: $\{x \mid x \neq 0\}$; R: $\{y \mid y \neq 5\}$
22. asymptotes: $x = 4$, $y = -1$; D: $\{x \mid x \neq 4\}$; R: $\{y \mid y \neq -1\}$

23–31. For graphs, see p. A37.

23. zeros: −2, 5; vertical asymptote: $x = 2$
24. zeros: −4, 2; vertical asymptote: $x = 1$
25. zeros: −2, 2; vertical asymptote: $x = -3$
26. zeros: −1, 2; vertical asymptote: $x = 1$
27. zero: 3; asymptotes: $x = -2$, $x = 2$, $y = 0$
28. zeros: $-\frac{1}{2}$, 0; asymptotes: $x = -1$, $x = 1$, $y = -2$

32b. See p. A37.

State Resources

go.hrw.com
State Resources Online
KEYWORD: MB7 Resources

Teaching Tip **Multiple Representations** In **Exercises 39–41**, suggest that students check their answers by graphing their functions on a graphing calculator.

Teaching Tip **Inclusion** You may wish to point out in **Exercise 44** that x represents the number of DVDs purchased and f represents the average cost per DVD. Since k is a constant, students can use the data in any row of the table to determine its value.

MULTI-STEP TEST PREP **Exercise 47** involves graphing a rational function to solve a problem about average speed. This exercise prepares students for the Multi-Step Test Prep on page 608.

Answers

33. zero: −1; asymptotes: $x = 0$, $y = 1$; hole at $x = 3$
34. hole at $x = 1$
35. zero: $\frac{5}{6}$; asymptotes: $x = \frac{2}{3}$, $y = -2$
36. zeros: −4, −2; asymptotes: $x = 0$; $y = 1$
37. zero: 0; asymptotes: $x = 3$, $x = -3$, $y = 0$
38. zeros: ±3; asymptotes: $x = 2$, $x = -2$, $y = 1$
39. Possible answer: $f(x) = \dfrac{(x+1)(x-3)}{x}$
40. Possible answer: $f(x) = \dfrac{(x-2)}{x(x+2)}$
41, 42a, 43a, 44a, 45–46, 47a–b. See p. A37.

Identify all zeros, asymptotes, and holes in the graph of each function.

33. $f(x) = \dfrac{x^2 - 2x - 3}{x^2 - 3x}$ **34.** $f(x) = \dfrac{x^3 - 1}{x - 1}$ **35.** $f(x) = \dfrac{6x - 5}{2 - 3x}$

36. $f(x) = \dfrac{x^2 + 6x + 8}{x^2}$ **37.** $f(x) = \dfrac{x}{x^2 - 9}$ **38.** $f(x) = \dfrac{x^2 - 9}{x^2 - 4}$

Write a rational function with the given characteristics.

39. zeros at −1 and 3 and vertical asymptote at $x = 0$

40. zero at 2, vertical asymptotes at $x = -2$ and $x = 0$, and horizontal asymptote at $y = 0$

41. zero at 2, vertical asymptote at $x = -1$, horizontal asymptote at $y = 1$, and hole at $x = -3$

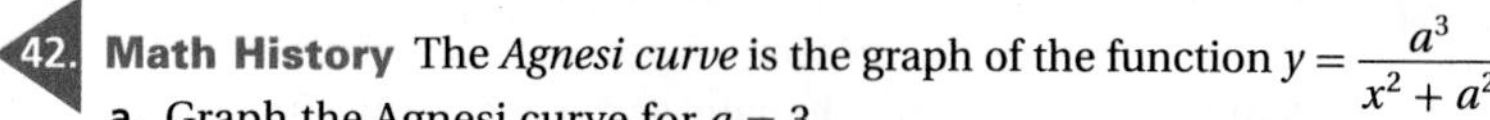

LINK **Math History**

The Agnesi curve is named for Maria Agnesi (1718–1799), a mathematician from Milan who wrote one of the earliest surviving mathematical works composed by a woman.

42. **Math History** The *Agnesi curve* is the graph of the function $y = \dfrac{a^3}{x^2 + a^2}$.

a. Graph the Agnesi curve for $a = 3$.

b. What are the domain and the range of the function? **D: ℝ; R: $\{y \mid 0 < y \le 3\}$**

c. Identify all asymptotes of the function. **$y = 0$**

43. **Chemistry** A chemist has 100 g of a 12% saline solution that she wants to strengthen to 25%. The percentage P of salt in the solution by mass can be modeled by $P(x) = \frac{100(12 + x)}{100 + x}$, where x is the number of grams of salt added.

a. Graph the function for $0 \le x \le 100$.

b. Use your graph to estimate how much salt the chemist must add to create a 25% solution. **≈ 17 g**

44. **Multi-Step** The average cost per DVD purchased from a movie club is a function of the number of DVDs a member buys.

a. Graph the data in the table.

b. The function that describes the data in the table has the form $f(x) = \frac{40}{x} + k$, where k is a constant. What is the value of k? **15**

c. What is the total cost of buying 15 DVDs from the club? **$265**

Number of DVDs	Average Cost ($)
1	55
2	35
4	25
5	23
10	19
20	17

45. **ERROR ANALYSIS** A student wrote the following description for the graph of $f(x) = \frac{(x-1)(2x-3)}{(x+1)(x-1)}$. Explain the error. Write a correct description.

The graph has vertical asymptotes at $x = 1$ and $x = -1$ and a horizontal asymptote at $y = 2$.

46. **Critical Thinking** Is it possible to have a rational function with no vertical asymptotes? Explain.

MULTI-STEP TEST PREP

47. This problem will prepare you for the Multi-Step Test Prep on page 608.

A race car driver makes a pit stop at the beginning of a lap. The time t in seconds that it takes the driver to complete the lap, including the pit stop, can be modeled by $t(r) = \frac{12r + 9000}{r}$, where r is the driver's average speed in miles per hour after the pit stop.

a. Graph the function.

b. What is the horizontal asymptote of the function, and what does it represent?

c. The driver's average speed after the pit stop is 200 mi/h. How long does it take the driver to complete the lap, including the pit stop? **57 s**

8-4 PRACTICE A

8-4 PRACTICE C

8-4 PRACTICE B

Using the graph of $f(x) = \frac{1}{x}$ as a guide, describe the transformation and graph the function.

1. $g(x) = \frac{2}{x+4}$

Translate 4 units left and vertically stretched by a factor of 2

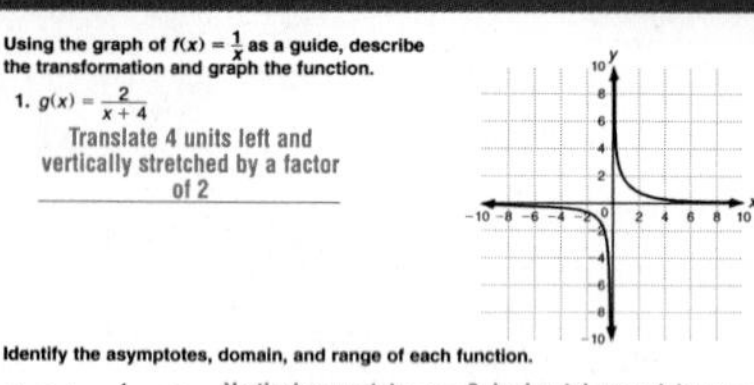

Identify the asymptotes, domain, and range of each function.

2. $g(x) = \frac{1}{x-3} + 5$ Vertical asymptote: $x = 3$; horizontal asymptote: $y = 5$; domain: $\{x \mid x \ne 3\}$; range: $\{y \mid y \ne 5\}$

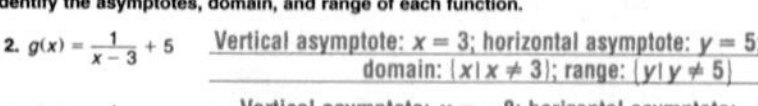

3. $g(x) = \frac{1}{x+8} - 1$ Vertical asymptote: $x = -8$; horizontal asymptote: $y = -1$; domain: $\{x \mid x \ne -8\}$; range: $\{y \mid y \ne -1\}$

Identify the zeros and asymptotes of the function. Then graph.

4. $f(x) = \frac{x^2 + 4x - 5}{x + 1}$

a. Zeros: Zeros: −5 and 1

b. Vertical asymptote: Vertical asymptote: $x = -1$

c. Horizontal asymptote: Horizontal asymptote: none

d. Graph.

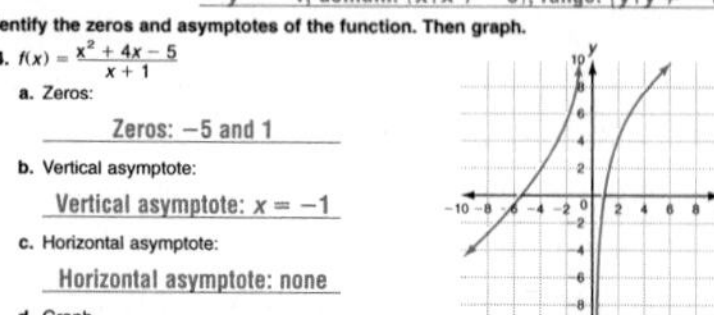

Solve.

5. The number, n, of daily visitors to a new store can be modeled by the function $n = \frac{(250x + 1000)}{x}$, where x is the number of days the store has been open.

a. What is the asymptote of this function and what does it represent? The asymptote is 250; it is the average number of people who will visit the store each day, long after the store opens.

b. To the nearest integer, how many visitors can be expected on day 30? 283

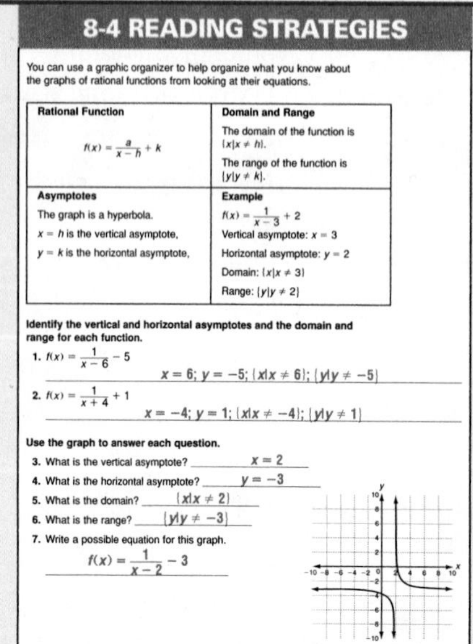

8-4 READING STRATEGIES

You can use a graphic organizer to help organize what you know about the graphs of rational functions from looking at their equations.

Rational Function	Domain and Range
$f(x) = \frac{a}{x-h} + k$	The domain of the function is $\{x \mid x \ne h\}$. The range of the function is $\{y \mid y \ne k\}$.
Asymptotes	**Example**
The graph is a hyperbola. $x = h$ is the vertical asymptote, $y = k$ is the horizontal asymptote,	$f(x) = \frac{1}{x-3} + 2$ Vertical asymptote: $x = 3$ Horizontal asymptote: $y = 2$ Domain: $\{x \mid x \ne 3\}$ Range: $\{y \mid y \ne 2\}$

Identify the vertical and horizontal asymptotes and the domain and range for each function.

1. $f(x) = \frac{1}{x-6} - 5$ $x = 6$; $y = -5$; $\{x \mid x \ne 6\}$; $\{y \mid y \ne -5\}$

2. $f(x) = \frac{1}{x+4} + 1$ $x = -4$; $y = 1$; $\{x \mid x \ne -4\}$; $\{y \mid y \ne 1\}$

Use the graph to answer each question.

3. What is the vertical asymptote? $x = 2$
4. What is the horizontal asymptote? $y = -3$
5. What is the domain? $\{x \mid x \ne 2\}$
6. What is the range? $\{y \mid y \ne -3\}$
7. Write a possible equation for this graph. $f(x) = \frac{1}{x-2} - 3$

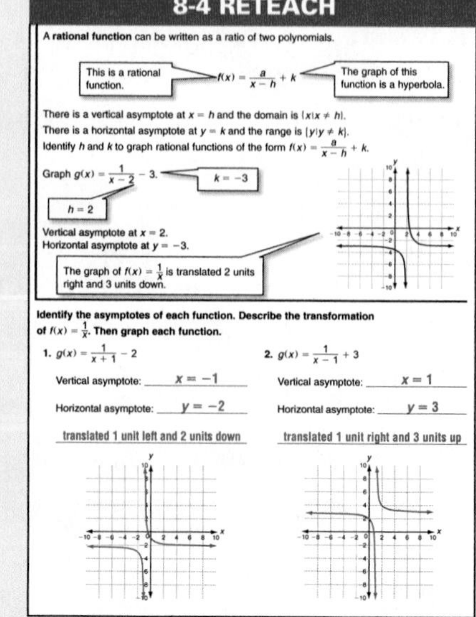

8-4 RETEACH

A **rational function** can be written as a ratio of two polynomials.

$f(x) = \frac{a}{x-h} + k$

There is a vertical asymptote at $x = h$ and the domain is $\{x \mid x \ne h\}$.
There is a horizontal asymptote at $y = k$ and the range is $\{y \mid y \ne k\}$.
Identify h and k to graph rational functions of the form $f(x) = \frac{a}{x-h} + k$.

Graph $g(x) = \frac{1}{x-2} - 3$.

Vertical asymptote at $x = 2$.
Horizontal asymptote at $y = -3$.

Identify the asymptotes of each function. Describe the transformation of $f(x) = \frac{1}{x}$. Then graph each function.

1. $g(x) = \frac{1}{x+1} - 2$

Vertical asymptote: $x = -1$

Horizontal asymptote: $y = -2$

translated 1 unit left and 2 units down

2. $g(x) = \frac{1}{x-1} + 3$

Vertical asymptote: $x = 1$

Horizontal asymptote: $y = 3$

translated 1 unit right and 3 units up

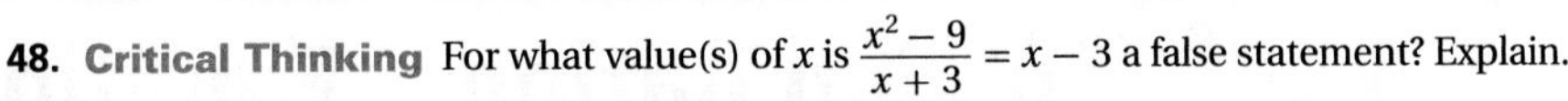

48. **Critical Thinking** For what value(s) of x is $\frac{x^2-9}{x+3} = x-3$ a false statement? Explain.

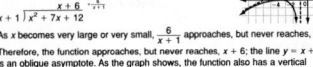

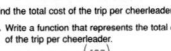

49. **Write About It** Explain how to identify the domain of a rational function. Possible answer: The domain of a rational function is all real numbers except the x-values of vertical asymptotes and holes.

TEST PREP

50. The graph of which of the following rational functions has a hole?

Ⓐ $f(x) = \frac{x^2+5x+4}{x^2+x-12}$ (circled)

Ⓒ $f(x) = \frac{x^2-9}{x^2-2x-7}$

Ⓑ $f(x) = \frac{x^2-2x+1}{x^2+7x-15}$

Ⓓ $f(x) = \frac{x^2+x-30}{x^2+5x-14}$

51. Which function is shown in the graph?

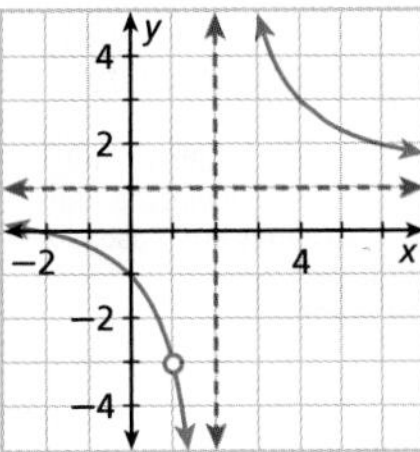

Ⓕ $f(x) = \frac{x^2+x-2}{x^2-3x+2}$ (circled)

Ⓗ $f(x) = \frac{x^2+x-2}{x^2+3x+2}$

Ⓖ $f(x) = \frac{x^2+3x+2}{x^2-x-2}$

Ⓙ $f(x) = \frac{x^2-3x+2}{x^2+x-2}$

52. What is the horizontal asymptote of $f(x) = \frac{(2x+4)(3x+6)}{(x-1)(x+6)}$?

Ⓐ $y = -6$

Ⓒ $y = 2$

Ⓑ $y = -2$

Ⓓ $y = 6$ (circled)

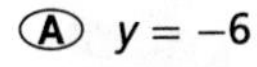

CHALLENGE AND EXTEND

Identify all zeros, asymptotes, and holes in the graph of each function. Then graph.

53. $f(x) = \frac{(x^2-3x+2)(x-3)}{(x-1)(x^2-5x+6)}$

54. $f(x) = \frac{(x^2-9)(3x+2)}{(x^2-4)(x-3)}$

55. Let $f(x) = \frac{1}{x^2-2x+c}$. Find c such that the graph of f has the given number of vertical asymptotes. Possible answers:

a. none 2 b. one 1 c. two 0

Write a rational function with the given characteristics.

56. no zeros, no vertical asymptotes, and a horizontal asymptote at $y = 1$

57. zero at 0, vertical asymptotes at $x = -3$ and $x = 3$, and holes at $x = -1$ and $x = 1$

SPIRAL REVIEW

58. **Sports** In the 1972–1973 school year, 817,073 females participated in high school sports in the United States. By the 2002–2003 school year, this number had increased to 2,856,358. To the nearest percent, what was the percent increase in the number of females participating in high school sports? *(Lesson 2-2)* 250%

Solve. *(Lesson 7-5)*

59. $\log_3(5x-2) = \log_3(2x+8)$ $\frac{10}{3}$

60. $\log_2 x^2 = 4$ ± 4

61. $\log_x \frac{1}{27} = 3$ $\frac{1}{3}$

62. $\log_4 48 - \log_4 4x = 4$ $\frac{3}{64}$

Add or subtract. Identify any x-values for which the expression is undefined. *(Lesson 8-3)*

63. $\frac{5x-7}{2x+1} + \frac{3x-6}{2x+1}$

$\frac{8x-13}{2x+1}$; $x \neq -\frac{1}{2}$

64. $\frac{x-1}{x+2} - \frac{x+1}{x-3}$

$\frac{-7x+1}{(x+2)(x-3)}$; $x \neq -2$ and $x \neq 3$

TEST PREP DOCTOR In Exercise 52, students who chose **A** probably confused horizontal and vertical asymptotes.

Answers

48, 53–54, 56–57. See p. A37.

Journal

Have students explain how to identify the zeros, asymptotes, and holes of rational functions.

ALTERNATIVE ASSESSMENT

Have students write and graph a rational equation that has exactly two real zeros, one vertical asymptote, and no horizontal asymptotes. Ask them to explain how they know that their function meets the requirements given above.

Power Presentations with PowerPoint®

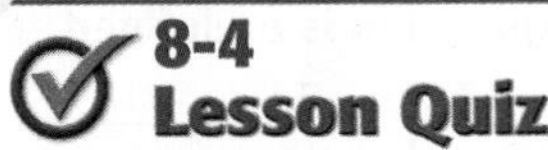

8-4 Lesson Quiz

1. Using the graph of $f(x) = \frac{1}{x}$ as a guide, describe the transformation and graph the function $g(x) = \frac{1}{x-4}$.

g is f translated 4 units right.

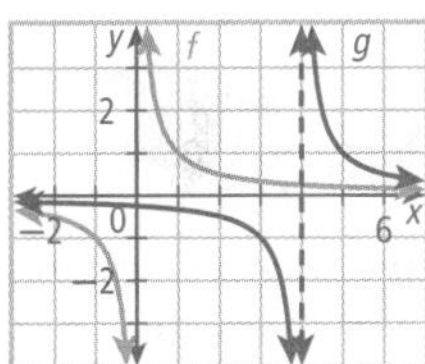

2. Identify the asymptotes, domain, and range of the function $g(x) = \frac{5}{x-1} + 2$.

asymptotes: $x = 1$, $y = 2$; D: $\{x \mid x \neq 1\}$; R: $\{y \mid y \neq 2\}$

3. Identify the zeros, asymptotes, and holes in the graph of $f(x) = \frac{x^2-3x+2}{x^2-x}$. Then graph.

zero: 2; asymptotes: $x = 0$, $y = 1$; hole at $x = 1$

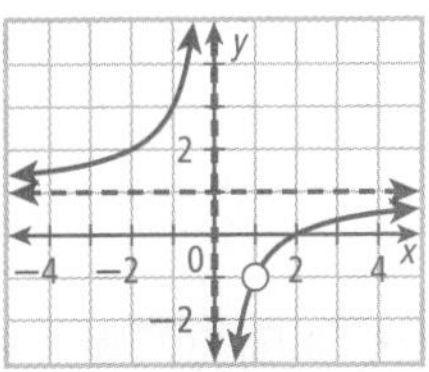

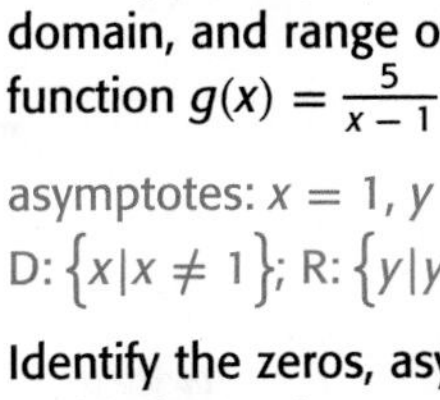

Also available on transparency

8-4 PROBLEM SOLVING

Members of a high school cheerleading squad plan a trip to support their robotics team at a regional competition. The trip will cost \$70 per person plus a \$420 deposit for the bus.

1. Find the total cost of the trip per cheerleader.
   a. Write a function that represents the total cost of the trip per cheerleader. $f(x) = \left(\frac{420}{x}\right) + 70$
   b. Graph the function on your graphing calculator. Sketch a graph to represent the function. 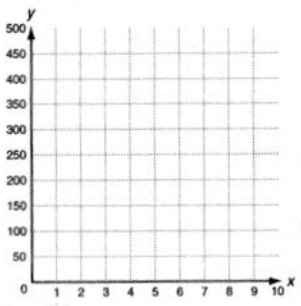
   c. Use your graph to determine the cost per person if
      5 cheerleaders go on the trip. \$154
      7 cheerleaders go on the trip. \$130
      10 cheerleaders go on the trip. \$112
   d. What is the horizontal asymptote of the function? What does it mean in terms of the cost per person of the trip?
      $y = 70$; possible answer: no matter how many people go on the trip, the cost per person cannot be less than \$70.
2. Stanton invites the cheerleaders to support the school's dive team at their next competition. The trip will cost \$145 per person plus a \$1000 deposit.
   a. Write a function to represent the cost of the trip per person. $f(x) = \left(\frac{1000}{x}\right) + 145$
   b. What is the cost per person if
      5 cheerleaders go on the trip? \$345.00
      7 cheerleaders go on the trip? \$287.86
      10 cheerleaders go on the trip? \$245.00
   c. What is the increased cost for each of 10 cheerleaders to go with the dive team rather than to go with the robotics team? \$133.00

Choose the letter for the best answer.

3. The deposit for the bus on the robotics trip increases to \$550. By how much does the cost per person increase if 10 cheerleaders go on the trip?
   Ⓐ \$13 (circled)
   B \$37
   C \$83
   D \$112

4. There are 15 cheerleaders signed up to go to the competition with the dive team. What is the cost per person to the nearest dollar?
   A \$76
   B \$103
   Ⓒ \$212 (circled)
   D \$304

8-4 CHALLENGE

An *asymptote* is a line that a graph approaches, but does not reach, as its x- or y- values become very large or very small.

You can find *vertical asymptotes* of the graph of a rational function by finding values for which the function is not defined.

You can find *horizontal asymptotes* of the graph of a rational function by comparing the degree of the polynomial function in the numerator to the degree of the polynomial function in the denominator.

If numerator degree < denominator degree, then $y = 0$ is a horizontal asymptote.
If numerator degree = denominator degree and the leading coefficients in the numerator and denominator are a and b, respectively, then $y = \frac{a}{b}$ is a horizontal asymptote.

Create a rational function that has the given lines as asymptotes.

1. $y = 0$, $x = -3$, $x = 0$, and $x = 2$ $y = \frac{1}{x^3+x^2-6x}$

2. $y = \frac{3}{2}$, $x = -1$, and $x = \frac{1}{2}$ $y = \frac{3x^2}{2x^2+x-1}$

If the degree of the numerator is greater than that of the denominator, the graph may have an *oblique asymptote*, an asymptote that is neither vertical nor horizontal.

Example

The function $y = \frac{x^2+7x+12}{x+1}$ has its numerator degree greater than its denominator degree. So the function has an oblique asymptote. Divide to find its equation.

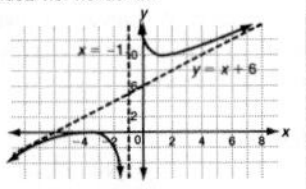

$x+1 \overline{)x^2+7x+12}$ quotient $x+6 + \frac{6}{x+1}$

As x becomes very large or very small, $\frac{6}{x+1}$ approaches, but never reaches, 0.

Therefore, the function approaches, but never reaches, $x+6$; the line $y = x+6$ is an oblique asymptote. As the graph shows, the function also has a vertical asymptote.

Is the nonvertical asymptote horizontal or oblique? Write its equation.

3. $y = \frac{2x+3}{x+4}$ horizontal; $y = 2$

4. $y = \frac{x^2+3x+1}{x-2}$ oblique; $y = x+5$

5. $y = \frac{5x^2-2x+1}{x-4}$ oblique; $y = 5x+18$

6. $y = \frac{2x^2-3x+6}{2x+1}$ oblique; $y = x-2$

8-5 Organizer

Pacing: Traditional 1 day
Block $\frac{1}{2}$ day

Objective: Solve rational equations and inequalities.

Online Edition
Graphing Calculator, Tutorial Videos, Interactivity, TechKeys

Countdown to Testing Week 18

Power Presentations with PowerPoint®

Warm Up

Find the least common multiple for each pair.

1. $2x^2$ and $4x^2 - 2x$ $\quad 2x^2(2x - 1)$

2. $x + 5$ and $x^2 - x - 30$
$(x + 5)(x - 6)$

Add or subtract. Identify any *x*-values for which the expression is undefined.

3. $\frac{1}{x-2} + \frac{1}{4x}$ $\quad \frac{5x-2}{4x(x-2)}$;
$x \neq 0, 2$

4. $\frac{1}{x^2} - \frac{1}{x}$ $\quad \frac{-(x-1)}{x^2}$; $x \neq 0$

Also available on transparency

Math Humor

Q: Why did the rational equation get a poor grade in chemistry?

A: It kept producing extraneous solutions.

8-5 Solving Rational Equations and Inequalities

A2.5.6 Solve problems that can be modeled using equations involving rational and radical functions, including problems of direct and inverse variation. Interpret . . . the solutions, and determine whether the solutions are reasonable.

Objective
Solve rational equations and inequalities.

Vocabulary
rational equation
extraneous solution
rational inequality

Who uses this?
Kayakers can use rational equations to determine how fast a river is moving. (See Example 3.)

A **rational equation** is an equation that contains one or more rational expressions. The time t in hours that it takes to travel d miles can be determined by using the equation $t = \frac{d}{r}$, where r is the average rate of speed. This equation is a rational equation.

To solve a rational equation, start by multiplying each term of the equation by the least common denominator (LCD) of all of the expressions in the equation. This step eliminates the denominators of the rational expressions and results in an equation you can solve by using algebra.

EXAMPLE 1 Solving Rational Equations

Solve the equation $x + \frac{8}{x} = 6$.

$x(x) + \frac{8}{x}(x) = 6(x)$	*Multiply each term by the LCD, x.*
$x^2 + 8 = 6x$	*Simplify. Note that $x \neq 0$.*
$x^2 - 6x + 8 = 0$	*Write in standard form.*
$(x - 2)(x - 4) = 0$	*Factor.*
$x - 2 = 0$ or $x - 4 = 0$	*Apply the Zero Product Property.*
$x = 2$ or $x = 4$	*Solve for x.*

Check

$x + \frac{8}{x}$	6
$2 + \frac{8}{2}$	6
6	6 ✓

$x + \frac{8}{x}$	6
$4 + \frac{8}{4}$	6
6	6 ✓

Remember!
Factoring is not the only method of solving the quadratic equation that results in Example 1. You could also complete the square or use the Quadratic Formula.

Solve each equation.

1a. $\frac{10}{3} = \frac{4}{x} + 2$ $\quad 3$ **1b.** $\frac{6}{x} + \frac{5}{4} = -\frac{7}{4}$ $\quad -2$ **1c.** $x = \frac{6}{x} - 1$ $\quad -3, 2$

An **extraneous solution** is a solution of an equation derived from an original equation that is not a solution of the original equation. When you solve a rational equation, it is possible to get extraneous solutions. These values should be eliminated from the solution set. Always check your solutions by substituting them into the original equation.

State Resources

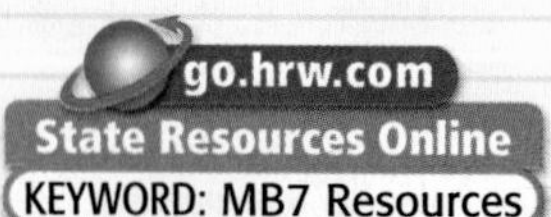

go.hrw.com
State Resources Online
KEYWORD: MB7 Resources

1 Introduce

EXPLORATION

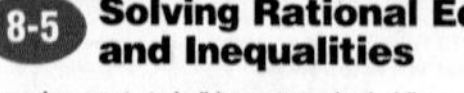

8-5 Solving Rational Equations and Inequalities

A rancher wants to build a rectangular holding pen.

1. The pen will have an area of 450 ft^2. Let w represent the width of the pen. Write an expression in terms of w for the length of the pen.
2. The length of the pen will be twice the width. Use this information to write a second expression in terms of w for the length of the pen.
3. Write an equation by setting the two expressions you wrote for the length of the pen equal to each other.
4. Solve the equation for w.
5. What will be the dimensions of the holding pen?

THINK AND DISCUSS

6. **Describe** the steps you used to solve the equation in Problem 4.
7. **Explain** how you could check your solution to the equation.
8. **Tell** how you knew which value of w to use for the width of the pen.

Motivate

Ask students what steps they would use to solve the equation $\frac{x}{3} + \frac{1}{4} = \frac{1}{2}$. Then ask how they might solve the equation $\frac{3}{x} + \frac{1}{4} = \frac{1}{2}$. Explain that in this lesson students will be learning to solve equations that contain fractions with variables in the denominator.

Explorations and answers are provided in the *Explorations* binder.

EXAMPLE 2 Extraneous Solutions

Solve each equation.

A $\frac{3x}{x-3} = \frac{2x+3}{x-3}$

$\frac{3x}{x-3}(x-3) = \frac{2x+3}{x-3}(x-3)$ *Multiply each term by the LCD, x − 3.*

$\frac{3x}{\cancel{x-3}}(\cancel{x-3}) = \frac{2x+3}{\cancel{x-3}}(\cancel{x-3})$ *Divide out common factors.*

$3x = 2x + 3$ *Simplify. Note that $x \neq 3$.*

$x = 3$ *Solve for x.*

The solution $x = 3$ is extraneous because it makes the denominators of the original equation equal to 0. Therefore, the equation has no solution.

Check Substitute 3 for x in the original equation.

$$\frac{3(3)}{3-3} = \frac{2(3)+3}{3-3}$$

$$\frac{9}{0} \;\Big|\; \frac{9}{0} \; ✗$$ *Division by 0 is undefined.*

Remember!

A rational expression is undefined for any value of a variable that makes a denominator in the expression equal to 0.

B $\frac{2x-9}{x-7} + \frac{x}{2} = \frac{5}{x-7}$

$\frac{2x-9}{x-7} \cdot 2(x-7) + \frac{x}{2} \cdot 2(x-7) = \frac{5}{x-7} \cdot 2(x-7)$ *Multiply each term by the LCD, 2(x − 7).*

$\frac{2x-9}{\cancel{x-7}} \cdot 2(\cancel{x-7}) + \frac{x}{\cancel{2}} \cdot \cancel{2}(x-7) = \frac{5}{\cancel{x-7}} \cdot 2(\cancel{x-7})$ *Divide out common factors.*

$2(2x-9) + x(x-7) = 5(2)$ *Simplify. Note that $x \neq 7$.*

$4x - 18 + x^2 - 7x = 10$ *Use the Distributive Property.*

$x^2 - 3x - 28 = 0$ *Write in standard form.*

$(x-7)(x+4) = 0$ *Factor.*

$x - 7 = 0 \text{ or } x + 4 = 0$ *Use the Zero Product Property.*

$x = 7 \text{ or } x = -4$ *Solve for x.*

The solution $x = 7$ is extraneous because it makes the denominators of the original equation equal to 0. The only solution is $x = -4$.

Check Write $\frac{2x-9}{x-7} + \frac{x}{2} = \frac{5}{x-7}$ as $\frac{2x-9}{x-7} + \frac{x}{2} - \frac{5}{x-7} = 0$. Graph the left side of the equation as **Y1** and identify the values of x for which **Y1** = 0.

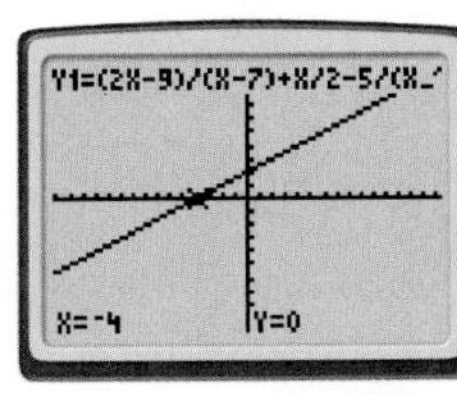

The graph intersects the x-axis only when $x = -4$. Therefore, $x = -4$ is the only solution.

Solve each equation.

2a. $\frac{16}{x^2-16} = \frac{2}{x-4}$ no solution

2b. $\frac{1}{x-1} = \frac{x}{x-1} + \frac{x}{6}$ −6

Additional Examples

Example 1

Solve the equation $x - \frac{18}{x} = 3$.

$x = -3$ or $x = 6$

Example 2

Solve each equation.

A. $\frac{5x}{x-2} = \frac{3x+4}{x-2}$

no solution

B. $\frac{2x-5}{x-8} + \frac{x}{2} = \frac{11}{x-8}$ $x = -4$

Also available on transparency

INTERVENTION

Questioning Strategies

EXAMPLE 1

- How do you determine the LCD of the expressions in the equation?
- Why should you multiply each term in the equation by the LCD?

EXAMPLE 2

- How can you tell whether a solution to a rational equation is extraneous?

2 Teach

Guided Instruction

Explain to students that they can solve a rational equation by rewriting it in a form that they already know how to solve, such as a linear or quadratic equation. To do so, they can multiply the equation by the LCD of each expression in the equation. Refer students back to **Lesson 8-3** if they need to review the steps for finding the LCD of rational expressions. Emphasize that students must always check for extraneous solutions when solving rational equations.

Reaching All Learners

Through Multiple Representations

Point out to students that they can use a graphing calculator to check their solutions to rational equations. They can enter the left side of the equation as **Y1** and the right side as **Y2**. Then, by using the table feature, they can verify that **Y1** and **Y2** have the same value for the values of x that they determined by using algebra. For example, the calculator screens shown at right provide support for the solution of **Example 1**.

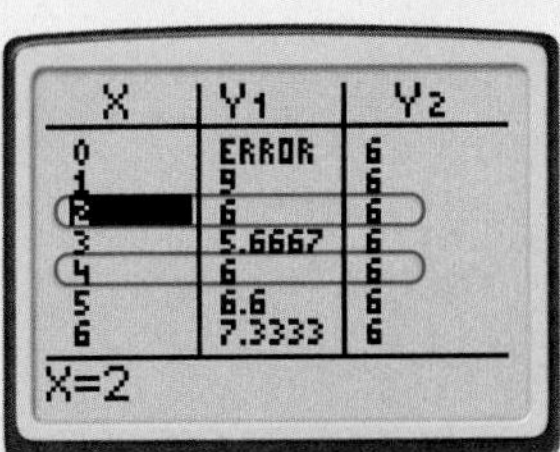

X	Y1	Y2
0	ERROR	6
1	9	6
2	6	6
3	5.6667	6
4	6	6
5	6.6	6
6	7.3333	6

X=2

Power Presentations with PowerPoint®

Additional Examples

Example 3

A jet travels 3950 mi from Chicago, Illinois, to London, England, and 3950 mi on the return trip. The total flying time is 16.5 h. The return trip takes longer due to winds that generally blow from west to east. If the jet's average speed with no wind is 485 mi/h, what is the average speed of the wind during the round-trip flight? Round to the nearest mile per hour. 55 mi/h

Also available on transparency

INTERVENTION

Questioning Strategies

EXAMPLE 3

- How can you use the information in the problem to write an equation that relates time, distance, and average speed?
- Why can one of the solutions of the rational equation be eliminated?

EXAMPLE 3 **Problem-Solving Application**

A kayaker spends an afternoon paddling on a river. She travels 3 mi upstream and 3 mi downstream in a total of 4 h. In still water, the kayaker can travel at an average speed of 2 mi/h. Based on this information, what is the average speed of the river's current? Is your answer reasonable?

1 Understand the Problem

The **answer** will be the average speed of the current.

List the **important information:**

- The kayaker spent 4 hours kayaking.
- She went 3 mi upstream and 3 mi downstream.
- Her average speed in still water is 2 mi/h.

2 Make a Plan

Let c represent the speed of the current. When the kayaker is going upstream, her speed is equal to her speed in still water minus c. When the kayaker is going downstream, her speed is equal to her speed in still water plus c.

	Distance (mi)	Average Speed (mi/h)	Time (h)
Up	3	$2 - c$	$\frac{3}{2-c}$
Down	3	$2 + c$	$\frac{3}{2+c}$

Helpful Hint

distance = rate × time
Therefore,
time = $\frac{\text{distance}}{\text{rate}}$.

total time = time upstream + time downstream

$$4 = \frac{3}{2-c} + \frac{3}{2+c}$$

3 Solve

$$4(2-c)(2+c) = \frac{3}{2-c}(2-c)(2+c) + \frac{3}{2+c}(2-c)(2+c)$$ *The LCD is $(2-c)(2+c)$.*

$$4(2-c)(2+c) = 3(2+c) + 3(2-c)$$ *Simplify. Note that $c \neq \pm 2$.*

$$16 - 4c^2 = 6 + 3c + 6 - 3c$$ *Use the Distributive Property.*

$$16 - 4c^2 = 12$$ *Combine like terms.*

$$-4c^2 = -4$$ *Solve for c.*

$$c = \pm 1$$

The speed of the current cannot be negative. Therefore, the average speed of the current is 1 mi/h.

4 Look Back

If the speed of the current is 1 mi/h, the kayaker's speed when going upstream is $2 - 1 = 1$ mi/h. It will take her 3 h to travel 3 mi upstream. Her speed when going downstream is $2 + 1 = 3$ mi/h. It will take her 1 hour to travel 3 mi downstream. The total trip will take 4 h, which is the given time.

Use the information given above to answer the following.

3. On a different river, the kayaker travels 2 mi upstream and 2 mi downstream in a total of 5 h. What is the average speed of the current of this river? Round to the nearest tenth. **1.5 mi/h**

EXAMPLE 4 *Work Application*

Jason can clean a large tank at an aquarium in about 6 hours. When Jason and Lacy work together, they can clean the tank in about 3.5 hours. About how long would it take Lacy to clean the tank if she works by herself?

Jason's rate: $\frac{1}{6}$ of the tank per hour

Lacy's rate: $\frac{1}{h}$ of the tank per hour, where h is the number of hours needed to clean the tank by herself

Jason's rate × hours worked	+	Lacy's rate × hours worked	=	1 complete job
$\frac{1}{6}(3.5)$	+	$\frac{1}{h}(3.5)$	=	1

$\frac{1}{6}(3.5)(6h) + \frac{1}{h}(3.5)(6h) = 1(6h)$ *Multiply by the LCD, 6h.*

$3.5h + 21 = 6h$ *Simplify.*

$21 = 2.5h$ *Solve for h.*

$8.4 = h$

It will take Lacy about 8.4 hours, or 8 hours 24 minutes, to clean the tank when working by herself.

4. Julien can mulch a garden in 20 minutes. Together, Julien and Remy can mulch the same garden in 11 minutes. How long will it take Remy to mulch the garden when working alone? **about 24 min**

A **rational inequality** is an inequality that contains one or more rational expressions. One way to solve rational inequalities is by using graphs and tables.

EXAMPLE 5 Using Graphs and Tables to Solve Rational Equations and Inequalities

Solve $\frac{x}{x-4} \le 2$ by using a graph and a table.

Use a graph. On a graphing calculator, let **Y1** $= \frac{x}{x-4}$ and **Y2** $= 2$.

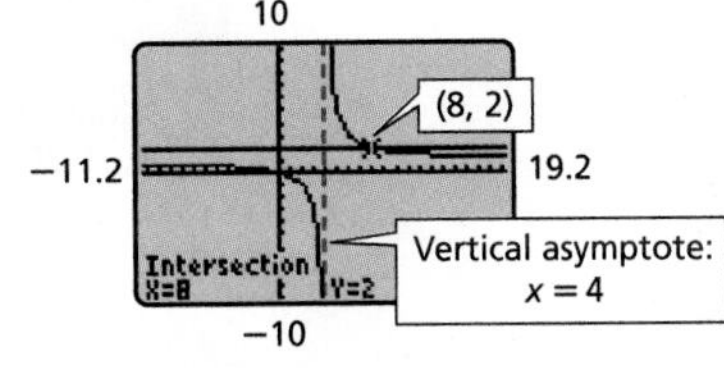

The graph of **Y1** is at or below the graph of **Y2** when $x < 4$ or when $x \ge 8$.

Remember!

The solution $x < 4$ or $x \ge 8$ can be written in set-builder notation as $\{x \mid x < 4 \cup x \ge 8\}$

Use a table. The table shows that **Y1** is undefined when $x = 4$ and that **Y1** $\le$ **Y2** when $x < 4$ or when $x \ge 8$.

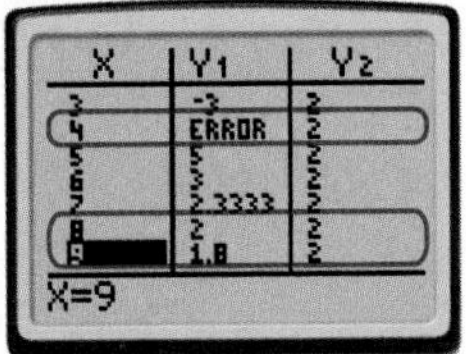

X	Y1	Y2
3	-3	2
4	ERROR	2
5	5	2
6	3	2
7	2.3333	2
8	2	2
9	1.8	2

X=9

The solution of the inequality is $x < 4$ or $x \ge 8$.

Solve by using a graph and a table.

5a. $\frac{x}{x-3} \ge 4$ **$3 < x \le 4$**

5b. $\frac{8}{x+1} = -2$ **$x = -5$**

COMMON ERROR ALERT

Students may sometimes forget to consider both cases when solving a rational inequality algebraically, as in **Example 6.** Point out that because the LCD of the inequality is a variable expression, its value could be positive or negative, depending on the value of the variable. Therefore, students must consider both of these cases when multiplying by the LCD to solve the inequality.

Power Presentations with PowerPoint®

Additional Examples

Example 4

Natalie can finish a 500-piece puzzle in about 8 hours. When Natalie and Renzo work together, they can finish a 500-piece puzzle in about 4.5 hours. About how long will it take Renzo to finish a 500-piece puzzle if he works by himself? about 10.3 h or 10 h 17 min

Example 5

Solve $\frac{x}{x-6} \le 3$ by using a graph and a table. $x < 6$ or $x \ge 9$

Also available on transparency

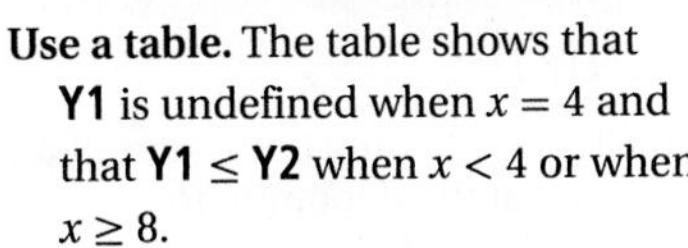

INTERVENTION
Questioning Strategies

EXAMPLE 4

- How do you write an expression for each person's rate?
- How do you set up the rational equation?

EXAMPLE 5

- How do you know which expressions to enter as **Y1** and **Y2**?
- How can you use the graph of **Y1** and **Y2** to determine the solution of the inequality?

Power Presentations with PowerPoint®

Additional Examples

Example 6

Solve the inequality $\frac{6}{x-8} \leq 3$ algebraically. $x < 8$ or $x \geq 10$

Also available on transparency

INTERVENTION

Questioning Strategies

EXAMPLE 6

- Why do you need to consider the sign of the LCD?
- How do you simplify a compound inequality like the one that results from Case 1?

Teaching Tip

Reading Math Emphasize that the word *and* in a compound inequality means that the value of the variable must satisfy both conditions of the inequality. These types of inequalities can often be simplified. Take, for example, the compound inequality $x > 2$ and $x > 5$. Both inequalities are true only when $x > 5$. Therefore, the compound inequality can be simplified to $x > 5$.

You can also solve rational inequalities algebraically. You start by multiplying each term by the least common denominator (LCD) of all the expressions in the inequality. However, you must consider two cases: the LCD is positive or the LCD is negative.

EXAMPLE 6 Solving Rational Inequalities Algebraically

Solve the inequality $\frac{8}{x+5} \leq 4$ algebraically. Check your answer for reasonableness.

Remember!

If you multiply or divide both sides of an inequality by a negative value, you must reverse the inequality symbol.

Case 1 LCD is positive.

Step 1 Solve for x.

$\frac{8}{x+5}(x+5) \leq 4(x+5)$ *Multiply by the LCD.*

$8 \leq 4x + 20$ *Simplify. Note that $x \neq -5$.*

$-12 \leq 4x$ *Solve for x.*

$-3 \leq x$

Step 2 Consider the sign of the LCD.

$x + 5 > 0$ *LCD is positive.*

$x > -5$ *Solve for x.*

For Case 1, the solution must satisfy $x \geq -3$ *and* $x > -5$, which simplifies to $x \geq -3$.

Case 2 LCD is negative.

Step 1 Solve for x.

$\frac{8}{x+5}(x+5) \geq 4(x+5)$ *Multiply by the LCD. Reverse the inequality.*

$8 \geq 4x + 20$ *Simplify. Note that $x \neq -5$.*

$-12 \geq 4x$ *Solve for x.*

$-3 \geq x$

Step 2 Consider the sign of the LCD.

$x + 5 < 0$ *LCD is negative.*

$x < -5$ *Solve for x.*

For Case 2, the solution must satisfy $x \leq -3$ *and* $x < -5$, which simplifies to $x < -5$.

The solution set of the original inequality is the union of the solutions to both Case 1 and Case 2. The solution to the inequality $\frac{8}{x+5} \leq 4$ is $x < -5$ or $x \geq -3$, or $\{x | x < -5 \cup x \geq -3\}$. The expression will be less than 4 when the denominator is negative or is very large, so the answer is reasonable.

CHECK IT OUT! **Solve each inequality algebraically.**

6a. $\frac{6}{x-2} \geq -4$ $x \leq \frac{1}{2}$ or $x > 2$

6b. $\frac{9}{x+3} < 6$ $x < -3$ or $x > -\frac{3}{2}$

THINK AND DISCUSS

1. Explain why multiplying both sides of a rational equation by the LCD eliminates all of the denominators.
2. Explain why rational equations may have extraneous solutions.
3. Describe two methods for solving the inequality $\frac{12}{x} > 3$.

4. **GET ORGANIZED** Copy and complete the graphic organizer. In each box, write the appropriate information related to rational equations.

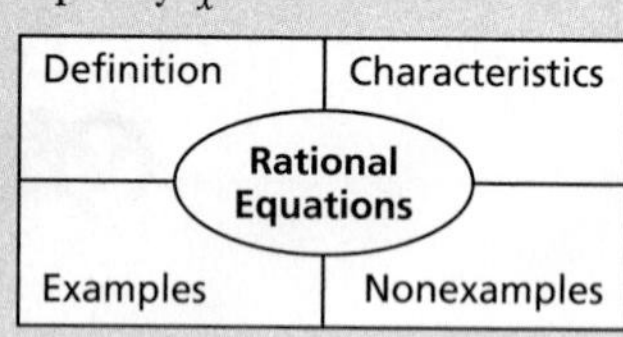

3 Close

Summarize

Ask students to describe the steps they would use to solve a rational equation or inequality. Make sure that they understand how to use the LCD of the expressions to derive an equation or inequality that they can solve by using methods from earlier chapters. Emphasize the importance of checking for extraneous solutions when solving rational equations and of considering the sign of the LCD when solving rational inequalities.

ONGOING ASSESSMENT and INTERVENTION

Diagnose ***Before*** **the Lesson**
8-5 Warm Up, TE p. 600

Monitor ***During*** **the Lesson**
Check It Out! Exercises, SE pp. 600–604
Questioning Strategies, TE pp. 601–604

Assess ***After*** **the Lesson**
8-5 Lesson Quiz, TE p. 607
Alternative Assessment, TE p. 607

Answers to *Think and Discuss*

Possible answers:

1. The LCD is a multiple of each denominator. Therefore, each denominator is a factor of the LCD.
2. When you multiply both sides of an equation by a variable expression, you may produce an equation with solutions that make denominators of the original equation equal to 0.
3. (1) Graph each side of the inequality. (2) Multiply both sides by x and consider two cases, x is positive or x is negative.
4. See p. A10.

8-5 Exercises

go.hrw.com
Homework Help Online
KEYWORD: MB7 8-5
Parent Resources Online
KEYWORD: MB7 Parent

GUIDED PRACTICE

1. **Vocabulary** How does a *rational expression* differ from a *rational equation*?

SEE EXAMPLE 1 p. 600

Solve each equation.

2. $\frac{1}{8}+\frac{2}{t}=\frac{17}{8t}$ 1
3. $7=\frac{1}{w}-4$ $\frac{1}{11}$
4. $\frac{1}{r-5}=\frac{7}{2r}$ 7
5. $\frac{1}{x}=\frac{x}{6}-\frac{5}{6}$ −1, 6
6. $m+\frac{12}{m}=7$ 3, 4
7. $k+\frac{1}{k}=2$ 1

SEE EXAMPLE 2 p. 601

8. $\frac{-2x}{x+2}+\frac{x}{3}=\frac{4}{x+2}$ 6
9. $\frac{x}{x-3}+\frac{x}{2}=\frac{6x}{2x-6}$ 0, 7
10. $\frac{3}{x(x+1)}-1=\frac{3}{x^2+x}$ no solution

SEE EXAMPLE 3 p. 602

11. **Transportation** A river barge travels at an average of 8 mi/h in still water. The barge travels 60 mi up the Mississippi River and 60 mi down the river in a total of 16.5 h. What is the average speed of the current in this section of the Mississippi River? Round to the nearest tenth. Is your answer reasonable? 2.4 mi/h

SEE EXAMPLE 4 p. 603

12. **Work** Each month Leo must make copies of a budget report. When he uses both the large and the small copier, the job takes 30 min. If the small copier is broken, the job takes him 50 min. How long will the job take if the large copier is broken? about 75 min, or $1\frac{1}{4}$ h

SEE EXAMPLE 5 p. 603

Solve by using a graph and a table.

13. $\frac{x-5}{x}>2$ $-5<x<0$
14. $\frac{3}{x+6}=3$ $x=-5$
15. $\frac{x+3}{2x}<2$ $x<0$ or $x>1$

SEE EXAMPLE 6 p. 604

Solve each inequality algebraically.

16. $\frac{4}{x+1}<4$ $x<-1$ or $x>0$
17. $\frac{12}{x-4}\le 3$ $x<4$ or $x\ge 8$
18. $\frac{10}{x+8}>2$ $-8<x<-3$

PRACTICE AND PROBLEM SOLVING

Independent Practice

For Exercises	See Example
19–24	1
25–27	2
28	3
29	4
30–32	5
33–35	6

Extra Practice
Skills Practice p. S19
Application Practice p. S39

Solve each equation.

19. $4+\frac{1}{x}=\frac{10}{2x}$ 1
20. $\frac{5}{4}=\frac{n-3}{n-4}$ 8
21. $\frac{1}{a-7}=3$ $\frac{22}{3}$
22. $\frac{1}{x}-\frac{3}{4}=\frac{x}{4}$ −4, 1
23. $\frac{14}{z}=9-z$ 2, 7
24. $x+\frac{4}{x}=4$ 2
25. $\frac{4x}{x-3}+\frac{x}{2}=\frac{12}{x-3}$ −8
26. $\frac{3x}{x+1}=\frac{2x-1}{x+1}$ no solution
27. $\frac{2}{x(x-1)}=1+\frac{2}{x-1}$ −2
28. **Multi-Step** A passenger jet travels from Los Angeles to Bombay, India, in 22 h. The return flight takes 17 h. The difference in flight times is caused by winds over the Pacific Ocean that blow primarily from west to east. If the jet's average speed in still air is 550 mi/h, what is the average speed of the wind during the round-trip flight? Round to the nearest mile per hour. Is your answer reasonable? 71 mi/h
29. **Art** A glassblower can produce a set of simple glasses in about 2 h. When the glassblower works with an apprentice, the job takes about 1.5 h. How long would it take the apprentice to make a set of glasses when working alone? about 6 h

Solve by using a graph and a table.

30. $\frac{1}{x}>1$ $0<x<1$
31. $\frac{x+1}{x+2}=2$ $x=-3$
32. $\frac{x}{x-5}\le 0$ $0\le x<5$

Answers

11. 2.4 mi/h; yes; an average current speed of 2.4 mi/h is close to 2 mi/h, so the barge would take about $\frac{60\text{ mi}}{8-2\text{ mi/h}}$, or 10 h, to travel upstream and about $\frac{60\text{ mi}}{8+2\text{ mi/h}}$, or 6 hr, to travel downstream. The trip should take about 16 h, which is close to the given time.

28. 71 mi/h; yes; an average wind speed of 71 mi/h is close to 70 mi/h. The plane travels about 22(550 − 70), or 10,560, mi on the flight to Bombay and about 22(550 + 70), or 10,540, mi on the flight to Los Angeles. Because the distances are approximately equal, the answer is reasonable.

8-5 Exercises

Assignment Guide

Assign *Guided Practice* exercises as necessary.

If you finished Examples 1–3
Basic 19–28, 38–43, 47–49
Average 19–28, 38–43, 47–49, 58
Advanced 19–28, 38–43, 47–49, 58–59

If you finished Examples 1–6
Basic 19–49, 51, 53–57, 63–67
Average 19–58, 63–67
Advanced 19–67

Homework Quick Check
Quickly check key concepts.
Exercises: 20, 26, 28, 29, 30, 34, 37

Teaching Tip

Measurement Point out in **Exercise 28** that when the jet travels from Los Angeles to Bombay, it is flying against the wind, so its speed is equal to its speed in still air minus the wind speed. When the jet travels from Bombay to Los Angeles, it is flying with the wind, so its speed is equal to its speed in still air plus the wind speed.

Answers

1. Possible answer: An equation is a statement that 2 expressions are equal. A rational expression is a quotient of 2 polynomials. A rational equation contains at least 1 rational expression.

State Resources

go.hrw.com
State Resources Online
KEYWORD: MB7 Resources

Teaching Tip

Sports Link For **Exercise 37,** note that batting averages are usually rounded to three decimal places, and that no leading zero is used to the left of the decimal point. You may wish to point out that in Major League Baseball the record for the highest batting average in a career is held by Ty Cobb, who batted .366 in a career that lasted from 1905 to 1928.

MULTI-STEP TEST PREP **Exercise 51** involves writing and solving a rational equation to determine the average speed of a race car. This exercise prepares students for the Multi-Step Test Prep on page 608.

Answers

36a. $P \le 2w + 2\left(\frac{17{,}000}{w}\right)$ or equivalent inequality

b. No; substituting 400 for P in the inequality results in nonreal values of w.

37b. Possible answer: $\frac{188 + h}{643 + h} = \frac{191}{614}$; 18 hits

53. Possible answer: Multiply both sides by the LCD of all the denominators. Solve the quadratic equation that results. Then check the solutions in the original equation.

66. $y = -\frac{10}{x}$

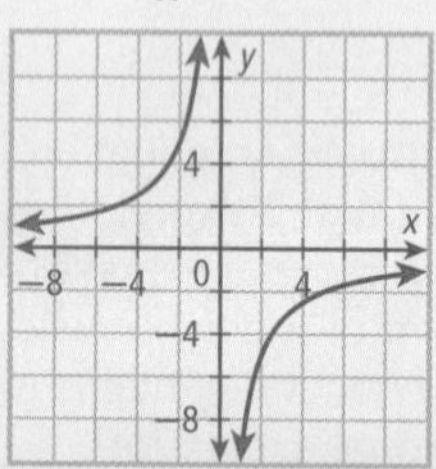

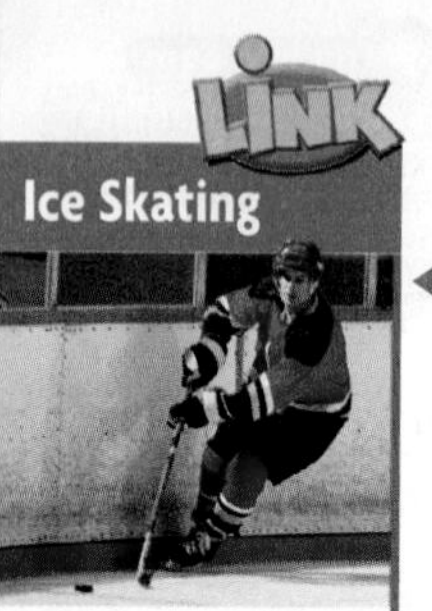

Ice Skating

The temperature of the ice in many indoor skating rinks is kept between 24°F and 28°F. Ice that is colder than these temperatures may chip too easily, and ice that is warmer may result in too much friction as skate blades pass over it.

37c. 170 hits; yes, he had 326 more at bats than hits, so he would need to reach a total of 326 hits.

Solve each inequality algebraically.

33. $\frac{1}{3x} < 2$ $x < 0$ or $x > \frac{1}{6}$

34. $\frac{9}{x-4} \ge -6$ $x \le 2.5$ or $x > 4$

35. $\frac{9}{x+10} > 3$ $-10 < x < -7$

36. **Ice Skating** A new skating rink will be approximately rectangular in shape and will have an area of no more than 17,000 square feet.

a. Write an inequality expressing the possible perimeter P of the skating rink in feet in terms of its width w.

b. Is 400 feet a reasonable value for the perimeter? Explain.

37. **Baseball** The baseball card shows statistics for a professional player during four seasons.

a. A player's batting average is equal to his number of hits divided by his number of at bats. For which year listed on the card did Derek Jeter have the greatest batting average? **2003**

b. Write and solve an equation to find how many additional consecutive hits h Jeter would have needed to raise his batting average in 2004 to that of his average in 2001.

c. **What if...?** How many additional hits in a row would Jeter have needed to raise his batting average in 2003 to .500? Check your answer for reasonableness.

YEAR	HITS	AT BATS
2001	191	614
2002	191	644
2003	156	482
2004	188	643

Solve each equation or inequality.

38. $\frac{15n}{n-3} = \frac{5}{n-3} - 8$ $\frac{29}{23}$

39. $\frac{z}{z+1} = \frac{z}{z-4}$ 0

40. $\frac{4}{x} + 6 = \frac{1}{x^2}$ $\frac{-2 \pm \sqrt{10}}{6}$

41. $\frac{8}{x} - \frac{3}{x} = \frac{6}{x-1}$ -5

42. $\frac{2(x+4)}{x-4} = \frac{3x}{x-4}$ 8

43. $\frac{1}{a-1} + \frac{4}{a+1} = \frac{7}{a^2-1}$ 2

44. $\frac{6}{r} \ge \frac{5}{2}$ $0 < r \le 2.4$

45. $\frac{8}{x+1} > 4$ $-1 < x < 1$

46. $x \ge \frac{4}{x}$ $-2 \le x < 0$ or $x \ge 2$

Use a graphing calculator to solve each rational equation. Round your answers to the nearest hundredth.

47. $\frac{1}{x^2} = 5$ ± 0.45

48. $\frac{1}{x^2} = x^2 - 1$ ± 1.27

49. $\frac{1}{x-1} = x - 1$ 0, 2

50. **Critical Thinking** The reciprocal of a number plus $\frac{7}{2}$ equals 2. Find the number. $-\frac{2}{3}$

51a. 2001 winner: $\frac{500}{s}$; 2002 winner: $\frac{500}{s+25}$

MULTI-STEP TEST PREP

51. This problem will prepare you for the Multi-Step Test Prep on page 608.

The average speed for the winner of the 2002 Indy 500 was 25 mi/h greater than the average speed for the 2001 winner. In addition, the 2002 winner completed the 500 mi race 32 min faster than the 2001 winner.

a. Let s represent the average speed of the 2001 winner in miles per hour. Write expressions in terms of s for the time in hours that it took the 2001 and 2002 winners to complete the race.

b. Write a rational equation that can be used to determine s. Solve your equation to find the average speed of the 2001 winner to the nearest mile per hour. **51b. Possible answer:** $\frac{500}{s} = \frac{500}{s+25} + \frac{32}{60}$; 141 mi/h

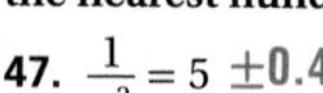

8-5 PRACTICE A

8-5 PRACTICE C

8-5 PRACTICE B

Solve each equation.

1. $x - \frac{6}{x} = 5$ $x = -1$ or $x = 6$

2. $\frac{15}{4} = \frac{6}{x} + 3$ $x = 8$

3. $x = \frac{3}{x} + 2$ $x = 3$ or $x = -1$

4. $\frac{4}{x^2-4} = \frac{1}{x-2}$ no solution.

Solve each inequality by using a graphing calculator and a table.

5. $\frac{6}{x+1} < -3$ $-3 < x < -1$

6. $\frac{x}{x-2} \ge 0$ $x \le 0$ or $x > 2$

7. $\frac{2x}{x+5} \le 0$ $-5 < x \le 0$

8. $\frac{-x}{x-3} \ge 0$ $0 \le x < 3$

Solve each inequality algebraically.

9. $\frac{12}{x+4} \le 4$ $x < -4$ or $x \ge -1$

10. $\frac{7}{x+3} < -5$ $-\frac{22}{5} < x < -3$

11. $\frac{x}{x-2} > 9$ $2 < x < \frac{9}{4}$

12. $\frac{2x}{x-5} \ge 3$ $5 < x \le 15$

Solve.

13. The time required to deliver and install a computer at a customer's location is $t = 4 + \frac{d}{r}$, where t is time in hours, d is the distance, in miles, from the warehouse to the customer's location, and r is the average speed of the delivery truck. If it takes 6.2 hours for the employee to deliver and install a computer for a customer located 100 miles from the warehouse, what is the average speed of the delivery truck?

About 45.5 miles per hour

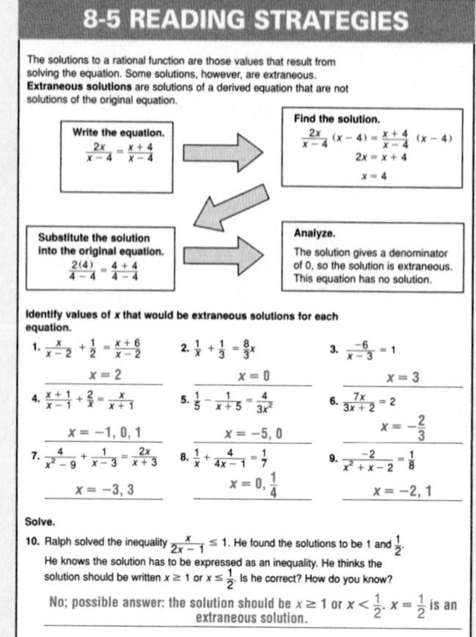

8-5 READING STRATEGIES

The solutions to a rational function are those values that result from solving the equation. Some solutions, however, are extraneous. **Extraneous solutions** are solutions of a derived equation that are not solutions of the original equation.

Write the equation. $\frac{2x}{x-4} = \frac{x+4}{x-4}$ → Find the solution. $\frac{2x}{x-4}(x-4) = \frac{x+4}{x-4}(x-4)$; $2x = x + 4$; $x = 4$ → Substitute the solution into the original equation. $\frac{2(4)}{4-4} = \frac{4+4}{4-4}$ → Analyze. The solution gives a denominator of 0, so the solution is extraneous. This equation has no solution.

Identify values of x that would be extraneous solutions for each equation.

1. $\frac{x}{x-2} + \frac{1}{2} = \frac{x+6}{x-2}$ $x = 2$

2. $\frac{1}{x} + \frac{1}{3} = \frac{8}{3}x$ $x = 0$

3. $\frac{-6}{x-3} = 1$ $x = 3$

4. $\frac{x+1}{x-1} + \frac{2}{x} = \frac{x}{x+1}$ $x = -1, 0, 1$

5. $\frac{1}{5} - \frac{1}{x+5} = \frac{4}{3x^2}$ $x = -5, 0$

6. $\frac{7x}{3x+2} = 2$ $x = -\frac{2}{3}$

7. $\frac{4}{x^2-9} + \frac{1}{x-3} = \frac{2x}{x+3}$ $x = -3, 3$

8. $\frac{1}{x} + \frac{4}{4x-1} = \frac{1}{7}$ $x = 0, \frac{1}{4}$

9. $\frac{-2}{x^2+x-2} = \frac{1}{8}$ $x = -2, 1$

Solve.

10. Ralph solved the inequality $\frac{x}{2x-1} \le 1$. He found the solutions to be 1 and $\frac{1}{2}$. He knows the solution has to be expressed as an inequality. He thinks the solution should be written $x \ge 1$ or $x \le \frac{1}{2}$. Is he correct? How do you know?

No; possible answer: the solution should be $x \ge 1$ or $x < \frac{1}{2}$. $x = \frac{1}{2}$ is an extraneous solution.

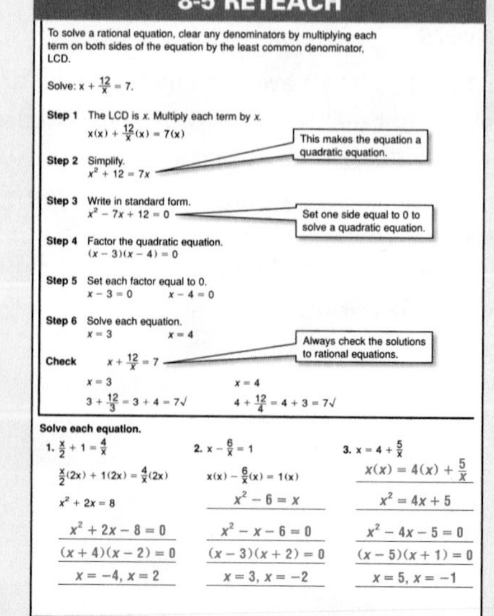

8-5 RETEACH

To solve a rational equation, clear any denominators by multiplying each term on both sides of the equation by the least common denominator, LCD.

Solve: $x + \frac{12}{x} = 7$.

Step 1 The LCD is x. Multiply each term by x. $x(x) + \frac{12}{x}(x) = 7(x)$ — This makes the equation a quadratic equation.

Step 2 Simplify. $x^2 + 12 = 7x$

Step 3 Write in standard form. $x^2 - 7x + 12 = 0$ — Set one side equal to 0 to solve a quadratic equation.

Step 4 Factor the quadratic equation. $(x-3)(x-4) = 0$

Step 5 Set each factor equal to 0. $x - 3 = 0$ $x - 4 = 0$

Step 6 Solve each equation. $x = 3$ $x = 4$

Check $x + \frac{12}{x} = 7$ — Always check the solutions to rational equations.

$x = 3$: $3 + \frac{12}{3} = 3 + 4 = 7$✓ $x = 4$: $4 + \frac{12}{4} = 4 + 3 = 7$✓

Solve each equation.

1. $\frac{x}{2} + 1 = \frac{4}{x}$; $\frac{x}{2}(2x) + 1(2x) = \frac{4}{x}(2x)$; $x^2 + 2x = 8$; $x^2 + 2x - 8 = 0$; $(x+4)(x-2) = 0$; $x = -4, x = 2$

2. $x - \frac{6}{x} = 1$; $x(x) - \frac{6}{x}(x) = 1(x)$; $x^2 - 6 = x$; $x^2 - x - 6 = 0$; $(x-3)(x+2) = 0$; $x = 3, x = -2$

3. $x = 4 + \frac{5}{x}$; $x(x) = 4(x) + \frac{5}{x}$; $x^2 = 4x + 5$; $x^2 - 4x - 5 = 0$; $(x-5)(x+1) = 0$; $x = 5, x = -1$

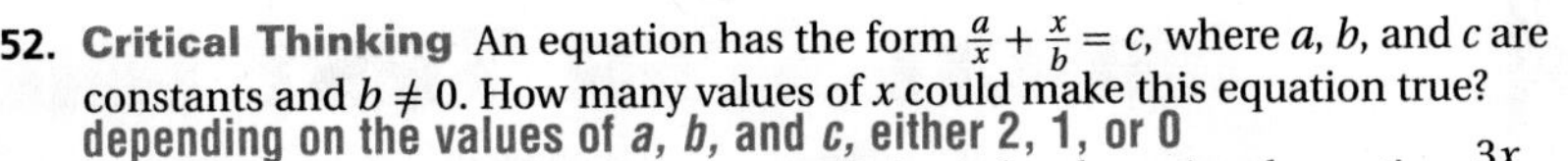
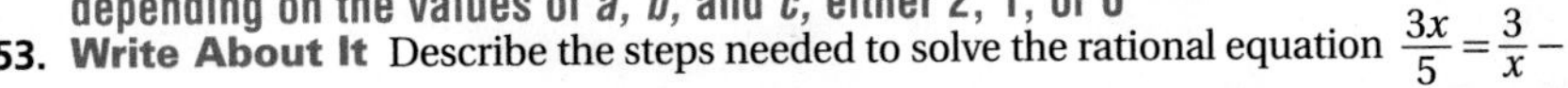

52. **Critical Thinking** An equation has the form $\frac{a}{x} + \frac{x}{b} = c$, where a, b, and c are constants and $b \neq 0$. How many values of x could make this equation true? **depending on the values of *a*, *b*, and *c*, either 2, 1, or 0**

53. **Write About It** Describe the steps needed to solve the rational equation $\frac{3x}{5} = \frac{3}{x} - 6$.

TEST PREP

54. What value of x makes the equation $\frac{1}{x} + \frac{3}{x+3} = \frac{6}{x}$ true?

Ⓐ $-\frac{15}{2}$ Ⓑ $-\frac{12}{5}$ Ⓒ $-\frac{3}{2}$ Ⓓ $-\frac{6}{7}$

55. How many solutions does the equation $\frac{x+2}{x-4} - \frac{1}{x} = \frac{4}{x^2 - 4x}$ have?

Ⓕ 0 Ⓖ 1 Ⓗ 2 Ⓙ 3

56. If $x \neq -2$, which is equivalent to $\frac{4x}{x-2} = 6 + \frac{10}{x-2}$?

Ⓐ $\frac{4x}{x-2} = \frac{16}{x-2}$ Ⓒ $4x = 6 + 10$

Ⓑ $4x = 6(x-2) + 10$ Ⓓ $\frac{4}{-2} = 6 + \frac{5}{x-1}$

57. **Short Response** Water flowing through both a small pipe and a large pipe can fill a water tank in 7 h. Water flowing through the small pipe alone can fill the tank in 15 h.

a. Write an equation that can be used to find the number of hours it would take to fill the tank using only the large pipe.

b. How many hours would it take to fill the tank using only the large pipe? Show your work, or explain how you determined your answer. **about 13 h**

57a. Possible answer: $\frac{1}{15}(7) + \frac{1}{h}(7) = 1$

CHALLENGE AND EXTEND

Solve each equation or inequality.

58. $\frac{4x}{x^2 + x - 6} = \frac{7x}{x^2 - 5x - 24}$ **−6, 0**

59. $\frac{1 - 4x^{-1} + 3x^{-2}}{1 - 9x^{-2}} = \frac{x-1}{x+3}$ **all real numbers except −3, 0, and 3**

60. $\frac{3x}{x+2} - \frac{2}{x+4} \geq 7$ $-5 \leq x < -4$ **or** $-3 \leq x < -2$

61. $\frac{6}{x-3} > \frac{x}{4} + 5$ $x < -21$ **or** $3 < x < 4$

62. Marcus and Will are painting a barn. Marcus paints about twice as fast as Will. On the first day, they have worked for 6 h and completed about $\frac{1}{3}$ of the job when Will gets injured. If Marcus has to complete the rest of the job by himself, about how many additional hours will it take him? **about 18 h**

SPIRAL REVIEW

63. Write and simplify an expression in terms of x that represents the area of the shaded portion of the rectangle. *(Previous course)* $4(x+4) - \frac{1}{2}(4x)$; $2x + 16$

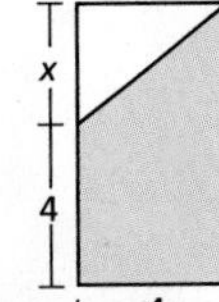

Simplify by rationalizing each denominator. *(Lesson 1-3)*

64. $\frac{-3\sqrt{3}}{\sqrt{8}}$ $\frac{-3\sqrt{6}}{4}$

65. $\frac{5}{4\sqrt{7}}$ $\frac{5\sqrt{7}}{28}$

Given: y varies inversely as x. Write and graph each inverse variation function. *(Lesson 8-1)*

66. $y = -2$ when $x = 5$

67. $y = 2$ when $x = \frac{3}{2}$ $y = \frac{3}{x}$

8-5 PROBLEM SOLVING

Norton and Jessie have a lawn service business. Sometimes they work by themselves, and sometimes they work together. They want to know if it is worthwhile to work together on some jobs.

1. Norton can mow a large lawn in about 4.0 hours. When Norton and Jesse work together, they can mow the same lawn in about 2.5 hours. Jesse wants to know how long it would take her to mow the lawn if she worked by herself.

a. Write an expression for Jessie's rate, using j for the number of hours she would take to mow the lawn by herself. $\frac{1}{j}$

b. Write an equation to show the amount of work completed when they work together. $\left[\frac{1}{4}(2.5)\right] + \left[\frac{1}{j}(2.5)\right] = 1$

c. How long would it take Jessie to mow the lawn by herself? $6\frac{2}{3}$ h

2. Jessie can weed a garden in about 30 minutes. When Norton helps her, they can weed the same garden in about 20 minutes. Norton wants to know how long it would take him to weed the garden if he worked by himself.

a. Write an expression for Norton's rate, using n for the number of hours he would take to weed the garden by himself. $\frac{1}{n}$

b. Write an equation to show the amount of work completed when they work together. $\left[\frac{1}{n}\left(\frac{1}{3}\right)\right] + \left[\frac{1}{\frac{1}{2}}\left(\frac{1}{3}\right)\right] = 1$

c. How long would it take Norton to weed the garden by himself? 1 h

Choose the letter for the best answer.

3. Norton can edge a large lawn in about 3.0 hours. Jessie can edge a similar lawn in about 2.5 hours. Which equation could be used to find the time it would take them to edge that lawn if they worked together?

A $\frac{1}{3} - \frac{1}{2.5} = \frac{1}{t}$

B $\frac{1}{3} - \frac{1}{2.5} = t$

Ⓒ $\frac{1}{3} + \frac{1}{2.5} = \frac{1}{t}$

D $\frac{1}{3} + \frac{1}{2.5} = t$

4. When Jessie helps Norton trim trees, they cut Norton's time to trim trees in half. What can be said about the time it would take Jessie to do the job alone?

Ⓐ Jessie would take the same amount of time as Norton.

B Jessie would take half the time that Norton takes.

C Jessie would take twice the time that Norton takes.

D There is not enough information.

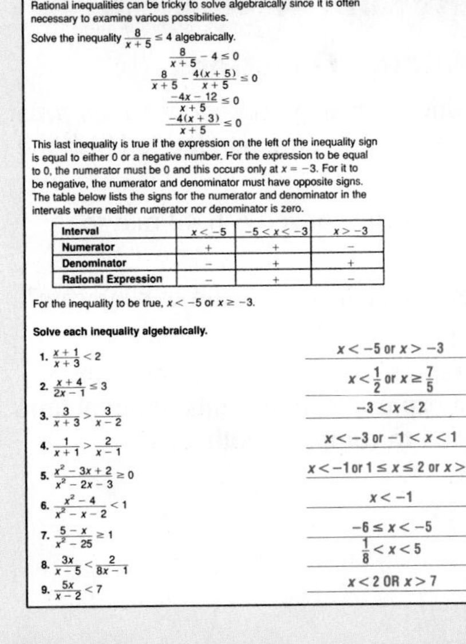

8-5 CHALLENGE

Rational inequalities can be tricky to solve algebraically since it is often necessary to examine various possibilities.

Solve the inequality $\frac{8}{x+5} \leq 4$ algebraically.

$$\frac{8}{x+5} - 4 \leq 0$$
$$\frac{8}{x+5} - \frac{4(x+5)}{x+5} \leq 0$$
$$\frac{-4x-12}{x+5} \leq 0$$
$$\frac{-4(x+3)}{x+5} \leq 0$$

This last inequality is true if the expression on the left of the inequality sign is equal to either 0 or a negative number. For the expression to be equal to 0, the numerator must be 0 and this occurs only at $x = -3$. For it to be negative, the numerator and denominator must have opposite signs. The table below lists the signs for the numerator and denominator in the intervals where neither numerator nor denominator is zero.

Interval	$x < -5$	$-5 < x < -3$	$x > -3$
Numerator	+	+	−
Denominator	−	+	+
Rational Expression	−	+	−

For the inequality to be true, $x < -5$ or $x \geq -3$.

Solve each inequality algebraically.

1. $\frac{x+1}{x+3} < 2$ $x < -5$ or $x > -3$
2. $\frac{x+4}{2x-1} \leq 3$ $x < \frac{1}{2}$ or $x \geq \frac{7}{5}$
3. $\frac{3}{x+3} > \frac{3}{x-2}$ $-3 < x < 2$
4. $\frac{1}{x+1} > \frac{2}{x-1}$ $x < -3$ or $-1 < x < 1$
5. $\frac{x^2-3x+2}{x^2-2x-3} \geq 0$ $x < -1$ or $1 \leq x \leq 2$ or $x > 3$
6. $\frac{x^2-4}{x^2-x-2} < 1$ $x < -1$
7. $\frac{5-x}{x^2-25} \geq 1$ $-6 \leq x < -5$
8. $\frac{3x}{x-5} < \frac{2}{8x-1}$ $\frac{1}{8} < x < 5$
9. $\frac{5x}{x-2} < 7$ $x < 2$ OR $x > 7$

TEST PREP DOCTOR If students have difficulty writing the equation for **Exercise 57,** you may want to point out that the small pipe can fill $\frac{1}{15}$ of the tank per hour and that the large pipe can fill $\frac{1}{h}$ of the tank per hour, where h is the number of hours it would take to fill the tank using only the large pipe.

Answers

67.

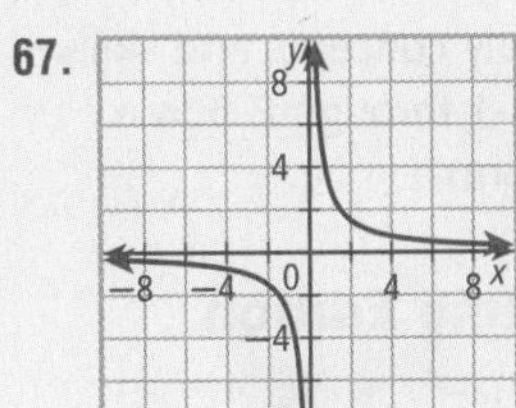

Journal

Have students explain why it is important that they be able to determine a common denominator of the expressions in a rational equation.

ALTERNATIVE ASSESSMENT

Have students write a rational equation or select one from the exercises. Ask students to describe the solution steps and to explain why each step is performed. Students should provide evidence that the solutions they find are not extraneous.

Power Presentations with PowerPoint®

8-5 Lesson Quiz

Solve each equation or inequality.

1. $\frac{x+2}{x} = \frac{x-1}{2}$ $x = -1$ or $x = 4$
2. $\frac{6x}{x+4} = \frac{7x+4}{x+4}$ no solution
3. $\frac{x+2}{x-3} + \frac{x}{5} = \frac{5}{x-3}$ $x = -5$
4. $\frac{4}{x-3} \geq 2$ $3 < x \leq 5$
5. A college basketball player has made 58 out of 82 attempted free-throws this season. How many additional free-throws must she make in a row to raise her free-throw percentage to 90%? 158

Also available on transparency

SECTION 8A MULTI-STEP TEST PREP

Organizer

Objective: Assess students' ability to apply concepts and skills in Lessons 8-1 through 8-5 in a real-world format.

 Online Edition

Resources

 ***Algebra II Assessments***

www.mathtekstoolkit.org

Problem	Text Reference
1	Lesson 8-1
2	Lesson 8-2
3	Lesson 8-4
4	Lesson 8-3
5	Lesson 8-5

State Resources

SECTION 8A

Rational Functions

Math in the Fast Lane The Indianapolis 500 is one of the most exciting events in sports. Each spring, 33 drivers compete in the 500 mi race, sometimes hitting speeds of more than 220 mi/h.

Winners of the Indianapolis 500		
Year	**Winner**	**Winning Time**
1911	Roy Harroun	6 h 42 min
1990	Arie Luyendyk	2 h 41 min 18 s
2004	Buddy Rice	3 h 15 s

1. Write a rational function that can be used to model the race, where the independent variable represents the average speed in miles per hour and the dependent variable represents the time in hours it takes to complete the race. What type of variation function is it? $t = \frac{500}{r}$; inverse variation

2. To the nearest mile per hour, how much faster was the average winning speed in 2004 than in 1911? 92 mi/h

3. In 1990, Arie Luyendyk set the record for the fastest Indy 500 average speed, about 186 mi/h. The time in hours to finish the race based on Arie Luyendyk's record can be modeled by the function $t = \frac{500}{186 + s}$, where s is the speed above 186 in miles per hour. Graph the function, and evaluate it for $s = 10$. What does this value of the function represent?

3. about 2.55; the time in hours needed to finish the Indy 500 at an average speed 10 mi/h faster than Luyendyk's record average speed

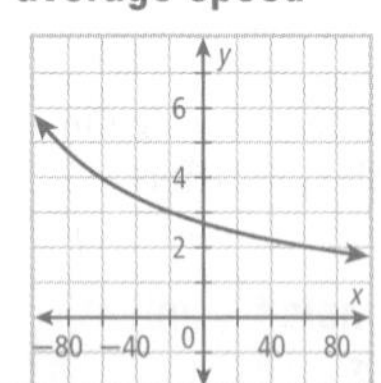

4. During the race, a driver completes one lap with an average speed of 200 mi/h and then completes the following lap at an average speed of 210 mi/h. What is the driver's average speed for the two laps, to the nearest tenth of a mile per hour? 204.9 mi/h

5. Each lap in the Indy 500 is 2.5 mi. A driver completes two laps in 1.5 min. The average speed during the second lap is 8 mi/h faster than the average speed during the first lap. Find the driver's average speed for each of the two laps, to the nearest mile per hour. 196 mi/h; 204 mi/h

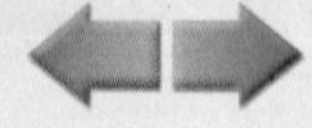

Scaffolding Questions

1. If a driver's average speed increases, what happens to the time needed to finish the race? The time decreases.
2. How can you convert 6 h 42 min to hours? Write it as $6 + \frac{42}{60}$, or 6.7, h.
3. What does a positive value of s indicate? an average speed greater than 186 mi/h
4. If d represents the length of one lap, what expression represents the total time needed to complete both laps? $\frac{d}{200} + \frac{d}{210}$
5. What equation can you use to determine f, the average speed of the first lap? $\frac{2.5}{f} + \frac{2.5}{f+8} = \frac{1.5}{60}$

Extension

A driver takes a 10 s pit stop during a 2.5 mi lap. The pit stop reduces her overall average speed during the lap to 130 mi/h. To the nearest mile per hour, what was the driver's average speed during the lap, not including the 10 s pit stop? 152 mi/h

READY TO GO ON?

Quiz for Lessons 8-1 Through 8-5

8-1 Variation Functions

1. The mass m in kilograms of a bronze statue varies directly as its volume V in cubic centimeters. If a statue made from 1000 cm^3 of bronze has a mass of 8.7 kg, what is the mass of a statue made from 4500 cm^3 of bronze? **39.15 kg**
2. The time t in hours needed to clean the rides at an amusement park varies inversely with the number of workers n. If 6 workers can clean the rides in 6 hours, how many hours will it take 10 workers to clean the rides? **3.6 h**

8-2 Multiplying and Dividing Rational Expressions

Simplify. Identify any x-values for which the expression is undefined.

3. $\dfrac{5x^3}{10x^2 + 5x}$ **$\dfrac{x^2}{2x+1}$; $x \neq -\dfrac{1}{2}$ and $x \neq 0$**
4. $\dfrac{x^2 - 2x - 3}{x^2 + 5x + 4}$ **$\dfrac{x-3}{x+4}$; $x \neq -4$ and $x \neq -1$**
5. $\dfrac{-x + 6}{x^2 - 3x - 18}$ **$\dfrac{-1}{x+3}$; $x \neq -3$ and $x \neq 6$**

Multiply or divide. Assume that all expressions are defined.

6. $\dfrac{x+3}{x+2} \cdot \dfrac{2x-4}{x^2-9}$
7. $\dfrac{9x^6y}{27x^2y^5} \div \dfrac{x}{6y^2}$ **$\dfrac{2x^3}{y^2}$**
8. $\dfrac{2x^3 - 18x}{x^2 - 2x - 8} \div \dfrac{x^2 + x - 12}{x^2 - 16}$ **$\dfrac{2x(x+3)}{x+2}$**

8-3 Adding and Subtracting Rational Expressions

Add or subtract. Identify any x-values for which the expression is undefined.

9. $\dfrac{3x+2}{x-2} - \dfrac{x+5}{x-2}$
10. $\dfrac{x^2 - x}{x^2 - 25} + \dfrac{3}{x+5}$
11. $\dfrac{x}{x-3} - \dfrac{1}{x+3}$
12. A plane's average speed when flying from one city to another is 550 mi/h and is 430 mi/h on the return flight. To the nearest mile per hour, what is the plane's average speed for the entire trip? **483 mi/h**

8-4 Rational Functions

Using the graph of $f(x) = \frac{1}{x}$ as a guide, describe the transformations and graph each function.

13. $g(x) = \dfrac{1}{x-4}$ **g is f translated 4 units right.**
14. $g(x) = \dfrac{1}{x+1} + 2$ **g is f translated 1 unit left and 2 units up.**

Identify the zeros and asymptotes of each function. Then graph.

15. $f(x) = \dfrac{x^2 - 16}{x - 3}$ **zeros: 4, −4; vertical asymptote: $x = 3$; horizontal asymptote: none**
16. $f(x) = \dfrac{2x}{x^2 - 4}$ **zero: 0; vertical asymptotes: $x = -2$, $x = 2$; horizontal asymptote: $y = 0$**

8-5 Solving Rational Equations and Inequalities

Solve each equation.

17. $y - \dfrac{10}{y} = 3$ **−2, 5**
18. $\dfrac{x}{x-8} = \dfrac{24 - 2x}{x - 8}$ **no solution**
19. $\dfrac{-3x}{3} - \dfrac{x+15}{x+9} = 1$ **−8, −3**
20. A restaurant has two pastry ovens. When both ovens are used, it takes about 3 hours to bake the bread needed for one day. When only the large oven is used, it takes about 4 hours to bake the bread for one day. Approximately how long would it take to bake the bread for one day if only the small oven were used? **12 h**

SECTION 8A

READY TO GO ON?

Organizer

Objective: Assess students' mastery of concepts and skills in Lessons 8-1 through 8-5.

Resources

Assessment Resources
Section 8A Quiz

Test & Practice Generator
One-Stop Planner®

INTERVENTION

Resources

***Ready to Go On? Intervention and Enrichment* Worksheets**

***Ready to Go On?* CD-ROM**

***Ready to Go On?* Online**
my.hrw.com

Answers

6. $\dfrac{2(x-2)}{(x+2)(x-3)}$
9. $\dfrac{2x-3}{x-2}$; $x \neq 2$

10–11. See p. A37.

13–16. For graphs, see p. A37.

READY TO GO ON?
Diagnose and Prescribe

NO
INTERVENE

Ready to Go On? Intervention	*Ready to Go On? Intervention,* Section 8A: Worksheets	CD-ROM	Online
Lesson 8-1	8-1 Intervention	Activity 8-1	Diagnose and Prescribe Online
Lesson 8-2	8-2 Intervention	Activity 8-2	
Lesson 8-3	8-3 Intervention	Activity 8-3	
Lesson 8-4	8-4 Intervention	Activity 8-4	
Lesson 8-5	8-5 Intervention	Activity 8-5	

YES
ENRICH

***Ready to Go On? Enrichment,* Section 8A**

Worksheets

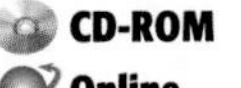

CD-ROM

Online

SECTION 8B

Radical Functions

One-Minute Section Planner

Lesson	Lab Resources	Materials
Lesson 8-6 Radical Expressions and Rational Exponents • Rewrite radical expressions by using rational exponents. • Simplify and evaluate radical expressions and expressions containing rational exponents. ☑ SAT-10 ☑ NAEP ☑ ACT ☑ SAT ☐ SAT Subject Tests		**Required** graphing calculator
Lesson 8-7 Radical Functions • Graph radical functions and inequalities. • Transform radical functions by changing parameters. ☐ SAT-10 ☐ NAEP ☐ ACT ☐ SAT ☐ SAT Subject Tests	***Technology Lab Activities*** 8-7 Technology Lab	**Required** graph paper and/or graphing calculator **Optional** blank transparency
Lesson 8-8 Solving Radical Equations and Inequalities • Solve radical equations and inequalities. ☑ SAT-10 ☐ NAEP ☐ ACT ☑ SAT ☐ SAT Subject Tests		**Required** graph paper and/or graphing calculator

MK = *Manipulatives Kit*

Section Overview

Professional Development

Radical Expressions and Rational Exponents

Lesson 8-6

Why? Radical expressions can be written with rational exponents.

Properties of *n*th Roots

For $a > 0$ and $b > 0$,

$$\sqrt[n]{ab} = \sqrt[n]{a} \cdot \sqrt[n]{b}$$

$$\sqrt[n]{\frac{a}{b}} = \frac{\sqrt[n]{a}}{\sqrt[n]{b}}$$

Rational Exponents

For any natural number n and integer m,

$$a^{\frac{1}{n}} = \sqrt[n]{a}$$

$$a^{\frac{m}{n}} = \left(\sqrt[n]{a}\right)^m = \sqrt[n]{a^m}$$

Rational exponents have the same properties as integer exponents.

Properties of Rational Exponents

For all nonzero real numbers a and b and rational numbers m and n,

$$a^m \cdot a^n = a^{m+n} \qquad \frac{a^m}{a^n} = a^{m-n} \qquad \left(\frac{a}{b}\right)^m = \frac{a^m}{b^m}$$

$$(ab)^m = a^m b^m \qquad (a^m)^n = a^{m \cdot n}$$

Radical Functions

Lesson 8-7

Being able to sketch the graph of a radical function makes it easier to understand the function's behavior and analyze its properties.

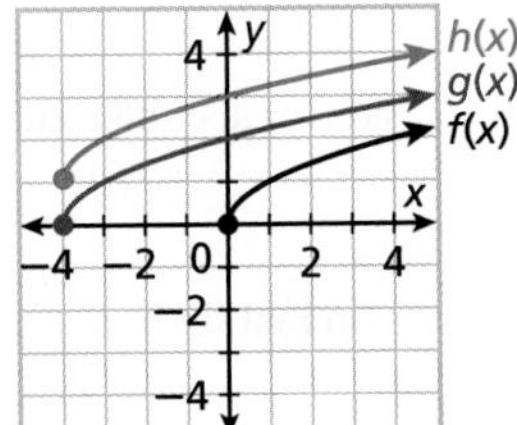

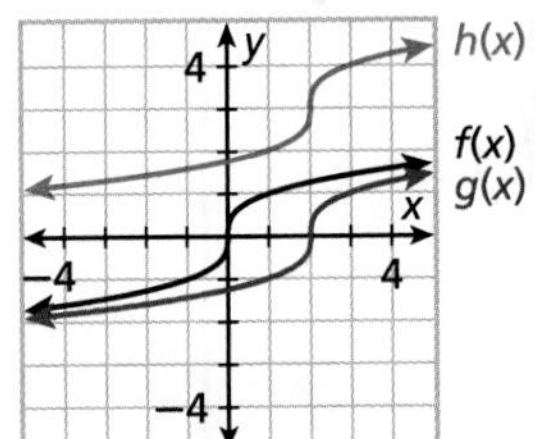

$f(x) = \sqrt{x}$ Domain: $\{x \mid x \geq 0\}$ Range: $\{y \mid y \geq 0\}$

$g(x) = \sqrt{x + 4}$ Domain: $\{x \mid x \geq -4\}$ Range: $\{y \mid y \geq 0\}$

$h(x) = \sqrt{x + 4} + 1$ Domain: $\{x \mid x \geq -4\}$ Range: $\{y \mid y \geq 1\}$

$f(x) = \sqrt[3]{x}$ Domain: $\mathbb{R}$ Range: $\mathbb{R}$

$g(x) = \sqrt[3]{x - 2}$ Domain: $\mathbb{R}$ Range: $\mathbb{R}$

$h(x) = \sqrt[3]{x - 2} + 3$ Domain: $\mathbb{R}$ Range: $\mathbb{R}$

Solving Radical Equations and Inequalities

Lesson 8-8

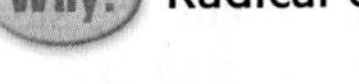

Radical equations and inequalities are found in many scientific formulas.

$$5\sqrt{2x + 4} = 30$$

$$\frac{5\sqrt{2x + 4}}{5} = \frac{30}{5}$$ *Isolate the radical expression.*

$$\left(\sqrt{2x + 4}\right)^2 = 6^2$$ *Raise both sides of the equation to the power equal to the index of the radical.*

$$2x + 4 = 36$$

$$x = 16$$

Check for extraneous solutions.

Check $5\sqrt{2x + 4} = 30$

$5\sqrt{2(16) + 4}$	30
$5\sqrt{36}$	30
30	30 ✓

8-6 Organizer

Pacing: Traditional 1 day
Block $\frac{1}{2}$ day

Objectives: Rewrite radical expressions by using rational exponents.

Simplify and evaluate radical expressions and expressions containing rational exponents.

Online Edition
Tutorial Videos, Interactivity

Countdown to Testing Week 18

Power Presentations with PowerPoint®

Warm Up

Simplify each expression.

1. $7^3 \cdot 7^2$ 16,807

2. $\frac{11^8}{11^6}$ 121

3. $(3^2)^3$ 729

4. $\sqrt{75}$ $5\sqrt{3}$

5. $\frac{\sqrt{20}}{\sqrt{7}}$ $\frac{2\sqrt{35}}{7}$

Also available on transparency

Math Humor

Q: How is an artificial tree like the fourth root of −68?

A: Neither has real roots.

8-6 Radical Expressions and Rational Exponents

A2.5.3 Understand the properties of rational exponents and use the properties to simplify, multiply, divide, and find powers of expressions containing negative and fractional . . . exponents. Relate expressions containing rational exponents to the corresponding radical expressions.

Objectives
Rewrite radical expressions by using rational exponents.

Simplify and evaluate radical expressions and expressions containing rational exponents.

Vocabulary
index
rational exponent

Who uses this?
Guitar makers use radical expressions to ensure that the strings produce the correct notes. (See Example 6.)

You are probably familiar with finding the square and square root of a number. These two operations are inverses of each other. Similarly, there are roots that correspond to larger powers.

5 and −5 are square roots of 25 because $5^2 = 25$ and $(-5)^2 = 25$.
2 is the cube root of 8 because $2^3 = 8$.
2 and −2 are fourth roots of 16 because $2^4 = 16$ and $(-2)^4 = 16$.
a is the nth root of b if $a^n = b$.

The nth root of a real number a can be written as the radical expression $\sqrt[n]{a}$, where n is the **index** (plural: *indices*) of the radical and a is the radicand. When a number has more than one real root, the radical sign indicates only the principal, or positive, root.

Reading Math
When a radical sign shows no index, it represents a square root.

Numbers and Types of Real Roots

Case	Roots	Example
Odd index	1 real root	The real 3rd root of 8 is 2.
Even index; positive radicand	2 real roots	The real 4th roots of 16 are ±2.
Even index; negative radicand	0 real roots	−16 has no real 4th roots.
Radicand of 0	1 root of 0	The 3rd root of 0 is 0.

EXAMPLE 1 Finding Real Roots

Find all real roots.

A **fourth roots of 81**
A positive number has two real fourth roots. Because $3^4 = 81$ and $(-3)^4 = 81$, the roots are 3 and −3.

B **cube roots of −125**
A negative number has one real cube root. Because $(-5)^3 = -125$, the root is −5.

C **sixth roots of −729**
A negative number has no real sixth roots.

Find all real roots.

1a. fourth roots of −256 no real roots **1b.** sixth roots of 1 ±1 **1c.** cube roots of 125 5

State Resources

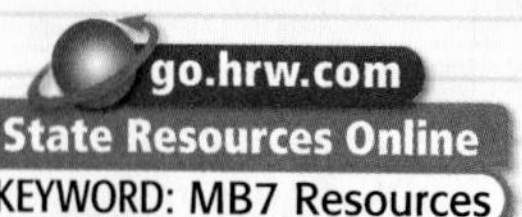

go.hrw.com
State Resources Online
KEYWORD: MB7 Resources

1 Introduce

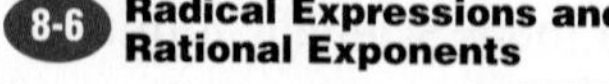

EXPLORATION

8-6 Radical Expressions and Rational Exponents

You can use a graphing calculator to investigate the meaning of cube roots. To enter cube roots, press MATH and select 4: ∛(.

1. Use your calculator to help you complete the table.

Cubes	Cube Roots
$1^3 =$	$\sqrt[3]{1} =$
$2^3 =$	$\sqrt[3]{8} =$
$3^3 =$	$\sqrt[3]{27} =$
$4^3 =$	$\sqrt[3]{64} =$
$5^3 =$	$\sqrt[3]{125} =$

2. Based on the pattern in the table, what is the cube root of 6^3?

THINK AND DISCUSS

3. Explain what is meant by the cube root of a real number a.

4. Discuss the meaning of the expression $\sqrt[3]{16}$ and how you could determine its value.

Motivate

Ask students how they can determine the side length of a square when given its area. by finding the square root of the area Draw a cube on the board and label its volume 8 ft³. Ask students to determine the side length of the cube and to justify their answer. The side length is 2 ft because $2^3 = 8$ ft³. Explain that 2 is said to be the cube root of 8 because $2^3 = 8$. Tell students that they will learn more about cube roots in this lesson.

Explorations and answers are provided in the *Explorations* binder.

The properties of square roots in Lesson 1-3 also apply to nth roots.

Properties of nth Roots

For $a > 0$ and $b > 0$,

WORDS	NUMBERS	ALGEBRA
Product Property of Roots The nth root of a product is equal to the product of the nth roots.	$\sqrt[3]{16} = \sqrt[3]{8} \cdot \sqrt[3]{2} = 2\sqrt[3]{2}$	$\sqrt[n]{ab} = \sqrt[n]{a} \cdot \sqrt[n]{b}$
Quotient Property of Roots The nth root of a quotient is equal to the quotient of the nth roots.	$\sqrt{\frac{25}{16}} = \frac{\sqrt{25}}{\sqrt{16}} = \frac{5}{4}$	$\sqrt[n]{\frac{a}{b}} = \frac{\sqrt[n]{a}}{\sqrt[n]{b}}$

EXAMPLE 2 Simplifying Radical Expressions

Simplify each expression. Assume that all variables are positive.

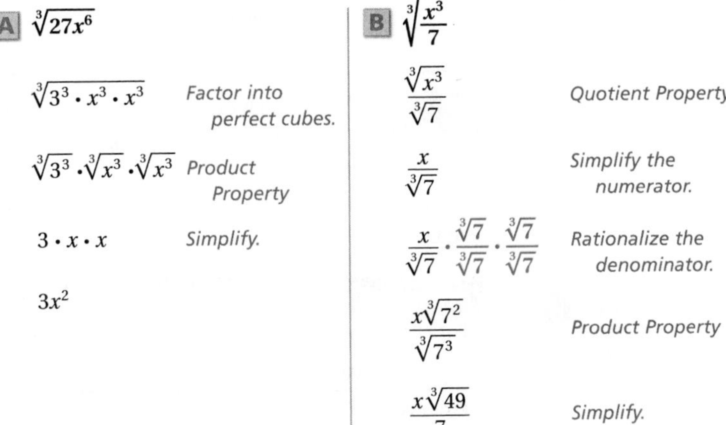

A $\sqrt[3]{27x^6}$

$\sqrt[3]{3^3 \cdot x^3 \cdot x^3}$ *Factor into perfect cubes.*

$\sqrt[3]{3^3} \cdot \sqrt[3]{x^3} \cdot \sqrt[3]{x^3}$ *Product Property*

$3 \cdot x \cdot x$ *Simplify.*

$3x^2$

B $\sqrt[3]{\frac{x^3}{7}}$

$\frac{\sqrt[3]{x^3}}{\sqrt[3]{7}}$ *Quotient Property*

$\frac{x}{\sqrt[3]{7}}$ *Simplify the numerator.*

$\frac{x}{\sqrt[3]{7}} \cdot \frac{\sqrt[3]{7}}{\sqrt[3]{7}} \cdot \frac{\sqrt[3]{7}}{\sqrt[3]{7}}$ *Rationalize the denominator.*

$\frac{x\sqrt[3]{7^2}}{\sqrt[3]{7^3}}$ *Product Property*

$\frac{x\sqrt[3]{49}}{7}$ *Simplify.*

Remember!

When an expression contains a radical in the denominator, you must rationalize the denominator. To do so, rewrite the expression so that the denominator contains no radicals.

Simplify each expression. Assume that all variables are positive.

2a. $\sqrt[4]{16x^4}$ **2b.** $\sqrt[4]{\frac{x^8}{3}}$ **2c.** $\sqrt[3]{x^7} \cdot \sqrt[3]{x^2}$

A **rational exponent** is an exponent that can be expressed as $\frac{m}{n}$, where m and n are integers and $n \neq 0$. Radical expressions can be written by using rational exponents.

Rational Exponents

For any natural number n and integer m,

WORDS	NUMBERS	ALGEBRA
The exponent $\frac{1}{n}$ indicates the nth root.	$16^{\frac{1}{4}} = \sqrt[4]{16} = 2$	$a^{\frac{1}{n}} = \sqrt[n]{a}$
The exponent $\frac{m}{n}$ indicates the nth root raised to the mth power.	$8^{\frac{2}{3}} = \left(\sqrt[3]{8}\right)^2 = 2^2 = 4$	$a^{\frac{m}{n}} = \left(\sqrt[n]{a}\right)^m = \sqrt[n]{a^m}$

2 Teach

Guided Instruction

This lesson extends concepts and properties that students have already learned. Start by reviewing square roots, including the Product and Quotient Properties of Square Roots. Then extend these concepts to include roots with higher indices. Before students apply the properties of exponents to rational exponents, make sure they remember how to use the properties with integer exponents.

Reaching All Learners

Through Auditory Cues

Ask students to work in pairs. Have one student in each pair write a radical expression with an index greater than 2. Then have partners read the radical expression aloud. For example, the expression $\sqrt[4]{7^3}$ can be read as "the principal fourth root of 7 cubed." Reading such expressions aloud can help students become familiar with the terminology associated with nth roots.

ENGLISH LANGUAGE LEARNERS

Power Presentations with PowerPoint®

Additional Examples

Example 1

Find all real roots.

A. sixth roots of 64 2, −2

B. cube roots of −216 −6

C. fourth roots of −1024 none

Example 2

Simplify each expression. Assume that all variables are positive.

A. $\sqrt[4]{81x^{12}}$ $3x^3$

B. $\sqrt[4]{\frac{16x^8}{5}}$ $\frac{2x^2\sqrt[4]{125}}{5}$

Also available on transparency

INTERVENTION

Questioning Strategies

EXAMPLE 1

- Which part of each expression represents the index? Which part represents the radicand?
- What properties of the index and the radicand help you determine the number of real roots?

EXAMPLE 2

- How can you use the Product Property of Roots or the Quotient Property of Roots to rewrite a radical expression?
- How do you rationalize the denominator of a radical expression?

Reading Math Example 1A shows that both 3 and −3 are fourth roots of 81. Note, however, that although $\sqrt[4]{81}$ is equal to 3, it is *not* also equal to −3. The radical symbol indicates the principal root, which is always nonnegative.

Inclusion To rationalize a denominator with an nth root, multiply the numerator and denominator by the nth root $n - 1$ times. In **Example 2B**, both the numerator and the denominator are multiplied by $\sqrt[3]{7}$ twice to rationalize the denominator $\sqrt[3]{7}$.

Power Presentations with PowerPoint®

Additional Examples

Example 3

Write the expression $(-32)^{\frac{3}{5}}$ in radical form and simplify.

$\left(\sqrt[5]{-32}\right)^3 = -8$

Example 4

Write each expression by using rational exponents.

A. $\sqrt[8]{13^4}$ $\quad 13^{\frac{1}{2}}$

B. $\sqrt[5]{3^{15}}$ $\quad 27$

Also available on transparency

INTERVENTION

Questioning Strategies

EXAMPLE 3

- What does the numerator of a rational exponent indicate? What does the denominator indicate?

EXAMPLE 4

- When rewriting a radical expression by using a rational exponent, where do you place the index of the radical?

EXAMPLE 3 Writing Expressions in Radical Form

Write the expression $(-125)^{\frac{2}{3}}$ in radical form, and simplify.

Writing Math

The denominator of a rational exponent becomes the index of the radical.

Method 1 Evaluate the root first.		**Method 2** Evaluate the power first.	
$\left(\sqrt[3]{-125}\right)^2$	*Write with a radical.*	$\sqrt[3]{(-125)^2}$	*Write with a radical.*
$(-5)^2$	*Evaluate the root.*	$\sqrt[3]{15{,}625}$	*Evaluate the power.*
25	*Evaluate the power.*	25	*Evaluate the root.*

CHECK IT OUT! Write each expression in radical form, and simplify.

3a. $64^{\frac{1}{3}}$ **4** $\qquad$ **3b.** $4^{\frac{5}{2}}$ **32** $\qquad$ **3c.** $625^{\frac{3}{4}}$ **125**

EXAMPLE 4 Writing Expressions by Using Rational Exponents

Write each expression by using rational exponents.

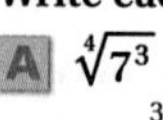

A $\sqrt[4]{7^3}$

$7^{\frac{3}{4}}$ $\qquad \sqrt[n]{a^m} = a^{\frac{m}{n}}$

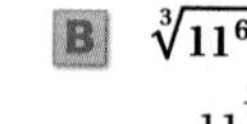

B $\sqrt[3]{11^6}$

$11^{\frac{6}{3}}$ $\qquad \sqrt[n]{a^m} = a^{\frac{m}{n}}$

$11^2 = 121$ $\qquad$ *Simplify.*

CHECK IT OUT! Write each expression by using rational exponents.

4a. $\left(\sqrt[4]{81}\right)^3$ $\mathbf{81^{\frac{3}{4}}}$ $\qquad$ **4b.** $\sqrt[3]{10^9}$ **1000** $\qquad$ **4c.** $\sqrt[4]{5^2}$ $\mathbf{5^{\frac{1}{2}}}$

Rational exponents have the same properties as integer exponents. (See Lesson 1-5.)

Know it! Note

Properties of Rational Exponents

For all nonzero real numbers *a* and *b* and rational numbers *m* and *n*,

WORDS	NUMBERS	ALGEBRA
Product of Powers Property To multiply powers with the same base, add the exponents.	$12^{\frac{1}{2}} \cdot 12^{\frac{3}{2}} = 12^{\frac{1}{2}+\frac{3}{2}} = 12^2 = 144$	$a^m \cdot a^n = a^{m+n}$
Quotient of Powers Property To divide powers with the same base, subtract the exponents.	$\dfrac{125^{\frac{2}{3}}}{125^{\frac{1}{3}}} = 125^{\frac{2}{3}-\frac{1}{3}} = 125^{\frac{1}{3}} = 5$	$\dfrac{a^m}{a^n} = a^{m-n}$
Power of a Power Property To raise one power to another, multiply the exponents.	$\left(8^{\frac{2}{3}}\right)^3 = 8^{\frac{2}{3}\cdot 3} = 8^2 = 64$	$(a^m)^n = a^{m \cdot n}$
Power of a Product Property To find the power of a product, distribute the exponent.	$(16 \cdot 25)^{\frac{1}{2}} = 16^{\frac{1}{2}} \cdot 25^{\frac{1}{2}} = 4 \cdot 5 = 20$	$(ab)^m = a^m b^m$
Power of a Quotient Property To find the power of a quotient, distribute the exponent.	$\left(\dfrac{16}{81}\right)^{\frac{1}{4}} = \dfrac{16^{\frac{1}{4}}}{81^{\frac{1}{4}}} = \dfrac{2}{3}$	$\left(\dfrac{a}{b}\right)^m = \dfrac{a^m}{b^m}$

Teaching Tip **Critical Thinking Example 3** demonstrates that when students find the value of a number raised to a rational power, they can evaluate either the root or the integer power first. It is often easier to evaluate the root first, since doing so enables students to work with smaller numbers.

Teaching Tip **Math Background** Before the invention of calculators, it was easier to estimate with radical expressions that were written with rationalized denominators. For example, it is easier to estimate $\frac{\sqrt{2}}{2} \approx \frac{1.4}{2} \approx 0.7$ than it is to estimate $\frac{1}{\sqrt{2}} \approx \frac{1}{1.4}$. Today, rationalizing the denominator will help students read integral tables when they take calculus.

EXAMPLE 5 Simplifying Expressions with Rational Exponents

Simplify each expression.

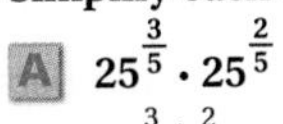

A $25^{\frac{3}{5}} \cdot 25^{\frac{2}{5}}$

$25^{\frac{3}{5}+\frac{2}{5}}$ *Product of Powers*

25^1 *Simplify.*

25 *Evaluate the power.*

Check Enter the expression in a graphing calculator.

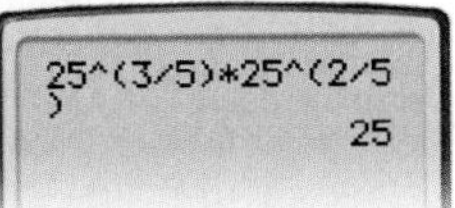

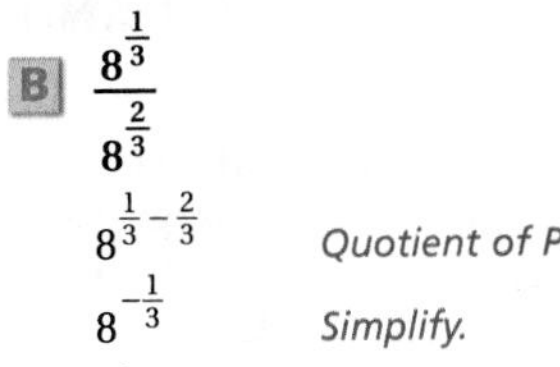

B $\dfrac{8^{\frac{1}{3}}}{8^{\frac{2}{3}}}$

$8^{\frac{1}{3}-\frac{2}{3}}$ *Quotient of Powers*

$8^{-\frac{1}{3}}$ *Simplify.*

$\dfrac{1}{8^{\frac{1}{3}}}$ *Negative Exponent Property*

$\dfrac{1}{2}$ *Evaluate the power.*

Check Enter the expression in a graphing calculator.

CHECK IT OUT! Simplify each expression.

5a. $36^{\frac{3}{8}} \cdot 36^{\frac{1}{8}}$ **5b.** $(-8)^{-\frac{1}{3}}$ **5c.** $\dfrac{5^{\frac{9}{4}}}{5^{\frac{1}{4}}}$

EXAMPLE 6 *Music Application*

Frets are small metal bars positioned across the neck of a guitar so that the guitar can produce the notes of a specific scale.

To find the distance a fret should be placed from the bridge, multiply the length of the string by $2^{-\frac{n}{12}}$, where n is the number of notes higher than the string's root note. Where should a fret be placed to produce a G note on the E string (3 notes higher)?

E string
Frets
64 cm
Bridge

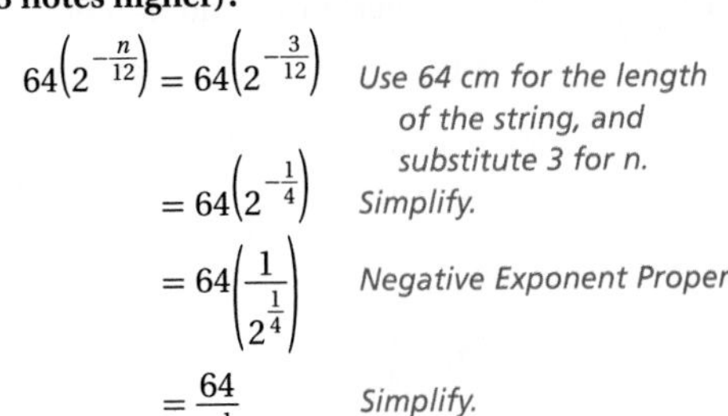

$64\left(2^{-\frac{n}{12}}\right) = 64\left(2^{-\frac{3}{12}}\right)$ *Use 64 cm for the length of the string, and substitute 3 for n.*

$= 64\left(2^{-\frac{1}{4}}\right)$ *Simplify.*

$= 64\left(\dfrac{1}{2^{\frac{1}{4}}}\right)$ *Negative Exponent Property*

$= \dfrac{64}{2^{\frac{1}{4}}}$ *Simplify.*

≈ 53.82 *Use a calculator.*

64/(2^(1/4))
53.81737058

The fret should be placed about 53.82 cm from the bridge.

CHECK IT OUT! **6.** Where should a fret be placed to produce the E note that is one octave higher on the E string (12 notes higher)?

COMMON ERROR ALERT

After learning the Product and Quotient Properties for nth roots, some students may incorrectly assume that there are similar properties for sums and differences. Show students by numerical example that $\sqrt[n]{a+b} \neq \sqrt[n]{a} + \sqrt[n]{b}$ and that $\sqrt[n]{a-b} \neq \sqrt[n]{a} - \sqrt[n]{b}$ for $a > 0$ and $b > 0$.

Power Presentations with PowerPoint®

Additional Examples

Example 5

Simplify each expression.

A. $7^{\frac{7}{9}} \cdot 7^{\frac{11}{9}}$ 49

B. $\dfrac{16^{\frac{3}{4}}}{16^{\frac{5}{4}}}$ $\dfrac{1}{4}$

Example 6

Radium-226 is a form of a radioactive element that decays over time. An initial sample of radium-226 has a mass of 500 mg. The mass of radium-226 remaining from the initial sample after t years is given by $500\left(2^{-\frac{t}{1600}}\right)$. To the nearest milligram, how much radium-226 would be left after 800 years? 354 mg

Also available on transparency

INTERVENTION
Questioning Strategies

EXAMPLE 5

- How do you multiply powers with the same base when the exponents are rational?
- How do you divide powers with the same base when the exponents are rational?

EXAMPLE 6

- How can you rewrite an expression with a negative exponent so that the exponent is positive?
- How do you enter an expression with a rational exponent on your calculator?

3 Close

Summarize

Review the properties of roots and exponents. Point out that the properties of roots apply only to radicals with the same index and that the properties of rational exponents apply only to powers with the same base. Ask students to describe the steps for converting between radical expressions and expressions with rational exponents. Remind students that when simplifying expressions involving nth roots, they can write the expressions using radicals or using rational exponents, whichever they find easier to use.

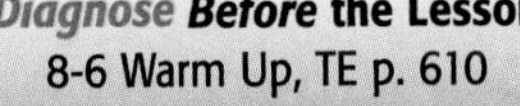

ONGOING ASSESSMENT and INTERVENTION

***Diagnose Before* the Lesson**
8-6 Warm Up, TE p. 610

***Monitor During* the Lesson**
Check It Out! Exercises, SE pp. 610–613
Questioning Strategies, TE pp. 611–613

***Assess After* the Lesson**
8-6 Lesson Quiz, TE p. 617
Alternative Assessment, TE p. 617

Answers to *Think and Discuss*

Possible answers:

1. When a and n are natural numbers, the expression $\sqrt[n]{a^n}$ can be written with a rational exponent: $a^{\frac{n}{n}}$. The exponent simplifies to 1, so the expression becomes a^1, or a.
2. See p. A10.

THINK AND DISCUSS

1. Explain why $\sqrt[n]{a^n}$ is equal to a for all natural numbers a and n.
2. **GET ORGANIZED** Copy and complete the graphic organizer. In each box, give a numeric and an algebraic example of the given property of rational exponents.

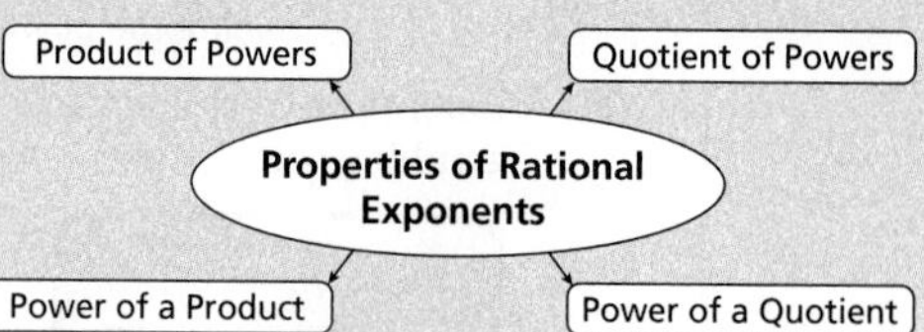

8-6 Exercises

Assignment Guide

Assign *Guided Practice* exercises as necessary.

If you finished Examples **1–3**
- **Basic** 30–44, 77–79, 82
- **Average** 30–44, 77–79, 82
- **Advanced** 30–44, 77–79, 82, 91

If you finished Examples **1–6**
- **Basic** 30–72, 77–82, 84–88, 93–100
- **Average** 30–90, 93–100
- **Advanced** 30–80, 82–100

Homework Quick Check

Quickly check key concepts.
Exercises: 32, 38, 42, 46, 54, 58, 72

Answers

26. $\frac{1}{7^{\frac{1}{2}}}$, or $\frac{\sqrt{7}}{7}$

State Resources

go.hrw.com
State Resources Online
KEYWORD: MB7 Resources

8-6 Exercises

GUIDED PRACTICE

1. **Vocabulary** The *index* of the expression $\sqrt[3]{4^2}$ is __?__. (2, 3, or 4) 3

SEE EXAMPLE 1 p. 610

Find all real roots.

2. cube roots of 27 3
3. fourth roots of 625 ± 5
4. cube roots of 0 0

SEE EXAMPLE 2 p. 611

Simplify each expression. Assume that all variables are positive.

5. $\sqrt[3]{8x^3}$ $2x$
6. $\sqrt[4]{\frac{32}{x^4}}$ $\frac{2\sqrt[4]{2}}{x}$
7. $\sqrt[3]{\frac{125x^6}{6}}$ $\frac{5x^2\sqrt[3]{36}}{6}$
8. $\sqrt{50x^3}$ $5x\sqrt{2x}$
9. $\sqrt[4]{x^8} \cdot \sqrt[3]{x^4}$ $x^3\sqrt[3]{x}$
10. $\sqrt[3]{\frac{x^5}{4}}$ $\frac{x\sqrt[3]{2x^2}}{2}$
11. $\frac{\sqrt{40x^4}}{\sqrt[3]{-x^3}}$ $-2x\sqrt{10}$
12. $\sqrt[4]{\frac{x^{12}y^4}{3}}$ $\frac{x^3y\sqrt[4]{27}}{3}$

SEE EXAMPLE 3 p. 612

Write each expression in radical form, and simplify.

13. $36^{\frac{3}{2}}$ 216
14. $32^{\frac{3}{5}}$ 8
15. $(-27)^{\frac{1}{3}}$ -3
16. $8^{\frac{2}{3}}$ 4

SEE EXAMPLE 4 p. 612

Write each expression by using rational exponents.

17. $\sqrt[5]{9^{10}}$ $9^{\frac{10}{5}} = 9^2 = 81$
18. $\sqrt{8^3}$ $8^{\frac{3}{2}}$
19. $(\sqrt[6]{5})^3$ $5^{\frac{1}{2}}$
20. $(\sqrt[3]{27})^2$ $27^{\frac{2}{3}}$

SEE EXAMPLE 5 p. 613

Simplify each expression.

21. $13^{\frac{1}{2}} \cdot 13^{\frac{3}{2}}$ 169
22. $\frac{9^{\frac{4}{3}}}{9^{\frac{2}{3}}}$ $81^{\frac{1}{3}}$, or $3\sqrt[3]{3}$
23. $\left(64^{\frac{1}{2}}\right)^{\frac{1}{3}}$ 2
24. $\left(\frac{8}{27}\right)^{\frac{1}{3}}$ $\frac{2}{3}$
25. $25^{-\frac{1}{2}}$ $\frac{1}{5}$
26. $7^{\frac{1}{4}} \cdot 7^{-\frac{3}{4}}$
27. $(-125)^{-\frac{1}{3}}$ $-\frac{1}{5}$
28. $\left(6^{\frac{1}{2}}\right)^6$ 216

SEE EXAMPLE 6 p. 613

29. **Geometry** The side length of a cube can be determined by finding the cube root of the volume. What is the side length to the nearest *inch* of the cube shown? 44 in.

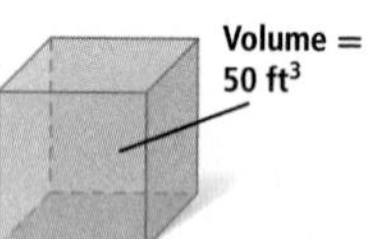

8-6 PRACTICE A

Answer each question.

1. List all of the square roots of 36. 6 and −6
2. What is the inverse of the square of a number? The square root
3. Express $n^{\frac{1}{2}}$ without a fractional exponent. $\sqrt{n}$
4. Express $n^{\frac{7}{4}}$ without a fractional exponent. $\sqrt[4]{n^7}$
5. Write the following root: the radicand is 10 and the index is 12. $\sqrt[12]{10}$

Find all real roots.

6. 4th roots of 1 ± 1
7. cube roots of 27 3
8. square roots of 81 ± 9

Write each expression in radical form, and simplify.

9. $6^{\frac{1}{2}}$ $\sqrt{6}$
10. $8^{\frac{2}{3}}$ $\sqrt[3]{8^2} = 4$
11. $5^{\frac{4}{3}}$ $\sqrt[3]{5^4}$

Write each expression by using rational exponents.

12. $\sqrt{7^2}$ 7^1 or 7
13. $\sqrt[4]{5^3}$ $5^{\frac{3}{4}}$
14. $\sqrt[3]{10^5}$ $10^{\frac{5}{3}}$

Simplify each expression. Assume all variables are positive.

15. $\sqrt[3]{8x^3}$ $2x$
16. $\sqrt{\frac{36}{16}}$ $\frac{3}{2}$
17. $2^2 \cdot 2^3$ 2^5 or 32
18. $\frac{(3x)^4}{(3x)^2}$ $9x^2$
19. $(5^2)^2$ 5^4 or 625
20. $\left(\frac{8x^3}{27}\right)^{\frac{1}{3}}$ $\frac{2x}{3}$
21. $\sqrt{\frac{8x^2}{2x^4}}$ $\frac{2}{x}$
22. $2 \cdot \left(\frac{1}{8}\right)^{\frac{1}{3}}$ 1
23. $(\sqrt{25x^2})^3$ $125x^3$

8-6 PRACTICE B

Simplify each expression. Assume all variables are positive.

1. $\sqrt[3]{125x^9}$ $5x^3$
2. $\sqrt[4]{\frac{x^8}{81}}$ $\frac{x^2}{3}$
3. $\sqrt[3]{\frac{64x^3}{8}}$ $2x$

Write each expression in radical form, and simplify.

4. $64^{\frac{5}{6}}$ 32
5. $27^{\frac{2}{3}}$ 9
6. $(-8)^{\frac{4}{3}}$ 16

Write each expression by using rational exponents.

7. $\sqrt[5]{51^4}$ $51^{\frac{4}{5}}$
8. $(\sqrt{169})^3$ $169^{\frac{3}{2}}$
9. $\sqrt[7]{36^{14}}$ 36^2

Simplify each expression.

10. $4^{\frac{3}{2}} \cdot 4^{\frac{5}{2}}$ 256
11. $\frac{27^{\frac{4}{3}}}{27^{\frac{2}{3}}}$ 9
12. $\left(125^{\frac{2}{3}}\right)^{\frac{1}{2}}$ 5
13. $(27 \cdot 64)^{\frac{2}{3}}$ 144
14. $\left(\frac{1}{243}\right)^{\frac{1}{5}}$ $\frac{1}{3}$
15. $64^{-\frac{1}{3}}$ $\frac{1}{4}$
16. $(-27x^6)^{\frac{1}{3}}$ $-3x^2$
17. $\frac{(25x)^{\frac{3}{2}}}{5 \cdot x^{\frac{1}{2}}}$ $25x$
18. $(4x)^{-\frac{1}{2}} \cdot (9x)^{\frac{1}{2}}$ $\frac{3}{2}$

Solve.

19. In every atom, electrons orbit the nucleus with a certain characteristic velocity known as the Fermi–Thomas velocity, equal to $\frac{Z^{\frac{2}{3}}}{137}c$, where Z is the number of protons in the nucleus and c is the speed of light. In terms of c, what is the characteristic Fermi-Thomas velocity of the electrons in Uranium, for which $Z = 92$? About $0.15c$

PRACTICE AND PROBLEM SOLVING

Independent Practice	
For Exercises	See Example
30–32	1
33–40	2
41–44	3
45–48	4
49–56	5
57	6

Extra Practice
Skills Practice p. S19
Application Practice p. S39

Find all real roots.

30. cube roots of -64 **31.** fifth roots of 32 **32.** fourth roots of -16

Simplify each expression. Assume that all variables are positive.

33. $\sqrt[3]{9x} \cdot \sqrt[3]{3x^2}$ **34.** $\sqrt[4]{324x^8}$ **35.** $\sqrt[3]{\frac{x^6}{250}}$ **36.** $\sqrt{\frac{x^5}{45}}$

37. $\sqrt[3]{56x^9}$ **38.** $\frac{\sqrt[4]{x^{10}}}{\sqrt[4]{x^4}}$ **39.** $\sqrt[5]{x^7} \cdot \sqrt[5]{x^6}$ **40.** $\sqrt[3]{-54x^9y^3}$

Write each expression in radical form, and simplify.

41. $64^{\frac{1}{2}}$ **42.** $216^{\frac{2}{3}}$ **43.** $(-1000)^{\frac{4}{3}}$ **44.** $6^{\frac{3}{2}}$

Write each expression by using rational exponents.

45. $\sqrt[3]{14^3}$ **46.** $(\sqrt[5]{-8})^4$ **47.** $(\sqrt[4]{144})^2$ **48.** $\sqrt{48^3}$

Simplify each expression.

49. $(8 \cdot 64)^{\frac{2}{3}}$ **50.** $144^{-\frac{1}{2}}$ **51.** $\left(\frac{2^3}{27}\right)^{\frac{1}{3}}$ **52.** $2^{\frac{1}{2}} \cdot 2^{\frac{1}{4}}$

53. $\left(\frac{49}{81}\right)^{-\frac{1}{2}}$ **54.** $\frac{12^{\frac{1}{4}}}{12^{\frac{3}{4}}}$ **55.** $\left(5^{\frac{1}{3}}\right)^{\frac{1}{3}}$ **56.** $\left(\frac{27}{27^{\frac{1}{3}}}\right)^{\frac{1}{2}}$

57. Banking The initial amount deposited in a savings account is \$1000. The amount a in dollars in the account after t years can be represented by the function $a(t) = 1000\left(2^{\frac{t}{24}}\right)$. To the nearest dollar, what will the amount in the account be after 6 years?

Biology

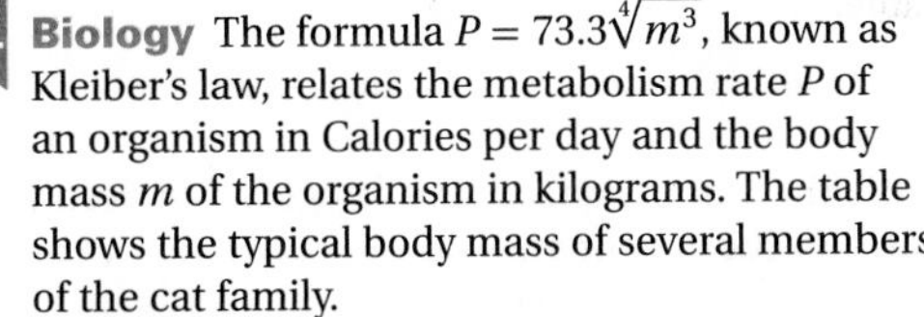

Suppose that a cheetah, a lion, a house cat, and the fastest human runner competed in a 100 m race. At top speed, the cheetah would finish in 3.20 s, the lion in 4.47 s, the house cat in 7.46 s, and the human in 9.77 s.

58. Biology The formula $P = 73.3\sqrt[4]{m^3}$, known as Kleiber's law, relates the metabolism rate P of an organism in Calories per day and the body mass m of the organism in kilograms. The table shows the typical body mass of several members of the cat family.

Typical Body Mass	
Animal	**Mass (kg)**
House cat	4.5
Cheetah	55.0
Lion	170.0

a. What is the metabolism rate of a cheetah to the nearest Calorie per day?

b. **Multi-Step** Approximately how many more Calories of food does a lion need to consume each day than a house cat does?

59. Medicine Iodine-131 is a radioactive material used to treat certain types of cancer. Iodine-131 has a half-life of 8 days, which means that it takes 8 days for half of an initial sample to decay. The percent of radioactive material that remains after t days can be determined from the expression $100\left(\frac{1}{2}\right)^{\frac{t}{h}}$, where h is the half-life in days.

a. What percent of a sample of iodine-131 will remain after 20 days?

b. **What if...?** Another form of radioactive iodine used in cancer treatment is iodine-125. Iodine-125 has a half-life of 59 days. A hospital has 20 g of iodine-125 and 20 g of iodine-131 left over from treating patients. How much more iodine-125 than iodine-131 will remain after a period of 30 days?

60. Meteorology The formula $W = 35.74 + 0.6215T - 35.75V^{\frac{4}{25}} + 0.4275TV^{\frac{4}{25}}$ relates the wind chill temperature W to the air temperature T in degrees Fahrenheit and the wind speed V in miles per hour. Use a calculator to find the wind chill to the nearest degree when the air temperature is 40°F and the wind speed is 35 mi/h.

When simplifying expressions such as those in **Exercises 51, 53,** and **56,** some students might forget that the exponent must also be applied to the denominator of the expression in parentheses. Remind students that the parentheses indicate that the entire expression is raised to a power; therefore, the exponent must be applied to the denominator as well as to the numerator.

Inclusion In **Exercise 59,** students must find the value of the expression $100\left(\frac{1}{2}\right)^{\frac{20}{8}}$. Point out that computations such as this can be made easier by first simplifying the rational exponent, if possible.

Answers

54. $\frac{1}{12^{\frac{1}{2}}}$, or $\frac{\sqrt{3}}{6}$

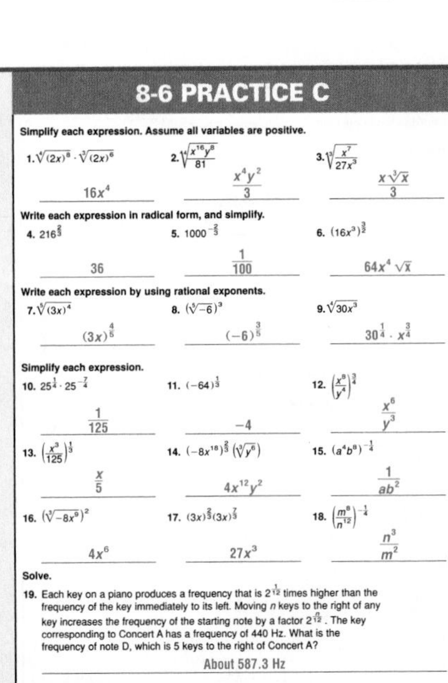

8-6 PRACTICE C

Simplify each expression. Assume all variables are positive.

1. $\sqrt[4]{(2x)^8} \cdot \sqrt[3]{(2x)^6}$ — $16x^4$
2. $\sqrt[4]{\frac{x^{16}y^8}{81}}$ — $\frac{x^4y^2}{3}$
3. $\sqrt[3]{\frac{x^7}{27x^3}}$ — $\frac{x\sqrt[3]{x}}{3}$

Write each expression in radical form, and simplify.

4. $216^{\frac{2}{3}}$ — 36
5. $1000^{-\frac{2}{3}}$ — $\frac{1}{100}$
6. $(16x^3)^{\frac{3}{2}}$ — $64x^4\sqrt{x}$

Write each expression by using rational exponents.

7. $\sqrt[5]{(3x)^4}$ — $(3x)^{\frac{4}{5}}$
8. $(\sqrt[5]{-6})^3$ — $(-6)^{\frac{3}{5}}$
9. $\sqrt[4]{30x^3}$ — $30^{\frac{1}{4}} \cdot x^{\frac{3}{4}}$

Simplify each expression.

10. $25^{\frac{1}{4}} \cdot 25^{-\frac{7}{4}}$ — $\frac{1}{125}$
11. $(-64)^{\frac{1}{3}}$ — -4
12. $\left(\frac{x^8}{y^4}\right)^{\frac{3}{4}}$ — $\frac{x^6}{y^3}$
13. $\left(\frac{x^3}{125}\right)^{\frac{1}{3}}$ — $\frac{x}{5}$
14. $(-8x^{18})^{\frac{2}{3}}(\sqrt[3]{y^6})$ — $4x^{12}y^2$
15. $(a^4b^8)^{-\frac{1}{4}}$ — $\frac{1}{ab^2}$
16. $(\sqrt[3]{-8x^9})^2$ — $4x^6$
17. $(3x)^{\frac{2}{3}}(3x)^{\frac{7}{3}}$ — $27x^3$
18. $\left(\frac{m^8}{n^{12}}\right)^{-\frac{1}{4}}$ — $\frac{n^3}{m^2}$

Solve.

19. Each key on a piano produces a frequency that is $2^{\frac{1}{12}}$ times higher than the frequency of the key immediately to its left. Moving n keys to the right of any key increases the frequency of the starting note by a factor $2^{\frac{n}{12}}$. The key corresponding to Concert A has a frequency of 440 Hz. What is the frequency of note D, which is 5 keys to the right of Concert A?

About 587.3 Hz

Exercise 61 involves simplifying and evaluating a radical expression representing the period of a pendulum. This exercise prepares students for the Multi-Step Test Prep on page 636.

Number Sense When students are asked to draw conclusions about algebraic equations such as those in **Exercises 73–76,** they often assume that the variables in the equations represent positive values. Remind them that unless stated otherwise, the variables can also represent negative values.

Answers

64. $(-9)^{\frac{4}{5}}x^{\frac{4}{3}}$

73. always; possible answer: $\sqrt[3]{x^6} = x^{\frac{6}{3}} = x^2$ for all real numbers

74. Never; possible answer: if x is positive, $(x)^{\frac{1}{3}}$ is positive and $(-x)^{\frac{1}{3}}$ is negative; therefore, $(x)^{\frac{1}{3}} \neq (-x)^{\frac{1}{3}}$. If x is negative, $(x)^{\frac{1}{3}}$ is negative and $(-x)^{\frac{1}{3}}$ is positive; therefore, $(x)^{\frac{1}{3}} \neq (-x)^{\frac{1}{3}}$.

75. Never; possible answer: simplify the left side of the equation: $-\sqrt[4]{x^8} = -x^{\frac{8}{4}} = -x^2$. The expression $-x^2$ is negative for all nonzero real numbers. Simplify the right side of the equation: $x^{-2} = \frac{1}{x^2}$. The expression $\frac{1}{x^2}$ is positive for all nonzero real numbers. Therefore, $-\sqrt[4]{x^8} \neq x^{-2}$.

76. Sometimes; possible answer: if x is positive, $-\sqrt[3]{x}$ is less than 0. If x is negative, $-\sqrt[3]{x}$ is greater than 0. Therefore, the inequality is true only for positive values of x.

77. 2 and 3; about 2.62

78. 3 and 4; about 3.76

79. –5 and –4; about –4.31

81. A is incorrect. The Quotient of Powers Property is incorrectly applied. To simplify $625^{\frac{1}{3}} \div 625^{\frac{4}{3}}$, you should subtract the exponents rather than dividing them.

83. Possible answer: Raise 10 to the $\frac{1}{6}$ power, or use the $\sqrt[x]{}$ function to find the sixth root of 10.

MULTI-STEP TEST PREP

61. This problem will prepare you for the Multi-Step Test Prep on page 636.
For a pendulum with a length L in meters, the expression $2\pi\sqrt{\frac{L}{g}}$ models the time in seconds for the pendulum to complete one back-and-forth swing. In this expression, g is the acceleration due to gravity, 9.8 m/s^2.
   a. Simplify the expression by rationalizing the denominator. $\frac{2\pi\sqrt{Lg}}{g}$
   b. To the nearest tenth of a second, how long does it take a pendulum with a length of 0.35 m to complete one back-and-forth swing? **1.2 s**

Write each expression by using rational exponents. Assume that all variables are positive.

62. $\sqrt[4]{20x^3}$ $20^{\frac{1}{4}}x^{\frac{3}{4}}$
63. $\sqrt{(5x)^7}$ $(5x)^{\frac{7}{2}}$
64. $\left(\sqrt[5]{-9\sqrt[3]{x}}\right)^4$
65. $\left(\sqrt[4]{11x^8}\right)^6$ $11^{\frac{3}{2}}x^{12}$

Simplify each expression, and write it by using a radical. Assume that all variables are positive.

66. $(-8x^{12})^{\frac{2}{3}}$ $4x^8$
67. $5^{\frac{7}{4}}x^{\frac{3}{4}}$ $5\sqrt[4]{125x^3}$
68. $(-12x^{15})^{\frac{3}{5}}$ $-2x^9\sqrt[5]{54}$
69. $(a^2b^4)^{\frac{1}{3}}$ $b\sqrt[3]{a^2b}$
70. $\left(\frac{a^4}{b}\right)^{\frac{1}{4}}$ $\frac{a\sqrt[4]{b^3}}{b}$
71. $a^{\frac{3}{4}}(4b^6)^{\frac{1}{4}}$ $b\sqrt[4]{4a^3b^2}$

72. **Botany** Duckweed is a quickly growing plant that floats on the surface of lakes and ponds. The initial mass of a population of duckweed plants is 100 kg. The mass of the population doubles every 60 h and can be represented by the function $m(t) = 100 \cdot 2^{\frac{t}{60}}$, where t is time in hours. To the nearest kilogram, what is the mass of the plants after 24 h? **132 kg**

Explain whether each statement is sometimes, always, or never true for nonzero values of the variable.

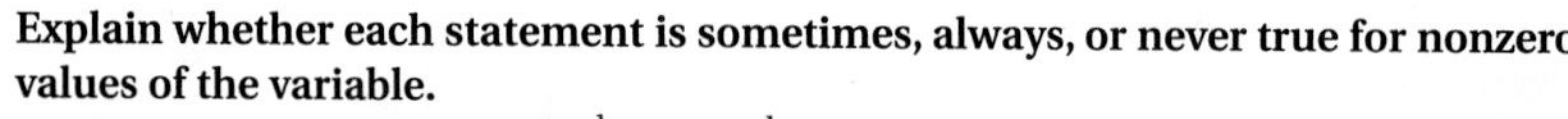

73. $\sqrt[3]{x^6} = x^2$
74. $(x)^{\frac{1}{3}} = (-x)^{\frac{1}{3}}$
75. $-\sqrt[4]{x^8} = x^{-2}$
76. $-\sqrt[3]{x} < 0$

Estimation **Identify the pair of consecutive integers that each value is between. Then use a calculator to check your answer.**

77. $\sqrt[3]{18}$
78. $\sqrt[4]{200}$
79. $\sqrt[3]{-80}$

80. **Physics** Air pressure decreases with altitude according to the formula $P = 14.7(10)^{-0.000014a}$, where P is the air pressure in pounds per square inch and a is the altitude in feet above sea level.
   a. Use the formula to estimate the air pressure in Denver, Colorado, which is 5280 ft above sea level. $\approx$ **12.4 psi**
   b. Use the formula to estimate the air pressure at the top of Mount Everest, which is 29,028 ft above sea level. $\approx$ **5.8 psi**

81. **ERROR ANALYSIS** Below are two methods of simplifying an expression. Which is incorrect? Explain the error.

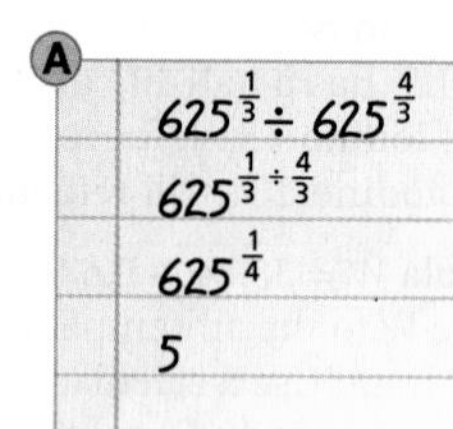

A
$625^{\frac{1}{3}} \div 625^{\frac{4}{3}}$
$625^{\frac{1}{3} \div \frac{4}{3}}$
$625^{\frac{1}{4}}$
5

B
$625^{\frac{1}{3}} \div 625^{\frac{4}{3}}$
$625^{\frac{1}{3} - \frac{4}{3}}$
625^{-1}
$\frac{1}{625}$

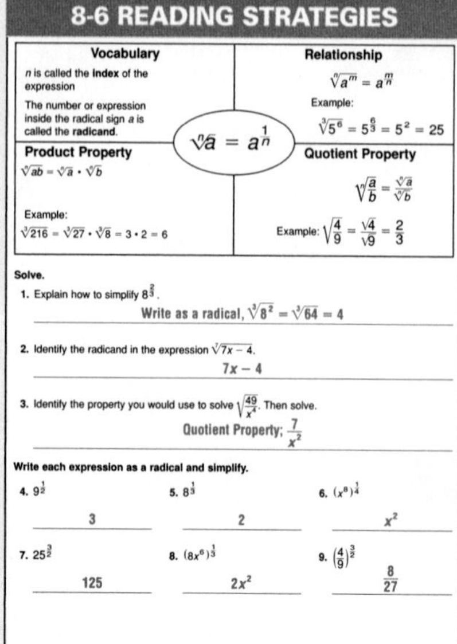

8-6 READING STRATEGIES

Vocabulary
n is called the **index** of the expression
The number or expression inside the radical sign a is called the **radicand**.

$\sqrt[n]{a} = a^{\frac{1}{n}}$

Relationship
$\sqrt[n]{a^m} = a^{\frac{m}{n}}$
Example: $\sqrt[3]{5^6} = 5^{\frac{6}{3}} = 5^2 = 25$

Product Property
$\sqrt[n]{ab} = \sqrt[n]{a} \cdot \sqrt[n]{b}$
Example: $\sqrt[3]{216} = \sqrt[3]{27} \cdot \sqrt[3]{8} = 3 \cdot 2 = 6$

Quotient Property
$\sqrt[n]{\frac{a}{b}} = \frac{\sqrt[n]{a}}{\sqrt[n]{b}}$
Example: $\sqrt{\frac{4}{9}} = \frac{\sqrt{4}}{\sqrt{9}} = \frac{2}{3}$

Solve.

1. Explain how to simplify $8^{\frac{2}{3}}$.
   Write as a radical, $\sqrt[3]{8^2} = \sqrt[3]{64} = 4$
2. Identify the radicand in the expression $\sqrt[7]{7x-4}$.
   $7x - 4$
3. Identify the property you would use to solve $\sqrt{\frac{49}{x^4}}$. Then solve.
   Quotient Property; $\frac{7}{x^2}$

Write each expression as a radical and simplify.

4. $9^{\frac{1}{2}}$ 3
5. $8^{\frac{1}{3}}$ 2
6. $(x^8)^{\frac{1}{4}}$ x^2
7. $25^{\frac{3}{2}}$ 125
8. $(8x^6)^{\frac{1}{3}}$ $2x^2$
9. $\left(\frac{4}{9}\right)^{\frac{3}{2}}$ $\frac{8}{27}$

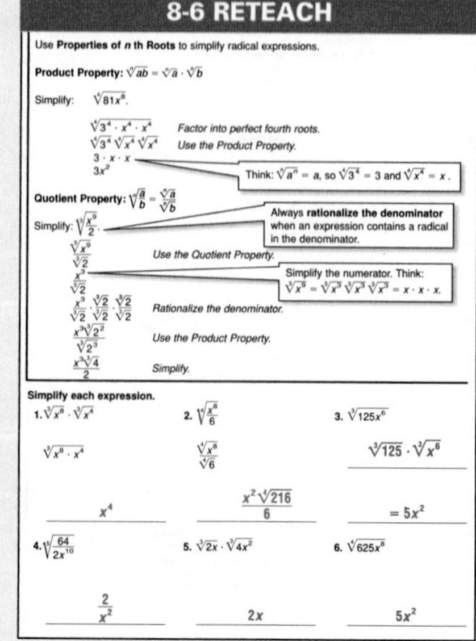

8-6 RETEACH

Use **Properties of n th Roots** to simplify radical expressions.

Product Property: $\sqrt[n]{ab} = \sqrt[n]{a} \cdot \sqrt[n]{b}$

Simplify: $\sqrt[4]{81x^8}$.

$\sqrt[4]{3^4 \cdot x^4 \cdot x^4}$ *Factor into perfect fourth roots.*
$\sqrt[4]{3^4}\sqrt[4]{x^4}\sqrt[4]{x^4}$ *Use the Product Property.*
$3 \cdot x \cdot x$
$3x^2$

Think: $\sqrt[n]{a^n} = a$, so $\sqrt[4]{3^4} = 3$ and $\sqrt[4]{x^4} = x$.

Quotient Property: $\sqrt[n]{\frac{a}{b}} = \frac{\sqrt[n]{a}}{\sqrt[n]{b}}$

Simplify: $\sqrt[3]{\frac{x^9}{2}}$.

Always **rationalize the denominator** when an expression contains a radical in the denominator.

$\frac{\sqrt[3]{x^9}}{\sqrt[3]{2}}$ *Use the Quotient Property.*
$\frac{x^3}{\sqrt[3]{2}}$

Simplify the numerator. Think: $\sqrt[3]{x^9} = \sqrt[3]{x^3}\sqrt[3]{x^3}\sqrt[3]{x^3} = x \cdot x \cdot x$.

$\frac{x^3}{\sqrt[3]{2}} \cdot \frac{\sqrt[3]{2}}{\sqrt[3]{2}} \cdot \frac{\sqrt[3]{2}}{\sqrt[3]{2}}$ *Rationalize the denominator.*
$\frac{x^3\sqrt[3]{2^2}}{\sqrt[3]{2^3}}$ *Use the Product Property.*
$\frac{x^3\sqrt[3]{4}}{2}$ *Simplify.*

Simplify each expression.

1. $\sqrt[3]{x^8} \cdot \sqrt[3]{x^4}$
   $\sqrt[3]{x^8 \cdot x^4}$
   x^4
2. $\sqrt[4]{\frac{x^8}{6}}$
   $\frac{\sqrt[4]{x^8}}{\sqrt[4]{6}}$
   $\frac{x^2\sqrt[4]{216}}{6}$
3. $\sqrt[3]{125x^6}$
   $\sqrt[3]{125} \cdot \sqrt[3]{x^6}$
   $= 5x^2$
4. $\sqrt[5]{\frac{64}{2x^{10}}}$
   $\frac{2}{x^2}$
5. $\sqrt[3]{2x} \cdot \sqrt[3]{4x^2}$
   $2x$
6. $\sqrt[4]{625x^8}$
   $5x^2$

82. How many different positive integer values of n result in a whole number nth root of 64? What are these values?

83. **Critical Thinking** Describe two ways to find the sixth root of 10 on a calculator.

84. **Write About It** Explain whether the expression $x^{2.4}$ contains a rational exponent.

TEST PREP

85. Which of the following represents a real number?

Ⓐ $6^{-\frac{4}{3}}$ Ⓑ $(-9)^{\frac{3}{2}}$ Ⓒ $\sqrt[4]{-11}$ Ⓓ $\left(\sqrt[4]{-14}\right)^3$

86. The surface area S of a sphere with volume V is $S = (4\pi)^{\frac{1}{3}}(3V)^{\frac{2}{3}}$. What effect does increasing the volume of a sphere by a factor of 8 have on its surface area?

Ⓕ The surface area doubles.
Ⓖ The surface area triples.
Ⓗ The surface area increases by a factor of 4.
Ⓙ The surface area increases by a factor of 8.

87. If $a = x^6$, what is $\sqrt[4]{a}$?

Ⓐ $(\sqrt{x})^3$ Ⓑ x^2 Ⓒ $x^2\sqrt{x}$ Ⓓ $x^{\frac{2}{3}}$

88. Which expression is equivalent to $\sqrt[3]{\frac{56a^6}{7}}$?

Ⓕ $2a^2$ Ⓖ $8a^2$ Ⓗ $2a^3$ Ⓙ $8a^3$

CHALLENGE AND EXTEND

89. Write an expression by using rational exponents for the square root of the square root of the square root of 20.

90. Simplify the expression $2^{\frac{1}{3}} \cdot 4^{\frac{1}{6}} \cdot 8^{\frac{1}{9}}$.

91. **Critical Thinking** For what real values of a is $\sqrt[3]{a}$ greater than a?

92. Any nonzero real number has three cube roots, only one of which is real. Show that the cube roots of 1 are 1, $\frac{-1 + i\sqrt{3}}{2}$, and $\frac{-1 - i\sqrt{3}}{2}$.

SPIRAL REVIEW

Add or subtract, if possible. *(Lesson 4-1)*

$A = \begin{bmatrix} -2 & -1 & 0 \\ 3 & 2 & 6 \end{bmatrix}$ $B = \begin{bmatrix} 1 & -1 \\ 0 & -2 \end{bmatrix}$ $C = \begin{bmatrix} 5 & 7 \\ 0 & -4 \end{bmatrix}$ $D = \begin{bmatrix} 9 & 8 & -2 \\ 6 & 3 & -1 \end{bmatrix}$

93. $A + D$ 94. $B - C$ 95. $B + C$

Use the description to write each quadratic function in vertex form. *(Lesson 5-1)*

96. The parent function $f(x) = x^2$ is vertically compressed by a factor of 3 and then translated 1 unit right to create g.

97. The parent function $f(x) = x^2$ is reflected across the x-axis and translated 3 units up to create h.

Identify the zeros and the asymptotes of each function. Then graph. *(Lesson 8-4)*

98. $f(x) = \frac{x^2 - 4}{x + 5}$ 99. $f(x) = \frac{x + 3}{x^2 + 6x + 5}$ 100. $f(x) = \frac{4x - 3}{x + 6}$

TEST PREP DOCTOR Students who chose **B, C,** or **D** in **Exercise 85** have forgotten that negative numbers do not have real roots for even indices.

If students have difficulty with **Exercise 86,** suggest that they start by replacing V with $8V$ in the formula for the surface area of a sphere. They can then use the properties of exponents to simplify the formula.

Answers

84. Possible answer: The exponent 2.4 is rational because it can be expressed as the ratio of 2 integers. For example, the exponent can be expressed as the ratio of the integers 24 and 10 because $2.4 = \frac{24}{10}$.

92, 98–100. See p. A37.

Journal

Ask students to use an example to explain the meaning of the negative sign, the numerator, and the denominator of a negative rational exponent.

ALTERNATIVE ASSESSMENT

Ask students to write and simplify a numerical expression for each of the following properties of rational exponents: Product of Powers, Quotient of Powers, Power of a Power, Power of a Product, and Power of a Quotient.

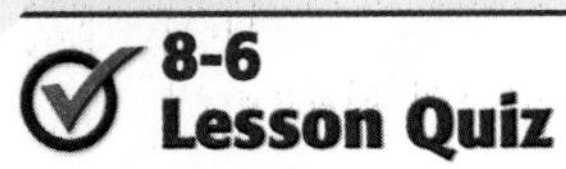

8-6 Lesson Quiz

Find all real roots.

1. fourth roots of 625 $-5, 5$
2. fifth roots of -243 -3

Simplify each expression.

3. $\frac{16^{\frac{3}{4}}}{16^{\frac{1}{2}}}$ 2
4. $\sqrt[4]{256y^8}$ $4y^2$
5. Write $(-216)^{\frac{2}{3}}$ in radical form and simplify. $\left(\sqrt[3]{-216}\right)^2 = 36$
6. Write $\sqrt[3]{21^5}$ using rational exponents. $21^{\frac{5}{3}}$
7. If \$2000 is invested at 4% interest compounded monthly, the value of the investment after t years is given by $2000\left(\frac{12.04}{12}\right)^{12t}$. What is the value of the investment after 3.5 years? \$2300.01

Also available on transparency

8-6 PROBLEM SOLVING

Louise is building a guitar-like instrument. It has small metal bars, called frets, positioned across its neck so that it can produce notes of a specific scale on each string. The distance a fret should be placed from the bridge is related to a string's root note length by the function $d(n) = r\left(2^{-\frac{n}{12}}\right)$, where r is the length of the root note string and n is the number of notes higher than that string's root note. Louise wants to know where to place frets to produce different notes on a 50-cm string.

1. Find the distance from the bridge for a fret that produces a note exactly one octave (12 notes) higher than the root note.
   a. Substitute values for r and n in the given function. $d(12) = 50\left(2^{-\frac{12}{12}}\right)$
   b. How far from the bridge should the fret be placed? 25 cm
   c. What fraction of the string length is the distance of this fret from the bridge? $\frac{1}{2}$

2. Complete the table to find the distance from the bridge, for frets that produce every other note of an entire scale on this string.

Notes Higher than the Root Note	2	4	6	8	10	12
Distance of Fret from Bridge (cm)	44.5	39.7	35.4	31.5	28.1	25

Choose the letter for the best answer.

3. Rafael made a ceramic cube in art class. The cube has a volume of 336 cm³. What is the side length of the cube to the nearest centimeter?
   Ⓐ 7
   B 12
   C 18
   D 56

4. Yolanda has an exercise ball with a volume of 7234 in.³. Find the radius of the exercise ball to the nearest inch.
   A 24
   B 21
   C 19
   Ⓓ 12

5. Which formula could you use to find the area of one side of a cube if the volume were given?
   A $A = V^{\frac{3}{2}}$ Ⓒ $A = V^{\frac{2}{3}}$
   B $A = V^{-\frac{3}{2}}$ D $A = V^{-\frac{2}{3}}$

6. A party tent in the shape of a hemisphere has a volume of 14,130 m³. What is the area of the ground that the tent covers in square meters?
   A 653.1 Ⓒ 1121.5
   B 706.5 D 1256.0

8-6 CHALLENGE

Rational exponents make it possible to simplify radical expressions. Consider the simple operation of multiplication of radicals. Is it possible to multiply the radical expression $\sqrt{2} \cdot \sqrt[3]{2}$? When written in radical form the answer is no, or at least it is very difficult. When written in exponent form it may be done as follows:

$$\sqrt{2} \cdot \sqrt[3]{2} = 2^{\frac{1}{2}} \cdot 2^{\frac{1}{3}} = 2^{\frac{1}{2}+\frac{1}{3}} = 2^{\frac{3}{6}+\frac{2}{6}} = 2^{\frac{5}{6}} = \sqrt[6]{2^5} = \sqrt[6]{32}.$$

When you look at the radicals, it may not be obvious that the first and last expressions are equal. The operation with rational exponents verifies the result. Other fraction operations are possible when using rational exponents instead of radicals.

$$\sqrt[3]{2} \cdot \sqrt[5]{3^2} = 2^{\frac{1}{3}} \cdot 3^{\frac{2}{5}} = 2^{\frac{5}{15}} \cdot 3^{\frac{6}{15}} = (2^5 \cdot 3^6)^{\frac{1}{15}} = \sqrt[15]{2^5 \cdot 3^6} = \sqrt[15]{23{,}328}$$

Once again, the radical operations are quite difficult, but the rational exponents greatly simplify the multiplication.

Simplify. Assume all variables have positive values.

1. $\sqrt{18} \cdot \sqrt[4]{18}$ — $3\sqrt[4]{72}$

2. $\sqrt{30} \cdot \sqrt[3]{900} \cdot \sqrt[5]{630}$ — $30\sqrt[30]{3^{17} \cdot 7^6 \cdot 10^{11}} \approx 30\sqrt[30]{1.52 \times 10^{24}}$

3. $\sqrt{35xy} \cdot \sqrt[4]{35x^2y^3}$ — $xy\sqrt[4]{35^3y} = xy\sqrt[4]{42{,}875y}$

4. $\sqrt{3xy} \cdot \sqrt[4]{75x^2y^3} \cdot \sqrt[3]{25x^2y}$ — $5xy\sqrt[12]{3^9 \cdot 5^2x^8y^7} = 5xy\sqrt[12]{492{,}075x^8y^7}$

5. $\sqrt{20} \div \sqrt[4]{20}$ — $\sqrt[4]{20}$

6. $\sqrt{210} \div \sqrt[4]{8820} \div \sqrt[5]{1296}$ — $\frac{\sqrt[20]{5^5 \cdot 6^4}}{6} = \frac{\sqrt[20]{4{,}050{,}000}}{6}$

7. $\sqrt{3xy} \div \sqrt[3]{3x^2y}$ — $\frac{\sqrt[6]{3y}}{\sqrt[6]{x}} = \frac{\sqrt[6]{3x^5y}}{x}$

8. $\sqrt{3xy} \div \sqrt[3]{75x^2y^2} \div \sqrt[6]{25x^3y^4}$ — $\frac{\sqrt[6]{3}}{5\sqrt[6]{x^4y^5}} = \frac{\sqrt[6]{3x^2y}}{5xy}$

9. $\frac{\sqrt{175} \cdot \sqrt[3]{175}}{\sqrt[5]{175}}$ — $175^{\frac{19}{30}} = 5\sqrt[30]{5^8 \cdot 7^{19}}$

10. $\frac{(\sqrt{75} \cdot 3\sqrt{108})\sqrt[3]{9}}{9\sqrt[4]{15}}$ — $6\sqrt[12]{5^9 \cdot 3^5} = 6\sqrt[12]{474{,}609{,}375}$

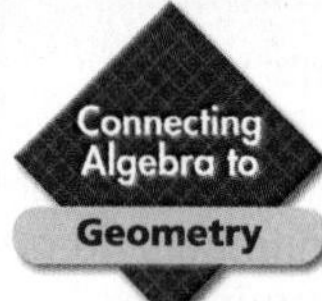

Organizer

See Skills Bank page S64

Pacing:

Traditional $\frac{1}{2}$ day

Block $\frac{1}{4}$ day

Objective: Apply skills with radical expressions to determine how changes in surface area and volume affect linear dimensions.

Teach

Remember

Students review and apply formulas for the surface area and volume of geometric figures.

INTERVENTION For additional review and practice on finding surface area and volume, see Skills Bank page S64.

Close

Assess

The ancient Greeks struggled with the problem of doubling the volume of a cube. Have students determine the factor by which the Greeks should have multiplied the side length of the cube. $\sqrt[3]{2}$

State Resources

Area and Volume Relationships

See Skills Bank page S64

When you change the linear dimensions of a solid figure, its surface area and volume may change in different ways.

Recall that when you multiply the side length of a cube by a constant a, the surface area increases by a factor of a^2 and the volume increases by a factor of a^3, as shown.

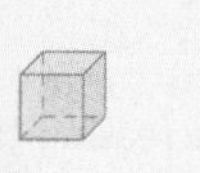

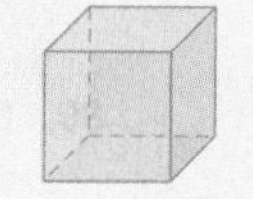

Side Length	$s = 1$ cm	$s = 2(1) = 2$ cm
Surface Area	$A = 6$ cm^2	$A = 2^2(6) = 24$ cm^2
Volume	$V = 1$ cm^3	$V = 2^3(1) = 8$ cm^3

When you want to change the surface area or volume of a figure but maintain the same linear proportions, you can use the reverse process. If the surface area increases by a factor of a, the linear dimensions increase by a factor of $\sqrt{a}$. If the volume increases by a factor of a, the linear dimensions increase by a factor of $\sqrt[3]{a}$.

Example

A cylindrical water storage tank has a radius of 5 ft and a height of 10 ft. A new tank similar to the first is constructed with 20% more capacity. What are the radius and height of the new tank?

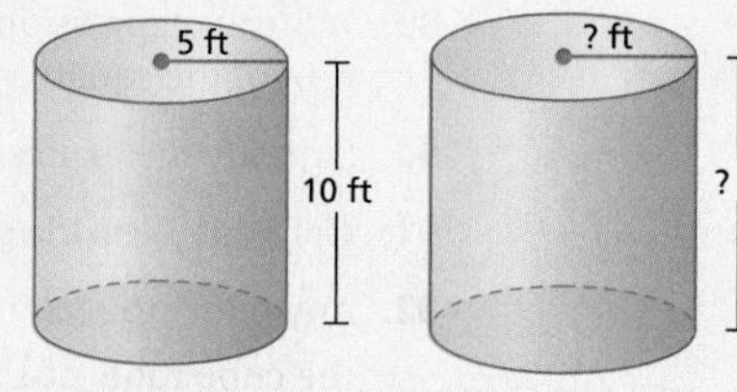

The capacity of the larger tank is 120% of the smaller tank. So, the volume is increased by a factor of 1.2.

Step 1 Find the scale factor for the linear dimensions.

$\sqrt[3]{1.2} \approx 1.0627$ — *Take the cube root.*

Step 2 Find the new dimensions.

$1.0627(5) \approx 5.31$

$1.0627(10) \approx 10.63$

Multiply the original dimensions by the scale factor.

The radius is about 5.31 ft, and the height is about 10.63 ft.

Try This

Solve each problem. If necessary, round your answers to the nearest thousandth.

1. Marsha wants to double the surface area of a circular pond. How should she change the radius? the diameter? **Multiply by $\sqrt{2}$ or 1.414.**
2. The volume of a sphere is increased by a factor of 100. The new radius is 30 cm. What was the radius of the original sphere? **$\approx$ 6.463 cm**
3. The surface area of a cube is decreased from 150 cm^2 to 96 cm^2. By what factor has the volume changed? **The volume has decreased by a factor of 0.512.**
4. A store owner wants to create giant ice-cream cones that contain 3 times the volume of a traditional cone. How should he change the radius and height of the traditional cone? **The radius and height should be increased by a factor of $\sqrt[3]{3}$, or 1.442.**

8-7 Radical Functions

A2.5.4 Analyze, describe and sketch graphs of square root and cube root functions by examining intercepts, zeros, domain and range and end behavior.

Objectives
Graph radical functions and inequalities.

Transform radical functions by changing parameters.

Vocabulary
radical function
square-root function

Who uses this?
Aerospace engineers use transformations of radical functions to adjust for gravitational changes on other planets. (See Example 5.)

Recall that exponential and logarithmic functions are inverse functions. Quadratic and cubic functions have inverses as well. The graphs below show the inverses of the quadratic parent function and the cubic parent function.

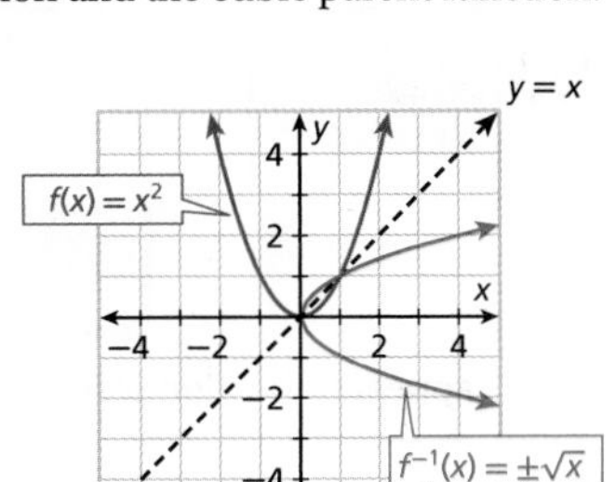

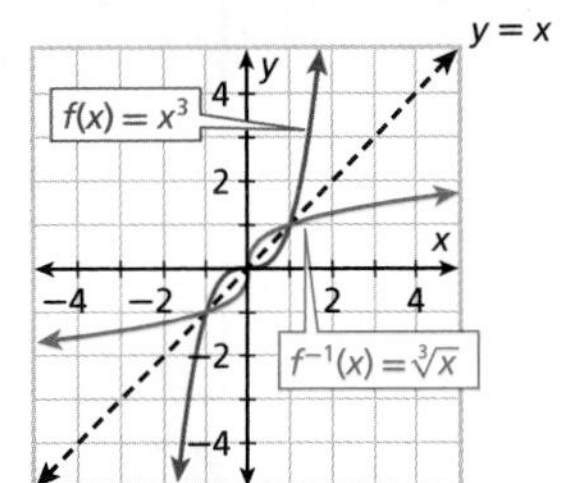

Notice that the inverse of $f(x) = x^2$ is not a function because it fails the vertical line test. However, if we limit the domain of $f(x) = x^2$ to $x \geq 0$, its inverse is the function $f^{-1}(x) = \sqrt{x}$.

A **radical function** is a function whose rule is a radical expression. A **square-root function** is a radical function involving $\sqrt{x}$. The square-root parent function is $f(x) = \sqrt{x}$. The cube-root parent function is $f(x) = \sqrt[3]{x}$.

EXAMPLE 1 Graphing Radical Functions

Graph the function, and identify its domain and range.

A $f(x) = \sqrt{x}$

Make a table of values. Plot enough ordered pairs to see the shape of the curve. Because the square root of a negative number is imaginary, choose only nonnegative values for x.

Helpful Hint
When using a table to graph square-root functions, choose x-values that make the radicands perfect squares.

x	$f(x) = \sqrt{x}$	$(x, f(x))$
0	$f(0) = \sqrt{0} = 0$	(0, 0)
1	$f(1) = \sqrt{1} = 1$	(1, 1)
4	$f(4) = \sqrt{4} = 2$	(4, 2)
9	$f(9) = \sqrt{9} = 3$	(9, 3)

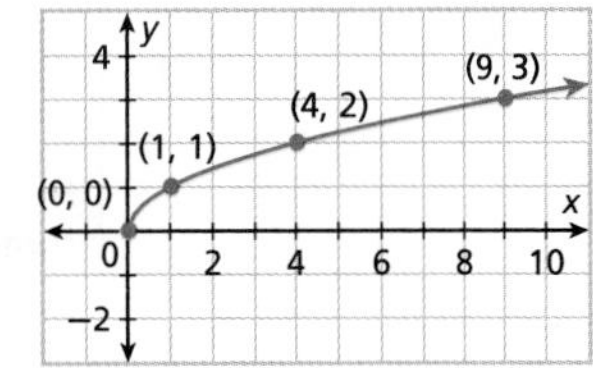

The domain is $\{x \mid x \geq 0\}$, and the range is $\{y \mid y \geq 0\}$.

8-7 Organizer

Pacing: Traditional $1\frac{1}{2}$ days
Block $\frac{3}{4}$ day

Objectives: Graph radical functions and inequalities.

Transform radical functions by changing parameters.

Technology Lab
In *Technology Lab Activities*

Online Edition
Graphing Calculator, Tutorial Videos

Countdown to Testing Week 18

Power Presentations with PowerPoint®

Warm Up

Identify the domain and range of each function.

1. $f(x) = x^2 + 2$ D: ℝ; R: $\{y \mid y \geq 2\}$

2. $f(x) = 3x^3$ D: ℝ; R: ℝ

Use the description to write the quadratic function *g* based on the parent function $f(x) = x^2$.

3. f is translated 3 units up.
$g(x) = x^2 + 3$

4. f is translated 2 units left.
$g(x) = (x + 2)^2$

Also available on transparency

Math Humor

Q: How can you predict how many protesters will show up at a rally?

A: By using a radical function.

1 Introduce

EXPLORATION

8-7 Radical Functions

You can explore the behavior of radical functions by using a graphing calculator.

1. Enter the function $f(x) = \sqrt{x}$ by pressing [key] and entering $\sqrt{x}$. Graph the function in the standard square window by pressing [ZOOM] and selecting **6:ZStandard** and by pressing [ZOOM] again and selecting **5:ZSquare**. Based on the graph, what is the domain of the function $f(x) = \sqrt{x}$?

2. Why is the function f restricted to this domain?

Graph each of the following functions on a graphing calculator and give its domain.

3. $f(x) = \sqrt{x - 2}$
4. $f(x) = \sqrt{x - 5}$
5. $f(x) = \sqrt{x + 4}$
6. $f(x) = \sqrt{x + 1}$

THINK AND DISCUSS

7. **Describe** how the graph of $y = \sqrt{x - h}$ is related to the graph of $y = \sqrt{x}$.
8. **Explain** how you can determine the domain of the function $y = \sqrt{x - h}$.

Motivate

Review with students how to use inverse operations to determine the inverse of a linear function, such as $f(x) = x + 3$. Ask students what they think the inverse operation of squaring or cubing a number is. taking the square root or cube root Explain that in this lesson, students will use roots to investigate the inverses of quadratic and cubic functions.

Explorations and answers are provided in the *Explorations* binder.

State Resources

go.hrw.com
State Resources Online
KEYWORD: MB7 Resources

Power Presentations with PowerPoint®

Additional Examples

Example 1

Graph each function and identify its domain and range.

A. $f(x) = \sqrt{x-3}$

D: $\{x \mid x \geq 3\}$; R: $\{y \mid y \geq 0\}$

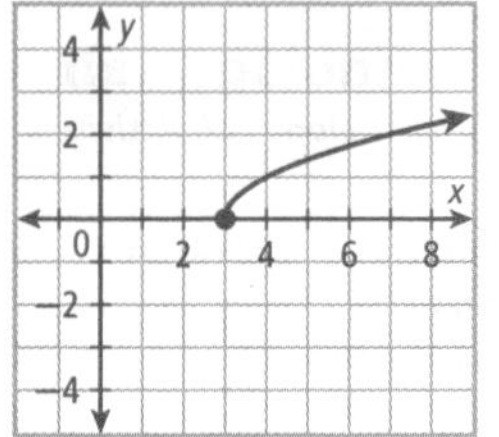

B. $f(x) = 2\sqrt[3]{x-2}$ D: $\mathbb{R}$; R: $\mathbb{R}$

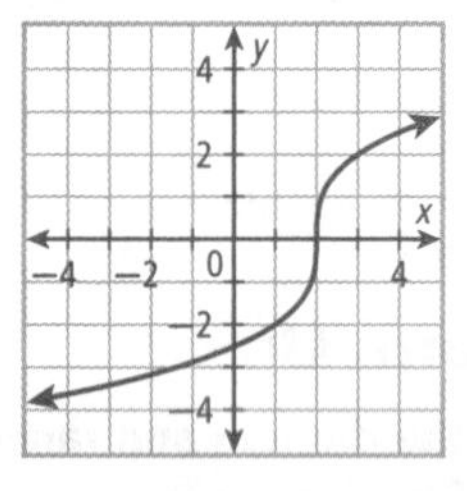

Also available on transparency

INTERVENTION

Questioning Strategies

EXAMPLE 1

- How can you determine the domain and range of a square-root function?
- Do you need to graph a cube-root function to determine its domain and range? Explain.

Math Background You may wish to point out that square-root and cube-root functions are not the only types of radical functions. There are also radical functions with higher indices, such as $f(x) = \sqrt[4]{x}$ and $f(x) = \sqrt[5]{x-2}$.

Answers to *Check It Out!*

1a.

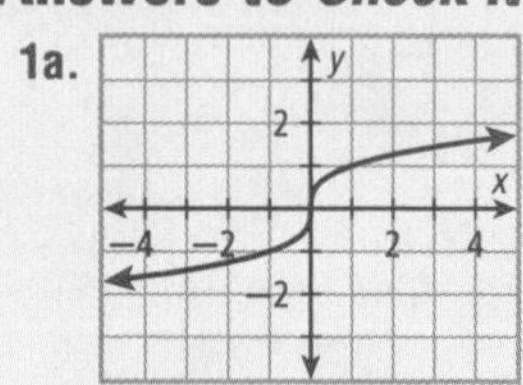

1b.

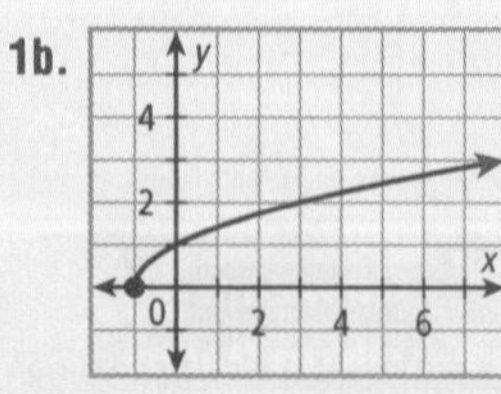

Graph the function, and identify its domain and range.

B $f(x) = 4\sqrt[3]{x+4}$

Make a table of values. Plot enough ordered pairs to see the shape of the curve. Choose both negative and positive values for x.

x	$4\sqrt[3]{x+4}$	$(x, f(x))$
−12	$4\sqrt[3]{-12+4} = 4\sqrt[3]{-8} = -8$	(−12, −8)
−5	$4\sqrt[3]{-5+4} = 4\sqrt[3]{-1} = -4$	(−5, −4)
−4	$4\sqrt[3]{-4+4} = 4\sqrt[3]{0} = 0$	(−4, 0)
−3	$4\sqrt[3]{-3+4} = 4\sqrt[3]{1} = 4$	(−3, 4)
4	$4\sqrt[3]{4+4} = 4\sqrt[3]{8} = 8$	(4, 8)

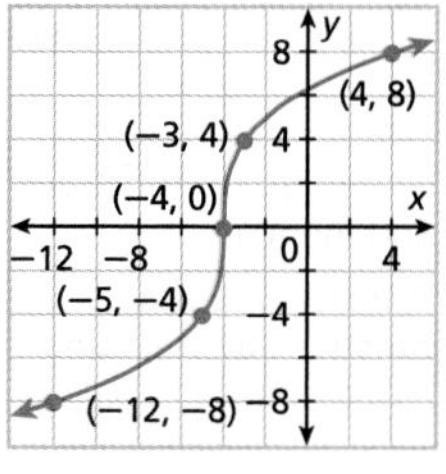

Helpful Hint

When using a table to graph cube-root functions, choose x-values that make the radicands perfect cubes.

The domain is the set of all real numbers. The range is also the set of all real numbers.

Check Graph the function on a graphing calculator.

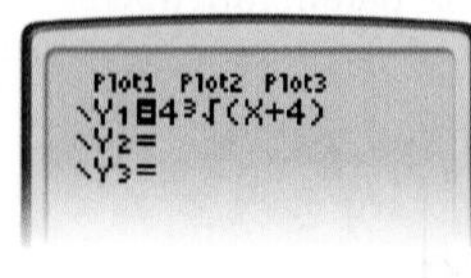

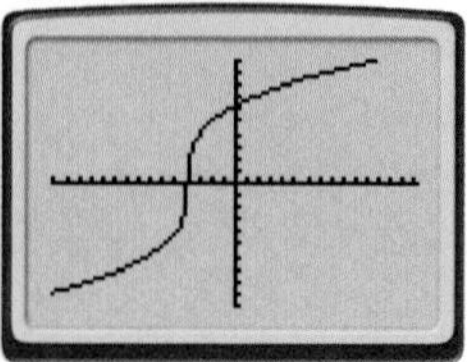

The graphs appear to be identical.

Graph each function, and identify its domain and range.

1a. $f(x) = \sqrt[3]{x}$

D: $\{x \mid x \in \mathbb{R}\}$; R: $\{y \mid y \in \mathbb{R}\}$

1b. $f(x) = \sqrt{x+1}$

D: $\{x \mid x \geq -1\}$; R: $\{y \mid y \geq 0\}$

The graphs of radical functions can be transformed by using methods similar to those used to transform linear, quadratic, polynomial, and exponential functions. This lesson will focus on transformations of square-root functions.

Transformations of the Square-Root Parent Function $f(x) = \sqrt{x}$

Transformation	$f(x)$ Notation	Examples
Vertical translation	$f(x) + k$	$y = \sqrt{x} + 3$ 3 units up $y = \sqrt{x} - 4$ 4 units down
Horizontal translation	$f(x - h)$	$y = \sqrt{x-2}$ 2 units right $y = \sqrt{x+1}$ 1 unit left
Vertical stretch/compression	$af(x)$	$y = 6\sqrt{x}$ vertical stretch by 6 $y = \frac{1}{2}\sqrt{x}$ vertical compression by $\frac{1}{2}$
Horizontal stretch/ compression	$f\left(\frac{1}{b}x\right)$	$y = \sqrt{\frac{1}{5}x}$ horizontal stretch by 5 $y = \sqrt{3x}$ horizontal compression by $\frac{1}{3}$
Reflection	$-f(x)$ $f(-x)$	$y = -\sqrt{x}$ across x-axis $y = \sqrt{-x}$ across y-axis

2 Teach

Guided Instruction

Before defining the square-root and cube-root functions, review with students the concept of inverse functions. Point out that the parameters used to transform radical functions are similar to those used to transform other types of functions.

Inclusion Remind students that if any horizontal line passes through more than one point on the graph of a function, the inverse relation is not itself a function.

Reaching All Learners

Through Modeling

Have students work in pairs. Each pair should place a transparency sheet over a sheet of graph paper with the axes labeled. Have them graph the radical function $f(x) = \sqrt{x-h} + k$ on the transparency for $h = 0$ and $k = 0$. Then have them move the transparency to represent changes in h and k, and write the function that represents the transformation. Students can use a graphing calculator to check their answers.

EXAMPLE 2 Transforming Square-Root Functions

Using the graph of $f(x) = \sqrt{x}$ as a guide, describe the transformation and graph each function.

A $g(x) = \sqrt{x} - 2$

$g(x) = f(x) - 2$

Translate f 2 units down.

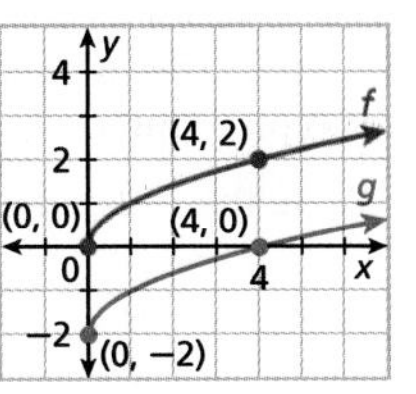

B $g(x) = 3\sqrt{x}$

$g(x) = 3 \cdot f(x)$

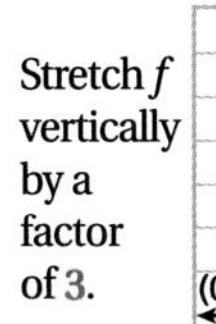

Stretch f vertically by a factor of 3.

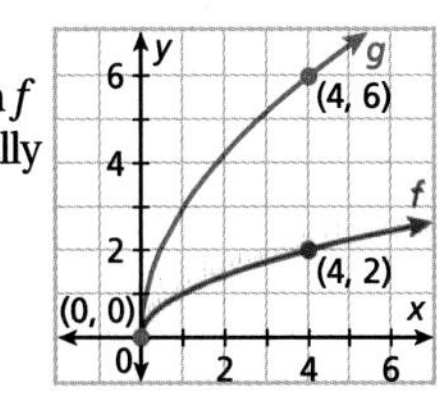

CHECK IT OUT! Using the graph of $f(x) = \sqrt{x}$ as a guide, describe the transformation and graph each function.

2a. $g(x) = \sqrt{x} + 1$ **2b.** $g(x) = \frac{1}{2}\sqrt{x}$

g is *f* translated 1 unit up.

Transformations of square-root functions are summarized below.

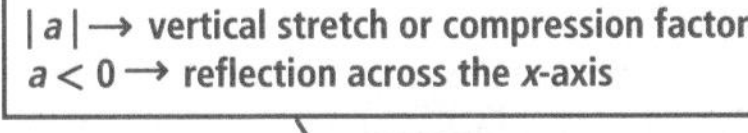

$|a| \rightarrow$ vertical stretch or compression factor
$a < 0 \rightarrow$ reflection across the *x*-axis

$h \rightarrow$ horizontal translation

$$f(x) = a\sqrt{\frac{1}{b}(x - h)} + k$$

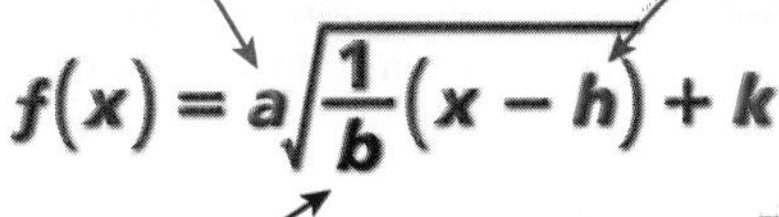

$|b| \rightarrow$ horizontal stretch or compression factor
$b < 0 \rightarrow$ reflection across the *y*-axis

$k \rightarrow$ vertical translation

EXAMPLE 3 Applying Multiple Transformations

Using the graph of $f(x) = \sqrt{x}$ as a guide, describe the transformation and graph each function.

A $g(x) = 2\sqrt{x + 3}$

Stretch f vertically by a factor of 2, and translate it 3 units left.

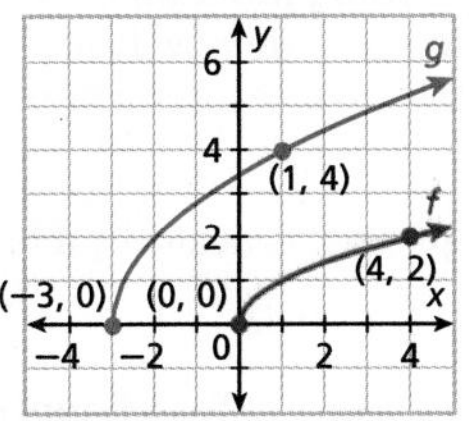

B $g(x) = \sqrt{-x} - 2$

Reflect f across the *y*-axis, and translate it 2 units down.

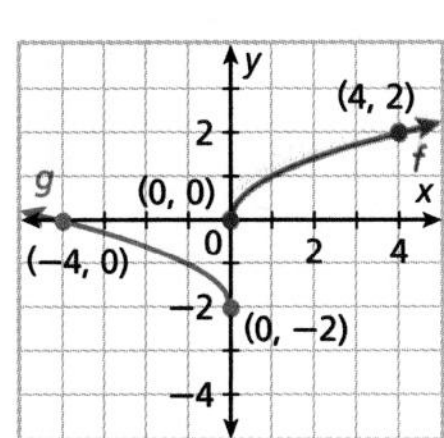

CHECK IT OUT! Using the graph of $f(x) = \sqrt{x}$ as a guide, describe the transformation and graph each function.

3a. $g(x) = \sqrt{-x} + 3$ **3b.** $g(x) = -3\sqrt{x} - 1$

Answers to Check It Out!

2a.

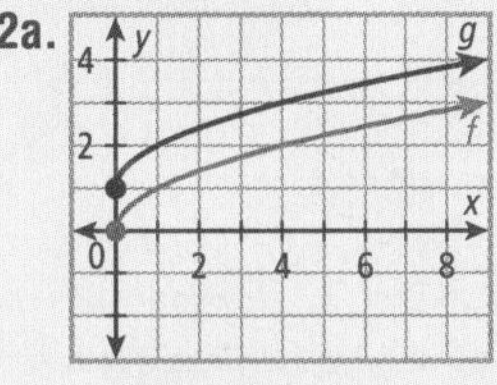

2b. *g* is *f* vertically compressed by a factor of $\frac{1}{2}$.

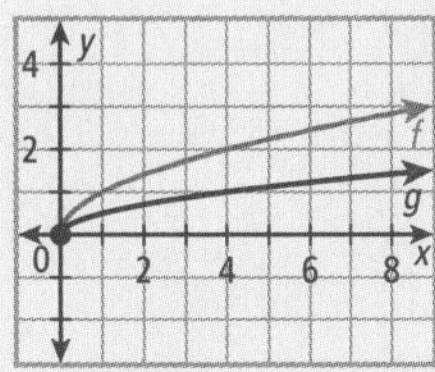

3a. *g* is *f* reflected across the *y*-axis and translated 3 units up.

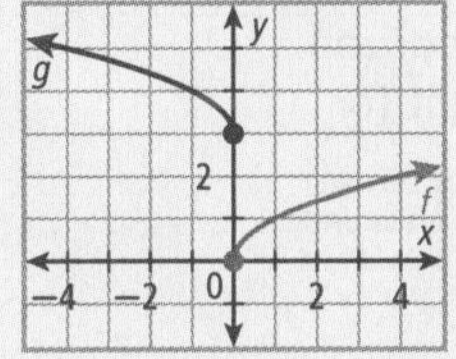

3b. *g* is *f* vertically stretched by a factor of 3, reflected across the *x*-axis, and translated 1 unit down.

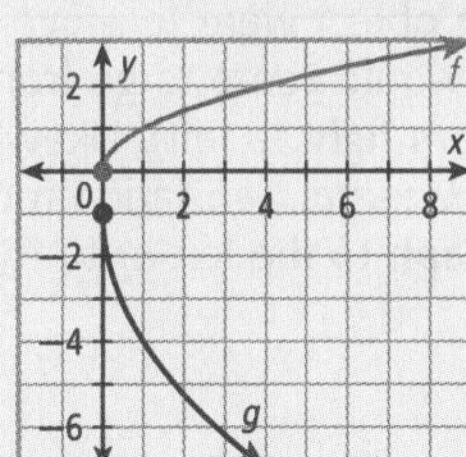

COMMON ERROR ALERT

Students may sometimes restrict the domain of cube-root functions to values of the variable that make the radicand nonnegative. Remind students that radicals with odd indices have real roots even when the radicand is negative. Therefore, they should graph cube-root functions for both positive and negative radicands.

Power Presentations with PowerPoint®

Additional Examples

Example 2

Using the graph of $f(x) = \sqrt{x}$ as a guide, describe the transformation and graph the function $g(x) = \sqrt{x} + 5$.

g is *f* translated up 5 units.

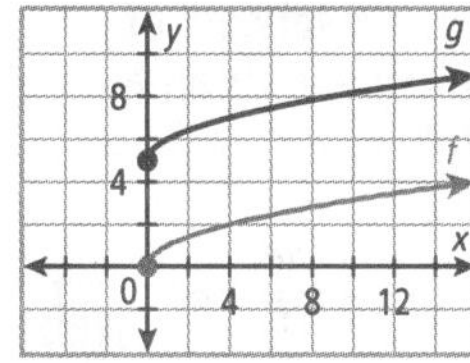

Example 3

Using the graph of $f(x) = \sqrt{x}$ as a guide, describe the transformation and graph the function $g(x) = -\sqrt{x - 4}$.

Reflect *f* across the *x*-axis and translate it 4 units right.

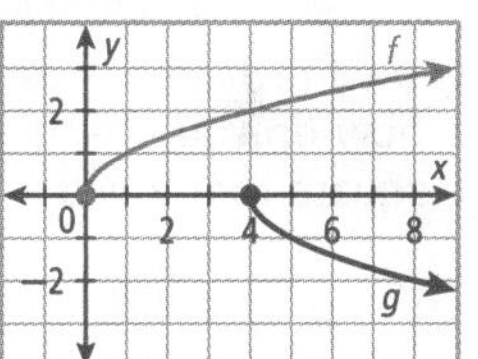

Also available on transparency

INTERVENTION

Questioning Strategies

EXAMPLE 2

- How can you determine the values of *a*, *h*, and *k* for a square-root function?
- What do these values indicate about the function's graph?

EXAMPLE 3

- How can you tell whether a square-root function has been reflected across the *y*-axis when compared with $f(x) = \sqrt{x}$? across the *x*-axis?

Power Presentations with PowerPoint®

Additional Examples

Example 4

Use the description to write the square-root function *g*.

The parent function $f(x) = \sqrt{x}$ is reflected across the x-axis, compressed vertically by a factor of $\frac{1}{5}$, and translated down 5 units.

$g(x) = -\frac{1}{5}\sqrt{x} - 5$

Example 5

A framing store uses the function $c(a) = 0.5\sqrt{a} + 0.2$ to determine the cost c in dollars of glass for a picture with an area a in square inches. The store charges an additional \$6.00 in labor to install the glass. Write the function d for the total cost of a piece of glass, including installation, and use it to estimate the total cost of glass for a picture with an area of 192 in². $d(a) = 0.5\sqrt{a} + 6.2$; \$13.13

Also available on transparency

INTERVENTION 

Questioning Strategies

EXAMPLE 4

- How can you use the description of the transformed function to determine the values of *a, b, h,* and *k*?
- Once you know the values of these parameters, how do you use them to write the square-root function?

EXAMPLE 5

- How do you find the value of a function for a given value of the independent variable?
- How can you check that your estimate is reasonable?

EXAMPLE 4 Writing Transformed Square-Root Functions

Use the description to write the square-root function *g*.

The parent function $f(x) = \sqrt{x}$ is stretched horizontally by a factor of 2, reflected across the y-axis, and translated 3 units left.

Step 1 Identify how each transformation affects the function.

Horizontal stretch by a factor of 2: $|b| = 2$ and Reflection across the y-axis: b is negative $\Big\}$ $b = -2$

Translation 3 units left: $h = -3$

Step 2 Write the transformed function.

$$g(x) = \sqrt{\frac{1}{b}(x - h)}$$

$$g(x) = \sqrt{\frac{1}{-2}[x-(-3)]} \quad \textit{Substitute } -2 \textit{ for b and } -3 \textit{ for h.}$$

$$g(x) = \sqrt{-\frac{1}{2}(x + 3)} \quad \textit{Simplify.}$$

Check Graph both functions on a graphing calculator. The graph of g indicates the given transformations of f.

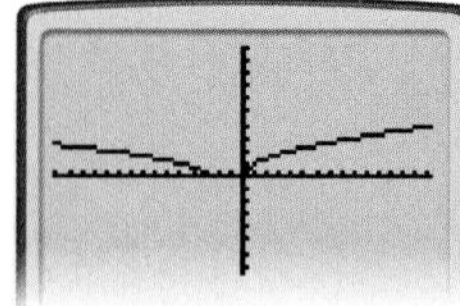

CHECK IT OUT! **Use the description to write the square-root function *g*.**

4. The parent function $f(x) = \sqrt{x}$ is reflected across the x-axis, stretched vertically by a factor of 2, and translated 1 unit up. $g(x) = -2\sqrt{x} + 1$

EXAMPLE 5 *Space Exploration Application*

Special airbags are used to protect scientific equipment when a rover lands on the surface of Mars. On Earth, the function $f(x) = \sqrt{64x}$ approximates an object's downward velocity in feet per second as the object hits the ground after bouncing x ft in height.

The corresponding function for Mars is compressed vertically by a factor of about $\frac{3}{5}$. Write the corresponding function g for Mars, and use it to estimate how fast a rover will hit Mars's surface after a bounce of 45 ft in height.

Step 1 To compress f vertically by a factor of $\frac{3}{5}$, multiply f by $\frac{3}{5}$.

$$g(x) = \frac{3}{5}f(x) = \frac{3}{5}\sqrt{64x}$$

Step 2 Find the value of g for a bounce height of 45 ft.

$$g(45) = \frac{3}{5}\sqrt{64(45)} \approx 32 \quad \textit{Substitute 45 for x and simplify.}$$

The rover will hit Mars's surface with a downward velocity of about 32 ft/s at the end of the bounce.

Teaching Tip **Language** The word *horizontal* is related to the word *horizon.* Point out that the horizon is the apparent line between the land and sky. If an object were to move along the horizon, it would seem to go from left to right (or from right to left). Likewise, a horizontal translation moves a graph to the left or to the right.

ENGLISH LANGUAGE LEARNERS

Use the information on the previous page to answer the following.

5. The downward velocity function for the Moon is a horizontal stretch of f by a factor of about $\frac{25}{4}$. Write the velocity function h for the Moon, and use it to estimate the downward velocity of a landing craft at the end of a bounce 50 ft in height.

$h(x) = \sqrt{\frac{256}{25}x}$; about 23 ft/s

In addition to graphing radical functions, you can also graph radical inequalities. Use the same procedure you used for graphing linear and quadratic inequalities.

EXAMPLE 6 Graphing Radical Inequalities

Graph the inequality $y < \sqrt{x} + 2$.

Step 1 Use the related equation $y = \sqrt{x} + 2$ to make a table of values.

x	0	1	4	9
y	2	3	4	5

Step 2 Use the table to graph the boundary curve. The inequality sign is $<$, so use a dashed curve and shade the area below it.

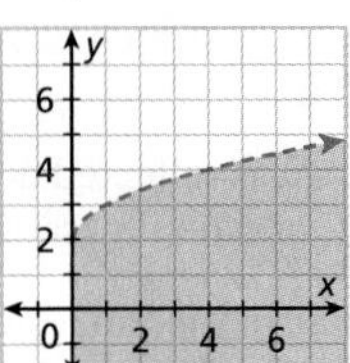

Because the value of x cannot be negative, do not shade left of the y-axis.

Check Choose a point in the solution region, such as $(1, 0)$, and test it in the inequality.

$y < \sqrt{x} + 2$

$0 \overset{?}{<} \sqrt{1} + 2$

$0 < 3$ ✔

Graph each inequality.

6a. $y > \sqrt{x + 4}$

6b. $y \geq \sqrt[3]{x - 3}$

THINK AND DISCUSS

1. Explain whether radical functions have asymptotes.
2. Explain how to determine the domain of the function $f(x) = \sqrt{2x + 2}$.

3. **GET ORGANIZED** Copy and complete the graphic organizer. In each box, give an example of the transformation of the square-root function $f(x) = \sqrt{x}$.

Transformation	Equation	Graph
Vertical translation		
Horizontal translation		
Reflection		
Vertical stretch		

Power Presentations with PowerPoint®

Additional Examples

Example 6

Graph the inequality $y > 2\sqrt{x} - 3$.

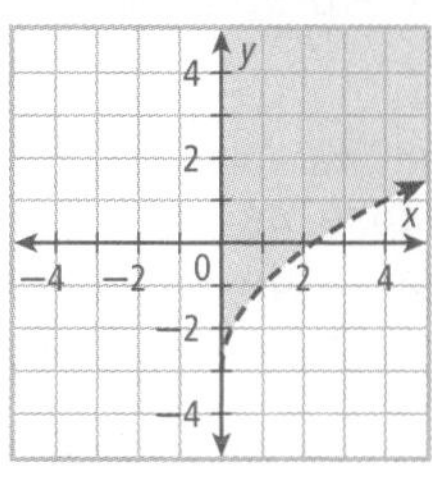

Also available on transparency

INTERVENTION
Questioning Strategies

EXAMPLE 6

- How do you know whether to make the boundary curve dashed or solid?
- How does the domain of the boundary curve affect the area of the graph that you shade?

Answers to *Check It Out!*

6a.

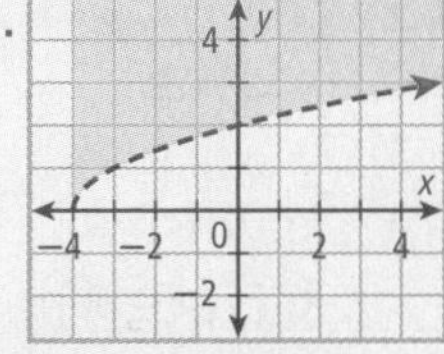

6b.

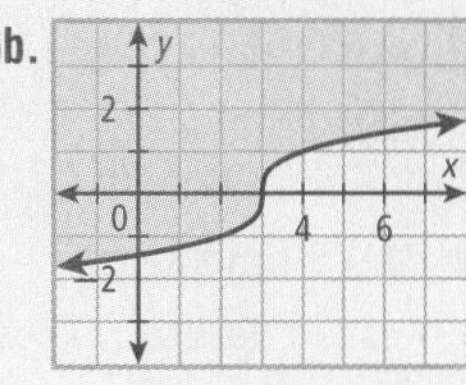

3 Close

Summarize

Ask students to describe each function as a transformation of $f(x) = \sqrt{x}$ without having first graphed the functions.

$g(x) = \frac{1}{5}\sqrt{x}$	vert. compression by $\frac{1}{5}$
$g(x) = \sqrt{x + 6}$	translation left 6
$g(x) = \sqrt{x} - 12$	translation down 12
$g(x) = -\sqrt{4x}$	reflection across x-axis and horiz. compression by $\frac{1}{4}$

ONGOING ASSESSMENT

and INTERVENTION

Diagnose **Before the Lesson**
8-7 Warm Up, TE p. 619

Monitor **During the Lesson**
Check It Out! Exercises, SE pp. 620–623
Questioning Strategies, TE pp. 620–623

Assess **After the Lesson**
8-7 Lesson Quiz, TE p. 627
Alternative Assessment, TE p. 627

Answers to *Think and Discuss*

Possible answers:

1. No; an asymptote is a line that a curve approaches as $|x|$ or $|y|$ becomes very large. There is no such line in the graphs of radical functions.
2. The radicand must be nonnegative, so $2x + 2$ must be greater than or equal to 0. Solve this inequality for x.
   $2x + 2 \geq 0$
   $x \geq -1$
   The domain of the function is $x \geq -1$.
3. See p. A10.

8-7 Exercises

Assignment Guide

Assign *Guided Practice* exercises as necessary.

If you finished Examples **1–3**
Basic 24–38, 48–54
Average 24–38, 48–54, 60–63
Advanced 24–38, 48–54, 60–63

If you finished Examples **1–6**
Basic 24–59, 64–69, 73–77, 80–88
Average 24–78, 80–88
Advanced 24–88

Homework Quick Check
Quickly check key concepts.
Exercises: 26, 30, 36, 40, 42, 46, 67

Answers

1. Possible answer: the function rule is a radical expression that contains a variable in the radicand.

2–11. For graphs, see p. A38.

2. D: $\{x|x \geq -6\}$; R: $\{y|y \geq 0\}$
3. D: $\{x|x \geq 0\}$; R: $\{y|y \geq -1\}$
4. D: $\{x|x \geq 3\}$; R: $\{y|y \geq 0\}$
5. D: $\{x|x \in \mathbb{R}\}$; R: $\{y|y \in \mathbb{R}\}$
6. D: $\{x|x \in \mathbb{R}\}$; R: $\{y|y \in \mathbb{R}\}$
7. D: $\{x|x \in \mathbb{R}\}$; R: $\{y|y \in \mathbb{R}\}$
8. g is f translated 7 units down.
9. h is f vertically stretched by a factor of 3.
10. j is f translated 5 units right.
11. g is f compressed vertically by a factor of $\frac{1}{2}$ and translated 1 unit down.

12–16, 20–37. See page A38.

State Resources

8-7 Exercises

go.hrw.com
Homework Help Online
KEYWORD: MB7 8-7
Parent Resources Online
KEYWORD: MB7 Parent

GUIDED PRACTICE

1. **Vocabulary** Explain why $f(x) = \sqrt{3x} + 4$ is a radical function.

SEE EXAMPLE 1 p. 619

Graph each function, and identify its domain and range.

2. $f(x) = \sqrt{x + 6}$
3. $f(x) = \sqrt{x} - 1$
4. $f(x) = 2\sqrt{x - 3}$
5. $f(x) = 3\sqrt[3]{x}$
6. $f(x) = \sqrt[3]{x} + 2$
7. $f(x) = \sqrt[3]{x - 2}$

SEE EXAMPLE 2 p. 621

Using the graph of $f(x) = \sqrt{x}$ as a guide, describe the transformation and graph each function.

8. $g(x) = \sqrt{x} - 7$
9. $h(x) = 3\sqrt{x}$
10. $j(x) = \sqrt{x - 5}$

SEE EXAMPLE 3 p. 621

11. $g(x) = \frac{1}{2}\sqrt{x} - 1$
12. $h(x) = \sqrt{\frac{1}{3}(x + 4)}$
13. $j(x) = \sqrt{-(x - 3)}$
14. $g(x) = -2\sqrt{x} - 4$
15. $h(x) = \sqrt{-2(x + 2)}$
16. $j(x) = 3\sqrt{x + 3} + 3$

SEE EXAMPLE 4 p. 622

Use the description to write the square-root function g.

17. The parent function $f(x) = \sqrt{x}$ is stretched vertically by a factor of 4 and then translated 5 units left and 2 units down. $g(x) = 4\sqrt{(x + 5)} - 2$
18. The parent function $f(x) = \sqrt{x}$ is reflected across the y-axis, then compressed horizontally by a factor of $\frac{1}{2}$, and finally translated 7 units right. $g(x) = \sqrt{-2(x - 7)}$

SEE EXAMPLE 5 p. 622

19. **Space Exploration** On Earth, the function $f(x) = \frac{6}{5}\sqrt{x}$ approximates the distance in miles to the horizon observed by a person whose eye level is x feet above the ground. The graph of the corresponding function for Mars is a horizontal stretch of f by a factor of about $\frac{9}{5}$. Write the corresponding function g for Mars, and use it to estimate the distance to the horizon for an astronaut whose eyes are 6 ft above Mars's surface. $g(x) = \frac{6}{5}\sqrt{\frac{5}{9}x}$; about 2.2 mi

SEE EXAMPLE 6 p. 623

Graph each inequality.

20. $y \geq \sqrt{x}$
21. $y \leq \sqrt{x - 4}$
22. $y < \sqrt{x} - 3$
23. $y > \sqrt[3]{x}$

PRACTICE AND PROBLEM SOLVING

Independent Practice

For Exercises	See Example
24–29	1
30–32	2
33–38	3
39–41	4
42	5
43–46	6

Extra Practice
Skills Practice p. S19
Application Practice p. S39

Graph each function, and identify its domain and range.

24. $f(x) = \sqrt{x - 2}$
25. $f(x) = -3\sqrt{x}$
26. $f(x) = 2\sqrt{x + 1} - 3$
27. $f(x) = \sqrt[3]{x + 1}$
28. $f(x) = \sqrt[3]{x} - 4$
29. $f(x) = -2\sqrt[3]{x - 3}$

Using the graph of $f(x) = \sqrt{x}$ as a guide, describe the transformation and graph each function.

30. $g(x) = \sqrt{x} + 2$
31. $h(x) = \sqrt{x - 4}$
32. $j(x) = 0.5\sqrt{x}$
33. $g(x) = \sqrt{3(x + 5)}$
34. $h(x) = \frac{1}{4}\sqrt{-x}$
35. $j(x) = \sqrt{x + 4} - 1$
36. $g(x) = -4\sqrt{x} + 1$
37. $h(x) = 3\sqrt{-x} + 2$
38. $j(x) = \frac{1}{3}\sqrt{-(x + 2)}$

Use the description to write the square-root function g.

39. The parent function $f(x) = \sqrt{x}$ is compressed vertically by a factor of $\frac{1}{3}$ and then translated 3 units left. $g(x) = \frac{1}{3}\sqrt{x + 3}$
40. The parent function $f(x) = \sqrt{x}$ is reflected across the y-axis, stretched horizontally by a factor of 6, and then translated 2 units right.

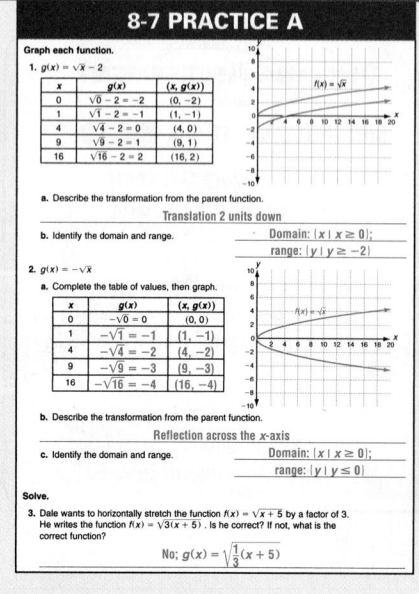

40. $g(x) = \sqrt{-\frac{1}{6}(x - 2)}$

8-7 PRACTICE A

Graph each function.

1. $g(x) = \sqrt{x} - 2$

x	$g(x)$	$(x, g(x))$
0	$\sqrt{0} - 2 = -2$	$(0, -2)$
1	$\sqrt{1} - 2 = -1$	$(1, -1)$
4	$\sqrt{4} - 2 = 0$	$(4, 0)$
9	$\sqrt{9} - 2 = 1$	$(9, 1)$
16	$\sqrt{16} - 2 = 2$	$(16, 2)$

$f(x) = \sqrt{x}$

a. Describe the transformation from the parent function. Translation 2 units down

b. Identify the domain and range. Domain: $\{x \mid x \geq 0\}$; range: $\{y \mid y \geq -2\}$

2. $g(x) = -\sqrt{x}$

a. Complete the table of values, then graph.

x	$g(x)$	$(x, g(x))$
0	$-\sqrt{0} = 0$	$(0, 0)$
1	$-\sqrt{1} = -1$	$(1, -1)$
4	$-\sqrt{4} = -2$	$(4, -2)$
9	$-\sqrt{9} = -3$	$(9, -3)$
16	$-\sqrt{16} = -4$	$(16, -4)$

$f(x) = \sqrt{x}$

b. Describe the transformation from the parent function. Reflection across the x-axis

c. Identify the domain and range. Domain: $\{x \mid x \geq 0\}$; range: $\{y \mid y \leq 0\}$

Solve.

3. Dale wants to horizontally stretch the function $f(x) = \sqrt{x + 5}$ by a factor of 3. He writes the function $f(x) = \sqrt{3(x + 5)}$. Is he correct? If not, what is the correct function?

No; $g(x) = \sqrt{\frac{1}{3}(x + 5)}$

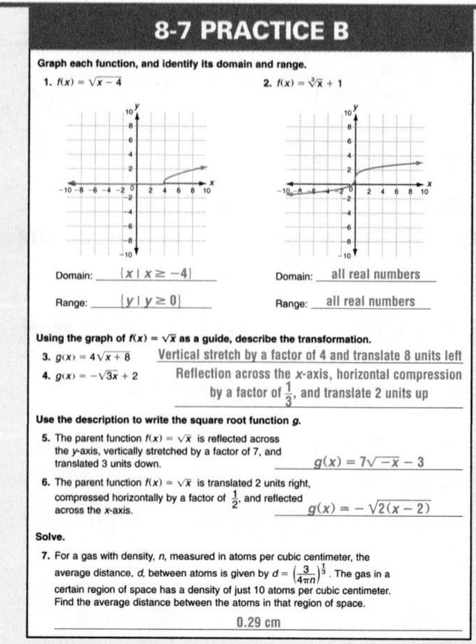

8-7 PRACTICE B

Graph each function, and identify its domain and range.

1. $f(x) = \sqrt{x - 4}$

Domain: $\{x \mid x \geq -4\}$
Range: $\{y \mid y \geq 0\}$

2. $f(x) = \sqrt[3]{x} + 1$

Domain: all real numbers
Range: all real numbers

Using the graph of $f(x) = \sqrt{x}$ as a guide, describe the transformation.

3. $g(x) = 4\sqrt{x + 8}$ Vertical stretch by a factor of 4 and translate 8 units left
4. $g(x) = -\sqrt{3x} + 2$ Reflection across the x-axis, horizontal compression by a factor of $\frac{1}{3}$, and translate 2 units up

Use the description to write the square root function g.

5. The parent function $f(x) = \sqrt{x}$ is reflected across the y-axis, vertically stretched by a factor of 7, and translated 3 units down. $g(x) = 7\sqrt{-x} - 3$
6. The parent function $f(x) = \sqrt{x}$ is translated 2 units right, compressed horizontally by a factor of $\frac{1}{2}$, and reflected across the x-axis. $g(x) = -\sqrt{2(x - 2)}$

Solve.

7. For a gas with density, n, measured in atoms per cubic centimeter, the average distance, d, between atoms is given by $d = \left(\frac{3}{4\pi n}\right)^{\frac{1}{3}}$. The gas in a certain region of space has a density of just 10 atoms per cubic centimeter. Find the average distance between the atoms in that region of space.

0.29 cm

41. The parent function $f(x) = \sqrt{x}$ is reflected across the x-axis and then translated 1 unit left and 4 units down. $g(x) = -\sqrt{x+1} - 4$

42. **Manufacturing** A company manufactures cans for pet food. The function $f(x) = \sqrt{\frac{x}{40}}$ models the radius in centimeters of a can holding x cm^3 of dog food. The graph of the corresponding function for cans of cat food is a horizontal compression of f by a factor of about $\frac{3}{5}$. Write the corresponding function g for cans of cat food, and use it to estimate the radius of a can holding 216 cm^3 of cat food. $g(x) = \sqrt{\frac{x}{24}}$; 3 cm

Okapi

Graph each inequality.

43. $y < \sqrt{x+5}$ 44. $y \geq \sqrt{x-1}$ 45. $y > \sqrt[3]{x} + 2$ 46. $y \leq \sqrt[3]{x+3}$

47. **Biology** The function $h(m) = 241m^{-\frac{1}{4}}$ can be used to approximate an animal's resting heart rate h in beats per minute, given its mass m in kilograms.
   a. A common shrew is one of the world's smallest mammals. What is the resting heart rate of a common shrew with a mass of 0.01 kg? $\approx$ 762 beats/min
   b. An okapi is an African animal related to the giraffe. What is the resting heart rate of an okapi with a mass of 300 kg? $\approx$ 58 beats/min

Describe how $f(x) = \sqrt{x}$ was transformed to produce each function.

48. $g(x) = 6\sqrt{x+1}$ 49. $h(x) = 3\sqrt{x-1} - 9$ 50. $j(x) = -\sqrt{x-3} - 7$

Match each function to its graph.

51. $f(x) = \sqrt{x+2} - 2$ D 52. $g(x) = \sqrt{x-2} + 2$ B

53. $h(x) = \sqrt{-(x+2)} + 2$ A 54. $j(x) = -\sqrt{x-2} - 2$ C

55. **Aviation** Pilots use the function $D(A) = 3.56\sqrt{A}$ to approximate the distance D in kilometers to the horizon from an altitude A in meters.
   a. What is the approximate distance to the horizon observed by a pilot flying at an altitude of 11,000 m? about 373 km
   b. **What if...?** How will the approximate distance to the horizon appear to change if the pilot descends by 4000 m? It will appear to decrease by about 76 km.

56. **Earth Science** The speed in miles per hour of a tsunami can be modeled by the function $s(d) = 3.86\sqrt{d}$, where d is the average depth in feet of the water over which the tsunami travels. Graph this function. Use the graph to predict the speed of a tsunami over water with a depth of 1500 feet. $\approx$ 150 mi/h

57. **Astrophysics** New stars can form inside an interstellar cloud of gas when a cloud fragment, called a clump, has a mass M that is greater than what is known as the Jean's mass. The Jean's mass M_J is given by $M_J = 100\sqrt{\frac{(T+273)^3}{n}}$, where T is the temperature of the gas in degrees Celsius and n is the density of the gas in molecules per cubic centimeter. An astronomer discovers a gas clump with $M = 137$, $T = -263$, and $n = 1000$. Will the clump form a star? Justify your answer.

58. **Multi-Step** The formula $v = \sqrt{4909gR}$ approximates the velocity in miles per hour necessary to escape the gravity of a planet with acceleration due to gravity g in ft/s^2 and radius R in miles. On Earth, which has a radius of 3960 mi, the acceleration due to gravity is 32 ft/s^2. On the Moon, which has a radius of 1080 mi, the acceleration due to gravity is about $\frac{1}{6}$ that on Earth. How much faster would a vehicle need to be traveling to escape Earth's gravity than to escape the Moon's gravity? about 19,624 mi/h faster on Earth than on the Moon

COMMON ERROR ALERT

It is easy to forget that when applying a horizontal stretch or compression to a square-root function, the reciprocal of the stretch or compression factor, and not the factor itself, is placed under the radical sign. Use **Exercises 18** and **19** as an opportunity to remind students of the proper procedure.

Inclusion When graphing inequalities, as in **Exercises 43–46,** remind students to check that the correct region has been shaded by testing a point in the shaded region. Students can simplify their computations by selecting a point whose x- or y-coordinate is 0.

Answers

38. j is f reflected across the y-axis, vertically compressed by a factor of $\frac{1}{3}$, and then translated 2 units left.

43. 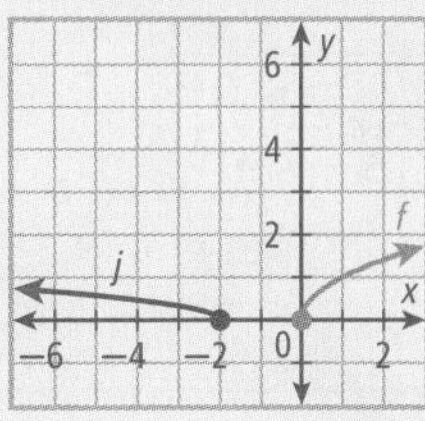

44. 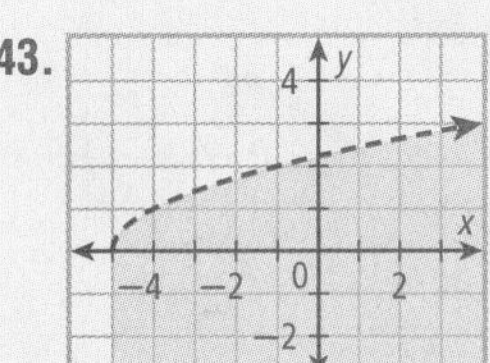

45. 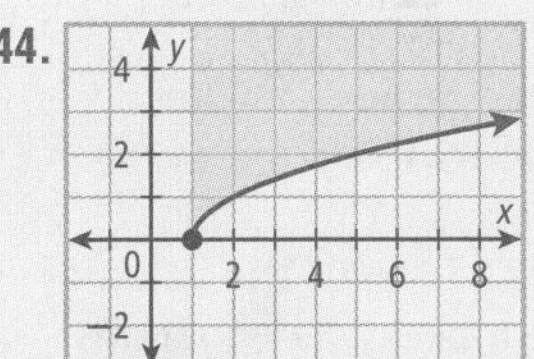

46. 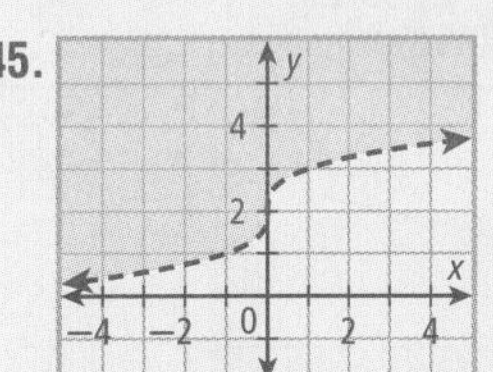

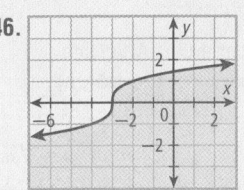

48. a vertical stretch by a factor of 6 followed by a translation 1 unit left

49. a vertical stretch by a factor of 3 followed by a translation 1 unit right and 9 units down

50. a reflection across the x-axis followed by a translation 3 units right and 7 units down

56. 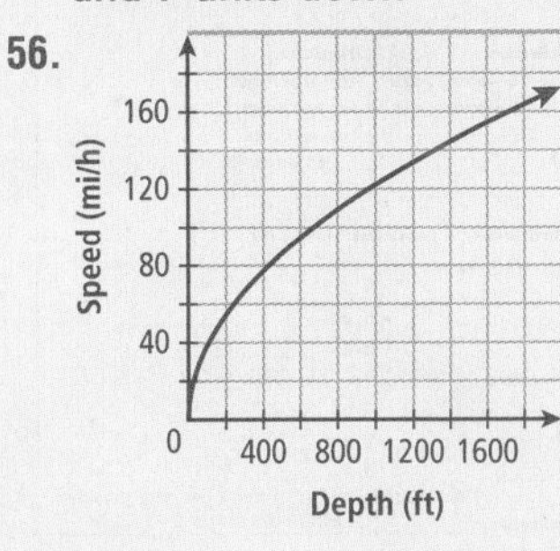

57. Yes; $M_J = 100\sqrt{\frac{(-263+273)^3}{1000}} = 100$ and so $M > M_J$.

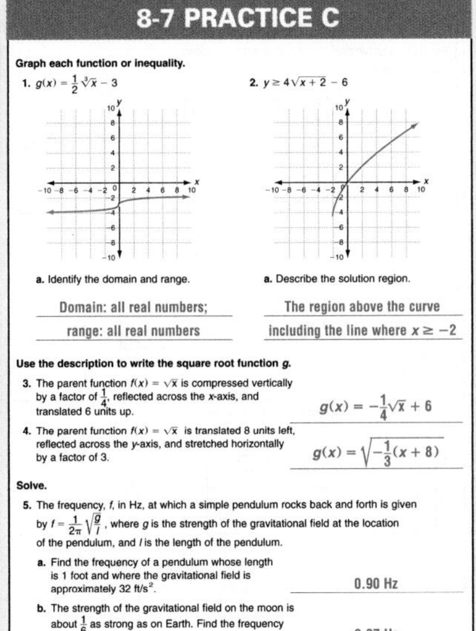

8-7 PRACTICE C

Graph each function or inequality.

1. $g(x) = \frac{1}{2}\sqrt[3]{x} - 3$
2. $y \geq 4\sqrt{x+2} - 6$

a. Identify the domain and range. Domain: all real numbers; range: all real numbers

a. Describe the solution region. The region above the curve including the line where $x \geq -2$

Use the description to write the square root function g.

3. The parent function $f(x) = \sqrt{x}$ is compressed vertically by a factor of $\frac{1}{4}$, reflected across the x-axis, and translated 6 units up. $g(x) = -\frac{1}{4}\sqrt{x} + 6$

4. The parent function $f(x) = \sqrt{x}$ is translated 8 units left, reflected across the y-axis, and stretched horizontally by a factor of 3. $g(x) = \sqrt{-\frac{1}{3}(x+8)}$

Solve.

5. The frequency, f, in Hz, at which a simple pendulum rocks back and forth is given by $f = \frac{1}{2\pi}\sqrt{\frac{g}{l}}$, where g is the strength of the gravitational field at the location of the pendulum, and l is the length of the pendulum.
   a. Find the frequency of a pendulum whose length is 1 foot and where the gravitational field is approximately 32 ft/s^2. 0.90 Hz
   b. The strength of the gravitational field on the moon is about $\frac{1}{6}$ as strong as on Earth. Find the frequency of the same pendulum on the moon. 0.37 Hz

MULTI-STEP TEST PREP Exercise 59 involves describing transformations of a square-root function related to a pendulum. This exercise prepares students for the Multi-Step Test Prep on page 636.

Answers

59a.

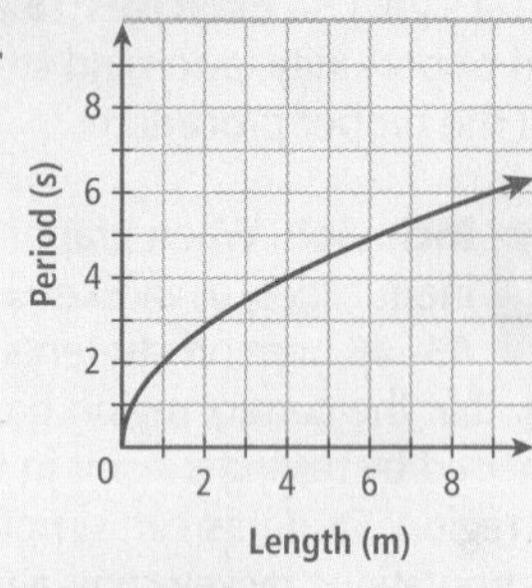

b. Possible answer: The graph of T is a vertical stretch of the graph of f by a factor of 2π and a horizontal stretch of the graph of f by a factor of 9.8.

64.

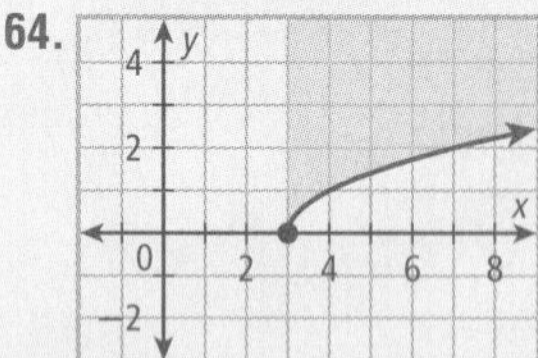

65–66. For graphs, see p. A39.

67a.

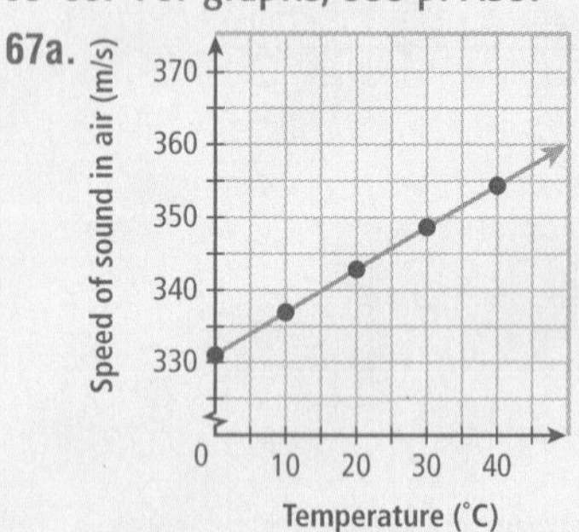

67c. Possible answer: because k is positive, the value of the function is 0 only when $T + 273.15 = 0$. The value of T that makes this equation true is -273.15.

68a.

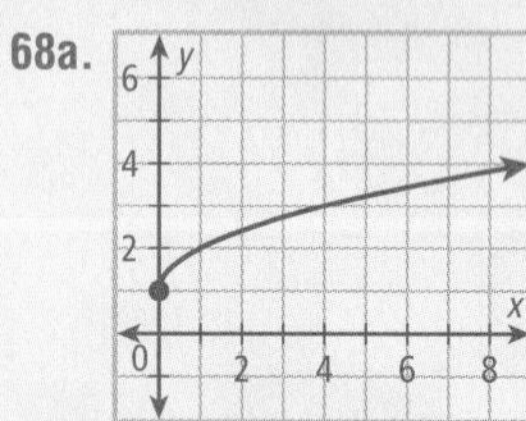

70. Possible answer: A vertical compression of the parent function by a factor of $\frac{1}{2}$ can be represented by $g(x) = \frac{1}{2}\sqrt{x}$. A horizontal stretch of the parent function by a factor of 4 can be represented by $h(x) = \sqrt{\frac{1}{4}x}$. The expression $\sqrt{\frac{1}{4}x}$ can be simplified as follows:

$$\sqrt{\frac{1}{4}x} = \sqrt{\frac{1}{4}} \cdot \sqrt{x} = \frac{1}{2} \cdot \sqrt{x}.$$

Therefore, $g(x) = h(x) = \frac{1}{2}\sqrt{x}$.

MULTI-STEP TEST PREP

59. This problem will prepare you for the Multi-Step Test Prep on page 636.

For a pendulum with length x in meters, the function $T(x) = 2\pi\sqrt{\frac{x}{9.8}}$ gives the period of the pendulum in seconds. The period of a pendulum is the time it takes the pendulum to complete one back-and-forth swing.

a. Graph the function.

b. Describe the graph of T as a transformation of $f(x) = \sqrt{x}$.

c. By what factor must the length of a pendulum be increased to double its period? **by a factor of 4**

Tell whether each statement is sometimes, always, or never true.

60. For $n > 0$, the value of $\sqrt{n}$ is greater than the value of $\sqrt[3]{n}$. **sometimes**

61. The domain of a radical function is all real numbers. **sometimes**

62. The range of $f(x) = a\sqrt[3]{x - h}$, where a and h are nonzero real numbers, is all real numbers. **always**

63. The range of $f(x) = a\sqrt{x} + k$, where a and k are nonzero real numbers, is all real numbers. **never**

Physics

A sonic boom is a shock wave produced by an aircraft flying at or above the speed of sound in air. Occasionally, an unusual cone-shaped cloud forms around a plane when the plane's speed is near that of sound, as shown above.

Graph each inequality, and tell whether the point $(1, 2)$ is a solution.

64. $f(x) \geq \sqrt{x - 3}$ **no**

65. $f(x) \leq \sqrt{x + 5}$ **yes**

66. $f(x) > \sqrt[3]{x} - 3$ **yes**

67. **Physics** The speed s of sound in air in meters per second is given by the function $s = \sqrt{k(T + 273.15)}$, where T is the air temperature in degrees Celsius and k is a positive constant. The table shows the speed of sound in air at a pressure of 1 atmosphere.

Temperature (°C)	Speed of Sound in Air (m/s)
0	331
10	337
20	343
30	348
40	354

a. Graph the data in the table.

b. Use your graph to predict the speed of sound in air at 25°C. **about 346 m/s**

c. Based on the function above, at what temperature would the speed of sound in air be 0 m/s? Explain. **−273.15°C**

68. **Medicine** A pharmaceutical company samples the raw materials it receives before they are used in the manufacture of drugs. For inactive ingredients, the company uses the function $s(x) = \sqrt{x} + 1$ to determine the number of samples s that should be taken from a shipment of x containers.

a. Describe the graph of s as a transformation of $f(x) = \sqrt{x}$. Then graph the function. ***s* is *f* translated 1 unit up.**

b. How many samples should be taken from a shipment of 45 containers of an inactive ingredient? **8**

69. **Multi-Step** The time t in seconds required for an object to fall from a certain height can be modeled by the function $t = \frac{\sqrt{h}}{4}$, where h is the initial height of the object in feet. To the nearest tenth of a second, how much longer will it take for a piece of an iceberg to fall to the ocean from a height of 240 ft than from a height of 100 ft? **1.4 s**

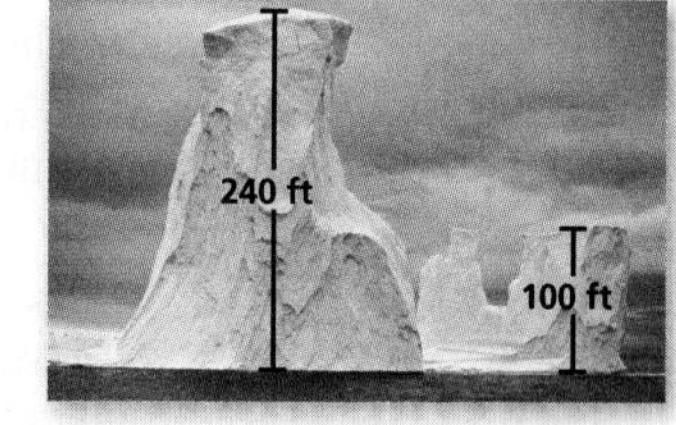

70. **Critical Thinking** Explain why a vertical compression of a square-root function by a factor of $\frac{1}{2}$ is equivalent to a horizontal stretch of a square-root function by a factor of 4.

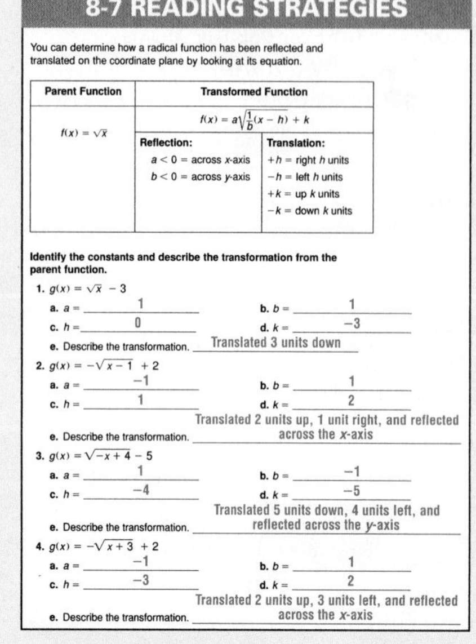

8-7 READING STRATEGIES

You can determine how a radical function has been reflected and translated on the coordinate plane by looking at its equation.

Parent Function	Transformed Function	
$f(x) = \sqrt{x}$	$f(x) = a\sqrt{\frac{1}{b}(x - h)} + k$	
	Reflection: $a < 0$ = across x-axis $b < 0$ = across y-axis	**Translation:** $+h$ = right h units $-h$ = left h units $+k$ = up k units $-k$ = down k units

Identify the constants and describe the transformation from the parent function.

1. $g(x) = \sqrt{x} - 3$
   a. $a =$ 1 b. $b =$ 1
   c. $h =$ 0 d. $k =$ −3
   e. Describe the transformation. Translated 3 units down
2. $g(x) = -\sqrt{x - 1} + 2$
   a. $a =$ −1 b. $b =$ 1
   c. $h =$ 1 d. $k =$ 2
   e. Describe the transformation. Translated 2 units up, 1 unit right, and reflected across the x-axis
3. $g(x) = \sqrt{-x + 4} - 5$
   a. $a =$ 1 b. $b =$ −1
   c. $h =$ −4 d. $k =$ −5
   e. Describe the transformation. Translated 5 units down, 4 units left, and reflected across the y-axis
4. $g(x) = -\sqrt{x + 3} + 2$
   a. $a =$ −1 b. $b =$ 1
   c. $h =$ −3 d. $k =$ 2
   e. Describe the transformation. Translated 2 units up, 3 units left, and reflected across the x-axis

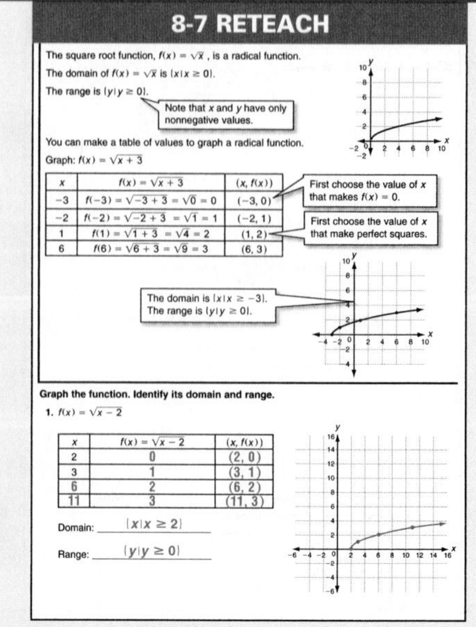

8-7 RETEACH

The square root function, $f(x) = \sqrt{x}$, is a radical function.

The domain of $f(x) = \sqrt{x}$ is $\{x \mid x \geq 0\}$.

The range is $\{y \mid y \geq 0\}$.

Note that x and y have only nonnegative values.

You can make a table of values to graph a radical function.

Graph: $f(x) = \sqrt{x + 3}$

x	$f(x) = \sqrt{x + 3}$	$(x, f(x))$
−3	$f(-3) = \sqrt{-3 + 3} = \sqrt{0} = 0$	(−3, 0)
−2	$f(-2) = \sqrt{-2 + 3} = \sqrt{1} = 1$	(−2, 1)
1	$f(1) = \sqrt{1 + 3} = \sqrt{4} = 2$	(1, 2)
6	$f(6) = \sqrt{6 + 3} = \sqrt{9} = 3$	(6, 3)

First choose the value of x that makes $f(x) = 0$.

First choose the value of x that make perfect squares.

The domain is $\{x \mid x \geq -3\}$.
The range is $\{y \mid y \geq 0\}$.

Graph the function. Identify its domain and range.

1. $f(x) = \sqrt{x - 2}$

x	$f(x) = \sqrt{x - 2}$	$(x, f(x))$
2	0	(2, 0)
3	1	(3, 1)
6	2	(6, 2)
11	3	(11, 3)

Domain: $\{x \mid x \geq 2\}$

Range: $\{y \mid y \geq 0\}$

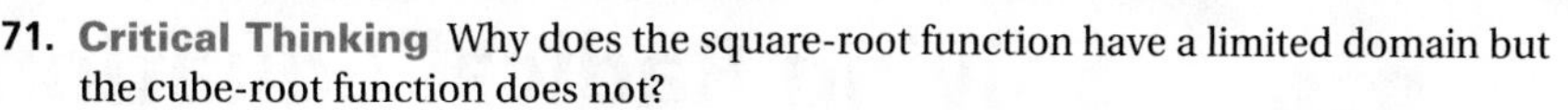

71. **Critical Thinking** Why does the square-root function have a limited domain but the cube-root function does not?

72. **Write About It** Describe how a horizontal translation and a vertical translation of the function $f(x) = \sqrt{x}$ each affects the function's domain and range.

TEST PREP

73. What is the domain of the function $f(x) = \sqrt{x - 9}$?

Ⓐ All real numbers　Ⓒ $x \geq 0$

Ⓑ $x \geq -9$　Ⓓ $x \geq 9$ (circled)

74. Which situation could best be modeled by a cube-root function?

Ⓕ The volume of a cube as a function of its edge length

Ⓖ The diameter of a circle as a function of its area

Ⓗ The edge length of a cube as a function of its surface area

Ⓙ The radius of a sphere as a function of its volume (circled)

75. The function g is a translation 2 units left and 5 units up of $f(x) = \sqrt{x}$. Which of the following represents g?

Ⓐ $g(x) = \sqrt{x + 2} + 5$ (circled)　Ⓒ $g(x) = \sqrt{x + 5} + 2$

Ⓑ $g(x) = 2\sqrt{x} + 5$　Ⓓ $g(x) = 5\sqrt{x - 2}$

76. Which function has a range of $\{y \mid y \leq -2\}$?

Ⓕ $f(x) = \sqrt{x} - 2$　Ⓗ $f(x) = \sqrt{-x} - 2$

Ⓖ $f(x) = \sqrt{x - 2}$　Ⓙ $f(x) = -\sqrt{x} - 2$ (circled)

77. **Short Response** Describe how the graph of $f(x) = \sqrt{x}$ was transformed to produce the graph shown. Then write the equation of the graphed function.

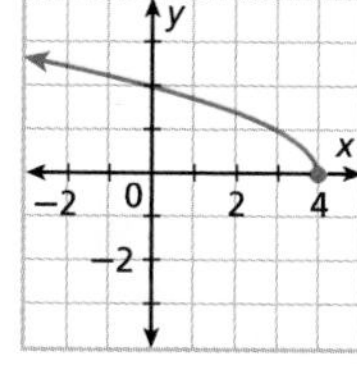

CHALLENGE AND EXTEND

78. The function $f(x) = \sqrt{x}$ is transformed solely by using translations and reflections to produce g. The domain of g is all real numbers greater than or equal to 3, and the range is all real numbers less than or equal to 2. What is the equation that represents g? $g(x) = -\sqrt{x - 3} + 2$

79. Write the equation of a square-root function whose graph has its endpoint at $(-3, 4)$ and passes through the point $(2, 2)$.

$f(x) = -2\sqrt{\frac{1}{5}(x + 3)} + 4$ or equivalent function

SPIRAL REVIEW

Solve and graph. *(Lesson 2-1)*

80. $-4x + 5 < -7$ $x > 3$

81. $12 \geq 4(x - 5)$ $x \leq 8$

82. $2(x + 1) \geq x - 2$ $x \geq -4$

Use substitution to solve each system of equations. *(Lesson 3-2)*

83. $\begin{cases} y = 2x - 10 \\ 2x + y = 14 \end{cases}$ $x = 6, y = 2$

84. $\begin{cases} y = 3x - 2 \\ 3x = 2y \end{cases}$ $x = \frac{4}{3}, y = 2$

85. $\begin{cases} -8x + y = 36 \\ y = x - 4 \end{cases}$ $x = -\frac{40}{7}, y = -\frac{68}{7}$

Solve each equation. *(Lesson 8-5)*

86. $\frac{7}{x} + x = \frac{16}{3}$ $\frac{7}{3}, 3$

87. $4 + \frac{2}{x} = \frac{9}{2}$ 4

88. $\frac{-5x^2}{x + 5} = \frac{3x - 2}{x + 5}$ $-1, \frac{2}{5}$

8-7 PROBLEM SOLVING

On Earth the distance, *d*, in kilometers that one can see to the horizon is a function of altitude, *a*, in meters, and can be found using the function $d(a) = 3.56\sqrt{a}$. To find the corresponding distance to the horizon on Mars, the function must be stretched horizontally by a factor of about $\frac{9}{5}$.

1. a. Write the function that corresponds to the given transformation.
   $d(a) = 3.56\sqrt{\frac{5}{9}a}$
   b. Use a graphing calculator to graph the function and the parent function. Sketch both curves on the coordinate plane.
   c. Use your graph to determine the approximate distance to the horizon from an altitude of 100 meters:
   on Earth 36 km
   on Mars 27 km

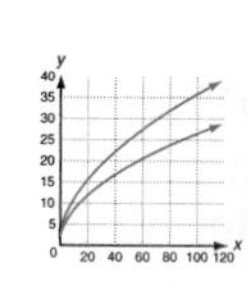

Choose the letter for the best answer.

2. Which equation represents the radius of a sphere as a function of the volume of the sphere?
   A $r = \sqrt[3]{\frac{3\pi}{4V}}$　C $r = \sqrt[3]{\frac{4V}{3\pi}}$
   Ⓑ $r = \sqrt[3]{\frac{3V}{4\pi}}$　D $r = \sqrt[3]{\frac{4\pi}{3V}}$

3. Alice graphed a function that is found only in the first quadrant. Which function could she have used?
   A $f(x) = \sqrt{x + 2}$　Ⓒ $f(x) = \sqrt{x} + 2$
   B $f(x) = -\sqrt{x}$　D $f(x) = \sqrt{x - 2}$

4. Harry made a symmetrical design by graphing four functions, one in each quadrant. The graph of which function is in the third quadrant?
   A $f(x) = 4\sqrt{x}$　C $f(x) = -4\sqrt{x}$
   B $f(x) = 4\sqrt{-x}$　Ⓓ $f(x) = -4\sqrt{-x}$

5. The side length of a cube can be represented by $s = \sqrt{\frac{T}{6}}$, where T is the surface area of the cube. What transformation is shown by $s = \sqrt{\frac{T}{3}}$?
   Ⓐ Horizontal compression by a factor of 0.5
   B Horizontal stretch by a factor of 2
   C Vertical compression by a factor of 0.5
   D Vertical stretch by a factor of 2

6. The hypotenuse of a right isosceles triangle can be written $H = \sqrt{2x^2}$, where x is the length of one of the legs. Which function models the hypotenuse when the legs are lengthened by a factor of 2?
   A $H = \sqrt{2x^2} + 2$　C $H = \sqrt{4x^2}$
   B $H = \sqrt{2x^2} + 4$　Ⓓ $H = \sqrt{8x^2}$

8-7 CHALLENGE

The first graph shows the function $y = \sqrt{x}$. Observe that both the domain and the range consist of the set of nonnegative numbers. The graph begins at the point (0, 0) and includes points (1, 1), (4, 2), and (9, 3). As x increases from 0 to 1, then from 1 to 4, and then from 4 to 9, the y value increases by 1 each time.

The second graph shows the function $y = \sqrt[3]{x}$. In this case the domain and range are both the set of real numbers. As x increases from 0 to 1, then from 1 to 8, and then from 8 to 27, the y-value increases by 1 each time.

Look at the third graph. You can determine the equation from the graph. The square root function has been reflected over the x-axis. The starting point is at (2, 6) so both a reflection and a translation are involved. As x increases from the starting point 1 unit to the right, the y-value decreases 4 units so a vertical stretch is also indicated. Putting all these transformations together gives $y = -4\sqrt{x - 2} + 6$.

Use these observations to write an equation for each graph. Note that the equations may not be unique since many times a vertical stretch or compression can also be written using a horizontal stretch or compression, respectively.

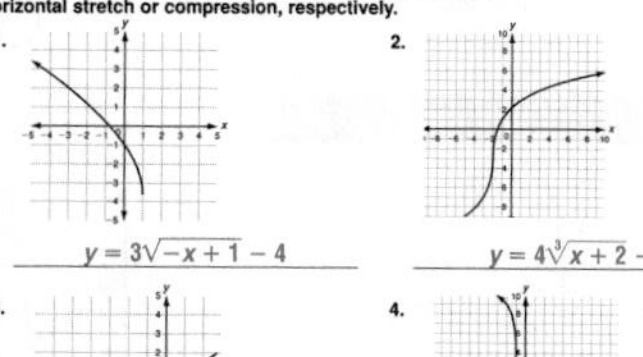

1. $y = 3\sqrt{-x + 1} - 4$

2. $y = 4\sqrt[3]{x + 2} - 3$

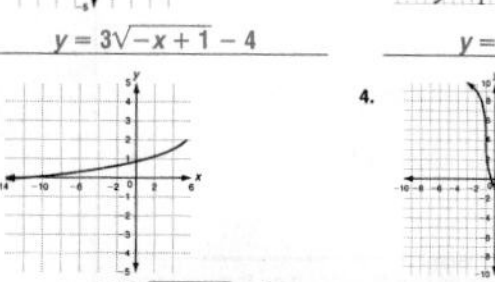

3. $y = -0.5\sqrt{-x + 5} + 2$

4. $y = 5\sqrt[3]{-x - 1} + 4$

TEST PREP DOCTOR In Exercise 77, students who wrote $g(x) = \sqrt{-(x + 4)}$ may have forgotten that h is the value subtracted from x, not the value added to x.

Answers

71–72, 77. See p. A39.

80–82. For graphs, see p. A39.

Journal

Have students describe the steps for graphing a radical inequality, such as $y \geq \sqrt{x + 5}$.

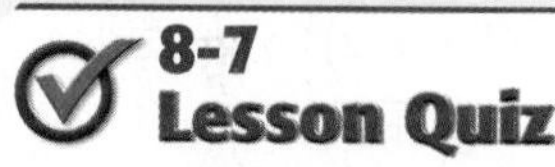

ALTERNATIVE ASSESSMENT

Have students create a radical function that involves two transformations of the graph of $f(x) = \sqrt{x}$. Ask students to describe the transformations and then graph the function.

Power Presentations with PowerPoint®

8-7 Lesson Quiz

1. Graph the function $f(x) = 2\sqrt{x + 4}$ and identify its domain and range.
   D: $\{x \mid x \geq -4\}$; R: $\{y \mid y \geq 0\}$

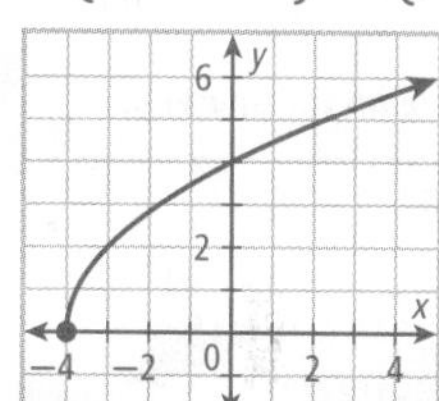

2. Using the graph of $f(x) = \sqrt{x}$ as a guide, describe the transformation and graph the function $g(x) = \sqrt{-x} + 3$. g is f reflected across the y-axis and translated 3 units up.

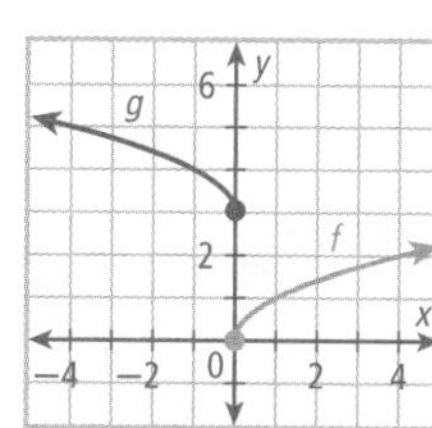

3. Graph the inequality $y \geq -\sqrt[3]{x} + 2$.

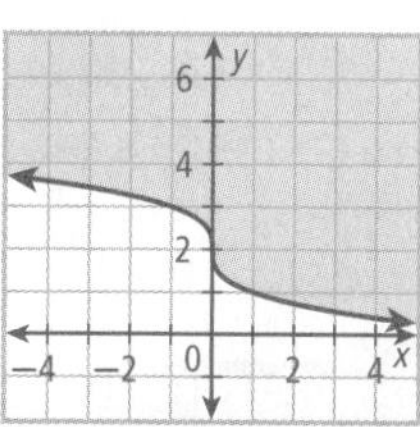

Also available on transparency

8-8 Organizer

Pacing: Traditional 1 day
Block $\frac{1}{2}$ day

Objective: Solve radical equations and inequalities.

Online Edition
Graphing Calculator, Tutorial Videos, TechKeys

Countdown to Testing Week 18

Power Presentations with PowerPoint®

Warm Up

Simplify each expression. Assume all variables are positive.

1. $2\sqrt{27x} + 3\sqrt{12x}$ $\quad 12\sqrt{3x}$
2. $\sqrt{72y^5}$ $\quad 6y^2\sqrt{2y}$
3. $\sqrt[3]{(x+2)^3}$ $\quad x + 2$
4. $\sqrt{2(48y)}$ $\quad 4\sqrt{6y}$

Write each expression in radical form.

5. $(x+6)^{\frac{1}{2}}$ $\quad \sqrt{x+6}$
6. $(3y+4)^{\frac{3}{5}}$ $\quad \sqrt[5]{(3y+4)^3}$

Also available on transparency

Math Humor

Teacher: Your behavior reminds me of $\sqrt{2}$.
Student: Why?
Teacher: Because it's completely irrational.

8-8 Solving Radical Equations and Inequalities

A2.5.5 Solve equations that contain radical expressions and identify extraneous roots when they occur.

Objective
Solve radical equations and inequalities.

Vocabulary
radical equation
radical inequality

Who uses this?
Police officers can use radical equations to determine whether a car is speeding. (See Example 6.)

IT'S AMAZING HOW PEOPLE SLOW DOWN WHEN YOU POINT A HAIR DRYER AT THEM.

A **radical equation** contains a variable within a radical. Recall that you can solve quadratic equations by taking the square root of both sides. Similarly, radical equations can be solved by raising both sides to a power.

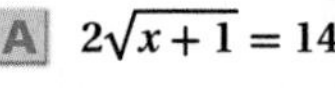

Solving Radical Equations

Steps	Example
1. Isolate the radical.	$\sqrt[3]{x} - 2 = 0$ $\sqrt[3]{x} = 2$
2. Raise both sides of the equation to the power equal to the index of the radical.	$(\sqrt[3]{x})^3 = (2)^3$
3. Simplify and solve.	$x = 8$

EXAMPLE 1 Solving Equations Containing One Radical

Solve each equation.

A $2\sqrt{x+1} = 14$

$\frac{2\sqrt{x+1}}{2} = \frac{14}{2}$ *Divide by 2.*

$\sqrt{x+1} = 7$ *Simplify.*

$\left(\sqrt{x+1}\right)^2 = 7^2$ *Square both sides.*

$x + 1 = 49$ *Simplify.*

$x = 48$ *Solve for x.*

Check $2\sqrt{x+1} = 14$

$2\sqrt{48+1}$	14
$2\sqrt{49}$	14
$2(7)$	14 ✓

B $5\sqrt[3]{4x+3} = 15$

$\frac{5\sqrt[3]{4x+3}}{5} = \frac{15}{5}$ *Divide by 5.*

$\sqrt[3]{4x+3} = 3$ *Simplify.*

$\left(\sqrt[3]{4x+3}\right)^3 = 3^3$ *Cube both sides.*

$4x + 3 = 27$ *Simplify.*

$4x = 24$ *Solve for x.*

$x = 6$

Check $5\sqrt[3]{4x+3} = 15$

$5\sqrt[3]{4(6)+3}$	15
$5\sqrt[3]{27}$	15
$5(3)$	15 ✓

Remember!
For a square root, the index of the radical is 2.
$\sqrt{x+1} = \sqrt[2]{x+1}$

Solve each equation.

1a. $4 + \sqrt{x-1} = 5$ **2** **1b.** $\sqrt[3]{3x-4} = 2$ **4** **1c.** $6\sqrt{x+10} = 42$ **39**

1 Introduce

EXPLORATION

8-8 Solving Radical Equations and Inequalities

An architect is designing the layout of an office building. One section of the building will consist of a row of 8 identical offices, each with a square-shaped floor.

1. Write an equation that represents the total area A of the offices in terms of s, the side length of each office.
2. Solve your equation from Problem 1 for s.
3. Use your calculator to help you complete the table.

Total Area (ft²)	Office Side Length (ft)
882	
968	
1058	
1152	
1250	

4. For what values of A does each office have a side length of at least 12 ft?

THINK AND DISCUSS

5. Give two equations you could use to determine the total area

Motivate

Ask students how they would solve the equation $x^2 = 49$. by taking the square root of both sides Then ask students how they think they could solve the equation $\sqrt{x} = 7$. by squaring both sides Lead students to realize that equality is preserved when they square both sides of this equation. Tell students that they will be using this property to solve radical equations.

Explorations and answers are provided in the *Explorations* binder.

State Resources

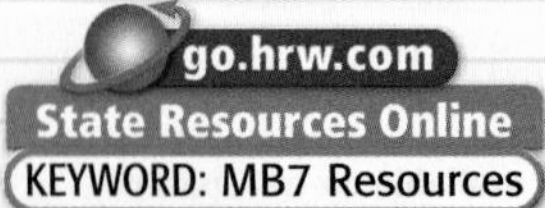

go.hrw.com State Resources Online KEYWORD: MB7 Resources

EXAMPLE 2 Solving Equations Containing Two Radicals

Solve $\sqrt{35x} = 5\sqrt{x+2}$.

$\left(\sqrt{35x}\right)^2 = \left(5\sqrt{x+2}\right)^2$ *Square both sides.*

$35x = 25(x+2)$ *Simplify.*

$35x = 25x + 50$ *Distribute 25.*

$10x = 50$ *Solve for x.*

$x = 5$

Check $\sqrt{35x} = 5\sqrt{x+2}$

$\sqrt{35 \cdot 5}$	$5\sqrt{5+2}$
$5\sqrt{7}$	$5\sqrt{7}$ ✔

CHECK IT OUT! Solve each equation.

2a. $\sqrt{8x+6} = 3\sqrt{x}$ 6 **2b.** $\sqrt[3]{x+6} = 2\sqrt[3]{x-1}$ 2

Raising each side of an equation to an even power may introduce extraneous solutions.

EXAMPLE 3 Solving Equations with Extraneous Solutions

Solve $\sqrt{x+18} = x - 2$.

Helpful Hint

You can also use the intersect feature on a graphing calculator to find the point where the two curves intersect.

Method 1 Use a graphing calculator. Let **Y1** $= \sqrt{x+18}$ and **Y2** $= x - 2$.

The graphs intersect in only one point, so there is exactly one solution.

The solution is $x = 7$.

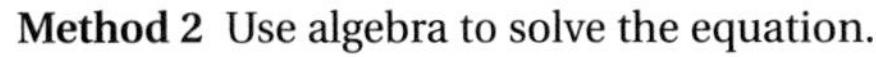

Method 2 Use algebra to solve the equation.

Step 1 Solve for x.

$\sqrt{x+18} = x - 2$

$\left(\sqrt{x+18}\right)^2 = (x-2)^2$ *Square both sides.*

$x + 18 = x^2 - 4x + 4$ *Simplify.*

$0 = x^2 - 5x - 14$ *Write in standard form.*

$0 = (x+2)(x-7)$ *Factor.*

$x + 2 = 0$ or $x - 7 = 0$ *Solve for x.*

$x = -2$ or $x = 7$

Step 2 Use substitution to check for extraneous solutions.

$\sqrt{x+18} = x - 2$

$\sqrt{-2+18}$	$-2-2$
$\sqrt{16}$	-4
4	-4 ✘

$\sqrt{x+18} = x - 2$

$\sqrt{7+18}$	$7-2$
$\sqrt{25}$	5
5	5 ✔

Because $x = -2$ is extraneous, the only solution is $x = 7$.

CHECK IT OUT! Solve each equation.

3a. $\sqrt{2x+14} = x + 3$ 1 **3b.** $\sqrt{-9x+28} = -x + 4$ −4, 3

2 Teach

Guided Instruction

Students have already solved many equations by performing the same operation on both sides to isolate the variable. Emphasize that they will be using the same procedure to solve radical equations. The only difference is that they will be adding a new operation—raising both sides of an equation to a power—and that this operation may introduce extraneous solutions.

Reaching All Learners

Through Communication

Discussing simple equations will help students understand why squaring both sides of a radical equation can produce extraneous solutions. Ask students why the equation $\sqrt{x} = -5$ has no real solution. The principal square root of a real number cannot be negative. Then square both sides to obtain $x = 25$. Discuss what happened when you squared both sides that "created" the extraneous solution of $x = 25$.

COMMON ERROR ALERT

When solving radical equations, students often forget that they must square the entire quantity on each side. Caution students not to square the terms individually when they are solving an equation like the one in **Example 3.** Point out that when both sides of this equation are squared, the right side becomes $(x-2)^2$, not $x^2 - 2^2$.

Power Presentations with PowerPoint®

Additional Examples

Example 1

Solve each equation.

A. $5 + \sqrt{x+1} = 16$ $x = 120$

B. $7\sqrt[3]{5x-7} = 84$ $x = 347$

Example 2

Solve $\sqrt{7x+2} = 3\sqrt{3x-2}$.

$x = 1$

Example 3

Solve $\sqrt{-3x+33} = 5 - x$.

$x = -1$

Also available on transparency

INTERVENTION

Questioning Strategies

EXAMPLE 1

- How do you isolate the radical?
- What is the index of the radical?

EXAMPLE 2

- How do you know to which power you should raise both sides of the equation?

EXAMPLE 3

- How can you tell whether the solution to a radical equation is extraneous?

Teaching Tip **Visual** Suggest that students circle or highlight the index of a radical equation so that they know to which power to raise each side of the equation when solving it. For square-root equations, they can write in the index of 2.

Power Presentations with PowerPoint®

Additional Examples

Example 4

Solve each equation.

A. $(5x + 7)^{\frac{1}{3}} = 3$ $x = 4$

B. $2x = (4x + 8)^{\frac{1}{2}}$ $x = 2$

Example 5

Solve $\sqrt{2x - 6} + 3 \le 9$.

$3 \le x \le 21$

Also available on transparency

INTERVENTION

Questioning Strategies

EXAMPLE 4

- How do you determine the reciprocal of an exponent?
- How do you rewrite an expression with a rational exponent in radical form?

EXAMPLE 5

- How can the intersect feature on your calculator help you solve radical inequalities by graphing?
- Why do you need to consider the sign of the radicand when solving radical inequalities algebraically?

You can use similar methods to solve equations containing rational exponents. You raise both sides of the equation to the reciprocal of the exponent. You can also rewrite any expressions with rational exponents in radical form and solve as you would other radical equations.

EXAMPLE 4 Solving Equations with Rational Exponents

Solve each equation.

A $(3x - 1)^{\frac{1}{5}} = 2$

$\sqrt[5]{3x - 1} = 2$ *Write in radical form.*

$\left(\sqrt[5]{3x - 1}\right)^5 = 2^5$ *Raise both sides to the fifth power.*

$3x - 1 = 32$ *Simplify.*

$3x = 33$ *Solve for x.*

$x = 11$

B $x = (x + 12)^{\frac{1}{2}}$

Step 1 Solve for x.

$x^2 = \left[(x + 12)^{\frac{1}{2}}\right]^2$ *Raise both sides to the reciprocal power.*

$x^2 = x + 12$ *Simplify.*

$x^2 - x - 12 = 0$ *Write in standard form.*

$(x + 3)(x - 4) = 0$ *Factor.*

$x + 3 = 0$ or $x - 4 = 0$ *Solve for x.*

$x = -3$ or $x = 4$

Step 2 Use substitution to check for extraneous solutions.

$x = (x + 12)^{\frac{1}{2}}$	
-3	$(-3 + 12)^{\frac{1}{2}}$
-3	$9^{\frac{1}{2}}$
-3	3 ✗

$x = (x + 12)^{\frac{1}{2}}$	
4	$(4 + 12)^{\frac{1}{2}}$
4	$16^{\frac{1}{2}}$
4	4 ✓

The only solution is $x = 4$.

Remember!

To find a power of a power, multiply the exponents.

$\left[(x + 12)^{\frac{1}{2}}\right]^2$

$(x + 12)^{\frac{1}{2} \cdot 2}$

$x + 12$

CHECK IT OUT! Solve each equation.

4a. $(x + 5)^{\frac{1}{3}} = 3$ **22** **4b.** $(2x + 15)^{\frac{1}{2}} = x$ **5** **4c.** $3(x + 6)^{\frac{1}{2}} = 9$ **3**

A **radical inequality** is an inequality that contains a variable within a radical. You can solve radical inequalities by graphing or by using algebra.

EXAMPLE 5 Solving Radical Inequalities

Solve $\sqrt{2x + 4} \le 4$.

Method 1 Use a graph and a table.

On a graphing calculator, let **Y1** $= \sqrt{2x + 4}$ and **Y2** $= 4$. The graph of **Y1** is at or below the graph of **Y2** for values of x between -2 and 6. Notice that **Y1** is undefined when $x < -2$.

The solution is $-2 \le x \le 6$.

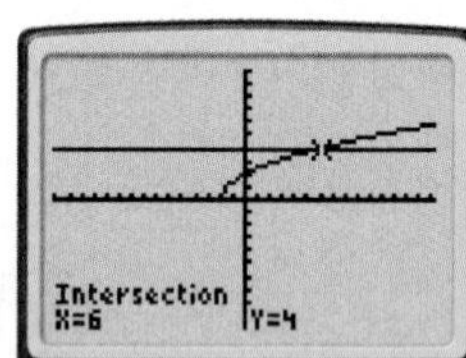

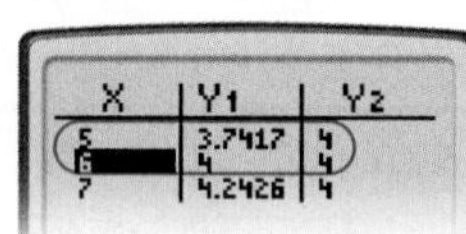

X	Y1	Y2
5	3.7417	4
6	4	4
7	4.2426	4

Teaching Tip **Critical Thinking** Extraneous solutions may be produced when both sides of an equation are raised to an even power, but not when they are raised to an odd power. For this reason, **Example 4B** was checked for extraneous solutions, but **Example 4A** was not. However, remind students that it is always a good idea to check their solutions to equations, regardless of whether the solutions might be extraneous.

Teaching Tip **Technology** For **Method 1** of **Examples 3** and **5,** discuss with students why they can conclude that the graphs of **Y1** and **Y2** intersect in only one point, based on the calculator screens shown. Point out that students can infer the behavior of both functions beyond the given window dimensions based on what they know about the parent functions of **Y1** and **Y2**.

Method 2 Use algebra to solve the inequality.

Step 1 Solve for x.

$\sqrt{2x+4} \le 4$

$\left(\sqrt{2x+4}\right)^2 \le (4)^2$ *Square both sides.*

$2x + 4 \le 16$ *Simplify.*

$2x \le 12$ *Solve for x.*

$x \le 6$

Step 2 Consider the radicand.

$2x + 4 \ge 0$ *The radicand cannot be negative.*

$2x \ge -4$ *Solve for x.*

$x \ge -2$

The solution of $\sqrt{2x+4} \le 4$ is $x \ge -2$ and $x \le 6$, or $-2 \le x \le 6$.

Remember!

A radical expression with an even index and a negative radicand has no real roots.

Solve each inequality.

5a. $\sqrt{x-3} + 2 \le 5$ $3 \le x \le 12$

5b. $\sqrt[3]{x+2} \ge 1$ $x \ge -1$

EXAMPLE 6 ***Automobile Application***

The speed s in miles per hour that a car is traveling when it goes into a skid can be estimated by using the formula $s = \sqrt{30fd}$, where f is the coefficient of friction and d is the length of the skid marks in feet.

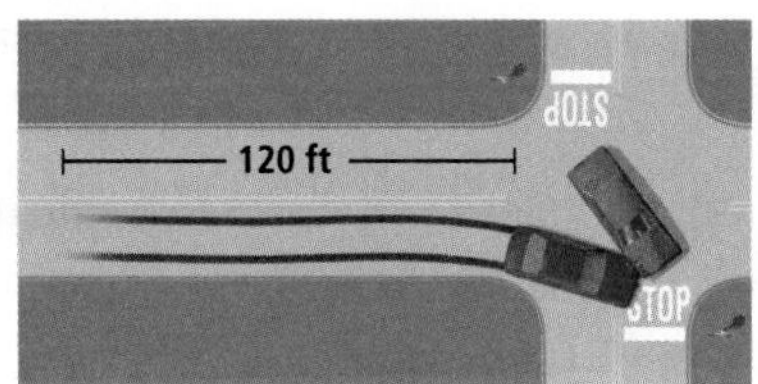

After an accident, a driver claims to have been traveling the speed limit of 45 mi/h. The coefficient of friction under accident conditions was 0.7. Is the driver telling the truth about his speed? Explain.

Use the formula to determine the greatest possible length of the driver's skid marks if he were traveling 45 mi/h.

$s = \sqrt{30fd}$

$45 = \sqrt{30(0.7)d}$ *Substitute 45 for s and 0.7 for f.*

$45 = \sqrt{21d}$ *Simplify.*

$(45)^2 = \left(\sqrt{21d}\right)^2$ *Square both sides.*

$2025 = 21d$ *Simplify.*

$96 \approx d$ *Solve for d.*

If the driver were traveling 45 mi/h, the skid marks would measure about 96 ft. Because the skid marks actually measure 120 ft, the driver must have been driving faster than 45 mi/h.

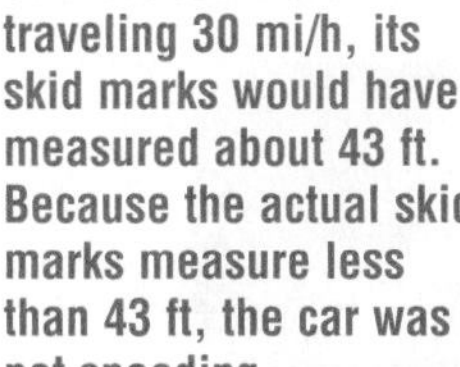

6. If the car were traveling 30 mi/h, its skid marks would have measured about 43 ft. Because the actual skid marks measure less than 43 ft, the car was not speeding.

6. A car skids to a stop on a street with a speed limit of 30 mi/h. The skid marks measure 35 ft, and the coefficient of friction was 0.7. Was the car speeding? Explain.

Power Presentations with PowerPoint®

Additional Examples

Example 6

The time t in seconds that it takes a car to travel a quarter mile when starting from a full stop can be estimated by using the formula $t = 5.825\sqrt[3]{\frac{w}{P}}$, where w is the weight of the car in pounds and P is the power delivered by the engine in horsepower. If the quarter-mile time for a 3590 lb car is 13.4 s, how much power does its engine deliver? Round to the nearest horsepower. 295 hp

Also available on transparency

INTERVENTION

Questioning Strategies

EXAMPLE 6

- For which variable do you need to solve the equation?
- How can you use the information in the problem to determine the values of the other variables?
- How can you check that your answer is reasonable?

Science Link In **Example 6,** point out that the coefficient of friction f depends on a number of factors, including the mass of the vehicle, the condition of its tires, and the condition and slope of the road.

3 Close

Summarize

Review the process for solving radical equations.

- If the equation contains a single radical, isolate the radical.
- Raise both sides of the equation to the power equal to the index of the radical.
- Simplify and solve for the variable.
- Check for extraneous solutions.

Review the similar process for solving square-root inequalities. Emphasize the importance of considering the sign of the radicand when solving these inequalities.

ONGOING ASSESSMENT and INTERVENTION

***Diagnose* Before the Lesson**
8-8 Warm Up, TE p. 628

***Monitor* During the Lesson**
Check It Out! Exercises, SE pp. 628–631
Questioning Strategies, TE pp. 629–631

***Assess* After the Lesson**
8-8 Lesson Quiz, TE p. 635
Alternative Assessment, TE p. 635

Answers to *Think and Discuss*

Possible answers:

1. The equation can be solved algebraically by squaring both sides, or it can be solved by graphing both sides of the equation.
2. To solve $x^2 = a$, take the square root of each side. To solve $\sqrt{x} = b$, square each side. The operations used to solve each equation are inverses of each other.
3. See p. A10.

THINK AND DISCUSS

1. Describe two methods that can be used to solve $\sqrt{x+2} = 6$.
2. Explain the relationship between solving a quadratic equation of the form $x^2 = a$ and a square-root equation of the form $\sqrt{x} = b$, where a and b are real numbers.

3. **GET ORGANIZED** Copy and complete the graphic organizer. In each box, write a step needed to solve a radical equation with extraneous solutions.

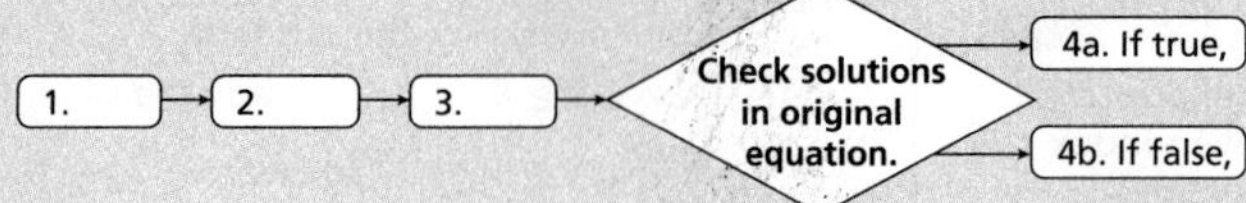

8-8 Exercises

8-8 Exercises

Assignment Guide

Assign *Guided Practice* exercises as necessary.

If you finished Examples **1–3**
Basic 27–38, 47–49
Average 27–38, 47–49
Advanced 27–38, 47–49

If you finished Examples **1–6**
Basic 27–59, 61–66, 75–81
Average 27–66, 74–81
Advanced 27–53, 55–81

Homework Quick Check
Quickly check key concepts.
Exercises: 28, 34, 36, 40, 42, 45, 46

GUIDED PRACTICE

1. **Vocabulary** Is $4x + \sqrt{9} = 5$ a *radical equation*? Explain. **No; the expression under the radical does not contain a variable.**

SEE EXAMPLE 1 p. 628

Solve each equation.

2. $\sqrt{x-9} = 5$ **34**
3. $\sqrt{3x} = 6$ **12**
4. $\sqrt[3]{x-2} = 2$ **10**

SEE EXAMPLE 2 p. 629

5. $\sqrt{3x-1} = \sqrt{2x+4}$ **5**
6. $2\sqrt{x} = \sqrt{x+9}$ **3**
7. $\sqrt[5]{x+4} = \sqrt[5]{3x-2}$ **3**
8. $2\sqrt[3]{x} = \sqrt[3]{x+7}$ **1**
9. $\sqrt{x+6} - \sqrt{2x-4} = 0$ **10**
10. $4\sqrt{x+1} = 3\sqrt{x+2}$ **$\frac{2}{7}$**

SEE EXAMPLE 3 p. 629

11. $\sqrt{x+56} = x$ **8**
12. $\sqrt{x+18} = x-2$ **7**
13. $\sqrt{3x-11} = x-3$ **4, 5**
14. $\sqrt{x+6} - x = 4$ **−2**
15. $\sqrt{-x-1} = x+1$ **−1**
16. $\sqrt{15x+10} = 2x+3$ **$-\frac{1}{4}$, 1**

SEE EXAMPLE 4 p. 630

17. $(x-5)^{\frac{1}{2}} = 3$ **14**
18. $(2x+1)^{\frac{1}{3}} = 2$ **$\frac{7}{2}$**
19. $(4x+5)^{\frac{1}{2}} = x$ **5**
20. $2(x-50)^{\frac{1}{3}} = -10$ **−75**
21. $2(x+1)^{\frac{1}{2}} = 1$ **$-\frac{3}{4}$**
22. $(45-9x)^{\frac{1}{2}} = x-5$ **5**

SEE EXAMPLE 5 p. 630

Solve each inequality.

23. $\sqrt{x+5} - 1 \le 4$
24. $\sqrt{2x} + 6 \le 10$
25. $\sqrt{2x+5} < 5$

SEE EXAMPLE 6 p. 631

26. **Stunts** The formula $s = \sqrt{21d}$ relates a stunt car's speed s in miles per hour at the beginning of a skid to the length d of the skid in feet. A stunt driver must skid her car to a stop just in front of a wall. When the driver starts her skid, she is traveling at 64 mi/h. When the driver comes to a stop, how many feet will be between her car and the wall? Round to the nearest foot. **5 ft**

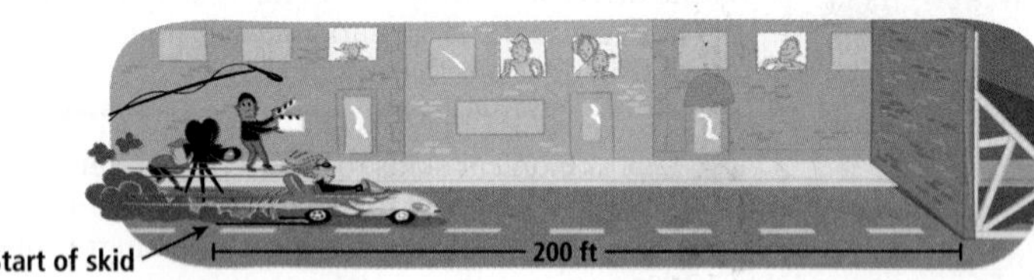

State Resources

8-8 PRACTICE A

Rewrite each equation to isolate the radical.

1. $\sqrt{x} - 6 = 0$ — $\sqrt{x} = 6$
2. $8 + \sqrt{3x} - x = 0$ — $\sqrt{3x} = x - 8$
3. $\sqrt{2x+1} - 17 = 3x$ — $\sqrt{2x+1} = 3x + 17$

Identify to what power each equation must be raised in order to solve. Then solve.

4. $\sqrt{x} = 4$ — $2;\ x = 16$
5. $\sqrt[4]{3x} = 12$ — $4;\ x = \frac{69}{2}$
6. $\sqrt[3]{x+1} = 4$ — $3;\ x = 63$

Solve the equation. Then identify any extraneous solutions.

7. $2\sqrt{x+2} = 4$ — $x = 2$; no extraneous solutions
8. $\sqrt{x+3} = x - 3$ — $x = 1$, $x = 6$; $x = 1$ is an extraneous solution.

Solve each equation or inequality.

9. $\sqrt{x+2} = 5$ — $x = 23$
10. $(4x)^{\frac{1}{2}} = 6$ — $x = 9$
11. $(x+1)^{\frac{1}{3}} = 3$ — $x = 26$
12. $2\sqrt{x-3} = 10$ — $x = 28$
13. $\sqrt{2x} - 6 < 0$ — $0 \le x < 18$
14. $\sqrt{3x+1} \ge 8$ — $x \ge 21$

Solve.

15. Ainsley and Ben each solve the inequality $\sqrt{x+3} + 5 \le 10$. Ainsley's solution is $x \le 22$. Ben's solution is $-3 \le x \le 22$. Why are their solutions different? Which is correct?

Ben's solution is correct. Ainsley forgot that the radicand cannot be negative.

8-8 PRACTICE B

Solve each equation.

1. $\sqrt{x+6} = 7$ — $x = 43$
2. $\sqrt{5x} = 10$ — $x = 20$
3. $\sqrt{2x+5} = \sqrt{3x-1}$ — $x = 6$
4. $\sqrt{x+4} = 3\sqrt{x}$ — $x = \frac{1}{2}$
5. $\sqrt[3]{x-6} = \sqrt[3]{3x+24}$ — $x = -15$
6. $3\sqrt[3]{x} = \sqrt[3]{7x+5}$ — $x = \frac{1}{4}$
7. $\sqrt{-14x+2} = x - 3$ — No solutions, since both −1 and −7 are extraneous
8. $(x+4)^{\frac{1}{2}} = 6$ — $x = 32$
9. $4(x-3)^{\frac{1}{2}} = 8$ — $x = 7$
10. $4(x-12)^{\frac{1}{3}} = -16$ — $x = -52$

Solve each inequality.

11. $\sqrt{3x+6} \le 3$ — $-2 \le x \le 1$
12. $\sqrt{x-4} + 3 > 9$ — $x > 40$
13. $\sqrt{x+7} \ge \sqrt{2x-1}$ — $\frac{1}{2} \le x \le 8$
14. $\sqrt{2x-7} > 9$ — $x > 44$

Solve.

15. A biologist is studying two species of animals in a habitat. The population, p_1, of one of the species is growing according to $p_1 = 500t^{\frac{3}{2}}$ and the population, p_2, of the other species is growing according to $p_2 = 100t^2$ where time, t, is measured in years. After how many years will the populations of the two species be equal?

25 years

PRACTICE AND PROBLEM SOLVING

Independent Practice	
For Exercises	See Example
27–32	1
33–35	2
36–38	3
39–41	4
42–44	5
45	6

Extra Practice

Skills Practice p. S19
Application Practice p. S39

Solve each equation.

27. $\sqrt{x-12}=9$ 93
28. $\sqrt[3]{2x+1}-3=0$ 13
29. $5\sqrt{x+7}=25$ 18
30. $\sqrt[4]{2x+6}=2$ 5
31. $3=\frac{1}{4}\sqrt{3x+30}$ 38
32. $-3=2\sqrt{x-7}-7$ 11
33. $\sqrt{4x+12}=\sqrt{6x}$ 6
34. $5\sqrt{x-1}=\sqrt{x+1}$ $\frac{13}{12}$
35. $\sqrt[3]{4x}=\sqrt[3]{x+7}$ $\frac{7}{3}$
36. $x+3=\sqrt{x+5}$ −1
37. $\sqrt{3x+13}+3=2x$ 4
38. $\sqrt{x+8}-x=-4$ 8
39. $(x-9)^{\frac{1}{2}}=4$ 25
40. $(5x+1)^{\frac{1}{4}}=4$ 51
41. $(3x+28)^{\frac{1}{2}}=x$ 7

Solve each inequality.

42. $\sqrt{3x+3}\le 6$ $-1\le x\le 11$
43. $\sqrt{x-3}\le 4$ $3\le x\le 19$
44. $\sqrt{8x+1}\ge 7$ $x\ge 6$

45. **Construction** The diameter d in inches of a rope needed to lift a weight of w tons is given by the formula $d=\frac{\sqrt{15w}}{\pi}$. How much weight can be lifted with a rope with a diameter of 1.5 in.? about 1.5 tons

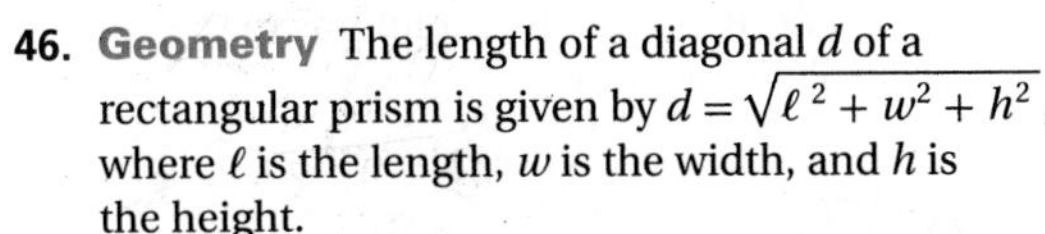

46. **Geometry** The length of a diagonal d of a rectangular prism is given by $d=\sqrt{\ell^2+w^2+h^2}$, where ℓ is the length, w is the width, and h is the height.

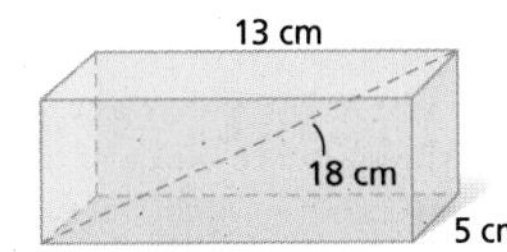

a. What is the height of the prism shown? Round to the nearest tenth. 11.4 cm

b. **What if...?** Suppose that the length, width, and height of the prism are doubled. What effect will this change have on the length of the diagonal? The length of the diagonal will double.

Solve each equation for the indicated variable.

47. $r=\sqrt{\frac{A}{\pi}}$ for A $A=\pi r^2$
48. $r=\sqrt[3]{\frac{3V}{4\pi}}$ for V $V=\frac{4}{3}\pi r^3$
49. $v=\sqrt{\frac{2E}{m}}$ for E $E=\frac{1}{2}mv^2$

LINK

Tornadoes

The Fujita Tornado Scale goes up to category F12, even though scientists expect that Earth's most powerful tornadoes will reach wind speeds of no higher than those of category F5.

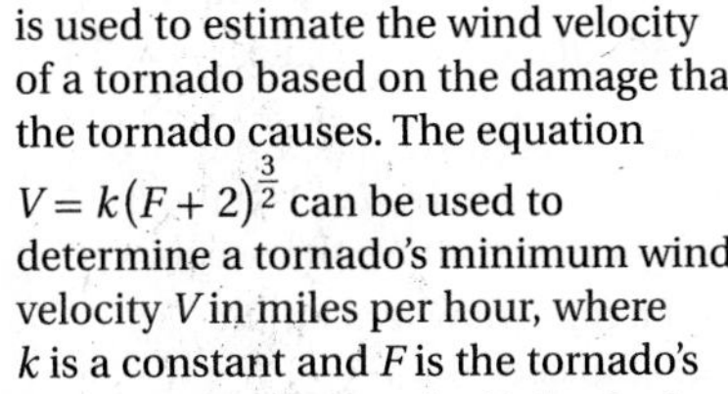

50. **Tornadoes** The Fujita Tornado Scale is used to estimate the wind velocity of a tornado based on the damage that the tornado causes. The equation $V=k(F+2)^{\frac{3}{2}}$ can be used to determine a tornado's minimum wind velocity V in miles per hour, where k is a constant and F is the tornado's category number on the Fujita Scale.

Fujita Tornado Scale

Damage Level	Category	Minimum Wind Velocity (mi/h)
Moderate	F1	73
Significant	F2	113
Severe	F3	158
Devastating	F4	207
Incredible	F5	261

a. Based on the information in the table, what is the value of the constant k? about 14

b. What would be the minimum wind velocity of an F6 tornado? about 317 mi/h

c. Winds on Neptune can reach velocities of more than 600 mi/h. Use the equation given above to determine the Fujita category of this wind velocity. F10

51. **Amusement Parks** For a spinning amusement park ride, the velocity v in meters per second of a car moving around a curve with a radius r meters is given by $v=\sqrt{ar}$, where a is the car's acceleration in m/s^2.

a. For safety reasons, a ride has a maximum acceleration of 39.2 m/s^2. If the cars on the ride have a velocity of 14 m/s, what is the smallest radius that any curve on the ride may have? 5 m

b. What is the acceleration of a car moving at 8 m/s around a curve with a radius of 2.5 m? 25.6 m/s^2

COMMON ERROR ALERT

When solving square-root inequalities, as in **Exercises 42–44,** students might forget that they must exclude any values of x that make the radicand negative. Remind students that they can determine these values by setting the radicand greater than or equal to 0 and then solving.

Teaching Tip

Geometry As an extension to **Exercise 46,** you may wish to have students derive the formula for the diagonal of a rectangular prism by using the Pythagorean Theorem: Let x represent the diagonal of the prism's base. By the Pythagorean Theorem, $x=\sqrt{\ell^2+w^2}$ and $d=\sqrt{x^2+h^2}$. By substitution,

$$d=\sqrt{\left(\sqrt{\ell^2+w^2}\right)^2+h^2}$$
$$=\sqrt{\ell^2+w^2+h^2}.$$

Answers

23. $-5\le x\le 20$
24. $0\le x\le 8$
25. $-\frac{5}{2}\le x<10$

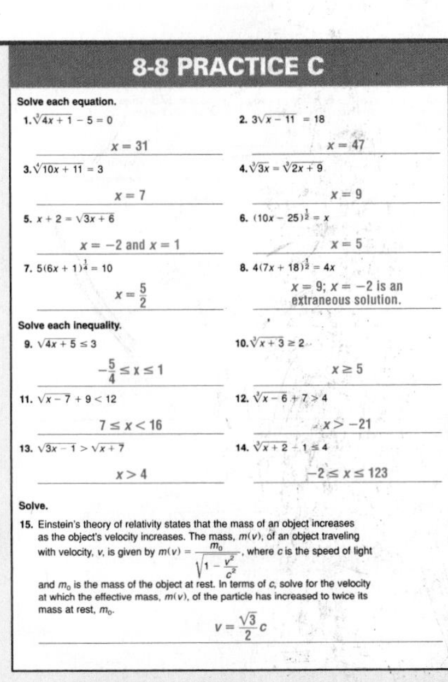

8-8 PRACTICE C

Solve each equation.

1. $\sqrt[3]{4x+1}-5=0$ — $x=31$
2. $3\sqrt{x-11}=18$ — $x=47$
3. $\sqrt[4]{10x+11}=3$ — $x=7$
4. $\sqrt[3]{3x}=\sqrt[3]{2x+9}$ — $x=9$
5. $x+2=\sqrt{3x+6}$ — $x=-2$ and $x=1$
6. $(10x-25)^{\frac{1}{2}}=x$ — $x=5$
7. $5(6x+1)^{\frac{1}{4}}=10$ — $x=\frac{5}{2}$
8. $4(7x+18)^{\frac{1}{2}}=4x$ — $x=9$; $x=-2$ is an extraneous solution.

Solve each inequality.

9. $\sqrt{4x+5}\le 3$ — $-\frac{5}{4}\le x\le 1$
10. $\sqrt[3]{x+3}\ge 2$ — $x\ge 5$
11. $\sqrt{x-7}+9<12$ — $7\le x<16$
12. $\sqrt[3]{x-6}+7>4$ — $x>-21$
13. $\sqrt{3x-1}>\sqrt{x+7}$ — $x>4$
14. $\sqrt[3]{x+2}-1\le 4$ — $-2\le x\le 123$

Solve.

15. Einstein's theory of relativity states that the mass of an object increases as the object's velocity increases. The mass, $m(v)$, of an object traveling with velocity, v, is given by $m(v)=\frac{m_0}{\sqrt{1-\frac{v^2}{c^2}}}$, where c is the speed of light and m_0 is the mass of the object at rest. In terms of c, solve for the velocity at which the effective mass, $m(v)$, of the particle has increased to twice its mass at rest, m_0. $v=\frac{\sqrt{3}}{2}c$

MULTI-STEP TEST PREP Exercise 52 involves solving a radical equation related to pendulums. This exercise prepares students for the Multi-Step Test Prep on page 636.

Answers

53a. $r \le \sqrt{\frac{A}{\pi}}$

b. No; if $A = 80$, then r must be less than or equal to about 5.04. Therefore, 20 would not be a reasonable value of r.

54. Solution B is incorrect. Possible answer: In the first step, the coefficient of the radical should have been squared along with the rest of the equation.

55. $x \approx 5.84$

56. $x \approx -2.38$ or $x \approx -12.42$

57. $x \approx 2.35$

60. Possible answer: Subtracting 5 from each side results in the equation $\sqrt{5x + 17} = -7$. Because the $\sqrt{\ }$ symbol indicates the principal, or nonnegative, square root, the value of the left side of the equation cannot be negative. Therefore, the equation has no real solution.

75b.

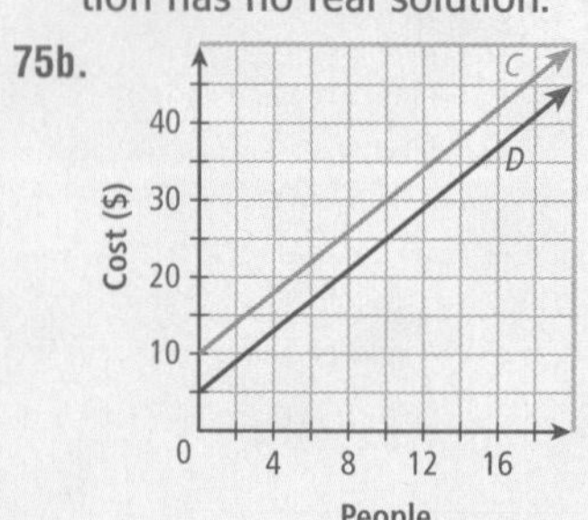

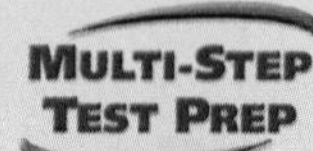

52. This problem will prepare you for the Multi-Step Test Prep on page 636.

The time T in seconds for a pendulum to complete one back-and-forth swing is given by $T = 2\pi\sqrt{\frac{L}{9.8}}$, where L is the length of the pendulum in meters.

a. Find the length of a pendulum that completes one back-and-forth swing in 2.2 s. Round to the nearest hundredth of a meter. **1.20 m**

b. A clockmaker needs a pendulum that will complete 120 back-and-forth swings in one minute. To the nearest hundredth of a meter, how long should the pendulum be? **0.06 m**

53. **Art** Gabriel plans to cover a circular area on a mural with yellow paint.

a. Write a radical inequality that can be used to determine the possible radius r of the circle given that Gabriel has enough paint to cover at most A ft^2.

b. If Gabriel can cover up to 80 ft^2, is 20 a reasonable value of r? Explain.

54. **///ERROR ANALYSIS///** Below are two solutions to the equation $2\sqrt{3x+3} = 12$. Which is incorrect? Explain the error.

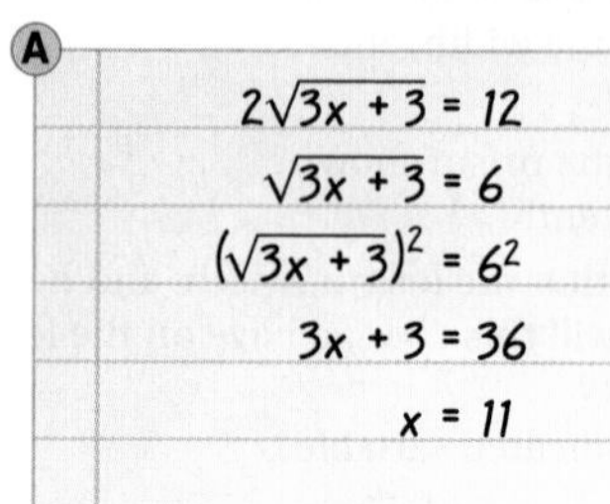

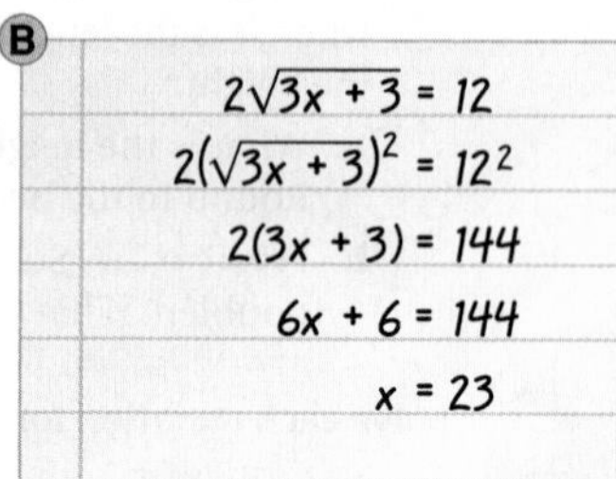

Graphing Calculator Use a graphing calculator to solve each equation. Graph each side of the equation on the same screen, and find the point(s) of intersection.

55. $1.6x - 4 = 1.4\sqrt{x + 8.7}$

56. $3(x + 7.4)^{\frac{2}{3}} = 8.8$

57. $\sqrt[3]{x^2 + 4.2} = 2.7x - 4.2$

58. **Multi-Step** On a clear day, the approximate distance d in miles that a person can see is given by $d = 1.2116\sqrt{h}$, where h is the person's height in feet above the ocean.

a. To the nearest tenth of a mile, how far can the captain on the clipper ship see? **4.7 mi**

b. How much farther, to the nearest tenth of a mile, will the sailor be able to see than will the captain? **8.6 mi farther**

c. A pirate ship is approaching the clipper ship at a relative speed of 10 mi/h. Approximately how many minutes sooner will the sailor be able to see the pirate ship than will the captain? **about 52 min sooner**

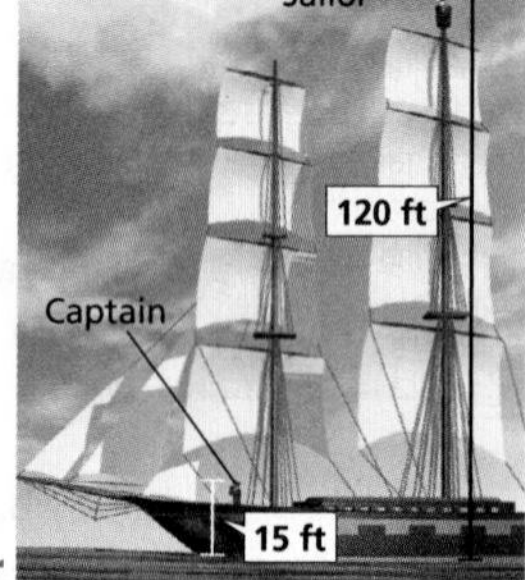

59. **Chemistry** The formula $s = \sqrt[3]{\frac{m}{\rho}}$ relates the side length s of a metal cube to its mass m and its density ρ. The density of gold is 19.30 g/cm^3, and the density of lead is 11.34 g/cm^3. How much greater is the mass of a cube of gold than the mass of a cube of lead if both cubes have a side length of 5 cm? **995 g**

60. **Critical Thinking** Without solving the equation, how can you tell that $\sqrt{5x + 17} + 5 = 2$ has no real solutions?

61. **Write About It** Describe how solving a radical equation is similar to solving a rational equation. **Possible answer: When solving both types of equations, you must check for extraneous solutions.**

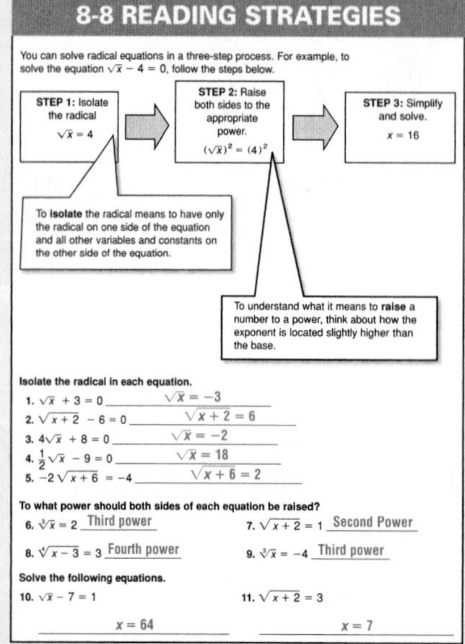

8-8 READING STRATEGIES

You can solve radical equations in a three-step process. For example, to solve the equation $\sqrt{x} - 4 = 0$, follow the steps below.

STEP 1: Isolate the radical
$\sqrt{x} = 4$

STEP 2: Raise both sides to the appropriate power.
$(\sqrt{x})^2 = (4)^2$

STEP 3: Simplify and solve.
$x = 16$

To **isolate** the radical means to have only the radical on one side of the equation and all other variables and constants on the other side of the equation.

To understand what it means to **raise** a number to a power, think about how the exponent is located slightly higher than the base.

Isolate the radical in each equation.

1. $\sqrt{x} + 3 = 0$ $\sqrt{x} = -3$
2. $\sqrt{x+2} - 6 = 0$ $\sqrt{x+2} = 6$
3. $4\sqrt{x} + 8 = 0$ $\sqrt{x} = -2$
4. $\frac{1}{2}\sqrt{x} - 9 = 0$ $\sqrt{x} = 18$
5. $-2\sqrt{x+6} = -4$ $\sqrt{x+6} = 2$

To what power should both sides of each equation be raised?

6. $\sqrt[3]{x} = 2$ Third power
7. $\sqrt{x+2} = 1$ Second Power
8. $\sqrt[4]{x-3} = 3$ Fourth power
9. $\sqrt[3]{x} = -4$ Third power

Solve the following equations.

10. $\sqrt{x} - 7 = 1$ $x = 64$
11. $\sqrt{x+2} = 3$ $x = 7$

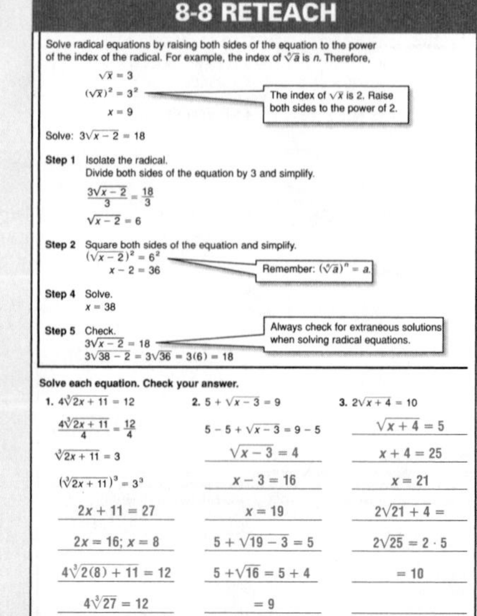

8-8 RETEACH

Solve radical equations by raising both sides of the equation to the power of the index of the radical. For example, the index of $\sqrt[n]{a}$ is n. Therefore,

$\sqrt{x} = 3$
$(\sqrt{x})^2 = 3^2$
$x = 9$

The index of $\sqrt{x}$ is 2. Raise both sides to the power of 2.

Solve: $3\sqrt{x-2} = 18$

Step 1 Isolate the radical.
Divide both sides of the equation by 3 and simplify.
$\frac{3\sqrt{x-2}}{3} = \frac{18}{3}$
$\sqrt{x-2} = 6$

Step 2 Square both sides of the equation and simplify.
$(\sqrt{x-2})^2 = 6^2$
$x - 2 = 36$

Remember: $(\sqrt[n]{a})^n = a$.

Step 4 Solve.
$x = 38$

Step 5 Check.
$3\sqrt{x-2} = 18$
$3\sqrt{38-2} = 3\sqrt{36} = 3(6) = 18$

Always check for extraneous solutions when solving radical equations.

Solve each equation. Check your answer.

1. $4\sqrt[3]{2x+11} = 12$
$\frac{4\sqrt[3]{2x+11}}{4} = \frac{12}{4}$
$\sqrt[3]{2x+11} = 3$
$(\sqrt[3]{2x+11})^3 = 3^3$
$2x + 11 = 27$
$2x = 16; x = 8$
$4\sqrt[3]{2(8)+11} = 12$
$4\sqrt[3]{27} = 12$

2. $5 + \sqrt{x-3} = 9$
$5 - 5 + \sqrt{x-3} = 9 - 5$
$\sqrt{x-3} = 4$
$x - 3 = 16$
$x = 19$
$5 + \sqrt{19-3} = 5$
$5 + \sqrt{16} = 5 + 4$
$= 9$

3. $2\sqrt{x+4} = 10$
$\sqrt{x+4} = 5$
$x + 4 = 25$
$x = 21$
$2\sqrt{21+4} =$
$2\sqrt{25} = 2 \cdot 5$
$= 10$

TEST PREP

62. Solve $\sqrt[3]{2x+4} = 3$.
(A) −0.5 (B) −1.5 (C) 2.5 **(D) 11.5**

63. How many solutions does $x - 1 = \sqrt{5x - 9}$ have?
(F) 0 (G) 1 **(H) 2** (J) 3

64. The surface area S of a cone is given by the formula $S = \pi\sqrt{r^2 + h^2}$, where r is the radius of the base and h is the height. What is the approximate height of a cone with a surface area of 40 square inches and a base radius of 8 inches?
(A) 5 inches (C) 15 inches
(B) 10 inches (D) 20 inches

65. The equation $V = \left(\frac{A}{6}\right)^{\frac{3}{2}}$ relates the volume V of a cube to its surface area A. Which of the following is equivalent to this equation?
(F) $A = 6V^{\frac{2}{3}}$ (G) $A = (6V)^{\frac{2}{3}}$ (H) $A = 36V^{\frac{1}{3}}$ (J) $A = (216V)^{\frac{1}{2}}$

66. **Gridded Response** What value of x makes $(2x - 3)^{\frac{1}{4}} = 3$ a true statement? **42**

CHALLENGE AND EXTEND

Indicate whether each of the following statements is sometimes, always, or never true. Equations of the form $\sqrt{x + a} = b$ have at least one real solution when

67. Both a and b are positive. **always true**

68. Both a and b are negative. **never true**

69. a is negative and b is positive. **always true**

70. a is positive and b is negative. **never true**

Solve each equation.

71. $\sqrt{x} = \frac{9}{\sqrt{x}}$ **9**

72. $\sqrt{\sqrt{x+2}} = 4$ **254**

73. $\sqrt{x^2 - 64} = x - 4$ **10**

74. **Biology** The surface area S of a human body in square meters can be approximated by $S = \sqrt{\frac{hm}{36}}$, where h is height in meters and m is mass in kilograms. Between the ages of 4 and 17, an athlete's height increased by 75% and mass increased by 350%. By approximately what percent did the surface area of the athlete's skin increase? **The surface area increased by about 181%.**

SPIRAL REVIEW

75. **Entertainment** The cost of driving through a safari park is \$2.00 per person and \$10.00 per car. For each car, the total cost C can be modeled by the function $C(n) = 2.00n + 10.00$, where n is the number of people. *(Lesson 2-6)*
   a. The manager of the park announces a half-price discount on the charge per car. Write the new cost function $D(n)$. Assume that the charge per person does not change. **$D(n) = 2.00n + 5.00$**
   b. Graph $C(n)$ and $D(n)$ in the same coordinate plane.
   c. Describe the transformation that has been applied. **vertical translation 5 units down**

Use inverse operations to write the inverse of each function. *(Lesson 7-2)*

76. $f(x) = \frac{x}{2} + 4$ **$f^{-1}(x) = 2x - 8$**

77. $f(x) = -3x - 1$ **$f^{-1}(x) = -\frac{1}{3}x - \frac{1}{3}$**

78. $f(x) = \frac{x-2}{7}$ **$f^{-1}(x) = 7x + 2$**

Simplify each expression. Assume that all variables are positive. *(Lesson 8-6)*

79. $\sqrt[3]{64x^9}$ **$4x^3$**

80. $\sqrt[4]{\frac{x^8}{81}}$ **$\frac{x^2}{3}$**

81. $\sqrt[3]{\frac{18x^2}{x^4}}$ **$\frac{\sqrt[3]{18x}}{x}$**

TEST PREP DOCTOR In **Exercise 62,** students who chose **A** may have forgotten to cube the right side of the equation. Students who chose **C** may have multiplied the right side of the equation by 3 instead of raising it to the third power.

Teaching Tip **Number Sense** In **Exercise 74,** point out that if the athlete's height increases by 75%, his new height is equal to $h + 0.75h$, or $1.75h$. If the athlete's mass increases by 350%, his new mass is equal to $m + 3.5m$, or $4.5m$.

Journal

Have students describe two methods that can be used to solve an equation with a rational exponent.

ALTERNATIVE ASSESSMENT

Have students create, or choose from the exercises, a radical equation and a radical inequality. Ask students to explain each step in the solution process of the equation and the inequality. Have them describe how they can check their answers.

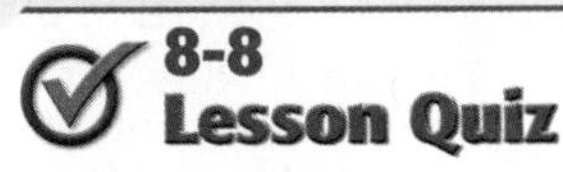

8-8 Lesson Quiz

Solve each equation or inequality.

1. $7 + \sqrt{2x + 4} = 13$ $x = 16$
2. $3\sqrt[3]{x + 4} = \sqrt[3]{2x - 17}$ $x = -5$
3. $\sqrt{2x + 12} = x + 2$ $x = 2$
4. $4(x - 5)^{\frac{1}{2}} = 12$ $x = 14$
5. $\sqrt[3]{x + 5} \geq 4$ $x \geq 59$
6. The radius r in feet of a spherical water tank can be determined by using the formula $r = \sqrt[3]{\frac{3V}{4\pi}}$, where V is the volume of the tank in cubic feet. To the nearest cubic foot, what is the volume of a spherical tank with a radius of 32 ft? 137,258 ft^3

Also available on transparency

8-8 PROBLEM SOLVING

The formula $s = \sqrt{30fd}$ can be used to estimate the speed, s, in miles per hour that a car is traveling when it goes into a skid, where f is the coefficient of friction and d is the length of the skid marks in feet.

1. How does the speed vary as the length of the skid marks? **Directly**
2. Kody skids to a stop on a street with a speed limit of 35 mi/h. His skid marks measure 52 ft, and the coefficient of friction is 0.7. Kody says that he was driving only about 30 mi/h. Kody wants to prove that he was not speeding.
   a. Solve the equation for d in terms of s. **$d = \frac{s^2}{30f}$**
   b. How long would the skid marks be if he had been driving at a speed of 35 mi/h? **About 58 ft**
   c. Was Kody speeding or not? Explain how you know. **No; possible answer: his skid marks were only 52 ft, not 58 ft.**
   d. Find his actual speed. **About 33 mi/h**
3. Ashley skids to a stop on a street with a speed limit of 15 mi/h to avoid a dog who runs into the street about 20 ft ahead of her. Ashley claims to have been going less than 15 mi/h. The coefficient of friction is 0.7.
   a. If Ashley were driving the speed limit, by what distance would she have missed the dog? **About 9 ft**
   b. If Ashley were driving less than 10 mi/h, by what distance would she have missed the dog? **By at least 15 ft**

Choose the letter for the best answer.

4. Barney was driving at 25 mi/h. A car pulls out 30 ft ahead of him. Which statement is true?
   A Barney hits the car.
   (B) Barney stops less than a foot from the car.
   C Barney misses the car by 3 ft.
   D Barney's skid marks measure 23 ft.
5. On a busy highway with a speed limit of 70 mi/h, a truck ahead of Verna jackknifes across the road. Verna skids to a stop 10 ft short of the truck. Her skid marks measure 260 ft. Was Verna speeding?
   (A) Yes; her speed was 73.9 mi/h.
   B Yes; her speed was 75.3 mi/h.
   C No; her speed was 70 mi/h.
   D No; her speed was only 63 mi/h.

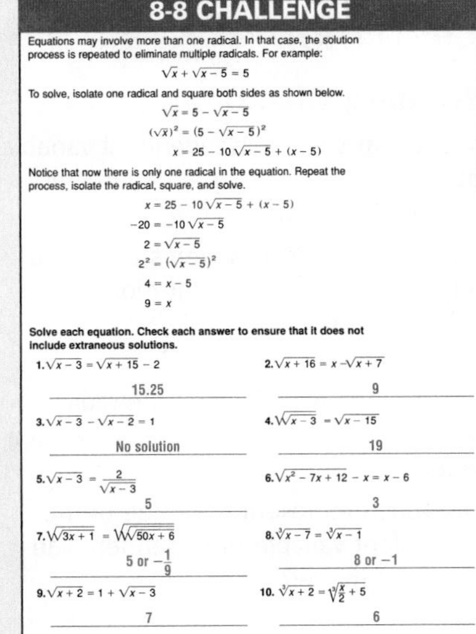

8-8 CHALLENGE

Equations may involve more than one radical. In that case, the solution process is repeated to eliminate multiple radicals. For example:

$$\sqrt{x} + \sqrt{x - 5} = 5$$

To solve, isolate one radical and square both sides as shown below.

$$\sqrt{x} = 5 - \sqrt{x-5}$$
$$(\sqrt{x})^2 = (5 - \sqrt{x-5})^2$$
$$x = 25 - 10\sqrt{x-5} + (x - 5)$$

Notice that now there is only one radical in the equation. Repeat the process, isolate the radical, square, and solve.

$$x = 25 - 10\sqrt{x-5} + (x - 5)$$
$$-20 = -10\sqrt{x-5}$$
$$2 = \sqrt{x-5}$$
$$2^2 = (\sqrt{x-5})^2$$
$$4 = x - 5$$
$$9 = x$$

Solve each equation. Check each answer to ensure that it does not include extraneous solutions.

1. $\sqrt{x-3} = \sqrt{x+15} - 2$ **15.25**
2. $\sqrt{x+16} = x - \sqrt{x+7}$ **9**
3. $\sqrt{x-3} - \sqrt{x-2} = 1$ **No solution**
4. $\sqrt{\sqrt{x-3}} = \sqrt{x-15}$ **19**
5. $\sqrt{x-3} = \frac{2}{\sqrt{x-3}}$ **5**
6. $\sqrt{x^2 - 7x + 12} - x = x - 6$ **3**
7. $\sqrt{\sqrt{3x+1}} = \sqrt{\sqrt{\sqrt{50x+6}}}$ **5 or $-\frac{1}{9}$**
8. $\sqrt[3]{x-7} = \sqrt[3]{x-1}$ **8 or −1**
9. $\sqrt{x+2} = 1 + \sqrt{x-3}$ **7**
10. $\sqrt[3]{x+2} = \sqrt[3]{\frac{x}{2} + 5}$ **6**

SECTION 8B MULTI-STEP TEST PREP

Organizer

Objective: Assess students' ability to apply concepts and skills in Lessons 8-6 through 8-8 in a real-world format.

Online Edition

Resources

Algebra II Assessments
www.mathtekstoolkit.org

For additional assessment activities, see www.utdanacenter.org.

Problems	Text Reference
1–3	Lesson 8-7
4	Lesson 8-6
5	Lesson 8-8
6	Lesson 8-7

Answers

1. See p. A39.
2. Possible answer: $y = 0.2\sqrt{x}$; the model is a vertical compression of $f(x) = \sqrt{x}$ by a factor of 0.2.
3. Possible answer: Real numbers greater than or equal to 0 and less than about 5000; the length of a pendulum cannot be negative and is unlikely to be longer than 5000 cm (50 m).
6. See p. A39.

State Resources

go.hrw.com
State Resources Online
KEYWORD: MB7 Resources

MULTI-STEP TEST PREP

SECTION 8B

Radical Functions

Tick Tock A pendulum clock keeps time by using weights, gears, and a pendulum. The length of the pendulum determines how fast it swings, and the speed of the pendulum determines how fast the hands of the clock advance.

A clockmaker is building a replica of an antique pendulum clock for a museum display and finds that it is running too slowly. As he attempts to fix the clock, he tries pendulums of different lengths. He records the pendulum length and period data shown in the table. The period of a pendulum is the time it takes for the pendulum to complete one back-and-forth swing.

Pendulum Swings

Length (cm)	Period (s)
10	0.6
20	0.9
30	1.1
40	1.3
50	1.4
60	1.6

1. Create a scatter plot of the data, using pendulum length as the independent variable and period as the dependent variable.
2. Experiment with a graphing calculator to find a function rule that models the data in the scatter plot. Describe your model as a transformation of $f(x) = \sqrt{x}$.
3. What is a reasonable domain for this situation? Explain.
4. Use your model to determine the period of a pendulum that has a length of 16 cm. Round to the nearest tenth of a second. $\approx$ **0.8 s**
5. From his observations, the clockmaker concludes that the pendulum needs to have a period of 1 s. To the nearest centimeter, how long should the pendulum be? $\approx$ **25 cm**
6. The function $y = 2\pi\sqrt{\frac{x}{9.8}}$ gives the period y of a pendulum in seconds in terms of the pendulum's length x in meters. Graph this function with the data from the table and explain whether the function is a reasonable model for the data.

636

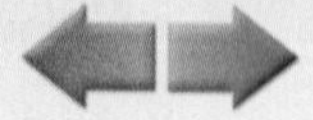

INTERVENTION

Scaffolding Questions

1. On which axis is the independent variable plotted? horizontal axis the dependent variable? vertical axis
2. What type of transformation should you apply to $f(x) = \sqrt{x}$ so that it more closely models the data? a vertical compression or a horizontal stretch
3. What are the restrictions on the radicand of the model? The radicand must be non-negative.
4. Does 16 cm represent the value of the independent variable or dependent variable of the model? independent
5. What equation can you solve to find the answer to this problem? Possible answer: $1 = 0.2\sqrt{x}$
6. How can you modify the function $y = 2\pi\sqrt{\frac{x}{9.8}}$ so that it gives the period of a pendulum in terms of the pendulum's length in centimeters instead of meters? Replace x with $\frac{x}{100}$.

Extension

A clock in Shinjuku, Japan, has a pendulum that is 22.5 m in length. Approximately how many back-and-forth swings does this pendulum make in one day? about 9075

READY TO GO ON?

CHAPTER 8

SECTION 8B

Quiz for Lessons 8-6 Through 8-8

8-6 Radical Expressions and Rational Exponents

Simplify each expression. Assume that all variables are positive.

1. $\sqrt{32x^3}$ $4x\sqrt{2x}$
2. $\sqrt[3]{8y^{12}z^6}$ $2y^4z^2$
3. $\sqrt[4]{\frac{a^4}{9}}$ $\frac{a\sqrt{3}}{3}$

Write each expression in radical form, and simplify.

4. $4^{\frac{3}{2}}$ $\sqrt{4^3}=8$
5. $16^{\frac{5}{4}}$ $\left(\sqrt[4]{16}\right)^5=32$
6. $(-27)^{\frac{2}{3}}$ $\left(\sqrt[3]{-27}\right)^2=9$

Write each expression by using rational exponents.

7. $\sqrt[4]{8^3}$ $8^{\frac{3}{4}}$
8. $\left(\sqrt[5]{243}\right)^2$ $243^{\frac{2}{5}}$
9. $\left(\sqrt[3]{-1000}\right)^2$ $(-1000)^{\frac{2}{3}}$
10. In an experiment involving fruit flies, the initial population is 112. The growth of the population can be modeled by the function $n(t)=112\cdot 2^{\frac{t}{50}}$, where n is the number of fruit flies and t is the time in hours. Based on this model, what is the population of fruit flies after 1 week? ≈ 1150

8-7 Radical Functions

Graph each function, and identify its domain and range.

11. $f(x)=-\sqrt{x}+4$
12. $f(x)=\sqrt[3]{x+1}$ D: $\mathbb{R}$; R: $\mathbb{R}$
13. Water is draining from a tank connected to two pipes. The speed f in feet per second at which water drains through the first pipe can be modeled by $f(x)=\sqrt{64(x-2)}$, where x is the depth of the water in the tank in feet. The graph of the corresponding function for the second pipe is a translation of f 4 units right. Write the corresponding function g, and use it to estimate the speed at which water drains through the second pipe when the depth of the water is 10 ft. $g(x)=\sqrt{64(x-6)}$; 16 ft/s
14. Use the description to write the square-root function g. The parent function $f(x)=\sqrt{x}$ is reflected across the x-axis and then translated 2 units right and 3 units down. $g(x)=-\sqrt{x-2}-3$

Graph each inequality.

15. $y>\sqrt{x}+4$
16. $y\le\sqrt{x-2}$

8-8 Solving Radical Equations and Inequalities

Solve each equation.

17. $-2\sqrt[3]{5x-5}=-10$ 26
18. $\sqrt{x+4}=x-8$ 12
19. $3\sqrt[3]{x-2}=\sqrt[3]{6x}$ $\frac{18}{7}$
20. The formula $d=\sqrt[3]{\frac{4w}{0.02847}}$ relates the average diameter d of a cultured pearl in millimeters to its weight w in carats. To the nearest tenth of a carat, what is the weight of a cultured pearl with an average diameter of 7 mm? 2.4 carats

Solve each inequality.

21. $\sqrt{x+5}<4$ $-5\le x<11$
22. $\sqrt[3]{2x}\ge -2$ $x\ge -4$
23. $\sqrt{x-6}-10\le 4$ $6\le x\le 202$

READY TO GO ON? SECTION 8B

Organizer

Objective: Assess students' mastery of concepts and skills in Lessons 8-6 through 8-8.

Resources

Assessment Resources

Section 8B Quiz

Test & Practice Generator

One-Stop Planner®

INTERVENTION

Resources

***Ready to Go On? Intervention and Enrichment* Worksheets**

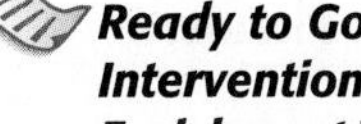

***Ready to Go On?* CD-ROM**

***Ready to Go On?* Online**

my.hrw.com

Answers

11–12, 15–16. See p. A39.

READY TO GO ON?

Diagnose and Prescribe

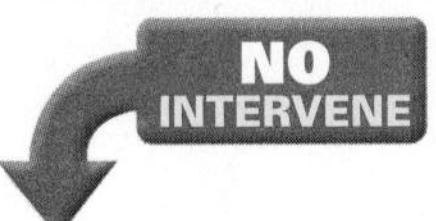

NO INTERVENE

Ready to Go On? Intervention	*Ready to Go On? Intervention*, Section 8B — Worksheets	CD-ROM	Online
Lesson 8-6	8-6 Intervention	Activity 8-6	Diagnose and Prescribe Online
Lesson 8-7	8-7 Intervention	Activity 8-7	
Lesson 8-8	8-8 Intervention	Activity 8-8	

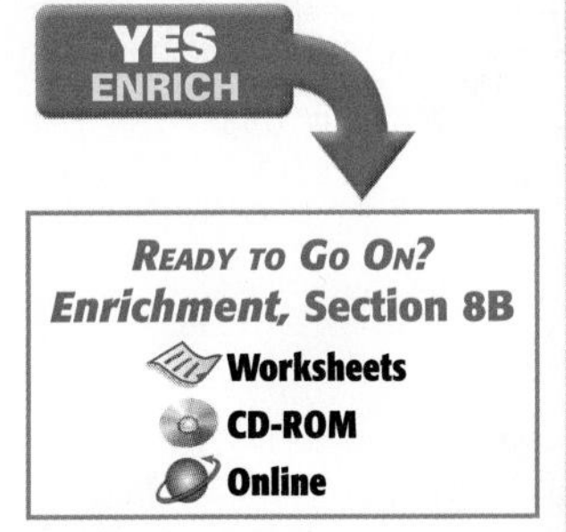

YES ENRICH

Ready to Go On? Enrichment, Section 8B

Worksheets

CD-ROM

Online

Organizer

Objective: Help students organize and review key concepts and skills presented in Chapter 8.

Online Edition
Multilingual Glossary

Resources

Puzzle Pro
One-Stop Planner®

***Multilingual Glossary* Online**
go.hrw.com
KEYWORD: MB7 Glossary

Lesson Tutorial Videos
CD-ROM

Test & Practice Generator
One-Stop Planner®

CHAPTER 8 Study Guide: Review

Vocabulary

Complete the sentences below with vocabulary words from the list above.

1. A(n) __?__ is a function whose rule is a ratio of two polynomials.
2. A(n) __?__ is a relationship that can be written in the form $y = kx$, where k is the __?__.

8-1 Variation Functions *(pp. 569–576)*

EXAMPLES

■ **The cost in dollars of apples a varies directly as the number of pounds p, and $a = 3.12$ when $p = 2.4$. Find p when $a = 1.04$.**

$\frac{a_1}{p_1} = \frac{a_2}{p_2}$ *Use a proportion.*

$\frac{3.12}{2.4} = \frac{1.04}{p_2}$ *Substitute.*

$3.12p = 2.4(1.04)$ *Find the cross products.*

$p = 0.8$ *Solve for p.*

Apples that cost \$1.04 have a weight of 0.8 lb.

■ **The base b of a parallelogram with fixed area varies inversely as the height h, and $b = 12$ cm when $h = 8$ cm. Find b when $h = 3$ cm.**

$b = \frac{k}{h}$ *b varies inversely with h.*

$12 = \frac{k}{8}$ *Substitute.*

$k = 96$ *Solve for k.*

$b = \frac{96}{h}$ *Substitute 96 for k.*

$b = \frac{96}{3}$ *Substitute 3 for h.*

$b = 32$ *Solve for b.*

The base is 32 cm when the height is 3 cm.

EXERCISES

Given: y varies directly as x. Write and graph each direct variation function.

3. $y = 2$ when $x = 6$
4. $y = 4$ when $x = 1$
5. The number of tiles n needed to cover a floor varies directly as the area a of the floor, and $n = 180$ when $a = 20$ ft^2. Find n when $a = 34$ ft^2.
6. The simple interest I earned over a particular period of time varies jointly as the principal P and rate r, and $I = \$264$ when $P = \$1100$ and $r = 0.12$. Find P when $I = \$360$ and $r = 0.09$.

Given: y varies inversely as x. Write and graph each inverse variation function.

7. $y = 3$ when $x = 2$
8. $y = 4$ when $x = 1$
9. For a fixed voltage, the current I flowing in a wire varies inversely as the resistance R of the wire. If the current is 8 amperes when the resistance is 15 ohms, what will the resistance be when the current is 5 amperes?
10. Determine whether the data set represents a direct variation, an inverse variation, or neither.

x	2	5	10
y	25	10	5

Answers

1. rational function
2. direct variation; constant of variation
3. $y = \frac{1}{3}x$

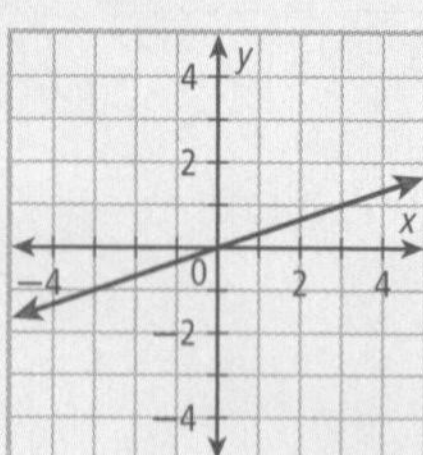

4. $y = 4x$

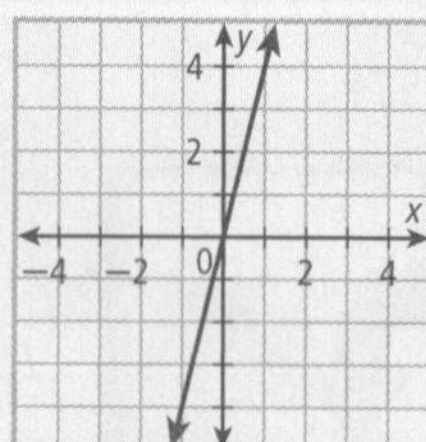

5. 306 tiles
6. \$2000
7. $y = \frac{6}{x}$

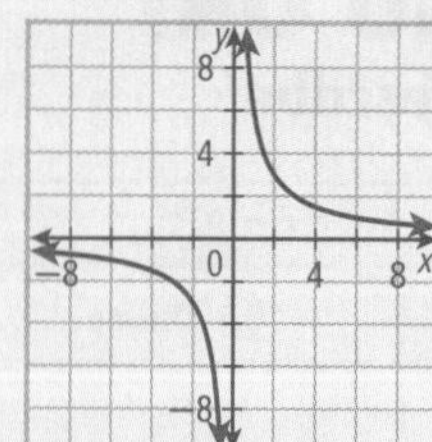

8. $y = \frac{4}{x}$

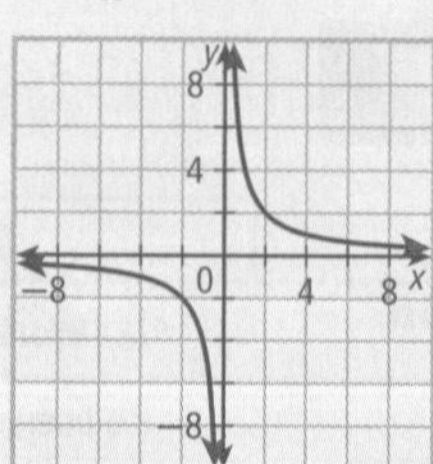

9. 24 ohms
10. inverse variation

8-2 Multiplying and Dividing Rational Expressions *(pp. 577–582)*

EXAMPLES

■ **Simplify $\frac{4-x}{x^2-x-20}$. Identify any x-values for which the expression is undefined.**

$$\frac{-1(x+4)}{(x-5)(x+4)} = \frac{-1}{x-5}$$ *Factor. Then divide out common factors.*

Undefined at $x = 5$ and $x = -4$

■ **Divide. Assume that all expressions are defined.**

$$\frac{x^2-9}{x+2} \div \frac{x+3}{x^2+7x+10}$$

$$\frac{x^2-9}{x+2} \cdot \frac{x^2+7x+10}{x+3}$$ *Rewrite as multiplication.*

$$\frac{(x-3)(x+3)}{x+2} \cdot \frac{(x+2)(x+5)}{x+3} = (x-3)(x+5)$$

EXERCISES

Simplify. Identify any x-values for which the expression is undefined.

11. $\frac{24x^{14}}{9x^{16}}$
12. $\frac{6x^3}{3x+12}$
13. $\frac{x^2+x-12}{x^2+5x+4}$

Multiply. Assume that all expressions are defined.

14. $\frac{x+5}{3x+1} \cdot \frac{9x+3}{x^2-25}$
15. $\frac{x}{x-4} \cdot \frac{-x+2}{x^2+x-6}$
16. $\frac{x^2+2x-3}{x^2-x-2} \cdot \frac{x-2}{x+3}$
17. $\frac{9x^2-1}{x^2-9} \cdot \frac{x+3}{3x+1}$

Divide. Assume that all expressions are defined.

18. $\frac{x^3y}{4xy^4} \div \frac{x}{8y^2}$
19. $\frac{x^2+2x-15}{x-2} \div \frac{x^2-9}{2x-4}$
20. $\frac{3x-21}{3x} \div \frac{x^2-49}{x^2+7x}$
21. $\frac{x^2+4x+3}{x^2+2x-8} \div \frac{3x+3}{x-2}$

8-3 Adding and Subtracting Rational Expressions *(pp. 583–590)*

EXAMPLES

■ **Add. Identify any x-values for which the expression is undefined.**

$$\frac{6x-3}{x^2-x-12} + \frac{x}{x+3}$$

$$\frac{6x-3}{(x-4)(x+3)} + \frac{x}{x+3}\left(\frac{x-4}{x-4}\right)$$

$$\frac{6x-3+x(x-4)}{(x-4)(x+3)}$$ *Add the numerators.*

$$\frac{x^2+2x-3}{(x-4)(x+3)}$$ *Simplify the numerator.*

$$\frac{(x+3)(x-1)}{(x-4)(x+3)} = \frac{x-1}{x-4}$$ *Factor the numerator.*

Undefined at $x = 4$ and $x = -3$

■ **Simplify. Assume that all expressions are defined.**

$$\frac{\frac{x+2}{6x}}{\frac{x}{x-4}} = \frac{\frac{x+2}{6x}(6x)(x-4)}{\frac{x}{x-4}(6x)(x-4)}$$ *The LCD is $(6x)(x-4)$.*

$$\frac{(x+2)(x-4)}{x(6x)} = \frac{(x+2)(x-4)}{6x^2}$$

EXERCISES

Add. Identify any x-values for which the expression is undefined.

22. $\frac{4}{x^2+4} + \frac{x^2+8}{x^2+4}$
23. $\frac{1}{x+3} + \frac{1}{x-3}$
24. $\frac{x}{x^2-4} + \frac{1}{x-2}$
25. $\frac{2x-3}{3x+7} + \frac{6}{4x-1}$

Find the least common multiple for each pair.

26. x^2-9 and x^2-6x+9
27. $x^2+2x-35$ and $x^2+9x+14$

Subtract. Identify any x-values for which the expression is undefined.

28. $\frac{2x}{x+4} - \frac{3}{x+4}$
29. $\frac{x}{x+5} - \frac{5}{x-5}$
30. $\frac{1}{x^2-x-6} - \frac{x}{x+2}$
31. $\frac{2x}{2x+1} - \frac{7}{3x-1}$

Simplify. Assume that all expressions are defined.

32. $\frac{\frac{x-6}{5}}{\frac{x+2}{8}}$
33. $\frac{\frac{x+3}{3x}}{\frac{x^2-9}{6x-9}}$
34. $\frac{\frac{x}{4}-\frac{1}{x}}{\frac{x+2}{x-2}}$

35. A jet's average speed is 520 mi/h when flying from Dallas to Chicago and 580 mi/h on the return trip. What is the jet's average speed for the entire trip?

Answers

11. $\frac{8}{3x^2}$; $x \neq 0$
12. $\frac{2x^3}{x+4}$; $x \neq -4$
13. $\frac{x-3}{x+1}$; $x \neq -4, x \neq -1$
14. $\frac{3}{x-5}$
15. $\frac{-x}{(x-4)(x+3)}$
16. $\frac{x-1}{x+1}$
17. $\frac{3x-1}{x-3}$
18. $\frac{2x}{y}$
19. $\frac{2(x+5)}{x+3}$
20. 1
21. $\frac{x+3}{3(x+4)}$
22. $\frac{x^2+12}{x^2+4}$
23. $\frac{2x}{(x+3)(x-3)}$; $x \neq \pm 3$
24. $\frac{2(x+1)}{(x+2)(x-2)}$; $x \neq \pm 2$
25. $\frac{8x^2+4x+45}{(3x+7)(4x-1)}$; $x \neq -\frac{7}{3}$, $x \neq \frac{1}{4}$
26. $(x-3)^2(x+3)$
27. $(x-5)(x+2)(x+7)$
28. $\frac{2x-3}{x+4}$; $x \neq -4$
29. $\frac{x^2-10x-25}{(x+5)(x-5)}$; $x \neq \pm 5$
30. $\frac{-(x^2-3x-1)}{(x-3)(x+2)}$; $x \neq -2, x \neq 3$
31. $\frac{6x^2-16x-7}{(2x+1)(3x-1)}$; $x \neq -\frac{1}{2}$, $x \neq \frac{1}{3}$
32. $\frac{8(x-6)}{5(x+2)}$
33. $\frac{2x-3}{x(x-3)}$
34. $\frac{(x-2)^2}{4x}$
35. ≈ 548 mi/h

Study Guide: Review 639

Answers

36. g is f translated 4 units right.

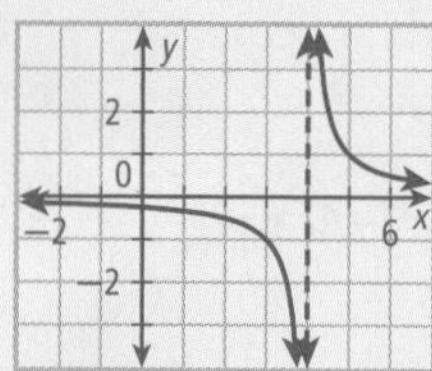

37. g is f translated 2 units right and 3 units up.

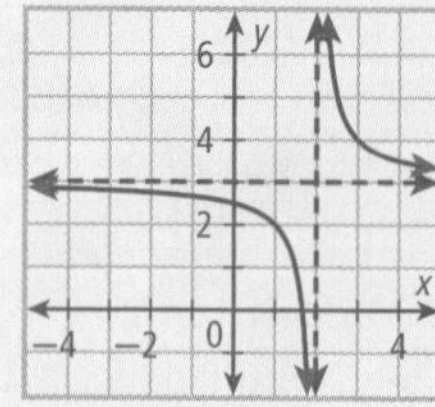

38. asymptotes: $x = 1$, $y = -3$; D: $\{x \mid x \neq 1\}$; R: $\{y \mid y \neq -3\}$

39. asymptotes: $x = -2$, $y = 1$; D: $\{x \mid x \neq -2\}$; R: $\{y \mid y \neq 1\}$

40. zeros: 0, 3; asymptote: $x = -4$

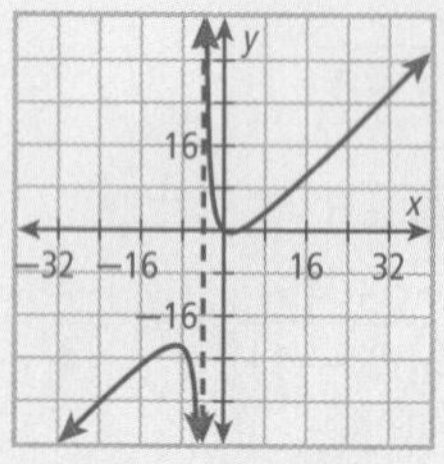

41. zero: 3; asymptotes: $x = -5$, $x = -1$, $y = 0$

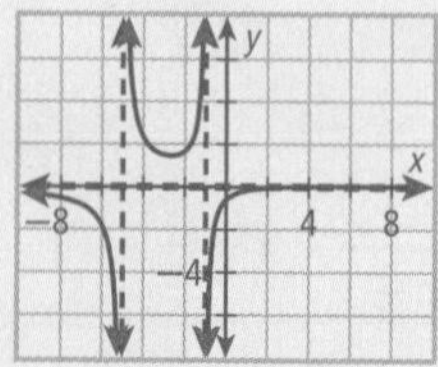

42. zero: 2; asymptotes: $x = -3$, $y = 2$

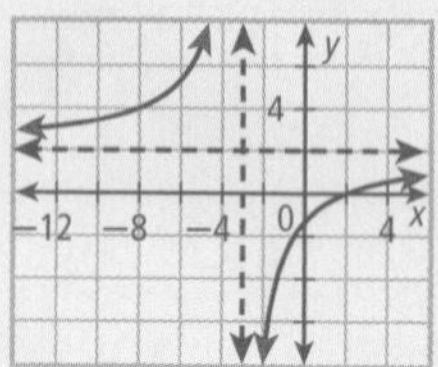

43. zeros: -3, 3; asymptote: $x = 2$

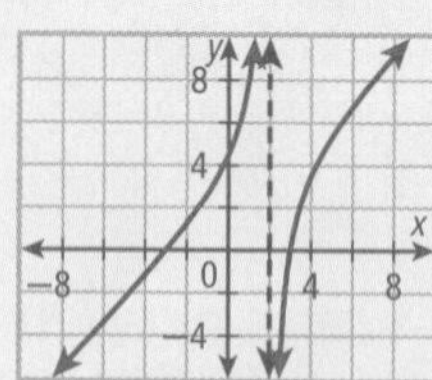

44. hole at $x = -3$

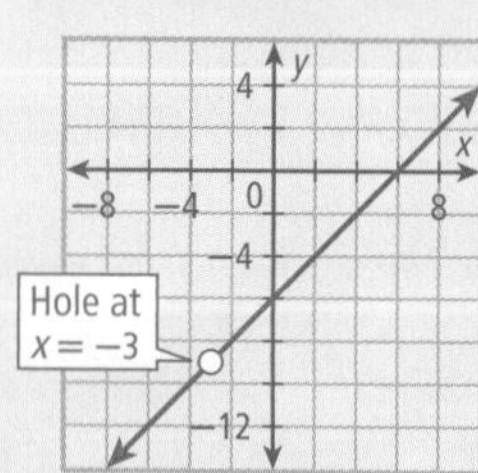

8-4 Rational Functions *(pp. 592–599)*

EXAMPLES

- **Using the graph of $f(x) = \frac{1}{x}$ as a guide, describe the transformation and graph $g(x) = \frac{1}{x} - 3$.**

  Because $k = -3$, translate f down 3 units.

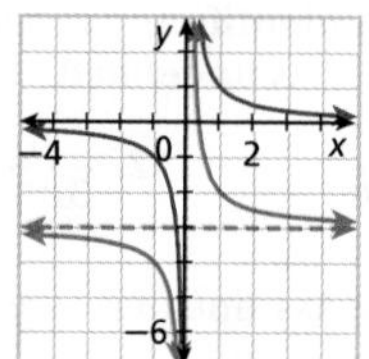

- **Identify the zeros and asymptotes of $f(x) = \frac{2x-4}{x+3}$. Then graph.**

  Zero: 2
  Vertical asymptote: $x = -3$
  Horizontal asymptote: $y = 2$

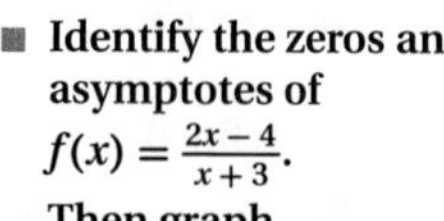

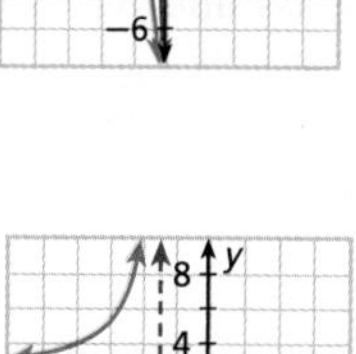

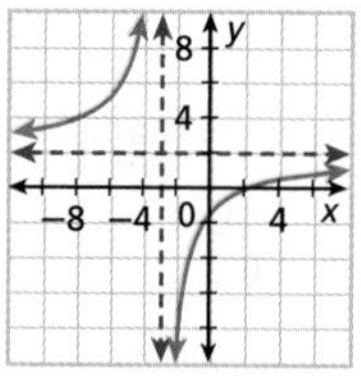

EXERCISES

Using the graph of $f(x) = \frac{1}{x}$ as a guide, describe the transformation and graph each function.

36. $g(x) = \frac{1}{x-4}$
37. $g(x) = \frac{1}{x-2} + 3$

Identify the asymptotes, domain, and range of each function.

38. $f(x) = \frac{2}{x-1} - 3$
39. $f(x) = \frac{3}{x+2} + 1$

Identify the zeros and asymptotes of each function. Then graph.

40. $f(x) = \frac{x^2 - 3x}{x+4}$
41. $f(x) = \frac{x-3}{x^2 + 6x + 5}$
42. $f(x) = \frac{2x-4}{x+3}$
43. $f(x) = \frac{x^2 - 9}{x-2}$
44. Identify holes in the graph of $f(x) = \frac{x^2 - 3x - 18}{x+3}$. Then graph.

8-5 Solving Rational Equations and Inequalities *(pp. 600–607)*

EXAMPLE

- **Solve the equation $\frac{30}{x+1} + x = 10$.**

$$\frac{30}{x+1}(x+1) + x(x+1) = 10(x+1)$$

$30 + x^2 + x = 10x + 10$ *Simplify. $x \neq -1$*

$x^2 - 9x + 20 = 0$ *Write in standard form.*

$(x-4)(x-5) = 0$ *Factor.*

$x = 4$ or $x = 5$ *Solve for x.*

EXERCISES

Solve each equation.

45. $x - \frac{6}{x} = 1$
46. $\frac{4x}{x-5} = \frac{3x+5}{x-5}$
47. $\frac{3x}{x+2} = \frac{2x+2}{x+2}$
48. $\frac{x}{x+4} + \frac{x}{2} = \frac{2x}{2x+8}$

Solve each inequality.

49. $\frac{x+4}{x} > -2$
50. $\frac{2}{x-3} < 4$

8-6 Radical Expressions and Rational Exponents *(pp. 610–617)*

EXAMPLES

Simplify each expression. Assume that all variables are positive.

- $\sqrt[3]{-8x^9} = \sqrt[3]{(-2^3)} \cdot \sqrt[3]{x^3} \cdot \sqrt[3]{x^3} \cdot \sqrt[3]{x^3} = -2x^3$

- $\sqrt[4]{8x^6} \cdot \sqrt[4]{2x^2} = \sqrt[4]{16x^8} = \sqrt[4]{2^4} \cdot \sqrt[4]{x^4} \cdot \sqrt[4]{x^4} = 2x^2$

- **Write the expression $(\sqrt{16})^3$ by using rational exponents.**

  $16^{\frac{3}{2}}$ $\quad (\sqrt[n]{a})^m = a^{\frac{m}{n}}$

EXERCISES

Simplify each expression. Assume that all variables are positive.

51. $\sqrt[3]{27x^6}$
52. $\sqrt[4]{81x^{12}}$
53. $\sqrt[3]{\frac{8x^3}{3}}$

Write each expression by using rational exponents.

54. $(\sqrt[3]{-27})^2$
55. $\sqrt[4]{16^3}$
56. $(\sqrt{9})^3$

Simplify each expression.

57. $17^{\frac{1}{3}} \cdot 17^{\frac{2}{3}}$
58. $(9^4)^{\frac{1}{2}}$
59. $\left(\frac{1}{16}\right)^{\frac{1}{4}}$

45. $x = -2$ or $x = 3$
46. no solution
47. $x = 2$
48. $x = 0$
49. $x < -\frac{4}{3}$ or $x > 0$
50. $x < 3$ or $x > \frac{7}{2}$
51. $3x^2$
52. $3x^3$
53. $2x\frac{\sqrt[3]{9}}{3}$
54. $(-27)^{\frac{2}{3}}$
55. $16^{\frac{3}{4}}$
56. $9^{\frac{3}{2}}$
57. 17
58. 81
59. $\frac{1}{2}$

8-7 Radical Functions (pp. 619–627)

EXAMPLE

■ **Graph $f(x) = \frac{\sqrt{x+8}}{2}$, and identify its domain and range.**

Make a table of values. Then graph.

x	y
−8	0
−7	0.5
−4	1
1	1.5
8	2

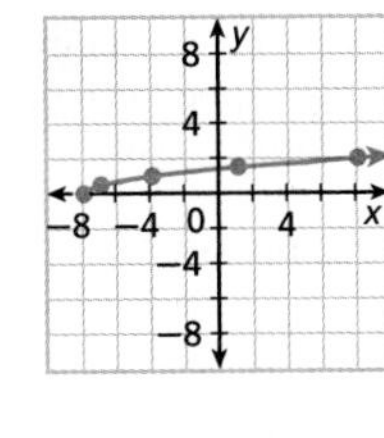

D: $\{x \mid x \geq -8\}$; R: $\{y \mid y \geq 0\}$

EXERCISES

Graph each function, and identify its domain and range.

60. $f(x) = \sqrt{x} + 5$

61. $f(x) = -4\sqrt[3]{x}$

Using the graph of $f(x) = \sqrt{x}$ as a guide, describe the transformation and graph each function.

62. $g(x) = -\sqrt{x} + 1$

63. $h(x) = \sqrt{4x}$

64. $j(x) = \sqrt{-(x-8)}$

65. $k(x) = -\frac{1}{2}\sqrt{x} + 1$

66. Use the description to write the square-root function g. The parent function $f(x) = \sqrt{x}$ is stretched vertically by a factor of 3 and translated 4 units left.

Graph each inequality.

67. $y < \sqrt{x}$

68. $y < \sqrt[3]{x+4}$

8-8 Solving Radical Equations and Inequalities (pp. 628–635)

EXAMPLES

Solve each equation.

■ $4\sqrt[3]{x-4} = 12$

$\sqrt[3]{x-4} = 3$ *Divide by 4.*

$\left(\sqrt[3]{x-4}\right)^3 = 3^3$ *Cube both sides.*

$x - 4 = 27$ *Simplify.*

$x = 31$ *Solve for x.*

■ $\sqrt{x+15} = x - 5$

$\left(\sqrt{x+15}\right)^2 = (x-5)^2$ *Square both sides.*

$x + 15 = x^2 - 10x + 25$

$x^2 - 11x + 10 = 0$ *Write in standard form.*

$(x-10)(x-1) = 0$ *Factor.*

$x = 10$ or $x = 1$ *Solve for x.*

Use substitution to check for extraneous solutions.

$\sqrt{x+15}$	$= x - 5$
$\sqrt{10+15}$	$10 - 5$
5	5 ✔

$\sqrt{x+15}$	$= x - 5$
$\sqrt{1+15}$	$1 - 5$
4	−4 ✘

The solution $x = 1$ is extraneous. The only solution is $x = 10$.

EXERCISES

Solve each equation.

69. $\sqrt{x+6} - 7 = -2$

70. $\frac{\sqrt[3]{2x-2}}{6} = 1$

71. $\sqrt{10x} = 3\sqrt{x+1}$

72. $2\sqrt[5]{x} = \sqrt[5]{64}$

73. $\sqrt{6x-12} = x - 2$

74. $\sqrt{x+1} = x - 5$

75. $(4x+7)^{\frac{1}{2}} = 3$

76. $(x-4)^{\frac{1}{4}} = 3$

77. $x = (2x+35)^{\frac{1}{2}}$

78. $(x+3)^{\frac{1}{3}} = -6$

Solve each inequality.

79. $\sqrt{x-4} \leq 3$

80. $\sqrt{2x+7} - 6 > -1$

81. $\sqrt{3x} - 4 < 2$

82. $\sqrt[3]{x-1} > -2$

83. The time T in seconds required for a pendulum to complete one back-and-forth swing can be determined from the formula $T = 2\pi\sqrt{\frac{L}{9.8}}$, where L is the length of the pendulum in meters. Estimate the length of a pendulum that completes one back-and-forth swing in 2.5 s.

84. A tetrahedron is a triangular pyramid with four congruent faces. The side length s in meters of a tetrahedron is given by the formula $s = \left(6V\sqrt{2}\right)^{\frac{1}{3}}$, where V is the volume of the tetrahedron in cubic meters. What is the volume of a tetrahedron with a side length of 8 m? Round to the nearest tenth.

Answers

60. D: $\{x \mid x \geq 0\}$; R: $\{y \mid y \geq 5\}$

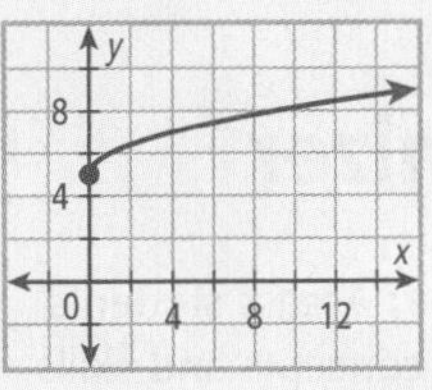

61. D: $\mathbb{R}$; R: $\mathbb{R}$

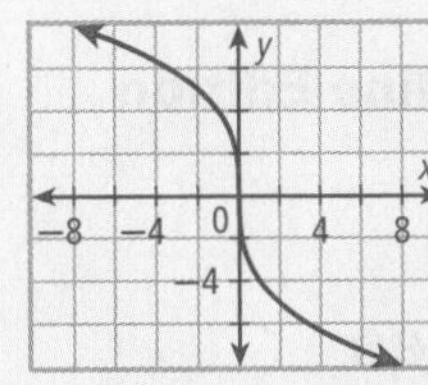

62. g is f reflected across the x-axis and translated 1 unit up.

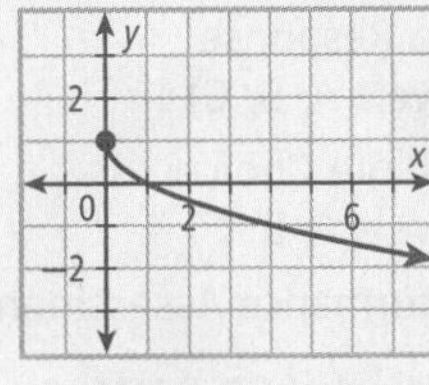

63. h is f compressed horizontally by a factor of $\frac{1}{4}$.

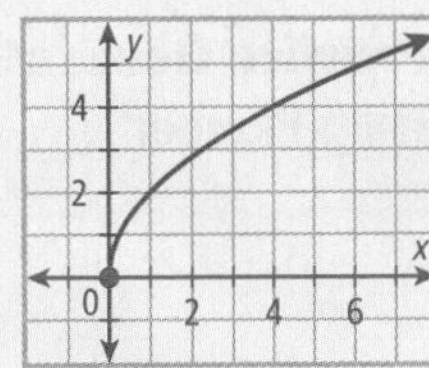

64. j is f reflected across the y-axis and translated 8 units right.

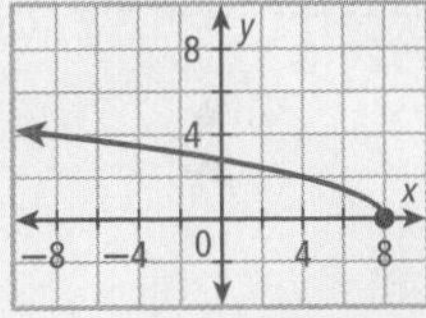

65. k is f reflected across the x-axis, compressed vertically by a factor of $\frac{1}{2}$, and translated 1 unit up.

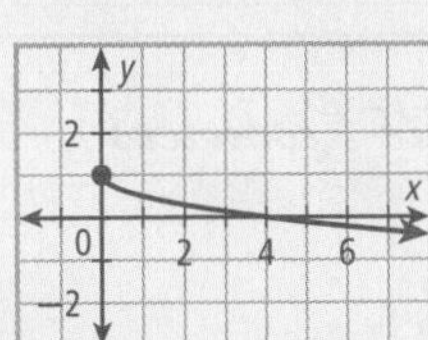

66. $g(x) = 3\sqrt{x+4}$

67.

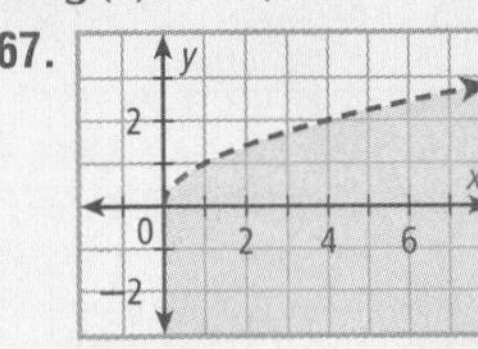

Answers

68.

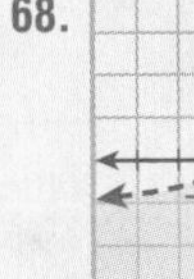
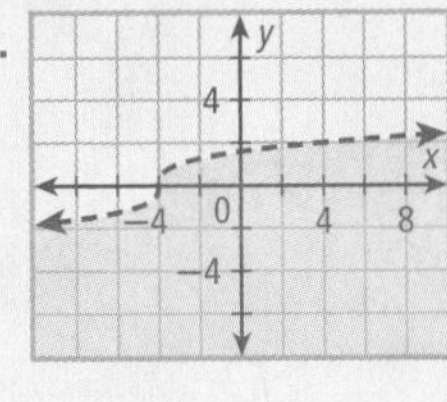

69. $x = 19$
70. $x = 109$
71. $x = 9$
72. $x = 2$
73. $x = 2$ or $x = 8$
74. $x = 8$
75. $x = 0.5$
76. $x = 85$
77. $x = 7$
78. $x = -219$
79. $4 \leq x \leq 13$
80. $x > 9$
81. $0 \leq x < 12$
82. $x > -7$
83. ≈ 1.6 m
84. 60.3 m^3

Organizer

Objective: Assess students' mastery of concepts and skills in Chapter 8.

Online Edition

Resources

Assessment Resources

Chapter 8 Tests

- Free Response (Levels A, B, C)
- Multiple Choice (Levels A, B, C)
- Performance Assessment

***IDEA Works!* CD-ROM**

Modified Chapter 8 Test

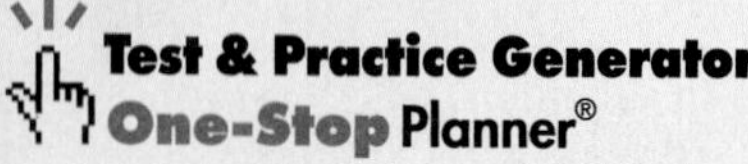

Answers

6. $\dfrac{x+10}{2(x-5)}$; $x \neq 5$

7. $\dfrac{-2(2x^2-42x+21)}{(x-7)(x+3)}$; $x \neq 7$ and $x \neq -3$

State Resources

1. The monthly minimum payment p due on a certain credit card with a fixed rate varies directly as the balance b, and $p = \$19.80$ when $b = \$1100$. Find p when $b = \$3000$. **\$54**

2. The time t that it takes Hannah to bike to school varies inversely as her average speed s. If she can bike to school in 25 min when her average speed is 6 mi/h, what would her average speed need to be to get to school in 20 min? **7.5 mi/h**

3. Simplify $\dfrac{x^2-x-6}{x^2-4x+3}$. Identify any x-values for which the expression is undefined. $\dfrac{x+2}{x-1}$; $x \neq 1$ and $x \neq 3$

Multiply or divide. Assume that all expressions are defined.

4. $\dfrac{x-9}{2x-10} \cdot \dfrac{x-5}{x^2-81}$ $\dfrac{1}{2(x+9)}$

5. $\dfrac{3x^3-9x^2}{x^2-16} \div \dfrac{2x-6}{x^2-8x+16}$ $\dfrac{3x^2(x-4)}{2(x+4)}$

Add or subtract. Identify any x-values for which the expression is undefined.

6. $\dfrac{5}{x-5} + \dfrac{x}{2x-10}$

7. $\dfrac{5x}{x-7} - \dfrac{9x-6}{x+3}$

8. Lorraine averaged 62 words per minute when typing the first 3 pages of a 6-page report. Her average typing speed for the last 3 pages was 45 words per minute. To the nearest word per minute, what was Lorraine's average typing speed for the entire report? **52 words/min**

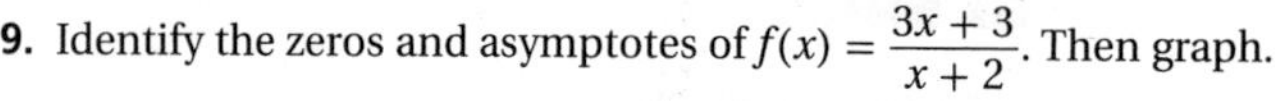

9. Identify the zeros and asymptotes of $f(x) = \dfrac{3x+3}{x+2}$. Then graph.
zero: -1; asymptotes: $x = -2$, $y = 3$

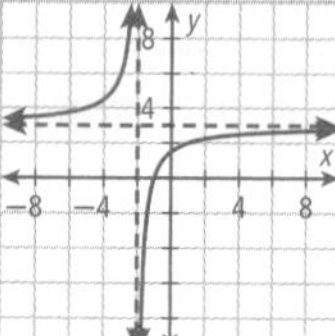

Solve each equation.

10. $2 + \dfrac{3}{x-1} = 10$ $\dfrac{11}{8}$

11. $\dfrac{x}{x-1} + \dfrac{x}{3} = \dfrac{5}{x-1}$ $-5, 3$

12. Beth can tile a floor in about 6 h. When Beth and Mike work together, they can tile a floor in about 2.4 h. About how long would it take Mike to tile a floor if he works by himself? **4 h**

Simplify each expression. Assume that all variables are positive.

13. $\sqrt[3]{-32x^6}$ $-2x^2(\sqrt[3]{4})$

14. $8^{-\frac{2}{3}}$ $\dfrac{1}{4}$

15. $\dfrac{27^{\frac{2}{3}}}{27^{\frac{1}{3}}}$ 3

16. Write the expression $\sqrt[5]{x^2}$ by using a rational exponent. $x^{\frac{2}{5}}$

17. Graph the function $f(x) = \sqrt{x+2} - 4$ and identify its domain and range.
D: $\{x \mid x \geq -2\}$; R: $\{y \mid y \geq -4\}$

18. Graph the inequality $y \leq \sqrt{x} - 2$.

18. 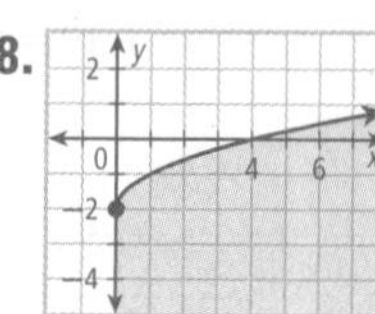

Solve each equation.

19. $\sqrt{x+7} = 5$ 18

20. $\sqrt{2x+1} = \sqrt{x+9}$ 8

21. $(3x+1)^{\frac{1}{3}} = -2$ -3

22. The formula $s = \sqrt{\dfrac{A}{4.828}}$ can be used to approximate the side length s of a regular octagon with area A. A stop sign is shaped like a regular octagon with a side length of 12.4 in. To the nearest square inch, what is the area of the stop sign? **742 in^2**

23. Solve the inequality $\sqrt{2x+1} > 3$. $x > 4$

17. 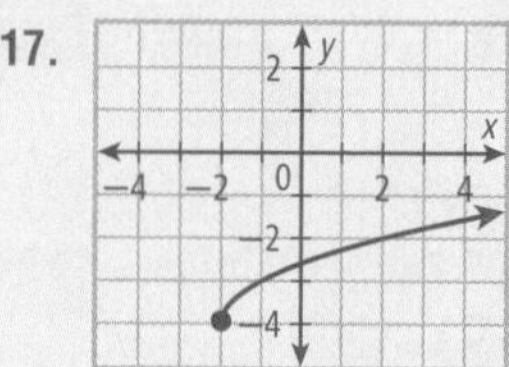

COLLEGE ENTRANCE EXAM PRACTICE

FOCUS ON SAT

There is a set of criteria that your calculator must meet in order for it to be allowed in the testing facility when you take the SAT. For example, calculators that make noise or have QWERTY keypads are not allowed. For complete guidelines, check www.collegeboard.com.

If you do not already have a graphing calculator, consider purchasing or borrowing one because it may give you an advantage when solving some problems on the SAT. Be sure to spend time getting used to any new calculator before test day.

You may want to time yourself as you take this practice test. It should take you about 6 minutes to complete.

1. Which of the following functions is graphed below?

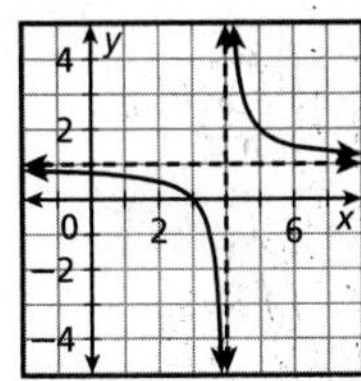

(A) $f(x) = (x + 3)(x - 4)$

(B) $f(x) = (x - 3)(x + 4)$

(C) $f(x) = \dfrac{x - 3}{x - 4}$

(D) $f(x) = \dfrac{x - 3}{x + 4}$

(E) $f(x) = \dfrac{x + 3}{x + 4}$

2. If each of the following expressions is defined, which is equivalent to $x - 1$?

(A) $\dfrac{(x + 1)(x - 1)}{x - 1}$

(B) $\dfrac{(x - 1)(x + 2)}{x + 1} \cdot \dfrac{x + 1}{x + 2}$

(C) $\dfrac{(x + 1)(x + 2)}{x - 2} \div \dfrac{x + 2}{x - 2}$

(D) $\dfrac{x + 1}{x + 2} + \dfrac{x - 1}{x + 2}$

(E) $\dfrac{2x - 2}{x - 2} - \dfrac{x - 1}{x - 2}$

3. The cube root of the square of a real number n is 16. What is the value of n?

(A) $\frac{4}{3}$

(B) $\frac{8}{3}$

(C) 4

(D) 12

(E) 64

4. If y varies inversely as the square of x and $y = 1$ when $x = 2$, what is the value of y when $x = -4$?

(A) -2

(B) $-\frac{1}{2}$

(C) $\frac{1}{4}$

(D) 4

(E) 16

5. If $\sqrt[3]{12x + 28} = 4$, what is the value of x^3?

(A) -8

(B) 3

(C) 12

(D) 27

(E) 64

Organizer

Objective: Provide practice for college entrance exams such as the SAT.

Online Edition

Resources

College Entrance Exam Practice

Questions on the SAT represent the following math content areas:

Number and Operation, 30–32%

Algebra and Functions, 28–32%

Geometry and Measurement, 27–30%

Data Analysis, Statistics, and Probability, 10–12%

Items on this page focus on:

- Number and Operation
- Algebra and Functions

Text References:

Item	1	2	3	4	5
Lesson	8-4	8-2	8-6	8-1	8-8

TEST PREP DOCTOR

1. Suggest that students start by identifying the asymptotes of the graph. They can then use the asymptotes to help them eliminate answer choices. For instance, because the graph has a vertical asymptote at $x = 4$, the function must be undefined at this x-value. Only choice **C** meets this requirement.

2. Students who chose **A** may have made a mistake in sign when simplifying the expression. Those who chose **C** may have multiplied by the divisor rather than by the reciprocal of the divisor.

3. Students may not know how to approach this problem. Suggest that they use the verbal description to write an equation. They can then either solve the equation algebraically or test each answer choice by using substitution.

4. Students who chose **B** assumed that y varies inversely as x rather than as the square of x. Students who chose **D** found the value of k rather than the value of y.

5. Point out that this problem has two steps. First students need to solve the equation to find the value of x. Then they need to use the value of x to evaluate the expression x^3. Note that students who chose **B** solved for x but did not complete the problem and find x^3.

Organizer

Objective: Provide opportunities to learn and practice common test-taking strategies.

Online Edition

Resources

 ***State Test Prep Workbook***

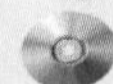 ***State Test Prep CD-ROM***

 ***State Test Practice Online***

KEYWORD: MB7 TestPrep

This Test Tackler reinforces the importance of using diagrams when solving problems. Point out that diagrams presented in test problems will often contain information that is not included in the text portion of the problems themselves. For this reason, students should pay close attention to all of the information presented in a diagram, including measurements, labels, and other visual cues.

Standardized Test Strategies

Any Question Type: Use a Diagram

Diagrams are often useful when you are solving problems. For some problems, a diagram is provided for you and you must correctly interpret it. In other situations, you can sketch your own diagram to help you visualize a problem.

EXAMPLE 

Short Response The height h of a square pyramid can be determined from the equation $h = \sqrt{\ell^2 - \left(\frac{s}{2}\right)^2}$, where ℓ is the slant height of the pyramid and s is the side length of the square base. What is the slant height ℓ of the square pyramid shown? Show your work.

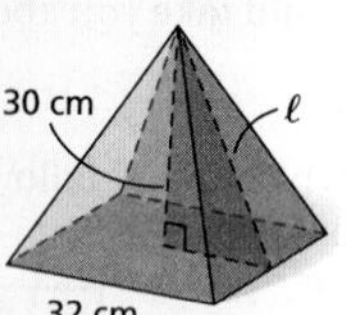

To solve this problem, you must use information from the diagram.

$30 = \sqrt{\ell^2 - \left(\frac{32}{2}\right)^2}$	*Substitute 30 for h and 32 for s.*
$30 = \sqrt{\ell^2 - 16^2}$	*Simplify.*
$900 = \ell^2 - 256$	*Square both sides.*
$1156 = \ell^2$	*Add 256 to both sides.*
$\pm 34 = \ell$	*Solve for ℓ.*

The slant height of the pyramid is 34 centimeters.

EXAMPLE 2

Multiple Choice A circular fountain with radius r feet is built into a square base with a side length of $3r$ feet. What is the probability that a penny hitting the square base at random will land in the circular fountain?

Ⓐ $\frac{\pi}{9}$ Ⓑ $\frac{\pi}{3}$ Ⓒ $\frac{1}{3}$ Ⓓ $\frac{1}{9}$

A diagram would be helpful with this problem. Sketch a square with side length 3r to represent the square base. Then sketch a circle inside it with radius r to represent the circular fountain.

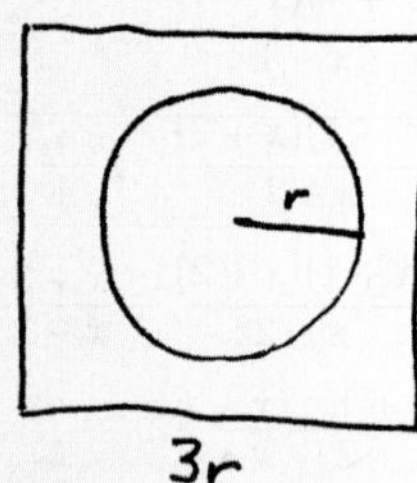

$\frac{\pi r^2}{(3r)^2}$	*The probability that the penny will land in the fountain is the ratio of the area of the fountain to the area of the base.*
$\frac{\pi r^2}{9r^2} = \frac{\pi}{9}$	*Simplify.*

The correct answer is A.

If you sketch your own diagram to help you solve a problem, be sure to label it with any measurements you are given.

Read each test item and answer the questions that follow.

Item A
Multiple Choice **What is the area of this composite figure?**

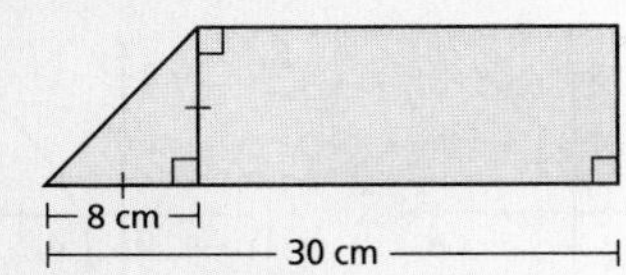

Ⓐ 176 cm^2 Ⓒ 240 cm^2

Ⓑ 208 cm^2 Ⓓ 272 cm^2

1. How can you use the information given in the diagram to determine the length of the rectangle?
2. Explain how you can use the diagram to determine the rectangle's width.
3. What is the area of the triangle? What is the area of the rectangle?

Item B
Multiple Choice **A square courtyard has a perimeter of 200 meters. What is the approximate length of a sidewalk that lies along one of the courtyard's diagonals?**

Ⓕ 50 meters Ⓗ 71 meters

Ⓖ 57 meters Ⓙ 87 meters

4. Sketch a diagram that can help you visualize the situation.
5. How can you use the information given in the problem to label each side of the courtyard in your diagram with its length?
6. Into what shapes does the diagonal sidewalk divide the courtyard?
7. What equation can you use to determine the length of the sidewalk?

Item C
Short Response **What are the measures of the three numbered angles of this triangle? Explain how you determined your answer.**

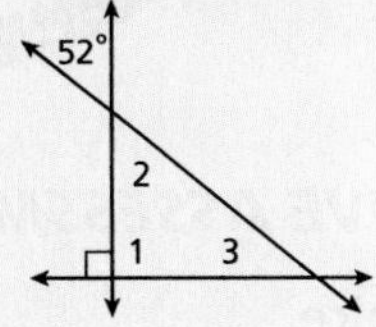

8. Based on the information in the diagram, what type of angle is $\angle 1$? What is its measure?
9. What is the relationship between the 52° angle and $\angle 2$? What is the measure of $\angle 2$?
10. How can you use the measures of $\angle 1$ and $\angle 2$ to determine the measure of $\angle 3$?

Item D
Extended Response **A rectangular pool is surrounded on all four sides by a tiled lounging area. The length of the pool is 5 feet greater than the width. The width of the lounging area is 10 feet greater than twice the width of the pool. The length of the lounging area is 5 times the width of the pool.**

a. Write a rational expression that represents the ratio of the area of the pool to the entire area of the pool and lounging area.

b. Determine the value of the ratio if the width of the pool is 30 feet.

11. Sketch a diagram that can help you visualize the situation.
12. Explain how you determined the labels for the dimensions of your diagram.
13. Is it necessary to draw your diagram to scale? Why or why not?
14. What expression represents the area of the pool? What expression represents the entire area of the pool and lounging area?

Answers

Possible answers:

1. Subtract the length of the leg of the right triangle from the length of the entire figure.
2. The marks on the diagram indicate that the legs of the right triangle are congruent. Because one of the legs measures 8 cm, the other leg does too. The length of the other leg is the same as the width of the rectangle. Therefore, the width of the rectangle is 8 cm.
3. 32 cm^2; 176 cm^2
4. 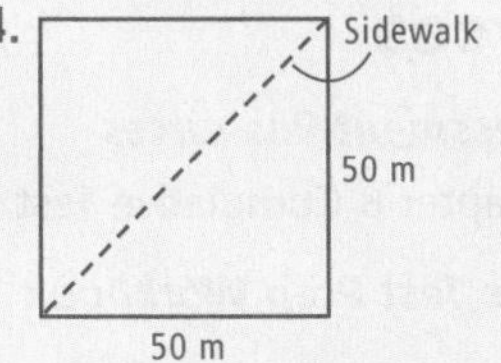

5. Because the courtyard is square, each of its sides has the same length. To find the side length of the courtyard, divide its perimeter by 4.
6. 2 right triangles
7. $50^2 + 50^2 = s^2$ or equivalent equation
8. a right angle; 90°
9. The 2 angles are vertical angles and are therefore congruent; 52°.
10. Subtract the sum of the measures of $\angle 1$ and $\angle 2$ from 180°.
11. 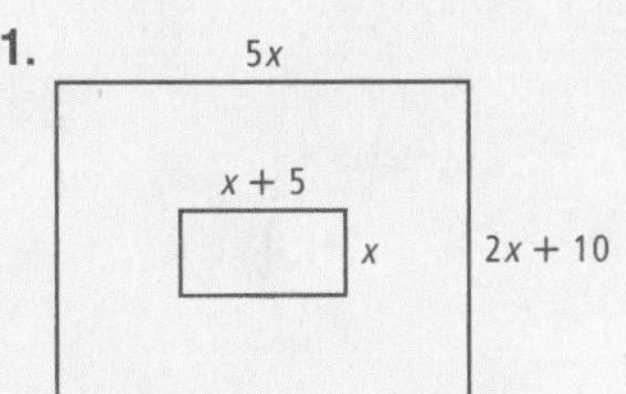

Answers to Test Items

A. B

B. H

C. $m\angle 1 = 90°$; $m\angle 2 = 52°$; $m\angle 3 = 38°$

Da. $\dfrac{x(x+5)}{(2x+10)(5x)}$ or equivalent expression

b. $\dfrac{1}{10}$

12. Let the width of the pool equal x ft. Then write expressions for each of the other dimensions in terms of x.
13. No; the diagram is simply a visual representation.
14. $x(x + 5)$ or equivalent expression; $5x(2x + 10)$ or equivalent expression

State Resources

go.hrw.com
State Resources Online
KEYWORD: MB7 Resources

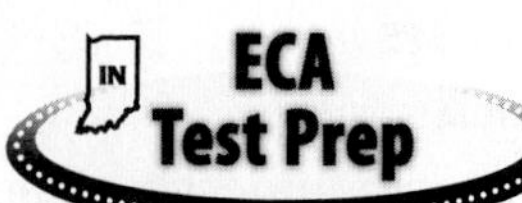

Organizer

Objective: Provide review and practice for Chapters 1–8 and standardized tests.

Resources

 ***Assessment Resources***

Chapter 8 Cumulative Test

 ***State Test Prep Workbook***

 ***State Test Prep CD-ROM***

 ***State Test Practice Online***

go.hrw.com
KEYWORD: MB7 TestPrep

Answers

1. D
2. C
3. B
4. C
5. A
6. C
7. A
8. D
9. D
10. C
11. B
12. A
13. D
14. A
15. A

 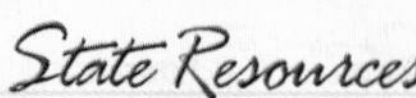

Core Standard	Items
1	13, 17
2	3
3	15, 18
4	11, 19
5	4, 12

CHAPTER 8

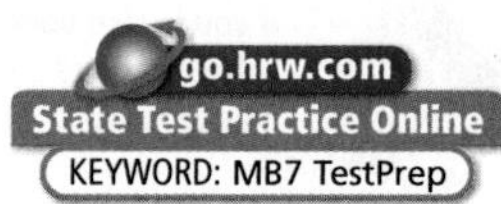

CUMULATIVE ASSESSMENT, CHAPTERS 1–8

Multiple Choice

1. Given: y varies jointly as x and z, and $y = 16$ when $x = \frac{1}{2}$ and $z = 8$. What equation represents the joint variation function?

A. $y = \frac{4x}{z}$

B. $y = 4x$

C. $y = \frac{1}{4}xz$

D. $y = 4xz$

2. What is the solution of the equation $\sqrt{3x + 2} = 3\sqrt{2x - 2}$?

A. $x = \frac{4}{15}$

B. $x = \frac{8}{15}$

C. $x = \frac{4}{3}$

D. $x = \frac{8}{3}$

3. Which is equivalent to $(3 - 5i)(2 + i)$?

A. 11

B. $11 - 7i$

C. $11 + 7i$

D. $1 - 7i$

4. Which is equivalent to $\frac{4x^2y^3}{5xy^2} \div \frac{2y}{10xy}$?

A. $\frac{4y}{25}$ **B.** $\frac{4x^2}{y}$

C. $4x^2y$ **D.** $4x^2y^5$

5. What is the slope of the line $3y = 2x + 9$?

A. $\frac{2}{3}$ **B.** $\frac{3}{2}$

C. 3 **D.** 9

6. Which expression can be simplified to a rational number?

A. $\sqrt{1} + \sqrt{8}$ **B.** $\sqrt{10} \cdot \sqrt{25}$

C. $(\sqrt{15})^2$ **D.** $\sqrt{\frac{20}{4}}$

7. Which is the graph of the function $f(x) = 4\sqrt{x + 2} - 3$?

A.

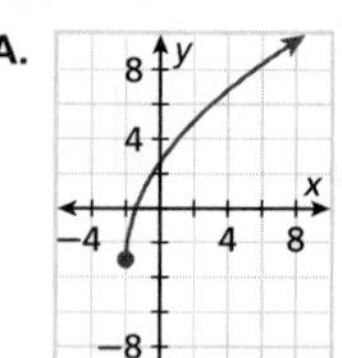

B.

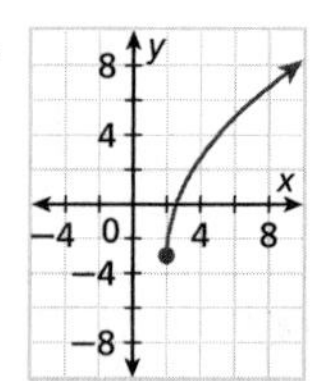

C.

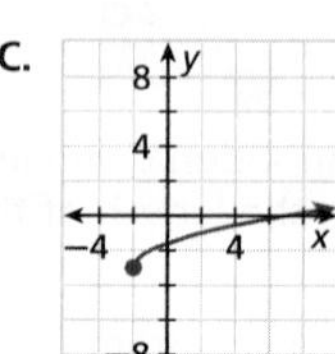

D.

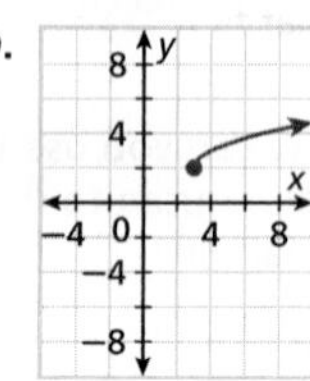

8. At track practice, Jamie ran 0.5 mile farther than twice the distance Rochelle ran. If x represents the distance in miles that Rochelle ran, which expression represents the distance that Jamie ran?

A. $0.5(2x)$ **B.** $0.5x + 2$

C. $2(x + 0.5)$ **D.** $2x + 0.5$

9. Which equation best describes the relationship between x and y shown in the table?

x	1	3	6	10	15
y	−1	5	14	26	41

A. $y = -3x + 2$

B. $y = -2x + 1$

C. $y = 2x - 3$

D. $y = 3x - 4$

10. A triangle with vertices at (1, 4), (−2, 3), and (5, 0) is translated 2 units right and 3 units down. Which are the coordinates of a vertex of the image?

A. (−5, 5) **B.** (−1, 1)

C. (0, 0) **D.** (3, 3)

TEST PREP DOCTOR

For **Item 7,** suggest that students choose a value for x and use it to determine the coordinates of a point on the function's graph. They can then use this point to eliminate one or more answer choices. For example, evaluating the function for $x = -2$ yields $f(-2) = 4\sqrt{-2 + 2} - 3 = -3$. Therefore, the correct graph must pass through the point (−2, −3), which eliminates all choices but **A** and **C.**

If you have extra time at the end of a test, go back and check your answers. Remember that you can always check the solution to an equation by substituting your answer to see if it makes the equation true.

11. What is the standard form of the expression $(2x^2 - x + 4) - (3x^3 + x^2 - 2x)$?

A. $-3x^3 - x^2 - 3x + 4$

B. $-3x^3 + x^2 + x + 4$

C. $x^2 + x + 4 - 3x^3$

D. $3x^3 + 3x^2 + 3x + 4$

12. At what point does the graph of $f(x) = \frac{2x^2 - x - 3}{x + 1}$ have a hole?

A. $(-1, -5)$ **B.** $(-1, 0)$

C. $(1.5, 0)$ **D.** $(1.5, 2.5)$

13. What function is graphed below?

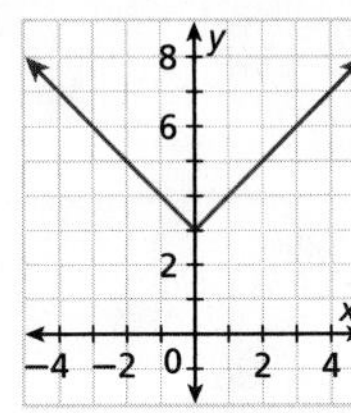

A. $f(x) = |3x|$ **B.** $f(x) = |x + 3|$

C. $f(x) = 3|x|$ **D.** $f(x) = |x| + 3$

14. What value of x makes the equation true?

$\frac{7}{4} = \frac{3}{x} + 1$

A. 4

B. 5

C. 6

D. 7

15. What value completes the square for the expression below?

$x^2 - 3x +$ ■

A. $\frac{9}{4}$

B. 9

C. 18

D. 36

Short Answer

16. The function $K = \frac{5}{9}(F - 32) + 273$ expresses temperature in kelvins K as a function of temperature in degrees Fahrenheit F.

Part A Find the inverse of the function.

Part B What does the inverse represent?

Part C Use the inverse to find the temperature in degrees Fahrenheit that is equivalent to 300 kelvins.

17. The WNBA Most Valuable Player award is given to the player with the greatest number of total points, which are tallied based on the number of first-, second-, and third-place votes that the player receives. The table shows the number of votes for the top three nominees in 2004. Find the number of points awarded for each vote.

Player	First-Place Votes	Second-Place Votes	Third-Place Votes	Total Points
L. Leslie	33	0	19	425
L. Jackson	15	18	15	351
D. Taurasi	0	13	7	126

18. The graph of $f(x) = \frac{1}{2}x^2 + c$ is a parabola with its vertex at $(0, 3)$.

Part A What is the value of c? Show or explain your work.

Part B Graph the function f.

Extended Response

19. The information in the table describes a polynomial function.

Leading Coefficient	1
Degree	3
Zeros	−1, 2, 4
Local Minimum	≈ −4.1
Local Maximum	≈ 8.2
y-intercept	8

Part A Describe the end behavior of the graph of the function. Show or explain your work.

Part B How many turning points does the graph of the function have? Show or explain your work.

Part C Sketch a graph of the function.

Short Answer Rubric

Items 16–18

Score 2 = Thorough understanding of mathematical concepts and processes.

Score 1 = Partial understanding of mathematical concepts and/or processes.

Score 0 = Limited or no understanding of the problem-solving concepts.

Blank = No written response.

Extended Response Rubric

Item 19

Score 4 = Thorough understanding of mathematical concepts and processes.

Score 3 = Demonstrated understanding of mathematical concepts and processes, but an error in computation or explanation.

Score 2 = Partial understanding of mathematical concepts and/or processes.

Score 1 = Limited understanding and execution of the problem-solving concepts.

Score 0 = No understanding of the problem-solving concepts.

Blank = No written response.

Answers

16. Part A: $F = \frac{9}{5}(K - 273) + 32$

Part B: The inverse expresses temperature in degrees Fahrenheit as a function of temperature in kelvins.

Part C: 80.6°F

17. 1st place: 10 points; 2nd place: 7 points; 3rd place: 5 points

18. Part A: 3; check students' explanations.

Part B:

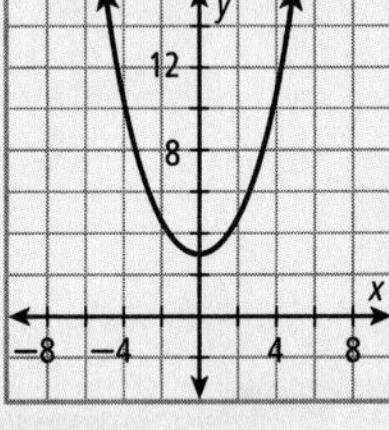

Answers

19. Part A: $P(x)$ is of odd degree with a positive leading coefficient. Therefore, as $x \to -\infty$, $P(x) \to -\infty$; as $x \to +\infty$, $P(x) \to +\infty$.

Part B: 2 turning points; possible answer: the function has a degree of 3 and 3 distinct real zeros; therefore, it has exactly 2 turning points.

Part C: Student's graphs should show a cubic polynomial function with zeros −1, 2, and 4, a y-intercept of 8, a local minimum of approximately −4.1 between the zeros −1 and 2, and a local maximum of approximately 8.2 between the zeros 2 and 4. Possible answer:

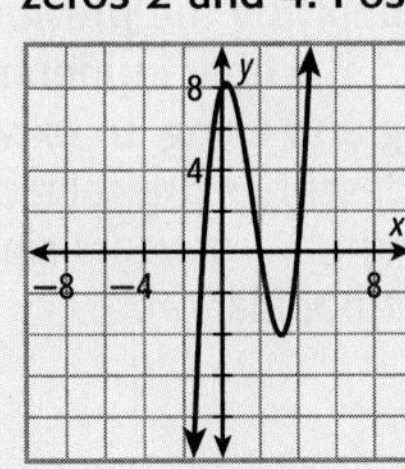

Problem Solving on Location

Organizer

Objective: Choose appropriate problem-solving strategies and use them with skills from Chapters 7 and 8 to solve real-world problems.

Online Edition

The Return of the Trumpeter Swan

Reading Strategies

Encourage students to list important information as they read a problem. In some cases, such as in **Problem 2,** students may find it helpful to use a table to organize the information about the number of trumpeter swans in each of the three main areas.

Using Data Before students do any calculations, have them examine the population data provided in the table. Ask students to "guesstimate" whether the population of trumpeter swans in 2004 was closer to 600, 700, or 800. Once students have determined an exponential model for the data, they can use it to verify their initial estimate.

State Resources

go.hrw.com
State Resources Online
KEYWORD: MB7 Resources

Problem Solving on Location

MICHIGAN

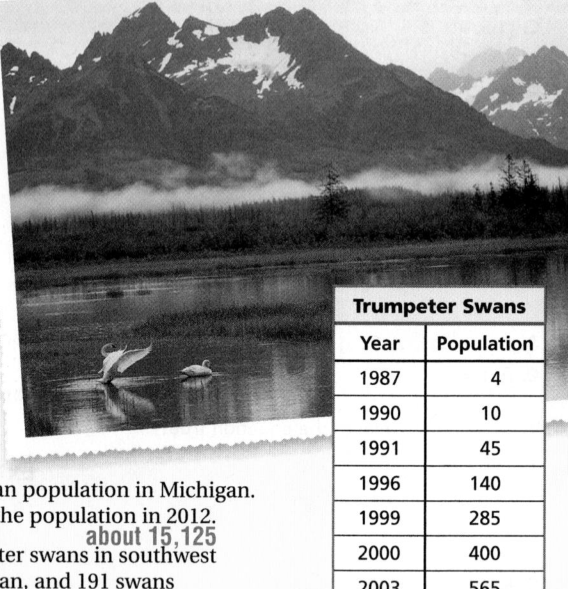

Trumpeter Swans	
Year	**Population**
1987	4
1990	10
1991	45
1996	140
1999	285
2000	400
2003	565

The Return of the Trumpeter Swan

The majestic trumpeter swan was once abundant throughout Michigan, but by 1900, the species had been hunted almost to extinction. Since 1985, the Detroit Zoo has been working with Michigan State University to reintroduce the species to Michigan's wetlands. The program has been a great success—the population of trumpeter swans continues to grow every year.

Choose one or more strategies to solve each problem. For 1–3, use the table.

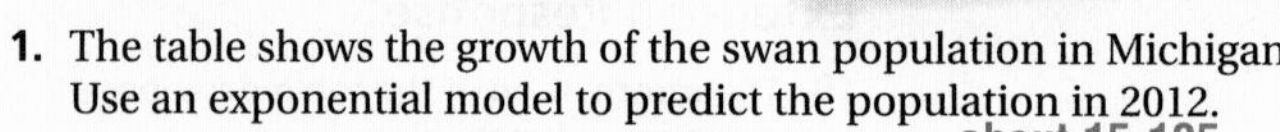

1. The table shows the growth of the swan population in Michigan. Use an exponential model to predict the population in 2012. **about 15,125**
2. In 2000, there were about 100 trumpeter swans in southwest Michigan, 50 swans in eastern Michigan, and 191 swans in Seney National Wildlife Refuge. If this population distribution continues, about how many swans will be in each region in 2012?
3. In what year do you predict that the total population of trumpeter swans in Michigan will exceed 6000? Justify your answer.
4. A cygnet is a young swan. In 1997, there were 60 trumpeter swan cygnets in Michigan. In each of the next 2 years, their population increased by 30% compared with the year before. If this rate of increase continues, in what year will the population of cygnets exceed 1500? **2010**

Problem-Solving Focus

Ask students to describe different strategies they can use to solve **Problem 4.** For example, some students may wish to make a table starting with the 1997 cygnet population and then calculate the population for each subsequent year by repeatedly multiplying the previous year's population by 1.3. Other students may suggest writing and using an exponential function that describes the relationship between the number of years since 1997 and the cygnet population.

Answers

2. southwest region: 3781; eastern region: 1891; Seney National Wildlife Refuge: 7222
3. 2010; possible answer: based on an exponential regression of the data, the population in 2009 will be 5912, and the population in 2010 will be 8085. Therefore, the population will exceed 6000 sometime in 2010.

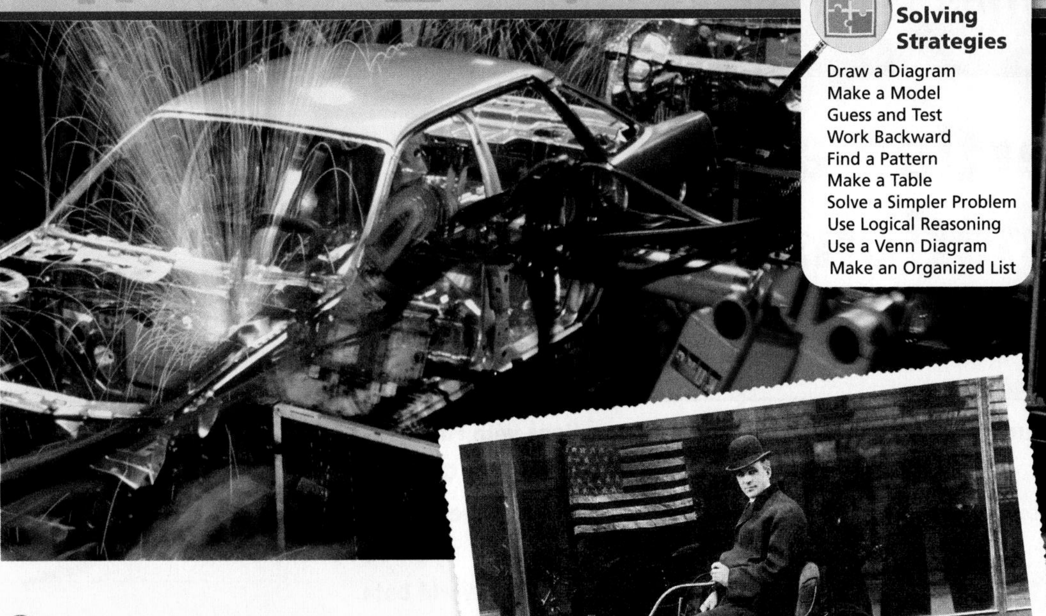

Problem Solving Strategies
Draw a Diagram
Make a Model
Guess and Test
Work Backward
Find a Pattern
Make a Table
Solve a Simpler Problem
Use Logical Reasoning
Use a Venn Diagram
Make an Organized List

The Motor City

In 1903, Henry Ford opened a small car company in Detroit that employed 10 people. Within a decade, Detroit had become the heart of America's automotive industry, earning it the nickname the "Motor City." Today, Detroit remains an important center for automotive research.

Choose one or more strategies to solve each problem. For 1–3, use the table.

1. Automotive engineers use the equation $s = \sqrt{30fd}$ to study the relationship between a vehicle's speed s in miles per hour and its stopping distance d in feet once the brakes have been applied. In this equation, f is the coefficient of friction, which depends in part on the condition of the road.
   a. Determine the coefficient of friction to the nearest tenth for dry pavement. 0.8
   b. Predict the stopping distance to the nearest foot for a vehicle moving at 65 mi/h. 176 ft

Stopping Distances on Dry Pavement	
Speed (mi/h)	Distance (ft)
10	4.2
20	16.8
30	37.8
40	67.2

2. For a vehicle on wet pavement, the coefficient of friction is 0.4. How does driving on wet pavement affect the stopping distance for a given speed?
3. Engineers want to design brakes that will reduce stopping distances by 10%. How would this change the equation relating speed and stopping distance?
4. The equation $v_{max} = \sqrt{14.88fr}$ gives the maximum velocity in miles per hour that a vehicle can safely travel around a curve that has a radius of r feet. If the velocity is greater than v_{max}, the tires will slip. Engineers find that under snowy conditions, $v_{max} = 15$ mi/h for a freeway off-ramp that has a radius of 50 ft. To the nearest tenth, what is the coefficient of friction for the off-ramp in these conditions? 0.3

Answers

2. Driving on wet pavement doubles the stopping distance for a given speed as compared with driving on dry pavement.
3. The new equation would be $s = \sqrt{30f(0.9d)}$, which simplifies to $s = \sqrt{27fd}$.

The Motor City

Reading Strategies

ENGLISH LANGUAGE LEARNERS

Be sure students understand the meaning of the word *friction* before they begin solving the problems. Explain that friction is a force that acts when one object, such as a tire, moves against another, such as a road. The force of friction acts to slow the tires' motion. Have students use the context of **Problem 1** to figure out what is meant by a coefficient of friction. a measure of the amount of friction between a vehicle's tires and the road

Using Data Have students briefly discuss the data in the table. You may wish to ask the following questions: How does stopping distance change as vehicle speed increases? Does the data generally fit students' own observations when driving or riding in a car? Does it seem reasonable that a car traveling at 40 mi/h would be able to stop in about 67 ft?

Problem-Solving Focus

For **Problem 2,** focus on the first two steps of the Problem-Solving Process.

(1) Understand the Problem: Ask students what type of answer is required. In this case, they will need to compare the function for stopping distance on wet pavement to the function for stopping distance on dry pavement.

(2) Make a Plan: Once students understand what type of answer is required, ask them how they can determine the function for stopping distance on wet pavement. by substituting 0.4 for f in the function given in **Problem 1** Ask how they can determine the function for stopping distance on dry pavement. by using the value of f for dry pavement calculated in **Problem 1** Point out that students can compare the values of these functions by evaluating them for a particular speed, such as 60 mi/h.

Properties and Attributes of Functions

Section 9A	Section 9B
Functions and Their Graphs	**Functional Relationships**
9-1 Multiple Representations of Functions	**9-4 Operations with Functions**
9-2 Piecewise Functions	**Connecting Algebra to Geometry** Geometric Formulas
9-2 Technology Lab Graph Piecewise Functions	**9-5 Functions and Their Inverses**
9-3 Transforming Functions	**9-6 Technology Lab** Explore Differences and Ratios
	9-6 Modeling Real-World Data

Pacing Guide for 45-Minute Classes

Chapter 9

Countdown to Testing Weeks 19, 20

DAY 1	DAY 2	DAY 3	DAY 4	DAY 5
9-1 Lesson	9-1 Lesson	9-2 Lesson	9-2 Technology Lab	9-3 Lesson
DAY 6	**DAY 7**	**DAY 8**	**DAY 9**	**DAY 10**
Multi-Step Test Prep Ready to Go On? 9-4 Lesson	9-4 Lesson Connecting Algebra to Geometry	9-5 Lesson	9-6 Technology Lab	9-6 Lesson
DAY 11	**DAY 12**			
9-6 Lesson Multi-Step Test Prep Ready to Go On?	Chapter 9 Test			

Pacing Guide for 90-Minute Classes

Chapter 9

DAY 1	DAY 2	DAY 3	DAY 4	DAY 5
Chapter 8 Test 9-1 Lesson	9-1 Lesson 9-2 Lesson	9-2 Technology Lab 9-3 Lesson	Multi-Step Test Prep Ready to Go On? 9-4 Lesson Connecting Algebra to Geometry	9-5 Lesson 9-6 Technology Lab
DAY 6	**DAY 7**			
9-6 Lesson Multi-Step Test Prep Ready to Go On?	Chapter 9 Test 10-1 Lesson			

ONGOING ASSESSMENT and INTERVENTION

	DIAGNOSE	PRESCRIBE
Assess Prior Knowledge	**Before Chapter 9**	
	Diagnose readiness for the chapter.	Prescribe intervention.
	Are You Ready? SE p. 651	***Are You Ready? Intervention*** Skills 58, 63, 64, 86
Formative Assessment	**Before Every Lesson**	
	Diagnose readiness for the lesson.	Prescribe intervention.
	Warm Up TE, every lesson	**Skills Bank** SE pp. S46–S73
		Reteach CRB, Ch. 1–9
	During Every Lesson	
	Diagnose understanding of lesson concepts.	Prescribe intervention.
	Check It Out! SE, every example	**Questioning Strategies** TE, every example
	Think and Discuss SE, every lesson	**Reading Strategies** CRB, every lesson
	Write About It SE, every lesson	***Success for ELL*** pp. 129–140
	Journal TE, every lesson	
	After Every Lesson	
	Diagnose mastery of lesson concepts.	Prescribe intervention.
	Lesson Quiz TE, every lesson	**Reteach** CRB, every lesson
	Alternative Assessment TE, every lesson	**Problem Solving** CRB, every lesson
	Test Prep SE, every lesson	**Test Prep Doctor** TE, every lesson
	Test and Practice Generator	***Homework Help Online***
	Before Chapter 9 Testing	
	Diagnose mastery of concepts in the chapter.	Prescribe intervention.
	Ready to Go On? SE pp. 682, 707	***Ready to Go On? Intervention*** pp. 146–160
	Multi-Step Test Prep SE pp. 681, 706	**Scaffolding Questions** TE pp. 680, 706
	Section Quizzes AR pp. 165–166	
	Test and Practice Generator	
	Before High Stakes Testing	
	Diagnose mastery of benchmark concepts.	Prescribe intervention.
	College Entrance Exam Practice SE p. 713	***College Entrance Exam Practice***
	Standardized Test Prep SE pp. 716–717	***State Test Prep Workbook***
	***State Test Prep* CD-ROM**	
Summative Assessment	**After Chapter 9**	
	Check mastery of chapter concepts.	Prescribe intervention.
	Multiple-Choice Tests (Forms A, B, C)	**Reteach** CRB, every lesson
	Free-Response Tests (Forms A, B, C)	***Lesson Tutorial Videos*** Chapter 9
	Performance Assessment AR pp. 167–180	
	Test and Practice Generator	
	Check mastery of benchmark concepts.	Prescribe intervention.
	AYP State Tests	***State Test Prep Workbook***
	College Entrance Exams	***College Entrance Exam Practice***

KEY: **SE** = *Student Edition* **TE** = *Teacher's Edition* **CRB** = *Chapter Resource Book* **AR** = *Assessment Resources*  Available on CD-ROM Available online

Supporting the Teacher

Chapter 9 Resource Book

Practice A, B, C
pp. 3–5, 11–13, 19–21, 27–29, 35–37, 43–45

Reading Strategies ELL
pp. 10, 18, 26, 34, 42, 50

Reteach
pp. 6–7, 14–15, 22–23, 30–31, 38–39, 46–47

Problem Solving
pp. 9, 17, 25, 33, 41, 49

Challenge
pp. 8, 16, 24, 32, 40, 48

Parent Letter pp. 1–2

Transparencies

Lesson Transparencies, Volume 3 .... Chapter 9
- Warm Ups
- Teaching Transparencies
- Additional Examples
- Lesson Quizzes

Alternate Openers: Explorations 65–70

Countdown to Testing 37–40

Know-It Notebook .... Chapter 9
- Graphic Organizers

Teacher Tools

Power Presentations®
Complete PowerPoint® presentations for Chapter 9 lessons

Lesson Tutorial Videos®
Holt authors Ed Burger and Freddie Renfro present tutorials to support the Chapter 9 lessons.

One-Stop Planner®
Easy access to all Chapter 9 resources and assessments, as well as software for lesson planning, test generation, and puzzle creation

IDEA Works!®
Key Chapter 9 resources and assessments modified to address special learning needs

Lesson Plans .... pp. 65–70

Solutions Key .... Chapter 9

Algebra Posters

TechKeys

Lab Resources 

Project Teacher Support

Parent Resources 

Workbooks

Homework and Practice Workbook
Teacher's Guide .... pp. 65–70

Know-It Notebook
Teacher's Guide .... Chapter 9

Problem Solving Workbook
Teacher's Guide .... pp. 65–70

State Test Prep Workbook
Teacher's Guide

Technology Highlights for the Teacher

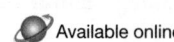

Power Presentations

Dynamic presentations to engage students. Complete PowerPoint® presentations for every lesson in Chapter 9.

2-1 Solving One-Step Equations

Isolate a variable by using inverse operations which "undo" operations on the variable.

An equation is like a balanced scale. To keep the balance, perform the same operation on both sides.

Inverse Operations	
Operation	**Inverse Operation**
Addition	Subtraction
Subtraction	Addition

One-Stop Planner

Easy access to Chapter 9 resources and assessments. Includes lesson-planning, test-generation, and puzzle-creation software.

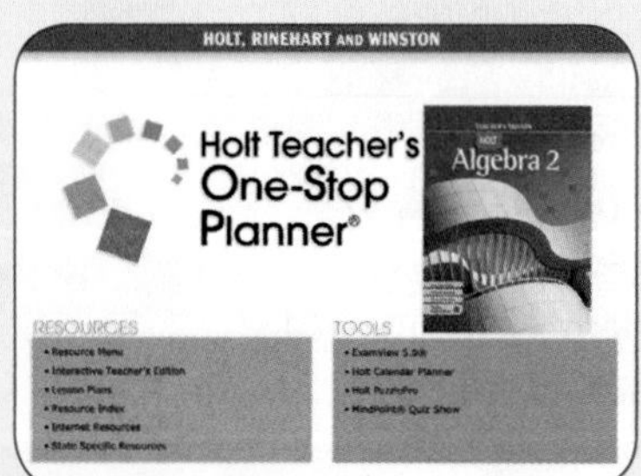

Premier Online Edition

Chapter 9 includes Tutorial Videos, Lesson Activities, Lesson Quizzes, Homework Help, and Chapter Project.

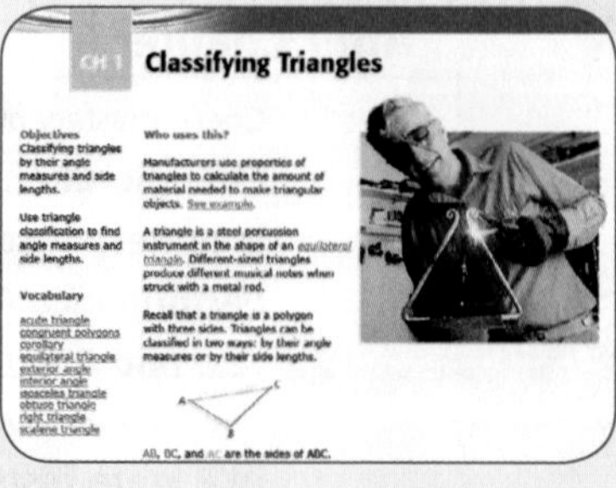

KEY: **SE** = *Student Edition* **TE** = *Teacher's Edition* ELL English Language Learners Available on CD-ROM Available online

CHAPTER 9

Reaching All Learners

Resources for All Learners

DEVELOPING LEARNERS

ON-LEVEL LEARNERS

ADVANCED LEARNERS

English Language Learners

ENGLISH LANGUAGE LEARNERS

Reaching All Learners Through...

Technology Highlights for Reaching All Learners

Lesson Tutorial Videos

Starring Holt authors Ed Burger and Freddie Renfro! Live tutorials to support every lesson in Chapter 9.

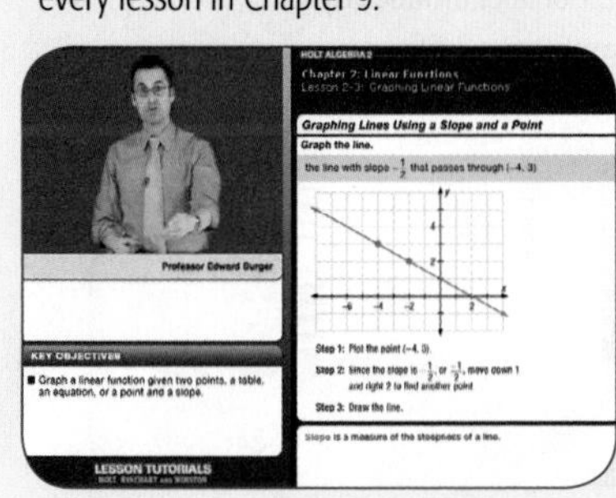

Multilingual Glossary

Searchable glossary includes definitions in English, Spanish, Vietnamese, Chinese, Hmong, Korean, and 4 other languages.

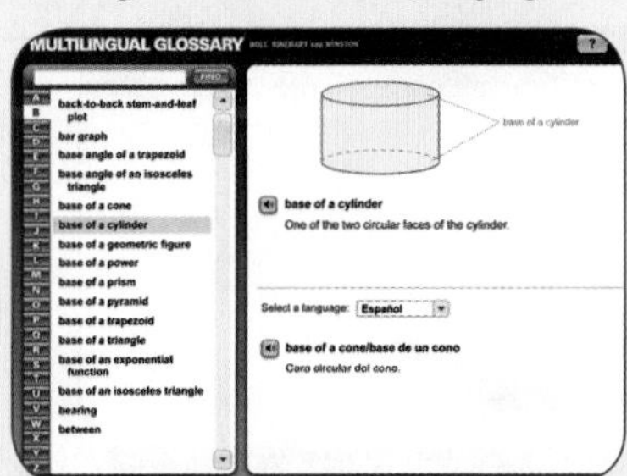

Online Interactivities

Interactive tutorials provide visually engaging alternative opportunities to learn concepts and master skills.

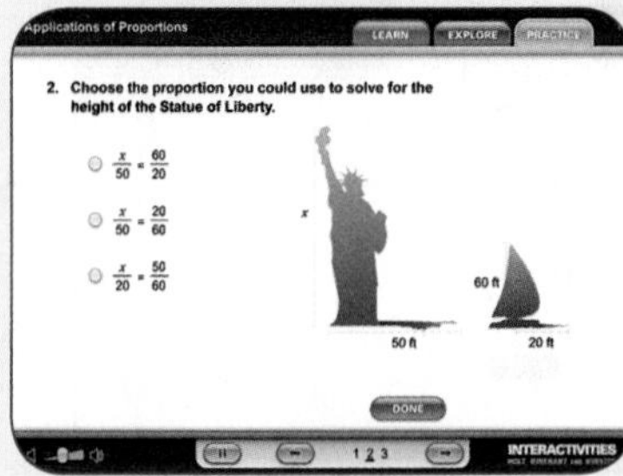

KEY: **SE** = *Student Edition* **TE** = *Teacher's Edition* **CRB** = *Chapter Resource Book* Available on CD-ROM 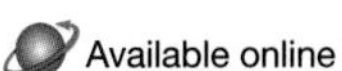 Available online

Ongoing Assessment

Assessing Prior Knowledge

Determine whether students have the required prerequisite concepts and skills for success in Chapter 9.

Are You Ready? SPANISH .... SE p. 651
Warm Up .... TE, every lesson

Test Preparation

Provide review and practice for Chapter 9 and standardized tests.

Multi-Step Test Prep .... SE pp. 681, 706
Study Guide: Review .... SE pp. 708–711
Test Tackler .... SE pp. 714–715
Standardized Test Prep .... SE pp. 716–717
College Entrance Exam Practice .... SE p. 713
***Countdown to Testing* Transparencies** 37–40
State Test Prep Workbook
***State Test Prep* CD-ROM**
IDEA Works!

Alternative Assessment

Assess students' understanding of Chapter 9 concepts and combined problem-solving skills.

Chapter 9 Project .... SE p. 650
Alternative Assessment .... TE, every lesson
Performance Assessment .... AR pp. 179–180
Portfolio Assessment .... AR p. xxxiv

Daily Assessment

Provide formative assessment for each day of Chapter 9.

Questioning Strategies .... TE, every example
Think and Discuss .... SE, every lesson
Check It Out! Exercises .... SE, every example
Write About It .... SE, every lesson
Journal .... TE, every lesson
Lesson Quiz .... TE, every lesson
Alternative Assessment .... TE, every lesson
Modified Lesson Quizzes .... *IDEA Works!*

Weekly Assessment

Provide formative assessment for each week of Chapter 9.

Multi-Step Test Prep .... SE pp. 681, 706
Ready to Go On? .... SE pp. 682, 707
Cumulative Assessment .... SE pp. 716–717
Test and Practice Generator .... *One-Stop Planner*

Formal Assessment

Provide summative assessment of Chapter 9 mastery.

Section Quizzes .... AR pp. 165–166
Chapter 9 Test .... SE p. 712
Chapter Test (Levels A, B, C) .... AR pp. 167–178
• Multiple Choice • Free Response
Cumulative Test .... AR pp. 181–184
Test and Practice Generator .... *One-Stop Planner*
Modified Chapter 9 Test .... *IDEA Works!*

Technology Highlights for Ongoing Assessment

Are You Ready? SPANISH

Automatically assess readiness and prescribe intervention for Chapter 9 prerequisite skills.

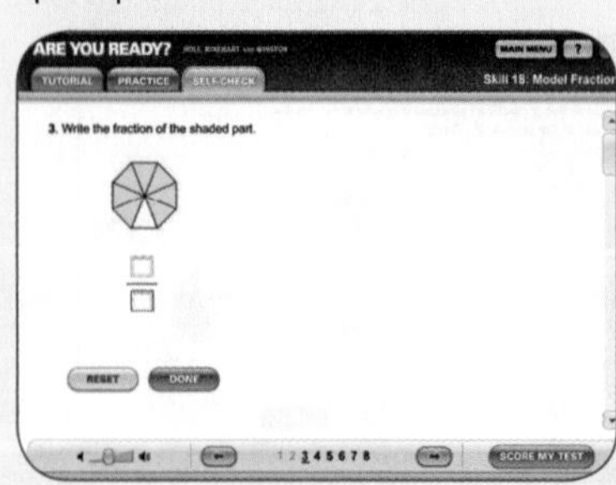

Ready to Go On?

Automatically assess understanding and prescribe intervention for Sections 9A and 9B.

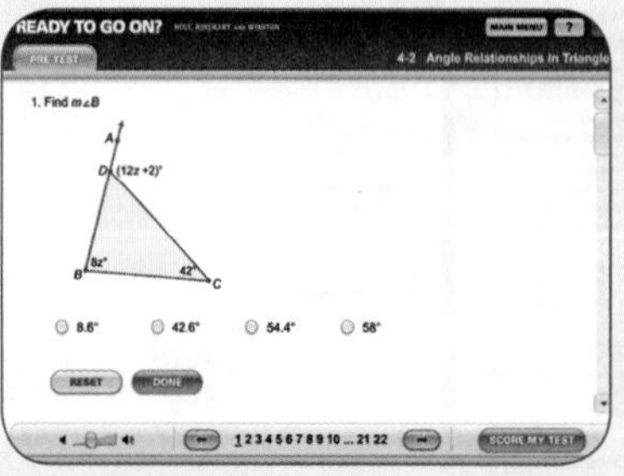

Test and Practice Generator

Use Chapter 9 problem banks to create assessments and worksheets to print out or deliver online. Includes dynamic problems.

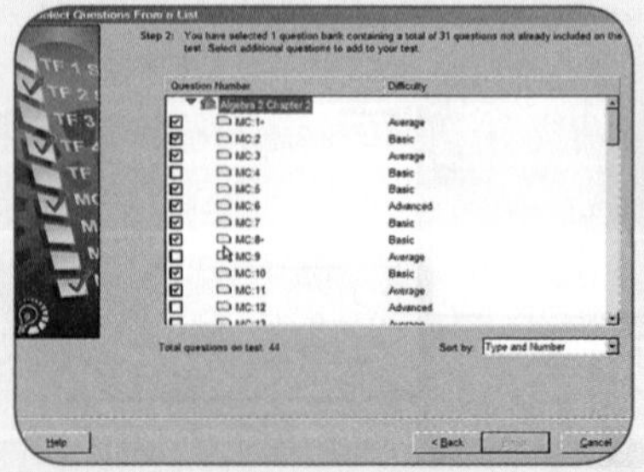

KEY: **SE** = *Student Edition* **TE** = *Teacher's Edition* **AR** = *Assessment Resources*  Spanish version available  Available on CD-ROM Available online

Formal Assessment

Three levels (A, B, C) of multiple-choice and free-response chapter tests are available in the *Assessment Resources.*

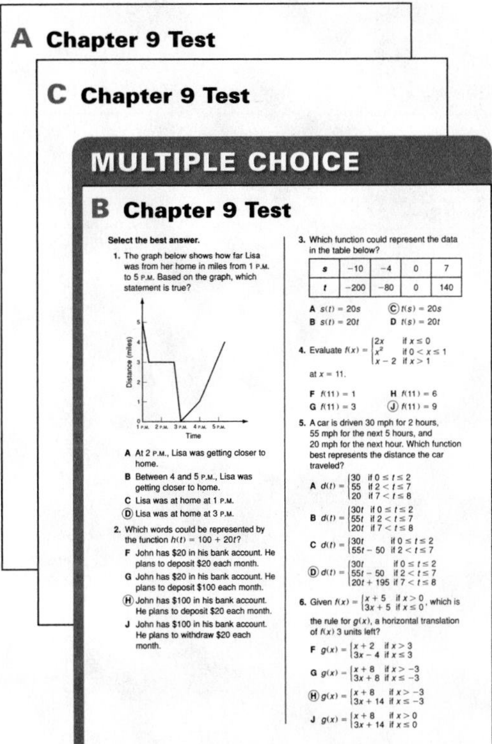

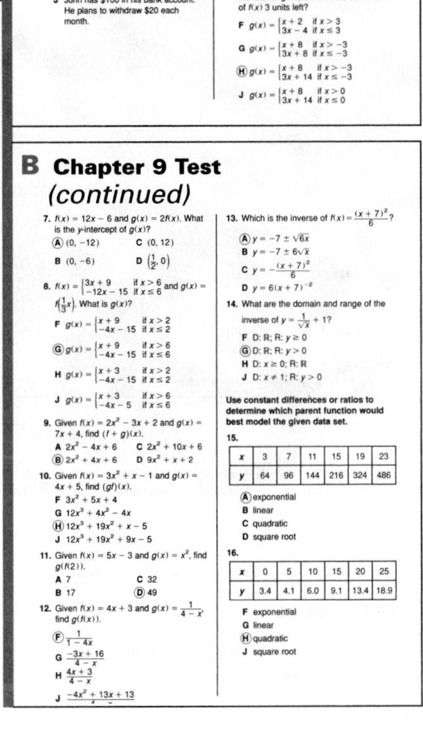

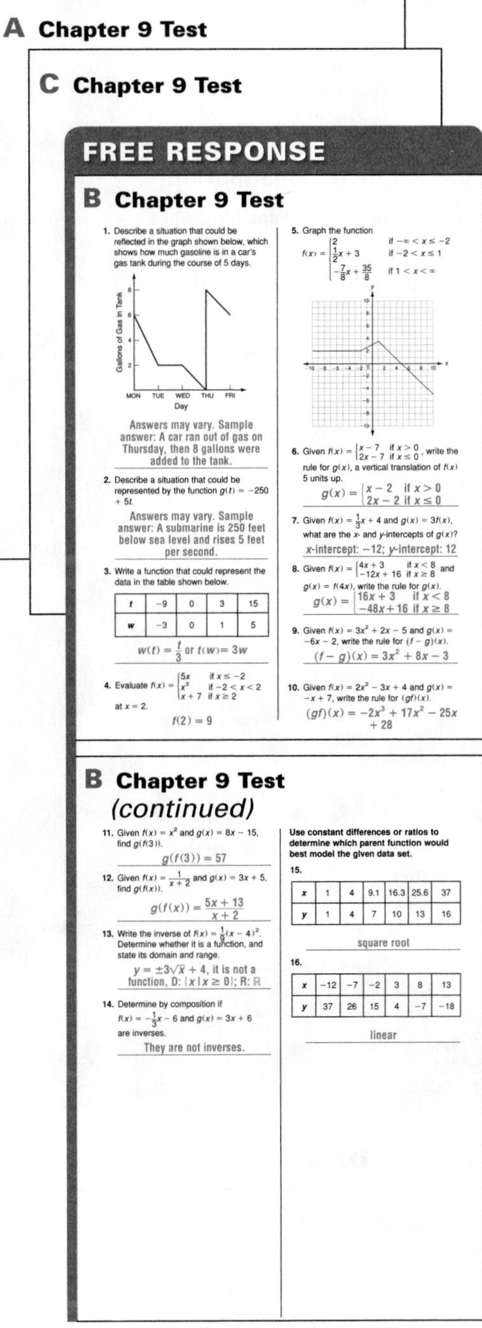

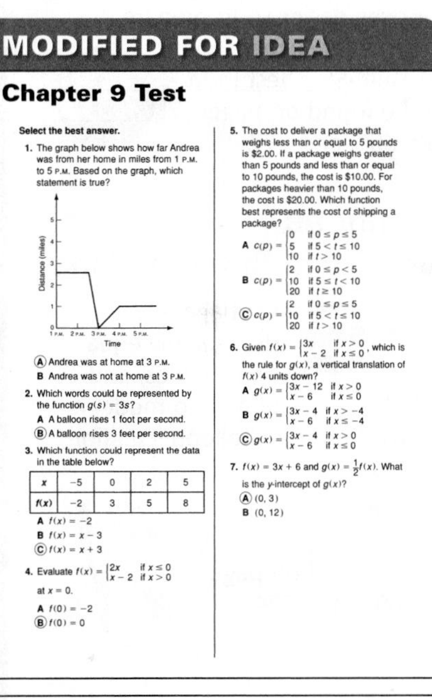

Test & Practice Generator
One-Stop Planner®

Create and customize Chapter 9 Tests. Instantly generate multiple test versions, answer keys, and practice versions of test items.

CHAPTER 9

SECTION 9A
Functions and Their Graphs

On page 680, students write, solve, and graph equations to model real-world reaction time situations.

Exercises designed to prepare students for success on the Multi-Step Test Prep can be found on pages 660, 668, and 677.

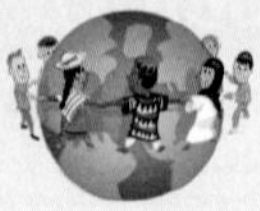

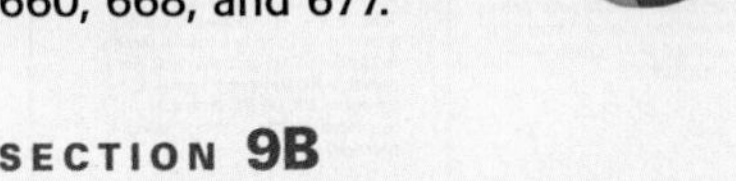

SECTION 9B
Functional Relationships

On page 706, students apply equations, tables, and graphs to model a real-world hot-air balloon situation.

Exercises designed to prepare students for success on the Multi-Step Test Prep can be found on pages 687, 695, and 704.

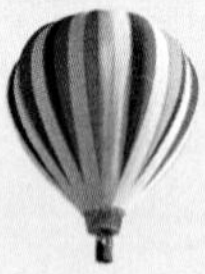

CHAPTER 9

Properties and Attributes of Functions

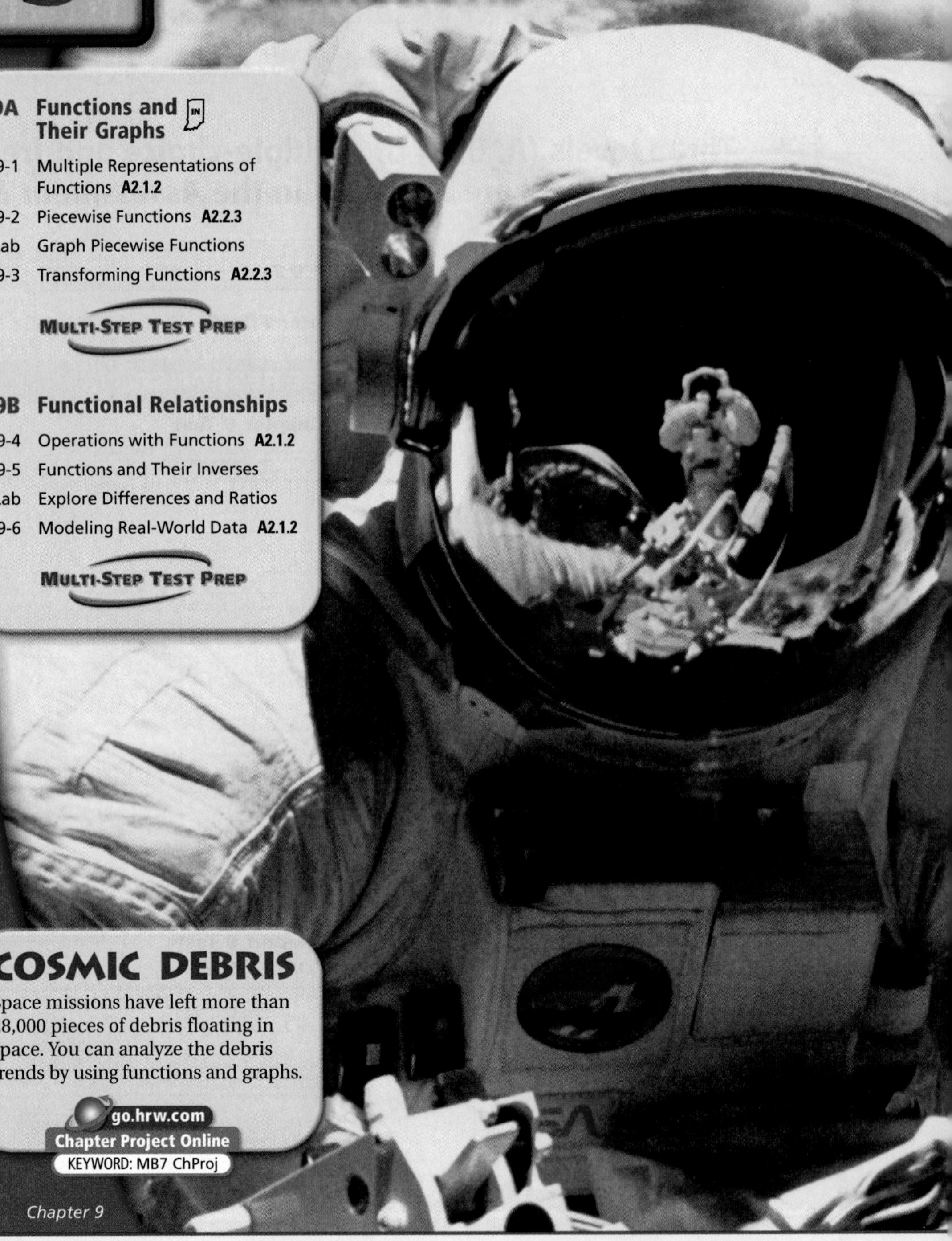

COSMIC DEBRIS

Space missions have left more than 28,000 pieces of debris floating in space. You can analyze the debris trends by using functions and graphs.

go.hrw.com
Chapter Project Online
KEYWORD: MB7 ChProj

Cosmic Debris

About the Project

In the Chapter Project, students analyze data involving the debris left behind by space missions. Students use the data to create a functional model that can be used to make predictions and answer questions about the growing amount of debris in space.

Project Resources

All project resources for teachers and students are provided online.

Materials:

- graphing calculator

ARE YOU READY?

Vocabulary

Match each term on the left with a definition on the right.

1. translation D
2. slope B
3. regression A
4. correlation E

A. the statistical study of the relationship between variables
B. the constant rate of change of a linear function
C. the ratio between two sets of measurements
D. a transformation that moves each point in a figure or graph the same distance in the same direction
E. a measure of the strength and direction of the linear relationship between two variables

Connect Words and Algebra

Write an equation to represent each situation.

5. The cost of renting a recording studio is \$30 for the first hour and \$20 for each additional hour. $c = 30 + 20(h - 1)$
6. The volume of water in a tank is equal to 30 gallons plus 8 gallons for every minute the pump is on. $V = 8m + 30$

Line Graphs

Find each value for the graph of $f(x)$ shown.

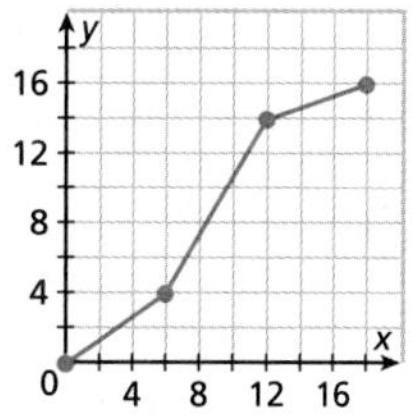

7. $f(6)$ 4
8. $f(15)$ 15
9. x such that $f(x) = 2$ 3
10. x such that $f(x) = 9$ 9
11. Find the slope of the line segment between $x = 6$ and $x = 12$. $\frac{5}{3}$
12. Find the slope of the line segment between $x = 12$ and $x = 18$. $\frac{1}{3}$

Multiply Binomials

Multiply. Then simplify.

13. $(x - 6)(x + 4)$ $x^2 - 2x - 24$
14. $(6 - x)(4 - x)$ $x^2 - 10x + 24$
15. $(5x + 8)(2x - 7)$ $10x^2 - 19x - 56$
16. $(x^2 - 7)(4x + 5)$ $4x^3 + 5x^2 - 28x - 35$
17. $(3x^2 + 8)(7x^2 + 8)$ $21x^4 + 80x^2 + 64$
18. $(x - 8)(x + 8)$ $x^2 - 64$

Simplify Polynomial Expressions

Simplify.

19. $8(3x^5) - (2x)^3(5x^2)$ $-16x^5$
20. $5(x + 3)^2 - 6(x + 3)$ $5x^2 + 24x + 27$
21. $3x(4 - x^3) - 6x^2(x + 4)$ $-3x^4 - 6x^3 - 24x^2 + 12x$
22. $3x^3(x^2 + 4) - x(x^4 - 5)$ $2x^5 + 12x^3 + 5x$

CHAPTER 9

ARE YOU READY?

Organizer

Objective: Assess students' understanding of prerequisite skills.

Prerequisite Skills

Connect Words and Algebra
Line Graphs
Multiply Binomials
Simplify Polynomial Expressions

Assessing Prior Knowledge

INTERVENTION

Diagnose and Prescribe

Use this page to determine whether intervention is necessary or whether enrichment is appropriate.

Resources

Are You Ready? Intervention and Enrichment **Worksheets**

Are You Ready? **CD-ROM**

Are You Ready? **Online**

my.hrw.com

ARE YOU READY?

Diagnose and Prescribe

NO INTERVENE

Prerequisite Skill	*Are You Ready? Intervention,* Chapter 9 Worksheets	CD-ROM	Online
Connect Words and Algebra	Skill 58	Activity 58	Diagnose and Prescribe Online
Line Graphs	Skill 86	Activity 86	
Multiply Binomials	Skill 64	Activity 64	
Simplify Polynomial Expressions	Skill 63	Activity 63	

Are You Ready? Enrichment, Chapter 9
Worksheets
CD-ROM
Online

Organizer

Objective: Help students organize the new concepts they will learn in Chapter 9.

Online Edition
Multilingual Glossary

Resources

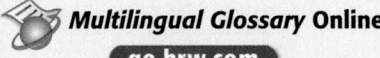

***Multilingual Glossary* Online**

go.hrw.com
KEYWORD: MB7 Glossary

Answers to *Vocabulary Connections*

1. Possible answer: A composition of functions is when you put 2 functions together.
2. Possible answer: No, a graph that looks like stairs would not be a function because of the vertical segments between steps. A step function might be like a set of steps with the vertical parts deleted.
3. Possible answer: A one-to-one function is a function where there is only 1 input for each output. A linear function, such as $f(x) = x + 1$, is one-to-one. A function of the prices for a number of items is one-to-one. Quadratic functions are not one-to-one because they can have 2 x-values for 1 y-value. A function of people to the number of letters in their names is not one-to-one because names may have the same number of letters.

CHAPTER 9 Study Guide: Preview

Where You've Been

Previously, you

- studied different functions, graphs, and equations.
- transformed linear, quadratic, exponential, and radical functions.
- performed operations on many types of expressions.
- used linear, quadratic, and exponential functions to model real-world data.

In This Chapter

You will study

- multiple representations of functions.
- transforming piecewise functions.
- performing operations on functions and function inverses.
- using various functions to model real-world data.

Where You're Going

You can use the skills in this chapter

- in all of your future math classes, including Calculus and Statistics.
- in other classes, such as Health, Chemistry, Physics, and Economics.
- outside of school to model data and make predictions in sports, travel, and finance.

Key Vocabulary/Vocabulario

composition of functions	composición de funciones
one-to-one function	función uno a uno
piecewise function	función a trozos
step function	función escalón

Vocabulary Connections

To become familiar with some of the vocabulary terms in the chapter, consider the following. You may refer to the chapter, the glossary, or a dictionary if you like.

1. One definition of the word *composition* is "the act or process of putting together." How can you use this definition of *composition* to understand **composition of functions** in mathematics?
2. Imagine looking at a set of stairs from the side. Would a graph that looked like stairs represent a function? What might a **step function** look like?
3. Recall the definition of a function. What do you think a **one-to-one function** is? Give examples of functions from mathematics and from real life that are one-to-one functions and that are not one-to-one functions.

652 Chapter 9

Reading Strategy: Read Problems for Understanding

Read a problem once to become aware of the concept being reviewed. Then read it again slowly and carefully to identify what the problem is asking. As you read, highlight key information given in the problem statement. When dealing with a multi-step problem, break the problem into parts and then make a plan to solve it.

19. Space Exploration On Earth, the function $f(x) = \frac{6}{5}\sqrt{x}$ approximates the distance in miles to the horizon observed by a person whose eye level is x feet above the ground. The graph of the corresponding function for Mars is a horizontal stretch of f by a factor of about $\frac{9}{5}$. Write the corresponding function g for Mars, and use it to estimate the distance to the horizon for an astronaut whose eyes are 6 ft above Mars's surface.

Step	Question	Answer
Step 1	What concept is being reviewed?	• transforming a rational function by changing its parameters
Step 2	What are you being asked to do?	• Rewrite the function to include the new parameter. • Evaluate the revised function for a given value.
Step 3	What is the key information needed to solve the problem?	• The function $f(x) = \frac{6}{5}\sqrt{x}$ represents the distance on Earth • The function for Mars is a horizontal stretch by a factor of $\frac{9}{5}$ • The astronaut's eye level on Mars is 6 ft.
Step 4	What is my plan to solve this multi-part problem?	• Revise the given function to account for horizontal stretch on Mars. • Evaluate the revised function for $x = 6$.

Try This

For each problem, complete each step in the four-step method described above.

1. A rectangle has a length of $(x + 5)$ units and a width of $(x + 4)$ units. Write and graph a rational function R to represent the ratio of the area to the perimeter. Identify a reasonable domain and range of the function.

2. The diameter d (in inches) of a rope needed to lift w tons is given by $d = \frac{\sqrt{15w}}{\pi}$. How much more can be lifted with a rope 1.25 inches in diameter than with a rope 0.75 inch in diameter?

Reading and Writing Math

Organizer

Objective: Help students apply strategies to understand and retain key concepts.

Resources

Chapter 9 Resource Book
Reading Strategies

ENGLISH LANGUAGE LEARNERS

Reading Strategy: Read Problems for Understanding

Discuss Reading a problem carefully can be critical, especially in complex problems containing extraneous information. In addition, reading a problem carefully can save students the work of solving a part of the problem that is not asked for.

Extend When developing piecewise functions to represent situations, students might easily miss an important detail if they do not approach problems methodically. As students work through the chapter, encourage them to try this approach with some of the more challenging exercises that are not already broken into steps.

Answers

1. **Step 1** rational functions; **Step 2** Write and graph a rational function, and identify a reasonable domain and range. **Step 3** rectangle: length $(x + 5)$ units, width $(x + 4)$ units; **Step 4** Find the area, find the perimeter, write a function representing the ratio of area to perimeter, graph the function, and then identify a reasonable domain and range.
2. **Step 1** solving radical equations; **Step 2** Find how much more can be lifted with a rope 1.25 in. in diameter than with a rope 0.75 in. in diameter. **Step 3** The diameter d in inches of a rope needed to lift w tons is given by $d = \frac{\sqrt{15w}}{\pi}$. How much more can be lifted with a rope 1.25 in. in diameter than with a rope 0.75 in. in diameter? **Step 4** Find w for $d = 1.25$ in., find w for $d = 0.75$ in., and then subtract the 2 values.

SECTION 9A

Functions and Their Graphs

One-Minute Section Planner

Lesson	Lab Resources	Materials
Lesson 9-1 Multiple Representations of Functions • Translate between the various representations of functions. • Solve problems by using the various representations of functions. ☐ SAT-10 ☑ NAEP ☑ ACT ☐ SAT ☑ SAT Subject Tests		**Optional** graphing calculator
Lesson 9-2 Piecewise Functions • Write and graph piecewise functions. • Use piecewise functions to describe real-world situations. ☐ SAT-10 ☐ NAEP ☐ ACT ☐ SAT ☑ SAT Subject Tests		
9-2 Technology Lab Graph Piecewise Functions • Use a graphing calculator to graph piecewise functions. ☐ SAT-10 ☐ NAEP ☐ ACT ☐ SAT ☑ SAT Subject Tests	***Technology Lab Activities*** 9-2 Lab Recording Sheet	**Required** graphing calculator
Lesson 9-3 Transforming Functions • Transform functions. • Recognize transformations of functions. ☐ SAT-10 ☐ NAEP ☑ ACT ☑ SAT ☑ SAT Subject Tests	***Algebra Lab Activities*** 9-3 Algebra Lab	**Optional** tracing paper or patty paper

MK = *Manipulatives Kit*

Section Overview

Multiple Representations of Functions — Lesson 9-1

Why? Sometimes one representation of a function is more useful than another.

A table can be used to show park attendance at specific times of the day.

Time	10:00 A.M.	2:00 P.M.	6:00 P.M.
Attendance	575	916	2172

A graph can be used to show *trends* in park attendance.

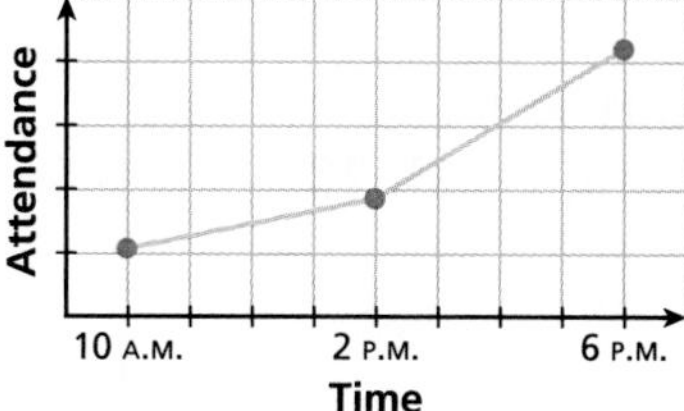

Piecewise Functions — Lesson 9-2

Why? Piecewise functions, functions that have different rules on different parts of their domain, are used to represent real-world situations.

A worker earns $8 per hour for the first 40 hours worked in one week. The worker earns time and a half, or $12, for each hour worked in excess of 40.

This piecewise function represents the worker's weekly wages as a function of the hours x worked in one week.

$$f(x) = \begin{cases} 8x & \text{if } 0 \le x \le 40 \\ 12x - 160 & \text{if } x > 40 \end{cases}$$

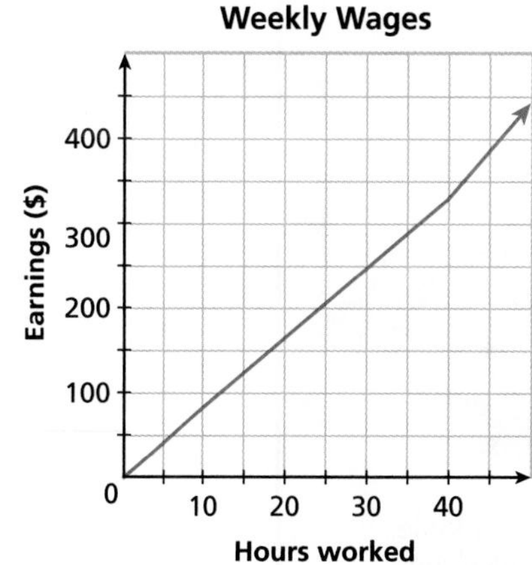

Transforming Functions — Lesson 9-3

Why? Students have seen transformations of various functions so far. All transformations of functions can be summarized.

Transformations of $f(x)$	
Horizontal Translation	**Vertical Translation**
$f(x) \rightarrow f(x - h)$ $h > 0$: right; $h < 0$: left	$f(x) \rightarrow f(x) + k$ $k > 0$: up; $k < 0$: down
Reflection Across y-axis	**Reflection Across x-axis**
$f(x) \rightarrow f(-x)$	$f(x) \rightarrow -f(x)$
Horizontal Stretch/Compression	**Vertical Stretch/Compression**
$f(x) \rightarrow f\left(\frac{x}{b}\right)$ $b > 1$: stretch; $0 < b < 1$: compression	$f(x) \rightarrow a \cdot f(x)$ $a > 1$: stretch; $0 < a < 1$: compression

9-1 Organizer

Pacing: Traditional 2 days
Block 1 day

Objectives: Translate between the various representations of functions.

Solve problems by using the various representations of functions.

Online Edition
Tutorial Videos, TechKeys

Countdown to Testing Week 19

Power Presentations with PowerPoint®

Warm Up

Create a table of values for each function.

1. $y = 2x - 3$

x	1	2	3	4	5
y	−1	1	3	5	7

2. $f(x) = 4x - x^2$

x	1	2	3	4	5
$f(x)$	3	4	3	0	−5

Also available on transparency

Math Humor

Teacher: Would you use a table, graph, or equation to solve this problem?

Student: A table . . . then I could sit down and eat while I worked.

9-1 Multiple Representations of Functions

A2.1.2 Use and interpret function notation, including evaluation of functions represented by tables, graphs, words, equations or a set of ordered pairs.

Objectives

Translate between the various representations of functions.

Solve problems by using the various representations of functions.

Who uses this?

An amusement park manager can use representations of functions, such as graphs and tables, to analyze ticket sales. (See Example 1.)

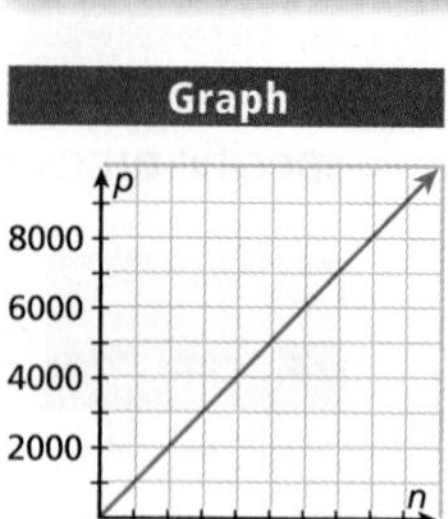

An amusement park manager estimates daily profits by multiplying the number of tickets sold by 20. This verbal description is useful, but other representations of the function may be more useful.

Equation

$p = 20n$

or

$p(n) = 20n$

Table

n	p
50	1000
100	2000
150	3000
200	4000

Graph

These different representations can help the manager set, compare, and predict prices.

EXAMPLE 1 ***Business Application***

A manager at an amusement park monitors the ticket sales at the park over a four-day weekend. Match each situation to one of the following graphs. Sketch a possible graph of the situation if the situation does not match any of the given graphs.

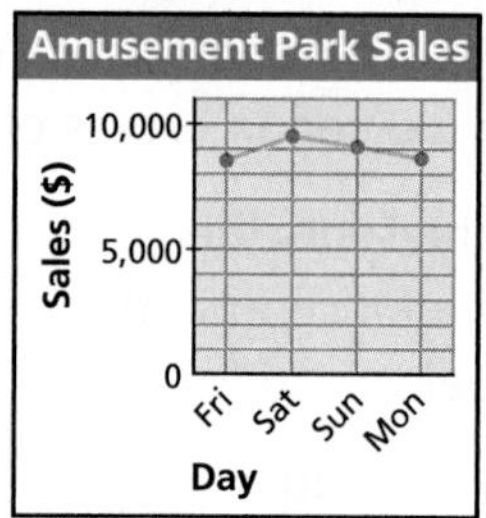

Graph 1

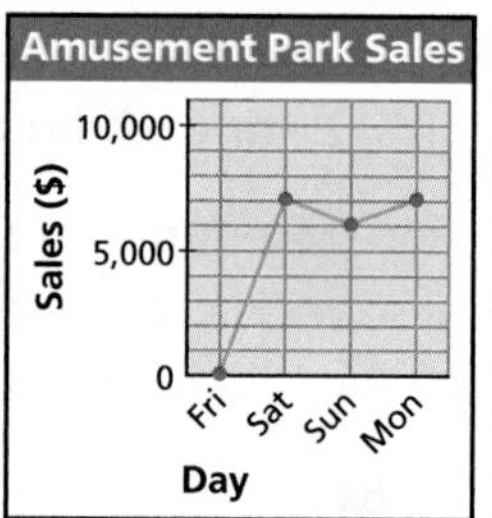

Graph 2

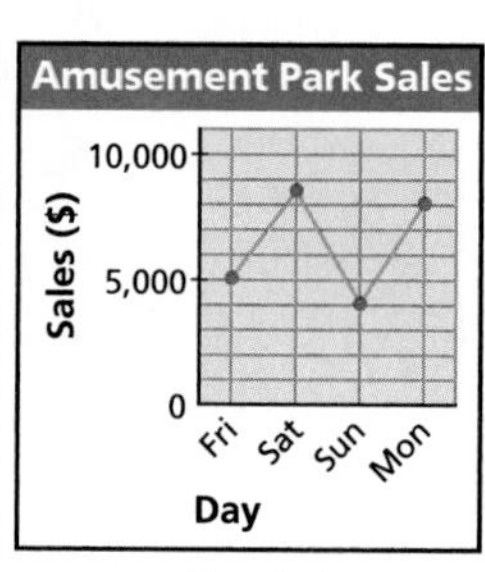

Graph 3

A **The park was closed on Friday for repairs.**
graph 2 *The graph shows no ticket sales on Friday.*

B **The park hosted a big concert on Saturday and a parade on Monday.**
graph 3 *The graph shows increased ticket sales on Saturday and Monday.*

C **The park was very busy during the holiday weekend.**
graph 1 *The graph shows high ticket sales every day.*

State Resources

go.hrw.com
State Resources Online
KEYWORD: MB7 Resources

1 Introduce

EXPLORATION

9-1 Multiple Representations of Functions

Many real-world situations can be represented with a verbal description, a graph, a table, and an equation.

1. Complete the table for the graph shown here.

Time (min)	Volume (gal)
0	
10	
20	
30	
40	

Volume of Water in Tank

2. Write a verbal description of the situation shown on the graph.
3. How many gallons are drained from the tank every 10 minutes? How many gallons are drained every minute?
4. Write an equation for the situation, where x is the time in minutes and y is the volume of water in the tank in gallons.

THINK AND DISCUSS

5. Discuss the advantages and disadvantages of using a graph to represent the situation.
6. Discuss the advantages and disadvantages of using an equation to represent the situation.

Motivate

Show students a quadratic function, its graph, and a table of values. Ask students to find the minimum and maximum. Discuss which representation makes answering the question easiest. Using the graph should be the easiest method. Explain that each representation has its advantages and disadvantages.

Explorations and answers are provided in the *Explorations* binder.

What if...? Sketch a possible graph to represent the following.

1a. The weather was beautiful on Friday and Saturday, but it rained all day on Sunday and Monday.

1b. Only $\frac{1}{2}$ of the rides were running on Friday and Sunday.

Because each representation of a function (words, equation, table, or graph) describes the same relationship, you can often use any representation to generate the others.

1a.

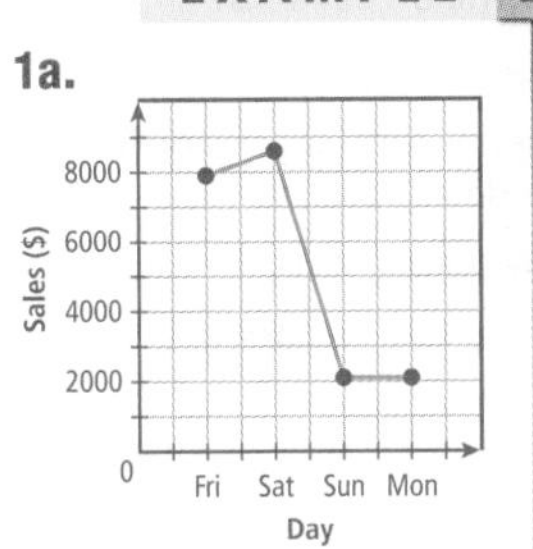

1b.

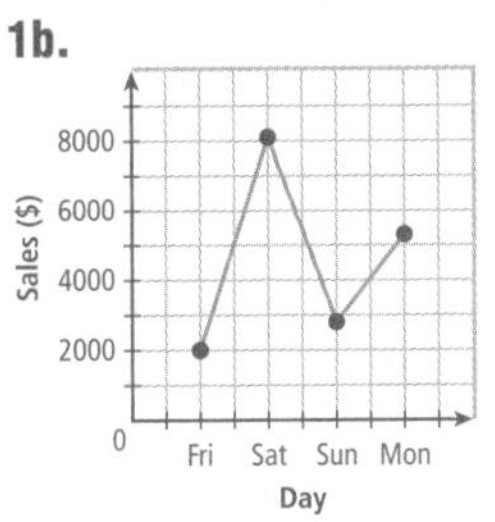

EXAMPLE 2 *Recreation Application*

Kurt is rappelling down a 500-foot cliff at a rate of 6 feet per second. Create a table, equation, and graph to represent Kurt's height from the ground with relation to time. When will Kurt reach the ground?

Step 1 Create a table.

Let t be the time in seconds and h be Kurt's height, in feet, from the ground.

Kurt begins at a height of 500 feet, and the height decreases by 6 feet each second.

t	h	
0	500	
1	494	500 − 6
2	488	500 − 6(2)
3	482	500 − 6(3)
4	476	500 − 6(4)
5	470	500 − 6(5)

Step 2 Write an equation.

Height	is equal to	500	minus	6 feet per second.
h	$=$	500	$-$	$6t$

Step 3 Find the intercepts and graph the equation.

h-intercept: 500

Solve for t when $h = 0$.

$h = 500 - 6t$

$0 = 500 - 6t$

$-500 = -6t$

$t = \frac{-500}{-6} = 83\frac{1}{3}$

t-intercept: $83\frac{1}{3}$

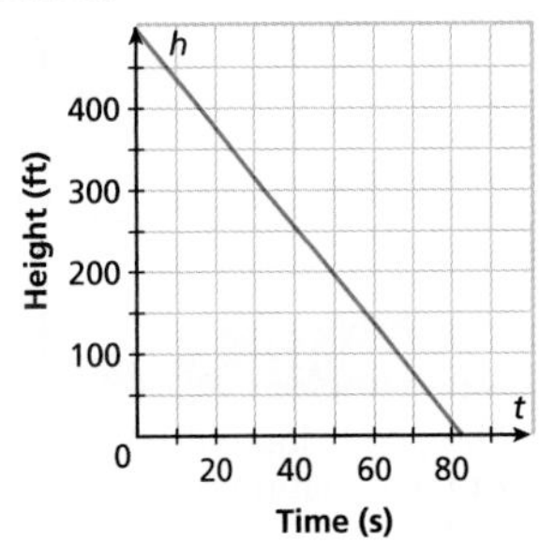

Kurt will reach the ground after $83\frac{1}{3}$ seconds.

2.

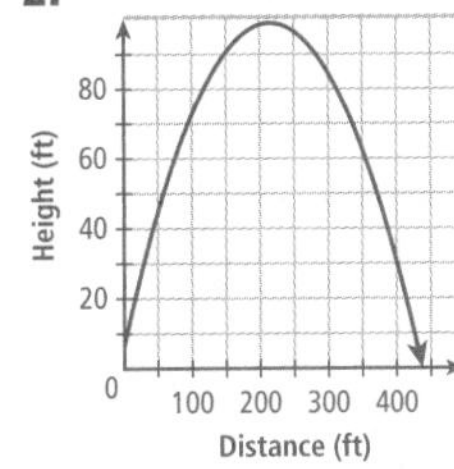

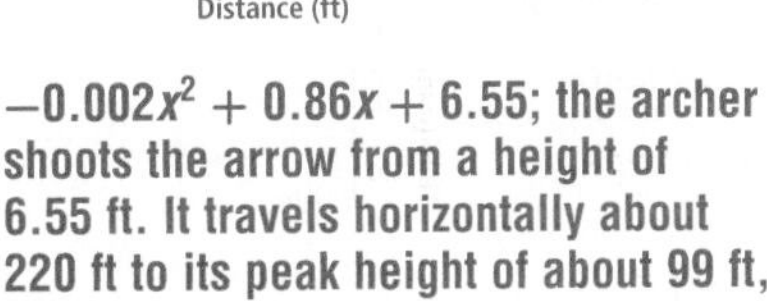

$-0.002x^2 + 0.86x + 6.55$; the archer shoots the arrow from a height of 6.55 ft. It travels horizontally about 220 ft to its peak height of about 99 ft, and then it lands on the ground about 500 ft away.

CHECK IT OUT!

2. The table shows the height, in feet, of an arrow in relation to its horizontal distance from the archer. Create a graph, an equation, and a verbal description to represent the height of the arrow with relation to its horizontal distance from the archer.

Arrow Distance and Height

Distance from Archer (ft)	0	75	150	225	300	375
Height (ft)	6.55	59.80	90.55	98.80	84.50	47.50

2 Teach

Guided Instruction

Explain to students how an equation, a table, and a graph can express the same relationship. While reviewing **Example 1,** make sure that students are able to analyze trends in graphs. Provide opportunities for students to practice translating between various representations of functions, and emphasize that one representation can be used to generate the others.

INTERVENTION
Questioning Strategies

EXAMPLE 1

- How does the shape of the graph relate to the sales each day?

EXAMPLE 2

- Could you solve the problem by creating a graph or an equation first?

Power Presentations with PowerPoint®

Additional Examples

Example 1

Sketch a possible graph to represent the following.

Ticket sales were good until a massive power outage happened on Saturday that was not repaired until late Sunday.

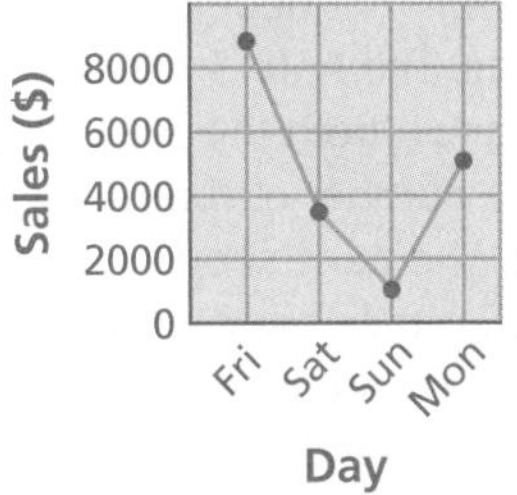

Example 2

Janet is rowing across an 80-meter-wide river at a rate of 3 meters per second. Create a table, an equation, and a graph of the distance that Janet has remaining before she reaches the other side. When will Janet reach the shore?

Time (s)	Distance (m)
0	80
1	77
2	74
3	71
4	68

$d = 80 - 3t$

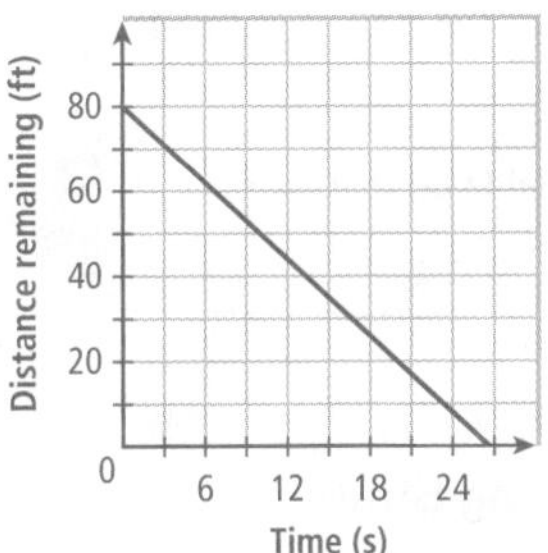

$26\frac{2}{3}$ s

Also available on transparency

Teaching Tip

Inclusion Have students create a poster of the table describing translation methods to display on the classroom wall. Students can reference the table during class discussions and while completing the exercises.

Power Presentations with PowerPoint®

Additional Examples

Example 3

A. A hotel manager knows that the number of rooms that guests will rent depends on the price. The hotel's revenue depends on both the price and the number of rooms rented. The table shows the hotel's average nightly revenue based on room price. Use a graph and an equation to find the price that the manager should charge in order to maximize his revenue.

Price per Room ($)	Revenue ($)
70	21,000
80	22,400
90	23,400
100	24,000

\$110

B. An investor buys a property for \$100,000. Experts expect the property to increase in value by about 6% per year. Use a table, a graph, and an equation to predict the number of years it will take for the property to be worth more than \$150,000. 7 yr

Also available on transparency

Know it! Note

Translating Between Multiple Representations	
When given a(n)...	**Try to...**
Table	• Find finite differences or ratios to determine which parent function best describes the data. • Graph points as ordered pairs and look for a pattern. • Match the data to the related parent function, if applicable, and perform a regression.
Graph	• Identify which parent function the graph most resembles, and then use key points (intercepts, maxima, minima, and so on) from the graph to help write an equation. • Locate several points on the graph and write them in a table. • Use slope; increasing, decreasing, or constant intervals; and intercepts to write a verbal description.
Equation	• Make a table of values. You may use a graphing calculator. • Make a graph by using transformations of parent functions or a graphing calculator.
Verbal Description	• Identify dependent and independent variables, and write an algebraic equation. • Generate a table of values by using the pattern described. • Sketch a graph of the situation by using hints from the description about increasing, decreasing, or constant intervals, as well as intercepts.

EXAMPLE 3 Using Multiple Representations to Solve Problems

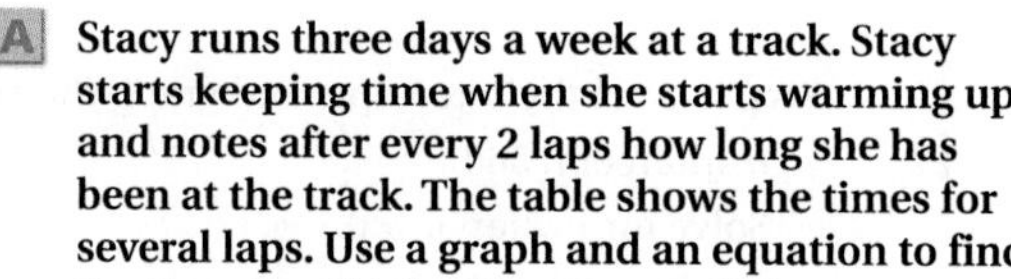

A **Stacy runs three days a week at a track. Stacy starts keeping time when she starts warming up and notes after every 2 laps how long she has been at the track. The table shows the times for several laps. Use a graph and an equation to find the time it will take Stacy to run 20 laps.**

Stacy's Time	
Laps	**Time (min)**
2	13
4	16
6	19
8	22
10	25

Step 1 Graph the data.

The data appear to be linear.

Step 2 Write a linear equation.

Let x = the number of laps and y = the time in minutes.

$m = \frac{y_2 - y_1}{x_2 - x_1} = \frac{16 - 13}{4 - 2} = \frac{3}{2}$ *Find the slope. Use any two points.*

$y - y_1 = m(x - x_1)$ *Point-slope form*

$y - 13 = \frac{3}{2}(x - 2)$ *Use (2, 13) and slope $\frac{3}{2}$.*

$y = \frac{3}{2}x + 10$ *Simplify.*

Step 3 Evaluate the function for 20 laps.

$y = \frac{3}{2}(20) + 10 = 40.$

It will take Stacy 40 minutes to complete 20 laps.

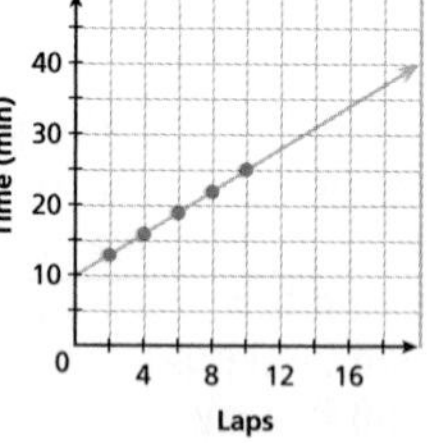

Remember!

The point-slope form of the equation of a line is $y - y_1 = m(x - x_1)$, where m is the slope and (x_1, y_1) is a point on the line. (Lesson 2-4)

INTERVENTION

Questioning Strategies

EXAMPLE 3

- What clues help you determine whether a function is linear, quadratic, or exponential?
- Does the order in which you choose to find multiple representations matter? Explain.

Reaching All Learners

Through Cooperative Learning

Have students work in small groups to come up with a situation that can be described by a function. One student in each group can create a graph, another a table, and another an equation. When the students are finished, each group can present its multiple representations to the entire class.

B **The owner of an orange grove finds that if 26 trees are planted per acre, each mature tree yields about 576 oranges per year. For each additional tree planted per acre, the number of oranges produced annually by each tree decreases by 12. Use a table, a graph, and an equation to find how many trees per acre should be planted to maximize the yield per acre.**

Make a table for an acre of orange trees. Because the orchard owner is interested in the total number of oranges, make a graph by using trees t as the independent variable and total oranges as the dependent variable.

Orange Tree Yield

Trees	Oranges per Tree	Total Oranges
26	576	14,976
27	564	15,228
28	552	15,456
29	540	15,660
30	528	15,840
31	516	15,996
32	504	16,128

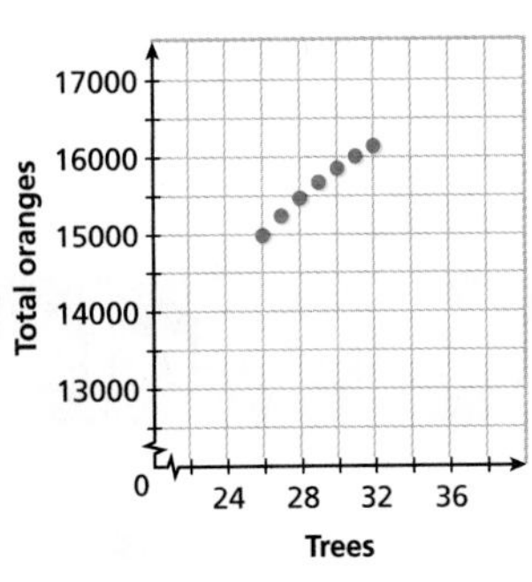

The data do not appear to be linear, so check finite differences.

Total oranges	14,976	15,228	15,456	15,660	15,840	15,996	16,128
First differences	252	228	204	180	156	132	
Second differences	−24	−24	−24	−24	−24		

Because the second differences are constant, a quadratic model is appropriate. Use a graphing calculator to perform a quadratic regression on the data.

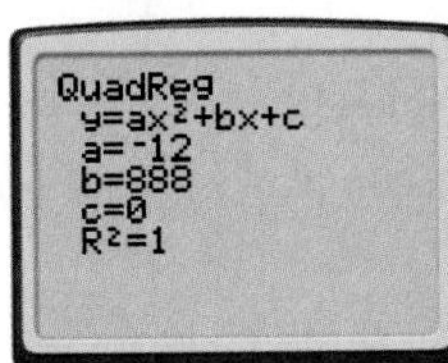

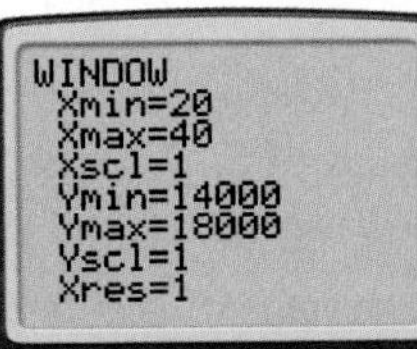

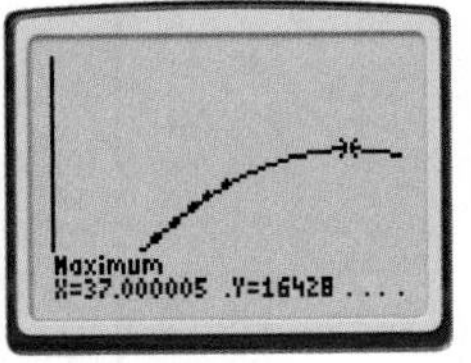

The equation $y = -12x^2 + 888x$ models the data, and the graph appears to fit. Use the **TRACE** or **MAXIMUM** feature to identify the maximum orange yield.

The maximum occurs when 37 trees are planted on each acre.

Remember!

First differences are constant in linear functions. Second differences are constant in quadratic functions. (Lesson 5-9)

3. Bartolo opened a new sporting goods business and has recorded his sales each week. To break even, Bartolo needs to sell $48,000 worth of merchandise in a week. Assuming the sales trend continues, use a graph and an equation to find the number of weeks before Bartolo breaks even.

Bartolo's Sales

Week	Sales ($)
1	25,000
2	27,500
3	30,250
4	33,275
5	36,603

3.

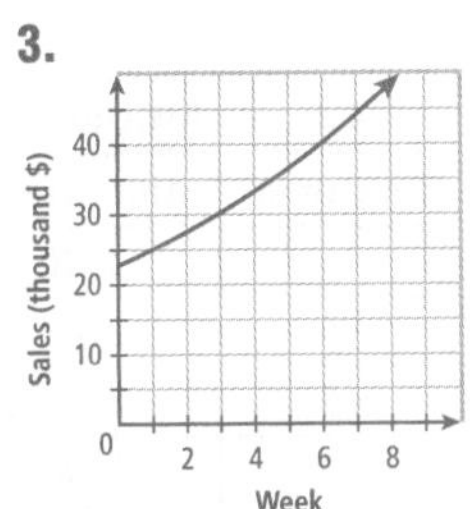

$f(x) \approx 22{,}727.15(1.1)^x$; 8 weeks

COMMON ERROR ALERT

Students may look at the graph in **Example 3B** and incorrectly assume that the data set is linear. A quick check of first differences will show that it is not linear but quadratic. Encourage students to use multiple representations to check their work.

Critical Thinking Students may use an alternate method to solve **Example 3B.** By letting x equal the number of additional trees planted, students can write the yield function $y = (24 + x)(600 - 12x)$, a factored form of the equation generated through a regression.

Reading Math For **Check It Out Problem 3,** remind students that to "break even" means to have sales revenue equal to costs.

ENGLISH LANGUAGE LEARNERS

3 Close

Summarize

Remind students that there are often multiple ways to represent a problem, including graphs, tables, equations, and verbal descriptions. Review the table on page 656. Remind students to consider which representation(s) would be most useful for solving a given problem.

ONGOING ASSESSMENT and INTERVENTION

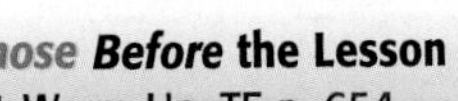

***Diagnose Before* the Lesson**
9-1 Warm Up, TE p. 654

***Monitor During* the Lesson**
Check It Out! Exercises, SE pp. 654–657
Questioning Strategies, TE pp. 655–656

***Assess After* the Lesson**
9-1 Lesson Quiz, TE p. 661
Alternative Assessment, TE p. 661

Answers to *Think and Discuss*

Possible answers:

1. A table can help you analyze a pattern in data. You can use a table to find finite differences or ratios.
2. A graph is useful when you want to show a change over time, such as the value of a stock.
3. See p. A10.

THINK AND DISCUSS

1. Explain how to use a table to help create an equation for a set of data.
2. Give an example of a real-world situation where a graph might be the most useful representation of a set of data.
3. **GET ORGANIZED** Copy and complete the graphic organizer. In each box give an example.

Know it! Note

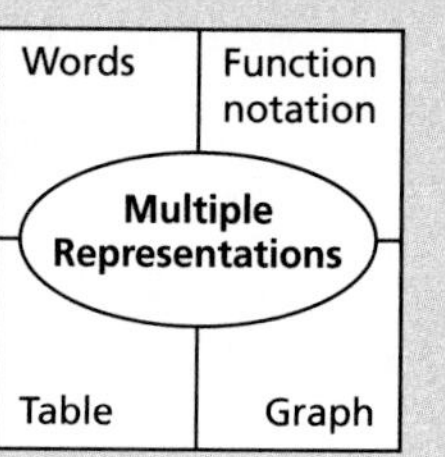

9-1 Exercises

Assignment Guide

Assign *Guided Practice* exercises as necessary.

If you finished Examples **1–3**

Basic 7–22, 24–27, 31–35

Average 7–28, 31–35

Advanced 7–35

Homework Quick Check

Quickly check key concepts.

Exercises: 8, 10, 12, 14, 20

Answers

4.

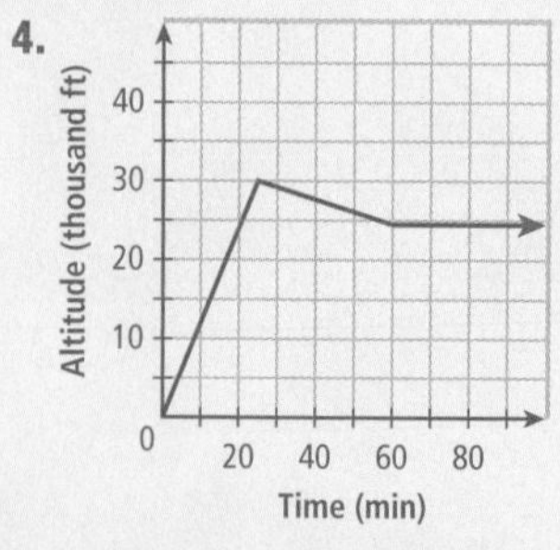

5–6. For graphs and tables, see p. A39.

State Resources

go.hrw.com
State Resources Online
KEYWORD: MB7 Resources

GUIDED PRACTICE

SEE EXAMPLE 1 p. 654

Match each situation to its corresponding graph. Sketch a possible graph of the situation if the situation does not match any of the given graphs.

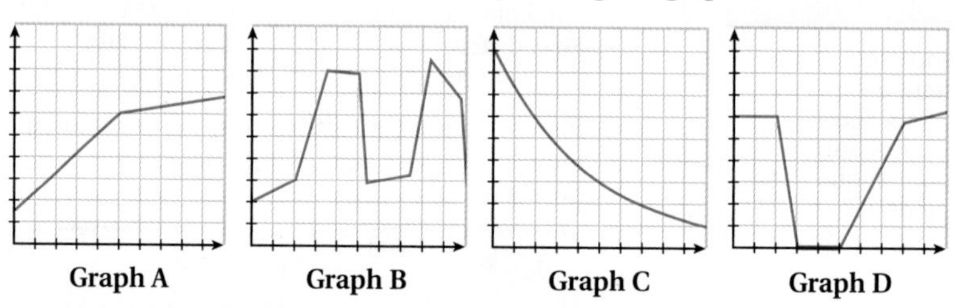

1. Due to a product recall, a company's profits drop sharply into a loss but rebound a few weeks later. **graph D**
2. The value of a car declines as the car gets older. **graph C**
3. A souvenir shop's sales are seasonal, with high sales in summer and winter and low sales in spring and fall. **graph B**
4. An airplane ascends to a peak height of 30,000 feet and then descends to a cruising altitude of 24,000 feet.

SEE EXAMPLE 2 p. 655

5. **Education** Part-time students at a university must pay an enrollment fee of \$179.35, plus \$218.40 per credit hour. Create a table, an equation, and a graph that give the total cost of enrollment as a function of credit hours. $C = 179.35 + 218.4x$

SEE EXAMPLE 3 p. 656

6. **Recreation** Claire is hiking up the South Kaibab Trail at the Grand Canyon. The table shows Claire's altitude above sea level every 15 minutes after she starts to hike. Use a graph and an equation to find how long it will take Claire to reach the rim of the canyon at 7260 feet. **231 min**

Claire's Altitude

Time (min)	Altitude (ft)
15	2940
30	3240
45	3540
60	3840
75	4140

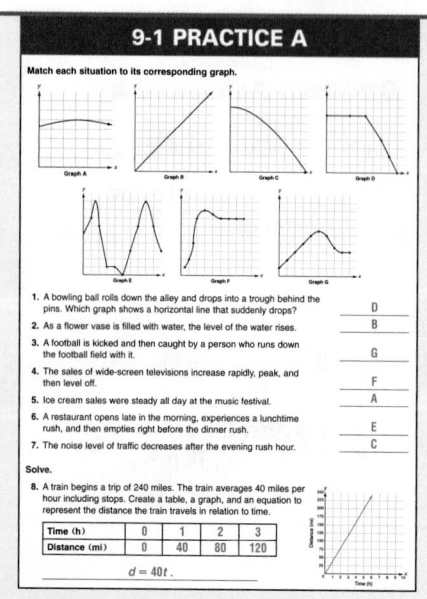

9-1 PRACTICE A

Match each situation to its corresponding graph.

Graph A Graph B Graph C Graph D Graph E Graph F Graph G

1. A bowling ball rolls down the alley and drops into a trough behind the pins. Which graph shows a horizontal line that suddenly drops? D
2. As a flower vase is filled with water, the level of the water rises. B
3. A football is kicked and then caught by a person who runs down the football field with it. G
4. The sales of wide-screen televisions increase rapidly, peak, and then level off. F
5. Ice cream sales were steady all day at the music festival. A
6. A restaurant opens late in the morning, experiences a lunchtime rush, and then empties right before the dinner rush. E
7. The noise level of traffic decreases after the evening rush hour. C

Solve.

8. A train begins a trip of 240 miles. The train averages 40 miles per hour including stops. Create a table, a graph, and an equation to represent the distance the train travels in relation to time.

Time (h)	0	1	2	3
Distance (mi)	0	40	80	120

$d = 40t$.

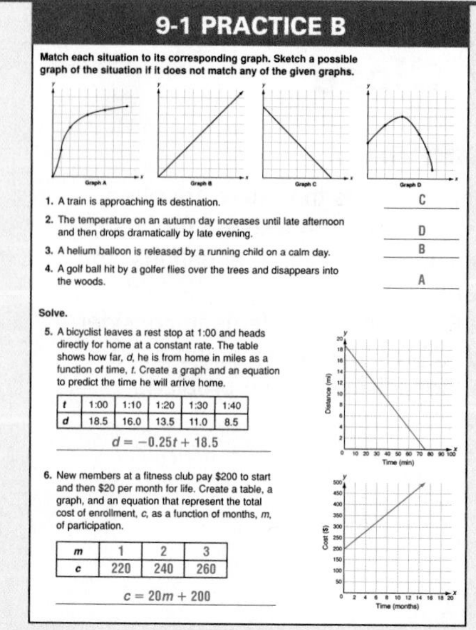

9-1 PRACTICE B

Match each situation to its corresponding graph. Sketch a possible graph of the situation if it does not match any of the given graphs.

Graph A Graph B Graph C Graph D

1. A train is approaching its destination. C
2. The temperature on an autumn day increases until late afternoon and then drops dramatically by late evening. D
3. A helium balloon is released by a running child on a calm day. B
4. A golf ball hit by a golfer flies over the trees and disappears into the woods. A

Solve.

5. A bicyclist leaves a rest stop at 1:00 and heads directly for home at a constant rate. The table shows how far, d, he is from home in miles as a function of time, t. Create a graph and an equation to predict the time he will arrive home.

t	1:00	1:10	1:20	1:30	1:40
d	18.5	16.0	13.5	11.0	8.5

$d = -0.25t + 18.5$

6. New members at a fitness club pay \$200 to start and then \$20 per month for life. Create a table, a graph, and an equation that represent the total cost of enrollment, c, as a function of months, m, of participation.

m	1	2	3
c	220	240	260

$c = 20m + 200$

PRACTICE AND PROBLEM SOLVING

Independent Practice	
For Exercises	See Example
7–10	1
11–12	2
13–14	3

Extra Practice
Skills Practice p. S20
Application Practice p. S40

Match each situation to its corresponding graph. Sketch a possible graph of the situation if the situation does not match any of the given graphs.

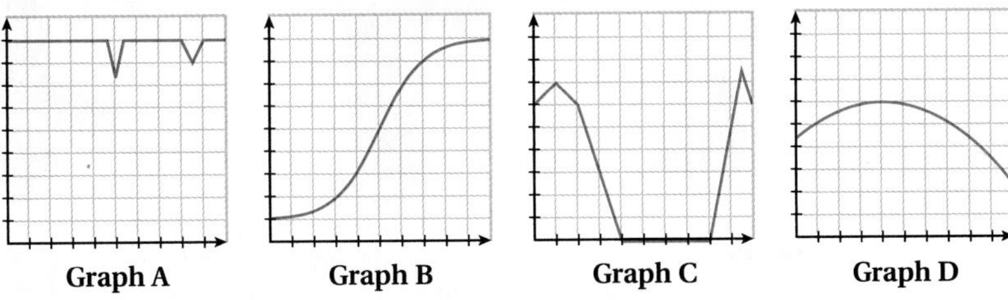

Graph A Graph B Graph C Graph D

graph C **7.** The sales of lift tickets at a ski resort are highest at the beginning and end of the year.

graph A **8.** The attendance at a pop singer's concerts is steadily high except on two nights.

graph D **9.** The population of a city peaked in the 1980s and has been decreasing slowly but steadily in the years since.

graph B **10.** Sales of a new type of cell phone increase rapidly and then level off.

11. Health Carl has a severe fever, so his doctor advises him to take his temperature every 4 hours until it falls below 100°F. The table shows Carl's temperature with relation to time. Create a graph, an equation, and a verbal description to represent Carl's temperature with relation to time. When will Carl's temperature drop below 100°F?

Carl's Temperature

Time (h)	Temperature (°F)
0	101.10
4	102.82
8	103.78
12	103.98
16	103.42
20	102.10

12. Transportation A truck begins a trip of 1675 miles. The truck averages 55 miles per hour, including stops. Create a table, a graph, and an equation to represent the distance that the truck has left to travel with relation to time.

Whales

Blue whales are the largest and loudest animals on Earth. Their calls can reach intensity levels of 180 decibels, louder than a jet airplane.

13. Whales Researchers are studying the growth of a young blue whale. The graph shows the approximate weight of the whale from birth to 8 months.

a. Find an equation for the weight of the whale as a function of time, and describe the relationship in words.

b. Will the weight of the whale continue to increase by the same amount each month? Explain your answer.

Weight of a Blue Whale from Birth

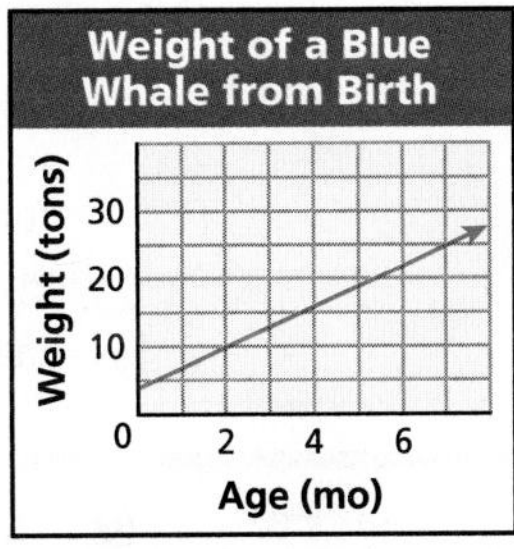

13a. $W(t) = 3t + 4$; The whale weighs 4 tons at birth and gains 3 tons per month.

b. No; as the whale reaches maturity its growth will probably slow down.

14. Business Alex is painting a house. When Alex starts work on Monday morning, there are 2452 square feet of surface area that remain to be painted. Alex can paint 64 square feet of surface area in an hour.

a. Write an equation for the amount of surface area that Alex has left to paint after t hours. $A(t) = 2452 - 64t$

b. If Alex works for 40 hours a week, will he be able to finish painting the house in a week? Yes; he will finish after about 38.5 hours.

15. Sports The owners of a minor league hockey team have found that when they charge $12 for a lower-level seat, they average 800 fans per game. For every $1 increase in ticket price, the attendance decreases by an average of 50 people. Find the ticket price that will maximize revenue for the team's owners. $14

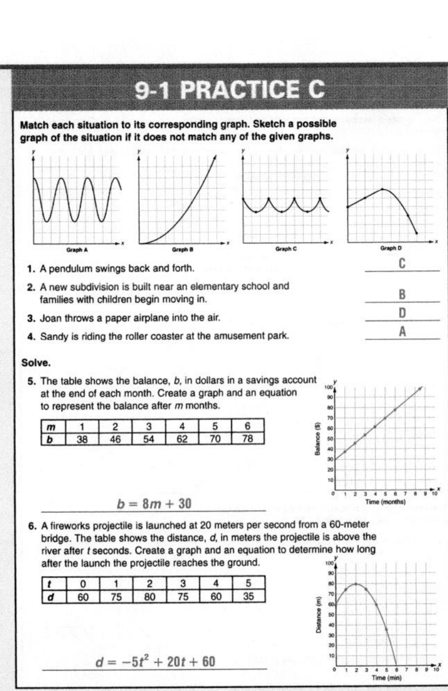

9-1 PRACTICE C

Match each situation to its corresponding graph. Sketch a possible graph of the situation if it does not match any of the given graphs.

Graph A Graph B Graph C Graph D

1. A pendulum swings back and forth. C
2. A new subdivision is built near an elementary school and families with children begin moving in. B
3. Joan throws a paper airplane into the air. D
4. Sandy is riding the roller coaster at the amusement park. A

Solve.

5. The table shows the balance, b, in dollars in a savings account at the end of each month. Create a graph and an equation to represent the balance after m months.

m	1	2	3	4	5	6
b	38	46	54	62	70	78

$b = 8m + 30$

6. A fireworks projectile is launched at 20 meters per second from a 60-meter bridge. The table shows the distance, d, in meters the projectile is above the river after t seconds. Create a graph and an equation to determine how long after the launch the projectile reaches the ground.

t	0	1	2	3	4	5
d	60	75	80	75	60	35

$d = -5t^2 + 20t + 60$

COMMON ERROR ALERT

In **Exercise 13,** students may assume that, because the data set on the blue whale weight is linear on the graph, it will remain linear throughout the whale's life cycle. Remind students that models are only approximations of a data set and are not necessarily accurate for the future.

Answers

11. $T(t) = -0.02375t^2 + 0.525t + 101.1$; Carl's temperature begins at 101.1°F, rises and peaks at 104°F after 11 h, and then begins to fall; after 24 h.

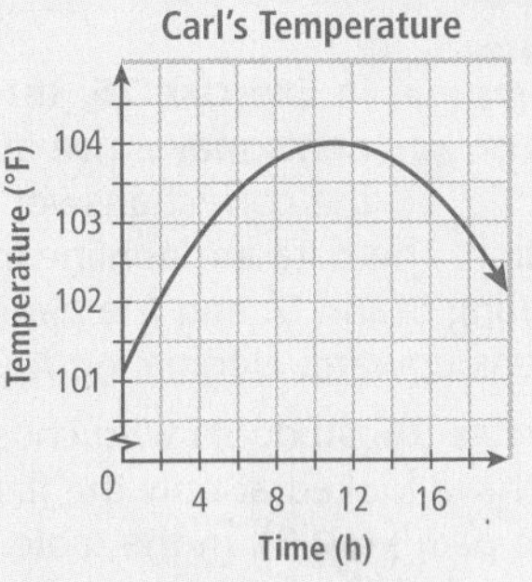

12. $d(t) = 1675 - 55t$

Time (h)	Distance Remaining (mi)
0	1675
1	1620
2	1565
3	1510
4	1455
5	1400

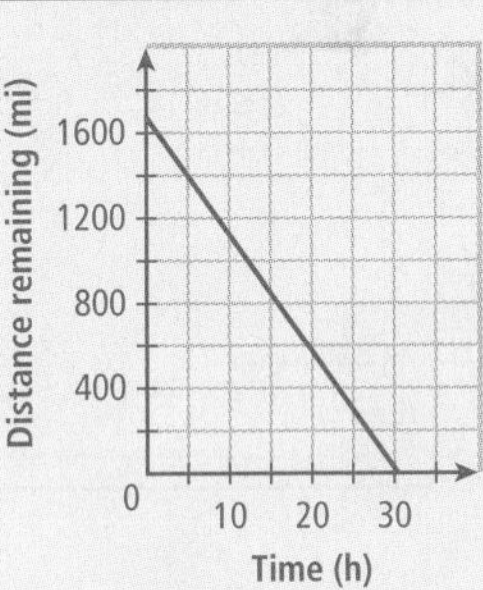

$d(t) = 1675 - 55t$

Teaching Tip **Math Background** It is worth noting that there may be several appropriate models for a small data set, such as the one given in **Exercise 21.** No model may be perfect or best. Emphasize to students that mathematical models based on real-world data are often only approximations and do not guarantee an accurate prediction.

MULTI-STEP TEST PREP **Exercise 24** involves using data in a table to produce a graph and find an appropriate function. This exercise prepares students for the Multi-Step Test Prep on page 680.

TEST PREP DOCTOR In **Exercise 25,** students may arrive at the correct answer by inspection. The data are nonlinear, eliminating **B** and **D,** and the parabola opens upward, eliminating **A.**

In **Exercise 26,** students who chose **D** may have looked at only the first ordered pair, (1, 0.5), in the table. Reinforce that they need to look at **all** of the other points before arriving at a conclusion.

Answers

16.

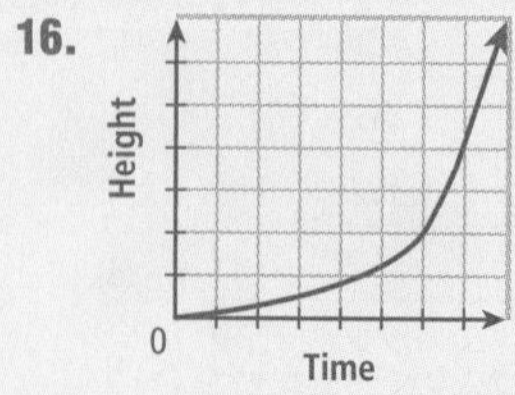

17.

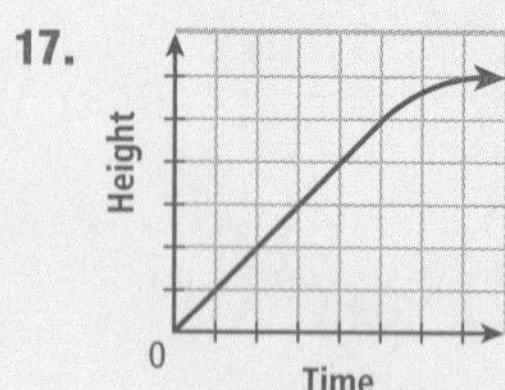

18.

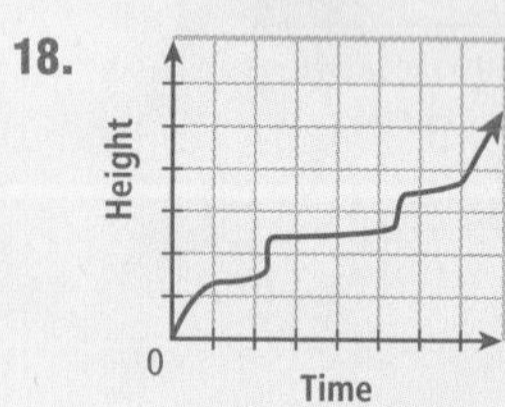

20–21. For graphs, see p. A40.
22–24a. See p. A40.
28–29, 34–35. For graphs, see p. A40.

Geometry Each container is filled at a constant rate. Sketch a graph of the height of water in each container as a function of time.

16. 17. 18.

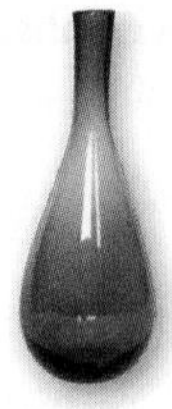

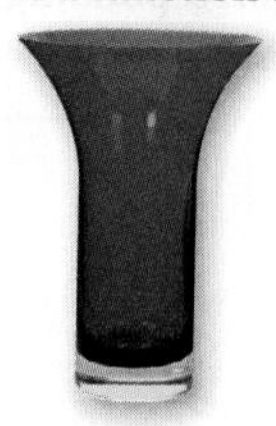

19. **Business** In order to better manage her restaurant, Rita counts the number of people who are in the restaurant at the end of every hour after the restaurant is opened. The results are shown in the graph.

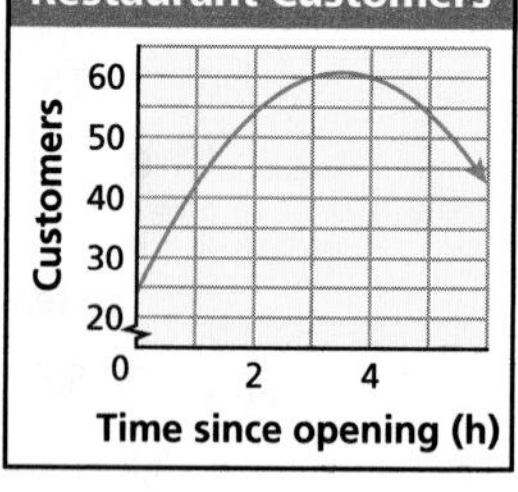

a. Write a function for the graph.
b. According to your function, what was the maximum number of customers in Rita's restaurant on this evening? ≈ 61
c. When will there be no customers in Rita's restaurant? 8 h after opening

19a. $C(t) = -3t^2 + 21t + 24$

20. **Hobbies** Susan collects antique dolls. In 2005, her collection contained 6 dolls. She plans to double the number of dolls in her collection every year. Use a table, a graph, and an equation to determine when Susan will have more than 100 dolls in her collection. $y(x) = 6(2^x)$; in the 5th year

21. **Forestry** The *Sorbus aucuparia*, or mountain ash tree, typically grows to the heights shown in the table.
a. Create a graph of height versus time.
b. Write a function that models the height.
c. During which year would you expect the height to reach 18 ft? during year 14

21b. $h(t) \approx 0.0071t^3 - 0.1714t^2 + 2.1t + 2.071$

Growth of Mountain Ash

Year	Height (ft)
1	4
3	7
6	10
10	13

22. **Write About It** Describe a different situation in which you would find each representation of a function, including a table, a graph, and an equation, useful.

23. **Critical Thinking** When would a graph give you more evidence about a relationship than a table would? When would a table give more evidence than a graph would?

MULTI-STEP TEST PREP

24. This problem will prepare you for the Multi-Step Test Prep on page 680.

A group of people stand in a circle and hold hands. One person squeezes the hand of the person on her left, who then squeezes the hand of the next person, and so on. The table shows the time that it takes the signal to go all the way around the circle.

Time for Hand Squeeze to Complete a Cycle

People	Time (s)
5	2.10
8	3.36
14	5.88
23	9.66

a. Create a graph of time versus the number of participants.
b. Write a function that models the situation. $y(x) = 0.42x$
c. Suppose the signal takes about a minute to go around the circle. How many participants are there? ≈ 143

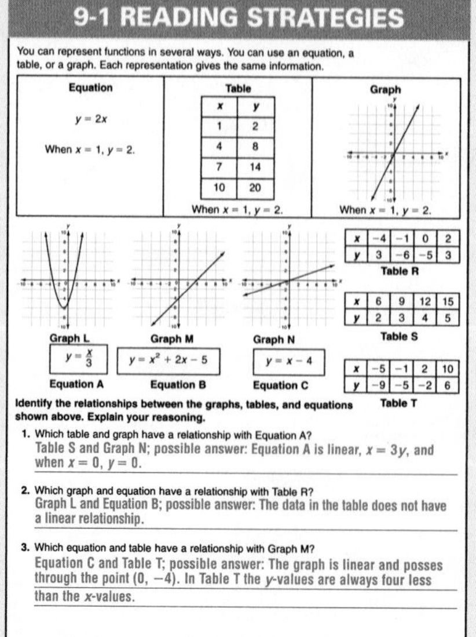

9-1 READING STRATEGIES

You can represent functions in several ways. You can use an equation, a table, or a graph. Each representation gives the same information.

Equation

$y = 2x$

When $x = 1$, $y = 2$.

Table

x	y
1	2
4	8
7	14
10	20

When $x = 1$, $y = 2$.

Graph

When $x = 1$, $y = 2$.

Graph L, Graph M, Graph N

Equation A: $y = \frac{x}{3}$

Equation B: $y = x^2 + 2x - 5$

Equation C: $y = x - 4$

Table R

x	−4	−1	0	2
y	3	−6	−5	3

Table S

x	6	9	12	15
y	2	3	4	5

Table T

x	−5	−1	2	10
y	−9	−5	−2	6

Identify the relationships between the graphs, tables, and equations shown above. Explain your reasoning.

1. Which table and graph have a relationship with Equation A?
Table S and Graph N; possible answer: Equation A is linear, $x = 3y$, and when $x = 0$, $y = 0$.

2. Which graph and equation have a relationship with Table R?
Graph L and Equation B; possible answer: The data in the table does not have a linear relationship.

3. Which equation and table have a relationship with Graph M?
Equation C and Table T; possible answer: The graph is linear and posses through the point (0, −4). In Table T the y-values are always four less than the x-values.

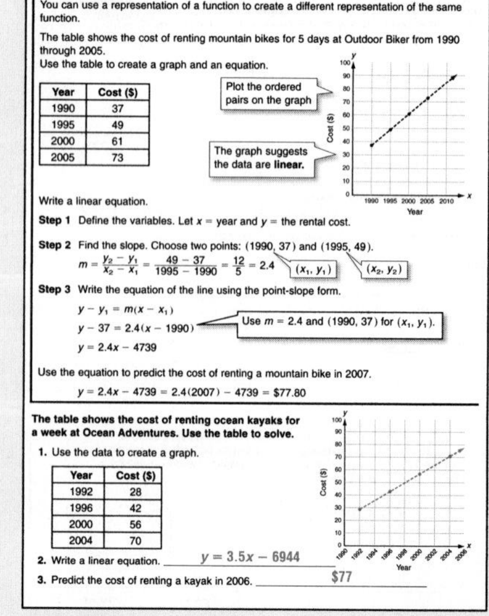

9-1 RETEACH

You can use a representation of a function to create a different representation of the same function.

The table shows the cost of renting mountain bikes for 5 days at Outdoor Biker from 1990 through 2005.
Use the table to create a graph and an equation.

Year	Cost ($)
1990	37
1995	49
2000	61
2005	73

Plot the ordered pairs on the graph

The graph suggests the data are **linear.**

Write a linear equation.

Step 1 Define the variables. Let x = year and y = the rental cost.

Step 2 Find the slope. Choose two points: (1990, 37) and (1995, 49).

$m = \frac{y_2 - y_1}{x_2 - x_1} = \frac{49 - 37}{1995 - 1990} = \frac{12}{5} = 2.4$ (x_1, y_1) (x_2, y_2)

Step 3 Write the equation of the line using the point-slope form.

$y - y_1 = m(x - x_1)$

$y - 37 = 2.4(x - 1990)$ Use $m = 2.4$ and (1990, 37) for (x_1, y_1).

$y = 2.4x - 4739$

Use the equation to predict the cost of renting a mountain bike in 2007.

$y = 2.4x - 4739 = 2.4(2007) - 4739 = \$77.80$

The table shows the cost of renting ocean kayaks for a week at Ocean Adventures. Use the table to solve.

1. Use the data to create a graph.

Year	Cost ($)
1992	28
1996	42
2000	56
2004	70

2. Write a linear equation. $y = 3.5x - 6944$

3. Predict the cost of renting a kayak in 2006. \$77

TEST PREP

25. **Business** This graph shows data on the number of olive slices on pizzas of different radii. Let r represent the radius of the pizza and n represent the number of olive slices. Identify the equation that best represents the relationship between the radius and the number of olive slices.

Number of Olive Slices on Pizzas

(Graph: Olive slices 0–120 vs. Radius (in.) 0–8)

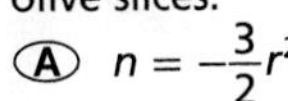

Ⓐ $n = -\frac{3}{2}r^2$ Ⓒ $n = \frac{3}{2}r^2$

Ⓑ $n = -6r$ Ⓓ $n = 6r$

26. A charity is selling American flags to celebrate Independence Day. The charity's profit in dollars is modeled by $p = \frac{1}{2}n$, where n is the number of flags sold. Which of the following choices identifies the same function?

Ⓐ The profit is \$2 per flag.

Ⓑ

n	1	2	3
p	2	4	6

Ⓒ For every 2 flags sold, the profit is \$1.

Ⓓ

n	1	2	3	4
p	0.5	1.5	2.5	3.5

27. **Short Response** Which type of function would best model the cost for carpeting a square room as a function of the room's width? Explain your answer.
A quadratic function would be the best model because the cost would depend on the area and the area is the square of the width.

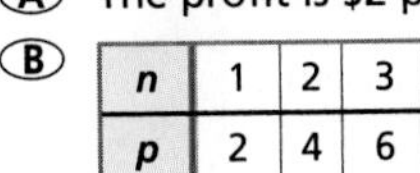

CHALLENGE AND EXTEND

Write an equation and create a graph for each situation described.

28. The volume of a box for a glass decoration is found by doubling the radius of the decoration, raising it to the third power, and then adding 10. $V(r) = (2r)^3 + 10$

29. The total cost of an item at a sale is found by taking off a 20% discount, subtracting a \$10-off coupon, and adding 6.5% sales tax. $C(p) = 1.065(0.8p - 10)$

30. **Finance** Sharmila was able to save \$500 from her summer job. She put the money into a mutual fund. This table shows how the value of Sharmila's money has grown.

a. Write an appropriate model for the amount that Sharmila will have in this mutual fund after t years. $V(t) = 500(1.09)^t$

b. Use your model to predict when Sharmila will have \$2000 in the mutual fund. ≈ 16.1 yr

Sharmila's Mutual Fund

Year	Value (\$)
1	545.00
2	594.00
3	647.51
4	705.79
5	769.31

SPIRAL REVIEW

Find the vertex of each function. *(Lesson 2-9)*

31. $f(x) = |x + 3| - 4$ $(-3, -4)$

32. $f(x) = -|x - 1| - 2$ $(1, -2)$

33. Tim paid \$200 to have his lawn fertilized. The lawn-care company charged \$0.25 per square foot. If Tim's lawn is a rectangle with a length that is twice its width, find the dimensions of the lawn. *(Lesson 5-4)* 40 ft × 20 ft

Graph each function, and identify its domain and range. *(Lesson 8-7)*

34. $f(x) = \sqrt{x + 3}$
D: $\{x \mid x \geq -3\}$; R: $\{y \mid y \geq 0\}$

35. $f(x) = 3\sqrt{x - 1}$
D: $\{x \mid x \geq 1\}$; R: $\{y \mid y \geq 0\}$

9-1 PROBLEM SOLVING

Yvonne opened a new video game store. The table shows a record of her sales for the first five weeks. To break even, she needs to sell at least \$12,500 worth of merchandise each week. She assumes the sales trend will continue and wants to know what to expect over the next weeks.

Weekly Store Sales	
Week	Sales (\$)
1	8470
2	8920
3	9360
4	9790
5	10,210

1. Graph the data using weeks as the independent variable and sales as the dependent variable.

2. Yvonne thinks she can model her sales data using a quadratic function. Is she correct? How do you know?
Yes, because second differences are constant. For a quadratic function, second differences are constant.

3. Use a graphing calculator to perform the appropriate regression on the data. Write the equation that models the data. $y = -5x^2 + 465x + 8010$

4. What sales can Yvonne expect in week 6? \$10,620

5. When will her sales exceed \$11,000 per week? Week 7

6. When will she break even? Week 11

7. When will sales be twice the sales of week 1? Week 28

Choose the letter for the best answer.

8. Which equation represents a steady increase of \$420 per week in sales from week 5 on?
A $y = -420x + 10{,}210$
Ⓑ $y = 420x + 10{,}210$
C $y = -5x^2 + 420x + 10{,}210$
D $y = -420x^2 + 10{,}210x$

9. During which week will Yvonne break even if the sales pattern changes and sales in week 6 and week 7 are \$10,640 and \$11,080, respectively?
F Week 9
G Week 10
Ⓗ Week 11
J Week 12

9-1 CHALLENGE

Some real-world problems can be modeled using functions. Consider a home owner in Maine faced with deciding which type of heating system to install in a new home. A solar system will cost \$20,000 to install, but the annual heating costs will be \$1000. A geothermal heat pump will cost \$15,000 to install with annual heating costs of \$1500. A conventional oil-fired furnace will cost \$6000 to install with annual heating costs of \$2400.

1. Write a function to represent the total cost of each system over t years.
$f(t) = 20{,}000 + 1000t$, $g(t) = 15{,}000 + 1500t$, $h(t) = 6000 + 2400t$

2. Graph each function over 20 years.

3. If the home owner plans to move within 7 years, which heating system is most economical?
Oil-fired furnace

4. Which system is better for a home owner who is planning to live in the house for 30 or more years? How do you know?
Solar system; after 10 years, this system is least expensive.

Consider the graph below. Three functions are shown: a linear function, $f(x)$, a quadratic function, $g(x)$, and a square root function, $h(x)$.

5. Identify three points on each graph.
a. $f(x)$ $f(x)$: (0, 15), (10, 10), (20, 5)
b. $g(x)$ $g(x)$: (5, 20), (15, 15), (25, 0)
c. $h(x)$ $h(x)$: (−5, 0), (4, 12), (20, 20)

6. Find an equation that models $f(t)$.
$f(x) = -0.5x + 15$

7. Find an equation that models $g(t)$. Remember, every quadratic function is of the form $y = ax^2 + bx + c$. Set up a system of equations and solve for a, b, and c.
$g(x) = -0.05(x - 5)^2 + 20 = -.05x^2 + 0.5x + 18.75$

8. Find an equation that models $h(t)$. A square root function can be modeled with $y = a\sqrt{x - h} + k$.
$h(x) = 4\sqrt{x + 5}$

Journal

Have students discuss the advantages and disadvantages of each of the three representations: graphs, tables, and equations.

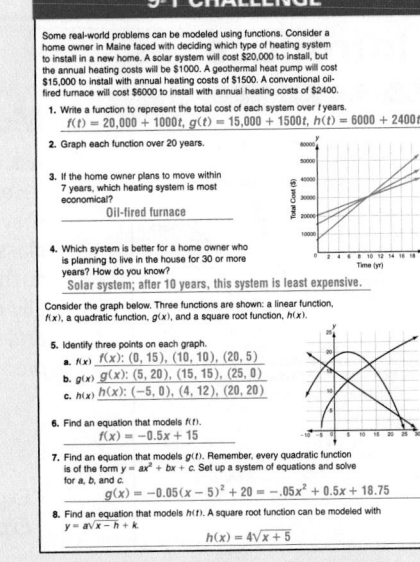

ALTERNATIVE ASSESSMENT

Have students describe a real-world situation involving a functional relationship. Have them represent the situation by using a table, a graph, and an equation.

Power Presentations with PowerPoint®

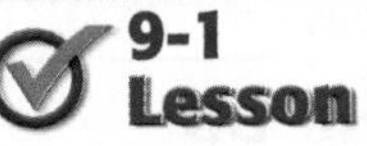

9-1 Lesson Quiz

1. The graph shows the number of cars in a high school parking lot on a Saturday, beginning at 10 A.M. and ending at 11 P.M. Give a possible interpretation for this graph.

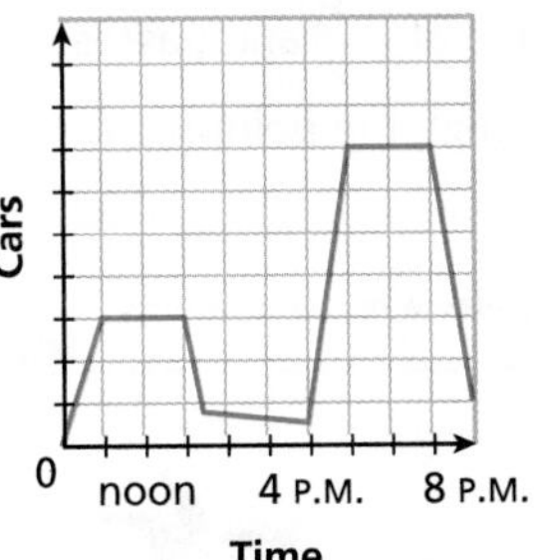

Possible answer: Football practice goes from 11:00 A.M. until 1:00 P.M. Families begin arriving at 4:00 P.M. for a play that begins at 5:00 and ends at 7:00. After the play, most people leave.

2. An online computer game company has 10,000 subscribers paying \$8 per month. Their research shows that for every 25-cent reduction in their fee, they will attract another 500 users. Use a table and an equation to find the fee that the company should charge to maximize their revenue.

Fee (\$)	Users	Revenue (\$)
\$8.00	10,000	\$80,000
\$7.75	10,500	\$81,375
\$7.50	11,000	\$82,500
\$7.25	11,500	\$83,375

$R(f) = -2000f^2 + 26{,}000f$; \$6.50

Also available on transparency

9-2 Organizer

Pacing: Traditional 1 day
Block $\frac{1}{2}$ day

Objectives: Write and graph piecewise functions.

Use piecewise functions to describe real-world situations.

Online Edition
Tutorial Videos, Interactivity

Countdown to Testing Week 19

Power Presentations with PowerPoint®

Warm Up

Write the equation of each line in slope-intercept form.

1. slope of 3 and passes through the point (50, 200)
   $y = 3x + 50$
2. slope of $-\frac{1}{2}$ and passes through the point (6, 40)
   $y = -\frac{1}{2}x + 43$

Also available on transparency

Math Humor

Teacher: This piecewise function begins with high profit but shows big losses as it continues.

Student: Sounds like a piece-*unwise* function to me.

9-2 Piecewise Functions

IN A2.2.3 Graph piecewise-defined functions.

Objectives
Write and graph piecewise functions.

Use piecewise functions to describe real-world situations.

Vocabulary
piecewise function
step function

Why learn this?
You can use piecewise functions to model an athlete's performance in a triathlon. (See Example 4.)

A **piecewise function** is a function that is a combination of one or more functions. The rule for a piecewise function is different for different parts, or pieces, of the domain. For instance, movie ticket prices are often different for different age groups. So the function for movie ticket prices would assign a different value (ticket price) for each domain interval (age group).

EXAMPLE 1 *Entertainment Application*

Create a table and a verbal description to represent the graph.

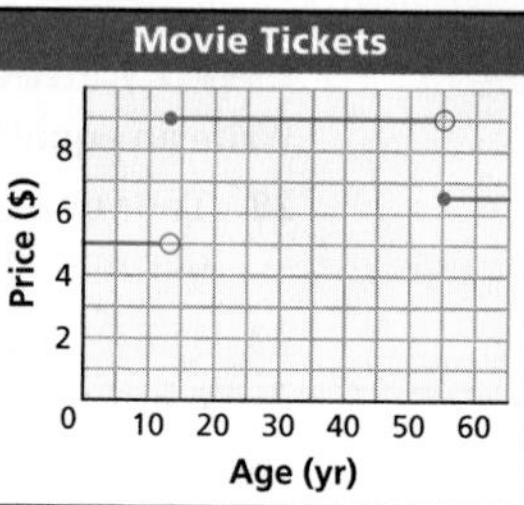

Step 1 Create a table.

Because the endpoints of each segment of the graph identify the intervals of the domain, use the endpoints and points close to them as the domain values in the table.

Remember!
When using interval notation, square brackets [ ] indicate an included endpoint, and parentheses ( ) indicate an excluded endpoint. (Lesson 1-1)

Movie Tickets	
Age	**Price ($)**
0–12	5.00
13–54	9.00
55+	6.50

The domain of the function is divided into three intervals:

Ages 12 and under ⟶ [0,13)
Ages 13 and under 55 ⟶ [13,55)
Ages 55 and over ⟶ [55,∞)

Step 2 Write a verbal description.

Use the domain intervals and the prices from the table.

Movie tickets are \$5.00 for children ages 12 and under, \$9.00 for people ages 13 through 54, and \$6.50 for seniors ages 55 years and older.

1. Create a table and a verbal description to represent the graph.

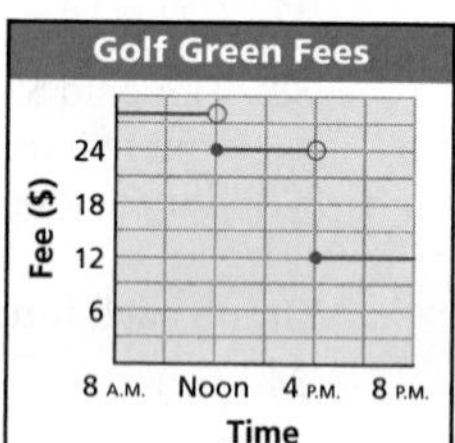

Time Range (h)	Green Fee ($)
[8 A.M. – noon)	28
[noon – 4 P.M.)	24
[4 P.M. – 9 P.M.)	12

The green fee is \$28 from 8 A.M. up to noon, \$24 from noon up to 4 P.M., and \$12 from 4 P.M. up to 9 P.M.

State Resources

go.hrw.com
State Resources Online
KEYWORD: MB7 Resources

1 Introduce

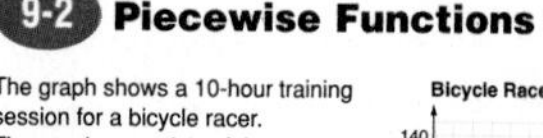

EXPLORATION

9-2 Piecewise Functions

The graph shows a 10-hour training session for a bicycle racer. The session consists of three different stages.

1. Write a verbal description of the training session.
2. What is the cyclist's speed during each stage of the training session?
3. Write a linear equation for each stage of the training session, where x represents the time in hours and y represents the cyclist's distance in miles. (Hint: Use the point-slope form for the equation of a line.)
4. What is the domain for each stage of the training session?

THINK AND DISCUSS

5. **Explain** how you can use only the graph to determine the stage during which the cyclist had the greatest speed.
6. **Describe** how the graph would have been different if the cyclist had maintained the same speed during all three stages.

Motivate

Ask students if any of them work, and if so if they receive overtime pay. Students who do not work may partner with a student who does. Ask the class if they could write a function to describe such a pay rate. Explain that the function is actually made up of two pieces: one for regular pay and one for overtime pay. This is an example of a *piecewise* function.

Explorations and answers are provided in the *Explorations* binder.

A piecewise function that is constant for each interval of its domain, such as the ticket price function, is called a **step function**. You can describe piecewise functions with a function rule. The rule for the movie ticket prices from Example 1 is shown.

$$f(x) = \begin{cases} 5 & \text{if } 0 < x < 13 \\ 9 & \text{if } 13 \le x < 55 \\ 6.5 & \text{if } x \ge 55 \end{cases}$$

Read this as "f of x is 5 if x is greater than 0 and less than 13, 9 if x is greater than or equal to 13 and less than 55, and 6.5 if x is greater than or equal to 55."

To evaluate any piecewise function for a specific input, find the interval of the domain that contains that input and then use the rule for that interval.

EXAMPLE 2

Evaluating a Piecewise Function

Evaluate each piecewise function for $x = -2$ and $x = 5$.

A $f(x) = \begin{cases} -5 & \text{if } x \le 0 \\ 4 & \text{if } 0 < x \le 3 \\ 12 & \text{if } x > 3 \end{cases}$

$f(-2) = -5$ — *Because $-2 \le 0$, use the rule for $x \le 0$.*

$f(5) = 12$ — *Because $5 > 3$, use the rule for $x > 3$.*

B $g(x) = \begin{cases} 3x + 4 & \text{if } x < 5 \\ x^2 - 3 & \text{if } x \ge 5 \end{cases}$

$g(-2) = 3(-2) + 4 = -2$ — *Because $-2 < 5$, use the rule for $x < 5$.*

$g(5) = 5^2 - 3 = 22$ — *Because $5 \ge 5$, use the rule for $x \ge 5$.*

Evaluate each piecewise function for $x = -1$ and $x = 3$.

2a $f(x) = \begin{cases} 12 & \text{if } x < -3 \\ 15 & \text{if } -3 \le x < 6 \\ 20 & \text{if } x \ge 6 \end{cases}$ 15; 15

2b $g(x) = \begin{cases} 3x^2 + 1 & \text{if } x < 0 \\ 5x - 2 & \text{if } x \ge 0 \end{cases}$ 4; 13

You can graph a piecewise function by graphing each piece of the function.

EXAMPLE 3

Graphing Piecewise Functions

Graph each function.

A $f(x) = \begin{cases} -4 & \text{if } x < 2 \\ 4 & \text{if } x \ge 2 \end{cases}$

The function is composed of two constant pieces that will be represented by horizontal rays. Because the domain is divided at $x = 2$, evaluate both branches of the function at $x = 2$. The function is -4 when $x < 2$, so plot the point $(2, -4)$ with an open circle and draw a horizontal ray to the left. The function is 4 when $x \ge 2$, so plot the point $(2, 4)$ with a solid dot and draw a horizontal ray to the right.

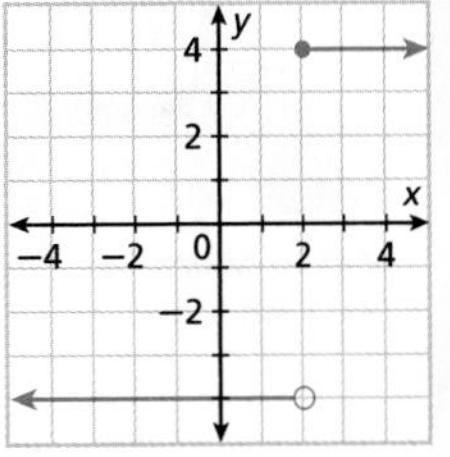

Power Presentations with PowerPoint®

Additional Examples

Example 1

Create a table and a verbal description to represent the graph.

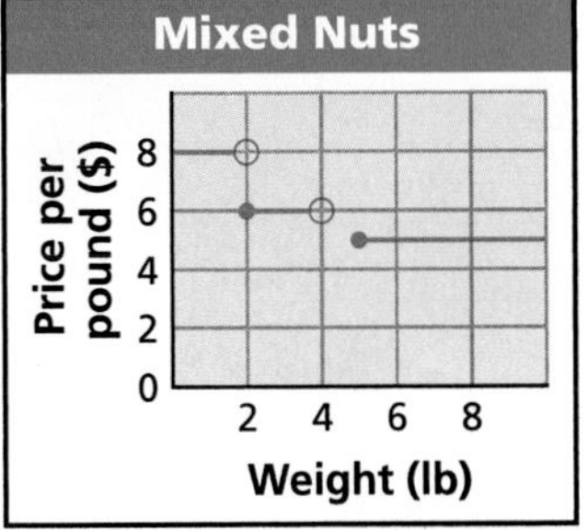

Weight (lb)	Price/lb ($)
0 to 1.99	8.00
2 to 4.99	6.00
5 or more	5.00

Mixed nuts cost \$8.00 per pound for less than 2 lb, \$6.00 per pound for 2 lb or more and less than 5 lb, and \$5.00 per pound for 5 or more pounds.

Example 2

Evaluate each piecewise function for $x = -1$ and $x = 4$.

A. $h(x) = \begin{cases} 2x + 1 & \text{if } x \le 2 \\ x^2 - 4 & \text{if } x > 2 \end{cases}$

-1; 12

B. $g(x) = \begin{cases} 2^x & \text{if } x \le -1 \\ 5x & \text{if } x > -1 \end{cases}$

$\frac{1}{2}$; 20

Also available on transparency

INTERVENTION

Questioning Strategies

EXAMPLE 1

- What do the open and closed circles on the graph indicate?

EXAMPLE 2

- How do you decide which rule to use when evaluating a piecewise function?

2 Teach

Guided Instruction

Review the slope-intercept and point-slope forms of linear functions. Make sure students understand that a closed endpoint on a graph shows an included point and an open endpoint shows an excluded point. Explain the connection between these points and the inequality symbols that indicate them. As you go through the steps of Example 4, make sure that students understand each step before proceeding.

Reaching All Learners

Through Modeling

Have students research and find an example of a real-world situation that can be modeled by a piecewise function. Common examples include postage or shipping rates, parking fees, and hourly wages. Have students create a table and a graph of these situations.

Power Presentations with PowerPoint®

Additional Examples

Example 3

Graph each function.

A. $g(x) = \begin{cases} \frac{1}{4}x + 3 & \text{if } x < 0 \\ -2x + 3 & \text{if } x \geq 0 \end{cases}$

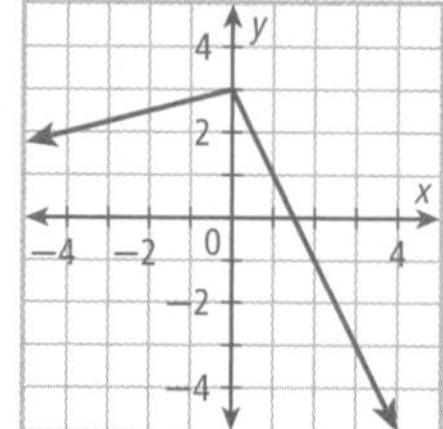

B.

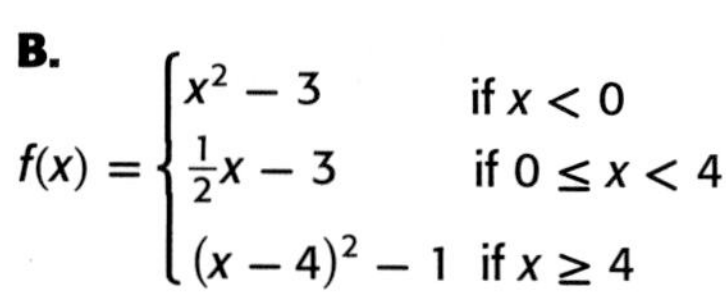

$f(x) = \begin{cases} x^2 - 3 & \text{if } x < 0 \\ \frac{1}{2}x - 3 & \text{if } 0 \leq x < 4 \\ (x-4)^2 - 1 & \text{if } x \geq 4 \end{cases}$

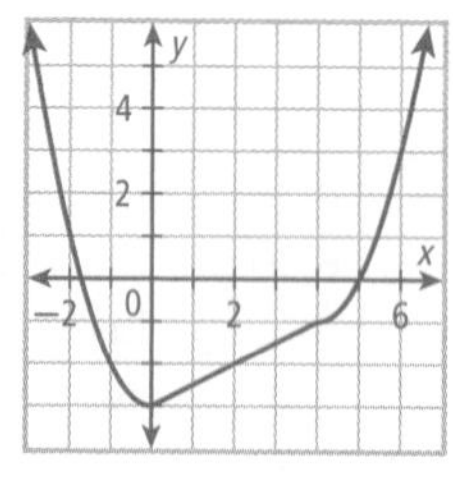

Also available on transparency

INTERVENTION

Questioning Strategies

EXAMPLE 3

- How can you tell where to put open and closed points on the graph of a piecewise function?
- In **Example 3B,** how do the shaded cells in the table relate to the domain of the function?

Graph each function.

B $g(x) = \begin{cases} 3x + 8 & \text{if } x \leq -3 \\ -2x & \text{if } -3 < x < 1 \\ x^2 - 3 & \text{if } x \geq 1 \end{cases}$

The function is composed of two linear pieces and a quadratic piece. The domain is divided at $x = -3$ and $x = 1$.

Use a table of values to graph each piece.

x	$g(x) = 3x + 8$	$g(x) = -2x$	$g(x) = x^2 - 3$
−4	−4		
−3	−1	6	
−2		4	
−1		2	
0		0	
1		−2	−2
2			1
3			6

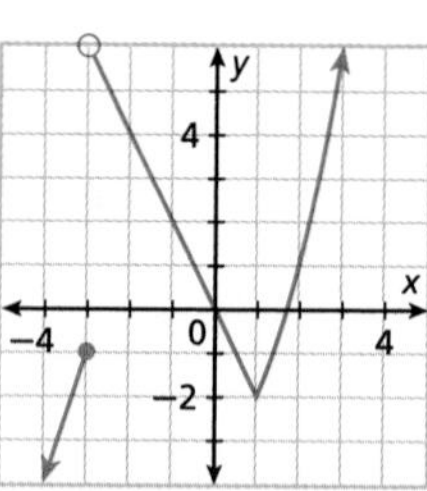

Add a closed circle at $(-3, -1)$ and an open circle at $(-3, 6)$ so that the graph clearly shows the function value when $x = -3$.

No circle is required at $(1, -2)$ because the function is connected at that point.

CHECK IT OUT! Graph each function.

3a $f(x) = \begin{cases} 4 & \text{if } x \leq -1 \\ -2 & \text{if } x > -1 \end{cases}$

3b $g(x) = \begin{cases} -3x & \text{if } x < 2 \\ x + 3 & \text{if } x \geq 2 \end{cases}$

3a.

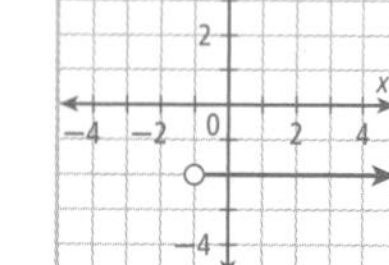

3b.

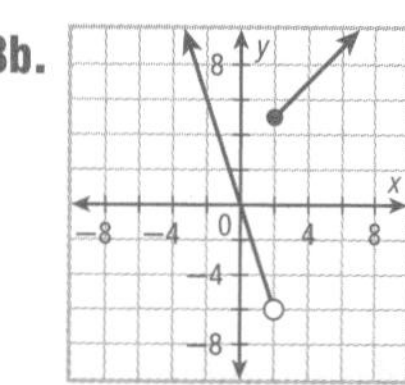

Notice that piecewise functions are not necessarily *continuous*, meaning that the graph of the function may have breaks or gaps.

To write the rule for a piecewise function, determine where the domain is divided and write a separate rule for each piece. Combine the pieces by using the correct notation.

Student to Student

Graphing Piecewise Functions

Mateo Morales
Lee High School

When I graph a piecewise function, I like to graph each piece like it's a separate function. Then I go back and erase the parts that are outside of the restricted domain.

Example: $f(x) = \begin{cases} x + 4 & \text{if } x < -2 \\ -2x & \text{if } x \geq -2 \end{cases}$

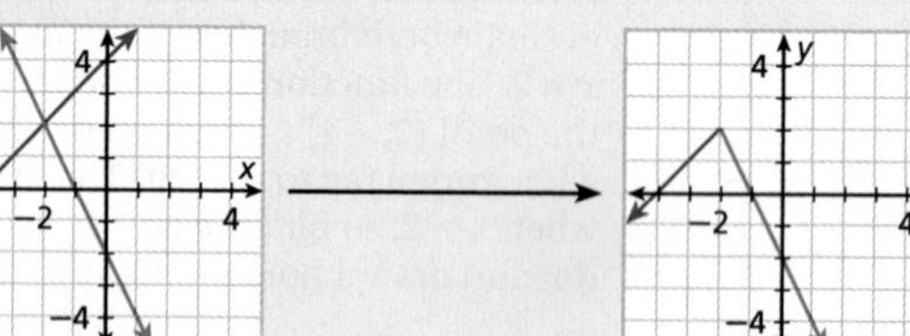

Teaching Tip

Science Link Piecewise functions often appear in science. For example, the height of a falling object is generally modeled with a quadratic function. In reality, it is a piecewise function because a falling object reaches a speed that it cannot exceed, called *terminal velocity.* At that point, the object's height is modeled by a linear function.

EXAMPLE 4 Sports Application

David is completing a 100-mile triathlon. He swims 2 miles in 1 hour, then bikes 80 miles in 4 hours, and finally he runs 18 miles in 3 hours. Sketch a graph of David's distance versus time. Then write a piecewise function for the graph.

Remember!

The distance formula $d = rt$ can be rearranged to find rates: $r = \frac{d}{t}$.

Step 1 Make a table to organize the data. Use the distance formula to find David's rate for each leg of the race.

David's Race

Activity	Time (h)	Distance (mi)	Rate (mi/h)
Swimming	1	2	2
Biking	4	80	20
Running	3	18	6

Step 2 Because time is the independent variable, determine the intervals for the function.

Swimming: $0 \le t \le 1$ — *He swims for 1 hour.*
Biking: $1 < t \le 5$ — *He bikes for the next 4 hours.*
Running: $5 < t \le 8$ — *He runs the final 3 hours.*

Step 3 Graph the function.

After 1 hour, David has covered 2 miles. On the next leg, he reaches a distance of 82 total miles after 5 total hours. Finally, he completes the 100 miles after 8 hours.

Triathlon Distance Covered

Step 4 Write a linear function for each leg.

Use point-slope form: $y - y_1 = m(x - x_1)$.

Swimming: $d = 2t$ — *Use $m = 2$ and $(0, 0)$.*
Biking: $d = 20t - 18$ — *Use $m = 20$ and $(5, 82)$.*
Running: $d = 6t + 52$ — *Use $m = 6$ and $(8, 100)$.*

The function rule is $d(t) = \begin{cases} 2t & \text{if } 0 \le t \le 1 \\ 20t - 18 & \text{if } 1 < t \le 5 \\ 6t + 52 & \text{if } 5 < t \le 8 \end{cases}$.

4.

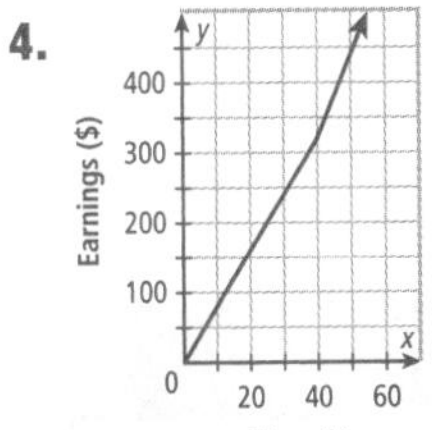

$f(h) = \begin{cases} 8h & \text{if } 0 \le h \le 40 \\ 12(h - 40) + 320 & \text{if } h > 40 \end{cases}$

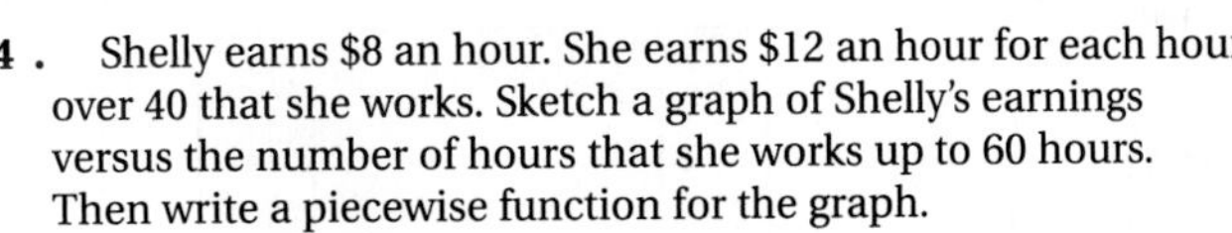

CHECK IT OUT! 4. Shelly earns \$8 an hour. She earns \$12 an hour for each hour over 40 that she works. Sketch a graph of Shelly's earnings versus the number of hours that she works up to 60 hours. Then write a piecewise function for the graph.

THINK AND DISCUSS

1. Tell whether it is possible to have a continuous step function.

2. **GET ORGANIZED** Copy and complete the graphic organizer. Describe the domain and range for each function. Then include an example.

Function	Domain	Range	Example
Piecewise			
Step			

Teaching Tip **Reading Math** Point out in **Example 4** that the prefix *tri-* in *triathlon* indicates that the race has three events. ENGLISH LANGUAGE LEARNERS

Power Presentations with PowerPoint®

Additional Examples

Example 4

Jennifer is completing a 15.5-mile triathlon. She swims 0.5 mile in 30 minutes, bicycles 12 miles in 1 hour, and runs 3 miles in 30 minutes. Sketch a graph of Jennifer's distance versus time. Then write a piecewise function for the graph.

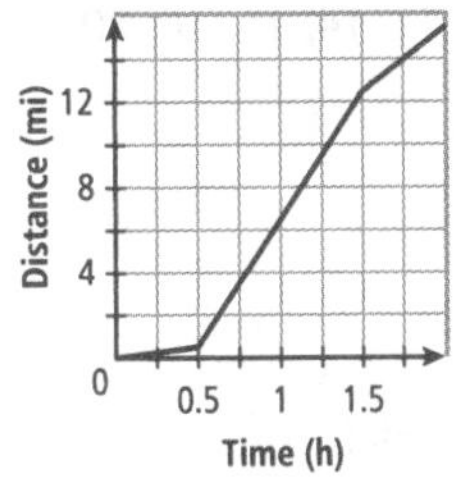

$d(t) = \begin{cases} t & \text{if } 0 \le t \le 0.5 \\ 12t - 5.5 & \text{if } 0.5 < t \le 1.5 \\ 6t - 3.5 & \text{if } 1.5 < t \le 2 \end{cases}$

Also available on transparency

INTERVENTION
Questioning Strategies

EXAMPLE 4

- How would the graph be different if the triathlete completed the three parts of the race in a different order? How would it be the same?

Teaching Tip **Inclusion** In a connected graph, the x-value where the function changes may be included with either interval. For example, when $x = 4$,

$\begin{cases} 2x & x < 4 \\ x + 4 & x \ge 4 \end{cases}$ and $\begin{cases} 2x & x \le 4 \\ x + 4 & x > 4 \end{cases}$

are equivalent.

3 Close

Summarize

Remind students that piecewise functions are combinations of types of functions that they have already studied. Emphasize that each piece is defined over a limited domain. Remind students that piecewise functions are often used for modeling real-world situations, including many pricing scales.

ONGOING ASSESSMENT

and INTERVENTION

Diagnose **Before** the Lesson
9-2 Warm Up, TE p. 662

Monitor **During** the Lesson
Check It Out! Exercises, SE pp. 662–665
Questioning Strategies, TE pp. 663–665

Assess **After** the Lesson
9-2 Lesson Quiz, TE p. 669
Alternative Assessment, TE p. 669

Answers to *Think and Discuss*

Possible answers:

1. No; because a step function is constant over each interval, the in-between values are never outputs of the function.
2. See p. A11.

9-2 Exercises

Assignment Guide

Assign *Guided Practice* exercises as necessary.

If you finished Examples **1–2**
- **Basic** 9–12
- **Average** 9–12, 28–29
- **Advanced** 9–12, 28–29, 36

If you finished Examples **1–4**
- **Basic** 9–30, 32–35, 38–45
- **Average** 9–35, 38–45
- **Advanced** 9–45

Homework Quick Check

Quickly check key concepts.

Exercises: 10, 12, 14, 15, 16, 20

Answers

2. The admission price is $5 for children under 7, $20 for children 7 to 11 years old, and $45 for everyone 12 years or older.

Admission Prices	
Price ($)	Age (yr)
5	$0 < x < 7$
20	$7 \le x < 12$
45	$x \ge 12$

3. The price per yard is $10 for less than 5 yd^3, $7 for 5 yd^3 up to 25 yd^3, and $4 for 25 yd^3 or more.

Topsoil Prices	
Price per Cubic Yard ($)	Volume (yd^3)
10	$0 \le x < 5$
7	$5 \le x < 25$
4	$x \ge 25$

State Resources

9-2 Exercises

go.hrw.com
Homework Help Online
KEYWORD: MB7 9-2
Parent Resources Online
KEYWORD: MB7 Parent

GUIDED PRACTICE

1. **Vocabulary** How are step functions related to piecewise functions?
Step functions are a subset of piecewise functions. A step function is a piecewise function that is constant over each interval in its domain.

SEE EXAMPLE 1 p. 662

Create a table and a verbal description to represent each graph.

2. 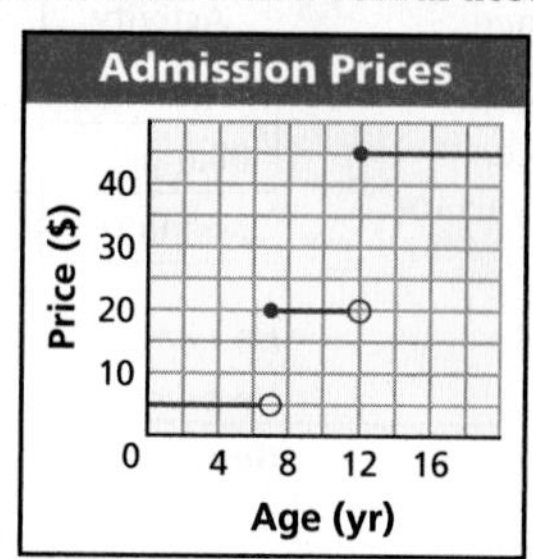

3. Topsoil Prices

Price rate ($/yd³); 8; 4; 0; 10; 20; Volume (yd³)

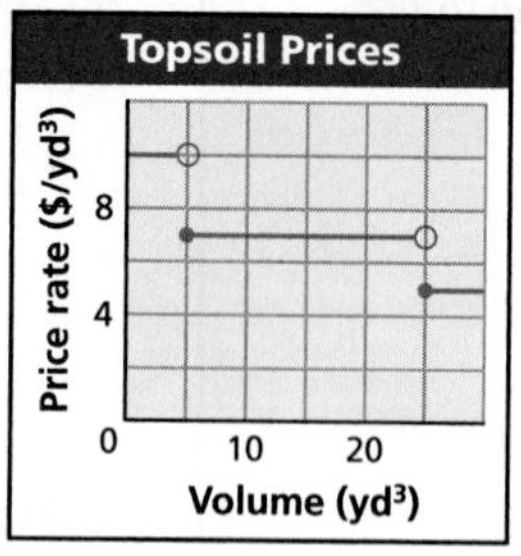

SEE EXAMPLE 2 p. 663

Evaluate each piecewise function for $x = -6$ and $x = 3$.

4. $f(x) = \begin{cases} -8 & \text{if } x \le -5 \\ 0 & \text{if } -5 < x < 5 \\ 5 & \text{if } x \ge 5 \end{cases}$ **−8; 0**

5. $g(x) = \begin{cases} 5x - 9 & \text{if } x < 2 \\ 4 - x^2 & \text{if } x \ge 2 \end{cases}$ **−39; −5**

SEE EXAMPLE 3 p. 663

Graph each function.

6. $f(x) = \begin{cases} 7 & \text{if } x < -2 \\ -2 & \text{if } x \ge -2 \end{cases}$

7. $g(x) = \begin{cases} -2x + 8 & \text{if } x \le 4 \\ \frac{1}{2}x & \text{if } x > 4 \end{cases}$

SEE EXAMPLE 4 p. 665

8. The cost of renting a canoe is $20 for the first 4 hours and $3 per hour for additional hours. Sketch a graph of the cost of renting a canoe from 0 to 8 hours. Then write a piecewise function for the graph.
$f(x) = \begin{cases} 20 & \text{if } 0 \le x < 4 \\ 3(h - 4) + 20 & \text{if } x \ge 4 \end{cases}$

PRACTICE AND PROBLEM SOLVING

Independent Practice	
For Exercises	See Example
9–10	1
11–12	2
13–14	3
15	4

Extra Practice
Skills Practice p. S20
Application Practice p. S40

Create a table and a verbal description to represent each graph.

9. 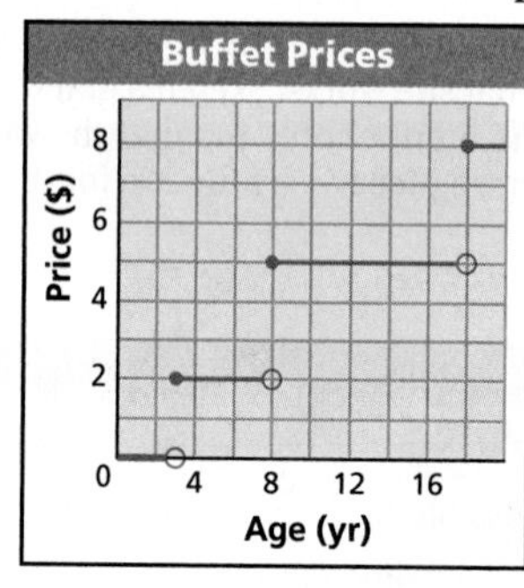

10. 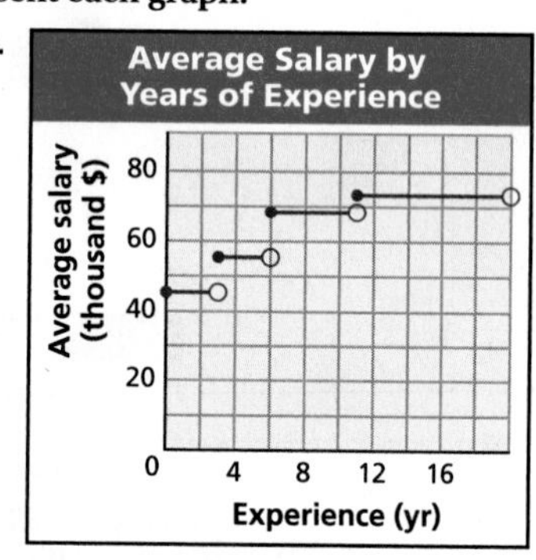

Evaluate each piecewise function for $x = -2$, $x = 2$, and $x = 6$.

11. $g(x) = \begin{cases} 9x - 2 & \text{if } x < -3 \\ x^2 - 3 & \text{if } -3 \le x < 1 \\ 5 & \text{if } x \ge 1 \end{cases}$ **1; 5; 5**

12. $f(x) = \begin{cases} 12 - 9x & \text{if } x \le 0 \\ x^2 + 3x & \text{if } 0 < x < 3 \\ 4^x & \text{if } x \ge 3 \end{cases}$ **30; 10; 4096**

6. 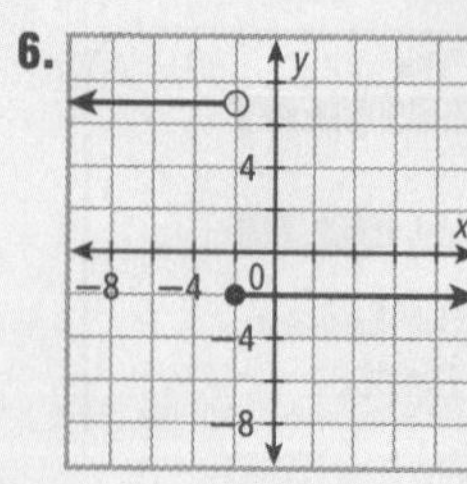

7. 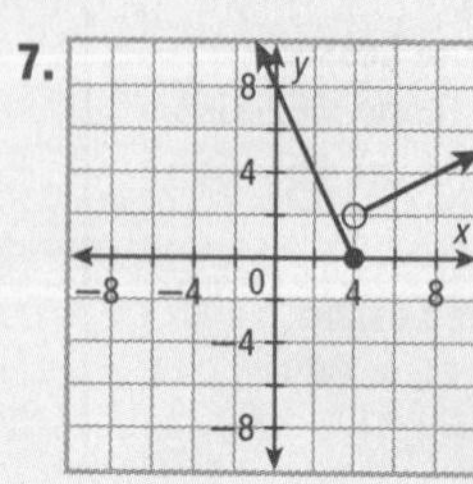

8. 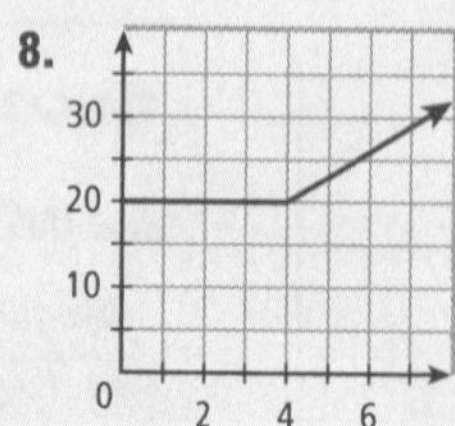

9.

Buffet Prices	
Price ($)	Age (yr)
0	$0 < x < 3$
2	$3 \le x < 8$
5	$8 \le x < 18$
8	$x \ge 18$

The buffet is free for children under 3, $2 for children from 3 up to 8, $5 for children from 8 up to 18, and $8 for adults.

10. See p. A40.

LINK

Pets

Dog grooming is a $2 billion industry in the United States. There is evidence that there were dog-grooming parlors in France as early as the 1700s.

Graph each function.

13. $f(x) = \begin{cases} \frac{3}{4}x + 1 & \text{if } x < 4 \\ \frac{3}{4}x - 2 & \text{if } x \geq 4 \end{cases}$

14. $g(x) = \begin{cases} -2x - 5 & \text{if } x < -2 \\ x^2 - 3 & \text{if } x \geq -2 \end{cases}$

15. **Pets** A dog groomer charges different prices based on the weight of the dog. Sketch a graph of the cost of grooming a dog from 0 to 100 pounds. Then write a piecewise function for the graph.

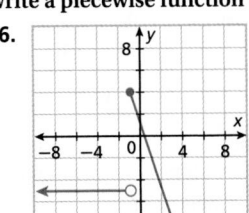

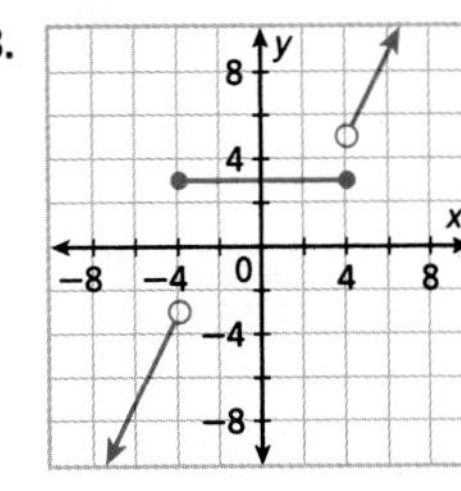

Grooming Prices	
Weight (lb)	**Price ($)**
15 and under	30
Over 15 and up to 50	50
Over 50	75

Write a piecewise function for each graph.

16.

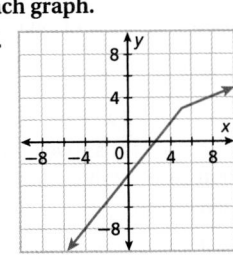

17.

18.

19. **Parking** A parking garage charges $6 for the first 4 hours that a car is parked in the lot. After that, the garage charges an additional $3 an hour. Write a piecewise function for the cost of parking a car in this garage for x hours.

20. **Travel** Derek and his friends drove from San Francisco to Lake Tahoe to go skiing. The average speed that they traveled during each leg of the trip is shown on the map. They drove 30 min in the city, 3 h on the highway, and 30 min up the mountain.

Average Speed

City 30 mi/h

Highway 60 mi/h

Mountain 45 mi/h

a. Write a piecewise function to represent the distance that Derek traveled during his 4 h trip.

b. Graph the function.

c. **What if...?** How much longer would the trip have taken if Derek had averaged 50 mi/h on the highway? **0.6 h, or 36 min**

Write each absolute-value function as a piecewise function.

21. $f(x) = |x|$

22. $g(x) = |x - 4|$

23. $h(x) = 2|x| - 4$

24. **Shipping** An overnight delivery service charges $11 for a package that weighs 2 pounds or less. The delivery service charges $3 for each additional pound. Sketch a graph of the cost of shipping a package from 0 to 8 pounds. Then write a piecewise function for the graph.

Graph each function.

25. $h(x) = \begin{cases} \frac{1}{2}x^2 & \text{if } x \leq 0 \\ 2^x - 4 & \text{if } 0 < x \leq 3 \\ 2x - 2 & \text{if } x > 3 \end{cases}$

26. $h(x) = \begin{cases} -3 & \text{if } x \leq 0 \\ 3^x - 4 & \text{if } x > 0 \end{cases}$

Answers

13.

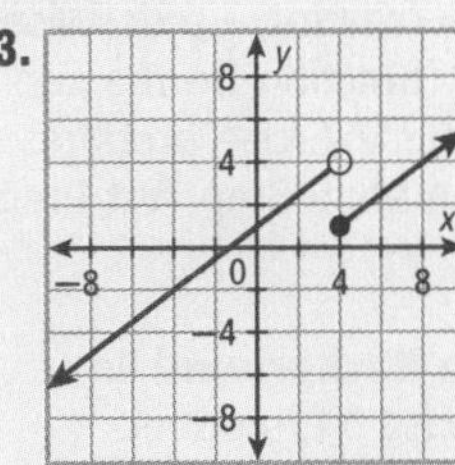

14.

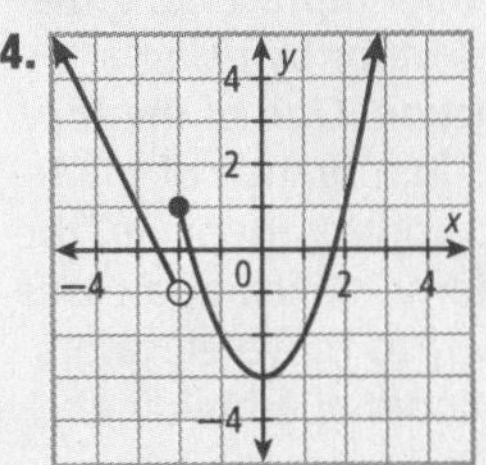

15.

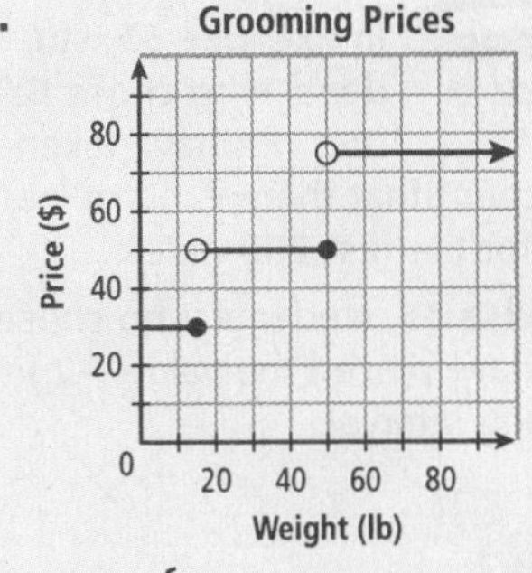

$f(x) = \begin{cases} 30 & \text{if } 0 < x \leq 15 \\ 50 & \text{if } 15 < x \leq 50 \\ 75 & \text{if } x > 50 \end{cases}$

16. $f(x) = \begin{cases} -5 & \text{if } x < -1 \\ -3x + 1 & \text{if } x \geq -1 \end{cases}$

17. $f(x) = \begin{cases} \frac{6}{5}x - 3 & \text{if } x < 5 \\ \frac{2}{5}x + 1 & \text{if } x \geq 5 \end{cases}$

18. $f(x) = \begin{cases} 2x + 5 & \text{if } x < -4 \\ 3 & \text{if } -4 \leq x \leq 4 \\ 2x - 3 & \text{if } x > 4 \end{cases}$

19. $f(x) = \begin{cases} 6 & \text{if } x \leq 4 \\ 6 + 3(x - 4) & \text{if } x > 4 \end{cases}$

9-2 PRACTICE A

9-2 PRACTICE C

9-2 PRACTICE B

Create a table for each graph. Then describe the graph in words.

1. a. Use the endpoints and points close to them as the domain values in the table.

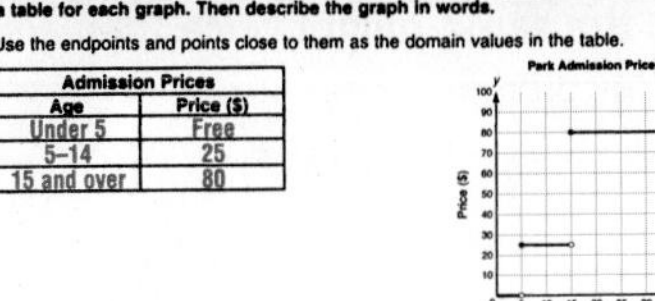

Admission Prices	
Age	Price ($)
Under 5	Free
5–14	25
15 and over	80

b. Use the domain intervals and the prices in the table to describe the graph.

Children less than 5 years of age get in free. Children between the ages of 5 and 14 pay $25. Those 15 and over pay $80.

2.

Dumpster Rental Fees	
Days	Fee ($)
Up to 4 days	400
More than 4 days and up to 8 days	600
More than 8 days and up to 14 days	800

Dumpster Rental Fees

A dumpster costs $400 for up to 4 days, $600 for more than 4 days and up to 8 days, and $800 for more than 8 days up to 14 days.

Evaluate each piecewise function for $x = -3$ and $x = 4$.

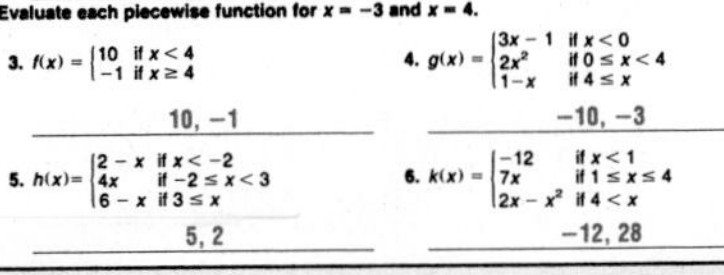

3. $f(x) = \begin{cases} 10 & \text{if } x < 4 \\ -1 & \text{if } x \geq 4 \end{cases}$ 10, −1

4. $g(x) = \begin{cases} 3x - 1 & \text{if } x < 0 \\ 2x^2 & \text{if } 0 \leq x < 4 \\ 1 - x & \text{if } 4 \leq x \end{cases}$ −10, −3

5. $h(x) = \begin{cases} 2 - x & \text{if } x < -2 \\ 4x & \text{if } -2 \leq x < 3 \\ 6 - x & \text{if } 3 \leq x \end{cases}$ 5, 2

6. $k(x) = \begin{cases} -12 & \text{if } x < 1 \\ 7x & \text{if } 1 \leq x \leq 4 \\ 2x - x^2 & \text{if } 4 < x \end{cases}$ −12, 28

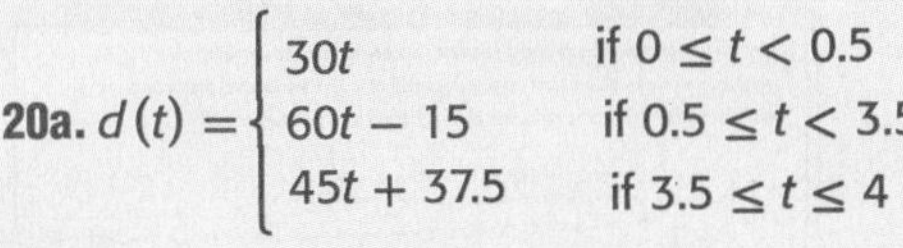

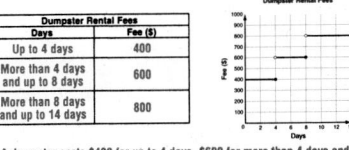

20a. $d(t) = \begin{cases} 30t & \text{if } 0 \leq t < 0.5 \\ 60t - 15 & \text{if } 0.5 \leq t < 3.5 \\ 45t + 37.5 & \text{if } 3.5 \leq t \leq 4 \end{cases}$

b.

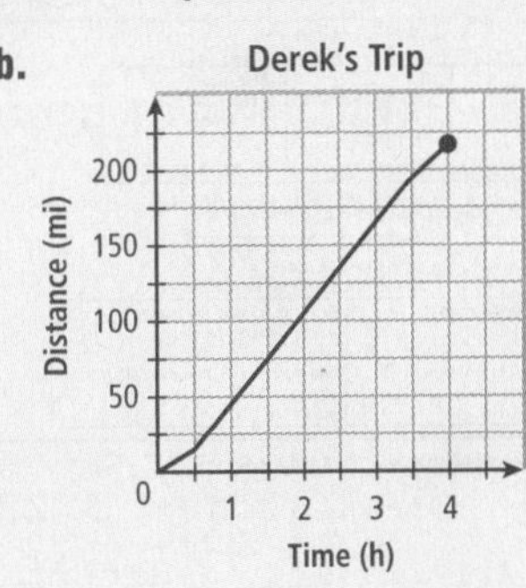

21. $f(x) = \begin{cases} x & \text{if } x \geq 0 \\ -x & \text{if } x < 0 \end{cases}$

22. $g(x) = \begin{cases} x - 4 & \text{if } x \geq 4 \\ -x + 4 & \text{if } x < 4 \end{cases}$

23. $h(x) = \begin{cases} 2x - 4 & \text{if } x \geq 0 \\ -2x - 4 & \text{if } x < 0 \end{cases}$

24.

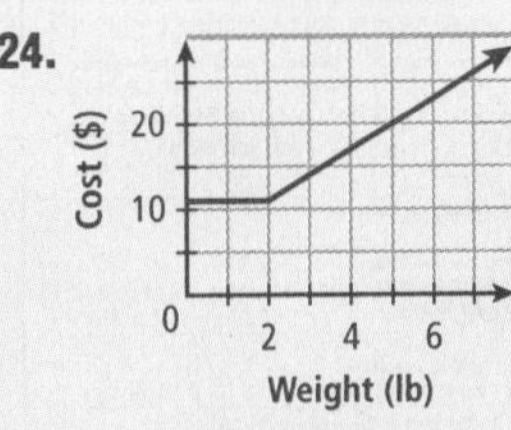

$f(x) = \begin{cases} 11 + 3(x - 2) & \text{if } x > 2 \\ 11 & \text{if } x \leq 2 \end{cases}$

25–26. See p. A40.

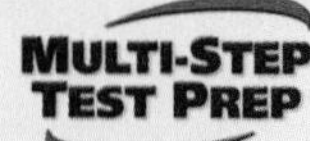

Exercise 27 involves creating a piecewise function from a verbal problem. This exercise prepares students for the Multi-Step Test Prep on page 680.

Math Background In **Exercise 31,** students consider representing the height of an elevator by using a piecewise function. One of the topics considered in a branch of mathematics called control theory is "the elevator problem," which addresses the optimal way to move elevators between the floors of a building.

In **Exercise 33,** students who chose **B** may not have taken into account that there is no mileage charge for the first 200 miles.

In **Exercise 35,** students who chose **D** may have placed the value −2 in the wrong interval.

Answers

27a. $d(t) = \begin{cases} 18t & \text{if } 0 \le t \le 10 \\ 16.5(t - 10) + 180 & \text{if } 10 < t \le 20 \end{cases}$

31. Possible answer: The elevator would ascend, then stop for a time, and then ascend again. The function would be different over each of the intervals. It would not be a step function because the elevator must pass through every height on its way up and down, so the graph would be connected.

32. Possible answer: Many real-world situations are better defined over separate intervals. For example, prices are often lower for large volume purchases. Also, some real-world situations change as time goes on. For example, people grow fairly quickly in the first years of life but stay the same height once they are adults.

MULTI-STEP TEST PREP

27. This problem will prepare you for the Multi-Step Test Prep on page 680.

A human chain is formed by 60 people standing with their arms outstretched, each holding the hand of the person on either side. The first 30 people in the chain have arm spans of 6 feet. The next 30 people have arm spans of 5.5 feet. At the word "go," the first person squeezes the hand of the second person, then the second person squeezes the hand of the third, and so on. Assume that each person takes $\frac{1}{3}$ second to pass along the signal.

a. Write a piecewise function for the distance that the signal travels in t seconds.

b. Does the signal travel faster in the first half of the chain or the second half? How is this shown in the function? **First half; the slope is steeper.**

28. D: ℝ; R: $\{y \mid y < -3 \text{ or } y \ge 3\}$ **29.** D: ℝ; R: $\{y \mid y \ge -4\}$

Find the domain and range of each piecewise function.

28. $f(x) = \begin{cases} -\frac{5}{2}x - 2 & \text{if } x \le -2 \\ -x - 5 & \text{if } x > -2 \end{cases}$

29. $g(x) = \begin{cases} x^2 - 2x - 3 & \text{if } x < 4 \\ 3x - 7 & \text{if } x \ge 4 \end{cases}$

30a. $400 plus 6% of the first $5000 she sells, and an additional 9% for every dollar over $5000 she sells.

b. $640

30. Sales Mary works at a jewelry store. She receives a base salary every week plus a commission based on how much she sells. Mary's income function can be modeled by $P(x) = \begin{cases} 400 + 0.06x & \text{if } 0 \le x \le 5000 \\ 700 + 0.09(x - 5000) & \text{if } x > 5000 \end{cases}$, where $P(x)$ is her income and x is the amount of her sales in dollars.

a. Write a description of Mary's income function.

b. How much will Mary earn in a week in which she sells $4000 worth of jewelry?

c. Find the value of the jewelry that Mary must sell in a week if she wants to earn $900 for that week. **$7222.22**

31. Critical Thinking Why would a piecewise function best describe the height of an elevator t seconds after it leaves the bottom floor of a building? Would the piecewise function also be a step function?

32. Write About It Explain why piecewise functions are often good for representing real-world situations. Include at least two examples.

33. A car rental agency charges $15 a day for driving a car 200 miles or less. If a car is driven over 200 miles, the renter must pay $0.05 for each mile over 200 driven. Which of the following functions represents the cost to drive a car from this agency x miles in a day?

Ⓐ $C(x) = \begin{cases} 15 & \text{if } 0 \le x \le 200 \\ 0.05x & \text{if } x > 200 \end{cases}$

Ⓒ $C(x) = \begin{cases} 15 & \text{if } 0 \le x \le 200 \\ 15 + 0.05(x - 200) & \text{if } x > 200 \end{cases}$

Ⓑ $C(x) = \begin{cases} 0.05 & \text{if } 0 \le x \le 200 \\ 15x & \text{if } x > 200 \end{cases}$

Ⓓ $C(x) = \begin{cases} 15 & \text{if } 0 \le x \le 200 \\ 15 + 0.05x & \text{if } x > 200 \end{cases}$

34. Which of the following is a continuous function?

Ⓕ $f(x) = \begin{cases} 3x - 4 & \text{if } x < 0 \\ -1 & \text{if } x \ge 0 \end{cases}$

Ⓗ $h(x) = \begin{cases} x^2 & \text{if } x < -2 \\ 2x & \text{if } x \ge -2 \end{cases}$

Ⓖ $g(x) = \begin{cases} 5x - 4 & \text{if } x < 3 \\ 2x + 5 & \text{if } x \ge 3 \end{cases}$

Ⓙ $j(x) = \begin{cases} 3x + 4 & \text{if } x \le -1 \\ 3^x + 4 & \text{if } x > -1 \end{cases}$

9-2 READING STRATEGIES

A **piecewise function** has different rules for different parts of the domain of the function. The toll to cross a bridge may be different depending on the weight of the vehicle. A car pays a different price than a tractor-trailer truck.

The function below is equal to $2x + 1$ if x is less than −1, it is equal to $x - 5$ if x is greater than or equal to −1 but less than or equal to 3, and it is equal to 8 if x is greater than 3.

$f(x) = \begin{cases} 2x + 1 & \text{if } x < -1 \\ x - 5 & \text{if } -1 \le x \le 3 \\ 8 & \text{if } x > 3 \end{cases}$

Answer each question.

1. Explain how the owner of a beach house could use a piecewise function in setting the rental fees for the summer.
   Possible answer: The owner could have different fees based on the length of stay: weekend, full week, full month, or entire summer.

2. a. Write a piecewise function to match the following description.
   The price per item is $2.99 if you buy fewer than 10 items. If you buy at least 10 items, the price per item is $2.50. If you buy at least 15 items, the price per item is $2.25.
   $f(x) = \begin{cases} 2.99x & \text{if } x < 10 \\ 2.50x & \text{if } 10 \le x < 15 \\ 2.25x & \text{if } x \ge 15 \end{cases}$
   b. Describe what the graph of this function looks like.
   A series of lines with slopes of 2.99 when $x < 10$, 2.50 when $10 \le x < 15$, and 2.25 when $x \ge 15$

3. Write a piecewise function to match the following description.
   The function is equal to $x - 3$ if x is less than or equal to 6.
   The function is equal to $\frac{1}{2}x$ if x is greater than 6.
   $f(x) = \begin{cases} x - 3 & \text{if } x \le 6 \\ \frac{1}{2}x & \text{if } x > 6 \end{cases}$

4. The notation for a piecewise function may remind you of a system of equations. How is the graph of a piecewise function different from the graph of a system of equations?
   Possible answer: The graph of a system of equations can be used to find the solution to the system, which is the point where the lines intersect. In a piecewise function, the graph is used to show the value of the function at the different domains.

9-2 RETEACH

A **piecewise function** has different rules for different parts of its domain.

To evaluate a piecewise function for a given value of x, find the interval that x belongs to. Then find the corresponding definition of the function for that interval.

$f(x) = \begin{cases} -6 & \text{if } x \le -1 \\ 2 & \text{if } -1 < x < 4 \\ 10 & \text{if } x \ge 4 \end{cases}$

When $x \le -1$, $f(x) = -6$.
When $-1 < x < 4$, $f(x) = 2$.
When $x \ge 4$, $f(x) = 10$.

At $x = -5$, x lies in the interval $x \le -1$, since $-5 < -1$. So, $f(-5) = -6$.	At $x = 0$, x lies in the interval $-1 < x < 4$, since $-1 < 0 < 4$. So, $f(0) = 2$.	At $x = 5$, x lies in the interval $x \ge 4$, since $5 > 4$. So, $f(5) = 10$.

$g(x) = \begin{cases} 4x - 1 & \text{if } x < 2 \\ x^2 + 3 & \text{if } x \ge 2 \end{cases}$

When $x < 2$, $g(x) = 4x - 1$.
When $x \ge 2$, $g(x) = x^2 + 3$.

At $x = -5$, x lies in the interval $x < 2$, since $-5 < 2$. Use $g(x) = 4x - 1$ to evaluate $g(-5)$. $g(-5) = 4(-5) - 1 = -21$	At $x = 5$, x lies in the interval $x \ge 2$, since $5 > 2$. Use $g(x) = x^2 + 3$ to evaluate $g(5)$. $g(5) = (5)^2 + 3 = 28$

Evaluate each piecewise function for $x = -2$ and $x = 4$.

1. $h(x) = \begin{cases} 0 & \text{if } x \le -3 \\ 2 & \text{if } -3 < x \le 1 \\ 6 & \text{if } x > 1 \end{cases}$
   $h(-2) =$ **2**
   $h(4) =$ **6**

2. $k(x) = \begin{cases} 2x^2 - 1 & \text{if } x \le -1 \\ 3x + 2 & \text{if } x > -1 \end{cases}$
   $k(-2) = 2($**−2**$)^2 - 1$
   7
   $k(4) = 3($**4**$) + 2$
   14

3. $p(x) = \begin{cases} 2x + 5 & \text{if } x < 0 \\ x^2 - 5 & \text{if } x \ge 0 \end{cases}$
   $p(-2) = 1$
   $p(4) = 11$

35. Let $f(x) = \begin{cases} 1 - 5x & \text{if } x < -5 \\ 3 - x^3 & \text{if } -5 \le x < -2 \\ 5 - x^2 & \text{if } x \ge -2 \end{cases}$. Find $f(-2)$.

Ⓐ −5 Ⓑ 1 (circled) Ⓒ 9 Ⓓ 11

CHALLENGE AND EXTEND

The *greatest integer function* returns the greatest integer less than or equal to a given number. The greatest integer function is written $f(x) = \lfloor x \rfloor$ and is often written as int(x) on graphing calculators. For example, if hamburgers cost $1.79 each, the function $f(x) = \left\lfloor \frac{x}{1.79} \right\rfloor$ would return the number of hamburgers you could buy for x dollars.

36. Write a function for the number of orders of fries that can be bought with x dollars if an order of fries costs $1.29. Then use your function to find the number of orders of fries that you can buy with $10. **$f(x) = \left\lfloor \frac{x}{1.29} \right\rfloor$; 7 orders**

The *least integer function* returns the least integer greater than or equal to a given number. The least integer function is written $f(x) = \lceil x \rceil$. For example, $f(2.9) = \lceil 2.9 \rceil = 3$.

37. At a parking garage, parking costs $4 for up to 1 hour. After that, it costs $1.50 for each additional hour or fraction thereof. Write a function to represent the cost of parking for x hours. Then use the function to find the cost of parking for 5 hours and 23 minutes. **$f(x) = 4 + 1.5(\lceil x \rceil - 1)$; $11.50**

SPIRAL REVIEW

38. **Geometry** There is a linear relationship between the number of sides in a regular polygon and the number of degrees in that polygon, as shown in the table. Write a function to represent the relationship. *(Lesson 2-4)* **$X = 180n - 360$**

Sides	3	4	5	6	8
Sum of Interior Angles (°)	180	360	540	720	1080

Identify the asymptotes, domain, and range of each function. *(Lesson 8-4)*

39. $f(x) = \frac{4}{x - 1} - 3$ 40. $f(x) = \frac{3}{x + 2} + 1$ 41. $f(x) = \frac{5}{x - 3} + 1$

39. vertical: $x = 1$; horizontal: $y = -3$; D: $\{x \mid x \neq 1\}$; R: $\{y \mid y \neq -3\}$

40. vertical: $x = -2$; horizontal: $y = 1$; D: $\{x \mid x \neq -2\}$; R: $\{y \mid y \neq 1\}$

41. vertical: $x = 3$; horizontal: $y = 1$; D: $\{x \mid x \neq 3\}$; R: $\{y \mid y \neq 1\}$

Match each situation with one of the following graphs. *(Lesson 9-1)*

A.

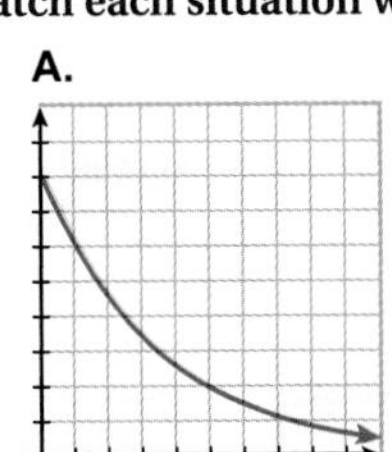

B.

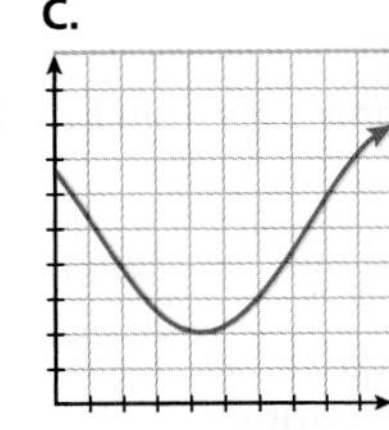

C.

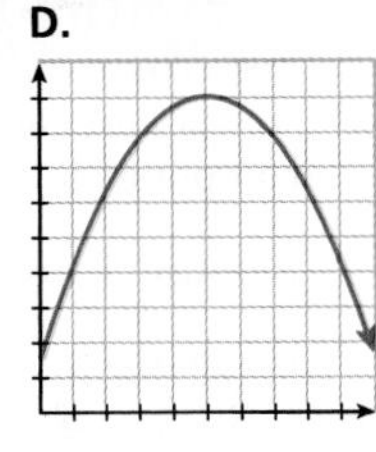

D.

42. A company releases a product without advertisement, and the profit drops. Then the company advertises, and the profit increases. **C**

43. The value of a computer declines over time. **A**

44. The sales for an ice cream store are low in winter, high in spring and fall, and extremely high in summer. **D**

45. The temperature rises steadily from 12:00 P.M. to 5:00 P.M. **B**

9-2 PROBLEM SOLVING

Roscoe earns $9.50 per hour at the woodcrafts store for up to 40 hours per week. For each hour over 40 hours he earns $13.00 per hour. Company policy limits his hours to no more than 60 per week. Roscoe wants to know how much he can earn in a week.

1. Complete the table to show his earnings for 30, 40, 50, and 60 hours per week.

Hours per Week (t)	Roscoe's Earnings, $E(t)$				
	Hours ≤ 40 ($9.50 per h)		Hours > 40 ($13.00 per h)		Total Earnings
30	30	$285	0	$0	$285
40	40	$380	0	0	$380
50	40	$380	10	$130	$510
60	40	$380	20	$260	$640

2. Graph earnings as a function of hours worked, using the data from the table. Roscoe thinks the points lie in a straight line. Is he correct?

No

3. Draw line segments to join the points, including the point that represents earnings for 0 hours worked. Describe the graph in terms of line segments and the slope of each segment. Explain the meaning of the slope in terms of rate of pay.

Possible answer: The graph shows two straight-line segments that intersect where $t = 40$. The slope of a segment is the rate of pay for that interval: 9.5 or 13.

4. Use the slope and a point on each line segment to write a piecewise function for earnings $E(t)$ as a function of hours worked (t). **$E(t) = \begin{cases} 9.5t & \text{if } 0 \le t \le 40 \\ 13(t - 40) + 380 & \text{if } 40 < t \le 60 \end{cases}$**

Choose the letter for the best answer.

5. How much will Roscoe earn if he works 56.5 hours in one week?
Ⓐ $594.50 (circled)
B $610.00
C $625.50
D $734.50

6. Roscoe earned $471 last week. How many hours did he work?
F 45
Ⓖ 47 (circled)
H 49
J 51

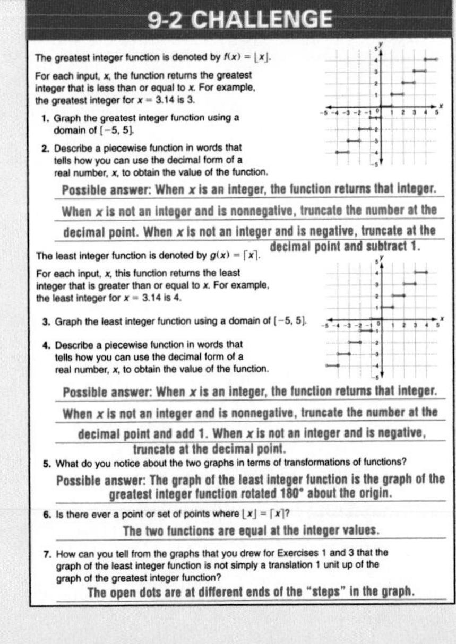

9-2 CHALLENGE

The greatest integer function is denoted by $f(x) = \lfloor x \rfloor$.

For each input, x, the function returns the greatest integer that is less than or equal to x. For example, the greatest integer for $x = 3.14$ is 3.

1. Graph the greatest integer function using a domain of $[-5, 5]$.

2. Describe a piecewise function in words that tells how you can use the decimal form of a real number, x, to obtain the value of the function.

Possible answer: When x is an integer, the function returns that integer. When x is not an integer and is nonnegative, truncate the number at the decimal point. When x is not an integer and is negative, truncate at the decimal point and subtract 1.

The least integer function is denoted by $g(x) = \lceil x \rceil$.

For each input, x, this function returns the least integer that is greater than or equal to x. For example, the least integer for $x = 3.14$ is 4.

3. Graph the least integer function using a domain of $[-5, 5]$.

4. Describe a piecewise function in words that tells how you can use the decimal form of a real number, x, to obtain the value of the function.

Possible answer: When x is an integer, the function returns that integer. When x is not an integer and is nonnegative, truncate the number at the decimal point and add 1. When x is not an integer and is negative, truncate at the decimal point.

5. What do you notice about the two graphs in terms of transformations of functions?

Possible answer: The graph of the least integer function is the graph of the greatest integer function rotated 180° about the origin.

6. Is there ever a point or set of points where $\lfloor x \rfloor = \lceil x \rceil$?

The two functions are equal at the integer values.

7. How can you tell from the graphs that you drew for Exercises 1 and 3 that the graph of the least integer function is not simply a translation 1 unit up of the graph of the greatest integer function?

The open dots are at different ends of the "steps" in the graph.

Journal

Have students describe the process of graphing a piecewise function, illustrated with an example.

ALTERNATIVE ASSESSMENT

Have students generate a piecewise function based on a real-world situation, such as a race or trip involving two different speeds. Have them include the equation, the graph, and the table for the function.

Power Presentations with PowerPoint®

9-2 Lesson Quiz

1. Graph the function, and evaluate at $x = 1$ and $x = 3$.

$$p(x) = \begin{cases} \frac{1}{2}x^2 + 2 & \text{if } x \le 2 \\ \frac{1}{2}x + 3 & \text{if } x > 2 \end{cases}$$

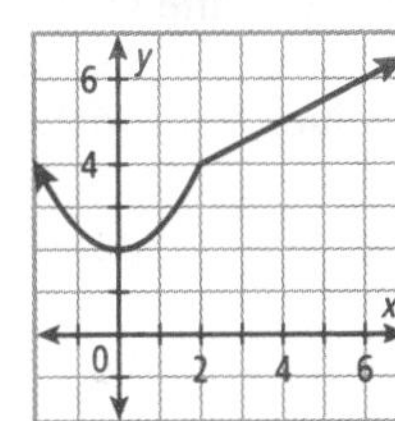

2.5; 4.5

2. Write and graph a piecewise function for the following situation. A house painter charges $12 per hour for the first 40 hours he works, time and a half for the 10 hours after that, and double time for all hours after that. How much does he earn for a 70-hour week?

$$f(x) = \begin{cases} 12x & \text{if } 0 \le x \le 40 \\ 18x - 240 & \text{if } 40 < x \le 50 \\ 24x - 540 & \text{if } x > 50 \end{cases}$$

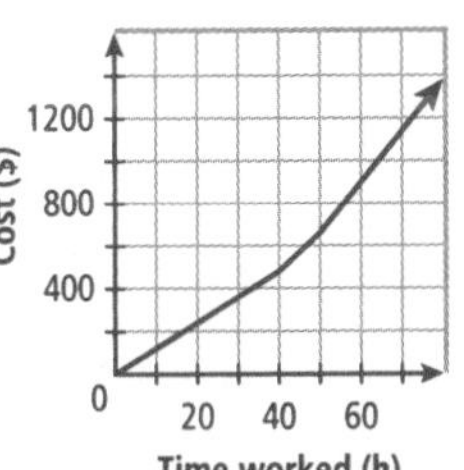

$1140

Also available on transparency

Technology LAB Organizer

Use with Lesson 9-2

Pacing:
Traditional 1 day
Block $\frac{1}{2}$ day

Objective: Use a graphing calculator to graph piecewise functions.

Materials: graphing calculator

Online Edition
TechKeys

Countdown to Testing Week 19

Resources

Technology Lab Activities
9-2 Lab Recording Sheet

Teach

Discuss

Discuss with students how to use logical tests to evaluate the truth value of inequalities. Then show students how logical tests are used to graph piecewise functions. Ask students what some of the graphs would look like if students did not use logical test values to restrict the domains.

State Resources

9-2 Technology LAB

Graph Piecewise Functions

You can graph piecewise functions on a graphing calculator by using logical tests to restrict the domain for each piece of the function.

Use with Lesson 9-2

Activity 1

A graphing calculator can determine whether mathematical statements, such as $5 > 3$, are true. You can enter these statements by using the **TEST** menu. The calculator returns a value of 1 if the statement is true and a value of 0 if the statement is false.

Determine whether the statement 5^7 is greater than or less than 50,000.

Enter the left side of the first expression. Access the **TEST** menu (as shown) by pressing 2nd MATH. Choose the less-than symbol (**5:<**), and then complete the expression. Enter the second expression, substituting the greater-than symbol (**3:>**).

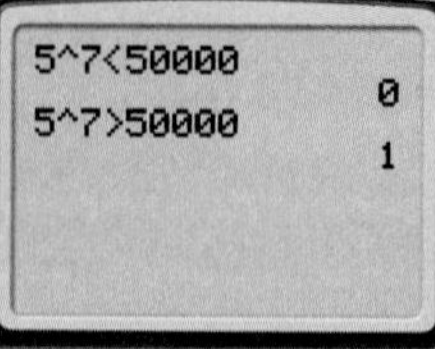

The first expression returns a value of 0, so it is false. The second expression returns a value of 1, so it is true. The expression 5^7 is greater than 50,000.

Try This

Use logical tests to determine whether each statement is true or false.

1. $4 - 3 = 3 - 4$ **false**
2. $(-6)^4 \geq 1000$ **true**
3. $\frac{3}{16} < 0.1875$ **false**
4. $\frac{3}{16} > 0.1875$ **false**
5. **Draw a Conclusion** What conclusion can you make about $\frac{3}{16}$ and 0.1875 based on the answers to Problems 3 and 4?
   They are equal.

Activity 2

You can use the commands from the **LOGIC** submenu of the **TEST** menu to create compound logical tests.

Determine whether the statement $3.14 < \pi < \frac{22}{7}$ is true.

Recall that the compound inequality $3.14 < \pi < \frac{22}{7}$ can be written as $3.14 < \pi$ and $\pi < \frac{22}{7}$. Enter the first expression, and then access the **LOGIC** submenu by pressing 2nd MATH ▶. Choose **1: and,** and then enter the second expression.

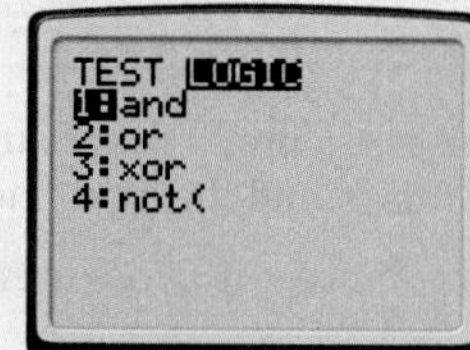

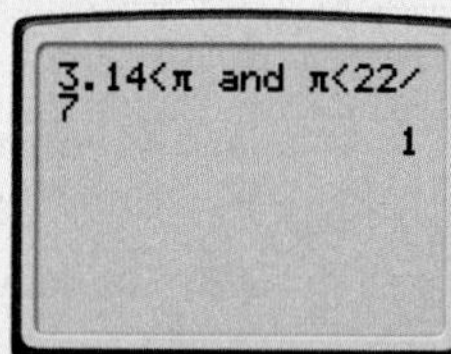

Because the statement returns a value of 1, the statement is true: $3.14 < \pi < \frac{22}{7}$. ✔

Try This

Use logical tests to determine whether each statement is true or false.

6. $-2^2 < -2 < (-2)^2$ true
7. $(-2)^1 < (-2)^2 < (-2)^3$ false
8. $\sqrt{2} < 2 < 2^2$ true
9. $\sqrt{\frac{1}{2}} < \frac{1}{2} < \left(\frac{1}{2}\right)^2$ false
10. **Make a Conjecture** What conjecture can you make about the relationship between a number, its square, and its square root if the number is greater than 1? What if the number is between 0 and 1? For $x > 1$, $x^2 > x > \sqrt{x}$. For $0 < x < 1$, $\sqrt{x} > x > x^2$.

Activity 3

Graph the piecewise function $f(x) = \begin{cases} 2x + 7 & \text{if } x \le -2 \\ 3 & \text{if } -2 < x \le 2 \\ x + 1 & \text{if } x > 2 \end{cases}$.

1. When you want to graph any piecewise function, change the calculator to dot mode. Press MODE, and then select **Dot**. This will prevent the calculator from showing extraneous lines.

2. Enter the first part of the rule, enclosed in parentheses, as **Y1**. If your calculator is not in dot mode, change the graph style so that three dots are shown. In a second set of parentheses, enter the logical test that will restrict the domain as indicated in the function rule.

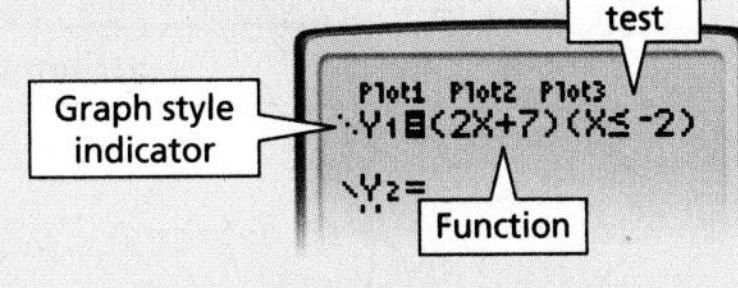

3. Use similar methods to enter the second part of the rule as **Y2**. Because the restriction is a compound inequality, you will have to use the **and** command from the **LOGIC** menu.

4. Finally, enter the third part of the rule as **Y3,** and graph in the standard square window.

Plot1 Plot2 Plot3
Y1(2X+7)(X≤-2)
Y2(3)(X>-2 and X≤2)
Y3(X+1)(X>2)
Y4=
Y5=

5. The table shows the function values for each function over the restricted domain. Outside of the restricted domain, each function shows values of zero.

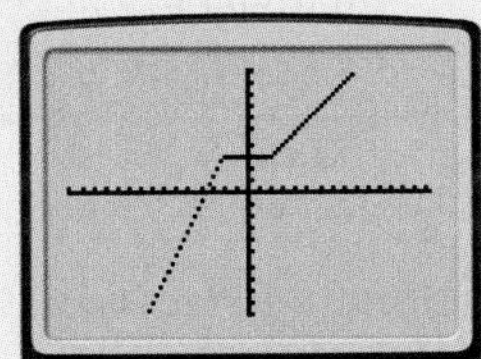

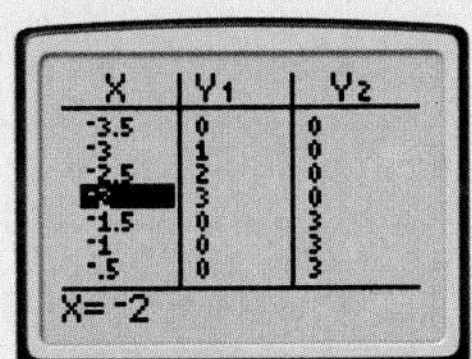

Try This

Graph each piecewise function.

11. $g(x) = \begin{cases} x & \text{if } x < 0 \\ -x & \text{if } x \ge 0 \end{cases}$
12. $h(x) = \begin{cases} 2x + 8 & \text{if } x \le -2 \\ x^2 & \text{if } x > -2 \end{cases}$
13. $f(x) = \begin{cases} -3x & \text{if } x < 1 \\ x - 4 & \text{if } 1 \le x < 5 \\ -\frac{1}{2}x + \frac{7}{2} & \text{if } x \ge 5 \end{cases}$
14. **Critical Thinking** Explain how multiplying the function by a logical test value visually restricts the domain of the function on your graph.
15. **Critical Thinking** Explain why you should use dot mode instead of connected mode when graphing piecewise functions.

Close

Key Concept

You can graph piecewise functions on a graphing calculator by using logical test values to restrict the domain for each piece of the piecewise function. Students must first understand how logical tests work before they can use them in graphs.

Assessment

Journal Give students the equation of a piecewise function, and have them explain how they would graph it on their calculators.

Answers

11.

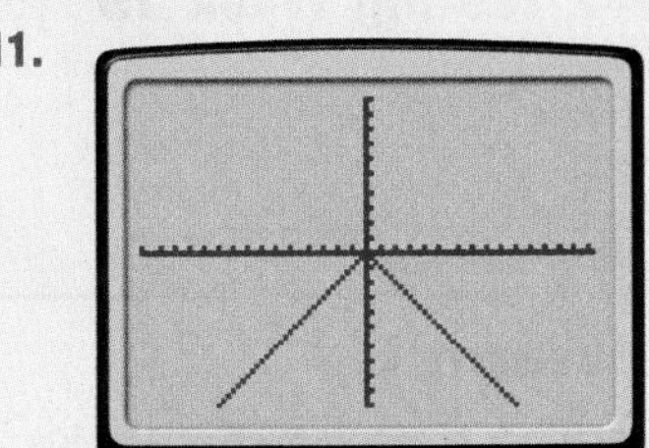

12.

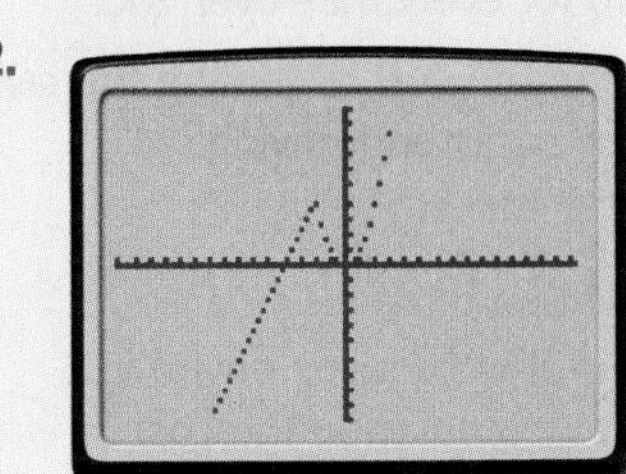

13.

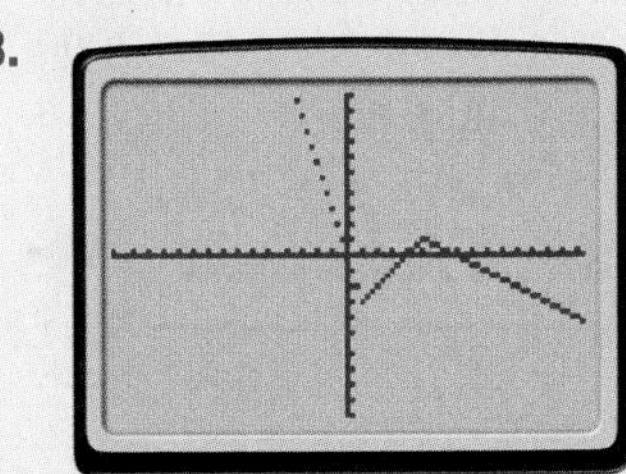

14. Possible answer: The logical test returns 1 if the statement is true and 0 if it is false. If the statement is false, the function is multiplied by 0 and all function values are 0. If the statement is true, the function is multiplied by 1 and all values stay the same.
15. Possible answer: The calculator gives the function a value of 0 when the x-values are not in the restricted domain. The connected mode would connect these values to the actual function values, creating extraneous lines.

9-3 Organizer

Pacing: Traditional 1 day
Block $\frac{1}{2}$ day

Objectives: Transform functions.

Recognize transformations of functions.

Algebra Lab
In *Algebra Lab Activities*

Online Edition
Tutorial Videos

Countdown to Testing Week 19

Power Presentations with PowerPoint®

Warm Up

A rental car costs \$45 per day plus \$0.10 for every mile over 200.

1. Find the cost of renting the car for a day and driving 250 miles. \$50
2. Write a function of d, the number of miles driven in a day, to describe the cost of renting the car for one day.

$$C(d) = \begin{cases} 45 & \text{if } 0 \le d \le 200 \\ 45 + 0.1(d - 200) & \text{if } d > 200 \end{cases}$$

Also available on transparency

Math Humor

Teacher: Why did you write "COUNT FINS" and "IN FUN COTS" all over your quiz?

Student: I wanted to show you that I could transform "FUNCTIONS."

State Resources

go.hrw.com
State Resources Online
KEYWORD: MB7 Resources

9-3 Transforming Functions

A2.2.3 Graph piecewise-defined functions.

Objectives
Transform functions.

Recognize transformations of functions.

Why learn this?
Transformations can be used to describe changes in college tuition fees. (See Example 4.)

"If you miss a payment, we show up and embarrass you in front of your friends."

In previous lessons, you learned how to transform several types of functions. You can transform piecewise functions by applying transformations to each piece independently. Recall the rules for transforming functions given in the table.

Transformations of $f(x)$

Horizontal Translation	Vertical Translation
$f(x) \to f(x - h)$ left for $h < 0$ right for $h > 0$	$f(x) \to f(x) + k$ down for $k < 0$ up for $k > 0$
Reflection Across y-axis	**Reflection Across x-axis**
$f(x) \to f(-x)$ The graph is reflected across the y-axis.	$f(x) \to -f(x)$ The graph is reflected across the x-axis.
Horizontal Stretch/Compression	**Vertical Stretch/Compression**
$f(x) \to f\left(\frac{1}{b}x\right)$ stretch for $b > 1$ compression for $0 < b < 1$	$f(x) \to af(x)$ stretch for $a > 1$ compression for $0 < a < 1$

Caution!
Horizontal translations change both the rules and the intervals of piecewise functions. Vertical translations change only the rules.

EXAMPLE 1 Transforming Piecewise Functions

Given $f(x) = \begin{cases} x + 3 & \text{if } x > 0 \\ 2x + 3 & \text{if } x \le 0 \end{cases}$, write the rule for $g(x)$, a horizontal translation of $f(x)$ 4 units right.

Each piece of $f(x)$ must be shifted 4 units right. Replace every x in the function with $(x - 4)$, and simplify.

$$g(x) = f(x - 4) = \begin{cases} (x - 4) + 3 & \text{if } (x - 4) > 0 \\ 2(x - 4) + 3 & \text{if } (x - 4) \le 0 \end{cases}$$

$$= \begin{cases} x - 1 & \text{if } x > 4 \\ 2x - 5 & \text{if } x \le 4 \end{cases}$$

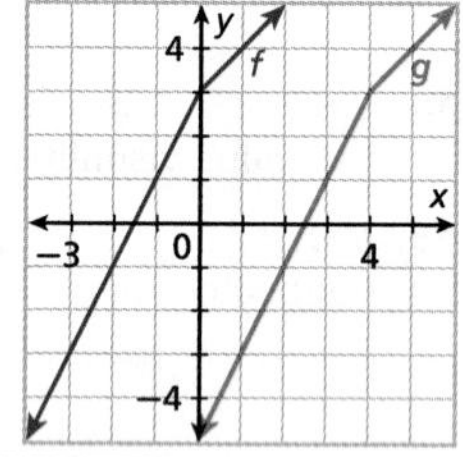

Check Graph both functions to support your answer.

1 Introduce

EXPLORATION

9-3 Transforming Functions

In this Exploration, you will investigate a transformation of a piecewise function.

1. Complete the table for the piecewise function in the graph.

x	y
−8	
−4	
0	
4	
8	

2. Add 2 to each x-value in the table and add 1 to each y-value. Plot the new points and connect them to graph the resulting piecewise function.
3. What are the intervals for the original piecewise function?
4. What are the intervals for the transformed function?

THINK AND DISCUSS

5. Explain how the graph of the transformed function compares

Motivate

Introduce a simple piecewise function, such as the cost of tickets to a play where students pay \$5 and adults pay \$8. Ask students to consider what happens if the prices are increased by 25%. Explain that this increase can be represented by a transformation of a piecewise function.

Explorations and answers are provided in the *Explorations* binder.

$$g(x) = \begin{cases} \left(\dfrac{x^2}{2}\right) & \text{if } x \le 0 \\ \dfrac{x}{2} - 3 & \text{if } x > 0 \end{cases}$$

1. Given $f(x) = \begin{cases} x^2 & \text{if } x \le 0 \\ x - 3 & \text{if } x > 0 \end{cases}$, write the rule for $g(x)$, a horizontal stretch of $f(x)$ by a factor of 2.

When functions are transformed, the intercepts may or may not change. By identifying the transformations, you can determine the intercepts, which can help you graph a transformed function.

Effects of Transformations on Intercepts of $f(x)$

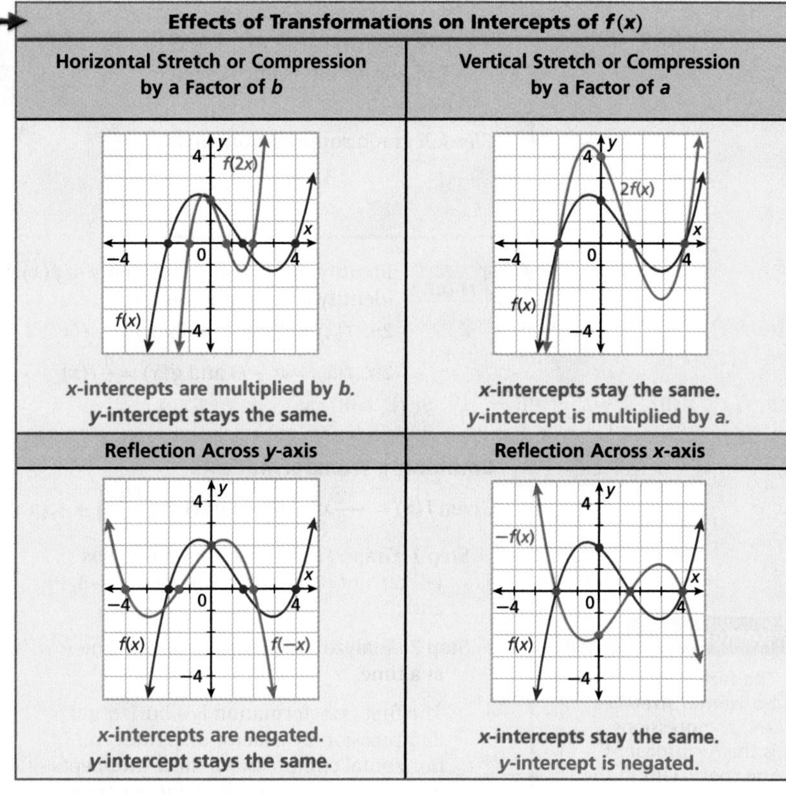

Horizontal Stretch or Compression by a Factor of b	Vertical Stretch or Compression by a Factor of a
x-intercepts are multiplied by b. y-intercept stays the same.	x-intercepts stay the same. y-intercept is multiplied by a.
Reflection Across y-axis	**Reflection Across x-axis**
x-intercepts are negated. y-intercept stays the same.	x-intercepts stay the same. y-intercept is negated.

EXAMPLE 2 Identifying Intercepts

Identify the x- and y-intercepts of $f(x)$. Without graphing $g(x)$, identify its x- and y-intercepts.

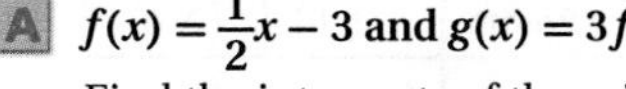

A $f(x) = \frac{1}{2}x - 3$ and $g(x) = 3f(x)$

Find the intercepts of the original function.

$f(0) = \frac{1}{2}(0) - 3 = -3$ $\qquad$ $0 = \frac{1}{2}x - 3$

$f(0) = -3$ $\qquad$ $6 = x$

The y-intercept is -3, and the x-intercept is 6. Note that $g(x)$ is a vertical stretch of $f(x)$ by a factor of 3. So the x-intercept of $g(x)$ is also 6. The y-intercept is $3(-3)$, or -9.

Check A graph supports your answer.

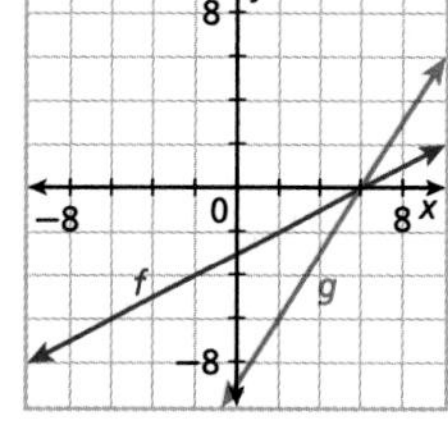

Power Presentations with PowerPoint®

Additional Examples

Example 1

Given $f(x) = \begin{cases} -\frac{1}{2}x & \text{if } x < 0 \\ \frac{1}{2}x^2 & \text{if } x \ge 0 \end{cases}$, write the rule for $g(x)$, a vertical stretch by a factor of 3.

$g(x) = \begin{cases} -\frac{3}{2}x & \text{if } x < -2 \\ \frac{3}{2}x^2 & \text{if } x \ge -2 \end{cases}$

Example 2

Identify the x- and y-intercepts of $f(x)$. Without graphing $g(x)$, identify its x- and y-intercepts.

A. $f(x) = -2x - 4$; $g(x) = f\left(\frac{1}{2}x\right)$

$f(x)$: x-int. $= -2$, y-int. $= -4$
$g(x)$: x-int. $= -4$, y-int. $= -4$

B. $f(x) = x^2 - 1$; $g(x) = f(-x)$

$f(x)$: x-ints. $= -1$ and 1, y-int. $= -1$
$g(x)$: x-ints. $= -1$ and 1, y-int. $= -1$

Also available on transparency

INTERVENTION

Questioning Strategies

EXAMPLE 1

- Which transformations will change the domain intervals of piecewise functions? Which will not?

EXAMPLE 2

- Which transformations affect only the x-intercepts? Which affect only the y-intercepts?

2 Teach

Guided Instruction

Use the table of transformations on p. 672 to review the transformations that students have already studied. Explain that transformations of piecewise functions follow the same rules. Use the table on p. 673 to show students how identifying the intercepts of a transformed function can make the function easier to visualize and to graph.

Reaching All Learners

Through Kinesthetic Experience

Reflections can be modeled by drawing a function on tracing paper or patty paper and then flipping the paper. Give students or small groups a few sheets of paper, and have them perform some reflections, such as $f(x) = x^3 + 2$, $g(x) = -(x^3 + 2)$, and $h(x) = (-x)^3 + 2$. You may want to do this activity before **Example 2** to let students discover the effects that reflections have on a function's x- and y-intercepts.

Power Presentations with PowerPoint®

Additional Examples

Example 3

Given $f(x) = \frac{1}{3}(x - 2)^2$ and $g(x) = 2f(x) - 3$, graph $g(x)$.

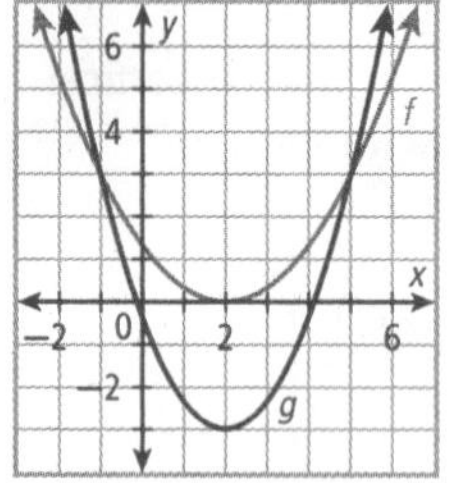

Also available on transparency

INTERVENTION

Questioning Strategies

EXAMPLE 3

- Describe how you can use algebra and graphing to check your work.

Answers to *Check it Out!*

3.

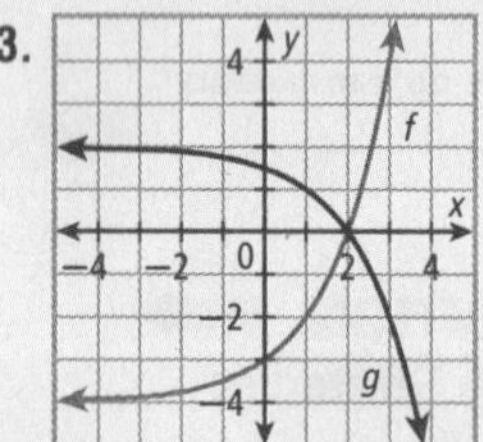

Identify the *x*- and *y*-intercepts of $f(x)$. Without graphing $g(x)$, identify its *x*- and *y*-intercepts.

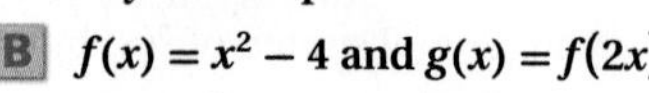

B $f(x) = x^2 - 4$ and $g(x) = f(2x)$

From the graph of $f(x)$, the *y*-intercept is -4 and the *x*-intercepts are -2 and 2.

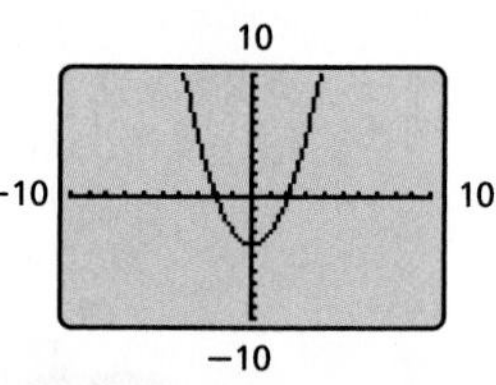

Note that $g(x)$ is a horizontal compression by a factor of $\frac{1}{2}$. So the *x*-intercepts of $g(x)$ will be $\frac{1}{2}(-2)$ and $\frac{1}{2}(2)$, or -1 and 1. The *y*-intercept is unchanged at -4.

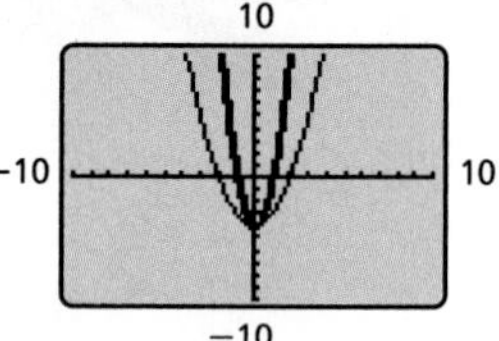

Check A graph supports your answer.

CHECK IT OUT! **Identify the *x*- and *y*-intercepts of $f(x)$. Without graphing $g(x)$, identify its *x*- and *y*-intercepts.**

2a. $f(x) = \frac{2}{3}x + 4$ and $g(x) = -f(x)$

2b. $f(x) = x^2 - 9$ and $g(x) = \frac{1}{3}f(x)$

2a. $f(x)$: *x*-int. $= -6$, *y*-int. $= 4$; $g(x)$: *x*-int. $= -6$, *y*-int. $= -4$

2b. $f(x)$: *x*-int. $= \pm 3$, *y*-int. $= -9$; $g(x)$: *x*-int. $= \pm 3$, *y*-int. $= -3$

EXAMPLE 3 Combining Transformations

Given $f(x) = -\frac{2}{3}x^2 + 6$ and $g(x) = f\left(\frac{3}{2}x\right) + 4$, graph $g(x)$.

Step 1 Graph $f(x)$. The graph of $f(x)$ has *y*-intercept $(0, 6)$ and *x*-intercepts $(-3, 0)$ and $(3, 0)$.

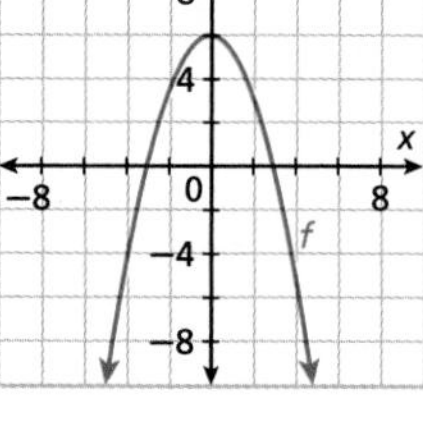

Step 2 Analyze each transformation one at a time.

The first transformation is a horizontal compression by a factor of $\frac{2}{3}$. After the horizontal compression, the *x*-intercepts will be -2 and 2, but the *y*-intercept will remain 6.

The second transformation is a vertical translation of 4 units up. Use a table to shift each identified point up 4 units.

Intercept Points	(−2, 0)	(2, 0)	(0, 6)
Shifted	(−2, 4)	(2, 4)	(0, 10)

Step 3 Graph the final result.

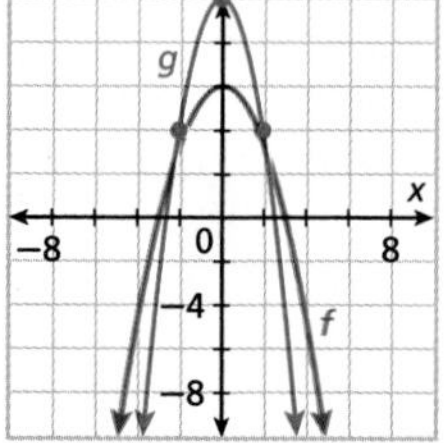

Remember!

The factor for horizontal stretches and compressions is the reciprocal of the coefficient in the equation.

$$\frac{1}{\frac{3}{2}} = \frac{2}{3}$$

CHECK IT OUT! **3.** Given $f(x) = 2^x - 4$ and $g(x) = -\frac{1}{2}f(x)$, graph $g(x)$.

EXAMPLE 4 Problem-Solving Application

A college charges different fees according to the number of credit hours in which students have enrolled. The fee scale is modeled by the piecewise function below, where x is the number of credit hours.

$$f(x) = \begin{cases} 110x & \text{if } 0 < x < 12 \\ 1320 & \text{if } 12 \le x \le 18 \\ 150(x - 18) + 1320 & \text{if } x > 18 \end{cases}$$

The college plans to increase all fees by 10% for the fall semester. In the spring semester, the college plans to add an administrative fee of $75 to each enrollment. Write the rule for the fee function for the spring semester.

1 Understand the Problem

The new fee function will include two changes, a 10% increase and an additional fee of $75. The 10% increase is equivalent to multiplying all of the parts of the function by 110%, or 1.1. This will be a vertical stretch by a factor of 1.1. The administrative fee will be a vertical translation of 75 units up.

2 Make a Plan

Perform each transformation, one at a time, and then write the new rule.

3 Solve

First find the fees for the fall semester.

$$f_{fall}(x) = (1.1)f(x) = \begin{cases} (1.1)110x & \text{if } 0 < x < 12 \\ (1.1)1320 & \text{if } 12 \le x \le 18 \\ (1.1)[150(x - 18) + 1320] & \text{if } x > 18 \end{cases}$$

Multiply all parts by 1.1.

$$= \begin{cases} 121x & \text{if } 0 < x < 12 \\ 1452 & \text{if } 12 \le x \le 18 \\ 165(x - 18) + 1452 & \text{if } x > 18 \end{cases}$$

Then find the fees for the spring semester.

$$f_{spring}(x) = f_{fall}(x) + 75 = \begin{cases} 121x + 75 & \text{if } 0 < x < 12 \\ 1452 + 75 & \text{if } 12 \le x \le 18 \\ 165(x - 18) + 1452 + 75 & \text{if } x > 18 \end{cases}$$

$$= \begin{cases} 121x + 75 & \text{if } 0 < x < 12 \\ 1527 & \text{if } 12 \le x \le 18 \\ 165(x - 18) + 1527 & \text{if } x > 18 \end{cases}$$

4 Look Back

Check your answer by trying a few values. For 20 hours, the original fee would have been $1620. A 10% increase plus a $75 fee would amount to $1857. Evaluate the function for $x = 20$ to check.

$f_{spring}(20) = \{165(20 - 18) + 1527 = 1857$ ✔

Continue by checking each piece of the function.

CHECK IT OUT! 4. A movie theater charges $5 for children under 12 and $7.50 for anyone 12 and over. The theater decides to increase its prices by 20%. It charges an additional $0.50 fee for online ticket purchases. Write a function for the online ticket prices.

$$f(x) = \begin{cases} 6.50 & \text{if } x < 12 \\ 9.50 & \text{if } x \ge 12 \end{cases}$$

Power Presentations with PowerPoint®

Additional Examples

Example 4

Coco's Coffee charges different prices based on the number of pounds purchased. The pricing scale is modeled by the function below, where w is the weight in pounds purchased.

$$p(w) = \begin{cases} 9w & \text{if } 0 < w < 3 \\ 27 + 7.5(w - 3) & \text{if } 3 \le w < 6 \\ 49.5 + 6(w - 6) & \text{if } w \ge 6 \end{cases}$$

Orders placed directly through the Web site are discounted by $\frac{1}{3}$, but a shipping fee of $2.50 is added. Write a pricing function for orders placed through the Web site.

$$p_w(w) = \begin{cases} 6w + 2.5 & \text{if } 0 < w < 3 \\ 20.5 + 5(w - 3) & \text{if } 3 \le w < 6 \\ 35.5 + 4(w - 6) & \text{if } w \ge 6 \end{cases}$$

Also available on transparency

INTERVENTION

Questioning Strategies

EXAMPLE 4

- Why is there no variable in the second interval of the given piecewise function?

Teaching Tip **Math Background** Have students note the use of the subscripts "fall" and "spring" in **Example 4.** Subscripts are common in higher-level math and science classes. They also help relate variables and functions to the real-world quantities or relationships that they represent.

3 Close

Summarize

Remind students that transforming piecewise functions is a combination of the processes used to transform other functions. Review the effects that transformations have on the x- and y-intercepts of functions. Emphasize that knowing the effects can make graphing the functions easier.

ONGOING ASSESSMENT and INTERVENTION

***Diagnose Before* the Lesson**
9-3 Warm Up, TE p. 672

***Monitor During* the Lesson**
Check It Out! Exercises, SE pp. 672–675
Questioning Strategies, TE pp. 673–675

***Assess After* the Lesson**
9-3 Lesson Quiz, TE p. 679
Alternative Assessment, TE p. 679

Answers to *Think and Discuss*

Possible answers:

1. reflections across y-axis, horizontal stretches, and horizontal compressions
2. Stretches and compressions are created by multiplying the input or output values by a number. If the input and output values are both 0, multiplying either by any number still yields 0.
3. See p. A11.

THINK AND DISCUSS

1. Identify the transformations that leave the y-intercept unchanged.
2. Explain why the point (0, 0) is unchanged under any stretch or compression.

3. **GET ORGANIZED** Copy and complete the graphic organizer. Identify the effects of each transformation on the intercepts.

Transformation	x-intercepts	y-intercept
Horizontal stretch or compression by a factor of b		
Vertical stretch or compression by a factor of a		
Reflection across y-axis		
Reflection across x-axis		

9-3 Exercises

Assignment Guide

Assign *Guided Practice* exercises as necessary.

If you finished Examples **1–2**
- **Basic** 8–16
- **Average** 8–16
- **Advanced** 8–16, 35

If you finished Examples **1–4**
- **Basic** 8–20, 22–27, 31–34, 37–41
- **Average** 8–34, 37–41
- **Advanced** 8–25, 27–41

Homework Quick Check

Quickly check key concepts.
Exercises: 8, 14, 18, 19, 20

State Resources

go.hrw.com
State Resources Online
KEYWORD: MB7 Resources

9-3 Exercises

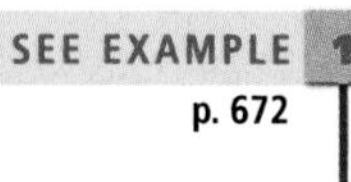

GUIDED PRACTICE

SEE EXAMPLE 1 p. 672

Given $f(x) = \begin{cases} x - 3 & \text{if } x \le 0 \\ 4x & \text{if } x > 0 \end{cases}$, write the rule for each function.

1. $g(x)$, a horizontal translation of $f(x)$ 6 units left $g(x) = \begin{cases} x + 3 & \text{if } x \le -6 \\ 4(x+6) & \text{if } x > -6 \end{cases}$
2. $h(x)$, a horizontal compression by a factor of $\frac{1}{4}$

SEE EXAMPLE 2 p. 673

Identify the x- and y-intercepts of $f(x)$. Without graphing $g(x)$, identify its x- and y-intercepts.

3. $f(x) = 4x + 12$ and $g(x) = \frac{1}{6}f(x)$ **3.** $f(x)$: x-int. $= -3$, y-int. $= 12$; $g(x)$: x-int. $= -3$, y-int. $= 2$
4. $f(x) = -x^2 + 16$ and $g(x) = f(4x)$ $f(x)$: x-int. $= \pm 4$, y-int. $= 16$; $g(x)$: x-int. $= \pm 1$, y-int. $= 16$

SEE EXAMPLE 3 p. 674

Given $f(x)$, graph $g(x)$.

5. $f(x) = -x^2 + 1$ and $g(x) = f(2x) - 1$
6. $f(x) = |x - 1| - 2$ and $g(x) = -2f(x)$

SEE EXAMPLE 4 p. 675

7. **Taxes** The state income tax in Connecticut is modeled by the function $T(x) = \begin{cases} 0.02x & \text{if } 0 < x \le 10{,}000 \\ 0.05x & \text{if } x > 10{,}000 \end{cases}$, where x is income in dollars. Suppose that Connecticut decided to increase its tax rates by 20% and add a filing fee of \$100 dollars. Write a function for the new state income tax.

PRACTICE AND PROBLEM SOLVING

Given $f(x) = \begin{cases} x^2 & \text{if } x < 1 \\ 4x & \text{if } x \ge 1 \end{cases}$, write the rule for each function.

8. $g(x)$, a vertical compression of $f(x)$ by a factor of $\frac{1}{4}$ $g(x) = \begin{cases} \frac{1}{4}x^2 & \text{if } x < 1 \\ x & \text{if } x \ge 1 \end{cases}$
9. $h(x)$, a horizontal stretch by a factor of 2
10. $p(x)$, a vertical translation 3 units down

Answers

2. $h(x) = \begin{cases} 4x - 3 & \text{if } x \le 0 \\ 16x & \text{if } x > 0 \end{cases}$

5.

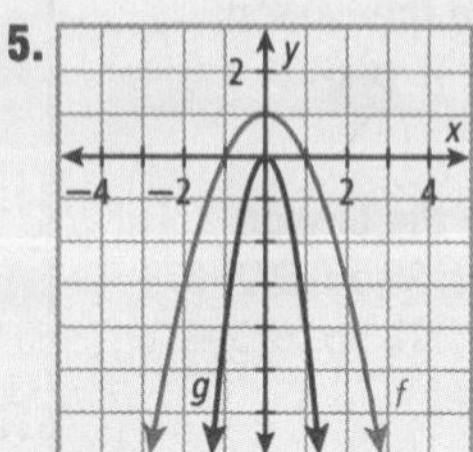

6.

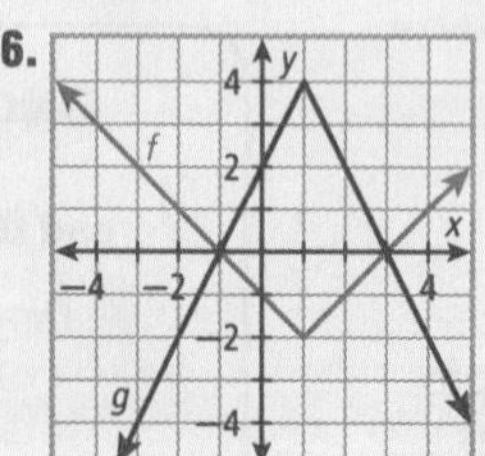

7. $T(x) = \begin{cases} 0.024x + 100 & \text{if } 0 < x \le 10{,}000 \\ 0.060x + 100 & \text{if } x > 10{,}000 \end{cases}$

9. $h(x) = \begin{cases} \left(\frac{x}{2}\right)^2 & \text{if } x < 2 \\ 2x & \text{if } x \ge 2 \end{cases}$

10. $p(x) = \begin{cases} x^2 - 3 & \text{if } x < 1 \\ 4x - 3 & \text{if } x \ge 1 \end{cases}$

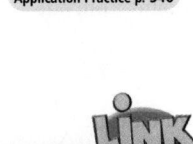

Independent Practice	
For Exercises	See Example
8–10	1
11–16	2
17–18	3
19	4

Extra Practice

Skills Practice p. S20

Application Practice p. S40

Identify the x- and y-intercepts of $f(x)$. Without graphing $g(x)$, identify its x- and y-intercepts.

11. $f(x) = -\frac{3}{2}x + 9$ and $g(x) = \frac{2}{3}f(x)$

12. $f(x) = x^2 - 25$ and $g(x) = f\left(\frac{5}{3}x\right)$

13. $f(x) = -\frac{2}{5}x + 2$ and $g(x) = f(2x)$

14. $f(x) = x^2 - 3x - 4$ and $g(x) = -f\left(\frac{1}{3}x\right)$

15. $f(x) = 3^x - 1$ and $g(x) = 2f(x) - 4$

16. $f(x) = x^3 + 8$ and $g(x) = f\left(-\frac{1}{2}x\right)$

Given $f(x)$, graph $g(x)$.

17. $f(x) = \frac{1}{2}x + 4$ and $g(x) = 3f(-x)$

18. $f(x) = \left(\frac{1}{2}\right)^x - 2$ and $g(x) = -f(2x)$

19. Business The amount that a caterer charges to cater a party for n people is given by the function $C(n) = \begin{cases} 18n & \text{if } n \le 50 \\ 400 + 10n & \text{if } n > 50 \end{cases}$.

a. During a sale, the caterer reduces the amount charged by 10%. Find the function for how much the caterer will charge during the sale.

b. If the caterer then decides to take an additional $2 off per person, find the function for how much the caterer will charge.

LINK

Safety

In some cities, automatic cameras are used to identify and photograph vehicles that are speeding. The first stationary speed camera in Washington, D.C., detected more than 10,000 speeding drivers in its first 15 days of operation.

20. Safety Speeding fines in Washington, D.C., are shown in the table.

a. Write a function to represent speeding fines.

b. If the speeding offense occurs in a school zone, the city adds a fine of $50. Write a function for the increased fines in a school zone.

c. **What if...?** The city is considering increasing speeding fines by 15%. Write a new function for the increased speeding fines.

Speeding Fines in Washington, D.C.

Speed Over Limit (mi/h)	Fine ($)
1–10	30
11–15	50
16–20	100
21–25	150
26–30	200

21. Critical Thinking Suppose that the graph of $f(x)$ has n x-intercepts.

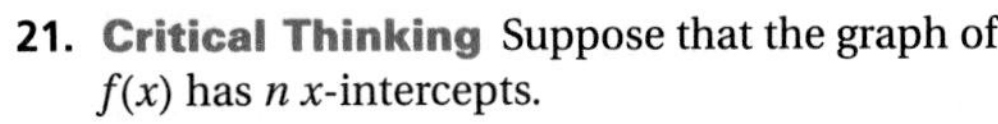

a. How many x-intercepts does the graph of $bf(ax)$ have? Explain.

b. Explain why you cannot tell how many x-intercepts the graph of $f(x - h) + k$ has.

22. Money A credit card company charges a person taking a cash advance on its credit card at an ATM a $6 transaction fee if $200 or less is withdrawn. For amounts over $200, the transaction fee is 3% of the amount withdrawn.

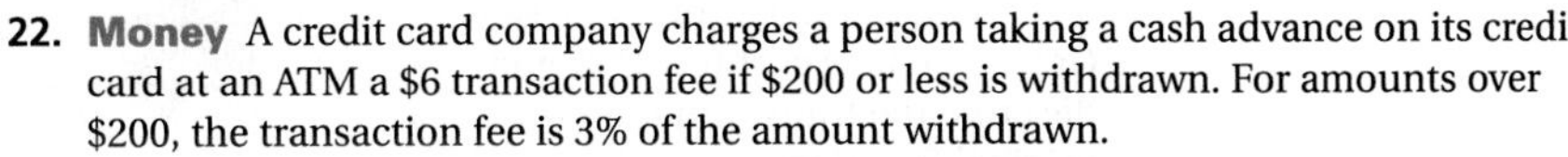

a. Write a function for the transaction fee to withdraw x dollars.

b. Suppose that the company wants to increase fees by 15% in order to reflect increased costs. Adjust your function to include the increase.

MULTI-STEP TEST PREP

23. This problem will prepare you for the Multi-Step Test Prep on page 680.

At a party, the host whispers a phrase into the ear of a guest who then whispers the phrase into the ear of the person standing next to him. The process is repeated down the line until the last person says the phrase out loud. The time in seconds for the phrase to move through the line is modeled by $T(n) = \begin{cases} 3.5n & \text{if } n \le 8 \\ 4.5n - 8 & \text{if } n > 8 \end{cases}$, where n is the number of guests in the line.

a. The second time that the game is played, each person's reaction time is 20% faster. Write a new function to model this situation.

b. Describe the effect of this improvement on the graph of $T(n)$.

MULTI-STEP TEST PREP Exercise 23 involves transforming a piecewise function. This exercise prepares students for the Multi-Step Test Prep on page 680.

Answers

11. $f(x)$: x-int. $= 6$, y-int. $= 9$; $g(x)$: x-int. $= 6$, y-int. $= 6$

12. $f(x)$: x-int. $= \pm 5$, y-int. $= -25$; $g(x)$: x-int. $= \pm 3$, y-int. $= -25$

13. $f(x)$: x-int. $= 5$, y-int. $= 2$; $g(x)$: x-int. $= 2.5$, y-int. $= 2$

14. $f(x)$: x-int. $= -1$ and 4, y-int. $= -4$; $g(x)$: x-int. $= -3$ and 12, y-int. $= 4$

15. $f(x)$: x-int. $= 0$, y-int. $= 0$; $g(x)$: x-int. $= 1$, y-int. $= -4$

16. $f(x)$: x-int. $= -2$, y-int. $= 8$; $g(x)$: x-int. $= 4$, y-int. $= 8$

17.

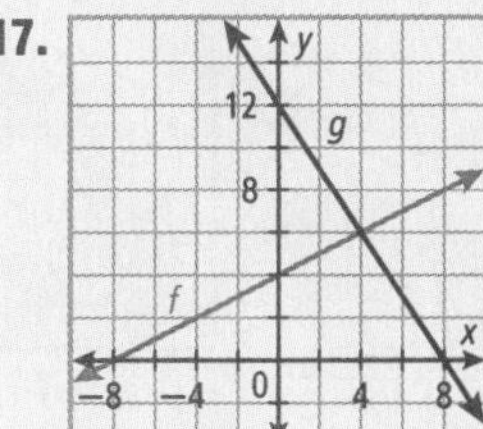

18.

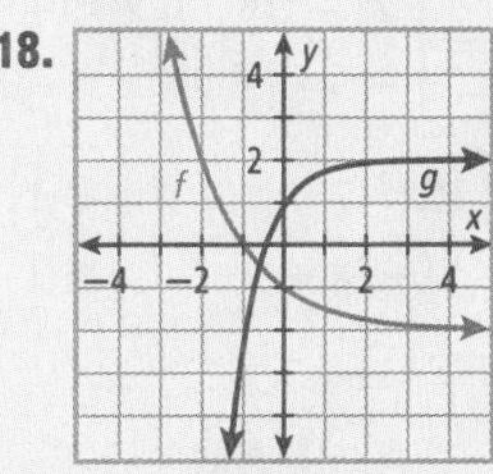

19a. $f(n) = \begin{cases} 16.2n & \text{if } n \le 50 \\ 360 + 9n & \text{if } n > 50 \end{cases}$

b. $f(n) = \begin{cases} 14.2n & \text{if } n \le 50 \\ 360 + 7n & \text{if } n > 50 \end{cases}$

20a. $f(v) = \begin{cases} 30 & \text{if } 1 \le v < 11 \\ 50 & \text{if } 11 \le v < 16 \\ 100 & \text{if } 16 \le v < 21 \\ 150 & \text{if } 21 \le v < 26 \\ 200 & \text{if } 26 \le v < 31 \end{cases}$

b. $f(v) = \begin{cases} 80 & \text{if } 1 \le v < 11 \\ 100 & \text{if } 11 \le v < 16 \\ 150 & \text{if } 16 \le v < 21 \\ 200 & \text{if } 21 \le v < 26 \\ 250 & \text{if } 26 \le v < 31 \end{cases}$

20c. $f(v) = \begin{cases} 34.5 & \text{if } 1 \le v < 11 \\ 57.5 & \text{if } 11 \le v < 16 \\ 115 & \text{if } 16 \le v < 21 \\ 172.5 & \text{if } 21 \le v < 26 \\ 230 & \text{if } 26 \le v < 31 \end{cases}$

21a. n x-intercepts; the intercepts may move, but the number of x-intercepts won't change.

b. A translation can move an intercept off the x-axis or move another point onto the x-axis, so the number of intercepts can change.

22–23. See p. A40.

9-3 PRACTICE A

9-3 PRACTICE C

9-3 PRACTICE B

Given $f(x) = \begin{cases} 5 - x & \text{if } x < 5 \\ 2x & \text{if } x \ge 5 \end{cases}$, write the rule for each function.

1. $d(x)$, a vertical translation of $f(x)$ 8 units down by adding -8 to each piece of the function $d(x) = \begin{cases} -x - 3 & \text{if } x < 5 \\ 2x - 8 & \text{if } x \ge 5 \end{cases}$

2. $p(x)$, a horizontal translation of $f(x)$ 3 units right $p(x) = \begin{cases} 8 - x & \text{if } x < 8 \\ 2x - 6 & \text{if } x \ge 8 \end{cases}$

3. $g(x)$, a horizontal stretch by a factor of 5 $g(x) = \begin{cases} 5 - \frac{x}{5} & \text{if } x < 5 \\ \frac{2x}{5} & \text{if } x \ge 5 \end{cases}$

4. $h(x)$, a reflection across the x-axis $h(x) = \begin{cases} x + 5 & \text{if } x > 5 \\ -2x & \text{if } x \le 5 \end{cases}$

5. $k(x)$, a vertical translation of $f(x)$ 4 units up $k(x) = \begin{cases} 9 - x & \text{if } x < 5 \\ 2x + 4 & \text{if } x \ge 5 \end{cases}$

Identify the x- and y-intercepts of $f(x)$. Then identify the x- and y-intercepts of $g(x)$.

6. $f(x) = -4x + 2$ and $g(x) = f(3x)$

a. Find the x-intercept for $f(x)$: $0 = -4x + 2$, so $x =$ 0.5

b. Find the y-intercept for $f(x)$: $f(0) = -4(0) + 2 =$ 2

c. $g(x)$ is a horizontal compression by a factor of $\frac{1}{3}$, so the x-intercept of $f(x)$ is divided by 3. The x-intercept of $g(x)$ is $\frac{1}{6}$

d. For a horizontal compression, the y-intercept does not change. The y-intercept of $g(x)$ is 2

7. $f(x) = x + 3$ $f(x)$: x-int. $= -3$, y-int. $= 3$; $g(x) = -f(x)$ $g(x)$: x-int. $= -3$, y-int. $= -3$

8. $f(x) = 4x + 4$ $f(x)$: x-int. $= -1$, y-int. $= 4$; $g(x) = f(-x)$ $g(x)$: x-int. $= 1$, y-int. $= 4$

Solve.

9. The function $T(x) = \begin{cases} 400x & \text{if } x < 12 \\ 350x & \text{if } x \ge 12 \end{cases}$, where x is the number of credit hours per semester, models tuition fees at a college. The school decides to add an energy surcharge fee of $200.

a. Write a function for the new tuition fees. $T(x) = \begin{cases} 400x + 200 & \text{if } x < 12 \\ 350x + 200 & \text{if } x \ge 12 \end{cases}$

b. How much will a student now pay for 16 credit hours? $5800

Teaching Tip **Language Arts Link** **Exercise 24** considers the process of *morphing.* Morph comes from the Greek *morphosis,* meaning "to form." To "morph," then, is to change form. The term is widely used in mathematics. ENGLISH LANGUAGE LEARNERS

TEST PREP DOCTOR In **Exercise 32,** students who chose **A** or **B** may have been confused by the reciprocal nature of the coefficient that indicates a horizontal stretch or compression. Remind them that a horizontal compression by a factor of $\frac{1}{4}$ is indicated by the expression $(4x)$ in the function.

Answers

24a.

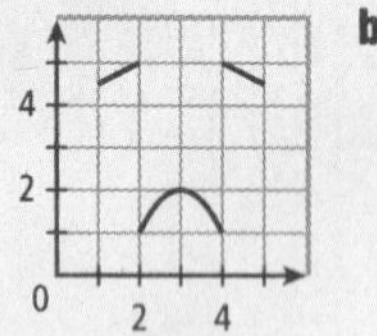

b.

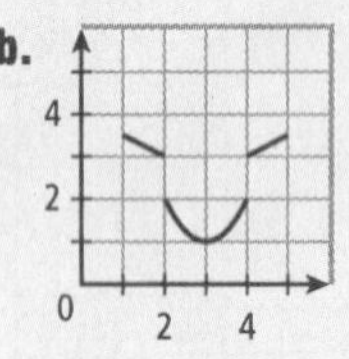

25. $f(x) - 7 = \begin{cases} 2^x - 8 & \text{if } x \leq -3 \\ -5x - 4 & \text{if } x > -3 \end{cases}$

26. $5f(x) = \begin{cases} 15x^2 & \text{if } x < 1 \\ 5(-2x + 4) & \text{if } x \geq 1 \end{cases}$

27a.

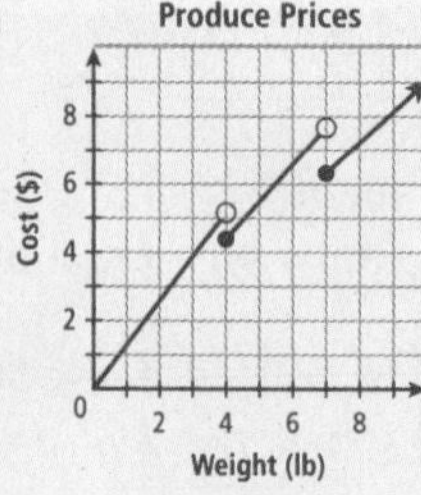

b. $C(x) = \begin{cases} 1.29x & \text{if } 0 < x < 4 \\ 0.85(1.29x) & \text{if } 4 \leq x < 7 \\ 0.7(1.29x) & \text{if } x \geq 7 \end{cases}$

c.

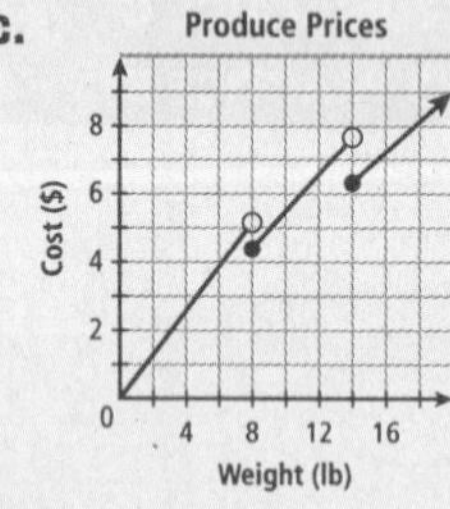

horizontal stretch by a factor of 2

30–31. See p. A40.

35. For graphs, see p. A40.

24. Technology Morphing is a computerized technique for making one picture turn into another picture. Morphing is created by transforming specific points from one location to another.

a. Graph the functions $f(x) = \left\{\frac{1}{2}x + 4 \text{ for } 1 \leq x \leq 2\right.$, $g(x) = \left\{-x^2 + 6x - 7 \text{ for } 2 \leq x \leq 4\right.$, and $h(x) = \left\{-\frac{1}{2}x + 7 \text{ for } 4 \leq x \leq 5\right.$ on the same coordinate grid.

b. Graph the transformed functions $f_{new}(x) = -f(x) + 8$, $g_{new}(x) = -g(x) + 3$, and $h_{new}(x) = -h(x) + 8$.

c. Describe the morph that you created.
The morph changed a sad face into a happy face.

For each function, give the new function rule after the given transformation.

25. $f(x) = \begin{cases} 2^x - 1 & \text{if } x \leq -3 \\ -5x + 3 & \text{if } x > -3 \end{cases}$ after a translation of 7 units down

26. $f(x) = \begin{cases} 3x^2 & \text{if } x < 1 \\ -2x + 4 & \text{if } x \geq 1 \end{cases}$ after a vertical stretch by a factor of 5

27. Food A farmers' market sells fruits and vegetables at a flat rate with discounts for larger purchases.

a. Sketch a graph of the cost of 0 to 10 pounds of produce.

b. Write a piecewise function for the cost of x pounds of produce.

c. **What if...?** During a sale, the market offers a buy-one-get-one-free sale. Graph the new cost function and describe the transformation from the original function.

28. Business A company's profit model is given by $P(n) = -0.002n^2 + 19n - 9000$, where $P(n)$ is the profit in dollars and n is the number of items produced. Based on some new data, the profit model for next year is predicted to be $R(n) = P(0.8n)$.

a. How will the change affect the number of items the company should produce to maximize its profit? **The number will increase by a factor of $\frac{5}{4}$, or 1.25.**

b. Find the number of items the company should produce to maximize profit under the new model. **5937 or 5938**

x-int: 2; y-int: 3 **29. Critical Thinking** A linear function has an x-intercept equal to 2 and a y-intercept equal to 3. The function is stretched vertically by a factor of 2, then translated 3 units down, and then stretched horizontally by a factor of 2. What are the new intercepts?

30. Critical Thinking Why does a vertical translation not affect the domain of a function but a horizontal translation might? Explain.

31. Write About It Can a graph that is not continuous be transformed into a continuous graph by using stretches and compressions only? Explain.

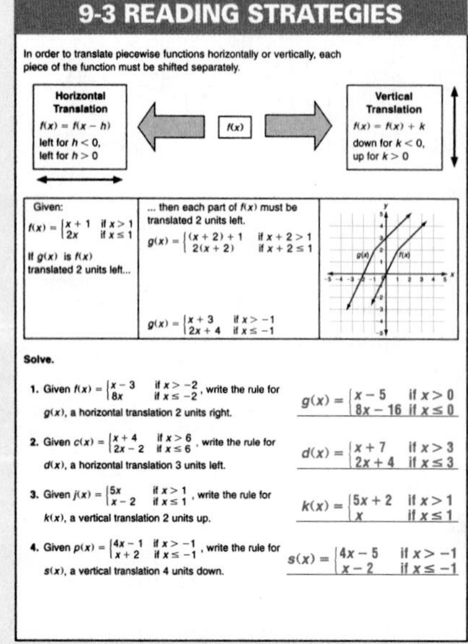

9-3 READING STRATEGIES

In order to translate piecewise functions horizontally or vertically, each piece of the function must be shifted separately.

Horizontal Translation
$f(x) = f(x - h)$
left for $h < 0$,
left for $h > 0$

$f(x)$

Vertical Translation
$f(x) = f(x) + k$
down for $k < 0$,
up for $k > 0$

Given:
$f(x) = \begin{cases} x + 1 & \text{if } x > 1 \\ 2x & \text{if } x \leq 1 \end{cases}$
If $g(x)$ is $f(x)$ translated 2 units left...

... then each part of $f(x)$ must be translated 2 units left.
$g(x) = \begin{cases} (x + 2) + 1 & \text{if } x + 2 > 1 \\ 2(x + 2) & \text{if } x + 2 \leq 1 \end{cases}$

$g(x) = \begin{cases} x + 3 & \text{if } x > -1 \\ 2x + 4 & \text{if } x \leq -1 \end{cases}$

Solve.

1. Given $f(x) = \begin{cases} x - 3 & \text{if } x > -2 \\ 8x & \text{if } x \leq -2 \end{cases}$, write the rule for $g(x)$, a horizontal translation 2 units right. $g(x) = \begin{cases} x - 5 & \text{if } x > 0 \\ 8x - 16 & \text{if } x \leq 0 \end{cases}$

2. Given $c(x) = \begin{cases} x + 4 & \text{if } x > 6 \\ 2x - 2 & \text{if } x \leq 6 \end{cases}$, write the rule for $d(x)$, a horizontal translation 3 units left. $d(x) = \begin{cases} x + 7 & \text{if } x > 3 \\ 2x + 4 & \text{if } x \leq 3 \end{cases}$

3. Given $j(x) = \begin{cases} 5x & \text{if } x > 1 \\ x - 2 & \text{if } x \leq 1 \end{cases}$, write the rule for $k(x)$, a vertical translation 2 units up. $k(x) = \begin{cases} 5x + 2 & \text{if } x > 1 \\ x & \text{if } x \leq 1 \end{cases}$

4. Given $p(x) = \begin{cases} 4x - 1 & \text{if } x > -1 \\ x + 2 & \text{if } x \leq -1 \end{cases}$, write the rule for $s(x)$, a vertical translation 4 units down. $s(x) = \begin{cases} 4x - 5 & \text{if } x > -1 \\ x - 2 & \text{if } x \leq -1 \end{cases}$

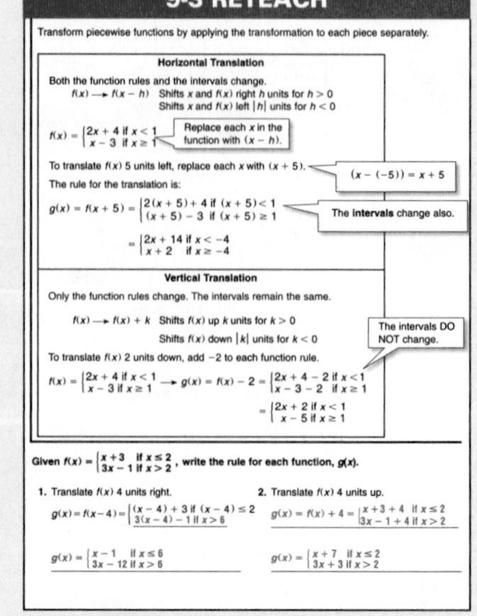

9-3 RETEACH

Transform piecewise functions by applying the transformation to each piece separately.

Horizontal Translation

Both the function rules and the intervals change.
$f(x) \rightarrow f(x - h)$ Shifts x and $f(x)$ right h units for $h > 0$
Shifts x and $f(x)$ left $|h|$ units for $h < 0$

$f(x) = \begin{cases} 2x + 4 & \text{if } x < 1 \\ x - 3 & \text{if } x \geq 1 \end{cases}$ Replace each x in the function with $(x - h)$.

To translate $f(x)$ 5 units left, replace each x with $(x + 5)$. $(x - (-5)) = x + 5$

The rule for the translation is:

$g(x) = f(x + 5) = \begin{cases} 2(x + 5) + 4 & \text{if } (x + 5) < 1 \\ (x + 5) - 3 & \text{if } (x + 5) \geq 1 \end{cases}$ The **intervals** change also.

$= \begin{cases} 2x + 14 & \text{if } x < -4 \\ x + 2 & \text{if } x \geq -4 \end{cases}$

Vertical Translation

Only the function rules change. The intervals remain the same.

$f(x) \rightarrow f(x) + k$ Shifts $f(x)$ up k units for $k > 0$
Shifts $f(x)$ down $|k|$ units for $k < 0$

The intervals DO NOT change.

To translate $f(x)$ 2 units down, add -2 to each function rule.

$f(x) = \begin{cases} 2x + 4 & \text{if } x < 1 \\ x - 3 & \text{if } x \geq 1 \end{cases} \rightarrow g(x) = f(x) - 2 = \begin{cases} 2x + 4 - 2 & \text{if } x < 1 \\ x - 3 - 2 & \text{if } x \geq 1 \end{cases}$

$= \begin{cases} 2x + 2 & \text{if } x < 1 \\ x - 5 & \text{if } x \geq 1 \end{cases}$

Given $f(x) = \begin{cases} x + 3 & \text{if } x \leq 2 \\ 3x - 1 & \text{if } x > 2 \end{cases}$, write the rule for each function, $g(x)$.

1. Translate $f(x)$ 4 units right.
$g(x) = f(x - 4) = \begin{cases} (x - 4) + 3 & \text{if } (x - 4) \leq 2 \\ 3(x - 4) - 1 & \text{if } x > 6 \end{cases}$
$g(x) = \begin{cases} x - 1 & \text{if } x \leq 6 \\ 3x - 12 & \text{if } x > 6 \end{cases}$

2. Translate $f(x)$ 4 units up.
$g(x) = f(x) + 4 = \begin{cases} x + 3 + 4 & \text{if } x \leq 2 \\ 3x - 1 + 4 & \text{if } x > 2 \end{cases}$
$g(x) = \begin{cases} x + 7 & \text{if } x \leq 2 \\ 3x + 3 & \text{if } x > 2 \end{cases}$

TEST PREP

32. For the graphs shown, which of the following is $g(x)$?

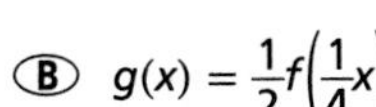

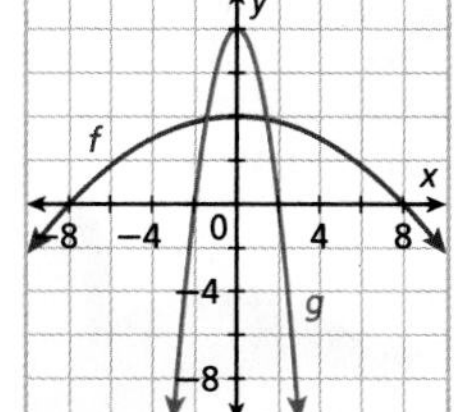

Ⓐ $g(x) = 2f\left(\frac{1}{4}x\right)$ Ⓒ $g(x) = 2f(4x)$

Ⓑ $g(x) = \frac{1}{2}f\left(\frac{1}{4}x\right)$ Ⓓ $g(x) = \frac{1}{2}f(4x)$

33. Suppose that $f(x) = \begin{cases} 2x & x > 8 \\ x^2 & x \le 8 \end{cases}$.

Which of the following is $g(x) = f(4x)$?

Ⓕ $g(x) = \begin{cases} \frac{x}{2} & \text{if } x > 2 \\ \frac{x^2}{16} & \text{if } x \le 2 \end{cases}$ Ⓗ $g(x) = \begin{cases} 8x & \text{if } x > 32 \\ 4x^2 & \text{if } x \le 32 \end{cases}$

Ⓖ $g(x) = \begin{cases} \frac{x}{2} & \text{if } x > 8 \\ \frac{x^2}{16} & \text{if } x \le 8 \end{cases}$  Ⓙ $g(x) = \begin{cases} 8x & \text{if } x > 2 \\ 16x^2 & \text{if } x \le 2 \end{cases}$

34. The y-intercept of $g(x) = \frac{3}{5}f(5x)$ is 15. Which of the following is the y-intercept of $f(x)$?

Ⓐ 3 Ⓑ 9 Ⓒ 25 Ⓓ 75

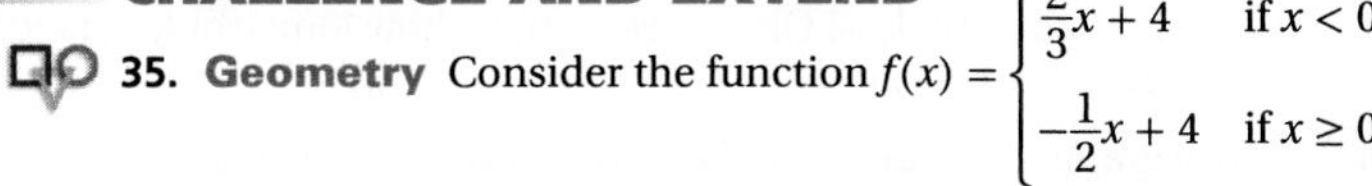

CHALLENGE AND EXTEND

35. **Geometry** Consider the function $f(x) = \begin{cases} \frac{2}{3}x + 4 & \text{if } x < 0 \\ -\frac{1}{2}x + 4 & \text{if } x \ge 0 \end{cases}$.

a. Graph the function, and find its intercepts. Then find the area bounded by the function and the x-axis. **28**

b. Graph the transformation $g(x) = 4f(2x)$. Find the area bounded by $g(x)$ and the x-axis. **56**

c. Write a function $h(x)$ that creates an area of 7 square units. **Possible answer: $\frac{1}{4}f(x)$**

36. Consider the functions $f(x) = 2x^3 - 3x^2 - 11x + 6$, $g(x) = 3f\left(\frac{1}{2}x\right)$, and $h(x) = -g\left(\frac{1}{2}x\right)$.

a. Find the x- and y-intercepts of $g(x)$. **x-int: −4, 1, 6; y-int: 18**

b. Find the x- and y-intercepts of $h(x)$. **x-int: −8, 2, 12; y-int: −18**

SPIRAL REVIEW

37. **Geology** An earthquake map claims that about 43% of the earthquakes in the United States between 1999 and 2002 occurred in California. There were 973 earthquakes between 1999 and 2002 in the United States. About how many earthquakes occurred in California? *(Lesson 2-2)* **about 418**

Find the maximum or minimum value of each function. Then state the domain and range of the function. *(Lesson 5-2)*

38. $f(x) = 4x^2 - 2x + 8$
7.75; D: ℝ; R: $\{y \mid y \ge 7.75\}$

39. $g(x) = -3x^2 + 6x - 9$
−6; D: ℝ; R: $\{y \mid y \le -6\}$

Evaluate each piecewise function for $x = -4$, $x = 0$, and $x = 5$. *(Lesson 9-2)*

40. $f(x) = \begin{cases} 3 & \text{if } x < 1 \\ x^2 - 4 & \text{if } x \ge 1 \end{cases}$ **3; 3; 21**

41. $f(x) = \begin{cases} 5 - 2x & \text{if } x < -3 \\ 4 + x & \text{if } x \ge -3 \end{cases}$ **13; 4; 9**

Teaching Tip **Geometry** For **Exercise 35,** remind students that the area of a triangle is $A = \frac{1}{2}bh$.

Journal

Is it possible to transform a continuous function into a discontinuous function? Explain why or why not. Provide an example to support your answer.

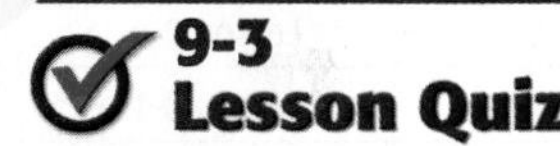

ALTERNATIVE ASSESSMENT

Have students research a real example of price changes that can be modeled as a transformation of a piecewise function, such as postal rates or prices at an area college or theater. Have students produce functions and graphs that illustrate both the old and new prices.

Power Presentations with PowerPoint®

9-3 Lesson Quiz

Consider the functions $f(x) = \frac{1}{2}x^2 - 2$, $g(x) = 4f(x)$, and $h(x) = f\left(\frac{1}{3}x\right) + 3$.

1. Identify the intercepts of $f(x)$ and $g(x)$.
$f(x)$: x-ints. = −2 and 2, y-int. = −2
$g(x)$: x-ints. = −2 and 2, y-int. = −8

2. Graph $f(x)$ and $h(x)$.

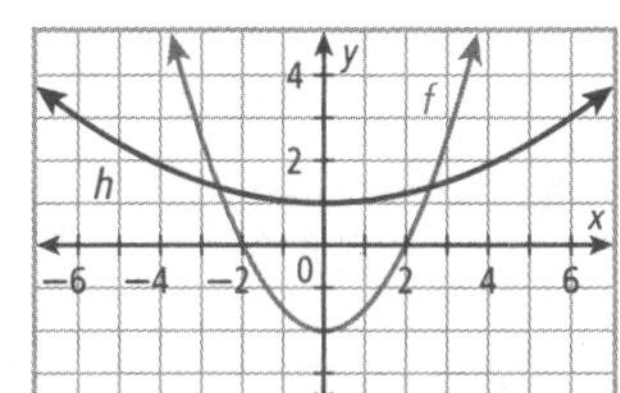

3. Ticket prices to a theater are modeled by the function below, where a is a person's age in years.

$$p(a) = \begin{cases} 4.50 & \text{if } 0 \le a < 12 \\ 7.00 & \text{if } a \ge 12 \end{cases}$$

They plan to raise all prices by \$1, but then they are going to offer a 25% discount to persons 55 and older. Write a function for their new prices.

$$p(a) = \begin{cases} 5.50 & \text{if } 0 \le a < 12 \\ 8.00 & \text{if } 12 \le a < 55 \\ 6.00 & \text{if } a \ge 55 \end{cases}$$

Also available on transparency

9-3 PROBLEM SOLVING

In March, Mei researches the sports clubs in her area. One club charges different rates according to the number of hours of use per month. The rate scale is modeled by the piecewise function below, where x is the number of hours of use.

$$f(x) = \begin{cases} 5x + 105 & \text{if } 0 \le x < 12 \\ 165 & \text{if } 12 \le x \le 20 \\ 7(x - 20) + 165 & \text{if } x > 20 \end{cases}$$

Mei learns that all rates will increase by 10% in June. In September the club is planning to add a \$5 monthly energy fee.

1. Describe the transformation of the fees in March, $f(x)$, to the fees in June, $g(x)$.
$g(x) = 1.1 \cdot f(x)$; vertical stretch by a factor of 1.1

2. Write the rules for the rates that will be effective in June.
$g(x) = \begin{cases} 5.5x + 115.5 & \text{if } 0 \le x < 12 \\ 181.50 & \text{if } 12 \le x \le 20 \\ 7.7x + 27.5 & \text{if } x > 20 \end{cases}$

3. Describe the transformation of the fees in June, $g(x)$, to the fees in September, $h(x)$.
$h(x) = g(x) + 5$; vertical translation 5 units up

4. Write the rules for the rates that will be effective in September.
$h(x) = \begin{cases} 5.5x + 120.5 & \text{if } 0 \le x < 12 \\ 186.50 & \text{if } 12 \le x \le 20 \\ 7.7x + 32.5 & \text{if } x > 20 \end{cases}$

Mei considers several options. Choose the letter for the best answer.

5. How much will she pay if she joins and uses the club for 10 hours in March?
A \$95.00
B \$110.00
Ⓒ \$155.00
D \$165.00

6. How much will she pay if she joins and uses the club for 10 hours in July?
F \$115.50
G \$165.50
Ⓗ \$170.50
J \$175.50

7. How much will she pay if she joins and uses the club between 12 and 20 hours in August?
A \$215.50
Ⓑ \$181.50
C \$165.00
D \$155.50

8. How much will she pay if she joins and uses the club for 25 hours in October?
F \$192.50
G \$208.00
H \$215.50
Ⓙ \$225.00

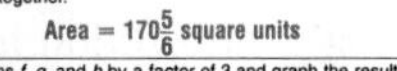

9-3 CHALLENGE

The area of the region bounded by a parabola and a horizontal line segment with endpoints on the parabola is given by the formula $A = \frac{2}{3}bh$, where b is the length of the line segment and h is the distance from the vertex of the parabola to that line segment.

1. Graph the following equations on the coordinate plane at right.
a. $f(x) = 25 - x^2$
b. $g(x) = 7x + 25$
c. $h(x) = x - 5$

2. Shade the largest region enclosed by the 3 functions. List the points of intersection.
Intersect at points (−5, −10), (0, 25), and (5, 0)

3. Find the area of the shaded region. Think of it as several different parts. Find the area of each part and then add the areas together.
Area = $170\frac{5}{6}$ square units

4. Vertically stretch functions f, g, and h by a factor of 3 and graph the resulting functions on a graphing calculator.
a. Give the values you used for x and y to place these graphs in an appropriate window. $-6 < x < 6$, $-45 < y < 90$
b. How do the x- and y-intercepts compare to those of the original functions?
x-intercepts are the same; y-intercepts have been tripled.
c. Find the area of the largest enclosed region.
Area is now 512.5 square units, three times that of original region.

5. Horizontally compress functions f, g, and h by a factor of $\frac{1}{3}$ and graph the resulting functions on a graphing calculator.
a. Give the values you used for x and y to place these graphs in an appropriate window. $-2 < x < 2$, $-45 < y < 90$
b. How do the x- and y-intercepts compare to those of the original functions?
x-intercepts are $\frac{1}{3}$ what they were; y-intercepts are the same.
c. Find the area of the largest enclosed region.
Area is now $56\frac{17}{18}$ square units, $\frac{1}{3}$ that of original region.

Organizer

Objective: Assess students' ability to apply concepts and skills in Lessons 9-1 through 9-3 in a real-world format.

Online Edition

Resources

Algebra II Assessments
www.mathtekstoolkit.org

Problem	Text Reference
1	Lesson 2-2
2–3	Lesson 9-1
4–5	Lesson 9-3
6	Lesson 9-2

Answers

3.

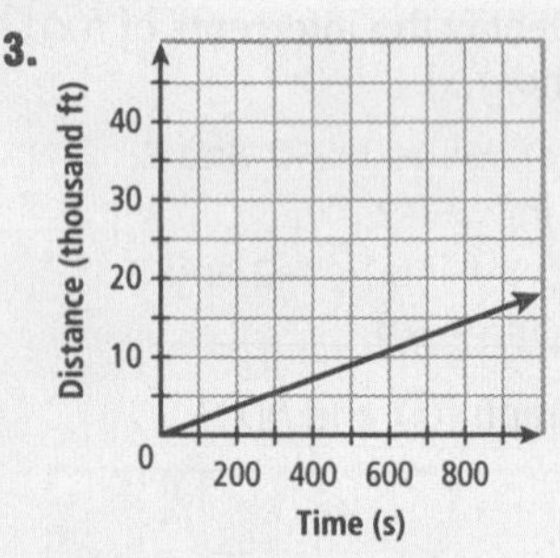

5–6. See p. A40.

State Resources

CHAPTER 9

MULTI-STEP TEST PREP

SECTION 9A

Functions and Their Graphs

Hands Around the World Imagine a human chain of people holding hands. Assume that each person stands with his or her arms fully outstretched.

1. Suppose that the chain could go all the way around the planet. Then the chain's length would be equal to the circumference of the earth at the equator (about 24,000 miles). Assuming that the average adult arm span is 6 feet, how many people would it take to make this human chain? **21,120,000**
2. At the word "go!" the first person in the chain squeezes the hand of the second person, who in turn immediately squeezes the hand of the third person, and so on. Given that it takes 20 seconds for the 60th person to react to having his or her hand squeezed, how many hours would it take the signal to travel all the way around the world? **≈ 1955.56 h, or about 81.5 days**
3. Sketch a graph of the distance in feet that the signal travels in the span of 0 to 1000 seconds. Identify the slope of the line. **18 ft/s**
4. Researchers at the University of British Columbia have measured muscle reaction times of 0.1 second for Olympic sprinters. If the human chain consisted entirely of Olympic sprinters, how long would it take for the signal to travel all the way around the world? **≈ 586.67 h, or about 24.4 days**
5. Create a graph of the distance the signal travels in the chain of Olympic sprinters. How does the slope compare to the graph in Problem 3? **The slope 60 ft/s is much greater than that in Problem 3.**
6. Suppose that the first half of a human chain is formed by 500 Olympic sprinters and the second half is formed by 500 people whose reaction time is 0.9 second. Write and graph a piecewise function that describes the distance traveled by the signal as a function of time.

INTERVENTION

Scaffolding Questions

1. How can you convert miles to feet? Multiply by 5280. Once you know the length of the chain in feet, how can you find the number of people in the chain? Divide by 6.
2. Can you use a proportion to find the time t in seconds? $\frac{20}{60} = \frac{t}{21,120,000}$ How can you convert the resulting time into hours? Divide by 3600.
3. What parent function models this situation? $f(x) = x$
4. Will the signal travel faster or slower in this case? faster About how many times as fast or as slow? about 3 times as fast
5. Is the graph steeper or flatter than the graph for **Problem 3**? steeper Why? The slope represents the rate, which is greater in this case.
6. Will the graph be a straight line? no Will it be continuous? yes What can you say about each portion of the piecewise function? Each portion of the function is linear.

Extension

The average height of players in the NBA is 6 ft 7 in. Assume each player's arm span equals his height. If the chain consists entirely of NBA players and the reaction time is as stated in **Problem 2,** how long does it take the signal to go around the world? 1782 h

READY TO GO ON?

CHAPTER 9

SECTION 9A

Quiz for Lessons 9-1 Through 9-3

9-1 Multiple Representations of Functions

1. Amanda must read a 294-page book for her history class over the next week. Amanda has found that she can read 42 pages in an hour. Create a table, a graph, and an equation to represent the number of pages that Amanda has left to read with relation to time. $f(x) = 294 - 42x$

2. The height of a rocket at different times after it was fired is shown in the table.

Time (s)	0	1	2	3	4	5
Height (m)	50.0	65.1	70.4	65.9	51.5	27.5

   a. Find an appropriate model for the height of the rocket. $h(t) = -4.9t^2 + 20t + 50$
   b. Find the maximum height of the rocket. about 70.41 ft
   c. How long will the rocket stay in the air? about 5.83 s

9-2 Piecewise Functions

Graph each function.

3. $f(x) = \begin{cases} 3 & \text{if } x < 0 \\ 2x + 3 & \text{if } x \geq 0 \end{cases}$

4. $h(x) = \begin{cases} -x + 1 & \text{if } x < -3 \\ -x & \text{if } -3 \leq x < 1 \\ -x - 1 & \text{if } x \geq 1 \end{cases}$

5. The cost of renting a mountain bike is \$25 for the first 3 hours and \$5 for each additional hour. Sketch a graph of the cost of renting a mountain bike for 0 to 8 hours. Then write a piecewise function for the graph.

Write a piecewise function for each graph.

6. 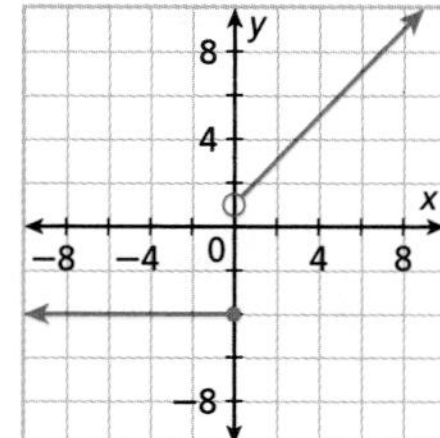

7. 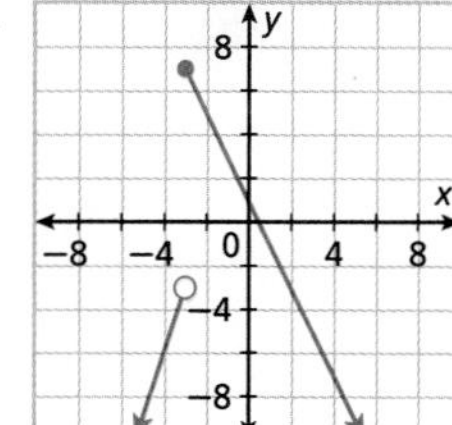

8. 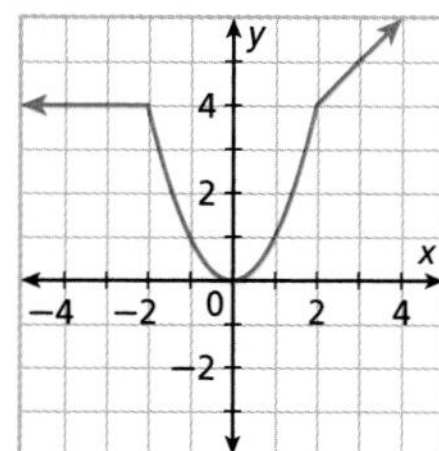

9-3 Transforming Functions

Identify the x- and y-intercepts of $f(x)$. Without graphing $g(x)$, identify its x- and y-intercepts.

9. $f(x) = 2x - 2$ and $g(x) = -f\left(\frac{1}{2}x\right)$

10. $f(x) = x^2 - 4$ and $g(x) = 2f(x)$

Given $f(x)$, graph $g(x)$.

11. $f(x) = |x| - 3$ and $g(x) = 2f(x) + 3$

12. $f(x) = x^2 + 1$ and $g(x) = -3f(x)$

READY TO GO ON?

SECTION 9A

Organizer

Objective: Assess students' mastery of concepts and skills in Lessons 9-1 through 9-3.

Resources

 ***Assessment Resources***
Section 9A Quiz

Test & Practice Generator
One-Stop Planner®

INTERVENTION 

Resources

 ***Ready to Go On? Intervention and Enrichment Worksheets***

 ***Ready to Go On? CD-ROM***

 ***Ready to Go On? Online***

my.hrw.com

Answers

1. For table and graph, see p. A41.

3–12. See p. A41.

READY TO GO ON? Diagnose and Prescribe

NO INTERVENE

YES ENRICH

Ready to Go On? Intervention	*Ready to Go On? Intervention, Section 9A* Worksheets	CD-ROM	Online
Lesson 9-1	9-1 Intervention	Activity 9-1	Diagnose and Prescribe Online
Lesson 9-2	9-2 Intervention	Activity 9-2	
Lesson 9-3	9-3 Intervention	Activity 9-3	

Ready to Go On? Enrichment, Section 9A
Worksheets
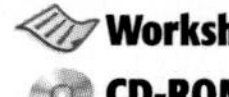 CD-ROM
 Online

SECTION **9B**

Functional relationships

One-Minute Section Planner

Lesson	Lab Resources	Materials
Lesson 9-4 Operations With Functions • Add, subtract, multiply, and divide functions. • Write and evaluate composite functions. ☐ SAT-10 ☐ NAEP ☐ ACT ☐ SAT ☐ SAT Subject Tests		
Lesson 9-5 Functions and Their Inverses • Determine whether the inverse of a function is a function. • Write rules for the inverses of functions. ☐ SAT-10 ☑ NAEP ☐ ACT ☐ SAT ☐ SAT Subject Tests		**Optional** tracing paper or patty paper
9-6 Technology Lab Explore Differences and Ratios • Use a spreadsheet to explore differences and ratios. ☑ SAT-10 ☑ NAEP ☑ ACT ☐ SAT ☑ SAT Subject Tests	***Technology Lab Activities*** 9-6 Lab Recording Sheet	**Required** spreadsheet software
Lesson 9-6 Modeling Real-World Data • Apply functions to problem situations. • Use mathematical models to make predictions. ☑ SAT-10 ☑ NAEP ☑ ACT ☑ SAT ☑ SAT Subject Tests	***Technology Lab Activities*** 9-6 Technology Lab ***Algebra Lab Activities*** 9-6 Algebra Lab	**Required** graphing calculator

MK = *Manipulatives Kit*

Section Overview

Operations with Functions

Lesson 9-4

A real-world function may be a combination of other functions or a composition of functions.

Operations with Functions	Composition of Functions
$(f+g)(x) = f(x) + g(x)$ $(f-g)(x) = f(x) - g(x)$ $(fg)(x) = f(x)g(x)$ $\left(\frac{f}{g}\right)(x) = \frac{f(x)}{g(x)}$	$(f \circ g)(x) = f(g(x))$ Use the value of $g(x)$ as the input into f.

Functions and Their Inverses

Lesson 9-5

Inverse functions are used to "undo" each other.

If $f(g(x)) = g(f(x)) = x$, then $f(x)$ and $g(x)$ are **inverse functions.**

When both a relation and its inverse are functions, the relation is called a **one-to-one function.**

One-to-One Function

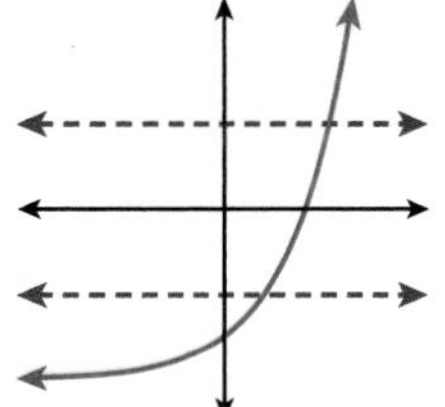

Any horizontal line passes through no more than one point on the graph.

Not a One-to-One Function

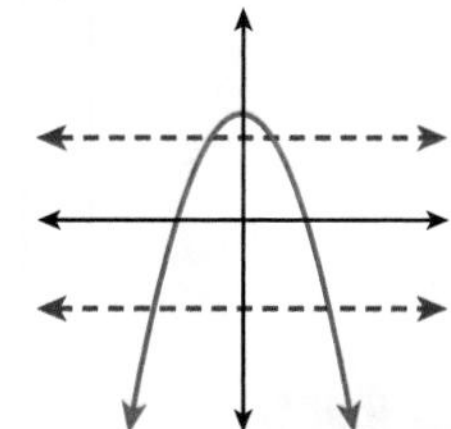

A horizontal line can be found that passes through more than one point on the graph.

Modeling Real-World Data

Lesson 9-6

Why? A mathematical model of a data set can be used to make predictions.

Families of Functions				
Family	Linear	Quadratic	Exponential	Square Root
Rule	$f(x) = x$	$f(x) = x^2$	$f(x) = b^x$, $b > 0$	$f(x) = \sqrt{x}$
Graph				
Constant Differences or Ratios	Constant first differences between y-values for evenly spaced x-values	Constant second differences between y-values for evenly spaced x-values	Constant ratios between y-values for evenly spaced x-values	Constant second differences between x-values for evenly spaced y-values

9-4 Organizer

Pacing: Traditional 1 day
Block $\frac{1}{2}$ day

Objectives: Add, subtract, multiply, and divide functions.

Write and evaluate composite functions.

Online Edition
Tutorial Videos

Countdown to Testing Week 19

Power Presentations with PowerPoint®

Warm Up

Simplify. Assume that all expressions are defined.

1. $(2x + 5) - (x^2 + 3x - 2)$
   $-x^2 - x + 7$
2. $(x - 3)(x + 1)^2$
   $x^3 - x^2 - 5x - 3$
3. $\dfrac{x^2 - x - 6}{x^2 - 4}$
   $\dfrac{x - 3}{x - 2}$

Also available on transparency

Math Humor

Student: I haven't figured out composite functions yet.

Teacher: Why not?

Student: I think my brain is in a $f \circ g$.

9-4 Operations with Functions

A2.1.2 Use and interpret function notation, including evaluation of functions represented by tables, graphs, words, equations or a set of ordered pairs.

Objectives
Add, subtract, multiply, and divide functions.

Write and evaluate composite functions.

Vocabulary
composition of functions

Who uses this?
Importers can use function operations to determine the costs of items that are purchased in foreign currencies. (See Example 5.)

You can perform operations on functions in much the same way that you perform operations on numbers or expressions. You can add, subtract, multiply, or divide functions by operating on their rules.

Know it! Note

Notation for Function Operations

Operation	Notation
Addition	$(f + g)(x) = f(x) + g(x)$
Subtraction	$(f - g)(x) = f(x) - g(x)$
Multiplication	$(fg)(x) = f(x) \cdot g(x)$
Division	$\left(\frac{f}{g}\right)(x) = \frac{f(x)}{g(x)}$, where $g(x) \neq 0$

EXAMPLE 1 Adding and Subtracting Functions

Given $f(x) = 2x^2 + 4x - 6$ and $g(x) = 2x - 2$, find each function.

A $(f + g)(x)$

$(f + g)(x) = f(x) + g(x)$
$= (2x^2 + 4x - 6) + (2x - 2)$ *Substitute function rules.*
$= 2x^2 + 6x - 8$ *Combine like terms.*

B $(f - g)(x)$

$(f - g)(x) = f(x) - g(x)$
$= (2x^2 + 4x - 6) - (2x - 2)$ *Substitute function rules.*
$= 2x^2 + 4x - 6 - 2x + 2$ *Distributive Property*
$= 2x^2 + 2x - 4$ *Combine like terms.*

Given $f(x) = 5x - 6$ and $g(x) = x^2 - 5x + 6$, find each function.

1a. $(f + g)(x)$ $\quad (f + g)(x) = x^2$

1b. $(f - g)(x)$ $\quad (f - g)(x) = -x^2 + 10x - 12$

When you divide functions, be sure to note any domain restrictions that may arise.

State Resources

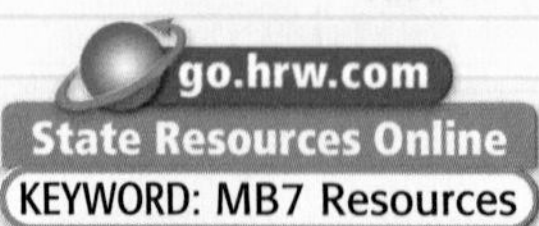
go.hrw.com
State Resources Online
KEYWORD: MB7 Resources

1 Introduce

EXPLORATION

9-4 Operations with Functions

Safety experts use functions to model the distance a car travels before stopping once the driver has noticed a hazard in the road. The table shows the reaction distance (the distance the car travels before the driver hits the brake pedal) and the braking distance (the distance the car travels once the brake has been applied).

Speed (mi/h)	Reaction Distance (ft)	Braking Distance (ft)
10	11	6
20	22	24
30	33	54
40	44	96
50	55	150

1. Determine a function R(x) for the reaction distance, where x is the car's speed in miles per hour.
2. The function for the braking distance B(x) is a quadratic function of the form $B(x) = ax^2$. Determine the value of a and write B(x).
3. Write a new function T(x) by adding the rules for R(x) and B(x).

THINK AND DISCUSS

Motivate

Ask students to find the total cost of 5 items that cost \$1.50 with a 6% sales tax. \$7.95 Have volunteers explain how they got their answers. Explain that this situation can be modeled by two functions: a cost-per-item function and a sales-tax function. Help them understand that the output of the cost function is the input for the sales-tax function. Explain that this is an example of a composite function.

Explorations and answers are provided in the *Explorations* binder.

EXAMPLE 2 Multiplying and Dividing Functions

Given $f(x) = 2x^2 + 4x - 6$ and $g(x) = 2x - 2$, find each function.

A $(gf)(x)$

$$(gf)(x) = g(x) \cdot f(x)$$

$= (2x - 2)(2x^2 + 4x - 6)$ *Substitute function rules.*

$= 2x(2x^2 + 4x - 6) - 2(2x^2 + 4x - 6)$ *Distributive Property*

$= 4x^3 + 8x^2 - 12x - 4x^2 - 8x + 12$ *Multiply.*

$= 4x^3 + 4x^2 - 20x + 12$ *Combine like terms.*

B $\left(\frac{f}{g}\right)(x)$

$$\left(\frac{f}{g}\right)(x) = \frac{f(x)}{g(x)}$$

$= \frac{2x^2 + 4x - 6}{2x - 2}$ *Set up the division as a rational expression.*

$= \frac{2(x-1)(x+3)}{2(x-1)}$ *Factor completely. Note that $x \neq 1$.*

$= \frac{\cancel{2(x-1)}(x+3)}{\cancel{2(x-1)}}$ *Divide out common factors.*

$= x + 3$, where $x \neq 1$ *Simplify.*

CHECK IT OUT! Given $f(x) = x + 2$ and $g(x) = x^2 - 4$, find each function.

2a. $(fg)(x)$ $\quad (fg)(x) = x^3 + 2x^2 - 4x - 8$

2b. $\left(\frac{g}{f}\right)(x)$ $\quad \left(\frac{g}{f}\right)(x) = x - 2,\ x \neq -2$

Another function operation uses the output from one function as the input for a second function. This operation is called the **composition of functions**.

Composition of Functions

The composition of functions f and g is notated

$$(f \circ g)(x) = f(g(x)).$$

The domain of $(f \circ g)(x)$ is all values of x in the domain of g such that $g(x)$ is in the domain of f.

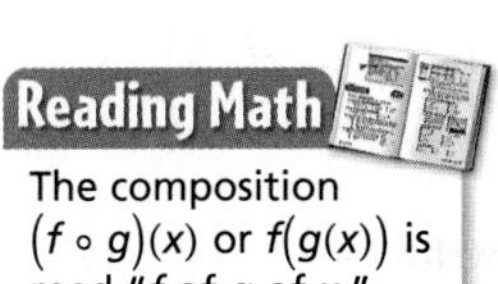

The composition $(f \circ g)(x)$ or $f(g(x))$ is read "f of g of x."

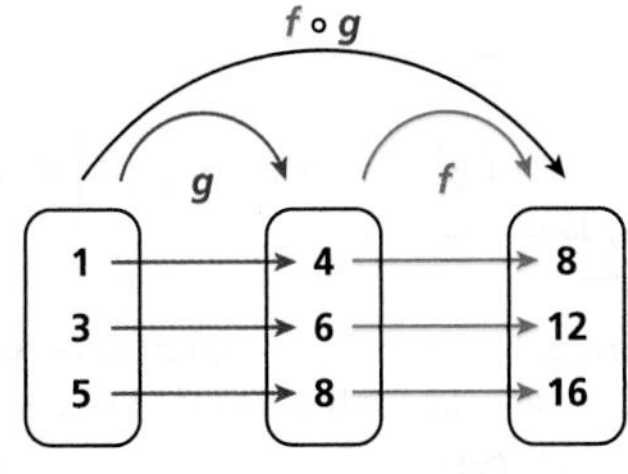

To find $(f \circ g)(1)$, first find $g(1)$.

$$g(1) = 4$$

Then use 4 as the input into f:

$$f(4) = 8$$

So $(f \circ g)(1) = f(g(1)) = 8$.

The order of function operations is the same as the order of operations for numbers and expressions. To find $f(g(3))$, evaluate $g(3)$ first and then substitute the result into f.

Power Presentations with PowerPoint®

Additional Examples

Example 1

Given $f(x) = 4x^2 + 3x - 1$ and $g(x) = 6x + 2$, find each function.

A. $(f + g)(x)$ $\quad 4x^2 + 9x + 1$

B. $(f - g)(x)$ $\quad 4x^2 - 3x - 3$

Example 2

Given $f(x) = 6x^2 - x - 12$ and $g(x) = 2x - 3$, find each function.

A. $(fg)(x)$

$12x^3 - 20x^2 - 21x + 36$

B. $\frac{f}{g}(x)$ $\quad 3x + 4$

Also available on transparency

INTERVENTION
Questioning Strategies

EXAMPLE 1

- Does the order of f and g matter in **Example 1A**? Does it matter in **Example 1B**?

EXAMPLE 2

- Does the order of f and g matter in **Example 2A**? Does it matter in **Example 2B**?

Reading Math Make sure that students note the difference between the open circle that indicates composition and the solid dot that indicates multiplication.

2 Teach

Guided Instruction

Before evaluating composite functions, make sure that students are comfortable evaluating a single function at any point. Throughout the lesson, encourage students to write out each step when writing composite functions, as many errors are made during simplification.

Reaching All Learners
Through Cognitive Strategies

Help students visualize a composite function as a series of "machines." For example, if $f(x) = x^2 - 3$ and $g(x) = 2x - 5$, then $f(g(4))$ looks like this:

$$4 \rightarrow \underset{g(x)}{\boxed{2x - 5}} \rightarrow 3 \rightarrow \underset{f(x)}{\boxed{x^2 - 3}} \rightarrow 6$$

Encourage students to draw a similar diagram to use as they complete the exercises.

Power Presentations with PowerPoint®

Additional Examples

Example 3

Given $f(x) = 2^x$ and $g(x) = 7 - x$, find each value.

A. $f(g(4))$ 8

B. $g(f(4))$ −9

Example 4

Given $f(x) = x^2 - 1$ and $g(x) = \frac{x}{1-x}$, write each composite function. State the domain of each.

A. $f(g(x))$

$$\left(\frac{x}{1-x}\right)^2 - 1 = \frac{-1+2x}{(1-x)^2}$$

$D: \{x \mid x \neq 1\}$

B. $g(f(x))$

$$\frac{x^2-1}{1-(x^2-1)} = \frac{x^2-1}{2-x^2}$$

$D: \{x \mid x \neq \pm\sqrt{2}\}$

Also available on transparency

INTERVENTION

Questioning Strategies

EXAMPLE 3

- How do you know which function to evaluate first?

EXAMPLE 4

- How can you determine the domain of a composite function?

Caution!

Be careful not to confuse the notation for multiplication of functions with composition.
$fg(x) \neq f(g(x))$

EXAMPLE 3 Evaluating Composite Functions

Given $f(x) = 3x + 1$ and $g(x) = x^3$, find each value.

A $f(g(2))$

Step 1 Find $g(2)$.

$g(2) = 2^3$ *$g(x) = x^3$*

$= 8$

Step 2 Find $f(8)$.

$f(8) = 3(8) + 1$ *$f(x) = 3x + 1$*

$= 25$

So $f(g(2)) = 25$.

B $g(f(2))$

Step 1 Find $f(2)$.

$f(2) = 3(2) + 1$ *$f(x) = 3(x) + 1$*

$= 7$

Step 2 Find $g(7)$.

$g(7) = 7^3$ *$g(x) = x^3$*

$= 343$

So $g(f(2)) = 343$.

Given $f(x) = 2x - 3$ and $g(x) = x^2$, find each value.

3a. $f(g(3))$ 15

3b. $g(f(3))$ 9

You can use algebraic expressions as well as numbers as inputs into functions. To find a rule for $f(g(x))$, substitute the rule for g into f.

EXAMPLE 4 Writing Composite Functions

Given $f(x) = 5x + 2$ and $g(x) = \frac{2}{x-1}$, write each composite function. State the domain of each.

A $f(g(x))$

$f(g(x)) = f\left(\frac{2}{x-1}\right)$ *Substitute the rule for g into f.*

$= 5\left(\frac{2}{x-1}\right) + 2$ *Use the rule for f. Note that $x \neq 1$.*

$= \frac{10}{x-1} + 2, x \neq 1$ *Simplify.*

The domain of $f(g(x))$ is $x \neq 1$ or $\{x \mid x \neq 1\}$ because $g(1)$ is undefined.

B $g(f(x))$

$g(f(x)) = g(5x + 2)$ *Substitute the rule for f into g.*

$= \frac{2}{(5x+2)-1}$ *Use the rule for g.*

$= \frac{2}{5x+1}, x \neq -\frac{1}{5}$ *Simplify. Note that $x \neq -\frac{1}{5}$.*

The domain of $g(f(x))$ is $x \neq -\frac{1}{5}$ or $\left\{x \mid x \neq -\frac{1}{5}\right\}$ because $f\left(-\frac{1}{5}\right) = 1$ and $g(1)$ is undefined.

Given $f(x) = 3x - 4$ and $g(x) = \sqrt{x} + 2$, write each composite function. State the domain of each.

4a. $f(g(x))$

$f(g(x)) = 3\sqrt{x} + 2, x \geq 0$

4b. $g(f(x))$

$g(f(x)) = \sqrt{3x-4} + 2, x \geq \frac{4}{3}$

Composite functions can be used to simplify a series of functions.

EXAMPLE 5 *Business Application*

Lisa imports scooters from Italy. The cost of the scooters is given in euros. The total cost of each scooter includes a 10% service charge and 75 euros for shipping.

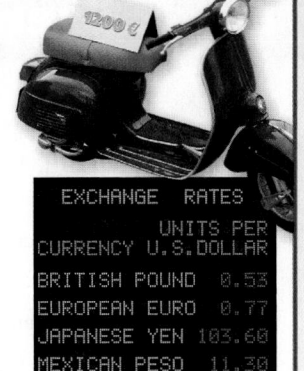

EXCHANGE RATES	
CURRENCY	UNITS PER U.S. DOLLAR
BRITISH POUND	0.53
EUROPEAN EURO	0.77
JAPANESE YEN	103.60
MEXICAN PESO	11.30

A **Write a composite function to represent the total cost of the scooter in dollars if the cost of the item is c euros.**

Step 1 Write a function for the total cost in euros.

$$E(c) = c + 0.1c + 75$$
$$= 1.1c + 75$$

Step 2 Write a function for the cost in dollars based on the cost in euros.

$$D(c) = \frac{c}{0.77}$$ *Use the exchange rate table.*

Step 3 Find the composition $D(E(c))$.

$$D(E(c)) = \frac{E(c)}{0.77}$$ *Substitute E(c) for c.*

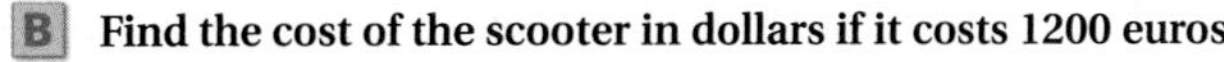

$$= \frac{1.1c + 75}{0.77}$$ *Replace E(c) with its rule.*

B **Find the cost of the scooter in dollars if it costs 1200 euros.**

Evaluate the composite function for $c = 1200$.

$$D(E(1200)) = \frac{1.1(1200) + 75}{0.77}$$
$$\approx 1811.69$$

The scooter would cost $1811.69, including all charges.

During a sale, a music store is selling all drum kits for 20% off. Preferred customers also receive an additional 15% off.

5a. Write a composite function to represent the final cost of a kit that originally cost c dollars. $f(c) = 0.68c$

5b. Find the cost of a drum kit priced at $248 that a preferred customer wants to buy. **$168.64**

THINK AND DISCUSS

1. Explain why $(f + g)x = (g + f)x$ for any functions f and g.
2. Find two functions such that $f(g(x)) = g(f(x))$.

3. **GET ORGANIZED** Copy and complete the graphic organizer. Write the correct notation for each function operation.

Operation	Notation
Addition	
Subtraction	
Multiplication	
Division	
Composition	

COMMON ERROR ALERT

Students may get confused by the multiple sets of parentheses in a composite function or value, such as $f(g(3))$. Remind students to follow the order of operations and work within the innermost parentheses first.

Power Presentations with PowerPoint®

Additional Examples

Example 5

Jake imports furniture from Mexico. The exchange rate is 11.30 pesos per U.S. dollar. The cost of each piece of furniture is given in pesos. The total cost of each piece of furniture includes a 15% service charge.

A. Write a composite function to represent the total cost of a piece of furniture in dollars if the cost of the item is c pesos.
$D(P(c)) = 1.15\left(\frac{c}{11.30}\right)$

B. Find the total cost of a table in dollars if it costs 1800 pesos.
$183.19

Also available on transparency

INTERVENTION
Questioning Strategies

EXAMPLE 5

- In this example, will you get the same answer if you create a composite function in reverse order? Why or why not?

3 Close

Summarize

Review the different function operations, taking care to emphasize the notation. Explain that composite functions are used to represent complicated relationships by combining simpler functions. Composite functions are useful when studying complex phenomena such as those encountered in physics, chemistry, and astronomy.

ONGOING ASSESSMENT and INTERVENTION

***Diagnose Before* the Lesson**
9-4 Warm Up, TE p. 682

***Monitor During* the Lesson**
Check It Out! Exercises, SE pp. 682–685
Questioning Strategies, TE pp. 683–685

***Assess After* the Lesson**
9-4 Lesson Quiz, TE p. 688
Alternative Assessment, TE p. 688

Answers to *Think and Discuss*

Possible answers:

1. Addition of real numbers is commutative.
2. $f(x) = x + 2$ and $g(x) = x - 2$; $f(x) = x^3$ and $g(x) = \sqrt[3]{x}$
3. See p. A11.

Assignment Guide

Assign *Guided Practice* exercises as necessary.

If you finished Examples **1–2**
- **Basic** 15–23
- **Average** 15–23
- **Advanced** 15–23, 51

If you finished Examples **1–5**
- **Basic** 15–34, 37–40, 44–48, 52–56
- **Average** 15–48, 52–56
- **Advanced** 16–34 even, 35–56

Homework Quick Check
Quickly check key concepts.
Exercises: 16, 20, 22, 26, 30, 37

Inclusion For **Exercise 14,** present the definitions of *net* and *gross* income for any students unfamiliar with these terms. ENGLISH LANGUAGE LEARNERS

Answers

1. Possible answer: Composition is like substituting 1 function into another, while the other operations are more similar to operations with numbers or expressions.

30. $\frac{4x}{x+3} + 3$; $x \neq -3$

State Resources

go.hrw.com
State Resources Online
KEYWORD: MB7 Resources

9-4 Exercises

go.hrw.com
Homework Help Online
KEYWORD: MB7 9-4
Parent Resources Online
KEYWORD: MB7 Parent

GUIDED PRACTICE

1. **Vocabulary** How is the *composition of functions* different from the other function operations?

SEE EXAMPLE 1 p. 682

Given $f(x) = 8x + 13$ and $g(x) = x^2 - 5x$, find each function.

2. $(f+g)(x)$ $x^2 + 3x + 13$
3. $(f-g)(x)$ $-x^2 + 13x + 13$
4. $(g-f)(x)$ $x^2 - 13x - 13$

SEE EXAMPLE 2 p. 683

Given $f(x) = 2x^2 + 2x$ and $g(x) = x + 1$, find each function.

5. $(fg)(x)$ $2x^3 + 4x^2 + 2x$
6. $\left(\frac{f}{g}\right)(x)$ $2x$, $x \neq -1$
7. $\left(\frac{g}{f}\right)(x)$ $\frac{1}{2x}$, $x \neq 0$ or -1

SEE EXAMPLE 3 p. 684

Given $f(x) = 3x^2$ and $g(x) = 7 - x$, find each value.

8. $f(g(5))$ 12
9. $g(f(5))$ -68
10. $f(g(-2))$ 243

SEE EXAMPLE 4 p. 684

Given $f(x) = x^2$, $g(x) = 2x - 3$, and $h(x) = \sqrt{x+1}$, write each composite function. State the domain of each.

11. $f(g(x))$ $4x^2 - 12x + 9$; $\mathbb{R}$
12. $g(f(x))$ $2x^2 - 3$; $\mathbb{R}$
13. $f(h(x))$ $x + 1$; $x \geq -1$

SEE EXAMPLE 5 p. 685

14. **Consumer Economics** Ron is saving money for college. Each month he deposits 10% of his net income plus an additional \$50 into a savings account. His net income, after taxes have been taken out, is 80% of his gross income.
    a. Write a composite function for the amount that Ron saves each month if his gross income is g. $S(g) = 0.1(0.8g) + 50$
    b. Find the amount that Ron saves in a month when his gross income is \$2400. \$242

PRACTICE AND PROBLEM SOLVING

Independent Practice	
For Exercises	See Example
15–18	1
19–23	2
24–29	3
30–32	4
33	5

Extra Practice
Skills Practice p. S21
Application Practice p. S40

Given $f(x) = 2x^2 - 8$, $g(x) = x^2 + 5x + 6$, and $h(x) = 2x + 4$, find each function.

15. $(f+g)(x)$ $3x^2 + 5x - 2$
16. $(f-g)(x)$ $x^2 - 5x - 14$
17. $(f+h)(x)$ $2x^2 + 2x - 4$
18. $(g-h)(x)$ $x^2 + 3x + 2$
19. $(fg)(x)$ $2x^4 + 10x^3 + 4x^2 - 40x - 48$
20. $\left(\frac{f}{g}\right)(x)$ $\frac{2x-4}{x+3}$, $x \neq -3$ or -2
21. $\left(\frac{h}{f}\right)(x)$ $\frac{1}{x-2}$, $x \neq -2$ or 2
22. $(gh)(x)$ $2x^3 + 14x^2 + 32x + 24$
23. $\left(\frac{g}{h}\right)(x)$ $\frac{x+3}{2}$, $x \neq -2$

Given $f(x) = 2\sqrt{x+3}$ and $g(x) = -3x + 1$, find each value.

24. $f(g(1))$ 2
25. $g(f(1))$ -11
26. $f(g(4))$ not a real number
27. $g(f(6))$ -17
28. $f\left(g\left(\frac{4}{3}\right)\right)$ 0
29. $g(f(97))$ -59

Given $f(x) = 4x + 3$, $g(x) = \frac{x}{x+3}$, and $h(x) = -x^2 - 2$, write each composite function. State the domain of each.

30. $f(g(x))$
31. $g(f(x))$ $\frac{4x+3}{4x+6}$; $x \neq -\frac{3}{2}$
32. $f(h(x))$ $-4x^2 - 5$; $\mathbb{R}$

33. **Business** The cost of carpeting a room is \$4 per square yard plus \$100. Each square yard is equal to 9 square feet.
    a. Write a composite function for the cost of carpeting a room that covers x square feet. $C(x) = 4\left(\frac{x}{9}\right) + 100$
    b. Find the square footage of a room that costs \$380 to carpet. 630 ft^2

9-4 READING STRATEGIES

Main Idea	Facts
Functions can be multiplied and divided just like numbers and expressions.	Multiplication: $(fg)(x) = f(x) \cdot g(x)$ Division: $\left(\frac{f}{g}\right)(x) = \frac{f(x)}{g(x)}$
Example	**Useful Hints**
$f(x) = x^2 + x - 6$ $g(x) = x + 3$ Multiplication: $(fg)(x) = f(x) \cdot g(x)$ $(fg)(x) = (x^2 + x - 6)(x + 3)$ $= x^3 + 4x^2 - 3x - 18$ Division: $\left(\frac{f}{g}\right)(x) = \frac{f(x)}{g(x)}$ $\left(\frac{f}{g}\right)(x) = \frac{x^2+x-6}{x+3} = \frac{(x+3)(x-2)}{x+3}$ $= x - 2$, where $x \neq -3$	When dividing functions, make sure you note any domain restrictions. In the example, $x \neq -3$ because at $x = -3$, the denominator of the function is 0.

Find each function. Note any domain restrictions.

1. Given $f(x) = x^2 + 9x + 20$ and $g(x) = x + 5$.
   a. Find $(gf)(x)$. $x^3 + 14x^2 + 65x + 100$
   b. Find $\left(\frac{f}{g}\right)(x)$. $x + 4$, where $x \neq -5$
2. Given $m(x) = 2x^2 - 2$ and $n(x) = 2x + 2$.
   a. Find $(mn)(x)$. $4x^3 + 4x^2 - 4x - 4$
   b. Find $\left(\frac{m}{n}\right)(x)$. $x - 1$, where $x \neq -1$
3. Given $c(x) = 2x - 8$ and $d(x) = 2x^2 - 4x - 16$.
   a. Find $(cd)(x)$. $4x^3 - 24x^2 + 128$
   b. Find $\left(\frac{d}{c}\right)(x)$. $x + 2$, where $x \neq 4$
4. Given $h(x) = x^2 + 7x + 6$ and $k(x) = x + 6$.
   a. Find $(hk)(x)$. $x^3 + 13x^2 + 48x + 36$
   b. Find $\left(\frac{h}{k}\right)(x)$. $x + 1$, where $x \neq -6$
5. Given $p(x) = x^3 - x$ and $q(x) = x^2 - x$.
   a. Find $(pq)(x)$. $x^5 - x^4 - x^3 + x^2$
   b. Find $\left(\frac{p}{q}\right)(x)$. $x + 1$, where $x \neq 0$ and $x \neq 1$

9-4 RETEACH

Follow these steps to perform operations with functions.

Step 1 Use the notation rule for the operation.
Step 2 Substitute each function into its rule.
Step 3 Simplify by combining like terms, using the Distributive Property, and/or factoring.

Let $f(x) = x^2 - 9$ and $g(x) = x - 3$.

Add	Subtract
$(f+g)(x) = f(x) + g(x)$ (Notation rule) $= (x^2 - 9) + (x - 3)$ $= x^2 + x - 12$	$(f-g)(x) = f(x) - g(x)$ $= (x^2 - 9) - (x - 3)$ $= x^2 - 9 - x + 3$ (Use the Distributive Property.) $= x^2 - x - 6$
Multiply	**Divide**
$(fg)(x) = f(x) \cdot g(x)$ $= (x^2 - 9) \cdot (x - 3)$ $= x^3 - 3x^2 - 9x + 27$ (Use FOIL.)	$\frac{f}{g}(x) = \frac{f(x)}{g(x)}$ $= \frac{x^2 - 9}{x - 3}$ $= \frac{(x-3)(x+3)}{(x-3)}$ (Factor and simplify the rational expression.) $= \frac{(x-3)(x+3)}{(x-3)}$ $= x + 3$ where $x \neq 3$

Given $f(x) = 4x^2 - 1$ and $g(x) = 2x - 1$, find each function.

1. $(f+g)(x)$
   $(f+g)(x) = f(x) + g(x)$
   $= 4x^2 - 1 + 2x - 1 = 4x^2 + 2x - 2$
2. $(f-g)(x)$
   $(f-g)(x) = f(x) - g(x)$
   $= 4x^2 - 1 - (2x - 1) = 4x^2 - 2x$
3. $(fg)(x)$
   $(fg)(x) = f(x) \cdot g(x)$
   $= (4x^2 - 1)(2x - 1)$
   $= 8x^3 - 4x^2 - 2x + 1$
4. $\frac{f}{g}(x)$
   $\frac{f}{g}(x) = \frac{f(x)}{g(x)} = \frac{4x^2 - 1}{2x - 1}$
   $= \frac{(2x+1)(2x-1)}{2x-1}$
   $= 2x + 1$, where $x \neq \frac{1}{2}$

34. This problem will prepare you for the Multi-Step Test Prep on page 706.

When the air in a hot-air balloon is heated to 100°F, each cubic foot of air can lift about 7 g.

a. Write a function $f(x)$ for the number of grams that can be lifted by a balloon containing x ft^3 of air.

b. The equation $g(x) = \frac{x}{453.6}$ converts x grams to pounds. Write a composite function for the number of pounds that can be lifted by a balloon containing x ft^3 of air.

c. Approximately how many cubic feet of air are needed to lift 1000 lb?

35d. 15%; she will save an extra \$1.50 if she uses the 15% first.

35. Consumer Economics Lanie has two coupons for a shoe store. One is for \$10 off, and the other is for 15% off.

a. Write a function $f(p)$ for the final cost of an item of original price p if Lanie uses only the \$10-off coupon. $f(p) = p - 10$

b. Write a function $g(p)$ for the final cost of an item of original price p if Lanie uses only the 15%-off coupon. $g(p) = 0.85p$

c. Find $f(g(p))$ and $g(f(p))$. $f(g(p)) = 0.85p - 10$; $g(f(p)) = 0.85p - 8.5$

d. Which coupon should Lanie apply first? Explain.

e. Find the lowest price that Lanie could pay for a pair of shoes priced at \$49. **\$31.65**

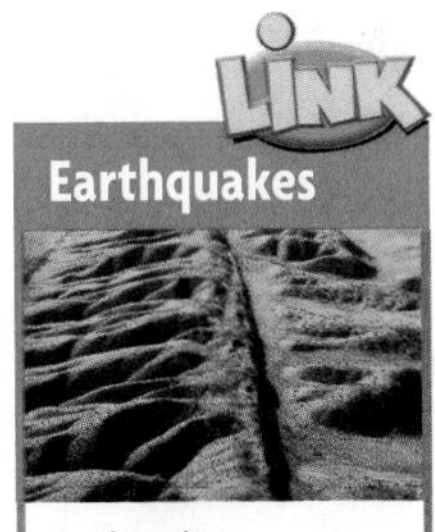

Earthquakes are generally caused by movement along faults. Faults are cracks in Earth's crust, the largest of which occur at tectonic plate boundaries.

36. Earthquakes The shock waves created from an earthquake travel away from the epicenter at a rate of 9 km/s. As the radius of the circular waves increases, more and more area is affected by the earthquake.

a. Find a function for the total area in square kilometers affected by the earthquake after t s. $A(t) = 81\pi t^2$

b. Geologists predict that the earthquake will be felt over an area of approximately 35,000 km^2. How long after the earthquake begins will this area be affected? $\approx$ **11.73 s**

37. Population The population of Las Vegas, Nevada, can be approximated by the function $p(t) = 160{,}000 \cdot 1.05^t$, where t is the number of years since 1980. The number of doctors in Las Vegas can be approximated by the function $d(p) = 0.0044p$, where p is the population.

a. Find a function for the number of doctors in Las Vegas as a function of the number of years t since 1980. $D(t) = 704 \cdot 1.05^t$

b. **Estimation** Estimate the number of doctors in Las Vegas in 2010. **about 3043**

37c. about 2020 c. Approximately when will the number of doctors in Las Vegas exceed 5000?

38. Critical Thinking Given $f(x) = x$ and given any function $g(x)$, is $f(g(x))$ always equal to $g(f(x))$? Explain.

Use the tables to find each value.

x	2	3	4	5
$f(x)$	0	1	2	3

x	1	2	3	4
$g(x)$	1	2	4	8

39. $(g \circ f)(5)$ 4 **40.** $(f \circ g)(3)$ 2

41. $g(f(4))$ 2 **42.** $f(g(2))$ 0

43. No; $g(4) = 8$, but $f(8)$ is not defined in the table.

43. Critical Thinking Can you use the tables to find $f(g(4))$? Explain your answer.

44. Write About It Is the sum of two linear functions also a linear function? Is the product of two linear functions also a linear function? Explain.

COMMON ERROR ALERT

Students may have difficulty finding the domain of a composite function, such as in **Exercises 30–32.** Encourage students to find domain restrictions of the function inside parentheses first and then to find the domain restrictions of the composition.

Exercise 34 involves writing composite functions to convert units. This exercise prepares students for the Multi-Step Test Prep on page 706.

Answers

34a. $f(x) = 7x$

b. $g(f(x)) = \frac{7x}{453.6} = \frac{x}{64.8}$

c. 64,800 ft^3

38. Yes; to create $f(g(x))$, you would replace x with $g(x)$, so $f(g(x)) = g(x)$. To create $g(f(x))$, you would replace x with itself, so $g(f(x)) = g(x)$. Both compositions equal $g(x)$.

44. Possible answer: The sum of 2 linear functions is also a linear function because the exponents of the variables don't change when terms are added. The product of 2 linear functions will be quadratic unless 1 of the functions is in the form $y = a$.

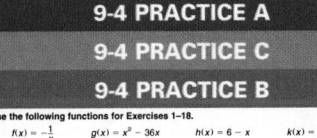

9-4 PROBLEM SOLVING

Andy is buying a new laptop computer. The store is offering a 15% discount on the model he wants. Andy also has a certificate from the manufacturer good for \$120 off his next computer purchase. Andy wants to know whether he will pay less if the certificate amount is deducted before or after the discount is applied.

1. Write a function, D, to represent the price of the computer after the discount is applied. Use p to represent the original price. $D(p) = p - 0.15p = 0.85p$
2. Write a function, R, to represent the price after the certificate amount is deducted. $R(p) = p - 120$
3. Find the composite function $R(D(p))$ and then describe what it means in terms of the final price of the computer.
   $R(D(p)) = R(0.85p) = 0.85p - 120$; means that the certificate amount is deducted after the discount is applied.
4. Find the composite function $D(R(p))$ and then describe what it means in terms of the final price of the computer.
   $D(R(p)) = D(p - 120) = 0.85p - 120$; means that the certificate amount is deducted after the discount is applied.
5. Will Andy pay less if the certificate amount is deducted before or after the discount is applied? Explain.
   Andy will pay less if the certificate amount is deducted after the discount is applied; $R(D(p)) < D(R(p))$.

Emily has a coupon from her favorite store for \$5 off any item this month. A sales tax of 8% is applied after the value of a coupon or discount is deducted. Let p represent the original price, $t(p)$ the price after tax, and $d(p)$ the price after the value of a coupon or discount is deducted. Choose the letter for the best answer.

6. Which function describes the final price of an item with price, p?
   A $td(p)$ C $d(t(p))$
   B $dt(p)$ (D) $t(d(p))$
7. Emily picks out a backpack with a price tag of p. Which expression gives the amount that Emily will pay?
   (F) $1.08(p - 5)$ H $0.92(p - 5)$
   G $(p - 5) + 0.08$ J $1.08p - 5$
8. If Emily uses her coupon to buy a pair of jeans that has been marked down to \$50, what will she pay?
   A \$41.40
   B \$45.00
   (C) \$48.60
   D \$49.00
9. A month later Emily buys a jacket on sale at 30% off. Which expression gives the amount that she pays after tax?
   F $(p - 0.3) + 1.08$
   (G) $1.08(0.7p)$
   H $0.7p + 1.08p$
   J $0.92(p - 0.3)$

9-4 CHALLENGE

Given any two real numbers, a and b, the maximum value of these numbers might be found by using the equation

$$\max[a, b] = \frac{a+b}{2} + \frac{|a-b|}{2}.$$

1. Find the maximum of 8 and 13. 13
2. Find the maximum of 18.6 and 12.8. 18.6

The concept of maximal value can also be applied to functions. Consider two functions, $f(x)$ and $g(x)$. The maximum function value of the two functions can be computed using the equation

$$\max[f(x), g(x)] = \frac{f(x)+g(x)}{2} + \frac{|f(x)-g(x)|}{2}.$$

This equation can be used in several ways. Consider the two functions $f(x) = 8 - x^2$ and $g(x) = 2^x$.

3. Find the maximum of $f(x)$ and $g(x)$ when $x = 1$. 7
4. Find the maximum of $f(x)$ and $g(x)$ when $x = -2$. $\frac{1}{4}$
5. Graph $f(x)$ on a calculator using x from -5 to 5 and y from -10 to 10.
6. Graph $g(x)$ on a calculator using x from -5 to 5 and y from -10 to 10.
7. Graph the function $\max[f(x), g(x)]$ on a calculator using x from -5 to 5 and y from -10 to 10. Sketch the graph on the coordinate plane at right. Describe the graph in words and as a piecewise function.
   The graph shows the greater of the two functions at different values of x; first the exponential, then the parabola, and finally the exponential function again.
   $$\max[f(x), g(x)] = \begin{cases} 2^x & x \geq 2 \\ 8 - x^2 & -2.8 \leq x \leq 2 \\ 2^x & x \leq -2.8 \end{cases}$$
8. How could you define a function to find the minimum value of two real numbers? Check your equation with the numbers 8 and 13.
   $$\min(a, b) = \frac{a+b}{2} - \frac{|a-b|}{2}$$
9. How could you define a function to find the minimum value of two functions? Check by graphing your minimum for functions $f(x)$ and $g(x)$ defined above on a calculator.
   $$\min[f(x), g(x)] = \frac{f(x)+g(x)}{2} - \frac{|f(x)-g(x)|}{2}$$

9-4 PRACTICE A

9-4 PRACTICE C

9-4 PRACTICE B

Use the following functions for Exercises 1–18.

$f(x) = -\frac{1}{x}$ $g(x) = x^2 - 36x$ $h(x) = 6 - x$ $k(x) = \sqrt{x}$

Find each function.

1. $(fg)(x)$ $-x + 36$
2. $(g + h)(x)$ $x^2 - 37x + 6$
3. $\left(\frac{g}{f}\right)(x)$ $-x^3 + 36x^2$

Find each value.

4. $f(g(-1))$ $-\frac{1}{37}$
5. $h(g(0))$ 6
6. $h(k(121))$ -5
7. $g(k(9))$ -99
8. $h(g(-3))$ -111
9. $g(h(-3))$ -243
10. $k(h(-10))$ 4
11. $k(f(-4))$ $\frac{1}{2}$
12. $f(h(1))$ $-\frac{1}{5}$

Write each composite function. State the domain of each.

13. $f(g(x))$ $f(g(x)) = -\frac{1}{x^2 - 36x}$; $\{x \mid x \neq 0 \text{ and } x \neq 36\}$
14. $k(h(x))$ $k(h(x)) = \sqrt{6 - x}$; $\{x \mid x \leq 6\}$
15. $h(k(x))$ $h(k(x)) = 6 - \sqrt{x}$; $\{x \mid x \geq 0\}$
16. $f(k(x))$ $f(k(x)) = -\frac{1}{\sqrt{x}}$; $\{x \mid x > 0\}$
17. $k(g(x))$ $k(g(x)) = \sqrt{x^2 - 36x}$; $\{x \mid x \geq 36 \text{ or } x \leq 0\}$
18. $h(g(x))$ $h(g(x)) = -x^2 + 36x + 6$; $\{x \mid x \text{ is a real number}\}$

Solve.

19. The cost of renting a banquet hall for an event is \$300 plus \$30 for each person attending the event. If the hall provides live music, the cost is 40% more per person.
   a. Write a function for the cost of an event that includes live music. $f(g(x)) = 300 + 42x$
   b. How much is the cost of an event for 125 people with live music? \$5550

TEST PREP DOCTOR In **Exercise 45,** students who chose **A** may have been confused about the order in which the functions are applied. Remind students that $(f \circ g)(x)$ means $f(g(x))$.

In **Exercise 48,** students who have trouble simplifying algebraic expressions may note that $(f+g)(2) = f(2) + g(2)$. Then they can evaluate each function for 2 and add the results.

Journal

Explain how function operations are similar to operations with numbers or algebraic expressions. Give some examples to illustrate your answer.

ALTERNATIVE ASSESSMENT

Have students choose two functions, f and g. Have them find the sum, difference, product, quotient, and compositions of the two functions. Ask students to determine which has the greatest value for the input $x = 10$.

Power Presentations with PowerPoint®

9-4 Lesson Quiz

Given $f(x) = 4x^2 - 1$ and $g(x) = 2x - 1$, find each function or value.

1. $(f+g)(x)$ $4x^2 + 2x - 2$
2. $(fg)(x)$ $8x^3 - 4x^2 - 2x + 1$
3. $\left(\frac{f}{g}\right)(x)$ $2x + 1;\ x \neq \frac{1}{2}$
4. $g(f(2))$ 29

Given $f(x) = x^2$ and $g(x) = \sqrt{x - 1}$, write each composite function. State the domain of each.

5. $f(g(x))$ $f(g(x)) = x - 1;$ $\{x \mid x \geq 1\}$
6. $g(f(x))$ $g(f(x)) = \sqrt{x^2 - 1};$ $\{x \mid x \leq -1 \text{ or } x \geq 1\}$

Also available on transparency

TEST PREP

45. If $(f \circ g)(x) = (3x + 4)^2$, which of the following could be true?
    - Ⓐ $f(x) = 3x + 4$ and $g(x) = x^2$
    - Ⓑ $f(x) = x^2$ and $g(x) = 3x + 4$
    - Ⓒ $f(x) = (3x)^2$ and $g(x) = 4^2$
    - Ⓓ $f(x) = 3x + 4$ and $g(x) = \sqrt{x}$

46. If $f(x) = 2x + 1$ and $g(x) = 5x - 2$, then which of the following is $(fg)(5)$?
    - Ⓕ 253
    - Ⓖ 53
    - Ⓗ 47
    - Ⓙ 13

47. Given $f(x) = 4 - x^2$ and $g(x) = \frac{1}{2}x - 2$, which of the following is $(f \circ g)(x)$?
    - Ⓐ $(f \circ g)(x) = -\frac{1}{2}x^2$
    - Ⓑ $(f \circ g)(x) = -\frac{1}{4}x^2 + 2x$
    - Ⓒ $(f \circ g)(x) = -\frac{1}{2}x^3 + 2x^2 + 2x - 8$
    - Ⓓ $(f \circ g)(x) = -x^2 + \frac{1}{2}x + 2$

48. **Gridded Response** Given that $f(x) = (x + 1)^2$ and $g(x) = 3x$, find $(f + g)(2)$. **15**

CHALLENGE AND EXTEND

49. $g(x) = \frac{3}{2}x^2 + 5$

50. $g(f(x)) = \begin{cases} 9x^2 + 48x + 64 & x < 0 \\ 15x + 42 & x \geq 0 \end{cases}$

49. Given $f(x) = 2x - 6$ and $f(g(x)) = 3x^2 + 4$, find $g(x)$.

50. Given $f(x) = 3x + 8$ and $g(x) = \begin{cases} x^2 & \text{if } x < 0 \\ 5x + 2 & \text{if } x \geq 0 \end{cases}$, find $g(f(x))$.

51. **Physics** When a ball is thrown up a hill, the height y of the ball is given by the function $y = -0.12x^2 + 2.8x$, where x is the horizontal distance from the thrower. The hill is represented by the linear function $y = \frac{2}{5}x$.
    a. Find the maximum height of the ball above the ground. **12 ft**
    b. Find the height of the ball when it hits the ground. **8 ft**

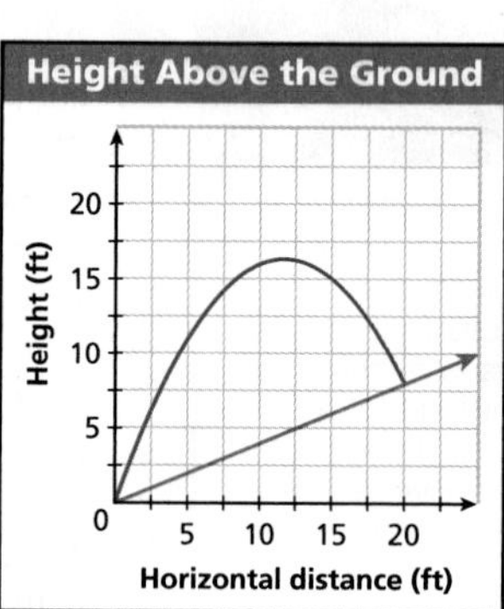

SPIRAL REVIEW

52. **Business** The value of a computer purchased for \$800 depreciates by 20% each year. *(Lesson 7-1)*
    a. Write a function to model the value of the computer after t years. $V(t) = 800(0.8)^t$
    b. How much will the computer be worth in 10 years? **\$85.90**

Decide whether the data set is exponential, and if it is, use exponential regression to find a function that models the data. *(Lesson 7-8)*

53.

x	2	3	4	5	6
y	5	10	20	40	80

$f(x) = 1.25(2^t)$

54.

x	1	2	3	4	5
y	5	10	15	20	25

not exponential

56. $h(x) = \begin{cases} 24x & x \geq 0 \\ 3x - 27 & x < 0 \end{cases}$

Given $f(x) = \begin{cases} 8x & x \geq 0 \\ x - 9 & x < 0 \end{cases}$, write the rule for each function. *(Lesson 9-3)*

55. $g(x)$, a horizontal translation of $f(x)$ 5 units to the left

56. $h(x)$, a vertical stretch by a factor of 3

55. $g(x) = \begin{cases} 8(x + 5) & x \geq -5 \\ x - 4 & x < -5 \end{cases}$

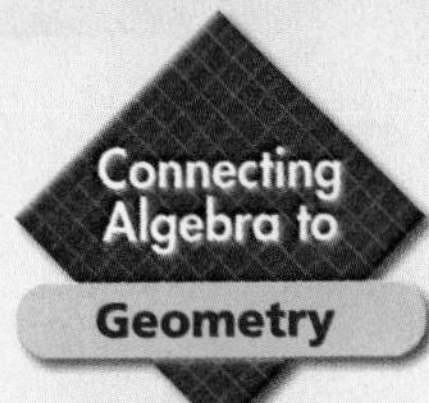

Using Geometric Formulas

See Skills Bank page S63

Geometric formulas can be used to find lengths of sides or edges. Solve the formula for the variable that you need. In these formulas, s is the length of a side or an edge and r is the radius.

Regular Hexagon	Regular Octagon	Regular Tetrahedron	Regular Octahedron	Sphere
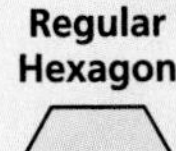  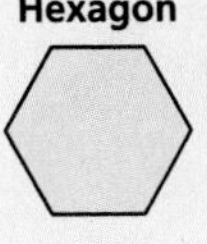	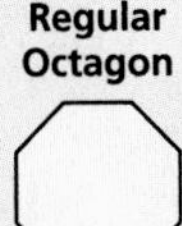  	 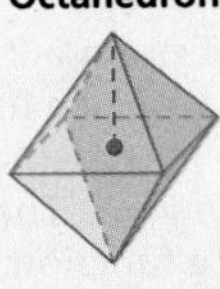	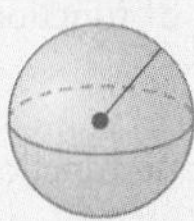	$A = 4\pi r^2$
$A = \frac{3s^2}{2}\sqrt{3}$	$A = 2s^2(\sqrt{2}+1)$	$V = \frac{s^3}{12}\sqrt{2}$	$V = \frac{s^3}{3}\sqrt{2}$	$V = \frac{4\pi r^3}{3}$

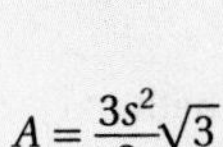

Example

A rectangle is 30 cm long and 10 cm wide. Find the length of the sides of a regular octagon that has the same area as this rectangle.

1. Find the area of the rectangle.

$30 \cdot 10 = 300$ *The area is 300 cm².*

2. Use the octagon formula. Solve for s, the length of one side.

$A = 2s^2(\sqrt{2}+1)$

$\frac{A}{2(\sqrt{2}+1)} = s^2$ *Divide both sides by $2(\sqrt{2}+1)$.*

$s = \sqrt{\frac{A}{2(\sqrt{2}+1)}}$ *Take the square root of both sides.*

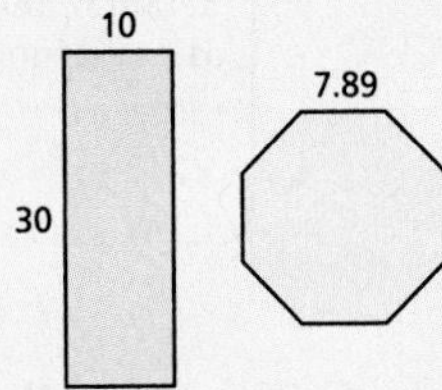

3. Substitute 300 for the area A, and solve for the side length.

$s \approx \sqrt{\frac{300}{2(1.41+1)}} \approx \sqrt{\frac{300}{4.82}} \approx \sqrt{62.24} \approx 7.89$ *Use 1.41 as an approximation for $\sqrt{2}$.*

Try This

Solve each problem. Start by solving the appropriate formula for s or r.

1. How large of a sphere could you build with 1000 cubic feet of clay? $r = \sqrt[3]{\frac{3V}{4\pi}}$; $r \approx 6.20$ ft
2. Jake used 540 square inches of mosaic tile to build a tabletop in the shape of a regular hexagon. How long is one edge of this tabletop?
3. A tent shaped like a tetrahedron has 30 cubic feet of air space. Describe the base of this tent.
4. Cyndi wants to construct an octahedron that has the same volume as a sphere with a radius of 9 cm. What length should she make each edge of the octahedron?

Answers

2. $s = \sqrt{\frac{2A}{3\sqrt{3}}}$; ≈ 14.42 in.

3. $s = \sqrt[3]{\frac{12V}{\sqrt{2}}}$; an equilateral triangle with side length ≈ 6.34 ft

4. $s = \sqrt[3]{\frac{3V}{\sqrt{2}}}$; ≈ 18.64 cm

Organizer

See Skills Bank page S63

Pacing:
Traditional $\frac{1}{2}$ day
Block $\frac{1}{4}$ day

Objective: Students apply procedures for finding inverse functions to using geometric formulas.

Online Edition

Countdown to Testing Week 20

Teach

Remember

Students review area and volume formulas for polygons and polyhedrons.

INTERVENTION For additional review and practice on using geometric formulas, see Skills Bank page S63.

Visual Point out that the faces of a tetrahedron and an octahedron are equilateral triangles.

Close

Assess

If you know the volume of a tetrahedron, you can use $V = \frac{s^2}{12}\sqrt{2}$ to find the length of one edge. Explain the steps used in applying this formula.

State Resources

9-5 Organizer

Pacing: Traditional 1 day
Block $\frac{1}{2}$ day

Objectives: Determine whether the inverse of a function is a function.

Write rules for the inverses of functions.

Online Edition
Tutorial Videos

Countdown to Testing Week 20

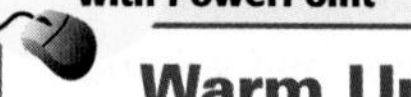

Power Presentations with PowerPoint®

Warm Up

Solve for *x* in terms of *y*.

1. $y = \frac{2}{3}x - 6$ $\quad x = \frac{3}{2}y + 9$
2. $y = (x + 2)^2$ $\quad x = \pm\sqrt{y} - 2$
3. $y = \sqrt{x + 10}$ $\quad x = y^2 - 10$
4. $y = 2\ln x$ $\quad x = e^{\frac{y}{2}}$

Also available on transparency

Math Humor

Parent: Why are you making all of your homework answers rhyme?

Student: I'm studying functions in verse.

9-5 Functions and Their Inverses

Objectives
Determine whether the inverse of a function is a function.

Write rules for the inverses of functions.

Vocabulary
one-to-one function

Who uses this?
Nurses can use inverse functions to approximate the ages of infants. (See Exercise 37.)

In Lesson 7-2, you learned that the inverse of a function $f(x)$ "undoes" $f(x)$. Its graph is a reflection across the line $y = x$. The inverse may or may not be a function.

Recall that the vertical-line test (Lesson 1-6) can help you determine whether a relation is a function. Similarly, the *horizontal-line test* can help you determine whether the inverse of a function is a function.

Know it! Note

Horizontal-line Test

WORDS	EXAMPLES	
If any horizontal line passes through more than one point on the graph of a relation, the inverse relation is not a function.	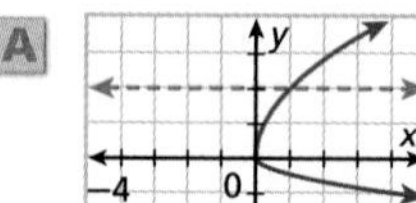 Inverse is a function.	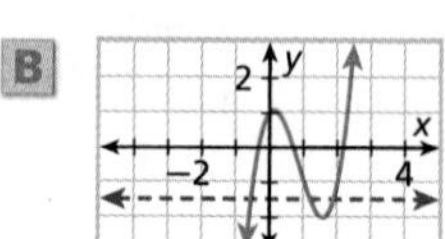 Inverse is not a function.

EXAMPLE 1 Using the Horizontal-Line Test

Use the horizontal-line test to determine whether the inverse of each relation is a function.

A

The inverse is a function because no horizontal line passes through two points on the graph.

B

The inverse is not a function because a horizontal line passes through more than one point on the graph.

CHECK IT OUT!

1. Use the horizontal-line test to determine whether the inverse of the relation is a function.

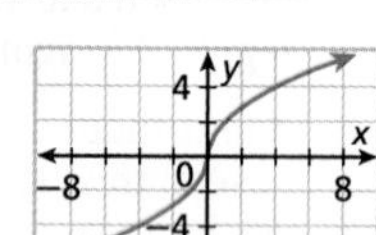

State Resources

go.hrw.com
State Resources Online
KEYWORD: MB7 Resources

1 Introduce

EXPLORATION

9-5 Functions and Their Inverses

For this Exploration, set your calculator to the decimal window by pressing ZOOM and selecting **4:ZDecimal**.

1. Enter the function $f(x) = x^4$ as **Y1** and view its graph.
2. To graph the inverse relation, return to the home screen, press 2nd DRAW, and select **8:DrawInv**. Then press VARS and use the arrows keys to move to the **Y-VARS** menu. Select **1:Function** and then **1:Y1**. Press ENTER to view the graph of $f(x)$ and its inverse.
3. Graph each function in the table. Tell whether there is a horizontal line that passes through more than one point on the graph. Then graph the inverse relation and tell whether it is a function.

Function	Is there a horizontal line that passes through more than one point on the graph?	Is the inverse relation a function?
$y = 2^x$		
$y = x^2 + 1$		
$y = x^3 + x - 1$		

Motivate

Ask students to recall what they know about inverse functions (from Lessons 7-2 and 8-7), including

- reflections across the line $y = x$.
- switching variables and solving for y.
- inverse parent functions: exponential and logarithmic, quadratic and square root.

Explorations and answers are provided in the *Explorations* binder.

Recall from Lesson 7-2 that to write the rule for the inverse of a function, you can exchange x and y and solve the equation for y. Because the values of x and y are switched, the domain of the function will be the range of its inverse and vice versa.

EXAMPLE 2 Writing Rules for Inverses

Find the inverse of $f(x) = \left(\frac{1}{2}x + 2\right)^2$. Determine whether it is a function, and state its domain and range.

Step 1 Graph the function.

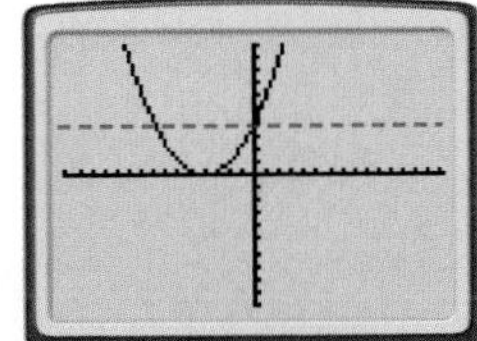

The horizontal-line test shows that the inverse is not a function. Note that the domain of f is all real numbers and the range is $\{y \mid y \geq 0\}$.

Step 2 Find the inverse.

$y = \left(\frac{1}{2}x + 2\right)^2$ *Rewrite the function using y instead of f(x).*

$x = \left(\frac{1}{2}y + 2\right)^2$ *Switch x and y in the equation.*

$\sqrt{x} = \sqrt{\left(\frac{1}{2}y + 2\right)^2}$ *Take the square root of both sides.*

$\pm\sqrt{x} = \frac{1}{2}y + 2$ *Note the domain restriction $x \geq 0$.*

$\pm\sqrt{x} - 2 = \frac{1}{2}y$ *Subtract 2 from each side.*

$y = 2(\pm\sqrt{x} - 2)$ *Isolate y.*

$y = \pm 2\sqrt{x} - 4$ *Simplify.*

Because of the $\pm$ symbol, there may be two y-values for an x-value. This confirms that the inverse is not a function. Because the inverse is not a function, you cannot use the notation $f^{-1}(x)$.

The domain of the inverse is the range of $f(x)$: $\{x \mid x \geq 0\}$. The range is the domain of $f(x)$: all real numbers.

Check Graph both relations to see that they are symmetric about $y = x$. To graph the inverse, you will have to graph the positive and negative cases separately.

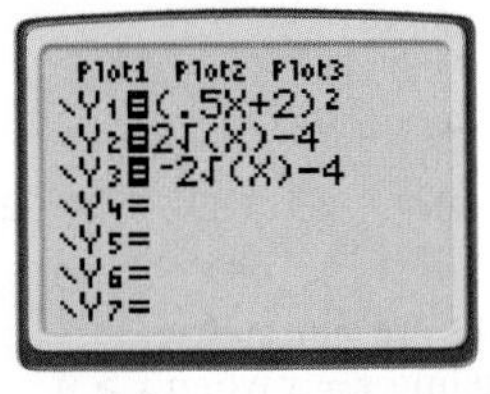

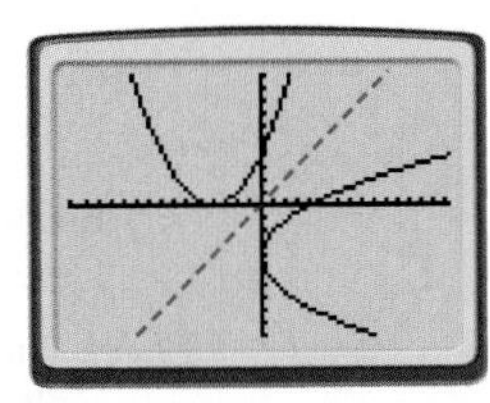

Caution!

When you take the square root of both sides of a quadratic equation be sure to add the $\pm$ symbol. (Lesson 5-4)

2. Find the inverse of $f(x) = x^3 - 2$. Determine whether it is a function, and state its domain and range.
$f^{-1}(x) = \sqrt[3]{x + 2}$; function; D: $\mathbb{R}$; R: $\mathbb{R}$

You have seen that the inverses of functions are not necessarily functions. When both a relation and its inverse are functions, the relation is called a *one-to-one function*. In a **one-to-one function**, each y-value is paired with exactly one x-value.

Power Presentations with PowerPoint®

Additional Examples

Example 1

Use the horizontal-line test to determine whether the inverse of each relation is a function.

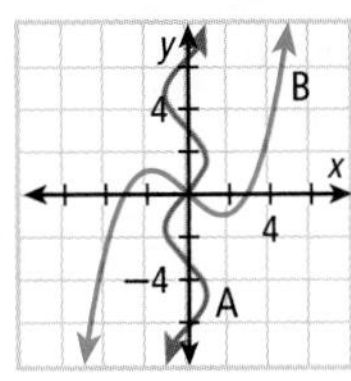

A. yes **B.** no

Example 2

Find the inverse of $f(x) = \sqrt[3]{x + 1}$. Determine whether it is a function, and state its domain and range.

$y = x^3 - 1$; function; D: $\mathbb{R}$; R: $\mathbb{R}$

Also available on transparency

INTERVENTION

Questioning Strategies

EXAMPLE 1

- Can a function pass both the horizontal- and vertical-line tests?

EXAMPLE 2

- How do you find the domain and range of a function and its inverse?

Teaching Tip **Multiple Representations** Encourage students to check their inverses by plugging in a few numbers. If they put a into a function and get b as the output, they should then be able to put b into the inverse and get a as the output.

Teaching Tip **Visual** Post a mapping diagram of a function and its inverse for students to reference while discussing the domain and range of inverse functions.

2 Teach

Guided Instruction

Review the vertical-line test from Lesson 1-6. Explain that the horizontal-line test is essentially the vertical-line test reflected over the line $y = x$. Encourage students to be careful with the algebra as they find and check inverse functions. Show students that the composition of two inverse functions is always equivalent to x.

Reaching All Learners

Through Kinesthetic Experience

Have students use tracing paper or patty paper to visualize the graphs of inverse functions. Have students follow these steps:

1. Graph the function and the line $y = x$ on graph paper.
2. Trace the function and the line on a piece of tracing or patty paper.
3. Flip the tracing over and align the lines.

The resulting curve is the inverse of the function.

Power Presentations with PowerPoint®

Additional Examples

Example 3

Determine by composition whether each pair of functions are inverses.

A. $f(x) = 3x - 1$ and $g(x) = \frac{1}{3}x + 1$ no

B. For $x \neq 1$ or 0, $f(x) = \frac{1}{x-1}$ and $g(x) = \frac{1}{x} + 1$. yes

Also available on transparency

INTERVENTION

Questioning Strategies

EXAMPLE 3

- How do you know if two functions are inverses by composition?

Teaching Tip **Math Background** Point out that composition of functions is not commutative, that is, $f(g(x)) \neq g(f(x))$. These two compositions are equal if $f(x)$ and $g(x)$ are inverses. However, the converse is *not* true. Just because $f(g(x)) = g(f(x))$, it does not mean that $f(x)$ and $g(x)$ are inverses.

You can use composition of functions to verify that two functions are inverses. Because inverse functions "undo" each other, when you compose two inverses the result is the input value x.

Identifying Inverse Functions

WORDS	ALGEBRA	EXAMPLE
If the compositions of two functions equal the input value, the functions are inverses.	If $f(g(x)) = g(f(x)) = x$, then $f(x)$ and $g(x)$ are inverse functions.	$f(x) = 3x$ and $g(x) = \frac{1}{3}x$ $f(g(x)) = 3\left(\frac{1}{3}x\right) = x$ $g(f(x)) = \frac{1}{3}(3x) = x$

EXAMPLE 3 Determining Whether Functions Are Inverses

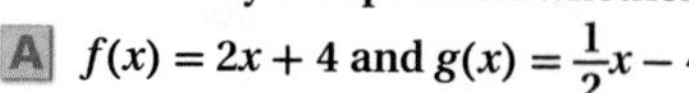

Determine by composition whether each pair of functions are inverses.

A $f(x) = 2x + 4$ and $g(x) = \frac{1}{2}x - 4$

Find the composition $f(g(x))$.

$$f(g(x)) = 2\left(\frac{1}{2}x - 4\right) + 4 \quad \textit{Substitute } \tfrac{1}{2}x - 4 \textit{ for x in f.}$$
$$= (x - 8) + 4 \quad \textit{Use the Distributive Property.}$$
$$= x - 4 \quad \textit{Simplify.}$$

Because $f(g(x)) \neq x$, f and g are not inverses. There is no need to check $g(f(x))$.

Check The graphs are not symmetric about the line $y = x$.

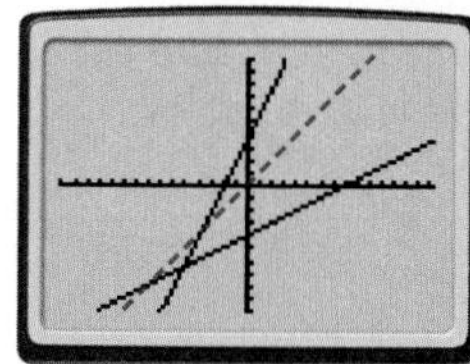

B For $x \geq 0$, $f(x) = \frac{1}{4}x^2$ and $g(x) = 2\sqrt{x}$.

Find the compositions $f(g(x))$ and $g(f(x))$.

$$f(g(x)) = \frac{1}{4}(2\sqrt{x})^2 \qquad g(f(x)) = 2\sqrt{\frac{1}{4}x^2}$$
$$= \frac{1}{4}(4x) \qquad = 2\left(\frac{1}{2}x\right)$$
$$= x, x \geq 0 \qquad = x$$

Because $f(g(x)) = g(f(x)) = x$ for $x \geq 0$, f and g are inverses.

Check The graphs are symmetric about the line $y = x$ when $x \geq 0$.

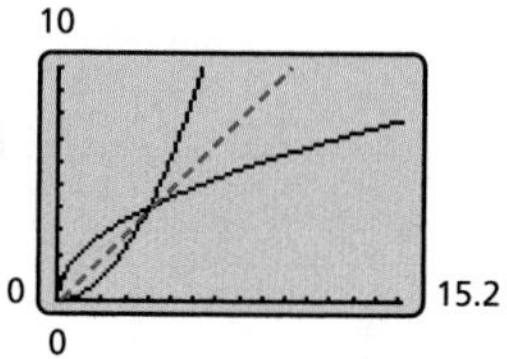

CHECK IT OUT! **Determine by composition whether each pair of functions are inverses.**

3a. $f(x) = \frac{2}{3}x + 6$ and $g(x) = \frac{3}{2}x - 9$ yes

3b. $f(x) = x^2 + 5$ and $g(x) = \sqrt{x} - 5$ for $x \geq 0$ no

3 Close

Summarize

Sometimes it makes sense to look at a relation in one way and sometimes in the other. By finding inverses of functions and relations, we have the flexibility to choose which makes more sense. For instance, it is useful to able to convert Fahrenheit to Celsius and vice versa. Ask students to think of other examples where it is useful to be able to go in either direction.

ONGOING ASSESSMENT and INTERVENTION

***Diagnose Before* the Lesson**
9-5 Warm Up, TE p. 690

***Monitor During* the Lesson**
Check It Out! Exercises, SE pp. 690–692
Questioning Strategies, TE pp. 691–692

***Assess After* the Lesson**
9-5 Lesson Quiz, TE p. 696
Alternative Assessment, TE p. 696

THINK AND DISCUSS

1. Explain why the horizontal-line test works.
2. Explain the relationship between the domain and range of a function and the domain and range of its inverse.
3. **GET ORGANIZED** Copy and complete the graphic organizer. Describe how each method or characteristic is used to find or verify inverses.

Vertical/horizontal-line test	Composition
Symmetry about $y = x$	Switching x and y

Inverses of Functions

Answers to *Think and Discuss*

Possible answers:

1. The inverse of a function is the reflection across the line $y = x$. When a horizontal line is reflected across the same line, it becomes a vertical line. So a horizontal-line test of a function is equivalent to a vertical-line test of its inverse.
2. The domain and range are switched.
3. See p. A11.

9-5 Exercises

GUIDED PRACTICE

SEE EXAMPLE 1 p. 690

Use the horizontal-line test to determine whether the inverse of each relation is a function.

1. 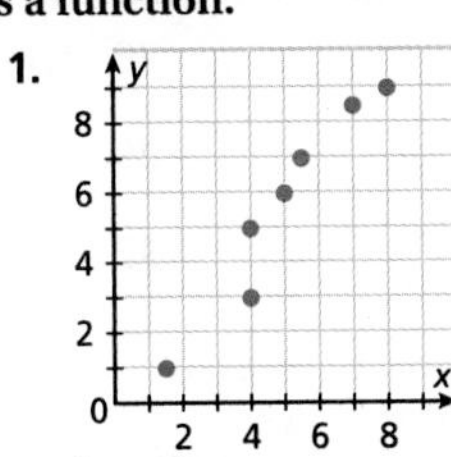 function

2. 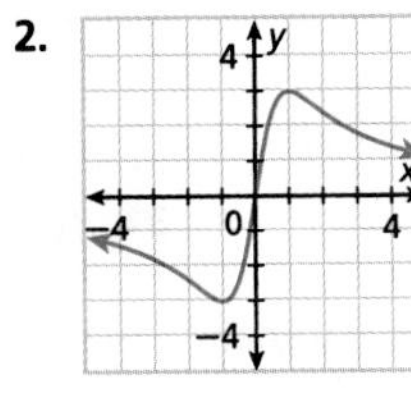 not a function

3. 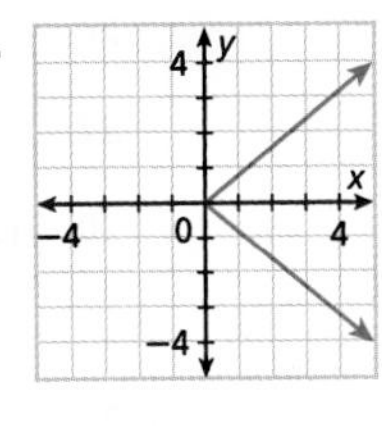 function

SEE EXAMPLE 2 p. 691

Find the inverse of each function. Determine whether the inverse is a function, and state its domain and range.

4. $f(x) = -3x + 21$
5. $g(x) = x^2 - 9$
6. $h(x) = \frac{x + 5}{8}$

SEE EXAMPLE 3 p. 692

Determine by composition whether each pair of functions are inverses.

7. $f(x) = 4x - 12$ and $g(x) = -4x + 8$ no
8. $f(x) = \sqrt{3x}$ and $g(x) = \frac{x^2}{3}$ for $x \geq 0$ yes

PRACTICE AND PROBLEM SOLVING

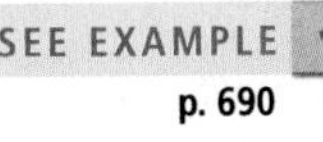

Independent Practice	
For Exercises	See Example
9–11	1
12–17	2
18–21	3

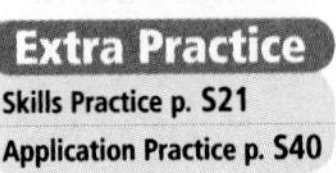

Extra Practice
Skills Practice p. S21
Application Practice p. S40

Use the horizontal-line test to determine whether the inverse of each relation is a function.

9. 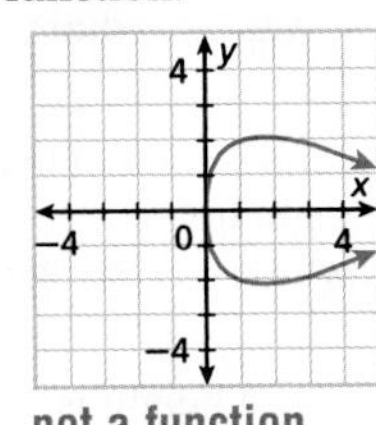 not a function

10. 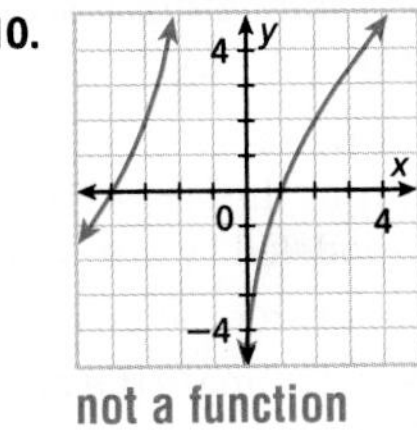 not a function

11. 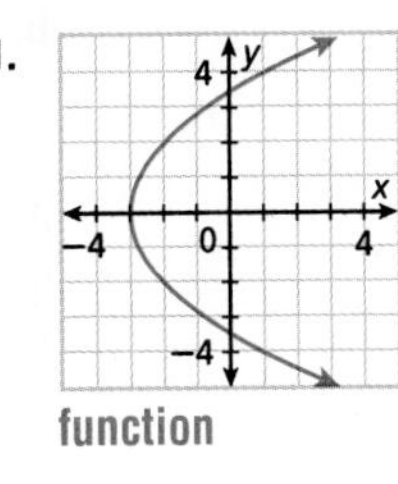 function

9-5 Exercises

Assignment Guide

Assign *Guided Practice* exercises as necessary.

If you finished Examples 1–3
Basic 9–41, 45–51, 57–63
Average 9–49, 56–63
Advanced 9–23, 24–36 even, 37–63

Homework Quick Check
Quickly check key concepts.
Exercises: 10, 14, 16, 18, 22

Answers

4. $f^{-1}(x) = -\frac{1}{3}x + 7$; function; D: $\mathbb{R}$; R: $\mathbb{R}$
5. $y = \pm\sqrt{x + 9}$; not a function; D: $\{x \mid x \geq -9\}$; R: $\mathbb{R}$
6. $h^{-1}(x) = 8x - 5$; function; D: $\mathbb{R}$; R: $\mathbb{R}$

State Resources

Answers

12. $f^{-1}(x) = \frac{5}{3}x$; function; D: $\mathbb{R}$; R: $\mathbb{R}$

13. $f^{-1}(x) = \frac{\sqrt[3]{x}}{2}$; function; D: $\mathbb{R}$; R: $\mathbb{R}$

14. $f^{-1}(x) = \frac{x}{1-x}$; function; D: $\{x \mid x \neq 1\}$; R: $\{y \mid y \neq -1\}$

15. $f^{-1}(x) = \frac{6}{5}x - \frac{9}{5}$; function; D: $\mathbb{R}$; R: $\mathbb{R}$

16. $y = \pm\sqrt{x} + 4$; not a function; D: $\{x \mid x \geq 0\}$; R: $\mathbb{R}$

17. $f^{-1}(x) = (x-5)^2 - 8$; function; D: $\{x \mid x \geq 5\}$; R: $\{y \mid y \geq -8\}$

22a. $F(N) = \frac{N+160}{4}$; the inverse gives the temperature in degrees Fahrenheit when a cricket chirps N times per minute.

23a. $d(t) = \frac{t-20}{2.5}$; d is the distance that the pizza can be delivered t minutes after it was ordered.

24. $y = -\frac{3}{8}x + \frac{7}{8}$; D: $\mathbb{R}$; R: $\mathbb{R}$

25. $y = \frac{5}{x} - 4$; D: $\{x \mid x \neq 0\}$; R: $\{y \mid y \neq -4\}$

26. $y = \pm\sqrt{\frac{x}{5}} - 6$; D: $\{x \mid x \geq 0\}$; R: $\mathbb{R}$

27. $y = x^3 + 12$; D: $\mathbb{R}$; R: $\mathbb{R}$

28. $y = \sqrt[3]{12x+5}$; D: $\mathbb{R}$; R: $\mathbb{R}$

29. $y = \log_7 x$; D: $\{x \mid x > 0\}$; R: $\mathbb{R}$

30. $y = e^x - 2$; D: $\mathbb{R}$; R: $\{y \mid y > -2\}$

31. $y = \ln\left(\frac{x}{3}\right) - 5$; D: $\{x \mid x > 0\}$; R: $\mathbb{R}$

32. $y = 10^{4x} - 8$; D: $\mathbb{R}$; R: $\{y \mid y > -8\}$

37a. $a(h) = \left(\frac{h-19}{3}\right)^2$; the inverse gives the age a in months of a girl with height h in inches.

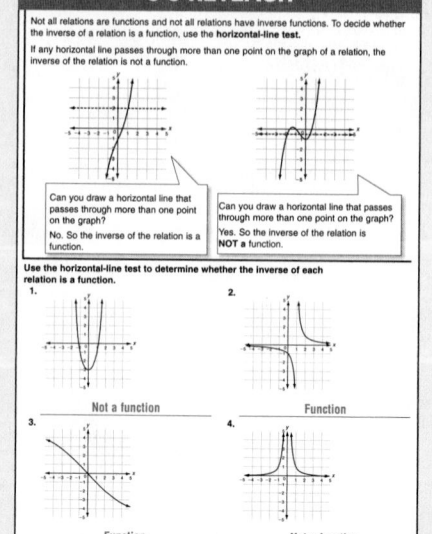

Find the inverse of each function. Determine whether the inverse is a function, and state its domain and range.

12. $f(x) = \frac{3}{5}x$ 13. $f(x) = 8x^3$ 14. $f(x) = \frac{x}{x+1}$

15. $f(x) = \frac{5x+9}{6}$ 16. $f(x) = (x-4)^2$ 17. $f(x) = 5 + \sqrt{x+8}$

LINK Biology

There are about 900 species of crickets worldwide. Many male crickets make chirping noises either by rubbing their wings together or by rubbing their wing cases against their hind legs.

Determine by composition whether each pair of functions are inverses.

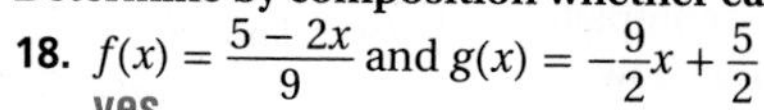

18. $f(x) = \frac{5-2x}{9}$ and $g(x) = -\frac{9}{2}x + \frac{5}{2}$ **yes**

19. $f(x) = \frac{5}{x+1}$ and $g(x) = \frac{x-1}{5}$ for $x \neq -1$ **no**

20. $f(x) = 3\sqrt{x}$ and $g(x) = \frac{1}{3}x^2$ for $x \geq 0$ **no**

21. $f(x) = \log\frac{x}{2}$ and $g(x) = 2(10^x)$ for $x > 0$ **yes**

22. **Biology** The number of times that a cricket chirps per minute can be found by using the function $N(F) = 4F - 160$, where F is the temperature in degrees Fahrenheit.

a. Find and interpret the inverse of $N(F)$.

b. What is the temperature when the cricket is chirping 60 times a minute? **55°F**

c. How many times will the cricket chirp in 1 minute at a temperature of 80°F? **160 times/min**

23. **Business** The managers of a pizza restaurant have found that the function $t(d) = 20 + 2.5d$ models the length of time in minutes, after it is ordered, for a pizza to be delivered a distance of d miles.

a. Write the inverse of $t(d)$, and explain what it represents.

b. How far away can a customer live and still get a pizza within 30 minutes of placing an order? **within 4 mi**

Write the rule for the inverse of each function. Then state its domain and range.

24. $f(x) = \frac{7-8x}{3}$ 25. $f(x) = \frac{5}{x+4}$ 26. $f(x) = 5(x+6)^2$

27. $f(x) = \sqrt[3]{x-12}$ 28. $f(x) = \frac{x^3-5}{12}$ 29. $f(x) = 7^x$

30. $f(x) = \ln(x+2)$ 31. $f(x) = 3e^{x+5}$ 32. $f(x) = \frac{\log(x+8)}{4}$

For each graph, determine which two functions are inverses.

33.

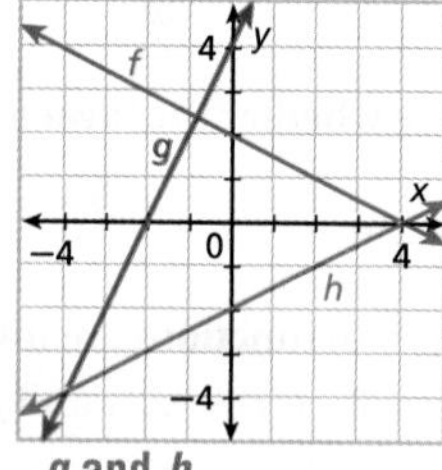

g and h

34.

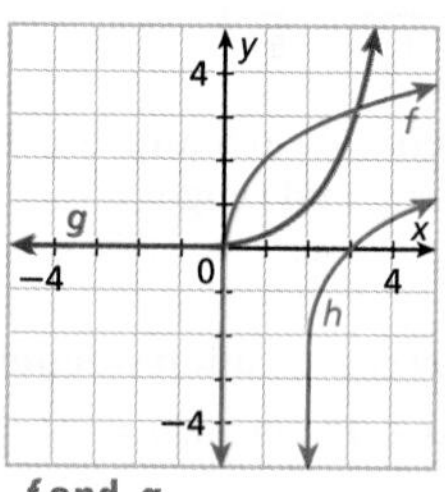

f and g

35.

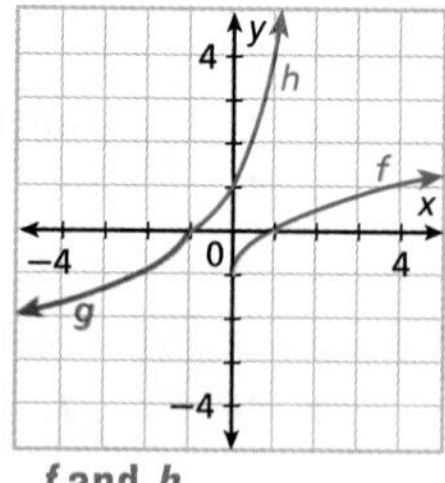

f and h

36. **Statistics** A person's standardized score on a test is given by the function $z(x) = \frac{x-250}{40}$, where x is the actual score on the test.

a. Find and interpret the inverse of $z(x)$.

b. If a person's standardized score on a test was 2.5, what was the person's actual score on the test? **350**

36a. $x(z) = 40z + 250$; **the inverse gives the actual score on a test with a given standardized score.**

37. **Medicine** Nurses carefully track the height and weight of infants to ensure that they are healthy as they grow. The average height in inches of a girl in the first 3 years of life can be modeled by $h(a) = 3\sqrt{a} + 19$, where a is the age of the girl in months.

a. Find and interpret the inverse of $h(a)$.

b. **Estimation** Estimate the age of a girl whose height is $32\frac{1}{2}$ inches. **about 20.25 mo**

9-5 READING STRATEGIES

Looking at the graph of a function, you can determine whether its inverse is a function. The vertical-line test is used to check whether the graph is a function. A **horizontal-line test** is used to check whether the inverse of the function is also a function. This test allows you to find whether the inverse is a function without drawing the graph of the inverse function.

Vertical-line Test	Horizontal-line Test
If any vertical line intersects the graph at only one point, then the graph represents a function.	If any horizontal line intersects the graph at only one point, then the inverse relation is a function.

Solve.

1. The function $f(x) = 3$ is a linear function. Explain whether the inverse of this graph is a function.
   The inverse is not a function. The graph of f is a horizontal line. So the horizontal line $y = 3$ intersects the graph of f at infinitely many points.

2. All linear functions $f(x) = mx + b$, where $m \neq 0$, have an inverse relation that is a function. Use the horizontal-line test to explain why.
   If the slope is not 0, then the graph is a straight line inclined at an angle. All horizontal lines will intersect the graph at only one point, so these graphs will all have inverse relations that are functions.

3. a. The points (−1, 4) and (5, 4) are on the graph of a function g. What happens if you draw a horizontal line $y = 4$ through the graph of the function?
   The line $y = 4$ will intersect the function at least at two points.

   b. Is the inverse of the function g also a function? Explain why.
   No; the function fails the horizontal-line test.

4. Suppose the graph of the inverse of a function is given. Would you use the horizontal-line test or the vertical-line test to determine whether the graph is a function? Explain.
   The vertical-line test should be used to test whether the graph represents a function.

9-5 RETEACH

Not all relations are functions and not all relations have inverse functions. To decide whether the inverse of a relation is a function, use the **horizontal-line test.**

If any horizontal line passes through more than one point on the graph of a relation, the inverse of the relation is not a function.

Can you draw a horizontal line that passes through more than one point on the graph?
No. So the inverse of the relation is a function.

Can you draw a horizontal line that passes through more than one point on the graph?
Yes. So the inverse of the relation is **NOT a** function.

Use the horizontal-line test to determine whether the inverse of each relation is a function.

1. Not a function

2. Function

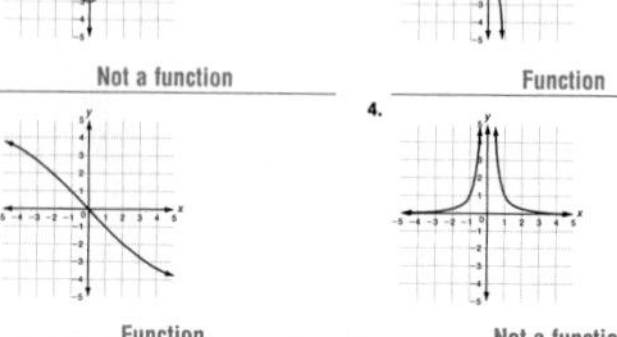

3. Function

4. Not a function

38. This problem will prepare you for the Multi-Step Test Prep on page 706.

If an object is dropped from a hot-air balloon at an altitude of 500 ft, the object's height after t seconds can be modeled by $h(t) = -16t^2 + 500$.

a. Find and interpret the inverse of $h(t)$.

b. How long does it take the object to hit the ground? $\approx$ **5.59 s**

c. How long does it take the object to fall if it lands on the roof of a building that is 128 ft tall? $\approx$ **4.82 s**

39. **Conservation** As a brown bear with a radio collar walks along a river, the distance from the bear to an observation post after t seconds is given by the function $d(t) = \sqrt{1600 + 9t^2}$.

a. Find and interpret the inverse of $d(t)$. **39b.** $\approx$ **1833.28 s (about 31 min)**

b. If the tracking equipment has a range of 5500 feet, how long will a person in the observation post be able to track the bear before having to move?

40. **Photography** The cost in dollars of enlarging a photo is given by the function $c = 0.1\ell^2$, where ℓ is the length of the enlargement in inches.

a. Write the inverse of the function, and explain what it represents.

b. Determine the length of an enlargement that costs $25.60. **16 in.**

40a. $l = \sqrt{10c}$; **the inverse gives the length of the enlargement for a given cost.**

41. **Manufacturing** The surface area of an aluminum can is given by the function $S(h) = 18\pi + 6\pi h$.

a. Find and interpret the inverse of $S(h)$.

b. Find the height to the nearest hundredth of a centimeter of a can with a surface area of 500 cm². **23.53 cm**

41a. $h(s) = \dfrac{s - 18\pi}{6\pi}$; **the inverse gives the height of the can for a given surface area.**

42. **Critical Thinking** Identify two functions that are their own inverses.

43. **Geometry** The area of a square is $A = s^2$, where s is the length of a side.

a. Find and interpret the inverse of the function.

b. Explain how an architect or city planner might use the inverse.

c. **Estimation** Estimate the side length of a square park that covers an area of 800,000 square feet.

44. **Critical Thinking** If a relation is not a function, can its inverse be a function? Use an example to illustrate your answer.

45. **Write About It** Describe two ways to determine whether two functions are inverses of each other. How would your methods apply to determining whether a function is its own inverse?

46. The formula for converting from degrees Celsius to degrees Fahrenheit is $F = \frac{9}{5}C + 32$. Which of the following formulas converts degrees Fahrenheit to degrees Celsius?

Ⓐ $C = \frac{9}{5}F - 32$

Ⓑ $C = \frac{9}{5}(F - 32)$

Ⓒ $C = \frac{5}{9}F + 32$

Ⓓ $C = \frac{5}{9}(F - 32)$

MULTI-STEP TEST PREP Exercise **38** involves finding the inverse of a function and using the inverse to solve a problem. This exercise prepares students for the Multi-Step Test Prep on page 706.

Answers

38a. $t(h) = \dfrac{\sqrt{500 - h}}{4}$; the inverse gives the time in seconds it takes an object to reach a given height.

39a. $t(d) = \dfrac{\sqrt{d^2 - 1600}}{3}$; the inverse gives the time it will take for the bear to reach a given distance.

42. Possible answer: $f(x) = x$ and $f(x) = \frac{1}{x}$

43a. $s = \sqrt{A}$; the inverse gives the side length for a square of given area.

b. Possible answer: If a town square had a target area, a planner could find its dimensions.

c. $\approx$ 894 ft

44. Possible answer: Yes; a relation such as $y = \pm\sqrt{x}$ is not a function, but its inverse $y = x^2$ is a function.

45. Possible answer: You can visually see whether the functions are reflections across the line $y = x$. You can also compose both functions. Functions that are symmetric about $y = x$ and whose compositions both equal x are inverses.

9-5 PROBLEM SOLVING

A juice drink manufacturer is designing an advertisement for a national sports event on its cans. The lateral surface area of the cans is given by the function $L(h) = 2.5\pi h$, where h is the height of the can. The total surface area of the can is given by the function $T(h) = 2.5\pi(h + 1.25)$.

1. The graphic designer needs to know how the height of the can varies as a function of the lateral surface area.

a. Find the inverse, $h(L)$, of the function $L(h)$.

$L(h) = 2.5\pi h$; $h(L) = \dfrac{L}{2.5\pi}$

b. Explain the meaning of the inverse function.

$h(L)$ gives the height of a can for a given lateral surface area.

c. If the lateral surface area of one can is 35.34 in², what is the height of this can? 4.5 in.

Choose the letter for the best answer.

2. The manufacturer produces cans in different sizes. The height of one can is 5.5 in. The designer is planning to use only half the lateral surface area of this can. What is this area?

A 8.8 in²
B 11.0 in²
Ⓒ 21.6 in²
D 43.2 in²

3. The designer is studying the possibility of using the total surface area of each can. Which function gives height, $h(T)$, as a function of total surface area, T?

Ⓕ $h(T) = \frac{T}{2.5\pi} - 1.25$
G $h(T) = \frac{T}{2.5\pi} + 1.25$
H $h(T) = (2.5\pi)(T - 1.25)$
J $h(T) = (2.5\pi)(T + 1.25)$

4. The total surface area of one size of can is 45.16 in². What is the height of this can?

A 3.5 in.
Ⓑ 4.5 in.
C 5.5 in.
D 6.5 in.

5. The designer updates an old advertisement that covers the lateral surface area, L, of a can to create a new advertisement that covers the total surface area, T, of the can. Which function gives this area?

F $T = (2.5\pi)(L + 1.25)$
G $T = (2.5\pi)(L - 1.25)$
H $T = L - 2.5\pi(1.25)$
Ⓙ $T = L + 2.5\pi(1.25)$

9-5 CHALLENGE

When both a relation and its inverse are functions, the relation is called a one-to-one function. The horizontal line test can be used to determine if the inverse of a relation is a function. But sometimes it is difficult to graph the relation in order to use the horizontal line test. Therefore, an alternate definition is useful.

A function is a one-to-one function if whenever a and b are in the domain of the function f and $a \neq b$, then $f(a) \neq f(b)$.

This definition may be used to determine whether a function is one-to-one or not. Consider the two functions $f(x) = 3x + 8$ and $g(x) = x^2 - 4$. The domain for both of the functions is the set of all real numbers.

For the function f, if $a \neq b$, then certainly $3a \neq 3b$ and likewise $3a + 8 \neq 3b + 8$; therefore, $f(a) \neq f(b)$ and f is a one-to-one function.

For the function g, does $a \neq b$ imply that $a^2 \neq b^2$? No since $-1 \neq 1$ but $g(-1) = g(1)$. Therefore, the function g is not a one-to-one function.

Use the horizontal line test and the definition of a one-to-one function given above to determine whether the following functions are one-to-one on the domain specified. Most of these may be graphed on a calculator, but remember to consider the domain specified and not the domain the calculator uses.

1. $f(x) = \frac{1}{2}x + 9$, domain is the set of real numbers.
Linear functions with a nonzero slope are always one-to-one.

2. $f(x) = \frac{1}{2}x + 9$, domain is the set of positive integers.
Linear functions with a nonzero slope are always one-to-one.

3. $f(x) = (x - \sqrt{2})^2$, domain is the set of real numbers.
Not one-to-one; fails the horizontal line test; also try $\sqrt{2} + 1$ and $\sqrt{2} - 1$ for a and b.

4. $f(x) = (x - \sqrt{2})^2$, domain is the set of integers. One-to-one

5. $f(x) = x^3 + x^2 - 2x - 1$, domain is the set of real numbers.
Fails horizontal line test, not one-to-one

6. $f(x) = x^3 + x^2 - 2x - 1$, domain is the set of integers. Not one-to-one, $f(-2) = f(0)$

7. $f(x) = \left\lfloor \frac{x}{2} \right\rfloor$, domain is the set of integers. Not one-to-one; $f(0) = f(1) = 0$

8. $f(x) = \lceil 2x \rceil$, domain is the set of integers. One-to-one

9. $f(x, y) = \max(x,y) = \frac{x + y}{2} + \frac{|x - y|}{2}$, where (x, y) are ordered pairs of positive integers.
Not one-to-one since $(3, 5)$ is not equal to $(4, 5)$ but $\max(3, 5) = 5 = \max(4, 5)$

9-5 PRACTICE A

9-5 PRACTICE C

9-5 PRACTICE B

Find the inverse of each function. Determine whether the inverse is a function and state its domain and range.

1. $A(x) = \frac{9 - 2x}{5}$
$A^{-1}(x) = -2.5x + 4.5$; function; domain: $(-\infty, +\infty)$; range: $(-\infty, +\infty)$

2. $B(x) = \frac{3 + x}{x}$
$B^{-1}(x) = \frac{3}{x - 1}$; function; domain: $(-\infty, 1)$ and $(1, +\infty)$; range: $(-\infty, 0)$ and $(0, +\infty)$

3. $C(x) = 25 - x^2$
$C^{-1}(x) = \pm\sqrt{25 - x}$; not a function; domain: $(-\infty, 25]$; range: $(-\infty, +\infty)$

4. $D(x) = 2 - \log x^3$
$D^{-1}(x) = \log^{-1}\left(\frac{-x + 2}{3}\right)$; not a function; domain: $(-\infty, +\infty)$; range: $(-\infty, 0)$ and $(0, +\infty)$.

5. $E(x) = \frac{x}{x + 2}$
$E^{-1}(x) = \frac{2x}{1 - x}$; not a function; domain: $(-\infty, -2)$ and $(-2, +\infty)$; range: $(-\infty, 1)$ and $(1, +\infty)$

6. $F(x) = 4 + \sqrt{2x - 1}$
$F^{-1}(x) = 0.5x^2 - 4x + 8.5$; function; domain: $[4, +\infty)$; range: $[0.5, +\infty)$

Determine by composition whether each pair of functions are inverses.

7. $p(x) = \sqrt{5 - x^2}$ for $|x| \leq 5$ and $q(x) = \sqrt{5 - x^2}$ for $|x| \leq 5$
no

8. $s(x) = \frac{-2x}{x - 2}$ and $t(x) = \frac{2x}{2 - x}$
yes

9. $u(x) = \frac{1}{(x - 3)^2}$, for $x > 3$ and $v(x) = 3 + \frac{\sqrt{x}}{x}$, for $x > 0$
yes

10. $b(x) = \log(x - 1)^4$ and $d(x) = 1 + 10^{\frac{x}{4}}$ for $x \geq 1$
yes

Solve.

11. The area of a regular octagon can be found by using the formula $A(s) = 2s^2(\sqrt{2} + 1)$, where s is the length of each side.

a. Find the inverse of $A(s)$. $s = \pm\sqrt{\dfrac{A}{2(\sqrt{2} + 1)}}$

b. What does the inverse represent? Side length

c. What is the side length of a regular octagon whose area is $(9.68\sqrt{2} + 9.68)$ m? 2.2 meters

In **Exercise 49,** students who chose **H** or **J** may not be sure about which values switch in an inverse relationship. Help students understand that the input of a function is the output of its inverse and vice versa.

47. Which of the following is true about the relation graphed?

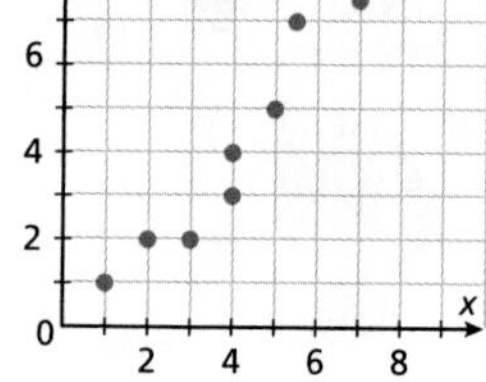

Ⓕ Both the relation and its inverse are functions.

Ⓖ The relation is a function, but its inverse is not a function.

Ⓗ The relation is not a function, but its inverse is a function.

Ⓙ Neither the relation nor its inverse is a function.

48. Which of the following is the inverse of $f(x) = \sqrt{x} + 1$?

Ⓐ $f^{-1}(x) = x^2 - 1, x \geq 0$ Ⓒ $f^{-1}(x) = x^2 + 1, x \geq 0$

Ⓑ $f^{-1}(x) = (x - 1)^2, x \geq 0$ Ⓓ $f^{-1}(x) = (x + 1)^2, x \geq 0$

49. For a certain function, $f(0) = 2$ and $f^{-1}(4) = 1$. Which of the following is also true?

Ⓕ $f^{-1}(0) = 2$ Ⓖ $f^{-1}(2) = 0$ Ⓗ $f(4) = 1$ Ⓙ $f(2) = 0$

50. Which function has an inverse that is NOT a function?

Ⓐ $f(x) = 2x^3 + 3$ Ⓒ $f(x) = x^2 - 1$

Ⓑ $f(x) = \sqrt{2x} + 5$ Ⓓ $f(x) = 3^x + 1$

51. **Short Response** Given that $f(x)$ is a quadratic function, is its inverse a function? Explain. **No; a quadratic function is a parabola that opens either upward or downward. The horizontal-line test will show that the inverse of a quadratic function is not a function.**

Journal

Decide whether you think that the following statement is always, sometimes, or never true: if a function and its inverse intersect, the intersection must be on the line $y = x$. Justify your decision.

CHALLENGE AND EXTEND

52. Use the Quadratic Formula to find a rule for the inverse of $f(x) = 3x^2 - 6x - 9$.

Find a rule for the inverse of each function.

53. $f(x) = \dfrac{3 + \ln x}{3 - \ln x}$ $y = e^{\frac{3x-3}{x+1}}$

54. $f(x) = \dfrac{5\log(x^3) - 3\log(x^2)}{3}$ $y = 10^{\frac{x}{3}}$

55. Is $f^{-1}(g^{-1}(x)) = (f(g(x)))^{-1}$ correct? Support your answer.

56. **Personal Finance** A financial manager predicts that if a person leaves \$1000 in his mutual fund, the value of the money after t years will be $V(t) = 1000(1.08^t)$.

a. Find and interpret the inverse of $V(t)$.

b. If a person puts \$1000 into this mutual fund, predict how much money the person will have in the fund in 10 years. **\$2158.92**

56c. $t \approx 18.01$; **about 18 yr** c. If a person puts \$1000 into this mutual fund, after how many years will the person have \$4000 in the fund?

ALTERNATIVE ASSESSMENT

Have students choose two functions: one quadratic and one exponential. For each function, have them identify the inverse, graph it, and state its domain and range.

SPIRAL REVIEW

57. **Geometry** Find a polynomial expression for the surface area of the cone that is shown (*Hint:* $S = B + \pi r\ell$) *(Lesson 6-1)* $2\pi x^2 + 2\pi x$

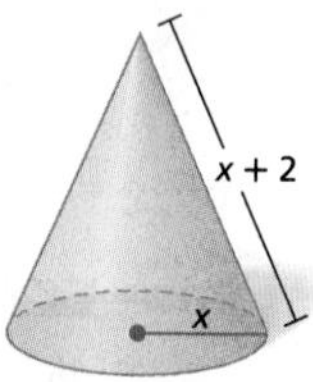

Find each product. *(Lesson 6-2)*

58. $(x + 2)(x^4 + x^2 + 1)$ $x^5 + 2x^4 + x^3 + 2x^2 + x + 2$

59. $(x + 3)(x^2 - 3x + 9)$ $x^3 + 27$

60. $(x^3 - x^2)(x^2 + 2x)$ $x^5 + x^4 - 2x^3$

Given $f(x) = 9x - 5$ and $g(x) = x^2 - x - 1$, find each function. *(Lesson 9-4)*

61. $(f + g)(x)$ $x^2 + 8x - 6$

62. $(f - g)(x)$ $-x^2 + 10x - 4$

63. $(g - f)(x)$ $x^2 - 10x + 4$

Power Presentations with PowerPoint®

9-5 Lesson Quiz

1. Use the horizontal-line test to determine whether the inverse of each relation is a function.

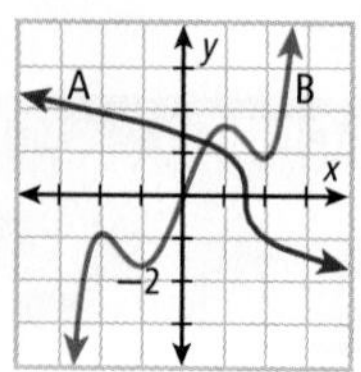

A: yes; B: no

2. Find the inverse of $f(x) = x^2 - 4$. Determine whether it is a function, and state its domain and range.

$f^{-1}(x) = \pm\sqrt{x + 4}$; no; D: $\{x \mid x \geq -4\}$; R: $\mathbb{R}$

3. Determine by composition whether $f(x) = 3(x - 1)^2$ and $g(x) = \sqrt{\dfrac{x}{3}} + 1$ are inverses for $x \geq 0$. yes

Also available on transparency

Answers

52. $y = \dfrac{6 \pm \sqrt{144 + 12x}}{6} = 1 \pm \dfrac{\sqrt{3x + 36}}{3}$

55. $f^{-1}(g^{-1}(x)) \neq (f(g(x)))^{-1}$; possible answer: let $f(x) = 2x$ and $g(x) = x + 1$. $f^{-1}(x) = \frac{1}{2}x$ and $g^{-1}(x) = x - 1$, so $f^{-1}(g^{-1}(x)) = \frac{x-1}{2}$. $f(g(x)) = 2x + 2$, so $(f(g(x)))^{-1} = \frac{x-2}{2}$. $\frac{x-1}{2} \neq \frac{x-2}{2}$, so by counterexample $f^{-1}(g^{-1}(x)) \neq (f(g(x)))^{-1}$.

56a. $t = \log_{1.08}\left(\dfrac{v}{1000}\right) = \dfrac{\log\left(\frac{v}{1000}\right)}{\log(1.08)}$; the inverse gives the time it takes to accumulate v dollars.

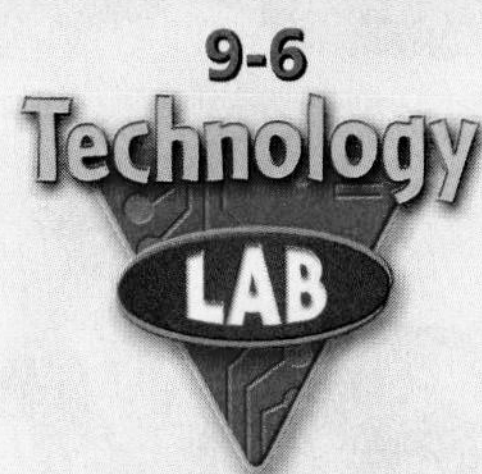

Explore Differences and Ratios

Recall that common differences or common ratios can help you determine which model is appropriate for a data set. You can use spreadsheets to quickly evaluate differences and ratios in data sets.

Use with Lesson 9-6

Activity

Consider the data set shown in the table. Use a spreadsheet to find the first differences, second differences, and ratios of the *y*-values. Identify which, if any, are constant.

x	5	6	7	8	9	10	11
y	1	3.4	6.6	10.6	15.4	21	27.4

Enter the row heads and the data into the spreadsheet as shown. Remember that the *x*-values must be evenly spaced.

1. Find first differences. In cell C3, enter the formula **=C2-B2** to find the difference of the first two *y*-values. Copy this formula into cells D3 through H3.

	A	B	C	D	E	F	G	H
1	x	5	6	7	8	9	10	11
2	y	1	3.4	6.6	10.6	15.4	21	27.4
3	1st differences		2.4	3.2	4	4.8	5.6	6.4
4	2nd differences							
5	Ratios							

2. Find second differences. In cell D4, enter the formula **=D3-C3** to find the first second difference. Copy this formula into cells E4 through H4.

	A	B	C	D	E	F	G	H
1	x	5	6	7	8	9	10	11
2	y	1	3.4	6.6	10.6	15.4	21	27.4
3	1st differences		2.4	3.2	4	4.8	5.6	6.4
4	2nd differences			0.8	0.8	0.8	0.8	0.8
5	Ratios							

3. Find the ratios. In cell C5, enter the formula **=C2/B2** to find the ratio of the first two *y*-values. Copy this formula into cells D5 through H5.

	A	B	C	D	E	F	G	H
1	x	5	6	7	8	9	10	11
2	y	1	3.4	6.6	10.6	15.4	21	27.4
3	1st differences		2.4	3.2	4	4.8	5.6	6.4
4	2nd differences			0.8	0.8	0.8	0.8	0.8
5	Ratios		3.4	1.94	1.61	1.45	1.36	1.3

For this data set, the second differences are constant. You can adjust the spreadsheet to include more data points if necessary.

1. 1st differences: 144, 240, 336, 432 2nd difference (constant): 96 ratios: −6.2, ≈ 2.94, ≈ 1.92, ≈ 1.62

2. 1st difference (constant): 1.17 ratios: ≈ 1.89, ≈ 1.47, ≈ 1.32, ≈ 1.24, ≈ 1.20

Try This

For each data set, find the first differences, second differences, and ratios of the *y*-values. Identify which, if any, are constant.

1.

x	2	4	6	8	10
y	−20	124	364	700	1132

2.

x	4	7	10	13	16	19
y	1.31	2.48	3.65	4.82	5.99	7.16

3.

x	3	4	5	6	7
y	8.96	35.84	143.36	573.44	2293.8

4.

x	1.5	3	4.5	6	7.5
y	−9	15	57	117	195

5. **Critical Thinking** What type of function might be an appropriate model for Problem 4? Justify your response.
quadratic; because quadratic functions have constant 2nd differences

Answers to *Try This*

3. 1st differences: 26.88, 107.52, 430.08, 1720.36
2nd differences: 80.64, 322.56, 1290.28
ratios (constant): 4

4. 1st differences: 24, 42, 60, 78
2nd difference (constant): 18
ratios: ≈ −1.67, 3.8, ≈ 2.05, ≈ 1.67

Technology LAB Organizer

Use with Lesson 9-6

Pacing:
Traditional 1 day
Block $\frac{1}{2}$ day

Objective: Use a spreadsheet to explore differences and ratios.

Materials: computer with spreadsheet software

Online Edition

Countdown to Testing Week 20

Resources

Technology Lab Activities
9-6 Lab Recording Sheet

Teach

Discuss

In situations involving large amounts of data, calculating differences and ratios to determine a parent function can become difficult and tedious. Using a spreadsheet's capabilities helps facilitate the process.

Close

Key Concept

You can use a spreadsheet to quickly evaluate differences and ratios in data sets.

Assessment

Journal Give students a data set that corresponds to the square root function, and have them explain how they would find first and second differences for *x*.

State Resources

9-6 Organizer

Pacing: Traditional $1\frac{1}{2}$ days
Block $\frac{3}{4}$ day

Objectives: Apply functions to problem situations.

Use mathematical models to make predictions.

Technology Lab
In *Technology Lab Activities*

Online Edition
Tutorial Videos, Interactivity, TechKeys

Countdown to Testing Week 20

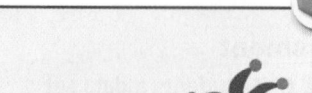

Warm Up

1. Use a calculator to perform quadratic and exponential regressions on the following data.

x	3	5	8	13
y	19	50	126	340

quadratic: $y \approx 2.13x^2 - 2x + 6.12$
exponential: $y \approx 10.57(1.32)^x$

Also available on transparency

Math Humor

Carmen was thrilled to learn that her new job title was $f(x) = -2x^2 + 1.6x + 4$. She had always wanted to grow up to be a model.

9-6 Modeling Real-World Data

A2.1.2 Use and interpret function notation, including evaluation of functions represented by tables, graphs, words, equations or a set of ordered pairs.

Objectives
Apply functions to problem situations.
Use mathematical models to make predictions.

Who uses this?
You can use mathematical models to analyze and predict the number of automated teller machines (ATMs) in use. (See Example 3.)

Much of the data that you encounter in the real world may form a pattern. Many times the pattern of the data can be modeled by one of the functions you have studied. You can then use the functions to analyze trends and make predictions. Recall some of the parent functions that you have studied so far.

Families of Functions

Family	Linear	Quadratic	Exponential	Square Root
Rule	$f(x) = x$	$f(x) = x^2$	$f(x) = b^x, b > 0$	$f(x) = \sqrt{x}$
Graph				
Constant Differences or Ratios	Constant first differences between y-values for evenly spaced x-values	Constant second differences between y-values for evenly spaced x-values	Constant ratios between y-values for evenly spaced x-values	Constant second differences between x-values for evenly spaced y-values

Helpful Hint
Because the square-root function is the inverse of the quadratic function, the constant differences for x- and y-values are switched.

EXAMPLE 1 Identifying Models by Using Constant Differences or Ratios

Use constant differences or ratios to determine which parent function would best model the given data set.

A **The length of a spring depends on the mass attached.**

Mass (kg)	4	5	6	7	8	9	10
Length (cm)	30.6	32	33.4	34.8	36.2	37.6	39

Notice that the mass data are evenly spaced. Check the first differences between the lengths to see if the data set is linear.

Length (cm)	30.6	32	33.4	34.8	36.2	37.6	39
First differences	1.4	1.4	1.4	1.4	1.4	1.4	

Because the first differences are a constant 1.4, a linear model will best model the data.

State Resources

1 Introduce

EXPLORATION

9-6 Modeling Real-World Data

For an object dropped from a height of x feet, the function $y = \frac{\sqrt{x}}{4}$ can be used to approximate the time in seconds that will pass before the object reaches the ground.

1. The table shows the heights of various objects. Complete the table by finding the time that passes before the object reaches the ground.

Height x	16	64	144	256	400	576
Time y						

2. What do you notice about the times?
3. Find the first differences and second differences of the heights.
4. What do you notice about the differences?
5. Plot the data points on a coordinate plane.
6. Describe the general shape of the graphed data.

THINK AND DISCUSS

Motivate

Ask students how long they think it will take them to get to school tomorrow. Then ask them how they came up with their answers. The answers are probably based on a pattern that has been established in the past. Explain that mathematicians and scientists use the same principles to develop mathematical models that can be used to describe and predict events.

Explorations and answers are provided in the *Explorations* binder.

Use constant differences or ratios to determine which parent function would best model the given data set.

B The age of a tree can be determined from its diameter.

Diameter (cm)	1.6	3.6	6.4	10.0	14.4	19.6	25.6
Age (yr)	2	3	4	5	6	7	8

Notice that the age data are evenly spaced. Check the first differences between diameters.

Diameter (cm)	1.6	3.6	6.4	10.0	14.4	19.6	25.6

First differences 2 2.8 3.6 4.4 5.2 6

Second differences 0.8 0.8 0.8 0.8 0.8

Because the second differences of the independent variable are constant when the dependent variables are evenly spaced, a square-root function will best model the data.

Check A scatter plot reveals a shape similar to the square-root parent function $f(x) = \sqrt{x}$.

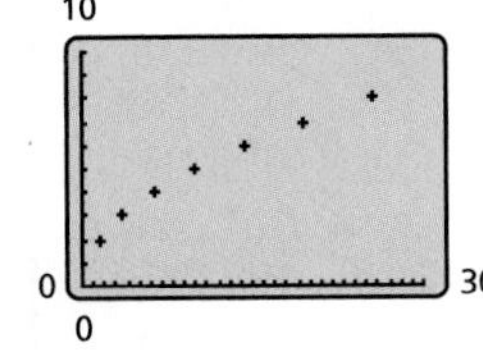

C The volume of a liquid remaining after evaporation depends on the time elapsed.

Time (h)	1	2	3	4	5	6
Volume (mL)	512	384	288	216	162	121.5

Because the time data are evenly spaced, check the differences between the volumes.

Volume (mL)	512	384	288	216	162	121.5

First differences −128 −96 −72 −54 −40.5

Second differences 32 24 18 13.5

Neither the first nor second differences are constant. Check ratios between the volumes.

$$\frac{384}{512} = 0.75, \frac{288}{384} = 0.75, \frac{216}{288} = 0.75, \frac{162}{216} = 0.75, \text{ and } \frac{121.5}{162} = 0.75.$$

Because the ratios between the values of the dependent variable are constant, an exponential function would best model the data.

Check A scatter plot reveals a shape similar to an exponential decay function.

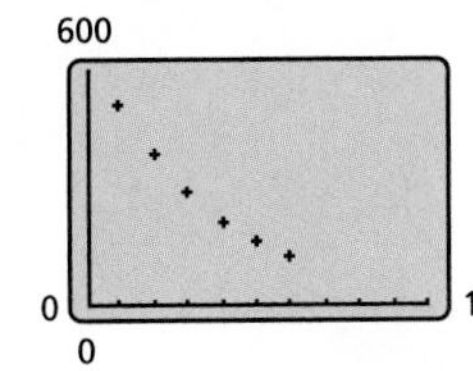

Use constant differences or ratios to determine which parent function would best model the given data set.

1a.

x	12	48	108	192	300
y	10	20	30	40	50

1b.

x	21	22	23	24
y	243	324	432	576

1a. square root; evenly-spaced y-values, constant second difference of x-values: 24

1b. exponential; constant ratio: $\frac{4}{3}$

Power Presentations with PowerPoint®

Additional Examples

Example 1

Use constant differences or ratios to determine which parent function would best model the given data set.

A.

Time (yr)	Height (in.)
5	58
10	93
15	128
20	163
25	198

linear

B.

Time (yr)	Population
4	10,000
8	9,600
12	9,216
16	8,847
20	8,493

exponential

C.

Time (s)	Height (m)
1	132
2	165
3	154
4	99
5	0

quadratic

Also available on transparency

INTERVENTION

Questioning Strategies

EXAMPLE 1

- How are the data sets of square root functions different from linear, quadratic, or exponential functions?

2 Teach

Guided Instruction

Review the families of functions with students, making sure that they understand the relationship each has with common differences or ratios. Explain to students that differences and ratios, graphs, and calculators are all helpful tools for creating mathematical models.

Reaching All Learners

Through Curriculum Integration

Have students research a topic from another subject and find a data set with time as the independent variable. Some examples might be the population of an endangered species or a city, the length or weight of an animal as it grows, the cost of a particular item, or a team's winning percentage. Have students find an appropriate model and present their findings to the class.

Power Presentations with PowerPoint®

Additional Examples

Example 2

A printing company prints advertising flyers and tracks its profits. Write a function that models the given data.

Flyers Printed	Profit ($)
100	10
200	70
300	175
400	312
500	500
600	720

$f(x) \approx 0.002x^2 + 0.007x - 11.2$

Also available on transparency

INTERVENTION

Questioning Strategies

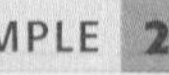

EXAMPLE 2

- How close to constant does the pattern of differences or ratios have to be to indicate an appropriate model?

Critical Thinking When possible, students should use multiple methods to establish the validity of a model. In **Example 2,** the second differences are not nearly constant, but if you perform a quadratic regression the r^2-value is fairly high, making it appear to be an appropriate model. Point out that the nearly constant ratios and the higher r^2-value of the exponential model show that it is a better model.

Real-world data rarely have differences or ratios that are mathematically constant, but you can analyze them to see if they are close to constant. You can also use a scatter plot to visually determine which model best suits a data set. Then you can perform a regression to find a function to model the data. Recall that the correlation coefficient *r* helps you see how well the model fits the data (Lesson 2-7).

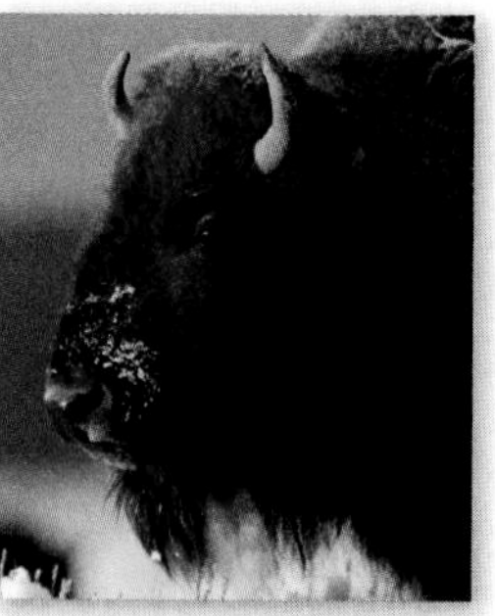

EXAMPLE 2 *Conservation Application*

A zoologist is monitoring the size of a herd of buffalo in the years since the herd was released into a wilderness area. Write a function that models the given data.

Time (yr)	5	6	7	8	9	10
Buffalo	124	150	185	213	261	322

Step 1 Make a scatter plot of the data.

The data appear to form a quadratic or an exponential pattern.

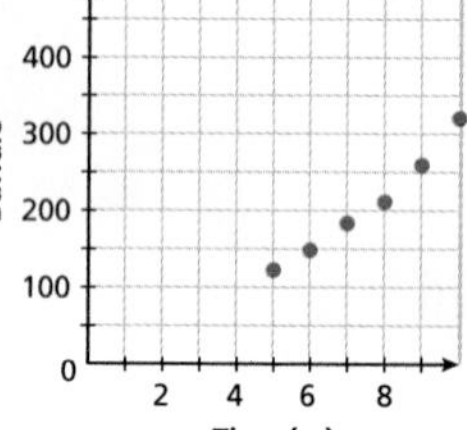

Step 2 Analyze differences.

Buffalo	124	150	185	213	261	322

First differences 26 35 28 48 61

Second differences 9 −7 20 13

Step 3 Neither the first nor the second differences are close to constant, so analyze the ratios.

$$\frac{150}{124} = 1.210, \frac{185}{150} = 1.233, \frac{213}{185} = 1.151, \frac{261}{213} = 1.225, \text{ and } \frac{322}{261} = 1.234$$

The ratios are all close to 1.2, indicating that an exponential model would be appropriate.

Step 4 Use your graphing calculator to perform an exponential regression.

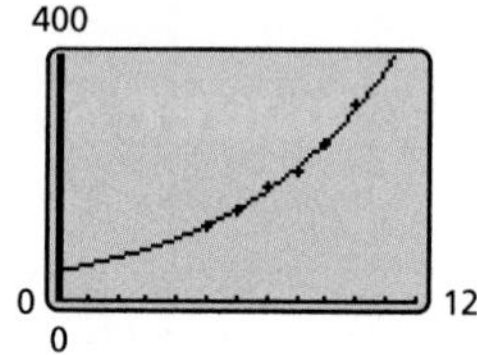

An exponential function that models the data is $f(x) = 48.581(1.207^x)$. The correlation coefficient *r* is very close to 1, which indicates a good fit.

Helpful Hint

To display the correlation coefficient *r* on some calculators, you must turn on the diagnostic mode.

Press 2nd CATALOG 0, and choose **DiagnosticOn**.

CHECK IT OUT! **2.** Write a function that models the given data.

x	12	14	16	18	20	22	24
y	110	141	176	215	258	305	356

$f(x) = \frac{1}{2}x^2 + \frac{5}{2}x + 8$

Reaching All Learners

Through Graphic Organizers

Have students create a poster by completing the table below.

Name	Degree	Constant Difference
Linear	1	First
Quadratic	2	Second
Cubic	3	Third
Quartic	4	Fourth

Help students see that for all *n*th-degree polynomial functions, the *n*th differences are constant.

Social Studies Link The type of function that fits a certain phenomenon can have profound implications for social scientists. In 1789, English economist Thomas Malthus predicted that mankind would eventually starve itself to extinction, based on his mathematical models. He noted that population was increasing exponentially, whereas food supplies tended to grow more linearly. Technological advances in food production have allowed humans to avoid Malthus's predictions for the most part, but hunger remains a serious global concern.

When data are not ordered or evenly spaced, you may have to try several models to determine which best approximates the data. Graphing calculators often indicate the value of the *coefficient of determination,* indicated by r^2 or R^2. The closer the coefficient is to 1, the better the model approximates the data.

EXAMPLE 3 ***Banking Application***

The data set shows the approximate number of automated teller machines (ATMs) in operation in the United States. Using 1990 as a reference year, write a function that models the data.

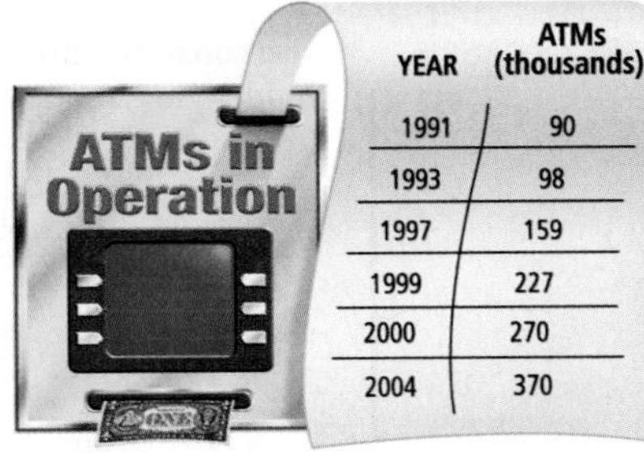

YEAR	ATMs (thousands)
1991	90
1993	98
1997	159
1999	227
2000	270
2004	370

The data are not evenly spaced, so you cannot analyze differences or ratios.

Create a scatter plot of the data. Use 1990 as year 0. The data appears to be quadratic, cubic, or exponential.

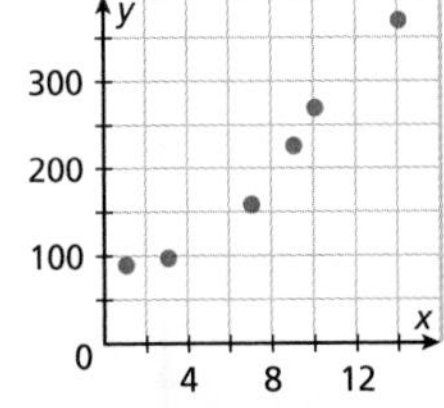

Use the calculator to perform each type of regression.

Compare the values of r^2. The cubic model seems to be the best fit. The function $f(x) \approx 0.2x^3 + 5.44x^2 - 22.13x + 110.07$ models the data.

3. Write a function that models the data.

Fertilizer/Acre (lb)	11	14	25	31	40	50
Yield/Acre (bushels)	245	302	480	557	645	705

$f(x) \approx -0.2x^2 + 23.99 + 5.28$

THINK AND DISCUSS

1. Explain the limitations of finding constant differences or ratios when working with real-world data.

2. GET ORGANIZED Copy and complete the graphic organizer. Explain how each method can help you determine which model best fits a data set.

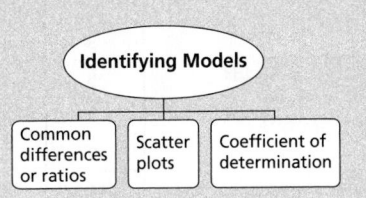

Identifying Models
- Common differences or ratios
- Scatter plots
- Coefficient of determination

Power Presentations with PowerPoint®

Additional Examples

Example 3

The data set shows the population of a small town since 1990. Using 1990 as a reference year, write a function that models the data.

Year	Population
1990	400
1993	490
1997	642
2000	787
2002	901
2005	1104
2006	1181

$f(x) \approx 399.94(1.07)^x$

Also available on transparency

INTERVENTION
Questioning Strategies

EXAMPLE 3

- Is it possible that two types of functions make appropriate models? How do you decide which is the better model?

3 Close

Summarize

From a data set, it is often possible to construct a model that is a good fit for the data. Using differences, ratios, graphs, and calculators can all be helpful in creating models. Remind students that there is often no "right" or "best" model for a data set, but appropriate models will most closely match the given data.

ONGOING ASSESSMENT and INTERVENTION

***Diagnose Before* the Lesson**
9-6 Warm Up, TE p. 698

***Monitor During* the Lesson**
Check It Out! Exercises, SE pp. 699–701
Questioning Strategies, TE pp. 699–701

***Assess After* the Lesson**
9-6 Lesson Quiz, TE p. 705
Alternative Assessment, TE p. 705

Answers to *Think and Discuss*

Possible answers:

1. The x-values must be in equally spaced intervals to use constant differences or ratios.
2. See p. A11.

9-6 Exercises

Assignment Guide

Assign *Guided Practice* exercises as necessary.

If you finished Examples **1–3**
Basic 6–12, 15–18, 20–23, 26–31
Average 6–23, 26–31
Advanced 6–31

Homework Quick Check
Quickly check key concepts.
Exercises: 8, 10, 12, 18

State Resources

9-6 Exercises

go.hrw.com
Homework Help Online
KEYWORD: MB7 9-6
Parent Resources Online
KEYWORD: MB7 Parent

GUIDED PRACTICE

SEE EXAMPLE 1 p. 698

Use constant differences or ratios to determine which parent function would best model the given data set.

1.

x	y
6	69.6
13	51.4
20	33.2
27	15
34	−3.2
41	−21.4

linear

2.

x	y
11	2
47	6
99	10
167	14
251	18
351	22

square root

3.

x	y
0	125
1	150
2	180
3	216
4	259.2
5	311.04

exponential

SEE EXAMPLE 2 p. 700

4. This table shows the mass in grams m of the radioactive substance iodine-131 remaining in a container t days after the beginning of an experiment.

Time t (days)	0	1	2	3	4	5	6
Mass m (g)	1000	917.40	841.62	772.10	708.33	649.82	596.14

a. Write a function that models the data. $M(t) \approx 1000(0.917^t)$

b. Use your model to predict the number of grams of iodine-131 that will be left after 20 days. ≈ 178.3 g

c. Use your model to predict when there will be less than 50 grams remaining. 35 days

SEE EXAMPLE 3 p. 701

5. The table shows the value of a stock at various points in the past 24 months since Carla bought the stock.

Time t (months)	0	4	9	12	15	20	24
Stock Value v ($)	62	54	45	48	55	53	60

a. Write a function that models the data. $V(t) \approx 0.08t^2 - 2.04t + 60.86$

b. Use your model to predict the stock price 6 months after Carla bought it.

b. about $51.68

c. Would you recommend that Carla use your model to predict the value of her stock a year from now? Why or why not? No; the model tells what happened in the past, not what is going to happen in the future. The stock might go down again.

PRACTICE AND PROBLEM SOLVING

Independent Practice

For Exercises	See Example
6–8	1
9	2
10	3

Extra Practice
Skills Practice p. S21
Application Practice p. S40

Use constant differences or ratios to determine which parent function would best model the given data set.

6.

x	y
1	380
3	343
5	310
7	279
9	252
11	228

6. exponential

7. quadratic

x	y
2	97
8	202
14	253
20	250
26	193
32	82

8. square root

x	y
4	4
9	6
16	8
25	10
36	12

Teacher to Teacher

It is a good idea to remind students how to make sure the regression coefficient shows on the calculator screen. It is not automatic on the TI-83 or later models of graphing calculators. Point out to students that the Helpful Hint on page 700 explains how to turn on the diagnostic mode so that the regression coefficient will be displayed.

Sarah Ritch
Carrollton, TX

9. **Agriculture** A farmer is experimenting with the amount of fertilizer to put on his corn fields. Different amounts of fertilizer are applied to each field, and the resulting yields are measured. Write a function that models the given data.

Fertilizer/Acre (lb)	45	70	90	115	125	135	150
Yield/Acre (bushels)	29	60	70	88	84	86	76

$f(x) \approx -0.009x^2 + 2.28x - 55.31$

10. **Biology** The table shows the estimated number of *E. coli* bacteria in a lab dish t minutes after the start of an experiment.

Time (min)	0	10	20	30	40	50	60
Bacteria	300	423	596	842	1188	1686	2354

a. Using t as the independent variable, find the model that best fits the data. $n(t) \approx 299.92(1.035^t)$

b. Use your model to predict the number of bacteria after 3 hours. about 146,940

c. How long does it take the population of *E. coli* to triple? about 32min

LINK

Math History

In 1806, French mathematician Adrien-Marie Legendre (1752–1833) modeled the orbit of a comet by fitting a quadratic curve to location data.

11. **Real Estate** The table shows the prices of some recent home sales compared with the area of the homes. $y \approx 34.37x + 85{,}851.76$

Area of Homes Sold

Area (ft²)	Price ($)
2675	179,000
1170	125,900
1486	136,750
2510	172,500
2444	169,900
2980	187,000

a. Using area as the independent variable, find a model for the data.

b. Use your model to predict the number of square feet in a house that is priced at $175,000. about 2594 ft²

c. How accurate do you think your answer to part **b** is?

12. **Economics** An economist is studying the median yearly income of workers by their ages.

Age (yr)	18	28	38	48	58	68
Median Income ($)	17,480	30,650	37,440	41,230	37,570	21,390

a. Find an appropriate model for the data.

b. Use your model to predict the median income for a worker who is 43 years old. about $40,780

13. **Data Collection** Use a graphing calculator and a motion detector to measure the distance of a ball or a toy car as it travels down a ramp. Set the motion detector at the top of the ramp and release the object to collect the data.

a. Find an appropriate model for distance versus time. Answers will vary.

b. Use your model to predict the distance the object would travel in 1 minute if the ramp continued indefinitely. Answers will vary.

14. **Health** The table shows the mean age of mothers in the United States when they had their first child.

Year	1980	1985	1990	1995	2000
Mean Age of Mother at First Birth	22.7	23.7	24.2	24.5	24.9

a. Using 1980 as a reference year, find both a quadratic and cubic model for the data.

b. Use both models to predict the mean age of a mother at first birth in 2010.

c. Explain which prediction you think is more accurate.

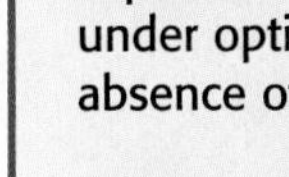
Science Link The model generated in **Exercise 10** accurately represents the exponential growth of *E. coli* bacteria under optimal conditions and in the absence of predators.

Data Collection To help students complete **Exercise 13**, see *Technology Lab Activities.*

Answers

11c. Possible answer: The model is pretty accurate, but there may be other factors, such as the age or condition of the house, that affect the sales price.

12a. $f(x) \approx -0.41x^3 + 18.95x^2 + 965.11x - 3321.21$

14a. quadratic: $f(x) \approx -0.004x^2 + 0.184x + 22.76$; cubic: $f(x) \approx 0.0004x^3 - 0.016x^2 + 0.27x + 22.7$

b. quadratic: 24.68; cubic: 27.2

c. Possible answer: The cubic prediction is more accurate because the data is increasing and there is no indication that it will begin to decline.

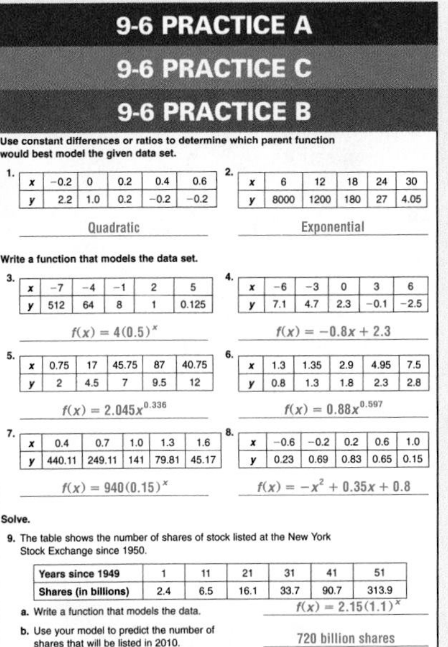
9-6 PRACTICE A

9-6 PRACTICE C

9-6 PRACTICE B

Use constant differences or ratios to determine which parent function would best model the given data set.

1.

x	-0.2	0	0.2	0.4	0.6
y	2.2	1.0	0.2	-0.2	-0.2

Quadratic

2.

x	6	12	18	24	30
y	8000	1200	180	27	4.05

Exponential

Write a function that models the data set.

3.

x	-7	-4	-1	2	5
y	512	64	8	1	0.125

$f(x) = 4(0.5)^x$

4.

x	-6	-3	0	3	6
y	7.1	4.7	2.3	-0.1	-2.5

$f(x) = -0.8x + 2.3$

5.

x	0.75	17	45.75	87	40.75
y	2	4.5	7	9.5	12

$f(x) = 2.045x^{0.336}$

6.

x	1.3	1.35	2.9	4.95	7.5
y	0.8	1.3	1.8	2.3	2.8

$f(x) = 0.88x^{0.597}$

7.

x	0.4	0.7	1.0	1.3	1.6
y	440.11	249.11	141	79.81	45.17

$f(x) = 940(0.15)^x$

8.

x	-0.6	-0.2	0.2	0.6	1.0
y	0.23	0.69	0.83	0.65	0.15

$f(x) = -x^2 + 0.35x + 0.8$

Solve.

9. The table shows the number of shares of stock listed at the New York Stock Exchange since 1950.

Years since 1949	1	11	21	31	41	51
Shares (in billions)	2.4	6.5	16.1	33.7	90.7	313.9

a. Write a function that models the data. $f(x) = 2.15(1.1)^x$

b. Use your model to predict the number of shares that will be listed in 2010. 720 billion shares

c. Use your model to determine the year in which the number of shares of stock listed first exceeded 10 billion. 1966

Exercise 15 involves finding a model based on scientific data. This exercise prepares students for the Multi-Step Test Prep on page 706.

Answers

15c. Possible answer: No; at a certain temperature the volume of the air would exceed the capacity of the balloon.

18a. $f(x) = 4.044x^2 - 76.656x - 306.496$

b. about 16,689 mi²

c. Not very accurate; the model is not an excellent fit, and there are probably many other factors that affect the relationship.

19. Possible answer: A quadratic model becomes more and more linear as the value of a gets close to 0. So the quadratic model for a roughly linear data set probably has an a-value close to 0.

20. Possible answer: A good fit does not mean that there is a cause-and-effect relationship between the variables. There might be other variables that influence both variables. For example, the number of flowers and the number of mosquitoes might both be affected by the amount of rainfall more than they are affected by each other.

26.

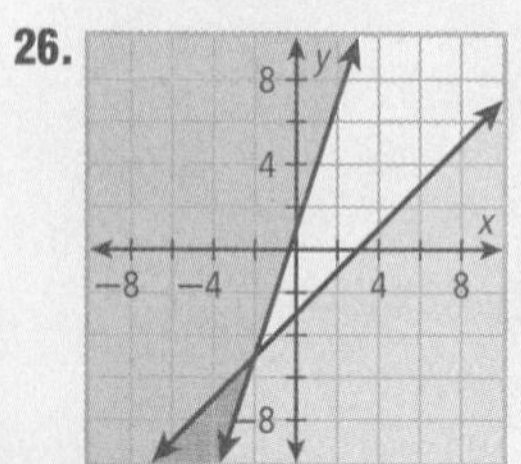

27.

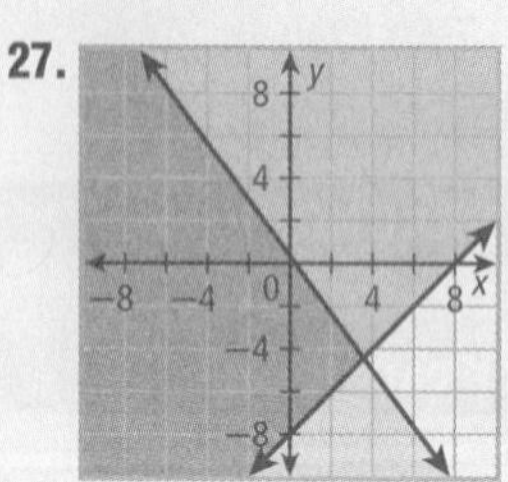

28.

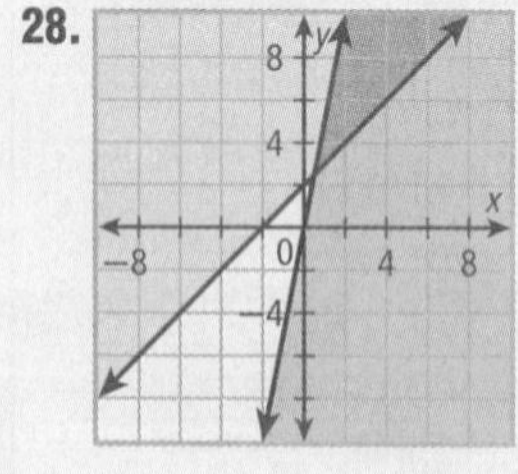

MULTI-STEP TEST PREP

$V(t) \approx 6126.9(1.016)^t$

15. This problem will prepare you for the Multi-Step Test Prep on page 706.

The table shows how the volume v of air in a hot-air balloon relates to the temperature t of the air.

Temperature (°F)	Volume (ft²)
100	30,000
106	33,000
112	36,300
118	39,930

a. Find an exponential model for the data.

b. Use your model to predict the volume of the air when its temperature is 109°F. **about 34,611 ft³**

c. Would your model be accurate for any air temperature greater than 118°F? Why or why not?

16a. Possible answer: $f(x) \approx 802.35(0.7704)^x$, **where x is millions of farms**

16c. about 248 acres

16. Agriculture The table shows the number and the average area of farms in the United States in the last century.

Number and Size of U.S. Farms

Year	Farms (millions)	Average Area (acres)
1910	6.4	139
1930	6.3	157
1950	5.4	216
1969	2.7	390
1987	2.1	462
1997	1.9	487

a. Using the number of farms as the independent variable, find a model for the average size of farms.

b. Use your model to predict the average size of the farms when the number of farms reaches 1 million. **about 618 acres**

c. Use your model to estimate the average size of the farms when there were 4.5 million farms.

17c. The model predicts $160.65, which is about $5 more than the actual FCI.

17e. The FCI has increased about 1.4 times as much as the inflation rate from 1991 to 2003.

17. Baseball The Fan Cost Index tracks the cost for a family of four to attend a Major League Baseball game.

Year	1991	1994	1997	2000	2003
FCI	$79.41	$96.41	$107.26	$132.44	$151.19

$f(x) \approx 75.95(1.055^x)$

a. Find a model for the data. Use 1990 as year 0.

b. How fast has the FCI been increasing according to your model? **about 5.5%/yr**

c. The FCI in 2004 was $155.52. How close is the actual value to the value predicted by your model?

d. Use your model to predict when the FCI will reach $200. **about 2008**

e. Because of inflation, something that cost $1.00 in 1991 cost $1.34 in 2003. How does the change in the FCI compare with inflation?

Green iguana

18. Biology The table shows the number of species of reptiles and amphibians and the area in square miles for some islands in the Caribbean.

Species	Area (mi²)
11	5
16	32
53	3,435
45	4,244
108	29,371
100	44,218

a. Using number of species as the independent variable, find an appropriate model for the data.

b. Use your model to predict the area of an island with 75 species of reptiles and amphibians.

c. How accurate do you think your prediction in part **b** is? Explain.

19. Critical Thinking Sometimes data that appear linear are better modeled by a quadratic function. What can you conclude about the value of a in the quadratic model of such a data set?

20. Write About It Suppose that a model can be found that provides a good fit for data on two variables. What evidence does the model give of a cause-and-effect relationship between the two variables? Use examples in your explanation.

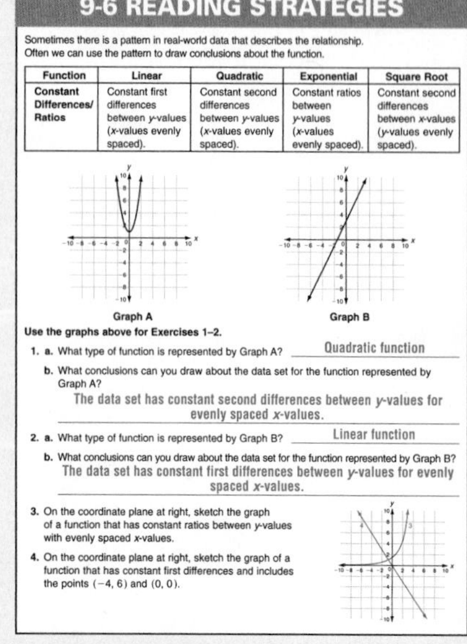

9-6 READING STRATEGIES

Sometimes there is a pattern in real-world data that describes the relationship. Often we can use the pattern to draw conclusions about the function.

Function	Linear	Quadratic	Exponential	Square Root
Constant Differences/ Ratios	Constant first differences between y-values (x-values evenly spaced).	Constant second differences between y-values (x-values evenly spaced).	Constant ratios between y-values (x-values evenly spaced).	Constant second differences between x-values (y-values evenly spaced).

Graph A

Graph B

Use the graphs above for Exercises 1–2.

1. a. What type of function is represented by Graph A? **Quadratic function**

b. What conclusions can you draw about the data set for the function represented by Graph A? **The data set has constant second differences between y-values for evenly spaced x-values.**

2. a. What type of function is represented by Graph B? **Linear function**

b. What conclusions can you draw about the data set for the function represented by Graph B? **The data set has constant first differences between y-values for evenly spaced x-values.**

3. On the coordinate plane at right, sketch the graph of a function that has constant ratios between y-values with evenly spaced x-values.

4. On the coordinate plane at right, sketch the graph of a function that has constant first differences and includes the points $(-4, 6)$ and $(0, 0)$.

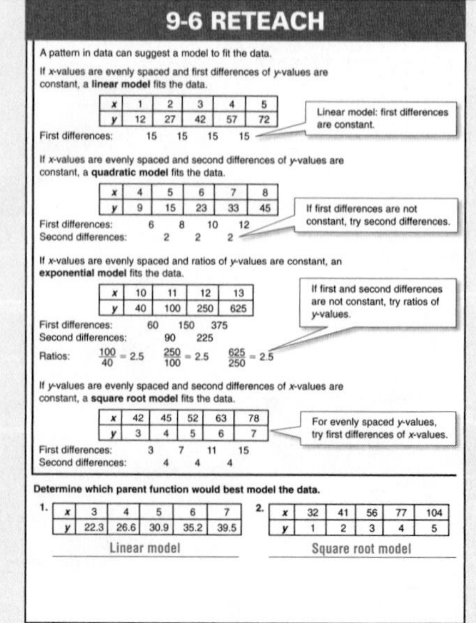

9-6 RETEACH

A pattern in data can suggest a model to fit the data.

If x-values are evenly spaced and first differences of y-values are constant, a **linear model** fits the data.

x	1	2	3	4	5
y	12	27	42	57	72

First differences: 15 15 15 15

Linear model: first differences are constant.

If x-values are evenly spaced and second differences of y-values are constant, a **quadratic model** fits the data.

x	4	5	6	7	8
y	9	15	23	33	45

First differences: 6 8 10 12
Second differences: 2 2 2

If first differences are not constant, try second differences.

If x-values are evenly spaced and ratios of y-values are constant, an **exponential model** fits the data.

x	10	11	12	13
y	40	100	250	625

First differences: 60 150 375
Second differences: 90 225
Ratios: $\frac{100}{40} = 2.5$ $\frac{250}{100} = 2.5$ $\frac{625}{250} = 2.5$

If first and second differences are not constant, try ratios of y-values.

If y-values are evenly spaced and second differences of x-values are constant, a **square root model** fits the data.

x	42	45	52	63	78
y	3	4	5	6	7

First differences: 3 7 11 15
Second differences: 4 4 4

For evenly spaced y-values, try first differences of x-values.

Determine which parent function would best model the data.

1.

x	3	4	5	6	7
y	22.3	26.6	30.9	35.2	39.5

Linear model

2.

x	32	41	56	77	104
y	1	2	3	4	5

Square root model

TEST PREP

21. Which of the following is true for the data in the table?
 - (A) The first differences of values of the dependent variable are constant.
 - **(B)** The second differences of values of the dependent variable are constant.
 - (C) The ratios of values of the dependent variable are constant.
 - (D) The ratios of values of the independent variable are constant.

x	y
3	2
4	23
5	50
6	83
7	122
8	167

22. Find n so that an exponential model will fit the data exactly.
 - (F) $n = 40$ (H) $n = 45$
 - **(G)** $n = 49$ (J) $n = 52$

x	5	6	7
y	16	28	n

23. Find n so that a quadratic model will fit the data exactly.
 - (A) $n = 60$ (C) $n = 80$
 - (B) $n = 70$ **(D)** $n = 90$

x	5	6	7	8
y	12	32	58	n

CHALLENGE AND EXTEND

24. The function $P(t) = \frac{a}{1 + be^{-kt}}$, called a *logistic function,* is often used when there are factors such as food or space that limit a population's growth. The number of fish in a stocked pond can be modeled by the function $F(t) = \frac{4000}{1 + 5.7e^{-0.2t}}$, where t is the number of months after the pond is stocked.
 - a. Predict the number of fish in the lake after 10 months. **about 2260 fish**
 - b. When will the population of fish reach 3000? **after about 14 mo**
 - c. Find the maximum number of fish that the pond can hold if the function is correct. **4000 fish**

25. **Graphing Calculator** Another type of regression you can perform is a power regression. Use the **PwrReg** feature to find a model for the given data. Which parent function best fits the data?
$f(x) \approx x^{0.5}$; $f(x) = \sqrt{x}$

x	1	24	41	74
y	1	4.9	6.4	8.6

SPIRAL REVIEW

Graph each system of inequalities. *(Lesson 3-3)*

26. $\begin{cases} y \geq 3x + 1 \\ y \leq x - 3 \end{cases}$

27. $\begin{cases} y \geq x - 8 \\ y \leq -\frac{4}{3}x + \frac{1}{3} \end{cases}$

28. $\begin{cases} y \leq 5x \\ y \geq x + 2 \end{cases}$

29. **Business** The profit for a company in thousands of dollars is modeled by the function $p(x) = -x^3 + 12x^2 - 12x - 80$, where x is the number of items produced in thousands. *(Lesson 5-5)*
 - a. Find the zeros of the function. **−2, 4, and 10**
 - b. Which zero represents the number of items that the company must produce to break even? **4 represents the 4000 items the company must produce to break even.**

Determine by composition whether each pair of functions are inverses. *(Lesson 9-5)*

30. $f(x) = x^2 + 1$ and $g(x) = \sqrt{x} + 1$
no

31. $f(x) = -4 + 5x$ and $g(x) = \frac{1}{5}x + \frac{4}{5}$
yes

TEST PREP DOCTOR In **Exercise 22,** students who chose **F** may have mistakenly used a linear model with a constant difference. Remind them that exponential models have a constant ratio.

Journal

Describe the process you would use for finding a model for a given data set containing pairs of values.

ALTERNATIVE ASSESSMENT

Have students find a real-world data set from a newspaper, magazine, or the Internet. Have them try to find an appropriate model for the data and have them explain their processes and conclusions.

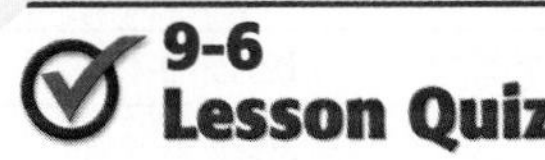

Power Presentations with PowerPoint®

9-6 Lesson Quiz

1. Use finite differences or ratios to determine which parent function would best model the given data set, and write a function that models the data.

Length (ft)	Cost ($)
5	102.50
10	290.00
15	602.50
20	1040.00
25	1602.50

quadratic; $C(\ell) = 2.5x^2 + 40$

2. Write a function that models the given data.

Time (min)	Volume (cm²)
0	1.2
2	3.9
4	15.7
6	64.2
8	256.5
10	1023.8

$f(x) \approx 1.085(1.977)^x$

Also available on transparency

9-6 PROBLEM SOLVING

The table shows the population of Lincoln Valley over the last 7 years. The town council is developing long range plans and is considering how the population might grow in the future if the current trend continues.

Lincoln Valley Population 2000–2006							
Year	1	2	3	4	5	6	7
Population	1049	1137	1229	1326	1434	1542	1662

1. Describe the data given in the table. What is the independent variable? What is the dependent variable? Assign x or y to each variable.
The independent variable (x) is the year. The dependent variable (y) is the population.

2. Make a scatter plot of the data. Do the data form a linear pattern? For this to be true, explain what must be true about finite differences.
Possible answer: The first few points appear to be linear, but the later points start a curve upward. For the data to be linear, the first differences must be constant.

3. Use the table of data.
 - a. Find the first differences. **88, 92, 97, 108, 108, 120**
 - b. Find the second differences. **4, 5, 11, 0, 12**
 - c. Find the third differences. **1, 6, −11, 12**
 - d. Find the ratios between y-values. **All ratios round to 1.08.**

4. What kind of function will best describe the data? Justify your conclusion.
Exponential function, because the ratios between y-values are almost constant

Choose the letter for the best answer.

5. Which function best models the given data?
 - A $y = 105.1x + 924.3$
 - B $y = 4.4x^2 + 69.6x + 977.4$
 - C $y = \sqrt{1049x}$
 - **(D)** $y = 970.2(1.08)^x$

6. Predict the population of Lincoln Valley in 2012.
 - F 2850
 - **(G)** 2640
 - H 2440
 - J 2260

9-6 CHALLENGE

Constant differences of the dependent variables can also be used to determine cubic, quartic, and higher degree polynomial functions.

Constant third differences indicate a cubic polynomial. Constant fourth differences indicate a quartic polynomial, and so on.

Once the degree of the polynomial is determined, polynomial interpolation can be used. For a cubic model an equation of the form $f(x) = ax^3 + bx^2 + cx + d$ will be appropriate. Substitute any four points from the data set to identify the constants a, b, c, and d by solving the appropriate system of linear equations.

For each data, determine the degree of the polynomial that is the best fit and then find the polynomial by interpolation.

1.

x	−4	−3	−2	−1	0	1	2	3	4
y	21	5	−5	−9	−7	1	15	35	61

Quadratic; $y = 3x^2 + 5x - 7$

2.

x	−4	−3	−2	−1	0	1	2	3	4
y	−795	−284	−61	12	25	20	−9	−116	−403

Quartic; $y = -2x^4 + 3x^3 - 7x^2 + x + 25$

3.

x	−4	−3	−2	−1	0	1	2	3	4
y	−348	−154	−52	−12	−4	2	36	128	308

Cubic; $y = 5x^3 - x^2 + 2x - 4$

4.

x	−4	−3	−2	−1	0	1	2	3	4
y	−1003	−222	−11	20	21	22	53	264	1045

Quintic; $y = x^5 + 21$

5.

x	−4	−3	−2	−1	0	1	2	3	4
y	1268	442	152	98	100	98	152	442	1268

Quartic; $y = 5x^4 - 7x^2 + 100$

SECTION 9B MULTI-STEP TEST PREP

Organizer

Objective: Assess students' ability to apply concepts and skills in Lessons 9-4 through 9-6 in a real-world format.

Online Edition

Resources

Algebra II Assessments
www.mathtekstoolkit.org

For additional assessment activities, see www.utdanacenter.org.

Problem	Text Reference
1–4	Lesson 9-6
5–6	Lesson 9-5
7	Lesson 9-4

Answers

2. Square-root function; dependent variables are evenly spaced, and second differences of the independent variable are constant.
5. $f^{-1}(x) = \frac{x^2}{12.96}$; the height of the balloon given the distance to the farthest object you can see

State Resources

go.hrw.com
State Resources Online
KEYWORD: MB7 Resources

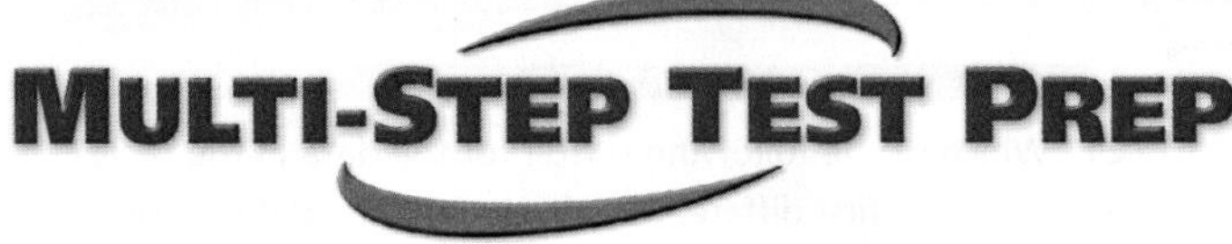

CHAPTER 9 MULTI-STEP TEST PREP

SECTION 9B

Functional Relationships

Full of Hot Air When you ride in a hot-air balloon that is rising vertically, the distance to the farthest object that you can see increases as the balloon's height increases. The table shows data that were collected on a hot-air balloon.

Balloon's Height (m)	7.8	31.3	70.5	125.4	196.0
Distance That You Can See (km)	10	20	30	40	50

1. Which is the independent variable? Why?
2. Which parent function best models the data set? Why?
3. Write a function $f(x)$ that models the data. $f(x) = 3.6\sqrt{x}$
4. If you are in a hot-air balloon at a height of 100 m, how far would you expect to be able to see? **36 km**
5. Write the inverse function of $f(x)$, and explain what it represents.
6. Find the approximate minimum height for a hot-air balloon if you want to be able to see objects that are 25 km away. **48.2 m**
7. The function $g(x) = 0.3x$ converts distances in feet to approximate distances in meters. Write a composite function for the distance that you can see in kilometers from a height of x feet.

1. Height; the distance you can see depends on the balloon's height.

$f(g(x)) = 3.6\sqrt{0.3x} \approx 1.97\sqrt{x}$

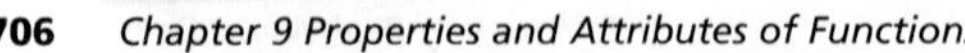

INTERVENTION

Scaffolding Questions

1. Which variable depends on the other? Distance depends on the height.
2. Is the data set linear? no What do you notice about the data points when you make a scatter plot? The shape is similar to $f(x) = \sqrt{x}$.
3. What is the general form for a square root function? $f(x) = a\sqrt{x-h} + k$ What assumptions can you make? $h = k = 0$
4. Does your answer seem reasonable given the data in the table? Why? yes; $70.5 < 100 < 125.4$ and $30 < 36 < 40$
5. What process can you use to write the inverse function? Write $y = 3.6\sqrt{x}$, then exchange x and y and solve for y.
6. How can you use the inverse function to write an inequality for this problem? $y \geq \frac{25^2}{12.96}$
7. Is $(f \circ g)(x)$ or $(g \circ f)(x)$ the correct composition? Why? $(f \circ g)(x)$; you first need to convert the height to meters in order to use $f(x)$.

Extension

The function $h(x) = 0.62x$ converts a distance x in kilometers to an approximately equivalent distance in miles. Explain how to write a composition of $f(x)$, $g(x)$, and $h(x)$ that gives the distance that you can see in miles when the balloon's height is x feet. $h(f(g(x))) = 1.22\sqrt{x}$

Quiz for Lessons 9-4 Through 9-6

9-4 Operations with Functions

Given $f(x) = \frac{5}{x+3}$, $g(x) = x - 6$, and $h(x) = x^2 - 4x - 12$, find each function or value.

1. $(f - g)(2)$ 5
2. $(g + h)(x)$ $x^2 - 3x - 18$
3. $\left(\frac{g}{h}\right)(8)$ 0.1
4. $\left(\frac{h}{g}\right)(x)$ $x + 2, x \neq 6$
5. $(gh)(5)$ 7
6. $(gf)(x)$ $\frac{5x - 30}{x + 3}$
7. $g(f(-2))$ −1
8. $h(g(x))$ $x^2 - 16x + 48$
9. Find $(f \circ g)(x)$. State the domain of the composite function.
10. Erin receives a 30% employee discount at the camera store where she works. During a sale, she receives an additional 20% off the discounted price. Write a composite function for the price Erin pays for an item with an original price of p dollars. $C(p) = 0.56p$

9-5 Functions and Their Inverses

State whether the inverse of each relation is a function.

11. 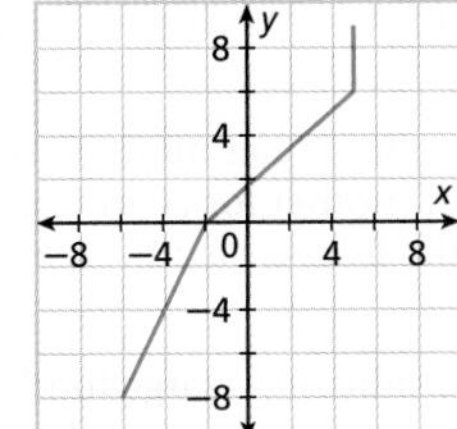 function

12. 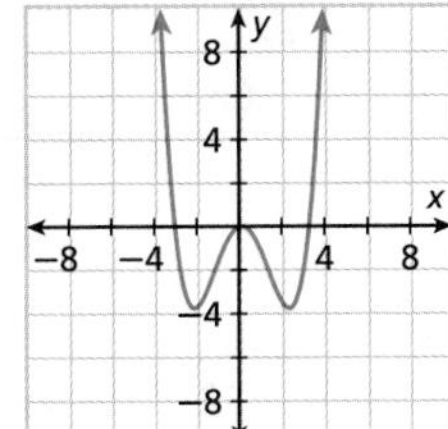 not a function

Write the rule for the inverse of each function. Then state the domain and range of the inverse.

13. $f(x) = \frac{2}{3}x - 12$ $f^{-1}(x) = \frac{3}{2}x + 18$; D: $\mathbb{R}$; R: $\mathbb{R}$
14. $g(x) = \frac{12}{x - 5}$ $g^{-1}(x) = \frac{12}{x} + 5$; D: $\{x \mid x \neq 0\}$; R: $\{y \mid y \neq 5\}$
15. $h(x) = x^2 - 4$ $y = \pm\sqrt{x + 4}$; D: $\{x \mid x \geq -4\}$; R: $\mathbb{R}$
16. $n(x) = 3^x$ $n^{-1}(x) = \log_3 x$; D: $\{x \mid x > 0\}$; R: $\mathbb{R}$

9-6 Modeling Real-World Data

17. Use finite differences or ratios to determine which parent function would best model this set of data. exponential

x	0	1	2	3	4
y	625	375	225	135	81

18. The table shows the average temperature in degrees Fahrenheit and the average utility bill for the households in a town in recent months. Using average temperature as the independent variable, find a model for the average bill. $f(x) \approx 0.101x^2 - 14.002x + 576.252$

Average Monthly Temperature (°F)	Average Monthly Utility Bill ($)
61	108
80	103
46	148
72	89
50	125
88	132

SECTION 9B

Organizer

Objective: Assess students' mastery of concepts and skills in Lessons 9-4 through 9-6.

Resources

Assessment Resources

Section 9B Quiz

Test & Practice Generator

One-Stop Planner®

INTERVENTION

Resources

Ready to Go On? Intervention and Enrichment Worksheets

Ready to Go On? **CD-ROM**

Ready to Go On? **Online**

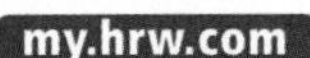

my.hrw.com

Answers

9. $(f \circ g)(x) = \frac{5}{x - 3}$; D: $\{x \mid x \neq 3\}$

READY TO GO ON?
Diagnose and Prescribe

NO INTERVENE

Ready to Go On? Intervention	Worksheets	CD-ROM	Online
	Ready to Go On? Intervention, Section 9B		
Lesson 9-4	9-4 Intervention	Activity 9-4	Diagnose and Prescribe Online
Lesson 9-5	9-5 Intervention	Activity 9-5	
Lesson 9-6	9-6 Intervention	Activity 9-6	

YES ENRICH

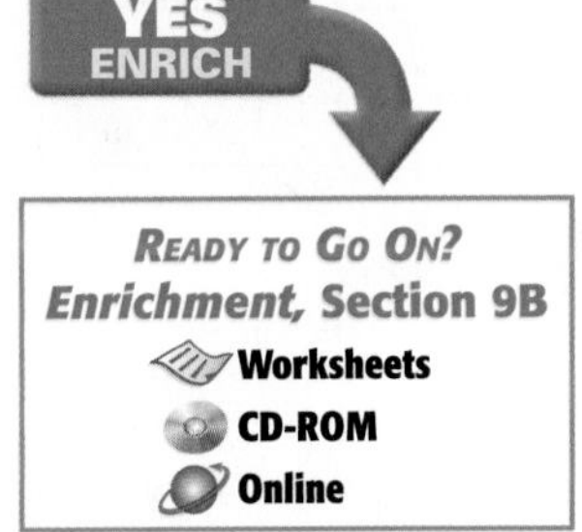

Ready to Go On? Enrichment, Section 9B

Worksheets

CD-ROM

Online

Organizer

Objective: Help students organize and review key concepts and skills presented in Chapter 9.

Online Edition
Multilingual Glossary

Countdown to Testing Week 20

Resources

***Multilingual Glossary* Online**

go.hrw.com
KEYWORD: MB7 Glossary

***Lesson Tutorial Videos* CD-ROM**

Answers

1. one-to-one function
2. step function
3. composition of functions
4.

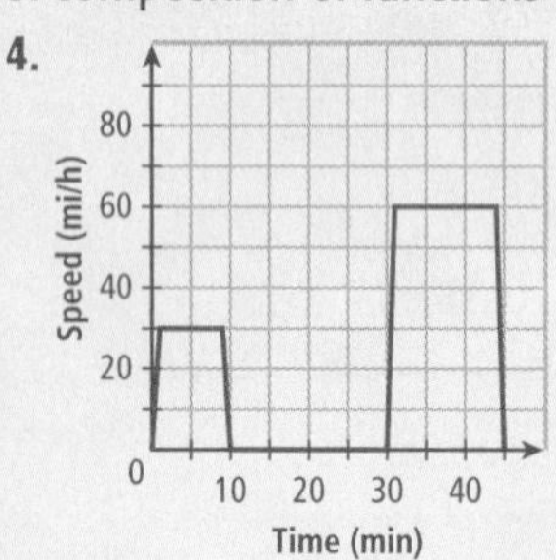

5.

Guests	10	20	30	40	50
Appetizers	160	200	240	280	320

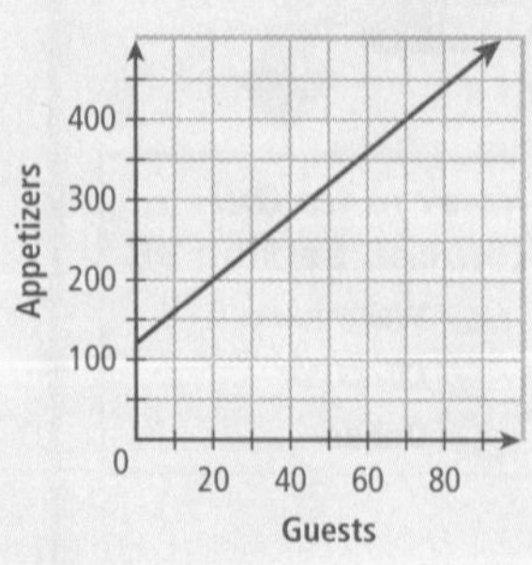

$y = 4x + 120$

6a.

Radius (in.)	1.5	2	2.5	3	4
Time (s)	3	5	7.5	10.5	18

$y = x^2 + \frac{1}{2}x$

b. 52.5 s

CHAPTER 9

Study Guide: Review

Vocabulary

Complete the sentences below with vocabulary words from the list above.

1. In a(n) ___?___, each y-value is paired with exactly one x-value.
2. A(n) ___?___ is a piecewise function that is constant for each interval of its domain.
3. The function operation that uses the output from one function as the input for a second function is the ___?___.

9-1 Multiple Representations of Functions *(pp. 654–661)*

EXAMPLE

■ **The managers of a town are interested in the cost of snow removal over the winter. The table shows the cost of removing various amounts of snow. Use a graph and an equation to find the cost to remove 24 inches of snow.**

Snowfall (in.)	Cost ($)
3	6,950
6	8,900
9	10,850
12	12,800

A scatter plot shows that the data is linear.

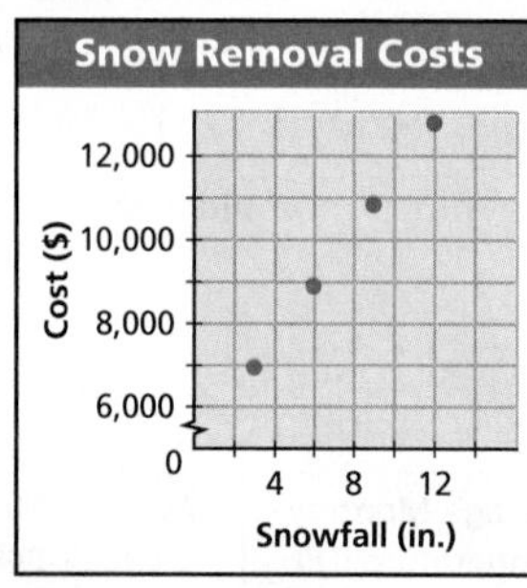

Find the slope of the line by using two points.

$$m = \frac{8900 - 6950}{6 - 3} = \frac{1950}{3} = 650$$

Write an equation by using one of the points.

$$y - 6950 = 650(x - 3)$$
$$y = 650x + 5000$$

The cost for removing 24 inches of snow is
$y = 5000 + 650(24) = \$20,600$.

EXERCISES

4. Draw a graph of speed versus time that represents the following situation.

   Avery drove 5 miles to her mother's house and visited with her mother for 20 minutes. Then she drove on the freeway for 15 minutes before arriving home.

5. A caterer is planning for a large fund-raising dinner. He plans to have 4 trays of 30 appetizers each on the buffet. In addition, he will prepare an additional 4 appetizers per guest. Create a table, a graph, and an equation to represent the number of appetizers with relation to the number of guests.

6. The scatter plot shows how long it takes to fill various cylindrical containers of different radii.

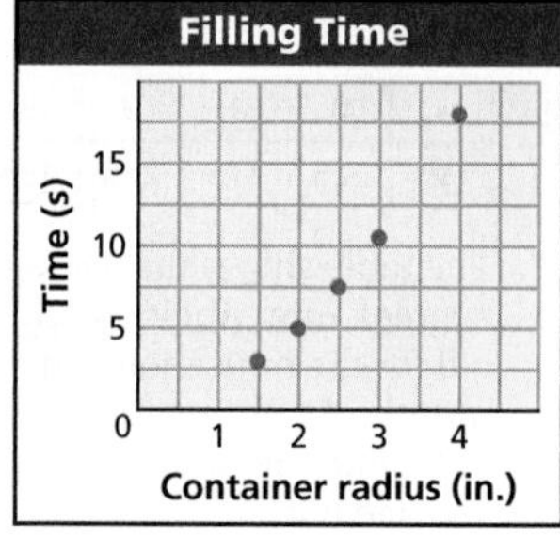

   a. Create a table and an equation for the data.
   b. Use your equation to predict the time that it would take to fill a cylindrical container with a radius of 7 inches.

9-2 Piecewise Functions *(pp. 662–669)*

EXAMPLES

■ **Evaluate** $f(x) = \begin{cases} 5x+2 & \text{if } x \le 1 \\ x^2 - 6 & \text{if } x > 1 \end{cases}$ **for** $x = -2$ **and** $x = 5$.

$f(-2) = 5(-2) + 2 = -8$ *Use the rule for* $x \le 1$.

$f(5) = 5^2 - 6 = 19$ *Use the rule for* $x > 1$.

■ **Graph** $g(x) = \begin{cases} 2x+4 & \text{if } x < -2 \\ -3x + 2 & \text{if } x \ge -2 \end{cases}$.

The domain of the function is split at $x = -2$. Use a table of values to graph both pieces.

x	$g(x) = 2x + 4$	$g(x) = -3x + 2$
−4	−4	
−3	−2	
−2	0	8
−1		5
0		2

Use an open circle at $(-2, 0)$ and a closed circle at $(-2, 8)$.

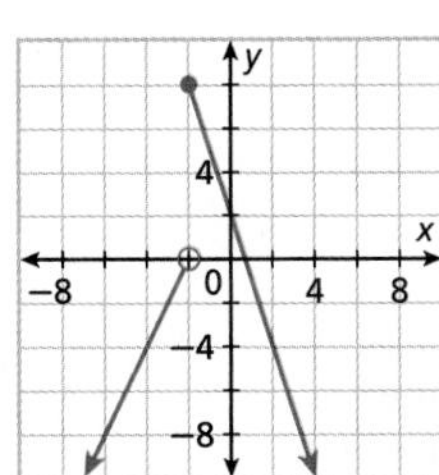

EXERCISES

7. Evaluate $f(x) = \begin{cases} \sqrt{5x+9} & \text{if } x \ge 4 \\ 9 - 7x & \text{if } x < 4 \end{cases}$ for $x = -6$ and $x = 8$.

Graph each function.

8. $f(x) = \begin{cases} 2x - 4 & \text{if } x < 0 \\ 5 & \text{if } x \ge 0 \end{cases}$

9. $g(x) = \begin{cases} \frac{3}{2}x - 1 & \text{if } x \le 2 \\ \sqrt{x+2} & \text{if } x > 2 \end{cases}$

10. Write a piecewise function for this graph.

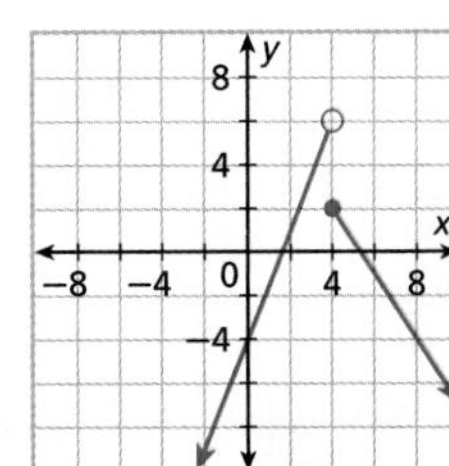

11. A bicycle delivery service charges $6 to deliver a package that weighs 8 ounces or less. For each additional ounce, the service charges $1.50 per ounce. Write a piecewise function for the amounts that this company charges to deliver packages that weigh 3 pounds or less.

9-3 Transforming Functions *(pp. 672–679)*

EXAMPLE

■ **Given** $f(x) = \begin{cases} 2x - 2 & \text{if } x \le 3 \\ -4x + 16 & \text{if } x > 3 \end{cases}$, **write the rule for** $g(x)$**, a horizontal translation of** $f(x)$ **5 units left.**

Each piece of $f(x)$ must be shifted 5 units left. Replace every x with $(x+5)$, and simplify.

$$g(x) = f(x+5) = \begin{cases} 2(x+5) - 2 & \text{if } (x+5) \le 3 \\ -4(x+5) + 16 & \text{if } (x+5) > 3 \end{cases}$$

$$= \begin{cases} 2x + 8 & \text{if } x \le -2 \\ -4x - 4 & \text{if } x > -2 \end{cases}$$

EXERCISES

12. Given $f(x) = \begin{cases} 2x - 2 & \text{if } x \le 3 \\ -4x + 16 & \text{if } x > 3 \end{cases}$, write the rule for $h(x)$, a vertical translation of $f(x)$ 2 units up.

13. Given $f(x) = \begin{cases} 3x + 2 & \text{if } x \le 0 \\ x^2 & \text{if } x > 0 \end{cases}$, write the rule for $g(x)$, a horizontal translation of $f(x)$ 7 units right.

14. Given $f(x) = 2x^2 + 1$ and $g(x) = f\left(\frac{1}{2}x\right) + 1$, graph $g(x)$.

Answers

7. 51; 7

8.

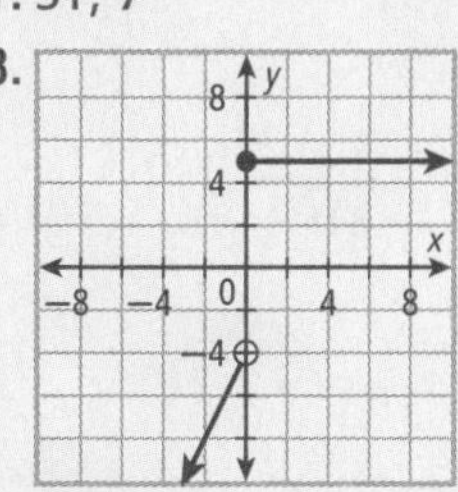

9.

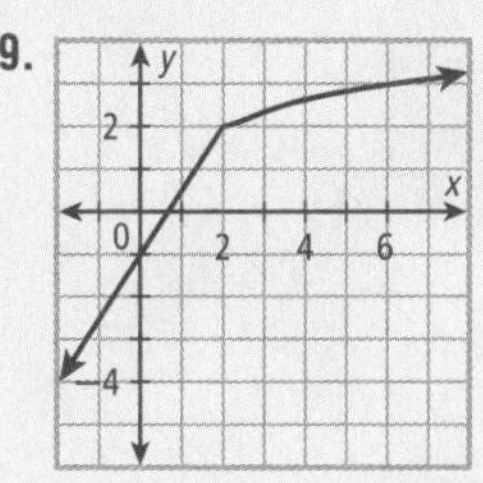

10. $f(x) = \begin{cases} \frac{5}{2}x - 4 & \text{if } x < 4 \\ -\frac{3}{2}x + 8 & \text{if } x \ge 4 \end{cases}$

11. $f(x) = \begin{cases} 6 & \text{if } 0 < x \le 8 \\ 6 + 1.5(x - 8) & \text{if } 8 < x \le 48 \end{cases}$

12. $h(x) = \begin{cases} 2x & \text{if } x \le 3 \\ -4x + 18 & \text{if } x > 3 \end{cases}$

13. $g(x) = \begin{cases} 3(x-7) + 2 & \text{if } x \le 7 \\ (x-7)^2 & \text{if } x > 7 \end{cases}$

14.

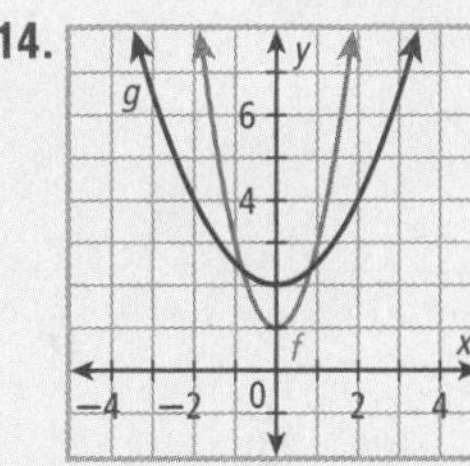

Answers

15. $x^2 - 4x - 21$
16. $x^2 - 6x - 7$
17. $-x^2 + 6x + 7$
18. $x^3 - 12x^2 + 21x + 98$
19. $x + 2, x \neq 7$
20. $\frac{1}{x+2}, x \neq 7$ or -2
21. $-10; -\frac{8}{3}$
22. 2; undefined
23. $g(f(x)) = \frac{8}{x-1}$; D: $\{x \mid x \neq 1\}$
24. $f(g(x)) = \frac{8}{x+1} - 2$;

    D: $\{x \mid x \neq -1\}$
25. $P(x) = 1.09(x + 30)$
26. function
27. $f^{-1}(x) = \frac{-x+5}{8}$; function;

    D: $\mathbb{R}$; R: $\mathbb{R}$
28. $y = \pm 3\sqrt{x} - 6$; not a function;

    D: $\{x \mid x \geq 0\}$; R: $\mathbb{R}$
29. $f^{-1}(x) = \frac{5}{2x} - 4$; function;

    D: $\{x \mid x \neq 0\}$; R: $\{y \mid y \neq -4\}$
30. $f^{-1}(x) = (x - 3)^2 + 5$; function;

    D: $\{x \mid x \geq 3\}$; R: $\{y \mid y \geq 5\}$

9-4 Operations with Functions *(pp. 682–688)*

EXAMPLES

Given $f(x) = x + 3$ and $g(x) = x^2 - 9$, find each function.

- $\left(\frac{g}{f}\right)(x)$

$$\left(\frac{g}{f}\right)(x) = \frac{g(x)}{f(x)} = \frac{x^2 - 9}{x + 3}$$
$$= \frac{(x+3)(x-3)}{x+3} = x - 3, x \neq -3$$

- **Given $f(x) = x + 6$ and $g(x) = \frac{18}{x+4}$, find $g(f(x))$. State its domain.**

$g(f(x)) = g(x + 6)$ *Substitute the rule for f into g.*

$= \frac{18}{(x+6)+4}$ *Use the rule for g.*

$= \frac{18}{x+10}$

The domain of $g(f(x))$ is $\{x \mid x \neq -10\}$ because the function is undefined at $x = -10$.

EXERCISES

Given $f(x) = x^2 - 5x - 14$ and $g(x) = x - 7$, find each function.

15. $(f + g)(x)$
16. $(f - g)(x)$
17. $(g - f)(x)$
18. $(fg)(x)$
19. $\left(\frac{f}{g}\right)(x)$
20. $\left(\frac{g}{f}\right)(x)$

Let $f(x) = x - 2$ and $g(x) = \frac{8}{x+1}$.

21. Find $f(g(-2))$ and $g(f(-2))$.
22. Find $f(g(1))$, and $g(f(1))$.
23. Find $g(f(x))$, and state its domain.
24. Find $f(g(x))$ and state its domain.
25. Because of high fuel costs, an airline begins adding a fuel surcharge of $30 to the price of each airline ticket the airline sells. Also, the airline must add 9% to the price for airport and sales taxes. Write a composite function for how much a person would pay for a ticket with this airline that is x dollars before surcharges and taxes.

9-5 Functions and Their Inverses *(pp. 690–696)*

EXAMPLES

- **Find the inverse of $f(x) = -3(x - 6)^2$. Determine whether it is a function, and state its domain and range.**

$y = -3(x - 6)^2$ *Rewrite the function by using y.*

$x = -3(y - 6)^2$ *Switch x and y in the equation.*

$-\frac{x}{3} = (y - 6)^2$ *Divide both sides by −3.*

$\pm\sqrt{-\frac{x}{3}} = y - 6$ *Take the square root of both sides.*

$y = \pm\sqrt{-\frac{x}{3}} + 6$ *Simplify.*

$f^{-1}(x) = \pm\sqrt{-\frac{x}{3}} + 6$ *Rewrite as $f^{-1}(x)$.*

Because there is a positive y-value and a negative y-value for any $x < 0$, the inverse is not a function. Because the radicand must be greater than or equal to 0, the domain is $\{x \mid x \leq 0\}$. The range is $\mathbb{R}$.

EXERCISES

26. Use the horizontal-line test to determine whether the inverse of the relation graphed is a function.

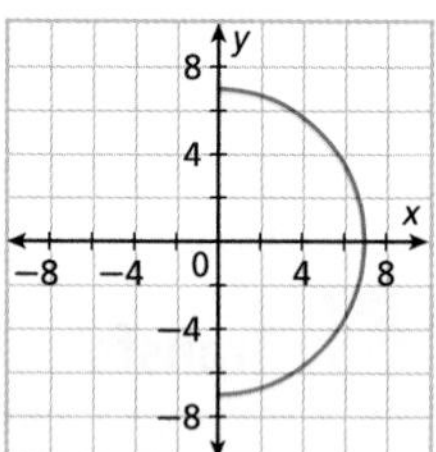

Find the inverse of each function. Determine whether the inverse is a function, and state its domain and range.

27. $f(x) = 5 - 8x$
28. $f(x) = \left(\frac{1}{3}x + 2\right)^2$
29. $f(x) = \frac{5}{2x+8}$
30. $f(x) = 3 + \sqrt{x - 5}$

EXAMPLES

- **Determine by composition whether $f(x) = \frac{1}{3}x - 4$ and $g(x) = 12 + 3x$ are inverses.**

Find both compositions.

$$f(g(x)) = \frac{1}{3}(12 + 3x) - 4 = 4 + x - 4 = x$$

$$g(f(x)) = 12 + 3\left(\frac{1}{3}x - 4\right) = 12 + x - 12 = x$$

Because $f(g(x)) = g(f(x)) = x$, f and g are inverses.

EXERCISES

Determine by composition whether each pair of functions are inverses.

31. $f(x) = 3x - 5$ and $g(x) = \frac{x - 3}{5}$

32. $f(x) = \sqrt[3]{x - 5}$ and $g(x) = x^3 + 5$

33. The formula for the surface area of a sphere with radius r is $A(r) = 4\pi r^2$. Find and interpret the inverse of $A(r)$.

9-6 Modeling Real-World Data *(pp. 698–705)*

EXAMPLE

- **The table shows the ticket prices to a minor league baseball game in relation to the number of years since the team began playing.**

Baseball Ticket Prices	
Year	**Price ($)**
1	9.50
2	10.25
3	11.10
4	12.00
5	12.92

Step 1 Check the first differences of the prices.

0.75 0.85 0.90 0.92

Because the first differences are not constant, a linear model is not a good fit.

Step 2 Check the second differences.

0.10 0.05 0.02

Because the second differences are not constant, a quadratic model is not a good fit.

Step 3 Check the ratios.

$\frac{10.25}{9.5} \approx 1.08$, $\frac{11.10}{10.25} \approx 1.08$, $\frac{12}{11.10} \approx 1.08$, $\frac{12.92}{12} \approx 1.08$

The ratios are close to 1.08. An exponential model is a good fit.

Step 4 Perform an exponential regression.

An appropriate model is $f(x) = 8.79(1.08)^x$.

EXERCISES

34. The table shows the city of Culver's water use in relation to daily high temperature.

Water Use in Culver	
Daily High Temperature (°F)	**Water Use (million gal)**
55	71.3
60	78.7
65	86.9
70	96
75	106
80	117

a. Find an appropriate model for this data. Use temperature t as the independent variable.

b. Use your model to predict the number of gallons that Culver will use when the high temperature is 85°F.

c. Use your model to predict the high temperature when the water use is 50 million gallons.

Answers

31. no

32. yes

33. $r = \sqrt{\frac{A}{4\pi}}$; r is the radius for a sphere with a given surface area.

34a. $f(x) \approx 23.96(1.02)^x$

b. about 129.0 million gal

c. about 37° F

Study Guide: Review **711**

Organizer

Objective: Assess students' mastery of concepts and skills in Chapter 9.

PREMIER Online Edition

Resources

Assessment Resources

Chapter 9 Tests

- Free Response (Levels A, B, C)
- Multiple Choice (Levels A, B, C)
- Performance Assessment

IDEA Works! CD-ROM

Modified Chapter 9 Test

Test & Practice Generator One-Stop Planner®

Answers

1. See p. A41.

2a. Height of Falling Stone

Height (m); Time (s)

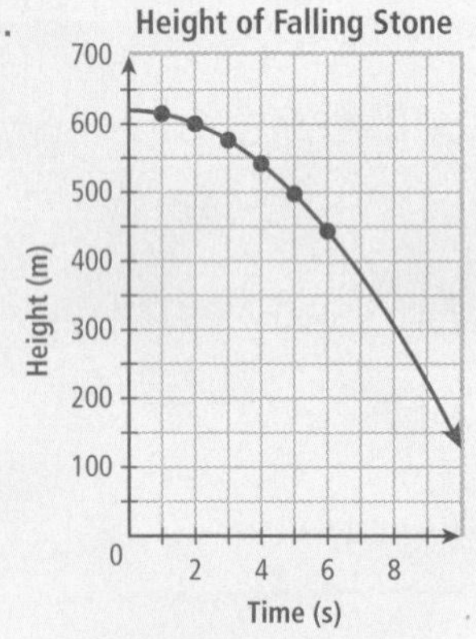

State Resources

go.hrw.com State Resources Online KEYWORD: MB7 Resources

CHAPTER 9 CHAPTER TEST

1. James receives a salary of \$300 per week plus a commission of 3% of the amount he sells. Create a table, a graph, and an equation to represent his weekly earnings on sales of 0 to 10,000 dollars.

2. While standing at the top of a cliff, Kurt accidentally knocks a stone loose. The table shows the height of the stone in meters after t seconds.

   a. Create a graph and an equation for the data by using time t as the independent variable. $h = -4.9t^2 + 620$

   b. How high is the cliff? **620 m**

   c. Find the height of the stone after 10 seconds. **130 m**

   d. When will the stone hit the ground? **about 11.25 s**

Height of Falling Stone	
Time (s)	**Height (m)**
1	615.1
2	600.4
3	575.9
4	541.6
5	497.5
6	443.6

Graph each function.

3. $f(x) = \begin{cases} -x - 3 & \text{if } x < 1 \\ 2x - 6 & \text{if } x \geq 1 \end{cases}$

4. $g(x) = \begin{cases} 5 & \text{if } x \leq -2 \\ -x^2 - 4x & \text{if } x > -2 \end{cases}$

Given $f(x)$, graph $g(x)$.

5. $f(x) = 2x - 4$ and $g(x) = -\frac{1}{2}f(x) - 1$

6. $f(x) = x^2 - 2$ and $g(x) = -f(x + 2)$

Given $f(x) = 4x^2 - 9$ and $g(x) = 2x + 3$, find each function or value.

7. $(f - g)(4)$ **44**

8. $g(f(3))$ **57**

9. $(fg)(5)$ **1183**

10. $\left(\frac{g}{f}\right)(x)$ $\frac{1}{2x - 3}, x \neq \pm\frac{3}{2}$

11. Ramon pays a 10% insurance fee for each piece of jewelry in his store. He then prices the item for sale at 150% of his total cost. Write a composite function for the price of an item with an original cost of c dollars. $P(c) = 1.65c$

Write the rule for the inverse of each function. Determine whether the inverse is a function, and state its domain and range.

12. $f(x) = 12 - 5x$

13. $g(x) = \frac{10}{x + 4}$

14. $h(x) = \frac{(x + 5)^2}{2}$

15. The table shows the average sales prices of houses and the houses' distances from downtown.

   a. Find an appropriate model for the data by using distance d as the independent variable. $P(x) = 128{,}800(0.959)^x$

   b. Use your model to predict the average sales prices of houses that are 20 miles from downtown. **\$55,949**

Sales Prices of Houses	
Distance from Downtown (mi)	**Average Sales Price (\$)**
2	118,496
4	109,016
6	100,295
8	92,271
10	84,890
12	78,098

Answers

3.

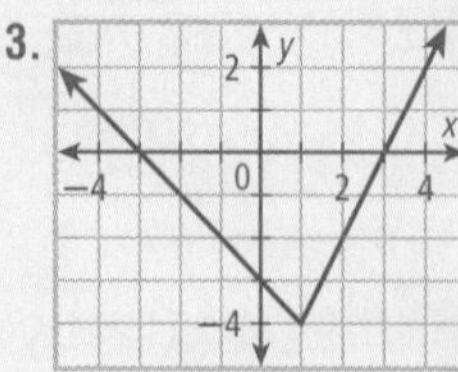

4.

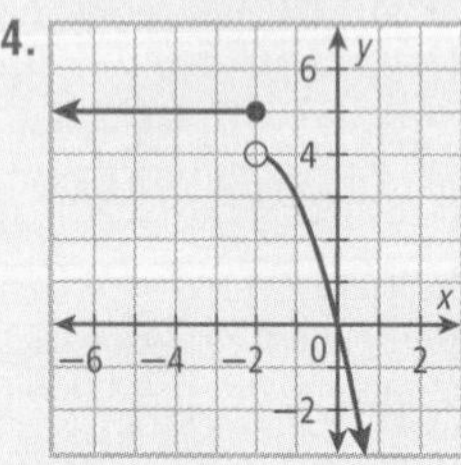

5.

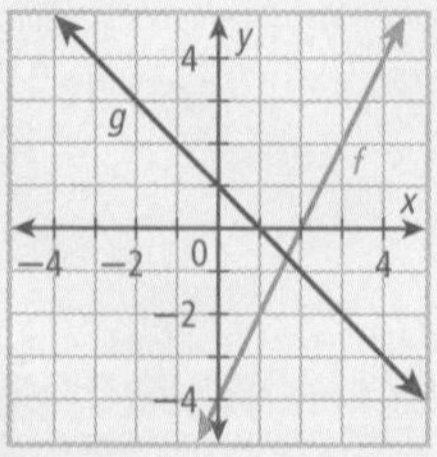

6.

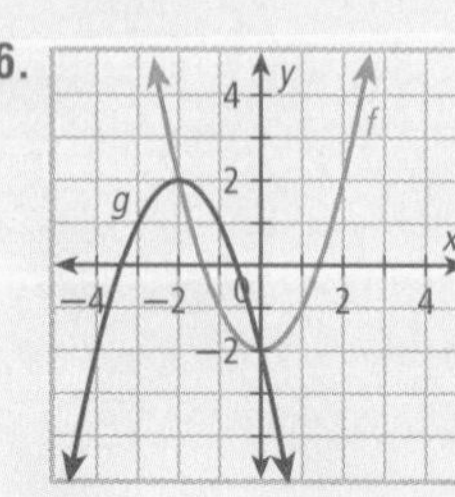

12. $f^{-1}(x) = \frac{-x + 12}{5}$; function; D: $\mathbb{R}$; R: $\mathbb{R}$

13. $g^{-1}(x) = \frac{10}{x} - 4$; function; D: $\{x \mid x \neq 0\}$; R: $\{y \mid y \neq -4\}$

14. $y = \pm\sqrt{2x} - 5$; not a function; $\{x \mid x \geq 0\}$; R: $\mathbb{R}$

College Entrance Exam Practice

FOCUS ON SAT STUDENT-PRODUCED RESPONSES

Some questions on the SAT require you to enter your answer in a special grid. Your answers must be positive integers, fractions, or decimals. You cannot enter negative numbers or mixed numbers in the grid.

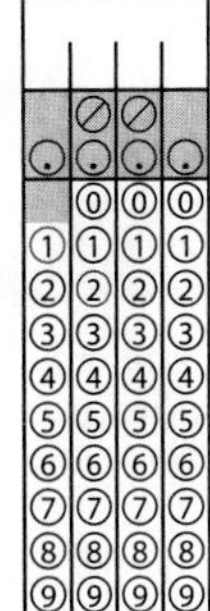

Some questions may have multiple answers; in these cases you may enter any one correct answer. If the solution is an inequality, be sure that you choose a number from the solution region.

You may want to time yourself as you take this practice test. It should take you about 9 minutes to complete.

1. If 5 less than 3 times a number is equal to 2 more than twice the number, what is the number? **7**

2. The graph of $f(x)$ is shown.

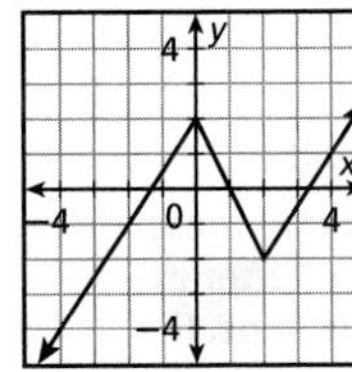

If $g(x) = -f(x) + 1$, what is $g(2)$? **3**

3. Give a possible value for x in the inequality $-4(2x - 3) > 4x - 24$.
any number less than 3

4. Let the operations ◆ and ♥ be defined for real numbers a and b as shown.

$a \blacklozenge b = 2a - b$

$a \heartsuit b = \frac{a+b}{2}$

What is the value of $(4 \heartsuit 9) \blacklozenge 3$? **10**

5. Maria drove to her grandmother's house at an average speed of 60 miles per hour. On the way home, she averaged only 45 miles per hour due to traffic. If she spent a total of $3\frac{1}{2}$ hours driving, how many miles is the trip to her grandmother's house? **90**

6. The table shows some values for the function f.

x	−2	0	2	4
$f(x)$	7	4	1	−2

What is the value of $f^{-1}(-2)$? **4**

COLLEGE ENTRANCE EXAM PRACTICE
CHAPTER 9

Organizer

Objective: Provide practice for college entrance exams such as the SAT.

PREMIER Online Edition

Resources

College Entrance Exam Practice

Questions on the SAT represent the following math strands:

Number and Operation, 30–32%

Algebra and Functions, 28–32%

Geometry and Measurement, 27–30%

Data Analysis, Statistics, and Probability, 10–12%

Items on this page focus on:
- Algebra and Functions

Text References:

Item	1	2	3	4	5	6
Lesson	9-1	9-3	2-1	9-4	8-7	9-5

TEST PREP DOCTOR

1. Students who answered 3.5 may have missed the word "twice" in the problem. Encourage students to read word problems carefully.
2. Students who answered −2 may have found $f(2)$ instead of $g(2)$. Encourage students to graph g before attempting to evaluate $g(2)$.
3. Students who answered 3 may have solved the inequality correctly ($x < 3$) but may not have realized that 3 is not included in the solution set.
4. Students who answered 1 may have applied the functions in the incorrect order. Instruct students to pay close attention to each symbol and follow the order of operations.
5. Students who answered 0.7 may have correctly set up the equation but forgotten to multiply both sides of the rational equation by the common denominator.
6. Students who answered 7 may have found $f(-2)$ instead of $f^{-1}(-2)$. Remind students that to evaluate an inverse, they should find the input value for the output value −2 in the table.

Organizer

Objective: Provide opportunities to learn and practice common test-taking strategies.

Online Edition

Resources

State Test Prep Workbook

***State Test Prep* CD-ROM**

***State Test Practice* Online**

go.hrw.com
KEYWORD: MB7 TestPrep

This Test Tackler focuses on using logic and mental math to eliminate answer choices in multiple choice test items. Although this strategy may not always help students find the specific answer, it may save students time by eliminating some of the choices. After students have read a multiple choice test item, have them first determine if any of the answer choices can be immediately eliminated, then solve the problem.

Standardized Test Strategies

Multiple Choice: Eliminate Answer Choices

With some multiple choice test items, you can use mental math or logic to quickly eliminate some of the answer choices before you begin solving the problem.

EXAMPLE 1

Tyler can install an air conditioning unit in 3 hours. If Laura helps him, the job is done in 2 hours. How many hours would it take Laura working alone?

Ⓐ 1 hour
Ⓑ 2 hours
Ⓒ 6 hours
Ⓓ 8 hours

*READ the question. Then try to **eliminate** some of the answer choices.*

Use logic:
When Tyler works alone, the job gets done in 3 hours. When working with Laura, the job takes only 2 hours. So, it is reasonable to assume that Laura working alone takes MORE THAN 2 hours to complete the job.

Based on this logic, **eliminate** choices A and B.
Set up and solve a rational equation to find the correct answer, C.

EXAMPLE 2

Ryanne swims six days a week. Her coach starts keeping time when Ryanne starts warming up and notes how long Ryanne has been at the pool after every 2 laps. The table shows the time that it takes for Ryanne to swim 12 laps. If Ryanne wants to swim 24 laps, how long will it take?

Laps	Time (min)
2	6
4	10
6	14
8	18
10	22
12	26

Ⓕ 28 minutes
Ⓖ 38 minutes
Ⓗ 48 minutes
Ⓙ 50 minutes

*LOOK at the data, and **eliminate** some answer choices.*

Use mental math and logic:
From the data in the table, you can tell that Ryanne swims 2 laps every 4 minutes. So it takes her 2 minutes to swim 1 lap.

So 24 laps would take $24(2) = 48$ minutes. You can eliminate any answer choice that is LESS THAN 48 minutes: choices F and G.

Before you select choice H as your answer, be careful. Look at the data in the table again. The first 2 laps that Ryanne swims take her **6** minutes, not 4 minutes, so your estimate of 48 laps is a bit low. Therefore, **eliminate** choice H. Choice J is the correct answer.

Try to eliminate unreasonable answer choices. Some choices may be too great or too small or may have incorrect units.

Read each test item and answer the questions that follow.

Item A

The width of a rectangle is 6 feet less than its length. Which of the following systems of equations can be used to find the dimensions of the rectangle if the perimeter of the rectangle is 56 feet?

Ⓐ $\ell = w - 6$, $2\ell + 2w = 56$

Ⓑ $w = \ell - 6$, $2(\ell + w) = 56$

Ⓒ $\ell = w - 6$, $\ell w = 56$

Ⓓ $w = \ell - 6$, $\ell w = \ell 6$

1. What is the perimeter formula for the area of a rectangle? Based on this formula, are there any choices that you can eliminate immediately? If so, which choices and why?
2. Read the first sentence of the test item again and write an expression. Are there any more answer choices that you can eliminate? Explain.

Item B

The volume V of a gas varies inversely with the pressure P and directly with the temperature T. A certain gas has a volume of 30 liters, a temperature of 345 kelvins, and a pressure of 1 atmosphere. If the gas is compressed to a volume of 20 liters and heated to 375 kelvins, what will the new pressure be?

Ⓕ 0.72 atmosphere

Ⓖ 0.72 liter

Ⓗ 1.5 atmospheres

Ⓙ 1.63 atmospheres

3. Are there any answer choices that logically do not make sense and can be eliminated? If so, which choices and why?
4. Because the volume of a gas varies inversely with the pressure, if the volume decreases, should the pressure increase or decrease? Can you eliminate any of the answer choices by using this information?

Item C

A moving truck company charges $125 a day for driving its truck 50 miles or less. The company charges an additional $0.05 per mile for all miles driven over 50 miles. Which of the following functions represents the fee for this moving truck for x miles in a day?

Ⓐ $C(x) = \begin{cases} 125 & \text{if } 0 \le x \le 50 \\ 2.5 & \text{if } x > 50 \end{cases}$

Ⓑ $C(x) = \begin{cases} 125 & \text{if } 0 \le x \le 50 \\ 125 + 0.05(x - 50) & \text{if } x > 50 \end{cases}$

Ⓒ $C(x) = \begin{cases} 50 & \text{if } 0 \le x \le 50 \\ 50 + 0.05x & \text{if } x > 50 \end{cases}$

Ⓓ $C(x) = \begin{cases} 0.05 & \text{if } 0 \le x \le 50 \\ 125x & \text{if } x > 50 \end{cases}$

5. Look at answer choice A. Why can it be eliminated immediately?
6. Sarah wants to eliminate choice C. Do you agree? Explain.

Item D

Which function corresponds to the graph?

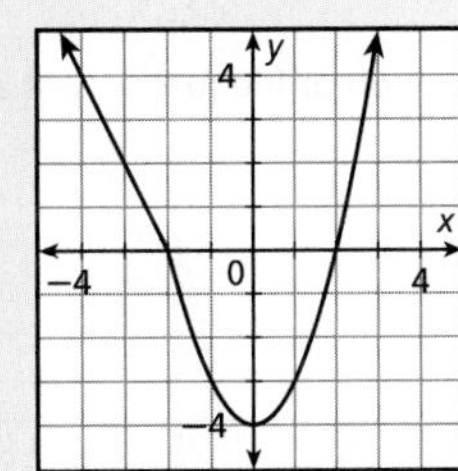

Ⓕ $g(x) = \begin{cases} x^2 - 4 & \text{if } x \ge 0 \\ -2x - 4 & \text{if } x < 0 \end{cases}$

Ⓖ $g(x) = \begin{cases} x - 4 & \text{if } x \ge -2 \\ -2x & \text{if } x < -2 \end{cases}$

Ⓗ $g(x) = \begin{cases} x^2 - 4 & \text{if } x \ge -2 \\ -2x - 4 & \text{if } x < -2 \end{cases}$

Ⓙ $g(x) = \begin{cases} x^2 & \text{if } x \ge -2 \\ -2x + 4 & \text{if } x < -2 \end{cases}$

7. Describe the functions on the graph. Which answer choice can be eliminated based on the shape of the function?
8. Kaye looked at the domain of the function and decided to eliminate choice F. Do you agree with Kaye's decision? Explain.

Answers

Possible answers:

1. $P = 2\ell + 2w$; yes; choices C and D because they use the area formula rather than the perimeter formula in one of their equations
2. $w = \ell - 6$; yes, choice A because the equation that represents the length does not correspond to the first sentence.
3. yes; choice G because the units given are in liters, and the new pressure is measured in atmospheres
4. increase; yes, choice F because 0.72 atm is less than 1 atm
5. Neither equation is given in terms of x.
6. Yes; the base fee is $125, not $50.
7. Linear and quadratic; choice G can be eliminated because both equations are linear. One equation needs to be quadratic.
8. Yes, the domain in choice F is incorrect.

Answers to Test Items

A. B
B. J
C. B
D. H

State Resources

go.hrw.com
State Resources Online
KEYWORD: MB7 Resources

Organizer

Objective: Provide review and practice for Chapters 1–9 and standardized tests.

Resources

 ***Assessment Resources***

Chapter 9 Cumulative Test

 ***State Test Prep Workbook***

 ***State Test Prep* CD-ROM**

***State Test Practice* Online**

KEYWORD: MB7 TestPrep

Answers

1. C
2. D
3. B
4. B
5. C
6. A
7. B
8. D
9. A
10. A

State Resources

Core Standard	Items
1	1
2	10
3	9, 11, 12, 13
4	7

CUMULATIVE ASSESSMENT, CHAPTERS 1–9

Multiple Choice

1. Which is the graph of $f(x) = |x + 1| - 2$?

A.

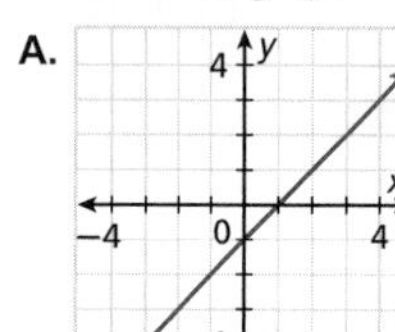

B.

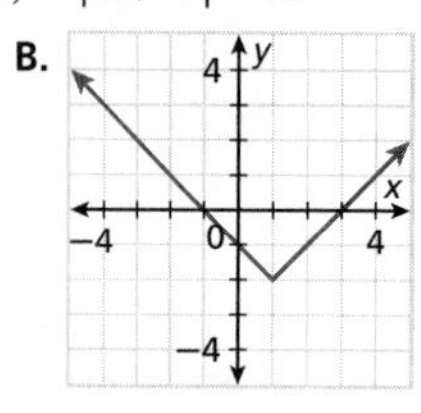

C.

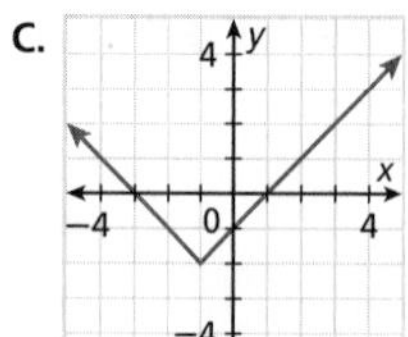

D.

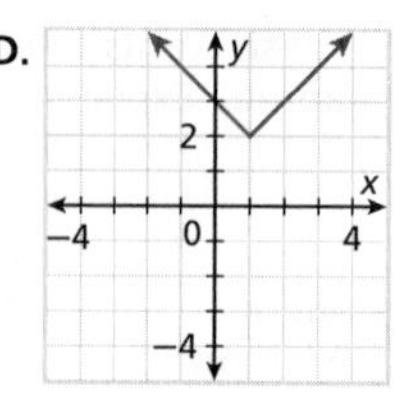

2. Which equation or inequality best represents the graph?

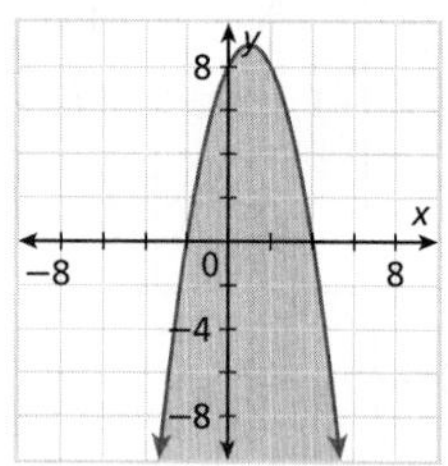

A. $y = x^2 + 2x + 8$

B. $y = -x^2 + 2x + 8$

C. $y \le x^2 + 2x + 8$

D. $y \le -x^2 + 2x + 8$

3. Which is the augmented matrix for this system of equations?

$$\begin{cases} -5y = 8 - x \\ y + 3x = 10 \end{cases}$$

A. $\left[\begin{array}{cc|c} -5 & 8 & -1 \\ 1 & 3 & 10 \end{array}\right]$ **B.** $\left[\begin{array}{cc|c} 1 & -5 & 8 \\ 3 & 1 & 10 \end{array}\right]$

C. $\left[\begin{array}{cc|c} 1 & -5 & 8 \\ 1 & 3 & 10 \end{array}\right]$ **D.** $\left[\begin{array}{cc|c} -5 & 8 & -1 \\ 3 & 1 & 10 \end{array}\right]$

4. Which description best reflects the graph shown?

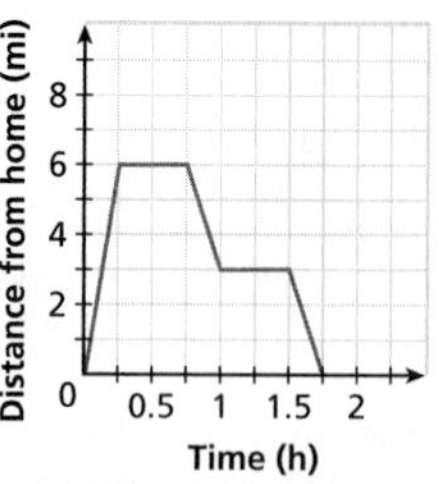

A. Lou drove 6 miles to the library, spent an hour there, and then drove straight home.

B. Lou drove 6 miles to the library, spent half an hour there, stopped by the video store for half an hour, and then drove home.

C. Lou drove 3 miles to the library, spent half an hour there, drove another 3 miles to the movie store, and then drove home.

D. Lou drove 6 miles to the library, spent half an hour there, drove another 3 miles to the video store, and spent an hour there.

5. Evaluate the piecewise function for $x = -1$.

$$f(x) = \begin{cases} x^2 + 4x - 8 & x < -1 \\ x^3 - x^2 + 5 & x \ge -1 \end{cases}$$

A. -13 **B.** -11

C. 3 **D.** 5

6. Solve for x.

$\sqrt{2x - 4} = x - 6$

A. $x = 10$ **B.** $x = 4$ and $x = 10$

C. $x = 2$ and $x = 20$ **D.** $x = 2$ and $x = 12$

7. Given $f(x) = 2x^2 - 7x - 30$ and $g(x) = x - 6$, find $\left(\frac{f}{g}\right)(x)$.

A. $2x - 5$ **B.** $2x + 5$

C. $\dfrac{(2x - 5)(x + 6)}{x - 6}$ **D.** $\dfrac{(2x - 10)(9x + 3)}{x - 6}$

Test Prep Doctor

For **Items 1** and **9,** students should use what they know about transformations of parent functions to eliminate choices right away. For **Item 1,** the − 2 outside of the absolute value bars indicates a vertical translation that shifts the vertex 2 units below the x-axis. This means that only choices **B** and **C** are possible answers. Knowing that + 1 inside of the absolute value bars means a shift to the left points the student to answer choice **C.**

For **Item 9,** because the quadratic term is negative, the parabola opens downward. The student can eliminate choices **B** and **D.** Then the student must use knowledge about compression and stretching to make the final choice.

8. Which transformation of triangle *ABD* creates an image with a vertex at $(-2, 1)$?

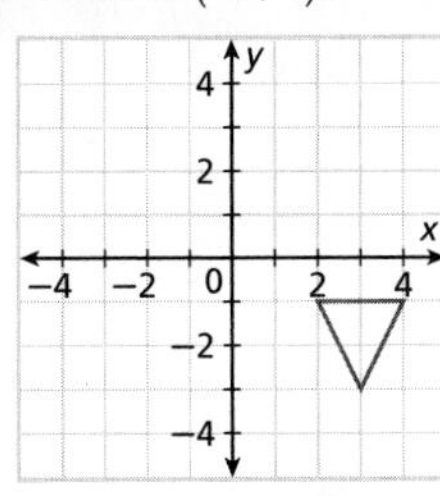

A. Reflect $\triangle ABC$ across the *x*-axis.

B. Reflect $\triangle ABC$ across the *y*-axis.

C. Translate $\triangle ABC$ 3 units left and 3 units up.

D. Rotate $\triangle ABC$ 180° about the origin.

In Item 9, examine one part of the function at a time, eliminating answer choices until you find a graph that matches all parts of the function.

9. Which is the graph of $f(x) = -\frac{1}{2}x^2 + 6$?

A.

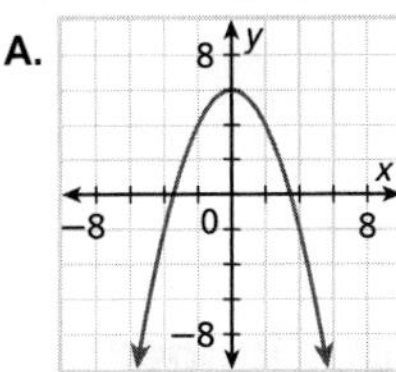

B.

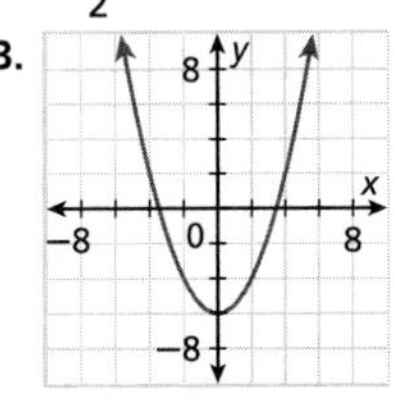

C.

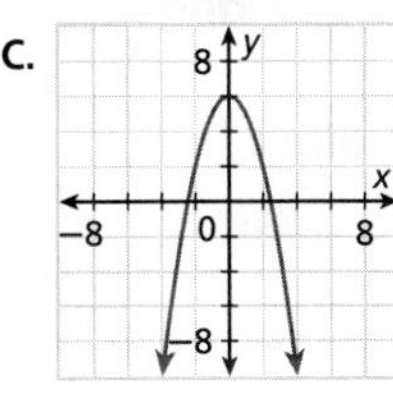

D.

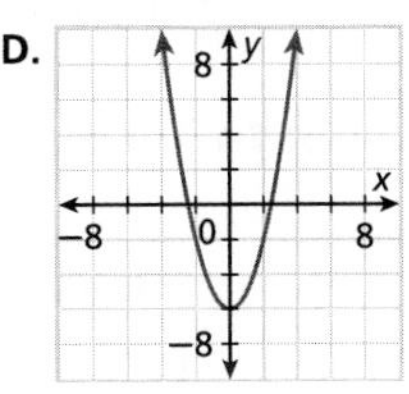

10. What is the value of *c* in the given equation?

$4(5i - 2) + 3 = 2(10i + c) - 7$

A. 1

B. 2

C. 3

D. 4

Short Answer

11. The equation $f(x) = x^2 + 1$ is a function.

Part A Find the inverse of the function.

Part B Graph $f(x) = x^2 + 1$ and its inverse.

Part C Explain whether the inverse is a function.

12. Use the points below.

$(0, 6)$, $(2, 2)$, and $(5, 11)$

Part A Write a quadratic function that fits the points.

Part B Check the quadratic function that you wrote by substituting the ordered pairs. Verify that each is a solution.

Part C Graph the equation.

Part D Find $f(7)$ and $f(-7)$.

13. Consider the function $f(x) = x^2 - 4$.

Part A Identify two different transformations of *f* so that the vertex would be $(1, 4)$.

Part B Identify two different transformations of *f* so that its graph would pass through $(0, 2)$ and $(-4, 2)$.

Extended Response

14. The volume of gas in a car depends on the number of miles that have been driven since the tank was last filled.

Distance driven (mi)	0	50	100	150	200
Gas (gal)	10	8	6	4	2

Part A Use constant differences or ratios to determine which parent function would best model the given data.

Part B Write the equation for the data.

Part C How many gallons are left after 75 miles?

Part D Can the car be driven for 300 miles? Why or why not?

Part E Find and interpret the inverse of the equation.

Short Answer Rubric

Items 11–13

Score 2 = Thorough understanding of mathematical concepts and processes.

Score 1 = Partial understanding of mathematical concepts and/or processes.

Score 0 = Limited or no understanding of the problem-solving concepts.

Blank = No written response.

Extended Response Rubric

Item 14

Score 4 = Thorough understanding of mathematical concepts and processes.

Score 3 = Demonstrated understanding of mathematical concepts and processes, but an error in computation or explanation.

Score 2 = Partial understanding of mathematical concepts and/or processes.

Score 1 = Limited understanding and execution of the problem-solving concepts.

Score 0 = No understanding of the problem-solving concepts.

Blank = No written response.

Answers

11. Part A: $y = \pm\sqrt{x - 1}$

Part B:

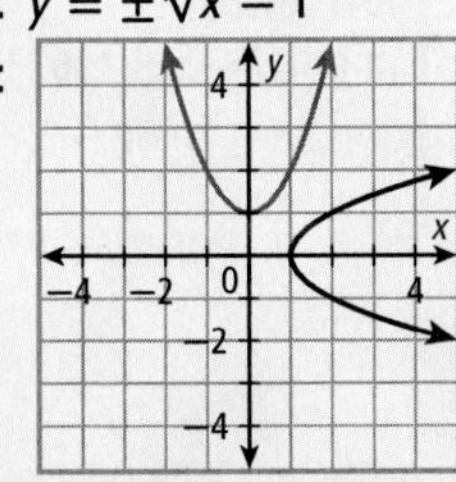

Part C: not a function because there are 2 *y*-values for any $x > 1$

12. Part A: $f(x) = x^2 - 4x + 6$

Part B: $f(2) = 2$; $f(0) = 6$; $f(5) = 11$

Part C:

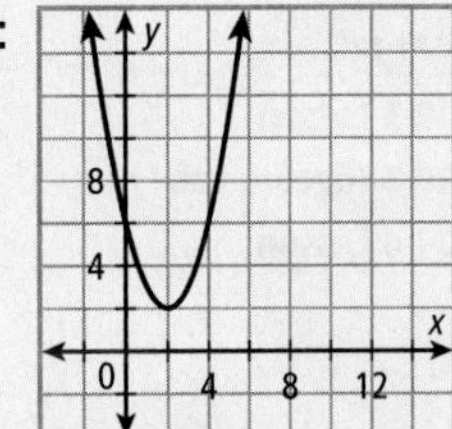

Part D: $f(7) = 27$; $f(-7) = 83$

13. Part A: Possible answers: a translation 8 units up and 1 unit right; a reflection across the *x*-axis and a translation 1 unit right

Part B: Possible answers: a translation 2 units up and 2 units left; a reflection across the *x*-axis and a translation 2 units up and 2 units left

14. Part A: $y = x$

Part B: $f(x) = -0.04x + 10$

Part C: 7 gal

Part D: No; the car would run out of gas at 250 ml

Part E: $f^{-1}(x) = -25x + 250$; the number of miles a car has driven when *x* gallons are left in the tank

CHAPTER 10 Conic Sections

Section 10A

Exploring Conic Sections

10-1 Introduction to Conic Sections
10-2 Circles
Connecting Algebra to Geometry Surface Area and Volume
10-3 Ellipses
10-3 Algebra Lab Locate the Foci of an Ellipse
10-4 Hyperbolas
10-5 Parabolas

Section 10B

Applying Conic Sections

10-6 Identifying Conic Sections
10-6 Technology Lab Conic-Section Art
10-7 Solving Nonlinear Systems

Pacing Guide for 45-Minute Classes

Chapter 10

Countdown to Testing Weeks 21, 22

DAY 1	DAY 2	DAY 3	DAY 4	DAY 5
10-1 Lesson	10-2 Lesson	Connecting Algebra to Geometry 10-3 Lesson	10-3 Lesson 10-3 Algebra Lab	10-4 Lesson
DAY 6	**DAY 7**	**DAY 8**	**DAY 9**	**DAY 10**
10-5 Lesson	10-5 Lesson Multi-Step Test Prep Ready to Go On?	10-6 Lesson	10-6 Technology Lab	10-7 Lesson
DAY 11	**DAY 12**			
10-7 Lesson Multi-Step Test Prep Ready to Go On?	Chapter 10 Test			

Pacing Guide for 90-Minute Classes

Chapter 10

DAY 1	DAY 2	DAY 3	DAY 4	DAY 5
Chapter 9 Test 10-1 Lesson	10-2 Lesson Connecting Algebra to Geometry 10-3 Lesson	10-3 Lesson 10-3 Algebra Lab 10-4 Lesson	10-5 Lesson Multi-Step Test Prep Ready to Go On?	10-6 Lesson 10-6 Technology Lab
DAY 6	**DAY 7**			
10-7 Lesson Multi-Step Test Prep Ready to Go On?	Chapter 10 Test 11-1 Lesson			

ONGOING ASSESSMENT and INTERVENTION

Assess Prior Knowledge

Before Chapter 10

DIAGNOSE	PRESCRIBE
Diagnose readiness for the chapter.	Prescribe intervention.
Are You Ready? SE p. 719	 ***Are You Ready? Intervention*** Skills 37, 38, 39, 82

Formative Assessment

Before Every Lesson

DIAGNOSE	PRESCRIBE
Diagnose readiness for the lesson.	Prescribe intervention.
Warm Up TE, every lesson	**Skills Bank** SE pp. S46–S73
	Reteach CRB, Ch. 1–10

During Every Lesson

DIAGNOSE	PRESCRIBE
Diagnose understanding of lesson concepts.	Prescribe intervention.
Check It Out! SE, every example	**Questioning Strategies** TE, every example
Think and Discuss SE, every lesson	**Reading Strategies** CRB, every lesson
Write About It SE, every lesson	***Success for ELL*** pp. 141–154
Journal TE, every lesson	

After Every Lesson

DIAGNOSE	PRESCRIBE
Diagnose mastery of lesson concepts.	Prescribe intervention.
Lesson Quiz TE, every lesson	**Reteach** CRB, every lesson
Alternative Assessment TE, every lesson	**Problem Solving** CRB, every lesson
Test Prep SE, every lesson	**Test Prep Doctor** TE, every lesson
Test and Practice Generator	***Homework Help* Online**

Before Chapter 10 Testing

DIAGNOSE	PRESCRIBE
Diagnose mastery of concepts in the chapter.	Prescribe intervention.
Ready to Go On? SE pp. 759, 777	***Ready to Go On? Intervention*** pp. 161–178
Multi-Step Test Prep SE pp. 758, 776	**Scaffolding Questions** TE pp. 758, 776
Section Quizzes AR pp. 185–186	
Test and Practice Generator	

Before High Stakes Testing

DIAGNOSE	PRESCRIBE
Diagnose mastery of benchmark concepts.	Prescribe intervention.
College Entrance Exam Practice SE p. 783	***College Entrance Exam Practice***
Standardized Test Prep SE pp. 786–787	***State Test Prep Workbook***
State Test Prep CD-ROM	

Summative Assessment

After Chapter 10

DIAGNOSE	PRESCRIBE
Check mastery of chapter concepts.	Prescribe intervention.
Multiple-Choice Tests (Forms A, B, C)	**Reteach** CRB, every lesson
Free-Response Tests (Forms A, B, C)	***Lesson Tutorial Videos*** Chapter 10
Performance Assessment AR pp. 187–200	
Test and Practice Generator	
Check mastery of benchmark concepts.	Prescribe intervention.
AYP State Tests	***State Test Prep Workbook***
College Entrance Exams	***College Entrance Exam Practice***

KEY: **SE** = *Student Edition* **TE** = *Teacher's Edition* **CRB** = *Chapter Resource Book* **AR** = *Assessment Resources* Available on CD-ROM  Available online

Supporting the Teacher

Chapter 10 Resource Book

Practice A, B, C
pp. 3–5, 11–13, 19–21, 27–29, 35–37, 43–45, 51–53

Reading Strategies ELL
pp. 10, 18, 26, 34, 42, 50, 58

Reteach
pp. 6–7, 14–15, 22–23, 30–31, 38–39, 46–47, 54–55

Problem Solving
pp. 9, 17, 25, 33, 41, 49, 57

Challenge
pp. 8, 16, 24, 32, 40, 48, 56

Parent Letter pp. 1–2

Transparencies

Lesson Transparencies, Volume 3 .... Chapter 10
- Warm Ups
- Teaching Transparencies
- Additional Examples
- Lesson Quizzes

Alternate Openers: Explorations 71–77

Countdown to Testing 41–44

Know-It Notebook .... Chapter 10
- Graphic Organizers

Teacher Tools

Power Presentations®
Complete PowerPoint® presentations for Chapter 10 lessons

Lesson Tutorial Videos®
Holt authors Ed Burger and Freddie Renfro present tutorials to support the Chapter 10 lessons.

One-Stop Planner®
Easy access to all Chapter 10 resources and assessments, as well as software for lesson planning, test generation, and puzzle creation

IDEA Works!®
Key Chapter 10 resources and assessments modified to address special learning needs

Lesson Plans .... pp. 71–77

Solutions Key .... Chapter 10

Algebra Posters

TechKeys 

Lab Resources 

Project Teacher Support

Parent Resources

Workbooks

Homework and Practice Workbook
Teacher's Guide .... pp. 71–77

Know-It Notebook
Teacher's Guide .... Chapter 10

Problem Solving Workbook
Teacher's Guide .... pp. 71–77

State Test Prep Workbook
Teacher's Guide

Technology Highlights for the Teacher

Power Presentations

Dynamic presentations to engage students. Complete PowerPoint® presentations for every lesson in Chapter 10.

2-1 Solving One-Step Equations

Isolate a variable by using inverse operations which "undo" operations on the variable.

An equation is like a balanced scale. To keep the balance, perform the same operation on both sides.

Inverse Operations	
Operation	**Inverse Operation**
Addition	Subtraction
Subtraction	Addition

One-Stop Planner

Easy access to Chapter 10 resources and assessments. Includes lesson-planning, test-generation, and puzzle-creation software.

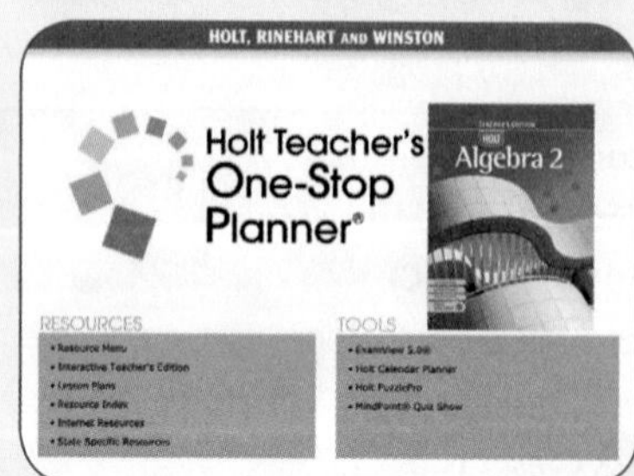

Premier Online Edition

Chapter 10 includes Tutorial Videos, Lesson Activities, Lesson Quizzes, Homework Help, and Chapter Project.

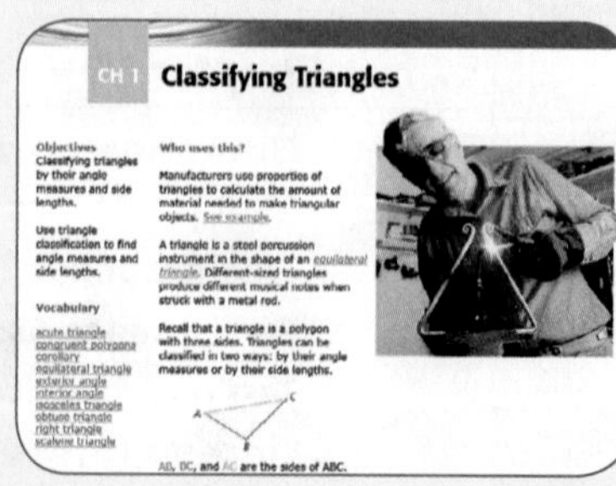

KEY: **SE** = *Student Edition* **TE** = *Teacher's Edition*  English Language Learners  Available on CD-ROM  Available online

CHAPTER 10

Reaching All Learners

Resources for All Learners

- *Algebra Lab Activities* .... Chapter 10
- *Technology Lab Activities* .... Chapter 10
- *Homework and Practice Workbook* .... pp. 71–77
- *Know-It Notebook* .... Chapter 10
- *Problem Solving Workbook* .... pp. 71–77

DEVELOPING LEARNERS

- **Practice A** .... CRB, every lesson
- **Reteach** .... CRB, every lesson
- **Inclusion** .... TE pp. 747, 756, 771
- **Questioning Strategies** .... TE, every example
- **Modified Chapter 10 Resources** .... *IDEA Works!*
- ***Homework Help Online***

ON-LEVEL LEARNERS

- **Practice B** .... CRB, every lesson
- **Multiple Representations** .... TE pp. 730, 731
- **Modeling** .... TE p. 745

ADVANCED LEARNERS

- **Practice C** .... CRB, every lesson
- **Challenge** .... CRB, every lesson
- **Reading and Writing Math EXTENSION** .... TE p. 721
- **Multi-Step Test Prep EXTENSION** .... TE pp. 758, 776
- **Critical Thinking** .... TE pp. 764, 765

English Language Learners

ENGLISH LANGUAGE LEARNERS

- **Are You Ready? Vocabulary** .... SE p. 719
- **Vocabulary Connections** .... SE p. 720
- **Lesson Vocabulary** .... SE pp. 722, 729, 736, 744, 751, 768
- **Vocabulary Exercises** . SE pp. 726, 732, 740, 748, 755, 772
- **Vocabulary Review** .... SE p. 778
- **English Language Learners** .... TE pp. 721, 723, 724, 738, 747, 762, 789
- **Reading Strategies** .... CRB, every lesson
- ***Success for English Language Learners*** .... pp. 141–154
- ***Multilingual Glossary***

Reaching All Learners Through...

- **Concrete Manipulatives** .... TE p. 723
- **Visual Cues** .... TE pp. 724, 763, 769
- **Multiple Representations** .... TE pp. 730, 731
- **Kinesthetic Experience** .... TE pp. 737, 753
- **Modeling** .... TE p. 745
- **Inclusion** .... TE pp. 747, 756, 771
- **Cooperative Learning** .... TE p. 752
- **Cognitive Strategies** .... TE p. 761
- **Critical Thinking** .... TE pp. 764–765
- **Test Prep Doctor** .... TE pp. 728, 734, 742, 750, 757, 766, 774, 783, 784, 786
- **Common Error Alerts** .... TE pp. 725, 731, 733, 761, 771
- **Scaffolding Questions** .... TE pp. 758, 776

Technology Highlights for Reaching All Learners

Lesson Tutorial Videos

Starring Holt authors Ed Burger and Freddie Renfro! Live tutorials to support every lesson in Chapter 10.

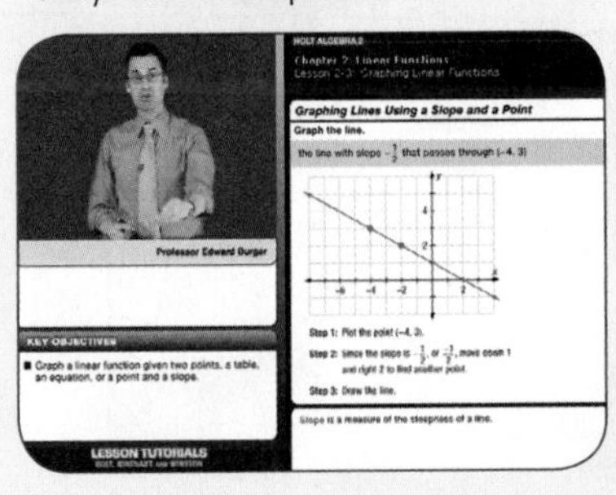

Multilingual Glossary

Searchable glossary includes definitions in English, Spanish, Vietnamese, Chinese, Hmong, Korean, and 4 other languages.

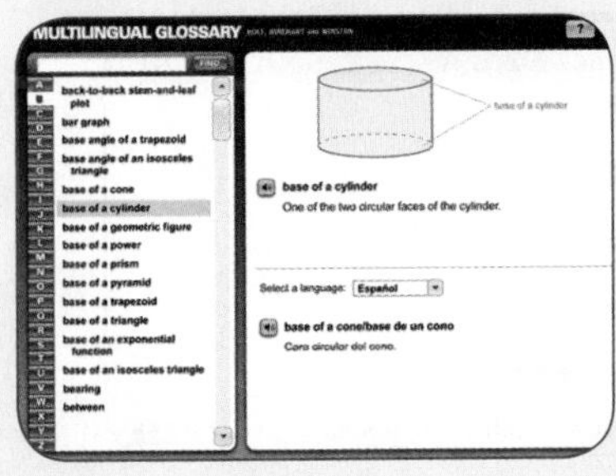

Online Interactivities

Interactive tutorials provide visually engaging alternative opportunities to learn concepts and master skills.

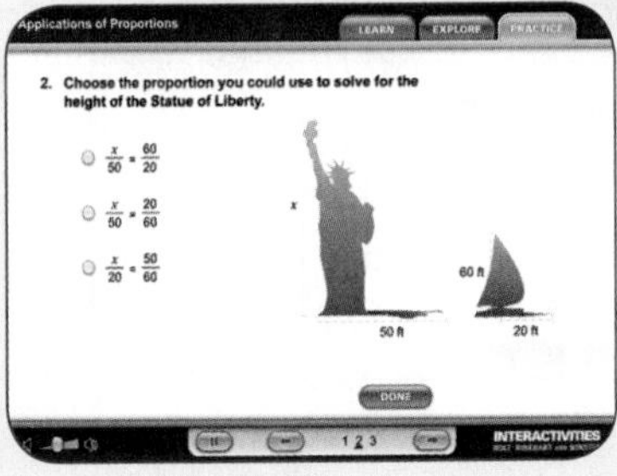

KEY: **SE** = *Student Edition* **TE** = *Teacher's Edition* **CRB** = *Chapter Resource Book* 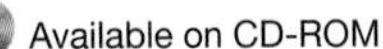 Available on CD-ROM  Available online

Ongoing Assessment

Assessing Prior Knowledge

Determine whether students have the required prerequisite concepts and skills for success in Chapter 10.

Are You Ready? SPANISH .... SE p. 719
Warm Up .... TE, every lesson

Test Preparation

Provide review and practice for Chapter 10 and standardized tests.

Multi-Step Test Prep .... SE pp. 758, 776
Study Guide: Review .... SE pp. 778–781
Test Tackler .... SE pp. 784–785
Standardized Test Prep .... SE pp. 786–787
College Entrance Exam Practice .... SE p. 783
***Countdown to Testing* Transparencies** 41–44
State Test Prep Workbook
***State Test Prep* CD-ROM**
IDEA Works!

Alternative Assessment

Assess students' understanding of Chapter 10 concepts and combined problem-solving skills.

Chapter 10 Project .... SE p. 718
Alternative Assessment .... TE, every lesson
Performance Assessment .... AR pp. 199–200
Portfolio Assessment .... AR p. xxxiv

Daily Assessment

Provide formative assessment for each day of Chapter 10.

Questioning Strategies .... TE, every example
Think and Discuss .... SE, every lesson
Check It Out! Exercises .... SE, every example
Write About It .... SE, every lesson
Journal .... TE, every lesson
Lesson Quiz .... TE, every lesson
Alternative Assessment .... TE, every lesson
Modified Lesson Quizzes .... *IDEA Works!*

Weekly Assessment

Provide formative assessment for each week of Chapter 10.

Multi-Step Test Prep .... SE pp. 758, 776
Ready to Go On? .... SE pp. 759, 777
Cumulative Assessment .... SE pp. 786–787
Test and Practice Generator .... *One-Stop Planner*

Formal Assessment

Provide summative assessment of Chapter 10 mastery.

Section Quizzes .... AR pp. 185–186
Chapter 10 Test .... SE p. 782
Chapter Test (Levels A, B, C) .... AR pp. 187–198
• Multiple Choice • Free Response
Cumulative Test .... AR pp. 201–204
Test and Practice Generator .... *One-Stop Planner*
Modified Chapter 10 Test .... *IDEA Works!*

Technology Highlights for Ongoing Assessment

Are You Ready? SPANISH

Automatically assess readiness and prescribe intervention for Chapter 10 prerequisite skills.

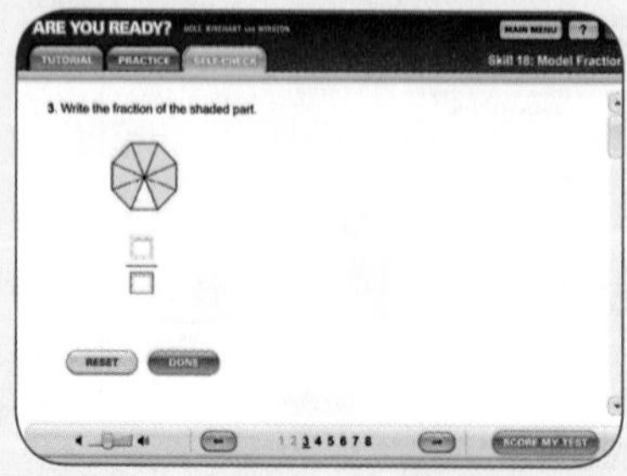

Ready to Go On?

Automatically assess understanding and prescribe intervention for Sections 10A and 10B.

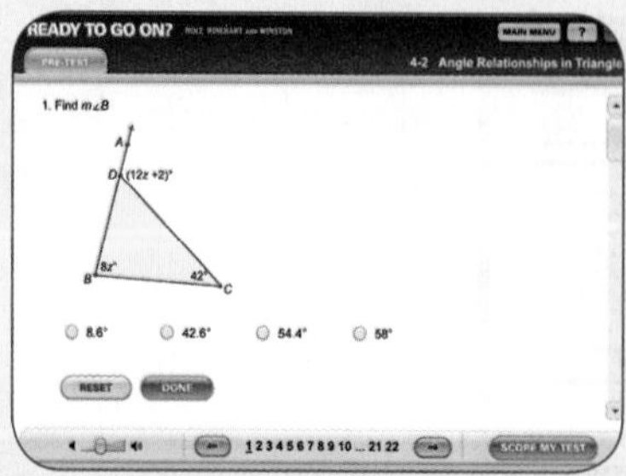

Test and Practice Generator

Use Chapter 10 problem banks to create assessments and worksheets to print out or deliver online. Includes dynamic problems.

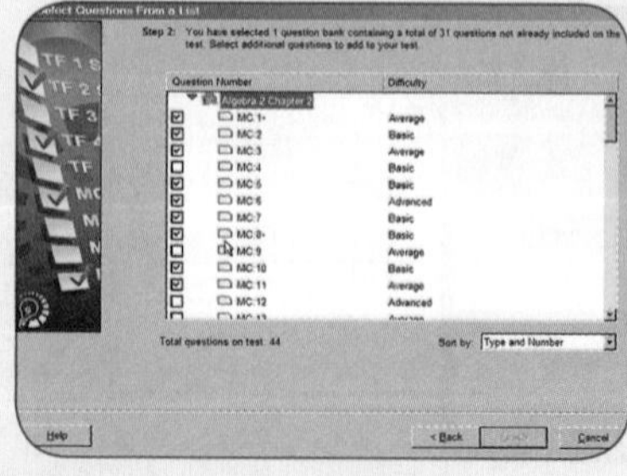

KEY: **SE** = *Student Edition* **TE** = *Teacher's Edition* **AR** = *Assessment Resources*  Spanish version available  Available on CD-ROM 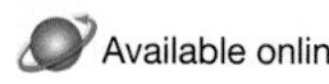

Formal Assessment

Three levels (A, B, C) of multiple-choice and free-response chapter tests are available in the *Assessment Resources*.

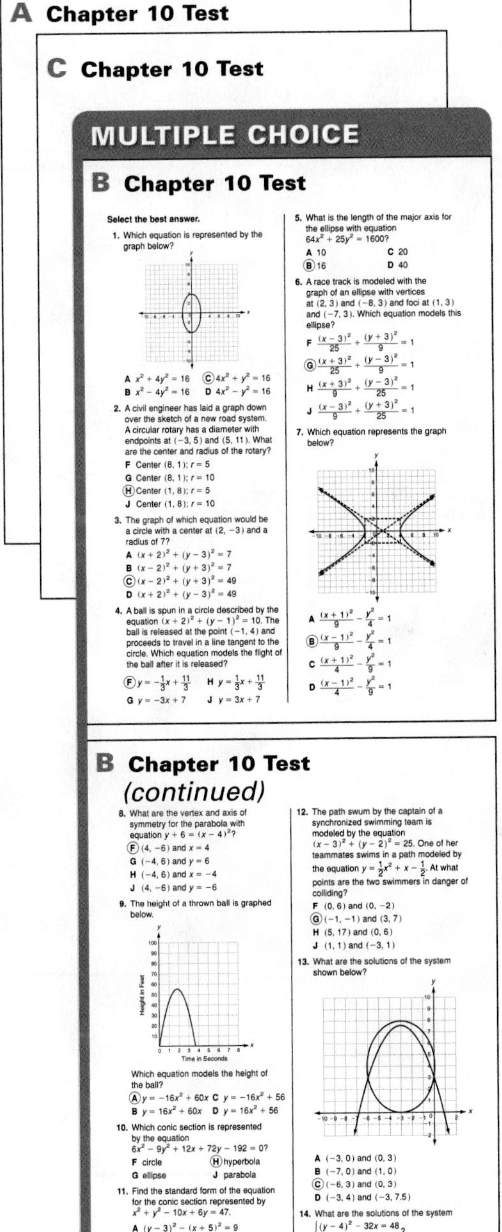

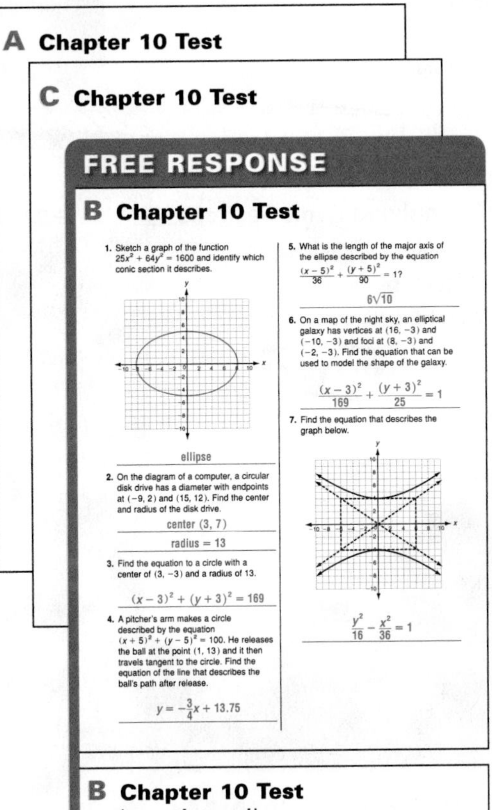

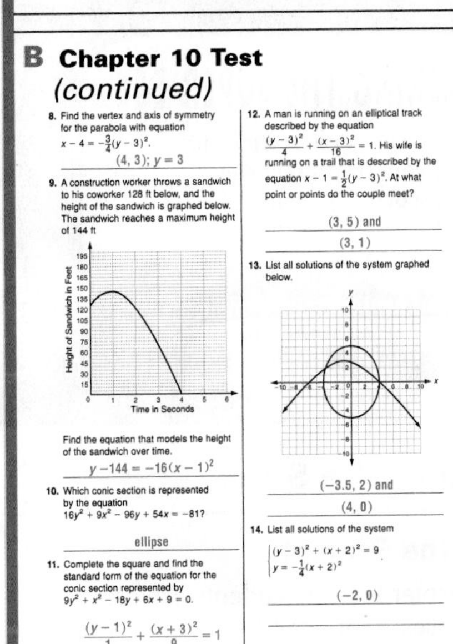

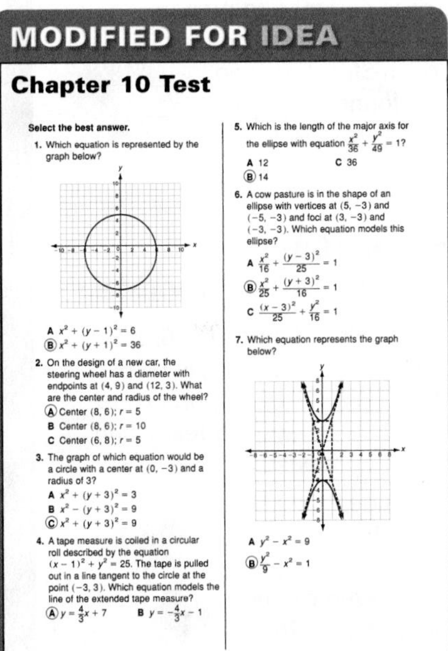

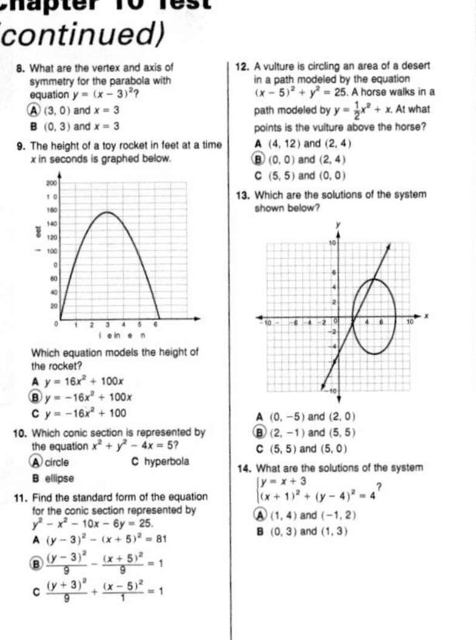

Test & Practice Generator
One-Stop Planner®

Create and customize Chapter 10 Tests. Instantly generate multiple test versions, answer keys, and practice versions of test items.

CHAPTER 10

SECTION 10A
Understanding Conic Sections

On page 758, students write, solve, and graph equations to model real-world events in our solar system.

Exercises designed to prepare students for success on the Multi-Step Test Prep can be found on pages 726, 733, 741, 749, and 756.

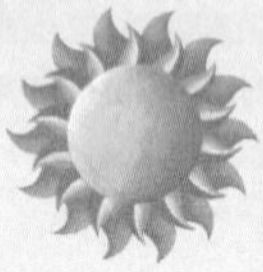

SECTION 10B
Applying Conic Sections

On page 776, students apply ratios and proportions to model a real-world water-skiing situation.

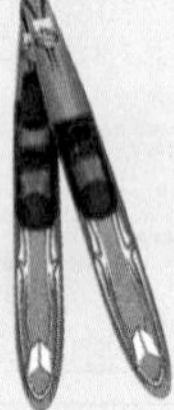

Exercises designed to prepare students for success on the Multi-Step Test Prep can be found on pages 765 and 773.

CHAPTER 10 Conic Sections

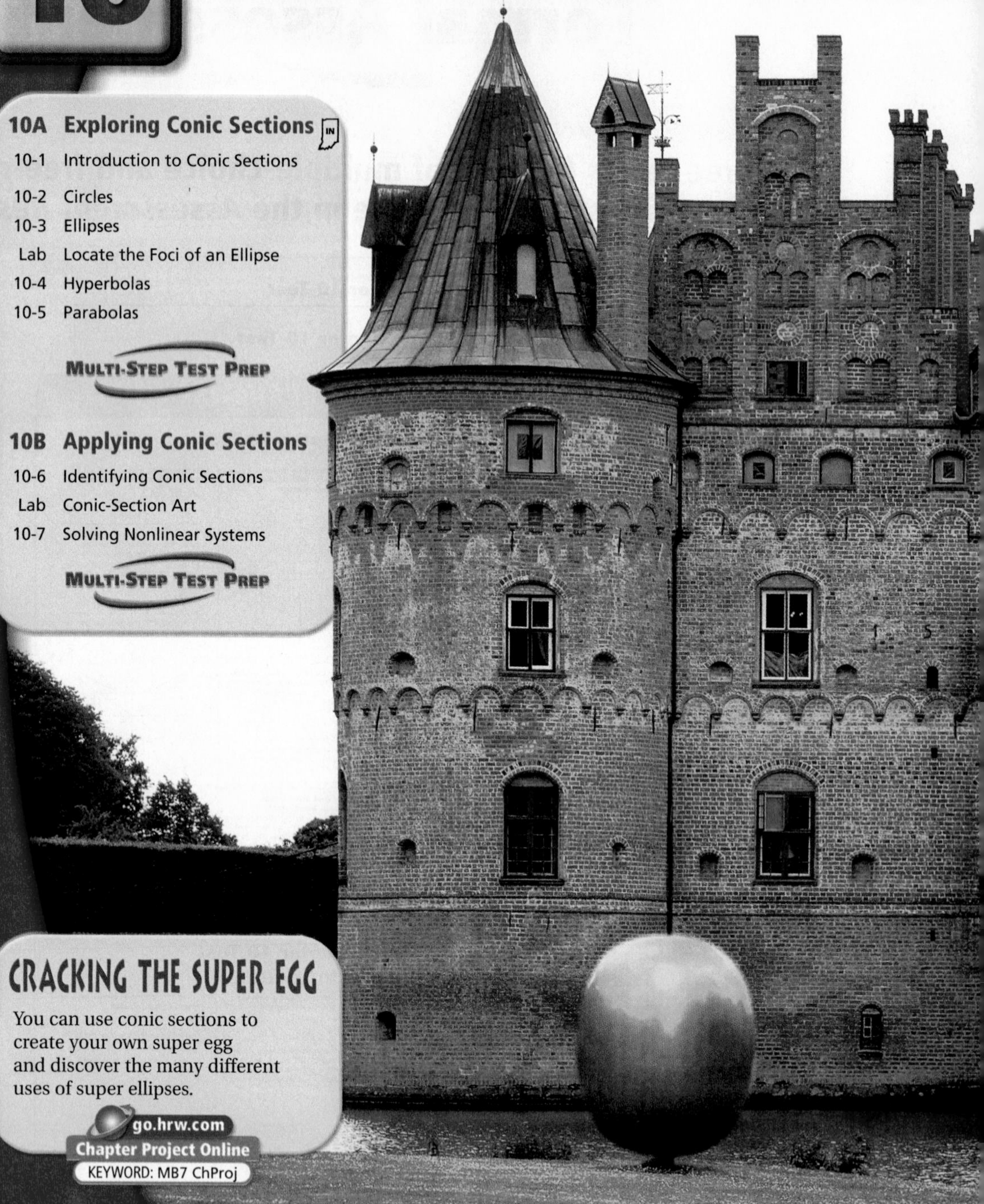

CRACKING THE SUPER EGG

You can use conic sections to create your own super egg and discover the many different uses of super ellipses.

go.hrw.com
Chapter Project Online
KEYWORD: MB7 ChProj

Cracking the Super Egg

About the Project

In the Chapter Project, students explore super-ellipses, geometric figures similar to ellipses, which are used to create many architectural and artistic structures. Students then construct their own three-dimensional super-eggs.

Project Resources

All project resources for teachers and students are provided online.

Materials:

- construction paper

ARE YOU READY?

Vocabulary

Match each term on the left with a definition on the right.

D 1. vertex of a parabola
A 2. axis of symmetry
E 3. solution set of a system of equations
B 4. asymptote

A. a line that divides a plane figure or a graph into two congruent reflected halves
B. a line approached by the graph of a function
C. a line that is neither horizontal nor vertical
D. the turning point of a parabola
E. the set of points that make all equations in a system true

Circumference and Area of Circles

Find the circumference and area of each circle.

5. 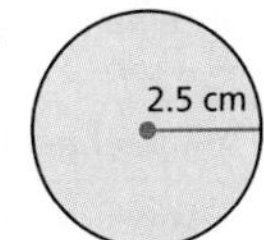

$C = 5\pi$ cm, $A = 6.25\pi$ cm^2

6. 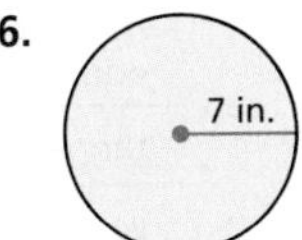

$C = 14\pi$ in, $A = 49\pi$ in^2

Area of Polygons

Find the area of each figure.

7. 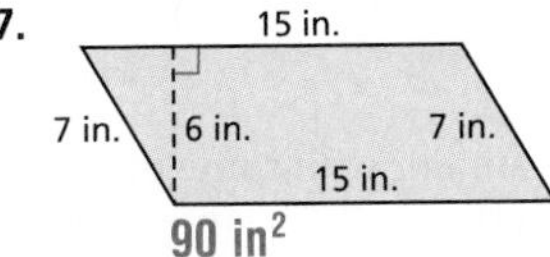

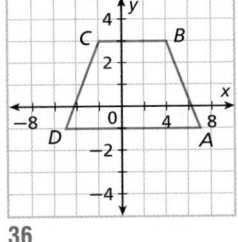

90 in^2

8. 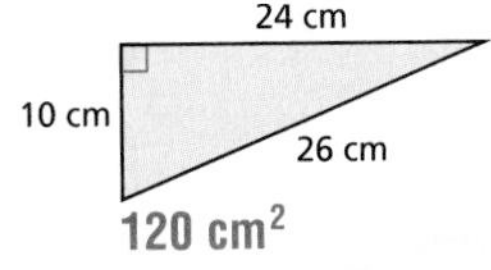

120 cm^2

9. 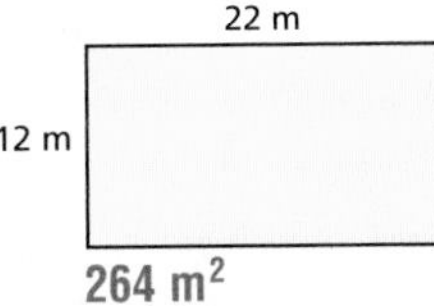

264 m^2

Find Areas in the Coordinate Plane

Find the area of each figure.

10. 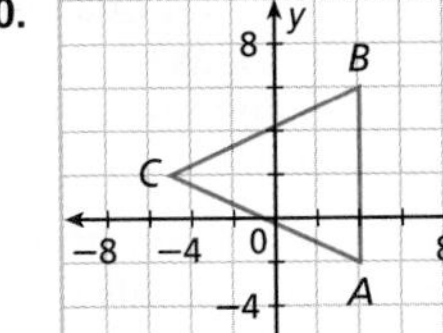

36

11. 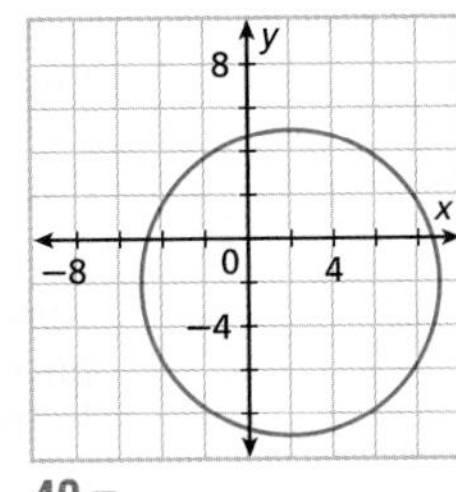

49π

12. 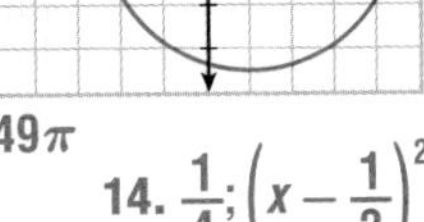

36

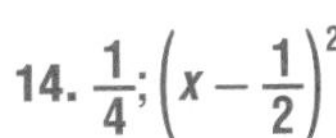

Complete the Square

Complete the square for each expression. Write the resulting expression as a binomial squared.

13. $x^2 - 4x + \blacksquare$ 4; $(x-2)^2$

14. $x^2 - x + \blacksquare$ 14. $\frac{1}{4}$; $\left(x - \frac{1}{2}\right)^2$

15. $x^2 + 6x + \blacksquare$ 9; $(x+3)^2$

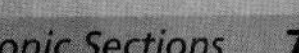

CHAPTER 10

ARE YOU READY?

Organizer

Objective: Assess students' understanding of prerequisite skills.

Prerequisite Skills

Circumference and Area of Circles
Area of Polygons
Find Areas in the Coordinate Plane
Complete the Square

Assessing Prior Knowledge

INTERVENTION 

Diagnose and Prescribe

Use this page to determine whether intervention is necessary or whether enrichment is appropriate.

Resources

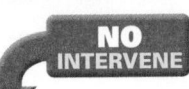

 ***Are You Ready? Intervention and Enrichment* Worksheets**

 ***Are You Ready?* CD-ROM**

 ***Are You Ready?* Online**

my.hrw.com

ARE YOU READY? Diagnose and Prescribe

NO — INTERVENE

Prerequisite Skill	*Are You Ready? Intervention*, Chapter 10 — Worksheets	CD-ROM	Online
Circumference and Area of Circles	Skill 39	Activity 39	Diagnose and Prescribe Online
Area of Polygons	Skill 37	Activity 37	
Find Areas in the Coordinate Plane	Skill 38	Activity 38	
Complete the Square	Skill 82	Activity 82	

YES — ENRICH

Are You Ready? Enrichment, Chapter 10

 Worksheets

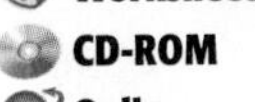 CD-ROM

Online

CHAPTER 10 Study Guide: Preview

Organizer

Objective: Help students organize the new concepts they will learn in Chapter 10.

Online Edition
Multilingual Glossary

Resources

***Multilingual Glossary* Online**

go.hrw.com
KEYWORD: MB7 Glossary

Answers to *Vocabulary Connections*

1. Possible answer: The focus is the central point of interest of a painting. The focus of a conic section must be a point that can be used to define the conic.
2. Possible answer: A vertex always represents a maximum or minimum value.
3. Once; yes; possible answer: the person took an idea from the conversation into a direction different than everyone else in the discussion.

CHAPTER 10

Study Guide: Preview

Where You've Been

Previously, you

- graphed parabolas defined by quadratic functions.
- studied graphs of piecewise functions.
- solved systems of linear equations.

In This Chapter

You will study

- graphs of parabolas and other conic sections that are not functions.
- graphs of conic sections represented by two functions together.
- methods for solving systems of nonlinear equations.

Where You're Going

You can use the skills in this chapter

- in all of your future math classes, including Calculus and Statistics.
- in other classes such as Chemistry, Physics, and Economics.
- outside of school in engineering, architecture, astronomy, photography, and communications.

Key Vocabulary/Vocabulario

circle	círculo
conic section	sección cónica
directrix	directriz
ellipse	elipse
foci of an ellipse	focos de una elipse
foci of a hyperbola	focos de una hipérbola
focus of a parabola	foco de una parábola
hyperbola	hipérbola
nonlinear system of equations	sistema no lineal de ecuaciones
tangent line	línea tangente
vertices of an ellipse	vértices de una elipse
vertices of a hyperbola	vértices de una hipérbola

Vocabulary Connections

To become familiar with some of the vocabulary terms in the chapter, consider the following. You may refer to the chapter, the glossary, or a dictionary if you like.

1. When you use the word *focus* in most contexts, you mean a center of activity or attention. What is the focus of a painting? How can this help you understand a **focus** of a conic section?
2. In the geometry book, you saw the term *vertex* used for triangles. In this book you have already seen the term *vertex* used for parabolas. In this chapter, you will see the term **vertex** used for ellipses and hyperbolas. Why is the same term used in all of these different situations?
3. How often does a *tangent* touch a circle? Can curves other than circles also have **tangents**? What do you mean when you say that someone went "off on a tangent" during a discussion?

Study Strategy: Learn Vocabulary

Understanding math terminology and vocabulary is important to learning and using new math concepts. You have already learned many new terms and as you progress in your studies of math, you will need to learn many more.

To learn new vocabulary:

- Look for the meaning of a new word through the context in which it is introduced.
- Use the prefix or suffix to determine the meaning of the root word.
- Relate the new term to familiar, everyday words.

Once you know what a word means, write its definition in your own words.

Vocabulary Word	Study Tips	Definition
Polynomial	*Prefix **poly-**, meaning "many"*	*A monomial or a sum or difference of monomials*
Conjunction	*Prefix **con-**, meaning "connect" or "together"*	*A compound statement that uses the word **and***
Extraneous Solution	*Relate to the word **extra**, meaning "not needed."*	*Extra roots that are not solutions to the original equation*
Slope	*Think of a **ski slope**.*	*The measure of the steepness of a line*

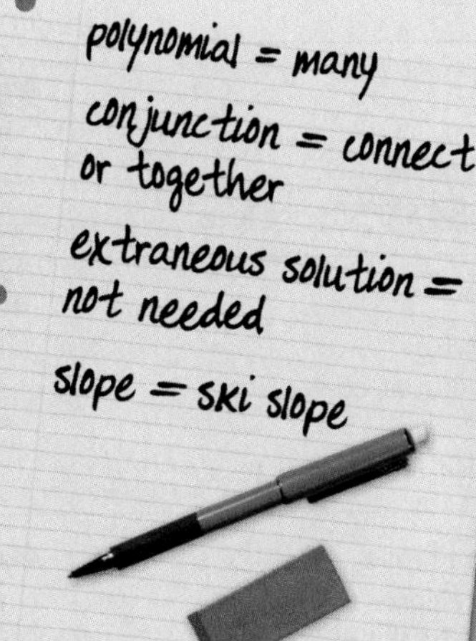

Try This

Fill in the chart with information that can help you learn the vocabulary words.

	Vocabulary Word	Study Tips	Definition
1.	Trinomial	■	■
2.	Disjunction	■	■
3.	Variable	■	■
4.	Multiplicity	■	■

Use the given prefix's meaning to write the definition of the corresponding vocabulary words.

5. *dia-* through, across, between: diameter; diagonal

6. *trans-* across, beyond, through: transformation; translation

Reading and Writing Math CHAPTER 10

Organizer

Objective: Help students apply strategies to understand and retain key concepts.

Online Edition

Resources

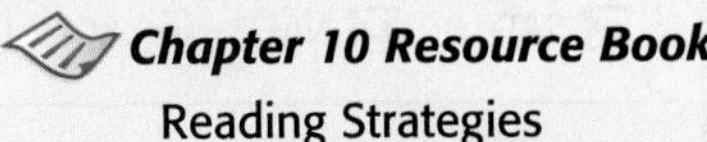

Chapter 10 Resource Book
Reading Strategies

ENGLISH LANGUAGE LEARNERS

Study Strategy: Learn Vocabulary

Discuss The process of learning mathematics involves building upon and extending earlier and simpler concepts. As concepts build, the language used to describe them also builds upon previous language.

Extend As students work through Chapter 10, have them pay close attention to the vocabulary at the beginning of each lesson. Have them attempt to deduce the meanings of new vocabulary words based on previous vocabulary before reading the definitions in the text.

Answers

1. Possible answer: prefix *tri-*, meaning "three"; a polynomial with only 3 terms
2. Possible answer: prefix *dis-*, meaning "apart" as in *disagree* or *disassemble;* a compound statement that uses the word or
3. Possible answer: related to the word *vary,* meaning "differ or fluctuate"; a quantity that can change
4. Possible answer: prefix *multi-*, meaning *many;* or relate to the word *multiple;* the number of times that a given polynomial equation has a root at a given point
5. the length of a straight line through the center of a circle connecting two points on the circumference; line segment joining 2 nonadjacent vertices of a polygon, or in a square matrix, the line of entries running northwest to southeast
6. movement of a figure from its original location; movement of all the points of a figure the same distance in the same direction

SECTION

10A Understanding Conic Sections

One-Minute Section Planner

Lesson	Lab Resources	Materials
Lesson 10-1 Introduction to Conic Sections • Recognize conic sections as intersections of planes and cones. • Use the distance and midpoint formulas to solve problems. ☑ SAT-10 ☑ NAEP ☑ ACT ☑ SAT ☑ SAT Subject Tests		**Required** graphing calculator **Optional** sheets of paper
Lesson 10-2 Circles • Write an equation for a circle. • Graph a circle, and identify its center and radius. ☑ SAT-10 ☐ NAEP ☑ ACT ☑ SAT ☑ SAT Subject Tests	***Algebra Lab Activities*** 10-2 Algebra Lab	**Optional** graphing calculator, compass and map, geometry software
Lesson 10-3 Ellipses • Write the standard equation for an ellipse. • Graph an ellipse, and identify its center, vertices, co-vertices, and foci. ☑ SAT-10 ☐ NAEP ☐ ACT ☐ SAT ☑ SAT Subject Tests	***Technology Lab Activities*** 10-3 Technology Lab	**Optional** graphing calculator, string, tacks
10-3 Algebra Lab Locate the Foci of an Ellipse • Use a compass to find the foci of a given ellipse. ☐ SAT-10 ☐ NAEP ☐ ACT ☐ SAT ☑ SAT Subject Tests	***Algebra Lab Activities*** 10-3 Lab Recording Sheet	**Required** compass, graph paper **Optional** graphing calculator
Lesson 10-4 Hyperbolas • Write the standard equation for a hyperbola. • Graph a hyperbola, and identify its vertices, co-vertices, center, foci, and asymptotes. ☑ SAT-10 ☐ NAEP ☐ ACT ☐ SAT ☑ SAT Subject Tests		**Optional** graphing calculator
Lesson 10-5 Parabolas • Write the standard equation for a parabola and its axis of symmetry. • Graph a parabola and identify its focus, directrix, and axis of symmetry. ☑ SAT-10 ☑ NAEP ☐ ACT ☐ SAT ☑ SAT Subject Tests		**Optional** graphing calculator, string, tacks, T square

MK = *Manipulatives Kit*

Section Overview

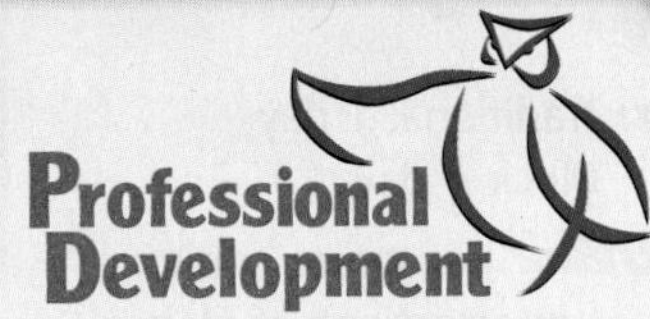

Introduction to Conic Sections

Lesson 10-1

Conic sections can be used to describe a variety of natural phenomena.

Conic sections cannot usually be represented by a single function.

Circles and Ellipses

Lessons 10-2, 10-3

The locations that are a given distance away from a location lie on a circle. The orbits of planets follow paths that are ellipses.

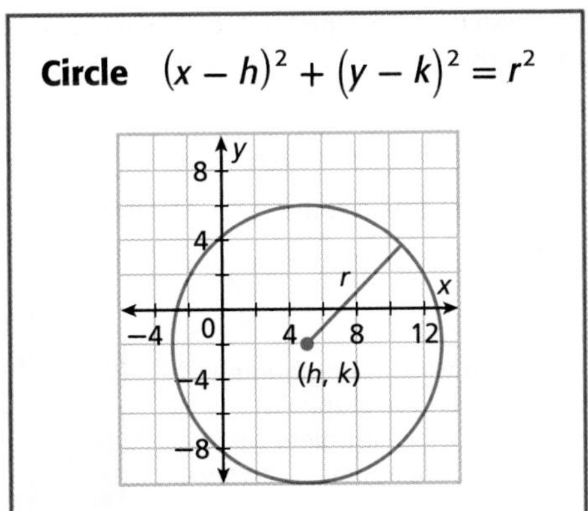

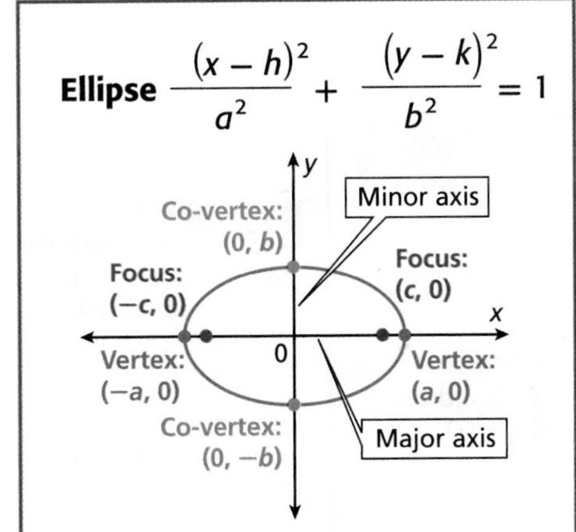

Hyperbolas and Parabolas

Lessons 10-4, 10-5

A hyperbola can be used to detect the source of a signal. Many microphones and antennas use parabolas to reflect and concentrate signals on a single point.

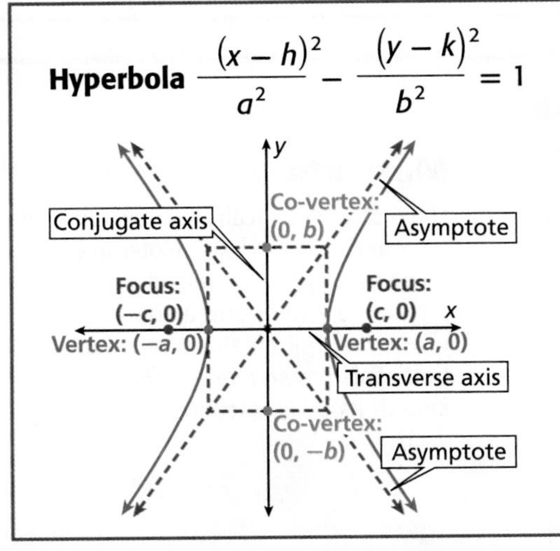

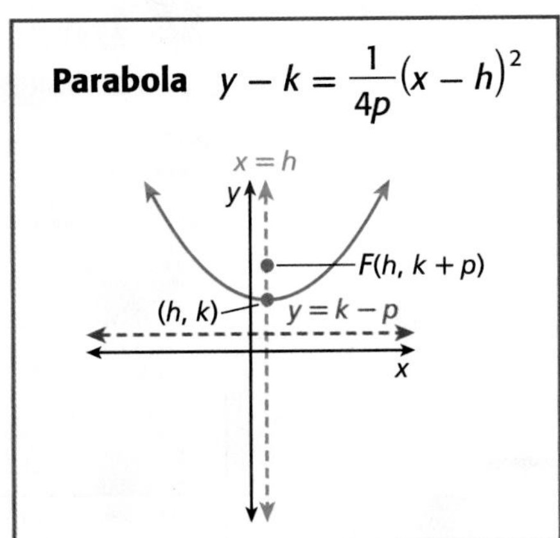

10-1 Organizer

Pacing: Traditional 1 day
Block $\frac{1}{2}$ day

Objectives: Recognize conic sections as intersections of planes and cones.

Use the distance and midpoint formulas to solve problems.

Online Edition
Graphing Calculator, Tutorial Videos, TechKeys

Countdown to Testing Week 21

Power Presentations with PowerPoint®

Warm Up

Solve for *y*.

1. $x^2 + y^2 = 1$ $y = \pm\sqrt{1 - x^2}$
2. $4x^2 - 9y^2 = 1$

$y = \pm\dfrac{\sqrt{4x^2 - 1}}{3}$

Also available on transparency

Math Humor

Parent: Why are you reading the Sunday paper when you should be doing your Algebra homework?

Student: It's ok, I'm reading the conic section.

10-1 Introduction to Conic Sections

Objectives
Recognize conic sections as intersections of planes and cones.
Use the distance and midpoint formulas to solve problems.

Vocabulary
conic section

Who uses this?
Archaeologists use distance and midpoint to organize excavation sites. (See Exercise 43.)

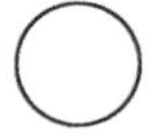

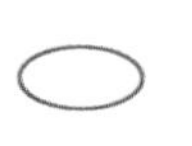

Circle Ellipse Parabola Hyperbola

In Chapter 5, you studied the parabola. The parabola is one of a family of curves called *conic sections.* **Conic sections** are formed by the intersection of a double right cone and a plane. There are four types of conic sections: circles, ellipses, hyperbolas, and parabolas.

Although the parabolas you studied in Chapter 5 are functions, most conic sections are not. This means that you often must use two functions to graph a conic section on a calculator.

A circle is defined by its center and its radius. An ellipse, an elongated shape similar to a circle, has two perpendicular axes of different lengths.

EXAMPLE 1 Graphing Circles and Ellipses on a Calculator

Graph each equation on a graphing calculator. Identify each conic section. Then describe the center and intercepts.

A $x^2 + y^2 = 25$

Step 1 Solve for y so that the expression can be used in a graphing calculator.

$y^2 = 25 - x^2$ *Subtract x^2 from both sides.*

$y = \pm\sqrt{25 - x^2}$ *Take the square root of both sides.*

Step 2 Use two equations to see the complete graph.

$y_1 = \sqrt{25 - x^2}$

$y_2 = -\sqrt{25 - x^2}$

Use a square window on your graphing calculator for an accurate graph. The graphs meet and form a complete circle, even though it may not appear that way on your calculator.

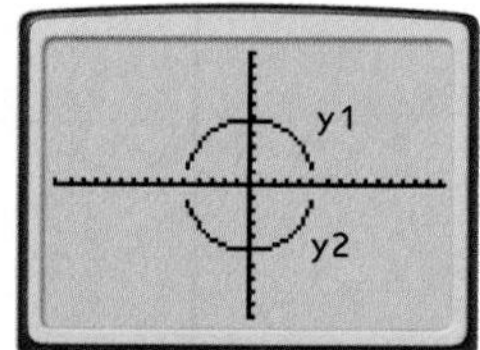

The graph is a circle with center $(0, 0)$ and intercepts $(5, 0)$, $(-5, 0)$, $(0, 5)$, and $(0, -5)$.

Check Use a table to confirm the intercepts.

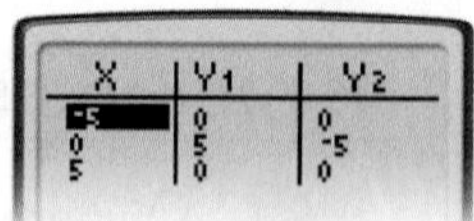

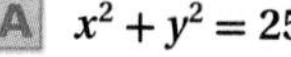

Remember!

When you take the square root of both sides of an equation, remember that you must include the positive and negative roots.

State Resources

go.hrw.com
State Resources Online
KEYWORD: MB7 Resources

1 Introduce

EXPLORATION

10-1 Introduction to Conic Sections

To graph any relation, you can begin by plotting a few points. Recall that not all graphs represent functions.

1. Complete the table for the equation $x^2 + y^2 = 25$. Be sure to find all the y-values for each x-value.

x	−5	−4	−3	0	3	4	5
y							

2. Plot the points and graph the relation.
3. What type of shape is the graph?
4. Complete the table for the equation $4x^2 + 9y^2 = 36$. Be sure to find all the y-values for each x-value. Round your answers to the nearest tenth if necessary.

x	−3	−2	−1	0	1	2	3
y							

5. Plot the points and graph the relation.

THINK AND DISCUSS

6. **Describe** the graph of $4x^2 + 9y^2 = 36$. How is it different from the graph of $x^2 + y^2 = 25$?
7. **Explain** whether the relations that you graphed are functions.

Motivate

Have students recall the function that represented a parabola. $y = x^2 + 1$ Note, in particular, that it involves an x^2-term. Introduce that if there is both a squared x-term and a squared y-term, such as $y^2 = x^2 + 1$, it creates a new curve called a hyperbola. This new curve is in the family of curves known as conic sections.

Explorations and answers are provided in the *Explorations* binder.

Graph each equation on a graphing calculator. Identify each conic section. Then describe the center and intercepts.

B $16x^2 + 9y^2 = 144$

Step 1 Solve for y so that the expression can be used in a graphing calculator.

$9y^2 = 144 - 16x^2$ *Subtract $16x^2$ from both sides.*

$y^2 = \frac{144 - 16x^2}{9}$ *Divide both sides by 9.*

$y = \pm\sqrt{\frac{144 - 16x^2}{9}}$ *Take the square root of both sides.*

Step 2 Use two equations to see the complete graph.

$y_1 = \sqrt{\frac{144 - 16x^2}{9}}$

$y_2 = -\sqrt{\frac{144 - 16x^2}{9}}$

Use a square window on your graphing calculator. The graphs meet and form a complete ellipse, even though it may not appear that way on your calculator.

The graph is an ellipse with center (0, 0) and intercepts (3, 0), (−3, 0), (0, 4), and (0, −4).

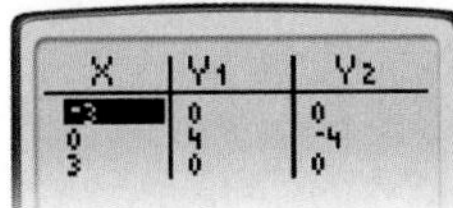

Check Use a table to confirm the intercepts.

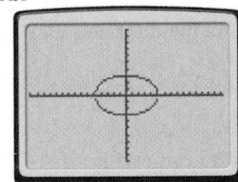

1a. circle; center: (0, 0); intercepts: (0, ±7), (±7, 0)

1b. ellipse; center: (0, 0); intercepts: (±5, 0) (0, ±3)

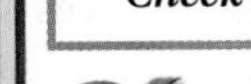

Graph each equation on a graphing calculator. Identify each conic section. Then describe the center and intercepts.

1a. $x^2 + y^2 = 49$ **1b.** $9x^2 + 25y^2 = 225$

A parabola is a single curve, whereas a hyperbola has two congruent branches. The equation of a parabola usually contains either an x^2 term or a y^2 term, but not both. The equations of the other conics will usually contain both x^2 and y^2 terms.

EXAMPLE 2 Graphing Parabolas and Hyperbolas on a Calculator

Graph each equation on a graphing calculator. Identify each conic section. Then describe the vertices and the direction that the graph opens.

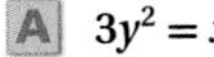

A $3y^2 = x$

Step 1 Solve for y so that the expression can be used in a graphing calculator.

$y^2 = \frac{x}{3}$ *Divide both sides by 3.*

$y = \pm\sqrt{\frac{x}{3}}$ *Take the square root of both sides.*

Step 2 Use two equations to see the complete graph.

$y_1 = \sqrt{\frac{x}{3}}$ and $y_2 = -\sqrt{\frac{x}{3}}$

The graph is a parabola with vertex (0, 0) that opens to the right.

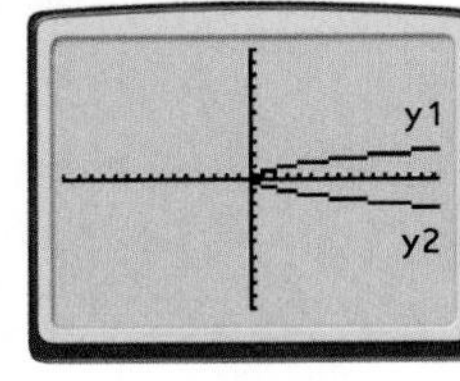

Power Presentations with PowerPoint®

Additional Examples

Example 1

Graph each equation on a graphing calculator. Identify each conic section. Then describe the center and intercepts.

A. $(x - 1)^2 + (y - 1)^2 = 1$

circle with center at (1, 1) and intercepts at (1, 0) and (0, 1).

B. $4x^2 + 25y^2 = 100$

ellipse with center at (0, 0) and intercepts at (±5, 0) and (0, ±2)

Example 2

Graph each equation on a graphing calculator. Identify each conic section. Then describe the vertices and the direction that the graph opens.

A. $y = -\frac{1}{2}x^2$

parabola with vertex at (0, 0) and opening downward

B. $y^2 - x^2 = 9$

hyperbola that opens vertically with vertices at (0, ±3)

Also available on transparency

INTERVENTION

Questioning Strategies

EXAMPLE 1

- Why can't you graph a circle or an ellipse by using a single function?

EXAMPLE 2

- How come there are two branches for a hyperbola but only one for a parabola?

2 Teach

Guided Instruction

First, students need to be comfortable solving conic equations for one variable so the equations can be graphed. Then explain that the graph of a relation may be made up of the graphs of two different functions.

Language Arts Each cone in the double right cone used to demonstrate conic sections is called a *nappe,* which is derived from a French word meaning "tablecloth," "sheet," or "napkin."

ENGLISH LANGUAGE LEARNERS

Reaching All Learners

Through Concrete Manipulatives

Have students create cones from sheets of paper.

Draw the four conic sections on the board and, using the model or a picture, ask the students if they can figure out the different ways that the cone might be sliced in order to produce these different figures.

Ask students to cut the paper cones to illustrate the conic sections.

Teaching Tip **Technology** Encourage students to watch carefully how the calculator draws the conics. Challenge students to explain why the four pieces of the hyperbola in **Example 2** are drawn in the order that they are.

Teaching Tip **Visual** This chart might help students understand how the equations for circles and ellipses reflect their similarities and differences.

Circles vs. Ellipses

Similarities	Differences
Closed curves	Compare axes
Circle: $4x^2 + 4y^2 = 25$	Circle: equal axes: $4x^2 + 4y^2 = 25$
Ellipse: $4x^2 + 9y^2 = 36$	Ellipse: different axes: $4x^2 + 9y^2 = 36$

Teaching Tip **Reading Math** The words *ellipse* and *ellipsis* come from the same root, the Greek *elleipsis,* "a falling short," or "deficit." An *ellipsis* is a placeholder for words left out of a sentence, usually ". . . ". For an *ellipse,* the cutting plane forms a smaller angle with the base of the cone than does the side of the cone (see diagram on p. 722). Hence, there is a "falling short." **English Language Learners**

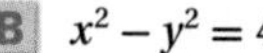

Graph each equation on a graphing calculator. Identify each conic section. Then describe the vertices and the direction that the graph opens.

B $x^2 - y^2 = 4$

Step 1 Solve for y so that the expression can be used in a graphing calculator.

$-y^2 = 4 - x^2$	*Subtract x^2 from both sides.*
$y^2 = -(4 - x^2)$	*Multiply both sides by −1.*
$y^2 = -4 + x^2$	*Distribute.*
$y^2 = x^2 - 4$	*Rearrange.*
$y = \pm\sqrt{x^2 - 4}$	*Take the square root of both sides.*

Helpful Hint

Because hyperbolas contain two curves that open in opposite directions, classify them as opening horizontally, vertically, or neither.

Step 2 Use two equations to see the complete graph.

$y_1 = \sqrt{x^2 - 4}$

$y_2 = -\sqrt{x^2 - 4}$

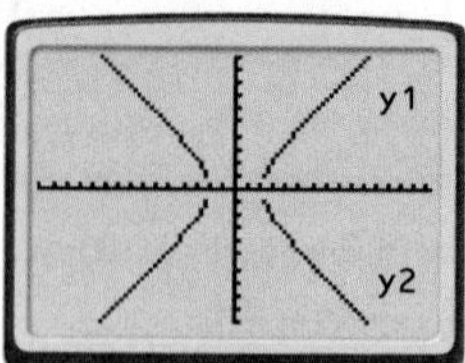

The graph is a hyperbola that opens horizontally with vertices at $(2, 0)$ and $(-2, 0)$.

CHECK IT OUT! **Graph each equation on a graphing calculator. Identify each conic section. Then describe the vertices and the direction that the graph opens.**

2a. $2y^2 = x$ **2b.** $x^2 - y^2 = 16$

2a.

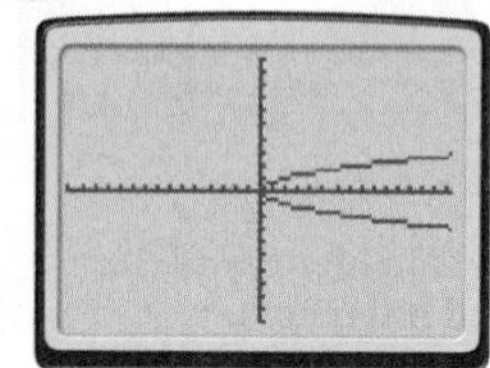

parabola; vertex: $(0, 0)$; opens right

2b.

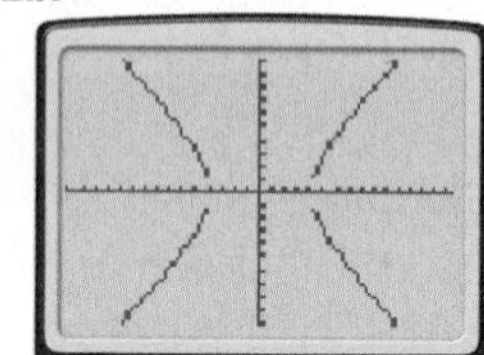

hyperbola; vertices: $(\pm 4, 0)$; opens horizontally

Every conic section can be defined in terms of distances. You can use the Midpoint and Distance Formulas to find the center and radius of a circle.

Midpoint and Distance Formulas

FORMULA	EXAMPLE	GRAPH
The **midpoint** (x_M, y_M) of the segment with endpoints (x_1, y_1) and (x_2, y_2) is $(x_M, y_M) = \left(\frac{x_1 + x_2}{2}, \frac{y_1 + y_2}{2}\right)$.	The midpoint of the segment with endpoints $(1, 2)$ and $(5, 8)$ is $\left(\frac{1+5}{2}, \frac{2+8}{2}\right) = (3, 5)$.	(5, 8); (3, 5); (1, 2)
The **distance** d between the points with coordinates (x_1, y_1) and (x_2, y_2) is $d = \sqrt{(x_2 - x_1)^2 + (y_2 - y_1)^2}$.	The distance between the points $(2, 1)$ and $(6, 4)$ is $\sqrt{(6-2)^2 + (4-1)^2} = 5$.	(6, 4); (2, 1); 5; $4 - 1 = 3$; $6 - 2 = 4$

Because a diameter must pass through the center of a circle, the midpoint of a diameter is the center of the circle. The radius of a circle is the distance from the center to any point on the circle and equal to half the diameter.

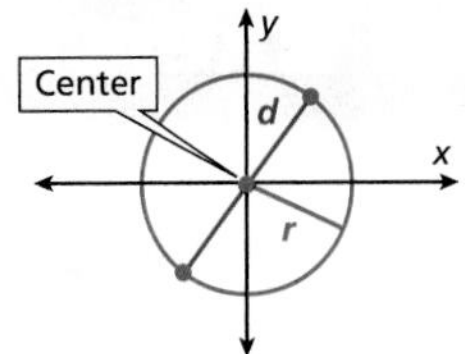

EXAMPLE 3 Finding the Center and Radius of a Circle

Find the center and radius of a circle that has a diameter with endpoints (3, 12) and (9, 4).

Step 1 Find the center of the circle.

Use the Midpoint Formula with the endpoints, (3, 12) and (9, 4).

$$\left(\frac{3+9}{2}, \frac{12+4}{2}\right) = (6, 8)$$

The center of the circle is (6, 8).

Step 2 Find the radius.

Use the Distance Formula with (6, 8) and (3, 12).

$$r = \sqrt{(6-3)^2 + (8-12)^2}$$
$$= \sqrt{3^2 + (-4)^2}$$
$$= \sqrt{9+16}$$
$$= 5$$

The radius of the circle is 5.

Check Use the other endpoint (9, 4) and the center (6, 8). The radius should equal 5 for any point on the circle.

$$r = \sqrt{(9-6)^2 + (4-8)^2} = 5 \checkmark$$

The radius is the same using (9, 4).

Helpful Hint

The midpoint formula uses averages. You can think of x_M as the average of the x-values and y_M as the average of the y-values.

CHECK IT OUT! 3. Find the center and radius of a circle that has a diameter with endpoints (2, 6) and (14, 22). **center: (8,14); $r = 10$**

THINK AND DISCUSS

1. If you know one endpoint and the midpoint of a line segment, how could you find the other endpoint of the segment?
2. Find the domain and range of each of the graphs in Examples 1 and 2.
3. **GET ORGANIZED** Copy and complete the graphic organizer. List the types of conic sections, and sketch an example of each.

COMMON ERROR ALERT

Students may choose incorrect viewing windows when graphing circles. The default window on graphing calculators is *not* usually the square grid. Circles may look like ellipses in a non-square window. To see the circle properly, it is necessary to choose **ZSquare** in the ZOOM menu, or the equivalent.

Power Presentations with PowerPoint®

Additional Examples

Example 3

Find the center and radius of a circle that has a diameter with endpoints at (5, 4) and (0, −8).

center: (2.5, −2); radius: 6.5

Also available on transparency

INTERVENTION Questioning Strategies

EXAMPLE 3

- Do you think it would be possible to find the equation for a circle if you had just two points on the circle that were *not* endpoints of the same diameter? How about if you had any three points on the circle?

3 Close

Summarize

Each of the four conic sections has its own characteristic equation. Each equation can be graphed on a graphing calculator by solving for y and, if necessary, breaking it into two functions.

ONGOING ASSESSMENT and INTERVENTION

***Diagnose Before* the Lesson**
10-1 Warm Up, TE p. 722

***Monitor During* the Lesson**
Check It Out! Exercises, SE pp. 723–725
Questioning Strategies, TE pp. 723, 725

***Assess After* the Lesson**
10-1 Lesson Quiz, TE p. 728
Alternative Assessment, TE p. 728

Answers to *Think and Discuss*

1. Possible answer: Use the midpoint formula. Substitute the values for the midpoint and known endpoint and solve for the unknown endpoint.
2. Example 1A: $\{x \mid -5 \le x \le 5\}$, $\{y \mid -5 \le y \le 5\}$
Example 1B: $\{x \mid -3 \le x \le 3\}$, $\{y \mid -4 \le y \le 4\}$
Example 2A: $\{x \mid x \ge 0\}$, $\{y \mid y \in \mathbb{R}\}$
Example 2B: $\{x \mid -2 \ge x \text{ or } x \ge 2\}$, $\{y \mid y \in \mathbb{R}\}$
3. See p. A11.

10-1 Exercises

Assignment Guide

Assign *Guided Practice* exercises as necessary.

If you finished Examples **1–3**

Basic 14–41, 44, 45, 49–53, 58–67

Average 14–55, 58–67

Advanced 14–36, 41–43, 45–67

Homework Quick Check

Quickly check key concepts.

Exercises: 14, 16, 24, 26, 32

Exercise 36 involves graphing and identifying a conic section. This exercise prepares students for the Multi-Step Test Prep on page 758.

Answers

2–10, 14–31. See p. A41.

32. center: $\left(16, \frac{27}{2}\right)$; $r = \frac{17}{2}$

33. center: $\left(\frac{7}{2}, \frac{11}{2}\right)$; $r = \sqrt{10}$

34. center: $\left(3, \frac{5}{2}\right)$; $r = \frac{17}{2}$

36a.

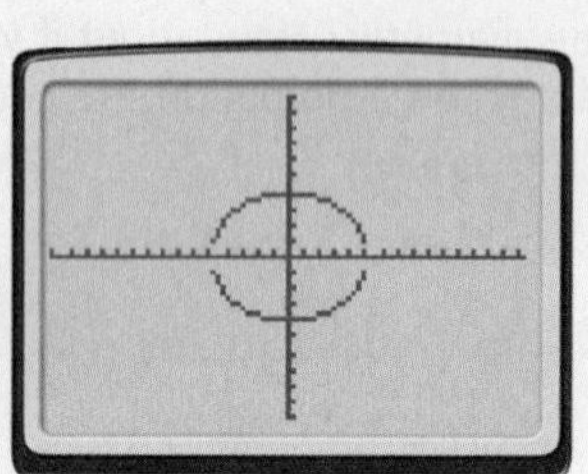

State Resources

go.hrw.com

State Resources Online

KEYWORD: MB7 Resources

10-1 Exercises

go.hrw.com

Homework Help Online

KEYWORD: MB7 10-1

Parent Resources Online

KEYWORD: MB7 Parent

GUIDED PRACTICE

1. **Vocabulary** What are the four different types of *conic sections*? **circles, ellipses, hyperbolas, and parabolas**

SEE EXAMPLE 1 p. 722

Graph each equation on a graphing calculator. Identify each conic section. Then describe the center and intercepts.

2. $3x^2 + 3y^2 = 48$
3. $9x^2 + 16y^2 = 144$
4. $x^2 + y^2 = 36$

SEE EXAMPLE 2 p. 723

Graph each equation on a graphing calculator. Identify each conic section. Then describe the vertices and the direction that the graph opens.

5. $5y^2 = x$
6. $x^2 = y^2 + 9$
7. $y^2 - x^2 = 25$
8. $12y = 6x^2$
9. $2x^2 - y^2 = 4$
10. $-y^2 = 4 + x$

SEE EXAMPLE 3 p. 725

Find the center and radius of a circle that has a diameter with the given endpoints.

11. $(3, 6)$ and $(13, 30)$ **center: $(8, 18)$; $r = 13$**
12. $(-4, 1)$ and $(-16, -8)$ **center: $(-10, -3.5)$; $r = 7.5$**
13. $(6, -9)$ and $(-8, 39)$ **center: $(-1, 15)$; $r = 25$**

PRACTICE AND PROBLEM SOLVING

Independent Practice

For Exercises	See Example
14–22	1
23–31	2
32–34	3

Extra Practice

Skills Practice p. S22
Application Practice p. S41

Graph each equation on a graphing calculator. Identify each conic section. Then describe the center and intercepts.

14. $49x^2 + 36y^2 = 1764$
15. $\frac{x^2}{9} + \frac{y^2}{9} = 1$
16. $243 - 3x^2 - 3y^2 = 0$
17. $\frac{x^2}{4} = 1 - \frac{y^2}{25}$
18. $4x^2 + 81y^2 = 324$
19. $\frac{4x^2}{25} + \frac{4y^2}{225} = 1$
20. $\frac{3}{4}x^2 + \frac{3}{4}y^2 = 75$
21. $4x^2 + 4y^2 = 81$
22. $x^2 + y^2 = \frac{4}{9}$

Graph each equation on a graphing calculator. Identify each conic section. Then describe the vertices and the direction that the graph opens.

23. $y = 2x^2$
24. $x^2 = y^2 + 64$
25. $x + 2y^2 = 0$
26. $x = \frac{2}{3}y^2$
27. $0 = 1 + \frac{x^2}{64} - \frac{y^2}{36}$
28. $5y^2 - 5x^2 = 180$
29. $x = 4y^2 - 3$
30. $y = 4 - \frac{x^2}{5}$
31. $9x^2 - 16y^2 = 144$

Find the center and radius of a circle that has a diameter with the given endpoints.

32. $(20, 21)$ and $(12, 6)$
33. $\left(\frac{9}{2}, \frac{5}{2}\right)$ and $\left(\frac{5}{2}, \frac{17}{2}\right)$
34. $(7, -5)$ and $(-1, 10)$

35. **Geometry** A circle has center $(-7, 10)$ and contains the point $(23, -6)$.
    a. Find the circumference and area of the circle. **$C = 68\pi$; $A = 1156\pi$**
    b. Find the other endpoint of the diameter with one endpoint $(23, -6)$. **$(-37, 26)$**

MULTI-STEP TEST PREP

36. This problem will prepare you for the Multi-Step Test Prep on page 758.
    The orbit of an asteroid can be modeled by the equation $16x^2 + 25y^2 = 400$. **ellipse**
    a. Graph the equation on a graphing calculator, and identify the conic section.
    b. Identify the x- and y-intercepts of the orbit. **$(0, \pm 4)$, $(\pm 5, 0)$**
    c. Suppose that each unit of the coordinate plane represents 50 million miles. What is the maximum width of the asteroid's orbit? **500 million mi**

10-1 READING STRATEGIES

You can use a graphic organizer to help organize what you know about the relationship between the radius, diameter, and center of a circle.

Main Idea	**Facts**
The diameter of a circle is a straight line segment that passes through the center of the circle. If you know the coordinates of the endpoints of the diameter of a circle, you can determine the location of the center of the circle and its radius.	Use the Midpoint Formula to find the coordinates of the center, (x, y). $(x, y) = \left(\frac{x_1 + x_2}{2}, \frac{y_1 + y_2}{2}\right)$ Use the Distance Formula to find the radius. $d = r = \sqrt{(x_2 - x_1)^2 + (y_2 - y_1)^2}$
Example	**Useful Hints**
For a circle with a diameter with endpoints $(2, 14)$ and $(5, 18)$, the center is located at $\left(\frac{2+5}{2}, \frac{14+18}{2}\right) = \left(\frac{7}{2}, 16\right)$ and the radius is $r = \sqrt{\left(5 - \frac{7}{2}\right)^2 + (18 - 16)^2} = \frac{5}{2}$.	You can make sure you calculated the radius correctly by using either endpoint of the diameter and the center of the circle in the Distance Formula. The radii you calculate using both endpoints should be the same.

Answer each question.

1. Could you calculate the length of the diameter of a circle given the coordinates of the center of the circle and the length of the radius? Explain.
   Yes; possible answer: to find the length of the diameter you only need to know the length of the radius, since the diameter is twice the radius.
2. Why is it possible to calculate the radius of the circle using the Distance Formula and either diameter endpoint?
   Possible answer: The endpoints of a diameter will be equidistant from the center of the circle. Both endpoints form radii when connected by a line segment to the center of the circle.
3. One diameter of a circle has endpoints $(-2, 8)$ and $(10, 8)$.
   a. What are the coordinates of the center of the circle? **$(4, 8)$**
   b. Find the length of the radius. **$r = 6$**
   c. Find the area of the circle. $(A = \pi r^2)$ **$A = 36\pi$**
   d. Find the circumference of the circle. $(C = 2\pi r)$ **$C = 12\pi$**
4. The center of a circle is at $(2, 0)$ and its radius is 3 units. Find the endpoints of one of its diameters. **Possible answer: $(-1, 0)$ and $(5, 0)$**

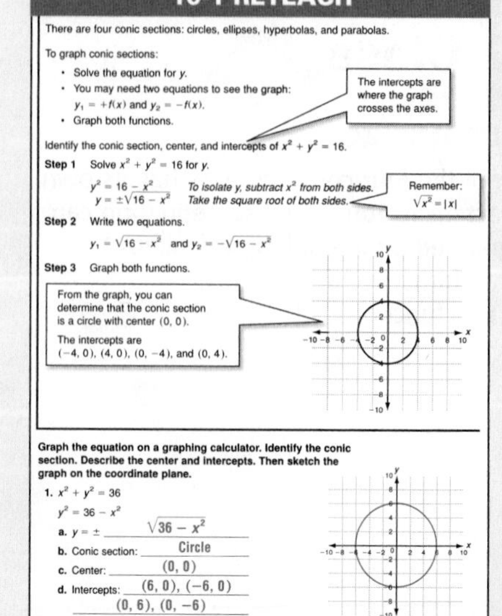

10-1 RETEACH

There are four conic sections: circles, ellipses, hyperbolas, and parabolas.

To graph conic sections:

- Solve the equation for y.
- You may need two equations to see the graph: $y_1 = +f(x)$ and $y_2 = -f(x)$.
- Graph both functions.

The intercepts are where the graph crosses the axes.

Identify the conic section, center, and intercepts of $x^2 + y^2 = 16$.

Step 1 Solve $x^2 + y^2 = 16$ for y.

$y^2 = 16 - x^2$ *To isolate y, subtract x^2 from both sides.*

$y = \pm\sqrt{16 - x^2}$ *Take the square root of both sides.*

Remember: $\sqrt{x^2} = |x|$

Step 2 Write two equations.

$y_1 = \sqrt{16 - x^2}$ and $y_2 = -\sqrt{16 - x^2}$

Step 3 Graph both functions.

From the graph, you can determine that the conic section is a circle with center $(0, 0)$.

The intercepts are $(-4, 0)$, $(4, 0)$, $(0, -4)$, and $(0, 4)$.

Graph the equation on a graphing calculator. Identify the conic section. Describe the center and intercepts. Then sketch the graph on the coordinate plane.

1. $x^2 + y^2 = 36$
   $y^2 = 36 - x^2$
   a. $y = \pm$ **$\sqrt{36 - x^2}$**
   b. Conic section: **Circle**
   c. Center: **$(0, 0)$**
   d. Intercepts: **$(6, 0)$, $(-6, 0)$, $(0, 6)$, $(0, -6)$**

Use your graphing calculator to match each equation to one of the following graphs.

42. Possible answer: The graph is a circle if $a = b$ and an ellipse if $a \neq b$.

43. C; the distance from A to B is $\sqrt{218}$, and the distance from A to C is $\sqrt{200}$.

A. 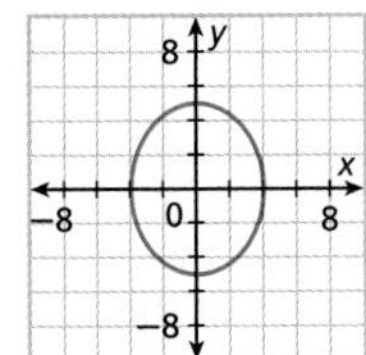

B. 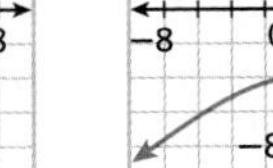

C. 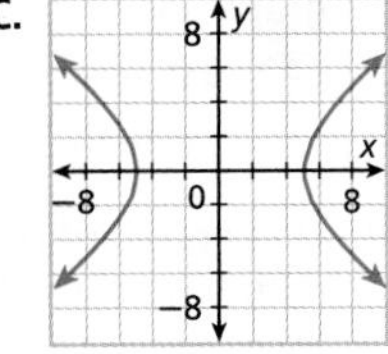

D. 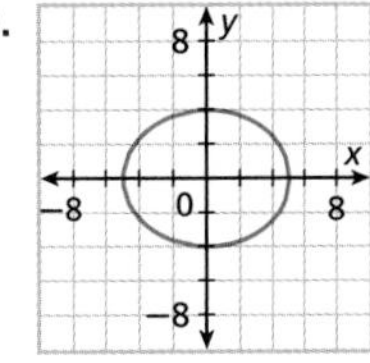

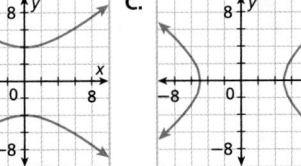

37. $16x^2 + 25y^2 = 400$ D
38. $16x^2 - 25y^2 = 400$ C
39. $25x^2 + 16y^2 = 400$ A
40. $25y^2 - 16x^2 = 400$ B

41. **Geometry** A quadrilateral has vertices $A(2, 3)$, $B(12, 3)$, $C(18, 11)$, and $D(8, 11)$.
   a. Find the length of each side. $\overline{AB} = 10$; $\overline{AD} = 10$; $\overline{BC} = 10$; $\overline{CD} = 10$
   b. Classify the figure $ABCD$. rhombus
   c. Find the area of $ABCD$. 80 square units

LINK Archaeology

Chichén Itzá, in Yucatán, Mexico, was a major city of the Maya civilization. Its city center covers about 2 square miles and was used primarily for religious ceremonies. Today the ruins are the most visited archaeological site in Mexico.

42. **Critical Thinking** How can you tell if the graph of an equation in the form $ax^2 + by^2 = c$ is a circle or an ellipse?

43. **Archaeology** Archaeologists exploring an underwater site have set up a grid so that they can precisely label where any artifacts they discover were found. The archaeologists have found two treasure chests at points B and C and a ship's wheel at point A. Which treasure is the wheel closer to? Explain.

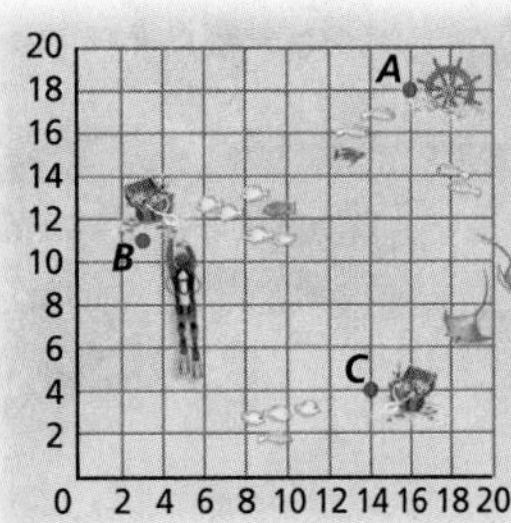

44. **ERROR ANALYSIS** Which solution is incorrect? Explain the error. Find the distance between $(0, 0)$ and $(2, 3)$.

A:
$d = \sqrt{(2-0)^2 + (3-0)^2}$
$d = \sqrt{2^2 + 3^2}$
$d = \sqrt{4 + 9}$
$d = \sqrt{13}$

B:
$d = \sqrt{(2-0)^2 + (3-0)^2}$
$d = \sqrt{2^2 + 3^2}$
$d = 2 + 3$
$d = 5$

B is incorrect. The square root of $2^2 + 3^2$ is not $2 + 3$.

45c. $\frac{12}{5}$; $\frac{12}{5}$; They are parallel.

45. **Geometry** A triangle has vertices $A(8, 2)$, $B(13, 14)$, and $C(-4, 6)$.
   a. Find the length of $\overline{AB}$. 13 units
   b. Find the length of the segment joining the midpoints of $\overline{BC}$ and $\overline{AC}$. 6.5 units
   c. Find the slopes of $\overline{AB}$ and the segment joining the midpoints of the other two sides. What do the slopes tell you about the two segments?

47. Sometimes true; the parabola $y = x^2$ has a domain of all real numbers, but the parabola $x = y^2$ has domain $x \geq 0$.

Tell whether each statement is sometimes, always, or never true. If it is sometimes true, give examples to support your answer.

46. A circle is a function. never true
47. The domain of a parabola is all real numbers.
48. The distance between two points is positive. always true
49. **Write About It** If a right triangle has a hypotenuse with length c and legs with lengths a and b, the Pythagorean Theorem states that $a^2 + b^2 = c^2$. Explain how the Distance Formula is related to the Pythagorean Theorem.

Teaching Tip **Geometry** For **Exercise 41,** review the types and properties of quadrilaterals such as rectangles, squares, trapezoids, and parallelograms.

Teaching Tip **Diversity Exercise 43** presents an archaeological application for the lesson content. The oldest known mathematical artifact is known as the Lebombo Bone. It is a baboon's fibula with 29 distinct notches cut into it. It dates from approximately 35,000 B.C. and was discovered in the 1970s in the Lebombo Mountains between South Africa and Swaziland. It may be a lunar calendar and resembles calendar sticks still in use by Bushmen clans in Namibia.

Teaching Tip **Geometry** For **Exercise 45,** review the Midsegment Theorem. A midsegment's endpoints are the midpoints of two sides, and the midsegment is parallel to the third side.

Answers

49. Possible answer: If you take the square root of both sides, the Pythagorean Theorem becomes $c = \sqrt{a^2 + b^2}$, where c could represent the distance between the origin and a point (a, b).

10-1 PROBLEM SOLVING

Hunter and Max draw a grid over a map of their town so that they can determine precisely where to set up a broadcast station. Hunter decides that locations A and B should be the endpoints of the diameter of a circle around the broadcast station.

1. Locate the center of the circle using the Midpoint Formula and points A and B. $\left(\frac{3}{2}, -1\right)$
2. Find the radius and the circumference of the circle.
   a. Name the coordinates of two points you can use with the Distance Formula to find the radius. Either (4,5) and $\left(\frac{3}{2}, -1\right)$, or (−1,−7) and $\left(\frac{3}{2}, -1\right)$
   b. Use the Distance Formula to find the radius. $6\frac{1}{2}$ units
   c. What is the circumference of the circle? 13π units
3. Hunter says that point C is within the circle. Max says that point C is on the circumference of the circle.
   a. Explain how they can use the Distance Formula to determine the answer. Possible answer: Find the distance between point C and the center of the circle; compare this distance to the radius.
   b. Who is correct? Why? Hunter is correct. Possible answer: The radius of the circle (6.5 units) is greater than the distance between point C and the center (about 5.4 units).

A broadcast station is set up at the location with coordinates (0, 2). The transmissions just reach a location with coordinates (8, 8). Choose the letter for the best answer.

4. Which point is farthest from the point (8, 8) and still within range of the broadcast station?
   Ⓐ (−8, −4) C (0, 10) B (−8, −8) D (10, 2)
5. What is the maximum distance the broadcast transmissions will reach?
   F 6 units G 8 units H 9 units Ⓙ 10 units
6. What is the area the broadcast transmissions will cover?
   A 20π Ⓒ 100π B 64π D 196π
7. The broadcast transmissions just reach the point $(x, 0)$. What is the value of x?
   F 8.4 H 9.2 G 8.8 Ⓙ 9.8

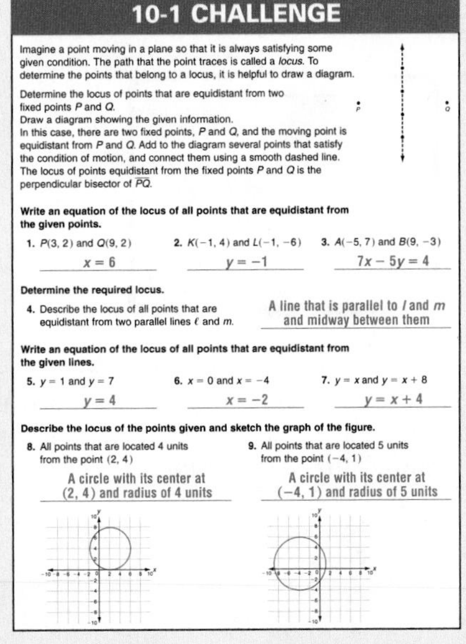

10-1 CHALLENGE

Imagine a point moving in a plane so that it is always satisfying some given condition. The path that the point traces is called a *locus*. To determine the points that belong to a locus, it is helpful to draw a diagram.

Determine the locus of points that are equidistant from two fixed points P and Q.
Draw a diagram showing the given information.
In this case, there are two fixed points, P and Q, and the moving point is equidistant from P and Q. Add to the diagram several points that satisfy the condition of motion, and connect them using a smooth dashed line.
The locus of points equidistant from the fixed points P and Q is the perpendicular bisector of $\overline{PQ}$.

Write an equation of the locus of all points that are equidistant from the given points.

1. $P(3, 2)$ and $Q(9, 2)$ $x = 6$
2. $K(-1, 4)$ and $L(-1, -6)$ $y = -1$
3. $A(-5, 7)$ and $B(9, -3)$ $7x - 5y = 4$

Determine the required locus.

4. Describe the locus of all points that are equidistant from two parallel lines ℓ and m. A line that is parallel to l and m and midway between them

Write an equation of the locus of all points that are equidistant from the given lines.

5. $y = 1$ and $y = 7$ $y = 4$
6. $x = 0$ and $x = -4$ $x = -2$
7. $y = x$ and $y = x + 8$ $y = x + 4$

Describe the locus of the points given and sketch the graph of the figure.

8. All points that are located 4 units from the point (2, 4) A circle with its center at (2, 4) and radius of 4 units
9. All points that are located 5 units from the point (−4, 1) A circle with its center at (−4, 1) and radius of 5 units

10-1 PRACTICE A
10-1 PRACTICE C
10-1 PRACTICE B

Graph each equation on a graphing calculator. Identify each conic section. Then describe the center and intercepts.

1. $5x^2 + 5y^2 = 45$ Circle; center: (0, 0); intercepts: (0, 3), (0, −3), (3, 0), (−3, 0)
2. $x^2 + 25y^2 = 25$ Ellipse; center (0, 0); intercepts: (0, 1), (0, −1), (5, 0), (−5, 0)
3. $4x^2 + 4y^2 = 64$ Circle; center (0, 0); intercepts: (0, 4), (0, −4), (4, 0), (−4, 0)
4. $49x^2 + 4y^2 = 196$ Ellipse; center (0, 0); intercepts: (0, 7), (0, −7), (2, 0), (−2, 0)

Graph each equation on a graphing calculator. Identify each conic section. Then describe the vertices and the direction that the graph opens.

5. $y = x^2 - 3$ Parabola; (0, −3); opens upward
6. $y^2 = x^2 + 4$ Hyperbola; (0, 2), (0, −2); vertically
7. $x^2 - y^2 = 1$ Hyperbola; (1, 0), (−1, 0); horizontally
8. $y^2 = x + 4$ Parabola; (−4, 0); opens right
9. $x^2 = y + 2$ Parabola; (0, −2); opens upward
10. $x = y^2 + 3$ Parabola; (3, 0); opens right

Find the center and radius of a circle that has a diameter with the given endpoints.

11. (−10, 5) and (−5, 17) Center (−7.5, 11); radius = 6.5
12. (8, 1) and (−4, 10) Center (2, 5.5); radius = 7.5
13. (−7, 12) and (11, −68) Center (2, −28); radius = 41

Solve.

14. The orbit of an asteroid is modeled by the equation $9x^2 + 36y^2 = 144$.
   a. Identify the conic section. Ellipse
   b. Identify the x- and y-intercepts of the orbit. (0, 2), (0, −2), (4, 0), (−4, 0)
   c. Suppose each unit of the coordinate plane represents 40 million miles. What is the maximum width of the asteroid's orbit? 320 million miles

TEST PREP DOCTOR If students have difficulty with **Exercise 51,** they could make a sketch. Choices **F, G,** and **H** are the result of computational errors. Choice **J** is the only choice that is visually feasible.

Journal

Have students explain how to find the center of a circle when given the radius and a point, or the radius when given the center and a point or the endpoints of a diameter.

ALTERNATIVE ASSESSMENT

Have students give an example of a graph of each of the four conic sections. Then students should describe how to differentiate between the graphs of circles and ellipses and between the graphs of parabolas and hyperbolas.

Power Presentations with PowerPoint®

10-1 Lesson Quiz

Graph each equation on a graphing calculator. Identify each conic section. Then describe the center and intercepts for circles and ellipses, or the vertices and direction that the graph opens for parabolas and hyperbolas.

1. $x^2 - 16y^2 = 16$

hyperbola; vertices: $(\pm 4, 0)$; opens horizontally

2. $4x^2 + 49y^2 = 196$

ellipse; center: $(0, 0)$; intercepts: $(\pm 7, 0)$, $(0, \pm 2)$

3. $x = 6y^2$

parabola; vertex: $(0, 0)$; opens right

4. $x^2 + y^2 = 0.25$

circle; center: $(0, 0)$; intercepts: $(\pm 0.5, 0)$, $(0, \pm 0.5)$

5. Find the center and radius of a circle that has a diameter with endpoints at $(3, 7)$ and $(-2, -5)$.

center: $(0.5, 1)$; radius: 6.5

Also available on transparency

TEST PREP

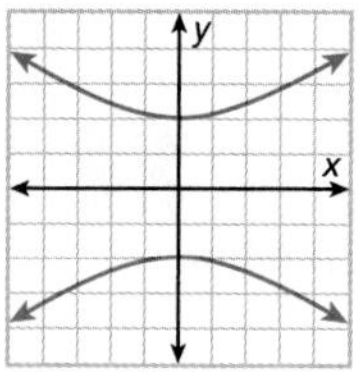

50. Which of the following could be the equation of the graph shown?

Ⓐ $9x^2 - 4y^2 = 36$ Ⓒ $9y^2 - 4x^2 = 36$

Ⓑ $4x^2 + 9y^2 = 36$ Ⓓ $9x^2 + 4y^2 = 36$

51. One endpoint of a line segment is $(-4, -8)$, and the midpoint of the line segment is $(2, -12)$. Which of the following is the other endpoint?

Ⓕ $(-1, -10)$ Ⓖ $(3, -2)$ Ⓗ $(-8, 16)$ Ⓙ $(8, -16)$

52. Which of the following are the x-intercepts of the graph of $4x^2 + 25y^2 = 100$?

Ⓐ $(2, 0)$ and $(-2, 0)$ Ⓒ $(5, 0)$ and $(-5, 0)$

Ⓑ $(4, 0)$ and $(-4, 0)$ Ⓓ $(10, 0)$ and $(-10, 0)$

53. What is the distance between the points $(-2, 6)$ and $(5, 30)$?

Ⓕ $3\sqrt{145}$ Ⓖ 31 Ⓗ $3\sqrt{65}$ Ⓙ 25

CHALLENGE AND EXTEND

Find a so that the two points are the given distance apart.

54. $(-5, 8)$ and $(3, a)$; 17 $a = 23$ or -7

55. $(4, -10)$ and $(a, 5)$; 39 $a = -32$ or 40

56. Multi-Step A degenerate conic is formed when a plane passes through the vertex of a hollow double cone. A point, a line, and a pair of intersecting lines are all degenerate conics.

a. The graph of $y^2 - x^2 = 0$ is a degenerate hyperbola. Graph $y^2 - x^2 = 0$.

b. What is the graph of $x^2 + y^2 = 0$? the point $(0, 0)$

c. Explain how a plane could intersect a hollow double cone to result in the graphs from parts **a** and **b**.

57. The midpoint and distance formulas can be extended to three dimensions by including an additional term in each formula for the variable z.

57a. $(9, 2, -11)$

a. Find the midpoint of the segment with endpoints $(6, -3, -9)$ and $(12, 7, -13)$.

b. Write a formula to find the midpoint of a segment in three dimensions.

57c. $d = \sqrt{101}$

c. Find the distance between the points $(1, 2, 3)$ and $(5, 8, 10)$.

d. Write a formula to find the distance between two points in three dimensions.

$d = \sqrt{(x_2 - x_1)^2 + (y_2 - y_1)^2 + (z_2 - z_1)^2}$

SPIRAL REVIEW

58. Construction A construction crew is repainting the center line on a 12 mi road. If the crew has completed 2.5 mi after 45 min, about how much more time should the painting take? *(Lesson 2-2)* 2 h 51 min

Find the zeros of each function by factoring. *(Lesson 5-3)*

59. $f(x) = x^2 - 2x - 48$ $x = -6, 8$

60. $f(x) = x^2 + 12x + 27$ $x = -9, -3$

61. $f(x) = x^2 - 11x + 28$ $x = 4, 7$

62. $f(x) = x^2 + 10x - 24$ $x = -12, 2$

63. $f(x) = 2x^2 - 25x + 33$ $x = 1.5, 11$

64. $f(x) = 3x^2 + 22x + 24$ $x = -6, -\frac{4}{3}$

Graph each exponential function. Find the y-intercept and the asymptote. Then describe how the graph transformed from the graph of its parent function $f(x) = 5^x$. *(Lesson 7-7)*

65. $f(x) = -\frac{1}{2}(5^x) + 3$

66. $f(x) = 4(5^x)$

67. $f(x) = 6(5^x) - 1$

Answers

56a.

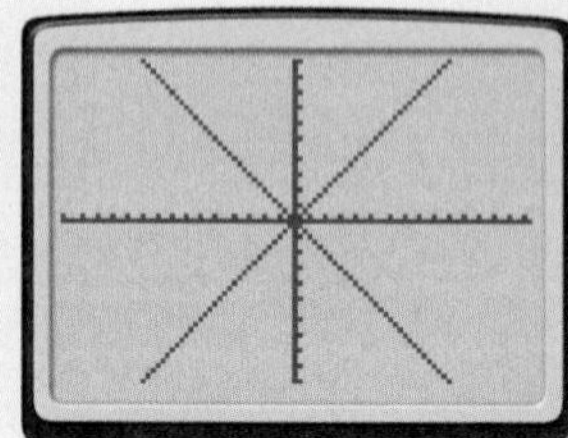

c. In part *a*, the plane passes through the vertex of the cone and is perpendicular to the base. In part *b*, the plane passes through the vertex of the cone and is parallel to the base.

57b. $\left(\frac{x_1 + x_2}{2}, \frac{y_1 + y_2}{2}, \frac{z_1 + z_2}{2}\right)$

65.

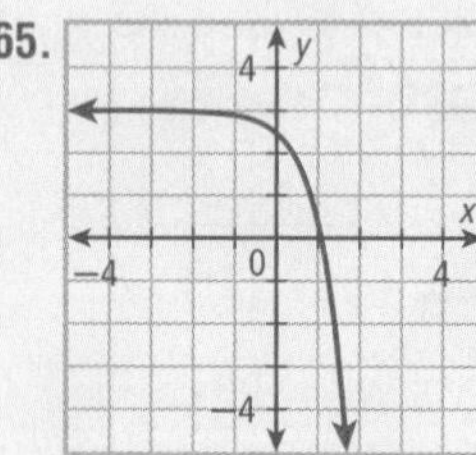

y-int.: 2.5; asymptote: $y = 3$; reflection across the x-axis, vertical compression by a factor of $\frac{1}{2}$, shift 3 units up

66, 67. See p. A42.

10-2 Circles

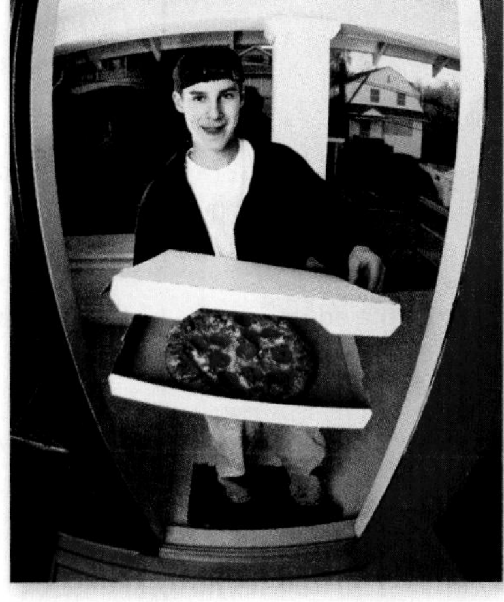

Objectives
Write an equation for a circle.

Graph a circle, and identify its center and radius.

Vocabulary
circle
tangent

Why learn this?
You can use circles to find locations within a given radius of an address. (See Example 3.)

A **circle** is the set of points in a plane that are a fixed distance, called the radius, from a fixed point, called the center. Because all of the points on a circle are the same distance from the center of the circle, you can use the Distance Formula to find the equation of a circle.

EXAMPLE 1 Using the Distance Formula to Write the Equation of a Circle

Write the equation of a circle with center $(2, 1)$ and radius $r = 5$.

Use the Distance Formula with $(x_2, y_2) = (x, y)$, $(x_1, y_1) = (2, 1)$, and distance equal to the radius, 5.

$$d = \sqrt{(x_2 - x_1)^2 + (y_2 - y_1)^2}$$ *Use the Distance Formula.*

$$5 = \sqrt{(x - 2)^2 + (y - 1)^2}$$ *Substitute.*

$$5^2 = (x - 2)^2 + (y - 1)^2$$ *Square both sides.*

$$25 = (x - 2)^2 + (y - 1)^2$$

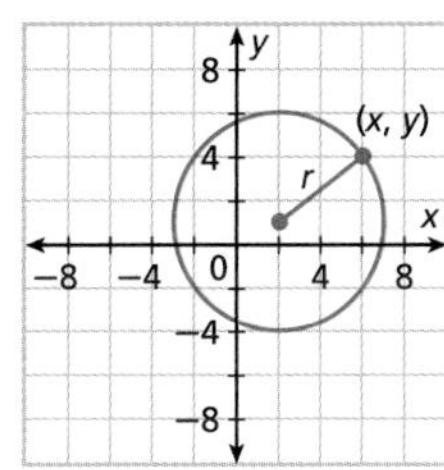

1. Write the equation of a circle with center $(4, 2)$ and radius $r = 7$. $(x - 4)^2 + (y - 2)^2 = 49$

Notice that r^2 and the center are visible in the equation of a circle. This leads to a general formula for a circle with center (h, k) and radius r.

Equation of a Circle

EQUATION	EXAMPLE	GRAPH
The equation of a circle with center (h, k) and radius r is $(x - h)^2 + (y - k)^2 = r^2$.	The equation of the circle with center $(5, -2)$ and radius $r = 8$ is $(x - 5)^2 + (y - (-2))^2 = 8^2$ or $(x - 5)^2 + (y + 2)^2 = 64$.	y, 4, r, x, −4, 0, 4, 8, 12, −4, (h, k), −8

10-2 Organizer

Pacing: Traditional 1 day
Block $\frac{1}{2}$ day

Objectives: Write an equation for a circle.

Graph a circle, and identify its center and radius.

Algebra Lab
In *Algebra Lab Activities*

Online Edition
Graphing Calculator, Tutorial Videos

Countdown to Testing Week 21

Power Presentations with PowerPoint®

Warm Up

Find the slope of the line that connects each pair of points.

1. $(5, 7)$ and $(-1, 6)$ $\frac{1}{6}$
2. $(3, -4)$ and $(-4, 3)$ -1

Find the distance between each pair of points.

3. $(-2, 12)$ and $(6, -3)$ 17
4. $(1, 5)$ and $(4, 1)$ 5

Also available on transparency

Math Humor

Q: What wild animal is good at algebra?

A: The tangent lion.

1 Introduce

EXPLORATION

10-2 Circles

You can use your calculator to discover properties of circles.

For example, to graph $(x - 1)^2 + (y - 2)^2 = 25$, first solve for y as shown.

$(x - 1)^2 + (y - 2)^2 = 25$
$(y - 2)^2 = 25 - (x - 1)^2$
$y - 2 = \pm\sqrt{25 - (x - 1)^2}$
$y = \pm\sqrt{25 - (x - 1)^2} + 2$

Enter the positive and negative functions in your calculator as **Y1** and **Y2** and graph these in a square window. The graph shows that the center of the circle is $(1, 2)$ and the radius is 5.

1. Graph each equation of a circle. Find the center and radius of each circle to complete the table.

Equation	Center	Radius
$x^2 + (y - 3)^2 = 9$		
$(x - 5)^2 + (y + 3)^2 = 16$		
$(x + 4)^2 + y^2 = 36$		

THINK AND DISCUSS

2. **Describe** how to find the center and radius of the circle $(x + 5)^2 + (y - 9)^2 = 4$ without graphing the equation.

Motivate

Present a state map. Ask students how they would figure out the distance between two cities. Are there any other cities in the state that are the same distance away from the first city? What shape do all of the points that are the same distance away from the first city form? circle

Explorations and answers are provided in the *Explorations* binder.

State Resources

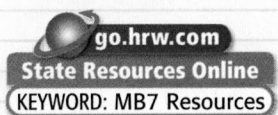

go.hrw.com
State Resources Online
KEYWORD: MB7 Resources

Power Presentations with PowerPoint®

Additional Examples

Example 1

Write the equation of the circle with center $(-3, 4)$ and radius 6.

$(x + 3)^2 + (y - 4)^2 = 36$

Example 2

Write the equation of each circle.

A. the circle with center $(0, 6)$ and radius 1

$x^2 + (y - 6)^2 = 1$

B. the circle with center $(-4, 11)$ and containing the point $(5, -1)$

$(x + 4)^2 + (y - 11)^2 = 225$

Example 3

Use the map given for **Example 3.** Which homes are within four miles of a restaurant located at $(-1, 1)$?

B, C, D, and E

Also available on transparency

INTERVENTION
Questioning Strategies

EXAMPLE 1

- What can you say about the equation $x^2 + y^2 = -16$?

EXAMPLE 2

- How can you find the center and radius of a circle from its graph?

EXAMPLE 3

- Are there any points on the grid that are within three miles of four different houses? zero houses?

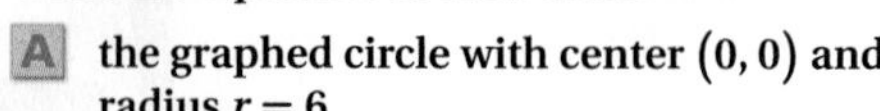

EXAMPLE 2 Writing the Equation of a Circle

Write the equation of each circle.

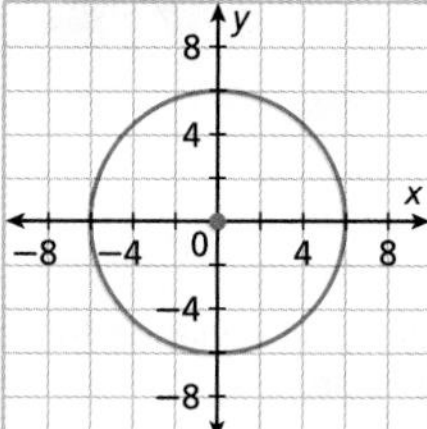

A the graphed circle with center $(0, 0)$ and radius $r = 6$

$(x - h)^2 + (y - k)^2 = r^2$ *Equation of a circle*

$(x - 0)^2 + (y - 0)^2 = 6^2$ *Substitute.*

$x^2 + y^2 = 36.$

Helpful Hint

If the center of the circle is at the origin, the equation simplifies to $x^2 + y^2 = r^2$.

B the circle with center $(2, 4)$ and containing the point $(8, 12)$

$r = \sqrt{(8 - 2)^2 + (12 - 4)^2}$ *Use the Distance Formula to find the radius.*

$= \sqrt{6^2 + 8^2}$

$= \sqrt{100} = 10$

$(x - 2)^2 + (y - 4)^2 = 10^2$ *Substitute the values into the equation of a circle.*

$(x - 2)^2 + (y - 4)^2 = 100$

CHECK IT OUT! **2.** Find the equation of the circle with center $(-3, 5)$ and containing the point $(9, 10)$. $(x + 3)^2 + (y - 5)^2 = 169$

The location of points in relation to a circle can be described by inequalities. The points inside the circle satisfy the inequality $(x - h)^2 + (y - k)^2 < r^2$. The points outside the circle satisfy the inequality $(x - h)^2 + (y - k)^2 > r^2$.

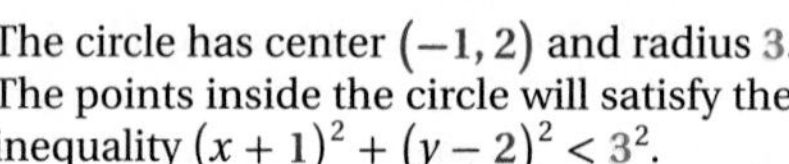

EXAMPLE 3 ***Consumer Application***

Raul and his friends are having a pizza party and will decide where to have the party based on the delivery area of the pizza restaurant. Suppose that the pizza restaurant is located at the point $(-1, 2)$ and the letters represent the homes of Raul and his friends. Use the equation of a circle to find the houses that are within a 3-mile radius and will get free delivery.

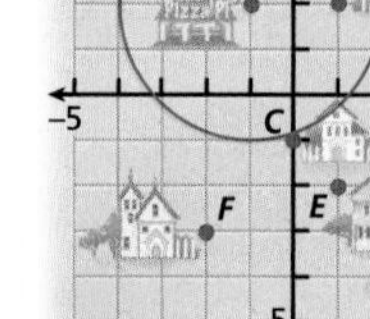

The circle has center $(-1, 2)$ and radius 3. The points inside the circle will satisfy the inequality $(x + 1)^2 + (y - 2)^2 < 3^2$.

Points D and B are within a 3-mile radius.

Check Point $C(0, -1)$ is near the boundary.

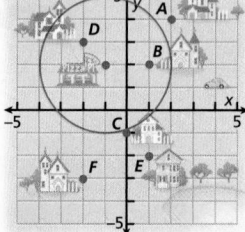

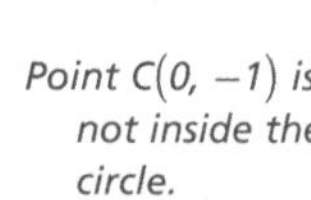

$(0 + 1)^2 + (-1 - 2)^2 < 3^2$

$(1)^2 + (-3)^2 < 3^2$

$1 + 9 < 9$ ✗ *Point C(0, −1) is not inside the circle.*

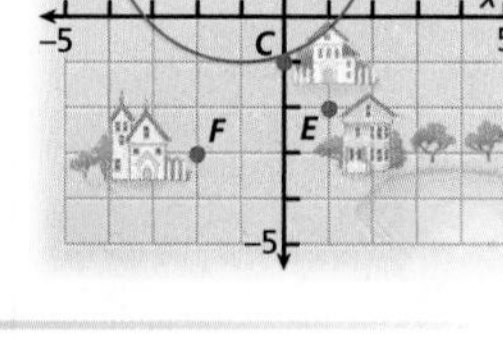

CHECK IT OUT! **3. What if...?** Which homes are within a 3-mile radius of a restaurant located at $(2, -1)$? *C, E*

2 Teach

Guided Instruction

Remind students of the Pythagorean Theorem and the formula for the distance between two points. As the lesson progresses, students will need to be able to recognize the equation for a circle in standard form. Then they need to be comfortable deriving an equation from a graph and vice versa.

Have students use a compass to reinforce the concept that a circle is a set of points a fixed distance away from a fixed center.

Reaching All Learners
Through Multiple Representations

A program such as *Geometer's Sketchpad* can be used to produce a dynamic demonstration of the line tangent to a circle at a given point. By dragging a point on the circle around the circle, students will be able to see the equation of the tangent line change.

ENGLISH LANGUAGE LEARNERS

A **tangent** is a line in the same plane as the circle that intersects the circle at exactly one point. Recall from geometry that a tangent to a circle is perpendicular to the radius at the point of tangency.

EXAMPLE 4 Writing the Equation of a Tangent

Write the equation of the line that is tangent to the circle $25 = x^2 + y^2$ at the point $(3, 4)$.

Step 1 Identify the center and radius of the circle.

From the equation $25 = x^2 + y^2$, the circle has center $(0, 0)$ and radius $r = 5$.

Step 2 Find the slope of the radius at the point of tangency and the slope of the tangent.

$m = \frac{y_2 - y_1}{x_2 - x_1}$ *Use the slope formula.*

$m = \frac{4 - 0}{3 - 0}$ *Substitute $(3, 4)$ for (x_2, y_2) and $(0, 0)$ for (x_1, y_1).*

$m = \frac{4}{3}$ *The slope of the radius is $\frac{4}{3}$.*

Because the slopes of perpendicular lines are negative reciprocals, the slope of the tangent is $-\frac{3}{4}$.

Remember!

To review linear functions, see Lesson 2-4.

Step 3 Find the slope-intercept equation of the tangent by using the point $(3, 4)$ and the slope $m = -\frac{3}{4}$.

$y - y_1 = m(x - x_1)$ *Use the point-slope formula.*

$y - 4 = -\frac{3}{4}(x - 3)$ *Substitute $(3, 4)$ for (x_1, y_1) and $-\frac{3}{4}$ for m.*

$y = -\frac{3}{4}x + \frac{25}{4}$ *Rewrite in slope-intercept form.*

The equation of the line that is tangent to $25 = x^2 + y^2$ at $(3, 4)$ is $y = -\frac{3}{4}x + \frac{25}{4}$.

Check Graph the circle and the line.

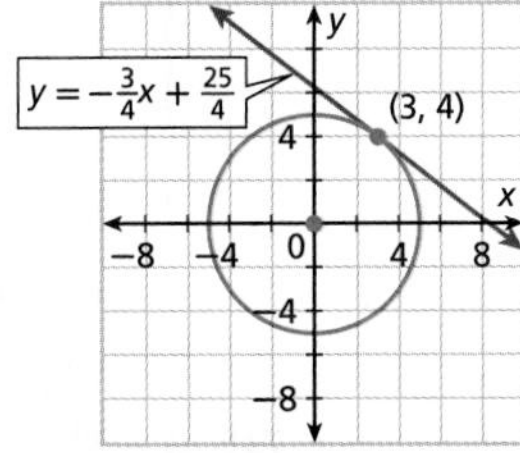

4. Write the equation of the line that is tangent to the circle $25 = (x - 1)^2 + (y + 2)^2$ at the point $(5, -5)$. $y = \frac{4}{3}x - \frac{35}{3}$

THINK AND DISCUSS

1. Explain the transformation of $x^2 + y^2 = 1$ that is necessary to get the equation $(x - h)^2 + (y - k)^2 = 1$.
2. Explain what happens to the radius if the equation of a circle changes from $x^2 + y^2 = 4$ to $x^2 + y^2 = 16$.

3. **GET ORGANIZED** Copy and complete the graphic organizer. Sketch each circle, and give its equation.

	$r = 1$	$r = 3$
Center (0, 0)		
Center (1, 2)		

COMMON ERROR ALERT

Students may sometimes forget to square the radius when forming the equation for a circle. Remind them that in the equation for a circle, every term is squared.

Power Presentations with PowerPoint®

Additional Examples

Example 4

Write the equation for the line tangent to the circle $x^2 + y^2 = 29$ at the point $(2, 5)$.

$y - 5 = -\frac{2}{5}(x - 2)$

Also available on transparency

INTERVENTION

Questioning Strategies

EXAMPLE 4

- Do you need the coordinates of the center of the circle in order to find the tangent line?
- Which is a better choice for a problem like this: point-slope form or slope-intercept form of a line? Why?

Multiple Representations You may wish to reinforce the meaning of the distance formula and the equation of a circle by using a right triangle having vertices opposite the right angle at the center of the circle and on the circle. Demonstrate the Pythagorean Theorem on this triangle and relate it to the equation of the circle.

3 Close

Summarize

Given the center and radius, or the center and a point on the circle, it is possible to write an equation for the circle. The equation is basically an application of the distance formula.

ONGOING ASSESSMENT and INTERVENTION

***Diagnose Before* the Lesson**
10-2 Warm Up, TE p. 729

***Monitor During* the Lesson**
Check It Out! Exercises, SE pp. 729–731
Questioning Strategies, TE pp. 730–731

***Assess After* the Lesson**
10-2 Lesson Quiz, TE p. 734
Alternative Assessment, TE p. 734

Answers to *Think and Discuss*

1. shift *h* units right and *k* units up
2. The radius doubles from 2 to 4.
3. See p. A11.

10-2 Exercises

Assignment Guide

Assign *Guided Practice* exercises as necessary.

If you finished Examples **1–2**
Basic 12–17
Average 12–17
Advanced 12–17, 27, 28

If you finished Examples **1–4**
Basic 12–21, 23–30, 33–35, 40–46
Average 12–36, 40–46
Advanced 12–46

Homework Quick Check
Quickly check key concepts.
Exercises: 12, 14, 16, 18, 20

State Resources

10-2 Exercises

GUIDED PRACTICE

1. **Vocabulary** How can you recognize a *tangent* of a circle?
Possible answer: A tangent line to a circle touches the circle at exactly 1 point.

SEE EXAMPLE 1 p. 729

Write the equation of each circle. **2.** $(x-6)^2+(y+5)^2=16$

2. center $(6, -5)$ and radius $r = 4$
3. center $(-11, 3)$ and radius $r = 9$ **3.** $(x+11)^2+(y-3)^2=81$

SEE EXAMPLE 2 p. 730

4. $x^2+y^2=64$
5. 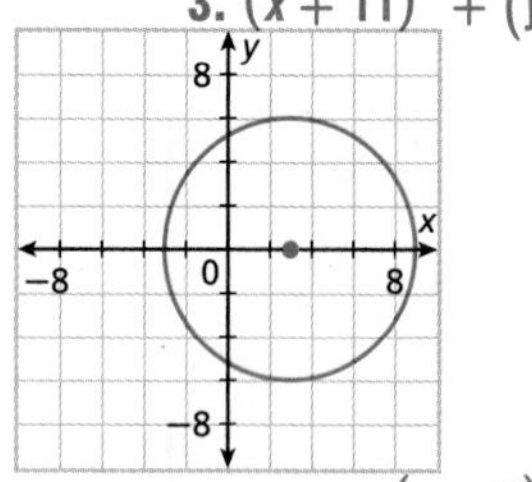

$(x-3)^2+y^2=36$

6. center $(-1, 9)$ and containing the point $(2, 5)$ $(x+1)^2+(y-9)^2=25$
7. center $(-2, -5)$ and containing the point $(-10, -20)$ $(x+2)^2+(y+5)^2=289$

SEE EXAMPLE 3 p. 730

Depending on its strength, an earthquake can be felt in locations miles away from the epicenter.

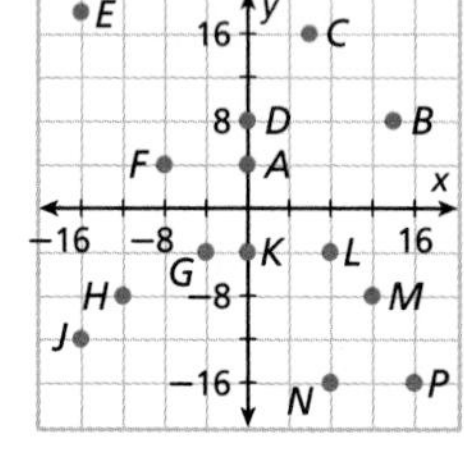

8. **Multi-Step** Suppose that the epicenter of the earthquake is located at the point $(5, -2)$ and is felt up to 10 mi away. Use the equation of a circle to find the locations that are affected. ***A, K, L, G, M***
9. **Multi-Step** Suppose that the epicenter of the earthquake is located at the point $(-5, -7)$ and is felt up to 8 mi away. Use the equation of a circle to find the locations that are affected. ***K, H, G***

SEE EXAMPLE 4 p. 731

Multi-Step **Write the equation of the line that is tangent to each circle at the given point.**

10. $x^2+y^2=100;\ (8, 6)$ $y=-\frac{4}{3}x+\frac{50}{3}$
11. $(x+6)^2+(y+4)^2=25;\ (-9, -8)$ $y=-\frac{3}{4}x-\frac{59}{4}$

12. $(x-3)^2+(y-2)^2=49$

PRACTICE AND PROBLEM SOLVING

Independent Practice	
For Exercises	See Example
12–13	1
14–17	2
18–19	3
20–21	4

Extra Practice
Skills Practice p. S22
Application Practice p. S41

Write the equation of each circle. **13.** $(x-5)^2+(y-1)^2=100$

12. center $(3, 2)$ and radius $r = 7$
13. center $(5, 1)$ and radius $r = 10$
14. 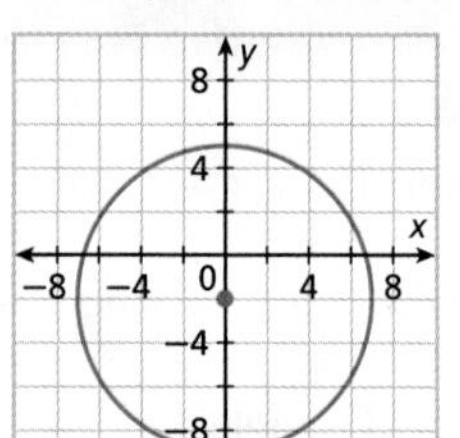

15.

14. $x^2+(y+2)^2=49$

16. center $(12, -3)$ and containing the point $(-12, 7)$ $(x-12)^2+(y+3)^2=676$
17. center $(-6, -4)$ and containing the point $(-2, -1)$ $(x+6)^2+(y+4)^2=25$

15. $(x+4)^2+(y-2)^2=64$

10-2 READING STRATEGIES

If you are given the length of the radius and the coordinates of the center of a circle, you can find the equation of the circle.

For a circle with its center at (3, 9) and a radius of 4 units, follow these steps to find the equation of the circle.

STEP 1 Write the standard form of the equation.	STEP 2 Substitute the coordinates of the center and the radius.	STEP 3 Square the radius.
$(x-h)^2+(y-k)^2=r^2$ where the center is at (h, k)	$h=3, k=9, r=4$ $(x-3)^2+(x-9)^2=(4)^2$	$(x-3)^2+(x-9)^2=16$

Answer each question.

1. A circle has center (1, 10) and radius 3.
   a. Give the values of h, k, and r. $h=1, k=10, r=3$
   b. Write the equation of the circle. $(x-1)^2+(y-10)^2=9$
2. A circle has center (−2, −3) and radius 12.
   a. Give the values of h, k, and r. $h=-2, k=-3, r=12$
   b. Write the equation of the circle. $(x+2)^2+(y+3)^2=144$
3. Explain how you can use the Distance Formula to write the equation of a circle if you know the radius of the circle and the coordinates of the center.
   Possible answer: Substitute the center coordinates in the Distance Formula in place of x_1 and y_1, and the radius for the distance. Then square both sides of the equation.
4. a. Describe how you could find the equation of the circle shown on the graph below.
   Possible answer: Use the graph to find the center of the circle (3, −5) and the radius, 4. Then use the standard form of the equation.
   b. What is the equation of the circle?
   $(x-3)^2+(y+5)^2=16$

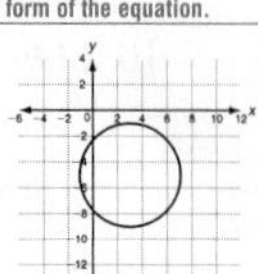

10-2 RETEACH

A **circle** is the set of points in the plane that are the same distance from a fixed point. The distance is defined as the **radius** of the circle and the fixed point is the **center** of the circle.

You can use the Distance Formula to write the equation of a circle with center (h, k) and radius r.

Step 1 Write the Distance Formula.
$d=\sqrt{(x_2-x_1)^2+(y_2-y_1)^2}$

Step 2 Let $(x_2, y_2)=(x, y)$ and $(x_1, y_1)=(h, k)$.
$d=\sqrt{(x-h)^2+(y-k)^2}$
Substitute (x, y) and (h, k) into the formula.

Step 3 The circle has radius r. This is the distance from the center (h, k) to any point (x, y) on the circle. So, substitute r for d in the formula.
$r=\sqrt{(x-h)^2+(y-k)^2}$

Step 4 Square both sides of the equation.
$r^2=(x-h)^2+(y-k)^2$
Think: $(\sqrt{a^2})^2=a^2$ if $a \geq 0$.

Use the Distance Formula. Write the equation of each circle with the given center and radius.

1. Center $(-1, 3)$ and radius $r=6$
   $d=\sqrt{(x_2-x_1)^2+(y_2-y_1)^2}$
   $d=\sqrt{(x-(-1))^2+(y-3)^2}$
   $6=\sqrt{(x+1)^2+(y-3)^2}$
   $6^2=\left(\sqrt{(x+1)^2+(y-3)^2}\right)^2$
   $(x+1)^2+(y-3)^2=36$
2. Center $(5, -2)$ and radius $r=4$
   $d=\sqrt{(x_2-x_1)^2+(y_2-y_1)^2}$
   $d=\sqrt{(x-5)^2+(y-(-2))^2}$
   $4=\sqrt{(x-5)^2+(y+2)^2}$
   $4^2=\left(\sqrt{(x-5)^2+(y+2)^2}\right)^2$
   $(x-5)^2+(y+2)^2=16$
3. Center $(4, 1)$ and radius $r=3$
   $3=\sqrt{(x-4)^2+(y-1)^2}$
   $(x-4)^2+(y-1)^2=9$
4. Center $(3, 7)$ and radius $r=8$
   $8=\sqrt{(x-3)^2+(y-7)^2}$
   $(x-3)^2+(y-7)^2=64$

Aida's puppy escaped from the backyard and is lost. Aida has created a map of places that the puppy may have gone.

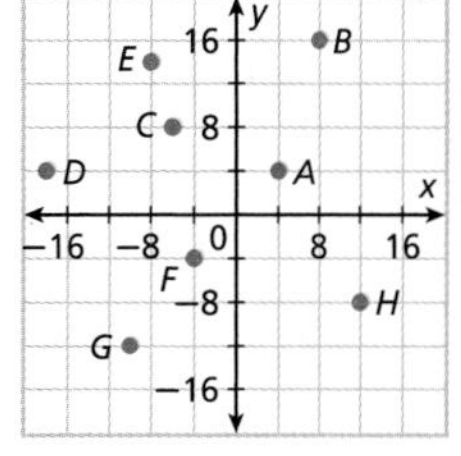

18. **Multi-Step** Suppose that Aida's house is located at the point $(3, 8)$. The puppy has been gone for 4 hours, and Aida estimates that the puppy cannot have traveled more than 12 miles. Use the equation of a circle to find the possible locations of the puppy. ***A, B, C***

19. **Multi-Step** Suppose that Aida's house is located at the point $(-6, 15)$. The puppy has been gone for 1 hour, and Aida estimates that the puppy cannot have traveled more than 3 miles. Use the equation of a circle to find the possible locations of the puppy. ***E***

Multi-Step **Write the equation of the line that is tangent to each circle at the given point.**

20. $x^2 + y^2 = 169, (-5, 12)$ $y = \frac{5}{12}x + \frac{169}{12}$

21. $(x - 2)^2 + (y - 4)^2 = 289, (-15, 4)$ $x = -15$

22. **History** The outermost ring of the ancient monument Stonehenge can be modeled by the equation $x^2 + y^2 = 27{,}225$. The Sarsen Circle, the center ring of stones usually associated with the monument, can be modeled by the equation $x^2 + y^2 = 2916$.
    a. The Heel Stone is located outside of the circles, approximately at the point $(0, 300)$. Find the maximum and minimum distances, in feet, to the Heel Stone from both the outer and inner circles. **465 ft, 135 ft; 354 ft, 246 ft**
    b. Graph the outer circle and the Sarsen Circle.
    c. Two Station Stones surrounded by circular ditches are located within the outer circle. One stone is located at approximately $(-100, 100)$ and is surrounded by a ditch of radius 12 ft. Write an equation to model the ditch around this Station Stone. $(x + 100)^2 + (y - 100)^2 = 144$

LINK

History

Stonehenge, in southern England, is thought to have been built in three stages, from 2950-1600 B.C.E. It is not a single structure but consists of many stone, earth, and wood constructions.

Find the domain and range of each relation.

23. $x^2 + y^2 = 36$

24. $(x - 2)^2 + (y + 7)^2 = 81$

25. $(x + 2)^2 + (y)^2 = 9$

26. **Geometry** The circle with center $(2, 3)$ and the circle with center $(-1, -1)$ are tangent at the point $(5, 7)$.
    a. Find an equation for the small circle.
    b. Find an equation for the large circle.
    c. Find the equation of the line that is tangent to both circles. $y = -\frac{3}{4}x + \frac{43}{4}$

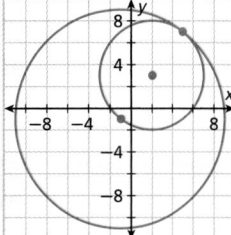

Geometry **Write the equation of each circle.**

27. center $(-4, 0)$ and circumference 16π $(x + 4)^2 + y^2 = 64$

28. center $\left(\frac{2}{3}, \frac{5}{8}\right)$ and area 49π $\left(x - \frac{2}{3}\right)^2 + \left(y - \frac{5}{8}\right)^2 = 49$

MULTI-STEP TEST PREP

29. This problem will prepare you for the Multi-Step Test Prep on page 758.

    The orbit of Venus is nearly circular. An astronomer develops a model for the orbit in which the Sun has coordinates $(-5, 20)$, the circular orbit of Venus passes through $(62, 20)$, and each unit of the coordinate plane represents 1 million miles.
    a. Write an equation for the orbit of Venus. $(x + 5)^2 + (y - 20)^2 = 4489$
    b. How far is Venus from the Sun? **67 million mi**
    c. How far does Venus travel as it makes one complete orbit of the Sun? **134π million mi**

COMMON ERROR ALERT

In **Exercises 24** and **25,** students may forget the center of the circle when finding the domain and range. Remind students that the center of the circle is also the center of the domain and range values.

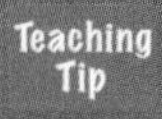

Language Arts The smaller circle in **Exercise 26,** which shares the same tangent line with the larger circle at (5, 7), is called an *osculating circle. Osculate* means "to kiss."

MULTI-STEP TEST PREP **Exercise 29** involves writing an equation for a circle. This exercise prepares students for the Multi-Step Test Prep on page 758.

Answers

22b.

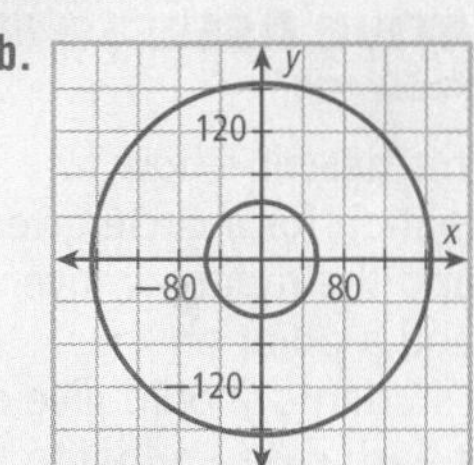

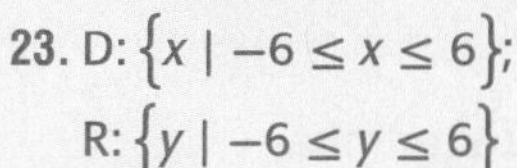

23. D: $\{x \mid -6 \le x \le 6\}$;
R: $\{y \mid -6 \le y \le 6\}$

24. D: $\{x \mid -7 \le x \le 11\}$;
R: $\{y \mid -16 \le y \le 2\}$

25. D: $\{x \mid -5 \le x \le 1\}$;
R: $\{y \mid -3 \le y \le 3\}$

26a. $(x - 2)^2 + (y - 3)^2 = 25$

b. $(x + 1)^2 + (y + 1)^2 = 100$

10-2 PROBLEM SOLVING

When Claire started her consulting business, she decided not to accept any clients located more than 10 miles from her home. On the graph below, her home is located at (5, 1), and her prospective clients are represented by the letters *P* through *W*.

1. Claire needs to know which prospective clients are located within a 10-mile radius of her home.
    a. Write the equation of a circle with center (5, 1) and radius 10. $(x - 5)^2 + (y - 1)^2 = 100$
    b. Which prospective clients are located within 10 miles of Claire's home? *P, S, W*
    c. Which prospective clients are located more than 10 miles from Claire's home? *Q, R, T, U, V*
2. Claire finds that she isn't earning enough to pay the expenses from her consulting business and she needs to find some additional clients. She decides that she will drive up to 15 miles from her home to visit a client. Which prospective clients are within a 15-mile radius of her home?
    a. Write the equation of a circle with center (5, 1) and radius 15. $(x - 5)^2 + (y - 1)^2 = 225$
    b. Which prospective clients are located within 15 miles of Claire's home? *P, Q, S, T, V, W*
    c. How far away is a prospective client located at (10, 15)? **14.9 units**

Claire rents an office at location (−2, −3). Choose the letter for the best answer.

3. Which of the prospective clients *P* through *W* are located more than 15 miles from Claire's office?
    A *R, V*
    B *R, S, V*
    (C) *Q, R, V*
    D *Q, R, S, V*
4. Which location is within 5 miles of Claire's office?
    F Post office at (2, 3)
    (G) Library at (2, −3)
    H Marina at (−3, 2)
    J Swimming pool at (−2, 3)

10-2 CHALLENGE

Every line has an equation of the form $ax + by = c$, where both a and b cannot be 0. Suppose that $a \neq 0$. Then dividing by a and setting $D = \frac{b}{a}$ and $E = \frac{c}{a}$ lead to the general form of a line, $x + Dy = E$. This shows that there are only two independent arbitrary constants, D and E. So, the equation of a line is determined algebraically by two independent conditions. This makes sense because you know that, geometrically, a line is determined by two points. You can explore the conditions that determine the equation of a circle.

1. Consider the standard equation of a circle, $(x - h)^2 + (y - k)^2 = r^2$.
    a. Name the constants in the equation. *h, k,* and *r*
    b. How many constants are there? 3
    c. Are the constants independent? Explain. Yes; possible answer: no algebraic operation will combine any two of the constants.
2. Consider the general equation of a circle, $x^2 + y^2 + Dx + Ey + F = 0$.
    a. How many independent constants are there? 3 b. How many points determine a circle? 3
3. Circle *O* passes through the three points (−1, 1), (3, 5), and (5, −3).
    a. Use the general equation of a circle to write a system of three equations in *D, E,* and *F*, which can be used to write an equation of circle *O*. $D - E - F = 2$; $3D + 5E + F = -34$; $5D - 3E + F = -34$
    b. Solve the system for *D, E,* and *F*. Write the equation of circle *O* in general form. $x^2 + y^2 - \frac{32}{5}x - \frac{8}{5}y - \frac{34}{5} = 0$
    c. Complete the squares in the equation. Write the coordinates of the center and the radius of circle *O*. Center $\left(\frac{16}{5}, \frac{4}{5}\right)$; radius $= \frac{\sqrt{442}}{5}$

The diagram at right shows a circle that passes through the origin and is tangent to the line $3x - 4y = 2$ at the point (2, 1).

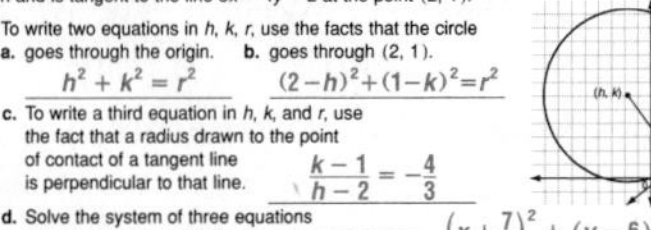

4. To write two equations in *h, k, r,* use the facts that the circle
    a. goes through the origin. $h^2 + k^2 = r^2$ b. goes through (2, 1). $(2-h)^2+(1-k)^2=r^2$
    c. To write a third equation in *h, k,* and *r*, use the fact that a radius drawn to the point of contact of a tangent line is perpendicular to that line. $\frac{k-1}{h-2} = -\frac{4}{3}$
    d. Solve the system of three equations in *h, k,* and *r*, and write the equation of the circle. $\left(x + \frac{7}{4}\right)^2 + (y - 6)^2 = \frac{625}{16}$
5. Determine the equation of the circle whose center lies on the line $3x + 7y = -2$ and that passes through the points (6, 2) and (8, 0). $(x - 4)^2 + (y + 2)^2 = 20$

10-2 PRACTICE A

10-2 PRACTICE C

10-2 PRACTICE B

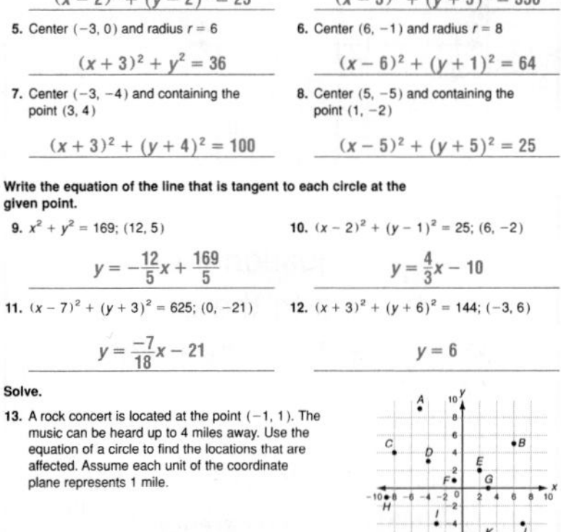

Write the equation of each circle.

1. Center (8, 9) and radius $r = 10$ $(x - 8)^2 + (y - 9)^2 = 100$
2. Center (−1, 5) and containing the point (23, −2) $(x + 1)^2 + (y - 5)^2 = 625$
3. Center (2, 2) and containing the point (−1, 6) $(x - 2)^2 + (y - 2)^2 = 25$
4. Center (3, −5) and containing the point (−7, 11) $(x - 3)^2 + (y + 5)^2 = 356$
5. Center (−3, 0) and radius $r = 6$ $(x + 3)^2 + y^2 = 36$
6. Center (6, −1) and radius $r = 8$ $(x - 6)^2 + (y + 1)^2 = 64$
7. Center (−3, −4) and containing the point (3, 4) $(x + 3)^2 + (y + 4)^2 = 100$
8. Center (5, −5) and containing the point (1, −2) $(x - 5)^2 + (y + 5)^2 = 25$

Write the equation of the line that is tangent to each circle at the given point.

9. $x^2 + y^2 = 169$; (12, 5) $y = -\frac{12}{5}x + \frac{169}{5}$
10. $(x - 2)^2 + (y - 1)^2 = 25$; (6, −2) $y = \frac{4}{3}x - 10$
11. $(x - 7)^2 + (y + 3)^2 = 625$; (0, −21) $y = \frac{-7}{18}x - 21$
12. $(x + 3)^2 + (y + 6)^2 = 144$; (−3, 6) $y = 6$

Solve.

13. A rock concert is located at the point (−1, 1). The music can be heard up to 4 miles away. Use the equation of a circle to find the locations that are affected. Assume each unit of the coordinate plane represents 1 mile. *D, E, F*

TEST PREP DOCTOR In **Exercise 33,** students must recall that the slope of the tangent is the negative reciprocal of the slope of the radius in order to see that **C** is the correct answer.

Journal

Have students discuss how they can tell from the equation for a circle whether the circle will include a given point in its interior.

ALTERNATIVE ASSESSMENT

Have students describe how to write an equation for a circle given the center and the radius or given the center and a point on the circle. Then students should give an example for each case and write the equation.

Power Presentations with PowerPoint®

10-2 Lesson Quiz

1. Write an equation for the circle with center $(1, -5)$ and a radius of $\sqrt{10}$.
   $(x-1)^2 + (y+5)^2 = 10$
2. Write an equation for the circle with center $(-4, 4)$ and containing the point $(-1, 16)$.
   $(x+4)^2 + (y-4)^2 = 153$
3. Which points on the graph shown are within 2 units of the point $(0, -2.5)$? C, F

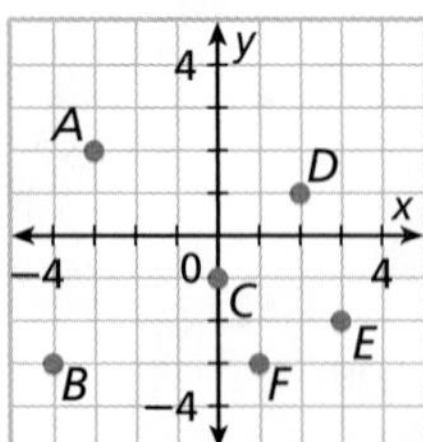

4. Write an equation for the line tangent to the circle $x^2 + y^2 = 17$ at the point $(4, 1)$.
   $y - 1 = -4(x - 4)$

Also available on transparency

30. **Entertainment** A radio station emits a signal that can be received by anyone within 120 miles of the station's transmitter. Write and graph an inequality for the region covered by the radio station with the transmitter located at $(0, 0)$.

31. **Critical Thinking** Is it possible to have two different lines that are tangent to the same circle at the same point? Explain.

32. **Write About It** How could you show that the line with equation $y = -\frac{5}{12}x + \frac{28}{3}$ is tangent to the circle with equation $169 = (x-3)^2 + (y+6)^2$ at the point $(8, 6)$?

TEST PREP

33. Which of the following lines is tangent at $(13, 9)$ to the circle with center $(5, 3)$?
    (A) $y = \frac{3}{4}x - \frac{3}{4}$ (B) $y = -\frac{3}{4}x + \frac{75}{4}$ (C) $y = -\frac{4}{3}x + \frac{79}{3}$ (D) $y = \frac{4}{3}x - \frac{25}{3}$

34. Which of the following points is inside the circle with the equation $121 = (x-5)^2 + (y+9)^2$?
    (F) $(12, 2)$ (G) $(-8, 6)$ (H) $(2, -6)$ (J) $(-9, -3)$

35. **Short Response** Give the equation of a circle with center $(-4, 8)$ and radius $r = 9$.
    $(x+4)^2 + (y-8)^2 = 81$

CHALLENGE AND EXTEND

36. Consider the circle with equation $100 = x^2 + (y-4)^2$
    a. Find the equation of the tangents of the circle at $(8, 10)$ and at $(8, -2)$.
    b. Find where the equations in part **a** intersect. $(12.5, 4)$
    c. Find the distance from the point of intersection to the tangent points. 7.5

36a. $y = -\frac{4}{3}x + \frac{62}{3}$; $y = \frac{4}{3}x - \frac{38}{3}$

37. The lines $y = -3x + 1$ and $y = 2x - 9$ each contain diameters of a particular circle. The point $(9, 19)$ is on the circle.
    a. Find the center of the circle. $(2, -5)$
    b. Write the equation of the circle. $(x-2)^2 + (y+5)^2 = 625$

Graph each system of inequalities.

38. $\begin{cases} x - 3y > -12 \\ (x-2)^2 + (y-1)^2 \le 49 \end{cases}$

39. $\begin{cases} (x-3)^2 + (y-2)^2 \le 36 \\ (x-4)^2 + (y+4)^2 \le 25 \end{cases}$

SPIRAL REVIEW

Write the equation of each line. *(Lesson 2-4)*

40. slope 2 through $(1, 4)$
41. slope $\frac{1}{2}$ through $(-2, 1)$
42. slope $\frac{4}{3}$ and y-intercept 1

40. $y = 2x + 2$
41. $y = \frac{1}{2}x + 2$
42. $y = \frac{4}{3}x + 1$

43. **Travel** Patrick drives a bus. When he picks up 20 passengers or fewer, his route takes him 15 minutes plus half a minute for each passenger. When Patrick picks up more than 20 passengers, his route takes him 20 minutes plus 1 minute for every passenger. *(Lesson 9-2)*
    a. Write a piecewise function for the amount of time that Patrick's route requires.
    b. Graph the function.
    c. How long does it take Patrick to pick up 20 passengers? 25 min

Graph each equation on a graphing calculator. Identify each conic section. Then describe the vertices and the direction that the graph opens. *(Lesson 10-1)*

44. $\frac{y^2}{3} = x$
45. $16y^2 = -x$
46. $4x^2 - 9y^2 = 36$

Answers

30. $x^2 + y^2 < 14{,}400$

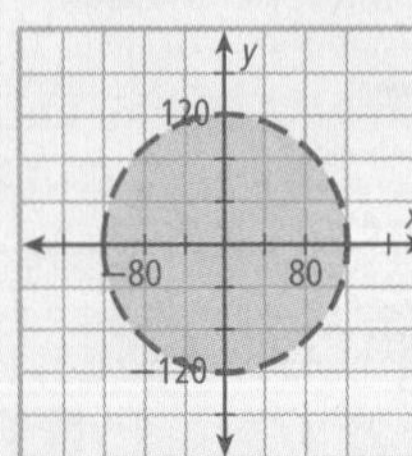

31. No; possible answer: a line with a different slope would not be perpendicular to the radius at that point and may intersect the circle more than once.

32. Possible answer: Verify that the point $(8, 6)$ is on the line, and then show that the slope of the line from the center to $(8, 6)$ is $\frac{12}{5}$.

38–39. See p. A42.

43a. $f(x) = \begin{cases} \frac{1}{2}x + 15 & 0 \le x \le 20 \\ x + 20 & x > 20 \end{cases}$

44. parabola; vertex: $(0, 0)$; opens right
45. parabola; vertex: $(0, 0)$; opens left
46. hyperbola; vertices: $(\pm 3, 0)$; opens horizontally

43b, 44–46. For graphs, see p. A42.

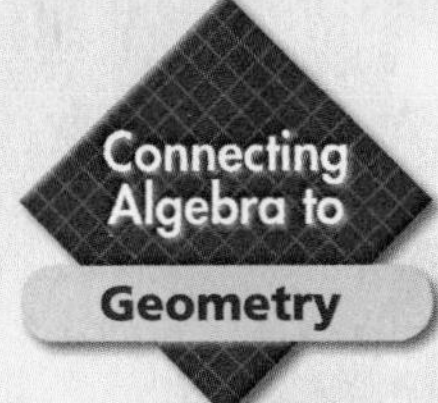

See Skills Bank page S64

Surface Area and Volume

You can use formulas to find the surface area and volume of three-dimensional figures such as cylinders, cones, and spheres.

	Cylinder with radius r and height h	Cone with radius r and height h	Sphere with radius r
Solid			
Volume	$V = \pi r^2 h$	$V = \frac{1}{3}\pi r^2 h$	$V = \frac{4}{3}\pi r^3$
Surface Area	$S = 2\pi r(r + h)$	$S = \pi r\sqrt{r^2 + h^2} + \pi r^2$	$S = 4\pi r^2$

Example

Find the surface area and volume of the cone shown.

In order to use the formulas, identify the radius and height of the cone. $r = 5$ and $h = 12$. Find the surface area. Use the formula.

$S = \pi r\sqrt{r^2 + h^2} + \pi r^2$ — *Formula for surface area of a cone.*

$S = \pi \cdot 5\sqrt{(5)^2 + (12)^2} + \pi(5)^2$ — *Substitute 5 for r and 12 for h.*

$S = 90\pi$ — *Simplify.*

Find the volume.

$V = \frac{1}{3}\pi r^2 h$ — *Formula for the volume of a cone.*

$V = \frac{1}{3}\pi(5)^2(12)$ — *Substitute 5 for r and 12 for h.*

$V = 100\pi$ — *Simplify.*

Try This

Find the surface area and volume of each figure.

1.

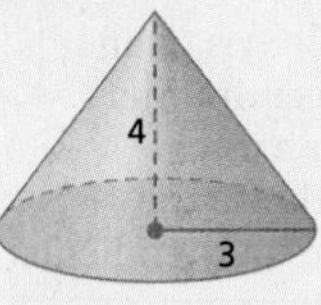

$S = 24\pi$; $V = 12\pi$

2.

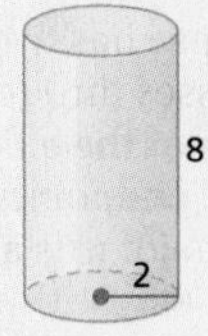

$S = 40\pi$; $V = 32\pi$

3.

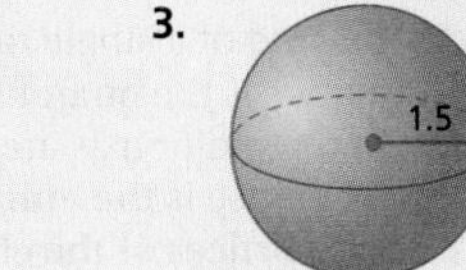

$S = 9\pi$; $V = 4.5\pi$

Organizer

Connecting Algebra to Geometry

See Skills Bank page S64

Pacing:
Traditional $\frac{1}{2}$ day
Block $\frac{1}{4}$ day

Objective: Find the surface area and volume of three-dimensional figures by using formulas.

Online Edition

Countdown to Testing Week 21

Teach

Remember

Students review and apply surface area and volume formulas for three-dimensional geometric figures.

INTERVENTION For additional review and practice on finding the surface area and volume, see Skills Bank page S64.

Close

Assess

Why is the volume or surface area of a cylinder, cone, or sphere sometimes an approximation rather than an exact answer? The formulas include π. If π is rounded, the result will also be an approximation.

State Resources

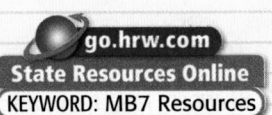

go.hrw.com
State Resources Online
KEYWORD: MB7 Resources

10-3 Organizer

Pacing: Traditional 1 day
Block $\frac{1}{2}$ day

Objectives: Write the standard equation for an ellipse.

Graph an ellipse, and identify its center, vertices, co-vertices, and foci.

Technology Lab
In *Technology Lab Activities*

Online Edition
Graphing Calculator, Tutorial Videos, Interactivity

Countdown to Testing Week 21

Warm Up

If $c^2 = a^2 - b^2$, find c if

1. $a = 13, b = 5$ $\quad c = \pm 12$

2. $a = 4, b = 3$ $\quad c = \pm\sqrt{7}$

Also available on transparency

Q: What is the hidden math term?

A: e-lips

10-3 Ellipses

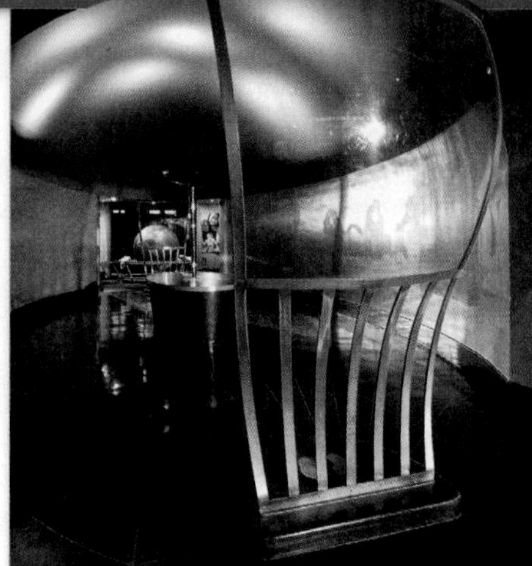

Objectives
Write the standard equation for an ellipse.

Graph an ellipse, and identify its center, vertices, co-vertices, and foci.

Vocabulary
ellipse
focus of an ellipse
major axis
vertices of an ellipse
minor axis
co-vertices of an ellipse

Who uses this?
The whispering gallery at the Chicago Museum of Science and Industry was designed by using an ellipse. (See Exercise 31.)

If you pulled the center of a circle apart into two points, it would stretch the circle into an ellipse.

An **ellipse** is the set of points $P(x, y)$ in a plane such that the sum of the distances from any point P on the ellipse to two fixed points F_1 and F_2, called the **foci** (singular: focus), is the constant sum $d = PF_1 + PF_2$. This distance d can be represented by the length of a piece of string connecting two pushpins located at the foci.

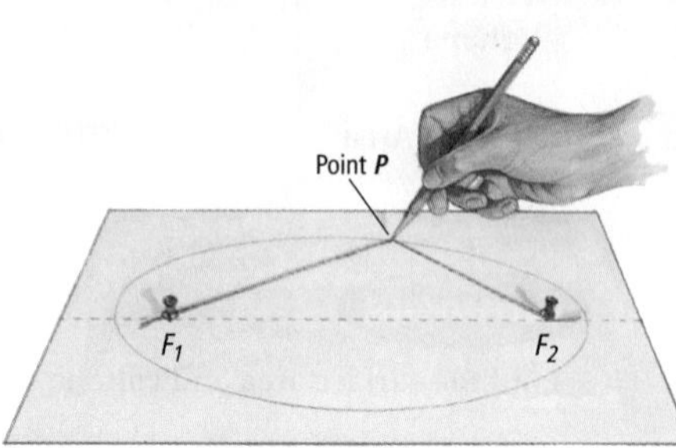

You can use the distance formula to find the constant sum of an ellipse.

EXAMPLE 1 Using the Distance Formula to Find the Constant Sum of an Ellipse

Find the constant sum for an ellipse with foci $F_1(-3, 0)$ and $F_2(3, 0)$ and the point on the ellipse $(0, 4)$.

$d = PF_1 + PF_2$ *Definition of the constant sum of an ellipse*

$d = \sqrt{(x_1 - x_3)^2 + (y_1 - y_3)^2} + \sqrt{(x_2 - x_3)^2 + (y_2 - y_3)^2}$ *Distance Formula*

$d = \sqrt{(-3 - 0)^2 + (0 - 4)^2} + \sqrt{(3 - 0)^2 + (0 - 4)^2}$ *Substitute.*

$d = \sqrt{25} + \sqrt{25}$ *Simplify.*

$d = 10$

The constant sum is 10.

1. Find the constant sum for an ellipse with foci $F_1(0, -8)$ and $F_2(0, 8)$ and the point on the ellipse $(0, 10)$. 20

Instead of a single radius, an ellipse has two axes. The longer axis of an ellipse is the **major axis** and passes through both foci. The endpoints of the major axis are the **vertices of the ellipse**. The shorter axis of an ellipse is the **minor axis**. The endpoints of the minor axis are the **co-vertices of the ellipse**. The major axis and minor axis are perpendicular and intersect at the center of the ellipse.

State Resources

State Resources Online
KEYWORD: MB7 Resources

1 Introduce

EXPLORATION

10-3 Ellipses

You can discover properties of ellipses by plotting a few points and sketching the graphs.

1. Complete the table for the equation $\frac{x^2}{25} + \frac{y^2}{9} = 1$. Then plot these points to help you sketch the graph of the ellipse.

x	y
0	
	0

2. Complete the table for the equation $\frac{y^2}{25} + \frac{x^2}{9} = 1$. Then plot these points to help you sketch the graph of the ellipse.

x	y
0	
	0

Use the above technique to sketch the graphs of the following ellipses. Look for patterns as you work.

3. $\frac{x^2}{16} + \frac{y^2}{4} = 1$

4. $\frac{y^2}{16} + \frac{x^2}{4} = 1$

5. $\frac{x^2}{49} + \frac{y^2}{36} = 1$

6. $\frac{y^2}{49} + \frac{x^2}{36} = 1$

THINK AND DISCUSS

7. Describe how the ellipses in Problems 1 and 2 are similar

Motivate

Have students consider walking from home to any location 2 miles away. Those locations are on a circle. Now have students consider the total distance walking from home, to the location, and back home. That will be a fixed distance, i.e., 4 miles. Introduce ellipses by discussing a trip from home, to a location, and then to school.

Have students brainstorm the resulting set of points if that trip were a fixed distance, say 4 miles. Connect the idea with the definition of an ellipse.

Explorations and answers are provided in the *Explorations* binder.

The standard form of an ellipse centered at (0, 0) depends on whether the major axis is horizontal or vertical.

Horizontal

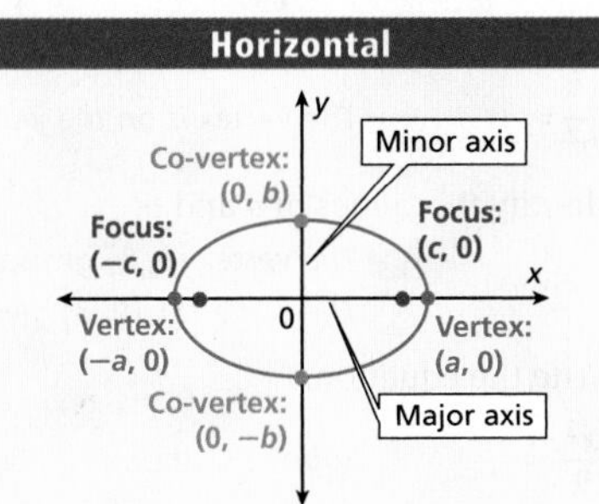

Vertical

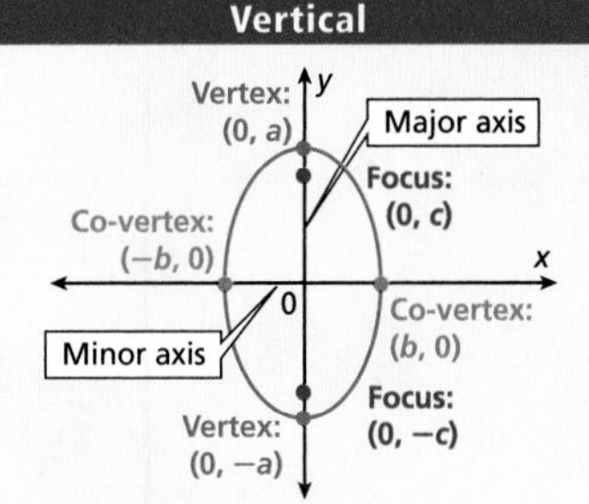

The values a, b, and c are related by the equation $c^2 = a^2 - b^2$. Also note that the length of the major axis is $2a$, the length of the minor axis is $2b$, and $a > b$.

Standard Form for the Equation of an Ellipse Center at (0, 0)

MAJOR AXIS	HORIZONTAL	VERTICAL
Equation	$\frac{x^2}{a^2} + \frac{y^2}{b^2} = 1$	$\frac{y^2}{a^2} + \frac{x^2}{b^2} = 1$
Vertices	$(a, 0), (-a, 0)$	$(0, a), (0, -a)$
Foci	$(c, 0), (-c, 0)$	$(0, c), (0, -c)$
Co-vertices	$(0, b), (0, -b)$	$(b, 0), (-b, 0)$

EXAMPLE 2 Using Standard Form to Write an Equation for an Ellipse

Write an equation in standard form for each ellipse with center (0, 0).

A

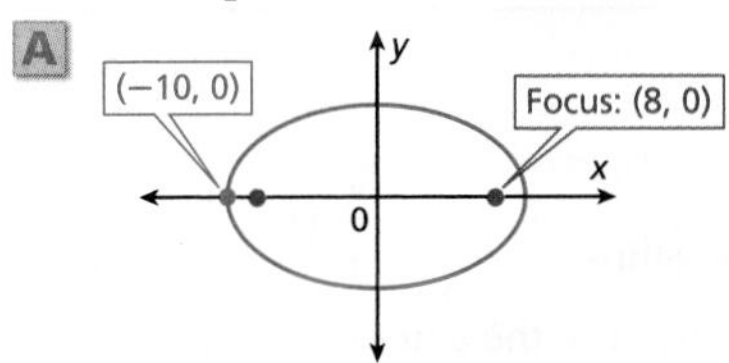

Step 1 Choose the appropriate form of equation.

$\frac{x^2}{a^2} + \frac{y^2}{b^2} = 1.$ *The horizontal axis is longer.*

Step 2 Identify the values of a and c.

$a = 10$ *The vertex $(-10, 0)$ gives the value of a.*

$c = 8$ *The focus $(8, 0)$ gives the value of c.*

Step 3 Use the relationship $c^2 = a^2 - b^2$ to find b^2.

$8^2 = 10^2 - b^2$ *Substitute 10 for a and 8 for c.*

$b^2 = 36$

Step 4 Write the equation.

$\frac{x^2}{100} + \frac{y^2}{36} = 1$ *Substitute the values into the equation of an ellipse.*

Power Presentations with PowerPoint®

Additional Examples

Example 1

Find the constant sum for an ellipse with foci $F_1(3, 0)$, $F_2(24, 0)$ and the point on the ellipse $(9, 8)$. 27

Example 2

Write an equation in standard form for each ellipse with center (0, 0).

A. Vertex at $(6, 0)$; co-vertex at $(0, 4)$

$\frac{x^2}{36} + \frac{y^2}{16} = 1$

B. Co-vertex at $(5, 0)$; focus at $(0, 3)$

$\frac{y^2}{34} + \frac{x^2}{25} = 1$

Also available on transparency

INTERVENTION
Questioning Strategies

EXAMPLE 1

- Once you find the constant sum d how can you locate the vertices?

EXAMPLE 2

- It appears that you need to know only two pieces of additional information (from among vertex, co-vertex, and focus) in order to write the equation for an ellipse. Is this true? Why or why not?

2 Teach

Guided Instruction

Introduce the equation for an ellipse in standard form by pointing out how it is similar to and different from the equation of a circle in standard form. Explain to students that because the two axes of an ellipse are different lengths, a radius is no longer relevant and is replaced in the equation by the values a and b.

Reaching All Learners
Through Kinesthetic Experience

Students can try drawing ellipses with the help of some string and two tacks as shown in the illustration on page 736. Students should repeat this activity to explore what happens to the ellipse as they change the distance between the tacks.

Power Presentations with PowerPoint®

Additional Examples

Example 3

Graph the ellipse

$$\frac{(x+4)^2}{49}+\frac{(y-3)^2}{16}=1.$$

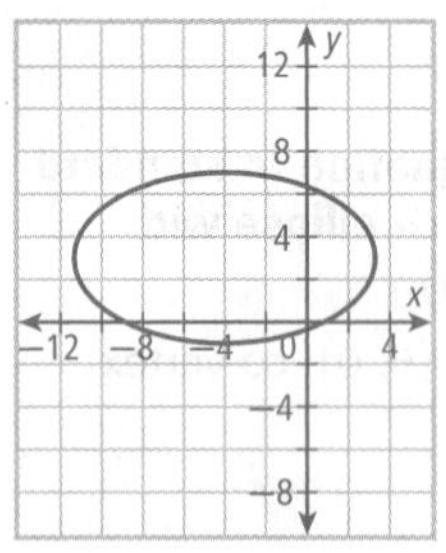

Also available on transparency

INTERVENTION

Questioning Strategies

EXAMPLE 3

- How can you locate the foci on the graph of an ellipse?

Reading Math Some of the plurals used in this lesson may pose difficulty for English Language Learners. Remind students that the plural of *vertex* is *vertices*, *axis* is *axes*, and *focus* is *foci*.

ENGLISH LANGUAGE LEARNERS

Write an equation in standard form for each ellipse with center (0, 0).

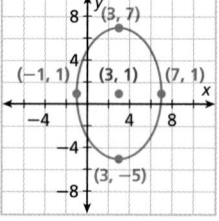

B **the ellipse with vertex (0, 8) and co-vertex (3, 0)**

Step 1 Choose the appropriate form of equation.

$$\frac{y^2}{a^2}+\frac{x^2}{b^2}=1$$ *The vertex is on the y-axis.*

Step 2 Identify the values of a and b.

$a=8$ *The vertex (0, 8) gives the value of a.*

$b=3$ *The co-vertex (0, 3) gives the value of b.*

Step 3 Write the equation.

$$\frac{y^2}{64}+\frac{x^2}{9}=1$$ *Substitute the values into the equation of an ellipse.*

Write an equation in standard form for each ellipse with center (0, 0).

2a. Vertex (9, 0) and co-vertex (0, 5) $\frac{x^2}{81}+\frac{y^2}{25}=1$

2b. Co-vertex (4, 0) focus (0, 3) $\frac{y^2}{25}+\frac{x^2}{16}=1$

Ellipses may also be translated so that the center is not the origin.

Standard Form for the Equation of an Ellipse Center at (h, k)

MAJOR AXIS	HORIZONTAL	VERTICAL
Equation	$\frac{(x-h)^2}{a^2}+\frac{(y-k)^2}{b^2}=1$	$\frac{(y-k)^2}{a^2}+\frac{(x-h)^2}{b^2}=1$
Vertices	$(h+a, k), (h-a, k)$	$(h, k+a), (h, k-a)$
Foci	$(h+c, k), (h-c, k)$	$(h, k+c), (h, k-c)$
Co-vertices	$(h, k+b), (h, k-b)$	$(h+b, k), (h-b, k)$

EXAMPLE 3 Graphing Ellipses

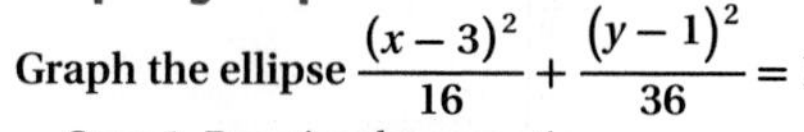

Graph the ellipse $\frac{(x-3)^2}{16}+\frac{(y-1)^2}{36}=1$.

Step 1 Rewrite the equation as

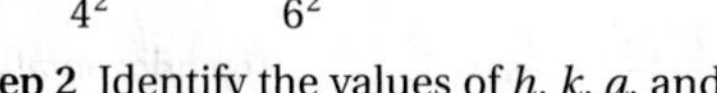

$$\frac{(x-3)^2}{4^2}+\frac{(y-1)^2}{6^2}=1.$$

Step 2 Identify the values of h, k, a, and b.

$h=3$ and $k=1$, so the center is $(3, 1)$.

$a=6$ and $b=4$; Because $6>4$, the major axis is vertical.

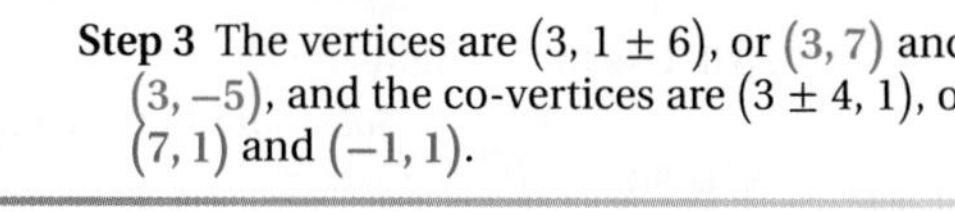

Step 3 The vertices are $(3, 1\pm 6)$, or $(3, 7)$ and $(3, -5)$, and the co-vertices are $(3\pm 4, 1)$, or $(7, 1)$ and $(-1, 1)$.

Graph each ellipse.

3a. $\frac{x^2}{64}+\frac{y^2}{25}=1$

3b. $\frac{(x-2)^2}{25}+\frac{(y-4)^2}{9}=1$

Answers

3a.

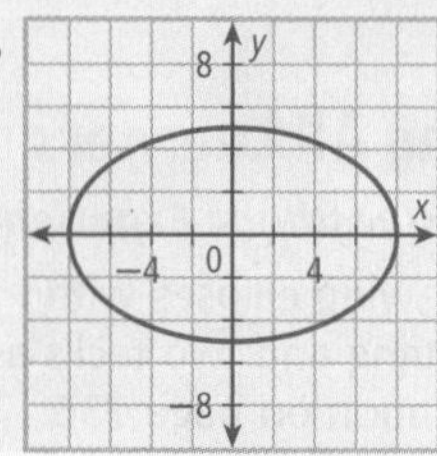

3b.

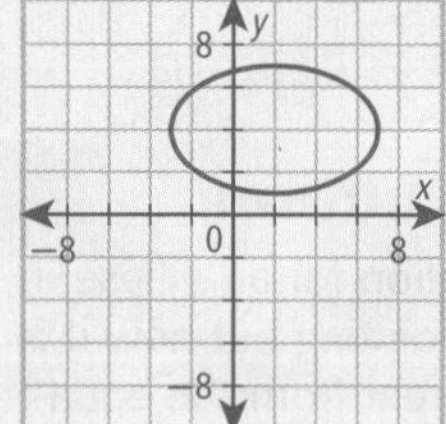

EXAMPLE 4 Engineering Application

A road passes through a tunnel in the form of a semi-ellipse. In order to widen the road to accommodate more traffic, engineers must design a larger tunnel that is twice as wide and 1.5 times as tall as the original tunnel. The design for the original tunnel can be modeled by the equation $\frac{x^2}{100} + \frac{y^2}{64} = 1$, measured in feet.

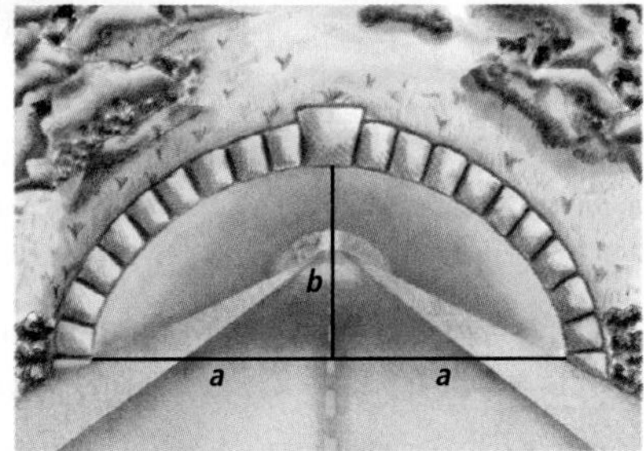

a. Find the dimensions of the larger tunnel.

Step 1 Find the dimensions of the original tunnel.

Because $100 > 64$, the major axis of the tunnel is horizontal.

$a^2 = 100$, so $a = 10$ and the width of the tunnel is $2a = 20$ ft.

$b^2 = 64$, so $b = 8$ and the height of the tunnel is 8 ft.

Step 2 Find the dimensions of the larger tunnel.

The width of the larger tunnel is $2(20) = 40$ ft.

The height is $1.5(8) = 12$ ft.

b. Write an equation for the design of the larger tunnel.

Step 1 Use the dimensions of the larger tunnel to find the values of a and b.

For the larger tunnel, $a = 20$ and $b = 12$.

Step 2 Write the equation.

The equation in standard form for the larger tunnel is $\frac{x^2}{20^2} + \frac{y^2}{12^2} = 1$, or $\frac{x^2}{400} + \frac{y^2}{144} = 1$.

Engineers have designed a tunnel with the equation $\frac{x^2}{64} + \frac{y^2}{36} = 1$, measured in feet. A design for a larger tunnel needs to be twice as wide and 3 times as tall.

4a. Find the dimensions for the larger tunnel. **width: 32 ft; height: 18 ft**

4b. Write an equation for the design of the larger tunnel.

$$\frac{x^2}{256} + \frac{y^2}{324} = 1$$

THINK AND DISCUSS

1. Explain where the foci are located in relation to the vertices.
2. Compare circles and ellipses by using lines of symmetry.
3. **GET ORGANIZED** Copy and complete the graphic organizer. Give an equation for each type of ellipse.

Know it! Note

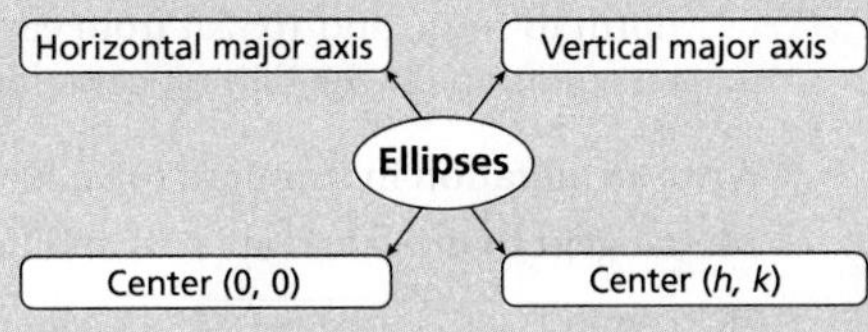

Power Presentations with PowerPoint®

Additional Examples

Example 4

A city park in the form of an ellipse with equation $\frac{x^2}{50} + \frac{y^2}{20} = 1$, measured in meters, is being renovated. The new park will have a length and width double that of the original park.

a. Find the dimensions of the new park.

width $20\sqrt{2}$, length $8\sqrt{5}$

b. Write an equation for the design of the new park.

$$\frac{x^2}{200} + \frac{y^2}{80} = 1$$

Also available on transparency

INTERVENTION
Questioning Strategies

EXAMPLE 4

- What is the relationship between the factors by which the dimensions of the ellipse change and the change in the coefficients of the equation?

3 Close

Summarize

Just as you need to know the center and radius to write the equation of a circle, you must know some key information to write the equation for an ellipse. The key information includes the vertices, co-vertices, foci, the center, the lengths of the major and minor axes, and a point on the ellipse. From the equation for an ellipse, it is possible to find everything else.

ONGOING ASSESSMENT and INTERVENTION

***Diagnose Before* the Lesson**
10-3 Warm Up, TE p. 736

***Monitor During* the Lesson**
Check It Out! Exercises, SE pp. 737–740
Questioning Strategies, TE pp. 737–739

***Assess After* the Lesson**
10-3 Lesson Quiz, TE p. 742
Alternative Assessment, TE p. 742

Answers to *Think and Discuss*

1. Possible answer: on the major axis with the vertices, but closer to the center
2. Possible answer: A circle has infinitely many lines of symmetry, but an ellipse has exactly 2 lines of symmetry.
3. See p. A11.

10-3 Exercises

Assignment Guide

Assign *Guided Practice* exercises as necessary.

If you finished Examples **1–2**
Basic 13–18
Average 13–18
Advanced 13–18, 41

If you finished Examples **1–4**
Basic 13–33, 35–40, 44–50
Average 13–42, 44–50
Advanced 13–50

Homework Quick Check
Quickly check key concepts.
Exercises: 14, 16, 20, 30

Answers

4. $\frac{x^2}{81} + \frac{y^2}{49} = 1$

5. $\frac{y^2}{625} + \frac{x^2}{225} = 1$

15. $\frac{x^2}{25} + \frac{y^2}{4} = 1$

16. $\frac{x^2}{100} + \frac{y^2}{64} = 1$

24. $\frac{(x-9)^2}{81} + \frac{(y+6)^2}{36} = 1$

25. $\frac{(y-7)^2}{100} + \frac{(x+4)^2}{51} = 1$

8–11, 19–22. See p. A43.

State Resources

10-3 Exercises

go.hrw.com
Homework Help Online
KEYWORD: MB7 10-3
Parent Resources Online
KEYWORD: MB7 Parent

GUIDED PRACTICE

1. **Vocabulary** How can you tell the difference between the *major axis* and the *minor axis* of an ellipse? **The major axis of an ellipse is always longer than the minor axis of an ellipse.**

SEE EXAMPLE 1 p. 736

Find the constant sum of an ellipse with the given foci and point on the ellipse.

2. $F_1(-5, 0)$, $F_2(5, 0)$, $P(0, -12)$ **26**
3. $F_1(0, -12)$, $F_2(0, 12)$, $P(9, 0)$ **30**

SEE EXAMPLE 2 p. 737

Multi-Step Write an equation in standard form for each ellipse with center $(0, 0)$.

4. vertex $(-9, 0)$, co-vertex $(0, 7)$
5. vertex $(0, 25)$, focus $(0, -20)$
6. co-vertex $(10, 0)$, focus $(0, 24)$ $\frac{y^2}{676} + \frac{x^2}{100} = 1$
7. vertex $(-7, 0)$, focus $(\sqrt{13}, 0)$ $\frac{x^2}{49} + \frac{y^2}{36} = 1$

SEE EXAMPLE 3 p. 738

Graph each ellipse.

8. $\frac{x^2}{36} + \frac{y^2}{81} = 1$
9. $\frac{x^2}{121} + \frac{y^2}{49} = 1$
10. $\frac{(x-5)^2}{16} + \frac{(y+2)^2}{36} = 1$
11. $\frac{(x+1)^2}{64} + \frac{(y-6)^2}{9} = 1$

SEE EXAMPLE 4 p. 739

12. **Engineering** Engineers are building semi-elliptical bridges across two rivers. The larger river is 4 times as wide as the smaller river and must accommodate boats that are 3 times as tall. The equation for the bridge over the smaller river is $\frac{x^2}{225} + \frac{y^2}{144} = 1$, measured in feet.
    a. Find the dimensions of the larger bridge. **width: 120 ft; height: 36 ft**
    b. Write an equation for the design of the larger bridge. $\frac{x^2}{3600} + \frac{y^2}{1296} = 1$

PRACTICE AND PROBLEM SOLVING

Independent Practice

For Exercises	See Example
13–14	1
15–18	2
19–22	3
23	4

Extra Practice
Skills Practice p. S22
Application Practice p. S41

Find the constant sum of an ellipse with the given foci and point on the ellipse.

13. $F_1(-20, 0)$, $F_2(20, 0)$, $P(-21, 0)$ **42**
14. $F_1(0, -8)$, $F_2(0, 8)$, $P(9, 13.6)$ **34**

Multi-Step Write an equation in standard form for each ellipse with center $(0, 0)$.

15. vertex $(5, 0)$, co-vertex $(0, -2)$
16. co-vertex $(0, -8)$, focus $(6, 0)$
17. co-vertex $(4, 0)$, focus $(0, -3)$ $\frac{y^2}{25} + \frac{x^2}{16} = 1$
18. vertex $(0, -9)$, focus $(0, 3\sqrt{5})$ $\frac{y^2}{81} + \frac{x^2}{36} = 1$

Graph each ellipse.

19. $\frac{(x+2)^2}{169} + \frac{(y-7)^2}{25} = 1$
20. $\frac{(x-6)^2}{36} + \frac{(y-4)^2}{100} = 1$
21. $\frac{x^2}{256} + \frac{y^2}{196} = 1$
22. $\frac{x^2}{225} + \frac{y^2}{289} = 1$

23. **National Parks** South of the White House in Washington, D.C., is the President's Park South, or the Ellipse, which hosts events such as the White House Garden Tours. The Ellipse is 880 ft from north to south and 1057 ft from east to west. Write an equation for the Ellipse, centered at the origin.

Write an equation in standard form for each ellipse.

24. tangent to the x-axis at $(9, 0)$ and tangent to the y-axis at $(0, -6)$
25. center $(-4, 7)$, vertex $(-4, -3)$, focus $(-4, 0)$

23. $\frac{x^2}{279{,}312.25} + \frac{y^2}{193{,}600} = 1$

10-3 READING STRATEGIES

The equation of an ellipse has one of two standard forms depending on how it is situated on the coordinate plane. The vertices and co-vertices of horizontal and vertical ellipses are computed differently.

Horizontal Ellipse Standard Equation $\frac{(x-h)^2}{a^2} + \frac{(y-k)^2}{b^2} = 1$		Vertical Ellipse Standard Equation $\frac{(y-k)^2}{a^2} + \frac{(x-h)^2}{b^2} = 1$	
Vertices $(h+a, k), (h-a, k)$	Co-vertices $(h, k+b), (h, k-b)$	Vertices $(h, k+a), (h, k-a)$	Co-vertices $(h+b, k), (h-b, k)$

Co-vertex $(-2, -1)$; Vertex $(-8, -4)$; Vertex $(4, -4)$; Co-vertex $(-2, -7)$

Vertex $(2, 7)$; Co-vertex $(0, 3)$; Co-vertex $(4, 3)$; Vertex $(2, -1)$

Answer each question.

1. $\frac{(x-5)^2}{2^2} + \frac{(y-4)^2}{1^2} = 1$
    a. Does this equation describe a horizontal or vertical ellipse? **Horizontal**
    b. Give the vertices of the ellipse. **(7, 4) and (3, 4)**
    c. Give the co-vertices of the ellipse. **(5, 5) and (5, 3)**
2. $\frac{(y+3)^2}{4^2} + \frac{(x-2)^2}{3^2} = 1$
    a. Does this equation describe a horizontal or vertical ellipse? **Vertical**
    b. Give the vertices of the ellipse. **(2, 1) and (2, −7)**
    c. Give the co-vertices of the ellipse. **(5, −3) and (−1, −3)**
3. What do you notice about the relative values of a and b?
    ***a* is always greater than *b*.**

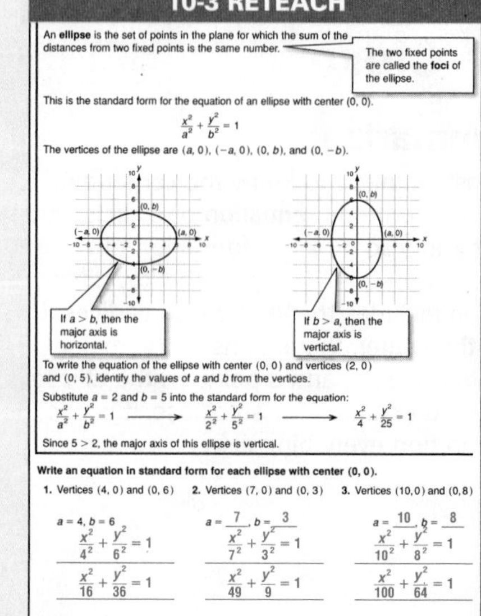

10-3 RETEACH

An **ellipse** is the set of points in the plane for which the sum of the distances from two fixed points is the same number.

The two fixed points are called the **foci** of the ellipse.

This is the standard form for the equation of an ellipse with center (0, 0).

$$\frac{x^2}{a^2} + \frac{y^2}{b^2} = 1$$

The vertices of the ellipse are $(a, 0)$, $(-a, 0)$, $(0, b)$, and $(0, -b)$.

If $a > b$, then the major axis is horizontal.

If $b > a$, then the major axis is vertictal.

To write the equation of the ellipse with center (0, 0) and vertices (2, 0) and (0, 5), identify the values of a and b from the vertices.

Substitute $a = 2$ and $b = 5$ into the standard form for the equation:

$$\frac{x^2}{a^2} + \frac{y^2}{b^2} = 1 \longrightarrow \frac{x^2}{2^2} + \frac{y^2}{5^2} = 1 \longrightarrow \frac{x^2}{4} + \frac{y^2}{25} = 1$$

Since $5 > 2$, the major axis of this ellipse is vertical.

Write an equation in standard form for each ellipse with center (0, 0).

1. Vertices (4, 0) and (0, 6)
    $a = 4, b = 6$
    $\frac{x^2}{4^2} + \frac{y^2}{6^2} = 1$
    $\frac{x^2}{16} + \frac{y^2}{36} = 1$
2. Vertices (7, 0) and (0, 3)
    $a = 7, b = 3$
    $\frac{x^2}{7^2} + \frac{y^2}{3^2} = 1$
    $\frac{x^2}{49} + \frac{y^2}{9} = 1$
3. Vertices (10,0) and (0,8)
    $a = 10, b = 8$
    $\frac{x^2}{10^2} + \frac{y^2}{8^2} = 1$
    $\frac{x^2}{100} + \frac{y^2}{64} = 1$

26. **Estimation** An ellipse has a vertex at the point $(2.4, -6.1)$, focus $(0.35, -6.1)$, and center $(-4.5, -6.1)$. Estimate the coordinates of the co-vertices.
Possible answer: $(-4.5, -1)$, $(-4.5, -11)$

Write an equation for each graph, and give the domain and range. (*Hint:* The domain and range depend on the center and the lengths of the major and minor axes.)

27. 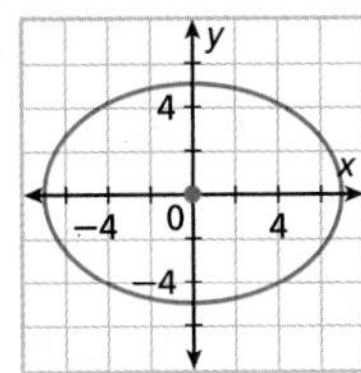

28. 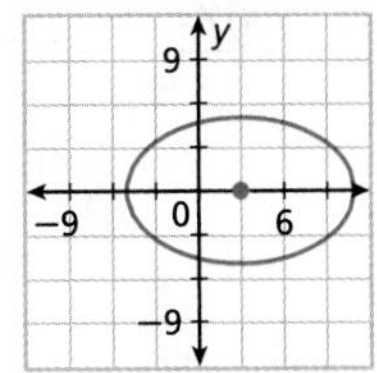

29. 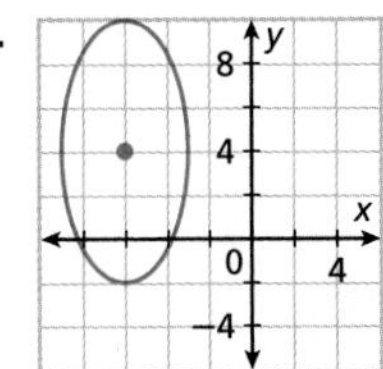

History

Located in Rome, Italy, the Colosseum was designed to hold as many as 50,000 spectators, who would arrive and leave through 80 entrances.

30. **History** The Roman Colosseum is shaped like a large ellipse, with an external width of 188 m and a length of 156 m. Write an equation that can be used to model the shape of the Colosseum.

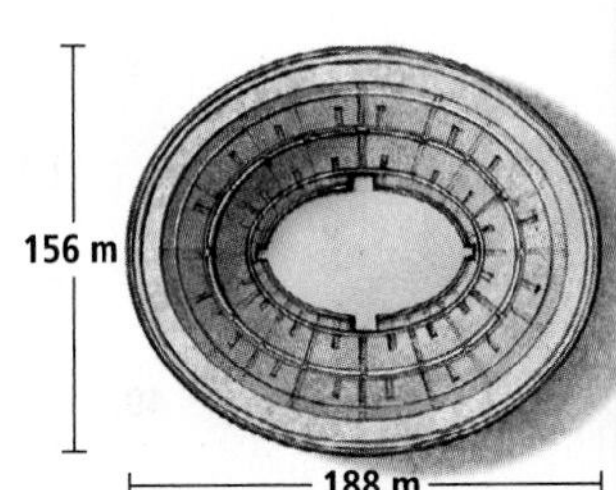

31. **Architecture** As a result of their unique elliptical shapes, whispering galleries enable the smallest sound generated at one focus to be carried across the room to the other focus. The whispering gallery at the Chicago Museum of Science and Industry is 47 ft 4 in. long and 13 ft 6 in. wide.
   a. Supposing that the center of the floor of the whispering gallery is located at the origin, write an equation for the gallery floor.
   Possible answer: $\frac{9x^2}{5041} + \frac{16y^2}{729} = 1$
   b. Find the coordinates of the foci. How far apart are they?
   $(\pm 22.68, 0)$; ~ 45.36 ft

30. $\frac{x^2}{8836} + \frac{y^2}{6084} = 1$

Find the center, vertices, co-vertices, foci, domain, and range of each ellipse.

32. $\frac{(x-1)^2}{225} + \frac{(y+5)^2}{324} = 1$

33. $9(x+9)^2 + 81(y+4)^2 = 729$

34. **Critical Thinking** An ellipse is defined by the distance $PF_1 + PF_2 = d$. Could the distance between the foci be less than $PF_1 + PF_2$? Explain.

35. **Geometry** The area of an ellipse in standard form is given by $A = \pi ab$.
   a. **Critical Thinking** How is the formula for the area of an ellipse related to the formula for the area of a circle?
   Instead of r^2, the formula for the area of an ellipse uses the values of a and b because an ellipse can be defined by a and b rather than a radius.
   b. Find the area of $\frac{(x+2)^2}{169} + \frac{(y-7)^2}{25} = 1$.
   65π

36. This problem will prepare you for the Multi-Step Test Prep on page 758.

The figure shows the elliptical orbit of Mars, where each unit of the coordinate plane represents 1 million kilometers. As shown, the planet's maximum distance from the Sun is 249 million kilometers and its minimum distance from the Sun is 207 million kilometers.

   a. The Sun is at one focus of the ellipse. What are the coordinates of the Sun? $(-21, 0)$
   b. What is the length of the minor axis of the ellipse? 454 million km
   c. Write an equation that models the orbit of Mars.
   $\frac{x^2}{51{,}984} + \frac{y^2}{51{,}543} = 1$

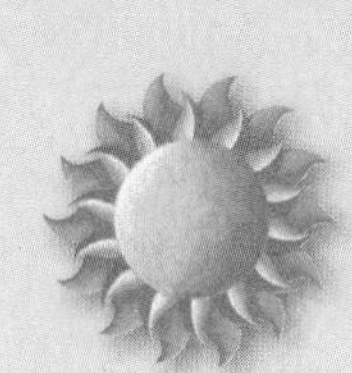

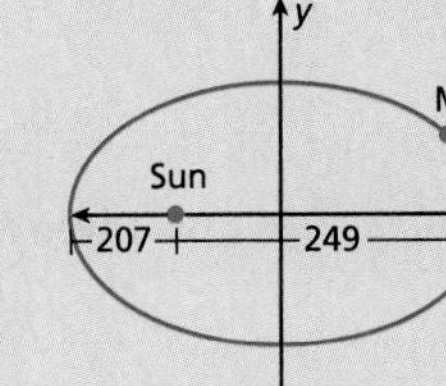

Teaching Tip **Science Link**

Exercise 31 discusses the elliptical Whispering Gallery in the Museum of Science and Industry in Chicago. One interesting property of ellipses is that the line from a focus F_1 to any tangent t form equal angles α with that tangent. Because of the laws of reflection, sound emanating from one focus will be reflected directly toward the other focus, F_2.

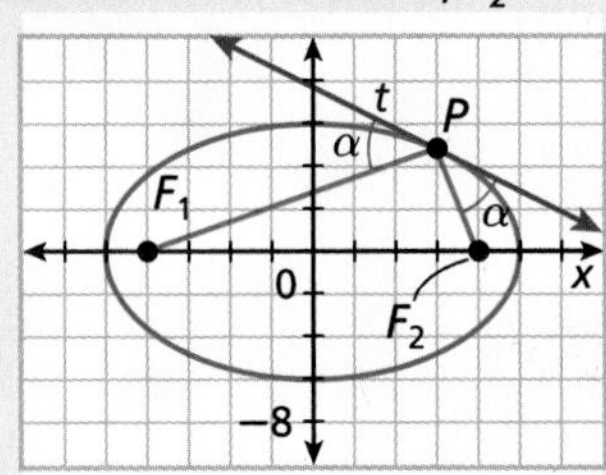

Students may wish to extend this idea to how billiard balls on an elliptical pool table or hockey pucks on an elliptical ice rink would behave.

MULTI-STEP TEST PREP Exercise 36 involves writing an equation for an ellipse. This exercise prepares students for the Multi-Step Test Prep on page 758.

Answers

27. $\frac{x^2}{49} + \frac{y^2}{25} = 1$;
D: $\{x \mid -7 \le x \le 7\}$;
R: $\{y \mid -5 \le y \le 5\}$

28. $\frac{(x-3)^2}{64} + \frac{y^2}{25} = 1$;
D: $\{x \mid -5 \le x \le 11\}$;
R: $\{y \mid -5 \le y \le 5\}$

29. $\frac{(y-4)^2}{36} + \frac{(x+6)^2}{9} = 1$;
D: $\{x \mid -9 \le x \le -3\}$;
R: $\{y \mid -2 \le y \le 10\}$

32–34. See p. A43.

10-3 PROBLEM SOLVING

Lenore and Zane study a drawing of an ornamental bridge such as the one shown at right. It shows an elliptical arch that spans a narrow strait of water. The arch they are studying can be modeled by the following equation.

$$\frac{x^2}{182.25} + \frac{y^2}{132.25} = 1$$

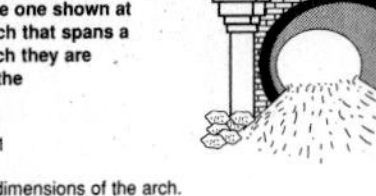

1. Lenore wants to know the dimensions of the arch.
   a. Which term in the equation defines the horizontal axis? $\frac{x^2}{182.25}$
   b. Write a comparative statement to show whether the major axis of the arch is horizontal or vertical.
   Since $182.25 > 132.25$, the major axis is horizontal.
   c. Lenore says that the width of the bridge is 13.5 feet. Is she correct? Explain.
   No; 13.5 ft is the distance from the center of the bridge to one side; so the width is 27 ft.
   d. Write an expression for the height of the bridge. $\sqrt{132.25}$; 11.5 ft
2. Zane notes that this bridge is hardly high enough to pass under while standing up in a moderate-size boat. If he were to build a bridge, it would be at least 1.3 times as wide and twice as high.
   a. Find the vertices and co-vertices of Zane's bridge design.
   Vertices: $(17.55, 0)$, $(-17.55, 0)$; co-vertices: $(0, 23)$, $(0, -23)$
   b. Write an equation for the design of Zane's bridge using his minimum dimensions. $\frac{x^2}{308.00} + \frac{y^2}{529.00} = 1$

Lenore finds architectural drawings for other bridges. Choose the letter for the best answer.

3. The equation for the arch of a bridge at the entrance to a wildlife park is $\frac{x^2}{225} + \frac{y^2}{324} = 1$. What is the width of this bridge?
   A 36 ft
   (B) 30 ft
   C 18 ft
   D 15 ft
4. The width and the height of one arch leading into part of an old town are both 17 feet. What is the equation for this bridge?
   (F) $\frac{x^2}{72.25} + \frac{y^2}{289} = 1$
   G $\frac{x^2}{72.25} + \frac{y^2}{72.25} = 1$
   H $\frac{x^2}{289} + \frac{y^2}{72.25} = 1$
   J $\frac{x^2}{289} + \frac{y^2}{289} = 1$

10-3 CHALLENGE

An ellipse is actually a circle that has undergone a stretch or a compression in a horizontal direction, a vertical direction, or in both directions.

The circle with equation $(x+1)^2 + (y-3)^2 = 36$ is stretched horizontally by a factor of 2 and vertically by a factor of 4. Applying the horizontal stretch to the x-values and the vertical stretch to the y-values gives

$$\left[\left(\tfrac{1}{2}\right)(x+1)\right]^2 + \left[\left(\tfrac{1}{4}\right)(y-3)\right]^2 = 36 \Rightarrow \frac{(x+1)^2}{4} + \frac{(y-3)^2}{16} = 36$$

The equation in standard form: $\frac{(x+1)^2}{144} + \frac{(y-3)^2}{576} = 1$

Write the equation of the ellipse that is the image of the given circle after the indicated scale change.

1. $x^2 + y^2 = 16$; horizontal stretch by a factor of 2 — $\frac{x^2}{64} + \frac{y^2}{16} = 1$
2. $(x-1)^2 + (y+2)^2 = 9$; horizontal stretch by a factor of 6 and a vertical stretch by a factor of 2 — $\frac{(x-1)^2}{324} + \frac{(y+2)^2}{36} = 1$
3. $3x^2 + 3y^2 = 75$; vertical compression by a factor of $\frac{1}{2}$ — $\frac{x^2}{25} + \frac{4y^2}{25} = 1$

Since the ellipse and the circle are related, you can write a formula for the area of an ellipse based on the area of a circle. In general, a scale change of a units in the horizontal direction and b units in the vertical direction multiplies the area of the pre-image by ab.

4. a. Consider a circle centered at the origin whose radius is 1 unit. What is the area of this circle? π square units
   b. Write the equation of the ellipse that is the image of that circle after a horizontal stretch by a factor of a and a vertical stretch by a factor of b, where $a > b$. $\frac{x^2}{a^2} + \frac{y^2}{b^2} = 1$
   c. What is the area of that ellipse? πab square units

Use the formula to determine the area of the given ellipse.

5. $\frac{x^2}{25} + \frac{y^2}{9} = 1$ — 15π square units
6. $36x^2 + 9y^2 = 324$ — 18π square units
7. $x^2 + 4y^2 - 12x = 0$ — 18π square units
8. $4x^2 + y^2 + 24x - 4y + 36 = 0$ — 2π square units

10-3 PRACTICE A

10-3 PRACTICE C

10-3 PRACTICE B

Find the constant sum of an ellipse with the given foci and point on the ellipse.

1. $F_1(40, 0)$, $F_2(-40, 0)$, $P(0, -9)$ — 82
2. $F_1(0, -20)$, $F_2(0, 20)$, $P(15, 0)$ — 50

Write an equation in standard form for each ellipse with center (0, 0).

3. Vertex $(15, 0)$, focus $(9, 0)$ — $\frac{x^2}{225} + \frac{y^2}{144} = 1$
4. Co-vertex $(0, -21)$, focus $(-75, 0)$ — $\frac{x^2}{6066} + \frac{y^2}{441} = 1$
5. Co-vertex $(-20, 0)$, focus $(0, 48)$ — $\frac{y^2}{2704} + \frac{x^2}{400} = 1$
6. Vertex $(61, 0)$, focus $(60, 0)$ — $\frac{x^2}{3721} + \frac{y^2}{121} = 1$

Graph each ellipse.

7. $\frac{(x+3)^2}{9} + \frac{(y-2)^2}{16} = 1$
8. $\frac{(x-4)^2}{36} + \frac{(y-1)^2}{25} = 1$

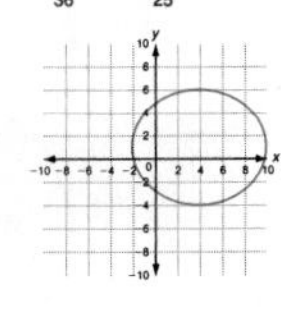

Solve.

9. Tom has a small semi-elliptical arch in his garden that he wants to enlarge. He wants to increase the height by a factor of 3 and increase the width by a factor of 2.5. The original arch can be modeled by the equation $\frac{y^2}{6.25} + \frac{x^2}{4} = 1$, measured in feet.
   a. Find the dimensions of the enlarged arch. 7.5 ft tall, 5 ft wide
   b. Write an equation to model the enlarged arch. $\frac{y^2}{56.25} + \frac{x^2}{25} = 1$

TEST PREP DOCTOR If students have difficulty with **Exercise 38**, they could try a few of the points that are on the ellipse, such as (9, 2) and (4, 10). Only choice **D** works for both.

Journal

Have students create a flowchart describing the process of graphing an ellipse from its equation.

ALTERNATIVE ASSESSMENT

Have students explain and illustrate how to write the equation for and graph an ellipse given any three of the following: vertex, co-vertex, focus, center.

Power Presentations with PowerPoint®

10-3 Lesson Quiz

1. Find the constant sum for an ellipse with foci $F_1(2, 0)$, $F_2(-6, 0)$ and the point on the ellipse $(2, 6)$. 16
2. Write an equation in standard form for each ellipse with the center at the origin.
   A. Vertex at $(0, 5)$; co-vertex at $(1, 0)$
   $\frac{y^2}{25} + x^2 = 1$
   B. Vertex at $(5, 0)$; focus at $(-2, 0)$
   $\frac{x^2}{25} + \frac{y^2}{21} = 1$
3. Graph the ellipse $\frac{(x-2)^2}{4} + \frac{(y+5)^2}{36} = 1$.

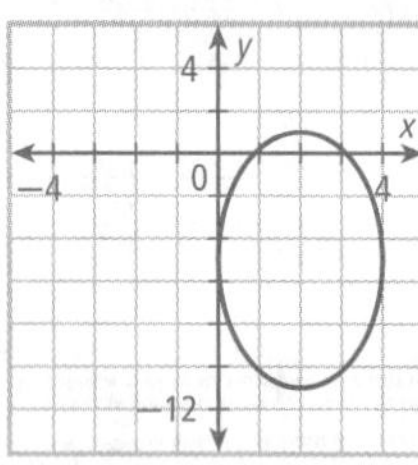

Also available on transparency

37. **Write About It** How is the distance $PF_1 + PF_2$ related to the length of the ellipse's major axis?
The length of an ellipse's major axis is equal to the distance $PF_1 + PF_2$.

TEST PREP

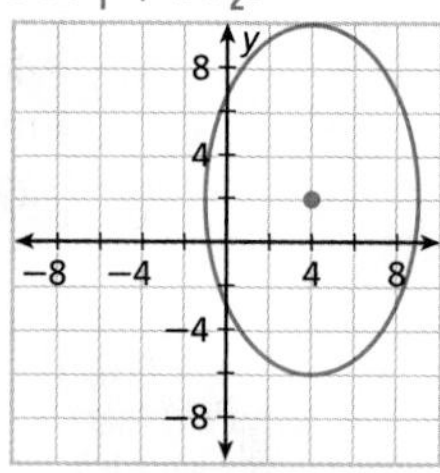

38. Which of the following is the equation for the graph?
    (A) $\frac{(x-4)^2}{25} - \frac{(y-2)^2}{64} = 1$
    (B) $25(x-4)^2 + 64(y-2)^2 = 1600$
    (C) $\frac{(x-4)^2}{64} + \frac{(y-2)^2}{25} = 1$
    (D) $64(x-4)^2 + 25(y-2)^2 = 1600$

39. The graph of which equation has the greatest distance between foci?
    (F) $\frac{(x-12)^2}{49} + \frac{(y+23)^2}{25} = 1$
    (G) $\frac{x^2}{625} + \frac{y^2}{576} = 1$
    (H) $\frac{(x-1)^2}{20} + \frac{(y-1)^2}{150} = 1$
    (J) $\frac{x^2}{175} + \frac{y^2}{225} = 1$

40. **Short Response** Give an equation for the ellipse with center $(2, -3)$, focus $(26, -3)$, and major axis length 50. $\frac{(y+3)^2}{49} + \frac{(x-2)^2}{625} = 1$

CHALLENGE AND EXTEND

41. The eccentricity of an ellipse is defined as $e = \frac{c}{a}$. Recall that $c^2 = a^2 - b^2$ for an ellipse in standard form.
    a. Find the eccentricity of the ellipse with equation $\frac{x^2}{841} + \frac{y^2}{400} = 1$. $\frac{21}{29}$
    b. Find the equation of the ellipse with vertices $(13, 0)$ and $(-13, 0)$ and $e = \frac{5}{13}$.
    c. What are the possible values for the eccentricity of an ellipse? $0 < e < 1$
    d. Describe the relationship between eccentricity and the shape of an ellipse.

41b. $\frac{x^2}{169} + \frac{y^2}{144} = 1$

41d. Possible answer: The closer the eccentricity is to 0, the more the ellipse resembles a circle. An eccentricity closer to 1 creates a long, thin ellipse.

42. **Astronomy** The path that the Moon travels around Earth is an ellipse with Earth at one focus. The length of the major axis is about 477,700 mi, and the length of the minor axis is about 476,980 mi.
    a. Write an equation for the Moon's orbit. $\frac{x^2}{(238{,}850)^2} + \frac{y^2}{(238{,}490)^2} = 1$
    b. Find the minimum and maximum distances from Earth to the Moon. 225,700 mi; 252,000 mi

43. Write an equation for an ellipse with foci $F_1(-3, 0)$ and $F_2(3, 0)$ and a constant sum of 10. (*Hint:* Use $d = PF_1 + PF_2$ and the point (x, y).) $\frac{x^2}{25} + \frac{y^2}{16} = 1$

SPIRAL REVIEW

44. **Recreation** Rhonda exercises no more than 60 minutes a day. She runs and lifts weights. *(Lesson 2-5)*
    a. Write and graph an inequality for the number of minutes that Rhonda can run and lift weights each day.
    b. How long does Rhonda lift weights if she runs for 25 minutes? no more than 35 min

44a. $x + y \le 60$

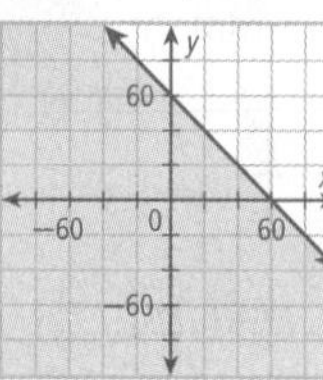

Given $f(x) = 2x^2 + 6$ and $g(x) = -\frac{1}{2}x + 4$, find each value. *(Lesson 9-4)*

45. $f(g(2))$ 24
46. $g(f(2))$ −3
47. $f(g(-2))$ 56
48. $g(f(-2))$ −3

Write the equation of each circle. *(Lesson 10-2)*

49. center $(0, -1)$, containing the point $(6, 7)$ $x^2 + (y+1)^2 = 100$
50. center $(-5, 9)$, radius $r = 6$ $(x+5)^2 + (y-9)^2 = 36$

Locate the Foci of an Ellipse

You have seen how an ellipse is defined by its foci and how to draw an ellipse given the foci. You can find the foci of a given ellipse by using a compass.

Use with Lesson 10-3

Activity

Find the foci of the ellipse with major axis length 20 and minor axis length 12.

1. Graph the ellipse so that the center is at $(0, 0)$. Mark the endpoints of the major axis: $(-10, 0)$ and $(10, 0)$. Mark the endpoints of the minor axis at $(0, -6)$ and $(0, 6)$. Draw the ellipse.

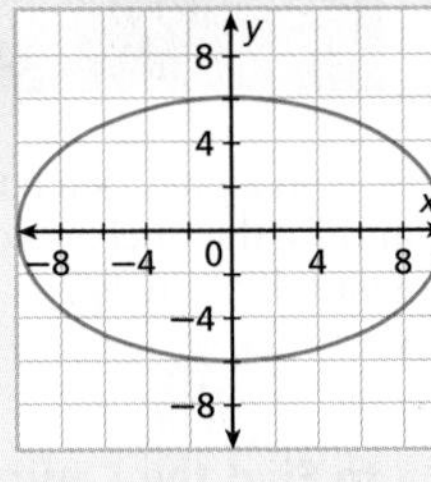

2. Use a compass to draw a circle with radius 10 units centered at $(0, 0)$.

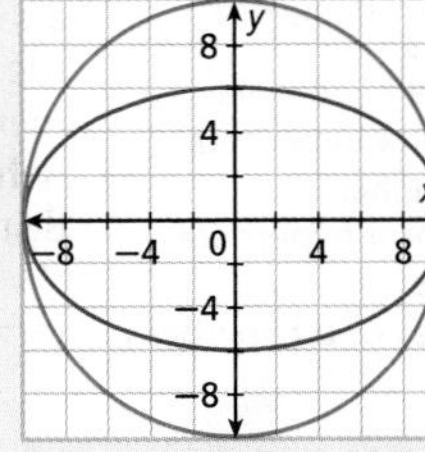

3. Draw the line with equation $y = 6$ on the graph. Mark the points where the line intersects the circle.

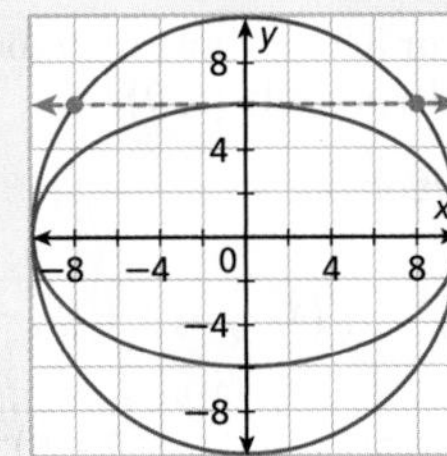

4. Draw lines from the points where $y = 6$ intersects the circle perpendicular to the x-axis. The foci of the ellipse are the points where the perpendicular lines intersect the x-axis. Where are the foci of your ellipse? Check by using the formula $c^2 = a^2 - b^2$.

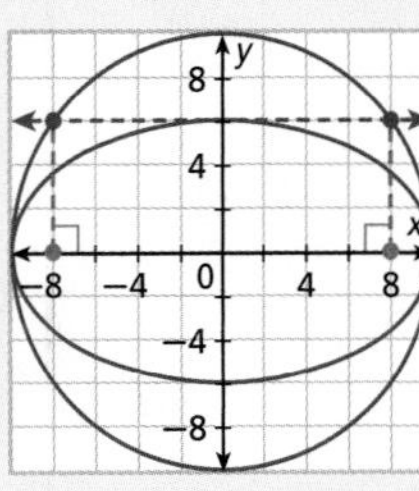

Try This

Use a compass to find the foci of each ellipse with a horizontal major axis.

1. major axis length 26, minor axis length 10 **$(\pm 12, 0)$**
2. major axis length 34, minor axis length 16 **$(\pm 15, 0)$**

Use a compass to find the foci of each ellipse with a vertical major axis.

3. major axis length 25, minor axis length 24 **$(0, \pm 3.5)$**
4. major axis length 20, minor axis length 12 **$(0, \pm 8)$**
5. **Critical Thinking** In Step 3 above, what other line could you have drawn to get the same foci? **the line parallel to the major axis through the other co-vertex**
6. **Critical Thinking** Why does this method of locating the foci of an ellipse work?

Answers

6. The line is drawn at $y = b$ or at $x = b$ and the circle has radius a. The intersection of the line and the circle is $(\pm c, b)$ or $(b, \pm c)$. The origin, the point where the line and circle intersect, and the point where the line intersects the major axis make a right triangle with hypotenuse length a. If the points where the lines meet have coordinates $(\pm c, 0)$ or $(0, \pm c)$, then by the Pythagorean Theorem, $c^2 = a^2 - b^2$.

Organizer

Use with Lesson 10-3

Pacing:

Traditional $\frac{1}{2}$ day

Block $\frac{1}{4}$ day

Objective: Use a compass to find the foci of a given ellipse.

Materials: Graph paper, compass, straightedge

Online Edition

Countdown to Testing Week 21

Resources

Algebra Lab Activities

10-3 Lab Recording Sheet

Teach

Discuss

Point out to students that this geometric construction provides an alternate approach to determining the coordinates of the foci of an ellipse.

Alternative Approach

Carry out the construction using a graphing calculator.

Close

Key Concept

The foci of an ellipse can be located by carrying out a simple geometric construction.

Assessment

Journal Have students describe how they would use the equation of the circle they constructed to find the x-coordinate of a point on the circle whose y-coordinate is b.

State Resources

10-4 Organizer

Pacing: Traditional 1 day
Block $\frac{1}{2}$ day

Objectives: Write the standard equation for a hyperbola.

Graph a hyperbola, and identify its vertices, co-vertices, center, foci, and asymptotes.

Online Edition
Graphing Calculator, Tutorial Videos

Countdown to Testing Week 22

Power Presentations with PowerPoint®

Warm Up

Multiply both sides of each equation by the least common multiple to eliminate the denominators.

1. $\frac{x^2}{9} - \frac{y^2}{4} = 1$ $4x^2 - 9y^2 = 36$

2. $\frac{y^2}{25} - \frac{x^2}{16} = 1$
$16y^2 - 25x^2 = 400$

Also available on transparency

Math Humor

Q: What do you call a snake after it drinks three cups of coffee?

A: A hyper boa.

10-4 Hyperbolas

Objectives
Write the standard equation for a hyperbola.

Graph a hyperbola, and identify its vertices, co-vertices, center, foci, and asymptotes.

Vocabulary
hyperbola
focus of a hyperbola
branch of a hyperbola
transverse axis
vertices of a hyperbola
conjugate axis
co-vertices of a hyperbola

Who uses this?
Biologists use hyperbolas to locate and track whales based on the sounds that the whales make. (See Exercise 33.)

What would happen if you pulled the two foci of an ellipse so far apart that they moved outside the ellipse? The result would be a *hyperbola*, another conic section.

A **hyperbola** is the set of points $P(x, y)$ in a plane such that the difference of the distances from P to fixed points F_1 and F_2, the **foci**, is constant. For a hyperbola, $d = |PF_1 - PF_2|$, where d is the constant difference. You can use the distance formula to find the equation of a hyperbola.

EXAMPLE 1 Using the Distance Formula to Find the Constant Difference of a Hyperbola

Find the constant difference for a hyperbola with foci $F_1(-5, 0)$ and $F_2(5, 0)$ and the point on the hyperbola $(4, 0)$.

$d = |PF_1 - PF_2|$ *Definition of the constant difference of a hyperbola*

$= \left|\sqrt{(x_1 - x_3)^2 + (y_1 - y_3)^2} - \sqrt{(x_2 - x_3)^2 + (y_2 - y_3)^2}\right|$ *Distance Formula*

$= \left|\sqrt{(-5 - 4)^2 + (0 - 0)^2} - \sqrt{(5 - 4)^2 + (0 - 0)^2}\right|$ *Substitute.*

$= \left|\sqrt{81} - \sqrt{1}\right|$ *Simplify.*

$= 8$

The constant difference is 8.

1. Find the constant difference for a hyperbola with foci at $F_1(0, -10)$ and $F_2(0, 10)$ and the point on the hyperbola $(6, 7.5)$. **12**

As the graphs in the following table show, a hyperbola contains two symmetrical parts called **branches**.

A hyperbola also has two axes of symmetry. The **transverse axis** of symmetry contains the vertices and, if it were extended, the foci of the hyperbola. The **vertices of a hyperbola** are the endpoints of the transverse axis.

The **conjugate axis** of symmetry separates the two branches of the hyperbola. The **co-vertices of a hyperbola** are the endpoints of the conjugate axis. The transverse axis is not always longer than the conjugate axis.

State Resources

go.hrw.com
State Resources Online
KEYWORD: MB7 Resources

1 Introduce

EXPLORATION

10-4 Hyperbolas

Use your calculator to investigate an equation in the form $\frac{x^2}{a^2} - \frac{y^2}{b^2} = 1$.

1. Solve the equation $\frac{x^2}{9} - \frac{y^2}{25} = 1$ for y.
2. Graph the positive and negative parts of the equation as **Y1** and **Y2**.
3. Describe the graph.
4. What are the x-intercepts of the graph?
5. Enter $y = \frac{5}{3}x$ as **Y3** and $y = -\frac{5}{3}x$ as **Y4**. Graph these lines in the same window as the previous graph.
6. How is the graph of $\frac{x^2}{9} - \frac{y^2}{25} = 1$ related to the graph of the lines represented by $y = \pm\frac{5}{3}x$?

THINK AND DISCUSS

7. **Compare** how the graph of $\frac{x^2}{9} - \frac{y^2}{25} = 1$ to the graph of $\frac{y^2}{9} - \frac{x^2}{25} = 1$.
8. **Explain** why the graph of $\frac{x^2}{...} - \frac{y^2}{...} = 1$ does not intersect...

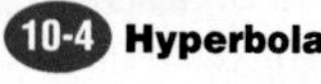

Motivate

Explain to students that an ellipse is the set of points where the sum of distances from points on the ellipse to two fixed points called foci is constant. A new conic section arises if the word *sum* in the definition of an ellipse is changed to *difference.* The resulting conic section is a hyperbola.

Explorations and answers are provided in the *Explorations* binder.

The standard form of the equation of a hyperbola depends on whether the hyperbola's transverse axis is horizontal or vertical.

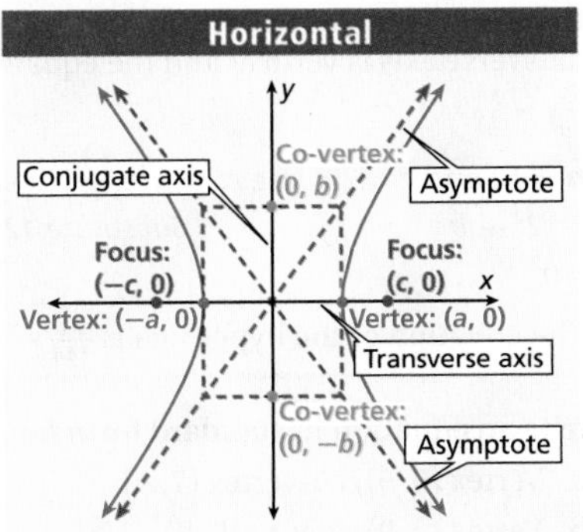

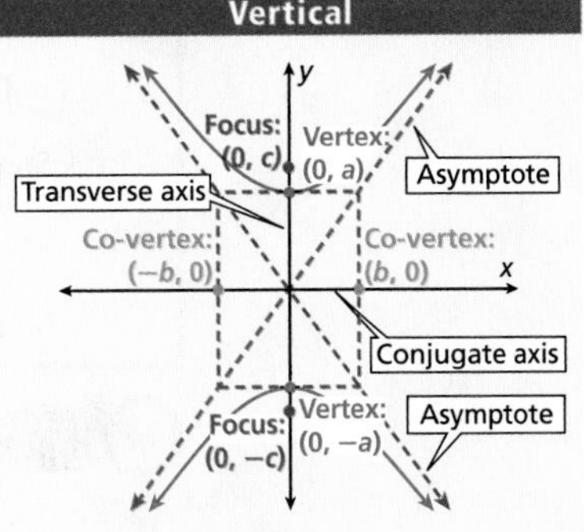

The values a, b, and c are related by the equation $c^2 = a^2 + b^2$. Also note that the length of the transverse axis is $2a$ and the length of the conjugate axis is $2b$.

Know it! Note

Standard Form for the Equation of a Hyperbola Center at (0, 0)

TRANSVERSE AXIS	HORIZONTAL	VERTICAL
Equation	$\frac{x^2}{a^2} - \frac{y^2}{b^2} = 1$	$\frac{y^2}{a^2} - \frac{x^2}{b^2} = 1$
Vertices	$(a, 0), (-a, 0)$	$(0, a), (0, -a)$
Foci	$(c, 0), (-c, 0)$	$(0, c), (0, -c)$
Co-vertices	$(0, b), (0, -b)$	$(b, 0), (-b, 0)$
Asymptotes	$y = \pm\frac{b}{a}x$	$y = \pm\frac{a}{b}x$

EXAMPLE 2 Writing Equations of Hyperbolas

Write an equation in standard form for each hyperbola.

A

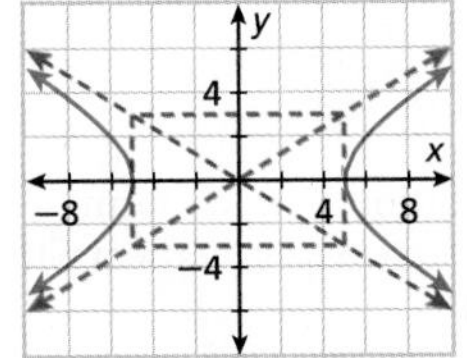

Step 1 Identify the form of the equation.

The graph opens horizontally, so the equation will be in the form $\frac{x^2}{a^2} - \frac{y^2}{b^2} = 1$.

Step 2 Identify the center and vertices.

The center of the graph is $(0, 0)$, the vertices are $(-5, 0)$ and $(5, 0)$, and the co-vertices are $(0, -3)$ and $(0, 3)$. So $a = 5$ and $b = 3$.

Step 3 Write the equation.

Because $a = 5$ and $b = 3$, the equation of the graph is $\frac{x^2}{5^2} - \frac{y^2}{3^2} = 1$, or $\frac{x^2}{25} - \frac{y^2}{9} = 1$.

Power Presentations with PowerPoint®

Additional Examples

Example 1

Find the constant difference for a hyperbola with foci $F_1(-8, 0)$ and $F_2(8, 0)$ and the point on the hyperbola $(8, 30)$. 4

Example 2

Write an equation in standard form for each hyperbola.

A.

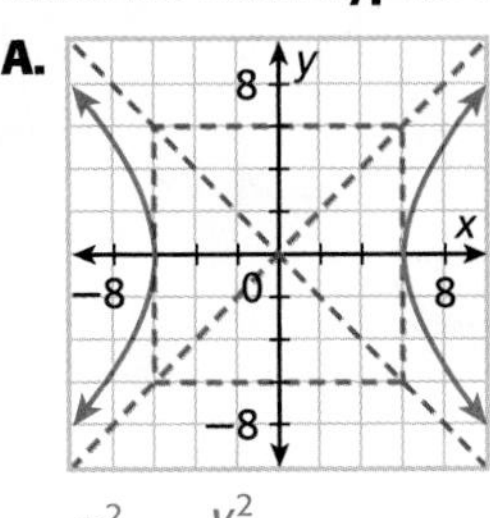

$\frac{x^2}{36} - \frac{y^2}{36} = 1$

B. The hyperbola with center at the origin, vertex $(4, 0)$, and focus at $(10, 0)$.

$\frac{x^2}{16} - \frac{y^2}{84} = 1$

Also available on transparency

INTERVENTION
Questioning Strategies

EXAMPLE 1

- If you know the foci and the common difference, how can you find the vertices?

EXAMPLE 2

- Can you write the equation if you know only the focus and the vertex? Why or why not?

2 Teach

Guided Instruction

As you work through the different examples, highlight the ways that hyperbolas and ellipses are similar and different. Encourage students to take time in drawing the box and asymptotes in order to create an accurate sketch of the hyperbola.

Reaching All Learners
Through Modeling

It may help illustrate the principle of the common difference by using the Pythagorean Theorem and distances. For example, $\frac{x^2}{4} - \frac{y^2}{12} = 1$ has foci at $(\pm4, 0)$ and vertices at $(\pm2, 0)$ and contains $(4, 6)$. A right triangle with vertices $(\pm4, 0)$ and $(4, 6)$, and a visual inspection of the points $(-4, 0)$, $(2, 0)$, and $(4, 0)$ can demonstrate the "constant difference" concept for two points on the hyperbola.

Power Presentations with PowerPoint®

Additional Examples

Example 3

Find the vertices, co-vertices, and asymptotes of each hyperbola, then graph.

A. $\frac{x^2}{49} - \frac{y^2}{9} = 1$

vertices: $(\pm 7, 0)$;

co-vertices: $(0, \pm 3)$;

asymptotes: $y = \pm\frac{3}{7}x$

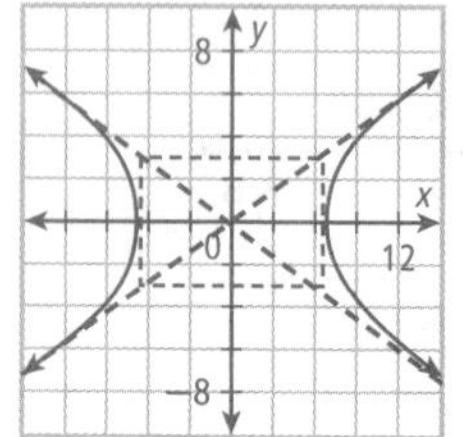

B. $\frac{(x-3)^2}{9} - \frac{(y+5)^2}{49} = 1$

vertices: $(0, -5)$, $(6, -5)$;

co-vertices: $(3, 2)$, $(3, -12)$;

asymptotes: $y + 5 = \pm\frac{7}{3}(x - 3)$

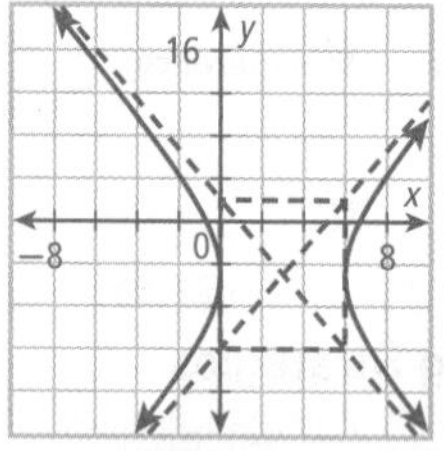

Also available on transparency

INTERVENTION

Questioning Strategies

EXAMPLE 3

- If you graph a hyperbola on a calculator with a very large viewing window, what will the hyperbola look like?

Write an equation in standard form for each hyperbola.

B the hyperbola with center $(0, 0)$, vertex $(0, 12)$, and focus $(0, 20)$

Step 1 Because the vertex and the focus are on the vertical axis, the transverse axis is vertical and the equation is in the form $\frac{y^2}{a^2} - \frac{x^2}{b^2} = 1$.

Step 2 $a = 12$ and $c = 20$; Use $c^2 = a^2 + b^2$ to solve for b^2.

$20^2 = 12^2 + b^2$ *Substitute 12 for a and 20 for c.*

$256 = b^2$

Step 3 The equation of the hyperbola is $\frac{y^2}{144} - \frac{x^2}{256} = 1$

Write an equation in standard form for each hyperbola.

2a. Vertex $(0, 9)$, co-vertex $(7, 0)$ $\frac{y^2}{81} - \frac{x^2}{49} = 1$

2b. Vertex $(8, 0)$, focus $(10, 0)$ $\frac{x^2}{64} - \frac{y^2}{36} = 1$

As with circles and ellipses, hyperbolas do not have to be centered at the origin.

Standard Form for the Equation of a Hyperbola Center at (h, k)

TRANSVERSE AXIS	HORIZONTAL	VERTICAL
Equation	$\frac{(x-h)^2}{a^2} - \frac{(y-k)^2}{b^2} = 1$	$\frac{(y-k)^2}{a^2} - \frac{(x-h)^2}{b^2} = 1$
Vertices	$(h + a, k)$, $(h - a, k)$	$(h, k + a)$, $(h, k - a)$
Foci	$(h + c, k)$, $(h - c, k)$	$(h, k + c)$, $(h, k - c)$
Co-vertices	$(h, k + b)$, $(h, k - b)$	$(h + b, k)$, $(h - b, k)$
Asymptotes	$y - k = \pm\frac{b}{a}(x - h)$	$y - k = \pm\frac{a}{b}(x - h)$

EXAMPLE 3 Graphing a Hyperbola

Find the vertices, co-vertices, and asymptotes of each hyperbola, and then graph.

A $\frac{y^2}{25} - \frac{x^2}{36} = 1$

Step 1 The equation is in the form $\frac{y^2}{a^2} - \frac{x^2}{b^2} = 1$, so the transverse axis is vertical with center $(0, 0)$.

Step 2 Because $a = 5$ and $b = 6$, the vertices are $(0, 5)$ and $(0, -5)$ and the co-vertices are $(6, 0)$ and $(-6, 0)$.

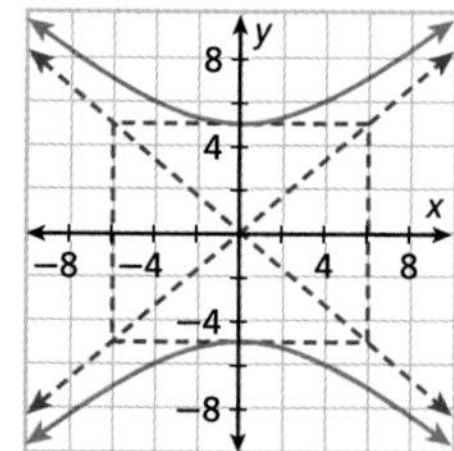

Step 3 The equations of the asymptotes are $y = \frac{5}{6}x$ and $y = -\frac{5}{6}x$.

Step 4 Draw a box by using the vertices and co-vertices. Draw the asymptotes through the corners of the box.

Step 5 Draw the hyperbola by using the vertices and the asymptotes.

Find the vertices, co-vertices, and asymptotes of each hyperbola, and then graph.

B $\frac{(x-2)^2}{16} - \frac{(y+3)^2}{49} = 1$

Step 1 The equation is in the form $\frac{(x-h)^2}{a^2} - \frac{(y-k)^2}{b^2} = 1$ so the transverse axis is horizontal with center $(2, -3)$.

Step 2 Because $a = 4$ and $b = 7$, the vertices are $(6, -3)$ and $(-2, -3)$ and the co-vertices are $(2, 4)$ and $(2, -10)$.

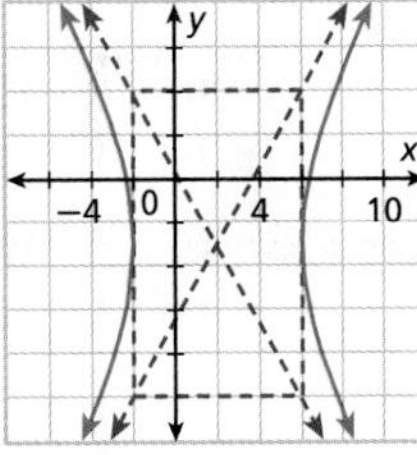

Step 3 The equations of the asymptotes are $y + 3 = \frac{7}{4}(x-2)$ and $y + 3 = -\frac{7}{4}(x-2)$.

Step 4 Draw a box by using the vertices and co-vertices. Draw the asymptotes through the corners of the box.

Step 5 Draw the hyperbola by using the vertices and the asymptotes.

Caution!

The graph of the hyperbola must pass through the vertices and approach both of the asymptotes.

3a. vertices: $(\pm 4, 0)$; co-vertices: $(0, \pm 6)$; asymptotes: $y = \pm\frac{3}{2}x$

3b. vertices: $(1, -4)$, $(1, -6)$; co-vertices: $(4, -5)$, $(-2, -5)$; asymptotes: $y = \pm\frac{1}{3}(x-1) - 5$

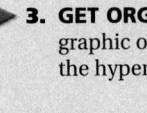

CHECK IT OUT! Find the vertices, co-vertices, and asymptotes of each hyperbola, and then graph.

3a. $\frac{x^2}{16} - \frac{y^2}{36} = 1$ **3b.** $\frac{(y+5)^2}{9} - \frac{(x-1)^2}{1} = 1$

Notice that as the parameters change, the graph of the hyperbola is transformed.

Parameter	Transformation
h	Translates the graph left for $h > 0$ and right for $h < 0$
k	Translates the graph up for $k > 0$ and down for $k < 0$
a	Stretches the graph in the direction of the transverse axis; as a increases, the vertices move farther apart.
b	Stretches the graph in the direction of the conjugate axis; as b increases, the co-vertices move farther apart.

THINK AND DISCUSS

1. When is the transverse axis of a hyperbola shorter than its conjugate axis?
2. How do you tell when a hyperbola has a horizontal transverse axis?

3. **GET ORGANIZED** Copy and complete the graphic organizer. Label all of the parts of the hyperbola.

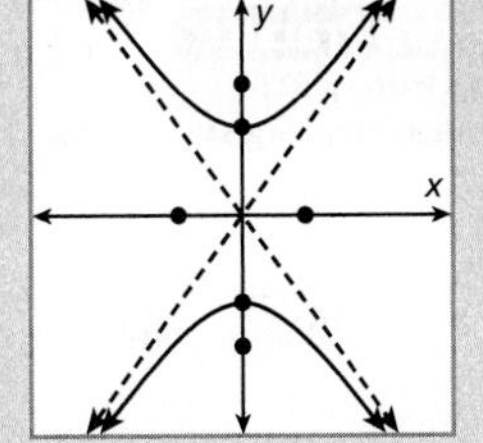

Teaching Tip **Language** The words *hyperbola* and *hyperbole* come from the same root, the Greek *hyperbole,* meaning "extravagance." In speech or writing, a *hyperbole* is an exaggeration. In the case of a *hyperbola*, the cutting plane forms a larger angle with the base of the cone than does the side of the cone see diagram on p. 722. ENGLISH LANGUAGE LEARNERS

Teaching Tip **Inclusion** Explain to students that they have seen hyperbolas when the class worked with rational functions. For example, $xy = 8$, or $y = \frac{8}{x}$ is a hyperbola with foci at (4, 4) and (−4, −4), vertices at $(\sqrt{8}, \sqrt{8})$ and $(-\sqrt{8}, -\sqrt{8})$, and the axes as asymptotes.

Answers

3a.

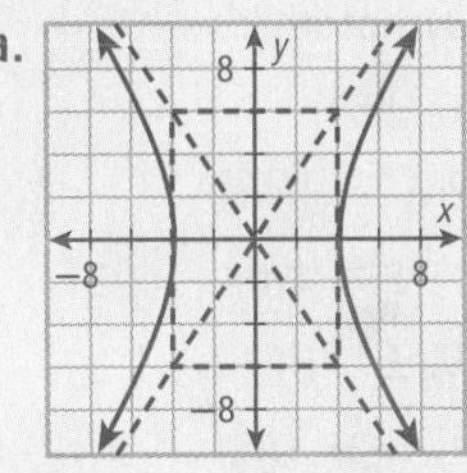

b.

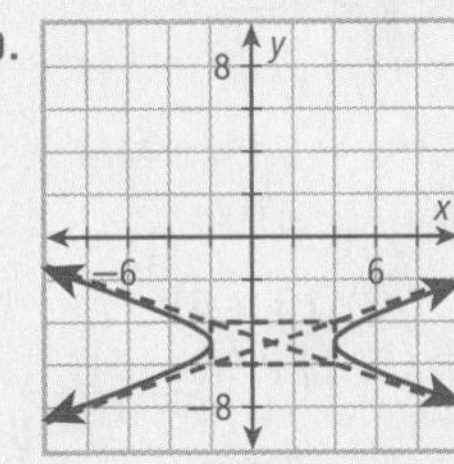

3 Close

Summarize

As with ellipses, it is possible to write an equation for a hyperbola given key information, such as the center, the foci, and a vertex. Given the equation, it is possible to identify the key features of the hyperbola, including the asymptotes, which aid in sketching a graph.

ONGOING ASSESSMENT and INTERVENTION

Diagnose **Before** the Lesson
10-4 Warm Up, TE p. 744

Monitor **During** the Lesson
Check It Out! Exercises, SE pp. 744–747
Questioning Strategies, TE pp. 745–746

Assess **After** the Lesson
10-4 Lesson Quiz, TE p. 750
Alternative Assessment, TE p. 750

Answers to *Think and Discuss*

1. when $a < b$
2. The y^2-term is negative for an equation in standard form.
3. See p. A12.

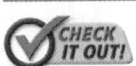

10-4 Exercises

Assignment Guide

Assign *Guided Practice* exercises as necessary.

If you finished Examples **1–3**
Basic 16–30, 36–41, 46–51
Average 16–41, 44, 46–51
Advanced 16–51

Homework Quick Check
Quickly check key concepts.
Exercises: 16, 18, 20, 22, 28

Answers

8–15. For graphs, see p. A43.

8. vertices: $(\pm 7, 0)$; co-vertices: $(0, \pm 6)$; asymptotes: $y = \pm\frac{6}{7}x$
9. vertices: $(\pm 5, 0)$; co-vertices: $(0, \pm 8)$; asymptotes: $y = \pm\frac{8}{5}x$
10. vertices: $(0, \pm 5)$; co-vertices: $(\pm 6, 0)$; asymptotes: $y = \pm\frac{5}{6}x$
11. vertices: $(0, \pm 10)$; co-vertices: $(\pm 9, 0)$; asymptotes: $y = \pm\frac{10}{9}x$
12. vertices: $(7, 3)$, $(1, 3)$; co-vertices: $(4, 11)$, $(4, -5)$; asymptotes: $y = \pm\frac{8}{3}(x-4)+3$
13. vertices: $(8, -6)$, $(0, -6)$; co-vertices: $(4, 1)$, $(4, -13)$; asymptotes: $y = \pm\frac{7}{4}(x-4)-6$
14. vertices: $(-3, -2)$, $(-3, -14)$; co-vertices: $(2, -8)$, $(-8, -8)$; asymptotes: $y = \pm\frac{6}{5}(x+3)-8$
15. vertices: $(0, -5)$, $(0, -9)$; co-vertices: $(\pm 5, -7)$; asymptotes: $y = \pm\frac{2}{5}x-7$

State Resources

10-4 Exercises

go.hrw.com
Homework Help Online
KEYWORD: MB7 10-4
Parent Resources Online
KEYWORD: MB7 Parent

GUIDED PRACTICE

1. **Vocabulary** The vertices of a hyperbola lie on the __?__ (*transverse axis* or *conjugate axis*). **transverse axis**

SEE EXAMPLE 1 p. 744

Find the constant difference for a hyperbola with the given foci and point on the hyperbola.

2. $F_1(-13, 0)$, $F_2(13, 0)$, $P(5, 0)$ **10**
3. $F_1(0, -17)$, $F_2(0, 17)$, $P(0, -15)$ **30**

SEE EXAMPLE 2 p. 745

Write an equation in standard form for each hyperbola.

4. center $(0, 0)$, vertex $(0, 5)$, and focus $(0, 13)$ $\frac{y^2}{25} - \frac{x^2}{144} = 1$
5. center $(0, 0)$, vertex $(9, 0)$, and co-vertex $(0, 7)$ $\frac{x^2}{81} - \frac{y^2}{49} = 1$
6. 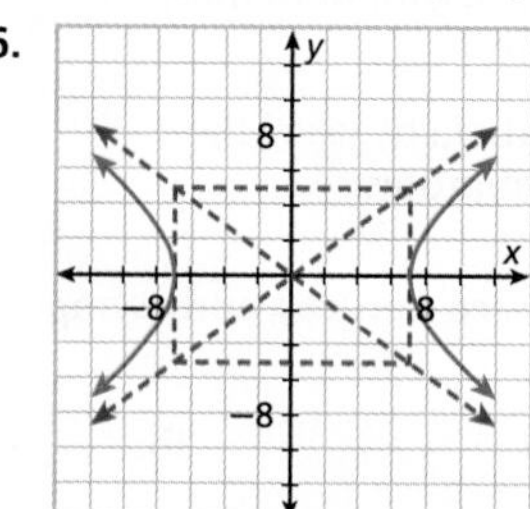 $\frac{x^2}{49} - \frac{y^2}{25} = 1$
7. 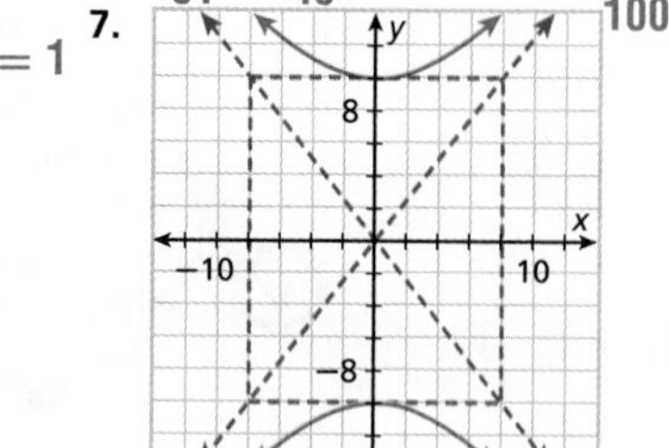 $\frac{y^2}{100} - \frac{x^2}{64} = 1$

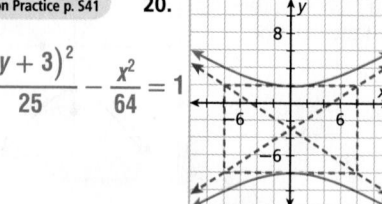

SEE EXAMPLE 3 p. 746

Find the vertices, co-vertices, and asymptotes of each hyperbola, and then graph.

8. $\frac{x^2}{49} - \frac{y^2}{36} = 1$
9. $\frac{x^2}{25} - \frac{y^2}{64} = 1$
10. $\frac{y^2}{25} - \frac{x^2}{36} = 1$
11. $\frac{y^2}{100} - \frac{x^2}{81} = 1$
12. $\frac{(x-4)^2}{9} - \frac{(y-3)^2}{64} = 1$
13. $\frac{(x-4)^2}{16} - \frac{(y+6)^2}{49} = 1$
14. $\frac{(y+8)^2}{36} - \frac{(x+3)^2}{25} = 1$
15. $\frac{(y+7)^2}{4} - \frac{x^2}{25} = 1$

PRACTICE AND PROBLEM SOLVING

Independent Practice	
For Exercises	See Example
16–17	1
18–21	2
22–29	3

Extra Practice
Skills Practice p. S22
Application Practice p. S41

Find the constant difference for a hyperbola with the given foci and point on the hyperbola.

16. $F_1(0, -10)$, $F_2(0, 10)$, $P(0, 6)$ **12**
17. $F_1(-29, 0)$, $F_2(29, 0)$, $P(21, 0)$ **42**

Write an equation in standard form for each hyperbola. 18. $\frac{x^2}{225} - \frac{y^2}{169} = 1$

18. center $(0, 0)$, vertex $(15, 0)$, co-vertex $(0, -13)$
19. center $(0, 0)$, vertex $(-8, 0)$, focus $(17, 0)$ $\frac{x^2}{64} - \frac{y^2}{225} = 1$
20. 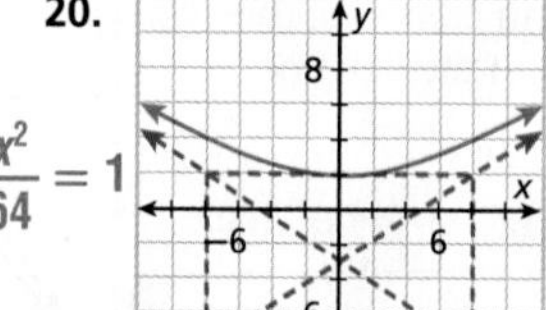 $\frac{(y+3)^2}{25} - \frac{x^2}{64} = 1$
21. 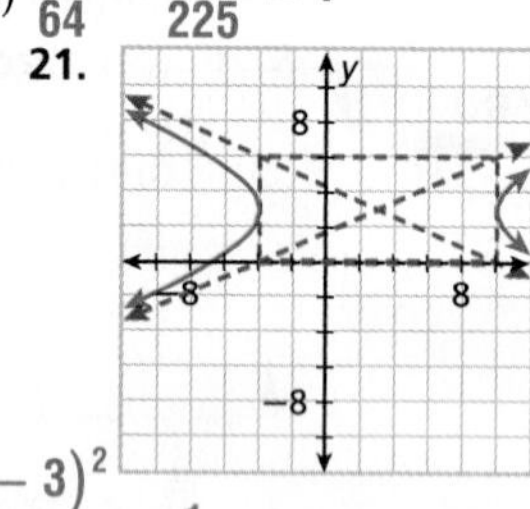 $\frac{(x-3)^2}{49} - \frac{(y-3)^2}{9} = 1$

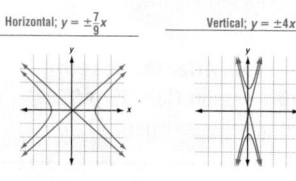

10-4 READING STRATEGIES

You can determine much about the graph of a hyperbola by looking at its equation. You can determine whether the hyperbola is horizontal or vertical, and you can determine the location of the asymptotes of the hyperbola.

$\frac{x^2}{a^2} - \frac{y^2}{b^2} = 1$
Asymptotes: $y = \pm\frac{b}{a}x$
The y^2 term is negative, so this hyperbola is horizontal.

$\frac{y^2}{a^2} - \frac{x^2}{b^2} = 1$
Asymptotes: $y = \pm\frac{a}{b}x$
The x^2 term is negative, so this hyperbola is vertical.

Determine whether each hyperbola is horizontal or vertical and give the asymptotes.

1. $\frac{y^2}{9} - \frac{x^2}{25} = 1$ Vertical; $y = \pm\frac{3}{5}x$
2. $\frac{x^2}{16} - \frac{y^2}{25} = 1$ Horizontal; $y = \pm\frac{5}{4}x$
3. $\frac{y^2}{81} - \frac{x^2}{9} = 1$ Vertical; $y = \pm 3x$

Sketch the asymptotes on the coordinate plane, and then draw the hyperbola.

4. $\frac{x^2}{81} - \frac{y^2}{49} = 1$ Horizontal; $y = \pm\frac{7}{9}x$
5. $\frac{y^2}{64} - \frac{x^2}{4} = 1$ Vertical; $y = \pm 4x$

10-4 RETEACH

The standard form for the equation of a **hyperbola** with center at (0, 0) depends on whether the graph opens horizontally or vertically.

Horizontal Opening	Vertical Opening
$\frac{x^2}{a^2} - \frac{y^2}{b^2} = 1$	$\frac{y^2}{a^2} - \frac{x^2}{b^2} = 1$
Vertices: $(a, 0)$ and $(-a, 0)$ lie on the x-axis. Co-vertices: $(0, b)$ and $(0, -b)$ lie on the y-axis.	Vertices: $(0, a)$ and $(0, -a)$ lie on the y-axis. Co-vertices: $(b, 0)$ and $(-b, 0)$ lie on the x-axis.

The graph opens horizontally. Vertices are $(2, 0)$ and $(-2, 0)$. Co-vertices are $(0, 4)$ and $(0, -4)$. So, $a = 2$ and $b = 4$. Substitute into the standard form equation and simplify. $\frac{x^2}{a^2} - \frac{y^2}{b^2} = 1 \rightarrow \frac{x^2}{4} - \frac{y^2}{16} = 1$

The graph opens vertically. Vertices are $(0, 2)$ and $(0, -2)$. Co-vertices are $(4, 0)$ and $(-4, 0)$. So, $a = 2$ and $b = 4$. Substitute into the standard form equation and simplify. $\frac{y^2}{a^2} - \frac{x^2}{b^2} = 1 \rightarrow \frac{y^2}{4} - \frac{x^2}{16} = 1$

Write an equation in standard form for each hyperbola.

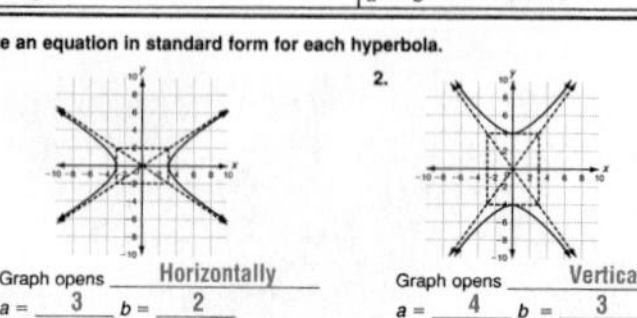

1. Graph opens Horizontally; $a = 3$, $b = 2$; $\frac{x^2}{9} - \frac{y^2}{4} = 1$
2. Graph opens Vertically; $a = 4$, $b = 3$; $\frac{y^2}{16} - \frac{x^2}{9} = 1$

31. Possible answers: The hyperbola becomes wider and flatter. The hyperbola becomes taller and thinner.

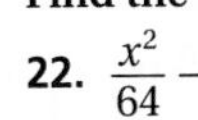

Find the vertices, co-vertices, and asymptotes of each hyperbola, and then graph.

22. $\frac{x^2}{64} - \frac{y^2}{36} = 1$ 23. $\frac{y^2}{25} - \frac{x^2}{81} = 1$ 24. $\frac{y^2}{81} - \frac{x^2}{16} = 1$ 25. $\frac{x^2}{4} - \frac{y^2}{121} = 1$

26. $\frac{(y-1)^2}{64} - \frac{(x+2)^2}{36} = 1$ 27. $\frac{(x+5)^2}{25} - \frac{(y-3)^2}{16} = 1$

28. $\frac{(y-8)^2}{25} - \frac{(x+6)^2}{36} = 1$ 29. $\frac{(x-6)^2}{9} - \frac{(y-2)^2}{16} = 1$

30. **Architecture** If the x-axis is placed at a height of 100 meters, the outer edge of a cooling tower can be modeled by the hyperbola $\frac{x^2}{900} - \frac{y^2}{1600} = 1$, measured in meters. If the tower is 150 meters tall, find the width of the cooling tower at the top. **96 m**

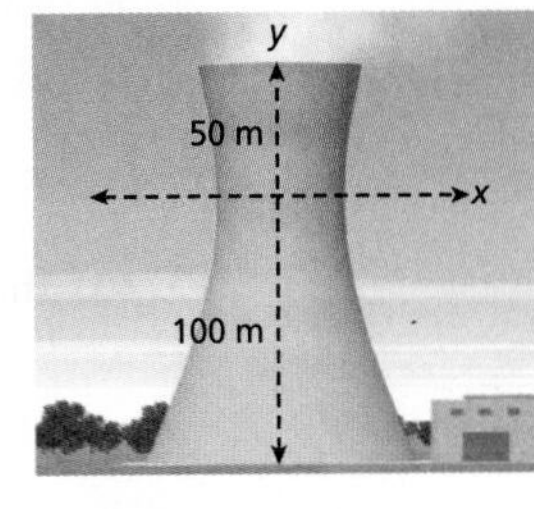

LINK

Physics

The saying "lightning never strikes twice in the same place" is often disproven. The Empire State Building is struck by lightning about 100 times each year and serves as a lightning rod for the surrounding area.

31. **Critical Thinking** What happens to the graph of $\frac{x^2}{a^2} - \frac{y^2}{16} = 1$ as the values of a increase? What happens to the graph of $\frac{x^2}{16} - \frac{y^2}{b^2} = 1$ as the values of b increase?

32. **Physics** Two people standing 10,000 feet apart see lightning strike. One person hears the thunder 5 seconds after the other person. Because sound travels at 1100 feet per second, one person is 5500 feet farther from the lightning strike than the other. The possible locations of the strike then form a hyperbola with the two people at the foci. Place the origin midway between the two people, and write an equation that could be used to represent the possible locations of the lightning strike.

33. **Biology** Two underwater listening devices 12,000 feet apart detect a whale call. One device detects the call 2 seconds before the other. The possible locations of the whale form a hyperbola with the two devices at the foci.
   a. If the speed of sound in water is 5000 feet per second, write an equation for the possible locations of the whale. (*Hint:* Place the origin midway between the devices.)
   b. **What if...?** Could the location of the whale be more precisely located if there were a third listening device? Explain.

32. Possible answer: $\frac{x^2}{2750^2} - \frac{y^2}{4176^2} = 1$

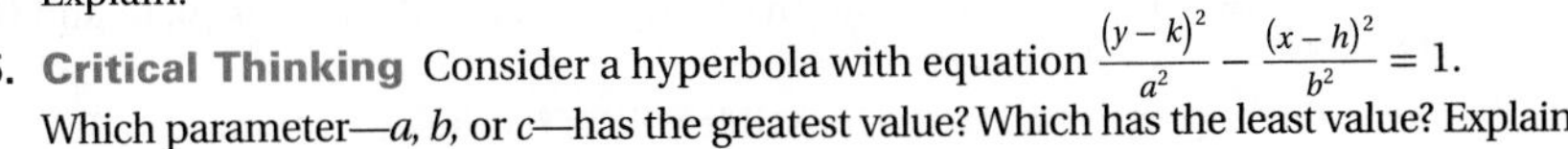

34. **Critical Thinking** How could you identify the domain and range of a hyperbola? Explain.

35. **Critical Thinking** Consider a hyperbola with equation $\frac{(y-k)^2}{a^2} - \frac{(x-h)^2}{b^2} = 1$. Which parameter—$a$, b, or c—has the greatest value? Which has the least value? Explain.

36. **Write About It** Suppose you have two hyperbolas that are the same except that the transverse axis and conjugate axis are switched. How does switching the axes affect the equations of the asymptotes for the two hyperbolas? Why?

MULTI-STEP TEST PREP

37. This problem will prepare you for the Multi-Step Test Prep on page 758.

A comet's path as it approaches the Sun is modeled by one branch of the hyperbola $\frac{y^2}{900} - \frac{x^2}{44{,}896} = 1$, where the Sun is at the corresponding focus. Each unit of the coordinate plane represents 1 million miles.
   a. Find the coordinates of the Sun, assuming that it is at the focus with nonnegative coordinates. **(0, 214)**
   b. How close does the comet come to the Sun? **184 million mi**
   c. When the comet is far from the Sun, the comet's path can be modeled by the hyperbola's asymptotes. Write the equations of the asymptotes. **$y \approx \pm 0.142x$**

Teaching Tip

Math Background
The shape of the cooling tower discussed in **Exercise 30** is called a *hyperboloid of one sheet*. It is the three-dimensional surface "swept out" when a hyperbola is rotated about its conjugate axis. If the same hyperbola is rotated about its transverse axis, an entirely different surface is formed, called a *hyperboloid of two sheets*.

MULTI-STEP TEST PREP **Exercise 37** involves identifying the important points on a hyperbola. This exercise prepares students for the Multi-Step Test Prep on page 758.

Answers

22–29. See p. A43.

33a. Possible answer: $\frac{x^2}{5000^2} - \frac{y^2}{3317^2} = 1$

b. Yes; possible answer: it would be possible to find the equation of a second hyperbola using a different combination of two of the stations; the whale would be located at the intersection of the two hyperbolas.

34. Possible answer: Use the vertices. For a hyperbola in standard form with a horizontal transverse axis, the domain is $\{x \mid x \le h - a \text{ or } x \ge h + a\}$, and the range is $\{y \mid y \in \mathbb{R}\}$.

35, 36. See p. A44.

10-4 PROBLEM SOLVING

A brochure for a new amusement park describes the design of the towers that characterize the park. The outline of the central and largest tower can be modeled by the hyperbola $\frac{x^2}{625} - \frac{y^2}{2025} = 1$, with dimensions in feet. The smaller towers are scaled-down versions of the central tower, and so their dimensions are in proportion to those of the central tower.

1. What is the diameter of the central tower at its narrowest part?
   a. Explain how to determine whether the transverse axis of a hyperbola is horizontal or vertical. Since the y^2 term is negative, the transverse axis is horizontal.
   b. Find the vertices and co-vertices. Vertices: (25, 0) and (−25, 0); co-vertices: (0, 45) and (0, −45)
   c. How can you use these data to answer the question? The diameter of the tower is equal to the distance between the vertices.
   d. What is the diameter of the tower at its narrowest part? 50 ft
2. The vertices of a smaller tower are (10, 0) and (−10, 0).
   a. Name the coordinates of the co-vertices. (0, 18), (0, −18)
   b. What is the equation for the outline of the smaller tower? $\frac{x^2}{100} - \frac{y^2}{324} = 1$
3. How do the asymptotes of the hyperbolas of the larger central tower and the smaller tower compare?
   a. Find the asymptotes of the two towers. $y = \pm 1.8x$; $y = \pm 1.8x$
   b. Compare the asymptotes of the two towers. The asymptotes are the same.

Choose the letter for the best answer.

4. The hyperbola that models a third tower has vertices (0, 9) and (0, −9) and focus (0, 15). The solution to which of the following equations gives the denominator of the y^2 term in the equation of the hyperbola?
   A $15^2 = a^2 - 9^2$
   B $15^2 = a^2 + 18^2$
   (C) $15^2 = b^2 + 9^2$
   D $15^2 = b^2 - 18^2$

5. The outline of a tower at the park's Welcome Center can be modeled by the equation $\frac{x^2}{25} - \frac{y^2}{81} = 1$. What are the asymptotes of the hyperbola?
   F $y = \pm 0.31x$
   G $y = \pm 0.56x$
   (H) $y = \pm 1.8x$
   J $y = \pm 3.24x$

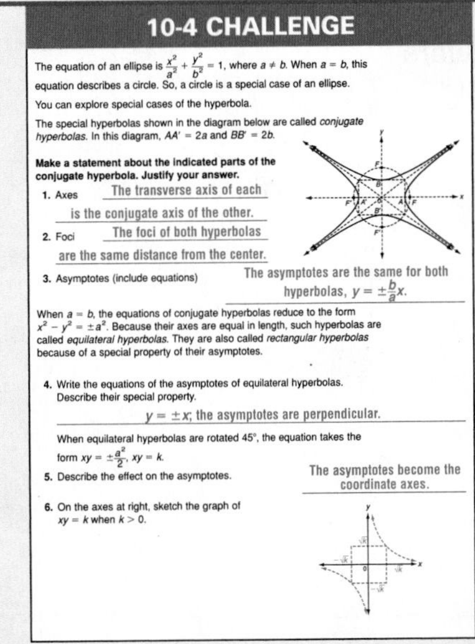

10-4 CHALLENGE

The equation of an ellipse is $\frac{x^2}{a^2} + \frac{y^2}{b^2} = 1$, where $a \ne b$. When $a = b$, this equation describes a circle. So, a circle is a special case of an ellipse.

You can explore special cases of the hyperbola.

The special hyperbolas shown in the diagram below are called *conjugate hyperbolas*. In this diagram, $AA' = 2a$ and $BB' = 2b$.

Make a statement about the indicated parts of the conjugate hyperbola. Justify your answer.

1. Axes The transverse axis of each is the conjugate axis of the other.
2. Foci The foci of both hyperbolas are the same distance from the center.
3. Asymptotes (include equations) The asymptotes are the same for both hyperbolas, $y = \pm\frac{b}{a}x$.

When $a = b$, the equations of conjugate hyperbolas reduce to the form $x^2 - y^2 = \pm a^2$. Because their axes are equal in length, such hyperbolas are called *equilateral hyperbolas*. They are also called *rectangular hyperbolas* because of a special property of their asymptotes.

4. Write the equations of the asymptotes of equilateral hyperbolas. Describe their special property. $y = \pm x$; the asymptotes are perpendicular.

When equilateral hyperbolas are rotated 45°, the equation takes the form $xy = \pm\frac{a^2}{2}$, $xy = k$.

5. Describe the effect on the asymptotes. The asymptotes become the coordinate axes.
6. On the axes at right, sketch the graph of $xy = k$ when $k > 0$.

10-4 PRACTICE A

10-4 PRACTICE C

10-4 PRACTICE B

Find the constant difference for a hyperbola with the given foci and point on the hyperbola.

1. $F_1(0, 11)$, $F_2(0, -11)$, $P(0, 7)$ 14
2. $F_1(-9, 0)$, $F_2(9, 0)$, $P(-8, 0)$ 16

Write an equation in standard form for each hyperbola with center (0, 0).

3. Co-vertex (−16, 0), focus (0, −20) $\frac{y^2}{144} - \frac{x^2}{256} = 1$
4. Vertex (24, 0), focus (−25, 0) $\frac{x^2}{576} - \frac{y^2}{49} = 1$
5. Vertex (0, −17), co-vertex (1, 0) $\frac{y^2}{289} - \frac{x^2}{1} = 1$
6. Vertex (30, 0), focus (−40, 0) $\frac{x^2}{900} - \frac{y^2}{700} = 1$

Find the vertices, co-vertices, and asymptotes of each hyperbola, and then graph.

7. $\frac{x^2}{196} - \frac{y^2}{49} = 1$
Vertices: (14, 0), (−14, 0); co-vertices: (0, 7), (0, −7); asymptotes: $y = \frac{1}{2}x$, $y = -\frac{1}{2}x$

8. $\frac{(y-4)^2}{36} - \frac{x^2}{81} = 1$
Vertices: (0, 10), (0, −2); co-vertices: (9, 4), (−9, 4); asymptotes: $y = \frac{2}{3}x + 4$, $y = -\frac{2}{3}x + 4$

Solve.

9. A comet's path as it approaches the sun is modeled by one branch of the hyperbola $\frac{y^2}{1122} - \frac{x^2}{39{,}355} = 1$, where the sun is at the corresponding focus. Each unit of the coordinate plane represents one million miles. How close does the comet come to the sun? 167.7 million miles

TEST PREP DOCTOR In **Exercise 40,** students should use the values of a and b to find the value of c. The hyperbola with the largest value of c will have the greatest distance between foci. Students who choose **A, B,** or **C** may not be using the relationship $a^2 + b^2 = c^2$.

Journal

Have students describe what they know about a hyperbola based on its equation, such as the orientation of the hyperbola and whether it curves sharply or gradually away from the conjugate axis.

ALTERNATIVE ASSESSMENT

Have students explain what a hyperbola is and give an example with a center that is not on either axis. Then students should describe how to graph a hyperbola given its equation and how to write the equation given a description that includes the center, a focus, and a vertex.

Power Presentations with PowerPoint®

10-4 Lesson Quiz

1. Find the constant difference for a hyperbola with foci $(-3.5, 0)$ and $(3.5, 0)$ and a point on the hyperbola $(3.5, 24)$. 1
2. Write an equation in standard form for a hyperbola with center $(4, 0)$, vertex $(10, 0)$, and focus $(12, 0)$.
$\frac{(x-4)^2}{36} - \frac{y^2}{28} = 1$
3. Find the vertices, co-vertices, and asymptotes of $\frac{y^2}{25} - \frac{(x+6)^2}{144} = 1$, then graph.
vertices: $(-6, \pm 5)$;
co-vertices: $(6, 0)$, $(-18, 0)$;
asymptotes: $y = \pm\frac{5}{12}(x+6)$

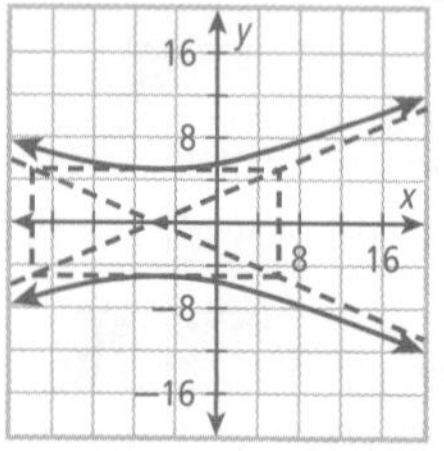

Also available on transparency

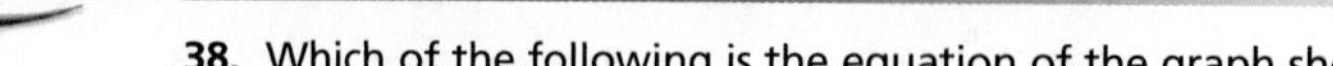

TEST PREP

38. Which of the following is the equation of the graph shown?

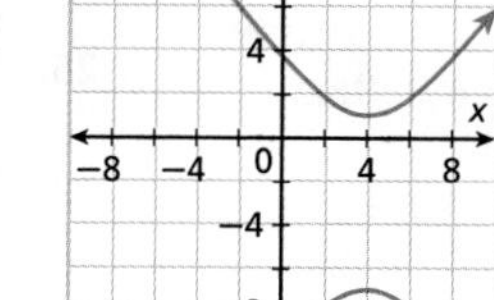

Ⓐ $\frac{(x-3)^2}{16} - \frac{(y+4)^2}{9} = 1$ Ⓒ $\frac{(y-3)^2}{16} - \frac{(x+4)^2}{9} = 1$

Ⓑ $\frac{(x+3)^2}{16} - \frac{(y-4)^2}{9} = 1$ Ⓓ $\frac{(y+3)^2}{16} - \frac{(x-4)^2}{9} = 1$ (circled)

39. Which of the following is an asymptote of the graph of $1 = \frac{x^2}{4} - \frac{y^2}{9}$?

Ⓕ $y = -\frac{2}{3}x$ Ⓖ $y = \frac{3}{2}x$ (circled) Ⓗ $y = -\frac{9}{4}x$ Ⓙ $y = \frac{4}{9}x$

40. The graph of which of the following equations will have the greatest distance between foci?

Ⓐ $\frac{(x-6)^2}{36} - \frac{(y+2)^2}{81} = 1$ Ⓒ $\frac{(y+115)^2}{49} - \frac{(x-225)^2}{100} = 1$

Ⓑ $\frac{(x+22)^2}{45} - \frac{(y-36)^2}{125} = 1$ Ⓓ $\frac{(y-59)^2}{90} - \frac{(x+76)^2}{95} = 1$ (circled)

41. What is the length of the conjugate axis of the hyperbola with equation $\frac{x^2}{49} - \frac{y^2}{121} = 1$?

Ⓕ 7 Ⓖ 11 Ⓗ 14 Ⓙ 22 (circled)

CHALLENGE AND EXTEND

Write an equation in standard form for each hyperbola.

42. co-vertex $(-12, 0)$, asymptote $y = -\frac{4}{3}x$ — 42. $\frac{y^2}{256} - \frac{x^2}{144} = 1$
43. vertex $(27, -9)$, asymptote $y + 9 = -\frac{3}{5}(x - 7)$ — $\frac{(x-7)^2}{400} - \frac{(y+9)^2}{144} = 1$
44. The eccentricity of a hyperbola is defined as $e = \frac{c}{a}$. Recall that $c^2 = a^2 + b^2$ for a hyperbola in standard form.
    a. Find the eccentricity of $\frac{(x-4)^2}{144} - \frac{(y+2)^2}{1225} = 1$. $e = \frac{37}{12}$
    b. Find the equation of a hyperbola with vertices $(0, 6)$ and $(0, -6)$, and eccentricity $e = \frac{4}{3}$. $\frac{y^2}{36} - \frac{x^2}{28} = 1$
    c. What are the possible values for the eccentricity of a hyperbola? $e > 1$
    d. Describe the relationship between eccentricity and the shape of a hyperbola. The greater the eccentricity, the more elongated the hyperbola is.
45. Use the distance formula to write the equation of a hyperbola with foci at $F_1(-5, 0)$ and $F_2(5, 0)$ and $d = 8$. (*Hint:* Use $d = PF_1 - PF_2$ and the point (x, y).) $\frac{x^2}{16} - \frac{y^2}{9} = 1$

SPIRAL REVIEW

Graph each function by using a table. *(Lesson 5-1)*

46. $f(x) = 2x^2 + 3x - 6$
47. $f(x) = -x^2 + 2x + 5$
48. $f(x) = x^2 - 5x + 4$
49. **Finance** Carlton's starting salary was \$30,000. Every year, he received a raise of \$3000. Let x represent years and y represent Carlton's salary. *(Lesson 9-1)*
    a. Write and graph an equation to represent this situation.
    b. After how many years will Carlton earn \$60,000? 10 yr

Write an equation in standard form for each ellipse with center (0, 0). *(Lesson 10-3)*

50. vertex $(5, 0)$, co-vertex $(0, 4)$ $\frac{x^2}{25} + \frac{y^2}{16} = 1$
51. vertex $(0, -2)$, focus $(0, \sqrt{2})$ $\frac{y^2}{4} + \frac{x^2}{2} = 1$

Answers

46.

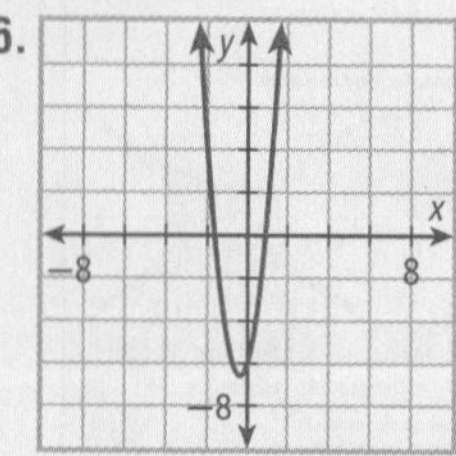

47.

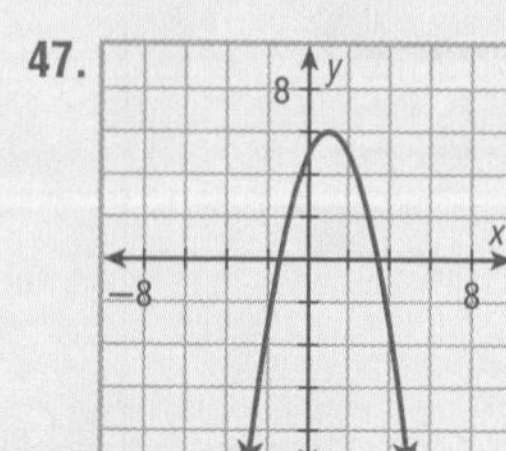

48.

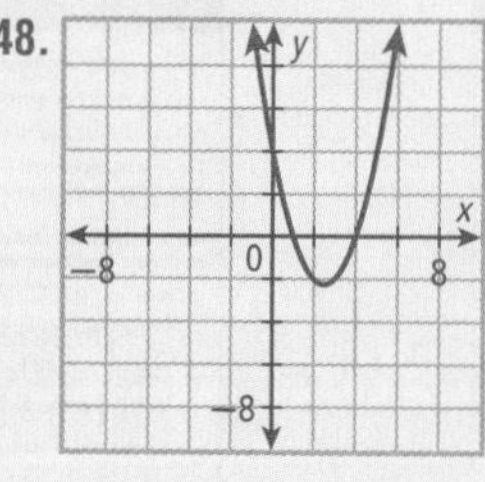

49a. $y = 30{,}000 + 3{,}000x$

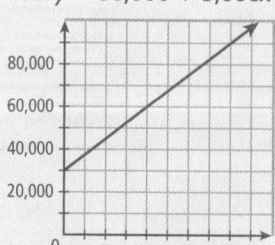

10-5 Parabolas

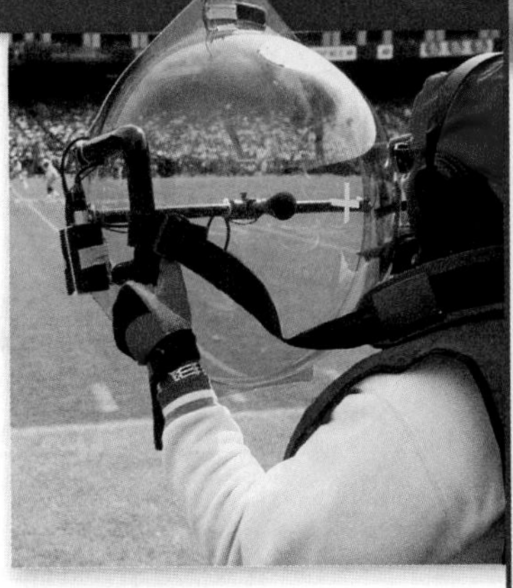

Objectives
Write the standard equation of a parabola and its axis of symmetry.
Graph a parabola, and identify its focus, directrix, and axis of symmetry.

Vocabulary
focus of a parabola
directrix

Why learn this?
Parabolas are used with microphones to pick up sounds from sports events. (See Example 4.)

In Chapter 5, you learned that the graph of a quadratic function is a parabola. Because a parabola is a conic section, it can also be defined in terms of distance.

A parabola is the set of all points $P(x, y)$ in a plane that are an equal distance from both a fixed point, the **focus**, and a fixed line, the **directrix**. A parabola has an axis of symmetry perpendicular to its directrix and that passes through its vertex. The vertex of a parabola is the midpoint of the segment connecting the focus and the directrix.

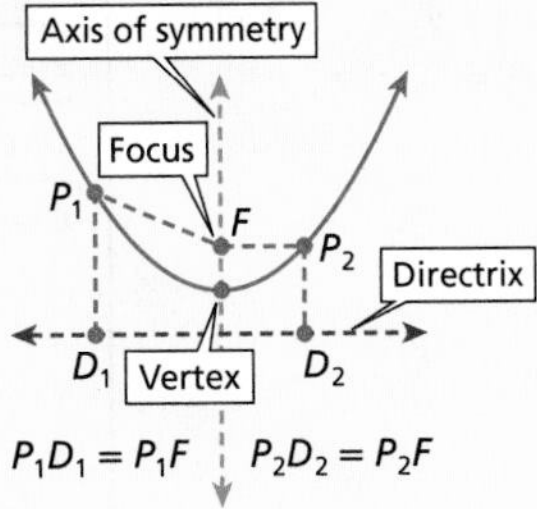

EXAMPLE 1 **Using the Distance Formula to Write the Equation of a Parabola**

Use the Distance Formula to find the equation of a parabola with focus $F(0, 3)$ and directrix $y = -3$.

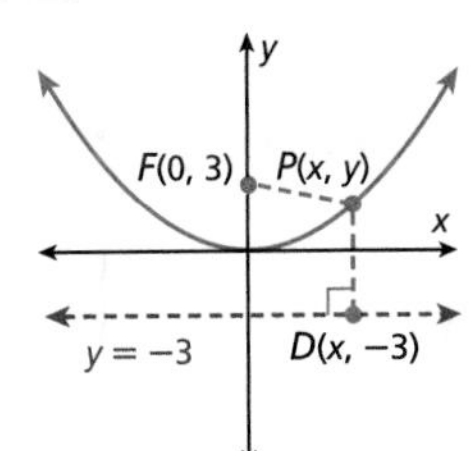

Remember!
The distance from a point to a line is defined as the length of the line segment from the point perpendicular to the line.

$PF = PD$	*Definition of a parabola*
$\sqrt{(x - x_1)^2 + (y - y_1)^2} = \sqrt{(x - x_2)^2 + (y - y_2)^2}$	*Distance Formula*
$\sqrt{(x - 0)^2 + (y - 3)^2} = \sqrt{(x - x)^2 + (y + 3)^2}$	*Substitute (0, 3) for (x_1, y_1) and (x, −3) for (x_2, y_2).*
$\sqrt{x^2 + (y - 3)^2} = \sqrt{(y + 3)^2}$	*Simplify.*
$x^2 + (y - 3)^2 = (y + 3)^2$	*Square both sides.*
$x^2 + y^2 - 6y + 9 = y^2 + 6y + 9$	*Expand.*
$x^2 - 6y = 6y$	*Subtract y^2 and 9 from both sides.*
$x^2 = 12y$	*Add 6y to both sides.*
$y = \frac{1}{12}x^2$	*Solve for y.*

CHECK IT OUT!

1. Use the Distance Formula to find the equation of a parabola with focus $F(0, 4)$ and directrix $y = -4$. $y = \frac{1}{16}x^2$

10-5 Organizer

Pacing: Traditional $1\frac{1}{2}$ days
Block $\frac{3}{4}$ day

Objectives: Write the standard equation for a parabola and its axis of symmetry.
Graph a parabola, and identify its focus, directrix, and axis of symmetry.

PREMIER **Online Edition**
Graphing Calculator, Tutorial Videos

Countdown to Testing Week 22

Power Presentations with PowerPoint®

Warm Up

1. Given $\frac{1}{4p} = c$, solve for p when $c = \left\{\frac{1}{32}, \frac{1}{4}, 1, 2\right\}$. $\left\{8, 1, \frac{1}{4}, \frac{1}{8}\right\}$

Find each distance.

2. from (0, 2) to (12, 7) 13
3. from the line $y = -6$ to (12, 7) 13

Also available on transparency

Math Humor

Q: What did the math student say when his pet bunny tried to steal his parabola?

A: Silly rabbit, directrix are for kids!

1 Introduce

EXPLORATION

10-5 Parabolas

The graph of an equation in the form $y = \frac{1}{4p}x^2$ or $x = \frac{1}{4p}y^2$ is a parabola. Use your calculator to explore how the value of p affects the shape and position of the parabola.

1. Use your calculator to graph each equation in the table. (Hint: For equations in the form $x = \frac{1}{4p}y^2$, solve for y and graph two separate functions.) Tell whether each parabola opens upward, downward, to the left, or to the right.

Equation	Parabola Opens
$y = \frac{1}{8}x^2$	
$y = -\frac{1}{8}x^2$	
$x = \frac{1}{8}y^2$	
$x = -\frac{1}{8}y^2$	

2. Graph $y = \frac{1}{4}x^2$, $y = \frac{1}{8}x^2$, $y = \frac{1}{12}x^2$, and $y = \frac{1}{16}x^2$ in the same window. What happens to the graph as the value of p increases in the equation $y = \frac{1}{4p}x^2$?

THINK AND DISCUSS

3. **Explain** how you can tell the direction in which a parabola opens by looking at its equation.
4. **Describe** how the graph of $x = \frac{1}{32}y^2$ compares to the graph of $x = -\frac{1}{32}y^2$.

Motivate

Review with students the connection between a parabola and quadratic functions. The equations $y = x^2$ and $y = -x^2$ represent both quadratic functions and parabolas. The equations $x = y^2$ and $x = -y^2$ represent parabolas only.

Explorations and answers are provided in the *Explorations* binder.

State Resources

Power Presentations with PowerPoint®

Additional Examples

Example 1

Use the distance formula to write the equation of a parabola with focus $F(2, 4)$ and directrix $y = -4$.

$y = \frac{1}{16}(x - 2)^2$

Example 2

Write the equation in standard form for each parabola.

A.

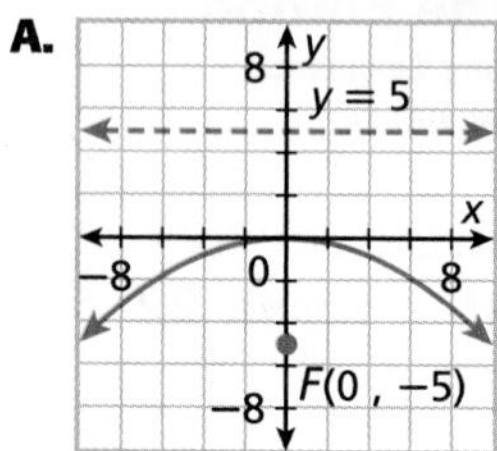

$y = -\frac{1}{20}x^2$

B. Vertex at $(0, 0)$, directrix at $x = -6$

$x = \frac{1}{24}y^2$

Also available on transparency

INTERVENTION

Questioning Strategies

EXAMPLE 1

- Is it possible to determine the equation of the parabola without using the distance formula? Explain.

EXAMPLE 2

- What is the distance between the focus and the directrix for the parent function $y = x^2$?

Previously, you have graphed parabolas with vertical axes of symmetry that open upward or downward. Parabolas may also have horizontal axes of symmetry and may open to the left or right.

The equations of parabolas use the parameter p. The $|p|$ gives the distance from the vertex to both the focus and the directrix.

Standard Form for the Equation of a Parabola Vertex at $(0, 0)$

AXIS OF SYMMETRY	HORIZONTAL $y = 0$	VERTICAL $x = 0$
Equation	$x = \frac{1}{4p}y^2$	$y = \frac{1}{4p}x^2$
Direction	Opens right if $p > 0$ Opens left if $p < 0$	Opens upward if $p > 0$ Opens downward if $p < 0$
Focus	$(p, 0)$	$(0, p)$
Directrix	$x = -p$	$y = -p$
Graph	y, D(−p, y), P(x, y), x, F(p, 0), x = −p	y, F(0, p), P(x, y), x, y = −p, D(x, −p)

EXAMPLE 2 **Writing Equations of Parabolas**

Write the equation in standard form for each parabola.

A

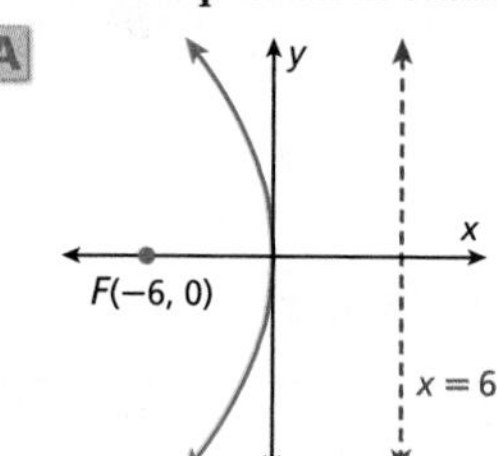

Step 1 Because the axis of symmetry is horizontal and the parabola opens to the left, the equation is in the form $x = \frac{1}{4p}y^2$ with $p < 0$.

Step 2 The distance from the focus $(-6, 0)$ to the vertex $(0, 0)$ is 6, so $p = -6$ and $4p = -24$.

Step 3 The equation of the parabola is $x = -\frac{1}{24}y^2$.

Check Use your graphing calculator. The graph of the equation appears to match.

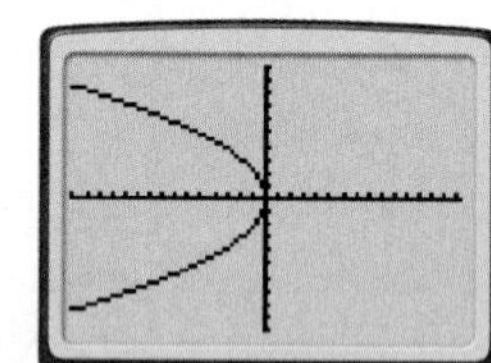

2 Teach

Guided Instruction

Students should first recount what they already know about parabolas from their earlier study of quadratic functions.

Then, have students compare a parabola of the form $y = x^2$ with a parabola of the form $x = y^2$ and experiment with different values of p.

Reaching All Learners

Through Cooperative Learning

Have students work in groups to research real-world examples where parabolas are used to focus and concentrate signals (e.g., satellite dishes, microphones, etc.). Also have students try to find examples of where the opposite principle is used, i.e., where a source is at the focus (e.g. on an automobile headlight). Students may wish to use the internet or the school library.

Write the equation in standard form for each parabola.

B the parabola with vertex $(0, 0)$ and directrix $y = -2.5$.

Step 1 Because the directrix is a horizontal line, the equation is in the form $y = \frac{1}{4p}x^2$. The vertex is above the directrix, so the graph will open upward.

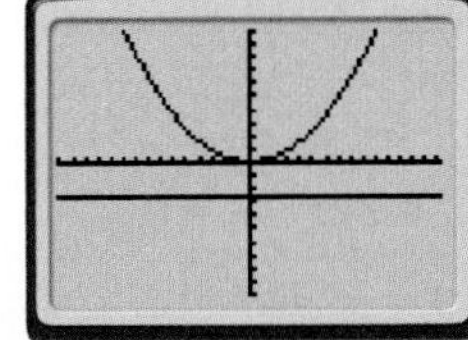

Step 2 Because the directrix is $y = -2.5$, $p = 2.5$ and $4p = 10$.

Step 3 The equation of the parabola is $y = \frac{1}{10}x^2$.

Check Use your graphing calculator.

Write the equation in standard form for each parabola.

2a. vertex $(0, 0)$, directrix $x = 1.25$ **2a.** $x = -\frac{1}{5}y^2$

2b. vertex $(0, 0)$, focus $(0, -7)$ **b.** $x = -\frac{1}{28}x^2$

The vertex of a parabola may not always be the origin. Adding or subtracting a value from x or y translates the graph of a parabola. Also notice that the values of p stretch or compress the graph.

Standard Form for the Equation of a Parabola Vertex at (h, k)

AXIS OF SYMMETRY	HORIZONTAL $y = k$	VERTICAL $x = h$
Equation	$x - h = \frac{1}{4p}(y - k)^2$	$y - k = \frac{1}{4p}(x - h)^2$
Direction	Opens right if $p > 0$ Opens left if $p < 0$	Opens upward if $p > 0$ Opens downward if $p < 0$
Focus	$(h + p, k)$	$(h, k + p)$
Directrix	$x = h - p$	$y = k - p$
Graph	y; y = k; F(h + p, k); (h, k); x; x = h − p	x = h; y; F(h, k + p); (h, k); y = k − p; x

EXAMPLE **3** **Graphing Parabolas**

Find the vertex, value of p, axis of symmetry, focus, and directrix of the parabola $x - 2 = -\frac{1}{16}(y + 5)^2$. Then graph.

Step 1 The vertex is $(2, -5)$.

Step 2 $\frac{1}{4p} = -\frac{1}{16}$, so $4p = -16$ and $p = -4$.

Step 3 The graph has a horizontal axis of symmetry, with equation $y = -5$, and opens left.

Power Presentations with PowerPoint®

Additional Examples

Example 3

Find the vertex, value of p, axis of symmetry, focus, and directrix of the parabola $y + 3 = \frac{1}{8}(x-2)^2$. Then graph.

vertex: $(2, -3)$; focus: $(2, -1)$; directrix: $y = -5$; $p = 2$; axis of symmetry: $x = 2$

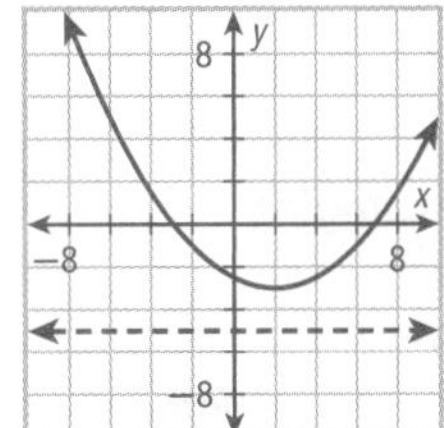

Also available on transparency

INTERVENTION

Questioning Strategies

EXAMPLE 3

- What part(s) of the standard form of the equation for a parabola would change if the focus is shifted toward the directrix?

Teaching Tip

Kinesthetic Show students how to draw a parabola by using a tack, some string, a T square, and a triangle. Place the tack at the focus and the T square on the directrix as shown. Use the point of the pencil to keep the string against the side of the triangle, and slide the triangle along the T square to draw a parabola. The distance from the pencil point to the tack (focus) is equal at all times to the distance from the pencil point to the T square (directrix).

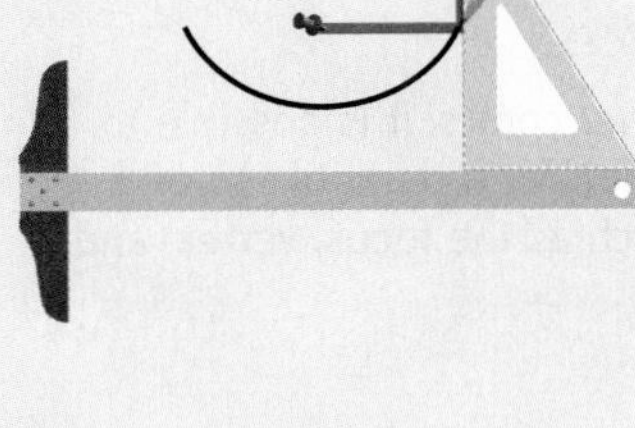

Power Presentations with PowerPoint®

Additional Examples

Example 4

The cross section of a larger parabolic microphone can be modeled by the equation $x = \frac{1}{132}y^2$.

What is the length of the feedhorn? 33 inches

Also available on transparency

INTERVENTION

Questioning Strategies

EXAMPLE 4

- Does it matter which way the parabola opens when modeling a microphone?

Answers

3a.

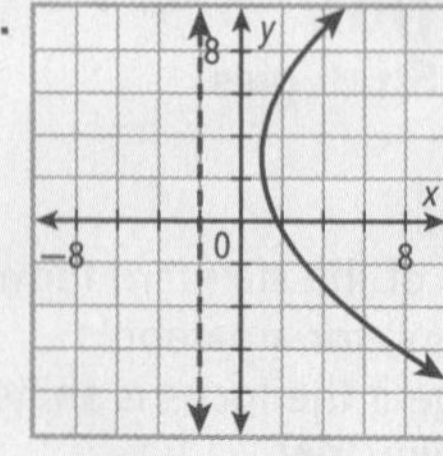

b.

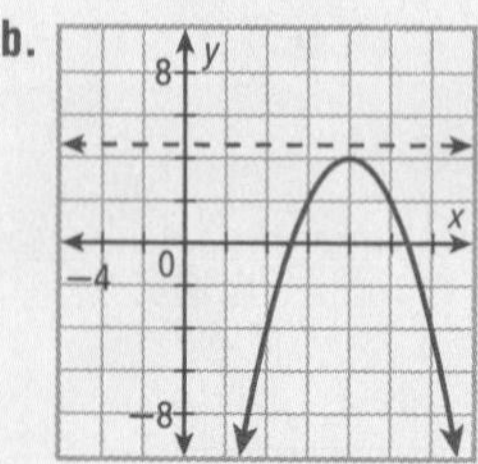

3a. vertex: $(1, 3)$; $p = 3$; axis of symmetry: $y = 3$; focus: $(4, 3)$; directrix: $x = -2$

3b. vertex: $(8, 4)$; $p = -\frac{1}{2}$; axis of symmetry: $x = 8$; focus: $(8, 3.5)$; directrix: $y = 4.5$

Step 4 The focus is $(2 + (-4), -5)$, or $(-2, -5)$.

Step 5 The directrix is a vertical line $x = 2 - (-4)$, or $x = 6$.

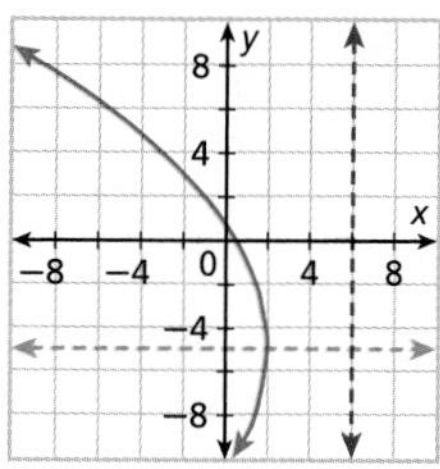

CHECK IT OUT! **Find the vertex, value of p, axis of symmetry, focus, and directrix of each parabola. Then graph.**

3a. $x - 1 = \frac{1}{12}(y - 3)^2$ **3b.** $y - 4 = -\frac{1}{2}(x - 8)^2$

Light or sound waves collected by a parabola will be reflected by the curve through the focus of the parabola, as shown in the figure. Waves emitted from the focus will be reflected out parallel to the axis of symmetry of a parabola. This property is used in communications technology.

EXAMPLE 4 Using the Equation of a Parabola

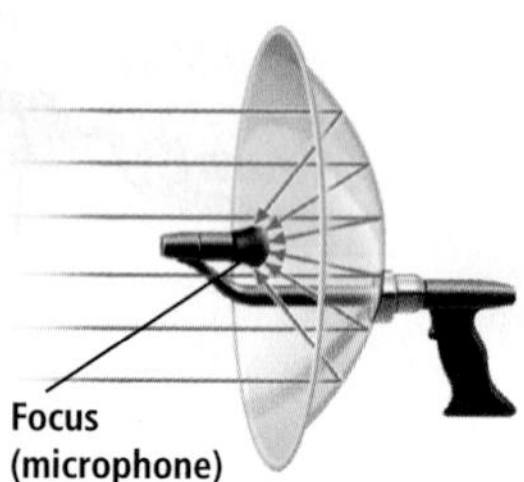

Engineers are constructing a parabolic microphone for use at sporting events. The surface of the parabolic microphone will reflect sounds to the focus of the microphone at the end of a part called a feedhorn. The equation for the cross section of the parabolic microphone dish is $x = \frac{1}{32}y^2$, measured in inches. How long should the engineers make the feedhorn?

The equation for the cross section is in the form $x = \frac{1}{4p}y^2$, so $4p = 32$ and $p = 8$. The focus should be 8 inches from the vertex of the cross section. Therefore, the feedhorn should be 8 inches long.

CHECK IT OUT! **4.** Find the length of the feedhorn for a microphone with a cross section equation $x = \frac{1}{44}y^2$. 11 in.

THINK AND DISCUSS

1. By using the standard form of a parabola's equation, how can you tell which direction a parabola opens?
2. How does knowing the value of p help you in finding the focus and the directrix of a parabola?
3. **GET ORGANIZED** Copy and complete the graphic organizer. Sketch an example and give an equation for each type of parabola.

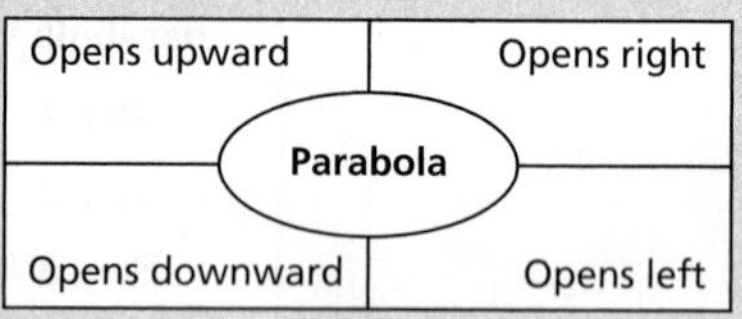

3 Close

Summarize

As with the other conics, it is possible to write an equation for a parabola given key information such as the focus, vertex, and directrix.

ONGOING ASSESSMENT and INTERVENTION

***Diagnose Before* the Lesson**
10-5 Warm Up, TE p. 751

***Monitor During* the Lesson**
Check It Out! Exercises, SE pp. 751–754
Questioning Strategies, TE pp. 752–754

***Assess After* the Lesson**
10-5 Lesson Quiz, TE p. 757
Alternative Assessment, TE p. 757

Answers to *Think and Discuss*

1. by looking at whether the x- or y-term is squared
2. You can add p to h or k to find the focus and subtract p from h or k to find the directrix.
3. See p. A12.

10-5 Exercises

go.hrw.com
Homework Help Online
KEYWORD: MB7 10-5
Parent Resources Online
KEYWORD: MB7 Parent

GUIDED PRACTICE

1. **Vocabulary** Describe the relationship between a parabola and its *directrix*.

SEE EXAMPLE 1 p. 751

Use the distance formula to find the equation of a parabola with the given focus and directrix.

2. $F(0, -5)$, $y = 5$ $\quad y = -\frac{1}{20}x^2$
3. $F(7, 0)$, $x = -7$ $\quad x = \frac{1}{28}y^2$
4. $F(-3, 0)$, $x = 6$ $\quad x - 1.5 = -\frac{1}{18}y^2$

SEE EXAMPLE 2 p. 752

Write the equation in standard form for each parabola.

5\. 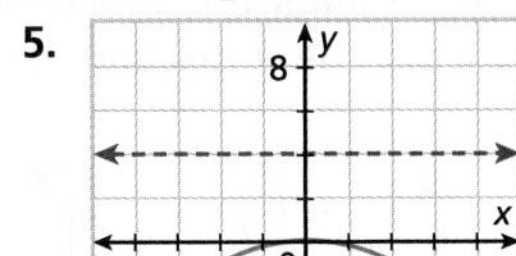

6\. 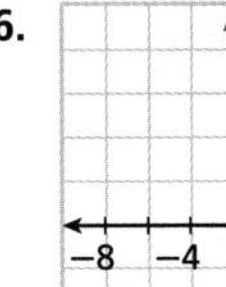 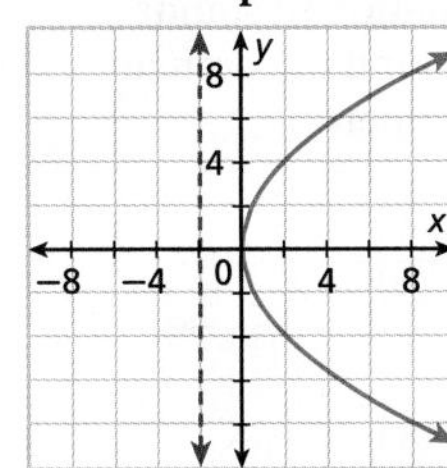

7\. 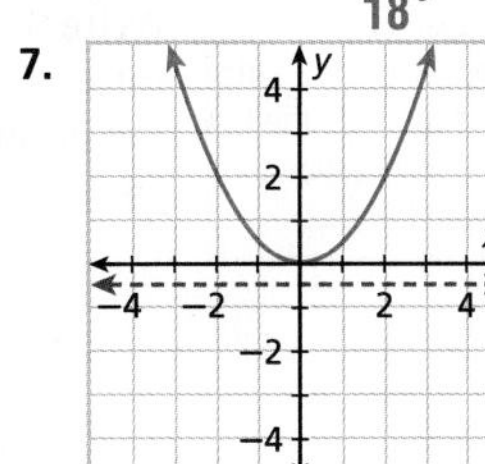

5. $y = -\frac{1}{16}x^2$
6. $x = \frac{1}{8}y^2$
7. $y = \frac{1}{2}x^2$

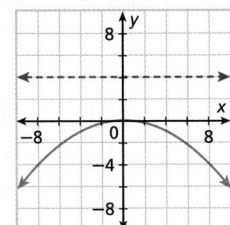

8. vertex $(0, 0)$, focus $(0, 1)$ $\quad y = \frac{1}{4}x^2$
9. vertex $(0, 0)$, focus $(-8, 0)$ $\quad x = -\frac{1}{32}y^2$

SEE EXAMPLE 3 p. 753

Find the vertex, value of p, axis of symmetry, focus, and directrix of each parabola, and then graph.

10. $y = \frac{1}{32}(x + 2)^2$
11. $x = \frac{1}{24}(y - 4)^2$
12. $y + 1 = \frac{1}{16}(x - 2)^2$

SEE EXAMPLE 4 p. 754

13. **Communications** The equation for the cross section of a parabolic satellite TV dish is $y = \frac{1}{38}x^2$, measured in inches. How far is the focus from the vertex of the cross section? **9.5 in.**

PRACTICE AND PROBLEM SOLVING

Independent Practice

For Exercises	See Example
14–16	1
17–21	2
22–24	3
25	4

Extra Practice

Skills Practice p. S23
Application Practice p. S41

Use the distance formula to find the equation of a parabola with the given focus and directrix.

14. $F(0, 3)$, $y = -5$ $\quad y + 1 = \frac{1}{16}x^2$
15. $F(-2, 0)$, $x = 8$ $\quad x - 3 = -\frac{1}{20}y^2$
16. $F(7, 0)$, $x = -1$ $\quad x - 3 = \frac{1}{16}y^2$

Write the equation in standard form for each parabola.

17\. 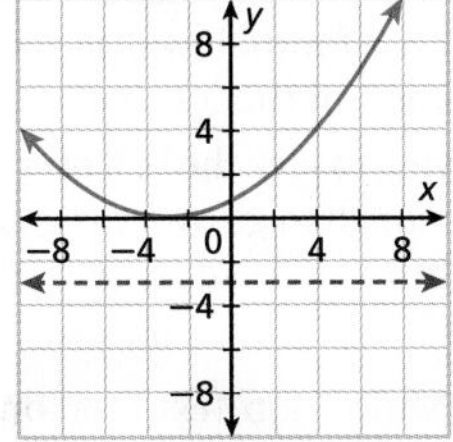

18\. 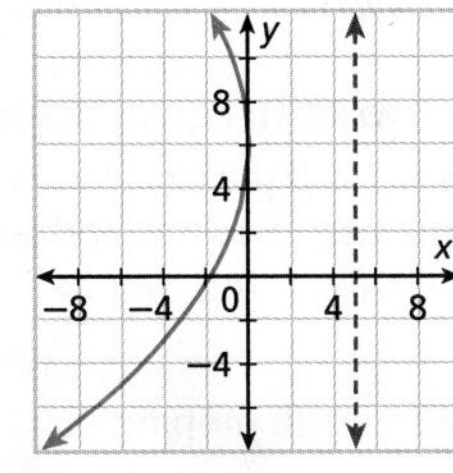

19\. 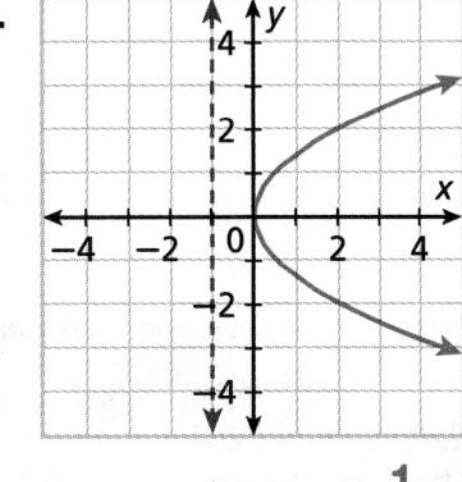

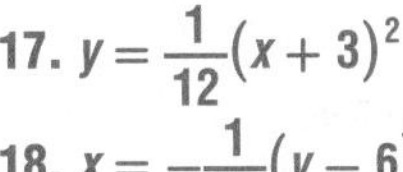

17. $y = \frac{1}{12}(x + 3)^2$
18. $x = -\frac{1}{20}(y - 6)^2$
19. $x = \frac{1}{4}y^2$

20. vertex $(0, 0)$, focus $\left(\frac{1}{2}, 0\right)$ $\quad x = \frac{1}{2}y^2$
21. vertex $(0, 0)$, focus $(0, -6)$ $\quad y = -\frac{1}{24}x^2$

Find the vertex, value of p, axis of symmetry, focus, and directrix of each parabola, and then graph.

22. $y = \frac{1}{8}(x - 1)^2$
23. $x = 2y^2 + 1$
24. $x - 2 = \frac{1}{2}(y + 1)^2$

10-5 READING STRATEGIES

A parabola is described in terms of its focus and directrix. A **parabola** is defined as a set of points in a plane that are an equal distance from a fixed point, the **focus**, and a fixed line, the **directrix**.

The **focus** is the point at $(0, p)$.

Vertical **parabolas** are in the form $y = \frac{1}{4p}x^2$.

The **directrix** is the line at $y = -p$.

For a vertical parabola, when $p > 0$, the parabola opens upward.

When $p < 0$, the parabola opens downward.

Answer each question.

1. $y = \frac{1}{32}x^2$
   a. How can you determine in which direction the parabola opens?
   Possible answer: From the equation, $\frac{1}{4p} = \frac{1}{32}$, so $p = 8$. Because p is positive, the parabola opens upward.
   b. What is the focus of the parabola? $(0, 8)$
   c. What is the directrix of the parabola? $y = -8$
2. $y = -\frac{1}{48}x^2$
   a. What is the value of p for this parabola? $p = -12$
   b. What is the focus of the parabola? $(0, -12)$
   c. What is the directrix of the parabola? $y = 12$
3. Explain the relationship between the focus and the directrix.
   Possible answer: The distance from the focus to the vertex of the parabola is the same as the distance from the vertex of the parabola to a point on the directrix. Both are based on the parameter p.
4. The standard equation for a horizontal parabola is $x = \frac{1}{4p}y^2$. How can you determine which direction the parabola opens?
   If $p > 0$, the parabola opens to the right; if $p < 0$, the parabola opens to the left.

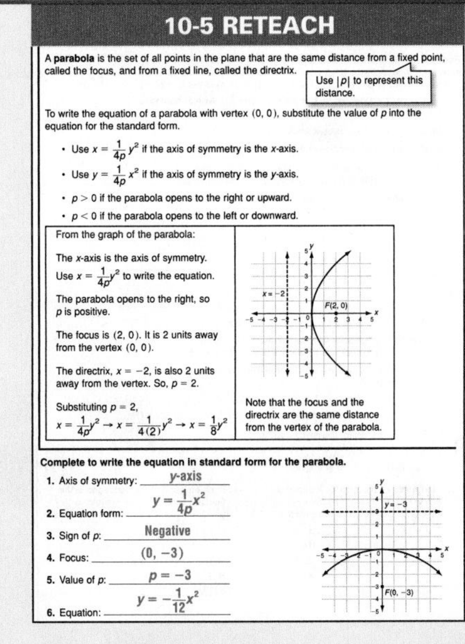

10-5 RETEACH

A **parabola** is the set of all points in the plane that are the same distance from a fixed point, called the focus, and from a fixed line, called the directrix.

Use $|p|$ to represent this distance.

To write the equation of a parabola with vertex $(0, 0)$, substitute the value of p into the equation for the standard form.

- Use $x = \frac{1}{4p}y^2$ if the axis of symmetry is the x-axis.
- Use $y = \frac{1}{4p}x^2$ if the axis of symmetry is the y-axis.
- $p > 0$ if the parabola opens to the right or upward.
- $p < 0$ if the parabola opens to the left or downward.

From the graph of the parabola:

The x-axis is the axis of symmetry. Use $x = \frac{1}{4p}y^2$ to write the equation.

The parabola opens to the right, so p is positive.

The focus is $(2, 0)$. It is 2 units away from the vertex $(0, 0)$.

The directrix, $x = -2$, is also 2 units away from the vertex. So, $p = 2$.

Substituting $p = 2$,
$x = \frac{1}{4p}y^2 \rightarrow x = \frac{1}{4(2)}y^2 \rightarrow x = \frac{1}{8}y^2$

Note that the focus and the directrix are the same distance from the vertex of the parabola.

Complete to write the equation in standard form for the parabola.

1. Axis of symmetry: y-axis
2. Equation form: $y = \frac{1}{4p}x^2$
3. Sign of p: Negative
4. Focus: $(0, -3)$
5. Value of p: $p = -3$
6. Equation: $y = -\frac{1}{12}x^2$

10-5 Exercises

Assignment Guide

Assign *Guided Practice* exercises as necessary.

If you finished Examples **1–2**
Basic 14–21
Average 14–21, 48
Advanced 14–21, 48–49

If you finished Examples **1–4**
Basic 14–41, 43–47, 52–60
Average 13–49, 52–60
Advanced 13–60

Homework Quick Check
Quickly check key concepts.
Exercises: 14, 18, 20, 22

Answers

1. Possible answer: The parabola never crosses or touches its directrix. The minimum distance between a parabola and its directrix is p.

10. vertex: $(-2, 0)$; $p = 8$; axis of symmetry: $x = -2$; focus: $(-2, 8)$; directrix: $y = -8$

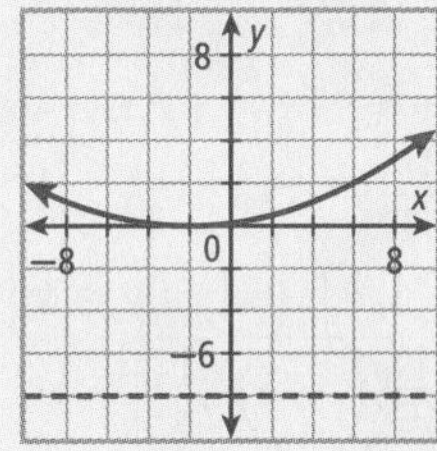

11, 12, 22–24. See p. A44.

State Resources

go.hrw.com
State Resources Online
KEYWORD: MB7 Resources

Math Background Although the cables of a suspension bridge form a parabola, as in **Exercise 26,** this is because they are supporting the weight of the bridge deck in addition to their own weight. If such a cable had no weight attached and was just hanging from its two ends, it would not form a parabola, but rather a similar curve called a *catenary.* The famous Gateway Arch in St. Louis is an inverted catenary.

Inclusion In **Exercises 27** and **28,** help students see that a parabola that opens upward or downward has a domain of all real numbers. A parabola that opens left or right has a range of all real numbers.

MULTI-STEP TEST PREP **Exercise 37** involves working with the equation for a parabola. This exercise prepares students for the Multi-Step Test Prep on page 758.

Answers

25. Possible answer: $y = \frac{1}{36}x^2$

27. $y + 6 = -\frac{1}{12}(x - 2)^2$; D: $\{x \mid x \in \mathbb{R}\}$; R: $\{y \mid y \le -6\}$

28. $x + 4 = \frac{1}{24}(y - 3)^2$; D: $\{x \mid x \ge -4\}$; R: $\{y \mid y \in \mathbb{R}\}$

29. $x + 7 = \frac{1}{36}(y + 3)^2$; D: $\{x \mid x \ge -7\}$; R: $\{y \mid y \in \mathbb{R}\}$

30. $y + 2 = -\frac{1}{24}(x - 5)^2$; D: $\{x \mid x \in \mathbb{R}\}$; R: $\{y \mid y \le -2\}$

31–34. See p. A44.

Engineering

The Akashi-Kaikyo Bridge is the longest suspension bridge in the world with a main span of 1991 m. Also known as the Pearl Bridge, it connects the Kobe region of Japan to Awaji Island.

25. **Communications** Find an equation for a cross section of a parabolic microphone whose feedhorn is 9 inches long if the end of the feedhorn is placed at the origin.

26. **Engineering** The main cables of a suspension bridge are ideally parabolic. The cables over a bridge that is 400 feet long are attached to towers that are 100 feet tall. The lowest point of the cable is 40 feet above the bridge.

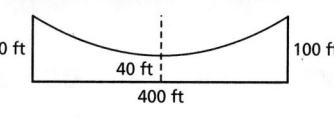

100 ft | 40 ft | 100 ft | 400 ft

   a. Find the coordinates of the vertex and the tops of the towers if the bridge represents the x-axis and the axis of symmetry is the y-axis. $(0, 40)$; $(\pm 200, 100)$
   b. Find an equation that can be used to model the cables. $y - 40 = 0.0015x^2$

Write the equation in standard form for each parabola, and give the domain and range. (*Hint:* Find the domain and range by using the vertex and the direction that the parabola opens.)

27. 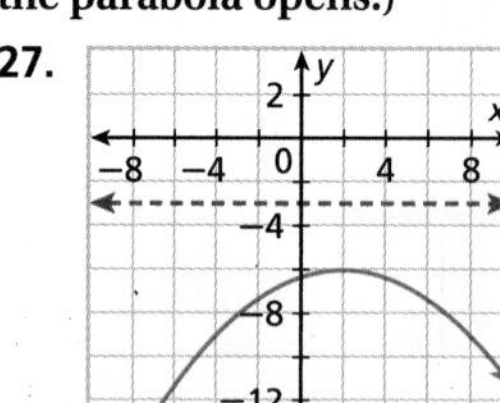

28. 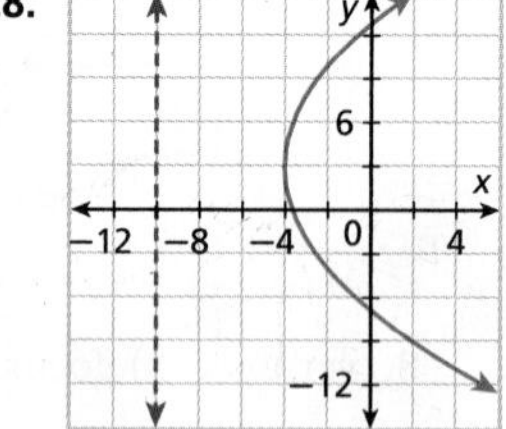

29. vertex $(-7, -3)$, focus $(2, -3)$
30. vertex $(5, -2)$, focus $(5, -8)$
31. focus $(0, 0)$, directrix $y = 10$
32. focus $(2, 6)$, directrix $y = -8$
33. focus $(4, -5)$, directrix $x = 12$
34. focus $(-3, 1)$, directrix $x = -15$

35. **Engineering** A spotlight has parabolic cross sections.
   a. Write an equation for a cross section of the spotlight if the bulb is 5 inches from the vertex and the vertex is placed at the origin.
   b. Write an equation for a cross section of the spotlight if the bulb is 4 inches from the vertex and the bulb is placed at the origin.
   c. If the spotlight has a diameter of 24 inches at its opening, find the depth of the spotlight if the bulb is 5 inches from the vertex. 7.2 in.

35a. Possible answer: $y = \frac{1}{20}x^2$

b. Possible answer: $y + 4 = \frac{1}{16}x^2$

36. **Sports** When a football is kicked, the path that the ball travels can be modeled by a parabola. $y - 8 = -0.0128(x - 25)^2$
   a. A placekicker kicks a football, which reaches a maximum height of 8 yards and lands 50 yards away. Assuming that the football was at the origin when it was kicked, write an equation for the height of the football.
   b. **What if...?** If the placekicker was trying to kick the ball over a 10-foot-high goalpost 40 yards away, was the football high enough to go over the goalpost? Explain. Yes; at 40 yd, the ball has a height of 5.12 yd, which is greater than 10 ft.

37. This problem will prepare you for the Multi-Step Test Prep on page 758.
The path of a comet is modeled by the parabola $y = -\frac{1}{532}(x + 96)^2 + 174$, where each unit of the coordinate plane represents 1 million kilometers. $(-96, 41)$
   a. The Sun is at the focus of the parabolic path. Find the coordinates of the Sun.
   b. How close does the comet come to the Sun? 133 million km
   c. What are the coordinates of the comet when it is at its closest point to the Sun? $(-96, 174)$

10-5 PRACTICE A

10-5 PRACTICE C

10-5 PRACTICE B

Use the Distance Formula to find the equation of a parabola with the given focus and directrix.

1. $F(6, 0)$, $x = -3$ $x = \frac{1}{18}y^2 + \frac{3}{2}$
2. $F(1, 0)$, $x = -4$ $x = 0.1y - 1.5$

Write the equation in standard form for each parabola.

3. Vertex $(0, 0)$, directrix $y = -2$ $y = \frac{1}{8}x^2$
4. Vertex $(0, 0)$, focus $(9, 0)$ $x = \frac{1}{36}y^2$
5. Focus $(-6, 0)$, directrix $x = 6$ $x = -\frac{1}{24}y^2$
6. Vertex $(0, 0)$, focus $(0, -3)$ $y = -\frac{1}{12}x^2$

Find the vertex, value of p, axis of symmetry, focus, and directrix of each parabola. Then graph.

7. $x - 1 = -\frac{1}{12}y^2$ Vertex $(1, 0)$; $p = -3$; axis of symmetry $y = 0$; focus $(-2, 0)$; directrix $x = 4$
8. $y + 2 = \frac{1}{4}(x - 1)^2$ Vertex $(1, -2)$; $p = 1$; axis of symmetry $x = 1$; focus $(1, -1)$; directrix $y = -3$

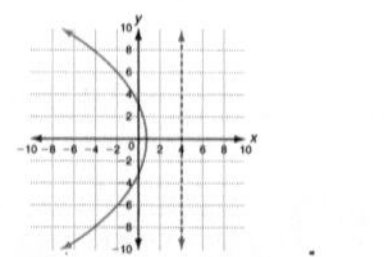

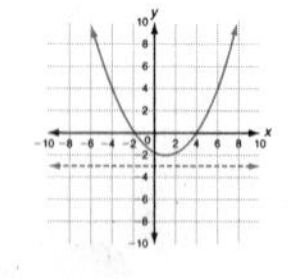

Solve.

9. A spotlight has parabolic cross sections.
   a. Write an equation for a cross section of the spotlight if the bulb is 6 inches from the vertex and the vertex is placed at the origin. $y = \frac{1}{24}x^2$
   b. If the spotlight has a diameter of 36 inches at its opening, find the depth of the spotlight if the bulb is 6 inches from the vertex. 13.5 inches

10-5 PROBLEM SOLVING

Rodrigo and Juan are constructing a model of the mirror grid in the solar wind concentrator used during the Genesis space mission to collect charged solar particles. They know that a cross section of the mirror grid can be modeled by the equation $y = \frac{x^2}{80}$, with dimensions in centimeters.

1. Draw a graph of the cross-sectional shape of the mirror grid.
   a. What are the coordinates of the vertex of the parabola? $(0, 0)$
   b. Find the distance, p, from the vertex to both the focus and the directrix of the parabola. Write an equation for p. $4p = 80$, $p = 20$
   c. Write an equation to represent the axis of symmetry. $x = 0$
   d. Find the coordinates of the focus. $(0, 20)$
   e. Write an equation to represent the directrix. $y = -20$
   f. Sketch a graph of the cross section of the mirror grid including the focus and the directrix.

2. Juan wants to construct a different parabolic mirror grid. He changes the focus to $(0, 5)$ and the directrix to $y = -5$.
   a. Explain why you can use the Distance Formula to find the equation for this parabola. Possible answer: A parabola is the set of points in a plane that are equidistant from the focus and the directrix.
   b. Find the equation for the new parabola. $y = \frac{1}{20}x^2$

Choose the letter for the best answer.

3. Juan writes an equation for a parabola with vertex $(0, 0)$ and directrix $x = -4$. Which equation could he have written?
   (A) $x = \frac{y^2}{16}$
   C $y = \frac{x^2}{16}$
   B $x = \frac{y^2}{4}$
   D $y = \frac{x^2}{4}$

4. If the equation of the mirror grid in the Genesis solar wind concentrator is $y - 2 = \frac{1}{15}(x - 3)^2$, where is the vertex of the parabola?
   F $(2, 3)$
   G $(2, -3)$
   H $(-3, 2)$
   (J) $(3, 2)$

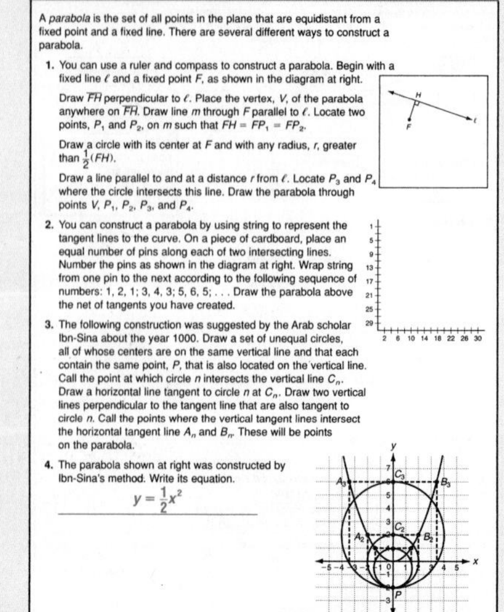

10-5 CHALLENGE

A *parabola* is the set of all points in the plane that are equidistant from a fixed point and a fixed line. There are several different ways to construct a parabola.

1. You can use a ruler and compass to construct a parabola. Begin with a fixed line ℓ and a fixed point F, as shown in the diagram at right.
Draw $\overline{FH}$ perpendicular to ℓ. Place the vertex, V, of the parabola anywhere on $\overline{FH}$. Draw line m through F parallel to ℓ. Locate two points, P_1 and P_2, on m such that $FH = FP_1 = FP_2$.
Draw a circle with its center at F and with any radius, r, greater than $\frac{1}{2}(FH)$.
Draw a line parallel to and at a distance r from ℓ. Locate P_3 and P_4 where the circle intersects this line. Draw the parabola through points V, P_1, P_2, P_3, and P_4.

2. You can construct a parabola by using string to represent the tangent lines to the curve. On a piece of cardboard, place an equal number of pins along each of two intersecting lines. Number the pins as shown in the diagram at right. Wrap string from one pin to the next according to the following sequence of numbers: 1, 2, 1; 3, 4, 3; 5, 6, 5; . . . Draw the parabola above the net of tangents you have created.

3. The following construction was suggested by the Arab scholar Ibn-Sina about the year 1000. Draw a set of unequal circles, all of whose centers are on the same vertical line and that each contain the same point, P, that is also located on the vertical line. Call the point at which circle n intersects the vertical line C_n. Draw a horizontal line tangent to circle n at C_n. Draw two vertical lines perpendicular to the tangent line that are also tangent to circle n. Call the points where the vertical tangent lines intersect the horizontal tangent line A_n and B_n. These will be points on the parabola.

4. The parabola shown at right was constructed by Ibn-Sina's method. Write its equation. $y = \frac{1}{2}x^2$

Graph each equation. Identify the vertex, value of p, axis of symmetry, focus, and directrix for each equation.

38. $20(y-2) = (x+6)^2$

39. $y = -2(x+4)^2 + 5$

40. $(y+7)^2 = \frac{x}{16}$

41. $x + 3 = \frac{1}{8}(y-2)^2$

42. **Critical Thinking** Find the distance d from the focus to the points on the parabola that are on the line perpendicular to the axis of symmetry and through the focus. Explain your answer.

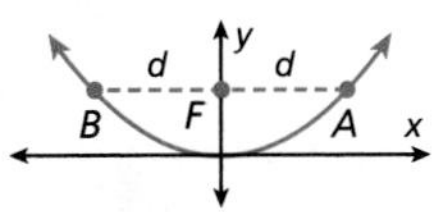

43. **Write About It** Explain how changing the value of p will affect the vertex, focus, and directrix of the parabola $y - k = \frac{1}{4p}(x-h)^2$.
Possible answer: The value of p does not affect the vertex, but it determines the distance between the vertex and the directrix or focus.

44. The graph of which of the following parabolas opens to the left?
Ⓐ $16y - 4x^2 = 12$ Ⓑ $16y + 4x^2 = 12$ Ⓒ $16x - 4y^2 = 12$ **Ⓓ** $16x + 4y^2 = 12$

45. Which of the following is the axis of symmetry for the graph of $x - 4 = \frac{1}{8}(y+2)^2$?
Ⓕ $x = 0$ **Ⓖ** $y = -2$ Ⓗ $x = 4$ Ⓙ $y = 8$

46. Which of the following graphs has the directrix $y = 4$?
Ⓐ $y + 3 = \frac{1}{4}(x-1)^2$
Ⓒ $x - 5 = \frac{1}{4}(y+4)^2$
Ⓑ $y - 5 = \frac{1}{4}(x+2)^2$
Ⓓ $x + 3 = \frac{1}{4}(y-2)^2$

47. **Short Response** What are the coordinates of the focus for the graph of $x - 3 = \frac{1}{16}y^2$? **(7, 0)**

49. $y - 7 = -\frac{1}{8}(x-6)^2$ or $y - 3 = \frac{1}{8}(x-6)^2$

CHALLENGE AND EXTEND

Write the equation in standard form for each parabola.

48. vertex (6, 8), contains the point (4, −2), axis of symmetry $x = 6$ **$y - 8 = -\frac{5}{2}(x-6)^2$**

49. focus (6, 5), axis of symmetry $x = 6$, contains the point (10, 5)

Multi-Step The latus rectum of a parabola is the line segment perpendicular to the axis of symmetry through the focus, with endpoints on the parabola. Find the length of the latus rectum of each parabola.

50. $y = \frac{1}{8}x^2$ **8**

51. $y - k = \frac{1}{4p}(x-h)^2$ **4p**

SPIRAL REVIEW

52. Write and graph a system of linear inequalities whose solution region is the triangle given by the vertices (0, 2), (1, 4), and (2, 1). *(Lesson 3-3)*

Find the inverse of each function. Tell whether the inverse is a function, and state its domain and range. *(Lesson 9-5)*

53. $f(x) = 4x + 22$

54. $f(x) = 3x^2 + 1$

55. $f(x) = \frac{x-2}{3}$

56. $f(x) = \frac{1}{x-1}$

Find the vertices, co-vertices, and asymptotes of each hyperbola, and then graph. *(Lesson 10-4)*

57. $\frac{x^2}{81} - \frac{y^2}{25} = 1$

58. $\frac{y^2}{9} - \frac{x^2}{16} = 1$

59. $\frac{y^2}{64} - \frac{x^2}{4} = 1$

60. $\frac{x^2}{49} - \frac{y^2}{36} = 1$

TEST PREP DOCTOR If students have difficulty with **Exercise 46,** encourage them to use the process of elimination. Because the directrix is a horizontal line, the graph must open up or down and choices **C** and **D** are excluded. Choice **A** has its vertex below the directrix and opens up and may also be excluded.

Journal

Have students describe their method for graphing a parabola when given its equation. Also have students describe how the value of c affects the graph.

ALTERNATIVE ASSESSMENT

Have students write a guide on how to find all of the relevant information about and graph a parabola given its equation. Have them include explanations of how to find the vertex, focus, directrix, p-value, and axis of symmetry.

Power Presentations with PowerPoint®

10-5 Lesson Quiz

1. Write an equation for the parabola with focus $F(0, 0)$ and directrix $y = 1$.
$y - \frac{1}{2} = -\frac{1}{2}x^2$

2. Find the vertex, value of p, axis of symmetry, focus, and directrix of the parabola $y - 2 = \frac{1}{12}(x-4)^2$, then graph.
vertex: (4, 2); focus: (4, 5); directrix: $y = -1$; $p = 3$; axis of symmetry: $x = 4$

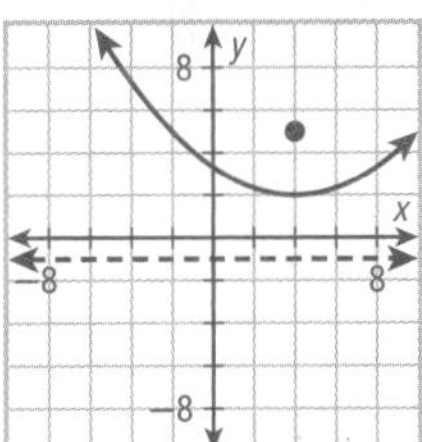

Also available on transparency

Answers

38. vertex: (−6, 2); $p = 5$; axis of symmetry: $x = -6$; focus: (−6, 7); directrix: $y = -3$

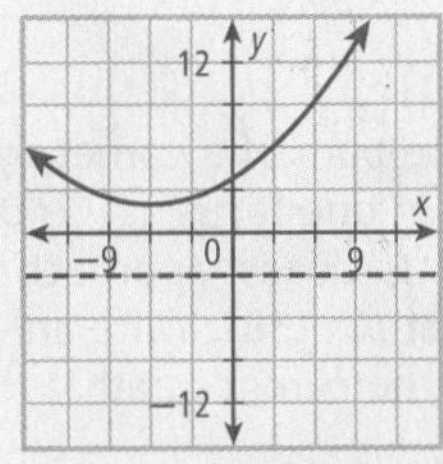

39. vertex: (−4, 5); $p = -\frac{1}{8}$; axis of symmetry: $x = -4$; focus: $\left(-4, 4\frac{7}{8}\right)$; directrix: $y = 5\frac{1}{8}$

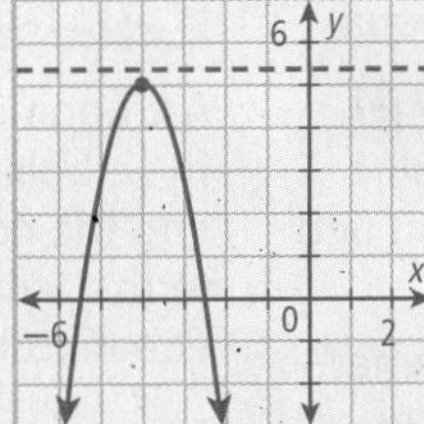

40. vertex: (0, −7); $p = \frac{1}{64}$; axis of symmetry: $y = -7$; focus: $\left(\frac{1}{64}, -7\right)$; directrix: $x = -\frac{1}{64}$

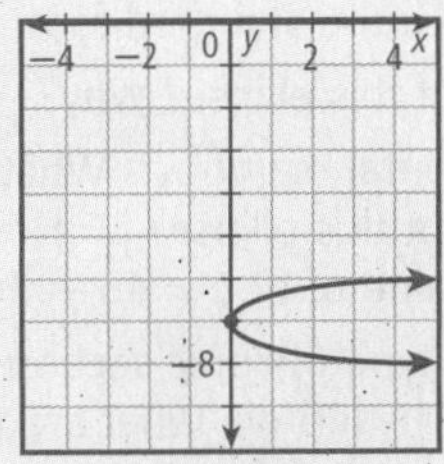

41, 42, 52–60. See p. A44.

Organizer

Objective: Assess students' ability to apply concepts and skills in Lessons 10-1 through 10-5 in a real-world format.

Online Edition

Resources

Algebra II Assessments

www.mathtekstoolkit.org

For additional assessment activities, see www.utdanacenter.org.

Problem	Text Reference
1	Lesson 10-2
2-3	Lesson 10-3
4	Lesson 10-4
5	Lesson 10-5

State Resources

go.hrw.com
State Resources Online
KEYWORD: MB7 Resources

CHAPTER 10

MULTI-STEP TEST PREP

SECTION 10A

Understanding Conic Sections

The Solar System Johannes Kepler (1571–1630) is generally credited as the first astronomer to recognize the role of the conic sections in describing our solar system. Kepler's first law of planetary motion states that the path of every planet is an ellipse with the Sun at one focus.

1. Although the orbit of Earth around the Sun is elliptical, it very closely resembles a circle. The orbit can be modeled by $x^2 + y^2 = 8649$, where the Sun is at the origin and each unit of the coordinate plane represents 1 million miles. How far does Earth travel in 1 year as it makes one complete orbit? **584.3 million mi**

2. The figure shows the elliptical orbit of Mercury, whose minimum distance to the Sun is 29 million miles and whose maximum distance to the Sun is 43 million miles. According to Kepler's laws, the average distance of a planet to the Sun is equal to half the length of the orbit's major axis. What is the average distance of Mercury to the Sun? **36 million mi**

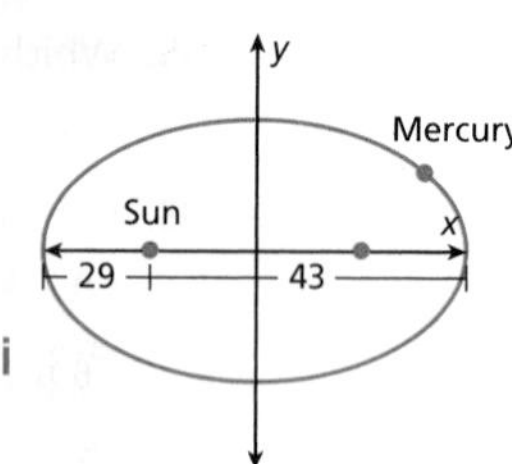

3. Write an equation that models the orbit of Mercury. $\frac{x^2}{1296} + \frac{y^2}{1247} = 1$

4. A comet that passes through the solar system just once has a path that is modeled by a hyperbola or a parabola. Astronomers discover a comet whose path is modeled by $\frac{x^2}{2500} - \frac{y^2}{37{,}500} = 1$, with the Sun at one focus. How close will the comet come to the Sun? **150 million mi**

5. The path of another comet is modeled by $336(x - 89) = (y - 62)^2$, with the Sun at the focus. In this model, what are the coordinates of the Sun? How close will this comet come to the Sun? **(173,62); 84 million mi**

INTERVENTION

Scaffolding Questions

1. What is the radius of the circular orbit? 93
2. What is the length of the major axis of the ellipse? 72
3. What is the standard form for the equation of this ellipse? Why? $\frac{x^2}{a^2} + \frac{y^2}{b^2} = 1$; horizontal major axis What is the value of a for this ellipse? 36 How can you find the value of c? $c = 43 - 36 = 7$
4. What type of conic section is the comet's path? hyperbola What are the vertices of the hyperbola? $(\pm 50, 0)$ How can you find the coordinates of the foci? Use $c^2 = a^2 + b^2$.
5. What type of conic section is this comet's path? parabola What is the vertex? (89, 62) How can you find the value of p? $p = 336 \div 4 = 84$

Extension

Astronomers model the path of a comet by a hyperbola. The Sun is at one focus, (0, 240), and the comet makes its closest approach to the Sun when it is at (0, 138). Write an equation that models the comet's path.

$$\frac{y^2}{19{,}044} - \frac{x^2}{38{,}556} = 1$$

READY TO GO ON?

CHAPTER 10

SECTION 10A

Quiz for Lessons 10-1 Through 10-5

10-1 Introduction to Conic Sections

1. The delivery area of a furniture store extends to the locations $(-7, 12)$ and $(5, -4)$. Write an equation for the delivery area of the store if a line between the locations represents a diameter of the delivery area. $(x+1)^2 + (y-4)^2 = 100$

Identify and describe each conic section.

2. $\frac{(x+2)^2}{64} + \frac{(y-8)^2}{64} = 1$
3. $25x^2 + 36y^2 = 900$
4. $x = \frac{y^2}{3} + 2$
5. $\frac{y^2}{25} - \frac{x^2}{25} = 1$

2. circle; center: $(-2, 8)$; radius $r = 8$ 3. ellipse; center: $(0, 0)$; vertices: $(\pm 6, 0)$; co-vertices $(0, \pm 5)$ 4. parabola; opens right; vertex $(2, 0)$ 5. hyperbola; opens vertically; center: $(0, 0)$; vertices: $(0, \pm 5)$

10-2 Circles

Write the equation of each circle.

6. center $(-3, 7)$ and radius $r = 12$ $(x+3)^2 + (y-7)^2 = 144$
7. center $(4, -2)$ and containing the point $(-4, 13)$ $(x-4)^2 + (y+2)^2 = 289$
8. Write the equation of the line that is tangent to $x^2 + y^2 = 225$ at $(9, -12)$. $y + 12 = \frac{3}{4}(x-9)$

10-3 Ellipses

Find the center, vertices, co-vertices, and foci of each ellipse. Then graph.

9. $\frac{x^2}{81} + \frac{y^2}{100} = 1$
10. $4(x-2)^2 + 16(y+3)^2 = 64$
11. Write the equation of the ellipse with center $(3, 5)$, vertex $(-10, 5)$, and focus $(8, 5)$. $\frac{(x-3)^2}{169} + \frac{(y-5)^2}{144} = 1$
12. A semi-elliptical bridge over a stream that is 30 feet wide must be 12 feet high at its highest point to accommodate boat traffic. Write an equation for a cross section of the bridge. $\frac{x^2}{225} + \frac{y^2}{144} = 1$

10-4 Hyperbolas

Find the center, vertices, co-vertices, foci, and asymptotes for each hyperbola. Then graph.

13. $\frac{y^2}{49} - \frac{x^2}{25} = 1$
14. $\frac{(x-5)^2}{36} - \frac{(y+3)^2}{9} = 1$
15. Write the equation of the hyperbola with vertices $(2, 3)$ and $(2, 9)$ and co-vertex $(7, 6)$. $\frac{(y-6)^2}{9} - \frac{(x-2)^2}{25} = 1$

10-5 Parabolas

Find the vertex, value of p, axis of symmetry, focus, and directrix for each parabola. Then graph.

16. $x = -\frac{1}{12}y^2$
17. $y = 2(x+3)^2 + 4$
18. Write the equation of the parabola with focus $(5, 2)$ and directrix $x = 1$. $x = \frac{1}{8}(y-2)^2 + 3$
19. A cross section of a parabolic microphone has the equation $35x = y^2$, where x and y are measured in inches. How far from the vertex of the microphone should the feedhorn be placed? 8.75 in.

READY TO GO ON? SECTION 10A

Organizer

Objective: Assess students' mastery of concepts and skills in Lessons 10-1 through 10-5.

Resources

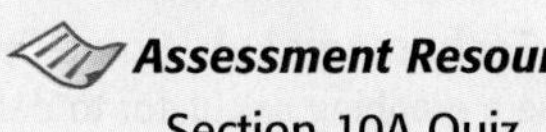

Assessment Resources

Section 10A Quiz

Test & Practice Generator
One-Stop Planner®

INTERVENTION

Resources

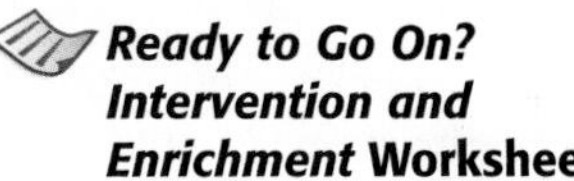

Ready to Go On? Intervention and Enrichment Worksheets

Ready to Go On? CD-ROM

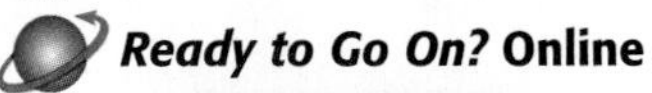

Ready to Go On? Online

my.hrw.com

Answers

9, 10, 13, 14, 16, 17. See p. A45.

READY TO GO ON? Diagnose and Prescribe

NO INTERVENE

Ready to Go On? Intervention	*Ready to Go On? Intervention,* Section 10A Worksheets	CD-ROM	Online
Lesson 10-1	10-1 Intervention	Activity 10-1	Diagnose and Prescribe Online
Lesson 10-2	10-2 Intervention	Activity 10-2	
Lesson 10-3	10-3 Intervention	Activity 10-3	
Lesson 10-4	10-4 Intervention	Activity 10-4	
Lesson 10-5	10-5 Intervention	Activity 10-5	

YES ENRICH

Ready to Go On? Enrichment, Section 10A
Worksheets
CD-ROM
Online

SECTION **10B**

Applying Conic Sections

One-Minute Section Planner

Lesson	Lab Resources	Materials
Lesson 10-6 Identifying Conic Sections • Identify and transform conic sections. • Use the method of completing the square to identify and graph conic sections. ☑ SAT-10 ☐ NAEP ☐ ACT ☐ SAT ☑ SAT Subject Tests		**Optional** graphing calculator
10-6 Technology Lab Conic-Section Art • Use a graphing calculator to design and create conic-section art. ☐ SAT-10 ☐ NAEP ☐ ACT ☐ SAT ☐ SAT Subject Tests	***Technology Lab Activities*** 10-6 Lab Recording Sheet	**Required** graphing calculator **Optional** graphing paper
Lesson 10-7 Solving Nonlinear Systems • Solve systems of equations in two variables that contain at least one second-degree equation. ☐ SAT-10 ☐ NAEP ☐ ACT ☐ SAT ☐ SAT Subject Tests		**Required** graphing calculator

MK = *Manipulatives Kit*

Section Overview

Identifying Conic Sections

Lesson 10-6

Identifying the conic section described by an equation that models a real-world scenario helps understand the nature of the phenomena.

Classifying Conic Sections	
For an equation of the **general form** $Ax^2 + Bxy + Cy^2 + Dx + Ey + F = 0$ (A, B, and C do not all equal 0).	
Conic Section	**Coefficients**
Circle	$B^2 - 4AC < 0$, $B = 0$, and $A = C$
Ellipse	$B^2 - 4AC < 0$ and either $B \neq 0$ or $A \neq C$
Hyperbola	$B^2 - 4AC > 0$
Parabola	$B^2 - 4AC = 0$

Solving Nonlinear Systems

Lesson 10-7

In many real-world situations, one or more equations in a system may be nonlinear.

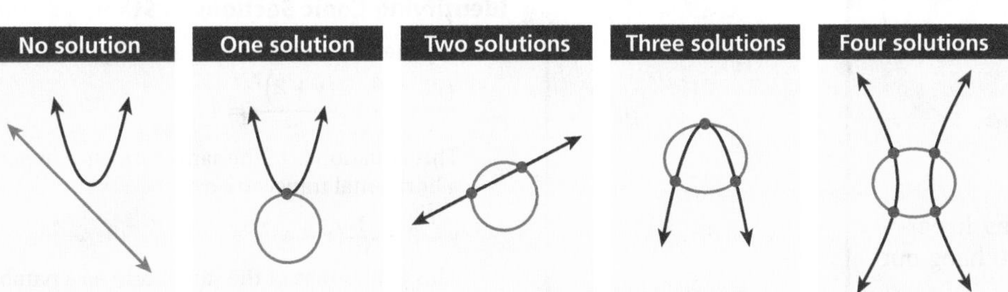

Solve $\begin{cases} y = \frac{1}{2}x^2 + 3 \\ x^2 + y^2 = 9 \end{cases}$ **by graphing.**

Use the intersect feature of your graphing calculator.

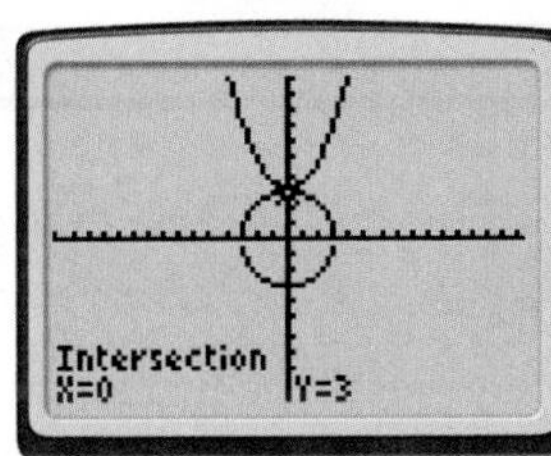

The solution is $(0, 3)$.

Solve $\begin{cases} x^2 - y^2 = 18 \\ 2x^2 + y^2 = 36 \end{cases}$ **by elimination.**

Step 1 Eliminate y.

$$\begin{array}{rl} x^2 - y^2 &= 18 \\ 2x^2 + y^2 &= 36 \\ \hline 3x^2 \qquad &= 54 \longrightarrow x^2 = 18, \text{ or } x = \pm 3\sqrt{2} \end{array}$$

Step 2 Substitute 18 for x^2 in the second equation to find the values for y.

$$2x^2 + y^2 = 36$$
$$2 \cdot 18 + y^2 = 36$$
$$y = 0$$

The solutions are $(3\sqrt{2}, 0)$ and $(-3\sqrt{2}, 0)$.

10-6 Organizer

Pacing: Traditional 1 day
Block $\frac{1}{2}$ day

Objectives: Identify and transform conic sections.

Use the method of completing the square to identify and graph conic sections.

Online Edition
Graphing Calculator, Tutorial Videos, Interactivity

Countdown to Testing Week 22

Power Presentations with PowerPoint®

Warm Up

Solve by completing the square.

1. $x^2 + 6x = 91$ $\quad x = -13$ or 7
2. $2x^2 + 8x - 90 = 0$
   $x = -9$ or 5

Also available on transparency

Math Humor

Q: Where do circles, ellipses, hyperbolas, and parabolas like to hang out in the summer?

A: Coney Island

10-6 Identifying Conic Sections

Objectives
Identify and transform conic sections.

Use the method of completing the square to identify and graph conic sections.

Why learn this?
The path of an airplane in a dive can be modeled by a branch of a hyperbola or a parabola. (See Example 4.)

In Lessons 10-2 through 10-5, you learned about the four conic sections. Recall the equations of conic sections in standard form. In these forms, the characteristics of the conic sections can be identified.

Know it! Note

Standard Forms for the Conic Sections with Center (h, k)

Circle	$(x-h)^2 + (y-k)^2 = r^2$	
	HORIZONTAL AXIS	**VERTICAL AXIS**
Ellipse	$\frac{(x-h)^2}{a^2} + \frac{(y-k)^2}{b^2} = 1$	$\frac{(x-h)^2}{b^2} + \frac{(y-k)^2}{a^2} = 1$
Hyperbola	$\frac{(x-h)^2}{a^2} - \frac{(y-k)^2}{b^2} = 1$	$\frac{(y-k)^2}{a^2} - \frac{(x-h)^2}{b^2} = 1$
Parabola	$x - h = \frac{1}{4p}(y-k)^2$	$y - k = \frac{1}{4p}(x-h)^2$

EXAMPLE 1 Identifying Conic Sections in Standard Form

Identify the conic section that each equation represents.

A $\frac{(x-7)^2}{5^2} - \frac{(y+2)^2}{2^2} = 1$

This equation is of the same form as a hyperbola with a horizontal transverse axis.

B $y - 3 = \frac{1}{12}(x-4)^2$

This equation is of the same form as a parabola with a vertical axis of symmetry.

C $\frac{(x-1)^2}{8^2} + \frac{(y-1)^2}{10^2} = 1$

This equation is of the same form as an ellipse with a vertical major axis.

CHECK IT OUT! **Identify the conic section that each equation represents.**

1a. $x^2 + (y+14)^2 = 11^2$ circle

1b. $\frac{(y-6)^2}{2^2} - \frac{(x-1)^2}{21^2} = 1$ hyperbola

State Resources

go.hrw.com
State Resources Online
KEYWORD: MB7 Resources

1 Introduce

EXPLORATION

10-6 Identifying Conic Sections

The equation of any conic section can be written in the general form $Ax^2 + Bxy + Cy^2 + Dx + Ey + F = 0$.

1. Sketch the graph of $\frac{(x-2)^2}{9} - \frac{(y-1)^2}{25} = 1$.
2. What type of conic section is this?
3. To write the equation of the conic section in general form, first multiply both sides of the equation by 225 (the LCM of 9 and 25), as shown.
   $\frac{(x-2)^2}{9} - \frac{(y-1)^2}{25} = 1$
   $25(x-2)^2 - 9(y-1)^2 = 225$
   Now expand the binomials and simplify to write the equation in general form.
4. What are the values of  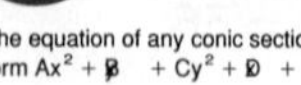 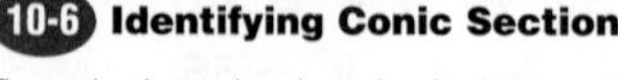 and F for this conic section?

THINK AND DISCUSS

5. **Explain** how to write the equation of the ellipse $\frac{(x-3)^2}{4} + \frac{(y+1)^2}{25} = 1$ in general form.
6. **Discuss** what type of conic section is represented

Motivate

Have students recall the two forms of a linear equation, point-slope and slope-intercept forms. One equation may have many different forms. Give an example of a conic section written in general form, such as $x^2 - y^2 - 4 = 0$. Ask students if they can determine which type of conic section it represents. hyperbola Make the connection to the standard form of the same hyperbola, $\frac{x^2}{4} - \frac{y^2}{4} = 1$.

Explorations and answers are provided in the *Explorations* binder.

Student to Student

Classifying Conic Sections

Mercedes Raya
Central High School

I can classify an equation in standard form just by looking. This is a good way for me to check my work.

Only one squared term →	*it's a parabola.*
A squared term minus a squared term →	*it's a hyperbola.*
A squared term plus a squared term →	*it's a circle or an ellipse.*

All conic sections can be written in the general form $Ax^2 + Bxy + Cy^2 + Dx + Ey + F = 0$. The conic section represented by an equation in general form can be determined by the coefficients.

Classifying Conic Sections

For an equation of the form $Ax^2 + Bxy + Cy^2 + Dx + Ey + F = 0$ (A, B, and C do not all equal 0.)

CONIC SECTION	COEFFICIENTS
Circle	$B^2 - 4AC < 0$, $B = 0$, and $A = C$
Ellipse	$B^2 - 4AC < 0$ and either $B \neq 0$ or $A \neq C$
Hyperbola	$B^2 - 4AC > 0$
Parabola	$B^2 - 4AC = 0$

EXAMPLE 2 Identifying Conic Sections in General Form

Identify the conic section that each equation represents.

A $6x^2 + 9y^2 + 12x - 15y - 25 = 0$

$A = 6, B = 0, C = 9$ — *Identify the values for A, B, and C.*

$B^2 - 4AC$

$0^2 - 4(6)(9)$ — *Substitute into $B^2 - 4AC$.*

-216 — *Simplify. The conic is either a circle or an ellipse.*

$A \neq C$ — *The conic is not a circle.*

Because $B^2 - 4AC < 0$ and $A \neq C$, the equation represents an ellipse.

B $4x^2 + 4xy + y^2 - 12x + 8y + 36 = 0$

$A = 4, B = 4, C = 1$ — *Identify the values for A, B, and C.*

$B^2 - 4AC$

$4^2 - 4(4)(1)$ — *Substitute into $B^2 - 4AC$.*

0 — *Simplify.*

Because $B^2 - 4AC = 0$, the equation represents a parabola.

CHECK IT OUT! **Identify the conic section that each equation represents.**

2a. $9x^2 + 9y^2 - 18x - 12y - 50 = 0$ **circle**

2b. $12x^2 + 24xy + 12y^2 + 25y = 0$ **parabola**

COMMON ERROR ALERT

Students may often think that any time a conic contains both x^2- and y^2-terms with positive coefficients, it must be a circle or ellipse. This is true only if there is no xy-term. When there is an xy-term, students must check the discriminant to identify the conic section.

Power Presentations with PowerPoint®

Additional Examples

Example 1

Identify the conic section that each equation represents.

A. $x + 4 = \frac{(y-2)^2}{10}$ parabola

B. $16(x-1)^2 = 144 + 9(y-2)^2$ hyperbola

C. $16(x-1)^2 = 81 - 16(y-2)^2$ circle

Example 2

Identify the conic section that each equation represents.

A. $4x^2 - 10xy + 5y^2 + 12x + 20y = 0$ hyperbola

B. $9x^2 - 12xy + 4y^2 + 6x - 8y = 0$ parabola

C. $8x^2 - 15xy + 6y^2 + x - 8y + 12 = 0$ hyperbola

Also available on transparency

INTERVENTION

Questioning Strategies

EXAMPLE 1

- How do you quickly distinguish between an ellipse and a circle?

EXAMPLE 2

- How do you quickly distinguish between an ellipse and a hyperbola?

2 Teach

Guided Instruction

First, review completing the square as a method for solving a quadratic equation. As you work with different equations in the form $Ax^2 + Bxy + Cy^2 + Dx + Ey + F = 0$, discuss with students ways to classify conic sections by observation of the equation, such as the ways given in the *Student to Student* feature.

Reaching All Learners

Through Cognitive Strategies

Students may notice that they have encountered the expression $B^2 - 4AC$ before, i.e., in the quadratic formula $\frac{-b \pm \sqrt{b^2 - 4ac}}{2a}$. The discriminant occurs in a wide variety of mathematical contexts but always characterizes properties of a quantity's roots. Have students compare and contrast the use of the discriminants for quadratics and conic sections.

Power Presentations with PowerPoint®

Additional Examples

Example 3

Find the standard form of each equation by completing the square. Then identify and graph each conic.

A. $x^2 + y^2 + 8x - 10y - 8 = 0$

$(x + 4)^2 + (y - 5)^2 = 49$; circle

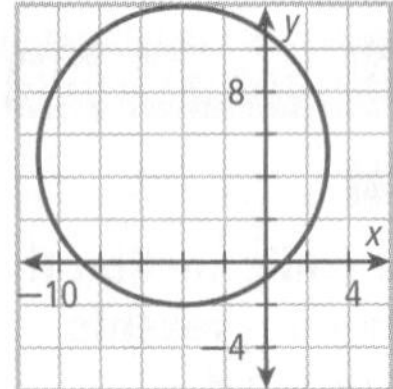

B. $5x^2 + 20y^2 + 30x + 40y - 15 = 0$

$\frac{(x + 3)^2}{16} + \frac{(y + 1)^2}{4} = 1$; ellipse

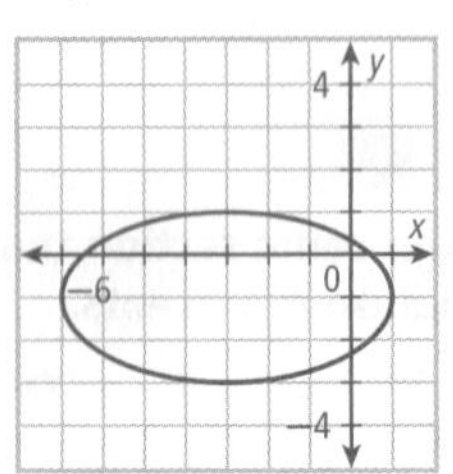

Also available on transparency

INTERVENTION

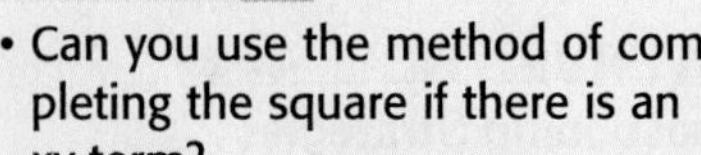

Questioning Strategies

EXAMPLE 3

- Can you use the method of completing the square if there is an xy-term?

Teaching Tip

Reading Math The *discriminant* allows you to *discriminate*, or classify, conic sections. Both words come from the Latin *discernere*, meaning "to distinguish between."

ENGLISH LANGUAGE LEARNERS

If you are given the equation of a conic in standard form, you can write the equation in general form by expanding the binomials.

If you are given the general form of a conic section, you can use the method of completing the square from Lesson 5-4 to write the equation in standard form.

EXAMPLE 3 Finding the Standard Form of the Equation for a Conic Section

Find the standard form of each equation by completing the square. Then identify and graph each conic.

A $x^2 - 12x - 16y + 36 = 0$

$x^2 - 12x + \blacksquare = 16y - 36 + \blacksquare$ *Prepare to complete the square in x.*

$x^2 - 12x + \left(\frac{-12}{2}\right)^2 = 16y - 36 + \left(\frac{-12}{2}\right)^2$ *Add $\left(-\frac{12}{2}\right)^2$, or 36, to both sides to complete the square.*

$(x - 6)^2 = 16y$ *Factor and simplify.*

$\frac{1}{16}(x - 6)^2 = y$ *Divide both sides by 16.*

$y = \frac{1}{16}(x - 6)^2$ *Rewrite in standard form.*

Because the conic is of the form $y - k = \frac{1}{4p}(x - h)^2$, it is a parabola with vertex $(6, 0)$ and $p = 4$, and it opens upward. The focus is $(6, 4)$ and the directrix is $y = -4$.

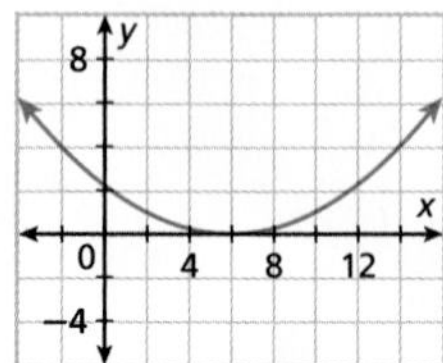

Remember!

You must factor out the leading coefficient of x^2 and y^2 before completing the square.

B $x^2 + 4y^2 + 4x - 24y + 36 = 0$

$x^2 + 4x + \blacksquare + 4y^2 - 24y + \blacksquare = -36 + \blacksquare + \blacksquare$ *Rearrange to prepare for completing the square in x and y.*

$x^2 + 4x + \blacksquare + 4(y^2 - 6y + \blacksquare) = -36 + \blacksquare + \blacksquare$ *Factor 4 from the y terms.*

$x^2 + 4x + \left(\frac{4}{2}\right)^2 + 4\left[y^2 - 6y + \left(-\frac{6}{2}\right)^2\right] = -36 + \left(\frac{4}{2}\right)^2 + 4\left(-\frac{6}{2}\right)^2$ *Complete both squares.*

$(x + 2)^2 + 4(y - 3)^2 = 4$ *Factor and simplify.*

$\frac{(x + 2)^2}{4} + \frac{(y - 3)^2}{1} = 1$ *Divide both sides by 4.*

Because the conic is of the form $\frac{(x - h)^2}{a^2} + \frac{(y - k)^2}{b^2} = 1$, it is an ellipse with center $(-2, 3)$, horizontal major axis length 4, and minor axis length 2. The co-vertices are $(-2, 4)$ and $(-2, 2)$, and the vertices are $(-4, 3)$ and $(0, 3)$.

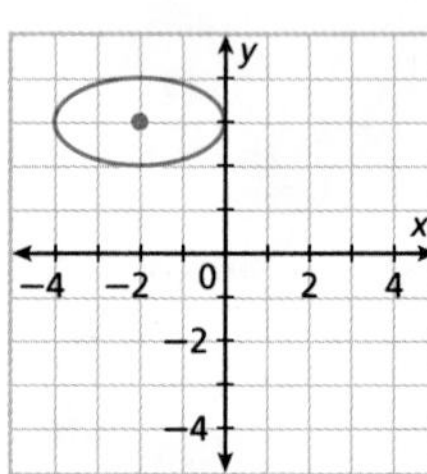

CHECK IT OUT! **Find the standard form of each equation by completing the square. Then identify and graph each conic.**

3a. $y^2 - 9x + 16y + 64 = 0$

3b. $16x^2 + 9y^2 - 128x + 108y + 436 = 0$

3a. $x = \frac{1}{9}(y + 8)^2$; parabola

3b. $\frac{(x - 4)^2}{9} + \frac{(y + 6)^2}{16} = 1$; ellipse

Answers

3a.

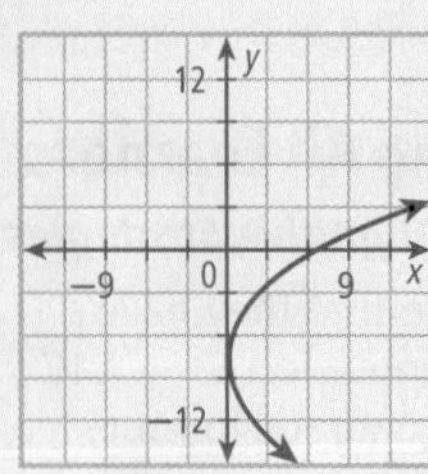

3b.

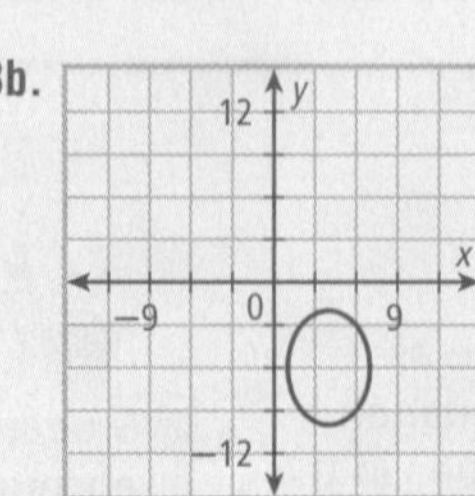

EXAMPLE 4 Aviation Application

At an air show, an airplane makes a dive that can be modeled by the equation $-4x^2 + 16y^2 - 16x + 32y - 64 = 0$, measured in hundreds of feet, with the ground represented by the x-axis. How close to the ground does the airplane pass?

The graph of $-4x^2 + 16y^2 - 16x + 32y - 64 = 0$ is a conic section. Write the equation in standard form.

$$-4x^2 - 16x + \blacksquare + 16y^2 + 32y + \blacksquare = 64 + \blacksquare + \blacksquare$$

Rearrange to prepare for completing the square in x and y.

$$-4\left(x^2 + 4x + \blacksquare\right) + 16\left(y^2 + 2y + \blacksquare\right) = 64 + \blacksquare + \blacksquare$$

Factor −4 from the x terms and 16 from the y terms.

$$-4\left[x^2 + 4x + \left(\frac{4}{2}\right)^2\right] + 16\left[y^2 + 2y + \left(\frac{2}{2}\right)^2\right] = 64 - 4\left(\frac{4}{2}\right)^2 + 16\left(\frac{2}{2}\right)^2$$

Complete both squares.

$16(y + 1)^2 - 4(x + 2)^2 = 64$ *Simplify.*

$\dfrac{(y + 1)^2}{4} - \dfrac{(x + 2)^2}{16} = 1$ *Divide both sides by 64.*

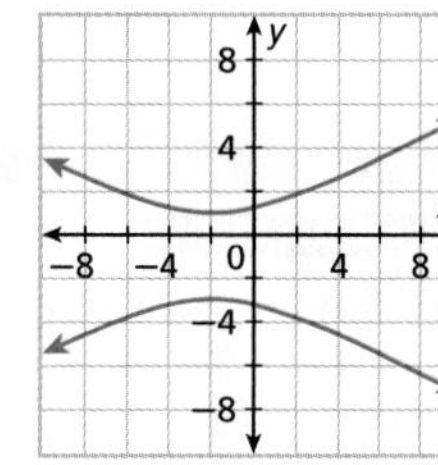

Because the conic is of the form $\dfrac{(y - k)^2}{a^2} - \dfrac{(x - h)^2}{b^2} = 1$, it is a hyperbola with vertical transverse axis length 4 and center $(-2, -1)$. The vertices are then $(-2, 1)$ and $(-2, -3)$. Because distance above ground is always positive, the airplane will be on the upper branch of the hyperbola. The relevant vertex is $(-2, 1)$ with y-coordinate 1.

The minimum height of the plane is 100 feet.

4. An airplane makes a dive that can be modeled by the equation $-16x^2 + 9y^2 + 96x + 36y - 252 = 0$, measured in hundreds of feet. How close to the ground does the airplane pass? **200 ft**

THINK AND DISCUSS

1. In the equation $Ax^2 + Bxy + Cy^2 + Dx + Ey + F = 0$, if $B = 0$, what must be true about either A or C for the equation to represent a parabola?

2. When solving by completing the square, what must be added to both sides of the equation if one side has $5x^2 - 30x$? Explain.

3. GET ORGANIZED Copy and complete the graphic organizer. Give an example of coefficients for each conic section in general form.

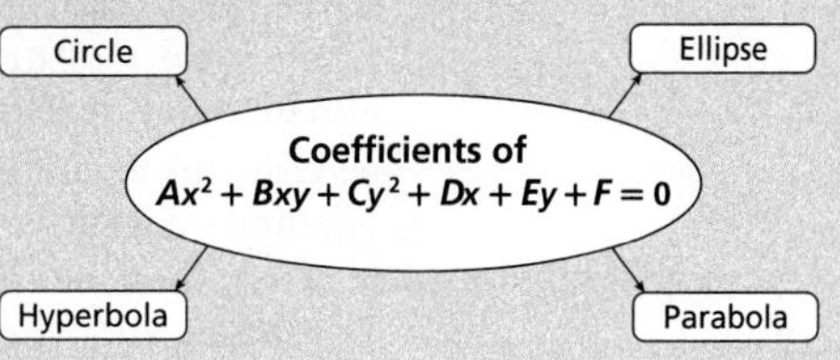

Power Presentations with PowerPoint®

Additional Examples

Example 4

An airplane makes a dive that can be modeled by the equation

$-9x^2 + 25y^2 + 18x + 50y - 209 = 0$

with dimensions in hundreds of feet. How close to the ground does the airplane pass?

200 feet

Also available on transparency

INTERVENTION Questioning Strategies

EXAMPLE 4

- Can you tell from looking at the equation whether the plane will crash into the ground? If so, how?
- What are the units for this problem, and how do they affect the final answer?

Teaching Tip **Visual** Have students create a flowchart for determining what kind of conic section is given by an equation in the form

$Ax^2 + Bxy + Cy^2 + Dx + Ey + F = 0.$

3 Close

Summarize

All conics and their transformations can be represented by the form

$Ax^2 + Bxy + Cy^2 + Dx + Ey + F = 0.$

Review with students how to recognize which conic is represented by a given equation, and put the equation into standard form so that it may be graphed.

ONGOING ASSESSMENT and INTERVENTION

***Diagnose Before* the Lesson**
10-6 Warm Up, TE p. 760

***Monitor During* the Lesson**
Check It Out! Exercises, SE pp. 760–763
Questioning Strategies, TE pp. 761–763

***Assess After* the Lesson**
10-6 Lesson Quiz, TE p. 766
Alternative Assessment, TE p. 766

Answers to *Think and Discuss*

1. Either A or C must equal 0.
2. 45; factor 5 from the terms and add 9 inside the parentheses to complete the square, the equivalent of adding $9 \cdot 5 = 45$.
3. See p. A12.

10-6 Exercises

Assignment Guide

Assign *Guided Practice* exercises as necessary.

If you finished Examples **1–2**
Basic 14–21
Average 14–21, 34
Advanced 14–21, 34–36

If you finished Examples **1–4**
Basic 14–41, 43–50, 55–61
Average 14–50, 55–61
Advanced 14–43, 46–61

Homework Quick Check
Quickly check key concepts.
Exercises: 16, 18, 22, 28, 30

Critical Thinking
For **Exercise 13,** pose the challenging question "Is the moth circling the light?"

Answers

9–12. For graphs, see p. A45.

9. $(x-8)^2+(y+5)^2=36$; circle

10. $y-4=\frac{1}{12}(x+7)^2$; parabola

11. $\frac{x^2}{9}+\frac{(y+4)^2}{25}=1$; ellipse

12. $\frac{(x+5)^2}{36}+\frac{(y-6)^2}{16}=1$; ellipse

22–23. For graphs, see p. A45.

22. $y=\frac{1}{4}(x+10)^2$; parabola

23. $x^2+(y-4)^2=49$; circle

24–31. See p. A45.

32a. $\frac{(x+17)^2}{64}+\frac{y^2}{225}=1$

State Resources

10-6 Exercises

go.hrw.com
Homework Help Online
KEYWORD: MB7 10-6
Parent Resources Online
KEYWORD: MB7 Parent

GUIDED PRACTICE

Identify the conic section that each equation represents.

SEE EXAMPLE 1 p. 760

1. $\frac{(x+4)^2}{2^2}+\frac{(y-3)^2}{3^2}=1$ **ellipse**
2. $\frac{(x-8)^2}{5^2}-\frac{y^2}{5^2}=1$ **hyperbola**
3. $y+9=4(x-1)^2$ **parabola**
4. $(x-2)^2+(y-6)^2=13^2$ **circle**

SEE EXAMPLE 2 p. 761

5. $12x^2+18y^2-8x+9y-10=0$ **ellipse**
6. $-4y^2+15x+12y-8=0$ **parabola**
7. $10x^2+15xy+10y^2+15x+25y+9=0$ **ellipse**
8. $6x^2=14x+12y^2-16y+20$ **hyperbola**

SEE EXAMPLE 3 p. 762

Find the standard form of each equation by completing the square. Then identify and graph each conic.

9. $x^2+y^2-16x+10y+53=0$
10. $x^2+14x-12y+97=0$
11. $25x^2+9y^2+72y-81=0$
12. $16x^2+36y^2+160x-432y+1120=0$

SEE EXAMPLE 4 p. 763

13. **Multi-Step** A moth is circling an outdoor light in a path that can be modeled by the equation $4x^2+9y^2-108y=-288$, measured in inches. How close does the moth pass to a lizard located at the origin? **4 in.**

PRACTICE AND PROBLEM SOLVING

Independent Practice	
For Exercises	See Example
14–17	1
18–21	2
22–31	3
32	4

Extra Practice
Skills Practice p. S23
Application Practice p. S41

Identify the conic section that each equation represents.

14. $\frac{(y-11)^2}{2^2}-\frac{(x+15)^2}{9^2}=1$ **hyperbola**
15. $x-4=\frac{1}{16}(y-3)^2$ **parabola**
16. $(x+2)^2+(y-4)^2=3^2$ **circle**
17. $\frac{(x+2)^2}{6^2}+\frac{(y-7)^2}{8^2}=1$ **ellipse**
18. $12x^2-18y^2-18x-12y+12=0$ **hyperbola**
19. $7x^2+28x-29y-16=0$ **parabola**
20. $-12x^2-3y^2+7x+9y-5=0$ **ellipse**
21. $12x^2+9y^2-2xy+9=8y-3y^2$ **ellipse**

Find the standard form of each equation by completing the square. Then identify and graph each conic.

22. $x^2+20x-4y+100=0$
23. $x^2+y^2-8y-33=0$
24. $9x^2+36y^2-72x-180=0$
25. $25x^2-4y^2-72y-424=0$
26. $x^2-2x-20y-79=0$
27. $x^2+y^2+10x+4y+9=0$
28. $64x^2+49y^2+256x-196y-2684=0$
29. $9x^2-4y^2+18x+56y-223=0$
30. $y^2+6x+12y-6=0$
31. $x^2+y^2-5x+9y+10.5=0$

32. **Astronomy** Scientists find that the path of a comet as it travels around the Sun can be modeled by the function $225x^2+64y^2+7650x+50{,}625=0$, with the Sun as one focus.
    a. Write the equation in standard form.
    b. If measurements are in millions of miles, about how close will the comet come to the sun? **about 2 million mi**

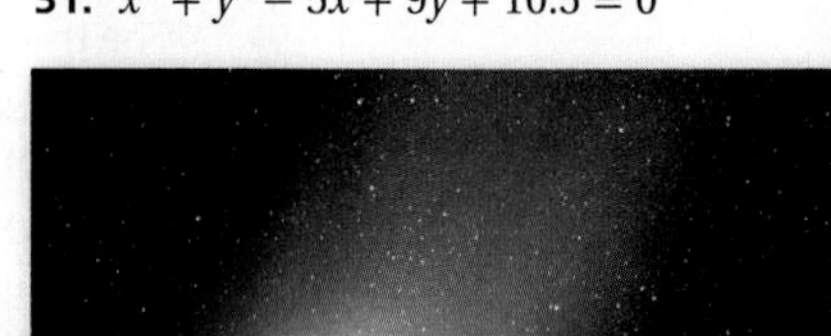

Comet C/2001 Q4

10-6 READING STRATEGIES

You can identify the different conic sections by looking at the standard form of their equations.

Conic	Standard Form	
	Horizontal	Vertical
Circle	$(x-h)^2+(y-k)^2=r^2$	
Ellipse	$\frac{(x-h)^2}{a^2}+\frac{(y-k)^2}{b^2}=1$	$\frac{(y-k)^2}{a^2}+\frac{(x-h)^2}{b^2}=1$
Hyperbola	$\frac{(x-h)^2}{a^2}-\frac{(y-k)^2}{b^2}=1$	$\frac{(y-k)^2}{a^2}-\frac{(x-h)^2}{b^2}=1$
Parabola	$x-h=\frac{1}{4p}(y-k)^2$	$y-k=\frac{1}{4p}(x-h)^2$

Answer each question.

1. What conclusion can you draw about a conic section equation that has just one squared term?
   The conic section is a parabola.
2. What conclusion can you draw about a conic section equation that is the difference of two squared terms?
   The conic section is a hyperbola.

Identify the conic section that each equation represents and explain your reasoning.

3. $x^2+(y+2)^2=4^2$ **Circle; sum of squared terms**
4. $\frac{(x-5)^2}{3^2}-\frac{(y+1)^2}{5^2}=1$ **Hyperbola; difference of squared terms**
5. $\frac{(x-4)^2}{6^2}+\frac{(y-7)^2}{5^2}=1$ **Ellipse; sum of squared terms, each of which has a divisor**
6. $(x-2)=\frac{1}{4}(y-3)^2$ **Parabola; only one squared term**
7. $\frac{(x+10)^2}{25}-\frac{(x-3)^2}{16}=1$ **Hyperbola; difference of squared terms**
8. $(x-7)^2+(y-1)^2=9$ **Circle; sum of squared terms**

10-6 RETEACH

Compare given equations of conic sections to equations in standard form to identify a conic section.

Standard Forms for Conic Sections with Center (h, k)		
Circle	$(x-h)^2+(y-k)^2=r^2$	
Ellipse	$\frac{(x-h)^2}{a^2}+\frac{(y-k)^2}{b^2}=1$	$\frac{(y-k)^2}{a^2}+\frac{(x-h)^2}{b^2}=1$
Hyperbola	$\frac{(x-h)^2}{a^2}-\frac{(y-k)^2}{b^2}=1$	$\frac{(y-k)^2}{a^2}-\frac{(x-h)^2}{b^2}=1$
Parabola	$x-h=\frac{1}{4p}(y-k)^2$	$y-k=\frac{1}{4p}(x-h)^2$

$\frac{(x-3)^2}{8^2}+\frac{(y+7)^2}{6^2}=1$ — Think: Sum of squared terms, coefficients of x^2 and y^2 will NOT be equal, with right side equal to 1. Ellipse

$(x+5)^2+(y-2)^2=9^2$ — Think: Sum of squared terms, coefficients of x^2 and y^2 will be equal, with right side NOT equal to 1. Circle

$\frac{(y-1)^2}{4^2}-\frac{(x-9)^2}{7^2}=1$ — Think: Difference of squared terms. Hyperbola

$x+6=\frac{1}{24}(y+5)^2$ — Think: Only one term will have a squared variable. Parabola

Identify the conic section that each equation represents.

1. $(x-4)^2+y^2=3^2$ **Circle**
2. $\frac{(x-6)^2}{2^2}+\frac{(y-4)^2}{10^2}=1$ **Ellipse**
3. $y+5=-\frac{1}{4}(x-7)^2$ **Parabola**
4. $\frac{(x-1)^2}{2^2}-\frac{(y+1)^2}{7^2}=1$ **Hyperbola**
5. $x-8=\frac{1}{16}(y-3)^2$ **Parabola**
6. $\frac{(y+3)^2}{6^2}-\frac{(x+4)^2}{8^2}=1$ **Hyperbola**

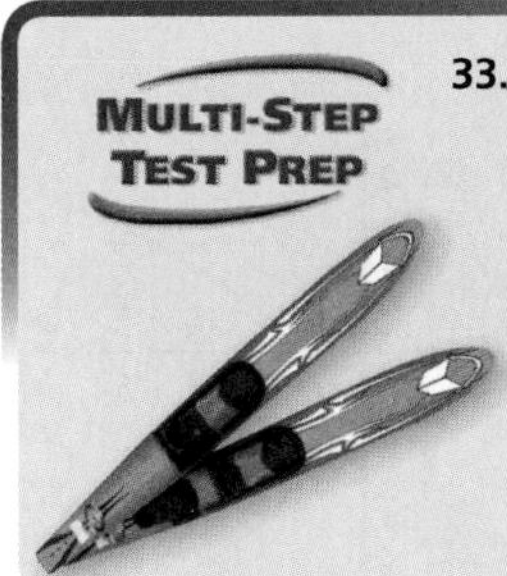

33. This problem will prepare you for the Multi-Step Test Prep on page 776.

A water-skier is towed along a path that can be modeled by $25x^2 + 4y^2 + 300x - 24y + 836 = 0$. Each unit of the coordinate plane represents 10 m.

a. What is the shape of the water-skier's path? **ellipse**

b. The edge of a dock is represented by the y-axis. How close does the water-skier come to the dock? **40 m**

c. A second water-skier is towed along the same path. What is the maximum possible distance between the two water-skiers? **100 m**

Write each equation in the form $Ax^2 + Bxy + Cy^2 + Dx + Ey + F = 0$.

34. $(x-7)^2 + (y+12)^2 = 81$ **$x^2 + y^2 - 14x + 24y + 112 = 0$**

35. $\frac{(x-5)^2}{25} + \frac{(y+8)^2}{36} = 1$ **35. $36x^2 + 25y^2 - 360x + 400y + 1600 = 0$**

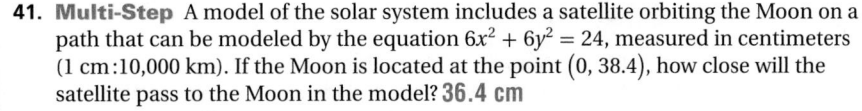

36. $\frac{(x+10)^2}{49} - \frac{(y-6)^2}{81} = 1$ **36. $81x^2 - 49y^2 + 1620x + 588y + 2367 = 0$**

Determine whether the origin lies inside, outside, or on the graph of each equation.

37. $36x^2 + 4y^2 - 432x + 1152 = 0$ **outside**

38. $4x^2 + 36y^2 - 48x = 0$ **on**

39. $16x^2 + 64y^2 - 192x + 16y - 447 = 0$ **inside**

40. $3x^2 + 3y^2 = 147$ **inside**

41. **Multi-Step** A model of the solar system includes a satellite orbiting the Moon on a path that can be modeled by the equation $6x^2 + 6y^2 = 24$, measured in centimeters (1 cm:10,000 km). If the Moon is located at the point (0, 38.4), how close will the satellite pass to the Moon in the model? **36.4 cm**

42. **Critical Thinking** What does the graph of $x^2 - xy = 0$ look like? Explain.

43. **Agriculture** A farmer is planning to fence in part of the farm. Placing the farmhouse at the origin, the farmer finds that the path for the fence can be modeled by the equation $x^2 + y^2 - 80x - 60y - 37{,}500 = 0$, measured in feet.

a. Write the equation in standard form. **$(x-40)^2 + (y-30)^2 = 40{,}000$**

b. Find the area enclosed by the fence. **$40{,}000\pi$**

c. Is the farmhouse inside or outside of the fence? **inside**

44. **ERROR ANALYSIS** In which case below was the conic section $4y^2 + 3x - 12y = 2x^2 + 18$ identified incorrectly? Explain the error.

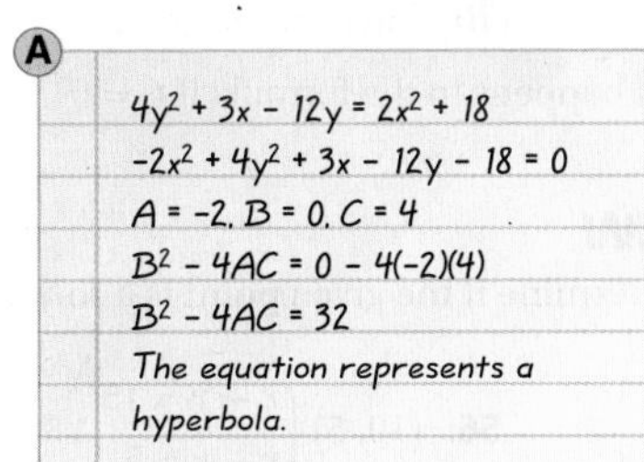

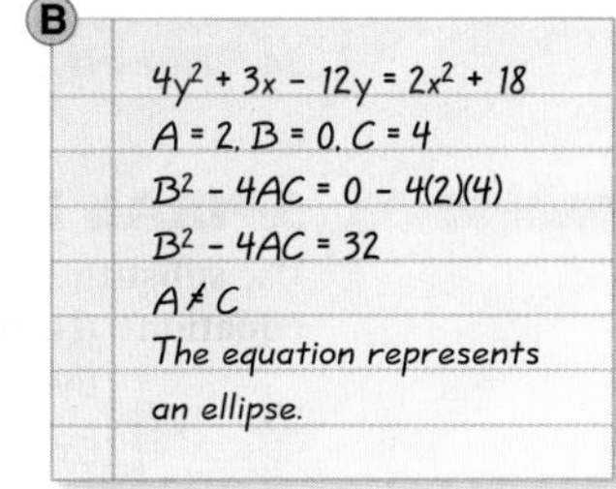

44. B is incorrect. The equation should be written in general form before the coefficients are identified.

45. **Sports** The path followed by a baseball after it is hit can be modeled by the equation $2x^2 - 800x + 1000y - 4000 = 0$, measured in feet.

a. Write the equation in standard form. **$y - 84 = -\frac{1}{500}(x - 200)^2$**

b. What is the maximum height of the ball? **84 ft**

c. What was the height of the ball when it was hit? **4 ft**

d. **What if...?** How would changing the 4000 in the equation to 5000 change your answers to parts **b** and **c**? **Each increases by 1 ft.**

46. **Write About It** Compare the equations and graphs of parabolas and hyperbolas.

46. Possible answer: A hyperbola has 2 branches and 2 squared terms while a parabola has only 1 branch and 1 squared term.

LINK Math History

In 1604, German astronomer Johannes Kepler introduced a new way of thinking about the conic sections—as a family of related curves. For example, the parabola could be considered simply a hyperbola with one focus at infinity.

Exercise 33 involves identifying and analyzing an unknown conic section. This exercise prepares students for the Multi-Step Test Prep on page 776.

Teaching Tip **Critical Thinking** In **Exercise 42,** the xy-term may be intimidating. Give students the hint that they must factor the equation and use the Zero Product Property.

Answers

42. Possible answer: The graph is two lines through the origin. The equation simplifies to $y = x$ or $x = 0$.

10-6 PROBLEM SOLVING

At a bungee-jumping contest, Gavin make a jump that can be modeled by the equation $x^2 - 12x - 12y + 84 = 0$, with dimensions in feet.

1. Gavin wants to know how close he came to the ground during his jump.

a. Classify the shape of his path. Identify the values for the coefficients of each term, and determine what conic section models his path. **$A = 1, B = 0, C = 0, B^2 - 4AC = 0$; parabola**

b. Write the equation of his path in standard form by completing the square. **$y - 4 = \left(\frac{1}{12}\right)(x - 6)^2$**

c. Which point on the path identifies the lowest point that Gavin reached? What are the coordinates of this point? How close to the ground was he? **Vertex; (6, 4); 4 ft off the ground**

2. Nicole makes a similar jump that can be modeled by the equation $x^2 - 4x - 8y + 84 = 0$. She wants to know whether she got closer to the ground than Gavin and by how much.

a. Write the equation of Nicole's path in standard form. **$y - 10 = \left(\frac{1}{8}\right)(x - 2)^2$**

b. How close to the ground did she get? **10 ft**

c. Did Nicole get closer to the ground than Gavin? **No; Gavin got 6 ft closer to the ground.**

The design for a new auto racetrack can be modeled by the equation $x^2 + 4y^2 - 20x - 32y + 160 = 0$, with dimensions in kilometers. Tracey tests the track. Choose the letter for the best answer.

3. What is the standard form of the equation for the path of the racetrack?

A $\frac{(x-10)^2}{1^2} + \frac{(y-4)^2}{2^2} = 1$

(B) $\frac{(x-10)^2}{2^2} + \frac{(y-4)^2}{1^2} = 1$

C $\frac{(x-4)^2}{2^2} + \frac{(y-10)^2}{1^2} = 1$

D $\frac{(x-4)^2}{1^2} + \frac{(y-10)^2}{2^2} = 1$

4. While driving around the track, what is the greatest distance that Tracey will reach from the center of the track?

F 1 km

(G) 2 km

H 10 km

J 16 km

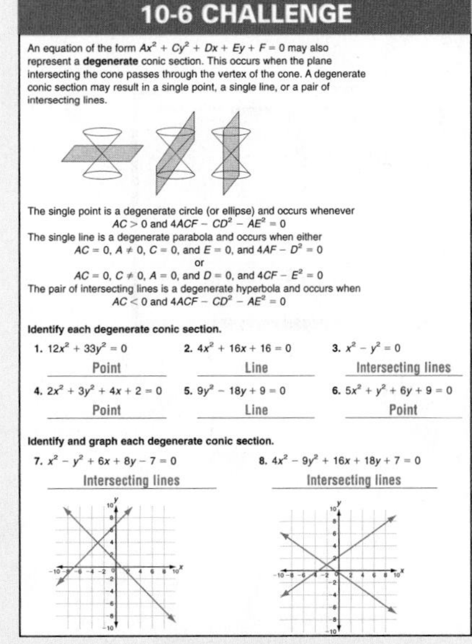

10-6 CHALLENGE

An equation of the form $Ax^2 + Cy^2 + Dx + Ey + F = 0$ may also represent a **degenerate** conic section. This occurs when the plane intersecting the cone passes through the vertex of the cone. A degenerate conic section may result in a single point, a single line, or a pair of intersecting lines.

The single point is a degenerate circle (or ellipse) and occurs whenever
$AC > 0$ and $4ACF - CD^2 - AE^2 = 0$

The single line is a degenerate parabola and occurs when either
$AC = 0, A \neq 0, C = 0$, and $E = 0$, and $4AF - D^2 = 0$
or
$AC = 0, C \neq 0, A = 0$, and $D = 0$, and $4CF - E^2 = 0$

The pair of intersecting lines is a degenerate hyperbola and occurs when
$AC < 0$ and $4ACF - CD^2 - AE^2 = 0$

Identify each degenerate conic section.

1. $12x^2 + 33y^2 = 0$ **Point**
2. $4x^2 + 16x + 16 = 0$ **Line**
3. $x^2 - y^2 = 0$ **Intersecting lines**
4. $2x^2 + 3y^2 + 4x + 2 = 0$ **Point**
5. $9y^2 - 18y + 9 = 0$ **Line**
6. $5x^2 + y^2 + 6y + 9 = 0$ **Point**

Identify and graph each degenerate conic section.

7. $x^2 - y^2 + 6x + 8y - 7 = 0$ **Intersecting lines**

8. $4x^2 - 9y^2 + 16x + 18y + 7 = 0$ **Intersecting lines**

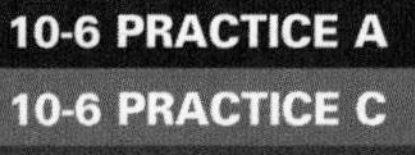

10-6 PRACTICE A
10-6 PRACTICE C
10-6 PRACTICE B

Identify the conic section that each equation represents.

1. $x - 1 = \frac{1}{4}(y - 8)^2$ **Parabola**
2. $\frac{(y+7)^2}{6^2} + \frac{(x-9)^2}{1^2} = 1$ **Ellipse**
3. $(x-9)^2 + (y+1)^2 = 3^2$ **Circle**
4. $y + 5 = -(x - 9)^2$ **Parabola**
5. $\frac{(y+4)^2}{4^2} - \frac{(x-4)^2}{3^2} = 1$ **Hyperbola**
6. $\frac{(x-2)^2}{6^2} + \frac{(y+8)^2}{4^2} = 1$ **Ellipse**
7. $y^2 + 8x + 2y + 57 = 0$ **Parabola**
8. $x^2 + y^2 - 4x + 4y - 17 = 0$ **Circle**
9. $x^2 - 9y^2 + 2x + 18y - 17 = 0$ **Hyperbola**
10. $x^2 + 4y^2 - 2x - 16y + 1 = 0$ **Ellipse**

Find the standard form of each equation by completing the square. Then identify and graph each conic.

11. $x^2 - 16y^2 + 4x + 96y - 124 = 0$ **$\frac{(y-3)^2}{1^2} - \frac{(x+2)^2}{4^2} = 1$; hyperbola**

12. $x^2 + 4y^2 = 16$ **$\frac{x^2}{4^2} + \frac{y^2}{2^2} = 1$; ellipse**

Solve.

13. A train takes a path around the town that can be modeled by the equation $x^2 + 28x + 16y = 348$. The town lies at the focus.

a. Write the equation in standard form. **$y - 34 = -\frac{1}{16}(x - 14)^2$**

b. If the measurement is in miles, how close does the train come to the town? **4 miles**

TEST PREP DOCTOR **Exercise 47** calls for process of elimination. **C** and **D** contain both x^2- and y^2-terms and so cannot be parabolas. Choice **B** is a parabola but opens vertically because of the x^2-term.

Journal

Have students describe the process for identifying and graphing a conic section given an equation in either standard or general form.

ALTERNATIVE ASSESSMENT

Have students create four equations in the form

$Ax^2 + Bxy + Cy^2 + Dx + Ey + F = 0$,

one for each type of conic section. For each conic section, have students show how it is transformed into standard form and graphed.

Power Presentations with PowerPoint®

10-6 Lesson Quiz

Identify the conic section that each equation represents.

1. $2x^2 - 8xy + 8y^2 + 11x - 5y = 0$ parabola

2. $4(x-1)^2 = 100 - 25(y-2)^2$ ellipse

3. $2x^2 - 6xy + 3y^2 + 12x + 18y - 2 = 0$ hyperbola

4. Find the standard form of $4x^2 + y^2 + 8x - 8y + 16 = 0$ by completing the square. Then identify and graph the conic.

$(x+1)^2 + \frac{(y-4)^2}{4} = 1$; ellipse

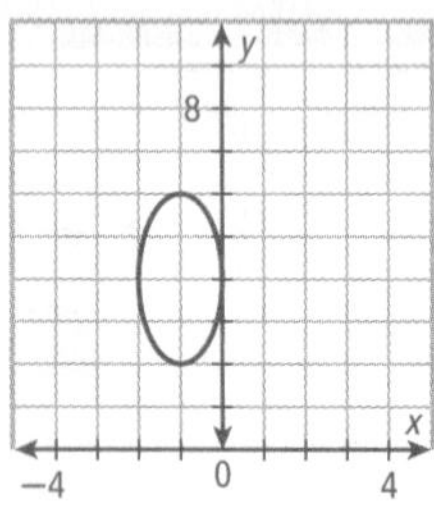

Also available on transparency

TEST PREP

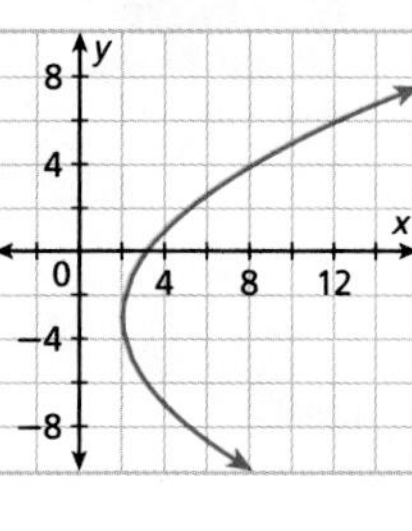

47. Which of the following is the equation for the graph shown?

Ⓐ $3y^2 - 24x + 18y + 75 = 0$ (circled)
Ⓑ $5x^2 + 30x - 40y + 125 = 0$
Ⓒ $2x^2 - 3y^2 + 18x - 24y + 75 = 0$
Ⓓ $3x^2 + 2y^2 - 24x + 18y + 125 = 0$

48. The graph of $9x^2 + 15x - 9y^2 - 15y + 25 = 0$ is which of the following?

Ⓕ Circle Ⓖ Ellipse
Ⓗ Hyperbola (circled) Ⓙ Parabola

49. Which of the following is the equation for the graph shown?

Ⓐ $25x^2 + 25y^2 - 150x + 32y - 159 = 0$
Ⓑ $25x^2 - 150x + 32y = 159$
Ⓒ $25x^2 - 150x = 16y^2 - 32y + 159$
Ⓓ $16y^2 + 32y - 159 = 150x - 25x^2$ (circled)

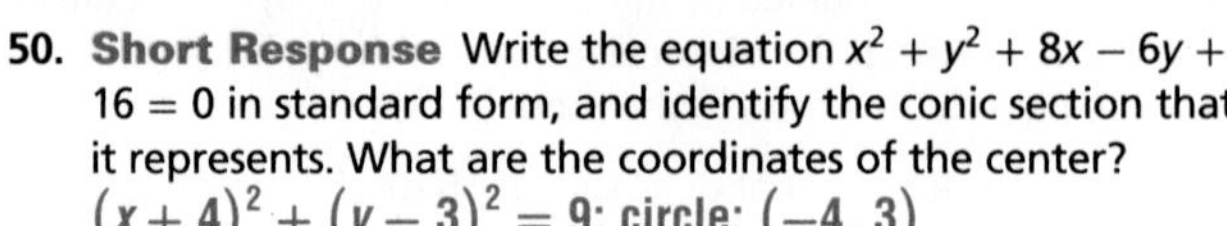

50. Short Response Write the equation $x^2 + y^2 + 8x - 6y + 16 = 0$ in standard form, and identify the conic section that it represents. What are the coordinates of the center? $(x+4)^2 + (y-3)^2 = 9$; circle; $(-4, 3)$

CHALLENGE AND EXTEND

In order to graph the general form of conic sections, $Ax^2 + Bxy + Cy^2 + Dx + Ey + F = 0$, use the quadratic formula,

$$y = \frac{-(Bx+E) \pm \sqrt{(Bx+E)^2 - 4C(Ax^2 + Dx + F)}}{2C}$$, **and a graphing calculator.**

51. Graph $4x^2 + 8xy - 9y^2 - 36 = 0$.

52. Graph $9x^2 - 12xy + 16y^2 - 144 = 0$.

53. What effect does the term Bxy have on the graph? It rotates the graph.

54. What if...? What happens to the formula if $C = 0$? The formula cannot be used if $C = 0$.

SPIRAL REVIEW

Use substitution to determine if the given point is a solution to the system of equations. *(Lesson 3-1)*

55. $(1, 2)\begin{cases}8y - 3x = 13\\5x + 6y = 18\end{cases}$ no

56. $(10, 5)\begin{cases}x + y = 15\\x - y = 5\end{cases}$ yes

57. $(-2, 4)\begin{cases}x = 8 - y\\2x - 7y = -32\end{cases}$ no

Use elimination to solve each system of equations. *(Lesson 3-2)*

58. $\begin{cases}7x - 2y = 20\\-7x + 10y = 12\end{cases}$ $(4, 4)$

59. $\begin{cases}3x + 4y = 16\\2x - 4y = 4\end{cases}$ $(4, 1)$

60. $\begin{cases}x + 5y = -13\\-2x - 7y = 14\end{cases}$ $(7, -4)$

61. Business In 1980, a baseball card was valued at \$1.65. The value of the baseball card increased at a rate of 5% per year. *(Lesson 7-1)*

a. Write an equation to model the value of the baseball card where t is the number of years since 1980. $f(x) = 1.65(1 + 0.05)^t$

b. What was the value of the baseball card in 2004? \$5.32

Answers

51.

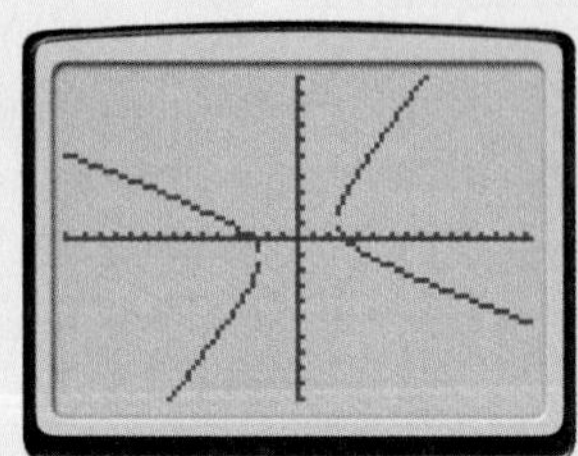

52.

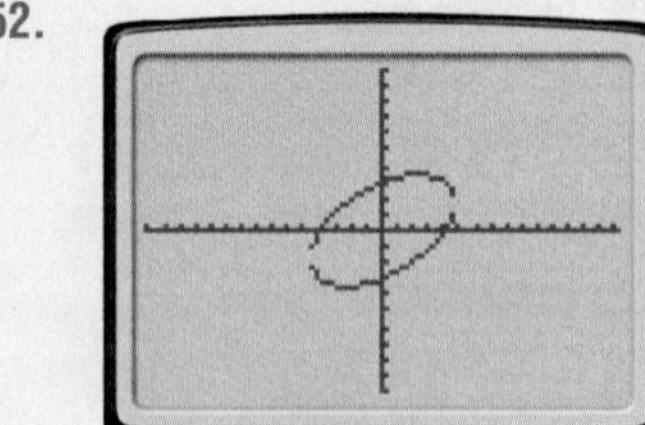

Conic-Section Art

You can use graphs of conic sections to design and create pictures on the coordinate grid.

Use with Lesson 10-6

Activity

Create a picture of a dragonfly by using one circle and six ellipses.

1. Graph the head by using $x^2 + (y-5)^2 = 1$.

   Solve for y, $y = \pm\sqrt{1 - x^2} + 5$, and graph. There are two ways to enter the two halves of the circle into the calculator.

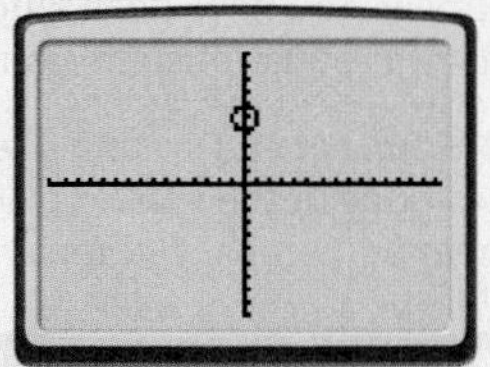

2. The part of the equation $\{-1, 1\}$ represents $\pm$ and can be used to graph both halves of a conic section at one time.

3. Graph the body parts and one right wing by using $x^2 + \frac{(y-2)^2}{4} = 1$, $x^2 + \frac{(y+4)^2}{16} = 1$, *and* $\frac{(x-6)^2}{25} + (y-1)^2 = 1$.

4. Graph the other right wing and left wings by using $\frac{(x-5)^2}{16} + (y-3)^2 = 1$, $\frac{(x+6)^2}{25} + (y-1)^2 = 1$, *and* $\frac{(x+5)^2}{16} + (y-3)^2 = 1$.

5. The dragonfly is now complete.

   Turn off the axes by using the **Format** function and setting **AxesOff**.

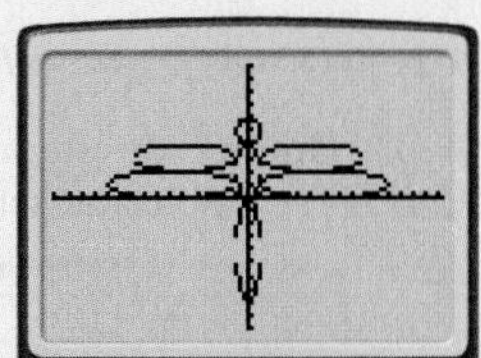

Try This

1. Create your own picture by using the graphs of conic sections. Use at least four conic sections. You may also use lines if necessary. **Check students' work.**
2. Trade equations with a classmate, and attempt to re-create his or her picture by using only the equations. **Check students' work.**

Teacher to Teacher

This is a great chapter. I have my students do a project with conic-section art as we work through the chapter. It is wonderful. It really pulls together everything that we've learned all year.

The students draw pictures using conic sections. I have my students write a program and everything.

Katie Smith
Greenville, SC

Organizer

Use with Lesson 10-6

Pacing:
Traditional 1 day
Block $\frac{1}{2}$ day

Objective: Use a graphing calculator to design and create conic section art.

Materials: Graphing calculator

Online Edition
Graphing Calculator, TechKeys

Countdown to Testing Week 22

Resources

Technology Lab Activities
10-6 Lab Recording Sheet

Teach

Discuss

Simple conic sections can be used to generate more complex pictures. Changing the parameters in the equations is the key to size and placement. Students may wish to brainstorm their designs on graph paper to help determine equations.

Close

Key Concept

Choosing the proper parameters in the equations of conic sections can allow you to change and combine graphs in a creative way.

Assessment

Journal Have students explain ways that they might add to their drawings by using points and lines (degenerate conic sections).

State Resources

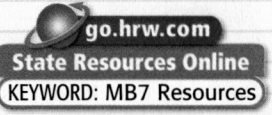

go.hrw.com
State Resources Online
KEYWORD: MB7 Resources

10-7 Organizer

Pacing: Traditional $1\frac{1}{2}$ days
Block $\frac{3}{4}$ day

Objectives: Solve systems of equations in two variables that contain at least one second-degree equation.

Online Edition
Graphing Calculator, Tutorial Videos, TechKeys

Countdown to Testing Week 22

Power Presentations with PowerPoint®

Warm Up

Solve by substitution.

1. $\begin{cases} 3x + 4y = 15 \\ x = 6y - 6 \end{cases}$ $x = 3; y = 1.5$

Solve by elimination.

2. $\begin{cases} 3x + 4y = 57 \\ 5x - 4y = -1 \end{cases}$ $x = 7; y = 9$

Also available on transparency

Math Humor

Q: Why won't the Circles invite the Ellipses over for dinner?

A: They're too eccentric.

10-7 Solving Nonlinear Systems

Objective
Solve systems of equations in two variables that contain at least one second-degree equation.

Vocabulary
nonlinear system of equations

Who uses this?
Harbormasters can solve nonlinear systems to ensure that ships traveling in a variety of patterns do not collide. (See Example 4.)

A **nonlinear system of equations** is a system in which at least one of the equations is not linear. You have been studying one class of nonlinear equations, the conic sections.

The solution set of a system of equations is the set of points that make all of the equations in the system true, or where the graphs intersect. For systems of nonlinear equations, you must be aware of the number of possible solutions.

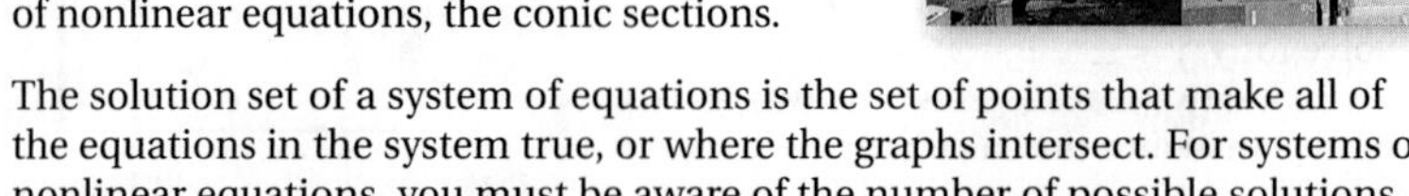

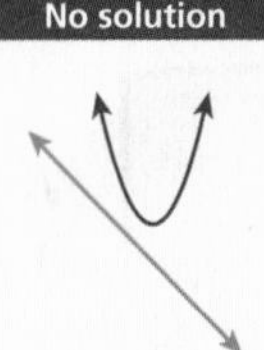
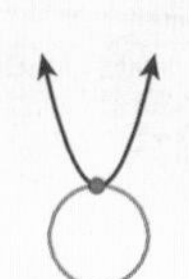
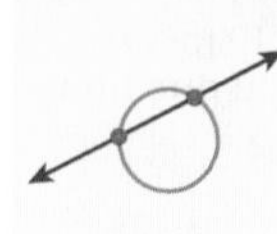
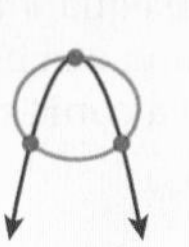
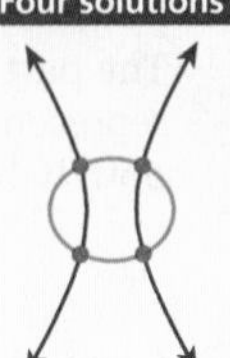

You can use your graphing calculator to find solutions to systems of nonlinear equations and to check algebraic solutions.

EXAMPLE 1 Solving a Nonlinear System by Graphing

Solve $\begin{cases} 2x - y = 1 \\ y + 7 = 2(x + 1)^2 \end{cases}$ by graphing.

The graph of the first equation is a line, and the graph of the second equation is a parabola, so there may be as many as two points of intersection.

Step 1 Solve each equation for *y*.

$y = 2x - 1$ *Solve the first equation for y.*

$y = 2(x + 1)^2 - 7$ *Solve the second equation for y.*

Step 2 Graph the system on your calculator, and use the intersect feature to find the solution set.

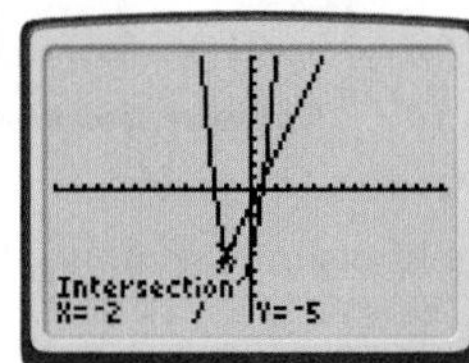

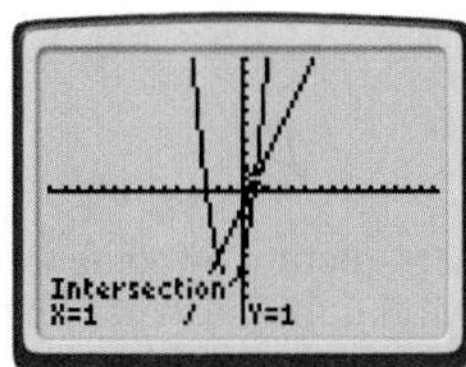

The points of intersection are $(-2, -5)$ and $(1, 1)$.

State Resources

go.hrw.com
State Resources Online
KEYWORD: MB7 Resources

1 Introduce

EXPLORATION

10-7 Solving Nonlinear Systems

Use a square window on your calculator for this Exploration.

1. Graph the line $y = -\frac{3}{4}x + \frac{25}{4}$.
2. Graph the circle $x^2 + y^2 = 25$ in the same window. What can you say about the relationship between the two graphs?
3. Use the intersect feature of your graphing calculator to find the point of intersection of the graphs. Press 2nd TRACE and select **5:intersect**. Use the arrow keys to move the cursor to the point of intersection. Note that you must use the positive part of the circle only.
4. What is the solution to the system of equations $\begin{cases} y = -\frac{3}{4}x + \frac{25}{4} \\ x^2 + y^2 = 25 \end{cases}$?
5. Use the above method to solve the system $\begin{cases} y = -\frac{3}{4}x \\ x^2 + y^2 = 25 \end{cases}$.

THINK AND DISCUSS

6. **Explain** what happens when you try to solve the system $\begin{cases} y = -\frac{3}{4}x + 7 \\ x^2 + y^2 = 25 \end{cases}$.
7. **Describe** the possible solutions for a system consisting of a line and a circle.

Motivate

What are the chances of a planet being struck by a meteor? Both of these objects travel in elliptical paths around the Sun. By finding the intersections of those paths, it is possible to calculate the possibility of such a collision.

Explorations and answers are provided in the *Explorations* binder.

Check Substitute the points into each equation.

Check $(-2, -5)$. Check $(1, 1)$.

y	$2x-1$
-5	$2(-2)-1$
-5	-5 ✔

y	$2(x+1)^2-7$
-5	$2(-2+1)^2-7$
-5	-5 ✔

y	$2x-1$
1	$2(1)-1$
1	1 ✔

y	$2(x+1)^2-7$
1	$2(1+1)^2-7$
1	1 ✔

The solution set of the system is $\{(-2, -5), (1, 1)\}$.

1. Solve $\begin{cases} 3x + y = 4.5 \\ y = \frac{1}{2}(x-3)^2 \end{cases}$ by graphing. **(0, 4.5)**

The substitution method for solving linear systems can also be used to solve nonlinear systems algebraically.

EXAMPLE 2 Solving a Nonlinear System by Substitution

Solve $\begin{cases} x^2 + y^2 = 25 \\ y + 5 = \frac{1}{2}x^2 \end{cases}$ by using the substitution method.

The graph of the first equation is a circle, and the graph of the second equation is a parabola. There may be as many as four points of intersection.

Step 1 It is simplest to solve for x^2 because both equations have x^2 terms.

$x^2 = 2y + 10$ *Solve for x^2 in the second equation.*

Step 2 Use substitution.

$(2y + 10) + y^2 = 25$ *Substitute this value into the first equation.*

$y^2 + 2y - 15 = 0$ *Simplify, and set equal to 0.*

$(y-3)(y+5) = 0$ *Factor.*

$y = 3$ or $y = -5$

Step 3 Substitute 3 and -5 into $x^2 = 2y + 10$ to find values for x.

$x^2 = 2(3) + 10$	$x^2 = 2(-5) + 10$
$x^2 = 16$	$x^2 = 0$
$x = \pm 4$	$x = 0$
$(4, 3)$ and $(-4, 3)$ are solutions.	$(0, -5)$ is a solution.

The solution set of the system is $\{(4, 3), (-4, 3), (0, -5)\}$.

Check Use a graphing calculator. The graph supports that there are three points of intersection.

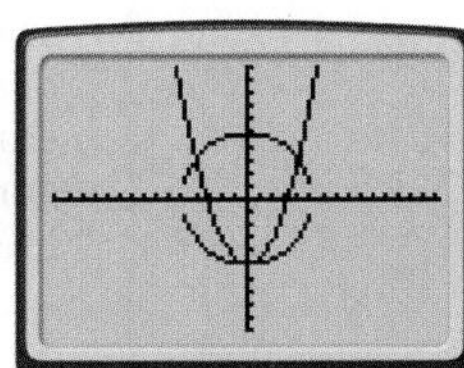

Solve each system of equations by using the substitution method.

2a. $\begin{cases} x + y = -1 \\ x^2 + y^2 = 25 \end{cases}$ **(−4, 3), (3, −4)**

2b. $\begin{cases} x^2 + y^2 = 25 \\ y - 5 = -x^2 \end{cases}$ **(0, 5), (±3, −4)**

Power Presentations with PowerPoint®

Additional Examples

Example 1

Solve $\begin{cases} x^2 + y^2 = 25 \\ 4x^2 + 9y^2 = 145 \end{cases}$ by graphing. $(\pm 4, \pm 3)$

Example 2

Solve $\begin{cases} x^2 + y^2 = 100 \\ y = \frac{1}{2}x^2 - 26 \end{cases}$ by substitution. $(\pm 8, 6), (\pm 6, -8)$

Also available on transparency

INTERVENTION
Questioning Strategies

EXAMPLE 1

- How can you tell if you have found all of the solutions to a system of nonlinear equations?

EXAMPLE 2

- What will happen if you substitute for y instead of substituting for x?

2 Teach

Guided Instruction

Before solving these nonlinear systems, review each of the three methods for solving a system using two linear equations. Point out that, in general, any method can be used to solve a system of nonlinear equations, but usually one method is simpler than the others.

Reaching All Learners
Through Visual Cues

Two conic sections may have 0, 1, 2, 3, or 4 points of intersection. Have students work in groups to sketch each case. Have groups share their sketches and discuss each case.

The elimination method can also be used to solve systems of nonlinear equations.

EXAMPLE 3 **Solving a Nonlinear System by Elimination**

Solve $\begin{cases} 25x^2 + 9y^2 = 225 \\ 16x^2 - 9y^2 = 144 \end{cases}$ by using the elimination method.

The graph of the first equation is an ellipse, and the graph of the second equation is a hyperbola. There may be as many as four points of intersection.

Remember!

In Example 3, you can check your work on a graphing calculator.

Step 1 Eliminate y.

$$\begin{array}{rl} 25x^2 + 9y^2 = 225 & \\ +\ 16x^2 - 9y^2 = 144 & \textit{Add the equations.} \\ \hline 41x^2 \qquad = 369 & \\ x^2 = 9, \text{ so } x = \pm 3 & \textit{Solve for x.} \end{array}$$

Step 2 Find the values for y.

$$\begin{array}{rl} 25(9) + 9y^2 = 225 & \textit{Substitute 9 for } x^2. \\ 225 + 9y^2 = 225 & \textit{Simplify.} \\ y = 0 & \end{array}$$

The solution set of the system is $\{(3, 0), (-3, 0)\}$.

3. Solve $\begin{cases} 25x^2 + 9y^2 = 225 \\ 25x^2 - 16y^2 = 400 \end{cases}$ by using the elimination method.

no solution

EXAMPLE 4 ***Problem-Solving Application***

A tour boat travels around a small island in a pattern that can be modeled by the equation $36x^2 + 25y^2 = 900$, with the island at the origin. Suppose that a fishing boat approaches the island on a path that can be modeled by the equation $y - 3 = \frac{1}{5}x^2$. Is there any danger of collision?

1 Understand the Problem

There is a potential danger of a collision if the two paths cross. The paths will cross if the graphs of the equations intersect.

List the important information:

- $36x^2 + 25y^2 = 900$ represents the path of the tour boat.
- $y - 3 = \frac{1}{5}x^2$ represents the path of the fishing boat.

Make a Plan

To see if the graphs intersect, solve the system $\begin{cases} 36x^2 + 25y^2 = 900 \\ y - 3 = \frac{1}{5}x^2 \end{cases}$

Power Presentations with PowerPoint®

Additional Examples

Example 3

Solve $\begin{cases} 4x^2 + 25y^2 = 41 \\ 36x^2 + 25y^2 = 169 \end{cases}$ by elimination. $(\pm 2, \pm 1)$

Example 4

Suppose that the paths of the boats are modeled by

$36x^2 + 25y^2 = 900$

$y = 0.25x^2 - 6$

How many possible collision points are there? 3

Also available on transparency

INTERVENTION

Questioning Strategies

EXAMPLE 3

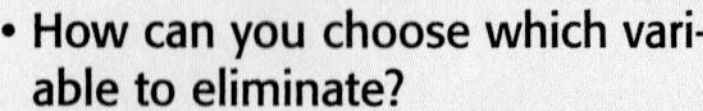

- How can you choose which variable to eliminate?

EXAMPLE 4

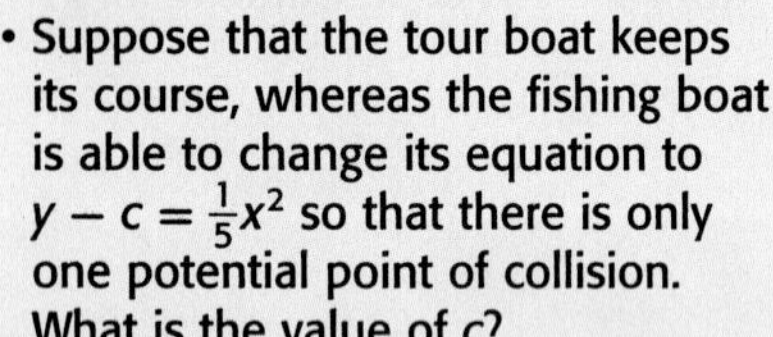

- Suppose that the tour boat keeps its course, whereas the fishing boat is able to change its equation to $y - c = \frac{1}{5}x^2$ so that there is only one potential point of collision. What is the value of c?

Teaching Tip **Inclusion** For **Example 4** clarify for students the difference between the paths of two objects crossing and the two objects colliding. If the paths cross, the objects may collide but not necessarily.

Teaching Tip **Technology** Designers of video games must have a thorough understanding of conic equations and their intersections. Many games involve the intersection of objects with conic paths, whether it is catching a ball traveling along a parabola or trying to rendezvous with a space station moving in an elliptical orbit.

3 Solve

The graph of the first equation is an ellipse, and the graph of the second equation is a parabola. There may be as many as four points of intersection.

$x^2 = 5y - 15$ *Solve the second equation for x^2.*

$36(5y - 15) + 25y^2 = 900$ *Substitute this value into the first equation.*

$25y^2 + 180y - 1440 = 0$ *Simplify, and set equal to 0.*

$$y = \frac{-180 \pm \sqrt{180^2 - 4(25)(-1440)}}{2(25)}$$ *Use the quadratic formula.*

$$y = \frac{-180 \pm 420}{50}, \text{ or } y = 4.8 \text{ and } y = -12$$

Substitute $y = 4.8$ and $y = -12$ into $x^2 = 5y - 15$ to find the values for x.

$x^2 = 5(4.8) - 15$ $\quad$ $x^2 = 5(-12) - 15$

$x^2 = 9$, or $x = \pm 3$ $\quad$ $x^2 = -75$ *There are no real values of $\sqrt{-75}$.*

The real solutions to the system are $(3, 4.8)$ and $(-3, 4.8)$.

4 Look Back

The graph supports that there are two points of intersection. Because the paths intersect, the boats are in danger of colliding if they arrive at the intersections $(3, 4.8)$ or $(-3, 4.8)$ at the same time.

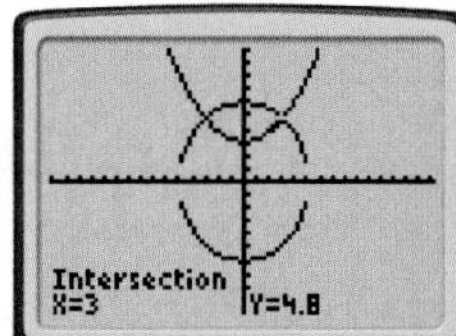

4. What if...? Suppose the paths of the boats can be modeled by the system $\begin{cases} 36x^2 + 25y^2 = 900 \\ y + 2 = -\frac{1}{10}x^2 \end{cases}$.

Is there any danger of collision? **yes, at $(\pm 4, -3.6)$**

THINK AND DISCUSS

1. What can you tell about the graphs if the system has no solution?

2. Describe the steps for solving a nonlinear system of equations by graphing.

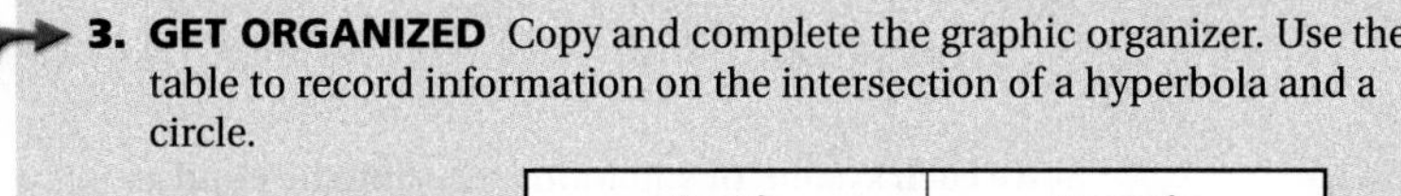

3. GET ORGANIZED Copy and complete the graphic organizer. Use the table to record information on the intersection of a hyperbola and a circle.

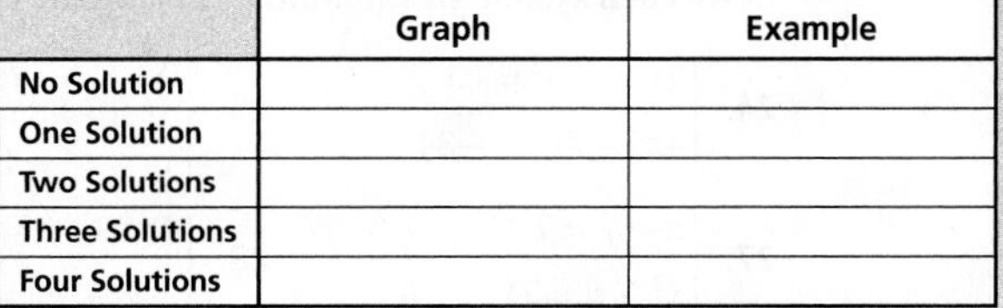

	Graph	Example
No Solution		
One Solution		
Two Solutions		
Three Solutions		
Four Solutions		

COMMON ERROR ALERT

When solving algebraically, students may forget to take both the positive and negative square roots, consequently losing one or more solutions of the system. Encourage students to consider the number of possible solutions before beginning.

Teaching Tip **Math Background** When a stone is thrown into a still pool, it sends out ripples in concentric circles. If two stones are thrown into a pool simultaneously, the two groups of concentric circles will intersect at many points. These points lie on both hyperbolas and ellipses and generate Moiré patterns.

3 Close

Summarize

To find the intersections of two conic sections, use the same techniques as used to find the intersections of lines.

1. Graph the equations.
2. Use substitution and solve.
3. Use elimination and solve.

ONGOING ASSESSMENT and INTERVENTION

Diagnose Before **the Lesson**
10-7 Warm Up, TE p. 768

Monitor During **the Lesson**
Check It Out! Exercises, SE pp. 768–771
Questioning Strategies, TE pp. 769–770

Assess After **the Lesson**
10-7 Lesson Quiz, TE p. 775
Alternative Assessment, TE p. 775

Answers to *Think and Discuss*

1. The graphs will never intersect.
2. Solve each equation for y and graph on the graphing calculator. Use the intersect feature to identify the points of intersection. The points of intersection are the solutions to the system.
3. See p. A12.

Assignment Guide

Assign *Guided Practice* exercises as necessary.

If you finished Examples **1–2**
- **Basic** 15–23
- **Average** 15–23, 45
- **Advanced** 15–23, 45

If you finished Examples **1–4**
- **Basic** 15–43, 45, 47–51, 55–69
- **Average** 15–56, 62–69
- **Advanced** 15–30, 37–69

Homework Quick Check
Quickly check key concepts.
Exercises: 16, 18, 24, 30

State Resources

10-7 Exercises

go.hrw.com
Homework Help Online
KEYWORD: MB7 10-7
Parent Resources Online
KEYWORD: MB7 Parent

GUIDED PRACTICE

1. **Vocabulary** How is a *nonlinear system of equations* different from a linear system of equations? **Possible answer: A nonlinear system of equations contains equations that are not lines.**

SEE EXAMPLE 1 p. 768

Solve each system of equations by graphing.

2. $\begin{cases} y + 3x = 0 \\ y - 6 = -3x^2 \end{cases}$ $(-1, 3), (2, -6)$

3. $\begin{cases} y + 2 = \frac{1}{4}(x - 4)^2 \\ x - y = 6 \end{cases}$ $(4, -2), (8, 2)$

4. $\begin{cases} y + 2x = 10 \\ x = \frac{1}{8}(y - 2)^2 \end{cases}$ $(8, -6), (2, 6)$

SEE EXAMPLE 2 p. 769

Solve each system of equations by using the substitution method.

5. $\begin{cases} y + x = 17 \\ x^2 + y^2 = 169 \end{cases}$ $(12, 5), (5, 12)$

6. $\begin{cases} x^2 + y^2 = 25 \\ y - x = 7 \end{cases}$ $(-3, 4), (-4, 3)$

7. $\begin{cases} x^2 + y^2 = 36 \\ x + 2y = 16 \end{cases}$ no solution

8. $\begin{cases} x^2 + y^2 = 100 \\ x + 2 = \frac{1}{8}y^2 \end{cases}$ $(6, \pm 8)$

9. $\begin{cases} x^2 + y^2 = 36 \\ y + 6 = \frac{1}{3}x^2 \end{cases}$ $(0, -6), (\pm 3\sqrt{3}, 3)$

10. $\begin{cases} x^2 + y^2 = 25 \\ y - 6.25 = -\frac{1}{4}x^2 \end{cases}$ $(\pm 5, 0), (\pm 3, 4)$

SEE EXAMPLE 3 p. 770

Solve each system of equations by using the elimination method.

11. $\begin{cases} x^2 + y^2 = 20 \\ 4x^2 + y^2 = 68 \end{cases}$ $(\pm 4, 2), (\pm 4, -2)$

12. $\begin{cases} 9x^2 + 5y^2 = 45 \\ 6y^2 - 27x^2 = 54 \end{cases}$ $(0, \pm 3)$

13. $\begin{cases} 4x^2 + 3y^2 = 12 \\ 5x^2 + 6y^2 = 30 \end{cases}$ no solution

SEE EXAMPLE 4 p. 770

14. **Radio** The range of a radio station is bounded by the circle with equation $x^2 + y^2 = 2025$. A stretch of highway near the station is modeled by the equation $y - 15 = \frac{1}{20}x^2$. At what points does a car on the highway enter or exit the broadcast range of the station? $(\pm 22, 39.2)$

15. $(0, 5), (-4, 3)$
16. $(0, 6), (4.5, -3)$
17. $(2.5, -6.5), (-4.5, 7.5)$

PRACTICE AND PROBLEM SOLVING

Independent Practice	
For Exercises	See Example
15–17	1
18–23	2
24–29	3
30	4

Extra Practice
Skills Practice p. S23
Application Practice p. S41

Solve each system of equations by graphing.

15. $\begin{cases} 2y - x = 10 \\ y - 3 = \frac{1}{8}(x + 4)^2 \end{cases}$

16. $\begin{cases} x - 6 = -\frac{1}{6}y^2 \\ 2x + y = 6 \end{cases}$

17. $\begin{cases} y^2 - x^2 = 36 \\ 2x + y = -\frac{3}{2} \end{cases}$

Solve each system of equations by using the substitution method.

18. $\begin{cases} x^2 + y^2 = 13 \\ x - y = 1 \end{cases}$ $(-2, -3), (3, 2)$

19. $\begin{cases} y^2 - 4x^2 = 16 \\ y - x = 4 \end{cases}$ $(0, 4), \left(\frac{8}{3}, \frac{20}{3}\right)$

20. $\begin{cases} x^2 - y^2 = 16 \\ x + y^2 = 4 \end{cases}$ $(4, 0), (-5, \pm 3)$

21. $\begin{cases} y = \frac{1}{4}(x - 3)^2 \\ 3x - 2y = 13 \end{cases}$ $(5, 1), (7, 4)$

22. $\begin{cases} -3 = 2x^2 - y \\ x^2 - 36 = 9y^2 \end{cases}$ no solution

23. $\begin{cases} x^2 + y^2 = 8 \\ x^2 - y = 6 \end{cases}$ $(\pm 2, -2), (\pm\sqrt{7}, 1)$

Solve each system of equations by using the elimination method.

24. $\begin{cases} 2x^2 + 3y^2 = 83 \\ 4x^2 - 2y^2 = -34 \end{cases}$ $(\pm 2, 5), (\pm 2, -5)$

25. $\begin{cases} \frac{x^2}{5} + \frac{y^2}{3} = 15 \\ x^2 + y^2 = 20 \end{cases}$ no solution

26. $\begin{cases} x^2 + y^2 = 16 \\ y^2 - 2x^2 = 16 \end{cases}$ $(0, \pm 4)$

27. $\begin{cases} x - y = 7 \\ x^2 - y = 7 \end{cases}$ $(0, -7), (1, -6)$

28. $\begin{cases} 4x^2 + y^2 = 1 \\ -x^2 + y^2 = 1 \end{cases}$ $(0, \pm 1)$

29. $\begin{cases} x^2 + y^2 = 9 \\ x^2 - 4y^2 = 4 \end{cases}$ $(2\sqrt{2}, \pm 1), (-2\sqrt{2}, \pm 1)$

10-7 PRACTICE A

Solve each system of equations by graphing.

1. $\begin{cases} (x - 2)^2 + y^2 = 5^2 \\ 3x + y = 11 \end{cases}$
   a. Solve each equation for y. $y = \sqrt{25 - (x - 2)^2}$, $y = -\sqrt{25 - (x - 2)^2}$, $y = -3x + 11$
   b. Graph each equation on a graphing calculator. How many points of intersection are there? 2
   c. Use the intersect feature on the calculator to find the coordinates of each solution. $(2, 5), (5, -4)$

2. $\begin{cases} 2y = 12 - x \\ x + 8 = 2(y - 4)^2 \end{cases}$ $(0, 6), (10, 1)$

3. $\begin{cases} 2x - y = 5 \\ (y - 1)^2 - (x - 3)^2 = 3 \end{cases}$ $(4, 3), (2, -1)$

Solve each system of equations by using substitution.

4. $\begin{cases} x - 2y = 0 \\ x^2 + y^2 = 125 \end{cases}$ $(10, 5), (-10, -5)$

5. $\begin{cases} 4y = x \\ x^2 - y^2 = 60 \end{cases}$ $(8, 2), (-8, -2)$

6. $\begin{cases} x^2 + y^2 = 100 \\ x - 7y = -50 \end{cases}$ $(6, 8), (-8, 6)$

7. $\begin{cases} 3y = x - 3 \\ x - 3 = \frac{1}{4}y^2 \end{cases}$ $(3, 0), (39, 12)$

Solve each system of equations by using elimination.

8. $\begin{cases} 2x^2 + 3y^2 = 59 \\ 3x^2 - y^2 = 39 \end{cases}$ $(4, 3), (4, -3), (-4, 3), (-4, -3)$

9. $\begin{cases} x^2 + y^2 = 97 \\ x^2 - y^2 = 65 \end{cases}$ $(9, 4), (9, -4), (-9, 4), (-9, -4)$

10. $\begin{cases} x^2 + 5y^2 = 501 \\ x^2 - y^2 = -99 \end{cases}$ $(1, 10), (1, -10), (-1, 10), (-1, -10)$

11. $\begin{cases} 2x^2 + 5y^2 = 148 \\ 4x^2 - 3y^2 = 244 \end{cases}$ $(8, 2), (8, -2), (-8, 2), (-8, -2)$

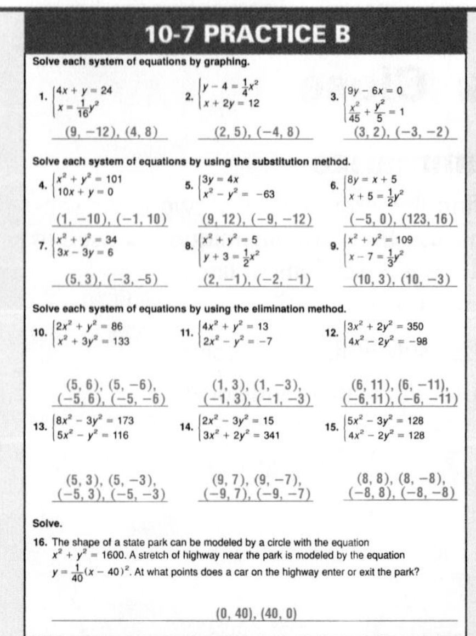

10-7 PRACTICE B

Solve each system of equations by graphing.

1. $\begin{cases} 4x + y = 24 \\ x = \frac{1}{16}y^2 \end{cases}$ $(9, -12), (4, 8)$

2. $\begin{cases} y - 4 = \frac{1}{4}x^2 \\ x + 2y = 12 \end{cases}$ $(2, 5), (-4, 8)$

3. $\begin{cases} 9y - 6x = 0 \\ \frac{x^2}{45} + \frac{y^2}{5} = 1 \end{cases}$ $(3, 2), (-3, -2)$

Solve each system of equations by using the substitution method.

4. $\begin{cases} x^2 + y^2 = 101 \\ 10x + y = 0 \end{cases}$ $(1, -10), (-1, 10)$

5. $\begin{cases} 3y = 4x \\ x^2 - y^2 = -63 \end{cases}$ $(9, 12), (-9, -12)$

6. $\begin{cases} 8y = x + 5 \\ x + 5 = \frac{1}{2}y^2 \end{cases}$ $(-5, 0), (123, 16)$

7. $\begin{cases} x^2 + y^2 = 34 \\ 3x - 3y = 6 \end{cases}$ $(5, 3), (-3, -5)$

8. $\begin{cases} x^2 + y^2 = 5 \\ y + 3 = \frac{1}{2}x^2 \end{cases}$ $(2, -1), (-2, -1)$

9. $\begin{cases} x^2 + y^2 = 109 \\ x - 7 = \frac{1}{3}y^2 \end{cases}$ $(10, 3), (10, -3)$

Solve each system of equations by using the elimination method.

10. $\begin{cases} 2x^2 + y^2 = 86 \\ x^2 + 3y^2 = 133 \end{cases}$ $(5, 6), (5, -6), (-5, 6), (-5, -6)$

11. $\begin{cases} 4x^2 + y^2 = 13 \\ 2x^2 - y^2 = -7 \end{cases}$ $(1, 3), (1, -3), (-1, 3), (-1, -3)$

12. $\begin{cases} 3x^2 + 2y^2 = 350 \\ 4x^2 - 2y^2 = -98 \end{cases}$ $(6, 11), (6, -11), (-6, 11), (-6, -11)$

13. $\begin{cases} 8x^2 - 3y^2 = 173 \\ 5x^2 - y^2 = 116 \end{cases}$ $(5, 3), (5, -3), (-5, 3), (-5, -3)$

14. $\begin{cases} 2x^2 - 3y^2 = 15 \\ 3x^2 + 2y^2 = 341 \end{cases}$ $(9, 7), (9, -7), (-9, 7), (-9, -7)$

15. $\begin{cases} 5x^2 - 3y^2 = 128 \\ 4x^2 - 2y^2 = 128 \end{cases}$ $(8, 8), (8, -8), (-8, 8), (-8, -8)$

Solve.

16. The shape of a state park can be modeled by a circle with the equation $x^2 + y^2 = 1600$. A stretch of highway near the park is modeled by the equation $y = \frac{1}{40}(x - 40)^2$. At what points does a car on the highway enter or exit the park? $(0, 40), (40, 0)$

30. **Multi-Step** While waiting to land, an airplane is traveling above the airport in a holding pattern that can be modeled by the equation $49x^2 + 64y^2 = 3136$, with the air traffic control tower at the origin. Suppose that another plane approaches the airport at the same altitude as the first plane on a path that can be modeled by the equation $y - 6 = \frac{1}{4}x^2$. Should the air traffic controller at the airport be concerned? If so, what are the possible points of collision? **Yes; the planes may intersect at $(\pm 1.8, 6.8)$.**

32. $(6, \pm 3)$, $(-6, \pm 3)$
38. $(\pm 4, 0)$
39. no solution
40. $(10, 0)$, $\left(-\frac{120}{13}, \frac{50}{13}\right)$
41. $(10, \pm 4)$, $(-10, \pm 4)$
42. $(0, 2)$, $(3, 0)$

Solve each system of equations by using any method.

31. $\begin{cases} y = x^2 \\ x = y^2 \end{cases}$ **$(0, 0), (1, 1)$**

32. $\begin{cases} 5x^2 + 4y^2 = 216 \\ 3x^2 + 6y^2 = 162 \end{cases}$

33. $\begin{cases} 8y - x = 2 \\ x - 10 = -4y^2 \end{cases}$ **$(6, 1), (-26, -3)$**

34. $\begin{cases} x^2 - 4y^2 = 9 \\ x - 4y = -3 \end{cases}$ **$(-3, 0), (5, 2)$**

35. $\begin{cases} x^2 + 4y^2 = 36 \\ x^2 + y^2 = 9 \end{cases}$ **$(0, \pm 3)$**

36. $\begin{cases} \frac{x^2}{16} - \frac{y^2}{9} = 1 \\ \frac{y^2}{25} - \frac{x^2}{4} = 1 \end{cases}$ **no solution**

37. $\begin{cases} x + 6 = \frac{1}{2}y^2 \\ x - 4 = -\frac{1}{8}y^2 \end{cases}$ **$(2, \pm 4)$**

38. $\begin{cases} \frac{x^2}{16} + \frac{y^2}{25} = 1 \\ \frac{x^2}{16} + \frac{y^2}{4} = 1 \end{cases}$

39. $\begin{cases} x - 3 = 2y^2 \\ y^2 - 9x^2 = 36 \end{cases}$

40. $\begin{cases} x^2 + y^2 = 100 \\ x + 5y = 10 \end{cases}$

41. $\begin{cases} 3x^2 - 6y^2 = 204 \\ 4x^2 - 2y^2 = 368 \end{cases}$

42. $\begin{cases} 4x^2 + 9y^2 = 36 \\ 2x + 3y = 6 \end{cases}$

43. **Physics** A speeding driver sees a parked police car at time $t = 0$ and starts to decelerate while the police car accelerates as the officer chases the driver. The distance that the driver has traveled in feet after t seconds can be modeled by the function $d(t) = 250 + 125t - 1.2t^2$. The distance that the police car has traveled in feet after t seconds can be modeled by the function $d(t) = 4.2t^2$. How long does it take the police car to catch the driver? **25 s**

LINK

Geology

One of the largest earthquakes ever recorded occurred in December 2004 off the coast of Indonesia. The quake caused a giant tsunami that wreaked havoc in Sri Lanka, Thailand, and other countries.

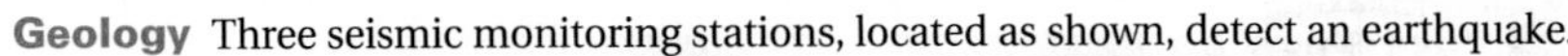

44. **Geology** Three seismic monitoring stations, located as shown, detect an earthquake.

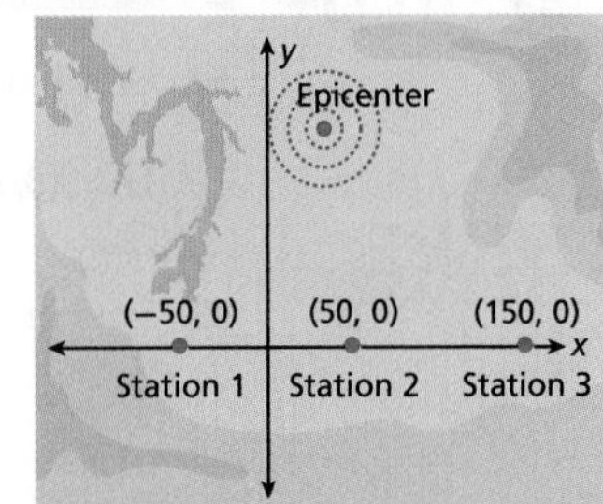

a. Suppose that the epicenter of the earthquake is 30 miles closer to station 2 than to station 1. Use 30 as the constant difference and Stations 1 and 2 as the foci to write an equation for the possible locations of the earthquake.

b. Suppose that the epicenter of the earthquake is 40 miles closer to station 2 than to station 3. Use 40 as the constant difference and stations 2 and 3 as the foci to write an equation for the possible locations of the earthquake.

c. Find the coordinates of the epicenter of the earthquake to the nearest mile.

45. $(2.8, -2.6)$, $(3.3, 2.9)(-7.9, -1.3)$, $(-8.1, 1.5)$

45. **Estimation** Use your graphing calculator to estimate the points of intersection of $x^2 - 4y^2 + 7x = 0$ and $x^2 - y + 5x - 24 = 0$.

46. **Critical Thinking** What must be true in order for two parabolas to have exactly four points of intersection? Explain. **The first parabola must open either upward or downward and the second parabola must open either left or right.**

MULTI-STEP TEST PREP

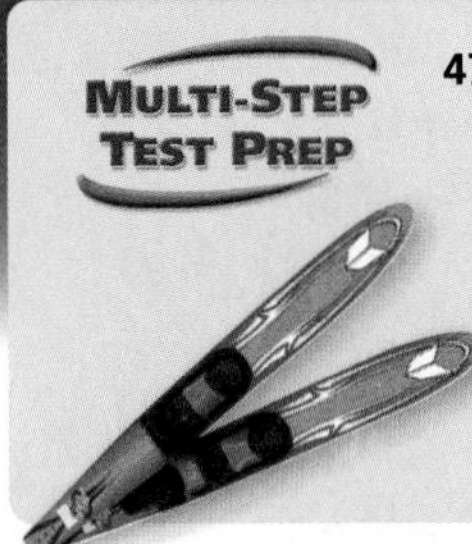

47. This problem will prepare you for the Multi-Step Test Prep on page 776.

A water-skiing exhibition takes place in a body of water modeled by the first and second quadrants of the coordinate plane. A water-skier is towed along a path that can be modeled by $-x^2 + 4y^2 + 8x - 8y - 16 = 0$.

a. What is the shape of the water-skier's path? **hyperbola**

b. A second water-skier's path is modeled by $x^2 + y^2 - 8x - 8y + 23 = 0$. Is there a chance that the two water-skiers will collide? If so, where? **yes; (6.69, 2.68), (1.31, 2.68)**

MULTI-STEP TEST PREP Exercise 47 involves solving a system of equations. This exercise prepares students for the Multi-Step Test Prep on page 776.

Answers

44a. $\frac{x^2}{225} - \frac{y^2}{2275} = 1$

b. $\frac{(x - 100)^2}{400} - \frac{y^2}{2100} = 1$

c. $(42, 125)$

10-7 PRACTICE C

Solve each system of equations by graphing.

1. $\begin{cases} y = -4x \\ x + 1 = \frac{1}{8}y^2 \end{cases}$ $(-0.5, 2), (1, -4)$

2. $\begin{cases} 4y = 5x \\ \frac{y^2}{9} - \frac{x^2}{9} = 1 \end{cases}$ $(4, 5), (-4, -5)$

3. $\begin{cases} 21x - 14y = 0 \\ \frac{3x^2}{16} + \frac{y^2}{36} = 1 \end{cases}$ $(2, 3), (-2, -3)$

Solve each system of equations by using the substitution method.

4. $\begin{cases} x^2 + y^2 = 346 \\ x - 2 = \frac{1}{25}y^2 \end{cases}$ $(11, 15), (11, -15)$

5. $\begin{cases} x^2 - y^2 = 40 \\ y + 10 = \frac{1}{7}x^2 \end{cases}$ $(7, -3), (-7, -3), (11.8, 10), (-11.8, 10)$

6. $\begin{cases} y^2 - x^2 = 119 \\ x + 19 = \frac{1}{6}y^2 \end{cases}$ $(5, 12), (5, -12)$

7. $\begin{cases} x - y = 6 \\ x^2 - y^2 = 132 \end{cases}$ $(14, 8)$

8. $\begin{cases} y^2 = x^2 - 9 \\ x^2 + y^2 = 41 \end{cases}$ $(5, 4), (5, -4), (-5, 4), (-5, -4)$

9. $\begin{cases} (x - 3)^2 + y^2 = 17 \\ y + 7 = \frac{1}{2}(x - 3)^2 \end{cases}$ $(3 + 2\sqrt{2}, -3), (3 - 2\sqrt{2}, -3), (7, 1), (-1, 1)$

Solve each system of equations by using the elimination method.

10. $\begin{cases} 7x^2 - y^2 = -36 \\ x^2 - y^2 = -60 \end{cases}$ $(2, 8), (2, -8), (-2, 8), (-2, -8)$

11. $\begin{cases} 3x^2 + 4y^2 = 1327 \\ x^2 + 2y^2 = 443 \end{cases}$ $(21, 1), (21, -1), (-21, 1), (-21, -1)$

12. $\begin{cases} 8x^2 + 7y^2 = 2143 \\ x^2 - 5y^2 = -20 \end{cases}$ $(15, 7), (15, -7), (-15, 7), (-15, -7)$

13. $\begin{cases} 4x^2 + 5y^2 = 445 \\ 5x^2 - 3y^2 = 473 \end{cases}$ $(10, 3), (10, -3), (-10, 3), (-10, -3)$

14. $\begin{cases} 8x^2 - 11y^2 = 252 \\ 6x^2 - 22y^2 = -306 \end{cases}$ $(9, 6), (9, -6), (-9, 6), (-9, -6)$

15. $\begin{cases} 7x^2 + 5y^2 = 363 \\ 3x^2 - 4y^2 = 131 \end{cases}$ $(7, 2), (7, -2), (-7, 2), (-7, -2)$

Solve.

16. Jordan is jogging on a path modeled by the equation $x^2 + y^2 = 2500$. Katherine is jogging on a path modeled by the equation $\frac{y^2}{60^2} + \frac{x^2}{40^2} = 1$. At what points do their paths intersect?

$(29.7, 40.2), (29.7, -40.2), (-29.7, 40.2), (-29.7, -40.2)$

If students have difficulty with **Exercise 53,** they should make a quick sketch of an ellipse centered at the origin and a parabola with its vertex at (0, 2). Unless the ellipse is very small, there will be two intersections.

In **Exercise 54,** graphing the system of equations for the various values of k is the most appropriate method. Students who choose **A** have incorrectly solved for y to graph.

Answers

51. If $a < 5$, there will be no points of intersection because the horizontal axis of the ellipse will be shorter than the transverse axis of the hyperbola. If $a = 5$, there will be exactly 2 points of intersection because the length of the horizontal axis of the ellipse will be equal to the length of the transverse axis of the hyperbola. If $a > 5$, there will be exactly 4 points of intersection because the horizontal axis of the ellipse will be longer than the transverse axis of the hyperbola.

58.

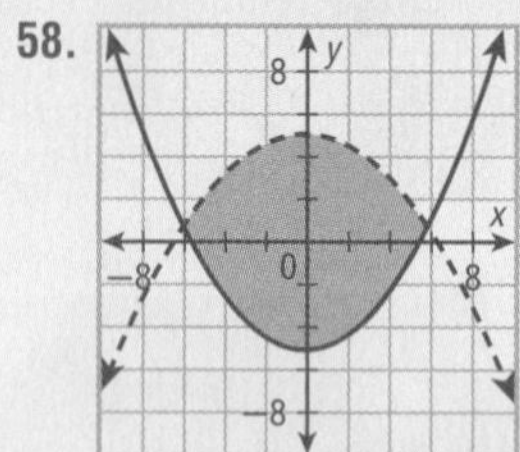

59.

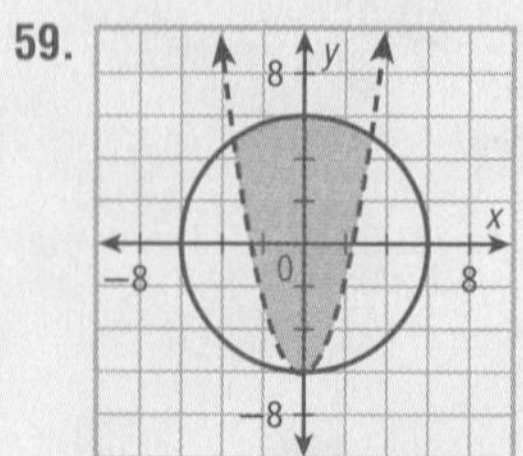

60.

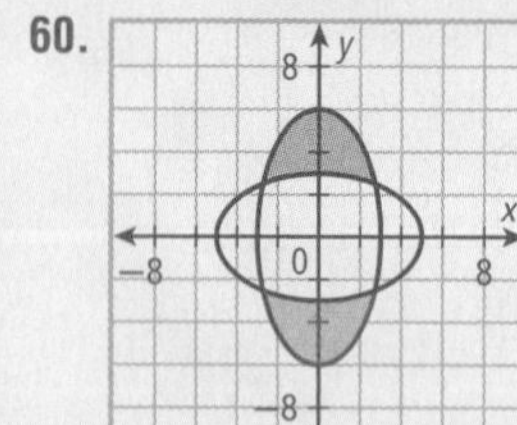

48. **Astronomy** An asteroid is traveling toward Earth on a path that can be modeled by the equation $y = \frac{1}{28}x^2 - 7$. It approaches a satellite in orbit on a path that can be modeled by the equation $\frac{x^2}{49} + \frac{y^2}{51} = 1$. What are the coordinates of the points where the satellite and asteroid might collide? $(\pm 1.91, -6.87)$

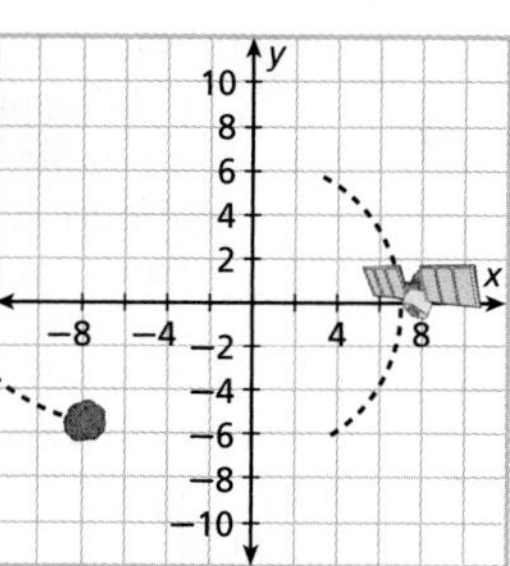

49. **Recreation** Ice skaters Bianca and Mark are performing a routine in which Bianca skates in a path that can be modeled by the equation $x + 2 = \frac{y^2}{4}$ and Mark skates in a path that can be modeled by the equation $\frac{(x+4)^2}{4} + \frac{y^2}{9} = 1$. When the pair meets, they will perform a lift. What are the coordinates of the point where the pair will perform a lift? $(-2, 0)$

50. **Multi-Step** The lake at a resort has an island near the center. A tour boat's path on the lake can be modeled by the equation $16x^2 + 9y^2 = 36$, with the island at the origin. If a canoe's path on the lake can be modeled by the equation $8x + 5y^2 = 20$, find the coordinates of the points on the lake where the boats might meet. $(0, \pm 2)$, $(0.9, \pm 1.6)$

51. **Write About It** How would the value of a in the system $\begin{cases} x^2 - y^2 = 25 \\ \frac{x^2}{a^2} + \frac{y^2}{9} = 1 \end{cases}$ affect the number of solutions for the system?

52. Which of the following points is a solution to the system $\begin{cases} 4x^2 + 5y^2 = 189 \\ 8y^2 - 2x = 60 \end{cases}$?

Ⓐ (3, −6) Ⓑ (−3, −6) **Ⓒ (6, −3)** Ⓓ (−6, −3)

53. How many solutions does the system $\begin{cases} \frac{x^2}{16} + \frac{y^2}{9} = 144 \\ x = 3(y-2)^2 \end{cases}$ have?

Ⓕ 1 **Ⓖ 2** Ⓗ 3 Ⓙ 4

54. For which value of k will the system $\begin{cases} x^2 + y^2 = 25 \\ 5(y + k) = x^2 \end{cases}$ have exactly one solution?

Ⓐ $k = -5$ Ⓑ $k = 0$ **Ⓒ $k = 5$** Ⓓ $k = 25$

CHALLENGE AND EXTEND

Solve each system of equations by any method.

55. $\begin{cases} x^2 + y^2 = 25 \\ 3x^2 + 2y^2 = 66 \\ x + y^2 = 13 \end{cases}$ $(4, \pm 3)$

56. $\begin{cases} 6x^2 - 3y^2 = 204 \\ y + 10 = \frac{1}{3}x^2 \\ 25x^2 - 36(y-2)^2 = 900 \end{cases}$ $(\pm 6, 2)$

57. $\begin{cases} x^2 + y^2 = 25 \\ xy = 12 \\ y^2 - x - 8y + 19 = 0 \end{cases}$ $(3, 4), (4, 3)$

Graph each system of inequalities.

58. $\begin{cases} y - 5 < -\frac{1}{8}x^2 \\ y + 5 \geq \frac{1}{6}x^2 \end{cases}$

59. $\begin{cases} x^2 + y^2 \leq 36 \\ y + 6 > x^2 \end{cases}$

60. $\begin{cases} \frac{x^2}{9} + \frac{y^2}{36} \leq 1 \\ \frac{x^2}{25} + \frac{y^2}{9} \geq 1 \end{cases}$

10-7 READING STRATEGIES

The solution set to a system of nonlinear equations is the set of points that make all the equations true. The maximum number of solutions corresponds to the number of points of intersection of the graphs of the equations.

How many solutions are possible for this system of equations?

$$\begin{cases} x^2 + y^2 = 13 \\ y - x = 1 \end{cases}$$

The first equation is a circle and the second equation is linear, so it must be a line.

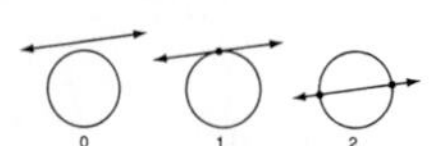

There are a maximum of 2 solutions for this system of equations.

Determine the maximum number of solutions for each system of equations by sketching the possible intersections of the graphs of each system.

1. $\begin{cases} x = 3y \\ y = \frac{1}{8}x^2 \end{cases}$ 2 possible solutions

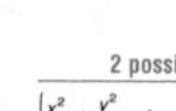

2. $\begin{cases} x^2 + y^2 = 25 \\ \frac{y^2}{25} + \frac{x^2}{16} = 1 \end{cases}$ 4 possible solutions

3. $\begin{cases} \frac{x^2}{49} + \frac{y^2}{36} = 1 \\ x^2 = 28y \end{cases}$ 4 possible solutions

4. $\begin{cases} \frac{y^2}{9} - \frac{x^2}{4} = 1 \\ y = 3x - 9 \end{cases}$ 2 possible solutions

10-7 RETEACH

You can use substitution to solve nonlinear systems of equations in much the same way you would solve linear systems.

Solve. $\begin{cases} x^2 - y^2 = 27 \\ x - 3 = \frac{1}{3}y^2 \end{cases}$ Because the first equation is a hyperbola and the second equation is a parabola, there may be four points of intersection.

Step 1 Look for the easiest way to substitute.

Solve the second equation for y^2, since y^2 appears in both equations.

$x - 3 = \frac{1}{3}y^2$

$3(x - 3) = y^2$ *Multiply to solve for y^2.*

$y^2 = 3x - 9$ *Simplify.*

Step 2 Substitute $3x - 9$ for y^2 in the first equation.

$x^2 - y^2 = 27$

$x^2 - (3x - 9) = 27$

$x^2 - 3x + 9 = 27$ *Use the Distributive Property to simplify.*

Step 3 Solve for x.

$x^2 - 3x - 18 = 0$ *Rewrite the equation to have 0 on one side.*

$(x - 6)(x + 3) = 0$ *Factor.*

$x = 6$ or $x = -3$

Step 4 Use the values of x to find the corresponding values of y in $y^2 = 3x - 9$.

For $x = 6$: $y^2 = 3x - 9 = 3(6) - 9 = 9$. So, $y = \pm\sqrt{9} = \pm 3$

For $x = -3$: $y^2 = 3x - 9 = 3(-3) - 9 = -18$. $y^2 = -18$ has no solution.

The solution to the system is (6, 3) and (6, −3).

Use the substitution method to solve the system of equations.

1. $\begin{cases} x^2 + y^2 = 20 \\ y + 6 = \frac{1}{2}x^2 \end{cases}$

a. Solve the second equation for x^2. $x^2 = 2y + 12$

b. Substitute the expression for x^2 into the first equation. $2y + 12 + y^2 = 20$

c. Rewrite to have one side of the equation equal to 0. $y^2 + 2y - 8 = 0$

d. Solve for y. $y = -4$ or $y = 2$

e. Solutions: $(-4, 2), (4, 2), (2, -4), (-2, -4)$

61. **Economics** Industry analysts predict that the demand curve for a new software product can be modeled by the function $D(p) = 5000 - 0.2p^2$, where p is the price of the product and $D(p)$ is the number of products that can be sold at p. The analysts also predict that the supply curve for the new product can be modeled by the function $S(p) = 0.3p^2$, where p is the price of the product and $S(p)$ is the number of products that companies will supply at p. Predict the price for the new product.
about \$100

SPIRAL REVIEW

Describe the three-dimensional figure that can be made from the given net. *(Previous course)*

62.

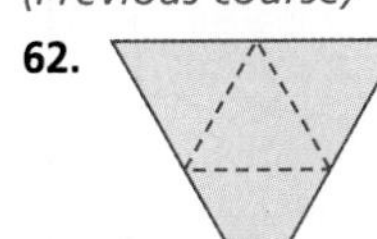

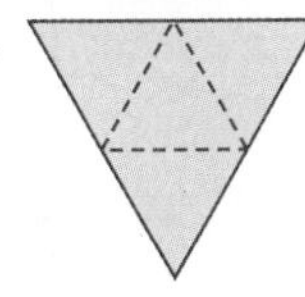

triangular pyramid

63.

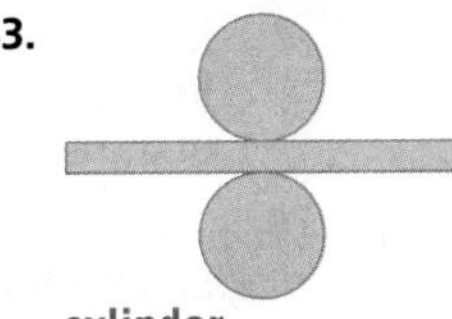

cylinder

Evaluate each expression for the given values of the variable. *(Lesson 1-4)*

64. $2x^2 + 3y - 6$ for $x = -1, y = 4$ **8**

65. $\frac{a^2 - b^2}{a - b}$ for $a = -2, b = 6$ **4**

66. $\frac{5s + 2t + st}{s + t}$ for $s = 7, t = -3$ **2**

67. $\frac{3w^2 - 4z}{2wz}$ for $w = 2, z = 5$ $-\frac{2}{5}$

Write a function that models the given data. *(Lesson 9-6)*

68.

x	−1	0	1	2	3	4
y	8	4	2	2	4	8

$f(x) = x^2 - 3x + 4$

69.

x	−2	−1	0	1	2	3
y	−12	−7	−2	3	8	13

$f(x) = 5x - 2$

Career Path

go.hrw.com
Career Resources Online
KEYWORD: MB7 Career

Shawn Innes
Actuarial Science major

Q: What math classes did you take in high school?
A: In high school, I took algebra, geometry, and precalculus.

Q: What do actuaries do?
A: Basically, actuaries evaluate the likelihood of certain events and try to find creative ways to reduce the chances of undesirable outcomes. Actuaries are involved in many different industries such as business and finance, health, retirement planning, and insurance.

Q: How do you become an actuary?
A: To become a full actuary, a series of exams must be completed. These exams cover topics like calculus, economics, and finance.

Q: What are your future plans?
A: I'd like to work at the consulting firm where I interned. They specialize in retirement planning and benefits. There, I tested formulas used to calculate pensions for client companies.

Journal

Have students describe how a system of nonlinear equations may have 0, 1, 2, 3, or 4 solutions.

ALTERNATIVE ASSESSMENT

Have students make up three problems to be solved: one by graphing, one by substitution, and one by elimination. Each of the four conic sections should be used in at least one of the problems.

10-7 PROBLEM SOLVING

Jim sets a course in his fishing boat that can be modeled by the equation $4x^2 + 9y^2 = 36$. Janice has her sailboat on a path that can be modeled by the equation $x - 2 = \left(\frac{1}{8}\right)y^2$.

1. Janice wonders whether there is a danger of them colliding.
   a. Explain which conic section models each boat's path and why. Jim's boat: ellipse; the sum of two squared terms; Janice's boat: parabola; only one squared term
   b. What is the maximum number of points of intersection between two such paths? 4
   c. To solve this system of equations using the quadratic formula, what expression can be substituted for y^2 in the equation of the path of Jim's boat? $8(x - 2)$
   d. Rewrite the equation of the path of Jim's boat in terms of x. $4x^2 + 72x - 180 = 0$
   e. Solve for x using the quadratic formula. $x = 2.2$ and -20.2
   f. Is there a possibility of collision? Is so, name the coordinates of the point(s) of intersection. Yes; points of possible collision are (2.2, 1.3) and (2.2, −1.3)
2. Janice changes course so that her sailboat now follows a path modeled by the equation $\frac{y^2}{4} - x^2 = 1$ in quadrants I and II. Is there now a possibility of collision?
   a. Sketch the system of equations represented by Jim's boat's course and Janice's boat's new course.
   b. Use your graph to determine if there is now a possibility of collision. If so, give the coordinates of the point(s). Yes; point of possible collision is (0, 2)

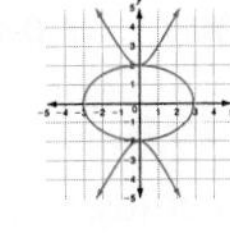

A trawler is on a course modeled by the equation $2x + y + 3 = 0$. Choose the letter for the best answer.

3. Which solution set represents possible points of collision between Jim's boat and the trawler's course?
   A (−2.2, 1.37)
   B (−0.5, −2)
   Ⓒ (−2.2, 1.37); (−0.5, −2)
   D There is no possible collision point.
4. Janice sees the trawler. Which equation models a path that avoids a possible collision of her boat with the trawler?
   Ⓕ $x - 1 = 0.5y^2$
   G $y = 0.5x + 2$
   H $y^2 - x^2 = 1$
   J $4x^2 + 3y^2 = 12$

10-7 CHALLENGE

The Global Positioning System (GPS) operates using the theory of conic sections. A simplified explanation is that a set of satellites is placed in orbit above Earth. Each of these satellites transmits a signal that is precisely synchronized among all the satellites. The GPS receiver on the ground receives the signals from the different satellites and records a time difference between the signals. This time difference is due to the various distances from the GPS receiver to the individual satellites.

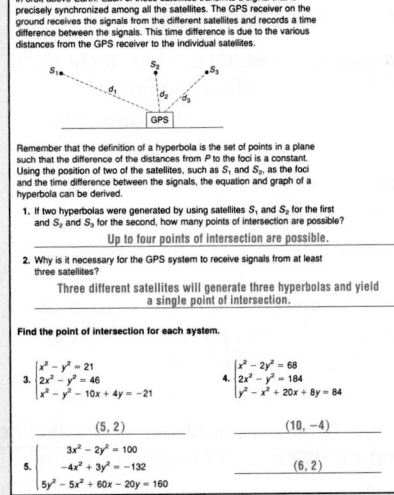

Remember that the definition of a hyperbola is the set of points in a plane such that the difference of the distances from P to the foci is a constant. Using the position of two of the satellites, such as S_1 and S_2, as the foci and the time difference between the signals, the equation and graph of a hyperbola can be derived.

1. If two hyperbolas were generated by using satellites S_1 and S_2 for the first and S_2 and S_3 for the second, how many points of intersection are possible? Up to four points of intersection are possible.
2. Why is it necessary for the GPS system to receive signals from at least three satellites? Three different satellites will generate three hyperbolas and yield a single point of intersection.

Find the point of intersection for each system.

3. $\begin{cases} x^2 - y^2 = 21 \\ 2x^2 - y^2 = 46 \\ x^2 - y^2 - 10x + 4y = -21 \end{cases}$ (5, 2)

4. $\begin{cases} x^2 - 2y^2 = 68 \\ 2x^2 - y^2 = 184 \\ y^2 - x^2 + 20x + 8y = 84 \end{cases}$ (10, −4)

5. $\begin{cases} 3x^2 - 2y^2 = 100 \\ -4x^2 + 3y^2 = -132 \\ 5y^2 - 5x^2 + 60x - 20y = 160 \end{cases}$ (6, 2)

Power Presentations with PowerPoint®

10-7 Lesson Quiz

1. Solve $\begin{cases} 4x^2 - 9y^2 = 108 \\ x^2 + y^2 = 40 \end{cases}$ by graphing. $(\pm6, \pm2)$
2. Solve $\begin{cases} 2x^2 + y^2 = 54 \\ x^2 - 3y^2 = 13 \end{cases}$ by substitution. $(\pm5, \pm2)$
3. Solve $\begin{cases} 4x^2 + 4y^2 = 52 \\ 9x^2 - 4y^2 = 65 \end{cases}$ by elimination. $(\pm3, \pm2)$

Also available on transparency

Organizer

Objective: Assess students' ability to apply concepts and skills in Lessons 10-6 through 10-7 in a real-world format.

 Online Edition

Resources

 ***Algebra II Assessments***

www.mathtekstoolkit.org

Problem	Text Reference
1-4	Lesson 10-6
5-7	Lesson 10-7

State Resources

CHAPTER 10

MULTI-STEP TEST PREP

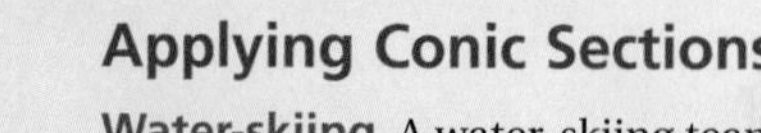

SECTION 10B

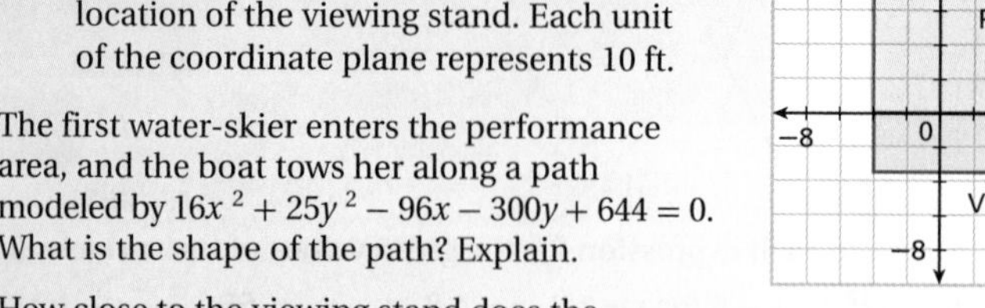

Applying Conic Sections

Water-skiing A water-skiing team is planning an exhibition on a lake. The figure shows the performance area that has been roped off on the lake and the location of the viewing stand. Each unit of the coordinate plane represents 10 ft.

1. The first water-skier enters the performance area, and the boat tows her along a path modeled by $16x^2 + 25y^2 - 96x - 300y + 644 = 0$. What is the shape of the path? Explain.

   1. Ellipse; $A = 16$, $B = 0$, and $C = 25$, so $B^2 - 4AC < 0$ and $A \neq C$; therefore, the path is an ellipse.

2. How close to the viewing stand does the water-skier pass? **20 ft**
3. During this routine, the water-skier will pass directly in front of what percentage of the viewers? **55.6%**
4. A second water-skier enters the performance area. The boat tows him along a path modeled by $x^2 + y^2 - 20x - 12y + 132 = 0$. What is the shape of the path? Explain.
5. Is there a chance that the second water-skier will collide with the first? If so, where? **yes; (8, 6)**
6. A third water-skier is towed along a path modeled by $x^2 - 14x - 8y + 129 = 0$. At what points does the water-skier enter and exit the performance area? **(3,12) and (11,12)**
7. Is there a chance that this water-skier will collide with the others? If so, where? **no**

4. Circle; $A = 1$, $B = 0$, $C = 1$, so $B^2 - 4AC < 0$, $B = 0$, and $A = C$; therefore, the path is a circle.

776

INTERVENTION

Scaffolding Questions

1. How can you identify a conic section based on an equation in general form? What are the values of *A*, *B*, and *C*? Find $B^2 - 4AC$; $A = 16$, $B = 0$, $C = 25$.
2. What do you need to do in order to solve this problem? Write the equation in standard form. $\frac{(x-3)^2}{25} + \frac{(y-6)^2}{16} = 1$
3. What information about the ellipse can help you solve this problem? What else do you need to know? length of major axis; length of the performance area
4. What can you say about this conic section based on its equation in general form? It is a circle.
5. What are some different ways to solve this system of equations? What are the possible numbers of solutions? by graphing, elimination, or substitution; 0, 1, 2, 3, or 4
6. What is the shape of this water-skier's path? parabola
7. What is the vertex of the parabola? Which way does it open? Does its graph intersect the other paths? (7, 10); up; no

Extension

What percentage of the viewers have a water-skier directly in front of them at some point during the exhibition? 77.8%

CHAPTER 10

SECTION 10B

Quiz for Lessons 10-6 Through 10-7

10-6 Identifying Conic Sections

Identify the conic section that each equation represents.

1. $\frac{6x^2}{9} + \frac{8y^2}{12} = 1$ circle
2. $8(y-4) - 3(x+4)^2 = 1$ parabola
3. $\frac{(y-2)^2}{9} = \frac{(x+5)^2}{16} + 1$ hyperbola
4. $(y-2)^2 - 3(x+7) = 0$ parabola
5. $2x^2 + 4y^2 - 12y = 18$ ellipse
6. $7x^2 - 5xy - 3y^2 + 7x - 6 = 0$ hyperbola
7. $9x^2 + 12xy + 16y^2 - 5x + 2y = 0$ ellipse
8. $x^2 + y^2 - 4x + 6y - 11 = 0$ circle

Write each equation in the form $Ax^2 + Bxy + Cy^2 + Dx + Ey + F = 0$.

9. $y - 5 = \frac{1}{4}(x+8)^2$ $\frac{1}{4}x^2 + 4x - y + 21 = 0$
10. $\frac{(y-3)^2}{9} - \frac{(x+5)^2}{5} = 1$ $-9x^2 + 5y^2 - 90x - 30y - 225 = 0$

Find the standard form of each equation by completing the square. Then identify the conic.

11. $x^2 + y^2 - 6x - 8y + 15 = 0$ $(x-3)^2 + (y-4)^2 = 10$; circle
12. $3x^2 + 4y^2 - 18x + 8y + 19 = 0$
13. $5y^2 - x - 60y + 176 = 0$ $x + 4 = 5(y-6)^2$; parabola
14. $2x^2 - 6y^2 - 16x - 24y = 4$ $\frac{(x-4)^2}{6} - \frac{(y+2)^2}{2} = 1$; hyperbola

10-7 Solving Nonlinear Systems

Solve each system of equations by graphing.

15. $\begin{cases} 8y + 3x^2 = 56 \\ y = \frac{1}{4}x^2 - 3 \end{cases}$ $(\pm 4, 1)$
16. $\begin{cases} 2x - 8 = y^2 \\ 3x - 3y = -12 \end{cases}$ no solution
17. $\begin{cases} x^2 + y^2 = 169 \\ 5y - 12x = 0 \end{cases}$ $(5, 12)$ and $(-5, -12)$

Solve each system by using the substitution or elimination method.

18. $\begin{cases} x^2 - 2y^2 = 28 \\ 3y - x = 0 \end{cases}$ $(6, 2)$ and $(-6, -2)$
19. $\begin{cases} 2x^2 + 3y^2 = 21 \\ x^2 - 9y = 0 \end{cases}$ $(\pm 3, 1)$
20. $\begin{cases} 8x^2 + 4y^2 = 32 \\ 10x^2 + 6y^2 = 60 \end{cases}$ no solution

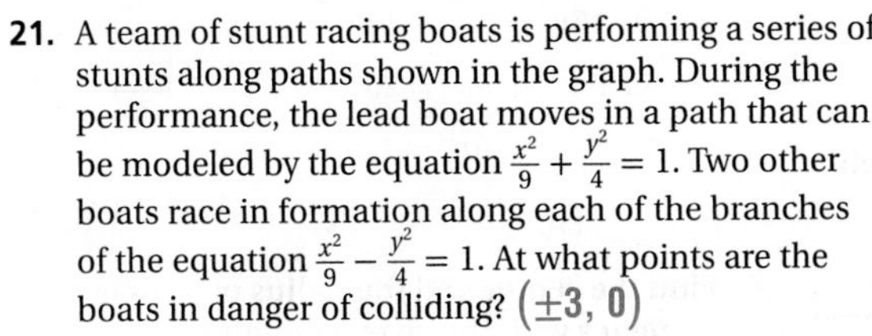

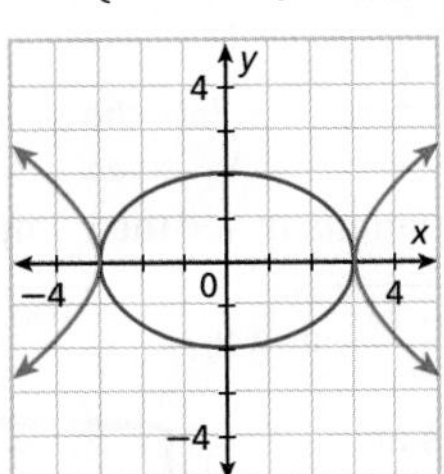

21. A team of stunt racing boats is performing a series of stunts along paths shown in the graph. During the performance, the lead boat moves in a path that can be modeled by the equation $\frac{x^2}{9} + \frac{y^2}{4} = 1$. Two other boats race in formation along each of the branches of the equation $\frac{x^2}{9} - \frac{y^2}{4} = 1$. At what points are the boats in danger of colliding? $(\pm 3, 0)$

22. Find n so that the system $\begin{cases} \frac{x^2}{9} + \frac{y^2}{16} = 1 \\ y - n = x^2 \end{cases}$ has exactly three solutions. $n = -4$

12. $\frac{(x-3)^2}{4} + \frac{(y+1)^2}{3} = 1$; ellipse

SECTION 10B

Organizer

Objective: Assess students' mastery of concepts and skills in Lessons 10-6 through 10-7.

Resources

Assessment Resources

Section 10B Quiz

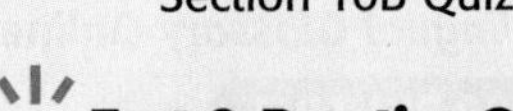

Test & Practice Generator One-Stop Planner®

INTERVENTION

Resources

Ready to Go On? Intervention and Enrichment **Worksheets**

Ready to Go On? **CD-ROM**

Ready to Go On? **Online**

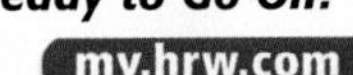

my.hrw.com

READY TO GO ON? Diagnose and Prescribe

NO INTERVENE

Ready to Go On? Intervention	Ready to Go On? Intervention, Section 10B: Worksheets	CD-ROM	Online
Lesson 10-6	10-6 Intervention	Activity 10-6	Diagnose and Prescribe Online
Lesson 10-7	10-7 Intervention	Activity 10-7	

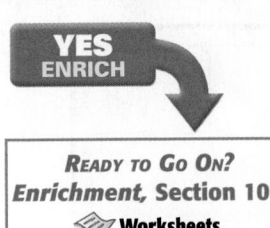

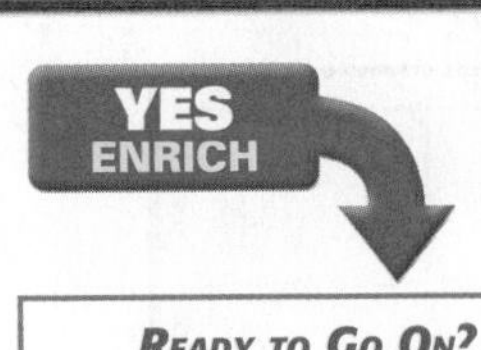

YES ENRICH

Ready to Go On? Enrichment, **Section 10B**

Worksheets

CD-ROM

Online

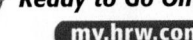

Organizer

Objective: Help students organize and review key concepts and skills presented in Chapter 10.

Online Edition
Multilingual Glossary

Resources

Puzzle Pro
One-Stop Planner®

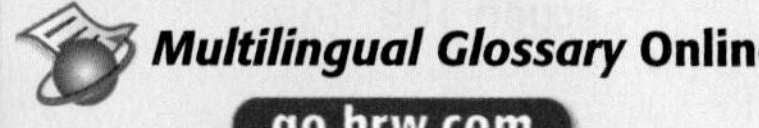
***Multilingual Glossary* Online**
go.hrw.com
KEYWORD: MB7 Glossary

Lesson Tutorial Videos
CD-ROM

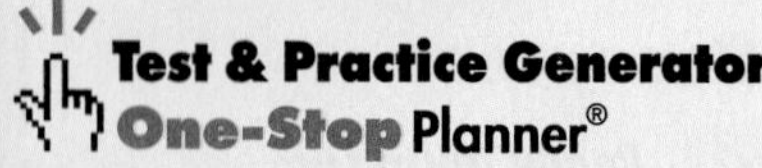
Test & Practice Generator
One-Stop Planner®

Answers

1. transverse axis
2. tangent line
3. focus; directrix
4. conic section
5. circle with center (0, 0) and radius $r = 9$

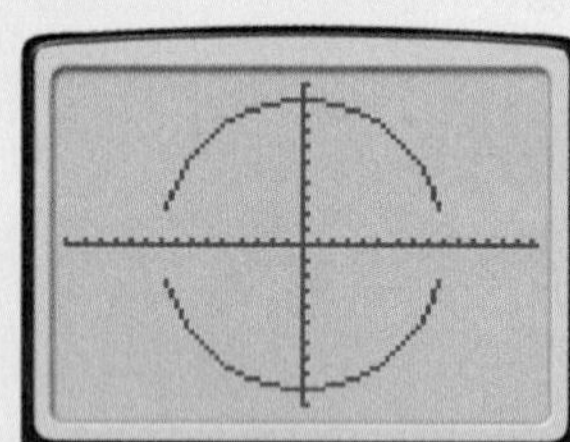

CHAPTER 10 Study Guide: Review

Vocabulary

Complete the sentences below with vocabulary words from the list above.

1. The line containing the vertices and the foci of a hyperbola is the ___?___ of symmetry of the hyperbola.
2. A line in the same plane as a circle that intersects the circle in exactly one point is a(n) ___?___.
3. A parabola is the set of all points P(*x*, *y*) that are equidistant from both a fixed point, called the ___?___, and a fixed line, called the ___?___.
4. A(n) ___?___ is formed by the intersection of a double right cone and a plane.

10-1 Introduction to Conic Sections *(pp. 722–728)*

EXAMPLE

- **Graph $4x^2 + 25y^2 = 100$ on a graphing calculator. Identify and describe the conic section.**

Solve for *y* so that the expression can be used in a graphing calculator.

$25y^2 = 100 - 4x^2$ *Subtract $4x^2$ from both sides.*

$y^2 = \frac{100 - 4x^2}{25}$ *Divide both sides by 25.*

$y = \pm\sqrt{\frac{100 - 4x^2}{25}}$ *Take the square root of both sides.*

Use two equations to see the complete graph.

$y_1 = \sqrt{\frac{100 - 4x^2}{25}}$ and $y_2 = -\sqrt{\frac{100 - 4x^2}{25}}$

The graph is an ellipse with center (0, 0), *y*-intercepts 2 and −2, and *x*-intercepts 5 and −5.

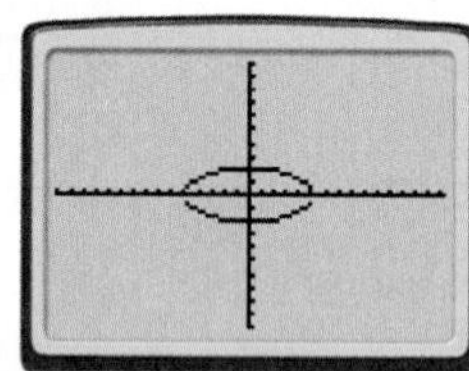

EXERCISES

Graph each equation on a graphing calculator. Identify and describe the conic section.

5. $x^2 + y^2 = 81$
6. $\frac{x^2}{25} - \frac{y^2}{4} = 1$
7. $x = \frac{1}{4}(y + 1)^2$
8. $8x^2 + 25y^2 = 98$
9. **Which equation is represented by the graph?**
   A. $16x^2 - 16y^2 = 256$
   B. $16y^2 = 9x^2 + 144$
   C. $9x^2 + 16y^2 = 256$
   D. $9y^2 - 16x^2 = 144$

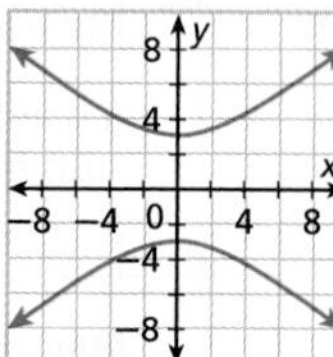

Find the center and the radius of a circle that has a diameter with the given endpoints.

10. (−9, −3) and (15, −3)
11. (−4, 1) and (20, −6)

6. hyperbola with center (0, 0) and intercepts (5, 0) and (−5, 0)

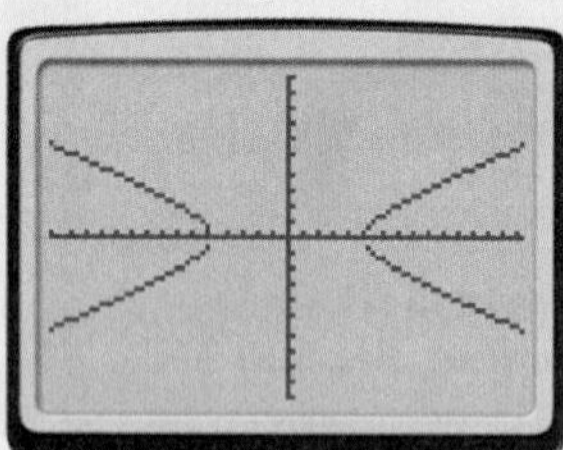

7. parabola with vertex (0, −1), opening in the positive *x*-direction

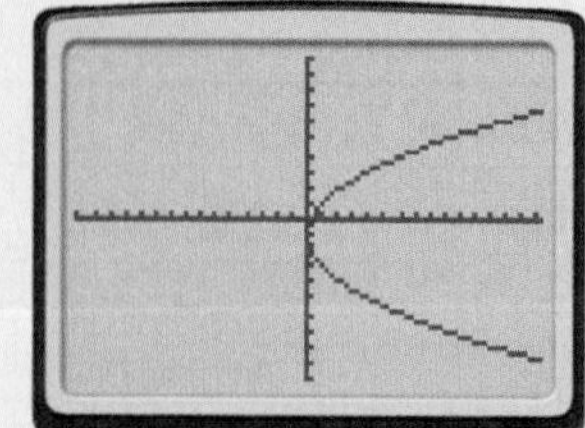

8. ellipse with center (0, 0), and intercepts (±3.5, 0) and (0, ≈ ±1.98)

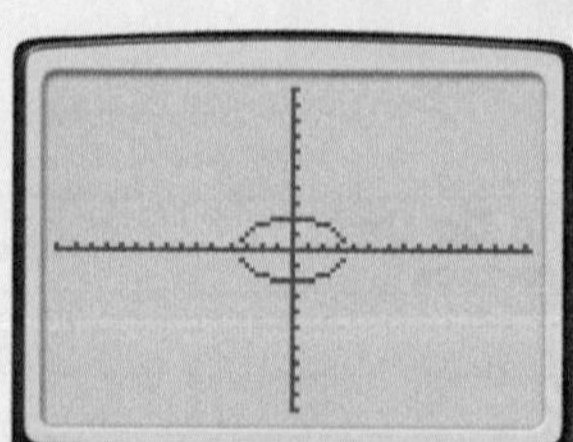

9. B
10. center: (3, −3); $r = 12$
11. center: (8, −2.5); $r = 12.5$

10-2 Circles *(pp. 729–734)*

EXAMPLES

- **Write the equation of the circle with center $(-5, 9)$ and radius $r = 16$.**

Substitute into the general equation of a circle, $(x - h)^2 + (y - k)^2 = r^2$.

$$\left(x - (-5)\right)^2 + (y - 9)^2 = 16^2$$

$$(x + 5)^2 + (y - 9)^2 = 256 \quad \textit{Simplify.}$$

- **Write an equation of the line that is tangent at (12, 9) to the circle with equation $x^2 + y^2 = 225$.**

The circle has center $(0, 0)$. The tangent is perpendicular to the radius at the point of tangency.

Find the slope of the radius and the slope of the tangent.

$m_r = \frac{9 - 0}{12 - 0} = \frac{9}{12} = \frac{3}{4}$ *The slope of the radius is $\frac{3}{4}$.*

$m_t = -\frac{4}{3}$ *Use the negative reciprocal.*

$y - 9 = -\frac{4}{3}(x - 12)$ *Use point-slope form.*

EXERCISES

Find the center and the radius of each circle.

12. $(x - 6)^2 + y^2 = 361$
13. $(x + 12)^2 + (y - 4)^2 = 15$

Write the equation of each circle.

14. center $(8, -7)$ and radius $r = 14$
15. center $(3, 6)$ and containing the point $(7, -2)$
16. diameter with endpoints $(2, 5)$ and $(-8, 11)$

Write an equation of the line that is tangent to the given circle at the given point.

17. $x^2 + y^2 = 34$ at $(3, 5)$
18. $(x + 3)^2 + y^2 = 16$ at $(-3, 4)$
19. $(x - 2)^2 + (y + 7)^2 = 44$ at $(6, -2)$
20. $(x + 4)^2 + (y - 1)^2 = 89$ at $(1, -7)$

10-3 Ellipses *(pp. 736–742)*

EXAMPLE

- **Graph $\frac{(x+1)^2}{25} + \frac{(y-4)^2}{9} = 1$. Then find the foci of the ellipse.**

Rewrite the equation as $\frac{(x+1)^2}{5^2} + \frac{(y-4)^2}{3^2} = 1$.

The center is $(-1, 4)$. Because $5 > 3$, the major axis is horizontal, $a = 5$ and $b = 3$. The vertices are $(-1 \pm 5, 4)$, or $(-6, 4)$ and $(4, 4)$. The co-vertices are $(-1, 4 \pm 3)$ or $(-1, 7)$ and $(-1, 1)$.

In an ellipse, $c^2 = a^2 - b^2$. In this ellipse, $c^2 = 5^2 - 3^2 = 16$, so $c = 4$.

The foci are $(-1 \pm 4, 4)$, or $(-5, 4)$ and $(3, 4)$.

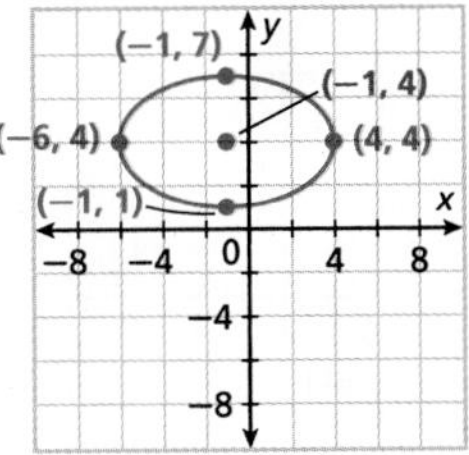

EXERCISES

Find the center, vertices, co-vertices, and foci of each ellipse. Then graph.

21. $\frac{x^2}{9} + \frac{y^2}{36} = 1$
22. $25x^2 + 64y^2 = 1600$
23. $\frac{(x-3)^2}{49} + \frac{(y+2)^2}{64} = 1$

Find the equation of each ellipse.

24.

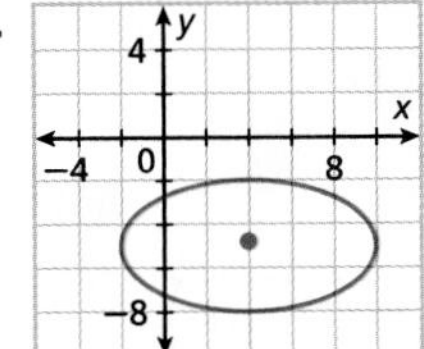

25. co-vertices at $(12, 0)$ and $(-12, 0)$ and major axis length 30
26. vertices at $(-8, 3)$ and $(4, 3)$ and foci at $(-5, 3)$ and $(1, 3)$

Answers

12. center: $(6, 0)$; $r = 19$
13. center: $(-12, 4)$; $r = \sqrt{15}$
14. $(x - 8)^2 + (y + 7)^2 = 196$
15. $(x - 3)^2 + (y - 6)^2 = 80$
16. $(x + 3)^2 + (y - 8)^2 = 34$
17. $y - 5 = -\frac{3}{5}(x - 3)$
18. $y = 4$
19. $y + 2 = -\frac{4}{5}(x - 6)$
20. $y + 7 = \frac{5}{8}(x - 1)$
21. center: $(0, 0)$; vertices: $(0, \pm 6)$; co-vertices: $(\pm 3, 0)$; foci: $(0, \pm 3\sqrt{3})$

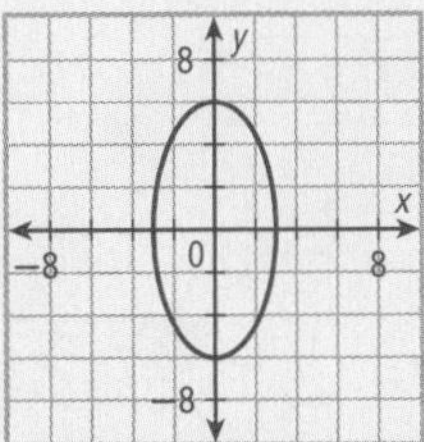

22. center: $(0, 0)$; vertices: $(\pm 8, 0)$; co-vertices: $(0, \pm 5)$; foci: $(\pm\sqrt{39}, 0)$

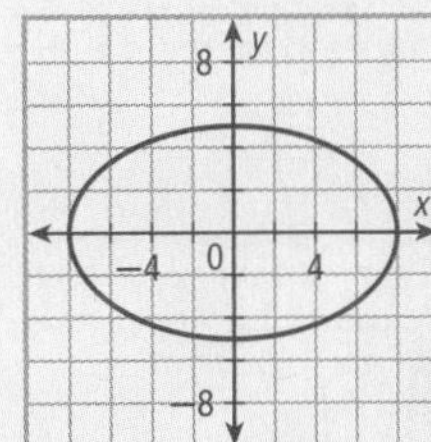

23. center: $(3, -2)$; vertices: $(3, 6)$, $(3, -10)$; co-vertices: $(10, -2)$, $(-4, -2)$; foci: $(3, -2 \pm \sqrt{15})$

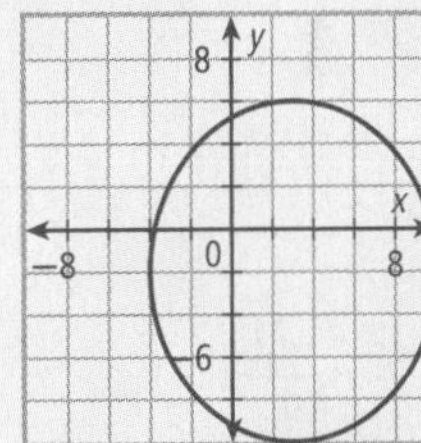

24. $\frac{(x - 4)^2}{36} + \frac{(y + 5)^2}{9} = 1$
25. $\frac{x^2}{144} + \frac{y^2}{225} = 1$
26. $\frac{(x + 2)^2}{36} + \frac{(y - 3)^2}{27} = 1$

Answers

27. center: $(0, 0)$; vertices: $(\pm5, 0)$; co-vertices: $(0, \pm7)$; foci: $(\pm\sqrt{74}, 0)$; asymptotes: $y = \pm\frac{7}{5}x$

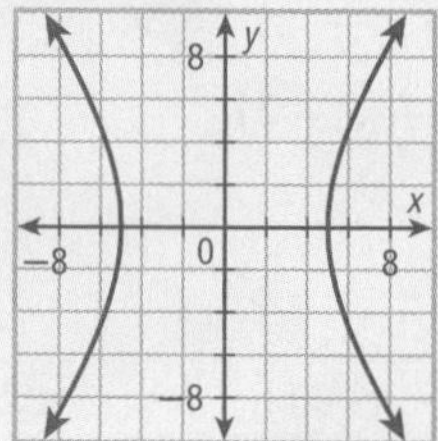

28. center: $(0, 0)$; vertices: $(0, \pm6)$; co-vertices: $(\pm8, 0)$; foci: $(0, \pm10)$; asymptotes: $y = \pm\frac{3}{4}x$

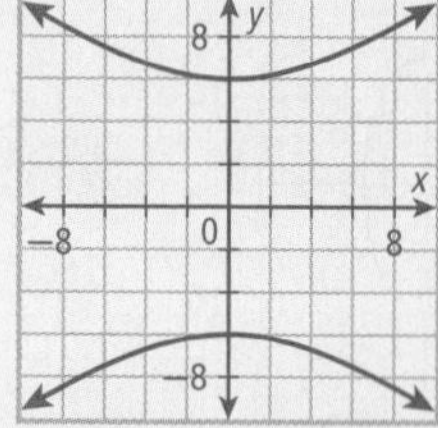

29. center: $(3, -6)$; vertices: $(5, -6)$, $(1, -6)$; co-vertices: $(3, 1)$, $(3, -13)$; foci: $(3 \pm \sqrt{53}, -6)$; asymptotes $y + 6 = \pm\frac{7}{2}(x - 3)$

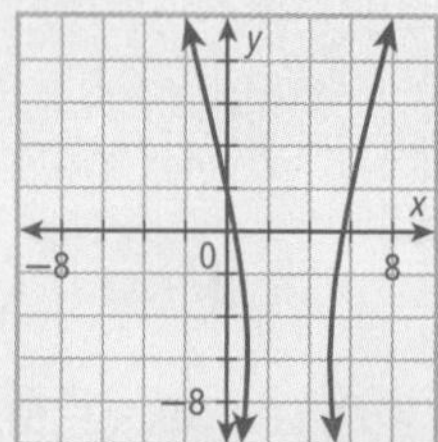

30. $\frac{x^2}{25} - \frac{y^2}{36} = 1$

31. $\frac{x^2}{121} - \frac{y^2}{16} = 1$

32. $\frac{y^2}{25} - \frac{x^2}{36} = 1$

33. $\frac{(y-5)^2}{25} - \frac{(x+7)^2}{144} = 1$

34. vertex: $(0, 0)$; $p = -3$; axis of symmetry: $x = 0$; focus: $(0, -3)$; directrix: $y = 3$

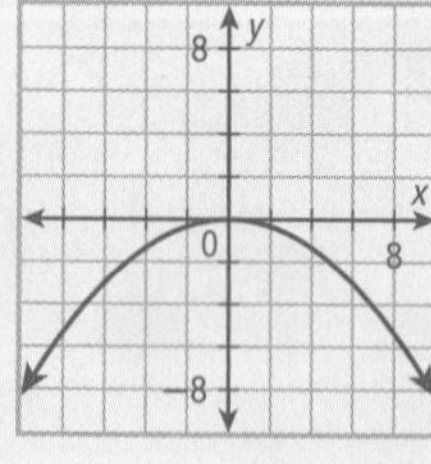

10-4 Hyperbolas *(pp. 744–750)*

EXAMPLE

- **Find the center, vertices, co-vertices, foci, and asymptotes of $\frac{y^2}{16} - \frac{x^2}{9} = 1$. Then graph.**

The equation is in the form $\frac{y^2}{a^2} - \frac{x^2}{b^2}$, so the transverse axis is vertical. The center is $(0, 0)$.

Because $a = 4$ and $b = 3$, the vertices are $(0, 4)$ and $(0, -4)$ and the co-vertices are $(3, 0)$ and $(-3, 0)$. The equations of the asymptotes are $y = \frac{4}{3}x$ and $y = -\frac{4}{3}x$.

In a hyperbola, $c^2 = a^2 + b^2$. In this hyperbola, $c^2 = 4^2 + 3^2 = 25$, so $c = 5$ and the foci are $(0, 5)$ and $(0, -5)$.

Draw a box by using the vertices and co-vertices. Draw the asymptotes through the corners of the box. Draw the hyperbola by using the vertices and the asymptotes.

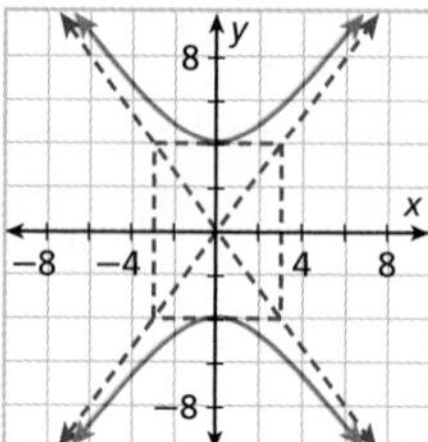

EXERCISES

Find the center, vertices, co-vertices, foci, and asymptotes of each hyperbola, and then graph.

27. $\frac{x^2}{25} - \frac{y^2}{49} = 1$

28. $64y^2 - 36x^2 = 2304$

29. $\frac{(x-3)^2}{4} - \frac{(y+6)^2}{49} = 1$

Write an equation in standard form for each hyperbola.

30.

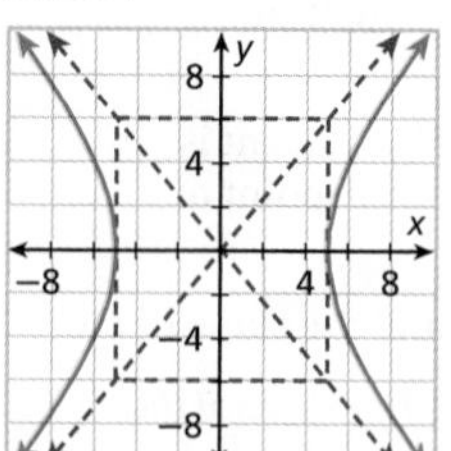

31. vertices $(11, 0)$ and $(-11, 0)$ and conjugate axis length 8

32. co-vertices $(6, 0)$ and $(-6, 0)$ and asymptotes $y = \frac{5}{6}x$ and $y = -\frac{5}{6}x$

33. length of transverse axis 10 and foci at $(-7, 18)$ and $(-7, -8)$

10-5 Parabolas *(pp. 751–757)*

EXAMPLE

- **Find the vertex, value of p, axis of symmetry, focus, and directrix of $x - 2 = -\frac{1}{16}(y + 3)^2$. Then graph.**

The equation is in the form $x - h = \frac{1}{4p}(y - k)^2$ with $p < 0$, so the graph opens to the left.

The vertex is $(2, -3)$, and the axis of symmetry is $y = -3$.

Because $\frac{1}{4p} = -\frac{1}{16}$, $p = -4$. The focus is $(2 - 4, -3)$, or $(-2, -3)$.

The directrix is $x = 2 + 4$, or $x = 6$.

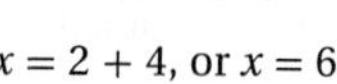

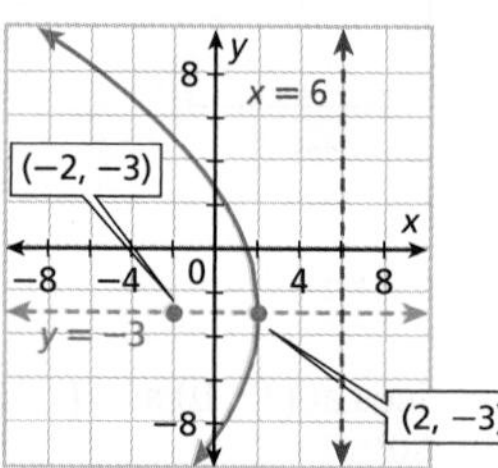

EXERCISES

Find the vertex, value of p, axis of symmetry, focus, and directrix for each parabola. Then graph.

34. $y = -\frac{1}{12}x^2$

35. $x = 2y^2$

36. $y - 5 = (x + 4)^2$

37. $x - 4 = -\frac{1}{6}(y + 2)^2$

Write the equation in standard form for each parabola.

38.

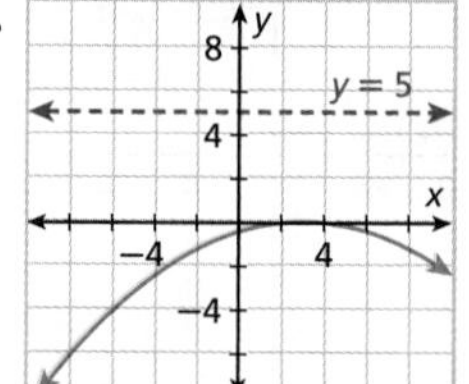

39. vertex $(4, 6)$, axis of symmetry $y = 6$, $p = -2.5$

40. focus $(12, -4)$ and directrix $x = 6$

35. vertex: $(0, 0)$; $p = \frac{1}{8}$; axis of symmetry: $y = 0$; focus: $\left(\frac{1}{8}, 0\right)$; directrix: $x = -\frac{1}{8}$

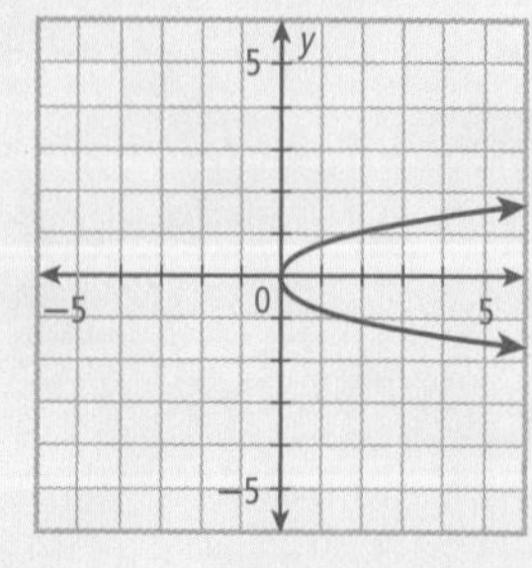

36. vertex: $(-4, 5)$; $p = \frac{1}{4}$; axis of symmetry: $x = -4$; focus: $\left(-4, 5\frac{1}{4}\right)$; directrix: $y = 4\frac{3}{4}$

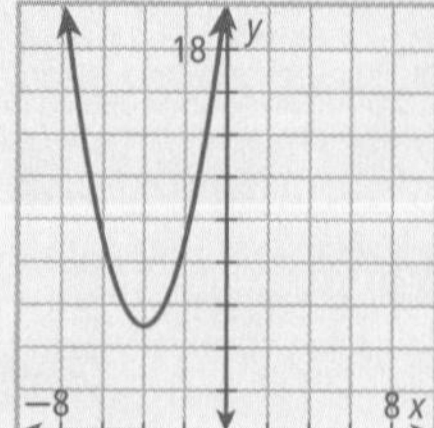

10-6 Identifying Conic Sections *(pp. 760–766)*

EXAMPLES

- **Identify the conic section represented by $3x^2 + 5xy - 8y^2 + 3x - 5y = 2$.**

$A = 3, B = 5, C = -8$ *Identify values of A, B, and C.*

$B^2 - 4AC = 5^2 - 4(3)(-8) = 121$ *Substitute.*

Because $B^2 - 4AC > 0$, the equation represents a hyperbola.

- **Find the standard form of the equation by completing the square. Then identify the conic.**

$y^2 - 4x - 10y = -13$

$y^2 - 10y + \blacksquare = 4x - 13 + \blacksquare$ *Rearrange.*

$y^2 - 10y + \left(\frac{10}{2}\right)^2 = 4x - 13 + \left(\frac{10}{2}\right)^2$ *Add $\left(\frac{10}{2}\right)^2$ to both sides.*

$(y-5)^2 = 4x + 12$ *Factor, and simplify.*

$x + 3 = \frac{1}{4}(y-5)^2$ *Rewrite in standard form.*

The equation represents a parabola.

EXERCISES

Identify the conic section that each equation represents.

41. $\frac{x^2}{12} = 1 - \frac{y^2}{9}$
42. $(x-5)^2 = \frac{2}{3}(y+4)^2 + 1$
43. $(x-8)^2 = \frac{1}{12}(y+5)$
44. $7x^2 + 7y^2 - 15x = 25$
45. $15x^2 - 6xy + 9y^2 - 12x - 12y + 15 = 0$

Find the standard form of each equation by completing the square. Then identify and graph each conic.

46. $y^2 - 4x + 12y = -24$
47. $2x^2 + 6y^2 + 16x = -20$
48. $x^2 + y^2 + 10x - 8y + 5 = 0$
49. $4x^2 - 8y^2 + 8x - 48y - 100 = 0$

10-7 Solving Nonlinear Systems *(pp. 768–775)*

EXAMPLE

- **Solve $\begin{cases} x^2 - y^2 = 16 \\ y^2 - x = 4 \end{cases}$ by using the substitution method.**

The graph of the first equation is a hyperbola. The graph of the second equation is a parabola. There may be as many as four points of intersection.

It is simplest to solve for y^2 because both equations have y^2 terms.

$y^2 = x + 4$ *Solve the second equation for y^2.*

$x^2 - (x+4) = 16$ *Substitute this value into the first equation.*

$(x-5)(x+4) = 0$ *Simplify, and factor.*

$x = 5$ or $x = -4$

$y^2 = 5 + 4 = 9$ or $y^2 = -4 + 4 = 0$ *Substitute.*

$y = \pm 3$ when $x = 5$ and $y = 0$ when $x = -4$. The solution set is $\{(5, 3), (5, -3), (-4, 0)\}$.

EXERCISES

Solve each system of equations by graphing.

50. $\begin{cases} y + 6 = \frac{1}{2}(x-2)^2 \\ y + 2x = -2 \end{cases}$
51. $\begin{cases} 25x^2 + 16y^2 = 400 \\ 16y = -5(x-4)^2 \end{cases}$

Solve each system by using the substitution method.

52. $\begin{cases} 2x^2 - 2y^2 = 56 \\ x^2 + y^2 = 100 \end{cases}$
53. $\begin{cases} 2x^2 - y^2 = 14 \\ y - 2x = -4 \end{cases}$

Solve each system by using the elimination method.

54. $\begin{cases} 4y^2 - 8x^2 = 16 \\ 4x^2 + 5y^2 = 20 \end{cases}$
55. $\begin{cases} 3x^2 - 2y^2 = 76 \\ 5x^2 + 3y^2 = 228 \end{cases}$

Solve each system by using any method.

56. $\begin{cases} 3x^2 + 5y^2 = 192 \\ 3y - x = 16 \end{cases}$
57. $\begin{cases} \frac{x^2}{25} - \frac{y^2}{16} = 1 \\ 30x^2 + 20y^2 = 600 \end{cases}$

Answers

37. vertex: $(4, -2)$; $p = -1.5$; axis of symmetry: $y = -2$; focus: $(2.5, -2)$; directrix: $x = 5.5$

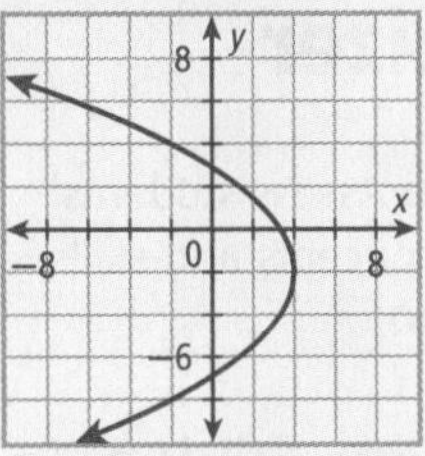

38. $y = -\frac{1}{20}(x-3)^2$
39. $x - 4 = -\frac{1}{10}(y-6)^2$
40. $x - 9 = \frac{1}{12}(y+4)^2$
41. ellipse
42. hyperbola
43. parabola
44. circle
45. ellipse
46. $x + 3 = \frac{1}{4}(y+6)^2$; parabola

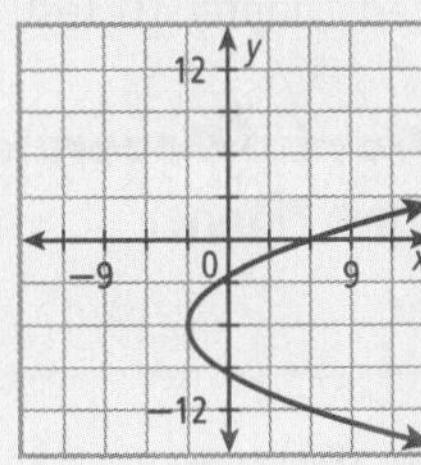

47. $\frac{(x+4)^2}{6} + \frac{y^2}{2} = 1$; ellipse

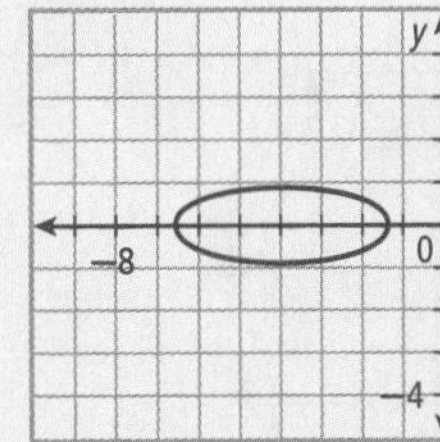

48. $(x+5)^2 + (y-4)^2 = 36$; circle

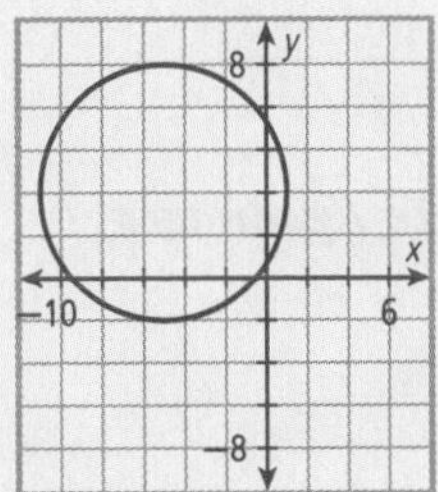

49. $\frac{(x+1)^2}{8} - \frac{(y+3)^2}{4} = 1$; hyperbola

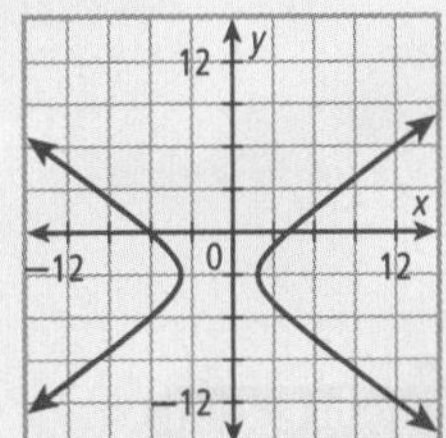

Answers

50. $(2, -6), (-2, 2)$
51. $(4, 0), (0, -5)$
52. $(8, \pm 6), (-8, \pm 6)$
53. $(3, 2), (5, 6)$
54. $(0, 2), (0, -2)$
55. $(6, 4), (6, -4), (-6, 4), (-6, -4)$
56. $(2, 6), (-7, 3)$
57. no solution

Organizer

Objective: Assess students' mastery of concepts and skills in Chapter 10.

Online Edition

Resources

Assessment Resources

Chapter 10 Tests
- Free Response (Levels A, B, C)
- Multiple Choice (Levels A, B, C)
- Performance Assessment

***IDEA Works!* CD-ROM**

Modified Chapter 10 Test

Test & Practice Generator One-Stop Planner®

Answers

3. center: $(-4, 2)$; vertices: $(-4, 9)$, $(-4, -5)$; co-vertices: $(-8, 2)$, $(0, 2)$; foci: $\left(-4, 2 \pm \sqrt{33}\right)$

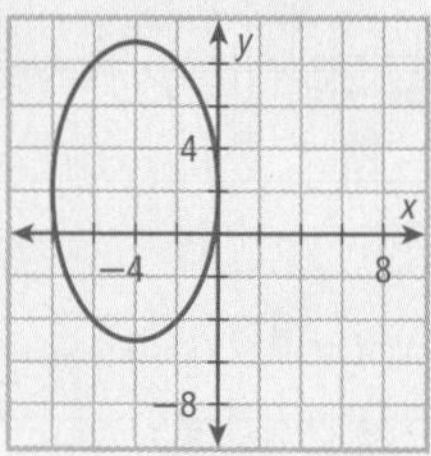

State Resources

1. The transmission of a radio signal can be received at the locations $(1, -10)$ and $(-11, 6)$. Write an equation for the range of the signal if a line between the locations represents a diameter of the range. $(x + 5)^2 + (y + 2)^2 = 100$
2. Write the equation of the line that is tangent to $(x + 2)^2 + (y - 8)^2 = 40$ at $(3, -1)$. $y + 1 = \frac{5}{9}(x - 3)$
3. Find the center, vertices, co-vertices, and foci of the ellipse with equation $49(x + 4)^2 + 16(y - 2)^2 = 784$. Then graph.
4. A shelter for a patch of young strawberry plants is constructed in the form of an ellipse. If the shelter is 4.5 feet high at its highest point and the patch is 19 feet wide, write an equation for the ellipse. $\frac{x^2}{90.25} + \frac{y^2}{20.25} = 1$
5. Find the center, vertices, co-vertices, foci, and asymptotes of the hyperbola with equation $\frac{x^2}{25} - \frac{y^2}{144} = 1$. Then graph.
6. Write the equation of the hyperbola with vertices $(0, 7)$ and $(0, -7)$ and conjugate axis length 28. $\frac{y^2}{49} - \frac{x^2}{196} = 1$
7. Find the vertex, value of p, axis of symmetry, focus, and directrix of the parabola with equation $y + 4 = \frac{1}{24}(x - 2)^2$. Then graph.
8. The filament of a flashlight bulb is located at the focus, which is 0.75 centimeters from the vertex of the flashlight's parabolic reflector. Write an equation for the cross section of the parabolic reflector if the vertex is at the origin and the reflector is pointed to the left. $x = -\frac{1}{3}y^2$

Identify the conic section that each equation represents.

9. $\frac{x - 2}{4} = \frac{(y + 5)^2}{12}$ parabola
10. $1 - \frac{(x + 5)^2}{8} = \frac{(y - 4)^2}{8}$ circle
11. $7x^2 + 5xy - 2y^2 + 8x - 26 = 0$ hyperbola

Find the standard form of each equation by completing the square. Then identify the conic.

12. $x^2 + y^2 - 16x + 20y + 124 = 0$ $(x - 8)^2 + (y + 10)^2 = 40$; circle
13. $6x^2 + 4y^2 + 84x - 24y + 306 = 0$

Find the solutions to the system by using the substitution or elimination method.

14. $\begin{cases} 2y - 3x = 1 \\ x + 4 = \frac{1}{4}(y - 2)^2 \end{cases}$
15. $\begin{cases} y + x = 2 \\ x^2 + y^2 = 52 \end{cases}$
16. $\begin{cases} 3x^2 - 4y^2 = 143 \\ 5x^2 - 5y^2 = 280 \end{cases}$
17. Two trapeze artists are swinging through the air along the paths shown in the graph. One performer releases the swing and travels in a path that can be modeled by the equation $y = -\frac{1}{4}x^2 + 16$. The performer's partner moves along a path that can be modeled by the equation $y = \frac{1}{2}x^2 + 16$. At what point will the performer be caught by his partner? $(0, 16)$

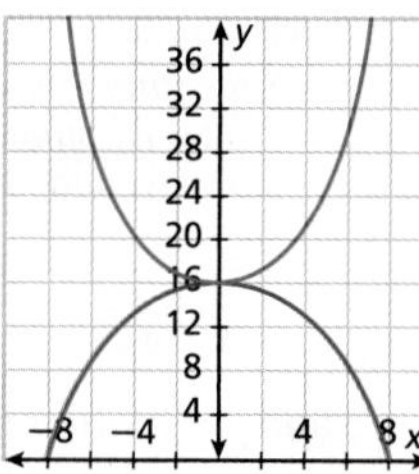

Answers

5.

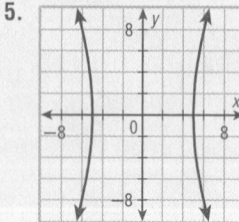

center: $(0, 0)$;
vertices: $(\pm 5, 0)$;
co-vertices: $(0, \pm 12)$;
foci: $(\pm 13, 0)$;
asymptotes: $y = \pm\frac{12}{5}x$

7. vertex: $(2, -4)$; $p = 6$; axis of symmetry: $x = 2$; focus: $(2, 2)$; directrix: $y = -10$

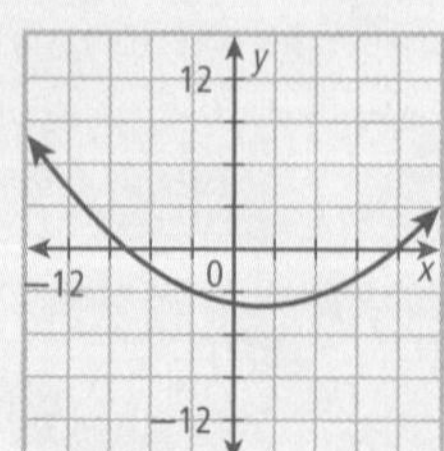

13. $\frac{(x + 7)^2}{4} + \frac{(y - 3)^2}{6} = 1$; ellipse
14. $(5, 8)$, $\left(-\frac{11}{9}, -\frac{4}{3}\right)$
15. $(6, -4)$, $(-4, 6)$
16. $(9, \pm 5)$, $(-9, \pm 5)$

College Entrance Exam Practice

FOCUS ON SAT MATHEMATICS SUBJECT TESTS

The topics covered on each SAT Mathematics Subject Tests vary only slightly each time the test is administered. You can find out the general distribution of questions across topics and then determine which areas need more of your attention when you are studying for the test.

HOT TIP! To prepare for the SAT Mathematics Subject Tests, start reviewing course material a couple of months before your test date. Take sample tests to find the areas you might need to focus on more. Remember that you are not expected to have studied all of the topics on the test.

You may want to time yourself as you take this practice test. It should take you about 6 minutes to complete.

1. The graph of the equation $x^2 + y^2 - 2x + 3y + 8 = 0$ is which of the following?
   (A) Parabola
   (B) Circle
   (C) Hyperbola
   (D) Ellipse
   (E) Point

2. What is the length of the major axis of the ellipse with equation $\frac{(x-1)^2}{4} + (y+3)^2 = 9$?
   (A) 2
   (B) 3
   (C) 4
   (D) 6
   (E) 12

3. What is the distance from the focus to the vertex of a parabola with equation $x = \frac{1}{12}(y-1)^2$?
   (A) 3
   (B) 6
   (C) 12
   (D) 48
   (E) 144

4. Which of the following is the equation of an asymptote of the graph of $\frac{(y+2)^2}{9} - \frac{(x-5)^2}{4} = 1$?
   (A) $y + 2 = \frac{3}{2}(x-5)$
   (B) $y + 2 = \frac{2}{3}(x-5)$
   (C) $y + 2 = \frac{9}{4}(x-5)$
   (D) $y = \frac{3}{2}x$
   (E) $y = \frac{2}{3}x$

5. The circle with equation $x^2 + y^2 + sx + ty + 33 = 0$ has center $(4, 5)$. What is $\frac{s}{t}$?
   (A) $-\frac{5}{4}$
   (B) $-\frac{4}{5}$
   (C) $\frac{4}{5}$
   (D) $\frac{5}{4}$
   (E) There is not enough information to determine the answer.

College Entrance Exam Practice CHAPTER 10

Organizer

Objective: Provide practice for college entrance exams such as the SAT Mathematics Subject Tests.

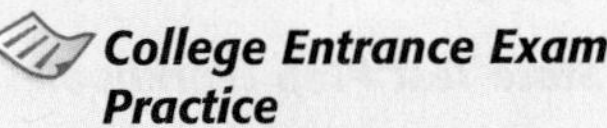

Resources

College Entrance Exam Practice

Questions on the SAT Mathematics Subject Tests Levels 1 and 2 represent the following math content areas:

	Level	
	IC	**IIC**
Algebra	30%	18%
Plane Euclidean Geometry	20%	0%
Coordinate Geometry	12%	12%
Three-dimensional Geometry	6%	8%
Trigonometry	8%	20%
Functions	12%	24%
Statistics/Probability	6%	6%
Miscellaneous	6%	12%

Items on this page focus on:
- Algebra

Text References:

Item	1	2	3	4	5
Lesson	10-6	10-3	10-5	10-4	10-2

Test Prep Doctor

1. Students may choose **C** because they identified the first three coefficients incorrectly as *A, B,* and *C.* Remind students that *A* is the coefficient of x^2, *B* is the coefficient of *xy*, and *C* is the coefficient of y^2.
2. Students may choose **D** because they found the length of the minor axis or forgot to double the value of *a* to find the length of the major axis. Point out that *a* is half the length of the major axis.
3. Students may choose **D** if they multiply by 4 instead of diving by 4. Review the equation of a parabola and the role of the parameter *p*.
4. Students who chose **B** may have reversed the roles of *a* and *b*. Remind students that *a* is always associated with the positive term of a hyperbola.
5. Students may not know how to approach solving this problem. Suggest that students use the given center and the general formula for a circle, then multiply out the squared terms to find the coefficients of the *x*- and *y*-terms.

Organizer

Objective: Provide opportunities to learn and practice common test-taking strategies.

Online Edition

Resources

State Test Prep Workbook

State Test Prep CD-ROM

***State Test Practice* Online**

go.hrw.com
KEYWORD: MB7 TestPrep

TEST PREP DOCTOR As students practice the strategy of solving context-based multiple-choice test items, review how students can also use the elimination method to quickly eliminate answer choices. For instance, in **Item A,** point out that if they know the equation for a parabola with a horizontal axis of symmetry, they can eliminate answer choices **A** and **B** because these equations are in the form of a vertical axis of symmetry.

Standardized Test Strategies

Multiple Choice: Context-Based Test Items

You will encounter some multiple-choice test items where the problem statement does not give you an actual problem to solve but requires you to use the answer choices provided to determine which choice fits the context of the problem statement. Depending on the problem, you can use a variety of methods, such as substitution, graphing, or elimination, to obtain the correct answer.

EXAMPLE 1

Which of the following equations, when graphed, has x-intercepts at $(5, 0)$ and $(-5, 0)$?

Ⓐ $2x^2 + 25y^2 = 150$

Ⓑ $8x^2 + 50y^2 = 200$

Ⓒ $5x^2 + 5y^2 = 100$

Ⓓ $4x^2 + 5y^2 = 50$

Although there are many equations that have x-intercepts at $(5, 0)$ and $(-5, 0)$, you need to select the equation from the four choices given. For this problem, you can use either of these two methods:

Substitution Method Substitute $x = 5$ and $y = 0$ into the equation, and simplify. Then substitute $x = -5$ and $y = 0$ into the equation, and simplify. Find which equation makes a true statement with the given x-intercepts.

Try choice A: $2x^2 + 25y^2 = 150$; $2(5)^2 + 25(0)^2 = 50$

Because the first equation does not make a true statement, $150 \neq 50$, choice A is incorrect.

Try choice B: $8x^2 + 50y^2 = 200$; $8(5)^2 + 50(0)^2 = 200$; $8(-5)^2 + 50(0)^2 = 200$

Because both equations make a true statement, choice B is correct.

Try choice C and choice D to confirm that you found the correct answer.

Graphing Method Solve each equation in the answer choices for y. Then graph each equation on a graphing calculator. Look for the graph that intersects the x-axis at $(5, 0)$ and $(-5, 0)$.

Try choice A: $2x^2 + 25y^2 = 150$

$$y = \pm\sqrt{\frac{(150 - 2x^2)}{25}}$$

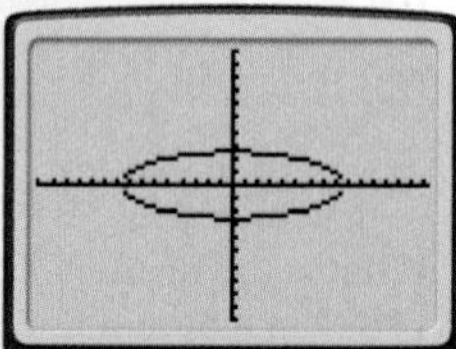

When graphed on a calculator, the graph crosses the x-axis at about (8.5, 0) and (−8.5, 0). Choice A is incorrect.

Try choice B: $8x^2 + 50y^2 = 200$

$$y = \pm\sqrt{\frac{(200 - 8x^2)}{50}}$$

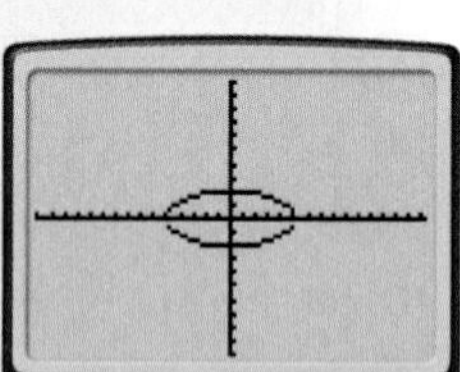

When graphed on a calculator, the graph crosses the x-axis at (5, 0) and (−5, 0). Choice B is the correct answer.

Try choice C and choice D to confirm that you found the correct answer.

Underline the context of the problem statement to make sure that you are clear about what is being asked.

Read each test item and answer the questions that follow.

Item A
Which equation, when graphed, is a parabola that opens to the right?

Ⓐ $4y - 2x^2 = 6$ Ⓒ $4x - 2y^2 = 6$

Ⓑ $4y + 2x^2 = 6$ Ⓓ $4x + 2y^2 = 6$

1. On a coordinate grid, sketch two or three parabolas that open to the right. Can they all be represented by the same equation? If not, what do these equations have in common?
2. From what you know about parabolas, can any of the answer choices be eliminated? Explain.
3. Describe how to determine which answer choice is correct.

Item B
The graph of which of the following ellipses has the smallest distance between foci?

Ⓕ $\frac{(x+16)^2}{64} + \frac{(y-9)^2}{25} = 1$

Ⓖ $\frac{x^2}{4} + \frac{y^2}{81} = 1$

Ⓗ $\frac{(x-1)^2}{1} + \frac{(y-1)^2}{100} = 1$

Ⓙ $\frac{x^2}{289} + \frac{y^2}{169} = 1$

4. If you read only the problem statement and not the answer choices, can you solve the problem? Explain.
5. How can you find the distance between foci if you know a and b?

Item C
Which of the following points is inside the circle described by the following equation?

$$(x-2)^2 + (y-6)^2 = 9$$

Ⓐ $(0, 0)$ Ⓒ $(5, 6)$

Ⓑ $(-2, 4)$ Ⓓ $(3, 5)$

6. Describe how you can use your graphing calculator to determine the correct answer.
7. Can you use algebra to determine the correct answer? If so, describe your method.

Item D
A power outage affects areas L, M, and N. Which of the following best describes the power outage?

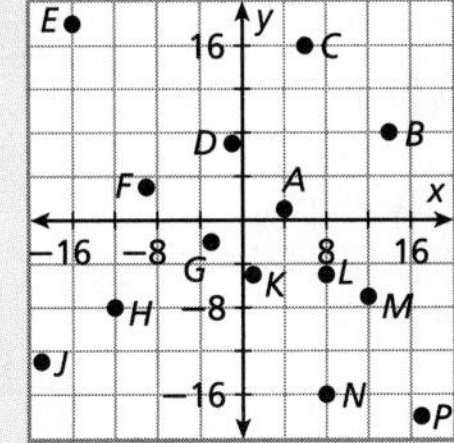
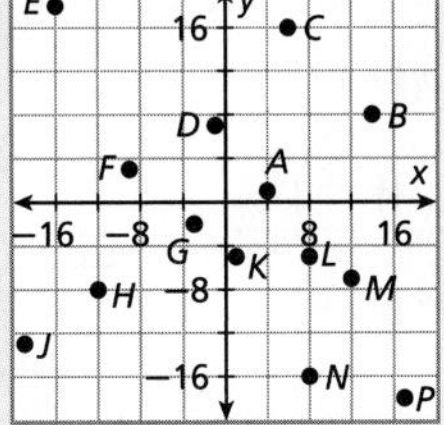

Ⓕ The main generator is located at $(12, -9)$ and shuts down power up to 9 miles away.

Ⓖ The main generator is located at $(4, -6)$ and shuts down power up to 8 miles away.

Ⓗ The main generator is located at $(10, -3)$ and shuts down power up to 5 miles away.

Ⓙ The main generator is located at $(-8, -15)$ and shuts down power up to 15 miles away.

8. What does the problem state about areas L, M, and N? What can you interpret about the areas not mentioned?
9. A student found that areas L and M are within the circle described by choice H. Can the student stop working and select choice H as the correct response? Explain.
10. Describe a method that you can use to determine the correct answer.

Answers

1. No; all of the equations have x equal to a y^2 term.
2. Yes, choices **A** and **B** can be eliminated because parabolas that have a horizontal axis of symmetry do not have an x-squared term.
3. Solve each equation in terms of y, and then graph on a graphing calculator. Determine which equation is a parabola that opens to the right. Or write each equation in terms of x, and determine which has a value of p greater than 0.
4. No, there is not enough information given.
5. Use $a^2 + b^2 = c^2$ and solve for c. This will give you each focus. Then find the distance between the foci. The one with the smallest distance is the correct choice.
6. Solve the equation for y and then graph it on a graphing calculator. Plot each ordered pair and determine which point lies within the circle.
7. Yes, substitute each ordered pair into the inequality, $(x-2)^2 + (y-6)^2 < 9$, and find which ordered pair makes a true statement.
8. It states that areas L, M, and N were affected. These three areas were all affected, but there might also be other areas affected that were not mentioned.
9. No; the student has to check for area N because the problem states that areas L, M, and N were affected.
10. Write an inequality for a circle described in each answer choice and substitute the ordered pairs for points L, M, and N into the inequality. Find the inequality that holds true for all 3 ordered pairs.

Answers to *Test Items*

A. C
B. F
C. D
D. F

State Resources

go.hrw.com
State Resources Online
KEYWORD: MB7 Resources

Organizer

Objective: Provide review and practice for Chapters 1–10 and standardized tests.

 **Online Edition**

Resources

 ***Assessment Resources***

Chapter 10 Cumulative Test

 ***State Test Prep Workbook***

 ***State Test Prep CD-ROM***

 ***State Test Practice Online***

go.hrw.com
KEYWORD: MB7 TestPrep

Answers

1. D
2. C
3. A
4. B
5. A
6. C
7. B
8. D
9. B
10. D
11. D
12. A

 *State Resources*

Core Standard	Items
3	14
4	6
5	8
6	7, 10, 16

CHAPTER 10

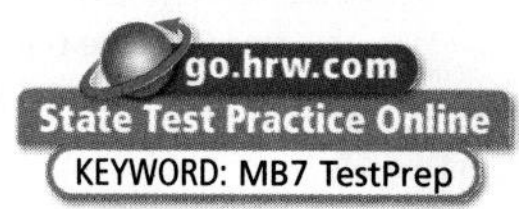

CUMULATIVE ASSESSMENT, CHAPTERS 1–10

Multiple Choice

1. Which conic section does the equation $\frac{x^2}{20} + \frac{y^2}{52} = 1$ represent?
   A. Circle
   B. Parabola
   C. Hyperbola
   D. Ellipse

2. Which is the graph of $(x + 2)^2 + (y - 2)^2 = 16$?

A. 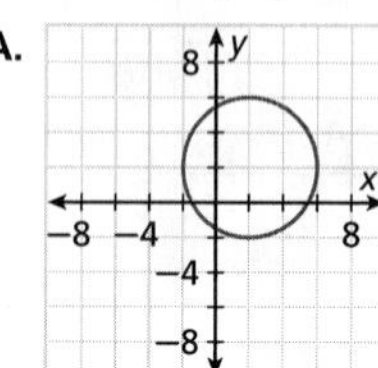

B. 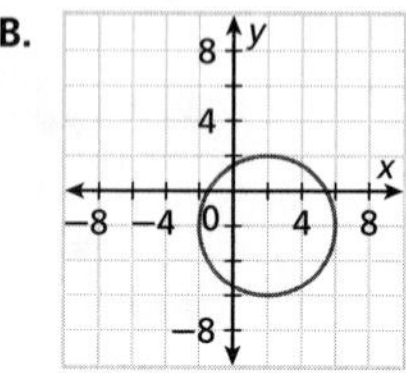

C. 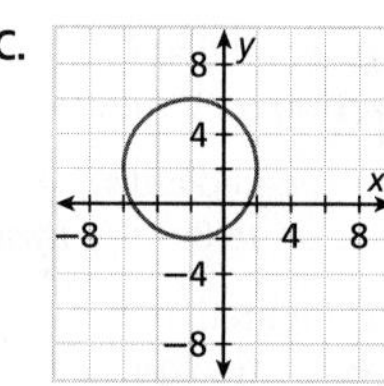

D. 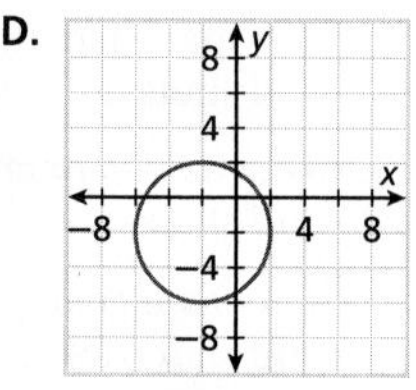

3. What system of linear inequalities can be used to represent the graph?

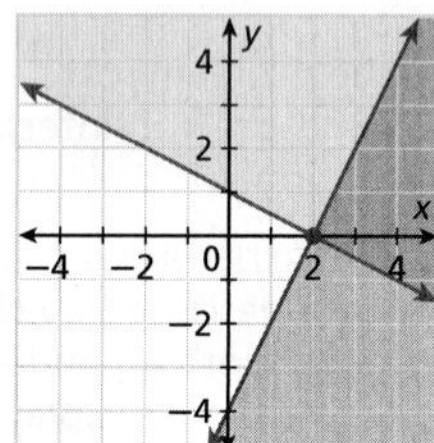

A. $\begin{cases} y \le 2x - 4 \\ 2y \ge -x + 2 \end{cases}$ B. $\begin{cases} y < 2x - 4 \\ 2y > -x + 2 \end{cases}$

C. $\begin{cases} y \le 2x - 4 \\ 2y \le -x + 2 \end{cases}$ D. $\begin{cases} y < 2x - 4 \\ 2y < -x + 2 \end{cases}$

4. What equation can be used to represent the graph?

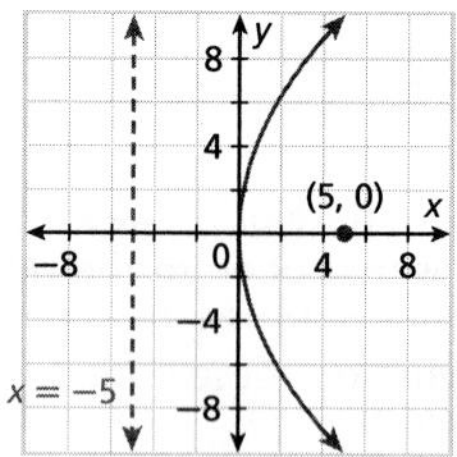

   A. $x = -\frac{1}{20}y^2$
   B. $x = \frac{1}{20}y^2$
   C. $y = \frac{1}{20}x^2$
   D. $y = -\frac{1}{20}x^2$

5. Solve $\begin{cases} x^2 + 4y^2 = 64 \\ x + 8 = \frac{1}{2}y^2 \end{cases}$ by using the substitution method.
   A. $\{(-8, 0), (0, 4), (0, -4)\}$
   B. $\{(0, -8), (4, 0), (-4, 0)\}$
   C. $\{(-8, 0), (0, 4)\}$
   D. $\{(0, 4), (0, -4)\}$

6. Find all of the roots of the polynomial equation $x^5 + x^4 - x^3 - x^2 - 20x - 20 = 0$.
   A. $\sqrt{5}, -\sqrt{5}, -1$
   B. $i, -i, \sqrt{5}, -\sqrt{5}, -1$
   C. $2i, -2i, \sqrt{5}, -\sqrt{5}, -1$
   D. $4i, -4i, \sqrt{5}, -\sqrt{5}, -1$

7. At age 20, Jon invested \$50 at 6.75% compounded continuously. Jon is now 50. What is the present value of Jon's investment?
   A. \$4,545.67
   B. \$378.81
   C. \$17,534.57
   D. \$2,314.46

TEST PREP DOCTOR

For **Item 7,** students must read the problem carefully. In order to determine which formula to use, students must identify that the investment is compounded continuously.

In Item 12, recall that the notation $(f \circ g)(x)$ is equivalent to $f(g(x))$. Begin by substituting the value for x into the function $g(x)$.

8. Simplify.

$\frac{x+1}{3x+4} + \frac{x-1}{4x-7}$

A. $\frac{2x}{7x-3}$

B. $\frac{7x^2-17x-11}{(3x+4)(4x-7)}$

C. $\frac{7x^2+17x-11}{(3x+4)(4x-7)}$

D. $\frac{7x^2-2x-11}{(3x+4)(4x-7)}$

9. What is the inverse of the function $f(x) = \frac{7x-4}{3}$?

A. $f^{-1}(x) = \frac{3}{7x-4}$

B. $f^{-1}(x) = \frac{3x+4}{7}$

C. $f^{-1}(x) = \frac{3}{7}x - \frac{3}{4}$

D. $f^{-1}(x) = \frac{3}{7}x - \frac{4}{7}$

10. Solve for x : $3^{2x-1} = 27^{x+4}$.

A. 5

B. $\frac{7}{5}$

C. -2

D. -13

11. Simplify.

$\left(\sqrt[3]{2^9}\right)^2$

A. 8

B. 16

C. 32

D. 64

12. Given $f(x) = 3x^2 - 1$ and $g(x) = \frac{1}{x+5}$, what is the value of $(f \circ g)(-1)$?

A. $-\frac{13}{16}$

B. $\frac{1}{7}$

C. $\frac{1}{4}$

D. $\frac{1}{2}$

Short Answer

13. A hyperbola has center $(3, -5)$, focus $(-10, -5)$, and vertex $(15, -5)$.

Part A Write the equation for the hyperbola.

Part B What are the equations of the asymptotes of the hyperbola?

14. The approximate heart rate of an adult can be modeled by $f(x) = -(x-5)^2 + 75$, where x is the age (in tens) of the person.

Part A Find the inverse for the function, and explain what it represents.

Part B Approximate the age of a person whose heart rate is 65.

15. The pentagon below has vertices at $(1, 2)$, $(2, 4)$, $(4, 5)$, $(5, 2)$, and $(4, -1)$.

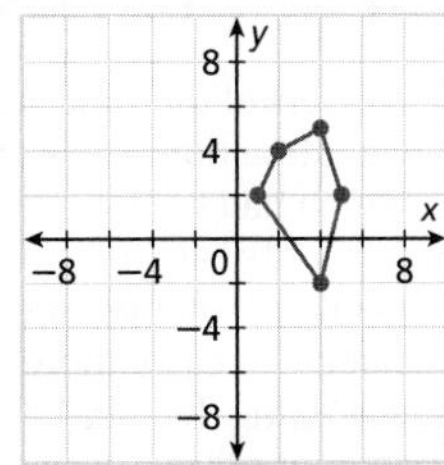

Part A Write the matrix used to transform the pentagon 3 units to the left and 5 units down.

Part B What are the coordinates of the transformed pentagon?

Extended Response

16. Joan's grandmother gave her a diamond necklace valued at \$4500. The value of the necklace is predicted to appreciate 7.5% per year.

Part A Write a function to model the predicted growth in the value of the necklace.

Part B Graph the function.

Part C What is the predicted value of the necklace in 10 years?

Part D Based on the model, what was the value of the necklace 30 years ago?

Short Answer Rubric

Items 13–15

Score 2 = Thorough understanding of mathematical concepts and processes.

Score 1 = Partial understanding of mathematical concepts and/or processes.

Score 0 = Limited or no understanding of the problem-solving concepts.

Blank = No written response.

Extended Response Rubric

Item 16

Score 4 = Thorough understanding of mathematical concepts and processes.

Score 3 = Demonstrated understanding of mathematical concepts and processes, but an error in computation or explanation.

Score 2 = Partial understanding of mathematical concepts and/or processes.

Score 1 = Limited understanding and execution of the problem-solving concepts.

Score 0 = No understanding of the problem-solving concepts.

Blank = No written response.

Answers

13. Part A: $\frac{(x-3)^2}{144} - \frac{(y+5)^2}{25} = 1$

Part B: $y + 5 = \pm\frac{5}{12}(x-3)$

14. Part A: $f^{-1}(x) = \sqrt{-x+75} + 5$; the inverse function represents the approximate age of a person (in tens) with a given heart rate.

Part B: between 81 and 82

15. Part A: $\begin{bmatrix} -3 & -3 & -3 & -3 & -3 \\ -5 & -5 & -5 & -5 & -5 \end{bmatrix}$

Part B: $(-2, -3)$, $(-1, -1)$, $(1, 0)$, $(2, -3)$, $(1, -6)$

16. Part A: $f(t) = 4500\,(1 + 0.075)^t$

Part B:

40,000
30,000
20,000
10,000
0 6 12 18 24

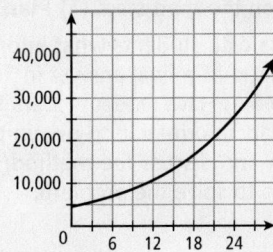

Part C: \$9274.64

Part D: \$513.99

Problem Solving on Location

Organizer

Objective: Choose appropriate problem-solving strategies and use them with skills from Chapters 9 and 10 to solve real-world problems.

PREMIER Online Edition

The First Ferris Wheel

Reading Strategies

As students read the introduction and the problems, have them make a list of the essential information that is needed to solve the problems. Also ask them to identify any mathematical or numerical information that is extraneous. For example, in **Problem 1,** the fact that each car could hold 60 passengers is not needed to solve the problem.

Using Data Have students modify the dates into appropriate independent variable values.

State Resources

go.hrw.com
State Resources Online
KEYWORD: MB7 Resources

Problem Solving on Location

ILLINOIS

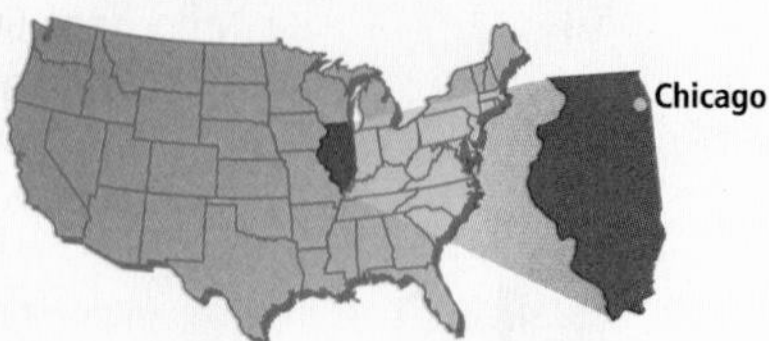

The First Ferris Wheel

The organizers of the 1893 World's Fair in Chicago wanted an attraction that would outdo the Eiffel Tower, which had been built four years earlier for the Paris World's Fair. A bridge builder named George Ferris met the challenge by designing a colossal wheel that could carry more than 2100 passengers at a time. During the fair, 1.5 million visitors paid the 50-cent fee for a 20-minute ride on Ferris's wheel.

Choose one or more strategies to solve each problem. For 1, use the table.

Building Ferris's Wheel	
Date	Total Number of Cars Attached
June 10, 1893	1
June 11, 1893	6
June 13, 1893	21

1. Each car of the wheel could carry up to 60 passengers. Because of the cars' enormous size, it took several days to hang all of the cars on the wheel. Develop a model to predict the number of cars that had been attached to the wheel by June 14, 1893. **31**
2. As the wheel revolved, the paths of the cars could be modeled by $x^2 + y^2 - 250y = 0$. Find the diameter of the wheel. **250 ft**
3. Approximately how many feet has a car traveled after one complete revolution of the wheel? **785 ft**
4. A car starts at the bottom of the wheel. After 2 min 15 s, the car's horizontal distance to the central axle is 125 ft. How long does it take the car to make one complete revolution? **9 min**

788

Problem-Solving Focus

Encourage students to use the four-step problem-solving process for the problems. Focus on the third step: **(3) Plan.**

Discuss with students what information is required as a final answer in **Problem 1.** Have students identify the necessary information to obtain the final answer and discuss the method(s) they will use to solve the problem.

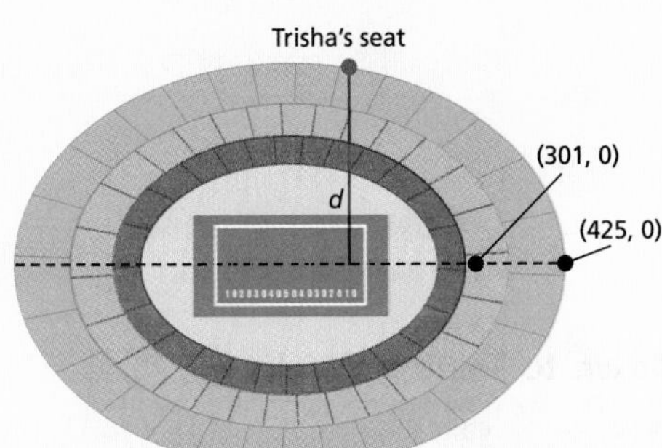

Soldier Field

Chicago's Soldier Field was built in 1924 as a multipurpose sports stadium. Since 1970, it has been the home of the National Football League's Chicago Bears. In 2003, a new 61,500-seat stadium was built within the shell of the original structure so that the historic colonnades and exterior walls of the old Soldier Field could be preserved.

Choose one or more strategies to solve each problem.

1. The renovated stadium can be modeled by an ellipse centered at the origin, a vertex at $(425, 0)$, and a focus at $(301, 0)$, measured in feet. Find the length and width of the stadium.
length: 850 ft; width: 600 ft

For 2, use the diagram.

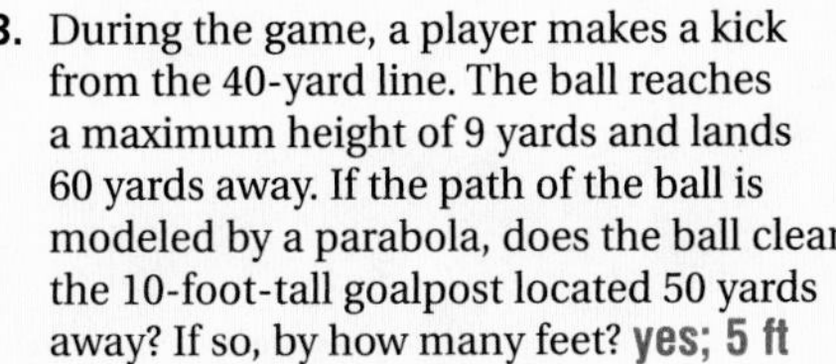

2. Trisha bought tickets to a Bears game. As shown, her seat is on the 20-yard line, in the last row of the stadium. What is the horizontal distance d from her seat to the middle of the playing field? **293 ft**

3. During the game, a player makes a kick from the 40-yard line. The ball reaches a maximum height of 9 yards and lands 60 yards away. If the path of the ball is modeled by a parabola, does the ball clear the 10-foot-tall goalpost located 50 yards away? If so, by how many feet? **yes; 5 ft**

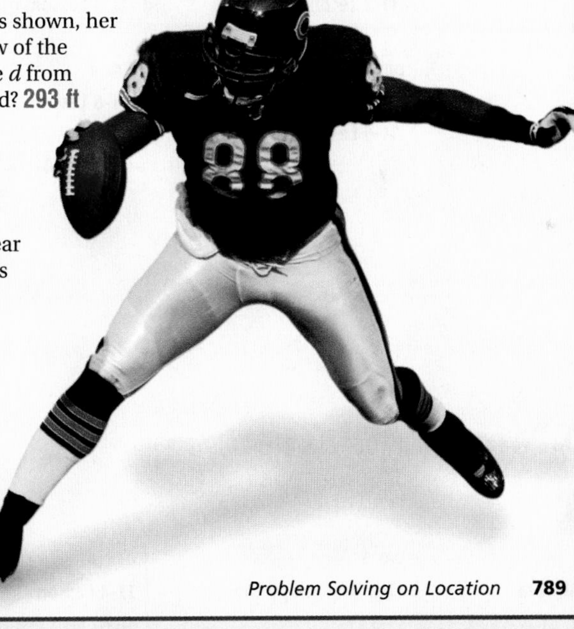

Soldier Field

Reading Strategies

Before they begin solving the problems, be sure all students are familiar with some of the basic terminology of football. You might ask a student who is a football fan to explain the layout of a field. In particular, students should understand that the field is 100 yards long, that the 50-yard line is in the middle of the field, and that the field is marked off in descending 10-yard increments on either side of this line. ENGLISH LANGUAGE LEARNERS

Using Data Have students identify some other places in the stadium by their coordinates.

Problem-Solving Focus

Encourage students to use the four-step problem-solving process for the problems. Focus on the fourth step: **(4) Look Back.**

Problems 2 and **3** of Soldier Field involve both feet and yards. Students may get incorrect answers if they don't pay attention to units. When students have completed these problems, ask them to check the units in their solutions and look back to see if these match the units in the problems.

Probability and Statistics

Section 11A

Probability

Section 11B

Data Analysis and Statistics

Pacing Guide for 45-Minute Classes

Chapter 11

Countdown to Testing Weeks 23, 24

DAY 1	DAY 2	DAY 3	DAY 4	DAY 5
11-1 Lesson	Connecting Algebra to Geometry 11-2 Lesson	11-2 Lesson 11-2 Technology Lab	11-2 Technology Lab 11-3 Lesson	11-3 Lesson 11-4 Lesson
DAY 6	**DAY 7**	**DAY 8**	**DAY 9**	**DAY 10**
11-4 Lesson Multi-Step Test Prep Ready to Go On?	11-5 Lesson	11-5 Algebra Lab 11-6 Lesson	11-6 Lesson Multi-Step Test Prep Ready to Go On?	Extension
DAY 11				
Chapter 11 Test				

Pacing Guide for 90-Minute Classes

Chapter 11

DAY 1	DAY 2	DAY 3	DAY 4	DAY 5
Chapter 10 Test 11-1 Lesson	Connecting Algebra to Geometry 11-2 Lesson 11-2 Technology Lab	11-2 Technology Lab 11-3 Lesson 11-4 Lesson	11-4 Lesson Multi-Step Test Prep Ready to Go On? 11-5 Lesson	11-5 Algebra Lab 11-6 Lesson Multi-Step Test Prep Ready to Go On?
DAY 6				
Extension Chapter 11 Test				

ONGOING ASSESSMENT and INTERVENTION

	DIAGNOSE	PRESCRIBE
Assess Prior Knowledge	**Before Chapter 11**	
	Diagnose readiness for the chapter.	Prescribe intervention.
	Are You Ready? SE p. 791	***Are You Ready? Intervention*** Skills 47, 48, 49, 84, 90
Formative Assessment	**Before Every Lesson**	
	Diagnose readiness for the lesson.	Prescribe intervention.
	Warm Up TE, every lesson	**Skills Bank** SE pp. S46–S73
		Reteach CRB, Ch. 1–11
	During Every Lesson	
	Diagnose understanding of lesson concepts.	Prescribe intervention.
	Check It Out! SE, every example	**Questioning Strategies** TE, every example
	Think and Discuss SE, every lesson	**Reading Strategies** CRB, every lesson
	Write About It SE, every lesson	***Success for ELL*** pp. 155–166
	Journal TE, every lesson	
	After Every Lesson	
	Diagnose mastery of lesson concepts.	Prescribe intervention.
	Lesson Quiz TE, every lesson	**Reteach** CRB, every lesson
	Alternative Assessment TE, every lesson	**Problem Solving** CRB, every lesson
	Test Prep SE, every lesson	**Test Prep Doctor** TE, every lesson
	Test and Practice Generator	***Homework Help* Online**
	Before Chapter 11 Testing	
	Diagnose mastery of concepts in the chapter.	Prescribe intervention.
	Ready to Go On? SE pp. 827, 845	***Ready to Go On? Intervention*** pp. 179–190
	Multi-Step Test Prep SE pp. 826, 844	**Scaffolding Questions** TE pp. 826, 844
	Section Quizzes AR pp. 205–206	
	Test and Practice Generator	
	Before High Stakes Testing	
	Diagnose mastery of benchmark concepts.	Prescribe intervention.
	College Entrance Exam Practice SE p. 853	***College Entrance Exam Practice***
	Standardized Test Prep SE pp. 856–857	***State Test Prep Workbook***
	 ***State Test Prep* CD-ROM**	
Summative Assessment	**After Chapter 11**	
	Check mastery of chapter concepts.	Prescribe intervention.
	Multiple-Choice Tests (Forms A, B, C)	**Reteach** CRB, every lesson
	Free-Response Tests (Forms A, B, C)	***Lesson Tutorial Videos*** Chapter 11
	Performance Assessment AR pp. 207–220	
	Test and Practice Generator	
	Check mastery of benchmark concepts.	Prescribe intervention.
	AYP State Tests	***State Test Prep Workbook***
	College Entrance Exams	***College Entrance Exam Practice***

KEY: **SE** = *Student Edition* **TE** = *Teacher's Edition* **CRB** = *Chapter Resource Book* **AR** = *Assessment Resources*  Available on CD-ROM Available online

Supporting the Teacher

Chapter 11 Resource Book

Practice A, B, C
pp. 3–5, 11–13, 19–21, 27–29, 35–37, 43–45

Reading Strategies ELL
pp. 10, 18, 26, 34, 42, 50

Reteach
pp. 6–7, 14–15, 22–23, 30–31, 38–39, 46–47

Problem Solving
pp. 9, 17, 25, 33, 41, 49

Challenge
pp. 8, 16, 24, 32, 40, 48

Parent Letter pp. 1–2

Transparencies

Lesson Transparencies, Volume 4 .... Chapter 11
- Warm Ups
- Teaching Transparencies
- Additional Examples
- Lesson Quizzes

Alternate Openers: Explorations 78–83

Countdown to Testing 45–48

Know-It Notebook .... Chapter 11
- Graphic Organizers

Teacher Tools

Power Presentations®
Complete PowerPoint® presentations for Chapter 11 lessons

Lesson Tutorial Videos®
Holt authors Ed Burger and Freddie Renfro present tutorials to support the Chapter 11 lessons.

One-Stop Planner®
Easy access to all Chapter 11 resources and assessments, as well as software for lesson planning, test generation, and puzzle creation

IDEA Works!®
Key Chapter 11 resources and assessments modified to address special learning needs

Lesson Plans .... pp. 78–83

Solutions Key .... Chapter 11

Algebra Posters

TechKeys

Project Teacher Support

Lab Resources

Parent Resources 

Workbooks

Homework and Practice Workbook
Teacher's Guide .... pp. 78–83

Know-It Notebook
Teacher's Guide .... Chapter 11

Problem Solving Workbook
Teacher's Guide .... pp. 78–83

State Test Prep Workbook
Teacher's Guide

Technology Highlights for the Teacher

Power Presentations

Dynamic presentations to engage students. Complete PowerPoint® presentations for every lesson in Chapter 11.

2-1 Solving One-Step Equations

Isolate a variable by using inverse operations which "undo" operations on the variable.

An equation is like a balanced scale. To keep the balance, perform the same operation on both sides.

Inverse Operations	
Operation	**Inverse Operation**
Addition	Subtraction
Subtraction	Addition

One-Stop Planner

Easy access to Chapter 11 resources and assessments. Includes lesson-planning, test-generation, and puzzle-creation software.

Premier Online Edition

Chapter 11 includes Tutorial Videos, Lesson Activities, Lesson Quizzes, Homework Help, and Chapter Project.

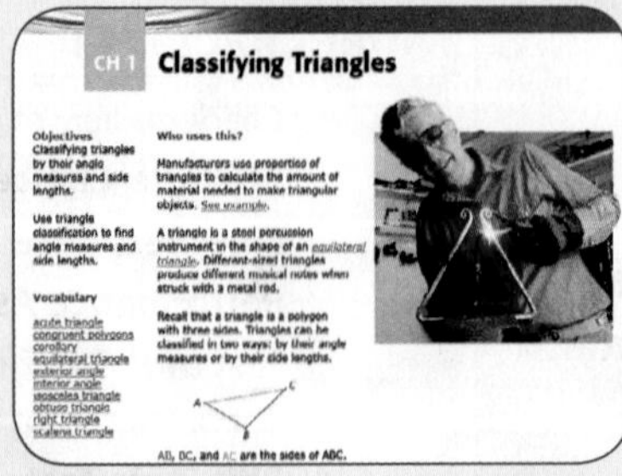

KEY: **SE** = *Student Edition* **TE** = *Teacher's Edition*  English Language Learners  Available on CD-ROM  Available online

Resources for All Learners

Algebra Lab Activities .... Chapter 11

Technology Lab Activities .... Chapter 11

Homework and Practice Workbook .... pp. 78–83

Know-It Notebook .... Chapter 11

Problem Solving Workbook .... pp. 78–83

DEVELOPING LEARNERS

Practice A .... CRB, every lesson

Reteach .... CRB, every lesson

Inclusion .... TE pp. 807, 820, 838

Questioning Strategies .... TE, every example

Modified Chapter 11 Resources .... *IDEA Works!*

Homework Help Online

ON-LEVEL LEARNERS

Practice B .... CRB, every lesson

Number Sense .... TE pp. 795, 816

Multiple Representations .... TE pp. 820

ADVANCED LEARNERS

Practice C .... CRB, every lesson

Challenge .... CRB, every lesson

Reading and Writing Math EXTENSION .... TE p. 793

Multi-Step Test Prep EXTENSION .... TE pp. 826, 844

Critical Thinking .... TE pp. 796, 813

English Language Learners

ENGLISH LANGUAGE LEARNERS

Are You Ready? Vocabulary .... SE p. 791

Vocabulary Connections .... SE p. 792

Lesson Vocabulary .... SE, every lesson

Vocabulary Exercises .... SE, every exercise set

Vocabulary Review .... SE p. 848

English Language Learners .... TE pp. 793, 796, 829, 838

Reading Strategies .... CRB, every lesson

Success for English Language Learners .... pp. 155–166

Multilingual Glossary

Reaching All Learners Through...

Graphic Organizers .... TE p. 838

Number Sense .... TE pp. 795, 817

Visual Cues .... TE pp. 795, 823, 846

Kinesthetic Experience .... TE pp. 795, 803, 812, 830

Critical Thinking .... TE pp. 796, 813

Inclusion .... TE pp. 807, 820, 838

Multiple Representations .... TE pp. 820

Curriculum Integration .... TE p. 829

Diversity .... TE p. 847

Test Prep Doctor .... TE pp. 800, 809, 817, 824, 834, 842, 853, 854, 856

Common Error Alerts .... TE pp. 797, 805, 807, 813, 817, 821, 823, 825, 831, 839, 841, 847

Scaffolding Questions .... TE pp. 826, 844

Technology Highlights for Reaching All Learners

Lesson Tutorial Videos

Starring Holt authors Ed Burger and Freddie Rentro! Live tutorials to support every lesson in Chapter 11.

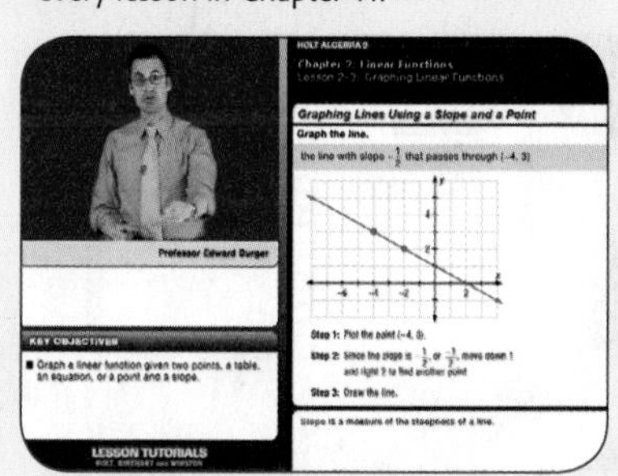

Multilingual Glossary

Searchable glossary includes definitions in English, Spanish, Vietnamese, Chinese, Hmong, Korean, and 4 other languages.

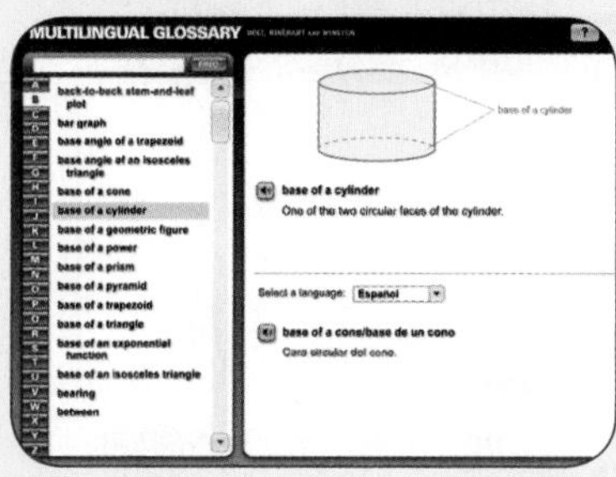

Online Interactivities

Interactive tutorials provide visually engaging alternative opportunities to learn concepts and master skills.

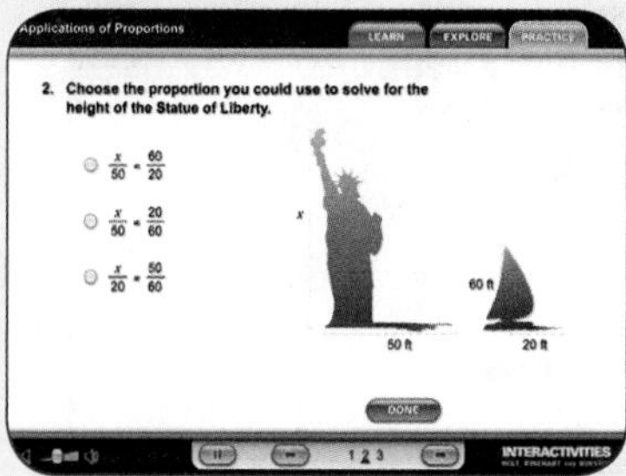

KEY: **SE** = *Student Edition* **TE** = *Teacher's Edition* **CRB** = *Chapter Resource Book* Available on CD-ROM Available online

Ongoing Assessment

Assessing Prior Knowledge

Determine whether students have the required prerequisite concepts and skills for success in Chapter 11.

Are You Ready? SPANISH .... SE p. 791
Warm Up .... TE, every lesson

Test Preparation

Provide review and practice for Chapter 11 and standardized tests.

Multi-Step Test Prep .... SE pp. 826, 844
Study Guide: Review .... SE pp. 848–851
Test Tackler .... SE pp. 854–855
Standardized Test Prep .... SE pp. 856–857
College Entrance Exam Practice .... SE p. 853
***Countdown to Testing* Transparencies** 45–48
State Test Prep Workbook
***State Test Prep* CD-ROM**
IDEA Works!

Alternative Assessment

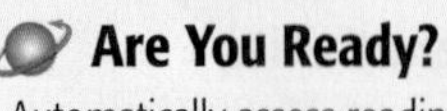

Assess students' understanding of Chapter 11 concepts and combined problem-solving skills.

Chapter 11 Project .... SE p. 790
Alternative Assessment .... TE, every lesson
Performance Assessment .... AR pp. 219–220
Portfolio Assessment .... AR p. xxxiv

Daily Assessment

Provide formative assessment for each day of Chapter 11.

Questioning Strategies .... TE, every example
Think and Discuss .... SE, every lesson
Check It Out! Exercises .... SE, every example
Write About It .... SE, every lesson
Journal .... TE, every lesson
Lesson Quiz .... TE, every lesson
Alternative Assessment .... TE, every lesson
Modified Lesson Quizzes .... *IDEA Works!*

Weekly Assessment

Provide formative assessment for each week of Chapter 11.

Multi-Step Test Prep .... SE pp. 826, 844
Ready to Go On? .... SE pp. 827, 845
Cumulative Assessment .... SE pp. 856–857
Test and Practice Generator .... *One-Stop Planner*

Formal Assessment

Provide summative assessment of Chapter 11 mastery.

Section Quizzes .... AR pp. 205–206
Chapter 11 Test .... SE p. 852
Chapter Test (Levels A, B, C) .... AR pp. 207–218
• Multiple Choice • Free Response
Cumulative Test .... AR pp. 221–224
Test and Practice Generator .... *One-Stop Planner*
Modified Chapter 11 Test .... *IDEA Works!*

Technology Highlights for Ongoing Assessment

Are You Ready? SPANISH

Automatically assess readiness and prescribe intervention for Chapter 11 prerequisite skills.

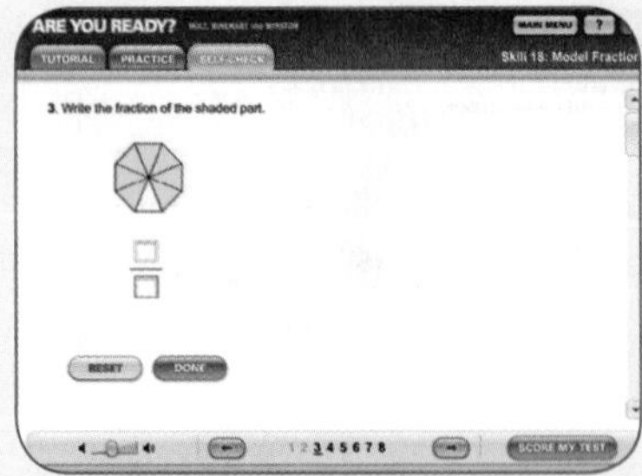

Ready to Go On?

Automatically assess understanding and prescribe intervention for Sections 11A and 11B.

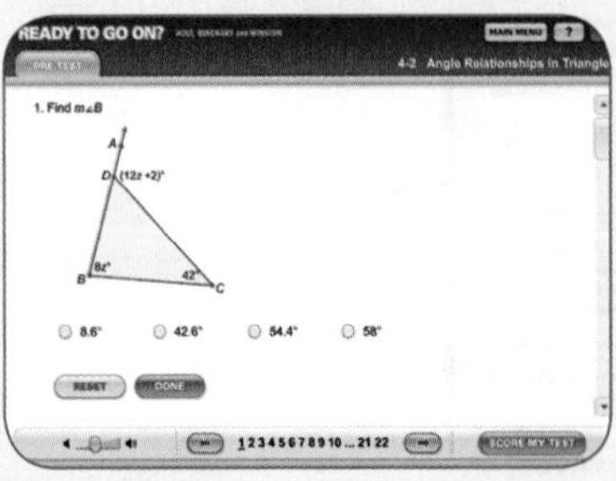

Test and Practice Generator

Use Chapter 11 problem banks to create assessments and worksheets to print out or deliver online. Includes dynamic problems.

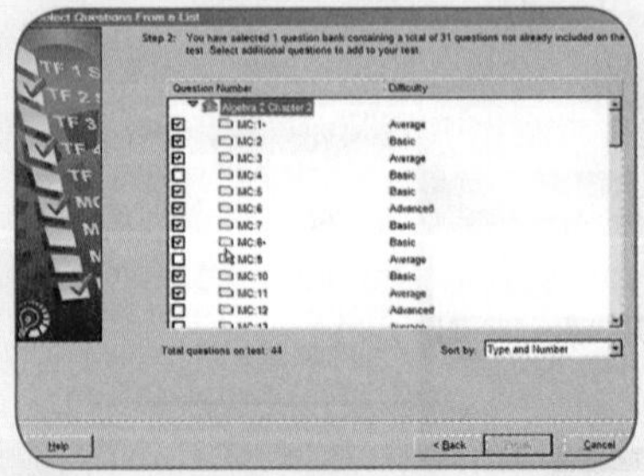

KEY: **SE** = *Student Edition* **TE** = *Teacher's Edition* **AR** = *Assessment Resources*  Spanish version available Available on CD-ROM  Available online

Formal Assessment

Three levels (A, B, C) of multiple-choice and free-response chapter tests are available in the *Assessment Resources.*

A Chapter 11 Test

C Chapter 11 Test

MULTIPLE CHOICE

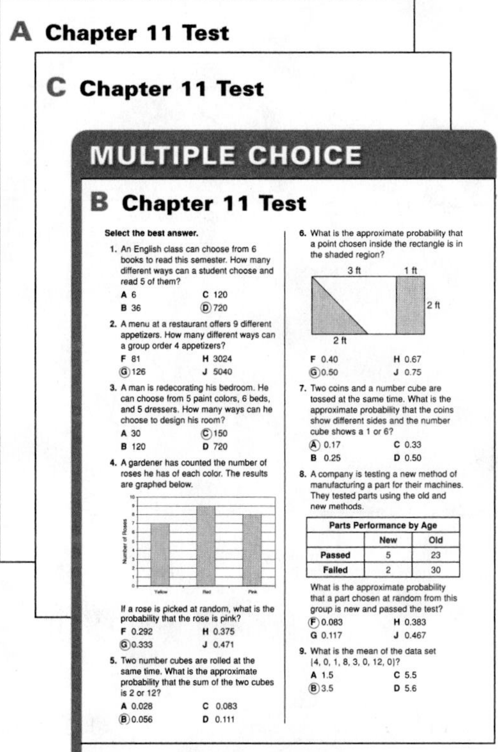

B Chapter 11 Test

Select the best answer.

1. An English class can choose from 6 books to read this semester. How many different ways can a student choose and read 5 of them?
A 6 C 120
B 36 (D) 720

2. A menu at a restaurant offers 9 different appetizers. How many different ways can a group order 4 appetizers?
F 81 H 3024
(G) 126 J 5040

3. A man is redecorating his bedroom. He can choose from 5 paint colors, 6 beds, and 5 dressers. How many ways can he choose to design his room?
A 30 (C) 150
B 120 D 720

4. A gardener has counted the number of roses he has of each color. The results are graphed below.
If a rose is picked at random, what is the probability that the rose is pink?
F 0.292 H 0.375
(G) 0.333 J 0.471

5. Two number cubes are rolled at the same time. What is the approximate probability that the sum of the two cubes is 2 or 12?
A 0.028 C 0.083
(B) 0.056 D 0.111

6. What is the approximate probability that a point chosen inside the rectangle is in the shaded region?
F 0.40 H 0.67
(G) 0.50 J 0.75

7. Two coins and a number cube are tossed at the same time. What is the approximate probability that the coins show different sides and the number cube shows a 1 or 6?
(A) 0.17 C 0.33
B 0.25 D 0.50

8. A company is testing a new method of manufacturing a part for their machines. They tested parts using the old and new methods.

Parts Performance by Age	New	Old
Passed	5	23
Failed	2	30

What is the approximate probability that a part chosen at random from this group is new and passed the test?
(F) 0.083 H 0.383
G 0.117 J 0.467

9. What is the mean of the data set {4, 0, 1, 8, 3, 0, 12, 0}?
A 1.5 C 5.5
(B) 3.5 D 5.6

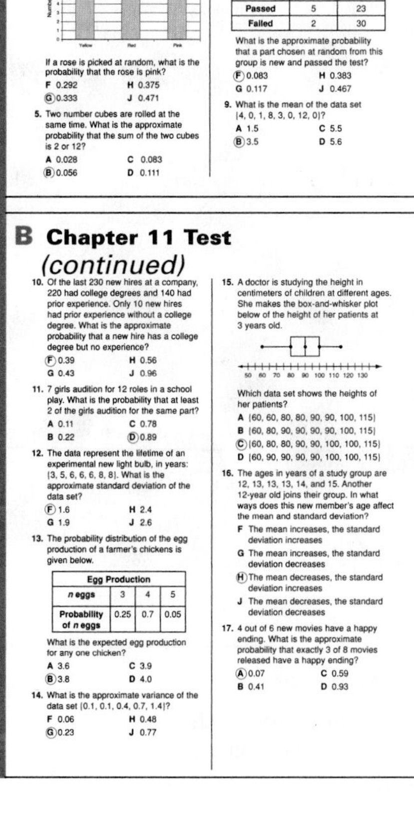

B Chapter 11 Test (continued)

10. Of the last 230 new hires at a company, 220 had college degrees and 140 had prior experience. Only 10 new hires had prior experience without a college degree. What is the approximate probability that a new hire has a college degree but no experience?
(F) 0.39 H 0.56
G 0.43 J 0.96

11. 7 girls audition for 12 roles in a school play. What is the probability that at least 2 of the girls audition for the same part?
A 0.11 C 0.78
B 0.22 (D) 0.89

12. The data represent the lifetime of an experimental new light bulb, in years: {3, 5, 6, 6, 6, 8, 8}. What is the approximate standard deviation of the data set?
(F) 1.6 H 2.4
G 1.9 J 2.6

13. The probability distribution of the egg production of a farmer's chickens is given below.

Egg Production			
n eggs	3	4	5
Probability of n eggs	0.25	0.7	0.05

What is the expected egg production for any one chicken?
A 3.6 C 3.9
(B) 3.8 D 4.0

14. What is the approximate variance of the data set {0.1, 0.1, 0.4, 0.7, 1.4}?
F 0.06 H 0.48
(G) 0.23 J 0.77

15. A doctor is studying the height in centimeters of children at different ages. She makes the box-and-whisker plot below of the height of her patients at 3 years old.
Which data set shows the heights of her patients?
A {60, 60, 80, 80, 90, 90, 100, 115}
B {60, 80, 90, 90, 90, 90, 100, 115}
(C) {60, 80, 80, 90, 90, 100, 100, 115}
D {60, 90, 90, 90, 90, 100, 100, 115}

16. The ages in years of a study group are 12, 13, 13, 13, 14, and 15. Another 12-year old joins their group. In what ways does this new member's age affect the mean and standard deviation?
F The mean increases, the standard deviation increases
G The mean increases, the standard deviation decreases
(H) The mean decreases, the standard deviation increases
J The mean decreases, the standard deviation decreases

17. 4 out of 6 new movies have a happy ending. What is the approximate probability that exactly 3 of 8 movies released have a happy ending?
(A) 0.07 C 0.59
B 0.41 D 0.93

A Chapter 11 Test

C Chapter 11 Test

FREE RESPONSE

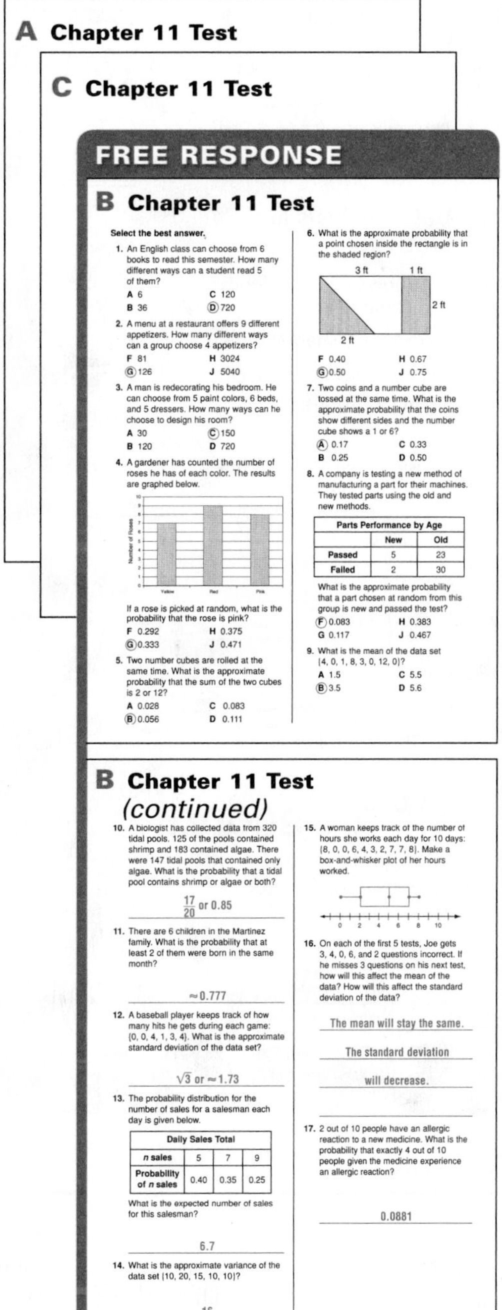

B Chapter 11 Test

Select the best answer.

1. An English class can choose from 6 books to read this semester. How many different ways can a student read 5 of them?
A 6 C 120
B 36 (D) 720

2. A menu at a restaurant offers 9 different appetizers. How many different ways can a group choose 4 appetizers?
F 81 H 3024
(G) 126 J 5040

3. A man is redecorating his bedroom. He can choose from 5 paint colors, 6 beds, and 5 dressers. How many ways can he choose to design his room?
A 30 (C) 150
B 120 D 720

4. A gardener has counted the number of roses he has of each color. The results are graphed below.
If a rose is picked at random, what is the probability that the rose is pink?
F 0.292 H 0.375
(G) 0.333 J 0.471

5. Two number cubes are rolled at the same time. What is the approximate probability that the sum of the two cubes is 2 or 12?
A 0.028 C 0.083
(B) 0.056 D 0.111

6. What is the approximate probability that a point chosen inside the rectangle is in the shaded region?
F 0.40 H 0.67
(G) 0.50 J 0.75

7. Two coins and a number cube are tossed at the same time. What is the approximate probability that the coins show different sides and the number cube shows a 1 or 6?
(A) 0.17 C 0.33
B 0.25 D 0.50

8. A company is testing a new method of manufacturing a part for their machines. They tested parts using the old and new methods.

Parts Performance by Age	New	Old
Passed	5	23
Failed	2	30

What is the approximate probability that a part chosen at random from this group is new and passed the test?
(F) 0.083 H 0.383
G 0.117 J 0.467

9. What is the mean of the data set {4, 0, 1, 8, 3, 0, 12, 0}?
A 1.5 C 5.5
(B) 3.5 D 5.6

B Chapter 11 Test (continued)

10. A biologist has collected data from 320 tidal pools. 125 of the pools contained shrimp and 183 contained algae. There were 147 tidal pools that contained only algae. What is the probability that a tidal pool contains shrimp or algae or both?
$\frac{17}{20}$ or 0.85

11. There are 6 children in the Martinez family. What is the probability that at least 2 of them were born in the same month?
≈ 0.777

12. A baseball player keeps track of how many hits he gets during each game: {0, 0, 4, 1, 3, 4}. What is the approximate standard deviation of the data set?
$\sqrt{3}$ or ≈ 1.73

13. The probability distribution for the number of sales for a salesman each day is given below.

Daily Sales Total			
n sales	5	7	9
Probability of n sales	0.40	0.35	0.25

What is the expected number of sales for this salesman?
6.7

14. What is the approximate variance of the data set {10, 20, 15, 10, 10}?
16

15. A woman keeps track of the number of hours she works each day for 10 days: {8, 0, 0, 6, 4, 3, 2, 7, 7, 8}. Make a box-and-whisker plot of her hours worked.

16. On each of the first 5 tests, Joe gets 3, 4, 0, 6, and 2 questions incorrect. If he misses 3 questions on his next test, how will this affect the mean of the data? How will this affect the standard deviation of the data?
The mean will stay the same.
The standard deviation will decrease.

17. 2 out of 10 people have an allergic reaction to a new medicine. What is the probability that exactly 4 out of 10 people given the medicine experience an allergic reaction?
0.0881

MODIFIED FOR IDEA

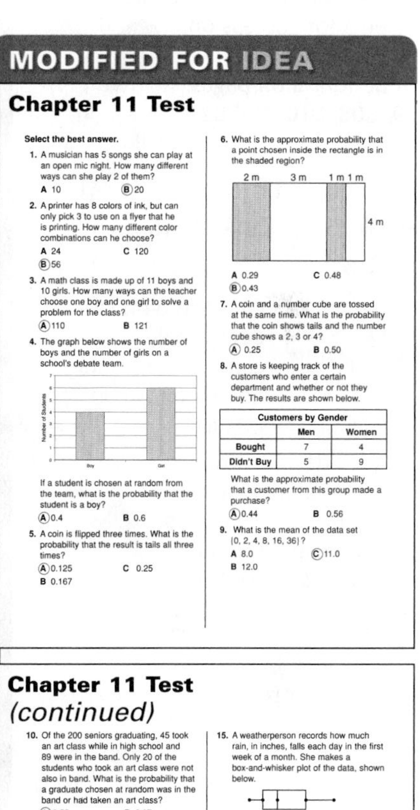

Chapter 11 Test

Select the best answer.

1. A musician has 5 songs she can play at an open mic night. How many different ways can she play 2 of them?
A 10
(B) 20

2. A printer has 8 colors of ink, but can only pick 3 to use on a flyer that he is printing. How many different color combinations can he choose?
A 24 C 120
(B) 56

3. A math class is made up of 11 boys and 10 girls. How many ways can the teacher choose one boy and one girl to solve a problem for the class?
(A) 110 B 121

4. The graph below shows the number of boys and the number of girls on a school's debate team.
If a student is chosen at random from the team, what is the probability that the student is a boy?
(A) 0.4 B 0.6

5. A coin is flipped three times. What is the probability that the result is tails all three times?
(A) 0.125 C 0.25
B 0.167

6. What is the approximate probability that a point chosen inside the rectangle is in the shaded region?
A 0.29 C 0.48
(B) 0.43

7. A coin and a number cube are tossed at the same time. What is the probability that the coin shows tails and the number cube shows a 2, 3 or 4?
(A) 0.25 B 0.50

8. A store is keeping track of the customers who enter a certain department and whether or not they buy. The results are shown below.

Customers by Gender	Men	Women
Bought	7	4
Didn't Buy	5	9

What is the approximate probability that a customer from this group made a purchase?
(A) 0.44 B 0.56

9. What is the mean of the data set {0, 2, 4, 8, 16, 36}?
A 8.0 (C) 11.0
B 12.0

Chapter 11 Test (continued)

10. Of the 200 seniors graduating, 45 took an art class while in high school and 89 were in the band. Only 20 of the students who took an art class were not also in band. What is the probability that a graduate chosen at random was in the band or had taken an art class?
(A) 0.55 B 0.67

11. If 4 friends are choosing from 8 different drinks at a refreshment stand, what is the probability that at least 2 of the friends order the same drink?
A 0.25
B 0.50
(C) 0.59

12. This data represent the number of books Sarah read each month: {1, 1, 3, 3, 4}. What is the approximate standard deviation of the data set?
(A) 1.2 B 2.4

13. The probability distribution of the number of piglets per litter on a farm is given below.

Piglet Births per Litter			
n piglets	4	5	6
Probability of n piglets	0.2	0.4	0.4

What is the expected number of piglets per litter on this farm?
A 4.8
B 5.0
(C) 5.2

14. What is the approximate variance of the data set {0, 0, 1, 2, 3}?
A 1.17
(B) 1.36
C 2.34

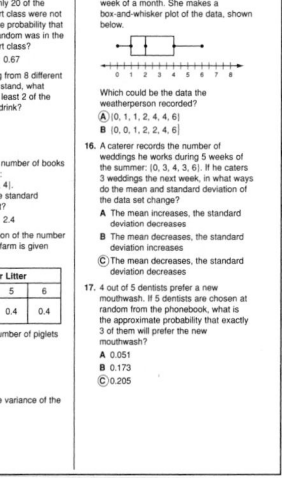

15. A weatherperson records how much rain, in inches, falls each day in the first week of a month. She makes a box-and-whisker plot of the data, shown below.
Which could be the data the weatherperson recorded?
(A) {0, 1, 1, 2, 4, 4, 6}
B {0, 0, 1, 2, 2, 4, 6}

16. A caterer records the number of weddings he works during 5 weeks of the summer: {0, 3, 4, 3, 6}. If he caters 3 weddings the next week, in what ways do the mean and standard deviation of the data set change?
A The mean increases, the standard deviation decreases
B The mean decreases, the standard deviation increases
(C) The mean decreases, the standard deviation decreases

17. 4 out of 5 dentists prefer a new mouthwash. If 5 dentists are chosen at random from the phonebook, what is the approximate probability that exactly 3 of them will prefer the new mouthwash?
A 0.051
B 0.173
(C) 0.205

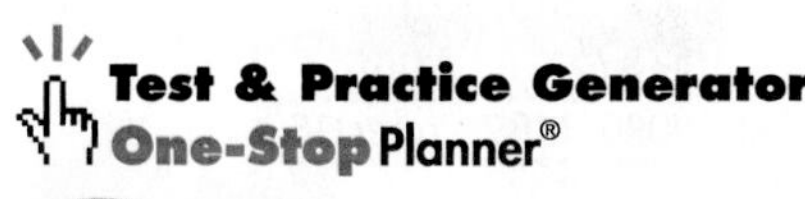

Test & Practice Generator
One-Stop Planner®

Create and customize Chapter 11 Tests. Instantly generate multiple test versions, answer keys, and practice versions of test items.

CHAPTER 11

SECTION 11A
Probability

On page 826, students use probability to analyze the outcomes of a game involving number cubes.

Exercises designed to prepare students for success on the Multi-Step Test Prep can be found on pages 799, 808, 816, and 824.

SECTION 11B
Data Analysis and Statistics

On page 844, students analyze and compare precipitation data for two U.S. cities.

Exercises designed to prepare students for success on the Multi-Step Test Prep can be found on pages 835 and 841.

CHAPTER 11

Probability and Statistics

APPROXIMATE WAIT TIME FROM HERE 14872 MINUTES

Wait a Second!

You can use probability and statistics to analyze *queuing*, the study of waiting in line.

go.hrw.com
Chapter Project Online
KEYWORD: MB7 ChProj

Wait a Second!

About the Project

In the Chapter Project, students create a simulation to investigate probabilities related to simple queues and waiting times.

Project Resources

All project resources for teachers and students are provided online.

Materials:

- graphing calculator

ARE YOU READY?

Vocabulary

Match each term on the left with a definition on the right.

1. mean **B**
2. median **E**
3. ratio **A**
4. mode **C**

A. a comparison of two quantities by division
B. the sum of the values in a set divided by the number of values
C. the value, or values, that occur most often
D. the result of addition
E. the middle value, or mean of the two middle values, of a set when the set is ordered numerically

Tree Diagrams

5. Natalie has three colors of wrapping paper (purple, blue, and yellow) and three colors of ribbon (gold, white, and red). Make a tree diagram showing all possible ways that she can wrap a present using one color of paper and one color of ribbon.

5.

Add and Subtract Fractions

Add or subtract.

6. $1 - \frac{14}{20}$ **$\frac{3}{10}$**
7. $\frac{3}{8} + \frac{5}{6}$ **$\frac{29}{24}$**
8. $\frac{8}{15} - \frac{2}{5}$ **$\frac{2}{15}$**
9. $\frac{1}{12} + \frac{1}{10}$ **$\frac{11}{60}$**

Multiply and Divide Fractions

Multiply or divide.

10. $\frac{1}{2} \cdot \frac{3}{7}$ **$\frac{3}{14}$**
11. $2\frac{1}{3} \cdot \frac{1}{4}$ **$\frac{7}{12}$**
12. $\frac{4}{5} \div \frac{1}{2}$ **$\frac{8}{5}$**
13. $5\frac{1}{3} \div \frac{1}{4}$ **$\frac{64}{3}$**

Percent Problems

Solve.

14. What number is 7% of 150? **10.5**
15. 90% of what number is 45? **50**
16. A $24 item receives a price increase of 12%. How much was the price increased? **$2.88**
17. Twenty percent of the water in a large aquarium should be changed weekly. How much water should be changed each week if an aquarium holds 65 gallons of water? **13 gal**

Find Measures of Central Tendency

Find the mean, median, and mode of each data set.

18. $\{9, 4, 2, 6, 4\}$ **5; 4; 4**
19. $\{1, 1, 1, 2, 2, 2\}$ **1.5; 1.5; 1, 2**
20. $\{1, 2, 3, 4, 5, 6\}$ **3.5; 3.5; none**
21. $\{18, 14, 20, 18, 14, 3, 18\}$ **15; 18; 18**

ARE YOU READY?

Organizer

Objective: Assess students' understanding of prerequisite skills.

Prerequisite Skills

Tree Diagrams
Add and Subtract Fractions
Multiply and Divide Fractions
Percent Problems
Find Measures of Central Tendency

Assessing Prior Knowledge

INTERVENTION

Diagnose and Prescribe

Use this page to determine whether intervention is necessary or whether enrichment is appropriate.

Resources

***Are You Ready? Intervention and Enrichment* Worksheets**

***Are You Ready?* CD-ROM**

***Are You Ready?* Online**

my.hrw.com

ARE YOU READY?
Diagnose and Prescribe

NO INTERVENE

Prerequisite Skill	*Are You Ready? Intervention,* Chapter 11		
	Worksheets	CD-ROM	Online
Tree Diagrams	Skill 90	Activity 90	Diagnose and Prescribe Online
Add and Subtract Fractions	Skill 48	Activity 48	
Multiply and Divide Fractions	Skill 47	Activity 47	
Percent Problems	Skill 49	Activity 49	
Find Measures of Central Tendency	Skill 84	Activity 84	

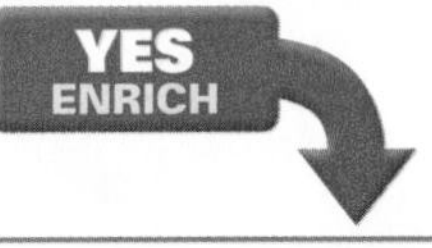

***Are You Ready? Enrichment,* Chapter 11**
Worksheets
CD-ROM
Online

Organizer

Objective: Help students organize the new concepts they will learn in Chapter 11.

Online Edition
Multilingual Glossary

Resources

Puzzle Pro
One-Stop Planner®

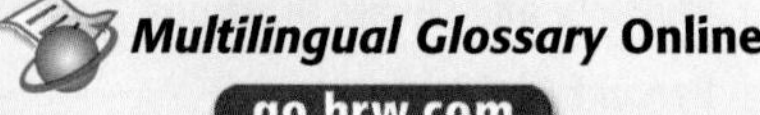

***Multilingual Glossary* Online**

go.hrw.com
KEYWORD: MB7 Glossary

Answers to *Vocabulary Connections*

1. multiplication
2. Possible answer: Theoretical probability is based on what should happen. Experimental probability is based on what actually happens.
3. dependent events, because they depend on something else being done first
4. 2; the prefix *bi-* indicates 2.

CHAPTER 11 Study Guide: Preview

Where You've Been

Previously, you

- made tree diagrams to find the number of possible combinations of a group of objects.
- made lists to count and arrange objects.
- calculated measures of central tendency.

In This Chapter

You will study

- solving problems involving counting and arranging.
- finding theoretical, experimental, and binomial probabilities.
- analyzing data to include expected value and standard deviation.

Where You're Going

You can use the skills in this chapter

- to find probabilities involved in games and events involving chance.
- to calculate and report appropriate measures when analyzing data.
- to form a solid foundation for studies in advanced statistics.

Key Vocabulary/Vocabulario

binomial experiment	experimento binomial
combination	combinación
conditional probability	probabilidad condicional
dependent events	sucesos dependientes
experimental probability	probabilidad experimental
factorial	factorial
independent events	sucesos independientes
outcome	resultado
permutation	permutación
theoretical probability	probabilidad teórica

Vocabulary Connections

To become familiar with some of the vocabulary terms in the chapter, consider the following. You may refer to the chapter, the glossary, or a dictionary if you like.

1. A number is the product of its *factors*. What operation do you think is involved in finding a **factorial** ?
2. A *theory* can be described as a sound and rational explanation. An *experiment* can be described as a procedure carried out in a controlled environment. Knowing this, how do you think **theoretical probability** differs from **experimental probability** ?
3. A *conditional* is used to describe something that will be done only if another thing is done. Do you think **conditional probability** is used with **independent events** or **dependent events** ? Why?
4. Each possible result of an experiment is an **outcome** . How many possible outcomes do you think a **binomial experiment** has? Why?

Writing Strategy: Translate Between Words and Math

It is important to correctly interpret the type of math being described by a verbal or written description. Listen/look for key words to help you translate between the words and the math.

15. In 1626, the Dutch bought Manhattan Island for $24 worth of merchandise. Suppose that, instead, $24 had been invested in an account that paid 3.5% interest compounded annually. Find the balance in 2008.

compounded: *Compounding indicates an exponential function.*

31. Gardeners check the pH level of soil to ensure a pH of 6 or 7. Soil is usually more acidic in areas where rainfall is high, whereas soil in dry areas is usually more alkaline. The pH level of a certain soil sample is 5.5. What is the difference in hydrogen ion concentration, or $[H^+]$, between the sample and an acceptable level?

pH

hydrogen ion concentration: *These terms indicate a logarithmic function.*

parabola: *A parabola indicates a quadratic function.*

27. You are given a parabola with two points that have the same *y*-value, $(-7, 11)$ and $(3, 11)$. Explain how to find the equation for the axis of symmetry of this parabola.

Try This

Identify the key word and the type of function being described.

1. Kelly invested $2000 in a savings account at a simple interest rate of 2.5%. How much money will she have in 8 months?
2. The diameter *d* in inches of a chain needed to move *p* pounds is given by the square root of 85*p*, divided by pi. How much more can be lifted with a chain 2.5 inches in diameter than by a rope 0.5 inch in diameter?
3. A technician took a blood sample from a patient and detected a toxin concentration of 0.01006 mg/cm^3. Two hours later, the technician took another sample and detected a concentration of 0.00881 mg/cm^3. Assume that the concentration varies exponentially with time. Write a function to model the data.
4. Students found that the number of mosquitoes per acre of wetland grows by about 10 to the power $\frac{1}{2}d + 2$, where *d* is the number of days since the last frost. Write and graph the function representing the number of mosquitoes on each day.

Reading and Writing Math CHAPTER 11

Organizer

Objective: Help students apply strategies to understand and retain key concepts.

PREMIER Online Edition

Resources

Chapter 11 Resource Book
Writing Strategies

ENGLISH LANGUAGE LEARNERS

Writing Strategy: Translate Between Words and Math

Discuss Point out that students are familiar with using key words to identify mathematical operations. For example, they know that a question beginning with the words *how many fewer* often indicates subtraction.

Explain to students that they can also use key words to identify the type of function that best models a situation given in a problem.

Extend As students work through Chapter 11, have them identify key words related to probability problems. For example, have them list words or phrases that can help recognize whether events are independent or dependent.

Answers to *Try This*

1. simple interest; linear function
2. square root; radical function
3. exponentially with time; exponential function
4. about 10 to the power; exponential function

SECTION

11A Probability

One-Minute Section Planner

Lesson	Lab Resources	Materials
Lesson 11-1 Permutations and Combinations • Solve problems involving the Fundamental Counting Principle. • Solve problems involving permutations and combinations. ☑ SAT-10 ☑ NAEP ☑ ACT ☐ SAT ☐ SAT Subject Tests		**Required** scientific calculator
Lesson 11-2 Theoretical and Experimental Probability • Find the theoretical probability of an event. • Find the experimental probability of an event. ☑ SAT-10 ☑ NAEP ☑ ACT ☑ SAT ☑ SAT Subject Tests	***Algebra Lab Activities*** 11-2 Algebra Lab	**Optional** scientific calculator, number cubes (MK), playing cards, globe, tape measure (MK)
11-2 Technology Lab Explore Simulations • Use a spreadsheet to simulate experimental probability. ☐ SAT-10 ☑ NAEP ☐ ACT ☐ SAT ☐ SAT Subject Tests	***Technology Lab Activities*** 11-2 Lab Recording Sheet	**Required** spreadsheet software
Lesson 11-3 Independent and Dependent Events • Determine whether events are independent or dependent. • Find the probability of independent and dependent events. ☑ SAT-10 ☑ NAEP ☑ ACT ☑ SAT ☑ SAT Subject Tests		**Optional** scientific calculator, number cubes (MK), playing cards
Lesson 11-4 Compound Events • Find the probability of mutually exclusive events. • Find the probability of inclusive events. ☑ SAT-10 ☑ NAEP ☑ ACT ☑ SAT ☑ SAT Subject Tests		**Optional** scientific calculator, number cubes (MK), playing cards

MK = *Manipulatives Kit*

Section Overview

Permutations and Combinations

Lesson 11-1

Permutations and combinations allow us to determine the number of possible outcomes in a situation involving various arrangements.

The **factorial** of a number is the product of the natural numbers less than or equal to the number. 0! is defined as 1.

$$n! = n \cdot (n-1) \cdot (n-2) \cdot (n-3) \cdot \ldots \cdot 1$$

A **permutation** is a selection of a group of items in which **order is important.**

The number of permutations of n items taken r at a time:

$${}_nP_r = \frac{n!}{(n-r)!}$$

A **combination** is a selection of a group of items in which **order does not matter.**

The number of combinations of n items taken r at a time:

$${}_nC_r = \frac{n!}{r!(n-r)!}$$

Probability and Dependence

Lessons 11-2, 11-3

Probabilities are often used in games or events involving chance.

Theoretical Probability

$$P(\text{event}) = \frac{\text{number of favorable outcomes}}{\text{number of outcomes in the sample space}}$$

Experimental Probability

$$P(\text{event}) = \frac{\text{number of times the event occurs}}{\text{number of trials}}$$

Probability of Independent Events

$$P(A \text{ and } B) = P(A) \cdot P(B)$$

Probability of Dependent Events

$$P(A \text{ and } B) = P(A) \cdot P(B \mid A)$$

where $P(B \mid A)$ is the probability of B given that A has occurred.

Compound Events

Lesson 11-4

Students must be able to distinguish between mutually exclusive and inclusive events in order to accurately compute the probability of compound events.

Mutually exclusive events are events that cannot both occur in the same trial of an experiment.

Example: Rolling a 1 and rolling a 2 on the same roll of a number cube are mutually exclusive events.

Inclusive events are events that have one or more outcomes in common.

Example: Rolling an even number and rolling a prime number on the same roll are inclusive events because the number 2 is both prime and even.

Probability of Mutually Exclusive Events

$$P(A \text{ or } B) = P(A) + P(B)$$

Probability of Inclusive Events

$$P(A \text{ or } B) = P(A) + P(B) - P(A \text{ and } B)$$

11-1 Organizer

Pacing: Traditional 1 day
Block $\frac{1}{2}$ day

Objectives: Solve problems involving the Fundamental Counting Principle.

Solve problems involving permutations and combinations.

Online Edition
Tutorial Videos

Countdown to Testing Week 23

Power Presentations with PowerPoint®

Warm Up

Evaluate.

1. $5 \cdot 4 \cdot 3 \cdot 2 \cdot 1$ 120
2. $7 \cdot 6 \cdot 5 \cdot 4 \cdot 3 \cdot 2 \cdot 1$ 5040
3. $\frac{4 \cdot 3 \cdot 2 \cdot 1}{3 \cdot 2}$ 4
4. $\frac{7 \cdot 6 \cdot 5 \cdot 4 \cdot 3 \cdot 2 \cdot 1}{4 \cdot 3 \cdot 2}$ 210
5. $\frac{5 \cdot 4 \cdot 3 \cdot 2 \cdot 1}{(2 \cdot 1)(3 \cdot 2 \cdot 1)}$ 10
6. $\frac{8 \cdot 7 \cdot 6 \cdot 5 \cdot 4 \cdot 3 \cdot 2 \cdot 1}{(4 \cdot 3 \cdot 2 \cdot 1)(4 \cdot 3 \cdot 2 \cdot 1)}$ 70

Also available on transparency

Math Humor

Q: How can you tell when a factorial is enthusiastic?

A: It's always enthusiastic—it has an exclamation point!

11-1 Permutations and Combinations

A2.8.3 Use permutations, combinations, and other counting methods to determine the number of ways that events can occur and to calculate probabilities including the probability of compound events.

Objectives
Solve problems involving the Fundamental Counting Principle.

Solve problems involving permutations and combinations.

Vocabulary
Fundamental Counting Principle
permutation
factorial
combination

Why learn this?
Permutations can be used to determine the number of ways to select and arrange artwork so as to give a new look each day. (See Example 2B.)

You have previously used tree diagrams to find the number of possible combinations of a group of objects. In this lesson, you will learn to use the **Fundamental Counting Principle**.

Fundamental Counting Principle

If there are n items and m_1 ways to choose a first item, m_2 ways to choose a second item after the first item has been chosen, and so on, then there are $m_1 \cdot m_2 \cdot \ldots \cdot m_n$ ways to choose n items.

EXAMPLE 1 Using the Fundamental Counting Principle

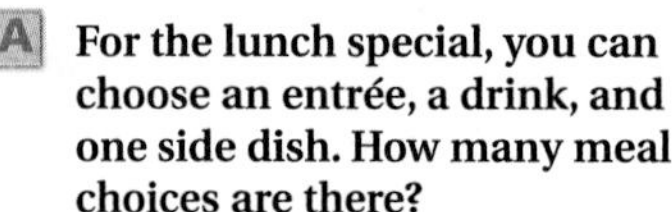

A **For the lunch special, you can choose an entrée, a drink, and one side dish. How many meal choices are there?**

number of main dishes	times	number of beverages	times	number of sides	equals	number of choices
3	×	4	×	3	=	36

There are 36 meal choices.

B **In Utah, a license plate consists of 3 digits followed by 3 letters. The letters *I*, *O*, and *Q* are not used, and each digit or letter may be used more than once. How many different license plates are possible?**

digit		*digit*		*digit*		*letter*		*letter*		*letter*	
10	×	10	×	10	×	23	×	23	×	23	= 12,167,000

There are 12,167,000 possible license plates.

Helpful Hint
In Example 1B, there are 10 possible digits and $26 - 3 = 23$ possible letters.

1a. A "make-your-own-adventure" story lets you choose 6 starting points, gives 4 plot choices, and then has 5 possible endings. How many adventures are there? **120**

1b. A password is 4 letters followed by 1 digit. Uppercase letters (A) and lowercase letters (a) may be used and are considered different. How many passwords are possible? **73,116,160**

State Resources

1 Introduce

EXPLORATION

11-1 Permutations and Combinations

At a juice bar, a customer who orders a smoothie gets to choose one type of fruit and one type of yogurt. For example, customers who order Simple Smoothies get to choose from 3 fruits (bananas, peaches, or blueberries) and 2 yogurts (plain or vanilla). The tree diagram shows that there are 6 possible Simple Smoothies.

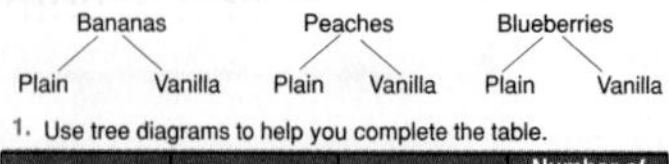

1. Use tree diagrams to help you complete the table.

Smoothie Name	Possible Fruits	Possible Yogurts	Number of Possible Smoothies
Berry Smoothie	strawberries, blueberries	raspberry, blackberry	
Choco Smoothie	bananas, raspberries, strawberries	chocolate	
Tropical Smoothie	papayas, mangos, bananas	coconut, lime, kiwi	

THINK AND DISCUSS

Motivate

Ask students to find the number of outfits possible from 3 different sweaters and 6 different shirts. 18 outfits Draw a tree diagram to verify the answer. Then ask students to consider how many different phone numbers are available in their town. Discuss the impracticality of using tree diagrams for situations like this that involve very large numbers. Explain that in this lesson, students will learn more efficient counting methods.

Explorations and answers are provided in the *Explorations* binder.

A **permutation** is a selection of a group of objects in which order is important.

There is one way to arrange one item A.

A second item B can be placed first or second.

A third item C can be first, second, or third for each order above.

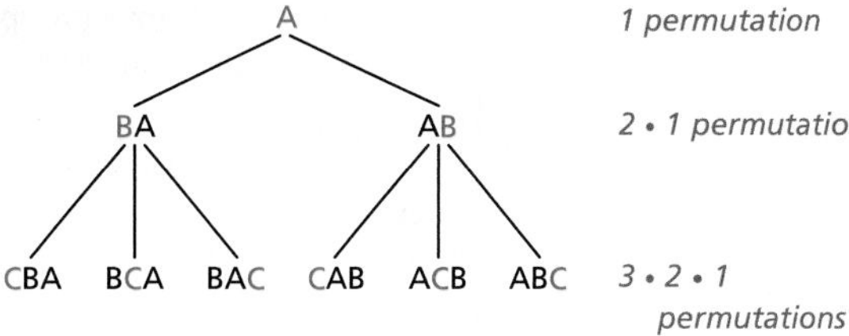

You can see that the number of permutations of 3 items is 3 • 2 • 1. You can extend this to permutations of n items, which is $n \cdot (n-1) \cdot (n-2) \cdot (n-3) \cdot \ldots \cdot 1$. This expression is called *n factorial*, and is written as $n!$.

n Factorial

For any whole number n,

WORDS	NUMBERS	ALGEBRA
The **factorial** of a number is the product of the natural numbers less than or equal to the number. 0! is defined as 1.	$6! = 6 \cdot 5 \cdot 4 \cdot 3 \cdot 2 \cdot 1 = 720$	$n! = n \cdot (n-1) \cdot (n-2) \cdot (n-3) \cdot \ldots \cdot 1$

Sometimes you may not want to order an entire set of items. Suppose that you want to select and order 3 people from a group of 7. One way to find possible permutations is to use the Fundamental Counting Principle.

First Person		Second Person		Third Person		*There are 7 people. You are choosing 3 of them in order.*
7 choices	•	6 choices	•	5 choices	=	210 permutations

Another way to find the possible permutations is to use factorials. You can divide the total number of arrangements by the number of arrangements that are not used. In the example above, there are 7 total people and 4 whose arrangements do not matter.

$$\frac{\text{arrangements of 7 people}}{\text{arrangements of 4 people}} = \frac{7!}{4!} = \frac{7 \cdot 6 \cdot 5 \cdot \cancel{4} \cdot \cancel{3} \cdot \cancel{2} \cdot \cancel{1}}{\cancel{4} \cdot \cancel{3} \cdot \cancel{2} \cdot \cancel{1}} = 210$$

This can be generalized as a formula, which is useful for large numbers of items.

Permutations

NUMBERS	ALGEBRA
The number of permutations of 7 items taken 3 at a time is $_7P_3 = \frac{7!}{(7-3)!} = \frac{7!}{4!}$.	The number of permutations of n items taken r at a time is $_nP_r = \frac{n!}{(n-r)!}$.

Power Presentations with PowerPoint®

Additional Examples

Example 1

A. To make a yogurt parfait, you choose one flavor of yogurt, one fruit topping, and one nut topping. How many parfait choices are there? 30

Yogurt Parfait (choose 1 of each)		
Flavor	**Fruit**	**Nuts**
Plain	Peaches	Almonds
Vanilla	Strawberries	Peanuts
	Bananas	Walnuts
	Raspberries	
	Blueberries	

B. A password for a site consists of 4 digits followed by 2 letters. The letters *A* and *Z* are not used, and each digit or letter may be used more than once. How many unique passwords are possible? 5,760,000

Also available on transparency

INTERVENTION
Questioning Strategies

EXAMPLE 1

- How does the Fundamental Counting Principle work in the example?
- How else could you find the total number of choices?

Teaching Tip **Visual** For **Example 1,** you may want to draw a tree diagram to help students visualize the Fundamental Counting Principle.

Teaching Tip **Number Sense** Students can use graphing calculators to check their calculations of permutations and combinations. These functions can be found by pressing MATH, scrolling right to the **PRB** menu, and then selecting **2:nPr** or **3:nCr.** Note that the value of n must be entered before selecting the function. Students can also use the calculator to quickly compare the number of permutations and combinations for a certain situation.

2 Teach

Guided Instruction

Use a tree diagram to introduce the Fundamental Counting Principle. Review factorials and permutations, making sure that students understand the method of dividing out common factors to simplify the calculations. Make sure that students understand the difference between permutations and combinations before beginning the exercises. Order is important in permutations but does not matter in combinations.

Reaching All Learners
Through Kinesthetic Experience

Have groups of 5 students model some of the different arrangements of selecting 3 students from a group of 5. Discuss the difference between choosing 3 class officers (order of positions matters) and choosing a committee of 3 students (order does not matter). Then ask students to find the corresponding permutation and combination.

$_5P_3 = 60$; $_5C_3 = 10$

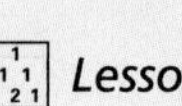

Critical Thinking Tell students that when you find permutations such as those in **Example 2,** the same factorials appear in both the numerator and denominator, so you can divide them out all at once.

Power Presentations with PowerPoint®

Additional Examples

Example 2

A. How many ways can a student government select a president, vice president, secretary, and treasurer from a group of 6 people? 360

B. How many ways can a stylist arrange 5 of 8 vases from left to right in a store display? 6720

Example 3

There are 12 different-colored cubes in a bag. How many ways can Randall draw a set of 4 cubes from the bag? 495

Also available on transparency

INTERVENTION
Questioning Strategies

EXAMPLE 2

- How can you recognize that the order matters?
- What is a similar problem in which the order does not matter?
- What patterns do you see in simplifying a permutation?

EXAMPLE 3

- How can you recognize that the order does not matter?
- What patterns can you use to simplify a combination?
- Do you expect more arrangements from a permutation or a combination? Explain.

Teaching Tip

Reading Math Permutations and combinations are generally read as "the number of permutations (or combinations) of n items taken r at a time." Combinations, such as $_6C_3$, are referred to in short as "6 choose 3."

ENGLISH LANGUAGE LEARNERS

EXAMPLE 2 Finding Permutations

A **How many ways can a club select a president, a vice president, and a secretary from a group of 5 people?**

This is the equivalent of selecting and arranging 3 items from 5.

$$_5P_3 = \frac{5!}{(5-3)!} = \frac{5!}{2!}$$

Substitute 5 for n and 3 for r in $\frac{n!}{(n-r)!}$.

$$= \frac{5 \cdot 4 \cdot 3 \cdot \cancel{2 \cdot 1}}{\cancel{2 \cdot 1}}$$

Divide out common factors.

$$= 5 \cdot 4 \cdot 3 = 60$$

There are 60 ways to select the 3 people.

Helpful Hint

The number of factors left after dividing is the number of items selected. In Example 2B, there are 4 paintings and 4 factors in $9 \cdot 8 \cdot 7 \cdot 6$.

B **An art gallery has 9 paintings from an artist and will display 4 from left to right along a wall. In how many ways can the gallery select and display the 4 paintings?**

 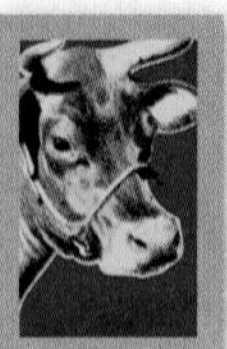  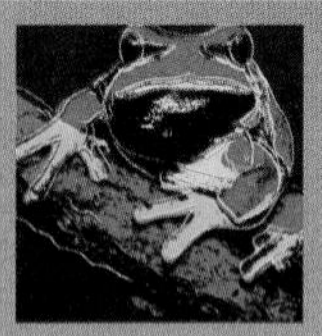

$$_9P_4 = \frac{9!}{(9-4)!} = \frac{9!}{5!} = \frac{9 \cdot 8 \cdot 7 \cdot 6 \cdot \cancel{5 \cdot 4 \cdot 3 \cdot 2 \cdot 1}}{\cancel{5 \cdot 4 \cdot 3 \cdot 2 \cdot 1}}$$

Divide out common factors.

$$= 9 \cdot 8 \cdot 7 \cdot 6$$
$$= 3024$$

There are 3024 ways that the gallery can select and display the paintings.

2a. Awards are given out at a costume party. How many ways can "most creative," "silliest," and "best" costume be awarded to 8 contestants if no one gets more than one award? **336**

2b. How many ways can a 2-digit number be formed by using only the digits 5–9 and by each digit being used only once? **20**

A **combination** is a grouping of items in which order does not matter. There are generally fewer ways to select items when order does not matter. For example, there are 6 ways to order 3 items, but they are all the same combination:

6 permutations → {ABC, ACB, BAC, BCA, CAB, CBA}

1 combination → {ABC}

To find the number of combinations, the formula for permutations can be modified.

$$\text{number of permutations} = \frac{\text{ways to arrange all items}}{\text{ways to arrange items not selected}}$$

Because order does not matter, divide the number of permutations by the number of ways to arrange the selected items.

$$\text{number of combinations} = \frac{\text{ways to arrange all items}}{(\text{ways to arrange selected items})(\text{ways to arrange items not selected})}$$

Teacher to Teacher

I like to show students an example of how to find the number of possible arrangements of repeating letters, such as the letters in the word *geese*.

Point out that $GE_1E_2SE_3$ is considered the same arrangement as $GE_2E_1SE_3$ because they both spell the same word. Including all 3! permutations of E_1, E_2, and E_3 would overcount the number of arrangements by 3!, or 6, times.

In fact, there are $\frac{5!}{3!} = 20$ arrangements of 5 items in which 3 of the items repeat.

Douglas Lohnas
Schenectady, NY

Combinations

NUMBERS	ALGEBRA
The number of combinations of 7 items taken 3 at a time is $_7C_3 = \frac{7!}{3!(7-3)!}$.	The number of combinations of n items taken r at a time is $_nC_r = \frac{n!}{r!(n-r)!}$.

When deciding whether to use permutations or combinations, first decide whether order is important. Use a permutation if order matters and a combination if order does not matter.

EXAMPLE 3 *Pet Adoption Application*

Katie is going to adopt kittens from a litter of 11. How many ways can she choose a group of 3 kittens?

Step 1 Determine whether the problem represents a permutation or combination.

The order does not matter. The group Kitty, Smoky, and Tigger is the same as Tigger, Kitty, and Smoky. It is a combination.

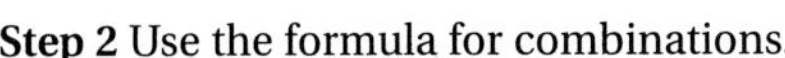

Step 2 Use the formula for combinations.

$$_{11}C_3 = \frac{11!}{3!(11-3)!} = \frac{11!}{3!(8!)} \quad n = 11 \text{ and } r = 3$$

$$= \frac{11 \cdot 10 \cdot 9 \cdot \cancel{8 \cdot 7 \cdot 6 \cdot 5 \cdot 4 \cdot 3 \cdot 2 \cdot 1}}{3 \cdot 2 \cdot 1(\cancel{8 \cdot 7 \cdot 6 \cdot 5 \cdot 4 \cdot 3 \cdot 2 \cdot 1})} \quad \text{Divide out common factors.}$$

$$= \frac{11 \cdot 10 \cdot 9}{3 \cdot 2 \cdot 1} = \frac{11 \cdot \cancel{10}^5 \cdot \cancel{9}^3}{{}_1\cancel{3} \cdot {}_1\cancel{2} \cdot 1} = 165$$

There are 165 ways to select a group of 3 kittens from 11.

Helpful Hint

You can find permutations and combinations by using **nPr** and **nCr**, respectively, on scientific and graphing calculators.

CHECK IT OUT!

3. The swim team has 8 swimmers. Two swimmers will be selected to swim in the first heat. How many ways can the swimmers be selected? 28

THINK AND DISCUSS

1. Give a situation in which order matters and one in which order does not matter.
2. Give the value of $_nC_n$, where n is any integer. Explain your answer.
3. Tell what $_3C_4$ would mean in the real world and why it is not possible.

4. **GET ORGANIZED** Copy and complete the graphic organizer.

	Fundamental Counting Principle	Permutation	Combination
Formula			
Examples			

COMMON ERROR ALERT

Students sometimes attempt to simplify permutations or combinations by canceling factorials. Remind students of the meaning of factorials, and suggest that students write out the multiplication to determine which factors actually cancel.

Teaching Tip **Math Background** *Combinatorics* is the branch of mathematics that involves counting and arranging finite collections of objects.

3 Close

Summarize

Review the three counting methods covered in the lesson: the fundamental counting principle, permutations, and combinations. Ask students to compare permutations with combinations. Possible answer: Both are used to count arrangements. In permutations, the order of the arrangement matters. In combinations, the order does not matter.

ONGOING ASSESSMENT and INTERVENTION

***Diagnose Before* the Lesson**
11-1 Warm Up, TE p. 794

***Monitor During* the Lesson**
Check It Out! Exercises, SE pp. 794, 796, 797
Questioning Strategies, TE pp. 795, 796

***Assess After* the Lesson**
11-1 Lesson Quiz, TE p. 800
Alternative Assessment, TE p. 800

Answers to *Think and Discuss*

1. Possible answers: selecting a 9-player batting order from 20 players; selecting 3 magazine subscriptions from a list of 20
2. 1; possible answer: there is only 1 way to choose the entire group from a group.
3. The number of ways to select 4 items from 3; you can't select more than the total number of items.
4. See p. A12.

11-1 Exercises

Assignment Guide

Assign *Guided Practice* exercises as necessary.

If you finished Examples **1–3**

Basic 9–14, 16–29, 35–37, 39–41, 44–50

Average 9–32, 34–37, 39–42, 44–50

Advanced 9–15, 24–25, 30–50

Homework Quick Check

Quickly check key concepts.
Exercises: 10, 12, 14, 24, 26

State Resources

11-1 Exercises

go.hrw.com
Homework Help Online
KEYWORD: MB7 11-1
Parent Resources Online
KEYWORD: MB7 Parent

GUIDED PRACTICE

1. **Vocabulary** When you open a rotating combination lock, order is __?__ (*important* or *not important*), so this is a __?__ (*permutation* or *combination*). **important; permutation**

SEE EXAMPLE 1 p. 794

2. Jamie purchased 3 blouses, 3 jackets, and 2 skirts. How many different outfits using a blouse, a jacket, and a skirt are possible? **18**
3. An Internet code consists of one digit followed by one letter. The number zero and the letter *O* are excluded. How many codes are possible? **225**

SEE EXAMPLE 2 p. 796

4. Nate is on a 7-day vacation. He plans to spend one day jet skiing and one day golfing. How many ways can Nate schedule the 2 activities? **42**
5. How many ways can you listen to 3 songs from a CD that has 12 selections? **1320**
6. Members from 6 different school organizations decorated floats for the homecoming parade. How many different ways can first, second, and third prize be awarded? **120**

SEE EXAMPLE 3 p. 797

7. A teacher wants to send 4 students to the library each day. There are 21 students in the class. How many ways can he choose 4 students to go to the library on the first day? **5985**
8. Gregory has a coupon for $1 off the purchase of 3 boxes of Munchie brand cereal. The store has 5 different varieties of Munchie brand cereal. How many ways can Gregory choose 3 boxes of cereal so that each box is a different variety? **10**

PRACTICE AND PROBLEM SOLVING

Independent Practice

For Exercises	See Example
9–10	1
11–13	2
14	3

Extra Practice

Skills Practice p. S24
Application Practice p. S42

9. **Hiking** A hiker can take 4 trails to the lake and then 3 trails from the lake to the cabins. How many routes are there from the lake to the cabins? **12**
10. The cheerleading squad is making posters. They have 3 different colors of poster board and 4 different colors of markers. How many different posters can be made by using one poster board and one marker? **12**
11. How many ways can you choose a manager and assistant from a 9-person task force? **72**
12. How many identification codes are possible by using 3 letters if no letter may be repeated? **15,600**
13. There are 5 airplanes ready to depart. Runway A and runway D are available. How many ways can 2 planes be assigned to runways without using the same runway? **20**
14. **Food** How many choices of 3 hamburger toppings are possible? **20**

15. **What if...?** In the United Kingdom's National Lottery, you must correctly select a group of 6 numbers from 49. Suppose that the contest were changed to selecting 7 numbers. How many more ways would there be to select the numbers? **71,916,768**

Evaluate.

16. ${}_6P_6$ **720**
17. ${}_5C_5$ **1**
18. ${}_9P_1$ **9**
19. ${}_6C_1$ **6**
20. $\frac{2!}{6!}$ $\mathbf{\frac{1}{360}}$
21. $\frac{4!3!}{2!}$ **72**
22. $\frac{9!}{7!}$ **72**
23. $\frac{8! - 5!}{(8-5)!}$ **6700**

11-1 READING STRATEGIES

Permutation	Combination
• Describes a grouping of objects in which order IS important	• Describes a grouping of objects in which order IS NOT important
• If John, Romeo, and Shelly all won prizes at the tennis tournament, it matters who won first prize, who won second prize, and who won third prize.	• If John, Romeo, and Shelly are chosen to compete in the tennis tournament, it doesn't matter in what order they are selected.
• The number of permutations of *x* items, chosen from a total of *n* items $${}_nP_x = \frac{n!}{(n-x)!}$$	• The number of combinations of *x* items, chosen from a total of *n* items $${}_nC_x = \frac{n!}{x!(n-x)!}$$
• *Example*: The number of ways that 3 objects can be selected from a total of 5 objects in a certain order. $${}_5P_3 = \frac{5!}{(5-3)!} = \frac{5 \cdot 4 \cdot 3 \cdot 2 \cdot 1}{2 \cdot 1} = 60$$	• *Example*: The number of ways that 3 objects can be selected from a total of 5 objects in no particular order. $${}_5C_3 = \frac{5!}{3!(5-3)!} = \frac{5 \cdot 4 \cdot 3 \cdot 2 \cdot 1}{3 \cdot 2 \cdot 1(2 \cdot 1)} = 10$$

Evaluate the following permutations and combinations.

1. ${}_4C_2$ 6
2. ${}_4P_2$ 12
3. ${}_5C_1$ 5
4. ${}_5P_1$ 5
5. ${}_3P_3$ 6
6. ${}_7C_6$ 7

Would you use a permutation or a combination to determine each of the following?

7. Nathan has a dozen eggs. He wants to decorate 4 eggs for an art project. Combination
8. Mr. Gunther is lining up 12 kindergarten students for a performance. Permutation
9. Rachel has 10 valuable baseball cards. She wants to select 2 of them to sell online. Combination
10. Don has 5 soccer trophies to line up on the mantel of his fireplace. Permutation
11. Bree has to select 5 photos from a box containing 25 photos to use in the yearbook. Combination

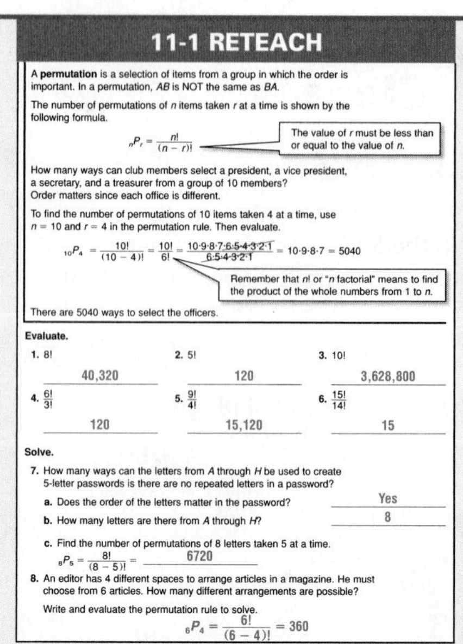

11-1 RETEACH

A **permutation** is a selection of items from a group in which the order is important. In a permutation, *AB* is NOT the same as *BA*.

The number of permutations of *n* items taken *r* at a time is shown by the following formula.

$${}_nP_r = \frac{n!}{(n-r)!}$$

The value of *r* must be less than or equal to the value of *n*.

How many ways can club members select a president, a vice president, a secretary, and a treasurer from a group of 10 members?
Order matters since each office is different.

To find the number of permutations of 10 items taken 4 at a time, use $n = 10$ and $r = 4$ in the permutation rule. Then evaluate.

$${}_{10}P_4 = \frac{10!}{(10-4)!} = \frac{10!}{6!} = \frac{10 \cdot 9 \cdot 8 \cdot 7 \cdot 6 \cdot 5 \cdot 4 \cdot 3 \cdot 2 \cdot 1}{6 \cdot 5 \cdot 4 \cdot 3 \cdot 2 \cdot 1} = 10 \cdot 9 \cdot 8 \cdot 7 = 5040$$

Remember that *n*! or "*n* factorial" means to find the product of the whole numbers from 1 to *n*.

There are 5040 ways to select the officers.

Evaluate.

1. 8! 40,320
2. 5! 120
3. 10! 3,628,800
4. $\frac{6!}{3!}$ 120
5. $\frac{9!}{4!}$ 15,120
6. $\frac{15!}{14!}$ 15

Solve.

7. How many ways can the letters from *A* through *H* be used to create 5-letter passwords is there are no repeated letters in a password?
   a. Does the order of the letters matter in the password? Yes
   b. How many letters are there from *A* through *H*? 8
   c. Find the number of permutations of 8 letters taken 5 at a time.
   ${}_8P_5 = \frac{8!}{(8-5)!} =$ 6720
8. An editor has 4 different spaces to arrange articles in a magazine. He must choose from 6 articles. How many different arrangements are possible?

   Write and evaluate the permutation rule to solve.

   $${}_6P_4 = \frac{6!}{(6-4)!} = 360$$

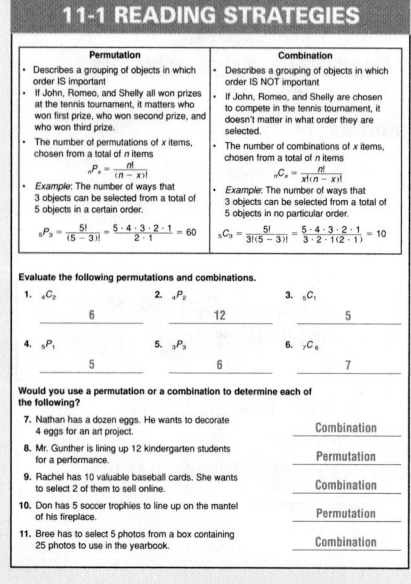

Geometry Find the number of ways that each selection can be made.

24. two marked points to determine slope **15**

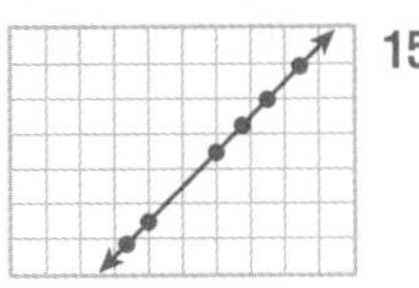

25. four points to form a quadrilateral **35**

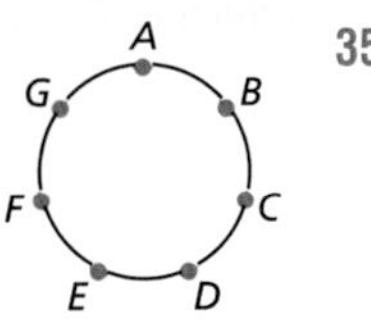

30. $n(n-1)! = n!$
$(1)(1-1)! = 1!$
$1(0)! = 1$
$0! = 1$

Compare. Write >, <, or =.

26. ${}_7P_3$ ■ ${}_7C_4$ **>**   27. ${}_7P_4$ ■ ${}_7P_3$ **>**   28. ${}_7C_3$ ■ ${}_7C_4$ **=**   29. ${}_{10}C_{10}$ ■ ${}_{10}P_{10}$ **<**

30. Copy and complete the table. Use the table to explain why 0! is defined as 1.

$n!$	4!	3!	2!	1!
$n(n-1)!$	4(3!) = 24	6	2	1

LINK

Music

There are many change-ringing societies and groups, especially in the United Kingdom. Bell ringers work together to follow patterns and called changes to avoid repeating sequences.

31. **Critical Thinking** Why are there more unique permutations of the letters in YOUNG than in GEESE?

32. **Music** In change ringing, a *peal* is the ringing of all possible sequences of a number of bells. Suppose that 8 bells are used and it takes 0.25 second to ring each bell. How long would it take to ring a complete peal? **10,080 s = 2.8 h**

33. **Multi-Step** Amy, Bob, Charles, Dena, and Esther are club officers.
    a. Copy and complete the table to show the ways that a president, a vice president, and a secretary can be chosen if Amy is chosen president. (Use first initials for names.)

President	A	A	A	A	A	A	A	A	A	A	A	A
Vice President	B	B	B	C	C	C	■	■	■	■	■	■
Secretary	C	D	E	■	■	■	■	■	■	■	■	■

    b. Extend the table to show the number of ways that the three officers can be chosen if Bob is chosen president. Make a conjecture as to the number of ways that a president, a vice president, and a secretary can be chosen.
    c. Use a formula to find the number of different ways that a president, a vice president, and a secretary can be chosen. Compare your result with part **b**.
    d. How many different ways can 3 club officers be chosen to form a committee? Compare this with the answer to part **c**. Which answer is a number of permutations? Which answer is a number of combinations?

34. **Critical Thinking** Use the formulas to divide ${}_nP_r$ by ${}_nC_r$. Predict the result of dividing ${}_6P_3$ by ${}_6C_3$. Check your prediction. What meaning does the result have?

35. **Write About It** Find ${}_9C_2$ and ${}_9C_7$. Find ${}_{10}C_6$ and ${}_{10}C_4$. Explain the results.
36, 36; 210, 210; $\frac{n!}{r!(n-r)!}$ is the same as $\frac{n!}{(n-r)!r!}$.

MULTI-STEP TEST PREP

36. This problem will prepare you for the Multi-Step Test Prep on page 826.

While playing the game of Yahtzee, Jen rolls 5 dice and gets the result shown at right.

a. How many different ways can she arrange the dice from left to right? **120**

b. How many different ways can she choose 3 of the dice to reroll? **10**

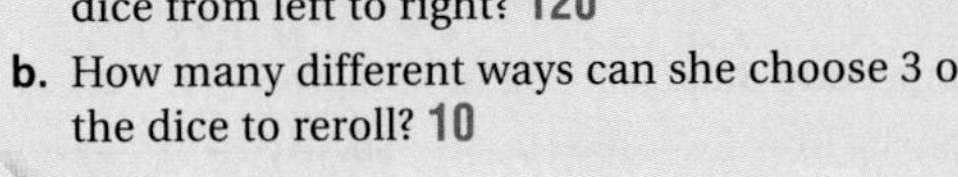

COMMON ERROR ALERT

In **Exercises 26–29,** students might make comparisons without referring back to the factorial forms of the permutations and combinations. Stress that the permutations and combinations should be written in their factorial forms before comparisons can be made.

Teaching Tip

Geometry In **Exercise 25,** remind students that a quadrilateral is a polygon with 4 sides that do not cross. So for each set of 4 points, there is only 1 possible quadrilateral (e.g., *ABCD* is a quadrilateral, but *ACBD* is not). Therefore, order does not matter.

Exercise 36 involves analyzing permutations and combinations involved in the game Yahtzee®. This exercise prepares students for the Multi-Step Test Prep on page 826.

Answers

31. The E's in GEESE are identical, so the order of the E's is not important.

33a–b. See p. A46.

c. $\frac{5!}{(5-3)!} = 60$

d. $\frac{5!}{3!(5-3)!} = 10; 60; 10$

34. Possible answer: $r!$; 6; ${}_6C_3 = \frac{{}_6P_3}{3!}$; the number of combinations of n items taken r at a time is the number of permutations of the items divided by the number of ways to order the r items.

11-1 PROBLEM SOLVING

Rosalie is looking at locks. The label *combination lock* confuses her. She wonders about the number of possible permutations or combinations a lock can have.

1. She looks at one circular lock with 12 positions. To open it she turns the dial clockwise to a first position, then counterclockwise to a second position, then clockwise to a third position
   a. Write an expression for the number of 3-position codes that are possible, if no position is repeated. **12 × 11 × 10 = 1320**
   b. Explain how this represents a combination or a permutation. **Permutation; possible answer: the order of the 3 numbers matters.** 
2. Rosalie looks at cable locks. Each position can be set from 0 to 9. How many different codes are possible for each lock if no digits are repeated in each code?
   a. a 3-digit cable lock **720 codes**
   b. a 4-digit cable lock **5040 codes**
   c. a 6-digit cable lock **151,200 codes**
3. Rosalie needs 2 cable locks, but there are 13 types of locks to choose from.
   a. In how many ways can she choose 2 different locks? **78 ways**
   b. Explain how this represents a permutation or a combination. **Combination; possible answer: the order in which she chooses the locks does not matter.**
4. Explain why you think Rosalie might be confused by the label *combination lock*. **Because order matters, *combination locks* represent permutations.**

Rosalie wants to lock her bicycle near the library. There are 7 slots still open in the bike rack. Choose the letter for the best answer.

5. Rosalie arrives at the same time as 2 other cyclists. In how many ways can they arrange their bikes in the open slots?
   A 7 (C) 210
   B 35 D 343
6. Suppose Rosalie arrived just ahead of the 2 other cyclists and selected a slot. In how many ways can the others arrange their bikes in the open slots?
   F 2 H 24
   G 15 (J) 30

11-1 CHALLENGE

A *permutation* is an arrangement of objects in a specific order. Sometimes there are also other conditions that must be satisfied. In such cases, you should deal with the special conditions first.

Using the letters in the word *square*, how many 6-letter arrangements with no repetitions are possible if vowels and consonants alternate, beginning with a vowel?

Of the 6 letters in the word, 3 are vowels (*u, a, e*) and 3 are consonants (*s, q, r*).

Beginning with a vowel, every other slot is to be filled by a vowel. There are 3 such slots and 3 vowels to be arranged in them. 3 × ___ × 2 × ___ × 1 × ___

The remaining 3 slots have 3 consonants to be arranged in them. 3 × 3 × 2 × 2 × 1 × 1

Multiply to determine the total number of arrangements. There are 36 possible arrangements.

The girls Amy, Ann, and Doris and the boys Al, Arnon, Bob, and Roy are in a nursery group. Determine the number of ways the children can be arranged in a line with the following conditions.

1. A girl is always at the head of the line. **2160**
2. Roy is always at the head of the line. **720**
3. A child whose name begins with *A* is always at the head of the line. **2880**
4. A child whose name begins with *A* is always at the head and the rear of the line. **1440**

The diamond suit from a standard deck of 52 playing cards is removed from the deck, shuffled, and laid out in a row. Determine the number of possible arrangements.

5. The first card is the ace. **479,001,600**
6. The first card is a face card. **1,437,004,800**

Use the digits 0, 1, 2, 3, 4 without repetition. Determine the number of ways to form each arrangement.

7. 3-digit numerals whose values are at least 100 **48**
8. 4-digit numerals whose values are at least 1000 and less than 4000 **72**

11-1 PRACTICE A
11-1 PRACTICE C
11-1 PRACTICE B

Use the Fundamental Counting Principle.

1. The soccer team is silk-screening T-shirts. They have 4 different colors of T-shirts and 2 different colors of ink. How many different T-shirts can be made using one ink color on a T-shirt? **8 T-shirts**
2. A travel agent is offering a vacation package. Participants choose the type of tour, a meal plan, and a hotel class from the table below.

Tour	Meal	Hotel
Walking	Restaurant	4-Star
Boat	Picnic	3-Star
Bicycle		2-Star
		1-Star

How many different vacation packages are offered? **24 packages**

Evaluate.

3. $\frac{3!6!}{3!}$ **720** 4. $\frac{10!}{7!}$ **720** 5. $\frac{9!-6!}{(9-6)!}$ **60,360**

Solve.

6. In how many ways can the debate team choose a president and a secretary if there are 10 people on the team? **90 ways**
7. A teacher is passing out first-, second-, and third-place prizes for the best student actor in a production of *Hamlet*. If there are 14 students in the class, in how many different ways can the awards be presented? **2184 ways**

Evaluate.

8. ${}_5P_4$ **120** 9. ${}_3C_2$ **3** 10. ${}_8P_3$ **336**

Solve.

11. Mrs. Marshall has 11 boys and 14 girls in her kindergarten class this year.
    a. In how many ways can she select 2 girls to pass out a snack? **91 ways**
    b. In how many ways can she select 5 boys to pass out new books? **462 ways**
    c. In how many ways can she select 3 students to carry papers to the office? **2300 ways**

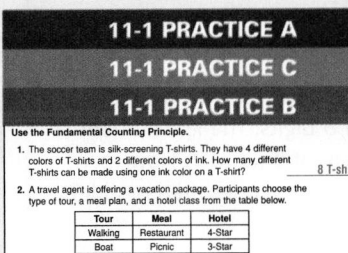

In **Exercise 39,** students who chose **B** or **C** may be looking for permutations instead of combinations. Remind students that choosing a group of 5 players does not involve the order or the choices.

In **Exercise 40,** students who select **F** or **H** might be equating permutations and combinations. Remind students that the two are different. Students who choose **G** might be assuming that the order of n and r does not matter. Stress that n cannot be less than r in either a permutation or a combination.

Journal

Have students cite real-world examples of permutations and combinations. Have them discuss why order does or does not matter in each one.

Have students give examples of a permutation and a combination based on the students in your classroom. Have them write each expression and calculate the value. Have students explain how they decided whether the order mattered in their examples.

Power Presentations with PowerPoint®

11-1 Lesson Quiz

1. Six different books will be displayed in the library window. How many different arrangements are there? 720
2. The code for a lock consists of 5 digits. The last number cannot be 0 or 1. How many different codes are possible? 80,000
3. The three best essays in a contest will receive gold, silver, and bronze stars. There are 10 essays. In how many ways can the prizes be awarded? 720
4. In a talent show, the top 3 performers of 15 will advance to the next round. In how many ways can this be done? 455

Also available on transparency

37. **ERROR ANALYSIS** Below are two solutions for "How many Internet codes can be made by using 3 digits if 0 is excluded and digits may not be repeated?" Which is incorrect? Explain the error. **A; order is important.**

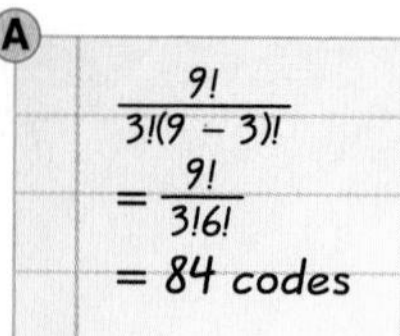

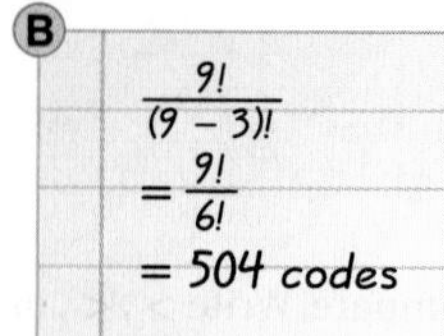

38. **Critical Thinking** Explain how to use the Fundamental Counting Principle to answer the question in Exercise 37.
Choosing 3 times from 9 digits: there are 9 possible choices the first time, 8 the second, and 7 the third, so the total number of permutations is $9 \times 8 \times 7 = 504$.

39. There are 14 players on the team. Which of the following expressions models the number of ways that the coach can choose 5 players to start the game?
   (A) $5!$ (B) $\frac{14!}{5!}$ (C) $\frac{14!}{9!}$ **(D)** $\frac{14!}{5!9!}$
40. Which of the following has the same value as ${}_9C_4$?
   (F) ${}_9P_4$ (G) ${}_4C_9$ (H) ${}_9P_5$ **(J)** ${}_9C_5$
41. **Short Response** Rene can choose 1 elective each of the 4 years that she is in high school. There are 15 electives. How many ways can Rene choose her electives? **1365**

CHALLENGE AND EXTEND

42. **Geometry** Consider a circle with two points, A and B. You can form exactly 1 segment, $\overline{AB}$. If there are 3 points, you can form 3 segments as shown in the diagram.

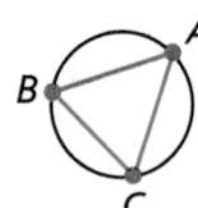

   a. How many segments can be formed from 4 points, 5 points, 6 points, and n points? Write your answer for n points as a permutation or combination. **6; 10; 15; ${}_nC_2$**
   b. How many segments can be formed from 20 points? **190**
43. **Government** How many ways can a jury of 12 and 2 alternate jurors be selected from a pool of 30 potential jurors? (*Hint:* Consider how order is both important and unimportant in selection.) Leave your answer in unexpanded notation.
   $({}_{30}C_{12})({}_{18}C_2)$

SPIRAL REVIEW

44. **Money** The cost to rent a boat increased from \$0.15 per mile to \$0.45 per mile. Write a function $p(x)$ for the initial cost and a function $P(x)$ for the cost after the price increase. Graph both functions on the same coordinate plane. Describe the transformation. *(Lesson 1-8)* **$p(x) = 0.15x$; $P(x) = 0.45x$**
   $P(x) = 3p(x)$ is a vertical stretch.

Solve each proportion. *(Lesson 2-2)*

45. $\frac{17}{n} = \frac{11}{77}$ **$n = 119$**
46. $\frac{2.9}{3.7} = \frac{x}{23.31}$ **$x = 18.27$**
47. $\frac{2.2}{n} = \frac{1.6}{9.5}$ **$n = 13.0625$**
48. $\frac{x}{36} = \frac{98}{18}$ **$x = 196$**

Identify the conic section that each equation represents. *(Lesson 10-6)*

49. $6x^2 + 3xy - 9y^2 + 5x - 2y - 16 = 0$ **hyperbola**
50. $8x^2 + 8y^2 - 6x + 7y - 9 = 0$ **circle**

Answers

44.
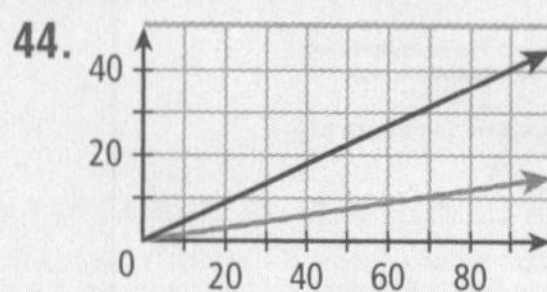

Relative Area

In *geometric probability*, the probability of an event corresponds to ratios of the areas (or lengths or volumes) or parts of one or more figures.

See Skills Bank page S62

In the spinners shown, the probability of landing on a color is based on relative area.

$\frac{1}{2}$ shaded $\frac{3}{8}$ shaded $\frac{1}{4}$ shaded

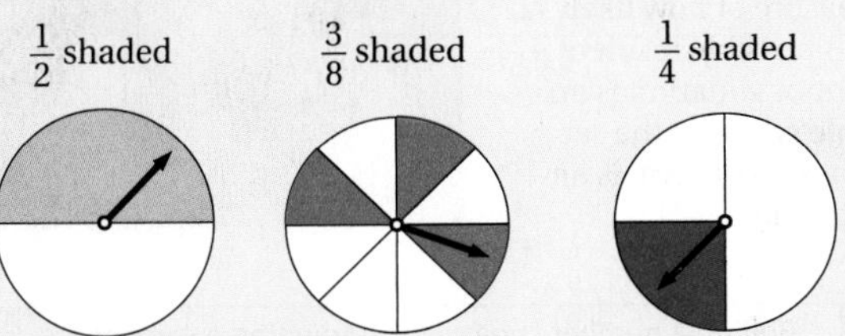

Area Formulas	
Figure	Formula
Rectangle	$A = bh$
Square	$A = s^2$
Triangle	$A = \frac{1}{2}bh$
Trapezoid	$A = \frac{1}{2}h(b_1 + b_2)$
Circle	$A = \pi r^2$

Use the area formulas at right to help you determine relative area.

Example

What portion of the rectangle is shaded? Write the relative area as a fraction, a decimal, and a percent.

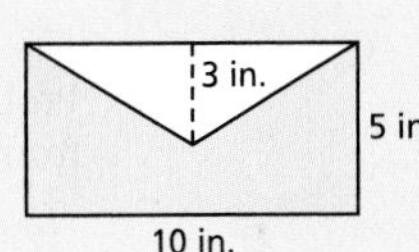

Find the ratio of the area of the shaded region to the area of the rectangle.

$A = 10(5) = 50 \text{ in}^2$ *Area of the rectangle: $A = bh$*

$A = \frac{1}{2}(3)(10) = 15 \text{ in}^2$ *Area of the unshaded triangle: $A = \frac{1}{2}bh$*

$$\frac{\text{area of shaded region}}{\text{area of the rectangle}} = \frac{50 - 15}{50} = \frac{35}{50} = \frac{7}{10} = 0.7\text{, or } 70\%$$

Try This

What portion of each figure is shaded? Write the relative area as a fraction, a decimal, and a percent.

1. 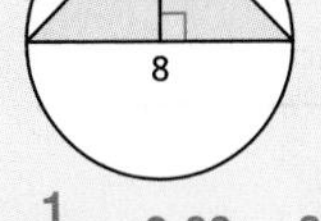

$\frac{1}{\pi} \approx 0.32 \approx 32\%$

2. 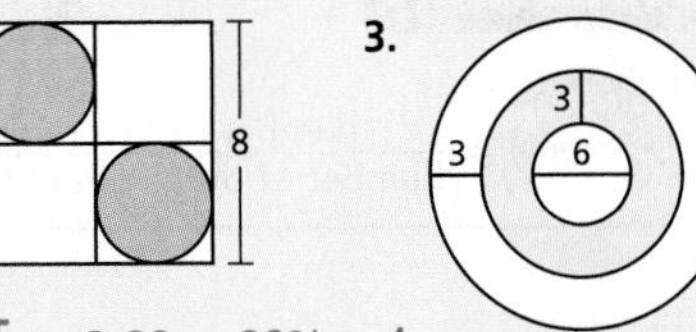

$\frac{\pi}{8} \approx 0.39 \approx 39\%$

3.

$\frac{1}{3} = 0.\overline{3} = 33.\overline{3}\%$

4. $\frac{2}{7} \approx 0.29 \approx 29\%$

5. Write the relative area of each sector of the spinner as a fraction, decimal, and percent.

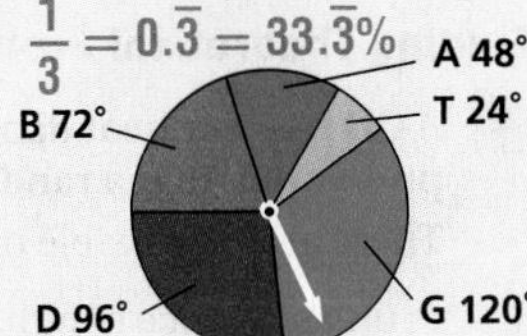

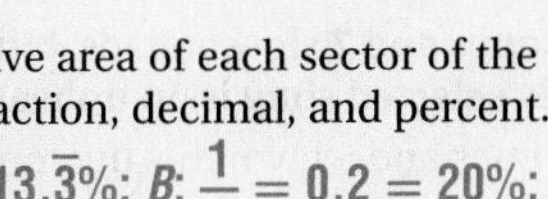
A: $\frac{2}{15} = 0.1\overline{3} = 13.\overline{3}\%$; B: $\frac{1}{5} = 0.2 = 20\%$;

D: $\frac{4}{15} = 0.2\overline{6} = 26.\overline{6}\%$; G: $\frac{1}{3} = 0.\overline{3} = 33.\overline{3}\%$; T: $\frac{1}{15} = 0.0\overline{6} = 6.\overline{6}\%$

Organizer

See Skills Bank page S62

Pacing:
Traditional $\frac{1}{2}$ day
Block $\frac{1}{4}$ day

Objective: Find relative areas of geometric figures.

Teach

Remember

Students review and apply area formulas for geometric figures.

INTERVENTION For additional review and practice using area formulas, see Skills Bank page S62.

Reading Math For **Exercise 5,** remind students that a *sector* of a circle is a region bounded by two radii and an intercepted arc.

Close

Assess

Have students describe two different ways in which they could determine the percent of the figure in **Exercise 4** that is not shaded.

State Resources

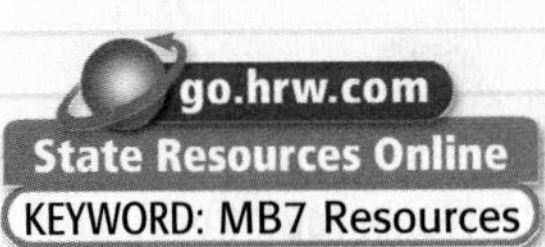

11-2 Organizer

Pacing: Traditional 1 day
Block $\frac{1}{2}$ day

Objectives: Find the theoretical probability of an event.

Find the experimental probability of an event.

Algebra Lab
In Algebra Lab Activities

Online Edition
Tutorial Videos, Interactivity

Countdown to Testing Week 23

Power Presentations with PowerPoint®

Warm Up

Write each fraction as a percent.

1. $\frac{1}{4}$ 25% **2.** $\frac{2}{3}$ $66\frac{2}{3}\%$

3. $\frac{3}{8}$ 37.5% **4.** $\frac{12}{12}$ 100%

Evaluate.

5. ${}_6P_3$ 120 **6.** ${}_5P_2$ 20

7. ${}_7C_4$ 35 **8.** ${}_8C_6$ 28

Also available on transparency

Math Humor

Su: My chances of winning are 1 in 10!

Bill: Your chances of NOT winning are 9 in 10.

Su: Go away!

Bill: Some people can't take a complement.

State Resources

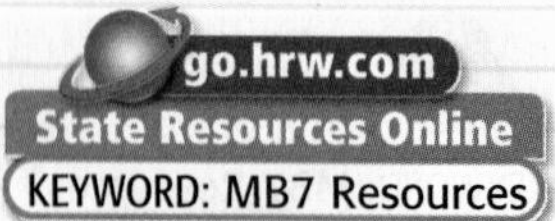

11-2 Theoretical and Experimental Probability

Objectives
Find the theoretical probability of an event.

Find the experimental probability of an event.

Vocabulary
probability
outcome
sample space
event
equally likely outcomes
favorable outcomes
theoretical probability
complement
geometric probability
experiment
trial
experimental probability

Why learn this?
You can use probability to find the chances of hitting or missing a target in the game Battleship. (See Example 2.)

Probability is the measure of how likely an event is to occur. Each possible result of a probability experiment or situation is an **outcome**. The **sample space** is the set of all possible outcomes. An **event** is an outcome or set of outcomes.

Experiment or Situation	Rolling a number cube	Spinning a spinner
	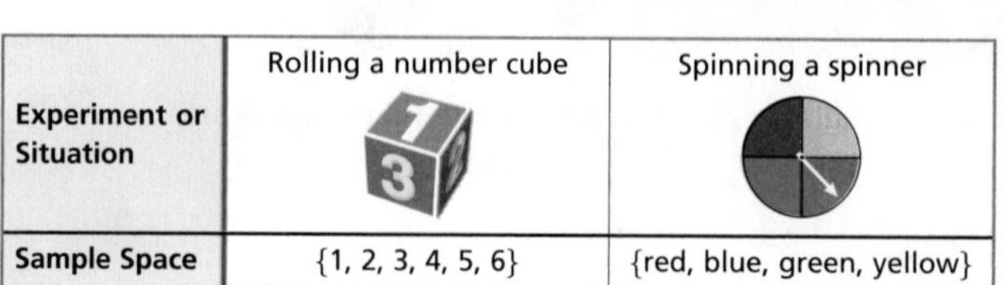	
Sample Space	{1, 2, 3, 4, 5, 6}	{red, blue, green, yellow}

Probabilities are written as fractions or decimals from 0 to 1, or as percents from 0% to 100%.

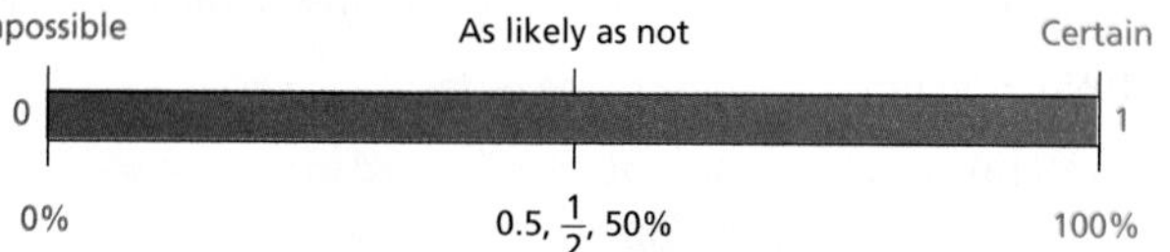

Equally likely outcomes have the same chance of occurring. When you toss a fair coin, heads and tails are equally likely outcomes. **Favorable outcomes** are outcomes in a specified event. For equally likely outcomes, the **theoretical probability** of an event is the ratio of the number of favorable outcomes to the total number of outcomes.

Know it! Note

Theoretical Probability

For equally likely outcomes,

$$P(\text{event}) = \frac{\text{number of favorable outcomes}}{\text{number of outcomes in the sample space}}.$$

EXAMPLE 1 Finding Theoretical Probability

A **A CD has 5 upbeat dance songs and 7 slow ballads. What is the probability that a randomly selected song is an upbeat dance song?**

There are 12 possible outcomes and 5 favorable outcomes.

$P(\text{upbeat dance song}) = \frac{5}{12} \approx 41.7\%$

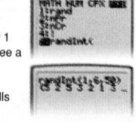

1 Introduce

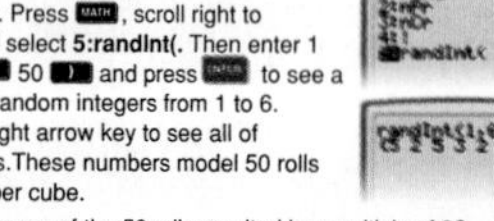

EXPLORATION

11-2 Theoretical and Experimental Probability

You can use a calculator to help you investigate probability.

1. A number cube has faces numbered 1 to 6. How many of the faces are numbered with a multiple of 3?
2. What fraction of the faces is labeled with a multiple of 3? This fraction represents the theoretical probability of rolling a multiple of 3 because it is based on p   outcomes.

You can model rolling a number cube by using the random integer feature of a calculator. Press MATH, scroll right to PRB, and select 5:randInt(. Then enter 1 , 6 , 50) and press ENTER to see a list of 50 random integers from 1 to 6. Use the right arrow key to see all of the results. These numbers model 50 rolls of a number cube.

3. How many of the 50 rolls resulted in a multiple of 3?
4. What fraction of the 50 rolls resulted in a multiple of 3? This fraction represents the experimental probability of rolling a multiple of 3 because it is based on a   outcomes.

THINK AND DISCUSS

5. **Discuss** what you think will happen to the experimental probability if you increase the number of rolls.

Motivate

Have a globe and tape measure (MK) available. Ask students "Suppose a satellite came down anywhere along the equator with an equal chance. Would you think it would come down on land or on water? Water is likely Estimate the chance that it falls on land." Have students examine the globe and revise their estimates. ≈ 20% chance

Explorations and answers are provided in the *Explorations* binder.

B **A red number cube and a blue number cube are rolled. If all numbers are equally likely, what is the probability that the sum is 10?**

There are 36 possible outcomes.

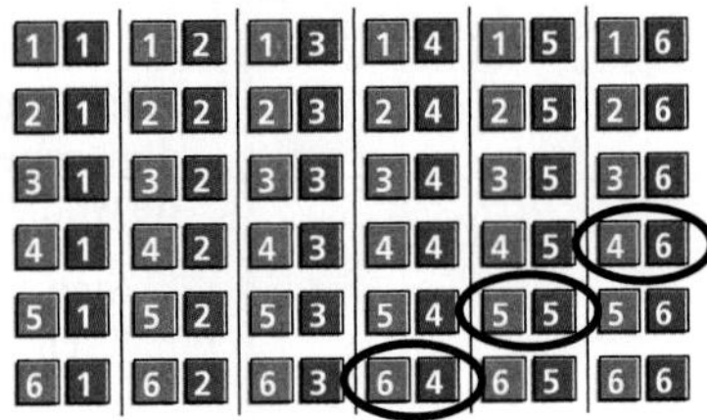

$$P(\text{sum is } 10) = \frac{\text{number of outcomes with sum of 10}}{36}$$

$$P(\text{sum is } 10) = \frac{3}{36} = \frac{1}{12}$$ *3 outcomes with a sum of 10: (4, 6) (5, 5), and (6, 4)*

A red number cube and a blue number cube are rolled. If all numbers are equally likely, what is the probability of each event?

1a. The sum is 6. $\frac{5}{36}$

1b. The difference is 6. 0

1c. The red cube is greater. $\frac{5}{12}$

The sum of all probabilities in the sample space is 1. The **complement** of an event E is the set of all outcomes in the sample space that are not in E.

Complement

The probability of the complement of event E is

$$P(\text{not } E) = 1 - P(E).$$

EXAMPLE 2 *Entertainment Application*

The game Battleship is played with 5 ships on a 100-hole grid. Players try to guess the locations of their opponent's ships and sink them. At the start of the game, what is the probability that the first shot misses all targets?

$P(\text{miss}) = 1 - P(\text{hit})$ *Use the complement.*

$P(\text{miss}) = 1 - \frac{17}{100}$ *There are 17 total holes covered by game pieces.*

$= \frac{83}{100}$, or 83%

There is an 83% chance of the first shot missing all targets.

Battleship Pieces

Game Piece	Number of Holes Covered
Destroyer	2
Cruiser	3
Submarine	3
Battleship	4
Carrier	5

2. Two integers from 1 to 10 are randomly selected. The same number may be chosen twice. What is the probability that both numbers are less than 9? $\frac{16}{25}$

2 Teach

Guided Instruction

Review the basic principles of theoretical probability. Define the complement of an event and give some examples. Explain that theoretical probability cannot be used in all situations. Experimental probability uses the pattern of past experiments to generate probabilities. Discuss the relationship between theoretical and experimental probability.

Reaching All Learners

Through Kinesthetic Experience

Have groups of students perform the simple experiment of flipping a thumbtack and recording how often it lands on the flat side. Have each group try to complete a table like the one below. Explain that in some cases, theoretical probability is not known and can only be estimated using experimental probability.

	$P(E)$	$P(\text{not } E)$
Theoretical		
Experimental		

Power Presentations with PowerPoint®

Additional Examples

Example 1

A. Each letter of the word PROBABLE is written on a separate card. The cards are placed face down and mixed up. What is the probability that a randomly selected card has a consonant? $\frac{5}{8} = 62.5\%$

B. Two number cubes are rolled. What is the probability that the difference between the two numbers is 4? $\frac{1}{9}$

Example 2

There are 25 students in study hall. The table shows the number of students who are studying a foreign language. What is the probability that a randomly selected student is not studying a foreign language?

$\frac{4}{25} = 16\%$

Language	Number
French	6
Spanish	12
Japanese	3

Also available on transparency

INTERVENTION

Questioning Strategies

EXAMPLE 1

- How do you find the number of favorable outcomes and the number of possible outcomes?
- How do you describe a situation with a probability of 1?
- How do you describe a situation with a probability of 0?

EXAMPLE 2

- Why do you use the complement in the first step?
- Is there another way to solve the problem? Explain.

Teaching Tip

Geometry Students might connect the complement of an event with the complement of an angle. The sum of the probabilities of an event and its complement is 1. The sum of the measures of an angle and its complement is 90°, 1 complete right angle.

Power Presentations with PowerPoint®

Additional Examples

Example 3

Each student receives a 5-digit locker combination. What is the probability of receiving a combination with all odd digits? $\frac{1}{32}$

Example 4

A figure is created by placing a rectangle inside a triangle inside a square as shown. If a point inside the figure is chosen at random, what is the probability that the point is inside the shaded region? $\frac{28.5}{81} \approx 0.352$

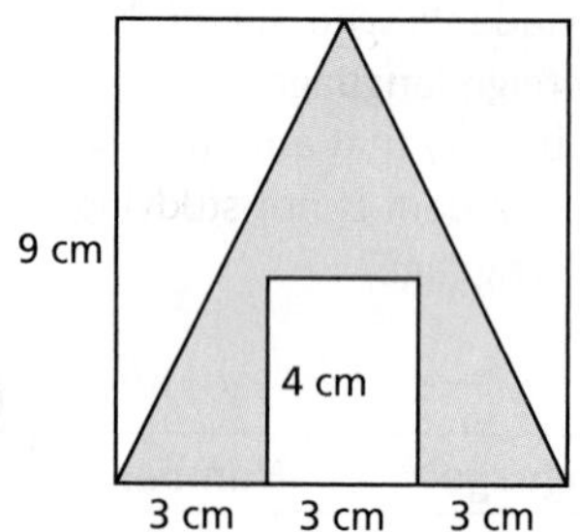

Also available on transparency

INTERVENTION

Questioning Strategies

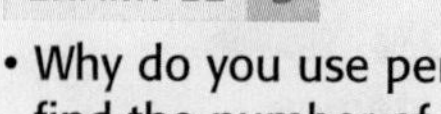

EXAMPLE 3

- Why do you use permutations to find the number of possible outcomes?
- How do you decide which permutations to find?

EXAMPLE 4

- How does the ratio for the geometrical probability relate to the definition of theoretical probability?

Teaching Tip **Science Link** Explain the similarities between a probability experiment and a scientific experiment. Both may have trials, data collection, analysis, prediction, and so on.

EXAMPLE 3 Finding Probability with Permutations or Combinations

Each student received a 4-digit code to use the library computers, with no digit repeated. Manu received the code 7654. What was the probability that he would receive a code of consecutive numbers?

Step 1 Determine whether the code is a permutation or a combination.
Order is important, so it is a permutation.

Step 2 Find the number of outcomes in the sample space.
The sample space is the number of permutations of 4 of 10 digits.

$${}_{10}P_4 = \frac{10!}{6!} = \frac{10 \cdot 9 \cdot 8 \cdot 7 \cdot \cancel{6 \cdot 5 \cdot 4 \cdot 3 \cdot 2 \cdot 1}}{\cancel{6 \cdot 5 \cdot 4 \cdot 3 \cdot 2 \cdot 1}} = 5040$$

Step 3 Find the favorable outcomes.
The favorable outcomes are the codes 0123, 1234, 2345, 3456, 4567, 5678, 6789, and the reverse of each of these numbers. There are 14 favorable outcomes.

Step 4 Find the probability.

$$P(\text{consecutive numbers}) = \frac{14}{5040} = \frac{1}{360}$$

The probability that Manu would receive a code of consecutive numbers was $\frac{1}{360}$.

3. A DJ randomly selects 2 of 8 ads to play before her show. Two of the ads are by a local retailer. What is the probability that she will play both of the retailer's ads before her show? $\frac{1}{28}$

Geometric probability is a form of theoretical probability determined by a ratio of lengths, areas, or volumes.

EXAMPLE 4 Finding Geometric Probability

Three semicircles with diameters 2, 4, and 6 cm are arranged as shown in the figure. If a point inside the figure is chosen at random, what is the probability that the point is inside the shaded region?

4 cm 2 cm 6 cm

Find the ratio of the area of the shaded region to the area of the entire semicircle. The area of a semicircle is $\frac{1}{2}\pi r^2$.

First, find the area of the entire semicircle.

$A_t = \frac{1}{2}\pi(3^2) = 4.5\pi$ *Total area of largest semicircle*

Next, find the unshaded area.

$A_u = \left[\frac{1}{2}\pi(2^2)\right] + \left[\frac{1}{2}\pi(1^2)\right] = 2\pi + 0.5\pi = 2.5\pi$ *Sum of areas of the unshaded semicircles*

Subtract to find the shaded area.

$A_s = 4.5\pi - 2.5\pi = 2\pi$ *Area of shaded region*

$\frac{A_s}{A_t} = \frac{2\pi}{4.5\pi} = \frac{2}{4.5} = \frac{4}{9}$ *Ratio of shaded region to total area*

The probability that the point is in the shaded region is $\frac{4}{9}$.

4. Find the probability that a point chosen at random inside the large triangle is in the small triangle. $\frac{16}{225}$

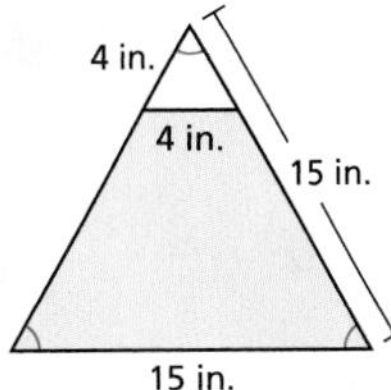

You can estimate the probability of an event by using data, or by **experiment**. For example, if a doctor states that an operation "has an 80% probability of success," 80% is an estimate of probability based on similar case histories.

Each repetition of an experiment is a **trial**. The sample space of an experiment is the set of all possible outcomes. The **experimental probability** of an event is the ratio of the number of times that the event occurs, the *frequency*, to the number of trials.

Experimental Probability

$$\text{experimental probability} = \frac{\text{number of times the event occurs}}{\text{number of trials}}$$

Experimental probability is often used to estimate theoretical probability and to make predictions.

EXAMPLE 5 Finding Experimental Probability

The bar graph shows the results of 100 tosses of an oddly shaped number cube. Find each experimental probability.

Results of 100 Rolls

(Bar graph: Frequency (0–20) vs. Number rolled (1–6))

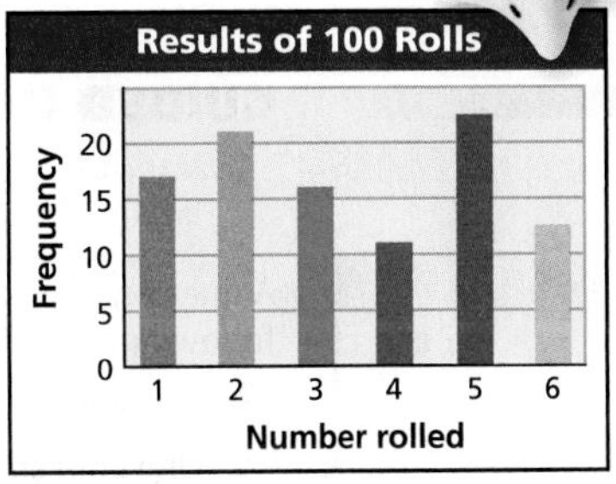

A rolling a 3

The outcome 3 occurred 16 times out of 100 trials.

$P(3) = \frac{16}{100} = \frac{4}{25} = 0.16$

Helpful Hint

Frequencies must be whole numbers, so they can be easily read from the graph in Example 5.

B rolling a perfect square

$P(\text{perfect square}) = \frac{17 + 11}{100}$ *The numbers 1 and 4 are perfect squares. 1 occurred 17 times and 4 occurred 11 times.*

$= \frac{28}{100} = \frac{7}{25} = 0.28$

C rolling a number other than 5

Use the complement.

$P(5) = \frac{22}{100}$ *5 occurred 22 times out of 100 trials.*

$1 - P(5) = 1 - \frac{22}{100} = \frac{78}{100} = \frac{39}{50} = 0.78$

5. The table shows the results of choosing one card from a deck of cards, recording the suit, and then replacing the card.

Card Suit	Hearts	Diamonds	Clubs	Spades
Number	5	9	7	5

5a. Find the experimental probability of choosing a diamond. $\frac{9}{26}$

5b. Find the experimental probability of choosing a card that is not a club. $\frac{19}{26}$

COMMON ERROR ALERT

Students may have trouble identifying some favorable outcomes. For example, when identifying outcomes on a pair of number cubes with a sum of 5, students may identify 1 + 4 and 2 + 3. They may not identify 4 + 1 and 3 + 2. Encourage students to carefully identify all favorable outcomes by using tables, lists, or diagrams.

Power Presentations with PowerPoint®

Additional Examples

Example 5

The table shows the results of a spinner experiment. Find each experimental probability.

Number	Occurrences
1	6
2	11
3	19
4	14

A. spinning a 4 $\frac{7}{25} = 28\%$

B. spinning a number greater than 2 $\frac{33}{50} = 66\%$

Also available on transparency

INTERVENTION

Questioning Strategies

EXAMPLE 5

- What is the first step toward finding probabilities based on the data in the graph?

Teaching Tip **Math Background** Two French mathematicians, Blaise Pascal (1623–1662) and Pierre de Fermat (1601–1665), are considered to be the founders of probability theory.

3 Close

Summarize

Ask students to explain how to find the theoretical probability of an event. Have them compare that definition with the definition of the experimental probability of an event. The theoretical probability of an event is the ratio of favorable outcomes to the total number of outcomes. The experimental probability of an event is the ratio of the number of times the event occurs to the total number of trials.

ONGOING ASSESSMENT and INTERVENTION

***Diagnose Before* the Lesson**
11-2 Warm Up, TE p. 802

***Monitor During* the Lesson**
Check It Out! Exercises, SE pp. 803–805
Questioning Strategies, TE pp. 803–805

***Assess After* the Lesson**
11-2 Lesson Quiz, TE p. 809
Alternative Assessment, TE p. 809

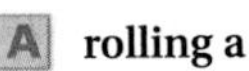
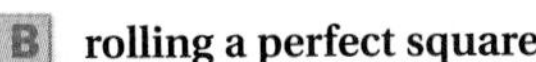

Answers to *Think and Discuss*

1. No, probability cannot exceed 1.
2. sum of 5 and sum of 9
3. experimental: $\frac{2}{5}$; theoretical: $\frac{1}{2}$
4. See p. A12.

11-2 Exercises

Assignment Guide

Assign *Guided Practice* exercises as necessary.

If you finished Examples **1–3**
- **Basic** 14–18
- **Average** 14–18, 22
- **Advanced** 14–18, 22, 24

If you finished Examples **1–5**
- **Basic** 14–22, 25–29, 33–40, 44–48
- **Average** 14–23, 25–31, 33, 35–40, 44–48
- **Advanced** 14–21, 23, 26, 27, 29–33, 35–48

Homework Quick Check
Quickly check key concepts.
Exercises: 14, 16, 18, 19, 20, 32

State Resources

go.hrw.com
State Resources Online
KEYWORD: MB7 Resources

THINK AND DISCUSS

1. Explain whether the probability of an event can be 1.5.
2. Tell which events have the same probability when two number cubes are tossed: sum of 7, sum of 5, sum of 9, and sum of 11.
3. Compare the theoretical and experimental probabilities of getting heads when tossing a coin if Joe got heads 8 times in 20 tosses of the coin.

4. **GET ORGANIZED** Copy and complete the graphic organizer. Give an example of each probability concept.

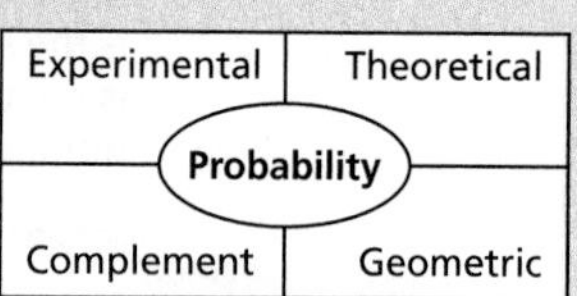

11-2 Exercises

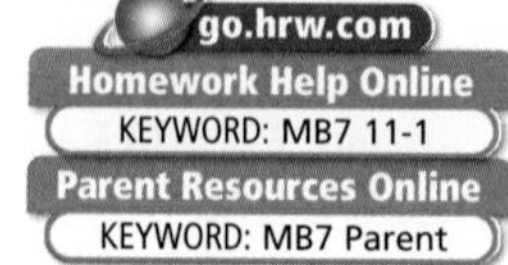

go.hrw.com
Homework Help Online
KEYWORD: MB7 11-1
Parent Resources Online
KEYWORD: MB7 Parent

GUIDED PRACTICE

1. **Vocabulary** A fair coin is tossed 8 times and lands heads up 3 times. The __?__ of landing heads is $\frac{1}{2}$. (*theoretical probability* or *experimental probability*) theoretical probability

SEE EXAMPLE 1 p. 802

A quarter, a nickel, and a penny are flipped. Find the probability of each of the following.

2. The quarter shows heads. $\frac{1}{2}$
3. The penny and nickel show heads. $\frac{1}{4}$
4. One coin shows heads. $\frac{3}{8}$
5. All three coins land the same way. $\frac{1}{4}$

SEE EXAMPLE 2 p. 803

6. What is the probability that a random 2-digit number (00-99) does not end in 5? $\frac{9}{10}$
7. What is the probability that a randomly selected date in one year is not in the month of December or January? $\frac{303}{365}$

SEE EXAMPLE 3 p. 804

8. A clerk has 4 different letters that need to go in 4 different envelopes. What is the probability that all 4 letters are placed in the correct envelopes? $\frac{1}{24}$
9. There are 12 balloons in a bag: 3 each of blue, green, red, and yellow. Three balloons are chosen at random. Find the probability that all 3 of the balloons are green. $\frac{1}{220}$

SEE EXAMPLE 4 p. 804

Use the diagram for Exercises 10 and 11. Find each probability.

10. that a point chosen at random is in the shaded area $\frac{1}{3}$
11. that a point chosen at random is in the smallest circle $\frac{1}{9}$

2 in.　2 in.　4 in.

SEE EXAMPLE 5 p. 805

Use the table for Exercises 12 and 13.

12. Find the experimental probability of spinning red. $\frac{1}{4}$
13. Find the experimental probability of spinning red or blue. $\frac{3}{5}$

Spinner Experiment

Color	Red	Green	Blue
Spins	5	8	7

11-2 PRACTICE A

Answer each question.

1. How many possible outcomes are there from tossing two number cubes labeled 1–6? 36 outcomes
2. Describe the sample space for a spinner with four equal sections of blue, red, green, and yellow. The sample space is blue, red, green, yellow.
3. How likely is it that an outcome with a probability of 1 will occur? Certain
4. How likely is it that an outcome with a probability of 0 will occur? Impossible

Solve.

5. A farmer has four sheepdogs and three beagles. If he randomly chooses a dog to accompany him on a walk, what is the probability of him taking a walk with a sheepdog? $\frac{4}{7}$
6. Gordon spins a spinner with equal-sized sections numbered 1–6. In one spin, what is the likelihood that the spinner will stop on a 1 or a 5? $\frac{1}{3}$
7. Oak trees shade 30% of the Fitzgeralds' backyard. What is the probability that someone standing at a random point in the backyard will NOT be in the shade? $\frac{7}{10}$
8. Find the probability that a point chosen at random inside the larger square shown here will also fall inside the smaller square. $\frac{1}{9}$

6 in.　2 in.

The table below shows the results of pulling one marble from a bag of marbles, recording its color, and replacing it in the bag.

Marble Color	Yellow	Red	Green
Times Pulled	53	17	30

Find the experimental probability of each event.

9. Choosing a yellow marble $\frac{53}{100}$
10. NOT choosing a red marble $\frac{83}{100}$
11. Choosing either a red or a green marble $\frac{47}{100}$
12. Which color marble is probably present in greatest number in the bag? Yellow

11-2 PRACTICE B

Solve.

1. A fruit bowl contains 4 green apples and 7 red apples. What is the probability that a randomly selected apple will be green? $\frac{4}{11}$
2. When two number cubes labeled 1–6 are rolled, what is the probability that the result will be two 4's? $\frac{1}{36}$
3. Joanne is guessing which day in November is Bess's birthday. Joanne knows that Bess's birthday does not fall on an odd-numbered day. What is the probability that Joanne will guess the correct day on her first try? $\frac{1}{15}$
4. Tom has a dollar's worth of dimes and a dollar's worth of nickels in his pocket.
   a. What is the probability he will randomly select a nickel from his pocket? $\frac{2}{3}$
   b. What is the probability he will randomly select a dime from his pocket? $\frac{1}{3}$
5. Clarice has 7 new CDs; 3 are classical music and the rest are pop music. If she randomly grabs 3 CDs to listen to in the car on her way to school, what is the probability that she will select only classical music? $\frac{1}{35}$
6. Find the probability that a point chosen at random inside the larger circle shown here will also fall inside the smaller circle. $\frac{9}{16}$

3 cm　4 cm

Frank is playing darts. The results of his throws are shown in the table below. Assume that his results continue to follow this trend.

Color Hit	Number of Throws
Blue	12
Red	5
White	2

Find the experimental probability of each event.

7. Frank's next throw will hit white. $\frac{2}{19}$
8. Frank's next throw will hit blue. $\frac{12}{19}$
9. Frank's next throw will hit either red or white. $\frac{7}{19}$
10. Frank's next throw will NOT hit red. $\frac{14}{19}$

PRACTICE AND PROBLEM SOLVING

Independent Practice

For Exercises	See Example
14–15	1
16	2
17–18	3
19	4
20	5

Extra Practice
Skills Practice p. S24
Application Practice p. S42

There are 3 green marbles, 7 red marbles, and 5 white marbles in a bag. Find the probability of each of the following.

14. The chosen marble is white. $\frac{1}{3}$

15. The chosen marble is red or white. $\frac{4}{5}$

16. Two integers from 1 to 8 are randomly selected. The same number can be chosen both times. What is the probability that both numbers are greater than 2? $\frac{9}{16}$

17. Swimming The coach randomly selects 3 swimmers from a team of 8 to swim in a heat. What is the probability that she will choose the three strongest swimmers?

18. Books There are 7 books numbered 1–7 on the summer reading list. Peter randomly chooses 2 books. What is the probability that Peter chooses books numbered 1 and 2?

17. $\frac{1}{56}$

18. $\frac{1}{21}$

19. Games In the game of corntoss, players throw corn-filled bags at a hole in a wooden platform. If a bag that hits the platform can hit any location with an equal likelihood, find the probability that a tossed bag lands in the hole. $\approx \frac{1}{42}$

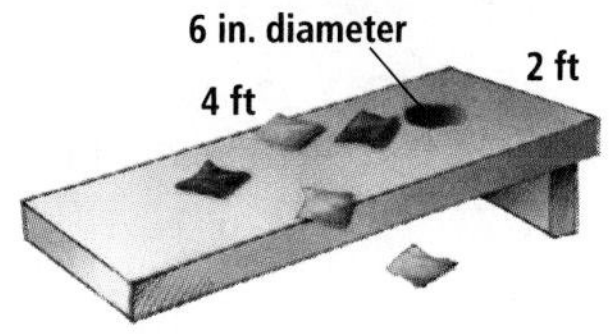

20. Cards An experiment consists of choosing one card from a standard deck and then replacing it. The experiment was done several times, and the results are: 8 hearts, 8 diamonds, 6 spades, and 6 clubs. Find the experimental probability that a card is red. $\frac{4}{7}$

21. Critical Thinking Explain whether the experimental probability of tossing tails when a fair coin is tossed 25 times is always, sometimes, or never equal to the theoretical probability.

KS MO IL IN KY TN OK AR MS AL GA TX LA FL

22. Games A radio station in Mississippi is giving away a trip to the Mississippi coast from any other state in the United States. Assuming an equally likely chance for a winner from any other state, what is the probability that the winner will be from a state that does not border Mississippi? $\frac{45}{49}$

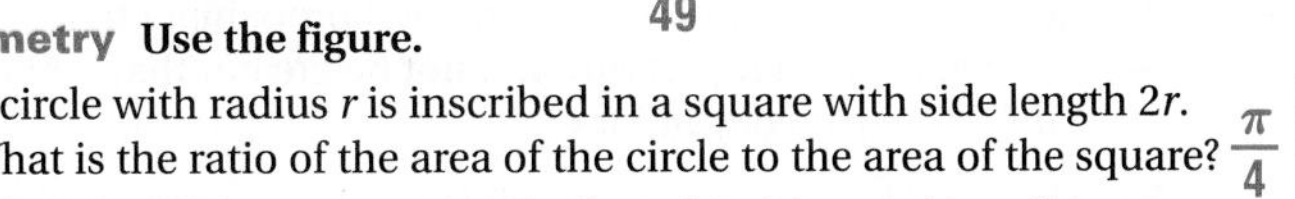

23. Geometry Use the figure.

a. A circle with radius r is inscribed in a square with side length $2r$. What is the ratio of the area of the circle to the area of the square? $\frac{\pi}{4}$

b. A square board has an inscribed circle with a 15 in. radius. A small button is dropped 10,000 times on the board, landing inside the circle 7852 times. How can you use this experiment to estimate a value for π?

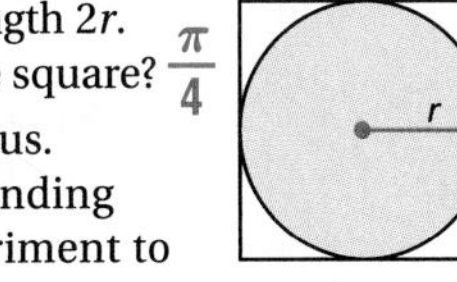

23b. Possible answer: $\frac{7852}{10{,}000} \approx \frac{\pi}{4}$, so $\pi \approx 4 \times \frac{7852}{10{,}000} \approx 3.141$.

24. Games The sides of a backgammon die are marked with the numbers 2, 4, 8, 16, 32, and 64. Describe an outcome that has a probability of $\frac{2}{3}$.

24. Possible answer: a roll of a die shows less than 20.

25. Computer A player in a computer basketball program has a constant probability of making each free throw. Jack notes the success rate over a period of time.

a. Find the experimental probability for each set of 25 attempts as a decimal. 0.68; 0.84; 0.76; 0.64

b. Find the experimental probability for the entire experiment. 0.73

c. What is the best estimate of the theoretical probability? Justify your answer.

0.73; The greater the number of experiments, the closer the experimental probability will be to the theoretical probability.

Free Throw Shooting

Attempts	Free Throws Made
1–25	17
26–50	21
51–75	19
76–100	16

COMMON ERROR ALERT

In **Exercise 21,** students might not consider the sample space. Suggest that students summarize the probability ratio using words before computing the probability.

Inclusion If students have difficulty with **Exercise 24,** suggest that they consider the total number of possible outcomes and the numerator that is needed to make an equivalent fraction using the given probability.

Answer

21. Never; the coin would need to land tails 12.5 times in 25 tosses for the experimental probability to be 0.5, the theoretical probability.

11-2 PRACTICE C

Solve.

1. A bowl contains 36 blue, 75 green, and 19 yellow jelly beans. What is the probability of randomly selecting a green jelly bean? $\frac{15}{26}$

2. Two spinners numbered 1–6 are spun. If all numbers are equally likely, what is the probability that the result will be two even numbers? $\frac{1}{4}$

3. Four quilters are preparing patches for a quilt. When finished, the quilt will contain 200 patches. The quilters' contributions thus far are in the table below.

Name	Number of Patches
Lia	65
Brian	17
Elle	88
Len	6

a. What is the probability that a randomly chosen patch will have been sewn by Elle? $\frac{1}{2}$

b. What is the probability that a randomly chosen patch will not have been sewn by Lia? $\frac{111}{176}$

c. What is the probability that a randomly chosen patch will have been sewn by Brian or Len? $\frac{23}{176}$

A hacker is trying to break into his school's computer system to change his F's to A's. The computer system access password is 5 digits.

4. If digits in the password are allowed to repeat, what is the probability that the hacker will guess the password correctly on the first try? $\frac{1}{100{,}000}$

5. The hacker learns that the password does not contain any repeated digits. What is the new probability that he will randomly guess the password correctly? $\frac{1}{30{,}240}$

6. If the password contains no repeated digits, what is the probability that the digits in the school password have a sum less than 10? 0

Use the diagram to find each probability.

7. That a random point is within the circle in the triangle $\frac{\pi}{12}$

8. That a random point is NOT within the circle in the triangle $1 - \frac{\pi}{12}$

10 m
2 m
16 m

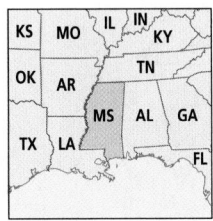

MULTI-STEP TEST PREP Exercise 26 involves finding probabilities associated with a second roll in the game Yahtzee. This exercise prepares students for the Multi-Step Test Prep on page 826.

Teaching Tip **Geometry** In **Exercise 32,** remind students of the definitions of *circumscribe* and *inscribe*. You may want to point out that the diagonal of the square is the diameter of the outer circle.

Answers

31. No; yes; a theoretical probability of 1 means all possible outcomes are favorable outcomes, but a theoretical probability of 0.99 means there is at least one unfavorable outcome.

34. college: female, $\frac{4100}{456900} > \frac{4500}{549500}$; pro: male, $\frac{44}{549500} > \frac{32}{456900}$

35. Possible answer: Theoretical probability is based on all possible outcomes, while experimental probability is based on sample results. The theoretical probability that a rolled number cube will show 4 is $\frac{1}{6}$. The experimental probability would be $\frac{3}{13}$ if it is rolled 13 times and shows 4 three times.

43. Possible answer:

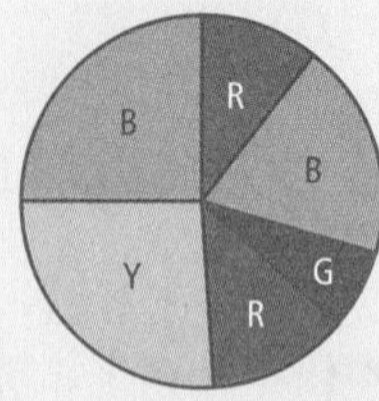

MULTI-STEP TEST PREP

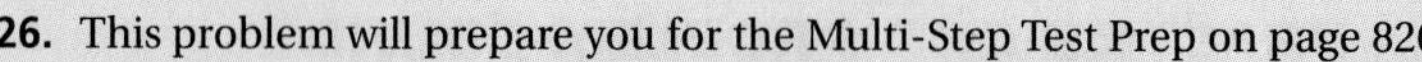

26. This problem will prepare you for the Multi-Step Test Prep on page 826.

While playing Yahtzee and rolling 5 dice, Mei gets the result shown at right. Mei decides to keep the three 4's and reroll the other 2 dice.

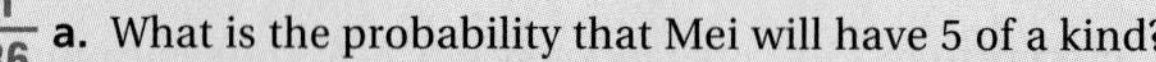

a. What is the probability that Mei will have 5 of a kind? $\frac{1}{36}$

b. What is the probability that she will have 4 of a kind (four 4's plus something else)? $\frac{5}{18}$

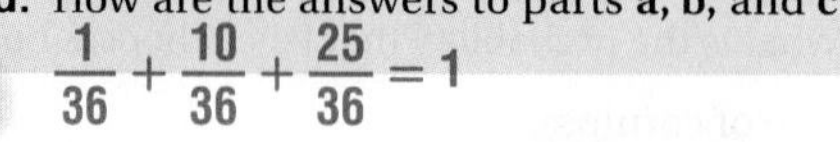

c. What is the probability that she will have exactly three 4's? $\frac{25}{36}$

d. How are the answers to parts **a**, **b**, and **c** related? $\frac{1}{36} + \frac{10}{36} + \frac{25}{36} = 1$

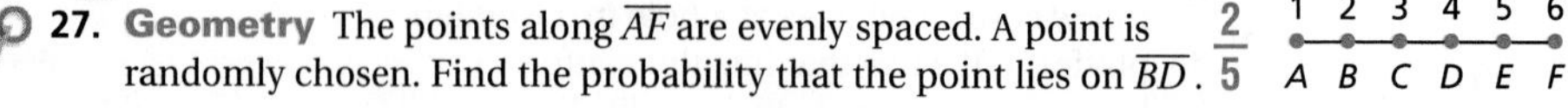

27. **Geometry** The points along $\overline{AF}$ are evenly spaced. A point is randomly chosen. Find the probability that the point lies on $\overline{BD}$. $\frac{2}{5}$

1 2 3 4 5 6
A B C D E F

Weather **Use the graph and the following information for Exercises 28–30.** The table shows the number of days that the maximum temperature was above 90°F in Death Valley National Park in 2002.

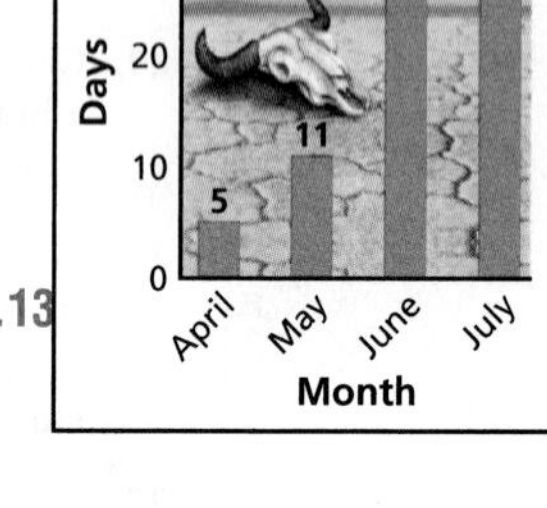

28. What is the experimental probability that the maximum temperature will be greater than 90°F on a given day in April? $\frac{1}{6} \approx 0.17$

29. For what month would you estimate the theoretical probability of a maximum temperature no greater than 90°F to be about 0.13? Explain. June; $1 - \frac{26}{30} \approx 0.13$

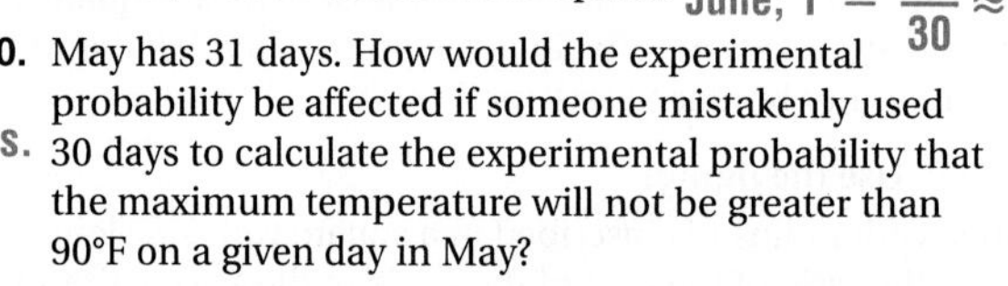

30. May has 31 days. How would the experimental probability be affected if someone mistakenly used 30 days to calculate the experimental probability that the maximum temperature will not be greater than 90°F on a given day in May? It would be slightly greater: $\frac{20}{31} \approx 0.645$ vs. $\frac{19}{30} \approx 0.634$.

31. **Critical Thinking** Is it possible for the experimental probability of an event to be 0 if the theoretical probability is 1? Is it possible for the experimental probability of an event to be 0 if the theoretical probability is 0.99? Explain.

32. **Geometry** The two circles circumscribe and inscribe the square. Find the probability that a random point in the large circle is within the inner circle. (*Hint:* Use the Pythagorean Theorem.) $\frac{1}{2}$

x

33. **Critical Thinking** Lexi tossed a fair coin 20 times, resulting in 12 heads and 8 tails. What is the theoretical probability that Lexi will get heads on the next toss? Explain. $\frac{1}{2}$; each toss is independent.

34. **Athletics** Do male or female high school basketball players have a better chance of playing on college teams? on professional teams? Explain.

U.S. Basketball Players		
	Men	Women
High School Players	549,500	456,900
College Players	4,500	4,100
College Players Drafted by Pro Leagues	44	32

Source: www.ncaa.org

35. **Write About It** Describe the difference between theoretical probability and experimental probability. Give an example in which they may differ.

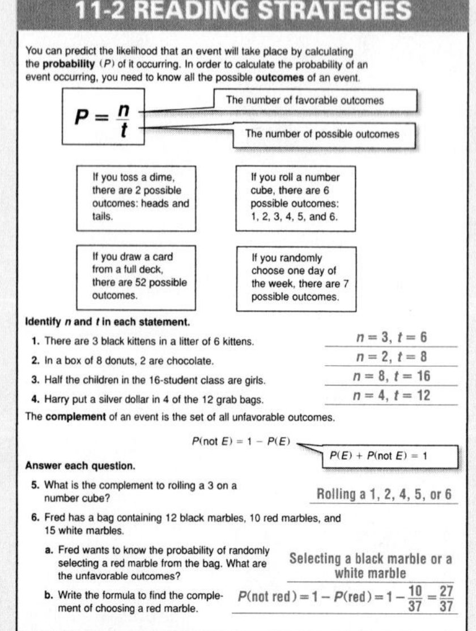

11-2 READING STRATEGIES

You can predict the likelihood that an event will take place by calculating the **probability** (*P*) of it occurring. In order to calculate the probability of an event occurring, you need to know all the possible **outcomes** of an event.

$P = \frac{n}{t}$

The number of favorable outcomes

The number of possible outcomes

If you toss a dime, there are 2 possible outcomes: heads and tails.

If you roll a number cube, there are 6 possible outcomes: 1, 2, 3, 4, 5, and 6.

If you draw a card from a full deck, there are 52 possible outcomes.

If you randomly choose one day of the week, there are 7 possible outcomes.

Identify *n* and *t* in each statement.

1. There are 3 black kittens in a litter of 6 kittens. $n = 3,\ t = 6$
2. In a box of 8 donuts, 2 are chocolate. $n = 2,\ t = 8$
3. Half the children in the 16-student class are girls. $n = 8,\ t = 16$
4. Harry put a silver dollar in 4 of the 12 grab bags. $n = 4,\ t = 12$

The **complement** of an event is the set of all unfavorable outcomes.

$P(\text{not } E) = 1 - P(E)$

$P(E) + P(\text{not } E) = 1$

Answer each question.

5. What is the complement to rolling a 3 on a number cube? Rolling a 1, 2, 4, 5, or 6
6. Fred has a bag containing 12 black marbles, 10 red marbles, and 15 white marbles.
   a. Fred wants to know the probability of randomly selecting a red marble from the bag. What are the unfavorable outcomes? Selecting a black marble or a white marble
   b. Write the formula to find the complement of choosing a red marble. $P(\text{not red}) = 1 - P(\text{red}) = 1 - \frac{10}{37} = \frac{27}{37}$

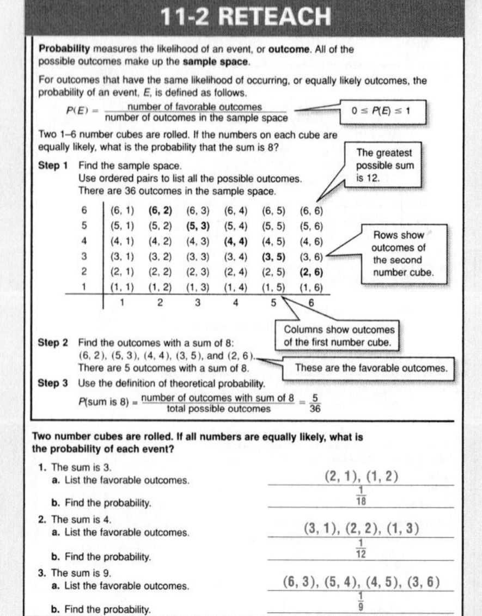

11-2 RETEACH

Probability measures the likelihood of an event, or **outcome**. All of the possible outcomes make up the **sample space**.

For outcomes that have the same likelihood of occurring, or equally likely outcomes, the probability of an event, *E*, is defined as follows.

$P(E) = \frac{\text{number of favorable outcomes}}{\text{number of outcomes in the sample space}}$

$0 \le P(E) \le 1$

Two 1–6 number cubes are rolled. If the numbers on each cube are equally likely, what is the probability that the sum is 8?

Step 1 Find the sample space.
Use ordered pairs to list all the possible outcomes.
There are 36 outcomes in the sample space.

The greatest possible sum is 12.

6	(6, 1)	**(6, 2)**	(6, 3)	(6, 4)	(6, 5)	(6, 6)
5	(5, 1)	(5, 2)	**(5, 3)**	(5, 4)	(5, 5)	(5, 6)
4	(4, 1)	(4, 2)	(4, 3)	**(4, 4)**	(4, 5)	(4, 6)
3	(3, 1)	(3, 2)	(3, 3)	(3, 4)	**(3, 5)**	(3, 6)
2	(2, 1)	(2, 2)	(2, 3)	(2, 4)	(2, 5)	**(2, 6)**
1	(1, 1)	(1, 2)	(1, 3)	(1, 4)	(1, 5)	(1, 6)
	1	2	3	4	5	6

Rows show outcomes of the second number cube.

Columns show outcomes of the first number cube.

Step 2 Find the outcomes with a sum of 8:
(6, 2), (5, 3), (4, 4), (3, 5), and (2, 6).
There are 5 outcomes with a sum of 8.

These are the favorable outcomes.

Step 3 Use the definition of theoretical probability.

$P(\text{sum is 8}) = \frac{\text{number of outcomes with sum of 8}}{\text{total possible outcomes}} = \frac{5}{36}$

Two number cubes are rolled. If all numbers are equally likely, what is the probability of each event?

1. The sum is 3.
   a. List the favorable outcomes. (2, 1), (1, 2)
   b. Find the probability. $\frac{1}{18}$
2. The sum is 4.
   a. List the favorable outcomes. (3, 1), (2, 2), (1, 3)
   b. Find the probability. $\frac{1}{12}$
3. The sum is 9.
   a. List the favorable outcomes. (6, 3), (5, 4), (4, 5), (3, 6)
   b. Find the probability. $\frac{1}{9}$

TEST PREP

36. A fair coin is tossed 25 times, landing tails up 14 times. What is the experimental probability of heads?

(A) 0.44 (circled) (B) 0.50 (C) 0.56 (D) 0.79

37. **Geometry** Find the probability that a point chosen at random in the large rectangle at right will lie in the shaded area, to the nearest percent.

(F) 18% (G) 45% (circled) (H) 55% (J) 71%

38. How many outcomes are in the sample space when a quarter, a dime, and a nickel are tossed?

(A) 3 (B) 6 (C) 8 (circled) (D) 12

39. Two number cubes are rolled. What is the theoretical probability that the sum is 5?

(F) $\frac{1}{3}$ (G) $\frac{1}{6}$ (H) $\frac{1}{9}$ (circled) (J) $\frac{1}{12}$

40. **Short Response** Find the probability that a point chosen at random on the part of the number line shown will lie between points B and C. $\frac{1}{5}$

CHALLENGE AND EXTEND

41. Possible answer: after a large number of trials, experimental probability approaches theoretical probability; check students' work

41. The graph illustrates a statistical property known as the *law of large numbers*. Make a conjecture about the effect on probability as the number of trials gets very large. Give an example of how the probability might be affected for a real-world situation.

42. Four trumpet players' instruments are mixed up, and the trumpets are given to the players just before a concert. What is the probability that *no one* gets his or her trumpet back? $\frac{3}{8}$

43. The table shows the data from a spinner experiment. Draw a reasonable spinner with 6 regions that may have been used for this experiment.

Experimental Probability

Spinner Experiment				
Color	Red	Blue	Green	Yellow
Occurrences	23	44	7	26

SPIRAL REVIEW

Find the minimum or maximum value of each function. *(Lesson 5-2)*

44. $f(x) = 0.25x^2 - 0.85x + 1$ min.: 0.2775

45. $f(x) = -2x^2 + 20x - 34$ max.: 16

Write the equation in standard form for each parabola. *(Lesson 10-5)*

46. vertex $(0, 0)$, directrix $x = -3$ $x = \frac{1}{12}y^2$

47. vertex $(0, 0)$, directrix $y = 5$ $y = -\frac{1}{20}x^2$

48. A coach chooses 5 players for a basketball team from a group of 11. *(Lesson 11-1)*

a. How many ways can she choose 5 players? ${}_{11}C_5 = 462$

b. How many ways can she choose 5 players to play different positions? ${}_{11}P_5 = 55,440$

TEST PREP DOCTOR In **Exercise 36,** students who chose **B** may be confusing experimental and theoretical probability. Students who chose **C** may have found the probability of tails instead of heads.

In **Exercise 38,** students who chose **A** may be confusing the number of coins with the number of outcomes. Students who chose **B** may have added the outcomes for each coin instead of multiplying them. Encourage students to use the fundamental counting principle to correctly count the outcomes.

Journal

Have students use their own words and an example to compare theoretical probability with experimental probability.

ALTERNATIVE ASSESSMENT

Have students create and solve a theoretical probability problem associated with a deck of cards. Then have students explain how they would conduct an experiment to compare experimental and theoretical probabilities. What results would they expect?

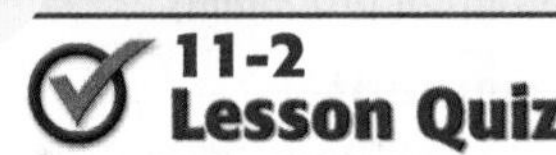

11-2 Lesson Quiz

1. In a box of 25 switches, 3 are defective. What is the probability of randomly selecting a switch that is not defective? $\frac{22}{25} = 88\%$

2. There are 12 E's among the 100 tiles in Scrabble. What is the probability of selecting all 4 E's when selecting 4 tiles? $\frac{1}{735}$

3. The table shows the results of rolling a die with unequal faces. Find the experimental probability of rolling 1 or 6. $\frac{11}{20} = 55\%$

Number	Occurrences
1	26
2	10
3	12
4	9
5	14
6	29

Also available on transparency

11-2 PROBLEM SOLVING

As part of a grant to improve bus routes to and from school, Hogan and Jane gather traffic flow statistics for one intersection. They make a table to show their findings for between 7:45 A.M. and 8:00 A.M. on a Monday morning.

Traffic Direction	Number of Vehicles
Straight through	282
Turn north	94
Turn south	188

1. Analyze the statistics.

a. Write and evaluate an expression for $P(N)$, the probability that a vehicle will turn north. $P(N) = \frac{94}{564}$ 0.17

b. Write and evaluate an expression for the probability that a vehicle will turn north or go straight through the intersection. $P(N \text{ or } through) = \frac{94 + 282}{564}$ 0.67

c. Write and evaluate an expression for the probability that a vehicle will not turn north. $1 - P(N) = 1 - 0.17$ 0.83

2. The police department gathers statistics on Tuesday. Officers count a total of 608 vehicles, of which 380 go straight through the intersection, 76 turn north, and the rest turn south.

a. What is the probability that a vehicle will turn north? $\frac{76}{608} = 0.125$

b. What is the probability that a vehicle will turn north or go straight through the intersection? $\frac{76 + 380}{608} = 0.75$

c. What is the probability that a vehicle will not turn north? $1 - 0.125 = 0.875$

3. Does this represent theoretical or experimental probability? Explain. Experimental; possible answer: the probabilities are based on actual data.

Math Assessment Survey				
Activity	Group projects	Keep a Journal	Multiple Choice	Word Problems
Student Response	57	18	35	10

A teacher surveys students on how they would prefer to have work assessed in math class. Choose the letter for the best answer.

4. What is the probability that a randomly chosen student prefers assessment through a group project?

A $\frac{1}{12}$ (C) $\frac{19}{40}$ (circled) B $\frac{53}{120}$ D $\frac{21}{40}$

5. Which expression gives the probability that a randomly chosen student will not want multiple-choice questions?

F $\frac{7}{24}$ (H) $1 - \frac{7}{24}$ (circled) G $1 + \frac{7}{24}$ J $35 - \frac{7}{24}$

11-2 CHALLENGE

The first means of generating random numbers used equipment similar to that in gambling casinos, so methods of using random numbers to simulate events are called *Monte Carlo methods*, named after the casino in the principality of Monaco. These methods can be used to approximate area under a curve.

To approximate the area of the ellipse shown in the diagram, choose a point at random in rectangle $ABCD$. The probability that this point also lies in the first-quadrant region of the ellipse is the ratio of the area of the quarter of the ellipse to the area of rectangle $ABCD$. You can find this probability experimentally by generating R random points in rectangle $ABCD$ and counting the number of points, N, that also lie in the ellipse.

As shown at right, set the area ratio approximately equal to $\frac{N}{R}$, the probability that a point lies inside the ellipse. $\frac{\text{area of quarter of ellipse}}{\text{area of rectangle } ABCD} \approx \frac{N}{R}$

Use the equation $\frac{x^2}{9} + \frac{y^2}{4} = 1$ for the ellipse. area of quarter of ellipse $\approx 6\left(\frac{N}{R}\right)$

Substitute the area, 6, for rectangle $ABCD$ in the area ratio. Then multiply by 4 to determine the area of the entire ellipse. area of ellipse $\approx 24\left(\frac{N}{R}\right)$

1. Use a graphing calculator to generate 25 points that lie in rectangle $ABCD$. Test whether these points lie inside the ellipse. Count the number of points, N, that are inside the ellipse.

a. Evaluate your ratio. $\frac{N}{25}$ Possible answer: $\frac{17}{25} = 0.68$

b. Approximate the area of the ellipse. Possible answer: 16.32 square units

c. Use the formula πab to calculate the area of the ellipse. 18.85 square units

d. How can you refine your approximation? Increase the number of random points in a simulation. Repeat the simulations a number of times and take the average of the results.

Carry out a simulation to calculate the area. Repeat your simulation 2 times and take the average of the 3 results. Determine a theoretical value by using an area formula. Compare.

2. the area enclosed by the circle $x^2 + y^2 = 16$ The area derived from the simulation will vary but should be close to 50.24 square units.

3. the area enclosed by the ellipse $\frac{y^2}{64} + \frac{x^2}{25} = 1$ above the x-axis The area derived from the simulation will vary but should be close to 62.8 square units

Organizer

Use with Lesson 11-2

Pacing:
Traditional 1 day
Block $\frac{1}{2}$ day

Objective: Use a spreadsheet to simulate experimental probability.

Materials: spreadsheet software

Online Edition

Resources

Technology Lab Activities
11-2 Lab Recording Sheet

Teach

Discuss

Explain to students that each row of the spreadsheet represents a trial and each column represents an attempt. For example, the entry in cell A1 represents the first attempt of the first trial.

Close

Key Concept

The random number function of a spreadsheet can be used to model experimental probability.

Assessment

Journal Have students explain how they could use a spreadsheet to generate a random integer from 1 to 25.

State Resources

go.hrw.com
State Resources Online
KEYWORD: MB7 Resources

11-2

Explore Simulations

Use with Lesson 11-2

A *simulation* is a model that uses random numbers to approximate experimental probability. You can use a spreadsheet to perform simulations. The **RAND( )** function generates random decimal values greater than or equal to 0 and less than 1. The **INT** function gives the greatest integer less than or equal to the input value. The functions can be used together to generate random integers as shown in the table

Random Numbers		
Formula	**Output**	**Example**
=RAND()	Decimal values $0 \le n < 1$	0.279606096
=100*RAND()	Decimal values $0 \le n < 100$	27.9606096
=INT(100*RAND())	Integers $0 \le n \le 99$	27
=INT(100*RAND())+1	Integers $1 \le n \le 100$	28

Activity

Use a simulation to find the experimental probability that a 65% free throw shooter will make at least 4 of his next 5 attempts.

1. To represent a percent, enter the formula for random integers from 1 to 100 into cell A1.

A1 ▾ fx =INT(100*RAND())+1

	A	B	C	D	E
1	38				

2. Let each row represent a trial of 5 attempts. Copy the formula from cell A1 into cells B1 through E1. Each time you copy the formula, the random values will change. To represent 10 trials, copy the formulas from row 1 into rows 2 through 10.

A1 ▾ fx =INT(100*RAND())+1

	A	B	C	D	E
1	72	98	34	74	87

3. Because the shooter makes 65% of his attempts, let the numbers 1 through 65 represent a successful attempt.

Identify the number of successful attempts in each row, or trial. There were 4 or more successes in trials 1, 3, 8, 9, and 10. So there is about a $\frac{5}{10}$, or 50%, experimental probability that the shooter will make at least 4 of his next 5 attempts.

Note that each time you run the simulation, you may get a different probability. The more trials you perform, the more reliable your estimate will be.

	A	B	C	D	E
1	✓ 25	✓ 2	✓ 62	✓ 26	✓ 38
2	✓ 30	✓ 32	66	88	✓ 9
3	✓ 27	✓ 18	✓ 9	✓ 9	93
4	98	✓ 34	✓ 10	86	99
5	87	✓ 64	✓ 4	74	✓ 36
6	✓ 5	97	69	83	✓ 51
7	✓ 39	✓ 39	80	95	97
8	✓ 32	✓ 64	✓ 51	✓ 64	✓ 46
9	✓ 52	81	✓ 39	✓ 5	✓ 36
10	✓ 48	✓ 46	✓ 45	69	✓ 21

Try This

Use a simulation to find each experimental probability.

1. An energy drink game advertises a 25% chance of winning with each bottle cap. Find the experimental probability that a 6-pack will contain at least 3 winners. $\approx$ **16.9%**
2. In a game with a 40% chance of winning, your friend challenges you to win 4 times in a row. Find the experimental probability of this happening in the next 4 games. $\approx$ **2.6%**
3. **Critical Thinking** How would you design a simulation to find the probability that a baseball player with a .285 batting average will get a hit in 5 of his next 10 at bats?
Possible answer: Use =INT(1000*RAND( )) 10 times. Consider numbers 0–284 successes.

11-3 Independent and Dependent Events

A2.8.2 Determine the probability of simple events involving independent and dependent events and conditional probability. Analyze probabilities to interpret odds and risk of events.

Objectives
Determine whether events are independent or dependent.

Find the probability of independent and dependent events.

Vocabulary
independent events
dependent events
conditional probability

Who uses this?
Political analysts can use demographic information and probabilities to predict the results of elections. (See Example 3.)

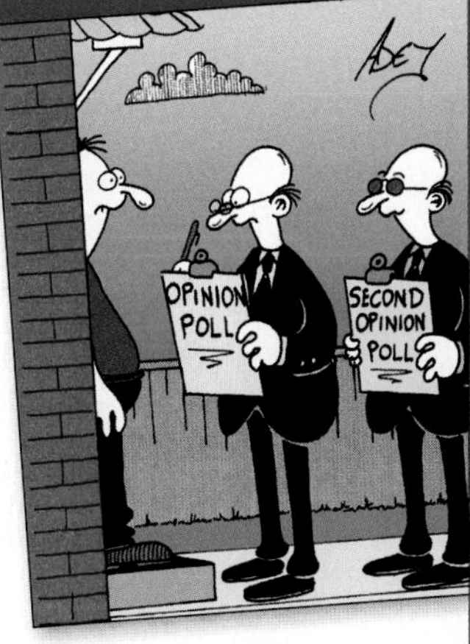

Events are **independent events** if the occurrence of one event does not affect the probability of the other.

If a coin is tossed twice, its landing heads up on the first toss and landing heads up on the second toss are independent events. The outcome of one toss does not affect the probability of heads on the other toss. To find the probability of tossing heads twice, multiply the individual probabilities, $\frac{1}{2} \cdot \frac{1}{2}$, or $\frac{1}{4}$.

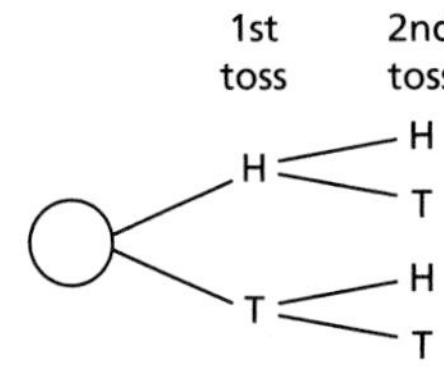
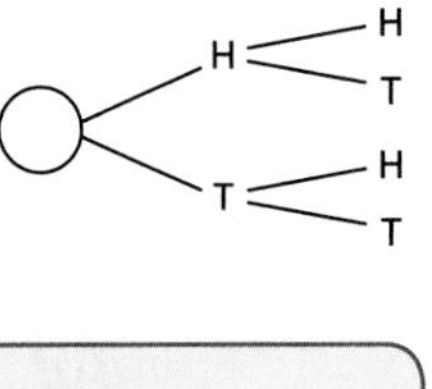

Know it! Note

Probability of Independent Events

If A and B are independent events, then $P(A \text{ and } B) = P(A) \cdot P(B)$.

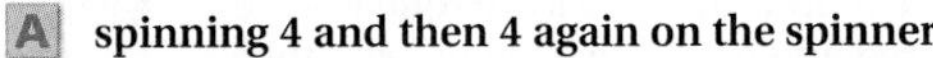

EXAMPLE 1 Finding the Probability of Independent Events

Find each probability.

A spinning 4 and then 4 again on the spinner

Spinning a 4 once does not affect the probability of spinning a 4 again, so the events are independent.

$P(4 \text{ and then } 4) = P(4) \cdot P(4)$

$\frac{3}{8} \cdot \frac{3}{8} = \frac{9}{64}$ *3 of the 8 equal sectors are labeled 4.*

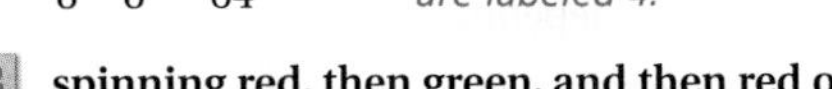

B spinning red, then green, and then red on the spinner

The result of any spin does not affect the probability of any other outcome.

$P(\text{red, then green, and then red}) = P(\text{red}) \cdot P(\text{green}) \cdot P(\text{red})$

$= \frac{1}{4} \cdot \frac{3}{8} \cdot \frac{1}{4} = \frac{3}{128}$ *2 of the 8 equal sectors are red; 3 are green.*

CHECK IT OUT! **Find each probability.**

1a. rolling a 6 on one number cube and a 6 on another number cube $\frac{1}{36}$

1b. tossing heads, then heads, and then tails when tossing a coin 3 times $\frac{1}{8}$

11-3 Organizer

Pacing: Traditional 1 day
Block $\frac{1}{2}$ day

Objectives: Determine whether events are independent or dependent.

Find the probability of independent and dependent events.

Online Edition
Tutorial Videos

Countdown to Testing Week 23

Power Presentations with PowerPoint®

Warm Up

There are 5 blue, 4 red, 1 yellow and 2 green beads in a bag. Find the probability that a bead chosen at random from the bag is:

1. blue. $\frac{5}{12}$ **2.** green. $\frac{1}{6}$

3. blue or red. $\frac{3}{4}$

4. blue or yellow. $\frac{1}{2}$

5. not red. $\frac{2}{3}$

6. not yellow. $\frac{11}{12}$

Also available on transparency

Math Humor

Q: What did the IRS couple consider the birth of their new baby?

A: A "dependent" event

1 Introduce

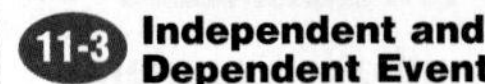

EXPLORATION

11-3 Independent and Dependent Events

Events are ___ if the occurrence of one event does not affect the probability of the other. Events are ___ if the occurrence of one event does affect the probability of the other.

1. Christie has 2 dimes and 1 penny in her pocket. If she takes one coin at random, what is the probability that it will be a dime? What is the probability that it will be a penny?

Christie takes a dime from her pocket.

2. What are the possible outcomes if she takes a second coin from her pocket without replacing the first coin?
3. What is the probability that the second coin will be a dime? What is the probability that it will be a penny?
4. If Christie tosses one of her dimes, what is the probability that it will land on heads?
5. Christie's first dime lands on heads. If she tosses the second dime, what is the probability that it will land on heads? What is the probability that it will land on tails?

THINK AND DISCUSS

6. **Explain** why the events described in Problems 2 and 3 are dependent events.

Motivate

Show students a coin. Ask them what the probability of tossing tails is. $\frac{1}{2}$ Toss the coin. Then show them another coin and repeat the question. Explain that no matter how many coins you toss in a row, the probability of tossing heads on any one of them is $\frac{1}{2}$ because they are *independent events.*

Explorations and answers are provided in the *Explorations* binder.

State Resources

go.hrw.com
State Resources Online
KEYWORD: MB7 Resources

Power Presentations with PowerPoint®

Additional Examples

Example 1

A six-sided cube is labeled with the numbers 1, 2, 2, 3, 3, and 3. Four sides are colored red, one side is white, and one side is yellow. Find each probability.

A. Tossing 2, then 2. $\frac{1}{9}$

B. Tossing red, then white, then yellow. $\frac{1}{54}$

Example 2

Two number cubes are rolled—one white and one yellow. Explain why the events are dependent. Then find the indicated probability.

A. The white cube shows a 6 and the sum is greater than 9.

$P(\text{sum} > 9)$ is different when it is known that a white 6 has occurred; $\frac{1}{12}$.

B. The yellow cube shows an even number and the sum is 5.

$P(\text{sum is } 5)$ is different when it is known that the yellow cube is even; $\frac{1}{18}$.

Also available on transparency

INTERVENTION
Questioning Strategies

EXAMPLE 1

- Why are the events independent?
- How is the multiplication rule for independent events extended to include more than two independent events?

EXAMPLE 2

- Why is the probability of dependent events different from the probability of independent events?
- How did you recognize that the events were dependent?
- How did you distinguish between events *A* and *B*?

Events are **dependent events** if the occurrence of one event affects the probability of the other. For example, suppose that there are 2 lemons and 1 lime in a bag. If you pull out two pieces of fruit, the probabilities change depending on the outcome of the first.

The tree diagram shows the probabilities for choosing two pieces of fruit from a bag containing 2 lemons and 1 lime.

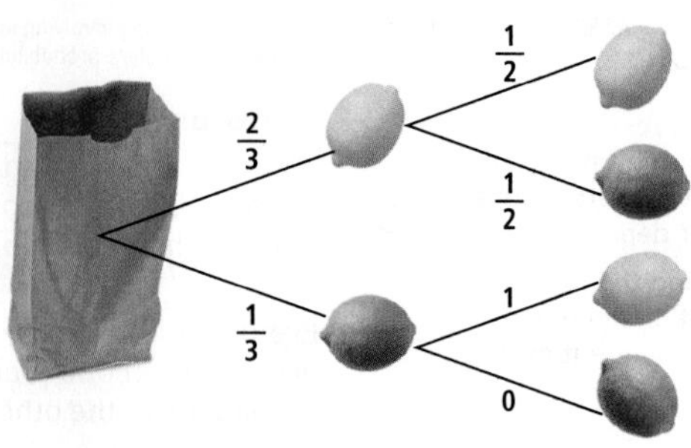

The probability of a specific event can be found by multiplying the probabilities on the branches that make up the event. For example, the probability of drawing two lemons is $\frac{2}{3} \cdot \frac{1}{2} = \frac{1}{3}$.

To find the probability of dependent events, you can use **conditional probability** $P(B \mid A)$, the probability of event *B*, given that event *A* has occurred.

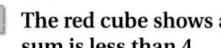

Know it! Note

Probability of Dependent Events

If *A* and *B* are dependent events, then $P(A \text{ and } B) = P(A) \cdot P(B \mid A)$, where $P(B \mid A)$ is the probability of *B*, given that *A* has occurred.

EXAMPLE 2 Finding the Probability of Dependent Events

Two number cubes are rolled—one red and one blue. Explain why the events are dependent. Then find the indicated probability.

A The red cube shows a 1, and the sum is less than 4.

Step 1 Explain why the events are dependent.

$P(\text{red } 1) = \frac{6}{36} = \frac{1}{6}$ *Of 36 outcomes, 6 have a red 1.*

$P(\text{sum} < 4 \mid \text{red } 1) = \frac{2}{6} = \frac{1}{3}$ *Of 6 outcomes with a red 1, 2 have a sum less than 4.*

The events "the red cube shows a 1" and "the sum is less than 4" are dependent because $P(\text{sum} < 4)$ is different when it is known that a red 1 has occurred.

Step 2 Find the probability.

$$P(A \text{ and } B) = P(A) \cdot P(B \mid A)$$

$$P(\text{red 1 and sum} < 4) = P(\text{red } 1) \cdot P(\text{sum} < 4 \mid \text{red } 1)$$

$$= \frac{1}{6} \cdot \frac{2}{3} = \frac{1}{18}$$

Helpful Hint

In Example 2A, you can check to see that 2 of the 36 outcomes, or $\frac{1}{18}$, have a red 1 and a sum less than 4: (1, 1) and (1, 2).

2 Teach

Guided Instruction

Explain the difference between independent and dependent events. A bag of marbles with and without replacement provides a simple example. Be sure that students understand the notation $P(B \mid A)$ as the probability of *B* given that *A* has occurred.

Reaching All Learners
Through Kinesthetic Experience

Break students into small groups. Give each group a set of 5 to 10 playing cards or numbered index cards. Have students lay out the cards face up and find the probabilities of independent and dependent events. Have students identify the favorable outcomes and the sample space for each event.

Explain why the events are dependent. Then find the indicated probability.

B **The blue cube shows a multiple of 3, and the sum is 8.**

The events are dependent because $P(\text{sum is } 8)$ is different when the blue cube shows a multiple of 3.

$P(\text{blue multiple of } 3) = \frac{2}{6} = \frac{1}{3}$ — *Of 6 outcomes for blue, 2 have a multiple of 3.*

$P(\text{sum is } 8 \mid \text{blue multiple of } 3) = \frac{2}{12} = \frac{1}{6}$ — *Of 12 outcomes that have a blue multiple of 3, 2 have a sum 8.*

$P(\text{blue multiple of 3 and sum is } 8) =$

$P(\text{blue multiple of } 3) \cdot P(\text{sum is } 8 \mid \text{blue multiple of } 3) = \left(\frac{1}{3}\right)\left(\frac{1}{6}\right) = \frac{1}{18}$

Two number cubes are rolled—one red and one black. Explain why the events are dependent, and then find the indicated probability.

2. The red cube shows a number greater than 4, and the sum is greater than 9. **$P(\text{sum is } 9)$ changes when it is known that the red cube is 4; $\frac{5}{36}$**

Conditional probability often applies when data fall into categories.

EXAMPLE 3 **Using a Table to Find Conditional Probability**

Largest Texas Counties' Votes for President 2004 (thousands)			
County	**Bush**	**Kerry**	**Other**
Harris	581	472	5
Dallas	345	336	4
Tarrant	349	207	3
Bexar	260	210	3
Travis	148	197	5

Tarrant
Dallas
Harris
Travis
Bexar

The table shows the approximate distribution of votes in Texas' five largest counties in the 2004 presidential election. Find each probability.

A **that a voter from Tarrant County voted for George Bush**

$P(\text{Bush} \mid \text{Tarrant}) = \frac{349}{559} \approx 0.624$ — *Use the Tarrant row. Of 559,000 Tarrant voters, 349,000 voted for Bush.*

B **that a voter voted for John Kerry and was from Dallas County**

$P(\text{Dallas} \mid \text{Kerry}) = \frac{336}{1422}$ — *Of 1,422,000 who voted for Kerry, 336,000 were from Dallas County.*

$P(\text{Kerry and Dallas} \mid \text{Kerry}) = \frac{1422}{3125} \cdot \frac{336}{1422}$ — *There were 3,125,000 total voters.*

≈ 0.108

Find each probability.

3a. that a voter from Travis county voted for someone other than George Bush or John Kerry $\approx$ **0.014**

3b. that a voter was from Harris county and voted for George Bush $\approx$ **0.186**

Teaching Tip **Critical Thinking**
In **Example 3A,** ask how the formula
$P(A \text{ and } B) = P(A) \cdot P(B \mid A)$ is used.
$P(\text{Tarrant and Bush}) =$
$P(\text{Tarrant}) \cdot P(\text{Bush} \mid \text{Tarrant})$
$\frac{349}{3125} = \frac{559}{3125} \cdot P(\text{Bush} \mid \text{Tarrant})$
So, $P(\text{Bush} \mid \text{Tarrant}) = \frac{349}{\cancel{3125}}\left(\frac{\cancel{3125}}{559}\right) = \frac{349}{559}.$

COMMON ERROR ALERT

Students may have trouble identifying dependent events involving number cubes. Have students copy the table that shows all possible outcomes, and use different colors to indicate desired outcomes. For example, first use red to circle all the combinations with a red 1. Then use blue to show all the combinations that have a sum less than 4.

Power Presentations with PowerPoint®

Additional Examples

Example 3

The table shows domestic migration from 1995 to 2000. A person is randomly selected. Find each probability.

Domestic Migration by Region (thousands)		
Region	**Immigrants**	**Emigrants**
Northeast	1537	2808
Midwest	2410	2951
South	5042	3243
West	2666	2654

A. that an emigrant is from the West $\frac{2654}{11,656} \approx 0.228$

B. that someone selected from the South region is an immigrant $\frac{5042}{8285} \approx 0.609$

C. that someone selected is an emigrant and is from the Midwest $\frac{2951}{23,311} \approx 0.127$

Also available on transparency

INTERVENTION
Questioning Strategies

EXAMPLE 3

- How is the table used to find each probability?
- Is the probability of B given A the same as the probability of A given B? Support your answer using data from the table.

Power Presentations with PowerPoint®

Additional Examples

Example 4

Two cards are drawn from a deck of 52. Determine whether the events are independent or dependent. Find the probability.

A. selecting two hearts when the first card is replaced

independent; $\frac{1}{16}$

B. selecting two hearts when the first card is not replaced

dependent; $\frac{1}{17}$

C. a queen is drawn, is not replaced, and then a king is drawn

dependent; $\frac{4}{663}$

Also available on transparency

INTERVENTION

Questioning Strategies

EXAMPLE 4

- How does replacement affect independence?
- Do you think that the multiplication rule for dependent events can be extended as it was for independent events? Explain.

In many cases involving random selection, events are independent when there is replacement and dependent when there is not replacement.

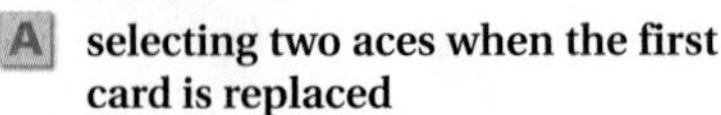

EXAMPLE 4 Determining Whether Events Are Independent or Dependent

Two cards are drawn from a deck of 52. Determine whether the events are independent or dependent. Find the probability.

> **Remember!**
> A standard card deck contains 4 suits of 13 cards each. The face cards are the jacks, queens, and kings.

A **selecting two aces when the first card is replaced**

Replacing the first card means that the occurrence of the first selection will not affect the probability of the second selection, so the events are independent.

$P(\text{ace} \mid \text{ace on first draw}) = P(\text{ace}) \cdot P(\text{ace})$

$= \frac{4}{52} \cdot \frac{4}{52} = \frac{1}{169}$ *4 of the 52 cards are aces.*

B **selecting a face card and then a 7 when the first card is not replaced**

Not replacing the first card means that there will be fewer cards to choose from, affecting the probability of the second selection, so the events are dependent.

$P(\text{face card}) \cdot P(7 \mid \text{first card was a face card})$

$= \frac{12}{52} \cdot \frac{4}{51} = \frac{4}{221}$ *There are 12 face cards, four 7's and 51 cards available for the second selection.*

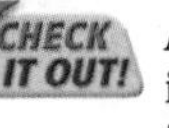

CHECK IT OUT! **A bag contains 10 beads—2 black, 3 white, and 5 red. A bead is selected at random. Determine whether the events are independent or dependent. Find the indicated probability.**

4a. selecting a white bead, replacing it, and then selecting a red bead — independent; $\frac{3}{20}$

4b. selecting a white bead, not replacing it, and then selecting a red bead — dependent; $\frac{1}{6}$

4c. selecting 3 nonred beads without replacement — dependent; $\frac{1}{12}$

THINK AND DISCUSS

1. Describe some independent events.
2. Extend the rule for the probability of independent events to more than two independent events. When might this be used?
3. **GET ORGANIZED** Copy and complete the graphic organizer. In each box, compare independent and dependent events and their related probabilities.

Probability of Independent Events vs. Probability of Dependent Events

Similarities | Differences

3 Close

Summarize

Ask students to explain the difference between independent and dependent events. Then have students tell how to find probabilities associated with independent and dependent events. Events are independent if the occurrence of one event does not affect the probability of the other. Events are dependent if the occurrence of one event affects the probability of the other.

Independent: $P(A \text{ and } B) = P(A) \cdot P(B)$

Dependent: $P(B \text{ and } A) = P(A) \cdot P(B|A)$

ONGOING ASSESSMENT and INTERVENTION

Diagnose ***Before*** **the Lesson**
11-3 Warm Up, TE p. 811

Monitor ***During*** **the Lesson**
Check It Out! Exercises, SE pp. 811, 813–814
Questioning Strategies, TE pp. 812–814

Assess ***After*** **the Lesson**
11-3 Lesson Quiz, TE p. 818
Alternative Assessment, TE p. 818

Answers to *Think and Discuss*

Possible answers:

1. a coin landing heads up on one flip and landing heads up on the next flip
2. For independent events A, B, and C, $P(A, \text{ then } B, \text{ then } C) = P(A) \cdot P(B) \cdot P(C)$; 3 coin flips: $P(\text{H, then H, then H})$
3. See p. A13.

11-3 Exercises

go.hrw.com
Homework Help Online
KEYWORD: MB7 11-3
Parent Resources Online
KEYWORD: MB7 Parent

GUIDED PRACTICE

1. **Vocabulary** Two events are __?__ if the occurrence of one event does not affect the probability of the other event. (*independent* or *dependent*) independent

SEE EXAMPLE 1 p. 811

Find each probability.

2. rolling a 1 and then another 1 when a number cube is rolled twice $\frac{1}{36}$
3. a coin landing heads up on every toss when it is tossed 3 times $\frac{1}{8}$

SEE EXAMPLE 2 p. 812

Two number cubes are rolled—one blue and one yellow. Explain why the events are dependent. Then find the indicated probability.

4. The blue cube shows a 4 and the product is less than 20. $\frac{1}{9}$
5. The yellow cube shows a multiple of 3, given that the product is 6. $\frac{1}{2}$

SEE EXAMPLE 3 p. 813

The table shows the results of a quality-control study of a lightbulb factory. A lightbulb from the factory is selected at random. Find each probability.

Lightbulb Quality		
	Shipped	Not Shipped
Defective	10	45
Not Defective	942	3

6. that a shipped bulb is not defective $\frac{471}{476}$
7. that a bulb is defective and shipped $\frac{1}{100}$

SEE EXAMPLE 4 p. 814

A bag contains 20 checkers—10 red and 10 black. Determine whether the events are independent or dependent. Find the indicated probability.

8. selecting 2 black checkers when they are chosen at random with replacement independent; $\frac{1}{4}$
9. selecting 2 black checkers when they are chosen at random without replacement dependent; $\frac{9}{38}$

PRACTICE AND PROBLEM SOLVING

Independent Practice	
For Exercises	See Example
10–11	1
12–14	2
15–16	3
17–18	4

Extra Practice
Skills Practice p. S24
Skills Practice p. S42

Find each probability.

10. choosing the same activity when two friends each randomly choose 1 of 4 extracurricular activities to participate in $\frac{1}{16}$
11. rolling an even number and then rolling a 6 when a number cube is rolled twice $\frac{1}{12}$

Two number cubes are rolled—one blue and one yellow. Explain why the events are dependent. Then find the indicated probability.

12. The yellow cube is greater than 5 and the product is greater than 24.
13. The blue cube is less than 3 and the product is 8. $\frac{1}{36}$
14. The table shows immigration to the United States from three countries in three different years. A person is randomly selected. Find each probability.

Immigration to the United States			
Country	1990	1995	2000
Cuba	10,645	17,937	20,831
Ghana	4,466	3,152	4,344
Spain	1,886	1,321	1,264

   a. that a selected person is from Cuba, given that the person immigrated in 1990 ≈ 0.63
   b. that a person came from Spain and immigrated in 2000 ≈ 0.019
   c. that a selected person immigrated in 1995, given that the person was from Ghana. ≈ 0.26

11-3 Exercises

Assignment Guide

Assign *Guided Practice* exercises as necessary.

If you finished Examples **1–2**
Basic 10–14, 20, 24
Average 10–14, 19, 20, 22, 24
Advanced 10–14, 19–22, 24

If you finished Examples **1–4**
Basic 10–23, 25–28, 31–34, 39–46
Average 10–28, 30–34, 37, 39–46
Advanced 10–18, 24–46

Homework Quick Check
Quickly check key concepts.
Exercises: 10, 12, 16, 18, 22, 28

Answers

4. The probability that the product is less than 20 decreases from $\frac{7}{9}$ if the blue cube shows 4; $\frac{1}{9}$.
5. The probability that the yellow cube shows a multiple of 3 increases from $\frac{1}{3}$ if the product is 6; $\frac{1}{2}$.
12. The probability that the product is greater than 24 increases from $\frac{1}{9}$ if the yellow cube is greater than 5; $\frac{1}{18}$.
13. The probability that the product is 8 decreases from $\frac{1}{18}$ if the blue cube is less than 3.

State Resources

Exercise 25 involves finding probabilities of independent and dependent events based on the game Yahtzee. This exercise prepares students for the Multi-Step Test Prep on page 826.

Teaching Tip

Geometry In **Exercise 22,** you may wish to review how to find the geometric probability of hitting the bull's-eye for a given radius of the dartboard. Then discuss why it is unlikely that the probability of hitting the bull's-eye is given by geometric probability alone.

Answers

24.

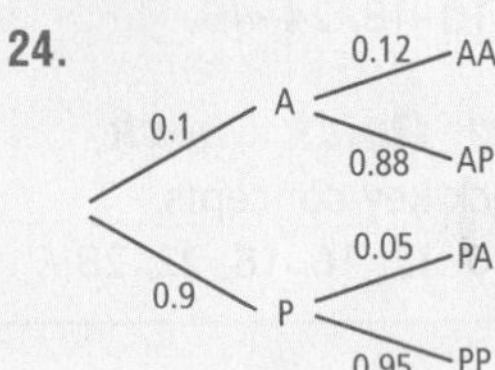

Employment Find each probability.

15. that a person with an advanced degree is employed ≈ **0.72**

16. that a person is not a high school graduate and is not employed ≈ **0.06**

Employment by Education Level, Ages 21–24		
Education Level	Employed (millions)	Not employed (millions)
Not a high school graduate	1.060	0.834
High school graduate	2.793	1.157
Some college	4.172	1.634
Bachelor's degree	1.53	0.372
Advanced degree	0.104	0.041

A bag contains number slips numbered 1 to 9. Determine whether the events are independent or dependent, and find the indicated probability.

17. selecting 2 even numbers when 2 slips are chosen without replacement **dependent; $\frac{1}{6}$**

18. selecting 2 even numbers when 2 slips are chosen with replacement **independent; $\frac{16}{81}$**

Determine whether the events are independent or dependent.

19. A coin comes up heads, and a number cube rolled at the same time comes up 6. **independent**

20. A 4 is drawn from a deck of cards, set aside, and then an ace is drawn. **dependent**

21. A 1 is rolled on a number cube, and then a 4 is rolled on the same number cube. **independent**

22. A dart hits the bull's-eye, and a second dart also hits the bull's eye. **independent**

Tennis

Wimbledon has been played annually since 1877 at the All England Lawn Tennis and Croquet Club.

23. **Tennis** In the 2004 Wimbledon Men's Tennis Championship final, Roger Federer defeated Andy Roddick in three sets.

a. What was the probability that Federer won the point when his second serve was in? ≈ **0.61**

b. When Federer lost a point, what was the probability that he *double faulted*? ≈ **0.05**

Roger Federer's Service Points	Won	Lost
First Serve In	64	31
Second Serve In	34	22
Second Serve Out (Double Fault)	0	3

24. **Multi-Step** At one high school, the probability that a student is absent today, given that the student was absent yesterday, is 0.12. The probability that a student is absent today, given that the student was present yesterday, is 0.05. The probability that a student was absent yesterday is 0.1. Draw a tree diagram to represent the situation. What is the probability that a randomly selected student was present yesterday and today? **0.855**

25. This problem will prepare you for the Multi-Step Test Prep on page 826.

While playing Yahtzee, Jake rolls 5 dice and gets the result shown at right. The rules allow him to reroll these dice 2 times. Jake decides to try for all 5's, so he rerolls the 2 and the 3.

a. What is the probability that Jake gets no additional 5's in either of the 2 rolls? **$\frac{625}{1296}$**

b. What is the probability that he gets all 5's on his first reroll of the 2 and the 3? **$\frac{1}{36}$**

c. What is the probability that he gets all 5's on his first reroll, given that at least one of the dice is a 5? **$\frac{1}{6}$**

816 *Chapter 11 Probability and Statistics*

11-3 PRACTICE A

11-3 PRACTICE C

11-3 PRACTICE B

Find each probability.

1. A bag contains 5 red, 3 green, 4 blue, and 8 yellow marbles. Find the probability of randomly selecting a green marble, and then a yellow marble if the first marble is replaced. **$\frac{3}{50}$**

2. A sock drawer contains 5 rolled-up pairs of each color of socks, white, green, and blue. What is the probability of randomly selecting a pair of blue socks, replacing it, and then randomly selecting a pair of white socks? **$\frac{1}{9}$**

Two 1–6 number cubes are rolled—one is black and one is white.

3. The sum of the rolls is greater than or equal to 6 and the black cube shows a 3.
   a. Explain why the events are dependent. **The events are dependent because $P(\text{sum} \geq 6)$ is different when it is known that a black 3 occurred.**
   b. Find the probability. **$\frac{1}{9}$**

4. The white cube shows an even number, and the sum is 8.
   a. Explain why the events are dependent. **The events are dependent because $P(\text{sum} = 8)$ is different when it is known that the white cube shows an even number.**
   b. Find the probability. **$\frac{1}{12}$**

The table below shows numbers of registered voters by age in the United States in 2004 based on the census. Find each probability in decimal form.

Age	Registered Voters (in thousands)	Not Registered to Vote (in thousands)
18–24	14,334	13,474
25–44	49,371	32,763
45–64	51,659	19,355
65 and over	26,706	8,033

5. A randomly selected person is registered to vote, given that the person is between the ages of 18 and 24. **0.52**

6. A randomly selected person is between the ages of 45 and 64 and is not registered to vote. **0.09**

7. A randomly selected person is registered to vote and is at least 65 years old. **0.12**

A bag contains 12 blue cubes, 12 red cubes, and 20 green cubes. Determine whether the events are independent or dependent, and find each probability.

8. A green cube and then a blue cube are chosen at random with replacement. **Independent; $\frac{15}{121}$**

9. Two blue cubes are chosen at random without replacement. **Dependent; $\frac{3}{43}$**

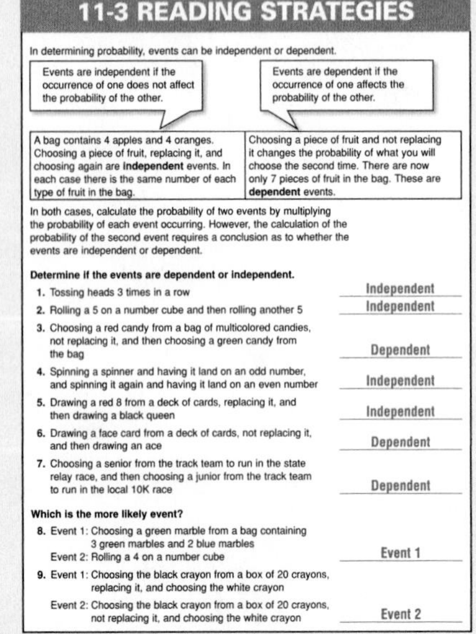

11-3 READING STRATEGIES

In determining probability, events can be independent or dependent.

Events are independent if the occurrence of one does not affect the probability of the other.

Events are dependent if the occurrence of one affects the probability of the other.

A bag contains 4 apples and 4 oranges. Choosing a piece of fruit, replacing it, and choosing again are **independent** events. In each case there is the same number of each type of fruit in the bag.	Choosing a piece of fruit and not replacing it changes the probability of what you will choose the second time. There are now only 7 pieces of fruit in the bag. These are **dependent** events.

In both cases, calculate the probability of two events by multiplying the probability of each event occurring. However, the calculation of the probability of the second event requires a conclusion as to whether the events are independent or dependent.

Determine if the events are dependent or independent.

1. Tossing heads 3 times in a row **Independent**
2. Rolling a 5 on a number cube and then rolling another 5 **Independent**
3. Choosing a red candy from a bag of multicolored candies, not replacing it, and then choosing a green candy from the bag **Dependent**
4. Spinning a spinner and having it land on an odd number, and spinning it again and having it land on an even number **Independent**
5. Drawing a red 8 from a deck of cards, replacing it, and then drawing a black queen **Independent**
6. Drawing a face card from a deck of cards, not replacing it, and then drawing an ace **Dependent**
7. Choosing a senior from the track team to run in the state relay race, and then choosing a junior from the track team to run in the local 10K race **Dependent**

Which is the more likely event?

8. Event 1: Choosing a green marble from a bag containing 3 green marbles and 2 blue marbles
   Event 2: Rolling a 4 on a number cube **Event 1**
9. Event 1: Choosing the black crayon from a box of 20 crayons, replacing it, and choosing the white crayon
   Event 2: Choosing the black crayon from a box of 20 crayons, not replacing it, and choosing the white crayon **Event 2**

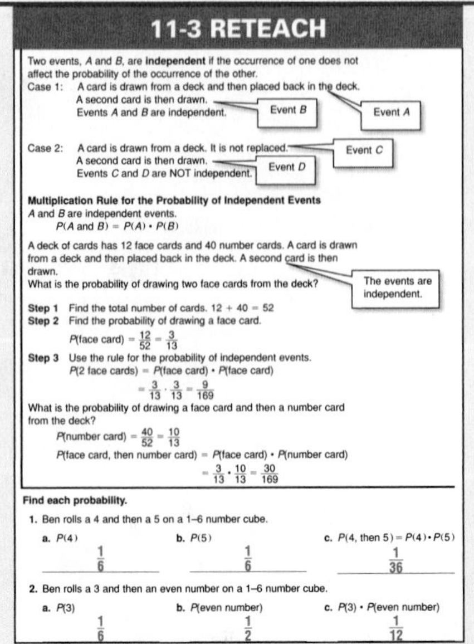

11-3 RETEACH

Two events, *A* and *B*, are **independent** if the occurrence of one does not affect the probability of the occurrence of the other.

Case 1: A card is drawn from a deck and then placed back in the deck. (Event *A*)
A second card is then drawn. (Event *B*)
Events *A* and *B* are independent.

Case 2: A card is drawn from a deck. It is not replaced. (Event *C*)
A second card is then drawn. (Event *D*)
Events *C* and *D* are NOT independent.

Multiplication Rule for the Probability of Independent Events
A and *B* are independent events.

$P(A \text{ and } B) = P(A) \cdot P(B)$

A deck of cards has 12 face cards and 40 number cards. A card is drawn from a deck and then placed back in the deck. A second card is then drawn. (The events are independent.)
What is the probability of drawing two face cards from the deck?

Step 1 Find the total number of cards. $12 + 40 = 52$

Step 2 Find the probability of drawing a face card.

$P(\text{face card}) = \frac{12}{52} = \frac{3}{13}$

Step 3 Use the rule for the probability of independent events.

$P(\text{2 face cards}) = P(\text{face card}) \cdot P(\text{face card})$

$= \frac{3}{13} \cdot \frac{3}{13} = \frac{9}{169}$

What is the probability of drawing a face card and then a number card from the deck?

$P(\text{number card}) = \frac{40}{52} = \frac{10}{13}$

$P(\text{face card, then number card}) = P(\text{face card}) \cdot P(\text{number card})$

$= \frac{3}{13} \cdot \frac{10}{13} = \frac{30}{169}$

Find each probability.

1. Ben rolls a 4 and then a 5 on a 1–6 number cube.
   a. $P(4)$ **$\frac{1}{6}$**
   b. $P(5)$ **$\frac{1}{6}$**
   c. $P(4, \text{then } 5) = P(4) \cdot P(5)$ **$\frac{1}{36}$**

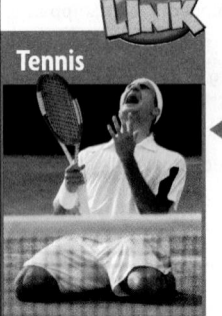

2. Ben rolls a 3 and then an even number on a 1–6 number cube.
   a. $P(3)$ **$\frac{1}{6}$**
   b. $P(\text{even number})$ **$\frac{1}{2}$**
   c. $P(3) \cdot P(\text{even number})$ **$\frac{1}{12}$**

Estimation Use the graph to estimate each probability.

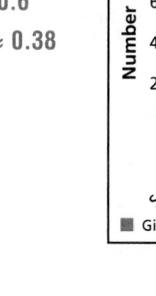

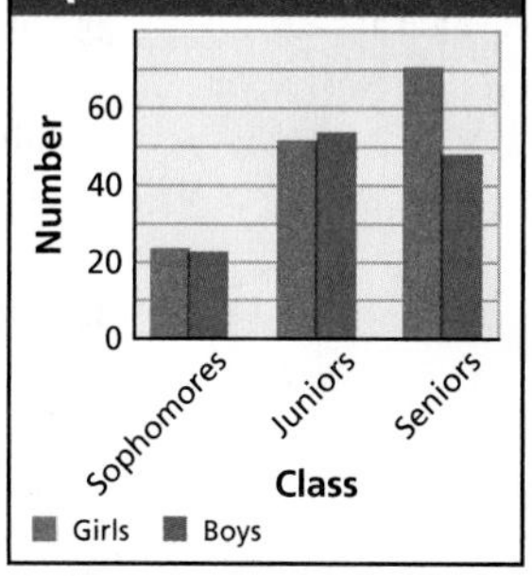

26. that a Spanish club member is a girl $\approx$ **0.54**
27. that a senior Spanish club member is a girl $\approx$ **0.6**
28. that a male Spanish club member is a senior $\approx$ **0.38**
29. **Critical Thinking** A box contains 100 balloons. Eighty are yellow, and 20 are green. Fifty are marked "Happy Birthday!" and 50 are not. A balloon is randomly chosen from the box. How many yellow "Happy Birthday!" balloons must be in the box if the event "a balloon is yellow" and the event "a balloon is marked 'Happy Birthday!'" are independent? **40**
30. **Travel** Airline information for three years is given in the table.
    a. Complete the table.
    b. What was the probability that a scheduled flight in 2004 was canceled? **$\frac{68}{4111} \approx 0.017$**
    c. An on-time flight is selected randomly for study. What is the probability that it was a flight from 2005? **$\frac{3237}{9536} \approx 0.339$**

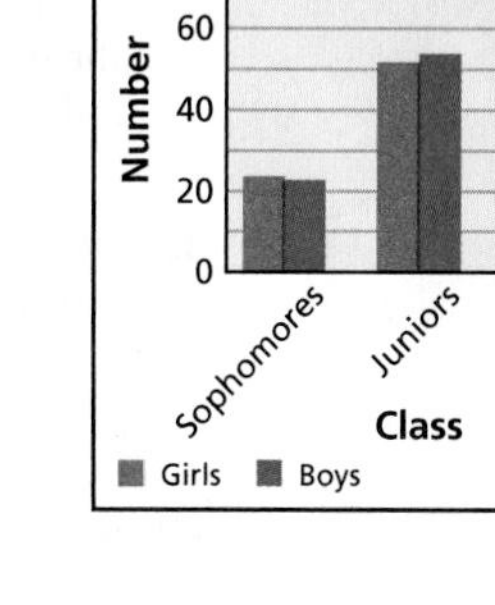

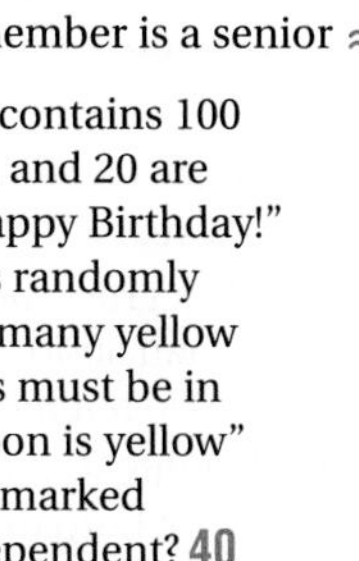

Scheduled Flights (thousands) January to July

	2003	2004	2005	Total
On Time	3102	3197	3237	9536
Delayed	598	846	877	2321
Canceled	61	68	82	211
Total	3761	4111	4196	12,068

Source: Bureau of Transportation Statistics

31. **Write About It** The "law of averages" is a nonmathematical term that means that events eventually "average out." So, if a coin comes up heads 10 tosses in a row, there is a greater probability that it will come up tails on the eleventh toss. Explain the error in this thinking.
    The events are not dependent. If the coin is fair, $P(H) = P(T) = 0.5$ for any toss.

TEST PREP

32. What is the probability that a person's birthday falls on a Saturday next year, given that it falls on a Saturday this year?
    (A) 0   (B) $\frac{1}{7}$ (C) $\frac{1}{2}$ (D) 1
33. Which of the following has the same probability as rolling doubles on 2 number cubes 3 times in a row?
    (F) A single number cube is rolled 3 times. The cube shows 5 each time.
    (G) Two number cubes are rolled 3 times. Each time the sum is 6.
    (H) Two number cubes are rolled 3 times. Each time the sum is greater than 2.
    (J) Three number cubes are rolled twice. Each time all cubes show the same number (triples).
34. **Extended Response** Use the tree diagram.

    a. Find $P(D \mid A)$, $P(D \mid B)$, and $P(D \mid C)$. **0.2; 0.2; 0.2**
    b. Does the tree diagram represent independent or dependent events? Explain your answer. **Independent; $P(D)$ and $P(E)$ do not change regardless of whether A, B, or C occurs first.**
    c. Describe a scenario for which the tree diagram could be used to find probabilities.
    Possible answer: a ball has a $0.\overline{3}$ probability of rolling into pipe A, B, or C. From any pipe, the probability of rolling to D is 0.2 and to E is 0.8.

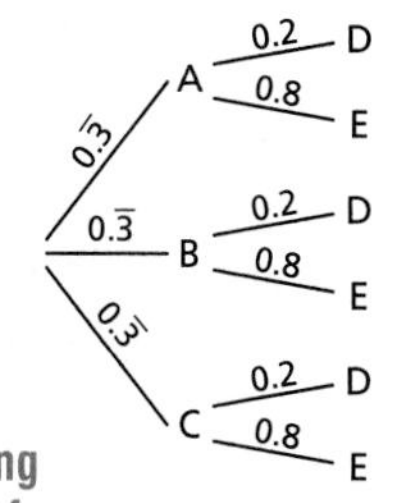

COMMON ERROR ALERT

In **Exercises 15, 16,** and **23,** students might forget to find the totals of each row or column and then be confused about the problem. Suggest that students copy each table and add a row and column in which to record the totals.

Teaching Tip **Number Sense** In **Exercises 26–28,** remind students that the frequencies in the bar graph must be whole numbers.

Teaching Tip **Math Background** After students complete **Exercise 31,** assure them that the coin has no memory of the previous 10 tosses. You may wish to contrast the "law of averages" with the Law of Large Numbers—as an experiment is repeated more times, the experimental probability of an event tends to approach the theoretical probability.

TEST PREP DOCTOR If students have difficulty with **Exercise 33,** suggest that they first decide whether the given events are dependent or independent. Then have them compute the probability and use it as a guide to select the answer. Students who select **G** or **H** may be confusing independent and dependent events.

11-3 PROBLEM SOLVING

The table shows student participation in different sports at a high school. Suppose a student is selected at random.

Sports Participation by Grade

	Track	Volleyball	Basketball	Tennis	No Sport
Grade 9	12	18	15	9	66
Grade 10	6	20	12	2	95
Grade 11	15	11	8	5	61
Grade 12	7	6	10	12	50

1. What is the probability that a student is in grade 10 and runs track?
   a. Find the probability that a student is in grade 10, $P(10)$. $P(10) = \frac{135}{440}$
   b. Find the probability that a student runs track, given that the student is in grade 10, $P(Tr \mid 10)$. $P(Tr \mid 10) = \frac{6}{135}$
   c. Find $P(10 \text{ and } Tr) = P(10) \cdot P(Tr \mid 10)$. $P(10 \text{ and } Tr) = \frac{6}{440} \approx 0.014$
2. What is the probability that a student is in grade 12 and runs track or plays tennis?
   a. Find the probability that a student is in grade 12, $P(12)$. $P(12) = \frac{85}{440}$
   b. Find the probability that a student runs track or plays tennis, given that the student is in grade 12, $P(Tr \text{ or } Te \mid 12)$. $P(Tr \text{ or } Te \mid 12) = \frac{7+12}{85} = \frac{19}{85}$
   c. Find $P(12 \text{ or } (Tr \text{ or } Te))$. $P(12 \text{ and } (Tr \text{ or } Te)) = \frac{19}{85} \cdot \frac{85}{440} \approx 0.043$
3. During a fire drill, the students are waiting in the parking lot. What is the probability that one student is in grade 12 and runs track or plays tennis, and the student standing next to her is in grade 10 and runs track?
   a. Find the probability for the first student. $\frac{19}{440}$
   b. Find the probability for the second student. $\frac{6}{439}$
   c. Find the probability for the event occurring. $\frac{19}{440} \cdot \frac{6}{439} \approx 0.0006$
   d. Are these events independent or dependent? Explain.
   Dependent; possible answer: the second student is one of the remaining 439 students.

Samantha is 1 of 17 students in a class of 85 who have decided to pursue a business degree. Each week, a student in the class is randomly selected to tutor younger students. Choose the letter for the best answer.

4. What is the probability of drawing a business student one week, replacing the name, and drawing the same name the next week?
   A 3.4   B 0.2   C 0.04   **(D)** 0.002
5. What is the probability of drawing Samantha's name one week, not replacing her name, and drawing the name of another business student the next week?
   (F) $\frac{1}{85} \cdot \frac{16}{84}$ G $\frac{1}{85} \cdot \frac{17}{84}$ H $\frac{17}{85} \cdot \frac{16}{84}$ J $\frac{17}{85} \cdot \frac{17}{84}$

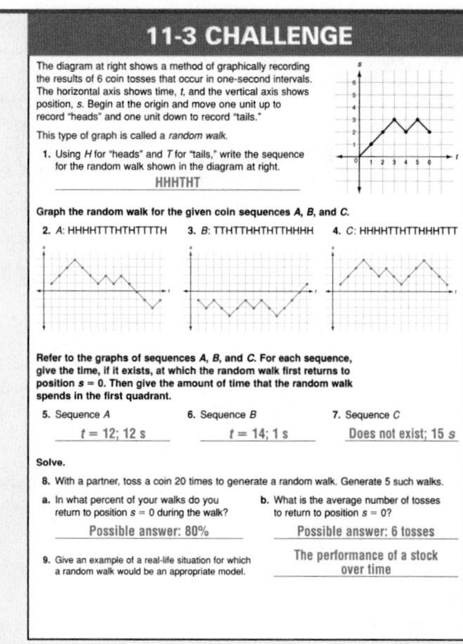

11-3 CHALLENGE

The diagram at right shows a method of graphically recording the results of 6 coin tosses that occur in one-second intervals. The horizontal axis shows time, t, and the vertical axis shows position, s. Begin at the origin and move one unit up to record "heads" and one unit down to record "tails."

This type of graph is called a *random walk.*

1. Using H for "heads" and T for "tails," write the sequence for the random walk shown in the diagram at right. HHHTHT

Graph the random walk for the given coin sequences A, B, and C.

2. A: HHHHTTTHTHTTTTH
   3. B: TTHTTHHTHTTHHHH
   4. C: HHHHTTHTTHHHTTT
   Refer to the graphs of sequences A, B, and C. For each sequence, give the time, if it exists, at which the random walk first returns to position $s = 0$. Then give the amount of time that the random walk spends in the first quadrant.

5. Sequence A $t = 12$; 12 s
6. Sequence B $t = 14$; 1 s
7. Sequence C Does not exist; 15 s

Solve.

8. With a partner, toss a coin 20 times to generate a random walk. Generate 5 such walks.
   a. In what percent of your walks do you return to position $s = 0$ during the walk? Possible answer: 80%
   b. What is the average number of tosses to return to position $s = 0$? Possible answer: 6 tosses
9. Give an example of a real-life situation for which a random walk would be an appropriate model. The performance of a stock over time

Journal

Have students use mathematical notation to define the probability of independent and dependent events. Then have students explain in their own words what the notation means and how to use it.

ALTERNATIVE ASSESSMENT

Have students describe a situation in which the probability of two events is independent. Have them formulate and answer a question about the probability. Repeat with dependent events.

Power Presentations with PowerPoint®

11-3 Lesson Quiz

1. Find the probability of rolling a number greater than 2 and then rolling a multiple of 3 when a number cube is rolled twice. $\frac{2}{9}$
2. A drawer contains 8 blue socks, 8 black socks, and 4 white socks. Socks are picked at random. Explain why the events picking a blue sock and then another blue sock are dependent. Then find the probability.

   $P(blue \mid blue)$ is different when it is known that a blue sock has been picked; $\frac{14}{95}$.
3. Two cards are drawn from a deck of 52. Determine whether the events are independent or dependent. Find the indicated probability.
   - **a.** selecting two face cards when the first card is replaced

     independent; $\frac{9}{169}$
   - **b.** selecting two face cards when the first card is not replaced

     dependent; $\frac{11}{221}$

Also available on transparency

CHALLENGE AND EXTEND

35. Two number cubes are rolled in succession and the numbers that they show are added together. What is the only sum for which the probability of the sum is independent of the number shown on the first roll? Explain.

36. Birthdays People born on February 29 have a birthday once every 4 years.

- **a.** What is the smallest group of people in which there is a greater than 50% chance that 2 people share a birthday? (Do not include February 29.) 23
- **b.** What is the probability that in a group of 150 people, none are born on February 29? $\left(\frac{1460}{1461}\right)^{150} \approx 0.90$
- **c.** What is the least number of people such that there is a greater than 50% chance that one of the people in the group has a birthday on February 29? 1013

37. There are 150 people at a play. Ninety are women, and 60 are men. Half are sitting in the lower level, and half are sitting in the upper level. There are 35 women sitting in the upper level. A person is selected at random for a prize. What is the probability that the person is sitting in the lower level, given that the person is a woman? Is the event "person is sitting in the lower level" independent of the event "person is a woman"? Explain. $\frac{11}{18}$; no, $P(\text{lower level}) \neq P(\text{lower level} \mid \text{woman})$

38. Medicine Suppose that strep throat affects 2% of the population and a test to detect it produces an accurate result 99% of the time.

- **a.** Complete the table.
- **b.** What is the probability that someone who tests positive actually has strep throat? $\frac{99}{148}$

Per 10,000 People Tested

	Have strep	Do not have strep	Total
Test Positive	198	98	296
Test Negative	2	9702	9704
Total	200	9800	10,000

SPIRAL REVIEW

39. Sports A basketball player averaged 18.3 points per game in the month of December. In January, the same basketball player averaged 32.5 points per game. *(Lesson 2-6)*

- **a.** Write the average number of points scored as a function of games played for both months, $p(d)$ and $p(j)$. $P(d) = 18.3g$; $P(j) = 32.5g$
- **b.** Graph $p(d)$ and $p(j)$ on the same coordinate plane.
- **c.** Describe the transformation that occurred. vertical stretch by a factor of ≈ 1.78

Solve each system of equations by graphing. Round your answer to the nearest tenth. *(Lesson 10-7)*

40. $\begin{cases} 2x^2 - 4y^2 = 12 \\ y = 2 \end{cases}$ **41.** $\begin{cases} 4x^2 - 2y^2 = 18 \\ -x^2 + 6y^2 = 22 \end{cases}$ **42.** $\begin{cases} x^2 + y^2 = 16 \\ 2y + 5x^2 = -3 \end{cases}$

Two number cubes are rolled. Find each probability. *(Lesson 11-2)*

43. The sum is 12. $\frac{1}{36}$

44. The sum is less than 5. $\frac{1}{6}$

45. At least one number is odd. $\frac{3}{4}$

46. At least one number is less than 3. $\frac{5}{9}$

Answers

35. 7; $P(\text{sum of } 7) = \frac{6}{36} = \frac{1}{6}$; after a roll, $P(\text{sum of } 7 \mid \text{1st roll} = 1, 2, 3, 4, 5, \text{or } 6) = \frac{1}{6}$

39b.

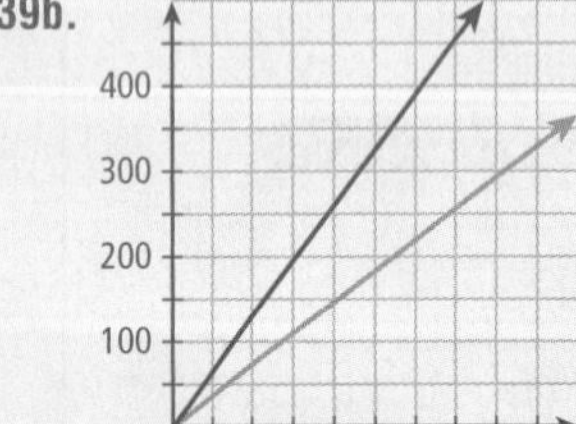

40.

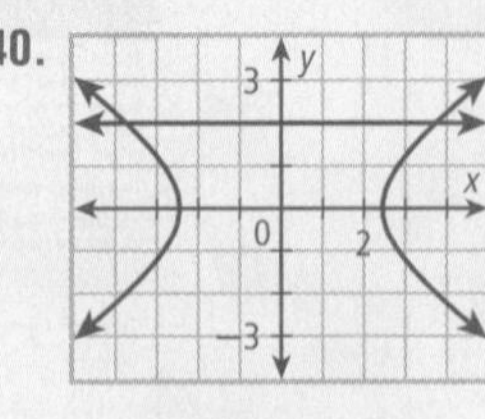

$x \approx \pm 3.7; y = 2$

41.

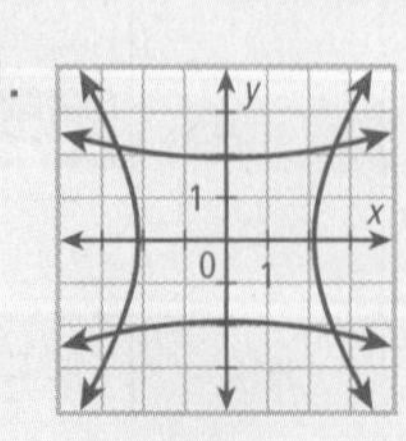

$x \approx \pm 2.6; y \approx \pm 2.2$

42.

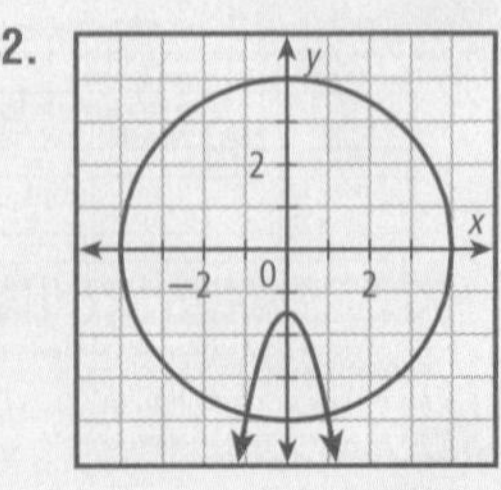

$x \approx \pm 1.0; y \approx -3.9$

11-4 Compound Events

A2.8.3 Use permutations, combinations, and other counting methods to determine the number of ways that events can occur and to calculate probabilities including the probability of compound events.

Objectives

Find the probability of mutually exclusive events.

Find the probability of inclusive events.

Vocabulary

simple event
compound event
mutually exclusive events
inclusive events

Why learn this?

You can use the probability of compound events to determine the likelihood that a person of a specific gender is color-blind. (See Example 3.)

A **simple event** is an event that describes a single outcome. A **compound event** is an event made up of two or more simple events. **Mutually exclusive events** are events that cannot both occur in the same trial of an experiment. Rolling a 1 and rolling a 2 on the same roll of a number cube are mutually exclusive events.

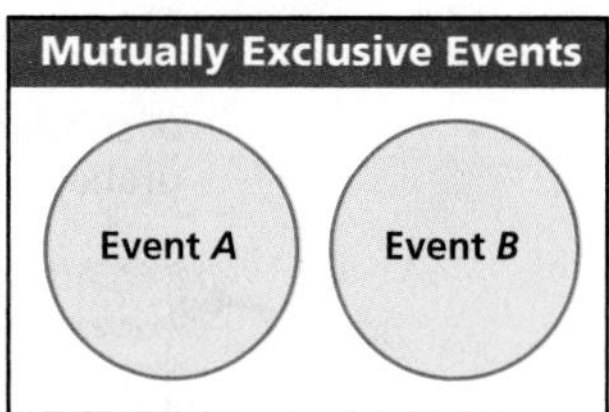

Mutually Exclusive Events

WORDS	ALGEBRA	EXAMPLE
The probability of two mutually exclusive events *A or B* occurring is the sum of their individual probabilities.	For two mutually exclusive events *A* and *B*, $P(A \cup B) = P(A) + P(B)$.	When a number cube is rolled, $P(\text{less than } 3) = P(1 \text{ or } 2) = P(1) + P(2) = \frac{1}{6} + \frac{1}{6} = \frac{1}{3}$.

Remember!

Recall that the union symbol ∪ means "or."

EXAMPLE 1 Finding Probabilities of Mutually Exclusive Events

A drink company applies one label to each bottle cap: "free drink," "free meal," or "try again." A bottle cap has a $\frac{1}{10}$ probability of being labeled "free drink" and a $\frac{1}{25}$ probability of being labeled "free meal."

a. Explain why the events "free drink" and "free meal" are mutually exclusive.

Each bottle cap has only one label applied to it.

b. What is the probability that a bottle cap is labeled "free drink" or "free meal"?

$$P(\text{free drink} \cup \text{free meal}) = P(\text{free drink}) + P(\text{free meal})$$
$$= \frac{1}{10} + \frac{1}{25} = \frac{5}{50} + \frac{2}{50} = \frac{7}{50}$$

1. Each student cast one vote for senior class president. Of the students, 25% voted for Hunt, 20% for Kline, and 55% for Vila. A student from the senior class is selected at random.

Each student can vote only once. **a.** Explain why the events "voted for Hunt," "voted for Kline," and "voted for Vila" are mutually exclusive.

75% **b.** What is the probability that a student voted for Kline or Vila?

11-4 Organizer

Pacing: Traditional 1 day
Block $\frac{1}{2}$ day

Objectives: Find the probability of mutually exclusive events.

Find the probability of inclusive events.

Online Edition
Tutorial Videos

Countdown to Testing Week 24

Power Presentations with PowerPoint®

Warm Up

One card is drawn from the deck. Find each probability.

1. selecting a two $\frac{1}{13}$
2. selecting a face card $\frac{3}{13}$

Two cards are drawn from the deck. Find each probability.

3. selecting two kings when the first card is replaced $\frac{1}{169}$
4. selecting two hearts when the first card is not replaced $\frac{1}{17}$

Also available on transparency

Q: Why did the mutually exclusive events break up?
A: They had nothing in common.

1 Introduce

EXPLORATION

11-4 Compound Events

The Math Club sponsors a booth at a school carnival. Visitors to the booth can win prizes by spinning the wheel shown.

Find each probability.

1. the wheel landing on an odd number
2. the wheel landing on a multiple of 4
3. the wheel landing on a prime number
4. During the morning, a player can win a prize if the player's spin lands on an odd number or a multiple of 4. Which numbers result in a player winning a prize?
5. What is the probability that a player will win a prize in one spin?
6. During the afternoon, a player can win a prize if the player's spin lands on an odd number or a prime number. Which numbers result in a player winning a prize?
7. What is the probability that a player will win a prize in one spin?

THINK AND DISCUSS

8. **Explain** whether the two possible winning events in the morning game are mutually exclusive.
cannot both occur in the same trial of an experiment.

Motivate

Conduct a quick survey about music. Ask students to raise their hands if they like hip-hop. Then ask them to raise their hands if they like rock. Ask how many like neither. Ask if the total number of hands raised equals the total number of students. Discuss how the data could be displayed in a Venn diagram. Those who like both hip-hop and rock would be in the intersection. Explain that they will learn how probability is affected by overlapping situations.

Explorations and answers are provided in the *Explorations* binder.

State Resources

go.hrw.com
State Resources Online
KEYWORD: MB7 Resources

Power Presentations with PowerPoint®

Additional Examples

Example 1

A group of students is donating blood during a blood drive. A student has a $\frac{9}{20}$ probability of having type O blood and a $\frac{2}{5}$ probability of having type A blood.

a. Explain why the events "type O" and "type A" blood are mutually exclusive.

A person can have only one blood type.

b. What is the probability that a student has type O or type A blood? $\frac{17}{20}$

Example 2

Find each probability on a number cube.

A. rolling a 4 or an even number $\frac{1}{2}$

B. rolling an odd number or a number greater than 2 $\frac{5}{6}$

Also available on transparency

INTERVENTION

Questioning Strategies

EXAMPLE 1

- Why is it important to determine whether events are mutually exclusive?
- How are mutually exclusive events different from independent events?

EXAMPLE 2

- How can you tell whether the events are inclusive?
- Why is the probability different if events are inclusive?

Inclusion Review the set notation used for $P(A \text{ or } B)$ and $P(A \text{ and } B)$. Discuss how "at least" translates into the complement.

Inclusive events are events that have one or more outcomes in common. When you roll a number cube, the outcomes "rolling an even number" and "rolling a prime number" are not mutually exclusive. The number 2 is both prime and even, so the events are inclusive.

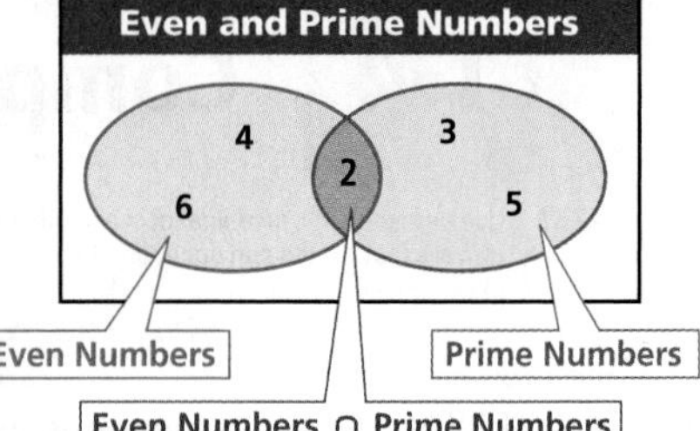

Remember!

Recall that the intersection symbol ∩ means "and."

There are 3 ways to roll an even number, $\{2, 4, 6\}$.

There are 3 ways to roll a prime number, $\{2, 3, 5\}$.

The outcome "2" is counted twice when outcomes are added $(3 + 3)$. The actual number of ways to roll an even number or a prime is $3 + 3 - 1 = 5$. The concept of subtracting the outcomes that are counted twice leads to the following probability formula.

Know it! Note

Inclusive Events

WORDS	The probability of two inclusive events *A* or *B* occurring is the sum of their individual probabilities minus the probability of *both* occurring.
ALGEBRA	For two inclusive events *A* and *B*, $P(A \cup B) = P(A) + P(B) - P(A \cap B)$.
EXAMPLE	When you roll a number cube, $P(\text{even number or prime}) =$ $P(\text{even or prime}) = P(\text{even}) + P(\text{prime}) - P(\text{even and prime})$ $= \frac{3}{6} + \frac{3}{6} - \frac{1}{6} = \frac{5}{6}$.

EXAMPLE 2 Finding Probabilities of Inclusive Events

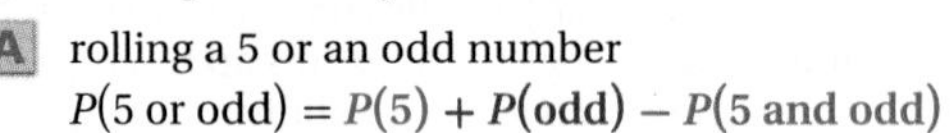

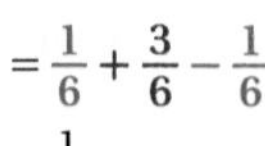

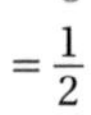

Find each probability on a die.

A rolling a 5 or an odd number

$P(5 \text{ or odd}) = P(5) + P(\text{odd}) - P(5 \text{ and odd})$

$= \frac{1}{6} + \frac{3}{6} - \frac{1}{6}$ *5 is also an odd number.*

$= \frac{1}{2}$

B rolling at least one 4 when rolling 2 dice

$P(4 \text{ or } 4) = P(4) + P(4) - P(4 \text{ and } 4)$

$= \frac{1}{6} + \frac{1}{6} - \frac{1}{36}$ *There is 1 outcome in 36 where both dice show 4.*

$= \frac{11}{36}$

CHECK IT OUT! **A card is drawn from a deck of 52. Find the probability of each.**

2a. drawing a king or a heart $\frac{4}{13}$

2b. drawing a red card (hearts or diamonds) or a face card (jack, queen, or king) $\frac{8}{13}$

2 Teach

Guided Instruction

Discuss the difference between finding the following probabilities when rolling a pair of number cubes:

(a) rolling doubles and each cube shows an odd number

(b) rolling doubles or each cube shows an odd number

Elicit that in (a) the overlap is 1, 1, 3, 3, and 5, 5. In (b), the solutions include doubles that are not odd numbers, 2, 2, 4, 4, and 6, 6, as well as odd numbers that are not doubles, such as 1, 3.

Reaching All Learners

Through Multiple Representations

Students may find it easier to visualize the relationships in **Example 3** by making a table or tree diagram. The totals provide a check as to whether the table is correctly filled in.

	Male	Female	Total
Not CB	1853	1554	3407
CB	97	6	103
Total	1950	1560	3510

Note: CB = color-blind

EXAMPLE 3 Health Application

Of 3510 drivers surveyed, 1950 were male and 103 were color-blind. Only 6 of the color-blind drivers were female. What is the probability that a driver was male or was color-blind?

Helpful Hint

As you work through Example 3, fill in the Venn diagram with information as you find it.

Step 1 Use a Venn diagram.

Label as much information as you know. Being male and being color-blind are inclusive events.

3510 total drivers

male drivers	overlap	color-blind drivers
1853	97	6

Step 2 Find the number in the overlapping region.

Subtract 6 from 103. This is the number of color-blind males, **97**.

Step 3 Find the probability.

$= P(\text{male} \cup \text{color-blind}) =$

$= P(\textbf{male}) + P(\textbf{color-blind}) - P(\textbf{male} \cap \textbf{color-blind})$

$= \frac{\mathbf{1950}}{3510} + \frac{\mathbf{103}}{3510} - \frac{\mathbf{97}}{3510} = \frac{1956}{3510} \approx 0.557$

The probability that a driver was male or was color-blind is about 55.7%.

3. Of 160 beauty spa customers, 96 had a hair styling and 61 had a manicure. There were 28 customers who had only a manicure. What is the probability that a customer had a hair styling or a manicure? **$\frac{31}{40}$**

Recall from Lesson 11-2 that the complement of an event with probability p, all outcomes that are not in the event, has a probability of $1 - p$. You can use the complement to find the probability of a compound event.

EXAMPLE 4 Book Club Application

There are 5 students in a book club. Each student randomly chooses a book from a list of 10 titles. What is the probability that at least 2 students in the group choose the same book?

$P(\text{at least 2 students choose same}) = 1 - P(\text{all choose different})$ *Use the complement.*

$$P(\text{all choose different}) = \frac{\text{number of ways 5 students can choose different books}}{\text{total number of ways 5 students can choose books}}$$

$$= \frac{{}_{10}P_5}{10^5}$$

$$= \frac{10 \cdot 9 \cdot 8 \cdot 7 \cdot 6}{10 \cdot 10 \cdot 10 \cdot 10 \cdot 10} = \frac{30{,}240}{100{,}000} = 0.3024$$

$P(\text{at least 2 students choose same}) = 1 - 0.3024 = 0.6976$

The probability that at least 2 students choose the same book is 0.6976, or 69.76%.

4. In one day, 5 different customers bought earrings from the same jewelry store. The store offers 62 different styles. Find the probability that at least 2 customers bought the same style. **≈ 0.1524**

COMMON ERROR ALERT

Students might treat inclusive events as mutually exclusive and double count a probability. A total probability > 1 could indicate this error. Remind students to consider whether the events can occur simultaneously before they choose the form of the addition rule to use.

Power Presentations with PowerPoint®

Additional Examples

Example 3

Of 1560 students surveyed, 840 were seniors and 630 read a daily paper. Only 215 of the paper readers were juniors. What is the probability that a student was a senior or read a daily paper?

$\frac{1055}{1560} \approx 0.676$, or about 67.6%

Example 4

Each of 6 students randomly chooses a butterfly from a list of 8 types. What is the probability that at least 2 students choose the same butterfly?

≈ 0.9231, or about 92.31%

Also available on transparency

INTERVENTION
Questioning Strategies

EXAMPLE 3

- How does a diagram or a table help you organize the data?
- Why are the events inclusive?

EXAMPLE 4

- Why can you use the complement to solve the problem?

3 Close

Summarize

Ask students to explain the difference between mutually exclusive events and inclusive events. Then have students tell how to find probabilities associated with the events. Events are mutually exclusive if they cannot occur simultaneously. If two events can occur at the same time, they are inclusive events.

Mutually exclusive: $P(A \text{ or } B) = P(A) + P(B)$

Inclusive: $P(A \text{ or } B) = P(A) + P(B) - P(A \text{ and } B)$

ONGOING ASSESSMENT and INTERVENTION

***Diagnose Before* the Lesson**
11-4 Warm Up, TE p. 819

***Monitor During* the Lesson**
Check It Out! Exercises, SE pp. 819–821
Questioning Strategies, TE pp. 820–821

***Assess After* the Lesson**
11-4 Lesson Quiz, TE p. 825
Alternative Assessment, TE p. 825

Teaching Tip

Communicating Math

Distinguish between evaluating $P(A \text{ or } B)$, when it is important to consider whether events are mutually exclusive, and $P(A \text{ and } B)$, when it is important to consider whether events are independent. The addition rule applies to finding the probability for a single trial, while the multiplication rule applies to finding the probability that event A will occur in one trial and event B will occur in another trial.

Math Background

$P(A) + P(B) - P(A \text{ and } B)$ can be used to find any probability $P(A \text{ or } B)$. For mutually exclusive events, $P(A \text{ and } B) = 0$.

Answers to *Think and Discuss*

1. If events A and B are mutually exclusive, $P(A \cap B) = 0$, so $P(A \cup B) = P(A) + P(B) - 0 = P(A) + P(B)$.
2. February 29 occurs only once every 4 years, and March 13 occurs once every year, so you are more likely to share a birthday with someone if you were born on March 13.
3. See p. A13.

THINK AND DISCUSS

1. Explain why the formula for inclusive events, $P(A \cup B) = P(A) + P(B) - P(A \cap B)$, also applies to mutually exclusive events.
2. Tell whether the probability of sharing a birthday with someone else in the room is the same whether your birthday is March 13 or February 29. Explain.

3. **GET ORGANIZED** Copy and complete the graphic organizer. Give at least one example for each.

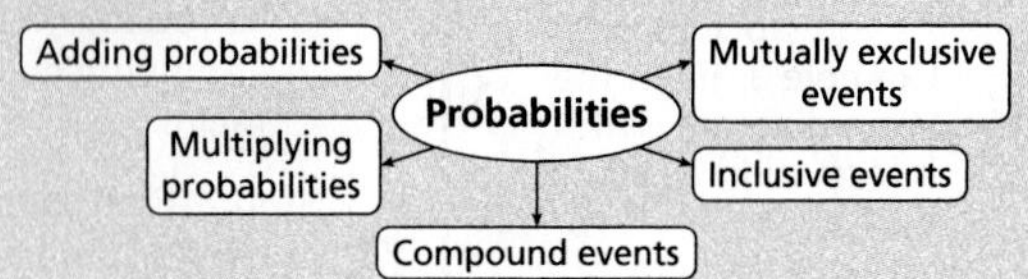

11-4 Exercises

11-4 Exercises

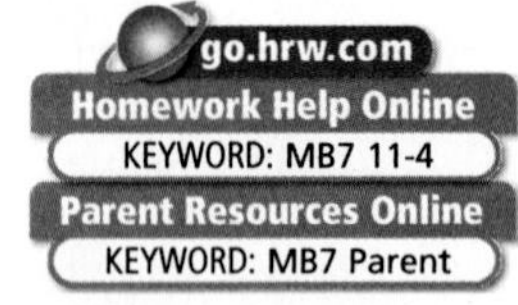

Assignment Guide

Assign *Guided Practice* exercises as necessary.

If you finished Examples **1–2**
- **Basic** 12–15
- **Average** 12–15, 19, 21
- **Advanced** 12–15, 19, 21

If you finished Examples **1–4**
- **Basic** 12–19, 21, 24–26, 29–34, 42–48
- **Average** 12–26, 28–34, 36, 42–48
- **Advanced** 12–20, 22–24, 26–28, 30–48

Homework Quick Check
Quickly check key concepts.
Exercises: 10, 12, 14, 17, 20

GUIDED PRACTICE

1. **Vocabulary** A compound event where one outcome overlaps with another is made up of two __?__. (*inclusive event* or *mutually exclusive events*) inclusive events

A bag contains 25 marbles: 10 black, 13 red, and 2 blue. A marble is drawn from the bag at random.

SEE EXAMPLE 1 p. 819

2. Explain why the events "getting a black marble" and "getting a red marble" are mutually exclusive. A marble is either black or red.
3. What is the probability of getting a red or a blue marble? $\frac{3}{5}$
4. A car approaching an intersection has a 0.1 probability of turning left and a 0.2 probability of turning right. Explain why the events are mutually exclusive. What is the probability that the car will turn? The car cannot turn both left and right; 0.3.

SEE EXAMPLE 2 p. 820

Numbers 1–10 are written on cards and placed in a bag. Find each probability.

5. choosing a number greater than 5 or choosing an odd number $\frac{4}{5}$
6. choosing an 8 or choosing a number less than 5 $\frac{1}{2}$
7. choosing at least one even number when selecting 2 cards from the bag $\frac{7}{9}$

SEE EXAMPLE 3 p. 821

Five years after 650 high school seniors graduated, 400 had a college degree and 310 were married. Half of the students with a college degree were married.

8. What is the probability that a student has a college degree or is married? $\frac{51}{65}$
9. What is the probability that a student has a college degree or is not married? $\frac{54}{65}$
10. What is the probability that a student does not have a college degree or is married? $\frac{9}{13}$

SEE EXAMPLE 4 p. 821

11. A vending machine offers 8 different drinks. One day, 6 employees each purchased a drink from the vending machine. Find the probability that at least 2 employees purchased the same drink. ≈ 0.92

State Resources

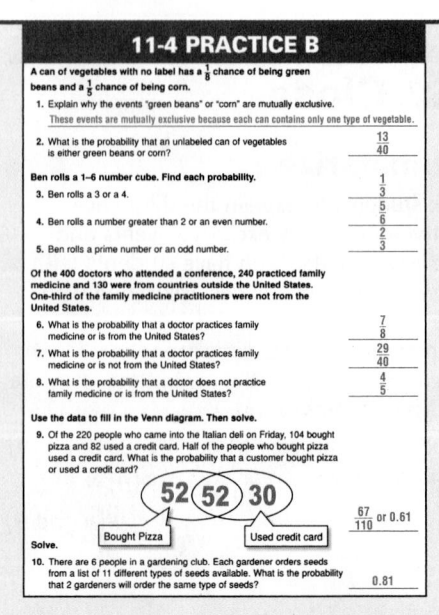

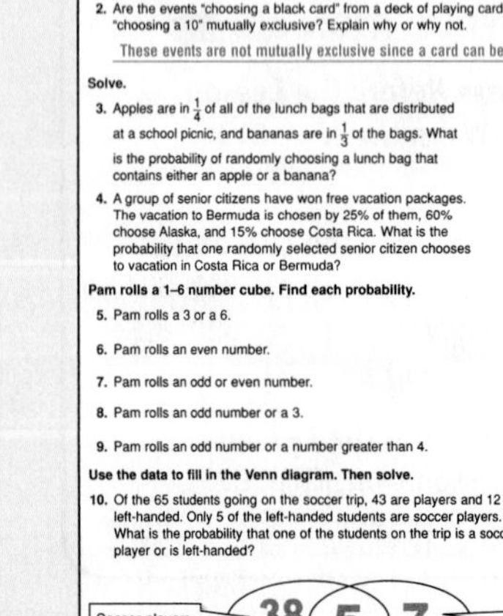

11-4 PRACTICE A

Determine which event(s) are mutually exclusive.

1. Students are forming 4 softball teams by each picking one of four different-color cards from a bag. Are the events "choosing a red card" and "choosing a blue card" mutually exclusive? Explain why or why not.
These events are mutually exclusive since each student can choose only one card.
2. Are the events "choosing a black card" from a deck of playing cards and "choosing a 10" mutually exclusive? Explain why or why not.
These events are not mutually exclusive since a card can be both black and a 10.

Solve.

3. Apples are in $\frac{1}{4}$ of all of the lunch bags that are distributed at a school picnic, and bananas are in $\frac{1}{3}$ of the bags. What is the probability of randomly choosing a lunch bag that contains either an apple or a banana? $\frac{7}{12}$
4. A group of senior citizens have won free vacation packages. The vacation to Bermuda is chosen by 25% of them, 60% choose Alaska, and 15% choose Costa Rica. What is the probability that one randomly selected senior citizen chooses to vacation in Costa Rica or Bermuda? $\frac{2}{5}$

Pam rolls a 1–6 number cube. Find each probability.

5. Pam rolls a 3 or a 6. $\frac{1}{3}$
6. Pam rolls an even number. $\frac{1}{2}$
7. Pam rolls an odd or even number. 1
8. Pam rolls an odd number or a 3. $\frac{1}{2}$
9. Pam rolls an odd number or a number greater than 4. $\frac{2}{3}$

Use the data to fill in the Venn diagram. Then solve.

10. Of the 65 students going on the soccer trip, 43 are players and 12 are left-handed. Only 5 of the left-handed students are soccer players. What is the probability that one of the students on the trip is a soccer player or is left-handed? $\frac{10}{13}$ or 0.77

Soccer players 38 | 5 | 7 Left-handed

11-4 PRACTICE B

A can of vegetables with no label has a $\frac{1}{8}$ chance of being green beans and a $\frac{1}{5}$ chance of being corn.

1. Explain why the events "green beans" or "corn" are mutually exclusive.
These events are mutually exclusive because each can contains only one type of vegetable.
2. What is the probability that an unlabeled can of vegetables is either green beans or corn? $\frac{13}{40}$

Ben rolls a 1–6 number cube. Find each probability.

3. Ben rolls a 3 or a 4. $\frac{1}{3}$
4. Ben rolls a number greater than 2 or an even number. $\frac{5}{6}$
5. Ben rolls a prime number or an odd number. $\frac{2}{3}$

Of the 400 doctors who attended a conference, 240 practiced family medicine and 130 were from countries outside the United States. One-third of the family medicine practitioners were not from the United States.

6. What is the probability that a doctor practices family medicine or is from the United States? $\frac{7}{8}$
7. What is the probability that a doctor practices family medicine or is not from the United States? $\frac{29}{40}$
8. What is the probability that a doctor does not practice family medicine or is from the United States? $\frac{4}{5}$

Use the data to fill in the Venn diagram. Then solve.

9. Of the 220 people who came into the Italian deli on Friday, 104 bought pizza and 82 used a credit card. Half of the people who bought pizza used a credit card. What is the probability that a customer bought pizza or used a credit card? $\frac{67}{110}$ or 0.61

Bought Pizza 52 | 52 | 30 Used credit card

Solve.

10. There are 6 people in a gardening club. Each gardener orders seeds from a list of 11 different types of seeds available. What is the probability that 2 gardeners will order the same type of seeds? 0.81

PRACTICE AND PROBLEM SOLVING

Independent Practice

For Exercises	See Example
12–13	1
14–15	2
16–18	3
19	4

Extra Practice

Skills Practice p. S24
Application Practice p. S42

Jump ropes are given out during gym class. A student has a $\frac{1}{6}$ chance of getting a red jump rope and a $\frac{1}{3}$ chance of getting a green jump rope. Meg is given a jump rope.

12. Explain why the events "getting a red jump rope" and "getting a green jump rope" are mutually exclusive. The jump rope is either red or green.

13. What is the probability that Meg gets a red or green jump rope? $\frac{1}{2}$

The letters *A–P* are written on cards and placed in a bag. Find the probability of each outcome.

14. choosing an *E* or choosing a *G* $\frac{1}{8}$

15. choosing an *E* or choosing a vowel $\frac{1}{4}$

Lincoln High School has 98 teachers. Of the 42 female teachers, 8 teach math. One-seventh of all of the teachers teach math.

16. What is the probability that a teacher is a woman or teaches math? $\frac{24}{49}$

17. What is the probability that a teacher is a man or teaches math? $\frac{32}{49}$

18. What is the probability that a teacher is a man or does not teach math? $\frac{45}{49}$

19. A card is drawn from a deck of 52 and recorded. Then the card is replaced, and the deck is shuffled. This process is repeated 13 times. What is the probability that at least one of the cards drawn is a heart? $1 - 0.75^{13} \approx 0.976$

20. **Critical Thinking** Events *A* and *B* are mutually exclusive. Must the complements of events *A* and *B* be mutually exclusive? Explain by example.

21. **Television** According to Nielsen Media Research, on June 21, 2005, from 9 to 10 P.M., the NBA Finals Game 7 between San Antonio and Detroit had a 22 *share* (was watched by 22% of television viewers), while *CSI* had a 15 share. What is the probability that someone who was watching television during this time watched the NBA Finals or *CSI*? Do you think that this is theoretical or experimental probability? Explain.

21. 0.37; experimental because it is based on a small sample

LINK Television

In 2004, about 109.6 million U.S. households had televisions. Nielsen's *rating points*, such as those for *CSI*, represent the percent of these households tuned to a show.

School Arts **Use the table for Exercises 22 and 23.**

22. What would you need to know to find the probability that a U.S. public school offers music or dance classes? the percent of schools that offer both music and dance classes

23. What is the minimum probability that a U.S. public school offers visual arts or drama? What is the maximum probability?
87%; 100%

Arts Offered by U.S. Public Schools

Class Type	Music	Visual arts	Dance	Drama and theater
Percent of Schools	94%	87%	20%	19%

24. **Geometry** A square dartboard contains a red square and a blue square that overlap. A dart hits a random point on the board.
    a. Find $P(\text{red} \cap \text{blue})$. $\frac{1}{36}$
    b. Find $P(\text{red})$. $\frac{1}{12}$
    c. Find $P(\text{red} \cup \text{blue})$. $\frac{91}{324}$
    d. Find $P(\text{yellow})$. $\frac{233}{324}$

9 in.
3 in.
3 in.
2.5 in.
2.5 in.
9 in.
4 in.
4 in.

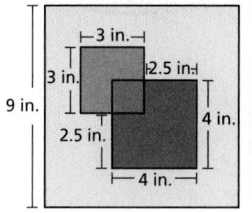

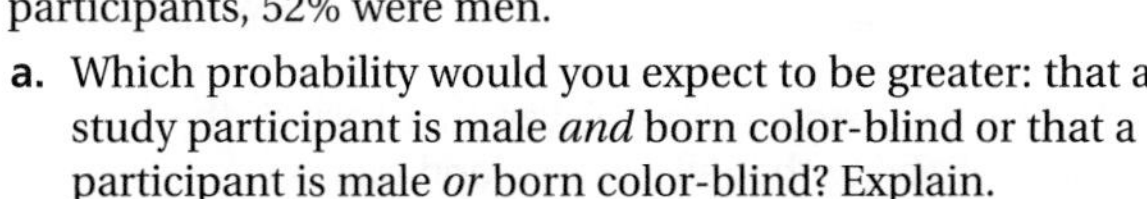

25. **Genetics** One study found that 8% of men and 0.5% of women are born color-blind. Of the study participants, 52% were men.
    a. Which probability would you expect to be greater: that a study participant is male *and* born color-blind or that a participant is male *or* born color-blind? Explain.
    b. What is the probability that a study participant is male and born color-blind? What is the probability that a study participant is male or born color-blind?
    4.16%; 52.24%

COMMON ERROR ALERT

In **Exercise 19,** students might have difficulty understanding how to use the complement to solve. Explain that the complement of "at least 1 heart" is "no hearts."

Teaching Tip

Geometry Remind students that the geometric probability is a ratio of each colored area to the total area in **Exercise 24.**

Answers

20. Possible answer: No; if event *A* is rolling a 3 on a number cube and event *B* is rolling a 4 on a number cube, then the outcomes 1, 2, 5, and 6 are common to both *A′* and *B′*.

21. 0.37; experimental because it is based on a small sample

25a. Possible answer: The probability that a person is born color-blind *or* male will be greater, because it includes more successful outcomes, such as color-blind females and non-color-blind males.

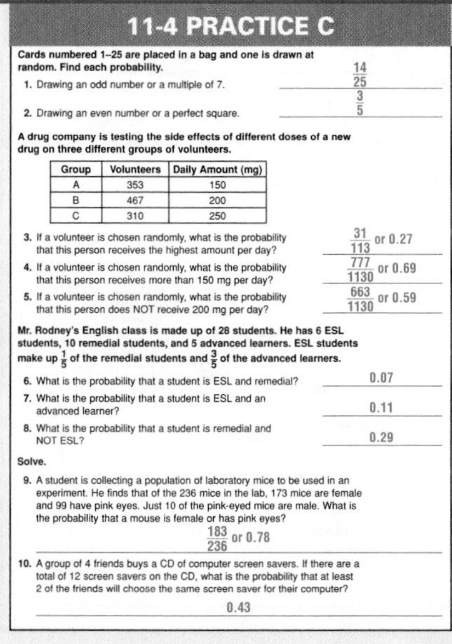

11-4 PRACTICE C

Cards numbered 1–25 are placed in a bag and one is drawn at random. Find each probability.

1. Drawing an odd number or a multiple of 7. $\frac{14}{25}$
2. Drawing an even number or a perfect square. $\frac{3}{5}$

A drug company is testing the side effects of different doses of a new drug on three different groups of volunteers.

Group	Volunteers	Daily Amount (mg)
A	353	150
B	467	200
C	310	250

3. If a volunteer is chosen randomly, what is the probability that this person receives the highest amount per day? $\frac{31}{113}$ or 0.27
4. If a volunteer is chosen randomly, what is the probability that this person receives more than 150 mg per day? $\frac{777}{1130}$ or 0.69
5. If a volunteer is chosen randomly, what is the probability that this person does NOT receive 200 mg per day? $\frac{663}{1130}$ or 0.59

Mr. Rodney's English class is made up of 28 students. He has 6 ESL students, 10 remedial students, and 5 advanced learners. ESL students make up $\frac{1}{5}$ of the remedial students and $\frac{3}{5}$ of the advanced learners.

6. What is the probability that a student is ESL and remedial? 0.07
7. What is the probability that a student is ESL and an advanced learner? 0.11
8. What is the probability that a student is remedial and NOT ESL? 0.29

Solve.

9. A student is collecting a population of laboratory mice to be used in an experiment. He finds that of the 236 mice in the lab, 173 mice are female and 99 have pink eyes. Just 10 of the pink-eyed mice are male. What is the probability that a mouse is female or has pink eyes? $\frac{183}{236}$ or 0.78
10. A group of 4 friends buys a CD of computer screen savers. If there are a total of 12 screen savers on the CD, what is the probability that at least 2 of the friends will choose the same screen saver for their computer? 0.43

Exercise 26 involves finding probabilities of compound events associated with rolling game cubes in the game Yahtzee. This exercise prepares students for finding probabilities in the Multi-Step Test Prep on page 826.

Visual A tree diagram may help students visualize how the probabilities are related in **Exercise 27.**

If students select **D** in **Exercise 31,** they are forgetting how to order fractions. Remind them that the greater denominator is the lesser unit fraction.

In **Exercise 32,** a choice of **H** suggests that the student is confusing mutually exclusive and independent events. Point out that the outcome of the first 3 tosses is known. The question relates only to the last—unknown—toss, which is different from finding the probability of 4 tosses landing on tails.

In **Exercise 33,** students who select **A** are finding only the probability of rolling 5. Have students reread the problem and use $P(A \text{ or } B)$ notation to set it up. This may help them recognize that the events are inclusive and discover how to find the probability.

Answers

30. Possible answer: There are a total of 4 outcomes: $\{HH, HT, TH, TT\}$. 3 of these have at least one heads, so the probability is $\frac{3}{4}$. The event "at least one heads" is the complement of the event "no heads," so the probability is $1 - \left(\frac{1}{2} \cdot \frac{1}{2}\right) = 1 - \frac{1}{4} = \frac{3}{4}$.

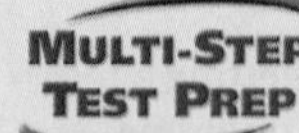

26. This problem will prepare you for the Multi-Step Test Prep on page 826.

While playing Yahtzee, Amanda rolls five dice and gets the result shown. She decides to keep the 1, 2, and 4, and reroll the 5 and 6.

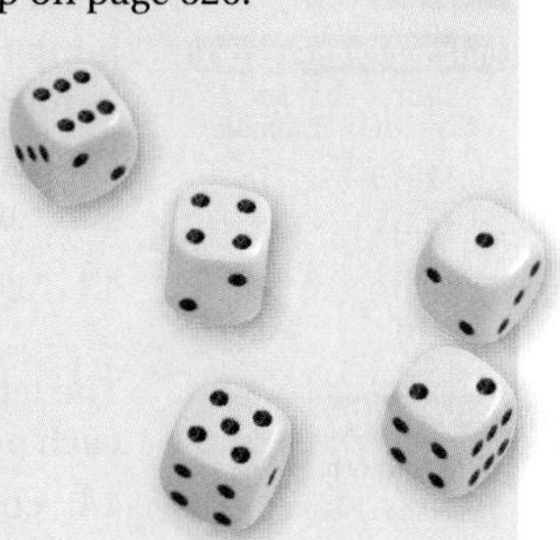

a. After rerolling the 5 and 6, what is the probability that Amanda will have a "large straight" (1-2-3-4-5) or three 4's? $\frac{1}{12}$

b. After rerolling the 5 and 6, what is the probability that Amanda will have a "small straight" (1-2-3-4 plus anything else) or a pair of 3's? $\frac{5}{18}$

27. Public Safety In a study of canine attacks, the probability that the victim was under 18 years of age was 0.8. The probability that the attack occurred on the dog owner's property was 0.64. The probability that the victim was under 18 years of age or the attack occurred on the owner's property was 0.95. What was the probability that the victim was under 18 years of age and the attack occurred on the owner's property? 0.49

28. Politics A 4-person leadership committee is randomly chosen from a group of 24 candidates. Ten of the candidates are men, and 14 are women.

a. What is the probability that the committee is all male or all female? ≈ 0.11

b. What is the probability that the committee has at least 1 man or at least 1 woman? 1

29. Multi-Step The game Scrabble contains letter tiles that occur in different numbers. Suppose that one tile is selected.

a. What is the probability of choosing a vowel if *Y* is not included? 0.42

b. What is the probability of choosing a *Y*? 0.02

c. What is the probability of choosing a vowel if *Y* is included? How does this relate to the answer to parts **a** and **b**? 0.44; it is the sum of the probabilities.

Distribution of Scrabble Tiles

Tiles	Frequency
J, K, Q, X, Z	1
B, C, F, H, M, P, V, W, Y, blank	2
G	3
D, L, S, U	4
N, R, T	6
O	8
A, I	9
E	12

30. Write About It Demonstrate two ways to find the probability of a coin's landing heads up at least once in 2 tosses of a coin.

31. For a quilt raffle, 2500 tickets numbered 0001–2500 are sold. Jamie has number 1527. The winning raffle number is read one digit at a time. The first winning number begins "One...". After the first digit is called, Jamie's chances of winning do which of the following?

Ⓐ Go to 0

Ⓑ Stay the same

Ⓒ Increase from $\frac{1}{2500}$ to $\frac{1}{1527}$

Ⓓ Increase from $\frac{1}{2500}$ to $\frac{1}{1000}$

32. A fair coin is tossed 4 times. Given that each of the first 3 tosses land tails up, what is the probability that all 4 tosses land tails up?

Ⓕ 0.5

Ⓖ Greater than 0.5

Ⓗ 0.5^4

Ⓙ Between 0.5^4 and 0.5

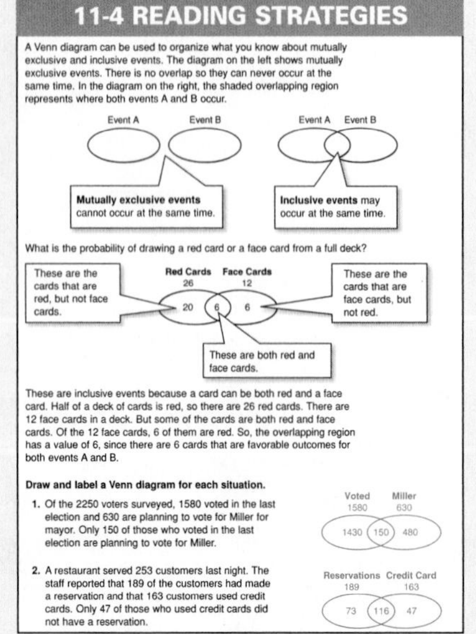

11-4 READING STRATEGIES

A Venn diagram can be used to organize what you know about mutually exclusive and inclusive events. The diagram on the left shows mutually exclusive events. There is no overlap so they can never occur at the same time. In the diagram on the right, the shaded overlapping region represents where both events A and B occur.

What is the probability of drawing a red card or a face card from a full deck?

These are inclusive events because a card can be both red and a face card. Half of a deck of cards is red, so there are 26 red cards. There are 12 face cards in a deck. But some of the cards are both red and face cards. Of the 12 face cards, 6 of them are red. So, the overlapping region has a value of 6, since there are 6 cards that are favorable outcomes for both events A and B.

Draw and label a Venn diagram for each situation.

1. Of the 2250 voters surveyed, 1580 voted in the last election and 630 are planning to vote for Miller for mayor. Only 150 of those who voted in the last election are planning to vote for Miller.

2. A restaurant served 253 customers last night. The staff reported that 189 of the customers had made a reservation and that 163 customers used credit cards. Only 47 of those who used credit cards did not have a reservation.

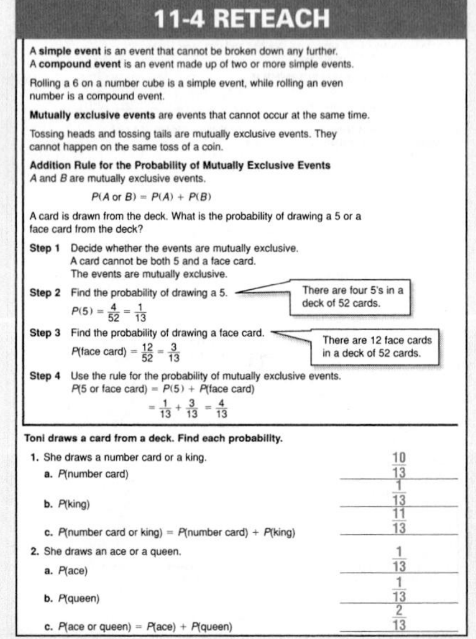

11-4 RETEACH

A **simple event** is an event that cannot be broken down any further.
A **compound event** is an event made up of two or more simple events.

Rolling a 6 on a number cube is a simple event, while rolling an even number is a compound event.

Mutually exclusive events are events that cannot occur at the same time.

Tossing heads and tossing tails are mutually exclusive events. They cannot happen on the same toss of a coin.

Addition Rule for the Probability of Mutually Exclusive Events
A and *B* are mutually exclusive events.

$$P(A \text{ or } B) = P(A) + P(B)$$

A card is drawn from the deck. What is the probability of drawing a 5 or a face card from the deck?

Step 1 Decide whether the events are mutually exclusive.
A card cannot be both 5 and a face card.
The events are mutually exclusive.

Step 2 Find the probability of drawing a 5. (There are four 5's in a deck of 52 cards.)
$P(5) = \frac{4}{52} = \frac{1}{13}$

Step 3 Find the probability of drawing a face card. (There are 12 face cards in a deck of 52 cards.)
$P(\text{face card}) = \frac{12}{52} = \frac{3}{13}$

Step 4 Use the rule for the probability of mutually exclusive events.
$P(5 \text{ or face card}) = P(5) + P(\text{face card})$
$= \frac{1}{13} + \frac{3}{13} = \frac{4}{13}$

Toni draws a card from a deck. Find each probability.

1. She draws a number card or a king.
   a. $P(\text{number card})$ $\frac{10}{13}$
   b. $P(\text{king})$ $\frac{1}{13}$
   c. $P(\text{number card or king}) = P(\text{number card}) + P(\text{king})$ $\frac{11}{13}$
2. She draws an ace or a queen.
   a. $P(\text{ace})$ $\frac{1}{13}$
   b. $P(\text{queen})$ $\frac{1}{13}$
   c. $P(\text{ace or queen}) = P(\text{ace}) + P(\text{queen})$ $\frac{2}{13}$

33. If Travis rolls a 5 on a number cube, he lands on "roll again." If Travis rolls a number greater than 3, he'll pass "start" and collect \$100. What is the probability that Travis rolls again or collects \$100?

Ⓐ $\frac{1}{6}$ Ⓑ $\frac{1}{5}$ Ⓒ $\frac{1}{4}$ ⓓ $\frac{1}{2}$

34. **Short Response** What is the probability of an event or its complement? Explain.
1; the complement of an event contains all unfavorable outcomes, so the probability of an event or its complement is the probability of all outcomes, 1.

CHALLENGE AND EXTEND

35. What is the probability that at least 2 people in a group of 10 people have the same birthday? (Assume no one in the group was born on February 29th.) $\approx$ **0.12**

Travel For Exercises 36–38, use the Venn diagram, which shows the transportation methods used by 162 travelers. Find each probability if a traveler is selected at random.

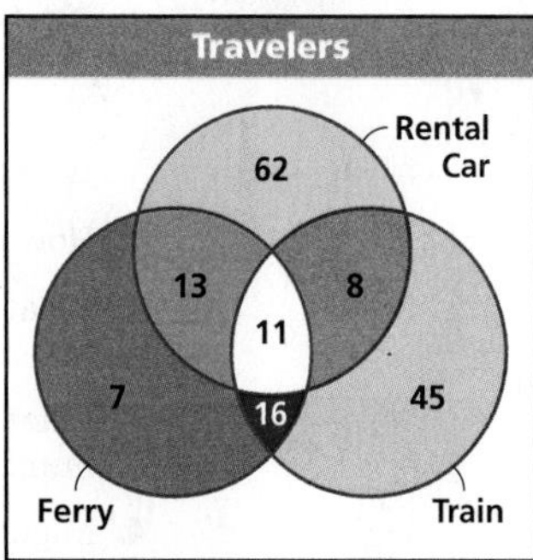

36. $P(\text{ferry or train})$ $\frac{50}{81}$

37. $P(\text{ferry or rental car})$ $\frac{13}{18}$

38. $P(\text{train and ferry, or train and rental car})$ $\frac{35}{162}$

Use the table of probabilities and the following information for Exercises 39–41. Hint: Draw a Venn diagram.

For any three events A, B, and C, $P(A \text{ or } B \text{ or } C) =$
$P(A) + P(B) + P(C) - P(A \cap B) - P(A \cap C) - P(B \cap C) + P(A \cap B \cap C)$

Event	$P(A)$	$P(B)$	$P(C)$	$P(A \cap B)$	$P(A \cap C)$	$P(B \cap C)$	$P(A \cap B \cap C)$
Probability	0.5	0.3	0.7	0.2	0.3	0.1	0.1

39. Find $P(B \cup C)$. **0.9**

40. Find $P(A \cup B \cup C)$. **1**

41. Find $P(B \cap (A \cup C))$. **0.2**

SPIRAL REVIEW

Write a cubic function for each graph. *(Lesson 6-9)*

42.

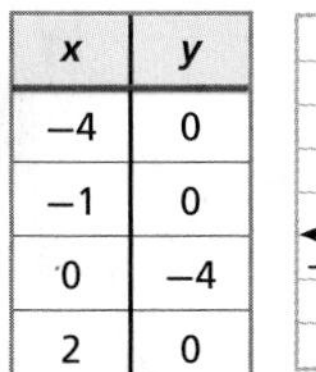

x	y
−4	0
−1	0
0	−4
2	0

$y = 0.5x^3 + 1.5x^2 - 3x - 4$

43.

x	y
−5	0
−2	0
−1	24
3	0

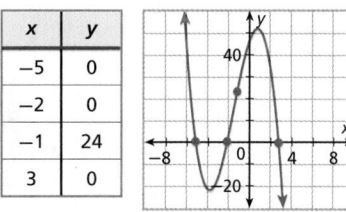

$y = -1.5x^3 - 6x^2 + 16.5x + 45$

Graph each function. *(Lesson 9-2)*

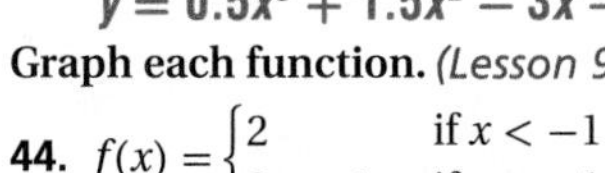

44. $f(x) = \begin{cases} 2 & \text{if } x < -1 \\ 2x + 4 & \text{if } x \geq -1 \end{cases}$

45. $g(x) = \begin{cases} 1 - x^2 & \text{if } x < 1 \\ x^2 - 1 & \text{if } x \geq 1 \end{cases}$

Find each probability. *(Lesson 11-3)*

46. A coin is tossed twice and it lands heads up both times. $\frac{1}{4}$

47. A coin is tossed 4 times and it lands heads up, heads up, tails up, and then tails up. $\frac{1}{16}$

48. Two number cubes are rolled. The sum is greater than 10. The first number cube is 6. $\frac{1}{18}$

11-4 PROBLEM SOLVING

Of 100 students surveyed, 44 are male and 54 are in favor of a change to a 9-period, 4-day school week. Of those in favor, 20 are female. One student is picked at random from those surveyed.

1. What is the probability that the student is male or favors the change? Use the Venn diagram.
   a. What is represented by the total of $A + B$? **The total number of male students; 44**
   b. What is represented by the total of $B + C$? **The total number of students in favor of the change; 54**
   c. How many of those in favor of the change are male? **54 − 20 = 34**
   d. Find the values for A, B, and C and label the diagram.
   e. Write and evaluate an expression for the probability that the student is male or favors the change. $\frac{44}{100} + \frac{54}{100} - \frac{34}{100} = \frac{64}{100} = 0.64$

School Week Survey: A10, B34, C20; Male Students; In Favor of the Change

2. What is the probability that the student is female or opposes the change?
   a. How many students are female? **100 − 44 = 56**
   b. How many students oppose the change? **100 − 54 = 46**
   c. If you draw a Venn diagram to show females and those opposed to the change, what is the meaning and value of the overlapping area? **The number of females who are opposed to the change; 36**
   d. Write and evaluate an expression for the probability that the student is female or opposes the change. $\frac{56}{100} + \frac{46}{100} - \frac{36}{100} = \frac{66}{100} = 0.66$

3. Of the students surveyed, 27 plan to start their own businesses. Of those, 18 are in favor of the change to the school week. Write and evaluate an expression for the probability that a student selected at random plans to start his or her own business or favors the change. $\frac{27}{100} + \frac{54}{100} - \frac{18}{100} = \frac{63}{100} = 0.63$

Sean asks each student to cast a vote for the type of class he or she would prefer. Of the students, 55% voted for online classes, 30% voted for projects, and 15% voted for following the textbook. Choose the letter for the best answer.

4. Which description best describes Sean's experiment?
   A Simple events
   B Compound events
   Ⓒ Mutually exclusive events
   D Inclusive events

5. What is the probability that a randomly selected student voted for online classes or projects?
   F $\frac{33}{200}$
   G $\frac{7}{10}$
   H $\frac{1}{4}$
   Ⓙ $\frac{17}{20}$

11-4 CHALLENGE

If A and B represent two events in the same sample space, then $P(A \text{ or } B) = P(A) + P(B) - P(A \text{ and } B)$ when A and B are inclusive events. When A and B are mutually exclusive events, this simplifies to $P(A \text{ or } B) = P(A) + P(B)$. This formula can also be extended to apply to probabilities involving three events.

Consider the following situation.

A certain drug causes a skin rash or hair loss in 35% of patients. Twenty-five percent of patients experience only a skin rash, and 5% experience both a skin rash and hair loss. Find the probability that a patient will experience hair loss only.

1. Using A to represent "experiences a skin rash" and B to represent "experiences hair loss," write a symbolic representation of the problem. $P(B) = P(A \text{ or } B) - P(A) + P(A \text{ and } B)$

2. Using the symbolic representation you wrote, write the answer to the question. **15%**

Consider the following situation.

Tawana and Sergio recorded a compact disc together. Each sang some solos, and the two sang some duets. Sergio recorded twice as many duets as solos, and Tawana recorded six more solos than duets. When a CD player selects one of these songs at random, the probability that it will select a duet is 25%.

3. Let s represent the number of solos that Sergio recorded.
   a. Write an equation to express the probability of randomly selecting a duet in terms of s. $\frac{1}{4} = \frac{2s}{5s + 6}$
   b. Solve the equation. Then determine the total number of songs recorded. **16 songs**
   c. Find the probability of selecting a solo by Tawana or a duet when a CD player selects one song at random. $\frac{7}{8}$

4. Explain how the shaded area in the diagram shown below is used in the formula for $P(A \text{ or } B)$.

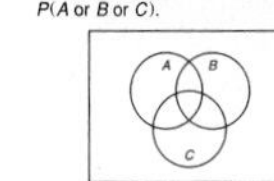

The probability of the shaded area is subtracted from the sum of the probabilities of the individual sets.

5. The diagram below represents three events in the same sample space. Use this diagram to write a formula for $P(A \text{ or } B \text{ or } C)$.

$P(A \text{ or } B \text{ or } C) = P(A) + P(B) + P(C) - P(A \text{ and } B) - P(A \text{ and } C) - P(B \text{ and } C) + P(A \text{ and } B \text{ and } C)$

COMMON ERROR ALERT

In **Exercises 36–38,** students might not understand how to use the Venn diagram to find the probabilities. Suggest that students copy only those parts of the diagram needed to solve each problem. Remind them not to double count probabilities.

Journal

Have students explain how the probabilities of mutually exclusive and inclusive events are really two versions of the same problem.

ALTERNATIVE ASSESSMENT

Have students describe a situation in which the probability of two events is mutually exclusive. Have them formulate and answer a question about the probability. Repeat with inclusive events.

Answers

44, 45. See p. A46.

Power Presentations with PowerPoint®

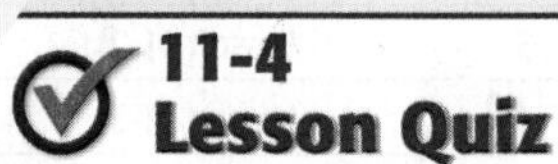

11-4 Lesson Quiz

You have a deck of 52 cards.

1. Explain why the events "choosing a club" and "choosing a heart" are mutually exclusive.
   A card can have only one suit.

2. What is the probability of choosing a club or a heart? $\frac{1}{2}$

The numbers 1–9 are written on cards and placed in a bag. Find each probability.

3. choosing a multiple of 3 or an even number $\frac{2}{3}$

4. choosing a multiple of 4 or an even number $\frac{4}{9}$

5. Of 570 people, 365 were male and 368 had brown hair. Of those with brown hair, 108 were female. What is the probability that a person was male or had brown hair?
   $\frac{473}{570} \approx 0.8298$

6. Each of 4 students randomly chooses a pen from 9 styles. What is the probability that at least 2 students choose the same style?
   ≈ 0.5391

Also available on transparency

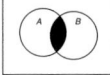

Organizer

Objective: Assess students' ability to apply concepts and skills in Lessons 11-1 through 11-4 in a real-world format.

 **Online Edition**

Resources

Algebra II Assessments
www.mathtekstoolkit.org

Problem	Text Reference
1	Lesson 11-1
2	Lesson 11-2
3	Lesson 11-2
4	Lesson 11-3
5	Lesson 11-3
6	Lesson 11-4
7	Lesson 11-4

State Resources

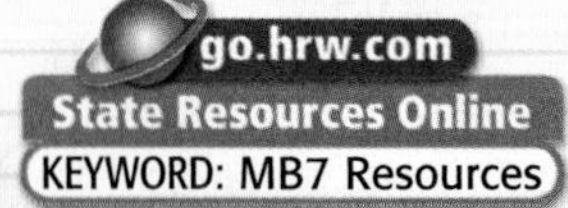

go.hrw.com
State Resources Online
KEYWORD: MB7 Resources

CHAPTER 11

MULTI-STEP TEST PREP

SECTION 11A

Probability

Roll Call Yahtzee is played with 5 dice. A player rolls all 5 dice and may choose to roll any or all of the dice a second time and then a third time. At that point, the player scores points for various combinations of dice, such as 3 of a kind, 4 of a kind, or 5 of a kind.

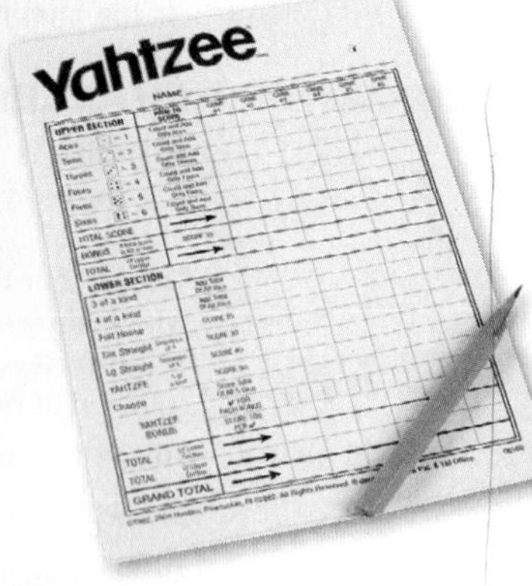

1. How many possible rolls of 5 dice are there?
2. What is the probability of rolling five 6's on the first roll of the dice?
3. What is the probability of rolling 5 of any one number on the first roll?
4. Miguel's first roll is shown at right. He decides to reroll the 6's. What is the probability that he has a 1, 2, 3, 4, and 5 after this roll?
5. What is the probability that Miguel has a 1, 2, 3, 4, and 5 after the roll, given that at least one of the dice comes up a 4?
6. What is the probability that Miguel has a 1, 2, 3, 4, and 5 or a pair of 2's after the roll in Problem 4?
7. What is the probability that Miguel has a 1, 2, 3, 4, and any other number or a pair of 4's after the roll in Problem 4?

Answers:
1. 7776
2. $\frac{1}{7776}$
3. $\frac{1}{1296}$
4. $\frac{1}{18}$
5. $\frac{2}{11}$
6. $\frac{13}{36}$
7. $\frac{11}{36}$

826

INTERVENTION

Scaffolding Questions

1. How many possible outcomes are there for a roll of 1 die? 6

2–3. In this situation, what are the favorable outcomes? **2.** five 6's; **3.** five 1's, five 2's, five 3's, five 4's, five 5's, five 6's How many favorable outcomes are there? **2.** 1; **3.** 6

4. How many outcomes are possible when Miguel rerolls the two 6's? 36 What are the favorable outcomes? 4, 5 and 5, 4
5. How many outcomes include at least one 4 when Miguel rolls two dice? 11

6–7. Are these events mutually exclusive or inclusive? 6. mutually exclusive; 7. mutually inclusive

Extension

What is the probability, to the nearest percent, of getting four of a kind (exactly four 1's, four 2's, four 3's, four 4's, four 5's, or four 6's) when rolling 5 dice? 2%

CHAPTER 11

SECTION 11A

Quiz for Lessons 11-1 Through 11-4

11-1 Permutations and Combinations

1. A security code consists of 5 digits (0–9), and a digit may not be used more than once. How many possible security codes are there? 30,240
2. Adric owns 8 pairs of shoes. How many ways can he choose 4 pairs of shoes to pack into his luggage? 70
3. A plumber received calls from 5 customers. There are 6 open slots on today's schedule. How many ways can the plumber schedule the customers? 720

11-2 Theoretical and Experimental Probability

4. A cooler contains 18 cans: 9 of lemonade, 3 of iced tea, and 6 of cola. Dee selects a can without looking. What is the probability that Dee selects iced tea? $\frac{1}{6}$
5. Jordan has 9 pens in his desk; 2 are out of ink. If his mom selects 2 pens from his desk, what is the probability that both are out of ink? $\frac{1}{36}$
6. Find the probability that a point chosen at random inside the figure shown is in the shaded area. $\frac{4}{15}$
7. A number cube is tossed 50 times, and a 2 is rolled 12 times. Find the experimental probability of not rolling a 2. $\frac{19}{25}$

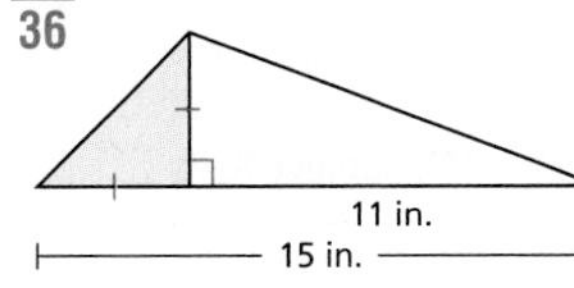

11-3 Independent and Dependent Events

8. Explain why the events "getting tails, then tails, then tails, then tails, then heads when tossing a coin 5 times" are independent, and find the probability.
9. Two number cubes are rolled—one red and one black. Explain why the events "the red cube shows a 6" and "the sum is greater than or equal to 10" are dependent, and find the probability.
10. The table shows the breakdown of math students for one school year. Find the probability that a Geometry student is in the 11th grade. $\frac{33}{127}$
11. A bag contains 25 checkers—15 red and 10 black. Determine whether the events "a red checker is selected, not replaced, and then a black checker is selected" are independent or dependent, and find the probability. dependent; $\frac{1}{4}$

Math Students by Grade

	Geometry	Algebra 2
9th Grade	26	0
10th Grade	68	24
11th Grade	33	94

11-4 Compound Events

Numbers 1–30 are written on cards and placed in a bag. One card is drawn. Find each probability.

12. drawing an even number or a 1 $\frac{8}{15}$
13. drawing an even number or a multiple of 7 $\frac{17}{30}$
14. Of a company's 85 employees, 60 work full time and 40 are married. Half of the full-time workers are married. What is the probability that an employee works part time or is not married? $\frac{11}{17}$

READY TO GO ON?

SECTION 11A

Organizer

Objective: Assess students' mastery of concepts and skills in Lessons 11-1 through 11-4.

Resources

 ***Assessment Resources***

Section 11A Quiz

INTERVENTION 

Resources

 ***Ready to Go On? Intervention and Enrichment* Worksheets**

***Ready to Go On?* CD-ROM**

 ***Ready to Go On?* Online**

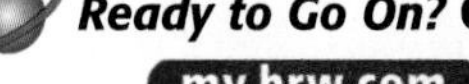

Answers

8. The result of a toss does not affect the probability of the next toss; $\frac{1}{32}$.
9. $P(\text{sum} \geq 10)$ changes after a red 6 has occurred. $P(\text{sum} \geq 10) = \frac{1}{6}$ and $P(\text{sum} \geq 10 \mid \text{red } 6) = \frac{1}{2}$

READY TO GO ON? Diagnose and Prescribe

Ready to Go On? Intervention	*Ready to Go On? Intervention,* Section 11A: Worksheets	CD-ROM	Online
Lesson 11-1	11-1 Intervention	Activity 11-1	Diagnose and Prescribe Online
Lesson 11-2	11-2 Intervention	Activity 11-2	
Lesson 11-3	11-3 Intervention	Activity 11-3	
Lesson 11-4	11-4 Intervention	Activity 11-4	

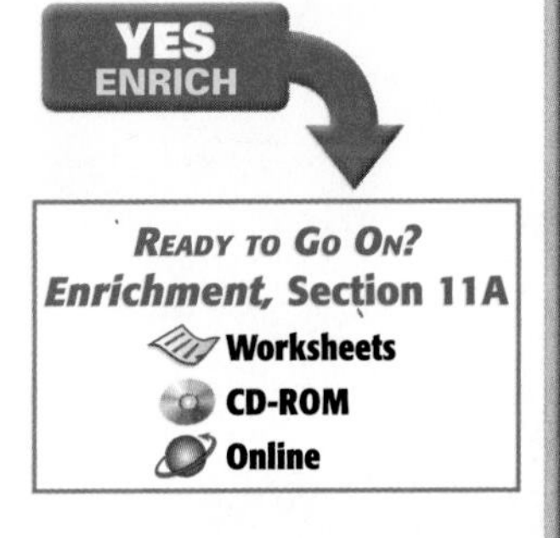

SECTION

11B Data Analysis and Statistics

One-Minute Section Planner

Lesson	Lab Resources	Materials
Lesson 11-5 Measures of Central Tendency and Variation • Find measures of central tendency and measures of variation for statistical data. • Examine the effects of outliers on statistical data. ☑ SAT-10 ☑ NAEP ☐ ACT ☑ SAT ☑ SAT Subject Tests	***Technology Lab Activities*** 11-5 Technology Lab	**Required** graphing calculator
11-5 Algebra Lab Collect Experimental Data • Generate, organize, and analyze data in order to form conjectures about probability. ☑ SAT-10 ☐ NAEP ☐ ACT ☐ SAT ☐ SAT Subject Tests	***Algebra Lab Activities*** 11-5 Lab Recording Sheet	**Required** number cubes (MK)
Lesson 11-6 Binomial Distributions • Use the Binomial Theorem to expand a binomial raised to a power. • Find binomial probabilities and test hypotheses. ☐ SAT-10 ☐ NAEP ☑ ACT ☐ SAT ☑ SAT Subject Tests		**Required** graphing calculator, graph paper
Extension Normal Distributions • Recognize normally distributed data. • Use the characteristics of the normal distribution to solve problems. ☑ SAT-10 ☑ NAEP ☑ ACT ☑ SAT ☑ SAT Subject Tests		

MK = *Manipulatives Kit*

Section Overview

Measures of Central Tendency and Variation

Lesson 11-5

Measures of central tendency and variation allow us to describe a data set efficiently.

Measures of Central Tendency

values that describe the center of a data set

Mean, $\bar{x}$: sum of the values in the set divided by the number of values

Median: middle value or the mean of the two middle values when the set is ordered numerically

Mode: value or values that occur most often

Measures of Variation

values that describe the spread of a data set

Range: difference between the least and greatest values in the data set

Interquartile Range (IQR): difference between the third and first quartiles (Quartiles are the medians of the lower and upper halves of the data set.)

Variance: average of the squared differences from the mean

Standard Deviation, σ: square root of the variance

Box-and-Whisker Plot

Displays the variation of a data set

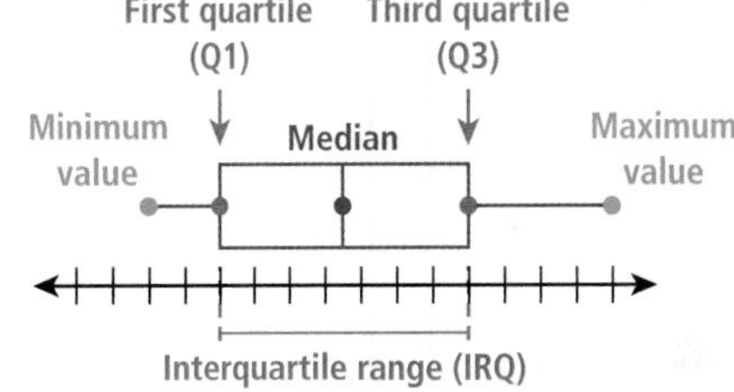

Binomial Distributions

Lesson 11-6

Why? Binomial experiments are used to model real-world situations in which there are two discrete possible outcomes.

A **binomial experiment** consists of n independent trials whose outcomes are either successes or failures.

Binomial Probability

of exactly $\boldsymbol{r}$ successes in $\boldsymbol{n}$ trials

$$P(r) = {}_nC_r \cdot p^r \cdot q^{n-r}$$

p is the probability of success.

q is $1-p$, the probability of failure.

11-5 Organizer

Pacing: Traditional 1 day
Block $\frac{1}{2}$ day

Objectives: Find measures of central tendency and measures of variation for statistical data.

Examine the effects of outliers on statistical data.

Technology Lab
In *Technology Lab Activities*

Online Edition
Graphing Calculator, Tutorial Videos, TechKeys

Countdown to Testing Week 24

Power Presentations with PowerPoint®

Warm Up

Simplify each expression.

1. $4\left(\frac{6}{27}\right)$ $\frac{8}{9}$
2. $\frac{136}{24}$ $\frac{17}{3}$
3. $\frac{3+4+8+7}{4}$ $5\frac{1}{2}$
4. $\sqrt{121}$ 11

Find the mean and median.

5. 1, 2, 87 30; 2
6. 3, 2, 1, 10 4; 2.5

Also available on transparency

Math Humor

A statistician with her feet in an oven and her head in ice will say that, on average, she feels fine.

State Resources

go.hrw.com
State Resources Online
KEYWORD: MB7 Resources

11-5 Measures of Central Tendency and Variation

Objectives
Find measures of central tendency and measures of variation for statistical data.

Examine the effects of outliers on statistical data.

Vocabulary
expected value
probability distribution
variance
standard deviation
outlier

Who uses this?
Statisticians can use measures of central tendency and variation to analyze World Series results. (See Example 2.)

Recall that the *mean*, *median*, and *mode* are measures of central tendency—values that describe the center of a data set.

The *mean* is the sum of the values in the set divided by the number of values. It is often represented as $\bar{x}$. The *median* is the middle value or the mean of the two middle values when the set is ordered numerically. The *mode* is the value or values that occur most often. A data set may have one mode, no mode, or several modes.

EXAMPLE 1 Finding Measures of Central Tendency

Helpful Hint

See the Skills Bank p. S68 for help with finding the mean, median, mode, and range for a set of data.

Find the mean, median, and mode of the data.

Number of days from mailing to delivery: 6, 4, 3, 4, 2, 5, 3, 4, 5, 2, 3, 4

Mean: $\frac{6+4+3+4+2+5+3+4+5+2+3+4}{12} = \frac{45}{12} = 3.75$ days

Median: 2 2 3 3 3 3 ¦ 4 4 4 5 5 6 $\frac{3+4}{2} = 3.5$ days

Mode: The most common result is 3 days.

CHECK IT OUT! **Find the mean, median, and mode of each data set.**

1a. $\{6, 9, 3, 8\}$ 6.5; 7; no mode

1b. $\{2, 5, 6, 2, 6\}$ 4.2; 5; 2 and 6

A *weighted average* is a mean calculated by using frequencies of data values. Suppose that 30 movies are rated as follows:

Movie Ratings					
Rating	★★★★	★★★	★★	★	no stars
Number of Movies	8	12	7	2	1

$$\textit{weighted average of stars} = \frac{8(4)+12(3)+7(2)+2(1)+1(0)}{8+12+7+2+1} = \frac{84}{30} = 2.8 \text{ stars}$$

For numerical data, the weighted average of all of those outcomes is called the **expected value** for that experiment. For example, the expected value for the number of stars of a randomly chosen movie from the group above is 2.8.

The **probability distribution** for an experiment is the function that pairs each outcome with its probability.

1 Introduce

EXPLORATION

11-5 Measures of Central Tendency and Dispersion

The advertised mass of a box of cereal is 453 grams. A quality control manager measures 13 boxes and records the following masses in grams.

450, 453, 451, 456, 455, 454, 456, 452, 452, 453, 495, 453, 456

Enter the data into a list in a calculator by pressing STAT and selecting **1:Edit...**. Then enter the data into list **L1**. Press 2nd MODE to return to the home screen.

1. Find the average, or mean, of the data by pressing 2nd STAT, scrolling right to **MATH**, and selecting **3:mean(**. Then press 2nd 1) ENTER.
2. Find the middle value, or median, of the data by using the procedure described above but select **4:median(** instead of **3:mean(**.
3. An outlier is a value that is much less than or much greater than the other values in a data set. Which value in the data set above is most likely to be considered an outlier?
4. How does the mean of the data set change if this outlier is removed? How does the median change?

Motivate

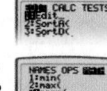

Discuss how we often use measures of central tendency with mental math without being aware of it. *Ask:* When we say that a CD costs "about $15" or that a movie is "generally 2 hours long," where do those numbers come from? What do they represent? averages, or means

Explorations and answers are provided in the *Explorations* binder.

EXAMPLE 2 Finding Expected Value

Helpful Hint

The sum of all of the probabilities in a probability distribution is 1. In Example 2,

$\frac{5}{27} + \frac{5}{27} + \frac{6}{27} + \frac{11}{27} = 1$

The probability distribution for the number of games played in each World Series for the years 1923–2004 is given below. Find the expected number of games in a World Series.

World Series Games				
Number of Games n in World Series	4	5	6	7
Probability of n Games	$\frac{5}{27}$	$\frac{5}{27}$	$\frac{6}{27}$	$\frac{11}{27}$

$$\text{expected value} = 4\left(\frac{5}{27}\right) + 5\left(\frac{5}{27}\right) + 6\left(\frac{6}{27}\right) + 7\left(\frac{11}{27}\right)$$ *Use the weighted average.*

$$= \frac{20}{27} + \frac{25}{27} + \frac{36}{27} + \frac{77}{27} = \frac{158}{27} \approx 5.85$$ *Simplify.*

The expected number of games in a World Series is about 5.85.

2. The probability distribution of the number of accidents in a week at an intersection, based on past data, is given below. Find the expected number of accidents for one week. **0.37**

Number of accidents n	0	1	2	3
Probability of n accidents	0.75	0.15	0.08	0.02

A *box-and-whisker plot* shows the spread of a data set. It displays 5 key points: the **minimum** and **maximum** values, the **median**, and the **first** and **third quartiles**.

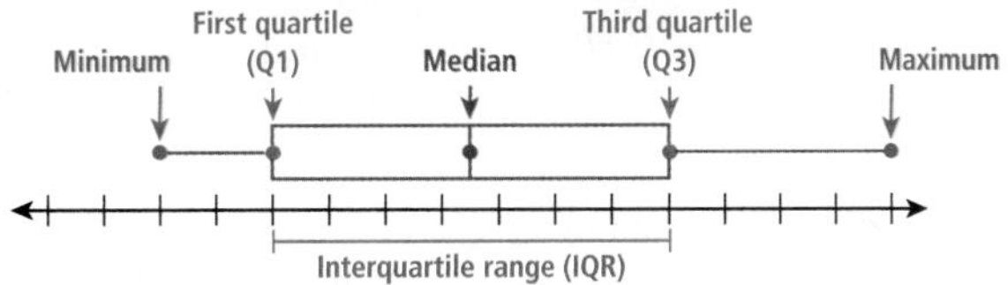

The quartiles are the medians of the lower and upper halves of the data set. If there are an odd number of data values, do not include the median in either half.

The *interquartile range*, or IQR, is the difference between the 1st and 3rd quartiles, or Q3 – Q1. It represents the middle 50% of the data.

Student to Student — *Box-and-Whisker Plots*

Jenny Rivera
Lincoln High School

I know I have to sort the data before I can make a box-and-whisker plot. I enter the data into my graphing calculator list. Then I use the STAT sort feature to sort the list in ascending order.

Other times, I'll use a spreadsheet and sort the data there.

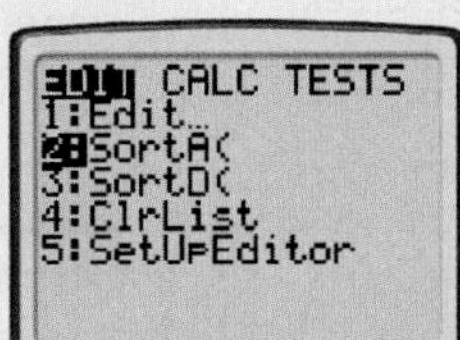

2 Teach

Guided Instruction

Review finding the mean, median, and mode. Discuss the need to describe the spread of data set as well as its center. Mention that box-and-whisker plots visually present the spread or clustering of data. Standard deviation expresses how tightly data are grouped and is greatly affected by outliers.

Reaching All Learners
Through Curriculum Integration

Have groups of students use the Internet to find the areas, in square miles, of the world's 10 largest lakes, deserts, and islands. Students should give the measures of central tendency and variation for their data. Have students describe their data sets visually, if possible (e.g., in a box-and-whisker plot) and mathematically without telling the actual data values.

Reading Math Tell students to look for key words. If you read the word *middle*, think "median." If you read *average*, think "mean." **ENGLISH LANGUAGE LEARNERS**

Power Presentations with PowerPoint®

Additional Examples

Example 1

Find the mean, median, and mode of the data.

deer at a feeder each hour: 3, 0, 2, 0, 1, 2, 4

mean ≈ 1.7; median = 2; two modes: 0 and 2

Example 2

The probability distribution of successful free throws for a practice set is given below. Find the expected number of successes for one set. 2.05

Number of Good Free Throws, n	0	1	2	3
Prob. of n Good Free Throws	$\frac{3}{20}$	$\frac{3}{20}$	$\frac{1}{5}$	$\frac{1}{2}$

Also available on transparency

INTERVENTION
Questioning Strategies

EXAMPLE 1

- Why do you order the data to calculate the median and mode but not the mean?

EXAMPLE 2

- Why is the calculated expected value not a whole number?

Sports Link Tell students that prior to 1922, there was no limit to the number of games in a Major League Baseball World Series and that it was possible to have a tied series. Point out that under those rules, it would have been impossible to calculate probabilities similar to those in **Example 2.**

Teaching Tip **Technology** The calculator refers to the first quartile as Q1 and third quartile as Q3. The median is considered to be the second quartile, Q2. The minimum can be considered Q0 and the maximum Q4.

Power Presentations with PowerPoint®

Additional Examples

Example 3

Make a box-and-whisker plot of the data. Find the interquartile range. $\{6, 8, 7, 5, 10, 6, 9, 8, 4\}$

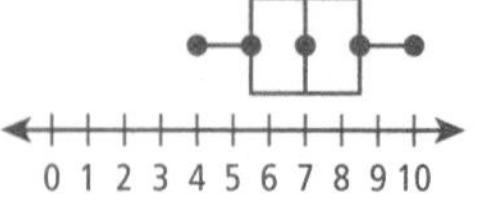

IQR = 3

Example 4

Find the mean and standard deviation for the data set of the number of people getting on and off a bus for several stops. $\{6, 8, 7, 5, 10, 6, 9, 8, 4\}$

mean: 7; std. dev. ≈ 1.8

Also available on transparency

INTERVENTION

Questioning Strategies

EXAMPLE 3

- What summary statement about the data can you make using the IQR? Explain.

EXAMPLE 4

- What are some examples of results (in mg) that might be usual in this situation, and what results might make you think there was something unusual about the result? Explain.

EXAMPLE 3 Making a Box-and-Whisker Plot and Finding the Interquartile Range

Make a box-and-whisker plot of the data. Find the interquartile range.
$\{5, 3, 9, 2, 14, 6, 8, 9, 5, 8, 13, 3, 15, 7, 4, 2, 12, 8\}$

Step 1 Order the data from least to greatest.

2, 2, 3, 3, 4, 5, 5, 6, 7, 8, 8, 8, 9, 9, 12, 13, 14, 15

Step 2 Find the minimum, maximum, median, and quartiles.

(2, 2, 3, 3, 4, 5, 5, 6, 7), (8, 8, 8, 9, 9, 12, 13, 14, 15)

Minimum — First quartile — Median 7.5 — Third quartile — Maximum

Step 3 Draw a box-and-whisker plot.

Draw a number line, and plot a point above each of the five values. Then draw the box from the first quartile to the third quartile with a line segment through the median. Draw whiskers from the box to the minimum and maximum.

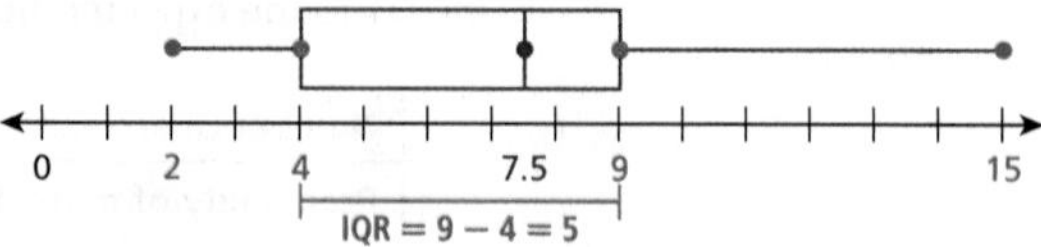

The interquartile range is 5, the length of the box in the diagram.

3. IQR = 5

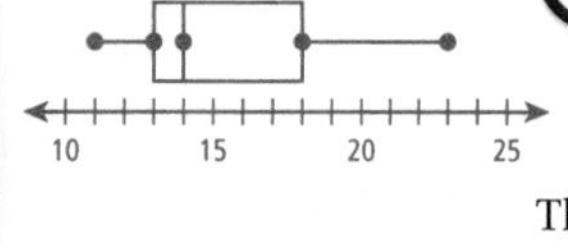

CHECK IT OUT! 3. Make a box-and-whisker plot of the data. Find the interquartile range.
$\{13, 14, 18, 13, 12, 17, 15, 12, 13, 19, 11, 14, 14, 18, 22, 23\}$

The data sets $\{19, 20, 21\}$ and $\{0, 20, 40\}$ have the same mean and median, but the sets are very different. The way that data are spread out from the mean or median is important in the study of statistics.

Reading Math

The symbol commonly used to represent the mean is $\bar{x}$, or "x bar." The symbol for standard deviation is the lowercase Greek letter *sigma*, σ.

A *measure of variation* is a value that describes the spread of a data set. The most commonly used measures of variation are the *range*, the interquartile range, the *variance*, and the *standard deviation*.

The **variance**, denoted by σ^2, is the average of the squared differences from the mean. **Standard deviation**, denoted by σ, is the square root of the variance and is one of the most common and useful measures of variation.

Low standard deviations indicate data that are clustered near the measures of central tendency, whereas high standard deviations indicate data that are spread out from the center.

Finding Variance and Standard Deviation
Step 1. Find the mean of the data, $\bar{x}$.
Step 2. Find the difference between the mean and each data value, and square it.
Step 3. Find the variance, σ^2, by adding the squares of all of the differences from the mean and dividing by the number of data values.
Step 4. Find the standard deviation, σ, by taking the square root of the variance.

Teaching Tip **Kinesthetic** To help students understand the concept of a box-and-whisker plot, have them copy the plot in **Example 3** and draw a cat face over it to show how the *box-and-whisker* plot got its name.

You can then briefly discuss all the parts—the nose (median), the ends of the mouth (quartiles), and the ends of the whiskers (minimum and maximum).

EXAMPLE 4 Finding the Mean and Standard Deviation

The data represent the number of milligrams of a substance in a patient's blood, found on consecutive doctor visits. Find the mean and the standard deviation of the data.

$\{14, 13, 16, 9, 3, 7, 11, 12, 11, 4\}$

Step 1 Find the mean.

$$\bar{x} = \frac{14 + 13 + 16 + 9 + 3 + 7 + 11 + 12 + 11 + 4}{10} = 10$$

Step 2 Find the difference between the mean and each data value, and square it.

Data Value x	14	13	16	9	3	7	11	12	11	4
$x - \bar{x}$	4	3	6	−1	−7	−3	1	2	1	−6
$(x - \bar{x})^2$	16	9	36	1	49	9	1	4	1	36

Step 3 Find the variance.

$$\sigma^2 = \frac{16 + 9 + 36 + 1 + 49 + 9 + 1 + 4 + 1 + 36}{10} = 16.2$$

Find the average of the last row of the table.

Step 4 Find the standard deviation.

$$\sigma = \sqrt{16.2} \approx 4.02$$

The standard deviation is the square root of the variance.

The mean is 10 mg, the standard deviation is about 4.02 mg.

4. Find the mean and standard deviation for the data set of the number of elevator stops for several rides. **1.4; ≈ 1.6**

$\{0, 3, 1, 1, 0, 5, 1, 0, 3, 0\}$

Remember!

Enter lists in the graphing calculator by pressing STAT and choosing **1:Edit...**

An **outlier** is an extreme value that is much less than or much greater than the other data values. Outliers have a strong effect on the mean and standard deviation. If an outlier is the result of measurement error or represents data from the wrong population, it is usually removed. There are different ways to determine whether a value is an outlier. One is to look for data values that are more than 3 standard deviations from the mean.

EXAMPLE 5 Examining Outliers

The number of electoral votes in 2004 for 11 western states are shown. Find the mean and the standard deviation of the data. Identify any outliers, and describe how they affect the mean and the standard deviation.

Step 1 Enter the data values into list **L1** on a graphing calculator.

Step 2 Find the mean and standard deviation.

On the graphing calculator, press STAT, scroll to the **CALC** menu, and select **1:1-Var Stats**.

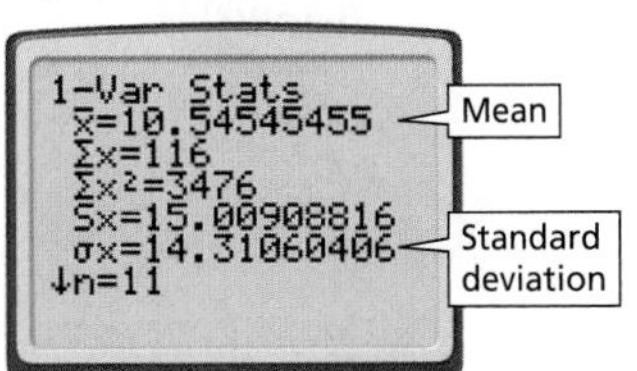

The mean is about 10.5, and the standard deviation is about 14.3.

COMMON ERROR ALERT

Students may forget to square the variation of each data point from the mean. To help students understand why this step is necessary, have them add the unsquared variations (which always total to zero).

Power Presentations with PowerPoint®

Additional Examples

Example 5

Find the mean and the standard deviation for the heights of 15 cans. Identify any outliers, and describe how they affect the mean and the standard deviation.

Can Heights (mm)		
92.8	92.8	92.9
92.9	92.9	92.8
92.7	92.9	92.1
92.7	92.8	92.9
92.9	92.7	92.8

$\bar{x}$: ≈ 92.77 mm; std. dev.: ≈ 0.19 mm; outlier: 92.1; removing outlier: $\bar{x}$: ≈ 92.82 mm; std. dev.: ≈ 0.08 mm

Also available on transparency

INTERVENTION

Questioning Strategies

EXAMPLE 5

- What questions might you ask about the reasons for an extreme value? Explain. For example, consider an extreme value for the number of cars passing through an intersection.

Teaching Tip

Technology Students might use the Sx calculator value rather than σx. Tell students that Sx is an adjusted standard deviation based on a sample rather than an entire set of numbers. It is used extensively in higher-level statistical analysis.

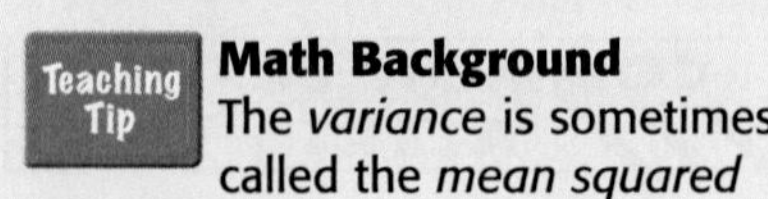

Math Background The *variance* is sometimes called the *mean squared deviation.*

Step 3 Identify the outliers.

Look for data values that are more than 3 standard deviations away from the mean in either direction.

Three standard deviations is about $3(14.3) = 42.9$.

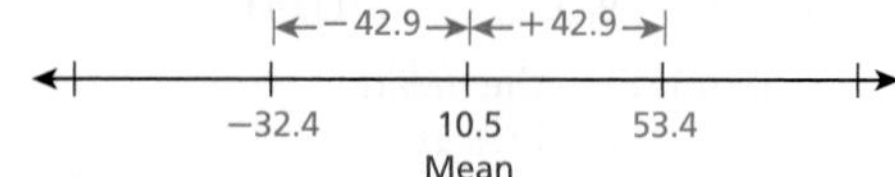

Values 42.9 units below the mean are negative and would not make sense in the problem (a state cannot have a negative number of electoral votes).

Values greater than 53.4 are outliers, so 55, the number of California electoral votes, is an outlier.

Check $\frac{\text{value} - \text{mean}}{\text{standard deviation}} = \frac{|55 - 10.5|}{14.3} \approx 3.1$ *55 is 3.1 standard deviations from the mean, so it is an outlier.*

Step 4 Remove the outlier to see the effect that it has on the mean and standard deviation.

All data **Without outlier**

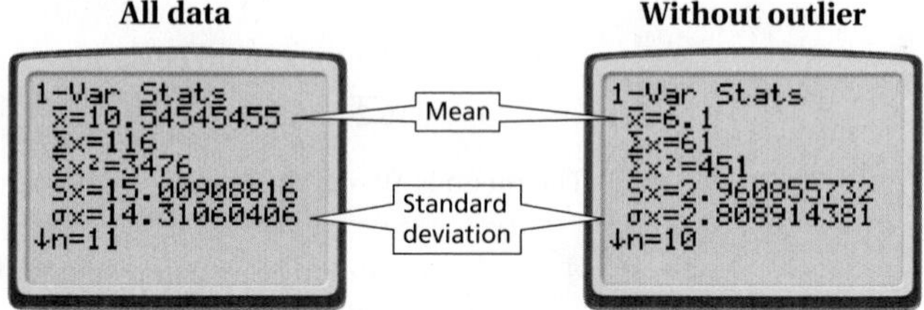

The outlier in the data set causes the mean to increase from 6.1 to 10.5 and the standard deviation to increase from ≈ 2.8 to ≈ 14.3.

5. In the 2003 and 2004 American League Championship Series, the New York Yankees scored the following numbers of runs against the Boston Red Sox: 2, 6, 4, 2, 4, 6, 6, 10, 3, 19, 4, 4, 2, 3. Identify the outlier, and describe how it affects the mean and standard deviation.
19; the mean increases from ≈ 4.3 to ≈ 5.4, and the standard deviation increases from ≈ 2.2 to ≈ 4.3.

THINK AND DISCUSS

1. Describe the effect of adding a constant to each data value on the mean.

2. Describe the effect of adding a constant to each data value on the standard deviation.

3. What effect does doubling the variance have on the standard deviation?

4. GET ORGANIZED Copy and complete the graphic organizer. In each box, define and give an example of each measure.

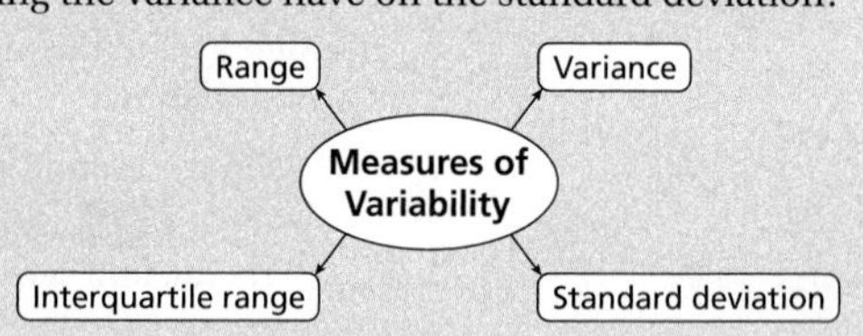

3 Close

Summarize

Ask students to name various measures of central tendency and variation and to explain how those measures might be used to summarize and compare large sets of data. mean: avg. value; median: middle value when set is ordered numerically; mode: most freq. value or values; first/third quartiles: medians of upper/lower halves; IQR: diff. between 3rd and 1st quartiles; variance: avg. of differences² from the mean; std dev.: √variance; outlier: extreme value

ONGOING ASSESSMENT and INTERVENTION

***Diagnose Before* the Lesson**
11-5 Warm Up, TE p. 828

***Monitor During* the Lesson**
Check It Out! Exercises, SE pp. 828–832
Questioning Strategies, TE pp. 829–831

***Assess After* the Lesson**
11-5 Lesson Quiz, TE p. 835
Alternative Assessment, TE p. 835

Answers to *Think and Discuss*

Possible answers:

1. The mean increases by the constant.
2. The standard deviation is unchanged.
3. The standard deviation is multiplied by $\sqrt{2}$.
4. See p. A13.

11-5 Exercises

go.hrw.com
Homework Help Online
KEYWORD: MB7 11-5
Parent Resources Online
KEYWORD: MB7 Parent

GUIDED PRACTICE

1. **Vocabulary** A measure of variation, or spread of a data set, is the __?__. (*variance* or *expected value*) variance

SEE EXAMPLE 1 p. 828

Find the mean, median, and mode of each data set.

2. $\{5, 7, 4, 7, 6, 7\}$ 6; 6.5; 7
3. $\{2, 4, 4, 6, 6, 6, 7, 8\}$ 5.375; 6; 6
4. $\{10, 14, 18, 22, 26\}$ 18; 18; no mode

SEE EXAMPLE 2 p. 829

5. Find the expected value of the prize. $0.36

Prize Giveaway

Value	$0	$1	$5	$20	$100	$1000
Probability	0.9359	0.05	0.01	0.003	0.001	0.0001

SEE EXAMPLE 3 p. 830

Make a box-and-whisker plot of the data. Find the interquartile range.

6. $\{3, 5, 2, 2, 8, 9, 1, 11\}$ IQR $= 6.5$
7. $\{2, 4, 1, 4, 2, 2, 7, 4\}$ IQR $= 2$
8. $\{33, 34, 31, 27, 22\}$ IQR $= 9$

SEE EXAMPLE 4 p. 831

Find the variance and standard deviation.

9. $\{3, 3, 4, 5, 5\}$ 0.8; 0.89
10. $\{10, 12, 14, 15, 18, 20, 23\}$ 18; 4.24
11. $\{7, 14, 21, 28, 35, 42\}$ 142.92; 11.95

SEE EXAMPLE 5 p. 831

12. **Measurement** Students in a fourth-grade class were asked to measure the widths of their desks in centimeters. They recorded the following measures: 49, 50, 49, 48, 49, 19, 50, 49, 48, 50, 49, and 50. Identify the outlier, and describe how it affects the mean and the standard deviation.
19; the mean decreases from ≈ 49.2 to $46.\overline{6}$, and the standard deviation increases from ≈ 0.72 to ≈ 8.4.

PRACTICE AND PROBLEM SOLVING

Independent Practice

For Exercises	See Example
13–15	1
16	2
17–19	3
20–22	4
23	5

Extra Practice
Skills Practice p. S25
Application Practice p. S42

Find the mean, median, and mode of each data set.

13. $\{4, 16, 25, 9, 36, 49\}$ $23.1\overline{6}$; 20.5; no mode
14. $\{1, 7, 7, 2, 3, 14, 127, 8\}$ 21.125; 7; 7
15. $\{5, 10, 15, 20, 25\}$ 15. 15; 15; no mode

16. Find the expected number of heads. 1.5

Three Coins Are Tossed

Number of Heads	0	1	2	3
Probability	$\frac{1}{8}$	$\frac{3}{8}$	$\frac{3}{8}$	$\frac{1}{8}$

Make a box-and-whisker plot of the data. Find the interquartile range.

17. $\{12, 15, 12, 6, 18, 29\}$ IQR $= 6$
18. $\{2, 2, 3, 8, 2, 8, 2, 42\}$ IQR $= 6$
19. $\{3, 4, 3, 1, 2\}$ IQR $= 2$

Find the variance and standard deviation.

20. $\{4, 4, 4, 4, 5\}$ 0.16; 0.4
21. $\{8, 12, 30, 35, 48, 50, 62\}$ ≈ 343.71; ≈ 18.54
22. $\{14, 26, 40, 52\}$ 205; ≈ 14.32
23. **Football** The 2004 Cincinnati Bengals scored 24, 16, 9, 17, 17, 23, 20, 26, 17, 14, 58, 27, and 28 points in their first 13 games. Find the mean and the standard deviation of the data. Identify the outlier, and describe how it affects the mean and the standard deviation. 58; the mean increases from ≈ 19.8 to ≈ 22.8, and the standard deviation increases from ≈ 5.6 to ≈ 11.5.
24. **Critical Thinking** Write a set of data in which neither the mean nor the median are data values. Possible answer: $\{3, 3, 9, 9\}$
25. **Shopping** You are at a store and want to purchase an accurate room thermometer. One says 73°F, six say 75°F, eight say 76°F, and one says 37°F. Which measure of central tendency would you be least likely to use to pick a thermometer? Explain.

25. the mean; 37° is an outlier and affects the mean greatly.

11-5 Exercises

Assignment Guide

Assign *Guided Practice* exercises as necessary.

If you finished Examples **1–3**
Basic 13–19, 38, 43
Average 13–19, 24, 38, 43
Advanced 13–19, 24, 35, 36, 38, 39, 43

If you finished Examples **1–5**
Basic 13–23, 25, 31–33, 37, 38, 40–43, 46–51
Average 13–25, 28–32, 36, 37, 40–43, 46–51
Advanced 13–36, 39–51

Homework Quick Check
Quickly check key concepts.
Exercises: 14, 16, 18, 22, 23, 28

Answers

6.

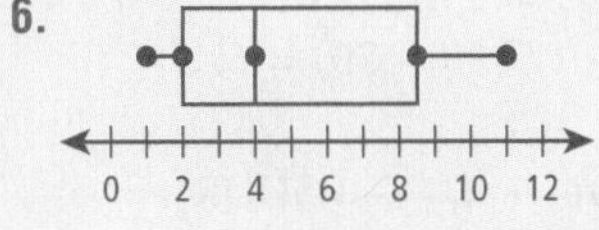

7.

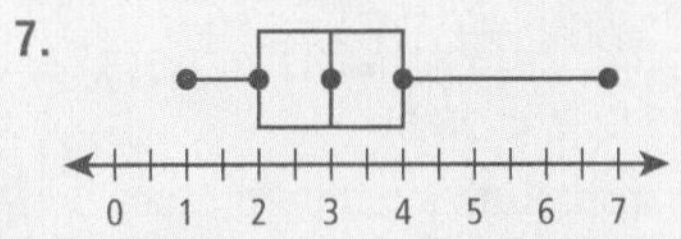

8.

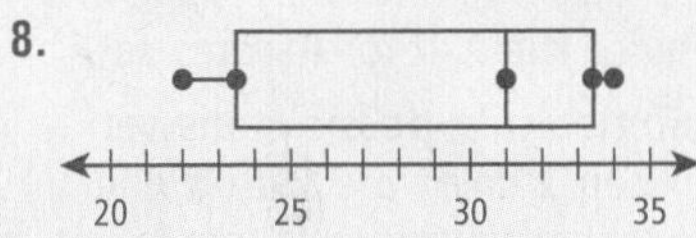

State Resources

go.hrw.com
State Resources Online
KEYWORD: MB7 Resources

Answers

17.
18.
19.

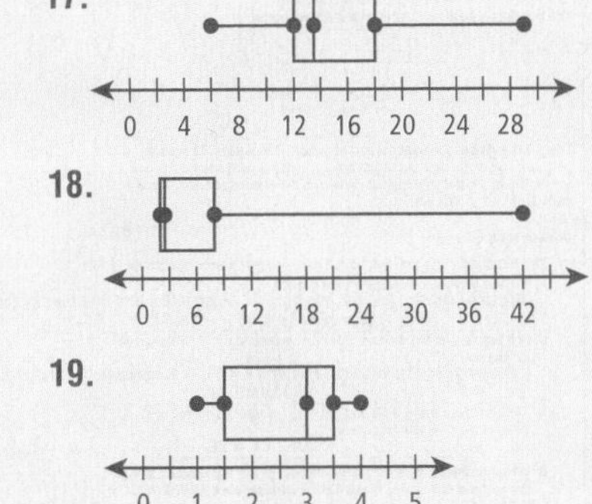

Science Link Before **Exercise 29,** explain that a geyser is a spring that throws forth intermittent jets of heated water and steam. Old Faithful was named for its continual and predictable erruptions.

TEST PREP DOCTOR In **Exercise 41,** have students look for data that is clustered. That eliminates choices **A** and **B.** In **C,** the values will be about 100 from the mean, so the answer is **D.**

In **Exercise 42,** comparing the ranges eliminates **G.** Testing the medians eliminates **J.** By using mental math (pairing 0 and 100, 48 and 52, etc.), students can find that the means are also equal, eliminating **F;** so the correct choice must be **H.**

In **Exercise 43,** have students read through all of the choices first. The mean of the set in **C** would be 37.5; so the answer is **C.**

Answers

26. 25; $Q_3 + 1.5(\text{IQR}) = 5 + 1.5(2) = 8$; $25 > 8$

27. 15; $Q_1 - 1.5(\text{IQR}) = 79 - 1.5(90 - 79) = 62.5$; $15 < 62.5$

28. 92 and 1; $Q_3 + 1.5(\text{IQR}) = 36 + 1.5(3) = 40.5$; $92 > 40.5$; $Q_1 - 1.5(\text{IQR}) = 33 - 1.5(3) = 28.5$; $1 < 28.5$

34. Aaron: Ruth's data are more spread out, and the set's IQR is twice the IQR for Aaron's set.

38. Sometimes; possible answer: when 2 coins are tossed, the expected number of heads is 1, a possible outcome. When 3 coins are tossed, the expected number, 1.5, is not a possible outcome.

11-5 PRACTICE A

11-5 PRACTICE C

11-5 PRACTICE B

Find the mean, median, and mode of each data set.

1. {12, 11, 17, 3, 9, 14, 16, 2}
   a. Mean **10.5**
   b. Median **11.5**
   c. Mode **None**

2. {6, 9, 9, 20, 4, 5, 9, 13, 10, 1}
   a. Mean **8.6**
   b. Median **9**
   c. Mode **9**

Make a box-and-whisker plot of the data. Find the interquartile range.

3. {3, 7, 7, 3, 10, 1, 6, 6}
   Interquartile range is 4.

4. {1, 2, 3, 5, 3, 5, 8, 2}
   Interquartile range is 3.

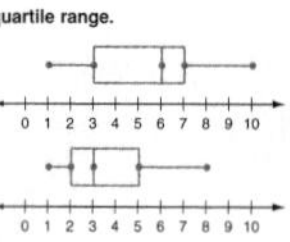

0 1 2 3 4 5 6 7 8 9 10

Find the variance and standard deviation.

5. {7, 4, 3, 9, 2}
   6.8; 2.6

6. {35, 67, 21, 16, 24, 51, 18, 32}
   278; 16.7

7. {19, 23, 17, 20, 25, 19, 15, 22}
   9.3; 3.0

8. {5, 12, 10, 13, 8, 11, 15, 12}
   8.4; 2.9

Solve.

9. The probability distribution for the amount of rain that falls on Boston in May each year is given below. Find the expected amount of rain for Boston in May. **7.01**

Inches of Rain, n	5	6	7	8
Probability	0.05	0.10	0.64	0.21

10. A biologist is growing bacteria in the lab. For a certain species of bacteria, she records these doubling times: 41 min, 45 min, 39 min, 42 min, 38 min, 88 min, 43 min, 40 min, 44 min, 39 min, 42 min, and 40 min.
    a. Find the mean of the data. **45.1**
    b. Find the standard deviation. **13.1**
    c. Identify any outliers. **88**
    d. Describe how any outlier affects the mean and the standard deviation. **The mean increases from ≈41.2 to ≈45.1, and the standard deviation increases from ≈2.1 to ≈13.1.**

The Old Faithful Geyser at Yellowstone National Park can send 8500 gallons of boiling water to a height of 185 feet.

For a data set with a first quartile of Q1 and a third quartile of Q3, a value less than Q1 – 1.5(IQR) or greater than Q3 + 1.5(IQR) may be considered to be an outlier. Use this rule to identify any outliers in each data set. Show your work.

26. $\{2, 3, 4, 5, 5, 25\}$ 27. $\{91, 90, 79, 15, 82, 90, 88\}$ 28. $\{1, 36, 34, 33, 35, 92\}$

Geology Use the graph of 222 eruptions of the Old Faithful Geyser for Exercises 29 and 30.

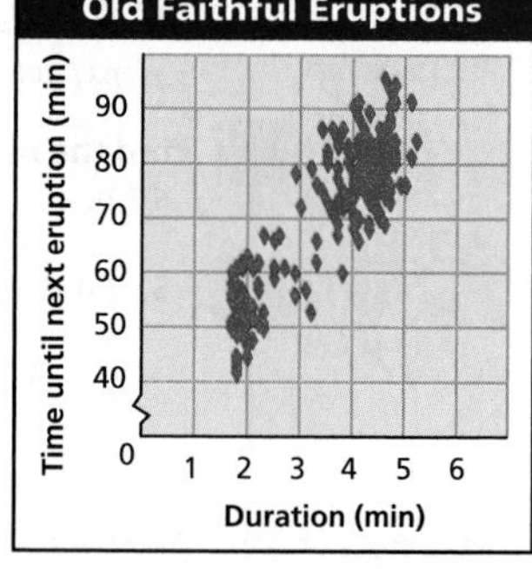

29. The duration has a mean of 3.6 min and a standard deviation of 1.1 min. What duration time intervals would be outliers? Describe any outliers for duration on the graph. **< 0.3 min or > 6.9 min; none**

30. The time between eruptions has a mean of 71 min and a standard deviation of 12.8 min. What time intervals would be outliers? Describe any outliers for time intervals on the graph. **< 32.6 min or > 109.4 min; none**

Estimation Use the box-and-whisker plots for Exercises 31–34.

Home Runs by Season

Babe Ruth

Hank Aaron

0 10 20 30 40 50 60

31. Which player hit the most home runs in a season? By approximately how many home runs did he do so? **Ruth; possible answer: 13**

32. Which player had the greater median number of home runs? Estimate how much greater.

33. Estimate the interquartile range for both players.

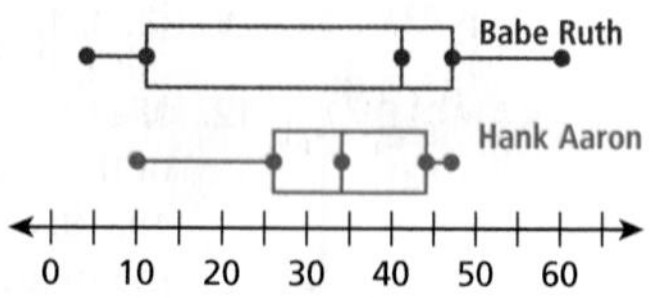

32. Ruth; possible answer: 6

33. Possible answer: Ruth: 36; Aaron: 18

34. Which data set has the smaller standard deviation? Explain.

35. You have a 0.1% chance of winning \$500 and a 99.9% chance of losing \$1. What is the expected value of your gain? (*Hint*: The two possible outcomes for this "experiment" are + 500 and –1.) **–\$0.499**

36. Suppose that you have a 10% chance of winning \$100, a 30% chance of losing \$2, and a 60% chance of breaking even. What is the expected value? **\$9.40**

37. **///ERROR ANALYSIS///** Two students attempt to find the standard deviation of 4, 6, 8, and 10. Which is incorrect? Explain the error. **B; the student should have squared the differences.**

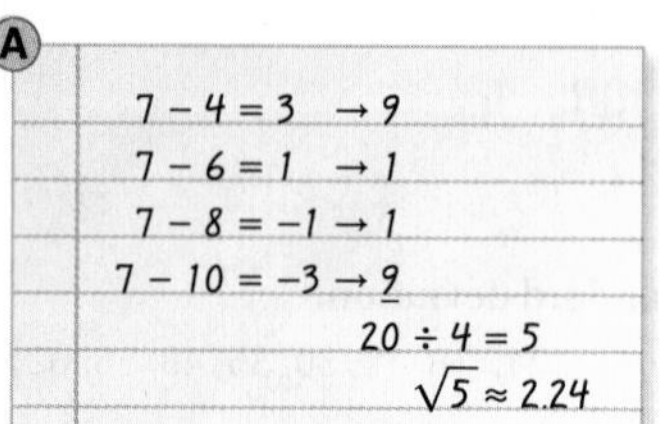

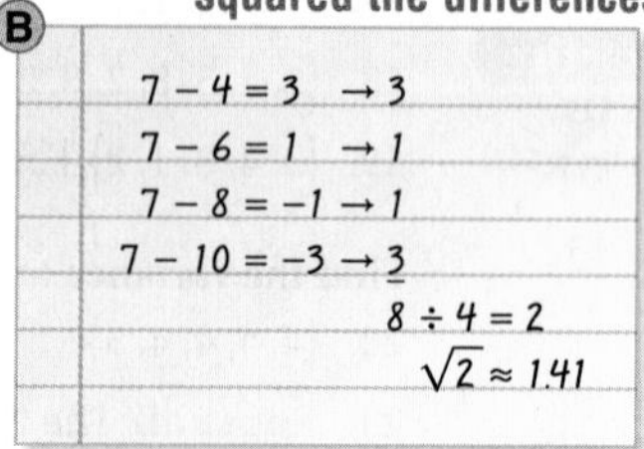

38. **Write About It** Is an expected value always, sometimes, or never a value in the data set? Give an example to justify your answer.

39. **Games** In a game, you multiply the values of two number cubes.
    a. What is the expected value of this product? **12.25**
    b. What is the probability that a product is greater than the expected value? $\mathbf{\frac{13}{36}}$
    c. What is the probability that a product is less than the expected value? $\mathbf{\frac{23}{36}}$
    d. Are the answers to parts **b** and **c** equal? Explain. **No; possible answer: the expected value is a mean, not a median value.**

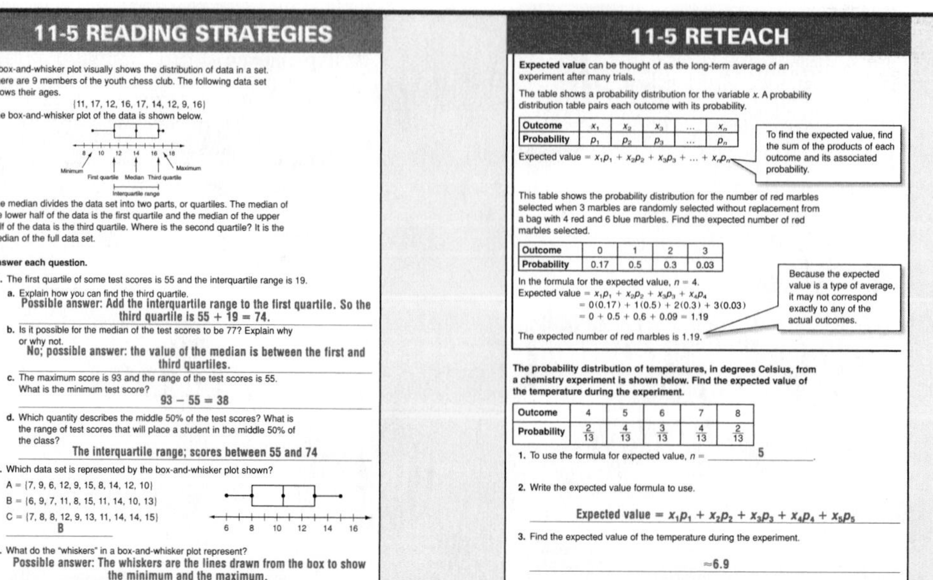

11-5 READING STRATEGIES

A box-and-whisker plot visually shows the distribution of data in a set. There are 9 members of the youth chess club. The following data set shows their ages.

{11, 17, 12, 16, 17, 14, 12, 9, 16}

The box-and-whisker plot of the data is shown below.

8 10 12 14 16 18

Minimum First quartile Median Third quartile Maximum

Interquartile range

The median divides the data set into two parts, or quartiles. The median of the lower half of the data is the first quartile and the median of the upper half of the data is the third quartile. Where is the second quartile? It is the median of the full data set.

Answer each question.

1. The first quartile of some test scores is 55 and the interquartile range is 19.
   a. Explain how you can find the third quartile. **Possible answer: Add the interquartile range to the first quartile. So the third quartile is 55 + 19 = 74.**
   b. Is it possible for the median of the test scores to be 77? Explain why or why not. **No; possible answer: the value of the median is between the first and third quartiles.**
   c. The maximum score is 93 and the range of the test scores is 55. What is the minimum test score? **93 − 55 = 38**
   d. Which quantity describes the middle 50% of the test scores? What is the range of test scores that will place a student in the middle 50% of the class? **The interquartile range; scores between 55 and 74**

2. Which data set is represented by the box-and-whisker plot shown?
   A = {7, 9, 6, 12, 9, 15, 8, 14, 12, 10}
   B = {6, 9, 7, 11, 8, 15, 11, 14, 10, 13}
   C = {7, 8, 8, 12, 9, 13, 11, 14, 14, 15}
   B

6 8 10 12 14 16

3. What do the "whiskers" in a box-and-whisker plot represent? **Possible answer: The whiskers are the lines drawn from the box to show the minimum and the maximum.**

11-5 RETEACH

Expected value can be thought of as the long-term average of an experiment after many trials.

The table shows a probability distribution for the variable x. A probability distribution table pairs each outcome with its probability.

Outcome	x_1	x_2	x_3	...	x_n
Probability	p_1	p_2	p_3	...	p_n

Expected value $= x_1p_1 + x_2p_2 + x_3p_3 + ... + x_np_n$

To find the expected value, find the sum of the products of each outcome and its associated probability.

This table shows the probability distribution for the number of red marbles selected when 3 marbles are randomly selected without replacement from a bag with 4 red and 6 blue marbles. Find the expected number of red marbles selected.

Outcome	0	1	2	3
Probability	0.17	0.5	0.3	0.03

In the formula for the expected value, $n = 4$.

Expected value $= x_1p_1 + x_2p_2 + x_3p_3 + x_4p_4$
$= 0(0.17) + 1(0.5) + 2(0.3) + 3(0.03)$
$= 0 + 0.5 + 0.6 + 0.09 = 1.19$

The expected number of red marbles is 1.19.

Because the expected value is a type of average, it may not correspond exactly to any of the actual outcomes.

The probability distribution of temperatures, in degrees Celsius, from a chemistry experiment is shown below. Find the expected value of the temperature during the experiment.

Outcome	4	5	6	7	8
Probability	$\frac{2}{13}$	$\frac{4}{13}$	$\frac{3}{13}$	$\frac{4}{13}$	$\frac{2}{13}$

1. To use the formula for expected value, $n =$ **5**.

2. Write the expected value formula to use.
   Expected value $= x_1p_1 + x_2p_2 + x_3p_3 + x_4p_4 + x_5p_5$

3. Find the expected value of the temperature during the experiment.
   ≈6.9

MULTI-STEP TEST PREP

40. This problem will prepare you for the Multi-Step Test Prep on page 844. The table shows the total annual precipitation for San Diego, California.

Year	1994	1995	1996	1997	1998
Precipitation (in.)	9.4	17.0	7.3	7.0	16.1

Year	1999	2000	2001	2002	2003
Precipitation (in.)	5.4	6.9	8.5	4.2	9.2

a. Find the mean annual precipitation and the standard deviation. **9.1 in.; ≈ 4.0**

b. In what years was the precipitation more than one standard deviation from the mean? **1995, 1998, and 2002**

c. Find the median and interquartile range for the data. **7.9 in.; 2.5**

TEST PREP

41. Which data set would give the smallest standard deviation?

Ⓐ $\{1, 5, 7, 50\}$
Ⓑ $\{2, 10, 102, 110\}$
Ⓒ $\{100, 200, 300, 400\}$
Ⓓ $\{100, 101, 102, 105\}$

42. Which of the following is NOT true about the data sets $\{0, 48, 49, 50, 51, 52, 100\}$ and $\{0, 1, 2, 50, 98, 99, 100\}$?

Ⓕ The means are equal.
Ⓖ The ranges are equal.
Ⓗ The variances are equal.
Ⓙ The medians are equal.

43. The mean score on a test is 50. Which cannot be true?

Ⓐ Half the scores are 0, and half the scores are 100.
Ⓑ The range is 50.
Ⓒ Half the scores are 25, and half the scores are 50.
Ⓓ Every score is 50.

CHALLENGE AND EXTEND

44. A data set has a mean of 4, a median of 3, and a standard deviation of 1.6.

a. Suppose that every value of the data set is multiplied by 5. What is the mean, median, and standard deviation of the new data set? **20; 15; 8**

b. Suppose that 5 is added to every value of the original data set. What is the mean, median, and standard deviation of the new data set? **9; 8; 1.6**

45. A deck of cards is shuffled. What is the expected number of cards that will be in the same position that they were in originally? (*Hint:* Look at decks of 1, 2, 3, and 4 cards.) **1**

SPIRAL REVIEW

46. **Business** Li was paid $725 a month plus $1.75 for every magazine she sold. Li earned $1425 one month. How many magazines did Li sell? *(Lesson 2-1)* **400**

Find each product. *(Lesson 6-2)*

47. $(2 - x^2)(2x^2 + 5x - 3)$
$\mathbf{-2x^4 - 5x^3 + 7x^2 + 10x - 6}$

48. $4xy^2(x^2y + 3x^2 - 2y)$
$\mathbf{4x^3y^3 + 12x^3y^2 - 8xy^3}$

A number cube is rolled. Find each probability. *(Lesson 11-4)*

49. an even number or a 1 $\mathbf{\frac{2}{3}}$

50. an odd number or a 4 $\mathbf{\frac{2}{3}}$

51. a number divisible by 2 or 6 $\mathbf{\frac{1}{2}}$

MULTI-STEP TEST PREP Exercise 40 involves finding measures of central tendency and variation for annual precipitation in San Diego. This exercise prepares students for the Multi-Step Test Prep on page 844.

Journal

Have students explain the meaning of *standard deviation* and describe some of the possible patterns of distribution that might occur in various data sets.

ALTERNATIVE ASSESSMENT

Have students write two different sets of integers less than 20 and find and compare the mean, median, mode, and standard deviation of the two sets.

Power Presentations with PowerPoint®

11-5 Lesson Quiz

Use the data set for 1 and 3–6: $\{9, 4, 7, 8, 5, 8, 24, 5\}$

1. Find the mean, median, and mode.
mean: 8.875, median: 7.5, modes: 5 and 8

2. The probability distribution of the number of people entering a store each day based on past data is given below. Find the expected number of people for one day. 85

Number of People n	76	84	98	89
Prob. of n People	0.3	0.2	0.1	0.4

3. Make a box-and-whisker plot of the data in 1. Find the interquartile range.

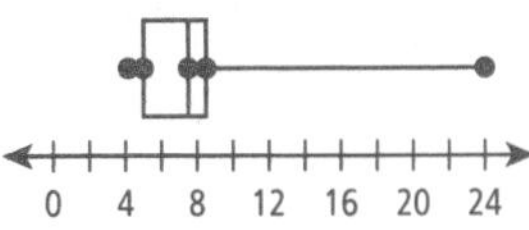

IQR: 3.5

4. Find the variance and the standard deviation of the data set. var: ≈ 35.94; std. dev.: ≈ 5.99

5. Use the standard deviation to identify any outliers in the data set. none by this method

Also available on transparency

11-5 PROBLEM SOLVING

Each week, Damien records the miles per gallon for his car, to the nearest whole number. Over a period of 10 weeks, the data are 18, 17, 19, 18, 18, 25, 29, 30, 26, 19. He wants to arrange and summarize his data so that he can analyze it.

1. Make a box-and-whisker plot of his data.

a. Order the data from least to greatest. **17, 18, 18, 18, 19, 19, 25, 26, 29, 30**

b. Identify the minimum, maximum, median, first quartile, and third quartile.
Minimum = 17; maximum = 30; median = 19; first quartile = 18; third quartile = 26

c. Use the number line to make a box-and-whisker plot of the data. Find and label the interquartile range.

14 18 22 26 30 34
IQR = 8

d. Explain what the interquartile range represents in terms of the car's miles per gallon.
Possible answer: Damien's car gets between 18 to 26 miles per gallon 50% of the time.

2. Find the standard deviation for the data.

a. Write an equation and solve to find the mean. **(18 + 17 + 19 + 18 + 18 + 25 + 29 + 30 + 26 + 19)/10 = 21.9**

b. Complete the table to show the difference between the mean and each data value, and the square of that difference.

Data Value, x	18	17	19	18	18	25	29	30	26	19
$x - \bar{x}$	−3.9	−4.9	−2.9	−3.9	−3.9	3.1	7.1	8.1	4.1	−2.9
$(x - \bar{x})^2$	15.21	24.01	8.41	15.21	15.21	9.61	50.41	65.61	16.81	8.41

c. Explain how to use the data from the table to find the standard deviation.
Find the square root of the mean of the $(x - \bar{x})^2$ terms.

d. What is the standard deviation for the data? **4.78**

e. Explain what the standard deviation represents in terms of the car's miles per gallon.
Possible answer: All but 3 data points are clustered within 1 standard deviation of the mean.

3. Damien thinks that the standard deviation is a more reliable measure of dispersion than the interquartile range. Is he correct? Explain.
He is correct; possible answer: the standard deviation depends on the entire set of data values; whereas the interquartile range depends on only 2 values, the first and third quartiles.

11-5 CHALLENGE

Cassie's job is to analyze a set of 100 integral value scores that range from 0 to 10 from a recent survey. The set of values includes exactly 6 scores that are zero. She decides not to include the 6 zero scores in the analysis, based on the false assumption that zero is not really a number since it has no value.

1. For the set of 94 values, excluding the zeros, Cassie correctly computes the mean. How does the mean for the 94 nonzero values compare to the mean for the 100 values? Is it greater than, less than, equal to, or is it impossible to determine? How do you know?
Greater than; the sum is the same for both, and in the first case you divide by 94 rather than 100.

2. For the set of 94 values, excluding the zeros, Cassie correctly computes the median. How does the median for the 94 nonzero values compare to the median for the 100 values? Is it greater than, less than, equal to, or is it impossible to determine? How do you know?
Impossible to determine; it may be the same or it may be greater depending on the distribution of the data.

3. For the set of 94 values, excluding the zeros, Cassie correctly computes the mode. How does the mode for the 94 nonzero values compare to the mode for the 100 values? Is it greater than, less than, equal to, or is it impossible to determine? How do you know?
Equal to; There were 6 zero scores. At least one value has to occur more than 10 times since 94 divided by 9 is greater than 10.

4. For the set of 94 values, excluding the zeros, Cassie correctly computes the standard deviation. How does the standard deviation for the 94 nonzero values compare to the standard deviation for the 100 values? Is it greater than, less than, equal to, or impossible to determine? How do you know?
Less than; The set of 94 values ranges from 1 to 10 and so is not as spread out as the set of 100 values.

The frequency distribution for the 100 survey scores is shown below.

Survey Value	0	1	2	3	4	5	6	7	8	9	10
Frequency	6	8	9	11	13		12	10	8	6	5

5. How many people answered with the value of 5 in the survey? How do you know?
12; the sum of the set of frequencies must equal 100.

6. If you randomly chose 1 of the 100 people surveyed, what answer would you expect that person to give?
The expected value is 4.81, which gives an expected result of 5.

7. Find the first and third quartiles and the interquartile range for this set of values.
Median is 5, Q1 is 3, Q3 is 7, and interquartile range is 4.

Organizer

Use with Lesson 11-5

Pacing:

Traditional $\frac{1}{2}$ day

Block $\frac{1}{4}$ day

Objective: Generate, organize, and analyze data in order to form conjectures about probability.

Materials: number cubes (MK)

Online Edition

Resources

Algebra Lab Activities

11-5 Lab Recording Sheet

Teach

Discuss

Before students complete the table in **Problem 2**, ask them to predict which sums are most and least likely.

Close

Key Concept

Although frequencies may diverge from expected frequencies as the number of trials increases, experimental probability approaches theoretical probability.

Assessment

Journal Have students explain how increasing the number of trials affects a probability distribution and its related frequencies.

State Resources

11-5

Collect Experimental Data

You can perform an experiment to generate, collect, organize, and analyze data in order to form mathematical conjectures.

Use with Lesson 11-5

Activity

Make a table of the sum of two number cubes.

Blue cube (columns); Red cube (rows)

	1	2	3	4	5	6
1	2	3	4	5	6	7
2	3	4	5	6	7	8
3	4	5	6	7	8	9
4	5	6	7	8	9	10
5	6	7	8	9	10	11
6	7	8	9	10	11	12

Try This

1. Describe any symmetry you notice in the table.
2. Make a probability distribution by using theoretical probabilities.

Sums	2	3	4	5	6	7	8	9	10	11	12
Probability	■	■	■	■	■	■	■	■	■	■	■

3. Find the expected value by using the theoretical probability distribution. **7**
4. Which sum is most likely? least likely? **7; 2 and 12**
5. Do any two different sums have the same probability? If so, what are those sums?
6. Roll two number cubes 36 times. Record the results in a table.
7. Make a probability distribution of your data.
8. Find the expected value by using your probability distribution. **Possible answer: 7.$\overline{3}$**

Answer the following questions based on your experiment.

9. Which sum was most likely? least likely? **Possible answer: 6; 2**
10. Did any two different sums have the same probability? If so, what are those sums?
11. Compare your results with the theoretical results.
12. Combine the results of your experiment with those of other students. How do the experimental results of the group compare with your results? with the theoretical results? **Check students' work.**

Answers to *Try This*

1. Possible answer: The numbers across the main diagonal are symmetric.
2. $\frac{1}{36}; \frac{1}{18}; \frac{1}{12}; \frac{1}{9}; \frac{5}{36}; \frac{1}{6}; \frac{5}{36}; \frac{1}{9}; \frac{1}{12}; \frac{1}{18}; \frac{1}{36}$
5. 2 and 12, 3 and 11, 4 and 10, 5 and 9, and 6 and 8
6. Possible answer:

Sums	2	3	4	5	6	7
Frequency	0	2	1	5	7	6
Sums	8	9	10	11	12	
Frequency	3	6	1	3	2	

7. Possible answer:

Sums	2	3	4	5	6	7
Probability	0	$\frac{1}{18}$	$\frac{1}{36}$	$\frac{5}{36}$	$\frac{7}{36}$	$\frac{1}{6}$
Sums	8	9	10	11	12	
Probability	$\frac{1}{12}$	$\frac{1}{6}$	$\frac{1}{36}$	$\frac{1}{12}$	$\frac{1}{18}$	

10. Possible answer: 7 and 9, 3 and 12, 4 and 10, and 8 and 11
11. The experimental probabilities and expected value differ from the theoretical.

11-6 Binomial Distributions

A2.4.2 Use the binomial theorem to expand binomial expressions raised to positive integer powers.

Objectives

Use the Binomial Theorem to expand a binomial raised to a power.

Find binomial probabilities and test hypotheses.

Vocabulary

Binomial Theorem
binomial experiment
binomial probability

Why learn this?

You can use binomial distributions to determine your chances of winning a marketing contest. (See Example 3.)

You used Pascal's triangle to find binomial expansions in Lesson 6-2. The coefficients of the expansion of $(x + y)^n$ are the numbers in Pascal's triangle, which are actually combinations.

Pascal's Triangle	Combinations (Binomial Coefficients)	Binomial Expansion
1	${}_0C_0$	$(x+y)^0 = 1$
1 1	${}_1C_0 \quad {}_1C_1$	$(x+y)^1 = x + y$
1 2 1	${}_2C_0 \quad {}_2C_1 \quad {}_2C_2$	$(x+y)^2 = x^2 + 2xy + y^2$
1 3 3 1	${}_3C_0 \quad {}_3C_1 \quad {}_3C_2 \quad {}_3C_3$	$(x+y)^3 = x^3 + 3x^2y + 3xy^2 + y^3$

The pattern in the table can help you expand any binomial by using the **Binomial Theorem**.

Binomial Theorem

For any whole number n,

$$(x+y)^n = {}_nC_0x^ny^0 + {}_nC_1x^{n-1}y^1 + {}_nC_2x^{n-2}y^2 + \cdots + {}_nC_{n-1}x^1y^{n-1} + {}_nC_nx^0y^n$$

EXAMPLE 1 Expanding Binomials

Remember!
In the expansion of $(x + y)^n$, the powers of x decrease from n to 0 and the powers of y increase from 0 to n. Also, the sum of the exponents is n for each term. (Lesson 6-2)

Use the Binomial Theorem to expand each binomial.

A $(x+y)^4$ *The sum of the exponents for each term is 4.*

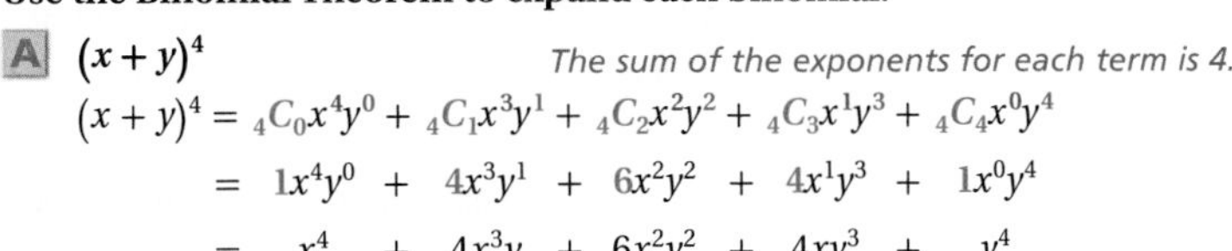

$$(x+y)^4 = {}_4C_0x^4y^0 + {}_4C_1x^3y^1 + {}_4C_2x^2y^2 + {}_4C_3x^1y^3 + {}_4C_4x^0y^4$$
$$= 1x^4y^0 + 4x^3y^1 + 6x^2y^2 + 4x^1y^3 + 1x^0y^4$$
$$= x^4 + 4x^3y + 6x^2y^2 + 4xy^3 + y^4$$

B $(3p+q)^3$

$$(3p+q)^3 = {}_3C_0(3p)^3q^0 + {}_3C_1(3p)^2q^1 + {}_3C_2(3p)^1q^2 + {}_3C_3(3p)^0q^3$$
$$= 1\cdot 27p^3\cdot 1 + 3\cdot 9p^2q + 3\cdot 3pq^2 + 1\cdot 1q^3$$
$$= 27p^3 + 27p^2q + 9pq^2 + q^3$$

CHECK IT OUT! **Use the Binomial Theorem to expand each binomial.**

1a. $(x-y)^5$ **1b.** $(a+2b)^3$

1a. $x^5 - 5x^4y + 10x^3y^2 - 10x^2y^3 + 5xy^4 - y^5$ **1b.** $a^3 + 6a^2b + 12ab^2 + 8b^3$

1 Introduce

EXPLORATION

11-6 Binomial Distributions

The figure shows the first few rows of Pascal's triangle. Each row begins and ends with 1. Any other entry in a row is the sum of the two entries to its upper left and upper right.

Row 0 1
Row 1 1 1
Row 2 1 2 1
Row 3 1 3 3 1

1. Write row 4 and row 5 of Pascal's triangle.
2. Recall that ${}_nC_r = \frac{n!}{r!(n-r)!}$. Calculate ${}_3C_0$, ${}_3C_1$, ${}_3C_2$, and ${}_3C_3$. How do these combinations relate to Pascal's triangle?
3. Calculate ${}_4C_0$, ${}_4C_1$, ${}_4C_2$, ${}_4C_3$ and ${}_4C_4$. How do these combinations relate to Pascal's triangle?
4. List the combinations that could be used to determine row 5 of Pascal's triangle.

THINK AND DISCUSS

5. **Discuss** whether the pattern of combinations holds for row 0 and row 1 of Pascal's triangle.
6. **Explain** how you could determine row n of Pascal's triangle, where n is a whole number.

Motivate

Ask students about a situation in which a coin is flipped 10 times. What are the possible results of a flip? heads or tails Ask if that is the same as "heads" or "not heads." yes Ask whether 10 heads is as likely as 5 heads and 5 tails. no Explain that there are many ways that the 5 heads and 5 tails can be distributed among the tosses but only 1 way for 10 heads. Tell students that this lesson will look at how these types of situations can be analyzed.

Explorations and answers are provided in the *Explorations* binder.

11-6 Organizer

Pacing: Traditional 1 day
Block $\frac{1}{2}$ day

Objectives: Use the Binomial Theorem to expand a binomial raised to a power.

Find binomial probabilities and test hypotheses.

Online Edition
Tutorial Videos, Interactivity

Countdown to Testing Week 24

Power Presentations with PowerPoint®

Warm Up

Expand each binomial.

1. $(a+b)^2$ $a^2 + 2ab + b^2$

2. $(x-3y)^2$ $x^2 - 6xy + 9y^2$

Evaluate each expression.

3. ${}_4C_3$ 4 **4.** $(0.25)^0$ 1

5. $\left(\frac{1}{3}\right)^3$ $\frac{1}{27}$ **6.** 23.2% of 37 8.584

Also available on transparency

Math Fact !!!

To escape the Great Plague in England in 1665, 23-year-old Isaac Newton stayed at his family's country home for 18 months. During that time, he developed his proof of the binomial theorem and made several other important discoveries.

State Resources

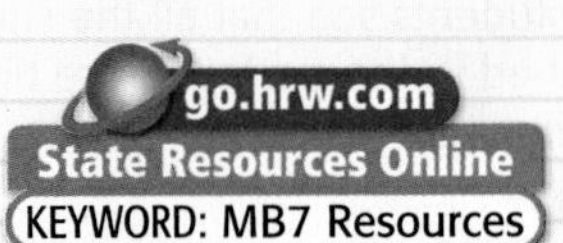

go.hrw.com
State Resources Online
KEYWORD: MB7 Resources

Power Presentations with PowerPoint®

Additional Examples

Example 1

Use the Binomial Theorem to expand each binomial.

A. $(a + b)^5$

$a^5 + 5a^4b + 10a^3b^2 + 10a^2b^3 + 5ab^4 + b^5$

B. $(2x + y)^3$

$8x^3 + 12x^2y + 6xy^2 + y^3$

Example 2

Jean usually makes half of her free throws in basketball practice. Today, she tries 3 free throws.

a. What is the probability that Jean will make exactly 1 of her free throws? ≈ 0.375

b. What is the probability that she will make at least 1 free throw? ≈ 0.875

Also available on transparency

INTERVENTION

Questioning Strategies

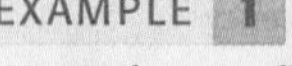

EXAMPLE 1

- How do you find the sign of each term in the expansion of $(x - y)^n$?

EXAMPLE 2

- Why are the probabilities multiplied by ${}_nC_r$?

Teaching Tip **Inclusion** Students can track the steps in their calculations by organizing work and labeling interim values. Students can exchange papers to determine whether an error is due to a miscalculation or is due to a mistake in a formula.

A **binomial experiment** consists of n independent trials whose outcomes are either successes or failures; the probability of success p is the same for each trial, and the probability of failure q is the same for each trial. Because there are only two outcomes, $p + q = 1$, or $q = 1 - p$. Below are some examples of binomial experiments:

Experiment	Success	Failure	P(success)	P(failure)
10 flips of a coin	Heads	Tails	$p = 0.5$	$q = 1 - p = 0.5$
100 rolls of a number cube	Roll a 3.	Roll any other number.	$p = \frac{1}{6}$	$q = \frac{5}{6}$

Suppose the probability of being left-handed is 0.1 and you want to find the probability that 2 out of 3 people will be left-handed. There are ${}_3C_2$ ways to choose the two left-handed people: LLR, LRL, and RLL. The probability of each of these occurring is 0.1(0.1)(0.9). This leads to the following formula.

Know it! Note

Binomial Probability

If a binomial experiment has n trials in which p is the probability of success and q is the probability of failure in any given trial, then the **binomial probability** that there will be exactly r successes is:

$$P(r) = {}_nC_r\, p^r q^{n-r}$$

EXAMPLE 2 **Finding Binomial Probabilities**

One in 5 boats going through a *slough* at midday will bypass the harbor and head out to sea. Four boats are going through the slough.

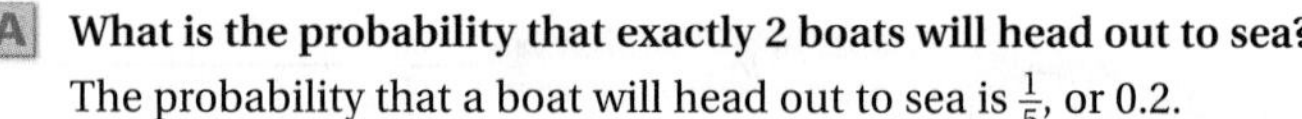

A What is the probability that exactly 2 boats will head out to sea?

The probability that a boat will head out to sea is $\frac{1}{5}$, or 0.2.

$P(r) = {}_nC_r p^r q^{n-r}$

$P(2) = {}_4C_2(0.2)^2(0.8)^{4-2}$ *Substitute 4 for n, 2 for r, 0.2 for p, and 0.8 for q.*

$= 6(0.04)(0.64) = 0.1536$

The probability that exactly 2 of the boats will head out to sea is about 15.4%.

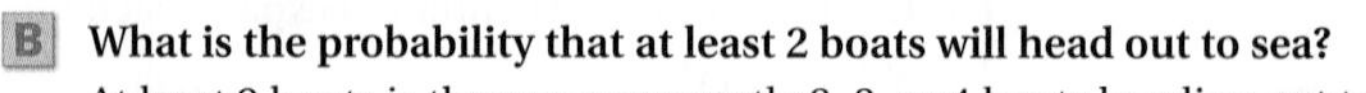

B What is the probability that at least 2 boats will head out to sea?

At least 2 boats is the same as exactly 2, 3, or 4 boats heading out to sea.

$P(2) + P(3) + P(4)$

$0.1536 + {}_4C_3(0.2)^3(0.8)^{4-3} + {}_4C_4(0.2)^4(0.8)^{4-4}$

$0.1536 + 0.0256 + 0.0016 = 0.1808$

The probability that at least 2 boats will head out to sea is about 18.1%.

CHECK IT OUT!

2a. Students are assigned randomly to 1 of 3 guidance counselors. What is the probability that Counselor Jenkins will get 2 of the next 3 students assigned? $\frac{2}{9} \approx 0.22$

2b. Ellen takes a multiple-choice quiz that has 5 questions, with 4 answer choices for each question. What is the probability that she will get at least 2 answers correct by guessing? $\frac{47}{128} \approx 0.37$

2 Teach

Guided Instruction

Go over the requirements for a binomial experiment.

1. Each trial has only two outcomes (sometimes designated "success" and "failure").
2. The probability of "success" is the same for every trial (the trials are independent).

Help students see that all the situations described in the examples are binomial experiments.

Reaching All Learners

Through Graphic Organizers

In **Example 2**, have students draw the ${}_4C_2 = 6$ ways that 2 of the 4 boats will go out to sea and include each probability.

– – Y Y $p = 0.8 \cdot 0.8 \cdot \mathbf{0.2} \cdot \mathbf{0.2}$

– Y – Y $p = 0.8 \cdot \mathbf{0.2} \cdot 0.8 \cdot \mathbf{0.2}$

– Y Y – $p = 0.8 \cdot \mathbf{0.2} \cdot \mathbf{0.2} \cdot 0.8$

Y – – Y $p = \mathbf{0.2} \cdot 0.8 \cdot 0.8 \cdot \mathbf{0.2}$

Y – Y – $p = \mathbf{0.2} \cdot 0.8 \cdot \mathbf{0.2} \cdot 0.8$

Y Y – – $p = \mathbf{0.2} \cdot \mathbf{0.2} \cdot 0.8 \cdot 0.8$

Teaching Tip **Reading Math** Point out that all the math phrases in the lesson beginning with *bi-* can be related to other terms containing that prefix, such as *bicycle* (two wheels) and *binary* (two-valued: 0 and 1). **English Language Learners**

EXAMPLE 3 Problem-Solving Application

Vince buys 10 juice drinks. What is the probability that he will get at least 2 prizes?

Sweepstakes Prizes Chances of Winning	
Free drink	1 in 5
Water bottle	1 in 22
T-shirt	1 in 250
Music player	1 in 100,000
Car	1 in 20,000,000
Any prize	1 in 4

1 Understand the Problem

The **answer** will be the probability that Vince will get at least 2 prizes.

List the important information:

- Vince buys 10 juice drinks.
- The binomial probability that each bottle wins a prize is $\frac{1}{4}$.

2 Make a Plan

The direct way to solve the problem is to calculate $P(2) + P(3) + P(4) + \cdots + P(10)$.

An easier way is to use the complement. "Getting 0 or 1 prize" is the complement of "getting at least 2 prizes." Find this probability, and then subtract the result from 1.

3 Solve

Step 1 Find $P(0 \text{ or } 1 \text{ prize})$.

$$P(0) \quad + \quad P(1)$$
$$= {}_{10}C_0\,(0.25)^0(0.75)^{10-0} + {}_{10}C_1\,(0.25)^1(0.75)^{10-1}$$
$$= 1(1)(0.75)^{10} + 10(0.25)(0.75)^9$$
$$\approx 0.0563 + 0.1877$$
$$\approx 0.2440$$

Step 2 Use the complement to find the probability.

$1 - 0.2440$ *Subtract from 1.*

≈ 0.7560

The probability that Vince will get at least 2 prizes is about 0.76.

4 Look Back

The answer is reasonable, as the expected number of winners is $\frac{1}{4}$ of 10, = 2.5, which is greater than 2. So the probability that Vince will get at least 2 prizes should be greater than 0.5.

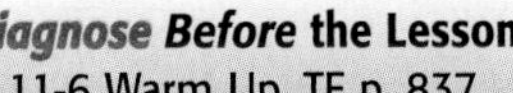

CHECK IT OUT!

3a. Wendy takes a multiple-choice quiz that has 20 questions. There are 4 answer choices for each question. What is the probability that she will get at least 2 answers correct by guessing? $\approx$ **0.98**

3b. A machine has a 98% probability of producing a part within acceptable tolerance levels. The machine makes 25 parts an hour. What is the probability that there are 23 or fewer acceptable parts? $\approx$ **0.09**

COMMON ERROR ALERT

Students might sometimes confuse p and q. Remind them that p is the probability of success and that q is the probability of failure, $1 - p$.

Power Presentations with PowerPoint®

Additional Examples

Example 3

You make 4 trips to a drawbridge. There is a 1 in 5 chance that the drawbridge will be raised when you arrive. What is the probability that the bridge will be down for at least 3 of your trips? 0.8192

Also available on transparency

INTERVENTION

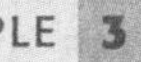

Questioning Strategies

EXAMPLE 3

- Why isn't the direct way to solve the problem also the easiest?
- How do you know when to use a complement?

Teaching Tip **Critical Thinking** In **Example 3,** students might think that a "1 in 4 chance of winning" means that a win is certain if you buy 4 drinks. Point out that because the trials are independent, all 4 could be winners or all 4 could be losers.

3 Close

Summarize

Ask: What does the Binomial Theorem tell you? When do you use binomial probabilities to solve a problem? The Binomial Theorem tells you the coefficients of any binomial expansion; it can be used to solve a probability problem involving trials of a binomial experiment, where each independent trial has 2 outcomes.

ONGOING ASSESSMENT and INTERVENTION

***Diagnose Before* the Lesson**
11-6 Warm Up, TE p. 837

***Monitor During* the Lesson**
Check It Out! Exercises, SE pp. 837–839
Questioning Strategies, TE pp. 838–839

***Assess After* the Lesson**
11-6 Lesson Quiz, TE p. 843
Alternative Assessment, TE p. 843

Answers to *Think and Discuss*

Possible answers:

1. 1; a binomial experiment has only 2 outcomes, and the probabilities of those outcomes are p and q. So $p + q = 1$.
2. ${}_nC_r$, p^r, and q^{n-r}
3. See p. A13.

11-6 Exercises

Assignment Guide

Assign *Guided Practice* exercises as necessary.

If you finished Examples **1–2**
Basic 9–14, 17, 18, 21, 31, 39
Average 9–14, 19, 20, 22–24, 30, 31, 33, 34, 37, 39
Advanced 9–14, 19, 20, 23–28, 30, 31, 33, 34, 39

If you finished Examples **1–3**
Basic 9–23, 26–28, 33, 38–39, 41–45, 51–58
Average 9–25, 29–38, 41–45, 47, 51–58
Advanced 9–16, 19, 23–36, 38–58

Homework Quick Check
Quickly check key concepts.
Exercises: 12, 14, 16, 28

Answers

2–5, 9–12. See p. A46.

State Resources

THINK AND DISCUSS

1. Describe and explain the sum of p and q for a binomial experiment.

2. Tell what three expressions are multiplied to find the probability that there will be r successes in a binomial experiment of n trials.

3. GET ORGANIZED Copy and complete the graphic organizer. Solve each problem that you include.

Binomial Experiments	
Probability	**Example**
Probability of r successes in n trials	
Probability of at least r successes	
Probability of at most r successes	
Probability using a complement	

11-6 Exercises

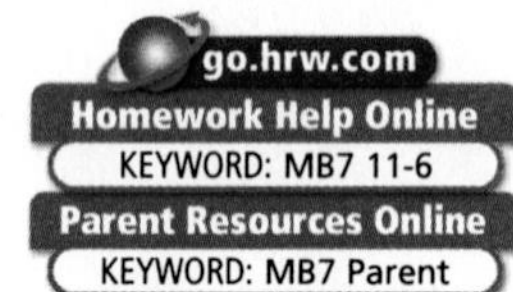

GUIDED PRACTICE

1. **Vocabulary** There are __?__ possible outcomes in each trial of a *binomial experiment.* 2

SEE EXAMPLE 1 p. 837

Use the Binomial Theorem to expand each binomial.

2. $(x+3)^4$ 3. $(3x+5)^3$ 4. $(p-2)^6$ 5. $(x+y)^6$

SEE EXAMPLE 2 p. 838

6. **School** The principal will randomly choose 6 students from a large school to represent the school in a newspaper photograph. The probability that a chosen student is an athlete is 30% (assume that this doesn't change). What is the probability that 4 athletes are chosen? What is the probability that at least 4 athletes are chosen? $\approx$ **0.060**; $\approx$ **0.070**

7. **Shopping** Wilma bought 4 boxes of Crunch-A-Lot cereal. One out of every 5 boxes has a coupon for a free box of Crunch-A-Lot. What is the probability that Wilma got 3 coupons? What is the probability that Wilma got at least 2 coupons? $\approx$ **0.026**; $\approx$ **0.181**

SEE EXAMPLE 3 p. 839

8. **Manufacturing** In a manufacturing plant, there is a 2% chance that a stamp will be placed on a box upside down. The plant shipped 30 boxes today. What is the probability that at least 2 of the boxes have an upside-down stamp? $\approx$ **0.121**

PRACTICE AND PROBLEM SOLVING

Use the Binomial Theorem to expand each binomial.

9. $(y+5)^4$ 10. $(2m-1)^3$ 11. $(4+3x)^5$ 12. $(2a+3c)^3$

13. **Civil Rights** In a survey of more than 100,000 high school students in 2004 by researchers at the University of Connecticut, 83% agreed with the statement "People should be allowed to express unpopular opinions." If 8 students are selected at random, what is the probability that at least 6 agree with the statement? $\approx$ **0.86**

11-6 PRACTICE A

Use the Binomial Theorem to expand each binomial.

1. $(x+y)^2$
   $x^2 + 2xy + y^2$
2. $(a+b)^3$
   $a^3 + 3a^2b + 3ab^2 + b^3$
3. $(2x+y)^2$
   $4x^2 + 4xy + y^2$
4. $(x+3y)^3$
   $x^3 + 9x^2 + 27xy^2 + 27y^3$

Solve.

5. A coin lands heads half of the time it is tossed.
   a. What is the probability that the coin will land heads? 0.5
   b. What is the probability that the coin will NOT land heads? 0.5
   c. If the coin is tossed 5 times, what is the probability that it will land heads twice? 0.31
   d. The probability that the coin will land heads either once or twice is given by $P(1 \text{ or } 2) = P(1) + P(2)$. Find the probability. 0.47
6. A survey showed that 1 in 3 people entering the post office are wearing glasses. At noon, 4 people enter the post office.
   a. What is the probability that one of those people is wearing glasses? 0.40
   b. What is the probability that one of those people is NOT wearing glasses? 0.60
   c. What is the probability that at least 2 of the 4 people are wearing glasses? 0.41
   d. The probability that at least 3 of the people are wearing glasses is given by $P(\geq 3) = P(3) + P(4)$. Find the probability. 0.11

11-6 PRACTICE B

Use the Binomial Theorem to expand each binomial.

1. $(x+y)^3$
   $x^3 + 3x^2y + 3xy^2 + y^3$
2. $(2x+y)^4$
   $16x^4 + 32x^3y + 24x^2y^2 + 8xy^3 + y^4$
3. $(m+3n)^3$
   $m^3 + 9m^2n + 27mn^2 + 27n^3$
4. $(p+q)^5$
   $p^5 + 5p^4q + 10p^3q^2 + 10p^2q^3 + 5pq^4 + q^5$

Solve.

5. Of the new cars in a car dealer's lot, 1 in 6 are white. Today, 4 cars were sold.
   a. What is the probability that 3 of the cars sold were white? 0.015
   b. What is the probability that at least 2 of the cars sold were white? 0.13
6. At a small college, $\frac{1}{3}$ of all of the students are vegetarians. There are 5 students in line at the cafeteria.
   a. What is the probability that all 5 students are vegetarians? 0.004
   b. What is the probability that just 1 of the students is a vegetarian? 0.33
7. Ellen plays 8 hands of a card game with her friends. She has a 1 in 3 chance of winning each hand. What is the probability that she will win exactly half of the hands played? 0.17
8. In a lottery, each ticket buyer has a 1 in 10 chance of winning a prize. If Chip buys 10 tickets, what is the probability that he will win at least 1 prize? 0.65

Independent Practice	
For Exercises	See Example
9–12	1
13–14	2
15–16	3

Extra Practice
Skills Practice p. S25
Application Practice p. S42

14. Five marbles are randomly selected with replacement. The probability that a black marble is chosen is 15%. What is the probability that 2 marbles are black? What is the probability that at least 2 marbles are black? ≈ 0.14; ≈ 0.16

15. **Genetics** A woman is expecting triplets. What is the probability that there are 2 girls and 1 boy? What is the probability that all 3 babies are girls?

16. **Botany** A tree has a 25% chance of flowering. In a random sample of 15 trees, what is the probability that at least 4 develop flowers? ≈ 0.54

Use the Binomial Theorem to expand each binomial.

17. $(x - y)^5$ 18. $(c + 6)^3$ 19. $(4k - 1)^4$ 20. $(p + q)^7$

Evaluate $P(r) = {}_nC_r\, p^r q^{n-r}$, where $q = 1 - p$.

21. $p = 0.8, n = 3, r = 2$ 0.384 22. $p = 0.5, n = 5, r = 1$ 0.15625 23. $p = \frac{1}{3}, n = 4, r = 2$ $\frac{8}{27} \approx 0.30$

24. **Travel** A small airline overbooks flights on the assumption that several passengers will not show up. Suppose that the probability that a passenger shows up is 0.91. What is the probability that a 20-seat flight with 22 tickets sold will be able to seat all passengers who arrive? ≈ 0.60

25. **Genetics** A hedgehog has a litter of 4. What is the probability that all 4 are male? What is the probability that at least 3 are male? $\frac{1}{16} = 0.0625$; $\frac{5}{16} = 0.3125$

Find each probability when a fair coin is tossed 10 times.

26. more than 7 heads ≈ 0.055 27. at least 2 heads ≈ 0.989 28. exactly 5 heads ≈ 0.25

29. **Quality Control** An auto part has a 95% chance of being made within its tolerance level and a 5% chance of being pulled as defective. What is the probability that in a box of 8 parts, no more than 1 is defective? ≈ 0.94

30. **Graphing Calculator** The **randBin** function simulates a binomial experiment and reports the number of successes. To simulate a binomial experiment with $n = 6$ and $p = 0.3$ five times, press MATH, move to **PRB**, select **randBin(** and enter 6, 0.3, and 5, separated by commas.
    a. Simulate a binomial experiment with $n = 5$ and $p = 0.8$ five times.
    b. Use the formula to find the probability of at least 4 successes. ≈ 0.74
    c. How do your simulation results compare? possible answer: $0.6 < 0.74$

31. **Multi-Step** For $P = 0.8$ and $n = 10$, use a calculator to find the binomial probabilities for $r = 0$ to $r = 10$. Round to the nearest hundredth. Construct a bar graph of the probabilities. Describe the shape of the graph. How does the graph relate to the expected value?

32. **Critical Thinking** Which is more likely, a family with 4 children of 2 girls and 2 boys or a family of 4 children with 3 of one gender and 1 of the other? Explain.

33a. $\frac{82}{365} \approx 0.22$

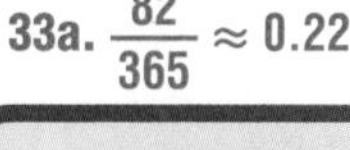

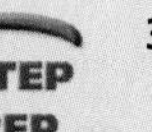

MULTI-STEP TEST PREP

33. This problem will prepare you for the Multi-Step Test Prep on page 844.

Based on historical data, the expected number of rainy days in San Antonio, Texas, during a calendar year is 82. Assume that rainy days are independent events.

a. What is the probability that there will be rain on any given day in San Antonio?
b. What is the probability that there will be exactly 3 rainy days during any given week? ≈ 0.14
c. What is the probability that there will be at least 3 rainy days during any given week? ≈ 0.19

11-6 PRACTICE C

Use the Binomial Theorem to expand each binomial.

1. $(x + y)^5$
   $x^5 + 5x^4y + 10x^3y^2 + 10x^2y^3 + 5xy^4 + y^5$
2. $(4x + y)^4$
   $256x^4 + 256x^3y + 96x^2y^2 + 16xy^3 + y^4$
3. $(2x + y)^5$
   $32x^5 + 80x^4y + 80x^3y^2 + 40x^2y^3 + 10xy^4 + y^5$
4. $(n + 2m)^4$
   $16m^4 + 32m^3n + 24m^2n^2 + 8mn^3 + n^4$

Solve.

5. At Hopewell High School, 1 in 7 students is on a sports team. There are 4 student council representatives in the school.
   a. What is the probability that 2 of the student council representatives are also on a sports team?
   0.09
   b. What is the probability that at least 3 of the student council representatives are on a sports team?
   0.01
6. Two in every 5 donuts in a package of donuts have a jelly filling. There are 5 donuts left in the package.
   a. What is the probability that all 5 donuts have a jelly filling?
   0.01
   b. What is the probability that none of the donuts has a jelly filling?
   0.08
7. Andrew is choosing CDs from a bag of free CDs without looking. He has a 1 in 5 chance of choosing a CD that he likes. He chooses 8 CDs in all. What is the probability that he will get 3 CDs that he likes?
   0.15
8. In a game of Bingo, the contestants have a 1 in 12 chance of winning each round. If Shirley plays 6 rounds, what is the probability that she will win at least half of them?
   0.01

In **Exercise 32**, students may only consider a family with 3 children of a specific gender and 1 of the other gender. Remind them that the reverse situation—1 child of that gender and 3 of the other—also qualifies.

MULTI-STEP TEST PREP **Exercise 33** involves finding binomial probabilities associated with rainy days during a calendar year. This exercise prepares students for the Multi-Step Test Prep on page 844.

Science Link Although **Exercises 15 and 32** assume that the chance of a male birth is 50%, the actual ratio of male to female births varies from region to region but is usually greater than 1.

Answers

15. $\frac{3}{8} = 0.375$; $\frac{1}{8} = 0.125$

17. $x^5 - 5x^4y + 10x^3y^2 - 10x^2y^3 + 5xy^4 - y^5$

18. $c^3 + 18c^2 + 108c + 216$

19. $256k^4 - 256k^3 + 96k^2 - 16k + 1$

20. $p^7 + 7p^6q + 21p^5q^2 + 35p^4q^3 + 35p^3q^4 + 21p^2q^5 + 7pq^6 + q^7$

30a. Possible answer: randBin(5, 0.8, 5);

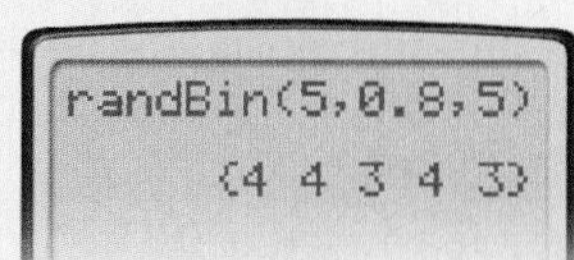

31.

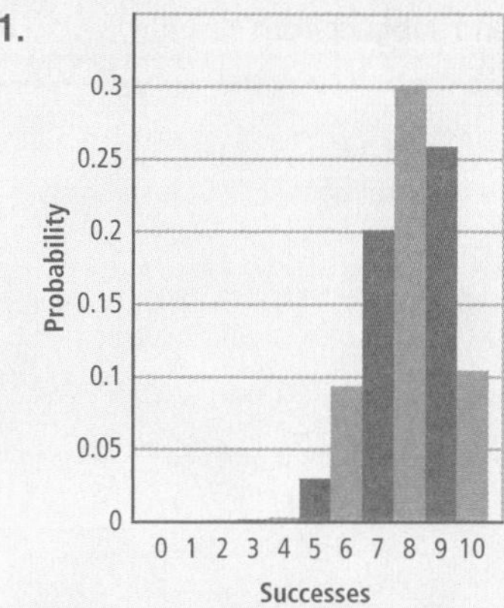

The bar heights increase nearly exponentially from 0 successes to 7 successes, maximize at 8, and drop at 10. The expected value is 8.

32. 3 of one and 1 of the other: $2 \cdot \frac{4}{16} = 0.5$
$\left(2 \text{ of each: } \frac{6}{16} = 0.375\right)$

TEST PREP DOCTOR If students have difficulty with **Exercise 41,** they might have overlooked the word *not* in the question. Have them review the parts of the definition of a binomial experiment, summarized in choices **A, C,** and **D,** leaving **B** as the correct answer.

In **Exercise 43,** students who choose **A** or **C** are missing the coefficient. Remind them that there are ${}_5C_3 = 10$ ways that there can be 3 successes in 5 trials: 123, 124, 125, 134, 135, 145, 234, 235, 245, and 345.

Teaching Tip **Math Background** **Exercise 47** is known as the Newton-Pepys (pronounced "peeps") problem because, in a 1693 letter to the famed mathematician Isaac Newton, Samuel Pepys, an English diarist, asked for advice about a wager he planned to make. Pepys asked which was more likely: 1. at least one 6 when 6 dice are rolled, 2. at least two 6's when 12 dice are rolled, or 3. at least three 6's when 18 dice are rolled.

Answers

36a. $\frac{3}{32} = 0.09375$

b. $\frac{9}{16} = 0.5625$

c. $\frac{7}{16} = 0.4375$

d. They are complements.

38. Possible answer: in 20 coin flips, the probability of getting fewer than 18 heads

40. Possible answer: ≈ 0.33; $P(0 \text{ successes}) \approx 0.017$, so solve $x^{10} = 0.017$ to find the complement, ≈ 0.67, and subtract from 1.

LINK Math History

The trials in a binomial experiment are often called Bernoulli trials after Italian mathematician Jacob Bernoulli (1654–1705).

34. There are 10 marbles in a bag. Half are striped, and half are not striped. Explain why choosing 3 marbles without replacement and noting whether they are striped does not fit the definition of a binomial experiment. **The trials are dependent.**

35. **Air Travel** In 2003, 20.46% of all direct flights from Dallas/Fort Worth to Los Angeles International Airport were delayed. Kelly flew that route 4 times and was on a delayed flight 3 times. What is the probability that she would have been on a delayed flight at least 3 times? $\approx$ **0.03**

36. **Games** As the ball drops, it has an equal chance of making a left turn or right turn at each peg.
    a. What is the probability of a home run?
    b. What is the probability of an out?
    c. What is the probability of a hit (a single, double, triple, or home run)?
    d. How are the answers to parts **b** and **c** related?

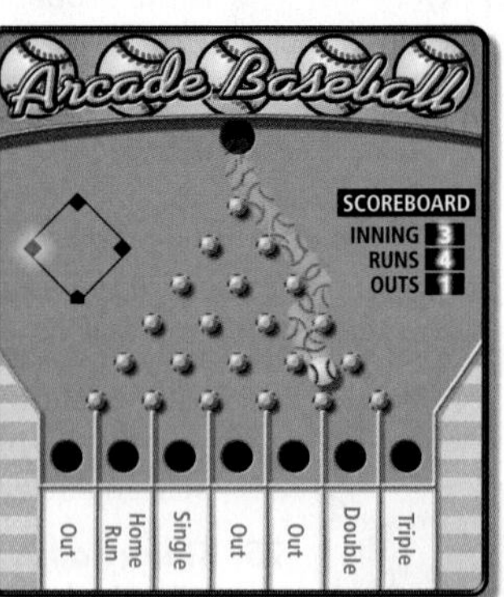

37. **Pets** A survey showed that 45% of dog owners take their dog with them on vacation. If 5 dog owners go on vacation, what is the probability that fewer than 3 take their dog? $\approx$ **0.59**

38. **Write About It** Describe a situation for which it would be beneficial to use the complement to find binomial probabilities.

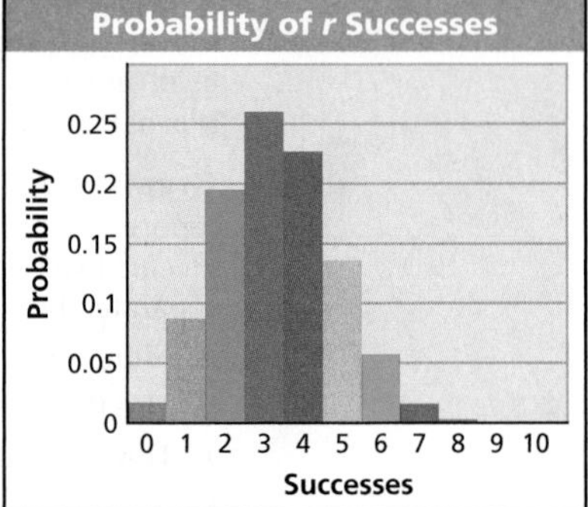

Estimation **Use the graph for Exercises 39 and 40. The graph shows the probability of *r* successes in 10 trials of a binomial experiment.**

39. Estimate the probability of 2 or fewer successes. $\approx$ **0.3**

40. Estimate the binomial probability p. Explain how you arrived at your answer.

TEST PREP

41. Which of the following is NOT true about a binomial experiment?
    (A) The outcomes are either successes or failures.
    (B) The trials are dependent.
    (C) The probability of success is constant.
    (D) The trials are identical.

42. In a binomial experiment with 2 trials and a probability of success on each trial of 40%, what is the probability of exactly 1 success?
    (F) 16% (G) 36% (H) 48% (J) 52%

43. In a binomial experiment, the probability of success is 20%. Which gives the probability of 3 successes in 5 trials?
    (A) $3(0.2)^3(0.8)^2$ (B) $10(0.2)^3(0.8)^2$ (C) $3(0.2)^2(0.8)^3$ (D) $10(0.2)^2(0.8)^3$

11-6 READING STRATEGIES

The probability that an event will happen r times can be determined by using a formula that involves the probability that the event will occur (p), the probability that it will not occur (q), a combination, and the total number of events taking place (n).

Example: In the senior class, 1 out of 4 students plays a sport. The principal chooses 2 students at random. What is the probability that both students play a sport?

Step 1	Identify n, p, q, and r.	$n = 2$; $p = \frac{1}{4}$; $q = 1 - \frac{1}{4} = \frac{3}{4}$; $r = 2$
Step 2	Write the equation and substitute for the variables.	Equation: $P(r) = {}_nC_r p^r q^{n-r}$ Substitute: $P(2) = {}_2C_2 \left(\frac{1}{4}\right)^2 \left(\frac{3}{4}\right)^0$
Step 3	Evaluate the combination.	${}_2C_2 = \frac{2!}{2!(2-2)!} = 1$
Step 4	Complete the solution.	$P(2) = 1\left(\frac{1}{4}\right)^2 \left(\frac{3}{4}\right)^0 = 1\left(\frac{1}{16}\right)1 = \frac{1}{16} \approx 0.0625$

Follow the procedure to solve.

1. Of the 6 kittens in the litter, 1 in 3 has blue eyes. What is the probability that if 2 kittens are picked at random, 1 will have blue eyes?
    a. Identify n, p, q, and r. $n = 2, p = \frac{1}{3}, q = \frac{2}{3}, r = 1$
    b. Write the equation and substitute for the variables. $P(r) = {}_nC_r p^r q^{n-r}$; $P(1) = {}_2C_1 \left(\frac{1}{3}\right)^1 \left(\frac{2}{3}\right)^1$
    c. Evaluate the combination. ${}_2C_1 = 2$
    d. Complete the solution. $P(1) = \frac{4}{9} \approx 0.44$

2. Jason sees that 2 out of every 5 cars that passed his house had windshield wipers on. What is the probability that of the next 4 cars that pass his house, 2 of them will have windshield wipers on?
    a. Identify n, p, q, and r. $n = 4, p = \frac{2}{5}, q = \frac{3}{5}, r = 2$
    b. Write the equation and substitute for the variables. $P(r) = {}_nC_r p^r q^{n-r}$; $P(2) = {}_4C_2 \left(\frac{2}{5}\right)^2 \left(\frac{3}{5}\right)^2$
    c. Evaluate the combination. ${}_4C_2 = 6$
    d. Complete the solution. $P(2) = \frac{216}{625} \approx 0.35$

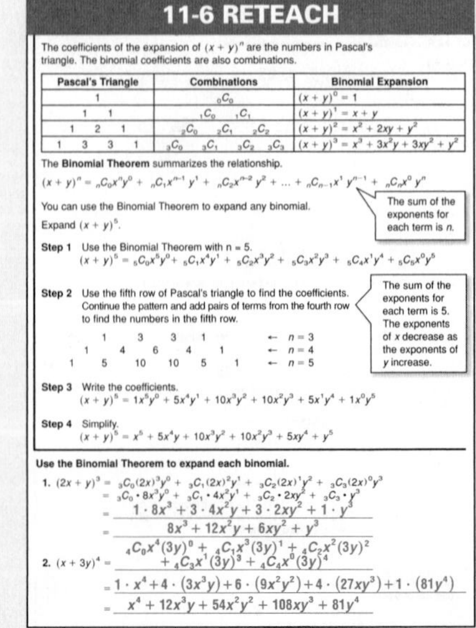

11-6 RETEACH

The coefficients of the expansion of $(x + y)^n$ are the numbers in Pascal's triangle. The binomial coefficients are also combinations.

Pascal's Triangle	Combinations	Binomial Expansion
1	${}_0C_0$	$(x+y)^0 = 1$
1 1	${}_1C_0$ ${}_1C_1$	$(x+y)^1 = x + y$
1 2 1	${}_2C_0$ ${}_2C_1$ ${}_2C_2$	$(x+y)^2 = x^2 + 2xy + y^2$
1 3 3 1	${}_3C_0$ ${}_3C_1$ ${}_3C_2$ ${}_3C_3$	$(x+y)^3 = x^3 + 3x^2y + 3xy^2 + y^3$

The **Binomial Theorem** summarizes the relationship.

$$(x+y)^n = {}_nC_0x^ny^0 + {}_nC_1x^{n-1}y^1 + {}_nC_2x^{n-2}y^2 + \dots + {}_nC_{n-1}x^1y^{n-1} + {}_nC_nx^0y^n$$

The sum of the exponents for each term is n.

You can use the Binomial Theorem to expand any binomial.

Expand $(x + y)^5$.

Step 1 Use the Binomial Theorem with n = 5.
$(x+y)^5 = {}_5C_0x^5y^0 + {}_5C_1x^4y^1 + {}_5C_2x^3y^2 + {}_5C_3x^2y^3 + {}_5C_4x^1y^4 + {}_5C_5x^0y^5$

Step 2 Use the fifth row of Pascal's triangle to find the coefficients. Continue the pattern and add pairs of terms from the fourth row to find the numbers in the fifth row.

1 3 3 1 ← $n = 3$
1 4 6 4 1 ← $n = 4$
1 5 10 10 5 1 ← $n = 5$

The sum of the exponents for each term is 5. The exponents of x decrease as the exponents of y increase.

Step 3 Write the coefficients.
$(x+y)^5 = 1x^5y^0 + 5x^4y^1 + 10x^3y^2 + 10x^2y^3 + 5x^1y^4 + 1x^0y^5$

Step 4 Simplify.
$(x+y)^5 = x^5 + 5x^4y + 10x^3y^2 + 10x^2y^3 + 5xy^4 + y^5$

Use the Binomial Theorem to expand each binomial.

1. $(2x+y)^3 = {}_3C_0(2x)^3y^0 + {}_3C_1(2x)^2y^1 + {}_3C_2(2x)^1y^2 + {}_3C_3(2x)^0y^3$
$= {}_3C_0 \cdot 8x^3y^0 + {}_3C_1 \cdot 4x^2y^1 + {}_3C_2 \cdot 2xy^2 + {}_3C_3 \cdot y^3$
$= 1 \cdot 8x^3 + 3 \cdot 4x^2y + 3 \cdot 2xy^2 + 1 \cdot y^3$
$= 8x^3 + 12x^2y + 6xy^2 + y^3$

2. $(x+3y)^4 = {}_4C_0x^4(3y)^0 + {}_4C_1x^3(3y)^1 + {}_4C_2x^2(3y)^2 + {}_4C_3x^1(3y)^3 + {}_4C_4x^0(3y)^4$
$= 1 \cdot x^4 + 4 \cdot (3x^3y) + 6 \cdot (9x^2y^2) + 4 \cdot (27xy^3) + 1 \cdot (81y^4)$
$= x^4 + 12x^3y + 54x^2y^2 + 108xy^3 + 81y^4$

44. **Gridded Response** A part has a 4% chance of being discarded for imperfections. Out of 10 randomly selected parts, what is the probability that no more than 1 has an imperfection? Round to the nearest whole percent. **94%**

45. **Short Response** About 18.8% of the people in the United States have one of the 100 most common last names. What is the probability that in a group of 10 randomly-selected people, 3 or more have one of these names? $\approx$ **0.29**

CHALLENGE AND EXTEND

46a. 65; number of people $\times$ probability left-handed

b. $\{n \mid 58 < n < 72\}$

46. **Genetics** There is about a 0.1 probability that a person is left-handed. There are 650 people in an auditorium.
    a. What is the expected number of left-handed people in the auditorium? Explain.
    b. The standard deviation for a binomial experiment with n trials is given by $\sqrt{npq}$. Describe the number of left-handed people that you would expect in the auditorium as an interval within 1 standard deviation of the expected number.

47. Find each probability. Which is greater?
    a. rolling at least one 1 in 6 rolls of a die $\approx$ **0.67**
    b. rolling at least two 1's in 12 rolls of a die $\approx$ **0.62**

48. **Calculator** The **binomcdf** function, found in 2nd CATALOG 0, computes the cumulative probability of r successes in a binomial experiment of n trials with a probability of success p. To compute the probability of at most 3 successes in a binomial experiment with $n = 6$ and $p = 0.3$, use **binomcdf**, enter 6, 0.3, and 3, separated by commas, and press ENTER. Use the **binomcdf** function to find the probability of *at least* 4 successes in a binomial experiment of 20 trials with probability of success 0.4. $\approx$ **0.984**

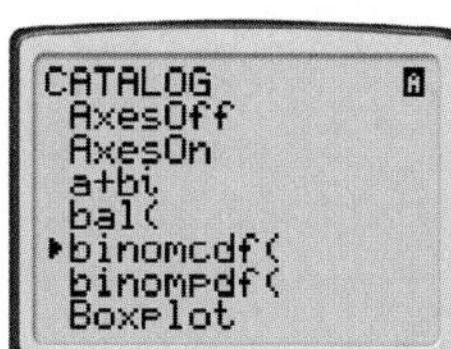

49. Show why any number ${}_{n+1}C_{r+1}$ in Pascal's triangle is the sum of the two numbers above it, ${}_nC_r$ and ${}_nC_{r+1}$ where r is not equal to 0 or n, and $n > 1$.

50. **Bowling** A bowler has a 0.4 probability of making exactly 1 strike in 2 frames, either in the first frame or the second frame. Assume that the bowler's probability p of getting a strike is the same for any frame.
    a. Write an equation and solve for p. $2p(1 - p) = 0.4$; ≈ 0.72 or ≈ 0.28
    b. Find the probability that the bowler makes strikes in both frames. ≈ 0.52 or ≈ 0.076

SPIRAL REVIEW

For each function, evaluate $f(-3)$, $f(0)$, and $f(2)$. *(Lesson 1-7)*

51. $f(x) = -x^2 + 2x - 4$ **−19; −4; −4**

52. $f(x) = (-x)^2 - 3x + 1$ **19; 1; −1**

Determine whether y is an exponential function of x. If so, use exponential regression to find a function that models the data. *(Lesson 7-8)*

53.

x	1	2	3	4	5
y	1.4	2.6	3.8	5.0	6.2

no

54.

x	1	2	3	4	5
y	10	22	36	52	70

no

Find the mean, median, and mode of each data set. *(Lesson 11-5)*

55. $\{2, 18, 15, 14, 18\}$ **13.4; 15; 18**

56. $\{6, 13, 9, 7, 6, 4\}$ **7.5; 6.5; 6**

57. $\{24, 20, 32, 24, 16, 34\}$ **25; 24; 24**

58. $\{10, 5, 15, 5, 8\}$ **8.6; 8; 5**

11-6 PROBLEM SOLVING

Sales records for the snack machines show that 1 out of every 6 students buys a bag of trail mix. There are 5 students waiting to use the machines. Melanie uses the formula for binomial probability, $P(r) = {}_nC_r p^r q^{n-r}$, to determine the number of students expected to buy trail mix.

1. What is the probability of exactly 3 students buying a bag of trail mix?
   a. What is the probability of each student buying a bag of trail mix? $\frac{1}{6}$
   b. Define each variable used in the formula and give its value. $n = 5$; $r = 3$; $p = \frac{1}{6}$; $q = \frac{5}{6}$
   c. Write the binomial formula using these values. $P(3) = {}_5C_3\left(\frac{1}{6}\right)^3\left(\frac{5}{6}\right)^2$
   d. Solve the equation to give the probability of exactly 3 students buying a bag of trail mix. 0.032
2. What is the probability of at least 1 student buying a bag of trail mix?
   a. Describe a method to solve involving the sum of probabilities. Find the sum of the probabilities of 1, 2, 3, 4, and 5 students buying a bag of trail mix, $P(1) + P(2) + P(3) + P(4) + P(5)$.
   b. Describe a method to solve that uses the formula $P(E) + P(\text{not } E) = 1$. Find the probability that no student will buy a bag of trail mix and subtract that probability from 1.
   c. Use either method to determine the probability of at least 1 student buying a bag of trail mix. 0.6
3. After school, 4 students line up to buy snacks from the machine. What is the probability that they will all buy a bag of trail mix? 0.0008

Sports drinks are purchased by 3 out of 4 students using the snack machines. There are 3 students at the machines now. Choose the letter for the best answer.

4. Which expression gives the probability of exactly 2 students buying an energy drink?
   (A) $P(2) = {}_3C_2\left(\frac{3}{4}\right)^2\left(\frac{1}{4}\right)^1$
   B $P(2) = {}_4C_3\left(\frac{2}{3}\right)^2\left(\frac{1}{3}\right)^1$
   C $P(3) = {}_3C_2\left(\frac{3}{4}\right)^1\left(\frac{1}{4}\right)^2$
   D $P(3) = {}_4C_3\left(\frac{2}{3}\right)^1\left(\frac{1}{3}\right)^2$
5. What is the probability that at least 2 of the students will buy an energy drink?
   F 42%
   G 50%
   H 75%
   (J) 84%

11-6 CHALLENGE

Antoine Gombauld, the Chevalier de Méré, was a seventeenth century French dice player. He was a successful gambler in one game of dice rolling and unsuccessful in another. He would bet that he could roll at least one 6 in 4 rolls of a single die. With this bet he made money in the long run. But he would also bet that he could roll at least one pair of 6s in 24 rolls of a pair of dice. He eventually lost money with this bet.

The first experiment is rolling at least one 6 in 4 rolls of a single die.

1. Is each of the 4 rolls of the single die independent of one another? Why or why not? Yes; the probability of a 6 is always $\frac{1}{6}$.
2. What is the probability of rolling at least one 6 in 4 rolls? This means rolling either one 6, two 6s, three 6s, or four 6s. $P(\text{1 six}) \approx 0.39$; $P(\text{2 sixes}) \approx 0.12$; $P(\text{3 sixes}) \approx 0.015$; $P(\text{4 sixes}) \approx 0.000778$; $P(\text{at least 1 six}) \approx 0.53$
3. What is the probability of rolling no 6s in the 4 rolls? How does your answer compare to your previous answer? $P(\text{0 sixes}) \approx 0.487$; it is the complement so the sum of the probabilities is equal to 1.
4. Predict the outcome of Gombauld's bets with this game over time. How much might he win or lose for each \$1 bet? Possible answer: win over time; $(1)(0.53) + (-1)(0.47) = 0.06$, so he would win an average of 6 cents for a \$1 bet on every game.

Consider the game of rolling at least one pair of 6s in 24 rolls of a pair of dice.

5. Is each of the 24 rolls of the pair of dice independent? Why or why not? Yes; the probability of rolling a pair of 6s when rolling a pair of dice is always $\frac{1}{36}$.
6. What is the probability of rolling at least one pair of 6s in 24 rolls of a pair of dice? How can you find this probability? You can use the complement of rolling no pairs of 6s; $\approx 1 - 0.51 = 0.49$.
7. Predict the outcome of Gombauld's bets with this game over time. How much might he win or lose for each \$1 bet? Possible answer: lose over time; $(1)(0.49) + (-1)(0.51) = -0.02$, so he would lose an average of 2 cents for a \$1 bet on every game.
8. How might Antoine Gombauld have changed the rules so that he could have had a positive expected return for this game? Possible answer: He could have changed the rules so that he rolls at least one pair of 6s in 25 (or more) rolls of a pair of dice. This makes his expected value positive.

Answers

49. See p. A46.

Journal

Have students summarize the conditions needed in a binomial experiment and give examples of binomial probabilities.

ALTERNATIVE ASSESSMENT

Have students design a binomial experiment and describe and calculate the probabilities of different outcomes, including those that use a complement.

Power Presentations with PowerPoint®

11-6 Lesson Quiz

Use the Binomial Theorem to expand each binomial.

1. $(x + 2)^4$
   $x^4 + 8x^3 + 24x^2 + 32x + 16$
2. $(2a - b)^5$
   $32a^5 - 80a^4b + 80a^3b^2 - 40a^2b^3 + 10ab^4 - b^5$

A binomial experiment has 4 trials, with $p = 0.3$.

3. What is the probability of 1 success? 0.4116
4. What is the probability of at least 2 successes? 0.3483
5. There is a 10% chance that Nila will have to wait for a train to pass as she heads for school. What is the probability that she will not have to wait for a train all 5 days this week? about 59%
6. Krissy has 3 arrows. The probability of her hitting the target is $\frac{2}{5}$. What is the probability that she will get at least one arrow on the target? 78.4%

Also available on transparency

Organizer

Objective: Assess students' ability to apply concepts and skills in Lessons 11-5 through 11-6 in a real-world format.

Online Edition

Resources

Algebra II Assessments
www.mathtekstoolkit.org

Problem	Text Reference
1	Lesson 11-5
2	Lesson 11-5
3	Lesson 11-5
4	Lesson 11-5
5	Lesson 11-6
6	Lesson 11-5

Answers

1. Seattle: mean: 39.68 in.; standard deviation: ≈ 6.2 in.; Atlanta: mean: 46.87 in.; standard deviation: ≈ 7.3 in.
2. Seattle
3. Seattle: 8.5; Atlanta: 13.9
4. Seattle
5. 0.32; 0.71
6. Possible answer: Although there is more rain in Atlanta, there are more rainy days in Seattle.

State Resources

go.hrw.com
State Resources Online
KEYWORD: MB7 Resources

CHAPTER 11

MULTI-STEP TEST PREP

SECTION 11B

Data Analysis and Statistics

Rain Reign Many people think of Seattle, Washington, as one of the rainiest cities in the United States. The table provides precipitation data for Seattle and Atlanta, Georgia, over a 10-year period. By analyzing this data set, you can decide for yourself whether Seattle deserves its soggy reputation.

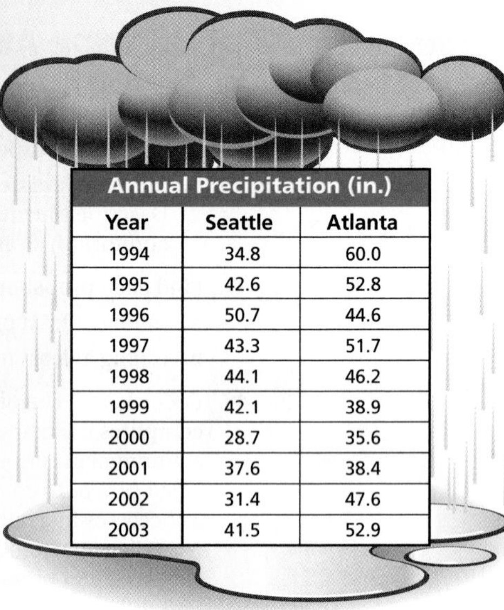

Annual Precipitation (in.)		
Year	**Seattle**	**Atlanta**
1994	34.8	60.0
1995	42.6	52.8
1996	50.7	44.6
1997	43.3	51.7
1998	44.1	46.2
1999	42.1	38.9
2000	28.7	35.6
2001	37.6	38.4
2002	31.4	47.6
2003	41.5	52.9

1. Find the mean annual precipitation and the standard deviation for Seattle and for Atlanta.
2. For which city do the data cluster more closely around the mean?
3. Find the interquartile range for Seattle and for Atlanta.
4. For which city do the data cluster more closely around the median?
5. During a calendar year, the expected number of rainy days in Atlanta is 115. Find the probability that it will rain on any given day. Then find the probability that it will rain there on at least 2 days during any given week.
6. Based on your findings, why do you think Seattle, rather than Atlanta, has a reputation as a rainy city?

844

INTERVENTION

Scaffolding Questions

1. Just by looking at the data, which city do you expect will have a greater mean? Atlanta
2. What does a low standard of deviation indicate? The data are clustered near the measures of central tendency.
3. How can you determine the quartiles of a data set? Find the medians of the upper and lower halves of the data set.
4. What does a low interquartile range indicate? The middle half of the data set is clustered near the median.
5. What is the complement of "rain on at least 2 days in a given week"? rain on 0 or 1 day
6. What factor may be more important than total amount when people form an opinion about how rainy a city is? the frequency of rain

Extension

Find the probability, to the nearest percent, that it will rain in Atlanta on exactly 10 days in a 30-day month. 15%

CHAPTER 11

SECTION 11B

Quiz for Lessons 11-5 Through 11-6

11-5 Measures of Central Tendency and Variation

1. Mr. Ortega took the following number of sick days per year for the last 5 years: 4, 2, 6, 3, 2. Find the mean, median, and mode of the data set. **mean: 3.4; median: 3; mode: 2**
2. The probability distribution for the number of defects in a shipment of alarm clocks, based on past data, is given below. Find the expected number of defects in a shipment of alarm clocks. **0.29**

Number of Defects, n	0	1	2	3	4
Probability of n Defects	0.82	0.11	0.04	0.02	0.01

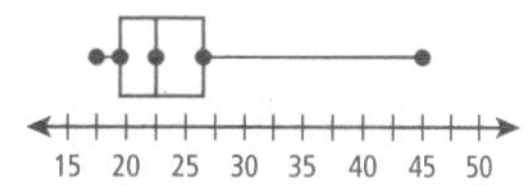

3. Make a box-and-whisker plot of the data. Find the interquartile range. Ages of employees at a movie theater: 17, 23, 18, 22, 45, 28, 21, 25 **interquartile range: 7**
4. The lengths of fish caught, in inches, during one fishing trip are given. Find the lengths within 1 standard deviation of the mean.

   Lengths of fish caught: 14, 28, 16, 20, 22, 33, 12, 30, 30, 25 **16.01 in. to 29.99 in.**

The data set shows the amount of money, rounded to the nearest dollar, spent by 20 consecutive shoppers at a home-improvement store.

35, 18, 49, 55, 280, 29, 42, 61, 19, 80, 33, 45, 67, 28, 71, 37, 48, 50, 31, 22

5. Find the mean and standard deviation of the data. **mean: 55; standard deviation: ≈ 54.3**
6. Identify the outlier, and describe how it affects the mean and standard deviation. **Outlier: 280; the mean increases from 43.2 to 55, and the standard deviation increases from ≈ 17.3 to ≈ 54.3.**

11-6 Binomial Distributions

7. Use the Binomial Theorem to expand $(m - 2n)^3$. $m^3 - 6m^2n + 12mn^2 - 8n^3$

The spinner shown is spun 10 times.

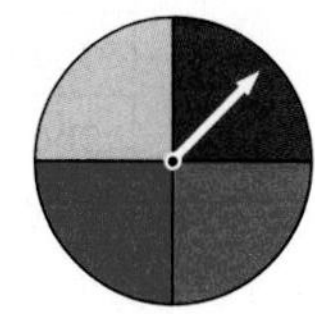

8. What is the probability that the spinner will land in the blue area exactly 5 times? ≈ **0.058**
9. What is the probability that the spinner will land in the blue area at least 3 times? ≈ **0.47**

A multiple-choice quiz has 5 questions. Each question has 3 possible answers. A student guesses the answer to each question. Find each probability.

10. The student answers all 5 questions correctly. ≈ **0.004**
11. The student answers exactly 1 question correctly. ≈ **0.33**
12. The student answers all 5 questions incorrectly. ≈ **0.13**
13. The student answers at least 1 question correctly. ≈ **0.87**

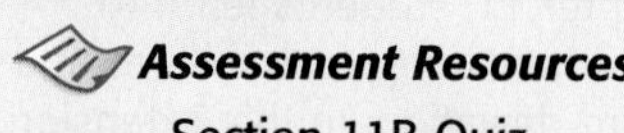

SECTION 11B

Organizer

Objective: Assess students' mastery of concepts and skills in Lessons 11-5 through 11-6.

Resources

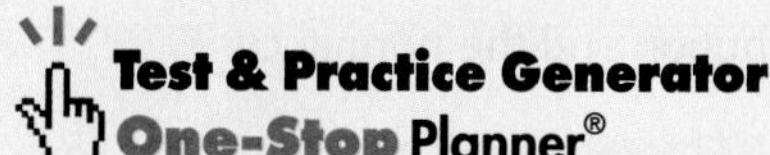

Assessment Resources
Section 11B Quiz

Test & Practice Generator
One-Stop Planner®

INTERVENTION

Resources

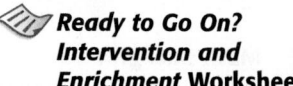

***Ready to Go On? Intervention and Enrichment* Worksheets**

***Ready to Go On?* CD-ROM**

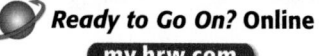

***Ready to Go On?* Online**
my.hrw.com

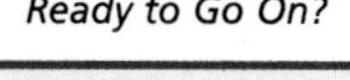

READY TO GO ON?
Diagnose and Prescribe

NO INTERVENE

Ready to Go On? Intervention	*Ready to Go On?* Intervention, Section 11B: Worksheets	CD-ROM	Online
Lesson 11-5	11-5 Intervention	Activity 11-5	Diagnose and Prescribe Online
Lesson 11-6	11-6 Intervention	Activity 11-6	

YES ENRICH

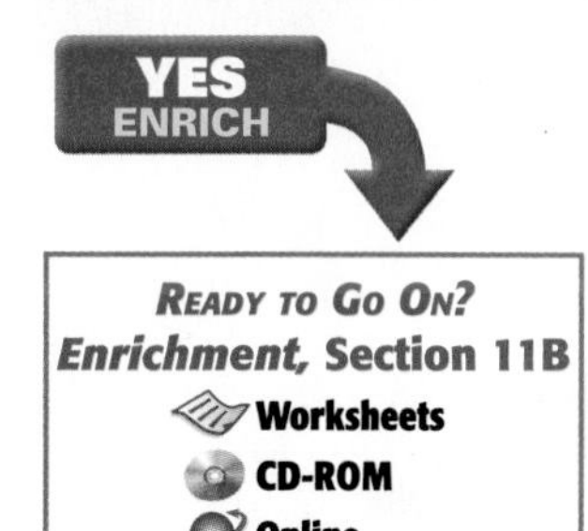

***Ready to Go On? Enrichment,* Section 11B**
Worksheets
CD-ROM
Online

CHAPTER 11 **Organizer**

Pacing: Traditional 1 day
Block $\frac{1}{2}$ day

Objectives: Recognize normally distributed data.

Use the characteristics of the normal distribution to solve problems.

Using the Extension

In Chapter 11, students learn to analyze data using probabilities and standard deviation. In this extension, students examine probability distribution and the normal curve.

Visual Help students see that a normal curve is a graphic representation of the concepts of mean and standard deviation. Have students identify those elements for the curves pictured in the lesson.

Math Background Point out that for continuous data, the mean rather than the median is used.

State Resources

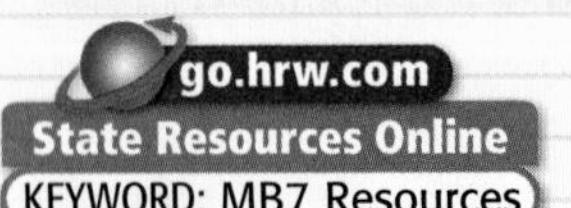

EXTENSION Normal Distributions

Objectives
Recognize normally distributed data.

Use the characteristics of the normal distribution to solve problems.

Standardized test results, like those used for college admissions, follow a *normal distribution.*

Probability distributions can be based on either *discrete* or *continuous* data. Usually discrete data result from counting and continuous data result from measurement.

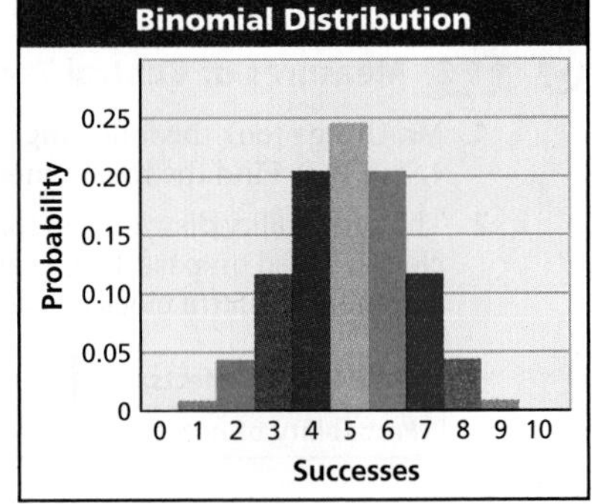

The binomial distributions that you studied in Lesson 11-6 were *discrete probability distributions* because there was a finite number of possible outcomes. The graph shows the probability distribution of the number of questions answered correctly when guessing on a true-false test.

In a *continuous probability distribution,* the outcome can be any real number—for example, the time it takes to complete a task.

You may be familiar with the bell-shaped curve called the *normal curve.* A *normal distribution* is a function of the mean and standard deviation of a data set that assigns probabilities to intervals of real numbers associated with continuous random variables.

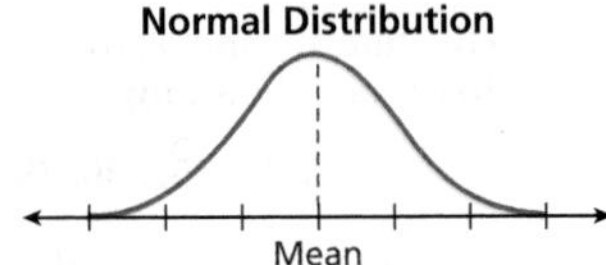

Normal Distributions
The probability assigned to a real-number interval is the area under the normal curve in that interval. Because the area under the curve represents probability, the total area under the curve is 1.
The maximum value of a normal curve occurs at the mean.
The normal curve is symmetric about a vertical line through the mean.
The normal curve has a horizontal asymptote at $y = 0$.

The figure shows the percent of data in a normal distribution that falls within a number of standard deviations from the mean.

0.1% 2.2% 13.6% 34.1% 34.1% 13.6% 2.2% 0.1%

Addition shows the following:

- About 68% lie within 1 standard deviation of the mean.
- About 95% lie within 2 standard deviations of the mean.
- Close to 99.8% lie within 3 standard deviations of the mean.

1 Introduce

Motivate

Determine whether students have ever heard of "grading on a curve" for a test.

Ask: If the tests of 100 students were graded on a curve, about how many of each grade–A, B, C, D, and F–would there be? Possible answer: 5, 20, 50, 20, and 5

Explain that the "curve" referred to is one pictured in this lesson.

2 Teach

Guided Instruction

Remind students that you can think of the standard deviation as the expected, or usual, variation of the data from the mean.

Reading Math Remind students that the word *normal,* as used in mathematics, does NOT mean the same thing as *good,* or *healthy,* as it does, for example, in the phrase "the patient's temperature is normal." A normal curve represents just one kind of distribution with certain characteristics.

ENGLISH LANGUAGE LEARNERS

EXAMPLE 1 Finding Normal Probabilities

The SAT is designed so that scores are normally distributed with a mean of 500 and a standard deviation of 100.

A **What percent of SAT scores are between 400 and 600?**

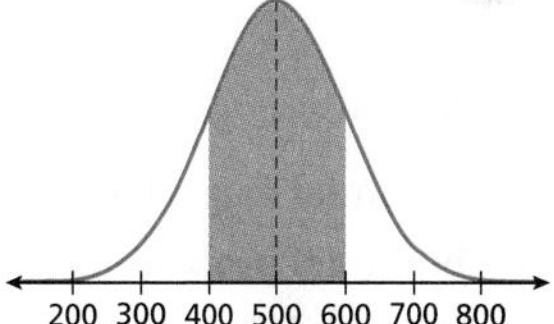

Both 400 and 600 are 1 standard deviation from the mean. Use the percents from the figure on the previous page.

34.1% + 34.1% = 68.2%

About 68.2% of the scores are between 400 and 600.

Each end of a normal distribution is called a *tail*.

B **What is the probability that an SAT score is above 600?**

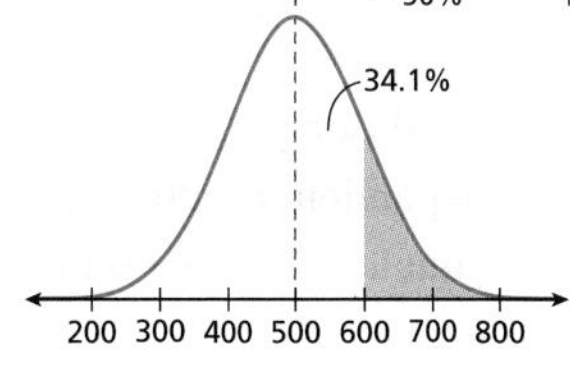

Because the graph is symmetric, the right side of the graph shows 50% of the data.

50% − 34.1% = 15.9%

The probability that an SAT score is above 600 is about 0.159, or 15.9%.

C **What is the probability that an SAT score is less than 300 or greater than 700?**

50% − (34.1% + 13.6%) = 2.3%

Because the curve is symmetric, the probability that an SAT score is less than 300 or greater than 700 is about 2(2.3%), or 4.6%.

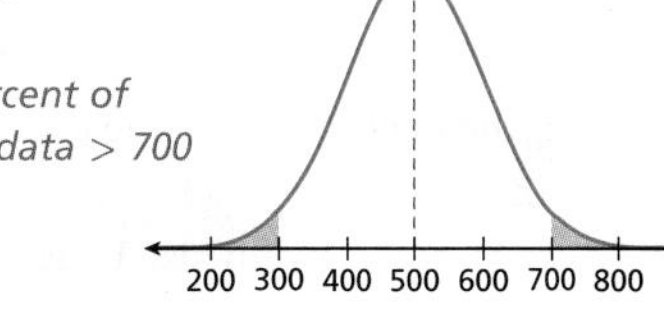

Use the information above to answer the following.

1. What is the probability that an SAT score is above 300? ≈ 97.7%

EXTENSION Exercises

A standardized test has a mean of 50 and a standard deviation of 4. Find the probability of test scores in the following ranges.

1. between 42 and 58 ≈ 95.4%
2. below 46 ≈ 15.9%
3. between 46 and 54 ≈ 68.2%

The amount of coffee in a can has a mean of 350 g and a standard deviation of 4 g.

4. What percent of cans have less than 338 g of coffee? ≈ 0.1%
5. What is the probability that a can has between 342 g and 350 g of coffee? ≈ 47.7%
6. What is the probability that a can has less than 342 g or more than 346 g of coffee? ≈ 86.4%

Flight 202's arrival time is normally distributed with a mean arrival time of 4:30 P.M. and a standard deviation of 15 minutes.

7. Find the probability that an arrival time is after 4:45 P.M. ≈ 15.9%
8. Find the probability that an arrival time is between 4:15 P.M. and 5:00 P.M. ≈ 81.8%

3 Close

Summarize

Have students list the characteristics of a normal curve. Then have students suggest data that could be summarized by a normal curve. Possible answers: Curve is a function of the mean and standard deviation of a data set; is continuous; the probability assigned to a real number interval is the area under the curve in that interval; maximum value occurs at the mean; curve is symmetrical about a vertical line through the mean; has a horizontal asymptote at $y = 0$; shoe sizes or hat sizes of very large populations.

COMMON ERROR ALERT

Students might confuse the mean in the graph of a normal curve with the y-axis in the coordinate system. To clear up this confusion, discuss the sign of the values to the left of the mean in **Example 1.**

Power Presentations with PowerPoint®

Additional Examples

Example 1

The SAT is designed so that scores are normally distributed with a mean of 500 and a standard deviation of 100.

A. What percent of SAT scores are between 300 and 500? about 47.7%

B. What is the probability that an SAT score is below 700? about 97.7%

C. What is the probability that an SAT score is less than 400 or greater than 600? about 31.8%

Also available on transparency

INTERVENTION Questioning Strategies

EXAMPLE 1

- If two normally distributed data sets have the same mean but one has a standard deviation of 2 and the other has a standard deviation of 7, how will the graph differ?

Diversity Tell students that although SAT used to be an acronym for Scholastic Aptitude Test, the name of the test is now simply SAT—the letters do not represent any words. The College Board, an association of 3200 high schools and colleges, oversees the exam.

Organizer

Objective: Help students organize and review key concepts and skills presented in Chapter 11.

Online Edition
Multilingual Glossary

Resources

***Multilingual Glossary* Online**
go.hrw.com
KEYWORD: MB7 Glossary

Tutorial Videos
CD-ROM

Answers

1. dependent events
2. expected value
3. permutation
4. 7,000,000
5. 792
6. 2,162,160
7. 604,800
8. 20

CHAPTER 11 Study Guide: Review

Vocabulary

binomial experiment 838
binomial probability 838
Binomial Theorem 837
combination 796
complement 803
compound event 819
conditional probability 812
dependent events 812
equally likely outcomes 802
event 802
expected value 828
experiment 805
experimental probability 805
factorial 795
favorable outcomes 802
Fundamental Counting Principle 794
geometric probability 804
inclusive events 820
independent events 811
mutually exclusive events . . . 819
outcome 802
outlier 831
permutation 795
probability 802
probability distribution 828
sample space 802
simple event 819
standard deviation 830
theoretical probability 802
trial 805
variance 830

Complete the sentences below with vocabulary words from the list above.

1. If the occurrence of one event affects the probability of the other, then the events are ___?___.
2. A(n) ___?___ can also be called a weighted average.
3. When arranging items, order is important when using a(n) ___?___.

11-1 Permutations and Combinations *(pp. 794–800)*

EXAMPLES

■ **If you have 8 vases to choose from, how many ways can you arrange 5 of them on a shelf?**

The order matters, so it is a permutation.

$$ {}_8P_5 = \frac{8!}{(8-5)!} = \frac{8 \cdot 7 \cdot 6 \cdot 5 \cdot 4 \cdot \cancel{3} \cdot \cancel{2} \cdot \cancel{1}}{\cancel{3} \cdot \cancel{2} \cdot \cancel{1}} = 8 \cdot 7 \cdot 6 \cdot 5 = 6720 $$

There are 6720 ways to arrange the vases.

■ **If 7 pizza toppings are available, how many ways can you choose 2 toppings?**

The order does not matter, so it is a combination.

$$ {}_7C_2 = \frac{7!}{2!(7-2)!} = \frac{7 \cdot 6 \cdot \cancel{5} \cdot \cancel{4} \cdot \cancel{3} \cdot \cancel{2} \cdot \cancel{1}}{2 \cdot 1(\cancel{5} \cdot \cancel{4} \cdot \cancel{3} \cdot \cancel{2} \cdot \cancel{1})} = \frac{42}{2} = 21 $$

There are 21 ways to choose the toppings.

EXERCISES

4. How many different 7-digit telephone numbers can be made if the first digit cannot be 7, 8, or 9?
5. From a group of 12 volunteers, a surveyor must choose 5 to complete an advanced survey. How many groups of 5 people can be chosen?
6. In one day, a salesman plans to visit 6 out of 14 companies that are in the neighborhood. How many ways can he plan the visits?
7. How many ways can 7 people arrange themselves inside a van that has 10 seats?
8. The caterer told Kathy that she can choose 3 entrées from the 6 listed on the menu. How many groups of 3 entrées can she choose?

11-2 Theoretical and Experimental Probability *(pp. 802–809)*

EXAMPLES

A paper clip holder has 100 paper clips: 30 are red, 20 are yellow, 25 are green, 15 are pink, and 10 are black. A paper clip is randomly chosen. Find each probability.

- The paper clip is green.

$$P(\text{green}) = \frac{\text{number of green paper clips}}{\text{total number of paper clips}}$$

$$= \frac{25}{100} = \frac{1}{4}$$

- The paper clip is not pink.

$$P(\text{not pink}) = 1 - P(\text{pink}) = 1 - \frac{15}{100} = \frac{17}{20}$$

- **Carl and Pedro each put their names in a hat for a door prize. Two names will be selected, and there are a total of 40 names in the hat. What is the probability that Carl wins the first prize and Pedro wins the second?**

The number of outcomes in the sample space is the number of ways that 2 people can be selected from 40 and then ordered.

$$P(\text{Carl, then Pedro}) = \frac{1}{{}_{40}P_2} = \frac{1}{1560}$$

- **A dart is randomly thrown at the dartboard. What is the probability that it lands in the outer ring?**

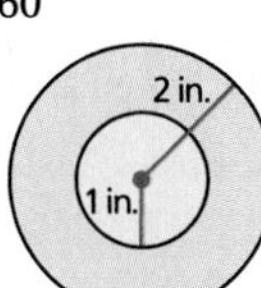

$$P(\text{outer ring}) = \frac{\text{area of outer ring}}{\text{area of dart board}}$$

$$= \frac{\text{area of large circle} - \text{area of inner circle}}{\text{area of large circle}}$$

$$= \frac{\pi(3)^2 - \pi(1)^2}{\pi(3)^2} = \frac{9\pi - 1\pi}{9\pi} = \frac{8\pi}{9\pi} = \frac{8}{9}$$

- **The table shows the results of 75 tosses of a number cube. Find the experimental probability of rolling a 4.**

1	2	3	4	5	6
10	12	16	15	9	13

$$P(4) = \frac{\text{number of times 4 occurred}}{\text{number of trials}} = \frac{15}{75}$$

$$= \frac{1}{5} = 0.2$$

EXERCISES

Two number cubes are rolled. What is the probability of each event?

9. Sum is 8.
10. Difference is 1.
11. Sum is even.
12. Product is less than 30.
13. The 10-member math team randomly selects 4 representatives to send to a meet. What is the probability that the 4 members chosen are the 4 with the lowest math grades?
14. A 5-digit code is given to all cashiers at a store to let them log onto the cash register. What is the probability that an employee receives a code with all 5 numbers the same?
15. Find the probability that a point chosen at random inside the rectangle is in the shaded area.

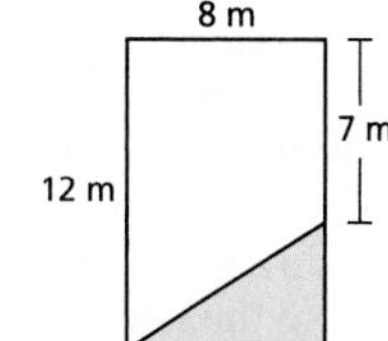

16. Find the probability that a point chosen at random inside the square is not inside the circle.

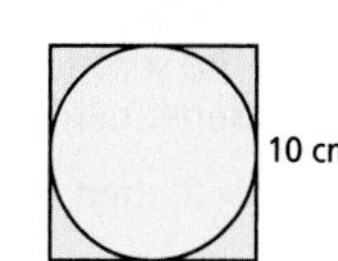

The bar graph shows the results of tossing two pennies 50 times. Find the experimental probability of each of the following.

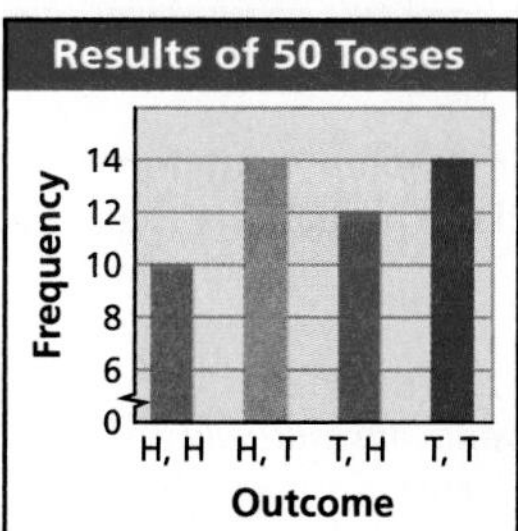

17. tossing 2 heads
18. tossing at least 1 tail
19. not tossing a head
20. tossing exactly 1 tail

Two pennies are tossed. Find the theoretical probability of each of the following.

21. tossing 2 heads
22. tossing at least 1 tail
23. not tossing a head
24. tossing exactly 1 tail

Answers

9. $\frac{5}{36}$
10. $\frac{5}{18}$
11. $\frac{1}{2}$
12. $\frac{11}{12}$
13. $\frac{1}{210}$
14. $\frac{1}{10{,}000}$
15. $\frac{5}{24}$
16. ≈ 0.21
17. $\frac{1}{5}$
18. $\frac{4}{5}$
19. $\frac{7}{25}$
20. $\frac{13}{25}$
21. $\frac{1}{4}$
22. $\frac{3}{4}$
23. $\frac{1}{4}$
24. $\frac{1}{2}$

Study Guide: Review **849**

Answers

25. The result of any roll does not affect the probability of any other outcome; $\frac{1}{216}$.
26. Replacing the first pen means the occurrence of the first selection does not affect the probability of the second selection; $\frac{6}{25}$.
27. $\frac{11}{21}$
28. $\frac{1}{13}$
29. $\frac{13}{31}$
30. $\frac{14}{99}$
31. Each coupon offers only 1 discount.
32. $\frac{5}{6}$
33. $\frac{7}{13}$
34. $\frac{1}{2}$
35. $\frac{7}{10}$

11-3 Independent and Dependent Events *(pp. 811–818)*

EXAMPLES

A bag contains slips of papers with the following numbers: 2, 2, 3, 3, 4, 5, 6. Determine whether the events are independent or dependent, and find the indicated probability.

- You select a 3, keep the paper, and then your friend selects a 3.

  Keeping the paper with the first 3 changes the number of 3's left in the bag for your friend to choose from, so the events are dependent.

  $P(3, \text{then } 3) = P(3) \cdot P(3 \mid 3)$.

  $= \frac{2}{7} \cdot \frac{1}{6} = \frac{2}{42} = \frac{1}{21}$

- You select a number greater than 3, replace the paper, and then your friend selects a number less than 3.

  Replacing the paper with the number greater than 3 means that your friend will also select from the same papers, so the occurrence of the first selection does not affect the probability of the second selection. The events are independent.

  $P(> 3, \text{then} < 3) = P(> 3) \cdot P(< 3)$

  $= \frac{3}{7} \cdot \frac{2}{7} = \frac{6}{49}$

EXERCISES

Explain why the events are independent, and find the probability.

25. rolling "doubles" 3 times in a row when rolling 2 number cubes
26. selecting a red pen and then a blue pen, when selecting 2 pens from a bag of 10 red and 15 blue pens with replacement

The table shows the age and marital status of the members of an environmental group. One person from the group is randomly selected. Find each probability.

Marital Status by Age

	18–34	35–50	51–65	66+
Married	6	20	22	4
Single	14	22	11	0

27. that the selected person is single, given that he or she is in the 35–50 age group
28. that a married person is 66 or older
29. that a person aged 18–50 is married
30. that a person in the group is single and in the 18–34 age group

11-4 Compound Events *(pp. 819–825)*

EXAMPLES

Andy is using his calculator to obtain a random number from 10 to 20. Find the probability that

- Andy gets a 15 or a multiple of 2.

  10 11 **12** 13 **14** **15** **16** 17 **18** 19 **20**

  $\frac{1}{11} + \frac{6}{11} = \frac{7}{11}$ *The events are mutually exclusive.*

- Andy gets a multiple of 3 or a multiple of 5.

  10 11 **12** 13 14 **15** 16 17 **18** 19 **20**

  $\frac{3}{11} + \frac{3}{11} - \frac{1}{11} = \frac{5}{11}$ *The events are inclusive.*

- Andy gets all different numbers if he has the calculator randomly select 5 numbers.

  $\frac{{}_{11}P_5}{11^5} = \frac{11 \cdot 10 \cdot 9 \cdot 8 \cdot 7}{11 \cdot 11 \cdot 11 \cdot 11 \cdot 11} = \frac{55{,}440}{161{,}051} \approx 0.3442$

EXERCISES

A store is handing out coupons. One-third of the coupons offer a 10% discount, half offer a 15% discount, and one-sixth offer a 20% discount. A customer is handed a coupon.

31. Explain why the events "10% discount" and "15% discount" are mutually exclusive.
32. What is the probability that the coupon offers a 10% discount or a 15% discount?

A card is drawn from a deck of 52. Find the probability of each outcome.

33. drawing a red card or drawing a 5
34. drawing a club or drawing a heart
35. Of 120 males and 180 females who took an eye exam, 170 passed. One-third of the males did not pass. What is the probability that a person who took the exam passed or was male?

11-5 Measures of Central Tendency and Variation (pp. 828–835)

EXAMPLES

- **The probability distribution for the number of substitute teachers needed is given. Find the expected number of substitute teachers needed on any given day.**

Number of Substitutes n	0	1	2	3	4
Probability of n Substitutes	0.05	0.08	0.38	0.41	0.08

$0(0.05)+1(0.08)+2(0.38)+3(0.41)+4(0.08)=2.39$

The expected number of substitutes is 2.39.

- **The number of books in each box shipped from a warehouse is given. Find the number within 1 standard deviation of the mean.**

12, 10, 4, 8, 24, 16, 14, 10, 10, 8, 16

Step 1 Find the mean.

$$\frac{12+10+4+8+24+16+14+10+10+8+16}{11}=12$$

Step 2 Find the variance. Add the squares of all the differences from the mean, and divide by the number of data values.

$$\frac{0+4+64+16+144+16+4+4+4+16+16}{11}\approx 26.2$$

Step 3 Take the square root: $\sqrt{26.2}\approx 5.1$

The number within 1 standard deviation of the mean is $\approx 12 \pm 5.1$, or $[6.9, 17.1]$.

EXERCISES

Find the mean, median, and mode of each data set.

36. 5, 8, 0, 8, 6

37. 12, 15, 13, 13, 15, 12

38. The probability distribution for the number of arrests made in a small town on one day is given below. Find the expected number of arrests on any one day.

Number of Arrests n	0	1	2	3
Probability of n Arrests	0.65	0.22	0.1	0.03

39. Make a box-and-whisker plot of the data. Then find the interquartile range.

33, 52, 65, 48, 83, 29, 33, 50, 71

40. The number of races that a runner won every year for 10 years is given. Find the number of wins within 1 standard deviation of the mean. 5, 7, 4, 11, 8, 10, 8, 6, 9, 7

41. The principal reported that the mean of a standardized test score for the school was 81.3 and the standard deviation was 4.4. Sharon scored 96. Is her score an outlier? Explain.

42. On 6 quizzes, Aaron scored 73, 88, 86, 90, 87, and 29. Find the mean and standard deviation of the data. On his seventh quiz, he scored 32. Describe how his seventh score affects the mean and standard deviation.

11-6 Binomial Distributions (pp. 837–843)

EXAMPLES

Sheila bought 5 energy bars. Each has a 1 in 10 chance of winning a free energy bar.

- What is the probability that Sheila will win 3 energy bars?

$P(3) = {}_5C_3(0.1)^3(0.9)^{5-3}$ $\quad P(r) = {}_nC_r p^r q^{n-r}$

$= 10(0.001)(0.81) = 0.0081$

- What is the probability that Sheila will win at least 1 energy bar?

$P(\text{at least } 1) = 1 - P(0)$

$P(0) = {}_5C_0(0.1)^0(0.9)^{5-0} \approx 0.5905$

$1 - 0.5905 = 0.4095$

EXERCISES

Use the Binomial Theorem to expand each binomial.

43. $(5+2x)^3$

44. $(x-2y)^4$

45. The probability of Ike making a free throw is 0.65. He shoots 75 free throws. Find the expected number of free throws made and the standard deviation.

46. A spinner is divided into 6 equal sections, numbered 1 through 6. It is spun 8 times. What is the probability that the spinner lands on 1 exactly 3 times? What is the probability that the spinner lands on 1 at least 2 times?

Answers

36. mean: 5.4; median: 6; mode: 8

37. mean: $13.\overline{3}$; median: 13; modes: 12, 13, and 15

38. 0.51

39.

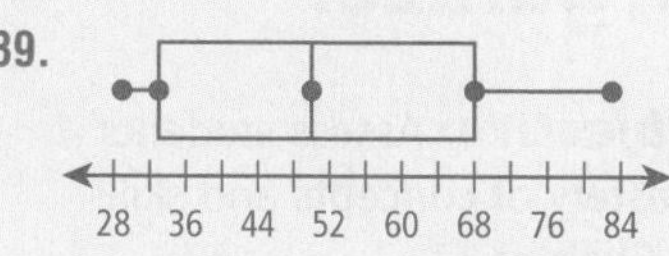

IQR = 35

40. [5.4, 9.6]

41. Yes; 3 standard deviations above the mean is 94.5. Her score is more than 3 standard deviations above the mean.

42. The mean decreases from 75.5 to 69.3, and the standard deviation increases from ≈ 21.5 to ≈ 25.1.

43. $125 + 150x + 60x^2 + 8x^3$

44. $x^4 - 8x^3y + 24x^2y^2 - 32xy^3 + 16y^4$

45. 48.75; ≈ 4.13

46. ≈ 0.10; ≈ 0.40

Study Guide: Review **851**

Organizer

Objective: Assess students' mastery of concepts and skills in Chapter 11.

Online Edition

Resources

Assessment Resources

Chapter 11 Tests
- Free Response (Levels A, B, C)
- Multiple Choice (Levels A, B, C)
- Performance Assessment

IDEA Works! **CD-ROM**

Modified Chapter 11 Test

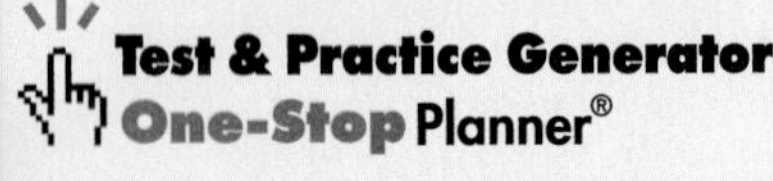

Answers

4. $\frac{3}{270{,}725} \approx 0.000011$

11. 29.5

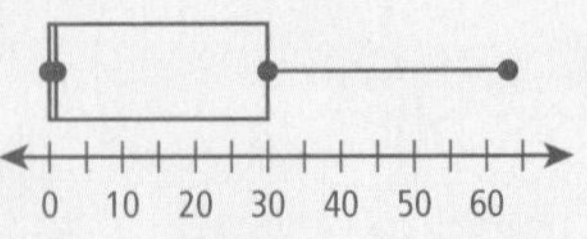

12. No; mean $\approx$ 15.6; standard deviation $\approx$ 20.5; 3 standard deviations above the mean $\approx$ 77.1, and 77.1 > 63.

State Resources

1. A mall employee is dressing a mannequin. There are 6 pairs of shoes, 4 types of jeans, and 8 sweaters. Using 1 of each, how many ways can the mannequin be dressed? **192**
2. How many ways can you award first, second, and third place to 8 contestants? **336**
3. How many ways can a group of 3 students be chosen from a class of 30? **4060**
4. Four cards are randomly selected from a standard deck of 52 playing cards. What is the probability that the cards are all jacks, all queens, or all kings?
5. The table shows the results of tossing 2 coins. Find the experimental probability of tossing 2 tails. $\frac{3}{10}$

HH	HT	TH	TT
3	6	5	6

Each letter of the alphabet is written on a card. The cards are placed into a bag. Determine whether the events are independent or dependent, and find the indicated probability.

6. The letter *D* is drawn, replaced in the bag, and then the letter *J* is drawn. **independent;** $\frac{1}{676}$
7. Three vowels are drawn without replacement. **dependent;** $\frac{1}{260}$

A card is drawn from a bag containing the 9 cards shown. Find each probability.

8. selecting a *C* or an even number $\frac{1}{3}$
9. selecting an odd number or a multiple of 3 $\frac{4}{9}$
10. The probability distribution for the number of absent students on any given day for a certain class is given. Find the expected number of absent students. **1.3**

Number of Students Absent *n*	0	1	2	3	4
Probability of *n* Absent Students	$\frac{7}{20}$	$\frac{5}{20}$	$\frac{4}{20}$	$\frac{3}{20}$	$\frac{1}{20}$

The number of known satellites of the planets in the solar system (as of 2005) is given.

	Mercury	Venus	Earth	Mars	Jupiter	Saturn	Uranus	Neptune	Pluto
Moons	0	0	1	2	63	33	27	13	1

Source: NASA Planetary Data System, 2005

11. Make a box-and-whisker plot of the data. Find the interquartile range.
12. Is 63 an outlier? Explain.
13. Identify the outlier in the following data set: 93, 107, 110, 103, 98, 95, 12, 111, 128, 99, 114, and 90. Describe how the outlier affects the mean and the standard deviation.
14. Use the Binomial Theorem to expand $(3x + y)^4$. $81x^4 + 108x^3y + 54x^2y^2 + 12xy^3 + y^4$

The probability of winning a carnival game is 15%. Elaine plays 10 times.

15. Find the probability that Elaine will win 2 times. $\approx$ **0.28**
16. Find the probability that Elaine will win at least 2 times. $\approx$ **0.46**

Answers

13. 12; the mean decreases from 104.4 to 96.7, and the standard deviation increases from $\approx$ 10.6 to $\approx$ 27.5.

COLLEGE ENTRANCE EXAM PRACTICE

CHAPTER 11

FOCUS ON SAT MATHEMATICS SUBJECT TESTS

The reference information at the beginning of a test is usually the same each time the test is given. Memorize this information so that you won't have to refer back to it during the test. When you take the test, note whether any information is different from what you expected.

You may want to time yourself as you take this practice test. It should take you about 6 minutes to complete.

If you do not know how to solve a general problem, try working out a simple example or two to see if a general solution method becomes apparent. But do not spend too much time on examples. If you are still stuck after a while, move on to the next problem.

1. Two cards are drawn from a standard deck of 52 cards. What is the probability that a king and a queen are drawn?

(A) $\frac{1}{169}$

(B) $\frac{2}{169}$

(C) $\frac{8}{663}$

(D) $\frac{14}{663}$

(E) $\frac{4}{169}$

2. A number cube is rolled twice. What is the probability of getting a 6 at least once?

(A) $\frac{1}{36}$

(B) $\frac{1}{6}$

(C) $\frac{11}{36}$

(D) $\frac{1}{3}$

(E) $\frac{5}{6}$

3. Your CD player can hold 6 CDs. You have 10 CDs to choose from, one of which is your favorite and is always in your player. How many ways can the player be filled if order does not matter?

(A) 126

(B) 210

(C) 720

(D) 15,120

(E) 151,200

4. Of 100 students, 37 play an instrument, 45 play sports, and 11 do both. What is the probability that a student neither plays an instrument nor plays sports?

(A) 0.145

(B) 0.18

(C) 0.29

(D) 0.40

(E) 0.82

5. A student's mean score after 4 quizzes was 72. After the fifth quiz, the mean increased to 75. What was the student's score on the fifth quiz?

(A) 60

(B) 72

(C) 84

(D) 87

(E) 100

COLLEGE ENTRANCE EXAM PRACTICE CHAPTER 11

Organizer

Objective: Provide practice for college entrance exams such as the SAT Mathematics Subject Tests.

Resources

Questions on the SAT Mathematics Subject Tests Levels 1 and 2 represent the following math content areas:

	Level	
	1	2
Algebra	30%	18%
Plane Euclidean Geometry	20%	0%
Coordinate Geometry	12%	12%
Three-dimensional Geometry	6%	8%
Trigonometry	8%	20%
Functions	12%	24%
Statistics/Probability	6%	6%
Miscellaneous	6%	12%

Items on this page focus on:
- Statistics
- Probability

Text References:

Item	1	2	3	4	5
Lesson	11-3	11-6	11-1	11-4	11-5

TEST PREP DOCTOR

1. Students may choose **B** because they assumed that the events are independent rather than dependent. Point out that after the first card is drawn, there is one fewer card left in the deck.

2. If students have difficulty with this problem, suggest that they start by making a table showing the sample space of rolling two number cubes. They can then circle all of the outcomes in the table that include at least one 6.

3. Students may choose **D** because they found the number of permutations instead of the number of combinations. Students may choose **B** because they did not take into account the fact that one place in the CD player is already filled.

4. Students may choose **B** because they did not take into account the number of students who do both activities. Suggest that students organize the information in the problem by making a Venn diagram.

5. Students who chose **A** or **B** did not check to make sure that their answer is reasonable. Ask students to explain why the fifth quiz score must be greater than the mean of the first 4 quizzes.

Organizer

Objective: Provide opportunities to learn and practice common test-taking strategies.

Resources

State Test Prep Workbook

State Test Prep **CD-ROM**

State Test Practice Online

go.hrw.com

KEYWORD: MB7 TestPrep

This test tackler focuses on choosing the best answer to multiple-choice questions. Reinforce to students that they should carefully read each answer choice as well as the problem statement. Point out that if students stop reading a test item after finding one correct answer, they may not realize that a choice such as *All of the above* might be a better answer.

Standardized Test Strategies

Multiple Choice: None of the Above or All of the Above

Given a multiple-choice test item where one of the answer choices is *none of the above* or *all of the above,* the correct response is the best, most-complete answer choice available.

To answer these types of test items, compare each answer choice with the question and determine if the answer is true or false. If you determine that more than one of the choices is true, then the correct choice is likely to be *all of the above.*

If you do not know how to solve the problem and have to guess at the answer, more often than not, *all of the above* is correct and *none of the above* is incorrect.

EXAMPLE 1

There are 8 players on the chess team. Which of the following models the number of ways that the coach can choose 2 players to start the game?

Ⓐ $_8C_2$
Ⓑ $\frac{8!}{2!(6!)}$
Ⓒ 28
Ⓓ All of the above

LOOK at each choice separately, and determine if it is true or false.

As you consider each choice, mark it "true" or "false."

Consider Choice A: *Because order does not matter, this is a combination problem. The number of combinations of 8 players, taken 2 at a time, is given by* $_nC_r$*, where* $n = 8$ *and* $r = 2$*. So,* $_8C_2$ *is a correct model of the combination.*

Choice A is *"true."* The answer could be choice A, but you need to check if choices B and C are also correct because the answer could be *all of the above.*

Consider Choice B: *The number of combinations of 8 players, taken two at a time, is given by* $_nC_r = \frac{n!}{r!(n-r)!}$*, where* $n = 8$ *and* $r = 2$*.*

$$_nC_r = \frac{n!}{r!(n-r)!} = \frac{8!}{2!(8-2)!} = \frac{8!}{2!(6)!}$$

Choice B is also a correct model of the combination. Choice B is *"true."* The answer is likely to be choice D, *all of the above,* but you still should check to see if choice C is true.

Consider Choice C: *The number of combinations of 8 players, taken two at a time, is given by* $_nC_r = \frac{n!}{r!(n-r)!}$*, where* $n = 8$ *and* $r = 2$*.*

$$_nC_r = \frac{n!}{r!(n-r)!} = \frac{8!}{2!(8-2)!} = \frac{8!}{2!(6)!} = 28$$

Choice C is also a correct model of the combination. Choice C is *"true."* Because choices A, B, and C are all *"true,"* the correct answer choice is choice D, *all of the above.*

Be careful of problems with double negatives. Read the problem statement and each answer choice twice before selecting an answer.

Read each test item and answer the questions that follow.

Item A

The mean score on a test is 68. Which can NOT be true about the scores?

Ⓐ Every score is 68.

Ⓑ Half are 68, and half are 0.

Ⓒ Half are 94, and half are 38.

Ⓓ None of these

1. What is the definition of *mean*?
2. Read the problem statement again. If an answer choice is true, is that the correct response? Explain.
3. Willie determined that both choices A and C could be true statements, so he chose choice D as his response. Do you agree? If not, what would you have done differently?

Item B

For a number cube, what is the probability of rolling a 2 or a number greater than 4?

Ⓕ 50%

Ⓖ $P(\text{rolling a 2} \cup \text{rolling 5 or 6}) = P(\text{rolling a 2}) + P(\text{rolling 5 or 6})$

Ⓗ $\frac{1}{6} + \frac{2}{6}$

Ⓙ All of the above

4. Is this event mutually exclusive or inclusive? How do you know? Determine if choice G is a true or false statement.
5. If you roll a number cube, what is the probability of rolling a 2? What is the probability of rolling a 5 or 6?
6. Simplify choice H to find its value. Is this value equivalent to any other answer choices?
7. How many answer choices are correct? What is the correct response?

Item C

Suppose that a dart lands at a random point on the circular dartboard. Find the probability that the dart lands inside only the dark gray or white region. The radius of the dartboard is 3 inches.

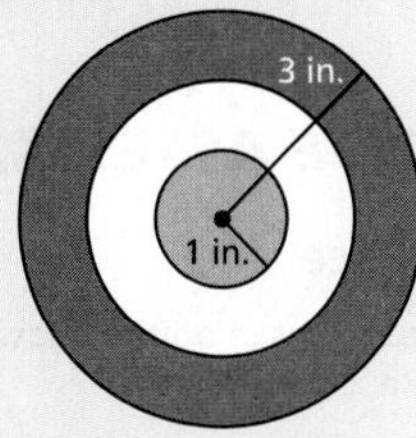

Ⓐ $\frac{1}{9}$

Ⓑ 8π

Ⓒ $\frac{8}{9}$

Ⓓ None of these

8. A student finds that both choice A and choice B are incorrect. To save time, he chooses choice D as his answer because he figures it is likely that choice C will also be incorrect. Do you think that this student made a wise decision? Explain.
9. What is the formula for the area of a circle? What is the area of this dartboard? How can you determine the area of the dark gray and white regions?
10. Find if choice A, B, or C is true, and determine the response to the test item.

Item D

Each gym member receives a 3-digit code to use for a locker combination with no digit repeated. Grace received the code 210. What was the probability that she would receive a code of consecutive numbers?

Ⓕ $1.\overline{6}\%$

Ⓖ $\frac{1}{45}$

Ⓗ $\frac{1}{{}_{10}P_3}$

Ⓙ All of the above

11. How can you determine if choice J is correct?
12. Are the values given in choices F, G, and H equivalent? What does this tell you about choice J?

Answers

1. the sum of the values in a data set divided by the number of values
2. No; the correct choice is the response that is not true.
3. No; determine whether **B** is true. Because **B** cannot be true, it is the correct response.
4. Mutually exclusive; because the events cannot occur at the same time in a roll; **G** is true.
5. $\frac{1}{6}$; $\frac{2}{6}$
6. $\frac{1}{2}$; equivalent to **F**
7. **F**, **G**, and **H** are correct, so the correct response is **J**.
8. No; because *none of the above* is usually not a correct response, it is better to determine whether **C** is incorrect before making that decision.
9. $A = \pi r^2$; 9π; subtract the area of the light gray region from the area of the dartboard
10. **A** is false, **B** is false, and **C** is true. The correct response is **C**.
11. Show that **F**, **G**, and **H** are all true.
12. No; **J** is not a correct response.

Answers to *Test Items*

A. B

B. J

C. B

D. G

State Resources

go.hrw.com
State Resources Online
KEYWORD: MB7 Resources

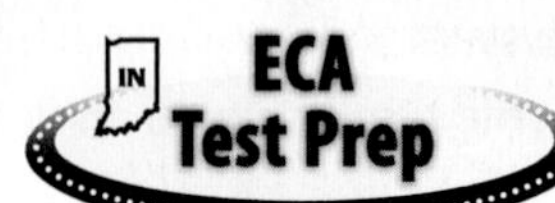

Organizer

Objective: Provide review and practice for Chapters 1–11 and standardized tests.

Resources

Assessment Resources

Chapter 11 Cumulative Test

State Test Prep Workbook

State Test Prep CD-ROM

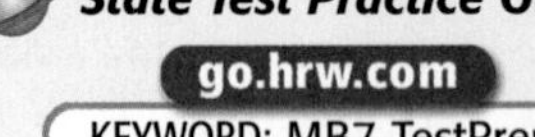
State Test Practice Online

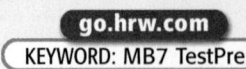

go.hrw.com
KEYWORD: MB7 TestPrep

Answers

1. C
2. C
3. A
4. B
5. B
6. D
7. A
8. C
9. D
10. A
11. B

Core Standard	Items
1	14
2	10
4	11, 13
6	4, 9
8	1

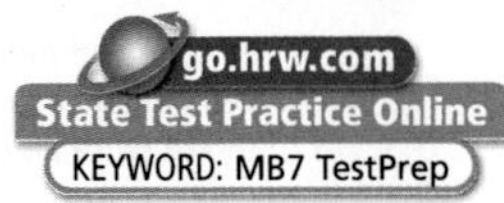

CUMULATIVE ASSESSMENT, CHAPTERS 1–11

Multiple Choice

1. There were 8 dogs in a litter. How many ways can Mike choose 2 dogs?

A. 20,160
B. 56
C. 28
D. $\frac{1}{28}$

2. What is the median of the test scores given: $\{97, 78, 61, 90, 95, 96, 80, 67, 86, 88, 90, 92\}$

A. 85
B. 88
C. 89
D. 90

3. The table shows the number of teachers, coaches, and students at a high school of each gender. What is the probability, to the nearest hundredth, that a coach is male?

School Population and Gender

	Male	Female
Teachers	12	24
Coaches	17	9
Students	429	453

A. 0.65
B. 0.35
C. 0.04
D. 0.02

4. For $f(x) = ab^x$, if x increases by 1, the value of $f(x)$ does which of the following?

A. $f(x)$ increases by b
B. $f(x)$ is multiplied by b
C. $f(x)$ increases by a
D. $f(x)$ is multiplied by a

5. A slice of an 18-inch diameter pizza that is cut into sixths sells for \$3.25. At this rate, how much should a slice that is one eighth of a 16-inch diameter pizza sell for, to the nearest \$0.05?

A. \$1.75
B. \$1.95
C. \$2.15
D. \$2.45

6. Which graph shows a line with a slope of $-\frac{4}{3}$ that passes through (5, 2)?

A.
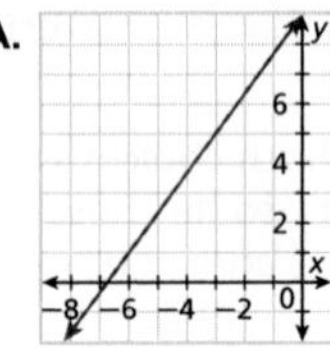

B.
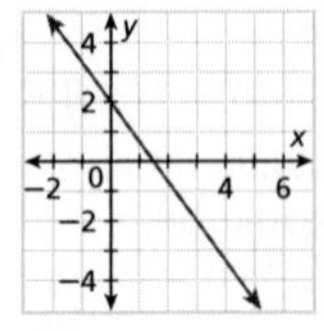

C.
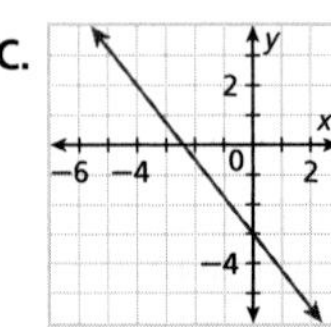

D.
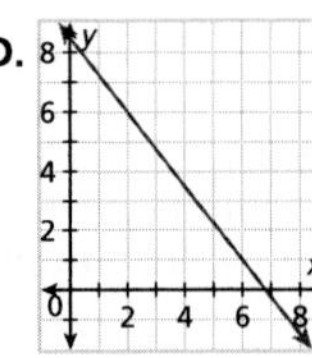

7. What is the inverse of $f(x) = 2(x - 3)^2$?

A. $y = \pm\sqrt{\frac{x}{2}} + 3$
B. $y = \sqrt{\frac{x}{2}} + 3$
C. $y = \pm\sqrt{\frac{x}{2} + 3}$
D. $y = \sqrt{\frac{x}{2} + 3}$

TEST PREP DOCTOR

For **Item 2,** students who answered **A** found the mean of the scores and those who answered **D** found the mode of the scores. Students who chose **B** did not order the test scores before finding the mean of the two middle values.

For **Item 3,** more information is given in the table than is needed to answer the question. Help students identify the necessary information by asking the following questions: How many male coaches does the school have? *17* How can you use the table to find the total number of coaches at the school? *Add the number of male coaches to the number of female coaches.* What information in the table is not needed to solve this problem? *the data about teachers and students*

8. Which conic section does the equation represent?
$2x^2 + 9xy + 10y^2 + 4x + 5y + 8 = 0$

A. Parabola

B. Hyperbola

C. Ellipse

D. Circle

In item 9, remember that a real number with a 0 exponent is 1. You can use mental math to quickly evaluate each function and compare your result to the corresponding value in the graphed function.

9. Which is the equation of the graph below?

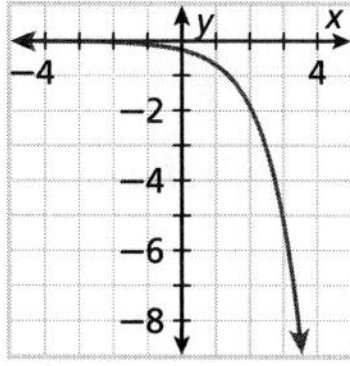

A. $f(x) = 0.25(2.75^x)$

B. $f(x) = -2.75(0.25^x)$

C. $f(x) = 2.75(0.25^x)$

D. $f(x) = -0.25(2.75^x)$

10. What value of x makes the equation true?
$6(x - i) - 2i = (4 - i)^2$

A. 2.5

B. 3

C. 3.5

D. 4

11. Use long division to find the coefficient of the x term in the quotient.
$(2x^3 + 5x^2 + 10x + 7) \div (x + 1)$

A. 2

B. 3

C. 7

D. 8

Short Answer

12. Find the center and the radius of a circle that has a diameter with the endpoints $(-2, 8)$ and $(4, 2)$.

Part A What is the length of the diameter?

Part B The endpoints $(4, 8)$ and $(-2, y)$ are located on the circle. Find the missing value of y.

13. The table below shows the number of students that graduated from a high school from 1920 to 2000, measured every 20 years.

x	1920	1940	1960	1980	2000
y	9	59	159	409	909

Part A Write a polynomial function for the data. Let x be the number of years since 1920. Round your answer to the nearest thousandth.

Part B At this rate how many students will graduate in 2020? Round your answer to the nearest student.

Part C About how many students graduated in 1990? Round your answer to the nearest student.

14. The Badgers won 70% of their games this season. They won 5 of the 12 games they played during their last road trip. Before the road trip, the Badgers had won 75% of their games.

Part A How many wins and losses did the Badgers have during the season?

Part B How many wins and losses did the Badgers have before their last road trip?

Extended Response

15. Randy wants to collect 515 baseball cards. Each week Randy buys 15 baseball cards.

Part A Create a table to represent this situation where t is the amount of time in weeks and c is the number of cards that Randy still wants to buy.

Part B Write an equation to model the data in the table.

Part C Graph the equation.

Part D After how many weeks will Randy meet his goal?

Short Answer Rubric

Items 12–14

Score 2 = Thorough understanding of mathematical concepts and processes.

Score 1 = Partial understanding of mathematical concepts and/or processes.

Score 0 = Limited or no understanding of the problem-solving concepts.

Blank = No written response.

Extended Response Rubric

Item 15

Score 4 = Thorough understanding of mathematical concepts and processes.

Score 3 = Demonstrated understanding of mathematical concepts and processes, but an error in computation or explanation.

Score 2 = Partial understanding of mathematical concepts and/or processes.

Score 1 = Limited understanding and execution of the problem-solving concepts.

Score 0 = No understanding of the problem-solving concepts.

Blank = No written response.

Answers

12. $(1, 5)$; $3\sqrt{2}$

Part A: $6\sqrt{2}$

Part B: 2

13. Part A. $f(x) = 0.002x^3 - 0.063x^2 + 2.917x + 9$

Part B: 1671

Part C: 590

14. Part A: 56 and 24

Part B: 51 and 17

15. PartA:

t	0	1	2	3	4	5
c	515	500	485	470	455	440

Part B: $c(t) = 515 + 15t$

Part C:

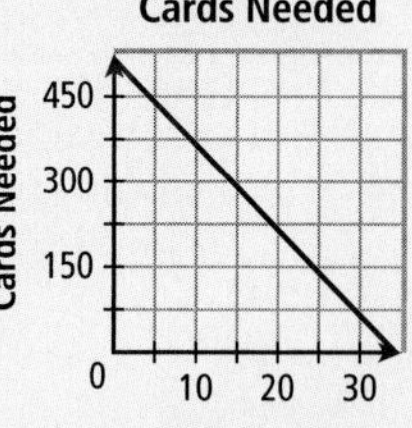

Part D: 35

Sequences and Series

Section 12A

Exploring Arithmetic Sequences and Series

12-1 Introduction to Sequences
Connecting Algebra to Geometry Geometric Patterns and Tessellations
12-2 Series and Summation Notation
12-2 Technology Lab Evaluate Sequences and Series
12-3 Arithmetic Sequences and Series

Section 12B

Exploring Geometric Sequences and Series

12-4 Geometric Sequences and Series
12-5 Algebra Lab Explore Infinite Geometric Series
12-5 Mathematical Induction and Infinite Geometric Series
EXTENSION Area Under a Curve

Pacing Guide for 45-Minute Classes

Chapter 12

DAY 1	DAY 2	DAY 3	DAY 4	DAY 5
12-1 Lesson	Connecting Algebra to Geometry	12-2 Lesson	12-2 Technology Lab	12-3 Lesson
DAY 6	**DAY 7**	**DAY 8**	**DAY 9**	**DAY 10**
Multi-Step Test Prep Ready to Go On? 12-4 Lesson	12-4 Lesson	12-5 Algebra Lab	12-5 Lesson	12-5 Lesson Multi-Step Test Prep Ready to Go On?
DAY 11	**DAY 12**			
EXTENSION	Chapter 12 Test			

Pacing Guide for 90-Minute Classes

Chapter 12

DAY 1	DAY 2	DAY 3	DAY 4	DAY 5
12-1 Lesson Connecting Algebra to Geometry	12-2 Lesson 12-2 Technology Lab	12-3 Lesson Multi-Step Test Prep Ready to Go On? 12-4 Lesson	12-4 Lesson 12-5 Algebra Lab	12-5 Lesson Multi-Step Test Prep Ready to Go On?
DAY 6				
EXTENSION Chapter 12 Test				

ONGOING ASSESSMENT and INTERVENTION

	DIAGNOSE	PRESCRIBE
Assess Prior Knowledge	**Before Chapter 12**	
	Diagnose readiness for the chapter.	Prescribe intervention.
	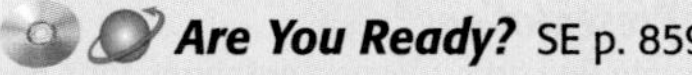 ***Are You Ready?*** SE p. 859	 ***Are You Ready? Intervention*** Skills 8, 53, 60, 72, 89
Formative Assessment	**Before Every Lesson**	
	Diagnose readiness for the lesson.	Prescribe intervention.
	Warm Up TE, every lesson	**Skills Bank** SE pp. S46–S73
		Reteach CRB, Ch. 1–12
	During Every Lesson	
	Diagnose understanding of lesson concepts.	Prescribe intervention.
	Check It Out! SE, every example	**Questioning Strategies** TE, every example
	Think and Discuss SE, every lesson	**Reading Strategies** CRB, every lesson
	Write About It SE, every lesson	***Success for ELL*** pp. 167–176
	Journal TE, every lesson	
	After Every Lesson	
	Diagnose mastery of lesson concepts.	Prescribe intervention.
	Lesson Quiz TE, every lesson	**Reteach** CRB, every lesson
	Alternative Assessment TE, every lesson	**Problem Solving** CRB, every lesson
	Test Prep SE, every lesson	**Test Prep Doctor** TE, every lesson
	Test and Practice Generator	***Homework Help* Online**
	Before Chapter 12 Testing	
	Diagnose mastery of concepts in the chapter.	Prescribe intervention.
	Ready to Go On? SE pp. 889, 909	***Ready to Go On? Intervention*** pp. 191–206
	Multi-Step Test Prep SE pp. 888, 908	**Scaffolding Questions** TE pp. 888, 908
	Section Quizzes AR pp. 225–226	
	Test and Practice Generator	
	Before High Stakes Testing	
	Diagnose mastery of benchmark concepts.	Prescribe intervention.
	College Entrance Exam Practice SE p. 917	***College Entrance Exam Practice***
	Standardized Test Prep SE pp. 920–921	***State Test Prep Workbook***
	***State Test Prep* CD-ROM**	
Summative Assessment	**After Chapter 12**	
	Check mastery of chapter concepts.	Prescribe intervention.
	Multiple-Choice Tests (Forms A, B, C)	**Reteach** CRB, every lesson
	Free-Response Tests (Forms A, B, C)	***Lesson Tutorial Videos*** Chapter 12
	Performance Assessment AR pp. 227–240	
	Test and Practice Generator	
	Check mastery of benchmark concepts.	Prescribe intervention.
	AYP State Tests	***State Test Prep Workbook***
	College Entrance Exams	***College Entrance Exam Practice***

KEY: **SE** = *Student Edition* **TE** = *Teacher's Edition* **CRB** = *Chapter Resource Book* **AR** = *Assessment Resources*  Available on CD-ROM Available online

Supporting the Teacher

Chapter 12 Resource Book

Practice A, B, C
pp. 3–5, 11–13, 19–21, 27–29, 35–37

Reading Strategies ELL
pp. 10, 18, 26, 34, 42

Reteach
pp. 6–7, 14–15, 22–23, 30–31, 38–39

Problem Solving
pp. 9, 17, 25, 33, 41

Challenge
pp. 8, 16, 24, 32, 40

Parent Letter pp. 1–2

Transparencies

Lesson Transparencies, Volume 4 .... Chapter 12
- Warm Ups
- Teaching Transparencies
- Additional Examples
- Lesson Quizzes

Alternate Openers: Explorations 84–88

Know-It Notebook .... Chapter 12
- Graphic Organizers

Teacher Tools

Power Presentations®
Complete PowerPoint® presentations for Chapter 12 lessons

Lesson Tutorial Videos®
Holt authors Ed Burger and Freddie Renfro present tutorials to support the Chapter 12 lessons.

One-Stop Planner®
Easy access to all Chapter 12 resources and assessments, as well as software for lesson planning, test generation, and puzzle creation

IDEA Works!®
Key Chapter 12 resources and assessments modified to address special learning needs

Lesson Plans .... pp. 84–88

Solutions Key .... Chapter 12

Algebra Posters

TechKeys **Lab Resources**

Project Teacher Support **Parent Resources**

Workbooks

Homework and Practice Workbook
Teacher's Guide .... pp. 84–88

Know-It Notebook
Teacher's Guide .... Chapter 12

Problem Solving Workbook
Teacher's Guide .... pp. 84–88

State Test Prep Workbook
Teacher's Guide

Technology Highlights for the Teacher

Power Presentations

Dynamic presentations to engage students. Complete PowerPoint® presentations for every lesson in Chapter 12.

2-1 Solving One-Step Equations

Isolate a variable by using inverse operations which "undo" operations on the variable.

An equation is like a balanced scale. To keep the balance, perform the same operation on both sides.

Inverse Operations	
Operation	**Inverse Operation**
Addition	Subtraction
Subtraction	Addition

One-Stop Planner

Easy access to Chapter 12 resources and assessments. Includes lesson-planning, test-generation, and puzzle-creation software.

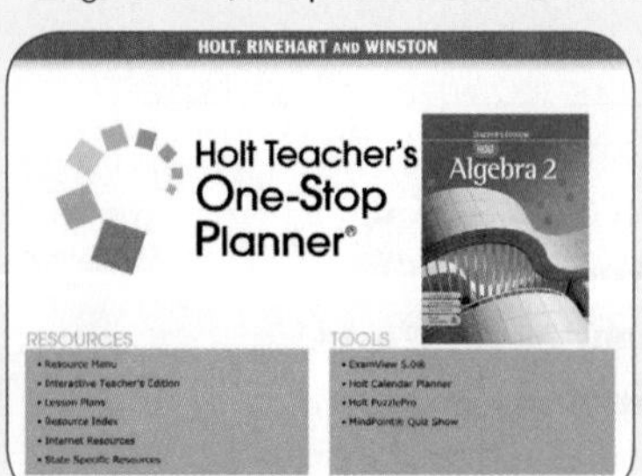

Premier Online Edition

Chapter 12 includes Tutorial Videos, Lesson Activities, Lesson Quizzes, Homework Help, and Chapter Project.

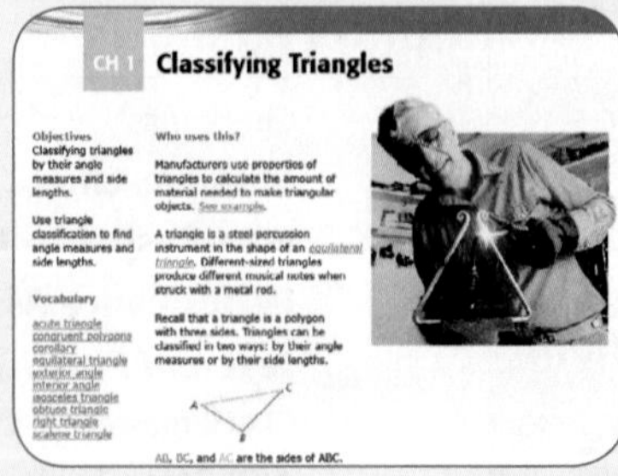

KEY: **SE** = *Student Edition* **TE** = *Teacher's Edition*  English Language Learners  Available on CD-ROM 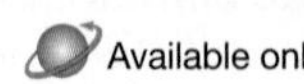 Available online

CHAPTER 12

Reaching All Learners

Resources for All Learners

Algebra Lab Activities	Chapter 12
Technology Lab Activities	Chapter 12
Homework and Practice Workbook	pp. 84–88
Know-It Notebook	Chapter 12
Problem Solving Workbook	pp. 84–88

DEVELOPING LEARNERS

Practice A	CRB, every lesson
Reteach	CRB, every lesson
Inclusion	TE pp. 891, 894
Questioning Strategies	TE, every example
Modified Chapter 12 Resources	*IDEA Works!*
Homework Help Online	

ON-LEVEL LEARNERS

Practice B	CRB, every lesson
Cognitive Strategies	TE p. 863
Multiple Representations	TE p. 901

ADVANCED LEARNERS

Practice C	CRB, every lesson
Challenge	CRB, every lesson
Reading and Writing Math EXTENSION	TE p. 861
Multi-Step Test Prep EXTENSION	TE pp. 888, 908
Critical Thinking	TE pp. 867, 875

English Language Learners

ENGLISH LANGUAGE LEARNERS

Are You Ready? Vocabulary	SE p. 859
Vocabulary Connections	SE p. 860
Lesson Vocabulary	SE, every lesson
Vocabulary Exercises	SE, every exercise set
Vocabulary Review	SE p. 912
English Language Learners	TE pp. 861, 871, 894, 906, 922, 923
Reading Strategies	CRB, every lesson
Success for English Language Learners	pp. 167–176
Multilingual Glossary	

Reaching All Learners Through...

Cognitive Strategies	TE p. 863
Number Sense	TE p. 864
Critical Thinking	TE pp. 867, 875
Cooperative Learning	TE p. 871
Visual Cues	TE pp. 872, 881
Modeling	TE p. 880
Inclusion	TE pp. 891, 894
Diversity	TE p. 896
Multiple Representations	TE p. 901
Test Prep Doctor	TE pp. 868, 876, 886, 897, 906, 917, 918, 920
Common Error Alerts	TE pp. 867, 873, 875, 877, 881, 883, 893, 901, 905, 911
Scaffolding Questions	TE pp. 888, 908

Technology Highlights for Reaching All Learners

Lesson Tutorial Videos

Starring Holt authors Ed Burger and Freddie Renfro! Live tutorials to support every lesson in Chapter 12.

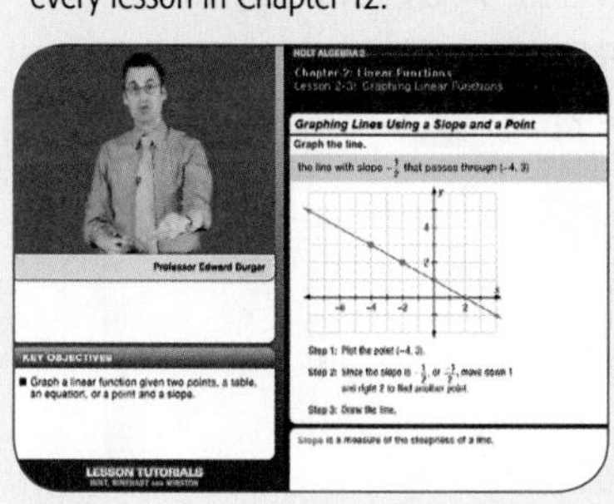

Multilingual Glossary

Searchable glossary includes definitions in English, Spanish, Vietnamese, Chinese, Hmong, Korean, and 4 other languages.

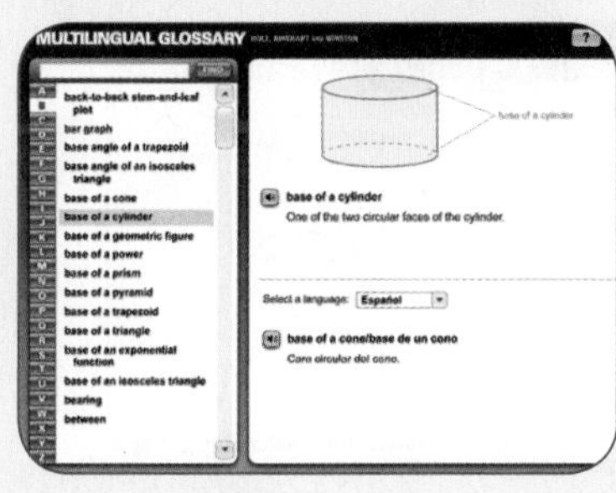

Online Interactivities

Interactive tutorials provide visually engaging alternative opportunities to learn concepts and master skills.

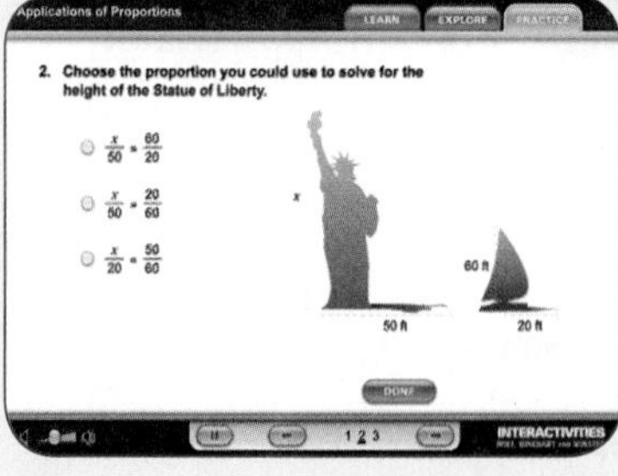

KEY: **SE** = *Student Edition* **TE** = *Teacher's Edition* **CRB** = *Chapter Resource Book* Available on CD-ROM Available online

Ongoing Assessment

Assessing Prior Knowledge

Determine whether students have the required prerequisite concepts and skills for success in Chapter 12.

Are You Ready? SPANISH .... SE p. 859
Warm Up .... TE, every lesson

Test Preparation

Provide review and practice for Chapter 12 and standardized tests.

Multi-Step Test Prep .... SE pp. 888, 908
Study Guide: Review .... SE pp. 912–915
Test Tackler .... SE pp. 918–919
Standardized Test Prep .... SE pp. 920–921
College Entrance Exam Practice .... SE p. 917
State Test Prep Workbook
***State Test Prep* CD-ROM**
IDEA Works!

Alternative Assessment

Assess students' understanding of Chapter 12 concepts and combined problem-solving skills.

Chapter 12 Project .... SE p. 858
Alternative Assessment .... TE, every lesson
Performance Assessment .... AR pp. 239–240
Portfolio Assessment .... AR p. xxxiv

Daily Assessment

Provide formative assessment for each day of Chapter 12.

Questioning Strategies .... TE, every example
Think and Discuss .... SE, every lesson
Check It Out! Exercises .... SE, every example
Write About It .... SE, every lesson
Journal .... TE, every lesson
Lesson Quiz .... TE, every lesson
Alternative Assessment .... TE, every lesson
Modified Lesson Quizzes .... *IDEA Works!*

Weekly Assessment

Provide formative assessment for each week of Chapter 12.

Multi-Step Test Prep .... SE pp. 888, 908
Ready to Go On? .... SE pp. 889, 909
Cumulative Assessment .... SE pp. 920–921
Test and Practice Generator .... *One-Stop Planner*

Formal Assessment

Provide summative assessment of Chapter 12 mastery.

Section Quizzes .... AR pp. 225–226
Chapter 12 Test .... SE p. 916
Chapter Test (Levels A, B, C) .... AR pp. 227–238
• Multiple Choice • Free Response
Cumulative Test .... AR pp. 241–244
Test and Practice Generator .... *One-Stop Planner*
Modified Chapter 12 Test .... *IDEA Works!*

Technology Highlights for Ongoing Assessment

Are You Ready? SPANISH

Automatically assess readiness and prescribe intervention for Chapter 12 prerequisite skills.

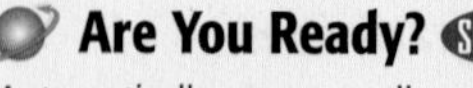

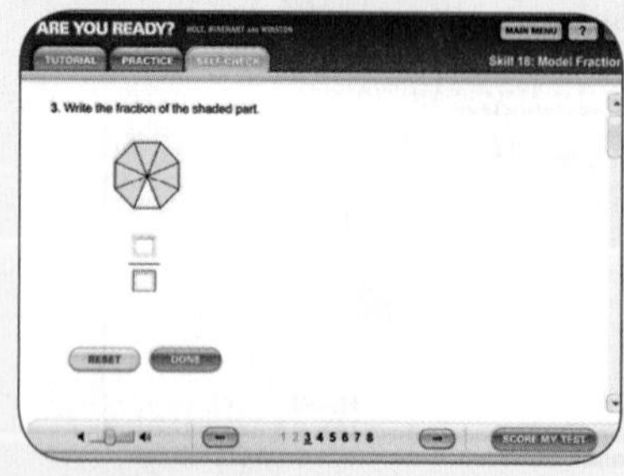

Ready to Go On?

Automatically assess understanding and prescribe intervention for Sections 12A and 12B.

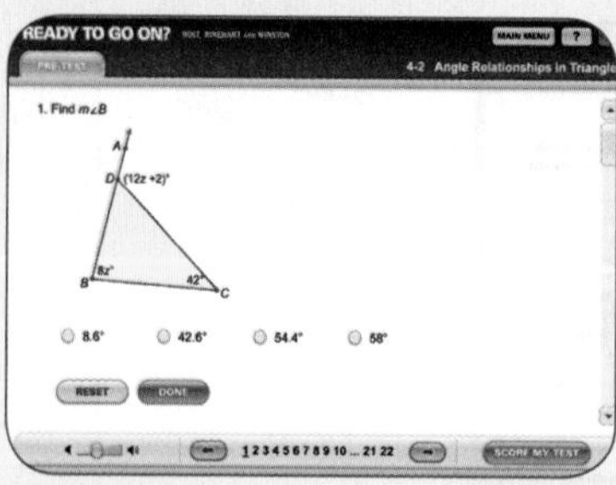

Test and Practice Generator

Use Chapter 12 problem banks to create assessments and worksheets to print out or deliver online. Includes dynamic problems.

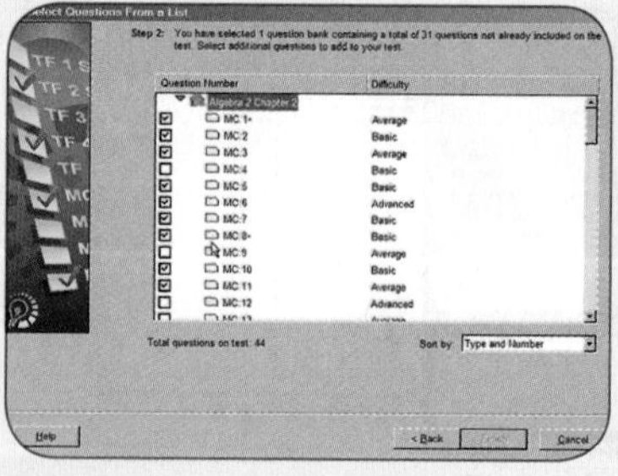

KEY: **SE** = *Student Edition* **TE** = *Teacher's Edition* **AR** = *Assessment Resources* SPANISH Spanish version available · Available on CD-ROM · Available online

Formal Assessment

Three levels (A, B, C) of multiple-choice and free-response chapter tests are available in the *Assessment Resources.*

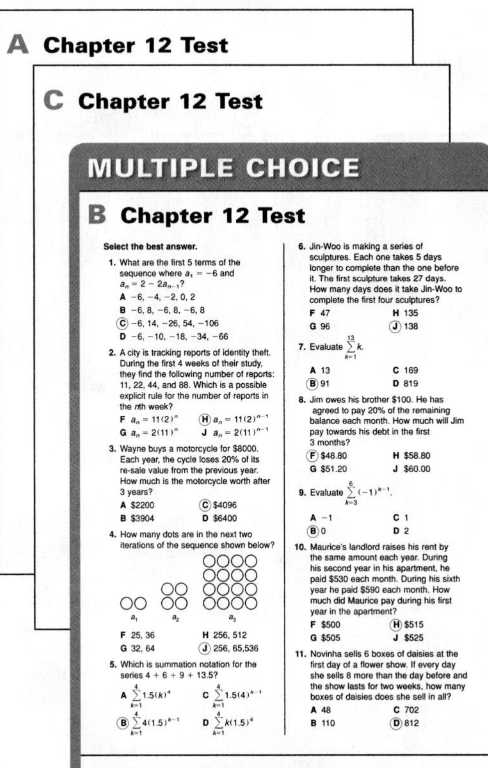

A Chapter 12 Test

C Chapter 12 Test

MULTIPLE CHOICE

B Chapter 12 Test

Select the best answer.

1. What are the first 5 terms of the sequence where $a_1 = -6$ and $a_n = 2 - 2a_{n-1}$?
A −6, −4, −2, 0, 2
B −6, 8, −6, 8, −6, 8
(C) −6, 14, −26, 54, −106
D −6, −10, −18, −34, −66

2. A city is tracking reports of identity theft. During the first 4 weeks of their study, they find the following number of reports: 11, 22, 44, and 88. Which is a possible explicit rule for the number of reports in the *n*th week?
F $a_n = 11(2)^n$ (H) $a_n = 11(2)^{n-1}$
G $a_n = 2(11)^n$ J $a_n = 2(11)^{n-1}$

3. Wayne buys a motorcycle for $8000. Each year, the cycle loses 20% of its re-sale value from the previous year. How much is the motorcycle worth after 3 years?
A $2200 (C) $4096
B $3904 D $6400

4. How many dots are in the next two iterations of the sequence shown below?
F 25, 36 H 256, 512
G 32, 64 (J) 256, 65,536

5. Which is summation notation for the series 4 + 6 + 9 + 13.5?
A $\sum_{k=1}^{4} 1.5(k)^k$ C $\sum_{k=1}^{4} 1.5(4)^{k-1}$
(B) $\sum_{k=1}^{4} 4(1.5)^{k-1}$ D $\sum_{k=1}^{4} k(1.5)^4$

6. Jin-Woo is making a series of sculptures. Each one takes 5 days longer to complete than the one before it. The first sculpture takes 27 days. How many days does it take Jin-Woo to complete the first four sculptures?
F 47 H 135
G 96 (J) 138

7. Evaluate $\sum_{k=1}^{13} k$.
A 13 C 169
(B) 91 D 819

8. Jim owes his brother $100. He has agreed to pay 20% of the remaining balance each month. How much will Jim pay towards his debt in the first 3 months?
(F) $48.80 H $58.80
G $51.20 J $60.00

9. Evaluate $\sum_{k=3}^{6} (-1)^{k-1}$.
A −1 C 1
(B) 0 D 2

10. Maurice's landlord raises his rent by the same amount each year. During his second year in his apartment, he paid $530 each month. During his sixth year he paid $590 each month. How much did Maurice pay during his first year in the apartment?
F $500 (H) $515
G $505 J $525

11. Novinha sells 6 boxes of daisies at the first day of a flower show. If every day she sells 8 more than the day before and the show lasts for two weeks, how many boxes of daisies does she sell in all?
A 48 C 702
B 110 (D) 812

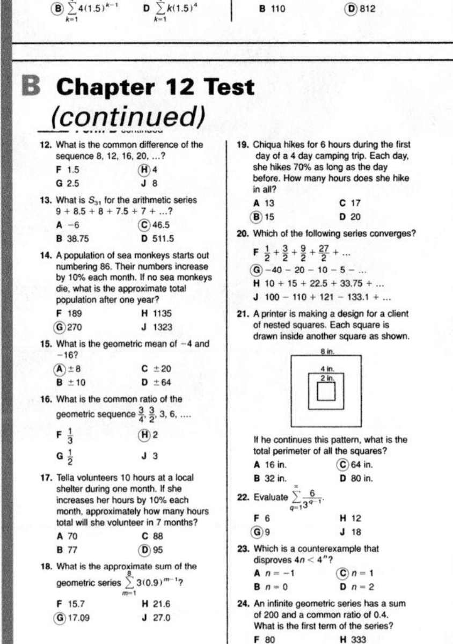

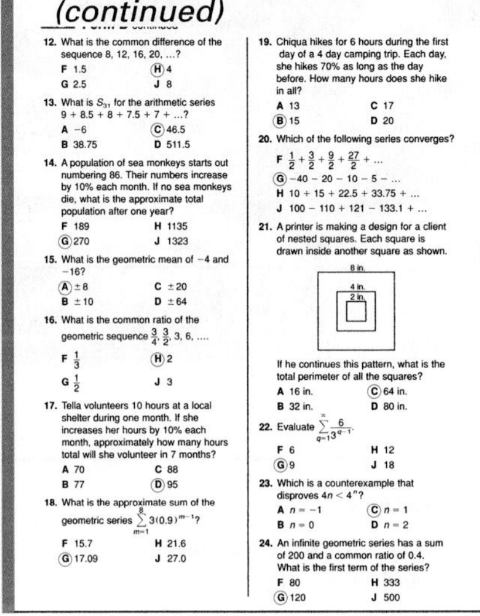

B Chapter 12 Test *(continued)*

12. What is the common difference of the sequence 8, 12, 16, 20, ...?
F 1.5 (H) 4
G 2.5 J 8

13. What is S_{11} for the arithmetic series 9 + 8.5 + 8 + 7.5 + 7 + ...?
A −6 (C) 46.5
B 38.75 D 511.5

14. A population of sea monkeys starts out numbering 86. Their numbers increase by 10% each month. If no sea monkeys die, what is the approximate total population after one year?
F 189 H 1135
(G) 270 J 1323

15. What is the geometric mean of −4 and −16?
(A) ±8 C ±20
B ±10 D ±64

16. What is the common ratio of the geometric sequence $\frac{3}{4}, \frac{3}{2}$, 3, 6, ...
F $\frac{1}{3}$ (H) 2
G $\frac{1}{2}$ J 3

17. Tella volunteers 10 hours at a local shelter during one month. If she increases her hours by 10% each month, approximately how many hours total will she volunteer in 7 months?
A 70 C 88
B 77 (D) 95

18. What is the approximate sum of the geometric series $\sum_{m=1}^{5} 3(0.9)^{m-1}$?
F 15.7 H 21.6
(G) 17.09 J 27.0

19. Chiqua hikes for 6 hours during the first day of a 4 day camping trip. Each day, she hikes 70% as long as the day before. How many hours does she hike in all?
A 13 C 17
(B) 15 D 20

20. Which of the following series converges?
F $\frac{1}{2} + \frac{3}{2} + \frac{9}{2} + \frac{27}{2} + ...$
(G) −40 − 20 − 10 − 5 − ...
H 10 + 15 + 22.5 + 33.75 + ...
J 100 − 110 + 121 − 133.1 + ...

21. A printer is making a design for a client of nested squares. Each square is drawn inside another square as shown.
If he continues this pattern, what is the total perimeter of all the squares?
A 16 in. (C) 64 in.
B 32 in. D 80 in.

22. Evaluate $\sum_{q=1}^{\infty} \frac{6}{3^{q-1}}$.
F 6 H 12
(G) 9 J 18

23. Which is a counterexample that disproves $4n < 4^n$?
A $n = -1$ (C) $n = 1$
B $n = 0$ D $n = 2$

24. An infinite geometric series has a sum of 200 and a common ratio of 0.4. What is the first term of the series?
F 80 H 333
(G) 120 J 500

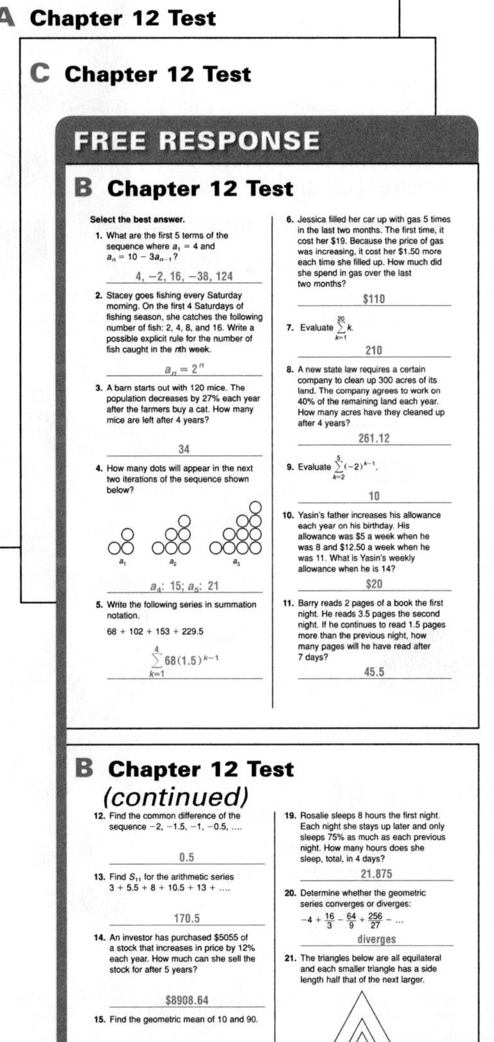

A Chapter 12 Test

C Chapter 12 Test

FREE RESPONSE

B Chapter 12 Test

Select the best answer.

1. What are the first 5 terms of the sequence where $a_1 = 4$ and $a_n = 10 - 3a_{n-1}$?
4, −2, 16, −38, 124

2. Stacey goes fishing every Saturday morning. On the first 4 Saturdays of fishing season, she catches the following number of fish: 2, 4, 8, and 16. Write a possible explicit rule for the number of fish caught in the *n*th week.
$a_n = 2^n$

3. A barn starts out with 120 mice. The population decreases by 27% each year after the farmers buy a cat. How many mice are left after 4 years?
34

4. How many dots will appear in the next two iterations of the sequence shown below?
a_4: 15; a_5: 21

5. Write the following series in summation notation.
68 + 102 + 153 + 229.5
$\sum_{k=1}^{4} 68(1.5)^{k-1}$

6. Jessica filled her car up with gas 5 times in the last two months. The first time, it cost her $19. Because the price of gas was increasing, it cost her $1.50 more each time she filled up. How much did she spend in gas over the last two months?
$110

7. Evaluate $\sum_{k=1}^{20} k$.
210

8. A new state law requires a certain company to clean up 300 acres of its land. The company agrees to work on 40% of the remaining land each year. How many acres have they cleaned up after 4 years?
261.12

9. Evaluate $\sum_{k=2}^{5} (-2)^{k-1}$.
10

10. Yasin's father increases his allowance each year on his birthday. His allowance was $5 a week when he was 8 and $12.50 a week when he was 11. What is Yasin's weekly allowance when he is 14?
$20

11. Barry reads 2 pages of a book the first night. He reads 3.5 pages the second night. If he continues to read 1.5 pages more than the previous night, how many pages will he have read after 7 days?
45.5

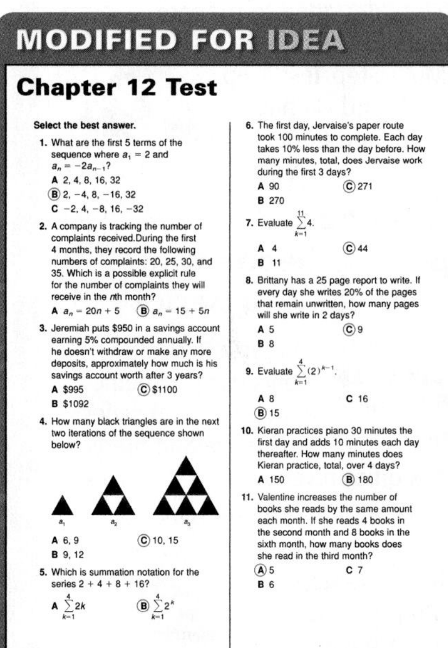

MODIFIED FOR IDEA

Chapter 12 Test

Select the best answer.

1. What are the first 5 terms of the sequence where $a_1 = 2$ and $a_n = -2a_{n-1}$?
A 2, 4, 8, 16, 32
(B) 2, −4, 8, −16, 32
C −2, 4, −8, 16, −32

2. A company is tracking the number of complaints received. During the first 4 months, they record the following numbers of complaints: 20, 25, 30, and 35. Which is a possible explicit rule for the number of complaints they will receive in the *n*th month?
A $a_n = 20n + 5$ (B) $a_n = 15 + 5n$

3. Jeremiah puts $950 in a savings account earning 5% compounded annually. If he doesn't withdraw or make any more deposits, approximately how much is his savings account worth after 3 years?
A $995 (C) $1100
B $1092

4. How many black triangles are in the next two iterations of the sequence shown below?
A 6, 9 (C) 10, 15
B 9, 12

5. Which is summation notation for the series 2 + 4 + 8 + 16?
A $\sum_{k=1}^{4} 2k$ (B) $\sum_{k=1}^{4} 2^k$

6. The first day, Jervaise's paper route took 100 minutes to complete. Each day takes 10% less than the day before. How many minutes, total, does Jervaise work during the first 3 days?
A 90 (C) 271
B 270

7. Evaluate $\sum_{k=1}^{11} 4$.
A 4 (C) 44
B 11

8. Brittany has a 25 page report to write. If every day she writes 20% of the pages that remain unwritten, how many pages will she write in 2 days?
A 5 (C) 9
B 8

9. Evaluate $\sum_{k=1}^{4} (2)^{k-1}$.
A 8 C 16
(B) 15

10. Kieran practices piano 30 minutes the first day and adds 10 minutes each day thereafter. How many minutes does Kieran practice, total, over 4 days?
A 150 (B) 180

11. Valentine increases the number of books she reads by the same amount each month. If she reads 4 books in the second month and 8 books in the sixth month, how many books does she read in the third month?
(A) 5 C 7
B 6

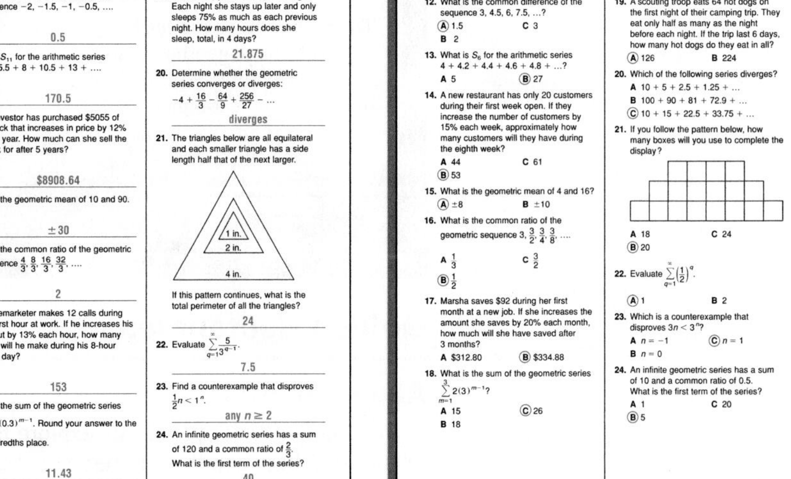

B Chapter 12 Test *(continued)*

12. Find the common difference of the sequence −2, −1.5, −1, −0.5, ...
0.5

13. Find S_{11} for the arithmetic series 3 + 5.5 + 8 + 10.5 + 13 + ...
170.5

14. An investor has purchased $5055 of a stock that increases in price by 12% each year. How much can she sell the stock for after 5 years?
$8908.64

15. Find the geometric mean of 10 and 90.
±30

16. Find the common ratio of the geometric sequence $\frac{4}{3}, \frac{8}{3}, \frac{16}{3}, \frac{32}{3}$, ...
2

17. A telemarketer makes 12 calls during his first hour at work. If he increases his output by 13% each hour, how many calls will he make during his 8-hour work day?
153

18. Find the sum of the geometric series $\sum_{m=1}^{7} 8(0.3)^{m-1}$. Round your answer to the hundredths place.
11.43

19. Rosalie sleeps 8 hours the first night. Each night she stays up later and only sleeps 75% as much as each previous night. How many hours does she sleep, total, in 4 days?
21.875

20. Determine whether the geometric series converges or diverges:
$-4 + \frac{16}{3} - \frac{64}{9} + \frac{256}{27} - ...$
diverges

21. The triangles below are all equilateral and each smaller triangle has a side length half that of the next larger.
If this pattern continues, what is the total perimeter of all the triangles?
24

22. Evaluate $\sum_{q=1}^{\infty} \frac{5}{3^{q-1}}$.
7.5

23. Find a counterexample that disproves $\frac{1}{2}n < 1^n$.
any $n \geq 2$

24. An infinite geometric series has a sum of 120 and a common ratio of $\frac{2}{3}$. What is the first term of the series?
40

Chapter 12 Test *(continued)*

12. What is the common difference of the sequence 3, 4.5, 6, 7.5, ...?
(A) 1.5 C 3
B 2

13. What is S_6 for the arithmetic series 4 + 4.2 + 4.4 + 4.6 + 4.8 + ...?
A 5 (B) 27

14. A new restaurant has only 20 customers during their first week open. If they increase the number of customers by 15% each week, approximately how many customers will they have during the eighth week?
A 44 C 61
(B) 53

15. What is the geometric mean of 4 and 16?
(A) ±8 B ±10

16. What is the common ratio of the geometric sequence 3, $\frac{3}{2}, \frac{3}{4}, \frac{3}{8}$, ...
A $\frac{1}{3}$ C $\frac{3}{2}$
(B) $\frac{1}{2}$

17. Marsha saves $92 during her first month at a new job. If she increases the amount she saves by 20% each month, how much will she have saved after 3 months?
A $312.80 (B) $334.88

18. What is the sum of the geometric series $\sum_{m=1}^{3} 2(3)^{m-1}$?
A 15 (C) 26
B 18

19. A scouting troop eats 64 hot dogs on the first night of their camping trip. They eat only half as many as the night before each night. If the trip last 6 days, how many hot dogs do they eat in all?
(A) 126 B 224

20. Which of the following series diverges?
A 10 + 5 + 2.5 + 1.25 + ...
B 100 + 90 + 81 + 72.9 + ...
(C) 10 + 15 + 22.5 + 33.75 + ...

21. If you follow the pattern below, how many boxes will you use to complete the display?
A 18 C 24
(B) 20

22. Evaluate $\sum_{q=1}^{\infty} \left(\frac{1}{2}\right)^q$.
(A) 1 B 2

23. Which is a counterexample that disproves $3n < 3^n$?
A $n = -1$ (C) $n = 1$
B $n = 0$

24. An infinite geometric series has a sum of 10 and a common ratio of 0.5. What is the first term of the series?
A 1 C 20
(B) 5

Create and customize Chapter 12 Tests. Instantly generate multiple test versions, answer keys, and practice versions of test items.

CHAPTER 12

SECTION 12A

Exploring Arithmetic Sequences and Series

On page 888, students use arithmetic sequences and series to analyze tetrahedral kites.

Exercises designed to prepare students for success on the Multi-Step Test Prep can be found on pages 867, 876, and 886.

SECTION 12B

Exploring Geometric Sequences and Series

On page 908, students use geometric sequences and series to analyze and predict the box office revenue of hit movies.

Exercises designed to prepare students for success on the Multi-Step Test Prep can be found on pages 897 and 906.

CHAPTER 12

Sequences and Series

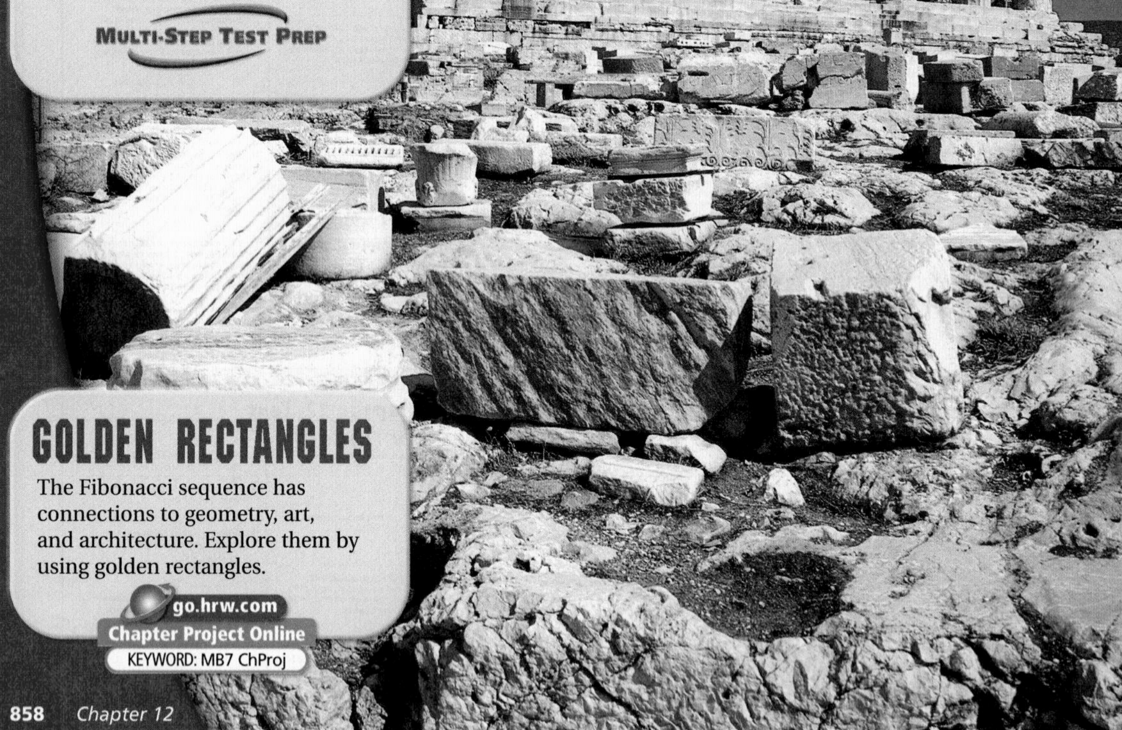

GOLDEN RECTANGLES

The Fibonacci sequence has connections to geometry, art, and architecture. Explore them by using golden rectangles.

go.hrw.com
Chapter Project Online
KEYWORD: MB7 ChProj

Golden Rectangles

About the Project

In the Chapter Project, students explore the relationship between the Fibonacci sequence and the golden ratio. Then they construct a golden rectangle and discover how its proportions relate to the golden ratio.

Project Resources

All project resources for teachers and students are provided online.

Materials:

- calculator
- compass and straightedge (MK)

go.hrw.com
Project Teacher Support
KEYWORD: MB7 ProjectTS

ARE YOU READY?

Vocabulary

Match each term on the left with a definition on the right.

1. exponential function E
2. function A
3. linear equation B
4. quadratic function D

A. a pairing in which there is exactly one output value for each input value
B. an equation whose graph is a straight line
C. a function defined by a quotient of two polynomials
D. a function of the form $f(x) = ax^2 + bx + c$, where $a \neq 0$
E. a function of the form $f(x) = ab^x$, where $a \neq 0$ and $b \neq 1$

Simplify Radical Expressions

Simplify each expression.

5. $\sqrt{25} \cdot \sqrt{36}$ 30
6. $\sqrt{121} - \sqrt{81}$ 2
7. $\sqrt{\frac{1}{49}}$ $\frac{1}{7}$
8. $\frac{\sqrt{16}}{\sqrt{64}}$ $\frac{1}{2}$

Evaluate Powers

Evaluate.

9. $(-3)^3$ -27
10. $(-5)^4$ 625
11. $1 - (-2^3)^3$ 513
12. $\frac{2^2 \cdot 2^7}{(2^2)^5}$ $\frac{1}{2}$

Solve for a Variable

Solve each equation for x.

13. $y = 12x - 5$ $x = \frac{y+5}{12}$
14. $y = -\frac{x}{3} + 1$ $x = -3y + 3$
15. $y = -9 + x^2$ $x = \pm\sqrt{y+9}$
16. $y = -4(x^2 - 9)$ $x = \pm\frac{\sqrt{36-y}}{2}$

Evaluate Expressions

Evaluate each expression for $x = 2$, $y = 12$, and $z = 24$.

17. $\frac{y(y+1)}{3x}$ 26
18. $z + (y - 1)x$ 46
19. $y\left(\frac{x+z}{2}\right)$ 156
20. $z\left(\frac{1-y}{1-x}\right)$ 264

Counterexamples Possible answers given.

Find a counterexample to show that each statement is false.

21. $n^2 = n$, where n is a real number $2^2 \neq 2$
22. $n^3 \geq n^2 \geq n$, where n is a real number $\left(\frac{1}{2}\right)^3 < \left(\frac{1}{2}\right)^2 < \left(\frac{1}{2}\right)^1$
23. $\frac{1}{n} > \frac{1}{n^2}$, where n is a real number $\frac{1}{1} = \frac{1}{1^2}$ or $\frac{1}{-2} < \frac{1}{(-2)^2}$
24. $\frac{2}{n} \neq \frac{n}{2}$, where n is a real number $\frac{2}{2} = \frac{2}{2}$

CHAPTER 12

ARE YOU READY?

Organizer

Objective: Assess students' understanding of prerequisite skills.

Prerequisite Skills

Simplify Radical Expressions
Evaluate Powers
Solve for a Variable
Evaluate Expressions
Counterexamples

Assessing Prior Knowledge

INTERVENTION 

Diagnose and Prescribe

Use this page to determine whether intervention is necessary or whether enrichment is appropriate.

Resources

 ***Are You Ready? Intervention and Enrichment* Worksheets**

***Are You Ready?* CD-ROM**

 ***Are You Ready?* Online**

my.hrw.com

ARE YOU READY? Diagnose and Prescribe

Prerequisite Skill	*Are You Ready? Intervention,* Chapter 12 Worksheets	CD-ROM	Online
Simplify Radical Expressions	Skill 53	Activity 53	Diagnose and Prescribe Online
Evaluate Powers	Skill 8	Activity 8	
Solve for a Variable	Skill 72	Activity 72	
Evaluate Expressions	Skill 60	Activity 60	
Counterexamples	Skill 89	Activity 89	

Are You Ready? Enrichment, Chapter 12
Worksheets
CD-ROM
Online

CHAPTER 12 Study Guide: Preview

Organizer

Objective: Help students organize the new concepts they will learn in Chapter 12.

Online Edition
Multilingual Glossary

Resources

Puzzle Pro
One-Stop Planner®

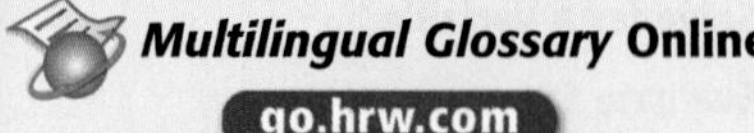

Multilingual Glossary **Online**

go.hrw.com
KEYWORD: MB7 Glossary

Answers to *Vocabulary Connections*

Possible answers:

1. *Sequence* relates to the order in which things are arranged. A number sequence might be numbers placed in a particular order.
2. There are a finite number of possible sums on a pair of number cubes. A finite sequence has an end.
3. You can combine colors in an infinite number of ways to create a painting. An infinite sequence continues without end.
4. A television series is a group of shows that follow each other. A mathematical series might be a set of numbers that follow each other.
5. Possible answer: Each term in a polynomial is separated by a + or − sign. A term of a sequence is probably one number in the sequence.

CHAPTER 12 Study Guide: Preview

Where You've Been

Previously, you

- studied sets of numbers, including natural numbers and perfect squares.
- used patterns of differences or ratios to classify data.
- graphed and evaluated linear and exponential functions.

In This Chapter

You will study

- patterns of numbers, called *sequences*, and their sums, called *series*.
- patterns to determine whether sequences are arithmetic or geometric.
- how to write and evaluate sequences and series.

Where You're Going

You can use the skills learned in this chapter

- in future math classes, especially Precalculus and Calculus.
- in Physics classes to model patterns, such as the heights of bouncing objects.
- outside of school to calculate the growth of financial investments.

Key Vocabulary/Vocabulario

converge	convergir
diverge	divergir
explicit formula	fórmula explícita
finite sequence	sucesión finita
infinite sequence	sucesión infinita
iteration	iteración
limit	límite
recursive formula	fórmula recurrente
sequence	sucesión
series	serie
term of a sequence	término de una sucesión

Vocabulary Connections

To become familiar with some of the vocabulary terms in the chapter, consider the following. You may refer to the chapter, the glossary, or a dictionary if you like.

1. What does the word **sequence** mean in everyday usage? What might a number sequence refer to?
2. The word *finite* means "having definite or definable limits." Give examples of sentences that use the word *finite*. Explain what a **finite sequence** might refer to.
3. Using the previous definition of *finite*, give examples of sentences that use the word *infinite*. Explain what an **infinite sequence** might refer to.
4. What does a television series refer to? What might a mathematical **series** mean?
5. State what a term of a polynomial refers to. Then write a possible description for a **term of a sequence**.

Writing Strategy: Write a Convincing Argument

Being able to write a convincing argument about a math concept shows that you understand the material well. You can use a four-step method to write an effective argument as shown in the response to the exercise below.

From Lesson 11-2

35. Write About It Describe the difference between theoretical probability and experimental probability. Give an example in which they may differ.

Step 1 **Identify the goal.**

The goal is to describe the difference between theoretical and experimental probability.

Step 2 **Provide a statement of response to the goal.**

Theoretical probability is based purely on mathematics, but experimental probability is based on the results of an experiment.

Step 3 **Provide the evidence to support your statement.**

In a coin toss, the theoretical probability of tossing heads is $\frac{\text{number of favorable outcomes}}{\text{number of outcomes in the sample space}} = \frac{1}{2}$.
The experimental probability of tossing heads is $\frac{\text{number of times the event occurs}}{\text{number of trials}}$.
In one trial, the result is either heads or tails, so the experimental probability will be 1 or 0. The theoretical probability is still $\frac{1}{2}$.

Step 4 **Summarize your argument.**

Because theoretical probability is based solely on the mathematical outcomes, it never changes. Experimental probability is based on actual results, so it may change with each trial of an experiment.

Try This

Use the four-step method described above to answer each question.

1. A number cube is rolled 20 times and lands on the number 3 twice. What is the fewest number of rolls needed for the experimental probability of rolling a 3 to equal the theoretical probability of rolling a 3? Explain how you got your answer.
2. Aidan has narrowed his college choices down to 9 schools. He plans to visit 3 or 4 schools before the end of his junior year. How many more ways can he visit a group of 4 schools than a group of 3 schools? Explain.

Organizer

Objective: Help students apply strategies to understand and retain key concepts.

Online Edition

Resources

Chapter 12 Resource Book
Reading Strategies

ENGLISH LANGUAGE LEARNERS

Writing Strategy: Write a Convincing Argument

Discuss Encourage students to suggest reasons why they might benefit from writing a convincing argument about a math concept. Help them realize that clearly articulating math concepts will enable them to understand the concepts more fully.

Extend As students work through Chapter 12, have them explain the new concepts in their own words. Suggest that the class work together to provide explanations that are as complete as possible. Ask students to suggest connections to concepts they have already learned and tell how those concepts are extended by the new material

Answers

1. Step 1: Find the least number of rolls for the experimental and theoretical probabilities to be equal. Step 2: Both probabilities are ratios that can be compared. Step 3: Theoretical P(3) $= \frac{1}{6}$, which is equivalent to $\frac{2}{12}$, $\frac{3}{18}$, $\frac{4}{24}$, etc. After 20 rolls, the first possible opportunity for the probabilities to be equal is at $\frac{4}{24}$, so at least 4 more rolls are needed.
   Step 4: If the number 3 is rolled 2 out of the next 4 rolls, the experimental probability would be $\frac{4}{24}$, which is equal to the theoretical probability, $\frac{1}{6}$.
2. See p. A46.

SECTION

12A Exploring Arithmetic Sequences and Series

One-Minute Section Planner

Lesson	Lab Resources	Materials
Lesson 12-1 Introduction to Sequences • Find the *n*th term of a sequence. • Write rules for sequences. ☑ SAT-10 ☑ NAEP ☑ ACT ☑ SAT ☑ SAT Subject Tests	***Algebra Lab Activities*** 12-1 Algebra Lab	**Optional** graphing calculator
Lesson 12-2 Series and Summation Notation • Evaluate the sum of a series expressed in sigma notation. ☑ SAT-10 ☐ NAEP ☐ ACT ☑ SAT ☑ SAT Subject Tests		**Optional** graphing calculator
12-2 Technology Lab Evaluate Sequences and Series • Use a graphing calculator to generate the terms of a sequence and find the sums of series. ☑ SAT-10 ☑ NAEP ☑ ACT ☑ SAT ☑ SAT Subject Tests	***Technology Lab Activities*** 12-2 Lab Recording Sheet	**Required** graphing calculator
Lesson 12-3 Arithmetic Sequences and Series • Find the indicated terms of an arithmetic sequence. • Find the sums of arithmetic series. ☑ SAT-10 ☑ NAEP ☑ ACT ☑ SAT ☑ SAT Subject Tests		**Optional** centimeter squares or cubes (MK), graphing calculator

MK = *Manipulatives Kit*

Section Overview

Sequences and Series

Lessons 12-1, 12-2

An introduction to finite sequences and series prepares students for infinite sequences and series they will encounter in calculus.

A **recursive formula** defines the nth term of a sequence a_n in terms of one or more previous terms, such as a_{n-1}.

Example: 1, 1, 2, 3, 5, 8, ... (Fibonacci sequence)

$a_1 = 1, a_2 = 1$, and $a_n = a_{n-2} + a_{n-1}$, $n \geq 3$

An **explicit formula** defines the nth term of a sequence a_n as a function of n.

Example: 2, 4, 6, 8, 10, ...

$a_n = 2n, n > 0$

Summation notation is used to represent a series.

$$\sum_{k=1}^{n} a_n = a_1 + a_2 + a_3 + \cdots + a_n$$

In the notation, k is the starting number, n is the last value, and a_n is an explicit formula of a sequence.

Example:

$$\sum_{k=3}^{5}(4 + k^2) = (4 + 3^2) + (4 + 4^2) + (4 + 5^2)$$
$$= 13 + 20 + 29$$
$$= 62$$

Arithmetic Sequences and Series

Lesson 12-3

Arithmetic sequences and series have applications that are easy to understand and recognize.

In an **arithmetic sequence**, the terms differ by a *common difference, d.*

Example: 8, 5, 2, −1, −4, ...

−3 −3 −3 −3 ← $d = -3$

The **7th term** of this arithmetic sequence is

$$a_n = a_1 + (n - 1)d$$
$$a_7 = 8 + (7 - 1)(-3)$$
$$= 8 + (-18)$$
$$= -10$$

An **arithmetic series** is the indicated sum of the terms of an arithmetic sequence.

Example: 8 + 5 + 2 + −1 + −4 + ...

The **sum of the first 7 terms** of this arithmetic series is

$$S_n = n\left(\frac{a_1 + a_n}{2}\right)$$
$$S_7 = 7\left(\frac{8 + (a_7)}{2}\right)$$
$$= 7\left(\frac{8 + (-10)}{2}\right)$$
$$= 7\left(\frac{-2}{2}\right) = -7$$

12-1 Organizer

Pacing: Traditional 1 day
Block $\frac{1}{2}$ day

Objectives: Find the *n*th term of a sequence.

Write rules for sequences.

Algebra Lab
In *Algebra Lab Activities*

Online Edition
Tutorial Videos

Power Presentations with PowerPoint®

Warm Up

Evaluate.

1. $(-1)^8$ 1 **2.** $(11)^2$ 121

3. $(-9)^3$ −729 **4.** $(3)^4$ 81

Evaluate each expression for $x = 4$.

5. $2x + 1$ 9

6. $0.5x + 1.5$ 3.5

7. $x^2 - 1$ 15

8. $2^x + 3$ 19

Also available on transparency

Math Humor

Q: Why did the fractal lose the dance contest?

A: Its third step was out of sequence.

12-1 Introduction to Sequences

A2.7.2 Write the formula for the general term for arithmetic and geometric sequences and make connections to linear and exponential functions.

Objectives
Find the *n*th term of a sequence.

Write rules for sequences.

Vocabulary
sequence
term of a sequence
infinite sequence
finite sequence
recursive formula
explicit formula
iteration

Who uses this?
Sequences can be used to model many natural phenomena, such as the changes in a rabbit population over time.

In 1202, Italian mathematician Leonardo Fibonacci described how fast rabbits breed under ideal circumstances. Fibonacci noted the number of pairs of rabbits each month and formed a famous pattern called the *Fibonacci sequence.*

A **sequence** is an ordered set of numbers. Each number in the sequence is a **term of the sequence**. A sequence may be an **infinite sequence** that continues without end, such as the natural numbers, or a **finite sequence** that has a limited number of terms, such as $\{1, 2, 3, 4\}$.

Reading Math
a_n is read "a sub *n*."

You can think of a sequence as a function with sequential natural numbers as the domain and the terms of the sequence as the range. Values in the domain are called *term numbers* and are represented by *n*. Instead of function notation, such as $a(n)$, sequence values are written by using subscripts. The first term is a_1, the second term is a_2, and the *n*th term is a_n. Because a sequence is a function, each number *n* has only one term value associated with it, a_n.

Term number	n	1	2	3	4	5	Domain
Term value	a_n	1	1	2	3	5	Range

In the Fibonacci sequence, the first two terms are 1 and each term after that is the sum of the two terms before it. This can be expressed by using the rule $a_1 = 1$, $a_2 = 1$, and $a_n = a_{n-2} + a_{n-1}$, where $n \geq 3$. This is a *recursive formula.* A **recursive formula** is a rule in which one or more previous terms are used to generate the next term.

EXAMPLE 1 Finding Terms of a Sequence by Using a Recursive Formula

Find the first 5 terms of the sequence with $a_1 = 5$ and $a_n = 2a_{n-1} + 1$ for $n \geq 2$.

The first term is given, $a_1 = 5$.

Substitute a_1 into the rule to find a_2. Continue using each term to find the next term.

n	$2a_{n-1} + 1$	a_n
1	Given	5
2	$2(5) + 1$	11
3	$2(11) + 1$	23
4	$2(23) + 1$	47
5	$2(47) + 1$	95

The first 5 terms are 5, 11, 23, 47, and 95.

Find the first 5 terms of each sequence.

1a. $a_1 = -5$, $a_n = a_{n-1} - 8$
−5, −13, −21, −29, −37

1b. $a_1 = 2$, $a_n = -3a_{n-1}$
2, −6, 18, −54, 162

State Resources

1 Introduce

EXPLORATION

12-1 Introduction to Sequences

A graphic designer uses software to enlarge a square repeatedly. The original dimensions of the square (stage 1) are 10 inches by 10 inches. The table shows the square's area as it is enlarged.

Stage	1	2	3	4	5
Area (in²)	100	110	121	133.1	146.41

1. Look for a pattern in the table. How is each value in the list of areas related to the previous one?
2. By how much does the software enlarge the square at each stage?
3. Find the area of the square at the next three stages.
4. What type of function models the data in the table? Why?
5. What is the domain of the function in this situation?

THINK AND DISCUSS

6. **Explain** how you can find the area of the square at stage 10.
7. **Explain** how you can find the area of the square at stage 11 once you know the area of the square at stage 10.

Motivate

Ask students to identify the next 3 terms in the pattern 2, 4, 6, 8, ... 10, 12, 14 Discuss how they decided on their answers. Then ask students to identify the next 3 terms in the pattern 2, 4, 8, 16, ... 32, 64, 128 Discuss how they decided on their answers. Explain that number patterns like these that follow a rule are called *sequences*.

Explorations and answers are provided in the *Explorations* binder.

go.hrw.com
State Resources Online
KEYWORD: MB7 Resources

In some sequences, you can find the value of a term when you do not know its preceding term. An **explicit formula** defines the nth term of a sequence as a function of n.

EXAMPLE 2 Finding Terms of a Sequence by Using an Explicit Formula

Find the first 5 terms of the sequence $a_n = 2^n - 3$.

Make a table. Evaluate the sequence for $n = 1$ through $n = 5$.

n	$2^n - 3$	a_n
1	$2^1 - 3$	−1
2	$2^2 - 3$	1
3	$2^3 - 3$	5
4	$2^4 - 3$	13
5	$2^5 - 3$	29

The first 5 terms are −1, 1, 5, 13, and 29.

Check Use a graphing calculator.
Enter $y = 2^x - 3$ and make a table.

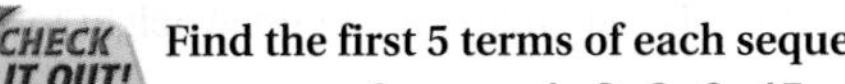

CHECK IT OUT! **Find the first 5 terms of each sequence.**

2a. $a_n = n^2 - 2n$ −1, 0, 3, 8, 15 **2b.** $a_n = 3n - 5$ −2, 1, 4, 7, 10

You can use your knowledge of functions to write rules for sequences.

EXAMPLE 3 Writing Rules for Sequences

Write a possible explicit rule for the nth term of each sequence.

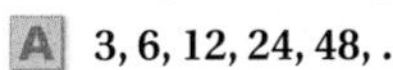

A 3, 6, 12, 24, 48, ...

Examine the differences and ratios.

Ratios		2	2	2	2
Terms	3	6	12	24	48
1st differences		3	6	12	24
2nd differences			3	6	12

The ratio is constant. The sequence is exponential with a base of 2.

Look for a pattern with powers of 2.

$a_1 = 3 = 3(2)^0$, $a_2 = 6 = 3(2)^1$, $a_3 = 12 = 3(2)^2$, ...

A pattern is $3(2)^{n-1}$. One explicit rule is $a_n = 3(2)^{n-1}$.

Remember!
Linear patterns have constant first differences. Quadratic patterns have constant second differences. Exponential patterns have constant ratios. (Lesson 9-6)

B 2.5, 4, 5.5, 7, 8.5, ...

Examine the differences.

Terms	2.5	4	5.5	7	8.5
1st differences		1.5	1.5	1.5	1.5

The first differences are constant, so the sequence is linear.

The first term is 2.5, and each term is 1.5 more than the previous.

A pattern is $2.5 + 1.5(n - 1)$, or $1.5n + 1$. One explicit rule is $a_n = 1.5n + 1$.

CHECK IT OUT! **Write a possible explicit rule for the nth term of each sequence.**

3a. 7, 5, 3, 1, −1, ... $a_n = 9 - 2n$

3b. $1, \frac{1}{2}, \frac{1}{3}, \frac{1}{4}, \frac{1}{5}, \ldots$ $a_n = \frac{1}{n}$

Power Presentations with PowerPoint®

Additional Examples

Example 1

Find the first 5 terms of the sequence with $a_1 = -2$ and $a_n = 3a_{n-1} + 2$ for $n \geq 2$.

−2, −4, −10, −28, −82

Example 2

Find the first 5 terms of the sequence $a_n = 3^n - 1$.

2, 8, 26, 80, 242

Example 3

Write a possible explicit rule for the nth term of each sequence.

A. 5, 10, 20, 40, 80, ...
$a_n = 5(2^{n-1})$

B. 1.5, 4, 6.5, 9, 11.5, ...
$a_n = 2.5n - 1$

Also available on transparency

INTERVENTION
Questioning Strategies

EXAMPLE 1

- Is the sequence increasing or decreasing?
- What effect would a negative multiplier have on the sequence? Explain.

EXAMPLE 2

- How is using an explicit formula different from using a recursive formula?

EXAMPLE 3

- How do differences or ratios help identify the explicit rule for the nth term?

Teaching Tip **Math Background** Remind students of functions they have already studied this year (linear, quadratic, and exponential) and of regression techniques to find the rules for sequences. You may wish to review Lesson 9-6.

2 Teach

Guided Instruction

Compare sequences with the functions students have already learned. Choose a simple linear function, such as $f(x) = 5x$. Have students evaluate the function for several consecutive integer values. Ask them to describe the results. counting by 5's or multiples of 5 Use the answer to explain the difference between recursive and explicit formulas.

Reaching All Learners
Through Cognitive Strategies

Students may need help with the new notation. Stress that n is the term number (also called the *index of a term*) and a_n is the nth term, so a_{n-1} is the previous term and a_{n+1} is the next term. To reinforce these concepts, have students identify some terms for a given n-value.
For example, which term is a_{n+2} when $n = 3$? fifth

Power Presentations with PowerPoint®

Additional Examples

Example 4

A ball is dropped and bounces to a height of 4 feet. The ball rebounds to 70% of its previous height after each bounce. Graph the sequence and describe its pattern. How high does the ball bounce on its 10th bounce?

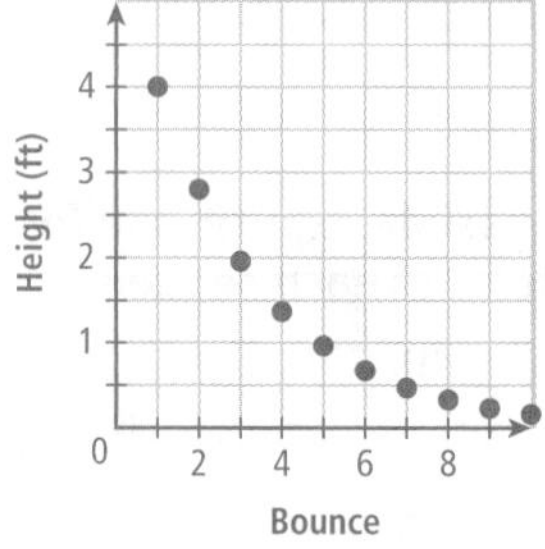

$a_n = 4(0.7)^{n-1}$; ≈ 0.161 ft, or ≈ 2 in.

Example 5

Find the number of triangles in the 7th and 8th iterations of the Sierpinski triangle. 729, 2187

Also available on transparency

INTERVENTION

Questioning Strategies

EXAMPLE 4

- How does the graph help identify the rule?
- Why would you find an explicit rule if you know the recursive rule?

EXAMPLE 5

- Why might you use a sequence to represent the iterations when you can draw pictures?

Number Sense To help students understand the discrete nature of the situation in **Example 4,** point out that 1.5 bounces would be impossible.

Math Background **Example 4** is an example of *Zeno's paradox.* According to the formula, the ball will never stop bouncing. Have students research this topic as an extension or challenge activity.

EXAMPLE 4 *Physics Application*

A ball is dropped and bounces to a height of 5 feet. The ball rebounds to 60% of its previous height after each bounce. Graph the sequence and describe its pattern. How high does the ball bounce on its 9th bounce?

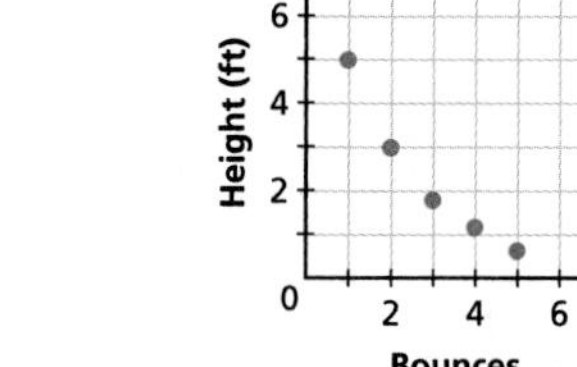

Because the ball first bounces to a height of 5 feet and then bounces to 60% of its previous height on each bounce, the recursive rule is $a_1 = 5$ and $a_n = 0.6a_{n-1}$. Use this rule to find some other terms of the sequence and graph them.

$a_2 = 0.6(5) = 3$

$a_3 = 0.6(3) = 1.8$

$a_4 = 0.6(1.8) = 1.08$

The graph appears to be exponential. Use the pattern to write an explicit rule.

$a_n = 5(0.6)^{n-1}$, where n is the bounce number

Use this rule to find the bounce height for the 9th bounce.

$a_9 = 5(0.6)^{9-1} \approx 0.084$ foot, or approximately 1 inch.

The ball is about 0.084 feet high on the 9th bounce.

Caution!

Do not connect the points on the graph because the number of bounces is limited to the set of natural numbers.

CHECK IT OUT!

4. An ultra-low-flush toilet uses 1.6 gallons every time it is flushed. Graph the sequence of total water used after n flushes, and describe its pattern. How many gallons have been used after 10 flushes?

The graph shows the points lie on a line with positive slope; 16 gal.

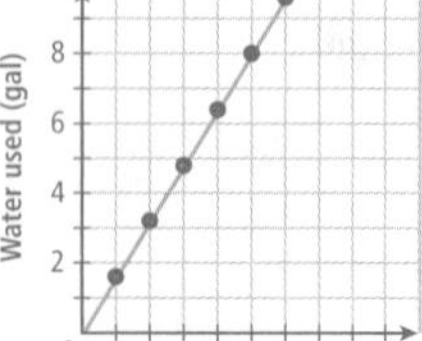

Recall that a fractal is an image made by repeating a pattern (Lesson 5-5). Each step in this repeated process is an **iteration**, the repetitive application of the same rule.

EXAMPLE 5 Iteration of Fractals

The Sierpinski triangle is a fractal made by taking an equilateral triangle, removing an equilateral triangle from the center, and repeating for each new triangle. Find the number of triangles in the next 2 iterations.

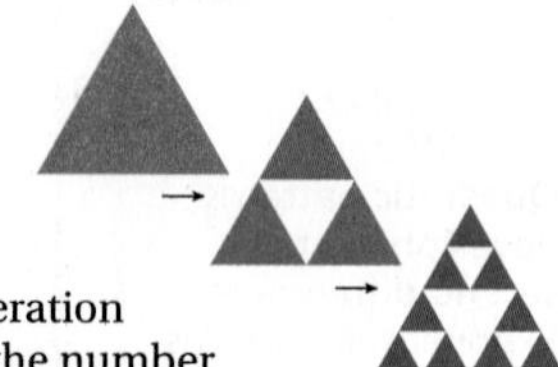

By removing the center of each triangle, each iteration turns every triangle into 3 smaller triangles. So the number of triangles triples with each iteration.

The number of triangles can be represented by the sequence $a_n = 3^{n-1}$.

The 4th and 5th terms are $a_4 = 3^{4-1} = 27$ and $a_5 = 3^{5-1} = 81$.

The next two iterations result in 27 and 81 triangles.

5. The Cantor set is a fractal formed by repeatedly removing the middle third of a line segment as shown. Find the number of segments in the next 2 iterations. 8, 16

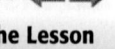

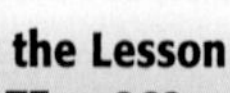

3 Close

Summarize

Ask students to define a sequence. A sequence is an ordered set of numbers. Then have them explain how to use a recursive formula and an explicit formula to find the terms of a sequence. A recursive formula uses previous terms to generate successive terms. An explicit formula defines the *n*th term of a sequence as a function of *n*.

ONGOING ASSESSMENT and INTERVENTION

Diagnose ***Before*** **the Lesson**
12-1 Warm Up, TE p. 862

Monitor ***During*** **the Lesson**
Check It Out! Exercises, SE pp. 862–864
Questioning Strategies, TE pp. 863–864

Assess ***After*** **the Lesson**
12-1 Lesson Quiz, TE p. 868
Alternative Assessment, TE p. 868

THINK AND DISCUSS

1. Explain the difference between a recursive rule and an explicit rule.
2. Identify three possible next terms for the sequence 1, 2, 4, ...
3. Describe how a sequence is a function. Do all sequences have the same domain? Explain.

4. **GET ORGANIZED** Copy and complete the graphic organizer. Summarize what you have learned about sequences.

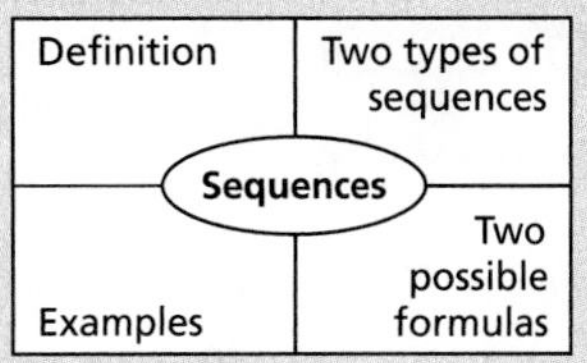

Answers to *Think and Discuss*

Possible answers:

1. A recursive rule uses one or more previous terms to find the value of a term. An explicit rule uses the first term and the term number to find the value.
2. 1, 7, 8
3. There is only one output, a_n, associated with each input, n. The domain of a sequence is the set of term numbers, but sequences do not necessarily have the same domain.
4. See p. A13.

12-1 Exercises

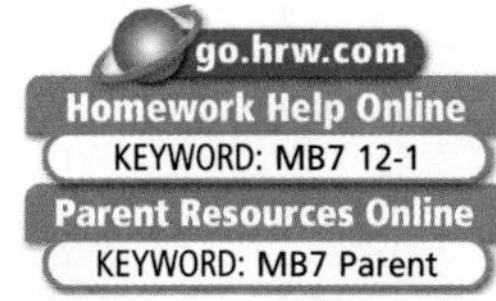

GUIDED PRACTICE

1. **Vocabulary** A formula that uses one or more previous terms to find the next term is a(n) __?__ formula. (*explicit* or *recursive*) recursive

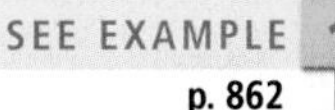

SEE EXAMPLE 1 p. 862

Find the first 5 terms of each sequence.

2. $a_1 = 1, a_n = 4a_{n-1} - 1$ 1, 3, 11, 43, 171
3. $a_1 = 3, a_n = a_{n-1} + 11$ 3, 14, 25, 36, 47
4. $a_1 = 500, a_n = \frac{a_{n-1}}{5}$ 500, 100, 20, 4, $\frac{4}{5}$

SEE EXAMPLE 2 p. 863

5. $a_n = 12(n - 2)$
6. $a_n = \left(-\frac{1}{2}\right)^{n-1}$
7. $a_n = -3n^2$
8. $a_n = n(n - 1)$ 0, 2, 6, 12, 20
9. $a_n = 4^{n-1}$ 1, 4, 16, 64, 256
10. $a_n = (n + 1)^2$ 4, 9, 16, 25, 36

SEE EXAMPLE 3 p. 863

Write a possible explicit rule for the *n*th term of each sequence.

11. 6, 9, 12, 15, 18, ... $a_n = 3 + 3n$
12. $\frac{1}{2}, \frac{2}{3}, \frac{3}{4}, \frac{4}{5}, \frac{5}{6}, \ldots$
13. 25, 15, 5, −5, −15, ... $a_n = 35 - 10n$

SEE EXAMPLE 4 p. 864

14. **Income** Billy earns $25,000 the first year and gets a 5% raise each year. Graph the sequence, and describe its pattern. How much will he earn per year after 5 years? 10 years? exponential growth; about $31,907; about $40,722

SEE EXAMPLE 5 p. 864

15. **Patterns** Find the number of segments in the next 2 terms of the pattern shown. 16, 32

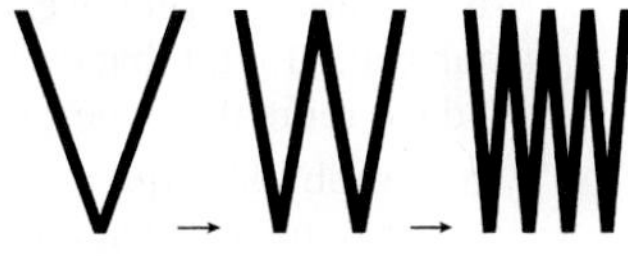

12. $a_n = \frac{n}{n+1}$

PRACTICE AND PROBLEM SOLVING

Find the first 5 terms of each sequence.

16. $a_1 = 7, a_n = a_{n-1} - 3$ 7, 4, 1, −2, −5
17. $a_n = \frac{1}{n^2}$ $1, \frac{1}{4}, \frac{1}{9}, \frac{1}{16}, \frac{1}{25}$
18. $a_1 = 4, a_n = 1.5a_{n-1} - 2$ 4, 4, 4, 4, 4
19. $a_n = (2)^{n-1} + 8$ 9, 10, 12, 16, 24
20. $a_n = 2n^2 - 12$ −10, −4, 6, 20, 38
21. $a_1 = -2, a_n = -3a_{n-1} - 1$ −2, 5, −16, 47, −142

12-1 Exercises

Assignment Guide

Assign *Guided Practice* exercises as necessary.

If you finished Examples 1–2
Basic 16–21, 27–29
Average 16–21, 27–31
Advanced 16–21, 27–32

If you finished Examples 1–5
Basic 16–29, 33–36, 43–46, 49–54, 59–66
Average 16–46, 49–54, 59–66
Advanced 16–33, 34–46 even, 47–66

Homework Quick Check
Quickly check key concepts.
Exercises: 16, 20, 22, 25, 26, 28

State Resources

go.hrw.com
State Resources Online
KEYWORD: MB7 Resources

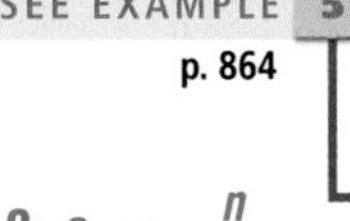

Teaching Tip **Technology** Students are taught to use the **seq(** function on graphing calculators in the Technology Lab following Lesson 12-2. You may want to teach the first part of that lab before or during this lesson.

Answers

5. −12, 0, 12, 24, 36
6. $1, -\frac{1}{2}, \frac{1}{4}, -\frac{1}{8}, \frac{1}{16}$
7. −3, −12, −27, −48, −75
14.

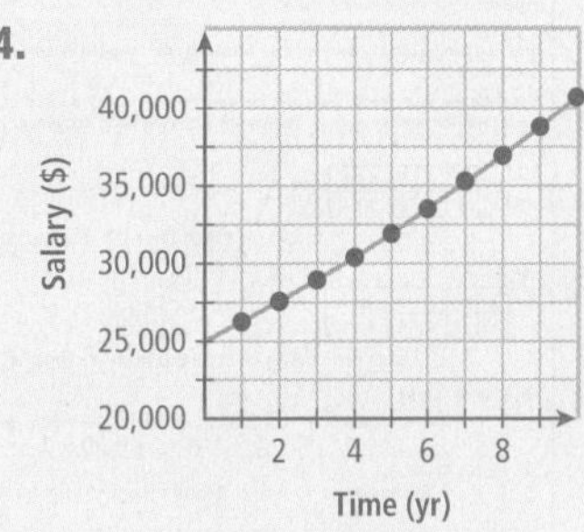

Teaching Tip **Geometry Link** In **Exercise 26,** students may want to draw the next two iterations of Cantor dust. Point out the difficulty of doing this by hand-there are too many small squares. If students want to visualize the iterations, suggest that they instead consider the number of squares formed along the side of the bigger square with each iteration.

Teaching Tip **Math Background** The sequence pictured in **Exercise 41** is the sequence of triangular numbers, and the sequence pictured in **Exercise 42** is the sequence of square numbers. Discuss why that is so.

Answers

25.

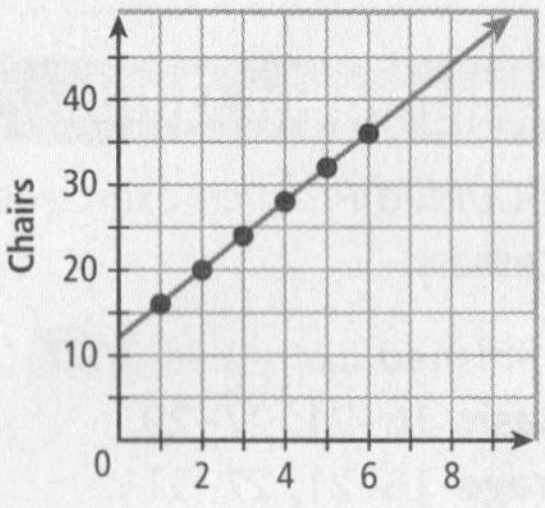

30. −10, −4, 6, 20, 38
31. 7.9, 7.8, 7.7, 7.6, 7.5
32. 5, −15, 45, −135, 405
34. $a_n = 16\left(\frac{1}{4}\right)^{n-1}; \frac{1}{16{,}384}$
35. $a_n = \frac{16}{9} - \frac{1}{9}n; \frac{2}{3}$
36. $a_n = -7.5 + 2.5n$; 17.5
37. $a_n = \frac{(-1)^{n+1}}{n}; -\frac{1}{10}$
38. $a_n = 0.04(10^{n-1})$; 40,000,000

Independent Practice	
For Exercises	See Example
16–18	1
19–21	2
22–24	3
25	4
26	5

Extra Practice
Skills Practice p. S26
Application Practice p. S43

24. $a_n = 5(0.1)^{n-1}$

27. 12, 8, 6, 5, $4\frac{1}{2}$

Write a possible explicit rule for the *n*th term of each sequence.

22. 2, 8, 18, 32, 50, … $a_n = 2n^2$
23. 9, 5, 1, −3, −7, … $a_n = 13 - 4n$
24. 5, 0.5, 0.05, 0.005, …

25. **Architecture** Chairs for an orchestra are positioned in a curved form with the conductor at the center. The front row has 16 chairs, and each successive row has 4 more chairs. Graph the sequence and describe its pattern. How many chairs are in the 6th row? **linear with a slope of 4; 36**

26. **Fractals** Find the number of squares in the next 2 iterations of Cantor dust as shown. **256, 1024**

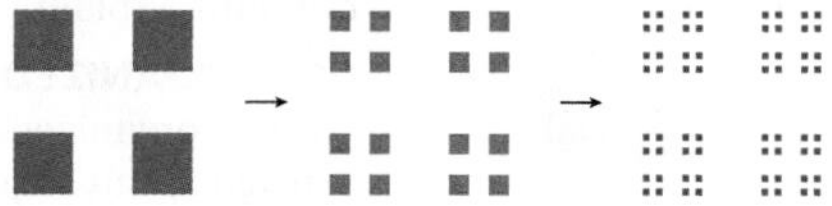

Find the first 5 terms of each sequence.

27. $a_1 = 12, a_n = \frac{1}{2}a_{n-1} + 2$
28. $a_1 = 1, a_n = \frac{2}{a_{n-1}}$ **1, 2, 1, 2, 1**
29. $a_1 = -10, a_n = -a_{n-1} + 10$ **−10, 20, −10, 20, −10**
30. $a_n = 2n^2 - 12$
31. $a_n = 8 - \frac{1}{10}n$
32. $a_n = 5(-1)^{n+1}(3)^{n-1}$

33. **ERROR ANALYSIS** Two attempts to find the first 5 terms of the sequence $a_1 = 3$ and $a_n = 2n + 1$ are shown. Which is incorrect? Explain the error. **B is incorrect. The formula is explicit, not recursive.**

(A)
3, 5, 7, 9, 11

(B)
3, 7, 15, 31, 63

Math History (LINK)

The Fibonacci sequence can also be used to discover the golden ratio. The ratios of successive terms become closer and closer to the golden ratio, $\frac{1+\sqrt{5}}{2}$.

Write a possible explicit rule for each sequence, and find the 10th term.

34. 16, 4, 1, $\frac{1}{4}$, $\frac{1}{16}$, …
35. $\frac{15}{9}$, $\frac{14}{9}$, $\frac{13}{9}$, $\frac{12}{9}$, $\frac{11}{9}$, …
36. −5.0, −2.5, 0, 2.5, 5.0, …
37. 1, $-\frac{1}{2}$, $\frac{1}{3}$, $-\frac{1}{4}$, $\frac{1}{5}$, …
38. 0.04, 0.4, 4, 40, 400, …
39. 24, 21, 16, 9, 0, … $a_n = 25 - n^2$; −75

40. **Fibonacci** Recall from the lesson that the Fibonacci sequence models the number of pairs of rabbits after a certain number of months. The sequence begins 1, 1, …, and each term after that is the sum of the two terms before it.
   a. Find the first 12 terms of the Fibonacci sequence. **1, 1, 2, 3, 5, 8, 13, 21, 34, 55, 89, 144**
   b. How many pairs of rabbits are produced under ideal circumstances at the end of one year? **144 rabbit pairs**

Find the number of dots in the next 2 figures for each dot pattern.

41. 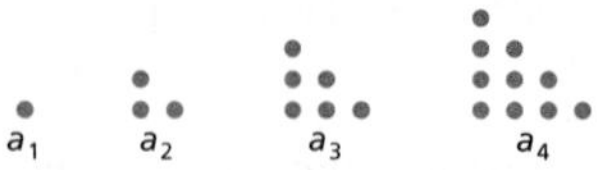

15, 21

42. 

25, 36

43. **Chess** Ronnie is scheduling a chess tournament in which each player plays every other player once. He created a table and found that each new player added more than one game.
   a. Graph the sequence and describe its pattern. What are the next 2 terms in the sequence? **15, 21**
   b. Use a regression to find an explicit rule for the sequence. $a_n = \frac{1}{2}n^2 - \frac{1}{2}n$
   c. **What if...?** How would the schedule change if each player played every other player *twice*? Make a table, and describe how the sequence is transformed.

Single-Play Chess Tournament	
Number of Players	Number of Games
1	0
2	1
3	3
4	6
5	10

12-1 PRACTICE A
12-1 PRACTICE C
12-1 PRACTICE B

Find the first 5 terms of each sequence.

1. $a_1 = 1, a_n = 3(a_{n-1})$ **1, 3, 9, 27, 81**
2. $a_1 = 2, a_n = 2(a_{n-1} + 1) - 5$ **2, 1, −1, −5, −13**
3. $a_1 = -2, a_n = (a_{n-1})^2 - 1$ **−2, 3, 8, 63, 3968**
4. $a_1 = 1, a_n = 6 - 2(a_{n-1})$ **1, 4, −2, 10, −14**
5. $a_1 = -1, a_n = (a_{n-1} - 1)^2 - 3$ **−1, 1, −3, 13, 141**
6. $a_1 = -2, a_n = \frac{2 - a_{n-1}}{2}$ **−2, 2, 0, 1, $\frac{1}{2}$**
7. $a_n = (n-2)(n+1)$ **−2, 0, 4, 10, 18**
8. $a_n = n(2n-1)$ **1, 6, 15, 28, 45**
9. $a_n = n^3 - n^2$ **0, 4, 18, 48, 100**
10. $a_n = \left(\frac{1}{2}\right)^{n-3}$ **4, 2, 1, $\frac{1}{2}$, $\frac{1}{4}$**
11. $a_n = (-2)^{n-1}$ **1, −2, 4, −8, 16**
12. $a_n = n^2 - 2n$ **−1, 0, 3, 8, 15**

Write a possible explicit rule for the *n*th term of each sequence.

13. 8, 16, 24, 32, 40, … $a_n = 8n$
14. 0.1, 0.4, 0.9, 1.6, 2.5, … $a_n = 0.1n^2$
15. 3, 6, 11, 18, 27, … $a_n = n^2 + 2$
16. $\frac{3}{2}, \frac{3}{4}, \frac{3}{8}, \frac{3}{16}, \frac{3}{32}$, … $a_n = 3\left(\frac{1}{2}\right)^n$
17. −2, 1, 4, 7, 10, … $a_n = 3n - 5$
18. 5, 1, 0.2, 0.04, 0.008, … $a_n = 5(0.2)^{n-1}$

Solve.

19. Find the number of line segments in the next two iterations. **31, 63**

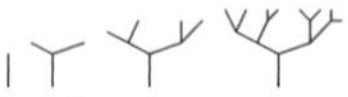

20. Jim charges $50 per week for lawn mowing and weeding services. He plans to increase his prices by 4% each year.
   a. Graph the sequence.
   b. Describe the pattern. **Exponential**
   c. To the nearest dollar, how much will he charge per week in 5 years? **$61 per week**

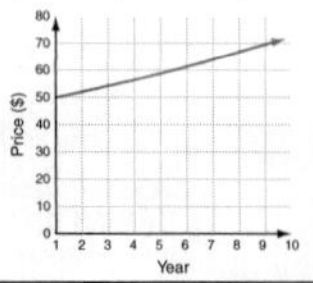

12-1 READING STRATEGIES

Sequences are ordered sets of numbers, such as 2, 3, 4, 5, 6, …, in which the terms follow a pattern.

Term Number	n	1	2	3	4	5
Value of the Term	a_n	2	3	4	5	6

The variable n denotes the term number. The value of each term is denoted by a_n. The relationship between the term number and the value of the term is the rule for the sequence. What is the relationship between the term number and the value of each term for the sequence above?

For each term in the sequence, the value of the term is 1 more than the corresponding term number.

$$a_n = n + 1$$

This rule can be used to determine an infinite number of terms in the sequence.

Describe the relationship between the term number and the value of each term for each sequence. Then write a rule for each sequence.

1.

n	1	2	3	4	5
a_n	0	1	2	3	4

Each term value is 1 less than the term number; $a_n = n - 1$.

2.

n	1	2	3	4	5
a_n	2	4	6	8	10

Each term value is twice the term number; $a_n = 2n$.

3. 5, 9, 13, 17, 21, … **Each term value is 5 plus 4 times the previous term number; $a_n = 5 + 4(n-1) = 4n + 1$.**
4. 75, 66, 57, 48, 39, … **Each term is 75 minus 9 times the previous term number; $a_n = 75 - 9(n-1) = 84 - 9n$.**

Write the next four terms, a_6 through a_9, for each sequence.

5. 31, 34, 37, 40, 43, … **46, 49, 52, 55**
6. 23, 16, 9, 2, −5, … **−12, −19, −26, −33**
7. 5, 17, 29, 41, 53, … **65, 77, 89, 101**

12-1 RETEACH

A **sequence** is an ordered set of numbers. Each number is called a **term**.
A **recursive formula** is a rule that tells you how to write the terms of a sequence, using the preceding terms of the sequence.

Find the first five terms of the sequence with $a_1 = 4$ and $a_n = 3a_{n-1} - 2$.

a_1 denotes the first term in the sequence.
a_{n-1} comes before a_n.
a_n denotes the nth term in the sequence

Make a table to list the terms in the sequence.

Term number — Recursive formula — Term value

n	$a_n = 3a_{n-1} - 2$	a_n
1	Given: $a_1 = 4$	4
2	$a_2 = 3a_{2-1} - 2 = 3a_1 - 2 = 3(4) - 2 = 10$	10
3	$a_3 = 3a_2 - 2 = 3(10) - 2 = 28$	28
4	$a_4 = 3a_3 - 2 = 3(28) - 2 = 82$	82
5	$a_5 = 3a_4 - 2 = 3(82) - 2 = 244$	244

Notice how the previous term is used each time to compute the next term.

The first five terms are 4, 10, 28, 82, and 244.

Find the first five terms of each sequence.

1. $a_1 = -8, a_n = a_{n-1} + 3$
   $a_2 = a_1 + 3 = -8 + 3 =$ **−5**
   $a_3 = a_2 + 3 =$ **−2**
   $a_4 =$ **1**
   $a_5 =$ **4**
2. $a_1 = 2, a_n = -5a_{n-1}$
   $a_2 = -5a_1 = -5(2) =$ **−10**
   $a_3 = -5a_2 =$ **50**
   $a_4 =$ **−250**
   $a_5 =$ **1250**
3. $a_1 = 6, a_n = 2a_{n-1} - 1$
   $a_2 = 11$
   $a_3 = 21$
   $a_4 = 41$
   $a_5 = 81$
4. $a_1 = -1, a_n = 4a_{n-1}$
   $a_2 = -4$
   $a_3 = -16$
   $a_4 = -64$
   $a_5 = -256$

44. This problem will prepare you for the Multi-Step Test Prep on page 888.

A kite is made with 1 tetrahedron in the first (top) layer, 3 tetrahedrons in the second layer, 6 tetrahedrons in the third layer, and so on. Each tetrahedron is made by joining six sticks of equal length.

a. The rule $a_n = a_{n-1} + 6n$ gives the number of sticks needed to make the nth layer of the kite, where $a_1 = 6$. Find the first five terms of the sequence. **6, 18, 36, 60, 90**

b. Use regression to find an explicit rule for the sequence. $a_n = 3n^2 + 3n$

c. How many sticks are needed to build the 10th layer of the kite? **330**

45. Geometry The sum of the interior angle measures for the first 5 regular polygons is shown.

Sum of Interior Angle Measures

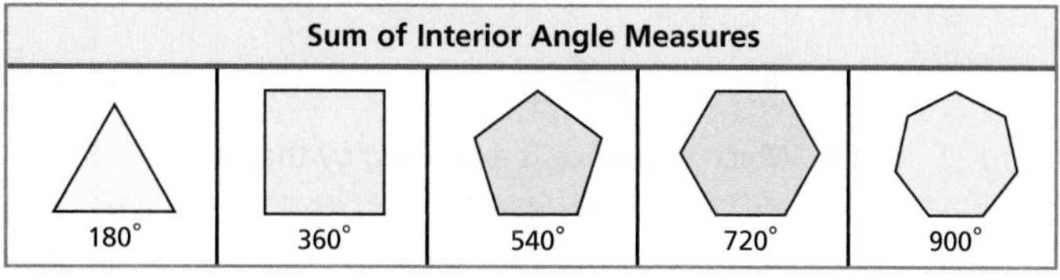

180°	360°	540°	720°	900°

a. Write an explicit rule for the nth term of the sequence of the sum of the angle measures. What is the sum of the measures of the interior angles of a 12-sided regular polygon? $a_n = 180(n - 2)$ **for** $n \geq 3$; **1800°**

b. Recall that all angles are congruent in a regular polygon. Make a table for the measure of an interior angle for each regular polygon. Graph the data, and describe the pattern.

c. Write an explicit rule for the nth term of the sequence described in part **b.**

d. Find the measure of an interior angle of a 10-sided regular polygon.

46. Possible answer: about 27; the first term is almost 8. Each term is about 1 more than the previous term and 8 + 19 is 27.

46. Estimation Estimate the 20th term of the sequence 7.94, 8.935, 9.93, 10.925, 11.92, ... Explain how you reached your estimate.

47. Music Music involves arranging different pitches through time. The musical notation below indicates the duration of various notes (and rests).

Symbols for Musical Notes and Rests

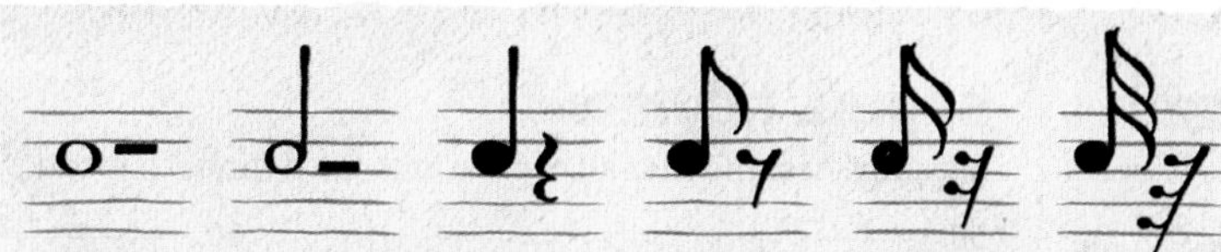

a. Write a numerical sequence that shows the progression of notes (and rests). Write a recursive formula and an explicit formula to generate this sequence.

b. In 4/4 time, a whole note represents 4 beats, a half note represents 2 beats, a quarter note represents 1 beat, and so on. Write a sequence for the number of beats that each note in the progression represents. Then write a recursive formula and an explicit formula to generate this sequence. How is this sequence related to the sequence in part **a**?

47a. $1, \frac{1}{2}, \frac{1}{4}, \frac{1}{8}, \frac{1}{16}, \frac{1}{32}$; $a_1 = 1, a_n = \frac{1}{2}a_{n-1}$; $a_n = \left(\frac{1}{2}\right)^{n-1}$

47b. $4, 2, 1, \frac{1}{2}, \frac{1}{4}, \frac{1}{8}$; $a_1 = 4, a_n = \frac{1}{2}a_{n-1}$; $a_n = 4\left(\frac{1}{2}\right)^{n-1}$; **possible answer: it follows the same pattern but starts at a different value.**

COMMON ERROR ALERT

In **Exercises 37** and **54,** students might have difficulty working with alternating signs. Remind them that the value of $(-1)^n$ is negative when n is odd and positive when n is even.

MULTI-STEP TEST PREP **Exercise 44** involves finding terms of a sequence and writing a rule for the sequence. This exercise prepares students for the Multi-Step Test Prep on page 888.

Teaching Tip **Critical Thinking** In **Exercise 45,** some students may remember the formula for the sum of the interior angle measures from geometry. Encourage those students to use the method presented in the problem to verify the formula they remember.

Answers

43a. It appears to be quadratic.

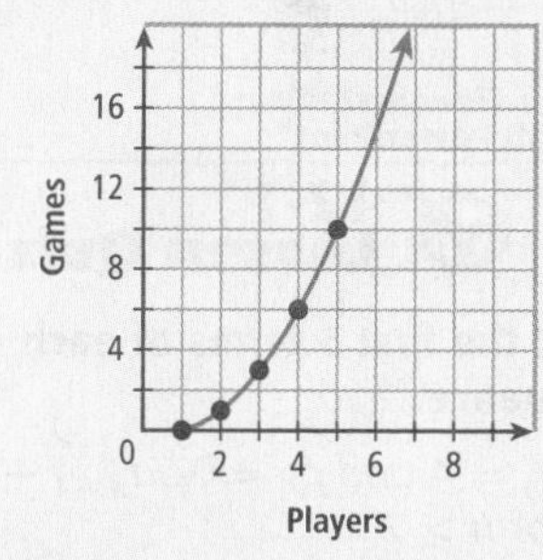

c.

Players	1	2	3	4	5
Games	0	2	6	12	20

The sequence is twice the previous sequence. The function is a vertical stretch by a factor of 2.

45b.

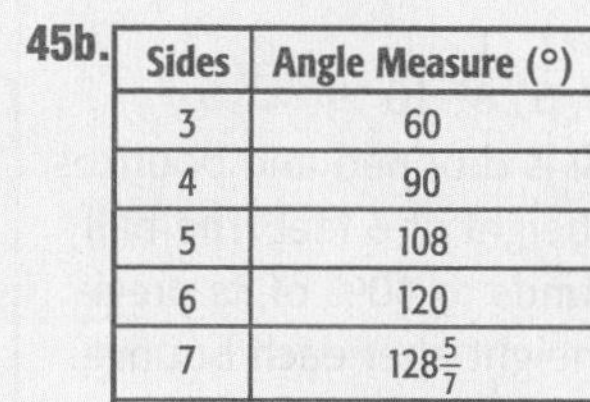

Sides	Angle Measure (°)
3	60
4	90
5	108
6	120
7	$128\frac{5}{7}$
8	135

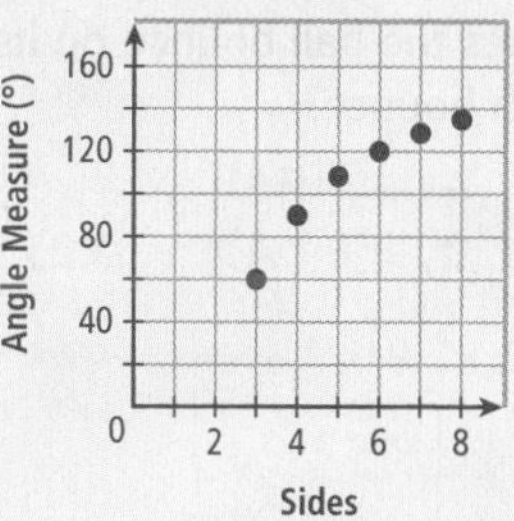

It appears to be a square-root or logarithmic curve.

c. $a_n = \frac{180(n-2)}{n}$ for $n \geq 3$

d. 144°

12-1 PROBLEM SOLVING

Tina is working on some home improvement projects involving repeated tasks. She wants to analyze her work patterns.

1. Tina is hammering nails into wallboard. With the first hit, a nail goes in 13.5 millimeters; with the second, it goes in an additional 9 mm; with the third, it goes in an additional 6 mm; and with the fourth it goes in 4 mm further. Suppose this pattern continues. Predict how far the nail would go in with the seventh hit.

   a. Complete the table to find first differences, second differences, and ratios.

Distance	13.5 mm	9 mm	6 mm	4 mm
Ratios	$\frac{2}{3}$	$\frac{2}{3}$	$\frac{2}{3}$	
First Differences	−4.5	−3	−2	
Second Differences	1.5	1		

   b. How do you know whether the rule for the sequence of distances that the nail goes in is linear, quadratic, or exponential? **The ratios are constant; so the sequence is exponential.**

   c. Write a possible rule for a_n, the nth term in the sequence. $a_n = 13.5\left(\frac{2}{3}\right)^{n-1}$

   d. If this pattern continues, how far would the nail go in with the seventh hit? **1.2 mm**

2. Tina builds a fence for her neighbor. It takes her 10 minutes to pound the first fence post into the ground. The neighbor predicts that Tina should improve her time on each successive fence post according to the rule $a_n = F - 2(n - 1)$, where F is the time for the first fence post, and a_n is the time it takes to pound in the nth post.

   a. Use the rule to find the time it should take Tina to pound each of the first 4 fence posts into the ground. **10 min, 8 min, 6 min, 4 min**

   b. If the rule that describes Tina's time on each successive post is $a_n = F - 1.5^{n-1}$, how long will it take her to pound the fourth fence post into the ground? **6.6 min**

The label on Pete's blue jeans states that, when washed, the jeans will lose 5% of their color. Choose the letter for the best answer.

3. Which rule describes the percent of color left in the blue jeans after n washings?
   A $a_n = 100(0.05)^n$
   (B) $a_n = 100(0.95)^n$
   C $a_n = 100(0.95)n$
   D $a_n = 100(0.05)n$

4. How much of the original color will be left after 8 washings?
   (F) 66%
   G 60%
   H 40%
   J 34%

12-1 CHALLENGE

Many sequences represent a constant-increase or a constant-decrease situation. The graph of such a sequence is a set of collinear points.

Consider the sequence defined by the recursive formula $a_1 = 7$ and $a_n = a_{n-1} - 2$.

1. Use the recursive formula to determine the first 5 terms of this sequence. **7, 5, 3, 1, −1**

2. Using the coordinates (n, a_n), graph the first 5 terms of this sequence on the coordinate plane at right.

3. Use the graph to determine the slope of the line that connects these points. **−2**

4. How is this slope reflected in the recursive formula for the sequence? **The slope of the line is equal to the constant difference in the recursive formula.**

5. a. Write an equation for the line that connects the set of points of this sequence. $y = -2x + 9$

   b. Use the equation of the line to determine the 20th term of this sequence. **−31**

   c. Verify your result by using the recursive formula to determine the 20th term of this sequence. $a_{20} = -31$

6. Explain how the equation of the graph of a sequence relates to the sequence. **The equation of the graph is equivalent to an explicit formula for the sequence.**

Write an equation in x and y for the line that connects the points of the given sequence.

7. $a_1 = 3$ and $a_n = a_{n-1} + 4$, where $n \geq 2$ — $y = 4x - 1$

8. $a_1 = -4$ and $a_n = a_{n-1} + 3$, where $n \geq 2$ — $y = 3x - 7$

An equation for the line that connects the points of a sequence is given. Write a recursive formula for the sequence.

9. $y = 3x + 1$ — $a_1 = 4$ and $a_n = a_{n-1} + 3$

10. $3y = x + 1$ — $a_1 = \frac{2}{3}$ and $a_n = a_{n-1} + \frac{1}{3}$

In **Exercise 50,** students who chose **A** might be subtracting in the wrong order to find the sequence rule.

In **Exercise 52,** students who choose **C** may be starting the sequence with 0 instead of 1. Remind them that the domain is the set of natural numbers, so the first term of a_n is a_1, in which $n = 1$.

Journal

Have students explain how fractals can be used to create patterns. Encourage them to include an example of a simple fractal.

ALTERNATIVE ASSESSMENT

Have students create rules for two different sequences—one in which the terms increase and one in which they decrease. Then have them find the first 5 terms of each sequence.

Power Presentations with PowerPoint®

12-1 Lesson Quiz

Find the first 5 terms of each sequence.

1. $a_1 = 4$ *and* $a_n = 0.5a_{n-1} + 1$ *for* $n \geq 2$
4, 3, 2.5, 2.25, 2.125

2. $a_n = 2^n - 5$ −3, −1, 3, 11, 27

Write a possible explicit rule for the *n*th term of each sequence.

3. 20, 40, 80, 160, 320 $a_n = 10(2^n)$

4. $\frac{1}{2}, \frac{1}{4}, \frac{1}{6}, \frac{1}{8}, \frac{1}{10}$ $a_n = \frac{1}{2n}$

5. A ball is dropped and bounces to a height of 6 feet. The ball rebounds to 40% of its previous height after each bounce. Graph the sequence and describe its pattern. How high does the ball bounce on its 7th bounce?

$a_n = 6(0.4)^{n-1}$;
$a_7 = 6(0.4)^6 \approx 0.025$ ft

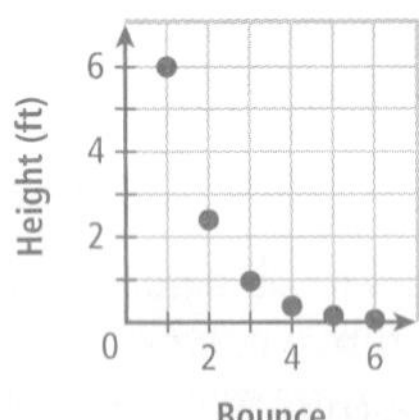

Also available on transparency

48. Critical Thinking Can the recursive rule and the explicit rule for a formula ever be the same?

49. Write About It Explain how an infinite sequence is different from a finite sequence.

TEST PREP

50. Which is the next term in the sequence −9, −6, −3, 0, ...?
Ⓐ −3 Ⓑ 0 Ⓒ 3 Ⓓ 6

51. Which rule describes the given sequence 4, 12, 36, 108, ...?
Ⓕ $a_n = 4 + 3n$
Ⓖ $a_n = 3 + 4n$
Ⓗ $a_1 = 4,\ a_n = 3a_{n-1},\ n \geq 2$
Ⓙ $a_1 = 3,\ a_n = 4a_{n-1},\ n \geq 2$

52. Which sequence is expressed by the rule $a_n = \frac{2n}{n+1}$?
Ⓐ $\frac{2}{3}, \frac{4}{5}, \frac{6}{7}, \frac{8}{9}, \frac{10}{11}, \ldots$
Ⓑ $1, \frac{4}{3}, \frac{3}{2}, \frac{8}{5}, \frac{5}{3}, \ldots$
Ⓒ $0, 1, 2, \frac{3}{2}, \frac{8}{5}, \ldots$
Ⓓ $2, \frac{3}{2}, \frac{8}{5}, \frac{5}{3}, \frac{12}{7}, \ldots$

53. Which sequence is expressed by the rule $a_1 = 6$ and $a_n = 12 - 2a_{n-1},\ n \geq 2$?
Ⓕ 6, 4, 2, 0, −2, −4, ...
Ⓖ 0, 12, −12, 36, −60, ...
Ⓗ 6, 0, 12, −12, 36, ...
Ⓙ 6, 0, −6, −12, −18, ...

54. Gridded Response Find the next term in the sequence −32, 16, −8, 4, −2, ... 1

CHALLENGE AND EXTEND

Write an explicit rule for each sequence and find the 10th term.

55. $-\frac{2}{3}, \frac{5}{3}, 8, \frac{61}{3}, \frac{122}{3}, \ldots$ **56.** −2, 6, −12, 20, −30, ... **57.** 0.9, 0.8, 0.6, 0.3, −0.1, ...

55. $a_n = \frac{n^3}{3} - 1$; $\frac{997}{3}$
56. $a_n = (-1)^n(n^2 + n)$; 110
57. $a_n = -0.05n^2 + 0.05n + 0.9$; −3.6

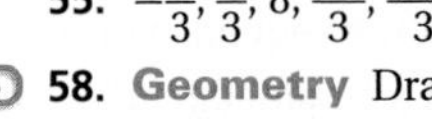

58. Geometry Draw 5 circles. Place 1 point on the first circle, 2 points on the second, 3 points on the third, and so forth. Then connect every point with every other point in each circle, and count the maximum number of nonoverlapping regions that are formed inside each circle.

a. Write the resulting sequence. 1, 2, 4, 8, 16, ...

b. Although the sequence appears to double, the sixth circle has less than 32 possible regions. Try to find them all by carefully drawing this figure. How many did you get? maximum of 31

SPIRAL REVIEW

Simplify. Assume that all expressions are defined. *(Lesson 8-2)*

59. $\frac{x^2 - 9}{x^2 + 5x + 6}$ $\frac{x-3}{x+2}$

60. $\frac{4x^2 - 5x}{8x^2 + 18x - 35}$ $\frac{x}{2x+7}$

61. $\frac{4x - 12}{x^2 - 25} \div \frac{8x - 24}{2x - 10}$ $\frac{1}{x+5}$

62. $\frac{x^2 - 5x - 6}{x^2 - 3x - 18} \cdot \frac{x^2 + x - 6}{x^2 - x - 2}$ 1

Add or subtract. *(Lesson 8-4)*

63. $\frac{2x - 3}{x + 1} + \frac{4x - 9}{x - 1}$

64. $\frac{9x}{8x - 4} - \frac{10x + 3}{12x - 6}$

65. $\frac{x^2}{2x + 7} - \frac{x}{x + 2}$

63. $\frac{2(3x^2 - 5x - 3)}{(x+1)(x-1)}$
64. $\frac{7x - 6}{12(2x - 1)}$
65. $\frac{x(x^2 - 7)}{(2x + 7)(x + 2)}$

66. Literature Christopher is reading a book containing 854 pages at a rate of 1.5 pages per minute. Create a table, equation, and graph to represent the number of pages remaining to be read *P* in relation to time *t*. *(Lesson 9-1)*

Answers

48. Possible answer: No, a recursive rule is based on one or more previous terms but an explicit rule is based on the term's *n*-value.

49. Possible answer: An infinite sequence has ellipsis points, or 3 dots, to indicate that the sequence continues without end. A finite sequence ends and has a last term.

66.

t	*P*
0	854
1	852.5
2	851
3	849.5
4	848
5	846.5

$P = 854 - 1.5t$

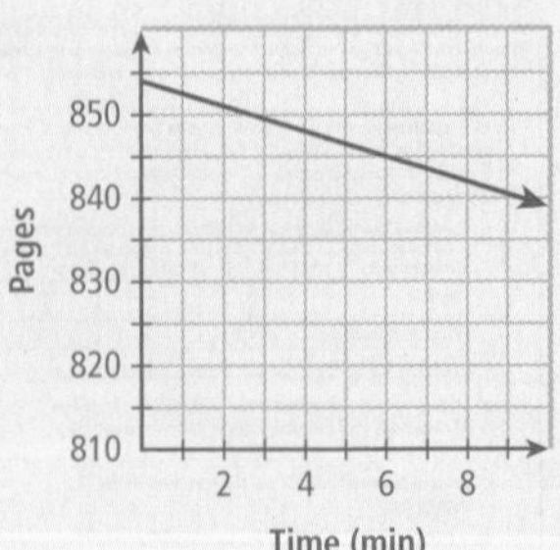

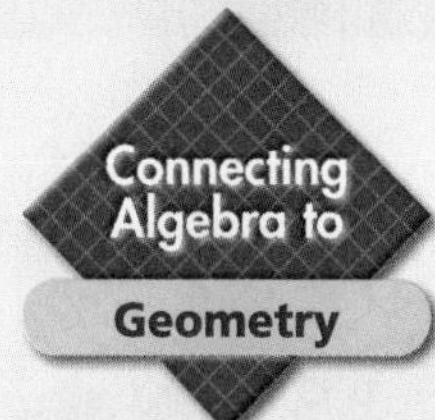

Geometric Patterns and Tessellations

See Skills Bank page S66

Sequences of figures can often be described with number patterns.

Polygonal numbers can be represented by dots arranged in the form of polygons. The first four hexagonal numbers are illustrated. The sums show a pattern. The sequence for the total number of dots is 1, 6, 15, 28, ...

$n = 1$ — 1

$n = 2$ — $1 + 5 = 6$

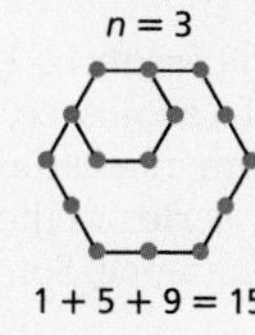

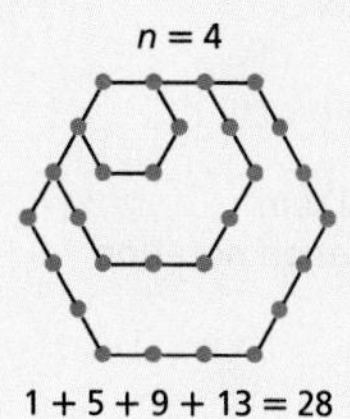

Example

The figure shows how regular hexagons can be used to tessellate, or cover, the plane. Write a sequence for the number of hexagons added at each stage. Describe the pattern in the sequence, and find the next term.

Show the number of hexagons added at each stage.

Level	1	2	3	4
Number of Hexagons	1	6	12	18

From the second term on, the number added appears to increase by 6 each time. The next level probably would have 24 hexagons. You can check your conjecture by constructing the next stage of the tessellation and counting the hexagons.

Try This

Write a sequence for the number of polygons added at each stage of the figure. Describe the pattern in the sequence, and find the next term.

1.

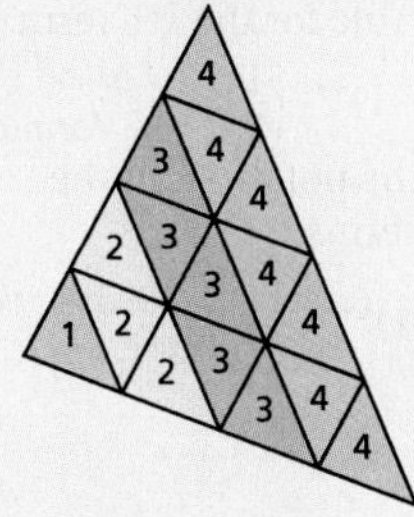

1, 3, 5, 7,...; consecutive odd numbers; 9

2.

4	4	4	4	4	4	4
4	3	3	3	3	3	4
4	3	2	2	2	3	4
4	3	2	1	2	3	4
4	3	2	2	2	3	4
4	3	3	3	3	3	4
4	4	4	4	4	4	4

1, 8, 16, 24,...; after the second term, each term increases by 8; 32.

3.

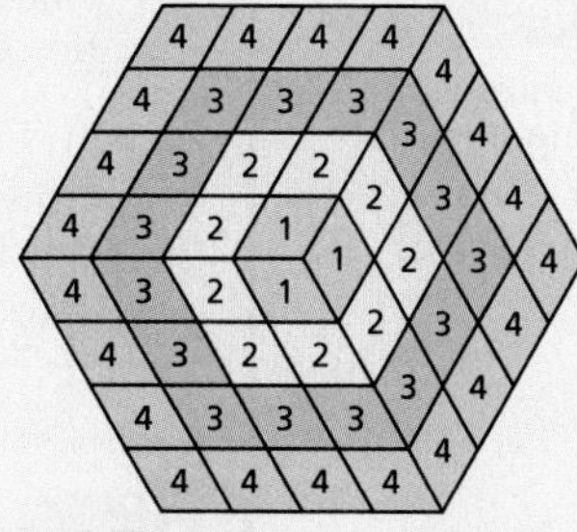

3, 9, 15, 21, ...; each term increases by 6; 27.

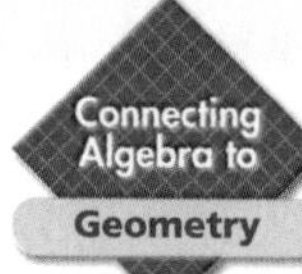

Organizer

See Skills Bank page S66

Pacing:
Traditional 1 day
Block $\frac{1}{2}$ day

Objective: Apply sequences to describe geometric patterns and tessellations.

Teach

Remember

Students review and apply geometric patterns.

INTERVENTION For additional review and practice on tessellations, see Skills Bank page S66.

Close

Assess

Have students create a pattern using an equilateral triangle. Then have them write a number sequence to describe the pattern.

State Resources

12-2 Organizer

Pacing: Traditional 1 day
Block $\frac{1}{2}$ day

Objective: Evaluate the sum of a series expressed in sigma notation.

Online Edition
Tutorial Videos

Power Presentations with PowerPoint®

Warm Up

Find the first 5 terms of each sequence.

1. $a_n = \frac{1}{n}$ $\quad 1, \frac{1}{2}, \frac{1}{3}, \frac{1}{4}, \frac{1}{5}$

2. $a_n = -n^2$ $\quad -1, -4, -9, -16, -25$

3. $a_n = 2^n$ $\quad 2, 4, 8, 16, 32$

4. $a_n = \left(\frac{1}{3}\right)^{n-1}$ $\quad 1, \frac{1}{3}, \frac{1}{9}, \frac{1}{27}, \frac{1}{81}$

5. $a_n = \frac{n}{n+1}$ $\quad \frac{1}{2}, \frac{2}{3}, \frac{3}{4}, \frac{4}{5}, \frac{5}{6}$

Write a possible explicit rule for the *n*th term of each sequence.

6. 1, 2, 4, 8, 16, ... $\quad a_n = 2^{n-1}$

7. 4, 7, 10, 13, 16, ... $\quad a_n = 3n + 1$

Also available on transparency

Math Humor

Q: Why do mathematicians watch so much TV?

A: They like all types of series.

12-2 Series and Summation Notation

A2.7.3 Find partial sums of arithmetic and geometric series.

Objective
Evaluate the sum of a series expressed in sigma notation.

Vocabulary
series
partial sum
summation notation

Why learn this?
You can use sums of sequences to find the size of a house of cards. (See Example 4.)

In Lesson 12-1, you learned how to find the nth term of a sequence. Often we are also interested in the sum of a certain number of terms of a sequence. A **series** is the indicated sum of the terms of a sequence. Some examples are shown in the table.

Sequence	1, 2, 3, 4	2, 4, 6, 8, ...	$\frac{1}{2}, \frac{1}{3}, \frac{1}{4}, \frac{1}{5}, \frac{1}{6}$
Series	$1 + 2 + 3 + 4$	$2 + 4 + 6 + 8 + \cdots$	$\frac{1}{2} + \frac{1}{3} + \frac{1}{4} + \frac{1}{5} + \frac{1}{6}$

Because many sequences are infinite and do not have defined sums, we often find partial sums. A **partial sum**, indicated by S_n, is the sum of a specified number of terms of a sequence.

For the even numbers:

$S_1 = 2$ *Sum of first term*
$S_2 = 2 + 4 = 6$ *Sum of first 2 terms*
$S_3 = 2 + 4 + 6 = 12$ *Sum of first 3 terms*
$S_4 = 2 + 4 + 6 + 8 = 20$ *Sum of first 4 terms*

A series can also be represented by using **summation notation**, which uses the Greek letter $\sum$ (capital *sigma*) to denote the sum of a sequence defined by a rule, as shown.

$$\sum_{k=1}^{5} 2k$$

5 ← Last value of *k*
$2k$ ← Explicit formula for sequence
$k=1$ ← First value of *k*

EXAMPLE 1 Using Summation Notation

Write each series in summation notation.

A $3 + 6 + 9 + 12 + 15$

Find a rule for kth term of the sequence.

$a_k = 3k$ *Explicit formula*

Write the notation for the first 5 terms.

$\sum_{k=1}^{5} 3k$ *Summation notation*

B $\frac{1}{2} - \frac{1}{4} + \frac{1}{8} - \frac{1}{16} + \frac{1}{32} - \frac{1}{64}$

Find a rule for the kth term.

$a_k = (-1)^{k+1}\left(\frac{1}{2}\right)^k$ *Explicit formula*

Write the notation for the first 6 terms.

$\sum_{k=1}^{6} (-1)^{k+1}\left(\frac{1}{2}\right)^k$ *Summation notation*

For sequences with alternating signs:
Use $(-1)^{k+1}$ if $a_1 = +$.
Use $(-1)^k$ if $a_1 = -$.

Write each series in summation notation.

1a. $\frac{2}{4} + \frac{2}{9} + \frac{2}{16} + \frac{2}{25} + \frac{2}{36}$ $\quad \sum_{k=1}^{5} \frac{2}{(k+1)^2}$

1b. $-2 + 4 - 6 + 8 - 10 + 12$ $\quad \sum_{k=1}^{6} (-1)^k(2k)$

State Resources

go.hrw.com
State Resources Online
KEYWORD: MB7 Resources

1 Introduce

EXPLORATION

12-2 Series and Summation Notation

The sequence given by the explicit formula $a_n = 2n - 1$ has some interesting properties.

1. Complete the table to find the first 5 terms of the sequence $a_n = 2n - 1$.

n	1	2	3	4	5
a_n					

2. Describe the sequence.
3. This table shows the sum of the first n terms of the above sequence. Complete the table.

n	1	2	3	4	5
Sum of first n terms of the sequence $a_n = 2n - 1$	1	4			

4. Describe any patterns you see in the table.
5. Predict the sum of the first 6 terms of the sequence $a_n = 2n - 1$.

THINK AND DISCUSS

6. **Explain** how you can use what you discovered to find the sum of the first 15 odd numbers.
7. **Describe** a sequence for which the sum of its terms is 81.

Motivate

Ask students if they have ever received any chain e-mails. Have them imagine that 2 people receive a chain e-mail on Monday, and each of those sends it to 2 people on Tuesday, and so on. How many people have received the e-mail at the end of one week? 254 Explain that the answer to this question is the sum of a sequence, or *series*.

Explorations and answers are provided in the *Explorations* binder.

EXAMPLE 2 Evaluating a Series

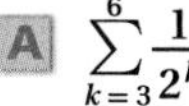

Expand each series and evaluate.

A $\sum_{k=3}^{6} \frac{1}{2^k}$

$\sum_{k=3}^{6} \frac{1}{2^k} = \frac{1}{2^3} + \frac{1}{2^4} + \frac{1}{2^5} + \frac{1}{2^6}$ *Expand the series by replacing k.*

$= \frac{1}{8} + \frac{1}{16} + \frac{1}{32} + \frac{1}{64}$ *Evaluate powers.*

$= \frac{8}{64} + \frac{4}{64} + \frac{2}{64} + \frac{1}{64} = \frac{15}{64}$ *Simplify.*

B $\sum_{k=1}^{4} (10 - k^2)$

$\sum_{k=1}^{4} (10 - k^2) = (10 - 1^2) + (10 - 2^2) + (10 - 3^2) + (10 - 4^2)$ *Expand.*

$= 9 + 6 + 1 + (-6)$ *Simplify.*

$= 10$

Caution!

Watch out! A series can have a first value other than $k = 1$, such as in Example 2A, where k begins at 3.

CHECK IT OUT! Expand each series and evaluate.

2a. $\sum_{k=1}^{4} (2k - 1)$ $1 + 3 + 5 + 7 = 16$

2b. $\sum_{k=1}^{5} -5(2)^{k-1}$ $-5 - 10 - 20 - 40 - 80 = -155$

Finding the sum of a series with many terms can be tedious. You can derive formulas for the sums of some common series.

In a *constant series,* such as $3 + 3 + 3 + 3 + 3$, each term has the same value.

$$\sum_{k=1}^{5} 3 = \underbrace{3 + 3 + 3 + 3 + 3}_{5 \text{ terms}} = 5 \cdot 3 = 15$$

The formula for the sum of a constant series is $\sum_{k=1}^{n} c = nc$, as shown.

$$\sum_{k=1}^{n} c = \underbrace{c + c + c + \cdots + c}_{n \text{ terms}} = nc$$

A *linear series* is a counting series, such as the sum of the first 10 natural numbers. Examine when the terms are rearranged.

$$\sum_{1}^{10} k = 1 + 2 + 3 + 4 + 5 + 6 + 7 + 8 + 9 + 10$$
$$= (1 + 10) + (2 + 9) + (3 + 8) + (4 + 7) + (5 + 6)$$
$$= \underbrace{11 + 11 + 11 + 11 + 11}_{5 \text{ terms}} = 5(11) = 55$$

Notice that 5 is half of the number of terms and 11 represents the sum of the first and the last term, $1 + 10$. This suggests that the sum of a linear series is $\sum_{k=1}^{n} k = \frac{n}{2}(1 + n)$, which can be written as $\sum_{k=1}^{n} k = \frac{n(n+1)}{2}$.

Similar methods will help you find the sum of a *quadratic series.*

Summation Formulas

CONSTANT SERIES	LINEAR SERIES	QUADRATIC SERIES
$\sum_{k=1}^{n} c = nc$	$\sum_{k=1}^{n} k = \frac{n(n+1)}{2}$	$\sum_{k=1}^{n} k^2 = \frac{n(n+1)(2n+1)}{6}$

2 Teach

Guided Instruction

Define a series and explain the relationship to a sequence. Review summation notation, and ask students to clarify what each variable or expression represents. Reinforce the notation verbally and visually because this material may be new for most students. Point out that the summation formulas on p. 871 are convenient ways to find the sums of common series.

Reaching All Learners

Through Cooperative Learning

Have groups of students create a sequence and a related series to model a real-world situation. Have them generate a question that draws on the terms of a sequence and a question that requires the sum of the related series. For example, cans are stacked in a pyramidal display with 1 in the top row, 2 in the 2nd row, 3 in the 3rd row, etc. How many cans are in the 5th row? sequence How many total cans are in a display with 10 rows? series

Power Presentations with PowerPoint®

Additional Examples

Example 1

Write each series in summation notation.

A. $4 + 8 + 12 + 16 + 20$

$\sum_{k=1}^{5} 4k$

B. $-1 + \frac{1}{4} - \frac{1}{9} + \frac{1}{16} - \frac{1}{25} + \frac{1}{36}$

$\sum_{k=1}^{6} (-1)^k \left(\frac{1}{k^2}\right)$

Example 2

Expand each series and evaluate.

A. $\sum_{k=2}^{5} \frac{1}{3^k}$ $\frac{1}{3^2} + \frac{1}{3^3} + \frac{1}{3^4} + \frac{1}{3^5} = \frac{40}{243}$

B. $\sum_{k=1}^{6} (k^2 - 10)$ $(1^2-10) + (2^2-10) + (3^2-10) + (4^2-10) + (5^2-10) + (6^2-10) = 31$

Also available on transparency

INTERVENTION

Questioning Strategies

EXAMPLE 1

- How do you use the terms of the series to help find the rule for the series?
- How do you know what to write for k in summation notation?

EXAMPLE 2

- How do you know the starting and ending values when you expand and evaluate a series?
- How does expanding a series differ from evaluating the series?

Teaching Tip

Reading Math Use words to help students read summation notation; for example, $\sum_{k=1}^{5} 2k$ represents "the sum from 1 to 5 of $2k$."

ENGLISH LANGUAGE LEARNERS

Power Presentations with PowerPoint®

Additional Examples

Example 3

Evaluate each series.

A. $\sum_{k=4}^{10} 6$ 42

B. $\sum_{k=1}^{8} k$ 36

C. $\sum_{k=1}^{12} k^2$ 650

Example 4

Sam is laying out patio stones in a triangular pattern. The first row has 2 stones and each row has 2 additional stones, as shown below. How many complete rows can he make with a box of 144 stones? 11

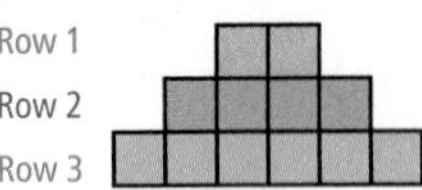

Also available on transparency

INTERVENTION

Questioning Strategies

EXAMPLE 3

- How do you recognize a constant, linear, or quadratic series?
- Are there types of series other than constant, linear, or quadratic? How do you know?

EXAMPLE 4

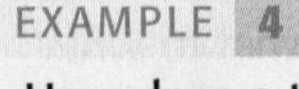

- How does a table or diagram help you identify a pattern?
- Why do you need to identify a pattern at all?
- How does the series represent the total?

EXAMPLE 3 Using Summation Formulas

Evaluate each series.

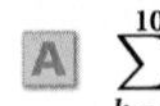

A $\sum_{k=5}^{10} 8$ *Constant series*

Method 1 Use the summation formula.

There are 6 terms.

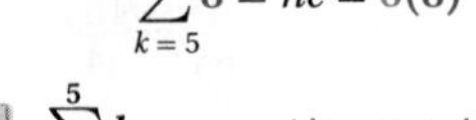

$$\sum_{k=5}^{10} 8 = nc = 6(8) = 48$$

Method 2 Expand and evaluate.

$$\sum_{k=5}^{10} 8 = \underbrace{8 + 8 + 8 + 8 + 8 + 8}_{6 \text{ terms}} = 48$$

Caution!

When counting the number of terms, you must include both the first and the last. For example, $\sum_{k=5}^{10} 8$ has six terms, not five.
$k = 5, 6, 7, 8, 9, 10$

B $\sum_{k=1}^{5} k$ *Linear series*

Method 1 Use the summation formula.

$$\sum_{k=1}^{5} k = \frac{n(n+1)}{2} = \frac{5(6)}{2} = 15$$

Method 2 Expand and evaluate.

$$\sum_{k=1}^{5} k = 1 + 2 + 3 + 4 + 5 = 15$$

C $\sum_{k=1}^{7} k^2$ *Quadratic series*

Method 1 Use the summation formula.

$$\sum_{k=1}^{7} k^2 = \frac{n(n+1)(2n+1)}{6}$$
$$= \frac{7(7+1)(2 \cdot 7 + 1)}{6}$$
$$= \frac{56(15)}{6}$$
$$= 140$$

Method 2 Use a graphing calculator.

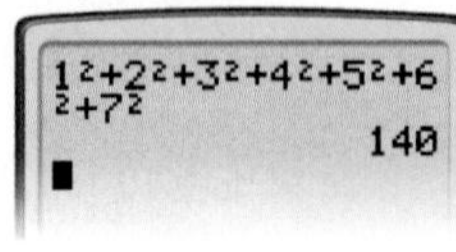

CHECK IT OUT! Evaluate each series.

3a. $\sum_{k=1}^{60} 4$ 240 **3b.** $\sum_{k=1}^{15} k$ 120 **3c.** $\sum_{k=1}^{10} k^2$ 385

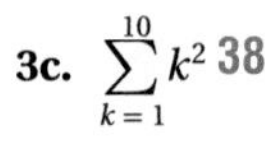

EXAMPLE 4 *Problem-Solving Application*

Ricky is building a card house similar to the one shown. He wants the house to have as many stories as possible with a deck of 52 playing cards. How many stories will Ricky's house have?

1 Understand the Problem

The **answer** will be the number of stories, or rows, in the card house.

List the important information:

- He has 52 playing cards.
- The house should have as many stories as possible.

2 Make a Plan

Make a diagram of the house to better understand the problem. Find a pattern for the number of cards in each story. Write and evaluate the series.

Reaching All Learners

Through Visual Cues

Have students create a poster of summation notation to display in the classroom. Have them use color coding to indicate that k is the value that changes with each new term in a series.

 **Solve**

Make a table and a diagram.

Row	1	2	3	4
Diagram	/\	/‾\/‾\	/‾\/‾\/‾\	/‾\/‾\/‾\/‾\
Cards	2	5	8	11

The number of cards increases by 3 in each row. Write a series to represent the total number of cards in n rows.

$\sum_{k=1}^{n}(3k-1)$, where k is the row number and n is the total number of rows

Evaluate the series for several n-values.

$$\sum_{k=1}^{4}(3k-1) = [3(1)-1]+[3(2)-1]+[3(3)-1]+[3(4)-1] = 26$$

$$\sum_{k=1}^{5}(3k-1) = [3(1)-1]+[3(2)-1]+[3(3)-1]+[3(4)-1]+[3(5)-1] = 40$$

$$\sum_{k=1}^{6}(3k-1) = [3(1)-1]+[3(2)-1]+[3(3)-1]+[3(4)-1]+[3(5)-1]+[3(6)-1] = 57$$

Because Ricky has only 52 cards, the house can have at most 5 stories.

 **Look Back**

Use the table to continue the pattern. The 5th row would have 14 cards. $S_5 = 2 + 5 + 8 + 11 + 14 = 40$. The next row would have more than 12 cards, so the total would be more than 52.

4. A flexible garden hose is coiled for storage. Each subsequent loop is 6 inches longer than the preceding loop, and the innermost loop is 34 inches long. If there are 6 loops, how long is the hose?

294 in., or $24\frac{1}{2}$ ft

THINK AND DISCUSS

1. Explain the difference between a sequence and a series.

2. Explain what each of the variables represents in the notation $\sum_{k=m}^{n} k$.

3. GET ORGANIZED Copy and complete the graphic organizer. Write the general notation and an example for each term.

	Sequence	Series
Notation		
Example		

COMMON ERROR ALERT

Students may attempt to find the partial sum of a series by evaluating the expression for only the final value of k. Stress that the notation means *sum*, so students should be adding at least two terms to evaluate a series.

Teaching Tip **Technology** Students are taught to use the **sum(** function on graphing calculators in the Technology Lab following Lesson 12-2. You may want to teach that lab before or during this lesson.

Teaching Tip **Statistics** The Greek letter Σ (capital *sigma*) denotes the sum of a sequence defined by a rule. The Greek letter σ (lower case *sigma*) denotes the standard deviation of a set of numbers.

3 Close

Summarize

Display an expression in summation notation, such as $\sum_{k=3}^{6}(5k-4)$. Ask students to describe how they would evaluate this sum, taking care to discuss each step. Have a volunteer complete each step as it is discussed. Possible answer: Identify the values of k that will be included: 3, 4, 5, and 6. Evaluate the expression for each of these terms and then find the sum: $11 + 16 + 21 + 26 = 74$.

ONGOING ASSESSMENT and INTERVENTION

***Diagnose Before* the Lesson**
12-2 Warm Up, TE p. 870

***Monitor During* the Lesson**
Check It Out! Exercises, SE pp. 870–873
Questioning Strategies, TE pp. 871–872

***Assess After* the Lesson**
12-2 Lesson Quiz, TE p. 877
Alternative Assessment, TE p. 877

Answers to *Think and Discuss*

Possible answers:

1. A sequence is an ordered list of terms. When the terms are added together, a series is created. The series is an indicated sum of the sequence.
2. m is the first replacement for k, n is the last replacement for k, and k is the explicit formula.
3. See p. A13.

12-2 Exercises

Assignment Guide

Assign *Guided Practice* exercises as necessary.

If you finished Examples **1–2**

Basic	13–19, 24–26, 36–39
Average	13–19, 24–29, 36–39
Advanced	13–19, 24–33, 36–39

If you finished Examples **1–4**

Basic	13–34, 36–42, 48–56, 62–68
Average	13–29, 34–46, 48–58, 62–68
Advanced	14–34 even, 35–68

Homework Quick Check
Quickly check key concepts.
Exercises: 16, 18, 20, 30, 34

Answers

8. $-25 - 30 - 35 - 40 - 45 - 50 = -225$

18. $4 - 8 + 16 - 32 + 64 - 128 = -84$

27. $\sum_{k=1}^{5} -800\left(\frac{1}{10}\right)^{k-1}$

28. $\sum_{k=1}^{4} 11.1 - 0.3k$

29. $\sum_{k=1}^{6} (-1)^{k+1}(k+2)^2$

30. $\sum_{k=1}^{5} (-1)^k(3.4 + 0.5k)$

31. $\sum_{k=1}^{5} 3.4k - 3.4$, or $\sum_{k=1}^{5} 3.4(k-1)$

State Resources

go.hrw.com
State Resources Online
KEYWORD: MB7 Resources

12-2 Exercises

go.hrw.com
Homework Help Online
KEYWORD: MB7 12-2
Parent Resources Online
KEYWORD: MB7 Parent

GUIDED PRACTICE

1. **Vocabulary** Give an example of *summation notation.* $\sum_{k=1}^{n} k$

SEE EXAMPLE 1 p. 870

Write each series in summation notation.

2. $1 + \frac{1}{4} + \frac{1}{9} + \frac{1}{16} + \frac{1}{25}$ $\sum_{k=1}^{5}\left(\frac{1}{k^2}\right)$

3. $-3 + 6 - 9 + 12 - 15$ $\sum_{k=1}^{6}(-1)^k(3k)$

4. $1 + 10 + 100 + 1000 + 10{,}000$ $\sum_{k=1}^{5}(10)^{k-1}$

5. $100 + 95 + 90 + 85 + 80$ $\sum_{k=1}^{5}[100 - 5(k-1)]$

SEE EXAMPLE 2 p. 871

Expand each series and evaluate.

6. $\sum_{k=1}^{5} k^3$ $1 + 8 + 27 + 64 + 125 = 225$

7. $\sum_{k=1}^{4}(-1)^{k+1}\frac{12}{k^2}$ $12 - 3 + \frac{4}{3} - \frac{3}{4} = 9\frac{7}{12}$

8. $\sum_{k=5}^{10} -5k$

SEE EXAMPLE 3 p. 872

Evaluate each series.

9. $\sum_{k=1}^{21} k$ **231**

10. $\sum_{k=1}^{20} k^2$ **2870**

11. $\sum_{k=15}^{35} 6$ **126**

SEE EXAMPLE 4 p. 872

12. **Finance** Melinda makes monthly car payments of $285 each month. How much will she have paid after 2 years? 5 years? **$6840; $17,100**

PRACTICE AND PROBLEM SOLVING

Independent Practice

For Exercises	See Example
13–16	1
17–19	2
20–22	3
23	4

Extra Practice
Skills Practice p. S26
Application Practice p. S43

Write each series in summation notation.

13. $1.1 + 2.2 + 3.3 + 4.4 + 5.5$ $\sum_{k=1}^{5} 1.1k$

14. $\frac{1}{2} + \frac{2}{3} + \frac{3}{4} + \frac{4}{5} + \frac{5}{6}$ $\sum_{k=1}^{5}\frac{k}{k+1}$

15. $11 - 12 + 13 - 14 + 15 - 16$ 15. $\sum_{k=1}^{6}(-1)^{k+1}(k+10)$

16. $1 + 2 + 4 + 8 + 16 + 32$ $\sum_{k=1}^{6} 2^{k-1}$

Expand each series and evaluate.

17. $\sum_{k=1}^{5}[8(k+1)]$ $16 + 24 + 32 + 40 + 48 = 160$

18. $\sum_{k=2}^{7}(-2)^k$

19. $\sum_{k=1}^{4}\frac{k-1}{k+1}$ $0 + \frac{1}{3} + \frac{2}{4} + \frac{3}{5} = \frac{43}{30}$

Evaluate each series.

20. $\sum_{k=1}^{99} k$ **4950**

21. $\sum_{k=11}^{88} 2.5$ **195**

22. $\sum_{k=1}^{25} k^2$ **5525**

23. **Retail** A display of soup cans is arranged with 1 can on top and each row having an additional can. How many cans are in a display of 20 rows? **210 cans**

Write each series in summation notation.

24. $-1 + 4 - 9 + 16 - 25 + 36$ $\sum_{k=1}^{6}(-1)^k k^2$

25. $25 + 24 + 23 + \cdots + 1$ $\sum_{k=1}^{25}(26 - k)$

26. $\frac{1}{3} + \frac{1}{9} + \frac{1}{27} + \frac{1}{81} + \frac{1}{243}$ $\sum_{k=1}^{5}\left(\frac{1}{3}\right)^k$

27. $-800 - 80 - 8 - 0.8 - 0.08$

28. $10.8 + 10.5 + 10.2 + 9.9$

29. $9 - 16 + 25 - 36 + 49 - 64$

30. $-3.9 + 4.4 - 4.9 + 5.4 - 5.9$

31. $0 + 3.4 + 6.8 + 10.2 + 13.6$

32. $3 + \frac{3}{2} + 1 + \frac{3}{4} + \frac{3}{5}$ $\sum_{k=1}^{5}\frac{3}{k}$

33. $1000 + 100 + 10 + 1 + \frac{1}{10}$ $\sum_{k=1}^{5}\frac{1000}{10^{k-1}}$

34. **Travel** The distance from St. Louis, Missouri, to Los Angeles, California, is 1596 miles. Michael plans to travel half the distance on the first day and half the remaining distance each day after that. Write a series in summation notation for the total distance he will travel in 5 days. How far will Michael travel in the 5 days?
$\sum_{k=1}^{5} 1596\left(\frac{1}{2}\right)^k$; $1546\frac{1}{8}$ mi

12-2 PRACTICE A

Use summation notation to write each series.

1. $2 + 4 + 8 + 16 + 32 + 64$
   a. Find a rule for the kth term. $a_k = 2^k$
   b. Write the notation for the first 6 terms. $\sum_{k=1}^{6} 2^k$

2. $-6 - 5 - 4 - 3 - 2$ $\sum_{k=1}^{5}(k-7)$

3. $4 + 7 + 10 + 13 + 16 + 19$ $\sum_{k=1}^{6}(3k+1)$

4. $2 + 8 + 18 + 32$ $\sum_{k=1}^{4}(2k^2)$

5. $-3 + 9 - 27 + 81 - 243$ $\sum_{k=1}^{5}(-3)^k$

6. $16 + 12 + 8 + 4 + 0 - 4 - 8$ $\sum_{k=1}^{7}(20 - 4k)$

7. $-1 - 4 - 9 - 16 - 25$ $\sum_{k=1}^{5} -(k^2)$

Expand each series. Then evaluate.

8. $\sum_{k=3}^{7} 2k^2$
   a. Expand by replacing k. $18 + 32 + 50 + 72 + 98$
   b. Simplify. 270

9. $\sum_{k=1}^{4}\frac{2}{k}$
   a. Expand. $2 + 1 + \frac{2}{3} + \frac{1}{2}$
   b. Simplify. $4\frac{1}{6}$

10. $\sum_{k=5}^{10}(k-7)$
   a. Expand. $-2 - 1 + 0 + 1 + 2 + 3$
   b. Simplify. 3

11. $\sum_{k=2}^{4} 5(2^k)$
   a. Expand. $20 + 40 + 80$
   b. Simplify. 140

12. $\sum_{k=21}^{25} 3(20 - k)$
   a. Expand. $-3 - 6 - 9 - 12 - 15$
   b. Simplify. -45

Solve.

13. Tracy deposits $16 into her savings account each week.
   a. Write a series to represent how much she will have deposited in n weeks. $\sum_{k=1}^{n} 16$
   b. Write a series to represent how much she will have deposited in one year. $\sum_{k=1}^{52} 16$
   c. How much will she have deposited in one year? $832

12-2 PRACTICE B

Write each series in summation notation.

1. $-2 + 4 - 8 + 16 - 32$ $\sum_{k=1}^{5}(-2)^k$

2. $\frac{1}{10} + \frac{1}{100} + \frac{1}{1{,}000} + \frac{1}{10{,}000}$ $\sum_{k=1}^{4}\left(\frac{1}{10}\right)^k$

3. $-6 - 1 + 4 + 9 + 14 + 19$ $\sum_{k=1}^{6}(5k - 11)$

4. $\frac{1}{3} + \frac{1}{6} + \frac{1}{9} + \frac{1}{12} + \frac{1}{15} + \frac{1}{18}$ $\sum_{k=1}^{6}\frac{1}{3k}$

5. $7 + 13 + 19 + 25 + 31$ $\sum_{k=1}^{5}(6k + 1)$

6. $-1 + 1 - 1 + 1 - 1 + 1 - 1$ $\sum_{k=1}^{7}(-1)^k$

Expand each series and evaluate.

7. $\sum_{k=4}^{8}\frac{k}{4}$
   a. Expand. $1 + \frac{5}{4} + \frac{6}{4} + \frac{7}{4} + 2$
   b. Simplify. $7\frac{1}{2}$

8. $\sum_{k=1}^{4} 5^{k-2}$
   a. Expand. $\frac{1}{5} + 1 + 5 + 25$
   b. Simplify. $31\frac{1}{5}$

9. $\sum_{k=2}^{6}(-2^k)$
   a. Expand. $4 - 8 + 16 - 32 + 64$
   b. Simplify. 44

10. $\sum_{k=30}^{39}(70 - 2k)$
   a. Expand. $10 + 8 + 6 + 4 + 2 + 0 - 2 - 4 - 6 - 8$
   b. Simplify. 10

Evaluate each series.

11. $\sum_{k=12}^{20} 3$ 27

12. $\sum_{k=1}^{40} k$ 820

13. $\sum_{k=1}^{10} k^2$ 385

Solve.

14. One day, Hannah starts a new online Internet club by convincing two of her friends to join. The next day, each member convinces two more people to join. The third day of the club, each member convinces two more people to join, and so on for a full week.
   a. Write a series that represents the number of club members at the end of n days. $\sum_{k=1}^{n} 3^k$
   b. Write a series that represents the number of club members at the end of one week. $\sum_{k=1}^{7} 3^k$
   c. How many members will the club have at the end of a week? 3279

35. **Safety** An employer uses a telephone tree to notify employees in the case of an emergency closing. When the office manager makes the decision to close, she calls 3 people. Each of these people calls 3 other people, and so on.

a. Make a tree diagram with 3 levels to represent the problem situation.

b. Write and evaluate a series to find the total number of people notified after 5 levels of calls.

c. **What if...?** Suppose that the phone tree involves calling 5 people at each level. How many more people would be notified after 5 levels of calls? **3542**

LINK
Math History

The Granger Collection, New York

At the age of 10, German mathematician Carl Friedrich Gauss discovered a quick method for adding the first 100 natural numbers. His method gave us the summation formula for a linear series.

Expand each series and evaluate.

36. $\sum_{k=1}^{6}(k^2+1)$

37. $\sum_{k=1}^{6}(-1)^k 5k$

38. $\sum_{k=3}^{6}\frac{1}{2k}$

39. $\sum_{k=1}^{6}(3k-2)$

40. $\sum_{k=6}^{11}12(k-2)$

41. $\sum_{k=1}^{5}\frac{k^2}{5k}$

42. **Architecture** A hotel is being built in the shape of a pyramid, as shown in the diagram. Each square floor is 10 feet longer and 10 feet wider than the floor above it.

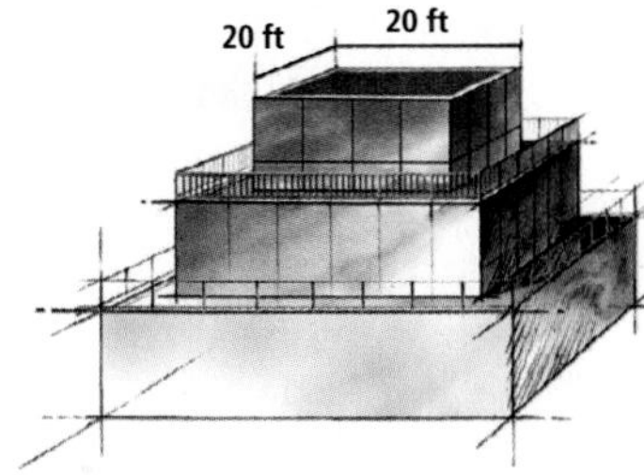

a. Write a series that represents the total area of n floors of the hotel.

b. How many stories must the hotel be to have at least 50,000 square feet of floor area? **10 stories**

42a. $\sum_{k=1}^{n}100(k+1)^2$

Estimation **Use mental math to estimate each sum. Then compare your answer to the sum obtained by using a calculator.**

43. $10 + 11 + 12 + \cdots + 29 + 30$ **420**

44. $1 + 3 + 5 + \cdots + 97 + 99$ **2500**

45. $-2 + (-4) + (-6) + \cdots + (-98) + (-100)$ **−2550**

46. **Physics** The distance that an object falls in equal time intervals is represented in the table. Rules created by Leonardo da Vinci and Galileo are shown. (In this general case, specific units do not apply to time or distance.)

Distance Fallen in Each Time Interval		
Time Interval	Leonardo's Rule	Galileo's Rule
1	1	1
2	2	3
3	3	5
4	4	7
5	5	9

a. Write the series for each rule for 5 intervals, and find the respective sums. What does the sum of the series for 5 intervals represent?

b. Write each series in summation notation. Then evaluate each series for $n = 10$.

c. By the current rule, the distance fallen in each interval is 1, 4, 9, 16, 25.... How do Leonardo's rule and Galileo's rule compare to the current rule?

47. **Critical Thinking** Some mathematical properties may be applied to series.

a. Evaluate $\sum_{k=1}^{10}3n$ and $3\sum_{k=1}^{10}n$. Make a conjecture based on your answer.

b. Evaluate $\sum_{k=1}^{10}n + \sum_{k=1}^{10}2$ and $\sum_{k=1}^{10}(n+2)$. Make a conjecture based on your answer.

COMMON ERROR ALERT

Students may have trouble with series in which the terms have alternating signs, such as **Exercises 24, 29,** and **30.** Remind them that each of these must contain either $(-1)^k$ if the first term is negative or $(-1)^{k+1}$ if the first term is positive.

Teaching Tip

Critical Thinking After students complete **Exercises 47** and **48,** have them consider whether the addition of series is commutative or associative.

Answers

35a.

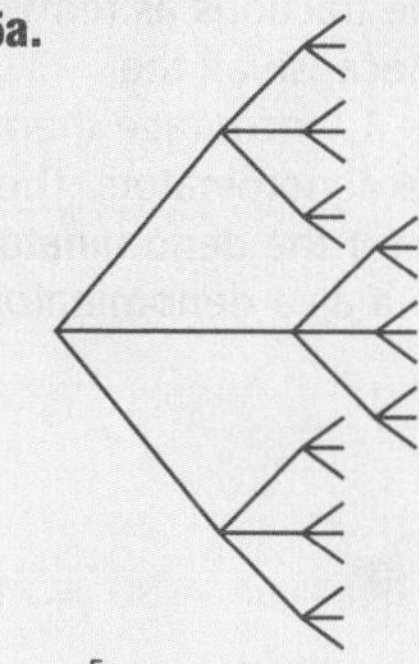

b. $\sum_{k=1}^{5}3^k = 3 + 9 + 27 + 81 + 243 = 363$

36. $2 + 5 + 10 + 17 + 26 + 37 = 97$

37. $-5 + 10 - 15 + 20 - 25 + 30 = 15$

38. $\frac{1}{6} + \frac{1}{8} + \frac{1}{10} + \frac{1}{12} = \frac{19}{40}$

39. $1 + 4 + 7 + 10 + 13 + 16 = 51$

40. $48 + 60 + 72 + 84 + 96 + 108 = 468$

41. $\frac{1}{5} + \frac{2}{5} + \frac{3}{5} + \frac{4}{5} + 1 = 3$

46a. Leonardo: $1 + 2 + 3 + 4 + 5 = 15$; Galileo: $1 + 3 + 5 + 7 + 9 = 25$; the total distance traveled in 5 equal units of time

b. Leonardo: $\sum_{k=1}^{n}k$; 55; Galileo: $\sum_{k=1}^{n}(2k-1)$; 100

c. Objects fall farther under the current rule.

47a. Both equal 165; $\sum_{k=1}^{n}ca_k = c\sum_{k=1}^{n}a_k$.

b. Both equal 75; $\sum_{k=1}^{n}(a_k + b_k) = \sum_{k=1}^{n}a_k + \sum_{k=1}^{n}b_k$.

12-2 PRACTICE C

Write each series in summation notation.

1. $6 + 12 + 24 + 48 + 96$ — $\sum_{k=1}^{5}3(2^k)$

2. $\frac{3}{2} + \frac{3}{4} + \frac{1}{2} + \frac{3}{8} + \frac{3}{10} + \frac{1}{4} + \frac{3}{14}$ — $\sum_{k=1}^{7}\frac{3}{2k}$

3. $1 - 1 + 1 - 1 + 1 - 1 + 1$ — $\sum_{k=1}^{7}(-1)^{k-1}$

4. $10 + 1 + \frac{1}{10} + \frac{1}{100} + \frac{1}{1000}$ — $\sum_{k=1}^{5}\left(\frac{1}{10}\right)^{k-2}$

5. $-\frac{1}{4} + 2 + \frac{23}{4} + 11 + \frac{71}{4} + 26$ — $\sum_{k=1}^{6}\left(\frac{3}{4}k^2 - 1\right)$

6. $0 + 2 + 6 + 12 + 20 + 30$ — $\sum_{k=1}^{6}(k^2 - k)$

Evaluate each series.

7. $\sum_{k=3}^{5}\frac{k+1}{k-2}$ — $8\frac{1}{2}$

8. $\sum_{k=4}^{8}(0.5k^2 - 3)$ — 80

9. $\sum_{k=2}^{6}(-3)^{k-4}$ — $6\frac{7}{9}$

10. $\sum_{k=7}^{22}8.1$ — 129.6

11. $\sum_{k=1}^{45}k$ — 1035

12. $\sum_{k=1}^{30}k^2$ — 9455

Solve.

13. Kate is unpacking boxes of books and arranging them on her new bookcases. She places 5 books on the top shelf. Each shelf contains 4 more books than the shelf above it. There are 6 shelves.

a. How many books are on the bottom shelf? 25 books

b. How many books are in the bookcase? 90 books

14. After a 20-minute jog on his treadmill, Trent cools down by gradually slowing until he reaches 0.5 mile per hour, the slowest speed on his treadmill. At minute 21, he moves his speed down 0.1 mile per hour. At minute 22, he moves his speed down 0.2 mile per hour. At minute 23, he moves his speed down 0.3 mile per hour. Each minute of cooldown his speed is reduced by 0.1 mile more than the previous minute.

a. Write a series representing the total reduction in speed at minute 30. $\sum_{k=21}^{30}\frac{(k-20)}{10}$

b. By how much has he reduced his speed after 10 minutes? 5.5 miles per hour

Exercise 48 involves expanding and evaluating the partial sum of a series that models the layers of a tetrahedral kite. This exercise prepares students for the Multi-Step Test Prep on page 888.

In **Exercise 52,** students who chose **A** or **D** probably did not recognize the effect that $(-1)^k$ has on the terms of the series. Students who chose **B** may be confusing the effect of odd and even exponents in that expression. Review how to evaluate $(-1)^k$ for odd and even values of k.

In **Exercise 53,** students may be confused by the fractions as terms of the series. Because all the numerators are 1, encourage them to focus on the denominators. They can find a rule for the denominators and then write it as a denominator under 1.

Answers

48a. $6 + 18 + 36 + 60 + 90 = 210$

b. $3\sum_{k=1}^{n} k^2 + 3\sum_{k=1}^{n} k$

50. Yes, both series have the same sum, 25. However, their summation notations are not the same because $\sum_{k=1}^{5}(2k-1) = 1 + 3 + 5 + 7 + 9$ and $\sum_{k=1}^{5}(11-2k) = 9 + 7 + 5 + 3 + 1$.

51. Possible answer: S_n represents a partial sum because it is the sum of only a specified number of terms. Many series are infinite and do not have actual sums.

56. Possible answer: A sequence would give the number of cans in the 20th row because each term in the sequence represents the number of cans in a row. A series would give the total number of cans in the stack.

59–61. See p. A46.

62–64. For graphs, see p. A46.

48. This problem will prepare you for the Multi-Step Test Prep on page 888.

The series $\sum_{k=1}^{n}(3k^2 + 3k)$ gives the total number of sticks needed to make a tetrahedral kite with n layers.

a. Expand and evaluate the series to find out how many sticks are needed to make a kite with 5 layers.

b. Use the properties $\sum_{k=1}^{n}(a_k + b_k) = \sum_{k=1}^{n} a_k + \sum_{k=1}^{n} b_k$ and $\sum_{k=1}^{n} ca_k = c\sum_{k=1}^{n} a_k$ to rewrite the series as a multiple of a quadratic series plus a multiple of a linear series.

c. Use summation formulas to determine how many sticks are needed to make a kite with 17 layers. **5814**

49. Multi-Step Examine the pattern made by toothpick squares with increasing side lengths.

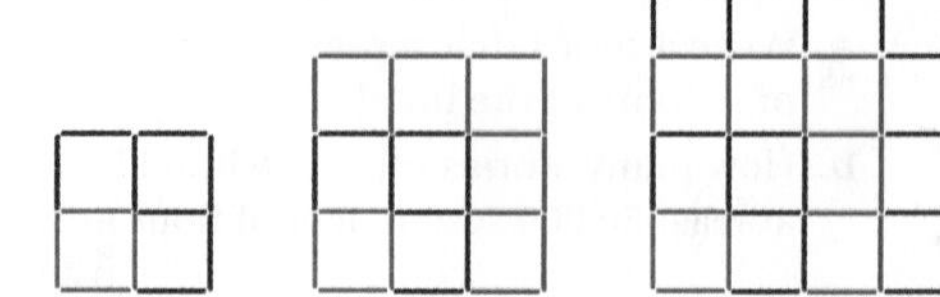

a. Write a sequence for the number of toothpicks added to form each new square. $a_n = 4n$

49b. $\sum_{k=1}^{6} 4k$; 84

b. Write and evaluate a series in summation notation to represent the total number of toothpicks in a square with a side length of 6 toothpicks.

50. Critical Thinking Are the sums of $1 + 3 + 5 + 7 + 9$ and $9 + 7 + 5 + 3 + 1$ the same? Do these series have the same summation notation? Explain.

51. Write About It Explain why S_n represents a partial sum and not a complete sum of the terms of a sequence.

52. Which notation accurately reflects the series $\sum_{k=1}^{7}(-1)^k(3k)$?

Ⓐ $3 + 6 + 9 + 12 + 15 + 18 + 21$

Ⓑ $3 - 6 + 9 - 12 + 15 - 18 + 21$

Ⓒ $-3 + 6 - 9 + 12 - 15 + 18 - 21$ (circled)

Ⓓ $-3 - 6 - 9 - 12 - 15 - 18 - 21$

53. Which notation accurately reflects the series $\frac{1}{2} + \frac{1}{4} + \frac{1}{6} + \frac{1}{8}$?

Ⓕ $\sum_{k=1}^{4}\frac{k}{2}$ Ⓖ $\sum_{k=1}^{4}\frac{1}{2^k}$ Ⓗ $\sum_{k=1}^{4}\frac{1}{2k}$ (circled) Ⓙ $\sum_{k=1}^{4}\frac{1}{k+2}$

54. What is the value of $\sum_{k=1}^{6} k^2$?

Ⓐ 36 Ⓑ 55 Ⓒ 91 (circled) Ⓓ 273

55. Find the sum of the series $\frac{1}{3} + \frac{1}{6} + \frac{1}{12} + \frac{1}{24}$?

Ⓕ $\frac{1}{45}$ Ⓖ $\frac{4}{45}$ Ⓗ $\frac{7}{12}$ Ⓙ $\frac{5}{8}$ (circled)

12-2 READING STRATEGIES

The sum of a certain number of terms of a sequence is described using the Greek letter sigma. You can use this symbol to show the sum of the terms of a sequence. The notation below is for the first 5 terms of the sequence with the rule that $a_k = \frac{k}{2}$. This method of denoting the sum of a series is called summation notation.

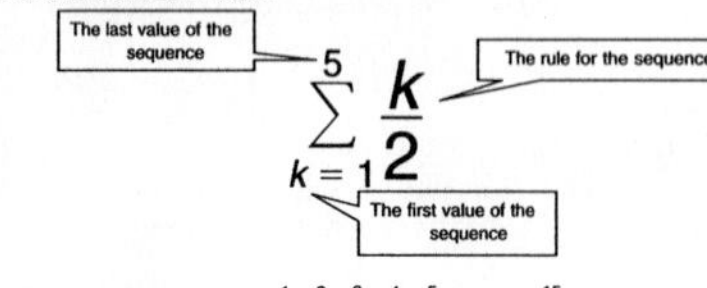

The expanded form of this series is $\frac{1}{2} + \frac{2}{2} + \frac{3}{2} + \frac{4}{2} + \frac{5}{2}$. The sum is $\frac{15}{2}$.

Answer each question.

1. $\sum_{k=1}^{4} k + 5$
   a. What is the rule for the sequence? $k + 5$
   b. What are the first and last values of k? 1 and 4
   c. Show an expanded series that fits this rule. $6 + 7 + 8 + 9$
2. $\sum_{k=1}^{5} 7k$
   a. What is the rule for the sequence? $7k$
   b. What are the first and last values of k? 1 and 5
   c. Show an expanded series that fits this rule. $7 + 14 + 21 + 28 + 35$
3. The series $-1 + 0 + 1 + 2 + 3 + 4$ follows the rule $k - 2$.
   a. What are the first and last values of k? 1 and 6
   b. Write the series in summation notation. $\sum_{k=1}^{6} k - 2$
4. The series $9 + 17 + 25 + 33 + 41$ follows the rule $8k + 1$.
   a. What are the first and last values of k? 1 and 5
   b. Write the series in summation notation. $\sum_{k=1}^{5} 8k + 1$

12-2 RETEACH

A series is the sum of the terms of a sequence. Summation notation is used to represent a series.

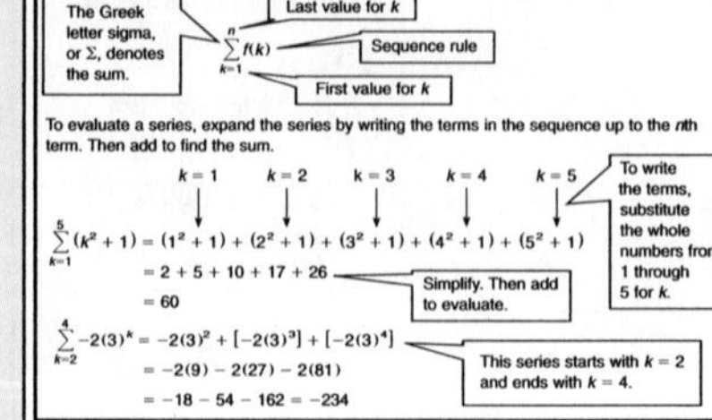

To evaluate a series, expand the series by writing the terms in the sequence up to the nth term. Then add to find the sum.

$$\sum_{k=1}^{5}(k^2+1) = (1^2+1) + (2^2+1) + (3^2+1) + (4^2+1) + (5^2+1)$$
$$= 2 + 5 + 10 + 17 + 26$$
$$= 60$$

To write the terms, substitute the whole numbers from 1 through 5 for k.

Simplify. Then add to evaluate.

$$\sum_{k=2}^{4} -2(3)^k = -2(3)^2 + [-2(3)^3] + [-2(3)^4]$$
$$= -2(9) - 2(27) - 2(81)$$
$$= -18 - 54 - 162 = -234$$

This series starts with $k = 2$ and ends with $k = 4$.

Expand each series and evaluate.

1. $\sum_{k=2}^{5}(4k-1) = (4(2)-1) + (4(3)-1) + (4(4)-1) + (4(5)-1)$
   $= 7 + 11 + 15 + 19$
   $= 52$
2. $\sum_{k=1}^{4}\frac{1}{k} = \frac{1}{1} + \frac{1}{2} + \frac{1}{3} + \frac{1}{4}$
   $= \frac{12}{12} + \frac{6}{12} + \frac{4}{12} + \frac{3}{12}$
   $= \frac{25}{12} = 2\frac{1}{12}$
3. $\sum_{k=1}^{4}(5)^{k-1} = (5)^{1-1} + (5)^{2-1} + (5)^{3-1} + (5)^{4-1}$
   $= 1 + 5 + 25 + 125$
   $= 156$
4. $\sum_{k=1}^{3}(2^k + 1)$
   $(2^1 + 1) + (2^2 + 1) + (2^3 + 1)$
   $= 3 + 5 + 9 = 17$
5. $\sum_{k=3}^{5}(2k^2 - 1)$
   $[2(3^2) - 1] + [2(4^2) - 1] + [2(5^2) - 1]$
   $= 17 + 31 + 49 = 97$

56. **Short Response** The number of cans in each row of a pyramidal stack is 1, 4, 9, 16, ... Would a sequence or series be used to find the number of cans in the 20th row? Explain.

CHALLENGE AND EXTEND

Write each series in summation notation. Then find the sum.

57. $1 + 2 + 3 + \cdots + 1000$ $\sum_{k=1}^{1000} k$; **500,500**

58. $1^2 + 2^2 + 3^2 + \cdots + 25^2$ $\sum_{k=1}^{25} k^2$; **5525**

Prove each summation property for the sequences a_k and b_k.

59. $\sum_{k=1}^{n} ca_k = c\sum_{k=1}^{n} a_k$

60. $\sum_{k=1}^{n} (a_k + b_k) = \sum_{k=1}^{n} a_k + \sum_{k=1}^{n} b_k$

61. **Critical Thinking** What might the sum of the sequence $1 - 1 + 1 - 1 + 1 - 1 + \cdots$ be if it continues forever? Explain.

SPIRAL REVIEW

Find the intercepts of each line, and graph the lines. *(Lesson 2-3)*

62. $3x - 4y = 12$

63. $-6x + 3y = -18$

64. $10x + 15y = -5$

62. *x*-int.: 4; *y*-int.: −3

63. *x*-int.: 3; *y*-int.: −6

64. *x*-int.: $-\frac{1}{2}$; *y*-int.: $-\frac{1}{3}$

65. **Architecture** The height in feet of an elevator above ground is modeled by $h(t) = 8|t - 6| + 10$, where t is the time in seconds. What is the minimum height of the elevator? *(Lesson 2-9)* **10 ft**

Find the first 5 terms of each sequence. *(Lesson 12-1)*

66. $a_n = \left(\frac{1}{2}n + 2\right)^2$ $\frac{25}{4}, 9, \frac{49}{4}, 16, \frac{81}{4}$

67. $a_1 = 2, a_n = (a_{n-1})^2 - 1$ **2, 3, 8, 63, 3968**

68. $a_n = \frac{4^n}{2}$ **2, 8, 32, 128, 512**

Career Path

go.hrw.com
Career Resources Online
KEYWORD: MB7 Career

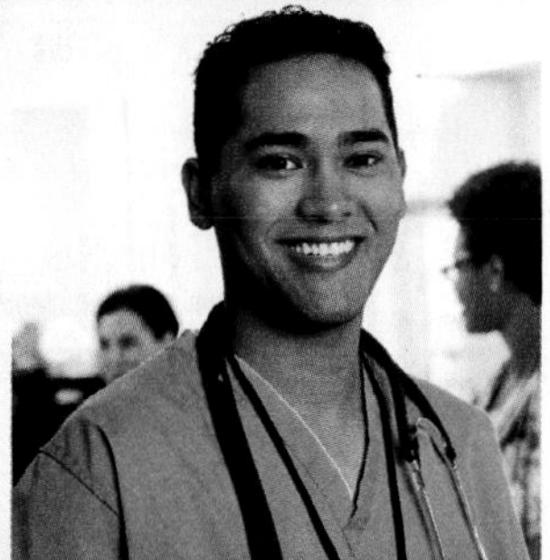

Steven Howe
Nursing student

Q: What high school math classes did you take?
A: Algebra 1, Geometry, Business Math, and Algebra 2

Q: Why did you decide to pursue a career in nursing?
A: I've always liked science, especially biology and anatomy. I also wanted a career where I can help people, so a job in medicine seemed perfect.

Q: How is math used in nursing?
A: Nurses have to make a lot of calculations to ensure that patients receive the correct dosages of medicine. They also use complicated instruments to measure and monitor different body functions.

Q: What are your future plans?
A: I'll finish my associate's degree in nursing at the end of the semester. I hope to get a job at one of the local hospitals.

COMMON ERROR ALERT

In **Exercise 48b,** some students might have difficulty recognizing how the properties correspond to the series $\sum_{k=1}^{n}(3k^2 + 3k)$. Point out that $a_k = 3k^2$ and $b_k = 3k$, so $\sum_{k=1}^{n}(3k^2 + 3k) = 3\sum_{k=1}^{n} k^2 + 3\sum_{k=1}^{n} k$. Now students can use the formulas to evaluate each part for $n = 17$ in **Exercise 48c.**

Journal

Have students explain summation notation using words and by providing an example. Encourage them to include an example of a partial sum as well.

ALTERNATIVE ASSESSMENT

Have students create two different series using summation notation. One should be a series with alternating signs. Have students expand and evaluate each series for several different values of k and n.

Power Presentations with PowerPoint®

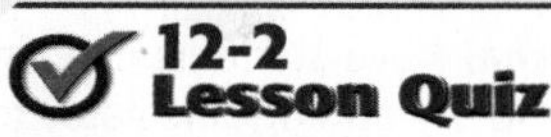

12-2 Lesson Quiz

Write each series in summation notation.

1. $1 - 10 + 100 - 1000 + 10{,}000$
2. $\frac{1}{5} + \frac{1}{10} + \frac{1}{15} + \frac{1}{20} + \frac{1}{25}$

1. $\sum_{k=1}^{5}(-10)^{k-1}$ 2. $\sum_{k=1}^{5}\frac{1}{5k}$

Evaluate each series.

3. $\sum_{k=4}^{8}(2k - 1)$ 55
4. $\sum_{k=10}^{25} 4$ 64
5. $\sum_{k=1}^{25} k$ 325
6. $\sum_{k=1}^{9} k^2$ 285
7. Ann is making a display of hand-held computer games. There will be 1 game on top. Each row will have 8 additional games. She wants the display to have as many rows as possible with 100 games. How many rows will Ann's display have? 5

Also available on transparency

12-2 PROBLEM SOLVING

Todd joins a fitness club. During the first week of training, his biceps increase by 4 millimeters. The trainer says Todd can expect his biceps to continue to increase each week, but only by about 90% of the increase of the week before.

1. Todd wants to know how much his biceps will increase in 8 weeks.
   a. Write a rule for the kth term in the sequence that represents the amount of muscle increase each week. $a_k = 4(0.9)^{k-1}$
   b. Write the summation notation using $\sum$ for the first 8 terms. $\sum_{k=1}^{8} 4(0.9)^{k-1}$
   c. Expand the series and evaluate to find the amount by which Todd's biceps will increase in 8 weeks. 22.8 mm
2. Todd thinks that, if he works out extra hard each week, his biceps should increase by at least an additional half-millimeter each week. If this is true, how much will his biceps increase after 8 weeks?
   a. Write a rule for the kth term in the sequence that represents the minimum amount of muscle increase each week. $a_k = 4(0.9)^{k-1} + \frac{1}{2}$
   b. Use summation notation to represent the minimum total amount of muscle increase after 8 weeks. $\sum_{k=1}^{8} 0.5 + 4(0.9)^{k-1}$
   c. What is the minimum increase in size in Todd's biceps after 8 weeks? 26.8 mm
   d. At this rate, how many weeks would it take to reach or exceed the total muscle increase predicted by the trainer? 7 weeks

Rodrigo puts his change into a bowl each evening. On Monday he puts 2 quarters in the bowl and decides to try and increase the amount each evening by at least 10 cents over the evening before. Choose the letter for the best answer.

3. Which series represents the minimum amount in the bowl Saturday morning?
   A $\sum_{k=1}^{5} 0.1(0.5)^{k-1}$
   B $\sum_{k=1}^{5} 0.5(0.1)^{k-1}$
   (C) $\sum_{k=1}^{5} 0.5 + 0.1(k-1)$
   D $\sum_{k=1}^{5} 0.1 + 0.5(k-1)$
4. What is the minimum amount in the bowl the following Monday morning?
   F \$3.50
   (G) \$5.60
   H \$6.80
   J \$7.60

12-2 CHALLENGE

Around 1675, the English physicist and mathematician Sir Isaac Newton developed a sequence whose terms approximate the square root of a positive number N. His recursive formula for the sequence is shown at right. $a_1 = \frac{N}{2}$ and $a_n = \frac{1}{2}\left(a_{n-1} + \frac{N}{a_{n-1}}\right)$

Use Newton's formula to approximate $\sqrt{10}$ by calculating a_5. Give the most accurate decimal value your calculator will display.

1. a_1 5
2. a_2 3.5
3. a_3 3.178571429
4. a_4 3.162319422
5. a_5 3.16227766
6. Compare your value of a_5 to the calculator value for $\sqrt{10}$ 3.16227766

The constant, linear, and quadratic series formulas are shown at right.

Constant Series $\sum_{k=1}^{n} c = nc$ *Linear Series* $\sum_{k=1}^{n} k = \frac{n(n+1)}{2}$ *Quadratic Series* $\sum_{k=1}^{n} k^2 = \frac{n(n+1)(2n+1)}{6}$

Now consider the formula for the cubic series, as shown at right. *Cubic Series* $\sum_{k=1}^{n} k^3 = \frac{n^2(n+1)^2}{4}$

Use the formulas shown above to evaluate $\sum_{m=1}^{5}(2m^3 + 3m^2 + 2m + 3)$.

7. $\sum_{m=1}^{5} 2m^3$ 450
8. $\sum_{m=1}^{5} 3m^2$ 165
9. $\sum_{m=1}^{5} 2m$ 30
10. $\sum_{m=1}^{5} 3$ 15
11. Use your results to write the value of $\sum_{m=1}^{5}(2m^3 + 3m^2 + 2m + 3)$. $450 + 165 + 30 + 15 = 660$
12. Verify your result by using a calculator to evaluate $2m^3 + 3m^2 + 2m + 3$ for $m = 1, 2, 3, 4, 5$, and add. $10 + 35 + 90 + 187 + 338 = 660$

Consider the series $\sum_{k=1}^{n}\frac{k(k+1)}{2}$.

13. Write the first 5 terms and determine their sum. $1 + 3 + 6 + 10 + 15 = 35$
14. Make a conjecture about a formula for the series. $\sum_{k=1}^{n}\frac{k(k+1)}{2} = \frac{n(n+1)(n+2)}{6}$
15. Use your formula to evaluate the sum when $n = 5$, and compare this result with your result from Exercise 13. $\frac{5 \cdot 6 \cdot 7}{6} = 35$

Organizer

Use with Lesson 12-2

Pacing:

Traditional 1 day

Block $\frac{1}{2}$ day

Objective: Use a graphing calculator to generate the terms of a sequence and find the sums of series.

Materials: graphing calculator

Online Edition

TechKeys

Resources

Technology Lab Activities

12-2 Lab Recording Sheet

Teach

Discuss

Have students use **seq(** to find the first 5 terms of $a_n = 2n^2$. Discuss the expressions that must be entered. Then have them use **sum(** to find the sum of the terms. Discuss why the sum is evaluated using **sum(seq(**.

Close

Key Concept

To evaluate the partial sum of a series by using the **sum(** and **seq(** functions on a graphing calculator

Assessment

Journal Have students explain how to use a graphing calculator to evaluate a sequence or a series.

State Resources

go.hrw.com

State Resources Online

KEYWORD: MB7 Resources

12-2

Evaluate Sequences and Series

Graphing calculators have built-in features that help you generate the terms of a sequence and find the sums of series.

Use with Lesson 12-2

Activity

Use a graphing calculator to find the first 7 terms of the sequence $a_n = 1.5n + 4$. Then find the sum of those terms.

1 Find the first 7 terms of the sequence.

Enter the **LIST** operations menu by pressing 2nd STAT (LIST) and scrolling right to the **OPS** menu. Then select the sequence command **5:seq(**.

NAMES OPS MATH
1:SortA(
2:SortD(
3:dim(
4:Fill(
5:seq(
6:cumSum(
7↓ΔList(

The sequence command takes the following four expressions separated by commas.

Explicit rule for the sequence

Variable (must match rule)

Number of the starting term

Number of the ending term

seq(1.5X+4,X,1,7)
{5.5 7 8.5 10 1…

Enter the rule, using x as the variable. Enter 1 for the starting term and 7 for the ending term. Close the parentheses, and then press ENTER.

seq(1.5X+4,X,1,7)
…0 11.5 13 14.5}

The terms of the sequence will be displayed in brackets. Use the arrow keys to scroll to see the rest of the terms.

The first 7 terms are 5.5, 7, 8.5, 10, 11.5, 13, and 14.5.

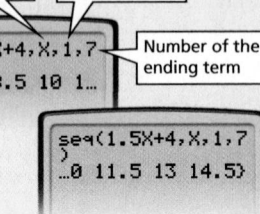

2 Find the sum of the terms.

Enter the **LIST** math menu by pressing 2nd STAT (LIST), and scrolling right to the **MATH** menu. Then select the sum command **5:sum(**.

Follow the steps for entering a sequence as shown in Step 1.

The sum of the first 7 terms is 70.

sum(seq(1.5X+4,X,1,7))
70

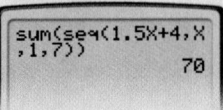

Try This

Find the first 8 terms of each sequence. Then find the sum of those 8 terms.

1. $a_n = 2n^2 - 5$
2. $a_n = \frac{1}{4}(2)^{n-1}$
3. $a_n = 0.3n + 1.6$
4. $a_n = 20n$
5. $a_n = n^3 - 2n$
6. $a_n = 0.1(5)^n$
7. **Critical Thinking** Find the next 5 terms of the sequence 200, 182, 164, 146, 128, ... Then find the sum of those 5 terms.

Answers to *Try This*

1. −3, 3, 13, 27, 45, 67, 93, 123; 368
2. 0.25, 0.5, 1, 2, 4, 8, 16, 32; 63.75
3. 1.9, 2.2, 2.5, 2.8, 3.1, 3.4, 3.7, 4; 23.6
4. 20, 40, 60, 80, 100, 120, 140, 160; 720
5. −1, 4, 21, 56, 115, 204, 329, 496; 1224
6. 0.5, 2.5, 12.5, 62.5, 312.5, 1562.5, 7812.5, 39,062.5; 48,828
7. 110, 92, 74, 56, 38; 370

12-3 Arithmetic Sequences and Series

A2.7.1 Write the recursive formula for arithmetic and geometric sequences and find specific terms of arithmetic and geometric sequences.

Objectives
Find the indicated terms of an arithmetic sequence.

Find the sums of arithmetic series.

Vocabulary
arithmetic sequence
arithmetic series

Who uses this?
You can use arithmetic sequences to predict the cost of mailing letters.

The cost of mailing a letter in 2005 gives the sequence 0.37,0.60,0.83,1.06, …. This sequence is called an **arithmetic sequence** because its successive terms differ by the same number d $(d \neq 0)$, called the *common difference.* For the mail costs, d is 0.23, as shown.

Term	a_1	a_2	a_3	a_4
Value	0.37	0.60	0.83	1.06

Differences 0.23 0.23 0.23

2005 U.S. Postage Costs

Cost ($): 0.50, 1.00, 1.50, 2.00
Weight (oz): 0, 2, 4, 6, 8

Recall that linear functions have a constant first difference. Notice also that when you graph the ordered pairs (n, a_n) of an arithmetic sequence, the points lie on a straight line. Thus, you can think of an arithmetic sequence as a linear function with sequential natural numbers as the domain.

EXAMPLE 1 Identifying Arithmetic Sequences

Determine whether each sequence could be arithmetic. If so, find the common first difference and the next term.

A $-3, 2, 7, 12, 17, \ldots$

$-3, \quad 2, \quad 7, \quad 12, \quad 17$

Differences 5 5 5 5

The sequence could be arithmetic with a common difference of 5. The next term is $17 + 5 = 22$.

B $-4, -12, -24, -40, -60, \ldots$

$-4, \quad -12, \quad -24, \quad -40, \quad -60$

Differences $-8 \quad -12 \quad -16 \quad -20$

The sequence is not arithmetic because the first differences are not common.

Determine whether each sequence could be arithmetic. If so, find the common difference and the next term.

1a. $1.9, 1.2, 0.5, -0.2, -0.9, \ldots$ arithmetic; -0.7; -1.6

1b. $\frac{11}{2}, \frac{11}{3}, \frac{11}{4}, \frac{11}{5}, \frac{11}{6}, \ldots$ not arithmetic

Each term in an arithmetic sequence is the sum of the previous term and the common difference. This gives the recursive rule $a_n = a_{n-1} + d$. You also can develop an explicit rule for an arithmetic sequence.

12-3 Organizer

Pacing: Traditional 1 day
Block $\frac{1}{2}$ day

Objectives: Find the indicated terms of an arithmetic sequence.

Find the sums of arithmetic series.

Online Edition
Tutorial Videos, Interactivity, TechKeys

Power Presentations with PowerPoint®

Warm Up

Find the 5th term of each sequence.

1. $a_n = n + 6$ 11

2. $a_n = 4 - n$ -1

3. $a_n = 3n + 4$ 19

Write a possible explicit rule for the nth term of each sequence.

4. 4, 5, 6, 7, 8, … $a_n = n + 3$

5. $-3, -1, 1, 3, 5, \ldots$ $a_n = 2n - 5$

6. $\frac{3}{2}, 2, \frac{5}{2}, 3, \frac{7}{2}, \ldots$ $a_n = \frac{n}{2} + 1$

Also available on transparency

Math Humor

Teacher: You have the terms of the sequence all mixed up.

Student: If you wanted them in order, why didn't you just say so?

1 Introduce

EXPLORATION

12-3 Arithmetic Sequences and Series

Bryan joins a DVD club that sends him 8 DVDs the first month and 3 DVDs every month thereafter.

1. Complete the table showing the number of DVDs Bryan buys through the club.

Month	Total Number of DVDs
1	8
2	
3	
4	
5	

2. Graph the data in the table.
3. What is the difference of the successive terms in the sequence formed by the total number of DVDs?
4. What type of function describes the data? Why?
5. Write an explicit formula for the nth term of the sequence formed by the total number of DVDs.

THINK AND DISCUSS

6. Show how you can use your rule to find the number of DVDs Bryan will have bought after 12 months.
7. Discuss how you can use your rule to determine whether or

Motivate

Pose this famous question to your students: "What is the sum of the first 100 natural numbers?" 5050 Explain that the sum is found by adding 50 pairs of numbers (1 + 100, 2 + 99, 3 + 98, …), each with a sum of 101. Explain that this method, discovered by a young Carl Friedrich Gauss (1777–1855), works for arithmetic sequences.

Explorations and answers are provided in the *Explorations* binder.

State Resources

go.hrw.com
State Resources Online
KEYWORD: MB7 Resources

Notice the pattern in the table. Each term is the sum of the first term and a multiple of the common difference.

This pattern can be generalized into a rule for all arithmetic sequences.

Postage Costs per Ounce	
n	a_n
1	$a_1 = 0.37 + 0(0.23)$
2	$a_2 = 0.37 + 1(0.23)$
3	$a_3 = 0.37 + 2(0.23)$
4	$a_4 = 0.37 + 3(0.23)$
n	$a_n = 0.37 + (n-1)(0.23)$

Know it! Note

General Rule for Arithmetic Sequences

The nth term a_n of an arithmetic sequence is given by

$$a_n = a_1 + (n-1)d$$

where a_1 is the first term and d is the common difference.

EXAMPLE 2 Finding the *n*th Term Given an Arithmetic Sequence

Find the 10th term of the arithmetic sequence 32, 25, 18, 11, 4, ...

Step 1 Find the common difference: $d = 25 - 32 = -7$.

Step 2 Evaluate by using the formula.

$a_n = a_1 + (n-1)d$ *General rule*

$a_{10} = 32 + (10-1)(-7)$ *Substitute 32 for a_1, 10 for n, and −7 for d.*

$= -31$ *Simplify.*

The 10th term is −31.

Check Continue the sequence.

n	1	2	3	4	5	6	7	8	9	10
a_n	32	25	18	11	4	−3	−10	−17	−24	−31 ✓

Find the 11th term of each arithmetic sequence.

2a. −3, −5, −7, −9, ... −23

2b. 9.2, 9.15, 9.1, 9.05, ... 8.7

Student to Student *Finding the nth Term*

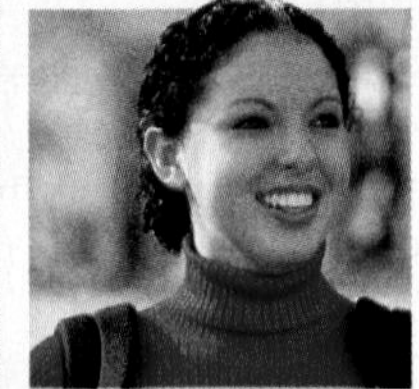

Diana Watson
Bowie High School

I like to check the value of a term by using a graphing calculator.

I enter the function for the nth, or general, term. For Example 2A, enter y = 32 + (x − 1)(−7).

I then use the table feature. Start at 1 (for n = 1), and use a step of 1. Then find the desired term (y-value) as shown for n = 10.

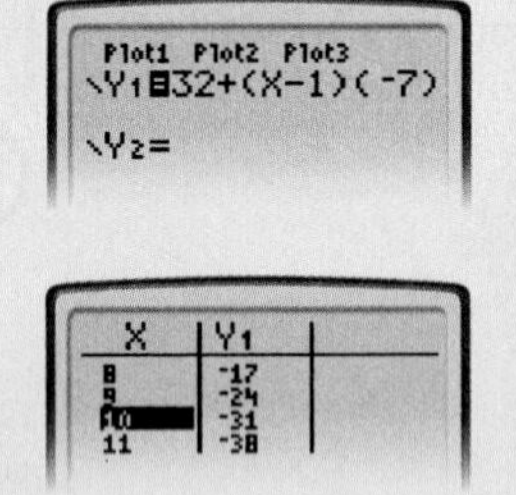

Power Presentations with PowerPoint®

Additional Examples

Example 1

Determine whether each sequence could be arithmetic. If so, find the common first difference and the next term.

A. −10, −4, 2, 8, 14, ... yes; 6; 20

B. −2, −5, −11, −20, −32, ... no

Example 2

Find the 12th term of the arithmetic sequence

20, 14, 8, 2, −4, ... −46

Also available on transparency

INTERVENTION

Questioning Strategies

EXAMPLE 1 

- Why do you have to find the first differences?
- How could you use the graph of a sequence to decide whether the sequence is arithmetic?

EXAMPLE 2

- What must you know to be able to find the *n*th term of a sequence? Explain.

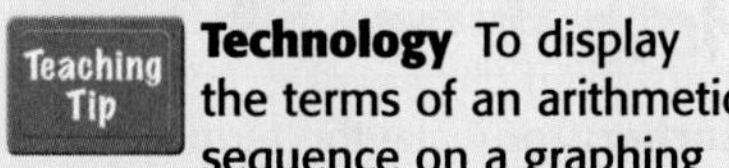

Teaching Tip **Technology** To display the terms of an arithmetic sequence on a graphing calculator, enter the first term, press ENTER, press +, enter the common difference, and press ENTER repeatedly.

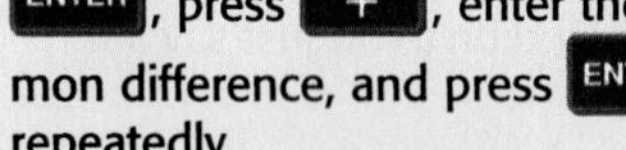

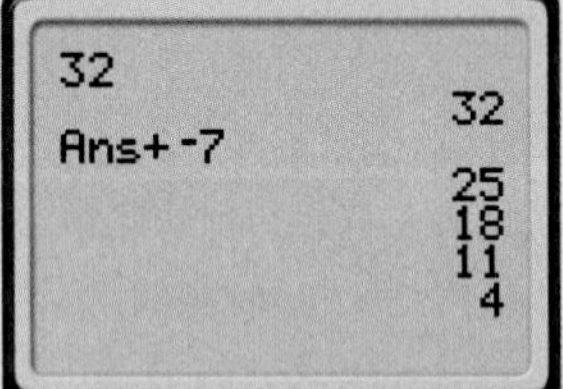

2 Teach

Guided Instruction

Introduce an arithmetic sequence such as 4, 7, 10, 13, ... Make the connection with linear functions that students have already studied. Show students how the general rule for an arithmetic sequence can be used in a number of ways as you review **Examples 2, 3,** and **4.** When introducing the sum formula for arithmetic series, you may want to remind students of the sum of a linear series (Lesson 12-2).

Reaching All Learners

Through Modeling

Separate students into small groups and give each group a set of small manipulatives, such as centimeter squares or cubes (MK). Have students create patterns by adding a specified number of items to each row. As they construct the model, have them write down the number of items in each row and the cumulative total for each row. Then have them write a rule for the sequence that describes their pattern.

EXAMPLE 3 Finding Missing Terms

Find the missing terms in the arithmetic sequence 11, ■, ■, ■, −17.

Step 1 Find the common difference.

$a_n = a_1 + (n-1)d$	*General rule*
$-17 = 11 + (5-1)d$	*Substitute −17 for a_n, 11 for a_1, and 5 for n.*
$-7 = d$	*Solve for d.*

Step 2 Find the missing terms using $d = -7$ and $a_1 = 11$.

$a_2 = 11 + (2-1)(-7)$	$a_3 = 11 + (3-1)(-7)$	$a_4 = 11 + (4-1)(-7)$
$= 4$	$= -3$	$= -10$

The missing terms are 4, −3, and −10.

3. Find the missing terms in the arithmetic sequence 2, ■, ■, ■, 0. $\frac{3}{2}, 1, \frac{1}{2}$

Because arithmetic sequences have a common difference, you can use any two terms to find the difference.

EXAMPLE 4 Finding the *n*th Term Given Two Terms

Find the 6th term of the arithmetic sequence with $a_9 = 120$ and $a_{14} = 195$.

Step 1 Find the common difference.

$a_n = a_1 + (n-1)d$	
$a_{14} = a_9 + (14-9)d$	*Let $a_n = a_{14}$ and $a_1 = a_9$. Replace 1 with 9.*
$a_{14} = a_9 + 5d$	*Simplify.*
$195 = 120 + 5d$	*Substitute 195 for a_{14} and 120 for a_9.*
$75 = 5d$	
$15 = d$	

Step 2 Find a_1.

$a_n = a_1 + (n-1)d$	*General rule*
$120 = a_1 + (9-1)(15)$	*Substitute 120 for a_9, 9 for n, and 15 for d.*
$120 = a_1 + 120$	*Simplify.*
$0 = a_1$	

Step 3 Write a rule for the sequence, and evaluate to find a_6.

$a_n = a_1 + (n-1)d$	*General rule*
$a_n = 0 + (n-1)(15)$	*Substitute 0 for a_1 and 15 for d.*
$a_6 = 0 + (6-1)15$	*Evaluate for n = 6.*
$= 75$	

The 6th term is 75.

Find the 11th term of each arithmetic sequence.

4a. $a_2 = -133$ and $a_3 = -121$ **−25**

4b. $a_3 = 20.5$ and $a_8 = 13$ **8.5**

COMMON ERROR ALERT

Students sometimes confuse a_n and a_1 or n and a_n. Emphasize the importance of writing the rule as the first step in using it to find missing terms. Discuss how n is different from a_n.

Power Presentations with PowerPoint®

Additional Examples

Example 3

Find the missing terms in the arithmetic sequence 17, ■, ■, ■, −7. 11, 5, −1

Example 4

Find the 5th term of the arithmetic sequence with $a_8 = 85$ and $a_{14} = 157$. 49

Also available on transparency

INTERVENTION

Questioning Strategies

EXAMPLE 3

- What is the first step in finding the common difference? Explain.
- After you find the common difference, is there a way to find the missing terms other than using the rule for the nth term? Explain.

EXAMPLE 4

- Why can you replace a_n and a_1 with other terms from the sequence?

Visual It often helps to visually represent the sequences with missing terms. For **Example 4,** you may want to show something like this.

120	■	■	■	■	195
a_9	a_{10}	a_{11}	a_{12}	a_{13}	a_{14}

Teacher to Teacher

I tell students that $a_n = a_1 + (n-1)d$ works with *any* two terms. For **Example 4:**

$$a_{14} = a_9 + (14-9)d$$
$$195 = 120 + 5d$$
$$75 = 5d$$
$$15 = d$$

Then solve for a_6 by using $a_9 = a_6 + (9-6)d$, where $a_9 = 120$ and $d = 15$. In a few steps, you find that $a_6 = 75$. You don't ever need to find a_1. Students really like this and it *always* works.

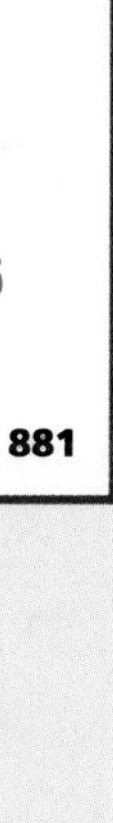

Dave Barker
Los Alamitos, CA

Math Background You may wish to show some additional numerical examples before the formal derivation of the sum of the first n terms of an arithmetic series. For example: $1 + 2 + 3 + 4 = \frac{4(1 + 4)}{2}$; and so on.

Power Presentations with PowerPoint®

Additional Examples

Example 5

Find the indicated sum for each arithmetic series.

A. S_{18} for $13 + 2 + (-9) + (-20) + \ldots$ -1449

B. $\sum_{k=1}^{15} (5 + 2k)$ 315

Example 6

The center section of a concert hall has 15 seats in the first row and 2 additional seats in each subsequent row.

A. How many seats are in the 20th row? 53

B. How many seats in total are in the first 20 rows? 680

Also available on transparency

INTERVENTION

Questioning Strategies

EXAMPLE 5

- How do you know which term(s) to find to evaluate the sum?
- When do you find the common difference to find the sum? Explain.

EXAMPLE 6

- Why do you use an arithmetic sequence to solve the problem?
- How do you know which part of the problem is solved using an arithmetic sequence and which is solved using an arithmetic series?

In Lesson 12-2 you wrote and evaluated series. An **arithmetic series** is the indicated sum of the terms of an arithmetic sequence. You can derive a general formula for the sum of an arithmetic series by writing the series in forward and reverse order and adding the results.

$$S_n = a_1 + (a_1 + d) + (a_1 + 2d) + \ldots + a_n$$

$$S_n = a_n + (a_n - d) + (a_n - 2d) + \ldots + a_1$$

$$2S_n = \underbrace{(a_1 + a_n) + (a_1 + a_n) + (a_1 + a_n) \ldots + (a_1 + a_n)}_{(a_1 + a_n) \text{ is added } n \text{ times}}$$

$$2S_n = n(a_1 + a_n)$$

$$S_n = \frac{n(a_1 + a_n)}{2}, \text{ or } S_n = n\left(\frac{a_1 + a_n}{2}\right)$$

Sum of the First n Terms of an Arithmetic Series

WORDS	NUMBERS	ALGEBRA
The sum of the first n terms of an arithmetic series is the product of the number of terms and the average of the first and last terms.	The sum of $2 + 4 + 6 + 8 + 10$ is $5\left(\frac{2 + 10}{2}\right) = 5(6) = 30.$	$S_n = n\left(\frac{a_1 + a_n}{2}\right)$, where n is the number of terms, a_1 is the first term, and a_n is the nth term.

EXAMPLE 5 **Finding the Sum of an Arithmetic Series**

Find the indicated sum for each arithmetic series.

A S_{15} for $25 + 12 + (-1) + (-14) + \cdots$

Find the common difference.

$d = 12 - 25 = -13$

Find the 15th term.

$a_{15} = 25 + (15 - 1)(-13)$
$= -157$

Find S_{15}.

$S_n = n\left(\frac{a_1 + a_n}{2}\right)$ *Sum formula*

$S_{15} = 15\left(\frac{25 + (-157)}{2}\right)$ *Substitute.*

$= 15(-66) = -990$

Check Use a graphing calculator.

B $\sum_{k=1}^{12} (3 + 4k)$

Find the 1st and 12th terms.

$a_1 = 3 + 4(1) = 7$

$a_{12} = 3 + 4(12) = 51$

Find S_{12}.

$S_n = n\left(\frac{a_1 + a_n}{2}\right)$

$S_{12} = 12\left(\frac{7 + 51}{2}\right)$

$= 348$

Check Use a graphing calculator.

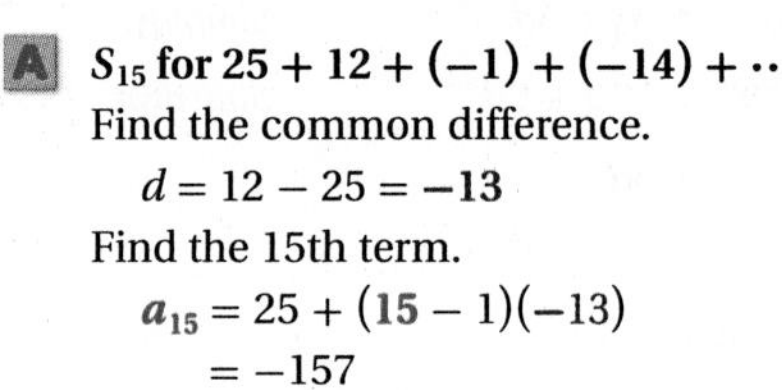

Remember!

These sums are actually *partial sums.* You cannot find the complete sum of an infinite arithmetic series because the term values increase or decrease indefinitely.

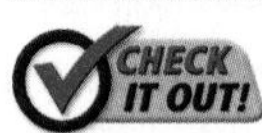

Find the indicated sum for each arithmetic series.

5a. S_{16} for $12 + 7 + 2 + (-3) + \cdots$ **−408**

5b. $\sum_{k=1}^{15} (50 - 20k)$ **−1650**

EXAMPLE 6 Theater Application

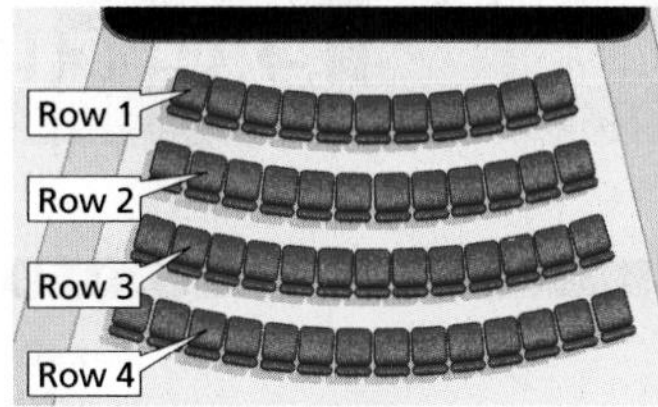

The number of seats in the first 14 rows of the center orchestra aisle of the Marquis Theater on Broadway in New York City form an arithmetic sequence as shown.

A How many seats are in the 14th row?

Write a general rule using $a_1 = 11$ and $d = 1$.

$a_n = a_1 + (n - 1)d$ *Explicit rule for nth term*

$a_{14} = 11 + (14 - 1)1$ *Substitute.*

$= 11 + 13$

$= 24$ *Simplify.*

There are 24 seats in the 14th row.

B How many seats in total are in the first 14 rows?

Find S_{14} using the formula for finding the sum of the first n terms.

$S_n = n\left(\frac{a_1 + a_n}{2}\right)$ *Formula for first n terms*

$S_{14} = 14\left(\frac{11 + 24}{2}\right)$ *Substitute.*

$= 14\left(\frac{35}{2}\right)$

$= 245$ *Simplify.*

There are 245 seats in rows 1 through 14.

CHECK IT OUT! 6. **What if...?** Suppose that each row after the first had 2 additional seats.

a. How many seats would be in the 14th row? **37 seats**

b. How many total seats would there be in the first 14 rows? **336 total seats**

THINK AND DISCUSS

1. Compare an arithmetic sequence with a linear function.
2. Describe the effect that a negative common difference has on an arithmetic sequence.
3. Explain how to find the 6th term in a sequence when you know the 3rd and 4th terms.
4. Explain how to find the common difference when you know the 7th and 12th terms of an arithmetic sequence.

5. **GET ORGANIZED** Copy and complete the graphic organizer. Write in each rectangle to summarize your understanding of arithmetic sequences.

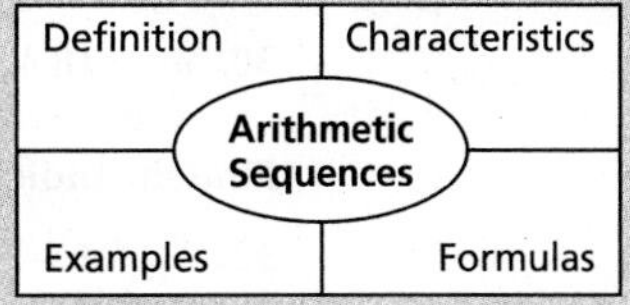

COMMON ERROR ALERT

Students sometimes confuse the sign of the common difference in an arithmetic sequence. Encourage students to check that the rule actually produces the terms of a sequence.

Teaching Tip **Technology** Before **Example 5,** you may wish to review how to use the **sum(seq(** features on a graphing calculator or have students look back at the Technology Lab that precedes this lesson. Calculators can help students check their work on difficult problems.

3 Close

Summarize

Ask students how to identify an arithmetic sequence. Then have them explain how to use the general rule for arithmetic sequences to find the nth term. An arithmetic sequence has a common first difference; to find the nth term, use $a_n = a_1 + (n - 1)d$, where a_1 is the first term and d is the common difference.

ONGOING ASSESSMENT and INTERVENTION

***Diagnose Before* the Lesson**
12-3 Warm Up, TE p. 879

***Monitor During* the Lesson**
Check It Out! Exercises, SE pp. 879–883
Questioning Strategies, TE pp. 880–882

***Assess After* the Lesson**
12-3 Lesson Quiz, TE p. 887
Alternative Assessment, TE p. 887

Answers to *Think and Discuss*

Possible answers:

1. An arithmetic sequence is a linear function with the domain restricted to the natural numbers.
2. decreases with each new term
3. Find d by subtracting $a_4 - a_3$, use the general rule to solve for a_1, and then evaluate for $n = 6$.
4. Substitute a_7 for a_1 and a_{12} for a_n in the general rule and solve for d.
5. See p. A13.

Assignment Guide

Assign *Guided Practice* exercises as necessary.

If you finished Examples **1–3**
Basic 21–28
Average 21–29
Advanced 21–29, 50

If you finished Examples **1–6**
Basic 21–37, 39–51 odd, 52–57, 62–69
Average 21–47, 50–58, 62–69
Advanced 21–36 even, 37–69

Homework Quick Check

Quickly check key concepts.
Exercises: 22, 24, 28, 30, 34, 36

State Resources

go.hrw.com
State Resources Online
KEYWORD: MB7 Resources

12-3 Exercises

go.hrw.com
Homework Help Online
KEYWORD: MB7 12-3
Parent Resources Online
KEYWORD: MB7 Parent

GUIDED PRACTICE

1. **Vocabulary** The expression 10 + 20 + 30 + 40 + 50 is an __?__. (*arithmetic sequence* or *arithmetic series*) **arithmetic series**

SEE EXAMPLE 1 p. 879

Determine whether each sequence could be arithmetic. If so, find the common difference and the next term.

2. 46, 39, 32, 25, 18, … **arithmetic; −7; 11**
3. 28, 21, 15, 10, 6, … **not arithmetic**
4. $\frac{12}{3}, \frac{10}{3}, \frac{8}{3}, \frac{6}{3}, \frac{4}{3}, \ldots$ **arithmetic; $-\frac{2}{3}$; $\frac{2}{3}$**

SEE EXAMPLE 2 p. 880

Find the 8th term of each arithmetic sequence.

5. 3, 8, 13, 18, … **38**
6. $10, 9\frac{3}{4}, 9\frac{1}{2}, 9\frac{1}{4}, \ldots$ **$8\frac{1}{4}$**
7. −3.2, −3.4, −3.6, −3.8, … **−4.6**

SEE EXAMPLE 3 p. 881

Find the missing terms in each arithmetic sequence.

8. 13, ▇, ▇, 25 **17, 21**
9. 9, ▇, ▇, ▇, 37 **16, 23, 30**
10. 1.4, ▇, ▇, ▇, −1 **0.8, 0.2, −0.4**

SEE EXAMPLE 4 p. 881

Find the 9th term of each arithmetic sequence.

11. $a_4 = 27$ and $a_5 = 19$ **−13**
12. $a_3 = 12.2$ and $a_4 = 12.6$ **14.6**
13. $a_3 = -5$ and $a_6 = -11$ **−17**
14. $a_{10} = 100$ and $a_{20} = 50$ **105**
15. $a_7 = -42$ and $a_{11} = -28$ **−35**
16. $a_4 = \frac{3}{4}$ and $a_8 = \frac{1}{2}$ **$\frac{7}{16}$**

SEE EXAMPLE 5 p. 882

Find the indicated sum for each arithmetic series.

17. S_{15} for $5 + 9 + 13 + 17 + \cdots$ **495**
18. $\sum_{k=1}^{12}(-2 + 6k)$ **444**
19. S_{18} for $3.2 + 2.9 + 2.6 + 2.3 + \cdots$ **11.7**

SEE EXAMPLE 6 p. 883

20. **Salary** Juan has taken a job with an initial salary of $26,000 and annual raises of $1250.
    a. What will his salary be in his 6th year? **$32,250**
    b. How much money in total will Juan have earned after six years? **$174,750**

PRACTICE AND PROBLEM SOLVING

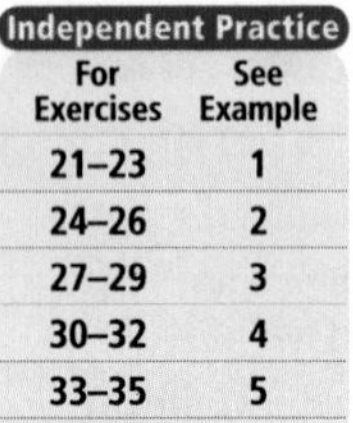

Independent Practice	
For Exercises	See Example
21–23	1
24–26	2
27–29	3
30–32	4
33–35	5
36	6

Extra Practice
Skills Practice p. S26
Application Practice p. S43

Determine whether each sequence could be arithmetic. If so, find the common difference and the next term.

21. 288, 144, 72, 36, 18, … **not arithmetic**
22. −2, −12, −22, −32, −42, … **arithmetic; −10; −52**
23. 0.99, 0.9, 0.81, 0.72, … **arithmetic; −0.09; 0.63**

Find the 11th term of each arithmetic sequence.

24. 12, 11.9, 11.8, 11.7, … **11**
25. $\frac{2}{5}, \frac{3}{5}, \frac{4}{5}, 1, \ldots$ **$\frac{12}{5}$**
26. −3.0, −2.5, −2.0, −1.5, … **2**

Find the missing terms in each arithmetic sequence.

27. 77, ▇, ▇, ▇, 33 **66, 55, 44**
28. −29, ▇, ▇, −2 **−20, −11**
29. 2.3, ▇, ▇, ▇, 1.5 **2.1, 1.9, 1.7**

Find the 12th term of each arithmetic sequence.

30. $a_4 = 18.4$ and $a_5 = 16.2$ **0.8**
31. $a_4 = -2$ and $a_8 = 46$ **94**
32. $a_{22} = -49$ and $a_{25} = -58$ **−19**

Find the indicated sum for each arithmetic series.

33. S_{15} for $-18 + (-16) + (-14) + \cdots$ **−60**
34. $\sum_{k=1}^{20}(88 - 3k)$ **1130**
35. $\sum_{k=1}^{14}\left(14 - \frac{1}{2}k\right)$ **143.5**

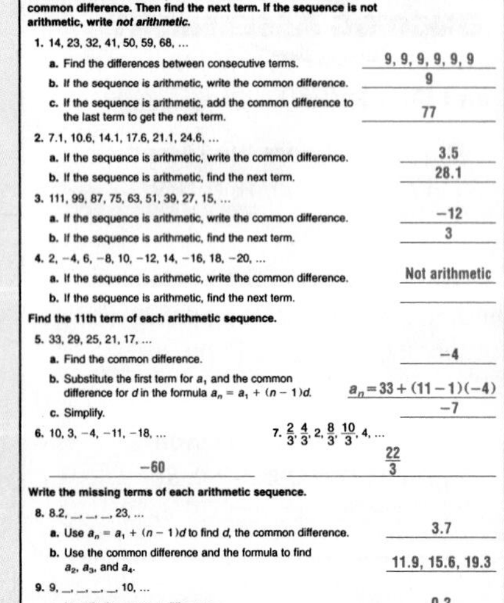

12-3 PRACTICE A

Determine whether the sequence is arithmetic. If it is, find the common difference. Then find the next term. If the sequence is not arithmetic, write *not arithmetic*.

1. 14, 23, 32, 41, 50, 59, 68, …
   a. Find the differences between consecutive terms. **9, 9, 9, 9, 9, 9**
   b. If the sequence is arithmetic, write the common difference. **9**
   c. If the sequence is arithmetic, add the common difference to the last term to get the next term. **77**
2. 7.1, 10.6, 14.1, 17.6, 21.1, 24.6, …
   a. If the sequence is arithmetic, write the common difference. **3.5**
   b. If the sequence is arithmetic, find the next term. **28.1**
3. 111, 99, 87, 75, 63, 51, 39, 27, 15, …
   a. If the sequence is arithmetic, write the common difference. **−12**
   b. If the sequence is arithmetic, find the next term. **3**
4. 2, −4, 6, −8, 10, −12, 14, −16, 18, −20, …
   a. If the sequence is arithmetic, write the common difference. **Not arithmetic**
   b. If the sequence is arithmetic, find the next term. ______

Find the 11th term of each arithmetic sequence.

5. 33, 29, 25, 21, 17, …
   a. Find the common difference. **−4**
   b. Substitute the first term for a_1 and the common difference for d in the formula $a_n = a_1 + (n - 1)d$. **$a_n = 33 + (11 - 1)(-4)$**
   c. Simplify. **−7**
6. 10, 3, −4, −11, −18, … **−60**
7. $\frac{2}{3}, \frac{4}{3}, 2, \frac{8}{3}, \frac{10}{3}, 4, \ldots$ **$\frac{22}{3}$**

Write the missing terms of each arithmetic sequence.

8. 8.2, __, __, __, 23, …
   a. Use $a_n = a_1 + (n - 1)d$ to find d, the common difference. **3.7**
   b. Use the common difference and the formula to find a_2, a_3, and a_4. **11.9, 15.6, 19.3**
9. 9, __, __, __, __, 10, …
   a. Identify the common difference. **0.2**
   b. Use the common difference to find the missing terms. **9.2, 9.4, 9.6, 9.8**

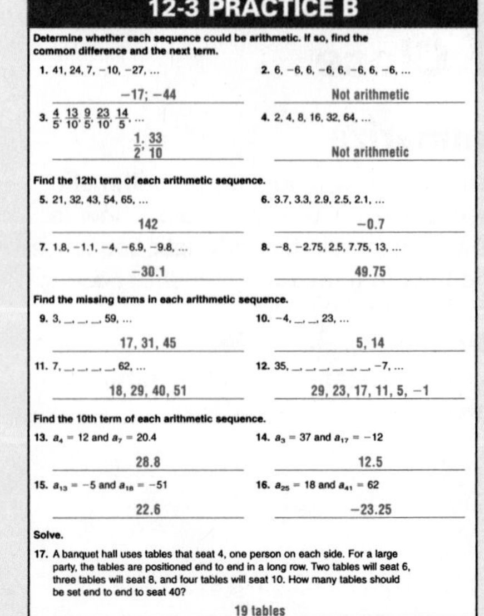

12-3 PRACTICE B

Determine whether each sequence could be arithmetic. If so, find the common difference and the next term.

1. 41, 24, 7, −10, −27, … **−17; −44**
2. 6, −6, 6, −6, 6, −6, 6, −6, … **Not arithmetic**
3. $\frac{4}{5}, \frac{13}{10}, \frac{9}{5}, \frac{23}{10}, \frac{14}{5}, \ldots$ **$\frac{1}{2}, \frac{33}{10}$**
4. 2, 4, 8, 16, 32, 64, … **Not arithmetic**

Find the 12th term of each arithmetic sequence.

5. 21, 32, 43, 54, 65, … **142**
6. 3.7, 3.3, 2.9, 2.5, 2.1, … **−0.7**
7. 1.8, −1.1, −4, −6.9, −9.8, … **−30.1**
8. −8, −2.75, 2.5, 7.75, 13, … **49.75**

Find the missing terms in each arithmetic sequence.

9. 3, __, __, __, 59, … **17, 31, 45**
10. −4, __, __, 23, … **5, 14**
11. 7, __, __, __, __, 62, … **18, 29, 40, 51**
12. 35, __, __, __, __, __, __, −7, … **29, 23, 17, 11, 5, −1**

Find the 10th term of each arithmetic sequence.

13. $a_4 = 12$ and $a_7 = 20.4$ **28.8**
14. $a_3 = 37$ and $a_{17} = -12$ **12.5**
15. $a_{13} = -5$ and $a_{18} = -51$ **22.6**
16. $a_{25} = 18$ and $a_{41} = 62$ **−23.25**

Solve.

17. A banquet hall uses tables that seat 4, one person on each side. For a large party, the tables are positioned end to end in a long row. Two tables will seat 6, three tables will seat 8, and four tables will seat 10. How many tables should be set end to end to seat 40? **19 tables**

Clocks

One of London's most recognizable landmarks, Big Ben sits atop the Palace of Westminister, where the British Parliament meets. The name Big Ben actually refers to the 13.8-ton bell that chimes the hours.

36. **Consumer Economics** Clarissa is buying a prom dress on layaway. She agrees to make a \$15 payment and increase the payment by \$5 each week.
    a. What will her payment be in the 9th week? **\$55**
    b. How much money in total will Clarissa have paid after 9 weeks? **\$315**

37. **Clocks** A clock chimes every hour. The clock chimes once at 1 o'clock, twice at 2 o'clock, and so on.
    a. How many times will the clock chime from 1 P.M. through midnight? in exactly one 24-hour period?
    b. **What if...?** Another clock also chimes once on every half hour. How does this affect the sequence and the total number of chimes per day?

Find the indicated sum for each arithmetic series.

38. $\sum_{k=1}^{16}(555 - 11k)$ **7384**
39. $\sum_{k=1}^{15}(4 - 0.5k)$ **0**
40. $\sum_{k=1}^{18}\left(-33 + \frac{5}{2}k\right)$ **−166.5**
41. S_{16} for $7.5 + 7 + 6.5 + 6.0 + \cdots$ **60**
42. S_{18} for $2 + 9 + 16 + 23 + \cdots$ **1107**

43. **Architecture** The Louvre pyramid in Paris, France, is built of glass panes. There are 4 panes in the top row, and each additional row has 4 more panes than the previous row.

    a. Write a series in summation notation to describe the total number of glass panes in n rows of the pyramid.
    b. If the pyramid were made of 18 complete rows, how many panes would it have? **684**
    c. The actual pyramid has 11 panes less than a complete 18-row pyramid because of the space for the entrance. Find the total number of panes in the Louvre pyramid. **673**

43a. $\sum_{k=1}^{n}4k$

44. **Physics** Water towers are tall to provide enough water pressure to supply all of the houses and businesses in the area of the tower. Each foot of height provides 0.43 psi (pounds per square inch) of pressure.
    a. Write a sequence for the pressure in psi for each foot of height. **0.43, 0.86, 1.29, 1.72, ...**
    b. What is the minimum height that supplies 50 psi, a typical minimum supply pressure? **about 116.3 ft**
    c. What is the minimum height that supplies 100 psi, which is a typical maximum pressure? **about 232.6 ft**
    d. Graph the sequence, and discuss the relationship between the height found for a pressure of 50 psi and the height found at 100 psi.

45. **Exercise** Sheila begins an exercise routine for 20 minutes each day. Each week she plans to add 5 minutes per day to the length of her routine.
    a. For how many minutes will she exercise each day of the 6th week? **45 minutes**
    b. What happens to the length of Sheila's exercise routine if she continues this increasing pattern for 2 years?

45b. after 2 years, her exercise routine would be over 8 h long, which is not realistic

46. **Geology** Every year the continent of North America moves farther away from Europe.
    a. How much farther from Europe will North America be in 50 years? **115 cm, or 1.15 m**
    b. How many years until an extra mile is added? (*Hint:* 1 mi ≈ 1609 m) ≈ **69,956 yr**

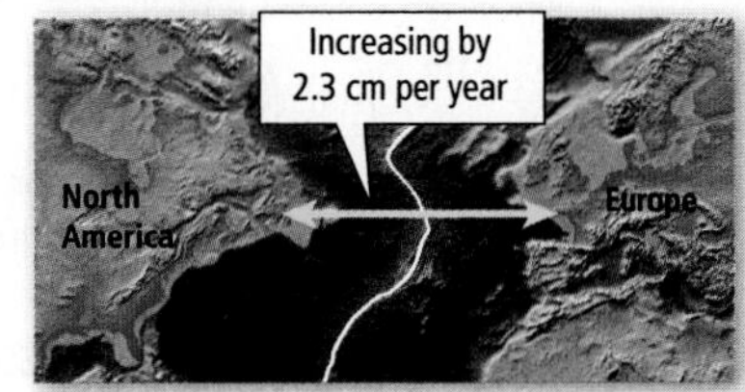

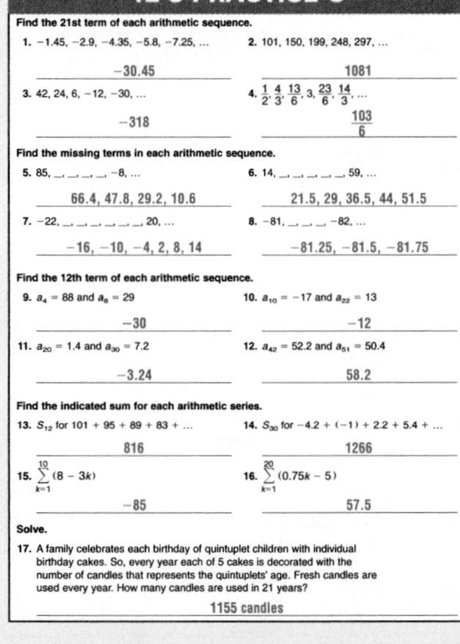

12-3 PRACTICE C

Find the 21st term of each arithmetic sequence.

1. −1.45, −2.9, −4.35, −5.8, −7.25, ... **−30.45**
2. 101, 150, 199, 248, 297, ... **1081**
3. 42, 24, 6, −12, −30, ... **−318**
4. $\frac{1}{2}, \frac{4}{3}, \frac{13}{6}, 3, \frac{23}{6}, \frac{14}{3}, \ldots$ **$\frac{103}{6}$**

Find the missing terms in each arithmetic sequence.

5. 85, __, __, __, __, −8, ... **66.4, 47.8, 29.2, 10.6**
6. 14, __, __, __, __, __, 59, ... **21.5, 29, 36.5, 44, 51.5**
7. −22, __, __, __, __, __, __, 20, ... **−16, −10, −4, 2, 8, 14**
8. −81, __, __, __, −82, ... **−81.25, −81.5, −81.75**

Find the 12th term of each arithmetic sequence.

9. $a_4 = 88$ and $a_8 = 29$ **−30**
10. $a_{10} = -17$ and $a_{22} = 13$ **−12**
11. $a_{20} = 1.4$ and $a_{30} = 7.2$ **−3.24**
12. $a_{42} = 52.2$ and $a_{51} = 50.4$ **58.2**

Find the indicated sum for each arithmetic series.

13. S_{12} for $101 + 95 + 89 + 83 + \ldots$ **816**
14. S_{30} for $-4.2 + (-1) + 2.2 + 5.4 + \ldots$ **1266**
15. $\sum_{k=1}^{10}(8 - 3k)$ **−85**
16. $\sum_{k=1}^{20}(0.75k - 5)$ **57.5**

Solve.

17. A family celebrates each birthday of quintuplet children with individual birthday cakes. So, every year each of 5 cakes is decorated with the number of candles that represents the quintuplets' age. Fresh candles are used every year. How many candles are used in 21 years? **1155 candles**

COMMON ERROR ALERT

Students may not know how to approach **Exercises 38–40.** Emphasize that the formula for the sum of an arithmetic series requires three values: the value of the first term, the value of the last term, and the number of terms included. If they can find these three values, they can use the formula to find the sum.

Answers

37a. 78; 156

b. adds 1 to each term of the sequence; adds 24 to the total number per day

44d.

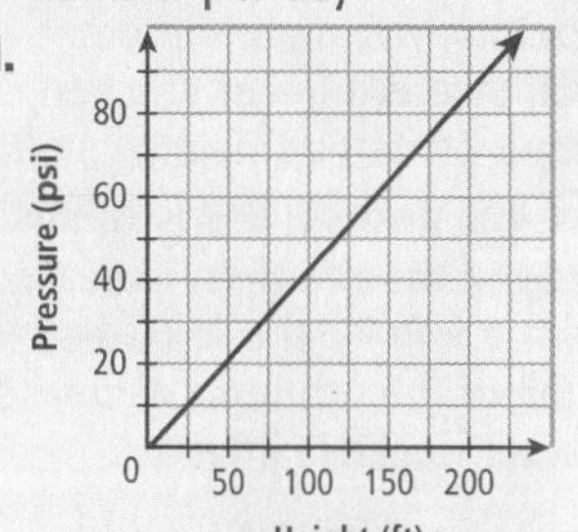

The height is twice as great because the graph represents a direct variation function.

MULTI-STEP TEST PREP **Exercise 47** involves using an arithmetic series to identify the number of tetrahedrons needed to make a kite. This exercise prepares students for the Multi-Step Test Prep on page 888.

TEST PREP DOCTOR In **Exercise 52,** students who choose **A, C,** or **D** may not recognize that arithmetic sequences must have a common difference. Remind students that they can check first differences to determine whether any sequence could be arithmetic.

Answers

50. Possible answer: 2 terms; 2 points; yes, an arithmetic sequence is a linear function with a limited domain.

51. Possible answer: If $d > 0$, the value of the nth term increases toward infinity. If $d < 0$, the value of the nth term decreases toward negative infinity.

58a.

$$\begin{aligned} a_n &= a_1 + (n-1)d \\ -\left(a_m \right. &= \left. a_1 + (m-1)d\right) \\ \hline a_n - a_m &= (n-1)d - (m-1)d \\ a_n - a_m &= nd - d - md + d \\ a_n - a_m &= nd - md \\ a_n - a_m &= (n-m)d \\ \frac{a_n - a_m}{n - m} &= d \end{aligned}$$

59. $S_n = n\left(\dfrac{2a_1 + (n-1)d}{2}\right)$; when you do not know the last term but know 2 of the 3 remaining variable quantities, S_n, n, or a_1

61. The equality states that the value of a term, such as a_6, is twice the value of the term that has half its term number, such as a_3. This gives $a_6 = 2a_3$. For this to be true, the first term must equal the common difference, or $a_1 = d$.

62.

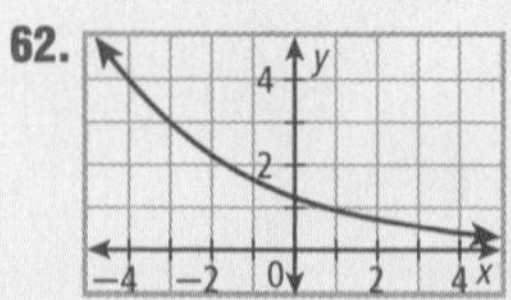

63.

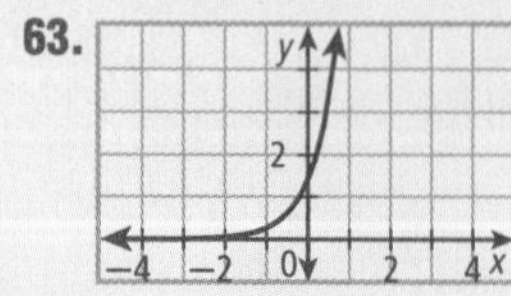

64.

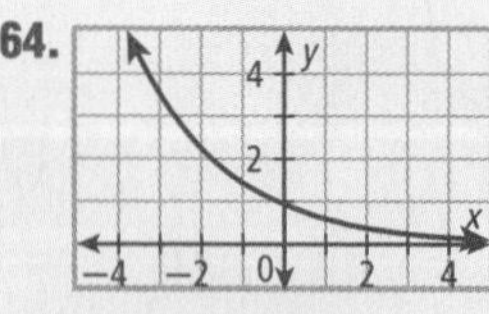

MULTI-STEP TEST PREP

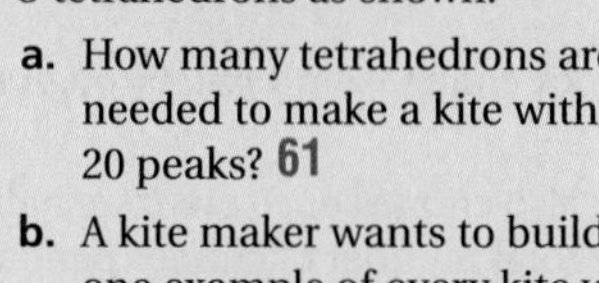

47. This problem will prepare you for the Multi-Step Test Prep on page 888.

You can make a simple tetrahedral kite with one peak by using 4 tetrahedrons. You can also make long kites with multiple peaks by successively adding 3 tetrahedrons as shown.

a. How many tetrahedrons are needed to make a kite with 20 peaks? **61**

b. A kite maker wants to build one example of every kite with 1 to 20 peaks. How many tetrahedrons will be needed? **650**

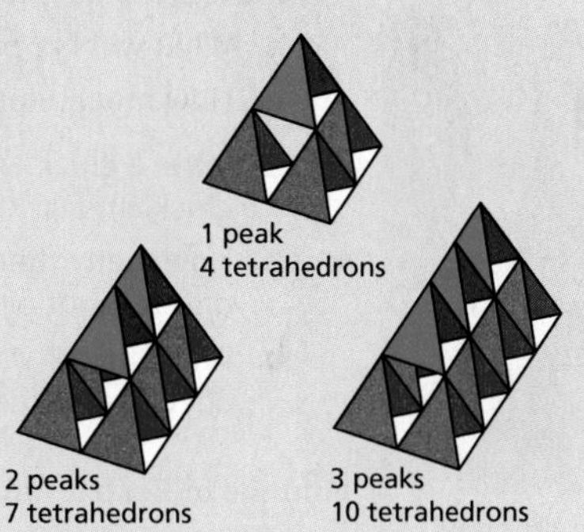

48. Finance The starting salary for a summer camp counselor is \$395 per week. In each of the subsequent weeks, the salary increases by \$45 to encourage experienced counselors to work for the entire summer. If the salary is \$710 in the last week of the camp, for how many weeks does the camp run? **8 weeks**

49. Sports A town is planning a 5K race. The race route will begin at 1st street, travel 30 blocks down Main Street, and finish on 31st Street. The race planners want to have water stations at each turn. In addition, they want to place 5 more water stations evenly distributed between 1st Street and 31st Street on Main Street.

a. At what street intersections should the water stations be placed?

49a. 6th, 11th, 16th, 21st, and 26th Streets

b. If each block is 0.1 mile, what is the maximum distance a runner will be from a water station while on Main Street? **0.25 mi**

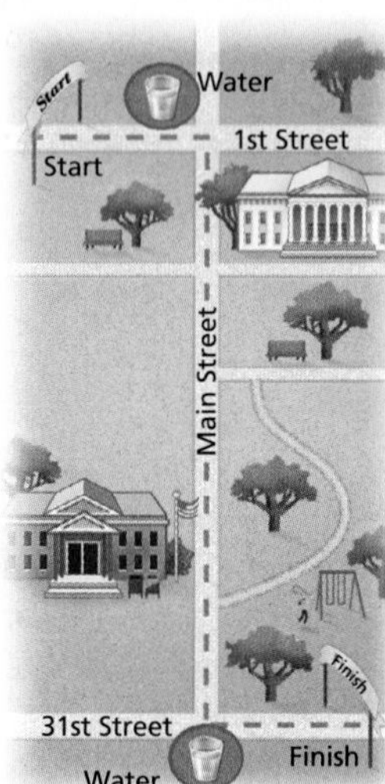

50. Critical Thinking What is the least number of terms you need to write the general rule for an arithmetic sequence? How many points do you need to write an equation of a line? Are these answers related? Explain.

51. Write About It An arithmetic sequence has a positive common difference. What happens to the nth term as n becomes greater and greater? What happens if the sequence has a negative common difference?

TEST PREP

52. Which sequence could be an arithmetic sequence?

Ⓐ $\frac{1}{2}, \frac{1}{3}, \frac{1}{4}, \frac{1}{5}, \ldots$ Ⓒ 2, 4, 8, 16, …

Ⓑ 2.2, 4.4, 6.6, 8.8, … Ⓓ 2, 4, 7, 11, …

53. A catering company charges a setup fee of \$45 plus \$12 per person. Which of the following sequences accurately reflects this situation?

Ⓕ $a_n = 45 + 12(n - 1)$ Ⓗ $a_n = 57 + 12n$

Ⓖ 45, 57, 69, 81, 93, … **Ⓙ** 57, 69, 81, 93, 105, …

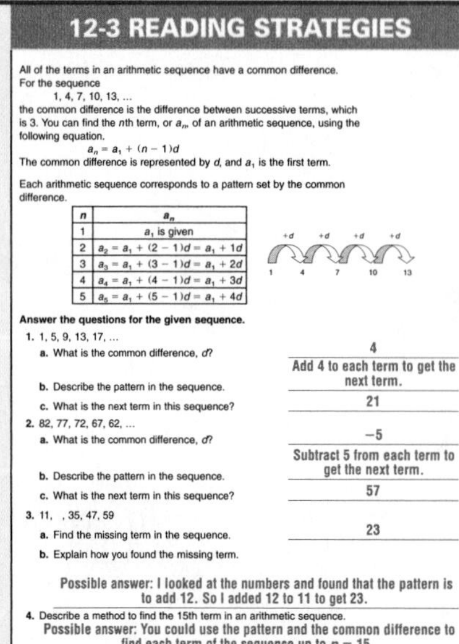

12-3 READING STRATEGIES

All of the terms in an arithmetic sequence have a common difference. For the sequence

1, 4, 7, 10, 13, …

the common difference is the difference between successive terms, which is 3. You can find the nth term, or a_n, of an arithmetic sequence, using the following equation.

$$a_n = a_1 + (n - 1)d$$

The common difference is represented by d, and a_1 is the first term.

Each arithmetic sequence corresponds to a pattern set by the common difference.

n	a_n
1	a_1 is given
2	$a_2 = a_1 + (2 - 1)d = a_1 + 1d$
3	$a_3 = a_1 + (3 - 1)d = a_1 + 2d$
4	$a_4 = a_1 + (4 - 1)d = a_1 + 3d$
5	$a_5 = a_1 + (5 - 1)d = a_1 + 4d$

+d +d +d +d
1 4 7 10 13

Answer the questions for the given sequence.

1. 1, 5, 9, 13, 17, …
   a. What is the common difference, d? **4**
   b. Describe the pattern in the sequence. **Add 4 to each term to get the next term.**
   c. What is the next term in this sequence? **21**
2. 82, 77, 72, 67, 62, …
   a. What is the common difference, d? **−5**
   b. Describe the pattern in the sequence. **Subtract 5 from each term to get the next term.**
   c. What is the next term in this sequence? **57**
3. 11, , 35, 47, 59
   a. Find the missing term in the sequence. **23**
   b. Explain how you found the missing term.
   Possible answer: I looked at the numbers and found that the pattern is to add 12. So I added 12 to 11 to get 23.
4. Describe a method to find the 15th term in an arithmetic sequence.
   Possible answer: You could use the pattern and the common difference to find each term of the sequence up to $n = 15$.

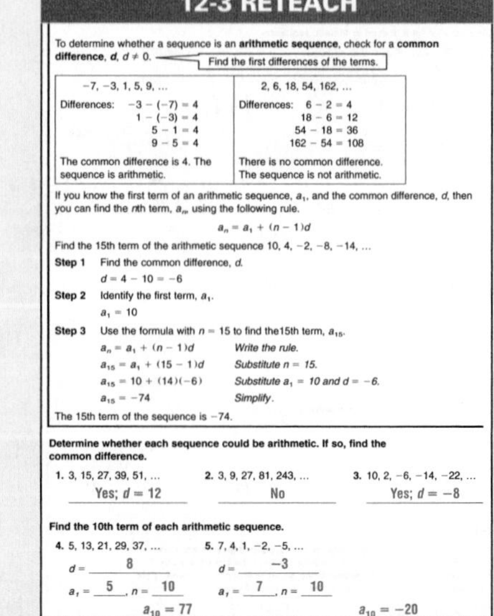

12-3 RETEACH

To determine whether a sequence is an **arithmetic sequence**, check for a **common difference, d, $d \neq 0$.** — Find the first differences of the terms.

−7, −3, 1, 5, 9, …	2, 6, 18, 54, 162, …
Differences: $-3 - (-7) = 4$; $1 - (-3) = 4$; $5 - 1 = 4$; $9 - 5 = 4$	Differences: $6 - 2 = 4$; $18 - 6 = 12$; $54 - 18 = 36$; $162 - 54 = 108$
The common difference is 4. The sequence is arithmetic.	There is no common difference. The sequence is not arithmetic.

If you know the first term of an arithmetic sequence, a_1, and the common difference, d, then you can find the nth term, a_n, using the following rule.

$$a_n = a_1 + (n - 1)d$$

Find the 15th term of the arithmetic sequence 10, 4, −2, −8, −14, …

Step 1 Find the common difference, d.
$d = 4 - 10 = -6$

Step 2 Identify the first term, a_1.
$a_1 = 10$

Step 3 Use the formula with $n = 15$ to find the15th term, a_{15}.

$a_n = a_1 + (n - 1)d$ *Write the rule.*
$a_{15} = a_1 + (15 - 1)d$ *Substitute $n = 15$.*
$a_{15} = 10 + (14)(-6)$ *Substitute $a_1 = 10$ and $d = -6$.*
$a_{15} = -74$ *Simplify.*

The 15th term of the sequence is −74.

Determine whether each sequence could be arithmetic. If so, find the common difference.

1. 3, 15, 27, 39, 51, … **Yes; $d = 12$**
2. 3, 9, 27, 81, 243, … **No**
3. 10, 2, −6, −14, −22, … **Yes; $d = -8$**

Find the 10th term of each arithmetic sequence.

4. 5, 13, 21, 29, 37, …
   $d =$ **8**
   $a_1 =$ **5**, $n =$ **10**
   $a_{10} = 77$
5. 7, 4, 1, −2, −5, …
   $d =$ **−3**
   $a_1 =$ **7**, $n =$ **10**
   $a_{10} = -20$

54. Which graph might represent the terms of an arithmetic sequence?

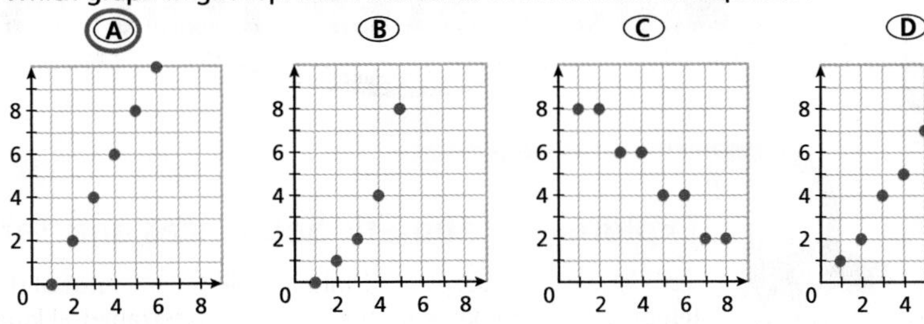

55. Given the arithmetic sequence 4, ■, ■, ■, 40, what are the three missing terms?

Ⓕ 11, 22, 33　　Ⓗ 14, 24, 34

Ⓖ 13, 22, 31 (circled)　　Ⓙ 16, 24, 36

56. Which represents the sum of the arithmetic series 19 + 16 + 13 + 10 + 7 + 4?

Ⓐ $\sum_{k=1}^{6} 19 - 3k$　　Ⓒ (circled) $\sum_{k=1}^{6} (22 - 3k)$

Ⓑ $\sum_{k=1}^{6} 19 - 4k$　　Ⓓ $\sum_{k=1}^{6} [22 - 3(k - 1)]$

57. **Gridded Response** What is the 13th term of the arithmetic sequence 54, 50, 46, 42, ...? **6**

CHALLENGE AND EXTEND

58. Consider the two terms of an arithmetic series a_n and a_m.
   a. Show that the common difference is $d = \frac{a_n - a_m}{n - m}$.
   b. Use the new formula to find the common difference for the arithmetic sequence with $a_{12} = 88$ and $a_{36} = 304$. **9**

59. Find a formula for the sum of an arithmetic sequence that does NOT include the last term. When might this formula be useful?

60. The sum of three consecutive terms of an arithmetic sequence is 60. If the product of these terms is 7500, what are the terms? **15, 20, 25 or 25, 20, 15**

61. **Critical Thinking** What does $a_{2n} = 2a_n$ mean and for what arithmetic sequences is it true?

SPIRAL REVIEW

Tell whether the function shows growth or decay. Then graph. *(Lesson 7-1)*

62. decay
63. growth
64. decay

62. $f(x) = 1.25(0.75)^x$　　63. $f(x) = 1.43(5.32)^x$　　64. $f(x) = 0.92(0.64)^x$

65. **Sound** The loudness of sound is given by $L = 10\log\left(\frac{I}{I_0}\right)$, where L is the loudness of sound in decibels, I is the intensity of sound, and I_0 is the intensity of the softest audible sound. A sound meter at an auto race had a relative intensity of $10^{9.2}\ I_0$. Find the loudness of the sound in decibels. *(Lesson 7-3)* **92 dB**

Write each series in summation notation. *(Lesson 12-2)*

66. $1 + \frac{1}{2} + \frac{1}{3} + \frac{1}{4} + \frac{1}{5}$　$\sum_{k=1}^{5} \frac{1}{k}$

67. $\frac{4}{5} + \frac{8}{5} + \frac{12}{5} + \frac{16}{5} + 4$　$\sum_{k=1}^{5} \frac{4k}{5}$

68. $-1 + 2 + 7 + 14 + 23$　$\sum_{k=1}^{5} (k^2 - 2)$

69. $-\frac{1}{3} - \frac{2}{3} - 1 - \frac{4}{3} - \frac{5}{3}$　$\sum_{k=1}^{5} -\frac{k}{3}$

Teaching Tip **Math Background** An alternative formula for the sum of an arithmetic series is $S_n = \frac{n}{2}[2a_1 + (n - 1)d]$. Students are asked to find this formula in **Exercise 59.**

Journal

Have students explain how to use the formula for the sum of the first *n* terms of an arithmetic series. Ask them to include an example.

ALTERNATIVE ASSESSMENT

Have students create an arithmetic sequence. Have them identify the common difference and several different terms of the sequence. Have them show how the general rule and the sum formula work with the sequence they have created.

Power Presentations with PowerPoint®

12-3 Lesson Quiz

1. Determine whether the sequence could be arithmetic. If so, find the first difference and the next term.
   −1, −4, −7, −10, −13, ...
   yes; −3, −16
2. Find the 10th term of the arithmetic sequence
   −2, −5, −8, −11, −14, ...
   −29
3. Find the missing terms in the arithmetic sequence
   15, ■, ■, ■, 17.
   15.5, 16, 16.5
4. Find the 6th term of the arithmetic sequence with $a_9 = 64$ and $a_{12} = 88$. 40
5. Find the indicated sum for $\sum_{k=1}^{12} (15 - 4k)$. −132
6. The side section of an auditorium has 12 seats in the first row and 3 additional seats in each subsequent row. How many seats are in the 10th row? How many seats in total are in the first 10 rows?
   39; 255

Also available on transparency

12-3 PROBLEM SOLVING

Violet has the book and the assignment for her literature class. Counting today, Monday, as day 1, she sees that she must read through page 385 by day 12, and through page 665 by day 20.

1. If Violet reads an equal number of pages each day, how many pages will she have read by this Friday?
   a. First write a rule for the *n*th term of an arithmetic sequence that represents the number of pages, a_n, that she will have read after *n* days. **$a_n = a_1 + (n-1)d$**
   b. Explain how to find the common difference by using the rule with the given data.
   Let $a_n = a_{20}$ and $a_1 = a_{12}$; replace 1 in $(n - 1)$ with 12; replace n in $(n - 1)$ with 20; substitute 385 and 665 for a_{12} and a_{20}; and calculate d.
   c. What is the common difference, and what does it mean in terms of Violet's assignment?
   35; possible answer: the number of pages Violet must read each day
   d. How many pages must Violet read today, Monday? Explain how you know this.
   0 pages; $385 = a_1 + (35)(12 - 1)$; so $a_1 = 0$; and a_1 represents the number of pages for day 1.
   e. Use the rule to find the number of pages Violet will have read by Friday. **$a_5 = 0 + (35)(5 - 1)$; 140 pages**
2. Violet looks at the table of contents in her book. She sees that each of the first 6 chapters is 2 pages longer than the preceding chapter, with the first chapter having 10 pages.
   a. How many pages are in the sixth chapter? Write a rule for the number of pages, a_n, in chapter *n*. Then solve for $n = 6$. **$a_n = a_1 + (n-1)(2)$; 20 pages**
   b. How pages are in the first 6 chapters? Use the formula for the sum of the first *n* terms of an arithmetic sequence. **$S_n = 6\left(\frac{10 + 20}{2}\right)$; 90 pages**

Choose the letter for the best answer.

3. Violet reads the first 385 pages by day 6. Which expression gives the minimum pages she must read each day to finish 665 pages by day 20?
   A $6\left(\frac{665 + 385}{2}\right)$
   B $\frac{665 - 385}{6}$
   C $14\left(\frac{665 + 385}{2}\right)$
   Ⓓ (circled) $\frac{665 - 385}{14}$
4. Page 385 of Violet's book is 15 pages before the end of a 40-page chapter. If chapter 1 contains 10 pages, which chapter contains page 385?
   F Chapter 15
   Ⓖ (circled) Chapter 16
   H Chapter 19
   J Chapter 25

12-3 CHALLENGE

A story told about the German mathematician Carl Friedrich Gauss (1777–1855) is that, as a child in third grade, he quickly solved the problem "Add the whole numbers from 1 to 100" when this task had been intended as a long punishment assignment for his class. Gauss recognized that to determine the sum of the first *n* terms of an arithmetic series, you simply multiply half the number of terms by the sum of the first and last terms, shown symbolically at right.

$$S_n = \frac{n}{2}(a_1 + a_n)$$

To determine the sum of a given number of terms of a particular series, you need values for the first and last terms. When these are not given, you can write an expression for the *n*th term of the series.

To determine the sum of the first *n* even integers, write an expression for the *n*th term, as shown at right. Since there is a constant difference of 2, the series of numbers is arithmetic. Apply the sum formula, using $a_1 = 2$ and $a_n = 2n$.

$$2 + 4 + 6 + \cdots + 2n$$
$$S_n = \frac{n}{2}(a_1 + a_n) = \frac{n}{2}(2 + 2n) = n(n + 1)$$

For each of the following:
a. Verify that the given sequence of numbers is arithmetic by stating the constant difference.
b. Write an expression for the *n*th term of the sequence.
c. Use your expression and the formula to determine the sum of the first *n* terms.

1. Odd integers	2. Positive multiples of 3	3. Positive multiples of k, with $k > 0$
a. **2**	a. **3**	a. **k**
b. **$2n - 1$**	b. **$3n$**	b. **nk**
c. **n^2**	c. **$\frac{3}{2}n(n + 1)$**	c. **$\frac{k}{2}n(n + 1)$**

4. Explain how to use the result of Exercise 3 to predict the sum of the first *n* terms of the series shown at right. State the sum.　$\log 10 + \log 100 + \log 1000 + \log 10{,}000 + \ldots$
   The series is equivalent to $\log 10 + \log 10^2 + \log 10^3 + \ldots + \log 10^n$ which by the Power Property of Logarithms, is equivalent to $\log 10 + 2\log 10 + 3\log 10 + \ldots + n\log 10$. By Exercise 3, the sum is $\frac{\log 10}{2}n(n + 1)$. Since $\log 10 = 1$, this reduces to $\frac{n}{2}(n + 1)$.

Use the results of Exercises 3 and 4 to find the sum of the first *n* terms of the given series.

5. $\ln e + \ln e^2 + \ln e^3 + \ln e^4 + \ldots$
   $\frac{\ln e}{2}n(n + 1)$ or $\frac{n}{2}(n + 1)$
6. $\log_b a + \log_b a^2 + \log_b a^3 + \log_b a^4 + \ldots$
   $\frac{\log_b a}{2}n(n + 1)$

MULTI-STEP TEST PREP

Organizer

Objective: Assess students' ability to apply concepts and skills in Lessons 12-1 through 12-3 in a real-world format.

Online Edition

Resources

Algebra II Assessments

www.mathtekstoolkit.org

Problem	Text Reference
1–4	Lesson 12-1
5–6	Lesson 12-2
7	Lessons 12-1, 12-2

State Resources

go.hrw.com
State Resources Online
KEYWORD: MB7 Resources

CHAPTER 12

MULTI-STEP TEST PREP

SECTION 12A

Exploring Arithmetic Sequences and Series

Go Fly a Kite! Alexander Graham Bell, the inventor of the telephone, is also known for his work with tetrahedral kites. In 1902, Bell used the kites to prove that it is possible to build an arbitrarily large structure that will fly. The kites are made up of tetrahedrons (four-sided triangular figures) with two sides covered with fabric. As shown in the figure, the size of a tetrahedral kite is determined by how many layers it has.

1 layer

1. The first layer of a tetrahedral kite has 1 tetrahedron, the second layer has 3 tetrahedrons, and the third layer has 6 tetrahedrons. Write a sequence that shows how many tetrahedrons are in each of the first 10 layers. **1, 3, 6, 10, 15, 21, 28, 36, 45, 55**
2. Write a recursive formula for the sequence. $a_n = a_{n-1} + n$
3. Write an explicit rule for the nth term of the sequence. $a_n = \frac{n(n+1)}{2}$
4. How many tetrahedrons are there in the 25th layer? **325**
5. Write a series in summation notation that gives the total number of tetrahedrons in a kite with 25 layers. $\sum_{k=1}^{25} \frac{k(k+1)}{2}$
6. Evaluate the series in problem 5 to find the total number of tetrahedrons in a kite with 25 layers. (*Hint:* Use the properties **2925**

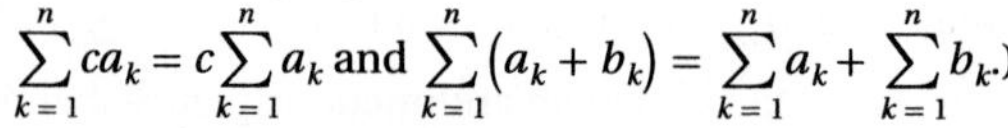

$\sum_{k=1}^{n} ca_k = c\sum_{k=1}^{n} a_k$ and $\sum_{k=1}^{n}(a_k + b_k) = \sum_{k=1}^{n} a_k + \sum_{k=1}^{n} b_k$.)

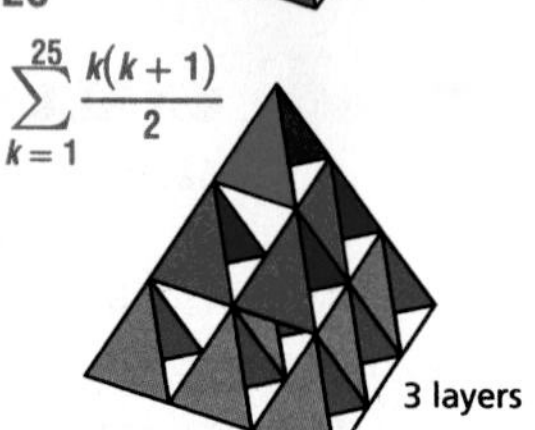

2 layers

3 layers

14; 560 7. You see someone flying a large tetrahedral kite at a kite festival. You look up and estimate that the bottom layer of the kite contains between 100 and 110 tetrahedrons. How many layers does the kite have? How many tetrahedrons did it take to build the kite?

888

INTERVENTION

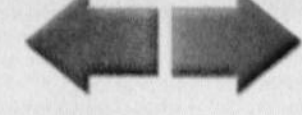

Scaffolding Questions

1. What pattern do you notice in the first few terms of the sequence? The first differences are 2, 3, and 4.
2. How can you find the 5th term when you know the 4th term? Add 5 to the 4th term.
3. What do the differences tell you about the sequence? It is quadratic.
4. How do you find the 25th term? Evaluate for $n = 25$.
5. How would you write the first few terms and the last term of this series in expanded notation? $1 + 3 + 6 + \ldots + 325$

6–7. How can you apply summation formulas to find the sum? Rewrite the series as the sum of a linear and a quadratic series.

Extension

Is it possible to make a tetrahedral kite in which the bottom layer has exactly 360 tetrahedrons? no

READY TO GO ON?

CHAPTER 12

SECTION 12A

Quiz for Lessons 12-1 Through 12-3

12-1 Introduction to Sequences

Find the first 5 terms of each sequence.

1. $a_n = \frac{2}{3}n$ $\frac{2}{3}, \frac{4}{3}, 2, \frac{8}{3}, \frac{10}{3}$
2. $a_n = 4^{n-1}$ 1, 4, 16, 64, 256
3. $a_1 = -1$ and $a_n = 2a_{n-1} - 12$ −1, −14, −40, −92, −196
4. $a_n = n^2 - 2n$ −1, 0, 3, 8, 15

Write a possible explicit rule for the nth term of each sequence.

5. 8, 11, 14, 17, 20, ... $a_n = 3n + 5$
6. −2, −8, −18, −32, −50, ... $a_n = -2n^2$
7. 1000, 200, 40, 8, $\frac{8}{5}$, ... $a_n = 1000\left(\frac{1}{5}\right)^{n-1}$
8. 437, 393, 349, 305, 261, ... $a_n = 437 - 44(n-1)$
9. A car traveling at 55 mi/h passes a mile marker that reads mile 18. If the car maintains this speed for 4 hours, what mile marker should the car pass? Graph the sequence for n hours, and describe its pattern. mile marker 238

12-2 Series and Summation Notation

Expand each series and evaluate.

10. $\sum_{k=1}^{4}(-14 - 2k)$ $-16 + (-18) + (-20) + (-22) = -76$
11. $\sum_{k=1}^{4}\left(\frac{k}{k+2}\right)$ $\frac{1}{3} + \frac{1}{2} + \frac{3}{5} + \frac{2}{3} = \frac{21}{10}$
12. $\sum_{k=1}^{5}(-1)^k(k^2 - 2)$ $1 + 2 - 7 + 14 - 23 = -13$

Evaluate each series.

13. $\sum_{k=1}^{5}\frac{1}{2}$ $\frac{5}{2}$
14. $\sum_{k=1}^{40}k^2$ 22,140
15. $\sum_{k=1}^{15}k$ 120
16. The first row of a theater has 20 seats, and each of the following rows has 3 more seats than the preceding row. How many seats are in the first 12 rows? 438

12-3 Arithmetic Sequences and Series

Find the 8th term of each arithmetic sequence.

17. 10.00, 10.11, 10.22, 10.33, ... 10.77
18. −5, −13, −21, −29, ... −61
19. $a_2 = 57.5$ and $a_5 = 80$ 102.5
20. $a_{10} = 141$ and $a_{13} = 186$ 111

Find the missing terms in each arithmetic sequence.

21. −23, ■, ■, −89 −45, −67
22. 31, ■, ■, ■, 79 43, 55, 67

Find the indicated sum for each arithmetic series

23. S_{10} for 40 + 30 + 20 + 10 + ⋯ −50
24. $\sum_{k=5}^{8}4k$ 104
25. $\sum_{k=1}^{11}(0.5k + 5.5)$ 93.5
26. S_{14} for −6 −1 + 4 + 9 + ⋯ 371
27. Suppose that you make a bank deposit of $1 the first week, $1.50 the second week, $2 the third week, and so on. How much will you contribute to the account on the last week of the year (52nd week)? What is the total amount that you have deposited in the bank after one year? $26.50; $715

SECTION 12A

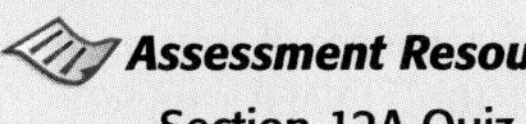

READY TO GO ON?

Organizer

Objective: Assess students' mastery of concepts and skills in Lessons 12-1 through 12-3.

Resources

Assessment Resources
Section 12A Quiz

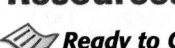

Test & Practice Generator One-Stop Planner®

INTERVENTION

Resources

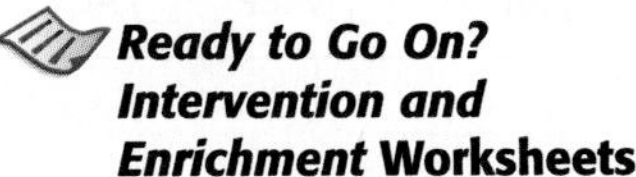

Ready to Go On? Intervention and Enrichment Worksheets

Ready to Go On? CD-ROM

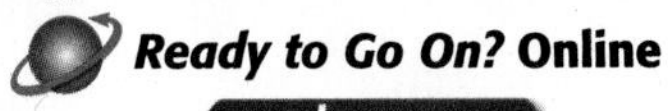

Ready to Go On? Online

my.hrw.com

Answers

9. For graph, see p. A46.

READY TO GO ON? Diagnose and Prescribe

NO INTERVENE

Ready to Go On? Intervention	Ready to Go On? Intervention, Section 12A: Worksheets	CD-ROM	Online
Lesson 12-1	12-1 Intervention	Activity 12-1	Diagnose and Prescribe Online
Lesson 12-2	12-2 Intervention	Activity 12-2	
Lesson 12-3	12-3 Intervention	Activity 12-3	

YES ENRICH

Ready to Go On? Enrichment, Section 12A
Worksheets
CD-ROM
Online

SECTION

12B Exploring Geometric Sequences and Series

One-Minute Section Planner

Lesson	Lab Resources	Materials
Lesson 12-4 Geometric Sequences and Series • Find terms of a geometric sequence, including geometric means. • Find the sums of geometric series. ☑ SAT-10 ☑ NAEP ☑ ACT ☑ SAT ☑ SAT Subject Tests	***Technology Lab Activities*** 12-4 Technology Lab	**Optional** graphing calculator
12-5 Algebra Lab Explore Infinite Geometric Series • Use a sequence of squares to explore an infinite geometric series. ☑ SAT-10 ☐ NAEP ☑ ACT ☑ SAT ☑ SAT Subject Tests	***Algebra Lab Activities*** 12-5 Lab Recording Sheet	**Required** graph paper, graphing calculator
Lesson 12-5 Mathematical Induction and Infinite Geometric Series • Find sums of infinite geometric series. • Use mathematical induction to prove statements. ☑ SAT-10 ☐ NAEP ☑ ACT ☑ SAT ☑ SAT Subject Tests		**Optional** dominoes or books, graphing calculator
Extension Area Under a Curve • Approximate area under a curve by using rectangles. ☐ SAT-10 ☐ NAEP ☐ ACT ☐ SAT ☐ SAT Subject Tests		**Optional** graphing calculator

MK = *Manipulatives Kit*

Section Overview

Geometric Sequences and Series — Lesson 12-4

Geometric sequences and series have applications in many areas, such as sound and video.

In a **geometric sequence,** the terms differ by a *common ratio, r.*

Example: 2, −8, 32, −128, 512, ...

$\frac{-8}{2}$ $\frac{32}{-8}$ $\frac{-128}{32}$ $\frac{512}{-128}$ ← $r = -4$

The **8th term** of this geometric sequence is:

$$a_n = a_1 r^{n-1}$$
$$a_8 = 2(-4)^{8-1}$$
$$= -32{,}768$$

A **geometric series** is the indicated sum of the terms of a geometric sequence.

Example: 2 + (−8) + 32 + (−128) + 512 + ...

The **sum of the first 8 terms** of this geometric sequence is:

$$S_n = a_1\left(\frac{1-r^n}{1-r}\right)$$
$$S_8 = a_1\left(\frac{1-(-4)^8}{1-(-4)}\right)$$
$$= 2\left(\frac{1-65{,}536}{5}\right) = -26{,}214$$

Geometric means are the terms between any two nonconsecutive terms of a geometric sequence.

Example: 7, 14, 28, **56**, 112, ...

56 is the geometric mean of 28 and 112.

If a and b are positive terms of a geometric sequence with exactly one term between them, the geometric mean is given by $\sqrt{ab}$.

The geometric mean of 28 and 112 is $\sqrt{(28)(112)} = 56$.

Infinite Geometric Series and Mathematical Induction — Lesson 12-5

Infinite geometric series introduce students to limits, an important concept for calculus.

An **infinite geometric series** has infinitely many terms. An infinite geometric series may converge or diverge.

Convergent Series

$$S_n = \frac{1}{2} + \frac{1}{4} + \frac{1}{8} + \frac{1}{16} + \frac{1}{32} + \dots \quad r = \frac{1}{2}$$

The partial sums get closer and closer to 1 as n increases.

When $|r| < 1$, the partial sums approach a fixed number, called a *limit.*

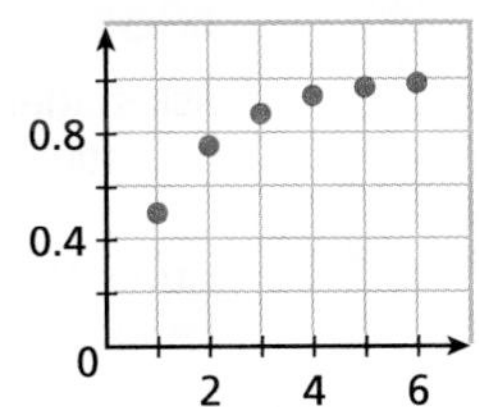

Divergent Series

$$R_n = \frac{1}{32} + \frac{1}{16} + \frac{1}{8} + \frac{1}{4} + \frac{1}{2} + \dots \quad r = 2$$

The partial sums increase toward infinity as n increases.

When $|r| > 1$, the partial sums do not approach a fixed number.

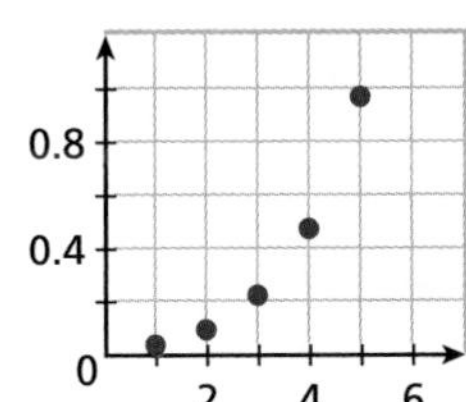

12-4 Organizer

Pacing: Traditional $1\frac{1}{2}$ days
Block $\frac{3}{4}$ day

Objectives: Find terms of a geometric sequence, including geometric means.

Find the sums of geometric series.

Technology Lab
In Technology Lab Activities

Online Edition
Tutorial Videos, TechKeys

Power Presentations with PowerPoint®

Warm Up

Simplify.

1. $\frac{18}{27}$ $\frac{2}{3}$ **2.** $128\left(\frac{3}{4}\right)$ 96

Evaluate.

3. $(-2)^8$ 256 **4.** $\left(\frac{1}{2}\right)^6$ $\frac{1}{64}$

Solve for *x*.

5. $x^2 = \frac{4}{25}$ $x = \pm\frac{2}{5}$

Also available on transparency

Math Humor

A math student came home at 3 A.M. His upset parents exclaimed, "You're late! You said you'd be home by 11:45!" The math student calmly replied, "I'm right on time. I said I'd be home by a quarter of twelve."

12-4 Geometric Sequences and Series

A2.7.1 Write the recursive formula for arithmetic and geometric sequences and find specific terms of arithmetic and geometric sequences.

Objectives
Find terms of a geometric sequence, including geometric means.

Find the sums of geometric series.

Vocabulary
geometric sequence
geometric mean
geometric series

Who uses this?
Sporting-event planners can use geometric sequences and series to determine the number of matches that must be played in a tournament. (See Example 6.)

Serena Williams was the winner out of 128 players who began the 2003 Wimbledon Ladies' Singles Championship. After each match, the winner continues to the next round and the loser is eliminated from the tournament. This means that after each round only half of the players remain.

The number of players remaining after each round can be modeled by a *geometric sequence.* In a **geometric sequence**, the ratio of successive terms is a constant called the *common ratio* r $(r \neq 1)$. For the players remaining, r is $\frac{1}{2}$.

Term	a_1	a_2	a_3	a_4
Value	128	64	32	16

Ratios $\frac{64}{128} = \frac{1}{2}$ $\frac{32}{64} = \frac{1}{2}$ $\frac{16}{32} = \frac{1}{2}$

Recall that exponential functions have a common ratio. When you graph the ordered pairs (n, a_n) of a geometric sequence, the points lie on an exponential curve as shown. Thus, you can think of a geometric sequence as an exponential function with sequential natural numbers as the domain.

EXAMPLE 1 Identifying Geometric Sequences

Determine whether each sequence could be geometric or arithmetic. If possible, find the common ratio or difference.

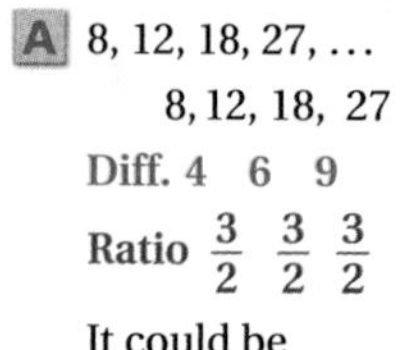

A 8, 12, 18, 27, ...

8, 12, 18, 27

Diff. 4 6 9

Ratio $\frac{3}{2}$ $\frac{3}{2}$ $\frac{3}{2}$

It could be geometric, with $r = \frac{3}{2}$.

B 8, 16, 24, 32, ...

8, 16 24, 32

Diff. 8 8 8

Ratio 2 $\frac{3}{2}$ $\frac{4}{3}$

It could be arithmetic, with $d = 8$.

C 6, 10, 15, 21, ...

6, 10, 15, 21

Diff. 4 5 6

Ratio $\frac{5}{3}$ $\frac{3}{2}$ $\frac{7}{5}$

It is neither.

Determine whether each sequence could be geometric or arithmetic. If possible, find the common ratio or difference.

1a. $\frac{1}{4}, \frac{1}{12}, \frac{1}{36}, \frac{1}{108}, \ldots$ geometric; $r = \frac{1}{3}$

1b. 1.7, 1.3, 0.9, 0.5, ... arithmetic; $d = -0.4$

1c. −50, −32, −18, −8, ... neither

State Resources

go.hrw.com
State Resources Online
KEYWORD: MB7 Resources

1 Introduce

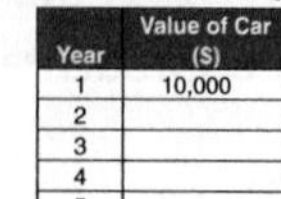

EXPLORATION

12-4 Geometric Sequences and Series

This year, Kate buys a used car worth $10,000. In each subsequent year, the car's value is 90% of the previous year's value.

1. Complete the table showing the yearly values of Kate's car.

Year	Value of Car ($)
1	10,000
2	
3	
4	
5	

2. Graph the data in the table.
3. What is the ratio of the successive terms in the sequence formed by the yearly values of Kate's car?
4. What type of function describes the data? Why?
5. Write an explicit formula for the nth term of the sequence formed by the yearly values of Kate's car.
6. Write a recursive formula for the nth term of the sequence.

THINK AND DISCUSS

7. Show how you can use the explicit formula to find the value of Kate's car in the 8th year.
8. Discuss whether the explicit formula or the recursive formula

Motivate

Ask students to consider the following situation: a collectible purchased for $100 increases in value by either $15 per year or 10% per year. Have students discuss which increase they would prefer and why. Possible answer: The 10% increase would be better after 10 years or more. Explain that this situation can compare an arithmetic sequence to a geometric sequence.

Explorations and answers are provided in the *Explorations* binder.

Each term in a geometric sequence is the product of the previous term and the common ratio, giving the recursive rule for a geometric sequence.

$$\underbrace{a_n}_{n\text{th term}} = \underbrace{a_{n-1}}_{\text{First term}}\underbrace{r}_{\text{Common ratio}}$$

You can also use an explicit rule to find the nth term of a geometric sequence. Each term is the product of the first term and a power of the common ratio as shown in the table.

Tennis Players in Each Round of Wimbledon					
Round	1	2	3	4	n
Players	128	64	32	16	a_n
Formula	$a_1 = 128\left(\frac{1}{2}\right)^0$	$a_2 = 128\left(\frac{1}{2}\right)^1$	$a_3 = 128\left(\frac{1}{2}\right)^2$	$a_4 = 128\left(\frac{1}{2}\right)^3$	$a_n = 128\left(\frac{1}{2}\right)^{n-1}$

This pattern can be generalized into a rule for all geometric sequences.

General Rule for Geometric Sequences

The nth term a_n of a geometric sequence is

$$a_n = a_1 r^{n-1},$$

where a_1 is the first term and r is the common ratio.

EXAMPLE 2 Finding the *n*th Term Given a Geometric Sequence

Find the 9th term of the geometric sequence −5, 10, −20, 40, −80, ...

Step 1 Find the common ratio.

$$r = \frac{a_2}{a_1} = \frac{10}{-5} = -2$$

Step 2 Write a rule, and evaluate for $n = 9$.

$a_n = a_1 r^{n-1}$ *General rule*

$a_9 = -5(-2)^{9-1}$ *Substitute −5 for a_1, 9 for n, and −2 for r.*

$= -5(256) = -1280$

The 9th term is −1280.

Check Extend the sequence.

$a_5 = -80$ *Given*

$a_6 = -80(-2) = 160$

$a_7 = 160(-2) = -320$

$a_8 = -320(-2) = 640$

$a_9 = 640(-2) = -1280$ ✓

Find the 9th term of each geometric sequence.

2a. $\frac{3}{4}, -\frac{3}{8}, \frac{3}{16}, -\frac{3}{32}, \frac{3}{64}, \ldots$ **$\frac{3}{1024}$**

2b. 0.001, 0.01, 0.1, 1, 10, ... **100,000**

Power Presentations with PowerPoint®

Additional Examples

Example 1

Determine whether each sequence could be geometric or arithmetic. If possible, find the common ratio or difference.

A. 100, 93, 86, 79, ... arithmetic; $d = -7$

B. 180, 90, 60, 15, ... neither

C. 5, 1, 0.2, 0.04, ... geometric; $r = 0.2$

Example 2

Find the 7th term of the geometric sequence 3, 12, 48, 192, ... 12,288

Also available on transparency

INTERVENTION

Questioning Strategies

EXAMPLE 1

- How would you determine whether a sequence is arithmetic or geometric?
- How could you try to find a possible rule for a sequence that is neither arithmetic nor geometric?

EXAMPLE 2

- How could you check the value you found for r, the common ratio?
- How could you predict the sign of the 9th term before you calculate it?

Technology To display the terms of a geometric sequence on a graphing calculator, enter the first term, press ENTER, press ×, enter the common ratio, and press ENTER repeatedly.

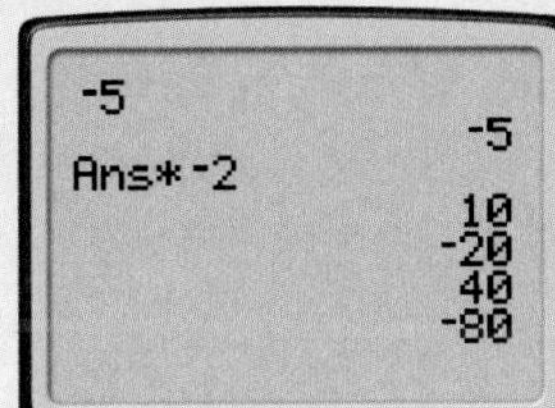

2 Teach

Guided Instruction

Review with students the domain and range for sequences with values in the form (n, a_n). Help students recall that the domain, or set of values for n, is the natural numbers, while the range is some set of real numbers.

Inclusion Make sure that students realize that r cannot be 0 and that the value of a_n cannot be 0.

Reaching All Learners

Through Graphic Organizers

Have students make a table for geometric sequences, labeling the rows so that the first row shows the values of n, the second row shows the value of a_n, and the third row shows the ratio between terms. The table for **Example 2** is shown below.

n	1	2	3	...
a_n	−5	10	−20	...
r	−2	−2	...	...

EXAMPLE 3 Finding the *n*th Term Given Two Terms

Find the 10th term of the geometric sequence with $a_5 = 96$ and $a_7 = 384$.

Step 1 Find the common ratio.

$a_7 = a_5 r^{(7-5)}$	*Use the given terms.*
$a_7 = a_5 r^2$	*Simplify.*
$384 = 96r^2$	*Substitute 384 for a_7 and 96 for a_5.*
$4 = r^2$	*Divide both sides by 96.*
$\pm 2 = r$	*Take the square root of both sides.*

Step 2 Find a_1.

Consider both the positive and negative values for r.

$a_n = a_1 r^{n-1}$		$a_n = a_1 r^{n-1}$	*General rule*
$96 = a_1(2)^{5-1}$	or	$96 = a_1(-2)^{5-1}$	*Use $a_5 = 96$ and $r = \pm 2$.*
$6 = a_1$		$6 = a_1$	

Step 3 Write the rule and evaluate for a_{10}.

Consider both the positive and negative values for r.

$a_n = a_1 r^{n-1}$		$a_n = a_1 r^{n-1}$	*General rule*
$a_n = 6(2)^{n-1}$	or	$a_n = 6(-2)^{n-1}$	*Substitute for a_1 and r.*
$a_{10} = 6(2)^{10-1}$		$a_{10} = 6(-2)^{10-1}$	*Evaluate for $n = 6$.*
$a_{10} = 3072$		$a_{10} = -3072$	

The 10th term is 3072 or −3072.

Caution!

When given two terms of a sequence, be sure to consider positive and negative values for r when necessary.

CHECK IT OUT! **Find the 7th term of the geometric sequence with the given terms.**

3a. $a_4 = -8$ and $a_5 = -40$ **−1000**

3b. $a_2 = 768$ and $a_4 = 48$ $\frac{3}{4}$ **or** $-\frac{3}{4}$

Geometric means are the terms between any two nonconsecutive terms of a geometric sequence.

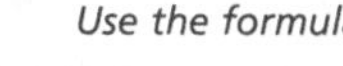

Geometric Mean

If a and b are positive terms of a geometric sequence with exactly one term between them, the geometric mean is given by the following expression.

$$\sqrt{ab}$$

EXAMPLE 4 Finding Geometric Means

Find the geometric mean of $\frac{1}{2}$ and $\frac{1}{32}$.

$$\sqrt{ab} = \sqrt{\left(\frac{1}{2}\right)\left(\frac{1}{32}\right)}$$

$$= \sqrt{\frac{1}{64}} = \frac{1}{8} \quad \textit{Use the formula.}$$

CHECK IT OUT! **4.** Find the geometric mean of 16 and 25. **20**

Power Presentations with PowerPoint®

Additional Examples

Example 3

Find the 8th term of the geometric sequence with $a_3 = 36$ and $a_5 = 324$. 8748 or −8748

Example 4

Find the geometric mean of $\frac{4}{9}$ and $\frac{25}{36}$. $\frac{5}{9}$

Also available on transparency

INTERVENTION
Questioning Strategies

EXAMPLE 3

- Will each term in a geometric sequence always be greater than the first term? Explain.
- Is the first term in a geometric sequence always positive? Explain.

EXAMPLE 4

- If a and b are nonconsecutive terms of a geometric sequence and there is exactly one term between them, can ab be less than 0? Explain.

The indicated sum of the terms of a geometric sequence is called a **geometric series**. You can derive a formula for the partial sum of a geometric series by subtracting the product of S_n and r from S_n as shown.

$$S_n = a_1 + a_1r + a_1r^2 + \cdots + a_1r^{n-1}$$
$$-rS_n = \quad -a_1r - a_1r^2 - \cdots - a_1r^{n-1} - a_1r^n$$
$$S_n - rS_n = a_1 \qquad -a_1r^n$$
$$S_n(1-r) = a_1(1-r^n)$$
$$S_n = a_1\left(\frac{1-r^n}{1-r}\right)$$

Sum of the First n Terms of a Geometric Series

The partial sum S_n of the first n terms of a geometric series $a_1 + a_2 + \cdots + a_n$ is given by

$$S_n = a_1\left(\frac{1-r^n}{1-r}\right),\ r \neq 1$$

where a_1 is the first term and r is the common ratio.

EXAMPLE 5 Finding the Sum of a Geometric Series

Find the indicated sum for each geometric series.

Remember!

These sums are partial sums because you are finding the sum of a finite number of terms. In Lesson 12-5, you will find the sums of infinite geometric series.

A S_7 for $3 - 6 + 12 - 24 + \cdots$

Step 1 Find the common ratio.

$$r = \frac{a_2}{a_1} = \frac{-6}{3} = -2$$

Step 2 Find S_7 with $a_1 = 3$, $r = -2$, and $n = 7$.

$$S_n = a_1\left(\frac{1-r^n}{1-r}\right) \quad \textit{Sum formula}$$

$$S_7 = 3\left(\frac{1-(-2)^7}{1-(-2)}\right) \quad \textit{Substitute.}$$

$$= 3\left(\frac{1-(-128)}{3}\right)$$

$$= 129$$

Check Use a graphing calculator.

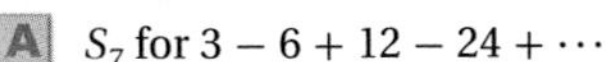

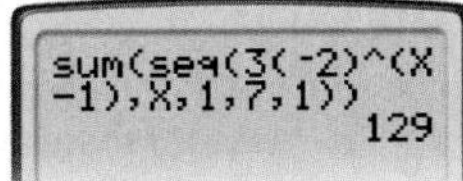

B $\sum_{k=1}^{5}\left(\frac{1}{3}\right)^{k-1}$

Step 1 Find the first term.

$$a_1 = \left(\frac{1}{3}\right)^{1-1} = \left(\frac{1}{3}\right)^0 = 1$$

Step 2 Find S_5.

$$S_n = a_1\left(\frac{1-r^n}{1-r}\right) \quad \textit{Sum formula}$$

$$S_5 = 1\left(\frac{1-\left(\frac{1}{3}\right)^5}{1-\left(\frac{1}{3}\right)}\right) \quad \textit{Substitute.}$$

$$= \left(\frac{1-\left(\frac{1}{243}\right)}{\frac{2}{3}}\right)$$

$$= \frac{242}{243}\cdot\frac{3}{2} = \frac{121}{81} \approx 1.49$$

Check Use a graphing calculator.

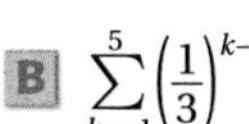

Find the indicated sum for each geometric series.

5a. S_6 for $2 + 1 + \frac{1}{2} + \frac{1}{4} + \cdots$ $\quad \frac{63}{16}$

5b. $\sum_{k=1}^{6} -3(2)^{k-1}$ $\quad -189$

COMMON ERROR ALERT

When applying the sum formula for geometric series, students may subtract the values in the numerator before applying the exponent. Remind them that exponents are evaluated before addition and subtraction in the order of operations.

Power Presentations with PowerPoint®

Additional Examples

Example 5

Find the indicated sum for each geometric series.

A. S_8 for $1 + 2 + 4 + 8 + 16 + \ldots$

255

B. $\sum_{k=1}^{6}\left(\frac{1}{2}\right)^{k-1}$ $\quad \frac{63}{32} \approx 1.97$

Also available on transparency

INTERVENTION

Questioning Strategies

EXAMPLE 5

- What are the first 5 terms of the geometric series in **Example 5B**? Explain.
- Can the sum of the first 5 terms of a geometric series ever be equal to zero? Explain.

Power Presentations with PowerPoint®

Additional Examples

Example 6

An online video game tournament begins with 1024 players. Four players play in each game, and in each game, only the winner advances to the next round. How many games must be played to determine the winner?
341

Also available on transparency

INTERVENTION

Questioning Strategies

EXAMPLE 6

- How can you tell how many games or matches will be required for the first round?
- How do you solve an exponential equation? Explain the steps.

Teaching Tip

Inclusion The notation of sequences and series can be confusing for some students. Encourage students to write down the value of each variable as they read through the problem. Then they can analyze the given information and determine what formulas to use. ENGLISH LANGUAGE LEARNERS

EXAMPLE 6 ***Sports Application***

The Wimbledon Ladies' Singles Championship begins with 128 players. The players compete until there is 1 winner. How many matches must be scheduled in order to complete the tournament?

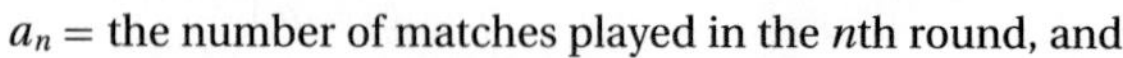

Remember!

For a review of solving exponential equations, see Lesson 7-5.

Step 1 Write a sequence.

Let n = the number of rounds,

a_n = the number of matches played in the nth round, and

S_n = the total number of matches played through n rounds.

$a_n = 64\left(\frac{1}{2}\right)^{n-1}$ *The first round requires 64 matches, so $a_1 = 64$. Each successive match requires $\frac{1}{2}$ as many, so $r = \frac{1}{2}$.*

Step 2 Find the number of rounds required.

$1 = 64\left(\frac{1}{2}\right)^{n-1}$ *The final round will have 1 match, so substitute 1 for a_n.*

$\frac{1}{64} = \left(\frac{1}{2}\right)^{n-1}$ *Isolate the exponential expression by dividing by 64.*

$\left(\frac{1}{2}\right)^{6} = \left(\frac{1}{2}\right)^{n-1}$ *Express $\frac{1}{64}$ as a power of $\frac{1}{2}$: $\frac{1}{64} = \left(\frac{1}{2}\right)^6$.*

$6 = n - 1$ *Equate the exponents.*

$7 = n$ *Solve for n.*

Step 3 Find the total number of matches after 7 rounds.

$$S_7 = 64\left(\frac{1-\left(\frac{1}{2}\right)^7}{1-\left(\frac{1}{2}\right)}\right) = 127$$ *Sum function for geometric series.*

127 matches must be scheduled to complete the tournament.

CHECK IT OUT! 6. **Real Estate** A 6-year lease states that the annual rent for an office space is $84,000 the first year and will increase by 8% each additional year of the lease. What will the total rent expense be for the 6-year lease? **$616,218.04**

THINK AND DISCUSS

1. Find the next three terms of the geometric sequence that begins 3, 6, ... Then find the next three terms of the arithmetic sequence that begins 3, 6, ...
2. Compare the geometric mean of 4 and 16 with the mean, or average.

3. **GET ORGANIZED** Copy and complete the graphic organizer. In each box, summarize your understanding of geometric sequences.

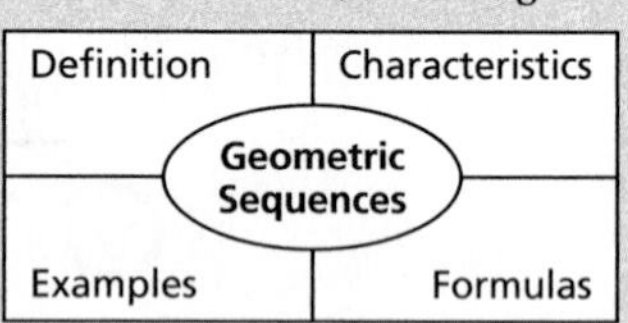

3 Close

Summarize

Ask students to explain the difference between arithmetic and geometric sequences. Ask students to explain the difference between a geometric sequence and a geometric series. Arithmetic sequences have a common difference, while geometric sequences have a common ratio. A geometric series is the indicated sum of the terms of such a sequence.

ONGOING ASSESSMENT and INTERVENTION

***Diagnose Before* the Lesson**
12-4 Warm Up, TE p. 890

***Monitor During* the Lesson**
Check It Out! Exercises, SE pp. 890–894
Questioning Strategies, TE pp. 891–894

***Assess After* the Lesson**
12-4 Lesson Quiz, TE p. 898
Alternative Assessment, TE p. 898

Answers to *Think and Discuss*

Possible answers:

1. geometric: 12, 24, 48; arithmetic: 9, 12, 15
2. Mean: 10; geometric mean: 8; either of the terms can be found by adding or subtracting 6 from the mean; either of the terms can be found by multiplying or dividing the geometric mean by 2.
3. See p. A13.

go.hrw.com
Homework Help Online
KEYWORD: MB7 12-4
Parent Resources Online
KEYWORD: MB7 Parent

GUIDED PRACTICE

1. **Vocabulary** The term between two given terms in a geometric sequence is the ___?___. (*geometric mean* or *geometric series*) geometric mean

SEE EXAMPLE 1 p. 890

Determine whether each sequence could be geometric or arithmetic. If possible, find the common ratio or difference.

2. $-10, -12, -14, -16, \ldots$ arithmetic; $d = -2$
3. $\frac{1}{2}, 1, 2, 3, \ldots$ neither
4. $-320, -80, -20, -5, \ldots$ geometric, $r = \frac{1}{4}$

SEE EXAMPLE 2 p. 891

Find the 10th term of each geometric sequence.

5. $2, 6, 18, 54, 162, \ldots$ 39,366
6. $5000, 500, 50, 5, 0.5, \ldots$ 0.000005
7. $-0.125, 0.25, -0.5, 1, -2, \ldots$ 64

SEE EXAMPLE 3 p. 892

Find the 6th term of the geometric sequence with the given terms.

8. $a_4 = -12, a_5 = -4$ $-\frac{4}{3}$
9. $a_2 = 4, a_5 = 108$ 324
10. $a_3 = 3, a_5 = 12$ 24 or −24

SEE EXAMPLE 4 p. 892

Find the geometric mean of each pair of numbers.

11. 6 and $\frac{3}{8}$ $\frac{3}{2}$
12. 2 and 32 8
13. 12 and 192 48

SEE EXAMPLE 5 p. 893

Find the indicated sum for each geometric series.

14. S_6 for $2 + 0.2 + 0.02 + \cdots$ 2.22222
15. $\sum_{k=1}^{5}(-3)^{k-1}$ 61
16. S_5 for $12 - 24 + 48 - 96 + \cdots$ 132
17. $\sum_{k=1}^{9}256\left(\frac{1}{2}\right)^{k-1}$ 511

SEE EXAMPLE 6 p. 894

18. **Salary** In his first year, a math teacher earned \$32,000. Each successive year, he earned a 5% raise. How much did he earn in his 20th year? What were his total earnings over the 20-year period? \$80,862.41; \$1,058,110.53

PRACTICE AND PROBLEM SOLVING

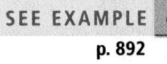

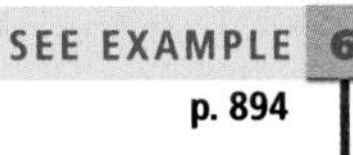

For Exercises	See Example
19–21	1
22–25	2
26–28	3
29–31	4
32–35	5
36	6

Extra Practice
Skills Practice p. S27
Application Practice p. S43

Determine whether each sequence could be geometric or arithmetic. If possible, find the common ratio or difference.

19. $-36, -49, -64, -81, \ldots$ neither
20. $-2, -6, -18, -54, \ldots$ geometric; $r = 3$
21. $2, 7, 12, 17, \ldots$ arithmetic; $d = 5$

Find the 9th term of each geometric sequence.

22. $\frac{1}{2}, \frac{1}{10}, \frac{1}{50}, \frac{1}{250}, \frac{1}{1250}, \ldots$ $\frac{1}{781{,}250}$
23. $3, -6, 12, -24, 48, \ldots$ 768
24. $3200, 1600, 800, 400, 200, \ldots$ 12.5
25. $8, 24, 72, 216, 648, \ldots$ 52,488

Find the 7th term of the geometric sequence with the given terms.

26. $a_4 = 54, a_5 = 162$ 1458
27. $a_5 = 13.5, a_6 = 20.25$ 30.375
28. $a_4 = -4, a_6 = -100$ 500 or −500

Find the geometric mean of each pair of numbers.

29. 9 and $\frac{1}{9}$ 1
30. 18 and 2 6
31. $\frac{1}{5}$ and 45 3

Find the indicated sum for each geometric series.

32. S_6 for $1 + 5 + 25 + 125 + \cdots$ 3906
33. S_8 for $10 + 1 + \frac{1}{10} + \frac{1}{100} + \cdots$ 11.111111
34. $\sum_{k=1}^{6}-1\left(\frac{1}{3}\right)^{k-1}$ $-\frac{364}{243}$
35. $\sum_{k=1}^{7}8(10)^{k-1}$ 8,888,888

12-4 Exercises

Assignment Guide

Assign *Guided Practice* exercises as necessary.

If you finished Examples 1–3
Basic 19–28
Average 19–28, 51
Advanced 19–28, 50–51

If you finished Examples 1–6
Basic 19–45, 49–51, 57–62, 68–75
Average 19–39, 43–51, 57–65, 68–75
Advanced 20–36 even, 40–75

Homework Quick Check
Quickly check key concepts.
Exercises: 20, 22, 26, 30, 34, 36

State Resources

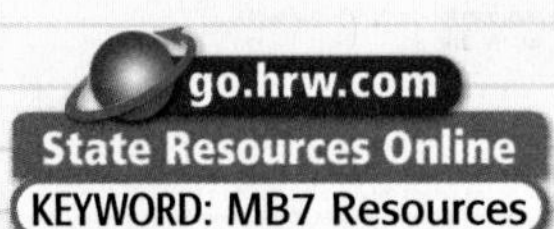

Diversity For **Exercise 36,** discuss the term *biological parents,* and be sure students understand that this limitation on the number of parents is used for mathematical reasons. Many people have varying numbers of stepparents or foster parents, as well as other extended family, but every person has exactly two biological parents.

ENGLISH LANGUAGE LEARNERS

Answers

37. $a_n = \frac{1}{16}(2)^{n-1}$; $a_{10} = 32$; $S_{10} = \frac{1023}{16} \approx 63.94$

38. $a_n = 4\left(\frac{1}{10}\right)^{n-1}$; $a_{10} = 0.000000004$; $S_{10} = 4.444444444$

39. $a_n = 8(2)^{n-1}$; $a_{10} = 4096$; $S_{10} = 8184$

40. $a_n = -22\left(\frac{1}{2}\right)^{n-1}$; $a_{10} = -\frac{11}{256}$; $S_{10} = -\frac{11,253}{256} \approx -43.96$

41. $a_n = 162\left(-\frac{1}{3}\right)^{n-1}$; $a_{10} = -\frac{2}{243}$; $S_{10} = 121\frac{121}{243} \approx 121.5$

42. $a_n = 12.5(5)^{n-1}$; $a_{10} = 24,414,062.5$; $S_{10} = 30,517,575$

43b. The shirt's value increases more in the second 4 years because the increase is a percentage of the value, which becomes greater every year.

44. \$1310.72; \$10,485.76; the money will probably not pay for 4 years of college.

36. **Genealogy** You have 2 biological parents, 4 biological grandparents, and 8 biological great grandparents.
    a. How many direct ancestors do you have in the 6 generations before you? 12 generations? **126; 8190**
    b. **What if...?** How does the explicit rule change if you are considered the first generation? **The exponent changes from n to $n-1$ such that $a_n = 2^n$ becomes $a_n = 2^{n-1}$.**

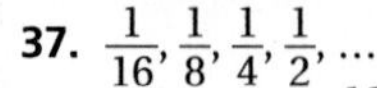

Collectibles

The most expensive rock'n'roll memorabilia ever purchased was John Lennon's Rolls Royce, with a price tag of \$2.2 million.

Given each geometric sequence, (a) write an explicit rule for the sequence, (b) find the 10th term, and (c) find the sum of the first 10 terms.

37. $\frac{1}{16}, \frac{1}{8}, \frac{1}{4}, \frac{1}{2}, \ldots$
38. $4, 0.4, 0.04, 0.004, \ldots$
39. $8, 16, 32, 64, \ldots$
40. $-22, -11, -\frac{11}{2}, -\frac{11}{4}, \ldots$
41. $162, -54, 18, -6, \ldots$
42. $12.5, 62.5, 312.5, 1562.5, \ldots$

43. **Collectibles** Louis bought a vintage Rolling Stones concert shirt for \$20. He estimates that the shirt will increase in value by 15% per year.
    a. How much is the shirt worth after 4 years? after 8 years? **\$34.98; \$61.18**
    b. Does the shirt increase more in value during the first 4 years or the second 4 years? Explain.

44. **College Tuition** New grandparents decide to pay for their granddaughter's college education. They give the girl a penny on her first birthday and double the gift on each subsequent birthday. How much money will the girl receive when she is 18? 21? Will the money pay for her college education? Explain.

45. **Technology** You receive an e-mail asking you to forward it to 5 other people to ensure good luck. Assume that no one breaks the chain and that there are no duplications among the recipients. How many e-mails will have been sent after 10 generations, including yours, have received and sent the e-mail? **2,441,406**

46. **Fractals** The Sierpinski carpet is a fractal based on a square. In each iteration, the center of each shaded square is removed.

    a. Given that the area of the original square is 1 square unit, write a sequence for the area of the nth iteration of the Sierpinski carpet. **$a_n = \left(\frac{8}{9}\right)^{n-1}$**
    b. In which iteration will the area be less than $\frac{1}{2}$ of the original area? **7th**

47a. 12.8 mm

47. **Paper** A piece of paper is 0.1 mm thick. When folded, the paper is twice as thick.
    a. Studies have shown that you can fold a piece of paper a maximum of 7 times. How thick will the paper be if it is folded on top of itself 7 times?
    b. Assume that you could fold the paper as many times as you want. How many folds would be required for the paper to be taller than Mount Everest (8850 m)? **27 folds**

48. **Measurement** Several common U.S. paper sizes are shown in the table.
    a. Examine the length and width measures for the different paper sizes. What interrelationships do you observe?
    b. How are the areas for each paper size (from A to E) mathematically related and what name is this relationship given?

Common U.S. Paper Sizes

U.S. Paper Size	Dimensions (in.)
A (letter)	$8\frac{1}{2} \times 11$
B (ledger)	11×17
C	17×22
D	22×34
E	34×44

12-4 PRACTICE A
12-4 PRACTICE C
12-4 PRACTICE B

Determine whether each sequence could be geometric or arithmetic. If possible, find the common ratio or difference.

1. 1.1, −3.3, 9.9, −29.7, 89.1, ... **Geometric; $r = -3$**
2. −18, −7, 4, 15, 26, ... **Arithmetic; $d = 11$**
3. 1, 2, 6, 24, 120, 720, ... **Neither**
4. 3125, 2500, 2000, 1600, 1280, ... **Geometric; $r = 0.8$**

Find the 10th term of each geometric sequence.

5. 1600, 800, 400, 200, ... **3.125**
6. 0.0000001, 0.00001, 0.001, 0.1, ... **100,000,000,000**
7. −64, 96, −144, 216, ... **2460.375**
8. 2, −6, 18, −54, ... **−39,366**

Find the 8th term of each geometric sequence with the given terms.

9. $a_3 = 12$ and $a_6 = 96$ **384**
10. $a_{15} = 100$ and $a_{17} = 25$ **±12,800**
11. $a_{11} = -4$ and $a_{13} = -36$ **$\pm\frac{4}{27}$**
12. $a_3 = -4$ and $a_5 = -36$ **±972**

Find the geometric mean of each pair of numbers.

13. 2 and 8 **±4**
14. 4 and 25 **±10**
15. 2 and 3 **$\pm\sqrt{6}$**

Find the indicated sum for each geometric series.

16. S_7 for 14, 42, 126, 378, ... **15,302**
17. $\sum_{k=1}^{8}(-4)^{k-1}$ **−13,107**

Solve.

18. Deanna received an e-mail asking her to forward it to 10 other people. Assume that no one breaks the chain and that there are no duplicate recipients. How many e-mails will have been sent after 8 generations, including Deanna's? **111,111,111**

12-4 READING STRATEGIES

You can use a graphic organizer to organize what you know about geometric sequences.

Definition	**Finding the nth Term**
In a geometric sequence, successive terms have a common ratio.	To find the nth term of a geometric sequence, use the formula $a_n = a_1r^{n-1}$, where a_1 = the first term, r = the common ratio
Example	**Example**
The sequence 200, 100, 50, 25 is geometric because successive terms have a common ratio of $\frac{1}{2}$. $200 \bullet \frac{1}{2} = 100$, $100 \bullet \frac{1}{2} = 50$	Find a_6 for the geometric sequence 200, 100, 50, 25. $a_6 = a_1\left(\frac{1}{2}\right)^{6-1} = 200\left(\frac{1}{2}\right)^5 = 6.25$

Answer each question.

1. Describe how to find the common ratio of a geometric sequence.
   Possible answer: Find the ratio of each term to the previous term.
2. Find the common ratio of each sequence.
   a. 81, 27, 9, 3, ... **$\frac{1}{3}$**
   b. 5, 25, 125, 625, ... **5**
   c. 10,000, 1000, 100, 10, ... **$\frac{1}{10}$**
   d. $1, \frac{1}{4}, \frac{1}{16}, \frac{1}{64}, \ldots$ **$\frac{1}{4}$**
3. Explain the difference between a geometric sequence and an arithmetic sequence.
   Possible answer: The terms of geometric sequences have common ratios; the terms of arithmetic sequences have common differences.
4. Complete each sentence to describe the graph of each type of sequence.
   a. The graph of a geometric sequence is **Exponential**.
   b. The graph of an arithmetic sequence is **Linear**.
5. $18, 6, 2, \frac{2}{3}, \frac{2}{9}$
   a. Find the common ratio. **$\frac{1}{3}$**
   b. What is a_1? **$a_1 = 18$**
   c. Find the value for a_7. **$\frac{2}{81}$**

12-4 RETEACH

To determine whether a sequence is a **geometric sequence**, check for a **common ratio, r ($r \neq 1$).**

−2, 6, −18, 54, −162, ... — Find the ratios of pairs of terms to decide whether the sequence is geometric.

Ratios: $\frac{6}{-2} = -3$ $\frac{-18}{6} = -3$ $\frac{54}{-18} = -3$ $\frac{-162}{54} = -3$

The common ratio is −3. The sequence is geometric.

If you know the first term of a geometric sequence, a_1, and the common ratio, r, then you can find the nth term, a_n, using the following rule.

$a_n = a_1r^{n-1}$

Find the 10th term of the geometric sequence 3, 12, 48, 192, 768, ...

Step 1 Find the common ratio, r.
$r = \frac{12}{3} = 4$

Step 2 Identify the first term, a_1.
$a_1 = 3$

Step 3 Use the formula with $r = 3$ to find the10th term, a_{10}.

$a_n = a_1r^{n-1}$	*Write the rule.*
$a_{10} = a_1r^{10-1}$	*Substitute $n = 10$.*
$a_{10} = 3(4)^9$	*Substitute $a_1 = 3$ and $r = 4$.*
$a_{10} = 3(262,144) = 786,432$	*Simplify.*

The 10th term of the sequence is 786,432.

Determine whether each sequence could be geometric. If so, find the common ratio.

1. −6, 12, −24, 48, −96, ... **Yes; $r = -2$**
2. 3, 9, 27, 81, 243, ... **Yes; $r = 3$**
3. 10, 60, 110, 160, 210, ... **No**

Find the 8th term of each geometric sequence.

4. −7, 14, −28, 56, −112, ...
   r = **−2**
   a_1 = **−7**, n = **8**
   $a_8 = 896$
5. 8, 24, 72, 216, 648, ...
   r = **3**
   a_1 = **8**, n = **8**
   $a_8 = 17,496$

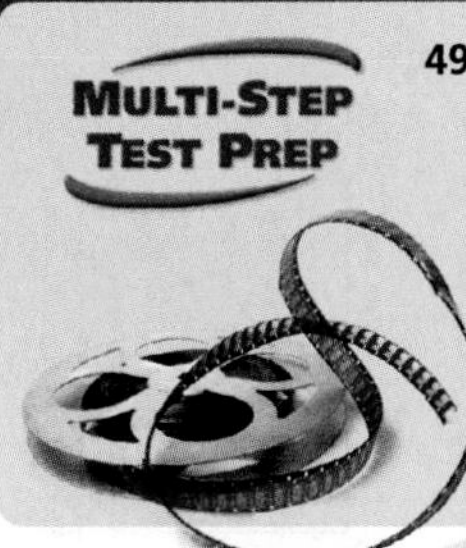

MULTI-STEP TEST PREP

49. This problem will prepare you for the Multi-Step Test Prep on page 908.

A movie earned \$60 million in its first week of release and \$9.6 million in the third week of release. The sales each week can be modeled by a geometric sequence.

a. Estimate the movie's sales in its second week of release. **\$24 million**

b. By what percent did the sales decrease each week? **60%**

c. In what week would you expect sales to be less than \$1 million? **week 6**

d. Estimate the movie's total sales during its 8-week release period. **about \$99.93 million**

50. Biology The population growth of bacteria in a petri dish each hour creates a geometric sequence. After 1 hour there were 4 bacteria cells, and after 5 hours there were 324 cells. How many cells were found at hours 2, 3, and 4? **12, 36, 108**

51. Critical Thinking Find an arithmetic sequence, a geometric sequence, and a sequence that is neither arithmetic nor geometric that begins 1, 4, ...

52. Finance Suppose that you pay \$750 in rent each month. Suppose also that your rent is increased by 10% each year thereafter.

a. Write a series that describes the total rent paid each year over the first 5 years, and find its sum.

b. Use sigma notation to represent the series for the total rent paid each year over the first 10 years, and evaluate it.

53. Music The frequencies produced by playing C notes in ascending octaves make up a geometric sequence. C0 is the lowest C note audible to the human ear.

a. The note commonly called middle C is C4. Find the frequency of middle C. **about 261.6 Hz**

b. Write a geometric sequence for the frequency of C notes in hertz where $n = 1$ represents C1. $a_n \approx 16.3(2)^n$

c. Humans cannot hear sounds with frequencies greater than 20,000 Hz. What is the first C note that humans cannot hear? **C11**

Scale of C's	
Note	Frequency (Hz)
C0	16.24
C1	32.7
C2	65.4
C3	130.8
C4	■

54. Medicine During a flu outbreak, a hospital recorded 16 cases the first week, 56 cases the second week, and 196 cases the third week.

a. Write a geometric sequence to model the flu outbreak. $a_n = 16(3.5)^{n-1}$

b. If the hospital did nothing to stop the outbreak, in which week would the total number infected exceed 10,000? **week 6**

55. Graphing Calculator Use the **SEQ** and **SUM** features to find each indicated sum of the geometric series $8 + 6 + 4.5 + \cdots$ to the nearest thousandth.

a. S_{10} **30.198** **b.** S_{20} **31.899** **c.** S_{30} **31.994** **d.** S_{40} **32.000**

e. Does the series appear to be approaching any particular value? Explain.

55e. Yes, the series appears to be approaching 32.

56. Critical Thinking If a geometric sequence has $r > 1$, what happens to the terms as n increases? What happens if $0 < r < 1$?

57. Write About It What happens to the terms of a geometric sequence when the first term is tripled? What happens to the sum of this geometric sequence?

TEST PREP

58. Find the sum of the first 6 terms for the geometric series $4.5 + 9 + 18 + 36 + \cdots$.

Ⓐ 67.5 Ⓑ 144 **Ⓒ 283.5** Ⓓ 445.5

MULTI-STEP TEST PREP Exercise 49 involves applying the model of a geometric sequence and finding a partial sum of a geometric series. This exercise prepares students for the Multi-Step Test Prep on page 908.

TEST PREP DOCTOR In **Exercise 58,** it may be helpful to write the 5th and 6th terms. Both **A** and **B** can be eliminated because the 6th term is 144 and the sum must be greater than this. Estimation shows that **C** is the correct choice.

For students who have difficulty with **Exercise 59,** remind them that the graph of a geometric sequence is similar in shape to the graph of an exponential function. Only choice **G** is close to this shape.

Answers

48a. Possible answer: The longer dimension becomes the shorter dimension in each subsequent paper size, and the shorter dimension is doubled to become the longer dimension.

b. Possible answer: Each paper size has twice as much area as the previous size. The areas form a geometric sequence with a common ratio of 2.

51. Possible answer: arithmetic: 1, 4, 7, 10, 13...; geometric: 1, 4, 16, 64, 256, ...; neither: 1, 4, 9, 16, 25, ...

52a. 9000 + 9900 + 10,890 + 11,979 + 13,176.90; \$54,945.90

b. $\sum_{k=1}^{10} 9000(1.1)^{k-1}$; \$143,436.82

56. Possible answer: For $r > 1$, the sequence increases or decreases without bound as n increases. For $0 < r < 1$, the sequence decreases toward a specific value as n increases.

57. Possible answer: Each term in the geometric sequence is tripled, and the sum of the series is also tripled.

12-4 PROBLEM SOLVING

Crystal works at a tree nursery during the summer. She wonders why the lower branches of one particular type of tree drop off. The nurseryman explains that each layer of branches absorbs about 10% of the sunlight and lets the rest through to the next layer. If a layer receives less than 25% of the sunlight, those branches will drop off.

1. Crystal counts 7 distinct healthy layers on one tree. She wants to know how many more layers the tree will grow before starting to lose layers of branches.

   a. Write the rule for the nth term, a_n, of a geometric sequence. $a_n = a_1(r^{n-1})$

   b. If a_n represents the percent of sunlight reaching layer n, what is the value of a_1? How do you know? $a_1 = 100$; because all the sunlight reaches layer 1

   c. What is the value of r? What does it represent? $r = 0.9$; r represents the fraction of sunlight that passes through a layer.

   d. Write the rule to find the percent of sunlight reaching layer 7. Solve for a_7. $a_7 = 100(0.9)^{(7-1)}$; 53%

   e. About how many layers of branches will this tree have before a bottom layer drops off? 15 layers

2. The nurseryman points to a denser type of tree and states that only about 75% of sunlight gets through to each lower layer, but that a layer of this type of tree needs only about 15% of the original sunlight to survive.

   a. What percent of sunlight gets through to layer 7 of this tree? 18%

   b. How many layers of branches could this type of tree support? 7 layers

Jackson usually runs 8 laps around the football field and consistently completes the first lap in 3 minutes. During one practice session, his coach notes that it takes him 15% longer to complete each lap than the previous lap. Choose the letter for the best answer.

3. How long does it take Jackson to complete the eighth lap?

   A 5.25 min
   B 6.03 min
   C 6.93 min
   Ⓓ 7.98 min

4. How long does it take Jackson to complete all 8 laps?

   F 9.18 min
   G 20.39 min
   Ⓗ 41.18 min
   J 61.18 min

12-4 CHALLENGE

Three numbers form a geometric sequence whose constant ratio is 3. If the first is decreased by 1, the second decreased by 3, and the third reduced to 2 less than half its value, the resulting three numbers form an arithmetic sequence. Determine the original three numbers.

Represent the 3 numbers that form a geometric sequence. $x \quad 3x \quad 9x$

Represent the 3 numbers that form an arithmetic sequence. $x - 1, 3x - 3, \frac{9}{2}x - 2$

Apply the constant-difference property of an arithmetic sequence. $(3x - 3) - (x - 1) = \left(\frac{9}{2}x - 2\right) - (3x - 3)$

Solve for x. $x = 6$

Evaluate x, $3x$, and $9x$ when $x = 6$ to obtain the original numbers; the original numbers are 6, 18, and 54.

1. Three numbers form a geometric sequence whose constant ratio is $\frac{1}{2}$. If the first is reduced to 10 more than $\frac{1}{4}$ its value, the second decreased by 10, and the third increased by 10 more than twice its value, the resulting three numbers form an arithmetic sequence. Determine the original three numbers. 160, 80, 40

2. Three numbers form an arithmetic sequence whose constant difference is 3. If the first number is increased by 1, the second increased by 6, and the third increased by 19, the resulting three numbers form a geometric sequence. Determine the original three numbers. 7, 10, 13

3. Insert two real numbers between 2 and 9 so that the first three terms form an arithmetic sequence and the last three terms form a geometric sequence. 2, 4, 6, 9 or 2, $\frac{1}{4}$, $-\frac{3}{2}$, 9

4. Determine the second term of an arithmetic sequence whose first term is 2 and whose first, third, and seventh terms form a geometric sequence. When $d = 0$, $a_2 = 2$. When $d = 1$, $a_2 = 3$.

5. Let a, b, and c represent real numbers that are not consecutive terms of an arithmetic sequence or of a geometric sequence. If $a < b < c$, determine a number that when added to a, b, and c yields consecutive terms of a geometric sequence.

$$x = \frac{ac - b^2}{2b - c - a}.$$

6. Show that if a and b are real numbers, the arithmetic mean of a^2 and b^2 and is greater than or equal to the absolute value of their geometric means. (Hint: $(a - b)^2 \geq 0$ and $(a + b)^2 \geq 0$) Possible answer: Arithmetic mean is $\frac{a^2 + b^2}{2}$. Geometric mean is ab or $-ab$. Show: $\frac{a^2 + b^2}{2} \geq ab$ and $\frac{a^2 + b^2}{2} \geq -ab$ Since all squares are nonnegative, $(a - b)^2 \geq 0$; so $a^2 - 2ab + b^2 \geq 0$ and $\frac{a^2 + b^2}{2} \geq ab$. Since all squares are nonnegative, $(a + b)^2 \geq 0$; so $a^2 + 2ab + b^2 \geq 0$ and $\frac{a^2 + b^2}{2} \geq -ab$.

59. Which graph might represent the terms of a geometric sequence?

Ⓕ 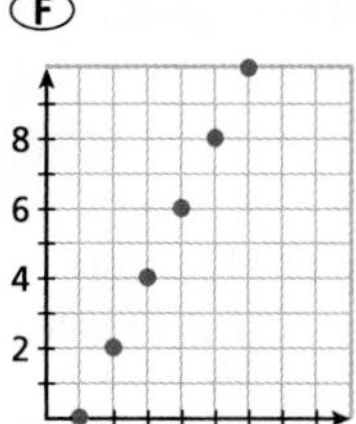

Ⓖ (circled)

Ⓗ 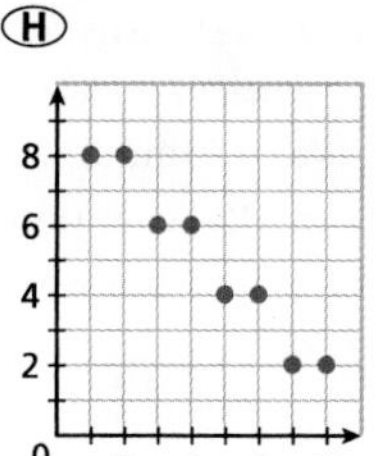

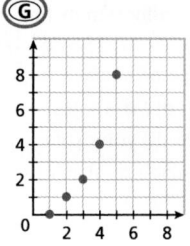

Ⓙ 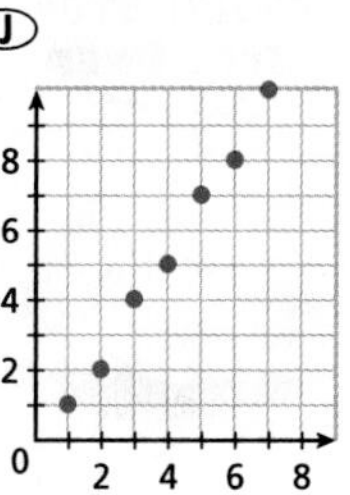

60. Find the first 3 terms of the geometric sequence with $a_7 = -192$ and $a_9 = -768$.

Ⓐ 3, −6, 12
Ⓑ −3, 12, −48
Ⓒ (circled) −3, 6, −12 or −3, −6, −12
Ⓓ 3, −12, 48 or −3, −12, −48

61. Which represents the sum of the series 10 − 15 + 22.5 − 33.75 + 50.625?

Ⓕ $\sum_{k=1}^{5} 10\left(\frac{3}{2}\right)^{k-1}$
Ⓗ $\sum_{k=1}^{5} -10\left(\frac{3}{2}\right)^{k-1}$
Ⓖ (circled) $\sum_{k=1}^{5} 10\left(-\frac{3}{2}\right)^{k-1}$
Ⓙ $\sum_{k=1}^{5} 10\left(-\frac{3}{2}\right)^{k}$

62. **Short Response** Why does the general rule for a geometric sequence use $n - 1$ instead of n? Explain.

CHALLENGE AND EXTEND

Graphing Calculator For each geometric sequence, find the first term with a value greater than 1,000,000.

63. $a_1 = 10$ and $r = 2$
64. $a_1 = \frac{1}{4}$ and $r = 4$
65. $a_1 = 0.01$ and $r = 3.2$

66. The sum of three consecutive terms of a geometric sequence is 73.5. If the product of these terms is 2744, what are the terms? **3.5, 14, 56, or 56, 14, 3.5**

67. Consider the geometric sequence whose first term is 55 with the common ratio $\frac{1+\sqrt{5}}{2}$.

a. Find the next 5 terms rounded to the nearest integer. **89, 144, 233, 377, 610**

b. Add each pair of successive terms together. What do you notice?

c. Make a conjecture about this sequence.

Beginning with 55, this sequence appears to round to the Fibonacci numbers.

67b. Their sum is the next term.

SPIRAL REVIEW

Identify the zeros and asymptotes of each function. *(Lesson 8-2)*

68. $f(x) = \frac{x^2 + 2x - 3}{x + 1}$
69. $f(x) = \frac{x + 5}{x^2 - x - 6}$
70. $f(x) = \frac{x^2 - 16}{4x}$

71. **Shopping** During a summer sale, a store gives a 20% discount on all merchandise. On Mondays, the store takes another 10% off of the sale price. *(Lesson 9-4)*

a. Write a composite function to represent the cost on Monday of an item with an original price of x dollars. $\mathbf{f(x) = 0.9(0.8x) = 0.72x}$

b. Find the cost on Monday of an item originally priced at $275. **$198**

Find the 10th term of each arithmetic sequence. *(Lesson 12-3)*

72. 78, 65, 52, 39, 26, ... **−39**
73. 1.7, 7.3, 12.9, 18.5, 24.1, ... **52.1**
74. 9.42, 9.23, 9.04, 8.85, 8.66, ... **7.71**
75. 16.4, 26.2, 36, 45.8, 55.6, ... **104.6**

Journal

Have students identify any confusion or difficulty they may have encountered in working with geometric sequences and series. Have students describe strategies for correcting or preventing them.

ALTERNATIVE ASSESSMENT

Have students write the first 5 terms of a geometric sequence, give its rule in both recursive and explicit form, find the 10th term, and find the sum of the first 8 terms.

Power Presentations with PowerPoint®

12-4 Lesson Quiz

1. Determine whether the sequence could be geometric or arithmetic. If possible, find the common ratio or difference. $\frac{1}{3}$, 2, 12, 72, ...
geometric; $r = 6$

2. Find the 8th term of the geometric sequence 1, −2, 4, −8, ... −128

3. Find the 9th term of the geometric sequence with $a_2 = 0.3$ and $a_6 = 0.00003$.
0.00000003

4. Find the geometric mean of $\frac{1}{2}$ and 18. 3

5. Find the indicated sum for the geometric series $\sum_{k=1}^{4} 3^{k-1}$.
40

6. A math tournament begins with 81 students. Students compete in groups of 3, with 1 person from each trio going on to the next round until there is 1 winner. How many matches must be played in order to complete the tournament? 40

Also available on transparency

Answers

62. Possible answer: The common ratio is not used to find the first term, so it is used only $n - 1$ times to find the nth term.

63. $a_{18} = 1{,}310{,}720$

64. $a_{12} = 1{,}048{,}576$

65. $a_{17} \approx 1{,}208{,}925.82$

68. zeros: 1 and −3; vertical asymptote: $x = -1$

69. zero: −5; vertical asymptotes: $x = -2$ and $x = 3$; horizontal asymptote: $y = 0$

70. zeros: 4 and −4; vertical asymptote: $x = 0$

Explore Infinite Geometric Series

You can explore infinite geometric series by using a sequence of squares.

Use with Lesson 12-5

Activity

1. On a piece of graph paper, draw a 16 × 16 unit square. Note that its perimeter is 64 units.
2. Starting at one corner of the original square, draw a new square with side lengths half as long, or in this case, 8 × 8 units. Note that its perimeter is 32 units.
3. Create a table as shown at right. Fill in the perimeters and the cumulative sum of the perimeters that you have found so far.

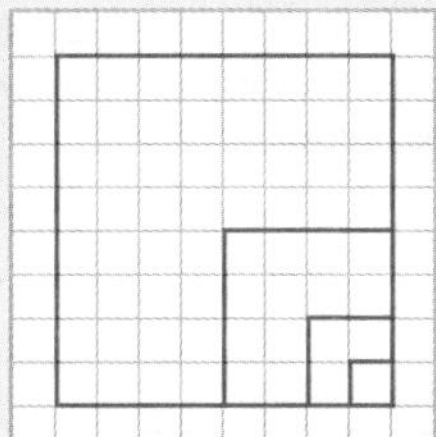

Square	Perimeter	Sum
16 × 16	64	64
8 × 8	32	96
4 × 4	16 ■	112 ■
2 × 2	8 ■	120 ■
1 × 1	4 ■	124 ■
$\frac{1}{2} \times \frac{1}{2}$	2 ■	126 ■

Try This

1. Copy the table, and complete the first 6 rows.
2. Use summation notation to write a geometric series for the perimeters. $\sum_{k=1}^{n} 64\left(\frac{1}{2}\right)^{k-1}$
3. Use a graphing calculator to find the sum of the first 20 terms of the series. **about 127.99988**
4. **Make a Conjecture** Make a conjecture about the sum of the perimeter series if it were to continue indefinitely. **Possible answer: The sum of the perimeters is 128.**
5. Evaluate $\frac{64}{1-\frac{1}{2}}$. How does this relate to your answer to Problem 4? **128; it is equal to the sum of the perimeters.**
6. Copy and complete the table by finding the area of each square and the cumulative sums.
7. Use summation notation to write a geometric series for the areas.
8. Use a graphing calculator to find the sum of the first 10 terms of the series. **about 341.333**
9. **Make a Conjecture** Make a conjecture about the sum of the area series if it were to continue indefinitely.
10. Evaluate $\frac{256}{1-\frac{1}{4}}$. How does this relate to your answer to Problem 9? **$341\frac{1}{3}$; it is equal to the sum of the areas.**
11. **Draw a Conclusion** Write a formula for the sum of an infinite geometric sequence. $S = \frac{a_1}{1-r}$

Square	Area	Sum
16 × 16	256 ■	256 ■
8 × 8	64 ■	320 ■
4 × 4	16 ■	336 ■
2 × 2	4 ■	340 ■
1 × 1	1 ■	341 ■
$\frac{1}{2} \times \frac{1}{2}$	$\frac{1}{4}$ ■	$341\frac{1}{4}$ ■

Answers to *Try This*

7. $\sum_{k=1}^{n} 256\left(\frac{1}{4}\right)^{k-1}$
9. Possible answer: The sum of the areas is $341\frac{1}{3}$.

Organizer

Use with Lesson 12-5

Pacing:
Traditional 1 day
Block $\frac{1}{2}$ day

Objective: Use a sequence of squares to explore infinite geometric series.

Materials: graph paper, graphing calculator

Online Edition

Resources

Algebra Lab Activities
12-5 Lab Recording Sheet

Teach

Discuss

Have students describe the pattern as the squares' sizes decrease.

Alternative Approach

Model the set with squares on a tiled floor or with square blocks.

Close

Key Concept

When $|r| < 1$, a formula can be used to find the sum of an infinite geometric sequence.

Assessment

Journal Have students explain why $|r| < 1$ must be true to find the sum of an infinite geometric sequence.

State Resources

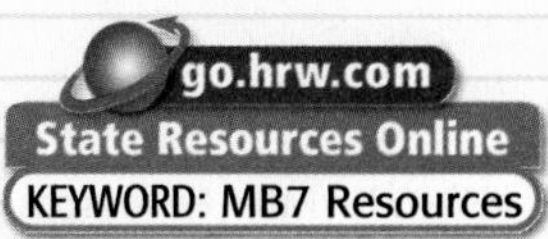

12-5 Organizer

Pacing: Traditional $1\frac{1}{2}$ days
Block $\frac{3}{4}$ day

Objectives: Find sums of infinite geometric series.

Use mathematical induction to prove statements.

Online Edition
Tutorial Videos, Interactivity, TechKeys

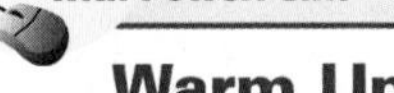

Warm Up

Evaluate.

1. $\dfrac{\frac{3}{5}}{6}$ $\frac{1}{10}$ **2.** $\dfrac{7}{1 - 0.3}$ 10

3. Write 0.6 as a fraction in simplest form. $\frac{3}{5}$

4. Find the indicated sum for the geometric series $\sum_{k=1}^{7} 3(-1)^{k-1}$. 3

Also available on transparency

Math Humor

Cat Theorem: A cat has nine tails.

Proof: No cat has eight tails. A cat has one tail more than no cat. Therefore, a cat has nine tails.

12-5 Mathematical Induction and Infinite Geometric Series

Objectives
Find sums of infinite geometric series.

Use mathematical induction to prove statements.

Vocabulary
infinite geometric series
converge
limit
diverge
mathematical induction

Why learn this?
You can use infinite geometric series to explore repeating patterns. (See Exercise 58.)

In Lesson 12-4, you found partial sums of geometric series. You can also find the sums of some infinite geometric series. An **infinite geometric series** has infinitely many terms. Consider the two infinite geometric series below.

$$S_n = \frac{1}{2} + \frac{1}{4} + \frac{1}{8} + \frac{1}{16} + \frac{1}{32} + \cdots$$

Partial Sums						
n	1	2	3	4	5	6
S_n	$\frac{1}{2}$	$\frac{3}{4}$	$\frac{7}{8}$	$\frac{15}{16}$	$\frac{31}{32}$	$\frac{63}{64}$

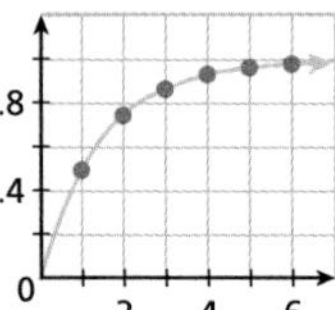

$$R_n = \frac{1}{32} + \frac{1}{16} + \frac{1}{8} + \frac{1}{4} + \frac{1}{2} + \cdots$$

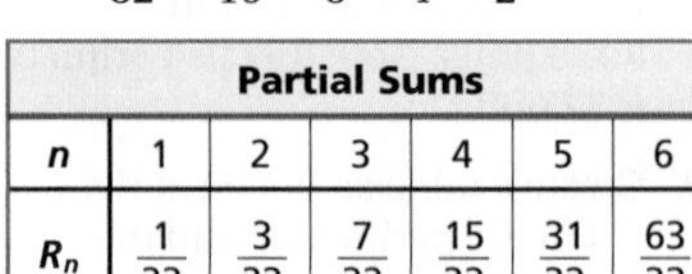

Partial Sums						
n	1	2	3	4	5	6
R_n	$\frac{1}{32}$	$\frac{3}{32}$	$\frac{7}{32}$	$\frac{15}{32}$	$\frac{31}{32}$	$\frac{63}{32}$

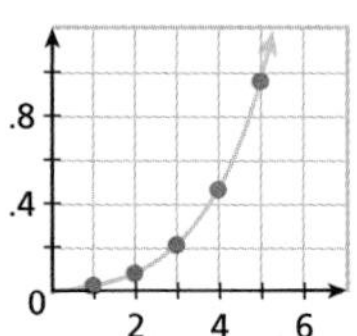

Notice that the series S_n has a common ratio of $\frac{1}{2}$ and the partial sums get closer and closer to 1 as n increases. When $|r| < 1$ and the partial sum approaches a fixed number, the series is said to **converge**. The number that the partial sums approach, as n increases, is called a **limit**.

For the series R_n, the opposite applies. Its common ratio is 2, and its partial sums increase toward infinity. When $|r| \geq 1$ and the partial sum does not approach a fixed number, the series is said to **diverge**.

EXAMPLE 1 Finding Convergent or Divergent Series

Determine whether each geometric series converges or diverges.

A $20 + 24 + 28.8 + 34.56 + \cdots$

$r = \frac{24}{20} = 1.2, |r| \geq 1$

The series diverges and does not have a sum.

B $1 + \frac{1}{3} + \frac{1}{9} + \frac{1}{27} + \frac{1}{81} + \cdots$

$r = \dfrac{\frac{1}{3}}{1} = \frac{1}{3}, |r| < 1$

The series converges and has a sum.

CHECK IT OUT! **Determine whether each geometric series converges or diverges.**

1a. $\frac{2}{3} + 1 + \frac{3}{2} + \frac{9}{4} + \frac{27}{8} + \cdots$ diverges

1b. $32 + 16 + 8 + 4 + 2 + \cdots$ converges

State Resources

State Resources Online
KEYWORD: MB7 Resources

1 Introduce

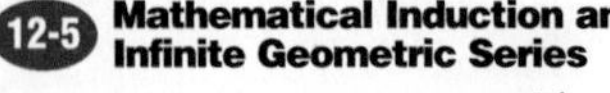

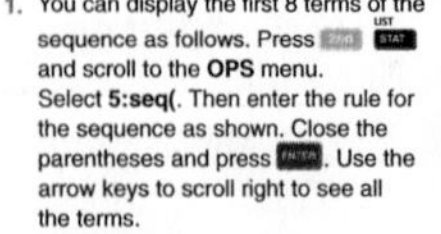

Use your calculator to explore the sequence $a_n = 0.9^{n-1}$.

1. You can display the first 8 terms of the sequence as follows. Press 2nd STAT and scroll to the **OPS** menu. Select **5:seq(**. Then enter the rule for the sequence as shown. Close the parentheses and press ENTER. Use the arrow keys to scroll right to see all the terms.

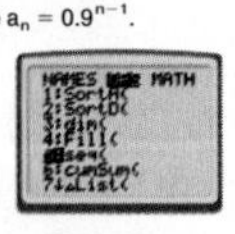

2. You can find the sum of the first 8 terms as follows. Press 2nd STAT and scroll to the **MATH** menu. Select **5:sum(**. Then enter the sequence as in Step 1, close the parentheses, and press ENTER.

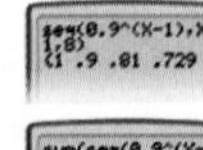

3. Use your calculator to find the sum of the first 20 terms of the sequence. Then find the sum of the first 50 terms, the first 100 terms, and the first 200 terms.

THINK AND DISCUSS

4. Describe what happens to the partial sums of the sequence as you add more and more terms.

Motivate

Set up a row of about 5 dominoes (or books set on edge), and discuss what must happen to make the last one fall if you knock over only the first one. Help students see that there are two conditions involved–the first domino must fall, and each domino must be placed so that when the one before it falls, it too will fall. Explain that this type of reasoning is used in proof by induction.

Explorations and answers are provided in the *Explorations* binder.

If an infinite series converges, we can find the sum. Consider the series $S_n = \frac{1}{2} + \frac{1}{4} + \frac{1}{8} + \frac{1}{16} + \frac{1}{32} + \cdots$ from the previous page. Use the formula for the partial sum of a geometric series with $a_1 = \frac{1}{2}$ and $r = \frac{1}{2}$.

$$S_n = a_1\left(\frac{1 - r^n}{1 - r}\right) = \frac{1}{2}\left(\frac{1 - \left(\frac{1}{2}\right)^n}{1 - \frac{1}{2}}\right) = \frac{1\left(1 - \left(\frac{1}{2}\right)^n\right)}{2\left(\frac{1}{2}\right)} = \frac{1 - \left(\frac{1}{2}\right)^n}{1} = 1 - \left(\frac{1}{2}\right)^n$$

Graph the simplified equation on a graphing calculator. Notice that the sum levels out and converges to 1.

As n approaches infinity, the term $\left(\frac{1}{2}\right)^n$ approaches zero. Therefore, the sum of the series is 1. This concept can be generalized for all convergent geometric series and proved by using calculus.

Sum of an Infinite Geometric Series

The sum of an infinite geometric series S with common ratio r and $|r| < 1$ is

$$S = \frac{a_1}{1 - r},$$

where a_1 is the first term.

EXAMPLE 2 Finding the Sums of Infinite Geometric Series

Find the sum of each infinite geometric series, if it exists.

A $5 + 4 + 3.2 + 2.56 + \cdots$

$r = 0.8$ *Converges: $|r| < 1$*

$S = \frac{a_1}{1 - r}$ *Sum formula*

$= \frac{5}{1 - 0.8} = \frac{5}{0.2} = 25$

Check Graph $y = 5\left(\frac{1 - (0.8)^x}{1 - 0.8}\right)$ on a graphing calculator. The graph approaches $y = 25$. ✔

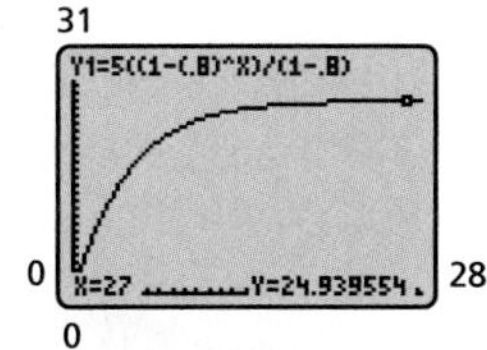

B $\sum_{k=1}^{\infty} \frac{2}{3^{k-1}}$

$\sum_{k=1}^{\infty} \frac{2}{3^{k-1}} = \frac{2}{1} + \frac{2}{3} + \frac{2}{9} + \cdots$ *Evaluate.*

$r = \frac{\frac{2}{3}}{2} = \frac{2}{6} = \frac{1}{3}$ *Converges: $|r| < 1$*

$S = \frac{a_1}{1 - r} = \frac{2}{1 - \frac{1}{3}} = \frac{2}{\frac{2}{3}} = \frac{6}{2} = 3$

Check Graph $y = 2\left(\frac{1 - \left(\frac{1}{3}\right)^x}{1 - \frac{1}{3}}\right)$ on a graphing calculator. The graph approaches $y = 3$. ✔

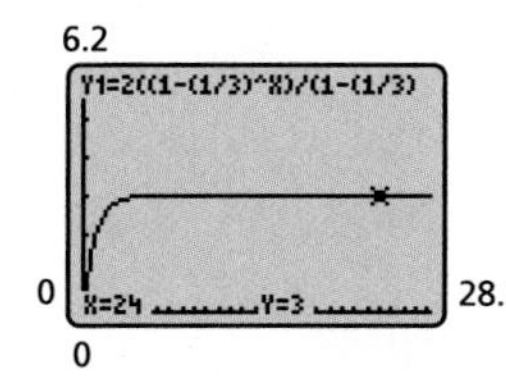

Helpful Hint

You can graph a geometric series by using the sum formula from Lesson 12-4: $S_n = a_1\left(\frac{1 - r^n}{1 - r}\right)$ with S_n as y and n as x and with values substituted for r and a_1.

CHECK IT OUT! **Find the sum of each infinite geometric series, if it exists.**

2a. $25 - 5 + 1 - \frac{1}{5} + \frac{1}{25} - \cdots$ **2b.** $\sum_{k=1}^{\infty} \left(\frac{2}{5}\right)^k$ $\frac{2}{3}$

2a. $\frac{125}{6}$

COMMON ERROR ALERT

Students may attempt to find the sum of an infinite series before knowing that the series converges. Remind students that only convergent geometric series have a finite sum.

Power Presentations with PowerPoint®

Additional Examples

Example 1

Determine whether each geometric series, converges or diverges.

A. $10 + 1 + 0.1 + 0.01 + \ldots$
converges

B. $4 + 12 + 36 + 108 + \ldots$
diverges

Example 2

Find the sum of each infinite geometric series, if it exists.

A. $1 - 0.2 + 0.04 - 0.008 + \ldots$
$0.8\overline{3}$

B. $\sum_{k=1}^{\infty} \left(\frac{1}{2}\right)^{k-1}$ 2

Also available on transparency

INTERVENTION
Questioning Strategies

EXAMPLE 1

- What do you look for in the graph of an infinite geometric series to help you determine whether it converges? Explain.

EXAMPLE 2

- How does a graph help you check the sum of an infinite geometric series?

2 Teach

Guided Instruction

Introduce the concepts of convergent and divergent series, and use several examples and graphs to reinforce the point. As students apply the sum formula, encourage them to check their answers by finding some partial sums. Explain that mathematical induction is an important method of proving that formulas work. Walk students through each step of the process because this will be new for most students.

Reaching All Learners

Through Multiple Representations

Have each student create or give each student an infinite geometric series that converges. Have them expand the series to 10 terms. Then have them create a table and a graph of the cumulative sums. Have them use their table and graph to estimate the sum of the series. Then have them use the formula to find the actual sum.

 **Technology** On a graphing calculator, the MATH, Frac command can be used to convert some decimals to fractions. To convert repeating decimals, students must enter at least 11 digits.

Power Presentations with PowerPoint®

Additional Examples

Example 3

Write $0.\overline{63}$ as a fraction in simplest form. $\frac{7}{11}$

Example 4

Use mathematical induction to prove that $1 + 4 + 7 + \cdots + (3n - 2) = \frac{n(3n-1)}{2}$.

1. $1 = \frac{1(3-1)}{2} = 1$.
2. $1 + 4 + \cdots + (3k - 2) = \frac{k(3k-1)}{2}$.
3. Add $3(k + 1) - 2$ to each side.

$$1 + \cdots + 3k - 2 + 3(k+1) - 2$$
$$= \frac{k(3k-1)}{2} + 3(k+1) - 2$$
$$= \frac{k(3k-1)}{2} + \frac{6(k+1)-4}{2}$$
$$= \frac{3k^2 - k + 6k + 2}{2}$$
$$= \frac{3k^2 + 5k + 2}{2}$$
$$= \frac{(k+1)(3k+2)}{2}$$
$$= \frac{(k+1)(3k+3-1)}{2}$$
$$= \frac{(k+1)[3(k+1)-1]}{2}.$$

Also available on transparency

You can use infinite series to write a repeating decimal as a fraction.

EXAMPLE 3 Writing Repeating Decimals as Fractions

Write 0.232323... as a fraction in simplest form.

Remember! Recall that every repeating decimal, such as 0.232323..., or $0.\overline{23}$, is a rational number and can be written as a fraction.

Step 1 Write the repeating decimal as an infinite geometric series.

$0.232323\ldots = 0.23 + 0.0023 + 0.000023 + \cdots$ *Use the pattern for the series.*

Step 2 Find the common ratio.

$$r = \frac{0.0023}{0.23}$$
$$= \frac{1}{100}, \text{ or } 0.01$$ *$|r| < 1$; the series converges to a sum.*

Step 3 Find the sum.

$$S = \frac{a_1}{1-r}$$ *Apply the sum formula.*
$$= \frac{0.23}{1-0.01} = \frac{0.23}{0.99} = \frac{23}{99}$$

Check Use a calculator to divide the fraction $\frac{23}{99}$. ✔

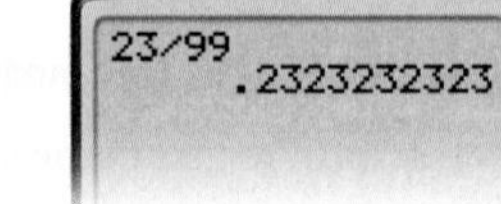

CHECK IT OUT! 3. Write 0.111... as a fraction in simplest form. $\frac{1}{9}$

You have used series to find the sums of many sets of numbers, such as the first 100 natural numbers. The formulas that you used for such sums can be proved by using a type of mathematical proof called **mathematical induction**.

Know it! Note

Proof by Mathematical Induction

To prove that a statement is true for all natural numbers n,

Step 1 The base case: Show that the statement is true for $n = 1$.

Step 2 Assume that the statement is true for a natural number k.

Step 3 Prove that the statement is true for the natural number $k + 1$.

EXAMPLE 4 Proving with Mathematical Induction

Use mathematical induction to prove that the sum of the first n natural numbers is $1 + 2 + 3 + \cdots + n = \frac{n(n+1)}{2}$.

Step 1 Base case: Show that the statement is true for $n = 1$.

$$1 = \frac{n(n+1)}{2} = \frac{1(1+1)}{2} = \frac{2}{2} = 1$$ *The base case is true.*

Step 2 Assume that the statement is true for a natural number k.

$$1 + 2 + 3 + \cdots + k = \frac{k(k+1)}{2}$$ *Replace n with k.*

INTERVENTION 

Questioning Strategies

EXAMPLE 3

- How can you estimate the repeating decimal for a fraction?

EXAMPLE 4

- If a statement is true for $n = 1$, $n = 2$, and $n = 3$, does that mean that it is true for every natural number n? Explain.

 **Math Background** There are other methods for finding a repeating decimal. For example, let $x = 0.\overline{23}$.

$$100x = 23.232323\ldots$$
$$-x = -0.232323\ldots$$
$$99x = 23$$
$$x = \frac{23}{99}$$

Step 3 Prove that it is true for the natural number $k+1$.

$$1+2+\cdots+k=\frac{k(k+1)}{2}$$

$$1+2+\cdots+k+(k+1)=\frac{k(k+1)}{2}+(k+1)$$ *Add the next term $(k+1)$ to each side.*

$$=\frac{k(k+1)}{2}+\frac{2(k+1)}{2}$$ *Find the common denominator.*

$$=\frac{k(k+1)+2(k+1)}{2}$$ *Add numerators.*

$$=\frac{(k+1)(k+2)}{2}$$ *Factor out $k+1$.*

$$=\frac{(k+1)[(k+1)+1]}{2}$$ *Write with $k+1$.*

Therefore, $1+2+3+\cdots+n=\frac{n(n+1)}{2}$.

4. Use mathematical induction to prove that the sum of the first n odd numbers is $1+3+5+\cdots+(2n-1)=n^2$.

Mathematical statements that seem to be true may in fact be false. By finding a counterexample, you can disprove a statement.

EXAMPLE 5 Using Counterexamples

Helpful Hint

Often counterexamples can be found using special numbers like 1, 0, negative numbers, or fractions.

Identify a counterexample to disprove $2^n \geq n^2$, where n is a real number.

$2^0 \geq (0)^2$	$2^1 \geq (1)^2$	$2^4 \geq (4)^2$	$2^{-1} \geq (-1)^2$
$1 \geq 0$ ✔	$2 \geq 1$ ✔	$24 \geq 16$ ✔	$\frac{1}{2} \geq 1$ ✘

$2^n \geq n^2$ is not true for $n=-1$, so it is not true for all real numbers.

5. Identify a counterexample to disprove $\frac{a^2}{2} \leq 2a+1$, where a is a real number.

when $a=5$: $\frac{5^2}{2} \overset{?}{\leq} 2(5)+1$

$12.5 \not\leq 11$

THINK AND DISCUSS

1. Explain how to determine whether a geometric series converges or diverges.

2. Explain how to represent the repeating decimal $0.8\overline{3}$ as an infinite geometric series.

3. GET ORGANIZED Copy and complete the graphic organizer. Summarize the different infinite geometric series.

	Example	Common Ratio	Sum
Convergent Series			
Divergent Series			

Power Presentations with PowerPoint®

Additional Examples

Example 5

Identify a counterexample to disprove $a^3 > a^2$, where a is a whole number. Possible answer: $a=0$ or $a=1$, so it is not true for all whole numbers

Also available on transparency

INTERVENTION

Questioning Strategies

EXAMPLE 5

- How many counterexamples does it take to disprove a statement? Explain.

Teaching Tip **Reading Math** Remind students that an ellipsis (...) at the end of a series indicates that it is an infinite series.

Answers to *Check It Out*

4. 1. $1=1^2$

2. $1+3+\ldots+(2k-1)=k^2$

3. $1+3+\ldots+(2k-1)+[2(k+1)-1]$
$=k^2+[2(k+1)-1]$
$=k^2+2k+1$
$=(k+1)^2$

3 Close

Summarize

Review infinite geometric series, stressing that only convergent series have a finite sum. Have students list the steps of a proof by mathematical induction.

ONGOING ASSESSMENT

and INTERVENTION

***Diagnose Before* the Lesson**
12-5 Warm Up, TE p. 900

***Monitor During* the Lesson**
Check It Out! Exercises, SE pp. 900–903
Questioning Strategies, TE pp. 901–903

***Assess After* the Lesson**
12-5 Lesson Quiz, TE p. 907
Alternative Assessment, TE p. 907

Answers to *Think and Discuss*

Possible answers:

1. Find the common ratio. If $|r|<1$, the series converges. If $|r| \geq 1$, the series diverges.
2. Write $0.8\overline{3}$ as 0.8 plus the infinite geometric series $0.03+0.003+\ldots$.
3. See p. A13.

12-5 Exercises

Assignment Guide

Assign *Guided Practice* exercises as necessary.

If you finished Examples **1–2**
Basic 15–20, 30–31
Average 15–20, 30–31, 46
Advanced 15–20, 30–31, 46

If you finished Examples **1–5**
Basic 15–33, 38–41, 45–47, 50–54, 61–65, 71–76
Average 15–38, 42–54, 59–65, 71–76
Advanced 16–38 even, 39–76

Homework Quick Check
Quickly check key concepts.
Exercises: 16, 18, 22, 24, 26, 38

Answers

11. 1. $2(1) = 1(1+1) = 2$
   2. $2 + 4 + \cdots + 2(k) = (k)(k+1)$
   3. $2 + 4 + \cdots + 2k + 2(k+1)$
   $= k(k+1) + 2(k+1)$
   $= k^2 + k + 2k + 2$
   $= k^2 + 3k + 2$
   $= (k+1)(k+2)$

State Resources

go.hrw.com
State Resources Online
KEYWORD: MB7 Resources

12-5 Exercises

go.hrw.com
Homework Help Online
KEYWORD: MB7 12-5
Parent Resources Online
KEYWORD: MB7 Parent

GUIDED PRACTICE

1. **Vocabulary** An infinite geometric series whose sum approaches a fixed number is said to ___?___. (*converge* or *diverge*) **converge**

SEE EXAMPLE 1 p. 900

Determine whether each geometric series converges or diverges.

2. $1 - \frac{1}{3} + \frac{1}{9} - \frac{1}{27} + \frac{1}{81} + \cdots$ **converges**
3. $1 - 5 + 25 - 125 + 625 + \cdots$ **diverges**
4. $27 + 18 + 12 + 8 + \cdots$ **converges**

SEE EXAMPLE 2 p. 901

Find the sum of each infinite geometric series, if it exists.

5. $\frac{3}{4} + \frac{1}{2} + \frac{1}{3} + \frac{2}{9} + \cdots$ $\mathbf{\frac{9}{4}}$
6. $\sum_{k=1}^{\infty} 4(0.25)^k$ $\mathbf{\frac{16}{3}}$
7. $800 + 200 + 50 + \cdots$ $\mathbf{1066\frac{2}{3}}$

SEE EXAMPLE 3 p. 902

Write each repeating decimal as a fraction in simplest form.

8. $0.888\ldots$ $\mathbf{\frac{8}{9}}$
9. $0.\overline{56}$ $\mathbf{\frac{56}{99}}$
10. $0.131313\ldots$ $\mathbf{\frac{13}{99}}$

SEE EXAMPLE 4 p. 902

11. Use mathematical induction to prove that the sum of the first n even numbers is $2 + 4 + 6 + \cdots + 2n = n(n+1)$.

SEE EXAMPLE 5 p. 903

Identify a counterexample to disprove each statement, where n is a real number.

12. $n^4 \ge 1$ $\mathbf{n = \frac{1}{2}}$
13. $\log n > 0$ $\mathbf{n = -1}$
14. $n^3 \le 3n^2$ $\mathbf{n = 5}$

PRACTICE AND PROBLEM SOLVING

Independent Practice	
For Exercises	See Example
15–17	1
18–20	2
21–23	3
24	4
25–27	5

Extra Practice
Skills Practice p. S27
Application Practice p. S43

Determine whether each geometric series converges or diverges.

15. $3 + \frac{3}{5} + \frac{3}{25} + \frac{3}{125} + \frac{3}{625} + \cdots$ **converges**
16. $5 + 10 + 20 + 40 + \cdots$ **diverges**
17. $2 - 4 + 8 - 16 + 32 + \cdots$ **diverges**

Find the sum of each infinite geometric series, if it exists.

18. $\sum_{k=1}^{\infty} 60\left(\frac{1}{10}\right)^k$ $\mathbf{\frac{20}{3}}$
19. $\frac{8}{5} - \frac{4}{5} + \frac{2}{5} - \frac{1}{5} + \cdots$ $\mathbf{\frac{16}{15}}$
20. $\sum_{k=1}^{\infty} 3.5^k$ **No sum exists.**

Write each repeating decimal as a fraction in simplest form.

21. $0.\overline{6}$ $\mathbf{\frac{2}{3}}$
22. $0.90909\ldots$ $\mathbf{\frac{10}{11}}$
23. $0.541541541\ldots$ $\mathbf{\frac{541}{999}}$

24. Use mathematical induction to prove
$$\frac{1}{1(2)} + \frac{1}{2(3)} + \frac{1}{3(4)} + \cdots + \frac{1}{n(n+1)} = \frac{n}{n+1}.$$

Identify a counterexample to disprove each statement, where a is a real number.

25–27. Possible answers are given.

25. $a^3 \ne -a^2$ $\mathbf{a = 0}$
26. $a^4 > 0$ $\mathbf{a = 0}$
27. $5a^2 > 2^a$ $\mathbf{a = 0}$

28. ***/// ERROR ANALYSIS ///*** Two possible sums for the series $\frac{1}{5} + \frac{2}{5} + \frac{4}{5} + \cdots$ are shown. Which is incorrect? Explain the error.

A
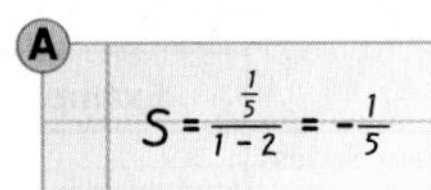

B
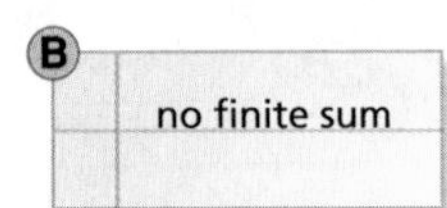

A, the sum formula was incorrectly applied to a divergent series.

12-5 PRACTICE A

Determine whether the geometric series converges or diverges.

1. $25 + 20 + 16 + 12.8 + \ldots$
   a. Find and simplify the common ratio. $\frac{4}{5}$
   b. Use the ratio to determine whether the series converges or diverges. **Converges**
2. $\frac{1}{16} + \frac{1}{8} + \frac{1}{4} + \frac{1}{2} + \cdots$ **Diverges**
3. $35.2 + 8.8 + 2.2 + 0.55 + \cdots$ **Converges**

Find the sum of each infinite geometric series, if it exists.

4. $864 + 576 + 384 + 256 + \cdots$
   a. Test the series for convergence. **Converges**
   b. Use the formula $S = \frac{a_1}{1-r}$ to find the sum. **2592**
5. $200 + 150 + 112.5 + 84.375 + \cdots$ **800**
6. $\frac{2}{5} - \frac{4}{25} + \frac{8}{125} - \frac{16}{625} + \cdots$ $\frac{2}{7}$
7. $\frac{2}{5} + \frac{4}{25} + \frac{8}{125} + \frac{16}{625} + \cdots$ $\frac{2}{3}$
8. $\frac{16}{625} - \frac{8}{125} + \frac{4}{25} - \frac{2}{5} + \cdots$ **Does not exist**

Write each repeating decimal as a fraction in simplest form.

9. $0.\overline{57}$
   a. Write the decimal as an infinite series. **0.57 + 0.0057 + 0.000057 + ...**
   b. Find the common ratio. **0.01**
   c. Use $S = \frac{a_1}{1-r}$ to write the fraction. $\frac{19}{33}$
10. $0.\overline{7}$ $\frac{7}{9}$
11. $0.8\overline{3}$ $\frac{5}{6}$
12. $0.\overline{23}$ $\frac{23}{99}$

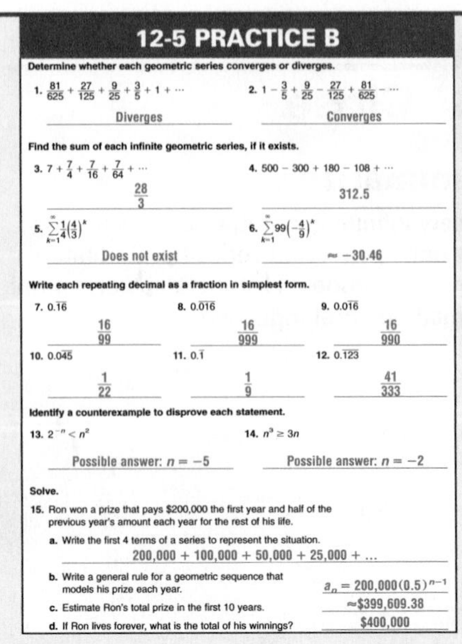

12-5 PRACTICE B

Determine whether each geometric series converges or diverges.

1. $\frac{81}{625} + \frac{27}{125} + \frac{9}{25} + \frac{3}{5} + 1 + \cdots$ **Diverges**
2. $1 - \frac{3}{5} + \frac{9}{25} - \frac{27}{125} + \frac{81}{625} - \cdots$ **Converges**

Find the sum of each infinite geometric series, if it exists.

3. $7 + \frac{7}{4} + \frac{7}{16} + \frac{7}{64} + \cdots$ $\frac{28}{3}$
4. $500 - 300 + 180 - 108 + \cdots$ **312.5**
5. $\sum_{k=1}^{\infty} \frac{1}{4}\left(\frac{4}{3}\right)^k$ **Does not exist**
6. $\sum_{k=1}^{\infty} 99\left(-\frac{4}{9}\right)^k$ **≈ −30.46**

Write each repeating decimal as a fraction in simplest form.

7. $0.\overline{16}$ $\frac{16}{99}$
8. $0.\overline{016}$ $\frac{16}{999}$
9. $0.0\overline{16}$ $\frac{16}{990}$
10. $0.0\overline{45}$ $\frac{1}{22}$
11. $0.\overline{1}$ $\frac{1}{9}$
12. $0.\overline{123}$ $\frac{41}{333}$

Identify a counterexample to disprove each statement.

13. $2^{-n} < n^2$ **Possible answer: $n = -5$**
14. $n^3 \ge 3n$ **Possible answer: $n = -2$**

Solve.

15. Ron won a prize that pays $200,000 the first year and half of the previous year's amount each year for the rest of his life.
   a. Write the first 4 terms of a series to represent the situation. **200,000 + 100,000 + 50,000 + 25,000 + ...**
   b. Write a general rule for a geometric sequence that models his prize each year. $a_n = 200{,}000(0.5)^{n-1}$
   c. Estimate Ron's total prize in the first 10 years. **≈$399,609.38**
   d. If Ron lives forever, what is the total of his winnings? **$400,000**

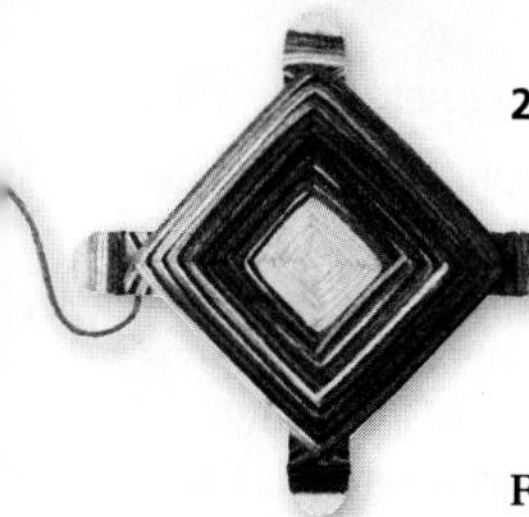

29. **Art** Ojos de Dios are Mexican holiday decorations. They are made of yarn, which is wrapped around sticks in a repeated square pattern. Suppose that the side length of the outer square is 8 inches. The side length of each inner square is 90% of the previous square's length. How much yarn will be required to complete the decoration? (Assume that the pattern is represented by an infinite geometric series.) **320 in., or $26\frac{2}{3}$ ft**

Find the sum of each infinite geometric series, if it exists.

30. $215 - 86 + 34.4 - 13.76 + \cdots$ **30.** $\frac{1075}{7} \approx 153.57$

31. $500 + 400 + 320 + \cdots$ **2500**

32. $8 - 10 + 12.5 - 15.625 + \cdots$ **No sum exists.**

33. $\sum_{k=1}^{\infty} -5\left(\frac{1}{8}\right)^{k-1}$ $-\frac{40}{7}$

34. $\sum_{k=1}^{\infty} 2\left(\frac{1}{4}\right)^{k-1}$ $\frac{8}{3}$

35. $\sum_{k=1}^{\infty} \left(\frac{5}{3}\right)^{k-1}$ **No sum exists.**

36. $-25 - 30 - 36 - 43.2 + \cdots$ **No sum exists.**

37. $\sum_{k=1}^{n} 200(0.6)^{k-1}$ **500**

38. **Geometry** A circle of radius r has smaller circles drawn inside it as shown. Each smaller circle has half the radius of the previous circle.

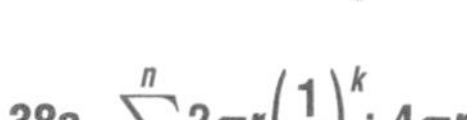

38a. $\sum_{k=1}^{n} 2\pi r\left(\frac{1}{2}\right)^k$; $4\pi r$

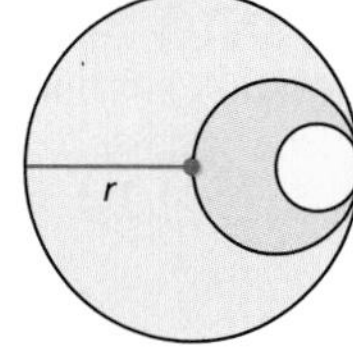

a. Write an infinite geometric series in terms of r that expresses the circumferences of the circles, and find its sum.

b. Find the sum of the circumferences for the infinite set of circles if the first circle has a radius of 3 cm. **$12\pi \approx 37.70$ cm**

Write each repeating decimal as a fraction in simplest form.

39. $0.\overline{4}$ $\frac{4}{9}$

40. $0.\overline{9}$ **1**

41. $0.\overline{123}$ $\frac{41}{333}$

42. $0.\overline{18}$ $\frac{2}{11}$

43. $0.\overline{5}$ $\frac{5}{9}$

44. $0.\overline{054}$ $\frac{2}{37}$

45. **Music** Due to increasing online downloads, CD sales have declined in recent years. Starting in 2001, the number of CDs shipped each year can be modeled by a geometric sequence.

a. Estimate the number of CDs that will be shipped in 2010. **about 415.0 million**

b. Estimate the total number of CDs shipped from 2001 through 2010. **about 6.2 billion**

c. Suppose that the geometric series continued indefinitely. Find the total number of CDs shipped from 2001. **about 11 billion**

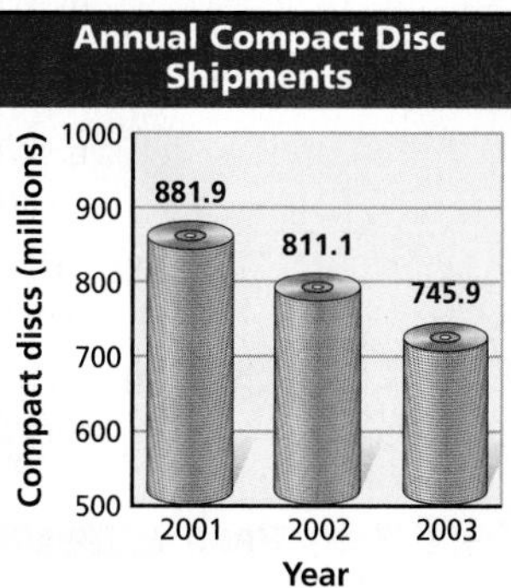

Use mathematical induction to prove each statement.

46. $1 + 2 + 4 + \cdots + 2^{n-1} = 2^n - 1$

47. $1 + 4 + \cdots + n^2 = \frac{n(n+1)(2n+1)}{6}$

48. $1(2) + 2(3) + 2(4) + \cdots + n(n+1) = \frac{n(n+1)(n+2)}{3}$

49. $\frac{1}{2} + \frac{1}{4} + \frac{1}{8} + \cdots + \left(\frac{1}{2}\right)^n = 1 - \left(\frac{1}{2}\right)^n$

COMMON ERROR ALERT

Some students might have difficulty finding counterexamples in **Exercises 25–27.** Remind them that a real number can be a negative number, a fraction, or an irrational number such as $\sqrt{2}$.

Geometry For **Exercise 38,** you may wish to remind students of the formula for the circumference of a circle: $C = \pi d$.

Answers

24. 1. $\frac{1}{1(1+1)} = \frac{1}{1+1} = \frac{1}{2}$

2. $\frac{1}{1(2)} + \cdots + \frac{1}{k(k+1)} = \frac{k}{k+1}$

3. $\frac{1}{1(2)} + \cdots + \frac{1}{k(k+1)} + \frac{1}{(k+1)(k+2)}$

$= \frac{k}{k+1} + \frac{1}{(k+1)(k+2)}$

$= \frac{k(k+2)}{(k+1)(k+2)} + \frac{1}{(k+1)(k+2)}$

$= \frac{k^2 + 2k + 1}{(k+1)(k+2)}$

$= \frac{\cancel{(k+1)}(k+1)}{\cancel{(k+1)}(k+2)}$

$= \frac{(k+1)}{(k+2)}$

46. 1. $2^{1-1} = 2^1 - 1 = 1$

2. $1 + \cdots + 2^{k-1} = 2^k - 1$

3. $1 + \cdots + 2^{k-1} + 2^{k+1-1}$

$= 2^k - 1 + 2^{k+1-1}$

$= 2^k - 1 + 2^k$

$= 2(2^k) - 1 = 2^{k+1} - 1$

47–49. See p. A47.

11-5 PRACTICE C

Find the sum of each infinite geometric series, if it exists.

1. $-10 + 0.4 - 0.016 + 0.00064 - \ldots$ $\frac{250}{26}$

2. $54 + 18 + 6 + 2 + \ldots$ 81

3. $\sum_{k=1}^{\infty} \frac{2}{3}\left(\frac{3}{2}\right)^k$ Does not exist

4. $\sum_{k=1}^{\infty} 100\left(-\frac{3}{4}\right)^k$ $-\frac{300}{7}$

Write each repeating decimal as a fraction in simplest form.

5. $0.\overline{72}$ $\frac{8}{11}$

6. $0.0\overline{72}$ $\frac{4}{55}$

7. $0.\overline{072}$ $\frac{8}{111}$

8. $3.6\overline{552}$ $\frac{6086}{1665}$

9. $1.4\overline{09}$ $\frac{31}{22}$

10. $0.\overline{714285}$ $\frac{5}{7}$

Use mathematical induction to prove.

11. $\sum_{k=1}^{n} \frac{2}{k(k+1)} = 1 + \frac{1}{3} + \ldots + \frac{2}{n(n+1)} = \frac{2n}{n+1}$

For $n = 1$: $\frac{2(1)}{(1)+1} = 1$ If the statement is true for $n = a$, then $\sum_{k=1}^{a} \frac{2}{k(k+1)} = \frac{2a}{a+1}$.

Let $n = a + 1$. $\sum_{k=1}^{a+1} \frac{2}{k(k+1)} = \frac{2a}{a+1} + \frac{2}{(a+1)(a+2)} = \frac{2a(a+2)+2}{(a+1)(a+2)} =$

$\frac{2(a+1)^2}{(a+1)(a+2)} = \frac{2(a+1)}{(a+1)+1}$; So $\sum_{k=1}^{n} \frac{2}{k(k+1)} = \frac{2n}{n+1}$.

Identify a counterexample to disprove each statement.

12. $(2n+1)^3 > n^2$ Possible answer: $n = -1$

13. $4n^2 \leq 2n^4$ Possible answer: $n = 1$

Solve.

14. A movie earned $60 million in the first week that it was released. In each successive week, sales declined by about 20%.

a. Write a general rule for a geometric sequence that models the movie's sales each week. $a_n = 60(0.8)^{n-1}$, where a_n represents millions of dollars

b. Estimate the movie's total sales in the first 8 weeks. ≈$249.67 million

c. If this pattern continued indefinitely, what would be the movie's total sales? $300 million

MULTI-STEP TEST PREP **Exercise 50** involves using a geometric sequence and sums for the corresponding series. This exercise prepares students for the Multi-Step Test Prep on page 908.

Teaching Tip **Geometry** For **Exercise 58,** you may wish to explain that *concentric* means having a common center.

ENGLISH LANGUAGE LEARNERS

TEST PREP DOCTOR In **Exercise 61,** if students have trouble identifying *r* from the formula, encourage them to find a few terms of each series. They should see that choices **A, C,** and **D** all have common ratios that are greater than 1.

In **Exercise 64,** the value of *y*, as *x* increases, continues to increase without limit in both **F** and **G,** so those choices could not represent a converging series. In **J,** the value of *y* decreases without limit, so the correct choice is **H.**

Answers

51. Possible answer: option B; option B gives the winner a total of \$2 million after 20 yr. Option A is an infinite geometric series with a sum of \$2 million, but in reality you would never collect the entire amount.

58d. perimeter: $\sum_{k=1}^{n} 4s\left(\frac{\sqrt{2}}{2}\right)^{k-1}$;

area: $\sum_{k=1}^{n} s^2\left(\frac{1}{2}\right)^{k-1}$

e. The sum of the areas decreases faster because it has a smaller common ratio (multiplier) than the perimeters, or $\frac{1}{2} < \frac{\sqrt{2}}{2}$.

59. For $a_1 > 0$, $S > S_n$, and both sums are positive. For $a_1 < 0$, $S_n > S$, and both sums are negative.

MULTI-STEP TEST PREP

50. This problem will prepare you for the Multi-Step Test Prep on page 908.

A movie earned \$80 million in the first week that it was released. In each successive week, sales declined by about 40%.

a. Write a general rule for a geometric sequence that models the movie's sales each week. $a_n = 80(0.6)^{n-1}$, where a_n represents millions of dollars

b. Estimate the movie's total sales in the first 6 weeks. about \$190.67 million

c. If this pattern continued indefinitely, what would the movie's total sales be? \$200 million

51. **Game Shows** Imagine that you have just won the grand prize on a game show. You can choose between two payment options as shown. Which would you choose, and why?

PRIZE PAYMENT OPTIONS

A.	B.
\$1 million the first year and half of the previous year's amount for eternity	\$100,000 a year for 20 years

52–57. Possible answers given.

Identify a counterexample to disprove each statement, where *x* is a real number.

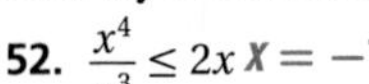

52. $\frac{x^4}{x^3} \le 2x$ $x = -1$

53. $x^4 - 1 \ge 0$ $x = \frac{1}{2}$

54. $\ln x^5 > \ln x$ $x = 0$

55. $2x^2 \le 3x^3$ $x = -2$

56. $2x^2 - x \ge 0$ $x = \frac{1}{4}$

57. $12x - x^2 > 25$ $x = 0$

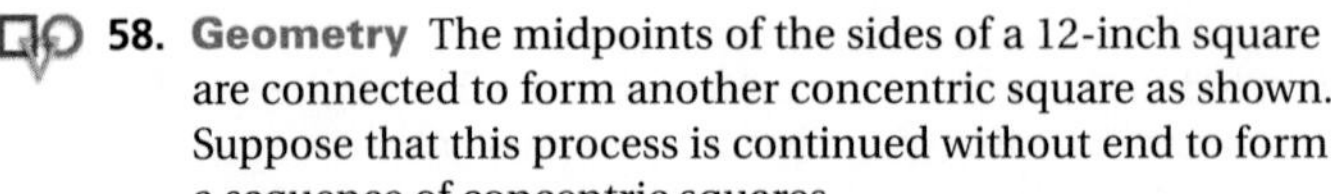

58. **Geometry** The midpoints of the sides of a 12-inch square are connected to form another concentric square as shown. Suppose that this process is continued without end to form a sequence of concentric squares.

a. Find the perimeter of the 2nd square. $24\sqrt{2} \approx 33.94$ in.

b. Find the sum of the perimeters of the squares. $96 + 48\sqrt{2} \approx 163.88$ in.

c. Find the sum of the areas of the squares. 288 in^2

d. Write the sum of the perimeters in summation notation for the general case of a square with side length *s*. Then write the sum of the areas for the general case.

e. Which series decreases faster, the sum of the perimeters or the sum of the areas? How do you know?

59. **Critical Thinking** Compare the partial-sum S_n with the sum S for an infinite geometric series when $a_1 > 0$ and $r = \frac{4}{5}$. Which is greater? What if $a_1 < 0$?

60. **Write About It** Why might the notation for a partial sum S_n change for the sum S for an infinite geometric series? The subscript *n* refers to a finite number of terms, but an infinite geometric series has an infinite number of terms.

TEST PREP

61. Which infinite geometric series converges?

Ⓐ $\sum_{k=1}^{\infty}\left(\frac{5}{4}\right)^k$ Ⓑ $\sum_{k=1}^{\infty}5\left(\frac{1}{4}\right)^k$ Ⓒ $\sum_{k=1}^{\infty}\frac{1}{4}(5)^k$ Ⓓ $\sum_{k=1}^{\infty}\left(\frac{1}{4}\right)^k 5^k$

62. What is the sum of the infinite geometric series $1 - \frac{1}{2} + \frac{1}{4} - \frac{1}{8} + \frac{1}{16} + \cdots$?

Ⓕ 2 Ⓖ $\frac{2}{3}$ Ⓗ $\frac{1}{2}$ Ⓙ $\frac{1}{3}$

63. An infinite geometric series has a sum of 180 and a common ratio of $\frac{2}{3}$. What is the first term of the series?

Ⓐ 60 Ⓑ 120 Ⓒ 270 Ⓓ 540

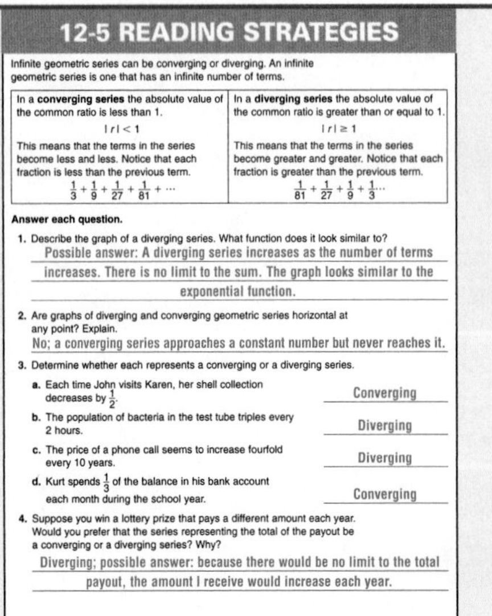

12-5 READING STRATEGIES

Infinite geometric series can be converging or diverging. An infinite geometric series is one that has an infinite number of terms.

In a **converging series** the absolute value of the common ratio is less than 1.	In a **diverging series** the absolute value of the common ratio is greater than or equal to 1.
$\|r\| < 1$	$\|r\| \ge 1$
This means that the terms in the series become less and less. Notice that each fraction is less than the previous term.	This means that the terms in the series become greater and greater. Notice that each fraction is greater than the previous term.
$\frac{1}{3} + \frac{1}{9} + \frac{1}{27} + \frac{1}{81} + \cdots$	$\frac{1}{81} + \frac{1}{27} + \frac{1}{9} + \frac{1}{3} \cdots$

Answer each question.

1. Describe the graph of a diverging series. What function does it look similar to?
Possible answer: A diverging series increases as the number of terms increases. There is no limit to the sum. The graph looks similar to the exponential function.

2. Are graphs of diverging and converging geometric series horizontal at any point? Explain.
No; a converging series approaches a constant number but never reaches it.

3. Determine whether each represents a converging or a diverging series.

a. Each time John visits Karen, her shell collection decreases by $\frac{1}{2}$. Converging

b. The population of bacteria in the test tube triples every 2 hours. Diverging

c. The price of a phone call seems to increase fourfold every 10 years. Diverging

d. Kurt spends $\frac{1}{3}$ of the balance in his bank account each month during the school year. Converging

4. Suppose you win a lottery prize that pays a different amount each year. Would you prefer that the series representing the total of the payout be a converging or a diverging series? Why?
Diverging; possible answer: because there would be no limit to the total payout, the amount I receive would increase each year.

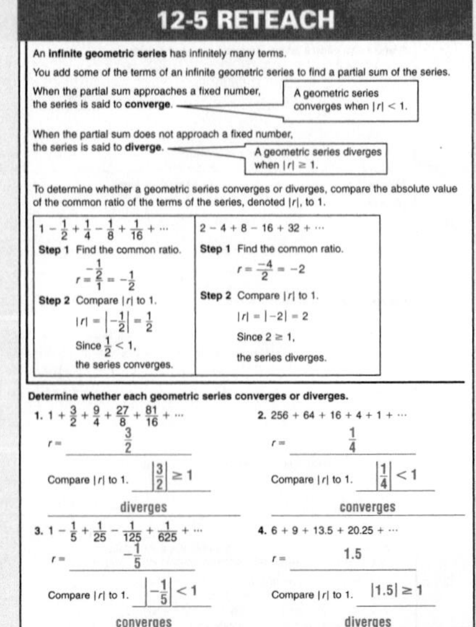

12-5 RETEACH

An **infinite geometric series** has infinitely many terms.

You add some of the terms of an infinite geometric series to find a partial sum of the series.

When the partial sum approaches a fixed number, the series is said to **converge**. — A geometric series converges when $|r| < 1$.

When the partial sum does not approach a fixed number, the series is said to **diverge**. — A geometric series diverges when $|r| \ge 1$.

To determine whether a geometric series converges or diverges, compare the absolute value of the common ratio of the terms of the series, denoted $|r|$, to 1.

$1 - \frac{1}{2} + \frac{1}{4} - \frac{1}{8} + \frac{1}{16} + \cdots$	$2 - 4 + 8 - 16 + 32 + \cdots$
Step 1 Find the common ratio. $r = \frac{-\frac{1}{2}}{1} = -\frac{1}{2}$	**Step 1** Find the common ratio. $r = \frac{-4}{2} = -2$
Step 2 Compare $\|r\|$ to 1. $\|r\| = \left\|-\frac{1}{2}\right\| = \frac{1}{2}$ Since $\frac{1}{2} < 1$, the series converges.	**Step 2** Compare $\|r\|$ to 1. $\|r\| = \|-2\| = 2$ Since $2 \ge 1$, the series diverges.

Determine whether each geometric series converges or diverges.

1. $1 + \frac{3}{2} + \frac{9}{4} + \frac{27}{8} + \frac{81}{16} + \cdots$
$r =$ $\frac{3}{2}$
Compare $|r|$ to 1. $\left|\frac{3}{2}\right| \ge 1$
diverges

2. $256 + 64 + 16 + 4 + 1 + \cdots$
$r =$ $\frac{1}{4}$
Compare $|r|$ to 1. $\left|\frac{1}{4}\right| < 1$
converges

3. $1 - \frac{1}{5} + \frac{1}{25} - \frac{1}{125} + \frac{1}{625} + \cdots$
$r =$ $-\frac{1}{5}$
Compare $|r|$ to 1. $\left|-\frac{1}{5}\right| < 1$
converges

4. $6 + 9 + 13.5 + 20.25 + \cdots$
$r =$ 1.5
Compare $|r|$ to 1. $|1.5| \ge 1$
diverges

64. Which graph represents a converging infinite geometric series?

F
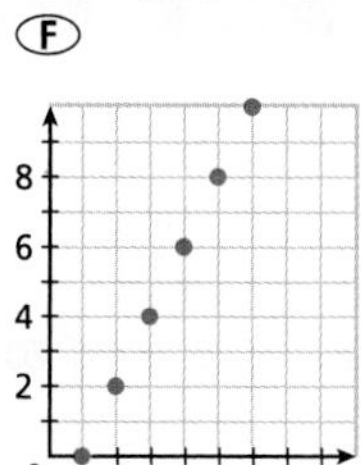

G
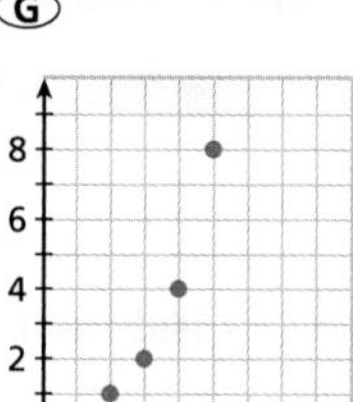

(H)
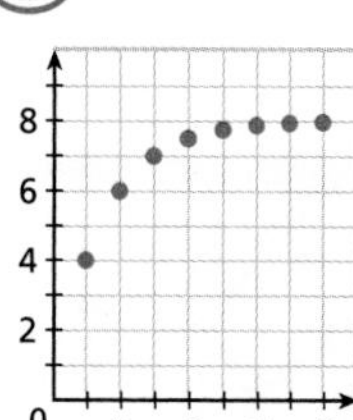

J
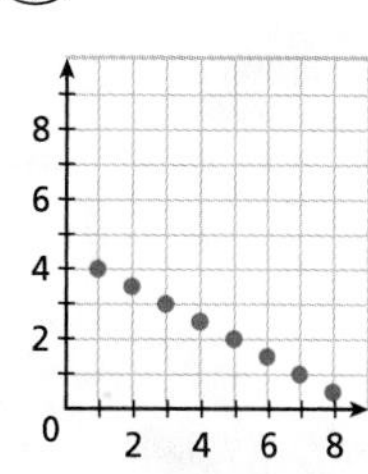

65. **Extended Response** Use mathematical induction to prove $3 + 5 + \cdots + (2n + 1) = n(n + 2)$. Show all of your work.

CHALLENGE AND EXTEND

Write each repeating decimal as a fraction in simplest form.

66. $0.1\overline{6}$ $\frac{1}{6}$ 67. $0.41\overline{6}$ $\frac{5}{12}$ 68. $0.5\overline{286}$ $\frac{2617}{4950}$

69. **Critical Thinking** Can an infinite arithmetic series approach a limit like an infinite geometric series? Explain why or why not.

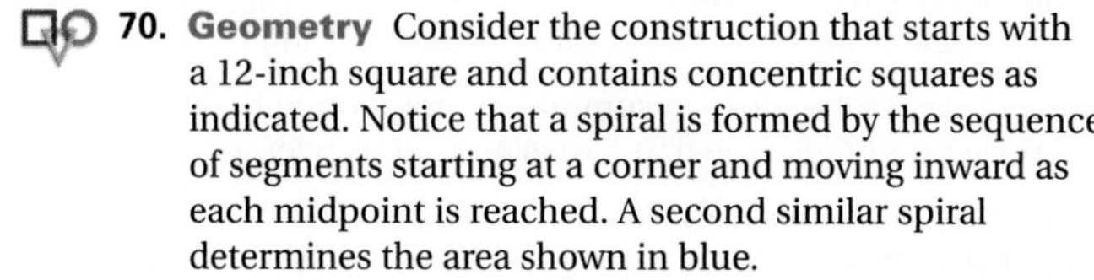

70. **Geometry** Consider the construction that starts with a 12-inch square and contains concentric squares as indicated. Notice that a spiral is formed by the sequence of segments starting at a corner and moving inward as each midpoint is reached. A second similar spiral determines the area shown in blue.

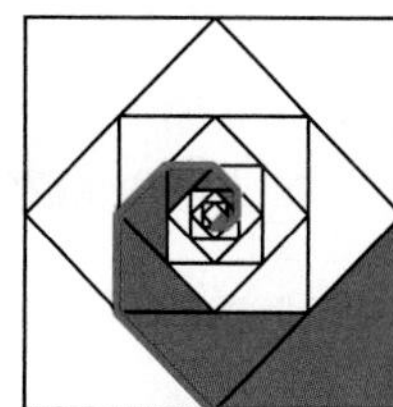

a. Use the sum of a series to find the length of the spiral indicated in red. $12 + 6\sqrt{2} \approx 20.485$ in.

b. Use the sum of a series to find the polygonal area indicated in blue. 36 in^2

c. Is your answer to the sum of the polygonal area in part **b** reasonable? Explain.
Yes; the area of the spiral is $\frac{1}{4}$ the area of the largest square.

SPIRAL REVIEW

71. **Football** A kickoff specialist kicks 80% of his kickoffs into the end zone. What is the probability that he kicks at least 4 out of 5 of his next kickoffs into the end zone? *(Lesson 11-6)* 73.728%

72. **Geometry** Consider the pattern of figures shown. *(Lesson 12-3)*

a. Find the number of dots in each of the next 3 figures in the pattern. 9, 11, 13

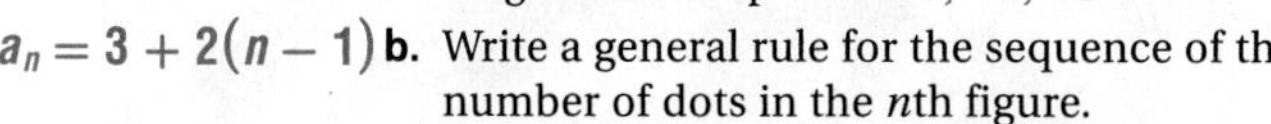

$a_n = 3 + 2(n - 1)$ b. Write a general rule for the sequence of the number of dots in the nth figure.

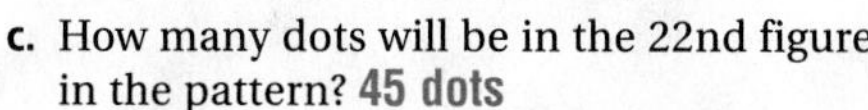

c. How many dots will be in the 22nd figure in the pattern? 45 dots

Determine whether each sequence could be geometric or arithmetic. If possible, find the common ratio or difference. *(Lesson 12-4)*

73. 297, 99, 33, 11, ... geometric; $r = \frac{1}{3}$

74. $\frac{4}{3}, \frac{8}{3}, 4, \frac{16}{3}, \ldots$ arithmetic; $d = \frac{4}{3}$

75. 25, 100, 250, 1000, ...
neither

76. 4, 4.8, 5.76, 6.912, ...
geometric; $r = \frac{6}{5}$

Answers

65. 1. $2(1) + 1 = 1(1 + 2) = 3$
2. $3 + \cdots + (2k + 1) = k(k + 2)$
3. $3 + \cdots + (2k + 1) + [2(k + 1) + 1]$
$= k(k + 2) + [2(k + 1) + 1]$
$= k^2 + 2k + (2k + 2 + 1)$
$= k^2 + 4k + 3$
$= (k + 1)(k + 3)$
$= (k + 1)(k + 1 + 2)$

69. No; the partial sums will approach infinity if $d > 0$ and negative infinity if $d < 0$.

Journal

Ask students to describe the process of proving a statement by mathematical induction.

ALTERNATIVE ASSESSMENT

Have students create a convergent geometric series and find its sum. Have them also write a divergent geometric series. Ask them to describe how a proof by induction is similar to a row of dominoes that falls if you knock down the first one.

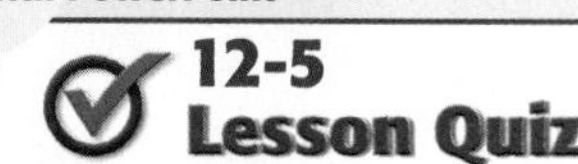

12-5 Lesson Quiz

Solve each equation.

1. Determine whether the geometric series $150 + 30 + 6 + \ldots$ converges or diverges, and find the sum if it exists. converges; 187.5

2. Write $0.\overline{0044}$ as a fraction in simplest form. $\frac{4}{909}$

3. Either prove by induction or provide a counterexample to disprove the following statement: $1 + 2 + 3 + 4 + \ldots + n = \frac{n^2 + 1}{2}$.
counterexample: $n = 2$

Also available on transparency

12-5 PROBLEM SOLVING

Diego drops a ball from different heights. He determines that after each bounce the ball rises to 80% of its previous height. He wants to find out how the total vertical distance that the ball falls before it comes to rest varies with the height from which it is dropped.

1. Diego drops the ball from a height of 8 feet and calculates the total vertical distance that the ball falls.

a. Find the total vertical distance that the ball has fallen by the third bounce, $a_1 + a_2 + a_3$.
19.52 ft

b. Is this a converging or diverging series? How do you know?
Converging because $|r| < 1$

c. Write a rule and solve for the total vertical distance that the ball falls. $S = \frac{a_1}{1 - r}$; 40 ft

2. Next Diego drops the ball from a height of 6 feet. What is the total vertical distance that the ball falls from this initial height? 30 ft

3. Complete the table.

Drop Height (ft)	Total Vertical Distance (ft)
12	60
8	40
6	30
3	15
1	5

4. Write an equation to show the relationship between the drop height and the total vertical distance that the ball travels.
Let x = drop height and y = total vertical distance; $y = 5x$

Kali notices that each year after the first year, a particular plant in her backyard adds only about 25% of the previous year's new growth to its height. The first year's growth from a seed was 3 feet. Choose the letter for the best answer.

5. Which statement describes the plant's ultimate height?
(A) Its height will converge to 4 ft.
B Its height will converge to 4.5 ft.
C Its height will converge to 12 ft.
D Its height will not converge.

6. In which year will new growth be less than 0.1 ft?
F First year
G Second year
H Third year
(J) Fourth year

12-5 CHALLENGE

Some series are neither arithmetic nor geometric. Study this series.

$$S = \frac{1}{1\cdot2} + \frac{1}{2\cdot3} + \frac{1}{3\cdot4} + \frac{1}{4\cdot5} + \frac{1}{5\cdot6} + \cdots + \frac{1}{99\cdot100} + \cdots$$

To find this sum of this series, first find a formula for the sum of the first n terms of the series. Then prove the formula always works by using mathematical induction.

1. Find the first partial sum, S_1. The first partial sum is the sum of the first fraction. $S_1 = \frac{1}{1\cdot2} = \frac{1}{2}$

2. Find the second partial sum, S_2. This is the sum of the first two fractions. $S_2 = \frac{1}{1\cdot2} + \frac{1}{2\cdot3} = \frac{1}{2} + \frac{1}{6} = \frac{2}{3}$

3. Find the third partial sum, S_3. This is the sum of the first three fractions. $S_3 = \frac{1}{2} + \frac{1}{6} + \frac{1}{12} = \frac{3}{4}$

4. Find the fourth partial sum, S_4. This is the sum of the first four fractions. $S_4 = \frac{1}{2} + \frac{1}{6} + \frac{1}{12} + \frac{1}{20} = \frac{4}{5}$

5. From the first four partial sums, make a conjecture about the fifth partial sum, S_5. Check your conjecture to make sure it is correct.
$S_5 = \frac{1}{2} + \frac{1}{6} + \frac{1}{12} + \frac{1}{20} + \frac{1}{30} = \frac{5}{6}$

6. What is a reasonable conjecture of the value of S_{99}?
$S_{99} = \frac{1}{1\cdot2} + \frac{1}{2\cdot3} + \frac{1}{3\cdot4} + \frac{1}{4\cdot5} + \frac{1}{5\cdot6} + \cdots + \frac{1}{98\cdot99} + \frac{1}{99\cdot100}$
$S_{99} = \frac{99}{100}$

7. Make a conjecture and write a formula for S_n.
$S_n = \frac{n}{n+1}$

8. Prove your conjecture using mathematical induction.
Step 1: $S_1 = \frac{1}{1\cdot2} = \frac{n}{n+1} = \frac{1}{2}$ Step 2: Assume $S_k = \frac{k}{k+1}$
Step 3: $S_{k+1} = S_k + \frac{1}{(k+1)(k+2)} = \frac{k(k+2)+1}{(k+1)(k+2)} =$
$\frac{(k+1)(k+1)}{(k+1)(k+2)} = \frac{k+1}{(k+1)+1}$ Since $S_k = \frac{k}{k+1}$ true implies
$S_{k+1} = \frac{k+1}{(k+1)+1}$, $S_n = \frac{n}{n+1}$

9. Predict the sum of this infinite series
$S = \frac{1}{1\cdot2} + \frac{1}{2\cdot3} + \frac{1}{3\cdot4} + \frac{1}{4\cdot5} + \frac{1}{5\cdot6} + \cdots$
$S = 1$

Organizer

Objective: Assess students' ability to apply concepts and skills in Lessons 12-4 through 12-5 in a real-world format.

Online Edition

Resources

Algebra II Assessments

www.mathtekstoolkit.org

Problem	Text Reference
1–4	Lesson 12-4
5	Lesson 12-5
6	Lessons 12-4, 12-5

Answers

1. *Spider-Man*: ≈ 0.62, ≈ 0.63; *Spider-Man 2*: ≈ 0.39, ≈ 0.55
2. $a_n = 114.9(0.625)^{n-1}$, where a_n represents sales in millions of dollars
6. Possible answer: No; the ratios for *Spider-Man 2* are not close to being constant, so it is very hard to develop an accurate geometric sequence.

State Resources

go.hrw.com
State Resources Online
KEYWORD: MB7 Resources

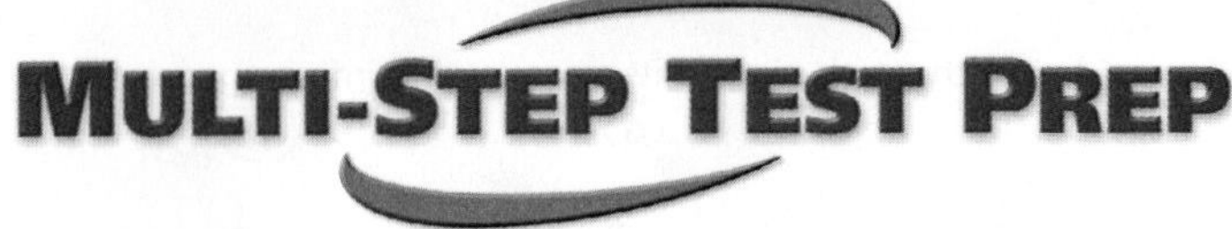

CHAPTER 12 MULTI-STEP TEST PREP

SECTION 12B

Exploring Geometric Sequences and Series

Sticky Business Big-budget movies often have their greatest sales in the first weekend, and then weekend sales decrease with each passing week. After a movie has been released for a few weeks, movie studios may try to predict the total sales that the movie will generate.

Weekend Box Office Sales (million $)		
Weekend	***Spider-Man***	***Spider-Man 2***
1	114.9	115.8
2	71.4	45.2
3	45.0	24.8

1. Find the ratios of the sequences of weekend sales for *Spider-Man* and *Spider-Man 2.*
2. Write the rule for a geometric sequence that could be used to estimate the sales for *Spider-Man* in a given weekend.
3. Use the sequence from Problem 2 to predict *Spider-Man's* weekend sales for weeks 4 and 5. **about \$28.1 million and \$17.5 million**
4. Write and evaluate a series in summation notation to find *Spider-Man's* total weekend sales for the first 5 weekends of its release. $\sum_{k=1}^{5} 114.9(0.625)^{k-1}$; **about \$277.2 million**
5. Suppose that the series from Problem 4 continued infinitely. Estimate the total weekend sales for *Spider-Man*. The actual total weekend sales for *Spider-Man* were about \$311.1 million. How does this compare with your estimate? **About \$306.4 million; the estimate is very close.**
6. Would a geometric sequence be a good model for the weekend sales of *Spider-Man 2*? Justify your answer.

INTERVENTION

Scaffolding Questions

1. How do you find common ratios? Divide each term by the previous term.
2. What must you know to write the rule for a geometric sequence? the first term and the common ratio
3. How can you find the 4th and 5th terms? Evaluate the series for $n = 4$ and $n = 5$.
4. What is the formula for the partial sum of a geometric series? $S_n = a_1\left(\frac{1-r^n}{1-r}\right)$
5. What is the formula for the sum of an infinite geometric series? $S_n = \frac{a_1}{1-r}$
6. What identifies a geometric sequence? common ratio

Extension

Have students find the box office data for a recent hit movie and determine whether a geometric sequence would be a good model for its weekend sales. Check students' work.

CHAPTER 12

SECTION 12B

Quiz for Lessons 12-4 Through 12-5

12-4 Geometric Sequences and Series

Find the 8th term of each geometric sequence.

1. $\frac{2}{5}, \frac{6}{5}, \frac{18}{5}, \frac{54}{5}, \ldots$ $\frac{4374}{5}$
2. $-16, -40, -100, -250, \ldots$ -9765.625
3. $-1, 11, -121, 1331, \ldots$ $19{,}487{,}171$
4. $2, 20, 200, 2000, \ldots$ $20{,}000{,}000$

Find the 10th term of each geometric sequence with the given terms.

5. $a_1 = 3.3$ and $a_2 = 33$
6. $a_4 = -1$ and $a_6 = -4$ -64
7. $a_6 = 20.25$ and $a_8 = 9$ 4
8. $a_3 = 57$ and $a_5 = 513$ $\pm 124{,}659$

5. $3{,}300{,}000{,}000$

Find the geometric mean of each pair of numbers.

9. $\frac{1}{3}$ and $\frac{1}{27}$ $\frac{1}{9}$
10. 4.5 and 450 45
11. 32 and $\frac{1}{8}$ 2

Find the indicated sum for each geometric series.

12. S_6 for $8 - 16 + 32 - 64 + \cdots$ -168
13. S_5 for $1 + \frac{2}{3} + \frac{4}{9} + \frac{8}{27} + \cdots$ $\frac{211}{81} \approx 2.60$
14. $\sum_{k=1}^{7} (8)^k$ $2{,}396{,}744$
15. $\sum_{k=1}^{5} 18\left(\frac{1}{6}\right)^{k-1}$ $\frac{1555}{72} \approx 21.60$
16. The cost for electricity is expected to rise at an annual rate of 8%. In its first year, a business spends $3000 for electricity.
    a. How much will the business pay for electricity in the 6th year? $4407.98
    b. How much in total will be paid for electricity over the first 6 years? $22,007.79

12-5 Mathematical Induction and Infinite Geometric Series

Find the sum of each infinite series, if it exists.

17. $25 + 20 + 16 + 12.8 + \cdots$ 125
18. $15 - 18 + 21.6 - 25.92 + \cdots$ No sum exists.
19. $\sum_{k=1}^{\infty} (-1)^k \left(\frac{2}{3}\right)^k$ -0.4
20. $\sum_{k=1}^{\infty} 4(0.22)^k$ $\frac{44}{39}$, or $1.\overline{128205}$

Use mathematical induction to prove $4 + 8 + 12 + \cdots + 4n = 2n(n + 1)$.

21. Step 1
22. Step 2
23. Step 3
24. A table-tennis ball is dropped from a height of 5 ft. The ball rebounds to 60% of its previous height after each bounce.
    a. Write an infinite geometric series to represent the distance that the ball travels after it initially hits the ground. (*Hint:* The ball travels up and down on each bounce.) $\sum_{k=1}^{\infty} 2(3)(0.6)^{k-1}$
    b. What is the total distance that the ball travels after it initially hits the ground? 15 ft

READY TO GO ON? SECTION 12B

Organizer

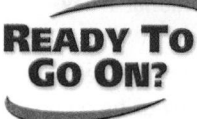

Objective: Assess students' mastery of concepts and skills in Lessons 12-4 through 12-5.

Resources

Assessment Resources
Section 12B Quiz

Test & Practice Generator One-Stop Planner®

INTERVENTION

Resources

***Ready to Go On? Intervention and Enrichment* Worksheets**

***Ready to Go On?* CD-ROM**

***Ready to Go On?* Online**
my.hrw.com

Answers

21. $4 = 2(1)(1 + 1) = 4$
22. $4 + \cdots + 4k = 2k(k + 1)$
23. $4 + \cdots + 4k + 4(k + 1)$
$= 2k(k + 1) + 4(k + 1)$
$= (k + 1)(2k + 4)$
$= 2(k + 1)(k + 2)$

READY TO GO ON? Diagnose and Prescribe

NO INTERVENE

Ready to Go On? Intervention	*Ready to Go On? Intervention, Section 12B*		
	Worksheets	CD-ROM	Online
Lesson 12-4	12-4 Intervention	Activity 12-4	Diagnose and Prescribe Online
Lesson 12-5	12-5 Intervention	Activity 12-5	

YES ENRICH

Ready to Go On? Enrichment, Section 12B

Worksheets
CD-ROM

Online

CHAPTER 12 **Organizer**

Pacing: Traditional 1 day
Block $\frac{1}{2}$ day

Objective: Approximate area under a curve by using rectangles.

Using the Extension

In Chapter 12, students learn about geometric sequences and series. In this extension, students use the partial sum of a series to estimate the area under a curve.

Technology The table function on a graphing calculator can be used to find the height of each rectangle. Set **Tblstart** to the center of the first rectangle and the **ΔTbl** to the width of each rectangle.

Precalculus The exact area under a curve can be found by finding the integral of a function over a given interval. On a graphing calculator, press 2nd CALC TRACE and then select **7:** $\int$**f(x)dx.**

State Resources

EXTENSION Area Under a Curve

Objective
Approximate area under a curve by using rectangles.

Finding the area under a curve is an important topic in higher mathematics, such as calculus. You can approximate the area under a curve by using a series of rectangles as shown in Example 1.

Remember!
Area is measured in square units.

EXAMPLE 1 Finding Area Under a Curve

Estimate the area under the curve $f(x) = -\frac{1}{2}x^2 + 2x + 3\frac{1}{8}$ over $0 \le x \le 5$.

Graph the function. Divide the area into 5 rectangles, each with a width of 1 unit.

Find the height of each rectangle by evaluating the function at the center of each rectangle, as shown in the table.

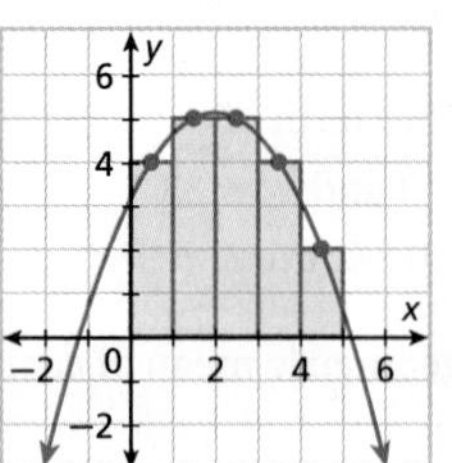

x	$f(x)$
0.5	4
1.5	5
2.5	5
3.5	4
4.5	2

Approximate the area by finding the sum of the areas of the rectangles.

$A \approx 1(4) + 1(5) + 1(5) + 1(4) + 1(2) = 20$

The estimate of 20 square units is very close to the actual area of $19\frac{19}{24}$ square units, which can be found by using calculus.

1. Estimate the area under the curve $f(x) = -x^2 + 5x + 5.75$ over $0 \le x \le 6$. Use 6 intervals.
53 square units

You can formalize the procedure for finding the area under the curve of a function by using the sum of a series.

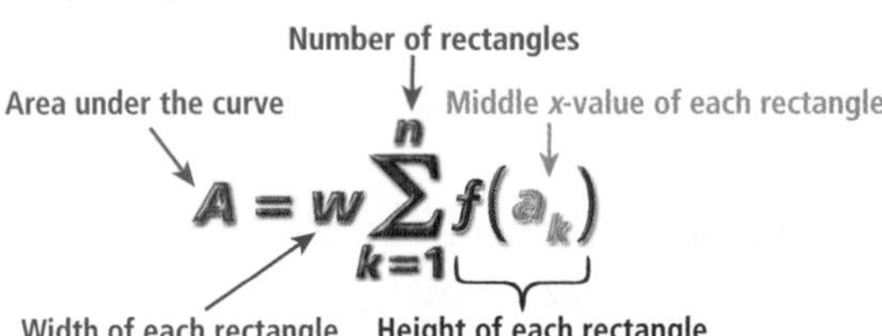

EXAMPLE 2 Finding Area Under a Curve by Using a Series

Use the sum of a series to estimate the area under the curve $f(x) = -x^2 + 50x$ over $0 \le x \le 50$.

Step 1 Graph the function.

Step 2 Divide the area into 5 rectangles, each with a width of 10 units.

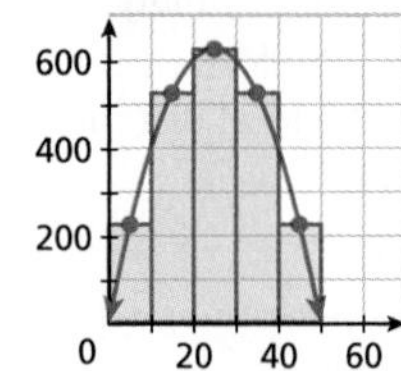

a_k	$f(a_k)$
$a_1 = 5$	225
$a_2 = 15$	525
$a_3 = 25$	625
$a_4 = 35$	525
$a_5 = 45$	225

1 Introduce

Motivate

Ask students to identify some figures for which they could easily find the area. square, triangle, rectangle, etc. Ask them to consider finding the area of a figure bounded by a curve, such as the entrance to a highway tunnel. Explain that series can be used to approximate areas such as these.

2 Teach

Guided Instruction

As you review the procedure for estimating the area under a curve, remind students that it is only an estimate. There are several different ways to draw rectangles that represent the area under the curve. Emphasize that calculus can be used to find the actual area.

Step 3 Find the value of the function at the center of each rectangle, as shown in the table.

Step 4 Write the sum that approximates the area.

$$A \approx 10\sum_{k=1}^{5} f(a_k) = 10\left[f(a_1) + f(a_2) + f(a_3) + f(a_4) + f(a_5)\right]$$
$$= 10\left[(225) + (525) + (625) + (525) + (225)\right]$$
$$= 10(2125) = 21{,}250$$

The estimated area is 21,250 square units.

2. Use the sum of a series to estimate the area under the curve $f(x) = -x^2 + 9x + 3$ over $0 \le x \le 9$. Use 3 intervals.
155.25 square units

EXTENSION Exercises

Estimate the area under each curve. Use 4 intervals.

1. $f(x) = -\frac{1}{2}x^2 + 12x + 2$ over $0 \le x \le 24$ **1236 square units**
2. $f(x) = -x^2 + 8x + 4$ over $0 \le x \le 8$ **120 square units**
3. $f(x) = -\frac{1}{4}x^2 + 5x$ over $0 \le x \le 16$ **304 square units**
4. $f(x) = -0.1x^2 + 20x$ over $0 \le x \le 200$ **137,500 square units**

Use the sum of a series to estimate the area under each curve. Use 5 intervals.

5. $f(x) = -x^2 + 10x + 5$ over $0 \le x \le 10$ **220 square units**
6. $f(x) = -x^2 + 30x$ over $0 \le x \le 20$ **3360 square units**
7. $f(x) = -\frac{1}{10}x^2 + 400$ over $0 \le x \le 50$ **15,875 square units**
8. $f(x) = -0.2x^2 + 28x + 300$ over $0 \le x \le 150$

8. 137,250 square units

9. **Physics** The graph shows a car's speed versus time as the car accelerates. This realistic curve can be approximated by $v(t) = -0.1t^2 + 7.3t$, where v is the velocity in feet per second and t is the time in seconds.
   a. Estimate the area under the curve for $0 \le t \le 35$.
   b. What does the area under the curve represent? Explain. (*Hint:* Consider the units of your answer to part **a.**)

Car Acceleration

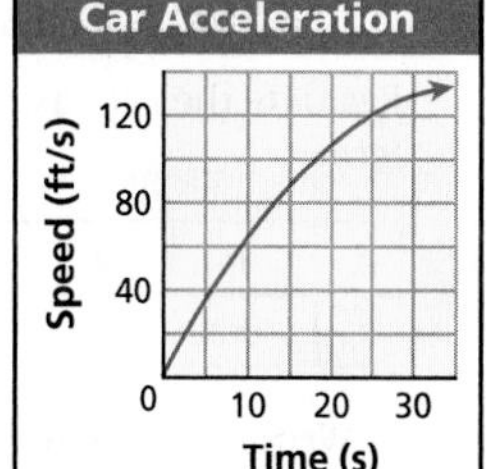

10. **Energy Conservation** Daily electricity use peaks in the early afternoon and can be approximated by a parabola. Suppose that the rate of electricity use in kilowatts (kW) is modeled by the function $f(x) = -1.25x^2 + 30x + 700$, where x represents the time in hours.
    a. Write a sum to represent the area under the curve for a domain of $0 \le x \le 24$.
    b. Estimate the area under the curve. **19,720 square units**

11. **Write About It** Explain how the units of the values on the x-axis and the units of the values on the y-axis can be used to find the units that apply to the area under a curve.
12. **Critical Thinking** For a given function and domain, how would increasing the number of rectangles affect the approximation of the area under the curve?

COMMON ERROR ALERT

Students may be confused by the units of the answer in **Exercises 9** and **10.** Explain that the graphs are only abstract representations of a function and that the area under the curve is not measured in common units of area, such as square feet.

Power Presentations with PowerPoint®

Additional Examples

Example 1

Estimate the area under the curve $f(x) = -\frac{1}{2}x^2 + 2x + 3\frac{1}{8}$ over $-1 \le x \le 2$. Use 3 intervals.

$\approx$ 11 square units

Example 2

Use the sum of a series to estimate the area under the curve $f(x) = -x^2 + 50x$ over $0 \le x \le 20$.

$\approx$ 7360 square units

Also available on transparency

INTERVENTION
Questioning Strategies

EXAMPLE 1

- How would your estimate of the area change if you made rectangles whose upper left corners were points on the curve?
- How does the number of rectangles affect your accuracy?

EXAMPLE 2

- Could you use the same function to find the area over an interval that does not start at zero, such as $20 \le x \le 50$? Explain.

Technology The area under a curve can be estimated on a graphing calculator by using the **sum(seq(** commands. For **Example 2,** let $Y1 = -x^2 + 50x$, and enter **10* sum(seq Y1, X, 5, 45, 10).**

3 Close

Summarize

Have students discuss how the accuracy of the estimate changes as the width of the rectangles decreases and the number of rectangles increases.

Answers

9a. about 3056 square units

b. Distance in feet traveled in t s; to find the area of each rectangle, you multiply speed (ft/s) by time (s), and the result is a distance (ft).

10a. Possible answer: $A = 4\sum_{k=1}^{6} f(a_k)$
$= 4(755 + 835 + 875 + 875 + 835 + 755)$

11. Possible answer: Because you find area by multiplying the length and the width, you multiply the units to find the units that apply to the area under the curve.

12. Possible answer: Increasing the number of rectangles would make the answer more accurate.

Organizer

Objective: Help students organize and review key concepts and skills presented in Chapter 12.

Resources

***Multilingual Glossary* Online**

go.hrw.com
KEYWORD: MB7 Glossary

***Lesson Tutorial Videos* CD-ROM**

Answers

1. arithmetic sequence; geometric sequence
2. diverges; converges
3. explicit formula; recursive formula
4. infinite sequence; finite sequence
5. iteration
6. −8, −7, −6, −5, −4
7. $\frac{1}{2}, 2, \frac{9}{2}, 8, \frac{25}{2}$
8. $1, -\frac{3}{2}, \frac{9}{4}, -\frac{27}{8}, \frac{81}{16}$
9. 55, 53, 51, 49, 47
10. $200, 40, 8, \frac{8}{5}, \frac{8}{25}$
11. −3, 10 ,−29, 88, −263
12. $a_n = -4n$
13. $a_n = 5(4)^{n-1}$
14. $a_n = 5n - 29$
15. $a_n = 27\left(\frac{2}{3}\right)^{n-1}$
16. 0.72 ft, or 8.6 in.; 0.12 ft, or 1.5 in.

Study Guide: Review

Vocabulary

arithmetic sequence 879
arithmetic series 882
converge 900
diverge 900
explicit formula 863
finite sequence 862
geometric mean 892
geometric sequence 890
geometric series 893
infinite geometric series 900
infinite sequence 862
iteration 864
limit 900
mathematical induction 902
partial sum 870
recursive formula 862
sequence 862
series 870
summation notation 870
term of a sequence 862

Complete the sentences below with vocabulary words from the list above.

1. A(n) __?__ has a common difference, and a(n) __?__ has a common ratio.
2. A series that has no limit __?__ , whereas a series that approaches a limit __?__ .
3. A(n) __?__ defines the *n*th term. A(n) __?__ defines the next term by using one or more of the previous terms.
4. A(n) __?__ continues without end, and a(n) __?__ has a last term.
5. Each step in a repeated process is called a(n) __?__ .

12-1 Introduction to Sequences *(pp. 862–868)*

EXAMPLES

- **Find the first 5 terms of the sequence with $a_1 = -52$; $a_n = 0.5a_{n-1} + 2$.**

Evaluate the rule using each term to find the next term.

n	1	2	3	4	5
a_n	−52	−24	−10	−3	0.5

- **Write an explicit rule for the *n*th term of 100, 72, 44, 16, −12, ….**

Examine the differences or ratios.

Terms	100	72	44	16	−12
1st differences		28	28	28	28

The first differences are constant, so the sequence is linear.

The first term is 100, and each term is 28 less than the previous term.

The explicit rule is $a_n = 100 - 28(n - 1)$.

EXERCISES

Find the first 5 terms of each sequence.

6. $a_n = n - 9$
7. $a_n = \frac{1}{2}n^2$
8. $a_n = \left(-\frac{3}{2}\right)^{n-1}$
9. $a_1 = 55$ and $a_n = a_{n-1} - 2$
10. $a_1 = 200$ and $a_n = \frac{1}{5}a_{n-1}$
11. $a_1 = -3$ and $a_n = -3a_{n-1} + 1$

Write a possible explicit rule for the *n*th term of each sequence.

12. −4, −8, −12, −16, −20, …
13. 5, 20, 80, 320, 1280, …
14. −24, −19, −14, −9, −4, …
15. 27, 18, 12, 8, $\frac{16}{3}$, …
16. **Sports** Suppose that a basketball is dropped from a height of 3 ft. If the ball rebounds to 70% of its height after each bounce, how high will the ball reach after the 4th bounce? the 9th bounce?

12-2 Series and Summation Notation (pp. 870–877)

EXAMPLES

- Expand $\sum_{k=1}^{5}(-1)^{n+1}(11-2n)$, and evaluate.

$\sum_{k=1}^{5}(-1)^{n+1}(11-2n) = (-1)^2(11-2)$
$+ (-1)^3(11-4) + (-1)^4(11-6)$
$+ (-1)^5(11-8) + (-1)^6(11-10)$
$= 9 - 7 + 5 - 3 + 1$
$= 5$ *Simplify.*

- Evaluate $\sum_{k=1}^{8} k^2$.

Use summation formula for a quadratic series.

$\sum_{k=1}^{8} k^2 = \frac{n(n+1)(2n+1)}{6}$

$= \frac{8(8+1)(2 \cdot 8 + 1)}{6} = \frac{72(17)}{6} = 204$

EXERCISES

Expand each series and evaluate.

17. $\sum_{k=1}^{4} k^2(-1)^k$
18. $\sum_{k=1}^{5}(0.5k + 4)$
19. $\sum_{k=1}^{5}(-1)^{k+1}(2k-1)$
20. $\sum_{k=1}^{4}\frac{5k}{k^2}$

Evaluate each series.

21. $\sum_{k=1}^{8} -5$
22. $\sum_{k=1}^{10} k^2$
23. $\sum_{k=1}^{12} k$
24. **Finance** A household has a monthly mortgage payment of $1150. How much is paid by the household after 2 years? 15 years?

12-3 Arithmetic Sequences and Series (pp. 879–887)

EXAMPLES

- **Find the 12th term for the arithmetic sequence 85, 70, 55, 40, 25, ...**

Find the common difference:
$d = 70 - 85 = -15$.

$a_n = a_1 + (n-1)d$ *General rule*

$a_{12} = 85 + (12-1)(-15)$ *Substitute.*

$= -80$ *Simplify.*

- **Find** $\sum_{k=1}^{11}(-2 - 33k)$.

Find the 1st and 11th terms.

$a_1 = -2 - 33(1) = -35$

$a_{11} = -2 - 33(11) = -365$

Find S_{11}.

$S_n = n\left(\frac{a_1 + a_n}{2}\right)$ *Sum formula*

$S_{11} = 11\left(\frac{-35 - 365}{2}\right)$ *Substitute.*

$= -2200$

EXERCISES

Find the 11th term of each arithmetic sequence.

25. 23, 19, 15, 11, ...
26. $\frac{1}{5}, \frac{3}{5}, 1, \frac{7}{5}, \frac{9}{5}, \ldots$
27. −9.2, −8.4, −7.6, −6.8, ...
28. $a_3 = 1.5$ and $a_4 = 5$
29. $a_6 = 47$ and $a_8 = 21$
30. $a_5 = -7$ and $a_9 = 13$

Find the indicated sum for each arithmetic series.

31. S_{18} for $-1 - 5 - 9 - 13 + \cdots$
32. S_{12} for $\frac{1}{3} + \frac{1}{6} + 0 - \frac{1}{6} + \cdots$
33. $\sum_{k=1}^{15}(-14 + 3k)$
34. $\sum_{k=1}^{15}\left(\frac{3}{2}k + 10\right)$
35. **Savings** Kelly has $50 and receives $8 a week for allowance. He wants to save all of his money to buy a new mountain bicycle that costs $499. Write an arithmetic sequence to represent the situation. Then find whether Kelly will be able to buy the new bicycle after one year (52 weeks).

Answers

17. $-1 + 4 - 9 + 16 = 10$
18. $4.5 + 5.0 + 5.5 + 6.0 + 6.5 = 27.5$
19. $1 - 3 + 5 - 7 + 9 = 5$
20. $5 + \frac{10}{4} + \frac{15}{9} + \frac{20}{16} = \frac{125}{12}$, or $10\frac{5}{12}$
21. −40
22. 385
23. 78
24. $27,600; $207,000
25. −17
26. $\frac{21}{5}$
27. −1.2
28. 29.5
29. −18
30. 23
31. −630
32. −7
33. 150
34. 330
35. 50, 58, 66, 74, ... ; no, because he will have a total savings of only $458

Answers

36. 0.000004
37. $\frac{243}{2}$
38. $-\frac{1}{8}$
39. 768
40. 98, 304
41. $\frac{512}{3}$
42. ± 32
43. 62,500
44. 5
45. 2
46. $\frac{\sqrt{3}}{24}$
47. $\frac{25}{36}$
48. $\frac{121}{81}$
49. 72,727.2
50. 21,845
51. −39,062
52. $\frac{315}{8} = 39.375$
53. $\frac{279}{8} = 34.875$
54. $1044.26
55a. $9847.32
b. $43,969.32

12-4 Geometric Sequences and Series *(pp. 890–898)*

EXAMPLES

■ **Find the 8th term of the geometric sequence 6, 24, 96, 384, ….**

Find the common ratio. $r = \frac{24}{6} = 4$

Write a rule, and evaluate for $n = 8$.

$a_n = a_1 r^{n-1}$ *General rule*

$a_8 = 6(4)^{8-1} = 98{,}304$

■ **Find the 8th term of the geometric sequence with $a_4 = -1000$ and $a_6 = -40$.**

Step 1 Find the common ratio.

$a_6 = a_4 r^{(6-4)}$ *Use the given terms.*

$-40 = -1000r^2$ *Substitute.*

$\frac{1}{25} = r^2$ *Simplify.*

$\pm\frac{1}{5} = r$

Step 2 Find a_1 using both possible values for r.

$-1000 = a_1\left(\frac{1}{5}\right)^{4-1}$ or $-1000 = a_1\left(-\frac{1}{5}\right)^{4-1}$

$a_1 = -125{,}000$ or $a_1 = 125{,}000$

Step 3 Write the rule and evaluate for a_8 by using both possible values for r.

$a_n = a_1 r^{n-1}$ $\quad a_n = a_1 r^{n-1}$

$a_n = -125{,}000\left(\frac{1}{5}\right)^{n-1}$ or $a_n = 125{,}000\left(-\frac{1}{5}\right)^{n-1}$

$a_8 = -125{,}000\left(\frac{1}{5}\right)^{8-1}$ $\quad a_8 = 125{,}000\left(-\frac{1}{5}\right)^{8-1}$

$a_8 = -1.6$ $\quad a_8 = -1.6$

■ **Find $\sum_{k=1}^{7} -2(5)^{k-1}$.**

Find the common ratio. $r = \frac{a_2}{a_1} = \frac{-6}{3} = -2$

Find S_7

$S_n = a_1\left(\frac{1-r^n}{1-r}\right)$ *Sum formula*

$S_7 = 3\left(\frac{1-(-2)^7}{1-(-2)}\right)$ *Substitute.*

$= 3\left(\frac{1-(-128)}{3}\right) = 129$

EXERCISES

Find the 8th term of each geometric sequence.

36. 40, 4, 0.4, 0.04, 0.004, …
37. $\frac{1}{18}, \frac{1}{6}, \frac{1}{2}, \frac{3}{2}, \ldots$
38. −16, −8, −4, −2, …
39. −6, 12, −24, 48, …

Find the 9th term of the geometric sequence with the given terms.

40. $a_3 = 24$ and $a_4 = 96$
41. $a_1 = \frac{2}{3}$ and $a_2 = -\frac{4}{3}$
42. $a_4 = -1$ and $a_6 = -4$
43. $a_3 = 4$ and $a_6 = 500$

Find the geometric mean of each pair of numbers.

44. 10 and 2.5
45. $\frac{1}{2}$ and 8
46. $\frac{\sqrt{3}}{96}$ and $\frac{\sqrt{3}}{6}$
47. $\frac{5}{12}$ and $\frac{125}{108}$

Find the indicated sum for each geometric series.

48. S_5 for $1 + \frac{1}{3} + \frac{1}{9} + \frac{1}{27} + \cdots$
49. S_6 for $-\frac{4}{5} + 8 - 80 + 800 + \cdots$
50. $\sum_{k=1}^{8} (4)^{k-1}$
51. $\sum_{k=1}^{7} -2(5)^{k-1}$
52. $\sum_{k=1}^{6} 60\left(-\frac{1}{2}\right)^{k-1}$
53. $\sum_{k=1}^{5} 18\left(\frac{1}{2}\right)^{k-1}$
54. **Depreciation** A new photocopier costs $9000 and depreciates each year such that it retains only 65% of its preceding year's value. What is the value of the photocopier after 5 years?
55. **Rent** A one-bedroom apartment rents for $650 a month. The rent is expected to increase by 6% per year.
    a. What will be the annual rent expense on the apartment after 5 years?
    b. What will be the total amount spent on rent if a person rents the apartment for the entire 5-year period?

12-5 Mathematical Induction and Infinite Geometric Series *(pp. 900–907)*

EXAMPLES

Find the sum of each infinite series, if it exists.

■ $-9261 + 441 - 21 + 1 + \cdots$

$r = \frac{441}{-9261} = -\frac{1}{21}$ *Converges: $|r| < 1$*

$S = \frac{a_1}{1 - r}$ *Sum formula*

$= \frac{-9261}{1 - \left(-\frac{1}{21}\right)} = \frac{-9261}{\frac{22}{21}}$

$= -\frac{194{,}481}{22}$, or $-8840.0\overline{45}$

■ $\sum_{k=1}^{\infty} -5\left(\frac{7}{10}\right)^{k-1}$

$= -5 - \frac{35}{10} - \frac{245}{100} + \cdots$ *Evaluate.*

$r = \frac{-\frac{35}{10}}{-5} = \frac{7}{10}$ *Converges: $|r| < 1$*

$S = \frac{a_1}{1 - r} = \frac{-5}{1 - \frac{7}{10}} = \frac{-5}{\frac{3}{10}} = -\frac{50}{3}$, or $-16.\overline{6}$

■ **Use mathematical induction to prove $2 + 5 + \cdots + (3n - 1) = \frac{n}{2}(3n + 1)$.**

Step 1 Base case: Show that the statement is true for $n = 1$.

$2 = \frac{n}{2}(3n + 1) = \frac{1}{2}(3 \cdot 1 + 1) = 2$ *True*

Step 2 Assume that the statement is true for a natural number k.

$2 + 5 + \cdots + (3k - 1) = \frac{k}{2}(3k + 1)$ *Replace n with k.*

Step 3 Prove that it is true for the natural number $k + 1$.

$2 + 5 + \ldots + (3k - 1) + 3(k + 1) - 1$ *Add to both sides.*

$= \frac{k}{2}(3k + 1) + 3(k + 1) - 1$

$= \frac{k(3k + 1)}{2} + (3k + 3 - 1)$ *Multiply.*

$= \frac{3k^2 + k}{2} + \frac{2(3k + 2)}{2}$ *Simplify and rewrite with like denominators.*

$= \frac{3k^2 + 7k + 4}{2}$ *Add.*

$= \frac{(k + 1)(3k + 4)}{2}$ *Factor.*

$= \frac{(k + 1)}{2}(3(k + 1) + 1)$ *Write with k + 1.*

EXERCISES

Find the sum of each infinite series, if it exists.

56. $-2700 + 900 - 300 + 100 + \cdots$
57. $-1.2 - 0.12 - 0.012 - 0.0012 + \cdots$
58. $-49 - 42 - 36 - \frac{216}{7} + \cdots$
59. $4 + \frac{4}{5} + \frac{4}{25} + \frac{4}{125} + \cdots$
60. $\sum_{k=1}^{\infty} \frac{9}{3^k}$
61. $\sum_{k=1}^{\infty} -7\left(\frac{3}{5}\right)^k$
62. $\sum_{k=1}^{\infty} (-1)^{k+1}\left(\frac{1}{8^k}\right)$
63. $\sum_{k=1}^{\infty} \left(\frac{4}{3}\right)^k$

Use mathematical induction to prove each statement.

64. $2 + 4 + 8 + \cdots + 2^n = 2^{n+1} - 2$
65. $1 + 5 + 25 + \cdots + 5^{n-1} = \frac{5^n - 1}{4}$
66. $\frac{1}{3} + \frac{1}{15} + \cdots + \frac{1}{4n^2 - 1} = \frac{n}{2n + 1}$
67. **Recreation** A child on a swing is let go from a vertical height so that the distance that he travels in the first back-and-forth swing is exactly 9 feet.
    a. If each swing decreases the distance by 85%, write an infinite geometric series that expresses the distance that the child travels in feet.
    b. What is the total distance that the child in the swing travels before the swing stops?

Answers

56. -2025
57. $-\frac{4}{3}$ or $-1.\overline{3}$
58. -343
59. 5
60. 4.5
61. $-\frac{21}{2}$
62. $\frac{1}{9}$
63. No sum exists.
64. 1. $2^1 = 2^{1+1} - 2 = 2$
    2. $2 + 4 + \ldots + 2^k = 2^{k+1} - 2$
    3. $2 + 4 + \ldots + 2^k + 2^{k+1}$
    $= 2^{k+1} - 2 + 2^{k+1}$
    $= 2(2^{k+1}) - 2$
    $= 2^{k+2} - 2$
    $= 2^{k+1+1} - 2$
65. 1. $5^{1-1} = \frac{5^1 - 1}{4} = 1$
    2. $1 + \cdots + 5^{k-1} = \frac{5^k - 1}{4}$
    3. $1 + \cdots + 5^{k-1} + 5^k$
    $= \frac{5^k - 1}{4} + 5^k$
    $= \frac{5^k - 1}{4} + \frac{4(5^k)}{4}$
    $= \frac{5^k + 4(5^k) - 1}{4}$
    $= \frac{5(5^k) - 1}{4} = \frac{5^{k+1} - 1}{4}$
66. 1. $\frac{1}{4(1^2) - 1} = \frac{1}{2(1) + 1} = \frac{1}{3}$
    2. $\frac{1}{3} + \ldots + \frac{1}{4k^2 - 1} = \frac{k}{2k + 1}$
    3. $\frac{1}{3} + \ldots + \frac{1}{4k^2 - 1} + \frac{1}{4(k + 1)^2 - 1}$
    $= \frac{k}{2k + 1} + \frac{1}{4(k + 1)^2 - 1}$
    $= \frac{k}{2k + 1} + \frac{1}{4k^2 + 8k + 3}$
    $= \frac{k}{2k + 1} + \frac{1}{(2k + 1)(2k + 3)}$
    $= \frac{k(2k + 3)}{(2k + 1)(2k + 3)} + \frac{1}{(2k + 1)(2k + 3)}$
    $= \frac{k(2k + 3) + 1}{(2k + 1)(2k + 3)}$
    $= \frac{2k^2 + 3k + 1}{(2k + 1)(2k + 3)}$
    $= \frac{\cancel{(2k + 1)}(k + 1)}{\cancel{(2k + 1)}(2k + 3)}$
    $= \frac{k + 1}{2k + 2 + 1}$
    $= \frac{k + 1}{2(k + 1) + 1}$

67a. $\sum_{k=1}^{\infty} 9(0.85)^{k-1}$
   b. 60 ft

Organizer

Objective: Assess students' mastery of concepts and skills in Chapter 12.

 **Online Edition**

Resources

 ***Assessment Resources***

Chapter 12 Tests
- Free Response (Levels A, B, C)
- Multiple Choice (Levels A, B, C)
- Performance Assessment

 ***IDEA Works!* CD-ROM**

Modified Chapter 12 Test

Find the first 5 terms of each sequence.

1. $a_n = n^2 - 4$ **−3, 0, 5, 12, 21**
2. $a_1 = 48$ and $a_n = \frac{1}{2}a_{n-1} - 8$ **48, 16, 0, −8, −12**

Write a possible explicit rule for the *n*th term of each sequence.

3. −4, −2, 0, 2, 4, ... $a_n = 2n - 6$
4. 54, 18, 6, 2, $\frac{2}{3}$, ... $a_n = 54\left(\frac{1}{3}\right)^{n-1}$

Expand each series and evaluate.

5. $\sum_{k=1}^{4} 5k^3$ $5 + 40 + 135 + 320 = 500$
6. $\sum_{k=1}^{7} (-1)^{k+1}(k)$ $1 - 2 + 3 - 4 + 5 - 6 + 7 = 4$

Find the 9th term of each arithmetic sequence.

7. −19, −13, −7, −1, ... **29**
8. $a_2 = 11.6$ and $a_5 = 5$ **−3.8**
9. Find 2 missing terms in the arithmetic sequence 125, ■, ■, 65. **105, 85**

Find the indicated sum for each arithmetic series.

10. S_{20} for 4 + 7 + 10 + 13 + ... **650**
11. $\sum_{k=1}^{12} (-9k + 8)$ **−606**
12. The front row of a theater has 16 seats and each subsequent row has 2 more seats than the row that precedes it. How many seats are in the 12th row? How many seats in total are in the first 12 rows? **38 seats; 324 seats**

Find the 10th term of each geometric sequence.

13. $\frac{3}{256}, \frac{3}{64}, \frac{3}{16}, \frac{3}{4}, \ldots$ **3072**
14. $a_4 = 2$ and $a_5 = 8$ **8192**
15. Find the geometric mean of 4 and 25. **10**

Find the indicated sum for each geometric series.

16. S_6 for $2 + 1 + \frac{1}{2} + \frac{1}{4} + \ldots$ $\frac{63}{16}$
17. $\sum_{k=1}^{6} 250\left(-\frac{1}{5}\right)^{k-1}$ **208.32**
18. You invest \$1000 each year in an account that pays 5% annual interest. How much is the first \$1000 you invested worth after 10 full years of interest payments? How much in total do you have in your account after 10 full years? **\$1628.89; \$13,206.79**

Find the sum of each infinite geometric series, if it exists.

19. 200 − 100 + 50 − 25 + ... $\frac{400}{3}$ or $133.\overline{3}$
20. $\sum_{k=1}^{\infty} 2\left(\frac{7}{8}\right)^k$ **14**

Use mathematical induction to prove $\frac{1}{2} + \frac{3}{2} + \frac{5}{2} + \cdots + \frac{2n-1}{2} = \frac{n^2}{2}$.

21. Step 1
22. Step 2
23. Step 3

Answers

21. $\frac{2(1)-1}{2} = \frac{1^2}{2} = \frac{1}{2}$

22. $\frac{1}{2} + \cdots + \frac{2k-1}{2} = \frac{k^2}{2}$

23. $\frac{1}{2} + \cdots + \frac{2k-1}{2} + \frac{2(k+1)-1}{2}$
$= \frac{k^2}{2} + \frac{2(k+1)-1}{2}$
$= \frac{k^2 + 2k + 2 - 1}{2}$
$= \frac{k^2 + 2k + 1}{2} = \frac{(k+1)^2}{2}$

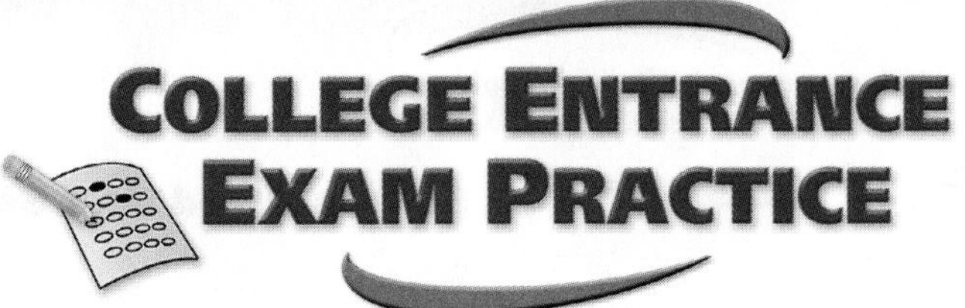

COLLEGE ENTRANCE EXAM PRACTICE

CHAPTER 12

FOCUS ON SAT

When you get your SAT scores, you are given the percentile in which your scores fall. This tells you the percentage of students that scored lower than you did on the same test. You'll see your percentile score at the national and state levels. They are usually not the same.

Read each problem carefully, and make sure that you understand what the question is asking. Before marking your final answer on the answer sheet, check that your answer makes sense in the context of the question.

You may want to time yourself as you take this practice test. It should take you about 8 minutes to complete.

1. The first term of a sequence is 6, and each successive term is 3 less than twice the preceding term. What is the sum of the first four terms of the sequence?
   - (A) 27
   - (B) 30
   - (C) 51
   - (D) 57
   - (E) 123

2. The first term of a sequence is 2, and the nth term is defined to be $3n - 1$. What is the average of the 7th, 10th, and 12th terms?
   - (A) 24.5
   - (B) 28
   - (C) 29
   - (D) 32
   - (E) 84

3. The first term of an arithmetic sequence is -5. If the common difference is 4, what is the 7th term of the sequence?
   - (A) $-20{,}480$
   - (B) -29
   - (C) 19
   - (D) 20
   - (E) 23

4. A population of 50 grows exponentially by doubling every 4 years. After how many years will the population have 1600 members?
   - (A) 20
   - (B) 16
   - (C) 10
   - (D) 6
   - (E) 5

5. Which of the following sequences can be expressed by the rule $a_n = \frac{n-1}{n+1}$?
   - (A) $3, 2, \frac{5}{3}, \frac{3}{2}, \frac{7}{5}, \ldots$
   - (B) $\frac{1}{2}, \frac{3}{4}, \frac{5}{6}, \frac{7}{8}, \frac{9}{10}, \ldots$
   - (C) $\frac{1}{3}, \frac{2}{4}, \frac{3}{5}, \frac{4}{6}, \frac{5}{7}, \ldots$
   - (D) $0, \frac{1}{3}, \frac{1}{2}, \frac{3}{5}, \frac{2}{3}, \ldots$
   - (E) $0, \frac{3}{2}, 3, \frac{5}{3}, 5, \ldots$

6. Which of the following sequences is a geometric sequence?
   - (A) $-7, 14, -28, 56, -112, \ldots$
   - (B) $-4, -6, -8, -10, -12, \ldots$
   - (C) $-3, 1, -3, 1, -3, \ldots$
   - (D) $4, 12, 48, 144, 576, \ldots$
   - (E) $1, 4, 9, 16, 25, \ldots$

COLLEGE ENTRANCE EXAM PRACTICE CHAPTER 12

Organizer

Objective: Provide practice for college entrance exams such as the SAT.

Resources

College Entrance Exam Practice

Questions on the SAT represent the following math content areas:

Number and Operation, 30–32%

Algebra and Functions, 28–32%

Geometry and Measurement, 27–30%

Data Analysis, Statistics, and Probability, 10–12%

Items on this page focus on:
- Number and Operation
- Algebra and Functions

Text References:

Item	1	2	3	4	5	6
Lesson	12-2	12-1	12-3	12-4	12-1	12-4

TEST PREP DOCTOR

1. Students may choose **A** because it is the fourth term of the sequence. Students may choose **B** because it is the sum of the first three terms. Remind students to read each question carefully.
2. Students may spend more time than is necessary on this problem if they find all the terms of the sequence from the 1st term through the 12th term. Encourage students to use a formula to find the 3 terms. Then remind them to find the average of these terms.
3. Students may choose **B** because they subtracted 4 from each successive term instead of adding 4 to each successive term. Students may choose **E** because it is the 7th term of the sequence after the first term.
4. Students may choose **D** because the population is 1600 after 5 doubling periods. Remind them that each period represents 4 years.
5. Students may choose **A** because it is close to the sequence given by the rule $\frac{n+1}{n-1}$. Students may choose **C** because it is the correct sequence but missing the first term.
6. Students may choose **B** if they do not know the difference between arithmetic and geometric sequences. Students may choose **D** because alternating terms have a common ratio.

Organizer

Objective: Provide opportunities to learn and practice common test-taking strategies.

Online Edition

Resources

State Test Prep Workbook

***State Test Prep* CD-ROM**

***State Test Practice* Online**

go.hrw.com

KEYWORD: MB7 TestPrep

This test tackler shows the benefits of outlining a response to either a short- or extended-response test item. Advise students that outlining a response to a multipart test item is similar to writing an outline for an essay in an English or history class. Remind students to include an answer check or verification of units as a step in the outline.

Encourage students to use short, concise statements or sentences in their outlines. Tell students that an outline is not just a restatement of the problem, but that it should include details of a plan for solving and explaining each step.

Standardized Test Strategies

Short/Extended Response: Outline Your Response

Answering short and extended response items on tests is a lot like writing essays in English class. You can use an outline to plan your response to the question. Outlines help you organize the main points and the order in which they will appear in your answer. Outlining your response will help ensure that your explanation is clearly organized and includes all necessary information.

EXAMPLE 1

Short Response Ariana is saving money for a new car. She saves \$40 the first week, \$45 the second week, \$50 the third week, and so on. Explain whether an arithmetic or geometric sequence would best represent this situation. Use a sequence or series to determine the amount that she will save in the 8th week and the total amount that she will have saved after 8 weeks.

Create an outline for your response.

Outline

1. *Explain whether arithmetic or geometric.*
2. *Write sequence and series.*
3. *Find amount saved in 8th week.*
4. *Find total saved after 8 weeks.*

Follow the outline, and write out your response.

Include evidence to explain the answer for the first step.

An arithmetic sequence would best represent this situation because Ariana is adding \$5 each week to the amount that she saves. This would be an arithmetic sequence where the first term is 40 and the common difference is 5.

Clearly indicate which is the sequence and which is the series for the second step.

The sequence for the amount saved each week is $a_n = 40 + 5(n - 1)$. The series for the total amount saved is $\sum_{k=1}^{n}[40 + 5(k - 1)]$.

Show how you found the answers for the last two steps.

The amount saved in the 8th week is $a_8 = 40 + 5(8 - 1) = \$75$.

The total saved after 8 weeks is $\sum_{k=1}^{8}[40 + 5(k - 1)] = \$460$.

When you finish your response, check it against your outline to make sure that you did not leave out any details.

Read each test item and answer the questions that follow.

Item A
Short Response Explain how to determine whether an infinite geometric series has a sum.

1. What should be included in an outline of the response for this test item?
2. Read the two different outlines below. Which outline is the most useful? Why?

Student A
I. Definition of an infinite geometric series and the common ratio r.
II. Definition of the sum of an infinite geometric series.
III. Explain for which values of r that a sum exists.

Student B
A. Geometric series has a common ratio.
B. Common ratio has to be less than 1.

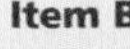

Item B
Extended Response
A pattern for stacking cereal boxes is shown at right.
a. Explain how many boxes are in a 9-row display.
b. If 91 boxes are to be stacked in this display, explain how many rows the display will have.

3. Read the outline below. Identify any areas that need improvement. Rewrite the outline to make it more useful.

Outline
1. Find the number of boxes if there are 9 rows.
2. Find the number of rows needed for 91 boxes.

Item C
Extended Response A pattern of squares is created by doubling the dimensions of the previous square. Explain how to find the sum of the perimeters of the first 8 squares if the first square is 5 cm wide.

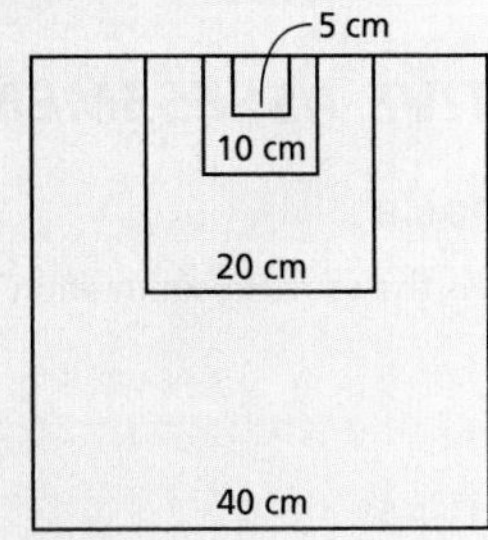

4. A student correctly gave the following response. Write an outline for a response to this question.

To find the perimeters of the first 8 squares, I need to determine the series.

$$4(5) + 4(10) + 4(20) + 4(40) + \cdots$$
$$4(5 + 10 + 20 + 40 + \cdots)$$
$$4 \cdot 5(1 + 2 + 4 + 8 + \cdots)$$
$$20(1 + 2 + 4 + 8 + \cdots)$$
$$20\sum_{n=1}^{8} 2^{(n-1)}$$

Now that I know that the first term is 20 and the common ratio is 2, I can use the formula $S_n = t_1\left(\frac{1-r^n}{1-r}\right)$, where t_1 is the first term and r is the common ratio.

$$S_n = 20\left(\frac{1-2^8}{1-2}\right)$$
$$= 20\left(\frac{1-256}{-1}\right)$$
$$= 20\left(\frac{-255}{-1}\right)$$
$$= 20(255) = 5100$$

So the sum of the perimeters of the first 8 squares is 5100 cm.

Answers to Test Items

See answers to related problems.

Answers

Possible answers:

1. Outlines should define an infinite geometric series and common ratio, define the sum of an infinite geometric series, and explain how the common ratio affects whether or not the series has a sum.
2. Student A's outline is most useful because it will guide the student to a more complete answer.
3. The outline only restates the directions. Improved outline:
   I. Identify the sequence by finding the differences between terms.
   II. Use the formula for the nth term of an arithmetic sequence to find the number of boxes in a 9-row display.
   III. Use the sum formula for an arithmetic series to find the number terms that have a sum of 91.
4. I. Find the perimeters of the first 4 squares.
   II. Write the sum of these perimeters as a series.
   III. Determine the first term of the series and the common ratio.
   IV. Use the formula $S_n = a_1\left(\frac{1-r^n}{1-r}\right)$, where a_1 is the first term and r is the common ratio, to determine the sum of the perimeters of the first 8 squares.

State Resources

go.hrw.com
State Resources Online
KEYWORD: MB7 Resources

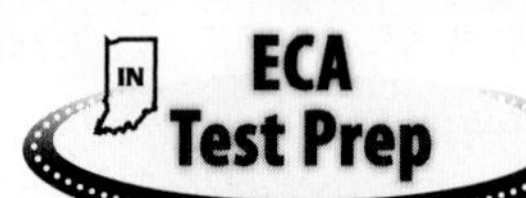

Organizer

Objective: Provide review and practice for Chapter 1–12 and standardized tests.

 Online Edition

Resources

 ***Assessment Resources***

Chapter 1 Cumulative Test

 ***State Test Prep Workbook***

 ***State Test Prep* CD-ROM**

 ***State Test Practice* Online**

go.hrw.com
KEYWORD: MB7 TestPrep

Answers

1. D
2. B
3. B
4. D
5. D
6. A
7. D
8. C
9. C
10. B
11. A
12. B
13. D

 *State Resources*

Core Standard	Items
3	11
4	2, 3
6	4, 5
7	1, 7, 8, 15, 16
8	12, 17

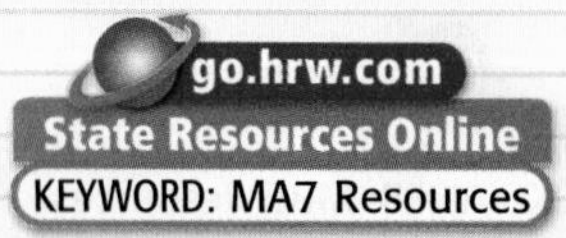

go.hrw.com
State Resources Online
KEYWORD: MA7 Resources

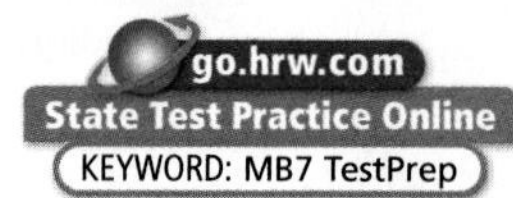

go.hrw.com
State Test Practice Online
KEYWORD: MB7 TestPrep

CUMULATIVE ASSESSMENT, CHAPTERS 1–12

Multiple Choice

1. Which shows the series in summation notation?

4, 6, 4, 6, 4

A. $\sum 24$

B. $\sum_{n=0}^{5} [(-1)^n + 5]$

C. $\sum_{n=1}^{4} [(-1)^n + 5]$

D. $\sum_{n=1}^{5} [(-1)^n + 5]$

2. What is the expanded binomial?

$(2x - y)^3$

A. $x^3 - 3x^2y + 3xy^2 - y^3$

B. $8x^3 - 12x^2y + 6xy^2 - y^3$

C. $x^3 + 3x^2y + 3xy^2 + y^3$

D. $8x^3 + 12x^2y + 6xy^2 + y^3$

3. Let $f(x) = x^3 + 2x^2 - 5x - 9$. Which function would show $f(x)$ reflected across the y-axis?

A. $g(x) = -x^3 - 2x^2 + 5x + 9$

B. $g(x) = -x^3 + 2x^2 + 5x - 9$

C. $g(x) = 2x^3 + 4x^2 - 10x - 18$

D. $g(x) = x^3 + 2x^2 - 5x - 5$

4. Which function shows exponential decay?

A. $f(x) = -5x$

B. $f(x) = 2.3(6.7)^x$

C. $f(x) = 0.49(7.9)^x$

D. $f(x) = 5.13(0.32)^x$

5. A ball is dropped from a height of 10 feet. On each bounce, the ball bounces 60% of the height of the previous bounce. Which expression represents the height in feet of the ball on the nth bounce?

A. $10(0.6n)$

B. $10(0.6)^{n-1}$

C. $\frac{10 - n}{0.6}$

D. $10(0.6)^n$

6. Which is the graph of the inequality $6x + 3y \geq 9x^2 - 3$?

A. 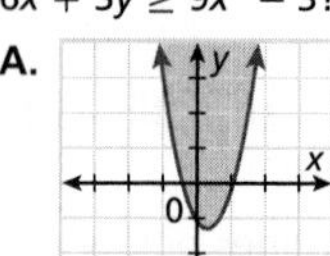

B. 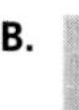 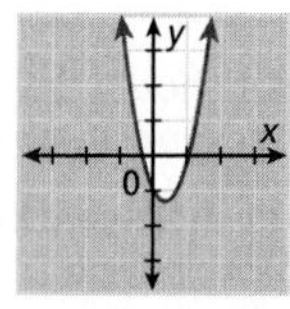

C. 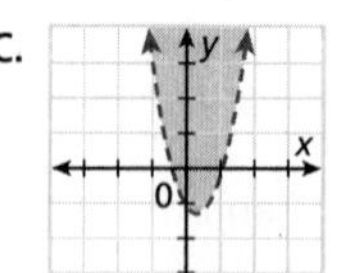

D. 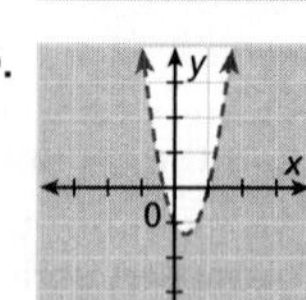

7. Gina opened a new deli. Her revenues for the first 4 weeks were \$2000, \$2400, \$2880, and \$3456. If the trend continues, which is the best estimate of Gina's revenues in the 6th week?

A. \$3856

B. \$4032

C. \$4147

D. \$4980

8. What is the 9th term in the sequence?

$a_n = \frac{1}{2}(2^{n-1}) + 4$

A. 36 **B.** 68

C. 132 **D.** 260

9. Find the inverse of $f(x) = 4x - 5$.

A. $f^{-1}(x) = -4x + 5$

B. $f^{-1}(x) = \frac{1}{4}x + 5$

C. $f^{-1}(x) = \frac{x + 5}{4}$

D. $f^{-1}(x) = 5x - 4$

TEST PREP DOCTOR

For **Item 12,** students will often forget that one of the 10 cards is also a diamond. Remind them that they must account for this by subtracting the probability of this one card from the combined probability.

10. What transformation has been applied to f to get g?

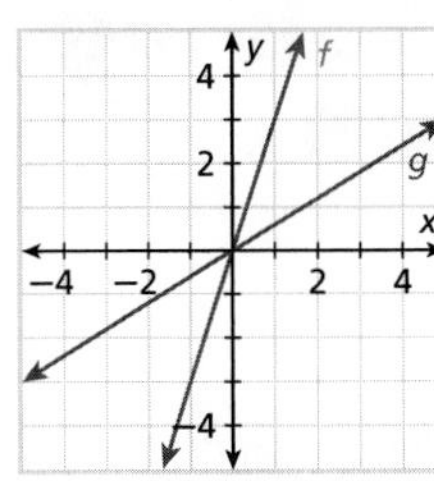

A. Horizontal compression by $\frac{1}{5}$

B. Horizontal stretch by 5

C. Vertical compression by $\frac{1}{3}$

D. Vertical stretch by 5

In Item 11, you may choose to graph, factor, complete the square, or use the Quadratic Formula to find the zeros.

11. Find the zeros of $f(x) = 2x^2 + 5x - 12$.

A. $-4, \frac{3}{2}$

B. $-2, 3$

C. $-\frac{3}{2}, 4$

D. $\frac{3}{2}, 2$

12. A card is drawn from a deck of 52. What is the probability of drawing a 10 or a diamond?

A. $\frac{1}{13}$

B. $\frac{4}{13}$

C. $\frac{5}{13}$

D. $\frac{17}{52}$

13. What is the y-value of the point that represents the solution to the given system of equations?

$$\begin{cases} 2y - 2 = 4x \\ 6 - x = 8y \end{cases}$$

A. $-\frac{13}{17}$

B. $-\frac{6}{17}$

C. $\frac{6}{17}$

D. $\frac{13}{17}$

Short Answer

14. Use the function $f(x) = \sqrt[3]{5x}$ to answer the following questions.

Part A What is the domain and range?

Part B What is the inverse of $f(x)$?

Part C What is the domain and range of the inverse function?

Part D Graph $f(x)$ and $f^{-1}(x)$ on the same coordinate plane.

15. Use the infinite geometric series $\sum_{n=1}^{\infty} \frac{5}{4^{n-1}}$ to answer the following questions.

Part A Determine if the series converges or diverges.

Part B Find the sum of the infinite series, if it exists.

16. A grocery store display contains 3 cans on the top row and an additional can in each row forming a triangular shape.

Part A Would you use a sequence or a series to represent the number of cans in the nth row? Show or explain your work.

Part B How many cans are in the 12th row?

Part C What does the series $\sum_{k=1}^{n} (k + 2)$ represent? Show or explain your work.

Extended Response

17. A test to be on a trivia show has two parts. 60% of contestants pass the first part, and 20% pass the second part.

Part A Draw a tree diagram that gives the probabilities for a contestant's possible outcomes on the test.

Part B If a contestant must pass both parts of the test to be on the show, how many contestants out of a group of 50 would likely make the show? Show or explain your work.

Part C Is it more likely that a contestant would pass both parts or fail both parts of the test? Show or explain your work.

Short Answer Rubric

Items 14–16

Score 2 = Thorough understanding of mathematical concepts and processes.

Score 1 = Partial understanding of mathematical concepts and/or processes.

Score 0 = Limited or no understanding of the problem-solving concepts.

Blank = No written response.

Extended Response Rubric

Item 17

Score 4 = Thorough understanding of mathematical concepts and processes.

Score 3 = Demonstrated understanding of mathematical concepts and processes, but an error in computation or explanation.

Score 2 = Partial understanding of mathematical concepts and/or processes.

Score 1 = Limited understanding and execution of the problem-solving concepts.

Score 0 = No understanding of the problem-solving concepts.

Blank = No written response.

Answers

14. Part A: $D: \mathbb{R}$; $R: \mathbb{R}$

Part B: $f^{-1}(x) = \frac{x^3}{5}$

Part C: $D: \mathbb{R}$; $R: \mathbb{R}$

Part D:

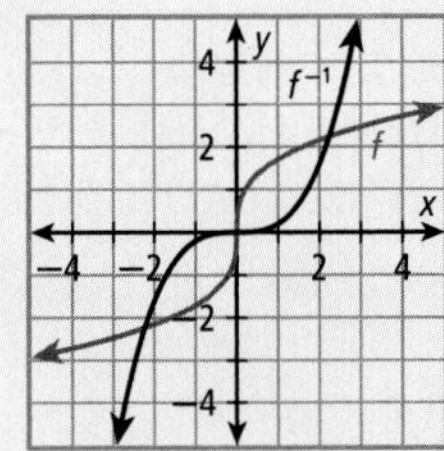

15. Part A: converges

Part B: $\frac{20}{3}$

16. Part A: a sequence because each term in the sequence represents the number of cans in each row

Part B: 14

Part C: the total number of cans in n rows

17. Part A:

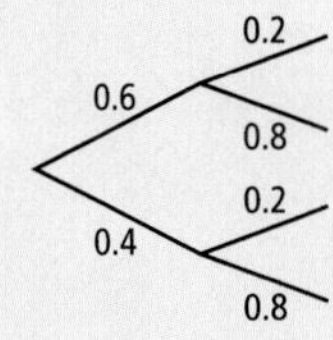

Part B: 6; the probability of passing both parts is 0.6(0.2) = 0.12. Out of 50 contestants, 0.12(50) = 6 would most likely pass.

Part C: It is more likely that a contestant fails both parts of the test. The probability of passing both parts is 12%, but the probability of failing both parts is 32%.

Problem Solving on Location

Organizer

Objective: Choose appropriate problem-solving strategies and use them with skills from Chapters 11 and 12 to solve real-world problems.

Online Edition

The Hoover Dam

Reading Strategies

As students read **Problem 1,** check that they understand the words *forecast* and *projection.* If students are unfamiliar with these terms, ask them to reread the problem and use context clues to guess the definitions. ENGLISH LANGUAGE LEARNERS

Using Data Ask students how they could estimate the total number of cars crossing the Hoover Dam in 2007. Multiply 16,300 by 365.

State Resources

go.hrw.com
State Resources Online
KEYWORD: MB7 Resources

Problem Solving on Location

NEVADA

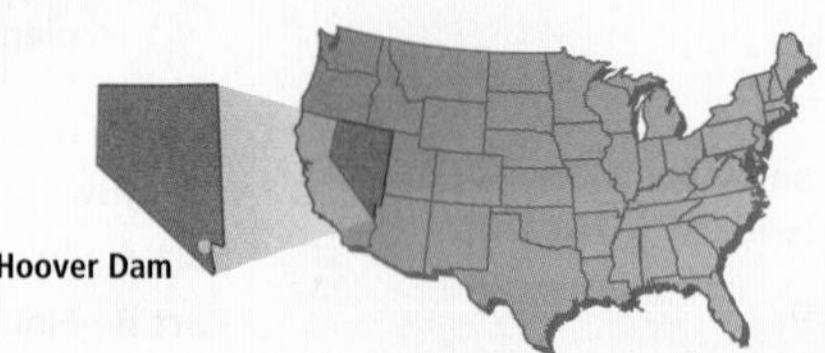

The Hoover Dam

Since its completion in 1935, the Hoover Dam has often been cited as one of the seven engineering wonders of the world. Its 6.6 million tons of concrete tame the waters of the Colorado River and form Lake Mead, the largest man-made reservoir in the United States.

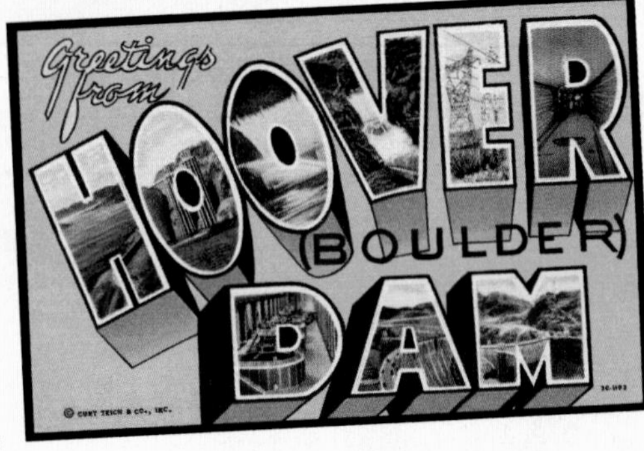

Choose one or more strategies to solve each problem. For 1 and 2, use the table.

Traffic Forecasts for the Hoover Dam			
Year	2007	2008	2009
Number of Cars per Day	16,300	16,780	17,260

1. The Hoover Dam serves as a bridge between the Nevada and Arizona sides of the Colorado River. Traffic analysts project that the traffic on the dam will increase according to an arithmetic sequence. How many cars, on average, would you predict to cross the dam each day in 2017? 21,100
2. Approximately how many vehicles will cross the dam in the years 2007 through 2017, inclusive? (*Hint:* Assume 365 days per year.) about 75 million
3. Small trucks make up 18% of the traffic on the dam, and RVs account for another 4%. All trucks and RVs are inspected before they are allowed to cross.
   a. Assuming that other types of vehicles are not inspected, what is the probability that three consecutive vehicles arriving at a checkpoint will be inspected? 0.01
   b. What is the probability that 3 out of 5 vehicles arriving at a checkpoint will need to be inspected? 0.06

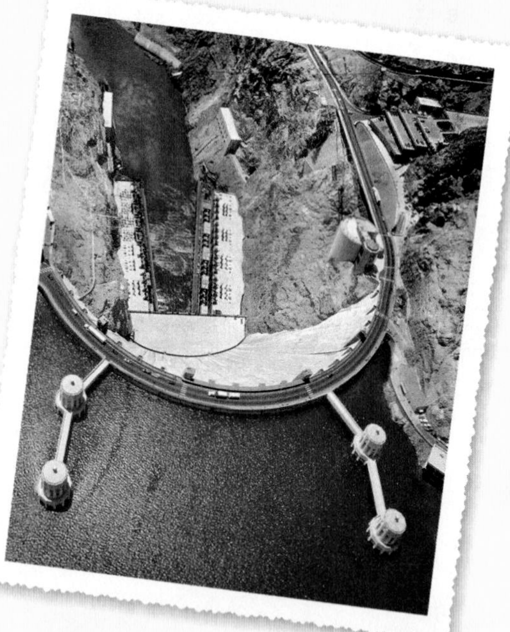

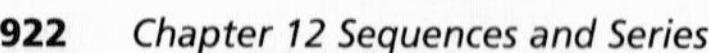

Problem-Solving Focus

Ask students what strategy they would use to solve **Problem 2.** Students may wish to use the strategy Solve a Simpler Problem and/or Make an Organized List. Finding the total number of cars for one year and multiplying by 11 will give students a good estimate to compare with their final answers.

Problem Solving Strategies

- Draw a Diagram
- Make a Model
- Guess and Test
- Work Backward
- Find a Pattern
- Make a Table
- Solve a Simpler Problem
- Use Logical Reasoning
- Use a Venn Diagram
- Make an Organized List

Silver and Gold Mining

Nevada's nickname is the Silver State, which is not surprising considering that more than 10 million ounces of the metal are mined in Nevada each year. Gold mining is also an essential part of Nevada's economy. In fact, if Nevada were a nation, it would rank third in the world in gold production behind South Africa and Australia.

Choose one or more strategies to solve each problem.

1. Nevada experienced a gold-mining boom from 1981 to 1990. During this period, the number of thousands of ounces of gold mined each year can be modeled by a geometric sequence in which $a_1 = 375$ (that is, 375,000 ounces were mined in 1981) and the common ratio is 1.35. Approximately how many ounces of gold were mined in 1990? 5,585,000 oz
2. What was the total gold production in the years 1981 through 1990, inclusive? 20,471,000 oz
3. In a particular mine, the probability of discovering a profitable quantity of gold in a sector is approximately 40%. What is the probability that the miners will discover a profitable quantity of gold in 3 of the next 4 sectors? 15.36%

For 4, use the table.

4. Nevada experienced a silver boom during the 1990s. An industry analyst is collecting detailed data for all of the years from 1991 to 2000 in which silver production was outside of 1 standard deviation of the mean. For which years should she collect this data?
1991, 1992, 1995, 1997, and 1999

Nevada Silver Production

Year	Production (million oz)
1991	18.6
1992	19.7
1993	23.2
1994	22.8
1995	24.6
1996	20.7
1997	24.7
1998	21.5
1999	19.5
2000	23.2

Silver and Gold Mining

Reading Strategies

ENGLISH LANGUAGE LEARNERS

Check that ELL students are familiar with the word *mining.* Students may recognize similarities to words in other languages. For example, the Spanish word for *miner* is *minero.*

Using Data In discussing the data presented in **Problem 1,** ask students to describe the annual rate of increase in gold production as a percent. 35% Before students do any calculations, ask them to make some ballpark predictions about gold production in 1990.

Problem-Solving Focus

Although students can use formulas to solve **Problems 1** and **2,** they may gain a deeper understanding of these problems if they also explore them using problem-solving strategies. For example, as part of the final step of the problem-solving process, **(4) Look Back,** ask students which strategy might be useful in checking the answers to these problems. Possible answer: Use the strategy Make a Table. To check the answer to **Problem 1,** look at the gold production for 1990 in the table. To check the answer to **Problem 2,** add all the values in the production column of the table.

Trigonometric Functions

Section 13A	Section 13B
Trigonometry and Angles	**Applying Trigonometric Functions**
Connecting Algebra to Geometry Special Right Triangles	**13-5 The Law of Sines**
13-1 Right-Angle Trigonometry	**13-6 The Law of Cosines**
13-2 Angles of Rotation	
13-3 Technology Lab Explore The Unit Circle	
13-3 The Unit Circle	
13-4 Inverses of Trigonometric Functions	

Pacing Guide for 45-Minute Classes

Chapter 13

DAY 1	DAY 2	DAY 3	DAY 4	DAY 5
Connecting Algebra to Geometry 13-1 Lesson	13-1 Lesson 13-2 Lesson	13-2 Lesson 13-3 Technology Lab	13-3 Lesson	13-4 Lesson
DAY 6	**DAY 7**	**DAY 8**	**DAY 9**	**DAY 10**
Multi-Step Test Prep Ready to Go On?	13-5 Lesson	13-5 Lesson	13-6 Lesson	Multi-Step Test Prep Ready to Go On?
DAY 11				
Chapter 13 Test				

Pacing Guide for 90-Minute Classes

Chapter 13

DAY 1	DAY 2	DAY 3	DAY 4	DAY 5
Connecting Algebra to Geometry 13-1 Lesson 13-2 Lesson	13-2 Lesson 13-3 Technology Lab 13-3 Lesson	13-4 Lesson Multi-Step Test Prep Ready to Go On?	13-5 Lesson	13-6 Lesson Multi-Step Test Prep Ready to Go On?
DAY 6				
Chapter 13 Test 14-1 Lesson				

ONGOING ASSESSMENT and INTERVENTION

Assess Prior Knowledge

Before Chapter 13

DIAGNOSE	PRESCRIBE
Diagnose readiness for the chapter.	Prescribe intervention.
Are You Ready? SE p. 925	***Are You Ready? Intervention*** Skills 12, 29, 30, 31

Formative Assessment

Before Every Lesson

DIAGNOSE	PRESCRIBE
Diagnose readiness for the lesson.	Prescribe intervention.
Warm Up TE, every lesson	**Skills Bank** SE pp. S46–S73
	Reteach CRB, Ch. 1–13

During Every Lesson

DIAGNOSE	PRESCRIBE
Diagnose understanding of lesson concepts.	Prescribe intervention.
Check It Out! SE, every example	**Questioning Strategies** TE, every example
Think and Discuss SE, every lesson	**Reading Strategies** CRB, every lesson
Write About It SE, every lesson	***Success for ELL*** pp. 177–188
Journal TE, every lesson	

After Every Lesson

DIAGNOSE	PRESCRIBE
Diagnose mastery of lesson concepts.	Prescribe intervention.
Lesson Quiz TE, every lesson	**Reteach** CRB, every lesson
Alternative Assessment TE, every lesson	**Problem Solving** CRB, every lesson
Test Prep SE, every lesson	**Test Prep Doctor** TE, every lesson
Test and Practice Generator	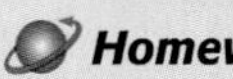 ***Homework Help* Online**

Before Chapter 13 Testing

DIAGNOSE	PRESCRIBE
Diagnose mastery of concepts in the chapter.	Prescribe intervention.
Ready to Go On? SE pp. 957, 975	***Ready to Go On? Intervention*** pp. 207–224
Multi-Step Test Prep SE pp. 956, 974	**Scaffolding Questions** TE pp. 956, 974
Section Quizzes AR pp. 245–246	
Test and Practice Generator	

Before High Stakes Testing

DIAGNOSE	PRESCRIBE
Diagnose mastery of benchmark concepts.	Prescribe intervention.
College Entrance Exam Practice SE p. 981	***College Entrance Exam Practice***
Standardized Test Prep SE pp. 984–985	***State Test Prep Workbook***
***State Test Prep* CD-ROM**	

Summative Assessment

After Chapter 13

DIAGNOSE	PRESCRIBE
Check mastery of chapter concepts.	Prescribe intervention.
Multiple-Choice Tests (Forms A, B, C)	**Reteach** CRB, every lesson
Free-Response Tests (Forms A, B, C)	***Lesson Tutorial Videos*** Chapter 13
Performance Assessment AR pp. 247–260	
Test and Practice Generator	
Check mastery of benchmark concepts.	Prescribe intervention.
AYP State Tests	***State Test Prep Workbook***
College Entrance Exams	***College Entrance Exam Practice***

KEY: **SE** = *Student Edition* **TE** = *Teacher's Edition* **CRB** = *Chapter Resource Book* **AR** = *Assessment Resources*  Available on CD-ROM Available online

Supporting the Teacher

Chapter 13 Resource Book

Practice A, B, C
pp. 3–5, 11–13, 19–21, 27–29, 35–37, 43–45

Reading Strategies ELL
pp. 10, 18, 26, 34, 42, 50

Reteach
pp. 6–7, 14–15, 22–23, 30–31, 38–39, 46–47

Problem Solving
pp. 9, 17, 25, 33, 41, 49

Challenge
pp. 8, 16, 24, 32, 40, 48

Parent Letter pp. 1–2

Transparencies

Lesson Transparencies, Volume 4 .... Chapter 13
- Warm Ups
- Teaching Transparencies
- Additional Examples
- Lesson Quizzes

Alternate Openers: Explorations 89–94

Know-It Notebook .... Chapter 13
- Graphic Organizers

Teacher Tools

Power Presentations®
Complete PowerPoint® presentations for Chapter 13 lessons

Lesson Tutorial Videos®
Holt authors Ed Burger and Freddie Renfro present tutorials to support the Chapter 13 lessons.

One-Stop Planner®
Easy access to all Chapter 13 resources and assessments, as well as software for lesson planning, test generation, and puzzle creation

IDEA Works!®
Key Chapter 13 resources and assessments modified to address special learning needs

Lesson Plans .... pp. 89–94

Solutions Key .... Chapter 13

Algebra Posters

TechKeys **Lab Resources**

Project Teacher Support **Parent Resources** 

Workbooks

Homework and Practice Workbook
Teacher's Guide .... pp. 89–94

Know-It Notebook
Teacher's Guide .... Chapter 13

Problem Solving Workbook
Teacher's Guide .... pp. 89–94

State Test Prep Workbook
Teacher's Guide

Technology Highlights for the Teacher

Power Presentations

Dynamic presentations to engage students. Complete PowerPoint® presentations for every lesson in Chapter 13.

2-1 Solving One-Step Equations

Isolate a variable by using inverse operations which "undo" operations on the variable.

An equation is like a balanced scale. To keep the balance, perform the same operation on both sides.

Inverse Operations	
Operation	Inverse Operation
Addition	Subtraction
Subtraction	Addition

One-Stop Planner

Easy access to Chapter 13 resources and assessments. Includes lesson-planning, test-generation, and puzzle-creation software.

Premier Online Edition

Chapter 13 includes Tutorial Videos, Lesson Activities, Lesson Quizzes, Homework Help, and Chapter Project.

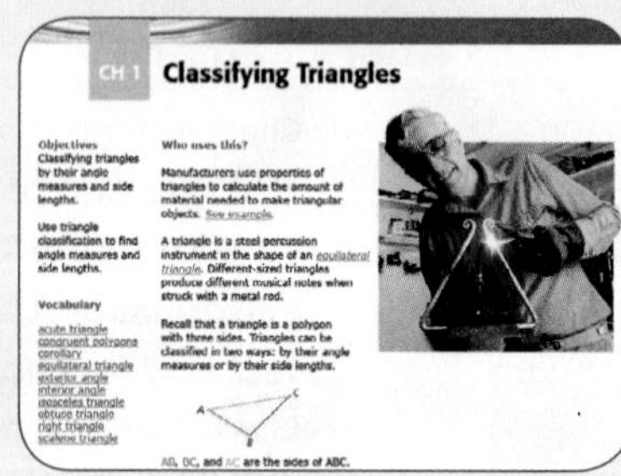

KEY: **SE** = *Student Edition* **TE** = *Teacher's Edition*  English Language Learners   Available on CD-ROM   Available online

Reaching All Learners

Resources for All Learners

Algebra Lab Activities ... Chapter 13
Technology Lab Activities ... Chapter 13
Homework and Practice Workbook ... pp. 89–94
Know-It Notebook ... Chapter 13
Problem Solving Workbook ... pp. 89–94

DEVELOPING LEARNERS

Practice A ... CRB, every lesson
Reteach ... CRB, every lesson
Inclusion ... TE pp. 928, 930, 938, 940, 944, 946, 948, 951, 960, 963, 967
Questioning Strategies ... TE, every example
Modified Chapter 13 Resources ... *IDEA Works!*
***Homework Help* Online**

ON-LEVEL LEARNERS

Practice B ... CRB, every lesson
Graphic Organizers ... TE p. 937
Cooperative Learning ... TE p. 959

ADVANCED LEARNERS

Practice C ... CRB, every lesson
Challenge ... CRB, every lesson
Reading and Writing Math EXTENSION ... TE p. 927
Multi-Step Test Prep EXTENSION ... TE pp. 956, 974
Critical Thinking ... TE pp. 948, 952, 972

English Language Learners

ENGLISH LANGUAGE LEARNERS

Are You Ready? Vocabulary ... SE p. 925
Vocabulary Connections ... SE p. 926
Lesson Vocabulary ... SE pp. 929, 936, 943, 950
Vocabulary Exercises ... SE pp. 933, 939, 947, 953
Vocabulary Review ... SE p. 976
English Language Learners ... TE pp. 927, 930
Reading Strategies ... CRB, every lesson
Success for English Language Learners ... pp. 177–188
Multilingual Glossary

Reaching All Learners Through...

Inclusion ... TE pp. 928, 930, 938, 940, 944, 946, 948, 951, 960, 963, 967
Auditory Cues ... TE p. 930
Graphic Organizers ... TE p. 937
Number Sense ... TE p. 939
Visual Cues ... TE p. 944
Critical Thinking ... TE pp. 948, 952, 972
Cognitive Strategies ... TE p. 959
Cooperative Learning ... TE p. 959
Kinesthetic Experience ... TE p. 961
Test Prep Doctor ... TE pp. 935, 941, 948, 955, 965, 973, 981, 982, 984
Common Error Alerts ... TE pp. 931, 935, 941, 945, 949, 963, 969, 971
Scaffolding Questions ... TE pp. 956, 974

Technology Highlights for Reaching All Learners

Lesson Tutorial Videos

Starring Holt authors Ed Burger and Freddie Renfro! Live tutorials to support every lesson in Chapter 13.

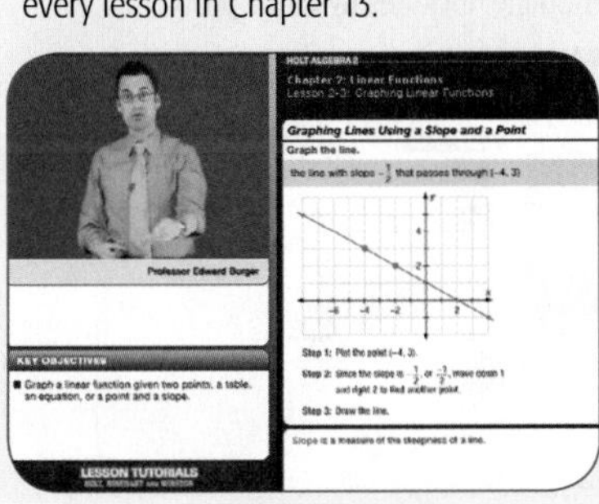

Multilingual Glossary

Searchable glossary includes definitions in English, Spanish, Vietnamese, Chinese, Hmong, Korean, and 4 other languages.

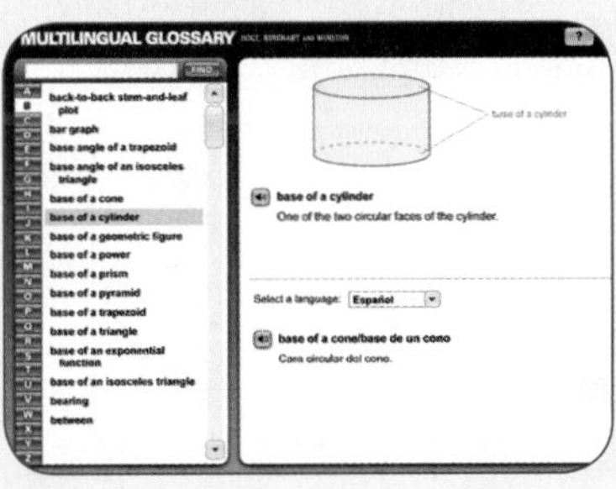

Online Interactivities

Interactive tutorials provide visually engaging alternative opportunities to learn concepts and master skills.

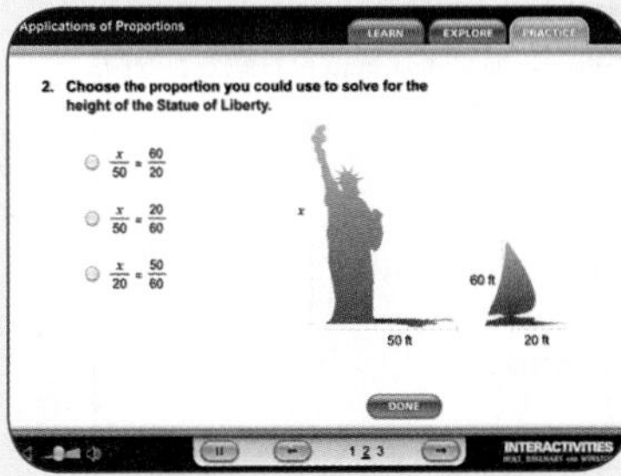

KEY: **SE** = *Student Edition* **TE** = *Teacher's Edition* **CRB** = *Chapter Resource Book*  Available on CD-ROM  Available online

CHAPTER 13

Ongoing Assessment

Assessing Prior Knowledge

Determine whether students have the required prerequisite concepts and skills for success in Chapter 13.

Are You Ready? SPANISH .... SE p. 925
Warm Up .... TE, every lesson

Test Preparation

Provide review and practice for Chapter 13 and standardized tests.

Multi-Step Test Prep .... SE pp. 956, 974
Study Guide: Review .... SE pp. 976–979
Test Tackler .... SE pp. 982–983
Standardized Test Prep .... SE pp. 984–985
College Entrance Exam Practice .... SE p. 981
State Test Prep Workbook
***State Test Prep* CD-ROM**
IDEA Works!

Alternative Assessment

Assess students' understanding of Chapter 13 concepts and combined problem-solving skills.

Chapter 13 Project .... SE p. 924
Alternative Assessment .... TE, every lesson
Performance Assessment .... AR pp. 259–260
Portfolio Assessment .... AR p. xxxiv

Daily Assessment

Provide formative assessment for each day of Chapter 13.

Questioning Strategies .... TE, every example
Think and Discuss .... SE, every lesson
Check It Out! Exercises .... SE, every example
Write About It .... SE, every lesson
Journal .... TE, every lesson
Lesson Quiz .... TE, every lesson
Alternative Assessment .... TE, every lesson
Modified Lesson Quizzes .... *IDEA Works!*

Weekly Assessment

Provide formative assessment for each week of Chapter 13.

Multi-Step Test Prep .... SE pp. 956, 974
Ready to Go On? .... SE pp. 957, 975
Cumulative Assessment .... SE pp. 984–985
Test and Practice Generator .... *One-Stop Planner*

Formal Assessment

Provide summative assessment of Chapter 13 mastery.

Section Quizzes .... AR pp. 245–246
Chapter 13 Test .... SE p. 980
Chapter Test (Levels A, B, C) .... AR pp. 247–258
• Multiple Choice • Free Response
Cumulative Test .... AR pp. 261–264
Test and Practice Generator .... *One-Stop Planner*
Modified Chapter 13 Test .... *IDEA Works!*

Technology Highlights for Ongoing Assessment

Are You Ready? SPANISH

Automatically assess readiness and prescribe intervention for Chapter 13 prerequisite skills.

Ready to Go On?

Automatically assess understanding and prescribe intervention for Sections 13A and 13B.

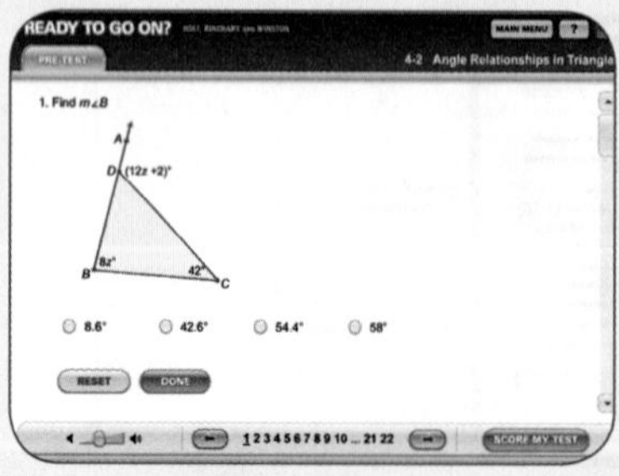

Test and Practice Generator

Use Chapter 13 problem banks to create assessments and worksheets to print out or deliver online. Includes dynamic problems.

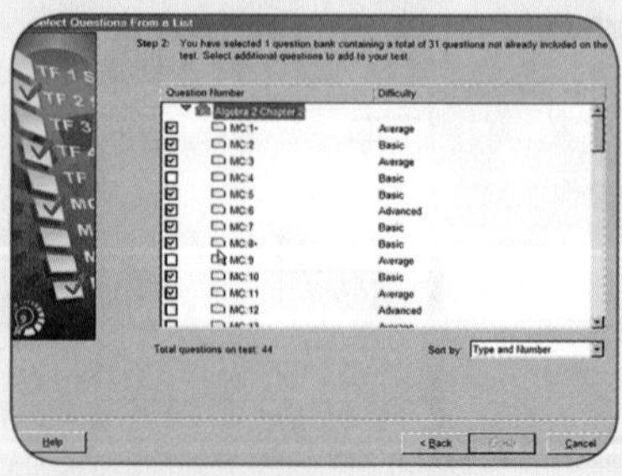

KEY: **SE** = *Student Edition* **TE** = *Teacher's Edition* **AR** = *Assessment Resources*  SPANISH Spanish version available Available on CD-ROM  Available online

Formal Assessment

Three levels (A, B, C) of multiple-choice and free-response chapter tests are available in the *Assessment Resources*.

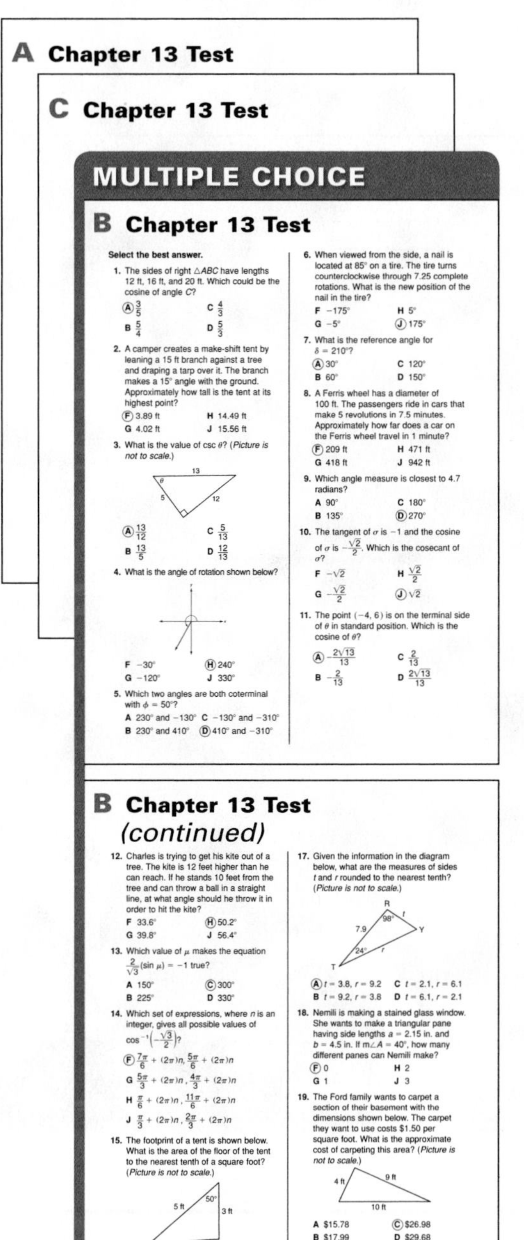

A Chapter 13 Test
C Chapter 13 Test
MULTIPLE CHOICE
B Chapter 13 Test
B Chapter 13 Test (continued)

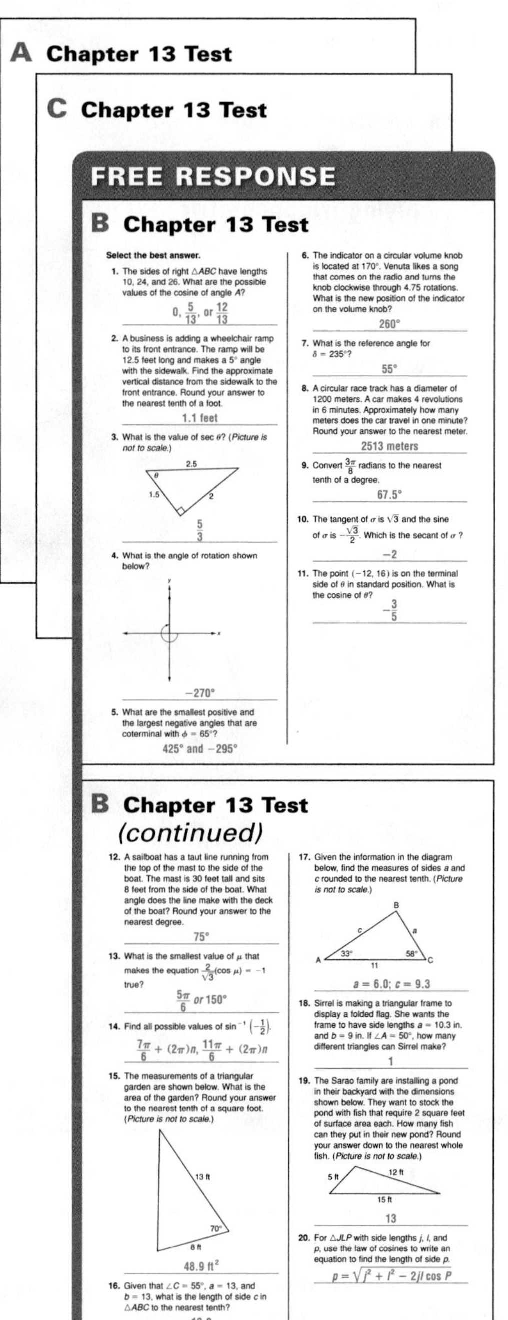

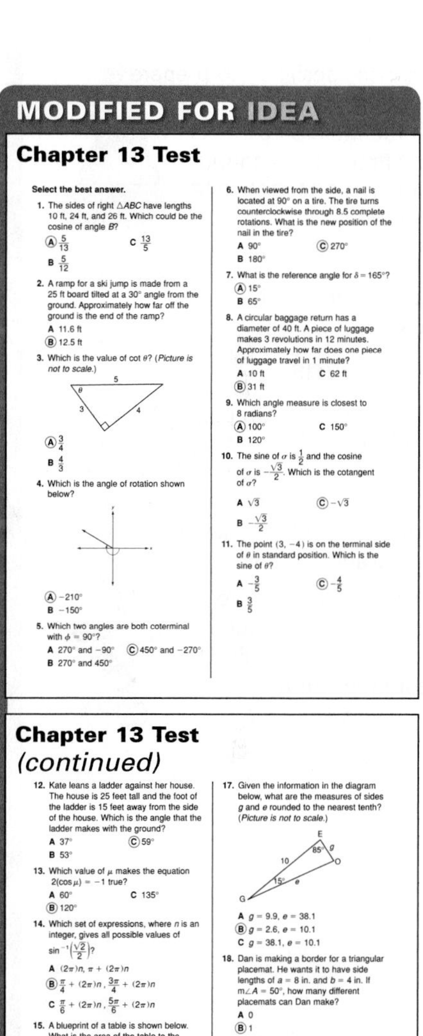

Create and customize Chapter 13 Tests. Instantly generate multiple test versions, answer keys, and practice versions of test items.

CHAPTER 13

SECTION 13A
Trigonometry and Angles

On page 956, students use trigonometry to solve real-world problems involving the Monterey Bay Aquarium.

Exercises designed to prepare students for success on the Multi-Step Test Prep can be found on pages 934, 940, 948, and 955.

SECTION 13B
Applying Trigonometric Functions

On page 974, students apply trigonometric functions to model a real-world situation involving triangulation and the location of a fire.

Exercises designed to prepare students for success on the Multi-Step Test Prep can be found on pages 964 and 972.

CHAPTER 13

Trigonometric Functions

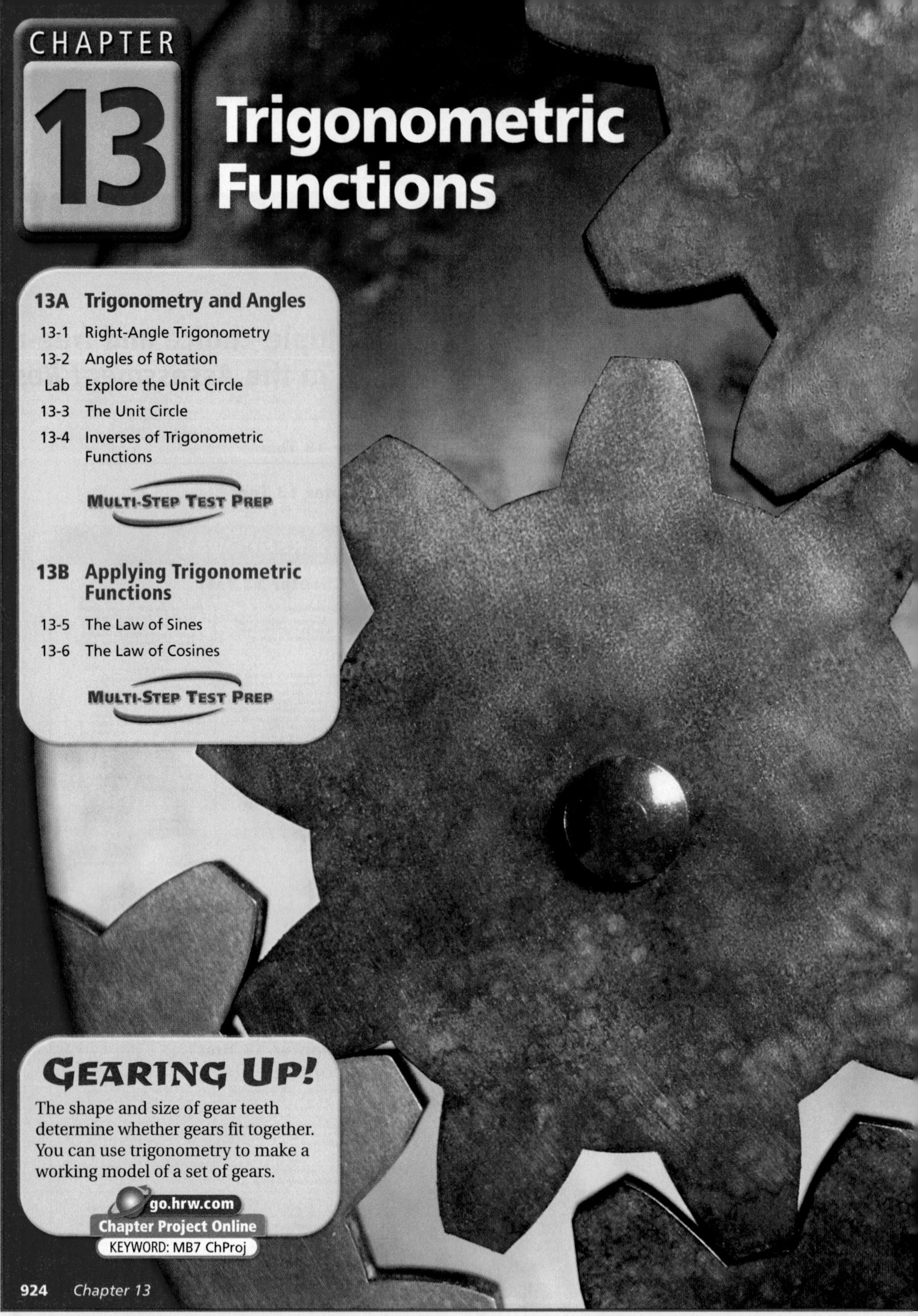

GEARING UP!

The shape and size of gear teeth determine whether gears fit together. You can use trigonometry to make a working model of a set of gears.

go.hrw.com
Chapter Project Online
KEYWORD: MB7 ChProj

Gearing Up!

About the Project

In the Chapter Project, students will use the Law of Cosines and rotation matrices to construct a template for a gear. They will then cut out two copies of the gear from cardboard to see how the gears work in tandem. Students' calculations and construction techniques must be precise in order for the gears to work together properly.

Project Resources

All project resources for teachers and students are provided online.

Materials:

- centimeter graph paper
- metric ruler
- compass
- graphing calculator
- cardboard or fiberboard
- pins

Vocabulary

Match each term on the left with a definition on the right.

1. acute angle D
2. function C
3. domain A
4. reciprocal E

A. the set of all possible input values of a relation or function
B. an angle whose measure is greater than 90°
C. a relation with at most one y-value for each x-value
D. an angle whose measure is greater than 0° and less than 90°
E. the multiplicative inverse of a number

Ratios

Use $\triangle ABC$ to write each ratio.

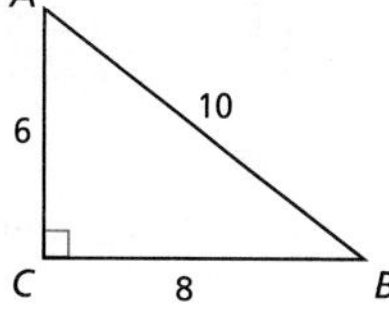

5. BC to AB $\frac{4}{5}$
6. AC to BC $\frac{3}{4}$
7. the length of the longest side to the length of the shortest side $\frac{5}{3}$
8. the length of the shorter leg to the length of the hypotenuse $\frac{3}{5}$

Classify Triangles

Classify each triangle as acute, right, or obtuse.

9. 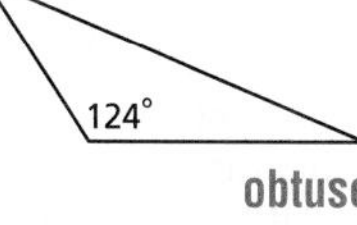

obtuse

10. 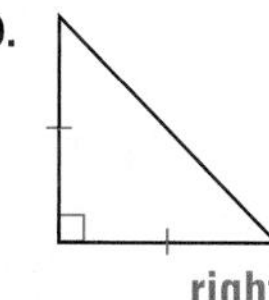
right

11. 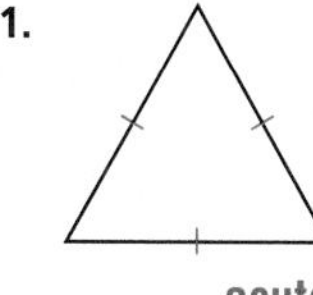
acute

Triangle Sum Theorem

Find the value of x in each triangle.

12. 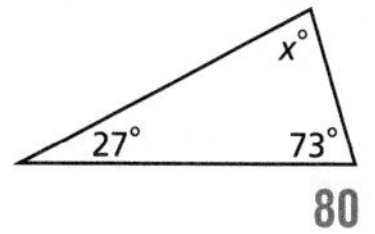

80

13. 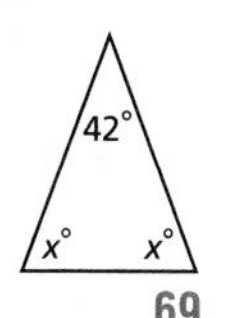

69

14. 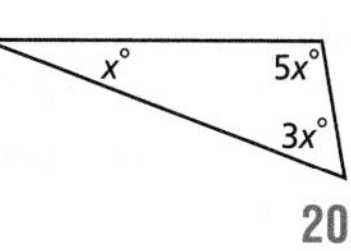

20

Pythagorean Theorem

Find the missing length for each right triangle with legs a and b and hypotenuse c. Round to the nearest tenth.

15. $a = 16, b = \blacksquare, c = 20$ 12
16. $a = 3, b = 5, c = \blacksquare$ 5.8
17. $a = 9, b = \blacksquare, c = 18$ 15.6
18. $a = 7, b = 14, c = \blacksquare$ 15.7

CHAPTER 13

ARE YOU READY?

Organizer

Objective: Assess students' understanding of prerequisite skills.

Prerequisite Skills

Ratios
Classify Triangles
Triangle Sum Theorem
Pythagorean Theorem

Assessing Prior Knowledge

INTERVENTION 

Diagnose and Prescribe

Use this page to determine whether intervention is necessary or whether enrichment is appropriate.

Resources

 ***Are You Ready? Intervention and Enrichment* Worksheets**

 ***Are You Ready?* CD-ROM**

 ***Are You Ready?* Online**
my.hrw.com

ARE YOU READY?
Diagnose and Prescribe

Prerequisite Skill	*Are You Ready? Intervention,* Chapter 13 — Worksheets	CD-ROM	Online
Ratios	Skill 12	Activity 12	Diagnose and Prescribe Online
Classify Triangles	Skill 29	Activity 29	
Triangle Sum Theorem	Skill 30	Activity 30	
Pythagorean Theorem	Skill 31	Activity 31	

***Are You Ready? Enrichment,* Chapter 13**
Worksheets
CD-ROM
Online

CHAPTER 13

Study Guide: Preview

Organizer

Objective: Help students organize the new concepts they will learn in Chapter 13.

Online Edition
Multilingual Glossary

Resources

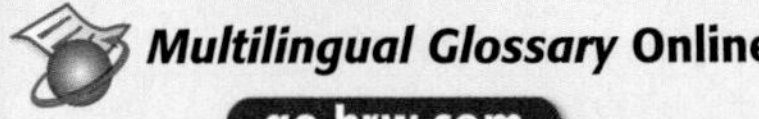

go.hrw.com
KEYWORD: MB7 Glossary

Answers to *Vocabulary Connections*

Possible answers:

1. problems involving side lengths and angle measures of triangles
2. a book, such as a dictionary or encyclopedia, that contains facts and information; an angle that provides information about something
3. a turn; an angle formed by turning one ray and keeping the other ray in place
4. 1 unit

CHAPTER 13

Study Guide: Preview

Where You've Been

Previously, you

- used inverses of functions.
- measured indirectly using ratios and proportional reasoning.
- found equations of circles on the coordinate plane.

In This Chapter

You will study

- using trigonometric functions and their inverses.
- measuring indirectly using side lengths and angles of triangles.
- using angles of rotation and finding arc lengths of circles.

Where You're Going

You can use the skills in this chapter

- in other math classes, such as Precalculus.
- in scientific fields such as astronomy, forensics, geology, and engineering.
- outside of school in navigation, surveying, drafting, architecture, landscaping, and aviation.

Key Vocabulary/Vocabulario

angle of rotation	ángulo de rotación
coterminal angle	ángulo coterminal
initial side	lado inicial
radian	radián
reference angle	ángulo de referencia
standard position	posición estándar
terminal side	lado terminal
trigonometric function	función trigonométrica
unit circle	círculo unitario

Vocabulary Connections

To become familiar with some of the vocabulary terms in the chapter, consider the following. You may refer to the chapter, the glossary, or a dictionary if you like.

1. The word *trigonometry* comes from Greek words meaning "triangle measurement." What types of problems might you be able to solve by using **trigonometric functions**?
2. What is a reference book? Based on this meaning of *reference*, what do you think a **reference angle** is?
3. What is a *rotation*? What do you think an **angle of rotation** is?
4. The origin of the word *unit* is a Latin word meaning "one." What do you think the radius of a **unit circle** is?

CHAPTER 13

Reading Strategy: Interpret and Read Diagrams

Diagrams are informational tools. Be sure to read and understand the information provided in these visual aids before you attempt to work a problem.

From Lesson 10-3

MULTI-STEP TEST PREP

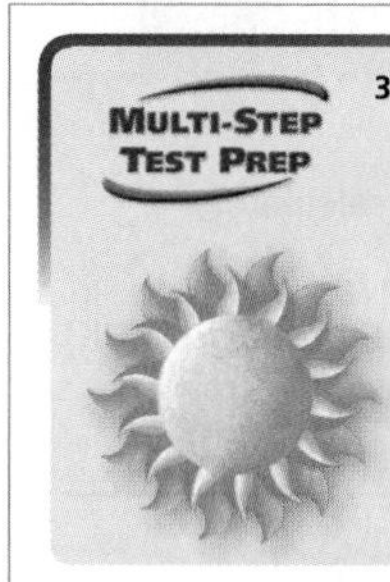

36. This problem will prepare you for the Multi-Step Test Prep on page 758.

The figure shows the elliptical orbit of Mars, where each unit of the coordinate plane represents 1 million kilometers. As shown, the planet's maximum distance from the Sun is 249 million kilometers and its minimum distance from the Sun is 207 million kilometers.

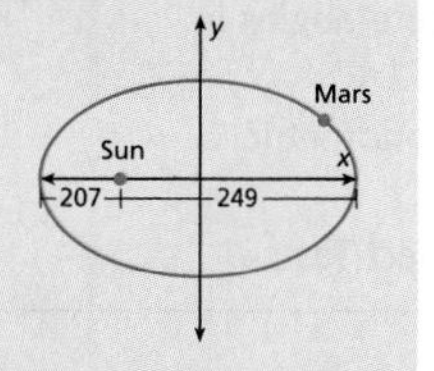

a. The Sun is at one focus of the ellipse. What are the coordinates of the Sun?

b. What is the length of the minor axis of the ellipse?

c. Write an equation that models the orbit of Mars.

1. **Examine the diagram.** A point labeled *Sun* lies on the major axis of what appears to be an ellipse. The distances from this point to the vertices are labeled 207 and 249.
2. **Reread the problem, and identify key information about the diagram.** Each unit represents 1 million kilometers. The Sun is at one focus of the ellipse.
3. **Interpret this information.** The labels 207 and 249 represent 207 million kilometers and 249 million kilometers. The length of the major axis can be found by adding these two measurements.
4. **Now you are ready to solve the problem.**

Try This

Read the problem from Chapter 10, and examine the diagram. Then answer the questions below.

26. Engineering The main cables of a suspension bridge are ideally parabolic. The cables over a bridge that is 400 feet long are attached to towers that are 100 feet tall. The lowest point of the cable is 40 feet above the bridge.

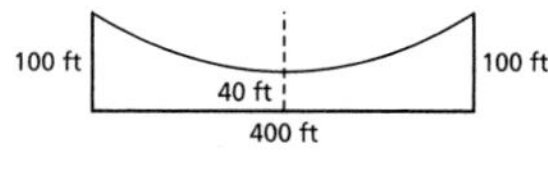

a. Find the coordinates of the vertex and the tops of the towers if the bridge represents the x-axis and the axis of symmetry is the y-axis.

1. What information is provided in the diagram?
2. What information regarding the diagram is provided in the problem?
3. What conclusions can you draw from the information related to the diagram?

Reading and Writing Math

CHAPTER 13

Organizer

Objective: Help students apply strategies to understand and retain key concepts.

Online Edition

Resources

Chapter 13 Resource Book

Reading Strategies

ENGLISH LANGUAGE LEARNERS

Reading Strategy: Interpret and Read Diagrams

Discuss Emphasize that being able to interpret diagrams is an essential part of problem solving. Point out that diagrams often contain information that is not included in the text of a problem. Discuss with students the types of information that may be presented in figures and diagrams, such as measurements, labels, and geometric relationships.

Extend As students work through Chapter 13, have them analyze diagrams (as well as tables, charts, and graphs) within the instructional text of the lessons. Discuss what information the diagrams convey and how students can use this information to help them understand the content of the lesson.

Answers to *Try This*

1. Possible answer: The diagram appears to show a parabola. The vertical distance between the vertex of the parabola and a horizontal segment is labeled 40 ft. The length of the horizontal segment is labeled 400 ft. Two vertical segments that intersect the parabola and the horizontal segment are labeled 100 ft.
2. Possible answer: The horizontal segment represents a bridge (and the x-axis). The vertical segments represent bridge towers. The parabola represents the bridge cable, and the axis of symmetry of the parabola represents the y-axis.
3. Possible answer: The 2 towers are the same distance from the lowest point of the cable, and therefore, the same distance from the y-axis.

SECTION

13A Trigonometry and Angles

One-Minute Section Planner

Lesson	Lab Resources	Materials
Lesson 13-1 Right-Angle Trigonometry • Understand and use trigonometric relationships of acute angles in triangles. • Determine side lengths of right triangles by using trigonometric functions. ☑ SAT-10 ☑ NAEP ☑ ACT ☑ SAT ☑ SAT Subject Tests	***Algebra Lab Activities*** 13-1 Algebra Lab	**Required** graphing calculator **Optional** ruler (MK), protractor (MK)
Lesson 13-2 Angles of Rotation • Draw angles in standard position. • Determine the values of the trigonometric functions for an angle in standard position. ☐ SAT-10 ☐ NAEP ☑ ACT ☑ SAT ☑ SAT Subject Tests		**Required** protractor (MK) **Optional** graph paper, graphing calculator
13-3 Technology Lab Explore the Unit Circle • Use a graphing calculator to graph the unit circle and find the sine and cosine of various angles. ☐ SAT-10 ☐ NAEP ☑ ACT ☐ SAT ☐ SAT Subject Tests	***Technology Lab Activities*** 13-3 Lab Recording Sheet	**Required** graphing calculator
Lesson 13-3 The Unit Circle • Convert angle measures between degrees and radians. • Find the values of trigonometric functions on the unit circle. ☐ SAT-10 ☐ NAEP ☐ ACT ☐ SAT ☑ SAT Subject Tests	***Algebra Lab Activities*** 13-3 Algebra Lab	**Required** protractor (MK) **Optional** graph paper, graphing calculator, blank unit circle, colored pencils (MK)
Lesson 13-4 Inverses of Trigonometric Functions • Evaluate inverse trigonometric functions. • Use trigonometric equations and inverse trigonometric functions to solve problems. ☐ SAT-10 ☐ NAEP ☐ ACT ☐ SAT ☐ SAT Subject Tests		**Required** graphing calculator **Optional** ruler or tape measure (MK), protractor (MK)

MK = *Manipulatives Kit*

Section Overview

Professional Development

Trigonometric Functions and Angles of Rotation — *Lessons 13-1, 13-2*

Trigonometric functions and their reciprocals are used in such fields as carpentry, drafting, navigating, and surveying.

For a point $P(x, y)$ on the terminal side of θ in standard position and $r = \sqrt{x^2 + y^2}$:

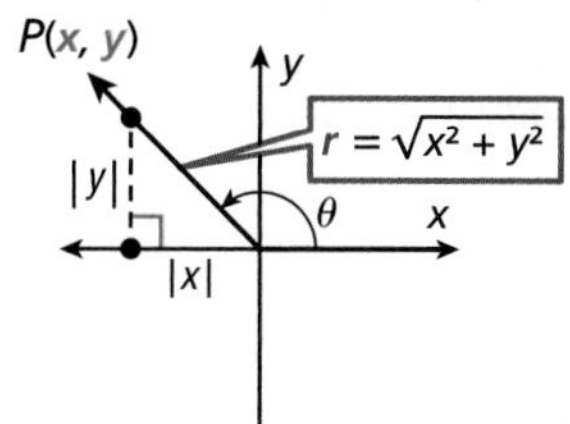

Trigonometric Functions	Reciprocal Trigonometric Functions
$\sin\theta = \dfrac{\text{opposite}}{\text{hypotenuse}} = \dfrac{y}{r}$	$\csc\theta = \dfrac{\text{hypotenuse}}{\text{opposite}} = \dfrac{r}{y}$
$\cos\theta = \dfrac{\text{adjacent}}{\text{hypotenuse}} = \dfrac{x}{r}$	$\sec\theta = \dfrac{\text{hypotenuse}}{\text{adjacent}} = \dfrac{r}{x}$
$\tan\theta = \dfrac{\text{opposite}}{\text{adjacent}} = \dfrac{y}{x}$	$\cot\theta = \dfrac{\text{adjacent}}{\text{opposite}} = \dfrac{x}{y}$

For an angle θ in standard position, the **reference angle** is the acute angle formed by the terminal side of θ and the x-axis.

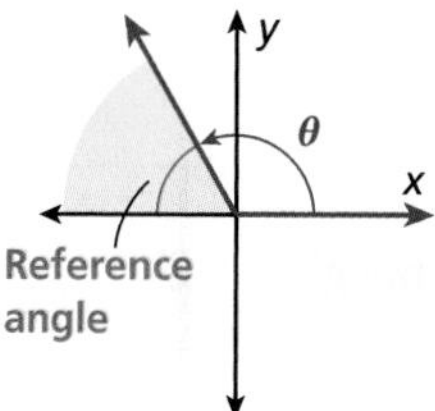

Use a reference angle to evaluate trigonometric functions.

$$\cos 135° = -\cos 45° = -\frac{\sqrt{2}}{2}$$

Radians — *Lesson 13-3*

In many applications, rotation is measured using radians rather than degrees. Radians have the advantage of being real-number measurements.

To convert from **degrees** d to **radians**:

$$d\left(\frac{\pi \text{ radians}}{180°}\right)$$

Example: $30° = 30°\left(\dfrac{\pi \text{ radians}}{180°}\right) = \dfrac{\pi}{6}$ radians

To convert from **radians** r to **degrees**:

$$r\left(\frac{180°}{\pi \text{ radians}}\right)$$

Example: $\dfrac{2\pi}{3} = \dfrac{2\pi}{3}\left(\dfrac{180°}{\pi \text{ radians}}\right) = 120°$

Inverse Trigonometric Functions — *Lesson 13-4*

Inverse trigonometric functions can be used to solve equations involving angle measures.

The ***domains*** of the trigonometric functions are ***restricted*** so that the inverse trigonometric relations can be defined as functions.

Inverse Sine Function	Inverse Cosine Function	Inverse Tangent Function
$\text{Sin}^{-1} a = \theta$, where $\text{Sin}\,\theta = a$	$\text{Cos}^{-1} a = \theta$, where $\text{Cos}\,\theta = a$	$\text{Tan}^{-1} a = \theta$, where $\text{Tan}\,\theta = a$
Domain: $\{-1 \le a \le 1\}$	Domain: $\{-1 \le a \le 1\}$	Domain: $\{-\infty < a < \infty\}$
Range: $\left\{-\dfrac{\pi}{2} \le \theta \le \dfrac{\pi}{2}\right\}$	Range: $\{0 \le \theta \le \pi\}$	Range: $\left\{-\dfrac{\pi}{2} < \theta < \dfrac{\pi}{2}\right\}$

Organizer

See Skills Bank page S60

Pacing:
Traditional $\frac{1}{2}$ day
Block $\frac{1}{4}$ day

Objective: Determine unknown side lengths of special right triangles.

Online Edition

Teach

Remember

Students review the relationships among the side lengths of 45°-45°-90° triangles and 30°-60°-90° triangles.

INTERVENTION For additional review and practice on finding side lengths of special right triangles, see Skills Bank page S60.

Inclusion Remind students that the legs of a right triangle are the two sides that form the right angle.

Close

Assess

Ask students to describe how they would find the lengths of the legs of a 30°-60°-90° triangle if they were given the length of the hypotenuse.

State Resources

Special Right Triangles

See Skills Bank page S60

Review the relationships of the side lengths of special right triangles below. You can use these relationships to find side lengths of special right triangles.

Special Right Triangles	
45°-45°-90° Triangle Theorem	In any 45°-45°-90° triangle, the length of the hypotenuse is $\sqrt{2}$ times the length of a leg. (Triangle: legs x, x; hypotenuse $x\sqrt{2}$; angles 45°, 45°) 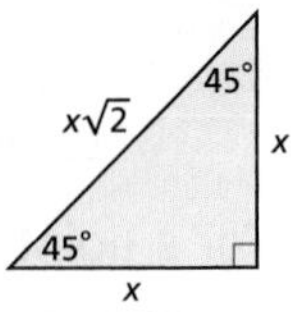
30°-60°-90° Triangle Theorem	In any 30°-60°-90° triangle, the length of the hypotenuse is 2 times the length of the shorter leg, and the length of the longer leg is $\sqrt{3}$ times the length of the shorter leg. (Triangle: shorter leg y; longer leg $y\sqrt{3}$; hypotenuse $2y$; angles 30°, 60°) 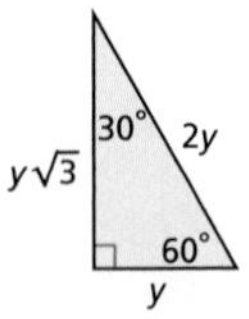

Example

Find the unknown side lengths for the triangle shown.

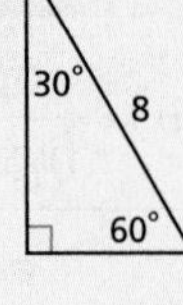

The triangle is a 30°-60°-90° triangle, and the length of the hypotenuse is 8.

Step 1 Find the length of the shorter leg.

$8 = 2y$ *hypotenuse = 2 • shorter leg*

$4 = y$ *Solve for y, the length of the shorter leg.*

Step 2 Find the length of the longer leg.

$4\sqrt{3}$ *longer leg = $\sqrt{3}$ • shorter leg*

The length of the shorter leg is 4, and the length of the longer leg is $4\sqrt{3}$.

Check Use the Pythagorean Theorem.

$4^2 + (4\sqrt{3})^2$	$= 8^2$
$16 + 48$	64
64	64 ✓

Try This

Find the unknown side lengths for each triangle.

1. 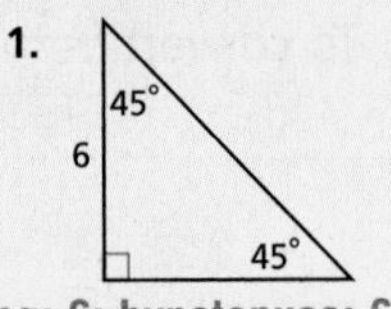

leg: 6; hypotenuse: $6\sqrt{2}$

2. 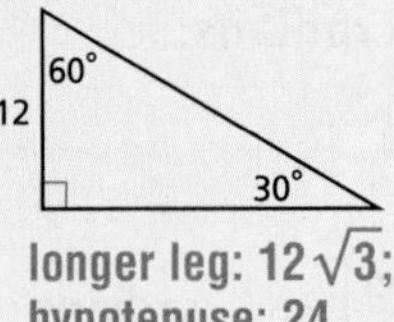

longer leg: $12\sqrt{3}$; hypotenuse: 24

3. 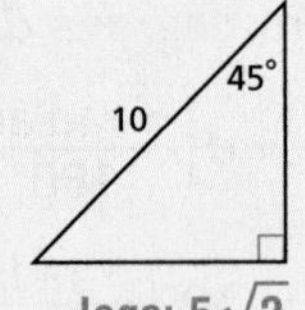

legs: $5\sqrt{2}$

4. 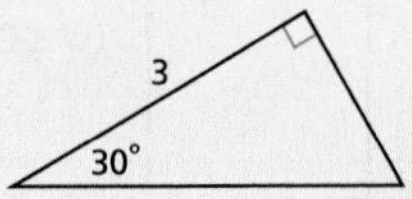 (Triangle: 3, 30°)
shorter leg: $\sqrt{3}$; hypotenuse: $2\sqrt{3}$

13-1 Right-Angle Trigonometry

Objectives
Understand and use trigonometric relationships of acute angles in triangles.

Determine side lengths of right triangles by using trigonometric functions.

Vocabulary
trigonometric function
sine
cosine
tangent
cosecant
secant
cotangent

Who uses this?
Trigonometry can be used to measure the heights of objects, such as an eruption of a geyser, that cannot be measured directly. (See Example 4.)

Trigonometry comes from Greek words meaning "triangle measurement." Trigonometry can be used to solve problems involving triangles.

A **trigonometric function** is a function whose rule is given by a trigonometric ratio. A *trigonometric ratio* compares the lengths of two sides of a right triangle. The Greek letter theta θ is traditionally used to represent the measure of an acute angle in a right triangle. The values of trigonometric ratios depend upon θ.

Know it! Note

Trigonometric Functions

WORDS	NUMBERS	SYMBOLS
The **sine** (sin) of angle θ is the ratio of the length of the opposite leg to the length of the hypotenuse.	$\sin\theta = \frac{4}{5}$	$\sin\theta = \frac{\text{opp.}}{\text{hyp.}}$
The **cosine** (cos) of angle θ is the ratio of the length of the adjacent leg to the length of the hypotenuse.	$\cos\theta = \frac{3}{5}$	$\cos\theta = \frac{\text{adj.}}{\text{hyp.}}$
The **tangent** (tan) of angle θ is the ratio of the length of the opposite leg to the length of the adjacent leg.	$\tan\theta = \frac{4}{3}$	$\tan\theta = \frac{\text{opp.}}{\text{adj.}}$

The triangle shown at right is similar to the one in the table because their corresponding angles are congruent. No matter which triangle is used, the value of $\sin\theta$ is the same. The values of the sine and other trigonometric functions depend only on angle θ and not on the size of the triangle.

$$\sin\theta = \frac{2}{2.5} = \frac{4}{5}$$

EXAMPLE 1 Finding Trigonometric Ratios

Find the value of the sine, cosine, and tangent functions for θ.

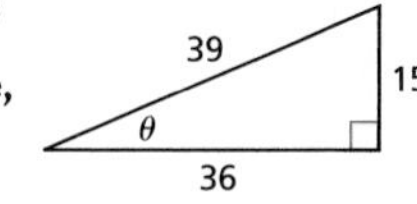

$$\sin\theta = \frac{\text{opp.}}{\text{hyp.}} = \frac{15}{39} = \frac{5}{13} \qquad \cos\theta = \frac{\text{adj.}}{\text{hyp.}} = \frac{36}{39} = \frac{12}{13} \qquad \tan\theta = \frac{\text{opp.}}{\text{adj.}} = \frac{15}{36} = \frac{5}{12}$$

1. Find the value of the sine, cosine, and tangent functions for θ.
$\sin\theta = \frac{15}{17}$; $\cos\theta = \frac{8}{17}$; $\tan\theta = \frac{15}{8}$

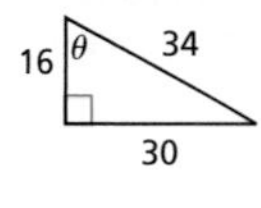

13-1 Organizer

Pacing: Traditional 1 day
Block $\frac{1}{2}$ day

Objectives: Understand and use trigonometric relationships of acute angles in triangles.

Determine side lengths of right triangles by using trigonometric functions.

Algebra Lab
In *Algebra Lab Activities*

Online Edition
Tutorial Videos

Power Presentations with PowerPoint®

Warm Up

Given the measure of one of the acute angles in a right triangle, find the measure of the other acute angle.

1. 45° 45° **2.** 60° 30°

3. 24° 66° **4.** 38° 52°

Find the unknown length for each right triangle with legs *a* and *b* and hypotenuse *c*.

5. $b = 12, c = 13$ $a = 5$

6. $a = 3, b = 3$ $c = 3\sqrt{2}$

Also available on transparency

Math Humor

Q: Why did the 30°-60°-90° triangle marry the 45°-45°-90° triangle?
A: They were right for each other.

1 Introduce

EXPLORATION

13-1 Right-Angle Trigonometry

You can use the Pythagorean Theorem to help you discover properties of special right triangles.

Use the Pythagorean Theorem to find the length of the hypotenuse c of each right triangle. Write your answers in simplest radical form.

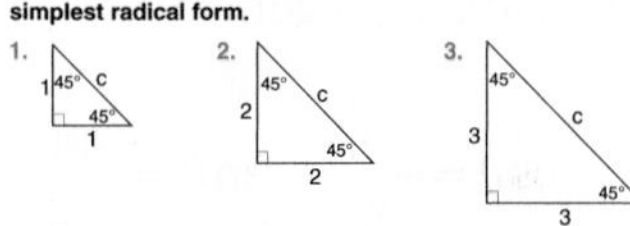

4. For each triangle in Problems 1–3, find the ratio of the length of a leg to the length of the hypotenuse.
5. What pattern do you notice about the ratios you calculated?

THINK AND DISCUSS

6. **Describe** how the side lengths are related to each other in a 45°-45°-90° triangle.
7. **Explain** how you can use the ratio you discovered above to find the value of x in this triangle.

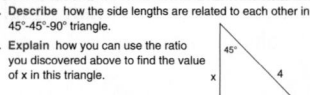

Motivate

Ask students how they would go about measuring the height of a skyscraper. Have them discuss the difficulties of making such a measurement directly. Explain that the height of a skyscraper can be determined much more easily by using relationships among the sides and angles of right triangles. These relationships can be used to measure an object's height indirectly.

Explorations and answers are provided in the *Explorations* binder.

State Resources

go.hrw.com
State Resources Online
KEYWORD: MB7 Resources

Power Presentations with PowerPoint®

Additional Examples

Example 1

Find the value of the sine, cosine, and tangent functions for θ.

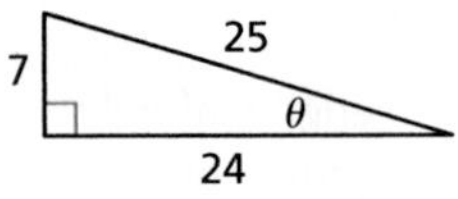

$\sin\theta = \frac{7}{25}$; $\cos\theta = \frac{24}{25}$; $\tan\theta = \frac{7}{24}$

Example 2

Use a trigonometric function to find the value of x. 37

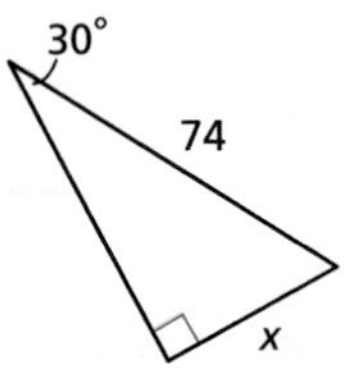

Also available on transparency

INTERVENTION

Questioning Strategies

EXAMPLE 1

- How do you tell which side is the hypotenuse? which is the leg opposite θ? which is the leg adjacent to θ?

EXAMPLE 2

- What information are you given in the diagram?
- How do you determine which trigonometric function to use?

Teaching Tip **Inclusion** Remind students that the hypotenuse of a right triangle is the longest side and is opposite the right angle. ENGLISH LANGUAGE LEARNERS

You will frequently need to determine the value of trigonometric ratios for 30°, 60°, and 45° angles as you solve trigonometry problems. Recall from geometry that in a 30°-60°-90° triangle, the ratio of the side lengths is $1:\sqrt{3}:2$, and that in a 45°-45°-90° triangle, the ratio of the side lengths is $1:1:\sqrt{2}$.

Trigonometric Ratios of Special Right Triangles

Diagram	Sine	Cosine	Tangent
60°, 2, 1, 30°, $\sqrt{3}$	$\sin 30° = \frac{1}{2}$ $\sin 60° = \frac{\sqrt{3}}{2}$	$\cos 30° = \frac{\sqrt{3}}{2}$ $\cos 60° = \frac{1}{2}$	$\tan 30° = \frac{1}{\sqrt{3}} = \frac{\sqrt{3}}{3}$ $\tan 60° = \frac{\sqrt{3}}{1} = \sqrt{3}$
45°, $\sqrt{2}$, 1, 45°, 1	$\sin 45° = \frac{1}{\sqrt{2}} = \frac{\sqrt{2}}{2}$	$\cos 45° = \frac{1}{\sqrt{2}} = \frac{\sqrt{2}}{2}$	$\tan 45° = \frac{1}{1} = 1$

EXAMPLE 2 Finding Side Lengths of Special Right Triangles

Use a trigonometric function to find the value of x.

$\sin\theta = \frac{\text{opp.}}{\text{hyp.}}$ *The sine function relates the opposite leg and the hypotenuse.*

$\sin 60° = \frac{x}{100}$ *Substitute 60° for θ, x for opp., and 100 for hyp.*

$\frac{\sqrt{3}}{2} = \frac{x}{100}$ *Substitute $\frac{\sqrt{3}}{2}$ for sin 60°.*

$50\sqrt{3} = x$ *Multiply both sides by 100 to solve for x.*

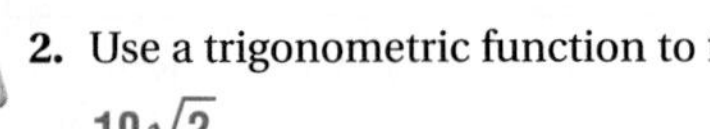

CHECK IT OUT! 2. Use a trigonometric function to find the value of x. $10\sqrt{2}$

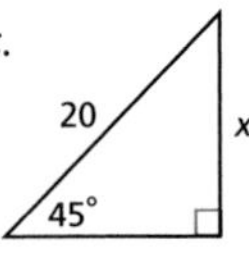

EXAMPLE 3 *Construction Application*

A builder is constructing a wheelchair ramp from the ground to a deck with a height of 18 in. The angle between the ground and the ramp must be 4.8°. To the nearest inch, what should be the distance d between the end of the ramp and the deck?

$\tan\theta = \frac{\text{opp.}}{\text{adj.}}$

$\tan 4.8° = \frac{18}{d}$ *Substitute 4.8° for θ, 18 for opp., and d for adj.*

$d(\tan 4.8°) = 18$ *Multiply both sides by d.*

$d = \frac{18}{\tan 4.8°}$ *Divide both sides by tan 4.8°.*

$d \approx 214$ *Use a calculator to simplify.*

```
18/tan(4.8)
      214.356283
```

The distance should be about 214 in., or 17 ft 10 in.

Caution! Make sure that your graphing calculator is set to interpret angle values as degrees. Press MODE. Check that **Degree** and not **Radian** is highlighted in the third row.

2 Teach

Guided Instruction

Emphasize that the value of trigonometric functions depends only on the value of θ. For example, draw a small and a large right triangle on the board, each with a 20° angle. Have students measure the side lengths of the triangles and use these measurements to determine that each 20° angle has the same sine value. Once students understand the relationships involved in trigonometric ratios, show them how these ratios can be used to determine side lengths of right triangles.

Reaching All Learners

Through Auditory Cues

Suggest that students use a mnemonic, such as SOH-CAH-TOA, to help them remember the following trigonometric ratios:

$\sin\theta = \frac{\text{opp.}}{\text{hyp.}}$ $\cos\theta = \frac{\text{adj.}}{\text{hyp.}}$ $\tan\theta = \frac{\text{opp.}}{\text{adj.}}$

Students who have trouble remembering SOH-CAH-TOA or who can't spell it may be able to remember, "Some old hen caught another hen taking oats away."

3. A skateboard ramp will have a height of 12 in., and the angle between the ramp and the ground will be 17°. To the nearest inch, what will be the length ℓ of the ramp? **41 in.**

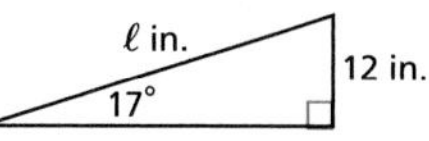

When an object is above or below another object, you can find distances indirectly by using the *angle of elevation* or the *angle of depression* between the objects.

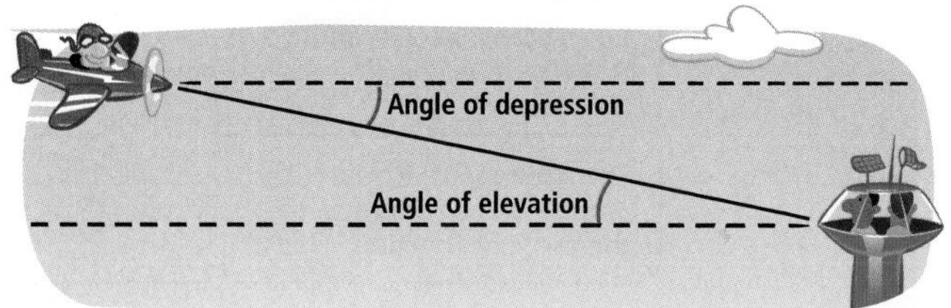

EXAMPLE 4 ***Geology Application***

A park ranger whose eye level is 5 ft above the ground measures the angle of elevation to the top of an eruption of Old Faithful geyser to be 34.6°. If the ranger is standing 200 ft from the geyser's base, what is the height of the eruption to the nearest foot?

Step 1 Draw and label a diagram to represent the information given in the problem.

Step 2 Let x represent the height of the eruption compared with the ranger's eye level. Determine the value of x.

$\tan\theta = \frac{\text{opp.}}{\text{adj.}}$	*Use the tangent function.*
$\tan 34.6° = \frac{x}{200}$	*Substitute 34.6° for θ, x for opp., and 200 for adj.*
$200(\tan 34.6°) = x$	*Multiply both sides by 200.*
$138 \approx x$	*Use a calculator to solve for x.*

Step 3 Determine the overall height of the eruption.

$x + 5 = 138 + 5$	*The ranger's eye level is 5 ft above the ground, so add 5 ft to x to find the overall height of the eruption.*
$= 143$	

The height of the eruption is about 143 ft.

4. A surveyor whose eye level is 6 ft above the ground measures the angle of elevation to the top of the highest hill on a roller coaster to be 60.7°. If the surveyor is standing 120 ft from the hill's base, what is the height of the hill to the nearest foot? **220 ft**

COMMON ERROR ALERT

Students may sometimes misidentify the adjacent leg, the opposite leg, and the hypotenuse when working with trigonometric ratios. Suggest that students first locate and label the hypotenuse—always opposite the right angle. Then they can identify and label the legs opposite and adjacent to the angle in question. Use one of the right triangles in the lesson to illustrate which leg is adjacent to and which leg is opposite a given angle.

Power Presentations with PowerPoint®

Additional Examples

Example 3

In a waterskiing competition, a jump ramp has the measurements shown. To the nearest foot, what is the height h above water that a skier leaves the ramp? 5 ft

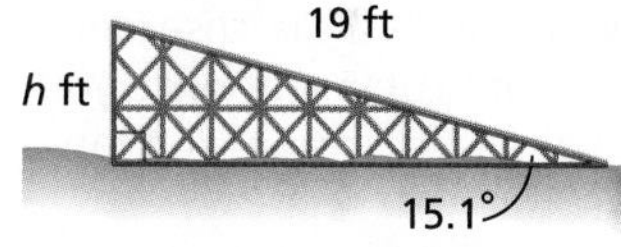

Example 4

A biologist whose eye level is 6 ft above the ground measures the angle of elevation to the top of a tree to be 38.7°. If the biologist is standing 180 ft from the tree's base, what is the height of the tree to the nearest foot? 150 ft

Also available on transparency

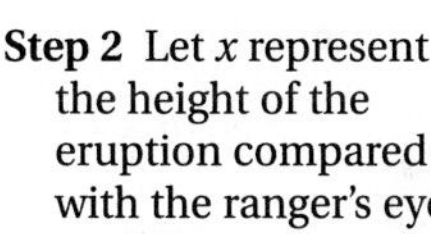

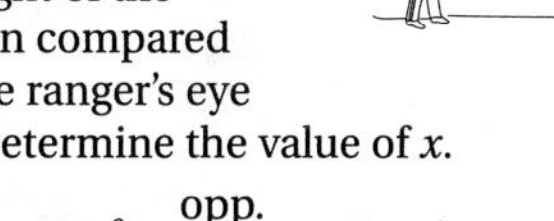

Teaching Tip

Geometry Point out that for a given problem situation, the angle of depression and the angle of elevation have the same measure. Ask volunteers to explain why this is true. Possible answer: The angles of depression and elevation are alternate interior angles formed by a pair of parallel lines and a transversal.

INTERVENTION

Questioning Strategies

EXAMPLE 3

- How can you use your calculator to determine the value of a trigonometric function?

EXAMPLE 4

- When you draw a diagram, how do you know which angle is the angle of elevation?
- How do you determine the overall height once you know the height compared to the observer's eye level?

Power Presentations with PowerPoint®

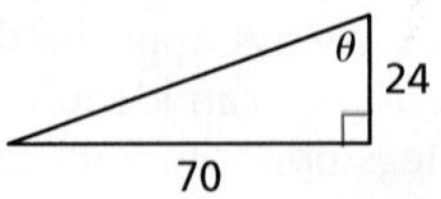

Additional Examples

Example 5

Find the values of the six trigonometric functions for θ.

$\sin\theta = \frac{35}{37}$; $\cos\theta = \frac{12}{37}$;

$\tan\theta = \frac{35}{12}$; $\csc\theta = \frac{37}{35}$;

$\sec\theta = \frac{37}{12}$; $\cot\theta = \frac{12}{35}$

Also available on transparency

INTERVENTION
Questioning Strategies

EXAMPLE 5

- How do you find the length of the third side of the triangle?
- How do you find the cosecant, secant, and cotangent once you know the sine, cosine, and tangent?

The reciprocals of the sine, cosine, and tangent ratios are also trigonometric ratios. They are the trigonometric functions *cosecant*, *secant*, and *cotangent*.

Reciprocal Trigonometric Functions

WORDS	NUMBERS	SYMBOLS
The **cosecant** (csc) of angle θ is the reciprocal of the sine function.	$\csc\theta = \frac{5}{4}$	$\csc\theta = \frac{1}{\sin\theta} = \frac{\text{hyp.}}{\text{opp.}}$
The **secant** (sec) of angle θ is the reciprocal of the cosine function.	$\sec\theta = \frac{5}{3}$	$\sec\theta = \frac{1}{\cos\theta} = \frac{\text{hyp.}}{\text{adj.}}$
The **cotangent** (cot) of angle θ is the reciprocal of the tangent function.	$\cot\theta = \frac{3}{4}$	$\cot\theta = \frac{1}{\tan\theta} = \frac{\text{adj.}}{\text{opp.}}$

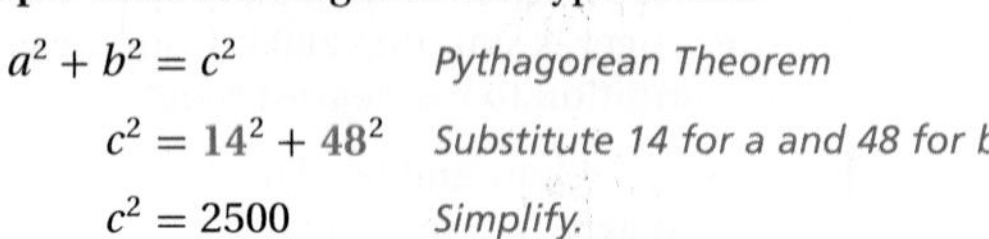

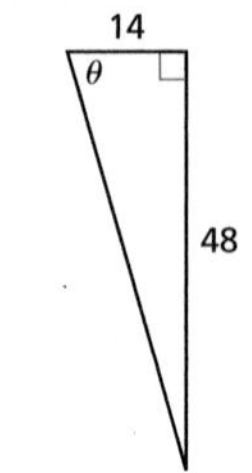

EXAMPLE 5 Finding All Trigonometric Ratios

Find the values of the six trigonometric functions for θ.

Helpful Hint

In each reciprocal pair of trigonometric functions, there is exactly one "*co*."

$$\textit{co}\text{secant}\,\theta = \frac{1}{\text{sine}\,\theta}$$
$$\text{secant}\,\theta = \frac{1}{\textit{co}\text{sine}\,\theta}$$
$$\textit{co}\text{tangent}\,\theta = \frac{1}{\text{tangent}\,\theta}$$

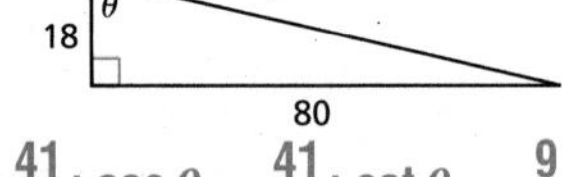

Step 1 Find the length of the hypotenuse.

$a^2 + b^2 = c^2$ *Pythagorean Theorem*

$c^2 = 14^2 + 48^2$ *Substitute 14 for a and 48 for b.*

$c^2 = 2500$ *Simplify.*

$c = 50$ *Solve for c. Eliminate the negative solution.*

Step 2 Find the function values.

$\sin\theta = \frac{48}{50} = \frac{24}{25}$ $\cos\theta = \frac{14}{50} = \frac{7}{25}$ $\tan\theta = \frac{48}{14} = \frac{24}{7}$

$\csc\theta = \frac{1}{\sin\theta} = \frac{25}{24}$ $\sec\theta = \frac{1}{\cos\theta} = \frac{25}{7}$ $\cot\theta = \frac{1}{\tan\theta} = \frac{7}{24}$

CHECK IT OUT! 5. Find the values of the six trigonometric functions for θ.

18, 80

$\sin\theta = \frac{40}{41}$; $\cos\theta = \frac{9}{41}$; $\tan\theta = \frac{40}{9}$; $\csc\theta = \frac{41}{40}$; $\sec\theta = \frac{41}{9}$; $\cot\theta = \frac{9}{40}$

THINK AND DISCUSS

1. The sine of an acute angle in a right triangle is 0.6. Explain why the cosine of the other acute angle in the triangle must be 0.6.
2. If the secant of an acute angle in a right triangle is 2, which trigonometric ratio for that angle has a value of 0.5? Explain.

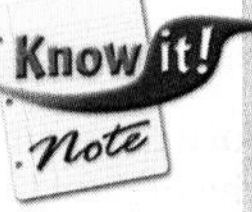

3. **GET ORGANIZED** Copy and complete the graphic organizer. For each trigonometric function, give the name, the side length ratio, and the reciprocal function.

	Sin	Cos	Tan
Function Name			
Side Length Ratio			
Reciprocal Function			

3 Close

Summarize

Ask students to orally define each of the six trigonometric functions in their own words. Then review the process for using trigonometric functions to find the side lengths of right triangles.

- Determine a trigonometric function that relates a given side length, the unknown side length, and a given angle measure.
- Substitute the known values.
- Solve for the unknown length.

ONGOING ASSESSMENT and INTERVENTION

***Diagnose Before* the Lesson**
13-1 Warm Up, TE p. 929

***Monitor During* the Lesson**
Check It Out! Exercises, SE pp. 929–932
Questioning Strategies, TE pp. 930–932

***Assess After* the Lesson**
13-1 Lesson Quiz, TE p. 935
Alternative Assessment, TE p. 935

Answers to *Think and Discuss*

Possible answers:

1. The leg opposite the first angle is the same as the leg adjacent to the second angle. Therefore, the sine of the first angle, $\frac{\text{opp.}}{\text{hyp.}}$, is equal to the cosine of the second angle, $\frac{\text{adj.}}{\text{hyp.}}$.
2. The reciprocal of 2 is 0.5. The reciprocal of the secant ratio is the cosine ratio. Therefore, if the secant of an angle is 2, its cosine is 0.5.
3. See p. A14.

13-1 Exercises

go.hrw.com
Homework Help Online
KEYWORD: MB7 13-1
Parent Resources Online
KEYWORD: MB7 Parent

GUIDED PRACTICE

1. **Vocabulary** The ratio of the length of the opposite leg to the length of the adjacent leg of an acute angle of a right triangle is the __?__ of the angle. (*tangent* or *cotangent*) **tangent**

SEE EXAMPLE 1 p. 929

Find the value of the sine, cosine, and tangent functions for θ.

2. 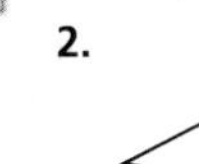
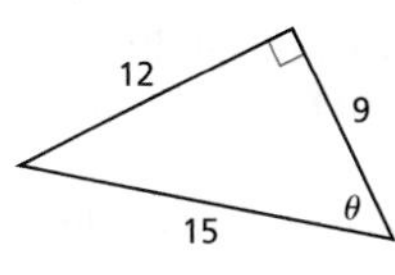

3. 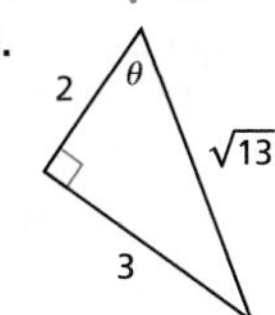

4. 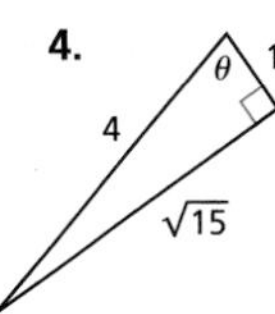

SEE EXAMPLE 2 p. 930

Use a trigonometric function to find the value of x.

5. 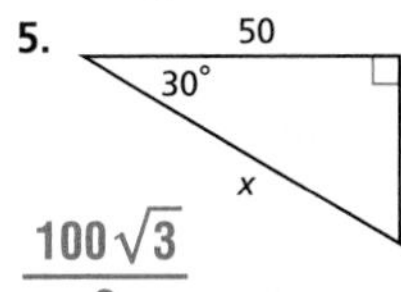

$\frac{100\sqrt{3}}{3}$

6. 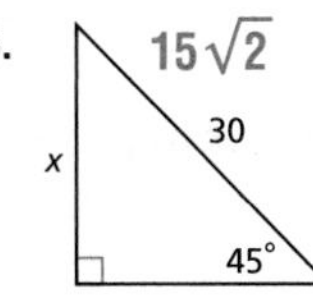

$15\sqrt{2}$

7. 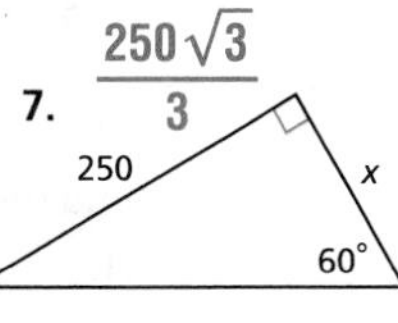

$\frac{250\sqrt{3}}{3}$

SEE EXAMPLE 3 p. 930

8. **Engineering** An escalator in a mall must lift customers to a height of 22 ft. If the angle between the escalator stairs and the ground floor will be 30°, what will be the length ℓ of the escalator? **44 ft**

SEE EXAMPLE 4 p. 931

9. **Recreation** The pilot of a hot-air balloon measures the angle of depression to a landing spot to be 20.5°. If the pilot's altitude is 90 m, what is the horizontal distance between the balloon and the landing spot? Round to the nearest meter. **241 m**

SEE EXAMPLE 5 p. 932

Find the values of the six trigonometric functions for θ.

10. 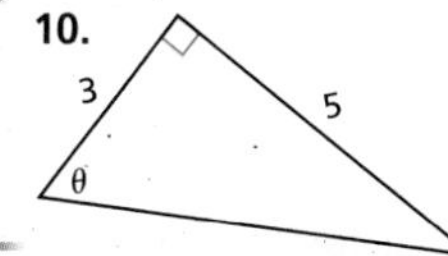

11. 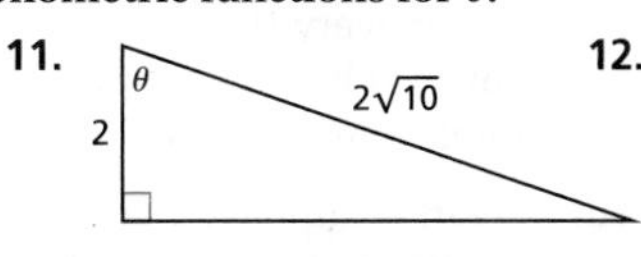

12. 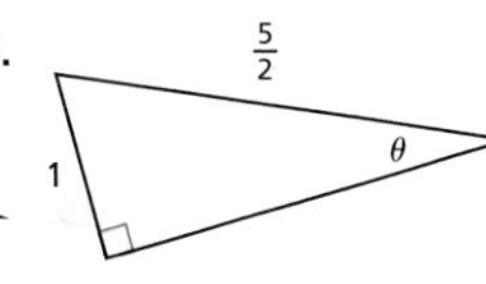

PRACTICE AND PROBLEM SOLVING

Independent Practice	
For Exercises	See Example
13–15	1
16–18	2
19	3
20	4
21–23	5

Extra Practice
Skills Practice p. S28
Application Practice p. S44

Find the value of the sine, cosine, and tangent functions for θ.

13. 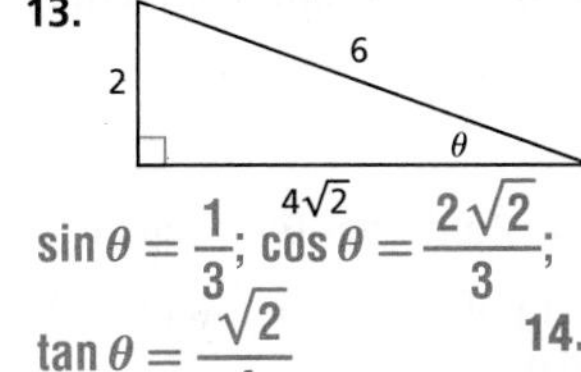

$\sin\theta = \frac{1}{3}$; $\cos\theta = \frac{2\sqrt{2}}{3}$; $\tan\theta = \frac{\sqrt{2}}{4}$

14. 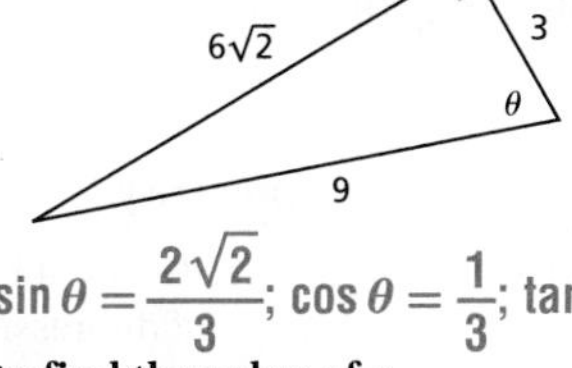

14. $\sin\theta = \frac{2\sqrt{2}}{3}$; $\cos\theta = \frac{1}{3}$; $\tan\theta = 2\sqrt{2}$

15. 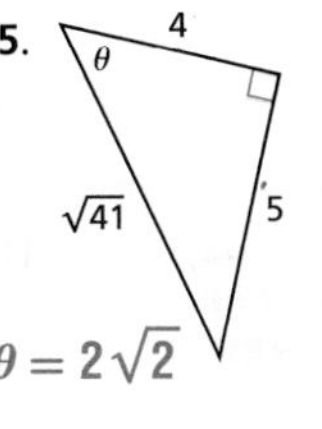

Use a trigonometric function to find the value of x.

16. 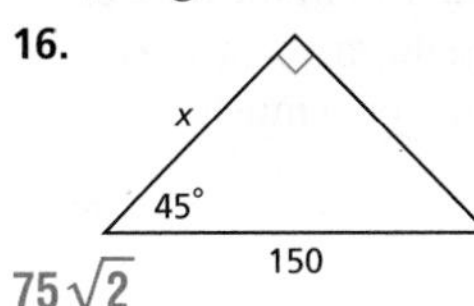

$75\sqrt{2}$

17. 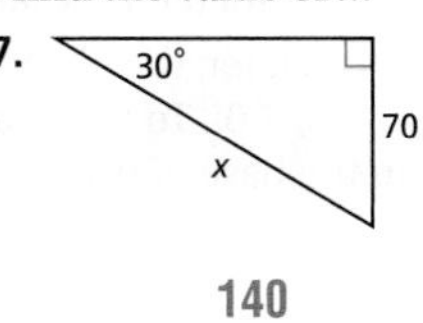

140

18. 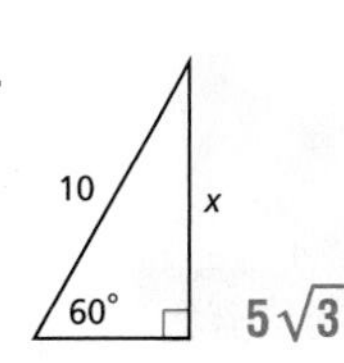

$5\sqrt{3}$

13-1 Exercises

Assignment Guide

Assign *Guided Practice* exercises as necessary.

If you finished Examples **1–3**
Basic 13–19, 27
Average 13–19, 27, 36
Advanced 13–19, 27, 33–36

If you finished Examples **1–5**
Basic 13–27, 30–32, 37–43
Average 13–32, 36–43
Advanced 13–43

Homework Quick Check
Quickly check key concepts.
Exercises: 14, 16, 19, 20, 22, 27

Answers

2. $\sin\theta = \frac{4}{5}$; $\cos\theta = \frac{3}{5}$; $\tan\theta = \frac{4}{3}$

3. $\sin\theta = \frac{3\sqrt{13}}{13}$; $\cos\theta = \frac{2\sqrt{13}}{13}$; $\tan\theta = \frac{3}{2}$

4. $\sin\theta = \frac{\sqrt{15}}{4}$; $\cos\theta = \frac{1}{4}$; $\tan\theta = \sqrt{15}$

10. $\sin\theta = \frac{5\sqrt{34}}{34}$; $\cos\theta = \frac{3\sqrt{34}}{34}$; $\tan\theta = \frac{5}{3}$; $\csc\theta = \frac{\sqrt{34}}{5}$; $\sec\theta = \frac{\sqrt{34}}{3}$; $\cot\theta = \frac{3}{5}$

State Resources

go.hrw.com
State Resources Online
KEYWORD: MB7 Resources

Answers

11. $\sin\theta = \frac{3\sqrt{10}}{10}$; $\cos\theta = \frac{\sqrt{10}}{10}$; $\tan\theta = 3$; $\csc\theta = \frac{\sqrt{10}}{3}$; $\sec\theta = \sqrt{10}$; $\cot\theta = \frac{1}{3}$

12. $\sin\theta = \frac{2}{5}$; $\cos\theta = \frac{\sqrt{21}}{5}$; $\tan\theta = \frac{2\sqrt{21}}{21}$; $\csc\theta = \frac{5}{2}$; $\sec\theta = \frac{5\sqrt{21}}{21}$; $\cot\theta = \frac{\sqrt{21}}{2}$

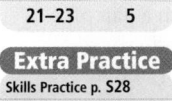

15. $\sin\theta = \frac{5\sqrt{41}}{41}$; $\cos\theta = \frac{4\sqrt{41}}{41}$; $\tan\theta = \frac{5}{4}$

Exercise 26 involves using trigonometric functions to determine the location of a sea otter. This exercise prepares students for the Multi-Step Test Prep on page 956.

Answers

21. $\sin\theta = \frac{4}{5}$; $\cos\theta = \frac{3}{5}$; $\tan\theta = \frac{4}{3}$; $\csc\theta = \frac{5}{4}$; $\sec\theta = \frac{5}{3}$; $\cot\theta = \frac{3}{4}$

22. $\sin\theta = \frac{\sqrt{17}}{17}$; $\cos\theta = \frac{4\sqrt{17}}{17}$; $\tan\theta = \frac{1}{4}$; $\csc\theta = \sqrt{17}$; $\sec\theta = \frac{\sqrt{17}}{4}$; $\cot\theta = 4$

23. $\sin\theta = \frac{\sqrt{2}}{2}$; $\cos\theta = \frac{\sqrt{2}}{2}$; $\tan\theta = 1$; $\csc\theta = \sqrt{2}$; $\sec\theta = \sqrt{2}$; $\cot\theta = 1$

24. Beginner: about 13 m; intermediate: about 27 m; advanced: about 52 m; possible answer: for each category, I estimated the typical slope angle by finding the mean of the least and greatest angle measures. Then I used the tangent ratio of the typical slope angle to find the distance the skier would descend.

28, 29, 33, 34, 36. See p. A47.

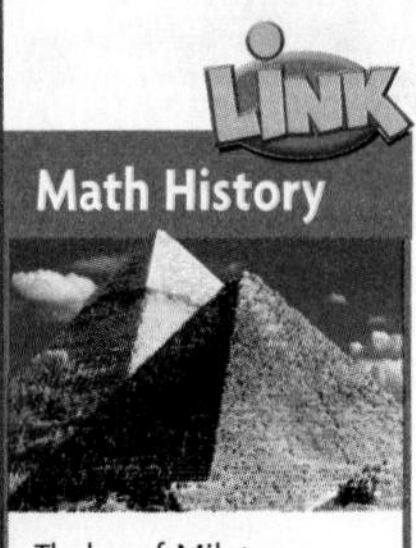

Thales of Miletus (624–547 B.C.E.) was a Greek mathematician reputed to have measured the height of the Egyptian pyramids by using the lengths of shadows and indirect measurement.

19. **History** Today, the Great Pyramid in Egypt is not as tall as when it was originally built. The square base of the pyramid has a side length of 230 m, and the sides of the pyramid meet the base at an angle of 52°.
    a. What was the original height of the pyramid to the nearest meter? **147 m**
    b. What was the original slant height of the pyramid to the nearest meter? **187 m**

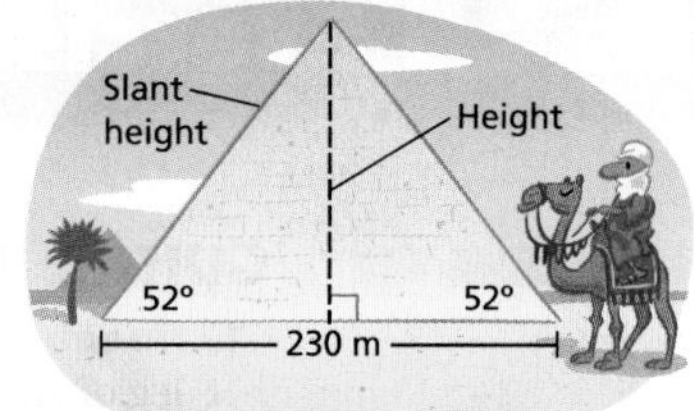

20. **Navigation** The top of the Matagorda Island Lighthouse in Texas is about 90 ft above sea level. The angle of elevation from a fishing boat to the top of the lighthouse is 10°.
    a. To the nearest foot, what is the distance d between the boat and the base of the lighthouse? **510 ft**
    b. **What if...?** After the boat drifts for half an hour, the angle of elevation has decreased to 4.5°. To the nearest foot, how much farther has the boat moved from the lighthouse? **633 ft**

Find the values of the six trigonometric functions for θ.

21. 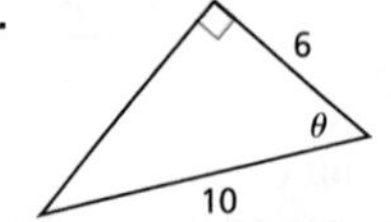

22. 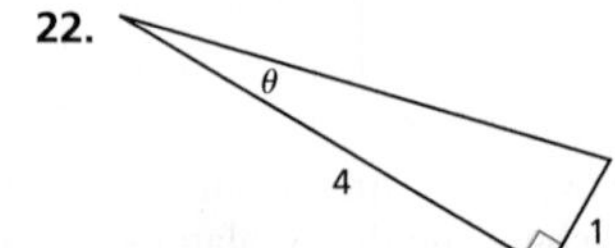

23. 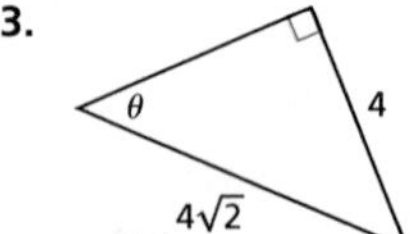

24. **Estimation** One factor that determines a ski slope's difficulty is the slope angle. The table shows the typical slope angles for the most common difficulty categories. For each category, estimate how many meters a skier descends for every 100 m that he or she moves forward horizontally. Explain how you determined your estimates.

Slope Ratings		
Symbol	Difficulty	Slope Angle
●	Beginner	5° to 10°
■	Intermediate	10° to 20°
◆	Expert	20° to 35°

25. **Multi-Step** A supply package will be dropped from an airplane to an Arctic research station. The plane's altitude is 2000 ft, and its horizontal speed is 235 ft/s. The angle of depression to the target is 14°.
    a. To the nearest foot, what is the plane's horizontal distance from the target? **8022 ft**
    b. The plane needs to drop the supplies when it is a horizontal distance of 500 ft from the target. To the nearest second, how long should the pilot wait before dropping the supplies? **32 s**

26. This problem will prepare you for the Multi-Step Test Prep on page 956.

    An observer on a sea cliff with a height of 12 m spots an otter through a pair of binoculars at an angle of depression of 5.7°.
    a. To the nearest meter, how far is the otter from the base of the cliff? **120 m**
    b. Five minutes later, the observer sights the same otter at an angle of depression of 7.6°. To the nearest meter, how much closer has the otter moved to the base of the cliff? **30 m**

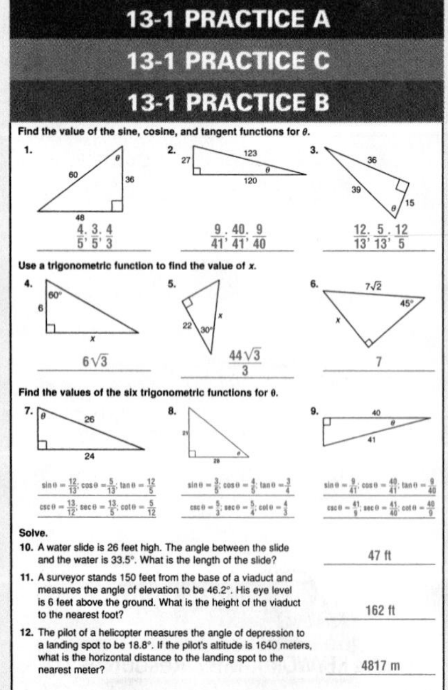

13-1 PRACTICE A

13-1 PRACTICE C

13-1 PRACTICE B

Find the value of the sine, cosine, and tangent functions for θ.

1. (triangle: 60, 36, 48) $\frac{4}{5}, \frac{3}{5}, \frac{4}{3}$
2. (triangle: 123, 27, 120) $\frac{9}{41}, \frac{40}{41}, \frac{9}{40}$
3. (triangle: 36, 39, 15) $\frac{12}{13}, \frac{5}{13}, \frac{12}{5}$

Use a trigonometric function to find the value of x.

4. (60°, 6, x) $6\sqrt{3}$
5. (22, 30°, x) $\frac{44\sqrt{3}}{3}$
6. ($7\sqrt{2}$, 45°, x) 7

Find the values of the six trigonometric functions for θ.

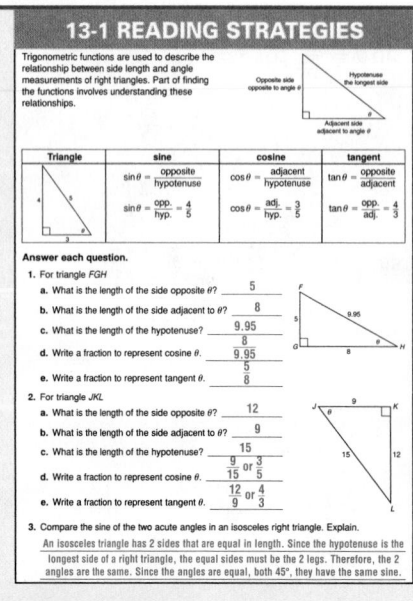

7. (26, 24) $\sin\theta = \frac{12}{13}$; $\cos\theta = \frac{5}{13}$; $\tan\theta = \frac{12}{5}$; $\csc\theta = \frac{13}{12}$; $\sec\theta = \frac{13}{5}$; $\cot\theta = \frac{5}{12}$
8. (21, 28) $\sin\theta = \frac{3}{5}$; $\cos\theta = \frac{4}{5}$; $\tan\theta = \frac{3}{4}$; $\csc\theta = \frac{5}{3}$; $\sec\theta = \frac{5}{4}$; $\cot\theta = \frac{4}{3}$
9. (40, 41) $\sin\theta = \frac{9}{41}$; $\cos\theta = \frac{40}{41}$; $\tan\theta = \frac{9}{40}$; $\csc\theta = \frac{41}{9}$; $\sec\theta = \frac{41}{40}$; $\cot\theta = \frac{40}{9}$

Solve.

10. A water slide is 26 feet high. The angle between the slide and the water is 33.5°. What is the length of the slide? **47 ft**
11. A surveyor stands 150 feet from the base of a viaduct and measures the angle of elevation to be 46.2°. His eye level is 6 feet above the ground. What is the height of the viaduct to the nearest foot? **162 ft**
12. The pilot of a helicopter measures the angle of depression to a landing spot to be 18.8°. If the pilot's altitude is 1640 meters, what is the horizontal distance to the landing spot to the nearest meter? **4817 m**

13-1 READING STRATEGIES

Trigonometric functions are used to describe the relationship between side length and angle measurements of right triangles. Part of finding the functions involves understanding these relationships.

Opposite side opposite to angle θ
Hypotenuse the longest side
Adjacent side adjacent to angle θ

Triangle	sine	cosine	tangent
(4, 5, 3)	$\sin\theta = \frac{\text{opposite}}{\text{hypotenuse}}$ $\sin\theta = \frac{\text{opp.}}{\text{hyp.}} = \frac{4}{5}$	$\cos\theta = \frac{\text{adjacent}}{\text{hypotenuse}}$ $\cos\theta = \frac{\text{adj.}}{\text{hyp.}} = \frac{3}{5}$	$\tan\theta = \frac{\text{opposite}}{\text{adjacent}}$ $\tan\theta = \frac{\text{opp.}}{\text{adj.}} = \frac{4}{3}$

Answer each question.

1. For triangle *FGH*
   a. What is the length of the side opposite θ? **5**
   b. What is the length of the side adjacent to θ? **8**
   c. What is the length of the hypotenuse? **9.95**
   d. Write a fraction to represent cosine θ. $\frac{8}{9.95}$
   e. Write a fraction to represent tangent θ. $\frac{5}{8}$
2. For triangle *JKL*
   a. What is the length of the side opposite θ? **12**
   b. What is the length of the side adjacent to θ? **9**
   c. What is the length of the hypotenuse? **15**
   d. Write a fraction to represent cosine θ. $\frac{9}{15}$ or $\frac{3}{5}$
   e. Write a fraction to represent tangent θ. $\frac{12}{9}$ or $\frac{4}{3}$
3. Compare the sine of the two acute angles in an isosceles right triangle. Explain.
   An isosceles triangle has 2 sides that are equal in length. Since the hypotenuse is the longest side of a right triangle, the equal sides must be the 2 legs. Therefore, the 2 angles are the same. Since the angles are equal, both 45°, they have the same sine.

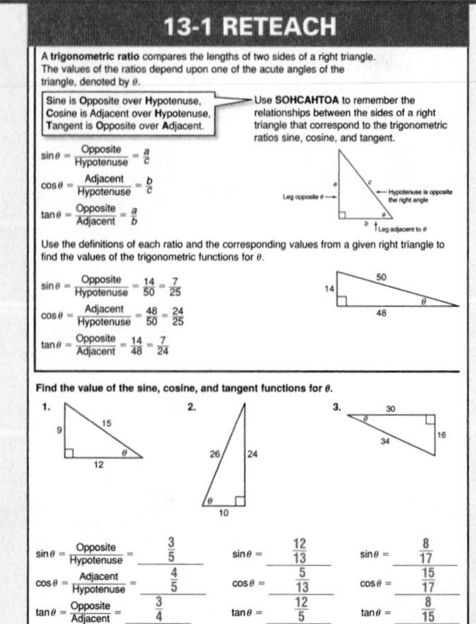

13-1 RETEACH

A **trigonometric ratio** compares the lengths of two sides of a right triangle. The values of the ratios depend upon one of the acute angles of the triangle, denoted by θ.

Sine is Opposite over Hypotenuse, Cosine is Adjacent over Hypotenuse, Tangent is Opposite over Adjacent.

Use **SOHCAHTOA** to remember the relationships between the sides of a right triangle that correspond to the trigonometric ratios sine, cosine, and tangent.

$\sin\theta = \frac{\text{Opposite}}{\text{Hypotenuse}} = \frac{a}{c}$

$\cos\theta = \frac{\text{Adjacent}}{\text{Hypotenuse}} = \frac{b}{c}$

$\tan\theta = \frac{\text{Opposite}}{\text{Adjacent}} = \frac{a}{b}$

Leg opposite θ — Hypotenuse is opposite the right angle — Leg adjacent to θ

Use the definitions of each ratio and the corresponding values from a given right triangle to find the values of the trigonometric functions for θ.

$\sin\theta = \frac{\text{Opposite}}{\text{Hypotenuse}} = \frac{14}{50} = \frac{7}{25}$

$\cos\theta = \frac{\text{Adjacent}}{\text{Hypotenuse}} = \frac{48}{50} = \frac{24}{25}$

$\tan\theta = \frac{\text{Opposite}}{\text{Adjacent}} = \frac{14}{48} = \frac{7}{24}$

Find the value of the sine, cosine, and tangent functions for θ.

1. (9, 15, 12) $\sin\theta = \frac{\text{Opposite}}{\text{Hypotenuse}} = \frac{3}{5}$; $\cos\theta = \frac{\text{Adjacent}}{\text{Hypotenuse}} = \frac{4}{5}$; $\tan\theta = \frac{\text{Opposite}}{\text{Adjacent}} = \frac{3}{4}$
2. (26, 24, 10) $\sin\theta = \frac{12}{13}$; $\cos\theta = \frac{5}{13}$; $\tan\theta = \frac{12}{5}$
3. (30, 34, 16) $\sin\theta = \frac{8}{17}$; $\cos\theta = \frac{15}{17}$; $\tan\theta = \frac{8}{15}$

27. **Surveying** Based on the measurements shown in the diagram, what is the width w of the river to the nearest foot? **135 ft**

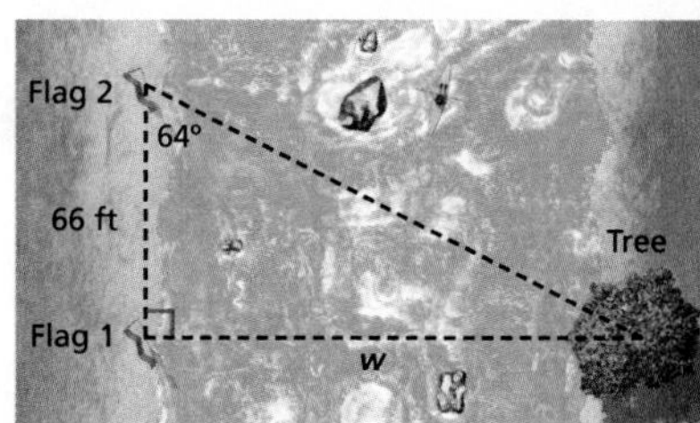

28. **Critical Thinking** Show that $\frac{\sin\theta}{\cos\theta} = \tan\theta$.

29. **Write About It** Suppose that you are given the measure of an acute angle in a right triangle and the length of the leg adjacent to this angle. Describe two different methods that you could use to find the length of the hypotenuse.

TEST PREP

Use the diagram for Exercises 30 and 31.

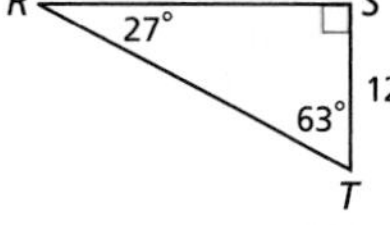

30. Which of the following is equal to $\cos 27°$?
    (A) $\csc 63°$
    (B) $\sec 63°$
    (C) $\tan 63°$
    (D) $\sin 63°$

31. Which expression represents the length of $\overline{RS}$?
    (F) $12\cot 27°$
    (G) $12\csc 27°$
    (H) $12\sin 27°$
    (J) $12\tan 27°$

32. If $\tan\theta = \frac{3}{4}$, what is $\cos\theta$?
    (A) $\frac{3}{5}$
    (B) $\frac{4}{5}$
    (C) $\frac{5}{4}$
    (D) $\frac{4}{3}$

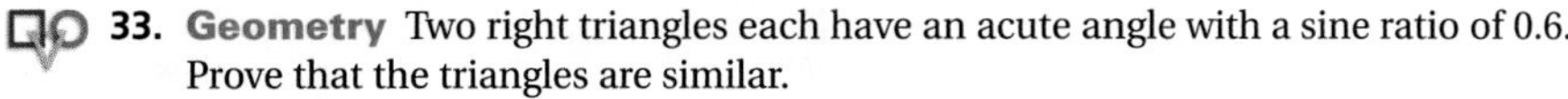

CHALLENGE AND EXTEND

33. **Geometry** Two right triangles each have an acute angle with a sine ratio of 0.6. Prove that the triangles are similar.

34. For an acute angle of a right triangle, which trigonometric ratios are always greater than 1? Which are always less than 1? Explain.

35. **Geometry** A regular hexagon with sides of length 3 ft is inscribed in a circle.
    a. Use a trigonometric ratio to find the radius of the circle. **3 ft**
    b. Determine the area of the hexagon. **$13.5\sqrt{3}$ ft²**

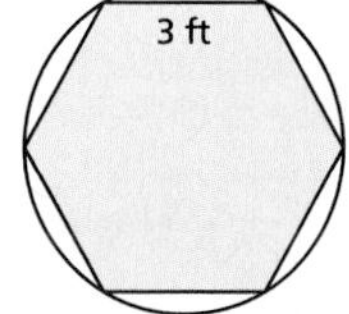

36. Explain why the sine of an acute angle is equal to the cosine of its complement.

SPIRAL REVIEW

Solve each proportion. *(Lesson 2-2)*

37. $\frac{4}{17} = \frac{x}{136}$ **32**
38. $\frac{60.3}{x} = \frac{6.7}{3}$ **27**
39. $\frac{196}{x} = \frac{0.05}{9.8}$ **38,416**

40. The students at a high school are randomly assigned a computer password. Each password consists of 4 characters, each of which can be a letter from A to Z or a digit from 0 to 9. What is the probability that a randomly chosen password will consist only of digits? *(Lesson 11-2)* **$\frac{625}{104{,}976}$**

Find the sum of each infinite series, if it exists. *(Lesson 12-5)*

41. $\sum_{n=1}^{\infty}\left(\frac{1}{3}\right)^n$ **$\frac{1}{2}$**
42. $\sum_{n=1}^{\infty} 3n - 5$ **The sum does not exist.**
43. $10 + 4 + 1.6 + 0.64 + \cdots$ **$16\frac{2}{3}$**

13-1 PROBLEM SOLVING

Kayla is fishing near the ferry landing near her home. She wonders how far the ferries actually travel when they cross the river. To find out, she puts a fishing pole upright on the riverbank directly across from the ferry landing. Then she walks down the bank 180 yards and measures an angle of 75°between the lines to her fishing pole and the ferry landing on the opposite bank.

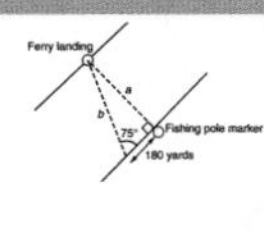

1. Find the distance directly across the river.
   a. On the diagram, name the side of the triangle that represents the distance Kayla wants to determine. **a**
   b. Write a trigonometric function that relates the known distance and angle to the required distance. **$\tan 75° = \frac{a}{180}$**
   c. Find the distance to the nearest yard directly across the river. **672 yd**

2. Kayla walks another 200 yards down the riverbank. At this point the ferries seem to come straight at her at an angle of 60° to the line to her fishing pole. If the boats travel along this line to compensate for the current, how far do they travel?
   a. How far is she from her fishing pole now? **380 yd**
   b. Write the trigonometric function that relates this distance and angle to the required distance, c. **$\cos 60° = \frac{380}{c}$**
   c. What is the distance that the ferries travel if they travel along this line? **760 yd**

At a hot-air balloon festival, Luis watches a hot-air balloon rise from a distance of 200 yards. Choose the letter for the best answer.

3. From Luis's position, the balloon seems to hover at an angle of elevation of 50°. Which trigonometric function gives the height of the balloon, h?
   A $200\sin 50°$
   (B) $200\tan 50°$
   C $\frac{200}{\cos 50°}$
   D $\frac{200}{\cot 50°}$

4. After a short while, the balloon seems to hover at an angle of 75°. How high is it off the ground now?
   F 193 yd
   G 207 yd
   (H) 746 yd
   J 773 yd

Olivia has a pool slide that makes an angle of 25° with the water. The top of the slide stands 4.5 feet above the surface of the water. Choose the letter for the best answer.

5. How far out into the pool will the slide reach?
   A 2.1 ft
   B 5.0 ft
   C 7.6 ft
   (D) 9.7 ft

6. The slide makes a straight line into the water. How long is the slide?
   F 5.0 ft
   G 7.6 ft
   H 9.7 ft
   (J) 10.6 ft

13-1 CHALLENGE

Trigonometry can be used to solve problems involving one or more right triangles. Different triangles can share common parts.

As shown in the diagram at right, a pole, $\overline{TF}$, is on the roof of a shed, $\overline{FB}$. From a point, P, on the ground 27 feet from the foot of the shed, the measure of the angle of elevation to the top of the pole, T, is 38°, and the measure of the angle of elevation to the foot of the pole, F, is 32°. Determine, to the nearest tenth of a foot, the height of the pole.

Since $\overline{TF}$ is not the side of a right triangle, first determine $\overline{TB}$ in right $\triangle TBP$ and $\overline{FB}$ in right $\triangle FBP$, and then subtract to determine $\overline{TF}$.

In right $\triangle TBP$:
$\tan 38° = \frac{\text{opp.}}{\text{adj.}} = \frac{\overline{TB}}{27}$
$\overline{TB} = 27\tan 38° \approx 21.09$

In right $\triangle FBP$:
$\tan 32° = \frac{\text{opp.}}{\text{adj.}} = \frac{\overline{FB}}{27}$
$\overline{FB} = 27\tan 32° \approx 16.87$

So, $\overline{TF} = \overline{TB} - \overline{FB} \approx 21.09 - 16.87 \approx 4.2$ feet.

As shown in the diagram at right, a ship is headed directly toward a coastline formed by a vertical cliff ($\overline{BC}$) that is 80 meters high. At point A, from the ship, the measure of the angle of elevation to the top of the cliff (B) is 10°.

A few minutes later, at point D, the measure of the angle of elevation to the top of the cliff has increased to 20°. Determine the following to the nearest meter.

1. $\overline{DC}$ **220 m**
2. $\overline{AC}$ **454 m**
3. The distance between the 2 sightings **234 m**

As shown in the diagram at right, the heights ($\overline{AB}$ and $\overline{CD}$) of buildings on opposite sides of a 90-foot-wide avenue are, respectively, 100 feet and 50 feet. From a point E on the avenue, the measure of the angle of elevation to B is 55°. Determine each of the following.

4. The distance from E to A to the nearest foot **70 ft**
5. The distance from E to D to the nearest foot **54 ft**

COMMON ERROR ALERT

In **Exercise 20 part a,** students may attempt to solve the problem by using the equation $\tan 10° = \frac{d}{90}$ rather than $\tan 10° = \frac{90}{d}$. Suggest that they draw a diagram to help them determine the relationship among the given measurements.

TEST PREP DOCTOR

In **Exercise 32,** students who chose **A, C,** or **D** may have confused the sine, secant, or cotangent functions with the cosine function. Have students review the definitions of the trigonometric functions.

Journal

Ask students to explain how to determine the sine of an acute angle of a right triangle when given only the lengths of the triangle's legs.

ALTERNATIVE ASSESSMENT

Ask students to draw a right triangle and label the length of one side and the measure of one acute angle. Then have them use trigonometric functions to find the lengths of the two other sides.

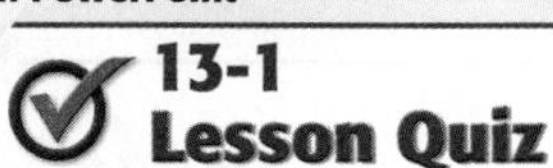

Power Presentations with PowerPoint®

13-1 Lesson Quiz

1. Find the values of the six trigonometric functions for θ.

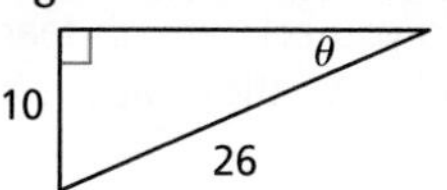

$\sin\theta = \frac{5}{13}$; $\cos\theta = \frac{12}{13}$;
$\tan\theta = \frac{5}{12}$; $\csc\theta = \frac{13}{5}$;
$\sec\theta = \frac{13}{12}$; $\cot\theta = \frac{12}{5}$

2. Use a trigonometric function to find the value of x. $30\sqrt{2}$

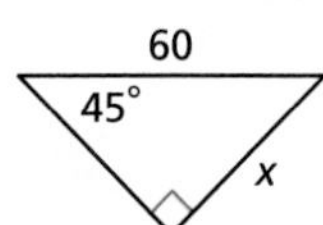

3. A helicopter's altitude is 4500 ft, and a plane's altitude is 12,000 ft. If the angle of depression from the plane to the helicopter is 27.6°, what is the distance between the two, to the nearest hundred feet? 16,200 ft

Also available on transparency

13-2 Organizer

Pacing: Traditional 1 day
Block $\frac{1}{2}$ day

Objectives: Draw angles in standard position.

Determine the values of the trigonometric functions for an angle in standard position.

Premier Online Edition
Tutorial Videos

Power Presentations with PowerPoint®

Warm Up

Find the measure of the supplement for each given angle.

1. 150° 30° **2.** 120° 60°

3. 135° 45° **4.** 95° 85°

5. Find the value of the sine, cosine, and tangent functions for θ.

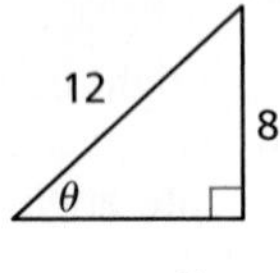

$\sin\theta = \frac{2}{3}$; $\cos\theta = \frac{\sqrt{5}}{3}$;

$\tan\theta = \frac{2\sqrt{5}}{5}$

Also available on transparency

Math Humor

Q: What do you call a math teacher who takes his vacations at the beach?
A: A tangent.

13-2 Angles of Rotation

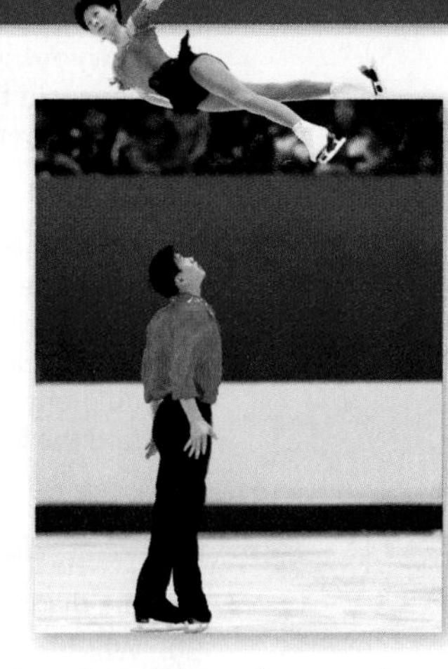

Objectives
Draw angles in standard position.

Determine the values of the trigonometric functions for an angle in standard position.

Vocabulary
standard position
initial side
terminal side
angle of rotation
coterminal angle
reference angle

Why learn this?
You can use angles of rotation to determine the rate at which a skater must spin to complete a jump. (See Exercise 51.)

In Lesson 13-1, you investigated trigonometric functions by using acute angles in right triangles. The trigonometric functions can also be evaluated for other types of angles.

An angle is in **standard position** when its vertex is at the origin and one ray is on the positive x-axis. The **initial side** of the angle is the ray on the x-axis. The other ray is called the **terminal side** of the angle.

Know it! Note

Positive Rotation

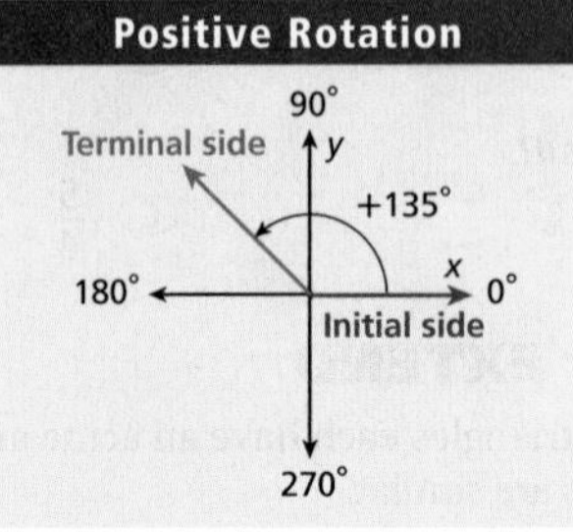

Negative Rotation

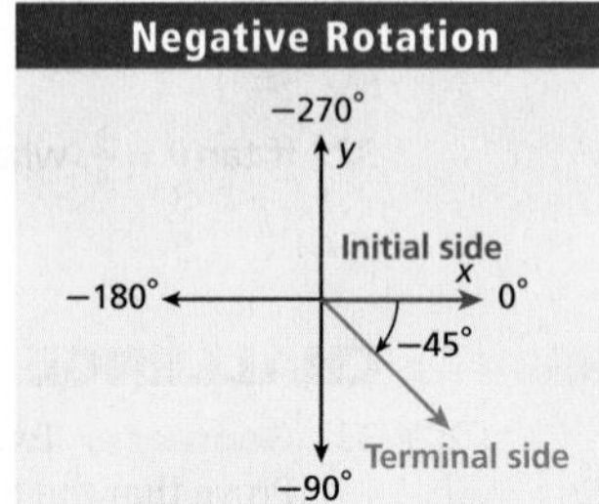

An **angle of rotation** is formed by rotating the terminal side and keeping the initial side in place. If the terminal side is rotated counterclockwise, the angle of rotation is positive. If the terminal side is rotated clockwise, the angle of rotation is negative. The terminal side can be rotated more than 360°.

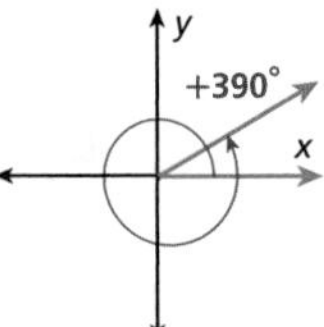

EXAMPLE 1 Drawing Angles in Standard Position

Remember!
A 360° rotation is a complete rotation. A 180° rotation is one-half of a complete rotation.

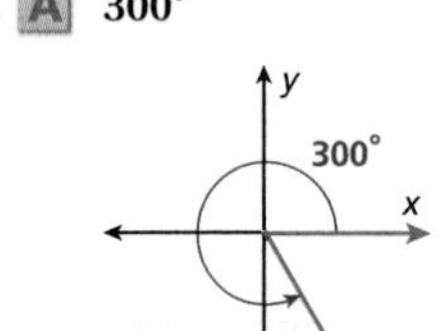

Draw an angle with the given measure in standard position.

A 300°

Rotate the terminal side 300° counterclockwise.

B −150°

Rotate the terminal side 150° clockwise.

C 900°

Rotate the terminal side 900° counterclockwise.
900° = 360° + 360° + 180°

CHECK IT OUT! Draw an angle with the given measure in standard position.

1a. 210° **1b.** 1020° **1c.** −300°

State Resources

1 Introduce

EXPLORATION

13-2 Angles of Rotation

Imagine a ray on the positive x-axis with its vertex at the origin. As the ray rotates counterclockwise about the origin, you can use what you know about angle measures to determine the number of degrees through which the ray rotates.

Find the number of degrees x through which each ray has rotated. (H : A complete rotation is equal to 360°.)

THINK AND DISCUSS

Motivate

Ask volunteers to describe the skateboarding moves called a "180," a "360," and a "900." In these moves, a skateboarder completes rotations of 180°, 360°, and 900° while in the air. Angles with these measures correspond to $\frac{1}{2}$, 1, and $2\frac{1}{2}$ revolutions, respectively. Have students discuss ways in which they might draw angles with these measures.

Explorations and answers are provided in the *Explorations* binder.

go.hrw.com
State Resources Online
KEYWORD: MB7 Resources

Coterminal angles are angles in standard position with the same terminal side. For example, angles measuring 120° and −240° are coterminal.

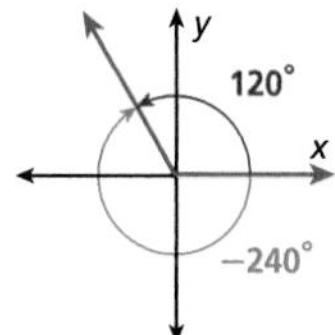

There are infinitely many coterminal angles. One way to find the measure of an angle that is coterminal with an angle θ is to add or subtract integer multiples of 360°.

EXAMPLE 2 Finding Coterminal Angles

Find the measures of a positive angle and a negative angle that are coterminal with each given angle.

A $\theta = 40°$

$40° + 360° = 400°$ *Add 360° to find a positive coterminal angle.*

$40° - 360° = -320°$ *Subtract 360° to find a negative coterminal angle.*

Angles that measure 400° and −320° are coterminal with a 40° angle.

B $\theta = 380°$

$380° - 360° = 20°$ *Subtract 360° to find a positive coterminal angle.*

$380° - 2(360°) = -340°$ *Subtract a multiple of 360° to find a negative coterminal angle.*

Angles that measure 20° and −340° are coterminal with a 380° angle.

Find the measures of a positive angle and a negative angle that are coterminal with each given angle.

2a. $\theta = 88°$ **2b.** $\theta = 500°$ **2c.** $\theta = -120°$

2a. Possible answer: 448°; −272°

2b. Possible answer: 860°; −220°

2c. Possible answer: 240°; −480°

For an angle θ in standard position, the **reference angle** is the positive acute angle formed by the terminal side of θ and the x-axis. In Lesson 13-3, you will learn how to use reference angles to find trigonometric values of angles measuring greater than 90° or less than 0°.

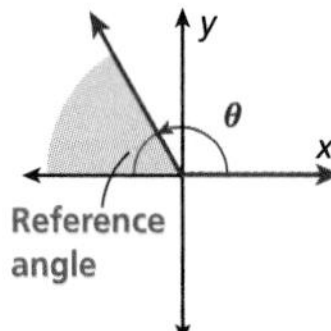

EXAMPLE 3 Finding Reference Angles

Find the measure of the reference angle for each given angle.

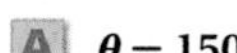

A $\theta = 150°$

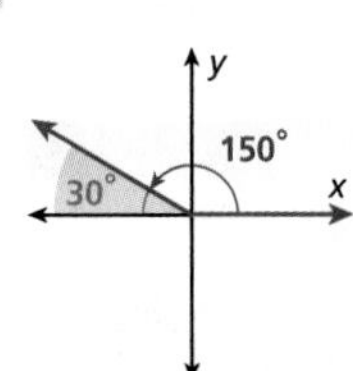

The measure of the reference angle is 30°.

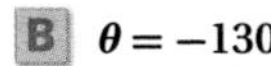

B $\theta = -130°$

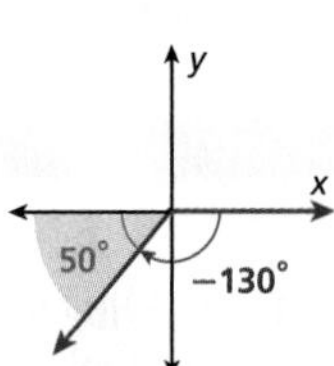

The measure of the reference angle is 50°.

C $\theta = 280°$

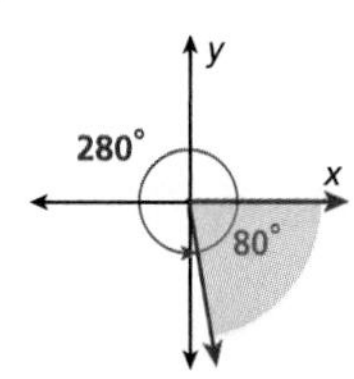

The measure of the reference angle is 80°.

Find the measure of the reference angle for each given angle.

3a. $\theta = 105°$ 75° **3b.** $\theta = -115°$ 65° **3c.** $\theta = 310°$ 50°

2 Teach

Guided Instruction

Angles of rotation will be a new concept to almost all students. Make sure that students understand how to represent angles in standard position and are familiar with the new vocabulary terms in this lesson before learning to determine the values of trigonometric functions for angles of rotation. It may be helpful to show students an angle of rotation that is not in standard position and discuss with them why this is so.

Reaching All Learners

Through Graphic Organizers

Have students complete a table like the one below that they can use to find the reference angle of an angle θ in standard position, given that $0° \le \theta < 360°$.

Quadrant of Terminal Side	Measure of Reference Angle
I	θ
II	$180° - \theta$
III	$\theta - 180°$
IV	$360° - \theta$

Power Presentations with PowerPoint®

Additional Examples

Example 1

Draw an angle with the given measure in standard position.

A. 320°

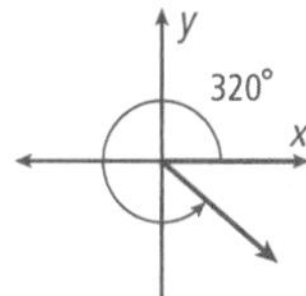

B. −110°

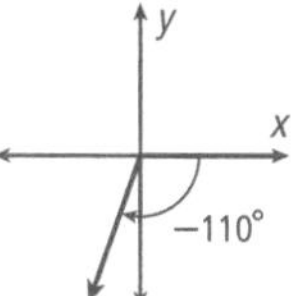

C. 990°

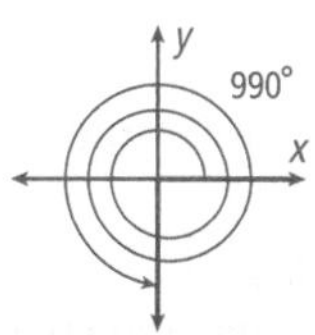

Example 2

Find the measures of a positive angle and a negative angle that are coterminal with each given angle. Possible answers:

A. $\theta = 65°$ 425°; −295°

B. $\theta = 410°$ 50°; −310°

Example 3

Find the measure of the reference angle for each given angle.

A. $\theta = 135°$ 45°

B. $\theta = -105°$ 75°

C. $\theta = 325°$ 35°

Also available on transparency

INTERVENTION

Questioning Strategies

EXAMPLE 1

- How do you know whether to rotate the terminal side clockwise or counterclockwise?

EXAMPLE 2

- How do you find a positive coterminal angle? a negative coterminal angle?

EXAMPLE 3

- When an angle is drawn in standard position, how do you know which angle is its reference angle?

Answers to *Check it Out!*

1a–1c. See p. A48.

Power Presentations with PowerPoint®

Additional Examples

Example 4

$P(-6, 9)$ is a point on the terminal side of θ in standard position. Find the exact value of the six trigonometric functions for θ.

$\sin\theta = \frac{3\sqrt{13}}{13}$; $\cos\theta = -\frac{2\sqrt{13}}{13}$;

$\tan\theta = -\frac{3}{2}$; $\csc\theta = \frac{\sqrt{13}}{3}$;

$\sec\theta = -\frac{\sqrt{13}}{2}$; $\cot\theta = -\frac{2}{3}$

Also available on transparency

INTERVENTION

Questioning Strategies

EXAMPLE 4

- How do you use the coordinates of point *P* to find the value of *r*?
- How do you use the values of *y*, *x*, and *r* to find the values of the trigonometric functions of θ?

Teaching Tip **Inclusion** Point out that the values of the trigonometric functions may be positive or negative depending upon the quadrant in which the terminal side of the angle lies. Therefore, it is important to include the signs of the *x*- and *y*-coordinates when determining the value of trigonometric functions.

To determine the value of the trigonometric functions for an angle θ in standard position, begin by selecting a point *P* with coordinates (x, y) on the terminal side of the angle. The distance *r* from point *P* to the origin is given by $\sqrt{x^2 + y^2}$.

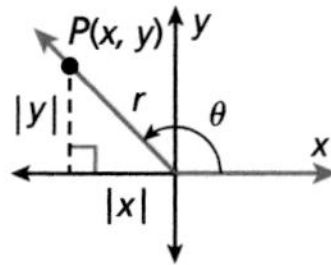

Know it! Note

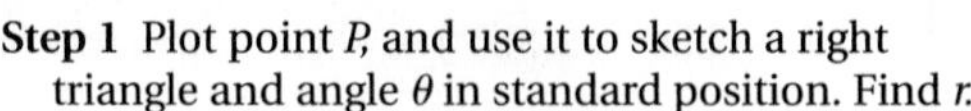

Trigonometric Functions

For a point $P(x, y)$ on the terminal side of θ in standard position and $r = \sqrt{x^2 + y^2}$,

SINE	COSINE	TANGENT
$\sin\theta = \frac{y}{r}$	$\cos\theta = \frac{x}{r}$	$\tan\theta = \frac{y}{x}, x \neq 0$

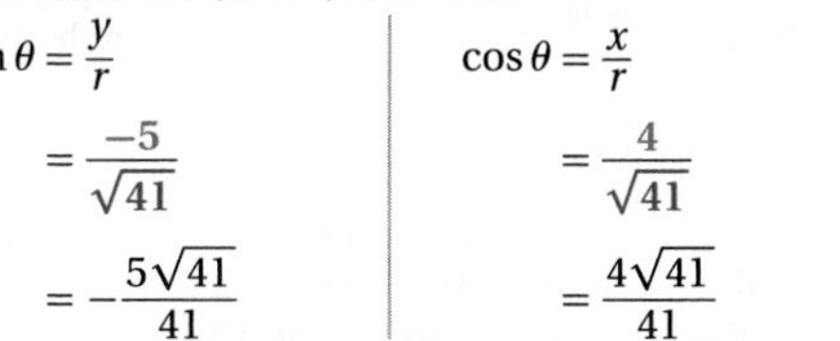

EXAMPLE 4 Finding Values of Trigonometric Functions

$P(4, -5)$ is a point on the terminal side of θ in standard position. Find the exact value of the six trigonometric functions for θ.

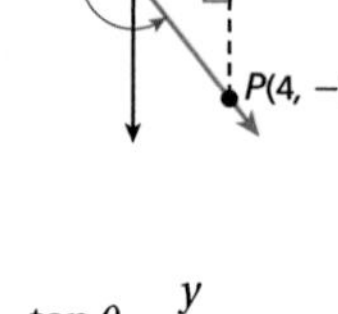

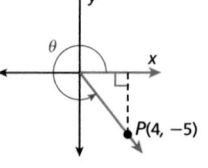

Step 1 Plot point *P*, and use it to sketch a right triangle and angle θ in standard position. Find *r*.

$$r = \sqrt{4^2 + (-5)^2} = \sqrt{16 + 25} = \sqrt{41}$$

Helpful Hint

Because *r* is a distance, its value is always positive, regardless of the sign of *x* and *y*.

Step 2 Find $\sin\theta$, $\cos\theta$, and $\tan\theta$.

$$\sin\theta = \frac{y}{r} = \frac{-5}{\sqrt{41}} = -\frac{5\sqrt{41}}{41}$$

$$\cos\theta = \frac{x}{r} = \frac{4}{\sqrt{41}} = \frac{4\sqrt{41}}{41}$$

$$\tan\theta = \frac{y}{x} = \frac{-5}{4} = -\frac{5}{4}$$

Step 3 Use reciprocals to find $\csc\theta$, $\sec\theta$, and $\cot\theta$.

$$\csc\theta = \frac{1}{\sin\theta} = -\frac{\sqrt{41}}{5} \quad \sec\theta = \frac{1}{\cos\theta} = \frac{\sqrt{41}}{4} \quad \cot\theta = \frac{1}{\tan\theta} = -\frac{4}{5}$$

CHECK IT OUT! **4.** $P(-3, 6)$ is a point on the terminal side of θ in standard position. Find the exact value of the six trigonometric functions for θ.

$\sin\theta = \frac{2\sqrt{5}}{5}$; $\cos\theta = -\frac{\sqrt{5}}{5}$; $\tan\theta = -2$; $\csc\theta = \frac{\sqrt{5}}{2}$; $\sec\theta = -\sqrt{5}$; $\cot\theta = -\frac{1}{2}$

THINK AND DISCUSS

1. Describe how to determine the reference angle of an angle whose terminal side is in Quadrant III.

2. GET ORGANIZED Copy and complete the graphic organizer. In each box, describe how to determine the given angle or position for an angle θ.

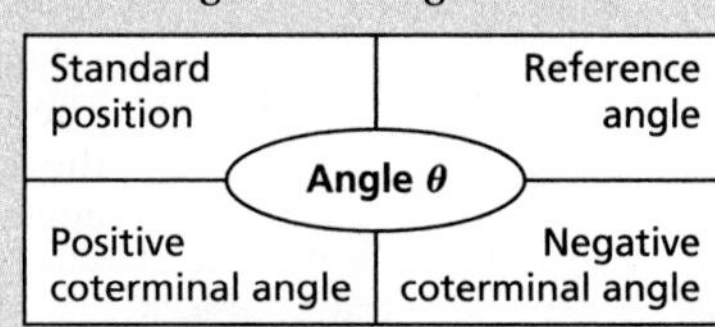

3 Close

Summarize

Review the steps for drawing an angle in standard position. Remind students that coterminal angles have the same terminal side and that a reference angle is the acute angle formed by the terminal side of a given angle and the *x*-axis. Review with students how to find the values of the trigonometric functions given a point on the terminal side of an angle in standard position.

ONGOING ASSESSMENT and INTERVENTION

***Diagnose Before* the Lesson**
13-2 Warm Up, TE p. 936

***Monitor During* the Lesson**
Check It Out! Exercises, SE pp. 936–938
Questioning Strategies, TE pp. 937–938

***Assess After* the Lesson**
13-2 Lesson Quiz, TE p. 941
Alternative Assessment, TE p. 941

Answers to *Think and Discuss*

1. Possible answer: If necessary, find a coterminal angle whose measure is between 270° and 360°. Then subtract 180° to find the measure of the reference angle.
2. See p. A14.

go.hrw.com
Homework Help Online
KEYWORD: MB7 13-2
Parent Resources Online
KEYWORD: MB7 Parent

GUIDED PRACTICE

1. **Vocabulary** If a 45° angle is in standard position, its __?__ side lies above the x-axis. (*initial* or *terminal*) terminal

SEE EXAMPLE 1 p. 936

Draw an angle with the given measure in standard position.

2. 60° 3. −135° 4. 450° 5. −1125°

SEE EXAMPLE 2 p. 937

Find the measures of a positive angle and a negative angle that are coterminal with each given angle.

6. $\theta = 75°$ 7. $\theta = 720°$ 8. $\theta = -25°$ 9. $\theta = -390°$

SEE EXAMPLE 3 p. 937

Find the measure of the reference angle for each given angle.

10. $\theta = 95°$ 85° 11. $\theta = -250°$ 70° 12. $\theta = 230°$ 50° 13. $\theta = -160°$ 20°
14. $\theta = 345°$ 15° 15. $\theta = -130°$ 50° 16. $\theta = -15°$ 15° 17. $\theta = 220°$ 40°

SEE EXAMPLE 4 p. 938

P is a point on the terminal side of θ in standard position. Find the exact value of the six trigonometric functions for θ.

18. $P(-3, 2)$ 19. $P(4, -2)$ 20. $P(0, -6)$ 21. $P(-3, -4)$
22. $P(5, -3)$ 23. $P(1, 6)$ 24. $P(-6, -5)$ 25. $P(-3, 6)$

PRACTICE AND PROBLEM SOLVING

Independent Practice

For Exercises	See Example
26–29	1
30–33	2
34–41	3
42–49	4

Extra Practice
Skills Practice p. S28
Application Practice p. S44

Draw an angle with the given measure in standard position.

26. −120° 27. 225° 28. −570° 29. 750°

Find the measures of a positive angle and a negative angle that are coterminal with each given angle.

30. $\theta = 254°$ 31. $\theta = 1020°$ 32. $\theta = -165°$ 33. $\theta = -610°$

Find the measure of the reference angle for each given angle.

34. $\theta = -25°$ 25° 35. $\theta = 50°$ 50° 36. $\theta = -185°$ 5° 37. $\theta = 200°$ 20°
38. $\theta = 390°$ 30° 39. $\theta = -95°$ 85° 40. $\theta = 160°$ 20° 41. $\theta = 325°$ 35°

P is a point on the terminal side of θ in standard position. Find the exact value of the six trigonometric functions for θ.

42. $P(2, -5)$ 43. $P(5, -2)$ 44. $P(-4, 5)$ 45. $P(4, 3)$
46. $P(-6, 2)$ 47. $P(3, -6)$ 48. $P(2, -4)$ 49. $P(5, 4)$

50. **Recreation** A carousel has eight evenly spaced seats shaped like animals. During each ride, the carousel makes between 8 and 9 clockwise revolutions. At the end of one ride, the carousel stops so that the lion is in the position where the zebra was when the ride started. Through how many degrees did the carousel rotate on this ride? 2970°

13-2 Exercises

Assignment Guide

Assign *Guided Practice* exercises as necessary.

If you finished Examples 1–2
Basic 26–33, 61–63
Average 26–33, 61–63, 72
Advanced 26–33, 61–63, 72

If you finished Examples 1–4
Basic 26–63, 66–68, 74–80
Average 26–68, 72, 74–80
Advanced 26–55, 57–80

Homework Quick Check
Quickly check key concepts.
Exercises: 26, 30, 36, 42, 50

Number Sense In **Exercises 42–49,** remind students that they should rationalize the denominators of their answers.

Answers

2.

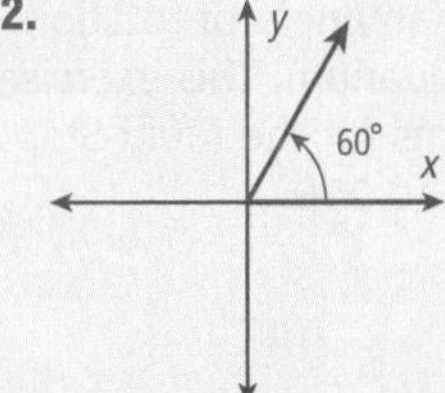

3.

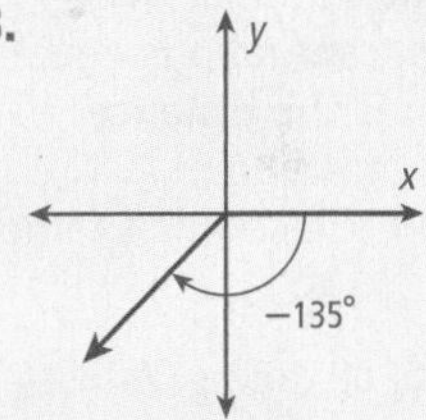

Answers

4.

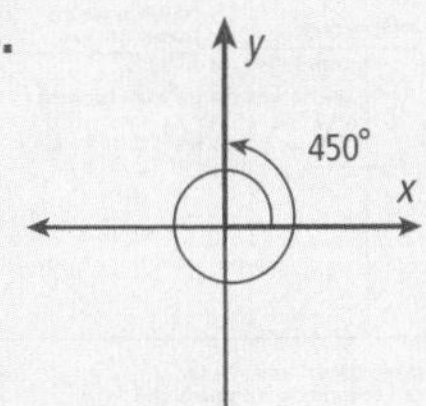

5.

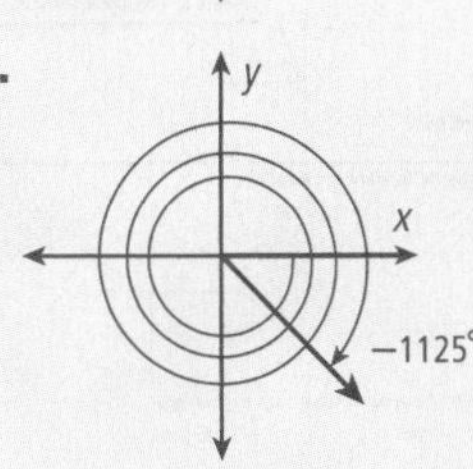

6. Possible answer: 435°; −285°
7. Possible answer: 360°; −360°
8. Possible answer: 335°; −385°
9. Possible answer: 330°; −30°

18. $\sin\theta = \frac{2\sqrt{13}}{13}$; $\cos\theta = -\frac{3\sqrt{13}}{13}$; $\tan\theta = -\frac{2}{3}$; $\csc\theta = \frac{\sqrt{13}}{2}$; $\sec\theta = -\frac{\sqrt{13}}{3}$; $\cot\theta = -\frac{3}{2}$

19–33, 42–49. See p. A48.

State Resources

go.hrw.com
State Resources Online
KEYWORD: MB7 Resources

Teaching Tip **Inclusion** In **Exercise 51,** explain that the average angular speed can be calculated by dividing the total number of degrees rotated by the time in which the rotation occurred.

Teaching Tip **Technology** In **Exercise 55,** you may wish to have students visualize the path of the firework by using a parametric graph on a graphing calculator. Press MODE and select **Par**. Then enter the equations, and graph as shown.

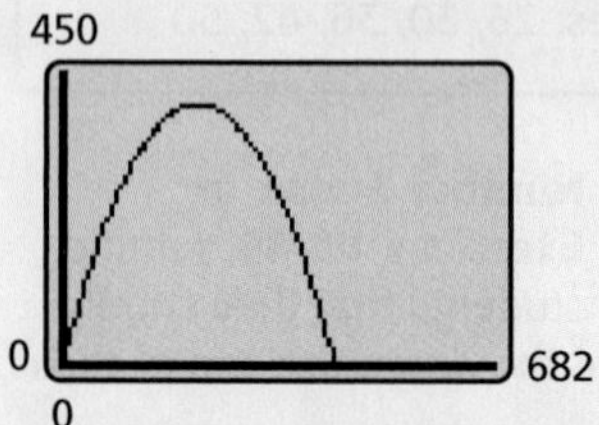

450
0
0
682

MULTI-STEP TEST PREP **Exercise 57** involves an application of an angle of rotation related to an aquarium. This exercise prepares students for the Multi-Step Test Prep on page 956.

Answers

56. A is incorrect. For a point $P(x, y)$ on the terminal side of θ, the cosecant ratio is equal to $\frac{r}{y}$, where r is the distance from the origin to point P. The ratio given in choice A is $\frac{r}{x}$ rather than $\frac{r}{y}$.

64, 65, 69–71, 73, 80. See p. A48.

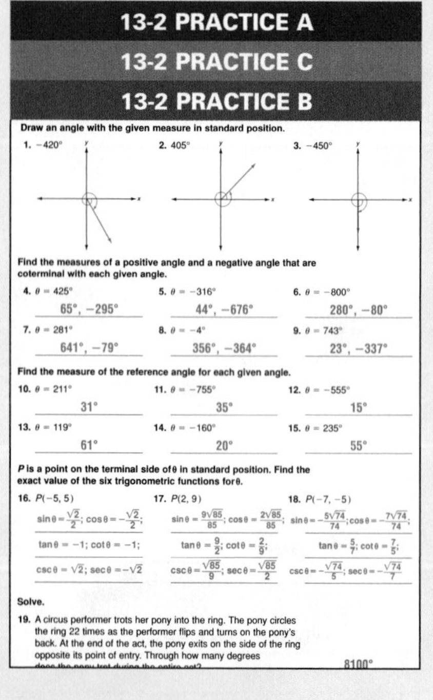
13-2 PRACTICE A

13-2 PRACTICE C

13-2 PRACTICE B

Draw an angle with the given measure in standard position.

1. −420° 2. 405° 3. −450°

Find the measures of a positive angle and a negative angle that are coterminal with each given angle.

4. $\theta = 425°$ 65°, −295°
5. $\theta = -316°$ 44°, −676°
6. $\theta = -800°$ 280°, −80°
7. $\theta = 281°$ 641°, −79°
8. $\theta = -4°$ 356°, −364°
9. $\theta = 743°$ 23°, −337°

Find the measure of the reference angle for each given angle.

10. $\theta = 211°$ 31°
11. $\theta = -755°$ 35°
12. $\theta = -555°$ 15°
13. $\theta = 119°$ 61°
14. $\theta = -160°$ 20°
15. $\theta = 235°$ 55°

***P* is a point on the terminal side of θ in standard position. Find the exact value of the six trigonometric functions for θ.**

16. $P(-5, 5)$ $\sin\theta = \frac{\sqrt{2}}{2}$; $\cos\theta = -\frac{\sqrt{2}}{2}$; $\tan\theta = -1$; $\cot\theta = -1$; $\csc\theta = \sqrt{2}$; $\sec\theta = -\sqrt{2}$

17. $P(2, 9)$ $\sin\theta = \frac{9\sqrt{85}}{85}$; $\cos\theta = \frac{2\sqrt{85}}{85}$; $\tan\theta = \frac{9}{2}$; $\cot\theta = \frac{2}{9}$; $\csc\theta = \frac{\sqrt{85}}{9}$; $\sec\theta = \frac{\sqrt{85}}{2}$

18. $P(-7, -5)$ $\sin\theta = -\frac{5\sqrt{74}}{74}$; $\cos\theta = -\frac{7\sqrt{74}}{74}$; $\tan\theta = \frac{5}{7}$; $\cot\theta = \frac{7}{5}$; $\csc\theta = -\frac{\sqrt{74}}{5}$; $\sec\theta = -\frac{\sqrt{74}}{7}$

Solve.

19. A circus performer trots her pony into the ring. The pony circles the ring 22 times as the performer flips and turns on the pony's back. At the end of the act, the pony exits on the side of the ring opposite its point of entry. Through how many degrees 8100°

51. Multi-Step A double axel is a figure-skating jump in which the skater makes 2.5 revolutions in the air. If a skater is in the air for 0.66 s during a double axel, what is her average angular speed to the nearest degree per second? **1364°/s**

Determine the exact coordinates of point *P*.

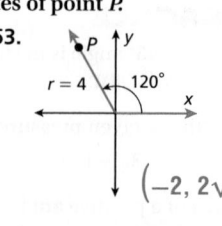

52. $r = 4\sqrt{2}$, 45° **(4, 4)**

53. $r = 4$, 120° $\mathbf{(-2, 2\sqrt{3})}$

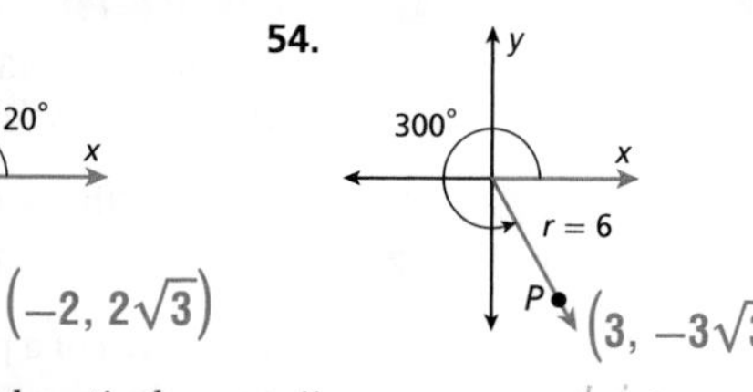
54. 300°, $r = 6$ $\mathbf{(3, -3\sqrt{3})}$

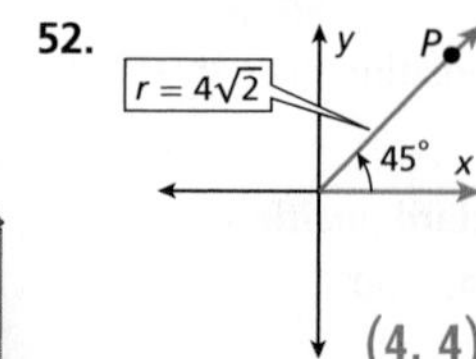

In professional fireworks displays, the chemicals that produce colored bursts of light are encased in spherical shells. In general, a firework rises about 100 ft for each inch of shell diameter.

55. Fireworks The horizontal distance x and vertical distance y in feet traveled by a firework can be modeled by the functions $x(t) = v(\cos\theta)t$ and $y(t) = -16t^2 + v(\sin\theta)t$. In these functions, v is the initial velocity of the firework, θ is the angle at which the firework is launched, and t is the time in seconds. A firework is launched with an initial velocity of 166 ft/s at an angle of 75°.

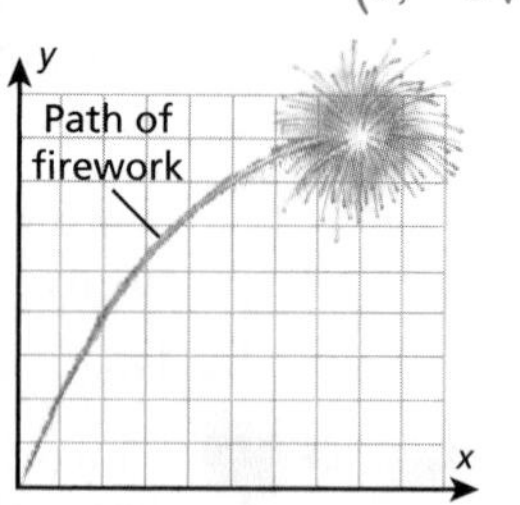

a. To the nearest foot, what is the maximum height that the firework will reach? **402 ft**

b. To achieve the greatest effect, the firework should explode when it reaches its maximum height. To the nearest second, how long after the launch should the firework explode? **5 s**

c. To the nearest foot, what is the horizontal distance that the firework will have traveled when the maximum height is reached? **215 ft**

d. **What if...?** To the nearest foot, how much higher would the firework travel if it were fired at an angle of 90°? **29 ft**

56. ERROR ANALYSIS $P(2, -2)$ is a point on the terminal side of an angle θ in standard position. Two attempts at finding $\csc\theta$ are shown below. Which is incorrect? Explain the error.

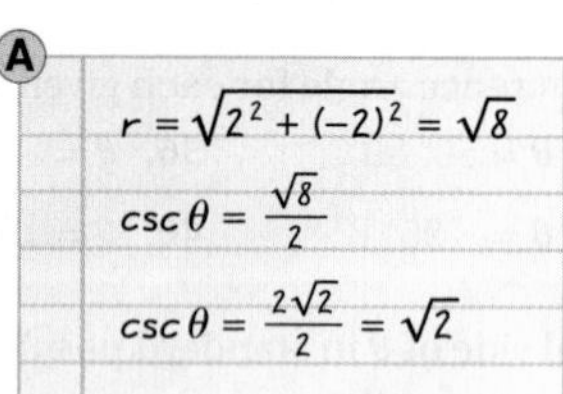

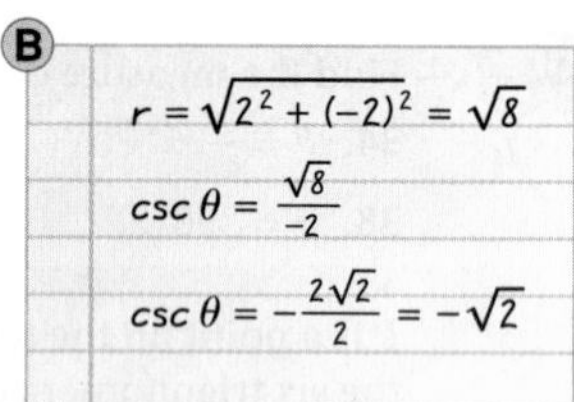

MULTI-STEP TEST PREP

57. This problem will prepare you for the Multi-Step Test Prep on page 956.

An aquarium has a cylindrical tank that rotates at a constant speed about an axis through the center of the cylinder's bases. In 1 minute, the tank rotates through an angle of 48°.

a. How long does it take the tank to make a complete rotation? **7.5 min**

b. The tank rotates only during the aquarium's operating hours. If the aquarium is open from 9:30 A.M. to 6:00 P.M., how many rotations does the tank make in one day? **68 rotations**

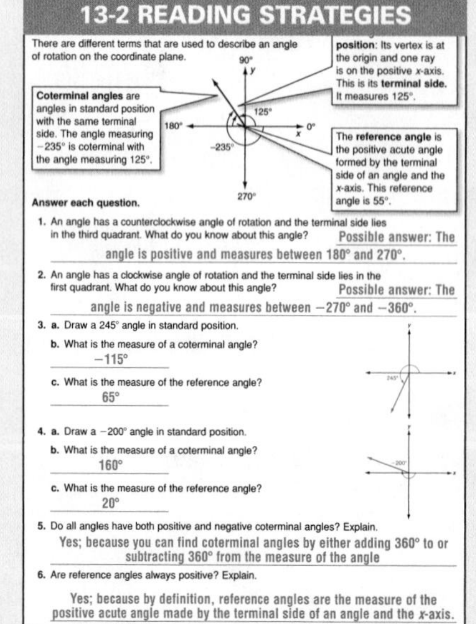
13-2 READING STRATEGIES

There are different terms that are used to describe an angle of rotation on the coordinate plane.

Coterminal angles are angles in standard position with the same terminal side. The angle measuring −235° is coterminal with the angle measuring 125°.

...**position**: Its vertex is at the origin and one ray is on the positive *x*-axis. This is its **terminal side.** It measures 125°.

The **reference angle** is the positive acute angle formed by the terminal side of an angle and the *x*-axis. This reference angle is 55°.

Answer each question.

1. An angle has a counterclockwise angle of rotation and the terminal side lies in the third quadrant. What do you know about this angle? Possible answer: The angle is positive and measures between 180° and 270°.

2. An angle has a clockwise angle of rotation and the terminal side lies in the first quadrant. What do you know about this angle? Possible answer: The angle is negative and measures between −270° and −360°.

3. a. Draw a 245° angle in standard position.
b. What is the measure of a coterminal angle? −115°
c. What is the measure of the reference angle? 65°

4. a. Draw a −200° angle in standard position.
b. What is the measure of a coterminal angle? 160°
c. What is the measure of the reference angle? 20°

5. Do all angles have both positive and negative coterminal angles? Explain. Yes; because you can find coterminal angles by either adding 360° to or subtracting 360° from the measure of the angle

6. Are reference angles always positive? Explain. Yes; because by definition, reference angles are the measure of the positive acute angle made by the terminal side of an angle and the *x*-axis.

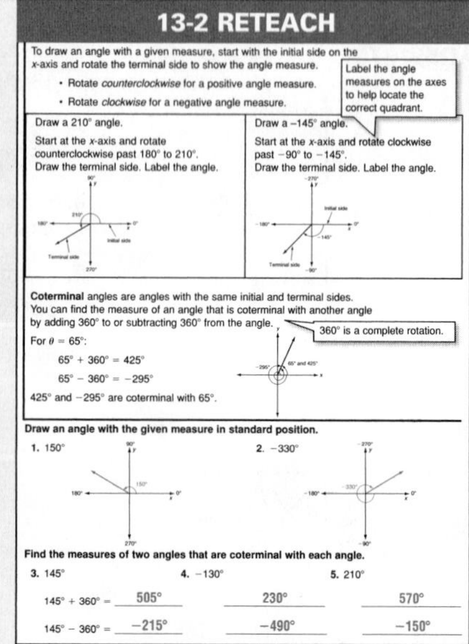
13-2 RETEACH

To draw an angle with a given measure, start with the initial side on the *x*-axis and rotate the terminal side to show the angle measure.

- Rotate *counterclockwise* for a positive angle measure.
- Rotate *clockwise* for a negative angle measure.

Label the angle measures on the axes to help locate the correct quadrant.

Draw a 210° angle. Start at the *x*-axis and rotate counterclockwise past 180° to 210°. Draw the terminal side. Label the angle.

Draw a −145° angle. Start at the *x*-axis and rotate clockwise past −90° to −145°. Draw the terminal side. Label the angle.

Coterminal angles are angles with the same initial and terminal sides. You can find the measure of an angle that is coterminal with another angle by adding 360° to or subtracting 360° from the angle.

360° is a complete rotation.

For $\theta = 65°$:

65° + 360° = 425°

65° − 360° = −295°

425° and −295° are coterminal with 65°.

Draw an angle with the given measure in standard position.

1. 150° 2. −330°

Find the measures of two angles that are coterminal with each angle.

3. 145° 145° + 360° = 505°; 145° − 360° = −215°
4. −130° 230°; −490°
5. 210° 570°; −150°

Use your calculator to find the value of each trigonometric function. Round to the nearest thousandth.

58. $\sin 260°$ -0.985 **59.** $\cos(-130°)$ -0.643 **60.** $\csc 200°$ -2.924

Find all values of θ that have a reference angle with the given measure for $0° \leq \theta < 360°$.

61. 30° — 30°, 150°, 210°, 330° **62.** 55° — 55°, 125°, 235°, 305° **63.** 82° — 82°, 98°, 262°, 278°

64. **Critical Thinking** Explain how the tangent of an angle in standard position is related to the slope of the terminal side of the angle.

65. **Write About It** Explain how to determine whether sin 225° is positive or negative without using a calculator.

TEST PREP

66. Which of the following angles have a reference angle with a measure of 30°?

I. $\theta = 120°$ II. $\theta = -150°$ III. $\theta = 330°$

(A) III only (B) I and II only **(C) II and III only** (D) I, II, and III

67. In standard position, the terminal side of $\angle P$ passes through point $(-3, 4)$, and the terminal side of $\angle Q$ passes through point $(3, 4)$. Which trigonometric function has the same value for both angles?

(F) sine (G) cosine (H) tangent (J) secant

68. Which angle in standard position is coterminal with an angle that measures $-120°$?

(A) $\theta = 60°$ (B) $\theta = 120°$ **(C) $\theta = 240°$** (D) $\theta = 300°$

CHALLENGE AND EXTEND

P is a point on the terminal side of θ in standard position. Find the value of the sine, cosine, and tangent of θ in terms of a and b. Assume that a and b are positive.

69. $P(a, b)$ **70.** $P\left(\frac{1}{a}, a\right)$ **71.** $P(a^2, ab)$

72. Write an expression that can be used to determine all of the coterminal angles of an angle that measures 50°. $50° + (360°)n$, where n is an integer

73. For what values of θ, if any, are the six trigonometric functions undefined?

SPIRAL REVIEW

Use finite differences to determine the degree of the polynomial that best describes the data. *(Lesson 6-9)*

74.

x	0	1	2	3	4	5
y	−3	−1	3	9	17	27

2

75.

x	0	1	2	3	4	5
y	2	−2	0	14	46	102

3

Given $f(x) = 2x - 2$ and $g(x) = x^2 + 1$, find each value. *(Lesson 9-4)*

76. $f(g(3))$ 18 **77.** $g(f(4))$ 37 **78.** $f(g(-1))$ 2

Find the value of the sine, cosine, and tangent functions for θ. *(Lesson 13-1)*

79.

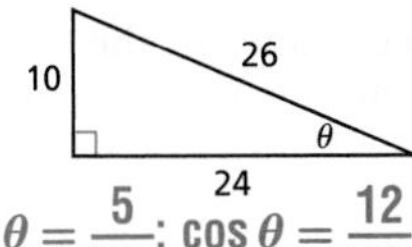

$\sin\theta = \frac{5}{13}$; $\cos\theta = \frac{12}{13}$; $\tan\theta = \frac{5}{12}$

80.

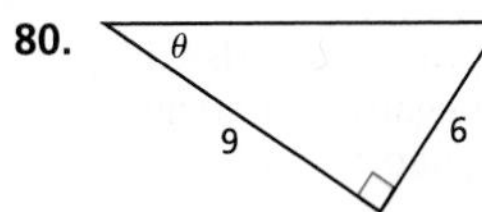

COMMON ERROR ALERT

Students may have difficulty identifying the reference angle in **Exercises 34–41.** Suggest that they draw θ in standard position and then draw a vertical segment from a point on the terminal side to the x-axis. Tell students that this segment passes through the reference angle.

TEST PREP DOCTOR In **Exercise 68,** students who chose **A, B,** or **D** may have confused coterminal angles with angles that are not coterminal but have the same reference angle.

Journal

Ask students to explain whether coterminal angles have the same reference angle.

ALTERNATIVE ASSESSMENT

Have students choose a point in Quadrant II, III, or IV and draw an angle in standard position whose terminal side passes through this point. Then have them determine the value of the six trigonometric functions of the angle.

13-2 Lesson Quiz

Draw an angle in standard position with the given measure.

1. 210° **2.** −160°

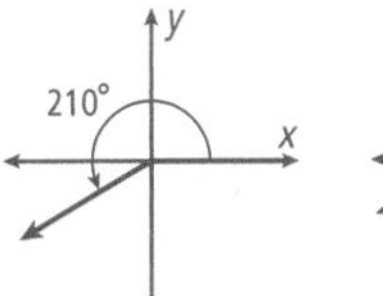

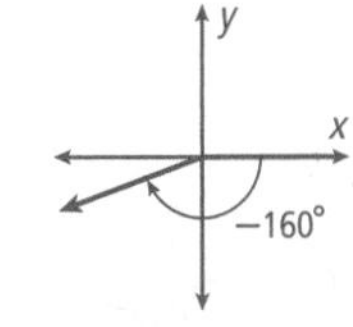

Find the measure of the reference angle for each given angle. 70° 15°

3. $\theta = 290°$ **4.** $\theta = -195°$

5. $P(1, -2)$ is a point on the terminal side of θ in standard position. Find the exact value of the six trigonometric functions for θ.

$\sin\theta = -\frac{2\sqrt{5}}{5}$, $\cos\theta = \frac{\sqrt{5}}{5}$,

$\tan\theta = -2$, $\csc\theta = -\frac{\sqrt{5}}{2}$,

$\sec\theta = \sqrt{5}$, $\cot\theta = -\frac{1}{2}$

Also available on transparency

13-2 PROBLEM SOLVING

Isabelle and Karl agreed to meet at the rotating restaurant at the top of a tower in the town center. The restaurant makes one full rotation each hour.

1. Isabelle waits for Karl, who arrives 30 minutes later. Through how many degrees does the restaurant rotate between the time that Isabelle arrives and the time that Karl arrives? 180°
2. Since the restaurant is busy, they don't get menus for another ten minutes. How much farther has the restaurant rotated? 60°
3. By the time they are served dinner, the restaurant has rotated to an angle 30° short of its orientation when Isabelle arrived.
   a. Write an expression for the length of time that Isabelle has been there. $\frac{330}{360} \times 60$ min
   b. How long has she been there? 55 min
   c. How long has Karl been there? 25 min
   d. How far has the restaurant rotated since Karl arrived? 150°
4. When their bill comes, it includes a note that the restaurant has rotated 840° since Isabelle arrived.
   a. How long has it been since they were served dinner? 2 h 20 min
   b. How many rotations has the restaurant made since Isabelle arrived? $2\frac{1}{3}$
   c. How far is the restaurant from its orientation when Karl arrived? 60°
5. On their way out, they stop and look at a map. A museum is located at a point northeast of the tower with coordinates (3, 2).
   a. Write the trigonometric function for the angle that the line from the tower to the museum makes with a line due north from the tower. $\tan\theta = \frac{3}{2}$
   b. Isabelle says that the museum is exactly 4 kilometers from the tower. How much farther north is the museum than the tower? 2.2 km

An advertisement on a kiosk near the bus stop rotates through 765° while Aaron waits for his bus. Choose the letter for the best answer.

6. What is the difference in the orientation of the advertisement between when Aaron arrived at the bus stop and when the bus came?
   (A) 45°
   B 90°
   C 315°
   D 405°
7. If the advertisement rotates at a rate of one rotation every 10 minutes, how long does Aaron wait for his bus?
   F Less than 2 min
   G Between 2 min and 10 min
   H Between 10 min and 20 min
   (J) More than 20 min

13-2 CHALLENGE

When a light ray passes from one medium, such as air, into another medium, such as glass, the light ray is bent, or *refracted*, at the boundary between the two media. The *index of refraction*, n, of a particular medium is given by the equation below.

$n = \frac{\sin\theta_i}{\sin\theta_r}$ θ_i is the incoming *angle of incidence* of the light ray; θ_r is the outgoing *angle of refraction*

Air
Glass

1. Measurements taken using a piece of crown glass gave an angle of incidence of 43.7° and an angle of refraction of 27.1°. Determine the index of refraction of crown glass. About 1.52

The Dutch physicist Willebrond Snell (1580–1626) discovered that the sine of the angle of incidence is proportional to the sine of the angle of refraction for any given interface between two media. As shown below, Snell's Law may be stated in terms of the indices of refraction of the media.

$n_1 \sin\theta_i = n_2 \sin\theta_r$ n_1 is the index of refraction of the first medium; n_2 is the index of refraction of the second medium

2. The measure of θ_i is 30° and the measure of θ_r for crown glass is 19.2°. Use the index of refraction of crown glass that you determined in Exercise 1. Find the index of refraction of air. 1.0

Snell's Law may be also be stated in terms of the velocity of light in the two media.

$\frac{\sin\theta_i}{\sin\theta_r} = \frac{v_1}{v_2}$ v_1 is the speed of light in the first medium; v_2 is the speed of light in the second medium

3. The measure of the angle of incidence with which a ray of light strikes crown glass is 30° and the measure of the angle of refraction is 19.2°. The speed of light in air is 3.0×10^8 meters per second. Find the speed of light in crown glass. 1.97×10^8 m per s

When light crosses a boundary and its speed increases in the second medium, the measure of the angle of refraction is greater than the measure of the angle of incidence. There is an angle of incidence, called the *critical angle* (θ_c), for which the corresponding angle of refraction is 90°, and the ray of light emerges parallel to the boundary. You can determine the measure of a critical angle when light passes from some medium into air by using the formula below.

$\sin\theta_c = \frac{1}{n}$, where n is the index of refraction of the first medium

4. When light passes from diamond to air the measure of the critical angle is 24.4°. Find the index of refraction of diamond. 2.42

Organizer

Use with Lesson 13-3

Pacing:

Traditional $\frac{1}{2}$ day
Block $\frac{1}{4}$ day

Objective: Use a graphing calculator to graph the unit circle and find the sine and cosine of various angles.

Materials: graphing calculator

Online Edition
Graphing Calculator, TechKeys

Resources

Technology Lab Activities
13-3 Lab Recording Sheet

Teach

Discuss

Tell students that because $r = 1$ for a point on the unit circle,
$\sin\theta = \frac{y}{r} = \frac{y}{1} = y$ and
$\cos\theta = \frac{x}{r} = \frac{x}{1} = x$.

Close

Key Concept

The coordinates of points on the unit circle can be used to determine the sine and cosine of angles.

Assessment

Journal Have students explain how to use the unit circle to determine the range of the sine and cosine functions.

State Resources

Explore the Unit Circle

Use with Lesson 13-3

A *unit circle* is a circle with a radius of 1 unit centered at the origin on the coordinate plane. You can use a graphing calculator to plot a unit circle based on the cosine and sine functions. You can then use the unit circle to explore the values of these functions for various angle measures.

Activity

Use the sine and cosine functions to graph a unit circle, and use it to determine sin 30° and cos 30°.

1. Press MODE and make sure that the angle mode is set to **Degree**. Set the graphing mode to **Par** (Parametric).

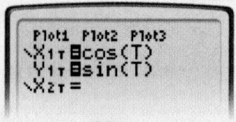

2. Press Y=, and enter **cos(T)** for X_{1T} and **sin(T)** for Y_{1T}.

```
Plot1 Plot2 Plot3
\X1T=cos(T)
 Y1T=sin(T)
\X2T=
```

3. Press WINDOW and set **Tmin** to 0, **Tmax** to 360, and **Tstep** to 2. Set **Xmin** and **Ymin** to −1, **Xmax** and **Ymax** to 1, and **Xscl** and **Yscl** to 0.1.

```
WINDOW
 Tmin=0
 Tmax=360
 Tstep=2
 Xmin=-1
 Xmax=1
 Xscl=.1
↓Ymin=-1
```

4. Press ZOOM and select **5:Zsquare**. A circle with a radius of 1 unit is displayed.

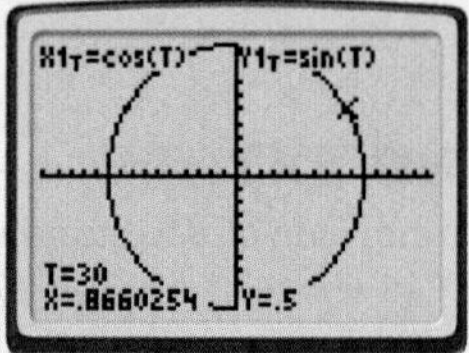

5. Press TRACE. Use the arrow keys to move the cursor to the point where **T=30**.

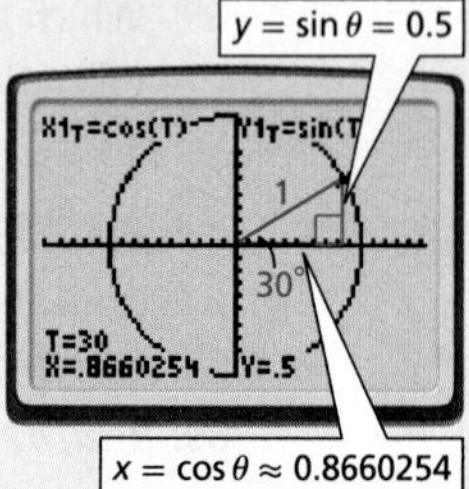

From Lesson 13-1, you know that $\sin 30° = \frac{1}{2} = 0.5$ and that $\cos 30° = \frac{\sqrt{3}}{2} \approx 0.8660254$. These values agree with those shown on the graph.

Notice that the unit circle can be used to define the cosine and sine functions. For an angle θ in standard position whose terminal side passes through point $P(x, y)$ on the unit circle, $\sin\theta = y$ and $\cos\theta = x$.

Try This

Use the unit circle on your graphing calculator to determine the values of the sine and cosine functions of each angle.

1. $\theta = 150°$
2. $\theta = 244°$
3. $\theta = 90°$
4. **Make a Conjecture** How can you verify that the unit circle displayed on your graphing calculator has a radius of 1 unit?
5. **Make a Conjecture** Use the graph of the unit circle to explain why the sine function is negative for an angle θ in standard position if the angle's terminal side lies in Quadrants III or IV.

Answers to *Try This*

1. $\sin 150° = 0.5$; $\cos 150° \approx -0.8660254$
2. $\sin 244° \approx -0.898794$; $\cos 244° \approx -0.4383711$
3. $\sin 90° = 1$; $\cos 90° = 0$
4. Possible answer: Use the TRACE feature to find the coordinates of the points where the circle crosses the axes. These points have coordinates (1, 0), (0, 1), (−1, 0), and (0, −1). The distance from each of these points to the origin is 1 unit. Therefore, the circle has a radius of 1 unit.
5. Possible answer: For an angle θ in standard position whose terminal side passes through point $P(x, y)$ on the unit circle, $\sin\theta = y$. The value of y is negative for points in Quadrants III or IV. Therefore, $\sin\theta$ is negative if the terminal side of θ lies in Quadrants III or IV.

13-3 The Unit Circle

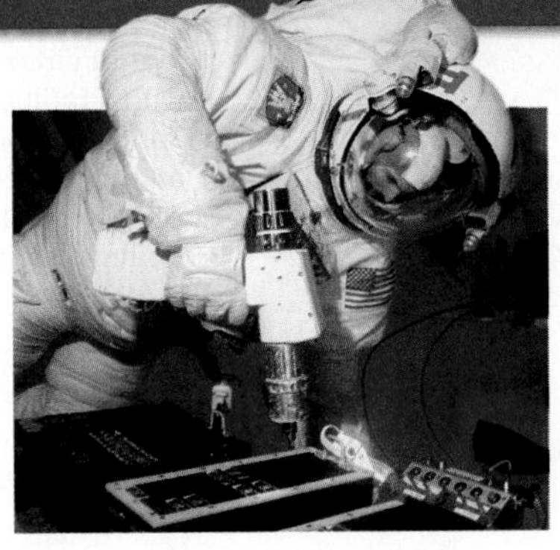

Objectives
Convert angle measures between degrees and radians.
Find the values of trigonometric functions on the unit circle.

Vocabulary
radian
unit circle

Who uses this?
Engineers can use angles measured in radians when designing machinery used to train astronauts. (See Example 4.)

So far, you have measured angles in degrees. You can also measure angles in *radians.*

A **radian** is a unit of angle measure based on arc length. Recall from geometry that an *arc* is an unbroken part of a circle. If a central angle θ in a circle of radius r intercepts an arc of length r, then the measure of θ is defined as 1 radian.

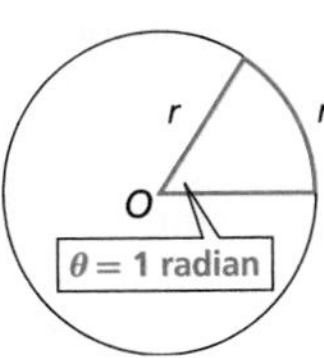

The circumference of a circle of radius r is $2\pi r$. Therefore, an angle representing one complete clockwise rotation measures 2π radians. You can use the fact that 2π radians is equivalent to 360° to convert between radians and degrees.

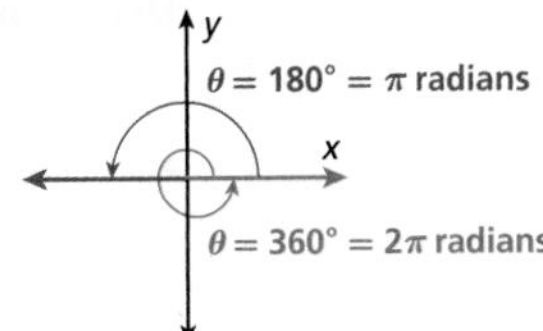

Converting Angle Measures

DEGREES TO RADIANS	RADIANS TO DEGREES
Multiply the number of degrees by $\left(\frac{\pi \text{ radians}}{180°}\right)$.	Multiply the number of radians by $\left(\frac{180°}{\pi \text{ radians}}\right)$.

EXAMPLE 1 Converting Between Degrees and Radians

Reading Math
Angles measured in radians are often not labeled with the unit. If an angle measure does not have a degree symbol, you can usually assume that the angle is measured in radians.

Convert each measure from degrees to radians or from radians to degrees.

A $-45°$

$$-45°\left(\frac{\pi \text{ radians}}{180°}\right) = -\frac{\pi}{4} \text{ radians} \qquad \textit{Multiply by } \left(\frac{\pi \text{ radians}}{180°}\right).$$

B $\frac{5\pi}{6}$ radians

$$\left(\frac{5\pi}{6} \text{ radians}\right)\left(\frac{180°}{\pi \text{ radians}}\right) = 150° \qquad \textit{Multiply by } \left(\frac{180°}{\pi \text{ radians}}\right).$$

CHECK IT OUT! Convert each measure from degrees to radians or from radians to degrees.

1a. 80° $\frac{4\pi}{9}$ radians **1b.** $\frac{2\pi}{9}$ radians 40° **1c.** $-36°$ $-\frac{\pi}{5}$ radians **1d.** 4π radians 720°

13-3 Organizer

Pacing: Traditional 1 day
Block $\frac{1}{2}$ day

Objectives: Convert angle measures between degrees and radians.

Find the values of trigonometric functions on the unit circle.

Algebra Lab
In *Algebra Lab Activities*

Online Edition
Tutorial Videos, Interactivity

Power Presentations with PowerPoint®

Warm Up

Find the measure of the reference angle for each given angle.

1. 120° 60° **2.** 225° 45°

3. $-150°$ 30° **4.** 315° 45°

Find the exact value of each trigonometric function.

5. $\sin 60°$ $\frac{\sqrt{3}}{2}$ **6.** $\tan 45°$ 1

7. $\cos 45°$ $\frac{\sqrt{2}}{2}$ **8.** $\cos 60°$ $\frac{1}{2}$

Also available on transparency

Math Humor

Q: Why is Ms. Radian such a good reporter?

A: She covers the story from every angle.

1 Introduce

13-3 The Unit Circle

A ______ is a circle with a radius of 1 unit. You can use trigonometric ratios to determine the coordinates of points on a unit circle that is centered at the origin.

1. The figure shows a unit circle and a 60° angle in standard position. What is the length of the hypotenuse of the 30°-60°-90° triangle? How do you know?
2. Use what you know about special right triangles to find the lengths of the legs of the 30°-60°-90° triangle.
3. What are the coordinates of point P?
4. What are the exact values of cos 60° and sin 60°?
5. How are the values of cos 60° and sin 60° related to the coordinates of point P?

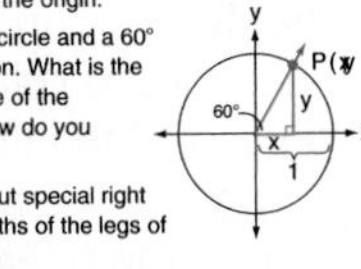

THINK AND DISCUSS

6. **Describe** how you can use a similar method to find the coordinates of point Q.
7. **Explain** how the values of cos 45° and sin 45° are related to the coordinates of point Q.

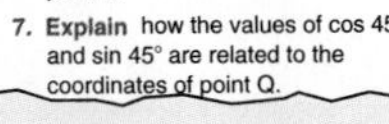

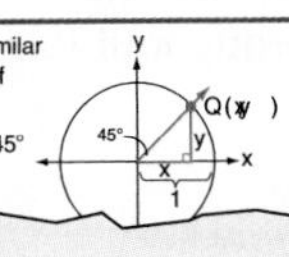

Motivate

Ask students to name various units in which they can measure an object's length. Possible answer: feet, yards, meters Then ask what unit they would use to measure the size of an angle. degrees Tell students that just as there is more than one unit in which to measure length, there is also more than one unit in which to measure angles. In this lesson, students will be learning about units of angle measure called radians.

Explorations and answers are provided in the *Explorations* binder.

State Resources

Power Presentations with PowerPoint®

Additional Examples

Example 1

Convert each measure from degrees to radians or from radians to degrees.

A. $-60°$ $\quad -\frac{\pi}{3}$ radians

B. $\frac{2\pi}{3}$ radians $\quad 120°$

Example 2

Use the unit circle to find the exact value of each trigonometric function.

A. $\cos 225°$ $\quad -\frac{\sqrt{2}}{2}$

B. $\tan \frac{5\pi}{6}$ $\quad -\frac{\sqrt{3}}{3}$

Also available on transparency

INTERVENTION

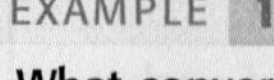

Questioning Strategies

EXAMPLE 1

- What conversion factor do you use to change from degrees to radians? from radians to degrees?

EXAMPLE 2

- How can you use the unit circle to identify a point through which an angle θ passes?
- How can you use the coordinates of this point to determine the values of trigonometric functions of θ?

Teaching Tip **Inclusion** Point out to students that they can also convert between degrees and radians by using the proportion $\frac{r \text{ radians}}{\pi \text{ radians}} = \frac{d°}{180°}$, where r is the measure of an angle θ in radians and d is its measure in degrees.

A **unit circle** is a circle with a radius of 1 unit. For every point $P(x, y)$ on the unit circle, the value of r is 1. Therefore, for an angle θ in standard position:

$$\sin\theta = \frac{y}{r} = \frac{y}{1} = y$$

$$\cos\theta = \frac{x}{r} = \frac{x}{1} = x$$

$$\tan\theta = \frac{y}{x}$$

So the coordinates of P can be written as $(\cos\theta, \sin\theta)$.

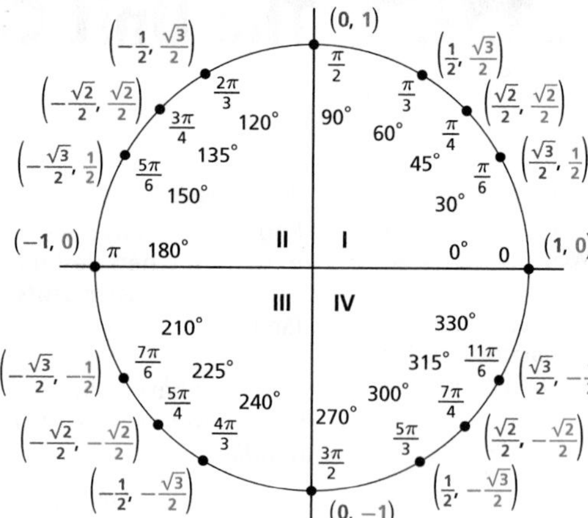

The diagram shows the equivalent degree and radian measures of special angles, as well as the corresponding x- and y-coordinates of points on the unit circle.

EXAMPLE 2 Using the Unit Circle to Evaluate Trigonometric Functions

Use the unit circle to find the exact value of each trigonometric function.

A $\cos 210°$

The angle passes through the point $\left(-\frac{\sqrt{3}}{2}, -\frac{1}{2}\right)$ on the unit circle.

$\cos 210° = x$ *Use* $\cos\theta = x$.

$= -\frac{\sqrt{3}}{2}$

B $\tan \frac{5\pi}{3}$

The angle passes through the point $\left(\frac{1}{2}, -\frac{\sqrt{3}}{2}\right)$ on the unit circle.

$\tan\frac{5\pi}{3} = \frac{y}{x}$ *Use* $\tan\theta = \frac{y}{x}$.

$= \frac{-\frac{\sqrt{3}}{2}}{\frac{1}{2}} = -\frac{\sqrt{3}}{2} \cdot \frac{2}{1} = -\sqrt{3}$

CHECK IT OUT! **Use the unit circle to find the exact value of each trigonometric function.**

2a. $\sin 315°$ $\quad -\frac{\sqrt{2}}{2}$ **2b.** $\tan 180°$ $\quad 0$ **2c.** $\cos\frac{4\pi}{3}$ $\quad -\frac{1}{2}$

You can use reference angles and Quadrant I of the unit circle to determine the values of trigonometric functions.

Know it! Note

Trigonometric Functions and Reference Angles	
To find the sine, cosine, or tangent of θ:	
Step 1	Determine the measure of the reference angle of θ.
Step 2	Use Quadrant I of the unit circle to find the sine, cosine, or tangent of the reference angle.
Step 3	Determine the quadrant of the terminal side of θ in standard position. Adjust the sign of the sine, cosine, or tangent based upon the quadrant of the terminal side.

2 Teach

Guided Instruction

Connect radian measure to the circumference of the unit circle. Because the radius of the unit circle is 1, the circumference is $C = 2\pi$, and the central angle that intercepts the circumference measures 2π radians. Be sure to point out that both of the methods shown in **Examples 2** and **3** can be used to determine the exact value of trigonometric functions. Encourage students to use whichever method they find easier.

Reaching All Learners

Through Visual Cues

Give students copies of blank unit circles to label as in the diagram on page 944. Suggest that students use colored pencils to help them organize the information. For example, they can write the measures of all angles with the same reference angle in the same color. Colored pencils can be found in the manipulatives kit (MK). Students may use their unit circles as a reference throughout this chapter.

The diagram shows how the signs of the trigonometric functions depend on the quadrant containing the terminal side of θ in standard position.

QII	$\sin\theta: +$ $\cos\theta: -$ $\tan\theta: -$	$\sin\theta: +$ $\cos\theta: +$ $\tan\theta: +$	QI
QIII	$\sin\theta: -$ $\cos\theta: -$ $\tan\theta: +$	$\sin\theta: -$ $\cos\theta: +$ $\tan\theta: -$	QIV

EXAMPLE 3 Using Reference Angles to Evaluate Trigonometric Functions

Use a reference angle to find the exact value of the sine, cosine, and tangent of 225°.

Step 1 Find the measure of the reference angle.

The reference angle measures 45°.

Step 2 Find the sine, cosine, and tangent of the reference angle.

$\sin 45° = \frac{\sqrt{2}}{2}$ *Use $\sin\theta = y$.*

$\cos 45° = \frac{\sqrt{2}}{2}$ *Use $\cos\theta = x$.*

$\tan 45° = 1$ *Use $\tan\theta = \frac{y}{x}$.*

Step 3 Adjust the signs, if needed.

$\sin 225° = -\frac{\sqrt{2}}{2}$ *In Quadrant III, $\sin\theta$ is negative.*

$\cos 225° = -\frac{\sqrt{2}}{2}$ *In Quadrant III, $\cos\theta$ is negative.*

$\tan 225° = 1$ *In Quadrant III, $\tan\theta$ is positive.*

Use a reference angle to find the exact value of the sine, cosine, and tangent of each angle.

3a. 270° **3b.** $\frac{11\pi}{6}$ **3c.** −30°

If you know the measure of a central angle of a circle, you can determine the length s of the arc intercepted by the angle.

$$\frac{\text{radian measure of } \theta}{\text{radian measure of circle}} \rightarrow \frac{\theta}{2\pi} = \frac{s}{2\pi r} \leftarrow \frac{\text{arc length intercepted by } \theta}{\text{arc length intercepted by circle}}$$

$\theta = \frac{s}{r}$ *Multiply each side by 2π.*

$s = r\theta$ *Solve for s.*

Arc Length Formula

For a circle of radius r, the arc length s intercepted by a central angle θ (measured in radians) is given by the following formula.

$s = r\theta$

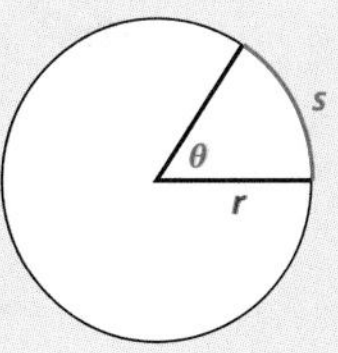

3a. $\sin 270° = -1$; $\cos 270° = 0$; $\tan 270°$: undefined

3b. $\sin\frac{11\pi}{6} = -\frac{1}{2}$; $\cos\frac{11\pi}{6} = \frac{\sqrt{3}}{2}$; $\tan\frac{11\pi}{6} = -\frac{\sqrt{3}}{3}$

3c. $\sin(-30°) = -\frac{1}{2}$; $\cos(-30°) = \frac{\sqrt{3}}{2}$; $\tan(-30°) = -\frac{\sqrt{3}}{3}$

COMMON ERROR ALERT

Students sometimes have trouble remembering how the signs of the trigonometric functions depend on the quadrant of the terminal side of θ. Emphasize that the value of the sine function represents the y-coordinate of a point on the unit circle; therefore, $\sin\theta$ is positive for positive y-coordinates (Quadrants I and II).

Likewise, the value of the cosine function represents the x-coordinate of a point on the unit circle; therefore, $\cos\theta$ is positive for positive x-coordinates (Quadrants I and IV).

Power Presentations with PowerPoint®

Additional Example

Example 3

Use a reference angle to find the exact value of the sine, cosine, and tangent of 330°.

$\sin 330° = -\frac{1}{2}$; $\cos 330° = \frac{\sqrt{3}}{2}$;

$\tan 330° = -\frac{\sqrt{3}}{3}$

Also available on transparency

INTERVENTION

Questioning Strategies

EXAMPLE 3

- How can you determine which quadrant contains the terminal side of the angle in standard position?
- How can you determine the sign of the trigonometric functions by knowing which quadrant contains the terminal side of the angle?

Teacher to Teacher

The mnemonic "**A**ll **S**tudents **T**ake **C**lasses" may help students remember which trigonometric ratios are positive in which quadrant.

Quadrant I: **A**ll
Quadrant II: **S**ine
Quadrant III: **T**angent
Quadrant IV: **C**osine

Mary Anderson
Downers Grove, IL

Power Presentations with PowerPoint®

Additional Example

Example 4

A tire of a car makes 653 complete rotations in 1 min. The diameter of the tire is 0.65 m. To the nearest meter, how far does the car travel in 1 s? 22 m

Also available on transparency

INTERVENTION

Questioning Strategies

EXAMPLE 4

- How do you find the values of r and θ used in the arc length formula?
- Why do you need to express the value of θ in radians rather than degrees?

Teaching Tip **Inclusion** In **Example 4,** point out that because 1 revolution is equivalent to an angle of rotation of 2π radians, the cab rotates through an angle of $32(2\pi)$ radians in 32 revolutions.

Teaching Tip **Math Background** It is important for students to become familiar with angles measured in radians because they will need to be able to use these units in more-advanced math classes, such as Calculus. For example, the processes of integration and differentiation that students will learn in these classes require that angles be measured in radians.

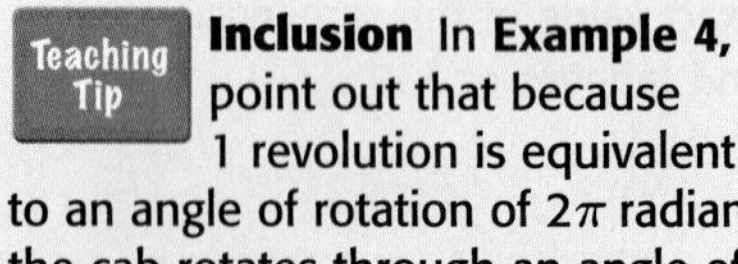

EXAMPLE 4 *Engineering Application*

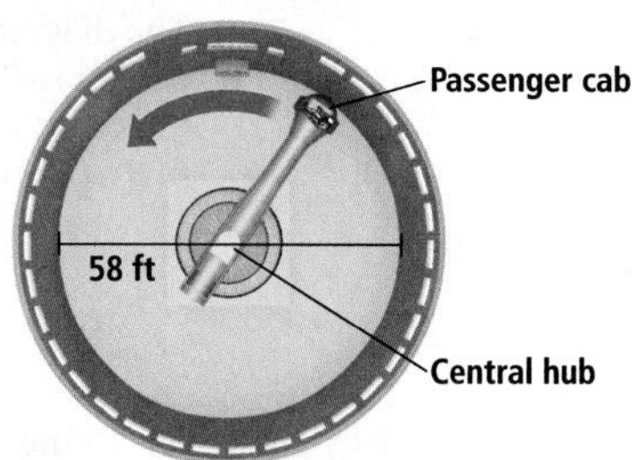

A human centrifuge is a device used in training astronauts. The passenger cab of the centrifuge shown makes 32 complete revolutions about the central hub in 1 minute. To the nearest foot, how far does an astronaut in the cab travel in 1 second?

Step 1 Find the radius of the centrifuge.

$r = \frac{58}{2} = 29$ ft *The radius is $\frac{1}{2}$ of the diameter.*

Step 2 Find the angle θ through which the cab rotates in 1 second.

$\frac{\text{radians rotated in 1 s}}{1\text{ s}} = \frac{\text{radians rotated in 60 s}}{60\text{ s}}$ *Write a proportion.*

$\frac{\theta \text{ radians}}{1\text{ s}} = \frac{32(2\pi)\text{ radians}}{60\text{ s}}$ *The cab rotates θ radians in 1 s and $32(2\pi)$ radians in 60 s.*

$60 \cdot \theta = 32(2\pi)$ *Cross multiply.*

$\theta = \frac{32(2\pi)}{60}$ *Divide both sides by 60.*

$\theta = \frac{16\pi}{15}$ *Simplify.*

Step 3 Find the length of the arc intercepted by $\frac{16\pi}{15}$ radians.

$s = r\theta$ *Use the arc length formula.*

$s = 29\left(\frac{16\pi}{15}\right)$ *Substitute 29 for r and $\frac{16\pi}{15}$ for θ.*

$s \approx 97$ *Simplify by using a calculator.*

The astronaut travels about 97 feet in 1 second.

4. An hour hand on Big Ben's Clock Tower in London is 14 ft long. To the nearest tenth of a foot, how far does the tip of the hour hand travel in 1 minute? **1.5 ft**

THINK AND DISCUSS

1. Explain why the tangent of a 90° angle is undefined.

2. Describe how to use a reference angle to determine the sine of an angle whose terminal side in standard position is in Quadrant IV.

3. GET ORGANIZED Copy and complete the graphic organizer. In each box, give an expression that can be used to determine the value of the trigonometric function.

	Acute Angle of Right Triangle	Angle of Rotation with *P(x, y)*	Angle with *P(x, y)* on Unit Circle
$\sin\theta$			
$\cos\theta$			
$\tan\theta$			

3 Close

Summarize

Review with students different methods that they have learned in this chapter for finding the values of trigonometric functions.

- by using the side lengths of right triangles
- by using a point on the terminal side of an angle in standard position
- by using the unit circle
- by using reference angles

ONGOING ASSESSMENT and INTERVENTION

***Diagnose Before* the Lesson**
13-3 Warm Up, TE p. 943

***Monitor During* the Lesson**
Check It Out! Exercises, SE pp. 943–946
Questioning Strategies, TE pp. 944–946

***Assess After* the Lesson**
13-3 Lesson Quiz, TE p. 949
Alternative Assessment, TE p. 949

Answers to *Think and Discuss*

Possible answers:

1. For a point $P(x, y)$ on the terminal side of a 90° angle, the value of x is always 0. Because division by 0 is undefined, $\tan\theta = \frac{y}{x}$ is undefined when θ is 90°.
2. The sine ratio is negative for an angle in standard position whose terminal side is in Quadrant IV. Therefore, the sine of the given angle is the negative of the sine of the reference angle.
3. See p. A14.

go.hrw.com
Homework Help Online
KEYWORD: MB7 13-3
Parent Resources Online
KEYWORD: MB7 Parent

GUIDED PRACTICE

1. **Vocabulary** What is the radius of a *unit circle*? the circumference? 1 unit; 2π units

SEE EXAMPLE 1 p. 943

Convert each measure from degrees to radians or from radians to degrees.

2. $30°$ $\frac{\pi}{6}$
3. $-75°$ $-\frac{5\pi}{12}$
4. $-150°$ $-\frac{5\pi}{6}$
5. $135°$ $\frac{3\pi}{4}$
6. $\frac{3\pi}{5}$ $108°$
7. $-\frac{5\pi}{8}$ $-112.5°$
8. $-\frac{\pi}{3}$ $-60°$
9. $\frac{4\pi}{9}$ $80°$

SEE EXAMPLE 2 p. 944

Use the unit circle to find the exact value of each trigonometric function.

10. $\sin 150°$ $\frac{1}{2}$
11. $\tan 315°$ -1
12. $\cot \frac{11\pi}{6}$ $-\sqrt{3}$
13. $\cos \frac{2\pi}{3}$ $-\frac{1}{2}$

SEE EXAMPLE 3 p. 945

Use a reference angle to find the exact value of the sine, cosine, and tangent of each angle.

14. $240°$
15. $120°$
16. $\frac{7\pi}{4}$
17. $\frac{\pi}{3}$

SEE EXAMPLE 4 p. 946

18. **Engineering** An engineer is designing a curve on a highway. The curve will be an arc of a circle with a radius of 1260 ft. The central angle that intercepts the curve will measure $\frac{\pi}{6}$ radians. To the nearest foot, what will be the length of the curve? 660 ft

PRACTICE AND PROBLEM SOLVING

Independent Practice

For Exercises	See Example
19–26	1
27–30	2
31–34	3
35	4

Extra Practice

Skills Practice p. S28
Application Practice p. S44

Convert each measure from degrees to radians or from radians to degrees.

19. $240°$ $\frac{4\pi}{3}$
20. $115°$ $\frac{23\pi}{36}$
21. $-25°$ $-\frac{5\pi}{36}$
22. $-315°$ $-\frac{7\pi}{4}$
23. $-\frac{\pi}{9}$ $-20°$
24. $\frac{2\pi}{5}$ $72°$
25. $\frac{7\pi}{2}$ $630°$
26. $-\frac{4\pi}{3}$ $-240°$

Use the unit circle to find the exact value of each trigonometric function.

27. $\tan 300°$ $-\sqrt{3}$
28. $\sin 120°$ $\frac{\sqrt{3}}{2}$
29. $\cos \frac{5\pi}{6}$ $-\frac{\sqrt{3}}{2}$
30. $\sec \frac{\pi}{3}$ 2

Use a reference angle to find the exact value of the sine, cosine, and tangent of each angle.

31. $225°$
32. $135°$
33. $\frac{11\pi}{6}$
34. $-\frac{5\pi}{6}$

35. **Geography** New York City is located about 40° north of the equator. If Earth's radius is about 4000 miles, approximately how many miles south would a plane need to fly from New York City to reach the equator? about 2793 mi

Draw an angle with the given measure in standard position. Then determine the measure of its reference angle.

36. $\frac{\pi}{3}$
37. $\frac{7\pi}{4}$
38. $\frac{5\pi}{6}$

39. **Electronics** A DVD rotates through an angle of 20π radians in 1 second. At this speed, how many revolutions does the DVD make in 1 minute? 600 revolutions/min

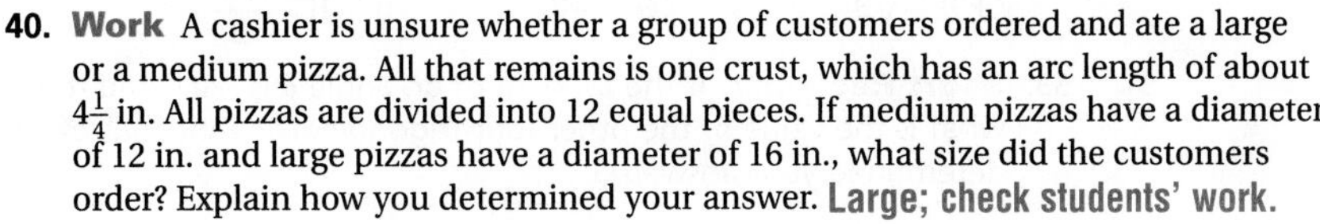

40. **Work** A cashier is unsure whether a group of customers ordered and ate a large or a medium pizza. All that remains is one crust, which has an arc length of about $4\frac{1}{4}$ in. All pizzas are divided into 12 equal pieces. If medium pizzas have a diameter of 12 in. and large pizzas have a diameter of 16 in., what size did the customers order? Explain how you determined your answer. Large; check students' work.

Assignment Guide

Assign *Guided Practice* exercises as necessary.

If you finished Examples **1–2**
- **Basic** 19–30, 36–38, 42–45
- **Average** 19–30, 36–38, 42–45
- **Advanced** 19–30, 36–38, 42–45, 54–56

If you finished Examples **1–4**
- **Basic** 19–48, 51–53, 59–68
- **Average** 19–53, 57, 59–68
- **Advanced** 19–68

Homework Quick Check
Quickly check key concepts.
Exercises: 20, 24, 28, 32, 35, 36

Teaching Tip **Social Studies Link** In **Exercise 35,** point out that because New York City is about 40° north of the equator, it has a latitude of about 40° north. Remind students that the equator has a latitude of 0° and the North and South Poles have latitudes of 90° north and 90° south, respectively.

Answers

14. $\sin 240° = -\frac{\sqrt{3}}{2}$; $\cos 240° = -\frac{1}{2}$; $\tan 240° = \sqrt{3}$

15. $\sin 120° = \frac{\sqrt{3}}{2}$; $\cos 120° = -\frac{1}{2}$; $\tan 120° = -\sqrt{3}$

16. $\sin\frac{7\pi}{4} = -\frac{\sqrt{2}}{2}$; $\cos\frac{7\pi}{4} = \frac{\sqrt{2}}{2}$; $\tan\frac{7\pi}{4} = -1$

State Resources

Answers

17. $\sin\frac{\pi}{3} = \frac{\sqrt{3}}{2}$; $\cos\frac{\pi}{3} = \frac{1}{2}$; $\tan\frac{\pi}{3} = \sqrt{3}$

31. $\sin 225° = -\frac{\sqrt{2}}{2}$; $\cos 225° = -\frac{\sqrt{2}}{2}$; $\tan 225° = 1$

32. $\sin 135° = \frac{\sqrt{2}}{2}$; $\cos 135° = -\frac{\sqrt{2}}{2}$; $\tan 135° = -1$

33. $\sin\frac{11\pi}{6} = -\frac{1}{2}$; $\cos\frac{11\pi}{6} = \frac{\sqrt{3}}{2}$; $\tan\frac{11\pi}{6} = -\frac{\sqrt{3}}{3}$

34. $\sin\left(-\frac{5\pi}{6}\right) = -\frac{1}{2}$; $\cos\left(-\frac{5\pi}{6}\right) = -\frac{\sqrt{3}}{2}$; $\tan\left(-\frac{5\pi}{6}\right) = \frac{\sqrt{3}}{3}$

36–38. See p. A49.

go.hrw.com
State Resources Online
KEYWORD: MB7 Resources

Exercise 41 involves the use of the arc length formula to solve a problem involving a deck at an aquarium. This exercise prepares students for the Multi-Step Test Prep on page 956.

Inclusion You may want to suggest that students review the definition of *coterminal angles* before they complete **Exercises 42–45.**

Teaching Tip **Critical Thinking** In **Exercise 46,** remind students to check that their answers are reasonable. By analyzing the data in the table, students can see that Earth is much larger than Pluto but has a shorter rotational period. Therefore, Pluto should rotate through a much smaller angle than Earth does in 1 hour.

In **Exercise 52,** students who chose **J** may not understand how to determine the sign of the value of a trigonometric function. Students who chose **G** may have determined the tangent of $\frac{5\pi}{6}$ rather than the cotangent.

Answers

42. Possible answer: $\frac{17\pi}{8}$

43. Possible answer: 3π

44. Possible answer: $\frac{11\pi}{4}$

45. Possible answer: $\frac{2\pi}{3}$

47. See p. A49.

49. Possible answer: when P lies on the unit circle

50, 53. See p. A49.

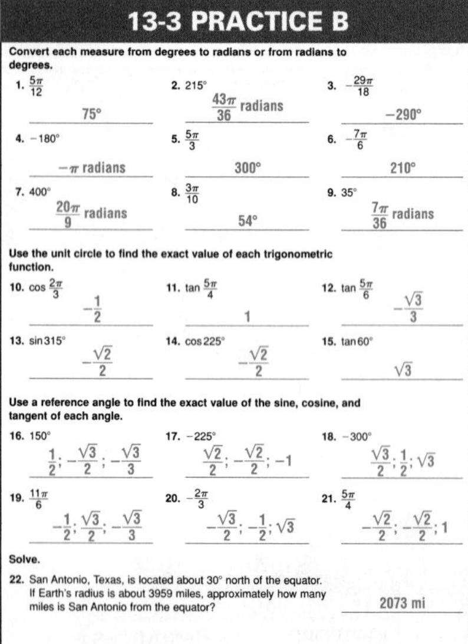

13-3 PRACTICE A

13-3 PRACTICE C

13-3 PRACTICE B

Convert each measure from degrees to radians or from radians to degrees.

1. $\frac{5\pi}{12}$ — 75°
2. 215° — $\frac{43\pi}{36}$ radians
3. $-\frac{29\pi}{18}$ — −290°
4. −180° — $-\pi$ radians
5. $\frac{5\pi}{3}$ — 300°
6. $\frac{7\pi}{6}$ — 210°
7. 400° — $\frac{20\pi}{9}$ radians
8. $\frac{3\pi}{10}$ — 54°
9. 35° — $\frac{7\pi}{36}$ radians

Use the unit circle to find the exact value of each trigonometric function.

10. $\cos\frac{2\pi}{3}$ — $-\frac{1}{2}$
11. $\tan\frac{5\pi}{4}$ — 1
12. $\tan\frac{5\pi}{6}$ — $-\frac{\sqrt{3}}{3}$
13. sin 315° — $-\frac{\sqrt{2}}{2}$
14. cos 225° — $-\frac{\sqrt{2}}{2}$
15. tan 60° — $\sqrt{3}$

Use a reference angle to find the exact value of the sine, cosine, and tangent of each angle.

16. 150° — $\frac{1}{2}; -\frac{\sqrt{3}}{2}; -\frac{\sqrt{3}}{3}$
17. −225° — $\frac{\sqrt{2}}{2}; -\frac{\sqrt{2}}{2}; -1$
18. −300° — $\frac{\sqrt{3}}{2}; \frac{1}{2}; \sqrt{3}$
19. $\frac{11\pi}{6}$ — $-\frac{1}{2}; \frac{\sqrt{3}}{2}; -\frac{\sqrt{3}}{3}$
20. $-\frac{2\pi}{3}$ — $-\frac{\sqrt{3}}{2}; -\frac{1}{2}; \sqrt{3}$
21. $\frac{5\pi}{4}$ — $-\frac{\sqrt{2}}{2}; -\frac{\sqrt{2}}{2}; 1$

Solve.

22. San Antonio, Texas, is located about 30° north of the equator. If Earth's radius is about 3959 miles, approximately how many miles is San Antonio from the equator? — 2073 mi

41. This problem will prepare you for the Multi-Step Test Prep on page 956.

A railing along an observation deck at an aquarium has a length of 22 ft. The railing is shaped like an arc that represents $\frac{1}{8}$ of a circle.

a. What is the measure, to the nearest degree, of the central angle that intercepts the railing? **45°**

b. To the nearest foot, what is the radius of the circle on which the railing is based? **28 ft**

Find the measure of an angle that is coterminal with each given angle.

42. $\theta = \frac{\pi}{8}$ **43.** $\theta = \pi$ **44.** $\theta = \frac{3\pi}{4}$ **45.** $\theta = -\frac{4\pi}{3}$

46. Astronomy The table shows the radius of Earth and Pluto and the number of hours that each takes to rotate on its axis.

	Radius at Equator (km)	Rotational Period (h)
Earth	6378	24
Pluto	1195	153

a. How many days does it take Earth to rotate through an angle of 2π radians? **1 day**

b. Through what angle, in radians, does each planet rotate in 1 hour? **Earth: $\frac{\pi}{12}$; Pluto: $\frac{2\pi}{153}$**

c. What if...? Suppose that a scientific expedition is sent to Pluto. In 1 hour, how much farther would a person at Earth's equator move than an astronaut at Pluto's equator, as a result of the planets' rotations? Round to the nearest kilometer. **1621 km**

47. Quadrantal angles are angles whose terminal sides lie on the x- or y-axis in standard position. Explain how to use the unit circle to determine the sine of the quadrantal angles 0, $\frac{\pi}{2}$, π, and $\frac{3\pi}{2}$ radians.

48. Multi-Step A rear windshield wiper moves through an angle of 135° on each swipe. To the nearest inch, how much greater is the length of the arc traced by the top end of the wiper blade than the length of the arc traced by the bottom end of the wiper blade? **33 in.**

Top end; 14 in.; Bottom end; 9 in.

49. Critical Thinking If P is a point on the terminal side of θ in standard position, under what conditions are the coordinates of P equal to $(\cos\theta, \sin\theta)$?

50. Write About It Explain how to determine the value of $\sin(-\theta)$ if you know the value of $\sin\theta$.

51. Which angle measure is closest to 2.5 radians?

(A) 90° (B) 120° **(C) 150°** (D) 225°

52. What is the value of $\cot\left(\frac{5\pi}{6}\right)$?

(F) $-\sqrt{3}$ (G) $-\frac{\sqrt{3}}{3}$ (H) $\frac{\sqrt{3}}{3}$ (J) $\sqrt{3}$

53. Short Response If the tangent of an angle θ is $-\sqrt{3}$ and the cosine of θ is $\frac{1}{2}$, what is the value of the other four trigonometric functions of θ? Explain how you determined your answer.

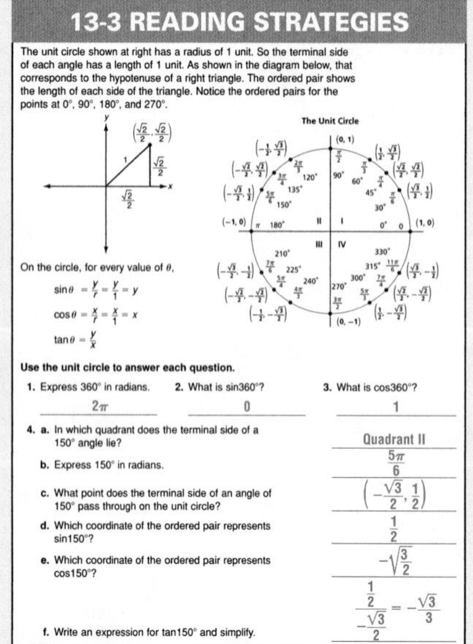

13-3 READING STRATEGIES

The unit circle shown at right has a radius of 1 unit. So the terminal side of each angle has a length of 1 unit. As shown in the diagram below, that corresponds to the hypotenuse of a right triangle. The ordered pair shows the length of each side of the triangle. Notice the ordered pairs for the points at 0°, 90°, 180°, and 270°.

On the circle, for every value of θ,

$\sin\theta = \frac{y}{r} = \frac{y}{1} = y$

$\cos\theta = \frac{x}{r} = \frac{x}{1} = x$

$\tan\theta = \frac{y}{x}$

Use the unit circle to answer each question.

1. Express 360° in radians. — 2π
2. What is sin 360°? — 0
3. What is cos 360°? — 1
4. a. In which quadrant does the terminal side of a 150° angle lie? — Quadrant II
   b. Express 150° in radians. — $\frac{5\pi}{6}$
   c. What point does the terminal side of an angle of 150° pass through on the unit circle? — $\left(-\frac{\sqrt{3}}{2}, \frac{1}{2}\right)$
   d. Which coordinate of the ordered pair represents sin 150°? — $\frac{1}{2}$
   e. Which coordinate of the ordered pair represents cos 150°? — $-\frac{\sqrt{3}}{2}$
   f. Write an expression for tan 150° and simplify. — $\frac{\frac{1}{2}}{-\frac{\sqrt{3}}{2}} = -\frac{\sqrt{3}}{3}$

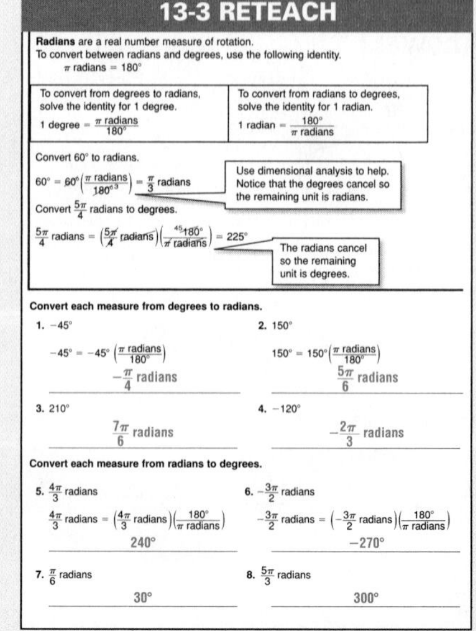

13-3 RETEACH

Radians are a real number measure of rotation.
To convert between radians and degrees, use the following identity.
π radians = 180°

To convert from degrees to radians, solve the identity for 1 degree.	To convert from radians to degrees, solve the identity for 1 radian.
1 degree = $\frac{\pi \text{ radians}}{180°}$	1 radian = $\frac{180°}{\pi \text{ radians}}$

Convert 60° to radians.

$60° = 60°\left(\frac{\pi \text{ radians}}{180°}\right) = \frac{\pi}{3}$ radians

Use dimensional analysis to help. Notice that the degrees cancel so the remaining unit is radians.

Convert $\frac{5\pi}{4}$ radians to degrees.

$\frac{5\pi}{4}$ radians $= \left(\frac{5\pi}{4} \text{ radians}\right)\left(\frac{180°}{\pi \text{ radians}}\right) = 225°$

The radians cancel so the remaining unit is degrees.

Convert each measure from degrees to radians.

1. −45° — $-45° = -45°\left(\frac{\pi \text{ radians}}{180°}\right)$ — $-\frac{\pi}{4}$ radians
2. 150° — $150° = 150°\left(\frac{\pi \text{ radians}}{180°}\right)$ — $\frac{5\pi}{6}$ radians
3. 210° — $\frac{7\pi}{6}$ radians
4. −120° — $-\frac{2\pi}{3}$ radians

Convert each measure from radians to degrees.

5. $\frac{4\pi}{3}$ radians — $\frac{4\pi}{3}$ radians $= \left(\frac{4\pi}{3} \text{ radians}\right)\left(\frac{180°}{\pi \text{ radians}}\right)$ — 240°
6. $-\frac{3\pi}{2}$ radians — $-\frac{3\pi}{2}$ radians $= \left(-\frac{3\pi}{2} \text{ radians}\right)\left(\frac{180°}{\pi \text{ radians}}\right)$ — −270°
7. $\frac{\pi}{6}$ radians — 30°
8. $\frac{5\pi}{3}$ radians — 300°

CHALLENGE AND EXTEND

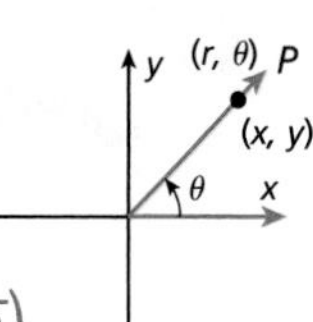

Polar Coordinates In the rectangular coordinate system, the coordinates of point P are (x, y). In the polar coordinate system, the coordinates of point P are (r, θ). Convert each point from polar coordinates to rectangular coordinates.

54. $\left(6\sqrt{2}, \frac{\pi}{4}\right)$ $(6, 6)$ **55.** $\left(10, \frac{7\pi}{6}\right)$ **56.** $\left(5, \frac{5\pi}{3}\right)$ $\left(2.5, -2.5\sqrt{3}\right)$

55. $\left(-5\sqrt{3}, -5\right)$

57. Photography A photographer taking nighttime photos of wildlife is using a searchlight attached to the roof of a truck. The light has a range of 250 m and can be rotated horizontally through an angle of 150°. Estimate the area of ground that can be lit by the searchlight without moving the truck. Explain how you determined your estimate.

58. What is the range of each of the six trigonometric functions for the domain $\{\theta \mid -90° < \theta < 90°\}$?

SPIRAL REVIEW

Graph each function, and identify its domain and range. *(Lesson 8-7)*

59. $f(x) = \sqrt{x+4}$ **60.** $f(x) = \sqrt[3]{x} - 3$ **61.** $f(x) = -3\sqrt{x}$

Find the 12th term of each geometric sequence. *(Lesson 12-4)*

62. 900, 180, 36, 7.2, ... 1.8432×10^{-5}

63. −6, 24, −96, 384, ... 25,165,824

64. $\frac{1}{8}, \frac{3}{8}, 1\frac{1}{8}, 3\frac{3}{8}, \ldots$ $22{,}143\frac{3}{8}$

Find the measure of the reference angle for each given angle. *(Lesson 13-2)*

65. $\theta = 135°$ 45°

66. $\theta = -295°$ 65°

67. $\theta = 175°$ 5°

68. $\theta = -155°$ 25°

Career Path

go.hrw.com
Career Resources Online
KEYWORD: MB7 Career

Darryl Wright
Surveying Assistant

Q: What high school math classes did you take?
A: Algebra 1, Geometry, Algebra 2, and Trigonometry

Q: What do you like about surveying?
A: I like being outside and being in the construction industry. It's cool to see a bridge or building built where there wasn't anything before. I also like the high-tech instruments we get to use.

Q: How is math used in surveying?
A: Surveying is basically measuring a lot of distances and angles, so we use trigonometry and geometry all the time. I also do unit conversions to make sure the measurements are in the correct form.

Q: What are your future plans?
A: I'm taking classes at a community college and working toward an associate's degree in surveying. At the same time, I'm gaining work experience that will eventually help me become a licensed surveyor.

COMMON ERROR ALERT

In **Exercises 31–34,** students may correctly find the sine, cosine, and tangent of the reference angle and then forget to adjust the sign of these values. Remind students that drawing θ in standard position can help them determine the quadrant of its terminal side. This quadrant determines the sign of the values of the trigonometric functions of θ.

Answers

57–61. See p. A49.

Journal

Have students explain how to convert from degrees to radians and from radians to degrees.

ALTERNATIVE ASSESSMENT

Have students choose one of the angle measures given in **Exercises 27–30** and determine the exact value of the other five trigonometric functions of this angle measure. Ask students to explain how they determined their answers.

Power Presentations with PowerPoint®

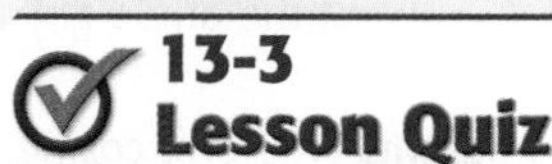

13-3 Lesson Quiz

Convert each measure from degrees to radians or from radians to degrees.

1. 100° $\frac{5\pi}{9}$ radians

2. $\frac{4\pi}{5}$ radians 144°

3. Use the unit circle to find the exact value of $\sin\frac{4\pi}{3}$. $-\frac{\sqrt{3}}{2}$

4. Use a reference angle to find the exact value of the sine, cosine, and tangent of $\frac{3\pi}{4}$. $\frac{\sqrt{2}}{2}; -\frac{\sqrt{2}}{2}; -1$

5. A carpenter is designing a curved piece of molding for the ceiling of a museum. The curve will be an arc of a circle with a radius of 3 m. The central angle that intercepts the curve will measure 120°. To the nearest tenth of a meter, what will be the length of the molding? 6.3 m

Also available on transparency

13-3 PROBLEM SOLVING

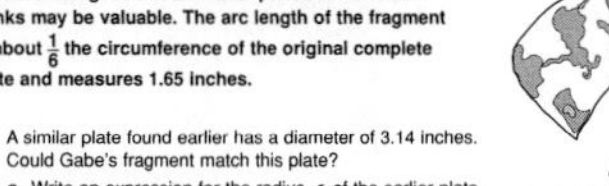

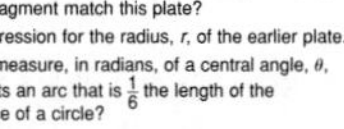

Gabe is spending two weeks on an archaeological dig. He finds a fragment of a circular plate that his leader thinks may be valuable. The arc length of the fragment is about $\frac{1}{6}$ the circumference of the original complete plate and measures 1.65 inches.

1. A similar plate found earlier has a diameter of 3.14 inches. Could Gabe's fragment match this plate?
   a. Write an expression for the radius, r, of the earlier plate. $r = \frac{\pi}{2}$
   b. What is the measure, in radians, of a central angle, θ, that intercepts an arc that is $\frac{1}{6}$ the length of the circumference of a circle? $\theta = \frac{2\pi}{6}$ or $\frac{\pi}{3}$
   c. Write an expression for the arc length, S, intercepted by this central angle. $S = r\theta = \frac{\pi}{2} \cdot \frac{\pi}{3} = \frac{\pi^2}{6}$
   d. How long would the arc length of a fragment be if it were $\frac{1}{6}$ the circumference of the plate? 1.64 in.
   e. Could Gabe's plate be a matching plate? Explain. Yes; possible answer: because the arc length of the fragment is very close to the arc length that would be expected for a plate of diameter π
2. Toby finds another fragment of arc length 2.48 inches. What fraction of the outer edge of Gabe's plate would it be if this fragment were part of Gabe's plate? $\frac{1}{4}$

The diameter of a merry-go-round at the playground is 12 feet. Elijah stands on the edge and his sister pushes him around. Choose the letter for the best answer

3. How far does Elijah travel if he moves through an angle of $\frac{5\pi}{4}$ radians?
   A 12.0 ft
   B 15.1 ft
   (C) 23.6 ft
   D 47.1 ft
4. Through what angle does Elijah move if he travels a distance of 80 feet around the circumference?
   F $\frac{40}{3}\pi$ radians
   G $\frac{80}{3}$ radians
   (H) $\frac{40}{3}$ radians
   J $\frac{20}{3}$ radians

Virgil sets his boat on a 1000-yard course keeping a constant distance from a rocky outcrop. Choose the letter for the best answer.

5. If Virgil keeps a distance of 200 yards, through what angle does he travel?
   A 5π radians
   (B) 5 radians
   C 10 radians
   D 10π radians
6. If Virgil keeps a distance of 500 yards, what fraction of the circumference of a circle does he cover?
   (A) $\frac{1}{\pi}$
   B $\frac{\pi}{3}$
   C $\frac{3}{4\pi}$
   D $\frac{3\pi}{4}$

13-3 CHALLENGE

Radians can be useful in application problems because of the close connection between radian measure for angles and arc length in a circle. Consider the formula for finding the length of an arc: $s = r\theta$

The variables s and r are both lengths, s is the length of the arc and r is the radius of the circle, and θ is an angle measured in radians. A radian is sometimes considered a unitless measure since it measures the distance around a circle using the radius as the measure of length. For instance, an angle of 2 radians is related to an arc of 2 radii around the circle. It makes no difference the size of the circle; an arc of 2 radii around the circle still produces the same angle.

Solve the following application problems by using the formula $s = r\theta$.

1. A captain at sea measures the distance his ship travels in nautical miles. A nautical mile is the length of the arc along the surface of Earth that is intercepted by an angle of 1 minute $\left(\frac{1}{60}\right)°$. If the radius of Earth is 3960 miles (1 land mile is 5280 feet), find the length of a nautical mile to the nearest 10 feet. 6080 ft
2. One year has approximately 365 days. Earth travels around the sun in an approximately circular orbit with a radius of 93 million miles. Find the distance Earth travels in its orbit each day. Calculate the speed of Earth in its orbit in miles per hour. Round answers to the nearest whole number. 1,600,921 mi; 66,705 mi/h
3. Use the formula for the area of a circle, $A = \pi r^2$, and derive the formula for the area of a sector using only the variables r and θ. Assume that θ is in radians. Area of circle $= \pi r^2$; A sector whose central angle has a measure of θ radians has an area of $\frac{\theta}{2\pi}$ times the area of the circle. So Area of sector $= \frac{\theta}{2\pi}(\pi r^2) = \frac{1}{2}\theta r^2$.
4. In the diagram below, find the area of the shaded sector. The circles are tangent to one another as shown in the diagram. $\frac{\pi}{4}$

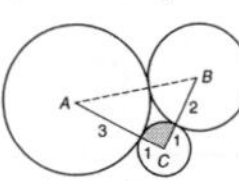

13-4 Organizer

Pacing: Traditional 1 day
Block $\frac{1}{2}$ day

Objectives: Evaluate inverse trigonometric functions.

Use trigonometric equations and inverse trigonometric functions to solve problems.

Online Edition Tutorial Videos

Power Presentations with PowerPoint®

Warm Up

Convert each measure from degrees to radians.

1. 120° $\frac{2\pi}{3}$ **2.** 180° π

3. 225° $\frac{5\pi}{4}$ **4.** −30° $-\frac{\pi}{6}$

Find the exact value of each trigonometric function.

5. $\cos\frac{2\pi}{3}$ $-\frac{1}{2}$ **6.** $\sin\frac{\pi}{4}$ $\frac{\sqrt{2}}{2}$

7. $\tan\frac{4\pi}{3}$ $\sqrt{3}$ **8.** $\cos(2\pi)$ 1

Also available on transparency

Math Humor

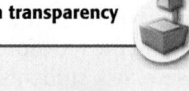

Q: Why couldn't the angle get a loan?

A: His parents wouldn't cosine.

13-4 Inverses of Trigonometric Functions

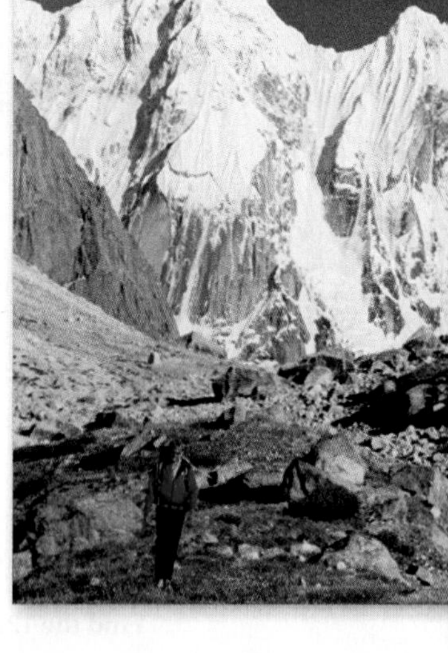

Objectives
Evaluate inverse trigonometric functions.

Use trigonometric equations and inverse trigonometric functions to solve problems.

Vocabulary
inverse sine function
inverse cosine function
inverse tangent function

Who uses this?
Hikers can use inverse trigonometric functions to navigate in the wilderness. (See Example 3.)

You have evaluated trigonometric functions for a given angle. You can also find the measure of angles given the value of a trigonometric function by using an *inverse trigonometric* relation.

Function	Inverse Relation
$\sin\theta = a$	$\sin^{-1} a = \theta$
$\cos\theta = a$	$\cos^{-1} a = \theta$
$\tan\theta = a$	$\tan^{-1} a = \theta$

Reading Math

The expression $\sin^{-1}$ is read as "the inverse sine." In this notation, $^{-1}$ indicates the *inverse* of the sine function, NOT the *reciprocal* of the sine function.

The inverses of the trigonometric functions are not functions themselves because there are many values of θ for a particular value of a. For example, suppose that you want to find $\cos^{-1}\frac{1}{2}$. Based on the unit circle, angles that measure $\frac{\pi}{3}$ and $\frac{5\pi}{3}$ radians have a cosine of $\frac{1}{2}$. So do all angles that are coterminal with these angles.

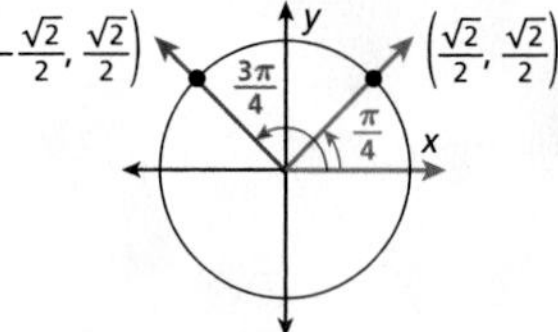

EXAMPLE 1 Finding Trigonometric Inverses

Find all possible values of $\sin^{-1}\frac{\sqrt{2}}{2}$.

Step 1 Find the values between 0 and 2π radians for which $\sin\theta$ is equal to $\frac{\sqrt{2}}{2}$.

$\left(-\frac{\sqrt{2}}{2}, \frac{\sqrt{2}}{2}\right)$ $\frac{3\pi}{4}$ $\frac{\pi}{4}$ $\left(\frac{\sqrt{2}}{2}, \frac{\sqrt{2}}{2}\right)$ y x

$$\frac{\sqrt{2}}{2} = \sin\frac{\pi}{4}, \qquad \frac{\sqrt{2}}{2} = \sin\frac{3\pi}{4}$$

Use y-coordinates of points on the unit circle.

Step 2 Find the angles that are coterminal with angles measuring $\frac{\pi}{4}$ and $\frac{3\pi}{4}$ radians.

$$\frac{\pi}{4} + (2\pi)n, \qquad \frac{3\pi}{4} + (2\pi)n$$

Add integer multiples of 2π radians, where n is an integer.

1. Find all possible values of $\tan^{-1}1$.
$\frac{\pi}{4} + (2\pi)n$ **or** $\frac{5\pi}{4} + (2\pi)n$**, where** n **is an integer**

Because more than one value of θ produces the same output value for a given trigonometric function, it is necessary to restrict the domain of each trigonometric function in order to define the inverse trigonometric functions.

State Resources

go.hrw.com
State Resources Online
KEYWORD: MB7 Resources

1 Introduce

EXPLORATION

13-4 Inverses of Trigonometric Functions

The inverse sine feature of a graphing calculator can be used to determine the measures of acute angles in right triangles.

To find the measure of an angle that has a sine of $\frac{1}{2}$, press 2nd SIN and enter $\frac{1}{2}$ as shown. The calculator shows that a 30° angle has a sine of $\frac{1}{2}$.

sin⁻¹(1/2) 30

For each triangle, write the exact value of the sine ratio for θ. Then use the inverse sine feature to find the value of θ to the nearest tenth of a degree.

1. 3, 5, θ
2. 18, 20, θ
3. 21, 9, θ
4. 14, 12, θ

THINK AND DISCUSS
5. Discuss how you could use the

Motivate

Give students the following situation: You want to determine the measure of an angle θ in a right triangle, but you do not have a protractor. Ask students how they could use a ruler to determine $\sin\theta$. Divide the length of the opposite leg by the length of the hypotenuse. Tell students that in this lesson, they will learn to use the sine of an angle to determine the angle's measure.

Explorations and answers are provided in the *Explorations* binder.

Trigonometric functions with restricted domains are indicated with a capital letter. The domains of the Sine, Cosine, and Tangent functions are restricted as follows.

$\text{Sin}\,\theta = \sin\theta$ for $\left\{\theta \mid -\frac{\pi}{2} \le \theta \le \frac{\pi}{2}\right\}$ *θ is restricted to Quadrants I and IV.*

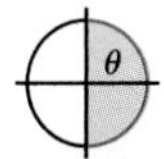

$\text{Cos}\,\theta = \cos\theta$ for $\left\{\theta \mid 0 \le \theta \le \pi\right\}$ *θ is restricted to Quadrants I and II.*

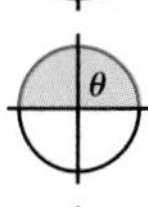

$\text{Tan}\,\theta = \tan\theta$ for $\left\{\theta \mid -\frac{\pi}{2} < \theta < \frac{\pi}{2}\right\}$ *θ is restricted to Quadrants I and IV.*

These functions can be used to define the inverse trigonometric functions. For each value of a in the domain of the inverse trigonometric functions, there is only one value of θ. Therefore, even though $\tan^{-1}1$ has many values, $\text{Tan}^{-1}1$ has only one value.

Know it! Note

Inverse Trigonometric Functions

WORDS	SYMBOL	DOMAIN	RANGE
The **inverse sine function** is $\text{Sin}^{-1}a = \theta$, where $\text{Sin}\,\theta = a$.	$\text{Sin}^{-1}a$	$\{a \mid -1 \le a \le 1\}$	$\left\{\theta \mid -\frac{\pi}{2} \le \theta \le \frac{\pi}{2}\right\}$ $\{\theta \mid -90° \le \theta \le 90°\}$
The **inverse cosine function** is $\text{Cos}^{-1}a = \theta$, where $\text{Cos}\,\theta = a$.	$\text{Cos}^{-1}a$	$\{a \mid -1 \le a \le 1\}$	$\{\theta \mid 0 \le \theta \le \pi\}$ $\{\theta \mid 0° \le \theta \le 180°\}$
The **inverse tangent function** is $\text{Tan}^{-1}a = \theta$, where $\text{Tan}\,\theta = a$.	$\text{Tan}^{-1}a$	$\{a \mid -\infty < a < \infty\}$	$\left\{\theta \mid -\frac{\pi}{2} < \theta < \frac{\pi}{2}\right\}$ $\{\theta \mid -90° < \theta < 90°\}$

Reading Math

The inverse trigonometric functions are also called the arcsine, arccosine, and arctangent functions.

EXAMPLE 2 Evaluating Inverse Trigonometric Functions

Evaluate each inverse trigonometric function. Give your answer in both radians and degrees.

A $\text{Cos}^{-1}\frac{1}{2}$

$\frac{1}{2} = \text{Cos}\,\theta$ *Find the value of θ for $0 \le \theta \le \pi$ whose Cosine is $\frac{1}{2}$.*

$\frac{1}{2} = \text{Cos}\frac{\pi}{3}$ *Use x-coordinates of points on the unit circle.*

$\text{Cos}^{-1}\frac{1}{2} = \frac{\pi}{3}$, or $\text{Cos}^{-1}\frac{1}{2} = 60°$

B $\text{Sin}^{-1}2$

The domain of the inverse sine function is $\{a \mid -1 \le a \le 1\}$. Because 2 is outside this domain, $\text{Sin}^{-1}2$ is undefined.

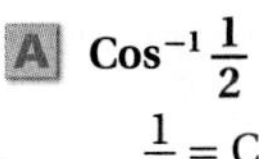

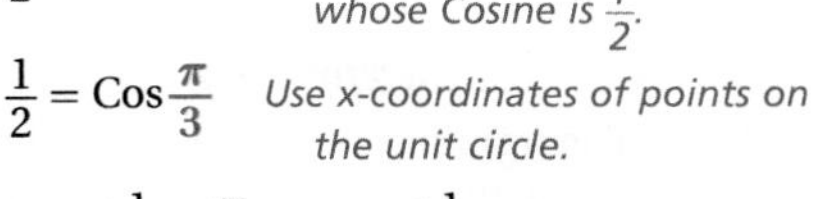

CHECK IT OUT! **Evaluate each inverse trigonometric function. Give your answer in both radians and degrees.**

2a. $\text{Sin}^{-1}\left(-\frac{\sqrt{2}}{2}\right)$ $-\frac{\pi}{4}$ **or −45°**

2b. $\text{Cos}^{-1}0$ $\frac{\pi}{2}$ **or 90°**

Power Presentations with PowerPoint®

Additional Examples

Example 1

Find all possible values of $\cos^{-1}\frac{\sqrt{3}}{2}$.

$\frac{\pi}{6} + (2\pi)n, \frac{11\pi}{6} + (2\pi)n$

Example 2

Evaluate each inverse trigonometric function. Give your answer in both radians and degrees.

A. $\text{Cos}^{-1}\left(-\frac{\sqrt{3}}{2}\right)$ $\frac{5\pi}{6}$, or 150°

B. $\text{Sin}^{-1}\frac{3}{2}$ undefined

Also available on transparency

INTERVENTION

Questioning Strategies

EXAMPLE 1

- How can you use the unit circle to find angles with a given value for a trigonometric function?
- How do you find the measures of all of the angles that are coterminal with a given angle?

EXAMPLE 2

- What is the domain of the inverse trigonometric function?
- How do you determine which quadrant contains the terminal side of θ?

Teaching Tip **Inclusion** In Lesson 13-2, students found the measures of coterminal angles by adding integer multiples of 360°. Point out that adding integer multiples of 2π radians is equivalent to this procedure.

2 Teach

Guided Instruction

Before beginning the lesson, remind students of the difference between a relation and a function. Then introduce the inverse trigonometric relations, and discuss with students why these relations are not functions. Emphasize how the domains of the trigonometric functions are restricted in order to define the inverse trigonometric functions and how these inverse functions can be used to find angle measures.

Reaching All Learners

Through Home Connection

Have students work outside of class to determine the angle that a wheelchair ramp makes with the ground. Instruct them to use only a ruler or tape measure (MK) and an inverse trigonometric function. Ask students to describe the steps they used to determine the angle measure. If possible, have students check their results by measuring the ramp angle with a protractor (MK).

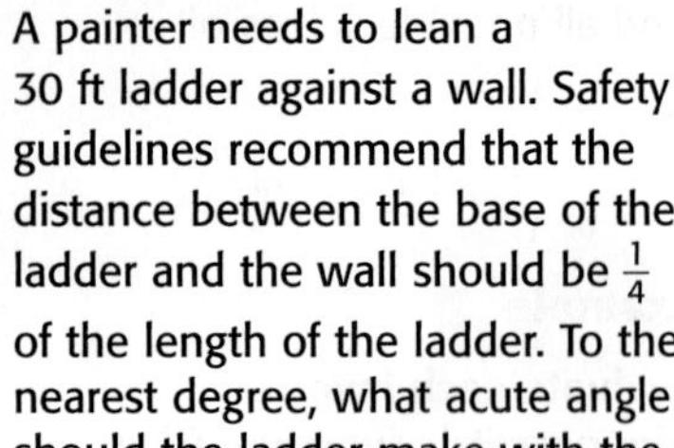

Additional Examples

Example 3

A painter needs to lean a 30 ft ladder against a wall. Safety guidelines recommend that the distance between the base of the ladder and the wall should be $\frac{1}{4}$ of the length of the ladder. To the nearest degree, what acute angle should the ladder make with the ground? 76°

Example 4

Solve each equation to the nearest tenth. Use the given restrictions.

A. $\sin\theta = 0.4$, for $-90° \le \theta \le 90°$

23.6°

B. $\sin\theta = 0.4$, for $90° \le \theta \le 270°$

156.4°

Also available on transparency

INTERVENTION

Questioning Strategies

EXAMPLE 3

- How can you use a right triangle to model the information in the problem?
- How do you determine which inverse trigonometric function to use?

EXAMPLE 4

- How do the restrictions indicate the quadrant of the terminal side of θ in standard position?
- For what values of θ can you solve the equation by using an inverse trigonometric function on your calculator?

Critical Thinking Ask students to explain why the value of the inverse tangent function cannot equal 90°. because the tangent function is undefined when $\theta = 90°$

Communicating Math Point out that when a problem asks for a heading, as in **Example 3,** students should give not only an angle measure but also a direction as their answer. For instance, the complete answer to **Example 3** is 14° north of east, not simply 14°.

You can solve trigonometric equations by using trigonometric inverses.

EXAMPLE 3 *Navigation Application*

A group of hikers plans to walk from a campground to a lake. The lake is 2 miles east and 0.5 mile north of the campground. To the nearest degree, in what direction should the hikers head?

Step 1 Draw a diagram.

The hikers' direction should be based on θ, the measure of an acute angle of a right triangle.

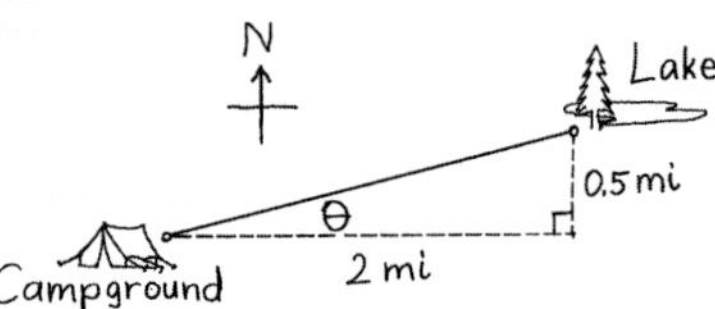

Step 2 Find the value of θ.

$\tan\theta = \frac{\text{opp.}}{\text{adj.}}$ *Use the tangent ratio.*

$\tan\theta = \frac{0.5}{2} = 0.25$ *Substitute 0.5 for opp. and 2 for adj. Then simplify.*

$\theta = \text{Tan}^{-1} 0.25$

$\theta \approx 14°$

The hikers should head 14° north of east.

tan⁻¹(.25)
14.03624347

Caution!

If the answer on your calculator screen is 0.2449786631 when you enter $\tan^{-1}(0.25)$, your calculator is set to radian mode instead of degree mode.

CHECK IT OUT! **Use the information given above to answer the following.**

3. An unusual rock formation is 1 mile east and 0.75 mile north of the lake. To the nearest degree, in what direction should the hikers head from the lake to reach the rock formation? 37° north of east

EXAMPLE 4 **Solving Trigonometric Equations**

Solve each equation to the nearest tenth. Use the given restrictions.

A $\cos\theta = 0.6$, **for** $0° \le \theta \le 180°$

The restrictions on θ are the same as those for the inverse cosine function.

$\theta = \text{Cos}^{-1}(0.6) \approx 53.1°$ *Use the inverse cosine function on your calculator.*

B $\cos\theta = 0.6$, **for** $270° < \theta < 360°$

The terminal side of θ is restricted to Quadrant IV. Find the angle in Quadrant IV that has the same cosine value as 53.1°.

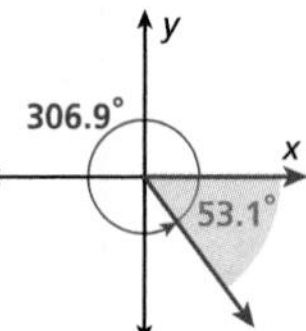

$\theta \approx 360° - 53.1° \approx 306.9°$ *θ has a reference angle of 53.1°, and $270° < \theta < 360°$.*

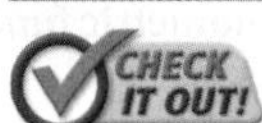

CHECK IT OUT! **Solve each equation to the nearest tenth. Use the given restrictions.**

4a. $\tan\theta = -2$, for $-90° < \theta < 90°$ −63.4°

4b. $\tan\theta = -2$, for $90° < \theta < 180°$ 116.6°

3 Close

Summarize

Remind students that the inputs of trigonometric functions are angle measures and the outputs are ratios. Therefore, the inputs of inverse trigonometric functions are ratios and the outputs are angle measures. Review with students the steps for determining the values of inverse trigonometric functions by using both the unit circle and a graphing calculator.

ONGOING ASSESSMENT and INTERVENTION

***Diagnose Before* the Lesson**
13-4 Warm Up, TE p. 950

***Monitor During* the Lesson**
Check It Out! Exercises, SE pp. 950–952
Questioning Strategies, TE pp. 951–952

***Assess After* the Lesson**
13-4 Lesson Quiz, TE p. 955
Alternative Assessment, TE p. 955

THINK AND DISCUSS

1. Given that θ is an acute angle in a right triangle, describe the measurements that you need to know to find the value of θ by using the inverse cosine function.
2. Explain the difference between $\tan^{-1}a$ and $\text{Tan}^{-1}a$.

3. **GET ORGANIZED** Copy and complete the graphic organizer. In each box, give the indicated property of the inverse trigonometric functions.

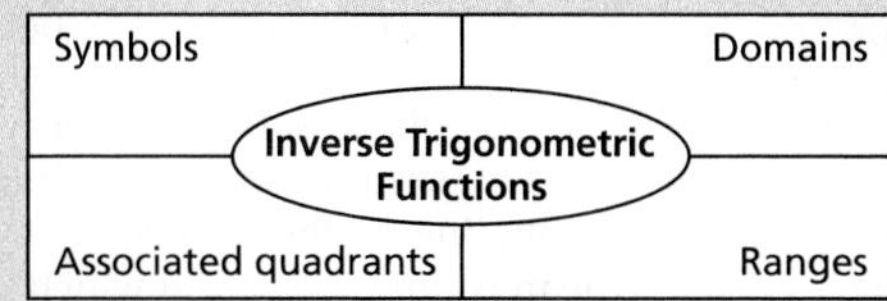

Answers to *Think and Discuss*

Possible answers:

1. You need to know the length of the leg adjacent to θ and the length of the hypotenuse.
2. Although $\text{Tan}^{-1}a$ is a function, $\tan^{-1}a$ is a relation. The function $\text{Tan}^{-1}a$ is defined for $-\frac{\pi}{2} < \theta < \frac{\pi}{2}$. For each value of a in this domain, there is exactly one value of $\text{Tan}^{-1}a$. The relation $\tan^{-1}a$ is defined for all values in the range of $\tan\theta$. For each value of a, there are multiple values of $\tan^{-1}a$.
3. See p. A14.

13-4 Exercises

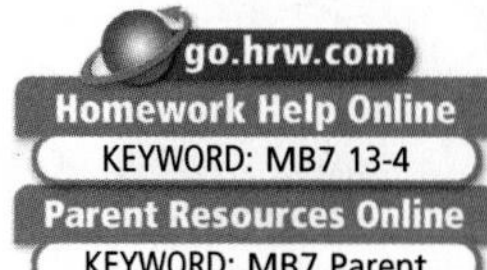

GUIDED PRACTICE

1. **Vocabulary** Explain how the inverse tangent function differs from the reciprocal of the tangent function.

SEE EXAMPLE 1 p. 950

Find all possible values of each expression.

2. $\sin^{-1}\left(-\frac{1}{2}\right)$
3. $\tan^{-1}\frac{\sqrt{3}}{3}$
4. $\cos^{-1}\left(-\frac{\sqrt{2}}{2}\right)$

SEE EXAMPLE 2 p. 951

Evaluate each inverse trigonometric function. Give your answer in both radians and degrees.

5. $\text{Cos}^{-1}\frac{\sqrt{3}}{2}$ $\frac{\pi}{6}$; 30°
6. $\text{Tan}^{-1}1$ $\frac{\pi}{4}$; 45°
7. $\text{Cos}^{-1}2$ undefined
8. $\text{Tan}^{-1}\left(-\sqrt{3}\right)$ $-\frac{\pi}{3}$; −60°
9. $\text{Sin}^{-1}\frac{\sqrt{2}}{2}$ $\frac{\pi}{4}$; 45°
10. $\text{Sin}^{-1}0$ 0; 0°

SEE EXAMPLE 3 p. 952

11. **Architecture** A point on the top of the Leaning Tower of Pisa is shifted about 13.5 ft horizontally compared with the tower's base. To the nearest degree, how many degrees does the tower tilt from vertical? 5°

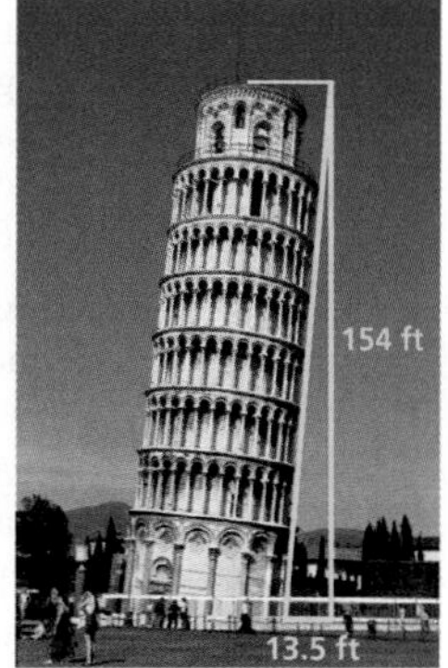

SEE EXAMPLE 4 p. 952

Solve each equation to the nearest tenth. Use the given restrictions.

12. $\tan\theta = 1.4$, for $-90° < \theta < 90°$ 54.5°
13. $\tan\theta = 1.4$, for $180° < \theta < 270°$ 234.5°
14. $\cos\theta = -0.25$, for $0 \le \theta \le 180°$ 104.5°
15. $\cos\theta = -0.25$, for $180° < \theta < 270°$ 255.5°

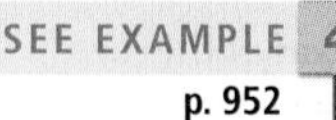

13-4 Exercises

Assignment Guide

Assign *Guided Practice* exercises as necessary.

If you finished Examples 1–2
Basic 16–24
Average 16–24, 34–36
Advanced 16–24, 34–36

If you finished Examples 1–4
Basic 16–33, 39–41, 46–53
Average 16–42, 46–53
Advanced 16–53

Homework Quick Check
Quickly check key concepts.
Exercises: 18, 20, 25, 26, 30, 31

State Resources

Answers

1. Possible answer: The inverse tangent function, $\text{Tan}^{-1}a$, gives the angle θ between −90° and 90° whose tangent is a. The reciprocal of the tangent function is equal to $\frac{1}{\tan\theta}$.
2. $\frac{7\pi}{6} + (2\pi)n$ and $\frac{11\pi}{6} + (2\pi)n$, where n is an integer
3. $\frac{\pi}{6} + (2\pi)n$ and $\frac{7\pi}{6} + (2\pi)n$, where n is an integer
4. $\frac{3\pi}{4} + (2\pi)n$ and $\frac{5\pi}{4} + (2\pi)n$, where n is an integer

Geometry In **Exercise 31,** point out that θ is an acute angle of a right triangle. Ask students how they can use the information in the table to determine the length of the leg opposite θ for each style of pool. by subtracting the depth of the shallow end from the depth of the deep end

Answers

17. $\frac{\pi}{3} + (2\pi)n$ and $\frac{2\pi}{3} + (2\pi)n$, where n is an integer

18. $\frac{3\pi}{4} + (2\pi)n$ and $\frac{7\pi}{4} + (2\pi)n$, where n is an integer

31a. style A: 7.5°; style B: 9.1°; style C: 5.1°

b. The pool with the steepest slope is the one for which the value of θ is greatest. Because 9.1° is greater than 7.5° or 5.1°, style B has the greatest slope.

37. See p. A49.

38. No; possible answer: The range of the inverse sine function is $\left\{\theta \mid -\frac{\pi}{2} \le \theta \le \frac{\pi}{2}\right\}$. Therefore, the statement is not true if θ is greater than $\frac{\pi}{2}$ radians or less than $-\frac{\pi}{2}$ radians.

45. $\frac{\pi}{8} \le \theta < \frac{\pi}{4}$
or $\frac{5\pi}{8} \le \theta < \frac{3\pi}{4}$
or $\frac{9\pi}{8} \le \theta < \frac{5\pi}{4}$
or $\frac{13\pi}{8} \le \theta < \frac{7\pi}{4}$

46, 47. For graphs, see p. A49.

46. cubic; vertical compression by a factor of $\frac{1}{2}$

47. linear; translation 5 units up (or 5 units left)

PRACTICE AND PROBLEM SOLVING

Independent Practice	
For Exercises	See Example
16–18	1
19–24	2
25	3
26–29	4

Extra Practice
Skills Practice p. S29
Application Practice p. S44

Find all possible values of each expression.

16. $\cos^{-1} 1$ $(2\pi)n$, where n is an integer
17. $\sin^{-1} \frac{\sqrt{3}}{2}$
18. $\tan^{-1}(-1)$

Evaluate each inverse trigonometric function. Give your answer in both radians and degrees.

19. $\text{Sin}^{-1} \frac{\sqrt{3}}{2}$ $\frac{\pi}{3}$; 60°
20. $\text{Cos}^{-1}(-1)$ π; 180°
21. $\text{Tan}^{-1}\left(-\frac{\sqrt{3}}{3}\right)$ $-\frac{\pi}{6}$; −30°
22. $\text{Cos}^{-1}\left(-\frac{\sqrt{3}}{2}\right)$ $\frac{5\pi}{6}$; 150°
23. $\text{Tan}^{-1} \sqrt{3}$ $\frac{\pi}{3}$; 60°
24. $\text{Sin}^{-1} \sqrt{3}$ undefined

25. **Volleyball** A volleyball player spikes the ball from a height of 2.44 m. Assume that the path of the ball is a straight line. To the nearest degree, what is the maximum angle θ at which the ball can be hit and land within the court? 75°

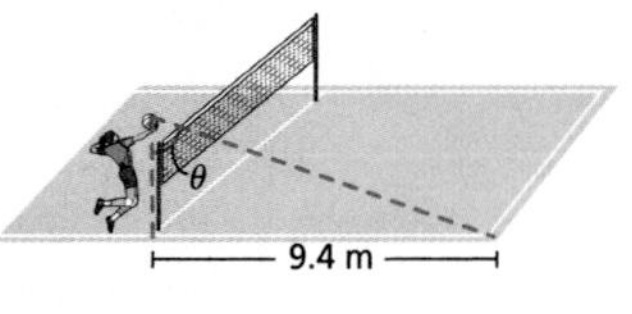

Solve each equation to the nearest tenth. Use the given restrictions.

26. $\sin \theta = -0.75$, for $-90° \le \theta \le 90°$ −48.6°
27. $\sin \theta = -0.75$, for $180° < \theta < 270°$ 228.6°
28. $\cos \theta = 0.1$, for $0° \le \theta \le 180°$ 84.3°
29. $\cos \theta = 0.1$, for $270° < \theta < 360°$ 275.7°

LINK
Aviation

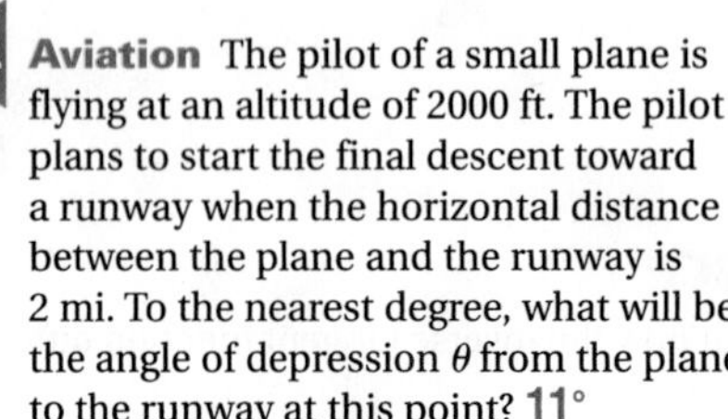

A flight simulator is a device used in training pilots that mimics flight conditions as realistically as possible. Some flight simulators involve full-size cockpits equipped with sound, visual, and motion systems.

30. **Aviation** The pilot of a small plane is flying at an altitude of 2000 ft. The pilot plans to start the final descent toward a runway when the horizontal distance between the plane and the runway is 2 mi. To the nearest degree, what will be the angle of depression θ from the plane to the runway at this point? 11°

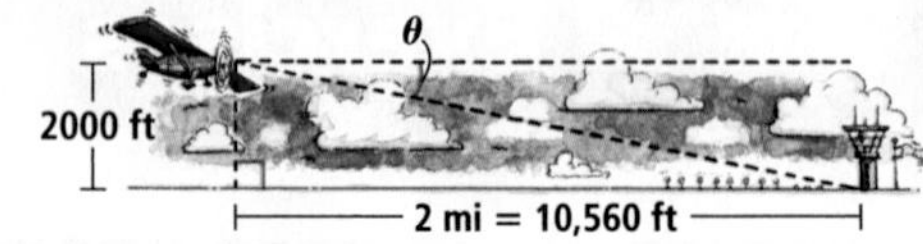

31. **Multi-Step** The table shows the dimensions of three pool styles offered by a construction company.

Pool Style	Length (ft)	Shallow End Depth (ft)	Deep End Depth (ft)
A	38	3	8
B	25	2	6
C	50	2.5	7

a. To the nearest tenth of a degree, what angle θ does the bottom of each pool make with the horizontal?

b. Which pool style's bottom has the steepest slope? Explain.

c. **What if...?** If the slope of the bottom of a pool can be no greater than $\frac{1}{6}$, what is the greatest angle θ that the bottom of the pool can make with the horizontal? Round to the nearest tenth of a degree. 9.5°

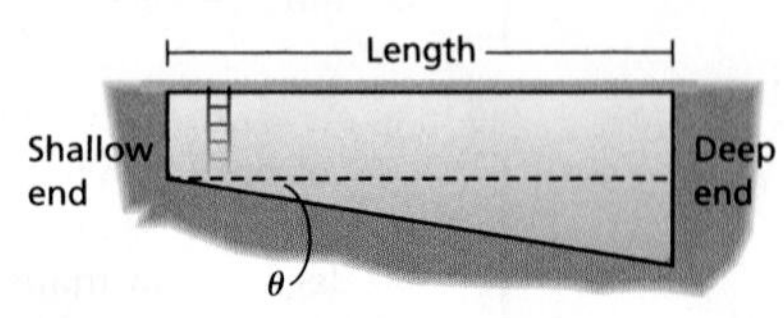

32. **Navigation** Lines of longitude are closer together near the poles than at the equator. The formula for the length ℓ of 1° of longitude in miles is $\ell = 69.0933 \cos \theta$, where θ is the latitude in degrees.

a. At what latitude, to the nearest degree, is the length of a degree of longitude approximately 59.8 miles? 30°N or S

b. To the nearest mile, how much longer is the length of a degree of longitude at the equator, which has a latitude of 0°, than at the Arctic Circle, which has a latitude of about 66°N? 41 mi

13-4 PRACTICE A
13-4 PRACTICE C
13-4 PRACTICE B

Find all possible values of each expression.

1. $\sin^{-1}\left(-\frac{\sqrt{3}}{2}\right)$ $\frac{4\pi}{3} + 2\pi n$; $\frac{5\pi}{3} + 2\pi n$
2. $\cos^{-1}\left(-\frac{1}{2}\right)$ $\frac{2\pi}{3} + 2\pi n$; $\frac{4\pi}{3} + 2\pi n$
3. $\tan^{-1} 0$ $0 + 2\pi n$; $\pi + 2\pi n$
4. $\sin^{-1}\left(-\frac{\sqrt{2}}{2}\right)$ $\frac{5\pi}{4} + 2\pi n$; $\frac{7\pi}{4} + 2\pi n$
5. $\cos^{-1}\left(-\frac{\sqrt{2}}{2}\right)$ $\frac{3\pi}{4} + 2\pi n$; $\frac{5\pi}{4} + 2\pi n$
6. $\tan^{-1}\left(\frac{\sqrt{3}}{3}\right)$ $\frac{\pi}{6} + 2\pi n$; $\frac{7\pi}{6} + 2\pi n$

Evaluate each inverse trigonometric function. Give your answer in both radians and degrees.

7. $\text{Sin}^{-1}(-1)$ $\frac{3\pi}{2}$; 270°
8. $\text{Tan}^{-1}(-\sqrt{3})$ $\frac{5\pi}{3}$; 300°
9. $\text{Cos}^{-1} 1$ 0; 0°
10. $\text{Sin}^{-1}\left(\frac{\sqrt{3}}{2}\right)$ $\frac{\pi}{3}$; 60°
11. $\text{Tan}^{-1}\left(-\frac{\sqrt{3}}{3}\right)$ $\frac{11\pi}{6}$; 330°
12. $\text{Cos}^{-1}\left(\frac{\sqrt{2}}{2}\right)$ $\frac{\pi}{4}$; 45°

Solve each equation to the nearest tenth. Use the given restrictions.

13. $\sin \theta = 0.45$, for $0° < \theta < 90°$ 26.7°
14. $\sin \theta = 0.801$, for $90° < \theta < 270°$ 233.2°
15. $\tan \theta = 2.42$, for $180° < \theta < 360°$ 247.5°
16. $\cos \theta = -0.334$, for $0° < \theta < 180°$ 109.5°
17. $\cos \theta = -0.181$, for $180° < \theta < 360°$ 259.6°
18. $\tan \theta = -10$, for $90° < \theta < 270°$ 95.7°

Solve.

19. A 21-foot ladder is leaning against a building. The base of the ladder is 7 feet from the base of a building. To the nearest degree, what is the measure of the angle that the ladder makes with the ground? 71°

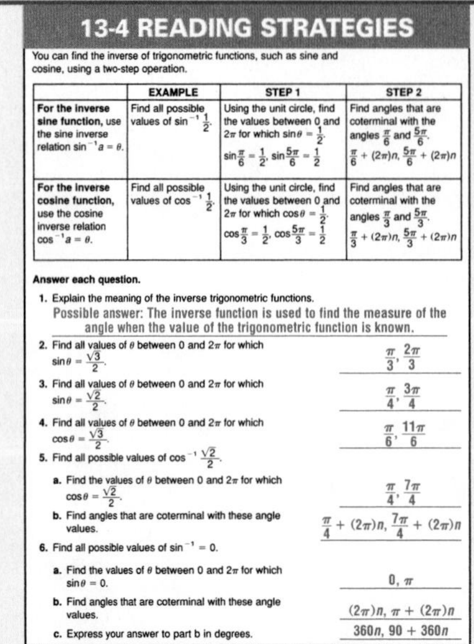

13-4 READING STRATEGIES

You can find the inverse of trigonometric functions, such as sine and cosine, using a two-step operation.

	EXAMPLE	STEP 1	STEP 2
For the inverse sine function, use the sine inverse relation $\sin^{-1} a = \theta$.	Find all possible values of $\sin^{-1} \frac{1}{2}$.	Using the unit circle, find the values between 0 and 2π for which $\sin \theta = \frac{1}{2}$. $\sin \frac{\pi}{6} = \frac{1}{2}$, $\sin \frac{5\pi}{6} = \frac{1}{2}$	Find angles that are coterminal with the angles $\frac{\pi}{6}$ and $\frac{5\pi}{6}$. $\frac{\pi}{6} + (2\pi)n$, $\frac{5\pi}{6} + (2\pi)n$
For the inverse cosine function, use the cosine inverse relation $\cos^{-1} a = \theta$.	Find all possible values of $\cos^{-1} \frac{1}{2}$.	Using the unit circle, find the values between 0 and 2π for which $\cos \theta = \frac{1}{2}$. $\cos \frac{\pi}{3} = \frac{1}{2}$, $\cos \frac{5\pi}{3} = \frac{1}{2}$	Find angles that are coterminal with the angles $\frac{\pi}{3}$ and $\frac{5\pi}{3}$. $\frac{\pi}{3} + (2\pi)n$, $\frac{5\pi}{3} + (2\pi)n$

Answer each question.

1. Explain the meaning of the inverse trigonometric functions.
Possible answer: The inverse function is used to find the measure of the angle when the value of the trigonometric function is known.
2. Find all values of θ between 0 and 2π for which $\sin \theta = \frac{\sqrt{3}}{2}$. $\frac{\pi}{3}, \frac{2\pi}{3}$
3. Find all values of θ between 0 and 2π for which $\sin \theta = \frac{\sqrt{2}}{2}$. $\frac{\pi}{4}, \frac{3\pi}{4}$
4. Find all values of θ between 0 and 2π for which $\cos \theta = \frac{\sqrt{3}}{2}$. $\frac{\pi}{6}, \frac{11\pi}{6}$
5. Find all possible values of $\cos^{-1} \frac{\sqrt{2}}{2}$.
   a. Find the values of θ between 0 and 2π for which $\cos \theta = \frac{\sqrt{2}}{2}$. $\frac{\pi}{4}, \frac{7\pi}{4}$
   b. Find angles that are coterminal with these angle values. $\frac{\pi}{4} + (2\pi)n$, $\frac{7\pi}{4} + (2\pi)n$
6. Find all possible values of $\sin^{-1} = 0$.
   a. Find the values of θ between 0 and 2π for which $\sin \theta = 0$. $0, \pi$
   b. Find angles that are coterminal with these angle values. $(2\pi)n$, $\pi + (2\pi)n$
   c. Express your answer to part b in degrees. $360n$, $90 + 360n$

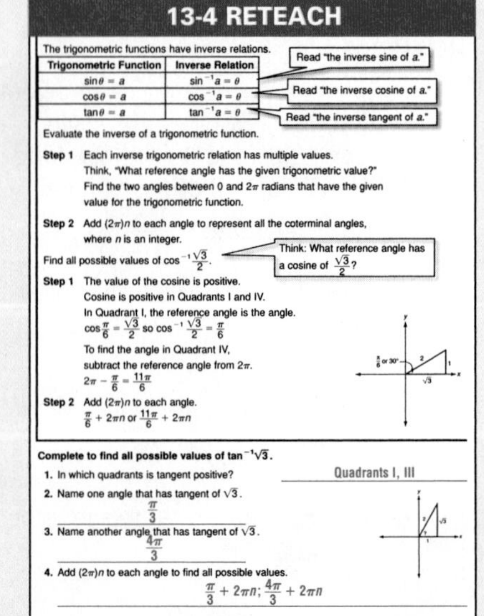

13-4 RETEACH

The trigonometric functions have inverse relations.

Trigonometric Function	Inverse Relation
$\sin \theta = a$	$\sin^{-1} a = \theta$
$\cos \theta = a$	$\cos^{-1} a = \theta$
$\tan \theta = a$	$\tan^{-1} a = \theta$

Read "the inverse sine of *a*."
Read "the inverse cosine of *a*."
Read "the inverse tangent of *a*."

Evaluate the inverse of a trigonometric function.

Step 1 Each inverse trigonometric relation has multiple values. Think, "What reference angle has the given trigonometric value?" Find the two angles between 0 and 2π radians that have the given value for the trigonometric function.

Step 2 Add $(2\pi)n$ to each angle to represent all the coterminal angles, where n is an integer.

Find all possible values of $\cos^{-1} \frac{\sqrt{3}}{2}$.

Think: What reference angle has a cosine of $\frac{\sqrt{3}}{2}$?

Step 1 The value of the cosine is positive. Cosine is positive in Quadrants I and IV. In Quadrant I, the reference angle is the angle. $\cos \frac{\pi}{6} = \frac{\sqrt{3}}{2}$ so $\cos^{-1} \frac{\sqrt{3}}{2} = \frac{\pi}{6}$
To find the angle in Quadrant IV, subtract the reference angle from 2π. $2\pi - \frac{\pi}{6} = \frac{11\pi}{6}$

Step 2 Add $(2\pi)n$ to each angle. $\frac{\pi}{6} + 2\pi n$ or $\frac{11\pi}{6} + 2\pi n$

Complete to find all possible values of $\tan^{-1}\sqrt{3}$.

1. In which quadrants is tangent positive? Quadrants I, III
2. Name one angle that has tangent of $\sqrt{3}$. $\frac{\pi}{3}$
3. Name another angle that has tangent of $\sqrt{3}$. $\frac{4\pi}{3}$
4. Add $(2\pi)n$ to each angle to find all possible values. $\frac{\pi}{3} + 2\pi n$; $\frac{4\pi}{3} + 2\pi n$

MULTI-STEP TEST PREP

33. This problem will prepare you for the Multi-Step Test Prep on page 956.

Giant kelp is a seaweed that typically grows about 100 ft in height, but may reach as high as 175 ft.

a. A diver positions herself 10 ft from the base of a giant kelp so that her eye level is 5 ft above the ocean floor. If the kelp is 100 ft in height, what would be the angle of elevation from the diver to the top of the kelp? Round to the nearest tenth of a degree. **84.0°**

b. The angle of elevation from the diver's eye level to the top of a giant kelp whose base is 30 ft away is 75.5°. To the nearest foot, what is the height of the kelp? **121 ft**

Find each value.

34. $\text{Cos}^{-1}(\cos 0.4)$ **0.4** **35.** $\tan(\text{Tan}^{-1} 0.7)$ **0.7** **36.** $\sin(\text{Cos}^{-1} 0)$ **1**

37. Critical Thinking Explain why the domain of the Cosine function is different from the domain of the Sine function.

38. Write About It Is the statement $\text{Sin}^{-1}(\sin \theta) = \theta$ true for all values of θ? Explain.

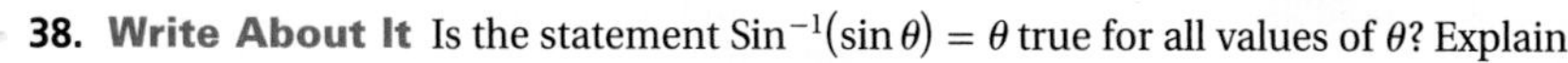

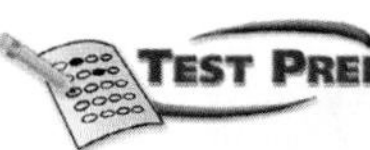

TEST PREP

39. For which equation is the value of θ in radians a positive value?

Ⓐ $\text{Cos}\,\theta = -\frac{1}{2}$ (circled) Ⓑ $\text{Tan}\,\theta = -\frac{\sqrt{3}}{3}$ Ⓒ $\text{Sin}\,\theta = -\frac{\sqrt{3}}{2}$ Ⓓ $\text{Sin}\,\theta = -1$

40. A caution sign next to a roadway states that an upcoming hill has an 8% slope. An 8% slope means that there is an 8 ft rise for 100 ft of horizontal distance. At approximately what angle does the roadway rise from the horizontal?

Ⓕ 2.2° Ⓖ 4.6° (circled) Ⓗ 8.5° Ⓙ 12.5°

41. What value of θ makes the equation $2\sqrt{2}(\text{Cos}\,\theta) = -2$ true?

Ⓐ 45° Ⓑ 60° Ⓒ 135° (circled) Ⓓ 150°

CHALLENGE AND EXTEND

42. If $\text{Sin}^{-1}\left(-\frac{\sqrt{2}}{2}\right) = -\frac{\pi}{4}$, what is the value of $\text{Csc}^{-1}(-\sqrt{2})$? $-\frac{\pi}{4}$

Solve each inequality for $\{\theta \mid 0 \le \theta \le 2\pi\}$.

43. $\cos\theta \le \frac{1}{2}$ $\frac{\pi}{3} \le \theta \le \frac{5\pi}{3}$ **44.** $2\sin\theta - \sqrt{3} > 0$ $\frac{\pi}{3} < \theta < \frac{2\pi}{3}$ **45.** $\tan 2\theta \ge 1$

SPIRAL REVIEW

Graph each function. Identify the parent function that best describes the set of points, and describe the transformation from the parent function. *(Lesson 1-9)*

46. $\{(-2, -4), (-1, -0.5), (0, 0), (1, 0.5), (2, 4)\}$ **47.** $\{(-4, 1), (-2, 3), (0, 5), (2, 7), (4, 9)\}$

Find the inverse of each function. Determine whether the inverse is a function, and state its domain and range. *(Lesson 9-5)*

48. $f(x) = 3(x+2)^2$ **49.** $f(x) = \frac{x}{4} + 1$ **50.** $f(x) = -2x^2 + 5$

Convert each measure from degrees to radians or from radians to degrees. *(Lesson 13-3)*

51. 240° $\frac{4\pi}{3}$ **52.** $-\frac{5\pi}{4}$ $-225°$ **53.** 420° $\frac{7\pi}{3}$

MULTI-STEP TEST PREP **Exercise 33** involves using the inverse tangent function to find an angle of elevation from a point on the ocean floor. This exercise prepares students for the Multi-Step Test Prep on page 956.

TEST PREP DOCTOR If students have difficulty with **Exercise 41,** point out that this problem can be solved by working backward. Students can substitute each answer choice into the equation to determine which value makes the equation true.

Answers

48. $f^{-1}(x) = \pm\sqrt{\frac{x}{3}} - 2$; not a function; D: $\{x \mid x \ge 0\}$; R: $\mathbb{R}$

49, 50. See p. A49.

Journal

Have students explain why the inverse of $\text{Sin}\,\theta$ is a function but the inverse of $\sin\theta$ is not a function.

ALTERNATIVE ASSESSMENT

Ask students to draw a right triangle and label the length of two of its sides. Then have students use inverse trigonometric functions to find the measures of the acute angles of the triangle.

Power Presentations with PowerPoint®

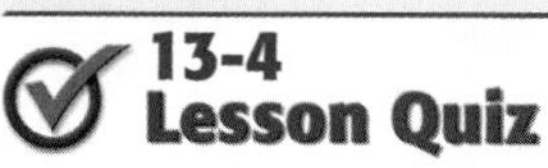

13-4 Lesson Quiz

1. Find all possible values of $\cos^{-1}(-1)$. $\pi + (2\pi)n$

2. Evaluate $\text{Sin}^{-1}\frac{\sqrt{3}}{2}$. Give your answer in both radians and degrees. $\frac{\pi}{3}$, or 60°

3. A road has a 5% grade, which means that there is a 5 ft rise for 100 ft of horizontal distance. At what angle does the road rise from the horizontal? Round to the nearest tenth of a degree. 2.9°

Solve each equation to the nearest tenth. Use the given restrictions.

4. $\cos\theta = 0.3$, for $0° \le \theta \le 180°$ $\theta \approx 72.5°$

5. $\cos\theta = 0.3$, for $270° < \theta < 360°$ $\theta \approx 287.5°$

Also available on transparency

13-4 PROBLEM SOLVING

Rafe is concerned that some recently constructed buildings in his town do not comply with code restrictions. New buildings are limited to a maximum of 40 feet in height.

1. When working with angles of elevation from his eye level, Rafe realizes that he must allow for his own height, 5 feet 9 inches, in his calculations. Explain how he can do this.
Possible answer: Subtract his height from any height measurements.

2. On the building plans, the height of the new bank is 33 feet. Rafe calculates what the angle of elevation should be from 100 feet away if the bank is 33 feet tall.

a. Label the diagram to show the height of the bank that Rafe will use in his calculations Mark the angle of elevation.

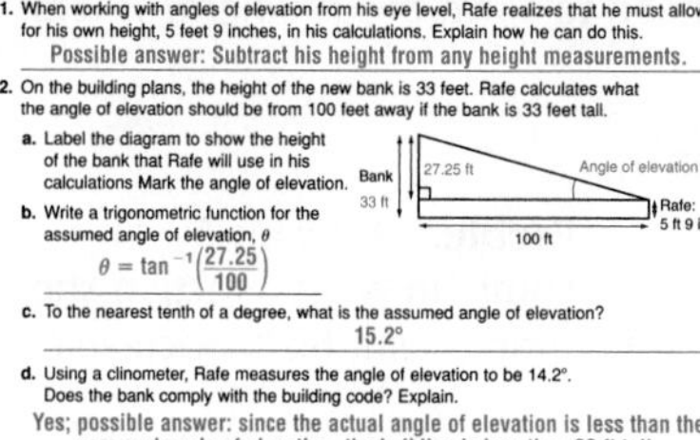

b. Write a trigonometric function for the assumed angle of elevation, θ
$\theta = \tan^{-1}\left(\frac{27.25}{100}\right)$

c. To the nearest tenth of a degree, what is the assumed angle of elevation? 15.2°

d. Using a clinometer, Rafe measures the angle of elevation to be 14.2°. Does the bank comply with the building code? Explain.
Yes; possible answer: since the actual angle of elevation is less than the assumed angle of elevation, the building is less than 33 ft tall.

3. On the plans, the height of the new inn is 39 feet. Rafe finds the angle of elevation and compares it to what he measures.

a. Predict the angle of elevation of the highest point on this building from a distance of 100 feet and allowing for Rafe's height. 18.4°

b. Predict the angle of elevation of the highest point on a building that is 40 feet tall, allowing for Rafe's height. 18.9°

c. If Rafe measures an angle of elevation of 19.0°, how does the height of the inn compare to its declared height of 39 feet? Explain.
The inn is more than 40 ft tall. Since the angle of elevation is greater than 18.9°, then the building is taller than 40 ft.

4. Carrie says the angle of elevation of the top of the flagpole at school is 55.9° from a distance of 20 feet away and allowing for her height of 5 feet 6 inches.

a. Write and evaluate an expression for the height of the flagpole to the nearest tenth of a foot. $20\tan 55.9° + 5.5 = 35.0$ ft

b. What should be the angle of elevation if Rafe measures it from a distance of 50 feet away? Write and evaluate an expression.
$\tan^{-1}\left(\frac{35 - 5.75}{50}\right) = 30.3°$

13-4 CHALLENGE

When evaluating an inverse trigonometric function, it is helpful to think of the result as an angle. For example, $\text{Sin}^{-1}x$ can be thought of as an angle whose sine is x. The other common notation for $\text{Sin}^{-1}x$ is arcsine x and is read as an angle whose sine is x.

Thinking of the inverse trigonometric functions in this manner will help you evaluate combinations of trigonometric functions and inverse trigonometric functions. For example, consider this expression.

$$\sin\left(\text{Cos}^{-1}\frac{3}{5}\right)$$

The expression directs you to find the sine of an angle θ such that $\theta = \text{Cos}^{-1}\frac{3}{5}$. This is interpreted as θ is an angle whose cosine is $\frac{3}{5}$. Think of θ as an angle in a right triangle as shown at right. The cosine of angle θ is $\frac{3}{5}$ since that is the ratio of the adjacent side to the hypotenuse. The third side of the triangle is 4, and the ratio of the opposite side to the hypotenuse is $\frac{4}{5}$. It follows that $\sin\left(\text{Cos}^{-1}\frac{3}{5}\right) = \frac{4}{5}$.

Evaluate each of the following.

1. $\sin\left(\text{Cos}^{-1}\frac{4}{5}\right)$ $\frac{3}{5}$
2. $\cos\left(\text{Tan}^{-1}\frac{3}{4}\right)$ $\frac{4}{5}$
3. $\tan\left(\text{Sin}^{-1}\frac{5}{13}\right)$ $\frac{5}{12}$
4. $\cos\left(\text{Sin}^{-1}\frac{12}{13}\right)$ $\frac{5}{13}$
5. $\sec\left(\text{Tan}^{-1}\frac{7}{24}\right)$ $\frac{25}{24}$
6. $\csc\left(\text{Sin}^{-1}\frac{9}{41}\right)$ $\frac{41}{9}$
7. $\cos(\text{Sin}^{-1}x)$ where $-1 \le x \le 1$
(*Hint:* Think of x as a ratio and use the Pythagorean Theorem.)
$\sqrt{1 - x^2}$
8. $\csc\left(\text{Tan}^{-1}\frac{1}{x}\right)$ where $x > 0$
(*Hint:* Draw a triangle and use the Pythagorean Theorem.)
$\sqrt{1 + x^2}$

Organizer

Objective: Assess students' ability to apply concepts and skills in Lessons 13-1 through 13-4 in a real-world format.

 Online Edition

Resources

 ***Algebra II Assessments***
www.mathtekstoolkit.org

Problems	Text Reference
1–2	Lesson 13-1
3	Lesson 13-3
4	Lesson 13-4

State Resources

go.hrw.com
State Resources Online
KEYWORD: MB7 Resources

CHAPTER 13

MULTI-STEP TEST PREP

SECTION 13A

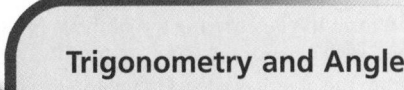

Trigonometry and Angles

By the Sea The Monterey Bay Aquarium in California is visited by almost 2 million people each year. The aquarium is home to more than 550 species of plants and animals.

54 ft
70°
70°
d
40°

1. The window in front of the aquarium's Outer Bay exhibit is 54 ft long. Maria's camera has a viewing angle of 40°, as shown. To the nearest foot, how far would Maria need to stand from the window in order to include the entire window in a photo? This distance is labeled d. **74 ft**
2. Warty sea cucumbers may be found in Monterey Bay to a depth of about 64 m. A research vessel is anchored to the seafloor by a 70 m chain that makes an angle of 56° with the ocean's surface. Is the research vessel located over water that is too deep for warty sea cucumbers? Justify your answer.
3. A crystal jellyfish in a cylindrical aquarium tank is carried by a current in a circular path with a diameter of 2.5 m. In 1 min, the jellyfish is carried 26 cm by the current. At this rate, how long will it take the current to move the jellyfish in a complete circle? Round to the nearest minute. **30 min**
4. A sea otter is released from the aquarium's rehabilitation program with a radio transmitter implanted in its abdomen. The transmitter indicates that the otter is 400 m west and 80 m south of an observation deck. How many degrees south of west should an aquarium worker standing on the deck aim his binoculars in order to see the otter? Round to the nearest degree. **11° south of west**

2. No, the water is only about 58 m deep.

INTERVENTION

Scaffolding Questions

1. What is the length of the shorter legs of the two congruent right triangles shown in the diagram? 27 ft
2. Which trigonometric function of 56° is equal to the ratio of the length of the anchor chain to the depth of the water? sine What is the water's depth? ≈ 58 m
3. How can you determine the circumference of the circular path? Multiply the diameter by π.
4. Which inverse trigonometric function do you need to solve this problem? inverse tangent

Extension

If the otter in **Problem 4** swims 50 m farther to the south, in what direction should the aquarium worker aim his binoculars? ≈ 18° south of west

CHAPTER 13

SECTION 13A

Quiz for Lessons 13-1 Through 13-4

13-1 Right-Angle Trigonometry

Find the values of the six trigonometric functions for θ.

1. 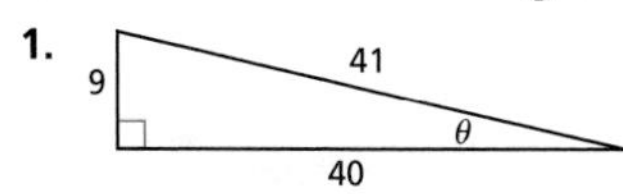

2. 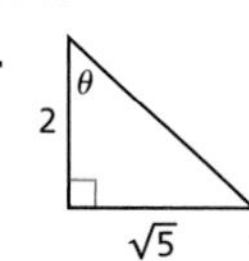

Use a trigonometric function to find the value of x.

3. 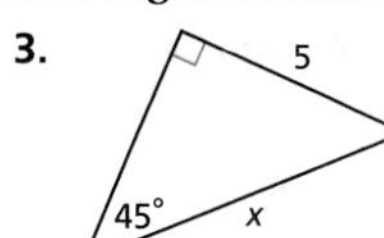 $5\sqrt{2}$

4. 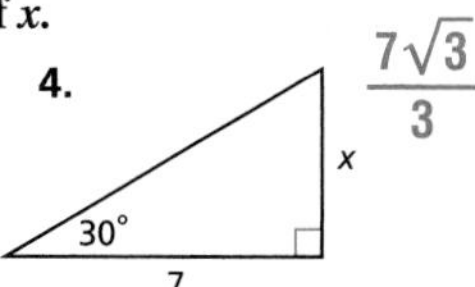 $\frac{7\sqrt{3}}{3}$

5. A biologist's eye level is 5.5 ft above the ground. She measures the angle of elevation to an eagle's nest on a cliff to be 66° when she stands 50 ft from the cliff's base. To the nearest foot, what is the height of the eagle's nest? **118 ft**

13-2 Angles of Rotation

Draw an angle with the given measure in standard position.

6. $-270°$
7. $405°$

Point P is a point on the terminal side of θ in standard position. Find the exact value of the six trigonometric functions for θ.

8. $P(12, -5)$
9. $P(-2, 7)$

13-3 The Unit Circle

Convert each measure from degrees to radians or from radians to degrees.

10. $-120°$ $-\frac{2\pi}{3}$
11. $63°$ $\frac{7\pi}{20}$
12. $\frac{3\pi}{8}$ $67.5°$
13. $-\frac{10\pi}{3}$ $-600°$

Use the unit circle to find the exact value of each trigonometric function.

14. $\cos 210°$ — 14. $-\frac{\sqrt{3}}{2}$
15. $\tan 120°$ $-\sqrt{3}$
16. $\cos\frac{\pi}{2}$ 0
17. $\tan\frac{5\pi}{4}$ 1
18. A bicycle tire rotates through an angle of 3.4π radians in 1 second. If the radius of the tire is 0.34 m, what is the bicycle's speed in meters per second? Round to the nearest tenth. **3.6 m/s**

13-4 Inverses of Trigonometric Functions

Evaluate each inverse trigonometric function. Give your answer in both radians and degrees.

19. $\text{Sin}^{-1}\frac{\sqrt{3}}{2}$ $60°; \frac{\pi}{3}$
20. $\text{Tan}^{-1}\left(-\frac{\sqrt{3}}{3}\right)$ $-30°; -\frac{\pi}{6}$
21. A driver uses a ramp when unloading supplies from his delivery truck. The ramp is 10 feet long, and the bed of the truck is 4 feet off the ground. To the nearest degree, what angle does the ramp make with the ground? **24°**

READY TO GO ON? SECTION 13A

Organizer

Objective: Assess students' mastery of concepts and skills in Lessons 13-1 through 13-4.

Resources

 ***Assessment Resources***
Section 13A Quiz

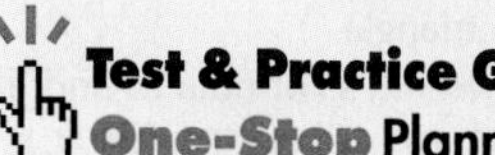

INTERVENTION 

Resources

 ***Ready to Go On? Intervention and Enrichment*** **Worksheets**

 ***Ready to Go On?*** **CD-ROM**

 ***Ready to Go On?*** **Online**

Answers

1. $\sin\theta = \frac{9}{41}$; $\cos\theta = \frac{40}{41}$; $\tan\theta = \frac{9}{40}$; $\csc\theta = \frac{41}{9}$; $\sec\theta = \frac{41}{40}$; $\cot\theta = \frac{40}{9}$

2, 6–9. See p. A49.

READY TO GO ON? Diagnose and Prescribe

Ready to Go On? Intervention	*Ready to Go On? Intervention*, Section 13A		
	Worksheets	CD-ROM	Online
Lesson 13-1	13-1 Intervention	Activity 13-1	Diagnose and Prescribe Online
Lesson 13-2	13-2 Intervention	Activity 13-2	
Lesson 13-3	13-3 Intervention	Activity 13-3	
Lesson 13-4	13-4 Intervention	Activity 13-4	

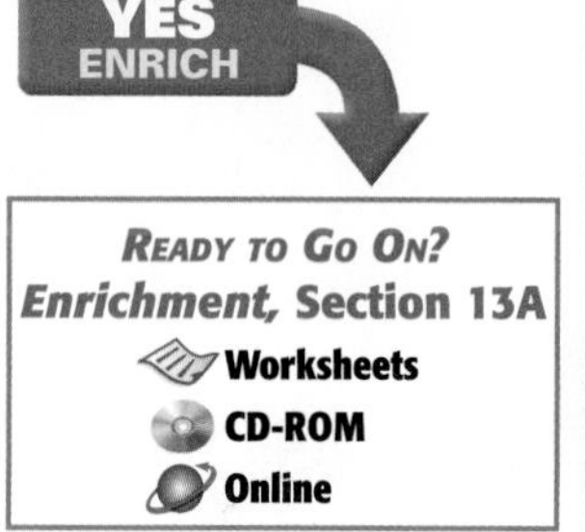

Ready to Go On? Enrichment, Section 13A
- Worksheets
- CD-ROM
- Online

SECTION
13B Applying Trigonometric Functions

One-Minute Section Planner

Lesson	Lab Resources	Materials
Lesson 13-5 The Law of Sines • Determine the area of a triangle given side-angle-side information. • Use the Law of Sines to find the side lengths and angle measures of a triangle. ☐ SAT-10 ☐ NAEP ☑ ACT ☑ SAT ☑ SAT Subject Tests		**Required** graphing calculator, graph paper **Optional** ruler (MK), protractor (MK), highlighters
Lesson 13-6 The Law of Cosines • Use the Law of Cosines to find the side lengths and angle measures of a triangle. • Use Heron's Formula to find the area of a triangle. ☐ SAT-10 ☐ NAEP ☑ ACT ☑ SAT ☑ SAT Subject Tests	***Technology Lab Activities*** 13-6 Technology Lab	**Required** graphing calculator **Optional** ruler (MK), note cards

MK = *Manipulatives Kit*

Section Overview

Professional Development

The Law of Sines

Lesson 13-5

Using the Law of Sines will enable students to determine measurements of a triangle that might otherwise be difficult to measure directly.

Area of a Triangle

For any $\triangle ABC$:

$$\text{Area} = \frac{1}{2}bc\sin A$$

$$\text{Area} = \frac{1}{2}ac\sin B$$

$$\text{Area} = \frac{1}{2}ab\sin C$$

Law of Sines

For any $\triangle ABC$:

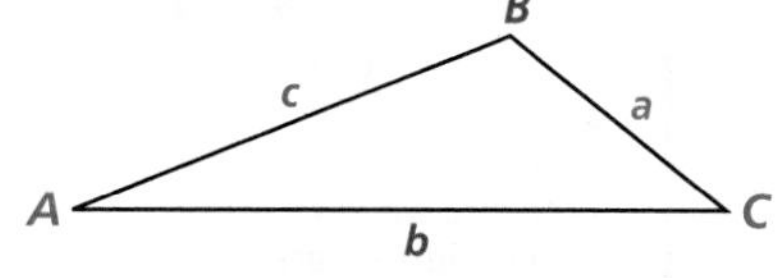

$$\frac{\sin A}{a} = \frac{\sin B}{b} = \frac{\sin C}{c}$$

You can use the Law of Sines to solve a triangle when you know

• AAS • ASA • SSA (ambiguous case)

Ambiguous Case When you use the Law of Sines to solve a triangle for which you know SSA, zero, one, or two triangles may be possible.

Given a, b, and $m\angle A$:

$\angle A$ is acute

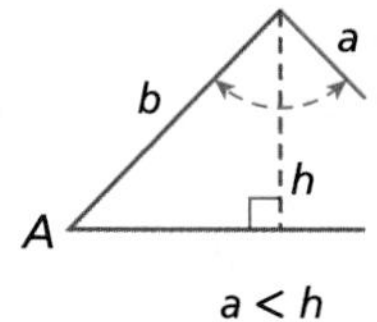

$a < h$
No triangle

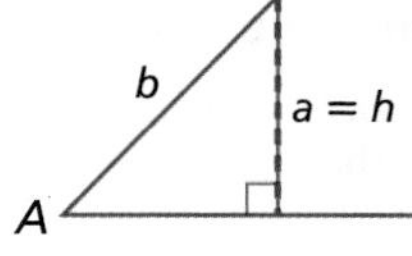

$a = h$
One triangle

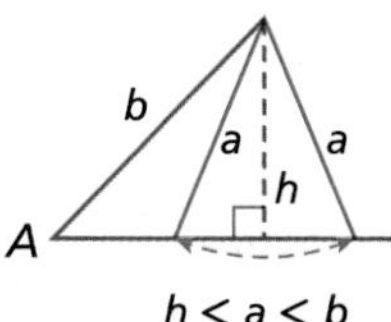

$h < a < b$
Two triangles

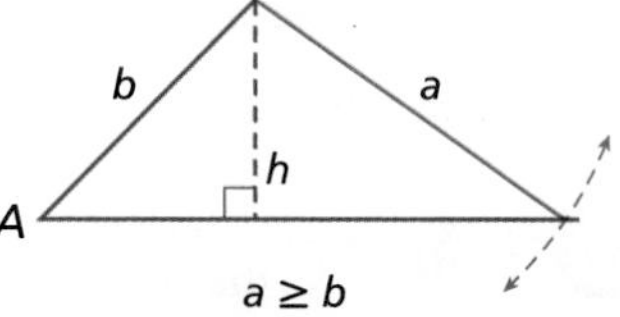

$a \geq b$
One triangle

$\angle A$ is right or obtuse

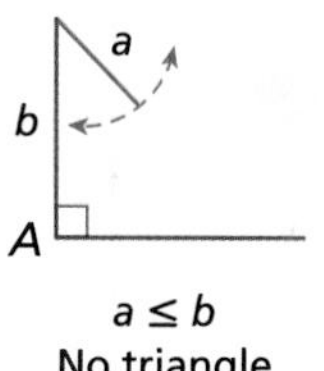

$a \leq b$
No triangle

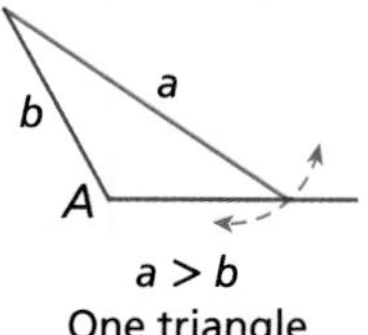

$a > b$
One triangle

The Law of Cosines

Lesson 13-6

The Law of Cosines and Heron's Formula are used in such fields as surveying, landscape architecture, and city planning.

Law of Cosines

For any $\triangle ABC$:

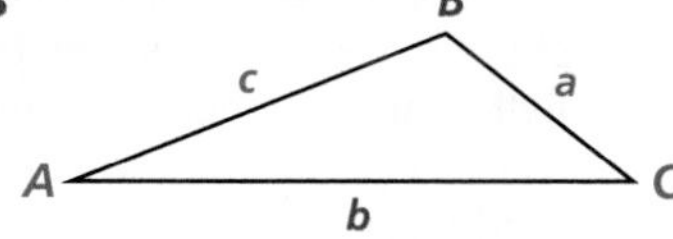

$$a^2 = b^2 + c^2 - 2bc\cos A$$

$$b^2 = a^2 + c^2 - 2ac\cos B$$

$$c^2 = a^2 + b^2 - 2ab\cos C$$

Heron's Formula

For any $\triangle ABC$, the area is

$$\sqrt{s(s-a)(s-b)(s-c)},$$

where $s = \frac{1}{2}(a + b + c)$.

13-5 Organizer

Pacing: Traditional 2 days
Block 1 day

Objectives: Determine the area of a triangle given side-angle-side information.

Use the Law of Sines to find the side lengths and angle measures of a triangle.

Online Edition
Tutorial Videos

Power Presentations with PowerPoint®

Warm Up

Find the area of each triangle with the given base and height.

1. $b = 10, h = 7$ 35 units^2

2. $b = 8, h = 4.6$ 18.4 units^2

Solve each proportion.

3. $\frac{12}{19} = \frac{18}{x}$ 28.5

4. $\frac{51}{15} = \frac{34}{x}$ 10

5. In $\triangle ABC$, $m\angle A = 122°$ and $m\angle B = 17°$. What is $m\angle C$? 41°

Also available on transparency

Math Humor

Q: How do you find the measures of the angles of an octagon?

A: By using the Law of Stop Signs.

13-5 The Law of Sines

Objectives
Determine the area of a triangle given side-angle-side information.

Use the Law of Sines to find the side lengths and angle measures of a triangle.

Who uses this?
Sailmakers can use sine ratios to determine the amount of fabric needed to make a sail. (See Example 1.)

A sailmaker is designing a sail that will have the dimensions shown in the diagram. Based on these dimensions, the sailmaker can determine the amount of fabric needed.

Helpful Hint
An angle and the side opposite that angle are labeled with the same letter. Capital letters are used for angles, and lowercase letters are used for sides.

The area of the triangle representing the sail is $\frac{1}{2}bh$. Although you do not know the value of h, you can calculate it by using the fact that $\sin A = \frac{h}{c}$, or $h = c \sin A$.

$$\text{Area} = \frac{1}{2}bh \qquad \textit{Write the area formula.}$$

$$\text{Area} = \frac{1}{2}bc\sin A \qquad \textit{Substitute } c \sin A \textit{ for } h.$$

This formula allows you to determine the area of a triangle if you know the lengths of two of its sides and the measure of the angle between them.

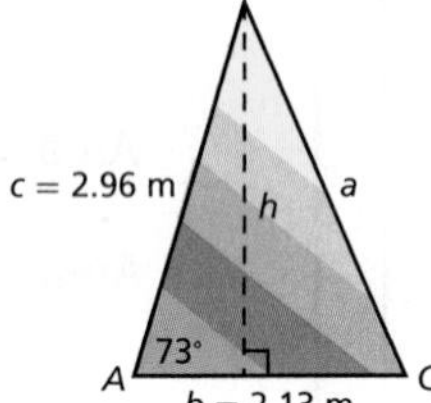

Know it! Note

Area of a Triangle

For $\triangle ABC$,

$\text{Area} = \frac{1}{2}bc \sin A$

$\text{Area} = \frac{1}{2}ac \sin B$

$\text{Area} = \frac{1}{2}ab \sin C$

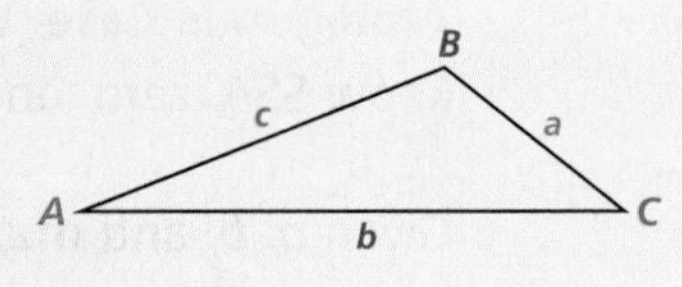

EXAMPLE 1 Determining the Area of a Triangle

Find the area of the sail shown at the top of the page. Round to the nearest tenth.

$\text{area} = \frac{1}{2}bc \sin A$ *Write the area formula.*

$= \frac{1}{2}(2.13)(2.96) \sin 73°$ *Substitute 2.13 for b, 2.96 for c, and 73° for A.*

≈ 3.014655113 *Use a calculator to evaluate the expression.*

The area of the sail is about 3.0 m^2.

1. Find the area of the triangle. Round to the nearest tenth. **47.9 ft^2**

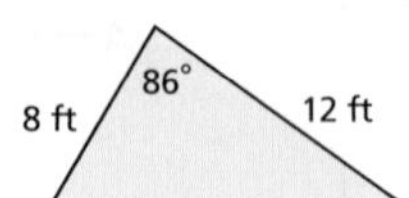

State Resources

go.hrw.com
State Resources Online
KEYWORD: MB7 Resources

1 Introduce

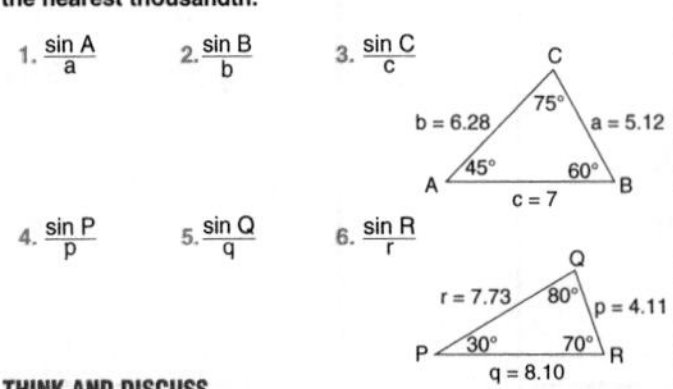
EXPLORATION

13-5 The Law of Sines

You can use a calculator to investigate the relationship between the sines of the angles of a triangle and the lengths of the opposite sides.

Use your calculator to find the value of each ratio. Round to the nearest thousandth.

1. $\frac{\sin A}{a}$ 2. $\frac{\sin B}{b}$ 3. $\frac{\sin C}{c}$

4. $\frac{\sin P}{p}$ 5. $\frac{\sin Q}{q}$ 6. $\frac{\sin R}{r}$

THINK AND DISCUSS

7. **Describe** the pattern you notice in the ratios for each triangle.

8. **Discuss** how you can use the pattern you observed to find the value of x.

Motivate

Present students with the triangle shown. Ask students why the Pythagorean Theorem cannot be used to determine the length of the third side. because the triangle is not a right triangle Tell students that in this lesson they will learn to use the sine function to determine measures of triangles that are not right triangles.

Explorations and answers are provided in the *Explorations* binder.

The area of $\triangle ABC$ is equal to $\frac{1}{2}bc\sin A$ or $\frac{1}{2}ac\sin B$ or $\frac{1}{2}ab\sin C$. By setting these expressions equal to each other, you can derive the Law of Sines.

$$\frac{1}{2}bc\sin A = \frac{1}{2}ac\sin B = \frac{1}{2}ab\sin C$$

$$bc\sin A = ac\sin B = ab\sin C \quad \text{Multiply each expression by 2.}$$

$$\frac{bc\sin A}{abc} = \frac{ac\sin B}{abc} = \frac{ab\sin C}{abc} \quad \text{Divide each expression by abc.}$$

$$\frac{\sin A}{a} = \frac{\sin B}{b} = \frac{\sin C}{c} \quad \text{Divide out common factors.}$$

Law of Sines

For $\triangle ABC$, the Law of Sines states that

$$\frac{\sin A}{a} = \frac{\sin B}{b} = \frac{\sin C}{c}.$$

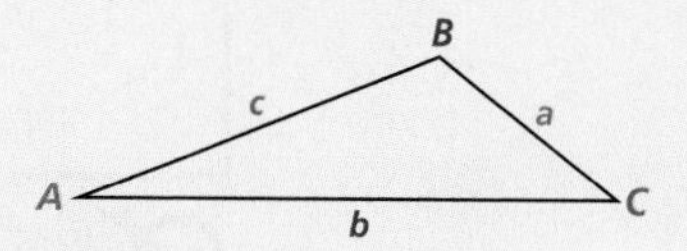

The Law of Sines allows you to solve a triangle as long as you know either of the following:

1. Two angle measures and any side length—angle-angle-side (AAS) or angle-side-angle (ASA) information
2. Two side lengths and the measure of an angle that is not between them—side-side-angle (SSA) information

EXAMPLE 2 **Using the Law of Sines for AAS and ASA**

Solve the triangle. Round to the nearest tenth.

A

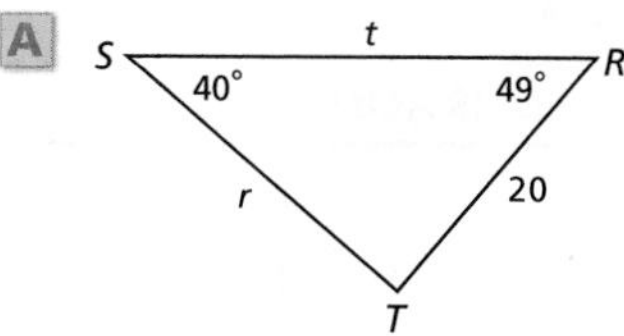

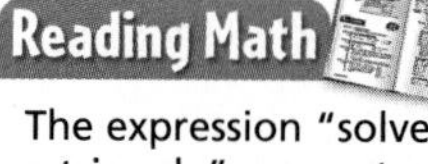

The expression "solve a triangle" means to find the measures of all unknown angles and sides.

Step 1 Find the third angle measure.

$m\angle R + m\angle S + m\angle T = 180°$ *Triangle Sum Theorem*

$49° + 40° + m\angle T = 180°$ *Substitute 49° for m∠R and 40° for m∠S.*

$m\angle T = 91°$ *Solve for m∠T.*

Step 2 Find the unknown side lengths.

$\frac{\sin R}{r} = \frac{\sin S}{s}$	*Law of Sines*	$\frac{\sin S}{s} = \frac{\sin T}{t}$
$\frac{\sin 49°}{r} = \frac{\sin 40°}{20}$	*Substitute.*	$\frac{\sin 40°}{20} = \frac{\sin 91°}{t}$
$r\sin 40° = 20\sin 49°$	*Cross multiply.*	$t\sin 40° = 20\sin 91°$
$r = \frac{20\sin 49°}{\sin 40°}$	*Solve for the unknown side.*	$t = \frac{20\sin 91°}{\sin 40°}$
$r \approx 23.5$		$t \approx 31.1$

2 Teach

Guided Instruction

Remind students that for an acute angle in a right triangle, the sine of the angle is equal to the ratio $\frac{\text{opp.}}{\text{hyp.}}$. Lead students through the derivations of both the area formula of a triangle and the Law of Sines. Make sure students can use the Law of Sines to solve triangles when given AAS or ASA information before introducing them to the ambiguous case of SSA information.

Reaching All Learners

Through Cooperative Learning

Have students work in pairs. Each student should draw a triangle and use a ruler (MK) and protractor (MK) to label it with AAS or ASA information. Then have partners use the Law of Sines to solve each other's triangles. Students can check their work by direct measurement of the unlabeled sides and angles.

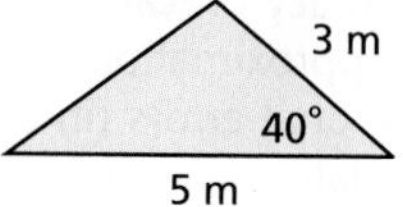

Additional Examples

Example 1

Find the area of the triangle. Round to the nearest tenth.

3 m, 40°, 5 m

4.8 m^2

Example 2

Solve each triangle. Round to the nearest tenth.

A.

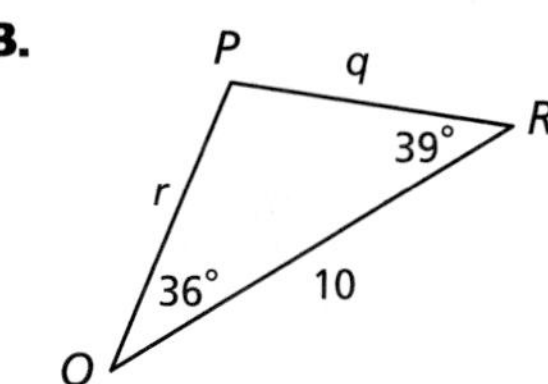

$m\angle E = 119°$; $d \approx 17.4$; $e \approx 27.9$

B.

P, q, R, 39°, r, 36°, 10, Q

$m\angle P = 105°$; $q \approx 6.1$; $r \approx 6.5$

Also available on transparency

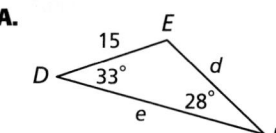

INTERVENTION 

Questioning Strategies

EXAMPLE 1

- How do you know which measurements to use for *b*, *c*, and $m\angle A$?

EXAMPLE 2

- How can you use the Triangle Sum Theorem to find the measure of the third angle of the triangle?
- Once you have substituted measurements into the Law of Sines, how do you solve for an unknown side length?

Geometry In **Example 2,** remind students that the Triangle Sum Theorem states that the sum of the measures of the angles of a triangle is 180°.

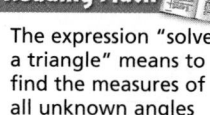

Teaching Tip **Measurement** In Example **2B,** some students may want to use the ratio $\frac{\sin E}{e}$ to determine the value of *f*. Point out that the ratio $\frac{\sin D}{d}$ should be used instead because both m∠*D* and *d* are known exactly. This provides greater accuracy (because the value of *e* is an approximation) and helps avoid additional errors (in case the student calculated *e* incorrectly).

Teaching Tip **Inclusion** Discuss with students how the height *h* of a triangle can be determined in the ambiguous case when given SSA information. Point out that $\sin A = \frac{h}{b}$; therefore, $h = b\sin A$.

Solve the triangle. Round to the nearest tenth.

B

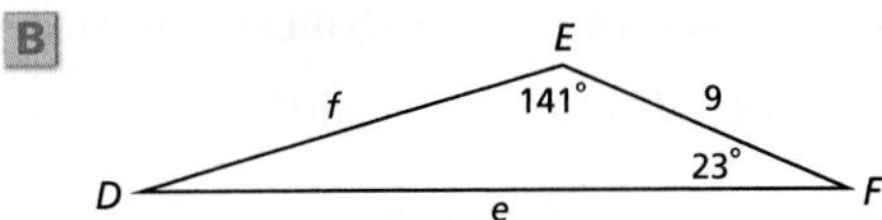

Step 1 Find the third angle measure.

$m\angle D = 180° - 141° - 23° = 16°$ *Triangle Sum Theorem*

Step 2 Find the unknown side lengths.

$\frac{\sin D}{d} = \frac{\sin E}{e}$ *Law of Sines* $\frac{\sin D}{d} = \frac{\sin F}{f}$

$\frac{\sin 16°}{9} = \frac{\sin 141°}{e}$ *Substitute.* $\frac{\sin 16°}{9} = \frac{\sin 23°}{f}$

$e = \frac{9\sin 141°}{\sin 16°} \approx 20.5$ $f = \frac{9\sin 23°}{\sin 16°} \approx 12.8$

Solve each triangle. Round to the nearest tenth.

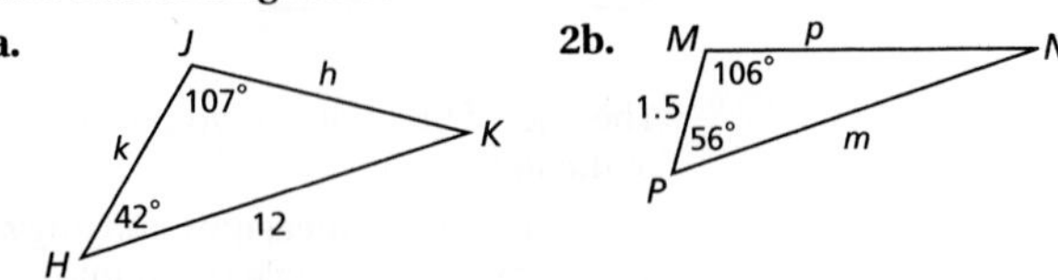

m∠*K* = 31°; *k* ≈ 6.5; *h* ≈ 8.4 m∠*N* = 18°; *m* ≈ 4.7; *p* ≈ 4.0

When you use the Law of Sines to solve a triangle for which you know side-side-angle (SSA) information, zero, one, or two triangles may be possible. For this reason, SSA is called the *ambiguous case*.

Ambiguous Case **Possible Triangles**

Given *a*, *b*, and m∠*A*,

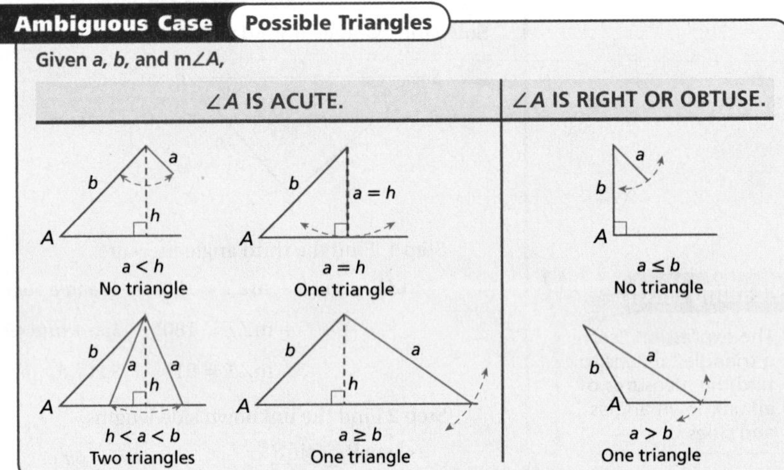

Remember!

When one angle in a triangle is obtuse, the measures of the other two angles must be acute.

Know it! Note

Solving a Triangle Given *a*, *b*, and m∠*A*
1. Use the values of *a*, *b*, and m∠*A* to determine the number of possible triangles.
2. If there is one triangle, use the Law of Sines to solve for the unknowns.
3. If there are two triangles, use the Law of Sines to find m∠B_1 and m∠B_2. Then use these values to find the other measurements of the two triangles.

EXAMPLE 3 Art Application

Maggie is designing a mosaic by using triangular tiles of different shapes. Determine the number of triangles that Maggie can form using the measurements $a = 11$ cm, $b = 17$ cm, and $m\angle A = 30°$. Then solve the triangles. Round to the nearest tenth.

Step 1 Determine the number of possible triangles. In this case, $\angle A$ is acute. Find h.

$$\sin 30° = \frac{h}{17} \qquad \textit{$\sin\theta = \frac{\text{opp.}}{\text{hyp.}}$}$$

$$h = 17\sin 30° \approx 8.5 \text{ cm} \qquad \textit{Solve for h.}$$

Because $h < a < b$, two triangles are possible.

Triangle 1

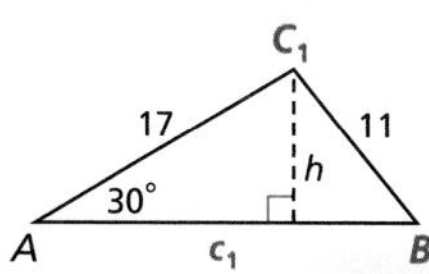

Triangle 2

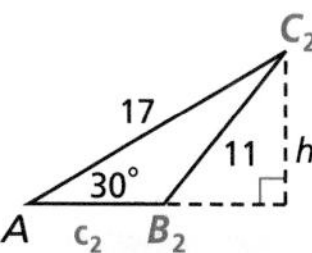

Step 2 Determine $m\angle B_1$ and $m\angle B_2$.

$$\frac{\sin A}{a} = \frac{\sin B}{b} \qquad \textit{Law of Sines}$$

$$\frac{\sin 30°}{11} = \frac{\sin B}{17} \qquad \textit{Substitute.}$$

$$\sin B = \frac{17\sin 30°}{11} \qquad \textit{Solve for sin B.}$$

$$\sin B \approx 0.773$$

Let $\angle B_1$ represent the acute angle with a sine of 0.773. Use the inverse sine function on your calculator to determine $m\angle B_1$.

$$m\angle B_1 = \text{Sin}^{-1}\left(\frac{17\sin 30°}{11}\right) \approx 50.6°$$

Let $\angle B_2$ represent the obtuse angle with a sine of 0.773.

$$m\angle B_2 = 180° - 50.6° = 129.4° \qquad \textit{The reference angle of $\angle B_2$ is 50.6°.}$$

Step 3 Find the other unknown measures of the two triangles.

Solve for $m\angle C_1$.

$$30° + 50.6° + m\angle C_1 = 180°$$
$$m\angle C_1 = 99.4°$$

Solve for $m\angle C_2$.

$$30° + 129.4° + m\angle C_2 = 180°$$
$$m\angle C_2 = 20.6°$$

Solve for c_1.

$$\frac{\sin A}{a} = \frac{\sin C_1}{c_1} \qquad \textit{Law of Sines}$$

$$\frac{\sin 30°}{11} = \frac{\sin 99.4°}{c_1} \qquad \textit{Substitute.}$$

$$c_1 = \frac{11\sin 99.4°}{\sin 30°} \qquad \textit{Solve for the unknown side.}$$

$$c_1 \approx 21.7 \text{ cm}$$

Solve for c_2.

$$\frac{\sin A}{a} = \frac{\sin C_2}{c_2}$$

$$\frac{\sin 30°}{11} = \frac{\sin 20.6°}{c_2}$$

$$c_2 = \frac{11\sin 20.6°}{\sin 30°}$$

$$c_2 \approx 7.7 \text{ cm}$$

3. Determine the number of triangles Maggie can form using the measurements $a = 10$ cm, $b = 6$ cm, and $m\angle A = 105°$. Then solve the triangles. Round to the nearest tenth.
1 triangle; $m\angle B \approx 35.4°$; $m\angle C \approx 39.6°$; $c \approx 6.6$ cm

Helpful Hint

Because $\angle B_1$ and $\angle B_2$ have the same sine value, they also have the same reference angle.

COMMON ERROR ALERT

Students may sometimes make mistakes with the Law of Sines by using the ratio of the sine of an angle and the length of a side that is *not* opposite that angle. Tell students that an angle and the side opposite that angle are called a side-angle pair. Suggest that students use highlighters to mark each side-angle pair in a triangle in the same color. This may help them set up equations correctly when using the Law of Sines.

Power Presentations with PowerPoint®

Additional Examples

Example 3

Determine the number of triangular banners that can be formed using the measurements $a = 50$, $b = 20$, and $m\angle A = 28°$. Then solve the triangles. Round to the nearest tenth.

one; $m\angle B \approx 10.8°$; $m\angle C \approx 141.2°$; $c \approx 66.8$

Also available on transparency

INTERVENTION
Questioning Strategies

EXAMPLE 3

- How do you determine the number of triangles that are possible?
- When two triangles are possible, how do you find the two possible measures of $\angle B$?

Kinesthetic You may wish to suggest that students use rulers (MK) and protractors (MK) to construct the two possible triangles in **Example 3.**

3 Close

Summarize

Review with students the requirements for using the Law of Sines to solve a triangle: two angle measures and any side length (AAS or ASA) or two side lengths and an angle measure that is not between them (SSA). Ask students to list the steps for solving a triangle in each of these cases. Remind students that before they use the Law of Sines to solve a triangle when given SSA information, they must first determine the number of triangles that can be formed.

ONGOING ASSESSMENT and INTERVENTION

***Diagnose Before* the Lesson**
13-5 Warm Up, TE p. 958

***Monitor During* the Lesson**
Check It Out! Exercises, SE pp. 958, 960, 961
Questioning Strategies, TE pp. 959, 961

***Assess After* the Lesson**
13-5 Lesson Quiz, TE p. 965
Alternative Assessment, TE p. 965

Answers to *Think and Discuss*

Possible answers:

1. Right-triangle trigonometry can be used to determine the height. Then the formula $A = \frac{1}{2}bh$ can be used to determine the triangle's area.
2. When given AAS or ASA, there is only 1 possible triangle. When given SSA, 0, 1, or 2 triangles are possible. For the ambiguous case of SSA, you must determine how many triangles are possible before using the Law of Sines.
3. See p. A14.

THINK AND DISCUSS

1. Explain how right triangle trigonometry can be used to determine the area of an obtuse triangle.
2. Explain why using the Law of Sines when given AAS or ASA is different than when given SSA.

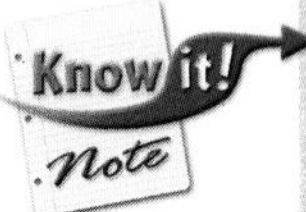

3. **GET ORGANIZED** Copy and complete the graphic organizer. In each box, give the conditions for which the ambiguous case results in zero, one, or two triangles.

SSA: Given a, b, and m∠A			
Angle A	**0 triangles**	**1 triangle**	**2 triangles**
Obtuse			
Acute			

13-5 Exercises

Assignment Guide

Assign *Guided Practice* exercises as necessary.

Basic 14–40, 42–45, 49–57
Average 14–46, 49–57
Advanced 14–38, 40–57

Homework Quick Check
Quickly check key concepts.
Exercises: 14, 18, 20, 24, 29, 34

Answers

12. 2 triangles; $m\angle B_1 \approx 40.2°$; $m\angle C_1 \approx 104.8°$; $c_1 \approx 13.5$ m; $m\angle B_2 \approx 139.8°$; $m\angle C_2 \approx 5.2°$; $c_2 \approx 1.3$ m

State Resources

13-5 Exercises

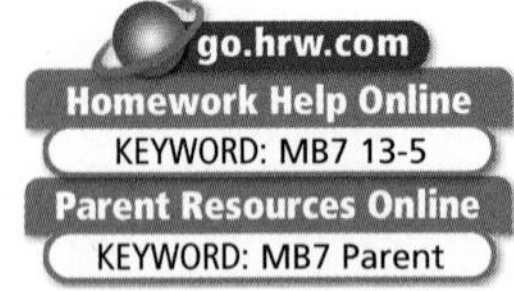

GUIDED PRACTICE

SEE EXAMPLE 1 p. 958

Find the area of each triangle. Round to the nearest tenth.

1.
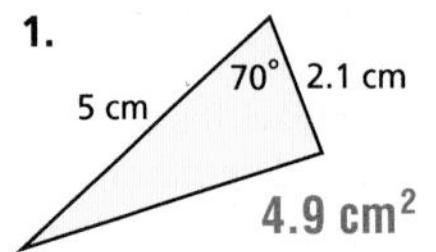

4.9 cm²

2.
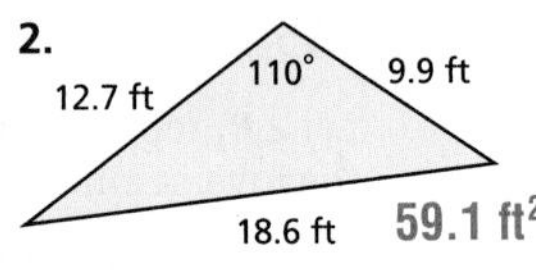

59.1 ft²

3.
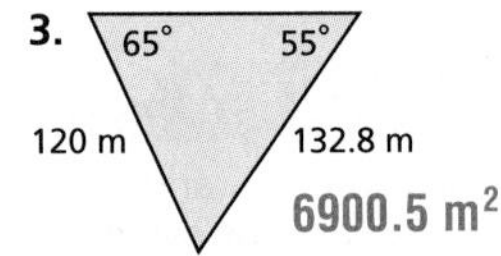

6900.5 m²

SEE EXAMPLE 2 p. 959

Solve each triangle. Round to the nearest tenth.

4. 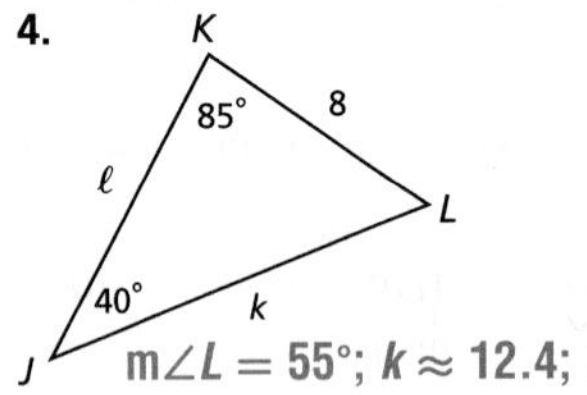 (Triangle JKL: $K = 85°$, $J = 40°$, $KL = 8$) **$m\angle L = 55°$; $k \approx 12.4$; $\ell \approx 10.2$**

5. 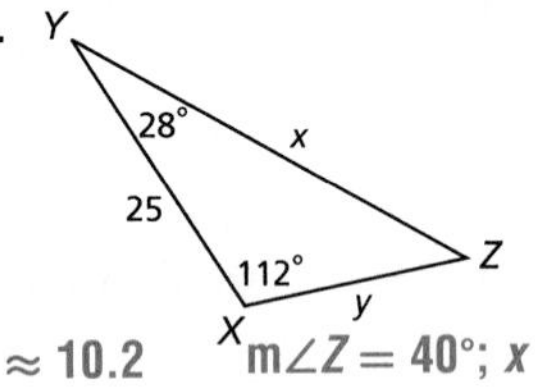 (Triangle XYZ: $Y = 28°$, $X = 112°$, $XY = 25$) **$m\angle Z = 40°$; $x \approx 36.1$; $y \approx 18.3$**

6.
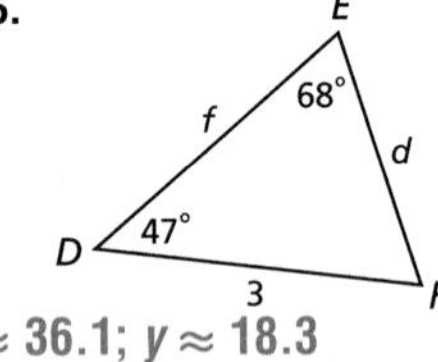

6. $m\angle F = 65°$; $d \approx 2.4$; $f \approx 2.9$

7. 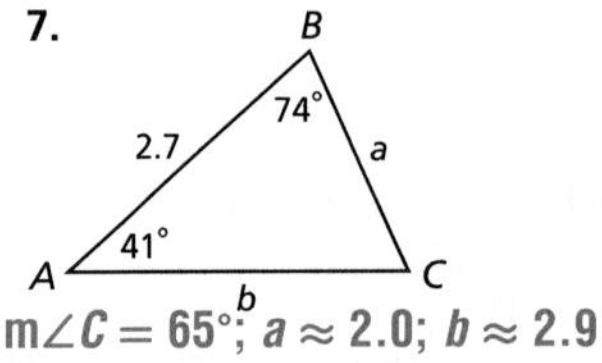 (Triangle ABC: $B = 74°$, $A = 41°$, $AB = 2.7$) **$m\angle C = 65°$; $a \approx 2.0$; $b \approx 2.9$**

8. 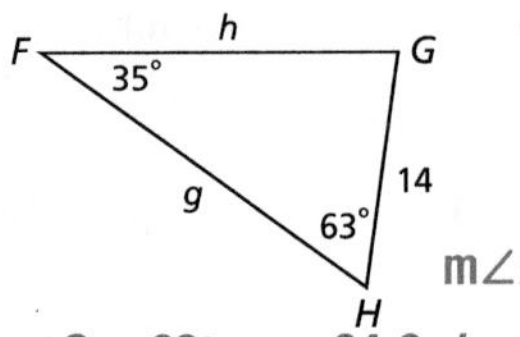 (Triangle FGH: $F = 35°$, $H = 63°$, $GH = 14$) **$m\angle G = 82°$; $g \approx 24.2$; $h \approx 21.7$**

9.
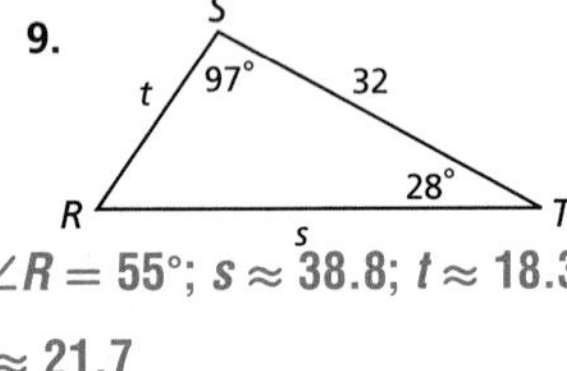

$m\angle R = 55°$; $s \approx 38.8$; $t \approx 18.3$

SEE EXAMPLE 3 p. 961

Gardening A landscape architect is designing triangular flower beds. Determine the number of different triangles that he can form using the given measurements. Then solve the triangles. Round to the nearest tenth.

10. $a = 6$ m, $b = 9$ m, $m\angle A = 55°$ **0 triangles**
11. $a = 10$ m, $b = 4$ m, $m\angle A = 120°$
12. $a = 8$ m, $b = 9$ m, $m\angle A = 35°$
13. $a = 7$ m, $b = 6$ m, $m\angle A = 45°$

11. 1 triangle; $m\angle B \approx 20.3°$; $m\angle C \approx 39.7°$; $c \approx 7.4$ m
13. 1 triangle; $m\angle B \approx 37.3°$; $m\angle C \approx 97.7°$; $c \approx 9.8$ m

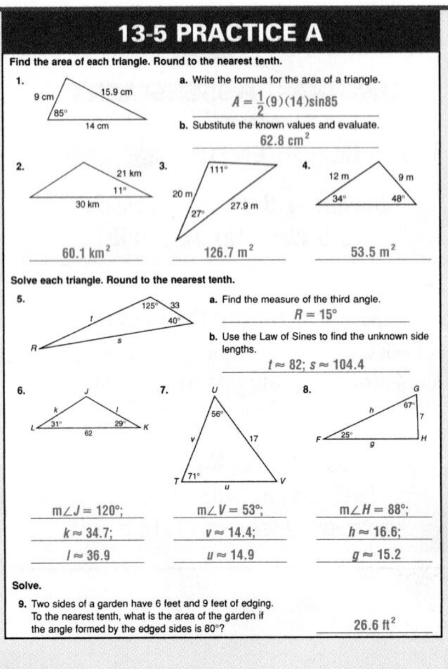

13-5 PRACTICE A

Find the area of each triangle. Round to the nearest tenth.

1. (9 cm, 85°, 14 cm, 15.9 cm)
   a. Write the formula for the area of a triangle. $A = \frac{1}{2}(9)(14)\sin 85$
   b. Substitute the known values and evaluate. 62.8 cm²
2. (21 km, 11°, 30 km) 60.1 km²
3. (111°, 20 m, 27°, 27.9 m) 126.7 m²
4. (12 m, 9 m, 34°, 48°) 53.5 m²

Solve each triangle. Round to the nearest tenth.

5. (125°, 33, 40°, t, s, R)
   a. Find the measure of the third angle. $R = 15°$
   b. Use the Law of Sines to find the unknown side lengths. $t \approx 82$; $s \approx 104.4$
6. $m\angle J = 120°$; $k \approx 34.7$; $l \approx 36.9$
7. $m\angle V = 53°$; $v \approx 14.4$; $u \approx 14.9$
8. $m\angle H = 88°$; $h \approx 16.6$; $g \approx 15.2$

Solve.

9. Two sides of a garden have 6 feet and 9 feet of edging. To the nearest tenth, what is the area of the garden if the angle formed by the edged sides is 80°? 26.6 ft²

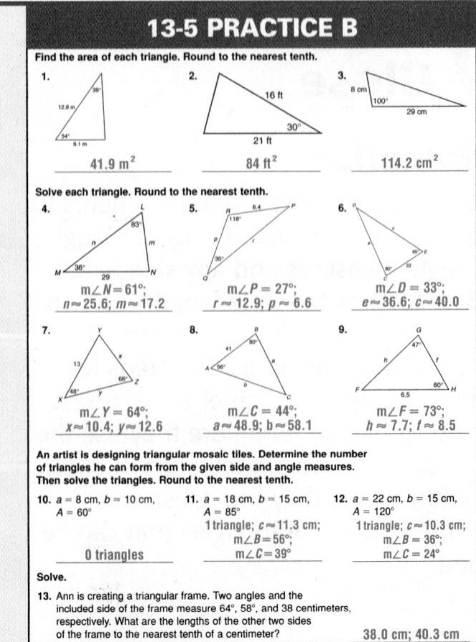

13-5 PRACTICE B

Find the area of each triangle. Round to the nearest tenth.

1. 41.9 m²
2. 84 ft²
3. 114.2 cm²

Solve each triangle. Round to the nearest tenth.

4. $m\angle N = 61°$; $n \approx 25.6$; $m \approx 17.2$
5. $m\angle P = 27°$; $r \approx 12.9$; $p \approx 6.6$
6. $m\angle D = 33°$; $e \approx 36.6$; $c \approx 40.0$
7. $m\angle Y = 64°$; $x \approx 10.4$; $y \approx 12.6$
8. $m\angle C = 44°$; $a \approx 48.9$; $b \approx 58.1$
9. $m\angle F = 73°$; $h \approx 7.7$; $f \approx 8.5$

An artist is designing triangular mosaic tiles. Determine the number of triangles he can form from the given side and angle measures. Then solve the triangles. Round to the nearest tenth.

10. $a = 8$ cm, $b = 10$ cm, $A = 60°$ — 0 triangles
11. $a = 18$ cm, $b = 15$ cm, $A = 85°$ — 1 triangle; $c \approx 11.3$ cm; $m\angle B = 56°$; $m\angle C = 39°$
12. $a = 22$ cm, $b = 15$ cm, $A = 120°$ — 1 triangle; $c \approx 10.3$ cm; $m\angle B = 36°$; $m\angle C = 24°$

Solve.

13. Ann is creating a triangular frame. Two angles and the included side of the frame measure 64°, 58°, and 38 centimeters, respectively. What are the lengths of the other two sides of the frame to the nearest tenth of a centimeter? 38.0 cm; 40.3 cm

PRACTICE AND PROBLEM SOLVING

Independent Practice

For Exercises	See Example
14–16	1
17–19	2
20–23	3

Extra Practice

Skills Practice p. S29

Application Practice p. S44

Find the area of each triangle. Round to the nearest tenth.

14. 41.7 in^2

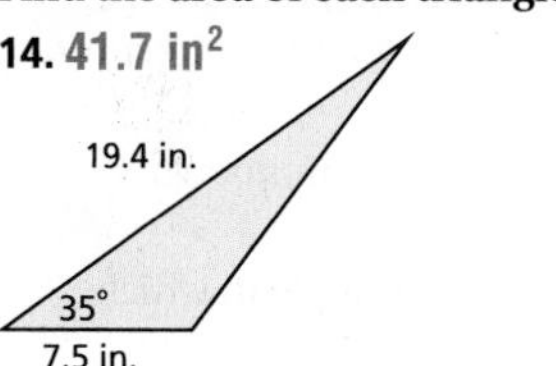

15. 1376.6 yd^2

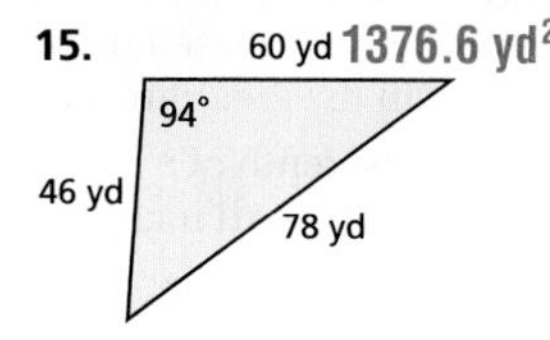

16. 638.5 m^2

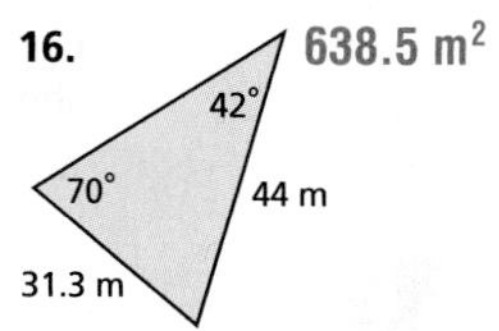

Solve each triangle. Round to the nearest tenth.

17.

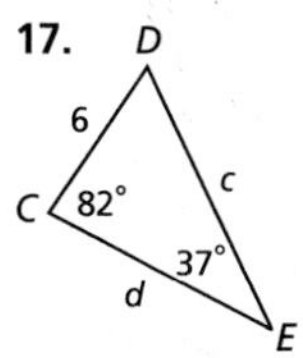

$m\angle D = 61°$; $c \approx 9.9$; $d \approx 8.7$

18.

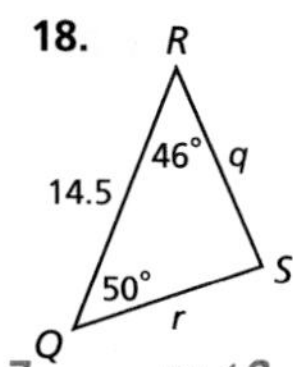

$m\angle S = 84°$; $q \approx 11.2$; $r \approx 10.5$

19.

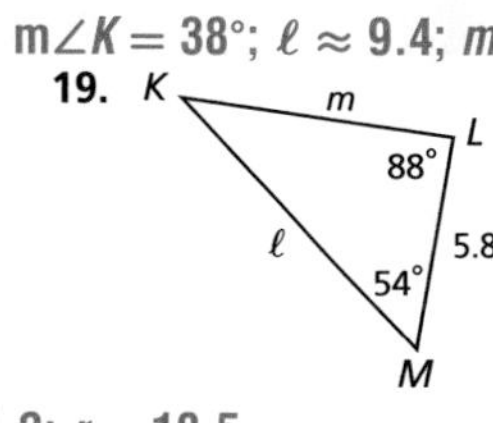

$m\angle K = 38°$; $\ell \approx 9.4$; $m \approx 7.6$

Art An artist is designing triangular mirrors. Determine the number of different triangles that she can form using the given measurements. Then solve the triangles. Round to the nearest tenth.

20. $a = 6$ cm, $b = 4$ cm, $m\angle A = 72°$

21. $a = 3.0$ in., $b = 3.5$ in., $m\angle A = 118°$ 0 triangles

22. $a = 4.2$ cm, $b = 5.7$ cm, $m\angle A = 39°$

23. $a = 7$ in., $b = 3.5$ in., $m\angle A = 130°$

24. **Astronomy** The diagram shows the relative positions of Earth, Mars, and the Sun on a particular date. What is the distance between Mars and the Sun on this date? Round to the nearest million miles. 133 million mi

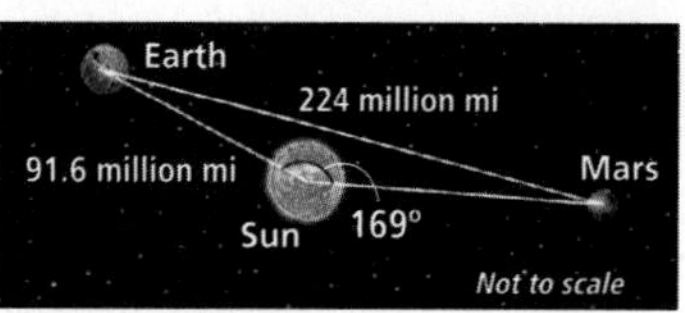

Use the given measurements to solve △ABC. Round to the nearest tenth.

25. $m\angle A = 54°$, $m\angle B = 62°$, $a = 14$
$m\angle C = 64°$; $b \approx 15.3$; $c \approx 15.6$

26. $m\angle A = 126°$, $m\angle C = 18°$, $c = 3$
$m\angle B = 36°$; $a \approx 7.9$; $b \approx 5.7$

27. $m\angle B = 80°$, $m\angle C = 41°$, $b = 25$
$m\angle A = 59°$; $a \approx 21.8$; $c \approx 16.7$

28. $m\angle A = 24°$, $m\angle B = 104°$, $c = 10$
$m\angle C = 52°$; $a \approx 5.2$; $b \approx 12.3$

29. **Rock Climbing** A group of climbers needs to determine the distance from one side of a ravine to another. They make the measurements shown. To the nearest foot, what is the distance d across the ravine? 21 ft

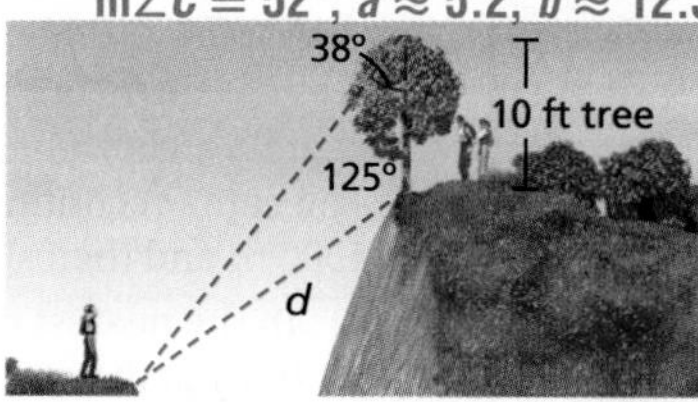

Determine the number of different triangles that can be formed using the given measurements. Then solve the triangles. Round to the nearest tenth.

30. $m\angle C = 45°$, $b = 10$, $c = 5$
0 triangles

31. $m\angle B = 135°$, $b = 12$, $c = 8$
31. 1 triangle; $m\angle A \approx 16.9°$; $m\angle C \approx 28.1°$; $a \approx 4.9$

32. $m\angle A = 60°$, $a = 9$, $b = 10$

33. $m\angle B = 30°$, $a = 6$, $b = 3$
1 triangle; $m\angle A = 90°$; $m\angle C = 60°$; $c \approx 5.2$

34. **Painting** Trey needs to paint a side of a house that has the measurements shown. What is the area of this side of the house to the nearest square foot? 508 ft^2

19.7 ft 125.6° 19.7 ft
10 ft
35 ft

COMMON ERROR ALERT

Students might make errors when solving triangles when given measurements without a diagram, as in **Exercises 30–33.** Suggest that students begin by sketching a triangle that is approximately to scale for the given measurements. Students should carefully label their sketches and double-check the labels before beginning to calculate.

Teaching Tip

Inclusion For **Exercises 20–23,** students can use the ambiguous case summary on page 960 to create a flowchart for determining the number of possible triangles. The first step might be checking whether the given angle is acute. The second step might be determining the value of h, and so forth.

Answers

20. 1 triangle; $m\angle B \approx 39.3°$; $m\angle C \approx 68.7°$; $c \approx 5.9$ cm

22. 2 triangles; $m\angle B_1 \approx 58.7°$; $m\angle C_1 \approx 82.3°$; $c_1 \approx 6.6$ cm; $m\angle B_2 \approx 121.3°$; $m\angle C_2 \approx 19.7°$; $c_2 \approx 2.2$ cm

23. 1 triangle; $m\angle B \approx 22.5°$; $m\angle C \approx 27.5°$; $c \approx 4.2$ in.

32. 2 triangles; $m\angle B_1 \approx 74.2°$; $m\angle C_1 \approx 45.8°$; $c_1 \approx 7.4$; $m\angle B_2 \approx 105.8°$; $m\angle C_2 \approx 14.2°$; $c_2 \approx 2.5$

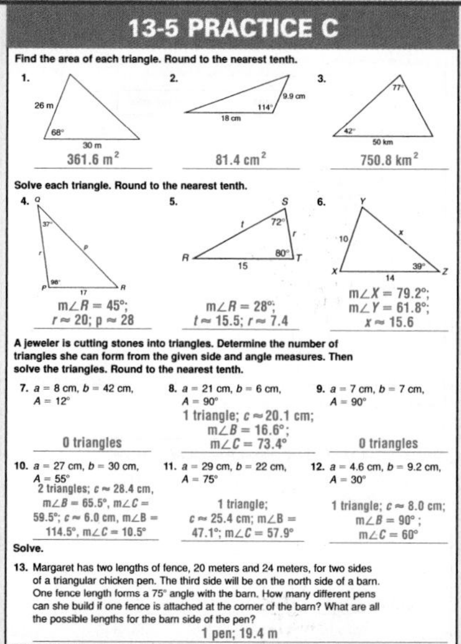

13-5 PRACTICE C

Find the area of each triangle. Round to the nearest tenth.

1. (26 m, 68°, 30 m) 361.6 m^2
2. (9.9 cm, 114°, 18 cm) 81.4 cm^2
3. (77°, 42°, 50 km) 750.8 km^2

Solve each triangle. Round to the nearest tenth.

4. (Q, 37°, r, p, 98°, P, 17, R) $m\angle R = 45°$; $r \approx 20$; $p \approx 28$
5. (S, t, 72°, r, R, 80°, T, 15) $m\angle R = 28°$; $t \approx 15.5$; $r \approx 7.4$
6. (Y, 10, x, X, 39°, Z, 14) $m\angle X = 79.2°$; $m\angle Y = 61.8°$; $x \approx 15.6$

A jeweler is cutting stones into triangles. Determine the number of triangles she can form from the given side and angle measures. Then solve the triangles. Round to the nearest tenth.

7. $a = 8$ cm, $b = 42$ cm, $A = 12°$
0 triangles

8. $a = 21$ cm, $b = 6$ cm, $A = 90°$
1 triangle; $c \approx 20.1$ cm; $m\angle B = 16.6°$; $m\angle C = 73.4°$

9. $a = 7$ cm, $b = 7$ cm, $A = 90°$
0 triangles

10. $a = 27$ cm, $b = 30$ cm, $A = 55°$
2 triangles; $c \approx 28.4$ cm, $m\angle B = 65.5°$, $m\angle C = 59.5°$; $c \approx 6.0$ cm, $m\angle B = 114.5°$, $m\angle C = 10.5°$

11. $a = 29$ cm, $b = 22$ cm, $A = 75°$
1 triangle; $c \approx 25.4$ cm; $m\angle B = 47.1°$; $m\angle C = 57.9°$

12. $a = 4.6$ cm, $b = 9.2$ cm, $A = 30°$
1 triangle; $c \approx 8.0$ cm; $m\angle B = 90°$; $m\angle C = 60°$

Solve.

13. Margaret has two lengths of fence, 20 meters and 24 meters, for two sides of a triangular chicken pen. The third side will be on the north side of a barn. One fence length forms a 75° angle with the barn. How many different pens can she build if one fence is attached at the corner of the barn? What are all the possible lengths for the barn side of the pen?
1 pen; 19.4 m

Exercise 35 involves a situation concerning the location of a fire in which students must apply the Law of Sines. This exercise prepares students for the Multi-Step Test Prep on page 974.

Answers

39. B is incorrect. Possible answer: The initial equation is set up incorrectly. Each ratio must compare the sine of an angle measure to the length of the opposite side, not to the length of an adjacent side.

41. Possible answer: A triangle cannot have more than one obtuse angle. Both $\angle A$ and $\angle B$ are obtuse.

42. Possible answer: Use the Triangle Sum Theorem to find the measure of the third angle. Then use the Law of Sines to find the length of a second side. Use the Law of Sines again to find the length of the third side.

48. ≈ 7 mi; Use the points to make a right triangle. Find its side lengths and angle measures. Use the stations and meteor location to make a new triangle. Find the distance between stations and angle measures, then use the Law of Sines to find the distance from station 1 to the meteor.

49. y-intercept: 5; x-intercept: 5

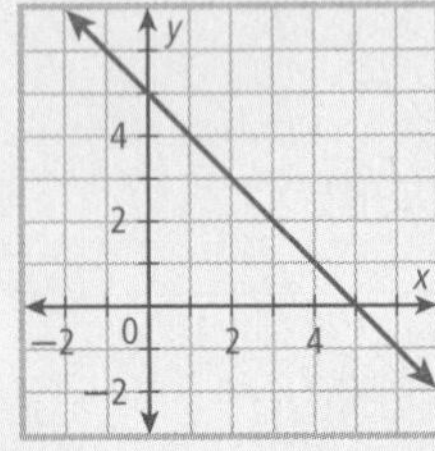

50. y-intercept: -9; x-intercept: 3

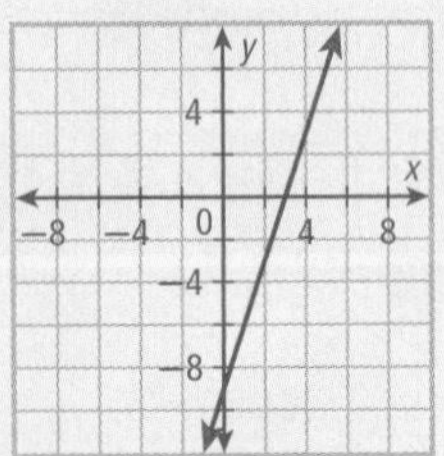

51. y-intercept: 2; x-intercept: 6

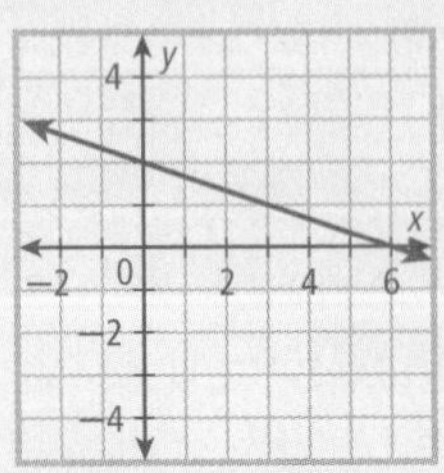

35. This problem will prepare you for the Multi-Step Test Prep on page 974.

An emergency dispatcher must determine the position of a caller reporting a fire. Based on the caller's cell phone records, she is located in the area shown.

a. To the nearest tenth of a mile, what are the unknown side lengths of the triangle?

b. What is the area in square miles of the triangle in which the caller is located? Round to the nearest tenth. **8.9 mi²**

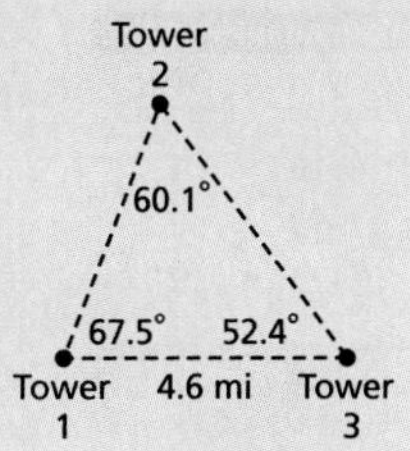

35a. distance from tower 1 to tower 2: 4.2 mi; distance from tower 2 to tower 3: 4.9 mi

Find the indicated measurement. Round to the nearest tenth.

36. Find $m\angle B$. **60.5°**

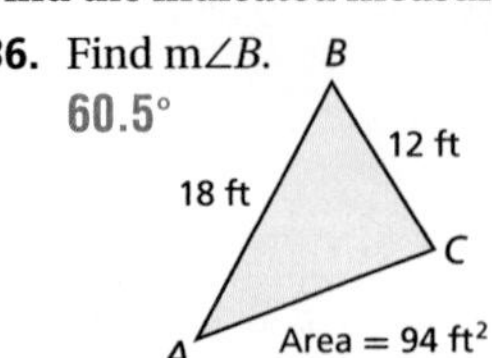

37. Find c. **16.7 cm**

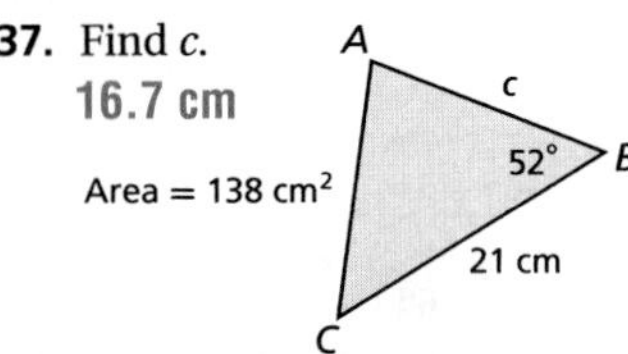

38. Multi-Step A new road will be built from a town to a nearby highway. So far, two routes have been proposed. To the nearest tenth of a mile, how much shorter is route 2 than route 1? **3.9 mi**

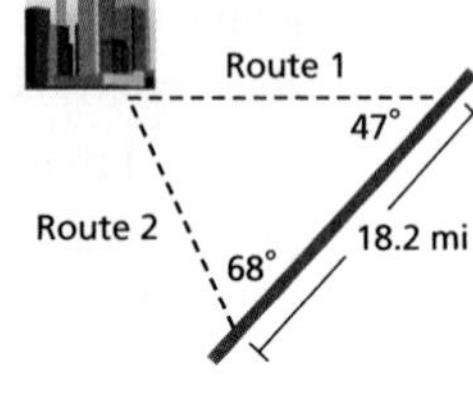

39. ///ERROR ANALYSIS/// Below are two attempts at solving $\triangle FGH$ for g. Which is incorrect? Explain the error.

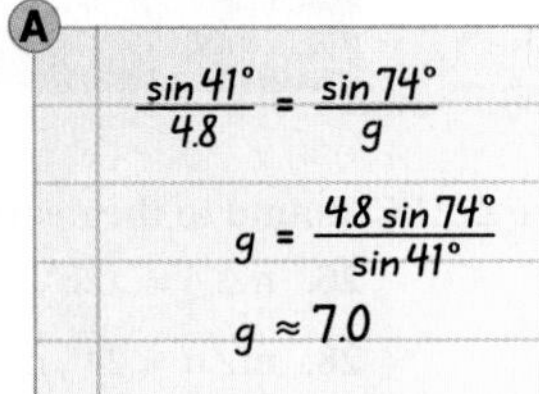

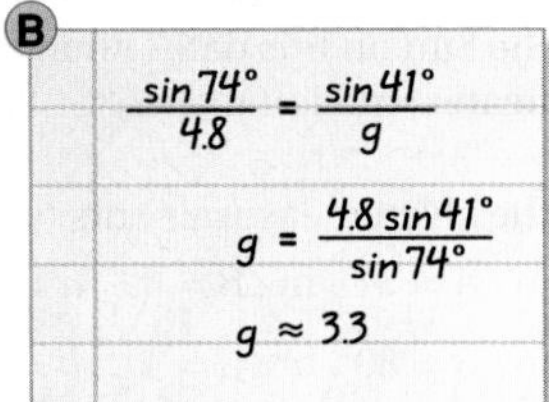

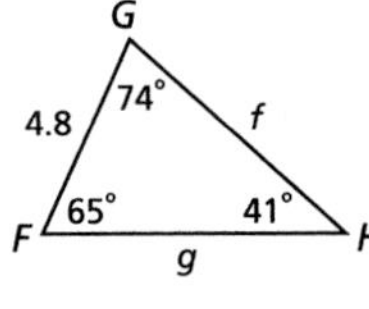

Navigation

Ship captains rely heavily on GPS technology. GPS stands for "Global Positioning System," a navigation system based on trigonometry and the use of satellites. The GPS can be used to determine information such as latitude and longitude.

40. Navigation As a tugboat travels along a channel, the captain sights a buoy at an angle of 28° to the boat's path. The captain continues on the same course for a distance of 1500 m and then sights the same buoy at an angle of 40°.

a. To the nearest meter, how far is the tugboat from the buoy at the second sighting? **3387 m**

b. To the nearest meter, how far was the tugboat from the buoy when the captain first sighted the bouy? **4637 m**

c. What if...? If the tugboat continues on the same course, what is the closest that it will come to the buoy? Round to the nearest meter. **2177 m**

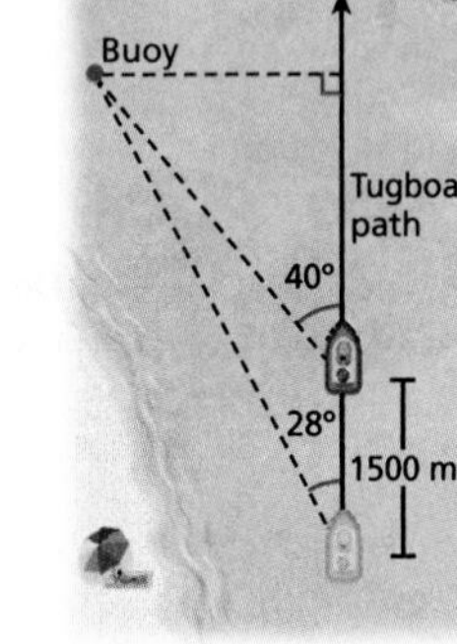

41. Critical Thinking How can you tell, without using the Law of Sines, that a triangle cannot be formed by using the measurements $m\angle A = 92°$, $m\angle B = 104°$, and $a = 18$?

42. Write About It Explain how to solve a triangle when angle-angle-side (AAS) information is known.

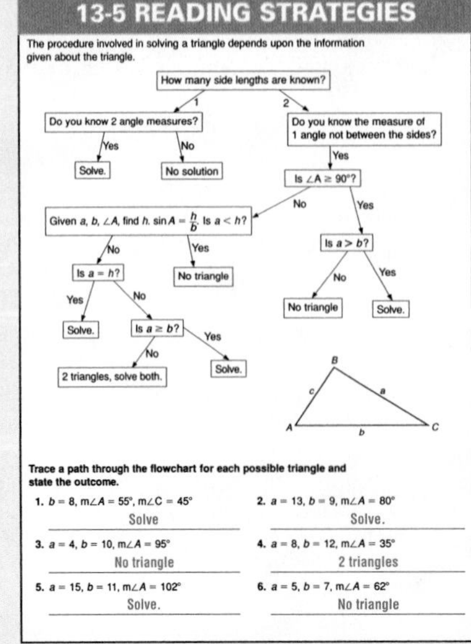

13-5 READING STRATEGIES

The procedure involved in solving a triangle depends upon the information given about the triangle.

How many side lengths are known?
1 → Do you know 2 angle measures?
Yes → Solve.
No → No solution
2 → Do you know the measure of 1 angle not between the sides?
Yes → Is $\angle A \ge 90°$?
No → Given a, b, $\angle A$, find h. $\sin A = \frac{h}{b}$. Is $a < h$?
Yes → No triangle
No → Is $a = h$?
Yes → Solve.
No → Is $a \ge b$?
Yes → Solve.
No → 2 triangles, solve both.
Yes → Is $a > b$?
Yes → Solve.
No → No triangle

B, c, a, A, b, C

Trace a path through the flowchart for each possible triangle and state the outcome.

1. $b = 8$, $m\angle A = 55°$, $m\angle C = 45°$ Solve
2. $a = 13$, $b = 9$, $m\angle A = 80°$ Solve.
3. $a = 4$, $b = 10$, $m\angle A = 95°$ No triangle
4. $a = 8$, $b = 12$, $m\angle A = 35°$ 2 triangles
5. $a = 15$, $b = 11$, $m\angle A = 102°$ Solve.
6. $a = 5$, $b = 7$, $m\angle A = 62°$ No triangle

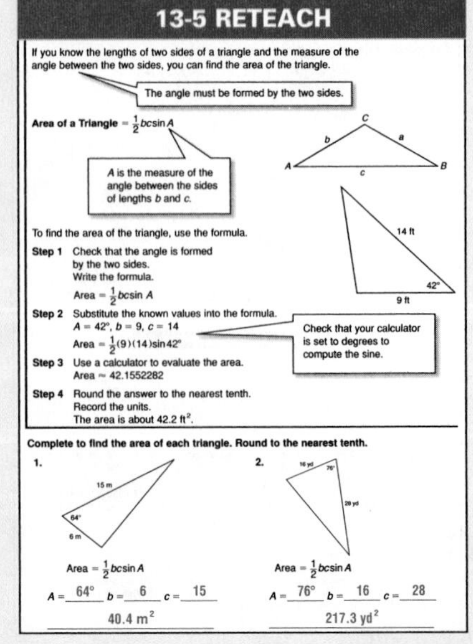

13-5 RETEACH

If you know the lengths of two sides of a triangle and the measure of the angle between the two sides, you can find the area of the triangle.

The angle must be formed by the two sides.

Area of a Triangle $= \frac{1}{2}bc\sin A$

A is the measure of the angle between the sides of lengths b and c.

C, b, a, A, c, B

14 ft, 42°, 9 ft

To find the area of the triangle, use the formula.

Step 1 Check that the angle is formed by the two sides. Write the formula. Area $= \frac{1}{2}bc\sin A$

Step 2 Substitute the known values into the formula. $A = 42°$, $b = 9$, $c = 14$. Area $= \frac{1}{2}(9)(14)\sin 42°$

Check that your calculator is set to degrees to compute the sine.

Step 3 Use a calculator to evaluate the area. Area ≈ 42.1552282

Step 4 Round the answer to the nearest tenth. Record the units. The area is about 42.2 ft².

Complete to find the area of each triangle. Round to the nearest tenth.

1. 15 m, 64°, 6 m
Area $= \frac{1}{2}bc\sin A$
$A =$ 64° $b =$ 6 $c =$ 15
40.4 m²

2. 16 yd, 76°, 28 yd
Area $= \frac{1}{2}bc\sin A$
$A =$ 76° $b =$ 16 $c =$ 28
217.3 yd²

TEST PREP

43. What is the area of $\triangle PQR$ to the nearest tenth of a square centimeter?

Ⓐ 2.4 cm² Ⓒ 23.5 cm²
Ⓑ 15.5 cm² Ⓓ 40.1 cm²

Q 75° P 45° R 7 cm

44. A bridge is 325 m long. From the west end, a surveyor measures the angle between the bridge and an island to be 38°. From the east end, the surveyor measures the angle between the bridge and the island to be 58°. To the nearest meter, what is the distance d between the bridge and the island?

Ⓕ 171 m Ⓗ 217 m
Ⓖ 201 m Ⓙ 277 m

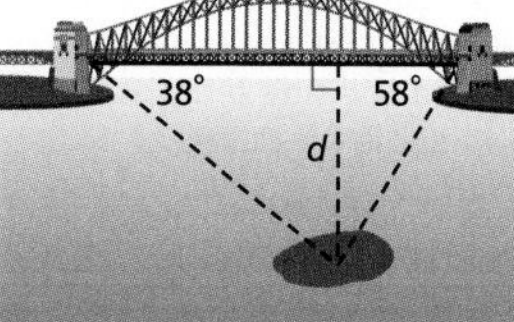

45. **Short Response** Examine $\triangle LMN$ at right.

45a. Possible answer: $\frac{16 \sin 32°}{\sin 64°}$

a. Write an expression that can be used to determine the value of m.

b. Is there more than one possible triangle that can be constructed from the given measurements? Explain your answer. No; in this case, AAS information is given so this triangle is not an example of the ambiguous case. There is only 1 triangle that can be constructed from the given measurements.

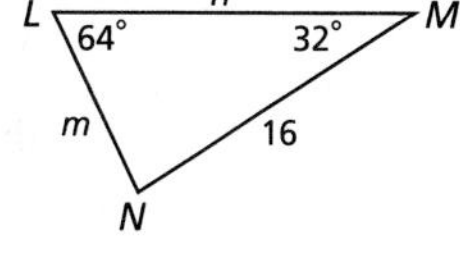

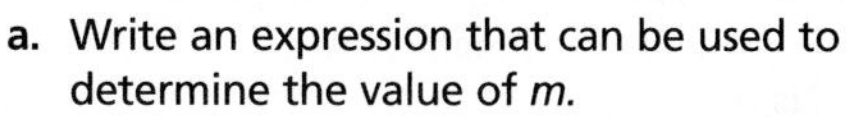

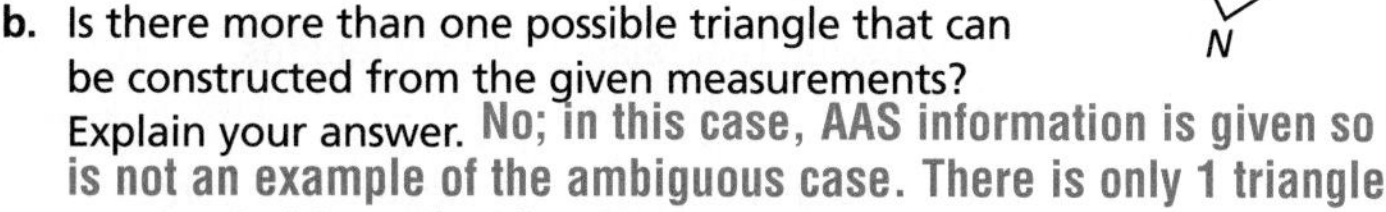

CHALLENGE AND EXTEND

46. What is the area of the quadrilateral at right to the nearest square unit? 76 square units

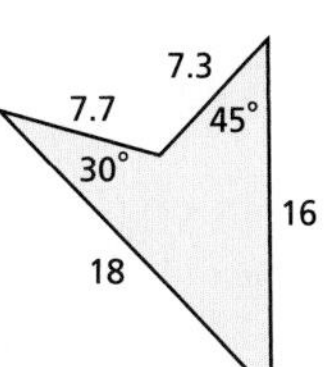

47. **Critical Thinking** The lengths of two sides of a triangle are $a = 3$ and $b = 2\sqrt{3}$. For what values of $m\angle A$ do two solutions exist when you solve the triangle by using the Law of Sines? $0° < m\angle A < 60°$

48. **Multi-Step** The map shows the location of two ranger stations. Each unit on the map represents 1 mile. A ranger at station 1 saw a meteor that appeared to land about 72° north of east. A ranger at station 2 saw the meteor appear to land about 45° north of west. Based on this information, about how many miles from station 1 did the meteor land? Explain how you determined your answer. about 7 mi

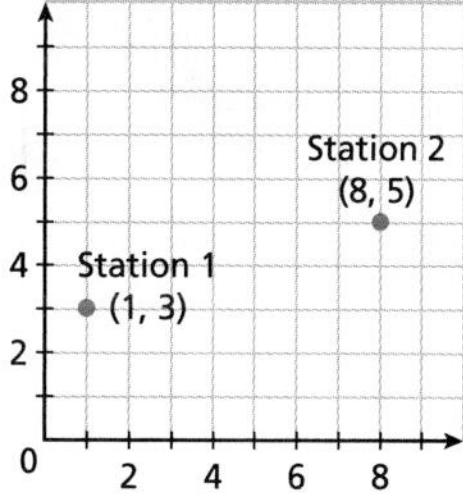

SPIRAL REVIEW

Find the intercepts of each line, and graph the line. *(Lesson 2-3)*

49. $x + y = 5$ 50. $3x - y = 9$ 51. $2x + 6y = 12$

Solve each equation. *(Lesson 8-5)*

52. $\frac{4x}{x-1} = \frac{2x+9}{x-1}$ $\frac{9}{2}$ 53. $\frac{7x-9}{x^2-4} = \frac{4}{x+2}$ $\frac{1}{3}$ 54. $\frac{x}{3} - \frac{4x}{7} = \frac{x-2}{3}$ $\frac{7}{6}$

Evaluate each inverse trigonometric function. Give your answer in both radians and degrees. *(Lesson 13-4)*

55. $\text{Cos}^{-1}\left(-\frac{\sqrt{2}}{2}\right)$ 135°; $\frac{3\pi}{4}$ radians 56. $\text{Tan}^{-1}\sqrt{3}$ 60°; $\frac{\pi}{3}$ radians 57. $\text{Sin}^{-1}\frac{1}{2}$ 30°; $\frac{\pi}{6}$ radians

TEST PREP DOCTOR If students have difficulty with **Exercise 43,** point out that they will need to know at least two of the side lengths of the triangle to determine its area. To find the length of a second side, they can use the Law of Sines.

Point out that there are multiple ways to solve **Exercise 44.** One way is to let e represent the distance from the east end of the bridge to the island. Use the Law of Sines to solve for e. Then find the value of d by using the equation $\sin 58° = \frac{d}{e}$.

Journal

Have students explain how to solve a triangle when given angle-side-angle (ASA) information.

ALTERNATIVE ASSESSMENT

Ask students to generate a set of side-side-angle (SSA) information for which there are two possible triangles. Then have students solve each triangle.

Power Presentations with PowerPoint®

13-5 Lesson Quiz

1. Find the area of the triangle. Round to the nearest tenth.

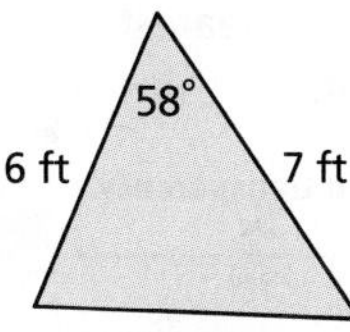

17.8 ft²

2. Solve the triangle. Round to the nearest tenth.

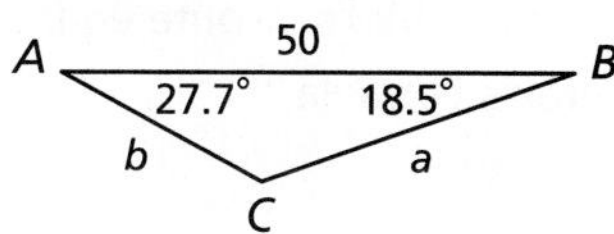

$a \approx 32.2$; $b \approx 22.0$; $m\angle C = 133.8°$

3. Determine the number of triangular quilt pieces that can be formed by using the measurements $a = 14$ cm, $b = 20$ cm, and $m\angle A = 39°$. Solve each triangle. Round to the nearest tenth.

2; $c_1 \approx 21.7$ cm; $m\angle B_1 \approx 64.0°$; $m\angle C_1 \approx 77.0°$; $c_2 \approx 9.4$ cm; $m\angle B_2 \approx 116.0°$; $m\angle C_2 \approx 25.0°$

13-5 PROBLEM SOLVING

In the middle of town, State and Elm streets meet at an angle of 40°. A triangular pocket park between the streets stretches 100 yards along State Street and 53.2 yards along Elm Street. Hoa and Cat walk around the pocket park every day at lunchtime.

West Ave Elm Street 53.2 yd 40° State Street 100 yd

1. Hoa would like to know the area of the pocket park.
   a. Write a formula for the area of the pocket park using the given dimensions. $A = \frac{1}{2}(100)(53.2)\sin(40°)$
   b. What is the area of the pocket park to the nearest tenth of a square yard? 1709.8 yd²
2. Cat determines that the total distance around the pocket park is 221.6 yards.
   a. Write and evaluate an expression for the length of the park along West Avenue. $221.6 - (100 + 53.2) = 68.4$ yd
   b. Use the Law of Sines to find $\angle S$ to the nearest degree, the angle that West Avenue makes with State Street. $\frac{\sin S}{53.2} = \frac{\sin 40°}{68.4}$; so $\angle S = 30°$
   c. Write an expression for the angle that West Avenue makes with Elm Street. Possible answer: $180° - (30° + 40°) = 110°$. Or, if student uses the Law of Sines, check the work.
3. West Avenue makes angles of 55° with Main Street and 80° with Third Street. The distance from Main to Third along West Avenue is 40 yards. Hoa contracts to design a pocket park for the acute-angled triangular area enclosed by these streets.
   a. What is the measure of the third angle of the triangular area? 45°
   b. Write and evaluate an expression for the distance from West Avenue to Third Street along Main Street. $\frac{40 \sin 80°}{\sin 45°} = 55.7$ yd

Choose the letter for the best answer.

4. Hoa wants to plant palm trees 8 feet apart along the side of the park on Third Street. Which expression gives the number of trees she will need?
   A $\frac{40 \sin 55°}{\sin 45°}$ C $\frac{5 \sin 45°}{\sin 55°}$
   Ⓑ $\frac{5 \sin 55°}{\sin 45°}$ D $\frac{40 \sin 45°}{\sin 55°}$
5. What is the area of the new pocket park that Hoa is designing?
   Ⓕ 913 yd²
   G 1004 yd²
   H 1207 yd²
   J 1398 yd²

13-5 CHALLENGE

The Law of Sines can be derived by a geometric argument. Consider the diagram below. The measure of $\angle ACB$ is $\frac{1}{2}$ the measure of $\angle AOB$. Right triangles AOD and BOD are congruent since they share a common leg (side OD) and each hypotenuse is a radius of the circle. So the $m\angle AOD = m\angle BOD = m\angle ACB$. Also $\overline{AD} = \overline{BD} = \frac{1}{2}c$.

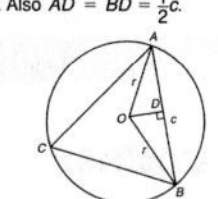

The following equation can be derived from the information given above.

$$\sin \angle AOD = \frac{AD}{AO} = \frac{\frac{c}{2}}{r} = \sin \angle ACB = \sin \angle C$$

This simplifies to $2r = \frac{c}{\sin \angle C}$, which tells us that that the ratio of the length of a side of a triangle to the sine of the opposite angle is equal to twice the radius of the circle circumscribed about the triangle. Thus we obtain the following, which leads immediately to the Law of Sines.

$$2r = \frac{a}{\sin \angle A} = \frac{b}{\sin \angle B} = \frac{c}{\sin \angle C}$$

Solve.

1. A buoy is anchored offshore to mark a sandbar. The straight shoreline at that location runs north and south. From two observation points on the shore 2.4 miles apart, the bearings to the buoy are S46°E and N22°E. How far is the buoy from the shore? What is the distance from the buoy to each of the observation points?
   about 0.70 mile from shore; about 0.97 mile from one point, about 1.86 miles from the second point.
2. The formula for the area of a triangle is Area $= \frac{1}{2}bh$, where b is the length of the base and h is the height of the triangle. Show that Area $= \frac{a^2 \sin B \sin C}{2 \sin A}$.
   In $\triangle ABC$, use $\overline{AC}$, which has length b, as the base. Draw a perpendicular segment from vertex B to line AC. The length h is the height of $\triangle ABC$ and $h = a \sin C$. By the Law of Sines, $\frac{\sin A}{a} = \frac{\sin B}{b}$, and $b = \frac{a \sin B}{\sin A}$.
   Substitute for h and b in the area formula; Area $= \frac{1}{2}\left(\frac{a \sin B}{\sin A}\right)(a \sin C)$; $= \frac{a^2 \sin B \sin C}{2 \sin A}$.

13-6 Organizer

Pacing: Traditional 1 day
Block $\frac{1}{2}$ day

Objectives: Use the Law of Cosines to find the side lengths and angle measures of a triangle.

Use Heron's Formula to find the area of a triangle.

Technology Lab
In *Technology Lab Activities*

Online Edition
Tutorial Videos, Interactivity

Power Presentations with PowerPoint®

Warm Up

Find each measure to the nearest tenth.

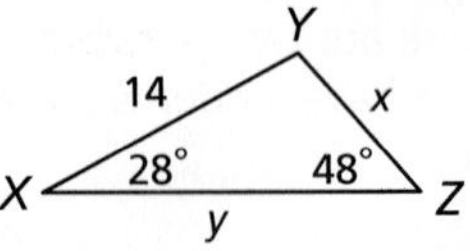

1. m∠Y 104°
2. x ≈ 8.8
3. y ≈ 18.3
4. What is the area of △XYZ? Round to the nearest square unit. 60 square units

Also available on transparency

Math Humor

Q: What is a bird's favorite equation?
A: Heron's Formula

State Resources

13-6 The Law of Cosines

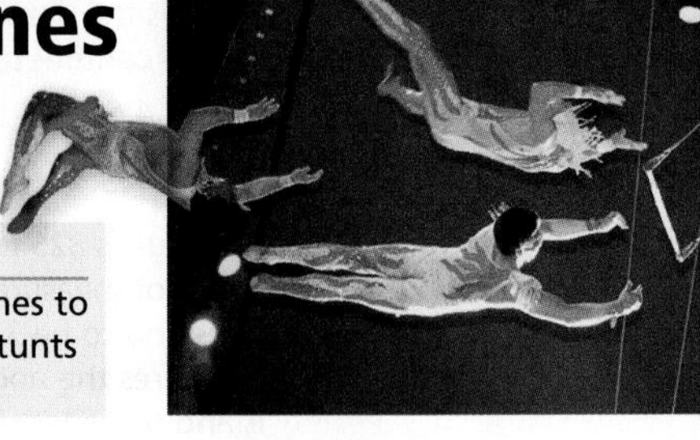

Objectives
Use the Law of Cosines to find the side lengths and angle measures of a triangle.

Use Heron's Formula to find the area of a triangle.

Who uses this?
Trapeze artists can use the Law of Cosines to determine whether they can perform stunts safely. (See Exercise 27.)

In the previous lesson, you learned to solve triangles by using the Law of Sines. However, the Law of Sines cannot be used to solve triangles for which side-angle-side (SAS) or side-side-side (SSS) information is given. Instead, you must use the Law of Cosines.

To derive the Law of Cosines, draw $\triangle ABC$ with altitude $\overline{BD}$. If x represents the length of $\overline{AD}$, the length of $\overline{DC}$ is $b - x$.

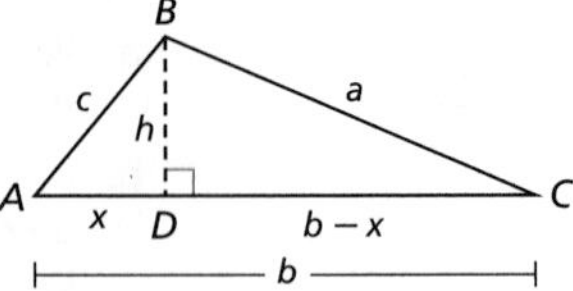

Write an equation that relates the side lengths of $\triangle DBC$.

$a^2 = (b - x)^2 + h^2$	*Pythagorean Theorem*
$a^2 = b^2 - 2bx + x^2 + h^2$	*Expand $(b - x)^2$.*
$a^2 = b^2 - 2bx + c^2$	*In $\triangle ABD$, $c^2 = x^2 + h^2$. Substitute c^2 for $x^2 + h^2$.*
$a^2 = b^2 - 2b(c\cos A) + c^2$	*In $\triangle ABD$, $\cos A = \frac{x}{c}$, or $x = c\cos A$. Substitute $c\cos A$ for x.*
$a^2 = b^2 + c^2 - 2bc\cos A$	

The previous equation is one of the formulas for the Law of Cosines.

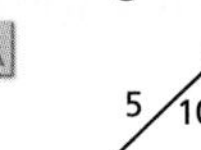

Law of Cosines

For $\triangle ABC$, the Law of Cosines states that

$a^2 = b^2 + c^2 - 2bc\cos A.$
$b^2 = a^2 + c^2 - 2ac\cos B.$
$c^2 = a^2 + b^2 - 2ab\cos C.$

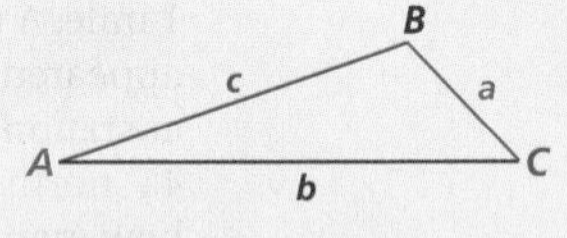

EXAMPLE 1 Using the Law of Cosines

Use the given measurements to solve $\triangle ABC$. Round to the nearest tenth.

A

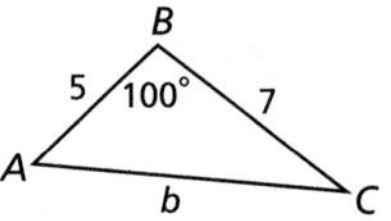

Step 1 Find the length of the third side.

$b^2 = a^2 + c^2 - 2ac\cos B$	*Law of Cosines*
$b^2 = 7^2 + 5^2 - 2(7)(5)\cos 100°$	*Substitute.*
$b^2 \approx 86.2$	*Use a calculator to simplify.*
$b \approx 9.3$	*Solve for the positive value of b.*

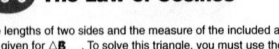

1 Introduce

EXPLORATION

13-6 The Law of Cosines

The lengths of two sides and the measure of the included angle are given for △ABC. To solve this triangle, you must use the Law of Cosines. For △ABC, the Law of Cosines states that $a^2 = b^2 + c^2 - 2bc\cos A$.

1. Substitute the known measures into the Law of Cosines and solve for the value of a. Round to the nearest tenth.
2. Use the Law of Sines to find the measure of ∠C to the nearest tenth of a degree.
3. Find the measure of ∠B to the nearest tenth of a degree. Explain how you determined your answer.

THINK AND DISCUSS

4. **Explain** why you cannot use the Law of Sines to find the value of a in △ABC.
5. **Describe** how you could use the Law of Sines to check that you solved △ABC correctly.

Motivate

Have students explain whether they could use the Law of Sines to determine the angle measures of a triangle with sides measuring 6 in., 7 in., and 8 in. No; you need to know at least one angle measure to use the Law of Sines. Explain that in this lesson, students will be learning the Law of Cosines, which can be used to solve triangles when given side-side-side (SSS) information.

Explorations and answers are provided in the *Explorations* binder.

Step 2 Find an angle measure.

$\frac{\sin A}{a} = \frac{\sin B}{b}$ *Law of Sines*

$\frac{\sin A}{7} = \frac{\sin 100°}{9.3}$ *Substitute.*

$\sin A = \frac{7 \sin 100°}{9.3}$ *Solve for sin A.*

$m\angle A = \text{Sin}^{-1}\left(\frac{7 \sin 100°}{9.3}\right) \approx 47.8°$ *Solve for m∠A.*

Step 3 Find the third angle measure.

$47.8° + 100° + m\angle C \approx 180°$ *Triangle Sum Theorem*

$m\angle C \approx 32.2°$ *Solve for m∠C.*

B

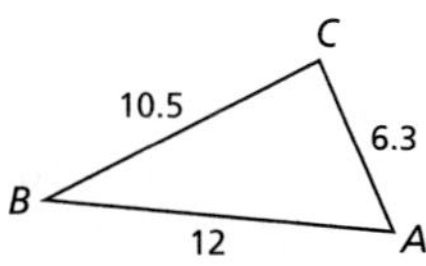

Step 1 Find the measure of the largest angle, ∠C.

$c^2 = a^2 + b^2 - 2ab \cos C$ *Law of Cosines*

$12^2 = 10.5^2 + 6.3^2 - 2(10.5)(6.3)\cos C$ *Substitute.*

$\cos C \approx 0.0449$ *Solve for cos C.*

$m\angle C \approx \text{Cos}^{-1}(0.0449) \approx 87.4°$ *Solve for m∠C.*

Step 2 Find another angle measure.

$b^2 = a^2 + c^2 - 2ac \cos B$ *Law of Cosines*

$6.3^2 = 10.5^2 + 12^2 - 2(10.5)(12)\cos B$ *Substitute.*

$\cos B \approx 0.8514$ *Solve for cos B.*

$m\angle B \approx \text{Cos}^{-1}(0.8514) \approx 31.6°$ *Solve for m∠B.*

Step 3 Find the third angle measure.

$m\angle A + 31.6° + 87.4° \approx 180°$ *Triangle Sum Theorem*

$m\angle A \approx 61.0°$ *Solve for m∠A.*

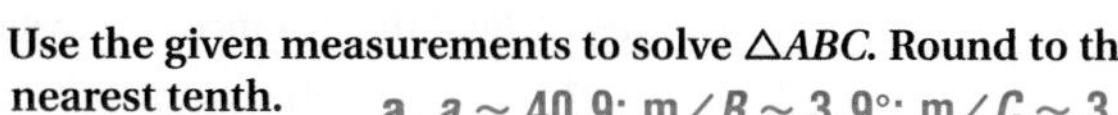

Use the given measurements to solve △ABC. Round to the nearest tenth.

1a. $b = 23, c = 18, m\angle A = 173°$ **1b.** $a = 35, b = 42, c = 50.3$

a. $a \approx 40.9$; $m\angle B \approx 3.9°$; $m\angle C \approx 3.1°$
b. $m\angle A \approx 43.4°$; $m\angle B \approx 55.6°$; $m\angle C \approx 81.0°$

Student to Student — *Solving Triangles*

Stefan Maric
Wylie High School

If I solve a triangle using the Law of Sines, I like to use the Law of Cosines to check my work. I used the Law of Sines to solve the triangle below.

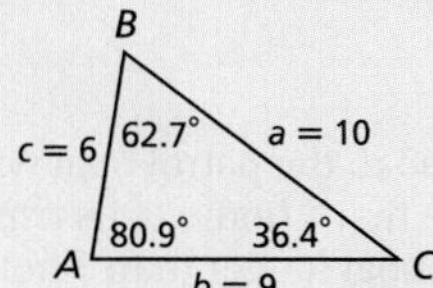

I can check that the length of side b really is 9 by using the Law of Cosines.

$b^2 = a^2 + c^2 - 2ac \cos B$

9^2	$10^2 + 6^2 - 2(10)(6)\cos 62.7°$
81	81.0 ✓

The Law of Cosines shows that I was right.

Power Presentations with PowerPoint®

Additional Examples

Example 1

Use the given measurements to solve △ABC. Round to the nearest tenth.

A. $a = 8, b = 5, m\angle C = 32.2°$

$c \approx 4.6$; $m\angle A \approx 112.5°$; $m\angle B \approx 35.3°$

B. $a = 8, b = 9, c = 7$

$m\angle A \approx 58.4°$; $m\angle B \approx 73.4°$; $m\angle C \approx 48.2°$

Also available on transparency

INTERVENTION

Questioning Strategies

EXAMPLE 1

- What information do you need to solve a triangle by using the Law of Cosines?
- How can you check that the answer obtained for the third angle measure is correct?

Inclusion Point out that m∠A in **Example 1A** could have been determined by using the Law of Cosines and that m∠B in **Example 1B** could have been determined by using the Law of Sines.

2 Teach

Guided Instruction

Explain to students that the Law of Cosines can be used to solve triangles that cannot be solved by using the Law of Sines alone. Stress that when students use the Law of Cosines to find angle measures, they should find the measure of the triangle's largest angle first, if it is not already known. By doing so, they will not need to worry about the ambiguous case if they use the Law of Sines to find another angle measure.

Reaching All Learners

Through Cognitive Strategies

Have students make note cards for each of the following cases: AAS, ASA, SAS, SSS, and SSA. For each case, have students list the steps they would use to solve a triangle if given this information. In the SSS case, for example, students might write the following:

1. Use the Law of Cosines twice to find the measures of the 2 largest angles.
2. Use the Triangle Sum Theorem to find the measure of the third angle.

Power Presentations with PowerPoint®

Additional Examples

Example 2

If a hiker travels at an average speed of 2.5 mi/h, how long will it take him to travel from the cave to the waterfall? Round to the nearest tenth of an hour.

1.7 h

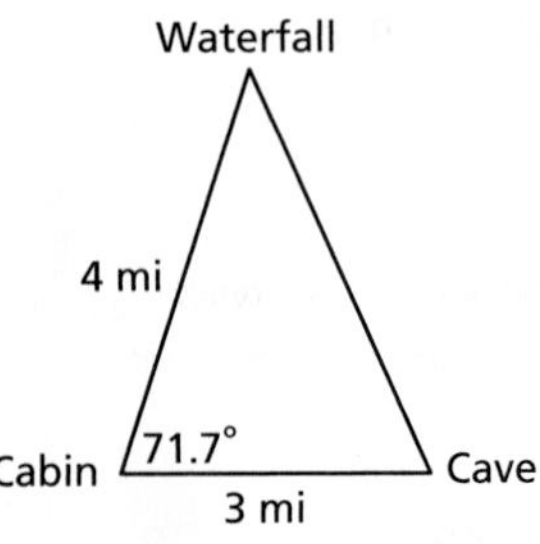

Also available on transparency

INTERVENTION
Questioning Strategies

EXAMPLE 2

- What distance do you need to determine in order to solve this problem?
- How can you use the Law of Cosines to find this distance?

Teaching Tip **Communicating Math** In **Example 2,** discuss with students why the negative value of *d* can be disregarded. Remind students that they should always consider the context of a problem when determining whether an answer is reasonable. In this case, *d* represents a distance between two boats, so a negative value of *d* does not make sense.

EXAMPLE 2 *Problem-Solving Application*

A coast guard patrol boat and a fishing boat leave a dock at the same time on the courses shown. The patrol boat travels at a speed of 12 nautical miles per hour (12 knots), and the fishing boat travels at a speed of 5 knots. After 3 hours, the fishing boat sends a distress signal picked up by the patrol boat. If the fishing boat does not drift, how long will it take the patrol boat to reach it at a speed of 12 knots?

1 Understand the Problem

The **answer** will be the number of hours that the patrol boat needs to reach the fishing boat.

List the important information:

- The patrol boat's speed is 12 knots. Its direction is 15° east of north.
- The fishing boat's speed is 5 knots. Its direction is 130° east of north.
- The boats travel 3 hours before the distress call is given.

2 Make a Plan

Determine the angle between the boats' courses and the distance that each boat travels in 3 hours. Use this information to draw and label a diagram. Then use the Law of Cosines to find the distance d between the boats at the time of the distress call. Finally, determine how long it will take the patrol boat to travel this distance.

3 Solve

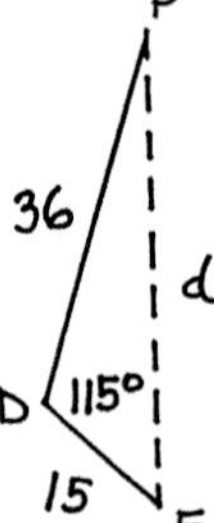

Step 1 Draw and label a diagram.

The angle between the boats' courses is 130° − 15° = 115°. In 3 hours, the patrol boat travels $3(12) =$ 36 nautical miles and the fishing boat travels $3(5) = 15$ nautical miles.

Step 2 Find the distance d between the boats.

$d^2 = p^2 + f^2 - 2pf\cos D$	*Law of Cosines*
$d^2 = 15^2 + 36^2 - 2(15)(36)\cos 115°$	*Substitute 15 for p, 36 for f, and 115° for D.*
$d^2 \approx 1977.4$	*Use a calculator to simplify.*
$d \approx 44.5$	*Solve for the positive value of d.*

Step 3 Determine the number of hours.

The patrol boat must travel about 44.5 nautical miles to reach the fishing boat. At a speed of 12 nautical miles per hour, it will take the patrol boat $\frac{44.5}{12} \approx 3.7$ hours to reach the fishing boat.

Helpful Hint

There are two solutions to $d^2 = 1977.4$. One is positive, and one is negative. Because d represents a distance, the negative solution can be disregarded.

4 Look Back

To reach the fishing boat, the patrol boat will have to travel a greater distance than it did during the first 3 hours of its trip. Therefore, it makes sense that it will take the patrol boat longer than 3 hours to reach the fishing boat. An answer of 3.7 hours seems reasonable.

2. A pilot is flying from Houston to Oklahoma City. To avoid a thunderstorm, the pilot flies 28° off of the direct route for a distance of 175 miles. He then makes a turn and flies straight on to Oklahoma City. To the nearest mile, how much farther than the direct route was the route taken by the pilot? 34 mi

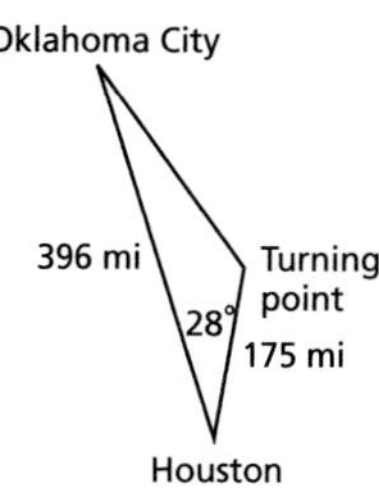

The Law of Cosines can be used to derive a formula for the area of a triangle based on its side lengths. This formula is called Heron's Formula.

Heron's Formula

For $\triangle ABC$, where s is half of the perimeter of the triangle, or $\frac{1}{2}(a + b + c)$,

Area $= \sqrt{s(s-a)(s-b)(s-c)}$

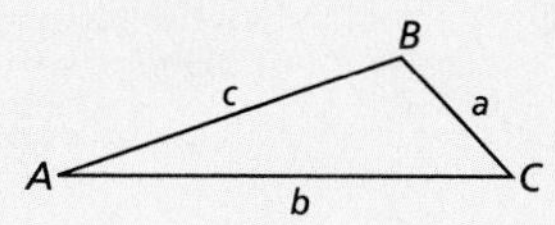

EXAMPLE 3 ***Architecture Application***

A blueprint shows a reception area that has a triangular floor with sides measuring 22 ft, 30 ft, and 34 ft. What is the area of the floor to the nearest square foot?

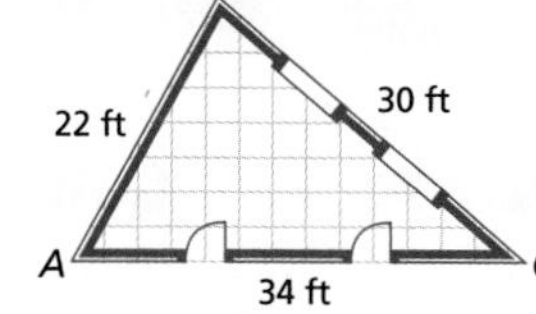

Step 1 Find the value of s.

$s = \frac{1}{2}(a + b + c)$ *Use the formula for half of the perimeter.*

$s = \frac{1}{2}(30 + 34 + 22) = 43$ *Substitute 30 for a, 34 for b, and 22 for c.*

Step 2 Find the area of the triangle.

$A = \sqrt{s(s-a)(s-b)(s-c)}$ *Heron's Formula*

$A = \sqrt{43(43-30)(43-34)(43-22)}$ *Substitute 43 for s.*

$A \approx 325$ *Use a calculator to simplify.*

The area of the floor is 325 ft^2.

Check Find the measure of the largest angle, $\angle B$.

$b^2 = a^2 + c^2 - 2ac\cos B$ *Law of Cosines*

$34^2 = 30^2 + 22^2 - 2(30)(22)\cos B$ *Substitute.*

$\cos B \approx 0.1727$ *Solve for cos B.*

$m\angle B \approx 80.1°$ *Solve for m∠B.*

Find the area of the triangle by using the formula area $= \frac{1}{2}ac\sin B$.

area $= \frac{1}{2}(30)(22)\sin 80.1° \approx 325$ ft^2 ✓

3. The surface of a hotel swimming pool is shaped like a triangle with sides measuring 50 m, 28 m, and 30 m. What is the area of the pool's surface to the nearest square meter? 367 m^2

COMMON ERROR ALERT

When using the Law of Cosines to determine a side length of a triangle, some students may solve for the square of the side length and then forget to take the positive square root of each side of the equation. Remind students that one way they can check that they have solved for the side length correctly is to substitute its value into their original equation to see whether it makes the equation true.

Power Presentations with PowerPoint®

Additional Examples

Example 3

A garden has a triangular flower bed with sides measuring 2 yd, 6 yd, and 7 yd. What is the area of the flower bed to the nearest tenth of a square yard? 5.6 yd^2

Also available on transparency

INTERVENTION

Questioning Strategies

EXAMPLE 3

- What does s represent in Heron's Formula? How do you find its value?

Teaching Tip **Math Background** Heron of Alexandria (also known as Hero) was a Greek mathematician of the first century. The formula named for him was included in his work *Metrica,* which compiled geometric knowledge from various ancient sources. *Metrica* includes a method of approximating square roots that is used today in a modified form by many computers.

3 Close

Summarize

Ask students to tell whether each of the following triangles could be solved by using the Law of Sines or the Law of Cosines and to justify their answers.

- $a = 14, b = 8, c = 9$
  Law of Cosines; SSS is given.
- $a = 26, m\angle A = 46°, m\angle B = 80°$
  Law of Sines; AAS is given.
- $b = 4, m\angle A = 27°, m\angle C = 100°$
  Law of Sines; ASA is given.
- $a = 12, b = 15, m\angle C = 45°$
  Law of Cosines; SAS is given.

ONGOING ASSESSMENT

and INTERVENTION

Diagnose Before **the Lesson**
13-6 Warm Up, TE p. 966

Monitor During **the Lesson**
Check It Out! Exercises, SE pp. 967, 969
Questioning Strategies, TE pp. 967–969

Assess After **the Lesson**
13-6 Lesson Quiz, TE p. 973
Alternative Assessment, TE p. 973

Answers to *Think and Discuss*

Possible answers:

1. All triangles that are similar to each other have the same AAA information. Therefore, you must know the length of at least 1 side of a triangle in order to solve it.
2. Use the Law of Cosines to find the length of the third side of the triangle. Then use the lengths of the 3 sides and Heron's Formula to find the area of the triangle.
3. See p. A14.

THINK AND DISCUSS

1. Explain why you cannot solve a triangle if you are given only angle-angle-angle (AAA) information.
2. Describe the steps that you could use to find the area of a triangle by using Heron's Formula when you are given side-angle-side (SAS) information.

3. **GET ORGANIZED** Copy and complete the graphic organizer. List the types of triangles that can be solved by using each law. Consider the following types of triangles: ASA, AAS, SAS, SSA, and SSS.

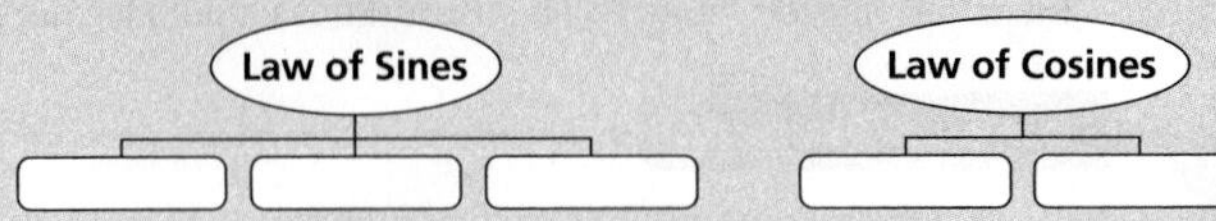

13-6 Exercises

Assignment Guide

Assign *Guided Practice* exercises as necessary.

Basic 9–34, 37–40, 44–52
Average 9–41, 44–52
Advanced 9–52

Homework Quick Check
Quickly check key concepts.
Exercises: 10, 15, 16, 24, 33

Answers

1. $q \approx 9.1$; $m\angle P \approx 40.5°$; $m\angle R \approx 59.5°$
2. $p \approx 25.0$; $m\angle Q \approx 15.0°$; $m\angle R \approx 42.0°$
3. $r \approx 11.6$; $m\angle P \approx 40.3°$; $m\angle R \approx 50.7°$
4. $m\angle P \approx 25.2°$; $m\angle Q \approx 96.4°$; $m\angle R \approx 58.4°$
5. $m\angle P \approx 43.2°$; $m\angle Q \approx 86.5°$; $m\angle R \approx 50.3°$
6. $m\angle P \approx 56.3°$; $m\angle Q \approx 29.9°$; $m\angle R \approx 93.8°$

State Resources

13-6 Exercises

go.hrw.com
Homework Help Online
KEYWORD: MB7 13-6
Parent Resources Online
KEYWORD: MB7 Parent

GUIDED PRACTICE

SEE EXAMPLE 1 p. 966

Use the given measurements to solve each triangle. Round to the nearest tenth.

1. 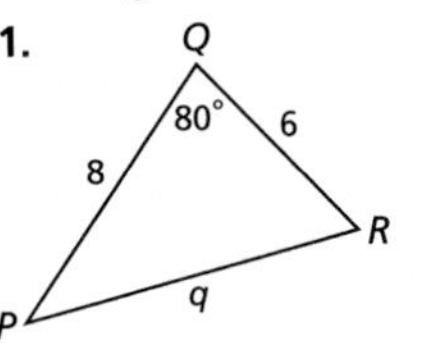

2. 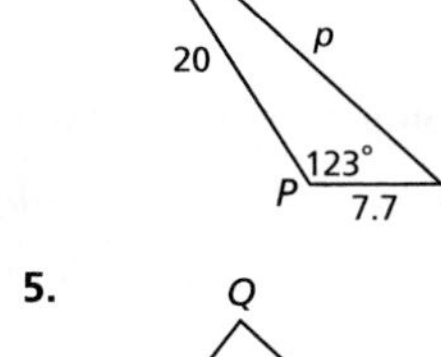

3. 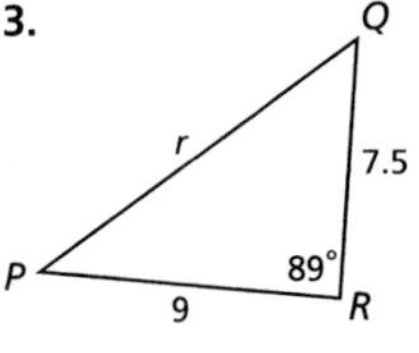

4. 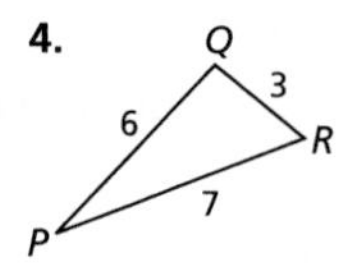

5. 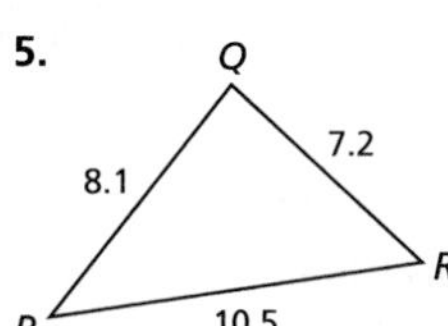

6. 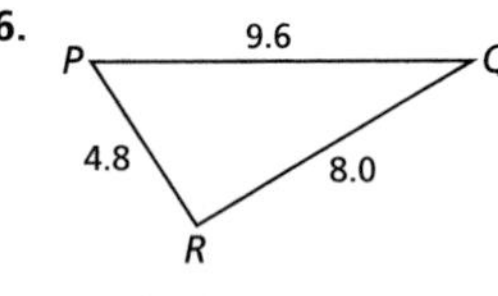

SEE EXAMPLE 2 p. 968

7. **Recreation** A triangular hiking trail is being built in the area shown. At an average walking speed of 2 m/s, how many minutes will it take a hiker to make a complete circuit around the triangular trail? Round to the nearest minute. **9 min**

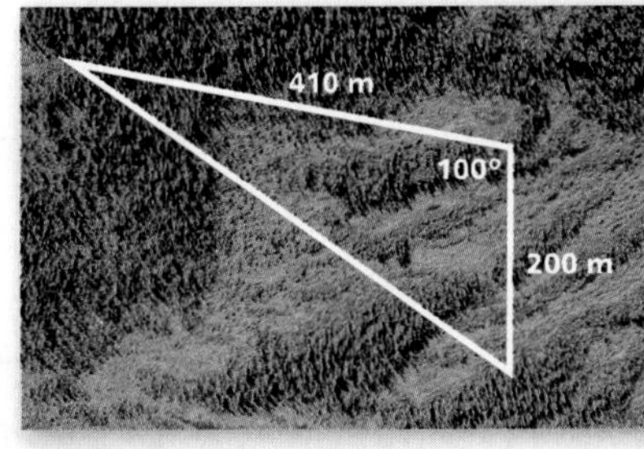

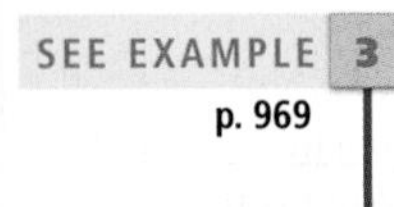

SEE EXAMPLE 3 p. 969

8. **Agriculture** A triangular wheat field has side lengths that measure 410 ft, 500 ft, and 420 ft. What is the area of the field to the nearest square foot? **82,795 ft²**

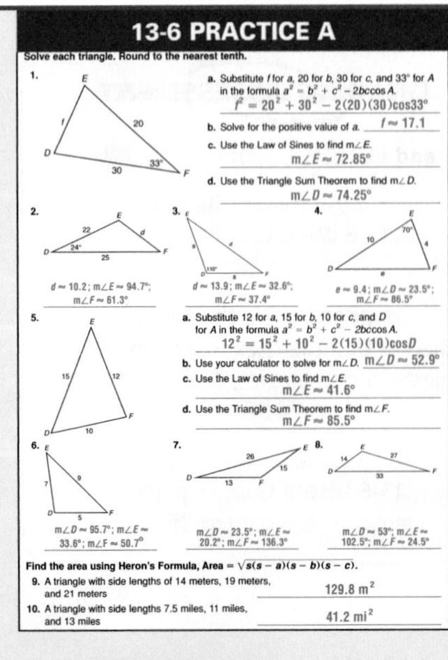

13-6 PRACTICE A

Solve each triangle. Round to the nearest tenth.

1. a. Substitute f for a, 20 for b, 30 for c, and 33° for A in the formula $a^2 = b^2 + c^2 - 2bc\cos A$. $f^2 = 20^2 + 30^2 - 2(20)(30)\cos 33°$
   b. Solve for the positive value of a. $f \approx 17.1$
   c. Use the Law of Sines to find $m\angle E$. $m\angle E \approx 72.85°$
   d. Use the Triangle Sum Theorem to find $m\angle D$. $m\angle D \approx 74.25°$
2. $d \approx 10.2$; $m\angle E \approx 94.7°$; $m\angle F \approx 61.3°$
3. $d \approx 13.9$; $m\angle E \approx 32.6°$; $m\angle F \approx 37.4°$
4. $e \approx 9.4$; $m\angle D \approx 23.5°$; $m\angle F \approx 86.5°$
5. a. Substitute 12 for a, 15 for b, 10 for c, and D for A in the formula $a^2 = b^2 + c^2 - 2bc\cos A$. $12^2 = 15^2 + 10^2 - 2(15)(10)\cos D$
   b. Use your calculator to solve for $m\angle D$. $m\angle D \approx 52.9°$
   c. Use the Law of Sines to find $m\angle E$. $m\angle E \approx 41.6°$
   d. Use the Triangle Sum Theorem to find $m\angle F$. $m\angle F \approx 85.5°$
6. $m\angle D \approx 95.7°$; $m\angle E \approx 33.6°$; $m\angle F \approx 50.7°$
7. $m\angle D \approx 23.5°$; $m\angle E \approx 20.2°$; $m\angle F \approx 136.3°$
8. $m\angle D \approx 53°$; $m\angle E \approx 102.5°$; $m\angle F \approx 24.5°$

Find the area using Heron's Formula, Area $= \sqrt{s(s-a)(s-b)(s-c)}$.

9. A triangle with side lengths of 14 meters, 19 meters, and 21 meters 129.8 m^2
10. A triangle with side lengths 7.5 miles, 11 miles, and 13 miles 41.2 mi^2

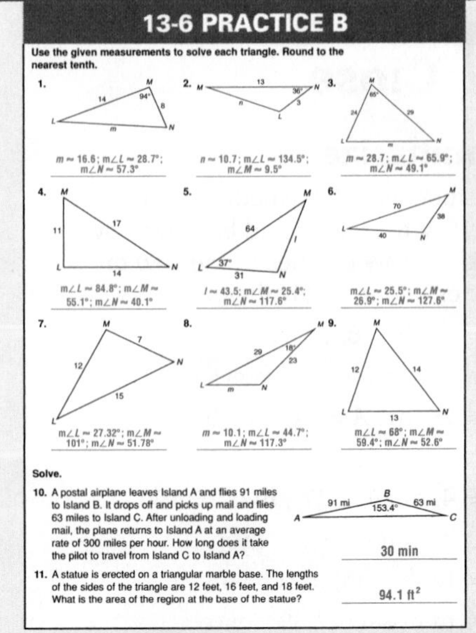

13-6 PRACTICE B

Use the given measurements to solve each triangle. Round to the nearest tenth.

1. $m \approx 16.6$; $m\angle L \approx 28.7°$; $m\angle N \approx 57.3°$
2. $n \approx 10.7$; $m\angle L \approx 134.5°$; $m\angle M \approx 9.5°$
3. $m \approx 28.7$; $m\angle L \approx 65.9°$; $m\angle N \approx 49.1°$
4. $m\angle L \approx 84.8°$; $m\angle M \approx 55.1°$; $m\angle N \approx 40.1°$
5. $l \approx 43.5$; $m\angle M \approx 25.4°$; $m\angle N \approx 117.6°$
6. $m\angle L \approx 25.5°$; $m\angle M \approx 26.9°$; $m\angle N \approx 127.6°$
7. $m\angle L \approx 27.32°$; $m\angle M \approx 101°$; $m\angle N \approx 51.78°$
8. $m \approx 10.1$; $m\angle L \approx 44.7°$; $m\angle N \approx 117.3°$
9. $m\angle L \approx 68°$; $m\angle M \approx 59.4°$; $m\angle N \approx 52.6°$

Solve.

10. A postal airplane leaves Island A and flies 91 miles to Island B. It drops off and picks up mail and flies 63 miles to Island C. After unloading and loading mail, the plane returns to Island A at an average rate of 300 miles per hour. How long does it take the pilot to travel from Island C to Island A? 30 min
11. A statue is erected on a triangular marble base. The lengths of the sides of the triangle are 12 feet, 16 feet, and 18 feet. What is the area of the region at the base of the statue? 94.1 ft^2

PRACTICE AND PROBLEM SOLVING

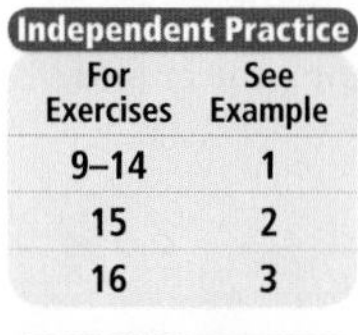

Independent Practice

For Exercises	See Example
9–14	1
15	2
16	3

Extra Practice

Skills Practice p. S29

Application Practice p. S44

Use the given measurements to solve each triangle. Round to the nearest tenth.

9. 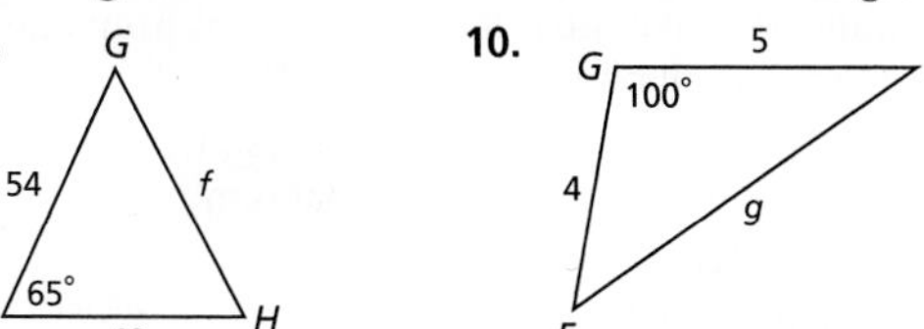

10. 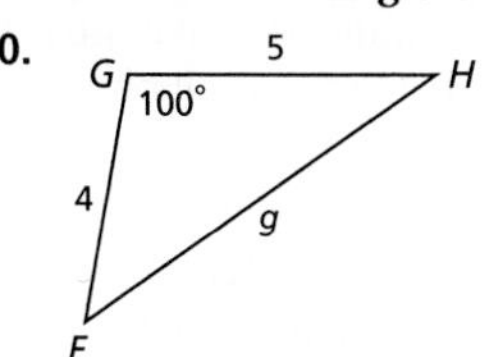

11. 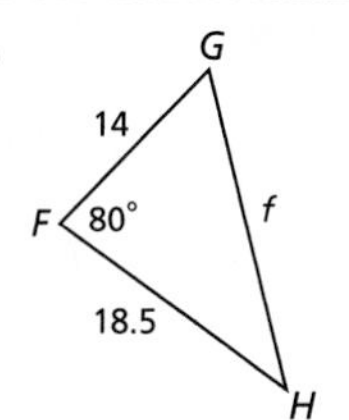

12. 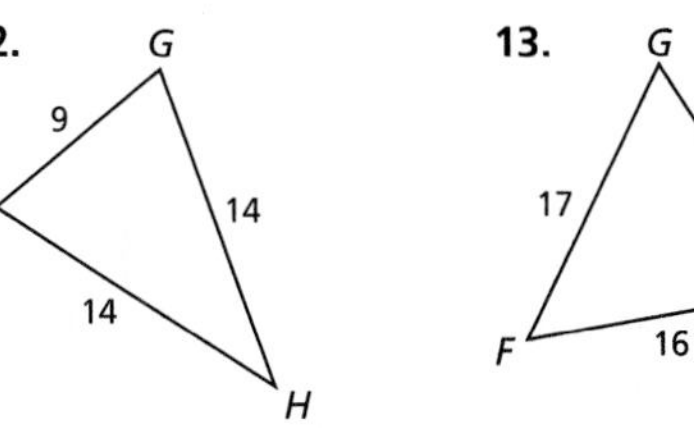

13.
G
17
15
F
16
H

14. 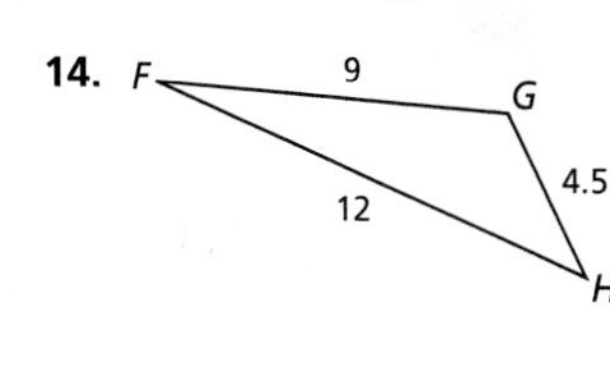

15. **Ecology** An ecologist is studying a pair of zebras fitted with radio-transmitter collars. One zebra is 1.4 mi from the ecologist, and the other is 3.5 mi from the ecologist. To the nearest tenth of a mile, how far apart are the two zebras? **3.8 mi**

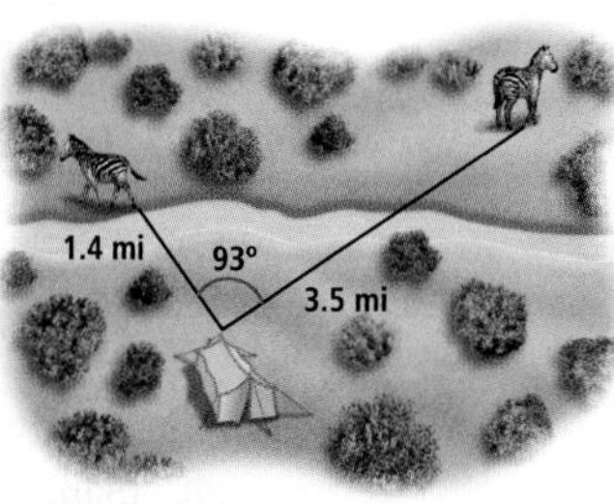

16. **Art** How many square meters of fabric are needed to make a triangular banner with side lengths of 2.1 m, 1.5 m, and 1.4 m? Round to the nearest tenth. **1.0 m²**

Use the given measurements to solve △*ABC*. Round to the nearest tenth.

17. $m\angle A = 120°$, $b = 16$, $c = 20$ **$m\angle B \approx 26.3°$; $m\angle C \approx 33.7°$; $a \approx 31.2$**
18. $m\angle B = 78°$, $a = 6$, $c = 4$ **$m\angle A \approx 64.9°$; $m\angle C \approx 37.1°$; $b \approx 6.5$**
19. $m\angle C = 96°$, $a = 13$, $b = 9$ **$m\angle A \approx 51.3°$; $m\angle B \approx 32.7°$; $c \approx 16.6$**
20. $a = 14$, $b = 9$, $c = 10$ **$m\angle A \approx 94.8°$; $m\angle B \approx 39.8°$; $m\angle C \approx 45.4°$**
21. $a = 5$, $b = 8$, $c = 6$ **$m\angle A \approx 38.6°$; $m\angle B \approx 92.9°$; $m\angle C \approx 48.5°$**
22. $a = 30$, $b = 26$, $c = 35$ **$m\angle A \approx 56.6°$; $m\angle B \approx 46.4°$; $m\angle C \approx 77.0°$**

23. **Commercial Art** A graphic artist is asked to draw a triangular logo with sides measuring 15 cm, 18 cm, and 20 cm. If she draws the triangle correctly, what will be the measures of its angles to the nearest degree? **74°, 46°, and 60°**

24. **Aviation** The course of a hot-air balloon takes the balloon directly over points *A* and *B*, which are 500 m apart. Several minutes later, the angle of elevation from an observer at point *A* to the balloon is 43.3°, and the angle of elevation from an observer at point *B* to the balloon is 58.2°. To the nearest meter, what is the balloon's altitude? **1133 m**

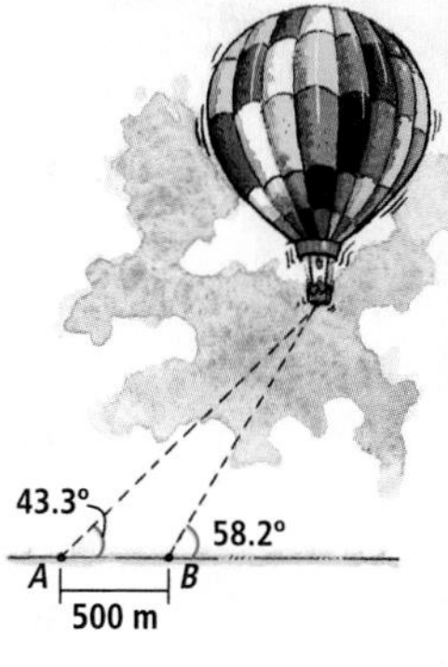

25. **Multi-Step** A student pilot takes off from a local airstrip and flies 70° south of east for 160 miles. The pilot then changes course and flies due north for another 80 miles before turning and flying directly back to the airstrip.
    a. How many miles is the third stage of the pilot's flight? Round to the nearest mile. **89 mi**
    b. To the nearest degree, what angle does the pilot turn the plane through in order to fly the third stage? **38°**

COMMON ERROR ALERT

When using Heron's Formula in problems such as **Exercises 8** and **16,** students may forget to divide the perimeter of the triangle by 2. To help students remember this step, point out that the *s* in Heron's Formula stands for *semiperimeter.* Explain that the semiperimeter is $\frac{1}{2}$ of the perimeter, just as a semicircle is $\frac{1}{2}$ of a circle.

Geometry Remind students that the shortest side of a triangle is opposite the smallest angle and the longest side is opposite the largest angle. Students can use this fact in problems such as **Exercises 9–14** to help them check whether their answers are reasonable.

Answers

9. $f \approx 55.5$; $m\angle G \approx 53.1°$; $m\angle H \approx 61.9°$
10. $g \approx 6.9$; $m\angle F \approx 45.5°$; $m\angle H \approx 34.5°$
11. $f \approx 21.2$; $m\angle G \approx 59.2°$; $m\angle H \approx 40.8°$
12. $m\angle F \approx 71.3°$; $m\angle G \approx 71.3°$; $m\angle H \approx 37.4°$
13. $m\angle F \approx 54.0°$; $m\angle G \approx 59.6°$; $m\angle H \approx 66.4°$
14. $m\angle F \approx 18.6°$; $m\angle G \approx 121.9°$; $m\angle H \approx 39.5°$

13-6 PRACTICE C

Use the given measurements to solve each triangle. Round to the nearest tenth.

1. $r \approx 13.3$; $m\angle S \approx 34.4°$; $m\angle T \approx 102.6°$
2. $t \approx 13.5$; $m\angle R \approx 40.1°$; $m\angle S \approx 61.9°$
3. $m\angle R \approx 127.2°$; $m\angle S \approx 32.1°$; $m\angle T \approx 20.7°$
4. $m\angle R \approx 47.7°$; $m\angle S \approx 76.9°$; $m\angle T \approx 55.4°$
5. $t \approx 12.4$; $m\angle R \approx 57.7°$; $m\angle S \approx 84.3°$
6. $m\angle R \approx 32.8°$; $m\angle S \approx 82.8°$; $m\angle T \approx 64.4°$
7. $m\angle R \approx 57°$; $m\angle S \approx 33.3°$; $m\angle T \approx 89.7°$
8. $r \approx 34$; $m\angle S \approx 23.1°$; $m\angle T \approx 49.1°$
9. $m\angle R \approx 51.4°$; $m\angle S \approx 70.8°$; $m\angle T \approx 57.8°$

Solve.

10. The rotunda of a shopping mall is in the shape of a triangle. Members of a local scout troop plan to walk around the outer edge of the rotunda 5 times to increase awareness of physical fitness. If they walk at an average speed of 3 miles per hour, how long should it take them to the nearest minute? **1 h 39 min**

11. There is a fountain in a triangular garden in front of City Hall. The lengths of the sides of the triangle are 14 meters, 15 meters, and 21 meters. What is the area of the garden? **104.9 m²**

Exercise 26 involves solving triangles by using the Law of Cosines in a problem situation concerning the location of a fire. This exercise prepares students for the Multi-Step Test Prep on page 974.

Geometry For **Exercise 32,** you may wish to draw a parallelogram on the board and review basic facts about parallelograms: opposite sides have the same length, opposite angles have the same measure, and adjacent angles are supplementary.

Critical Thinking For **Exercise 36,** remind students that the Triangle Inequality Theorem states that the sum of the lengths of any two sides of a triangle is greater than the length of the third side. Students can use this theorem to help them prove that $\frac{1}{2}(a + b + c) > a$, where a is the longest side of $\triangle ABC$.

Answers

27a. $m\angle A = 43°$; $m\angle B = 44°$
b. $m\angle A = 28°$; $m\angle B = 41°$

32. About 3.5 cm and 6 cm; check students' work.

34. The angle between Kauai and Molokai with Lanai at the vertex is 40°. The angle between Kauai and Lanai with Molokai at the vertex is 134°. The angle between Molokai and Lanai with Kauai at the vertex is 6°.

35. Possible answer: If $\angle C$ is a right angle, then its measure is 90°.
$c^2 = a^2 + b^2 - 2ab \cos C$
$c^2 = a^2 + b^2 - 2ab \cos 90°$
$c^2 = a^2 + b^2 - 2ab(0)$
$c^2 = a^2 + b^2$

36. No. Possible answer: If s were less than the length of the longest side of a triangle, the expression under the radical in Heron's Formula would be negative. Because the square root of a negative number is not a real value, s cannot be less than the length of the longest side.

37. Possible answer: (1) Use the Law of Cosines to find the measure of the largest angle. Then use the Law of Cosines again to find the measure of a second angle. Finally, use the Triangle Sum Theorem to find the measure of the third angle. (2) Use the Law of Cosines to find the measure of the largest angle. Then use the Law of Sines to find the measure of a second angle. Finally, use the Law of Sines again to find the measure of the third angle.

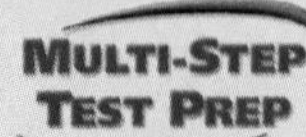

26. This problem will help prepare you for the Multi-Step Test Prep on page 974.

Phone records indicate that a fire is located 2.5 miles from one cell phone tower and 3.2 miles from a second cell phone tower.

a. To the nearest degree, what are the measures of the angles of the triangle shown in the diagram?

b. Tower 2 is directly east of tower 1. How many miles north of the towers is the fire? This distance is represented by n in the diagram. **about 1.7 mi**

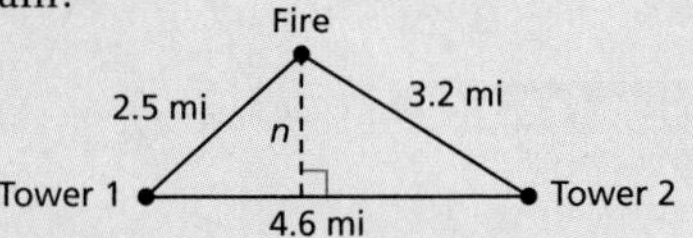

26a. angle with vertex at tower 1: 42°; angle with vertex at tower 2: 31°; angle with vertex at fire: 107°

27. **Entertainment** Two performers hang by their knees from trapezes, as shown.

a. To the nearest degree, what acute angles A and B must the cords of each trapeze make with the horizontal if the performer on the left is to grab the wrists of the performer on the right and pull her away from her trapeze?

b. **What if...?** Later, the performer on the left grabs the trapeze of the performer on the right and lets go of his trapeze. To the nearest degree, what angles A and B must the cords of each trapeze make with the horizontal for this trick to work?

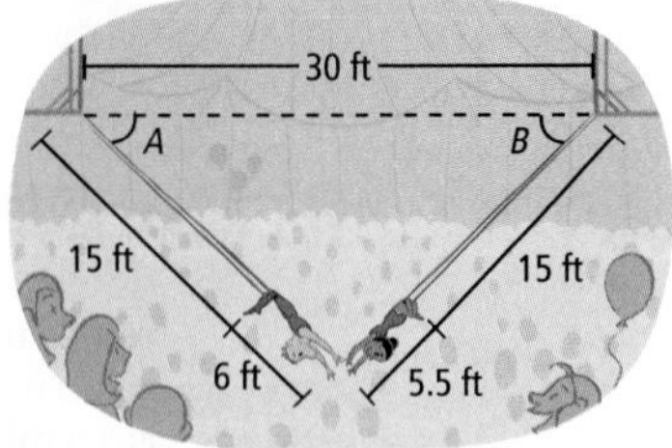

Find the area of the triangle with the given side lengths. Round to the nearest tenth.

28. 15 in., 18 in., 24 in. **134.8 in²**

29. 30 cm, 35 cm, 47 cm **524.6 cm²**

30. 28 m, 37 m, 33 m **444.5 m²**

31. 3.5 ft, 5 ft, 7.5 ft **7.3 ft²**

32. **Estimation** The adjacent sides of a parallelogram measure 3.1 cm and 3.9 cm. The measures of the acute interior angles of the parallelogram are 58°. Estimate the lengths of the diagonals of the parallelogram without using a calculator, and explain how you determined your estimates.

33. **Surveying** Barrington Crater in Arizona was produced by the impact of a meteorite. Based on the measurements shown, what is the diameter d of Barrington Crater to the nearest tenth of a kilometer? **1.2 km**

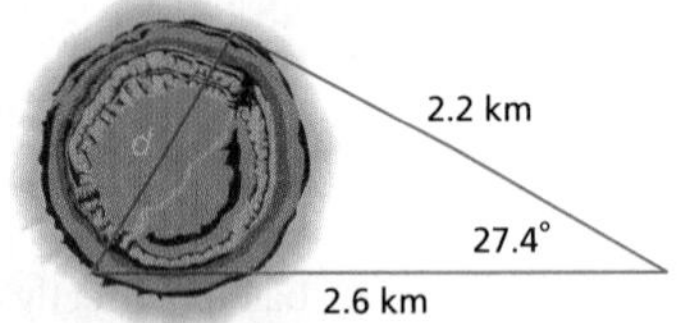

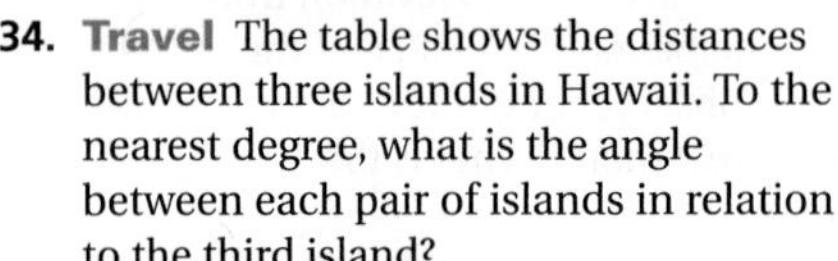

34. **Travel** The table shows the distances between three islands in Hawaii. To the nearest degree, what is the angle between each pair of islands in relation to the third island?

Distances Between Islands (mi)

	Kauai	Molokai	Lanai
Kauai	0	155.7	174.8
Molokai	155.7	0	26.1
Lanai	174.8	26.1	0

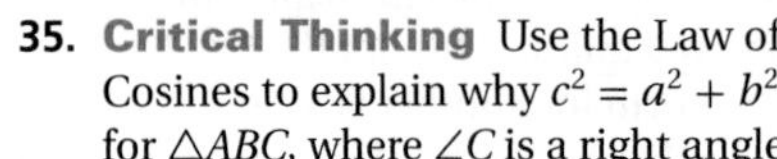

35. **Critical Thinking** Use the Law of Cosines to explain why $c^2 = a^2 + b^2$ for $\triangle ABC$, where $\angle C$ is a right angle.

36. **Critical Thinking** Can the value of s in Heron's Formula ever be less than the length of the longest side of a triangle? Explain.

37. **Write About It** Describe two different methods that could be used to solve a triangle when given side-side-side (SSS) information.

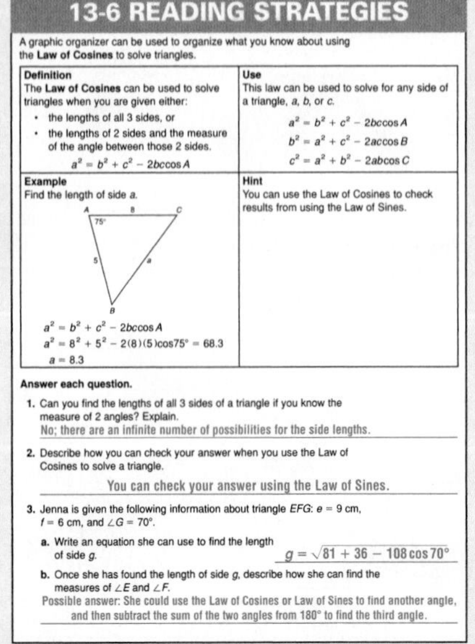

13-6 READING STRATEGIES

A graphic organizer can be used to organize what you know about using the **Law of Cosines** to solve triangles.

Definition The **Law of Cosines** can be used to solve triangles when you are given either: • the lengths of all 3 sides, or • the lengths of 2 sides and the measure of the angle between those 2 sides. $a^2 = b^2 + c^2 - 2bc\cos A$	**Use** This law can be used to solve for any side of a triangle, a, b, or c. $a^2 = b^2 + c^2 - 2bc\cos A$ $b^2 = a^2 + c^2 - 2ac\cos B$ $c^2 = a^2 + b^2 - 2ab\cos C$
Example Find the length of side a. $a^2 = b^2 + c^2 - 2bc\cos A$ $a^2 = 8^2 + 5^2 - 2(8)(5)\cos 75° = 68.3$ $a = 8.3$	**Hint** You can use the Law of Cosines to check results from using the Law of Sines.

Answer each question.

1. Can you find the lengths of all 3 sides of a triangle if you know the measure of 2 angles? Explain.
No; there are an infinite number of possibilities for the side lengths.

2. Describe how you can check your answer when you use the Law of Cosines to solve a triangle.
You can check your answer using the Law of Sines.

3. Jenna is given the following information about triangle EFG: $e = 9$ cm, $f = 6$ cm, and $\angle G = 70°$.
a. Write an equation she can use to find the length of side g. $g = \sqrt{81 + 36 - 108\cos 70°}$
b. Once she has found the length of side g, describe how she can find the measures of $\angle E$ and $\angle F$.
Possible answer: She could use the Law of Cosines or Law of Sines to find another angle, and then subtract the sum of the two angles from 180° to find the third angle.

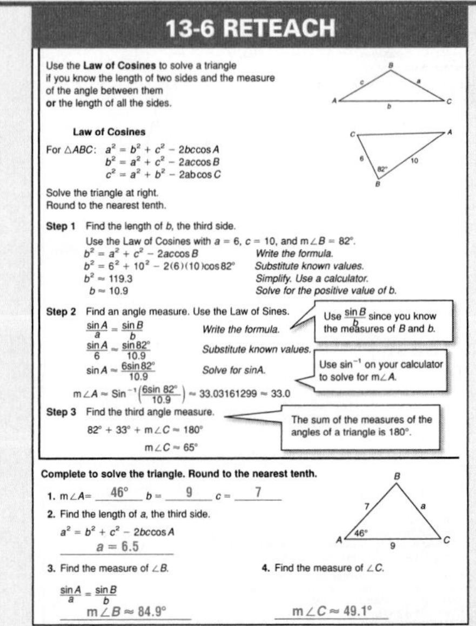

13-6 RETEACH

Use the **Law of Cosines** to solve a triangle if you know the length of two sides and the measure of the angle between them **or** the length of all the sides.

Law of Cosines

For $\triangle ABC$: $a^2 = b^2 + c^2 - 2bc\cos A$
$b^2 = a^2 + c^2 - 2ac\cos B$
$c^2 = a^2 + b^2 - 2ab\cos C$

Solve the triangle at right.
Round to the nearest tenth.

Step 1 Find the length of b, the third side.
Use the Law of Cosines with $a = 6$, $c = 10$, and $m\angle B = 82°$.
$b^2 = a^2 + c^2 - 2ac\cos B$ *Write the formula.*
$b^2 = 6^2 + 10^2 - 2(6)(10)\cos 82°$ *Substitute known values.*
$b^2 \approx 119.3$ *Simplify. Use a calculator.*
$b \approx 10.9$ *Solve for the positive value of b.*

Step 2 Find an angle measure. Use the Law of Sines.
$\frac{\sin A}{a} = \frac{\sin B}{b}$ *Write the formula.* (Use $\frac{\sin B}{b}$ since you know the measures of B and b.)
$\frac{\sin A}{6} \approx \frac{\sin 82°}{10.9}$ *Substitute known values.*
$\sin A \approx \frac{6\sin 82°}{10.9}$ *Solve for sinA.* (Use $\sin^{-1}$ on your calculator to solve for $m\angle A$.)
$m\angle A \approx \text{Sin}^{-1}\left(\frac{6\sin 82°}{10.9}\right) \approx 33.03161299 \approx 33.0$

Step 3 Find the third angle measure. (The sum of the measures of the angles of a triangle is 180°.)
$82° + 33° + m\angle C \approx 180°$
$m\angle C \approx 65°$

Complete to solve the triangle. Round to the nearest tenth.

1. $m\angle A =$ 46° $b =$ 9 $c =$ 7

2. Find the length of a, the third side.
$a^2 = b^2 + c^2 - 2bc\cos A$
$a = 6.5$

3. Find the measure of $\angle B$.
$\frac{\sin A}{a} = \frac{\sin B}{b}$
$m\angle B \approx 84.9°$

4. Find the measure of $\angle C$.
$m\angle C \approx 49.1°$

TEST PREP

38. What is the approximate measure of $\angle K$ in the triangle shown?

K 12 L 4 J 9.6

Ⓐ 30° Ⓒ 54°
Ⓑ 45° (circled) Ⓓ 60°

39. For $\triangle RST$ with side lengths r, s, and t, which equation can be used to determine r?

Ⓕ $r = \sqrt{s^2 + t^2 - 2st \sin R}$ Ⓗ (circled) $r = \sqrt{s^2 + t^2 - 2st \cos R}$
Ⓖ $r = \sqrt{s^2 - t^2 - 2st \sin R}$ Ⓙ $r = \sqrt{s^2 - t^2 - 2st \cos R}$

40. A team of archaeologists wants to dig for fossils in a triangular area marked by three stakes. The distances between the stakes are shown in the diagram. Which expression represents the dig area in square feet?

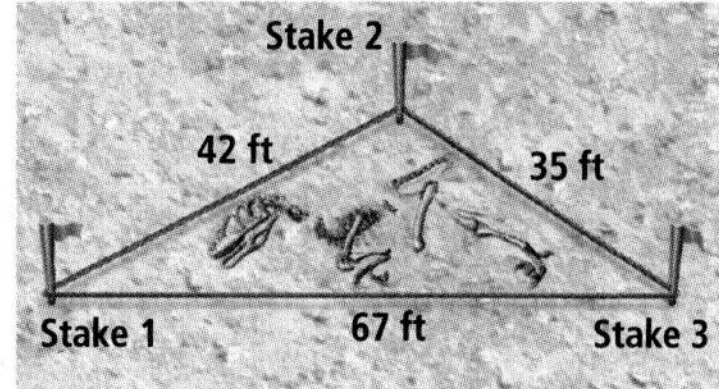

Ⓐ (circled) $\sqrt{72(30)(37)(5)}$
Ⓑ $\sqrt{48(6)(13)(19)}$
Ⓒ $\sqrt{144(42)(35)(67)}$
Ⓓ $\sqrt{144(102)(109)(77)}$

CHALLENGE AND EXTEND

41. Abby uses the Law of Cosines to find $m\angle A$ when $a = 2$, $b = 3$, and $c = 5$. The answer she gets is 0°. Did she make an error? Explain.

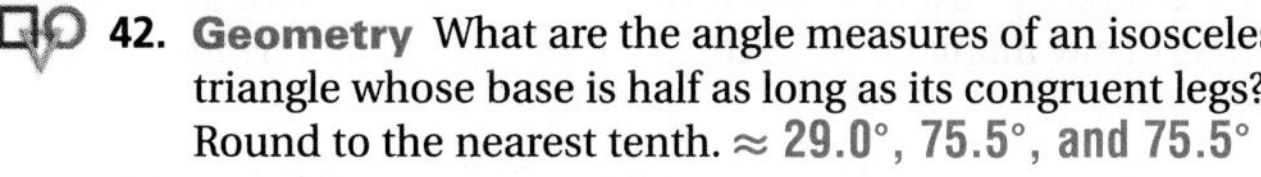

42. **Geometry** What are the angle measures of an isosceles triangle whose base is half as long as its congruent legs? Round to the nearest tenth. $\approx$ **29.0°, 75.5°, and 75.5°**

43. Use the figure shown to solve for x. Round to the nearest tenth. **9.9**

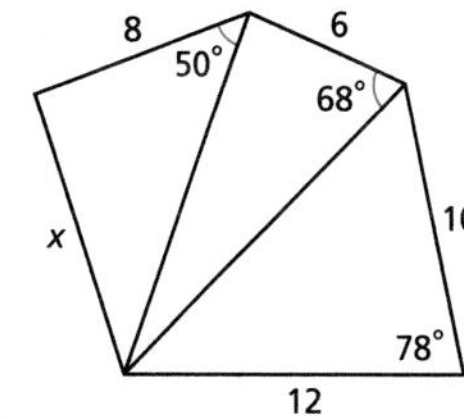

SPIRAL REVIEW

Solve each equation. *(Lesson 5-5)*

44. $x^2 + 25 = 0$ $\pm 5i$
45. $3x^2 = -48$ $\pm 4i$
46. $\frac{1}{2}x^2 + 18 = 0$ $\pm 6i$

Identify the x- and y-intercepts of $f(x)$. Without graphing $g(x)$, identify its x- and y-intercepts. *(Lesson 9-3)*

47. $f(x) = 2x - 8$ and $g(x) = \frac{1}{2}f(x)$
48. $f(x) = x^2 - 4$ and $g(x) = -f(x)$
49. $f(x) = \frac{1}{2}x + 6$ and $g(x) = f(3x)$
50. $f(x) = x^3 + 1$ and $g(x) = -4f(x)$

Solve each triangle. Round to the nearest tenth. *(Lesson 13-5)*

51.

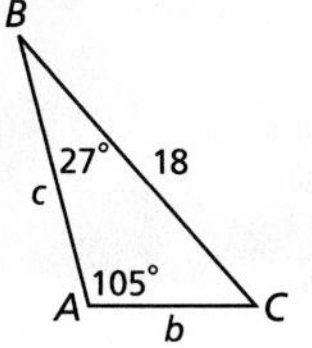

$m\angle C = 48°$; $b \approx 8.5$; $c \approx 13.8$

52.

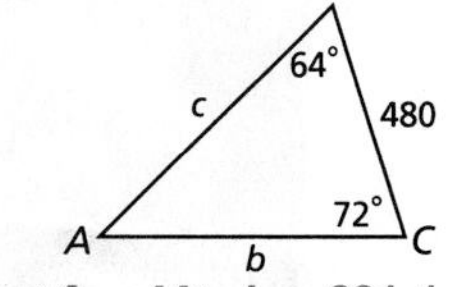

$m\angle A = 44°$; $b \approx 621.1$; $c \approx 657.2$

TEST PREP DOCTOR For **Exercise 38,** stress that students should not estimate the measure of $\angle K$ just by looking at the diagram. Instead, they should use the Law of Cosines to calculate an approximate measure.

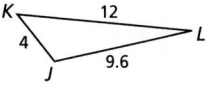

In **Exercise 39,** students should carefully compare the choices to the Law of Cosines. Choices **F** and **G** incorrectly use $\sin R$ instead of $\cos R$. Choice **J** includes $s^2 - t^2$ instead of $s^2 + t^2$, which leaves **H** as the correct choice.

Answers

41, 47–50. See p. A50.

Journal

Have students explain how the Law of Cosines enables them to solve a triangle when given SAS information.

ALTERNATIVE ASSESSMENT

Have students use a ruler (MK) to draw an SSS triangle. Then have them solve the triangle and find its area.

Power Presentations with PowerPoint®

13-6 Lesson Quiz

Use the given measurements to solve $\triangle ABC$. Round to the nearest tenth.

1. $a = 18$, $b = 40$, $m\angle C = 82.5°$
$c \approx 41.7$; $m\angle A \approx 25.4°$; $m\angle B \approx 72.1°$

2. $a = 18$, $b = 10$, $c = 9$
$m\angle A \approx 142.6°$; $m\angle B \approx 19.7°$; $m\angle C \approx 17.7°$

3. Two model planes take off from the same spot. The first plane travels 300 ft due west before landing, and the second plane travels 170 ft southeast before landing. To the nearest foot, how far apart are the planes when they land? 437 ft

4. An artist needs to know the area of a triangular piece of stained glass with sides measuring 9 cm, 7 cm, and 5 cm. What is the area to the nearest square centimeter?
17 cm²

Also available on transparency

13-6 PROBLEM SOLVING

Standing on a small bluff overlooking a local pond, Clay wants to calculate the width of the pond.

1. From point C, Clay walks the distances $\overline{CA}$ and $\overline{CB}$. Then he measures the angle between these line segments.

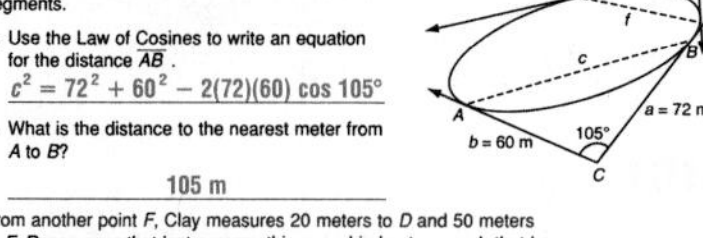

a. Use the Law of Cosines to write an equation for the distance $\overline{AB}$.
$c^2 = 72^2 + 60^2 - 2(72)(60)\cos 105°$

b. What is the distance to the nearest meter from A to B?
105 m

2. From another point F, Clay measures 20 meters to D and 50 meters to E. Reece says that last summer this area dried out so much that he could walk the 49 meters from D to E.

a. Use the Law of Cosines to write an equation for the measure of the angle between $\overline{DF}$ and $\overline{EF}$.
$\angle F = \cos^{-1}\left(\frac{(50^2 + 20^2 - 49^2)}{2(50)(20)}\right)$

b. What is the measure of this angle? 75.6°

3. Reece tells Clay that when the area defined by ΔDEF dries out, it becomes covered with a grass native to this area of the country. Clay wants to know the area of this section.

a. Use Heron's Formula to write an expression for the area.
$A = \sqrt{59.5(9.5)(39.5)(10.5)}$

b. Find the area to the nearest tenth of a square meter. 484.2 m²

A local naturalist says that a triangular area on the north sides of the pond is a turtle habitat. The lengths of the sides of this area are 15 meters, 25 meters, and 36 meters. Choose the letter for the best answer.

4. What is the area of this triangular turtle habitat?
Ⓐ (circled) 150.7 m²
B 213.2 m²
C 1012.9 m²
D 3075 m²

5. Which expression gives the measure of the angle between the sides of the habitat that measure 15 meters and 25 meters?
Ⓕ (circled) $\cos^{-1}(-0.595)$
G $\cos(-0.595)$
H $\cos(0.595)$
J $\cos^{-1}(0.595)$

13-6 CHALLENGE

The Law of Cosines can be derived by a geometric argument. Consider triangle ABC below. Vertex B is placed at the center of a circle, vertex C is located on the circle, and side a is the radius of the circle. Sides AC and BC are extended so that they intersect the circle at points A' and B'. Since $B'C$ is a diameter of the circle, triangle $A'B'C$ is a right triangle since $\angle A'$ intercepts a semicircle.

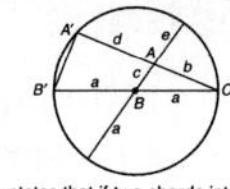

A theorem from geometry states that if two chords intersect inside a circle, then the product of the two segments of one chord is equal to the product of the two segments of the other chord. For the two chords that intersect at point A, we therefore have $bd = (a + c)e$.

Justify each step in the derivation of the Law of Cosines.

1. $bd = (a + c)(a - c)$ $c + e = a$, so $e = a - c$

2. $b(2a\cos C - b) = a^2 - c^2$
$\cos C = \frac{\text{adj.}}{\text{hyp.}} = \frac{d + b}{2a}$, so $2a\cos C = d + b$, and $2a\cos C - b = d$; the right side of the equation is the FOIL method.

3. $2ab\cos C - b^2 = a^2 - c^2$
Distributive Property simplifies the left side; the right side is unchanged.

4. $c^2 = a^2 + b^2 - 2ab\cos C$
Solve for c^2 to obtain the Law of Cosines.

5. A worker is installing an infrared security scanning device in the corner of a living room 6 inches below the ceiling as shown in the figure at right. She needs to set the scan angle on the scanning device so that it will scan from one corner of the room to the opposite corner of the room. The room measures 18 feet by 14 feet and is 9 feet high. What is the angle θ that the device should be set to scan?

9 ft 14 ft 18 ft θ

Appropriate diagonals are of length 16.4 ft, 19.9 ft, and 22.8 ft; from the Law of Cosines, the angle is then $\theta = \cos^{-1}\left(\frac{c^2 - a^2 - b^2}{-2ab}\right)$
$= \cos^{-1}\left(\frac{22.8^2 - 19.9 - 16.4^2}{-2(19.9)(16.4)}\right) \approx 77°$.

SECTION 13B MULTI-STEP TEST PREP

Organizer

Objective: Assess students' ability to apply concepts and skills in Lessons 13-5 through 13-6 in a real-world format.

Online Edition

Resources

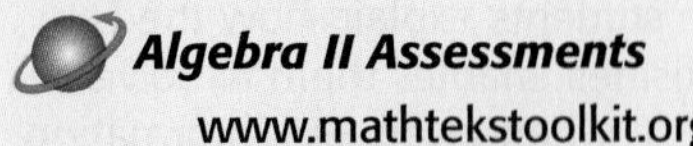

Algebra II Assessments

www.mathtekstoolkit.org

Problems	Text Reference
1–2	Lesson 13-5
3–5	Lesson 13-6

Answers

1. distance between tower 1 and tower 3: 2.8 mi; distance between tower 2 and tower 3: 3.2 mi
3. angle with tower 1 at vertex: 38.0°; angle with tower 2 at vertex: 25.8°; angle with driver at vertex: 116.2°

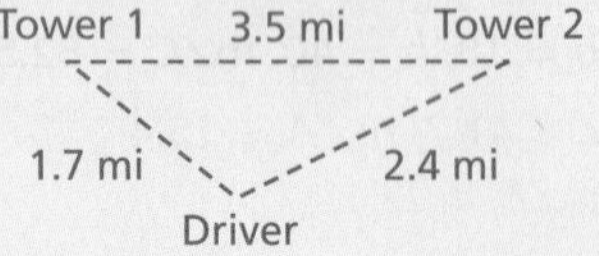

5. See p. A50.

State Resources

CHAPTER 13

MULTI-STEP TEST PREP

SECTION 13B

Applying Trigonometric Functions

Where's the Fire? A driver dials 9-1-1 on a cell phone to report smoke coming from a building. Before the driver can give the building's address, the call is cut short. The 9-1-1 dispatcher is still able to determine the driver's location based on the driver's position in relation to nearby cell phone towers.

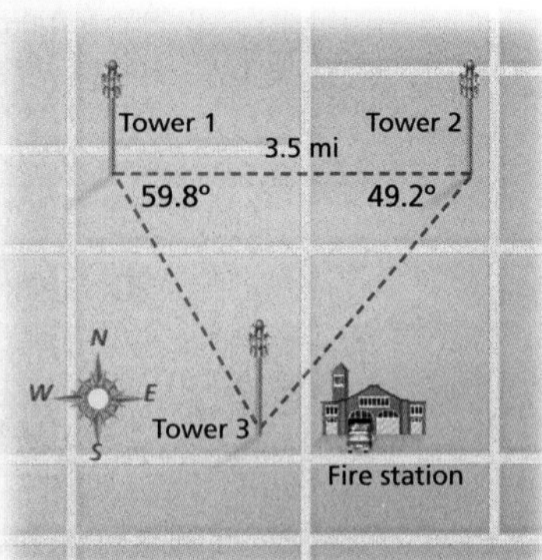

1. When the driver makes the call, he is located in the triangular area between the three cell phone towers shown. To the nearest tenth of a mile, what is the distance between tower 3 and each of the other towers?
2. What is the area in square miles of the triangle with the three cell phone towers at its vertices? Round to the nearest tenth. **4.2 mi²**
3. The driver is 1.7 miles from tower 1 and 2.4 miles from tower 2 when the call is made. Make a sketch of the triangle with tower 1, tower 2, and the driver at its vertices. To the nearest tenth of a degree, what are the measures of the angles of this triangle?
4. Tower 2 is directly east of tower 1. How many miles east of tower 1 is the driver? How many miles south of tower 1 is the driver? Round to the nearest tenth. **1.3 mi east; 1.0 mi south**
5. A fire station is located 1 block from tower 3. Estimate the distance between the fire station and the fire. Explain how you determined your estimate.

INTERVENTION

Scaffolding Questions

1. What is the measure of the angle of the triangle with tower 3 at its vertex? 71.0°
2. What formula can you use to find the area of the triangle? Possible answer: area $= \frac{1}{2}bc \sin A$
3. Which law can you use to find an angle measure of a triangle given side-side-side information? Law of Cosines
4. Which trigonometric ratio can you use to determine how far east of tower 1 the driver is? Possible answer: cosine
5. How can you determine the distance between the fire and tower 3? Possible answer: Solve a triangle with the fire, tower 1, and tower 3 at its vertices.

Extension

If a fire truck leaves the station and travels at an average speed of 35 mi/h, will it reach the fire in less than 5 min? Justify your answer. Yes, the fire truck has to travel a little more than 1.4 mi. It should take the truck less than 3 min to travel this distance.

READY TO GO ON?

Quiz for Lessons 13-5 Through 13-6

13-5 The Law of Sines

Find the area of each triangle. Round to the nearest tenth.

1. 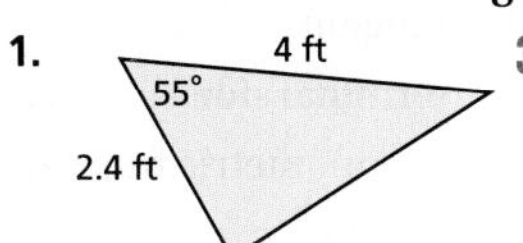

3.9 ft^2

2. 8.2 cm, 10.4 cm, 48°, 36°
42.4 cm^2

Solve each triangle. Round to the nearest tenth.

3. 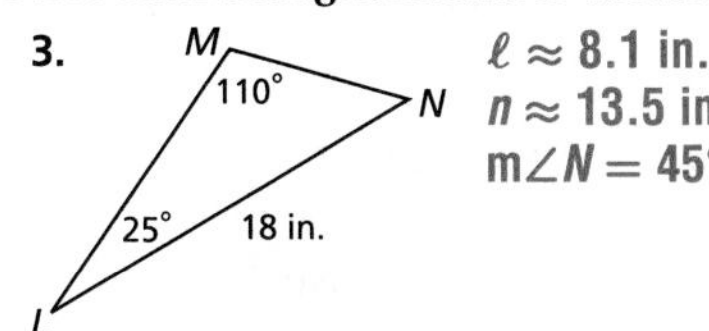

$\ell \approx 8.1$ in.; $n \approx 13.5$ in; $m\angle N = 45°$

4. 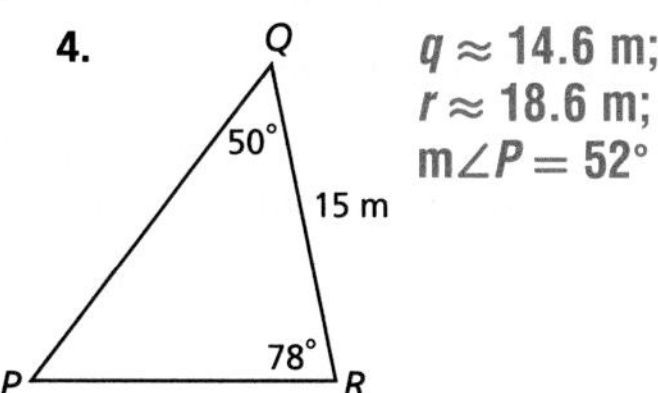

$q \approx 14.6$ m; $r \approx 18.6$ m; $m\angle P = 52°$

Derrick is designing triangular panes for a stained glass window. Determine the number of different triangles that he can form using the given measurements. Then solve the triangles. Round to the nearest tenth.

5. $a = 2.1$ cm, $b = 1.8$ cm, $m\angle A = 42°$
6. $a = 3$ cm, $b = 4.6$ cm, $m\angle A = 95°$ 0 triangles
7. The rangers at two park stations spot a signal flare at the same time. Based on the measurements shown in the diagram, what is the distance between each park station and the point where the flare was set off? Round to the nearest tenth.
distance from station 1: 6.2 km; distance from station 2: 7.0 km

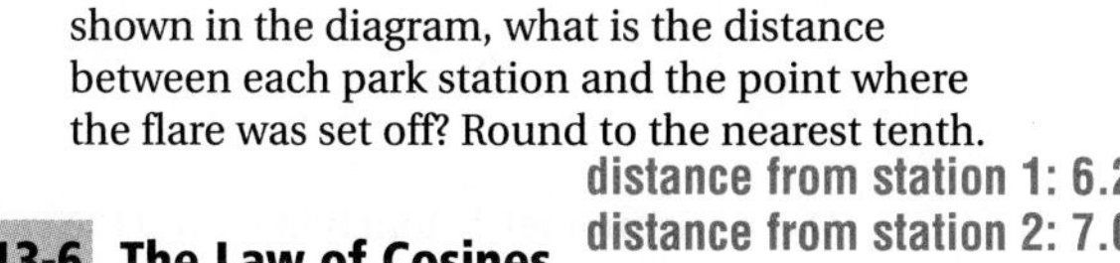

13-6 The Law of Cosines

Use the given measurements to solve each triangle. Round to the nearest tenth.

8. B, 21, a, 85°, A, 15, C

9. 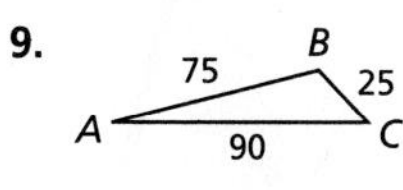

10. A civil engineer is working on plans for a new road called Pine Avenue. This road will intersect Market Boulevard and 3rd Street as shown. To the nearest degree, what is the measure of the angle that Pine Avenue will make with Market Boulevard? 94°

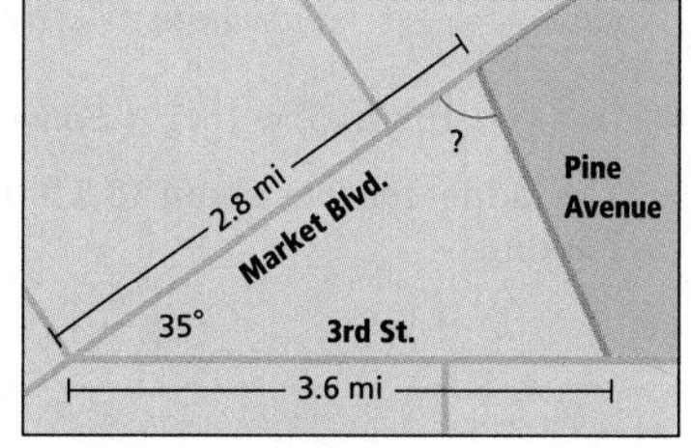

11. A school courtyard is shaped like a triangle. Its sides measure 25 yards, 27.5 yards, and 32 yards. What is the area of the courtyard to the nearest square yard? 332 yd^2

READY TO GO ON? SECTION 13B

Organizer

Objective: Assess students' mastery of concepts and skills in Lessons 13-5 through 13-6.

Resources

Assessment Resources
Section 13B Quiz

Test & Practice Generator
One-Stop Planner®

INTERVENTION Resources

***Ready to Go On? Intervention and Enrichment* Worksheets**

***Ready to Go On?* CD-ROM**

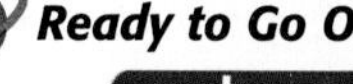

***Ready to Go On?* Online**
my.hrw.com

Answers

5. 1 triangle; $c \approx 3.1$ cm; $m\angle B \approx 35.0°$; $m\angle C \approx 103.0°$
8. $a \approx 24.7$; $m\angle B \approx 37.2°$; $m\angle C \approx 57.8°$
9. $m\angle A \approx 14.0°$; $m\angle B \approx 119.6°$; $m\angle C \approx 46.4°$

READY TO GO ON? Diagnose and Prescribe

Ready to Go On? Intervention	*Ready to Go On? Intervention,* Section 13B		
	Worksheets	CD-ROM	Online
Lesson 13-5	13-5 Intervention	Activity 13-5	Diagnose and Prescribe Online
Lesson 13-6	13-6 Intervention	Activity 13-6	

Organizer

Objective: Help students organize and review key concepts and skills presented in Chapter 13.

Online Edition
Multilingual Glossary

Resources

Puzzle Pro
One-Stop Planner®

***Multilingual Glossary* Online**

go.hrw.com
KEYWORD: MB7 Glossary

***Lesson Tutorial Videos* CD-ROM**

Test & Practice Generator
One-Stop Planner®

Answers

1. radian
2. cosecant
3. standard position
4. $\sin\theta = \frac{3}{5}$; $\cos\theta = \frac{4}{5}$; $\tan\theta = \frac{3}{4}$; $\csc\theta = \frac{5}{3}$; $\sec\theta = \frac{5}{4}$; $\cot\theta = \frac{4}{3}$
5. $\sin\theta = \frac{2}{3}$; $\cos\theta = \frac{\sqrt{5}}{3}$; $\tan\theta = \frac{2\sqrt{5}}{5}$; $\csc\theta = \frac{3}{2}$; $\sec\theta = \frac{3\sqrt{5}}{5}$; $\cot\theta = \frac{\sqrt{5}}{2}$
6. $12\sqrt{3}$
7. $\frac{9\sqrt{2}}{2}$
8. 18 ft
9. 178 m

Study Guide: Review

Vocabulary

angle of rotation 936	inverse cosine function 951	sine 929
cosecant 932	inverse sine function 951	standard position 936
cosine 929	inverse tangent function 951	tangent 929
cotangent 932	radian 943	terminal side 936
coterminal angle 937	reference angle 937	trigonometric function 929
initial side 936	secant 932	unit circle 944

Complete the sentences below with vocabulary words from the list above.

1. A(n) ___?___ is a unit of angle measure based on arc length.
2. The ___?___ of an acute angle in a right triangle is the ratio of the length of the hypotenuse to the length of the opposite leg.
3. An angle in ___?___ has its vertex at the origin and one ray on the positive x-axis.

13-1 Right-Angle Trigonometry *(pp. 929–935)*

EXAMPLES

■ **Find the values of the sine, cosine, and tangent functions for θ.**

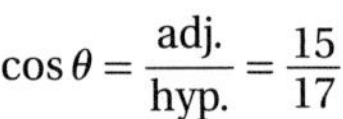

$$\sin\theta = \frac{\text{opp.}}{\text{hyp.}} = \frac{8}{17}$$

$$\cos\theta = \frac{\text{adj.}}{\text{hyp.}} = \frac{15}{17}$$

$$\tan\theta = \frac{\text{opp.}}{\text{adj.}} = \frac{8}{15}$$

■ **A 16 ft ladder is leaned against a building as shown. How high up the building does the ladder reach?**

h ft
16 ft
75°

$$\sin\theta = \frac{\text{opp.}}{\text{hyp.}}$$

$\sin 75° = \frac{h}{16}$ *Substitute.*

$h = 16\sin 75° \approx 15.5$ *Solve for h.*

The ladder reaches about 15.5 ft up the building.

EXERCISES

Find the values of the six trigonometric functions for θ.

4.
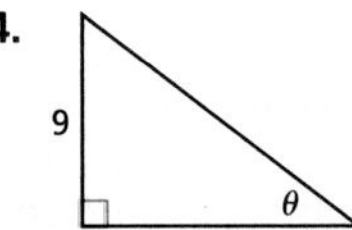

5.
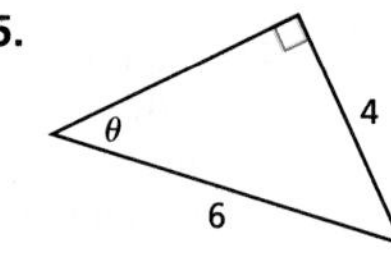

Use a trigonometric function to find the value of x.

6.
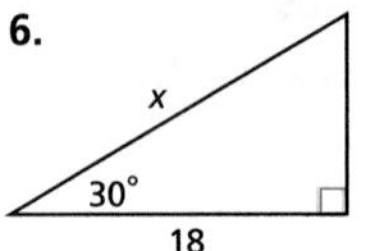

7.
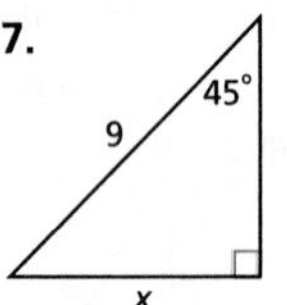

8. A support wire is being attached to a telephone pole as shown in the diagram. To the nearest foot, how long does the wire need to be?

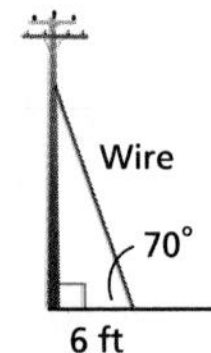

9. The angle of depression from a watchtower to a forest fire is 8°. If the watchtower is 25 m high, what is the distance between the base of the tower and the fire to the nearest meter?

Answers

10.
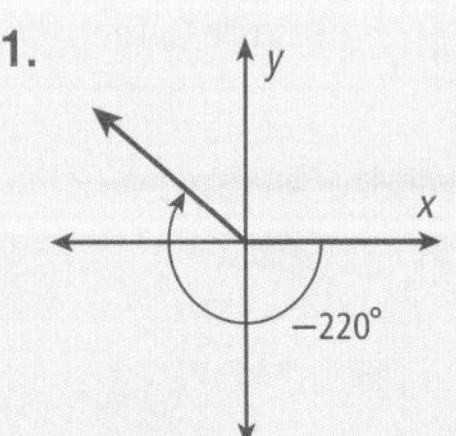

11.
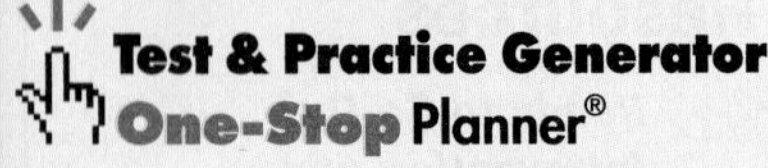

12.
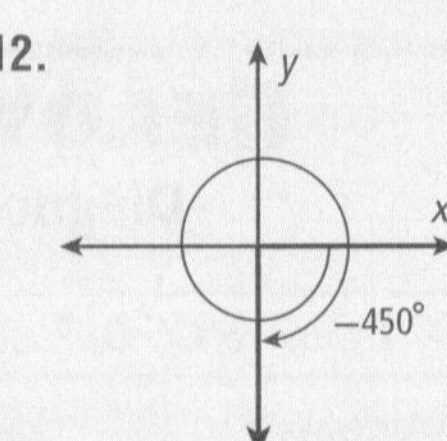

13-2 Angles of Rotation *(pp. 936–941)*

EXAMPLES

- **Draw a $-290°$ angle in standard position.**

  Rotate the terminal side 290° clockwise.

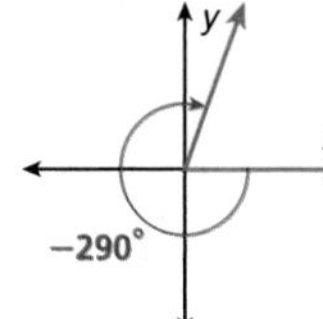

- **$P(-5, 12)$ is a point on the terminal side of θ in standard position. Find the exact value of the six trigonometric functions of θ.**

  $r = \sqrt{(-5)^2 + (12)^2} = 13$ *Find r.*

  $\sin\theta = \frac{y}{r} = \frac{12}{13}$ $\cos\theta = \frac{x}{r} = \frac{-5}{13} = -\frac{5}{13}$

  $\tan\theta = \frac{y}{x} = \frac{12}{-5} = -\frac{12}{5}$ $\csc\theta = \frac{1}{\sin\theta} = \frac{13}{12}$

  $\sec\theta = \frac{1}{\cos\theta} = -\frac{13}{5}$ $\cot\theta = \frac{1}{\tan\theta} = -\frac{5}{12}$

EXERCISES

Draw an angle with the given measure in standard position.

10. $195°$ **11.** $-220°$ **12.** $-450°$

Find the measures of a positive angle and a negative angle that are coterminal with each given angle.

13. $\theta = 115°$ **14.** $\theta = 382°$ **15.** $\theta = -135°$

Find the measure of the reference angle for each given angle.

16. $\theta = 84°$ **17.** $\theta = 127°$ **18.** $\theta = -105°$

***P* is a point on the terminal side of θ in standard position. Find the exact value of the six trigonometric functions for θ.**

19. $P(-4, 3)$ **20.** $P(5, 12)$ **21.** $P(-15, -8)$

22. $P(8, -3)$ **23.** $P(-9, -1)$ **24.** $P(-5, 10)$

13-3 The Unit Circle *(pp. 943–949)*

EXAMPLES

Convert each measure from degrees to radians or from radians to degrees.

- $-60°$

  $-60°\left(\frac{\pi \text{ radians}}{180°}\right) = -\frac{\pi}{3}$ radians

- $\frac{5\pi}{3}$ radians

  $\left(\frac{5\pi}{3} \text{ radians}\right)\left(\frac{180°}{\pi \text{ radians}}\right) = 300°$

- **Use a reference angle to find the exact value of $\tan 150°$.**

  Step 1 The reference angle measures 30°.

  Step 2 Find the tangent of the reference angle.

  $\tan 30° = \frac{\sqrt{3}}{3}$

  Step 3 Adjust the sign, if needed.

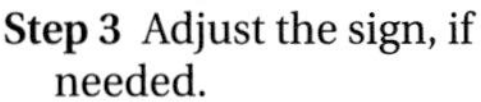

  The tangent ratio is negative if the terminal side of the angle is in Quadrant II.

  $\tan 150° = -\frac{\sqrt{3}}{3}$

EXERCISES

Convert each measure from degrees to radians or from radians to degrees.

25. $270°$ **26.** $-120°$ **27.** $400°$

28. $\frac{\pi}{6}$ **29.** $-\frac{\pi}{9}$ **30.** $\frac{9\pi}{4}$

Use the unit circle to find the exact value of each trigonometric function.

31. $\cos 240°$ **32.** $\tan\frac{3\pi}{4}$ **33.** $\sec 300°$

Use a reference angle to find the exact value of the sine, cosine, and tangent of each angle measure.

34. $\frac{7\pi}{6}$ **35.** $300°$ **36.** $-\frac{\pi}{3}$

37. A circle has a radius of 16 in. To the nearest inch, what is the length of an arc of the circle that is intercepted by a central angle of 80°?

38. The minute hand on a clock on a town hall tower is 1.5 meters in length.

a. Find the angle in radians through which the minute hand rotates in 10 minutes.

b. To the nearest tenth of a meter, how far does the tip of the minute hand travel in 10 minutes?

Answers

13. Possible answer: 475°; –245°
14. Possible answer: 22°; –338°
15. Possible answer: 225°; –495°
16. 84°
17. 53°
18. 75°
19. $\sin\theta = \frac{3}{5}$; $\cos\theta = -\frac{4}{5}$; $\tan\theta = -\frac{3}{4}$; $\csc\theta = \frac{5}{3}$; $\sec\theta = -\frac{5}{4}$; $\cot\theta = -\frac{4}{3}$
20. $\sin\theta = \frac{12}{13}$; $\cos\theta = \frac{5}{13}$; $\tan\theta = \frac{12}{5}$; $\csc\theta = \frac{13}{12}$; $\sec\theta = \frac{13}{5}$; $\cot\theta = \frac{5}{12}$
21. $\sin\theta = -\frac{8}{17}$; $\cos\theta = -\frac{15}{17}$; $\tan\theta = \frac{8}{15}$; $\csc\theta = -\frac{17}{8}$; $\sec\theta = -\frac{17}{15}$; $\cot\theta = \frac{15}{8}$
22. $\sin\theta = -\frac{3\sqrt{73}}{73}$; $\cos\theta = \frac{8\sqrt{73}}{73}$; $\tan\theta = -\frac{3}{8}$; $\csc\theta = -\frac{\sqrt{73}}{3}$; $\sec\theta = \frac{\sqrt{73}}{8}$; $\cot\theta = -\frac{8}{3}$
23. $\sin\theta = -\frac{\sqrt{82}}{82}$; $\cos\theta = -\frac{9\sqrt{82}}{82}$; $\tan\theta = \frac{1}{9}$; $\csc\theta = -\sqrt{82}$; $\sec\theta = -\frac{\sqrt{82}}{9}$; $\cot\theta = 9$
24. $\sin\theta = \frac{2\sqrt{5}}{5}$; $\cos\theta = -\frac{\sqrt{5}}{5}$; $\tan\theta = -2$; $\csc\theta = \frac{\sqrt{5}}{2}$; $\sec\theta = -\sqrt{5}$; $\cot\theta = -\frac{1}{2}$
25. $\frac{3\pi}{2}$ radians
26. $-\frac{2\pi}{3}$ radians
27. $\frac{20\pi}{9}$ radians
28. 30°
29. –20°

Answers

30. 405°
31. $-\frac{1}{2}$
32. –1
33. 2
34. $\sin\frac{7\pi}{6} = -\frac{1}{2}$; $\cos\frac{7\pi}{6} = -\frac{\sqrt{3}}{2}$; $\tan\frac{7\pi}{6} = \frac{\sqrt{3}}{3}$

Answers

35. $\sin 300° = -\frac{\sqrt{3}}{2}$; $\cos 300° = \frac{1}{2}$; $\tan 300° = -\sqrt{3}$
36. $\sin\left(-\frac{\pi}{3}\right) = -\frac{\sqrt{3}}{2}$; $\cos\left(-\frac{\pi}{3}\right) = \frac{1}{2}$; $\tan\left(-\frac{\pi}{3}\right) = -\sqrt{3}$
37. 22 in.

38a. $\frac{\pi}{3}$ radians

b. 1.6 m

Answers

39. $\frac{\pi}{3} + (2\pi)n$ and $\frac{4\pi}{3} + (2\pi)n$, where n is an integer
40. $\frac{5\pi}{6} + (2\pi)n$ and $\frac{7\pi}{6} + (2\pi)n$, where n is an integer
41. $\frac{5\pi}{4} + (2\pi)n$ and $\frac{7\pi}{4} + (2\pi)n$, where n is an integer
42. $\frac{5\pi}{6} + (2\pi)n$ and $\frac{11\pi}{6} + (2\pi)n$, where n is an integer
43. $-30°$; $-\frac{\pi}{6}$ radians
44. $30°$; $\frac{\pi}{6}$ radians
45. $180°$; π radians
46. $45°$; $\frac{\pi}{4}$ radians
47. 34°
48. 41°
49. 17.5°
50. 162.5°
51. 65.6°
52. 245.6°
53. 5.4 m²
54. 4953.1 ft²
55. 24.0 in²
56. 112.5 cm²

13-4 Inverses of Trigonometric Functions *(pp. 950–955)*

EXAMPLES

■ **Evaluate $\text{Sin}^{-1}\left(-\frac{\sqrt{3}}{2}\right)$. Give your answer in both radians and degrees.**

$-\frac{\sqrt{3}}{2} = \text{Sin}\,\theta$ *Find the value of θ for $-\frac{\pi}{2} \le \theta \le \frac{\pi}{2}$.*

$-\frac{\sqrt{3}}{2} = \text{Sin}\left(-\frac{\pi}{3}\right)$ *Use y-coordinates of points on the unit circle.*

$$\text{Sin}^{-1}\left(-\frac{\sqrt{3}}{2}\right) = -\frac{\pi}{3}, \text{ or } \text{Sin}^{-1}\left(-\frac{\sqrt{3}}{2}\right) = -60°$$

■ **A boat is 2.8 miles east and 1.3 miles north of a dock. To the nearest degree, in what direction should the boat head to reach the dock?**

Step 1 Draw a diagram.

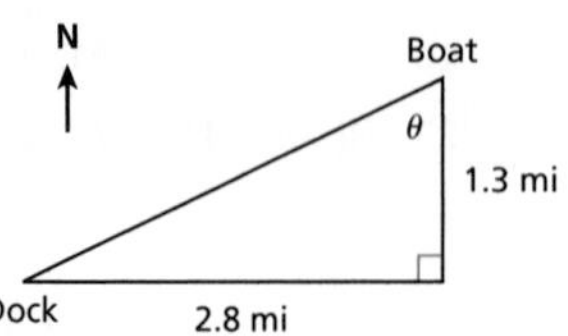

Step 2 Find the value of θ.

$\tan\theta = \frac{\text{opp.}}{\text{adj.}}$ *Use the tangent ratio.*

$\tan\theta = \frac{2.8}{1.3}$ *Substitute.*

$\theta = \text{Tan}^{-1}\left(\frac{2.8}{1.3}\right) \approx 65°$ *Solve for θ.*

The boat should head 65° west of south.

EXERCISES

Find all possible values of each expression.

39. $\tan^{-1}\sqrt{3}$
40. $\cos^{-1}\left(-\frac{\sqrt{3}}{2}\right)$
41. $\sin^{-1}\left(-\frac{\sqrt{2}}{2}\right)$
42. $\tan^{-1}\left(-\frac{\sqrt{3}}{3}\right)$

Evaluate each inverse trigonometric function. Give your answer in both radians and degrees.

43. $\text{Sin}^{-1}\left(-\frac{1}{2}\right)$
44. $\text{Tan}^{-1}\frac{\sqrt{3}}{3}$
45. $\text{Cos}^{-1}(-1)$
46. $\text{Sin}^{-1}\frac{\sqrt{2}}{2}$
47. A skateboard ramp is 39 inches long and rises to a height of 22 inches. To the nearest degree, what angle does the ramp make with the ground?
48. A parasail is a parachute that lifts a person into the air when he or she is towed by a boat. Shelley is parasailing at a height of 100 feet. If 152 feet of towline attaches her to the boat, what is the angle of depression from Shelley to the boat? Round to the nearest degree.

Solve each equation to the nearest tenth. Use the given restrictions.

49. $\sin\theta = 0.3$, for $-90° \le \theta \le 90°$
50. $\sin\theta = 0.3$, for $90° \le \theta \le 180°$
51. $\tan\theta = 2.2$, for $-90° < \theta < 90°$
52. $\tan\theta = 2.2$, for $180° \le \theta \le 270°$

13-5 The Law of Sines *(pp. 958–965)*

EXAMPLES

■ **Find the area of the triangle. Round to the nearest tenth.**

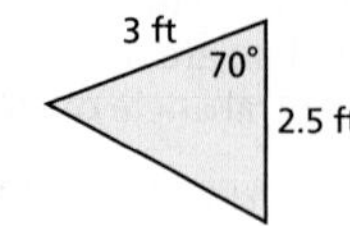

$\text{Area} = \frac{1}{2}ab\sin C$ *Use the area formula*

$= \frac{1}{2}(3)(2.5)\sin 70°$ *Substitute.*

$\approx 3.5 \text{ ft}^2$ *Evaluate.*

EXERCISES

Find the area of each triangle. Round to the nearest tenth.

53.

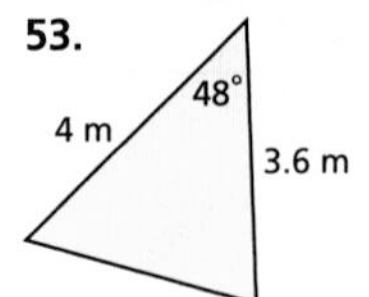

54.

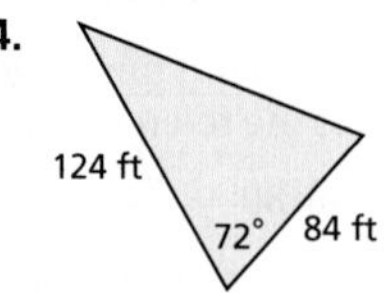

55.

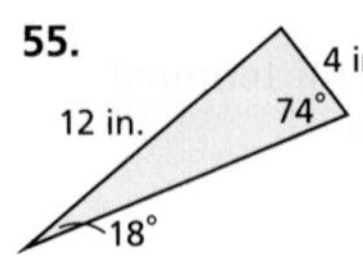

56.

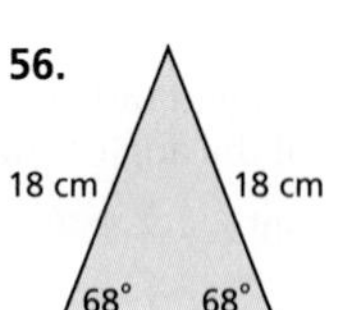

- **Solve the triangle. Round to the nearest tenth.**

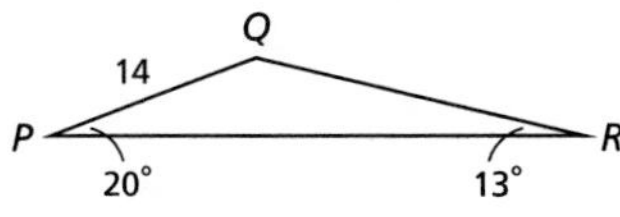

Step 1 Find the third angle measure.

$m\angle Q° = 180° - 20° - 13° = 147°$

Step 2 Use the Law of Sines to find the unknown side lengths.

$\frac{\sin P}{p} = \frac{\sin R}{r}$ $\frac{\sin Q}{q} = \frac{\sin R}{r}$

$\frac{\sin 20°}{p} = \frac{\sin 13°}{14}$ $\frac{\sin 147°}{q} = \frac{\sin 13°}{14}$

$p = \frac{14 \sin 20°}{\sin 13°}$ $q = \frac{14 \sin 147°}{\sin 13°}$

$p \approx 21.3$ $q \approx 33.9$

Solve each triangle. Round to the nearest tenth.

57.

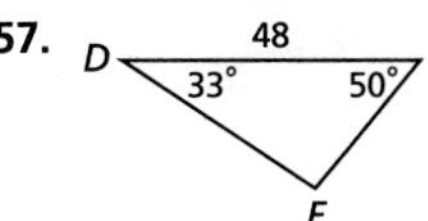

58.

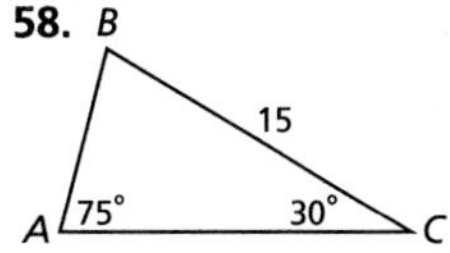

59.

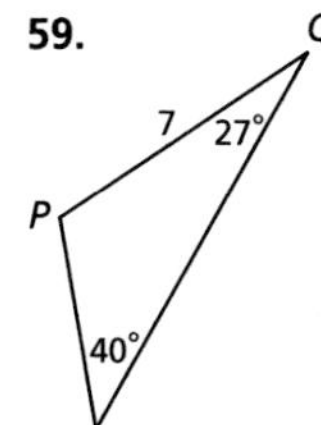

60.

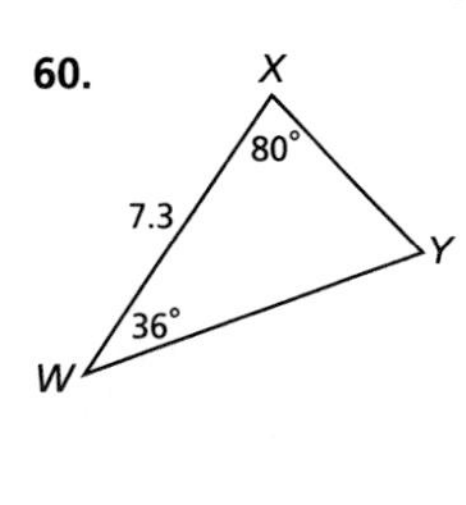

61. A graphic artist is designing a triangular logo. Determine the number of different triangles that he can form using the measurements $a = 14$ cm, $b = 16$ cm, and $m\angle A = 55°$. Then solve the triangles. Round to the nearest tenth.

13-6 The Law of Cosines *(pp. 966–973)*

EXAMPLES

- **Use the given measurements to solve $\triangle ABC$. Round to the nearest tenth.**

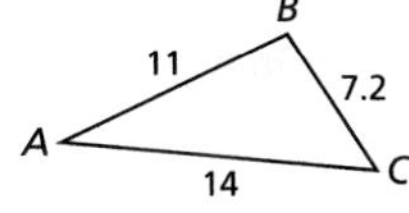

Step 1 Find the measure of the largest angle, $\angle B$.

$b^2 = a^2 + c^2 - 2ac\cos B$

$14^2 = 7.2^2 + 11^2 - 2(7.2)(11)\cos B$

$m\angle B \approx 98.4°$

Step 2 Find another angle measure.

$a^2 = b^2 + c^2 - 2bc\cos A$

$7.2^2 = 14^2 + 11^2 - 2(14)(11)\cos A$

$m\angle A \approx 30.6°$

Step 3 Find the third angle measure.

$m\angle C \approx 180° - 30.6° - 98.4° \approx 51.0°$

- **A triangular tile has sides measuring 4 in., 5 in., and 8 in. What is the area of the tile to the nearest square inch?**

$s = \frac{1}{2}(4 + 5 + 8) = 8.5$ *Find the value of s.*

$A = \sqrt{s(s-a)(s-b)(s-c)}$ *Heron's Formula*

$A = \sqrt{8.5(8.5-4)(8.5-5)(8.5-8)} \approx 8.2 \text{ in}^2$

EXERCISES

Use the given measurements to solve $\triangle ABC$. Round to the nearest tenth.

62. $m\angle C = 29°$, $a = 14$, $b = 30$

63. $m\angle A = 110°$, $b = 18$, $c = 12$

64. $a = 12$, $b = 3$, $c = 10$

65. $a = 7$, $b = 9$, $c = 11$

66. A bicycle race has a triangular course with the dimensions shown.

a. To the nearest tenth of a kilometer, how long is the race?

b. At an average speed of 28 km/h, how many hours will it take a rider to complete the race? Round to the nearest tenth.

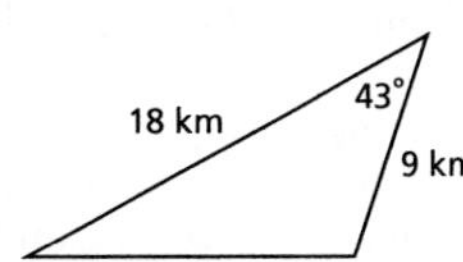

67. A triangular wading pool has side lengths that measure 10 ft, 12 ft, and 16 ft. What is the area of the pool's surface to the nearest square foot?

68. A triangular pennant has side lengths that measure 24 in., 24 in., and 8 in. What is the area of the pennant to the nearest square inch?

Answers

57. $m\angle F = 97°$; $d \approx 26.3$; $e \approx 37.0$

58. $m\angle B = 75°$; $b = 15$; $c \approx 7.8$

59. $m\angle P = 113°$; $p \approx 10.0$; $q \approx 4.9$

60. $m\angle Y = 64°$; $w = 4.8$; $x = 8.0$

61. 2 triangles; $m\angle B_1 \approx 69.4°$; $m\angle C_1 \approx 55.6°$; $c_1 \approx 14.1$ cm; $m\angle B_2 \approx 110.6°$; $m\angle C_2 \approx 14.4°$; $c_2 \approx 4.3$ cm

62. $m\angle A \approx 20.9°$; $m\angle B \approx 130.1°$; $c \approx 19.0$

63. $m\angle B \approx 43.0°$; $m\angle C \approx 27.0°$; $a \approx 24.8$

64. $m\angle A \approx 125.7°$; $m\angle B \approx 11.7°$; $m\angle C \approx 42.6°$

65. $m\angle A \approx 39.4°$; $m\angle B \approx 54.7°$; $m\angle C \approx 85.9°$

66a. 40.0 km

b. 1.4 h

67. 60 ft^2

68. 95 in^2

CHAPTER 13

Organizer

Objective: Assess students' mastery of concepts and skills in Chapter 13.

Online Edition

Resources

Assessment Resources

Chapter 13 Tests

- Free Response (Levels A, B, C)
- Multiple Choice (Levels A, B, C)
- Performance Assessment

***IDEA Works!* CD-ROM**

Modified Chapter 13 Test

Test & Practice Generator
One-Stop Planner®

Answers

1. $\sin\theta = \frac{24}{25}$; $\cos\theta = \frac{7}{25}$; $\tan\theta = \frac{24}{7}$; $\csc\theta = \frac{25}{24}$; $\sec\theta = \frac{25}{7}$; $\cot\theta = \frac{7}{24}$

2. $\sin\theta = \frac{2\sqrt{13}}{13}$; $\cos\theta = \frac{3\sqrt{13}}{13}$; $\tan\theta = \frac{2}{3}$; $\csc\theta = \frac{\sqrt{13}}{2}$; $\sec\theta = \frac{\sqrt{13}}{3}$; $\cot\theta = \frac{3}{2}$

State Resources

go.hrw.com
State Resources Online
KEYWORD: MB7 Resources

CHAPTER 13

CHAPTER TEST

Find the values of the six trigonometric functions for θ.

1.

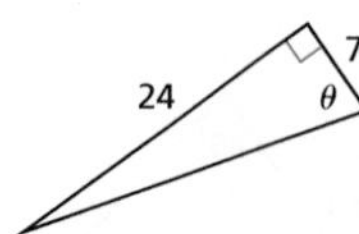

2.

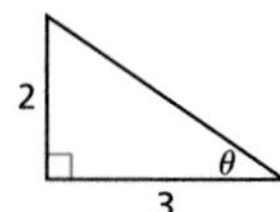

3. Katrina is flying a kite on 150 ft of string. The string makes an angle of 62° with the horizontal. If Katrina holds the end of the string 5 ft above the ground, how high is the kite? Round to the nearest foot. **137 ft**

Draw an angle with the given measure in standard position.

4. 100°

5. −210°

***P* is a point on the terminal side of θ in standard position. Find the exact value of the six trigonometric functions of θ.**

6. $P(-32, 24)$

7. $P(-3, -7)$

Convert each measure from degrees to radians or from radians to degrees.

8. 310° $\frac{31\pi}{18}$ **radians**

9. −36° $-\frac{\pi}{5}$ **radians**

10. $\frac{2\pi}{9}$ **40°**

11. $-\frac{5\pi}{6}$ **−150°**

Use the unit circle to find the exact value of each trigonometric function.

12. $\cos 210°$ $-\frac{\sqrt{3}}{2}$

13. $\tan\frac{11\pi}{6}$ $-\frac{\sqrt{3}}{3}$

Evaluate each inverse trigonometric function. Give your answer in both radians and degrees.

14. $\text{Cos}^{-1}\frac{\sqrt{2}}{2}$ $\frac{\pi}{4}$ **radians; 45°**

15. $\text{Sin}^{-1}\left(-\frac{\sqrt{3}}{2}\right)$ $-\frac{\pi}{3}$ **radians; −60°**

16. A limestone cave is 6.2 mi south and 1.4 mi east of the entrance of a national park. To the nearest degree, in what direction should a group at the entrance head in order to reach the cave? **77° south of east**

17. Find the area of $\triangle DEF$. Round to the nearest tenth. **425.8 cm²**

18. Use the given measurements to solve $\triangle DEF$. Round to the nearest tenth. $m\angle D \approx 26.2°$; $m\angle F \approx 71.8°$; $e \approx 44.8$ **cm**

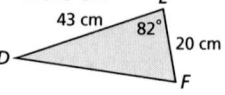

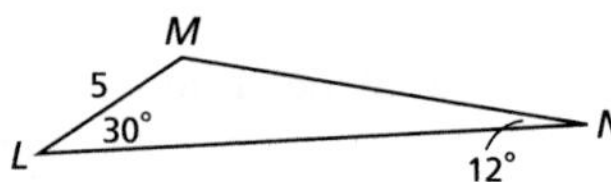

19. An artist is designing a wallpaper pattern based on triangles. Determine the number of different triangles she can form using the measurements $a = 28$, $b = 13$, and $m\angle A = 102°$. Then solve the triangles. Round to the nearest tenth. **1 triangle;** $m\angle B \approx 27.0°$; $m\angle C \approx 51.0°$; $c \approx 22.2$ **cm**

20. Solve $\triangle LMN$. Round to the nearest tenth. $m\angle M = 138°$; $\ell \approx 12.0$; $m \approx 16.1$

M
5
30°
L
N
12°

21. A lawn next to an office building is shaped like a triangle with sides measuring 16 ft, 24 ft, and 30 ft. What is the area of the lawn to the nearest square foot? **191 ft²**

Answers

4.

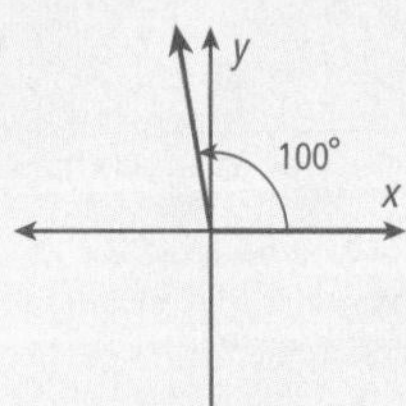

5.

y
x
−210°

6. $\sin\theta = \frac{3}{5}$; $\cos\theta = -\frac{4}{5}$; $\tan\theta = -\frac{3}{4}$; $\csc\theta = \frac{5}{3}$; $\sec\theta = -\frac{5}{4}$; $\cot\theta = -\frac{4}{3}$

7. $\sin\theta = -\frac{7\sqrt{58}}{58}$; $\cos\theta = -\frac{3\sqrt{58}}{58}$; $\tan\theta = \frac{7}{3}$; $\csc\theta = -\frac{\sqrt{58}}{7}$; $\sec\theta = -\frac{\sqrt{58}}{3}$; $\cot\theta = \frac{3}{7}$

COLLEGE ENTRANCE EXAM PRACTICE

FOCUS ON SAT MATHEMATICS SUBJECT TESTS

Though both the SAT Mathematics Subject Tests Level 1 and Level 2 may include questions involving basic trigonometric functions, only the Level 2 test may include questions involving the Law of Sines, the Law of Cosines, and radian measure.

You may want to time yourself as you take this practice test. It should take you about 6 minutes to complete.

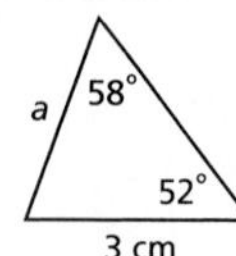

If you take the Level 1 test, make sure that your calculator is set to degree mode, because no questions will require you to use radians. If you take the Level 2 test, you will need to determine whether to use degree or radian mode as appropriate.

1. A right triangle has an angle measuring 22°. The shorter leg of the triangle has a length of 3 inches. What is the area of the triangle?

(A) 1.8 in^2

(B) 4.2 in^2

(C) 7.4 in^2

(D) 11.1 in^2

(E) 12.0 in^2

2. If $0 \le \theta \le \frac{\pi}{2}$ and $\cos^{-1}(\sin\theta) = \frac{\pi}{3}$, then what is the value of θ?

(A) $\frac{\pi}{6}$

(B) $\frac{\pi}{2}$

(C) $\frac{5\pi}{6}$

(D) $\frac{4\pi}{3}$

(E) $\frac{3\pi}{2}$

3. A triangle has side lengths of 7, 26, and 31. What is the measure of the smallest angle of the triangle?

(A) 8°

(B) 10°

(C) 26°

(D) 30°

(E) 40°

4. A manufacturer must produce a metal bar with a triangular cross section that meets the specifications shown. What is the length of side a?

a, 58°, 52°, 3 cm

Note: Figure not drawn to scale

(A) 2.4 cm

(B) 2.6 cm

(C) 2.8 cm

(D) 3.2 cm

(E) 3.6 cm

5. If $\sin B = \frac{5}{9}$ in the figure below, what is $\tan A$?

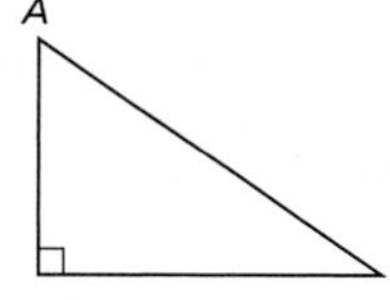

Note: Figure not drawn to scale

(A) 0.45

(B) 0.67

(C) 0.83

(D) 1.50

(E) 1.80

COLLEGE ENTRANCE EXAM PRACTICE CHAPTER 13

Organizer

Objective: Provide practice for college entrance exams such as the SAT Mathematics Subject Test Level 2.

Resources

Questions on the SAT Mathematics Subject Test Level 2 represent the following math content areas:

Algebra, 18%

Coordinate Geometry, 12%

Three-dimensional Geometry, 8%

Trigonometry, 20%

Functions, 24%

Statistics/Probability, 6%

Miscellaneous, 12%

Items on this page focus on:

- Trigonometry

Text References:

Item	1	2	3	4	5
Lesson	13-1	13-4	13-6	13-5	13-1

TEST PREP DOCTOR

1. Students who chose **A** may have assumed that the shorter leg is adjacent to the 22° angle rather than opposite it. Students who chose **C** may have found the length of the longer leg and then forgotten to find the area of the triangle.

2. Students who chose **C** found a value of θ that satisfies the equation but not the condition $0 \le \theta \le \frac{\pi}{2}$. Point out that three of the answer choices, **C, D,** and **E,** can be automatically eliminated because they do not meet the restrictions on the value of θ.

3. Students who chose **E** correctly found the measure of an angle of the triangle but not the smallest angle. Remind students that the smallest angle is opposite the shortest side.

4. Students who chose **D** may have switched the expressions $\sin 52°$ and $\sin 58°$ when substituting into the Law of Sines.

5. Remind students that they need to know the length of the legs to evaluate $\tan A$. Suggest that students use the value of $\sin B$ to label the lengths of two of the triangle's sides. Students can then use the Pythagorean Theorem to determine the length of the third side.

Organizer

Objective: Provide opportunities to learn and practice common test-taking strategies.

 Online Edition

Resources

 ***State Test Prep Workbook***

 ***State Test Prep CD-ROM***

 ***State Test Practice Online***

go.hrw.com
KEYWORD: MB7 TestPrep

TEST PREP DOCTOR This Test Tackler focuses on using spatial reasoning to visualize geometric figures. Make sure that students are familiar with basic solid figures such as prisms, cylinders, and pyramids and that they can recognize the two-dimensional shapes that make up the faces, bases, and surfaces of these figures.

Standardized Test Strategies

Multiple Choice: Spatial-Reasoning Problems

Some problems test your ability to use spatial reasoning. To solve these problems, you must be able to recognize different views of geometric figures. Orthographic drawings and nets are two common ways of representing three-dimensional objects. An *orthographic drawing* usually presents three views of a three-dimensional object: top, front, and side. A *net* is a diagram that can be folded to form a three-dimensional figure.

EXAMPLE 1

The drawing shows the top view of a structure made from cubes as well as the number of cubes in each column of the structure. Which three-dimensional view represents the same structure?

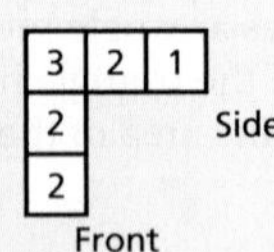

Ⓐ 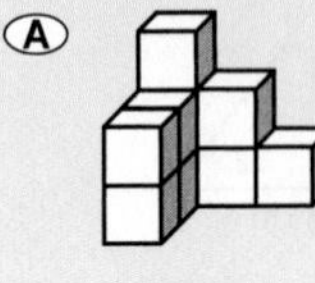

Ⓒ 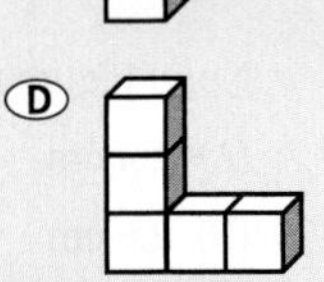

Ⓑ 

Ⓓ

Start by sketching the top view of each answer choice.

Choice A 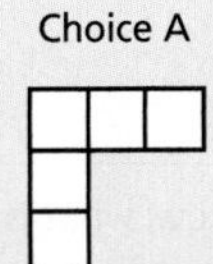

Choice B 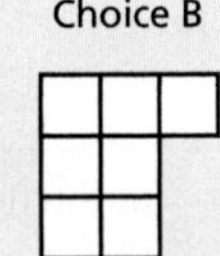

Choice C 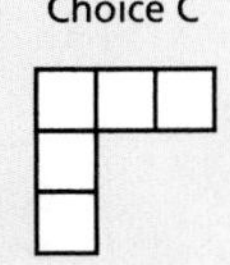

Choice D 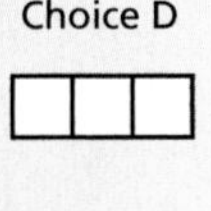

Choices B and D can be eliminated because their top views do not match the one given in the problem. Next, count the number of cubes in each column of choices A and C.

Choice A 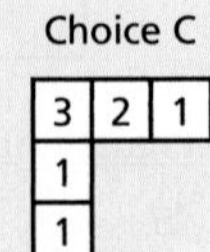

Choice C

3	2	1
1		
1		

The two front columns of choice C have only 1 cube each instead of 2. Therefore, choice C can be eliminated. Each column of choice A, however, has the correct number of cubes.

The correct answer is choice A.

If you have trouble visualizing the geometric figures, make a quick sketch. Your sketch does not need to be exact, but it should show the sides or faces of the figures in the correct relationships to each other.

Read each test item and answer the questions that follow.

Item A
The front, top, and side views of a solid are shown below. What is the volume of the solid?

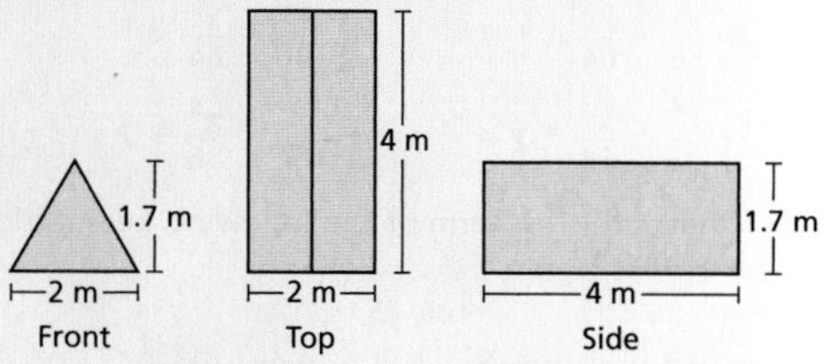

1.7 m, 2 m — Front; 4 m, 2 m — Top; 1.7 m, 4 m — Side

Ⓐ 6.8 m^3 Ⓒ 13.6 m^3

Ⓑ 9.1 m^3 Ⓓ 16.5 m^3

1. Make a sketch of the figure. What type of figure do the three views show?
2. How can you determine the volume of this figure?

Item B
What three-dimensional figure does this net represent?

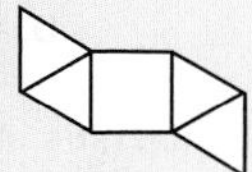

Ⓕ Square pyramid
Ⓖ Triangular pyramid
Ⓗ Rectangular prism
Ⓙ Triangular prism

3. What type and number of faces does the figure have?
4. What type and number of faces does each of the answer choices have?

Item C
Which of the following is the front view of the figure shown?

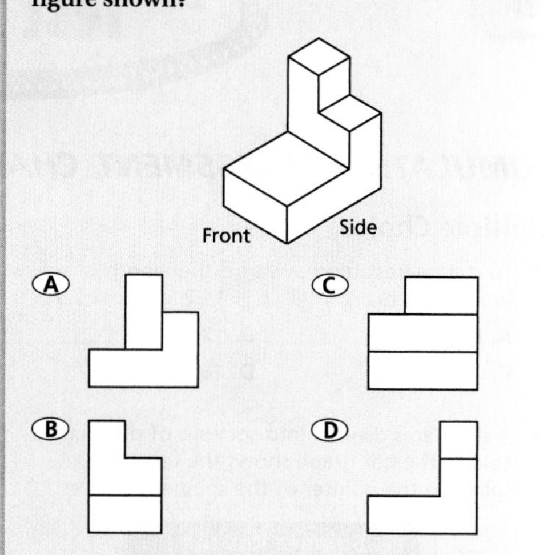

5. Make a sketch of the figure. Shade the faces on the front of the figure.
6. Describe the shapes of these faces.

Item D
Which is a true statement about the net of the cube shown?

Ⓕ The face with the star and the face with the circle are parallel.
Ⓖ The face with the heart and the face with the circle are perpendicular.
Ⓗ The faces with the triangles are parallel.
Ⓙ The face with the number 5 and the face with the star are perpendicular.

7. Which faces of the cube are opposite each other? Are opposite faces parallel or perpendicular to each other?
8. Can faces that share an edge be parallel to each other? Explain.

Answers

1. triangular prism

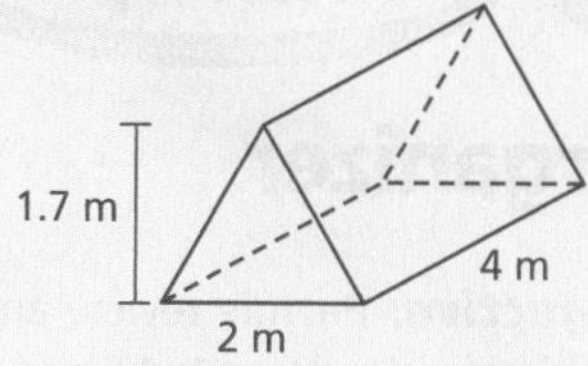

2. Possible answer: Find the area of a triangular base of the prism by using the formula $A = \frac{1}{2}bh$. Then multiply this area by the height of the prism when resting on a base.
3. 1 square face and 4 triangular faces
4. choice F: 1 square face and 4 triangular faces; choice G: 4 triangular faces; choice H: 6 rectangular faces; choice J: 2 triangular faces and 3 rectangular faces
5. 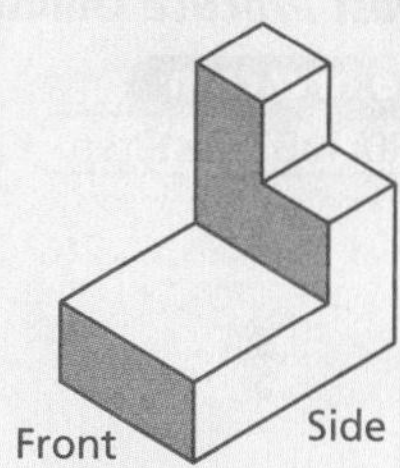

6. a rectangle and an L-shaped polygon
7. the face with a 5 and a face with a triangle; the face with the star and a face with a triangle; the face with the heart and the face with a circle; parallel
8. No; faces that are parallel do not intersect.

Answers to Test Items

A. A
B. F
C. B
D. J

State Resources

go.hrw.com
State Resources Online
KEYWORD: MB7 Resources

CHAPTER 13

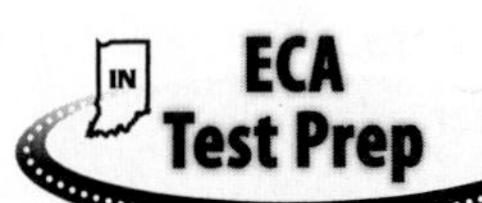

Organizer

Objective: Provide review and practice for Chapters 1–13 and standardized tests.

Resources

Assessment Resources

Chapter 13 Cumulative Test

State Test Prep Workbook

State Test Prep CD-ROM

State Test Practice Online

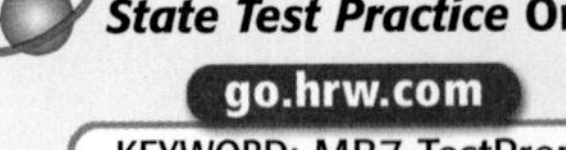

Answers

1. D
2. D
3. A
4. A
5. B
6. C
7. B
8. B
9. D
10. D
11. D
12. B
13. C
14. D

Core Standard	Items
3	7
4	11
5	18
7	6

CHAPTER 13

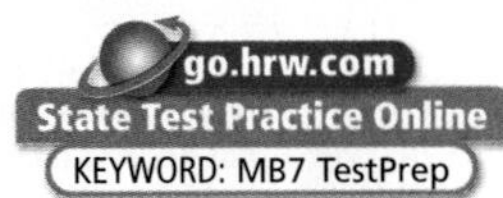

CUMULATIVE ASSESSMENT, CHAPTERS 1–13

Multiple Choice

1. To the nearest tenth, what is the length of side a in $\triangle ABC$ if $m\angle A = 98°$, $b = 14.2$, and $c = 5.9$?

A. 8.4 **B.** 12.9

C. 15.4 **D.** 16.1

2. A spinner is divided into sections of different colors. The bar graph shows the results of spinning the pointer of the spinner 50 times.

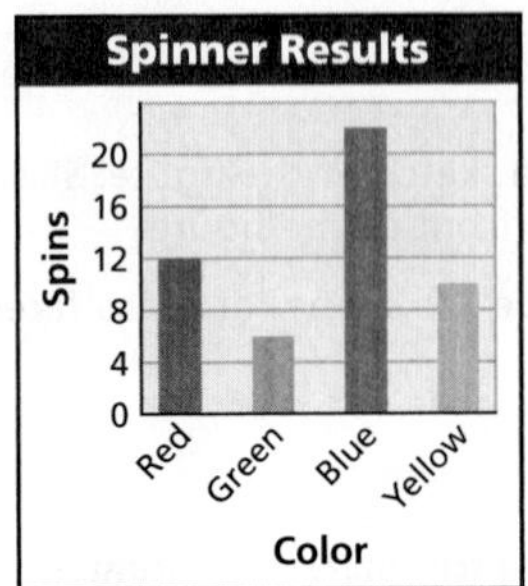

What is the experimental probability that the pointer of the spinner will land on a blue section?

A. 0.05 **B.** 0.22

C. 0.25 **D.** 0.44

3. If $-\frac{\pi}{2} \le \theta \le \frac{\pi}{2}$, what value of θ makes the equation $\sin^{-1}\left(\frac{1}{2}\right) = \theta$ true?

A. $\frac{\pi}{6}$ **B.** $\frac{\pi}{4}$

C. $\frac{\pi}{3}$ **D.** $\frac{5\pi}{6}$

4. What is the inverse of the matrix $\begin{bmatrix} -3 & 4 \\ 0 & -1 \end{bmatrix}$?

A. $\begin{bmatrix} -\frac{1}{3} & -\frac{4}{3} \\ 0 & -1 \end{bmatrix}$ **B.** $\begin{bmatrix} 1 & 0 \\ -4 & 3 \end{bmatrix}$

C. $\begin{bmatrix} -\frac{1}{3} & \frac{1}{4} \\ 0 & -1 \end{bmatrix}$ **D.** $\begin{bmatrix} -1 & -4 \\ 0 & -3 \end{bmatrix}$

5. What is the equation of a hyperbola with center (0, 0), a vertex at (0, 6), and a focus at (0, 10)?

A. $\frac{x^2}{36} - \frac{y^2}{64} = 1$ **B.** $\frac{y^2}{36} - \frac{x^2}{64} = 1$

C. $\frac{y^2}{36} + \frac{x^2}{64} = 1$ **D.** $\frac{y^2}{64} - \frac{x^2}{36} = 1$

6. What is the 7th term of the following geometric sequence?

125, 25, 5, 1, ...

A. 0.2 **B.** 0.04

C. 0.008 **D.** 0.0016

7. What type of function best models the data in the table?

x	−2	−1	0	1	2
y	6.35	11.6	29.35	59.6	102.35

A. linear **B.** quadratic

C. cubic **D.** square root

8. If $f(x) = \frac{3}{2}x - 4$ and $g(x) = \frac{1}{2}f(x)$, what is the y-intercept of $g(x)$?

A. −4 **B.** −2

C. $\frac{1}{2}$ **D.** $\frac{8}{3}$

9. What is the common ratio of the exponential function represented by the table?

x	−2	−1	0	1	2
y	2.56	3.2	4	5	6.25

A. 0.16 **B.** 0.25

C. 0.64 **D.** 1.25

10. What effect does a translation 3 units right have on the graph of $f(x) = 2x - 5$?

A. The slope increases.

B. The slope decreases.

C. The value of the y-intercept increases.

D. The value of the y-intercept decreases.

TEST PREP DOCTOR

For **Item 1,** students who chose **C** may have used the Pythagorean Theorem rather than the Law of Cosines to find the length of the third side. Remind students that the Pythagorean Theorem applies only to right triangles.

For **Item 12,** students who chose **A** may have found $\tan\theta$ and students who chose **C** may have found $\sin\theta$. Remind students that for a point $P(x, y)$ on the terminal side of θ in standard position, $\cos\theta = \frac{x}{r}$.

Answers

15. Part A: $f(x) = \begin{cases} 12 & \text{if } 0 < x < 13 \\ 20 & \text{if } 13 \le x \le 60 \\ 15 & \text{if } x > 60 \end{cases}$

Part B:

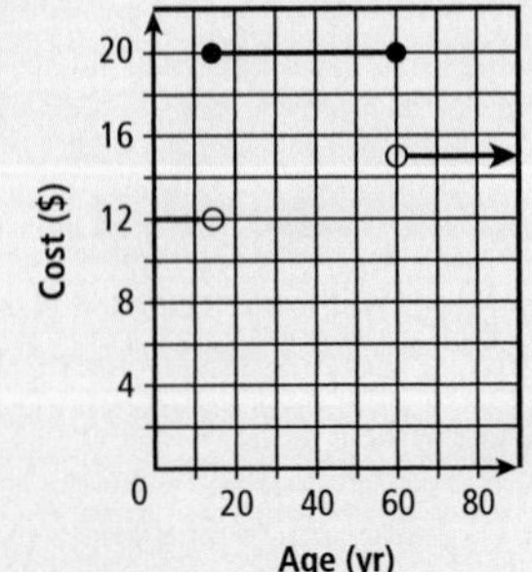

One way to check whether two expressions are equivalent is to substitute the same value for the variable in each expression. If the expressions simplify to different values, then they are *not* equivalent.

11. Which of the following is equivalent to $(x + 4)^3$?

A. $x^3 + 64$

B. $x^3 + 8x + 16$

C. $4x^3 + 32x^2 + 64x$

D. $x^3 + 12x^2 + 48x + 64$

12. What is $\cos\theta$?

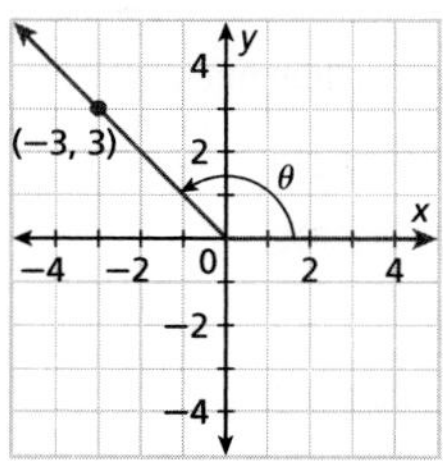

A. -1 **B.** $-\frac{\sqrt{2}}{2}$

C. $\frac{\sqrt{2}}{2}$ **D.** 1

13. What is the measure in degrees of an angle that measures $\frac{3\pi}{4}$ radians?

A. 45° **B.** 90°

C. 135° **D.** 180°

14. To the nearest hundredth, what is the value of x in the triangle below?

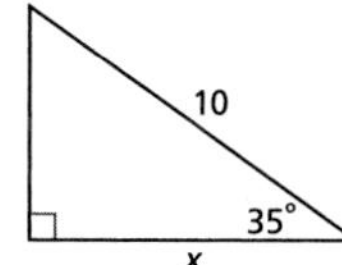

A. 3.86

B. 5.74

C. 7.00

D. 8.19

Short Answer

15. Tickets for the water park cost $12 for children under 13, $20 for people ages 13 to 60, and $15 for people over 60 years of age.

Part A Write a function to represent the cost y in dollars of a ticket to the water park given a person's age x in years.

Part B Graph the function.

16. What are the constraints on the region bounded by the quadrilateral below?

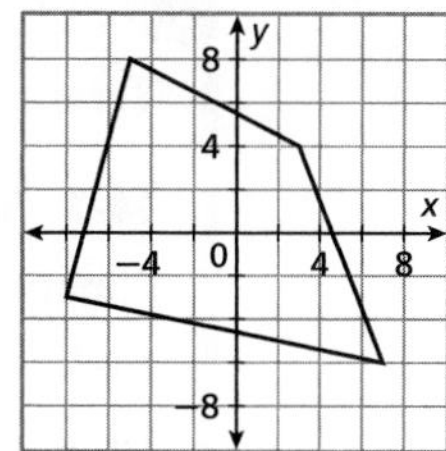

17. The table shows the number of Atlantic hurricanes for the years 1997–2004.

Atlantic Hurricanes			
Year	**Number**	**Year**	**Number**
1997	3	2001	9
1998	10	2002	4
1999	8	2003	7
2000	8	2004	9

Part A Make a box-and-whisker plot of the hurricane data.

Part B What is the mean number of hurricanes per year for the time period shown in the table?

Extended Response

18. The choir director at a high school wants to rent an auditorium for an upcoming performance. To pay for the auditorium, $550 must be raised in ticket sales. The cost of the tickets will depend on the number of people who are expected to attend the performance.

Part A Write a function to represent the number of dollars y a ticket should cost when x is the number of people who are expected to attend the performance.

Part B What are the asymptotes of the function?

Part C Graph the function.

Part D What is a reasonable domain and range for the function? Show or explain your work.

Part E How much should tickets cost if 250 people are expected to attend the performance?

Short Answer Rubric

Items 15–17

Score 2 = Thorough understanding of mathematical concepts and processes.

Score 1 = Partial understanding of mathematical concepts and/or processes.

Score 0 = Limited or no understanding of the problem-solving concepts.

Blank = No written response.

Extended Response Rubric

Item 18

Score 4 = Thorough understanding of mathematical concepts and processes.

Score 3 = Demonstrated understanding of mathematical concepts and processes, but an error in computation or explanation.

Score 2 = Partial understanding of mathematical concepts and/or processes.

Score 1 = Limited understanding and execution of the problem-solving concepts.

Score 0 = No understanding of the problem-solving concepts.

Blank = No written response.

16. $\begin{cases} 2y + x \le 11 \\ 2y + 5x \le 23 \\ 5y + x \ge -23 \\ 3y - 11x \le 79 \end{cases}$

17. Part A:

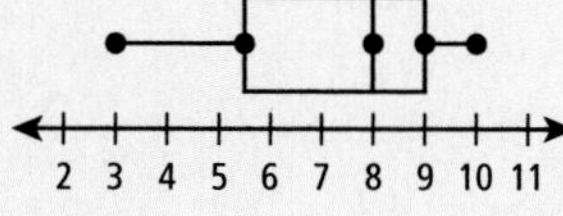

Part B: 7.25

18. Part A: $y = \frac{550}{x}$

Part B: $x = 0$; $y = 0$

Part C:

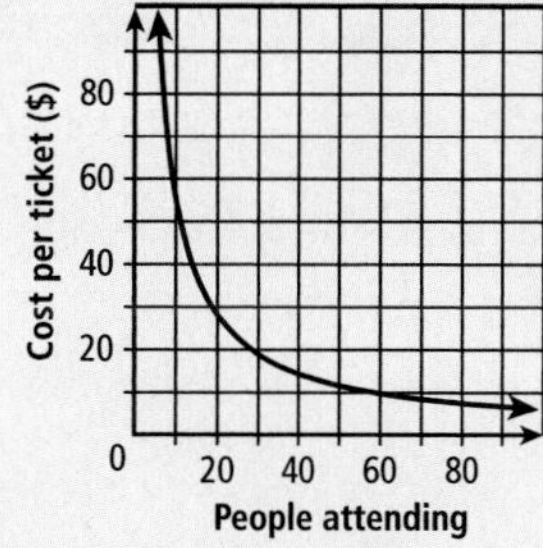

Part D: D: $\{x \mid x \in \mathbb{N}\}$; R: $\{y \mid y > 0\}$; x represents a number of people, so x must be a natural number. y represents the cost of a ticket, so y must be greater than 0.

Part E: $2.20

CHAPTER 14 Trigonometric Graphs and Identities

Section 14A

Exploring Trigonometric Graphs

14-1 Graphs of Sine and Cosine
14-2 Graphs of Other Trigonometric Functions

Section 14B

Trigonometric Identities

14-3 Technology Lab Graph Trigonometric Identities
Connecting Algebra to Geometry Angle Relationships
14-3 Fundamental Trigonometric Identities
14-4 Sum and Difference Identities
14-5 Double-Angle and Half-Angle Identities
14-6 Solving Trigonometric Equations

Pacing Guide for 45-Minute Classes

Chapter 14

DAY 1	DAY 2	DAY 3	DAY 4	DAY 5
14-1 Lesson	14-2 Lesson	14-2 Lesson	Multi-Step Test Prep Ready to Go On? 14-3 Technology Lab	Connecting Algebra to Geometry 14-3 Lesson
DAY 6	**DAY 7**	**DAY 8**	**DAY 9**	**DAY 10**
14-3 Lesson 14-4 Lesson	14-4 Lesson 14-5 Lesson	14-5 Lesson 14-6 Lesson	14-6 Lesson Multi-Step Test Prep Ready to Go On?	Chapter 14 Test

Pacing Guide for 90-Minute Classes

Chapter 14

DAY 1	DAY 2	DAY 3	DAY 4	DAY 5
14-1 Lesson 14-2 Lesson	14-2 Lesson Multi-Step Test Prep Ready to Go On? 14-3 Technology Lab	Connecting Algebra to Geometry 14-3 Lesson 14-4 Lesson	14-4 Lesson 14-5 Lesson 14-6 Lesson	14-6 Lesson Multi-Step Test Prep Ready to Go On? Chapter 14 Test

ONGOING ASSESSMENT and INTERVENTION

Assess Prior Knowledge

Before Chapter 14

DIAGNOSE	PRESCRIBE
Diagnose readiness for the chapter.	Prescribe intervention.
Are You Ready? SE p. 987	***Are You Ready? Intervention*** Skills 47, 53, 64, 65

Formative Assessment

Before Every Lesson

DIAGNOSE	PRESCRIBE
Diagnose readiness for the lesson.	Prescribe intervention.
Warm Up TE, every lesson	**Skills Bank** SE pp. S46–S73
	Reteach CRB, Ch. 1–14

During Every Lesson

DIAGNOSE	PRESCRIBE
Diagnose understanding of lesson concepts.	Prescribe intervention.
Check It Out! SE, every example	**Questioning Strategies** TE, every example
Think and Discuss SE, every lesson	**Reading Strategies** CRB, every lesson
Write About It SE, every lesson	***Success for ELL*** pp. 189–200
Journal TE, every lesson	

After Every Lesson

DIAGNOSE	PRESCRIBE
Diagnose mastery of lesson concepts.	Prescribe intervention.
Lesson Quiz TE, every lesson	**Reteach** CRB, every lesson
Alternative Assessment TE, every lesson	**Problem Solving** CRB, every lesson
Test Prep SE, every lesson	**Test Prep Doctor** TE, every lesson
Test and Practice Generator	**Homework Help Online**

Before Chapter 14 Testing

DIAGNOSE	PRESCRIBE
Diagnose mastery of concepts in the chapter.	Prescribe intervention.
Ready to Go On? SE pp. 1005, 1035	***Ready to Go On? Intervention*** pp. 225–242
Multi-Step Test Prep SE pp. 1004, 1034	**Scaffolding Questions** TE pp. 1004, 1034
Section Quizzes AR pp. 265–266	
 ***Test and Practice Generator***	

Before High Stakes Testing

DIAGNOSE	PRESCRIBE
Diagnose mastery of benchmark concepts.	Prescribe intervention.
College Entrance Exam Practice SE p. 1041	***College Entrance Exam Practice***
Standardized Test Prep SE pp. 1044–1045	***State Test Prep Workbook***
State Test Prep CD-ROM	

Summative Assessment

After Chapter 14

DIAGNOSE	PRESCRIBE
Check mastery of chapter concepts.	Prescribe intervention.
Multiple-Choice Tests (Forms A, B, C)	**Reteach** CRB, every lesson
Free-Response Tests (Forms A, B, C)	***Lesson Tutorial Videos*** Chapter 14
Performance Assessment AR pp. 267–280	
Test and Practice Generator	
Check mastery of benchmark concepts.	Prescribe intervention.
AYP State Tests	***State Test Prep Workbook***
College Entrance Exams	***College Entrance Exam Practice***

KEY: **SE** = *Student Edition* **TE** = *Teacher's Edition* **CRB** = *Chapter Resource Book* **AR** = *Assessment Resources* Available on CD-ROM  Available online

CHAPTER 14

Supporting the Teacher

Chapter 14 Resource Book

Practice A, B, C
pp. 3–5, 11–13, 19–21, 27–29, 35–37, 43–45

Reading Strategies ELL
pp. 10, 18, 26, 34, 42, 50

Reteach
pp. 6–7, 14–15, 22–23, 30–31, 38–39, 46–47

Problem Solving
pp. 9, 17, 25, 33, 41, 49

Challenge
pp. 8, 16, 24, 32, 40, 48

Parent Letter pp. 1–2

Transparencies

Lesson Transparencies, Volume 4 .... Chapter 14
- Warm Ups
- Teaching Transparencies
- Additional Examples
- Lesson Quizzes

Alternate Openers: Explorations 95–100

Know-It Notebook .... Chapter 14
- Graphic Organizers

Teacher Tools

Power Presentations®
Complete PowerPoint® presentations for Chapter 14 lessons

Lesson Tutorial Videos®
Holt authors Ed Burger and Freddie Renfro present tutorials to support the Chapter 14 lessons.

One-Stop Planner®
Easy access to all Chapter 14 resources and assessments, as well as software for lesson planning, test generation, and puzzle creation

IDEA Works!®
Key Chapter 14 resources and assessments modified to address special learning needs

Lesson Plans .... pp. 95–100

Solutions Key .... Chapter 14

Algebra Posters

TechKeys

Lab Resources

Project Teacher Support

Parent Resources 

Workbooks

Homework and Practice Workbook
Teacher's Guide .... pp. 95–100

Know-It Notebook
Teacher's Guide .... Chapter 14

Problem Solving Workbook
Teacher's Guide .... pp. 95–100

State Test Prep Workbook
Teacher's Guide

Technology Highlights for the Teacher

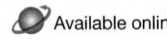 **Power Presentations**

Dynamic presentations to engage students. Complete PowerPoint® presentations for every lesson in Chapter 14.

2-1 Solving One-Step Equations

Isolate a variable by using inverse operations which "undo" operations on the variable.

An equation is like a balanced scale. To keep the balance, perform the same operation on both sides.

Inverse Operations	
Operation	Inverse Operation
Addition	Subtraction
Subtraction	Addition

 **One-Stop Planner**

Easy access to Chapter 14 resources and assessments. Includes lesson-planning, test-generation, and puzzle-creation software.

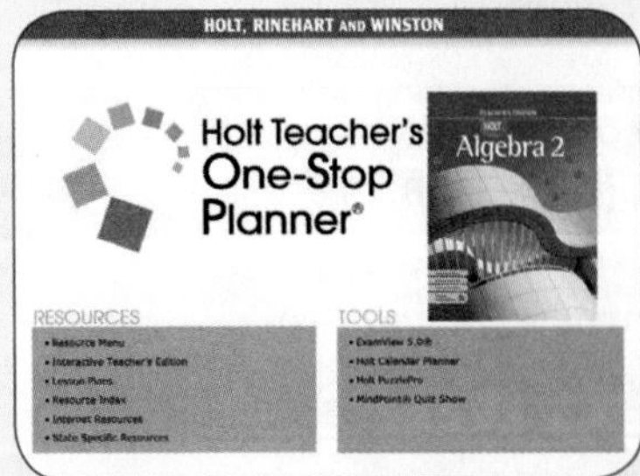

Premier Online Edition

Chapter 14 includes Tutorial Videos, Lesson Activities, Lesson Quizzes, Homework Help, and Chapter Project.

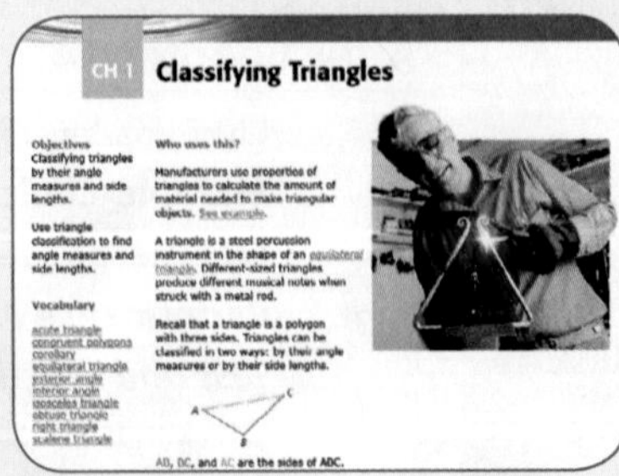

KEY: **SE** = *Student Edition* **TE** = *Teacher's Edition*  English Language Learners Available on CD-ROM Available online

Reaching All Learners

Resources for All Learners

Algebra Lab Activities	Chapter 14
Technology Lab Activities	Chapter 14
Homework and Practice Workbook	pp. 95–100
Know-It Notebook	Chapter 14
Problem Solving Workbook	pp. 95–100

DEVELOPING LEARNERS

Practice A	CRB, every lesson
Reteach	CRB, every lesson
Inclusion	TE p. 996
Questioning Strategies	TE, every example
Modified Chapter 14 Resources (CD-ROM)	*IDEA Works!*
Homework Help Online (online)	

ON-LEVEL LEARNERS

Practice B	CRB, every lesson
Multiple Representations	TE pp. 991, 1018
Modeling	TE p. 999

ADVANCED LEARNERS

Practice C	CRB, every lesson
Challenge	CRB, every lesson
Reading and Writing Math EXTENSION	TE p. 989
Multi-Step Test Prep EXTENSION	TE pp. 1004, 1034
Critical Thinking	TE pp. 1016, 1021

English Language Learners

ENGLISH LANGUAGE LEARNERS

Are You Ready? Vocabulary	SE p. 987
Vocabulary Connections	SE p. 988
Lesson Vocabulary	SE pp. 990, 1014
Vocabulary Exercises	SE pp. 995, 1017
Vocabulary Review	SE p. 1037
English Language Learners	TE pp. 989, 993, 1018, 1046
Reading Strategies	CRB, every lesson
Success for English Language Learners	pp. 189–200
Multilingual Glossary (online)	

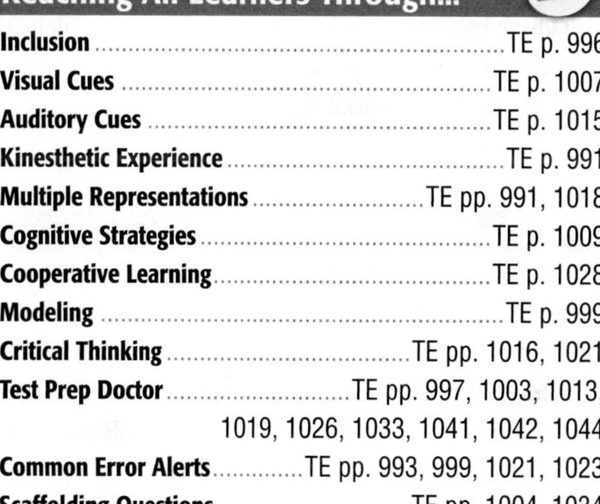

Reaching All Learners Through...

Inclusion	TE p. 996
Visual Cues	TE p. 1007
Auditory Cues	TE p. 1015
Kinesthetic Experience	TE p. 991
Multiple Representations	TE pp. 991, 1018
Cognitive Strategies	TE p. 1009
Cooperative Learning	TE p. 1028
Modeling	TE p. 999
Critical Thinking	TE pp. 1016, 1021
Test Prep Doctor	TE pp. 997, 1003, 1013, 1019, 1026, 1033, 1041, 1042, 1044
Common Error Alerts	TE pp. 993, 999, 1021, 1023
Scaffolding Questions	TE pp. 1004, 1034

Technology Highlights for Reaching All Learners

Lesson Tutorial Videos

Starring Holt authors Ed Burger and Freddie Renfro! Live tutorials to support every lesson in Chapter 14.

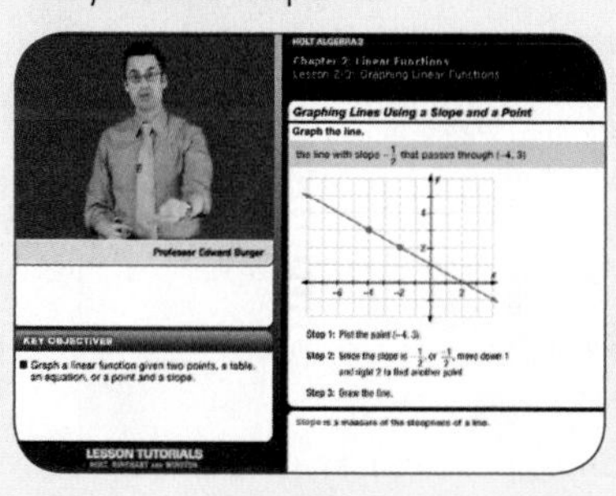

Multilingual Glossary

Searchable glossary includes definitions in English, Spanish, Vietnamese, Chinese, Hmong, Korean, and 4 other languages.

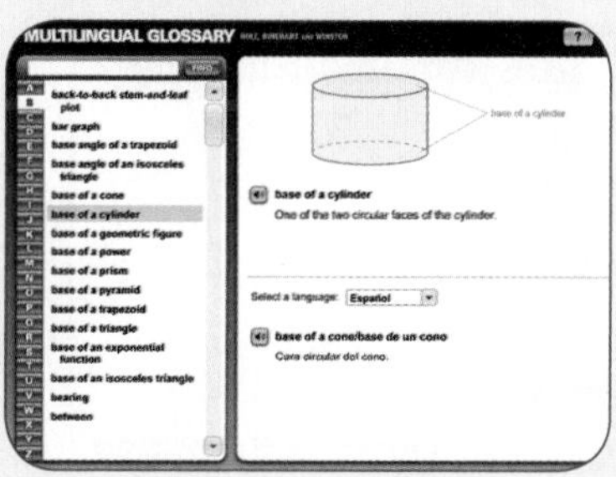

Online Interactivities

Interactive tutorials provide visually engaging alternative opportunities to learn concepts and master skills.

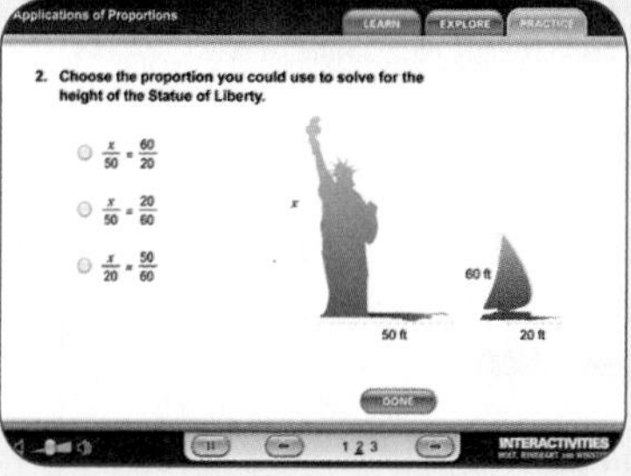

KEY: **SE** = *Student Edition* **TE** = *Teacher's Edition* **CRB** = *Chapter Resource Book* (CD icon) Available on CD-ROM (online icon) Available online

Ongoing Assessment

Assessing Prior Knowledge

Determine whether students have the required prerequisite concepts and skills for success in Chapter 14.

Are You Ready? SPANISH .... SE p. 987
Warm Up .... TE, every lesson

Test Preparation

Provide review and practice for Chapter 14 and standardized tests.

Multi-Step Test Prep .... SE pp. 1004, 1034
Study Guide: Review .... SE pp. 1036–1039
Test Tackler .... SE pp. 1042–1043
Standardized Test Prep .... SE pp. 1044–1045
College Entrance Exam Practice .... SE p. 1041
State Test Prep Workbook
***State Test Prep* CD-ROM**
IDEA Works!

Alternative Assessment

Assess students' understanding of Chapter 14 concepts and combined problem-solving skills.

Chapter 14 Project .... SE p. 986
Alternative Assessment .... TE, every lesson
Performance Assessment .... AR pp. 279–280
Portfolio Assessment .... AR p. xxxiv

Daily Assessment

Provide formative assessment for each day of Chapter 14.

Questioning Strategies .... TE, every example
Think and Discuss .... SE, every lesson
Check It Out! Exercises .... SE, every example
Write About It .... SE, every lesson
Journal .... TE, every lesson
Lesson Quiz .... TE, every lesson
Alternative Assessment .... TE, every lesson
Modified Lesson Quizzes .... *IDEA Works!*

Weekly Assessment

Provide formative assessment for each week of Chapter 14.

Multi-Step Test Prep .... SE pp. 1004, 1034
Ready to Go On? .... SE pp. 1005, 1035
Cumulative Assessment .... SE pp. 1044–1045
Test and Practice Generator .... *One-Stop Planner*

Formal Assessment

Provide summative assessment of Chapter 14 mastery.

Section Quizzes .... AR pp. 265–266
Chapter 14 Test .... SE p. 1040
Chapter Test (Levels A, B, C) .... AR pp. 267–278
• Multiple Choice • Free Response
Cumulative Test .... AR pp. 281–284
Test and Practice Generator .... *One-Stop Planner*
Modified Chapter 14 Test .... *IDEA Works!*

Technology Highlights for Ongoing Assessment

Are You Ready? SPANISH

Automatically assess readiness and prescribe intervention for Chapter 14 prerequisite skills.

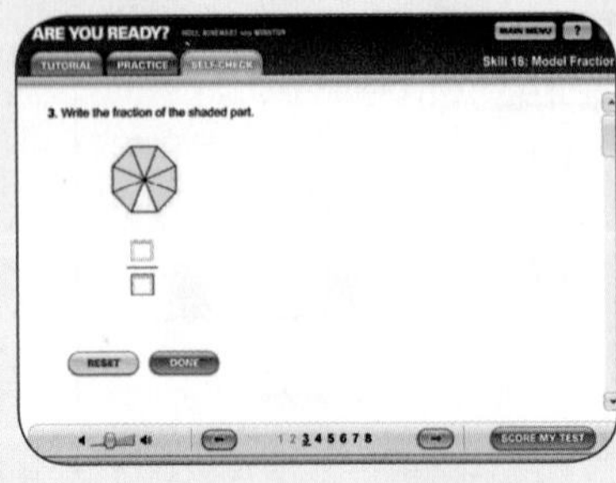

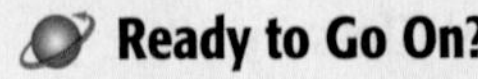

Ready to Go On?

Automatically assess understanding and prescribe intervention for Sections 14A and 14B.

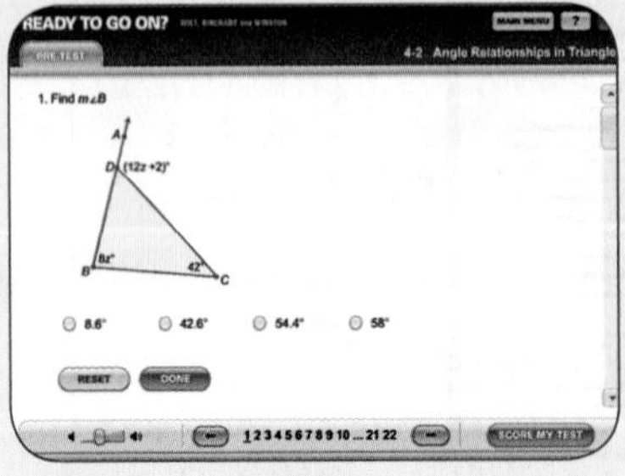

Test and Practice Generator

Use Chapter 14 problem banks to create assessments and worksheets to print out or deliver online. Includes dynamic problems.

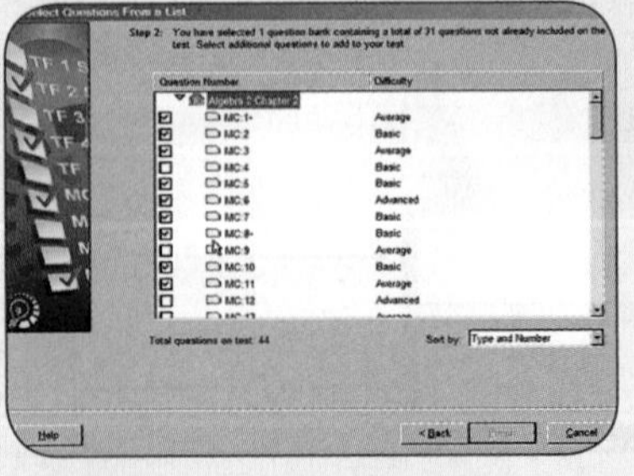

KEY: **SE** = *Student Edition* **TE** = *Teacher's Edition* **AR** = *Assessment Resources*  SPANISH Spanish version available   Available on CD-ROM 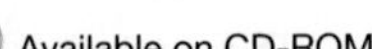 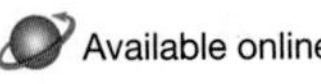 Available online

CHAPTER 14

Formal Assessment

Three levels (A, B, C) of multiple-choice and free-response chapter tests are available in the *Assessment Resources.*

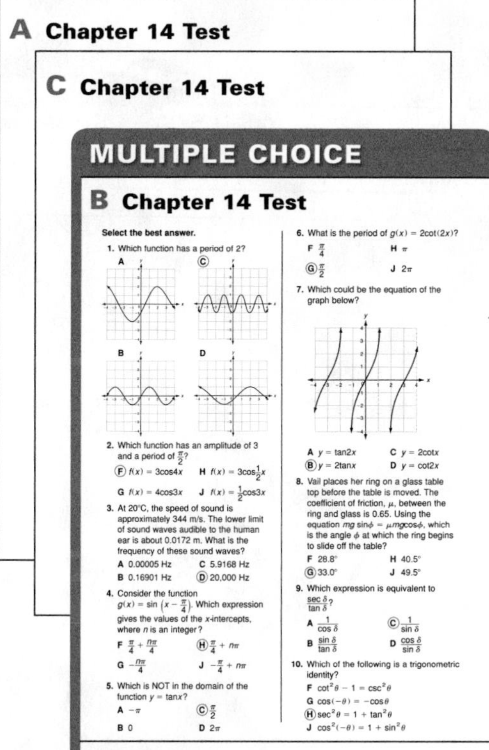

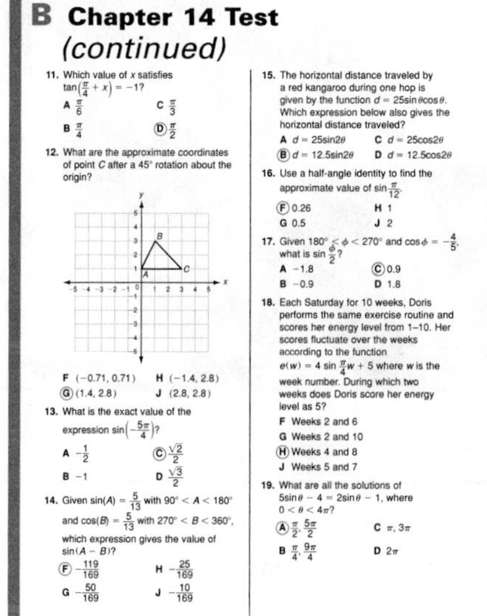

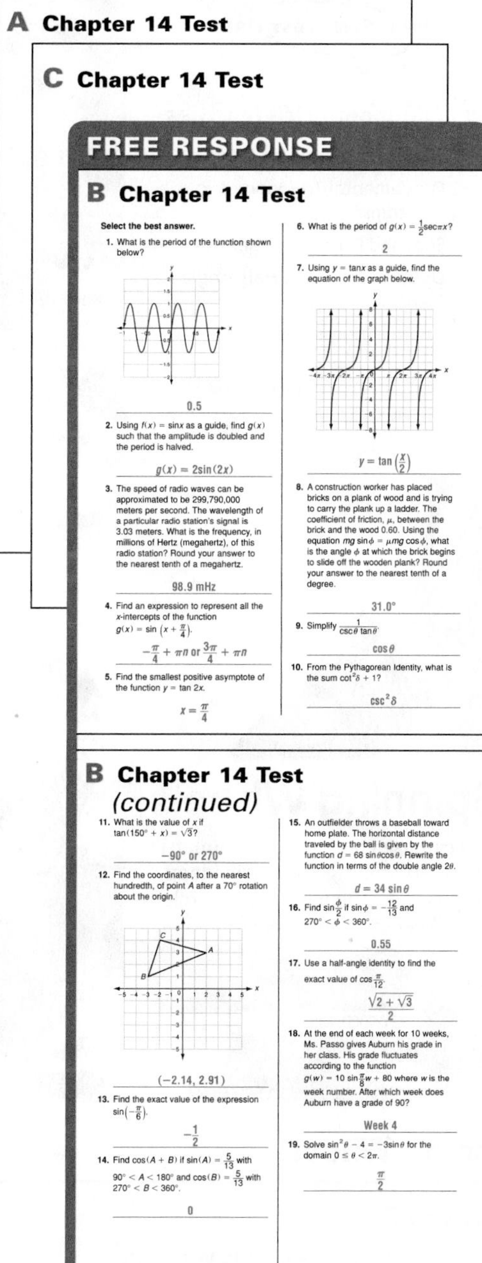

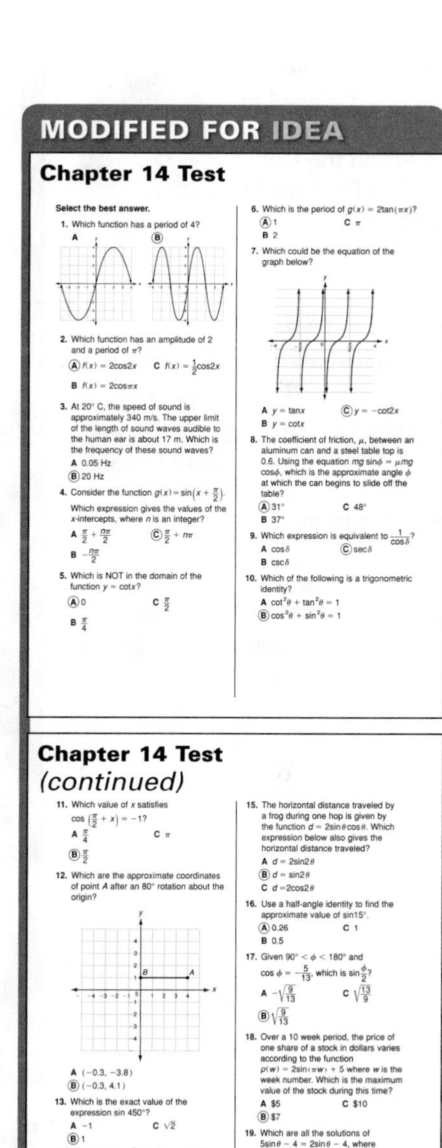

Test & Practice Generator
One-Stop Planner®

Create and customize Chapter 14 Tests. Instantly generate multiple test versions, answer keys, and practice versions of test items.

CHAPTER 14

SECTION 14A
Exploring Trigonometric Graphs

On page 1004, students write and graph functions to model real-world movement of tides.

Exercises designed to prepare students for success on the Multi-Step Test Prep can be found on pages 996 and 1002.

SECTION 14B
Trigonometric Identities

On page 1034, students apply trigonometric identities and solve trigonometric equations to model real-world motion of springs.

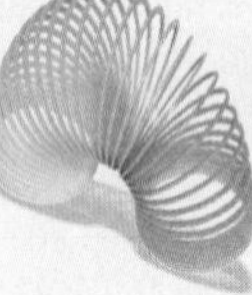

Exercises designed to prepare students for success on the Multi-Step Test Prep can be found on pages 1012, 1018, 1025, and 1032.

CHAPTER 14

Trigonometric Graphs and Identities

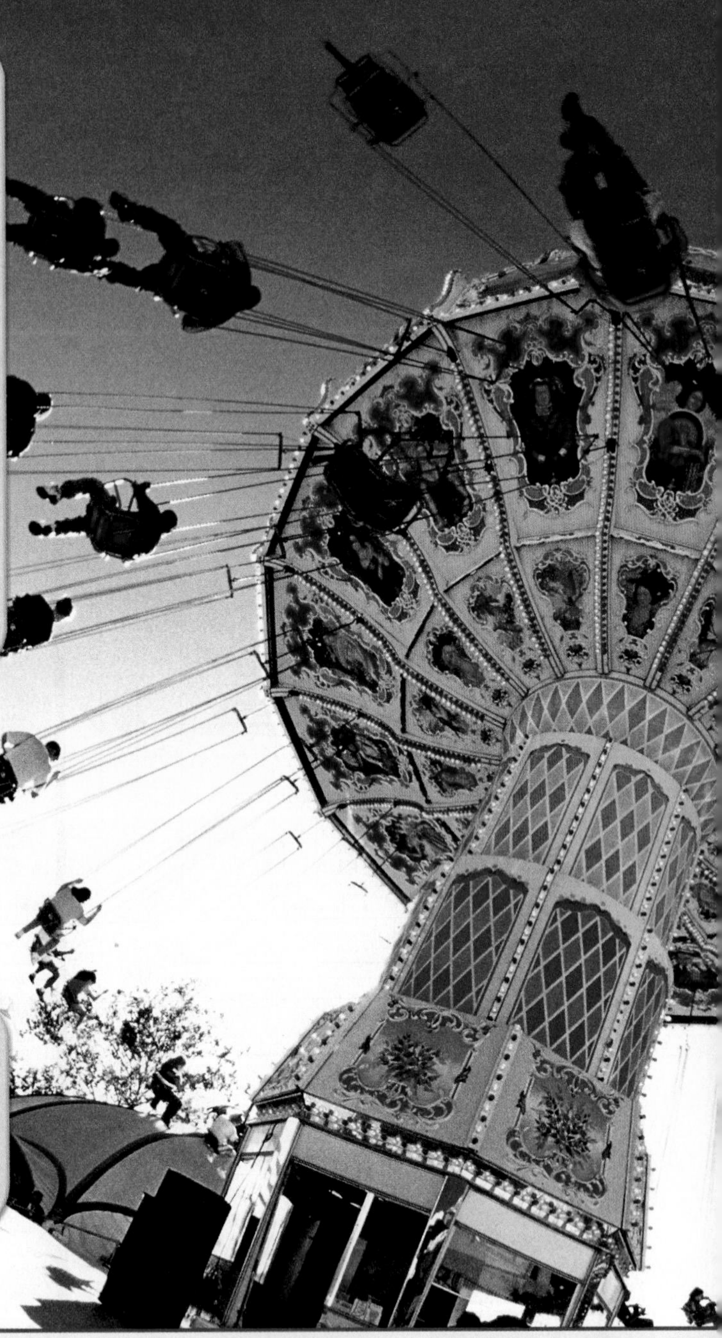

Spinning Wheels

You can use graphs of trigonometric functions and trigonometric identities to model the motion of a circle or a wheel in a variety of situations.

go.hrw.com
Chapter Project Online
KEYWORD: MB7 ChProj

Spinning Wheels

About the Project

In the Chapter Project, students write and graph functions to model the circular motion of a wheel. Students then investigate an unusual trigonometric identity.

Project Resources

All project resources for teachers and students are provided online.

Materials:

- ruler
- graphing calculator

Are You Ready?

Vocabulary

Match each term on the left with a definition on the right.

1. cosecant D
2. cosine B
3. hypotenuse E
4. tangent of an angle C

A. the ratio of the length of the leg adjacent the angle to the length of the opposite leg
B. the ratio of the length of the leg adjacent the angle to the length of the hypotenuse
C. the ratio of the length of the leg opposite the angle to the length of the adjacent leg
D. the ratio of the length of the hypotenuse to the length of the leg opposite the angle
E. the side opposite the right angle

Divide Fractions

Divide.

5. $\frac{\frac{3}{5}}{\frac{5}{2}}$ $\frac{6}{25}$
6. $\frac{\frac{3}{4}}{\frac{1}{2}}$ $\frac{3}{2}$
7. $\frac{-\frac{3}{8}}{\frac{1}{8}}$ -3
8. $\frac{\frac{2}{3}}{-\frac{7}{4}}$ $-\frac{8}{21}$

Simplify Radical Expressions

Simplify each expression.

9. $\sqrt{6} \cdot \sqrt{2}$ $2\sqrt{3}$
10. $\sqrt{100 - 64}$ 6
11. $\frac{\sqrt{9}}{\sqrt{36}}$ $\frac{1}{2}$
12. $\sqrt{\frac{4}{25}}$ $\frac{2}{5}$

Multiply Binomials

Multiply.

13. $(x + 11)(x + 7)$ $x^2 + 18x + 77$
14. $(y - 4)(y - 9)$ $y^2 - 13y + 36$
15. $(2x - 3)(x + 5)$ $2x^2 + 7x - 15$
16. $(k + 3)(3k - 3)$ $3k^2 + 6k - 9$
17. $(4z - 4)(z + 1)$ $4z^2 - 4$
18. $(y + 0.5)(y - 1)$ $y^2 - 0.5y - 0.5$

Special Products of Binomials

Multiply.

19. $(2x + 5)^2$ $4x^2 + 20x + 25$
20. $(3y - 2)^2$ $9y^2 - 12y + 4$
21. $(4x - 6)(4x + 6)$ $16x^2 - 36$
22. $(2m + 1)(2m - 1)$ $4m^2 - 1$
23. $(s + 7)^2$ $s^2 + 14s + 49$
24. $(-p + 4)(-p - 4)$ $p^2 - 16$

CHAPTER 14

Are You Ready?

Organizer

Objective: Assess students' understanding of prerequisite skills.

Prerequisite Skills

Multiply and Divide Fractions
Simplify Radical Expressions
Multiply Binomials
Special Products of Binomials

Assessing Prior Knowledge

INTERVENTION

Diagnose and Prescribe

Use this page to determine whether intervention is necessary or whether enrichment is appropriate.

Resources

Are You Ready? Intervention and Enrichment **Worksheets**

Are You Ready? **CD-ROM**

Are You Ready? **Online**

my.hrw.com

Are You Ready?

Diagnose and Prescribe

NO INTERVENE

YES ENRICH

Prerequisite Skill	*Are You Ready? Intervention*, Chapter 14: Worksheets	CD-ROM	Online
Multiply and Divide Fractions	Skill 47	Activity 47	Diagnose and Prescribe Online
Simplify Radical Expressions	Skill 53	Activity 53	
Multiply Binomials	Skill 64	Activity 64	
Special Products of Binomials	Skill 65	Activity 65	

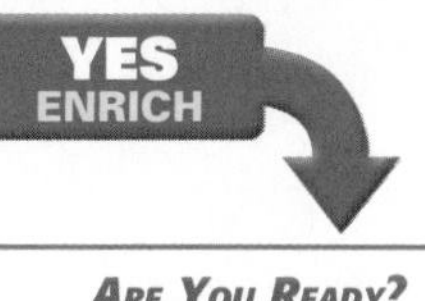

***Are You Ready? Enrichment*, Chapter 14**
Worksheets
CD-ROM
Online

Organizer

Objective: Help students organize the new concepts they will learn in Chapter 14.

Online Edition
Multilingual Glossary

Resources

Puzzle Pro
One-Stop Planner®

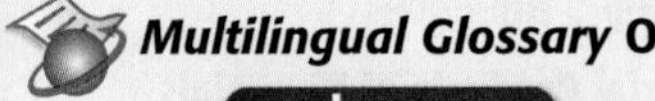
***Multilingual Glossary* Online**
go.hrw.com
KEYWORD: MB7 Glossary

Answers to *Vocabulary Connections*

Possible answers:

1. to increase in amount or importance; a measure of the size or amount of its swing
2. something that repeats itself or returns to the same point; The yearly cycle refers to the movement of Earth around the Sun or the sequence of the seasons. A washing machine cycle refers to a sequence of operations–filling, agitation, rinsing, and spinning.
3. blinking; 15 blinks per minute
4. a length of time; a function that repeats at regular intervals
5. a rotation of whatever is operated on by the rotation matrix

CHAPTER 14 Study Guide: Preview

Where You've Been

In previous chapters, you

- solved problems involving triangles and trigonometric ratios.
- factored to solve quadratic equations.
- applied function models to solve real-world problems.
- solved equations by using algebra and graphs.

In This Chapter

You will study

- problems involving trigonometric functions.
- factoring to solve trigonometric equations.
- trigonometric function models of real-world problems.
- solving trigonometric equations by using algebra and graphs.

Where You're Going

You can use the skills in this chapter

- in your future math classes, particularly Calculus.
- in other classes, such as Physics, Biology, and Economics.
- outside of school to observe cyclical patterns and make conjectures.

Key Vocabulary/Vocabulario

amplitude	amplitud
cycle	ciclo
frequency	frecuencia
period	periodo
periodic function	función periódica
phase shift	cambio de fase
rotation matrix	matriz de rotación

Vocabulary Connections

To become familiar with some of the vocabulary terms in the chapter, consider the following. You may refer to the chapter, the glossary, or a dictionary if you like.

1. What does the word *amplify* mean? What might the **amplitude** of a pendulum swing refer to?
2. What does a **cycle** refer to in everyday language? Give examples of cyclical phenomena.
3. Give an example of something that occurs *frequently*. To describe how often something occurs, like brushing our teeth, we can say "we brush twice a day." Describe the **frequency** of your example.
4. What does **period** mean in everyday language? What might a **periodic function** refer to?
5. What result might you expect from using a **rotation matrix**?

Study Strategy: Prepare for Your Final Exam

Math is a cumulative subject, so your final exam will probably cover all of the material that you have learned from the beginning of the course. Preparation is essential for you to be successful on your final exam. It may help you to make a study timeline like the one below.

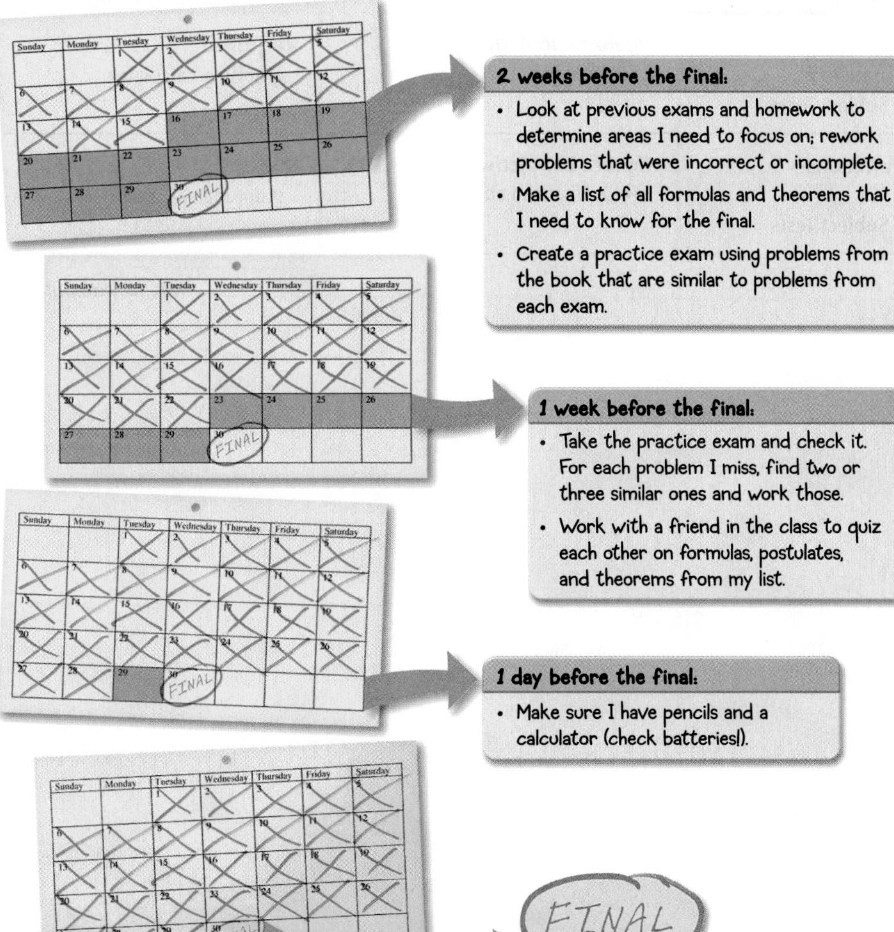

Try This

1. Create a timeline that you will use to study for your final exam.

Organizer

Objective: Help students apply strategies to understand and retain key concepts.

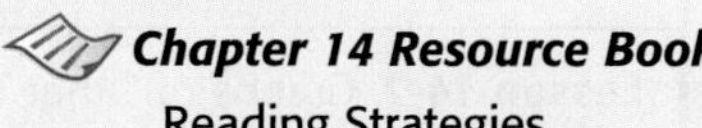

Resources

Chapter 14 Resource Book
Reading Strategies

ENGLISH LANGUAGE LEARNERS

Study Strategy: Prepare for Your Final Exam

Discuss Students benefit from adequate preparation for a final exam. Planning a study strategy as early as possible can help reduce the anxiety of taking a final exam as it draws nearer and allow students to concentrate on course content.

Encourage students to share their strategies with fellow students.

Extend As students work through Chapter 14, have them create a timeline that they will use to study for the Chapter 14 Test. Have them consider how that timeline could be generalized into one that could be used for their final exam. In particular, have students think about how the schedule of the timeline would have to be altered for them to prepare for a test that covers all of the material in the course.

Answers to *Try This*

1. Check students' work.

SECTION

14A Exploring Trigonometric Graphs

One-Minute Section Planner

Lesson	Lab Resources	Materials
Lesson 14-1 Graphs of Sine and Cosine • Recognize and graph periodic and trigonometric functions. ☐ SAT-10 ☐ NAEP ☑ ACT ☐ SAT ☐ SAT Subject Tests	***Algebra Lab Activities*** 14-1 Algebra Lab	**Required** graphing calculator
Lesson 14-2 Graphs of Other Trigonometric Functions • Recognize and graph trigonometric functions. ☐ SAT-10 ☐ NAEP ☑ ACT ☐ SAT ☐ SAT Subject Tests	***Algebra Lab Activities*** 14-2 Algebra Lab	**Required** graphing calculator

MK = *Manipulatives Kit*

Section Overview

Graphs of Sine and Cosine — *Lesson 14-1*

Why? Many natural phenomena, such as sound waves, can be modeled by periodic functions such as the sine and cosine functions.

Graphs of Sine and Cosine		
Function	$y = \sin x$	$y = \cos x$
Graph	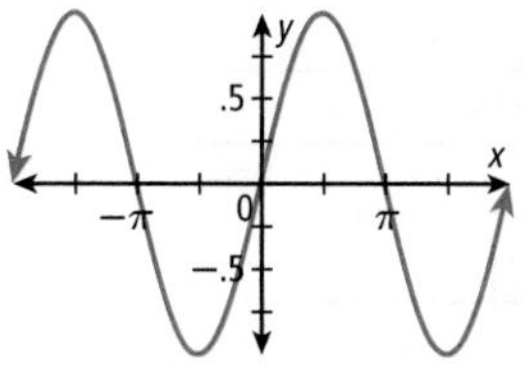	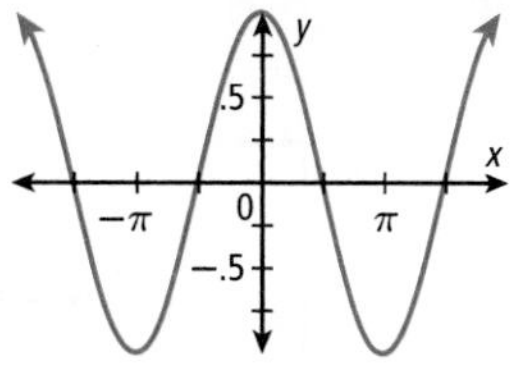
Domain	$\{x \mid x \in \mathbb{R}\}$	$\{x \mid x \in \mathbb{R}\}$
Range	$\{y \mid -1 \leq y \leq 1\}$	$\{y \mid -1 \leq y \leq 1\}$
Period	2π	2π
Amplitude	1	1

Transformations of Sine or Cosine

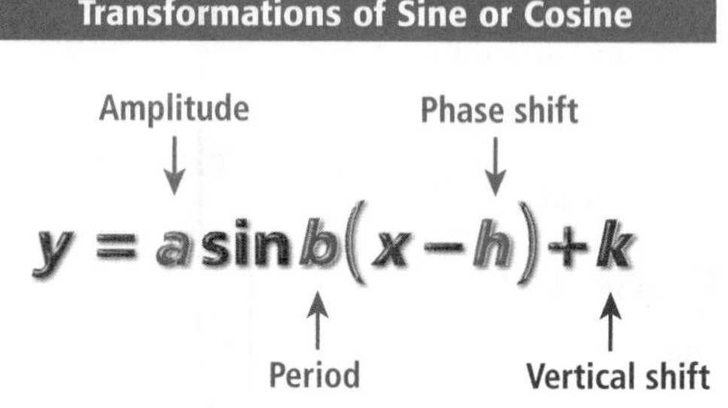

Graphs of Other Trigonometric Functions — *Lesson 14-2*

Why? Other trigonometric functions can also be used to model real-world phenomena such as rotating objects and tides.

Graphs of Tangent and Cotangent		
Function	$y = \tan x$	$y = \cot x$
Graph	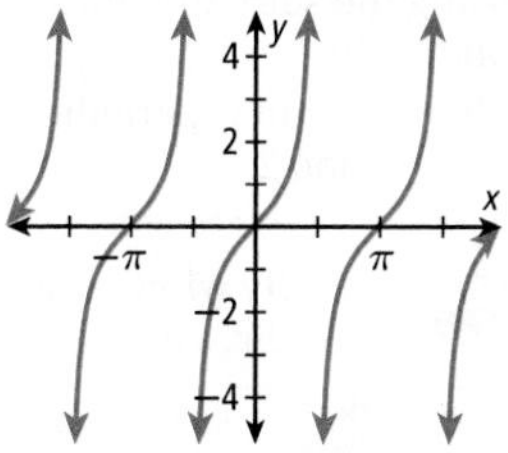	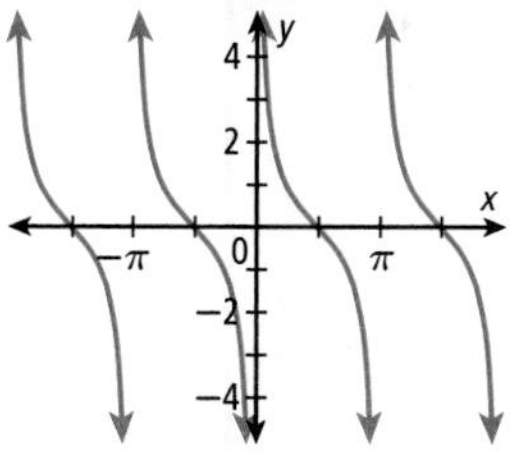
Domain	$\{x \mid x \neq \frac{\pi}{2} + \pi n$, where n is an integer$\}$	$\{x \mid x \neq \pi n$, where n is an integer$\}$
Range	$\{y \mid -\infty < y < \infty\}$	$\{y \mid -\infty < y < \infty\}$
Period	π	π
Amplitude	Undefined	Undefined

Graphs of Secant and Cosecant		
Function	$y = \sec x$	$y = \csc x$
Graph	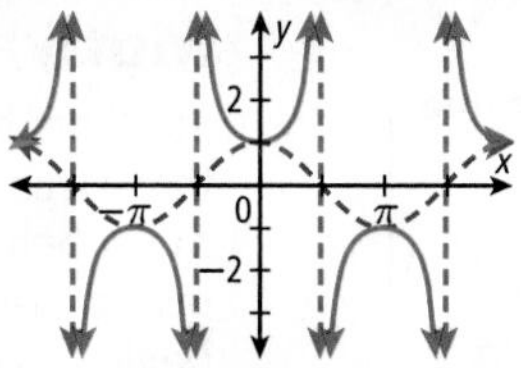	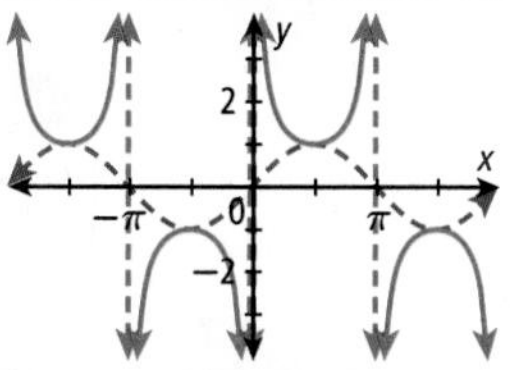
Domain	$\{x \mid x \neq \frac{\pi}{2} + \pi n$, where n is an integer$\}$	$\{x \mid x \neq \pi n$, where n is an integer$\}$
Range	$\{y \mid y \leq -1$ or $y \geq 1\}$	$\{y \mid y \leq -1$ or $y \geq 1\}$
Period	2π	2π
Amplitude	Undefined	Undefined

14-1 Organizer

Pacing: Traditional 1 day
Block $\frac{1}{2}$ day

Objectives: Recognize and graph periodic and trigonometric functions.

Algebra Lab
In *Algebra Lab Activities*

Online Edition
Graphing Calculator, Tutorial Videos, Interactivity

Power Presentations with PowerPoint®

Warm Up

Evaluate.

1. $\sin\frac{\pi}{6}$ 0.5 **2.** $\cos\frac{\pi}{2}$ 0

3. $\cos\frac{\pi}{3}$ 0.5 **4.** $\sin\frac{\pi}{4}$ $\frac{\sqrt{2}}{2}$

Find the measure of the reference angle for each given angle.

5. 145° 35° **6.** 317° 43°

Also available on transparency

Math Humor

Student: I think I've done enough problems about frequency.

Teacher: How do you know?

Student: My brain hertz.

14-1 Graphs of Sine and Cosine

A2.1.2 Use and interpret function notation, including evaluation of functions represented by tables, graphs, words, equations or a set of ordered pairs.

Objective
Recognize and graph periodic and trigonometric functions.

Vocabulary
periodic function
cycle
period
amplitude
frequency
phase shift

Why learn this?
Periodic phenomena such as sound waves can be modeled with trigonometric functions. (See Example 3.)

Periodic functions are functions that repeat exactly in regular intervals called **cycles**. The length of the cycle is called its **period**. Examine the graphs of the periodic function and nonperiodic function below. Notice that a cycle may begin at any point on the graph of a function.

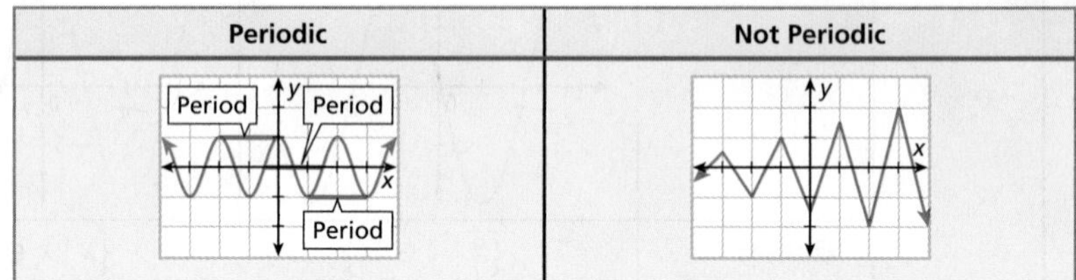

EXAMPLE 1 Identifying Periodic Functions

Identify whether each function is periodic. If the function is periodic, give the period.

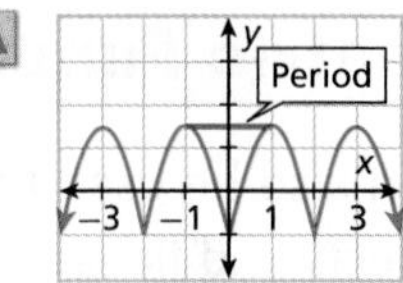

The pattern repeats exactly, so the function is periodic. Identify the period by using the start and finish of one cycle.

This function is periodic with period 2.

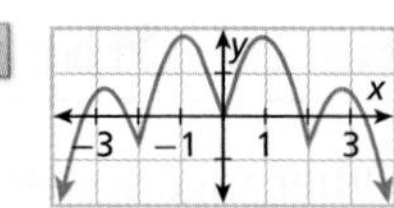

Although there is some symmetry, the pattern does not repeat exactly.

This function is not periodic.

Identify whether each function is periodic. If the function is periodic, give the period.

1a.

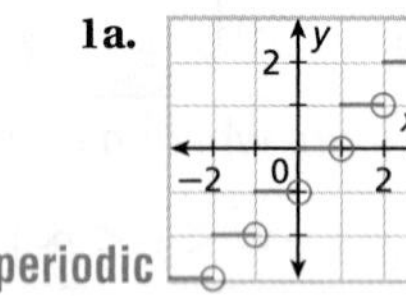

not periodic

1b.

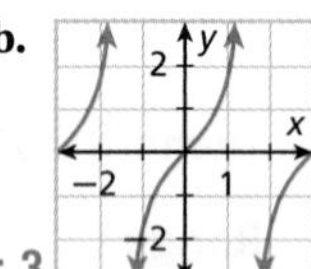

periodic; 3

State Resources

go.hrw.com
State Resources Online
KEYWORD: MB7 Resources

1 Introduce

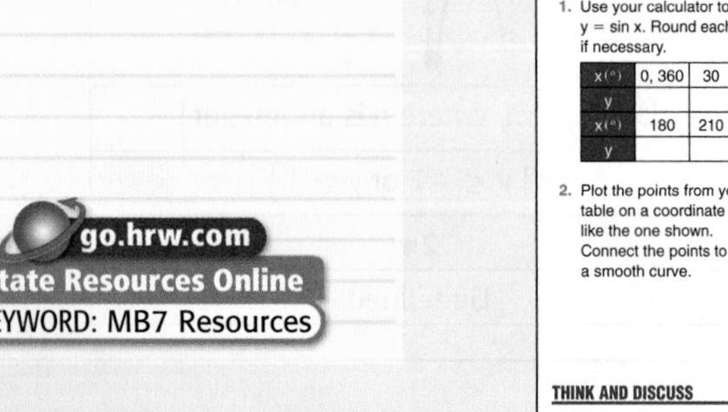
EXPLORATION

14-1 Graphs of Sine and Cosine

You can investigate the graph of the function y = sin x by making a table of values and plotting points.

1. Use your calculator to complete the table for the function y = sin x. Round each y-value to the nearest hundredth if necessary.

x(°)	0, 360	30	45	60	90	120	135	150
y								
x(°)	180	210	225	240	270	300	315	330
y								

2. Plot the points from your table on a coordinate plane like the one shown. Connect the points to form a smooth curve.

THINK AND DISCUSS

3. Describe the maximum and minimum values of the function.

Motivate

Students have modeled many types of behavior that exhibit growth or decay. However, a great many behaviors are *periodic,* that is, they repeat over a specific period of time. Have students begin to consider periodic functions by brainstorming examples of periodic behavior. Possible answers: temperatures and weather, tides and waves, and orbits of planets

Explorations and answers are provided in the *Explorations* binder.

The trigonometric functions that you studied in Chapter 13 are periodic. You can graph the function $f(x) = \sin x$ on the coordinate plane by using y-values from points on the unit circle where the independent variable x represents the angle θ in standard position.

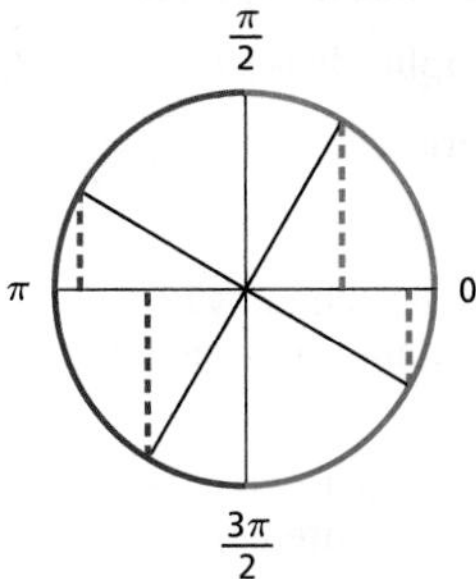

$x(=\theta)$	y
$\frac{\pi}{3}$	$\frac{\sqrt{3}}{2}$
$\frac{5\pi}{6}$	$\frac{1}{2}$
$\frac{4\pi}{3}$	$-\frac{\sqrt{3}}{2}$
$\frac{11\pi}{6}$	$-\frac{1}{2}$

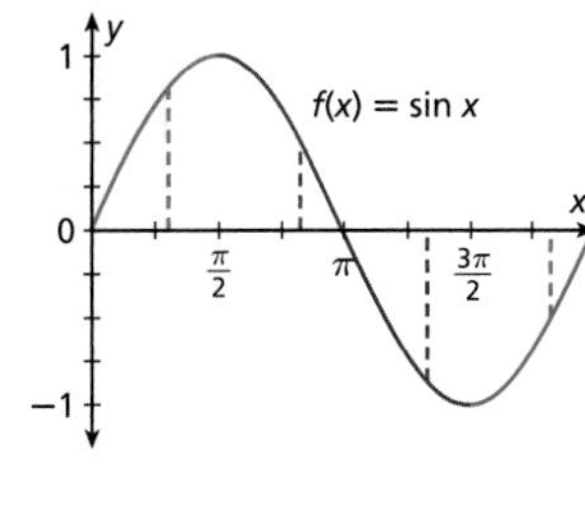

Similarly, the function $f(x) = \cos x$ can be graphed on the coordinate plane by using x-values from points on the unit circle.

The **amplitude** of sine and cosine functions is half of the difference between the maximum and minimum values of the function. The amplitude is always positive.

Characteristics of the Graphs of Sine and Cosine

FUNCTION	$y = \sin x$	$y = \cos x$
GRAPH		
DOMAIN	$\{x \mid x \in \mathbb{R}\}$	$\{x \mid x \in \mathbb{R}\}$
RANGE	$\{y \mid -1 \le y \le 1\}$	$\{y \mid -1 \le y \le 1\}$
PERIOD	2π	2π
AMPLITUDE	1	1

Helpful Hint

The graph of the sine function passes through the origin. The graph of the cosine function has y-intercept 1.

You can use the parent functions to graph transformations $y = a \sin bx$ and $y = a \cos bx$. Recall that a indicates a vertical stretch $(|a| > 1)$ or compression $(0 < |a| < 1)$, which changes the amplitude. If a is less than 0, the graph is reflected across the x-axis. The value of b indicates a horizontal stretch or compression, which changes the period.

Transformations of Sine and Cosine Graphs

For the graphs of $y = a \sin bx$ or $y = a \cos bx$ where $a \neq 0$ and x is in radians,

- the amplitude is $|a|$.
- the period is $\frac{2\pi}{|b|}$.

2 Teach

Guided Instruction

Introduce the graph of sine and cosine by first drawing the unit circle and choosing values with which to plot points. Be sure to include the quadrantal angle values, as these correspond to maxima, minima, and x-intercepts.

Discuss how the types of transformations that students learned in previous chapters are applied to graphs of sine and cosine.

Reaching All Learners

Through Multiple Representations

Have students work in groups to create large drawings of the unit circle to post in the classroom. Ask students to discuss the connection between the sine and the cosine functions and coordinates of points on the unit circle.

Power Presentations with PowerPoint®

Additional Examples

Example 1

Identify whether each function is periodic. If the function is periodic, give the period.

A.

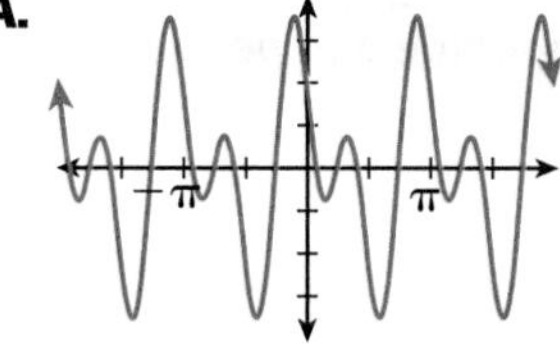

yes; π

B.

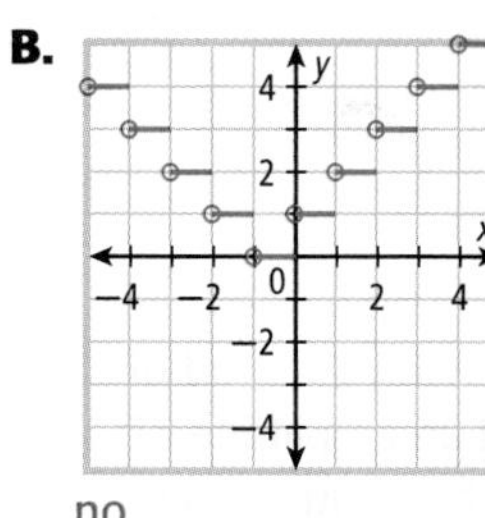

no

Also available on transparency

INTERVENTION

Questioning Strategies

EXAMPLE 1

- How much of the curve do you need to see before you can conclude that it is periodic?
- How can you determine the period?

Teaching Tip

Kinesthetic Have students trace the circumference of the unit circle with a finger and note where the y-coordinates are positive, negative, increasing, and decreasing and then trace along the graph of sine to make the connection with the y-coordinate. Repeat for cosine.

Power Presentations with PowerPoint®

Additional Examples

Example 2

Using $f(x) = \sin x$ as a guide, graph the function $g(x) = \frac{1}{2}\sin\left(\frac{1}{2}x\right)$. Identify the amplitude and period.

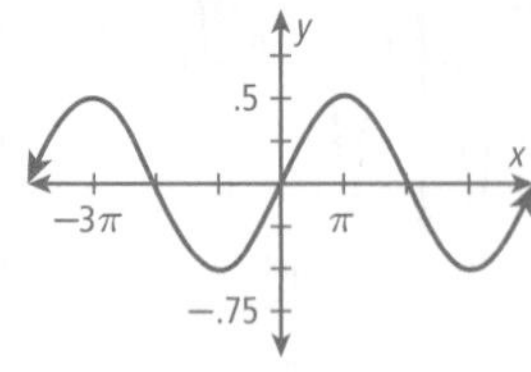

amplitude: $\frac{1}{2}$; period: 4π

Example 3

Use a sine function to graph a sound wave with a period of 0.002 s and an amplitude of 3 cm. Find the frequency in hertz for this sound wave.

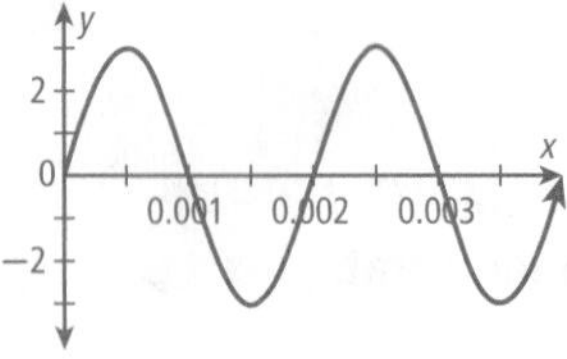

frequency: 500 Hz

Also available on transparency

INTERVENTION

Questioning Strategies

EXAMPLE 2

- How do horizontal or vertical compressions of sine and cosine graphs compare to these transformations of other functions?

EXAMPLE 3

- What are the frequencies of the parent curves $f(x) = \sin x$ and $g(x) = \cos x$?

EXAMPLE 2 Stretching or Compressing Sine and Cosine Functions

Using $f(x) = \sin x$ as a guide, graph the function $g(x) = 3\sin 2x$. Identify the amplitude and period.

Step 1 Identify the amplitude and period.

Because $a = 3$, the amplitude is $|a| = |3| = 3$.

Because $b = 2$, the period is $\frac{2\pi}{|b|} = \frac{2\pi}{|2|} = \pi$.

Step 2 Graph.

The curve is vertically stretched by a factor of 3 and horizontally compressed by a factor of $\frac{1}{2}$.

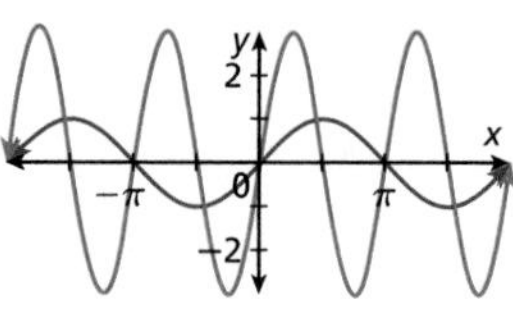

The parent function f has x-intercepts at multiples of π and g has x-intercepts at multiples of $\frac{\pi}{2}$.

The maximum value of g is 3, and the minimum value is −3.

CHECK IT OUT! **2.** Using $f(x) = \cos x$ as a guide, graph the function $h(x) = \frac{1}{3}\cos 2x$. Identify the amplitude and period.

2.

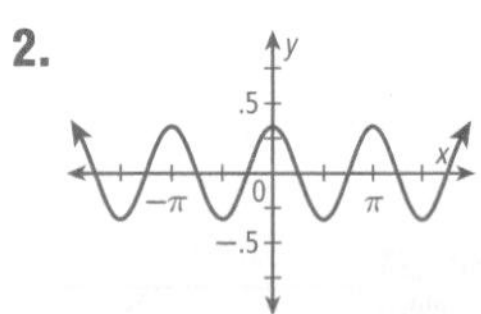

amplitude: $\frac{1}{3}$; period: π

Sine and cosine functions can be used to model real-world phenomena, such as sound waves. Different sounds create different waves. One way to distinguish sounds is to measure *frequency*. **Frequency** is the number of cycles in a given unit of time, so it is the reciprocal of the period of a function.

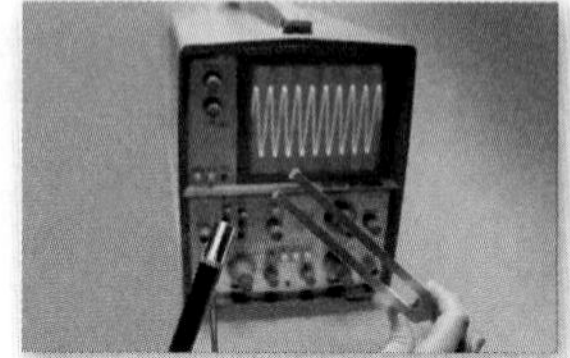

Hertz (Hz) is the standard measure of frequency and represents one cycle per second. For example, the sound wave made by a tuning fork for middle A has a frequency of 440 Hz. This means that the wave repeats 440 times in 1 second.

EXAMPLE 3 *Sound Application*

Use a sine function to graph a sound wave with a period of 0.005 second and an amplitude of 4 cm. Find the frequency in hertz for this sound wave.

Use a horizontal scale where one unit represents 0.001 second. The period tells you that it takes 0.005 seconds to complete one full cycle. The maximum and minimum values are given by the amplitude.

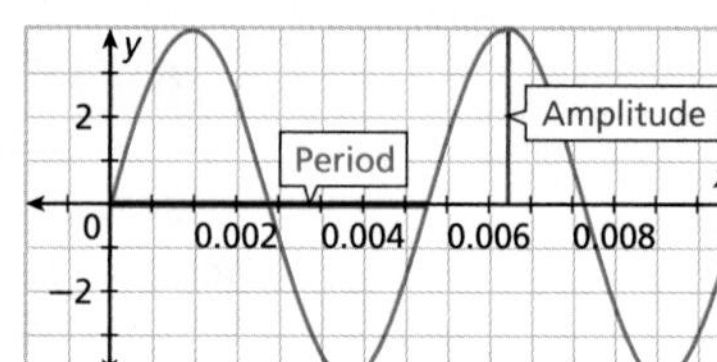

$$\text{frequency} = \frac{1}{\text{period}}$$

$$= \frac{1}{0.005} = 200 \text{ Hz}$$

The frequency of the sound wave is 200 Hz.

CHECK IT OUT! **3.** Use a sine function to graph a sound wave with a period of 0.004 second and an amplitude of 3 cm. Find the frequency in hertz for this sound wave.

3.

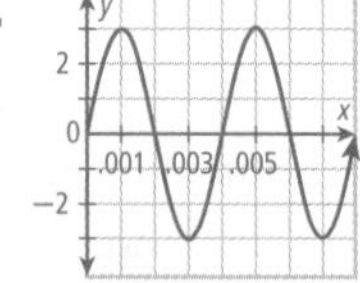

frequency: 250 Hz

Teaching Tip **Science Link** You may wish to have students reinforce their understanding of *amplitude* and *frequency* by investigating the meanings of these terms in broadcast media. Radio signals are broadcast on AM (amplitude modulation) and FM (frequency modulation) bands.

Sine and cosine can also be translated as $y = \sin(x - h) + k$ and $y = \cos(x - h) + k$. Recall that a vertical translation by k units moves the graph up $(k > 0)$ or down $(k < 0)$.

A **phase shift** is a horizontal translation of a periodic function. A phase shift of h units moves the graph left $(h < 0)$ or right $(h > 0)$.

EXAMPLE 4 Identifying Phase Shifts for Sine and Cosine Functions

Using $f(x) = \sin x$ as a guide, graph $g(x) = \sin\left(x + \frac{\pi}{2}\right)$. Identify the x-intercepts and phase shift.

Step 1 Identify the amplitude and period.

Amplitude is $|a| = |1| = 1$.

The period is $\frac{2\pi}{|b|} = \frac{2\pi}{|1|} = 2\pi$.

Step 2 Identify the phase shift.

$x + \frac{\pi}{2} = x - \left(-\frac{\pi}{2}\right)$ *Identify h.*

Because $h = -\frac{\pi}{2}$, the phase shift is $\frac{\pi}{2}$ radians to the left.

All x-intercepts, maxima, and minima of $f(x)$ are shifted $\frac{\pi}{2}$ units to the left.

Step 3 Identify the x-intercepts.

The first x-intercept occurs at $-\frac{\pi}{2}$. Because $\sin x$ has two x-intercepts in each period of 2π, the x-intercepts occur at $-\frac{\pi}{2} + n\pi$, where n is an integer.

Step 4 Identify the maximum and minimum values.

The maximum and minimum values occur between the x-intercepts. The maxima occur at $2\pi n$ and have a value of 1. The minima occur at $\pi + 2\pi n$ and have a value of -1.

Step 5 Graph using all of the information about the function.

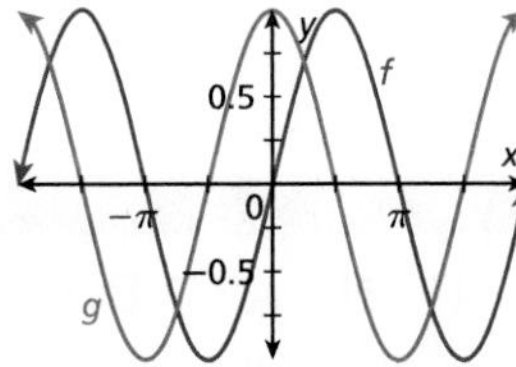

4. Using $f(x) = \cos x$ as a guide, graph $g(x) = \cos(x - \pi)$. Identify the x-intercepts and phase shift.

You can combine the transformations of trigonometric functions. Use the values of a, b, h, and k to identify the important features of a sine or cosine function.

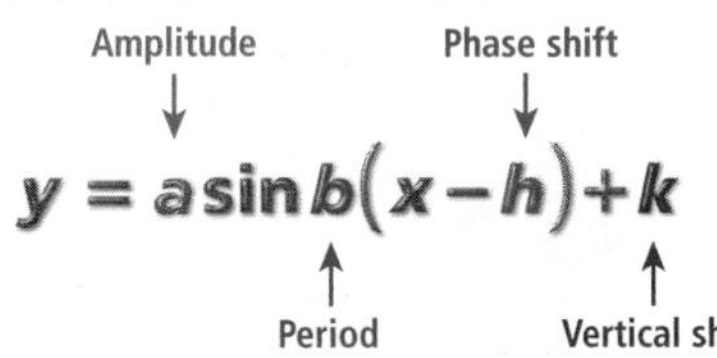

Helpful Hint

The repeating pattern is maximum, intercept, minimum, intercept,.... So intercepts occur twice as often as maximum or minimum values.

4. x-intercepts: $\frac{\pi}{2} + \pi n$; phase shift: π right

COMMON ERROR ALERT

It is worth noting that an expression such as $\sin \frac{\pi}{15}(t - 7.5)$ is equivalent to $\sin\left\{\frac{\pi}{15}(t - 7.5)\right\}$ and **not** to $\left(\sin \frac{\pi}{15}\right) \cdot (t - 7.5)$. The use of the extra brackets may be cumbersome, but it serves to eliminate confusion.

Power Presentations with PowerPoint®

Additional Examples

Example 4

Using $f(x) = \sin x$ as a guide, graph $g(x) = \sin\left(x - \frac{\pi}{4}\right)$. Identify the x-intercepts and phase shift.

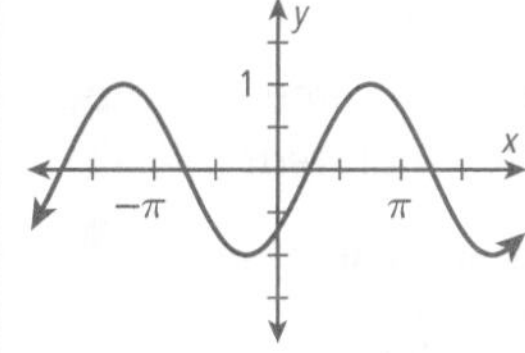

x-intercepts: $\frac{\pi}{4} + n\pi$; phase shift: $\frac{\pi}{4}$ units to the right

Also available on transparency

INTERVENTION
Questioning Strategies

EXAMPLE 4

- How could sine be shifted so that its graph looks like that of cosine?

Teaching Tip **Reading Math** Point out to students the word *sinusoidal.* Discuss with them the meaning "of, relating to, or varying according to a sine curve." Also note that a cosine function, because it is shaped similar to a sine function, is sinusoidal.

ENGLISH LANGUAGE LEARNERS

Power Presentations with PowerPoint®

Additional Examples

Example 5

The number of people, in thousands, employed in a resort town can be modeled by $g(x) = 1.5\sin\frac{\pi}{6}(x + 2) + 5.2$, where x is the month of the year.

A. Graph the number of people employed in the town for one complete period.

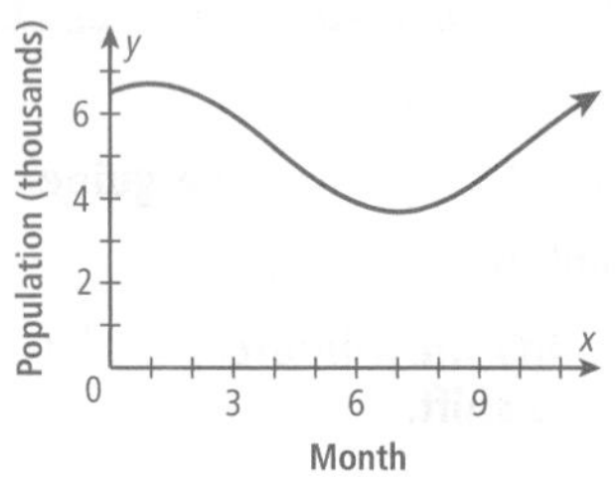

B. What is the maximum number of people employed? 6700

Also available on transparency

Questioning Strategies

EXAMPLE 5

- How can you find the radius of the Ferris wheel from the function that describes the wheel's height?

EXAMPLE 5 ***Entertainment Application***

The Ferris wheel at the landmark Navy Pier in Chicago takes 7 minutes to make one full rotation. The height H in feet above the ground of one of the six-person gondolas can be modeled by $H(t) = 70\sin\frac{2\pi}{7}(t - 1.75) + 80$, where t is time in minutes.

a. Graph the height of a cabin for two complete periods.

$H(t) = 70\sin\frac{2\pi}{7}(t - 1.75) + 80$ $a = 70,\ b = \frac{2\pi}{7},\ h = 1.75,\ k = 80$

Step 1 Identify the important features of the graph.

Amplitude: 70

Period: $\frac{2\pi}{|b|} = \frac{2\pi}{\left|\frac{2\pi}{7}\right|} = 7$

The period is equal to the time required for one full rotation.

Phase shift: 1.75 minutes right

Vertical shift: 80

There are no x-intercepts.

Maxima: $80 + 70 = 150$ at 3.5 and 10.5

Minima: $80 - 70 = 10$ at 0, 7, and 14

Step 2 Graph using all of the information about the function.

b. What is the maximum height of a cabin?

The maximum height is $80 + 70 = 150$ feet above the ground.

5a.

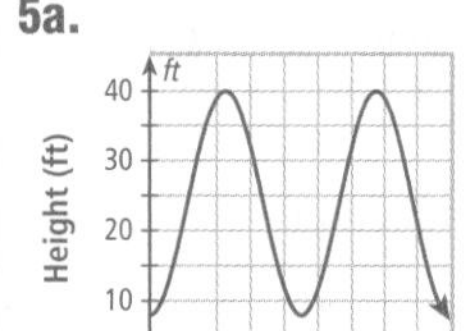

5. **What if...?** Suppose that the height H of a Ferris wheel can be modeled by $H(t) = -16\cos\frac{\pi}{45}t + 24$, where t is the time in seconds.

a. Graph the height of a cabin for two complete periods.

b. What is the maximum height of a cabin? **40 ft**

THINK AND DISCUSS

1. **DESCRIBE** how the frequency and period of a periodic function are related. How does this apply to the graph of $f(x) = \cos x$?

2. **EXPLAIN** how the maxima and minima are related to the amplitude and period of sine and cosine functions.

3. **GET ORGANIZED** Copy and complete the graphic organizer. For each type of transformation, give an example and state the period.

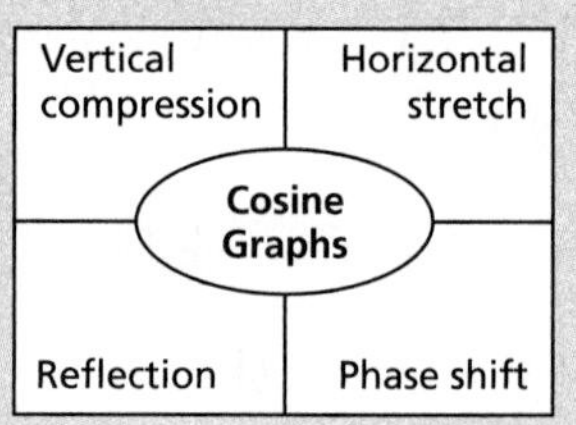

3 Close

Summarize

The graphs of $f(x) = \sin x$ and $g(x) = \cos x$ are periodic, which is not surprising because they represent the movement of a point around a circle. They may be transformed in the same way as other previously studied graphs. In the function $f(x) = a\sin b(x - h) + k$, a and b are used to identify the amplitude and the period. A horizontal translation of a sine or cosine function is called a *phase shift.*

ONGOING ASSESSMENT and INTERVENTION

Diagnose Before **the Lesson**
14-1 Warm Up, TE p. 990

Monitor During **the Lesson**
Check It Out! Exercises, SE pp. 990–994
Questioning Strategies, TE pp. 991–994

Assess After **the Lesson**
14-1 Lesson Quiz, TE p. 997
Alternative Assessment, TE p. 997

Answers to *Think and Discuss*

1. The frequency of a periodic function is the reciprocal of the period. The period of $f(x) = \cos x$ is 2π, and the frequency is $\frac{1}{2\pi}$.
2. The period of sine and cosine functions tells how often the maxima and minima occur. The amplitude affects the value of the maxima and minima.
3. See p. A14.

14-1 Exercises

go.hrw.com
Homework Help Online
KEYWORD: MB7 14-1
Parent Resources Online
KEYWORD: MB7 Parent

GUIDED PRACTICE

1. **Vocabulary** Periodic functions repeat in regular intervals called __?__. *(cycles or periods)* cycles

SEE EXAMPLE 1 p. 990

Identify whether each function is periodic. If the function is periodic, give the period.

2.

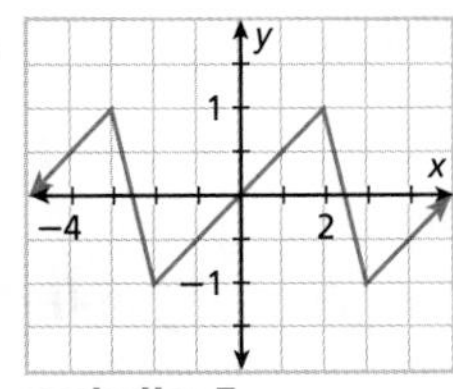

periodic; 5

3.

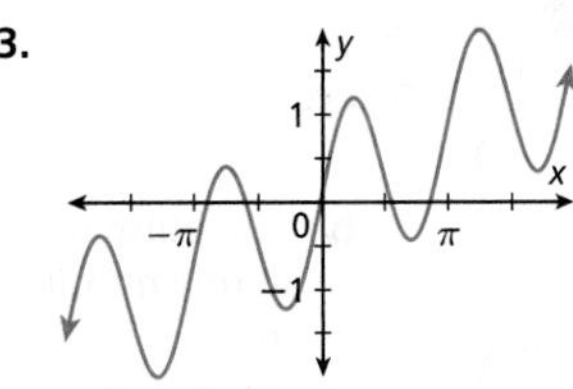

not periodic

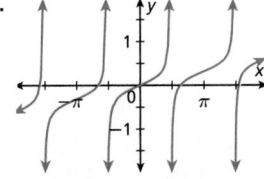

SEE EXAMPLE 2 p. 992

Using $f(x) = \sin x$ or $f(x) = \cos x$ as a guide, graph each function. Identify the amplitude and the period.

4. $f(x) = 2\sin\frac{1}{2}x$
5. $h(x) = \frac{1}{4}\cos x$
6. $k(x) = \sin \pi x$

SEE EXAMPLE 3 p. 992

7. **Sound** Use a sine function to graph a sound wave with a period of 0.01 second and an amplitude of 6 in. Find the frequency in hertz for this sound wave. 100 Hz

SEE EXAMPLE 4 p. 993

Using $f(x) = \sin x$ or $f(x) = \cos x$ as a guide, graph each function. Identify the x-intercepts and the phase shift.

8. $f(x) = \sin\left(x + \frac{3\pi}{2}\right)$
9. $g(x) = \cos\left(x - \frac{\pi}{2}\right)$
10. $h(x) = \sin\left(x - \frac{\pi}{4}\right)$

SEE EXAMPLE 5 p. 994

11. **Recreation** The height H in feet above the ground of the seat of a playground swing can be modeled by $H(\theta) = -4\cos\theta + 6$, where θ is the angle that the swing makes with a vertical extended to the ground. Graph the height of a swing's seat for $0° \le \theta \le 90°$. How high is the swing when $\theta = 60°$? 4 ft

PRACTICE AND PROBLEM SOLVING

Independent Practice

For Exercises	See Example
12–13	1
14–17	2
18	3
19–22	4
23	5

Extra Practice
Skills Practice p. S30
Application Practice p. S45

Identify whether each function is periodic. If the function is periodic, give the period.

12.

not periodic

13.

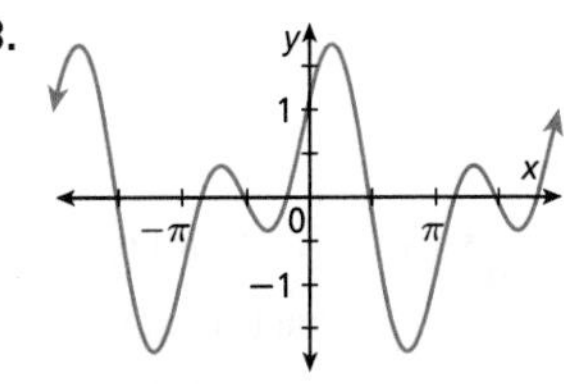

periodic; 2π

Using $f(x) = \sin x$ or $f(x) = \cos x$ as a guide, graph each function. Identify the amplitude and period.

14. $f(x) = 4\cos x$
15. $g(x) = \frac{3}{2}\sin x$
16. $g(x) = -\cos 4x$
17. $j(x) = 6\sin\frac{1}{3}x$

18. **Sound** Use a sine function to graph a sound wave with a period of 0.025 seconds and an amplitude of 5 in. Find the frequency in hertz for this sound wave. 40 Hz

14-1 Exercises

Assignment Guide

Assign *Guided Practice* exercises as necessary.

If you finished Examples **1–2**
Basic 12–17, 29–32
Average 12–17, 29–32
Advanced 12–17, 29–32, 44

If you finished Examples **1–5**
Basic 12–37, 39–43, 48–53
Average 12–44, 48–53
Advanced 12–53

Homework Quick Check
Quickly check key concepts.
Exercises: 12, 14, 20, 28

Answers

4.

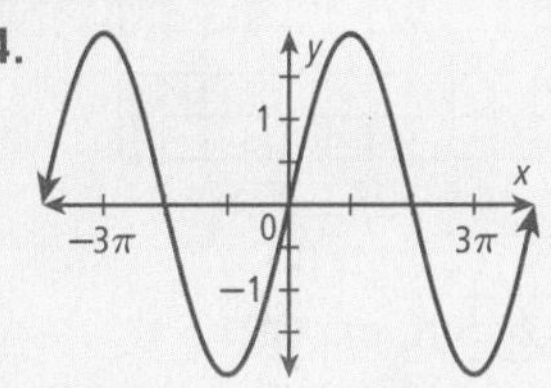

amplitude: 2; period: 4π

5.

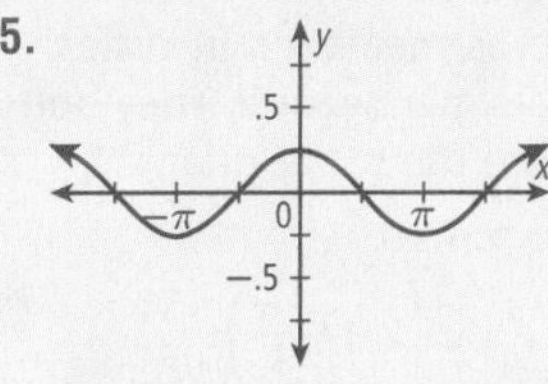

amplitude: $\frac{1}{4}$; period: 2π

6.

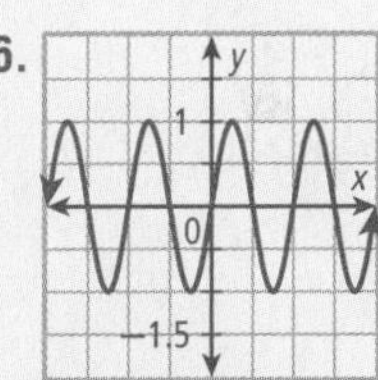

amplitude: 1; period: 2

State Resources

7.

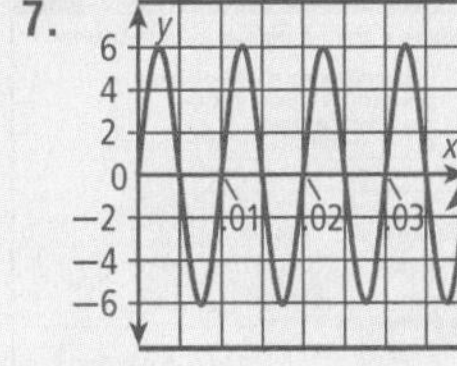

8.

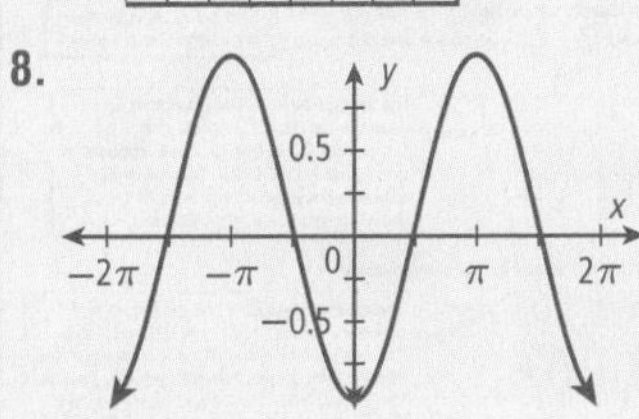

x-intercepts: $n\pi$;

phase shift: $\frac{3\pi}{2}$ left

9.

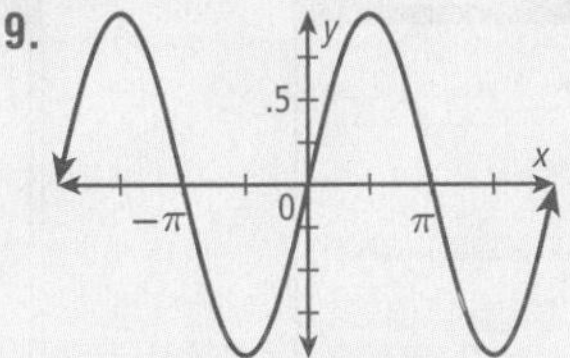

x-intercepts: $n\pi$;

phase shift: $\frac{\pi}{2}$ right

10.

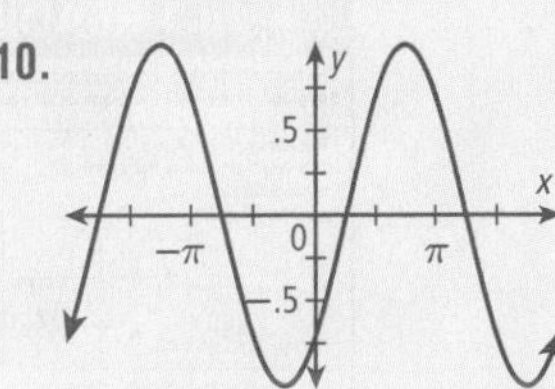

x-intercepts: $\frac{\pi}{4} + \pi n$;

phase shift: $\frac{\pi}{4}$ right

11, 14–18. For graphs, see p. A50.

14. amplitude: 4; period: 2π
15. amplitude: $\frac{3}{2}$; period: 2π
16. amplitude: 1; period: $\frac{\pi}{2}$
17. amplitude: 6; period: 6π

go.hrw.com
State Resources Online
KEYWORD: MB7 Resources

Inclusion In **Exercise 23,** to find the minimum and maximum values of the sine function, remind students that the range of sin(x) is from −1 to 1. Then they simply note that the extreme values will be $\frac{3}{2}(-1) + 23$ and $\frac{3}{2}(1) + 23$.

MULTI-STEP TEST PREP **Exercise 37** involves graphing and interpreting sine functions. This exercise prepares students for the Multi-Step Test Prep on page 1004.

Answers

19–22. See p. A50.

23.

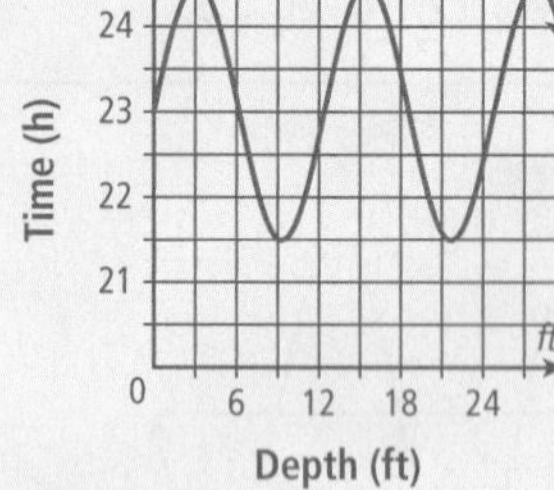

max.: 24.5 ft; min.: 21.5 ft

24d. The pulse rate is measured in beats per minute and the frequency is measured in cycles, or beats, per second. They both measure the same quantity.

25–28. See p. A50.

34. $f(x) = \frac{1}{4}\sin\left(x + \frac{2\pi}{3}\right)$

35. $f(x) = -4\sin 2x$; $g(x) = 4\cos 2\left(x + \frac{\pi}{4}\right)$

36. $f(x) = -\frac{1}{4}\sin\frac{1}{2}x + 1$; $g(x) = \frac{1}{4}\cos\frac{1}{2}(x - \pi) + 1$

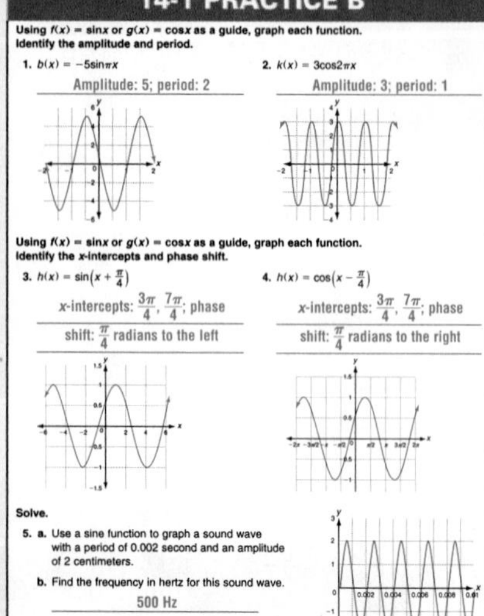

14-1 PRACTICE A

14-1 PRACTICE C

14-1 PRACTICE B

Using f(x) = sinx or g(x) = cosx as a guide, graph each function. Identify the amplitude and period.

1. $b(x) = -5\sin\pi x$ Amplitude: 5; period: 2

2. $k(x) = 3\cos 2\pi x$ Amplitude: 3; period: 1

Using f(x) = sinx or g(x) = cosx as a guide, graph each function. Identify the x-intercepts and phase shift.

3. $h(x) = \sin\left(x + \frac{\pi}{4}\right)$ x-intercepts: $\frac{3\pi}{4}, \frac{7\pi}{4}$; phase shift: $\frac{\pi}{4}$ radians to the left

4. $h(x) = \cos\left(x - \frac{\pi}{4}\right)$ x-intercepts: $\frac{3\pi}{4}, \frac{7\pi}{4}$; phase shift: $\frac{\pi}{4}$ radians to the right

Solve.

5. a. Use a sine function to graph a sound wave with a period of 0.002 second and an amplitude of 2 centimeters.

b. Find the frequency in hertz for this sound wave. 500 Hz

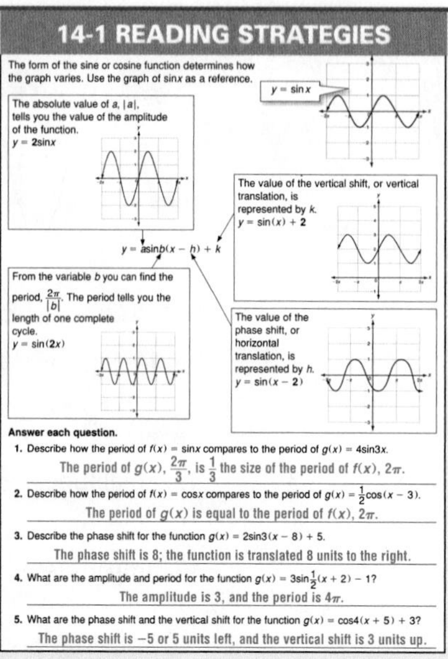

Using $f(x) = \sin x$ or $f(x) = \cos x$ as a guide, graph each function. Identify the x-intercepts and phase shift.

19. $f(x) = \sin(x + \pi)$

20. $h(x) = \cos(x - 3\pi)$

21. $g(x) = \sin\left(x + \frac{3\pi}{4}\right)$

22. $j(x) = \cos\left(x + \frac{\pi}{4}\right)$

23. **Oceanography** The depth d in feet of the water in a bay at any time is given by $d(t) = \frac{3}{2}\sin\left(\frac{5\pi}{31}t\right) + 23$, where t is the time in hours. Graph the depth of the water. What are the maximum and minimum depths of the water?

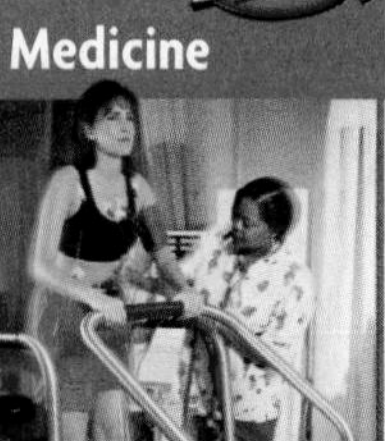

LINK Medicine

An EKG measures the electrical signals that control the rhythm of a beating heart. EKGs are used to diagnose and monitor heart disease.

24. **Medicine** The figure shows a normal adult electrocardiogram, known as an EKG. Each cycle in the EKG represents one heartbeat.

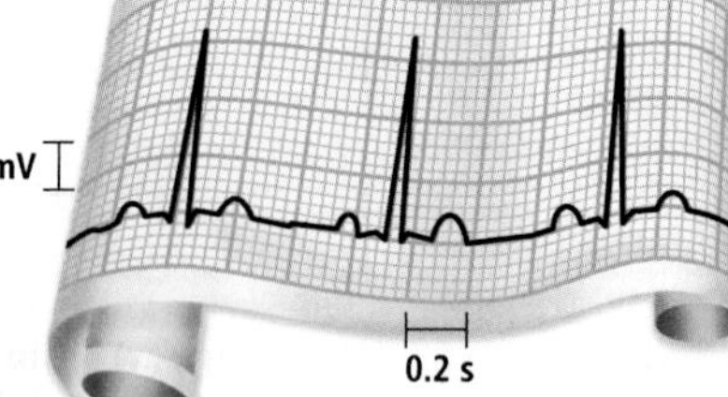

a. What is the period of one heartbeat? ≈ 0.8 s

b. The pulse rate is the number of beats in one minute. What is the pulse rate indicated by the EKG? 75 beats/min

c. What is the frequency of the EKG? 1.25 Hz

d. How does the pulse rate relate to the frequency in hertz?

Determine the amplitude and period for each function. Then describe the transformation from its parent function.

25. $f(x) = \sin\left(x + \frac{\pi}{4}\right) - 1$

26. $h(x) = \frac{3}{4}\cos\frac{\pi}{4}x$

27. $h(x) = \cos(2\pi x) - 2$

28. $j(x) = -3\sin 3x$

Estimation Use a graph of sine or cosine to estimate each value.

29. $\sin 160° \approx 0.3$

30. $\cos 50° \approx 0.6$

31. $\sin 15° \approx 0.25$

32. $\cos 95° \approx -0.1$

Write both a sine and a cosine function for each set of conditions.

33. amplitude of 6, period of π $f(x) = 6\sin 2x$; $f(x) = 6\cos 2x$

34. amplitude of $\frac{1}{4}$, phase shift of $\frac{2}{3}\pi$ left

Write both a sine and a cosine function that could be used to represent each graph.

35.

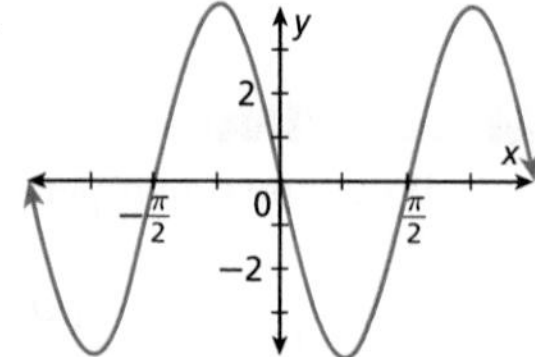

36.

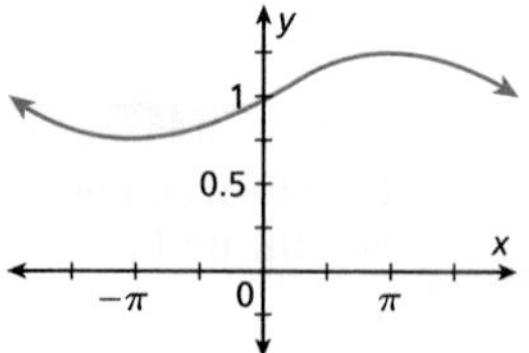

MULTI-STEP TEST PREP

37. This problem will prepare you for the Multi-Step Test Prep on page 1004.

The tide in a bay has a maximum height of 3 m and a minimum height of 0 m. It takes 6.1 hours for the tide to go out and another 6.1 hours for it to come back in. The height of the tide h is modeled as a function of time t.

a. What are the period and amplitude of h? What are the maximum and minimum values? period: 12.2; amplitude: 1.5; max.: 3; min.: 0

b. Assume that high tide occurs at $t = 0$. What are $h(0)$ and $h(6.1)$? b. $h(0) = 3$; $h(6.1) = 0$

c. Write h in the form $h(t) = a\cos bt + k$. $h(t) = 1.5\cos\frac{2\pi}{12.2}t + 1.5$

14-1 READING STRATEGIES

The form of the sine or cosine function determines how the graph varies. Use the graph of sinx as a reference.

The absolute value of a, |a|, tells you the value of the amplitude of the function. y = 2sinx

The value of the vertical shift, or vertical translation, is represented by k. y = sin(x) + 2

y = asinb(x − h) + k

From the variable b you can find the period, $\frac{2\pi}{|b|}$. The period tells you the length of one complete cycle. y = sin(2x)

The value of the phase shift, or horizontal translation, is represented by h. y = sin(x − 2)

Answer each question.

1. Describe how the period of f(x) = sinx compares to the period of g(x) = 4sin3x. The period of g(x), $\frac{2\pi}{3}$, is $\frac{1}{3}$ the size of the period of f(x), 2π.

2. Describe how the period of f(x) = cosx compares to the period of $g(x) = \frac{1}{2}\cos(x - 3)$. The period of g(x) is equal to the period of f(x), 2π.

3. Describe the phase shift for the function g(x) = 2sin3(x − 8) + 5. The phase shift is 8; the function is translated 8 units to the right.

4. What are the amplitude and period for the function $g(x) = 3\sin\frac{1}{2}(x + 2) - 1$? The amplitude is 3, and the period is 4π.

5. What are the phase shift and the vertical shift for the function g(x) = cos4(x + 5) + 3? The phase shift is −5 or 5 units left, and the vertical shift is 3 units up.

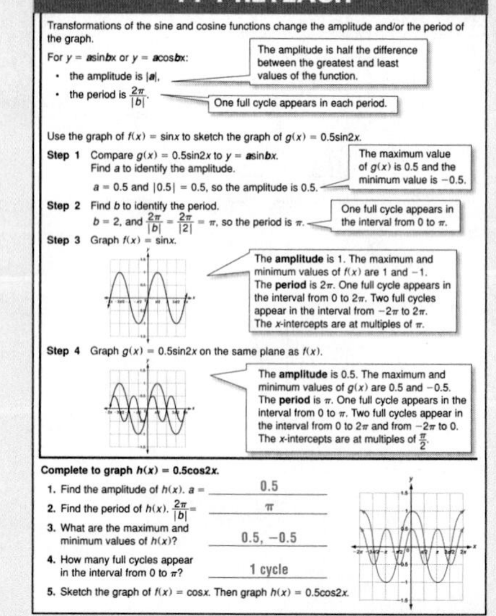

14-1 RETEACH

Transformations of the sine and cosine functions change the amplitude and/or the period of the graph.

For y = asinbx or y = acosbx:
- the amplitude is |a|, (The amplitude is half the difference between the greatest and least values of the function.)
- the period is $\frac{2\pi}{|b|}$. (One full cycle appears in each period.)

Use the graph of f(x) = sinx to sketch the graph of g(x) = 0.5sin2x.

Step 1 Compare g(x) = 0.5sin2x to y = asinbx. Find a to identify the amplitude. a = 0.5 and |0.5| = 0.5, so the amplitude is 0.5. (The maximum value of g(x) is 0.5 and the minimum value is −0.5.)

Step 2 Find b to identify the period. b = 2, and $\frac{2\pi}{|b|} = \frac{2\pi}{|2|} = \pi$, so the period is π. (One full cycle appears in the interval from 0 to π.)

Step 3 Graph f(x) = sinx. (The amplitude is 1. The maximum and minimum values of f(x) are 1 and −1. The period is 2π. One full cycle appears in the interval from 0 to 2π. Two full cycles appear in the interval from −2π to 2π. The x-intercepts are at multiples of π.)

Step 4 Graph g(x) = 0.5sin2x on the same plane as f(x). (The amplitude is 0.5. The maximum and minimum values of g(x) are 0.5 and −0.5. The period is π. One full cycle appears in the interval from 0 to π. Two full cycles appear in the interval from 0 to 2π and from −2π to 0. The x-intercepts are at multiples of $\frac{\pi}{2}$.)

Complete to graph h(x) = 0.5cos2x.

1. Find the amplitude of h(x). a = 0.5
2. Find the period of h(x). $\frac{2\pi}{|b|}$ = π
3. What are the maximum and minimum values of h(x)? 0.5, −0.5
4. How many full cycles appear in the interval from 0 to π? 1 cycle
5. Sketch the graph of f(x) = cosx. Then graph h(x) = 0.5cos2x.

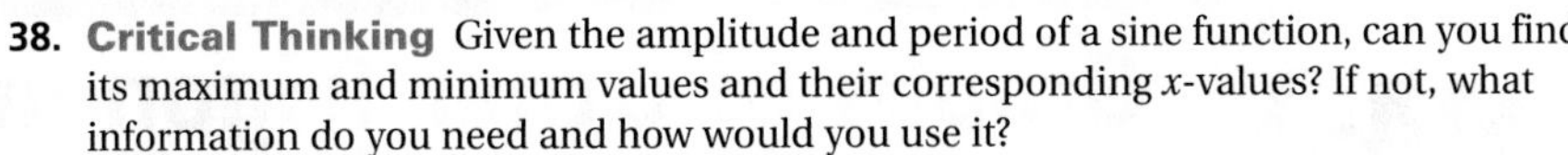

38. **Critical Thinking** Given the amplitude and period of a sine function, can you find its maximum and minimum values and their corresponding x-values? If not, what information do you need and how would you use it?

39. **Write About It** What happens to the period of $f(x) = \sin b\theta$ when $b > 1$? $b < 1$? Explain.

TEST PREP

40. Which trigonometric function best matches the graph?

Ⓐ $y = \frac{1}{2}\sin x$ Ⓒ $y = \frac{1}{2}\sin 2x$

Ⓑ $y = 2\sin x$ Ⓓ $y = 2\sin\frac{1}{2}x$ (circled)

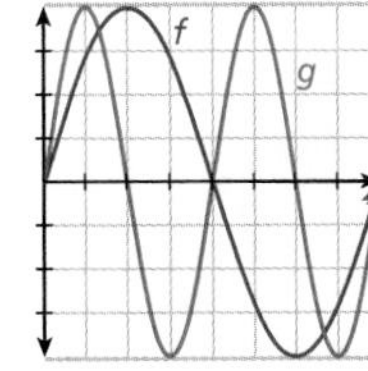

41. What is the amplitude for $y = -4\cos 3\pi x$?

Ⓕ -4 Ⓗ 4 (circled)

Ⓖ 3 Ⓙ 3π

42. Based on the graphs, what is the relationship between f and g?

Ⓐ f has twice the amplitude of g.

Ⓑ f has twice the period of g. (circled)

Ⓒ f has twice the frequency of g.

Ⓓ f has twice the cycle of g.

43. **Short Response** Using $y = \sin x$ as a guide, graph $y = -4\sin 2(x - \pi)$ on the interval $[0, 2\pi]$ and describe the transformations.

43. 

phase shift π right, horizontal compression, vertical stretch, and reflection across the x-axis; amplitude: 4; period: π; x-intercepts: $0, \frac{\pi}{2}, \pi, \frac{3\pi}{2}$, and 2π; max.: 4; min.: -4

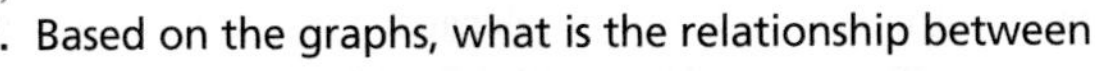

CHALLENGE AND EXTEND

44. Graph $f(x) = \text{Sin}^{-1}x$ and $g(x) = \text{Cos}^{-1}x$. (*Hint:* Use what you learned about graphs of inverse functions in Lesson 9-5 and inverse trigonometric functions in Lesson 13-4.)

Consider the functions $f(\theta) = \frac{1}{2}\sin\theta$ and $g(\theta) = 2\cos\theta$ for $0° \le \theta \le 360°$.

45. On the same set of coordinate axes, graph $f(\theta)$ and $g(\theta)$.

46. What are the approximate coordinates of the points of intersection of $f(\theta)$ and $g(\theta)$?

46. $(256°, -0.485)$ and $(76°, 0.485)$

47. When is $f(\theta) > g(\theta)$? $76° < \theta < 256°$

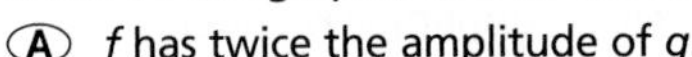

SPIRAL REVIEW

Use interval notation to represent each set of numbers. *(Lesson 1-1)*

48. $-7 < x \le 5$ $(-7, 5]$

49. $x \le -2$ or $1 \le x < 13$

49. $(-\infty, -2]$ or $[1, 13)$

50. $0 \le x \le 9$ $[0, 9]$

51. **Flowers** Adam has $100 to purchase a combination of roses, lilies, and carnations. Roses cost $6 each, lilies cost $2 each, and carnations cost $4 each. *(Lesson 3-5)*

Roses	6	4	3	7
Lilies	10	8	5	3
Carnations	11	15	18	13

a. Write a linear equation in three variables to represent this situation. $6r + 2\ell + 4c = 100$

b. Complete the table.

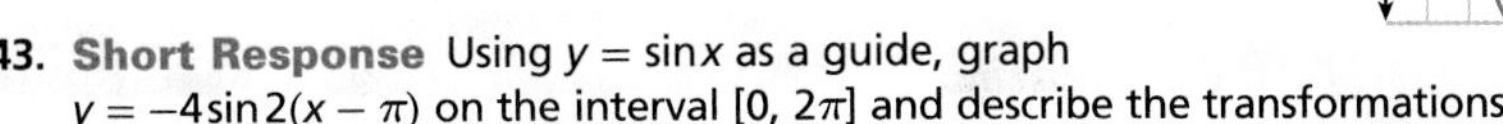

Use the given measurements to solve $\triangle ABC$. Round to the nearest tenth. *(Lesson 13-6)*

52. $b = 20$, $c = 11$, $m\angle A = 165°$
$a = 30.8$; $m\angle B = 9.7°$; $m\angle C = 5.3°$

53. $a = 11.9$, $b = 14.7$, $c = 26.1$
$m\angle A = 10°$; $m\angle B = 12.4°$; $m\angle C = 157.$

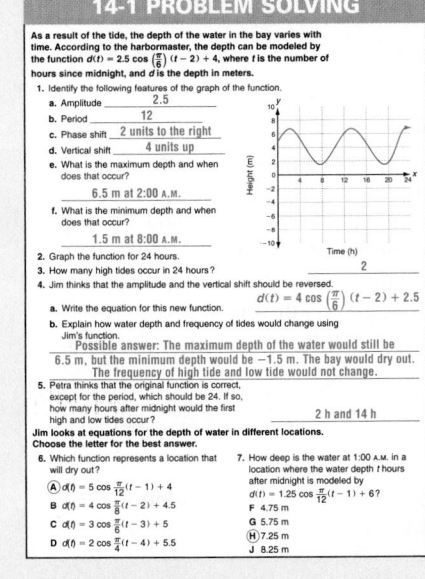

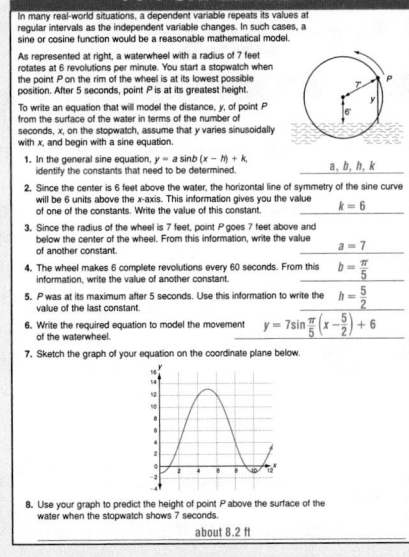

TEST PREP DOCTOR If students have difficulty with **Exercise 40,** they can test a key point on the curve, such as $(\pi, 2)$, which fits only choice **D.**

Answers

38. No; possible answer: you would also need to know whether there is a phase shift or vertical shift. The phase shift and period give the location of the maxima and minima. The amplitude and vertical shift give the values of the maxima and minima.

39. The period decreases for $b > 1$ and increases for $b < 1$ because the period is given by $\frac{2\pi}{b}$.

44, 45. See p. A50.

Journal

Have students describe how to identify the period and the phase shift of a sine or cosine function.

ALTERNATIVE ASSESSMENT

Have students explain and give examples of the roles of a, b, h, and k for $f(x) = a\cos b(x - h) + k$.

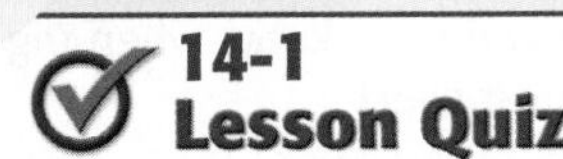

Power Presentations with PowerPoint®

14-1 Lesson Quiz

1. Using $f(x) = \cos x$ as a guide, graph $g(x) = 1.5\cos 2x$.

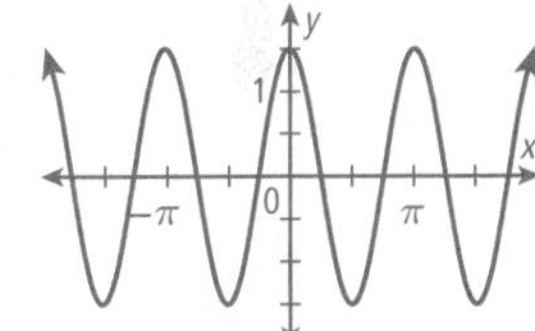

Suppose that the height, in feet, above ground of one of the cabins of a Ferris wheel at t minutes is modeled by

$$H(t) = 30\sin\left(\frac{2\pi}{3}\left(t - \frac{3}{4}\right)\right) + 36.$$

2. Graph the height of the cabin for two complete revolutions.

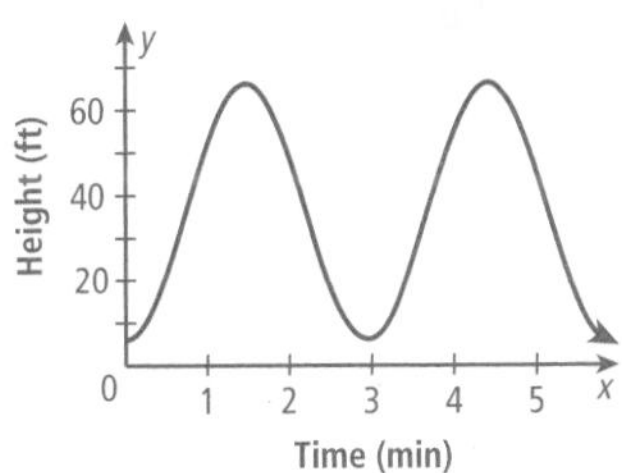

3. What is the radius of this Ferris wheel? 30 ft

Also available on transparency

14-1 PROBLEM SOLVING

As a result of the tide, the depth of the water in the bay varies with time. According to the harbormaster, the depth can be modeled by the function $d(t) = 2.5\cos\left(\frac{\pi}{6}\right)(t - 2) + 4$, where t is the number of hours since midnight, and d is the depth in meters.

1. Identify the following features of the graph of the function.
   a. Amplitude 2.5
   b. Period 12
   c. Phase shift 2 units to the right
   d. Vertical shift 4 units up
   e. What is the maximum depth and when does that occur? 6.5 m at 2:00 A.M.
   f. What is the minimum depth and when does that occur? 1.5 m at 8:00 A.M.
2. Graph the function for 24 hours.
3. How many high tides occur in 24 hours? 2
4. Jim thinks that the amplitude and the vertical shift should be reversed.
   a. Write the equation for this new function. $d(t) = 4\cos\left(\frac{\pi}{6}\right)(t - 2) + 2.5$
   b. Explain how water depth and frequency of tides would change using Jim's function.
   Possible answer: The maximum depth of the water would still be 6.5 m, but the minimum depth would be -1.5 m. The bay would dry out. The frequency of high tide and low tide would not change.
5. Petra thinks that the original function is correct, except for the period, which should be 24. If so, how many hours after midnight would the first high and low tides occur? 2 h and 14 h

Jim looks at equations for the depth of water in different locations. Choose the letter for the best answer.

6. Which function represents a location that will dry out?
   Ⓐ $d(t) = 5\cos\frac{\pi}{12}(t - 1) + 4$ (circled)
   B $d(t) = 4\cos\frac{\pi}{8}(t - 2) + 4.5$
   C $d(t) = 3\cos\frac{\pi}{6}(t - 3) + 5$
   D $d(t) = 2\cos\frac{\pi}{4}(t - 4) + 5.5$
7. How deep is the water at 1:00 A.M. in a location where the water depth t hours after midnight is modeled by $d(t) = 1.25\cos\frac{\pi}{12}(t - 1) + 6$?
   F 4.75 m
   G 5.75 m
   Ⓗ 7.25 m (circled)
   J 8.25 m

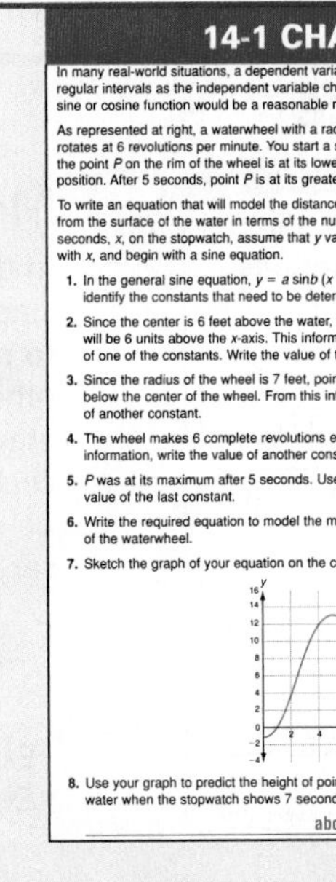

14-1 CHALLENGE

In many real-world situations, a dependent variable repeats its values at regular intervals as the independent variable changes. In such cases, a sine or cosine function would be a reasonable mathematical model.

As represented at right, a waterwheel with a radius of 7 feet rotates at 6 revolutions per minute. You start a stopwatch when the point P on the rim of the wheel is at its lowest possible position. After 5 seconds, point P is at its greatest height.

To write an equation that will model the distance, y, of point P from the surface of the water in terms of the number of seconds, x, on the stopwatch, assume that y varies sinusoidally with x, and begin with a sine equation.

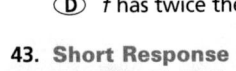

1. In the general sine equation, $y = a\sin b(x - h) + k$, identify the constants that need to be determined. a, b, h, k
2. Since the center is 6 feet above the water, the horizontal line of symmetry of the sine curve will be 6 units above the x-axis. This information gives you the value of one of the constants. Write the value of this constant. $k = 6$
3. Since the radius of the wheel is 7 feet, point P goes 7 feet above and below the center of the wheel. From this information, write the value of another constant. $a = 7$
4. The wheel makes 6 complete revolutions every 60 seconds. From this information, write the value of another constant. $b = \frac{\pi}{5}$
5. P was at its maximum after 5 seconds. Use this information to write the value of the last constant. $h = \frac{5}{2}$
6. Write the required equation to model the movement of the waterwheel. $y = 7\sin\frac{\pi}{5}\left(x - \frac{5}{2}\right) + 6$
7. Sketch the graph of your equation on the coordinate plane below.
8. Use your graph to predict the height of point P above the surface of the water when the stopwatch shows 7 seconds. about 8.2 ft

14-2 Organizer

Pacing: Traditional 2 days
Block 1 day

Objectives: Recognize and graph trigonometric functions.

Algebra Lab
In Algebra Lab Activities

Online Edition
Graphing Calculator, Tutorial Videos

Power Presentations with PowerPoint®

Warm Up

If $\sin A = \frac{3}{5}$, evaluate:

1. $\cos A$ $\frac{4}{5}$ **2.** $\tan A$ $\frac{3}{4}$

3. $\cot A$ $\frac{4}{3}$ **4.** $\sec A$ $\frac{5}{4}$

5. $\csc A$ $\frac{5}{3}$

Also available on transparency

Math Humor

Q: How do you know when trig class is almost over?

A: When time starts getting asymptotically close to the end of the period.

State Resources

go.hrw.com
State Resources Online
KEYWORD: MB7 Resources

14-2 Graphs of Other Trigonometric Functions

A2.1.2 Use and interpret function notation, including evaluation of functions represented by tables, graphs, words, equations or a set of ordered pairs.

Objective
Recognize and graph trigonometric functions.

Why learn this?
You can use the graphs of reciprocal trigonometric functions to model rotating objects such as lights. (See Exercise 25.)

The tangent and cotangent functions can be graphed on the coordinate plane. The tangent function is undefined when $\theta = \frac{\pi}{2} + \pi n$, where n is an integer. The cotangent function is undefined when $\theta = \pi n$. These values are excluded from the domain and are represented by vertical asymptotes on the graph. Because tangent and cotangent have no maximum or minimum values, amplitude is undefined.

To graph tangent and cotangent, let the variable x represent the angle θ in standard position.

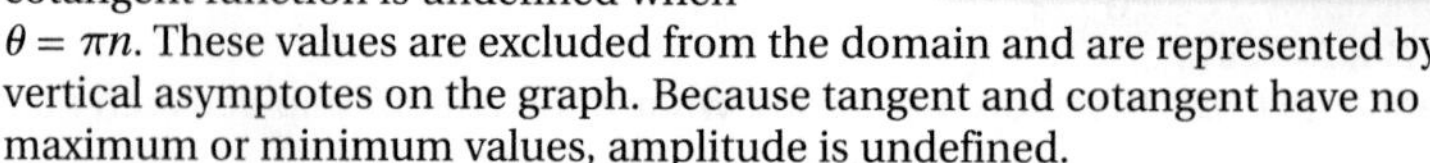

Know it! Note

Characteristics of the Graphs of Tangent and Cotangent

FUNCTION	$y = \tan x$	$y = \cot x$
GRAPH	[graph]	[graph]
DOMAIN	$\left\{x \mid x \neq \frac{\pi}{2} + \pi n,\right.$ where n is an integer$\left.\right\}$	$\{x \mid x \neq \pi n,$ where n is an integer$\}$
RANGE	$\{y \mid -\infty < y < \infty\}$	$\{y \mid -\infty < y < \infty\}$
PERIOD	π	π
AMPLITUDE	undefined	undefined

Like sine and cosine, you can transform the tangent function.

Know it! Note

Transformations of Tangent Graphs

For the graph of $y = a \tan bx$, where $a \neq 0$ and x is in radians,

- the period is $\frac{\pi}{|b|}$.
- the asymptotes are located at $x = \frac{\pi}{2|b|} + \frac{\pi n}{|b|}$, where n is an integer.

1 Introduce

EXPLORATION

14-2 Graphs of Other Trigonometric Functions

You can investigate the graph of the function y = tan x by making a table of values and plotting points.

1. Use your calculator to complete the table for the function y = tan x. Round each y-value to the nearest hundredth if necessary.

x(°)	−90	−60	−45	−30	0	30	45	60	90
y									

2. Plot the points from your table on a coordinate plane like the one shown. Connect the points to form a smooth curve.

THINK AND DISCUSS

3. **Explain** what happens when x approaches 90° or −90°.

4. **Describe** what you think would happen if you continued the

Motivate

In the previous lesson, students investigated the sine and cosine functions, which can be used to model certain types of periodic behavior. The other four trigonometric functions also have graphs that are periodic and based on the unit circle values. The graphs of sine and cosine can be used to sketch graphs of tangent, cotangent, secant, and cosecant.

Explorations and answers are provided in the *Explorations* binder.

EXAMPLE 1 Transforming Tangent Functions

Using $f(x) = \tan x$ as a guide, graph $g(x) = \tan 2x$. Identify the period, x-intercepts, and asymptotes.

Step 1 Identify the period.

Because $b = 2$, the period is $\frac{\pi}{|b|} = \frac{\pi}{|2|} = \frac{\pi}{2}$.

Step 2 Identify the x-intercepts.

The first x-intercept occurs at $x = 0$. Because the period is $\frac{\pi}{2}$, the x-intercepts occur at $\frac{\pi}{2}n$, where n is an integer.

Step 3 Identify the asymptotes.

Because $b = 2$, the asymptotes occur at $x = \frac{\pi}{2|2|} + \frac{\pi n}{|2|}$, or $x = \frac{\pi}{4} + \frac{\pi n}{2}$.

Step 4 Graph using all of the information about the function.

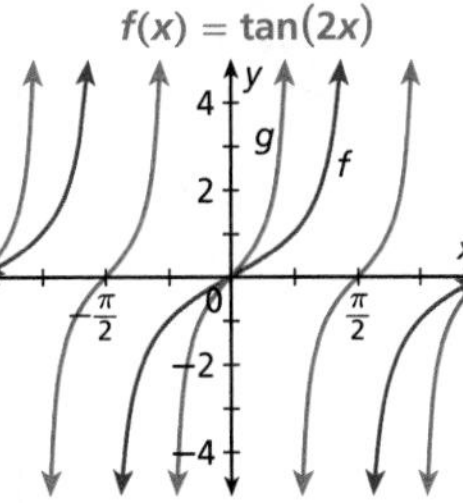

1\. period: 2π; x-intercepts: $2\pi n$; asymptotes: $\pi + 2\pi n$

1. Using $f(x) = \tan x$ as a guide, graph $g(x) = 3\tan\frac{1}{2}x$. Identify the period, x-intercepts, and asymptotes.

Transformations of Cotangent Graphs

For the graph of $y = a\cot bx$, where $a \neq 0$ and x is in radians,

- the period is $\frac{\pi}{|b|}$.
- the asymptotes are located at $x = \frac{\pi n}{|b|}$, where n is an integer.

EXAMPLE 2 Graphing the Cotangent Function

Using $f(x) = \cot x$ as a guide, graph $g(x) = \cot 0.5x$. Identify the period, x-intercepts, and asymptotes.

Step 1 Identify the period.

Because $b = 0.5$, the period is $\frac{\pi}{|b|} = \frac{\pi}{|0.5|} = 2\pi$.

Step 2 Identify the x-intercepts.

The first x-intercept occurs at $x = \pi$. Because the period is 2π, the x-intercepts occur at $x = \pi + 2\pi n$, where n is an integer.

Step 3 Identify the asymptotes.

Because $b = 0.5$, the asymptotes occur at $x = \frac{\pi n}{|0.5|} = 2\pi n$.

Step 4 Graph using all of the information about the function.

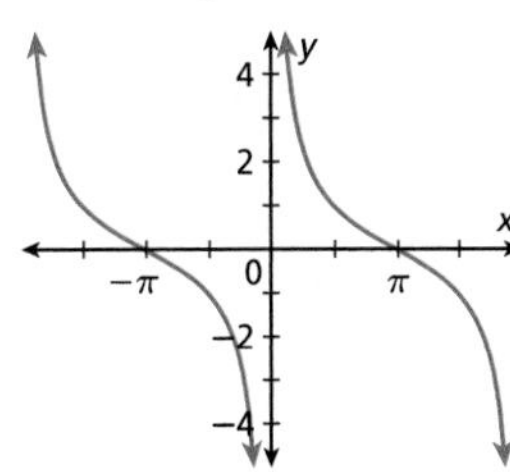

COMMON ERROR ALERT

Students may forget to include negative values of n when determining the domain of tangent and cotangent functions. Remind students that n is an integer, not a natural number.

Power Presentations with PowerPoint®

Additional Examples

Example 1

Using $f(x) = \tan x$ as a guide, graph $gx = \frac{1}{2}\tan\left(\frac{1}{3}x\right)$. Identify the period, x-intercepts, and asymptotes.

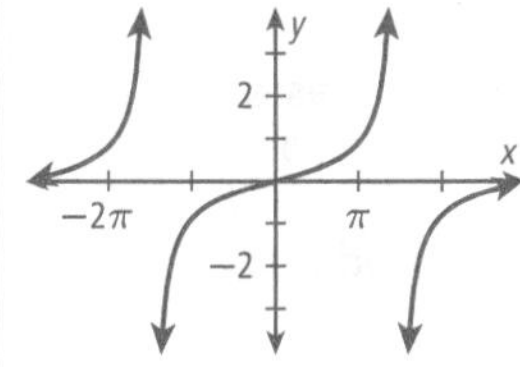

period: 3π; x-intercepts: $3\pi n$; asymptotes: $x = \frac{3\pi}{2} + 3\pi n$

Also available on transparency

INTERVENTION

Questioning Strategies

EXAMPLE 1

- What determines the location of the asymptotes on the graph of a tangent function?

2 Teach

Guided Instruction

Introduce the graphs of tangent and cotangent by first drawing the unit circle and choosing values with which to plot points. Be sure to include the angle values that correspond to x-intercepts and asymptotes.

Reaching All Learners

Through Modeling

Have students plot the sine curve, then have them carefully construct the cosecant curve by taking a series of points from the sine curve and plotting the reciprocal of each point.

Power Presentations with PowerPoint®

Additional Examples

Example 2

Using $f(x) = \cot x$ as a guide, graph $g(x) = \frac{1}{2}\cot 3x$. Identify the period, x-intercepts, and asymptotes.

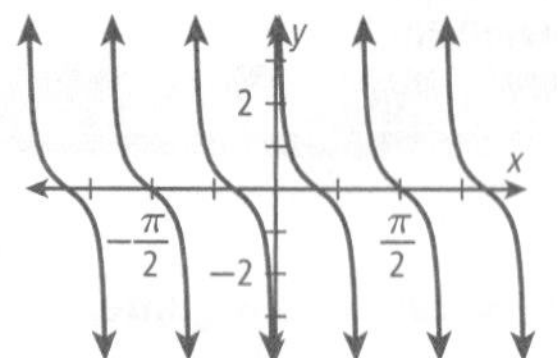

period: $\frac{\pi}{3}$; x-intercepts: $\frac{\pi}{6} + \frac{\pi}{3}n$; asymptotes: $x = \frac{\pi}{3}n$

Example 3

Using $f(x) = \cos x$ as a guide, graph $g(x) = \frac{1}{2}\sec\left(\frac{1}{2}x\right)$. Identify the period and asymptotes.

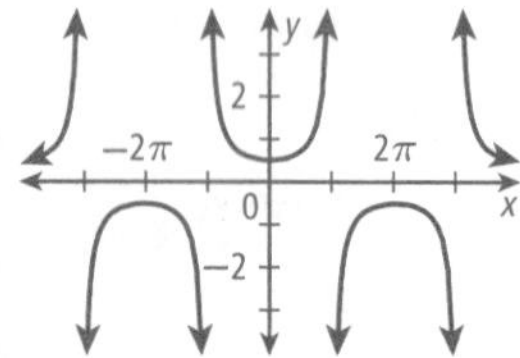

period: 4π; asymptotes: $x = \pi + 2\pi n$

Also available on transparency

INTERVENTION
Questioning Strategies

EXAMPLE 2

- Compare the graph of cotangent to the graph of tangent.

EXAMPLE 3

- What determines the location of the asymptotes on the graph of a secant or cosecant function?

2. Using $f(x) = \cot x$ as a guide, graph $g(x) = -\cot 2x$. Identify the period, x-intercepts, and asymptotes.

2. period: $\frac{\pi}{2}$; x-intercepts: $\frac{\pi}{4} + \frac{\pi}{2}n$; asymptotes: $\frac{\pi}{2}n$

Recall that $\sec\theta = \frac{1}{\cos\theta}$. So, secant is undefined where cosine equals zero and the graph will have vertical asymptotes at those locations. Secant will also have the same period as cosine. Sine and cosecant have a similar relationship. Because secant and cosecant have no absolute maxima or minima, amplitude is undefined.

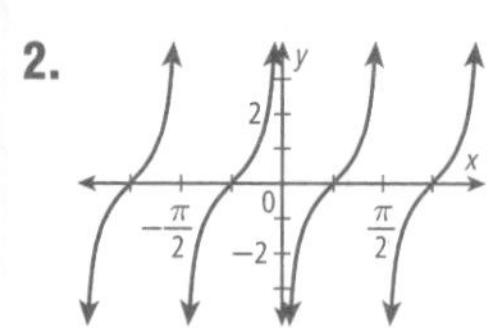

Characteristics of the Graphs of Secant and Cosecant

FUNCTION	$y = \sec x$	$y = \csc x$
GRAPH		
DOMAIN	$\{x \mid x \neq \frac{\pi}{2} + \pi n$, where n is an integer$\}$	$\{x \mid x \neq \pi n$, where n is an integer$\}$
RANGE	$\{y \mid y \leq -1, \text{ or } y \geq 1\}$	$\{y \mid y \leq -1, \text{ or } y \geq 1\}$
PERIOD	2π	2π
AMPLITUDE	undefined	undefined

You can graph transformations of secant and cosecant by using what you learned in Lesson 14-1 about transformations of graphs of cosine and sine.

EXAMPLE 3 Graphing Secant and Cosecant Functions

Using $f(x) = \cos x$ as a guide, graph $g(x) = \sec 2x$. Identify the period and asymptotes.

Step 1 Identify the period.

Because $\sec 2x$ is the reciprocal of $\cos 2x$, the graphs will have the same period.

Because $b = 2$ for $\cos 2x$, the period is $\frac{2\pi}{|b|} = \frac{2\pi}{|2|} = \pi$.

Step 2 Identify the asymptotes.

Because the period is π, the asymptotes occur at $x = \frac{\pi}{2|2|} + \frac{\pi}{|2|}n = \frac{\pi}{4} + \frac{\pi}{2}n$, where n is an integer.

Step 3 Graph using all of the information about the function.

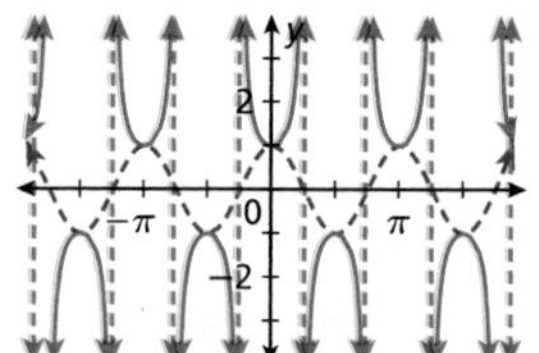

3. period: 2π; asymptotes: πn

3. Using $f(x) = \sin x$ as a guide, graph $g(x) = 2\csc x$. Identify the period and asymptotes.

ONGOING ASSESSMENT and INTERVENTION

Diagnose ***Before*** **the Lesson**
14-2 Warm Up, TE p. 998

Monitor ***During*** **the Lesson**
Check It Out! Exercises, SE pp. 999–1000
Questioning Strategies, TE pp. 999–1000

Assess ***After*** **the Lesson**
14-2 Lesson Quiz, TE p. 1003
Alternative Assessment, TE p. 1003

3 Close

Summarize

Remind students that the cotangent, secant, and cosecant functions are, respectively, reciprocals of the tangent, cosine, and sine functions. They are subject to all of the same transformations as any other curve.

THINK AND DISCUSS

1. **EXPLAIN** why $f(x) = \sin x$ can be used to graph $g(x) = \csc x$.
2. **EXPLAIN** how the zeros of the cosine function relate to the vertical asymptotes of the graph of the tangent function.

3. **GET ORGANIZED** Copy and complete the graphic organizer.

Function	Zeros	Asymptotes	Period
$y = \sec x$			
$y = \csc x$			
$y = \cot x$			
$y = \tan x$			

Answers to *Think and Discuss*

Possible answers:

1. Cosecant is the reciprocal of the sine function, so the graphs are related.
2. By using the unit circle, you can see that tangent is undefined at the same values where cosine is equal to 0. An undefined value corresponds to an asymptote, so the zeros of cosine correspond to the asymptotes of tangent.
3. See p. A14.

14-2 Exercises

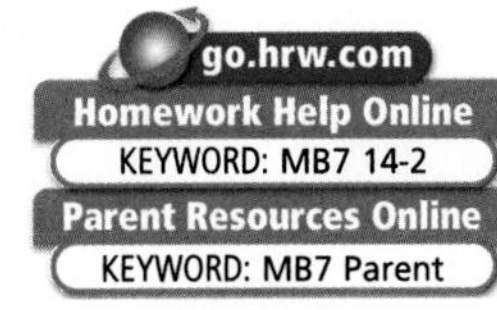

go.hrw.com
Homework Help Online
KEYWORD: MB7 14-2
Parent Resources Online
KEYWORD: MB7 Parent

GUIDED PRACTICE

SEE EXAMPLE 1 p. 999

Using $f(x) = \tan x$ as a guide, graph each function. Identify the period, x-intercepts, and asymptotes.

1. $k(x) = 2\tan(3x)$
2. $g(x) = \tan\frac{1}{4}x$
3. $h(x) = \tan 2\pi x$

SEE EXAMPLE 2 p. 999

Using $f(x) = \cot x$ as a guide, graph each function. Identify the period, x-intercepts, and asymptotes.

4. $j(x) = 0.25\cot x$
5. $p(x) = \cot 2x$
6. $g(x) = \frac{3}{2}\cot x$

SEE EXAMPLE 3 p. 1000

Using $f(x) = \cos x$ or $f(x) = \sin x$ as a guide, graph each function. Identify the period and asymptotes.

7. $g(x) = \frac{1}{2}\sec x$
8. $q(x) = \sec 4x$
9. $h(x) = 3\csc x$

PRACTICE AND PROBLEM SOLVING

Independent Practice

For Exercises	See Example
10–13	1
14–16	2
17–19	3

Extra Practice
Skills Practice p. S30
Application Practice p. S45

Using $f(x) = \tan x$ as a guide, graph each function. Identify the period, x-intercepts, and asymptotes.

10. $p(x) = \tan\frac{3}{2}x$
11. $g(x) = \tan\left(x + \frac{\pi}{4}\right)$
12. $h(x) = \frac{1}{2}\tan 4x$
13. $j(x) = -2\tan\frac{\pi}{2}x$

Using $f(x) = \cot x$ as a guide, graph each function. Identify the period, x-intercepts, and asymptotes.

14. $h(x) = 4\cot x$
15. $g(x) = \cot\frac{1}{4}x$
16. $j(x) = 0.1\cot x$

Using $f(x) = \cos x$ or $f(x) = \sin x$ as a guide, graph each function. Identify the period and asymptotes.

17. $g(x) = -\sec x$
18. $k(x) = \frac{1}{2}\csc x$
19. $h(x) = \csc(-x)$

14-2 Exercises

Assignment Guide

Assign *Guided Practice* exercises as necessary.

Basic 10-33, 35-40, 51-59
Average 10-43, 51-59
Advanced 10-59

Homework Quick Check
Quickly check key concepts.
Exercises: 10, 12, 14, 18

Answers

1–19. See p. A50.

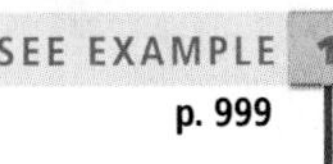

Teacher to Teacher

I have my advanced students read a chapter or excerpts about the development of the six trigonometric functions over time from the book *Trigonometric Delights* by Eli Maor. Students are usually quite surprised to find out that the trigonometric functions were not all discovered at one time.

Mary Lane Blomquist
Kewaskum, WI

State Resources

go.hrw.com
State Resources Online
KEYWORD: MB7 Resources

MULTI-STEP TEST PREP Exercise 20 involves graphing and interpreting cosecant functions. This exercise prepares students for the Multi-Step Test Prep on page 1004.

Answers

20a.

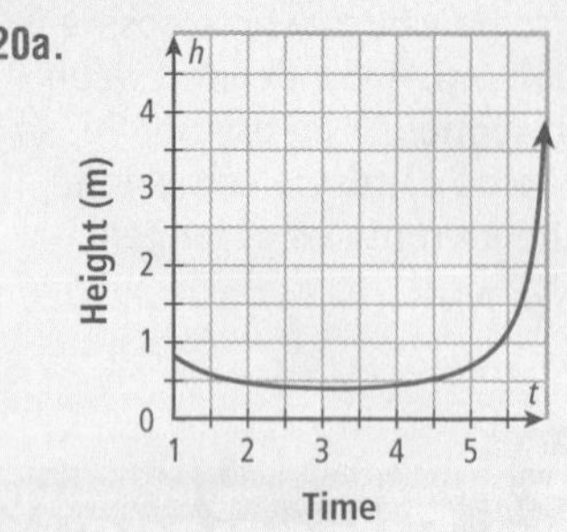

25b.

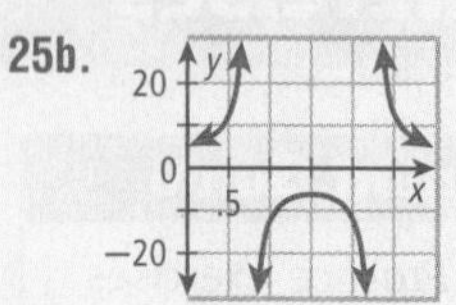

26b.

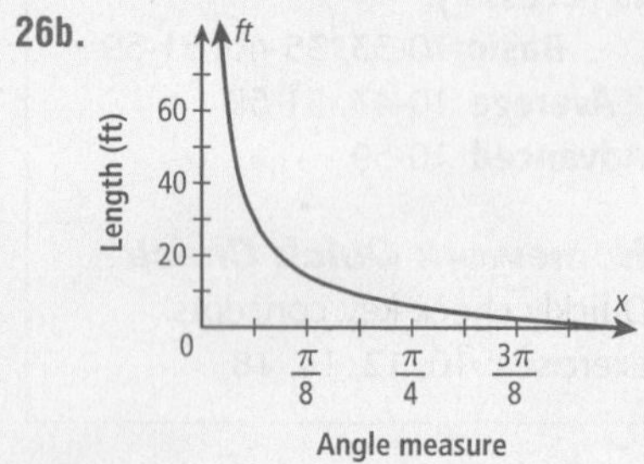

22. $-\pi$; 0; π; 2π

24. $-\pi$; 0; π; 2π

33. Possible answer: For reciprocal pairs of trigonometric functions, when one increases, the other decreases and vice versa.

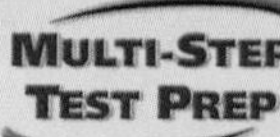

MULTI-STEP TEST PREP

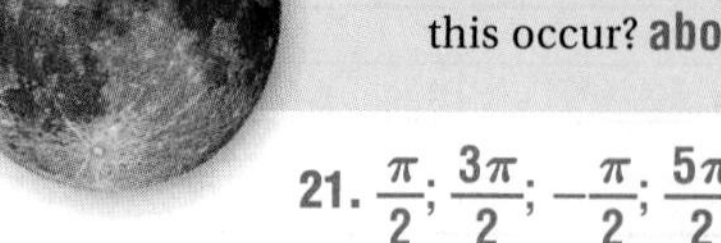

20. This problem will prepare you for the Multi-Step Test Prep on page 1004.

    Between 1:00 P.M. ($t = 1$) and 6:00 P.M. ($t = 6$), the height (in meters) of the tide in a bay is modeled by $h(t) = 0.4\csc \frac{5\pi}{31}t$.

    a. Graph the function for the range $1 \le t \le 6$.

    b. At what time does low tide occur? **about 3:06 P.M. ($t = 3.1$)**

    c. What is the height of the tide at low tide? **0.4 m**

    d. What is the maximum height of the tide during this time span? When does this occur? **about 3.95 m; 6:00 P.M.**

21. $\frac{\pi}{2}; \frac{3\pi}{2}; -\frac{\pi}{2}; \frac{5\pi}{2}$

23. $\frac{\pi}{2}; \frac{3\pi}{2}; -\frac{\pi}{2}; \frac{5\pi}{2}$

Find four values for which each function is undefined.

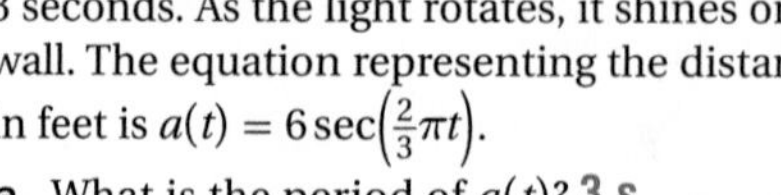

21. $f(\theta) = \tan\theta$ 22. $g(\theta) = \cot\theta$ 23. $h(\theta) = \sec\theta$ 24. $j(\theta) = \csc\theta$

25. **Law Enforcement** A police car is parked on the side of the road next to a building. The flashing light on the car is 6 feet from the wall and completes one full rotation every 3 seconds. As the light rotates, it shines on the wall. The equation representing the distance a in feet is $a(t) = 6\sec\left(\frac{2}{3}\pi t\right)$.

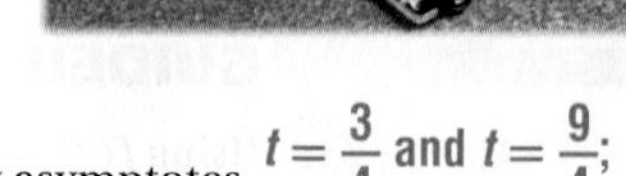

    a. What is the period of $a(t)$? **3 s**

    b. Graph the function for $0 \le t \le 3$.

    c. **Critical Thinking** Identify the location of any asymptotes. **$t = \frac{3}{4}$ and $t = \frac{9}{4}$;** What do the asymptotes represent? **Possible answer: The asymptotes represent the time when the light shines parallel to the wall.**

LINK

Math History

The Greek gnomon was a tall staff, but gnomon is also the part of a sundial that casts a shadow. Based on the variation of shadows at high noon, a gnomon can be used to determine the day of the year, in addition to the time of day.

26. **Math History** The ancient Greeks used a *gnomon,* a type of tall staff, to tell the time of day based on the lengths of shadows and the altitude θ of the sun above the horizon.

    a. Use the figure to write a cotangent function that can be used to find the length of the shadow s in terms of the height of the gnomon h and the angle θ. **$s = h\cot\theta$**

    b. Graph your answer to part **a** for a gnomon of height 6 ft.

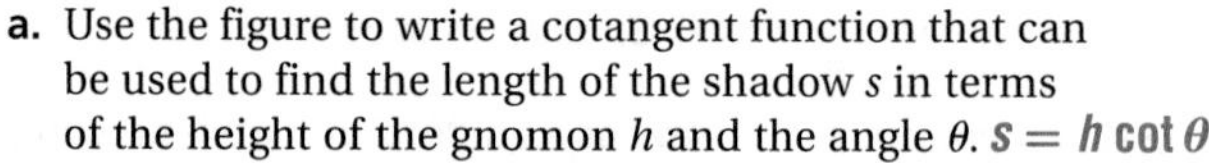

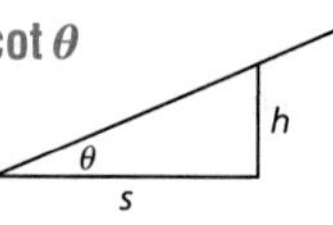

Complete the table by labeling each function as increasing or decreasing.

		$0 < x < \frac{\pi}{2}$	$\frac{\pi}{2} < x < \pi$	$\pi < x < \frac{3\pi}{2}$	$\frac{3\pi}{2} < x < 2\pi$
27.	sin x	inc.	dec.	dec.	inc.
28.	csc x	dec.	inc.	inc.	dec.
29.	cos x	dec.	dec.	inc.	inc.
30.	sec x	inc.	inc.	dec.	dec.
31.	tan x	inc.	inc.	inc.	inc.
32.	cot x	dec.	dec.	dec.	dec.

33. **Critical Thinking** Based on the table above, what do you observe about the increasing/decreasing relationship between reciprocal pairs of trigonometric functions?

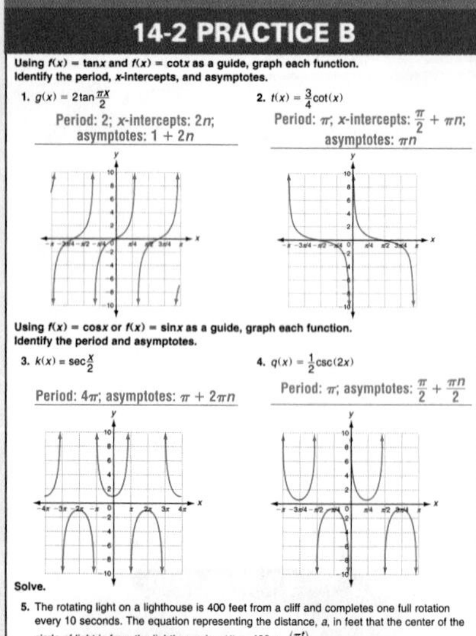

14-2 PRACTICE A

14-2 PRACTICE C

14-2 PRACTICE B

Using $f(x) = \tan x$ and $f(x) = \cot x$ as a guide, graph each function. Identify the period, x-intercepts, and asymptotes.

1. $g(x) = 2\tan\frac{\pi x}{2}$ Period: 2; x-intercepts: $2n$; asymptotes: $1 + 2n$

2. $f(x) = \frac{3}{4}\cot(x)$ Period: π; x-intercepts: $\frac{\pi}{2} + \pi n$; asymptotes: πn

Using $f(x) = \cos x$ or $f(x) = \sin x$ as a guide, graph each function. Identify the period and asymptotes.

3. $k(x) = \sec\frac{x}{2}$ Period: 4π; asymptotes: $\pi + 2\pi n$

4. $q(x) = \frac{1}{2}\csc(2x)$ Period: π; asymptotes: $\frac{\pi}{2} + \frac{\pi n}{2}$

Solve.

5. The rotating light on a lighthouse is 400 feet from a cliff and completes one full rotation every 10 seconds. The equation representing the distance, a, in feet that the center of the circle of light is from the lighthouse is $a(t) = 400\sec\left(\frac{\pi t}{5}\right)$.

a. What is the period of $a(t)$? 10

b. Find the value of the function at $t = 10$. 400 ft

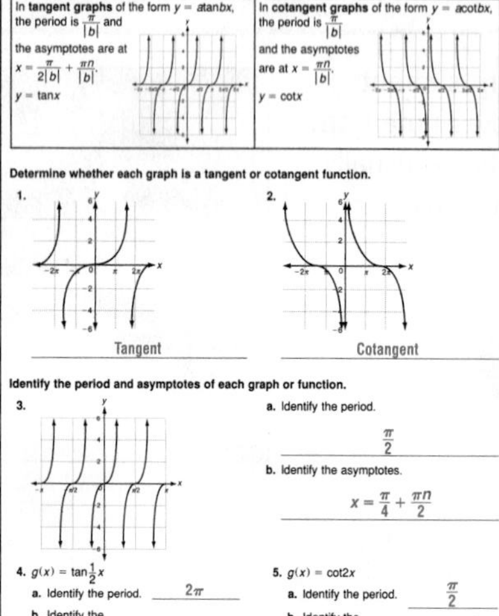

14-2 READING STRATEGIES

Tangent and cotangent graphs have different characteristics.

In **tangent graphs** of the form $y = a\tan bx$, the period is $\frac{\pi}{\lvert b\rvert}$ and the asymptotes are at $x = \frac{\pi}{2\lvert b\rvert} + \frac{\pi n}{\lvert b\rvert}$. $y = \tan x$	In **cotangent graphs** of the form $y = a\cot bx$, the period is $\frac{\pi}{\lvert b\rvert}$ and the asymptotes are at $x = \frac{\pi n}{\lvert b\rvert}$. $y = \cot x$

Determine whether each graph is a tangent or cotangent function.

1. Tangent

2. Cotangent

Identify the period and asymptotes of each graph or function.

3. a. Identify the period. $\frac{\pi}{2}$

b. Identify the asymptotes. $x = \frac{\pi}{4} + \frac{\pi n}{2}$

4. $g(x) = \tan\frac{1}{2}x$

a. Identify the period. 2π

b. Identify the asymptotes. $x = \pi + 2\pi n$

5. $g(x) = \cot 2x$

a. Identify the period. $\frac{\pi}{2}$

b. Identify the asymptotes. $x = \frac{\pi n}{2}$

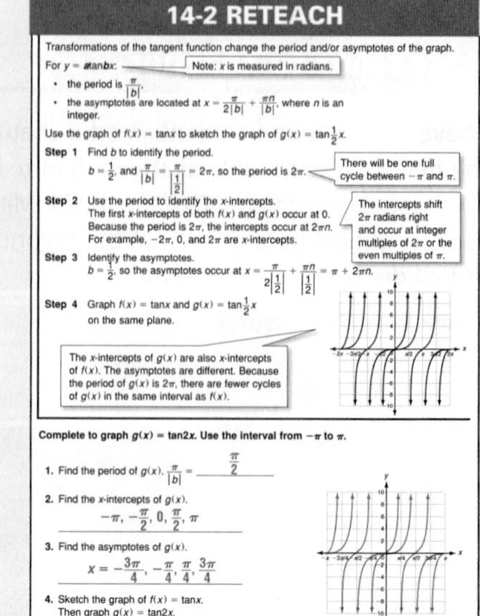

14-2 RETEACH

Transformations of the tangent function change the period and/or asymptotes of the graph.

For $y = a\tan bx$: Note: x is measured in radians.

- the period is $\frac{\pi}{\lvert b\rvert}$.
- the asymptotes are located at $x = \frac{\pi}{2\lvert b\rvert} + \frac{\pi n}{\lvert b\rvert}$, where n is an integer.

Use the graph of $f(x) = \tan x$ to sketch the graph of $g(x) = \tan\frac{1}{2}x$.

Step 1 Find b to identify the period.
$b = \frac{1}{2}$, and $\frac{\pi}{\lvert b\rvert} = \frac{\pi}{\left|\frac{1}{2}\right|} = 2\pi$, so the period is 2π. There will be one full cycle between $-\pi$ and π.

Step 2 Use the period to identify the x-intercepts.
The first x-intercepts of both $f(x)$ and $g(x)$ occur at 0. Because the period is 2π, the intercepts occur at $2\pi n$. For example, -2π, 0, and 2π are x-intercepts. The intercepts shift 2π radians right and occur at integer multiples of 2π or the even multiples of π.

Step 3 Identify the asymptotes.
$b = \frac{1}{2}$, so the asymptotes occur at $x = \frac{\pi}{2\left|\frac{1}{2}\right|} + \frac{\pi n}{\left|\frac{1}{2}\right|} = \pi + 2\pi n$.

Step 4 Graph $f(x) = \tan x$ and $g(x) = \tan\frac{1}{2}x$ on the same plane.

The x-intercepts of $g(x)$ are also x-intercepts of $f(x)$. The asymptotes are different. Because the period of $g(x)$ is 2π, there are fewer cycles of $g(x)$ in the same interval as $f(x)$.

Complete to graph $g(x) = \tan 2x$. Use the interval from $-\pi$ to π.

1. Find the period of $g(x)$. $\frac{\pi}{\lvert b\rvert} =$ $\frac{\pi}{2}$

2. Find the x-intercepts of $g(x)$. $-\pi, -\frac{\pi}{2}, 0, \frac{\pi}{2}, \pi$

3. Find the asymptotes of $g(x)$. $x = -\frac{3\pi}{4}, -\frac{\pi}{4}, \frac{\pi}{4}, \frac{3\pi}{4}$

4. Sketch the graph of $f(x) = \tan x$. Then graph $g(x) = \tan 2x$.

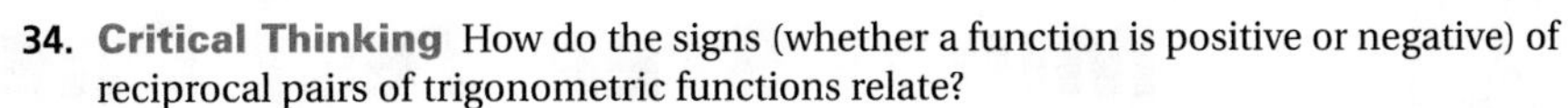

34. **Critical Thinking** How do the signs (whether a function is positive or negative) of reciprocal pairs of trigonometric functions relate?

35. **Write About It** Describe how to graph $f(x) = 3\sec 4x$ by using the graph of $g(x) = 3\cos 4x$.

TEST PREP

36. Which is NOT in the domain of $y = \cot x$?
    Ⓐ $-\frac{\pi}{2}$ Ⓑ (circled) 0 Ⓒ $\frac{\pi}{2}$ Ⓓ $\frac{3\pi}{2}$

37. What is the range of $f(x) = 3\csc 2\theta$?
    Ⓕ $\{y \mid y \le -1 \text{ or } y \ge 1\}$ Ⓗ $\{y \mid y \le -2 \text{ or } y \ge 2\}$
    Ⓖ (circled) $\{y \mid y \le -3 \text{ or } y \ge 3\}$ Ⓙ $\{y \mid y \le -\frac{1}{2} \text{ or } y \ge \frac{1}{2}\}$

38. Which could be the equation of the graph?
    Ⓐ $y = \tan 2x$ Ⓒ $y = 2\tan x$
    Ⓑ (circled) $y = \cot 2x$ Ⓓ $y = 2\cot x$

39. What is the period of $y = \tan\frac{1}{2}x$?
    Ⓕ $\frac{\pi}{2}$ Ⓗ (circled) 2π
    Ⓖ π Ⓙ 4π

40. The graph of which function has a period of $\frac{2\pi}{3}$ and an asymptote at $x = \frac{\pi}{2}$?
    Ⓐ $y = \sec\frac{3}{2}x$ Ⓒ $y = \csc\frac{3}{2}x$
    Ⓑ (circled) $y = \sec 3x$ Ⓓ $y = \csc 3x$

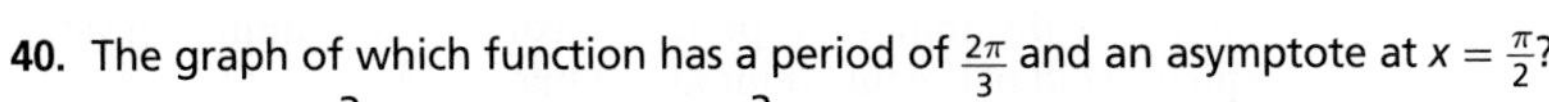

CHALLENGE AND EXTEND

Describe the period, local maximum and minimum values, and phase shift.

41. $f(x) = 4 - 3\csc\pi(x - 1)$ 42. $g(x) = 4\cot\frac{1}{2}\left(x - \frac{\pi}{2}\right)$ 43. $h(x) = 0.5\sec 2\left(x + \frac{\pi}{4}\right)$

44. $f(x) = 9 + 2\tan 3(x + \pi)$ 45. $g(x) = 0.62 + 0.76\sec x$ 46. $h(x) = \csc\frac{\pi}{2}\left(x + \frac{5}{7}\right)$

Graph each trigonometric function and its inverse. Identify the domain and range of the corresponding inverse function.

47. $f(x) = \operatorname{Sec} x$ for $0 \le x \le \pi$ and $x \ne \frac{\pi}{2}$ 48. $f(x) = \operatorname{Tan} x$ for $-\frac{\pi}{2} < x < \frac{\pi}{2}$

49. $g(x) = \operatorname{Csc} x$ for $-\frac{\pi}{2} \le x \le \frac{\pi}{2}$ and $x \ne 0$ 50. $g(x) = \operatorname{Cot} x$ for $0 < x < \pi$

SPIRAL REVIEW

Find the additive and multiplicative inverse for each number. *(Lesson 1-2)*

51. $-\frac{1}{10}$ **$\frac{1}{10}$; -10** 52. 0.2 **-0.2; 5** 53. $-3\sqrt{5}$ **$3\sqrt{5}$; $-\frac{\sqrt{5}}{15}$** 54. $\frac{4}{9}$ **$-\frac{4}{9}$; $\frac{9}{4}$**

55. **Technology** Marjorie's printer prints 30 pages per minute. How many pages does Marjorie's printer print in 22 seconds? *(Lesson 2-2)* **11 pages**

Convert each measure from degrees to radians or from radians to degrees. *(Lesson 13-3)*

56. $45°$ **$\frac{\pi}{4}$ radians** 57. $\frac{3\pi}{4}$ radians **$135°$** 58. $225°$ **$\frac{5\pi}{4}$ radians** 59. $-\frac{\pi}{3}$ radians **$-60°$**

TEST PREP DOCTOR Identifying stretches and compressions of tangent and cotangent graphs can be difficult. If students have difficulty with **Exercise 38,** they should focus on the shape and the period. The shape and period indicate that the correct answer is choice **B.**

Answers

34, 35, 41–50. See p. A51.

Journal

Have students explain how the domain and range of each of the six trigonometric graphs relates to right triangles.

ALTERNATIVE ASSESSMENT

Give students the graphs of the functions $f(x) = 2\csc\left(\frac{3}{4}x\right)$, $g(x) = \cot\left(x + \frac{\pi}{4}\right)$, and $h(x) = 3\sec\left(\frac{\pi}{2}x\right)$, and ask them to write the function rule.

Power Presentations with PowerPoint®

14-2 Lesson Quiz

1. Using $f(x) = \tan x$ as a guide, graph $g(x) = -\tan\left(\frac{1}{2}x\right)$. Identify the period, x-intercepts, and asymptotes.

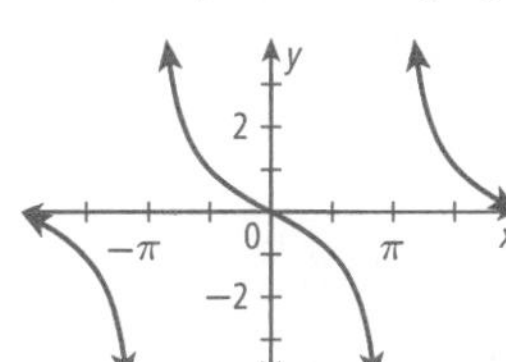

period: 2π; x-intercepts: $2\pi n$; asymptotes: $x = \pi + 2\pi n$

2. Using $f(x) = \sin(x)$ as a guide, graph $g(x) = \frac{1}{3}\csc\left(\frac{1}{3}x\right)$. Identify the period and asymptotes.

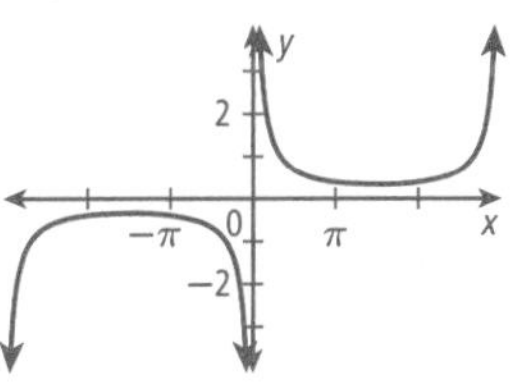

period: 6π; asymptotes: $x = 3\pi n$

Also available on transparency

14-2 PROBLEM SOLVING

As the sign outside the community youth center rotates, the light on it traces a path on the center's wall. The distance in feet of the light to the point on the wall where it shines varies with time, t, and can be modeled by the function $g(t) = 9\csc\left(\frac{3\pi}{4}t\right)$, where t is measured in seconds.

1. Identify the period of the function.
   a. What is the coefficient of t in the equation of the function? $\frac{3\pi}{4}$
   b. Write and evaluate an expression for the period of the function. $\frac{2\pi}{\left(\frac{3\pi}{4}\right)} = \frac{8}{3}$
   c. Explain what the period of the function means in terms of the time for one rotation of the light.
   Possible answer: It takes $2\frac{2}{3}$ s for the light to make one full rotation.
   d. How does the graph of the function vary based on the period?
   Possible answer: The graph repeats every $2\frac{2}{3}$ seconds.
2. a. This function has asymptotes at points where what other function is equal to 0? $\sin\left(\frac{3\pi}{4}t\right)$
   b. What are the asymptotes of the function? $t = \frac{4}{3}n$
3. What is the significance of 9 in the equation for the function?
   Possible answers: It is the shortest distance from the light to the point on the wall where it shines; or it is the value of $g(t)$ when $\csc\left(\frac{3\pi}{4}t\right) = 1$.
4. Graph the function using all the information about the function.

Toni changes the rotation rate of the light so that it rotates once every 4 seconds. Choose the letter for the best answer.

5. Which equation represents the distance of the light to the point on the wall where it shines, as a function of time, t?
   A $g(t) = 9\csc\left(\frac{\pi}{4}t\right)$
   B (circled) $g(t) = 9\csc\left(\frac{\pi}{2}t\right)$
   C $g(t) = 9\csc(2\pi t)$
   D $g(t) = 9\csc(4\pi t)$
6. Which pair of parameters describes this new function?
   F (circled) period: 4 s; vertical asymptotes at $\pm 2n$ s
   G period: 2 s; vertical asymptotes at $\pm n$ s
   H period: 2 s; horizontal asymptotes at $\pm 2n$ s
   J period: 4 s; horizontal asymptotes at $\pm n$ s

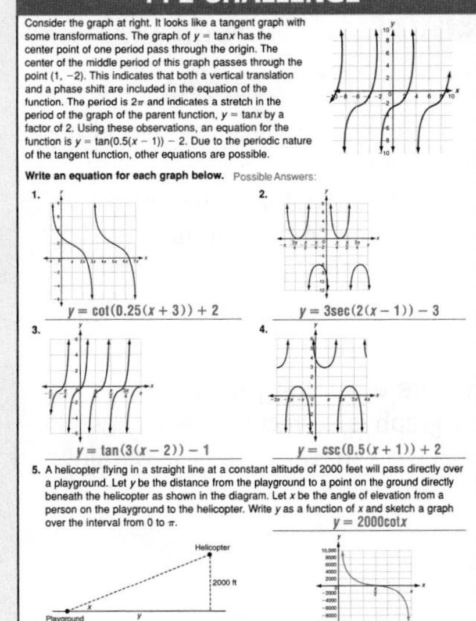

14-2 CHALLENGE

Consider the graph at right. It looks like a tangent graph with some transformations. The graph of $y = \tan x$ has the center point of one period pass through the origin. The center of the middle period of this graph passes through the point $(1, -2)$. This indicates that both a vertical translation and a phase shift are included in the equation of the function. The period is 2π and indicates a stretch in the period of the graph of the parent function, $y = \tan x$ by a factor of 2. Using these observations, an equation for the function is $y = \tan(0.5(x - 1)) - 2$. Due to the periodic nature of the tangent function, other equations are possible.

Write an equation for each graph below. Possible Answers:

1. $y = \cot(0.25(x + 3)) + 2$
2. $y = 3\sec(2(x - 1)) - 3$
3. $y = \tan(3(x - 2)) - 1$
4. $y = \csc(0.5(x + 1)) + 2$
5. A helicopter flying in a straight line at a constant altitude of 2000 feet will pass directly over a playground. Let y be the distance from the playground to a point on the ground directly beneath the helicopter as shown in the diagram. Let x be the angle of elevation from a person on the playground to the helicopter. Write y as a function of x and sketch a graph over the interval from 0 to π. $y = 2000\cot x$

SECTION 14A MULTI-STEP TEST PREP

Organizer

Objective: Assess students' ability to apply concepts and skills in Lessons 14-1 and 14-2 in a real-world format.

Online Edition

Resources

Algebra II Assessments

www.mathtekstoolkit.org

Problem	Text Reference
1–6	Lesson 14-1

Answers

3.

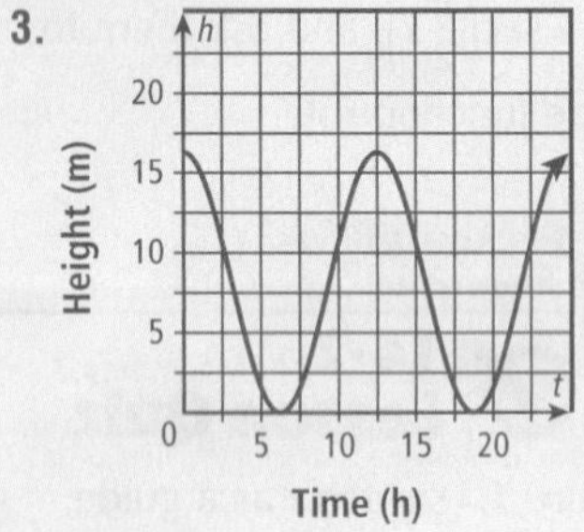

State Resources

MULTI-STEP TEST PREP

SECTION 14A

Trigonometric Graphs

The Tide Is Turning Tides are caused by several factors, but the main factor is the gravitational pull of the Moon. As the Moon revolves around Earth, the Moon causes large bodies of water to swell toward it resulting in rising and falling tides. You can use trigonometric functions to develop a model of a simplified tide. $h(t) = 8.15\cos\frac{4\pi}{25}t + 8.15$

1. The highest tides in the world have been measured at the Bay of Fundy, in Nova Scotia, Canada. As shown in the table, high tides in the bay can reach heights of 16.3 m. Assume that it takes 6.25 hours for the tide to completely retreat and then another 6.25 hours for the tide to come back in. Write a periodic function based on the cosine function that models the height of the tide over time.

Tides at the Bay of Fundy

	Time (h)	Height (m)
High Tide	$t = 0$	16.3
Low Tide	$t = 6.25$	0

2. What are the amplitude, period, maximum and minimum values, and phase shift of the function? amplitude: 8.15; period: 12.5; maximum: 16.3; minimum: 0; phase shift: none

3. Graph the function.

4. At time $t = 0$, the tide is at 16.3 m. What is the tide's height after 3 hours? after 9 hours? about 8.66 m; about 6.62 m

5. Will a high tide occur at the same time each day at the Bay of Fundy? Why or why not?

5. No; the period of the function is 12.5 h, which is not a factor of 24 h.

6. It is possible to write a function that models the height of the tide based on the sine function. What is the function? What is the phase shift?

yes; $h(t) = 8.15\sin\left(\frac{4\pi}{25}t + \frac{\pi}{2}\right) + 8.15$; $\frac{\pi}{2}$ left

INTERVENTION

Scaffolding Questions

1. What information gives the period of the tide function? the time between high and low tide What information gives the amplitude of the tide function? the heights of high and low tide
2. How do you know there is no phase shift? High tide occurs exactly at $t = 0$.
3. What are ways that you can check that your graph is correct? Possible answer: Check for a maximum at $t = 0$; minimum value should be 0, so the graph should touch, but not cross, the x-axis.
4. How can you make a rough estimate of the height of the tide at $t = 3$? It is halfway between16.3 m and 0 m, about 8 m.
5. If the high tide occurred at the same time each day, what would be true of the period? It would be a divisor of 24.
6. What phase shift makes a sine graph equivalent to a cosine graph? $\frac{\pi}{2}$ left

Extension

At what time is the height of the tide exactly 8.15 m? 3.125 hr, or 3 hr 7.5 min

Quiz for Lessons 14-1 Through 14-2

14-1 Graphs of Sine and Cosine

Identify whether each function is periodic. If the function is periodic, give the period.

1. 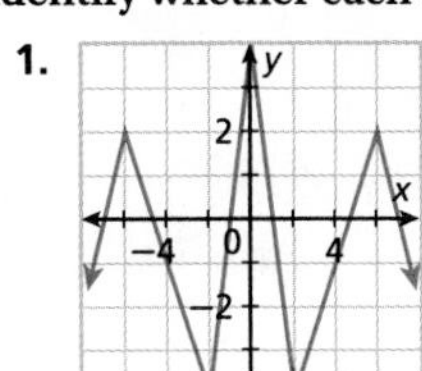
not periodic

2. 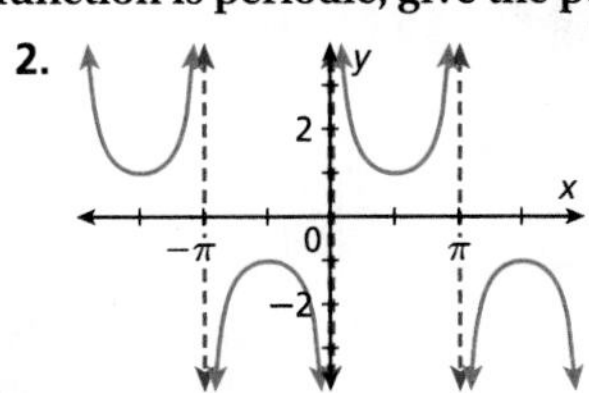
periodic; 2π

3. 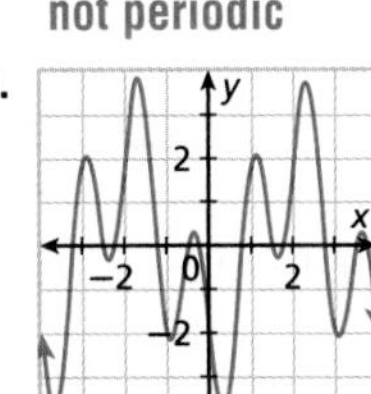
periodic; 4

4. 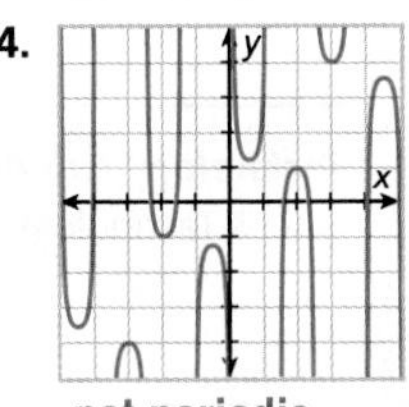
not periodic

Using $f(x) = \sin x$ or $f(x) = \cos x$ as a guide, graph each function. Identify the amplitude and period.

5. $f(x) = \sin 4x$
6. $g(x) = -3\sin x$
7. $h(x) = 0.25\cos \pi x$

Using $f(x) = \sin x$ or $f(x) = \cos x$ as a guide, graph each function. Identify the x-intercepts and phase shift.

8. $f(x) = \cos\left(x - \frac{3\pi}{2}\right)$
9. $g(x) = \sin\left(x - \frac{3\pi}{4}\right)$
10. $h(x) = \cos\left(x + \frac{5\pi}{4}\right)$

11. The torque τ applied to a bolt is given by $\tau(x) = Fr\sin x$, where r is the length of the wrench in meters, F is the applied force in newtons, and x is the angle between F and r in radians. Graph the torque for a 0.5 meter wrench and a force of 500 newtons for $0 \le x \le \frac{\pi}{2}$. What is the torque for an angle of $\frac{\pi}{3}$?

14-2 Graphs of Other Trigonometric Functions

Using $f(x) = \tan x$ as a guide, graph each function. Identify the period, x-intercepts, and asymptotes.

12. $f(x) = \frac{1}{2}\tan 4x$
13. $g(x) = -2\tan\frac{1}{2}x$
14. $h(x) = \tan\frac{1}{2}\pi x$

Using $f(x) = \cot x$ as a guide, graph each function. Identify the period, x-intercepts, and asymptotes.

15. $g(x) = -2\cot x$
16. $h(x) = \cot 0.5x$
17. $j(x) = \cot 4x$

Using $f(x) = \cos x$ or $f(x) = \sin x$ as a guide, graph each function. Identify the period and asymptotes.

18. $f(x) = -2\sec x$
19. $g(x) = \frac{1}{4}\csc x$
20. $h(x) = \sec \pi x$

Organizer

Objective: Assess students' mastery of concepts and skills in Lessons 14-1 and 14-2.

 Online Edition

Resources

 *Assessment Resources*
Section 14A Quiz

Test & Practice Generator
One-Stop Planner®

INTERVENTION

Resources

 *Ready to Go On? Intervention and Enrichment Worksheets*

 *Ready to Go On?* CD-ROM

 *Ready to Go On?* Online

my.hrw.com

Answers

5–20. See p. A52.

READY TO GO ON? Diagnose and Prescribe

NO — INTERVENE

Ready to Go On? Intervention	Ready to Go On? Intervention, Section 14A — Worksheets	CD-ROM	Online
Lesson 14-1	14-1 Intervention	Activity 14-1	Diagnose and Prescribe Online
Lesson 14-2	14-2 Intervention	Activity 14-2	

YES — ENRICH

Ready to Go On? Enrichment, Section 14A
Worksheets
CD-ROM
Online

SECTION

14B Trigonometric Identities

One-Minute Section Planner

Lesson	Lab Resources	Materials
14-3 Technology Lab Graph Trigonometric Identities • Use a graphing calculator to compare graphs and make conjectures about trigonometric identities. ☐ SAT-10 ☐ NAEP ☑ ACT ☐ SAT ☐ SAT Subject Tests	***Technology Lab Activities*** 14-3 Lab Recording Sheet	**Required** graphing calculator
Lesson 14-3 Fundamental Trigonometric Identities • Use fundamental trigonometric identities to simplify and rewrite expressions and to verify other identities. ☐ SAT-10 ☐ NAEP ☑ ACT ☐ SAT ☑ SAT Subject Tests	***Technology Lab Activities*** 14-3 Technology Lab	**Optional** graphing calculator
Lesson 14-4 Sum and Difference Identities • Evaluate trigonometric expressions by using sum and difference identities. • Use matrix multiplication with sum and difference identities to perform rotations. ☐ SAT-10 ☐ NAEP ☑ ACT ☐ SAT ☑ SAT Subject Tests		**Optional** graphing calculator
Lesson 14-5 Double-Angle and Half-Angle Identities • Evaluate and simplify expressions by using double-angle and half-angle identities. ☐ SAT-10 ☐ NAEP ☐ ACT ☐ SAT ☑ SAT Subject Tests		**Optional** graphing calculator
Lesson 14-6 Solving Trigonometric Equations • Solve equations involving trigonometric functions. ☐ SAT-10 ☐ NAEP ☑ ACT ☐ SAT ☑ SAT Subject Tests		**Required** graphing calculator

MK = *Manipulatives Kit*

Section Overview

Fundamental Trigonometric Identities — *Lesson 14-3*

Many of the equations used in physics to model characteristics such as friction and displacement can be simplified using trigonometric identities.

Fundamental Trigonometric Identities			
Reciprocal Identities	**Tangent and Cotangent Ratio Identities**	**Pythagorean Identities**	**Negative-Angle Identities**
$\csc\theta = \frac{1}{\sin\theta}$	$\tan\theta = \frac{\sin\theta}{\cos\theta}$	$\cos^2\theta + \sin^2\theta = 1$	$\sin(-\theta) = -\sin\theta$
$\sec\theta = \frac{1}{\cos\theta}$	$\cot\theta = \frac{\cos\theta}{\sin\theta}$	$1 + \tan^2\theta = \sec^2\theta$	$\cos(-\theta) = \cos\theta$
$\cot\theta = \frac{1}{\tan\theta}$		$\cot^2\theta + 1 = \csc^2\theta$	$\tan(-\theta) = -\tan\theta$

Other Trigonometric Identities — *Lessons 14-4, 14-5*

Other trigonometric identities can be used to solve trigonometric equations involving image rotations and projectile trajectories.

To rotate any point $P(x, y)$ θ degrees counterclockwise about the origin, use a rotation matrix as shown.

$$\begin{bmatrix} \cos\theta & -\sin\theta \\ \sin\theta & \cos\theta \end{bmatrix}\begin{bmatrix} x \\ y \end{bmatrix} = \begin{bmatrix} x' \\ y' \end{bmatrix}$$

Sum and Difference Identities	
Sum Identities	**Difference Identities**
$\sin(A + B) = \sin A\cos B + \cos A\sin B$	$\sin(A - B) = \sin A\cos B - \cos A\sin B$
$\cos(A + B) = \cos A\cos B - \sin A\sin B$	$\cos(A - B) = \cos A\cos B + \sin A\sin B$
$\tan(A + B) = \frac{\tan A + \tan B}{1 - \tan A\tan B}$	$\tan(A - B) = \frac{\tan A - \tan B}{1 + \tan A\tan B}$

Double-Angle Identities		
$\sin 2\theta = 2\sin\theta\cos\theta$	$\cos 2\theta = 2\cos^2\theta - \sin^2\theta$ $\cos 2\theta = 2\cos^2\theta - 1$ $\cos 2\theta = 1 - 2\sin^2\theta$	$\tan 2\theta = \frac{2\tan\theta}{1 - \tan^2\theta}$

Solving Trigonometric Equations — *Lesson 14-6*

Trigonometric equations can be used to model periodic phenomena, such as planetary motion.

Using trigonometric identities, you can solve trigonometric equations by
- factoring.
- using the Quadratic Formula.
- applying inverses.

You can support your solutions by graphing.

Number of solutions of a trigonometric equation:
- 0
- 1
- 2
- Infinitely many

Organizer

Use with Lesson 14-3

Pacing:
Traditional $\frac{1}{2}$ day
Block $\frac{1}{4}$ day

Objective: Use a graphing calculator to compare graphs and make conjectures about trigonometric identities.

Materials: graphing calculator

Online Edition
Graphing Calculator, TechKeys

Resources

Technology Lab Activities
14-3 Lab Recording Sheet

Teach

Discuss

Discuss the limitations of using a graph to determine whether an equation is an identity. Include topics such as domain and viewing windows.

Close

Key Concept

When you graph both sides of a trigonometric equation together and their graphs coincide, then the equation is most likely an identity.

Assessment

Journal Have students explain why graphing shows that an equation is only *most likely* an identity.

State Resources

go.hrw.com
State Resources Online
KEYWORD: MB7 Resources

14-3

Graph Trigonometric Identities

You can use a graphing calculator to compare graphs and make conjectures about trigonometric identities.

Use with Lesson 14-3

go.hrw.com
Lab Resources Online
KEYWORD: MB7 Lab14

Activity

Determine whether $\frac{\sin^2 x}{1-\cos x} = 1 + \cos x$ is a possible identity.

If the equation is an identity, there should be no visible difference in the graphs of the left- and right-hand sides of the equation.

1. Enter $\frac{\sin^2 x}{1-\cos x}$ as **Y1** and $1 + \cos x$ as **Y2**. For **Y2**, select the mode represented by the 0 with a line through it. This will help you see the path of the graph.

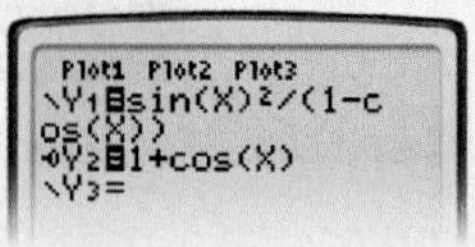

2. Set the graphing window by using ZOOM and **7:ZTrig**.

3. Watch the calculator as the graphs are generated. As **Y2** is being graphed, a circle will move along the path of the graph.

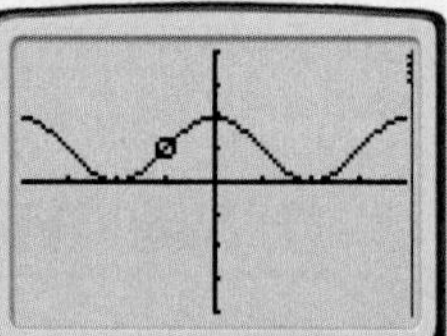

4. The path of the circle, **Y2**, traced the graph of **Y1**. The graphs appear to be the same.

   Because the graphs appear to be identical, $\frac{\sin^2 x}{1-\cos x} = 1 + \cos x$ is most likely an identity. Use algebra to confirm.

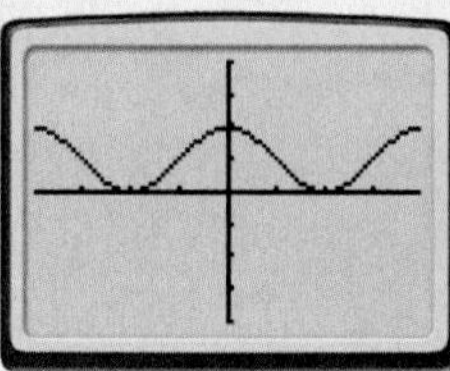

Try This

1. **Make a Conjecture** Determine whether $\sec x - \tan x \sin x = \cos x$ is a possible identity. It is a possible identity.
2. Prove or disprove your answer to Problem 1 by using algebra.
3. **Make a Conjecture** Determine whether $\frac{1+\tan x}{1+\cot x} = \tan x$ is a possible identity. It is a possible identity.
4. Prove or disprove your answer to Problem 3 by using algebra.

Answers to *Try This*

2. $\sec x - \tan x \sin x$
$= \frac{1}{\cos x} - \frac{\sin^2 x}{\cos x}$
$= \frac{1-\sin^2 x}{\cos x}$
$= \frac{\cos^2 x}{\cos x} = \cos x$

4. $\frac{1+\tan x}{1+\cot x}$
$= \frac{1+\frac{\sin x}{\cos x}}{1+\frac{\cos x}{\sin x}}$
$= \frac{\frac{\cos x+\sin x}{\cos x}}{\frac{\sin x+\cos x}{\sin x}}$
$= \frac{\cos x+\sin x}{\cos x} \cdot \frac{\sin x}{\sin x+\cos x}$
$= \frac{\sin x}{\cos x} = \tan x$

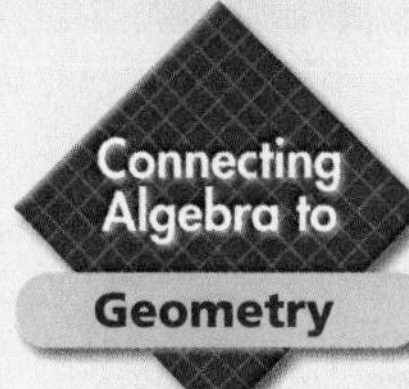

Angle Relationships

Angle relationships in circles and polygons can be used to solve problems.

See Skills Bank page S62

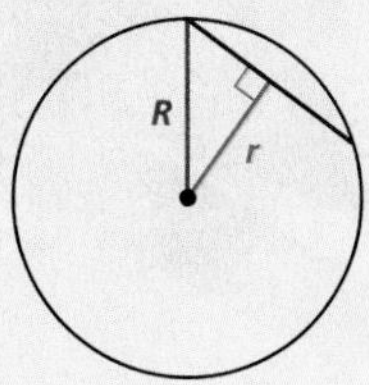

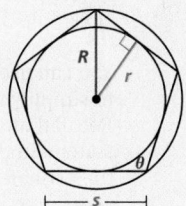

R radius

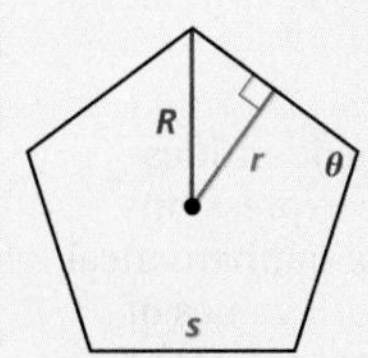

r apothem
s length of side
θ interior angle
n number of sides

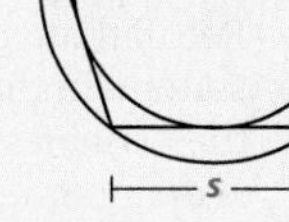

R radius of circumscribed circle
r radius of inscribed circle

The figures show regular polygons. A **regular polygon** has sides of equal length and equal interior angles. Here are some useful relationships for regular polygons.

R bisects θ. $\quad \theta = \left(\frac{n-2}{n}\right)180°$ $\quad r = R\cos\left(\frac{180}{n}\right)$ $\quad s = 2r\tan\left(\frac{180}{n}\right) = 2R\sin\left(\frac{180}{n}\right)$

Example

A regular octagon is inscribed in a circle with a radius of 5 cm. What is the length of each side of the octagon?

Make a sketch of the problem.

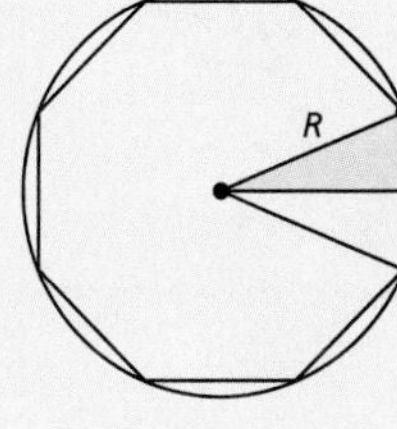

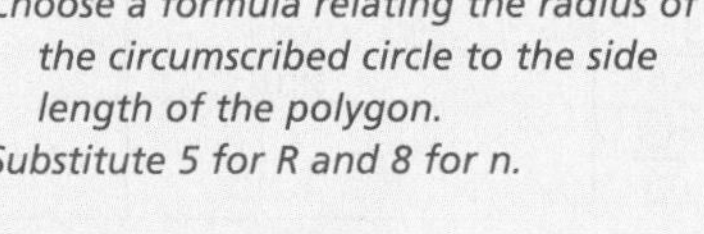

$s = 2R\sin\left(\frac{180}{n}\right)$ *Choose a formula relating the radius of the circumscribed circle to the side length of the polygon.*

$s = 2(5)\sin\left(\frac{180}{8}\right)$ *Substitute 5 for R and 8 for n.*

$s = 10\sin 22.5° \approx 3.83$ cm

Try This

Solve each problem. Round each answer to the nearest hundredth.

1. A circle is inscribed in an equilateral triangle with 8 in. sides. What is the diameter of the circle? What is the altitude of the triangle?
2. An isosceles right triangle is inscribed in a semicircle with a radius of 20 cm. What are the lengths of the three sides of the triangle?
3. The interior angles of a regular polygon each measure 150°. If this polygon is inscribed in a circle with a 10 in. diameter, how long is each side of the polygon? **2.59 in.**
4. Use the figure to find the side lengths of all three shaded triangles if the diameter of the circle is 10 cm. **pink triangle: 5 cm, 4.10 cm, 2.87 cm; yellow triangle: 5 cm, 3.83 cm, 3.21 cm; blue triangle: 3.30 cm, 7.07 cm, and 7.80 cm**

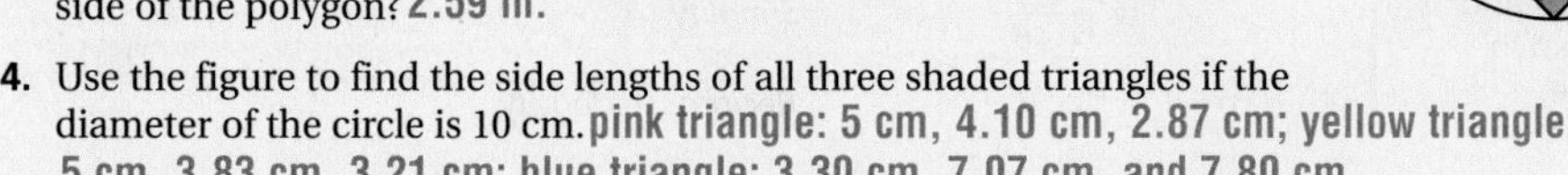

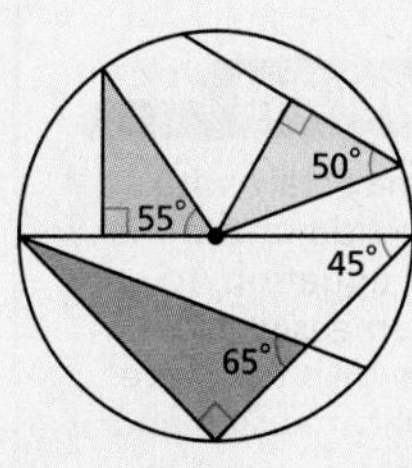

Answers

1. 4.62 in.; 6.93 in.
2. 28.28 cm, 28.28 cm, and 40 cm

Organizer

See Skills Bank page S62

Pacing: Traditional $\frac{1}{2}$ day
Block $\frac{1}{4}$ day

Objective: Apply trigonometric functions to solving problems involving inscribed and circumscribed polygons.

Teach

Remember

Students review and apply the Pythagorean Theorem and angle relationships in circles and polygons.

INTERVENTION For additional review and practice on solving problems involving inscribed and circumscribed polygons, see Skills Bank page S62.

Visual Point out that there are two radii on the top right figure. R is the radius of the circumscribed circle. r is the radius of the inscribed circle and is called the apothem.

Close

Assess

Ask students to find the value of θ and the side length for a regular hexagon circumscribing a circle of radius 3 cm. $\theta = 120°$; $s \approx 3.46$ cm

State Resources

14-3 Organizer

Pacing: Traditional 1 day
Block $\frac{1}{2}$ day

Objectives: Use fundamental trigonometric identities to simplify and rewrite expressions and to verify other identities.

Technology Lab
In Technology Lab Activities

Online Edition
Graphing Calculator, Tutorial Videos

Power Presentations with PowerPoint®

Warm Up

Simplify.

1. $\left(\frac{\sin A}{\cos A}\right)\left(\frac{\cos^2 A}{\sin A}\right)$ $\cos A$

2. $\tan A\left(\frac{\sin A}{\tan A}\right)\left(\frac{1}{\sin A}\right)$ 1

Also available on transparency

Math Humor

Student: Superheroes would be in big trouble if villains knew trig.

Parent: Why is that?

Student: Because then the villains could figure out the superheroes' secret identities.

14-3 Fundamental Trigonometric Identities

Objective
Use fundamental trigonometric identities to simplify and rewrite expressions and to verify other identities.

Who uses this?
Ski supply manufacturers can use trigonometric identities to determine the type of wax to use on skis. (See Example 3.)

You can use trigonometric identities to simplify trigonometric expressions. Recall that an identity is a mathematical statement that is true for all values of the variables for which the statement is defined.

A derivation for a Pythagorean identity is shown below.

$$x^2 + y^2 = r^2 \quad \textit{Pythagorean Theorem}$$

$$\frac{x^2}{r^2} + \frac{y^2}{r^2} = 1 \quad \textit{Divide both sides by } r^2.$$

$$\cos^2\theta + \sin^2\theta = 1 \quad \textit{Substitute } \cos\theta \textit{ for } \frac{x}{r} \textit{ and } \sin\theta \textit{ for } \frac{y}{r}.$$

Fundamental Trigonometric Identities

Reciprocal Identities	Tangent and Cotangent Ratio Identities	Pythagorean Identities	Negative-Angle Identities
$\csc\theta = \frac{1}{\sin\theta}$	$\tan\theta = \frac{\sin\theta}{\cos\theta}$	$\cos^2\theta + \sin^2\theta = 1$	$\sin(-\theta) = -\sin\theta$
$\sec\theta = \frac{1}{\cos\theta}$	$\cot\theta = \frac{\cos\theta}{\sin\theta}$	$1 + \tan^2\theta = \sec^2\theta$	$\cos(-\theta) = \cos\theta$
$\cot\theta = \frac{1}{\tan\theta}$		$\cot^2\theta + 1 = \csc^2\theta$	$\tan(-\theta) = -\tan\theta$

To prove that an equation is an identity, alter one side of the equation until it is the same as the other side. Justify your steps by using the fundamental identities.

EXAMPLE  **1 Proving Trigonometric Identities**

Helpful Hint
You may start with either side of the given equation. It is often easier to begin with the more complicated side and simplify it to match the simpler side.

Prove each trigonometric identity.

A $\sec\theta = \csc\theta\tan\theta$

$$\sec\theta = \csc\theta\tan\theta \quad \textit{Choose the right-hand side to modify.}$$

$$= \left(\frac{1}{\sin\theta}\right)\left(\frac{\sin\theta}{\cos\theta}\right) \quad \textit{Reciprocal and ratio identities}$$

$$= \frac{1}{\cos\theta} \quad \textit{Simplify.}$$

$$= \sec\theta \quad \textit{Reciprocal identity}$$

State Resources

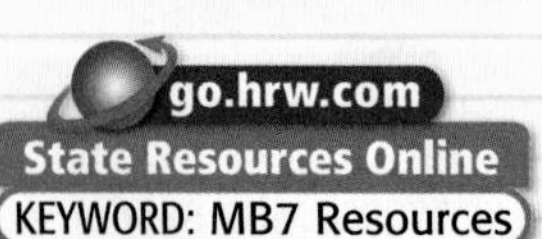

go.hrw.com
State Resources Online
KEYWORD: MB7 Resources

1 Introduce

EXPLORATION

14-3 Fundamental Trigonometric Identities

You can discover properties of trigonometric functions by evaluating expressions.

Evaluate each of the following expressions.

1. $\sin^2\left(\frac{\pi}{6}\right) + \cos^2\left(\frac{\pi}{6}\right)$
2. $\sin^2\left(\frac{\pi}{4}\right) + \cos^2\left(\frac{\pi}{4}\right)$
3. $\sin^2\left(\frac{\pi}{3}\right) + \cos^2\left(\frac{\pi}{3}\right)$
4. What do you notice about the expressions in 1–3?
5. Enter the function $y = \sin^2 x + \cos^2 x$ into your calculator and view a table of values. What do you find?

THINK AND DISCUSS

6. **Derive** a new identity by investigating the expression $\sec^2 x - \tan^2 x$.

Motivate

Recall that the vertex form and the standard form of a quadratic function are equivalent but have different uses: the vertex form gives the vertex and the standard form gives the y-intercept. The same holds true for many trigonometric expressions; one form may be more useful than another for a given situation. Trigonometric identities can be used to rewrite expressions.

Explorations and answers are provided in the *Explorations* binder.

Prove each trigonomentric identity.

B $\csc(-\theta) = -\csc\theta$

$\csc(-\theta) = -\csc\theta$	*Choose the left-hand side to modify.*
$\dfrac{1}{\sin(-\theta)} =$	*Reciprocal identity*
$\dfrac{1}{-\sin\theta} =$	*Negative-angle identity*
$-\left(\dfrac{1}{\sin\theta}\right) = -\csc\theta$	
$-\csc\theta = -\csc\theta$	*Reciprocal identity*

Prove each trigonometric identity.

1a. $\sin\theta\cot\theta = \cos\theta$ **1b.** $1 - \sec(-\theta) = 1 - \sec\theta$

You can use the fundamental trigonometric identities to simplify expressions.

EXAMPLE 2 Using Trigonometric Identities to Rewrite Trigonometric Expressions

Rewrite each expression in terms of $\cos\theta$, and simplify.

Helpful Hint

If you get stuck, try converting all of the trigonometric functions into sine and cosine functions.

A $\dfrac{\sin^2\theta}{1 - \cos\theta}$

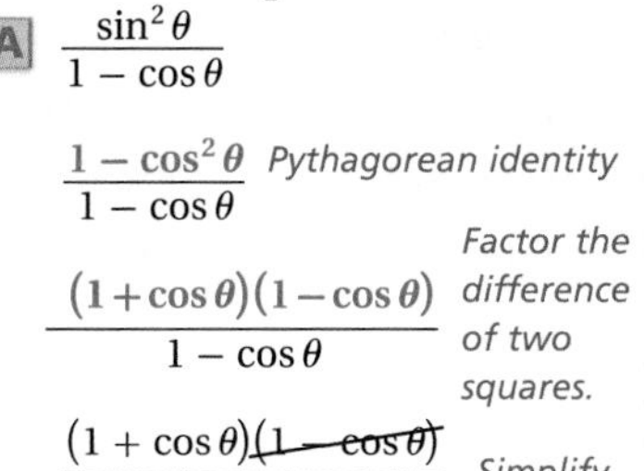

$\dfrac{1 - \cos^2\theta}{1 - \cos\theta}$	*Pythagorean identity*
$\dfrac{(1+\cos\theta)(1-\cos\theta)}{1 - \cos\theta}$	*Factor the difference of two squares.*
$\dfrac{(1 + \cos\theta)\cancel{(1 - \cos\theta)}}{\cancel{1 - \cos\theta}}$	*Simplify.*
$1 + \cos\theta$	

B $\sec\theta - \tan\theta\sin\theta$

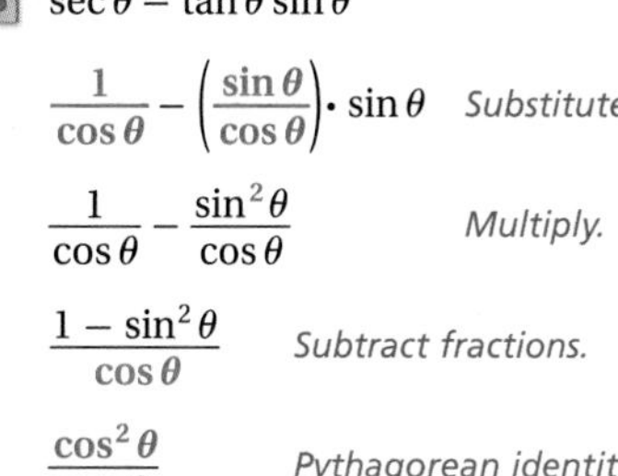

$\dfrac{1}{\cos\theta} - \left(\dfrac{\sin\theta}{\cos\theta}\right)\cdot\sin\theta$	*Substitute.*
$\dfrac{1}{\cos\theta} - \dfrac{\sin^2\theta}{\cos\theta}$	*Multiply.*
$\dfrac{1 - \sin^2\theta}{\cos\theta}$	*Subtract fractions.*
$\dfrac{\cos^2\theta}{\cos\theta}$	*Pythagorean identity*
$\cos\theta$	*Simplify.*

Rewrite each expression in terms of $\sin\theta$, and simplify.

2a. $\dfrac{\cos^2\theta}{1 - \sin\theta}$ $1 + \sin\theta$ **2b.** $\cot^2\theta$ $\dfrac{1}{\sin^2\theta} - 1$

Student to Student — *Graphing to Check for Equivalent Expressions*

Julia Zaragoza
Oak Ridge
High School

I like to use a graphing calculator to check for equivalent expressions.

For Example 2A, enter $y = \dfrac{\sin^2\theta}{(1 - \cos\theta)}$ *and* $y = 1 + \cos\theta$*. Graph both functions in the same viewing window.*

The graphs appear to coincide, so the expressions are most likely equivalent.

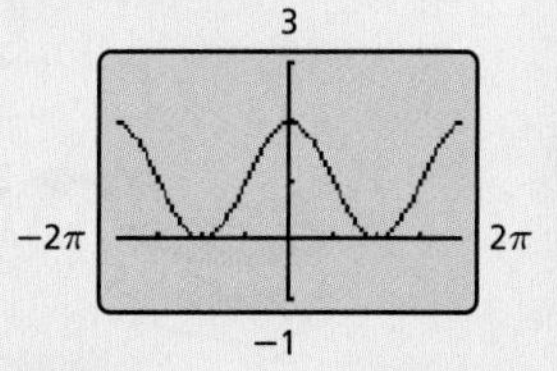

2 Teach

Guided Instruction

Guide students through the table on p. 1008 containing the Fundamental Trigonometric Identities. Remind students that an identity is an equation that is true for all values of the variable. To prove an identity, students must make substitutions using other, previously proven identities.

Reaching All Learners
Through Cognitive Strategies

Have students work in groups to derive the Pythagorean identities $1 + \cot^2\theta = \csc^2\theta$ and $1 + \tan^2\theta = \sec^2\theta$ so that students can recall the identities by understanding.

For example, $\dfrac{\sin^2\theta}{\sin^2\theta} + \dfrac{\cos^2\theta}{\sin^2\theta} = \dfrac{1}{\sin^2\theta}$ yields $1 + \cot^2\theta = \csc^2\theta$.

Power Presentations with PowerPoint®

Additional Examples

Example 1

Prove each trigonometric identity.

A. $\tan\theta = \dfrac{\sec\theta}{\csc\theta}$

$= \dfrac{\left(\dfrac{1}{\cos\theta}\right)}{\left(\dfrac{1}{\sin\theta}\right)}$

$= \dfrac{1}{\cos\theta}\cdot\sin\theta = \tan\theta$

B. $1 - \cot\theta = 1 + \cot(-\theta)$

$= 1 + \dfrac{1}{\tan(-\theta)}$

$= 1 + \dfrac{1}{-\tan\theta}$

$= 1 + (-\cot\theta)$

$= 1 - \cot\theta$

Example 2

Rewrite each expression in terms of $\cos\theta$, and simplify.

A. $\sec\theta\,(1 - \sin^2\theta)$ $\cos\theta$

B. $\sin\theta\cos\theta\,(\tan\theta + \cot\theta)$ 1

Also available on transparency

INTERVENTION
Questioning Strategies

EXAMPLE 1

- How can the identity in **Example 1B** be demonstrated by using the unit circle?

EXAMPLE 2

- How do you know when you should use one of the Pythagorean identities?

Answers to *Check It Out!*

1a. $\sin\theta\cot\theta = \sin\theta\left(\dfrac{\cos\theta}{\sin\theta}\right)$

$= \cos\theta$

b. $1 - \sec(-\theta) = 1 - \dfrac{1}{\cos(-\theta)}$

$= 1 - \dfrac{1}{\cos\theta}$

$= 1 - \sec\theta$

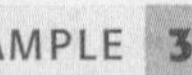

Precalculus Many aspects of trigonometry become important when students begin their study of calculus. In calculus, students will encounter situations in which expressions must be modified in order to solve problems.

Power Presentations with PowerPoint®

Additional Examples

Example 3

At what angle will a wooden block on a concrete incline start to move if the coefficient of friction is 0.62?

$\theta \approx 32°$

Also available on transparency

INTERVENTION

Questioning Strategies

EXAMPLE 3

- If you knew the angle at which the block began to slide, how could you find the coefficient of friction?

EXAMPLE 3 Sports Application

A ski supply company is testing the friction of a new ski wax by placing a waxed wood block on an inclined plane of wet snow. The incline plane is slowly raised until the wood block begins to slide.

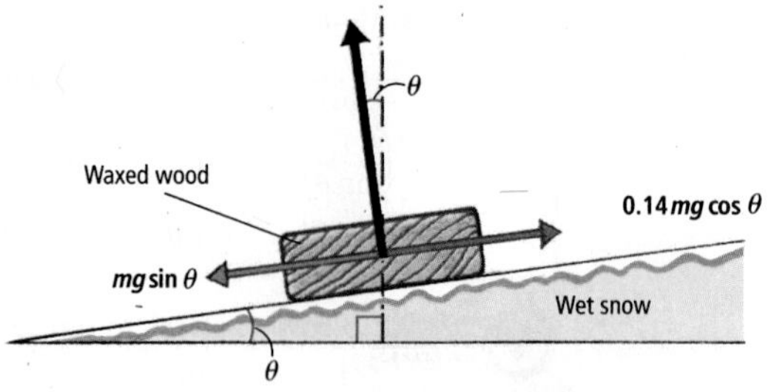

Reading Math

The symbol μ is read as "mu."

At the instant the block starts to slide, the component of the weight of the block parallel to the incline, $mg\sin\theta$, and the resistive force of friction, $\mu mg\cos\theta$, are equal. μ is the coefficient of friction. At what angle will the block start to move if $\mu = 0.14$?

Set the expression for the weight component equal to the expression for the force of friction.

$mg\sin\theta = \mu mg\cos\theta$

$\sin\theta = \mu\cos\theta$	*Divide both sides by mg.*
$\sin\theta = 0.14\cos\theta$	*Substitute 0.14 for μ.*
$\frac{\sin\theta}{\cos\theta} = 0.14$	*Divide both sides by $\cos\theta$.*
$\tan\theta = 0.14$	*Ratio identity*
$\theta \approx 8°$	*Evaluate inverse tangent.*

The wood block will start to move when the wet snow incline is raised to an angle of about 8°.

CHECK IT OUT! **3.** Use the equation $mg\sin\theta = \mu mg\cos\theta$ to determine the angle at which a waxed wood block on a wood incline with $\mu = 0.4$ begins to slide. $\theta \approx 22°$

THINK AND DISCUSS

1. **DESCRIBE** how you prove that an equation is an identity.
2. **EXPLAIN** which identity can be used to prove that $(1 - \cos\theta)(1 + \cos\theta) = \sin^2\theta$.
3. **GET ORGANIZED** Copy and complete the graphic organizer by writing the three Pythagorean identities.

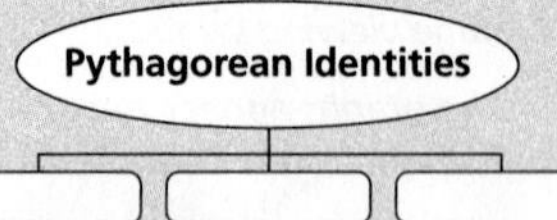

3 Close

Summarize

Trigonometric identities can be proven true by substituting simpler trigonometric identities. Tell students that when they are proving an identity, it is good practice to work with only one side of an equation at a time. Converting all terms to sine and cosine may be a good strategy if students become stuck.

ONGOING ASSESSMENT and INTERVENTION

***Diagnose Before* the Lesson**
14-3 Warm Up, TE p. 1008

***Monitor During* the Lesson**
Check It Out! Exercises, SE pp. 1009–1010
Questioning Strategies, TE pp. 1009–1010

***Assess After* the Lesson**
14-3 Lesson Quiz, TE p. 1013
Alternative Assessment, TE p. 1013

Answers to *Think and Discuss*

Possible answers:

1. Use identities to modify one side of the equation until it is written in the same form as the other side of the equation.
2. After multiplying the left side of the equation and simplifying by combining like terms, use the Pythagorean identity $\sin^2\theta + \cos^2\theta = 1$.
3. See p. A14.

14-3 Exercises

go.hrw.com
Homework Help Online
KEYWORD: MB7 14-3
Parent Resources Online
KEYWORD: MB7 Parent

GUIDED PRACTICE

SEE EXAMPLE 1 p. 1008

Prove each trigonometric identity.

1. $\sin\theta\sec\theta = \tan\theta$
2. $\cot(-\theta) = -\cot\theta$
3. $\cos^2\theta(\sec^2\theta - 1) = \sin^2\theta$

SEE EXAMPLE 2 p. 1009

Rewrite each expression in terms of $\cos\theta$, and simplify.

4. $\csc\theta\tan\theta$ $\frac{1}{\cos\theta}$
5. $(1 + \sec^2\theta)(1 - \sin^2\theta)$ $1 + \cos^2\theta$
6. $\sin^2\theta + \cos^2\theta + \tan^2\theta$ 6. $\frac{1}{\cos^2\theta}$

SEE EXAMPLE 3 p. 1010

7. **Physics** Use the equation $mg\sin\theta = \mu mg\cos\theta$ to determine the angle at which a glass-top table can be tilted before a glass plate on the table begins to slide. Assume $\mu = 0.94$. $\theta \approx 43°$

PRACTICE AND PROBLEM SOLVING

Independent Practice	
For Exercises	See Example
8–11	1
12–15	2
16	3

Extra Practice
Skills Practice p. S31
Application Practice p. S45

Prove each trigonometric identity.

8. $\sec\theta\cot\theta = \csc\theta$
9. $\frac{\sin\theta - \cos\theta}{\sin\theta} = 1 - \cot\theta$
10. $\tan\theta\sin\theta = \sec\theta - \cos\theta$
11. $\sec^2\theta(1 - \cos^2\theta) = \tan^2\theta$

Rewrite each expression in terms of $\sin\theta$, and simplify.

12. $\frac{\cos^2\theta}{1 + \sin\theta}$ $1 - \sin\theta$
13. $\frac{\tan\theta}{\cot\theta}$ $\frac{\sin^2\theta}{1 - \sin^2\theta}$
14. $\cos\theta\cot\theta + \sin\theta$ $\frac{1}{\sin\theta}$
15. $\frac{\sec^2\theta - 1}{1 + \tan^2\theta}$ $\sin^2\theta$
16. **Physics** Use the equation $mg\sin\theta = \mu mg\cos\theta$ to determine the steepest slope of the street shown on which a car with rubber tires can park without sliding. $\theta \approx 42°$

Multi-Step Rewrite each expression in terms of a single trigonometric function.

17. $\tan\theta\cot\theta$ 1
18. $\sin\theta\cot\theta\tan\theta$ $\sin\theta$
19. $\cos\theta + \sin\theta\tan\theta$ $\sec\theta$
20. $\sin\theta\csc\theta - \cos^2\theta$ $\sin^2\theta$
21. $\cos^2\theta\sec\theta\csc\theta$
22. $\cos\theta(\tan^2\theta + 1)$
23. $\csc\theta(1 - \cos^2\theta)$
24. $\csc\theta\cos\theta\tan\theta$ 1
25. $\frac{\sin\theta}{1 - \cos^2\theta}$ $\csc\theta$
26. $\frac{\sin^2\theta}{1 - \cos^2\theta}$ 1
27. $\frac{\tan\theta}{\sin\theta\sec\theta}$ 1
28. $\frac{\cos\theta}{\sin\theta\cot\theta}$ 1
29. $\tan\theta(\tan\theta + \cot\theta)$ $\sec^2\theta$
30. $\sin^2\theta + \cos^2\theta + \cot^2\theta$ $\csc^2\theta$
31. $\sin^2\theta\sec\theta\csc\theta$ $\tan\theta$

21. $\cot\theta$
22. $\sec\theta$
23. $\sin\theta$

Verify each identity.

32. $\frac{\cos\theta - 1}{\cos^2\theta} = \sec\theta - \sec^2\theta$
33. $\sin^2\theta(\csc^2\theta - 1) = \cos^2\theta$
34. $\tan\theta + \cot\theta = \sec\theta\csc\theta$
35. $\frac{\cos\theta}{1 - \sin^2\theta} = \sec\theta$
36. $\frac{1 - \cos^2\theta}{\tan\theta} = \sin\theta\cos\theta$
37. $\frac{\csc^2\theta}{1 + \tan^2\theta} = \cot^2\theta$

Prove each fundamental identity without using any of the other fundamental identities. (*Hint:* Use the trigonometric ratios with *x*, *y*, and *r*.)

38. $\tan\theta = \frac{\sin\theta}{\cos\theta}$
39. $\cot\theta = \frac{\cos\theta}{\sin\theta}$
40. $1 + \cot^2\theta = \csc^2\theta$
41. $\csc\theta = \frac{1}{\sin\theta}$
42. $\sec\theta = \frac{1}{\cos\theta}$
43. $1 + \tan^2\theta = \sec^2\theta$

10. $\tan\theta\sin\theta = \frac{\sin^2\theta}{\cos\theta}$
$= \frac{1 - \cos^2\theta}{\cos\theta}$
$= \sec\theta - \cos\theta$

11. $\sec^2\theta(1 - \cos^2\theta) = \left(\frac{1}{\cos^2\theta}\right)(\sin^2\theta)$
$= \frac{\sin^2\theta}{\cos^2\theta}$
$= \tan^2\theta$

32. $\frac{\cos\theta - 1}{\cos^2\theta} = \frac{\cos\theta}{\cos^2\theta} - \frac{1}{\cos^2\theta}$
$= \frac{1}{\cos\theta} - \frac{1}{\cos^2\theta}$
$= \sec\theta - \sec^2\theta$

33. $\sin^2\theta(\csc^2\theta - 1) = \sin^2\theta\cot^2\theta$
$= \sin^2\theta\left(\frac{\cos^2\theta}{\sin^2\theta}\right)$
$= \cos^2\theta$

34. $\tan\theta + \cot\theta = \frac{\sin\theta}{\cos\theta} + \frac{\cos\theta}{\sin\theta}$
$= \frac{\sin^2\theta + \cos^2\theta}{\sin\theta\cos\theta}$
$= \frac{1}{\sin\theta\cos\theta}$
$= \left(\frac{1}{\sin\theta}\right)\left(\frac{1}{\cos\theta}\right)$
$= \sec\theta\csc\theta$

35–43. See p. A52.

14-3 Exercises

Assignment Guide

Assign *Guided Practice* exercises as necessary.

Basic 8–22, 32–34, 44–50, 56–61, 70–75
Average 8–16, 17–43 odd, 44–63, 70–75
Advanced 8–44 even, 45–75

Homework Quick Check
Quickly check key concepts.
Exercises: 8, 10, 12, 14, 16

Answers

1. $\sin\theta\sec\theta = \sin\theta\left(\frac{1}{\cos\theta}\right)$
$= \frac{\sin\theta}{\cos\theta}$
$= \tan\theta$

2. $\cot(-\theta) = \frac{\cos(-\theta)}{\sin(-\theta)} = \frac{\cos\theta}{-\sin\theta}$
$= -\left(\frac{\cos\theta}{\sin\theta}\right)$
$= -\cot\theta$

3. $\cos^2\theta(\sec^2\theta - 1) = \cos^2\theta(\tan^2\theta)$
$= \cos^2\theta\left(\frac{\sin\theta}{\cos\theta}\right)^2$
$= \cos^2\theta\left(\frac{\sin^2\theta}{\cos^2\theta}\right)$
$= \sin^2\theta$

8. $\sec\theta\cot\theta = \left(\frac{1}{\cos\theta}\right)\left(\frac{\cos\theta}{\sin\theta}\right)$
$= \frac{1}{\sin\theta}$
$= \csc\theta$

9. $\frac{\sin\theta - \cos\theta}{\sin\theta} = \frac{\sin\theta}{\sin\theta} - \frac{\cos\theta}{\sin\theta}$
$= 1 - \cot\theta$

State Resources

go.hrw.com
State Resources Online
KEYWORD: MB7 Resources

Exercise 44 involves solving trigonometric equations. This exercise prepares students for the Multi-Step Test Prep on page 1034.

Answers

56. Because $\tan\theta = \frac{\sin\theta}{\cos\theta}$, $\tan(-\theta) = \frac{\sin(-\theta)}{\cos(-\theta)}$. Use $\sin(-\theta) = -\sin\theta$ and $\cos(-\theta) = \cos\theta$ to get $\tan(-\theta) = \frac{-\sin\theta}{\cos\theta} = -\tan\theta$.

44. This problem will prepare you for the Multi-Step Test Prep on page 1034.

The displacement y of a mass attached to a spring is modeled by $y(t) = 5\sin t$, where t is the time in seconds. The displacement z of another mass attached to a spring is modeled by $z(t) = 2.6\cos t$.

a. The two masses are set in motion at $t = 0$. When do the masses have the same displacement for the first time? **≈ 0.48 s**

b. What is the displacement at this time? **≈ 2.31**

c. At what other times will the masses have the same displacement? **≈ 0.48 + πn where n is an integer**

Graphing Calculator Use a graphing calculator to determine whether each of the following equations represents an identity. (*Hint:* You may need to rewrite the equations in terms of sine, cosine, and tangent.)

45. $(\csc\theta - 1)(\csc\theta + 1) = \tan^2\theta$ **no**

46. $\sec\theta - \cos\theta = \sin\theta$ **no**

47. $\cos\theta(\sec\theta + \cos\theta\csc^2\theta) = \csc^2\theta$ **yes**

48. $\cot\theta(\cos\theta + \sin\theta\tan\theta) = \csc\theta$ **yes**

49. $\cos\theta = 0.99\cos\theta$ **no**

50. $\sin\theta\cos\theta = \tan\theta - \tan\theta\sin^2\theta$ **yes**

51. Physics A conical pendulum is created by a pendulum that travels in a circle rather than side to side and traces out the shape of a cone. The radius r of the base of the cone is given by the formula $r = \frac{g\tan\theta}{\omega^2}$, where g represents the force of gravity and ω represents the angular velocity of the pendulum.

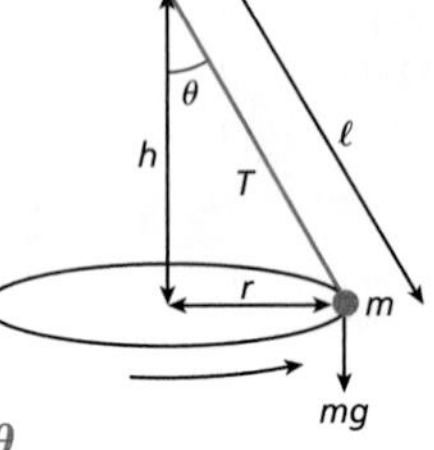

a. Use $\omega = \sqrt{\frac{g}{\ell\cos\theta}}$ and fundamental trigonometric identities to rewrite the formula for the radius. $r = \ell\sin\theta$

b. Find a formula for ℓ in terms of g, ω, and a single trigonometric function. $\ell = \frac{g}{\omega^2}\sec\theta$

52. odd: sine, tangent, cotangent, cosecant; even: cosine, secant

53. The graphs of even functions show reflection symmetry across the y-axis. Odd functions show 180° rotational symmetry about the origin, or both a reflection across the x-axis and the y-axis.

55. an infinite number of equivalent forms; $\tan\theta = \frac{\sin\theta}{\cos\theta}$, $\cos\theta = \frac{\sin\theta}{\tan\theta}$, $\sin\theta = \tan\theta\cos\theta$

Critical Thinking A function is called odd if $f(-x) = -f(x)$ and even if $f(-x) = f(x)$.

52. Which of the six trigonometric functions are odd? Which are even?

53. What distinguishes the graph of an odd function from an even function or a function that is neither odd nor even?

54. Determine whether the following functions are odd, even, or neither.

a. 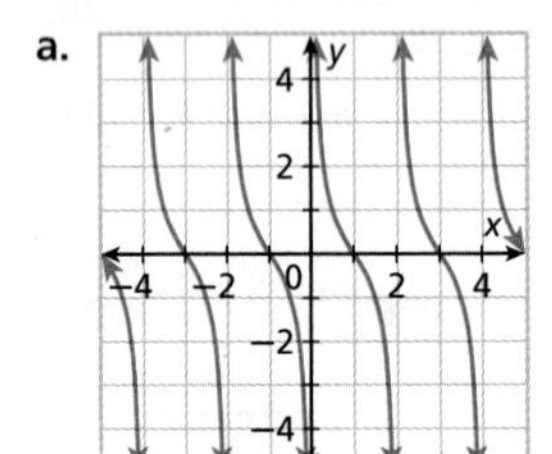

odd

b. 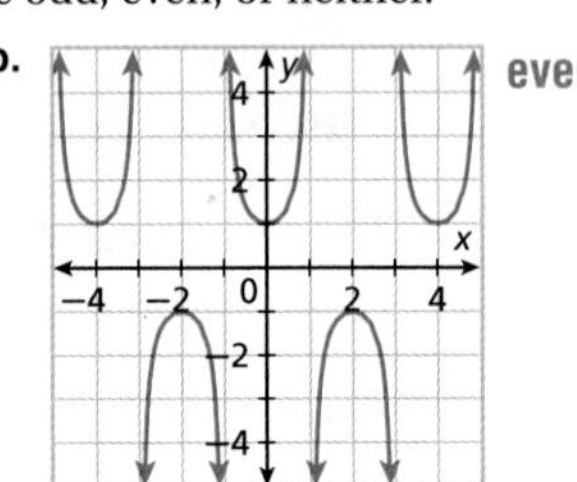

even

55. Critical Thinking In how many equivalent forms can $\tan\theta = \frac{\sin\theta}{\cos\theta}$ be expressed? Write at least three of its forms.

56. Write About It Use the fact that $\sin(-\theta) = -\sin\theta$ and $\cos(-\theta) = \cos\theta$ to explain why $\tan(-\theta) = -\tan\theta$.

14-3 PRACTICE A
14-3 PRACTICE C
14-3 PRACTICE B

Prove each trigonometric identity.

1. $\sin^2\theta + \sin^2\theta\cot^2\theta = 1$

$\sin^2\theta + \sin^2\theta\cot^2\theta = 1$
$\sin^2\theta(1 + \cot^2\theta) = 1$
$\sin^2\theta(\csc^2\theta) = 1$
$\sin^2\theta\left(\frac{1}{\sin^2\theta}\right) = 1$
$1 = 1$

2. $\cot^2\theta\cos^2\theta = \cot^2\theta - \cos^2\theta$

$\cot^2\theta\cos^2\theta = \cot^2\theta - \cos^2\theta = \frac{\cos^2\theta}{\sin^2\theta} - \cos^2\theta =$
$\frac{\cos^2\theta}{\sin^2\theta} - \frac{\sin^2\theta\cos^2\theta}{\sin^2\theta} = \frac{\cos^2\theta - \sin^2\theta\cos^2\theta}{\sin^2\theta} =$
$\frac{\cos^2\theta(1 - \sin^2\theta)}{\sin^2\theta} = \left(\frac{\cos^2\theta}{\sin^2\theta}\right)(1 - \sin^2\theta) =$
$\cot^2\theta(1 - \sin^2\theta) = \cot^2\theta(\cos^2\theta + \sin^2\theta - \sin^2\theta) =$
$\cot^2\theta\cos^2\theta$

3. $\tan^2\theta - \tan^2\theta\sin^2\theta = \sin^2\theta$

$\tan^2\theta - \tan^2\theta\sin^2\theta = \sin^2\theta$
$\tan^2\theta(1 - \sin^2\theta) = \sin^2\theta$
$\tan^2\theta(\cos^2\theta) = \sin^2\theta$
$\frac{\sin^2\theta}{\cos^2\theta}(\cos^2\theta) = \sin^2\theta$
$(\sin^2\theta)\frac{\cos^2\theta}{\cos^2\theta} = \sin^2\theta$
$\sin^2\theta = \sin^2\theta$

4. $\frac{\sin\theta + \cos\theta}{\sin\theta\cos\theta} = \sec\theta + \csc\theta$

$\frac{\sin\theta + \cos\theta}{\sin\theta\cos\theta} = \sec\theta + \csc\theta$
$\frac{\sin\theta}{\sin\theta\cos\theta} + \frac{\cos\theta}{\sin\theta\cos\theta} = \sec\theta + \csc\theta$
$\left(\frac{\sin\theta}{\sin\theta}\right)\frac{1}{\cos\theta} + \frac{1}{\sin\theta}\left(\frac{\cos\theta}{\cos\theta}\right) = \sec\theta + \csc\theta$
$(1)\frac{1}{\cos\theta} + \frac{1}{\sin\theta}(1) = \sec\theta + \csc\theta$
$\frac{1}{\cos\theta} + \frac{1}{\sin\theta} = \sec\theta + \csc\theta$
$\sec\theta + \csc\theta = \sec\theta + \csc\theta$

Rewrite each expression in terms of cos θ. Then simplify.

5. $2\sin\theta\cos\theta\cot\theta$

$2\sin\theta\cos\theta\cot\theta =$
$2\sin\theta\cos\theta \cdot \frac{\cos\theta}{\sin\theta} =$
$2\cos^2\theta$

6. $\frac{1 + \cot\theta}{\cot\theta(\sin\theta + \cos\theta)}$

$\frac{1 + \cot\theta}{\cot\theta(\sin\theta + \cos\theta)} = \frac{1 + \frac{\cos\theta}{\sin\theta}}{\frac{\cos\theta}{\sin\theta}(\sin\theta + \cos\theta)} = \frac{\frac{\sin\theta + \cos\theta}{\sin\theta}}{\frac{\cos\theta(\sin\theta + \cos\theta)}{\sin\theta}} = \frac{\sin\theta + \cos\theta}{\cos\theta(\sin\theta + \cos\theta)} = \frac{1}{\cos\theta}$

7. $\cos^4\theta - \sin^4\theta + \sin^2\theta$

$\cos^4\theta - \sin^4\theta + \sin^2\theta$
$= (\cos^2\theta + \sin^2\theta)$
$(\cos^2\theta - \sin^2\theta) + \sin^2\theta$
$(1)(\cos^2\theta - \sin^2\theta) +$
$\sin^2\theta = \cos^2\theta$

Solve.

8. Use the equation $mg\sin\theta = \mu mg\cos\theta$ to determine the angle at which a waxed wood block on an inclined plane of wet snow begins to slide. Assume $\mu = 0.17$. 9.6°

14-3 READING STRATEGIES

The trigonometric identities are relationships that we can use to rewrite and simplify trigonometric functions.

Reciprocal Identities	Ratio Identities
$\csc\theta = \frac{1}{\sin\theta}$	$\tan\theta = \frac{\sin\theta}{\cos\theta}$
$\sec\theta = \frac{1}{\cos\theta}$	$\cot\theta = \frac{\cos\theta}{\sin\theta}$
$\cot\theta = \frac{1}{\tan\theta}$	

Answer each question.

1. Which identities are like inverse relationships? Explain.
Possible answer: the cosecant, secant, and cotangent functions because they are the opposite of the sine, cosine, and tangent functions

2. Rewrite each as its reciprocal identity.
a. sec85° $\frac{1}{\cos 85°}$
b. csc150° $\frac{1}{\sin 150°}$
c. cot22° $\frac{1}{\tan 22°}$

3. Rewrite each as its ratio identity.
a. tan340° $\frac{\sin 340°}{\cos 340°}$
b. $\frac{1}{\tan 230°}$ $\frac{\cos 230°}{\sin 230°}$
c. $\frac{1}{\cot 45°}$ $\frac{\sin 45°}{\cos 45°}$

Rewrite each expression (a) using reciprocal identities, and then (b) simplify using ratio identities.

4. $\csc\theta - \cot\theta$ a. $\frac{1}{\sin\theta} - \frac{1}{\tan\theta}$ b. $\frac{1 - \cos\theta}{\sin\theta}$
5. $\sec\theta + \frac{1}{\cot\theta}$ a. $\frac{1}{\cos\theta} + \tan\theta$ b. $\frac{1 + \sin\theta}{\cos\theta}$
6. $\cot\theta + 2(\csc\theta)$ a. $\frac{1}{\tan\theta} + \frac{2}{\sin\theta}$ b. $\frac{\cos\theta + 2}{\sin\theta}$

Rewrite each expression in terms of sine and cosine using reciprocal identities and ratio identities.

7. $\frac{1}{\cot\theta}$ $\frac{\sin\theta}{\cos\theta}$
8. $\frac{1}{\csc\theta} + \tan\theta$ $\sin\theta + \frac{\sin\theta}{\cos\theta}$
9. $\frac{1}{\tan\theta} + \csc\theta$ $\frac{\cos\theta + 1}{\sin\theta}$
10. $\frac{1}{\sec\theta} + \tan\theta$ $\cos\theta + \frac{\sin\theta}{\cos\theta}$

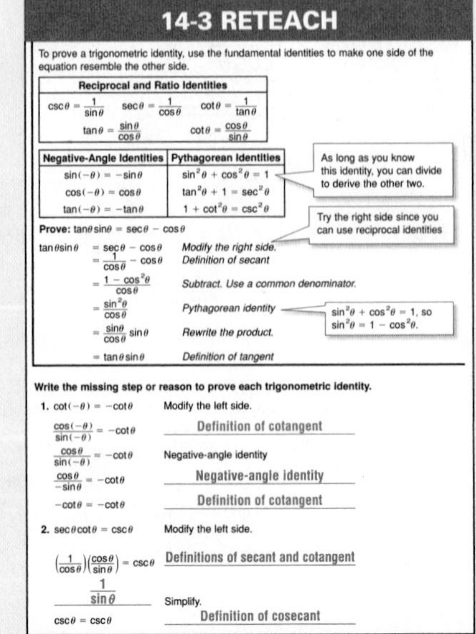

14-3 RETEACH

To prove a trigonometric identity, use the fundamental identities to make one side of the equation resemble the other side.

Reciprocal and Ratio Identities		
$\csc\theta = \frac{1}{\sin\theta}$	$\sec\theta = \frac{1}{\cos\theta}$	$\cot\theta = \frac{1}{\tan\theta}$
$\tan\theta = \frac{\sin\theta}{\cos\theta}$		$\cot\theta = \frac{\cos\theta}{\sin\theta}$

Negative-Angle Identities	Pythagorean Identities
$\sin(-\theta) = -\sin\theta$	$\sin^2\theta + \cos^2\theta = 1$
$\cos(-\theta) = \cos\theta$	$\tan^2\theta + 1 = \sec^2\theta$
$\tan(-\theta) = -\tan\theta$	$1 + \cot^2\theta = \csc^2\theta$

As long as you know this identity, you can divide to derive the other two.

Prove: $\tan\theta\sin\theta = \sec\theta - \cos\theta$

Try the right side since you can use reciprocal identities

$\tan\theta\sin\theta = \sec\theta - \cos\theta$ *Modify the right side.*
$= \frac{1}{\cos\theta} - \cos\theta$ *Definition of secant*
$= \frac{1 - \cos^2\theta}{\cos\theta}$ *Subtract. Use a common denominator.*
$= \frac{\sin^2\theta}{\cos\theta}$ *Pythagorean identity*
$= \frac{\sin\theta}{\cos\theta}\sin\theta$ *Rewrite the product.*
$= \tan\theta\sin\theta$ *Definition of tangent*

$\sin^2\theta + \cos^2\theta = 1$, so $\sin^2\theta = 1 - \cos^2\theta$.

Write the missing step or reason to prove each trigonometric identity.

1. $\cot(-\theta) = -\cot\theta$ Modify the left side.
$\frac{\cos(-\theta)}{\sin(-\theta)} = -\cot\theta$ Definition of cotangent
$\frac{\cos\theta}{\sin(-\theta)} = -\cot\theta$ Negative-angle identity
$\frac{\cos\theta}{-\sin\theta} = -\cot\theta$ Negative-angle identity
$-\cot\theta = -\cot\theta$ Definition of cotangent

2. $\sec\theta\cot\theta = \csc\theta$ Modify the left side.
$\left(\frac{1}{\cos\theta}\right)\left(\frac{\cos\theta}{\sin\theta}\right) = \csc\theta$ Definitions of secant and cotangent
$\frac{1}{\sin\theta}$ Simplify.
$\csc\theta = \csc\theta$ Definition of cosecant

57. Which expression is equivalent to $\sec\theta \sin\theta$?

Ⓐ $\sin\theta$ Ⓑ $\cos\theta$ Ⓒ $\csc\theta$ Ⓓ $\tan\theta$ (circled)

58. Which expression is NOT equivalent to the other expressions?

Ⓕ $\sec\theta\csc\theta$ Ⓖ $\dfrac{1}{\sin\theta\cos\theta}$ Ⓗ $\dfrac{\tan\theta}{\sin^2\theta}$ Ⓙ $\dfrac{\cos^2\theta}{\cot\theta}$ (circled)

59. Which trigonometric statement is NOT an identity?

Ⓐ $1 + \cos^2\theta = \sin^2\theta$ (circled) Ⓒ $1 + \tan^2\theta = \sec^2\theta$

Ⓑ $\csc^2\theta - 1 = \cot^2\theta$ Ⓓ $1 - \sin^2\theta = \cos^2\theta$

60. Which is equivalent to $1 - \sec^2\theta$?

Ⓕ $\tan^2\theta$ Ⓖ $-\tan^2\theta$ (circled) Ⓗ $\cot^2\theta$ Ⓙ $-\cot^2\theta$

61. **Short Response** Verify that $\sin\theta + \cot\theta\cos\theta = \csc\theta$ is an identity. Write the justification for each step.

CHALLENGE AND EXTEND

Write each expression as a single fraction.

62. $\dfrac{1}{\cos\theta} + \dfrac{1}{\cos^2\theta}$ $\dfrac{\cos\theta + 1}{\cos^2\theta}$

63. $\dfrac{\cos\theta}{\sin\theta} + \dfrac{\sin\theta}{\cos\theta}$ $\dfrac{1}{\sin\theta\cos\theta}$

64. $1 - \dfrac{\cos\theta}{\sin\theta}$ $\dfrac{\sin\theta - \cos\theta}{\sin\theta}$

65. $\dfrac{1}{1-\cos\theta} - \dfrac{\cos\theta}{1-\cos^2\theta}$ $\dfrac{1}{1-\cos^2\theta}$

Simplify.

66. $\dfrac{\frac{1}{\sin^2\theta} - 1}{\frac{\cos^2\theta}{\sin^2\theta}}$ 1

67. $\dfrac{\frac{1}{\sin\theta} + \frac{1}{\cos\theta}}{\frac{1}{\sin\theta\cos\theta}}$ $\sin\theta + \cos\theta$

68. $\dfrac{\frac{1}{\sin\theta} - \frac{1}{\cos\theta}}{\frac{\sin\theta}{\cos\theta} - \frac{\cos\theta}{\sin\theta}}$ $\dfrac{-1}{\sin\theta + \cos\theta}$

69. $\dfrac{1 - \frac{1}{\sin\theta}}{1 - \frac{1}{\sin^2\theta}}$ $\dfrac{\sin\theta}{\sin\theta + 1}$

SPIRAL REVIEW

70. **Travel** A statistician kept a record of the number of tourists in Hawaii for six months. Match each situation to its corresponding graph. *(Lesson 9-1)*

A

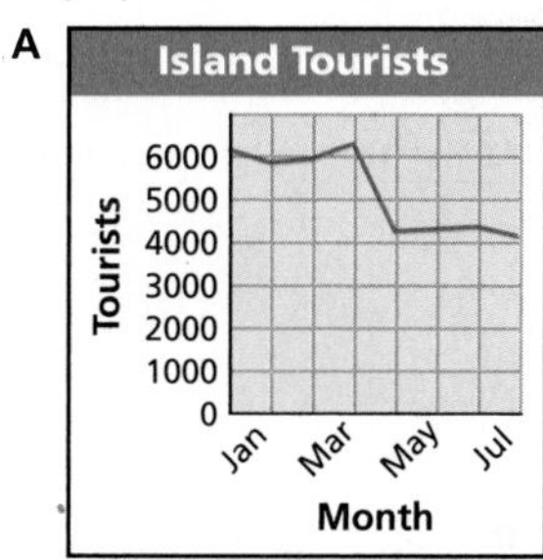

B

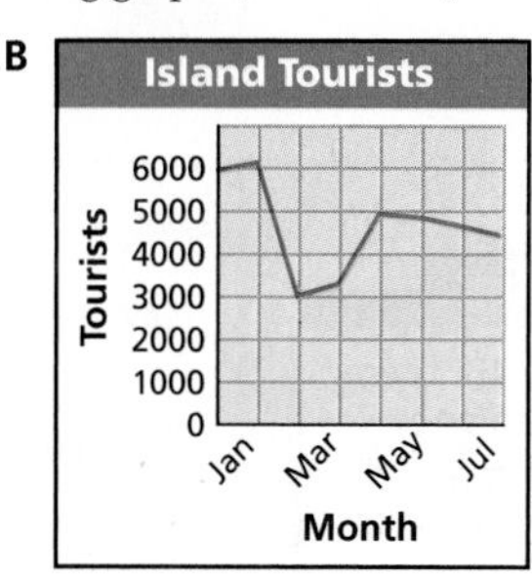

a. There were predictions of hurricanes in March and April. **graph B**

b. High airfares and high temperatures cause tourism to drop off in the summer. **graph A**

Find each probability. *(Lesson 11-3)*

71. rolling a 4 on a number cube and a 4 on another number cube $\dfrac{1}{36}$

72. getting heads on both tosses when a coin is tossed 2 times $\dfrac{1}{4}$

Find four values for which each function is undefined. *(Lesson 14-2)*

73. $y = -\tan\theta$ $\dfrac{\pi}{2}, \dfrac{3\pi}{2}, -\dfrac{\pi}{2}, -\dfrac{3\pi}{2}$

74. $y = \sec(0.5\theta)$ $\pi, 3\pi, -\pi, -3\pi$

75. $y = -\csc\theta$ $0, \pi, -\pi, 2\pi$

14-3 PROBLEM SOLVING

The advertisement for a new shoe promises runners less slip. The coefficient of friction (μ) between concrete and a new material used in the sole of this shoe is 1.5. The force of friction that causes slip is equal to $mg \sin\theta$, where m is a runner's mass and g is the acceleration due to gravity. The force that prevents slip is $\mu mg \cos\theta$.

Shoe

Concrete

1. Mukisa wants to know what this new shoe will do for his performance.

   a. At the instant of slip, the force that causes slip is equal to the force that prevents it. Write an equation to show this relationship. $mg\sin\theta = \mu mg\cos\theta$

   b. Rewrite the equation with trigonometric expressions on one side of the equation, and substitute the coefficient of friction for the new material. $\dfrac{\sin\theta}{\cos\theta} = 1.5$

   c. Use a trigonometric identity to rewrite the equation using only the tangent function. $\tan\theta = 1.5$

   d. Solve for θ, the angle at which the new shoe will start to slip. $56.3°$

2. Mukisa wonders how his old shoes compare to these new shoes. The label on the box of his old shoes states that the coefficient of friction is 1.3.

   a. Write an equation to find the angle at which a shoe with a coefficient of friction of 1.3 will slip. $mg\sin\theta = (1.3)mg\cos\theta$

   b. At what angle will this shoe start to slip? $52.4°$

   c. Suggest how the new shoes might improve Mukisa's performance.

   Possible answer: With the new shoes he should be able to push off at a greater angle (by about 4°) to the vertical.

An advertisement states, "Use this wax and your skis will slide better than silk on silk!" The coefficient of friction for silk on silk is 0.25. The coefficient of friction for waxed wood on wet snow is 0.14. The equation $mg\sin\theta = \mu mg\cos\theta$ can be used to find the angle at which a material begins to slide. Choose the letter for the best answer.

3. Which expression gives the angle at which silk begins to slide on silk?

   A $\cos^{-1}(0.25)$

   B $\sin\left(\dfrac{1}{0.25}\right)$

   C $\tan\left(\dfrac{1}{0.25}\right)$

   Ⓓ $\tan^{-1}(0.25)$

4. At what angle would a waxed wooden ski begin to slide on wet snow?

   F 2°

   Ⓖ 8°

   H 12°

   J 14°

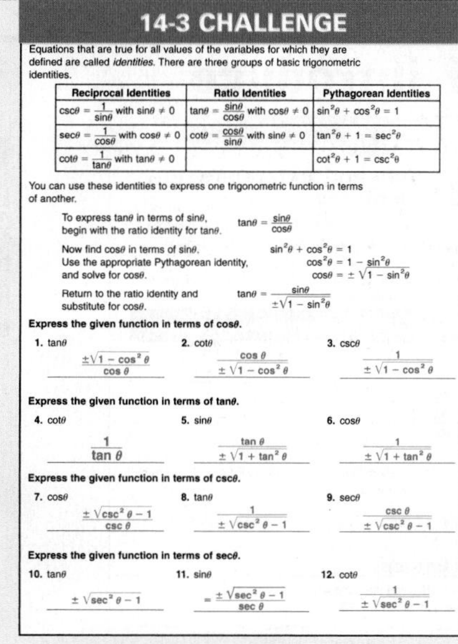

14-3 CHALLENGE

Equations that are true for all values of the variables for which they are defined are called *identities*. There are three groups of basic trigonometric identities.

Reciprocal Identities	Ratio Identities	Pythagorean Identities
$\csc\theta = \dfrac{1}{\sin\theta}$ with $\sin\theta \neq 0$	$\tan\theta = \dfrac{\sin\theta}{\cos\theta}$ with $\cos\theta \neq 0$	$\sin^2\theta + \cos^2\theta = 1$
$\sec\theta = \dfrac{1}{\cos\theta}$ with $\cos\theta \neq 0$	$\cot\theta = \dfrac{\cos\theta}{\sin\theta}$ with $\sin\theta \neq 0$	$\tan^2\theta + 1 = \sec^2\theta$
$\cot\theta = \dfrac{1}{\tan\theta}$ with $\tan\theta \neq 0$		$\cot^2\theta + 1 = \csc^2\theta$

You can use these identities to express one trigonometric function in terms of another.

To express $\tan\theta$ in terms of $\sin\theta$, begin with the ratio identity for $\tan\theta$. $\tan\theta = \dfrac{\sin\theta}{\cos\theta}$

Now find $\cos\theta$ in terms of $\sin\theta$. Use the appropriate Pythagorean identity, and solve for $\cos\theta$.

$$\sin^2\theta + \cos^2\theta = 1$$
$$\cos^2\theta = 1 - \sin^2\theta$$
$$\cos\theta = \pm\sqrt{1 - \sin^2\theta}$$

Return to the ratio identity and substitute for $\cos\theta$. $\tan\theta = \dfrac{\sin\theta}{\pm\sqrt{1 - \sin^2\theta}}$

Express the given function in terms of $\cos\theta$.

1. $\tan\theta$ $\dfrac{\pm\sqrt{1-\cos^2\theta}}{\cos\theta}$

2. $\cot\theta$ $\dfrac{\cos\theta}{\pm\sqrt{1-\cos^2\theta}}$

3. $\csc\theta$ $\dfrac{1}{\pm\sqrt{1-\cos^2\theta}}$

Express the given function in terms of $\tan\theta$.

4. $\cot\theta$ $\dfrac{1}{\tan\theta}$

5. $\sin\theta$ $\dfrac{\tan\theta}{\pm\sqrt{1+\tan^2\theta}}$

6. $\cos\theta$ $\dfrac{1}{\pm\sqrt{1+\tan^2\theta}}$

Express the given function in terms of $\csc\theta$.

7. $\cos\theta$ $\dfrac{\pm\sqrt{\csc^2\theta-1}}{\csc\theta}$

8. $\tan\theta$ $\dfrac{1}{\pm\sqrt{\csc^2\theta-1}}$

9. $\sec\theta$ $\dfrac{\csc\theta}{\pm\sqrt{\csc^2\theta-1}}$

Express the given function in terms of $\sec\theta$.

10. $\tan\theta$ $\pm\sqrt{\sec^2\theta-1}$

11. $\sin\theta$ $= \dfrac{\pm\sqrt{\sec^2\theta-1}}{\sec\theta}$

12. $\cot\theta$ $\dfrac{1}{\pm\sqrt{\sec^2\theta-1}}$

TEST PREP DOCTOR Students having difficulty with **Exercise 58** should remember to change everything to sine and cosine. Students having difficulty with **Exercise 60** should begin with the identity $1 + \tan^2\theta = \sec^2\theta$ and try to solve from there.

Answers

61. $\sin\theta + \cot\theta\cos\theta$

$= \sin\theta + \left(\dfrac{\cos\theta}{\sin\theta}\right)\cos\theta$ Given, ratio identity

$= \dfrac{\sin^2\theta}{\sin\theta} + \dfrac{\cos^2\theta}{\sin\theta}$ Common denominators

$= \dfrac{\sin^2\theta + \cos^2\theta}{\sin\theta}$ Add fractions.

$= \dfrac{1}{\sin\theta}$ Pythagorean identity

$= \csc\theta$ Ratio identity

Journal

Have students use an example to explain how to choose which side of an identity to begin working with and how to choose which identity to use.

ALTERNATIVE ASSESSMENT

Have students create three of their own trigonometric identities including all six trigonometric functions by working backwards from a true statement such as $\sin\theta = \sin\theta$ and substituting for each side, e.g., from $\sin\theta = \sin\theta$ to $\dfrac{1}{\csc\theta} = \tan\theta\cos\theta$.

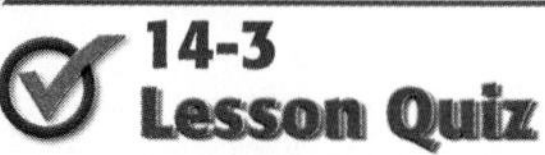

14-3 Lesson Quiz

Prove each trigonometric identity.

1. $\sin\theta\sec\theta = \dfrac{1-\cos^2\theta}{\sin\theta\cos\theta}$

$= \left(\dfrac{\sin^2\theta}{\sin\theta\cos\theta}\right)$

$= \dfrac{\sin\theta}{\cos\theta}$

$= \sin\theta\sec\theta$

2. $\sec^2\theta = 1 + \sin^2\theta\sec^2\theta$

$= 1 + \dfrac{\sin^2\theta}{\cos^2\theta}$

$= 1 + \tan^2\theta$

$= \sec^2\theta$

Rewrite each expression in terms of $\cos\theta$, and simplify.

3. $\sin^2\theta\cot^2\theta\sec\theta$ $\cos\theta$

4. $\dfrac{2(\csc^2\theta - \cot^2\theta)}{\sec\theta}$ $2\cos\theta$

Also available on transparency

14-4 Organizer

Pacing: Traditional 1 day
Block $\frac{1}{2}$ day

Objectives: Evaluate trigonometric expressions by using sum and difference identities.

Use matrix multiplication with sum and difference identities to perform rotations.

Online Edition
Tutorial Videos

Power Presentations with PowerPoint®

Warm Up

Find each product, if possible.

$$A = \begin{bmatrix} \frac{1}{2} & -\frac{\sqrt{3}}{2} \\ \frac{\sqrt{3}}{2} & \frac{1}{2} \end{bmatrix} \quad B = \begin{bmatrix} \sqrt{3} & 1 \\ 1 & \sqrt{3} \end{bmatrix}$$

1. $AB \begin{bmatrix} 0 & -1 \\ 2 & \sqrt{3} \end{bmatrix}$ **2.** $BA \begin{bmatrix} \sqrt{3} & -1 \\ 2 & 0 \end{bmatrix}$

Also available on transparency

Math Humor

"A good mathematical joke is better, and better mathematics, than a dozen mediocre papers."
J. E. Littlewood

14-4 Sum and Difference Identities

Objectives
Evaluate trigonometric expressions by using sum and difference identities.

Use matrix multiplication with sum and difference identities to perform rotations.

Vocabulary
rotation matrix

Why learn this?
You can use sum and difference identities and matrices to form images made from rotations. (See Example 4.)

Matrix multiplication and sum and difference identities are tools to find the coordinates of points rotated about the origin on a plane.

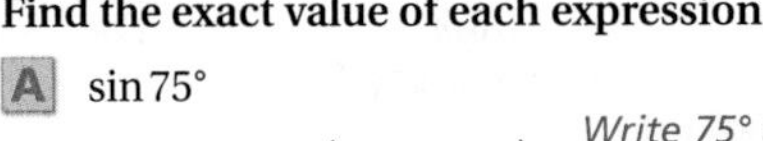

Know it! Note

Sum and Difference Identities	
Sum Identities	**Difference Identities**
$\sin(A+B) = \sin A\cos B + \cos A\sin B$	$\sin(A-B) = \sin A\cos B - \cos A\sin B$
$\cos(A+B) = \cos A\cos B - \sin A\sin B$	$\cos(A-B) = \cos A\cos B + \sin A\sin B$
$\tan(A+B) = \dfrac{\tan A + \tan B}{1 - \tan A\tan B}$	$\tan(A-B) = \dfrac{\tan A - \tan B}{1 + \tan A\tan B}$

EXAMPLE 1 **Evaluating Expressions with Sum and Difference Identities**

Find the exact value of each expression.

A $\sin 75°$

$\sin 75° = \sin(30° + 45°)$ *Write 75° as the sum 30° + 45° because trigonometric values of 30° and 45° are known.*

$= \sin 30°\cos 45° + \cos 30°\sin 45°$ *Apply identity for sin(A + B).*

$= \frac{1}{2}\cdot\frac{\sqrt{2}}{2} + \frac{\sqrt{3}}{2}\cdot\frac{\sqrt{2}}{2}$ *Evaluate.*

$= \frac{\sqrt{2}}{4} + \frac{\sqrt{6}}{4} = \frac{\sqrt{2}+\sqrt{6}}{4}$ *Simplify.*

B $\cos\left(-\frac{\pi}{12}\right)$

$\cos\left(-\frac{\pi}{12}\right) = \cos\left(\frac{\pi}{6} - \frac{\pi}{4}\right)$ *Write $-\frac{\pi}{12}$ as the difference $\frac{\pi}{6} - \frac{\pi}{4}$.*

$= \cos\frac{\pi}{6}\cos\frac{\pi}{4} + \sin\frac{\pi}{6}\sin\frac{\pi}{4}$ *Apply the identity for cos(A − B).*

$= \frac{\sqrt{3}}{2}\cdot\frac{\sqrt{2}}{2} + \frac{1}{2}\cdot\frac{\sqrt{2}}{2}$ *Evaluate.*

$= \frac{\sqrt{6}}{4} + \frac{\sqrt{2}}{4} = \frac{\sqrt{2}+\sqrt{6}}{4}$ *Simplify.*

Helpful Hint

In Example 1B, there is more than one way to get $-\frac{\pi}{12}$. For example, $\left(\frac{\pi}{6} - \frac{\pi}{4}\right)$ or $\left(\frac{\pi}{4} - \frac{\pi}{3}\right)$.

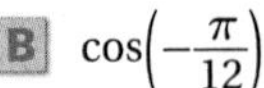

CHECK IT OUT! **Find the exact value of each expression.**

1a. $\tan 105°$ $-2 - \sqrt{3}$ **1b.** $\sin\left(-\frac{11\pi}{12}\right)$ $\frac{\sqrt{2}-\sqrt{6}}{4}$

State Resources

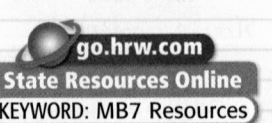

go.hrw.com
State Resources Online
KEYWORD: MB7 Resources

1 Introduce

EXPLORATION

14-4 Sum and Difference Identities

You can use patterns to discover new trigonometric identities.

1. In each row of the table, the measures of two angles, ∠A and ∠B, are given. Use your calculator to evaluate sin(A + B), sin A cos B, and cos A sin B. Round each value to the nearest thousandth if necessary.

m∠A	m∠B	sin(A + B)	sin A cos B	cos A sin B
10°	20°			
25°	40°			
50°	15°			
60°	20°			
100°	150°			

2. Look for a pattern in the table. How is sin(A + B) related to sin A cos B, and cos A sin B?

3. Write an identity based on your answer to Problem 2.

THINK AND DISCUSS

4. Explain what happens when you use your identity to evaluate sin(45° + 45°).

Motivate

Have students consider the parabolas $y = x^2$ and $x = y^2$. Have students brainstorm the type of transformation that would be necessary to transform one of these parabolas into the other. The transformation is a rotation, and its methods and techniques will be investigated in this lesson.

Explorations and answers are provided in the *Explorations* binder.

Shifting the cosine function right π radians is equivalent to reflecting it across the x-axis. A proof of this is shown in Example 2 by using a difference identity.

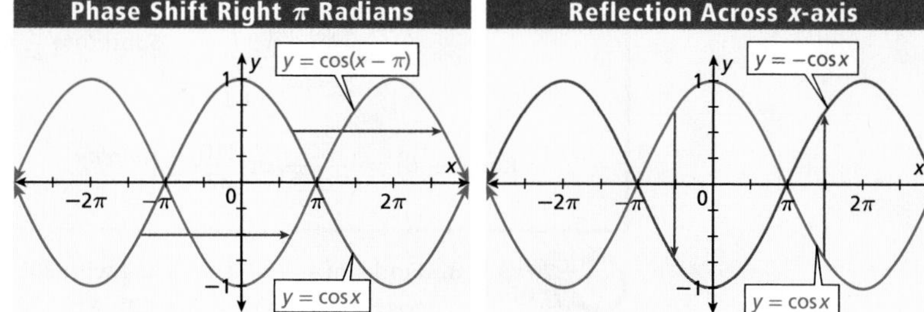

EXAMPLE 2 **Proving Identities with Sum and Difference Identities**

Prove the identity $\cos(x - \pi) = -\cos x$.

$\cos(x - \pi) = -\cos x$	*Choose the left-hand side to modify.*
$\cos x \cos \pi + \sin x \sin \pi =$	*Apply the identity for* $\cos(A - B)$.
$-1 \cdot \cos x + 0 \cdot \sin x =$	*Evaluate.*
$-\cos x = -\cos x$	*Simplify.*

CHECK IT OUT! **2.** Prove the identity $\cos\left(x + \frac{\pi}{2}\right) = -\sin x$.

EXAMPLE 3 **Using the Pythagorean Theorem with Sum and Difference Identities**

Find $\tan(A + B)$ if $\sin A = -\frac{7}{25}$ with $180° < A < 270°$ and if $\cos B = \frac{8}{17}$ with $0° < B < 180°$.

Remember!
Refer to Lessons 13-2 and 13-3 to review reference angles.

Step 1 Find $\tan A$ and $\tan B$.

Use reference angles and the ratio definitions $\sin A = \frac{y}{r}$ and $\cos B = \frac{x}{r}$. Draw a triangle in the appropriate quadrant and label x, y, and r for each angle.

In Quadrant III (QIII), $180° < A < 270°$ and $\sin A = -\frac{7}{25}$.

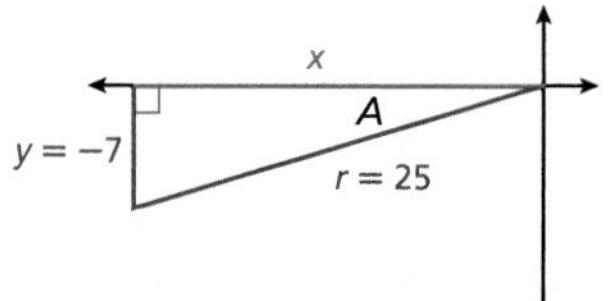

$x^2 + (-7)^2 = 25^2$

$x = -\sqrt{625 - 49} = -24$

Thus, $\tan A = \frac{y}{x} = \frac{7}{24}$.

In Quadrant I (QI), $0° < B < 180°$ and $\cos B = \frac{8}{17}$.

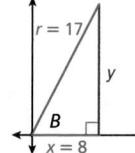

$8^2 + y^2 = 17^2$

$y = \sqrt{289 - 64} = 15$

Thus, $\tan B = \frac{y}{x} = \frac{15}{8}$.

Power Presentations with PowerPoint®

Additional Examples

Example 1

Find the exact value of each expression.

A. $\cos 15°$ $\quad \frac{\sqrt{6} + \sqrt{2}}{4}$

B. $\tan\left(\frac{11\pi}{12}\right)$ $\quad \sqrt{3} - 2$

Example 2

Prove the identity.

$$\tan\left(\theta + \frac{\pi}{4}\right) = \frac{1 + \tan\theta}{1 - \tan\theta}$$

$$\tan\left(\theta + \frac{\pi}{4}\right) = \frac{\tan\theta + \tan\frac{\pi}{4}}{1 - \tan\theta\tan\frac{\pi}{4}} = \frac{1 + \tan\theta}{1 - \tan\theta}$$

Example 3

Find $\cos(A - B)$ if $\sin A = \frac{1}{3}$ with $0 < A < \frac{\pi}{2}$ and if $\tan B = \frac{3}{4}$ with $0 < B < \frac{\pi}{2}$. $\quad \frac{8\sqrt{2} + 3}{15}$

Also available on transparency

INTERVENTION

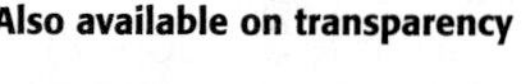

Questioning Strategies

EXAMPLE 1

- How can you decide whether to add or subtract values?

EXAMPLE 2

- How can you decide what values to use for A and B in the sum and difference formulas?

EXAMPLE 3

- How can you check to see if your answer is reasonable?

Answers to *Check It Out!*

2. $\cos\left(\frac{\pi}{2} + x\right)$
$= \cos\left(\frac{\pi}{2}\right)\cos x - \sin\left(\frac{\pi}{2}\right)\sin x$
$= (0)\cos x - (1)\sin x$
$= -\sin x$

2 Teach

Guided Instruction

Introduce the sum and difference identities for sine, cosine, and tangent. Practice with students adding and subtracting angle measures from the unit circle to help identify what angle measures can be evaluated with the sum and difference identities.

Reaching All Learners

Through Auditory Cues

To help students remember the sum and difference formulas, show students the following:

For **s**ines, the formulas are the **s**ame:

$\sin(A + B) = \sin A \cos B + \sin B \cos A$

$\sin(A - B) = \sin A \cos B - \sin B \cos A$

For **co**sines, the formulas **co**ntradict:

$\cos(A + B) = \cos A \cos B - \sin A \sin B$

$\cos(A - B) = \cos A \cos B + \sin A \sin B$

Step 2 Use the angle-sum identity to find $\tan(A+B)$.

$$\tan(A+B) = \frac{\tan A + \tan B}{1 - \tan A \tan B} \quad \textit{Apply identity for } \tan(A+B).$$

$$= \frac{\left(\frac{7}{24}\right) + \left(\frac{15}{8}\right)}{1 - \left(\frac{7}{24}\right)\left(\frac{15}{8}\right)} \quad \textit{Substitute } \tfrac{7}{24} \textit{ for } \tan A \textit{ and } \tfrac{15}{8} \textit{ for } \tan B.$$

$$\tan(A+B) = \frac{\frac{52}{24}}{1 - \frac{35}{64}}, \text{ or } \frac{416}{87} \quad \textit{Simplify.}$$

3. Find $\sin(A-B)$ if $\sin A = \frac{4}{5}$ with $90° < A < 180°$ and if $\cos B = \frac{3}{5}$ with $0° < B < 90°$. $\frac{24}{25}$

To rotate a point $P(x,y)$ through an angle θ, use a **rotation matrix**.

The sum identities for sine and cosine are used to derive the system of equations that yields the rotation matrix.

Using a Rotation Matrix

If $P(x, y)$ is any point in a plane, then the coordinates $P'(x', y')$ of the image after a rotation of θ degrees counterclockwise about the origin can be found by using the rotation matrix:

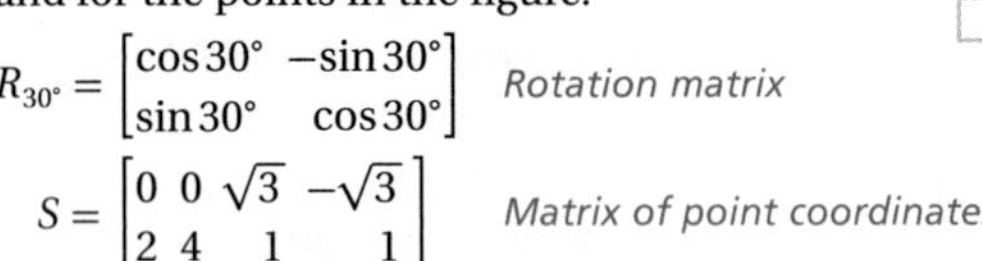

$$\begin{bmatrix} \cos\theta & -\sin\theta \\ \sin\theta & \cos\theta \end{bmatrix} \begin{bmatrix} x \\ y \end{bmatrix} = \begin{bmatrix} x' \\ y' \end{bmatrix}$$

EXAMPLE 4 **Using a Rotation Matrix**

Find the coordinates, to the nearest hundredth, of the points in the figure shown after a 30° rotation about the origin.

Step 1 Write matrices for a 30° rotation and for the points in the figure.

$$R_{30°} = \begin{bmatrix} \cos 30° & -\sin 30° \\ \sin 30° & \cos 30° \end{bmatrix} \quad \textit{Rotation matrix}$$

$$S = \begin{bmatrix} 0 & 0 & \sqrt{3} & -\sqrt{3} \\ 2 & 4 & 1 & 1 \end{bmatrix} \quad \textit{Matrix of point coordinates}$$

Step 2 Find the matrix product.

$$R_{30°} \times S = \begin{bmatrix} \cos 30° & -\sin 30° \\ \sin 30° & \cos 30° \end{bmatrix} \begin{bmatrix} 0 & 0 & \sqrt{3} & -\sqrt{3} \\ 2 & 4 & 1 & 1 \end{bmatrix}$$

$$= \begin{bmatrix} -1 & -2 & 1 & -2 \\ \sqrt{3} & 2\sqrt{3} & \sqrt{3} & 0 \end{bmatrix}$$

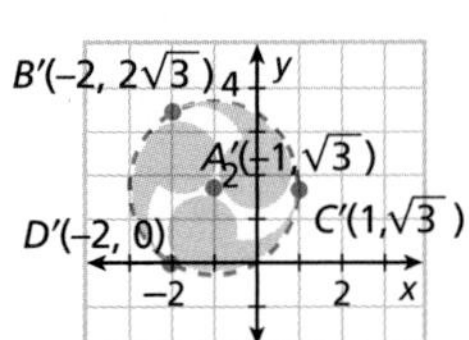

Step 3 The approximate coordinates of the points after a 30° rotation are $A'(-1, \sqrt{3})$, $B'(-2, 2\sqrt{3})$, $C'(1, \sqrt{3})$, and $D'(-2, 0)$.

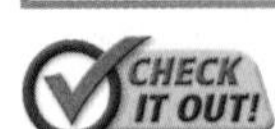

4. Find the coordinates, to the nearest hundredth, of the points in the original figure after a 60° rotation about the origin. $A'(-\sqrt{3}, 1)$, $B'(-2\sqrt{3}, 2)$, $C'(0, 2)$, $D'(-\sqrt{3}, -1)$

Power Presentations with PowerPoint®

Additional Examples

Example 4

Find the coordinates to the nearest hundredth of the points (1, 1) and (2, 0) after a 40° rotation about the origin.

(0.12, 1.41), (1.53, 1.29)

Also available on transparency

INTERVENTION

Questioning Strategies

EXAMPLE 4

- What are the coordinates of the point (1, 0) after a rotation of θ?

Critical Thinking Students may wonder how to show a *clockwise* rotation. This rotation can be shown by multiplying by $\begin{bmatrix} \cos\theta & \sin\theta \\ -\sin\theta & \cos\theta \end{bmatrix}$.

Tell students that the clockwise rotation is equivalent to a $(360 - \theta)°$ counterclockwise rotation.

ONGOING ASSESSMENT and INTERVENTION

Diagnose ***Before*** **the Lesson**
14-4 Warm Up, TE p. 1014

Monitor ***During*** **the Lesson**
Check It Out! Exercises, SE pp. 1014–1016
Questioning Strategies, TE pp. 1015–1016

Assess ***After*** **the Lesson**
14-4 Lesson Quiz, TE p. 1019
Alternative Assessment, TE p. 1019

3 Close

Summarize

By using angle sum and difference formulas, it is possible to evaluate trigonometric functions for additional angles without resorting to a calculator. By using rotation matrices, you can rotate a point or a figure about the origin.

THINK AND DISCUSS

1. **DESCRIBE** three different ways that you can use the difference identity to find the exact value of $\sin 15°$.
2. **EXPLAIN** the similarities and differences between the identity formulas for sine and cosine. How do the signs of the terms relate to whether the identity is a sum or a difference?

3. **GET ORGANIZED** Copy and complete the graphic organizer. For each type of function, give the sum and difference identity and an example.

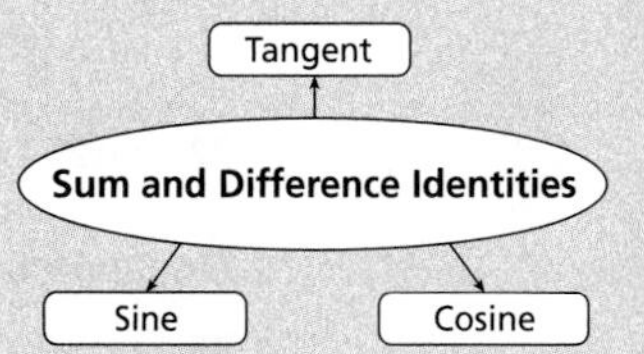

14-4 Exercises

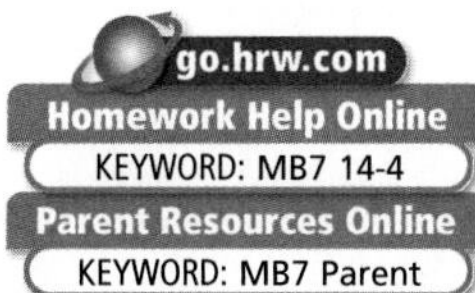

GUIDED PRACTICE

1. **Vocabulary** A geometric rotation requires that a center point of rotation be defined. Which point and which direction does a rotation matrix such as R_θ assume?
A rotation matrix assumes a counterclockwise rotation about the origin.

SEE EXAMPLE 1 p. 1014

Find the exact value of each expression.

2. $\cos 105°$ $\frac{\sqrt{2}-\sqrt{6}}{4}$
3. $\sin\frac{11\pi}{12}$ $\frac{\sqrt{6}-\sqrt{2}}{4}$
4. $\tan\frac{\pi}{12}$ $2-\sqrt{3}$
5. $\cos(-75°)$ $\frac{\sqrt{6}-\sqrt{2}}{4}$

SEE EXAMPLE 2 p. 1015

Prove each identity.

6. $\sin\left(\frac{\pi}{2}+x\right)=\cos x$
7. $\tan(\pi+x)=\tan x$
8. $\cos\left(\frac{3\pi}{2}-x\right)=-\sin x$

SEE EXAMPLE 3 p. 1015

Find each value if $\sin A=-\frac{12}{13}$ with $180°<A<270°$ and if $\sin B=\frac{4}{5}$ with $90°<B<180°$.

9. $\sin(A+B)$ $\frac{16}{65}$
10. $\cos(A-B)$ $\frac{-33}{65}$
11. $\tan(A+B)$ $\frac{16}{63}$
12. $\tan(A-B)$ $-\frac{56}{33}$

SEE EXAMPLE 4 p. 1016

13. Find the coordinates, to the nearest hundredth, of the vertices of triangle ABC with $A(0, 2)$, $B(0, -1)$, and $C(3, 0)$ after a 120° rotation about the origin.
$A'(-1.73, -1)$, $B'(0.87, 0.5)$, $C'(-1.5, 2.60)$

PRACTICE AND PROBLEM SOLVING

Independent Practice

For Exercises	See Example
14–17	1
18–20	2
21–24	3
25	4

Extra Practice
Skills Practice p. S31
Application Practice p. S45

Find the exact value of each expression.

14. $\sin\frac{7\pi}{12}$ $\frac{\sqrt{6}+\sqrt{2}}{4}$
15. $\tan 165°$ $\sqrt{3}-2$
16. $\sin 195°$ $\frac{\sqrt{2}-\sqrt{6}}{4}$
17. $\cos\frac{11\pi}{12}$ $\frac{-\sqrt{2}-\sqrt{6}}{4}$

Prove each identity.

18. $\cos\left(\frac{3\pi}{2}+x\right)=\sin x$
19. $\sin\left(\frac{3\pi}{2}+x\right)=-\cos x$
20. $\tan(x-2\pi)=\tan x$

Find each value if $\cos A=-\frac{12}{13}$ with $90°<A<180°$ and if $\sin B=-\frac{4}{5}$ with $270°<B<360°$.

21. $\sin(A+B)$ $\frac{63}{65}$
22. $\tan(A-B)$ $\frac{33}{56}$
23. $\cos(A+B)$ $-\frac{16}{65}$
24. $\cos(A-B)$ $-\frac{56}{65}$

Answers to *Think and Discuss*

Possible answers:

1. Evaluate $\sin(60°-45°)$, $\sin(45°-30°)$, or $\sin(135°-120°)$.
2. Both the sine and cosine identities are in the form of a sum or difference of 2 products. The products each involve the 2 different angles given in the same order (A then B).
In sine identities, a cosine is multiplied by a sine, and the sign of the second term matches the sign between A and B. In cosine identities, cosines are multiplied by each other, sines are multiplied by each other, and the signs are opposites.
3. See p. A14.

14-4 Exercises

Assignment Guide

Assign *Guided Practice* exercises as necessary.

If you finished Examples 1–2
Basic 14–20
Average 14–20, 26–28
Advanced 14–20, 26–31, 54

If you finished Examples 1–4
Basic 14–25, 35–37, 41, 43–52, 60–67
Average 14–28, 35–53, 58–67
Advanced 14–67

Homework Quick Check
Quickly check key concepts.
Exercises: 14, 18, 22, 24

Answers

6. $\sin\left(\frac{\pi}{2}+x\right)$
$=\sin\frac{\pi}{2}\cos x+\cos\frac{\pi}{2}\sin x$
$=(1)\cos x-(0)\sin x$
$=\cos x$

7. $\tan(\pi+x)$
$=\frac{\tan\pi+\tan x}{1-\tan\pi\tan x}$
$=\frac{0+\tan x}{1-0}$
$=\tan x$

8. $\cos\left(\frac{3\pi}{2}-x\right)$
$=\cos\frac{3\pi}{2}\cos x+\sin\frac{3\pi}{2}\sin x$
$=(0)\cos x+(-1)\sin x$
$=-\sin x$

18. $\cos\left(\frac{3\pi}{2}+x\right)$
$=\cos\frac{3\pi}{2}\cos x-\sin\frac{3\pi}{2}\sin x$
$=(0)\cos x-(-1)\sin x$
$=\sin x$

19, 20. See p. A53.

State Resources

Language For **Exercise 38,** ensure that students know that, in this context, to *offset* is to displace or move out of position.

ENGLISH LANGUAGE LEARNERS

Multiple Representations Matrices like the one in **Exercise 41** can be used to represent other transformations. For example, a 180° rotation is equivalent to a reflection about the *x*- and *y*-axes.

Exercise 43 involves applying trigonometric identities. This exercise prepares students for the Multi-Step Test Prep on page 1034.

Answers

41a. $\begin{bmatrix} 0 & -1 \\ 1 & 0 \end{bmatrix}; \begin{bmatrix} -1 & 0 \\ 0 & -1 \end{bmatrix}; \begin{bmatrix} 0 & 1 \\ -1 & 0 \end{bmatrix}$

b. $P'(0, 0), Q'(-1, 1), R'(0, 4), S'(1, 1)$;
$P''(0, 0), Q''(-1, -1), R''(-4, 0), S''(-1, 1)$;
$P'''(0, 0), Q'''(1, -1), R'''(0, -4), S'''(-1, -1)$

c.

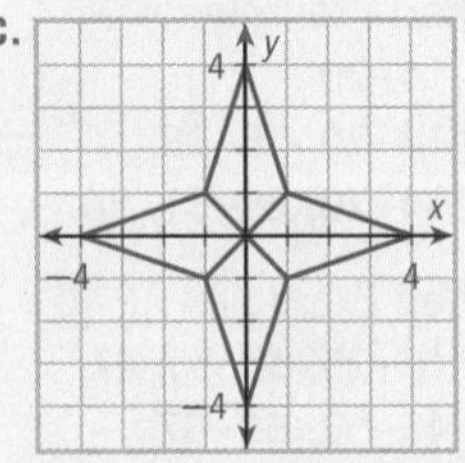

42. Possible answer: No; $\frac{11\pi}{24}$ cannot be expressed as a sum or difference of values from the unit circle.

26. $\frac{\sqrt{6}-\sqrt{2}}{4}$

28. $\frac{-\sqrt{2}-\sqrt{6}}{4}$

29. $\frac{\sqrt{2}-\sqrt{6}}{4}$

30. $\frac{\sqrt{6}-\sqrt{2}}{4}$

32. $\frac{-\sqrt{6}-\sqrt{2}}{4}$

34. $\frac{\sqrt{2}+\sqrt{6}}{4}$

38a. $\Delta = (1 - \cot\theta_i \tan\theta_r)t$

39. $\frac{204}{253}; -\frac{253}{325}; \frac{36}{325}$

40. $\frac{54-25\sqrt{2}}{28}; \frac{4+6\sqrt{2}}{15}; \frac{-3-8\sqrt{2}}{15}$

25. Find the coordinates, to the nearest hundredth, of the vertices of figure *ABC* with $A(0, 2)$, $B(1, 2)$, and $C(0, 1)$ after a 45° rotation about the origin. $A'(-1.41, 1.41)$, $B'(-0.71, 2.12)$, $C'(-0.71, 0.71)$

Find the exact value of each expression.

26. $\sin 165°$
27. $\tan(-105°)$ $2+\sqrt{3}$
28. $\cos 195°$
29. $\sin(-15°)$
30. $\cos\frac{19\pi}{12}$
31. $\tan\frac{5\pi}{12}$ $2+\sqrt{3}$
32. $\sin 255°$
33. $\tan 195°$ $2-\sqrt{3}$
34. $\cos\frac{\pi}{12}$

Find the value for each unknown angle given that $0° \le \theta \le 180°$.

35. $\cos(\theta - 30°) = \frac{1}{2}$ $\theta = 90°$
36. $\cos(20° + \theta) = \frac{\sqrt{2}}{2}$ $\theta = 25°$
37. $\sin(180° - \theta) = \frac{1}{2}$ $\theta = 30°$ or $150°$

38. **Physics** Light enters glass of thickness t at an angle θ_i and leaves the glass at the same angle θ_i. However, the exiting ray of light is offset from the initial ray by a distance $\Delta = \left(\frac{\sin(\theta_i - \theta_r)}{\sin\theta_i \cos\theta_r}\right)t$, indicated in the figure shown.

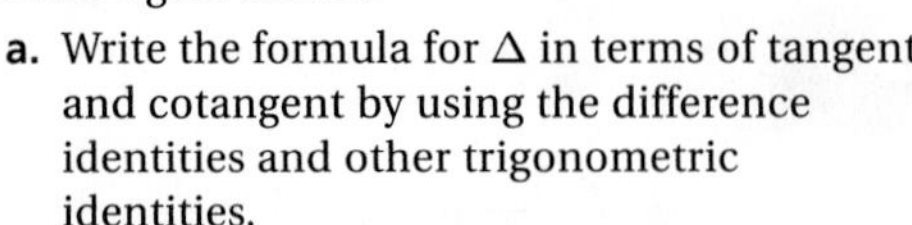

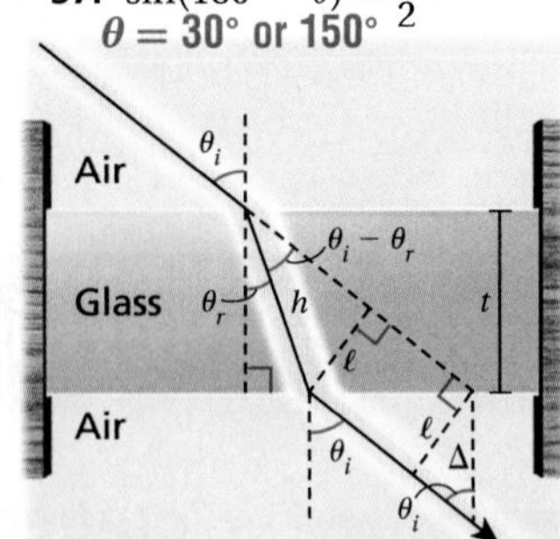

a. Write the formula for Δ in terms of tangent and cotangent by using the difference identities and other trigonometric identities.

b. Use the figure to write a ratio for $\sin(\theta_i - \theta_r)$. $\sin(\theta_i - \theta_r) = \frac{\ell}{h}$

Multi-Step Find $\tan(A + B)$, $\cos(A + B)$, and $\sin(A - B)$ for each situation.

39. $\sin A = -\frac{7}{25}$ with $180° < A < 270°$ and $\cos B = \frac{12}{13}$ with $0° < B < 90°$

40. $\sin A = -\frac{1}{3}$ with $270° < A < 360°$ and $\sin B = \frac{4}{5}$ with $0° < B < 90°$

41. The figure *PQRS* will be rotated about the origin repeatedly to create the logo for a new product.

a. Write the rotation matrices for 90°, 180°, and 270° rotations.

b. Use your answers to part **a** to find the coordinates of the vertices of the figure after each of the three rotations.

c. Graph the three rotations on the same graph as *PQRS* to create the logo.

y
4
2
Q(1, 1)
P(0, 0)
x
−4
−2
0
R(4, 0)
−2
S(1, −1)
−4

42. **Critical Thinking** Is it possible to find the exact value of $\sin\left(\frac{11\pi}{24}\right)$ by using sum or difference identities? Explain.

MULTI-STEP TEST PREP

43. This problem will prepare you for the Multi-Step Test Prep on page 1034.

The displacement y of a mass attached to a spring is modeled by $y(t) = 4.2\sin\left(\frac{2\pi}{3}t - \frac{\pi}{2}\right)$, where t is the time in seconds.

a. What are the amplitude and period of the function? 4.2; 3

b. Use a trigonometric identity to write the displacement, using only the cosine function. $y(t) = -4.2\cos\frac{2\pi}{3}t$

c. What is the displacement of the mass when $t = 8$ s? 2.1

14-4 PRACTICE A
14-4 PRACTICE C
14-4 PRACTICE B

Find the exact value of each expression.

1. $\cos 120°$ $-\frac{1}{2}$
2. $\sin 315°$ $-\frac{\sqrt{2}}{2}$
3. $\tan 255°$ $2+\sqrt{3}$
4. $\tan\frac{7\pi}{6}$ $\frac{\sqrt{3}}{3}$
5. $\sin\frac{\pi}{12}$ $\frac{\sqrt{6}-\sqrt{2}}{4}$
6. $\cos\frac{3\pi}{4}$ $-\frac{\sqrt{2}}{2}$

Prove each identity.

7. $\sin\left(x - \frac{3\pi}{2}\right) = \cos x$

$\sin\left(x - \frac{3\pi}{2}\right) = \cos x$;
$\sin x \cos\left(\frac{3\pi}{2}\right) - \sin\left(\frac{3\pi}{2}\right)\cos x = \cos x$
$\sin x \bullet 0 - (-1)\cos x = \cos x$;
$\cos x = \cos x$

8. $\cos\left(x - \frac{\pi}{2}\right) = \sin x$

$\cos\left(x - \frac{\pi}{2}\right) = \sin x$
$\cos x \cos\left(\frac{\pi}{2}\right) + \sin x \sin\left(\frac{\pi}{2}\right) = \sin x$
$\cos x \bullet 0 + \sin x \bullet 1 = \sin x$
$\sin x = \sin x$

Find each value if $\cos A = \frac{12}{13}$ with $0° \le A \le 90°$ and if $\sin B = \frac{8}{17}$ with $90° \le B \le 180°$.

9. $\sin(A + B)$ $\frac{21}{221}$
10. $\cos(A + B)$ $-\frac{220}{221}$
11. $\tan(A + B)$ $-\frac{21}{220}$
12. $\sin(A - B)$ $-\frac{171}{221}$
13. $\cos(A - B)$ $-\frac{140}{221}$
14. $\tan(A - B)$ $\frac{171}{140}$

Solve.

15. Find the coordinates, to the nearest hundredth, of the vertices of triangle *ABC* with $A(1, 0)$, $B(10, 0)$, and $C(2, 6)$ after a 60° rotation about the origin.

a. Write the matrices for the rotation and for the points. $\begin{bmatrix} \cos 60° & -\sin 60° \\ \sin 60° & \cos 60° \end{bmatrix}\begin{bmatrix} 1 & 10 & 2 \\ 0 & 0 & 6 \end{bmatrix}$

b. Find the matrix product. $\begin{bmatrix} 0.50 & 5.00 & -4.20 \\ 0.87 & 8.66 & 4.73 \end{bmatrix}$

c. Write the coordinates. $A'(0.50, 0.87)$, $B'(5, 8.66)$, $C'(-4.2, 4.73)$

16. A hill rises from the horizontal at a 15° angle. The road leading straight up the hill is 800 meters long. How much higher is the top of the hill than the base of the hill? 207 m

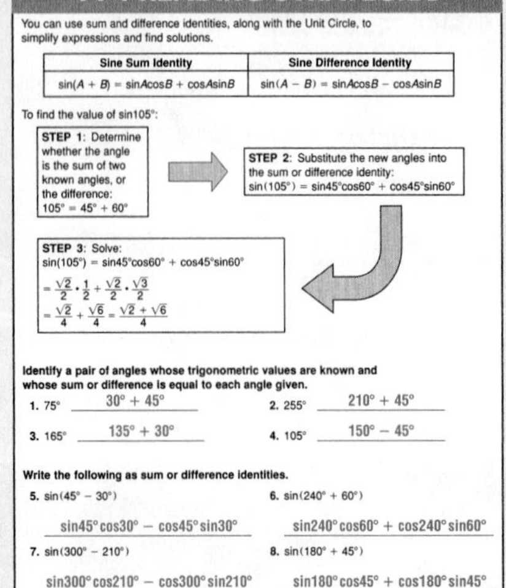

14-4 READING STRATEGIES

You can use sum and difference identities, along with the Unit Circle, to simplify expressions and find solutions.

Sine Sum Identity	Sine Difference Identity
$\sin(A + B) = \sin A\cos B + \cos A\sin B$	$\sin(A - B) = \sin A\cos B - \cos A\sin B$

To find the value of $\sin 105°$:

STEP 1: Determine whether the angle is the sum of two known angles, or the difference: $105° = 45° + 60°$

STEP 2: Substitute the new angles into the sum or difference identity: $\sin(105°) = \sin 45°\cos 60° + \cos 45°\sin 60°$

STEP 3: Solve: $\sin(105°) = \sin 45°\cos 60° + \cos 45°\sin 60°$
$= \frac{\sqrt{2}}{2}\cdot\frac{1}{2} + \frac{\sqrt{2}}{2}\cdot\frac{\sqrt{3}}{2}$
$= \frac{\sqrt{2}}{4} + \frac{\sqrt{6}}{4} = \frac{\sqrt{2}+\sqrt{6}}{4}$

Identify a pair of angles whose trigonometric values are known and whose sum or difference is equal to each angle given.

1. 75° $30° + 45°$
2. 255° $210° + 45°$
3. 165° $135° + 30°$
4. 105° $150° - 45°$

Write the following as sum or difference identities.

5. $\sin(45° - 30°)$ $\sin 45°\cos 30° - \cos 45°\sin 30°$
6. $\sin(240° + 60°)$ $\sin 240°\cos 60° + \cos 240°\sin 60°$
7. $\sin(300° - 210°)$ $\sin 300°\cos 210° - \cos 300°\sin 210°$
8. $\sin(180° + 45°)$ $\sin 180°\cos 45° + \cos 180°\sin 45°$
9. $\sin(90° - 60°)$ $\sin 90°\cos 60° - \cos 90°\sin 60°$
10. $\sin(225° - 135°)$ $\sin 225°\cos 135° - \cos 225°\sin 135°$

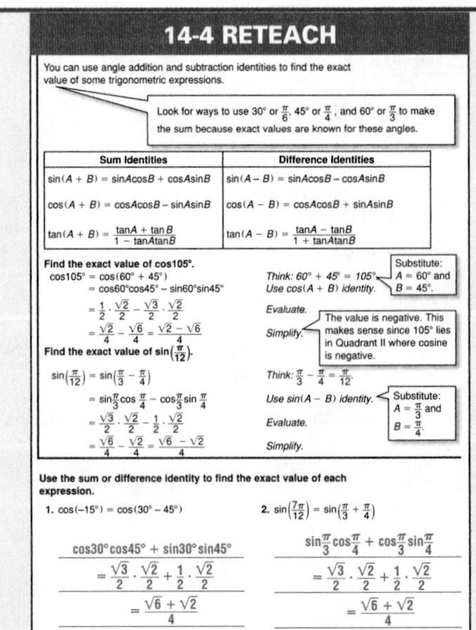

14-4 RETEACH

You can use angle addition and subtraction identities to find the exact value of some trigonometric expressions.

Look for ways to use 30° or $\frac{\pi}{6}$, 45° or $\frac{\pi}{4}$, and 60° or $\frac{\pi}{3}$ to make the sum because exact values are known for these angles.

Sum Identities	Difference Identities
$\sin(A + B) = \sin A\cos B + \cos A\sin B$	$\sin(A - B) = \sin A\cos B - \cos A\sin B$
$\cos(A + B) = \cos A\cos B - \sin A\sin B$	$\cos(A - B) = \cos A\cos B + \sin A\sin B$
$\tan(A + B) = \frac{\tan A + \tan B}{1 - \tan A\tan B}$	$\tan(A - B) = \frac{\tan A - \tan B}{1 + \tan A\tan B}$

Find the exact value of $\cos 105°$.

$\cos 105° = \cos(60° + 45°)$ — *Think: $60° + 45° = 105°$.* Substitute: $A = 60°$ and $B = 45°$.
$= \cos 60°\cos 45° - \sin 60°\sin 45°$ — *Use $\cos(A + B)$ identity.*
$= \frac{1}{2}\cdot\frac{\sqrt{2}}{2} - \frac{\sqrt{3}}{2}\cdot\frac{\sqrt{2}}{2}$ — *Evaluate.*
$= \frac{\sqrt{2}}{4} - \frac{\sqrt{6}}{4} = \frac{\sqrt{2}-\sqrt{6}}{4}$ — *Simplify.* The value is negative. This makes sense since 105° lies in Quadrant II where cosine is negative.

Find the exact value of $\sin\left(\frac{\pi}{12}\right)$.

$\sin\left(\frac{\pi}{12}\right) = \sin\left(\frac{\pi}{3} - \frac{\pi}{4}\right)$ — *Think: $\frac{\pi}{3} - \frac{\pi}{4} = \frac{\pi}{12}$.*
$= \sin\frac{\pi}{3}\cos\frac{\pi}{4} - \cos\frac{\pi}{3}\sin\frac{\pi}{4}$ — *Use $\sin(A - B)$ identity.* Substitute: $A = \frac{\pi}{3}$ and $B = \frac{\pi}{4}$.
$= \frac{\sqrt{3}}{2}\cdot\frac{\sqrt{2}}{2} - \frac{1}{2}\cdot\frac{\sqrt{2}}{2}$ — *Evaluate.*
$= \frac{\sqrt{6}}{4} - \frac{\sqrt{2}}{4} = \frac{\sqrt{6}-\sqrt{2}}{4}$ — *Simplify.*

Use the sum or difference identity to find the exact value of each expression.

1. $\cos(-15°) = \cos(30° - 45°)$
$\cos 30°\cos 45° + \sin 30°\sin 45°$
$= \frac{\sqrt{3}}{2}\cdot\frac{\sqrt{2}}{2} + \frac{1}{2}\cdot\frac{\sqrt{2}}{2}$
$= \frac{\sqrt{6}+\sqrt{2}}{4}$

2. $\sin\left(\frac{7\pi}{12}\right) = \sin\left(\frac{\pi}{3} + \frac{\pi}{4}\right)$
$\sin\frac{\pi}{3}\cos\frac{\pi}{4} + \cos\frac{\pi}{3}\sin\frac{\pi}{4}$
$= \frac{\sqrt{3}}{2}\cdot\frac{\sqrt{2}}{2} + \frac{1}{2}\cdot\frac{\sqrt{2}}{2}$
$= \frac{\sqrt{6}+\sqrt{2}}{4}$

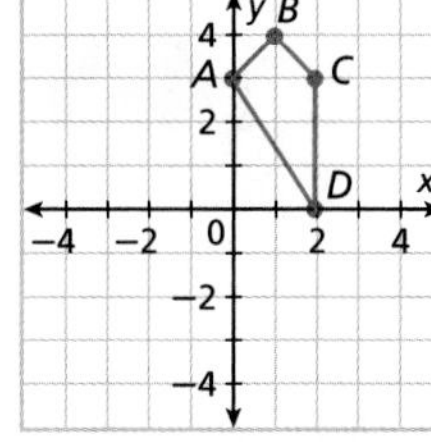

Geometry Find the coordinates, to the nearest hundredth, of the vertices of figure $ABCD$ with $A(0, 3)$, $B(1, 4)$, $C(2, 3)$, and $D(2, 0)$ after each rotation about the origin.

44. 45° **45.** 60°

46. 120° **47.** −30°

48. Write About It In general, does $\sin(A + B) = \sin A + \sin B$? Give an example to support your response.

TEST PREP

49. Which is the value of $\cos 15° \cos 45° - \sin 15° \sin 45°$?

(A) $\frac{1}{2}$ (B) $\frac{\sqrt{2}}{2}$ (C) $-\frac{\sqrt{2}}{2}$ (D) $\frac{2+\sqrt{2}}{2}$

50. Which gives the value for x if $\sin\left(\frac{\pi}{2} + x\right) = \frac{1}{2}$?

(F) $\frac{\pi}{6}$ (G) $\frac{\pi}{4}$ (H) $\frac{\pi}{3}$ (J) $\frac{\pi}{2}$

51. Given $\sin A = \frac{1}{2}$ with $0° < A < 90°$ and $\cos B = \frac{3}{5}$ with $0° < B < 90°$, which expression gives the value of $\cos(A - B)$?

(A) $\frac{3\sqrt{3}+4}{10}$ (B) $\frac{3\sqrt{3}-4}{10}$ (C) $\frac{3+4\sqrt{3}}{10}$ (D) $\frac{3-4\sqrt{3}}{10}$

52. Short Response Find the exact value for $\sin(-15°)$. Show your work.

CHALLENGE AND EXTEND

53. Verify that the rotation matrix for θ is the inverse of the rotation matrix for $-\theta$.

54. Derive the identity for $\tan(A + B)$.

55. Derive the rotation matrix by using the sum identities for sine and cosine and recalling from Lesson 13-2 that any point $P(x, y)$ can be represented as $(r\cos\alpha, r\sin\alpha)$ by using a reference angle.

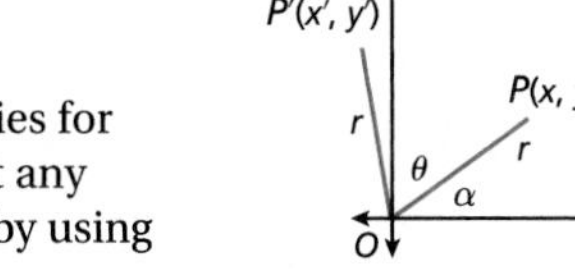

Find the angle by which a figure ABC with vertices $A(1, 0)$, $B(0, 2)$, and $C(-1, 0)$ was rotated to get $A'B'C'$.

56. $A'(0, 1)$, $B'(-2, 0)$, $C'(0, -1)$ **90°**

57. $A'\left(\frac{\sqrt{2}}{2}, \frac{\sqrt{2}}{2}\right)$, $B'(-\sqrt{2}, 2)$, $C'\left(-\frac{\sqrt{2}}{2}, -\frac{\sqrt{2}}{2}\right)$ **45°**

58. $A'(-1, 0)$, $B'(0, -2)$, $C'(1, 0)$ **180°**

59. $A'\left(\frac{\sqrt{3}}{2}, \frac{1}{2}\right)$, $B'(-1, \sqrt{3})$, $C'\left(-\frac{\sqrt{3}}{2}, -\frac{1}{2}\right)$ **30°**

SPIRAL REVIEW

Divide. Assume that all expressions are defined. *(Lesson 8-2)*

60. $\frac{3x^2}{7y^3} \div \frac{6x}{21y}$ $\mathbf{\frac{3x}{2y^2}}$

61. $\frac{x^2+x-2}{x^2-2x-8} \div \frac{x^2+3x+2}{x^2-3x-4}$ $\mathbf{\frac{x-1}{x+2}}$

62. $\frac{9x^3y^2}{15xy^4} \div \frac{6x^4y}{3x^2y^5}$ $\mathbf{\frac{3y^2}{10}}$

Identify the conic section that each equation represents. *(Lesson 10-6)*

63. $x^2 + 2xy + y^2 + 12x - 25 = 0$ **parabola**

64. $5x^2 + 5y^2 + 20x - 15y = 0$ **circle**

Rewrite each expression in terms of a single trigonometric function. *(Lesson 14-3)*

65. $\frac{\cot\theta\sec\theta}{\sin\theta\cos\theta}$

66. $\cot\theta\tan\theta\csc\theta$ $\mathbf{\csc\theta}$

67. $\frac{\tan\theta}{\sec\theta}\sin\theta$ $\mathbf{\sin^2\theta}$

65. $\mathbf{\frac{1}{\cos\theta - \cos^3\theta}}$

TEST PREP DOCTOR Students having difficulty with **Exercise 49** should condense the expression into $\cos(15° + 45°)$ rather than evaluating $\cos 15°$ and $\sin 15°$.

Students having difficulty with **Exercise 50** may wish to refer to the unit circle as a guide. If $\sin\left(\frac{\pi}{2} + x\right) = \frac{1}{2}$, then $\frac{\pi}{2} + x = \frac{5\pi}{6}$.

Answers

44–48, 52–55. See p. A53.

Journal

Have students explain how the sum formulas can be used to show that adding 360° has no effect on the values of sine, cosine, or tangent.

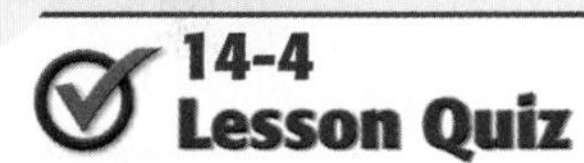

ALTERNATIVE ASSESSMENT

Have students create their own quiz modeled after the one below, and have them supply complete answers. The quiz should use sine, cosine, and tangent formulas.

Power Presentations with PowerPoint®

14-4 Lesson Quiz

1. Find the exact value of $\cos 75°$.
$\frac{\sqrt{6}-\sqrt{2}}{4}$

2. Prove the identity $\sin\left(\frac{\pi}{2} - \theta\right) = \cos\theta$.
$= \sin\frac{\pi}{2}\cos\theta - \cos\frac{\pi}{2}\sin\theta$
$= \cos\theta - 0 = \cos\theta$

3. Find $\tan(A - B)$ for $\sin A = \frac{12}{13}$ with $0 < A < \frac{\pi}{2}$ and $\cos B = \frac{8}{17}$ with $0 < B < \frac{\pi}{2}$.
$\frac{21}{220}$

4. Find the coordinates to the nearest hundredth of the point $(3, 4)$ after a 60° rotation about the origin.
$\approx \begin{bmatrix} -1.96 \\ 4.60 \end{bmatrix}$

Also available on transparency

14-4 PROBLEM SOLVING

Caitlin is designing a rotating graphic for her website. She explores what it will look like if it flashes in different positions.

1. Use rotation matrices to find the coordinates of the figure $PQRS$ after a 60° rotation about the origin.

a. Write matrices for a 60° rotation and for the points P, Q, R, and S in the figure.

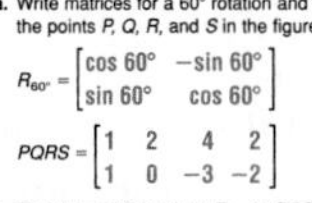

$R_{60°} = \begin{bmatrix} \cos 60° & -\sin 60° \\ \sin 60° & \cos 60° \end{bmatrix}$

$PQRS = \begin{bmatrix} 1 & 2 & 4 & 2 \\ 1 & 0 & -3 & -2 \end{bmatrix}$

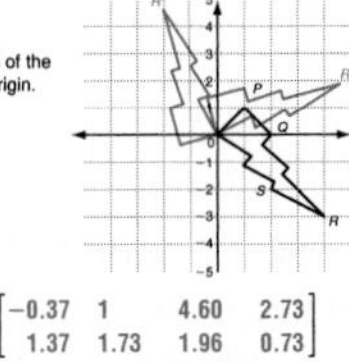

b. Find the matrix product. $R_{60°} \times PQRS \approx \begin{bmatrix} -0.37 & 1 & 4.60 & 2.73 \\ 1.37 & 1.73 & 1.96 & 0.73 \end{bmatrix}$

c. Name the coordinates of P', Q', R', S' to the nearest hundredth after a 60° rotation.
$P'(-0.37, 1.37)$, $Q'(1, 1.73)$, $R'(4.60, 1.96)$, and $S'(2.73, 0.73)$

2. a. Write the matrix product that gives the coordinates of the figure after a rotation of 150°.
$R_{150°} \times PQRS = \begin{bmatrix} -1.37 & -1.73 & -1.96 & -0.73 \\ -0.37 & 1 & 4.60 & 2.73 \end{bmatrix}$

b. Name the coordinates of $P''Q''R''S''$ to the nearest hundredth.
$P''(-1.37, -0.37)$, $Q''(-1.73, 1)$, $R''(-1.96, 4.60)$, and $S''(-0.73, 2.73)$

3. Graph the two rotations on the plane above to see where Caitlin's rotating graphic will flash. Label R' and R''.

Choose the letter for the best answer.

4. Which expression gives the exact value of $\sin 150°$?
(A) $\sin 90°\cos 60° + \cos 90°\sin 60°$
B $\sin 90°\cos 60° - \cos 90°\sin 60°$
C $\cos 180°\cos 30° + \sin 180°\sin 30°$
D $\cos 180°\cos 30° - \sin 180°\sin 30°$

5. What is the exact value of $\cos 75°$?
F $\frac{\sqrt{2}-\sqrt{6}}{2}$
G $\frac{\sqrt{6}+\sqrt{2}}{4}$
(H) $\frac{\sqrt{6}-\sqrt{2}}{4}$
J $\frac{\sqrt{6}+\sqrt{2}}{2}$

14-4 CHALLENGE

The diagram at right provides a geometric proof of the trigonometric identity $\sin(x + y) = \sin x\cos y + \cos x\sin y$. Angles x and y are located at the origin with angle y in standard position and the initial side of angle x located on the terminal side of angle y. The circle has $r = 1$. All other sides of the triangle are marked.

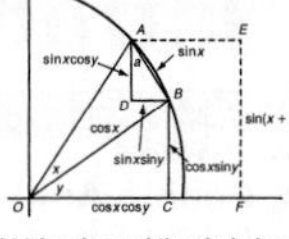

1. Using the properties of right triangles and the definitions of the trigonometric functions, justify the lengths of the sides of triangles AOB and BOC.
Possible answer: Since the triangles are right triangles and the circle has a radius of 1, the length of the side opposite angle x is $\sin x$ and the length of the adjacent side is $\cos x$. In the right triangle with angle y, the length of the hypotenuse is $\cos x$ so the length of the side opposite angle y is $\cos x\sin y$ and the adjacent side is $\cos x\cos y$.

2. Prove that angle a in triangle ABD is equal in measure to angle y.
Possible answer: $m\angle OAD + a = 90° - x$; $x + y = 90° - m\angle OAD$; so $a = 90° - x - m\angle OAD$ and $y = 90° - m\angle OAD - x$; therefore, $a = y$.

3. Using the properties of right triangles and the definitions of the trigonometric functions, justify the lengths of the sides of triangle ABD.
Possible answer: Triangle ABD is a right triangle, therefore, $AD = AB\cos a$ and $BD = AB\sin a$. But $AB = \sin x$ and $a = y$, so $AD = \sin x\cos y$ and $BD = \sin x\sin y$.

4. Now prove the identity for the sine of a sum, $\sin(x + y) = \sin x\cos y + \cos x\sin y$.
Possible answer: In right triangle OBC, $OB = \cos x$ and $BC = OB\sin y = \cos x\sin y$. From the diagram, it is clear why the length EF is, as the label indicates, equal to $\sin(x + y)$. But $EF = AD + BC$. Substitution of the expressions for EF, AD, and BC gives $\sin(x + y) = \sin x\cos y + \cos x\sin y$.

5. Use this information to prove the sum identity for cosines, $\cos(x + y) = \cos x\cos y - \sin x\sin y$.
Possible answer: Extend segment AD to intersect segment OC at a point P. The segment AP will be perpendicular to segment OC so it follows that $OP = \cos(x + y)$. But $OP + PC = OC$, and hence $OP = OC - PC$. Since $OC = \cos x\cos y$ and $PC = BD = \sin x\sin y$, it follows that $\cos(x + y) = \cos x\cos y - \sin x\sin y$.

14-5 Organizer

Pacing: Traditional 1 day
Block $\frac{1}{2}$ day

Objectives: Evaluate and simplify expressions by using double-angle and half-angle identities.

Online Edition
Tutorial Videos

Power Presentations with PowerPoint®

Warm Up

Find $\tan\theta$ for $0 \le \theta \le 90°$, if

1. $\sin\theta = \frac{3}{5}$. $\tan\theta = \frac{3}{4}$
2. $\sin\theta = \frac{1}{3}$. $\tan\theta = \frac{\sqrt{2}}{4}$
3. $\cos\theta = x$. $\tan\theta = \frac{\sqrt{1-x^2}}{x}$

Also available on transparency

Math Humor

Teacher: Why is your answer $\sin\frac{\theta}{2}$ when the problem asks for $\sin 2\theta$?

Student: I guess it's a case of mistaken identity.

14-5 Double-Angle and Half-Angle Identities

Objective
Evaluate and simplify expressions by using double-angle and half-angle identities.

Who uses this?
Double-angle formulas can be used to find the horizontal distance for a projectile such as a golf ball. (See Exercise 49.)

You can use sum identities to derive the *double-angle identities.*

$$\sin 2\theta = \sin(\theta + \theta)$$
$$= \sin\theta\cos\theta + \cos\theta\sin\theta$$
$$= 2\sin\theta\cos\theta$$

You can derive the double-angle identities for cosine and tangent in the same way. There are three forms of the identity for $\cos 2\theta$, which are derived by using $\sin^2\theta + \cos^2\theta = 1$. It is common to rewrite expressions as functions of θ only.

Know it! Note

Double-Angle Identities		
$\sin 2\theta = 2\sin\theta\cos\theta$	$\cos 2\theta = \cos^2\theta - \sin^2\theta$ $\cos 2\theta = 2\cos^2\theta - 1$ $\cos 2\theta = 1 - 2\sin^2\theta$	$\tan 2\theta = \frac{2\tan\theta}{1-\tan^2\theta}$

EXAMPLE 1 Evaluating Expressions with Double-Angle Identities

Find $\sin 2\theta$ and $\cos 2\theta$ if $\cos\theta = -\frac{3}{4}$ and $90° < \theta < 180°$.

Step 1 Find $\sin\theta$ to evaluate $\sin 2\theta = 2\sin\theta\cos\theta$.

Method 1 Use the reference angle.

In QII, $90° < \theta < 180°$, and $\cos\theta = -\frac{3}{4}$.

$(-3)^2 + y^2 = 4^2$ *Use the Pythagorean Theorem.*

$y = \sqrt{16-9} = \sqrt{7}$ *Solve for y.*

$\sin\theta = \frac{\sqrt{7}}{4}$

r = 4
y
θ
x = −3

Method 2 Solve $\sin^2\theta = 1 - \cos^2\theta$.

$\sin^2\theta = 1 - \cos^2\theta$

$\sin\theta = \sqrt{1 - \left(-\frac{3}{4}\right)^2}$ *Substitute $-\frac{3}{4}$ for cosθ.*

$= \sqrt{1 - \frac{9}{16}} = \frac{\sqrt{7}}{4}$ *Simplify.*

$\sin\theta = \frac{\sqrt{7}}{4}$

Caution!
The signs of *x* and *y* depend on the quadrant for angle θ.

	sin	cos
QI	+	+
QII	+	−
QIII	−	−
QIV	−	+

State Resources

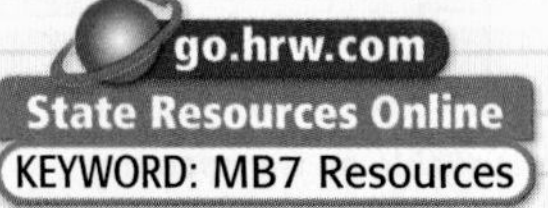

1 Introduce

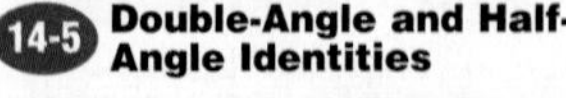

14-5 Double-Angle and Half-Angle Identities

It is often useful to rewrite trigonometric expressions involving 2θ in terms of θ only. You can use your calculator to develop an identity for sin 2θ.

1. In each row of the table, the measure of angle θ is given. Use your calculator to find sin 2θ and sin θ cos θ. Round each value to the nearest thousandth if necessary.

θ	sin 2θ	sin θ cos θ
10°		
30°		
65°		
80°		
150°		

2. Look for a pattern in the table. How is sin 2θ related to sin θ cos θ?
3. Write an identity based on your findings.

THINK AND DISCUSS

4. **Explain** how you could use a graph or table to verify the identity you discovered.
5. **Describe** what happens when θ = 45° in the identity.

Motivate

Ask students how they might find the exact value of sin 22.5°. Giving exact trigonometric function values for angles other than those on the unit circle may be necessary sometimes. In addition to using sum and difference identities, you can use the double-angle and half-angle identities.

Explorations and answers are provided in the *Explorations* binder.

Step 2 Find $\sin 2\theta$.

$\sin 2\theta = 2\sin\theta\cos\theta$	*Apply the identity for $\sin 2\theta$.*
$= 2\left(\frac{\sqrt{7}}{4}\right)\left(-\frac{3}{4}\right)$	*Substitute $\frac{\sqrt{7}}{2}$ for $\sin\theta$ and $-\frac{3}{4}$ for $\cos\theta$.*
$= -\frac{3\sqrt{7}}{8}$	*Simplify.*

Step 3 Find $\cos 2\theta$.

$\cos 2\theta = 2\cos^2\theta - 1$	*Select a double-angle identity.*
$= 2\left(-\frac{3}{4}\right)^2 - 1$	*Substitute $-\frac{3}{4}$ for $\cos\theta$.*
$= 2\left(\frac{9}{16}\right) - 1$	*Simplify.*
$= \frac{1}{8}$	

1. Find $\tan 2\theta$ and $\cos 2\theta$ if $\cos\theta = \frac{1}{3}$ and $270° < \theta < 360°$. $\frac{4\sqrt{2}}{7}$; $-\frac{7}{9}$

You can use double-angle identities to prove trigonometric identities.

EXAMPLE 2 Proving Identities with Double-Angle Identities

Prove each identity.

A $\sin^2\theta = \frac{1}{2}(1 - \cos 2\theta)$

$\sin^2\theta = \frac{1}{2}(1 - \cos 2\theta)$	*Choose the right-hand side to modify.*
$= \frac{1}{2}\left(1 - \left(1 - 2\sin^2\theta\right)\right)$	*Apply the identity for $\cos 2\theta$.*
$= \frac{1}{2}\left(2\sin^2\theta\right)$	*Simplify.*
$\sin^2\theta = \sin^2\theta$	

B $(\cos\theta + \sin\theta)^2 = 1 + \sin 2\theta$

$(\cos\theta + \sin\theta)^2 = 1 + \sin 2\theta$	*Choose the left-hand side to modify.*
$\cos^2\theta + 2\cos\theta\sin\theta + \sin^2\theta =$	*Expand the square.*
$(\cos^2\theta + \sin^2\theta) + (2\cos\theta\sin\theta) =$	*Regroup.*
$1 + \sin 2\theta =$	*Rewrite using $1 = \cos^2\theta + \sin^2\theta$ and $\sin 2\theta = 2\sin\theta\cos\theta$.*
$1 + \sin 2\theta = 1 + \sin 2\theta$	

Helpful Hint

Choose to modify either the left side or the right side of an identity. Do not work on both sides at once.

Prove each identity.

2a. $\cos^4\theta - \sin^4\theta = \cos 2\theta$ **2b.** $\sin 2\theta = \frac{2\tan\theta}{1 + \tan^2\theta}$

2b. Possible answer:

$$\frac{2\tan\theta}{1+\tan^2\theta} = \frac{2\left(\frac{\sin\theta}{\cos\theta}\right)}{\sec^2\theta} = \frac{2\left(\frac{\sin\theta}{\cos\theta}\right)}{\frac{1}{\cos^2\theta}} \cdot \frac{\left(\frac{\cos^2\theta}{1}\right)}{\left(\frac{\cos^2\theta}{1}\right)} = 2\left(\frac{\sin\theta}{\cos\theta}\right)\left(\frac{\cos^2\theta}{1}\right) = 2\sin\theta\cos\theta = \sin 2\theta$$

You can use double-angle identities for cosine to derive the *half-angle identities* by substituting $\frac{\theta}{2}$ for θ. For example, $\cos 2\theta = 2\cos^2\theta - 1$ can be rewritten as $\cos\theta = 2\cos^2\frac{\theta}{2} - 1$. Then solve for $\cos\frac{\theta}{2}$.

COMMON ERROR ALERT

Students may consider $\sin 2\theta$ to be a function of only θ. Although θ is the only variable, the intent of the rewriting is to move the constants away from θ.

Power Presentations with PowerPoint®

Additional Examples

Example 1

Find $\sin 2\theta$ and $\tan 2\theta$ if $\sin\theta = \frac{2}{5}$ and $0° < \theta < 90°$.

$\frac{4\sqrt{21}}{25}$; $\frac{4\sqrt{21}}{17}$

Example 2

Prove each identity.

A. $\sin 2\theta = 2\tan\theta - 2\tan\theta\sin^2\theta$
$= 2\tan\theta\left(1 - \sin^2\theta\right)$
$= 2\tan\theta\cos^2\theta$
$= 2\left(\tan\theta\cos\theta\right)\cos\theta$
$= 2\sin\theta\cos\theta$
$= \sin 2\theta$

B. $\cos 2\theta = \left(2 - \sec^2\theta\right)\left(1 - \sin^2\theta\right)$
$= \left(2 - \sec^2\theta\right)\left(\cos^2\theta\right)$
$= 2\cos^2\theta - 1$
$= \cos 2\theta$

Also available on transparency

INTERVENTION
Questioning Strategies

EXAMPLE 1

- When will the signs for sine, cosine, and tangent of 2θ be the same as the signs for sine, cosine, and tangent of θ?

EXAMPLE 2

- How do you decide what to do first when proving an identity?

2 Teach

Guided Instruction

Introduce the half-angle and double-angle identities. To help students identify the value of θ, encourage them to set up simple equations for each problem, such as $\frac{\theta}{2} = 120°$, or $2\theta = 120°$.

Reaching All Learners
Through Critical Thinking

Have students show that the double-angle identities are special cases of the angle sum and difference identities from Lesson 14-4. For example, begin with $\sin(2\theta) = \sin(\theta + \theta)$ to derive the double-angle identity for sine.

Answers to *Check It Out!*

2a. Possible answer:

$\cos^4\theta - \sin^4\theta$
$= \left(\cos^2\theta + \sin^2\theta\right)\left(\cos^2\theta - \sin^2\theta\right)$
$= (1)(\cos 2\theta)$
$= \cos 2\theta$

Power Presentations with PowerPoint®

Additional Examples

Example 3

Use half-angle identities to find the exact value of each trigonometric expression.

A. $\cos 15°$ $\quad \dfrac{\sqrt{\sqrt{3}+2}}{2}$

B. $\tan\dfrac{7\pi}{8}$ $\quad -\sqrt{3-2\sqrt{2}}$

Example 4

Find $\cos\dfrac{\theta}{2}$ and $\tan\dfrac{\theta}{2}$ if $\tan\theta = \dfrac{7}{24}$ and $0 < \theta < \dfrac{\pi}{2}$.

$\dfrac{7\sqrt{2}}{10}$; $\dfrac{1}{7}$

Also available on transparency

INTERVENTION

Questioning Strategies

EXAMPLE 3

- How do you decide which sign to select when evaluating an expression by using the half-angle identity?

EXAMPLE 4

- What is the connection between the half-angle formulas and the corresponding difference formulas from Lesson 14-4?

Half-Angle Identities

$\sin\dfrac{\theta}{2} = \pm\sqrt{\dfrac{1-\cos\theta}{2}}$	$\cos\dfrac{\theta}{2} = \pm\sqrt{\dfrac{1+\cos\theta}{2}}$	$\tan\dfrac{\theta}{2} = \pm\sqrt{\dfrac{1-\cos\theta}{1+\cos\theta}}$

Choose + or − depending on the location of $\frac{\theta}{2}$.

Half-angle identities are useful in calculating exact values for trigonometric expressions.

EXAMPLE 3 Evaluating Expressions with Half-Angle Identities

Use half-angle identities to find the exact value of each trigonometric expression.

A $\cos 165°$

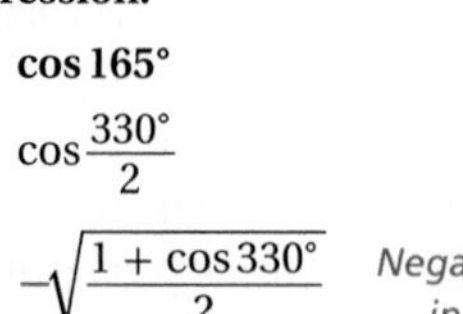

$\cos\dfrac{330°}{2}$

$-\sqrt{\dfrac{1+\cos 330°}{2}}$ *Negative in QII*

$-\sqrt{\dfrac{1+\left(\frac{\sqrt{3}}{2}\right)}{2}}$ $\quad \cos 330° = \dfrac{\sqrt{3}}{2}$

$-\sqrt{\left(\dfrac{2+\sqrt{3}}{2}\right)\left(\dfrac{1}{2}\right)}$ *Simplify.*

$-\dfrac{\sqrt{2+\sqrt{3}}}{2}$

Check Use your calculator.

B $\sin\dfrac{\pi}{8}$

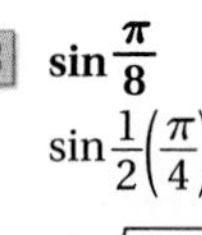

$\sin\dfrac{1}{2}\left(\dfrac{\pi}{4}\right)$

$+\sqrt{\dfrac{1-\cos\left(\frac{\pi}{4}\right)}{2}}$ *Positive in QI*

$\sqrt{\dfrac{1-\frac{\sqrt{2}}{2}}{2}}$ $\quad \cos\dfrac{\pi}{4} = \dfrac{\sqrt{2}}{2}$

$\sqrt{\left(\dfrac{2-\sqrt{2}}{2}\right)\left(\dfrac{1}{2}\right)}$ *Simplify.*

$\dfrac{\sqrt{2-\sqrt{2}}}{2}$

Check Use your calculator.

Reading Math

In Example 3, the expressions $-\dfrac{\sqrt{2+\sqrt{3}}}{2}$ and $\dfrac{\sqrt{2-\sqrt{2}}}{2}$ are in reduced form and cannot be simplified further.

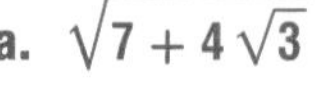

3a. $\sqrt{7+4\sqrt{3}}$

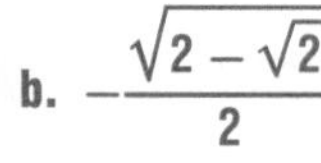

b. $-\dfrac{\sqrt{2-\sqrt{2}}}{2}$

Use half-angle identities to find the exact value of each trigonometric expression.

3a. $\tan 75°$ **3b.** $\cos\dfrac{5\pi}{8}$

EXAMPLE 4 Using the Pythagorean Theorem with Half-Angle Identities

Find $\sin\frac{\theta}{2}$ and $\tan\frac{\theta}{2}$ if $\sin\theta = -\frac{5}{13}$ and $180° < \theta < 270°$.

Step 1 Find $\cos\theta$ to evaluate the half-angle identities.

Use the reference angle.

In QIII, $180° < \theta < 270°$, and $\sin\theta = -\frac{5}{13}$.

$x^2 + (-5)^2 = 13^2$ *Pythagorean Theorem*

$x = -\sqrt{169-25} = -12$ *Solve for the missing side x.*

Thus, $\cos\theta = -\dfrac{12}{13}$.

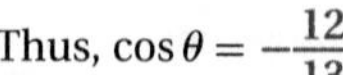

Step 2 Evaluate $\sin\frac{\theta}{2}$.

$\sin\frac{\theta}{2}$

$+\sqrt{\frac{1-\cos\theta}{2}}$ *Choose + for $\sin\frac{\theta}{2}$ where $90° < \frac{\theta}{2} < 135°$.*

$\sqrt{\frac{1-\left(-\frac{12}{13}\right)}{2}}$ *Evaluate.*

$\sqrt{\left(\frac{25}{13}\right)\left(\frac{1}{2}\right)}$ *Simplify.*

$\sqrt{\frac{25}{26}}$

$\frac{5\sqrt{26}}{26}$

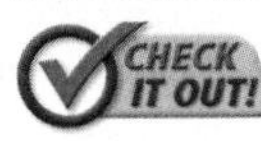

Caution!

Be careful to choose the correct sign for $\sin\frac{\theta}{2}$ and $\cos\frac{\theta}{2}$. If $180° < \theta < 270°$, then $90° < \frac{\theta}{2} < 135°$.

Step 3 Evaluate $\tan\frac{\theta}{2}$.

$\tan\frac{\theta}{2}$

$-\sqrt{\frac{1-\cos\theta}{1+\cos\theta}}$ *Choose − for $\tan\frac{\theta}{2}$ where $90° < \frac{\theta}{2} < 135°$.*

$-\sqrt{\frac{1-\left(-\frac{12}{13}\right)}{1+\left(-\frac{12}{13}\right)}}$ *Evaluate.*

$-\sqrt{\left(\frac{25}{13}\right)\left(\frac{13}{1}\right)}$ *Simplify.*

$-\sqrt{25}$

-5

CHECK IT OUT! 4. Find $\sin\frac{\theta}{2}$ and $\cos\frac{\theta}{2}$ if $\tan\theta = \frac{4}{3}$ and $0° < \theta < 90°$. $\frac{\sqrt{5}}{5}; \frac{2\sqrt{5}}{5}$

THINK AND DISCUSS

1. **EXPLAIN** which double-angle identity you would use to simplify $\frac{\cos 2\theta}{\sin\theta + \cos\theta}$.
2. **DESCRIBE** how to determine the sign of the value for $\sin\frac{\theta}{2}$ and for $\cos\frac{\theta}{2}$.

3. **GET ORGANIZED** Copy and complete the graphic organizer. In each box, write one of the identities.

COMMON ERROR ALERT

In problems such as **Example 3,** students may drop or combine the radicals. The nature of the calculations is such that the answers will often contain radicals inside of other radicals. Remind students that these expressions are in simplest form.

Teaching Tip **Math Background** To avoid confusion, you may wish to encourage students to work on only one side of an equation at a time when proving identities. However, for more organized students, it is legitimate to manipulate both sides of the identity until they are equal.

3 Close

Summarize

Expressions in terms of twice an angle or half an angle can be rewritten as expressions in terms of the angle by using double-angle and half-angle identities.

ONGOING ASSESSMENT and INTERVENTION

***Diagnose Before* the Lesson**
14-5 Warm Up, TE p. 1020

***Monitor During* the Lesson**
Check It Out! Exercises, SE pp. 1021–1023
Questioning Strategies, TE pp. 1021–1022

***Assess After* the Lesson**
14-5 Lesson Quiz, TE p. 1026
Alternative Assessment, TE p. 1026

Answers to *Think and Discuss*

Possible answers:

1. $\cos 2\theta = \cos^2\theta - \sin^2\theta$, because it can be factored into $(\cos\theta + \sin\theta)(\cos\theta - \sin\theta)$, and the factor $(\cos\theta + \sin\theta)$ can be divided out to eliminate the denominator
2. Determine the quadrant that $\frac{\theta}{2}$ lies in based on the quadrant that θ lies in, and identify the sign of sine (or cosine) in that quadrant.
3. See p. A14.

14-5 Exercises

Assignment Guide

Assign *Guided Practice* exercises as necessary.

If you finished Examples **1–2**
Basic 13–18, 29–30
Average 13–18, 29–32
Advanced 13–18, 29–32, 57

If you finished Examples **1–4**
Basic 13–24, 29–37, 48, 49, 51–56, 65–74
Average 13–37, 44–57, 65–74
Advanced 14–34 even, 35–74

Homework Quick Check
Quickly check key concepts.
Exercises: 14, 16, 18, 20, 24

Answers

3. $2\cos 2\theta = 2(2\cos^2\theta - 1)$
$= 4\cos^2\theta - 2$

4. $\sin^2\theta = 1 - \cos^2\theta$
$= 1 - \dfrac{2\cos^2\theta}{2}$
$= 1 - \dfrac{(2\cos^2\theta - 1) + 1}{2}$
$= 1 - \dfrac{\cos 2\theta + 1}{2}$

5. $\dfrac{1 + \cos 2\theta}{\sin 2\theta} = \dfrac{1 + (2\cos^2\theta - 1)}{(2\sin\theta\cos\theta)}$
$= \dfrac{2\cos^2\theta}{2\sin\theta\cos\theta}$
$= \dfrac{\cos\theta}{\sin\theta}$
$= \cot\theta$

6, 15–18. See p. A53.
27. $\cos\theta\,(1 - 4\sin^2\theta)$
28. $\sin^4\theta + \cos^4\theta - 6\sin^2\theta\cos^2\theta$

State Resources

14-5 Exercises

go.hrw.com
Homework Help Online
KEYWORD: MB7 14-5
Parent Resources Online
KEYWORD: MB7 Parent

GUIDED PRACTICE

SEE EXAMPLE 1 p. 1020

Find $\sin 2\theta$, $\cos 2\theta$, and $\tan 2\theta$ for each set of conditions.

1. $\cos\theta = -\frac{5}{13}$ and $\frac{\pi}{2} < \theta < \pi$ $\quad -\frac{120}{169}; -\frac{119}{169}; \frac{120}{119}$
2. $\sin\theta = \frac{4}{5}$ and $0° < \theta < 90°$ $\quad \frac{24}{25}; -\frac{7}{25}; -\frac{24}{7}$

SEE EXAMPLE 2 p. 1021

Prove each identity.

3. $2\cos 2\theta = 4\cos^2\theta - 2$
4. $\sin^2\theta = 1 - \frac{\cos 2\theta + 1}{2}$
5. $\frac{1 + \cos 2\theta}{\sin 2\theta} = \cot\theta$
6. $\sin 2\theta = \frac{2\tan\theta}{1 + \tan^2\theta}$

SEE EXAMPLE 3 p. 1022

Use half-angle identities to find the exact value of each trigonometric expression.

7. $\cos 67.5°$ $\quad \frac{\sqrt{2 - \sqrt{2}}}{2}$
8. $\cos\frac{\pi}{12}$ $\quad \frac{\sqrt{2 + \sqrt{3}}}{2}$
9. $\tan\frac{3\pi}{8}$ $\quad \sqrt{\frac{2 + \sqrt{2}}{2 - \sqrt{2}}}$
10. $\sin 112.5°$ $\quad \frac{\sqrt{2 + \sqrt{2}}}{2}$

SEE EXAMPLE 4 p. 1022

Find $\sin\frac{\theta}{2}$, $\cos\frac{\theta}{2}$, and $\tan\frac{\theta}{2}$ for each set of conditions.

11. $\sin\theta = -\frac{24}{25}$ and $180° < \theta < 270°$ $\quad \frac{4}{5}; -\frac{3}{5}; -\frac{4}{3}$
12. $\cos\theta = \frac{1}{4}$ and $270° < \theta < 360°$ $\quad \frac{\sqrt{6}}{4}; -\frac{\sqrt{10}}{4}; -\frac{\sqrt{15}}{5}$

PRACTICE AND PROBLEM SOLVING

Independent Practice	
For Exercises	See Example
13–14	1
15–18	2
19–22	3
23–24	4

Extra Practice
Skills Practice p. S31
Application Practice p. S45

Find $\sin 2\theta$, $\cos 2\theta$, and $\tan 2\theta$ for each set of conditions.

13. $\cos\theta = -\frac{7}{25}$ and $90° < \theta < 180°$ $\quad -\frac{336}{625}; -\frac{527}{625}; \frac{336}{527}$
14. $\tan\theta = \frac{20}{21}$ and $0 \le \theta \le \frac{\pi}{2}$ $\quad \frac{840}{841}; \frac{41}{841}; \frac{840}{41}$

Prove each identity.

15. $\frac{\sin 2\theta}{\sin\theta} = 2\cos\theta$
16. $\cos^2\theta = \frac{1}{2}(1 + \cos 2\theta)$
17. $\tan\theta = \frac{1 - \cos 2\theta}{\sin 2\theta}$
18. $\tan\theta = \frac{\sin 2\theta}{1 + \cos 2\theta}$

Use half-angle identities to find the exact value of each trigonometric expression.

19. $\sin\frac{7\pi}{12}$
20. $\cos\frac{5\pi}{12}$
21. $\sin 22.5°$
22. $\tan 15°$

19. $\frac{\sqrt{2 + \sqrt{3}}}{2}$
20. $\frac{\sqrt{2 - \sqrt{3}}}{2}$
21. $\frac{\sqrt{2 - \sqrt{2}}}{2}$
22. $\sqrt{\frac{2 - \sqrt{3}}{2 + \sqrt{3}}}$
23. $\frac{\sqrt{37}}{37}; -\frac{6\sqrt{37}}{37}; -\frac{1}{6}$

Find $\sin\frac{\theta}{2}$, $\cos\frac{\theta}{2}$, and $\tan\frac{\theta}{2}$ for each set of conditions.

24. $\frac{3\sqrt{10}}{10}; -\frac{\sqrt{10}}{10}; -3$

23. $\tan\theta = -\frac{12}{35}$ and $\frac{3\pi}{2} < \theta < 2\pi$
24. $\sin\theta = -\frac{3}{5}$ and $180° < \theta < 270°$

25. $3\sin\theta\cos^2\theta - \sin^3\theta$
26. $4\sin\theta\cos^3\theta - 4\cos\theta\sin^3\theta$

Multi-Step Rewrite each expression in terms of trigonometric functions of θ rather than multiples of θ. Then simplify.

25. $\sin 3\theta$
26. $\sin 4\theta$
27. $\cos 3\theta$
28. $\cos 4\theta$
29. $\cos 2\theta + 2\sin^2\theta$ $\quad 1$
30. $\cos 2\theta + 1$ $\quad 2\cos^2\theta$
31. $\tan 2\theta(2 - \sec^2\theta)$ $\quad 2\tan\theta$
32. $\frac{\cos 2\theta}{\cos\theta + \sin\theta}$ $\quad \cos\theta - \sin\theta$
33. $\frac{\cos\theta\sin 2\theta}{1 + \cos 2\theta}$ $\quad \sin\theta$
34. $\frac{\cos 2\theta - 1}{\sin^2\theta}$ $\quad -2$

14-5 READING STRATEGIES

You can use double-angle identities and half-angle identities to evaluate expressions and find exact values. One step is to find the sign of the functions of the angle.

Use the diagram above to determine the sign of each function of θ in each quadrant. Write + or – next to the function name.

	Quadrant I	Quadrant II	Quadrant III	Quadrant IV
1.	sin +	sin +	sin –	sin –
2.	cos +	cos –	cos –	cos +
3.	tan +	tan –	tan +	tan –

Determine the quadrant and sign of each trigonometric expression.

4. sin330° QIV, –
5. cos210° QIII, –
6. sin150° QII, +
7. tan123° QII, –
8. sin290° QIV, –
9. cos13° QI, +
10. sin194° QIII, –
11. cos359° QIV, +
12. tan275° QIV, –
13. cos178° QII, –
14. tan205° QIII, +
15. sin85° QI, +

14-5 RETEACH

There are special double-angle formulas for $\sin 2\theta$, $\cos 2\theta$, and $\tan 2\theta$.

Double-Angle Identities
$\sin 2\theta = 2\sin\theta\cos\theta$
$\cos 2\theta = \cos^2\theta - \sin^2\theta$
$\cos 2\theta = 2\cos^2\theta - 1$
$\cos 2\theta = 1 - 2\sin^2\theta$
$\tan 2\theta = \frac{2\tan\theta}{1 - \tan^2\theta}$

The double angle is twice θ, or 2θ.

There are three equivalent forms of the identity for $\cos 2\theta$. If you know one form, you can use $\sin^2\theta + \cos^2\theta = 1$ to derive the other forms.

Find $\sin 2\theta$ and $\cos 2\theta$ if $\cos\theta = -\frac{2}{3}$ and $180° < \theta < 270°$.

Notice the interval in which θ lies. Cosine and sine are both negative in Quadrant III.

Step 1 Find $\sin\theta$.
$\sin^2\theta = 1 - \cos^2\theta$ — Pythagorean identity
$\sin^2\theta = 1 - \left(-\frac{2}{3}\right)^2$ — Substitute $\cos\theta = -\frac{2}{3}$.
$\sin^2\theta = \frac{5}{9}$ — Evaluate.
$\sin\theta = -\frac{\sqrt{5}}{3}$ — Solve for $\sin\theta$.

Use the negative value since θ lies in Quadrant III.

Step 2 Find $\sin 2\theta$.
$\sin 2\theta = 2\sin\theta\cos\theta$ — Write the formula.
$\sin 2\theta = 2\left(-\frac{\sqrt{5}}{3}\right)\left(-\frac{2}{3}\right)$ — Substitute values for sine and cosine.
$\sin 2\theta = \frac{4\sqrt{5}}{9}$ — Simplify.

Step 3 Find $\cos 2\theta$.
$\cos 2\theta = 2\cos^2\theta - 1$ — Choose a formula.
$\cos 2\theta = 2\left(-\frac{2}{3}\right)^2 - 1$ — Substitute the value for $\cos\theta$.
$\cos 2\theta = \frac{8}{9} - 1 = -\frac{1}{9}$ — Simplify.

Evaluate each expression if $\cos\theta = \frac{1}{4}$ and $270° < \theta < 360°$.

1. $\sin\theta$ — Use $\sin^2\theta = 1 - \cos^2\theta$. $\quad -\frac{\sqrt{15}}{4}$
2. $\cos 2\theta$ — Use $\cos 2\theta = 1 - 2\sin^2\theta$. $\quad -\frac{7}{8}$
3. $\tan\theta$ — Use $\tan\theta = \frac{\sin\theta}{\cos\theta}$. $\quad -\sqrt{15}$
4. $\tan 2\theta$ — Use $\tan 2\theta = \frac{2\tan\theta}{1 - \tan^2\theta}$. $\quad \frac{\sqrt{15}}{7}$

35. This problem will prepare you for the Multi-Step Test Prep on page 1034.

The displacement y of a mass attached to a spring is modeled by $y(t) = 3.1\sin 2t$, where t is the time in seconds.

a. Rewrite the function by using a double-angle identity. $y(t) = 6.2\sin t\cos t$

b. The displacement w of another mass attached to a spring is given by $w(t) = 3.8\cos t$. The two masses are set in motion at $t = 0$. When do the masses have the same displacement for the first time? about 0.66 s

c. What is the displacement at this time? about 3.00 m

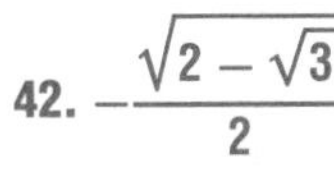

42. $-\dfrac{\sqrt{2-\sqrt{3}}}{2}$

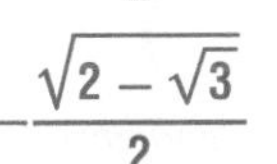

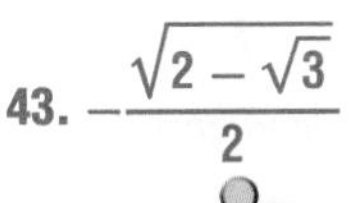

43. $-\dfrac{\sqrt{2-\sqrt{3}}}{2}$

Multi-Step Find $\sin 2\theta$, $\cos 2\theta$, $\tan 2\theta$, $\sin\frac{\theta}{2}$, $\cos\frac{\theta}{2}$, and $\tan\frac{\theta}{2}$ for each set of conditions.

36. $\cos\theta = \frac{3}{8}$ and $\frac{\pi}{2} < \theta < \pi$

37. $\cos\theta = -\frac{\sqrt{5}}{3}$ and $180° < \theta < 270°$

38. $\sin\theta = \frac{2}{5}$ and $0° < \theta < 90°$

39. $\tan\theta = -\frac{1}{2}$ and $\frac{3\pi}{2} < \theta < 2\pi$

Use half-angle identities to find the exact value of each trigonometric expression.

40. $\cos\frac{7\pi}{8}$ $\quad -\dfrac{\sqrt{2+\sqrt{2}}}{2}$

41. $\sin\frac{11\pi}{12}$ $\quad \dfrac{\sqrt{2-\sqrt{3}}}{2}$

42. $\cos 105°$

43. $\sin(-15°)$

Physics

The Tevatron at Fermi National Accelerator Lab in Batavia, Illinois, uses superconducting magnets to study subatomic particles by colliding matter and antimatter inside of a ring with a diameter of 6.3 km.

44. Physics The change in momentum of a scattered nuclear particle is given by $\Delta P = P_f - P_i$, where P_f is the final momentum, and P_i is the initial momentum.

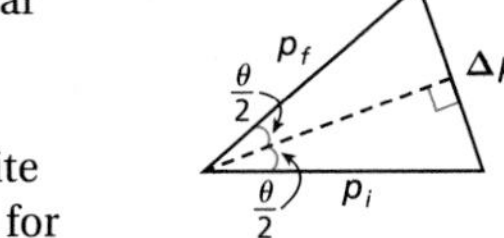

a. Use the diagram and the Pythagorean Theorem to write a formula for ΔP in terms of P_i. Then write a formula for ΔP in terms of P_f.

b. Compare your two answers to part **a.** What does this tell you about the magnitude, or size, of the momentum before and after the "collision"? It does not change.

c. Write the formula for ΔP in terms of $\cos\theta$. $\Delta P = 2P_f\sqrt{\dfrac{1-\cos\theta}{2}}$

Prove each identity.

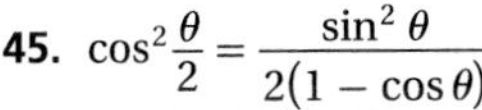

45. $\cos^2\frac{\theta}{2} = \dfrac{\sin^2\theta}{2(1-\cos\theta)}$

46. $\cos 2\theta = \dfrac{1-\tan^2\theta}{1+\tan^2\theta}$

47. $\dfrac{\tan\theta + \sin\theta}{2\tan\theta} = \cos^2\frac{\theta}{2}$

48. Graphing Calculator Graph $y = \dfrac{(\cos x)(1-\cos 2x)}{\sin 2x}$ to discover an identity. Then prove the identity.

49. Multi-Step A golf ball is hit with an initial velocity of v_0 in feet per second at an angle of elevation θ. The function $d(\theta) = \dfrac{v_0^2\sin\theta\cos\theta}{16}$ gives the horizontal distance d in feet that the ball travels.

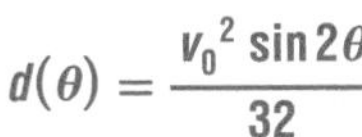

$d(\theta) = \dfrac{v_0^2\sin 2\theta}{32}$

a. Rewrite the function in terms of the double angle 2θ.

b. Calculate the horizontal distance for an initial velocity of 80 ft/s for angles of 15°, 30°, 45°, 60°, and 75°. 100 ft; ≈ 173 ft; 200 ft; ≈ 173 ft; 100 ft

c. For a given velocity, what angle gives the maximum horizontal distance? 45°

d. **What if...?** If the initial velocity is 80 ft/s, through what approximate range of angles will the ball travel horizontally at least 175 ft? $30.52° < \theta < 59.48°$

50. Critical Thinking Explain how to find the exact value for $\sin 7.5°$.

51. Write About It How do you know when to use a double-angle or a half-angle identity?

Possible answer: If θ is multiplied by 2, use a double-angle identity. If θ is divided by 2, use a half-angle identity.

Exercise 35 involves applying double-angle identities. This exercise prepares students for the Multi-Step Test Prep on page 1034.

Answers

36. $-\frac{3\sqrt{55}}{32}$; $-\frac{23}{32}$; $\frac{3\sqrt{55}}{23}$; $\frac{\sqrt{11}}{4}$; $\frac{\sqrt{5}}{4}$; $\frac{\sqrt{55}}{5}$

37. $\frac{4\sqrt{5}}{9}$; $\frac{1}{9}$; $4\sqrt{5}$; $\frac{\sqrt{18+6\sqrt{5}}}{6}$; $-\frac{\sqrt{18-6\sqrt{5}}}{6}$; $-\frac{\sqrt{3+\sqrt{5}}}{\sqrt{3-\sqrt{5}}}$

38. $\frac{4\sqrt{21}}{25}$; $\frac{17}{25}$; $\frac{4\sqrt{21}}{17}$; $\frac{\sqrt{50-10\sqrt{21}}}{10}$; $\frac{\sqrt{50+10\sqrt{21}}}{10}$; $\frac{\sqrt{5-\sqrt{21}}}{\sqrt{5+\sqrt{21}}}$

39. $-\frac{4}{5}$; $\frac{3}{5}$; $-\frac{4}{3}$; $\sqrt{\frac{5-2\sqrt{5}}{10}}$; $-\sqrt{\frac{5+2\sqrt{5}}{10}}$; $-\sqrt{\frac{5-2\sqrt{5}}{5+2\sqrt{5}}}$

44a. $\Delta P = 2P_i\sin\left(\frac{\theta}{2}\right)$; $\Delta P = 2P_f\sin\left(\frac{\theta}{2}\right)$

45–48. See p. A53.

50. First find $\sin 15°$ by using $\sin\frac{30°}{2}$, and then find $\sin 7.5°$ by using $\sin\frac{15°}{2}$.

14-5 PROBLEM SOLVING

Chris set a new personal best in football with a 35-yard kick. He wants to improve his distance. His coach suggests using the formula $d(\theta) = \dfrac{3v_0^2\sin\theta\cos\theta}{16}$, which gives the horizontal distance, d, in yards, as a function of the angle of elevation, θ, at which the ball is kicked with an initial velocity of v_0 yards per second.

1. What is the angle of elevation of the ball when Chris kicks it with an initial velocity of 20 yards per second and the ball covers 35 yards.
   a. What double-angle identity can you use to rewrite the function in terms of $\sin 2\theta$? $\sin 2\theta = 2\sin\theta\cos\theta$
   b. Rewrite the function in terms of $\sin 2\theta$. $d(\theta) = \dfrac{3v_0^2\sin 2\theta}{32}$
   c. Substitute the known values in the equation. $35 = \dfrac{3(20)^2\sin 2\theta}{32}$
   d. Solve for $\sin 2\theta$. $\sin 2\theta = 0.933$
   e. What is the angle at which he kicked the ball? 34.5°
2. Chris wonders how the horizontal distance would change if he kicked the ball with the same velocity but at a different angle.
   a. Complete the table to show the horizontal distance, to the nearest hundredth yard, for the given angles.
   b. At what angle must Chris kick the ball to cover the greatest horizontal distance? 45°

Angle of Elevation (°)	Horizontal Distance (yd)
15	18.75
25	28.73
35	35.24
45	37.50
55	35.24

3. What is the least angle at which Chris must kick the ball if he wants to cover at least 30 yards horizontally? 26.5°
4. Chris thinks he can kick the ball with an initial velocity of 18 yards per second and make a horizontal distance of 40 yards. Is he correct? Explain.
   Possible answer: For this initial velocity and target distance, $\sin 2\theta \approx 1.32$, which is outside the possible range of values for the sine of an angle; so he is incorrect.

Choose the letter for the best answer.

5. If Chris kicks the ball with an initial velocity of only 15 yards per second and an angle of elevation of 45°, what is the maximum horizontal distance the ball will cover?
   A 12.06 yd
   B 14.92 yd
   (C) 21.09 yd
   D 29.83 yd
6. At what angle can Chris kick the ball to cover a horizontal distance of 36 yards, if he kicks the ball with an initial velocity of 20 yards per second?
   F 18.5°
   (G) 36.9°
   H 44.1°
   J 73.7°

14-5 CHALLENGE

Double-angle and half-angle identities for sine and cosine are shown below.

Double-Angle Identities: $\sin 2A = 2\sin A\cos A$; $\cos 2A = \cos^2 A - \sin^2 A$

Half-Angle Identities: $\sin\frac{A}{2} = \pm\sqrt{\frac{1-\cos A}{2}}$; $\cos\frac{A}{2} = \pm\sqrt{\frac{1+\cos A}{2}}$

You can use these identities to derive double-angle and half-angle identities for tangent.

1. a. Use a ratio identity to express $\tan 2A$ in terms of $\sin 2A$ and $\cos 2A$. $\tan 2A = \dfrac{\sin 2A}{\cos 2A}$
   b. Use identities for $\sin 2A$ and $\cos 2A$ to rewrite the right side in terms of $\sin A$ and $\cos A$. $\tan 2A = \dfrac{2\sin A\cos A}{\cos^2 A - \sin^2 A}$
   c. Divide numerator and denominator of the right side by $\cos^2 A$. $\tan 2A = \dfrac{\frac{2\sin A\cos A}{\cos^2 A}}{\frac{\cos^2 A}{\cos^2 A} - \frac{\sin^2 A}{\cos^2 A}}$
   d. Simplify, and rewrite the right side in terms of $\tan A$. $\tan 2A = \dfrac{2\tan A}{1-\tan^2 A}$
2. Verify the result of Exercise 1 by using the identity shown below to obtain an identity for $\tan 2A$. $\tan(A+B) = \dfrac{\tan A + \tan B}{1 - \tan A\tan B}$
   $\tan 2A = \tan(A+A) = \dfrac{\tan A + \tan A}{1 - \tan A\tan A} = \dfrac{2\tan A}{1-\tan^2 A}$
3. Angle A is in Quadrant II and $\sin A = \frac{4}{5}$.
   a. Use your identity to determine $\tan 2A$. $\tan 2A = \frac{24}{7} \approx 3.43$
   b. Use a calculator to verify your result. $m\angle A = 127°$, $\tan 254° \approx 3.49$
4. Show that $2\cot 2A = \cot A - \tan A$ is an identity by
   a. expressing $2\cot 2A$ in terms of $\tan A$. $2\cot 2A = \dfrac{1-\tan^2 A}{\tan A}$
   b. expressing $\cot A - \tan A$ as a single fraction in terms of $\tan A$. $\cot A - \tan A = \dfrac{1-\tan^2 A}{\tan A}$
5. Derive an identity for $\tan\frac{A}{2}$ in terms of $\cos A$. $\tan\frac{A}{2} = \pm\sqrt{\dfrac{1-\cos A}{1+\cos A}}$
6. a. Use your identity to determine $\tan 22.5°$. $\tan 22.5° = \sqrt{\dfrac{2-\sqrt{2}}{2+\sqrt{2}}}$
   b. Verify that your result is equivalent to $\sqrt{2} - 1$. $\sqrt{\dfrac{2-\sqrt{2}}{2+\sqrt{2}}\cdot\dfrac{2-\sqrt{2}}{2-\sqrt{2}}} = \dfrac{2-\sqrt{2}}{\sqrt{2}}\cdot\dfrac{\sqrt{2}}{\sqrt{2}} = \sqrt{2} - 1$
7. Show that $\tan\frac{A}{2}$ is equivalent to $\frac{1-\cos A}{\sin A}$. $\tan\frac{A}{2} = \sqrt{\dfrac{1-\cos A}{1+\cos A}\cdot\dfrac{1-\cos A}{1-\cos A}} = \sqrt{\dfrac{(1-\cos A)^2}{\sin^2 A}} = \dfrac{1-\cos A}{\sin A}$

14-5 PRACTICE A

14-5 PRACTICE C

14-5 PRACTICE B

Find $\sin 2\theta$, $\cos 2\theta$, and $\tan 2\theta$ for each.

1. $\cos\theta = -\frac{12}{13}$ for $\pi < \theta < \frac{3\pi}{2}$ $\quad \frac{120}{169}$; $\frac{119}{169}$; $\frac{120}{119}$
2. $\sin\theta = \frac{\sqrt{6}}{10}$ for $0 < \theta < \frac{\pi}{2}$ $\quad \frac{\sqrt{141}}{25}$; $\frac{22}{25}$; $\frac{\sqrt{141}}{22}$
3. $\sin\theta = -\frac{2}{3}$ for $\frac{3\pi}{2} < \theta < 2\pi$ $\quad -\frac{4\sqrt{5}}{9}$; $\frac{1}{9}$; $-4\sqrt{5}$
4. $\tan\theta = -\frac{5}{6}$ for $\frac{\pi}{2} < \theta < \pi$ $\quad -\frac{60}{61}$; $-\frac{11}{61}$; $-\frac{60}{11}$

Prove each identity.

5. $2\cos^2\theta = \cos 2\theta + 1$
   $2\cos^2\theta = \cos 2\theta + 1$
   $2\cos^2\theta = \cos^2\theta - \sin^2\theta + 1$
   $2\cos^2\theta = \cos^2\theta - (1 - \cos^2\theta) + 1$
   $2\cos^2\theta = \cos^2\theta - 1 + \cos^2\theta + 1$
   $2\cos^2\theta = 2\cos^2\theta$
6. $\tan\theta = \dfrac{1-\cos 2\theta}{\sin 2\theta}$
   $\tan\theta = \dfrac{1-\cos 2\theta}{\sin 2\theta}$;
   $\tan\theta = \dfrac{1-(1-2\sin^2\theta)}{2\sin\theta\cos\theta}$;
   $\tan\theta = \dfrac{1-1+2\sin^2\theta}{2\sin\theta\cos\theta}$;
   $\tan\theta = \dfrac{\sin\theta}{\cos\theta}$; $\tan\theta = \tan\theta$

Use half-angle identities to find the exact value of each trigonometric expression.

7. $\tan 22.5°$ $\quad \sqrt{\dfrac{2-\sqrt{2}}{2+\sqrt{2}}}$
8. $\cos\frac{7\pi}{12}$ $\quad -\dfrac{\sqrt{2-\sqrt{3}}}{2}$
9. $\sin\frac{11\pi}{12}$ $\quad \dfrac{\sqrt{2-\sqrt{3}}}{2}$

Find $\sin\frac{\theta}{2}$, $\cos\frac{\theta}{2}$, and $\tan\frac{\theta}{2}$ for each.

10. $\cos\theta = \frac{3}{5}$ and $270° < \theta < 360°$ $\quad \frac{\sqrt{5}}{5}$; $-\frac{2\sqrt{5}}{5}$; $-\frac{1}{2}$
11. $\sin\theta = -\frac{\sqrt{5}}{3}$ and $180° < \theta < 270°$ $\quad \frac{\sqrt{30}}{6}$; $-\frac{\sqrt{6}}{6}$; $-\sqrt{5}$

Solve.

12. A water-park slide covers 100 feet of horizontal space and is 36 feet high.
    a. Write a trigonometric relation in terms of θ, the angle that the slide makes with the water surface. $\tan\theta = \frac{9}{25}$
    b. A new replacement slide will create an angle with the water surface that measures twice that of the original slide. The new slide will use the same horizontal space as the old slide. Write an expression that can be evaluated to find the height of the new slide. $\dfrac{100\cdot 2\left(\frac{9}{25}\right)}{1-\left(\frac{9}{25}\right)^2}$
    c. What is the height of the new slide to the nearest foot? 83 ft

TEST PREP DOCTOR In **Exercise 55,** students who have difficulty should refer to the unit circle. The answer must be a positive number because 157.5° is in quadrant 2. The value must also be closer to zero than it is to one. These characteristics apply to only choice **G.**

Answers

56. Possible answer:

$$\frac{\cos 2\theta}{\sin\theta + \cos\theta} = \frac{(\cos^2\theta - \sin^2\theta)}{\sin\theta + \cos\theta}$$

$$= \frac{(\cos\theta - \sin\theta)(\cos\theta + \sin\theta)}{\sin\theta + \cos\theta}$$

$$= \cos\theta - \sin\theta$$

59. $\tan\left[\frac{1}{2}\left(\frac{30°}{2}\right)\right]$

$$= \sqrt{\frac{2 - \sqrt{2 + \sqrt{3}}}{2 + \sqrt{2 + \sqrt{3}}}}$$

Journal

Have students show that, given the first double-angle identity for cosines, $\cos 2\theta = \cos^2\theta - \sin^2\theta$, they can derive the other two double-angle identities by using the Pythagorean identities.

ALTERNATIVE ASSESSMENT

Have students present, preferably to the class, a derivation of one double-angle identity. They should also include a numerical example of the identity in use.

Power Presentations with PowerPoint®

14-5 Lesson Quiz

1. Find $\cos\frac{\theta}{2}$ and $\cos 2\theta$ if $\sin\theta = \frac{5}{8}$ and $0 < \theta < \frac{\pi}{2}$.

   $\frac{\sqrt{\sqrt{39} + 8}}{4}$; $\frac{7}{32}$

2. Prove the following identity:

$$\tan\theta = \frac{\sin 2\theta}{2 - 2\sin^2\theta}$$

$$= \frac{2\sin\theta\cos\theta}{2(1 - \sin^2\theta)}$$

$$= \frac{\sin\theta\cos\theta}{\cos^2\theta}$$

$$= \tan\theta$$

3. Find the exact value of $\cos 22.5°$.

   $\frac{\sqrt{\sqrt{2} + 2}}{2}$

Also available on transparency

TEST PREP

52. What is the value of $\sin 2\theta$ if $\cos\theta = -\frac{\sqrt{2}}{2}$ and $90° < \theta < 180°$?

    (A) $\frac{1}{2}$ (B) $\frac{\sqrt{2}}{2}$ (C) 1 **(D) −1**

53. What is the value for $\cos 2\theta$ if $\sin\theta = \cos\theta$?

    (F) 0 (G) 1 (H) $2\sin^2\theta$ (J) $2\cos^2\theta$

54. What is the value for $\sin\frac{\theta}{2}$ if $\cos\theta = -\frac{12}{13}$ and $90° < \theta < 180°$?

    (A) $\frac{\sqrt{26}}{26}$ (B) $-\frac{\sqrt{26}}{26}$ **(C) $\frac{5\sqrt{26}}{26}$** (D) $-\frac{5\sqrt{26}}{26}$

55. What is the exact value for $\sin 157.5°$?

    (F) $-\frac{\sqrt{2 - \sqrt{2}}}{2}$ **(G) $\frac{\sqrt{2 - \sqrt{2}}}{2}$** (H) $-\frac{\sqrt{2 + \sqrt{2}}}{2}$ (J) $\frac{\sqrt{2 + \sqrt{2}}}{2}$

56. **Short Response** Verify that $\frac{\cos 2\theta}{\sin\theta + \cos\theta} = \cos\theta - \sin\theta$ for $0 \le \theta \le \frac{\pi}{2}$. Show each step in your justification process.

CHALLENGE AND EXTEND

57. Derive the double-angle formula for $\tan 2\theta$ by using the ratio identity for tangent and the double-angle identities for sine and cosine.

58. Derive the half-angle formula for $\tan\frac{\theta}{2}$ by using the ratio identity for tangent.

Use half-angle identities to find the exact value of each expression.

59. $\tan 7.5°$ 60. $\tan\frac{\pi}{16}$ 61. $\sin\frac{\pi}{24}$ 62. $\cos 11.25°$

63. **Write About It** For what values of θ is $\sin 2\theta = 2\sin\theta$ true? Explain first by using graphs and then by solving the equation.

64. Derive the product-to-sum formulas $\sin A \sin B = \frac{1}{2}\left[\cos(A - B) - \cos(A + B)\right]$ and $\cos A \cos B = \frac{1}{2}\left[\cos(A + B) + \cos(A - B)\right]$ by using the angle sum and difference formulas.

SPIRAL REVIEW

Use the vertical-line test to determine whether each relation is a function. *(Lesson 1-6)*

65. 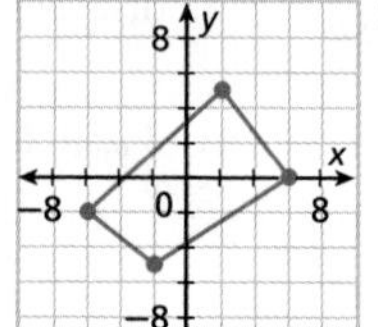

no

66. 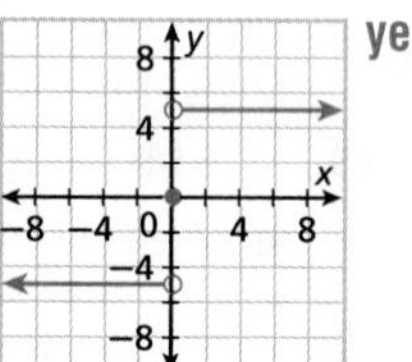

yes

Add or subtract. Identify any x-values for which the expression is undefined. *(Lesson 8-3)*

67. $\frac{3x - 2}{x + 7} + \frac{2x + 14}{x + 7}$ $\frac{5x + 12}{x + 7}$; $x \ne -7$

68. $\frac{4x - 1}{x} + \frac{6x - 2}{2x}$ $\frac{7x - 2}{x}$; $x \ne 0$

69. $\frac{7x + 4}{x + 1} - \frac{5x + 8}{x - 3}$ $\frac{2x^2 - 30x - 20}{(x + 1)(x - 3)}$; $x \ne -1, 3$

70. $\frac{x + 9}{x^2} - \frac{x}{x + 2}$ $\frac{-x^3 + x^2 + 11x + 18}{x^2(x + 2)}$; $x \ne -2, 0$

Find the exact value of each expression. *(Lesson 14-4)*

71. $\sin\left(-\frac{\pi}{12}\right)$ $\frac{\sqrt{2} - \sqrt{6}}{4}$

72. $\sin 105°$ $\frac{\sqrt{2} + \sqrt{6}}{4}$

73. $\cos\frac{7\pi}{12}$ $\frac{\sqrt{2} - \sqrt{6}}{4}$

74. $\cos 255°$ $\frac{\sqrt{2} - \sqrt{6}}{4}$

60. $\tan\left[\frac{1}{2}\left(\frac{1}{2}\cdot\frac{\pi}{4}\right)\right] = \sqrt{\frac{2 - \sqrt{2 + \sqrt{2}}}{2 + \sqrt{2 + \sqrt{2}}}}$

61. $\sin\left[\frac{1}{2}\left(\frac{1}{2}\cdot\frac{\pi}{6}\right)\right] = \frac{1}{2}\sqrt{2 - \sqrt{2 + \sqrt{3}}}$

62. $\cos\left[\frac{1}{2}\left(\frac{45°}{2}\right)\right] = \frac{1}{2}\sqrt{2 + \sqrt{2 + \sqrt{2}}}$

63. πn, where n is an integer; possible answer:

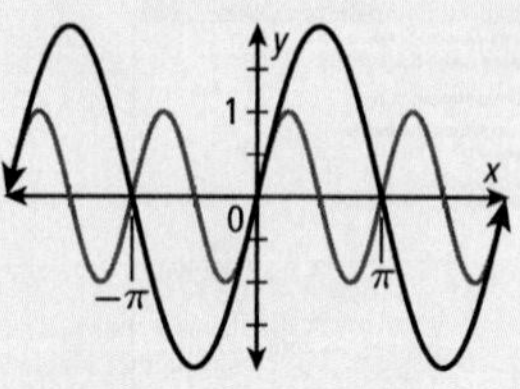

Solve the equation:

$\sin 2\theta = 2\sin\theta$

$2\sin\theta\cos\theta - 2\sin\theta = 0$

$2\sin\theta(\cos\theta - 1) = 0$

So $\cos\theta = 1$ or $\sin\theta = 0$, which are both true when $\theta = \pi n$, where n is an integer.

57, 58, 64. See p. A53.

14-6 Solving Trigonometric Equations

Objectives
Solve equations involving trigonometric functions.

Why learn this?
You can use trigonometric equations to determine the day of the year that the sun will rise at a given time. (See Example 4.)

Unlike trigonometric identities, most trigonometric equations are true only for certain values of the variable, called *solutions*. To solve trigonometric equations, apply the same methods used for solving algebraic equations.

EXAMPLE 1 Solving Trigonometric Equations with Infinitely Many Solutions

Find all of the solutions of $3\tan\theta = \tan\theta + 2$.

Method 1 Use algebra.

Solve for θ over one cycle of the tangent, $-90° < \theta < 90°$.

$$3\tan\theta = \tan\theta + 2$$

$3\tan\theta - \tan\theta = 2$ — *Subtract $\tan\theta$ from both sides.*

$2\tan\theta = 2$ — *Combine like terms.*

$\tan\theta = 1$ — *Divide by 2.*

$\theta = \tan^{-1}1$ — *Apply the inverse tangent.*

$\theta = 45°$ — *Find θ when $\tan\theta = 1$.*

Find all real number values of θ, where n is an integer.

$\theta = 45° + 180°n$ — *Use the period of the tangent function.*

Method 2 Use a graph.

Graph $y = 3\tan\theta$ and $y = \tan\theta + 2$ in the same viewing window for $-90° \le \theta \le 90°$.

Use the intersect feature of your graphing calculator to find the points of intersection.

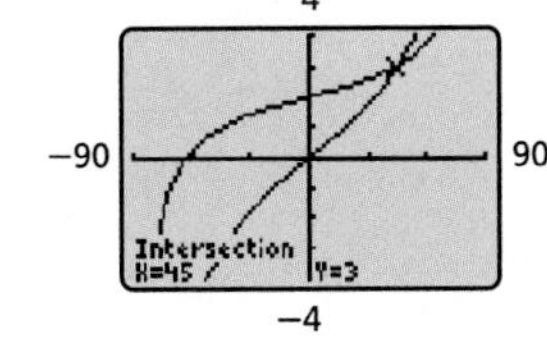

The graphs intersect at $\theta = 45°$. Thus, $\theta = 45° + 180°n$, where n is an integer.

Helpful Hint

Compare Example 1 with this solution:

$$3x = x + 2$$
$$3x - x = 2$$
$$2x = 2$$
$$x = 1$$

CHECK IT OUT! **1.** Find all of the solutions of $2\cos\theta + \sqrt{3} = 0$.
$150° + 360°n$, $210° + 360°n$

Some trigonometric equations can be solved by applying the same methods used for quadratic equations.

14-6 Organizer

Pacing: Traditional 1 day
Block $\frac{1}{2}$ day

Objectives: Solve equations involving trigonometric functions.

Online Edition
Graphing Calculator, Tutorial Videos, Interactivity, TechKeys

Power Presentations with PowerPoint®

Warm Up

Solve.

1. $x^2 + 3x - 4 = 0$ $x = 1$ or -4

2. $3x^2 + 7x = 6$ $x = \frac{2}{3}$ or -3

Evaluate each inverse trigonometric function.

3. $\text{Tan}^{-1}1$ $45°$

4. $\text{Sin}^{-1}-\frac{\sqrt{3}}{2}$ $-60°$

Also available on transparency

Math Humor

"Do not worry about your difficulties in mathematics. I can assure you that mine are still greater."
Albert Einstein

1 Introduce

EXPLORATION

14-6 Solving Trigonometric Equations

You can use your calculator to help you solve trigonometric equations. Set your calculator to the trigonometry window by pressing ZOOM and selecting **7:ZTrig**. The x-axis will now display values from -2π to 2π if you are in **RADIAN** mode.

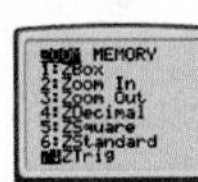

1. Solve the equation $\cos\theta = -1$ for values of θ within this viewing window by entering the functions $y = \cos\theta$ and $y = -1$ and finding all the points of intersection.
2. How many solutions are there if you do not restrict the possible values of θ? What are the solutions?
3. Use the same method to find all the solutions of the equation $\sin\theta\cos\theta = -\sin\theta$.
4. You can also solve $\sin\theta\cos\theta = -\sin\theta$ algebraically by adding $\sin\theta$ to both sides of the equation and then factoring. Show that this method results in the same set of solutions.

THINK AND DISCUSS

5. **Explain** how the solutions of $\cos\theta = -1$ are related to the period of the cosine function.
6. **Explain** why you cannot solve $\sin\theta\cos\theta = -\sin\theta$ by simply dividing both sides by $\sin\theta$ and then solving $\cos\theta = -1$.

Motivate

Remind students of properties of the real numbers such as the Distributive Property. Point out that these properties are in fact *algebraic* identities and were the basic tools used for solving *algebraic* equations. In this lesson, the *trigonometric* identities that have been studied will be used to solve *trigonometric* equations. Also, some methods used to solve algebraic equations will be used to solve trigonometric equations.

Explorations and answers are provided in the *Explorations* binder.

State Resources

Power Presentations with PowerPoint®

Additional Examples

Example 1

Find all solutions for $\sin\theta = \frac{1}{2}\sin\theta + \frac{1}{4}$.

$\theta = \{30° + 360°n,\ 150° + 360°n\}$

Example 2

Solve each equation for the given domain.

A. $4\tan^2\theta - 7\tan\theta + 3 = 0$ for $0 \le \theta \le 360°$.

$(\tan\theta - 1)(4\tan\theta - 3) = 0$
$\theta = 45°$ or $225°$, or $\theta \approx 36.9$ or 216.9

B. $2\cos^2\theta - \cos\theta = 1$ for $0 \le \theta \le \pi$.

$(2\cos\theta + 1)(\cos\theta - 1) = 0$
$\theta = \frac{2\pi}{3}$ or $\theta = 0$

Also available on transparency

INTERVENTION

Questioning Strategies

EXAMPLE 1

- If a trigonometric equation with no domain restriction has at least one solution, will it always have infinitely many solutions?

EXAMPLE 2

- What are possible numbers of solutions for a quadratic trigonometric equation with one variable $0 < \theta < 360°$?

Caution!

A trigonometric equation may have zero, one, two, or an infinite number of solutions, depending on the equation and domain of θ.

EXAMPLE 2 Solving Trigonometric Equations in Quadratic Form

Solve each equation for the given domain.

A $\sin^2\theta - 2\sin\theta = 3$ **for** $0 \le \theta < 2\pi$

$\sin^2\theta - 2\sin\theta - 3 = 0$ *Subtract 3 from both sides.*

$(\sin\theta + 1)(\sin\theta - 3) = 0$ *Factor the quadratic expression by comparing it with $x^2 - 2x - 3 = 0$.*

$\sin\theta = -1$ or $\sin\theta = 3$ *Apply the Zero Product Property.*

$\sin\theta = 3$ has no solution because $-1 \le \sin\theta \le 1$.

$\theta = \frac{3\pi}{2}$ *The only solution will come from $\sin\theta = -1$.*

B $\cos^2\theta + 2\cos\theta - 1 = 0$ **for** $0° \le \theta < 360°$

The equation is in quadratic form but cannot easily be factored. Use the Quadratic Formula.

$\cos\theta = \frac{-(2) \pm \sqrt{(2)^2 - 4(1)(-1)}}{2(1)}$ *Substitute 1 for a, 2 for b, and −1 for c.*

$\cos\theta = -1 \pm \sqrt{2}$ *Simplify.*

$-1 - \sqrt{2} < -1$ so $\cos\theta = -1 - \sqrt{2}$ has no solution.

$\theta = \cos^{-1}(-1 + \sqrt{2})$ *Apply the inverse cosine.*

$\approx 65.5°$ or $294.5°$ *Use a calculator. Find both angles for $0° \le \theta < 360°$.*

Solve each equation for $0 \le \theta < 2\pi$**.**

2a. $\cos^2\theta + 2\cos\theta = 3$ **0**

2b. $\sin^2\theta + 5\sin\theta - 2 = 0$ **≈ 21.9°, ≈ 158.1°**

You can often write trigonometric equations involving more than one function as equations of only one function by using trigonometric identities.

EXAMPLE 3 Solving Trigonometric Equations with Trigonometric Identities

Use trigonometric identities to solve each equation for $0 \le \theta < 2\pi$**.**

A $2\cos^2\theta = \sin\theta + 1$

$2(1 - \sin^2\theta) - \sin\theta - 1 = 0$ *Substitute $1 - \sin^2\theta$ for $\cos^2\theta$ by the Pythagorean identity.*

$-2\sin^2\theta - \sin\theta + 2 - 1 = 0$ *Simplify.*

$2\sin^2\theta + \sin\theta - 1 = 0$ *Multiply by −1.*

$(2\sin\theta - 1)(\sin\theta + 1) = 0$ *Factor.*

$\sin\theta = \frac{1}{2}$ or $\sin\theta = -1$ *Apply the Zero Product Property.*

$\theta = \frac{\pi}{6}$ or $\frac{5\pi}{6}$ or $\theta = \frac{3\pi}{2}$

Check Use the intersect feature of your graphing calculator. A graph supports your answer.

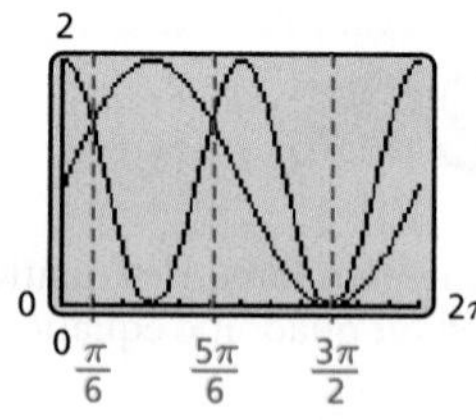

2 Teach

Guided Instruction

Before solving quadratic trigonometric equations, some students may need to review solving basic quadratic equations. Make the connection between a trigonometric equation and an algebraic equation by replacing sine or cosine with x. Demonstrate that the process of factoring and isolating the variable will remain the same.

Reaching All Learners

Through Cooperative Learning

When solving equations or systems of equations, students may use different approaches to arrive at the correct answer. Have students work in small groups to discuss and share the techniques that they used on specific problems, and the way that they decided which method to use.

Use trigonometric identities to solve each equation for $0° \leq \theta < 360°$.

B $\cos 2\theta + 3\cos\theta + 2 = 0$

$2\cos^2\theta - 1 + 3\cos\theta + 2 = 0$ — *Substitute $2\cos^2\theta - 1$ for $\cos 2\theta$ by the double-angle identity.*

$2\cos^2\theta + 3\cos\theta + 1 = 0$ — *Combine like terms.*

$(2\cos\theta + 1)(\cos\theta + 1) = 0$ — *Factor.*

$\cos\theta = -\frac{1}{2}$ — *Apply the Zero Product Property.*

or

$\cos\theta = -1$

$\theta = 120°$ or $240°$ or $\theta = 180°$

Check Use the intersect feature of your graphing calculator. A graph supports your answer.

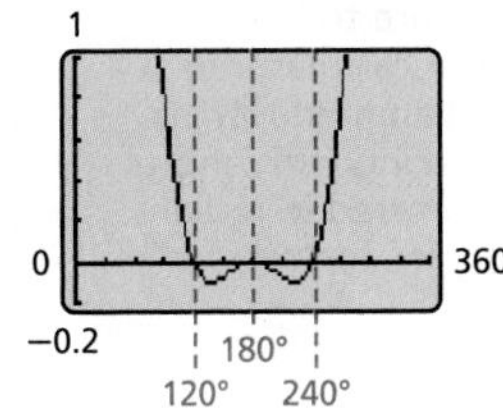

Use trigonometric identities to solve each equation for the given domain.

3a. $4\sin^2\theta + 4\cos\theta = 5$ for $0° \leq \theta < 360°$ **60°, 300°**

3b. $\sin 2\theta = -\cos\theta$ for $0 \leq \theta < 2\pi$ **90°, 210°, 270°, 330°**

EXAMPLE 4 *Problem-Solving Application*

The first sunrise in the United States each day is observed from Cadillac Mountain on Mount Desert Island in Maine. The time of the sunrise can be modeled by $t(m) = 1.665\sin\frac{\pi}{6}(m + 3) + 5.485$, where t is hours after midnight and m is the number of months after January 1. When does the sun rise at 7 A.M.?

1 Understand the Problem

The **answer** will be months of the year.

List the important information:

- The function model is $t(m) = 1.665\sin\frac{\pi}{6}(m + 3) + 5.485$.
- Sunrise is at 7 A.M., which is represented by $t = 7$.
- m represents the number of months after January 1.

2 Make a Plan

Substitute 7 for t in the model. Then solve the equation for m by using algebra.

Power Presentations with PowerPoint®

Additional Examples

Example 3

Use trigonometric identities to solve each equation.

A. $\tan^2\theta + \sec^2\theta = 3$ for $0 \leq \theta \leq 2\pi$.

$\theta = \left\{\frac{\pi}{4}, \frac{3\pi}{4}, \frac{5\pi}{4}, \frac{7\pi}{4}\right\}$

B. $\cos^2\theta = 1 + \sin^2\theta$ for $0 \leq \theta \leq 360°$.

$\theta = 0°$ or $180°$ or $360°$

Also available on transparency

INTERVENTION

Questioning Strategies

EXAMPLE 3

- How do you determine which identity will help solve an equation or whether one is even necessary?
- Is it possible to solve an equation containing more than one trigonometric function without converting everything to the same function?

Power Presentations with PowerPoint®

Additional Examples

Example 4

When does the sun rise at 4 A.M. on Cadillac Mountain? Use the equation from **Example 4.**

early June and late July

Also available on transparency

INTERVENTION

Questioning Strategies

EXAMPLE 4

- How do you know what month the value of m corresponds to?

Caution!

Be sure to have your calculator in radian mode when working with angles expressed in radians.

3 Solve

$$7 = 1.665\sin\frac{\pi}{6}(m+3) + 5.485 \quad \textit{Substitute 7 for t.}$$

$$\frac{7-5.485}{1.665} = \sin\frac{\pi}{6}(m+3) \quad \textit{Isolate the sine term.}$$

$$\sin^{-1}(0.9\overline{099}) = \frac{\pi}{6}(m+3) \quad \textit{Apply the inverse sine.}$$

Sine is positive in Quadrants I and II. Compute both values.

QI: $\sin^{-1}(0.9\overline{099}) = \frac{\pi}{6}(m+3)$

$1.143 \approx \frac{\pi}{6}(m+3)$

$\left(\frac{6}{\pi}\right)1.143 \approx m+3$

$-0.817 \approx m$

QII: $\pi - \sin^{-1}(0.9\overline{099}) = \frac{\pi}{6}(m+3)$

$\pi - 1.143 \approx \frac{\pi}{6}(m+3)$

$\left(\frac{6}{\pi}\right)(\pi - 1.143) \approx m+3$

$0.817 \approx m$

The value $m = 0.817$ corresponds to late January and the value $m = -0.817$ corresponds to early December.

4 Look Back

Check your answer by using a graphing calculator. Enter $y = 1.665\sin\frac{\pi}{6}(x+3) + 5.485$ and $y = 7$. Graph the functions on the same viewing window, and find the points of intersection.

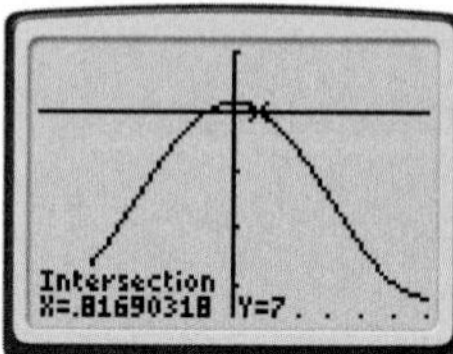

The graphs intersect at about 0.817 and -0.817.

CHECK IT OUT!

4. The number of hours h of sunlight in a day at Cadillac Mountain can be modeled by $h(d) = 3.31\sin\frac{\pi}{182.5}(d - 85.25) + 12.22$, where d is the number of days after January 1. When are there 12 hours of sunlight?

late March and late September

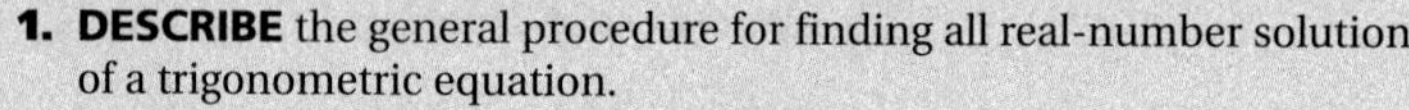

THINK AND DISCUSS

1. **DESCRIBE** the general procedure for finding all real-number solutions of a trigonometric equation.

2. **GET ORGANIZED** Copy and complete the graphic organizer. Write when each method is most useful, and give an example.

Method	Most useful when...	Example
Graphing		
Solving linear equations		
Factoring		
Quadratic Formula		
Identity substitution		

3 Close

Summarize

Review with students the different methods for solving trigonometric equations, such as graphing, factoring, and substituting by using trigonometric identities.

ONGOING ASSESSMENT and INTERVENTION

***Diagnose Before* the Lesson**
14-6 Warm Up, TE p. 1027

***Monitor During* the Lesson**
Check It Out! Exercises, SE pp. 1027–1030
Questioning Strategies, TE pp. 1028–1030

***Assess After* the Lesson**
14-6 Lesson Quiz, TE p. 1033
Alternative Assessment, TE p. 1033

Answers to *Think and Discuss*

Possible answers:

1. First solve the equation for a restricted domain equal to the period of the given function. Then use an understanding of the periodicity of the given function to find all solutions.
2. See p. A14.

14-6 Exercises

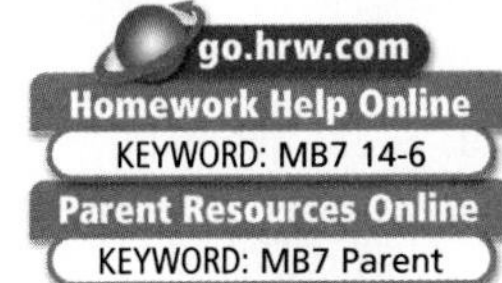

GUIDED PRACTICE

SEE EXAMPLE 1 p. 1027

Find all of the solutions of each equation.

1. $6\cos\theta - 1 = 2$ $60° + 360°n$, $300° + 360°n$
2. $2\sin\theta - \sqrt{3} = 0$ $60° + 360°n$, $120° + 360°n$
3. $\cos\theta = \sqrt{3} - \cos\theta$ $30° + 360°n$, $330° + 360°n$

SEE EXAMPLE 2 p. 1028

Solve each equation for the given domain.

4. $2\sin^2\theta + 3\sin\theta = -1$ for $0 \le \theta < 2\pi$
5. $\cos^2\theta - 4\cos\theta + 1 = 0$ for $0° \le \theta < 360°$ $\approx 74.5°$ or $285.5°$

SEE EXAMPLE 3 p. 1028

Multi-Step Use trigonometric identities to solve each equation for the given domain.

6. $2\sin^2\theta - \cos 2\theta = 0$ for $0° \le \theta < 360°$ $30°, 150°, 210°, 330°$
7. $\sin^2\theta + \cos\theta = -1$ for $0 \le \theta < 2\pi$ π

SEE EXAMPLE 4 p. 1029

8. **Heating** The amount of energy from natural gas used for heating a manufacturing plant is modeled by $E(m) = 350\sin\frac{\pi}{6}(m + 1.5) + 650$, where E is the energy used in dekatherms, and m is the month where $m = 0$ represents January 1. When is the gas usage 825 dekatherms? Assume an average of 30 days per month. mid-April and mid-December

PRACTICE AND PROBLEM SOLVING

Independent Practice	
For Exercises	See Example
9–12	1
13–14	2
15–16	3
17	4

Extra Practice
Skills Practice p. S31
Application Practice p. S45

Find all of the solutions of each equation.

9. $1 - 2\cos\theta = 0$ $60° + 360°n$, $300° + 360°n$
10. $\sqrt{3}\tan\theta - 3 = 0$ $60° + 180°n$
11. $2\cos\theta + \sqrt{3} = 0$ $150° + 360°n$, $210° + 360°n$
12. $2\sin\theta + 1 = 2 + \sin\theta$ $90° + 360°n$

Solve each equation for the given domain.

13. $2\cos^2\theta + \cos\theta - 1 = 0$ for $0 \le \theta < 2\pi$
14. $\sin^2\theta + 2\sin\theta - 2 = 0$ for $0° \le \theta < 360°$ $\approx 47.1°$, $\approx 132.9°$

Multi-Step Use trigonometric identities to solve each equation for the given domain.

15. $\cos 2\theta + \cos\theta + 1 = 0$ for $0° \le \theta < 360°$ $90°, 120°, 240°, 270°$
16. $\cos 2\theta = \sin\theta$ for $0 \le \theta < 2\pi$ $\frac{\pi}{6}, \frac{5\pi}{6}, \frac{3\pi}{2}$

13. $\frac{\pi}{3}$, π, or $\frac{5\pi}{3}$

17. **Multi-Step** The amount of energy used by a large office building is modeled by $E(t) = 100\sin\frac{\pi}{12}(t - 8) + 800$, where E is the energy in kilowatt-hours, and t is the time in hours after midnight. 17a. 10:00 A.M. and 6:00 P.M.
    a. During what time in the day is the electricity use 850 kilowatt-hours?
    b. When are the least and greatest amounts of electricity used? Are your answers reasonable? Explain.

Solve each equation algebraically for $0° \le \theta < 360°$.

18. $2\sin^2\theta = \sin\theta$ $0°, 30°, 150°, 180°$
19. $2\cos^2\theta = \sin\theta + 1$ $30°, 150°, 270°$
20. $\cos 2\theta - 2\sin\theta + 2 = 0$ $\approx 55.4°$, $\approx 124.6°$
21. $2\cos^2\theta + 3\sin\theta = 3$ $30°, 90°, 150°$
22. $\cos^2\theta + \sin\theta - 1 = 0$ $0°, 90°, 180°$
23. $2\sin^2\theta + \sin\theta = 0$ $0°, 180°, 210°, 330°$

24. $0, \frac{\pi}{2}, \pi$

27. $\frac{7\pi}{6}, \frac{11\pi}{6}$

28. no solution

Solve each equation algebraically for $0 \le \theta < 2\pi$.

24. $\sin^2\theta - \sin\theta = 0$
25. $\cos^2\theta - 3\cos\theta = 4$ π
26. $\cos\theta(0.5 + \cos\theta) = 0$ $\frac{\pi}{2}, \frac{2\pi}{3}, \frac{4\pi}{3}, \frac{3\pi}{2}$
27. $2\sin^2\theta - 3\sin\theta = 2$
28. $\cos^2\theta + \frac{1}{2}\cos\theta = 5$
29. $\sin^2\theta + 3\sin\theta + 3 = 0$ no solution
30. $\cos^2\theta + 4\cos\theta - 3 = 0$ ≈ 0.869, ≈ 5.414
31. $\tan^2\theta = \sqrt{3}\tan\theta$ $0, \frac{\pi}{3}, \pi, \frac{4\pi}{3}$

14-6 Exercises

Assignment Guide

Assign *Guided Practice* exercises as necessary.

If you finished Examples **1–2**
Basic 9–14, 18–23
Average 9–14, 18–23, 52
Advanced 9–14, 18–23, 52, 55

If you finished Examples **1–4**
Basic 9–27, 33–51, 58–64
Average 9–51, 52, 56, 58–64
Advanced 9–34, 36–64

Homework Quick Check
Quickly check key concepts.
Exercises: 10, 12, 14, 16, 17

Teaching Tip

Science Link For **Exercise 8,** note that the metric prefix *deka-* is sometimes written *deca-*. A *therm* is equivalent to 100,000 Btu. One Btu (British thermal unit) is the amount of heat required to raise the temperature of 1 pound of water 1 degree Fahrenheit.

Answers

4. $\frac{3\pi}{2}, \frac{7\pi}{6}, \frac{11\pi}{6}$

17b. Possible answer: The minimum electricity use is at 2:00 A.M., when no one is at work. The maximum electricity use is at 2:00 P.M., when the building is fully occupied. 2:00 P.M. is also near the hottest time of the day, so the building's electricity use may be very high because of air conditioning. The answers are reasonable.

State Resources

go.hrw.com
State Resources Online
KEYWORD: MB7 Resources

Teaching Tip

Science Link
Exercise 34 points out that the length of a *tidal day,* a period containing two complete cycles of high and low tides, is not 24 hours. The actual factors contributing to tidal patterns include the gravitational pulls of both the Sun and the Moon, centrifugal force that causes a bulge on the dark side of Earth, frictional forces that delay tides, and irregularities in the paths of all of the objects involved. The average length of a tidal day is actually about 24 hours and 50 minutes.

Exercise 38 involves solving and interpreting a trigonometric equation. This exercise prepares students for the Multi-Step Test Prep on page 1034.

Answers

32b. $\approx 36°$; The other answer of 144° is not reasonable because it implies that the ball is thrown in the opposite direction.

36. Possible answer: An equation that includes trigonometric functions is a trigonometric equation, such as $\sin^2\theta - \sin\theta = 0$, and may be true only for some values. A trigonometric identity is a trigonometric equation that is true for all values, such as $\tan\theta = \frac{\sin\theta}{\cos\theta}$.

32a. $\approx 30°$ and $\approx 60°$

32. Sports A baseball is thrown with an initial velocity of 96 feet per second at an angle θ degrees with a horizontal.

a. The horizontal range R in feet that the ball travels can be modeled by $R(\theta) = \frac{v^2 \sin 2\theta}{32}$. At what angle(s) with the horizontal will the ball travel 250 feet?

b. The maximum vertical height H_{max} in feet that the ball travels upward can be modeled by $H_{max}(\theta) = \frac{v^2 \sin^2\theta}{64}$. At what angle(s) with the horizontal will the ball travel 50 feet?

LINK Performing Arts

Traditional Japanese kabuki theaters were round and were able to be rotated to change scenes. The stages were also equipped with trapdoors and bridges that led through the audience.

33. Performing Arts A theater has a rotating stage that can be turned for different scenes. The stage has a radius of 18 feet, and the area in square feet of the segment of the circle formed by connecting two radii as shown is $A = \frac{r^2}{2}(\theta - \sin\theta)$, with θ in radians.

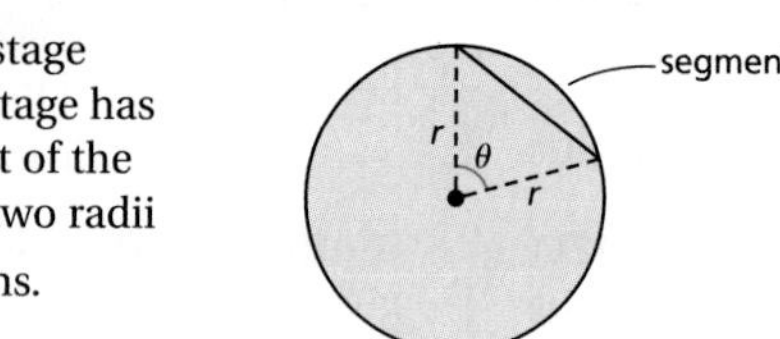

a. What angle gives a segment area of 92 square feet? How many such sets can simultaneously fit on the full rotating stage?

b. What angle gives a segment area of 50 square feet? About how many such sets can simultaneously fit on the full rotating stage?

a. $\approx \frac{\pi}{2}$; 4 sets b. $\approx \frac{2\pi}{5}$; 5 sets

34. Oceanography The height of the water on a certain day at a pier in Cape Cod, Massachusetts, can be modeled by $h(t) = 4.5\sin\frac{\pi}{6.25}(t + 4) + 7.5$, where h is the height in feet and t is the time in hours after midnight.

a. On this particular day, when is the height of the water 5 feet?

b. How much time is there between high and low tides? 6.25 h

c. What is the period for the tide? 12.5 h

d. Does the cycle of tides fit evenly in a 24-hour day? Explain.

34a. 3:25 A.M., 7:20 A.M., 3:55 P.M., and 7:50 P.M.

d. No; the period of the model is 12.5 h.

35. ///ERROR ANALYSIS/// Below are two solution procedures for solving $\sin^2\theta - \frac{1}{2}\sin\theta = 0$ for $0° \le \theta < 360°$. Which is incorrect? Explain the error.

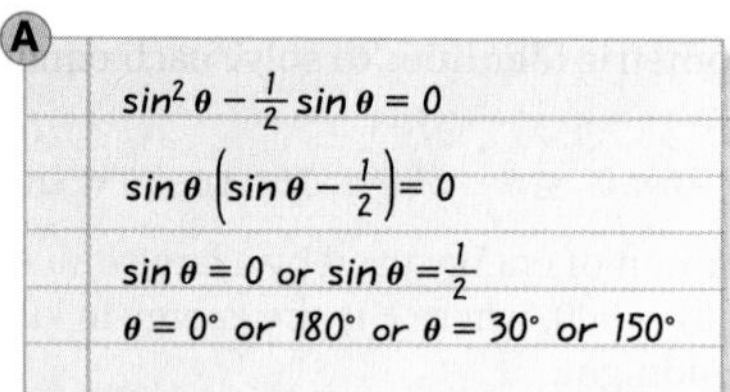

A
$\sin^2\theta - \frac{1}{2}\sin\theta = 0$
$\sin\theta\left(\sin\theta - \frac{1}{2}\right) = 0$
$\sin\theta = 0$ or $\sin\theta = \frac{1}{2}$
$\theta = 0°$ or $180°$ or $\theta = 30°$ or $150°$

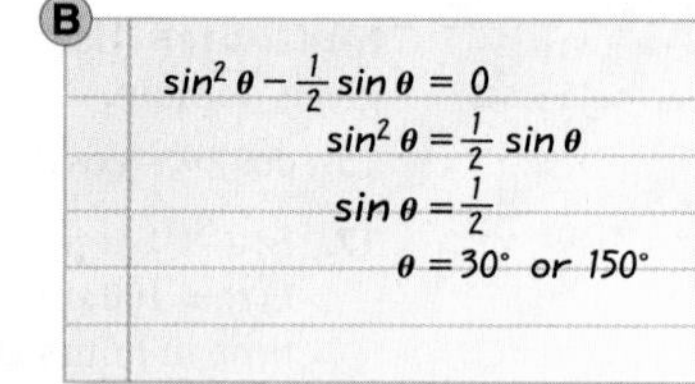

B
$\sin^2\theta - \frac{1}{2}\sin\theta = 0$
$\sin^2\theta = \frac{1}{2}\sin\theta$
$\sin\theta = \frac{1}{2}$
$\theta = 30°$ or $150°$

35. B is incorrect; Possible answer: Division by $\sin\theta$ eliminates the solution when $\sin\theta = 0$.

36. Critical Thinking What is the difference between a trigonometric equation and a trigonometric identity? Explain by using examples.

37. Graphing Calculator Use your graphing calculator to find all solutions of the equation $2\cos x = 0.25x$. $x \approx -4.165, -1.797, 1.395, 5.464, 6.831$

38. This problem will prepare you for the Multi-Step Test Prep on page 1034.

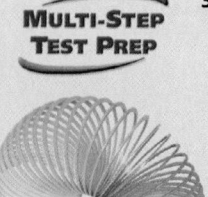

The displacement in centimeters of a mass attached to a spring is modeled by $y(t) = 2.9\cos\left(\frac{2\pi}{3}t + \frac{\pi}{4}\right) + 3$, where t is the time in seconds.

a. What are the maximum and minimum displacements of the mass? 5.9 cm; 0.1 cm

b. The mass is set in motion at $t = 0$. When is the displacement of the mass equal to 1 cm for the first time? 0.74 s

c. At what other times will the displacement be 1 cm?
0.74 + 3*n* and 1.51 + 3*n* where *n* is an integer

14-6 PRACTICE A

14-6 PRACTICE C

14-6 PRACTICE B

Find all of the solutions of each equation.

1. $4\tan\theta = 5\tan\theta + \sqrt{3}$ — $120° + 180°n$
2. $\sqrt{2} - 2\sin\theta = 0$ — $45° + 360°n, 135° + 360°n$
3. $7\cos\theta - 1 = 9\cos\theta$ — $120° + 360°n, 240° + 360°n$
4. $2\tan\theta + \sqrt{3} = 5\tan\theta$ — $30° + 180°n$

Solve each equation for the given domain.

5. $\tan^2\theta - 2\tan\theta = -1$ for $0° \le \theta \le 360°$ — 45°, 225°
6. $2\sin^2\theta = 1$ for $0° \le \theta \le 360°$ — 45°, 135°, 225°, 315°
7. $4\cos^2\theta = 3\cos\theta$ for $90° \le \theta \le 180°$ — 90°
8. $2\sqrt{3}\cos^2\theta - \cos\theta = 2\sqrt{3}$ for $\pi \le \theta \le 2\pi$ — $\frac{7\pi}{6}$
9. $3\tan^2\theta = 2\tan\theta + 1$ for $0° \le \theta \le 90°$ — 45°
10. $5\tan^2\theta = 2\tan\theta + 6$ for $180° \le \theta \le 360°$ — 232.7°, 317.6°

Use trigonometric identities to solve each equation for the given domain.

11. $\sin\theta + \sin 2\theta = 0$ for $0° \le \theta \le 360°$ — 0°, 120°, 180°, 240°, 360°
12. $\cos^2\theta = \sin^2\theta$ for $0° \le \theta \le 360°$ — 45°, 135°, 225°, 315°
13. $\frac{\cos 2\theta}{\sin^2\theta} = 0$ for $0° \le \theta \le 360°$ — 45°, 135°, 225°, 315°
14. $\cos 2\theta = \frac{1}{2}\sin\theta$ for $0° \le \theta \le 90°$ — $\approx 36.4°, \approx 57.5°$

Solve.

15. The height of the water at a pier on a certain day can be modeled by $h(t) = 4.8\sin\frac{\pi}{6}(t + 3.5) + 9$, where h is the height in feet and t is the time in hours after midnight. When is the height of the water 6 feet?
3:47 A.M., 7:13 A.M., 3:47 P.M., 7:13 P.M.

14-6 READING STRATEGIES

You can solve trigonometric equations in the same way as you solve algebraic equations.

Linear Algebraic Equations	Linear Trigonometric Equations
$3x = x + 2$ $3x - x = 2$ $2x = 2$ $x = 1$	$3\tan\theta = \tan\theta + 2$ $3\tan\theta - \tan\theta = 2$ $2\tan\theta = 2$ $\tan\theta = 1$
Quadratic Algebraic Equations	**Quadratic Trigonometric Equations**
$x^2 + 3x - 10 = 0$ $(x + 5)(x - 2) = 0$ $x + 5 = 0$ or $x - 2 = 0$ $x = -5$ or $x = 2$	$2\cos^2\theta - \cos\theta - 1 = 0$ $(2\cos\theta + 1)(\cos\theta - 1) = 0$ $2\cos\theta + 1 = 0$ or $\cos\theta - 1 = 0$ $\cos\theta = -\frac{1}{2}$ or $\cos\theta = 1$

Solve.

1. $3\cot\theta = \cot\theta + 1$ — $\cot\theta = \frac{1}{2}$
2. $2\sec\theta = 6\sec\theta - 3$ — $\sec\theta = \frac{3}{4}$
3. $\frac{5}{2}\cos\theta + \frac{3}{2}\cos\theta - 4 = 0$ — $\cos\theta = 1$
4. $5\tan\theta + 3 = 4\tan\theta - \frac{1}{3}$ — $\tan\theta = -\frac{10}{3}$
5. $6\sin\theta = 3\sin\theta + 3$ — $\sin\theta = 1$
6. $\frac{1}{2}\cot\theta = -\frac{5}{2}\cot\theta + 2$ — $\cot\theta = \frac{2}{3}$
7. $3\cos^2\theta - 1 = 2\cos^2\theta - \frac{3}{4}$ — $\cos\theta = \pm\frac{1}{2}$
8. $\sin^2\theta + 3\sin\theta + 5 = \sin\theta + 4 + \sin^2\theta$ — $\sin\theta = -\frac{1}{2}$
9. $3\tan^2\theta = \tan\theta$ — $\tan\theta = 0$ or $\frac{1}{3}$
10. $4\cos^2\theta = 1 - 3\cos\theta$ — $\cos\theta = -1$ or $\frac{1}{4}$

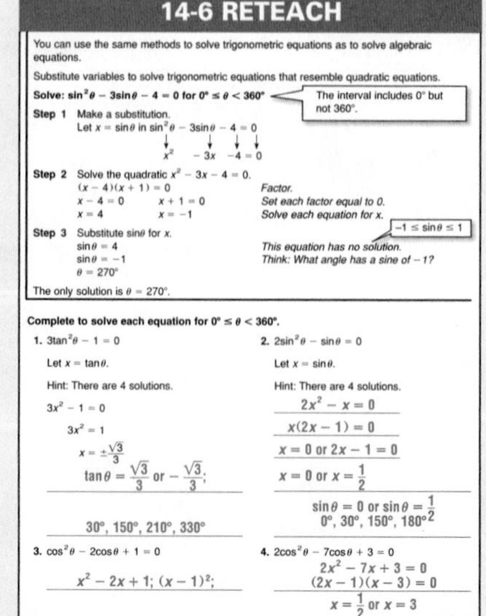

14-6 RETEACH

You can use the same methods to solve trigonometric equations as to solve algebraic equations.

Substitute variables to solve trigonometric equations that resemble quadratic equations.

Solve: $\sin^2\theta - 3\sin\theta - 4 = 0$ for $0° \le \theta < 360°$ (The interval includes 0° but not 360°.)

Step 1 Make a substitution.
Let $x = \sin\theta$ in $\sin^2\theta - 3\sin\theta - 4 = 0$
$x^2 - 3x - 4 = 0$

Step 2 Solve the quadratic $x^2 - 3x - 4 = 0$.
$(x - 4)(x + 1) = 0$ *Factor.*
$x - 4 = 0$ $x + 1 = 0$ *Set each factor equal to 0.*
$x = 4$ $x = -1$ *Solve each equation for x.*

Step 3 Substitute $\sin\theta$ for x.
$\sin\theta = 4$ *This equation has no solution.* ($-1 \le \sin\theta \le 1$)
$\sin\theta = -1$ *Think: What angle has a sine of −1?*
$\theta = 270°$

The only solution is $\theta = 270°$.

Complete to solve each equation for $0° \le \theta < 360°$.

1. $3\tan^2\theta - 1 = 0$
Let $x = \tan\theta$.
Hint: There are 4 solutions.
$3x^2 - 1 = 0$
$3x^2 = 1$
$x = \pm\frac{\sqrt{3}}{3}$
$\tan\theta = \frac{\sqrt{3}}{3}$ or $-\frac{\sqrt{3}}{3}$;
30°, 150°, 210°, 330°

2. $2\sin^2\theta - \sin\theta = 0$
Let $x = \sin\theta$.
Hint: There are 4 solutions.
$2x^2 - x = 0$
$x(2x - 1) = 0$
$x = 0$ or $2x - 1 = 0$
$x = 0$ or $x = \frac{1}{2}$
$\sin\theta = 0$ or $\sin\theta = \frac{1}{2}$
0°, 30°, 150°, 180°

3. $\cos^2\theta - 2\cos\theta + 1 = 0$
$x^2 - 2x + 1; (x - 1)^2;$
$\cos\theta = 1; 0°$

4. $2\cos^2\theta - 7\cos\theta + 3 = 0$
$2x^2 - 7x + 3 = 0$
$(2x - 1)(x - 3) = 0$
$x = \frac{1}{2}$ or $x = 3$
60°, 300°

Estimation Use a graphing calculator to approximate the solution to each equation to the nearest tenth of a degree for $0° \le \theta < 360°$.

39. $\tan\theta - 12 = -1$ **≈ 84.8°, ≈ 264.8°**

40. $\sin\theta + \cos\theta + 1.25 = 0$ **≈ 197.1°, ≈ 252.9°**

41. $4\sin^2(2\theta - 30) = 4$ **60°, 150°, 240°, 330°**

42. $\tan^2\theta + \tan\theta = 3$ **52.5°, 113.5°, 232.5°, 293.5°**

43. $\sin^2\theta + 5\sin\theta = 3.5$ **38.5°, 141.5°**

44. $\cos^2\theta - \cos 2\theta + 1 = 0$ **no solution**

45. Write About It How many solutions can a trigonometric equation have? Explain by using examples. **Possible answer: A trigonometric equation may have no solution, such as $\sin x = 2$, or an infinite number of solutions, such as $\sin x = 1$, or any given number of solutions if there are restrictions on the domain.**

TEST PREP

46. Which values are solutions of $2\cos\theta + \sqrt{3} = 2\sqrt{3}$ for $0° \le \theta < 360°$?

- (A) 30° or 150°
- (C) 60° or 120°
- **(B) 30° or 330°** (circled)
- (D) 60° or 320°

47. Which gives an approximate solution to $5\tan\theta - \sqrt{3} = \tan\theta$ for $-90° \le \theta \le 90°$?

- (F) −23.4°
- (G) −19.1°
- (H) 19.1°
- **(J) 23.4°** (circled)

48. Which value for θ is NOT a solution to $\sin^2\theta = \sin\theta$?

- (A) 0°
- (B) 90°
- (C) 180°
- **(D) 270°** (circled)

49. Which gives all of the solutions of $\cos\theta - 1 = -\frac{1}{2}$ for $0 \le \theta < 2\pi$?

- (F) $\frac{2\pi}{3}$ or $\frac{5\pi}{3}$
- (H) $\frac{2\pi}{3}$ or $\frac{4\pi}{3}$
- (G) $\frac{\pi}{3}$ or $\frac{2\pi}{3}$
- **(J) $\frac{\pi}{3}$ or $\frac{5\pi}{3}$** (circled)

50. Which gives the solution to $\sin^2\theta - \sin\theta - 2 = 0$ for $0° \le \theta < 360°$?

- (A) 90°
- (C) 90° or 270°
- **(B) 270°** (circled)
- (D) No solution

51. Short Response Solve $2\cos^2\theta + \cos\theta - 2 = 0$ algebraically. Show the steps in the solution process.

CHALLENGE AND EXTEND

Solve each equation algebraically for $0° \le \theta < 360°$.

52. $9\cos^3\theta - \cos\theta = 0$ **90°, 270°, 109.5°, 250.5°, 70.5°, 289.5°**

53. $4\cos^3\theta - \cos\theta = 0$ **90°, 270°, 120°, 240°, 60°, 300°**

54. $16\sin^4\theta - 16\sin^2\theta + 3 = 0$ **60°, 150°, 240°, 330°, 30°, 120°, 210°, 300°**

55. $\sin^2\theta - 4.5\sin\theta = 2.5$ **210°, 330°**

56. $|\sin\theta| = \frac{1}{2}$ **30°, 150°, 210°, 330°**

57. $|\cos\theta| = \frac{\sqrt{3}}{2}$ **30°, 150°, 210°, 330°**

SPIRAL REVIEW

Order the given numbers from least to greatest. *(Lesson 1-1)*

58. $\frac{\sqrt{3}}{2}, -1, 0.8\overline{6}, 1, \frac{5}{6}$ **$-1, \frac{5}{6}, \frac{\sqrt{3}}{2}, 0.8\overline{6}, 1$**

59. $2\sqrt{5}, \frac{19}{4}, 4.\overline{47}, \sqrt{21}, \frac{\pi}{0.65}$ **$2\sqrt{5}, 4.\overline{47}, \sqrt{21}, \frac{19}{4}, \frac{\pi}{0.65}$**

60. Technology An e-commerce company constructed a Web site for a local business. Each time a customer purchases a product on the Web site, the e-commerce company receives 5% of the sale. Write a function to represent the e-commerce company's revenue based on total website sales per day. What is the value of the function for an input of 259, and what does it represent? *(Lesson 1-7)* **$f(x) = 0.05x$; \$12.95; 5% of \$259, the e-commerce company's revenue from web sales of \$259**

Simplify each expression by writing it only in terms of θ. *(Lesson 14-5)*

61. $\cos 2\theta - 2\cos^2\theta$ **−1**

62. $\frac{\sin 2\theta}{2\sin\theta}$ **$\cos\theta$**

63. $\cos 2\theta + \sin^2\theta$ **$\cos^2\theta$**

64. $\frac{\cos 2\theta + 1}{2}$ **$\cos^2\theta$**

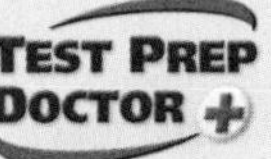

TEST PREP DOCTOR In Exercises **46** and **50**, students can substitute the answer choices into the equations to eliminate choices.

Answers

51. $\cos\theta = \frac{-1 \pm \sqrt{(1)^2 - 4(2)(-2)}}{2(2)}$

$= \frac{-1 \pm \sqrt{17}}{4}$

$\theta = \cos^{-1}\left(\frac{-1 + \sqrt{17}}{4}\right)$ or

$\theta = \cos^{-1}\left(\frac{-1 - \sqrt{17}}{4}\right)$

$\theta \approx 38.7°$ or $321.3°$ or no solution. Thus, $\theta \approx 38.7°$ or $321.3°$.

Journal

Have students describe how they choose which method to use when solving a trigonometric equation, including when to use a graphing calculator and when an exact solution is possible.

ALTERNATIVE ASSESSMENT

Have students create three different trigonometric equations with solutions worked out. At least one equation should be quadratic, and at least one should involve a Pythagorean or double-angle identity. At least two of them should be solvable without a calculator.

Power Presentations with PowerPoint®

14-6 Lesson Quiz

1. Find all solutions for $\cos\theta = \sqrt{2} - \cos\theta$.

$\theta = 45° + n \cdot 360°$ or $315° + n \cdot 360°$

2. Solve $3\sin^2\theta - 4\sin\theta - 4 = 0$ for $0 \le \theta \le 360°$.

$\theta \approx 221.8°$ or $318.2°$

3. Solve $\cos 2\theta = 3\sin\theta + 2$ for $0 \le \theta \le 2\pi$.

$\theta = \left\{\frac{7\pi}{6}, \frac{3\pi}{2}, \frac{11\pi}{6}\right\}$

Also available on transparency

14-6 PROBLEM SOLVING

Jon watches his sister Jessica skateboard. When she jumps and launches herself into the air with an initial speed of v_0 feet per second, her path in terms of time, t, in seconds, is represented by these equations.

Equation 1 $x(t) = v_0 t\cos\theta$

Equation 2 $y(t) = v_0 t\sin\theta - 16t^2$

The first equation models the horizontal distance, $x(t)$, that the skateboarder travels, and the second equation models the vertical height, $y(t)$, that the skateboarder attains.

1. Jessica attains a height of 4.7 feet above the launch and landing ramps after 1 second. Her initial velocity is 25 feet per second. Find the angle of her launch.
   a. Which equation can you use with the given information to solve for θ? **Equation 2**
   b. Substitute the known values and solve for θ. **$4.7 = 25(1)\sin\theta - 16(1)^2$; $\theta = 55.9°$**
   c. What is Jessica's height above the launch and landing ramps after 0.5 second? **6.4 ft**
   d. What distance has Jessica traveled after 1 second? **14 ft**
2. Jon attains a height of 5.2 feet above the launch and landing ramps after 1 second. His initial velocity is 28 feet per second. Find the angle of his launch.
   a. Write and evaluate an expression for Jon's launch angle. **$5.2 = 28(1)\sin\theta - 16(1)^2$; $\theta = 49.2°$**
   b. Write and evaluate an expression for his height above the launch and landing ramps after 0.5 second. **$y(t) = 28(0.5)\sin 49.2° - 16(0.5)^2$; $y(t) = 6.6$ ft**

Choose the letter for the best answer.

3. How far does Jon travel in 1 second?
   - A 14.5 ft
   - B 16.7 ft
   - **C 18.3 ft** (circled)
   - D 21.2 ft
4. Jessica increases her initial velocity to 30 feet per second. She attains a height of 5.5 feet after 1 second. Which expression represents her launch angle?
   - F $\cos^{-1}\left(\frac{10.5}{30}\right)$
   - G $\cos^{-1}\left(\frac{21.5}{30}\right)$
   - H $\sin^{-1}\left(\frac{10.5}{30}\right)$
   - **J $\sin^{-1}\left(\frac{21.5}{30}\right)$** (circled)

14-6 CHALLENGE

A *trigonometric equation* contains one or more trigonometric functions of an angle. Such an equation must first be solved for a function of the angle and then for the measure of the angle. Some trigonometric equations contain radicals.

1. Solve $2\cos\theta = \sqrt{8\sin\theta - 1}$ for $0° \le \theta < 360°$.
   a. Since the radical is isolated, square both sides of the equation. **$4\cos^2\theta = 8\sin\theta - 1$**
   b. Use an identity to express the equation in terms of a single trigonometric function. **$4(1 - \sin^2\theta) = 8\sin\theta - 1$**
   c. Solve for θ and check. **30°**

Solve each equation for $0° \le \theta < 360°$. Check your results.

2. $\sqrt{\frac{\sin\theta}{2}} = \sin\theta$ **0°, 30°, 150°, 180°**
3. $\sqrt{2 + 3\cot^2\theta} = \tan\theta$ **60°, 240°**
4. $\sin\theta + \sin\frac{\theta}{2} = 0$
   a. Use an identity to replace $\sin\frac{\theta}{2}$. **$\sin\theta \pm \sqrt{\frac{1 - \cos\theta}{2}} = 0$**
   b. Isolate the radical and square both sides. **$\sin^2\theta = \frac{1 - \cos\theta}{2}$**
   c. Use an identity to express the equation in terms of a single trigonometric function. **$1 - \cos^2\theta = \frac{1 - \cos\theta}{2}$**
   d. Solve for θ and check. **0°, 240°**
5. $\cos\theta = \sin\frac{\theta}{2}$ **60°, 300°**
6. $\sin\theta = 2\sin\frac{\theta}{2}$ **0°**

As opposed to the equations in Exercises 4–6, where you first had to get the angles to be of the same multiple of θ, the angles in Exercises 7 and 8 are already of the same multiple. So, you do not need to use radicals.

Solve each equation for $0° \le \theta < 360°$.

7. $\cos\frac{\theta}{2} + \sin\frac{\theta}{2} = 1$ **0°, 180°**
8. $2\sin\theta\cos\theta + 2\sin\theta - \cos\theta - 1 = 0$ **30°, 150°, 180°**

Organizer

Objective: Assess students' ability to apply concepts and skills in Lessons 14-3 through 14-6 in a real-world format.

Online Edition

Resources

Algebra II Assessments
www.mathtekstoolkit.org

Problem	Text Reference
1	Lesson 14-1
2–3	Lesson 14-6
4	Lesson 14-3
5–6	Lesson 14-6

State Resources

go.hrw.com
State Resources Online
KEYWORD: MB7 Resources

CHAPTER 14

MULTI-STEP TEST PREP

SECTION 14B

Trigonometric Identities

Spring into Action Simple harmonic motion refers to motion that repeats in a regular pattern. The bouncing motion of a mass attached to a spring is a good example of simple harmonic motion. As shown in the figure, the displacement y of the mass as a function of time t in seconds is a sine or cosine function. The amplitude is the distance from the center of the motion to either extreme. The period is the time that it takes to complete one full cycle of the motion.

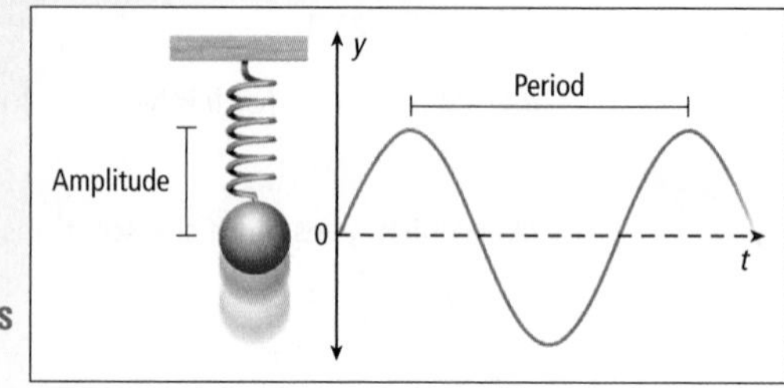

1. The displacement in inches of a mass attached to a spring is modeled by $y_1(t) = 3\sin\left(\frac{2\pi}{5}t + \frac{\pi}{2}\right)$, where t is the time in seconds. What is the amplitude of the motion? What is the period? **3 in.; 5 s**
2. What is the initial displacement when $t = 0$ s? How long does it take until the displacement is 1.8 in.? **3 in.; 0.74 s**
3. At what other times will the displacement be 1.8 in.? **$5n \pm 0.74$ s where n is an integer**
4. Use trigonometric identities to write the displacement by using only the cosine function. **$y(t) = 3\cos\frac{2\pi}{5}t$**
5. The displacement of a second mass attached to a spring is modeled by $y_2(t) = \sin\frac{2\pi}{5}t$. Both masses are set in motion at $t = 0$ s. How long does it take until both masses have the same displacement? **about 0.99 s**
6. The displacement of a third mass attached to a spring is modeled by $y_3(t) = \cos\frac{\pi}{5}t$. The second and third masses are set in motion at $t = 0$ s. How long does it take until both masses have the same displacement? **about 0.83 s**

1034

INTERVENTION

Scaffolding Questions

1. What are the maximum and minimum values of the function? 3, −3
2. What equation should you solve in order to determine when the displacement is 1.8 in.? $1.8 = 3\sin\left(\frac{2\pi}{5}t + \frac{\pi}{2}\right)$
3. How can you use the period to find when the displacement will be 1.8 in. again? Add 5 s to the answer from Problem 2.
4. What type of identity should you use to rewrite the function? sum identity
5. What equation do you need to solve? $3\cos\frac{2\pi}{5}t = \sin\frac{2\pi}{5}t$
6. What equation do you need to solve? $\sin\frac{2\pi}{5}t = \cos\frac{\pi}{5}t$

Extension

At what times will the second and third masses have the same displacement? $t = 2.5 + 5n$, $t = 0.83 + 10n$, and $t = 4.16 + 10n$, for $n \in \mathbb{Z}$

CHAPTER 14

SECTION 14B

Quiz for Lessons 14-3 Through 14-6

14-3 Fundamental Trigonometric Identities

Prove each trigonometric identity.

1. $\sin^2\theta \sec\theta \csc\theta = \tan\theta$
2. $\sin(-\theta)\sec\theta\cot\theta = -1$
3. $\dfrac{\cot^2\theta - 1}{\cot^2\theta + 1} = 1 - 2\sin^2\theta$

Rewrite each expression in terms of a single trigonometric function.

4. $\cot\theta\sec\theta$ $\csc\theta$
5. $\dfrac{1}{\cos(-\theta)}$ $\sec\theta$
6. $\dfrac{\csc^2\theta}{\tan\theta + \cot\theta}$ $\cot\theta$

14-4 Sum and Difference Identities

Find the exact value of each expression.

7. $\cos\frac{5\pi}{12}$ $\dfrac{\sqrt{6} - \sqrt{2}}{4}$
8. $\sin(-75°)$ $\dfrac{-\sqrt{6} - \sqrt{2}}{4}$
9. $\tan 75°$ $2 + \sqrt{3}$

Find each value if $\sin A = \frac{1}{4}$ with $90° < A < 180°$ and if $\cos B = \frac{12}{13}$ with $270° < B < 360°$.

10. $\sin(A + B)$ $\dfrac{12 + 5\sqrt{15}}{52}$
11. $\cos(A + B)$ $\dfrac{-12\sqrt{15} + 5}{52}$
12. $\cos(A - B)$ $\dfrac{-12\sqrt{15} - 5}{52}$
13. Find the coordinates, to the nearest hundredth, of the vertices of figure $ABCD$ with $A(0, 0)$, $B(4, 1)$, $C(0, 2)$, and $D(-1, 1)$ after a 120° rotation about the origin.

(0, 0), (−2.87, 2.96), (−1.73, −1), (−0.37, −1.37)

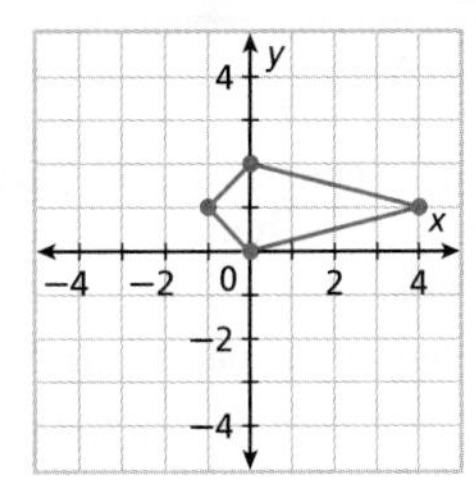

14-5 Double-Angle and Half-Angle Identities

Find each expression if $\cos\theta = -\frac{4}{5}$ and $180° < \theta < 270°$.

14. $\sin 2\theta$ $\frac{24}{25}$
15. $\cos 2\theta$ $\frac{7}{25}$
16. $\tan 2\theta$ $\frac{24}{7}$
17. $\sin\frac{\theta}{2}$ $\dfrac{3\sqrt{10}}{10}$
18. $\cos\frac{\theta}{2}$ $-\dfrac{\sqrt{10}}{10}$
19. $\tan\frac{\theta}{2}$ -3
20. Use half-angle identities to find the exact value of $\cos 22.5°$. $\dfrac{\sqrt{2 + \sqrt{2}}}{2}$

14-6 Solving Trigonometric Equations

21. Find all solutions of $1 + 2\sin\theta = 0$ where θ is in radians. $\frac{7\pi}{6} + 2\pi n$, $\frac{11\pi}{6} + 2\pi n$

Solve each equation for $0° \le \theta < 360°$.

22. $\cos 2\theta + 2\cos\theta = 3$
    0°
23. $8\sin^2\theta - 2\sin\theta = 1$
    30°, 150°, ≈ 194.5°, ≈ 345.5°

Use trigonometric identities to solve each equation for $0 \le \theta < 2\pi$.

24. $\cos 2\theta = 3\cos\theta + 1$ $\frac{2\pi}{3}$, $\frac{4\pi}{3}$
25. $\sin^2\theta + \cos\theta + 1 = 0$ π
26. The average daily *minimum* temperature for Houston, Texas, can be modeled by $T(x) = -15.85\cos\frac{\pi}{6}(x - 1) + 76.85$, where T is the temperature in degrees Fahrenheit, x is the time in months, and $x = 0$ is January 1. When is the temperature 65°F? 85°F? mid-March and mid-December; early June and late September

READY TO GO ON? SECTION 14B

Organizer

Objective: Assess students' mastery of concepts and skills in Lessons 14-3 through 14-6.

PREMIER Online Edition

Resources

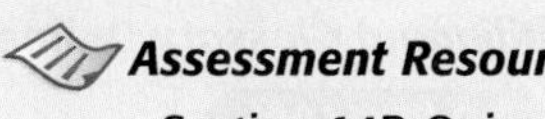
Assessment Resources
Section 14B Quiz

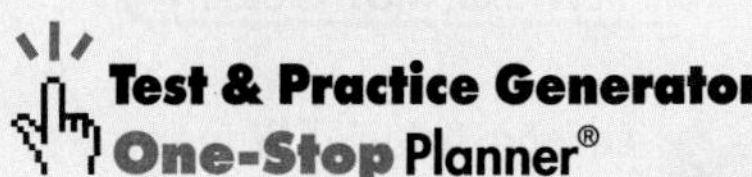
Test & Practice Generator
One-Stop Planner®

INTERVENTION

Resources

Ready to Go On? Intervention and Enrichment Worksheets

Ready to Go On? CD-ROM

Ready to Go On? Online

my.hrw.com

Answers

1–3. See p. A54.

READY TO GO ON?

Diagnose and Prescribe

Ready to Go On? Intervention	*Ready to Go On? Intervention, Section 14B*		
	Worksheets	CD-ROM	Online
Lesson 14-3	14-3 Intervention	Activity 14-3	Diagnose and Prescribe Online
Lesson 14-4	14-4 Intervention	Activity 14-4	
Lesson 14-5	14-5 Intervention	Activity 14-5	
Lesson 14-6	14-6 Intervention	Activity 14-6	

YES
ENRICH
Ready to Go On? Enrichment, Section 14B
Worksheets
CD-ROM
Online

Organizer

Objective: Help students organize and review key concepts and skills in Chapter 14.

Online Edition
Multilingual Glossary

Resources

***Multilingual Glossary* Online**

go.hrw.com
KEYWORD: MB7 Glossary

Lesson Tutorial Videos
CD-ROM

CHAPTER 14 Study Guide: Review

Vocabulary

Complete the sentences below with vocabulary words from the list above.

1. The shortest repeating portion of a periodic function is known as a(n) ___?___.
2. The number of cycles in a given unit of time is called ___?___.
3. The ___?___ gives the length of a complete cycle for a periodic function.
4. A horizontal translation of a periodic function is known as a(n) ___?___.

14-1 Graphs of Sine and Cosine *(pp. 990–997)*

EXAMPLES

■ **Using $f(x) = \cos x$ as a guide, graph $g(x) = -2\cos\frac{\pi}{2}x$. Identify the amplitude and period.**

Step 1 Identify the period and amplitude.

Because $a = -2$, amplitude is $|a| = |-2| = 2$.

Because $b = \frac{\pi}{2}$, the period is $\frac{2\pi}{|b|} = \frac{2\pi}{\left|\frac{\pi}{2}\right|} = 4$.

Step 2 Graph.

The curve is reflected over the x-axis.

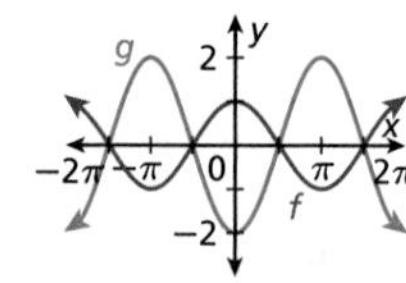

■ **Using $f(x) = \sin x$ as a guide, graph $g(x) = \sin\left(x - \frac{5\pi}{4}\right)$. Identify the x-intercepts and phase shift.**

The amplitude is 1. The period is 2π.

$-\frac{5\pi}{4}$ indicates a shift $\frac{5\pi}{4}$ units right.

The first x-intercept occurs at $\frac{\pi}{4}$. Thus, the intercepts occur at $\frac{\pi}{4} + n\pi$, where n is an integer.

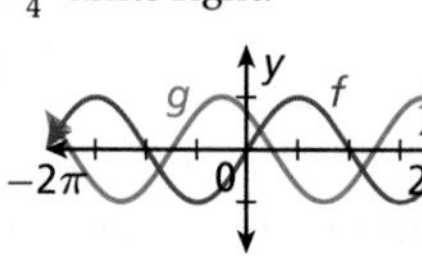

EXERCISES

Using $f(x) = \sin x$ or $f(x) = \cos x$ as a guide, graph each function. Identify the amplitude and period.

5. $f(x) = \cos 3x$
6. $g(x) = \cos\frac{1}{2}x$
7. $h(x) = -\frac{1}{3}\sin x$
8. $j(x) = 2\sin \pi x$
9. $f(x) = \frac{1}{2}\cos 2x$
10. $g(x) = \frac{\pi}{2}\sin \pi x$

Using $f(x) = \sin x$ or $f(x) = \cos x$ as a guide, graph each function. Identify the x-intercepts and phase shift.

11. $f(x) = \cos(x + \pi)$
12. $g(x) = \sin\left(x + \frac{\pi}{4}\right)$
13. $h(x) = \sin\left(x - \frac{3\pi}{2}\right)$
14. $j(x) = \cos\left(x + \frac{3\pi}{2}\right)$

Biology In photosynthesis, a plant converts carbon dioxide and water to sugar and oxygen. This process is studied by measuring a plant's carbon assimilation C (in micromoles of CO_2 per square meter per second). For a bean plant, $C(t) = 1.2\sin\frac{\pi}{12}(t - 6) + 7$, where t is time in hours starting at midnight.

15. Graph the function for two complete cycles.
16. What is the period of the function?
17. What is the maximum and at what time does it occur?

Answers

1. cycle
2. frequency
3. period
4. phase shift
5. amplitude: 1; period: $\frac{2\pi}{3}$

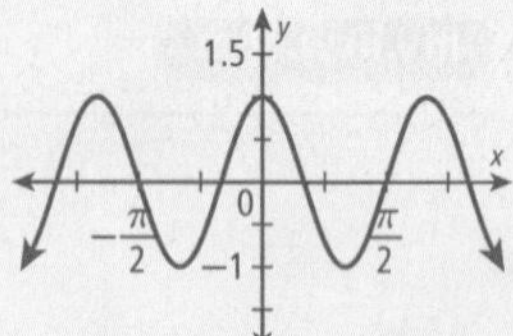

6. amplitude: 1; period: 4π

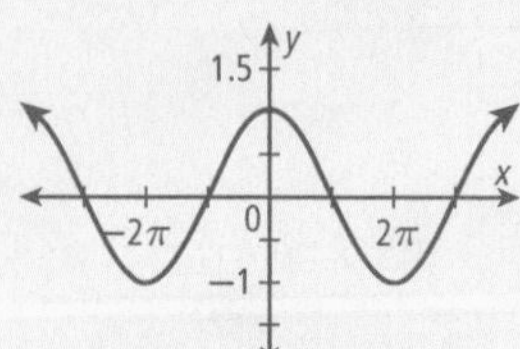

7. amplitude: $\frac{1}{3}$; period: 2π

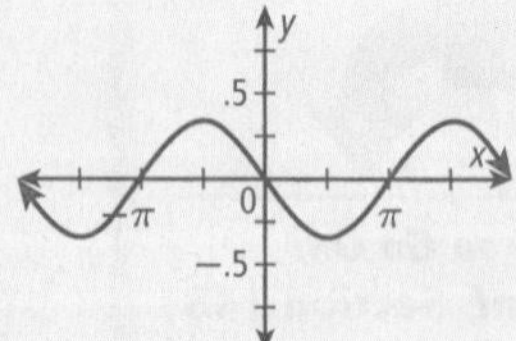

8. amplitude: 2; period: 2

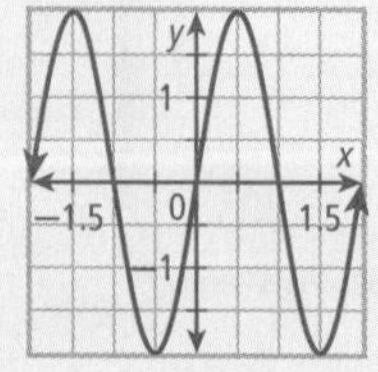

9. amplitude: $\frac{1}{2}$; period: π

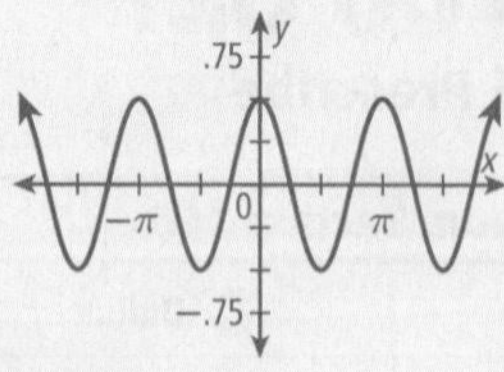

10. amplitude: $\frac{\pi}{2}$; period: 2

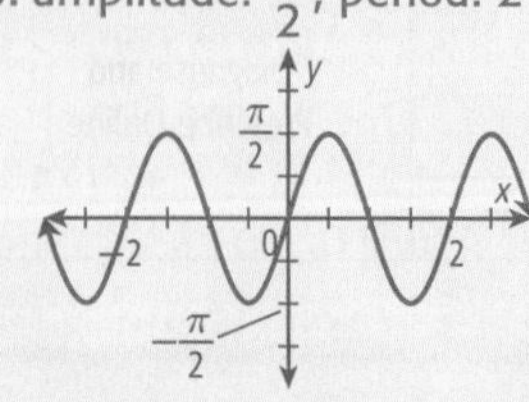

11. x-intercepts: $\frac{\pi}{2} + n\pi$; phase shift: π left

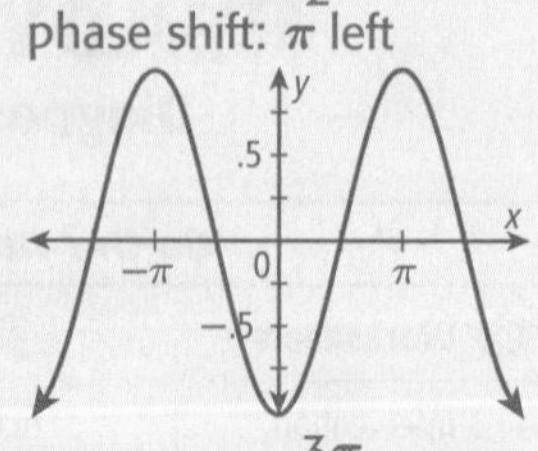

12. x-intercepts: $\frac{3\pi}{4} + \pi n$; phase shift: $\frac{\pi}{4}$ left

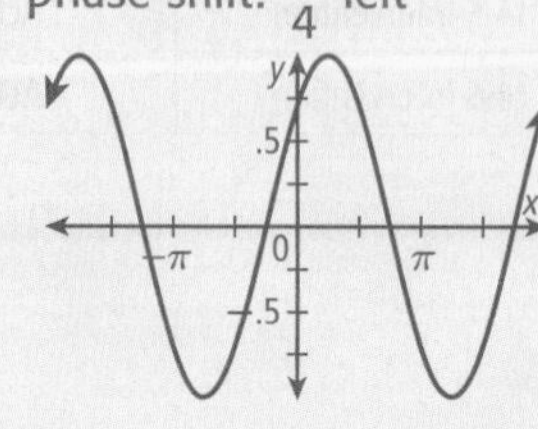

13. x-intercepts: $\frac{\pi}{2} + \pi n$; phase shift: $\frac{3\pi}{2}$ right

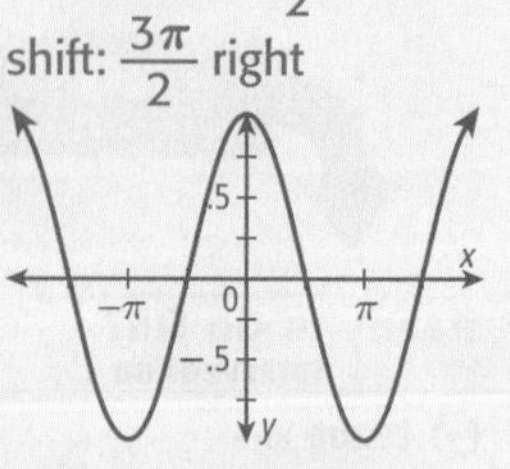

14. x-intercepts: πn; phase shift: $\frac{3\pi}{2}$ left

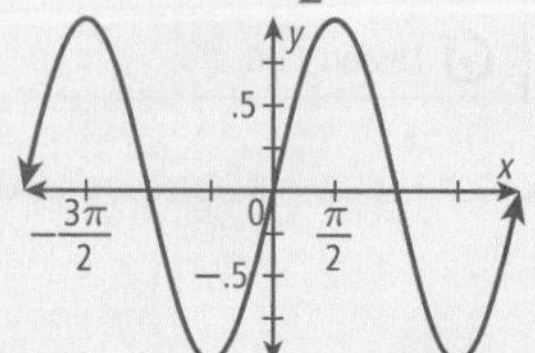

14-2 Graphs of Other Trigonometric Functions *(pp. 998–1003)*

EXAMPLE

- **Using $f(x) = \cot x$ as a guide, graph $g(x) = \cot \frac{\pi}{2}x$. Identify the period, x-intercepts, and asymptotes.**

Step 1 Identify the period.

Because $b = \frac{\pi}{2}$, the period is $\frac{\pi}{|b|} = \frac{\pi}{\left|\frac{\pi}{2}\right|} = 2$.

Step 2 Identify the x-intercepts.

The first x-intercept occurs at 1. Thus, the x-intercepts occur at $1 + 2n$, where n is an integer.

Step 3 Identify the asymptotes.

The asymptotes occur at $x = \frac{\pi n}{|b|} = \frac{\pi n}{\left|\frac{\pi}{2}\right|} = 2n$.

Step 4 Graph.

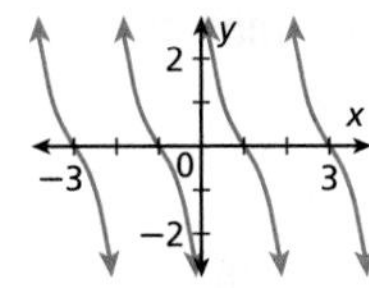

EXERCISES

Using $f(x) = \tan x$ or $f(x) = \cot x$ as a guide, graph each function. Identify the period, x-intercepts, and asymptotes.

18. $f(x) = \frac{1}{4}\tan x$

19. $g(x) = \tan \pi x$

20. $h(x) = \tan \frac{1}{2}\pi x$

21. $g(x) = 5\cot x$

22. $j(x) = -0.5\cot x$

23. $j(x) = \cot \pi x$

Using $f(x) = \cos x$ or $f(x) = \sin x$ as a guide, graph each function. Identify the period and asymptotes.

24. $f(x) = 2\sec x$

25. $g(x) = \csc 2x$

26. $h(x) = 4\csc x$

27. $j(x) = 0.2\sec x$

28. $h(x) = \sec(-x)$

29. $j(x) = -2\csc x$

14-3 Fundamental Trigonometric Identities *(pp. 1008–1013)*

EXAMPLES

- **Prove $\frac{\tan\theta}{1-\cos^2\theta} = \sec\theta\csc\theta$.**

$\dfrac{\left(\frac{\sin\theta}{\cos\theta}\right)}{(\sin^2\theta)} =$	*Modify the left side. Apply the ratio and Pythagorean identities.*
$\left(\frac{\sin\theta}{\cos\theta}\right)\left(\frac{1}{\sin^2\theta}\right) =$	*Multiply by the reciprocal.*
$\left(\frac{1}{\cos\theta}\right)\left(\frac{1}{\sin\theta}\right) =$	*Simplify.*
$\sec\theta\csc\theta$	*Reciprocal identities*

- **Rewrite $\frac{\cot\theta + \tan\theta}{\csc\theta}$ in terms of a single trigonometric function, and simplify.**

$(\cot\theta + \tan\theta)\sin\theta$	*Given.*
$\left(\frac{\cos\theta}{\sin\theta} + \frac{\sin\theta}{\cos\theta}\right)\sin\theta$	*Ratio identities*
$\frac{\cos^2\theta + \sin^2\theta}{\cos\theta}$	*Add fractions and simplify.*
$\frac{1}{\cos\theta} = \sec\theta$	*Pythagorean and reciprocal identities*

EXERCISES

Prove each trigonometric identity.

30. $\sec\theta\sin\theta\cot\theta = 1$

31. $\frac{\sin^2(-\theta)}{\tan\theta} = \sin\theta\cos\theta$

32. $(\sec\theta + 1)(\sec\theta - 1) = \tan^2\theta$

33. $\cos\theta\sec\theta + \cos^2\theta\csc^2\theta = \csc^2\theta$

34. $(\tan\theta + \cot\theta)^2 = \sec^2\theta + \csc^2\theta$

35. $\tan\theta + \cot\theta = \sec\theta\csc\theta$

36. $\sin^2\theta\tan\theta = \tan\theta - \sin\theta\cos\theta$

37. $\frac{\tan\theta}{1-\cos^2\theta} = \sec\theta\csc\theta$

Rewrite each expression in terms of a single trigonometric function, and simplify.

38. $\cot\theta\sec\theta$

39. $\frac{\sec\theta\sin\theta}{\cot\theta}$

40. $\frac{\tan(-\theta)}{\cot\theta}$

41. $\frac{\cos\theta\cot\theta}{\csc^2\theta - 1}$

Answers

15.

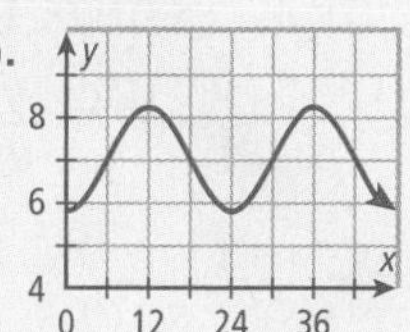

16. 24 h

17. 8.2; noon

18. period: π; x-intercepts: πn; asymptotes: $\frac{\pi}{2} + \pi n$

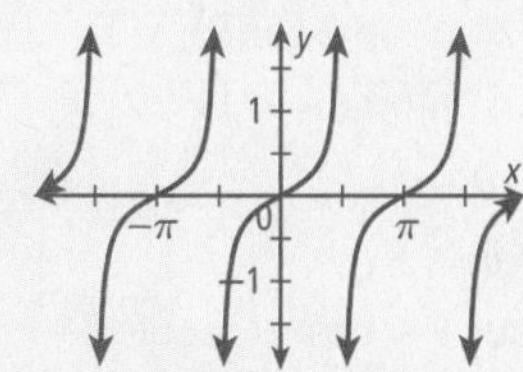

19. period: 1; x-intercepts: n; asymptotes: $\frac{1}{2} + n$

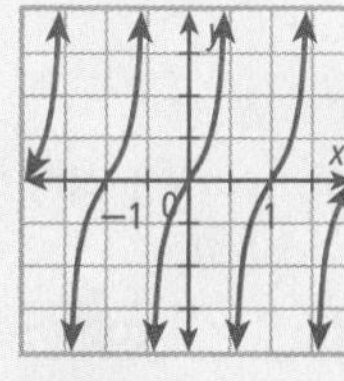

20. period: 2; x-intercepts: $2n$; asymptotes: $1 + 2n$

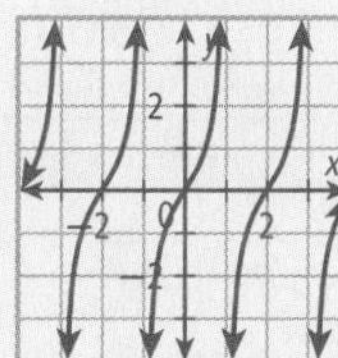

21. period: π; x-intercepts: $\frac{\pi}{2} + \pi n$; asymptotes: πn

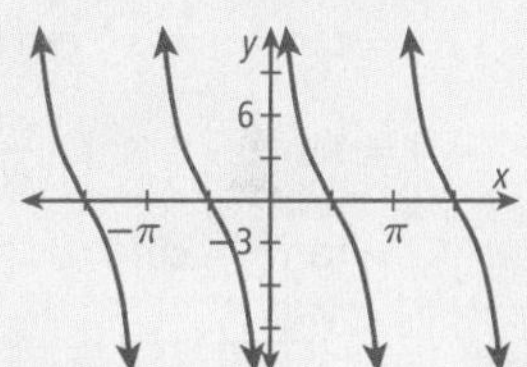

22. period: π; x-intercepts: $\frac{\pi}{2} + \pi n$; asymptotes: πn

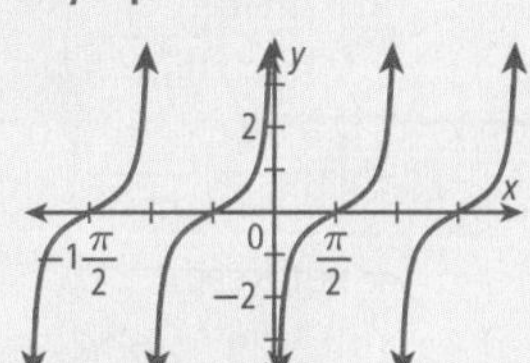

23. period: 1; x-intercepts: $\frac{1}{2} + n$; asymptotes: n

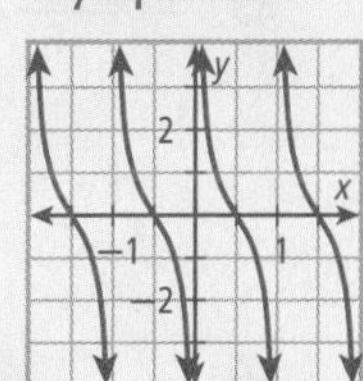

24. period: 2π; asymptotes: $\frac{\pi}{2} + \pi n$

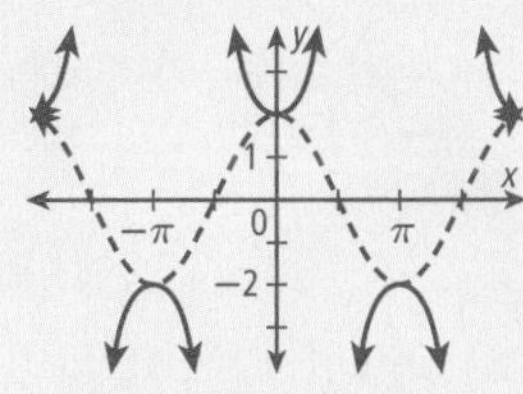

25. period: π; asymptotes: $\frac{\pi}{2}n$

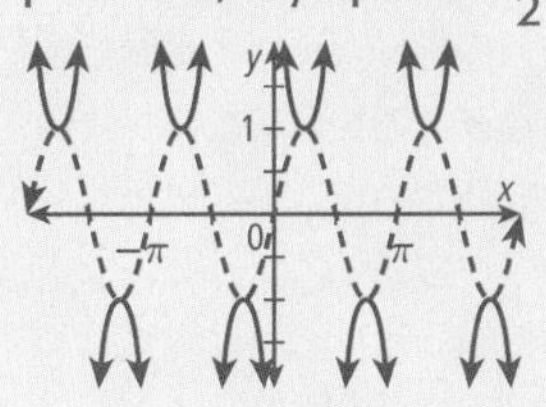

26. period: 2π; asymptotes: $\pi + \pi n$

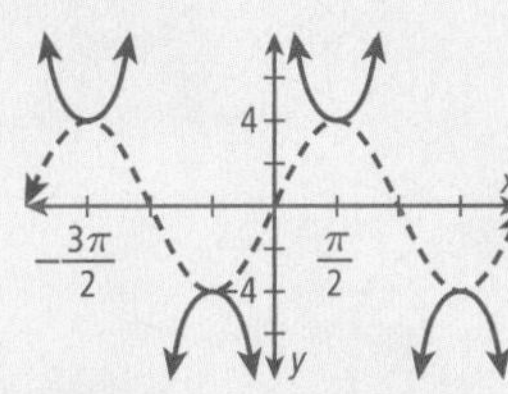

27. period: 2π; asymptotes: $\frac{\pi}{2} + \pi n$

28. period: 2π; asymptotes: $\frac{\pi}{2} + \pi n$

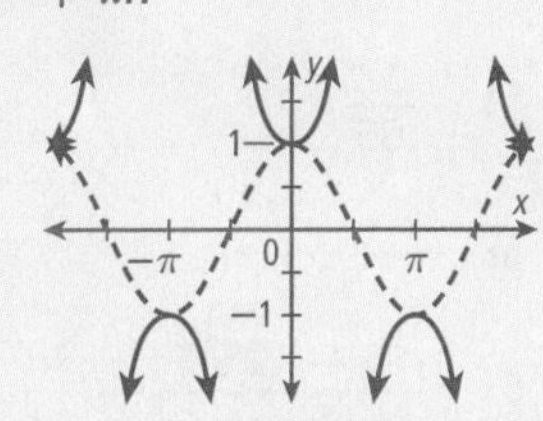

29. period: 2π; asymptotes: $\pi + \pi n$

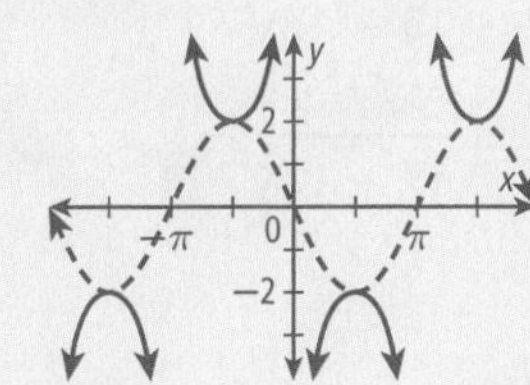

Answers

30.

$$\sec\theta\sin\theta\cot\theta = \left(\frac{1}{\cos\theta}\right)\sin\theta\left(\frac{\cos\theta}{\sin\theta}\right)$$
$$= \left(\frac{\cos\theta}{\cos\theta}\right)\left(\frac{\sin\theta}{\sin\theta}\right) = 1$$

31.
$$\frac{\sin^2(-\theta)}{\tan\theta} = \frac{(-\sin\theta)(-\sin\theta)}{\frac{\sin\theta}{\cos\theta}}$$
$$= (\sin\theta)(\sin\theta)\left(\frac{\cos\theta}{\sin\theta}\right)$$
$$= \sin\theta\cos\theta$$

32. $(\sec\theta + 1)(\sec\theta - 1)$
$$= \sec^2\theta - 1$$
$$= \tan^2\theta$$

33. $\cos\theta\sec\theta + \cos^2\theta\csc^2\theta$
$$= 1 + \cos^2\theta\left(\frac{1}{\sin^2\theta}\right)$$
$$= 1 + \cot^2\theta$$
$$= \csc^2\theta$$

34. $(\tan\theta + \cot\theta)^2$
$$= \tan^2\theta + 2\tan\theta\cot\theta + \cot^2\theta$$
$$= \tan^2\theta + 2 + \cot^2\theta$$
$$= (\tan^2\theta + 1) + (1 + \cot^2\theta)$$
$$= \sec^2\theta + \csc^2\theta$$

35. $\tan\theta + \cot\theta = \frac{\sin\theta}{\cos\theta} + \frac{\cos\theta}{\sin\theta}$
$$= \frac{\sin^2\theta + \cos^2\theta}{\sin\theta\cos\theta}$$
$$= \frac{1}{\sin\theta\cos\theta}$$
$$= \sec\theta\csc\theta$$

36. $\sin^2\theta\tan\theta = (1 - \cos^2\theta)\tan\theta$
$$= \tan\theta - \cos^2\tan\theta$$
$$= \tan\theta - \cos^2\theta\left(\frac{\sin\theta}{\cos\theta}\right)$$
$$= \tan\theta - \sin\theta\cos\theta$$

37.
$$\frac{\tan\theta}{1 - \cos^2\theta} = \frac{\left(\frac{\sin\theta}{\cos\theta}\right)}{(\sin^2\theta)}$$
$$= \left(\frac{\sin\theta}{\cos\theta}\right)\left(\frac{1}{\sin^2\theta}\right)$$
$$= \left(\frac{1}{\cos\theta}\right)\left(\frac{1}{\sin\theta}\right)$$
$$= \sec\theta\csc\theta$$

14-4 Sum and Difference Identities *(pp. 1014–1019)*

EXAMPLES

■ **Find $\sin(A + B)$ if $\cos A = -\frac{1}{3}$ with $180° < A < 270°$ and if $\sin B = \frac{4}{5}$ with $90° < B < 180°$.**

Step 1 Find $\sin A$ and $\cos B$ by using the Pythagorean Theorem with reference triangles.

$180° < A < 270°$ $\quad$ $90° < B < 180°$

$\cos A = -\frac{1}{3}$ $\quad$ $\sin B = \frac{4}{5}$

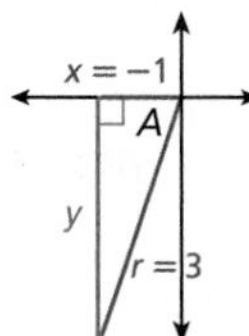

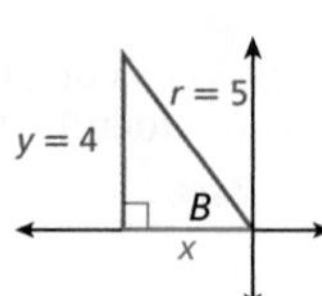

$y = -\sqrt{8}$, $\sin A = \frac{-\sqrt{8}}{3}$ $\quad$ $x = -3$, $\cos B = \frac{-3}{5}$

Step 2 Use the angle-sum identity.

$$\sin(A + B) = \sin A\cos B + \cos A\sin B$$
$$= \left(\frac{-\sqrt{8}}{3}\right)\left(\frac{-3}{5}\right) + \left(-\frac{1}{3}\right)\left(\frac{4}{5}\right)$$
$$= \frac{3\sqrt{8} - 4}{15}$$

■ **Find the coordinates to the nearest hundredth of the vertices of figure ABC with $A(0, 2)$, $B(1, 2)$, and $C(0, 1)$ after a 60° rotation about the origin.**

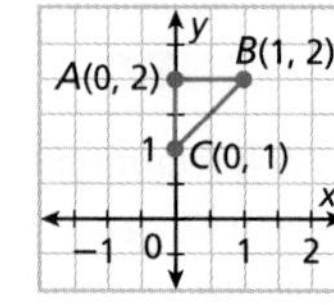

Step 1 Write matrices for a 60° rotation and for the points in the figure.

$$R_{60°} = \begin{bmatrix} \cos 60° & -\sin 60° \\ \sin 60° & \cos 60° \end{bmatrix} \quad \textit{Rotation matrix}$$

$$S = \begin{bmatrix} 0 & 1 & 0 \\ 2 & 2 & 1 \end{bmatrix} \quad \textit{Matrix of points}$$

Step 2 Find the matrix product.

$$R_{60°} \times S = \begin{bmatrix} \cos 60° & -\sin 60° \\ \sin 60° & \cos 60° \end{bmatrix}\begin{bmatrix} 0 & 1 & 0 \\ 2 & 2 & 1 \end{bmatrix}$$
$$\approx \begin{bmatrix} -1.73 & -1.23 & -0.87 \\ 1 & 1.87 & 0.5 \end{bmatrix}$$

Step 3 The approximate coordinates of the points after a 60° rotation are $A'(-1.73, 1)$, $B'(-1.23, 1.87)$, and $C'(-0.87, 0.5)$.

EXERCISES

Find the exact value of each expression.

42. $\sin\frac{19\pi}{12}$
43. $\cos 165°$
44. $\cos 15°$
45. $\tan\frac{\pi}{12}$

Find each value if $\tan A = \frac{3}{4}$ with $0° < A < 90°$ and if $\tan B = -\frac{5}{12}$ with $90° < B < 180°$.

46. $\sin(A + B)$
47. $\cos(A + B)$
48. $\tan(A - B)$
49. $\tan(A + B)$
50. $\sin(A - B)$
51. $\cos(A - B)$

Find each value if $\sin A = \frac{\sqrt{7}}{4}$ with $0° < A < 90°$ and if $\cos B = -\frac{5}{13}$ with $90° < B < 180°$.

52. $\sin(A + B)$
53. $\cos(A + B)$
54. $\tan(A - B)$
55. $\tan(A + B)$
56. $\sin(A - B)$
57. $\cos(A - B)$

Find the coordinates, to the nearest hundredth, of the vertices of figure $ABCD$ with $A(0, 0)$, $B(3, 0)$, $C(4, 2)$, and $D(1, 2)$ after each rotation about the origin.

58. 30° rotation
59. 45° rotation
60. 60° rotation
61. 90° rotation

Find the coordinates, to the nearest hundredth, of the vertices of figure $ABCD$ with $A(0, 0)$, $B(5, 2)$, $C(0, 4)$, and $D(-5, 2)$ after each rotation about the origin.

62. 120° rotation
63. 180° rotation
64. 240° rotation
65. 270° rotation

38. $\csc\theta$
39. $\tan^2\theta$
40. $-\tan^2\theta$
41. $\sin\theta$
42. $\frac{-\sqrt{2} - \sqrt{6}}{4}$
43. $\frac{-\sqrt{2} - \sqrt{6}}{4}$
44. $\frac{\sqrt{6} + \sqrt{2}}{4}$
45. $2 - \sqrt{3}$
46. $-\frac{16}{65}$
47. $-\frac{63}{65}$
48. $\frac{56}{33}$
49. $\frac{16}{63}$
50. $-\frac{56}{65}$
51. $-\frac{33}{65}$
52. $\frac{36 - 5\sqrt{7}}{52}$
53. $\frac{-15 - 12\sqrt{7}}{52}$
54. $\frac{5\sqrt{7} + 36}{15 - 12\sqrt{7}}$
55. $\frac{5\sqrt{7} - 36}{15 + 12\sqrt{7}}$

14-5 Double-Angle and Half-Angle Identities (pp. 1020–1026)

EXAMPLES

Find each expression if $\sin\theta = \frac{1}{4}$ and $270° < \theta < 360°$.

- $\sin 2\theta$

For $\sin\theta = \frac{1}{4}$ in QIV, $\cos\theta = -\frac{\sqrt{15}}{4}$.

$\sin 2\theta = 2\sin\theta\cos\theta$ *Identity for sin 2θ*

$= 2\left(\frac{1}{4}\right)\left(-\frac{\sqrt{15}}{4}\right) = -\frac{\sqrt{15}}{8}$ *Substitute.*

- $\cos\frac{\theta}{2}$

$\cos\frac{\theta}{2} = \pm\sqrt{\frac{1+\cos\theta}{2}}$ *Identity for $\cos\frac{\theta}{2}$*

$= -\sqrt{\frac{1+\left(-\frac{\sqrt{15}}{4}\right)}{2}}$ *Negative for $\cos\frac{\theta}{2}$ in QII*

$= -\sqrt{\left(\frac{4-\sqrt{15}}{4}\right)\left(\frac{1}{2}\right)} = -\frac{\sqrt{4-\sqrt{15}}}{\sqrt{8}}$

EXERCISES

Find each expression if $\tan\theta = \frac{4}{3}$ and $0° < \theta < 90°$.

66. $\sin 2\theta$ **67.** $\cos 2\theta$

68. $\tan\frac{\theta}{2}$ **69.** $\sin\frac{\theta}{2}$

Find each expression if $\cos\theta = \frac{3}{4}$ and $\frac{3\pi}{2} < \theta < 2\pi$.

70. $\tan 2\theta$ **71.** $\cos 2\theta$

72. $\cos\frac{\theta}{2}$ **73.** $\sin\frac{\theta}{2}$

Use half-angle identities to find the exact value of each trigonometric expression.

74. $\sin\frac{\pi}{12}$ **75.** $\cos 75°$

14-6 Solving Trigonometric Equations (pp. 1027–1033)

EXAMPLES

- **Find all of the solutions of $3\cos\theta - \sqrt{3} = \cos\theta$.**

$3\cos\theta - \sqrt{3} = \cos\theta$

$3\cos\theta - \cos\theta = \sqrt{3}$ *Subtract tan θ.*

$2\cos\theta = \sqrt{3}$ *Combine like terms.*

$\cos\theta = \frac{\sqrt{3}}{2}$ *Divide by 2.*

$\theta = \cos^{-1}\left(\frac{\sqrt{3}}{2}\right)$ *Apply the inverse cosine.*

$\theta = 30°$ or $330°$ *Find θ for $0° \le \theta < 360°$.*

$\theta = 30° + 360°n$ or $330° + 360°n$

- **Solve $6\sin^2\theta + 5\sin\theta = -1$ for $0° \le \theta < 360°$.**

$6\sin^2\theta + 5\sin\theta + 1 = 0$ *Set equal to 0.*

$(2\sin\theta + 1)(3\sin\theta + 1) = 0$ *Factor.*

$\sin\theta = -1$ or $\sin\theta = 3$ *Zero Product Property*

$\theta = 210°, 330°$ or $\approx 199.5°, 340.5°$ *$\sin\theta = 3$ has no solution since $-1 \le \sin\theta \le 1$.*

EXERCISES

Find all of the solutions of each equation.

76. $\sqrt{2}\cos\theta + 1 = 0$ **77.** $\cos\theta = 2 + 3\cos\theta$

78. $\tan^2\theta + \tan\theta = 0$ **79.** $\sin^2\theta - \cos^2\theta = \frac{1}{2}$

Solve each equation for $0 \le \theta < 2\pi$.

80. $2\cos^2\theta - 3\cos\theta = 2$ **81.** $\cos^2\theta + 5\cos\theta - 6 = 0$

82. $\sin^2\theta - 1 = 0$ **83.** $2\sin^2\theta - \sin\theta = 3$

Use trigonometric identities to solve each equation for $0 \le \theta < 2\pi$.

84. $\cos 2\theta = \cos\theta$ **85.** $\sin 2\theta + \cos\theta = 0$

86. Earth Science The number of minutes of daylight for each day of the year can be modeled with a trigonometric function. For Washington, D.C., S is the number of minutes of daylight in the model $S(d) = 180\sin(0.0172d - 1.376) + 720$, where d is the number of days since January 1.

a. What is the maximum number of daylight minutes, and when does it occur?

b. What is the minimum number of daylight minutes, and when does it occur?

Answers

56. $\frac{-36 - 5\sqrt{7}}{52}$

57. $\frac{-15 + 12\sqrt{7}}{52}$

58. $\approx \begin{bmatrix} 0 & 2.60 & 2.46 & -0.13 \\ 0 & 1.50 & 3.73 & 2.23 \end{bmatrix}$

59. $\approx \begin{bmatrix} 0 & 2.12 & 1.41 & -0.71 \\ 0 & 2.12 & 4.24 & 2.12 \end{bmatrix}$

60. $\approx \begin{bmatrix} 0 & 1.5 & 0.27 & -1.23 \\ 0 & 2.60 & 4.46 & 1.87 \end{bmatrix}$

61. $\approx \begin{bmatrix} 0 & 0 & -2 & -2 \\ 0 & 3 & 4 & 1 \end{bmatrix}$

62. $\approx \begin{bmatrix} 0 & -4.23 & -3.46 & 0.77 \\ 0 & 3.33 & -2 & -5.33 \end{bmatrix}$

63. $\approx \begin{bmatrix} 0 & -5 & 0 & 5 \\ 0 & -2 & -4 & -2 \end{bmatrix}$

64. $\approx \begin{bmatrix} 0 & -0.77 & 3.46 & 4.23 \\ 0 & -5.33 & -2 & 3.33 \end{bmatrix}$

65. $\approx \begin{bmatrix} 0 & 2 & 4 & 2 \\ 0 & -5 & 0 & 5 \end{bmatrix}$

66. $\frac{24}{25}$ 67. $-\frac{7}{25}$

68. $\frac{1}{2}$ 69. $\frac{\sqrt{5}}{5}$

70. $-3\sqrt{7}$ 71. $\frac{1}{8}$

72. $-\frac{\sqrt{14}}{4}$ 73. $\frac{\sqrt{2}}{4}$

74. $\frac{\sqrt{2-\sqrt{3}}}{2}$ 75. $\frac{\sqrt{2-\sqrt{3}}}{2}$

76. $135° + 360°n$, $225° + 360°n$

77. $180° + 360°n$

78. $0° + 180°n$, $135° + 180°n$

79. $60° + 180°n$, $120° + 180°n$

80. $\frac{2\pi}{3}, \frac{4\pi}{3}$

81. 0

82. $\frac{\pi}{2}, \frac{3\pi}{2}$

83. $\frac{3\pi}{2}$

84. $0, \frac{2\pi}{3}, \frac{4\pi}{3}$

85. $\frac{\pi}{2}, \frac{7\pi}{6}, \frac{3\pi}{2}, \frac{11\pi}{6}$

86a. 900 min; late June

b. 540 min; late December

Organizer

Objective: Assess students' mastery of concepts and skills in Chapter 14.

 **Online Edition**

Resources

 ***Assessment Resources***

Chapter 14 Tests

- Free Response (Levels A, B, C)
- Multiple Choice (Levels A, B, C)
- Performance Assessment

 ***IDEA Works!* CD-ROM**

Modified Chapter 14 Test

Test & Practice Generator One-Stop Planner®

Answers

1.

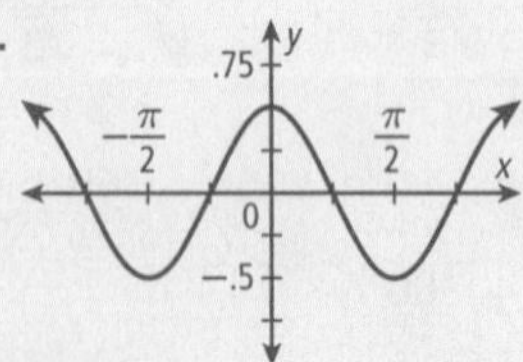

amplitude: $\frac{1}{2}$; period: π

State Resources

go.hrw.com State Resources Online KEYWORD: MB7 Resources

CHAPTER 14 CHAPTER TEST

1. Using $f(x) = \cos x$ as a guide, graph $g(x) = \frac{1}{2}\cos 2x$. Identify the amplitude and period.
2. Using $f(x) = \sin x$ as a guide, graph $g(x) = \sin\left(x + \frac{\pi}{3}\right)$. Identify the x-intercepts and phase shift.
3. A torque τ in newton meters (N•m) applied to an object is given by $\tau(\theta) = Fr\sin\theta$, where r is the length of the lever arm in meters, F is the applied force in newtons, and θ is the angle between F and r in degrees. Find the amount and angle for the maximum torque and the minimum torque for a lever arm of 0.5 m and a force of 500 newtons, where $0° \le \theta \le 90°$. **max.: 250 N•m at 90°; min.: 0 N•m at 0°**
4. Using $f(x) = \tan x$ as a guide, graph $g(x) = 2\tan \pi x$. Identify the period, x-intercepts, and asymptotes.
5. Using $f(x) = \cot x$ as a guide, graph $g(x) = \cot 4x$. Identify the period, x-intercepts, and asymptotes.
6. Using $f(x) = \sin x$ as a guide, graph $g(x) = \frac{1}{4}\csc x$. Identify the period and asymptotes.
7. Prove the trigonometric identity $\cot\theta = \cos^2\theta\sec\theta\csc\theta$. $\cos^2\theta\sec\theta\csc\theta = \cos^2\theta\left(\frac{1}{\cos\theta}\right)\left(\frac{1}{\sin\theta}\right) = \frac{\cos\theta}{\sin\theta} = \cot\theta$

Rewrite each expression in terms of a single trigonometric function.

8. $(\sec\theta + 1)(\sec\theta - 1)$ $\tan^2\theta$
9. $\frac{\sin(-\theta)}{\cos(-\theta)}$ $-\tan\theta$

Find each value if $\tan A = \frac{3}{4}$ with $0° < A < 90°$ and if $\sin B = -\frac{12}{13}$ with $180° < B < 270°$.

10. $\sin(A + B)$ $-\frac{63}{65}$
11. $\cos(A - B)$ $-\frac{56}{65}$
12. Find the coordinates, to the nearest hundredth, of the vertices of figure $ABCD$ with $A(0, 1)$, $B(2, 1)$, $C(3, 3)$, and $D(-1, 3)$ after a 30° rotation about the origin. **(−0.50, 0.87), (1.23, 1.87), (1.10, 4.10), (−2.37, 2.10)**

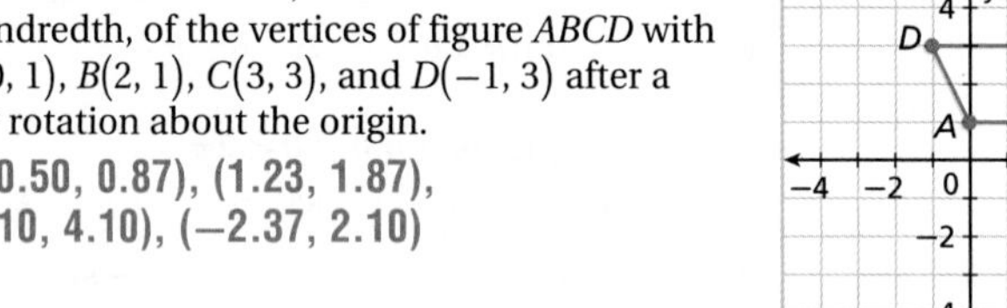
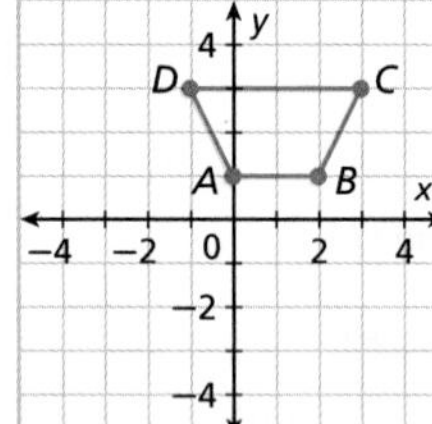

Find each expression if $\tan\theta = -\frac{12}{5}$ and $90° < \theta < 180°$.

13. $\sin 2\theta$ $-\frac{120}{169}$
14. $\cos 2\theta$ $-\frac{119}{169}$
15. $\cos\frac{\theta}{2}$ $\frac{2\sqrt{13}}{13}$
16. Use half-angle identities to find the exact value of $\sin\frac{3\pi}{8}$. $\frac{\sqrt{2+\sqrt{2}}}{2}$
17. Find all of the solutions of $\tan\theta + \sqrt{3} = 0$.
18. Solve $2\sin^2\theta = \sin\theta$ for $0° \le \theta < 360°$. **0°, 30°, 150°, 180°**
19. Use trigonometric identities to solve $2\cos^2\theta + 3\sin\theta = 0$ for $0 \le \theta < 2\pi$. $\frac{7\pi}{6}, \frac{11\pi}{6}$
20. The voltage at a wall plug in a home can be modeled by $V(t) = 156\sin 2\pi(60t)$, where V is the voltage in volts and t is time in seconds. At what times is the voltage equal to 110 volts? $\approx 0.0021 + n\frac{1}{60}$ s, $\approx 0.0063 + n\frac{1}{60}$ s

17. $120° + 180°n$, $\frac{2\pi}{3} + \pi n$

Answers

2.

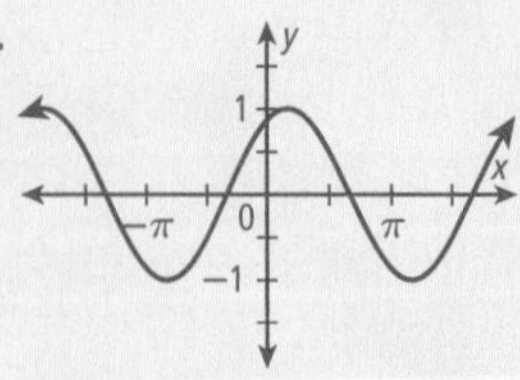

x-intercepts: $\frac{2\pi}{3} + \pi n$;

phase shift: $\frac{\pi}{3}$ left

4.

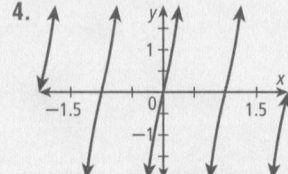

period: 1; intercepts: n;

asymptotes: $\frac{1}{2} + n$

5.

period: $\frac{\pi}{4}$;

intercepts: $\frac{\pi}{8} + \frac{\pi}{4}n$;

asymptotes: $\frac{\pi}{4}n$

6.

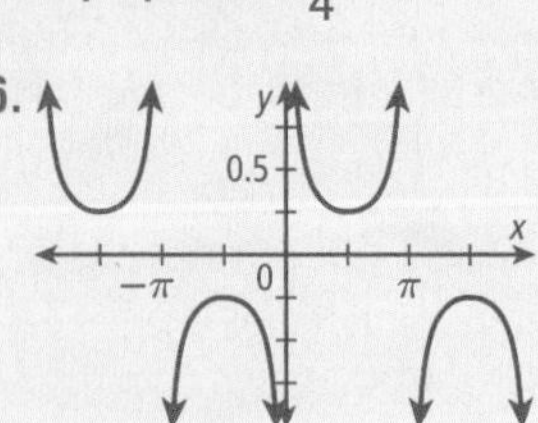

period: 2π;
asymptotes: πn

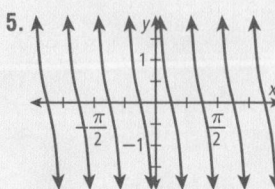

COLLEGE ENTRANCE EXAM PRACTICE

FOCUS ON SAT MATHEMATICS SUBJECT TESTS

To help decide which standardized tests you should take, make a list of colleges that you might like to attend. Find out the admission requirements for each school. Make sure that you register for and take the appropriate tests early enough for colleges to receive your scores.

You may want to time yourself as you take this practice test. It should take you about 6 minutes to complete.

HOT TIP! If your calculator malfunctions while you are taking an SAT Mathematics Subject Test, you may be able to have your score for that test canceled. To do so, you must inform a supervisor at the test center immediately when the malfunction occurs.

1. Identify the range of $f(x) = 3\sin x$.

(A) $-1 \le f(x) \le 1$

(B) $-3 < f(x) < 3$

(C) $0 \le f(x) \le 3$

(D) $-3 \le f(x) \le 3$

(E) $-\infty < f(x) < \infty$

2. If $2\sin^2\theta + 5\sin\theta = 3$, what could the value of θ be?

(A) $\frac{\pi}{6}$

(B) $\frac{\pi}{3}$

(C) $\frac{2\pi}{3}$

(D) $\frac{7\pi}{6}$

(E) $\frac{11\pi}{6}$

3. If $\sec\theta = 4$, what is $\tan^2\theta$?

(A) $\frac{1}{16}$

(B) 3

(C) 5

(D) 15

(E) 17

4. Given the figure, what is the value of $\cos(A - B)$?

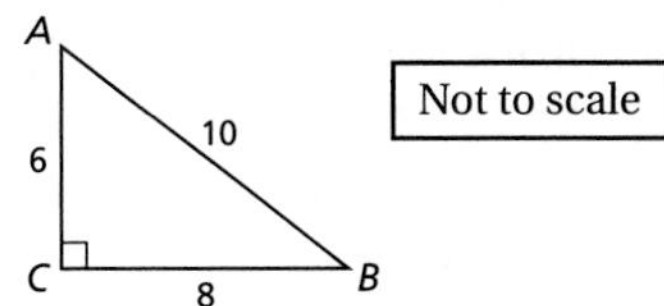

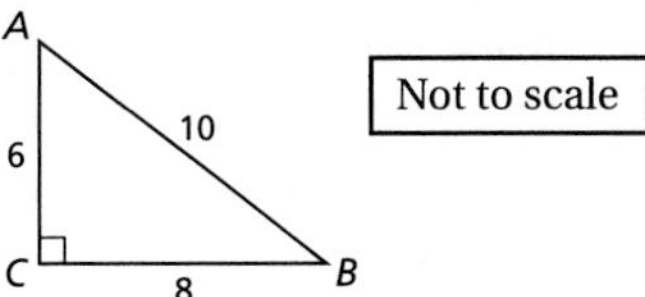

(A) 0

(B) $\frac{7}{25}$

(C) $\frac{24}{25}$

(D) 1

(E) $\frac{28}{25}$

5. If $\sin\theta = \frac{7}{9}$, what is $\cos 2\theta$?

(A) $-\frac{8\sqrt{2}}{9}$

(B) $-\frac{17}{81}$

(C) $\frac{17}{81}$

(D) $\frac{56\sqrt{2}}{81}$

(E) $\frac{8\sqrt{2}}{9}$

COLLEGE ENTRANCE EXAM PRACTICE CHAPTER 14

Organizer

Objective: Provide practice for college entrance exams such as the SAT Mathematics Subject Tests.

Online Edition

Resources

College Entrance Exam Practice

Questions on the SAT Mathematics Subject Tests Levels 1 and 2 represent the following math content areas:

	Level 1	Level 2
Algebra	30%	18%
Plane Euclidean Geometry	20%	0%
Coordinate Geometry	12%	12%
Three-dimensional Geometry	6%	8%
Trigonometry	8%	20%
Functions	12%	24%
Statistics/Probability	6%	6%
Miscellaneous	6%	12%

Items on this page focus on:
- Algebra
- Trigonometry

Text References:

Item	1	2	3	4	5
Lesson	1	6	3	4	5

TEST PREP DOCTOR

1. Students may choose answer **C** because they found the amplitude of the function and then selected only half of the range.

2. Students may choose answers **D** or **E** because they found the correct reference angle but forgot that the sine function is negative in the third and fourth quadrants.

3. Students may choose answer **E** because they have added 1 to $\sec^2\theta$ instead of subtracted 1.

4. Students may choose answer **A** because they found the value of $\cos(A + B)$.

5. Students may choose answer **C** because they have reversed the order of the terms in one of the equivalent forms of the double-angle formula for cosine.

Organizer

Objective: Provide opportunities to learn and practice common test-taking strategies.

Online Edition

Resources

State Test Prep Workbook

***State Test Prep* CD-ROM**

***State Test Practice* Online**

go.hrw.com

KEYWORD: MB7 TestPrep

TEST PREP DOCTOR This Test Tackler focuses on choosing the best answer when there are multiple correct answers or combinations of answers. Reinforce students to read the problem statement and answer choices thoroughly. Encourage students to investigate each possibility.

As students practice this strategy, remind them to choose the best, most complete answer, not just the first correct answer that they discover. Review the elimination strategy, and guide students to use logic to eliminate any obvious answer choice. If students are struggling with organization, show them how a table can be used to organize their process.

Standardized Test Strategies

Multiple Choice: Choose Answer Combinations

You may be given a test item in which you are asked to choose from a combination of statements. To answer these types of test items, try comparing each given statement with the question and determining whether the statement is true or false. If you determine that more than one of the statements is correct, choose the combination that contains each correct statement.

EXAMPLE 1

Which exact solution makes the equation $2\cos^2\theta - 3\cos\theta = 2$ true?

I. $\theta = 2°$
II. $\theta = 120°$
III. $\theta = 240°$

Look at each statement separately, and determine if it is true or false.

Ⓐ I only　　Ⓒ II only

Ⓑ II and III　　Ⓓ I, II, and III

As you consider each statement, mark it true or false.

Consider statement I: Substitute 2° for θ in the equation.

$2\cos^2(2°) - 3\cos(2°) \approx -1.0006$
$\neq 2$

Statement I is false.
So, the answer is ***not*** choice A or D.

Consider statement II: Substitute 120° for θ in the equation.

$2\cos^2(120°) - 3\cos(120°) = 2$

Statement II is true.
The answer *could be* choice B or C.

Consider statement III: Substitute 240° for θ in the equation.

$2\cos^2(240°) - 3\cos(240°) = 2$

Statement III is true.

Because both statements II and III are true, choice B is the correct response.

You can also use a table to keep track of whether the statements are true or false.

Statement	True/False
I	False
II	True
III	True

As you eliminate a statement, cross out the corresponding answer choice(s).

Read each test item and answer the questions that follow.

Item A

Which expression is equivalent to $\tan^2\theta$?

I. $\sec^2\theta - 1$

II. $\sec^2\theta + 1$

III. $\dfrac{1}{\csc^2\theta - 1}$

IV. $\dfrac{1-\cos^2\theta}{1-\sin^2\theta}$

Ⓐ I and II

Ⓑ II and III

Ⓒ I and III

Ⓓ I, III, and IV

1. What are some of the identities that involve the tangent function?
2. Determine whether statements I, II, III, and IV are true or false. Explain your reasoning.
3. Sally realized that statement III was true and selected choice B as her response. Do you agree? If not, what would you have done differently?

Item B

For the graph of $f(x) = 3\sin x + 2$, which of the statements are true?

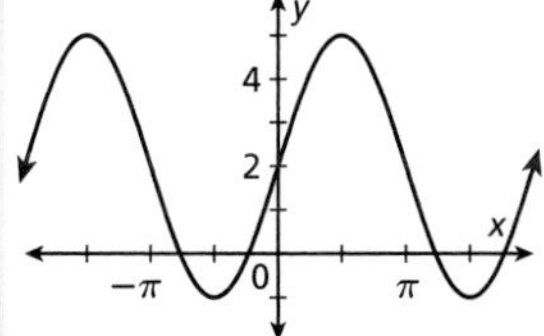

I. The function has a period of $\frac{2\pi}{3}$.

II. The function has an amplitude of 3.

III. The function has a period of 2π.

Ⓕ I only

Ⓖ III only

Ⓗ II only

Ⓙ II and III

4. How do you determine the period of a trigonometric function?
5. How do you determine the amplitude of a trigonometric function?
6. Using your response to Problems 4 and 5, which of the three statements are true? Explain.

Item C

Which identities do you need to use to prove that $\tan\theta\csc\theta = \sec\theta$?

I. $\tan\theta = \dfrac{\sin\theta}{\cos\theta}$

II. $\sec^2\theta = \tan^2\theta + 1$

III. $\csc\theta = \dfrac{1}{\sin\theta}$

Ⓐ I only

Ⓑ II only

Ⓒ I and II

Ⓓ I and III

7. Is statement I true or false? Can any answer choice be eliminated? Explain.
8. Is statement II true or false? Should you select the answer choice yet? Explain.
9. Is statement III true or false? Explain.
10. Which combination of statements is correct? How do you know?

Item D

For the graph of the function $f(x) = \sec 4x$, which are equations of some of the asymptotes?

I. $x = \dfrac{\pi}{8}$

II. $x = \dfrac{\pi}{2}$

III. $x = -\dfrac{3\pi}{4}$

Ⓕ I only

Ⓖ II and III

Ⓗ I, II, and III

Ⓙ I and III

11. Create a table, and determine whether each statement is true or false.
12. Using your table, which choice is the most accurate?

Answers

Possible answers:

1. Some of the identities that involve the tangent function are $\tan\theta = \dfrac{\sin\theta}{\cos\theta}$, $\sec^2\theta = \tan^2\theta + 1$, and $\cot\theta = \dfrac{1}{\tan\theta}$.
2. Statement I is true because it is a fundamental identity. Statement II is false because $\tan^2\theta = \sec^2\theta - 1$. Statement III is true because $\dfrac{1}{\csc^2\theta - 1} = \dfrac{1}{\cot^2\theta} = \tan^2\theta$. Statement IV is true because $\dfrac{1-\cos^2\theta}{1-\sin^2\theta} = \dfrac{\sin^2\theta}{\cos^2\theta} = \tan^2\theta$.
3. No; check if Statements I and IV are true before selecting an answer choice.
4. The period of a trigonometric function in the form $f(x) = a\sin bx$ is equal to $\dfrac{2\pi}{|b|}$.
5. The amplitude of a trigonometric function in the form $f(x) = a\sin bx$ is equal to $|a|$.
6. Statements II and III are true because the given values are true for the period and for the amplitude.
7. Statement I is true because you can substitute $\frac{\sin\theta}{\cos\theta}$ for $\tan\theta$. Statement II can be eliminated because there are no squared terms.
8. Statement II is false because you cannot use an expression for $\tan^2\theta$ in this identity. No; It is necessary to determine if Statement III is true or false first.

State Resources

go.hrw.com
State Resources Online
KEYWORD: MB7 Resources

Answers to Test Items

A. D

B. J

C. D

D. F

Possible answers:

9. Statement III is true because you can substitute $\dfrac{1}{\sin\theta}$ for $\csc\theta$.
10. Statements I and III are true because you need both of these identities in order to prove that $\tan\theta\csc\theta = \sec\theta$.
11.

Statement	True/False
I	True
II	False
III	False

12. F

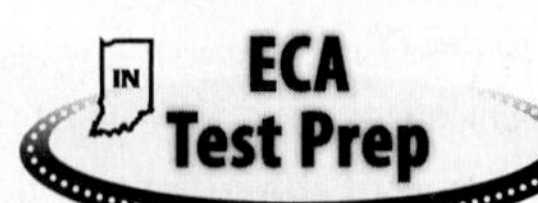

Organizer

Objective: Provide review and practice for Chapters 1–14 and standardized tests.

Resources

 ***Assessment Resources***

Chapter 14 Cumulative Test

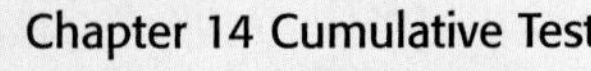

 **State Test Prep CD-ROM**

 ***State Test Practice* Online**

KEYWORD: MB7 TestPrep

Answers

1. D
2. B
3. D
4. A
5. B
6. D
7. C
8. D
9. C
10. A
11. A
12. C
13. A

State Resources

Core Standard	Items
3	8
4	5
7	15
8	4, 14

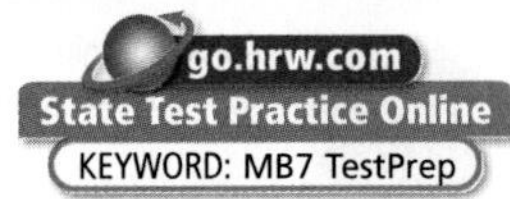

CUMULATIVE ASSESSMENT, CHAPTERS 1–14

Multiple Choice

1. What is the exact value of $\tan 15°$?

A. $\frac{\sqrt{6}-\sqrt{2}}{4}$

B. $\frac{\sqrt{6}+\sqrt{2}}{4}$

C. $2+\sqrt{3}$

D. $2-\sqrt{3}$

2. Where do the asymptotes occur in the given equation?

$y = \frac{1}{3}\cot 2x$

A. $2\pi n$

B. $\frac{\pi n}{2}$

C. $3\pi n$

D. $\frac{\pi n}{3}$

3. What is the period of the given equation?

$y = 5\cos\frac{1}{3}x$

A. $\frac{2\pi}{5}$

B. $\frac{5}{3}$

C. $\frac{2\pi}{3}$

D. 6π

4. A movie has 14 dialogue scenes and 10 action scenes. If these are the only two types of scenes, what is the probability that a randomly selected scene will be an action scene?

A. $\frac{5}{12}$

B. $\frac{7}{12}$

C. $\frac{5}{7}$

D. $\frac{7}{5}$

5. What is the value of $f(x) = 3x^3 + 4x^2 + 7x + 10$ for $x = -2$?

A. -44

B. -12

C. 0

D. 36

6. Which is the graph of a function when $y = 2$ and $x = -1$ if y varies inversely as x?

A.

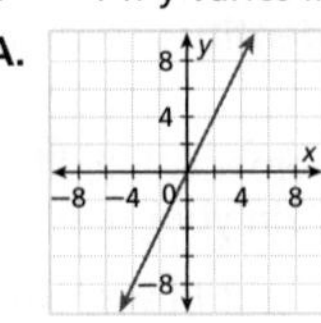

B.

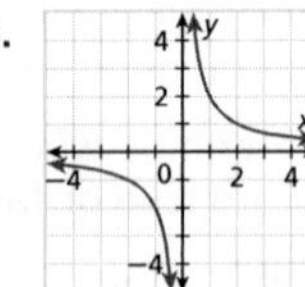

C.

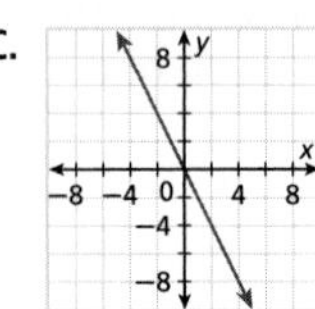

D.

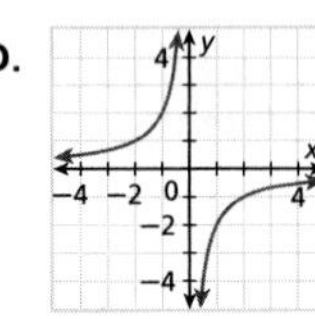

7. What is the exact value of $\cos 157.5°$ using half-angle identities?

A. $-\frac{\sqrt{2-\sqrt{2}}}{2}$

B. $\frac{\sqrt{2-\sqrt{2}}}{2}$

C. $-\frac{\sqrt{2+\sqrt{2}}}{2}$

D. $\frac{\sqrt{2+\sqrt{2}}}{2}$

8. What are the coordinates of the vertex of the parabola given by the equation $f(x) = -x^2 + 6x - 4$?

A. $(0, -4)$

B. $(-3, -13)$

C. $(-3, 5)$

D. $(3, 5)$

TEST PREP DOCTOR

For **Item 2,** students may have trouble identifying the location of the asymptotes. For instance, if students chose **D,** they may have chosen the wrong value to find the period of the function. If students chose **A,** they may have multiplied instead of divided by 2. Encourage students to graph the function to confirm their answer.

When answering **Item 12,** students might use the wrong ratio definition for cosine because all side lengths are labeled. Encourage students to think carefully and to use a memory device such as SOH-CAH-TOA to make sure that they have chosen the correct ratio.

9. Which is a solution of $2\cos\theta = 2\sin\theta$ for $\pi \le \theta \le 3\pi$?

Ⓕ $\frac{\pi}{4}$

Ⓖ π

Ⓗ $\frac{5\pi}{4}$

Ⓙ 3π

10. Which is the equation of a circle with center (3, 2) and radius 5?

Ⓐ $25 = (x-3)^2 + (y-2)^2$

Ⓑ $5 = (x-3)^2 + (y-2)^2$

Ⓒ $25 = (x+3)^2 + (y+2)^2$

Ⓓ $5 = (x+3)^2 + (y+2)^2$

Gridded Response

11. What is the value of x?

$$5\sqrt{2x-7} + 4 = 9$$

12. What is the value of $\cos\theta$? Round to the nearest thousandth.

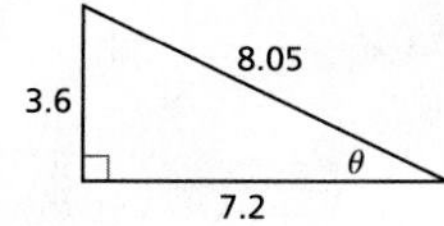

In Item 13, the answer will be a *y*-value only. It will be quickest and most efficient to isolate *x* in one equation and substitute for *x* in the second equation because then the first variable for which you obtain a value will be *y*.

13. What is the y-value of the solution of the following system of nonlinear equations?

$$\begin{cases} x - 4 = \frac{1}{4}y^2 \\ \frac{(x+1)^2}{25} + \frac{y^2}{36} = 1 \end{cases}$$

14. Find the sum of the arithmetic series $\sum_{k=1}^{14}(3k - 5)$.

Short Response

15. The chart below shows the names of the students on the academic bowl team.

Robin	Drew	Jim
Greg	Sarah	Mindy
Ashley	Tina	Justin
David	Amy	Kevin

a. Only 2 students can be chosen for the final academic bowl. How many different ways can the students be selected?

b. Explain why you solved the problem the way that you did.

16. Given the sequence:

4, 12, 36, 108, 324, ...

a. Write the explicit rule for the nth term.

b. Find the 10th term.

Extended Response

17. The chart below shows the grades in Mr. Bradshaw's class.

90	85	72	86	94	96
85	95	94	68	71	85
93	98	84	83	80	89

Round each answer to the nearest tenth.

a. Find the mean.

b. Find the median.

c. Find the mode.

d. Find the variance.

e. Find the standard deviation.

f. Find the range.

Short-Response Rubric

Items 15–16

2 Points = The student's answer is an accurate and complete execution of the task or tasks.

1 Point = The student's answer contains attributes of an appropriate response but is flawed.

0 Points = The student's answer contains no attributes of an appropriate response.

Extended-Response Rubric

Item 17

4 Points = The student correctly finds the value of each measure in parts **a–f** and rounds to the nearest tenth correctly.

3 Points = The student correctly finds the value of at least 5 of the values in parts **a–f** or makes errors in rounding.

2 Points = The student correctly finds the value of at least 3 of the values in parts **a–f.**

1 Point = The student correctly finds the value of 1 or 2 of the values in parts **a–f.**

0 Points = The student does not answer correctly and does not attempt all parts of the problem.

Answers

11. 4

12. 0.894

13. 0

14. 245

15a. 66

b. Possible answer: I used the combination formula with the values $n = 12$ and $r = 2$ because the order in which the students are selected does not matter.

16a. $4(3^{n-1})$

b. 78,732

17a. 86

b. 85.5

c. 85

d. 73.6

e. 8.6

f. 30

Problem Solving on Location

Organizer

Objective: Choose appropriate problem-solving strategies, and use them with skills from Chapters 13 and 14 to solve real-world problems.

The Rock and Roll Hall of Fame

Reading Strategies

ENGLISH LANGUAGE LEARNERS

Make sure students understand the word *façade* in **Problem 1.** Ask ELL students to identify and define similar words in other languages (for example, the Spanish word *fachada* means "front").

Using Data Be sure students understand that an angle of depression is measured down from the horizontal. Ask students whether the angle of depression from the 200 ft tower will be greater than or less than the angle of depression from the 162 ft tower. greater

State Resources

Problem Solving on Location

OHIO

The Rock and Roll Hall of Fame

The Rock and Roll Hall of Fame in downtown Cleveland traces the history of rock music through live performances and interactive exhibits. Designed by renowned architect I. M. Pei, the 50,000-square-foot exhibition space houses everything from vintage posters to handwritten lyrics to John Lennon's report card.

Choose one or more strategies to solve each problem.
For 1 and 2, use the diagram.

1. Visitors enter the museum through an enormous glass entryway in the shape of a tetrahedron. The figure shows the dimensions of the tetrahedron. What is the pitch of the tetrahedron's slanted facade? (*Hint:* The pitch is shown in the figure by angle θ.) $\approx 35°$

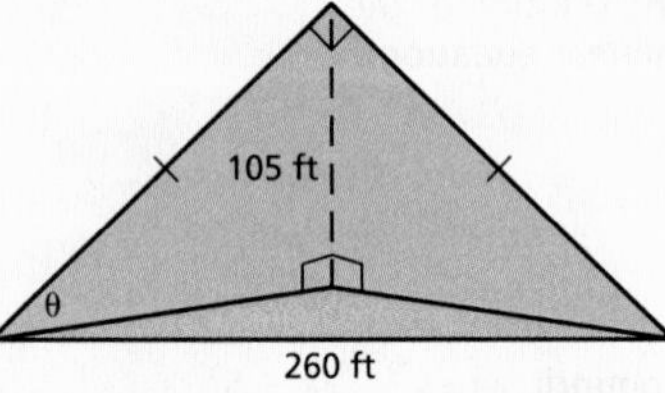

2. What is the area of the triangular floor space enclosed by the glass tetrahedron? about 9964.5 ft^2

3. The Hall of Fame exhibits are displayed in an eight-story, 162-foot tower. Pei originally designed a 200-foot tower but had to reduce its height in order to meet the requirements of a nearby airport. From the top of the existing tower, an observer sights the entrance to the museum's plaza with an angle of depression of 18°. What would be the angle of depression to the entrance of the plaza from Pei's original tower? $\approx 21.9°$

Problem-Solving Focus

Encourage students to use the four-step probelm-solving process for the problems. Focus on the first step: **(1) Understand the Problem.**

Discuss with students how they could organize the information about the building in **Problem 3.** Suggest that students draw a diagram that shows towers of both heights and the line of sight from the top of each tower to the entrance of the plaza in order to visualize the problem.

Problem Solving Strategies

- Draw a Diagram
- Make a Model
- Guess and Test
- Work Backward
- Find a Pattern
- Make a Table
- Solve a Simpler Problem
- Use Logical Reasoning
- Use a Venn Diagram
- Make an Organized List

Marblehead Lighthouse

Since its construction in 1821, Marblehead Lighthouse has stood at the entrance to Sandusky Bay, guiding sailors along Lake Erie's rocky shores. The 65-foot tower is one of Ohio's best-known landmarks and the oldest continuously operating lighthouse on the Great Lakes.

Choose one or more strategies to solve each problem.

1. The range of a lighthouse is the maximum distance at which its light is visible. In the figure, point A is the farthest point from which it is possible to see the light at the top of the lighthouse L. The distance along Earth s is the range. Assuming that the radius of Earth is 4000 miles, find the range of Marblehead Lighthouse. **about 9.9 mi**

L
s
A
4000 mi
E

2. In 1897, a new lighting system was installed in the lighthouse. A set of descending weights rotated the tower's lantern to produce a flashing light. The rotation could be modeled by the function $f(x) = \sin\frac{\pi}{5}x$, where x is the time in seconds since the weights were released. The light briefly flashed on whenever $f(x) = 1$. How many times per minute did the light flash? **6**

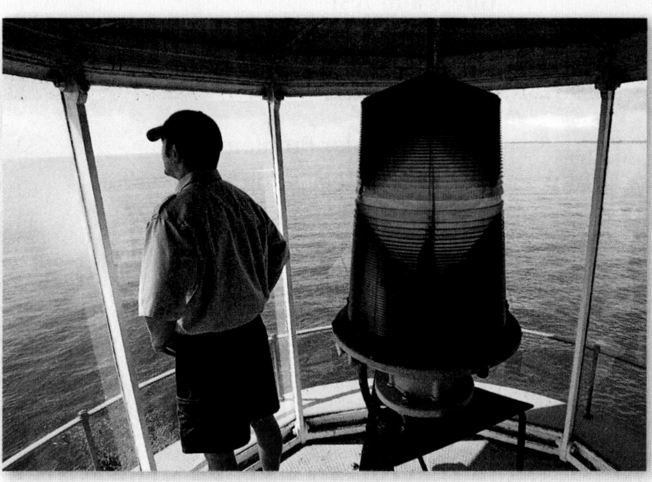

3. Today the flashing light of Marblehead Lighthouse can be modeled by $g(x) = \sin\frac{\pi}{3}x$. How many seconds are there between each flash? Does the light flash more or less frequently than in 1897? **6 s; more frequently**

Marblehead Lighthouse

Reading Strategies

ENGLISH LANGUAGE LEARNERS

Have students restate **Problem 1** in their own words. Then ask them what values they will need to find in order to determine the lighthouse's range. Students will need to find m$\angle LEA$. Then they can use $s = r\theta$ to find the range.

Using Data Ask students what additional information they can add to the figure for **Problem 1.** For example, $AE = 4000$ mi and $LE = 4000.0123$ mi because the height of the lighthouse is 65 ft, which equals 0.0123 mi.

Problem-Solving Focus

Encourage students to use the four-step problem-solving process for the problems. Focus on the second step: **(2) Make a Plan.**

Discuss with students the strategies that might be useful in solving the problem, such as making a table or graphing $f(x)$ from $x = 0$ to $x = 60$.

Student Handbook

Extra Practice

Extra Practice

Chapter 1 ■ Skills Practice

Lesson 1-1

Order the given numbers from least to greatest. Then classify each number by the subsets of the real numbers to which it belongs. 1–3. See p. A54.

1. $2.3, \frac{5}{2}, \sqrt{10}, 2.\overline{4}, 2\sqrt{3}$
2. $-3, -\sqrt{12}, \frac{2}{5}, -2\pi, -\pi$
3. $\sqrt{9}, 3.0\overline{2}, 3\frac{1}{16}, 3\frac{2}{30}, \pi$

Use interval notation to represent each set of numbers.

4. $-40 \le x < -12$ $[-40, -12)$
5. $-1 < x < 5$ or $x \ge 13$ $(-1, 5)$ or $[13, \infty)$
6. 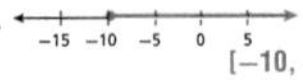 $[-10, \infty)$

Rewrite each set in the indicated notation.

7. $x \le 0$ or $4 < x < 8$; set-builder notation $\{x \mid x \le 0 \text{ or } 4 < x < 8\}$
8. all odd natural numbers; roster notation $\{1, 3, 5, 7, 9, \dots\}$

Lesson 1-2

Identify the property demonstrated by each equation.

9. $12 + a = a + 12$ Commutative Property of Addition
10. $3 \cdot (9 \cdot 2) = (3 \cdot 9) \cdot 2$ Associative Property of Multiplication
11. $2(\sqrt{10} + 4) = 2(\sqrt{10}) + 2(4)$ Distributive Property

Use mental math to find each value.

12. a 15% tip on a bill of \$34.60 \$5.19
13. a 30% discount on a \$67.80 item \$20.34

Classify each statement as sometimes, always, or never true. Give examples or properties to support your answer. 14–16. See p. A54.

14. $a + 4 = b + 4$
15. $12b = 6b + 6b$
16. $ab = ac$

Lesson 1-3

Estimate to the nearest tenth.

17. $\sqrt{90}$ 9.5
18. $\sqrt{62}$ 7.9
19. $-\sqrt{48}$ −6.9
20. $\sqrt{23}$ 4.8

Simplify each expression.

21. $\frac{\sqrt{242}}{\sqrt{2}}$ 11
22. $\frac{\sqrt{20}}{\sqrt{120}}$ $\frac{\sqrt{6}}{6}$
23. $2\sqrt{5} + 4\sqrt{20}$ $10\sqrt{5}$
24. $2\sqrt{72} - \sqrt{18}$ $9\sqrt{2}$

Lesson 1-4

Write an algebraic expression to represent each situation.

25. the area in square inches of a triangle with base b inches and height 12 inches $6b$
26. the amount in dollars remaining from \$55 after spending d dollars $55 - d$

Evaluate each expression for the given values of the variables.

27. $2a^2 + 5a - 3b$ for $a = 4$ and $b = -3$ 61
28. $\frac{x + y}{2xy + 2}$ for $x = 3$ and $y = 5$ $\frac{1}{4}$

Simplify each expression.

29. $3n + 5n - 2(n + 2)$ $6n - 4$
30. $3(x - 7) + 4x^2$ $4x^2 + 3x - 21$
31. $-4a + 2(12 - 4a)$ $-12a + 24$

Lesson 1-5

Simplify each expression. Assume all variables are nonzero.

32. 4^0 1
33. $3^2 \cdot 3^{-5}$ $\frac{1}{27}$
34. $(3x^2y)^4$ $81x^8y^4$
35. $\frac{(5x)^2}{5y^{-4}}$ $5x^2y^4$

Simplify each expression. Write the answer in scientific notation.

36. $(1.4 \times 10^{12})(2.2 \times 10^3)$ 3.08×10^{15}
37. $\frac{(9.9 \times 10^6)}{(2.2 \times 10^3)}$ 4.5×10^3
38. $\frac{24 \times 10^{-5}}{6 \times 10^4}$ 4×10^{-9}

Chapter 1 ■ Skills Practice

Lesson 1-6

Give the domain and range for each relation.

39. 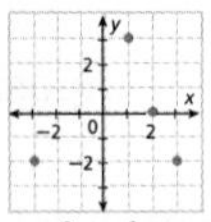

D: $\{-3, 1, 2, 3\}$; R: $\{-2, 0, 3\}$

40.

x	y
−5	−10
−2	−2
0	5
4	19

D: $\{-5, -2, 0, 4\}$; R: $\{-10, -2, 5, 19\}$

41. 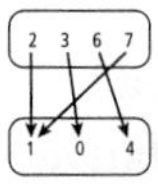

D: $\{2, 3, 6, 7\}$; R: $\{0, 1, 4\}$

Determine whether each relation is a function.

42.

Average Regular Gasoline Prices August 2005				
Date	8/8	8/15	8/22	8/29
Cost (\$/gal)	2.37	2.55	2.61	2.61

function

43. from a person's age to his or her height not a function

Lesson 1-7

For each function, evaluate $f(0)$, $f(3)$, and $f(-2)$.

44. $f(x) = -4x + 10$ 10; −2; 18
45. $f(x) = \frac{1}{2}x^2$ $0; \frac{9}{2}; 2$
46. $f(x) = x^2 - 2x + 5$ 5; 8; 13

Graph each function.

47. $g(x) = \frac{1}{2}x - 4$
48.

x	1	2	3	4
y	1	3	5	7

49. $h(x) = -2x + 5$

47–49. See p. A54.

Lesson 1-8

Perform the given translation on the point $(-3, 4)$. Give the coordinates of the translated point.

50. 3 units right $(0, 4)$
51. 5 units up $(-3, 9)$
52. 2 units left, 2 units down $(-5, 2)$

Use a table to perform each transformation of $y = f(x)$. Use the same coordinate plane as the original function. 53–55. See p. A54.

53. reflection across the y-axis
54. translation 2 units up
55. vertical compression by a factor of $\frac{1}{2}$

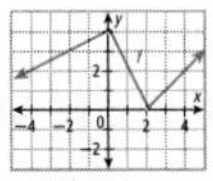

Lesson 1-9

Identify the parent function for g from its function rule. Then graph g on your calculator and describe what transformation of the parent function it represents.

56. $g(x) = (x + 3)^3$ cubic; translation 3 units left
57. $g(x) = \sqrt{x - 4}$ square root; translation 4 units right
58. $g(x) = x^2 + 3$ quadratic; translation 3 units up

Graph the data from the table. Describe the parent function and the transformation that best approximates the data set. 59, 60. For graphs, see p. A54.

59.

x	−2	−1	0	1	2
y	−4	−0.5	0	0.5	4

cubic; vertical compression by a factor of $\frac{1}{2}$

60.

x	1	3	5	7	9
y	16	4	0	4	16

quadratic; translation 5 units right

Chapter 2 ■ Skills Practice

Lesson 2-1

Solve.

1. $4(x - 3) = 48$ $x = 15$
2. $6x + 10 = -2x + 26$ $x = 2$
3. $\frac{1}{2}(10a + 12) = a - 6$ $a = -3$
4. $3z + 12 = \frac{1}{2}(4z + 4)$ $z = -10$
5. $11w + 4 = 58 - 7w$ $w = 3$
6. $-5p + 32 = 2(p - 2)$ $p = \frac{36}{7}$

Solve and graph. 7–9. For graphs, see p. A54.

7. $3x + 7 < 28$ $x < 7$
8. $12y - 3 \le 57$ $y \le 5$
9. $2(4 - x) < 10$ $x > -1$

Lesson 2-2

Solve each proportion.

10. $\frac{3x}{15} = \frac{3}{5}$ $x = 3$
11. $\frac{8}{5x} = \frac{2}{11}$ $x = 8.8$
12. $\frac{-4}{5} = \frac{14}{y}$ $y = -17.5$
13. $\frac{2.2}{3} = \frac{n}{5}$ $n = \frac{11}{3}$
14. $\frac{9.5}{3} = \frac{6 + m}{6}$ $m = 13$
15. $\frac{-1}{9} = \frac{1.5}{3 - x}$ $x = 16.5$

Lesson 2-3

Determine whether each data set could represent a linear function.

16.

x	−2	1	4	7
f(x)	−14	−5	4	13

yes

17.

x	−2	−1	0	1
f(x)	6	0	−2	0

no

Graph each line. 18–23. For graphs, see p. A54.

18. slope $\frac{2}{3}$; passes through $(3, 4)$
19. slope $-\frac{5}{3}$; passes through $(6, -1)$

Find the intercepts of each line, and graph the lines.

20. $-2y + x = 8$ $(0, -4)$ and $(8, 0)$
21. $3x + y = 6$ $(0, 6)$ and $(2, 0)$

Write each function in slope-intercept form. Then graph the function.

22. $3y - 2x = 3$ $y = \frac{2}{3}x + 1$
23. $4y + 3x = 20$ $y = -\frac{3}{4}x + 5$

Lesson 2-4

Find the slope of each line.

24.

x	−2	1	4	7
f(x)	−14	−5	4	13

3

25. a line through $(-1, 20)$ and $(3, -4)$ −6

Write the equation of each line in slope-intercept form.

26. a line with slope 3 and x-intercept $\frac{4}{3}$ $y = 3x - 4$
27. a line with slope $-\frac{3}{2}$ passing through $(4, 1)$ 27. $y = -\frac{3}{2}x + 7$

28.

x	−2	0	5	6
f(x)	14	15	17.5	18

$y = \frac{1}{2}x + 15$

29.

x	7	10	13	16
f(x)	−6	−3	0	3

$y = x - 13$

30. 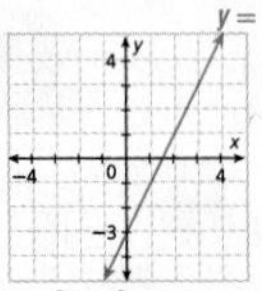

$y = 2x - 3$

31. 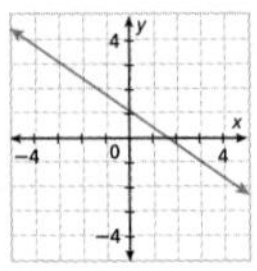

$y = -\frac{2}{3}x + 1$

Chapter 2 ■ Skills Practice

Lesson 2-5

Graph each inequality using intercepts. 32–37. For graphs, see p. A54.

32. $y - x > 4$
33. $2y - 8x \le -4$
34. $4y + 3x \ge 12$

Solve each inequality for y. Graph the solution.

35. $6x + 6y < 18$ $y < -x + 3$
36. $12 > 2(x - 3y)$ $y > \frac{1}{3}x - 2$
37. $6y \le 9x - 36$ $y \le \frac{3}{2}x - 6$

Lesson 2-6

Let $g(x)$ be the indicated transformation of $f(x)$. Write the rule for $g(x)$.

38. $f(x) = \frac{4}{7}x + 1$; vertical translation 3 units down 38. $g(x) = \frac{4}{7}x - 2$
39. $f(x) = -4x + 9$; horizontal stretch by a factor of 4 $g(x) = -x + 9$
40. linear function defined in the table; reflection across the y-axis $g(x) = -6x - 11$

x	−1	0	2	5
y	−17	−11	1	19

Let $g(x)$ be the indicated transformation of $f(x) = x$. Write the rule for $g(x)$.

41. vertical stretch by a factor of 2 followed by a horizontal shift 2 units right $g(x) = 2x - 4$
42. horizontal shift 5 units left followed by a reflection across the x-axis $g(x) = -x - 5$
43. vertical stretch by a factor of $\frac{3}{2}$ followed by a vertical shift 8 units down $g(x) = \frac{3}{2}x - 8$

Lesson 2-7

44. If the points in a scatter plot have a positive correlation, then the r-value is __?__. If the points have no correlation, then the r-value is __?__. positive; approximately zero
45. Make a scatter plot of the data shown in the table. 45, 46. For graphs, see p. A55.

x	0	2	3	4	6	9
y	18	15	14	10	5	1

46. Find the correlation coefficient and the equation of the line of best fit. Draw the line of best fit on your scatter plot. $y \approx -2.02x + 18.58$; $r = -0.987$

Lesson 2-8

Solve each compound inequality. Then graph the solution set. 47, 48. For graphs, see p. A55.

47. $3 - x > 4$ or $2x + 7 \ge 17$ $x < -1$ or $x \ge 5$
48. $8x \le 0$ and $4x + 6 \ge -10$ $-4 \le x \le 0$

Solve each equation.

49. $|x - 9| = 1$ $x = 8$ or $x = 10$
50. $|5x + 5| = 20$ $x = 3$ or $x = -5$
51. $4|-2x| = 48$ $x = \pm 6$

Solve each inequality. Then graph the solution set. 52–54. For graphs, see p. A55.

52. $|x + 7| > 4$ $x > -3$ or $x < -11$
53. $|2x - 5| < 21$ $-8 < x < 13$
54. $3\left|\frac{1}{2}x + 1\right| \ge 12$ $x \le -10$ or $x \ge 6$

Lesson 2-9

Let $g(x)$ be the indicated transformation of $f(x) = |x|$. Write the rule for $g(x)$.

55. 7 units up $g(x) = |x| + 7$
56. 3 units right $g(x) = |x - 3|$

Translate $f(x) = |x|$ so that the vertex is at the given point. Then graph. 57–61. For graphs, see p. A55.

57. $(1, 4)$ $g(x) = |x - 1| + 4$
58. $(-3, 2)$ $g(x) = |x + 3| + 2$
59. $(1.5, -2.5)$ $g(x) = |x - 1.5| - 2.5$

Perform each transformation. Then graph.

60. Stretch $f(x) = |x - 1|$ vertically by a factor of 2. $g(x) = 2|x - 1|$
61. Reflect $f(x) = |x + 4| - 1$ across the y-axis. $g(x) = |-x + 4| - 1$

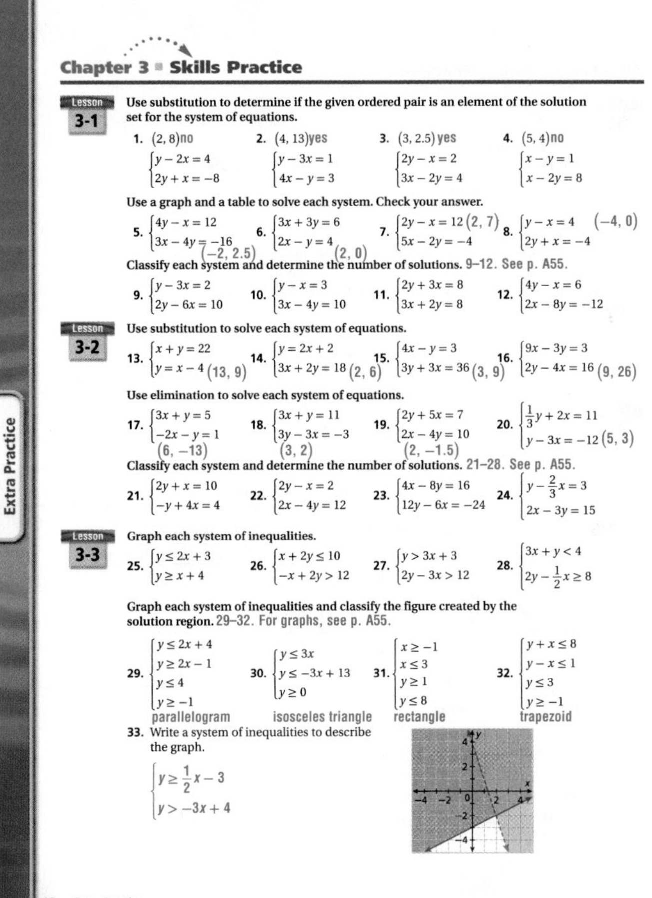

Chapter 3 ■ Skills Practice

Lesson 3-1 Use substitution to determine if the given ordered pair is an element of the solution set for the system of equations.

1. $(2, 8)$ no $\begin{cases} y - 2x = 4 \\ 2y + x = -8 \end{cases}$
2. $(4, 13)$ yes $\begin{cases} y - 3x = 1 \\ 4x - y = 3 \end{cases}$
3. $(3, 2.5)$ yes $\begin{cases} 2y - x = 2 \\ 3x - 2y = 4 \end{cases}$
4. $(5, 4)$ no $\begin{cases} x - y = 1 \\ x - 2y = 8 \end{cases}$

Use a graph and a table to solve each system. Check your answer.

5. $\begin{cases} 4y - x = 12 \\ 3x - 4y = -16 \end{cases}$ $(-2, 2.5)$
6. $\begin{cases} 3x + 3y = 6 \\ 2x - y = 4 \end{cases}$ $(2, 0)$
7. $\begin{cases} 2y - x = 12 \\ 5x - 2y = -4 \end{cases}$ $(2, 7)$
8. $\begin{cases} y - x = 4 \\ 2y + x = -4 \end{cases}$ $(-4, 0)$

Classify each system and determine the number of solutions. 9–12. See p. A55.

9. $\begin{cases} y - 3x = 2 \\ 2y - 6x = 10 \end{cases}$
10. $\begin{cases} y - x = 3 \\ 3x - 4y = 10 \end{cases}$
11. $\begin{cases} 2y + 3x = 8 \\ 3x + 2y = 8 \end{cases}$
12. $\begin{cases} 4y - x = 6 \\ 2x - 8y = -12 \end{cases}$

Lesson 3-2 Use substitution to solve each system of equations.

13. $\begin{cases} x + y = 22 \\ y = x - 4 \end{cases}$ $(13, 9)$
14. $\begin{cases} y = 2x + 2 \\ 3x + 2y = 18 \end{cases}$ $(2, 6)$
15. $\begin{cases} 4x - y = 3 \\ 3y + 3x = 36 \end{cases}$ $(3, 9)$
16. $\begin{cases} 9x - 3y = 3 \\ 2y - 4x = 16 \end{cases}$ $(9, 26)$

Use elimination to solve each system of equations.

17. $\begin{cases} 3x + y = 5 \\ -2x - y = 1 \end{cases}$ $(6, -13)$
18. $\begin{cases} 3x + y = 11 \\ 3y - 3x = -3 \end{cases}$ $(3, 2)$
19. $\begin{cases} 2y + 5x = 7 \\ 2x - 4y = 10 \end{cases}$ $(2, -1.5)$
20. $\begin{cases} \frac{1}{3}y + 2x = 11 \\ y - 3x = -12 \end{cases}$ $(5, 3)$

Classify each system and determine the number of solutions. 21–28. See p. A55.

21. $\begin{cases} 2y + x = 10 \\ -y + 4x = 4 \end{cases}$
22. $\begin{cases} 2y - x = 2 \\ 2x - 4y = 12 \end{cases}$
23. $\begin{cases} 4x - 8y = 16 \\ 12y - 6x = -24 \end{cases}$
24. $\begin{cases} y - \frac{2}{3}x = 3 \\ 2x - 3y = 15 \end{cases}$

Lesson 3-3 Graph each system of inequalities.

25. $\begin{cases} y \le 2x + 3 \\ y \ge x + 4 \end{cases}$
26. $\begin{cases} x + 2y \le 10 \\ -x + 2y > 12 \end{cases}$
27. $\begin{cases} y > 3x + 3 \\ 2y - 3x > 12 \end{cases}$
28. $\begin{cases} 3x + y < 4 \\ 2y - \frac{1}{2}x \ge 8 \end{cases}$

Graph each system of inequalities and classify the figure created by the solution region. 29–32. For graphs, see p. A55.

29. $\begin{cases} y \le 2x + 4 \\ y \ge 2x - 1 \\ y \le 4 \\ y \ge -1 \end{cases}$ parallelogram
30. $\begin{cases} y \le 3x \\ y \le -3x + 13 \\ y \ge 0 \end{cases}$ isosceles triangle
31. $\begin{cases} x \ge -1 \\ x \le 3 \\ y \ge 1 \\ y \le 8 \end{cases}$ rectangle
32. $\begin{cases} y + x \le 8 \\ y - x \le 1 \\ y \le 3 \\ y \ge -1 \end{cases}$ trapezoid

33. Write a system of inequalities to describe the graph.

$\begin{cases} y \ge \frac{1}{2}x - 3 \\ y > -3x + 4 \end{cases}$

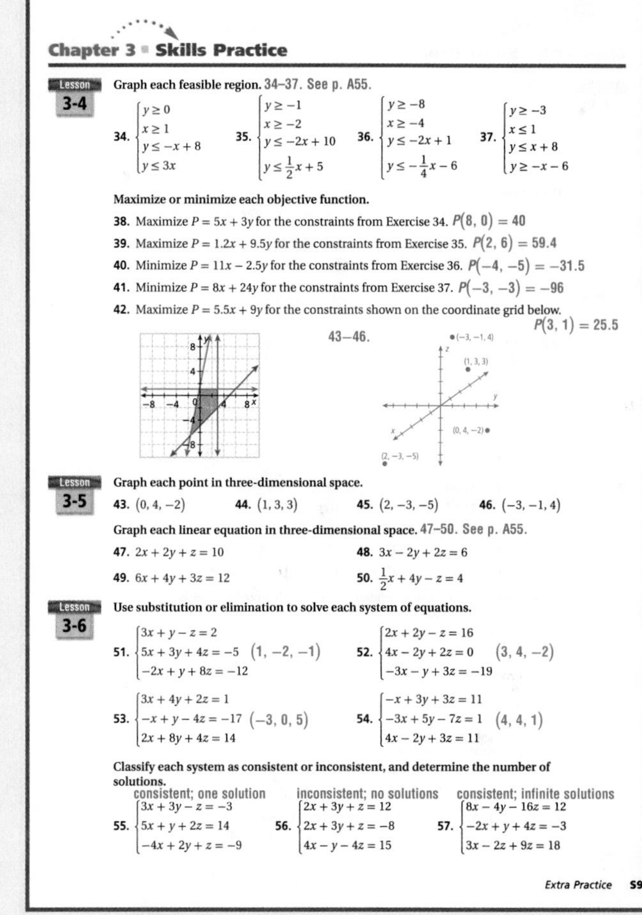

Chapter 3 ■ Skills Practice

Lesson 3-4 Graph each feasible region. 34–37. See p. A55.

34. $\begin{cases} y \ge 0 \\ x \ge 1 \\ y \le -x + 8 \\ y \le 3x \end{cases}$
35. $\begin{cases} y \ge -1 \\ x \ge -2 \\ y \le -2x + 10 \\ y \le \frac{1}{2}x + 5 \end{cases}$
36. $\begin{cases} y \ge -8 \\ x \ge -4 \\ y \le -2x + 1 \\ y \le -\frac{1}{4}x - 6 \end{cases}$
37. $\begin{cases} y \ge -3 \\ x \le 1 \\ y \le x + 8 \\ y \ge -x - 6 \end{cases}$

Maximize or minimize each objective function.

38. Maximize $P = 5x + 3y$ for the constraints from Exercise 34. $P(8, 0) = 40$
39. Maximize $P = 1.2x + 9.5y$ for the constraints from Exercise 35. $P(2, 6) = 59.4$
40. Minimize $P = 11x - 2.5y$ for the constraints from Exercise 36. $P(-4, -5) = -31.5$
41. Minimize $P = 8x + 24y$ for the constraints from Exercise 37. $P(-3, -3) = -96$
42. Maximize $P = 5.5x + 9y$ for the constraints shown on the coordinate grid below. $P(3, 1) = 25.5$

43–46.

Lesson 3-5 Graph each point in three-dimensional space.

43. $(0, 4, -2)$
44. $(1, 3, 3)$
45. $(2, -3, -5)$
46. $(-3, -1, 4)$

Graph each linear equation in three-dimensional space. 47–50. See p. A55.

47. $2x + 2y + z = 10$
48. $3x - 2y + 2z = 6$
49. $6x + 4y + 3z = 12$
50. $\frac{1}{2}x + 4y - z = 4$

Lesson 3-6 Use substitution or elimination to solve each system of equations.

51. $\begin{cases} 3x + y - z = 2 \\ 5x + 3y + 4z = -5 \\ -2x + y + 8z = -12 \end{cases}$ $(1, -2, -1)$
52. $\begin{cases} 2x + 2y - z = 16 \\ 4x - 2y + 2z = 0 \\ -3x - y + 3z = -19 \end{cases}$ $(3, 4, -2)$
53. $\begin{cases} 3x + 4y + 2z = 1 \\ -x + y - 4z = -17 \\ 2x + 8y + 4z = 14 \end{cases}$ $(-3, 0, 5)$
54. $\begin{cases} -x + 3y + 3z = 11 \\ -3x + 5y - 7z = 1 \\ 4x - 2y + 3z = 11 \end{cases}$ $(4, 4, 1)$

Classify each system as consistent or inconsistent, and determine the number of solutions.

55. $\begin{cases} 3x + 3y - z = -3 \\ 5x + y + 2z = 14 \\ -4x + 2y + z = -9 \end{cases}$ consistent; one solution
56. $\begin{cases} 2x + 3y + z = 12 \\ 2x + 3y + z = -8 \\ 4x - y - 4z = 15 \end{cases}$ inconsistent; no solutions
57. $\begin{cases} 8x - 4y - 16z = 12 \\ -2x + y + 4z = -3 \\ 3x - 2z + 9z = 18 \end{cases}$ consistent; infinite solutions

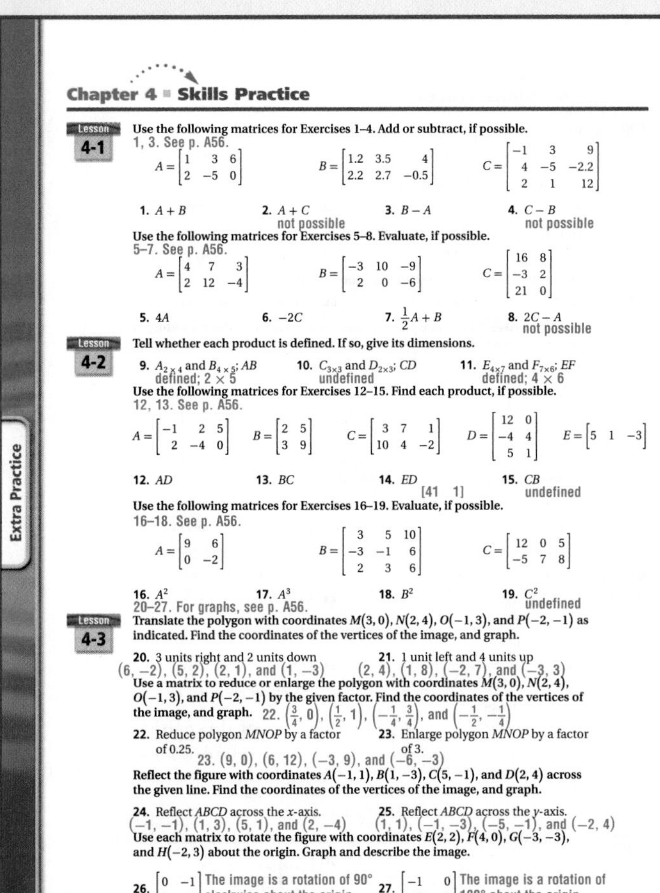

Chapter 4 ■ Skills Practice

Lesson 4-1 Use the following matrices for Exercises 1–4. Add or subtract, if possible. 1, 3. See p. A56.

$A = \begin{bmatrix} 1 & 3 & 6 \\ 2 & -5 & 0 \end{bmatrix}$ $B = \begin{bmatrix} 1.2 & 3.5 & 4 \\ 2.2 & 2.7 & -0.5 \end{bmatrix}$ $C = \begin{bmatrix} -1 & 3 & 9 \\ 4 & -5 & -2.2 \\ 2 & 1 & 12 \end{bmatrix}$

1. $A + B$
2. $A + C$ not possible
3. $B - A$
4. $C - B$ not possible

Use the following matrices for Exercises 5–8. Evaluate, if possible. 5–7. See p. A56.

$A = \begin{bmatrix} 4 & 7 & 3 \\ 2 & 12 & -4 \end{bmatrix}$ $B = \begin{bmatrix} -3 & 10 & -9 \\ 2 & 0 & -6 \end{bmatrix}$ $C = \begin{bmatrix} 16 & 8 \\ -3 & 2 \\ 21 & 0 \end{bmatrix}$

5. $4A$
6. $-2C$
7. $\frac{1}{2}A + B$
8. $2C - A$ not possible

Lesson 4-2 Tell whether each product is defined. If so, give its dimensions.

9. $A_{2 \times 4}$ and $B_{4 \times 5}$; AB defined; 2×5
10. $C_{3 \times 3}$ and $D_{2 \times 3}$; CD undefined
11. $E_{4 \times 7}$ and $F_{7 \times 6}$; EF defined; 4×6

Use the following matrices for Exercises 12–15. Find each product, if possible. 12, 13. See p. A56.

$A = \begin{bmatrix} -1 & 2 & 5 \\ 2 & -4 & 0 \end{bmatrix}$ $B = \begin{bmatrix} 2 & 5 \\ 3 & 9 \end{bmatrix}$ $C = \begin{bmatrix} 3 & 7 & 1 \\ 10 & 4 & -2 \end{bmatrix}$ $D = \begin{bmatrix} 12 & 0 \\ -4 & 4 \\ 5 & 1 \end{bmatrix}$ $E = \begin{bmatrix} 5 & 1 & -3 \end{bmatrix}$

12. AD
13. BC
14. ED $[41 \quad 1]$
15. CB undefined

Use the following matrices for Exercises 16–19. Evaluate, if possible. 16–18. See p. A56.

$A = \begin{bmatrix} 9 & 6 \\ 0 & -2 \end{bmatrix}$ $B = \begin{bmatrix} 3 & 5 & 10 \\ -3 & -1 & 6 \\ 2 & 3 & 6 \end{bmatrix}$ $C = \begin{bmatrix} 12 & 0 & 5 \\ -5 & 7 & 8 \end{bmatrix}$

16. A^2
17. A^3
18. B^2
19. C^2 undefined

Lesson 4-3 20–27. For graphs, see p. A56. Translate the polygon with coordinates $M(3, 0)$, $N(2, 4)$, $O(-1, 3)$, and $P(-2, -1)$ as indicated. Find the coordinates of the vertices of the image, and graph.

20. 3 units right and 2 units down $(6, -2)$, $(5, 2)$, $(2, 1)$, and $(1, -3)$
21. 1 unit left and 4 units up $(2, 4)$, $(1, 8)$, $(-2, 7)$, and $(-3, 3)$

Use a matrix to reduce or enlarge the polygon with coordinates $M(3, 0)$, $N(2, 4)$, $O(-1, 3)$, and $P(-2, -1)$ by the given factor. Find the coordinates of the vertices of the image, and graph. 22. $\left(\frac{3}{4}, 0\right)$, $\left(\frac{1}{2}, 1\right)$, $\left(-\frac{1}{4}, \frac{3}{4}\right)$, and $\left(-\frac{1}{2}, -\frac{1}{4}\right)$

22. Reduce polygon $MNOP$ by a factor of 0.25.
23. Enlarge polygon $MNOP$ by a factor of 3. 23. $(9, 0)$, $(6, 12)$, $(-3, 9)$, and $(-6, -3)$

Reflect the figure with coordinates $A(-1, 1)$, $B(1, -3)$, $C(5, -1)$, and $D(2, 4)$ across the given line. Find the coordinates of the vertices of the image, and graph.

24. Reflect $ABCD$ across the x-axis. $(-1, -1)$, $(1, 3)$, $(5, 1)$, and $(2, -4)$
25. Reflect $ABCD$ across the y-axis. $(1, 1)$, $(-1, -3)$, $(-5, -1)$, and $(-2, 4)$

Use each matrix to rotate the figure with coordinates $E(2, 2)$, $F(4, 0)$, $G(-3, -3)$, and $H(-2, 3)$ about the origin. Graph and describe the image.

26. $\begin{bmatrix} 0 & -1 \\ 1 & 0 \end{bmatrix}$ The image is a rotation of 90° clockwise about the origin.
27. $\begin{bmatrix} -1 & 0 \\ 0 & -1 \end{bmatrix}$ The image is a rotation of 180° about the origin.

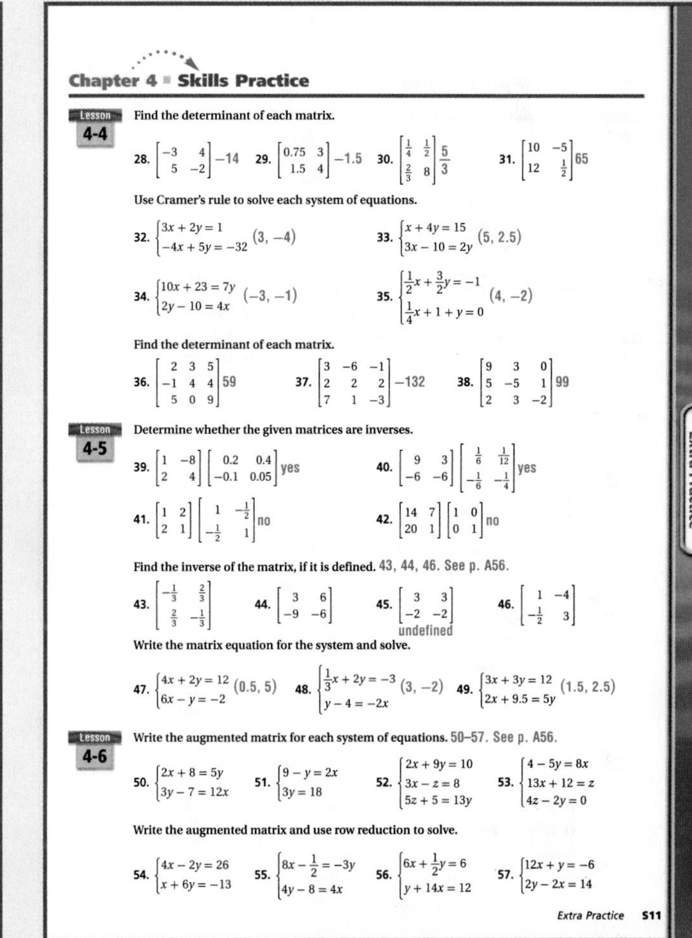

Chapter 4 ■ Skills Practice

Lesson 4-4 Find the determinant of each matrix.

28. $\begin{bmatrix} -3 & 4 \\ 5 & -2 \end{bmatrix}$ -14
29. $\begin{bmatrix} 0.75 & 3 \\ 1.5 & 4 \end{bmatrix}$ -1.5
30. $\begin{bmatrix} \frac{1}{4} & \frac{1}{2} \\ \frac{2}{3} & 8 \end{bmatrix}$ $\frac{5}{3}$
31. $\begin{bmatrix} 10 & -5 \\ 12 & \frac{1}{2} \end{bmatrix}$ 65

Use Cramer's rule to solve each system of equations.

32. $\begin{cases} 3x + 2y = 1 \\ -4x + 5y = -32 \end{cases}$ $(3, -4)$
33. $\begin{cases} x + 4y = 15 \\ 3x - 10 = 2y \end{cases}$ $(5, 2.5)$
34. $\begin{cases} 10x + 23 = 7y \\ 2y - 10 = 4x \end{cases}$ $(-3, -1)$
35. $\begin{cases} \frac{1}{2}x + \frac{3}{2}y = -1 \\ \frac{1}{4}x + 1 + y = 0 \end{cases}$ $(4, -2)$

Find the determinant of each matrix.

36. $\begin{bmatrix} 2 & 3 & 5 \\ -1 & 4 & 4 \\ 5 & 0 & 9 \end{bmatrix}$ 59
37. $\begin{bmatrix} 3 & -6 & -1 \\ 2 & 2 & 2 \\ 7 & 1 & -3 \end{bmatrix}$ -132
38. $\begin{bmatrix} 9 & 3 & 0 \\ 5 & -5 & 1 \\ 2 & 3 & -2 \end{bmatrix}$ 99

Lesson 4-5 Determine whether the given matrices are inverses.

39. $\begin{bmatrix} 1 & -8 \\ 2 & 4 \end{bmatrix} \begin{bmatrix} 0.2 & 0.4 \\ -0.1 & 0.05 \end{bmatrix}$ yes
40. $\begin{bmatrix} 9 & 3 \\ -6 & -6 \end{bmatrix} \begin{bmatrix} \frac{1}{6} & \frac{1}{12} \\ -\frac{1}{6} & -\frac{1}{4} \end{bmatrix}$ yes
41. $\begin{bmatrix} 1 & 2 \\ 2 & 1 \end{bmatrix} \begin{bmatrix} 1 & -\frac{1}{2} \\ -\frac{1}{2} & 1 \end{bmatrix}$ no
42. $\begin{bmatrix} 14 & 7 \\ 20 & 1 \end{bmatrix} \begin{bmatrix} 1 & 0 \\ 0 & 1 \end{bmatrix}$ no

Find the inverse of the matrix, if it is defined. 43, 44, 46. See p. A56.

43. $\begin{bmatrix} -\frac{1}{3} & \frac{2}{3} \\ \frac{2}{3} & -\frac{1}{3} \end{bmatrix}$
44. $\begin{bmatrix} 3 & 6 \\ -9 & -6 \end{bmatrix}$
45. $\begin{bmatrix} 3 & 3 \\ -2 & -2 \end{bmatrix}$ undefined
46. $\begin{bmatrix} 1 & -4 \\ -\frac{1}{2} & 3 \end{bmatrix}$

Write the matrix equation for the system and solve.

47. $\begin{cases} 4x + 2y = 12 \\ 6x - y = -2 \end{cases}$ $(0.5, 5)$
48. $\begin{cases} \frac{1}{3}x + 2y = -3 \\ y - 4 = -2x \end{cases}$ $(3, -2)$
49. $\begin{cases} 3x + 3y = 12 \\ 2x + 9.5 = 5y \end{cases}$ $(1.5, 2.5)$

Lesson 4-6 Write the augmented matrix for each system of equations. 50–57. See p. A56.

50. $\begin{cases} 2x + 8 = 5y \\ 3y - 7 = 12x \end{cases}$
51. $\begin{cases} 9 - y = 2x \\ 3y = 18 \end{cases}$
52. $\begin{cases} 2x + 9y = 10 \\ 3x - z = 8 \\ 5z + 5 = 13y \end{cases}$
53. $\begin{cases} 4 - 5y = 8x \\ 13x + 12 = z \\ 4z - 2y = 0 \end{cases}$

Write the augmented matrix and use row reduction to solve.

54. $\begin{cases} 4x - 2y = 26 \\ x + 6y = -13 \end{cases}$
55. $\begin{cases} 8x - \frac{1}{2} = -3y \\ 4y - 8 = 4x \end{cases}$
56. $\begin{cases} 6x + \frac{1}{2}y = 6 \\ y + 14x = 12 \end{cases}$
57. $\begin{cases} 12x + y = -6 \\ 2y - 2x = 14 \end{cases}$

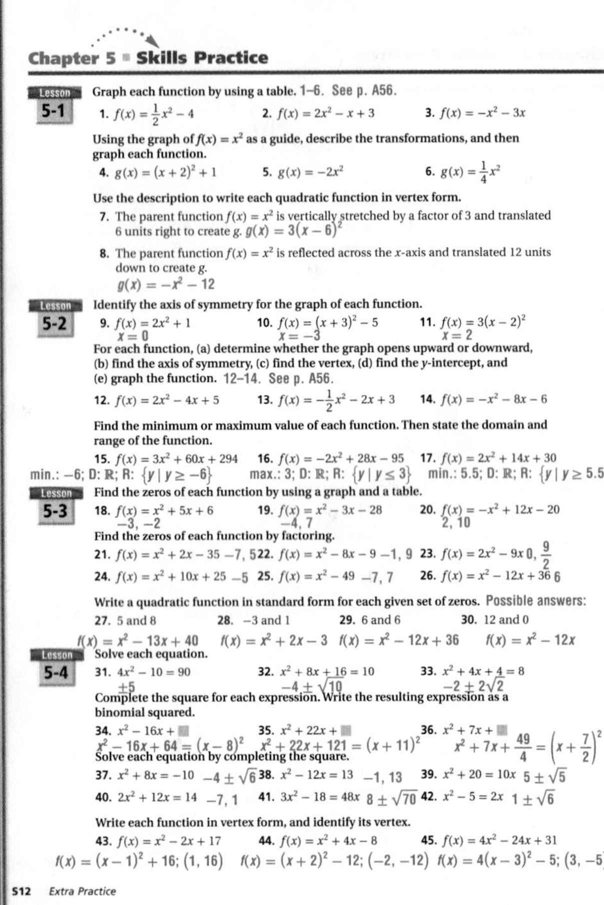

Chapter 5 ■ Skills Practice

Lesson 5-1 Graph each function by using a table. 1–6. See p. A56.

1. $f(x) = \frac{1}{2}x^2 - 4$ 2. $f(x) = 2x^2 - x + 3$ 3. $f(x) = -x^2 - 3x$

Using the graph of $f(x) = x^2$ as a guide, describe the transformations, and then graph each function.

4. $g(x) = (x + 2)^2 + 1$ 5. $g(x) = -2x^2$ 6. $g(x) = \frac{1}{4}x^2$

Use the description to write each quadratic function in vertex form.

7. The parent function $f(x) = x^2$ is vertically stretched by a factor of 3 and translated 6 units right to create g. $g(x) = 3(x - 6)^2$
8. The parent function $f(x) = x^2$ is reflected across the x-axis and translated 12 units down to create g. $g(x) = -x^2 - 12$

Lesson 5-2 Identify the axis of symmetry for the graph of each function.

9. $f(x) = 2x^2 + 1$ $x = 0$ 10. $f(x) = (x + 3)^2 - 5$ $x = -3$ 11. $f(x) = 3(x - 2)^2$ $x = 2$

For each function, (a) determine whether the graph opens upward or downward, (b) find the axis of symmetry, (c) find the vertex, (d) find the y-intercept, and (e) graph the function. 12–14. See p. A56.

12. $f(x) = 2x^2 - 4x + 5$ 13. $f(x) = -\frac{1}{2}x^2 - 2x + 3$ 14. $f(x) = -x^2 - 8x - 6$

Find the minimum or maximum value of each function. Then state the domain and range of the function.

15. $f(x) = 3x^2 + 60x + 294$ min.: -6; D: $\mathbb{R}$; R: $\{y \mid y \geq -6\}$
16. $f(x) = -2x^2 + 28x - 95$ max.: 3; D: $\mathbb{R}$; R: $\{y \mid y \leq 3\}$
17. $f(x) = 2x^2 + 14x + 30$ min.: 5.5; D: $\mathbb{R}$; R: $\{y \mid y \geq 5.5\}$

Lesson 5-3 Find the zeros of each function by using a graph and a table.

18. $f(x) = x^2 + 5x + 6$ $-3, -2$ 19. $f(x) = x^2 - 3x - 28$ $-4, 7$ 20. $f(x) = -x^2 + 12x - 20$ $2, 10$

Find the zeros of each function by factoring.

21. $f(x) = x^2 + 2x - 35$ $-7, 5$ 22. $f(x) = x^2 - 8x - 9$ $-1, 9$ 23. $f(x) = 2x^2 - 9x$ $0, \frac{9}{2}$
24. $f(x) = x^2 + 10x + 25$ -5 25. $f(x) = x^2 - 49$ $-7, 7$ 26. $f(x) = x^2 - 12x + 36$ 6

Write a quadratic function in standard form for each given set of zeros. Possible answers:

27. 5 and 8 $f(x) = x^2 - 13x + 40$ 28. -3 and 1 $f(x) = x^2 + 2x - 3$ 29. 6 and 6 $f(x) = x^2 - 12x + 36$ 30. 12 and 0 $f(x) = x^2 - 12x$

Lesson 5-4 Solve each equation.

31. $4x^2 - 10 = 90$ ± 5 32. $x^2 + 8x + 16 = 10$ $-4 \pm \sqrt{10}$ 33. $x^2 + 4x + 4 = 8$ $-2 \pm 2\sqrt{2}$

Complete the square for each expression. Write the resulting expression as a binomial squared.

34. $x^2 - 16x + ■$ $x^2 - 16x + 64 = (x - 8)^2$ 35. $x^2 + 22x + ■$ $x^2 + 22x + 121 = (x + 11)^2$ 36. $x^2 + 7x + ■$ $x^2 + 7x + \frac{49}{4} = \left(x + \frac{7}{2}\right)^2$

Solve each equation by completing the square.

37. $x^2 + 8x = -10$ $-4 \pm \sqrt{6}$ 38. $x^2 - 12x = 13$ $-1, 13$ 39. $x^2 + 20 = 10x$ $5 \pm \sqrt{5}$
40. $2x^2 + 12x = 14$ $-7, 1$ 41. $3x^2 - 18 = 48x$ $8 \pm \sqrt{70}$ 42. $x^2 - 5 = 2x$ $1 \pm \sqrt{6}$

Write each function in vertex form, and identify its vertex.

43. $f(x) = x^2 - 2x + 17$ $f(x) = (x - 1)^2 + 16$; $(1, 16)$
44. $f(x) = x^2 + 4x - 8$ $f(x) = (x + 2)^2 - 12$; $(-2, -12)$
45. $f(x) = 4x^2 - 24x + 31$ $f(x) = 4(x - 3)^2 - 5$; $(3, -5)$

S12 Extra Practice

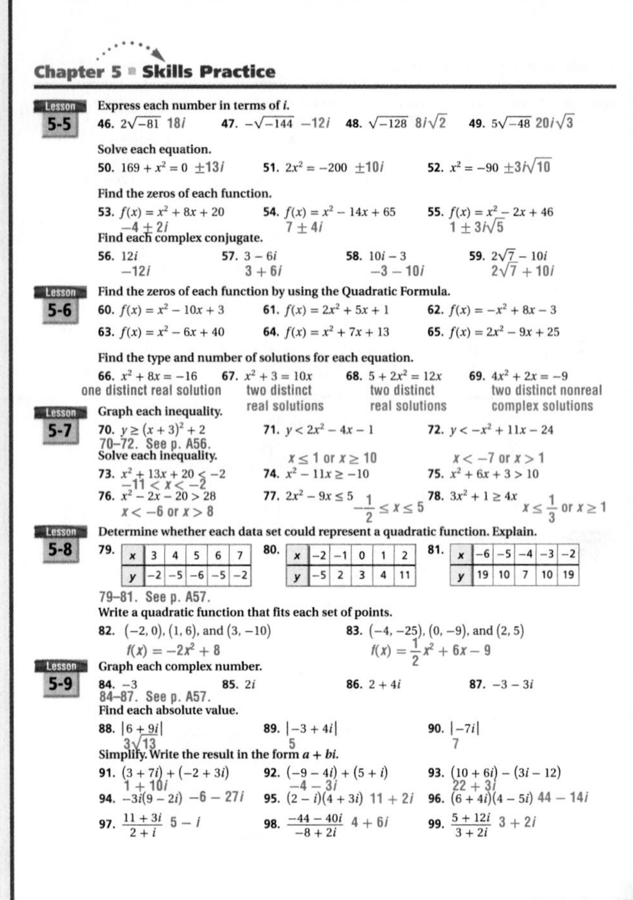

Chapter 5 ■ Skills Practice

Lesson 5-5 Express each number in terms of i.

46. $2\sqrt{-81}$ $18i$ 47. $-\sqrt{-144}$ $-12i$ 48. $\sqrt{-128}$ $8i\sqrt{2}$ 49. $5\sqrt{-48}$ $20i\sqrt{3}$

Solve each equation.

50. $169 + x^2 = 0$ $\pm 13i$ 51. $2x^2 = -200$ $\pm 10i$ 52. $x^2 = -90$ $\pm 3i\sqrt{10}$

Find the zeros of each function.

53. $f(x) = x^2 + 8x + 20$ $-4 \pm 2i$ 54. $f(x) = x^2 - 14x + 65$ $7 \pm 4i$ 55. $f(x) = x^2 - 2x + 46$ $1 \pm 3i\sqrt{5}$

Find each complex conjugate.

56. $12i$ $-12i$ 57. $3 - 6i$ $3 + 6i$ 58. $10i - 3$ $-3 - 10i$ 59. $2\sqrt{7} - 10i$ $2\sqrt{7} + 10i$

Lesson 5-6 Find the zeros of each function by using the Quadratic Formula.

60. $f(x) = x^2 - 10x + 3$ 61. $f(x) = 2x^2 + 5x + 1$ 62. $f(x) = -x^2 + 8x - 3$
63. $f(x) = x^2 - 6x + 40$ 64. $f(x) = x^2 + 7x + 13$ 65. $f(x) = 2x^2 - 9x + 25$

Find the type and number of solutions for each equation.

66. $x^2 + 8x = -16$ one distinct real solution 67. $x^2 + 3 = 10x$ two distinct real solutions 68. $5 + 2x^2 = 12x$ two distinct real solutions 69. $4x^2 + 2x = -9$ two distinct nonreal complex solutions

Lesson 5-7 Graph each inequality.

70. $y \geq (x + 3)^2 + 2$ 71. $y < 2x^2 - 4x - 1$ 72. $y < -x^2 + 11x - 24$

70–72. See p. A56.

Solve each inequality.

73. $x^2 + 13x + 20 \leq -2$ $-11 \leq x \leq -2$ 74. $x^2 - 11x \geq -10$ $x \leq 1$ or $x \geq 10$ 75. $x^2 + 6x + 3 > 10$ $x < -7$ or $x > 1$
76. $x^2 - 2x - 20 > 28$ $x < -6$ or $x > 8$ 77. $2x^2 - 9x \leq 5$ $-\frac{1}{2} \leq x \leq 5$ 78. $3x^2 + 1 \geq 4x$ $x \leq \frac{1}{3}$ or $x \geq 1$

Lesson 5-8 Determine whether each data set could represent a quadratic function. Explain.

79.

x	3	4	5	6	7
y	−2	−5	−6	−5	−2

80.

x	−2	−1	0	1	2
y	−5	2	3	4	11

81.

x	−6	−5	−4	−3	−2
y	19	10	7	10	19

79–81. See p. A57.

Write a quadratic function that fits each set of points.

82. $(-2, 0)$, $(1, 6)$, and $(3, -10)$ $f(x) = -2x^2 + 8$
83. $(-4, -25)$, $(0, -9)$, and $(2, 5)$ $f(x) = \frac{1}{2}x^2 + 6x - 9$

Lesson 5-9 Graph each complex number.

84. -3 85. $2i$ 86. $2 + 4i$ 87. $-3 - 3i$

84–87. See p. A57.

Find each absolute value.

88. $|6 + 9i|$ $3\sqrt{13}$ 89. $|-3 + 4i|$ 5 90. $|-7i|$ 7

Simplify. Write the result in the form $a + bi$.

91. $(3 + 7i) + (-2 + 3i)$ $1 + 10i$ 92. $(-9 - 4i) + (5 + i)$ $-4 - 3i$ 93. $(10 + 6i) - (3i - 12)$ $22 + 3i$
94. $-3i(9 - 2i)$ $-6 - 27i$ 95. $(2 - i)(4 + 3i)$ $11 + 2i$ 96. $(6 + 4i)(4 - 5i)$ $44 - 14i$
97. $\frac{11 + 3i}{2 + i}$ $5 - i$ 98. $\frac{-44 - 40i}{-8 + 2i}$ $4 + 6i$ 99. $\frac{5 + 12i}{3 + 2i}$ $3 + 2i$

Extra Practice S13

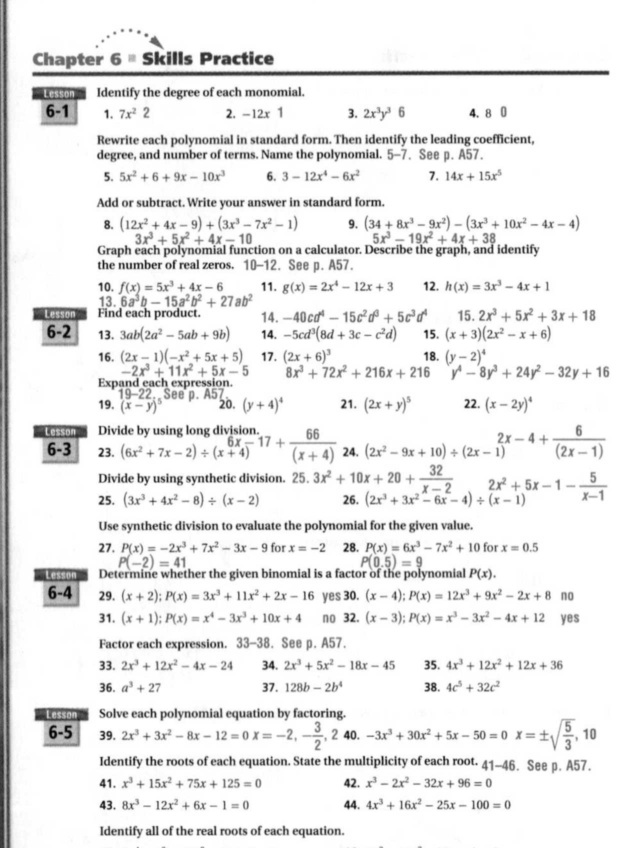

Chapter 6 ■ Skills Practice

Lesson 6-1 Identify the degree of each monomial.

1. $7x^2$ 2 2. $-12x$ 1 3. $2x^3y^3$ 6 4. 8 0

Rewrite each polynomial in standard form. Then identify the leading coefficient, degree, and number of terms. Name the polynomial. 5–7. See p. A57.

5. $5x^2 + 6 + 9x - 10x^3$ 6. $3 - 12x^4 - 6x^2$ 7. $14x + 15x^5$

Add or subtract. Write your answer in standard form.

8. $(12x^2 + 4x - 9) + (3x^3 - 7x^2 - 1)$ $3x^3 + 5x^2 + 4x - 10$
9. $(34 + 8x^3 - 9x^2) - (3x^3 + 10x^2 - 4x - 4)$ $5x^3 - 19x^2 + 4x + 38$

Graph each polynomial function on a calculator. Describe the graph, and identify the number of real zeros. 10–12. See p. A57.

10. $f(x) = 5x^3 + 4x - 6$ 11. $g(x) = 2x^4 - 12x + 3$ 12. $h(x) = 3x^3 - 4x + 1$

Lesson 6-2 Find each product.

13. $3ab(2a^2 - 5ab + 9b)$ $6a^3b - 15a^2b^2 + 27ab^2$
14. $-5cd^3(8d + 3c - c^2d)$ $-40cd^4 - 15c^2d^3 + 5c^3d^4$
15. $(x + 3)(2x^2 - x + 6)$ $2x^3 + 5x^2 + 3x + 18$
16. $(2x - 1)(-x^2 + 5x + 5)$ $-2x^3 + 11x^2 + 5x - 5$
17. $(2x + 6)^3$ $8x^3 + 72x^2 + 216x + 216$
18. $(y - 2)^4$ $y^4 - 8y^3 + 24y^2 - 32y + 16$

Expand each expression. 19–22. See p. A57.

19. $(x - y)^5$ 20. $(y + 4)^4$ 21. $(2x + y)^5$ 22. $(x - 2y)^4$

Lesson 6-3 Divide by using long division.

23. $(6x^2 + 7x - 2) \div (x + 4)$ $6x - 17 + \frac{66}{(x + 4)}$ 24. $(2x^2 - 9x + 10) \div (2x - 1)$ $2x - 4 + \frac{6}{(2x - 1)}$

Divide by using synthetic division.

25. $(3x^3 + 4x^2 - 8) \div (x - 2)$ $3x^2 + 10x + 20 + \frac{32}{x - 2}$ 26. $(2x^3 + 3x^2 - 6x - 4) \div (x - 1)$ $2x^2 + 5x - 1 - \frac{5}{x - 1}$

Use synthetic division to evaluate the polynomial for the given value.

27. $P(x) = -2x^3 + 7x^2 - 3x - 9$ for $x = -2$ $P(-2) = 41$ 28. $P(x) = 6x^3 - 7x^2 + 10$ for $x = 0.5$ $P(0.5) = 9$

Lesson 6-4 Determine whether the given binomial is a factor of the polynomial $P(x)$.

29. $(x + 2)$; $P(x) = 3x^3 + 11x^2 + 2x - 16$ yes 30. $(x - 4)$; $P(x) = 12x^3 + 9x^2 - 2x + 8$ no
31. $(x + 1)$; $P(x) = x^4 - 3x^3 + 10x + 4$ no 32. $(x - 3)$; $P(x) = x^3 - 3x^2 - 4x + 12$ yes

Factor each expression. 33–38. See p. A57.

33. $2x^3 + 12x^2 - 4x - 24$ 34. $2x^3 + 5x^2 - 18x - 45$ 35. $4x^3 + 12x^2 + 12x + 36$
36. $a^3 + 27$ 37. $128b - 2b^4$ 38. $4c^5 + 32c^2$

Lesson 6-5 Solve each polynomial equation by factoring.

39. $2x^3 + 3x^2 - 8x - 12 = 0$ $x = -2, -\frac{3}{2}, 2$ 40. $-3x^3 + 30x^2 + 5x - 50 = 0$ $x = \pm\sqrt{\frac{5}{3}}, 10$

Identify the roots of each equation. State the multiplicity of each root. 41–46. See p. A57.

41. $x^3 + 15x^2 + 75x + 125 = 0$ 42. $x^3 - 2x^2 - 32x + 96 = 0$
43. $8x^3 - 12x^2 + 6x - 1 = 0$ 44. $4x^3 + 16x^2 - 25x - 100 = 0$

Identify all of the real roots of each equation.

45. $2x^4 - x^3 - 14x^2 - 5x + 6 = 0$ 46. $6x^3 - 11x^2 - 19x - 6 = 0$

S14 Extra Practice

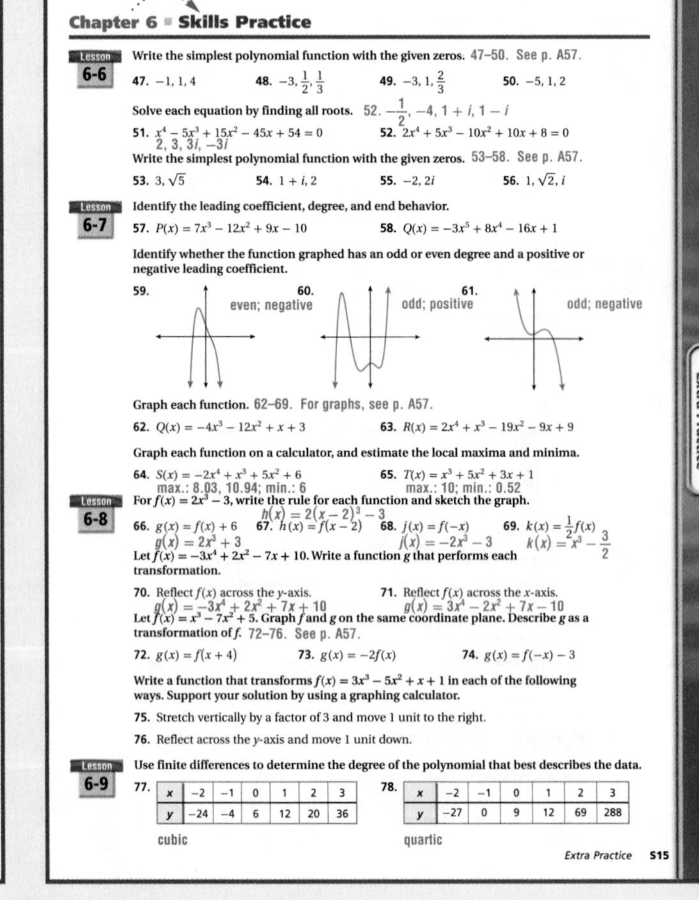

Chapter 6 ■ Skills Practice

Lesson 6-6 Write the simplest polynomial function with the given zeros. 47–50. See p. A57.

47. $-1, 1, 4$ 48. $-3, \frac{1}{2}, \frac{1}{3}$ 49. $-3, 1, \frac{2}{3}$ 50. $-5, 1, 2$

Solve each equation by finding all roots.

51. $x^4 - 5x^3 + 15x^2 - 45x + 54 = 0$ $2, 3, 3i, -3i$ 52. $2x^4 + 5x^3 - 10x^2 + 10x + 8 = 0$ $-\frac{1}{2}, -4, 1 + i, 1 - i$

Write the simplest polynomial function with the given zeros. 53–58. See p. A57.

53. $3, \sqrt{5}$ 54. $1 + i, 2$ 55. $-2, 2i$ 56. $1, \sqrt{2}, i$

Lesson 6-7 Identify the leading coefficient, degree, and end behavior.

57. $P(x) = 7x^3 - 12x^2 + 9x - 10$ 58. $Q(x) = -3x^5 + 8x^4 - 16x + 1$

Identify whether the function graphed has an odd or even degree and a positive or negative leading coefficient.

59. even; negative 60. odd; positive 61. odd; negative

Graph each function. 62–69. For graphs, see p. A57.

62. $Q(x) = -4x^3 - 12x^2 + x + 3$ 63. $R(x) = 2x^4 + x^3 - 19x^2 - 9x + 9$

Graph each function on a calculator, and estimate the local maxima and minima.

64. $S(x) = -2x^4 + x^3 + 5x^2 + 6$ max.: 8.03, 10.94; min.: 6 65. $T(x) = x^3 + 5x^2 + 3x + 1$ max.: 10; min.: 0.52

Lesson 6-8 For $f(x) = 2x^3 - 3$, write the rule for each function and sketch the graph.

66. $g(x) = f(x) + 6$ $g(x) = 2x^3 + 3$ 67. $h(x) = f(x - 2)$ $h(x) = 2(x - 2)^3 - 3$ 68. $j(x) = f(-x)$ $j(x) = -2x^3 - 3$ 69. $k(x) = \frac{1}{2}f(x)$ $k(x) = x^3 - \frac{3}{2}$

Let $f(x) = -3x^4 + 2x^2 - 7x + 10$. Write a function g that performs each transformation.

70. Reflect $f(x)$ across the y-axis. $g(x) = -3x^4 + 2x^2 + 7x + 10$ 71. Reflect $f(x)$ across the x-axis. $g(x) = 3x^4 - 2x^2 + 7x - 10$

Let $f(x) = x^3 - 7x^2 + 5$. Graph f and g on the same coordinate plane. Describe g as a transformation of f. 72–76. See p. A57.

72. $g(x) = f(x + 4)$ 73. $g(x) = -2f(x)$ 74. $g(x) = f(-x) - 3$

Write a function that transforms $f(x) = 3x^3 - 5x^2 + x + 1$ in each of the following ways. Support your solution by using a graphing calculator.

75. Stretch vertically by a factor of 3 and move 1 unit to the right.
76. Reflect across the y-axis and move 1 unit down.

Lesson 6-9 Use finite differences to determine the degree of the polynomial that best describes the data.

77.

x	−2	−1	0	1	2	3
y	−24	−4	6	12	20	36

cubic

78.

x	−2	−1	0	1	2	3
y	−27	0	9	12	69	288

quartic

Extra Practice S15

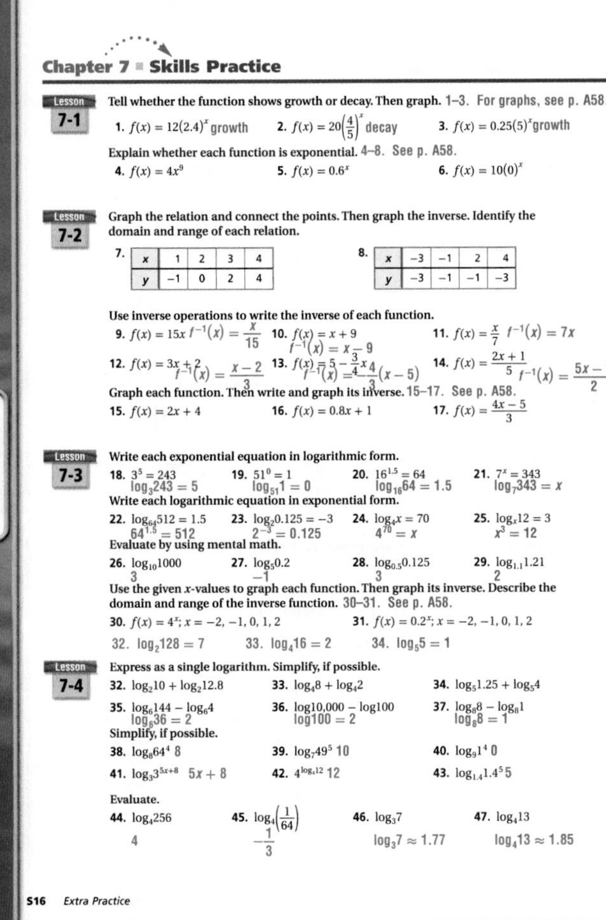

Chapter 7 ■ Skills Practice

Lesson 7-1

Tell whether the function shows growth or decay. Then graph. 1–3. For graphs, see p. A58.

1. $f(x) = 12(2.4)^x$ growth
2. $f(x) = 20\left(\frac{4}{5}\right)^x$ decay
3. $f(x) = 0.25(5)^x$ growth

Explain whether each function is exponential. 4–8. See p. A58.

4. $f(x) = 4x^9$
5. $f(x) = 0.6^x$
6. $f(x) = 10(0)^x$

Lesson 7-2

Graph the relation and connect the points. Then graph the inverse. Identify the domain and range of each relation.

7.

x	1	2	3	4
y	−1	0	2	4

8.

x	−3	−1	2	4
y	−3	−1	−1	−3

Use inverse operations to write the inverse of each function.

9. $f(x) = 15x$ $f^{-1}(x) = \frac{x}{15}$
10. $f(x) = x + 9$ $f^{-1}(x) = x - 9$
11. $f(x) = \frac{x}{7}$ $f^{-1}(x) = 7x$
12. $f(x) = 3x + 2$ $f^{-1}(x) = \frac{x-2}{3}$
13. $f(x) = 5 - \frac{3}{4}x$ $f^{-1}(x) = -\frac{4}{3}(x-5)$
14. $f(x) = \frac{2x+1}{5}$ $f^{-1}(x) = \frac{5x-1}{2}$

Graph each function. Then write and graph its inverse. 15–17. See p. A58.

15. $f(x) = 2x + 4$
16. $f(x) = 0.8x + 1$
17. $f(x) = \frac{4x-5}{3}$

Lesson 7-3

Write each exponential equation in logarithmic form.

18. $3^5 = 243$ $\log_3 243 = 5$
19. $51^0 = 1$ $\log_{51} 1 = 0$
20. $16^{1.5} = 64$ $\log_{16} 64 = 1.5$
21. $7^x = 343$ $\log_7 343 = x$

Write each logarithmic equation in exponential form.

22. $\log_{64} 512 = 1.5$ $64^{1.5} = 512$
23. $\log_2 0.125 = -3$ $2^{-3} = 0.125$
24. $\log_4 x = 70$ $4^{70} = x$
25. $\log_x 12 = 3$ $x^3 = 12$

Evaluate by using mental math.

26. $\log_{10} 1000$ 3
27. $\log_5 0.2$ −1
28. $\log_{0.5} 0.125$ 3
29. $\log_{1.1} 1.21$ 2

Use the given x-values to graph each function. Then graph its inverse. Describe the domain and range of the inverse function. 30–31. See p. A58.

30. $f(x) = 4^x$; $x = -2, -1, 0, 1, 2$
31. $f(x) = 0.2^x$; $x = -2, -1, 0, 1, 2$

32. $\log_2 128 = 7$ 33. $\log_4 16 = 2$ 34. $\log_5 5 = 1$

Lesson 7-4

Express as a single logarithm. Simplify, if possible.

32. $\log_2 10 + \log_2 12.8$
33. $\log_4 8 + \log_4 2$
34. $\log_5 1.25 + \log_5 4$
35. $\log_6 144 - \log_6 4$ $\log_6 36 = 2$
36. $\log 10{,}000 - \log 100$ $\log 100 = 2$
37. $\log_8 8 - \log_8 1$ $\log_8 8 = 1$

Simplify, if possible.

38. $\log_8 64^4$ 8
39. $\log_7 49^5$ 10
40. $\log_9 1^4$ 0
41. $\log_3 3^{5x+8}$ $5x + 8$
42. $4^{\log_4 12}$ 12
43. $\log_{1.4} 1.4^5$ 5

Evaluate.

44. $\log_4 256$ 4
45. $\log_4\left(\frac{1}{64}\right)$ $-\frac{1}{3}$
46. $\log_3 7$ $\log_3 7 \approx 1.77$
47. $\log_4 13$ $\log_4 13 \approx 1.85$

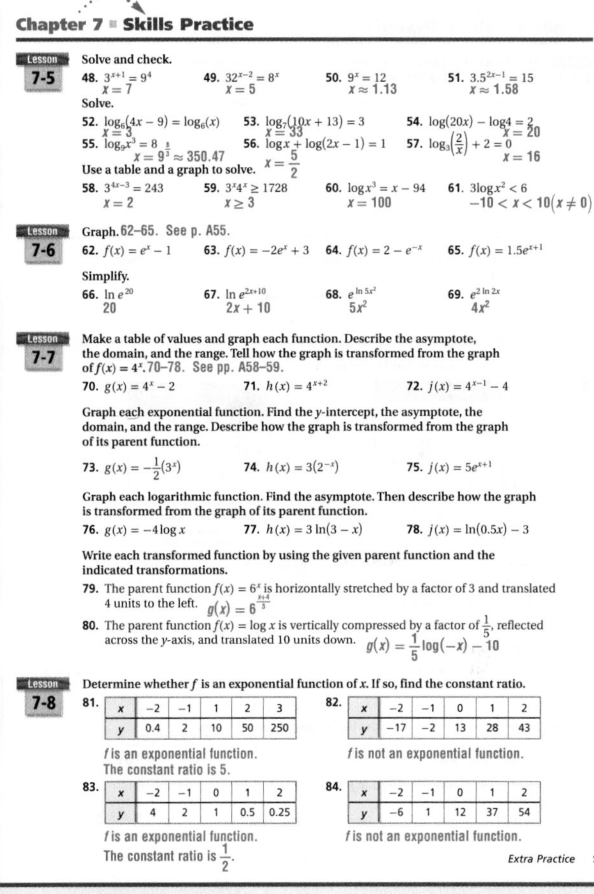

Chapter 7 ■ Skills Practice

Lesson 7-5

Solve and check.

48. $3^{x+1} = 9^4$ $x = 7$
49. $32^{x-2} = 8^x$ $x = 5$
50. $9^x = 12$ $x \approx 1.13$
51. $3.5^{2x-1} = 15$ $x \approx 1.58$

Solve.

52. $\log_6(4x - 9) = \log_6(x)$ $x = 3$
53. $\log_7(10x + 13) = 3$ $x = 33$
54. $\log(20x) - \log 4 = 2$ $x = 20$
55. $\log_9 x^3 = 8$ $x = 9^{\frac{8}{3}} \approx 350.47$
56. $\log x + \log(2x - 1) = 1$ $x = \frac{5}{2}$
57. $\log_3\left(\frac{2}{x}\right) + 2 = 0$ $x = 16$

Use a table and a graph to solve.

58. $3^{4x-3} = 243$ $x = 2$
59. $3^x 4^x \geq 1728$ $x \geq 3$
60. $\log x^3 = x - 94$ $x = 100$
61. $3\log x^2 < 6$ $-10 < x < 10 (x \neq 0)$

Lesson 7-6

Graph. 62–65. See p. A55.

62. $f(x) = e^x - 1$
63. $f(x) = -2e^x + 3$
64. $f(x) = 2 - e^{-x}$
65. $f(x) = 1.5e^{x+1}$

Simplify.

66. $\ln e^{20}$ 20
67. $\ln e^{2x+10}$ $2x + 10$
68. $e^{\ln 5x^2}$ $5x^2$
69. $e^{2\ln 2x}$ $4x^2$

Lesson 7-7

Make a table of values and graph each function. Describe the asymptote, the domain, and the range. Tell how the graph is transformed from the graph of $f(x) = 4^x$. 70–78. See pp. A58–59.

70. $g(x) = 4^x - 2$
71. $h(x) = 4^{x+2}$
72. $j(x) = 4^{x-1} - 4$

Graph each exponential function. Find the y-intercept, the asymptote, the domain, and the range. Describe how the graph is transformed from the graph of its parent function.

73. $g(x) = -\frac{1}{2}(3^x)$
74. $h(x) = 3(2^{-x})$
75. $j(x) = 5e^{x+1}$

Graph each logarithmic function. Find the asymptote. Then describe how the graph is transformed from the graph of its parent function.

76. $g(x) = -4\log x$
77. $h(x) = 3\ln(3 - x)$
78. $j(x) = \ln(0.5x) - 3$

Write each transformed function by using the given parent function and the indicated transformations.

79. The parent function $f(x) = 6^x$ is horizontally stretched by a factor of 3 and translated 4 units to the left. $g(x) = 6^{\frac{x+4}{3}}$
80. The parent function $f(x) = \log x$ is vertically compressed by a factor of $\frac{1}{5}$, reflected across the y-axis, and translated 10 units down. $g(x) = \frac{1}{5}\log(-x) - 10$

Lesson 7-8

Determine whether f is an exponential function of x. If so, find the constant ratio.

81.

x	−2	−1	1	2	3
y	0.4	2	10	50	250

f is an exponential function. The constant ratio is 5.

82.

x	−2	−1	0	1	2
y	−17	−2	13	28	43

f is not an exponential function.

83.

x	−2	−1	0	1	2
y	4	2	1	0.5	0.25

f is an exponential function. The constant ratio is $\frac{1}{2}$.

84.

x	−2	−1	0	1	2
y	−6	1	12	37	54

f is not an exponential function.

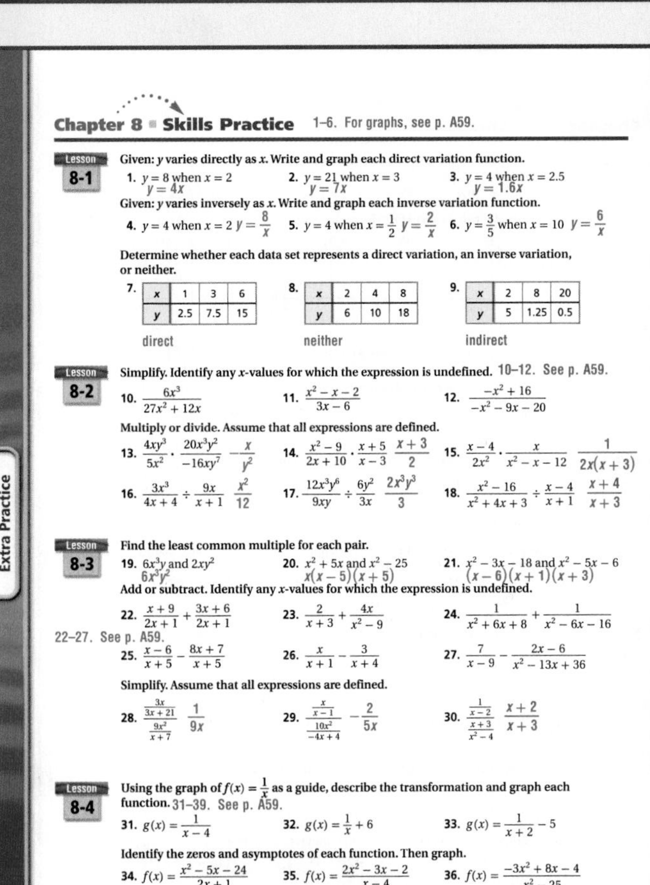

Chapter 8 ■ Skills Practice

1–6. For graphs, see p. A59.

Lesson 8-1

Given: y varies directly as x. Write and graph each direct variation function.

1. $y = 8$ when $x = 2$ $y = 4x$
2. $y = 21$ when $x = 3$ $y = 7x$
3. $y = 4$ when $x = 2.5$ $y = 1.6x$

Given: y varies inversely as x. Write and graph each inverse variation function.

4. $y = 4$ when $x = 2$ $y = \frac{8}{x}$
5. $y = 4$ when $x = \frac{1}{2}$ $y = \frac{2}{x}$
6. $y = \frac{3}{5}$ when $x = 10$ $y = \frac{6}{x}$

Determine whether each data set represents a direct variation, an inverse variation, or neither.

7.

x	1	3	6
y	2.5	7.5	15

direct

8.

x	2	4	8
y	6	10	18

neither

9.

x	2	8	20
y	5	1.25	0.5

indirect

Lesson 8-2

Simplify. Identify any x-values for which the expression is undefined. 10–12. See p. A59.

10. $\frac{6x^3}{27x^2 + 12x}$
11. $\frac{x^2 - x - 2}{3x - 6}$
12. $\frac{-x^2 + 16}{-x^2 - 9x - 20}$

Multiply or divide. Assume that all expressions are defined.

13. $\frac{4xy^3}{5x^2} \cdot \frac{20x^3y^2}{-16xy^7}$ $-\frac{x}{y^2}$
14. $\frac{x^2 - 9}{2x + 10} \cdot \frac{x + 5}{x - 3}$ $\frac{x+3}{2}$
15. $\frac{x - 4}{2x^2} \cdot \frac{x}{x^2 - x - 12}$ $\frac{1}{2x(x+3)}$
16. $\frac{3x^3}{4x + 4} \div \frac{9x}{x + 1}$ $\frac{x^2}{12}$
17. $\frac{12x^3y^6}{9xy} \div \frac{6y^2}{3x}$ $\frac{2x^3y^3}{3}$
18. $\frac{x^2 - 16}{x^2 + 4x + 3} \div \frac{x - 4}{x + 1}$ $\frac{x+4}{x+3}$

Lesson 8-3

Find the least common multiple for each pair.

19. $6x^3y$ and $2xy^2$ $6x^3y^2$
20. $x^2 + 5x$ and $x^2 - 25$ $x(x-5)(x+5)$
21. $x^2 - 3x - 18$ and $x^2 - 5x - 6$ $(x-6)(x+1)(x+3)$

Add or subtract. Identify any x-values for which the expression is undefined.

22. $\frac{x + 9}{2x + 1} + \frac{3x + 6}{2x + 1}$
23. $\frac{2}{x + 3} + \frac{4x}{x^2 - 9}$
24. $\frac{1}{x^2 + 6x + 8} + \frac{1}{x^2 - 6x - 16}$

22–27. See p. A59.

25. $\frac{x - 6}{x + 5} - \frac{8x + 7}{x + 5}$
26. $\frac{x}{x + 1} - \frac{3}{x + 4}$
27. $\frac{7}{x - 9} - \frac{2x - 6}{x^2 - 13x + 36}$

Simplify. Assume that all expressions are defined.

28. $\frac{\frac{3x}{3x+21}}{\frac{9x^2}{x+7}}$ $\frac{1}{9x}$
29. $\frac{\frac{x}{x-1}}{\frac{10x^2}{-4x+4}}$ $-\frac{2}{5x}$
30. $\frac{\frac{1}{x-2}}{\frac{x+3}{x^2-4}}$ $\frac{x+2}{x+3}$

Lesson 8-4

Using the graph of $f(x) = \frac{1}{x}$ as a guide, describe the transformation and graph each function. 31–39. See p. A59.

31. $g(x) = \frac{1}{x - 4}$
32. $g(x) = \frac{1}{x} + 6$
33. $g(x) = \frac{1}{x + 2} - 5$

Identify the zeros and asymptotes of each function. Then graph.

34. $f(x) = \frac{x^2 - 5x - 24}{2x + 1}$
35. $f(x) = \frac{2x^2 - 3x - 2}{x - 4}$
36. $f(x) = \frac{-3x^2 + 8x - 4}{x^2 - 25}$

Identify holes in the graph of each function. Then graph.

37. $f(x) = \frac{x^2 - 4x - 21}{x + 3}$
38. $f(x) = \frac{x^2 - 4x - 5}{x^2 - 25}$
39. $f(x) = \frac{x^2 - 3x}{4x - 12}$

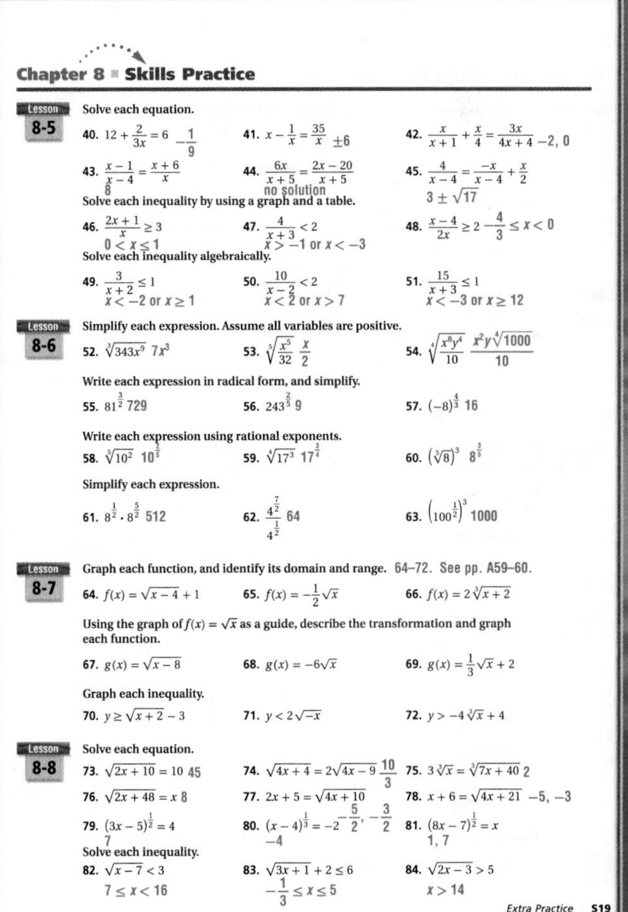

Chapter 8 ■ Skills Practice

Lesson 8-5

Solve each equation.

40. $12 + \frac{2}{3x} = 6$ $-\frac{1}{9}$
41. $x - \frac{1}{x} = \frac{35}{x}$ ± 6
42. $\frac{x}{x + 1} + \frac{x}{4} = \frac{3x}{4x + 4}$ $-2, 0$
43. $\frac{x - 1}{x - 4} = \frac{x + 6}{x}$ 8
44. $\frac{6x}{x + 5} = \frac{2x - 20}{x + 5}$ no solution
45. $\frac{4}{x - 4} = \frac{-x}{x - 4} + \frac{x}{2}$ $3 \pm \sqrt{17}$

Solve each inequality by using a graph and a table.

46. $\frac{2x + 1}{x} \geq 3$ $0 < x \leq 1$
47. $\frac{4}{x + 3} < 2$ $x > -1$ or $x < -3$
48. $\frac{x - 4}{2x} \geq 2$ $-\frac{4}{3} \leq x < 0$

Solve each inequality algebraically.

49. $\frac{3}{x + 2} \leq 1$ $x < -2$ or $x \geq 1$
50. $\frac{10}{x - 2} < 2$ $x < 2$ or $x > 7$
51. $\frac{15}{x + 3} \leq 1$ $x < -3$ or $x \geq 12$

Lesson 8-6

Simplify each expression. Assume that all variables are positive.

52. $\sqrt[3]{343x^9}$ $7x^3$
53. $\sqrt[5]{\frac{x^5}{32}}$ $\frac{x}{2}$
54. $\sqrt[4]{\frac{x^8y^4}{10}}$ $\frac{x^2y\sqrt[4]{1000}}{10}$

Write each expression in radical form, and simplify.

55. $81^{\frac{3}{2}}$ 729
56. $243^{\frac{2}{5}}$ 9
57. $(-8)^{\frac{4}{3}}$ 16

Write each expression using rational exponents.

58. $\sqrt[3]{10^2}$ $10^{\frac{2}{3}}$
59. $\sqrt[4]{17^3}$ $17^{\frac{3}{4}}$
60. $(\sqrt[3]{8})^3$ $8^{\frac{3}{3}}$

Simplify each expression.

61. $8^{\frac{1}{2}} \cdot 8^{\frac{5}{2}}$ 512
62. $\frac{4^{\frac{7}{2}}}{4^{\frac{1}{2}}}$ 64
63. $\left(100^{\frac{1}{2}}\right)^3$ 1000

Lesson 8-7

Graph each function, and identify its domain and range. 64–72. See pp. A59–60.

64. $f(x) = \sqrt{x - 4} + 1$
65. $f(x) = -\frac{1}{2}\sqrt{x}$
66. $f(x) = 2\sqrt[3]{x + 2}$

Using the graph of $f(x) = \sqrt{x}$ as a guide, describe the transformation and graph each function.

67. $g(x) = \sqrt{x - 8}$
68. $g(x) = -6\sqrt{x}$
69. $g(x) = \frac{1}{3}\sqrt{x} + 2$

Graph each inequality.

70. $y \geq \sqrt{x + 2} - 3$
71. $y < 2\sqrt{-x}$
72. $y > -4\sqrt[3]{x} + 4$

Lesson 8-8

Solve each equation.

73. $\sqrt{2x + 10} = 10$ 45
74. $\sqrt{4x + 4} = 2\sqrt{4x - 9}$ $\frac{10}{3}$
75. $3\sqrt[3]{x} = \sqrt[3]{7x + 40}$ 2
76. $\sqrt{2x + 48} = x$ 8
77. $2x + 5 = \sqrt{4x + 10}$ $-\frac{5}{2}, -\frac{3}{2}$
78. $x + 6 = \sqrt{4x + 21}$ $-5, -3$
79. $(3x - 5)^{\frac{1}{2}} = 4$ 7
80. $(x - 4)^{\frac{1}{3}} = -2$ −4
81. $(8x - 7)^{\frac{1}{2}} = x$ 1, 7

Solve each inequality.

82. $\sqrt{x - 7} < 3$ $7 \leq x < 16$
83. $\sqrt{3x + 1} + 2 \leq 6$ $-\frac{1}{3} \leq x \leq 5$
84. $\sqrt{2x - 3} > 5$ $x > 14$

Extra Practice

Chapter 9 ■ Skills Practice

Lesson 9-1

Match each situation to its corresponding graph. Sketch a possible graph of the situation if the situation does not match any of the given graphs.

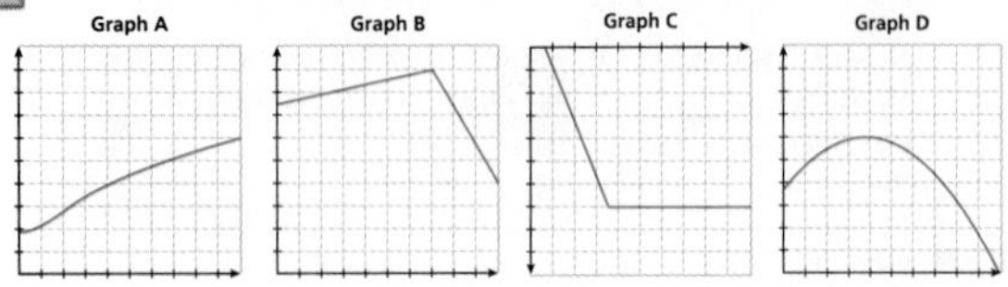

Graph A Graph B Graph C Graph D

1. A state senator's high approval rating is rising steadily but then drops sharply after a scandal. graph B
2. The value of an antique chair increases steadily. graph A
3. Sales of a valuable stock dip and then recover. See p. A60.
4. A scuba diver descends to 60 ft below sea level and swims around at that depth. graph C

Lesson 9-2

Create a table and a verbal description to represent each graph. 5–6. See p. A60.

5. Hat Prices (Price Per Hat ($); Hats Ordered: 0, 20, 40, 60, 80)

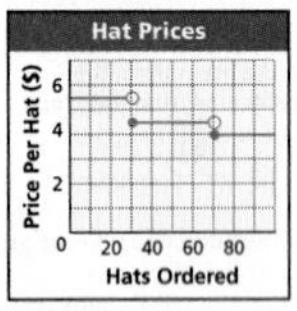

6. Swimming Pool Admission (Price ($); Time of Day: 8 A.M., Noon, 4 P.M., 8 P.M.)

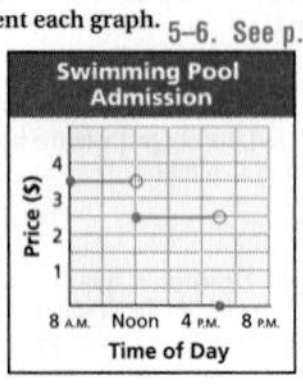

Evaluate each piecewise function for $x = -2$ and $x = 5$.

7. $f(x) = \begin{cases} 10 & \text{if } x \le -4 \\ 7 & \text{if } -4 < x \le 2 \\ 3 & \text{if } x > 2 \end{cases}$ $f(-2) = 7$; $f(5) = 3$
8. $g(x) = \begin{cases} x + 2 & \text{if } x < 0 \\ 4 - x & \text{if } x \ge 0 \end{cases}$ $g(-2) = 0$; $g(5) = -1$
9. $h(x) = \begin{cases} x^2 - 3 & \text{if } x \le 2 \\ x + 1 & \text{if } x > 2 \end{cases}$ $h(-2) = 1$; $h(5) = 6$

Graph each function. 10–16. See p. A60.

10. $f(x) = \begin{cases} 4 & \text{if } x < -1 \\ -1 & \text{if } x \ge -1 \end{cases}$
11. $g(x) = \begin{cases} 2x - 4 & \text{if } x \le 2 \\ -2x + 2 & \text{if } x > 2 \end{cases}$
12. $h(x) = \begin{cases} 2 & \text{if } x < 3 \\ x^2 - 7 & \text{if } x \ge 3 \end{cases}$

Lesson 9-3

Given $f(x) = \begin{cases} 2x - 2 & \text{if } x < 1 \\ -3x & \text{if } x \ge 1 \end{cases}$, write the rule for each function.

13. $g(x)$, a vertical stretch by a factor of 3
14. $h(x)$, a reflection across the y-axis

Identify the x- and y-intercepts of $f(x)$. Without graphing $g(x)$, identify its x- and y-intercepts.

15. $f(x) = -3x + 6$ and $g(x) = f(-2x)$
16. $f(x) = (x - 3)^2$ and $g(x) = -2f(x)$

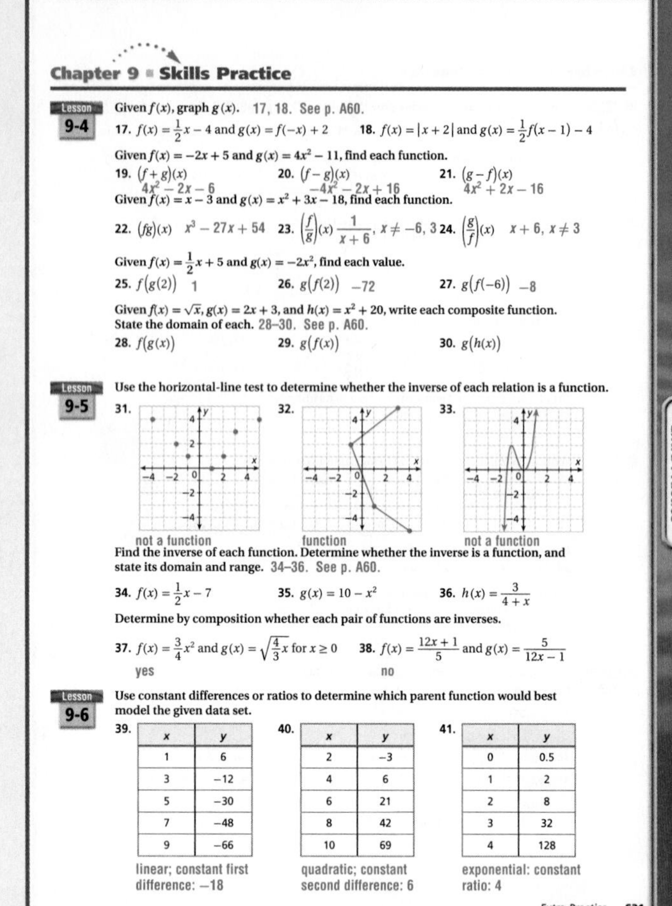

Chapter 9 ■ Skills Practice

Lesson 9-4

Given $f(x)$, graph $g(x)$. 17, 18. See p. A60.

17. $f(x) = \frac{1}{2}x - 4$ and $g(x) = f(-x) + 2$
18. $f(x) = |x + 2|$ and $g(x) = \frac{1}{2}f(x - 1) - 4$

Given $f(x) = -2x + 5$ and $g(x) = 4x^2 - 11$, find each function.

19. $(f + g)(x)$ $4x^2 - 2x - 6$
20. $(f - g)(x)$ $-4x^2 - 2x + 16$
21. $(g - f)(x)$ $4x^2 + 2x - 16$

Given $f(x) = x - 3$ and $g(x) = x^2 + 3x - 18$, find each function.

22. $(fg)(x)$ $x^3 - 27x + 54$
23. $\left(\frac{f}{g}\right)(x)$ $\frac{1}{x + 6}$, $x \ne -6, 3$
24. $\left(\frac{g}{f}\right)(x)$ $x + 6$, $x \ne 3$

Given $f(x) = \frac{1}{2}x + 5$ and $g(x) = -2x^2$, find each value.

25. $f(g(2))$ 1
26. $g(f(2))$ −72
27. $g(f(-6))$ −8

Given $f(x) = \sqrt{x}$, $g(x) = 2x + 3$, and $h(x) = x^2 + 20$, write each composite function. State the domain of each. 28–30. See p. A60.

28. $f(g(x))$
29. $g(f(x))$
30. $g(h(x))$

Lesson 9-5

Use the horizontal-line test to determine whether the inverse of each relation is a function.

31. not a function
32. function
33. not a function

Find the inverse of each function. Determine whether the inverse is a function, and state its domain and range. 34–36. See p. A60.

34. $f(x) = \frac{1}{2}x - 7$
35. $g(x) = 10 - x^2$
36. $h(x) = \frac{3}{4 + x}$

Determine by composition whether each pair of functions are inverses.

37. $f(x) = \frac{3}{4}x^2$ and $g(x) = \sqrt{\frac{4}{3}x}$ for $x \ge 0$ yes
38. $f(x) = \frac{12x + 1}{5}$ and $g(x) = \frac{5}{12x - 1}$ no

Lesson 9-6

Use constant differences or ratios to determine which parent function would best model the given data set.

39.

x	y
1	6
3	−12
5	−30
7	−48
9	−66

linear; constant first difference: −18

40.

x	y
2	−3
4	6
6	21
8	42
10	69

quadratic; constant second difference: 6

41.

x	y
0	0.5
1	2
2	8
3	32
4	128

exponential: constant ratio: 4

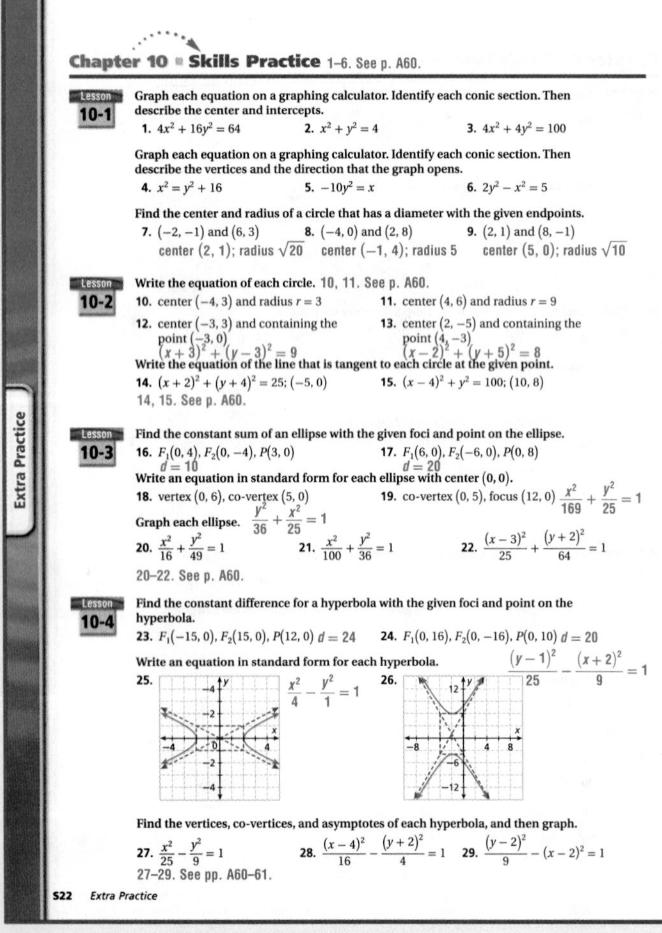

Chapter 10 ■ Skills Practice 1–6. See p. A60.

Lesson 10-1

Graph each equation on a graphing calculator. Identify each conic section. Then describe the center and intercepts.

1. $4x^2 + 16y^2 = 64$
2. $x^2 + y^2 = 4$
3. $4x^2 + 4y^2 = 100$

Graph each equation on a graphing calculator. Identify each conic section. Then describe the vertices and the direction that the graph opens.

4. $x^2 = y^2 + 16$
5. $-10y^2 = x$
6. $2y^2 - x^2 = 5$

Find the center and radius of a circle that has a diameter with the given endpoints.

7. $(-2, -1)$ and $(6, 3)$ center $(2, 1)$; radius $\sqrt{20}$
8. $(-4, 0)$ and $(2, 8)$ center $(-1, 4)$; radius 5
9. $(2, 1)$ and $(8, -1)$ center $(5, 0)$; radius $\sqrt{10}$

Lesson 10-2

Write the equation of each circle. 10, 11. See p. A60.

10. center $(-4, 3)$ and radius $r = 3$
11. center $(4, 6)$ and radius $r = 9$
12. center $(-3, 3)$ and containing the point $(-3, 0)$ $(x + 3)^2 + (y - 3)^2 = 9$
13. center $(2, -5)$ and containing the point $(4, -3)$ $(x - 2)^2 + (y + 5)^2 = 8$

Write the equation of the line that is tangent to each circle at the given point.

14. $(x + 2)^2 + (y + 4)^2 = 25$; $(-5, 0)$
15. $(x - 4)^2 + y^2 = 100$; $(10, 8)$

14, 15. See p. A60.

Lesson 10-3

Find the constant sum of an ellipse with the given foci and point on the ellipse.

16. $F_1(0, 4)$, $F_2(0, -4)$, $P(3, 0)$ $d = 10$
17. $F_1(6, 0)$, $F_2(-6, 0)$, $P(0, 8)$ $d = 20$

Write an equation in standard form for each ellipse with center $(0, 0)$.

18. vertex $(0, 6)$, co-vertex $(5, 0)$ $\frac{y^2}{36} + \frac{x^2}{25} = 1$
19. co-vertex $(0, 5)$, focus $(12, 0)$ $\frac{x^2}{169} + \frac{y^2}{25} = 1$

Graph each ellipse.

20. $\frac{x^2}{16} + \frac{y^2}{49} = 1$
21. $\frac{x^2}{100} + \frac{y^2}{36} = 1$
22. $\frac{(x - 3)^2}{25} + \frac{(y + 2)^2}{64} = 1$

20–22. See p. A60.

Lesson 10-4

Find the constant difference for a hyperbola with the given foci and point on the hyperbola.

23. $F_1(-15, 0)$, $F_2(15, 0)$, $P(12, 0)$ $d = 24$
24. $F_1(0, 16)$, $F_2(0, -16)$, $P(0, 10)$ $d = 20$

Write an equation in standard form for each hyperbola.

25. $\frac{x^2}{4} - \frac{y^2}{1} = 1$
26. $\frac{(y - 1)^2}{25} - \frac{(x + 2)^2}{9} = 1$

Find the vertices, co-vertices, and asymptotes of each hyperbola, and then graph.

27. $\frac{x^2}{25} - \frac{y^2}{9} = 1$
28. $\frac{(x - 4)^2}{16} - \frac{(y + 2)^2}{4} = 1$
29. $\frac{(y - 2)^2}{9} - (x - 2)^2 = 1$

27–29. See pp. A60–61.

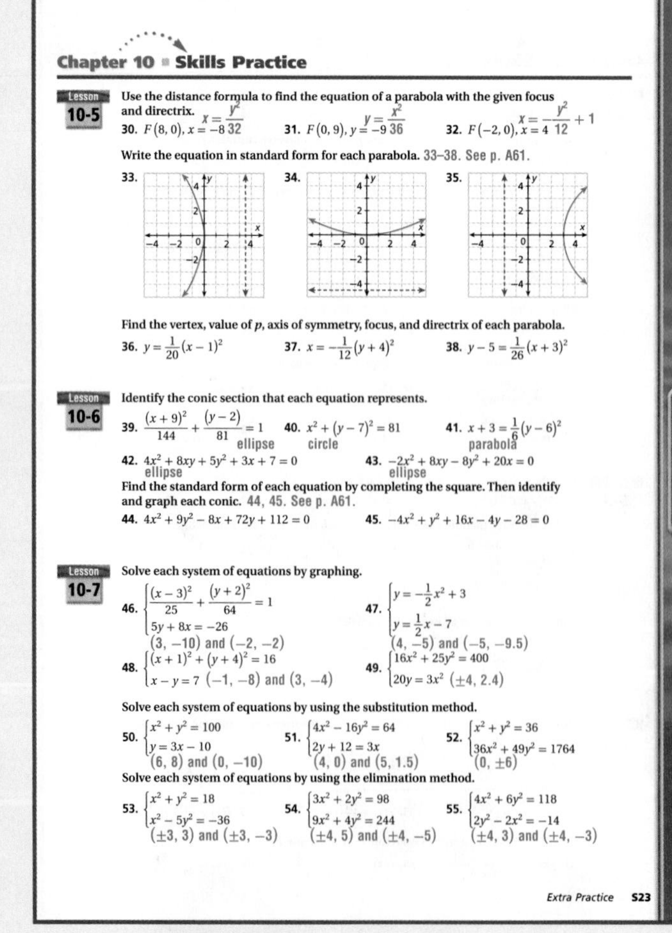

Chapter 10 ■ Skills Practice

Lesson 10-5

Use the distance formula to find the equation of a parabola with the given focus and directrix.

30. $F(8, 0)$, $x = -8$ $x = \frac{y^2}{32}$
31. $F(0, 9)$, $y = -9$ $y = \frac{x^2}{36}$
32. $F(-2, 0)$, $x = 4$ $x = -\frac{y^2}{12} + 1$

Write the equation in standard form for each parabola. 33–38. See p. A61.

33. 34. 35.

Find the vertex, value of p, axis of symmetry, focus, and directrix of each parabola.

36. $y = \frac{1}{20}(x - 1)^2$
37. $x = -\frac{1}{12}(y + 4)^2$
38. $y - 5 = \frac{1}{26}(x + 3)^2$

Lesson 10-6

Identify the conic section that each equation represents.

39. $\frac{(x + 9)^2}{144} + \frac{(y - 2)}{81} = 1$ ellipse
40. $x^2 + (y - 7)^2 = 81$ circle
41. $x + 3 = \frac{1}{6}(y - 6)^2$ parabola
42. $4x^2 + 8xy + 5y^2 + 3x + 7 = 0$ ellipse
43. $-2x^2 + 8xy - 8y^2 + 20x = 0$ ellipse

Find the standard form of each equation by completing the square. Then identify and graph each conic. 44, 45. See p. A61.

44. $4x^2 + 9y^2 - 8x + 72y + 112 = 0$
45. $-4x^2 + y^2 + 16x - 4y - 28 = 0$

Lesson 10-7

Solve each system of equations by graphing.

46. $\begin{cases} \frac{(x - 3)^2}{25} + \frac{(y + 2)^2}{64} = 1 \\ 5y + 8x = -26 \end{cases}$ $(3, -10)$ and $(-2, -2)$
47. $\begin{cases} y = -\frac{1}{2}x^2 + 3 \\ y = \frac{1}{2}x - 7 \end{cases}$ $(4, -5)$ and $(-5, -9.5)$
48. $\begin{cases} (x + 1)^2 + (y + 4)^2 = 16 \\ x - y = 7 \end{cases}$ $(-1, -8)$ and $(3, -4)$
49. $\begin{cases} 16x^2 + 25y^2 = 400 \\ 20y = 3x^2 \end{cases}$ $(\pm 4, 2.4)$

Solve each system of equations by using the substitution method.

50. $\begin{cases} x^2 + y^2 = 100 \\ y = 3x - 10 \end{cases}$ $(6, 8)$ and $(0, -10)$
51. $\begin{cases} 4x^2 - 16y^2 = 64 \\ 2y + 12 = 3x \end{cases}$ $(4, 0)$ and $(5, 1.5)$
52. $\begin{cases} x^2 + y^2 = 36 \\ 36x^2 + 49y^2 = 1764 \end{cases}$ $(0, \pm 6)$

Solve each system of equations by using the elimination method.

53. $\begin{cases} x^2 + y^2 = 18 \\ x^2 - 5y^2 = -36 \end{cases}$ $(\pm 3, 3)$ and $(\pm 3, -3)$
54. $\begin{cases} 3x^2 + 2y^2 = 98 \\ 9x^2 + 4y^2 = 244 \end{cases}$ $(\pm 4, 5)$ and $(\pm 4, -5)$
55. $\begin{cases} 4x^2 + 6y^2 = 118 \\ 2y^2 - 2x^2 = -14 \end{cases}$ $(\pm 4, 3)$ and $(\pm 4, -3)$

Chapter 11 ■ Skills Practice

Lesson 11-1

1. When text messaging on a telephone, pressing a 3 types D, E, F, or 3. Pressing a 7 types P, Q, R, S, or 7. How many messages are possible by pressing a 3, a 7, and then a 3? 80
2. At a company, each employee has an ID that consists of 2 digits followed by a letter. The letters Q and X are not used. How many employee IDs are possible? 2400
3. If there are 8 finalists in a talent show, how many ways can a winner and a runner-up be chosen? 56
4. Jim's soccer team has 18 members. How many ways can the coach choose a right forward, a center forward, and a left forward? 4896
5. Erin's health club offers 7 types of aerobics classes. She plans to attend 4 classes this week. How many ways can she choose 4 classes that are all different? 35
6. Francesca can take 4 of her 14 books on a trip. How many ways can she choose them? 1001

Lesson 11-2

Two number cubes are rolled. Find each probability.

7. Both cubes roll the same number. $\frac{1}{6}$
8. The sum is greater than 8. $\frac{5}{18}$
9. The sum is 8 or less. $\frac{13}{18}$
10. Both cubes roll even numbers. $\frac{1}{4}$
11. What is the probability that a random 2-digit number is a multiple of 7? $\frac{13}{90}$
12. What is the probability that a randomly selected day in January is after the 20th? $\frac{11}{31}$
13. A mother is making different lunches for each of her 3 children. If each child grabs a lunch bag at random, what is the probability that all 3 children will get the correct bag? $\frac{1}{6}$
14. A teacher writes MATHEMATICS on a piece of paper and then cuts out each letter and puts them all in a bag. She will draw two letters at random. What is the probability that she will select an M and an A? $\frac{4}{55}$

The shaded region is vertically centered in the flag. Find each probability.

35 in.
14 in.
2 in.

15. a random point inside the flag is in the shaded region $\frac{1}{7}$
16. a random point inside the flag is above the shaded region $\frac{3}{7}$

A marble is drawn from a bag and then its color is recorded in the table.

17. Find the experimental probability of drawing a blue marble. 0.32 or 32%
18. Find the experimental probability of drawing a pink or a yellow marble. 0.48 or 48%

Marble Drawing Experiment	
Color	**Times Drawn**
Pink	12
Green	10
Blue	16
Yellow	12

Chapter 11 ■ Skills Practice

Lesson 11-3

Find each probability.

19. rolling a number greater than or equal to 4 on a number cube twice in a row $\frac{1}{4}$
20. drawing a face card from a deck, replacing it, and drawing a number card $\frac{30}{169}$
21. Two number cubes are rolled—one blue and one yellow. Find the probability that the yellow cube is even, and the sum is 7. Explain why the events are dependent. See p. A56.

The table shows the results of a schoolwide survey on the homecoming dance. Find each probability.

Homecoming Dance Location Survey		
	Girls	**Boys**
Gymnasium	67	58
Cafeteria	53	37

22. A student who prefers the cafeteria is a girl. 0.589, or 58.9%
23. A surveyed student is male and prefers the gymnasium. 0.270, or 27%

A bag contains 18 beads—5 blue, 6 yellow, and 7 red. Determine whether the events are independent or dependent. Find the indicated probability.

24. selecting a yellow and then a blue bead when they are chosen with replacement independent; $\frac{5}{54}$
25. selecting a yellow and then a blue bead when they are chosen without replacement dependent; $\frac{5}{51}$

Lesson 11-4

26. A table was chosen at random in the cafeteria, and there were 2 freshmen, 5 sophomores, 7 juniors, and 2 seniors eating there. A student is chosen at random from the table. What is the probability of choosing a freshman or a senior? $\frac{1}{4}$

The numbers 1–20 are written on cards and placed in a bag. Find each probability.

27. choosing a number less than 10 or choosing a multiple of 5 $\frac{3}{5}$
28. choosing 20 or choosing an odd number $\frac{11}{20}$
29. In an apartment building with 50 residents, 16 residents have cats, 28 residents are students, and 9 of the students have cats. What is the probability that a resident is a student or has a cat? $\frac{7}{10}$
30. There are 8 couples in a dance competition, and each of the 3 judges must pick the couple they believe should win. Suppose the judges picked randomly. What is the probability that at least 2 judges picked the same couple? $\frac{11}{32}$

Lesson 11-5

Find the mean, median, and mode of each data set. 31–33. See p. A61.

31. $\{3, 7, 8, 2, 8, 4\}$
32. $\{12, 9, 8, 15, 16, 12, 13\}$
33. $\{7, 31, 20, 12, 18\}$
34. Find the expected value of the raffle prize. \$6.00

Raffle Prizes				
Value	\$0	\$5	\$20	\$200
Probability	0.76	0.16	0.06	0.02

Make a box-and-whisker plot of the data. Find the interquartile range.

35–36. See p. A61.

35. $\{3, 5, 7, 6, 5, 2, 3\}$
36. $\{12, 15, 18, 10, 9, 15, 16\}$

Find the variance and standard deviation.

37. $\{8, 12, 10, 6, 9\}$ $\sigma^2 = 4$; $\sigma = 2$
38. $\{14, 15, 10, 8, 12, 13\}$ $\sigma^2 = 5\frac{2}{3}$; $\sigma = \sqrt{5\frac{2}{3}} \approx 2.38$
39. $\{6, 33, 37, 28, 1\}$ $\sigma^2 = 214.8$; $\sigma = \sqrt{214.8} \approx 14.66$

Lesson 11-6

Use the Binomial Theorem to expand each binomial. 40–42. See p. A61.

40. $(x + 4)^5$
41. $(2x - 3)^4$
42. $(2a + 7b)^3$
43. Patrick takes a multiple-choice quiz that has 4 questions. There are 5 answer choices for each question. What is the probability that he will get at least 2 answers correct by guessing? 0.1808

Chapter 12 ■ Skills Practice

Lesson 12-1

Find the first 5 terms of each sequence.

1. $a_1 = 16, a_n = 0.25a_{n-1}$ $16, 4, 1, \frac{1}{4}, \frac{1}{16}$
2. $a_1 = -1, a_n = 3a_{n-1} + 1$ $-1, -2, -5, -14, -41$
3. $a_1 = 2, a_2 = 5, a_n = 2a_{n-1} + a_{n-2}$ $2, 5, 7, 12, 31$
4. $a_n = 5(n - 1)$ $0, 5, 10, 15, 20$
5. $a_n = 3^n - 4$ $-1, 5, 23, 77, 239$
6. $a_n = (n + 2)^2$ $9, 16, 25, 36, 49$

Write a possible explicit rule for the *n*th term of each sequence.

7. $5, 1, -3, -7, -11, \ldots$ $a_n = -4n + 9$
8. $7, 9, 13, 21, 37, \ldots$ $a_n = 2^n + 5$
9. $\frac{3}{4}, \frac{3}{2}, \frac{9}{4}, 3, \frac{15}{4}, \ldots$ $a_n = \frac{3n}{4}$
10. $60, 30, 15, \frac{15}{2}, \ldots$ $a_n = 120\left(\frac{1}{2}\right)^n$

Lesson 12-2

Write each series in summation notation.

11. $\frac{1}{2} + \frac{1}{4} + \frac{1}{6} + \frac{1}{8} + \frac{1}{10}$ $\sum_{k=1}^{5} \frac{1}{2k}$
12. $0 + 3 + 8 + 15 + 24 + 35$ $\sum_{k=1}^{6} (k^2 - 1)$
13. $50 + 41 + 32 + 23 + 14 + 5$ $\sum_{k=1}^{6} [50 - 9(k - 1)]$
14. $-4 - 2 + 0 + 2 + 4$ $\sum_{k=1}^{5} [-4 + 2(k - 1)]$

Expand each series and evaluate. 15–17. See p. A61.

15. $\sum_{k=1}^{5}(12k - 7)$
16. $\sum_{k=1}^{4}\frac{(2k)^2}{2}$
17. $\sum_{k=1}^{5}\frac{k - 2}{k + 1}$

Evaluate each series.

18. $\sum_{k=1}^{55} k$ 1540
19. $\sum_{k=15}^{25} 12$ 132
20. $\sum_{k=1}^{18} k^2$ 2109

Lesson 12-3

Determine whether each sequence could be arithmetic. If so, find the common difference and the next term.

21. $15.5, 28, 40.5, 53, 65.5, \ldots$ arithmetic; 12.5, 78
22. $9.67, 9.34, 9.01, 8.68, \ldots$ arithmetic; −0.33, 8.35
23. $\frac{1}{2}, 2, \frac{9}{2}, 8, \frac{25}{2}, \ldots$ not arithmetic
24. $2, 4, 6, 4, 2, \ldots$ not arithmetic

Find the 8th term of each arithmetic sequence.

25. $4.5, 6, 7.5, 9, 10.5, \ldots$ 15
26. $74, 68, 62, 56, 50, \ldots$ 32
27. $5, 5\frac{2}{5}, 5\frac{4}{5}, 6\frac{1}{5}, 6\frac{3}{5}, \ldots$ $7\frac{4}{5}$

Find the missing terms in each arithmetic sequence.

28. 13, ■, ■, 37, ... 21, 29
29. 9.5, ■, ■, ■, −0.5, ... 7, 4.5, 2
30. 10, ■, ■, ■, 26, ... 14, 18, 22

Find the 9th term of each arithmetic sequence.

31. $a_3 = 29$ and $a_6 = 56$ 83
32. $a_4 = 16$ and $a_7 = -2$ −14
33. $a_{10} = 30.5$ and $a_{14} = 38.5$ 28.5
34. $a_5 = 3\frac{1}{3}$ and $a_7 = 2\frac{2}{3}$ 2

Find the indicated sum for each arithmetic series.

35. S_{12} for 18, 21, 24, 27, 30, ... 414
36. S_{15} for 20, 18.5, 17, 15.5, 14, ... 142.5
37. $\sum_{k=1}^{9}(5k + 8)$ 297
38. $\sum_{k=1}^{20}(-2.75k + 15)$ −277.5

Chapter 12 ■ Skills Practice

Lesson 12-4

Determine whether each sequence could be geometric or arithmetic. If possible, find the common ratio or difference.

39. $7, 14, 28, 56, 112, \ldots$ geometric, with $r = 2$
40. $7, 14, 21, 28, 35, \ldots$ arithmetic, with $d = 7$
41. $\frac{2}{3}, 1\frac{1}{3}, 2\frac{2}{3}, 5\frac{1}{3}, 10\frac{2}{3}, \ldots$ geometric, with $r = 2$
42. $25.5, 31, 36.5, 42, 47.5, \ldots$ arithmetic, with $d = 5.5$
43. $-3, 6, 21, 42, 69, \ldots$ neither
44. $4, 1, \frac{1}{4}, \frac{1}{16}, \frac{1}{64}, \ldots$ geometric, with $r = \frac{1}{4}$

Find the 7th term of each geometric sequence.

45. $5, 10, 20, 40, 80, \ldots$ 320
46. $200, 100, 50, 25, 12.5, \ldots$ 3.125
47. $-1, 3, -9, 27, -81, \ldots$ −729
48. $7, 70, 700, 7000, \ldots$ 7,000,000

Find the 8th term of the geometric sequence with the given terms.

49. $a_4 = 4, a_5 = 8$ 64
50. $a_4 = 16, a_6 = 256$ 4096
51. $a_3 = 125, a_5 = 5$ $\pm\frac{1}{25}$
52. $a_4 = 4, a_7 = 864$ 5184

Find the geometric mean of each pair of numbers.

53. 4 and 36 12
54. $\frac{1}{4}$ and $\frac{1}{9}$ $\frac{1}{6}$
55. 72 and 288 144
56. 10 and 20 $10\sqrt{2}$

Find the indicated sum for each geometric series.

57. S_8 for 5, −15, 45, −135, ... −8200
58. S_6 for $\frac{3}{4}$, 3, 12, 48, ... $1023\frac{3}{4}$
59. $\sum_{k=1}^{5}12(2)^{k-1}$ 372
60. $\sum_{k=1}^{7}(-4)^{k-1}$ 3277

Lesson 12-5

Determine whether each geometric series converges or diverges.

61. $\frac{5}{2}, \frac{5}{8}, \frac{5}{32}, \frac{5}{128}, \ldots$ converges and has a sum
62. $0.1, 0.5, 2.5, 12.5, 62.5, \ldots$ diverges and does not have a sum
63. $1, 1.3, 1.69, 2.197, 2.8561, \ldots$ diverges and does not have a sum
64. $1, 0.7, 0.49, 0.343, 0.2401, \ldots$ converges and has a sum

Find the sum of each infinite geometric series, if it exists.

65. $1.1, 1.21, 1.331, 1.4641, \ldots$ no sum exists
66. $1.8, 1.62, 1.458, 1.3122, \ldots$ 18
67. $7, 0.7, 0.07, 0.007, \ldots$ $\frac{70}{9}$
68. $\sum_{k=1}^{\infty}\frac{1}{2}\left(\frac{3}{2}\right)^k$ no sum exists
69. $\sum_{k=1}^{\infty}8\left(\frac{4}{10}\right)^k$ $5\frac{1}{3}$
70. $\sum_{k=1}^{\infty}100(0.95)^k$ 1900

Write each repeating decimal as a fraction in simplest form.

71. $0.\overline{4}$ $\frac{4}{9}$
72. $0.\overline{26}$ $\frac{26}{99}$
73. $0.\overline{892}$ $\frac{892}{999}$

Identify a counterexample to disprove each statement, where the variable is a real number.

74. $4a^3 \geq 8a^2$ $a = 1$
75. $5^{2n} \geq 5^n$ $n = -1$
76. $x^2 > (x - 1)^2$ $x = -1$
77. $|x + 1| \geq |x|$ $x = -1$

Extra Practice

Chapter 13 ■ Skills Practice

Lesson 13-1

Find the value of the sine, cosine, and tangent functions for θ. 1–17. See p. A61.

1. (12, 5, 13, θ) 2. ($\sqrt{61}$, 5, 6, θ) 3. ($2\sqrt{3}$, 2, 4, θ)

Use a trigonometric function to find the value of x.

4. (3, 45°, x) 5. (25, 60°, x) 6. (x, 10, 30°)

Find the values of the six trigonometric functions for θ.

7. (5, 8, θ) 8. (5, $\sqrt{34}$, θ) 9. (1, $\sqrt{5}$, θ)

Lesson 13-2

Draw an angle with the given measure in standard position.

10. −30° 11. 240° 12. 410° 13. −350°

Find the measures of a positive angle and a negative angle that are coterminal with each given angle.

14. $\theta = 20°$ 15. $\theta = 400°$ 16. $\theta = -125°$ 17. $\theta = -385°$

Find the measure of the reference angle for each given angle.

18. $\theta = -120°$ 60° 19. $\theta = 175°$ 5° 20. $\theta = 110°$ 70° 21. $\theta = 385°$ 25°

P is a point on the terminal side of θ in standard position. Find the exact value of the six trigonometric functions for θ. 22–25. See p. A61.

22. $P(2, 3)$ 23. $P(-1, 4)$ 24. $P(-1, -1)$ 25. $P(2, -8)$

Lesson 13-3

Convert each measure from degrees to radians or from radians to degrees.

26. 60° $\frac{\pi}{3}$ 27. −135° $-\frac{3\pi}{4}$ 28. 90° $\frac{\pi}{2}$ 29. −10° $-\frac{\pi}{18}$

30. $-\frac{3\pi}{2}$ −270° 31. $\frac{\pi}{10}$ 18° 32. $\frac{\pi}{18}$ 10° 33. $-\frac{3\pi}{8}$ −67.5°

Use the unit circle to find the exact value of each trigonometric function.

34. $\cos 150°$ $-\frac{\sqrt{3}}{2}$ 35. $\tan \frac{7\pi}{4}$ −1 36. $\sin \frac{7\pi}{6}$ $-\frac{1}{2}$ 37. $\cos 315°$ $\frac{\sqrt{2}}{2}$

38. $\sin \frac{2\pi}{3}$ $\frac{\sqrt{3}}{2}$ 39. $\cos 270°$ 0 40. $\csc \frac{4\pi}{3}$ $-\frac{2\sqrt{3}}{3}$ 41. $\cot 225°$ 1

Use a reference angle to find the exact value of the sine, cosine, and tangent of each angle.

42. −150° 43. 210° 44. 315° 45. 330°

46. $\frac{\pi}{4}$ 47. $-\frac{7\pi}{6}$ 48. $\frac{5\pi}{4}$ 49. $\frac{5\pi}{3}$

42–49. See p. A62.

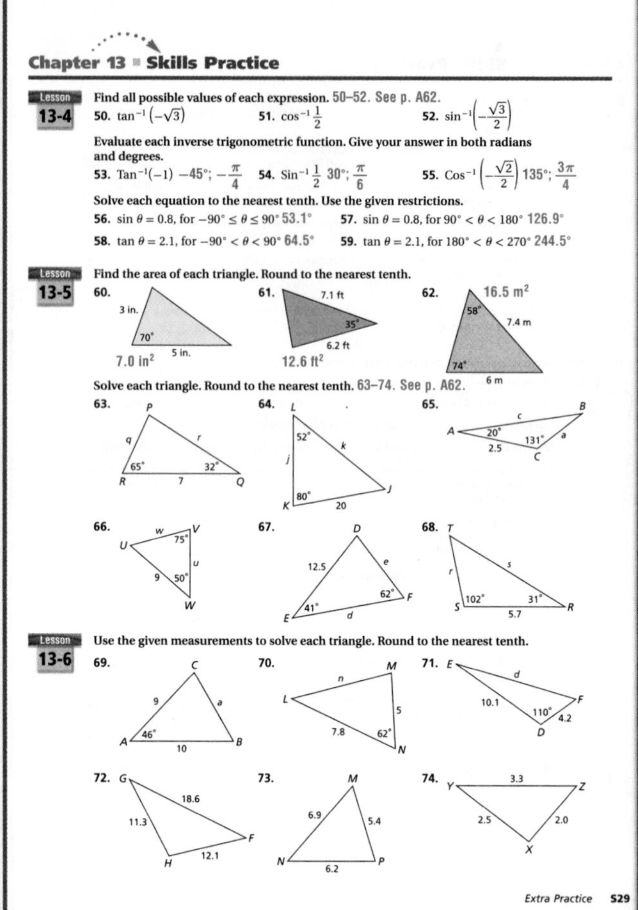

Chapter 13 ■ Skills Practice

Lesson 13-4

Find all possible values of each expression. 50–52. See p. A62.

50. $\tan^{-1}(-\sqrt{3})$ 51. $\cos^{-1}\frac{1}{2}$ 52. $\sin^{-1}\left(-\frac{\sqrt{3}}{2}\right)$

Evaluate each inverse trigonometric function. Give your answer in both radians and degrees.

53. $\text{Tan}^{-1}(-1)$ −45°; $-\frac{\pi}{4}$ 54. $\text{Sin}^{-1}\frac{1}{2}$ 30°; $\frac{\pi}{6}$ 55. $\text{Cos}^{-1}\left(-\frac{\sqrt{2}}{2}\right)$ 135°; $\frac{3\pi}{4}$

Solve each equation to the nearest tenth. Use the given restrictions.

56. $\sin\theta = 0.8$, for $-90° \le \theta \le 90°$ 53.1° 57. $\sin\theta = 0.8$, for $90° < \theta < 180°$ 126.9°

58. $\tan\theta = 2.1$, for $-90° < \theta < 90°$ 64.5° 59. $\tan\theta = 2.1$, for $180° < \theta < 270°$ 244.5°

Lesson 13-5

Find the area of each triangle. Round to the nearest tenth.

60. 7.0 in² 61. 12.6 ft² 62. 16.5 m²

Solve each triangle. Round to the nearest tenth. 63–74. See p. A62.

63. 64. 65.

66. 67. 68.

Lesson 13-6

Use the given measurements to solve each triangle. Round to the nearest tenth.

69. 70. 71.

72. 73. 74.

Extra Practice S29

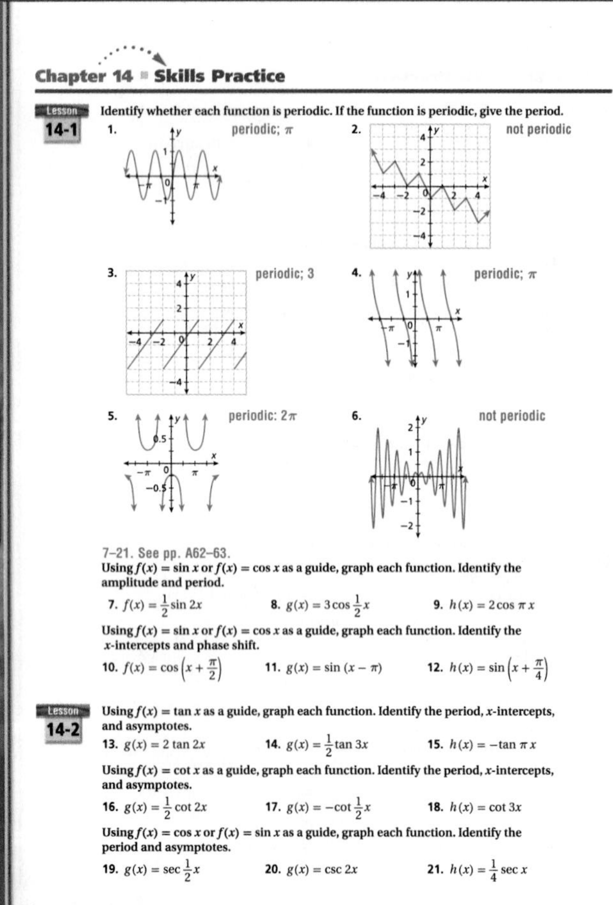

Chapter 14 ■ Skills Practice

Lesson 14-1

Identify whether each function is periodic. If the function is periodic, give the period.

1. periodic; π 2. not periodic

3. periodic; 3 4. periodic; π

5. periodic: 2π 6. not periodic

7–21. See pp. A62–63.

Using $f(x) = \sin x$ or $f(x) = \cos x$ as a guide, graph each function. Identify the amplitude and period.

7. $f(x) = \frac{1}{2}\sin 2x$ 8. $g(x) = 3\cos\frac{1}{2}x$ 9. $h(x) = 2\cos \pi x$

Using $f(x) = \sin x$ or $f(x) = \cos x$ as a guide, graph each function. Identify the x-intercepts and phase shift.

10. $f(x) = \cos\left(x + \frac{\pi}{2}\right)$ 11. $g(x) = \sin(x - \pi)$ 12. $h(x) = \sin\left(x + \frac{\pi}{4}\right)$

Lesson 14-2

Using $f(x) = \tan x$ as a guide, graph each function. Identify the period, x-intercepts, and asymptotes.

13. $g(x) = 2\tan 2x$ 14. $g(x) = \frac{1}{2}\tan 3x$ 15. $h(x) = -\tan \pi x$

Using $f(x) = \cot x$ as a guide, graph each function. Identify the period, x-intercepts, and asymptotes.

16. $g(x) = \frac{1}{2}\cot 2x$ 17. $g(x) = -\cot\frac{1}{2}x$ 18. $h(x) = \cot 3x$

Using $f(x) = \cos x$ or $f(x) = \sin x$ as a guide, graph each function. Identify the period and asymptotes.

19. $g(x) = \sec\frac{1}{2}x$ 20. $g(x) = \csc 2x$ 21. $h(x) = \frac{1}{4}\sec x$

S30 Extra Practice

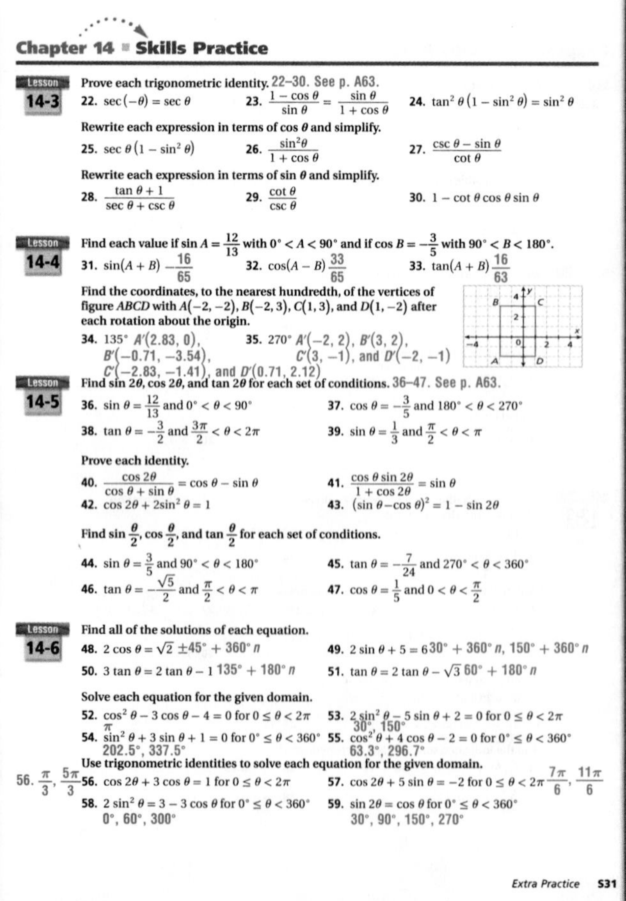

Chapter 14 ■ Skills Practice

Lesson 14-3

Prove each trigonometric identity. 22–30. See p. A63.

22. $\sec(-\theta) = \sec\theta$ 23. $\frac{1 - \cos\theta}{\sin\theta} = \frac{\sin\theta}{1 + \cos\theta}$ 24. $\tan^2\theta(1 - \sin^2\theta) = \sin^2\theta$

Rewrite each expression in terms of $\cos\theta$ and simplify.

25. $\sec\theta(1 - \sin^2\theta)$ 26. $\frac{\sin^2\theta}{1 + \cos\theta}$ 27. $\frac{\csc\theta - \sin\theta}{\cot\theta}$

Rewrite each expression in terms of $\sin\theta$ and simplify.

28. $\frac{\tan\theta + 1}{\sec\theta + \csc\theta}$ 29. $\frac{\cot\theta}{\csc\theta}$ 30. $1 - \cot\theta\cos\theta\sin\theta$

Lesson 14-4

Find each value if $\sin A = \frac{12}{13}$ with $0° < A < 90°$ and if $\cos B = -\frac{3}{5}$ with $90° < B < 180°$.

31. $\sin(A + B)$ $-\frac{16}{65}$ 32. $\cos(A - B)$ $\frac{33}{65}$ 33. $\tan(A + B)$ $\frac{16}{63}$

Find the coordinates, to the nearest hundredth, of the vertices of figure $ABCD$ with $A(-2, -2)$, $B(-2, 3)$, $C(1, 3)$, and $D(1, -2)$ after each rotation about the origin.

34. 135° $A'(2.83, 0)$, $B'(-0.71, -3.54)$, $C'(-2.83, -1.41)$, and $D'(0.71, 2.12)$ 35. 270° $A'(-2, 2)$, $B'(3, 2)$, $C'(3, -1)$, and $D'(-2, -1)$

Lesson 14-5

Find $\sin 2\theta$, $\cos 2\theta$, and $\tan 2\theta$ for each set of conditions. 36–47. See p. A63.

36. $\sin\theta = \frac{12}{13}$ and $0° < \theta < 90°$ 37. $\cos\theta = -\frac{3}{5}$ and $180° < \theta < 270°$

38. $\tan\theta = -\frac{3}{2}$ and $\frac{3\pi}{2} < \theta < 2\pi$ 39. $\sin\theta = \frac{1}{3}$ and $\frac{\pi}{2} < \theta < \pi$

Prove each identity.

40. $\frac{\cos 2\theta}{\cos\theta + \sin\theta} = \cos\theta - \sin\theta$ 41. $\frac{\cos\theta\sin 2\theta}{1 + \cos 2\theta} = \sin\theta$

42. $\cos 2\theta + 2\sin^2\theta = 1$ 43. $(\sin\theta - \cos\theta)^2 = 1 - \sin 2\theta$

Find $\sin\frac{\theta}{2}$, $\cos\frac{\theta}{2}$, and $\tan\frac{\theta}{2}$ for each set of conditions.

44. $\sin\theta = \frac{3}{5}$ and $90° < \theta < 180°$ 45. $\tan\theta = -\frac{7}{24}$ and $270° < \theta < 360°$

46. $\tan\theta = -\frac{\sqrt{5}}{2}$ and $\frac{\pi}{2} < \theta < \pi$ 47. $\cos\theta = \frac{1}{5}$ and $0 < \theta < \frac{\pi}{2}$

Lesson 14-6

Find all of the solutions of each equation.

48. $2\cos\theta = \sqrt{2}$ ±45° + 360° n 49. $2\sin\theta + 5 = 6$ 30° + 360° n, 150° + 360° n

50. $3\tan\theta = 2\tan\theta - 1$ 135° + 180° n 51. $\tan\theta = 2\tan\theta - \sqrt{3}$ 60° + 180° n

Solve each equation for the given domain.

52. $\cos^2\theta - 3\cos\theta - 4 = 0$ for $0 \le \theta < 2\pi$ π 53. $2\sin^2\theta - 5\sin\theta + 2 = 0$ for $0 \le \theta < 2\pi$ 30°, 150°

54. $\sin^2\theta + 3\sin\theta + 1 = 0$ for $0° \le \theta < 360°$ 202.5°, 337.5° 55. $\cos^2\theta + 4\cos\theta - 2 = 0$ for $0° \le \theta < 360°$ 63.3°, 296.7°

Use trigonometric identities to solve each equation for the given domain.

56. $\frac{\pi}{3}$, $\frac{5\pi}{3}$ 56. $\cos 2\theta + 3\cos\theta = 1$ for $0 \le \theta < 2\pi$ 57. $\cos 2\theta + 5\sin\theta = -2$ for $0 \le \theta < 2\pi$ $\frac{7\pi}{6}$, $\frac{11\pi}{6}$

58. $2\sin^2\theta = 3 - 3\cos\theta$ for $0° \le \theta < 360°$ 0°, 60°, 300° 59. $\sin 2\theta = \cos\theta$ for $0° \le \theta < 360°$ 30°, 90°, 150°, 270°

Extra Practice S31

Extra Practice

Chapter 1 ■ Applications Practice 1, 4, 9, 11. See p. A63.

Sports **Use the following information for Exercises 1–3.**

In women's boxing, some of the official weight classes in pounds are defined in the table below. Each class includes the lightest weight in the range but not the heaviest weight. *(Lesson 1-1)*

Middleweight 154–160	Featherweight 122–126
Jr. Middleweight 147–154	Bantamweight 115–118
Super Lightweight 135–140	Welterweight 140–147

1. Order the weight classes from lightest to heaviest.
2. Use interval notation to represent the set of weights in pounds that define the Super Lightweight class. $[135, 140)$
3. Use set-builder notation to represent the set of weights in pounds that define the Welterweight class. $\{x \mid 140 \le x < 147\}$
4. **Commerce** A sweater is on sale for 20% off. The regular price of the sweater is $60. Use mental math to determine the sale price of the sweater. Explain how you determined your answer. *(Lesson 1-2)*
5. **Construction** A builder is covering a rectangular floor with square tiles. A row of 46 tiles fits along the length of the room, and a row of 26 tiles fits along the width of the room. If each tile covers 20.25 in^2, what are the dimensions of the room in feet? *(Lesson 1-3)* 17.25 ft by 9.75 ft

Money **Use the following information for Exercises 6 and 7.**

Charles pays $1.25 for a newspaper using only quarters and dimes. Let q represent the number of quarters he uses. *(Lesson 1-4)*

6. Write an expression in terms of q for the number of dimes Charles uses. $12.5 - 2.5q$ or equivalent expression
7. If Charles uses 3 quarters, how many dimes does he use? 5

13.

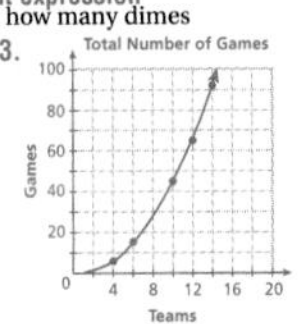

8. **Astronomy** The diameter of the Sun is 1.392×10^6 km. What is the radius of the Sun in kilometers? Express your answer in scientific notation. *(Lesson 1-5)* 6.96×10^5 km
9. **Shipping** The table shows the cost of shipping packages that weigh up to 3 lb. Is the relation from weight to cost a function? Is the relation from cost to weight a function? Explain. *(Lesson 1-6)*

Weight (lb)	Cost ($)
Up to 1 lb	3.69
More than 1 lb and up to 2 lb	3.85
More than 2 lb and up to 3 lb	4.65

Communication **Use the following information for Exercises 10 and 11.**

A cell phone plan charges $2.99 per month for 300 text messages plus $0.05 for each additional text message. *(Lesson 1-7)* $f(x) = 2.99 + 0.05(x - 300)$ or equivalent function

10. Write a function to represent the monthly charge in dollars for x text messages.
11. What is the value of the function for an input of 450, and what does it represent?
12. **Recreation** A bowling alley charges $4.00 to rent shoes and $2.75 per game. As part of a promotion, the alley lowers the price of shoes to $3.00. What kind of transformation describes the change in the total cost of bowling x games per person? *(Lesson 1-8)* translation 1 unit down
13. **Sports** Each team in a soccer league plays each of the other teams one time during a season. Graph the relationship between the number of teams and the total number of games and identify which parent function best describes the data. Then use the graph to estimate the total number of games per season when there are 8 teams in the league. *(Lesson 1-9)* quadratic; 28

Total Number of Games per Season					
Teams	4	6	10	12	14
Games	6	15	45	66	91

Chapter 2 ■ Applications Practice 3–6. See p. A63.

1. **Poetry** An English sonnet is made up of 14 lines of text. Rebecca is working on a poetry project for her English class that must be at least 100 lines long. Rebecca has already written 61 lines of haiku, free-verse poems, and limericks, and she plans to write the rest in sonnet form. How many sonnets must she write to complete the project? *(Lesson 2-1)* 3
2. **Nutrition** Tom follows a strict diet in which he gets 22% of his daily Calories from fat. His diet contains 363 Calories of fat each day. What is his total daily caloric intake? *(Lesson 2-2)* 1650 Calories

Home Economics **Use the following information for Exercises 3 and 4.**

Jonathan owes his parents $150 for car repairs. For each hour of chores he does, Jonathan's parents credit him $8 toward his debt. *(Lesson 2-3)*

3. Make a graph showing the amount that Jonathan owes his parents versus the number of hours he does chores.
4. What are the intercepts of the graph? What do they mean?

Consumer Economics **Use the following information for Exercises 5 and 6.**

The table below shows the cost of several long-distance calls made using the same calling plan. *(Lesson 2-4)*

Time (min)	7	12	15	24
Cost ($)	$1.80	$2.55	$3.00	$4.35

5. Find the function that represents the data and write it in slope-intercept form. What do the slope and y-intercept represent?
6. Make a graph to show the cost of all phone calls up to 20 minutes.
7. **Sports** The basketball team is losing by 8 points. They score either 2 points or 3 points for each basket they make. Write and graph an inequality for the number of 2-point and 3-point baskets the team needs to make in order to win the game if the other team scores 16 more points. *(Lesson 2-5)* Let r = regular baskets and t = three-point baskets. $2r + 3t \ge 24$

Careers **Use the following information for Exercises 8 and 9.**

At a spa each masseur earns $80 per day plus $15 per massage. Starting next month, the per-massage fee will be raised to $30. *(Lesson 2-6)*

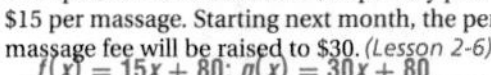

$f(x) = 15x + 80$; $g(x) = 30x + 80$

8. Write $f(x)$ to represent the original earnings and $g(x)$ to represent the new earnings. $g(x)$ is a vertical stretch by a factor of 2.
9. Graph $f(x)$ and $g(x)$ on the same coordinate plane. Describe the transformation. 9, 10. For graphs, see p. A63.
10. **Astronomy** The table below shows the distances from four planets to the Sun and the time it takes in Earth days for each planet to complete its revolution around the Sun.

Planet	Mercury	Venus	Earth	Mars
Distance (million km)	58	108	150	228
Revolution (Earth days)	88	225	365	687

Make a scatter plot using distance as the independent variable. Find the line of best fit and correlation coefficient. *(Lesson 2-7)* $y \approx 3.552x - 141.774$; $r = 0.995$

11. **Meteorology** A meteorologist predicts that Sunday's high temperature will be 76°F. Her predictions are generally accurate to within 4°F. Write and solve an absolute-value inequality to find the possible high temperatures. *(Lesson 2-8)*
12. **Architecture** The TransAmerica Pyramid in San Francisco is 324 meters high and 81 meters wide at its base. The diagram shows a side view of the building. The vertex is at $(40.5, 324)$. Write an absolute-value equation to describe the graph. *(Lesson 2-9)*

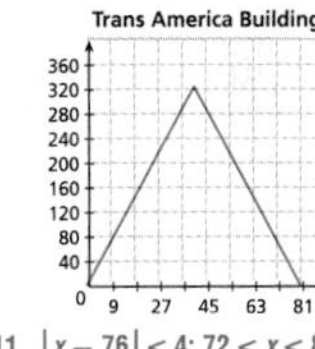

11. $|x - 76| \le 4$; $72 \le x \le 80$
12. $y = -8|x - 40.5| + 324$

Chapter 3 ■ Applications Practice 1, 6, 8–10, 12. See pp. A63–64.

Oceanography **Use the following information for Exercises 1–3.**

A dolphin and a shark are swimming toward the same fish. The dolphin is 88 meters away and is swimming at a rate of 10.7 meters per second. The shark is 100 meters away and is swimming at a rate of 12.2 meters per second. *(Lesson 3-1)*

1. Write and graph a system of equations that could be used to model the distance of both the dolphin and the shark from the fish.
2. In how many seconds will the dolphin and the shark be the same distance from the fish? 8 seconds
3. What will that distance be? 2.4 meters
4. **Chemistry** A chemist needs 16 ounces of a 10% potassium chloride solution. Solution A contains 12% potassium chloride, and solution B contains 8% potassium chloride. How much of each solution must the chemist combine? *(Lesson 3-2)* 8 ounces of Solution A and 8 ounces of Solution B
5. **Consumer Economics** At the hardware store, Leslie bought 2 boxes of nails and 3 boxes of screws and paid $13.95 before tax. Michael bought 4 boxes of nails and 1 box of screws and paid $12.15 before tax. Find the cost of a box of nails and the cost of a box of screws. *(Lesson 3-2)* A box of nails costs $2.25, and a box of screws costs $3.15.
6. **Entertainment** Hillary and Rob are at a multimedia store buying CDs and DVDs. The CDs cost $14 each, and the DVDs cost $12 each. Their total budget is $150, and Hillary wants to make sure that they buy at least as many DVDs as they buy CDs. Write and graph a system of inequalities that describes the possible number of CDs and DVDs they can buy. *(Lesson 3-3)*
7. **Construction** The Moua family is building a toy train using two types of cars. Passenger cars cost $30 and are 6 inches long. Freight cars cost $25 and are 9 inches long. They cannot spend more than $350, and the train must not be more than 9 feet long. Write and graph a system of inequalities that describes the possible number of each type of car they can use to make their train. *(Lesson 3-3)*

Let x = passenger cars and y = freight cars, then

$$\begin{cases} 30x + 25y \le 350 \\ 6x + 9y \le 108 \end{cases}$$

Business **Use the following information for Exercises 8 and 9.**

Leona owns a small business selling earrings and necklaces. Each pair of earrings takes 30 minutes to make and yields $3 of profit. Each necklace takes 1 hour to make and yields $7 of profit. Leona works no more than 7 hours per day, and she always makes at least 4 pairs of earrings each day. *(Lesson 3-4)*

8. Write a system of inequalities and graph the feasible region for how many earrings and necklaces Leona can make in a day.
9. Write an equation describing Leona's profit P. How many of each product should she make each day to maximize her profits?

Interior Design **Use the following information for Exercises 10 and 11.**

Mrs. Walsh has $150 to spend on decorations for her living room. She plans to buy candles, picture frames, and decorative pillows. The candles are 3 for $20, the picture frames cost $15 each, and the pillows cost $25 each. *(Lesson 3-5)*

10. Write a linear equation in three variables to represent this situation.
11. If Mrs. Walsh buys 6 candles and 4 frames, how many pillows can she buy? 2 pillows

Fitness **Use the following information for Exercises 12 and 13.**

Each day at the gym, Jaya cycles on the stationary bicycle, lifts weights, and swims laps. The table shows the number of minutes she spent doing each activity and the number of Calories she burned on 3 different days. *(Lesson 3-6)*

Day	Cycling	Weight Lifting	Swimmimg	Total Calories
1	30	30	20	455
2	25	45	15	432.5
3	25	20	30	495

12. How many Calories per minute does each activity burn?
13. How many Calories would Jaya burn if she spent 40 minutes cycling, 20 minutes lifting weights, and 20 minutes swimming? 470 Calories

Chapter 4 ■ Applications Practice 1, 2, 5, 7–11. See p. A64.

Transportation **Use the following information for Exercises 1 and 2.**

The table shows the costs for different bus tickets from San Antonio to Dallas. *(Lesson 4-1)*

Category	Child	Student	Adult	Senior
One-Way	$18.00	$23.50	$41.00	$34.50
Round-Trip	$34.00	$45.00	$79.00	$66.00

1. Next year, the bus company will raise the price of each ticket by 3%. Use a scalar product to find the new ticket prices.
2. Due to a rise in gas prices this month, the bus company is temporarily charging passengers an extra $2.50 per one-way ticket and $4.50 per round-trip ticket. Use matrix addition to find the new ticket prices.
3. **Taxes** Different portions of Mr. Waller's income are taxed at different rates. Use matrix multiplication to find the total amount of taxes he paid each year. *(Lesson 4-2)* 2004: $7152.50; 2005: $7792.00

Tax Rates			Mr. Waller's Income		
Year	Job	Home Business	Source	2004	2005
2004	23%	31%	Job	$23,550	$25,750
2005	24%	31%	Home Business	$5,600	$5,200

4. **Design** The Fishing Club's new logo is shaped like a fish on a fishing line. On a coordinate plane, the vertices of the image are $(-1, 1)$, $(2, -3)$, $(0, -5)$, $(4, -5)$, $(5, 1)$, $(2, 5)$ and $(2, 10)$. Find the vertices of the figure after it is enlarged by a factor of 2 and reflected across the x-axis. *(Lesson 4-3)*

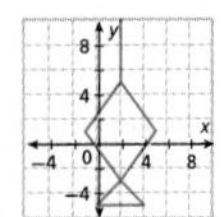

$(-2, -2)$, $(4, 6)$, $(0, 10)$, $(8, 10)$, $(10, -2)$, and $(4, -10)$

Gardening **Use the following information for Exercises 5 and 6.**

Mrs. Alarcón bought 3 geraniums, 2 ferns, and 2 petunias for $67.00. Mrs. Muñiz bought 4 geraniums, 4 petunias, and 1 fern for $89.50. The geraniums cost $3.50 more than the ferns. *(Lesson 4-4)*

5. Write the coefficient matrix for the problem.
6. Use Cramer's rule to find the cost of each type of plant. Geraniums are $11, petunias are $9.50, and ferns are $7.50.

Sports **Use the following information for Exercises 7–9.**

The gymnastics coach kept track of how many of each type of deduction some of his gymnasts received during the balance beam exercise at their last meet. *(Lesson 4-5)*

	Stepping Out of Bounds	Heavy Brush of Hands/ Feet	Out of Sync with Music	Total Points Lost
Amber	2	1	1	0.55
Marcia	1	2	1	0.75
Jenna	3	1	2	0.70

7. Write the appropriate matrix equation.
8. Find the inverse of the coefficient matrix.
9. Solve the matrix equation to find the amount of each deduction.

Manufacturing **Use the following information for Exercises 10 and 11.**

A manufacturing company makes wooden boxes in small, medium, and large sizes out of the same wood. The table shows how many of each box were made and how much wood was used on 3 different days. *(Lesson 4-6)*

	Small	Medium	Large	Wood Used
Mon	10	12	8	4468 in^2
Tue	7	15	10	5068 in^2
Wed	20	9	5	4298 in^2

10. Write an augmented matrix to describe the situation.
11. Use row operations to find the amount of wood used to make each size of box.

Chapter 5 ■ Applications Practice

Construction **Use the following information for Exercises 1 and 2.**

A landscape designer is using square stepping stones in a backyard. The function $f(x) = 8x^2$ represents the area in square inches that will be covered by 8 stepping stones with side length x inches. *(Lesson 5-1)*

1. Write a function g for the area that will be covered by 16 stepping stones with side length x inches. Describe g as a transformation of f.
2. The landscape designer decides to use smaller stones with a side length of $(x - 2)$ inches. Write a function h for the area that will be covered by 8 of the smaller stones. Describe h as a transformation of f.

Entertainment **Use the following information for Exercises 3 and 4.**

Part of a roller coaster's path can be modeled by the function $f(x) = -\frac{4}{49}x^2 + \frac{40}{7}x$, where x is the horizontal distance in feet the roller coaster has traveled and f is its height in feet above the ground. *(Lesson 5-2)*

3. What is the roller coaster's maximum height above the ground on this part of the path? 100 ft
4. How far has the roller coaster traveled horizontally when it reaches its maximum height? 35 ft

Sports **Use the following information for Exercises 5–7.**

A kickball player kicks a ball from ground level with an initial vertical velocity of 24 ft/s.

5. Write a function in standard form for the ball's height h in feet, where t is the time in seconds after the ball is thrown. *(Lesson 5-3)* $h(t) = -16t^2 + 24t$
6. How long is the ball in the air? *(Lesson 5-3)* 1.5 s
7. Complete the square to rewrite h in vertex form. What is the ball's maximum height? *(Lesson 5-4)*

1. $g(x) = 16x^2$; g is a vertical stretch of f by a factor of 2.
2. $h(x) = 8(x - 2)^2$; h is f translated 2 units right.
7. $h(x) = -16\left(t - \frac{3}{4}\right)^2 + 9$; 9 ft

8. **School** In a student's science fair project, he claims that the height h in feet above the ground of an object shot from a catapult can be modeled by $h(t) = 16t^2 - 32t + 32$, where t is the time in seconds after the object is shot. What are the zeros of this function? Explain why the values of the zeros indicate that the student's model is incorrect. *(Lesson 5-5)*
9. **Forestry** A wind gust blows a cone from a branch on a redwood tree. The cone's height h in meters above the ground can be modeled by $h(t) = -4.9t^2 - t + 75$, where t is the time in seconds since the cone broke from the branch. To the nearest tenth of a second, how long does the cone fall before hitting the ground? *(Lesson 5-6)* 3.8 s
10. **Business** The weekly profit p in dollars generated by a smoothie stand can be modeled by the function $p(c) = -302c^2 + 1635c - 1712$, where c is the cost in dollars per smoothie. For what range of smoothie costs will the stand generate at least \$450 per week? *(Lesson 5-7)* between \$2.30 and \$3.11, inclusive
11. **Law Enforcement** The table shows the cost of speeding tickets in a certain town, based on how many miles per hour over the speed limit the driver was traveling. Find a quadratic model for the fine given the number of miles per hour over the speed limit. Estimate the fine for a driver traveling 8 mi/h over the speed limit. *(Lesson 5-8)* $f(x) = 0.2x^2 + 50$; \$62.80

Miles per Hour over the Speed Limit	Fine (\$)
5	55
10	70
15	95
20	130

12. **Fractals** A fractal can be generated from the formula $Z_{n+1} = (Z_n)^2 + 0.4$. Find the value of Z_2 for this fractal given that $Z_1 = 0.5 - 0.5i$ and $Z_2 = (Z_1)^2 + 0.4$. $0.4 - 0.5i$

8. $1 \pm i$; the zeros of the function are not real, so according to the model, the object would never hit the ground.

Chapter 6 ■ Applications Practice 4, 6, 10–13. See p. A64.

Manufacturing **Use the following information for Exercises 1 and 2.**

A company produces globes in two different sizes. The large globes have a radius of x inches, and the small globes have a radius of $x - 2$ inches. *(Lesson 6-1)*

1. Write functions to find the volume of each globe size.
2. Evaluate each function for $x = 8$.

1. $L(x) = \frac{4}{3}\pi x^3$; $S(x) = \frac{4}{3}\pi(x - 2)^3$
2. $L(8) \approx 2144.7$ in.^{3}, $S(6) \approx 904.8$ in.^{3}

Business **Use the following information for Exercises 3 and 4.**

Mr. Schwartz models the number of items his business sold during its first 10 years as $N(x) = 0.07x^3 + 9x^2 - 16x + 80$. His average profit per item (in dollars) can be modeled as $P(x) = 0.5x + 10$. *(Lesson 6-2)*

3. Write a polynomial $T(x)$ that can be used to model the total profit for his company during these years. $T(x) = 0.035x^4 + 5.2x^3 + 82x^2 - 120x + 800$
4. Evaluate $T(4)$ and explain its significance.
5. **Entertainment** The concert attendance for a music group can be described by the function $F(x) = \frac{1}{4}x^3 + 2x^2 + 50$, where x is the number of concerts since its debut. Use synthetic division to find the number of people who attended the fourth concert. *(Lesson 6-3)* 98 people

Sports **Use the following information for Exercises 6 and 7.**

The manager of a basketball team charted the team's progress for the season. For each game, she took the team's points and subtracted the points that the other team scored. The team's performance can be modeled by the function $P(x) = x^3 - 9x^2 + 18x$, where x represents the number of games since the start of the season. *(Lesson 6-4)*

6. Find the zeros of the function. What do they represent?
7. Write the function in factored form. $P(x) = x(x - 3)(x - 6)$
8. **Packaging** A company packages its ink pens in a box whose length is 3 inches longer than its width and whose height is 2 inches shorter than its width. The volume of the box is 18 in^3. What are the dimensions of the box? *(Lesson 6-5)* 3 in. × 6 in. × 1 in.
9. **Medicine** A medicine capsule is shaped like a cylinder with a hemisphere at each end. The cylindrical portion of the capsule is 3 cm long, and the volume is $\frac{9}{4}\pi$ cm^3. Find the radius of the capsule. *(Lesson 6-6)* $r = \frac{3}{4}$ cm

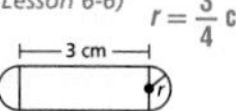

Investing **Use the following information for Exercises 10–12.**

Sharon tracked the closing value of a stock that she owns each day over a 25-day period. On average, the stock followed the curve $F(x) = -0.005x^3 + 0.05x^2 + x + 31.25$. *(Lesson 6-7)*

10. Graph the function on a graphing calculator.
11. What is the maximum value that the stock hit, and on approximately what day did it occur?
12. What is the y-intercept of the graph, and what does it signify?

School **Use the following information for Exercises 13 and 14.**

The enrollment of students at a school each year since 2000 can be modeled by the function $S(x) = -0.005x^5 + 0.07x^4 - 0.5x^2 + 278$. *(Lesson 6-8)*

13. Write the function $T(x) = S(x) - 50$.
14. Graph S and T on the same coordinate plane. Describe T as a transformation of S.
15. **Government** The table below shows the number of city employees during a 6-year period. Use a polynomial model to estimate the number of city employees in 2007. *(Lesson 6-9)* 606

Year	City Employees
2000	165
2001	168
2002	181
2003	210
2004	261
2005	340

14. vertical translation

Chapter 7 ■ Applications Practice 2, 14. See p. A64.

School **Use the following information for Exercises 1–3.**

A school's honor society was founded in 1970 with 120 members. Since then, the society membership has increased by about 10% each year. *(Lesson 7-1)*

1. Write a function representing the number of members each year since the club's founding (1970 = year 0). $f(x) = 120(1.1)^t$
2. Graph the function through the year 2005.
3. In which year did the number of members exceed 1000? 1993

Chemistry **Use the following information for Exercises 4–6.**

A glass was filled with 6 inches of water and left out on the counter. The amount of water in inches left in the glass after d days is $f(d) = 6 - 0.2d$. *(Lesson 7-2)*

4. Write the inverse function $f^{-1}(d)$. $f^{-1}(d) = 5(6 - d)$
5. After how many days was there 3.4 inches of water left in the glass? 13 days
6. After how many days was the glass empty? 30 days

Biology **Use the following information for Exercises 7 and 8.**

The number of bacteria in a culture after t hours is $f(t) = 3^{\frac{t}{2}}$. *(Lesson 7-3)*

7. How many bacteria are in the culture after 10 hours? 243
8. Replace $f(t)$ with y and write the function in logarithmic form. $\log_3 y = \frac{t}{2}$

Sound **Use the following information for Exercises 9 and 10.**

The loudness L of sound in decibels is given by $L = 10 \log\left(\frac{I}{I_0}\right)$, where I is the intensity of sound and I_0 is the intensity of the softest audible sound. *(Lesson 7-4)*

9. Rewrite this equation as the difference of two logarithms.
10. When is the equation undefined? The equation is undefined when $I = 0$.

9. $L = 10(\log I - \log I_0)$ or $L = 10 \log I - 10 \log I_0$

11. **Investing** A stock is losing value at a rate of 5% per month. An investor made an initial purchase of \$1500 worth of stock. The value of her shares of stock after m months is $A = 1500(0.95)^m$. Solve for m to find how many months it will take for the stockholder's shares to be worth less than \$1000. *(Lesson 7-5)* 8 mo
12. **Economics** Ivy's parents invested \$2700 for college in an account that receives 3.5% interest compounded continuously. What will the total amount of their investment be when Ivy starts college in 8 years? *(Lesson 7-6)* \$3572.45
13. **Physics** Americium-241, a radioactive element used in smoke detectors, has a half-life of 7370 years. Find the decay constant, then use the decay function $N(t) = N_0 e^{-kt}$ to determine the amount of atoms that remain from a sample of 1000 atoms after 20,000 years. *(Lesson 7-6)* $k = 9.4 \times 10^{-5}$; ≈ 152 atoms

Art **Use the following information for Exercises 14–16.**

A small painting by Mondrian was valued at \$10,500 in the year 2000. Since then its value has been increasing by 3% each year. The value of the painting x years after the year 2000 is $V = 10{,}500(1.03)^x$. Write a function for each transformation described below and explain the effect on the graph of the parent function. *(Lesson 7-7)*

14. The initial value in 2000 is adjusted to \$9500.
15. The value is \$1500 more each year.
16. The value of the painting increases by 3% every 2 years.
17. **Business** The table gives the number of employees at a company in the years since it was founded. Find a logarithmic model for the data. Predict when the company will have 60 employees. *(Lesson 7-8)* $E(t) \approx 12 + 20 \ln t$; 11 yr after its founding

Company Employees						
Years since Founding	1	2	3	4	5	6
Employees	12	26	34	40	44	48

15. $V_3 = 10{,}500(1.03)^x + 1500$; the graph is translated 1500 units up.
16. $V_4 = 10{,}500(1.03)^{\frac{x}{2}}$; the graph is stretched horizontally by a factor of 2.

Chapter 8 ■ Applications Practice

1. **Physics** The amount of force F exerted by an object varies directly as the object's acceleration a. An object accelerating at 5 m/s^2 exerts a force of 10 Newtons. How much force would the same object exert at an acceleration of 7 m/s^2? *(Lesson 8-1)* 14 Newtons
2. **Transportation** The time t required for a bus to travel a certain distance varies inversely as its average speed r. It takes the bus 2.2 h to travel between two cities at 50 mi/h. How long would the same drive take at 40 mi/h? *(Lesson 8-1)* 2.75 h

Recreation **Use the following information for Exercises 3 and 4.**

At a carnival booth, contestants can win a prize by throwing a dart at a square board. The total area of the board in square feet can be represented by the expression $4x^2 + 24x + 36$. *(Lesson 8-2)*

4. $\frac{x + 8}{4(x + 3)}$

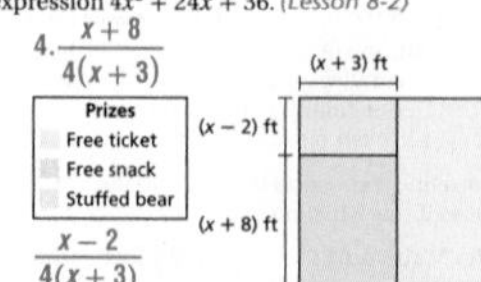

3. $\frac{x - 2}{4(x + 3)}$

3. If a dart hits the board at random, what is the probability in terms of x of winning a bear?
4. If a dart hits the board at random, what is the probability in terms of x of winning a snack?
5. **Fitness** Geoff ran a 6 mi race for charity. During the first 4 mi of the race, he averaged 6 mi/h. During the last 2 mi, he averaged 5.5 mi/h. What was Geoff's average speed in miles per hour for the entire race? Round to the nearest hundredth. *(Lesson 8-3)* 5.82 mi/h

School **Use the following information for Exercises 6 and 7.**

A science class is taking a field trip to a planetarium. Admission costs \$8 per student, plus there is a tour charge of \$80 per class. *(Lesson 8-4)*

6. Write and graph a function to represent the total average cost of the field trip per student.
7. Find the total average cost per student if 25 students go on the field trip. \$11.20

8. **Travel** A tour boat travels 12 mi up a river and 12 mi down the river in a total of 5.5 h. In still water, the boat travels at an average speed of 5.5 mi/h. Based on this information, what is the speed of the river's current? *(Lesson 8-5)* 2.5 mi/h
9. **Carpentry** A carpenter can build a cabinet in 4 h. When his son assists him, they can build the same type of cabinet in 2.5 h. About how long would it take the carpenter's son to build a cabinet by himself? *(Lesson 8-5)* $6\frac{2}{3}$ h, or 6 h 40 min
10. **Measurement** A large cubic storage box has a volume of $166\frac{3}{8}$ ft^3. The box is labeled with a strip of tape that wraps once around the entire box. What is the length of the tape that labels the box? *(Lesson 8-6)* 22 ft

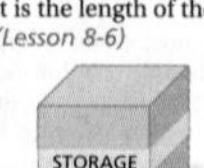

Physics **Use the following information for Exercises 11 and 12.**

The period of a pendulum is the time it takes for the pendulum to complete one back-and-forth swing. The function $f(x) = 2\pi\sqrt{\frac{x}{32}}$ gives the period f of a pendulum in seconds where x is the length of the pendulum in feet. *(Lesson 8-7)*

11. Write a function g for the period of a pendulum of length $(x + 2)$ ft. $g = 2\pi\sqrt{\frac{x + 2}{32}}$
12. Describe the function g as a transformation of f. g is f translated 2 units left.
13. **Geometry** The length of a diagonal d of a rectangular prism is given by $d = \sqrt{\ell^2 + w^2 + h^2}$, where ℓ is the length, w is the width, and h is the height. What is the minimum height in inches of a box with a length of 15 in. and a width of 12 in. that will hold a 20 in. baton? Round your answer to the nearest tenth. *(Lesson 8-8)* 5.6 in.

6. $f(x) = \frac{80}{x} + 8$

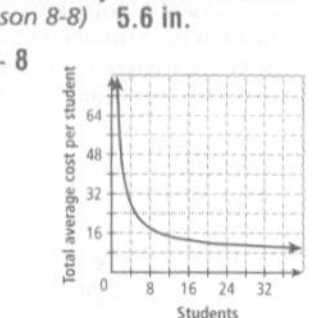

Chapter 9 ■ Applications Practice 1–3, 5. See p. A64.

1. **Ecology** The table shows the population of a colony of penguins over a 6-year period. Use a graph and an equation to predict the number of penguins in the colony in 2010. *(Lesson 9-1)*

Penguin Colony Population

Year	Population
2000	112
2001	123
2002	135
2003	149
2004	164
2005	180

Shipping **Use the following information for Exercises 2 and 3.**

A shipping company charges different rates depending on the weight of the package to be shipped. *(Lesson 9-2)*

Shipping Costs

Weight (lb)	Cost ($)
Under 2	$3.50
2 to 7	$6.00
More than 7	$9.00

2. Write a piecewise function to represent shipping costs for packages up to 10 lb.
3. Graph the function.

Recreation **Use the following information for Exercises 4 and 5.**

The zoo charges $7.00 per person for admittance. For groups of 20 people or more, the zoo charges $6.00 per person plus a one-time administrative fee of $10. *(Lesson 9-3)*

4. Write a function to represent the cost of admittance to the zoo for x people.
5. The zoo decides to raise the group administrative fee by $5. Write the resulting function. How does this affect the graph of the function?

4. $f(x) = \begin{cases} 7x & \text{if } 0 < x < 20 \\ 6x + 10 & \text{if } x \geq 20 \end{cases}$

6. $g(f(x)) = \frac{2}{3}\left(\frac{6}{10}x\right) = \frac{2}{5}x$

Politics **Use the following information for Exercises 6 and 7.**

Approximately 2 in 3 people surveyed support a bill to raise the salaries of local police officers. Of those who support the bill, 60% also support a raise in taxes to pay for the bill. *(Lesson 9-4)*

6. Write a composite function for the number of people who support the bill and think that taxes should be raised.
7. The total number of people who support both the bill and the tax is 90. How many people were surveyed?
225

Scouting **Use the following information for Exercises 8–10.**

The graph shows the number of merit badges that scouts from the same troop have earned, based on the number of years they have been in the troop. *(Lesson 9-5)*

8. 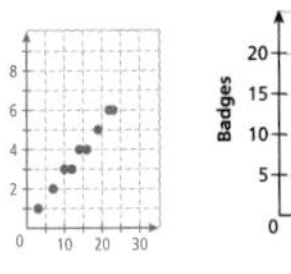

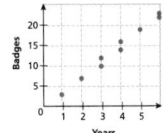

8. Graph the inverse of $f(x)$.
9. Is $f(x)$ a function? Is its inverse a function?
$f(x)$: no; $f^{-1}(x)$: yes
10. Use your graph to predict how long a scout has been in the troop if he has earned 36 badges.
9 yr

Nutrition **Use the following information for Exercises 11 and 12.**

The table shows the number of Calories and grams of fat in selected sandwiches. *(Lesson 9-6)*

Sandwich Nutrition Information

Fat (g)	6	8	12	15	20
Calories	372	396	442	477	535

11. Write a function that models the data.
$f(x) \approx 11.6x + 302.6$
12. Use your model to predict the number of Calories in a sandwich containing 25 grams of fat.
593 Calories

Chapter 10 ■ Applications Practice

Geometry **Use the following information for Exercises 1–3.**

A circle has center $(7, 8)$ and contains the point $(11, 11)$. *(Lesson 10-1)*

1. Find the circumference of the circle.
10π
2. Find the area of the circle.
25π
3. Find the other endpoint of the diameter with one endpoint $(11, 5)$.
$(3, 11)$

Design **Use the following information for Exercises 4–6.**

Grace is designing a courtyard for a client. The courtyard will include a small circular fountain inside a large circular patio, which will be surrounded by a square fence. The plans have been overlaid on a coordinate plane, as shown below. *(Lesson 10-2)*

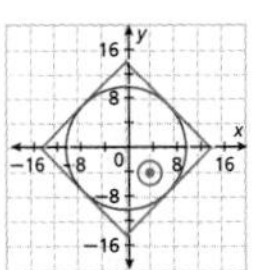

4. Find an equation for the fountain.
$(x - 4)^2 + (y + 4)^2 = 4$
5. Find an equation for the circular patio.
$x^2 + y^2 = 100$
6. Each side of the fence is tangent to the patio. Find the equation for the part of the fence that passes through the point $(-5\sqrt{2}, 5\sqrt{2})$.
$y = x + 10\sqrt{2}$

Architecture **Use the following information for Exercises 7 and 8.**

The Oval Office in the White House has a major axis 35 ft 10 in. long and a minor axis 29 ft long. *(Lesson 10-3)*

7. Suppose that the center of the floor of the Oval Office is located at the origin. Write an equation that can be used to model the office floor.
8. Find the coordinates of the foci.
Possible answer: $(\pm 10.52, 0)$

7. Possible answer: $\frac{x^2}{321} + \frac{y^2}{210.25} = 1$

9. Possible answer: $\frac{x^2}{302{,}500} - \frac{y^2}{697{,}500} = 1$

9. **Sports** Two people watching a baseball game are seated 2000 feet apart. One person hears the crack of the bat 1 second before the other person. Because sound travels at 1100 feet per second, one person must be 1100 feet closer to the bat than the other. The possible locations of the batter form a hyperbola with the two people as foci. Write an equation that could be used to represent the possible locations of the batter. (*Hint:* Place the origin midway between the two people.) *(Lesson 10-4)*
10. **Recreation** A half-pipe, similar to those used by skateboarders, is parabolic in shape. Use the intersection of the ground and the center of the half-pipe as the origin and write an equation to model the shape of the curved interior of the structure. *(Lesson 10-5)*

10. $y - 1 = \frac{1}{40}x^2$

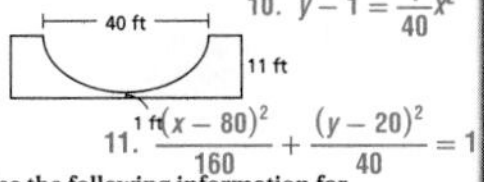

11. $\frac{(x - 80)^2}{160} + \frac{(y - 20)^2}{40} = 1$

Fitness **Use the following information for Exercises 11 and 12.**

A runner is running on a track. His path in yards can be modeled by the equation $x^2 - 160x + 4y^2 - 160y + 7840 = 0$. *(Lesson 10-6)*

11. Write the equation in standard form by completing the square.
12. There is a drinking fountain in the center of the track. What are the coordinates of the fountain? What is the farthest distance that a runner would have to travel from the track to the fountain?
13. **Ecology** A water tank has spilled, and the flooded area in square feet can be modeled by the equation $x^2 + y^2 = 225$. Near the spilled tank, there is a garden whose shape can be modeled by the equation $\frac{(x - 9)^2}{25} + \frac{(y - 6)^2}{36} = 1$. At what points do the boundaries of the spill and the garden intersect? *(Lesson 10-7)*
$(9, 12)$ and $(13.98, 5.44)$

12. The fountain is at $(80, 20)$; the farthest a runner would have to travel from the track to the fountain is 80 yards.

Chapter 11 ■ Applications Practice

Music **Use the following information for Exercises 1 and 2.**

Serialism is a form of music in which the composer arranges each of the 12 tones in an octave to form a musical phrase. *(Lesson 11-1)*

1. How many ways can the 12 tones of an octave be arranged?
$12! = 479{,}001{,}600$
2. How many different musical phrases could a composer create by arranging only 5 of the 12 tones of an octave?
95,040
3. **Drama** A drama class is performing the Greek tragedy *Antigone*, by Sophocles. Of the 15 students in the class, 6 will make up the chorus. How many different ways can the chorus be selected? *(Lesson 11-1)*
3,603,600
4. **Holidays** Of December's 31 days, the 25th and the 31st are holidays. What is the probability that a randomly chosen day in December is not a holiday? *(Lesson 11-2)*
$\approx 93.55\%$
5. **Games** If Sara's dart lands in a red equilateral triangle, she wins a prize. Each triangle has a base of 2 in. If all locations on the 12 in. diameter target are equally likely, what is the probability that Sara wins a prize? *(Lesson 11-2)*
≈ 0.046

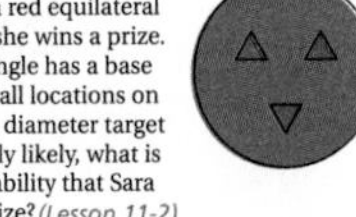

Literature **Use the following information for Exercises 6 and 7.**

The works of Chilean poet Pablo Neruda have been published in many languages. The school library has copies of two of his books in both English and Spanish. The table shows how many times each book has been checked out. *(Lesson 11-3)*

Books Checked Out

	Canto General	*Extravagario*
English	23	27
Spanish	17	14

6. What is the probability that *Canto General* was checked out in Spanish?
42.5%
7. What is the probability that a student who checked out a Pablo Neruda book selected *Extravagario* in English?
33.33%

Immigration **Use the following information for Exercises 8 and 9.**

A group of 100 immigrants was studied over a one-year period. During the study, 63 of the immigrants found jobs, and 14 returned to their country of origin. Of the immigrants who found jobs, 6 of them returned to their countries before the end of the study. *(Lesson 11-4)*

8. What is the probability that an immigrant found a job or returned to his or her country of origin? $\frac{71}{100} = 71\%$
9. What is the probability that an immigrant did not find a job or returned to his country of origin? $\frac{51}{100} = 51\%$

Basketball **Use the following information for Exercises 10–12.**

The table below shows the number of points scored by Tracy McGrady and Yao Ming of the Houston Rockets during the same 5 games of the 2005 season. *(Lesson 11-5)*

Points Scored

Game	1	2	3	4	5
Tracy McGrady	28	36	25	37	27
Yao Ming	15	20	30	8	33

10. Find the mean of both sets of data.
McGrady: 30.6; Ming: 21.2
11. Find the standard deviation of both sets of data.
McGrady: ≈ 4.923; Ming: ≈ 9.282
12. Determine whether there is an outlier. If so, describe how it affects the mean and standard deviation.
no outlier

Nutrition **Use the following information for Exercises 13 and 14.**

At a frozen yogurt store, 75% of customers ask for a cup, while the others ask for a cone. At closing time, the store has 7 people waiting and only 2 cones left. *(Lesson 11-6)*

13. What is the probability that exactly 2 people will want cones?
≈ 0.311
14. What is the probability that no more than 2 people will want cones?
≈ 0.756

Chapter 12 ■ Applications Practice

Housing **Use the following information for Exercises 1 and 2.**

Lily moved into her apartment in 2001, when the rent was $650. Every year since then, the landlord has raised the rent by 5%. *(Lesson 12-1)*

1. Graph the sequence and describe its pattern.
2. How much will Lily's rent be in 2010?
$1008.36
3. **Fractals** Find the number of red circles in the next 2 terms of the fractal. *(Lesson 12-1)*
8, 16

  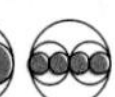

4. **Awards** A local charity started its Volunteer Hall of Fame by inducting the first honoree in 1997. The next year it inducted 2 new members, and in 1999 it inducted 3 new members. Each year since then, it has added one more member than it did the previous year. How many members will the Volunteer Hall of Fame have in 2009? *(Lesson 12-2)*
91

Fractals **Use the following information for Exercises 5 and 6.**

The number of circles in the first iteration of the fractal is $3^0 = 1$. The number of circles in the second iteration of the fractal is $3^0 + 3^1 = 4$. The number of circles in the third iteration of the fractal is $3^0 + 3^1 + 3^2 = 13$. *(Lesson 12-2)*

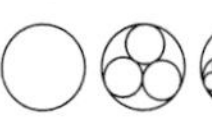

5. Use summation notation to write an expression for the number of circles in the nth iteration of the fractal. $\sum_{k=1}^{n} 3^{k-1}$
6. Find the number of circles in the 5th iteration of the fractal.
121

1. The graph appears to be growing at an exponential rate.

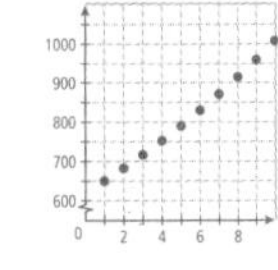

Fitness **Use the following information for Exercises 7–9.**

When a member first joins a health club, he or she pays $240 for the first year. Each year after that, the yearly fee is reduced by $10. *(Lesson 12-3)*

7. What is the yearly fee for the 7th year?
$180
8. How much will a member have paid after belonging to the health club for 10 years?
$1950
9. If a member has paid a total of $2450 in fees, how long has she been a member of the health club?
14 yr

Communication **Use the following information for Exercises 10–12.**

The Parent Teacher Association spreads news using a phone tree. The president and vice president start the phone tree by calling 3 people each. Each of the 6 people called then have 3 new people to call, and so on, until every member of the PTA has been called. *(Lesson 12-4)*

10. Write a sequence to describe the phone tree.
$a_n = 2(3)^{n-1}$
11. How many people are on the 5th row of the phone tree?
162
12. It takes a total of 6 rows to finish the phone tree. Write an expression in summation notation to express the number of people called in the entire phone tree. How many members does the Parent Teacher Association have? $\sum_{k=1}^{6} 2(3)^{k-1}$; the PTA has 728 members.

Business **Use the following information for Exercises 13 and 14.**

The table shows the annual revenue generated by a new product in its first 4 years. *(Lesson 12-5)*

Annual Revenue

Year	2001	2002	2003	2004
Sales (thousand $)	375	225	135	81

13. Assume that the trend continues. Estimate the revenue generated in 2008.
approximately $10.5 thousand
14. Assume that the sales trend continues indefinitely. Estimate the total revenue the product will generate.
approximately $938 thousand

Extra Practice

Chapter 13 ■ Applications Practice

1. **Aviation** A plane is flying at an altitude of 6500 ft. The pilot sights the runway of an airport at an angle of depression of 6°. To the nearest tenth of a mile, what is the horizontal distance from the plane to the runway? *(Lesson 13-1)*
11.7 mi
2. **Architecture** Thomas stands 250 m from the base of the Sears Tower in Chicago. His eye level is 1.75 m above the ground, and he measures the angle of elevation to the top of the tower to be 60.4°. Based on this information, what is the height of the Sears Tower to the nearest meter? *(Lesson 13-1)*
442 m

Recreation **Use the following information for Exercises 3 and 4.**

A Ferris wheel makes one complete revolution in 40 s. *(Lesson 13-2)*

3. Through what angle, in degrees, does a car of the Ferris wheel rotate in 70 s?
630°
4. How long does it take a car of the Ferris wheel to rotate through an angle of 792°?
88 s
5. **Landscape Design** A path through a park is shaped like an arc of a circle with a radius of 25 ft. The central angle that intercepts the path measures $\frac{\pi}{2}$ radians. To the nearest foot, how long is the path? *(Lesson 13-3)*
39 ft
6. **Entertainment** A standard circus ring is 42 ft in diameter. A clown on a bicycle rides once around the circumference of the ring in 10 s. To the nearest tenth of a foot, how far does the clown travel in 1 second? *(Lesson 13-3)*
13.2 ft
7. **Astronomy** Venus is approximately 108 million km from the Sun and takes 225 days to complete an orbit. Based on this information, how far does Venus travel in its nearly circular orbit around the Sun in 1 day? Round to the nearest million kilometers. *(Lesson 13-3)*
3 million km
8. **Construction** The entrance to a store is 6 in. above the level of the sidewalk. A contractor is building an access ramp to the entrance that will cover a horizontal distance of 6 ft. To the nearest degree, what angle will the ramp make with the sidewalk? *(Lesson 13-4)*
5°
9. **Safety** The "1-to-4" rule states that when a ladder is leaning against a wall, the bottom of the ladder should be 1 ft away from the wall for every 4 ft that the top of the ladder rises on the wall. To the nearest degree, what angle should the ladder make with the ground? *(Lesson 13-4)*
76°
10. **Surveying** A surveyor is measuring a triangular plot of land, as shown. To the nearest foot, what is the distance between stakes 1 and 2? *(Lesson 13-5)*
52 ft

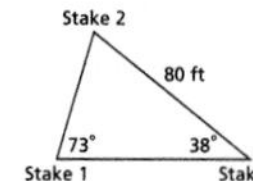

Hobbies **Use the following information for Exercises 11 and 12.**

Andrew uses pieces of wood to build triangular picture frames. Determine the number of triangles he can form using the given side and angle measurements. Then solve the triangles. Round to the nearest tenth. *(Lesson 13-5)*

11. $a = 10.5$ cm, $b = 12$ cm, $m\angle A = 60°$
12. $a = 8$ cm, $b = 15$ cm, $m\angle A = 44°$
No triangles
13. **Hiking** Anne and Keisha leave their campsite at the same time. Anne hikes due east at 2 mi/h. Keisha heads 65° east of north at 3 mi/h. To the nearest tenth of a mile, what is the distance d between the hikers after 3 hours? *(Lesson 13-6)*
4.4 mi

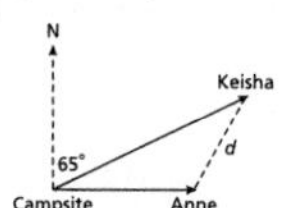

14. A museum has a triangular window with sides measuring 9 ft, 11 ft, and 14 ft. What is the area of the window to the nearest square foot? *(Lesson 13-6)*
49 ft^2

11. 2 triangles; $m\angle B_1 \approx 81.8°$; $m\angle C_1 \approx 38.2°$; $c_1 = 7.5$ cm; $m\angle B_2 \approx 98.2°$; $m\angle C_2 \approx 21.8$; $c_2 = 4.5$ cm

Chapter 14 ■ Applications Practice

1, 2, 5, 7, 13. For graphs, see p. A64.

1. **Sound** Use a sine function to graph a sound wave with a period of 0.006 second and an amplitude of 5 cm. Find the frequency in hertz for this sound wave. *(Lesson 14-1)* $166\frac{2}{3}$ Hz

Recreation **Use the following information for Exercises 2–4.**

As a cyclist rides her bike, the height in inches above the ground of one of the pedals is modeled by $H(t) = 6\cos 2\pi t + 12$, where t is the time in seconds. *(Lesson 14-1)*

2. Graph the height of the pedal for two complete periods.
3. What is the maximum and minimum height of the pedal?
18 in.; 6 in.
4. How many complete revolutions does the pedal make in one minute?
60

Use the following information for Exercises 5 and 6.

As a swimming pool is drained, the depth of the water in feet is modeled by $D(t) = 1.05 \cot \frac{\pi}{8}\left(t + \frac{1}{2}\right)$, where t is the time in hours. *(Lesson 14-2)*

5. Graph the depth of the water in the swimming pool for $0 \le t \le 3$.
6. What is the starting depth of the water? Round to the nearest inch.
5 ft 3 in.

Use the following information for Exercises 7 and 8.

The minute hand of a clock begins on the 12 and moves around the dial. The slope of the line represented by the minute hand is given by the function $S(t) = -\tan 2\pi(t - 0.25)$, where t is the time in hours. *(Lesson 14-2)*

7. Graph the slope of the minute hand for six complete periods.
8. What is the period of the function? $\frac{1}{2}$ h
9. **Physics** Use the equation $mg \sin\theta = \mu mg \cos\theta$ to determine the angle at which a steel table can be tilted before a copper pan on the table begins to slide. Assume $\mu = 0.53$ and round your answer to the nearest degree. *(Lesson 14-3)*
28°

Geometry **Use the following information for Exercises 10 and 11.**

Find the coordinates, to the nearest hundredth, of the vertices of $\triangle ABC$ after the given rotation. *(Lesson 14-4)*

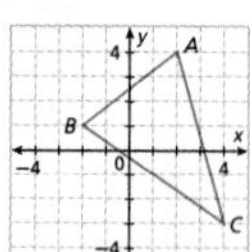

10. A 60° rotation about the origin
11. A 135° rotation about the origin

Physics **Use the following information for Exercises 12 and 13.**

The horizontal component of the acceleration of an object sliding down a frictionless inclined plane is $a(\theta) = 9.8 \sin\theta \cos\theta$, where θ is the angle of the inclined plane and where acceleration is measured in meters per second per second $\left(\frac{m}{s^2}\right)$. *(Lesson 14-5)*

12. Rewrite the function in terms of the double angle 2θ. $a(\theta) = 4.9\sin 2\theta$
13. Graph the function for $0 \le \theta \le \frac{\pi}{2}$. For what angle does the object have the greatest acceleration in the horizontal direction? $\frac{\pi}{4}$
14. The population in thousands of a seaside town is modeled by $P(t) = 10\sin\frac{\pi}{180}(t - 160) + 15$, where t is the day of the year and $t = 0$ represents January 1. How many days after January 1 is the population equal to 22,000? *(Lesson 14-6)*
204 and 296
15. The temperature in New York City during one day in the summer is modeled by $F(t) = 16\sin\frac{\pi}{12}(t - 8) + 68$, where F is the temperature in degrees Fahrenheit and t is the time in hours after midnight. At what times during the day is the temperature 80°F? *(Lesson 14-6)*
11:14 A.M. and 4:45 P.M.

10. $A'(-2.46, 3.73)$, $B'(-1.87, -1.23)$, $C'(4.60, 1.96)$
11. $A'(-4.24, -1.41)$, $B'(0.71, -2.12)$, $C'(-0.71, 4.95)$

Problem-Solving Handbook

Problem Solving Handbook

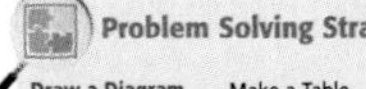

Draw a Diagram

You can draw a diagram that represents the information in a problem to help you understand and solve the problem.

Problem Solving Strategies

Draw a Diagram	Make a Table
Make a Model	Solve a Simpler Problem
Guess and Test	Use Logical Reasoning
Work Backward	Use a Venn Diagram
Find a Pattern	Make an Organized List

EXAMPLE

Carmen is participating in an online contest to win a car. She is given a choice of three doors. Each door leads to another level with three doors, and each of those leads to another level with three doors. Behind one of those final doors is the grand prize of a new car. What is the probability of winning the car if she chooses doors at random?

1 Understand the Problem

List the important information.

- She begins with three doors.
- Each of those doors leads to three other doors, and each of those doors leads to another three doors.
- One of the final doors leads to the car.
- The probability of winning is the number of cars divided by the total number of final door choices.

The answer will be the probability of finding the car.

2 Make a Plan

Use a tree diagram to show the possible door choices. This will show the number of possible paths Carmen could choose.

3 Solve

Draw the tree diagram. Draw three doors to represent the original three doors. Draw three more doors for each door and connect them with lines. Repeat to have three rows of doors.

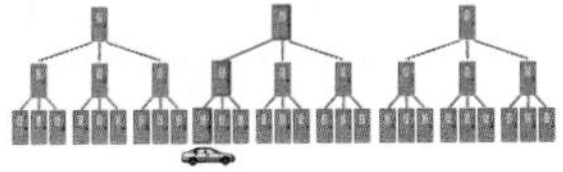

The highlighted path shows that there is exactly one way to win the car.

The total number of paths is 27.

The probability of winning the car is $\frac{1}{27} \approx 3.7\%$.

4 Look Back

Check that you drew your diagram correctly. Does the diagram accurately represent the information given in the question?

PRACTICE

1. Bob has a green, a blue, a red, and a yellow marble in a bag. He randomly selects one marble at a time from the bag until the bag is empty. What is the probability that the blue marble is chosen immediately before the red one? $\frac{1}{4}$

Make a Model

For problems that involve objects, it is sometimes useful to make a model to help you solve the problem.

Problem Solving Strategies

Draw a Diagram	Make a Table
Make a Model	Solve a Simpler Problem
Guess and Test	Use Logical Reasoning
Work Backward	Use a Venn Diagram
Find a Pattern	Make an Organized List

EXAMPLE

Ryan created a pyramid with a square base out of cans of soup for a store display. When he had finished, he needed to know the number of cans that he had used. The pyramid has four levels. The top level has one can, and each row beneath it has one additional can added to each side length. How many cans are in the pyramid?

1 Understand the Problem

List the important information.

- There are four levels.
- The top level has one can.
- The side length increases by one as you go down each level.

The answer will be the number of cans in the pyramid.

2 Make a Plan

You can use blocks to make a model of the problem. Use the blocks to create the pyramid in the problem. Remember to count the number of blocks as you go.

3 Solve

Since each level has one can added to the side length, the side length of the bottom level is 4. Make a 4-by-4 square of blocks for the base. Count the number of blocks used. The level above has side lengths of 3, so make a 3-by-3 square on top of the base. Count the number of blocks used in this level. Continue to the top of the pyramid. The total number of blocks is the sum of the blocks at each level: 16 + 9 + 4 + 1 = 30.

4 Look Back

Make sure the pyramid matches the given information. There should be four levels increasing by one in side length as you go down the pyramid.

PRACTICE

1. Paul wants to make a pyramid with an equilateral triangle base out of cans. Paul has 25 cans. He wants the pyramid to have one can on the top, and he wants the number of cans on each side of the following triangle layers to increase by one. How tall can Paul make the pyramid? How many cans will he have left over? The tallest possible pyramid is 4 layers tall, and he will have 5 cans left over.
2. A display of cereal boxes is arranged with 1 box on top and each row having an additional box. How many boxes are in a display of 9 rows? 45 boxes

Guess and Test

One way to solve a problem is to guess the answer and test to see whether it is correct. You can continue to guess and test until you find the correct answer.

Problem Solving Strategies

Draw a Diagram	Make a Table
Make a Model	Solve a Simpler Problem
Guess and Test	Use Logical Reasoning
Work Backward	Use a Venn Diagram
Find a Pattern	Make an Organized List

EXAMPLE

Tom is playing a game where he draws marbles out of a bag. Red marbles are worth 3 points, and blue ones are worth 2 points. Tom drew 8 marbles and won 20 points. How many marbles of each color does Tom have?

1 Understand the Problem

List the important information.

- Red marbles are worth 3 points.
- Blue marbles are worth 2 points.
- The total number of points is 20.
- The total number of marbles is 8.

2 Make a Plan

Start with a guess in which the total number of marbles is 8. Test to see whether the total number of points is 20.

3 Solve

Make a first guess of 3 red and 5 blue, and find the total number of points.

Guess: 3 red and 5 blue

Test: $(3 \times 3) + (5 \times 2) = 19$

The number of points is too small. Increase the number of red marbles and decrease the number of blue marbles.

Guess: 5 red and 3 blue

Test: $(5 \times 3) + (3 \times 2) = 21$

The number of points is too high. Decrease the number of red marbles and increase the number of blue marbles.

Guess: 4 red and 4 blue

Test: $(4 \times 3) + (4 \times 2) = 20$

Tom should have drawn 4 red marbles and 4 blue marbles.

4 Look Back

Test the answer to see whether the number of marbles satisfies the question.

4 red marbles and 4 blue marbles are 8 marbles and are worth 20 points.

PRACTICE

1. Fred has 7 coins. All the coins are nickels or dimes. The total value of the coins is \$0.55. How many of each type of coin does he have? There are 3 nickels and 4 dimes.
2. The sum of Beth's age and Brian's age is 20. Three times Beth's age plus 2 times Brian's age is 55. How old are Beth and Brian? Beth is 15, and Brian is 5.

Work Backward

Sometimes in a problem you are given an end result and asked to find a fact that leads to the result. In these cases, you can work backward to solve the problem.

Problem Solving Strategies

Draw a Diagram	Make a Table
Make a Model	Solve a Simpler Problem
Guess and Test	Use Logical Reasoning
Work Backward	Use a Venn Diagram
Find a Pattern	Make an Organized List

EXAMPLE

Laura is delivering meals to retirement communities. She dropped off 2 less than $\frac{1}{2}$ of the meals at the first community. Then she dropped off $\frac{1}{3}$ of the remaining meals plus 2 at the second community. She has 8 meals left. How many meals did she have to start?

1 Understand the Problem

List the important information.

- Laura delivered $\frac{1}{2}$ of the meals minus 2 at the first community.
- Laura delivered $\frac{1}{3}$ of the meals plus 2 at the second community.
- She has 8 meals left.

The answer will be the number of meals that she had at the start.

2 Make a Plan

Start with the 8 meals and work backward through the given information to determine the beginning number of meals.

3 Solve

She has 8 meals at the end, so start with 8 meals.

She delivered $\frac{1}{3}$ of the meals plus 2 at the second community, so add 2 to the number of meals and multiply by $\frac{3}{2}$ to undo giving $\frac{1}{3}$ away. $\frac{3}{2}(8 + 2) = 15$

She had 15 meals before she visited the second community.

She delivered $\frac{1}{2}$ of the meals minus 2 at the first community, so subtract 2 and multiply by 2 to undo giving $\frac{1}{2}$ away. $2(15 - 2) = 26$

Laura started with 26 meals.

4 Look Back

Use the starting amount of 26 meals and work from the beginning of the problem following the steps.

Start: 26

Subtract $\frac{1}{2}$ of the meals plus 2 more: 15

Subtract $\frac{1}{3}$ of the meals minus 2 more: 8

PRACTICE

1. A tree is growing in Danny's yard. When Danny first observed the tree, he noticed that the number of branches on the tree had doubled that year. The year after, the number of branches tripled minus 3. The year after that, the tree doubled its number of branches, plus 6. How many branches did the tree originally have if it currently has 120 branches? The tree originally had 10 branches.

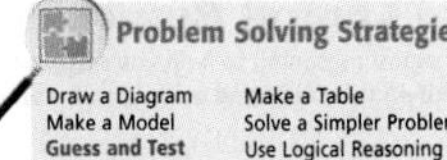

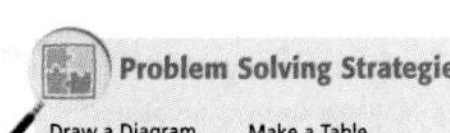

Find a Pattern

When the pieces of information in a problem have a relationship, you can find a pattern to help solve the problem.

Problem Solving Strategies

Draw a Diagram	Make a Table
Make a Model	Solve a Simpler Problem
Guess and Test	Use Logical Reasoning
Work Backward	Use a Venn Diagram
Find a Pattern	Make an Organized List

EXAMPLE

Fred has 3 homework problems the first day of school. The second day he has 5. The third day he has 7. The fourth day he has 9. If this pattern continues, how many homework problems will Fred have on the tenth day of school?

1 Understand the Problem

List the important information.

- On day 1 he has 3 homework problems, on day 2 he has 5 homework problems, on day 3 he has 7 homework problems, and on day 4 he has 9 homework problems.

The answer will be the number of homework problems Fred will have on day 10.

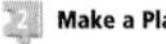

2 Make a Plan

Find a pattern by comparing the number of homework problems Fred has each day. Then use this pattern to determine the number of homework problems he will have on day 10.

3 Solve

Organize the data and find the pattern.

Day	Number of Homework Problems	Pattern
1	3	$3 + 2(1 - 1)$
2	5	$3 + 2(2 - 1)$
3	7	$3 + 2(3 - 1)$
4	9	$3 + 2(4 - 1)$

The pattern is that he gains 2 homework problems each day. Since he has 3 problems the first day and the number of days that have passed is the day number minus 1, the number of homework problems Fred has on the day n is $3 + 2(n - 1)$.

The number of homework problems Fred will have on day 10 is $3 + 2(10 - 1) = 21$.

4 Look Back

Since the pattern is that he gains 2 homework problems each day, continue the data in a table to make sure that he will have 21 homework problems on the tenth day. Check that the formula you developed satisfies the information given in the question.

PRACTICE

1. Joseph is making signs for his student council election campaign. He made 1 sign the first day, 4 signs the second day, 7 signs the third day, and 10 signs the fourth day. How many signs will he make on the tenth day? 28
2. A flower is growing in a field. In year 1 there are two flowers in the field, in year 2 there are 3, in year 3 there are 5, in year 4 there are 9, in year 5 there are 17, and in year 6 there are 33. How many flowers will there be in year 11? 1025

Make a Table

When you are solving problems that involve a large amount of data, it is often useful to make a table to organize and analyze the data.

Problem Solving Strategies

Draw a Diagram	**Make a Table**
Make a Model	Solve a Simpler Problem
Guess and Test	Use Logical Reasoning
Work Backward	Use a Venn Diagram
Find a Pattern	Make an Organized List

EXAMPLE

Peter, Michael, and Lisa work at the same shop. Peter works every 2 days, Michael works every 4 days, and Lisa works every 5 days. They all worked today. In how many days will they all work together again? How many days will each person work between now and when they all work together next?

1 Understand the Problem

List the important information.

- Peter works every 2 days, Michael every 4 and Lisa every 5.
- They all worked together today.

The answers will be:

- the number of days until they work together again and
- the number of days each person will work between now and then.

2 Make a Plan

Make a table, using ✔'s to show the days each person works.

3 Solve

Start with a ✔ in each person's row on day 0. For Peter, place a ✔ every 2 days. For Michael, place a ✔ every 4 days. For Lisa, place a ✔ every 5 days.

Day	0	1	2	3	4	5	6	7	8	9	10	11	12	13	14	15	16	17	18	19	20
Peter	✔		✔		✔		✔		✔		✔		✔		✔		✔		✔		✔
Michael	✔				✔				✔				✔				✔				✔
Lisa	✔					✔					✔					✔					✔

They will all work together again in 20 days. Peter will work nine, Michael will work 4, and Lisa will work 3 days between now and then.

4 Look Back

Check the information in the table. Make sure that no mistakes have been made in counting and that the data matches the information given in the question.

PRACTICE

1. If Peter works every 3 days, Michael works every 5 days, and Lisa works every 6 days, when will the next day be that they all work together if they all worked together today? How many days will each person work between now and when they all work together next? 30 days; Peter will work 9 days, Michael will work 5 days, and Lisa will work 4 days.
2. A restaurant receives a shipment of produce every 2 days, a shipment of meat every 9 days, and a shipment of frozen food every 12 days. When will be the next day that all three shipments arrive if all three shipments arrived today? How many of each type of shipment will the restaurant receive between now and then. 36 days; 17 produce shipments, 3 meat shipments, and 2 frozen food shipments

Solve a Simpler Problem

When solving a complex problem, it is sometimes helpful to write a simpler problem, solve it, and then use a similar method to solve the complex problem.

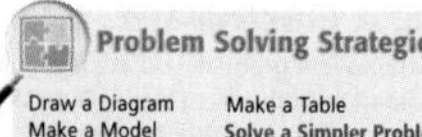

Problem Solving Strategies

Draw a Diagram	Make a Table
Make a Model	**Solve a Simpler Problem**
Guess and Test	Use Logical Reasoning
Work Backward	Use a Venn Diagram
Find a Pattern	Make an Organized List

EXAMPLE

In a garden, there are 2 flowers, 1 red and 1 blue. Each year, the number of red flowers increases by 1 and the number of blue flowers increases by 2. What percent of the flowers will be red 10 years from now?

1 Understand the Problem

List the important information.

- The field begins with 1 red and 1 blue flower.
- Each year, the number of red flowers increases by 1.
- Each year, the number of blue flowers increases by 2.

The answer will be the percent of red flowers after 10 years have passed.

2 Make a Plan

Solve a simpler problem: Find the pattern in the number of red flowers and the total number of flowers in ten years.

3 Solve

Make a table. Separate the two patterns. Identify each pattern and develop a formula.

Year	Red Flowers	Pattern	Blue Flowers	Total Flowers	Pattern
0	1	$1 + (0)$	1	2	$2 + 3(0)$
1	2	$1 + (1)$	3	5	$2 + 3(1)$
2	3	$1 + (2)$	5	8	$2 + 3(2)$
3	4	$1 + (3)$	7	11	$2 + 3(3)$

If n is the nth year, then the number of red flowers is $1 + n$ and the total number of flowers is $2 + 3n$. The percent of flowers that are red is the ratio of the number of red flowers to the total number of flowers.

So the percent of red flowers in the nth year is $\frac{1 + n}{2 + 3n}$, and in 10 years the percent of flowers that are red is $\frac{1 + 10}{2 + 3(10)} = \frac{11}{32} = 34.375\%$.

4 Look Back

Check that the answer is reasonable. Since the blue flowers grow faster than the red flowers and the garden starts with an equal number of each, there should be more blue flowers than red flowers. Therefore, the percent of red flowers should be less than 50%.

PRACTICE

1. In a field of flowers, there are 2 flowers; 1 yellow and 1 orange. Each year, the number of yellow flowers increases by 3, and the number of orange flowers increases by 4. What percent of the flowers will be yellow in 20 years? approximately 43%

Use Logical Reasoning

Use logical reasoning to help you solve problems by identifying the facts and using them to draw conclusions.

Problem Solving Strategies

Draw a Diagram	Make a Table
Make a Model	Solve a Simpler Problem
Guess and Test	**Use Logical Reasoning**
Work Backward	Use a Venn Diagram
Find a Pattern	Make an Organized List

EXAMPLE

Friends Jeff, Luca, Linda, and Blair are each a different age between 11 and 14. Each person has a different favorite color and sport. The sports are baseball, football, tennis and hockey. The colors are red, blue, green, and yellow. Jeff is 11 and likes to play baseball. The football player is the oldest and dislikes red. The hockey player's favorite color is blue. Linda does not play football. Blair likes the color green, plays tennis, and is a year younger than Linda. Find each person's age, favorite color, and sport.

1 Understand the Problem

List the important information.

- Jeff is 11 and likes to play baseball.
- The football player is the oldest and dislikes red.
- The hockey player's favorite color is blue.
- Linda does not play football.
- Blair likes the color green, plays tennis, and is a year younger than Linda.

The answer will be each person's age, favorite color, and sport.

2 Make a Plan

Start with the given clues. Use logical reasoning to make a table of the facts.

3 Solve

Make a table. Work with the clues one at a time. Place a ✔ in a box if the clue matches the person and an ✗ if it does not.

	R	Bl	G	Y	Ba	F	T	H	11	12	13	14
Jeff	✔	✗	✗	✗	✔	✗	✗	✗	✔	✗	✗	✗
Luca	✗	✗	✗	✔	✗	✔	✗	✗	✗	✗	✗	✔
Linda	✗	✔	✗	✗	✗	✗	✗	✔	✗	✗	✔	✗
Blair	✗	✗	✔	✗	✗	✗	✔	✗	✗	✔	✗	✗

Jeff is 11, plays baseball, and likes red. Luca is 14, plays football, and likes yellow. Linda is 13, plays hockey, and likes blue. Blair is 12, plays tennis, and likes green.

4 Look Back

Compare your answer to the clues in the problem. Make sure none of the conclusions conflict with the clues.

PRACTICE

1. Friends Bob, Gary, Roxanne, and Robin have last names that begin with the letters *B*, *S*, *T*, and *H*. Their ages are 10, 12, 14, and 16, and their hair colors are blond, black, brown, and red. Bob's last initial is *B*. Robin is a teenager. Roxanne does not have red hair. Bob is 2 years older than Roxanne. The oldest has the last initial *S* and brown hair. Gary's last initial comes before Roxanne's in the alphabet. Gary is 10 and has black hair. Find each person's last initial, age, and hair color. Bob: B, 14, red; Gary: H, 10, black; Roxanne: T, 12, blond; Robin: S, 16, brown

Use a Venn Diagram

Venn diagrams can be useful in solving problems with sets that overlap each other.

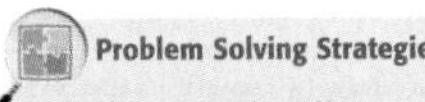

Problem Solving Strategies

Draw a Diagram	Make a Table
Make a Model	Solve a Simpler Problem
Guess and Test	Use Logical Reasoning
Work Backward	**Use a Venn Diagram**
Find a Pattern	Make an Organized List

EXAMPLE

There were three science lectures that students could attend, one on physics, one on chemistry, and one on biology. Four students attended all lectures, 6 students went to both the biology and physics lectures, 10 students went to both the chemistry and physics lectures, and 16 students went to both the chemistry and biology lectures. If a total of 30 students attended the physics lecture, 50 students attended the chemistry lecture, and 60 students attended the biology lecture, how many students went to at least one lecture?

1 Understand the Problem

List the important information.

- all lectures: 4
- biology and physics: 6
- chemistry and physics: 10
- chemistry and biology: 16
- physics: total of 30
- chemistry: total of 50
- biology: total of 50

The answer will be the number of students that went to at least one lecture.

2 Make a Plan

Use a Venn diagram to show the number of students that attended each lecture.

3 Solve

Draw and label three overlapping circles. In the section where all the circles overlap, place a 4 because 4 students attended all the lectures. In each section where only two circles overlap, place the number of students that went to both those two lectures. Calculate the number of students that went to only one lecture by taking the number of students that attended each lecture and subtracting the number that also attended other lectures. The sum of the numbers in each circle should be the total number of students that attended that lecture.

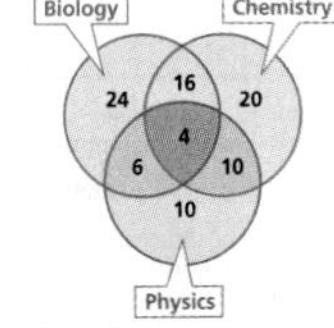

The total number of students is the sum of the numbers in all the circles. Therefore, the number of students is $24 + 6 + 10 + 16 + 4 + 10 + 20 = 90$.

4 Look Back

Check your Venn diagram against the initial data to make certain that the diagram agrees with the question asked.

PRACTICE

1. In summer school the math courses offered were Algebra, Geometry, and Calculus. Three students took all three courses, 5 students took only Algebra and Geometry, 1 student took only Calculus and Geometry, and 10 students took only Algebra and Calculus. If there were 28 students in Algebra, 24 students in Geometry, and 30 students in Calculus, how many students took at least one math course? 60

Make an Organized List

When you are solving a problem that contains a lot of information, it may be helpful to make an organized list to record the possible outcomes.

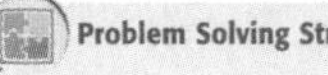

Problem Solving Strategies

Draw a Diagram	Make a Table
Make a Model	Solve a Simpler Problem
Guess and Test	Use Logical Reasoning
Work Backward	Use a Venn Diagram
Find a Pattern	**Make an Organized List**

EXAMPLE

Pete's Pizza has four toppings to choose from: pepperoni, ham, extra cheese, and mushrooms. How many possible pizzas are there if you can have 0, 1, 2, 3, or 4 toppings and cannot get the same topping twice?

1 Understand the Problem

List the important information.

- There are 4 possible toppings.
- A pizza can have 0 to 4 toppings.
- You cannot have the same topping twice.

The answer will be the number of pizzas that are possible.

2 Make a Plan

Make an organized list of the possible combinations of toppings. List all the possible combinations.

3 Solve

Make a column for each number of toppings on the pizza. Let P = pepperoni, H = ham, C = extra cheese, and M = mushrooms.

0 Toppings	1 Topping	2 Toppings	3 Toppings	4 Toppings
Plain Cheese	P	PH	PHC	PHCM
	H	PC	PHM	
	C	PM	PCM	
	M	HC	HCM	
		HM		
		CM		

Adding the number of choices yields 16 possible pizzas.

4 Look Back

Make sure all the possible choices are shown in the table and that none repeat.

PRACTICE

1. Pete's Pizza has decided that customers may repeat toppings but choose no more than a total of two toppings per pizza. How many pizzas are now possible? 15
2. Calvin has a bag with 5 balls inside. The balls are all distinct and labeled A through E. How many three-letter "words" can he create by randomly removing a ball and not replacing it? (Consider a word to be any permutation of three letters.) 60
3. Matty is going to run some errands. She may stop by the cleaners, the video store, and the grocery store. If she plans to make at least 1 stop, how many possible routes can she take? 15

Problem-Solving Handbook

Skills Bank

Skills Bank

Estimation

You can use estimation to find approximate values and determine whether your answers are reasonable.

EXAMPLE 1 **Estimate 4218 + 788.**

Round each value to a number that is easy to add.

$4218 + 788 \approx 4200 + 800 = 5000$ *Round 4218 to 4200 and 788 to 800. Add.*

4128 + 788 is about 5000.

EXAMPLE 2 **Estimate 157 ÷ 28.**

Round each value to a number that is easy to divide and will leave no remainder.

$157 \div 28 \approx 150 \div 30 = 5$ *Round 157 to 150 and 29 to 30. Divide.*

157 ÷ 28 is about 5.

PRACTICE

Estimate. Possible answers:

1. 12.616 + 16.791 30
2. 11,624 + 396 12,000
3. 32.56 + 108.44 140
4. 12.84 − 6.11 7
5. 6581 − 477 6000
6. 533 − 29.1 500
7. 106 · 69 7000
8. 5.23 · 14.86 75
9. 215 · 19 4000
10. 7.86 ÷ 1.94 4
11. 18,274 ÷ 1011 18
12. 561 ÷ 47 11

Percent Increase and Decrease

Percent change is an increase or decrease given as a percent of the original amount. Percent increase describes an amount that has grown. Percent decrease describes an amount that has been reduced.

EXAMPLE 1 **Find the percent increase or decrease from 24 to 31.2.**

$$\frac{\text{amount of change}}{\text{original amount}} = \frac{31.2 - 24}{24} = \frac{7.2}{24} = 0.3 = 30\%$$

From 24 to 31.2 is a 30% increase.

EXAMPLE 2 **Find the percent increase or decrease from 8.2 to 6.97.**

$$\frac{\text{amount of change}}{\text{original amount}} = \frac{8.2 - 6.97}{8.2} = \frac{1.23}{8.2} = 0.15 = 15\%$$

From 8.2 to 6.97 is a 15% decrease.

PRACTICE

Find each percent increase or decrease.

1. from 36 to 43.2 20% increase
2. from 100 to 19 81% decrease
3. from 5.5 to 7.26 32% increase
4. from 42 to 39.9 5% decrease
5. from 220 to 327.8 49% increase
6. from 9 to 10.35 15% increase
7. from 0.66 to 0.594 10% decrease
8. from 78 to 25.74 67% decrease
9. from 685 to 506.9 26% decrease
10. from 11 to 12.43 13% increase
11. from 1.54 to 2.31 50% increase
12. from 51 to 13.77 73% decrease

Accuracy, Precision, and Error

The accuracy of a measurement refers to how close the measurement is to the actual value of the quantity. The precision of a measurement refers to the number of significant digits in the measured value. Use relative error to make judgments about measurements. Recall that relative error $= \frac{\text{measurement} - \text{actual value}}{\text{actual value}}$.

EXAMPLE **A 1.29-foot-long object was measured as both 1.23 feet and 1.3 feet. Which measurement was more accurate? Which was more precise?**

Calculate the relative errors.

$$\text{Error for 1.23 ft} = \frac{1.23\text{ ft} - 1.29\text{ ft}}{1.29\text{ ft}} \approx -0.465 \approx -4.65\%$$

$$\text{Error for 1.3 ft} = \frac{1.3\text{ ft} - 1.29\text{ ft}}{1.29\text{ ft}} \approx 0.00775 \approx 0.775\%$$

The 1.3 ft measurement is more accurate because its relative error has a smaller magnitude. The 1.23 ft measurement is more precise because it is measured to more decimal places.

PRACTICE

Determine which measurements are more accurate and which are more precise.

1. measurements: 12.56 in. and 12.7 in.
   actual: 12.66 in.
   12.7 in. is more accurate. 12.56 in. is more precise.
2. measurements: 4.0 m and 4.24 m
   actual: 4.19 m
   4.24 m is more accurate and more precise.
3. measurements: 0.67 s and 0.79 s
   actual: 0.73 s
   The measurements are equally precise and accurate.
4. measurements: 155 lb and 160 lb
   actual: 158 lb
   160 lb is more accurate. 155 lb is more precise.

Dimensional Analysis and Unit Conversions

Use unit conversion factors to change one unit of measure to another. Dimensional analysis requires choosing the appropriate conversion factor.

EXAMPLE **Convert 5 m/s to km/h.**

Use conversion factors relating meters to kilometers and seconds to hours. There are 1000 meters in a kilometer, so the conversion factor is $\frac{1\text{ km}}{1000\text{ m}}$. There are 60 seconds in a minute and 60 minutes in an hour, so the conversion factor is $\frac{3600\text{ s}}{1\text{ h}}$.

$$\left(5\frac{\text{m}}{\text{s}}\right)\left(\frac{1\text{ km}}{1000\text{ m}}\right)\left(\frac{3600\text{ s}}{1\text{ h}}\right) = 18\text{ km/h}$$ *Multiply by the conversion factors.*

A speed of 5 m/s is equivalent to 18 km/h.

PRACTICE

Convert.

1. 19 ft/h to mi/s ≈ 0.000001 mi/s
2. 3.65 m^2/yr to m^2/day ≈ 0.01 m^2/day
3. 9.8 m/s^2 to ft/s^2 ≈ 32.2 ft/s^2
4. 12 mL/s to L/h ≈ 43.2 L/h
5. 6552 in. to yd 182 yd
6. 9 gal to pt 72 pt
7. 11,232 s to h 3.12 h
8. 792 ft^2 to in^2 114,048 in^2
9. 484 mg to kg 0.000484 kg
10. 18 in./day to mi/yr ≈ 0.10 mi/yr

Measure Angles

You can use a protractor to measure angles. Be sure to use the correct scale on the protractor when reading an angle's measure.

EXAMPLE **Find the measure of the angle by using a protractor.**

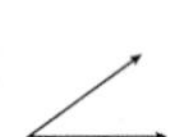

The angle measures 35°.

PRACTICE

Find the measure of each angle by using a protractor.

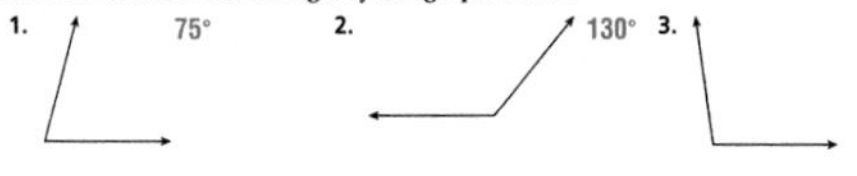

1. 75°
2. 130°
3. 98°

Parallel Lines and Transversals

If two parallel lines are intersected by a transversal, the angle pairs shown below are congruent.

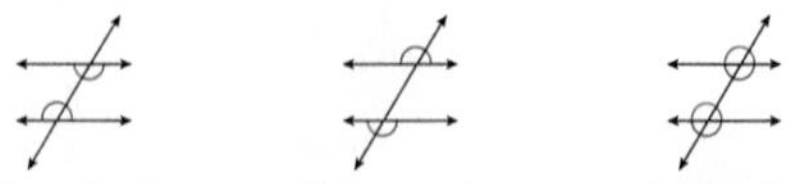

Alternate interior Alternate exterior Corresponding

EXAMPLE **In the figure, line *m* is parallel to line *n*. Name three angles that are congruent to ∠1. Justify your answers.**

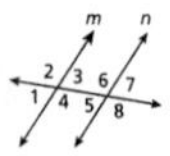

∠7: ∠1 and ∠7 are alternate exterior angles.

∠5: ∠1 and ∠5 are corresponding angles.

∠3: ∠1 ≅ ∠7, and ∠7 and ∠3 are corresponding angles.

PRACTICE

In the figure, line *s* is parallel to line *t*. Name three angles that are congruent to each given angle. Justify your answers.

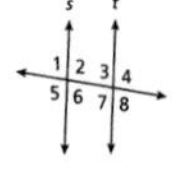

1. ∠2
   ∠7: ∠2 and ∠7 are alternate interior angles; ∠4: ∠2 and ∠4 are corresponding angles; ∠5: ∠2 ≅ ∠7, and ∠7 and ∠5 are corresponding angles.
2. ∠8
   ∠1: ∠8 and ∠1 are alternate exterior angles; ∠6: ∠8 and ∠6 are corresponding angles; ∠3: ∠8 ≅ ∠1, and ∠1 and ∠3 are corresponding angles.

Angle Relationships

Complementary angles are two angles whose measures add to 90°. **Supplementary angles** are two angles whose measures add to 180°.

Vertical angles are a pair of opposite angles formed by intersecting lines. Vertical angles are congruent. **Adjacent angles** have a common vertex, a common side, and do not overlap.

In the figure shown, ∠1 and ∠3 are vertical angles, and ∠2 and ∠4 are vertical angles. Two angles adjacent to ∠1 are ∠2 and ∠4.

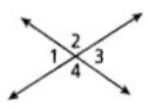

EXAMPLE

A **Name two angles adjacent to ∠*CFD*.**

∠*BFC* *∠CFD and ∠BFC share vertex F and side $\overrightarrow{FC}$.*

∠*EFD* *∠CFD and ∠EFD share vertex F and side $\overrightarrow{FD}$.*

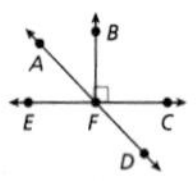

B **If m∠*CFD* = 43°, find m∠*AFB*.**

m∠*AFE* = 43° *∠AFE and ∠CFD are vertical angles and are congruent.*

m∠*EFB* = 90° *∠EFB is supplementary to ∠BFC, and m∠BFC = 90°.*

m∠*AFE* + m∠*AFB* = m∠*EFB* *If point A is in the interior of ∠EFB, then m∠AFE + m∠AFB = m∠EFB.*

43° + m∠*AFB* = 90° *Substitute.*

m∠*AFB* = 47° *Solve for m∠AFB.*

PRACTICE

Find the measure of the complement of an angle with each given measure.

1. 23° 67°
2. 16° 74°
3. 42° 48°
4. 87° 3°
5. 35° 55°

Find the measure of the supplement of an angle with each given measure.

6. 120° 60°
7. 74° 106°
8. 94° 86°
9. 27° 153°
10. 156° 24°

Use the figure for Exercises 11–13.

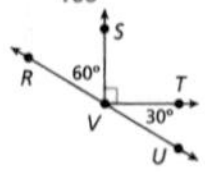

11. Name two angles adjacent to ∠*RVS*.
    Possible answer: ∠SVT and ∠SVU
12. Name a pair of complementary angles.
    ∠RVS and ∠TVU
13. Name two pairs of supplementary angles.
    ∠RVS and ∠SVU; ∠RVT and ∠TVU

In the figure, m∠*JQK* = 38°. Find each angle measure.

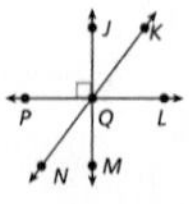

14. m∠*PQK* 128°
15. m∠*MQN* 38°
16. m∠*KQL* 52°
17. m∠*NQP* 52°
18. m∠*LQM* 90°
19. m∠*KQM* 142°
20. Name two angles adjacent to ∠*KQL*.
    Possible answer: ∠JQK and ∠LQM
21. Name two pairs of vertical angles.
    Possible answer: ∠JQK and ∠MQN; ∠KQL and ∠NQP
22. Name a pair of complementary angles.
    Possible answer: ∠JQK and ∠KQL

Mean, Median, Mode, and Range

The **mean** of a data set is the sum divided by the number of values. The **median** is the middle value in a numerically ordered set. The **mode** is the value or values that occur most often. The **range** is the difference between the greatest and the least values.

EXAMPLE **Find the mean, median, mode, and range of the data.** $\{4, 6, 1, 6, 2, 7, 8, 2, 7, 2\}$

Mean: Add all the values and divide by the number of values.

$\text{mean} = \frac{45}{10} = 4.5$ *The sum is 45. There are 10 values.*

Median: First, order the values from least to greatest. $\{1, 2, 2, 2, 4, 6, 6, 7, 7, 8\}$

$\text{median} = \frac{4+6}{2} = 5$ *Since there are an even number of values, 10, the median is the average of the 5th and 6th values.*

Mode: Find the value that repeats the most. $\{1, 2, 2, 2, 4, 6, 6, 7, 7, 8\}$

$\text{mode} = 2$ *The value 2 occurs most often.*

Range: Find the difference between the largest and smallest value: range $= 8 - 1 = 7$

PRACTICE

Find the mean, median, mode, and range of each data set.

1. $\{5, 1, 5\}$ mean: $3\frac{2}{3}$; median: 5; mode: 5; range: 4
2. $\{7, 5, 3, 25\}$ mean: 10; median: 6; no mode; range: 22
3. $\{2, 0, 0, 3, 0, 1, 0\}$ mean: $\frac{6}{7}$; median: 0; mode: 0; range: 3
4. $\{15, 17, 171, 4, 0, 15, 2, 4\}$ mean: $28\frac{1}{2}$; median: $9\frac{1}{2}$; modes: 4 and 15; range: 171

Data Displays

Stem-and-leaf plots group the data by place value. Box-and-whisker plots show the least and greatest values, the median, the first quartile (the median of the lower half of the data), and the third quartile (the median of the upper half of the data).

EXAMPLE **Use the data.** $\{45, 47, 39, 30, 29, 37, 10, 50, 28, 49, 47, 36, 39, 28, 44\}$

A Draw a stem-and-leaf plot of the data.

Sort the data:

10, 28, 28, 29, 30, 36, 37, 39, 39, 44, 45, 47, 47, 49, 50

The stems represent the tens digit, and the leaves represent the ones digit—the number 10 is shown in red.

Stems	Leaves
1	0
2	8 8 9
3	0 6 7 9 9
4	4 5 7 7 9
5	0

B Draw a box-and-whisker plot of the data.

The least value is 10; the greatest value is 50; the median is 39; the first quartile is 29 (the median of 10, 28, 28, 29, 30, 36, and 37); and the upper quartile is 47.

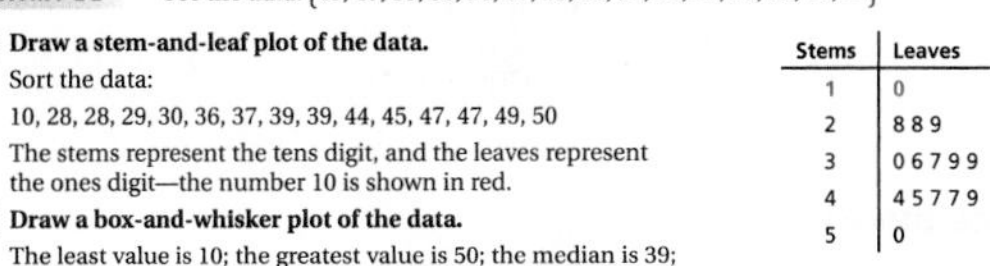
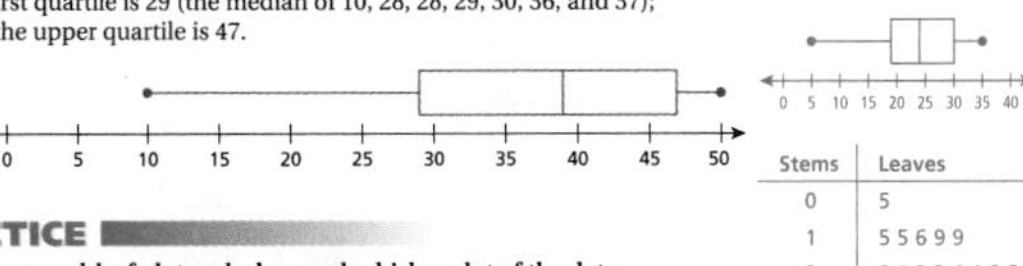

PRACTICE

Draw a stem-and-leaf plot and a box-and-whisker plot of the data.

1. $\{35, 30, 21, 19, 15, 29, 28, 15, 24, 20, 34, 30, 23, 29, 16, 19, 24, 28, 31, 33, 22, 5\}$

0 5 10 15 20 25 30 35 40

Stems	Leaves
0	5
1	5 5 6 9 9
2	0 1 2 3 4 4 8 8 9 9
3	0 0 1 3 4 5

Statistical Graphs

Statistical graphs include bar graphs, circle graphs, and line graphs. Bar graphs compare numerical amounts; circle graphs compare parts of a whole; and line graphs show changes in data, such as over time.

EXAMPLE **Make a line graph of the data.**

Year	2006	2007	2008	2009	2010	2011
Sales (million $)	5.2	4.9	6.8	7.1	12.9	11.4

Use "Year" evenly spaced on the horizontal axis and use "Sales (million $)" on the vertical axis. The vertical axis should go from 0 to at least 12.9 to accommodate all the data.

Total Sales

Sales (million $)
12 10 8 6 4 2 0
2006 2007 2008 2009 2010 2011
Year

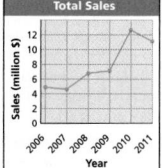

PRACTICE

1. Draw a bar graph and a circle graph of the data. See p. A65.

Students in 11th-Grade Classrooms						
Classroom	A	B	C	D	E	Total
Students	21	28	17	30	24	120

Sampling Methods and Bias

There are several sampling methods you can use when collecting a random sample of data from a population.

Random Sampling	Each member of the population has an equal chance of being selected.
Systematic Sampling	A rule or formula is used, such as surveying every nth person.
Stratified Sampling	The population is divided into groups, and then sampling is done within each group.

These sampling techniques are designed to reduce the **bias** in taking surveys. Bias is any factor that prevents an accurate representation of the population. Systematic and stratified sampling may or may not be random.

EXAMPLE **Hal asks every third person wearing a blue shirt for their favorite color. Identify the sampling method and explain whether the survey is biased.**

Surveying every third person is systematic sampling but is not random. The survey is biased because people wearing blue shirts might have a greater probability of liking blue than the rest of the population.

PRACTICE

Identify the sampling method or methods and explain whether the survey is biased.

1. Lisa asks the first 10 boys and the first 10 girls who arrive at school in the morning what method of transportation they take to get to school.

1. Stratified and systematic sampling; biased because early arrivals will likely use different forms of transportation than late arrivals

Pascal's Triangle

Pascal's triangle is a triangle of numbers.

- Each row has one more number than the row above it.
- Each number is the sum of the two numbers directly to the left and right above it.
- The first and last numbers of a row are each 1.
- Each row is symmetric.

Row 0 →	1
Row 1 →	1 1
Row 2 →	1 2 1
Row 3 →	1 3 □ 1
Row 4 →	1 4 □ □ 1
Row 5 →	1 5 10 □ 5 1

EXAMPLE **Find the missing number in row 3.**

Method 1 Add the two numbers above it in row 2.

Row 2 → 1 2 1
Row 3 → 1 3 [3] 1

Method 2 Since the row is symmetric, it is the same as the second term in row 3.

Row 3 → 1 3 → [3] 1

PRACTICE

1. Complete the first 5 rows above.
2. Part of Pascal's triangle is shown. Find the missing number. 252

   120 210 □
   330 462 462

3. Find the first two numbers in row 27. 1; 27
4. The third number in row 12 is 220. Find the last three numbers in row 12. 220; 12; 1
5. What row gives the coefficients of $(x + 1)^2$ when written in standard form? row 2

1.
1
1 1
1 2 1
1 3 3 1
1 4 6 4 1
1 5 10 10 5 1

Exponents in Probability Formulas

If the probability of an event p is always the same, the probability that it occurs 3 times in succession is $p \cdot p \cdot p$, or p^3. The probability P that it occurs n times in succession is p^n.

EXAMPLE **What is the probability of getting 3 tails in a row when flipping a coin?**

$P = p^n$ *Write the probability formula.*

$P = 0.5^3$ *Substitute 0.5 for p and 3 for n.*

$P = 0.125$

The probability of getting 3 tails in a row is 0.125.

PRACTICE

1. Find P if $p = 0.7$ and $n = 4$. 0.2401
2. There is a 60% chance Cal will get home on time each day. What is the probability he will get home on time all 5 days this week? 0.07776
3. What is the probability of getting 2 ones in a row when rolling a number cube twice? $\frac{1}{36}$

Proofs

A proof is an argument that uses logic to show that a conclusion is true. There are several different techniques that you can use to prove a conclusion is true.

The goal in a proof is to reach a statement that is either always or never true and either confirms or contradicts the desired conclusion.

EXAMPLE 1 **Prove $(x-3)(x+2) = x^2 - x - 6$.**

Begin with $(x-3)(x+2)$ and multiply to show it equals $x^2 - x - 6$.

$$\begin{aligned}(x-3)(x+2) &= x \cdot x + (-3) \cdot x + 2 \cdot x + (-3) \cdot 2 \\ &= x^2 - 3x + 2x - 6 \\ &= x^2 - x - 6 \checkmark\end{aligned}$$

EXAMPLE 2 **Prove $(x-3)(x-1) = (x-2)^2 - 1$.**

Simplify each side to obtain equivalent expressions.

Left Side	Right Side
$(x-3)(x-1)$	$(x-2)^2 - 1$
$x^2 - 3x - x + 3$	$x^2 - 2x - 2x + 4 - 1$
$x^2 - 4x + 3$	$x^2 - 4x + 3$

$(x-3)(x-1) = x^2 - 4x + 3 = (x-2)^2 - 1 \checkmark$

EXAMPLE 3 **Disprove $x(x-4) + 4 = (x+1)(x-5)$.**

Assume that $x(x-4) + 4 = (x+1)(x-5)$. Then simplify.

$$\begin{aligned}x(x-4) + 4 &= (x+1)(x-5) \\ x^2 - 4x + 4 &= x^2 - 4x - 5 \\ -4x + 4 &= -4x - 5 && \textit{Subtract } x^2 \textit{ from both sides.} \\ 4 &= -5 ✗ && \textit{Add 4x to both sides.}\end{aligned}$$

Since $4 \neq -5$, the assumption must be false.

$x(x-4) + 4 \neq (x+1)(x-5)$

PRACTICE

Prove or disprove each statement.

1. $(a+b)^3 = a^3 + 3a^2b + 3ab^2 + b^3$
2. $(x+1)^3 = (x^3+1) + 3x(x+1)$
3. $\frac{1}{x+2} + \frac{1}{x-2} = \frac{2x}{x^2-4}$
4. $\sqrt{4x^6} = \sqrt[3]{8x^9}$, where $x \geq 0$
5. $(x+4)^2 = x^2 + 8x + 8$
6. $x^2(x+1) + 3(x-1) = x(x^2+3) + (x-2)(x+2)$
7. $(x+2)(x+8) = (x+5)^2 - 9$
8. $(x+1)(x-6)(x+7) = x^3 + 2x^2 - 41x - 42$

Possible answers:

1. $(a+b)^3 = (a+b)(a+b)(a+b)$
$= (a^2 + 2ab + b^2)(a+b)$
$= a^3 + 3a^2b + 3ab^2 + b^3$

2.

Left Side	Right Side
$(x+1)^3$	$(x^3+1) + 3x(x+1)$
$x^3 + 3x^2 + 3x + 1$	$x^3 + 3x^2 + 3x + 1$

3. $\frac{1}{x+2} + \frac{1}{x-2}$
$= \frac{x-2}{(x+2)(x-2)} + \frac{x+2}{(x+2)(x-2)}$
$= \frac{2x}{x^2-4}$

4.

Left Side	Right Side
$\sqrt{4x^6}$	$\sqrt[3]{8x^9}$
$2x^3$	$2x^3$

5. Assume $(x+4)^2 = x^2 + 8x + 8$.
$(x+4)^2 = x^2 + 8x + 8$
$x^2 + 8x + 16 = x^2 + 8x + 8$
$16 = 8$ ✗
$(x+4)^2 \neq x^2 + 8x + 8$

6. Assume $x^2(x+1) + 3(x-1) = x(x^2+3) + (x-2)(x+2)$.
$x^2(x+1) + 3(x-1) = x(x^2+3) + (x-2)(x+2)$
$x^3 + x^2 + 3x - 3 = x^3 + 3x + x^2 - 4$
$-3 = -4$ ✗
$x^2(x+1) + 3(x-1) \neq x(x^2+3) + (x-2)(x+2)$

7, 8. See p. A65.

Logical Reasoning and Conditional Statements

Logical reasoning is a process of making conclusions based upon given information. When using logical reasoning it is sometimes best to write the given information as conditional statements. A conditional statement is a statement that can be written in the form "if p, then q," where p is the hypothesis and q is the conclusion.

EXAMPLE **Use logical reasoning to draw a conclusion from the given premises. If Aaron joins the baseball team, then Brandon will join the team. If Brandon joins the baseball team, then Corey will not join the team. Aaron joins the baseball team.**

Because Aaron joins the team, Brandon also joins. Because Brandon joins the team, Corey will not join. Conclusion: Corey does not join the team.

PRACTICE

Use logical reasoning to draw a conclusion from the given premises.

1. If it is raining, then the sun does not shine. It is raining.
   The sun does not shine.
2. If it is Friday, then we go out for dinner. If we go out for dinner, then we eat pasta. It is Friday.
   We eat pasta.
3. If a quadrilateral is a square, then it has 4 right angles. If a quadrilateral has 4 right angles, then it is a rectangle.
   If a quadrilateral is a square, then it is a rectangle.

Venn Diagrams

A Venn diagram is used to show relationships between sets.

EXAMPLE **Draw a Venn diagram of the relationships between the following sets:**
A: factors of 20 **B: factors of 75** **C: factors of 18**

Find the elements of each set:

A: $\{1, 2, 4, 5, 10, 20\}$ B: $\{1, 3, 5, 15, 25, 75\}$ C: $\{1, 2, 3, 6, 9, 18\}$

Draw three overlapping circles. Label one circle for each set. Place each element in the appropriate circle or overlapping region.

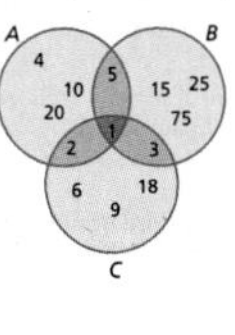

1. 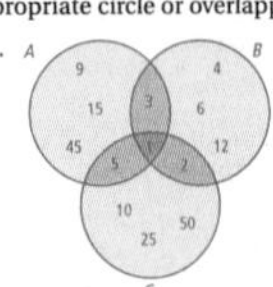

2. 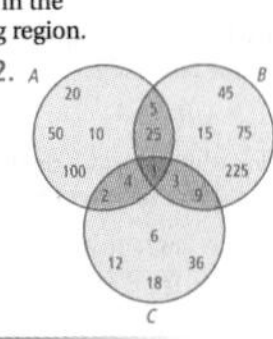

PRACTICE

Draw a Venn diagram for each of the following sets.

1. Set A: factors of 45 Set B: factors of 12 Set C: factors of 50
2. Set A: factors of 100 Set B: factors of 225 Set C: factors of 36

Graph Theory: Euler and Hamiltonian Paths

A vertex-edge graph is a set of points, or vertices, that are connected by a set of lines, or edges. If you trace through the graph from vertex to vertex along the edges, you create a path.

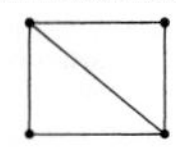

An Euler path includes every edge in the graph exactly once. Not every graph has an Euler path.

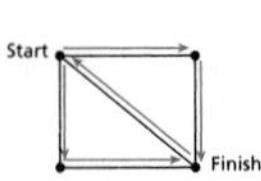

A Hamiltonian path includes every vertex in the graph exactly once. Not every graph has a Hamiltonian path.

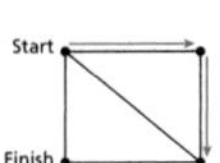

EXAMPLE **Find an Euler path and a Hamiltonian path for the graph, if possible.**

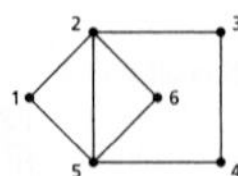

Try the vertices in sequence. To complete the path, revisit vertices 2, 5, and 1. This is an Euler path.

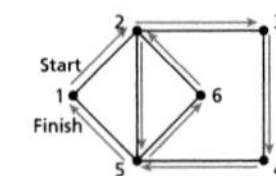

Try the vertices in sequence. Stop at vertex 6. This is a Hamiltonian path.

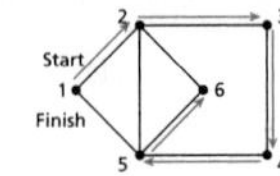

PRACTICE

Find an Euler path and a Hamiltonian path for each graph, if possible.

1. 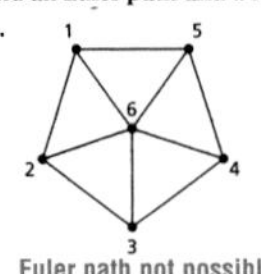

Euler path not possible; Hamiltonian path: 1-2-3-4-5-6

2. 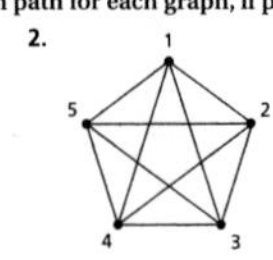

Euler path: 1-2-3-4-5-1-3-5-2-4-1; Hamiltonian path: 1-2-3-4-5

3. 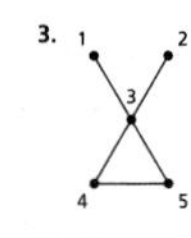

Euler path: 1-3-4-5-3-2; Hamiltonian path not possible

Selected Answers

Selected Answers

Chapter 1

1-1

Check It Out! 1a. $-2, -\sqrt{3}, -0.321, \frac{3}{2}, \pi$ b. −2: ℝ, ℚ, ℤ; $-\sqrt{3}$: ℝ, irrational; −0.321: ℝ, ℚ; $\frac{3}{2}$: ℝ, ℚ; π: ℝ, irrational 2a. $(-\infty, -1]$ b. $(-\infty, 2]$ or $(3, 11]$ 3a. even numbers between 1 and 9 b. {3, 4, 5, 6, 7} c. $\{x \mid x \geq 99\}$

Exercises 1. roster notation 3. $-\frac{100}{4}, -6.897, \frac{1}{8}, \sqrt{4}, \sqrt{6}$; $-\frac{100}{4}$: ℝ, ℚ, ℤ; −6.897: ℝ, ℚ; $\frac{1}{8}$: ℝ, ℚ; $\sqrt{4}$: ℝ, ℚ, ℤ, W, ℕ; $\sqrt{6}$: ℝ, irrational 5. $(-10, 10]$ 7. $[1, 20)$ or $(30, \infty)$ 9. $\{x \mid -5 \leq x < 3\}$ 11. {−5, −4, −3, −2, −1, 0, 1, 2, 3, 4, 5} 13. $-2, -\sqrt{2}, -1.\overline{25}, \frac{\sqrt{2}}{3}, \frac{1}{2}$; −2: ℝ, ℚ, ℤ; $-\sqrt{2}$: ℝ, irrational; $-1.\overline{25}$: ℝ, ℚ; $\frac{\sqrt{2}}{3}$: ℝ, irrational; $\frac{1}{2}$: ℝ, ℚ 15. $(-\infty, 5)$ or $(5, \infty)$ 17. $[-3, 3]$ 19. {11, 22, 33, 44, 55, 66, 77, ...} 21. $\{x \mid -9 \leq x \leq -1$ and x is odd$\}$ 23. ℚ 27. numbers greater than or equal to −4 and less than 8; cannot be expressed in roster notation; $\{x \mid -4 \leq x < 8\}$ 29. numbers greater than 0 and less than 1; cannot be expressed in roster notation; $(0, 1)$ 31. $(-\infty, 2)$ or $(2, \infty)$; $\{x \mid x \neq 2\}$ 33. $(1, 10)$; $\{x \mid 1 < x < 10\}$ 35. $(-\infty, 5)$ or $(5, 10]$; $\{x \mid x < 5$ or $5 < x \leq 10\}$ 37. false 39. true 41. $\{x \mid 11 \leq x \leq 12\}$; $\{x \mid 12 \leq x \leq 13\}$; $\{x \mid 14 \leq x \leq 16\}$ 45. $(-\infty, -1]$ or $(3, 6)$ or $[9, \infty)$ 47. −2 0 2 4 6 8 10 12 49. −2 −1 0 1 2 3 4 5 51. −3 −2 −1 0 1 2 3 4 53. N 55. W 57a. interior designer, police officer, pediatric nurse, marine biologist, astronaut b. The order would not change. c. The order would not change. d. {46,000, 52,900, 59,800, 79,350, 106,950} 63. D 65. B 67. finite; ℚ 69. finite; ℚ, ℤ, W, ℕ 75. \$20, \$20, and \$10

1-2

Check It Out! 1a. $-500; \frac{1}{500}$ b. 0.01; −100 2a. Commutative Property of Multiplication b. Associative Property of Multiplication 3. \$3.12 4a. always true by the Additive Inverse Property b. sometimes true; possible answer: true when $a = 0$, $b = 1$, and $c = 2$; false when $a = 1$, $b = 2$, and $c = 3$

Exercises 1. 36; $-\frac{1}{36}$ 3. $-2\sqrt{2}$; $\frac{1}{2\sqrt{2}}$ 5. $\frac{1}{500}$; −500 7. Associative Property of Multiplication 9. Commutative Property of Multiplication 11. \$7.33 13. sometimes true 15. 2.5; $-\frac{2}{5}$ 17. -2π; $\frac{1}{2\pi}$ 19. $-\frac{1}{20}$; 20 21. Distributive Property 23. Additive Identity Property 25. \$9.80 27. never true by the Multiplicative Inverse Property 29. $4(11.99) - 2(8.88) = \$30.20$ 31. $3(0.9)(9.96) + 5(0.75)(11.99) = 71.8545 \approx \$71.85$ 33. ≈ 2 loops 35. 5; Associative Property of Addition 37. 0; Additive Identity Property 39. $\frac{5}{4}$; Multiplicative Inverse Property 41. yes 45. Multiplicative Identity Property 47. Distributive Property; Associative Property of Addition 49. Distributive Property 53. D 55. C 57. $n = 2$ 59. 66.7% 61. $-4\sqrt{2}$ 63. $(-10, 0]$ 65. cannot be notated

1-3

Check It Out! 1. −7.4 2a. $4\sqrt{3}$ b. $\frac{3}{2}$ c. 10 d. 7 3a. $\frac{3\sqrt{35}}{7}$ b. $\frac{\sqrt{10}}{2}$ 4a. $13\sqrt{5}$ b. $-\sqrt{5}$

Exercises 1. radicand 3. 4.5 5. 3.6 7. 12 9. $4\sqrt{5}$ 11. $-5\sqrt{2}$ 13. $-\frac{\sqrt{7}}{7}$ 15. $5\sqrt{2}$ 17. $\sqrt{2}$ 19. −3.9 21. 9.9 23. $-\frac{1}{11}$ 25. $-8\sqrt{5}$ 27. $5\sqrt{17}$ 29. $-3\sqrt{21}$ 31. $\frac{9\sqrt{2}}{4}$ 33. $\frac{\sqrt{3}}{30}$ 35. $7\sqrt{7}$ 37. $23\sqrt{3}$ 39. $8\sqrt{7}$ 41. $-3\sqrt{6}$ 43. 33.9 cm 45. 99.0 in. 47. about 50 in. by 50 in. 49. 180 51. $2\sqrt{5} - 5\sqrt{2}$ 53. $\frac{3\sqrt{35} + \sqrt{5}}{5}$ 55. $\frac{16\sqrt{10}}{5}$ 57. 600 ft by 600 ft 59. 7467.3 ft 61. 8167.7 ft 63. always true 65. no 67a. ≈ 7.81 s 67b. ≈ 3.20 s 69. H 71. 8.9 73a. 6 in.; $6\sqrt{5}$ in. b. 54 in² c. $18 + 6\sqrt{2} + 6\sqrt{5}$ in. 75. tetrahedron or triangular pyramid 77. triangular prism 79. $1.5 < x < 8$ 81. $\frac{3}{4} < x < \frac{5}{2}$ 83. Commutative Property of Addition 85. Distributive Property

1-4

Check It Out! 1a. $18 + y$ b. $3600h$ 2. −15 3. $-6x - 8xy - 9y$ 4a. $8000 - 30h$ b. \$7160

Exercises 1. $0.79c$ 3. 9 5. $-12a + 9$ 7. $1 + 5ab - 25a - b^2$ 9. $(180 - x)°$ 11. −18 13. 115 15. $3x - 12y + 2$ 17. $5 - 3m - 2n$ 19a. $500 - 20m$ b. 460 min or 7 h 40 min 21. $5g^2 - 6g + 1$; 28 23. $\frac{a^2 - 2b^2 + 2a}{2 + a}$; −7 25.

x	$(x-4)^2$	x^2+16	$x^2-8x+16$
1	9	17	9
0	4	20	4
2	1	25	1
4	0	32	0

$(x - 4)^2 = x^2 - 8x + 16$ 27. $7a + 4b$ 29a. $4125 - 175d$ b. \$3250 c. They save \$175 per day. 31. $y = -40$; $y = -25$; $y = -7$; $y = -5$; $y = -10$ 33. $y = 7$; $y = 15$; $y = 1$; $y = -13$; $y = -5$ 37. G 39. $a = 8$ 41. $a = 22$ 43a. 4; undefined; −48; undefined; 36; $\frac{147}{8}$ b. $x = 1$ and $x = 3$ c. $\{x \mid x \neq 1$ and $x \neq 3\}$ 45. square pyramid 47. ℚ 49. irrational 51. $3\sqrt{6}$ 53. 14

1-5

Check It Out! 1a. $(2a)(2a)(2a)(2a)(2a)$ b. $3 \cdot b \cdot b \cdot b \cdot b$ c. $-(2x - 1)(2x - 1)(2x - 1) \cdot y \cdot y$ 2a. 9 b. $-\frac{1}{3125}$ 3a. $125x^{18}$ b. $-\frac{1}{8a^9b^3}$ 4a. 2.5×10^{-4} b. 1.24×10^{-9} 5. ≈ 8.33 min

Exercises 3. $(12xy)(12xy)(12xy)(12xy)$ 5. $\left(-\frac{1}{2}d\right)\left(-\frac{1}{2}d\right)\left(-\frac{1}{2}d\right)$ 7. 1 9. $\frac{1}{10}$ 11. cd^6 13. $\frac{10y^{10}}{x^4}$ 15. $-4m^4n^6$ 17. $\frac{y^3}{x^4}$ 19. 3×10^{11} 21. 400 23. $5 \cdot x \cdot x \cdot x$ 25. $2a(-b^2 - a)(-b^2 - a)$ 27. $-\frac{4}{3}$ 29. −1 31. $-x^{20}y^{10}$ 33. $-16a^5b^7$ 35. 1.5×10^9 37. 1.55 min 39. $2^6, 2^2, 2^5, 2^{-8}; 16^{-2}, 4^1, 2^5, 8^2$ 41. $-2^6, 2^0, 2^4, 2^{-2}; -8^2, 2^{-2}, 4^0, 16^1$ 43. $3m^5n^4$ 45. $\frac{3x}{2y^3}$ 47. $-24a^5b^7$ 49. $\frac{9m^2}{25n^2}$ 51. 1296 53. 1728 55a. 3742 km/h b. ≈ 288,609 times as fast c. ≈ 1.28 s 57. $-\frac{7x^3}{4y^2}$ 59. $\frac{100}{x^4z^6}$ 61. $\frac{8m^4}{n^2}$ 63. Laos; 25.6 65. Vietnam; 615.6 67. ≈ 2.84×10^9 beats 69. ≈ 1.27×10^5 hairs 71. Power of a Product Property or Power of a Power Property 73. Power of a Quotient Property or Power of a Power Property 77. 6.5×10^{-15} 79. 3.5×10^{14} 81. 1.1346×10^{24} 83. C 85. C 87. ≈ 2.0363×10^{-4} 91. $\frac{1}{3}$ 93. 8 95. $-\frac{1}{3}$

1-6

Check It Out! 1. D: {−2, −1, 0, 1, 2, 3}; R: {−3, −2, −1, 0, 1, 2} 2a. function b. not a function 3a. function b. not a function; (1, 2) and (1, −2)

Exercises 1. range 3. D: {2000, 2001, 2002, 2003}; R: {5.39, 5.65, 5.80, 6.03} 5. not a function 7. function 9. D: {Irene, Anna, Lea, Kate}; R: {12, 16, 22} 11. function 13. not a function 15. function 17. D: {−2, −1, 0, 1, 2}; R: {−2, 0, 2} 19. D: {jumbo, extra large, large, medium}; R: {1.75, 2, 2.25, 2.5} 21a. function b. function c. not a function d. function e. not a function 23. D: {a, b, c, d}; R: {1, 2, 4}; function 25. D: {1, 3, 5, 7, 9}; R: {3}; function 27. D: {3, 4, 5, 6, 7}; R: {−1, 2, 3}; function 29. D: {Monday, Tuesday, Wednesday, Thursday, Friday, Saturday, Sunday}; R: {24}; function 31. B to A 33. A to B 35. B to A 37. both 39. No; the relation is not a function. 41a. Yes, the relation is a function. b. It is a function. c. 2d: ≈ 0.0183 oz; 3d: ≈ 0.0282 oz; 4d: ≈ 0.0506 oz; 5d: ≈ 0.0590 oz; 6d: ≈ 0.0884 oz 45. F 47. $b \in$ ℝ and $a \neq \{-1, 0, 1, 2\}$ 49. One to one; each length in feet corresponds to only one length in inches. 51. 288 ft 53. $36\pi \approx 113.1$ ft² 55. 4.7 57. 9.5 59. $\frac{20}{w}$ 61. $\frac{x^{21}}{z^7}$

1-7

Check It Out! 1a. $f(0) = 0$; $f\left(\frac{1}{2}\right) = -\frac{7}{4}$; $f(-2) = 12$ b. $f(0) = 1$; $f\left(\frac{1}{2}\right) = 0$; $f(-2) = 5$ 2a. b. 3a. $f(x) = 0.27x$ b. 6.48; the price to develop 24 prints, in dollars

Exercises 1. independent 3. $f(0) = 9$; $f(1.5) = 11.25$; $f(-4) = 25$ 5. $f(0) = 3$; $f(1.5) = 4$; $f(-4) = 4$ 7. $f(0) = -5$; $f(1.5) = 1$; $f(-4) = 1$ 9.

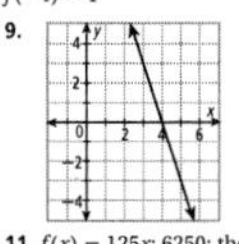

11. $f(x) = 125x$; 6250; the loss if 50 customers purchase the living room set, in dollars 13. $f(0) = 0$; $f\left(\frac{3}{2}\right) = -\frac{3}{4}$; $f(-1) = -2$ 15. $f(0) = 2$; $f\left(\frac{3}{2}\right) = 5$; $f(-1) = 0$ 17. $f(0) = 0$; $f\left(\frac{3}{2}\right) = 3$; $f(-1) = \frac{1}{2}$ 19. 21. $f(m) = 160 + 4m$; 192; a fine of \$192 for driving 8 mi/h over the speed limit 23. $f(-3.5) = -16.5$; $f(-1) = -9$; $f\left(\frac{1}{4}\right) = -5.25$; $f(2) = 0$; $f(11) = 27$ 25. $f(-4) = -3$; $f(0) = -\frac{1}{3}$; $f\left(\frac{1}{2}\right) = 0$; $f(5) = 3$ 27. $f(-2)0 = -1$; $f(-1) = 2$; $f(1) = 2$; $f(2) = -1$ 29. D: $\{A \mid A \geq 0\}$; R: $\{y \mid y \in W\}$ 31. D: $\{t \mid t \geq 0\}$; R: $\{y \mid -16 < y \leq 32.8\}$ 33. $t = 35$; the number of years it takes for plan h to reach a value of \$7500 35. $t = 40$; the time when plan g is worth $\frac{1}{2}$ the value of plan h 37. $h(40) - g(40) = 5000$; the difference in the value of the plans after 40 years 39. When $x = 3$, $f(x) = \frac{1}{x-3} = \frac{1}{0}$, but division by 0 is undefined. 41. For $-5 < x < 0$, x represents negative hours, and distance traveled would be negative. 43. independent: number of shirts; dependent: total cost; domain: $x \geq 15$ 45. $f(x) = 2.37x$ 47. $f(x) = 0.8x$ 51. H 53. 31 55. $g\left(-\frac{h}{4}\right) = 1$ 57. $r(t^4) = \frac{\sqrt{t^{16} + 4}}{t^4}$ 59. $12x - xy + 8$ 61. $\frac{c-2}{c}$ 63. b is any value. 65. yes

1-8

Check It Out! 1a. (3, 3) b. (−2, 1) 2a.

$x + 3$	x	y
1	−2	4
2	−1	0
3	0	2
5	2	2

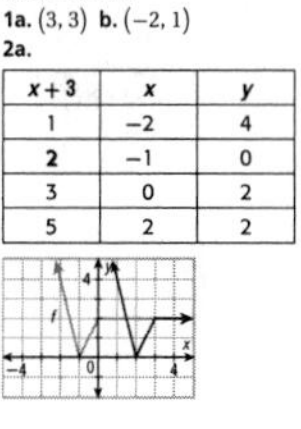

b.

x	y	$-y$
−2	4	−4
−1	0	0
0	2	−2
2	2	−2

3.

x	y	$2y$
−1	3	6
0	0	0
2	2	4
4	2	4

4. vertical compression by a factor of $\frac{3}{4}$

Recording Studio Fees

Exercises 1. compression 3. (4, −1) 5. 7. 9. 11. vertical compression by a factor of $\frac{1}{2}$ 13. horizontal shift right 5 units 15. (3, 5) 17. 21. 25. vertical shift down 5 units 27. horizontal stretch by a factor of 2 29. 10 square units; the same as the original 31. 7 square units; smaller than the original 33. 10 square units; the same as the original 35. 30 square units; larger than the original 37a. vertical translation b. horizontal compression c. the increase in the per-hour labor rate 39.

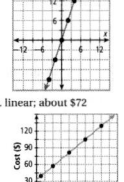

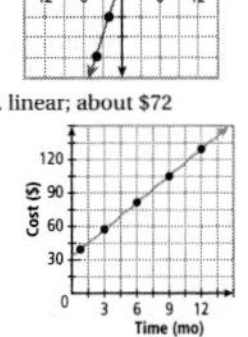

41. 43. The library is half as far from Roberta's house. 47. H 49. H 53a. $c(n) = 0.37n$ b. vertical stretch c. 15 in 1999 and 13 in 2002 d. The number of letters that can be mailed for \$5.00 must be rounded down to the nearest whole number. 55. 110 57. yes 59. $f(1) = -\frac{1}{2}$; $f(-3) = -\frac{17}{2}$; $f\left(\frac{1}{4}\right) = -2$ 61. $f(1) = 0$; $f(-3) = 64$; $f\left(\frac{1}{4}\right) = \frac{225}{256}$

1-9

Check It Out! 1a. cubic; translation 2 units up b. quadratic; reflection across the y-axis 2. linear; vertical stretch by a factor of 3 3. linear; about \$72

Exercises 3. quadratic; translation 1 unit left 5. square root; translation 3 units left 7. linear; translation $\sqrt{2}$ units down 9. cubic; vertical compression or horizontal stretch 11. quadratic; translation 1 unit down 13. cubic; translation 3 units up 15. square root; vertical stretch or horizontal compression 17. D: $\{x \mid x \geq 0\}$; R: $\{y \mid y \geq 0\}$; vertical stretch by a factor of 3 19. D: $\{x \mid x \geq 0\}$; R: $\{y \mid y \leq 0\}$; reflection across the x-axis 21. D: $\{x \mid x \in$ ℝ$\}$; R: $\{y \mid y \leq 1\}$; reflection across the x-axis and then a vertical shift up 1 unit 23. \$195 25. quadratic; horizontal shift right 7 units 27. linear; reflection across the y-axis and a vertical shift down 1 unit 29. linear; ≈ 1500 pixels 31. quadratic; ≈ 1417 pixels 33. Cubic; D: $\{\ell \mid \ell \geq 0\}$; R: $\{y \mid y \geq 0\}$; the domain and range are restricted. 35. Linear; D: $\{n \mid n \in$ ℕ$\}$; R: $\{y \mid y \in$ ℕ$\}$; the domain and range are restricted. 37. Square root; D: $\{a \mid a \geq 0\}$; R: $\{y \mid y \geq 0\}$; the domain and range are the same. 39a. linear b. cubic c. quadratic d. square root

e. linear; horizontal stretch by a factor of 2 and a vertical shift up 3 units 43. H 45. G 47. quadratic 49. linear 51. 7.5×10^8 53. 2.0×10^{-25} 55. $f(-5) = 15$; $f\left(-\frac{2}{3}\right) = -\frac{8}{9}$; $f(1.6) = 5.76$; $f(4) = 24$ 57. (4, −10)

Study Guide: Review

1. domain; range 2. $\{x \mid x \geq -5\}$ 3. $(-1, 5]$ 4. {4, 5, 6, 7, ...} 5. $\{x \mid x < -2$ or $x > 5\}$ 6. integers greater than −4 and less than or equal to 5 7. [5.5, 5.6] 8. Commutative Property of Multiplication 9. Distributive Property 10. −0.55; $\frac{1}{0.55}$ 11. $\frac{7}{8}$; $-\frac{8}{7}$ 12. $-1.\overline{2}$; $\frac{1}{1.\overline{2}}$ or $\frac{9}{11}$ 13. 3.5 14. 7.4 15. 8.6 16. 5.4 17. $4\sqrt{2}$ 18. 4 19. $-4\sqrt{2}$ 20. $3\sqrt{7}$ 21. $\frac{7\sqrt{2}}{2}$ 22. $\frac{\sqrt{10}}{5}$ 23. −96 24. 14 25. $\frac{1}{8}$ 26. $11x - 3y$ 27. $18 - 5a + b$ 28. $-3x - 12y$ 29. $a^2c + 2bc$ 30. $\frac{-8x^{15}}{y^9}$ 31. $-\frac{12x^7}{7y^9}$ 32. $\frac{r^4}{s^4}$ 33. $\frac{4m^6}{n^4}$ 34. 7×10^7 35. 5.4×10^1 36. D: {3, 5, 7}; R: {−1, 0, 9}; not a function 37. D: $[-2, \infty)$; R: $[-4, \infty)$; not a function 38. D: {−2, 0, 3, 4}; R: {3, 4}; function 39. D: {5, 10, 15, 20, 25}; R: {−5, −4, −3, −2, −1}; function 40. D: {a, b, c}; R: {Alabama, Alaska, Arizona, Arkansas, California, Colorado, Connecticut}; not a function 41. $f(2) = -2$; $f\left(\frac{1}{2}\right) = \frac{7}{4}$; $f(-2) = -2$ 42. $f(2) = -16$; $f\left(\frac{1}{2}\right) = -\frac{17}{2}$; $f(-2) = 4$ 43. $f(2) = -1$; $f\left(\frac{1}{2}\right) = 1$; $f(-2) = 2$ 44. $f(2) = \frac{1}{2}$; $f\left(\frac{1}{2}\right) = 2$; $f(-2) = -\frac{1}{2}$ 45. 46. 47. $A(s) = 6s^2$, where A is the surface area in square units and s is the side length in linear units; $A(10) = 600$; the surface area for a cube of side length 10 cm is 600 cm². 48. (0, −5) 49. (5, 1) 50. vertical compression by a factor of $\frac{1}{2}$ 51. vertical stretch by a factor of 1.1 52. translation 1 unit up 53. quadratic function; translation 1 unit down 54. square-root function; reflection across the x-axis 55. linear function; about 90 psi

Chapter 2

2-1

Check It Out! 1. 44 2a. $p = -4$ b. $r = \frac{1}{2}$ 3. $w = 3$ 4a. ∅ b. ℝ −5 −4 −3 −2 −1 0 1 2 3 5. $x \leq -3$

Exercises 1. identity 3. $x = 14$ 5. $x = -6$ 7. $x = -3$ 9. $x = 2$ 11. $r = -6$ 13. ∅ 15. ℝ 17. ∅ 19. $x > \frac{7}{3}$ 21. 28 s 23. $x = 16$ 25. $x = \frac{19}{2}$ 27. $n = 6$ 29. $x = 2$ 31. $t = -8$ 33. ∅ 35. ∅ 37. $x \geq -2$ −4 −3 −2 −1 0 1 2 3 4 39. $x \leq -12$ 41. \$0.04 43a. no more than 10 b. no more than 21 c. no more than 13 45. $m\angle D = 70°$; $m\angle E = 20°$ 47. 10 tragedies; 17 comedies; 10 histories. 49. $k = -10$ 53. C 55. D 57. 12 59. ℝ −4 −3 −2 −1 0 1 2 3 4 61a. ≈ 111 min b. ≈ 75 min 63. $8\sqrt{10}$ 65. $2\sqrt{15}$ 67. function 69. Yes

2-2

Check It Out! 1a. $y = 11$ b. $x = 42$ 2. 1240 students 3. ≈ 53 in. 4. 5. 27 ft

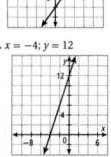

Exercises 1. rate 3. $n = 8$ 5. $t = 54$ 7. $x = 20$ 9. $x = -21$ 11. 24 mi/gal 13. 52.5 ft 15. $y = 6.2$ 17. $x = 10$ 19. \$1.22 21. 36 ft 23. $t = 0.168$ 25. $u = 8$ 27. $h = -30$ 29. $x = 0$ 33. The person would be 22 ft tall. 35a. ≈ 128.57 35b. ≈ 128.59 times as long 37. ≈ 0.0018% 39. 5.4 in. 41. $AB = 16\frac{2}{3}$; $EF = 22\frac{1}{2}$ 43. HO 45. 145 ft 49. G 51. G 53. $h = 8.6$ 55. $z = 8$ or $z = -8$ 57. no 59. 3 61. 350 63. 0.025 65. cone 67. hexagonal prism or cylinder 69. $f(x) = \sqrt{x}$; vertical translation, up 4, then stretch by a scale factor of 3 71. $f(x) = \sqrt{x}$; horizontal translation, left 1, then reflection.

2-3

Check It Out! 1a. yes b. no 2. 3. $x = -4$; $y = 12$

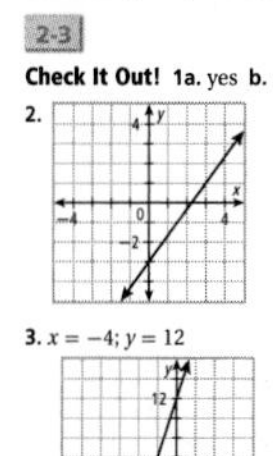

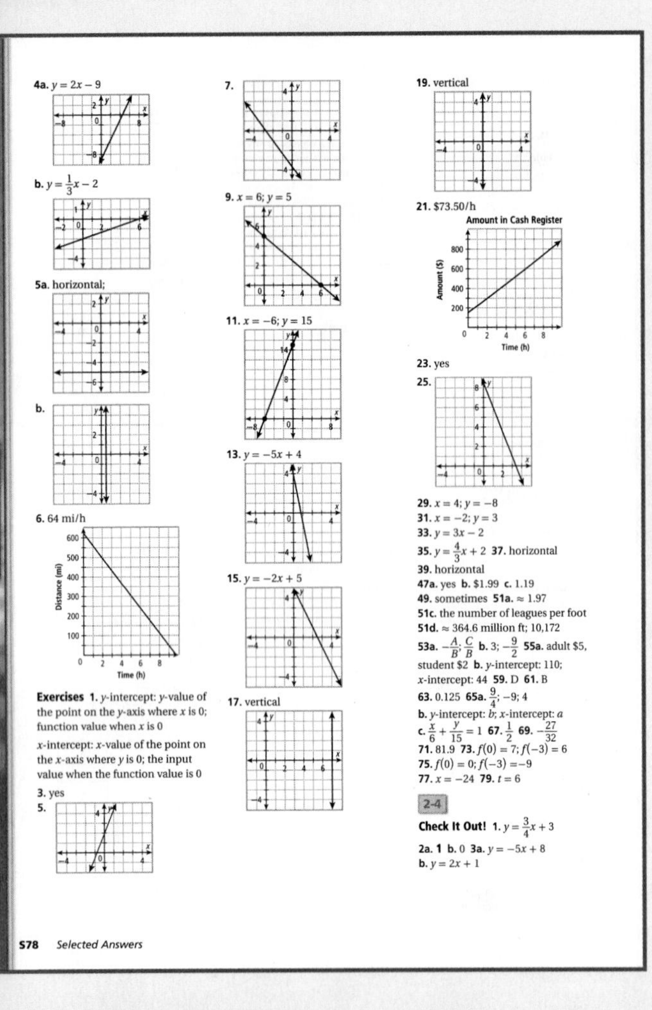

4a. $y = 2x - 9$

b. $y = \frac{1}{3}x - 2$

5a. horizontal;

b.

6. 64 mi/h

Exercises 1. y-intercept: y-value of the point on the y-axis where x is 0; function value when x is 0

x-intercept: x-value of the point on the x-axis where y is 0; the input value when the function value is 0

3. yes

5.

7.

9. $x = 6$; $y = 5$

11. $x = -6$; $y = 15$

13. $y = -5x + 4$

15. $y = -2x + 5$

17. vertical

19. vertical

21. \$73.50/h

23. yes

25.

29. $x = 4$; $y = -8$
31. $x = -2$; $y = 3$
33. $y = 3x - 2$
35. $y = \frac{4}{3}x + 2$ **37.** horizontal
39. horizontal
47a. yes **b.** \$1.99 **c.** 1.19
49. sometimes **51a.** ≈ 1.97
51c. the number of leagues per foot
51d. $\approx$ 364.6 million ft; 10,172
53a. $-\frac{A}{B}; \frac{C}{B}$ **b.** 3; $-\frac{9}{2}$ **55a.** adult \$5, student \$2 **b.** y-intercept: 110; x-intercept: 44 **59.** D **61.** B
63. 0.125 **65a.** $\frac{9}{4}$; -9; 4
b. y-intercept: b; x-intercept: a
c. $\frac{x}{6} + \frac{y}{15} = 1$ **67.** $\frac{1}{2}$ **69.** $-\frac{27}{32}$
71. 81.9 **73.** $f(0) = 7; f(-3) = 6$
75. $f(0) = 0; f(-3) = -9$
77. $x = -24$ **79.** $t = 6$

2-4

Check It Out! 1. $y = \frac{3}{4}x + 3$

2a. 1 b. 0 **3a.** $y = -5x + 8$
b. $y = 2x + 1$

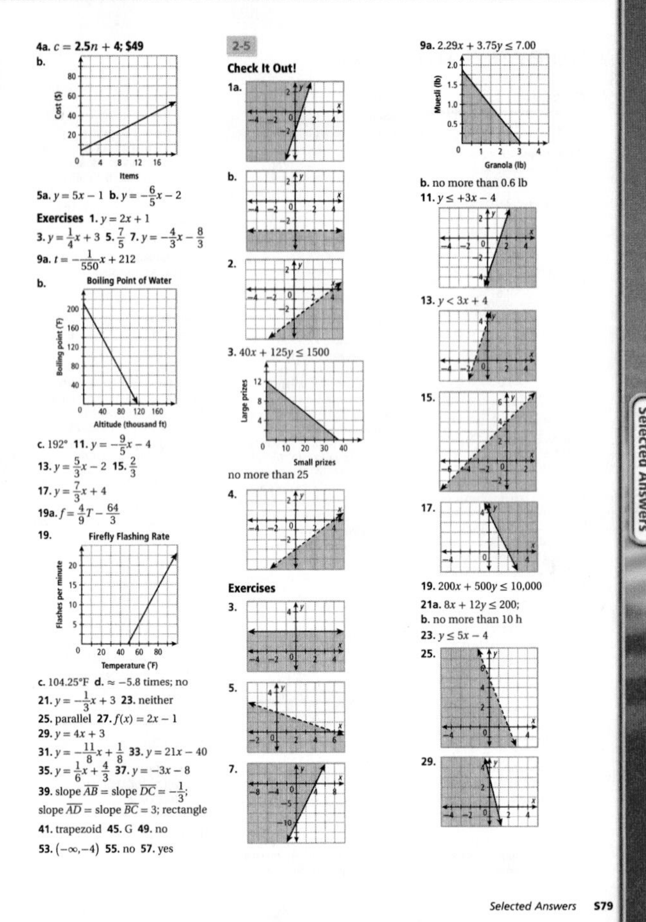

4a. $c = 2.5n + 4$; \$49

b.

5a. $y = 5x - 1$ **b.** $y = -\frac{6}{5}x - 2$

Exercises 1. $y = 2x + 1$
3. $y = \frac{1}{4}x + 3$ **5.** $\frac{7}{5}$ **7.** $y = -\frac{4}{3}x - \frac{8}{3}$
9a. $t = -\frac{1}{550}x + 212$

b. Boiling Point of Water

c. 192° **11.** $y = -\frac{9}{5}x - 4$
13. $y = \frac{5}{3}x - 2$ **15.** $\frac{2}{3}$
17. $y = \frac{7}{3}x + 4$
19a. $f = \frac{4}{9}T - \frac{64}{3}$

19. Firefly Flashing Rate

c. 104.25°F **d.** ≈ -5.8 times; no
21. $y = -\frac{1}{3}x + 3$ **23.** neither
25. parallel **27.** $f(x) = 2x - 1$
29. $y = 4x + 3$
31. $y = -\frac{11}{8}x + \frac{1}{8}$ **33.** $y = 21x - 40$
35. $y = \frac{1}{6}x + \frac{4}{3}$ **37.** $y = -3x - 8$
39. slope $\overline{AB}$ = slope $\overline{DC} = -\frac{1}{3}$; slope $\overline{AD}$ = slope $\overline{BC}$ = 3; rectangle
41. trapezoid **45.** G **49.** no
53. $(-\infty, -4)$ **55.** no **57.** yes

2-5

Check It Out!

1a.

b.

2.

3. $40x + 125y \le 1500$

no more than 25

4.

Exercises

3.

5.

7.

9a. $2.29x + 3.75y \le 7.00$

b. no more than 0.6 lb
11. $y \le +3x - 4$

13. $y < 3x + 4$

15.

17.

19. $200x + 500y \le 10{,}000$
21a. $8x + 12y \le 200$;
b. no more than 10 h
23. $y \le 5x - 4$

25.

29.

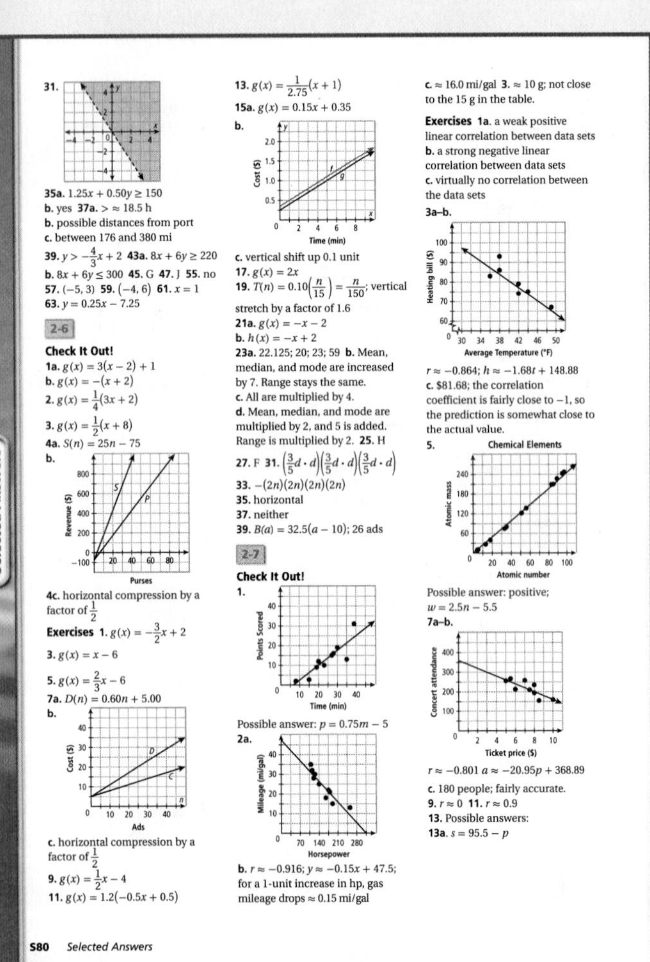

31.

35a. $1.25x + 0.50y \ge 150$
b. yes **37a.** $> \approx 18.5$ h
b. possible distances from port
c. between 176 and 380 mi
39. $y > -\frac{4}{3}x + 2$ **43a.** $8x + 6y \ge 220$
b. $8x + 6y \le 300$ **45.** G **47.** J **55.** no
57. $(-5, 3)$ **59.** $(-4, 6)$ **61.** $x = 1$
63. $y = 0.25x - 7.25$

2-6

Check It Out!
1a. $g(x) = 3(x - 2) + 1$
b. $g(x) = -(x + 2)$
2. $g(x) = \frac{1}{4}(3x + 2)$
3. $g(x) = \frac{1}{2}(x + 8)$
4a. $S(n) = 25n - 75$
b.

4c. horizontal compression by a factor of $\frac{1}{2}$
Exercises 1. $g(x) = -\frac{3}{2}x + 2$
3. $g(x) = x - 6$
5. $g(x) = \frac{2}{3}x - 6$
7a. $D(n) = 0.60n + 5.00$
b.

c. horizontal compression by a factor of $\frac{1}{2}$
9. $g(x) = \frac{1}{2}x - 4$
11. $g(x) = 1.2(-0.5x + 0.5)$

13. $g(x) = \frac{1}{2.75}(x + 1)$
15a. $g(x) = 0.15x + 0.35$
b.

c. vertical shift up 0.1 unit
17. $g(x) = 2x$
19. $T(n) = 0.10\left(\frac{n}{15}\right) = \frac{n}{150}$; vertical stretch by a factor of 1.6
21a. $g(x) = -x - 2$
b. $h(x) = -x + 2$
23a. 22.125; 20; 23; 59 **b.** Mean, median, and mode are increased by 7. Range stays the same.
c. All are multiplied by 4.
d. Mean, median, and mode are multiplied by 2, and 5 is added. Range is multiplied by 2. **25.** H
27. F **31.** $\left(\frac{3}{5}d \cdot d\right)\left(\frac{3}{5}d \cdot d\right)\left(\frac{3}{5}d \cdot d\right)$
33. $-(2n)(2n)(2n)(2n)$
35. horizontal
37. neither
39. $B(a) = 32.5(a - 10)$; 26 ads

2-7

Check It Out!
1.

Possible answer: $p = 0.75m - 5$
2a.

b. $r \approx -0.916$; $y \approx -0.15x + 47.5$; for a 1-unit increase in hp, gas mileage drops $\approx$ 0.15 mi/gal

c. $\approx$ 16.0 mi/gal **3.** $\approx$ 10 g; not close to the 15 g in the table.
Exercises 1a. a weak positive linear correlation between data sets
b. a strong negative linear correlation between data sets
c. virtually no correlation between the data sets
3a–b.

$r \approx -0.864$; $h \approx -1.68t + 148.88$
c. \$81.68; the correlation coefficient is fairly close to -1, so the prediction is somewhat close to the actual value.
5. Chemical Elements

Possible answer: positive; $w = 2.5n - 5.5$
7a–b.

$r \approx -0.801$ $a \approx -20.95p + 368.89$
c. 180 people; fairly accurate.
9. $r \approx 0$ **11.** $r \approx 0.9$
13. Possible answers:
13a. $s = 95.5 - p$

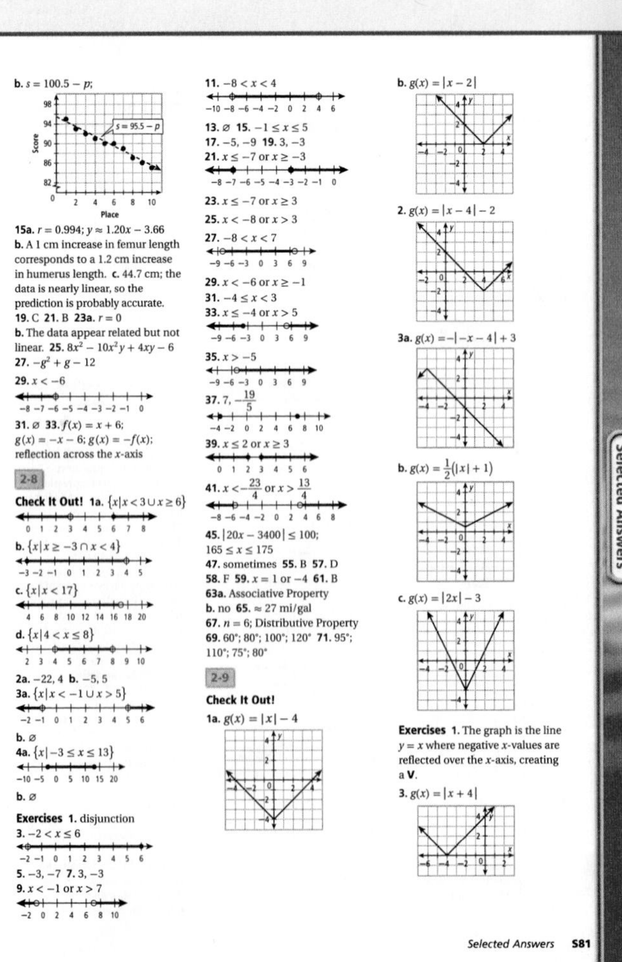

b. $s = 100.5 - p$;

15a. $r = 0.994$; $y \approx 1.20x - 3.66$
b. A 1 cm increase in femur length corresponds to a 1.2 cm increase in humerus length. **c.** 44.7 cm; the data is nearly linear, so the prediction is probably accurate.
19. C **21.** B **23a.** $r = 0$
b. The data appear related but not linear. **25.** $8x^2 - 10x^2y + 4xy - 6$
27. $-g^2 + g - 12$
29. $x < -6$

31. $\varnothing$ **33.** $f(x) = x + 6$; $g(x) = -x - 6$; $g(x) = -f(x)$; reflection across the x-axis

2-8

Check It Out! 1a. $\{x \mid x < 3 \cup x \ge 6\}$

b. $\{x \mid x \ge -3 \cap x < 4\}$

c. $\{x \mid x < 17\}$

d. $\{x \mid 4 < x \le 8\}$

2a. $-22, 4$ **b.** $-5, 5$
3a. $\{x \mid x < -1 \cup x > 5\}$

b. $\varnothing$
4a. $\{x \mid -3 \le x \le 13\}$

b. $\varnothing$

Exercises 1. disjunction
3. $-2 < x \le 6$

5. $-3, -7$ **7.** $3, -3$
9. $x < -1$ or $x > 7$

11. $-8 < x < 4$

13. $\varnothing$ **15.** $-1 \le x \le 5$
17. $-5, -9$ **19.** $3, -3$
21. $x \le -7$ or $x \ge -3$

23. $x \le -7$ or $x \ge 3$
25. $x < -8$ or $x > 3$
27. $-8 < x < 7$

29. $x < -6$ or $x \ge -1$
31. $-4 \le x < 3$
33. $x \le -4$ or $x > 5$

35. $x > -5$

37. $7, -\frac{19}{5}$

39. $x \le 2$ or $x \ge 3$

41. $x < -\frac{23}{4}$ or $x > \frac{13}{4}$

45. $|20x - 3400| \le 100$; $165 \le x \le 175$
47. sometimes **55.** B **57.** D
58. F **59.** $x = 1$ or -4 **61.** B
63a. Associative Property
b. no **65.** $\approx$ 27 mi/gal
67. $n = 6$; Distributive Property
69. 60°; 80°; 100°; 120° **71.** 95°; 110°; 75°; 80°

2-9

Check It Out!
1a. $g(x) = |x| - 4$

b. $g(x) = |x - 2|$

2. $g(x) = |x - 4| - 2$

3a. $g(x) = -|-x - 4| + 3$

b. $g(x) = \frac{1}{2}(|x| + 1)$

c. $g(x) = |2x| - 3$

Exercises 1. The graph is the line $y = x$ where negative x-values are reflected over the x-axis, creating a **V**.
3. $g(x) = |x + 4|$

5. $g(x) = |x - 1| + 6$

7. $g(x) = 2|x + 3|$

9. $g(x) = |x - 2|$

11. $g(x) = |x + 4|$
13. $g(x) = |x - 1.5| + 4.5$
15. $g(x) = -|x - 5| - 2$
17. $f(x) = \left|2\left(\frac{2}{3}x\right)\right| - 3$
19. translated down 6 units
21. translated right 1 unit and vertically stretched by a factor of 2
23. $(-5, 9)$ 27. $f(x) = |x - 2| - 4$
29. $f(x) = -|x - 4|$ 33. D 35. B
37. B 41. $f(x) = 2|x + 3|$
43. 7.5×10^8 45. 6.561×10^7
47. 2.0×10^{-25} 49. $(1, 1)$
51. $(6, -5)$ 53. $(4, -10)$
55. $\varnothing$

Study Guide: Review

1. contradiction 2. point-slope form 3. correlation 4. $x = \frac{13}{2}$
5. $\mathbb{R}$ 6. $x = -\frac{4}{7}$ 7. $x = \frac{31}{2}$ 8. $x = \frac{51}{41}$
9. 140 10. $x \le 7$ 11. $x < -\frac{32}{3}$
12. $x \le 9$ 13. $19.95 + 2.75x < 50$; fewer than 11 times 14. $x = 33$
15. $x = -15$ 16. $x = -\frac{11}{3}$
17. $x = \frac{19}{18}$ 18. 4.5 ft 19. yes
20. $(5, 0)$; $(0, 2)$
21. $(3, 0)$; $(0, -2)$
22. $(-2.25, 0)$; $(0, 1.5)$
23. $(1.5, 0)$; $(0, 6)$
24. $y = -2x + 5$
25. $y = \frac{5}{3}x + 3$
26. $y = -\frac{3}{2}x + 2$
27. $y = -\frac{2}{3}x + 9$
28. vertical 29. horizontal
30. $-27.5t + 500$
31. $y = \frac{1}{2}x + 4$
32. $y = 3x$
33. $y = \frac{3}{2}x - 8$
34. $y = -\frac{2}{3}x + 2$
35. $y > -3$
36. $y \le x + 3$
37. $y > -\frac{1}{2}x - 3$
38. $y < 3x - 4$
39. $y < -2x + 3$
40. $12x + 21y \le 2520$
41. $g(x) = x - 8$
42. $g(x) = 3x + 15$
43. $g(x) = x - 4$
44. $g(x) = -x - 5$
45. $g(x) = -x - 12$
46a.

b. $r = 0.800$; $P = 1.279I + 35.074$
47. $x = 28$ or $x = -12$
48. $x = 66$ or $x = -54$
49. $\varnothing$
50. $\{x \mid x < -5 \cup x > 3\}$
51. $\{x \mid -2 \le x \le 5\}$
52. $\{x \mid 1 < x < 3\}$
53. $\{x \mid x \le -8 \cup x \ge 4\}$
54. $g(x) = |x + 5| + 7$
55. $g(x) = |x - 6| - 9$
56. $g(x) = |-x - 4| + 1$
57. $g(x) = \frac{|3x + 1|}{3}$
58. $g(x) = -|x - 3| - 5$

Chapter 3

3-1

Check It Out! 1a. solution. b. not a solution. 2a. $(0, -3)$ b. $(4, 4)$ c. $(-1, 4)$ 3a. consistent, dependent; infinite number of solutions b. inconsistent; no solution 4. 10 min

Exercises 1. inconsistent 3. not a solution 5. solution 7. $(-2, 5)$ 9. $(2, 3)$ 11. consistent, dependent; infinite number of solutions 13. inconsistent; no solution 15. solution 17. not a solution 19. $(3, 1)$ 21. $(1, -4)$ 23. consistent, dependent; infinite number of solutions 25. consistent, independent; one solution 27. 10 system sales 29. solution 31. not a solution; $(-3, 0)$

33a. $\begin{cases} \ell = 10{,}000 - 200x \\ m = 5{,}000 + 50x \end{cases}$ b. 20 min c. 6000 ft

35. $\begin{cases} y = 2x - 3 \\ y = -x + 6 \end{cases}$ consistent, independent; $(3, 3)$

37. $\begin{cases} y = 3x - 3 \\ y = 3x + 1 \end{cases}$ inconsistent; no solution

39. $(-0.25, 4)$ 41. $(2.831, -30.403)$ 45. Consistent, independent 47. D 49. B 51. $\left(\frac{100}{7}, \frac{6200}{7}\right)$ 53. infinite number of solutions 55. The solution has no meaning in the real world. 57. $\frac{2\sqrt{3}}{3}$ 59. $\frac{\sqrt{2}}{2}$ 61. -3 63. $40h$

3-2

Check It Out! 1a. $(4, 7)$ b. $(3, -4)$ 2a. $\left(\frac{3}{4}, -4\right)$ b. $(6, -4)$ 3a. consistent, dependent; infinite number of solutions b. inconsistent; no solution 4. 18.75 lb of Sumatra beans and 31.25 lb of Kona beans

Exercises 1. elimination 3. $(8, -11)$ 5. $(-2, -1)$ 7. $(-55, -21)$ 9. $(-2, 5)$

11. inconsistent; no solution 13. consistent, dependent; infinite number of solutions 15. $\left(-6, \frac{3}{2}\right)$ 17. $\left(\frac{1}{4}, 1\right)$ 19. $(-7, -6)$ 21. $(-2.45, -4.8)$ 23. consistent, dependent; infinite number of solutions 25. consistent, dependent; infinite number of solutions 27. $x + y = 1200$; $x = \frac{1}{2}y$; $(400, 800)$ 29. $(6, 2)$ 31. $(20, -3)$ 33a. 22 b. The total number of coins increases. c. 12 dimes and 18 nickels 35a. 266.5 mi b. $y = 128.43x$ c. ≈ 7.12 mi 37. student = \$5.50 and adult = \$7.50 41. G 43. $(2, -1)$; independent, consistent 47a. $p = 22\frac{7}{9}$; $q = 8\frac{8}{9}$ b. $p = 17\frac{2}{3}$; $q = 29\frac{1}{3}$ 49. $28c^2 + 1$; 253 51. $\frac{2}{9y^2}$; $\frac{2}{81}$ 53. $f(x) = -1.5x - 0.5$ 55.

3-3

Check It Out!
1a.

b.

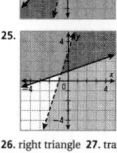

2. $\begin{cases} d + s \le 40 \\ 2d + 2.5s \ge 90 \end{cases}$

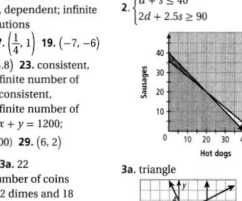

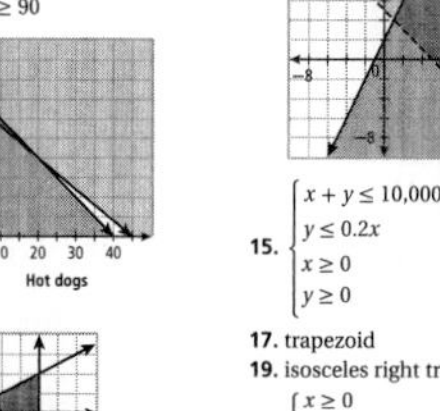

3a. triangle

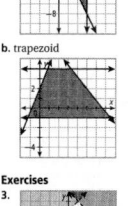

b. trapezoid

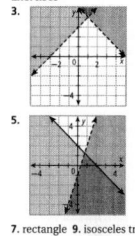

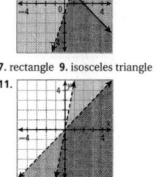

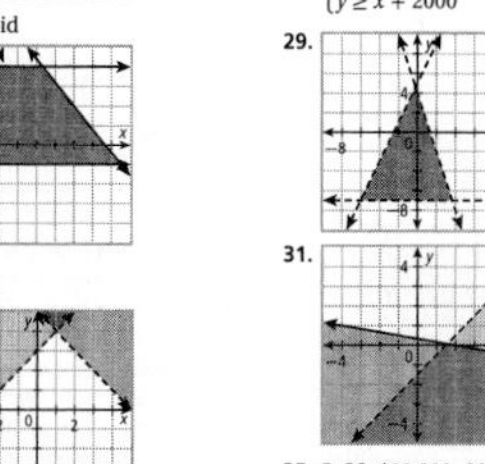

Exercises
3.

5.

7. rectangle 9. isosceles triangle
11.

13.

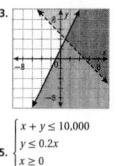

15. $\begin{cases} x + y \le 10{,}000 \\ y \le 0.2x \\ x \ge 0 \\ y \ge 0 \end{cases}$

17. trapezoid
19. isosceles right triangle

27. $\begin{cases} x \ge 0 \\ y \ge 0 \\ x + y \le 114{,}650 \\ x + y \ge 56{,}801 \\ y \ge x + 2000 \end{cases}$

29.

31.

35. G 39. \$20,000 41. $\frac{3}{4}$; $-\frac{4}{3}$ 43. 1; -1 45. $y = -3$ 47. $y = -\frac{1}{3}x + 9$ 49. $y = -x + 5$

3-4

Check It Out!
1.

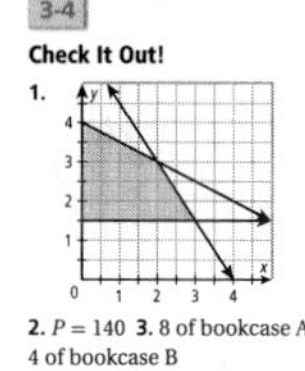

2. $P = 140$ 3. 8 of bookcase A and 4 of bookcase B

Exercises
1. Constraints
3.

5. $P = 106$ 7. $P = 3.9$
9.

11.

13. $P = -36$ 15. 60 radio and 24 prime-time television commercials 17. 32 h

19. right triangle; $\begin{cases} y \le x + 2 \\ y \ge 2x \\ y \ge -\frac{1}{2}x \end{cases}$

21. 20 stops 23. 40 Soy Joy and 20 Vitamin Boost 27. D 29. G
31. $f(7) = \frac{1}{11}$; $f\left(-\frac{1}{2}\right) = -\frac{1}{4}$
33. $f(7) = 8$; $f\left(-\frac{1}{2}\right) = \frac{1}{2}$
37. right triangle

3-5

Check It Out!
1.

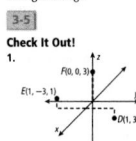

2.

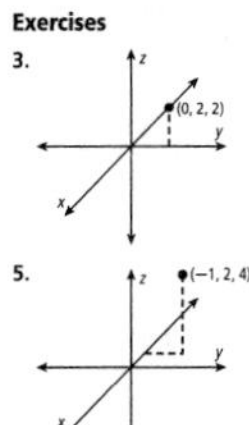

3a. $3.5x + 1.5y + 0.75z = 61.5$ b. 15

Exercises
3.

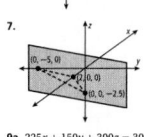

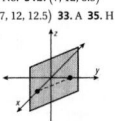

5.

7.

9a. $225x + 150y + 300z = 3000$ b. 1; 6; 6; 0 c. 20
11.

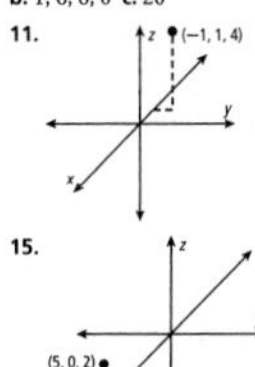

15.

19.

23.

29. No. 31b. $(7, 12, 8.5)$ c. $(7, 12, 12.5)$ 33. A 35. H
37.

41. $x + 2y - 4z = 4$ 43. square pyramid 45. sphere 47. $x = 10$; $y = 2$ 49. $x = 5$; $y = \frac{1}{3}$

3-6

Check It Out!
1. $x = -2, y = 1, z = 2$
2. first place—3 points; second place—2 points; third place—1 point
3a. consistent; infinite number of solutions b. inconsistent; no solution

Exercises
1. $x = -4, y = 3, z = 3$
3. $x = 1, y = 3, z = 1$
5. inconsistent; no solution
7. inconsistent; no solution
9. $x = 3, y = 1, z = 6$
11. Talent—30%; Presentation—20%; Star Quality—50%
13. inconsistent; no solution
15. $m\angle A = 120°$; $m\angle B = 45°$; $m\angle A = 15°$ 19a. $(5, -2, 50)$ b. 50 ft c. $(5, -2, 0)$ 21. J
23. $w = 1, x = -2, y = -1, z = 3$
25. $(3, 3)$ 27. 7.15 m by 5.2 m
29. $y = \frac{2}{3}x - 4$

Extension

Check It Out!
1a. $\begin{cases} x = 5t \\ y = 20t \end{cases}$

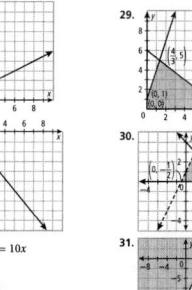

b. At $t = 10$, the helicopter has a ground distance of 50 ft from its takeoff point and an altitude of 200 ft. 2. $y = 4x$

Exercises
1.

3.

5. $y = \frac{2}{3}x$ 7. $y = 10x$
9a. $\begin{cases} x = 1.8t \\ y = -0.9t \end{cases}$
b. -45 m c. $-77{,}760$ m

Study Guide: Review

1. dependent 2. elimination 3. system of linear inequalities; feasible region 4. three-dimensional coordinate system; ordered triple 5. consistent 6. $(5, 10)$ 7. $(4, 2)$ 8. $(-4, -1)$ 9. $(0, -2)$ 10. independent; one solution 11. dependent; infinitely many solutions 12. inconsistent; no solution 13. independent; 1 solution 14. 3 locks 15. $(1, 3)$ 16. $(6, 5)$ 17. $(-2, -8)$ 18. $(4, -2)$ 19. $(4, 5)$ 20. $(3, 4)$ 21. $(5, 2)$ 22. $(2, 1)$ 23. 48 oz pine; 32 oz lavender

24.

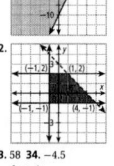

25.

26. right triangle 27. trapezoid
28. $\begin{cases} x + y \le 120 \\ 8x + 11.5y < 1200 \end{cases}$
29.

30.

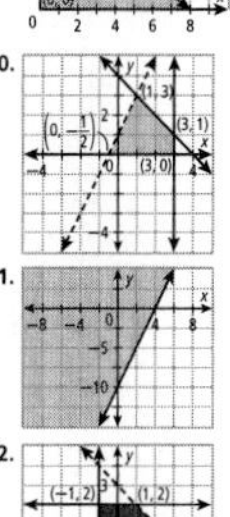

31.

32.

33. 58 34. -4.5
35. $\begin{cases} x \ge 0 \\ y \ge 0 \\ 6x + 4y \le 720 \\ x \ge 2y \end{cases}$
36. $P = 8x + 9y$ 37. \$1125
38. 25 phones with contracts and 5 without contracts

39–42.

43.

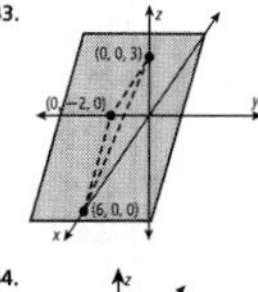

44.

45.

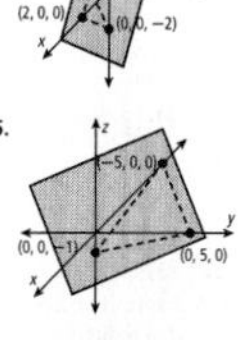

46.

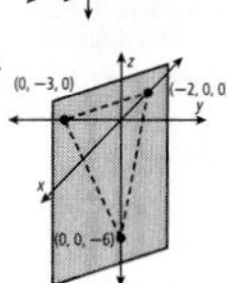

47. $2d + 9p + 4c = 35$, where d = drinks, p = pizza, c = ice cream 48. $(1, 2, 3)$ 49. $(1, -1, 2)$ 50. inconsistent, no solution 51. dependent, infinitely many solutions

Chapter 4

4-1

Check It Out!
1a. 3×4 b. 11 c. m_{14} and m_{23}
2a. $\begin{bmatrix} 4 & 0 & -8 \\ 6 & 2 & 18 \end{bmatrix}$

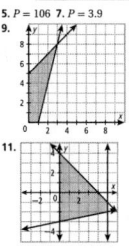

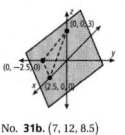

b. not possible
c. $\begin{bmatrix} -4 & 2 & 2 \\ 0 & -2 & 2 \end{bmatrix}$

3.

Ticket Service Prices		
Day	**Plaza**	**Balcony**
Days 1–2	$120	$70
Days 3–8	$100	$56
Days 9–10	$160	$90

4a. not possible
b. $\begin{bmatrix} -1 & -10 \\ -6 & 47 \end{bmatrix}$ **c.** $\begin{bmatrix} -9 & 4.5 & 12 \end{bmatrix}$

Exercises

1. entry **3.** $\begin{bmatrix} 1.5 & 7.8 & 4 \\ -1.2 & 0.4 & 1 \end{bmatrix}$

5. $\begin{bmatrix} -1.5 & 0.2 & -2 \\ 1.2 & -4.4 & 1 \end{bmatrix}$

7. $P_T = \begin{bmatrix} 9.74 & 14.07 & 15.16 \\ 6.50 & 10.28 & 11.91 \\ 16.24 & 22.73 & 24.90 \\ 5.41 & 8.12 & 9.20 \end{bmatrix}$

9. $\begin{bmatrix} -\frac{1}{2} & \frac{1}{2} & 3 \\ 2 & 0 & \frac{1}{2} \\ \frac{1}{2} & 1 & \frac{1}{2} \end{bmatrix}$ **11.** not possible

13. $F - E = \begin{bmatrix} -7.4 & 0 \\ 37 & -2.4 \end{bmatrix}$

15. not possible
17. $\begin{bmatrix} 29{,}061 & 13{,}483 & 20{,}147 \end{bmatrix}$
19. not possible **21.** not possible
23. never true **27.** always true
29. $a = -6$; $b = 11$; $c = 4$
31. no **33.** F **35.** $\frac{1}{2}$

39. $\begin{bmatrix} 2.5 & -4 \\ 1 & -7 \end{bmatrix}$ **41.** $20n$ **43.** no

4-2

Check It Out!

1a. no **b.** no **c.** 4×3

2a. $\begin{bmatrix} 67 & 5 \\ 62 & 72 \\ 66 & -6 \end{bmatrix}$ **2b.** $\begin{bmatrix} 3 & 41 & 97 \\ -30 & 78 & 128 \end{bmatrix}$

3. $\begin{bmatrix} 2436 & 1196 & 1240 \\ 1605 & 786 & 819 \end{bmatrix}$; 819

4a. not possible

b. $A^3 = \begin{bmatrix} 259 & 129 \\ -86 & -42 \end{bmatrix}$

c. $B^3 = \begin{bmatrix} 82 & 103 & 2 \\ 125 & 33 & -39 \\ 17 & -12 & 34 \end{bmatrix}$

d. $I^4 = \begin{bmatrix} 1 & 0 \\ 0 & 1 \end{bmatrix}$

Exercises

1. multiplicative identity matrix
3. no **5.** yes; 5×5 **7.** yes; 2×2

9. $\begin{bmatrix} -2 & -18 & -9 \\ 4 & 29 & 15 \\ -2 & 3 & 0 \end{bmatrix}$ **11.** not possible

13. $\begin{bmatrix} 4 & 2 \\ 1 & -3 \end{bmatrix}$ **15.** $\begin{bmatrix} -1 & 2 \\ -1 & -2 \end{bmatrix}$

17. not possible **19.** no
21. yes; 3×1 **23.** no
25. not possible

27. $\begin{bmatrix} 27 & -10 \\ -10 & 3 \\ -5 & 1 \end{bmatrix}$ **29.** $\begin{bmatrix} -2 & 3 & -4 \\ 1 & -1 & 1 \\ 4 & 1 & 3 \end{bmatrix}$

31. $\begin{bmatrix} -1 & 2 \\ -1 & -2 \end{bmatrix}$ **33.** $\begin{bmatrix} 6 & 2 & 1 \\ 5 & 4 & 1 \\ 7 & 3 & 3 \end{bmatrix}$

35. not possible

37. $\begin{bmatrix} 5 & 11 \\ 7 & 27 \end{bmatrix}$ **39.** $\begin{bmatrix} -2 & 8 & 12 \\ 6 & 0 & 4 \end{bmatrix}$

41a. $SD = \begin{bmatrix} 122.8 & 124.5 & 160.2 & 148.1 \\ 161.85 & 160.4 & 207.8 & 191.95 \\ 131.45 & 130.3 & 168.4 & 155.85 \\ 168.95 & 169.0 & 217.8 & 201.65 \end{bmatrix}$

b. Ted: 122.8; Chloe: 160.4; Biko: 168.4; Hana: 201.65
43. sometimes true
45. sometimes true **47.** −8
49. Madison: 122; Devyn: 113.5; Ali: 69.5 **51.** Tristan Island **55.** G
57. *BA* **59a.** yes **b.** p_{12} and p_{21}
61. 10 **63.** 11 **69.** not possible

4-3

Check It Out!

1. $G'(5, 3)$, $H'(6, 0)$, $J'(4, -2)$

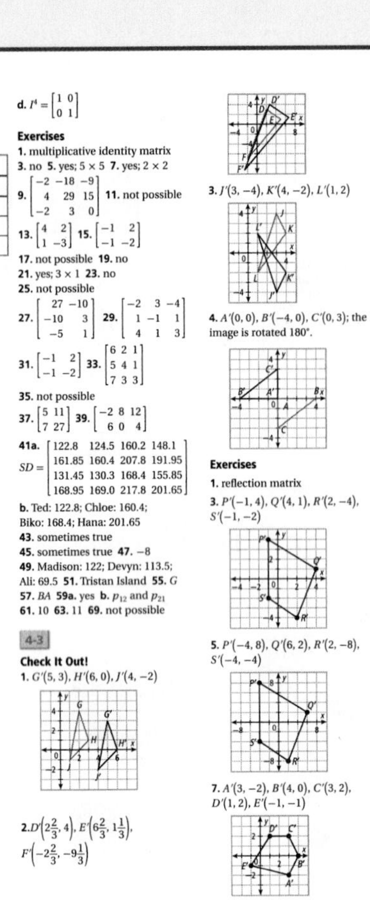

2. $D'\left(2\frac{2}{3}, 4\right)$, $E'\left(6\frac{2}{3}, 1\frac{1}{3}\right)$, $F'\left(-2\frac{2}{3}, -9\frac{1}{3}\right)$

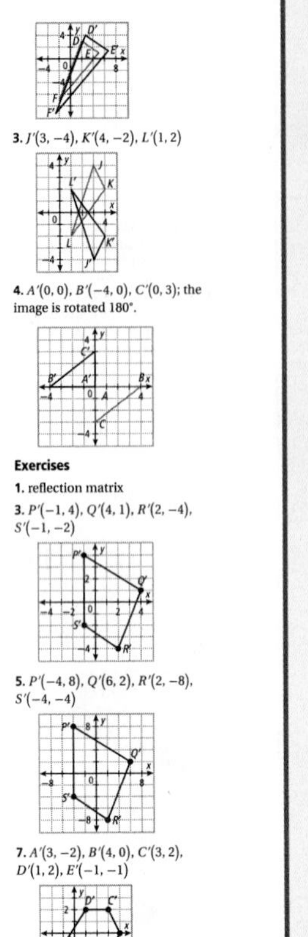

3. $J'(3, -4)$, $K'(4, -2)$, $L'(1, 2)$

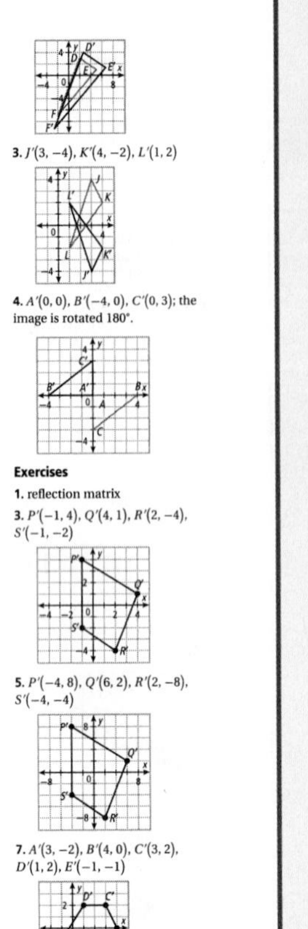

4. $A'(0, 0)$, $B'(-4, 0)$, $C'(0, 3)$; the image is rotated 180°.

Exercises

1. reflection matrix
3. $P'(-1, 4)$, $Q'(4, 1)$, $R'(2, -4)$, $S'(-1, -2)$

5. $P'(-4, 8)$, $Q'(6, 2)$, $R'(2, -8)$, $S'(-4, -4)$

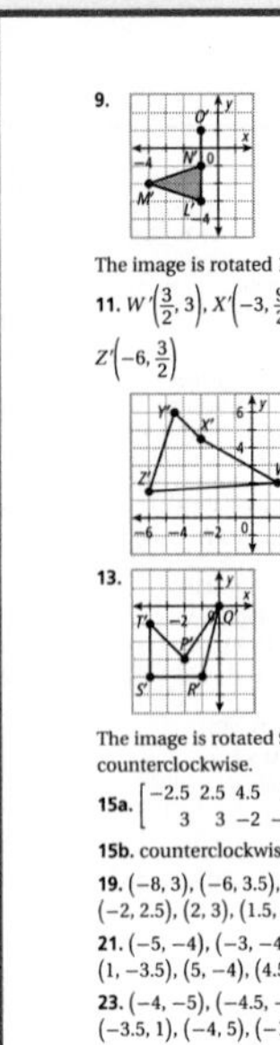

7. $A'(3, -2)$, $B'(4, 0)$, $C'(3, 2)$, $D'(1, 2)$, $E'(-1, -1)$

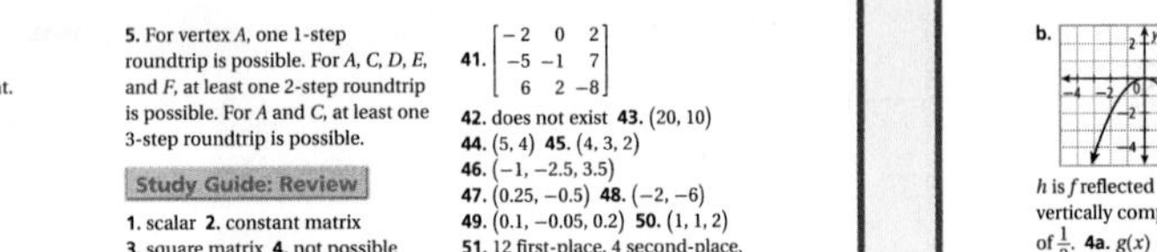

9.

The image is rotated 180°.

11. $W'\left(\frac{3}{2}, 3\right)$, $X'\left(-3, \frac{9}{2}\right)$, $Y'\left(-\frac{9}{2}, 6\right)$, $Z'\left(-6, \frac{3}{2}\right)$

13.

The image is rotated 90° counterclockwise.

15a. $\begin{bmatrix} -2.5 & 2.5 & 4.5 & 0.5 & -4 \\ 3 & 3 & -2 & -4.5 & -1.5 \end{bmatrix}$

15b. counterclockwise
19. $(-8, 3)$, $(-6, 3.5)$, $(-4, 3)$, $(-2, 2.5)$, $(2, 3)$, $(1.5, 0)$, $(-1, 0)$
21. $(-5, -4)$, $(-3, -4.5)$, $(-1, -4)$, $(1, -3.5)$, $(5, -4)$, $(4.5, -1)$, $(2, -1)$
23. $(-4, -5)$, $(-4.5, -3)$, $(-4, -1)$, $(-3.5, 1)$, $(-4, 5)$, $(-1, 4.5)$, $(-1, 2)$

25. $\begin{bmatrix} 1 & 0 \\ 0 & -1 \end{bmatrix}$; $\begin{bmatrix} -1 & 0 \\ 0 & 1 \end{bmatrix}$

27. B **29.** A **33.** yes **35.** yes
37. not possible

4-4

Check It Out!

1a. 10 **b.** $-2\frac{1}{4}$ **c.** $\pi - \frac{1}{2}$

2. $D = \begin{vmatrix} 6 & -2 \\ 3 & -1 \end{vmatrix} = 0$

$\begin{vmatrix} c_1 & b_1 \\ c_2 & b_2 \end{vmatrix} = \begin{vmatrix} 14 & -2 \\ 7 & -1 \end{vmatrix} = 0$

dependent; infinitely many solutions.
3. 75 **4.** 240 g protein, 380 g carbohydrates, and 80 g fat

Exercises

1. A 0 entry in a coefficient matrix corresponds to a coefficient of 0 for one variable in one equation.
3. 2.25 **5.** 0 **7.** no solution

9. $\left(2\frac{1}{2}, -\frac{1}{4}\right)$ **11.** 0

13. trail mix $2.99; mixed nuts $6.98; dried fruit $3.99 **15.** −1
17. $\pi r^2 - 2r^2$ **19.** $(\approx 1.27, \approx 1.11)$
21. $\left(-4\frac{2}{3}, \frac{7}{9}\right)$ **23.** 1.2
25. bicycling: 420 Cal/h; racquetball: 540 Cal/h; swimming: 600 Cal/h **27.** 17 square units
29. 1 point: 9 voters; 2 points: 11 voters; 3 points: 18 voters **31.** −16
33. a. 235 dimes, 190 nickels
b. $33 **37.** D **39.** 2.5, or $\frac{5}{2}$ **43.** 254
45. $\left(-\frac{4}{3}, -4\right)$ **47.** $\left(-\frac{1}{3}, -\frac{2}{3}\right)$
49. $D'(1, -1)$, $E'(4, 2)$, $F'(-2, 3)$, $G'(-1, 1)$
51. $D'(3, 3)$, $E'(12, -6)$, $F'(-6, -9)$, $G'(-3, -3)$

4-5

Check It Out!

1. yes

2. $\begin{bmatrix} \frac{1}{6} & \frac{1}{6} \\ \frac{1}{4} & -\frac{1}{4} \end{bmatrix}$ **3.** $\begin{bmatrix} 1 & 1 \\ 2 & 3 \end{bmatrix}\begin{bmatrix} x \\ y \end{bmatrix} = \begin{bmatrix} 4 \\ 9 \end{bmatrix}$; $(3, 1)$

4. smarty pants

Exercises

1. Set the product of the coefficient matrix and the variable matrix equal to the constant matrix. **3.** no

5. $\begin{bmatrix} 2 & 0 \\ 1 & 3 \end{bmatrix}$ **7.** no inverse **9.** $\begin{bmatrix} 8 & -7 \\ -9 & 8 \end{bmatrix}$

11. $\begin{bmatrix} 5 & 9 \\ -4 & -7 \end{bmatrix}\begin{bmatrix} x \\ y \end{bmatrix} = \begin{bmatrix} 1 \\ 2 \end{bmatrix}$; $(-25, 14)$

13. $\begin{bmatrix} 7 & -4 \\ -5 & 3 \end{bmatrix}$; in New Delhi

15. yes **17.** $\begin{bmatrix} 8 & -2 \\ -6 & 1 \end{bmatrix}$

19. $\begin{bmatrix} 8 & -3 \\ -5 & 2 \end{bmatrix}$ **21.** $\begin{bmatrix} -11 & -3 \\ 7 & 2 \end{bmatrix}$

23. $\begin{bmatrix} 1 & 2 \\ 2 & 1 \end{bmatrix}\begin{bmatrix} x \\ y \end{bmatrix} = \begin{bmatrix} 6 \\ 9 \end{bmatrix}$; $(4, 1)$

25. $\begin{bmatrix} 4 & -3 \\ -9 & 7 \end{bmatrix}$; Monday early

27a. $\begin{bmatrix} 6 & 2 \\ 1 & 1 \end{bmatrix}$ **b.** $\begin{bmatrix} 6 & 2 \\ 1 & 1 \end{bmatrix}\begin{bmatrix} x \\ y \end{bmatrix} = \begin{bmatrix} 34 \\ 7 \end{bmatrix}$

c. $\begin{bmatrix} \frac{1}{4} & -\frac{1}{2} \\ -\frac{1}{4} & \frac{3}{2} \end{bmatrix}$

d. 5 six-person boats and 2 two-person boats
31. 46 $50 bills and 27 $100 bills
33a. They are halved. **37.** $\begin{bmatrix} \frac{1}{a} \end{bmatrix}$
39. The two matrices are inverses of each other. **41.** H **43.** F
45. points/game: 2; assists/game: 5; turnovers/game: −4; steals/game: 3
47a. play to win

b. $\begin{bmatrix} 1 & -1 & 0 \\ 0 & 1 & -1 \\ 0 & 0 & 1 \end{bmatrix}$

c. $\begin{bmatrix} -3 & -12 & 23 & -11 \\ -6 & -13 & 0 & 20 \\ 18 & 25 & 0 & 0 \end{bmatrix}$

49. 0.175 **51.** $(1, 1, 0)$
53. 8.5 **55.** −43

4-6

Check It Out!

1a. $\left[\begin{array}{cc|c} -1 & -1 & 0 \\ -1 & -1 & -2 \end{array}\right]$

b. $\left[\begin{array}{ccc|c} -5 & -4 & 0 & 12 \\ 1 & 0 & 1 & 3 \\ 0 & 4 & 3 & 10 \end{array}\right]$

2a. $\left[\begin{array}{cc|c} 4 & 4 & 32 \\ 1 & 3 & 16 \end{array}\right]$; $(4, 4)$

b. $\left[\begin{array}{cc|c} 9 & 3 & 15 \\ -6 & -2 & 10 \end{array}\right]$; no solution

3a. $\left[\begin{array}{ccc|c} 3 & -1 & 5 & -1 \\ 1 & 0 & 2 & 1 \\ 1 & 3 & -1 & 25 \end{array}\right]$; $(5, 6, -2)$

b. $t = 820$; $d = 1600$; 1600 days.

Exercises

1. The coefficients are in columns to the left of the vertical bar that separates them from the constant terms.

3. $\left[\begin{array}{ccc|c} 1 & 1 & 1 & 10 \\ 2 & 0 & 1 & 12 \\ 0 & -1 & 1 & 3 \end{array}\right]$

5. $\left[\begin{array}{ccc|c} -3 & 1 & 0 & -2 \\ 0 & \frac{1}{4} & -1 & -1 \\ -\frac{1}{2} & 0 & 1 & 8 \end{array}\right]$

7. $\left[\begin{array}{cc|c} -1 & 8 & 7 \\ \frac{1}{2} & 3 & 0 \end{array}\right]$; $\left(-3, \frac{1}{2}\right)$

9. $\left[\begin{array}{cc|c} 1 & -1 & -4 \\ 4 & -4 & -3 \end{array}\right]$; the system is inconsistent.

11. $\left[\begin{array}{ccc|c} \frac{1}{2} & \frac{3}{2} & -1 & 0 \\ -2 & 1 & 0 & 4 \\ 1 & 1 & 1 & 3 \end{array}\right]$

13. $\left[\begin{array}{ccc|c} 0.1 & 0.2 & 0.15 & 1.0 \\ 1 & 1 & -1 & 0 \\ 1.3 & -2 & 0 & 0 \end{array}\right]$

15. $\left[\begin{array}{cc|c} 5 & -1 & 2 \\ 1 & -1 & -4 \end{array}\right]$; $(1.5, 5.5)$

17. 12 roosters, 4 hens, and 84 chicks.

23. $\left[\begin{array}{cc|c} 3 & -1 & -9 \\ -4 & 7 & 12 \end{array}\right]$; $(-3, 0)$

25. $\left[\begin{array}{ccc|c} 2 & 5 & -1 & 0 \\ -1 & 3 & 0 & -7 \\ 1 & 0 & 7 & 25 \end{array}\right]$; $(4, -1, 3)$

27b. first-place: 3 points, second-place: 2 points, third-place: 1 point.
29. $(-1, 4, 2)$ **31.** $\left(\frac{5}{6}, \frac{5}{6}, -\frac{5}{2}\right)$

33a. $\begin{cases} 2x + 7y = 24 \\ 4x + 13y = 46 \end{cases}$

33b. $\left[\begin{array}{cc|c} 2 & 7 & 24 \\ 4 & 13 & 46 \end{array}\right]$ **33c.** $(5, 2)$

33d. meal: 5 tickets, ride: 2 tickets
35. A **37.** C **41.** a reduction by a factor of $\frac{3}{8}$ **43.** $P = 6$ at $(0, 3)$

45. $\begin{bmatrix} 3 & -1 \\ 1 & 2 \end{bmatrix}\begin{bmatrix} x \\ y \end{bmatrix} = \begin{bmatrix} 0 \\ 7 \end{bmatrix}$; $(1, 3)$

Extension

Check it Out!

1. $A^3 = \begin{bmatrix} 6 & 1 & 0 & 0 & 5 \\ 3 & 4 & 1 & 3 & 5 \\ 3 & 1 & 1 & 1 & 3 \\ 4 & 1 & 2 & 6 & 2 \\ 2 & 2 & 1 & 4 & 2 \end{bmatrix}$;

5 3-step paths from *B* to *F* and from *F* to itself

Exercises

1. $\begin{bmatrix} 1 & 0 & 1 & 0 & 0 & 1 \\ 0 & 0 & 1 & 1 & 0 & 0 \\ 1 & 0 & 0 & 1 & 0 & 0 \\ 0 & 0 & 1 & 0 & 0 & 0 \\ 0 & 0 & 0 & 0 & 0 & 1 \\ 0 & 1 & 0 & 0 & 2 & 0 \end{bmatrix}$

3. *A* to *D*, *A* to *E*, *B* to *A*, *B* to *C*, *C* to *D*, *C* to *E*, *D* to *C*, *E* to *F*, *F* to *B*

5. For vertex *A*, one 1-step roundtrip is possible. For *A*, *C*, *D*, *E*, and *F*, at least one 2-step roundtrip is possible. For *A* and *C*, at least one 3-step roundtrip is possible.

Study Guide: Review

1. scalar **2.** constant matrix
3. square matrix **4.** not possible

5. $\begin{bmatrix} 0.4 & 0.6 \\ 0.8 & 1 \end{bmatrix}$ **6.** $\begin{bmatrix} 2 & -\frac{7}{3} & \frac{4}{3} \\ -\frac{11}{3} & \frac{2}{3} & 1 \end{bmatrix}$

7. $\begin{bmatrix} 6 & -9 & 4 \\ -9 & 2 & 5 \end{bmatrix}$ **11.** $\begin{bmatrix} -4 & -3 & 5 \\ 4 & 2 & -8 \\ -2 & -4 & -5 \end{bmatrix}$

12. $\begin{bmatrix} -7 & 9 \\ -3 & -3 \\ -8 & -1 \end{bmatrix}$ **13.** not defined

14. $\begin{bmatrix} -3 & 5 & 10 \\ -12 & 2 & 9 \end{bmatrix}$ **15.** not possible

16. $\begin{bmatrix} 15 & 1 & 7 \\ -1 & 5 & 5 \\ -7 & 5 & 9 \end{bmatrix}$ **17.** $\begin{bmatrix} 71 & -7 \\ 70 & -6 \end{bmatrix}$

18a. $A = \begin{bmatrix} 5 & 2.5 \\ 7.5 & 4.25 \\ 9 & 5.75 \end{bmatrix}$;

$B = \begin{bmatrix} 67 & 196 & 245 \\ 104 & 75 & 154 \end{bmatrix}$

18b. Thursday: $595; Friday: $1788.75; Saturday: $3090.50
18c. adults: $4010; students: $1464.25 **19.** $(0, 0)$, $(1, 4)$, $(4, 5)$, and $(2, 1)$ **20.** $(-3, -1.5)$, $(-1.5, 4.5)$, $(3, 6)$, and $(0, 0)$
21. $(-2, 1)$, $(-1, -3)$; $(2, -4)$, $(0, 0)$; reflected across the *x*-axis.
22. $(-1, 2)$, $(3, 1)$, $(4, -2)$, and $(0, 0)$; rotated 90°clockwise.
23. 2 **24.** 0 **25.** $\frac{1}{2}$ **26.** 22 **27.** −31
28. 0 **29.** $(5, 4)$ **30.** $(2, -5)$
31. infinitely many solutions
32. $(2, 4, -3)$ **33.** no solution
34. $(0.5, 2, 1.5)$ **35a.** $\begin{vmatrix} 2 & 3 \\ -1 & 1 \end{vmatrix} = 5$
35b. $(1, 2)$ **36b.** 72 small, 18 medium, and 12 large

37. $\begin{bmatrix} 0.15 & -0.1 \\ 0.05 & 0.3 \end{bmatrix}$ **38.** $\begin{bmatrix} \frac{4}{3} & \frac{8}{3} \\ 0 & 5 \end{bmatrix}$

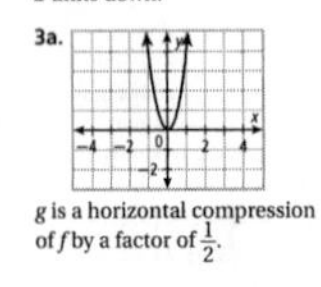

39. no inverse

40. $\begin{bmatrix} -0.25 & -0.25 & 0.5 \\ 1.5 & 0.5 & -1 \\ -2.25 & -0.25 & 1.5 \end{bmatrix}$

41. $\begin{bmatrix} -2 & 0 & 2 \\ -5 & -1 & 7 \\ 6 & 2 & -8 \end{bmatrix}$

42. does not exist **43.** $(20, 10)$
44. $(5, 4)$ **45.** $(4, 3, 2)$
46. $(-1, -2.5, 3.5)$
47. $(0.25, -0.5)$ **48.** $(-2, -6)$
49. $(0.1, -0.05, 0.2)$ **50.** $(1, 1, 2)$
51. 12 first-place, 4 second-place, 11 third-place

Chapter 5

5-1

Check It Out!

1.

x	−1	1	3	5	7
$g(x)$	−15	−3	1	−3	−15

2a.

g is *f* translated 5 units down.

b.

h is *f* translated 3 units left and 2 units down.

3a.

g is a horizontal compression of *f* by a factor of $\frac{1}{2}$.

b.

h is *f* reflected across the *x*-axis and vertically compressed by a factor of $\frac{1}{2}$. **4a.** $g(x) = \frac{1}{3}(x - 2)^2 - 4$
b. $g(x) = -(x + 5)^2 + 1$ **5.** Vertical compression by a factor of $\frac{13}{15}$; the braking distance will be less with optimally inflated new tires than with tires having more wear.

Exercises **1.** vertex

3.

5. *d* is *f* translated 4 units right.
7. *h* is *f* translated 1 unit left and 3 units down. **9.** *h* is a horizontal stretch of *f* by a factor of 8.
11. *h* is *f* reflected across the *x*-axis and horizontally compressed by a factor of $\frac{1}{5}$. **13.** *d* is *f* reflected across the *x*-axis and vertically compressed by a factor of $\frac{2}{3}$.
15. $h(x) = -x^2 - 6$

17.

19.

21. *h* is *f* translated 5 units left.
23. *g* is *f* translated 4 units left and 3 units down. **25.** *j* is *f* translated 4 units right and 9 units down.
27. *h* is *f* reflected across the *x*-axis and vertically stretched by a factor of 20. **29.** $g(x) = -\frac{1}{2}(x - 1)^2$

31. Vertical translation; at any given speed, the gas mileage for an SUV is 18 mi/gal less than for a compact car. **33.** *p* is *f* reflected across the *x*-axis and translated 4 units right. **35.** *h* is *f* vertically stretched by a factor of 4 and translated 2 units down. **37.** *g* is *f* horizontally compressed by a factor of $\frac{1}{3}$ and translated 1 unit up.
39. C **41.** A **43.** horizontal line; linear or constant function
45a. vertical compression by a factor of 0.38 and translation 3.5 units right and 59 units up
b. $y = -6.08(t - 4)^2 + 95$ **47.** J
49. G **51.** translation 6 units right and 6 units up: $y = -3(x - 3)^2 + 3$
55. $f(x) = \sqrt{x}$ **57.** $y = 2x + 10$

5-2

Check It Out! **1.** $x = 3$

2a.

downward; $x = -1$; $(-1, 2)$; 0

b.

upward; $x = -\frac{3}{2}$; $\left(-\frac{3}{2}, -\frac{13}{4}\right)$; −1

3a. minimum: −6; D: $\mathbb{R}$; R: $\{y \mid y \ge -6\}$ **b.** maximum: −4; D: $\mathbb{R}$; R: $\{y \mid y \le -4\}$ **4.** 30.0 mi/gal at 49 mi/h

Exercises **1.** minimum **3.** $x = 0$
5. downward; $x = -1$; $(-1, -7)$; −8 **7.** downward; $x = 2$; $(2, 3)$; −1
9. maximum: $\frac{1}{4}$; D: $\mathbb{R}$; R: $\left\{y \mid y \le \frac{1}{4}\right\}$
11. 3.125 m **13.** $x = 1$ **15.** upward; $x = -\frac{1}{2}$; $\left(-\frac{1}{2}, -\frac{9}{4}\right)$; −2 **17.** upward; $x = 2$; $(2, -6)$; −4 **19.** upward; $x = -\frac{1}{3}$; $\left(-\frac{1}{3}, -\frac{25}{3}\right)$; −8
21. downward; $x = 0$; $(0, -2)$; −2
23. upward; $x = -2$; $(-2, 1)$; 2
25. maximum: 9; D: $\mathbb{R}$; R: $\{y \mid y \le 9\}$
27. maximum: −4; D: $\mathbb{R}$; R: $\{y \mid y \le -4\}$
29. minimum: 0; D: $\mathbb{R}$; R: $\{y \mid y \ge 0\}$

31. 64 ft **33a.** 562.5 mm
b. 93.75 to 1 **c.** 168.75 m
35. minimum: ≈ -3.029771
37. minimum: ≈ -1.253333
41a. about 1.6 s **b.** about 45 ft
43. G **45.** G **51.** $60\sqrt{2}$ **53.** $\frac{3\sqrt{5}}{5}$
55. $f(0) = 10$; $f\left(\frac{1}{2}\right) = \frac{29}{4}$; $f(-2) = 26$
57. $f(0) = -20$; $f\left(\frac{1}{2}\right) = -22$; $f(-2) = -12$ **59.** $y + 4 = 3(x - 1)$
61. $y - 5 = -2(x - 3)$

5-3

Check It Out! **1.** −3,1 **2a.** −1, 6 **b.** 0, 8 **3.** 3 s **4a.** $x = 2$ **b.** $x = -\frac{3}{5}$, $x = \frac{3}{5}$ **5.** Possible answer: $f(x) = x^2 - 25$

Exercises **1.** roots **3.** 2, 4 **5.** 1, 6
7. −4, 0 **9.** −2, 8 **11.** 4 s **13.** $x = 2$
19. −3, 2 **21.** −8, −3 **23.** 0, 9
25. −8, 1 **27.** 4 s **29.** $x = -\frac{9}{2}$, $x = \frac{9}{2}$ **31.** $x = -\frac{1}{2}$, $x = \frac{1}{2}$
33. $x = \frac{2}{7}$ **37.** 0, 6 **39.** 6 **41.** 11
43. 5, 6 **45.** −7, −2 **47a.** $h(t) = -16t^2 + 16t + 5$ **b.** 1.25 s
49. $x = -5$, $x = -1$ **51.** $x = -\frac{1}{3}$
53. $x = -2$, $x = 3$ **55a.** $(0, -16)$
b. −16 **c.** −4, 4 **57a.** $(1, 2)$ **b.** 0
c. 0, 2 **59a.** $\left(-\frac{1}{6}, -4\frac{1}{12}\right)$ **b.** −4
c. $-1\frac{1}{3}$, 1 **61.** 20 ft by 4 ft
63. 10 m by 5 m **67.** B **69.** C
71. $x = 0$, $x = \frac{3}{2}$ **73.** $x = \frac{1}{4}$, $x = \frac{1}{2}$
75a. $(a + b)(a^2 - ab + b^2) = a^3 - a^2b + ab^2 + a^2b - ab^2 + b^3 = a^3 + b^3$ **b.** $(2x + 3)(4x^2 - 6x + 9)$
c. $a^3 - b^3 = (a - b)(a^2 + ab + b^2)$
d. $(x - 1)(x^2 + x + 1)$ **77.** 8.64×10^{12}
79. 6.5×10^{-10} **81.** $w = 2.2$
83. *h* is a vertical compression of *f* by a factor of 0.5. **85.** *g* is *f* translated 1 unit left.

5-4

Check It Out! **1a.** $x = \pm\frac{5}{2}$
b. $x = -11$, $x = 3$ **2a.** $x^2 + 4x + 4 = (x + 2)^2$ **b.** $x^2 - 4x + 4 = (x - 2)^2$
c. $x^2 + 3x + \frac{9}{4} = \left(x + \frac{3}{2}\right)^2$
3a. $x = \frac{9 \pm \sqrt{89}}{2}$ **b.** $x = -1$, $x = 9$

4a. $f(x)=(x+12)^2+1; (-12, 1)$
b. $g(x)=5(x-5)^2+3; (5, 3)$

Exercises 1. $\left(\frac{b}{2}\right)^2$ 3. $x=1, x=9$
5. $x^2+14x+49=(x+7)^2$
7. $x^2-9x+\frac{81}{4}=\left(x-\frac{9}{2}\right)^2$
9. $x=2, x=4$ 11. $x=-2\pm2\sqrt{7}$
13. $x=-2\pm\frac{\sqrt{46}}{2}$ 15. $g(x)=(x-5)^2-14; (5, -14)$ 17. $f(x)=(x+4)^2-26; (-4, -26)$ 19. $h(x)=3(x-2)^2-16; (2, -16)$ 21. $x=-7, x=13$ 23. $x^2-18x+81=(x-9)^2$ 25. $x^2-\frac{1}{2}x+\frac{1}{16}=\left(x-\frac{1}{4}\right)^2$ 27. $x=2\pm\sqrt{3}$ 29. $x=2, x=6$ 31. $x=-1\pm\frac{2\sqrt{3}}{3}$ 33. $g(x)=(x+7)^2+22; (-7, 22)$ 35. $f(x)=(x+2)^2-11; (-2, -11)$ 37. $h(x)=2(x+1.5)^2+20.5; (-1.5, 20.5)$
39a. about 12.3 s b. about 2.3 s
41. $x=\pm\sqrt{3}$ 43. $x=\pm5$ 45. $x=-13\pm\sqrt{7}$ 47. $x=\frac{-3\pm5\sqrt{2}}{2}$
49. $x=\frac{-3\pm\sqrt{5}}{3}$ 51. $x=-5, x=-3$
53. $x=\frac{-2\pm\sqrt{7}}{3}$ 55. $x=\frac{7\pm\sqrt{57}}{2}$
57. $x=-3\pm\sqrt{5}$ 59. $x=4\pm2\sqrt{10}$
61a. 1.7 s b. 71 ft/s 65. $x=\pm7.416$
67. $x=\pm4.192$ 69. $x=\pm1.528$
73. B 75. A 77. 2.5 79. $b=\pm24$
81. $b=\pm18$ 83. $2\sqrt{5}\pm1$
85a. 135,000 ft^2 b. 450 ft by 300 ft
c. 129,600 ft^2 87. $\{x \mid -6\le x\le14\}$
89. $\{x \mid -1\le x\le5\}$ 91. 3×3
93. 1368; the amount in dollars the Hernandez family budgeted for housing 95. $x=0; (0, -1)$

5-5

Check It Out! 1a. $2i\sqrt{3}$ b. $12i$
c. $-i\sqrt{7}$ 2a. $x=\pm6i$ b. $x=\pm4i\sqrt{3}$
c. $x=\pm\frac{5}{3}i$ 3a. $x=-4; y=-\frac{3}{10}$
b. $x=-\frac{8}{5}; y=-\frac{\sqrt{6}}{6}$ 4a. $-2\pm3i$
b. $4\pm i\sqrt{2}$ 5a. $9+i$ b. $\sqrt{3}-i$ c. $8i$

Exercises 1. imaginary 3. $2i$
5. $12i$ 7. $x=\pm6i$ 9. $x=\pm11i$
11. $x=1; y=-1$ 13. $-3\pm5i$
15. $\sqrt{5}-5i$ 17. $6-i\sqrt{2}$ 19. $-i\sqrt{10}$
21. $5i\sqrt{2}$ 23. $x=\pm4i$ 25. $x=\pm8i$
27. $x=-3; y=-5$ 29. $\frac{3\pm i\sqrt{7}}{8}$
31. $\frac{3\pm i\sqrt{21}}{3}$ 33. $-\frac{\sqrt{3}}{2}+2i$

35. $-1-\frac{i}{10}$ 37. $1-14i$
39. $-2\sqrt{5}-4i$ 41. $9+i\sqrt{2}$
43. $c=0, d=5$ 45. $c=\pm2, d=4$
47. $x=\pm9i$ 49. $x=\pm12i$
51. $x=\pm2i\sqrt{2}$ 53. $x=-5\pm2i$
55. $x=-1\pm2i$ 57. $x=12\pm i\sqrt{5}$
59. always true 61. sometimes true 63. sometimes true
65. sometimes true 67. $-1\pm4i$
69. $-8\pm3i$ 71. $8\pm2i$
73. The complex conjugate of a real number a is the number a.
75a. $t=\frac{7}{2}\pm\frac{\sqrt{3}}{2}i$ b. no c. 196 ft
77. F 79. G 81. When $a<0$, the 2 solutions are imaginary and complex. When $a>0$, the 2 solutions are real and complex.
85. $T^2=\begin{bmatrix}12&-3&5\\2&7&-1\\-4&4&-2\end{bmatrix}$
87. not defined 89a. upward
b. $x=-2.5$ c. $(-2.5, -11.25)$
d. -10 91a. upward b. $x=-1$
c. $(-1, -5)$ d. -3 93. $x=-7, x=2$
95. $x=\frac{3}{4}, x=3$ 97. $x=-8, x=-3$

5-6

Check It Out! 1a. $\frac{-3\pm\sqrt{37}}{2}$
b. $4\pm\sqrt{6}$ 2. $\frac{1}{6}\pm\frac{\sqrt{95}}{6}i$
3a. 1 distinct real solution
b. 2 distinct nonreal complex solutions c. 2 distinct real solutions 4. 449 ft

Exercises 3. $\frac{2\pm\sqrt{7}}{3}$ 5. $-6, 1$
7. $\pm\frac{\sqrt{38}}{2}$ 9. $-3\pm i\sqrt{3}$ 11. $-2\pm i\sqrt{6}$
13. $\frac{-7\pm i\sqrt{111}}{20}$ 15. 2 distinct real solutions 17. 14 in. and 20 in.
19. $-6, 0$ 21. $-1\pm\sqrt{10}$ 23. $\pm\frac{\sqrt{21}}{7}$
25. $\frac{-1\pm i\sqrt{3}}{2}$ 27. $\frac{-7\pm3\sqrt{17}}{4}$
29. $\frac{2\pm2i\sqrt{2}}{3}$ 31. 2 distinct real solutions 33. 1 distinct real solution
35. 2 distinct real solutions
37a. 9 s b. 6 s 39. $\frac{1\pm\sqrt{3}}{2}$
41. $\frac{-3\pm\sqrt{17}}{4}$ 43. $\frac{1\pm i\sqrt{87}}{2}$
45. $x=-2, x=5$ 47. $x=-2.5, x=1.5$ 49. $x=-3, x=7$
51. $x=\pm5$ 53. $x=8$ 55. 3 in.
57. $c=-36$ 61. B 63. C

65. 15 cm and 8 cm
73. $\left[\begin{array}{cc|c}2&-3&-7\\1&-6&1\end{array}\right]; x=-5; y=-1$
75. $\left[\begin{array}{cc|c}4&5&-1\\2&-7&9\end{array}\right]; x=1; y=-1$
77. $x=4\pm\sqrt{14}$

5-7

Check It Out!
1a. 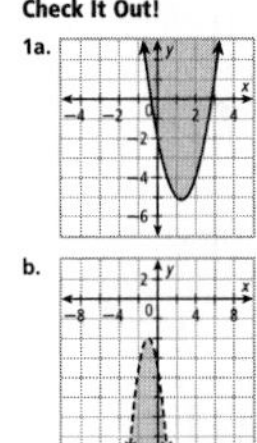
b.
2a. $-1<x<2$ b. $x\le0$ or $x\ge2.5$
3a. $x\le2$ or $x\ge4$ b. $x<-1$ or $x>2.5$
4. fewer than 14 or more than 36 people

Exercises
3. 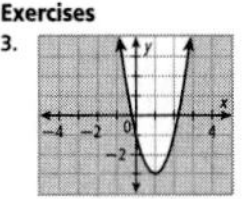
5. $0\le x\le5$ 7. $1.5\le x\le3$
9. $-8<x<-5$ 11. a range of costs between about \$21.78 and \$48.22
13. 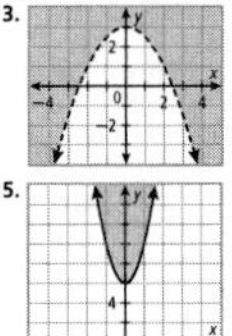
15.

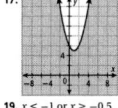

17.
19. $x\le-1$ or $x\ge-0.5$
21. $x<-2$ or $x>4$ 23. $2<x<10$
25. $-1\le x\le2.5$ 27. at distances less than about 3 ft and at distances greater than about 102 ft
29. 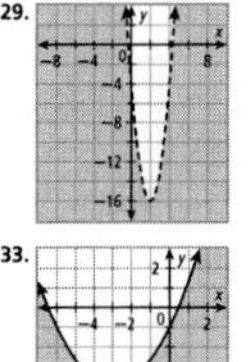
33.
35. $-3\le x\le8$
37. $\frac{-1-\sqrt{17}}{4}<x<\frac{-1+\sqrt{17}}{4}$
39. $-1-\frac{\sqrt{6}}{3}<x<-1+\frac{\sqrt{6}}{3}$
41. $\frac{-5-\sqrt{61}}{6}\le x\le\frac{-5+\sqrt{61}}{6}$
43. $x\le\frac{1-\sqrt{6}}{5}$ or $x\ge\frac{1+\sqrt{6}}{5}$
45. $x<3$ or $x>9$ 47. a distance between 0 ft and about 31 ft
49. A 51a. $A(x)=-\frac{1}{2}x^2+10x$
b. $3.7\le x\le16.3$ c. $0<x\le5.5$ or $14.5\le x\le20$ 53b. a width between 5 ft and 15 ft c. a width of 10 ft 55. $0.9\le x\le14.1$
57. $x\le-2.2$ or $x\ge0.7$ 59. It is not 63. J 65. $x<-3$ or $x>-1$
67. $\frac{5-\sqrt{17}}{4}<x<\frac{5+\sqrt{17}}{4}$
69. 121.5 square units
75. $c=9$

5-8

Check It Out! 1a. Quadratic; second differences are constant for equally spaced x-values.
b. Not quadratic; first differences are constant so the function is linear. 2. $f(x)=-x^2+4x-3$

3. $L(d)\approx14.3d^2-112.4d+430.1$; about 446 ft

Exercises 3. Not quadratic; second differences are not constant for equally spaced x-values.
5. $y=x^2-2x-3$ 7. $y=x^2-3x+4$
9. $y=-\frac{1}{2}x^2+4x-3$ 11. $C(x)\approx0.0098x^2+0.62x+3.8$; about \$31.20
13. Quadratic; second differences are constant for equally spaced x-values. 15. $y=\frac{4}{3}x^2-x-\frac{7}{3}$
17. $y=0.5x^2-3x-8$
19. $y\approx-3.7x^2+216x+781$; about \$3290 million, or \$3.29 billion
21. The function is $A(b)=\left(\frac{1}{2}h\right)b$, which is linear. 23. The function is $A(s)=s^2$, which is quadratic.
25. -3 27. -1
29a. $p(s)=-0.125s^2+5.25s-35.05$ b. \$18.95 c. a maximum point; the price and size of the most expensive pizza
d. \$9.95; $-\$1.05$ 31. not quadratic
33. quadratic; $y=5x^2+2x$
35. not quadratic 39a. $y\approx-10.7x+208.1$ b. no c. linear; $y=4x+8$
41. $t(n)=\frac{1}{2}n^2+\frac{1}{2}n$
43b. $y\approx0.5x+3$
c. $y\approx-0.13x^2+2.8x-6$
45. B 47. D
49. $y=2x^2-5$ 53. yes
55. The matrix is undefined.
57. $\begin{bmatrix}\frac{1}{3}&-\frac{8}{3}\\0&-2\end{bmatrix}$ 59. $\pm3i$

5-9

Check It Out!
1. 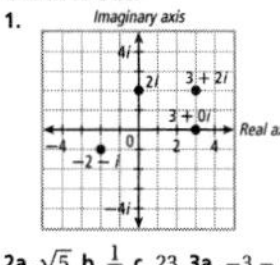

2a. $\sqrt{5}$ b. $\frac{1}{2}$ c. 23 3a. $-3-i$
b. $-3-3i$ c. 8

4a. $4+i$
b. $-2-3i$
5a. $10+6i$ b. $20-28i$
c. 13 6a. $-\frac{1}{2}i$ b. -1
7a. $-8+3i$ b. $\frac{7}{5}+\frac{1}{5}i$
Exercises 1. real; imaginary
3, 5. 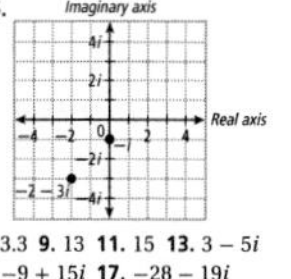
7. 33.3 9. 13 11. 15 13. $3-5i$
15. $-9+15i$ 17. $-28-19i$
19. $-3-i$ 21. 5 23. $37-5i$
25. $8+6i$ 27. $-i$ 29. -1 31. $\frac{21}{10}+\frac{17}{10}i$
33. $4-i$ 35. $-2+\frac{1}{2}i$
37, 39. 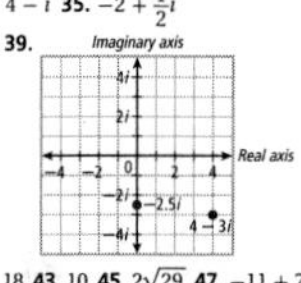
41. 18 43. 10 45. $2\sqrt{29}$ 47. $-11+7i$
49. $28+41i$ 51. $-4+9i$ 53. $4+6i$
55. $48+12i$ 57. 53 59. $24+78i$
61. $-i$ 63. -5 65. $\frac{13}{10}-\frac{11}{10}i$
67. $4+i$ 69. $\frac{3}{4}+\frac{9}{4}i$ 71. $3i$
73. $-2-i$ 75. $\sqrt{10}$ 77. $2\sqrt{10}$
79. 0 81. $\frac{\sqrt{10}}{2}$ 83. $\sqrt{11}$ 85. $9.5+2.9i$
87. $-9.7+1.3i$ 89. $-1+4i$
91. $-5+12i$ 93. $10-5i$ 95. 0

97. $1-12i$ 99. $\frac{26}{37}+\frac{8}{37}i$ 101. $\frac{8}{13}+\frac{12}{13}i$ 103. $Z_{eq}=\frac{7}{4}-i$
105. always true 107. always true
109. A is incorrect. 113. D 115. C
119. $\frac{ac+bd}{c^2+d^2}+\frac{(bc-ad)}{c^2+d^2}i$
121. $0\le x\le2$ 123. $-5\le x\le\frac{3}{2}$
125. Yes

Study Guide: Review

1. imaginary number; complex number 2. zero of a function
3. vertex of a parabola
4. discriminant 5. minimum value
6. 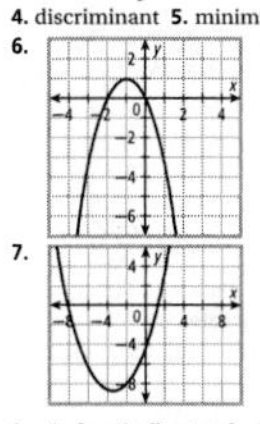
7.
8. g is f vertically stretched by a factor of 4 and translated 2 units right. 9. g is f reflected across the x-axis, vertically stretched by a factor of 2, and translated 1 unit left. 10. g is f vertically compressed by a factor of $\frac{1}{3}$ and translated 3 units down. 11. g is f reflected across the x-axis and translated 2 units left and 6 units up.
12. Possible answer: $g(x)=-x^2-3$
13. Possible answer: $g(x)=2(x-4)^2$
14. Possible answer: $g(x)=\frac{1}{4}(x+1)^2$
15. opens upward; $x=2$; $(2, -1)$; 3
16. opens upward; $x=-1$; $(-1, 2)$; 3
17. opens upward; $x=1.5$; $(1.5, -2.25)$; 0 18. opens upward; $x=2$; $(2, 2)$; 4 19. minimum: 5
20. maximum: 4.5 21. minimum: -5.25 22. maximum: 18
23. maximum: 12 24. minimum: 7
25. $x=-1$ or $x=8$ 26. $x=2$ or $x=3$ 27. $x=-12$ or $x=12$
28. $x=0$ or $x=21$ 29. $x=2$
30. $x=-1$ or $x=-3$ 31. $x=2$ or $x=-16$ 32. $x=-\frac{1}{3}$ 33. Possible answer: $f(x)=x^2+x-6$

34. Possible answer: $f(x)=x^2-1$
35. Possible answer: $f(x)=x^2-9x+20$ 36. Possible answer: $f(x)=x^2+5x+6$ 37. Possible answer: $f(x)=x^2+10x+25$
38. Possible answer: $f(x)=x^2-9x$
39. $x=4$ or $x=12$ 40. $x=-14$ or $x=-6$ 41. $x=-2$ or $x=8$
42. $x=7\pm\sqrt{62}$ 43. $f(x)=(x-2)^2+5$; $(2, 5)$ 44. $g(x)=(x+1)^2-8$; $(-1, -8)$ 45. $x=\pm9i$ 46. $x=\pm5i$
47. $x=-3\pm i$ 48. $x=-6\pm3i$
49. $x=7\pm i\sqrt{26}$ 50. $x=11\pm2i\sqrt{3}$
51. $-5i-4$ 52. $3-i\sqrt{5}$
53. $\frac{3\pm\sqrt{41}}{2}$ 54. $5\pm2i\sqrt{3}$
55. $\frac{5}{2}\pm\frac{i\sqrt{11}}{2}$ 56. $-\frac{3}{2}\pm i\frac{\sqrt{3}}{2}$
57. $\frac{5}{2}\pm i\frac{\sqrt{15}}{2}$ 58. 1 distinct real solution 59. 2 real solutions
60. 2 nonreal complex solutions
61. 2 real solutions 62. 2 nonreal complex solutions 63. 2 nonreal complex solutions
64. 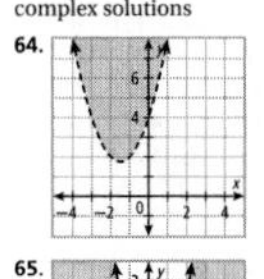
65.
66. $x\le-3$ or $x\ge1$ 67. $-4<x<-1$
68. $x<1$ or $x>5$ 69. $-3\le x\le3$
70. $-\sqrt{3}<x<\sqrt{3}$ 71. $-2\le x\le\frac{2}{3}$
72. $y=-x^2-3x+6$ 73. $y=-2x^2+x$
74. $y\approx0.000188x^2-0.0112x+0.182$
75. ≈0.074 in. 76. $y\approx0.360x^2-11.9x+105$ 77. ≈37.8 ohms
78. 3 79. $2\sqrt{5}$ 80. 20 81. 7
82. $7+4i$ 83. $6+2i$ 84. -6
85. $-20-15i$ 86. $46+28i$
87. 13 88. $9-19i$
89. $-57-51i$ 90. 1 91. $-5i$
92. $-\frac{9}{2}+i$ 93. $\frac{7}{25}+\frac{26}{25}i$
94. $2-6i$ 95. $4+5i$

Chapter 6

6-1

Check It Out! 1a. 3 b. 0 c. 5 d. 9 2a. $-2x^2+4x+2$; -2; 2; 3; quadratic trinomial
b. x^3-18x^2+2x-5; 1; 3; 4; cubic polynomial with 4 terms
3a. $16x^3-30x^2+6x-16$
b. $5x^3-9x^2-3x+14$
4. $f(4)=3.8398$; $f(17)=1.6368$; the concentration of dye after 4 s; the concentration of dye after 17 s
5a. From left to right, the graph increases, decreases slightly, and then increases again. It crosses the x-axis 3 times, so there appear to be 3 real zeros.
b. From right to left, the graph decreases and then increases. It does not cross the x-axis, so there are no real zeros.
c. From left to right, the graph decreases and then increases. It crosses the x-axis twice, so there appear to be 2 real zeros.
d. From left to right, the graph alternately decreases and increases, changing direction 3 times. It crosses the x-axis 4 times, so there appear to be 4 real zeros.

Exercises 1. The leading coefficient of a polynomial is the number being multiplied by the variable with the greatest degree. 3. 5 5. 6 7. $3x^2+5x-4$; 3; 2; 3; quadratic trinomial
9. $4x^4+8x^2-3x+1$; 4; 4; 4; quartic with 4 terms
11. $3x^2+12x+3$
13. $-5x^2-7x-5$ 15. From left to right, the graph increases. It crosses the x-axis once, so there appears to be 1 real zero. 17. From left to right, the graph decreases. It crosses the x-axis once, so there appears to be 1 real zero. 19. 8
21. 0 23. $2x^4+3x^3+x^2-7x$; 2; 4; 4; quartic with 4 terms
25. $2x^3+10x-9$; 2; 3; 3; cubic trinomial 27. x^3+x^2
29. $5y^3-3y^2+2y+2$
31a. $d(1)=-3$; $d(2)=-28$
33. From left to right, the graph increases. There is 1 real zero.

35. The graph decreases, increases, and then decreases. There is 1 real zero. 41. $S(x)=4\pi x^2+8\pi x$
43. $S(x)=5\pi x^2+\frac{31}{2}\pi x+12\pi$
45a. \$12.04 b. \$27.52 47. sometimes true 49. sometimes true
51a. The x-intercepts are -3, 1, and 4. b. The x-intercepts are -1, -2, 3, and 1. c. The x-intercepts are 0, -1, and 2. d. The x-intercepts are -2 and 3. e. The x-intercepts are $-\frac{1}{2}$, 0, and $\frac{1}{2}$. 53. Yes 55. J 57. J
67. vertical 69. horizontal
71. shift left 3 units and up 2 units

6-2

Check It Out!
1a. $12c^3d^3-18c^2d^3+42c^2d^4$
b. $6x^2y^4+x^2y^3-28x^2y^2+30x^2y$
2a. $9b^3-9b^2c-4bc^2+4c^3$
b. $x^4+x^3-21x^2+13x-2$
3. $T(x)=-0.00008x^4-0.0028x^3+0.028x^2+0.3x+9$
4a. $x^4+16x^3+96x^2+256x+256$
b. $8x^3-12x^2+6x-1$
5a. $x^3+6x^2+12x+8$
b. $x^5-20x^4+160x^3-640x^2+1280x-1024$
c. $81x^4+108x^3+54x^2+12x+1$

Exercises
1. $-20c^3d^5-12c^4d^4$
3. $5x^3y+8x^2y-7xy$
5. $x^3+x^2y-3xy^2+y^3$
7. $3x^5+15x^4+16x^3-3x^2+6x-2$
9. $-0.02x^4-0.3x^3+4.4x^2-14.2x+20$
11. $x^4+4x^3y+6x^2y^2+4xy^3+y^4$
13. $x^3-9x^2y+27xy^2-27y^3$
15. $16x^4+32x^3y+24x^2y^2+8xy^3+y^4$
17. $32x^5-80x^4y+80x^3y^2-40x^2y^3+10xy^4-y^5$
19. $6x^4+27x^3-18x^2$
21. $12r^5+28r^4-60r^3+28r^2$
23. $6x^3+7x^2y-16xy^2+10y^3$
25. $12x^4+17x^3+8x^2+x-2$
27. $8x^3-24x^2+24x-8$
29. $x^4-4x^3y+6x^2y^2-4xy^3+y^4$
31. $x^4-12x^3y+54x^2y^2-108xy^3+81y^4$ 33. $x^5+5x^4y+10x^3y^2+10x^2y^3+5xy^4+y^5$
35. equivalent 37. not equivalent
39. $T(x)=-0.0003x^4-0.0164x^3+2.572x^2-14.12x+116.2$
41. $p^3-6p^2q+12pq^2-8q^3$
43. $x^6+x^4y^3+x^3y^3+xy^6$

45. $5x^3y+x^2y-9xy+10x^3+2x^2-18x$
47. $3x^4-24x^3+72x^2-96x+48$
49. $-x^5-14x^3-45x^2+30x-450$
51. $2x^6-3x^5-8x^4+12x^3+14x-21$
53. No
55a. $f(n)=\frac{1}{4}n^4+n^3+\frac{5}{4}n^2+\frac{1}{2}n$
b. 7098 59. J 61. H
63. $x^{10}-10x^9+45x^8-120x^7+210x^6-252x^5+210x^4-120x^3+45x^2-10x+1$
65. $m^6-3m^4n^2+3m^2n^4-n^6$
67. $B(x)=x-3$
69. $B(x)=x^3+1$
71. $\begin{bmatrix}8&1\\4&13\end{bmatrix}$
73. $\begin{bmatrix}4&-2&10\\-4&10&6\\-4&-6&6\end{bmatrix}$
75. $4x^4-6x^3+5x^2+3x$; 4; 4; 4; quartic with 4 terms
77. $3x^5-4x^2-2x+9$; 3; 5; 4; quintic with 4 terms

6-3

Check It Out!
1a. $5x+1-\frac{13}{3x+1}$
b. $x+8-\frac{4}{x-3}$
2a. $6x-23+\frac{63}{x+3}$ b. $x+3$
3a. $P(-3)=4$
b. $P\left(\frac{1}{5}\right)=5$ 4. $y-5$

Exercises 3. $x+2+\frac{1}{x-1}$
5. $7x-2$ 7. $x-6$
9. $P(-8)=42$ 11. $P(-1)=6$
13. $x+4$ 15. x^2-1
17. $\frac{1}{2}x^3-2x^2-\frac{7}{2}$
19. $x+4+\frac{2}{x+1}$
21. $x+1-\frac{2}{x+8}$
23. $2x+14-\frac{1}{x-\frac{1}{2}}$
25. $P(4)=9$
27. $P\left(-\frac{1}{3}\right)=\frac{5}{3}$
29. $I(t)=0.5t^2+4t$
31. $a=2; b=8; c=29$
33. $a=3; b=9; c=-4$
35. $x-2$
37. $D(h)=\frac{1}{\pi}-\frac{4}{\pi h}+\frac{20}{\pi h^2}$
39. y^2+5 41. $x^2-5x-12$

43. $t-4$ 45. $x^3+3x^2-10x-1$
47. $x^3-x^2+3x-4+\frac{1}{x-6}$
49. Solution B is correct. 53. B
55. D 57. $P(-4)=-1{,}189{,}150$
59. $P(1)=0$ 61. $k=18$
65. max = 1.25; D: $\mathbb{R}$; R: $\{y \mid y\le1.25\}$
67. min = -2; D: $\mathbb{R}$; R: $\{y \mid y\ge-2\}$
69. $12x^3y^3+24x^3y+20x^2y^4$
71. $4x^3-8x^2y+8xy^2-4y^3$

6-4

Check It Out!
1a. no b. yes
2a. $(x+3)(x-3)(x-2)$
b. $(x^2+4)(2x+1)$
3a. $(2+z^2)(4-2z^2+z^4)$
b. $2x^2(x-2)(x^2+2x+4)$
4. $x=1, 3, 4$; $V(x)=(x-1)(x-3)(x-4)$

Exercises
1. yes 3. yes
5. $(x+2)(x-2)(x+5)$
7. $2(x+2)(x-2)(x-1)$
9. $3(x-2)(4x+1)$
11. $2t^4(t+3)(t^2-3t+9)$
13. $(3+x)(9-3x+x^2)$
15. $(y-5)(y^2+5y+25)$
17. no 19. yes
21. $(b+2)(b-2)(4b+3)$
23. $(x+3)(x-3)(3x+1)$
25. $(x+2)(x-2)(5x-1)$
27. $(s-1)(s+1)(s^2+s+1)(s^2-s+1)$
29. $6x(x-3)(x^2+3x+9)$
31. $y^2(y+3)(y^2-3y+9)$
33. $x^2(x^2-7)(x^2-7)$
35. $(x-2)(x+2)(4x+1)$
37. $x(2x^2-1)(2x^2-3)(2x^2+3)$
39. $a=3; d=72$
41. $P(x)=(x-2)(x^3+5x+1)$
43. $P(x)=(x+2)(2x^4-6x+3)$
45a. $f(t)=-t(t-8)(t-18)$ b. \$2,535,000
c. $f(15)=-945$
47. $B(x)=x^3-2x^2+4x-8$ 51. J
53. $[(x-3)+2][(x-3)^2-2(x-3)+4]$; $(x-1)(x^2-8x+19)$

57. $(3x-5)(3x-5)$
59. $\left(x-\frac{22}{3}\right)\left(x+\frac{35}{6}\right)$ 61. 20
63. $\frac{19}{26}+\frac{17}{26}i$ 65. $P(5)=64$
67. $P(-1)=20$

6-5

Check It Out!
1a. $x=0,-1,6$ b. $x=-5,2,5$
2a. $x=2$ with multiplicity 4
b. $x=0$ with multiplicity 3; $x=-1$ with multiplicity 1; $x=6$ with multiplicity 2 3. 2 ft
4. $x=-\frac{1}{2}, 1\pm\sqrt{5}$

Exercises
3. $x=6,-6,1,-1$
5. $x=0,\frac{1}{3},-4$
7. $x=-5,-2,2,5$
9. $x=-2,2$ with multiplicity 3
11. $x=-6,\pm\sqrt{5}$ 13. $x=-5,1,4$
15. $x=-3,3$ 17. $x=-8,0,8$
19. $x=\frac{5}{2},\pm\sqrt{2}$ 21. $x=0$ with multiplicity 2; $x=8$ with multiplicity 3 23. 3 in. by 3 in.
25. $x=-\frac{4}{3},\pm\sqrt{2}$ 27a. $\pm1,\pm2,\pm4$
b. $x=-2,2$ c. 2 d. $x=-2.62, -0.38$ 29. $x=3, 2\pm\sqrt{2}$
31. $x=-5,-2,3,5$
33. $x=-1,0,1,2\pm\sqrt{5}$ 35a. 126 ft
b. The coaster passes through 2 tunnels within the first 100 s.
c. Possible answer: $h(t)=3(t-3)(t-5)$ 41. F 43. H
45. $k=-18$ 47. $k=6$
49. $x<-3$ or $x>2$ 51. $-1<x<1$
53. $4(2x+1)(x+1)(x-1)$

6-6

Check It Out!
1a. $P(x)=x^3-4x^2-4x+16$
1b. $x^3-\frac{11}{3}x^2+2x$
2. $x=-5,1,2i,-2i$
3. $P(x)=x^5-5x^4+9x^3-17x^2+20x+12$ 4. $r=9$ ft

Exercises
1. $P(x)=x^3-\frac{10}{3}x^2+3x-\frac{2}{3}$
3. $P(x)=x^3-\frac{1}{2}x^2-4x+2$
5. $x=2, \frac{2\pm\sqrt{2i}}{3}$
7. $P(x)=x^3-4x^2+6x-4$
9. $P(x)=x^5-2x^4+2x^3-4x^2-8x+16$
11. $P(x)=x^3-3x-2$
13. $P(x)=x^3+3x^2-6x-8$
15. $x=1,3$ 17. $x=\frac{3}{2},2i,-2i$
19. $x=1,-1,\pm\sqrt{3}$
21. $P(x)=x^5+3x^4-13x^3-39x^2+40x+120$ 23. $r=9$ ft
25. $x=2,-4,-1$
27. $x=-1$ 29. $x=3,\frac{-1\pm i\sqrt{3}}{2}$
31. $x=0,7,3\pm2i$
33. $x=\pm3i,\pm i\sqrt{5}$ 35. $x=-1,2,3$
37a. $x^3-6x^2-243=0$ b. 9 m
c. They are complex.
39. $P(x)=x^4+12x^2-64$
41. $P(x)=x^3-4x^2+5x-2$
43. $P(x)=x^4-6x^3+18x^2-54x+81$
45. never true 47. Sometimes true
49. $x=0$ or $x\approx\pm0.537$
51. $x\approx-0.782, 0.975, 3.965$
53. $r=6$ 57. B 59. D 61. D
63. $f(3i)=0; f(-\sqrt{3})=-36-12\sqrt{3}$ 65. $x=\pm3i$
67. $(a+bi)(a-bi)$
69. $(a+bi)(a-bi)(a^4-2a^2b^2+b^4)$
71. $x^4+2x^2+1=0;\pm i$
73. shift right 2 units, reflection across x-axis, and shift up 3 units
75. $(9,-3)$ 77. $x=0,42,1$
79. $x=0,-8,2$

6-7

Check It Out!
1a. 2; 5; as $x\to-\infty, P(x)\to-\infty$, as $x\to+\infty, P(x)\to\infty$ b. -3; 2; as $x\to-\infty$, $P(x)\to-\infty$ as $x\to+\infty, P(x)\to-\infty$
2a. odd; negative b. even; positive
3a.
b.
4a.
min $=-4.0887$; max $=-1.9113$
b.
min $=6$
5. 420.1 ft^3

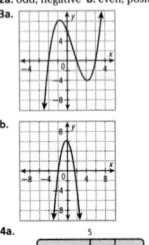

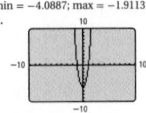

Exercises
1. A graph "turns around" at a turning point.
3. -2; 7; $x\to-\infty$ $Q\to+\infty$, $x\to+\infty$ $Q\to-\infty$ 5. 3; 2; $x\to\infty$ $S\to+\infty$, $x\to+\infty$ $S\to+\infty$ 7. even; positive
9. even; negative
11.
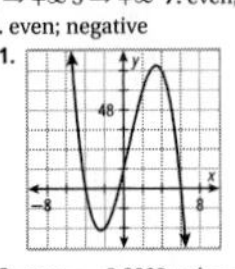
13. max $=-2.9098$; min $=-14.0902$
15. 2; 3; $x\to-\infty$ $P\to-\infty$, $x\to+\infty$ $P\to+\infty$
17. -1; 5; $x\to-\infty$ $R\to\infty$ $x\to+\infty$ $R\to+\infty$
19. even; negative 21. odd; negative
23.
25.
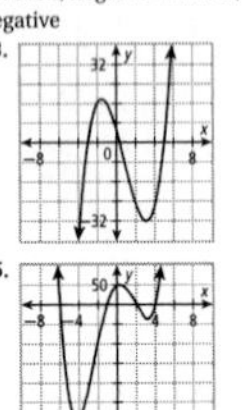
27. min $=20$ 29. max $=-1$
31. 3.425 L; 0.5 s 33. B 35. A
37. $+\infty$; $+\infty$ 39. $+\infty$; $+\infty$
41. $-\infty$; $-\infty$
45a. $V(x)=-\frac{1}{3}x^3+\frac{10}{3}x^2$
b. 49.4 in^3 c. 6.7 in. × 3.3 in. × 6.7 in.
49. H
57. no 59. $h(t)=-16(t-2)^2+70$; vertex $(2,70)$ 61. $10x-2+\frac{8}{x+1}$

6-8

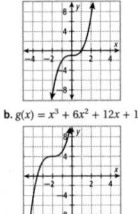

Check It Out!
1a. $g(x)=x^3-1$
b. $g(x)=x^3+6x^2+12x+12$
2a. $g(x)=-x^3+2x^2+x-2$
b. $g(x)=-x^3-2x^2+x+2$
3a. vertical compression
b. horizontal stretch
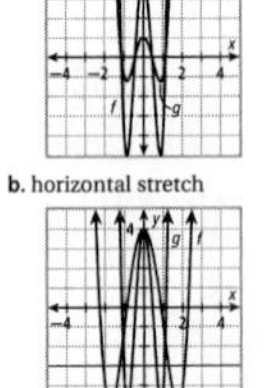
4a. $g(x)=4(x-3)^3-1 = 4x^3-3x^2+108x-109$
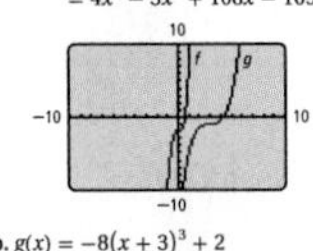
b. $g(x)=-8(x+3)^3+2 = -8x^3-96x^2-384x-510$
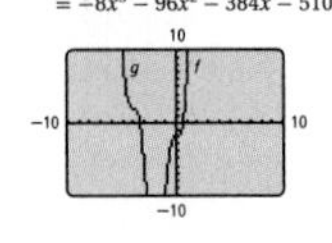
5. $g(x)=0.01x^3+0.55x^2-5.85x+134.25$
Possible answer: The model represents the number of sales since March.

Exercises
1. $g(x)=x^4-4$ 3. $j(x)=81x^4-8$
5. $g(x)=x^3+3x^2+2x+1$
7. horizontal stretch 9. horizontal compression and vertical shift
11. $g(x)=-32x^3+2$
13. $c(x)=4x^3-6x+60$; the cost has doubled.
15. $h(x)=x^3-9x^2+27x-31$
17. $g(x)=-x^3+2x^2-5x+3$
19. vertical stretch
21. horizontal stretch
23. $g(x)=\frac{1}{3}x^4-1$
25. $V\left(\frac{2}{3}x\right)=\frac{8}{27}x^3+\frac{4}{3}x^2+\frac{2}{3}x+8$
27a. $v>2.04$ b. $G(v)=0.24v^2+2.4v+6$; a shift 5 units left
c. $v\geq0$ d. a vertical stretch
31. B 33. B 35. shift right 2 units
37. shift right 3 units and up 8 units
39. $w(t)=60t$; yes 41. $3x^5-3x^4+5x^2-4x$ 43. $x=-2,1,\pm i\sqrt{5}$
45. $x=-4,-1,2,\pm2i\sqrt{2}$

6-9

Check It Out!
1. cubic 2. $f(x)=0.001x^3-0.113x^2+4.134x-24.867$
3. \$11,482.84

Exercises 1. linear 3. quartic
5. 831 patients 7. quartic
9. $f(x)=0.821x^2-1.821x+23.357$
13a. $f(x)=0.019x^3-0.185x^2+0.95x+12.056$; $R^2=0.9944$
b. $f(x)=0.0075x^4-0.071x^3+0.143x^2+0.604x+12.083$; $R^2=0.9967$ c. no 15. yes 17. C
19. $f(x)=x^3-5x+4$
25. $4a-25a^3$ 27. cubic parent function; shift right 1 unit and up 2 units. 29. 4; 5; $x\to-\infty$, $f(x)\to-\infty$; $x\to+\infty, f(x)\to+\infty$

Study Guide: Review

1. monomial 2. synthetic division
3. multiplicity 4. end behavior
5. $-3x^3+4x^2+6x+7$; -3; 3; 4: cubic polynomial with 4 terms
6. $-x^5+2x^4+5x^3+8x$; -1; 5; 4: quintic polynomial with 4 terms
7. $9x^2-11x+1$; 9; 2; 3: quadratic trinomial 8. x^4-6x^2; 1; 4; 2: quartic binomial 9. $8x^3+x^2-4x$
10. $-5x^3+6x^2+10x-1$
11. $-6x^2-x+9$ 12. $-4x^4-x^3-3$
13. From left to right, it alternately increases and decreases, changing direction 3 times and crossing the x-axis 2 times. There appear to be 2 real zeros. 14. From left to right, it increases, decreases slightly, and then increases again. It crosses the x-axis 1 time. There appears to be 1 real zero. 15. From left to right, it alternately decreases and increases, changing direction 3 times. It crosses the x-axis 4 times. There appear to be 4 real zeros.
16. From left to right, it increases, decreases, and then increases again. It crosses the x-axis 3 times. There appear to be 3 real zeros.
17. $15x^3-10x^2$
18. $-6t^3+18t^2-3t$
19. $a^3b^2-a^2b^2+a^2b^3$
20. x^3-4x^2+x+6
21. $2x^4+3x^3-5x^2+2x+5$
22. $x^3-9x^2+27x-27$
23. $x^5+4x^4-3x^3-11x^2+4x$
24. $16x^4+32x^3+24x^2+8x+1$
25. $4\pi x^4-4\pi x^3-12\pi x^2$
26. $x^2-7x+16-\frac{39}{x+2}$
27. $4x^3+2x^2+4x+1+\frac{5}{2x-1}$
28. $x^2-x+\frac{2}{x-3}$
29. $x^2+2x+6+\frac{11}{x-2}$
30. x^2+2x+2 in.; remainder 2 in. 31. no 32. yes 33. yes
34. $(x-1)(x-4)(x+4)$
35. $(x-2)(2x-1)(2x+1)$
36. $3(x+3)(x^2-3x+9)$
37. $2(2x-1)(4x^2+2x+1)$
38. 1, 2 39. $-2,-2\pm\sqrt{3}$
40. -1 41. $-3,3,\pm\sqrt{3}$ 42. $-1,\pm\sqrt{2}$
43. $1,2\pm2\sqrt{2}$ 44. 2 m
45. $P(x)=x^3-3x^2-10x+24$
46. $P(x)=x^3-\frac{1}{2}x^2-\frac{13}{2}x-3$
47. $P(x)=x^3+x^2-2x-2$
48. $P(x)=x^3+3x^2+x+3$
49. $P(x)=x^4-5x^2+6$
50. $P(x)=x^4-2x^3+2x^2-8x-8$
51. $1,-2i,2i$ 52. $-i,i,-\sqrt{2},\sqrt{2}$
53. $\pm4,\pm\frac{1}{2}i$ 54. $\pm\sqrt{5},-3$
55. -2; 3; as $x\to-\infty, f(x)\to+\infty$; as $x\to+\infty, f(x)\to-\infty$

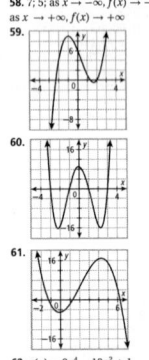

56. 1; 4; as $x\to\pm\infty, f(x)\to+\infty$
57. -3; 6; as $x\to\pm\infty, f(x)\to-\infty$
58. 7; 5; as $x\to-\infty, f(x)\to-\infty$, as $x\to+\infty, f(x)\to+\infty$
59.
60.
61.
62. $g(x)=2x^4-12x^2+1$
63. $g(x)=-x^4+6x^2+6$
64. $g(x)=(-x-3)^4+6(-x-3)^2-4$
65. $f(x)\approx-6\frac{2}{3}x^4+80x^3-328\frac{1}{3}x^2+575x-72$
66. $f(x)\approx80.5x^3-523.5x^2+1790x+544$

Chapter 7

7-1

Check It Out!
1. growth
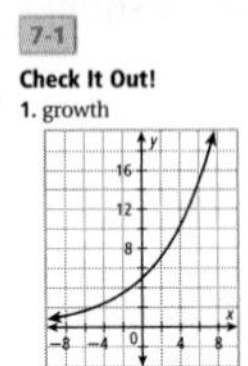
2. $P(t)=350(1.14)^t$
30.9 yr
3. $v(t)=1000(0.85)^t$
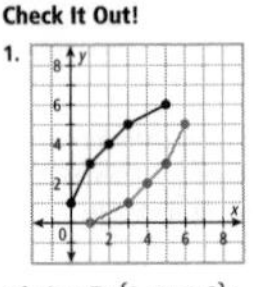
14.2 yr
Exercises 1. exponential decay. 3. growth
5a. $f(x)=150(2^x)$
b.
c. ≈ 600,000
7. decay 9. growth
11a. $f(x)=10(0.95)^t$ c. ≈ 6 units
d. 13.6 min. 13. no
15. ≈ \$12,000,000 17. ≈ 5.8 yr
19. 15.63; 6.25; ...; 0.03; 0.01
21a. ≈ 3146 b. 12th month
25. (34.868, 100] 27a. 17%
b. $A(t)=500(0.83)^t$ c. ≈ 36.8 mg
29. 3^x 31. B 37. $x>22.76$
39. 2; (2, 4), (≈ −0.767, ≈ 0.588)
43. D: ℝ; R: $\{y|y\leq1\}$;
$f(x)=x^2$ reflected across x-axis and shifted 1 unit up 47. odd; positive 49. even; negative

7-2

Check It Out!
1.
relation: D: $\{1\leq x\leq6\}$; R: $\{0\leq y\leq5\}$
inverse: D: $\{0\leq y\leq5\}$; R: $\{1\leq x\leq6\}$
2a. $f^{-1}(x)=3x$ b. $f^{-1}(x)=x-\frac{2}{3}$
3. $f^{-1}(x)=\frac{x+7}{5}$
4. $f^{-1}(x)=\frac{2}{3}x-3$
5. inverse: $z=6t-6$; 36 oz of water

Exercises
1. relation
3.
relation: D: $\{-1\leq x\leq4\}$; R: $\{-4\leq y\leq-1\}$
inverse: D: $\{-4\leq y\leq-1\}$; R: $\{-1\leq x\leq4\}$
5. $f^{-1}(x)=\frac{1}{4}x$ 7. $f^{-1}(x)=x+2\frac{1}{2}$
9. $f^{-1}(x)=2(x-3)$
11. $f^{-1}(x)=-\frac{2}{3}x+1$
13. $f^{-1}(x)=\frac{2}{3}x+\frac{5}{3}$

15.
$f^{-1}(x)=4(x-2)$
17. $F=\frac{9}{5}C+32$; 61° F
19.
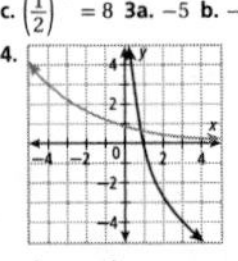
relation: D: $\{-4\leq x\leq4\}$; R: $\{-2\leq y\leq2\}$
inverse: D: $\{-2\leq y\leq2\}$; R: $\{-4\leq x\leq4\}$
21. $f^{-1}(x)=x+1\frac{3}{4}$
23. $f^{-1}(x)=-\frac{1}{32}x+\frac{21}{32}$
25. $f^{-1}(x)=5x-60$
27. $f^{-1}(x)=-3x+6$
29. 22 31a. $f^{-1}(x)=\frac{212-x}{1.85}$
b. 6500 ft c. 27,946 ft
33. (4, 2), (2, 4), (−3, −1), (−1, −3)
35. $f(x)=\frac{10}{12.59}x$; $f^{-1}(x)=1.259x$; 31.48 s 37. B 39. yes 41. always
43. never 45. always
47a. $P=\frac{147}{340}d+14.7$
b. D: $\{d|d\geq0\}$; R: $\{P|P\geq14.7\}$
c. $d=\frac{340}{147}P-34$; depth as a function of pressure 49. F
51.

x	1	2	3	4	5
y	0	1	2	3	4

53. $y=-\frac{b}{a}x+\frac{c}{a}$
61. $2x^3-14x+12=0$
63. $2x^3-8x^2+12x-8=0$
65. decay 67. growth

7-3

Check It Out! 1a. $\log_9 81=2$
b. $\log_3 27=3$ c. $\log_x 1=0$
2a. $10^1=10$ b. $12^2=144$
c. $\left(\frac{1}{2}\right)^{-3}=8$ 3a. -5 b. -1
4.
D: $\{x|x>0\}$; R: ℝ 5. 3.8

Exercises
1. x 3. $\log_4 8=1.5$ 5. $\log_3 243=x$
7. $x^3=-16$ 9. $6^3=x$ 11. -2 13. 2
15. $f(x)$: D: ℝ, R: $\{y|y>0\}$; $f^{-1}(x)$: D: $\{x|x>0\}$; R: ℝ
17. $\log_4 32=2.5$ 19. $\log_{1.2}1=0$
21. $5^4=625$ 23. $4.5^0=1$ 25. 0 27. 3
29. $f(x)$: D: ℝ, R: $\{y|y>0\}$; $f^{-1}(x)$: D: $\{x|x>0\}$; R: ℝ 31. no 33. 1
35. yes 37a. orange b. lemon
c. grapefruit 39. C 41. A 43. 6
47a. $2^{11}=2048$ Hz, $\log_2 2048=11$
b. 3 octaves lower 49. $\frac{2s}{t^2}$
51. $21a^{-1}b^4+28a^{-3}b^5$
53. 0.35; 0.59; 1; 1.7; 2.89
55. 11.11; 3.33; 1; 0.3; 0.09

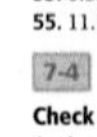
7-4

Check It Out!
1a. $\log_5(625\cdot25)=6$
b. $\log_{\frac{1}{3}}3=-1$ 2. $\log_7 7=1$
3a. $4\log10=4$ b. $4\log_5 5=4$
c. $-5\log_2 2=-5$ 4a. 0.9 b. $8x$
5a. 1.5 b. $1.\overline{3}$ 6. ≈ 63

Exercises
1. $\log_5 3125=5$ 3. $\log_3 81=4$
5. $\log100=2$ 7. 2 9. 6 11. $\frac{x}{2}+5$
13. 5 15. -1.5 17. ≈ 1.43
19. 2 times as large 21. $\log10=1$
23. $\log10=1$ 25. $\log_{1.5}3.375=3$
27. 0.2 29. $7+x$ 31. 4 33. 1.5
35. ≈ 3.16 times as intense
37. $\log_b m+\log_b n=\log_b mn$
39. $n\log_b b^m=mn$
41. 0 43. $-\frac{3}{2}$ 45. 1
47. $10^{-7}-10^{-7.6}$
49. $t=\log_{1.08}\left(\frac{50}{40}\right)$; 2.9
55a. ≈ 0.2 b. ≈ 2.6 c. ≈ 2.4
57. sometimes 59. always
61. always 63. sometimes 65. B
67. H 71. $\{x|x>1\}$ 73. $\{x|x>0\}$
75. $\{x|-1\leq x<0\}$ 77. x 79. ∅
81. 17 83. 7 85. $12i$ 87. $8i\sqrt{2}$
89. $\log_5 125=3$ 91. $\log_{36}6=0.5$
93. 0 95. 0.5

7-5

Check It Out!
1a. 1.5 b. ≈ −1.565 c. ≈ 1.302
2. day 18 3a. 5 b. 2 4a. $x=2$
b. $x<2$ c. $x=1000$

Exercises
1. exponential equation 3. $x=-2$
5. $x\approx1.661$ 7. $x\approx0.503$ 9. $x=\frac{1}{8}$
11. $x=108$ 13. $x=\frac{9}{13}$ 15. $x=2$
17. $x=3.5$ 19. $x=100$ 21. $x=-5$
23. $x=0.8$ 25. ≈ 7.595
27. ≈ 41 min 29. $x=30$ 31. ≈ 2.73
33. $x=20$ 35. $x<1$ 37. $x=4$
39. $x=4$ 41. 24 keys below concert A 43. 0 47a. 11 km; 25 km b. greater 49. J 51. no
53. $\{x|0<x<12\}$ 55. 26 57. 3
59. $f^{-1}(x)=\frac{1}{4}x-\frac{3}{4}$
61. $f^{-1}(x)=3x-27$

7-6

Check It Out!
1.
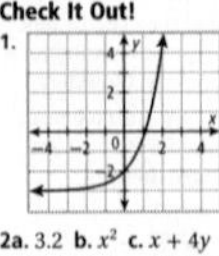
2a. 3.2 b. x^2 c. $x+4y$
3. \$132.31 4. ≈ 47.6 days

Exercises
1. $f(x)=\ln x$; natural logarithm
3.
5.
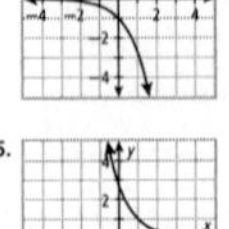

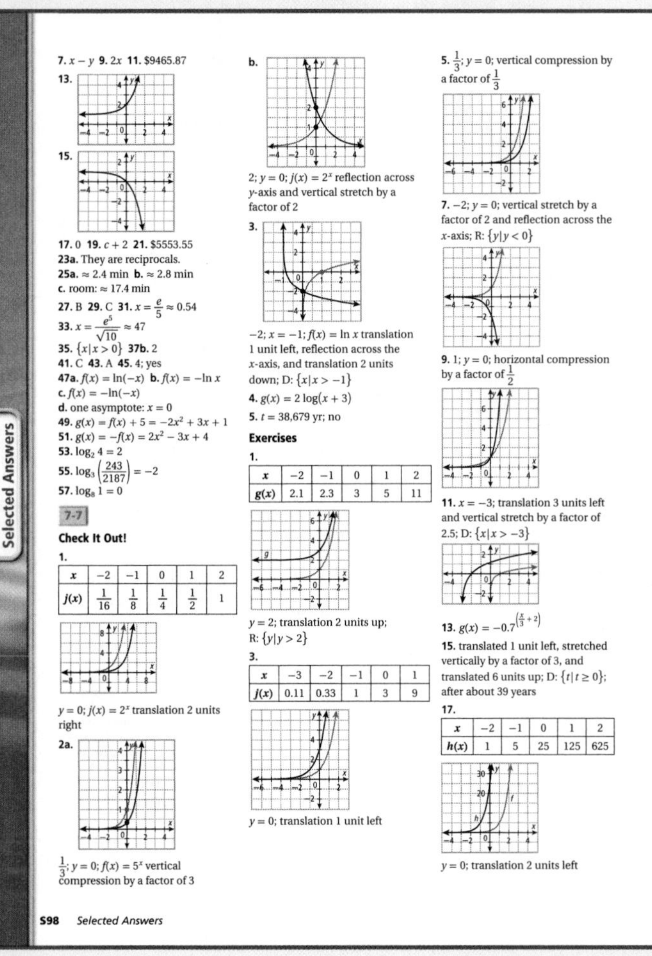

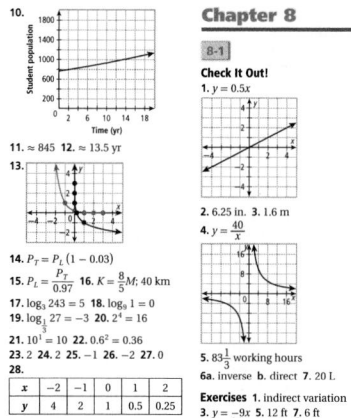

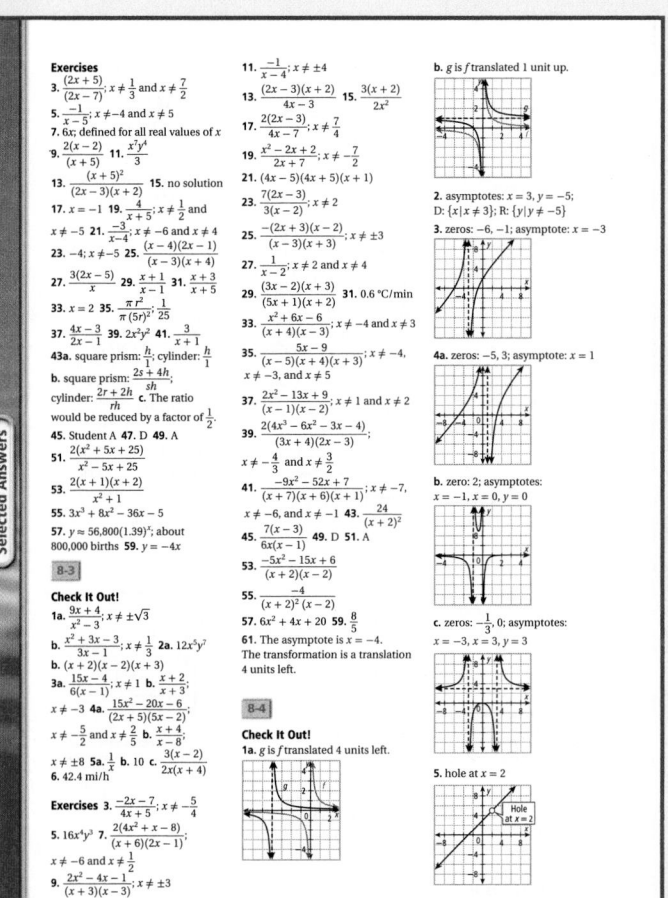

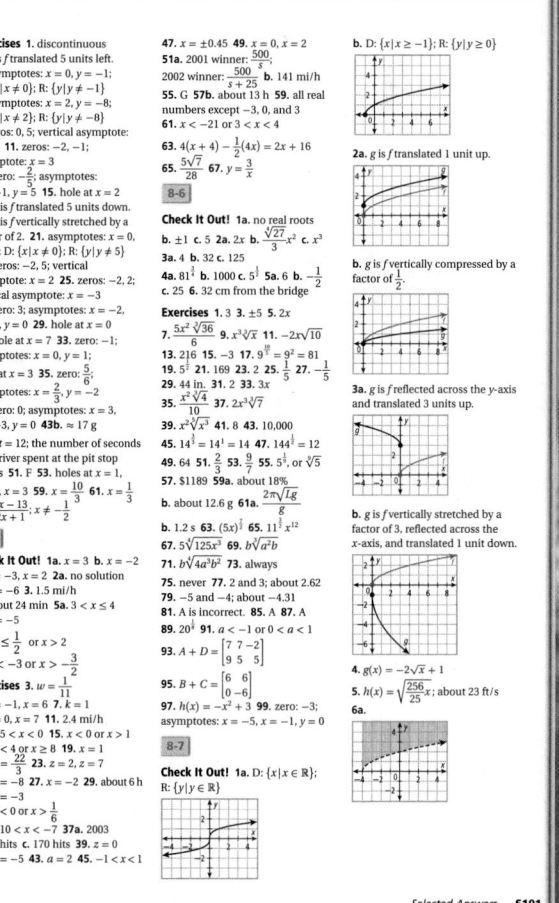

7. $x - y$ **9.** $2x$ **11.** \$9465.87

13. [graph]

15. [graph]

17. 0 **19.** $c + 2$ **21.** \$5553.55
23a. They are reciprocals.
25a. ≈ 2.4 min **b.** ≈ 2.8 min
c. room: ≈ 17.4 min
27. B **29.** C **31.** $x = \frac{e}{5} \approx 0.54$
33. $x = \frac{e^5}{\sqrt{10}} \approx 47$
35. $\{x \mid x > 0\}$ **37b.** 2
41. C **43.** A **45.** 4; yes
47a. $f(x) = \ln(-x)$ **b.** $f(x) = -\ln x$
c. $f(x) = -\ln(-x)$
d. one asymptote: $x = 0$
49. $g(x) = f(x) + 5 = -2x^2 + 3x + 1$
51. $g(x) = -f(x) = 2x^2 - 3x + 4$
53. $\log_2 4 = 2$
55. $\log_3\left(\frac{243}{2187}\right) = -2$
57. $\log_8 1 = 0$

7-7

Check It Out!

1.

x	-2	-1	0	1	2
$j(x)$	$\frac{1}{16}$	$\frac{1}{8}$	$\frac{1}{4}$	$\frac{1}{2}$	1

$y = 0$; $j(x) = 2^x$ translation 2 units right

2a. [graph]

$\frac{1}{3}$; $y = 0$; $f(x) = 5^x$ vertical compression by a factor of 3

b. [graph]

2; $y = 0$; $j(x) = 2^x$ reflection across y-axis and vertical stretch by a factor of 2

3. [graph]

-2; $x = -1$; $f(x) = \ln x$ translation 1 unit left, reflection across the x-axis, and translation 2 units down; D: $\{x \mid x > -1\}$
4. $g(x) = 2\log(x + 3)$
5. $t = 38{,}679$ yr; no

Exercises

1.

x	-2	-1	0	1	2
$g(x)$	2.1	2.3	3	5	11

$y = 2$; translation 2 units up; R: $\{y \mid y > 2\}$

3.

x	-3	-2	-1	0	1
$j(x)$	0.11	0.33	1	3	9

$y = 0$; translation 1 unit left

5. $\frac{1}{3}$; $y = 0$; vertical compression by a factor of $\frac{1}{3}$

7. -2; $y = 0$; vertical stretch by a factor of 2 and reflection across the x-axis; R: $\{y \mid y < 0\}$

9. 1; $y = 0$; horizontal compression by a factor of $\frac{1}{2}$

11. $x = -3$; translation 3 units left and vertical stretch by a factor of 2.5; D: $\{x \mid x > -3\}$

13. $g(x) = -0.7^{\left(\frac{x}{3} + 2\right)}$
15. translated 1 unit left, stretched vertically by a factor of 3, and translated 6 units up; D: $\{t \mid t \geq 0\}$; after about 39 years
17.

x	-2	-1	0	1	2
$h(x)$	1	5	25	125	625

$y = 0$; translation 2 units left

19. 4; $y = 0$; vertical stretch by a factor of 4 **21.** -0.25; $y = 0$; vertical compression by a factor of 0.25 and reflection across the x-axis; R: $\{y \mid y < 0\}$ **23.** 4; $y = 0$; vertical stretch by a factor of 4 and reflection across the y-axis
25. $x = 5$; translation 5 units right; D: $\{x \mid x > 5\}$ **27.** $x = 0$; vertical stretch by a factor of 4 and reflection across the x-axis
29. $f(x) = \ln(4x + 3) - 0.5$
31. ≈ 47 yr **33.** A **35.** D **37.** F
39. B and F **41.** always
43. sometimes **45.** C **47.** B
51a. $N(t) = 419(0.99)^t$
b. $N(t) = 419(0.99)^{\frac{m}{12}}$
c. 413 **53.** H **59.** min: $\left(-\frac{1}{8}, -\frac{81}{16}\right)$; D: $\mathbb{R}$; R: $\{y \mid y \geq -5\}$
61. $f(x) \approx 0.032x^3 - 0.0076x^2 + 0.073x + 1.30$ **63.** $-5x$ **63.** $\frac{x}{4}$

7-8

Check It Out!
1a. yes; 1.5 **b.** no
2. $B(t) \approx 199(1.25)^t$; ≈ 10.3 min
3. $S(t) \approx 0.59 + 2.64 \ln t$; ≈ 16.6 min

Exercises
1. exponential regression **3.** yes; $\frac{2}{3}$
5. yes; $\frac{4}{3}$ **7.** $P(t) \approx 621.6 + 1221 \ln t$; ≈ 421 mo **9.** no **11.** yes; $\frac{1}{2}$
13. $T(t) \approx 4.45(1.165)^t$; ≈ 2011
15. yes; $f(x) = 1.55(7.54)^x$
19. $s(t) = 68.24(3.69)^t$; ≈ 46.5 million **23a.** 20.5 mi/h; 36.8 mi/h; 84.0 mi/h **b.** $s = 100(0.8^t)$
25a. exponential **b.** linear **27.** F
29. $f(x) = 7.68(2.5)^x$ **33.** $x = -4$
35. $x = \pm\frac{9}{4}$ **37.** $x = -8, 0$
39. $x = -12, 3$ **41.** $x = \frac{4}{3}$ **43.** $x = 0$

Study Guide: Review
1. natural logarithmic function
2. asymptote
3. inverse relation
4. growth **5.** growth
6. decay **7.** growth
8. growth
9. $P(t) = 765(1.02)^t$

10. [graph: Student population vs. Time (yr)]

11. ≈ 845 **12.** ≈ 13.5 yr
13. [graph]

14. $P_T = P_L(1 - 0.03)$
15. $P_L = \frac{P_T}{0.97}$ **16.** $K = \frac{8}{5}M$; 40 km
17. $\log_3 243 = 5$ **18.** $\log_8 1 = 0$
19. $\log_{\frac{1}{3}} 27 = -3$ **20.** $2^4 = 16$
21. $10^1 = 10$ **22.** $0.6^2 = 0.36$
23. 2 **24.** 2 **25.** -1 **26.** -2 **27.** 0
28.

x	-2	-1	0	1	2
y	4	2	1	0.5	0.25

D: $\{x \mid x > 0\}$; R: $\mathbb{R}$
29. $\log_2 128 = 7$
30. $\log 1{,}000{,}000 = 6$
31. $\log_2 64 = 6$ **32.** $\log 100 = 2$
33. $\log_5 5^4 = 4$ **34.** $9 \log 10 = 9$
35. 10 times **36.** -1 **37.** $x \geq -6$
38. $x > 10$ **39.** 17.67 quarters, or 4.4 yr **40.** $k = 0.0346$
41. $g(x) = -3e^x - 2$ **42.** 0.6; $y = 0$; vertically compressed by a factor of $\frac{3}{5}$ and horizontally compressed by a factor of $\frac{1}{6}$ **43.** -0.5; $x = 0.5$; translated $\frac{1}{2}$ unit left and vertically stretched by a factor of 2
44. $V(t) = 5300(1 - 0.35)^t$
45. vertically stretched by a factor of 3500 **46.** $f(x) \approx 11.26(1.05)^x$
47. $f(x) \approx -97.8 + 56.4 \ln x$
48. The exponential function; $r^2 \approx 0.94$ versus $r^2 \approx 0.60$ for the logarithmic function

Chapter 8

8-1

Check It Out!
1. $y = 0.5x$

2. 6.25 in. **3.** 1.6 m
4. $y = \frac{40}{x}$

5. $83\frac{1}{3}$ working hours
6a. inverse **b.** direct **7.** 20 L

Exercises **1.** indirect variation
3. $y = -9x$ **5.** 12 ft **7.** 6 ft
9. $y = \frac{14}{x}$ **11.** $y = -\frac{5}{x}$ **13.** neither
15. direct **17.** $y = \frac{1}{2}x$ **19.** $y = -3x$
21. 88 Cal **23.** 0.2 kg **25.** $y = \frac{10.5}{x}$
27. 5 days **29.** neither
31. 1.375 atm **33.** sometimes
35. always **37a.** $s = \frac{6300}{t}$ **b.** 30 s
39a. $I = 0.02Pt$ **b.** True Federal Bank **c.** \$30 **41.** $x = 5$; $y = 4.4$; $z = 2$ **45.** D **47.** D **49.** 24 **51.** $y \approx 7$
53. $y = \frac{5}{4}x + \frac{1}{4}$ **55.** asymptote: $y = -2$; vertically compressed by a factor of $\frac{1}{2}$ and translated 2 units down

8-2

Check It Out!
1a. $2x^8$; $x \neq 0$ **b.** $\frac{1}{x-1}$; $x \neq -\frac{4}{3}$ and $x \neq 1$ **c.** $\frac{(2x+1)}{(2x-3)}$; $x \neq -\frac{2}{3}$ and $x \neq \frac{3}{2}$ **2a.** -2; $x \neq 5$ **b.** $\frac{-x}{2x-1}$; $x \neq 3$ and $x \neq \frac{1}{2}$ **3a.** $\frac{2x^3}{3}$ **b.** $\frac{2}{x-2}$
4a. $\frac{3y}{x^2}$ **b.** $\frac{4(x-4)}{x+3}$
5a. no solution **b.** $x = 4$

Exercises
3. $\frac{(2x+5)}{(2x-7)}$; $x \neq \frac{1}{3}$ and $x \neq \frac{7}{2}$
5. $\frac{-1}{x-5}$; $x \neq -4$ and $x \neq 5$
7. $6x$; defined for all real values of x
9. $\frac{2(x-2)}{(x+5)}$ **11.** $\frac{x^7y^4}{3}$
13. $\frac{(x+5)^2}{(2x-3)(x+2)}$ **15.** no solution
17. $x = -1$ **19.** $\frac{4}{x+5}$; $x \neq \frac{1}{2}$ and $x \neq -5$ **21.** $\frac{-3}{x-4}$; $x \neq -6$ and $x \neq 4$
23. -4; $x \neq -5$ **25.** $\frac{(x-4)(2x-1)}{(x-3)(x+4)}$
27. $\frac{3(2x-5)}{x}$ **29.** $\frac{x+1}{x-1}$ **31.** $\frac{x+3}{x+5}$
33. $x = 2$ **35.** $\frac{\pi r^2}{\pi(5r)^2}$; $\frac{1}{25}$
37. $\frac{4x-3}{2x-1}$ **39.** $2x^2y^2$ **41.** $\frac{3}{x+1}$
43a. square prism: $\frac{h}{1}$; cylinder: $\frac{h}{1}$
b. square prism: $\frac{2s+4h}{sh}$; cylinder: $\frac{2r+2h}{rh}$ **c.** The ratio would be reduced by a factor of $\frac{1}{2}$.
45. Student A **47.** D **49.** A
51. $\frac{2(x^2+5x+25)}{x^2-5x+25}$
53. $\frac{2(x+1)(x+2)}{x^2+1}$
55. $3x^3 + 8x^2 - 36x - 5$
57. $y \approx 56{,}800(1.39)^x$; about 800,000 births **59.** $y = -4x$

8-3

Check It Out!
1a. $\frac{9x+4}{x^2-3}$; $x \neq \pm\sqrt{3}$
b. $\frac{x^2+3x-3}{3x-1}$; $x \neq \frac{1}{3}$ **2a.** $12x^5y^7$
b. $(x+2)(x-2)(x+3)$
3a. $\frac{15x-4}{6(x-1)}$; $x \neq 1$ **b.** $\frac{x+2}{x+3}$; $x \neq -3$ **4a.** $\frac{15x^2-20x-6}{(2x+5)(5x-2)}$; $x \neq -\frac{5}{2}$ and $x \neq \frac{2}{5}$ **b.** $\frac{x+4}{x-8}$; $x \neq \pm 8$ **5a.** $\frac{1}{x}$ **b.** 10 **c.** $\frac{3(x-2)}{2x(x+4)}$
6. 42.4 mi/h

Exercises **3.** $\frac{-2x-7}{4x+5}$; $x \neq -\frac{5}{4}$
5. $16x^4y^3$ **7.** $\frac{2(4x^2+x-8)}{(x+6)(2x-1)}$; $x \neq -6$ and $x \neq \frac{1}{2}$
9. $\frac{2x^2-4x-1}{(x+3)(x-3)}$; $x \neq \pm 3$

11. $\frac{-1}{x-4}$; $x \neq \pm 4$
13. $\frac{(2x-3)(x+2)}{4x-3}$ **15.** $\frac{3(x+2)}{2x^2}$
17. $\frac{2(2x-3)}{4x-7}$; $x \neq \frac{7}{4}$
19. $\frac{x^2-2x+2}{2x+7}$; $x \neq -\frac{7}{2}$
21. $(4x-5)(4x+5)(x+1)$
23. $\frac{7(2x-3)}{3(x-2)}$; $x \neq 2$
25. $\frac{-(2x+3)(x-2)}{(x-3)(x+3)}$; $x \neq \pm 3$
27. $\frac{1}{x-2}$; $x \neq 2$ and $x \neq 4$
29. $\frac{(3x-2)(x+3)}{(5x+1)(x+2)}$ **31.** 0.6 °C/min
33. $\frac{x^2+6x-6}{(x+4)(x-3)}$; $x \neq -4$ and $x \neq 3$
35. $\frac{5x-9}{(x-5)(x+4)(x+3)}$; $x \neq -4$, $x \neq -3$, and $x \neq 5$
37. $\frac{2x^2-13x+9}{(x-1)(x-2)}$; $x \neq 1$ and $x \neq 2$
39. $\frac{2(4x^3-6x^2-3x-4)}{(3x+4)(2x-3)}$; $x \neq -\frac{4}{3}$ and $x \neq \frac{3}{2}$
41. $\frac{-9x^2-52x+7}{(x+7)(x+6)(x+1)}$; $x \neq -7$, $x \neq -6$, and $x \neq -1$ **43.** $\frac{24}{(x+2)^2}$
45. $\frac{7(x-3)}{6x(x-1)}$ **49.** D **51.** A
53. $\frac{-5x^2-15x+6}{(x+2)(x-2)}$
55. $\frac{-4}{(x+2)^2(x-2)}$
57. $6x^2 + 4x + 20$ **59.** $\frac{8}{5}$
61. The asymptote is $x = -4$. The transformation is a translation 4 units left.

8-4

Check It Out!
1a. g is f translated 4 units left.

b. g is f translated 1 unit up.

2. asymptotes: $x = 3$, $y = -5$; D: $\{x \mid x \neq 3\}$; R: $\{y \mid y \neq -5\}$
3. zeros: $-6, -1$; asymptote: $x = -3$

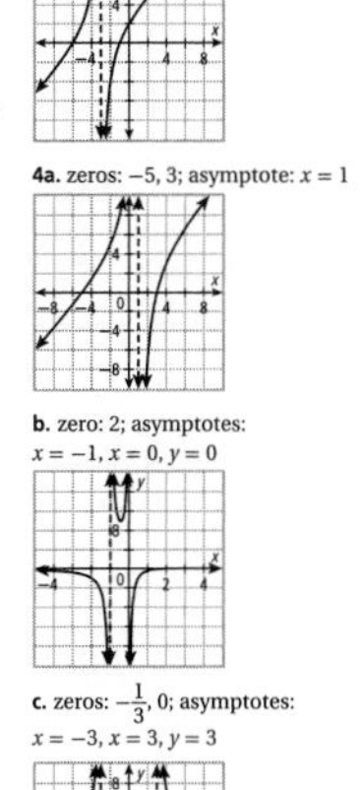

4a. zeros: $-5, 3$; asymptote: $x = 1$

b. zero: 2; asymptotes: $x = -1$, $x = 0$, $y = 0$

c. zeros: $-\frac{1}{3}$, 0; asymptotes: $x = -3$, $x = 3$, $y = 3$

5. hole at $x = 2$

Hole at $x = 2$

Exercises **1.** discontinuous
3. g is f translated 5 units left.
5. asymptotes: $x = 0$, $y = -1$; D: $\{x \mid x \neq 0\}$; R: $\{y \mid y \neq -1\}$
7. asymptotes: $x = 2$, $y = -8$; D: $\{x \mid x \neq 2\}$; R: $\{y \mid y \neq -8\}$
9. zeros: 0, 5; vertical asymptote: $x = 2$ **11.** zeros: $-2, -1$; asymptote: $x = 3$
13. zero: $-\frac{2}{5}$; asymptotes: $x = -1$, $y = 5$ **15.** hole at $x = 2$
17. g is f translated 5 units down.
19. g is f vertically stretched by a factor of 2. **21.** asymptotes: $x = 0$, $y = 5$; D: $\{x \mid x \neq 0\}$; R: $\{y \mid y \neq 5\}$
23. zeros: $-2, 5$; vertical asymptote: $x = 2$ **25.** zeros: $-2, 2$; vertical asymptote: $x = -3$
27. zero: 3; asymptotes: $x = -2$, $x = 2$, $y = 0$ **29.** hole at $x = 0$
31. hole at $x = 7$ **33.** zero: -1; asymptotes: $x = 0$, $y = 1$; hole at $x = 3$ **35.** zero: $\frac{5}{6}$; asymptotes: $x = \frac{2}{3}$, $y = -2$
37. zero: 0; asymptotes: $x = 3$, $x = -3$, $y = 0$ **43b.** ≈ 17 g
47b. $t = 12$; the number of seconds the driver spent at the pit stop
c. 57 s **51.** F **53.** holes at $x = 1$, $x = 2$, $x = 3$ **59.** $x = \frac{10}{3}$ **61.** $x = \frac{1}{3}$
63. $\frac{8x-13}{2x+1}$; $x \neq -\frac{1}{2}$

8-5

Check It Out! **1a.** $x = 3$ **b.** $x = -2$
c. $x = -3$, $x = 2$ **2a.** no solution
b. $x = -6$ **3.** 1.5 mi/h
4. about 24 min **5a.** $3 < x \leq 4$
b. $x = -5$
6a. $x \leq \frac{1}{2}$ or $x > 2$
b. $x < -3$ or $x > -\frac{3}{2}$

Exercises **3.** $w = \frac{1}{11}$
5. $x = -1$, $y = 6$ **7.** $k = 1$
9. $x = 0$, $x = 7$ **11.** 2.4 mi/h
13. $-5 < x < 0$ **15.** $x < 0$ or $x > 1$
17. $x < 4$ or $x \geq 8$ **19.** $x = 1$
21. $a = \frac{22}{3}$ **23.** $z = 2$, $z = 7$
25. $x = -8$ **27.** $x = -2$ **29.** about 6 h
31. $x = -3$
33. $x < 0$ or $x > \frac{1}{6}$
35. $-10 < x < -7$ **37a.** 2003
b. 18 hits **c.** 170 hits **39.** $z = 0$
41. $x = -5$ **43.** $a = 2$ **45.** $-1 < x < 1$

47. $x = \pm 0.45$ **49.** $x = 0$, $x = 2$
51a. 2001 winner: $\frac{500}{s}$; 2002 winner: $\frac{500}{s+25}$ **b.** 141 mi/h
55. G **57b.** about 13 h **59.** all real numbers except -3, 0, and 3
61. $x < -21$ or $3 < x < 4$
63. $4(x+4) - \frac{1}{2}(4x) = 2x + 16$
65. $\frac{5\sqrt{7}}{28}$ **67.** $y = \frac{3}{x}$

8-6

Check It Out! **1a.** no real roots
b. ± 1 **c.** 5 **2a.** $2x$ **b.** $\frac{\sqrt[3]{27}}{3}x^2$ **c.** x^3
3a. 4 **b.** 32 **c.** 125
4a. $81^{\frac{1}{4}}$ **b.** 1000 **c.** $5^{\frac{1}{3}}$ **5a.** 6 **b.** $-\frac{1}{2}$
c. 25 **6.** 32 cm from the bridge

Exercises **1.** 3 **3.** ± 5 **5.** $2x$
7. $\frac{5x^2\sqrt[3]{36}}{6}$ **9.** $x^3\sqrt[4]{x}$ **11.** $-2x\sqrt{10}$
13. 216 **15.** -3 **17.** $9^{\frac{6}{3}} = 9^2 = 81$
19. $5^{\frac{1}{3}}$ **21.** 169 **23.** 2 **25.** $\frac{1}{5}$ **27.** $-\frac{1}{5}$
29. 44 In. **31.** 2 **33.** $3x$
35. $\frac{x^2\sqrt[4]{4}}{10}$ **37.** $2x^3\sqrt[4]{7}$
39. $x^2\sqrt[4]{x^3}$ **41.** 8 **43.** 10,000
45. $14^{\frac{3}{3}} = 14^1 = 14$ **47.** $144^{\frac{1}{2}} = 12$
49. 64 **51.** $\frac{2}{3}$ **53.** $\frac{9}{5}$ **55.** $5^{\frac{1}{5}}$, or $\sqrt[5]{5}$
57. \$1189 **59a.** about 18%
b. about 12.6 g **61a.** $2\pi\sqrt{\frac{l}{g}}$
b. 1.2 s **63.** $(5x)^{\frac{1}{3}}$ **65.** $11^{\frac{1}{3}}x^{12}$
67. $5\sqrt[4]{125x^3}$ **69.** $b\sqrt[3]{a^2b}$
71. $b\sqrt[4]{4a^3b^2}$ **73.** always
75. never **77.** 2 and 3; about 2.62
79. -5 and -4; about -4.31
81. A is incorrect. **85.** A **87.** A
89. $20^{\frac{1}{4}}$ **91.** $a < -1$ or $0 < a < 1$
93. $A + D = \begin{bmatrix} 7 & 7 & -2 \\ 9 & 5 & 5 \end{bmatrix}$
95. $B + C = \begin{bmatrix} 6 & 6 \\ 0 & -6 \end{bmatrix}$
97. $h(x) = -x^2 + 3$ **99.** zero: -3; asymptotes: $x = -5$, $x = -1$, $y = 0$

8-7

Check It Out! **1a.** D: $\{x \mid x \in \mathbb{R}\}$; R: $\{y \mid y \in \mathbb{R}\}$

b. D: $\{x \mid x \geq -1\}$; R: $\{y \mid y \geq 0\}$

2a. g is f translated 1 unit up.

b. g is f vertically compressed by a factor of $\frac{1}{2}$.

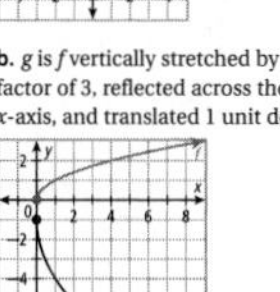

3a. g is f reflected across the y-axis and translated 3 units up.

b. g is f vertically stretched by a factor of 3, reflected across the x-axis, and translated 1 unit down.

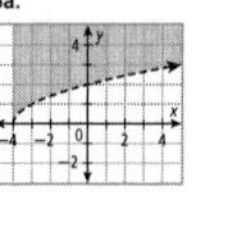

4. $g(x) = -2\sqrt{x} + 1$
5. $h(x) = \sqrt{\frac{256}{25}x}$; about 23 ft/s
6a.

b.

Exercises 3. D: $\{x|x \ge 0\}$; R: $\{y|y \ge -1\}$ 5. D: $\{x|x \in \mathbb{R}\}$; R: $\{y|y \in \mathbb{R}\}$ 7. D: $\{x|x \in \mathbb{R}\}$; R: $\{y|y \in \mathbb{R}\}$ 9. h is f vertically stretched by a factor of 3. 11. g is f compressed vertically by a factor of $\frac{1}{2}$ and translated 1 unit down. 13. j is f reflected across the y-axis and then translated 3 units right. 15. h is f reflected across the y-axis, horizontally compressed by a factor of $\frac{1}{2}$, and then translated 2 units left. 17. $g(x) = 4\sqrt{(x+5)} - 2$

19. $g(x) = \frac{6}{5}\sqrt{\frac{5}{9}x}$; about 2.2 mi

21.

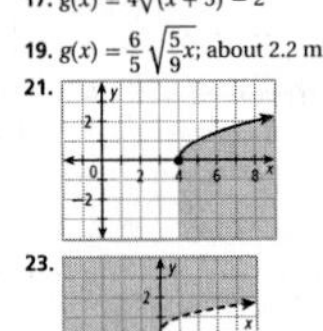

23.

25. D: $\{x|x \ge 0\}$; R: $\{y|y \le 0\}$
27. D: $\{x|x \in \mathbb{R}\}$; R: $\{y|y \in \mathbb{R}\}$
29. D: $\{x|x \in \mathbb{R}\}$; R: $\{y|y \in \mathbb{R}\}$
31. h is f translated 4 units right.
33. g is f horizontally compressed by a factor of $\frac{1}{3}$ and then translated 5 units left. 35. j is f translated 4 units left and 1 unit down.
37. h is f reflected across the y-axis, vertically stretched by a factor of 3, and then translated 2 units up.
39. $g(x) = \frac{1}{3}\sqrt{x+3}$
41. $g(x) = -\sqrt{x+1} - 4$
43.

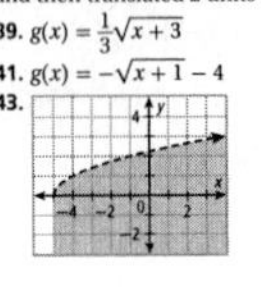

45.

47a. ≈ 762 beats/min b. ≈ 58 beats/min 49. a vertical stretch by a factor of 3 followed by a translation 1 unit right and 9 units down 51. D 53. A 55a. about 373 km b. It will appear to decrease by about 76 km. 57. yes 59c. by a factor of 4 61. sometimes 63. never 65. yes 67b. about 346 m/s c. -273.15°C 69. 1.4 s 73. D 75. A 79. $f(x) = -2\sqrt{\frac{1}{5}(x+3)} + 4$ 81. $x \le 8$ 83. $x = 6, y = 2$ 85. $x = -\frac{40}{7}, y = -\frac{68}{7}$ 87. $x = 4$

8-8

Check It Out! 1a. $x = 2$ b. $x = 4$ c. $x = 39$ 2a. $x = 6$ b. $x = 2$ 3a. $x = 1$ b. $x = -4, x = 3$ 4a. $x = 22$ b. $x = 5$ c. $x = 3$ 5a. $3 \le x \le 12$ b. $x \ge -1$ 6. If the car were traveling 30 mi/h, its skid marks would have measured about 43 ft. Because the actual skid marks measure less than 43 ft, the car was not speeding.

Exercises 1. No; the expression under the radical does not contain a variable. 3. $x = 12$ 5. $x = 5$ 7. $x = 3$ 9. $x = 10$ 11. $x = 8$ 13. $x = 4, x = 5$ 15. $x = -1$ 17. $x = 14$ 19. $x = 5$ 21. $x = -\frac{3}{4}$ 23. $-5 \le x \le 20$ 25. $\frac{-5}{2} \le x < 10$ 27. $x = 93$ 29. $x = 18$ 31. $x = 38$ 33. $x = 6$ 35. $x = \frac{7}{3}$ 37. $x = 4$ 39. $x = 25$ 41. $x = 7$ 43. $3 \le x \le 19$ 45. about 1.5 tons 47. $A = \pi r^2$ 49. $E = \frac{1}{2}mv^2$ 51a. 5 m b. 25.6 m/s² 53a. $r \le \sqrt{\frac{A}{\pi}}$ b. no 55. $x \approx 5.84$ 57. $x \approx 2.35$ 59. 995 g 63. H 65. F 67. always true 69. always true 71. $x = 9$ 73. $x = 10$ 75a. $D(n) = 2.00n + 5.00$ c. vertical translation 5 units down 77. $f^{-1}(x) = -\frac{1}{3}x - \frac{1}{3}$ 79. $4x^3$ 81. $\frac{\sqrt[3]{18x}}{x}$

Study Guide: Review

1. rational function 2. direct variation; constant of variation 3. $y = \frac{1}{3}x$ 4. $y = 4x$ 5. 306 tiles 6. $2000 7. $y = \frac{6}{x}$ 8. $y = \frac{4}{x}$ 9. 24 ohms 10. inverse variation 11. $\frac{8}{3x^2}$; $x \ne 0$ 12. $\frac{2x^3}{x+4}$; $x \ne -4$ 13. $\frac{x-3}{x+1}$; $x \ne -4, x \ne -1$ 14. $\frac{3}{x-5}$ 15. $\frac{-x}{(x-4)(x+3)}$ 16. $\frac{x-1}{x+1}$ 17. $\frac{3x-1}{x-3}$ 18. $\frac{2x}{y}$ 19. $\frac{2(x+5)}{x+3}$ 20. 1 21. $\frac{x+3}{3(x+4)}$ 22. $\frac{x^2+12}{x^2+4}$ 23. $\frac{2x}{(x+3)(x-3)}$; $x \ne \pm 3$ 24. $\frac{2(x+1)}{(x+2)(x-2)}$; $x \ne \pm 2$ 25. $\frac{8x^2+4x+45}{(3x+7)(4x-1)}$; $x \ne -\frac{7}{3}$, $x \ne \frac{1}{4}$ 26. $(x-3)^2(x+3)$ 27. $(x-5)(x+2)(x+7)$ 28. $\frac{2x-3}{x+4}$; $x \ne -4$ 29. $\frac{x^2-10x-25}{(x+5)(x-5)}$; $x \ne \pm 5$ 30. $\frac{-(x^2-3x-1)}{(x-3)(x+2)}$; $x \ne -2, x \ne 3$ 31. $\frac{6x^2-16x-7}{(2x+1)(3x-1)}$; $x \ne -\frac{1}{2}$, $x \ne \frac{1}{3}$ 32. $\frac{8(x-6)}{5(x+2)}$ 33. $\frac{2x-3}{x(x-3)}$ 34. $\frac{(x-2)^2}{4x}$ 35. ≈ 548 mi/h 36. g is f translated 4 units right. 37. g is f translated 2 units right and 3 units up. 38. asymptotes: $x = 1, y = -3$; D: $\{x|x \ne 1\}$; R: $\{y|y \ne -3\}$ 39. asymptotes: $x = -2, y = 1$; D: $\{x|x \ne -2\}$; R: $\{y|y \ne 1\}$ 40. zeros: 0, 3; asymptote: $x = -4$ 41. zero: 3; asymptotes: $x = -5, x = -1, y = 0$ 42. zero: 2; asymptotes: $x = -3$, $y = 2$ 43. zeros: -3, 3; asymptote: $x = 2$ 44. hole at $x = -3$ 45. $x = -2$ or $x = 3$ 46. no solution 47. $x = 2$ 48. $x = 0$ 49. $x < -\frac{4}{3}$ or $x > 0$ 50. $x < 3$ or $x > \frac{7}{2}$ 51. $3x^2$ 52. $3x^3$ 53. $2x\frac{\sqrt[3]{9}}{3}$ 54. $(-27)^{\frac{2}{3}}$ 55. $16^{\frac{3}{4}}$

56. $9^{\frac{3}{2}}$ 57. 17 58. 81 59. $\frac{1}{2}$ 60. D: $\{x|x \ge 0\}$; R: $\{y|y \ge 5\}$ 61. D: $\mathbb{R}$; R: $\mathbb{R}$ 62. g is f reflected across the x-axis and translated 1 unit up. 63. h is f compressed horizontally by a factor of $\frac{1}{4}$. 64. j is f reflected across the y-axis and translated 8 units right. 65. k is f reflected across the x-axis, compressed vertically by a factor of $\frac{1}{2}$, and translated 1 unit up. 66. $g(x) = 3\sqrt{x+4}$

67.

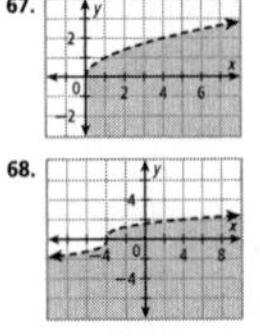

68.

69. $x = 19$ 70. $x = 109$ 71. $x = 9$ 72. $x = 2$ 73. $x = 2$ or $x = 8$ 74. $x = 8$ 75. $x = 0.5$ 76. $x = 85$ 77. $x = 7$ 78. $x = -219$ 79. $4 \le x \le 13$ 80. $x > 9$ 81. $0 \le x < 12$ 82. $x > -7$ 83. ≈ 1.6 m 84. 60.3 m³

Chapter 9

9-1

Check It Out! 1.

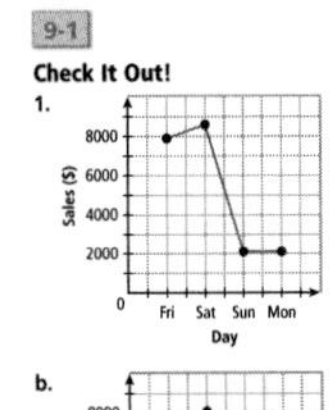

b.

2.

$h(x) = -0.002x^2 + 0.86x + 6.55$

3.

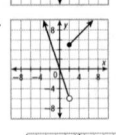

$f(x) \approx 22{,}727.15(1.1)^x$; 8 weeks

Exercises 1. graph D 3. graph B

5.

Enrollment Costs	
Credit Hours	Cost ($)
1	397.75
2	616.15
3	834.55
4	1053.00
5	1271.40

$C = 179.35 + 218.4x$

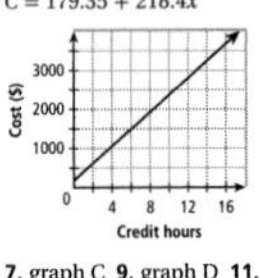

7. graph C 9. graph D 11. $T(t) = -0.02375t^2 + 0.525t + 101.1$ 13a. $W(t) = 3t + 4$; The whale weighs 4 tons at birth and gains 3 tons per month. 15. $14

17.

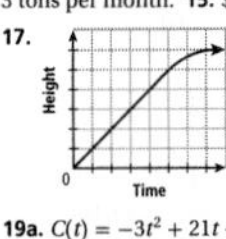

19a. $C(t) = -3t^2 + 21t + 24$ b. ≈ 61 c. 8 h after opening 21b. $h(t) \approx 0.0071t^3 - 0.1714t^2 + 2.1t + 2.071$ c. during year 14 25. C 29. $C(p) = 1.065(0.8p - 10)$

31. $(-3, -4)$ 33. 40 × 20 ft 35. D: $\{x|x \ge 1\}$; R: $\{y|y \ge 0\}$

9-2

Check It Out! 1.

Time Range (h)	Green Fee ($)
8 A.M. – noon	28
noon – 4 P.M.	24
4 P.M. – 9 P.M.	12

The green fee is $28 from 8 A.M. up to noon, $24 from noon up to 4 P.M., and $12 from 4 P.M. up to 9 P.M.

2a. 15; 15 b. 4; 13

3a.

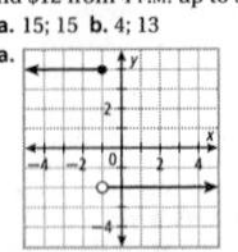

b.

4.

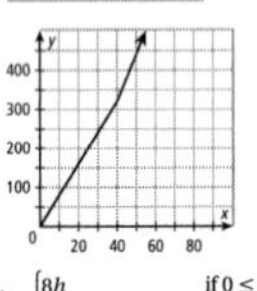

$f(h) = \begin{cases} 8h & \text{if } 0 \le h \le 40 \\ 12(h-40) + 320 & \text{if } h > 40 \end{cases}$

Exercises 1. Step functions are a subset of piecewise functions. A step function is a piecewise function that is constant over each interval in its domain. 3. The price per yard is $10 for less than 5 yd³, $7 for 5 yd³ up to 25 yd³, and $4 for 25 yd³ or more.

Topsoil Prices	
Price per Cubic Yard ($)	Volume (yd³)
10	$0 \le x < 5$
7	$5 \le x < 25$
4	$x \ge 25$

5. -39; -5

7.

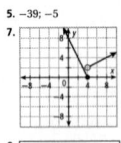

9.

Buffet Prices	
Price ($)	Age (yr)
0	$0 < x < 3$
2	$3 \le x < 8$
5	$8 \le x < 18$
8	$18 \le x$

The buffet is free for children under 3, $2 for children from 3 up to 8, $5 for children from 8 up to 18, and $8 for adults. 11. 1; 5; 5

13.

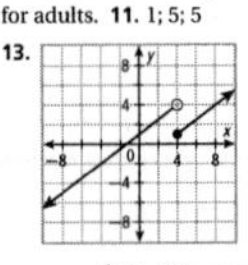

15. $f(x) = \begin{cases} 30 & \text{if } 0 < x \le 15 \\ 50 & \text{if } 15 < x \le 50 \\ 75 & \text{if } x > 50 \end{cases}$

17. $f(x) = \begin{cases} \frac{6}{5}x - 3 & \text{if } x < 5 \\ \frac{2}{5}x + 2 & \text{if } x \ge 5 \end{cases}$

19. $f(x) = \begin{cases} 6 & \text{if } x \le 4 \\ 6 + 3(x-4) & \text{if } x > +4 \end{cases}$

21. $f(x) = \begin{cases} +x & \text{if } x \ge 0 \\ -x & \text{if } x < 0 \end{cases}$

23. $h(x) = \begin{cases} 2x - 4 & \text{if } x \ge 0 \\ -2x - 4 & \text{if } x < 0 \end{cases}$

27a. $d(t) = \begin{cases} 18t & \text{if } 0 \le t \le 10 \\ 16.5(t-10) + 180 & \text{if } 10 < t \le 20 \end{cases}$

b. First half; the slope is steeper. 29. D: $\mathbb{R}$; R: $\{y|y \ge -4\}$ 33. C 35. B 37. $f(x) = 4 + 1.5(\lceil x \rceil - 1)$; $11.50 39. vertical: $x = 1$; horizontal: $y = -3$; D: $\{x|x \ne 1\}$; R: $\{y|y \ne -3\}$ 41. vertical: $x = 3$; horizontal: $y = 1$; D: $\{x|x \ne 3\}$; R: $\{y|y \ne 1\}$ 43. A 45. B

9-3

Check It Out!

1. $g(x) = \begin{cases} \left(\frac{x}{2}\right)^2 & \text{if } x \le 0 \\ \frac{x}{2} - 3 & \text{if } x > 0 \end{cases}$

2a. $f(x)$: x-int. $= -6$, y-int. $= 4$; $g(x)$: x-int. $= -6$, y-int. $= -4$
b. $f(x)$: x-int. $= \pm 3$, y-int. $= -9$; $g(x)$: x-int. $= \pm 3$, y-int. $= -3$

3.

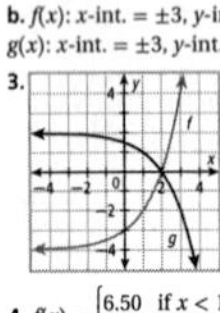

4. $f(x) = \begin{cases} 6.50 & \text{if } x < 12 \\ 9.50 & \text{if } x \ge 12 \end{cases}$

Exercises

1. $g(x) = \begin{cases} x + 3 & \text{if } x \le -6 \\ 4(x+6) & \text{if } x > -6 \end{cases}$

3. $f(x)$: x-int. $= -3$, y-int. $= 12$; $g(x)$: x-int. $= -3$, y-int. $= 2$

5.

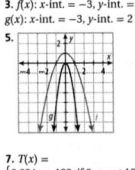

7. $T(x) = \begin{cases} 0.024x + 100 & \text{if } 0 < x \le 10{,}000 \\ 0.060x + 100 & \text{if } x > 10{,}000 \end{cases}$

9. $h(x) = \begin{cases} \left(\frac{x}{2}\right)^2 & \text{if } x < 2 \\ 2x & \text{if } x \ge 2 \end{cases}$

11. $f(x)$: x-int. $= 6$, y-int. $= 9$; $g(x)$: x-int. $= 6$, y-int. $= 6$
13. $f(x)$: x-int. $= 5$, y-int. $= 2$; $g(x)$: x-int. $= 2.5$, y-int. $= 2$
15. $f(x)$: x-int. $= 0$, y-int. $= 0$; $g(x)$: x-int. $= 1$, y-int. $= -4$

17.

19a. $f(n) = \begin{cases} 16.2n & \text{if } n \le 50 \\ 360 + 9n & \text{if } n > 50 \end{cases}$

b. $f(n) = \begin{cases} 14.2n & \text{if } n \le 50 \\ 360 + 7n & \text{if } n > 50 \end{cases}$

21a. n x-intercepts

23a. $T(n) = \begin{cases} 2.8n & \text{if } n \le 8 \\ 3.6n - 6.4 & \text{if } n > 8 \end{cases}$

25. $f(x) - 7 = \begin{cases} 2^x - 8 & \text{if } x \le -3 \\ -5x - 4 & \text{if } x > -3 \end{cases}$

27b. $C(x) = \begin{cases} 1.29x & \text{if } 0 < x < 4 \\ 0.85(1.29x) & \text{if } 4 \le x < 7 \\ 0.7(1.29x) & \text{if } x \ge 7 \end{cases}$

c. horizontal stretch by a factor of 2 29. x-int: 2; y-int: 3 33. J 35a. 28 b. 56 37. about 418 39. -6; D: $\mathbb{R}$; R: $\{y|y \le -6\}$ 41. 13; 4; 9

9-4

Check It Out! 1a. $(f+g)(x) = x^2$ b. $(f-g)(x) = -x^2 + 10x - 12$ 2a. $(fg)(x) = x^3 + 2x^2 - 4x - 8$ b. $\left(\frac{g}{f}\right)(x) = x - 2$, $x \ne -2$ 3a. 15 b. 9 4a. $f(g(x)) = 3\sqrt{x} + 2$, $x \ge 0$ b. $g(f(x)) = \sqrt{3x-4} + 2$, $x \ge \frac{4}{3}$ 5a. $f(c) = 0.68c$ b. $168.64

Exercises 3. $-x^2 + 13x + 13$ 5. $2x^3 + 4x^2 + 2x$ 7. $\frac{1}{2x}$, $x \ne 0$ or -1 9. -68 11. $4x^2 - 12x + 9$; $\mathbb{R}$ 13. $x + 1$; $x \ge -1$ 15. $3x^2 + 5x - 2$ 17. $2x^2 + 2x - 4$ 19. $2x^4 + 10x^3 + 4x^2 - 40x - 48$ 21. $\frac{1}{x-2}$, $x \ne -2$ or 2 23. $\frac{x+3}{2}$, $x \ne -2$ 25. -11 27. -17 29. -59 31. $\frac{4x+3}{4x+6}$; $x \ne -\frac{3}{2}$ 33a. $C(x) = 4\left(\frac{x}{9}\right) + 100$ b. 630 ft² 35a. $f(p) = p - 10$ b. $g(p) = 0.85p$ c. $f(g(p)) = 0.85p - 10$; $g(f(p)) = 0.85p - 8.5$ d. 15% e. $31.65 37a. $D(t) = 704 \cdot 1.05^t$ b. about 3043 c. about 2020 39. 4 41. 2 43. no 45. B 47. B 49. $g(x) = \frac{3}{2}x^2 + 5$ 51a. 12 ft b. 8 ft 53. $f(x) = 1.25(2^t)$ 55. $g(x) = \begin{cases} 8(x+5) & x \ge -5 \\ x - 4 & x < -5 \end{cases}$

9-5

Check It Out! 1. function 2. $f^{-1}(x) = \sqrt[3]{x+2}$; function; D: $\mathbb{R}$; R: $\mathbb{R}$ 3a. yes b. no

Exercises 1. function 3. function 5. $y = \pm\sqrt{x+9}$; not a function; D: $\{x|x \ge -9\}$; R: $\mathbb{R}$ 7. no 9. not a function 11. function 13. $f^{-1}(x) = \frac{\sqrt[3]{x}}{2}$; function; D: $\mathbb{R}$; R: $\mathbb{R}$ 15. $f^{-1}(x) = \frac{6}{5}x - \frac{9}{5}$; function; D: $\mathbb{R}$; R: $\mathbb{R}$ 17. $f^{-1}(x) = (x-5)^2 - 8$; function; D: $\{x|x \ge 5\}$; R: $\{y|y \ge -8\}$ 19. no 21. yes 23a. $d(t) = \frac{t-20}{2.5}$ b. within 4 mi 25. $y = \frac{5}{x} - 4$; D: $\{x|x \ne 0\}$; R: $\{y|y \ne -4\}$ 27. $y = x^3 + 12$; D: $\mathbb{R}$; R: $\mathbb{R}$ 29. $y = \log_7 x$; D: $\{x|x > 0\}$; R: $\mathbb{R}$ 31. $y = \ln\left(\frac{x}{3}\right) - 5$; D: $\{x|x > 0\}$; R: $\mathbb{R}$ 33. g and h 35. f and h 37a. $a(h) = \left(\frac{h-19}{3}\right)^2$ b. about 20.25 mo 39a. $t(d) = \frac{\sqrt{d^2 - 1600}}{3}$ b. ≈ 1833.28 s (about 31 min) 41a. $h(s) = \frac{s - 18\pi}{6\pi}$ b. 23.53 cm 43a. $s = \sqrt{A}$ c. ≈ 894 ft 47. J 49. G 53. $y = e^{\frac{3x-3}{x+1}}$ 55. $f^{-1}(g^{-1}(x)) \ne (f(g(x)))^{-1}$ 57. $2\pi x^2 + 2\pi x$ 59. $x^3 + 27$ 61. $x^2 + 8x - 6$ 63. $x^2 - 10x + 4$

9-6

Check It Out! 1a. square root b. exponential 2. $f(x) = \frac{1}{2}x^2 + \frac{5}{2}x + 8$ 3. $f(x) \approx -0.2x^2 + 23.99x + 5.28$

Exercises 1. linear 3. exponential 5a. $V(t) \approx 0.08t^2 - 2.04t + 60.86$ b. about $51.68 7. quadratic 9. $f(x) \approx -0.009x^2 + 2.28x - 55.31$ 11a. $y \approx 34.37x + 85{,}851.76$ b. about 2594 ft² 15a. $V(t) \approx 6126.9(1.016)^t$ b. about 34,611 ft³ 17a. $f(x) \approx 75.95(1.055^x)$ b. about 5.5%/yr c. The model predicts $160.65, which is about $5 more than the actual FCI. d. about 2008 21. B 23. D

25. $f(x) \approx x^{0.5}$; $f(x) = \sqrt{x}$ 29. a. -2, 4, and 10 31. yes

Study Guide: Review

1. one-to-one function 2. step function 3. composition of functions

4.

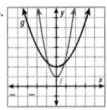

5.

Guests	10	20	30	40	50
Appetizers	160	200	240	280	320

$y = 4x + 120$

6a.

Radius (in.)	1.5	2	2.5	3	4
Time (s)	3	5	7.5	10.5	18

$y = x^2 + \frac{1}{2}x$ b. 52.5 s 7. 51; 7

8.

9.

10. $f(x) = \begin{cases} \frac{5}{2}x - 4 & \text{if } x < 4 \\ -\frac{3}{2}x + 8 & \text{if } x \ge 4 \end{cases}$

11. $f(x) = \begin{cases} 6 & 0 < x \le 8 \\ 6 + 1.5(x-8) & 8 < x \le 48 \end{cases}$

12. $h(x) = \begin{cases} 2x & \text{if } x \le 3 \\ -4x + 18 & \text{if } x > 3 \end{cases}$

13. $g(x) = \begin{cases} 3(x-7) + 2 & \text{if } x \le 7 \\ (x-7)^2 & \text{if } x > 7 \end{cases}$

14.

15. $x^2 - 4x - 21$ 16. $x^2 - 6x - 7$ 17. $-x^2 + 6x + 7$ 18. $x^3 - 12x^2 + 21x + 98$ 19. $x + 2$, $x \ne 7$ 20. $\frac{1}{x+2}$, $x \ne 7$ or -2 21. -10; $-\frac{8}{3}$ 22. 2; undefined 23. $g(f(x)) = \frac{8}{x-1}$; D: $\{x|x \ne 1\}$ 24. $f(g(x)) = \frac{8}{x+1} - 2$; D: $\{x|x \ne -1\}$ 25. $P(x) = 1.09(x + 30)$ 26. function 27. $f^{-1}(x) = \frac{-x+5}{8}$; function; D: $\mathbb{R}$; R: $\mathbb{R}$ 28. $y = \pm 3\sqrt{x} - 6$; not a function; D: $\{x|x \ge 0\}$; R: $\mathbb{R}$ 29. $f^{-1}(x) = \frac{5}{2x} - 4$; function; D: $\{x|x \ne 0\}$; R: $\{y|y \ne -4\}$ 30. $f^{-1}(x) = (x-3)^2 + 5$; function; D: $\{x|x \ge 3\}$; R: $\{y|y \ge 5\}$ 31. no 32. yes 33. $r = \sqrt{\frac{A}{4\pi}}$; r is the radius for a sphere with a given surface area. 34a. $f(x) = 23.96(1.02)^x$ b. ≈ 129.0 million gal c. ≈ 37°F

Chapter 10

10-1

Check It Out! 1a.

circle; center: (0, 0); intercepts: $(0, \pm 7)$, $(\pm 7, 0)$

b. 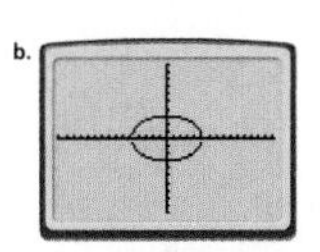

ellipse; center: (0, 0); intercepts: (±5, 0), (0, ±3)

2a. 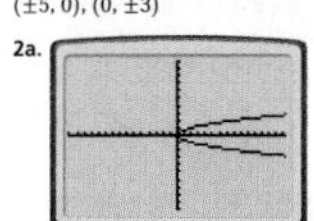

parabola; vertex: (0, 0); opens right

b. 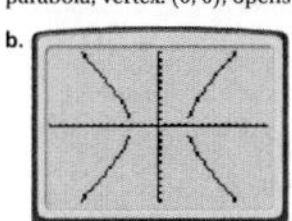

hyperbola; vertices: (±4, 0); opens horizontally **3.** Center: (8, 14); $r = 10$

Exercises 1. circles, ellipses, hyperbolas, and parabolas **3.** ellipse; center: (0, 0); intercepts: (0, ±3), (±4, 0) **5.** parabola; vertex: (0, 0); opens right **7.** hyperbola; vertices: (0, ±5); opens vertically **9.** hyperbola; vertices: $(\pm\sqrt{2}, 0)$; opens horizontally **11.** center: (8, 18); $r = 13$ **13.** center: (−1, 15); $r = 25$ **15.** circle; center: (0, 0); intercepts: (0, ±3), (±3, 0) **17.** ellipse; center: (0, 0); intercepts: (0, ±5), (±2, 0) **19.** ellipse; center: (0, 0); intercepts: $\left(0, \pm\frac{15}{2}\right)$, $\left(\pm\frac{5}{2}, 0\right)$ **21.** circle; center: (0, 0); intercepts: $\left(0, \pm\frac{9}{2}\right)$, $\left(\pm\frac{9}{2}, 0\right)$ **23.** parabola; vertex: (0, 0); opens upward **25.** parabola; vertex: (0, 0); opens left **27.** hyperbola; vertices: (0, ±6); opens vertically **29.** parabola; vertex: (−3, 0); opens right **31.** hyperbola; vertices: (±4, 0); opens horizontally **33.** center: $\left(\frac{7}{2}, \frac{11}{2}\right)$; $r = \sqrt{10}$ **35a.** $C = 68\pi$; $A = 1156\pi$

b. (−37, 26) **37.** D **39.** A **41a.** $AB = 10$; $AD = 10$; $BC = 10$; $CD = 10$ **b.** rhombus **c.** 80 square units **43.** C **45a.** 13 units **b.** 6.5 units **c.** $\frac{12}{5}$; $\frac{12}{5}$ **47.** Sometimes true **51.** J **53.** J **55.** $a = -32$ or 40 **57. a.** (9, 2, −11) **b.** $\left(\frac{x_1 + x_2}{2}, \frac{y_1 + y_2}{2}, \frac{z_1 + z_2}{2}\right)$ **c.** $d = \sqrt{101}$ **d.** $d = \sqrt{(x_2 - x_1)^2 + (y_2 - y_1)^2 + (z_2 - z_1)^2}$ **59.** $x = -6, 8$ **61.** $x = 4, 7$ **63.** $x = 1.5, 11$ **65.** y-int.: 2.5; asymptote: $y = 3$; reflection across the x-axis, vertical compression by a factor of $\frac{1}{2}$, shift 3 units up **67.** y-int.: 5; asymptote: $y = -1$; vertical stretch by a factor of 6, shift 1 unit down

10-2

Check It Out!
1. $(x - 4)^2 + (y - 2)^2 = 49$
2. $(x + 3)^2 + (y - 5)^2 = 169$
3. C, E **4.** $y = \frac{4}{3}x - \frac{35}{3}$

Exercises
3. $(x + 11)^2 + (y - 3)^2 = 81$
5. $(x - 3)^2 + y^2 = 36$
7. $(x + 2)^2 + (y + 5)^2 = 289$
9. K, H, G **11.** $y = -\frac{3}{4}x - \frac{59}{4}$
13. $(x - 5)^2 + (y - 1)^2 = 100$
15. $(x + 4)^2 + (y - 2)^2 = 64$
17. $(x + 6)^2 + (y + 4)^2 = 25$
19. E **21.** $x = -15$
23. $\{x \mid -6 \le x \le 6\}$; $\{y \mid -6 \le y \le 6\}$
25. $\{x \mid -5 \le x \le 1\}$; $\{y \mid -3 \le y \le 3\}$
27. $(x + 4)^2 + y^2 = 64$
29a. $(x + 5)^2 + (y - 20)^2 = 4489$
b. 67 million mi **c.** 134π million mi
31. No **33.** C **35.** $(x + 4)^2 + (y - 8)^2 = 81$ **37a.** (2, −5)
b. $(x - 2)^2 + (y + 5)^2 = 625$
41. $y = \frac{1}{2}x + 2$
43a. $f(x) = \begin{cases} \frac{1}{2}x + 15 & 0 \le x \le 20 \\ x + 20 & x > 20 \end{cases}$
c. 25 min **45.** parabola; vertex: (0, 0); opens left

10-3

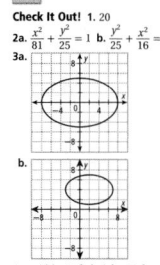

Check It Out! 1. 20
2a. $\frac{x^2}{81} + \frac{y^2}{25} = 1$ **b.** $\frac{y^2}{25} + \frac{x^2}{16} = 1$
3a.
b.
4a. width: 32 ft; height: 18 ft
b. $\frac{x^2}{256} + \frac{y^2}{324} = 1$

Exercises 1. The major axis of an ellipse is always longer than the minor axis of an ellipse. **3.** 30
5. $\frac{y^2}{625} + \frac{x^2}{225} = 1$ **7.** $\frac{x^2}{49} + \frac{y^2}{36} = 1$
9. 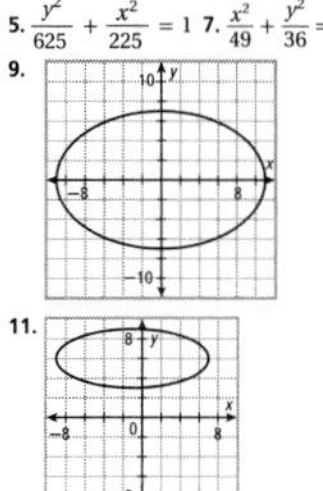

11.
13. 42 **15.** $\frac{x^2}{25} + \frac{y^2}{4} = 1$
17. $\frac{y^2}{25} + \frac{x^2}{16} = 1$
19. 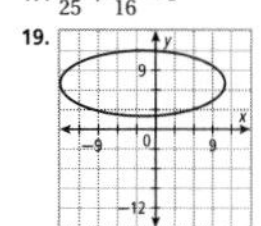

21.
23. $\frac{x^2}{279{,}312.25} + \frac{y^2}{193{,}600} = 1$
25. $\frac{(y - 7)^2}{100} + \frac{(x + 4)^2}{51} = 1$
27. $\frac{x^2}{49} + \frac{y^2}{25} = 1$; D: $\{x \mid -7 \le x \le 7\}$; R: $\{y \mid -5 \le y \le 5\}$
29. $\frac{(y - 4)^2}{36} + \frac{(x + 6)^2}{9} = 1$; $\{x \mid -9 \le x \le -3\}$, $\{y \mid -2 \le y \le 10\}$
31a. $\frac{9x^2}{5041} + \frac{16y^2}{729} = 1$
b. (±22.68, 0); ≈45.36 ft **33.** center: (−9, −4); vertices: (0, −4), (−18, −4); co-vertices: (−9, −7), (−9, −1); foci: $(-9 \pm 6\sqrt{2}, -4)$; D: $\{x \mid -18 \le x \le 0\}$; R: $\{y \mid -7 \le y \le -1\}$ **35a.** Instead of r^2, the formula for the area of an ellipse uses the values of a and b because an ellipse can be defined by a and b rather than a radius. **b.** 65π **37.** The length of an ellipse's major axis is equal to the distance $PF_1 + PF_2$. **39.** H
41a. $\frac{21}{29}$ **b.** $\frac{x^2}{169} + \frac{y^2}{144} = 1$
c. $0 < e < 1$ **43.** $\frac{x^2}{25} + \frac{y^2}{16} = 1$
45. 24 **47.** 56
49. $x^2 + (y + 1)^2 = 100$

10-4

Check It Out! 1. 12
2a. $\frac{y^2}{81} - \frac{x^2}{49} = 1$ **b.** $\frac{x^2}{64} - \frac{y^2}{36} = 1$
3a. vertices: (±4, 0); co-vertices: (0, ±6); asymptotes: $y = \pm\frac{3}{2}x$

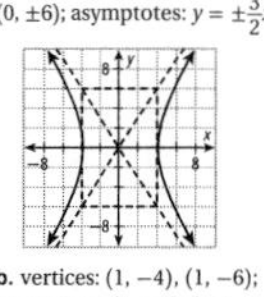

b. vertices: (1, −4), (1, −6); co-vertices: (4, −5), (−2, −5); asymptotes: $y = \pm\frac{1}{3}(x - 1) - 5$

Exercises 1. transverse axis **3.** 30 **5.** $\frac{x^2}{81} - \frac{y^2}{49} = 1$ **7.** $\frac{y^2}{100} - \frac{x^2}{64} = 1$ **9.** vertices: (±5, 0); co-vertices: (0, ±8); asymptotes: $y = \pm\frac{8}{5}x$ **11.** vertices: (0, ±10); co-vertices: (±9, 0); asymptotes: $y = \pm\frac{10}{9}x$ **13.** vertices: (8, −6), (0, −6); co-vertices: (4, 1), (4, −13); asymptotes: $y = \pm\frac{7}{4}(x - 4) - 6$ **15.** vertices: (0, −5), (0, −9); co-vertices: (±5, −7); asymptotes: $y = \pm\frac{2}{5}x - 7$ **17.** 42 **19.** $\frac{x^2}{64} - \frac{y^2}{225} = 1$ **21.** $\frac{(x - 3)^2}{49} - \frac{(y - 3)^2}{9} = 1$ **23.** vertices: (0, ±5); co-vertices: (±9, 0); asymptotes: $y = \pm\frac{5}{9}x$ **25.** vertices: (±2, 0); co-vertices: (0, ±11); asymptotes: $y = \pm\frac{11}{2}x$ **27.** vertices: (0, 3), (−10, 3); co-vertices: (−5, 7), (−5, −1); asymptotes: $y = \pm\frac{4}{5}(x + 5) + 3$ **29.** vertices: (9, 2), (3, 2); co-vertices: (6, 6), (6, −2); asymptotes: $y = \pm\frac{4}{3}(x - 6) + 2$ **33b.** Yes **35.** $c^2 = a^2 + b^2$, so c always has the greatest value. There is not enough information given to determine whether a or b has the least value. **37a.** (0, 214) **b.** 184 million mi **c.** $y \approx \pm 0.142x$ **39.** G **41.** J **43.** $\frac{(x - 7)^2}{400} - \frac{(y + 9)^2}{144} = 1$ **45.** $\frac{x^2}{16} - \frac{y^2}{9} = 1$ **47.**

49a. $y = 30{,}000 + 3{,}000x$ **b.** 10 yr **51.** $\frac{y^2}{4} + \frac{x^2}{2} = 1$

10-5

Check It Out! 1. $y = \frac{1}{16}x^2$ **2. a.** $x = -\frac{1}{5}y^2$ **b.** $y = -\frac{1}{28}x^2$ **3a.** vertex: (1, 3); $p = 3$; axis of symmetry: $y = 3$; focus: (4, 3); directrix: $x = -2$

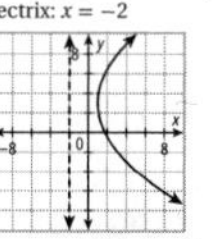

b. vertex: (8, 4); $p = -\frac{1}{2}$; axis of symmetry: $x = 8$; focus: (8, 3.5); directrix: $y = 4.5$

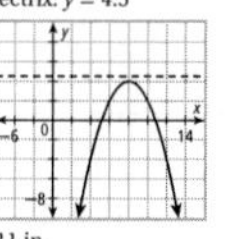

4. 11 in.

Exercises 3. $x = \frac{1}{28}y^2$ **5.** $y = -\frac{1}{16}x^2$ **7.** $y = \frac{1}{2}x^2$ **9.** $x = -\frac{1}{32}y^2$ **11.** vertex: (0, 4); $p = 6$; axis of symmetry: $y = 4$; focus: (6, 4); directrix: $x = -6$ **13.** 9.5 in **15.** $x - 3 = -\frac{1}{20}y^2$ **17.** $y = \frac{1}{12}(x + 3)^2$ **19.** $x = \frac{1}{4}y^2$ **21.** $y = -\frac{1}{24}x^2$ **23.** vertex: (1, 0); $p = \frac{1}{8}$; axis of symmetry: $y = 0$; focus: $\left(\frac{9}{8}, 0\right)$; directrix: $x = \frac{7}{8}$ **27.** $y + 6 = -\frac{1}{12}(x - 2)^2$; D: $\{x \mid x \in \mathbb{R}\}$; R: $\{y \mid y \le -6\}$ **29.** $x + 7 = \frac{1}{36}(y + 3)^2$; D: $\{x \mid x \ge -7\}$; R: $\{y \mid y \in \mathbb{R}\}$ **31.** $y - 5 = -\frac{1}{20}x^2$; D: $\{x \mid x \in \mathbb{R}\}$; R: $\{y \mid y \le 5\}$ **33.** $x - 8 = -\frac{1}{16}(y + 5)^2$; D: $\{x \mid x \le 8\}$; R: $\{y \mid y \in \mathbb{R}\}$ **35a.** $y = \frac{1}{20}x^2$ **b.** $y + 4 = \frac{1}{16}x^2$ **c.** 7.2 in **37a.** (−96, 41) **b.** 133 million km **c.** (−96, 174) **39.** vertex: (−4, 5);

$p = -\frac{1}{8}$; axis of symmetry: $x = -4$; focus: $\left(-4, 4\frac{7}{8}\right)$; directrix: $y = 5\frac{1}{8}$ **41.** vertex: (−3, 2); $p = 2$; axis of symmetry: $y = 2$; focus: (−1, 2); directrix: $x = -5$ **45.** G **47.** (7, 0) **49.** $y - 7 = -\frac{1}{8}(x - 6)^2$ or $y - 3 = \frac{1}{8}(x - 6)^2$ **51.** $4p$ **53.** $f^{-1}(x) = \frac{x - 22}{4}$; D: $\{x \mid x \in \mathbb{R}\}$; R: $\{y \mid y \in \mathbb{R}\}$; function **55.** $f^{-1}(x) = 3x + 2$; D: $\{x \mid x \in \mathbb{R}\}$; R: $\{y \mid y \in \mathbb{R}\}$; function **57.** vertices: (±9, 0); co-vertices: (0, ±5); asymptotes: $y = \pm\frac{5}{9}x$ **59.** vertices: (0, ±8); co-vertices: (±2, 0); asymptotes: $y = \pm 4x$

10-6

Check It Out! 1a. circle **b.** hyperbola **2a.** circle **b.** parabola
3a. $x = \frac{1}{9}(y + 8)^2$; parabola

b. $\frac{(x - 4)^2}{9} + \frac{(y + 6)^2}{16} = 1$; ellipse

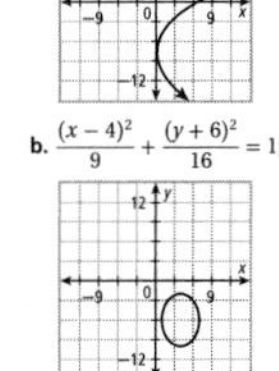

4. 200 ft

Exercises 1. ellipse **3.** parabola **5.** ellipse **7.** ellipse **9.** $(x - 8)^2 + (y + 5)^2 = 36$; circle **11.** $\frac{x^2}{9} + \frac{(y + 4)^2}{25} = 1$; ellipse **13.** 4 in **15.** parabola **17.** ellipse **19.** parabola **21.** ellipse **23.** $x^2 + (y - 4)^2 = 49$; circle **25.** $\frac{x^2}{4} - \frac{(y + 9)^2}{25} = 1$; hyperbola **27.** $(x + 5)^2 + (y + 2)^2 = 20$; circle **29.** $\frac{(x + 1)^2}{4} - \frac{(y - 7)^2}{9} = 1$; hyperbola **31.** $(x - 2.5)^2 + (y + 4.5)^2 = 16$; circle

33a. ellipse **b.** 40 m **c.** 100 m **35.** $36x^2 + 25y^2 - 360x + 400y + 1600 = 0$ **37.** outside **39.** inside **41.** 36.4 cm **43a.** $(x - 40)^2 + (y - 30)^2 = 40{,}000$ **b.** $40{,}000\pi$ **c.** inside **45a.** $y - 84 = -\frac{1}{500}(x - 200)^2$ **b.** 84 ft **c.** 4 ft **47.** A **49.** D **53.** It rotates the graph. **55.** no **57.** no **59.** (4, 1) **61a.** $f(x) = 1.65(1 + 0.05)^t$ **b.** $5.32

10-7

Check It Out! 1. (0, 4.5) **2a.** (−4, 3), (3, −4) **b.** (0, 5), (±3, −4) **3.** no solution **4.** yes, at (±4, −3.6)

Exercises 3. (4, −2), (8, 2) **5.** (12, 5), (5, 12) **7.** no solution **9.** (0, −6), $(\pm 3\sqrt{3}, 3)$ **11.** (±4, 2), (±4, −2) **13.** no solution **15.** (0, 5), (−4, 3) **17.** (2.5, −6.5), (−4.5, 7.5) **19.** (0, 4), $\left(\frac{8}{3}, \frac{20}{3}\right)$ **21.** (5, 1), (7, 4) **23.** (±2, −2), $(\pm\sqrt{7}, 1)$ **25.** no solution **27.** (0, −7), (1, −6) **29.** $(2\sqrt{2}, \pm 1)$, $(-2\sqrt{2}, \pm 1)$ **31.** (0, 0), (1, 1) **33.** (6, 1), (−26, −3) **35.** (0, ±3) **37.** (2, ±4) **39.** no solution **41.** (10, ±4), (−10, ±4) **43.** 25 s **45.** (2.8, −2.6), (3.3, 2.9), (−7.9, −1.3), (−8.1, 1.5) **47a.** hyperbola **b.** yes; (6.69, 2.68), (1.31, 2.68) **49.** (−2, 0) **53.** G **55.** (4, ±3) **57.** (3, 4), (4, 3) **61.** about $100 **63.** cylinder **65.** 4 **67.** $-\frac{2}{5}$ **69.** $f(x) = 5x - 2$

Study Guide: Review

1. transverse axis **2.** tangent line **3.** focus; directrix **4.** conic section **5.** circle with center (0, 0) and radius $r = 9$ **6.** hyperbola with center (0, 0) and intercepts (5, 0) and (−5, 0) **7.** parabola with vertex (0, −1), opening in the positive x-direction **8.** ellipse with center (0, 0), and intercepts (±3.5, 0), and (0, ≈ ±1.98) **9.** B **10.** center: (3, −3); $r = 12$ **11.** center: (8, −2.5); $r = 12.5$ **12.** center: (6, 0); $r = 19$ **13.** center: (−12, 4); $r = \sqrt{15}$

14. $(x - 8)^2 + (y + 7)^2 = 196$
15. $(x - 3)^2 + (y - 6)^2 = 80$
16. $(x + 3)^2 + (y - 8)^2 = 34$
17. $y - 5 = -\frac{3}{5}(x - 3)$
18. $y = 4$ **19.** $y + 2 = -\frac{4}{5}(x - 6)$
20. $y + 7 = \frac{5}{8}(x - 1)$
21. center: (0, 0); vertices: (0, ±6); co-vertices: (±3, 0); foci: $(0, \pm 3\sqrt{3})$
22. center: (0, 0); vertices: (±8, 0); co-vertices: (0, ±5); foci: $(\pm\sqrt{39}, 0)$
23. center: (3, −2); vertices: (3, 6), (3, −10); co-vertices: (10, −2), (−4, −2); foci: $(3, -2 \pm \sqrt{15})$
24. $\frac{(x - 4)^2}{36} + \frac{(y + 5)^2}{9} = 1$
25. $\frac{x^2}{144} + \frac{y^2}{225} = 1$
26. $\frac{(x + 2)^2}{36} + \frac{(y - 3)^2}{27} = 1$
27. center: (0, 0); vertices: (±5, 0); co-vertices: (0, ±7); foci: $(\pm\sqrt{74}, 0)$; asymptotes: $y = \pm\frac{7}{5}x$
28. center: (0, 0); vertices: (0, ±6); co-vertices: (±8, 0); foci: (0, ±10); asymptotes: $y = \pm\frac{3}{4}x$ **29.** center: (3, −6); vertices: (5, −6), (1, −6); co-vertices: (3, 1), (3, −13); foci: $(3 \pm \sqrt{53}, -6)$; asymptotes: $y + 6 = \pm\frac{7}{2}(x - 3)$ **30.** $\frac{x^2}{25} - \frac{y^2}{36} = 1$
31. $\frac{x^2}{121} - \frac{y^2}{16} = 1$ **32.** $\frac{y^2}{25} - \frac{x^2}{36} = 1$
33. $\frac{(y - 5)^2}{25} - \frac{(x + 7)^2}{144} = 1$
34. vertex: (0, 0); $p = -3$; axis of symmetry: $x = 0$; focus: (0, −3); directrix: $y = 3$ **35.** vertex: (0, 0); $p = \frac{1}{8}$; axis of symmetry: $y = 0$; focus: $\left(\frac{1}{8}, 0\right)$; directrix: $x = -\frac{1}{8}$
36. vertex: (−4, 5); $p = \frac{1}{4}$; axis of symmetry: $x = -4$; focus: $\left(-4, 5\frac{1}{4}\right)$; directrix: $y = 4\frac{3}{4}$ **37.** vertex: (4, −2); $p = -1.5$; axis of symmetry: $y = -2$; focus: (2.5, −2); directrix: $x = 5.5$
38. $y = -\frac{1}{20}(x - 3)^2$
39. $x - 4 = -\frac{1}{10}(y - 6)^2$
40. $x - 9 = \frac{1}{12}(y + 4)^2$ **41.** ellipse
42. hyperbola **43.** parabola
44. circle **45.** ellipse
46. $x + 3 = \frac{1}{4}(y + 6)^2$; parabola

47. $\frac{(x + 4)^2}{6} + \frac{y^2}{2} = 1$; ellipse
48. $(x + 5)^2 + (y - 4)^2 = 36$; circle
49. $\frac{(x + 1)^2}{8} - \frac{(y + 3)^2}{4} = 1$; hyperbola **50.** (2, −6), (−2, 2)
51. (4, 0), (0, −5)
52. (8, ±6), (−8, ±6)
53. (3, 2), (5, 6) **54.** (0, 2), (0, −2)
55. (6, 4), (6, −4), (−6, 4), (−6, −4)
56. (2, 6), (−7, 3) **57.** no solution

Chapter 11

11-1

Check It Out! 1a. 120 **b.** 73,116,160 **2a.** 336 **b.** 20 **3.** 28

Exercises 1. important; permutation **3.** 225 **5.** 1320 **7.** 5985 **9.** 12 **11.** 72 **13.** 20 **15.** 71,916,768 **17.** 1 **19.** 6 **21.** 72 **23.** 6700 **25.** 35 **27.** > **29.** <
33a.

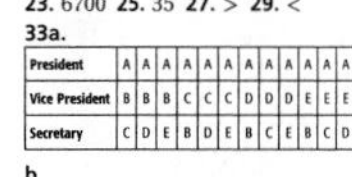

President	A	A	A	A	A	A	A	A	A	A	A	A
Vice President	B	B	B	C	C	C	D	D	D	E	E	E
Secretary	C	D	E	B	D	E	B	C	E	B	C	D

b.

President	B	B	B	B	B	B	B	B	B	B	B	B
Vice President	A	A	A	C	C	C	D	D	D	E	E	E
Secretary	C	D	E	A	D	E	A	C	E	A	C	D

60 ways
c. 60 **d.** 10; 60; 10 **37.** A **39.** D
41. 1365 **43.** $({}_{30}C_{12})({}_{18}C_2)$
45. $n = 119$ **47.** $n = 13.0625$
49. hyperbola

11-2

Check It Out! 1a. $\frac{5}{36}$ **b.** 0 **c.** $\frac{5}{12}$ **2.** $\frac{16}{25}$ **3.** $\frac{1}{28}$ **4.** $\frac{16}{225}$ **5a.** $\frac{9}{26}$ **b.** $\frac{19}{26}$

Exercises 1. theoretical probability **3.** $\frac{1}{4}$ **5.** $\frac{1}{4}$ **7.** $\frac{303}{365}$ **9.** $\frac{1}{220}$ **11.** $\frac{1}{9}$ **13.** $\frac{3}{5}$ **15.** $\frac{4}{5}$ **17.** $\frac{1}{56}$ **19.** $\approx\frac{1}{42}$ **21.** never **23a.** $\frac{\pi}{4}$ **25a.** 0.68; 0.84; 0.76; 0.64 **b.** 0.73 **27.** $\frac{2}{5}$ **29.** June; ≈ 0.13 **31.** no; yes **33.** $\frac{1}{2}$ **37.** G **39.** H **45.** max.: 16 **47.** $y = -\frac{1}{20}x^2$

11-3

Check It Out! 1a. $\frac{1}{36}$ **b.** $\frac{1}{8}$ **2.** $\frac{5}{36}$ **3a.** ≈ 0.014 **b.** ≈ 0.186 **4a.** independent; $\frac{3}{20}$ **b.** dependent; $\frac{1}{6}$ **c.** dependent; $\frac{1}{12}$

Exercises 1. independent **3.** $\frac{1}{8}$ **5.** The probability that the yellow cube shows a multiple of 3 increases from $\frac{1}{3}$ if the product is 6; $\frac{1}{2}$ **7.** $\frac{1}{100}$ **9.** dependent; $\frac{9}{38}$ **11.** $\frac{1}{12}$ **13.** The probability that the product is 8 increases from $\frac{1}{18}$ if the blue cube is less than 3; $\frac{1}{36}$ **15.** ≈ 0.72 **17.** dependent; $\frac{1}{6}$ **19.** independent **21.** independent **23a.** ≈ 0.61 **b.** ≈ 0.05 **25a.** $\frac{625}{1296}$ **b.** $\frac{1}{36}$ **c.** $\frac{1}{6}$ **27.** ≈ 0.6 **29.** 40 **33.** F **35.** 7 **37.** $\frac{11}{18}$; no **39a.** $P(d) = 18.3$g; $P(j) = 32.5$g **c.** vertical stretch by a factor of ≈ 1.78 **41.** $x \approx \pm 2.6$; $y \approx \pm 2.2$ **43.** $\frac{1}{36}$ **45.** $\frac{3}{4}$

11-4

Check It Out! 1a. Each student can vote only once. **b.** 75% **2a.** $\frac{4}{13}$ **b.** $\frac{8}{13}$ **3.** $\frac{31}{40}$ **4.** ≈ 0.1524

Exercises 1. inclusive events **3.** $\frac{3}{5}$ **5.** $\frac{4}{5}$ **7.** $\frac{7}{9}$ **9.** $\frac{54}{65}$ **11.** ≈ 0.92 **13.** $\frac{1}{2}$ **15.** $\frac{1}{4}$ **17.** $\frac{32}{49}$ **19.** $1 - 0.75^{13} \approx 0.976$ **21.** 0.37; experimental **23.** 87%; 100% **25b.** 4.16%; 52.24% **27.** 0.49 **29a.** 0.42 **b.** 0.02 **c.** 0.44; it is the sum of the probabilities. **31.** D **33.** D **35.** ≈ 0.12 **37.** $\frac{13}{18}$ **39.** 0.9 **41.** 0.2 **43.** $y = -1.5x^3 - 6x^2 + 16.5x + 45$ **47.** $\frac{1}{16}$

11-5

Check It Out! 1a. 6.5; 7; no mode **b.** 4.2; 5; 2 and 6 **2.** 0.37
3.
IQR = 5

4. 1.4; ≈ 1.6 **5.** 19; the mean increases from ≈ 4.3 to ≈ 5.4, and the standard deviation increases from ≈ 2.2 to ≈ 4.3.

Exercises 1. variance **3.** 5.375; 6; 6 **5.** $0.36
7.
IQR = 2
9. 0.8; 0.89 **11.** 142.92; 11.95
13. $23.1\overline{6}$; 20.5; no mode
15. 15; 15; no mode
17.
IQR = 6
19.
IQR = 2
21. 343.71; 18.54 **23.** 58; the mean increases from ≈ 19.8 to ≈ 22.8, and the standard deviation increases from ≈ 5.6 to ≈ 11.5. **25.** the mean; 37° is an outlier and affects the mean greatly. **27.** 15; $Q_1 - 1.5(IQR) = 79 - 1.5(90 - 79) = 62.5$; $15 < 62.5$ **29.** < 0.3 min or > 6.9 min; none **31.** Ruth **35.** − $0.499 **37.** B **39a.** 12.25 **b.** $\frac{13}{36}$ **c.** $\frac{23}{36}$ **d.** no **41.** D **43.** C **45.** 1 **47.** $-2x^4 - 5x^3 + 7x^2 + 10x - 6$ **49.** $\frac{2}{3}$ **51.** $\frac{1}{2}$

11-6

Check It Out! 1a. $x^5 - 5x^4y + 10x^3y^2 - 10x^2y^3 + 5xy^4 - y^5$ **b.** $a^3 + 6a^2b + 12ab^2 + 8b^3$ **2a.** $\frac{2}{9} \approx 0.22$ **b.** $\frac{47}{128} \approx 0.37$ **3a.** ≈ 0.98 **b.** ≈ 0.09

Exercises 1. 2 **3.** $27x^3 + 135x^2 + 225x + 125$ **5.** $x^6 + 6x^5y + 15x^4y^2 + 20x^3y^3 + 15x^2y^4 + 6xy^5 + y^6$ **7.** ≈ 0.026 ≈ 0.181 **9.** $y^4 + 20y^3 + 150y^2 + 500y + 625$ **11.** $1024 + 3840x + 5760x^2 + 4320x^3 + 1620x^4 + 243x^5$ **13.** ≈ 0.86 **15.** $\frac{3}{8}$; $\frac{1}{8}$

17. $x^5 - 5x^4y + 10x^3y^2 - 10x^2y^3 + 5xy^4 - y^5$ 19. $256k^4 - 256k^3 + 96k^2 - 16k + 1$ 21. 0.384 23. $\frac{8}{27}$
25. $\frac{1}{16}$; $\frac{5}{16}$ 27. ≈ 0.989
29. ≈ 0.94 33a. $\frac{82}{365}$ b. ≈ 0.14
c. ≈ 0.19 35. ≈ 0.03 37. ≈ 0.59
39. ≈ 0.3 41. B 43. B 45. ≈ 0.29
47a. ≈ 0.67 b. ≈ 0.62 51. −19; −4; −4 53. no 55. 13.4; 15; 18
57. 25; 24; 24

Extension

Check it Out! 1. ≈ 97.7%
Exercises 1. ≈ 95.4% 3. ≈ 68.2%
5. ≈ 47.7% 7. ≈ 15.9%

Study Guide: Review

1. dependent events
2. expected value
3. permutation 4. 7,000,000
5. 792 6. 2,162,160 7. 604,800
8. 20 9. $\frac{5}{36}$ 10. $\frac{5}{18}$ 11. $\frac{1}{2}$
12. $\frac{11}{12}$ 13. $\frac{1}{210}$ 14. $\frac{1}{10{,}000}$
15. $\frac{5}{24}$ 16. ≈ 0.21 17. $\frac{1}{5}$
18. $\frac{4}{5}$ 19. $\frac{7}{25}$ 20. $\frac{13}{25}$ 21. $\frac{1}{4}$
22. $\frac{3}{4}$ 23. $\frac{1}{4}$ 24. $\frac{1}{2}$ 25. $\frac{1}{216}$
26. $\frac{6}{25}$ 27. $\frac{11}{21}$ 28. $\frac{1}{13}$
29. $\frac{13}{31}$ 30. $\frac{14}{99}$ 31. Each coupon offers only 1 discount. 32. $\frac{5}{6}$
33. $\frac{7}{13}$ 34. $\frac{1}{2}$ 35. $\frac{7}{10}$
36. mean: 5.4; median: 6; mode: 8 37. mean: $13.\overline{3}$; median: 13; modes: 12, 13, and 15
38. 0.51
39.
28 36 44 52 60 68 76 84
IQR = 35
40. [5.4, 9.6] 41. yes 42. The mean decreases from 75.5 to 69.3, and the standard deviation increases from ≈ 21.5 to ≈ 25.1.
43. $125 + 150x + 60x^2 + 8x^3$
44. $x^4 - 8x^3y + 24x^2y^2 - 32xy^3 + 16y^4$ 45. 48.75; ≈ 4.13
46. ≈ 0.10; ≈ 0.40

Chapter 12

12-1

Check It Out! 1a. −5, −13, −21, −29, −37 b. 2, −6, 18, −54, 162
2a. −1, 0, 3, 8, 15 b. −2, 1, 4, 7, 10
3a. $a_n = 9 - 2n$ b. $a_n = \frac{1}{n}$
4.

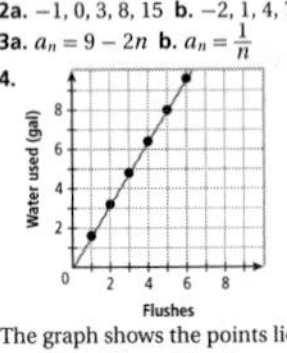

The graph shows the points lie on a line with positive slope; 16 gal. 5. 8, 16

Exercises 1. recursive 3. 3, 14, 25, 36, 47 5. −12, 0, 12, 24, 36
7. −3, −12, −27, −48, −75 9. 1, 4, 16, 64, 256 11. $a_n = 3 + 3n$
13. $a_n = 35 - 10n$ 15. 16, 32
17. −2, 5, −16, 47, −142 19. 9, 10, 12, 16, 24 21. 1, $\frac{1}{4}$, $\frac{1}{9}$, $\frac{1}{16}$, $\frac{1}{25}$
23. $a_n = 13 - 4n$ 25. linear with a slope of 4; 36 27. 12, 8, 6, 5, $4\frac{1}{2}$ 29. 10, 20, −10, 20, −10
31. 7.9, 7.8, 7.7, 7.6, 7.5 33. B is incorrect. The formula is explicit, not recursive. 35. $a_n = \frac{16}{9} - \frac{1}{9}n$; $\frac{2}{3}$ 37. $a_n = \frac{(-1)^{n+1}}{n}$; $-\frac{1}{10}$
39. $a_n = 25 - n^2$; −75 41. 15, 21
43a. 15, 21 b. $a_n = \frac{1}{2}n^2 - \frac{1}{2}n$
c.

Players	1	2	3	4	5
Games	0	2	6	12	20

The sequence is twice the previous sequence. The function is a vertical stretch by a factor of 2.
45a. $a_n = 180(n-2)$ for $n \geq 3$; 1800°
c. $a_n = \frac{180(n-2)}{n}$ for $n \geq 3$
47a. 1, $\frac{1}{2}$, $\frac{1}{4}$, $\frac{1}{8}$, $\frac{1}{16}$, $\frac{1}{32}$;
$a_1 = 1$, $a_n = \frac{1}{2}a_{n-1}$; $a_n = \left(\frac{1}{2}\right)^{n-1}$
b. 4, 2, 1, $\frac{1}{2}$, $\frac{1}{4}$, $\frac{1}{8}$;
$a_1 = 4$, $a_n = \frac{1}{2}a_{n-1}$; $a_n = 4\left(\frac{1}{2}\right)^{n-1}$
51. H 53. H 55. $a_n = \frac{n^3}{3} - 1$; $\frac{997}{3}$

57. $a_n = -0.05n^2 + 0.05n + 0.9$; −3.6 59. $\frac{x-3}{x+2}$ 61. $\frac{1}{x+5}$
63. $\frac{2(3x^2 - 5x - 3)}{(x+1)(x-1)}$
65. $\frac{x(x^2-7)}{(2x+7)(x+2)}$

12-2

Check It Out! 1a. $\sum_{k=1}^{5} \frac{2}{(k+1)^2}$
b. $\sum_{k=1}^{6} (-1)^k(2k)$
2a. 1 + 3 + 5 + 7 = 16
b. −5 − 10 − 20 − 40 − 80 = −155
3a. 240 b. 120 c. 385 4. 294 in., or $24\frac{1}{2}$ ft
Exercises 1. $\sum_{k=1}^{n} k$
3. $\sum_{k=1}^{5} (-1)^k(3k)$
5. $\sum_{k=1}^{5} [100 - 5(k-1)]$
7. $12 - 3 + \frac{4}{3} - \frac{3}{4} = 9\frac{7}{12}$
9. 231 11. 126 13. $\sum_{k=1}^{5} 1.1k$
15. $\sum_{k=1}^{5} (-1)^{k+1}(k+10)$
17. 16 + 24 + 32 + 40 + 48 = 160
19. $0 + \frac{1}{3} + \frac{2}{4} + \frac{3}{5} = \frac{43}{30}$ 21. 195
23. 210 cans 25. $\sum_{k=1}^{25} (26-k)$
27. $\sum_{k=1}^{5} -800\left(\frac{1}{10}\right)^{k-1}$
29. $\sum_{k=1}^{5} (-1)^{k+1}(k+2)^2$
31. $\sum_{k=1}^{5} 3.4k - 3.4$, or $\sum_{k=1}^{5} 3.4(k-1)$
33. $\sum_{k=1}^{5} \frac{1000}{10^{k-1}}$ 35b. $\sum_{k=1}^{5} 3^k =$ 3 + 9 + 27 + 81 + 243 = 363
c. 3542
37. −5 + 10 − 15 + 20 − 25 + 30 = 15
39. 1 + 4 + 7 + 10 + 13 + 16 = 51
41. $\frac{1}{5} + \frac{2}{5} + \frac{3}{5} + \frac{4}{5} + 1 = 3$
43. 420 45. −2550
47a. Both equal 165; $\sum_{k=1}^{n} ca_k = c\sum_{k=1}^{n} a_k$.
b. Both equal 75; $\sum_{k=1}^{n} (a_k + b_k) = \sum_{k=1}^{n} a_k + \sum_{k=1}^{n} b_k$. 49. a. $a_n = 4n$
b. $\sum_{k=1}^{n} 4k$; 84 toothpicks 53. H

55. J 57. $\sum_{k=1}^{1000} k$; 500, 500
59. $\sum_{k=1}^{n} ca_k = ca_1 + ca_2 + \cdots + ca_n$
$= c(a_1 + a_2 + \cdots + a_n)$
$= c\sum_{k=1}^{n} a_k$
63. x-int.: 3; y-int.: −6 65. 10 ft
67. 2, 3, 8, 63, 3968

12-3

Check It Out! 1a. arithmetic; $d = -0.7$; −1.6 b. not arithmetic
2a. −23 b. 8.7 3. $\frac{3}{2}$, 1, $\frac{1}{2}$ 4a. −25
b. 8.5 5a. −408 b. −1650
6a. 37 seats b. 336 total seats
Exercises 1. arithmetic series
3. not arithmetic 5. 38 7. −4.6
9. 16, 23, 30 11. −13 13. −17
15. −35 17. 495 19. 11.7
21. not arithmetic 23. arithmetic; −0.09; 0.63 25. $\frac{12}{5}$ 27. 66, 55, 44
29. 2.1, 1.9, 1.7 31. 94 33. −60
35. 143.5 37a. 78; 156 b. adds 1 to each term of the sequence; adds 24 to the total number per day
39. 0 41. 60 43a. $\sum_{k=1}^{n} 4k$ b. 684
c. 673 45. 45 minutes; after 2 years, her exercise routine would be over 8 h long, which is not realistic. 47a. 61 b. 650 49a. 6th, 11th, 16th, 21st, and 26th Streets
b. 0.25 mi 53. J 55. G 57. 6
63. growth 65. 92 dB 67. $\sum_{k=1}^{5} \frac{4k}{5}$
69. $\sum_{k=1}^{5} -\frac{k}{3}$

12-4

Check It Out! 1a. geometric; $r = \frac{1}{3}$ b. arithmetic; $d = -0.4$
c. neither 2a. $\frac{3}{1024}$ b. 100,000
3a. −1000 b. $\frac{3}{4}$ or $-\frac{3}{4}$ 4. 20
5a. $\frac{63}{16}$ b. −189 6. $616,218.04
Exercises 1. geometric mean
3. neither 5. 39,366 7. 64 9. 324
11. $\frac{3}{2}$ 13. 48 15. 61 17. 511
19. neither 21. arithmetic; $d = 5$
23. 768 25. 52,488 27. 30.375
29. 1 31. 3 33. 11.111111
35. 8,888,888 37. $a_n = \frac{1}{16}(2)^{n-1}$; $a_{10} = 32$; $S_{10} = \frac{1023}{16} \approx 63.94$
39. $a_n = 8(2)^{n-1}$; $a_{10} = 4096$; $S_{10} = 8184$ 41. $a_n = 162\left(-\frac{1}{3}\right)^{n-1}$; $a_{10} = -\frac{2}{243}$; $S_{10} = 121\frac{121}{243} \approx 121.5$ 43a. $34.98; $61.18
45. 2,441,406 47a. 12.8 mm
b. 27 folds 49a. $24 million
b. 60% c. week 6 d. about $99.93 million 53a. about 261.6 Hz
b. $a_n \approx 16.3(2)^n$ c. C11
55a. 30.198 b. 31.899 c. 31.994
d. 32.000 e. Yes, the series appears to be approaching 32.
59. G 61. G 63. $a_{18} = 1{,}310{,}720$
65. $a_{17} \approx 1{,}208{,}925.82$ 67a. 89, 144, 233, 377, 610 b. Their sum is the next term. 69. zero: −5; vertical asymptotes: $x = -2$ and $x = 3$; horizontal asymptote: $y = 0$
71a. $f(x) = 0.9(0.8x) = 0.72x$
b. $198 73. 52.1 75. 104.6

12-5

Check It Out! 1a. diverges
b. converges 2a. $\frac{125}{6}$ b. $\frac{2}{3}$ 3. $\frac{1}{9}$
4. Step 1: $\sum_{k=1}^{1} (2k-1) = 1$; $1^2 = 1$
Step 2: $1 + 3 + \cdots + (2k-1) = k^2$
Step 3: $1 + 3 + \cdots + (2k-1) + [2(k+1)-1]$
$= k^2 + [2(k+1)-1]$
$= k^2 + 2k + 1$
$= (k+1)^2$
5. $a = 5$: $\frac{5^2}{4} \stackrel{?}{\geq} 2(5) + 1$
$12.5 \ngeq 11$
Exercises 1. converge 3. diverges
5. $\frac{9}{4}$ 7. $1066\frac{2}{3}$ 9. $\frac{56}{99}$
11. Step 1: $2 \cdot 1 = n(n+1)$
$= 1(1+1) = 2$
Step 2: $2 + 4 + \cdots + 2(k)$
$= (k)(k+1)$
Step 3: $2 + 4 + \cdots + 2k + 2(k+1) = k(k+1) + 2(k+1)$
$= k^2 + k + 2k + 2$
$= k^2 + 3k + 2$
$= (k+1)(k+2)$
13. $n = -1$ 15. converges
17. diverges 19. $\frac{16}{15}$ 21. $\frac{2}{3}$
23. $\frac{541}{999}$ 25. $a = 0$
27. $a = 0$ 29. 320 in., or $26\frac{2}{3}$ ft
31. 2500 33. $-\frac{40}{7}$ 35. No sum exists. 37. 500 39. $\frac{4}{9}$ 41. $\frac{41}{333}$
43. $\frac{5}{9}$ 45a. about 415.0 million
b. about 6.2 billion c. about 11 billion 53. $x = \frac{1}{2}$
55. $x = -2$ 57. $x = 0$ 59. For $a_1 > 0$, $S > S_n$, and both sums are positive. For $a_1 < 0$, $S_n > S$, and both sums are negative.
61. B 63. A 67. $\frac{5}{12}$ 69. No; the partial sums will approach infinity if $d > 0$ and negative infinity if $d < 0$. 71. 73.728 %
73. geometric; $r = \frac{1}{3}$
75. geometric; $r = 0.25$

Extension

Check It Out! 1. 53 square units
2. 155.25 square units
Exercises 1. 1236 square units
3. 304 square units 5. 220 square units 7. 15,875 square units
9a. about 3056 square units

Study Guide: Review

1. arithmetic; geometric
2. diverges; converges
3. explicit formula; recursive formula 4. infinite sequence; finite sequence 5. iteration
6. −8, −7, −6, −5, −4
7. $\frac{1}{2}$, 2, $\frac{9}{2}$, 8, $\frac{25}{2}$ 8. 1, $-\frac{3}{2}$, $\frac{9}{4}$, $-\frac{27}{8}$, $\frac{81}{16}$ 9. 55, 53, 51, 49, 47 10. 200, 40, 8, $\frac{8}{5}$, $\frac{8}{25}$ 11. −3, 10, −29, 88, −263
12. $a_n = -4n$ 13. $a_n = 5(4)^{n-1}$
14. $a_n = 5n - 29$ 15. $a_n = 27\left(\frac{2}{3}\right)^{n-1}$
16. 0.72 ft, or 8.6 in.; 0.12 ft, or 1.5 in.
17. −1 + 4 − 9 + 16 = 10
18. 4.5 + 5.0 + 5.5 + 6.0 + 6.5 = 27.5
19. 1 − 3 + 5 − 7 + 9 = 5
20. $5 + \frac{5}{2} + \frac{5}{3} + \frac{5}{4} = \frac{125}{12}$
21. −40 22. 385 23. 78
24. $27,600; $207,000 25. 17 26. $\frac{21}{5}$
27. −1.2 28. 29.5 29. −18 30. 23
31. −630 32. −7 33. 150 34. 330
35. 50, 58, 66, 74,...; no, because he will have a total savings of only $458
36. 0.000004 37. $\frac{243}{2}$ 38. $-\frac{1}{8}$
39. 768 40. 98,304 41. $\frac{512}{3}$
42. ±32 43. 62,500 44. 5 45. 2
46. $\frac{\sqrt{3}}{24}$ 47. $\frac{25}{36}$ 48. $\frac{121}{81}$
49. 72,727.2 50. 21,845 51. −39,062
52. $\frac{315}{8} = 39.375$ 53. $\frac{279}{8} = 34.875$
54. $1044.26 55. $9847.32; $43,969.32
56. −2025 57. $-\frac{4}{3}$ or $-1.\overline{3}$

58. −343 59. 5 60. 4.5 61. $-\frac{21}{2}$
62. $\frac{1}{9}$ 63. No sum exists.
64. Step 1: $2^1 = 2^{1+1} - 2 = 2$
Step 2: $2 + \cdots + 2^k = 2^{k+1} - 2$
Step 3: $2 + \cdots + 2^k + 2^{k+1}$
$= 2^{k+1} - 2 + 2^{k+1}$
$= 2(2^{k+1}) - 2$
$= 2^{k+2} - 2 = 2^{k+1+1} - 2$
65. Step 1: $5^{1-1} = \frac{5^1 - 1}{4} = 1$
Step 2: $1 + \cdots + 5^{k-1} = \frac{5^k - 1}{4}$
Step 3: $1 + \cdots + 5^{k-1} + 5^k$
$= \frac{5^k - 1}{4} + 5^k$
$= \frac{5^k - 1}{4} + \frac{4(5^k)}{4}$
$= \frac{5^k + 4(5^k) - 1}{4}$
$= \frac{5(5^k) - 1}{4} = \frac{5^{k+1} - 1}{4}$
66. Step 1: $\frac{1}{4(1^2) - 1}$
$= \frac{1}{2(1) + 1}$
$= \frac{1}{3}$
Step 2: $\frac{1}{3} + \cdots + \frac{1}{4k^2 - 1}$
$= \frac{k}{2k+1}$
Step 3: $\frac{1}{3} + \cdots + \frac{1}{4k^2 - 1} + \frac{1}{4(k+1)^2 - 1}$
$= \frac{k}{2k+1} + \frac{1}{4(k+1)^2 - 1}$
$= \frac{k}{2k+1} + \frac{1}{4k^2 + 8k + 3}$
$= \frac{k}{2k+1} + \frac{1}{(2k+1)(2k+3)}$
$= \frac{k(2k+3)}{(2k+1)(2k+3)} + \frac{1}{(2k+1)(2k+3)}$
$= \frac{k(2k+3) + 1}{(2k+1)(2k+3)}$
$= \frac{2k^2 + 3k + 1}{(2k+1)(2k+3)}$
$= \frac{(2k+1)(k+1)}{(2k+1)(2k+3)}$
$= \frac{k+1}{2k+2+1}$
$= \frac{k+1}{2(k+1)+1}$
67a. $\sum_{k=1}^{\infty} 9(0.85)^{k-1}$ b. 60 ft

Chapter 13

13-1

Check It Out! 1. $\sin\theta = \frac{15}{17}$; $\cos\theta = \frac{8}{17}$; $\tan\theta = \frac{15}{8}$ 2. $x = 10\sqrt{2}$
3. 41 in. 4. 220 ft 5. $\sin\theta = \frac{40}{41}$; $\cos\theta = \frac{9}{41}$; $\tan\theta = \frac{40}{9}$; $\csc\theta = \frac{41}{40}$; $\sec\theta = \frac{41}{9}$; $\cot\theta = \frac{9}{40}$
Exercises 1. tangent
3. $\sin\theta = \frac{3\sqrt{13}}{13}$; $\cos\theta = \frac{2\sqrt{13}}{13}$; $\tan\theta = \frac{3}{2}$ 5. $x = \frac{100\sqrt{3}}{3}$
7. $x = \frac{250\sqrt{3}}{3}$ 9. 241 m
11. $\sin\theta = \frac{3\sqrt{10}}{10}$; $\cos\theta = \frac{\sqrt{10}}{10}$; $\tan\theta = 3$; $\csc\theta = \frac{\sqrt{10}}{3}$; $\sec\theta = \sqrt{10}$; $\cot\theta = \frac{1}{3}$ 13. $\sin\theta = \frac{1}{3}$; $\cos\theta = \frac{2\sqrt{2}}{3}$; $\tan\theta = \frac{\sqrt{2}}{4}$ 15. $\sin\theta = \frac{5\sqrt{41}}{41}$; $\cos\theta = \frac{4\sqrt{41}}{41}$; $\tan\theta = \frac{5}{4}$
17. $x = 140$ 19a. 147 m b. 187 m
21. $\sin\theta = \frac{4}{5}$; $\cos\theta = \frac{3}{5}$; $\tan\theta = \frac{4}{3}$; $\csc\theta = \frac{5}{4}$; $\sec\theta = \frac{5}{3}$; $\cot\theta = \frac{3}{4}$
23. $\sin\theta = \frac{\sqrt{2}}{2}$; $\cos\theta = \frac{\sqrt{2}}{2}$; $\tan\theta = 1$; $\csc\theta = \sqrt{2}$; $\sec\theta = \sqrt{2}$; $\cot\theta = 1$ 25a. 8022 ft b. 32 s
27. 135 ft 31. F 35a. 3 ft
b. $13.5\sqrt{3}$ ft² 37. $x = 32$
39. $x = 38{,}416$ 41. $\frac{1}{2}$ 43. $16\frac{2}{3}$

13-2

Check It Out!
1a.
b.

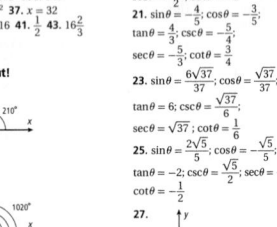

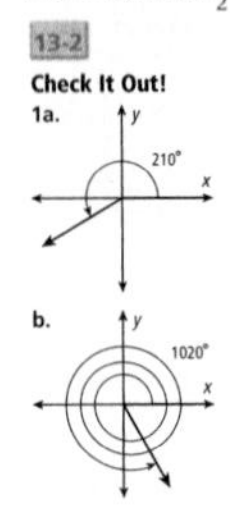

c. −300°
2a. Possible answer: 448°; −272°
b. Possible answer: 860°; −220°
c. Possible answer: 240°; −480°
3a. 75° b. 65° c. 50°
4. $\sin\theta = \frac{2\sqrt{5}}{5}$; $\cos\theta = -\frac{\sqrt{5}}{5}$; $\tan\theta = -2$; $\csc\theta = \frac{\sqrt{5}}{2}$; $\sec\theta = -\sqrt{5}$; $\cot\theta = -\frac{1}{2}$
Exercises 1. terminal
3. −135°
5.

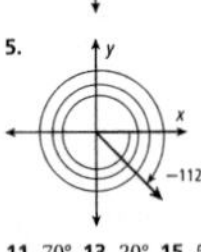

11. 70° 13. 20° 15. 50° 17. 40°
19. $\sin\theta = -\frac{\sqrt{5}}{5}$; $\cos\theta = \frac{2\sqrt{5}}{5}$; $\tan\theta = -\frac{1}{2}$; $\csc\theta = -\sqrt{5}$; $\sec\theta = \frac{\sqrt{5}}{2}$; $\cot\theta = -2$
21. $\sin\theta = -\frac{4}{5}$; $\cos\theta = -\frac{3}{5}$; $\tan\theta = \frac{4}{3}$; $\csc\theta = -\frac{5}{4}$; $\sec\theta = -\frac{5}{3}$; $\cot\theta = \frac{3}{4}$
23. $\sin\theta = \frac{6\sqrt{37}}{37}$; $\cos\theta = \frac{\sqrt{37}}{37}$; $\tan\theta = 6$; $\csc\theta = \frac{\sqrt{37}}{6}$; $\sec\theta = \sqrt{37}$; $\cot\theta = \frac{1}{6}$
25. $\sin\theta = \frac{2\sqrt{5}}{5}$; $\cos\theta = -\frac{\sqrt{5}}{5}$; $\tan\theta = -2$; $\csc\theta = \frac{\sqrt{5}}{2}$; $\sec\theta = -\sqrt{5}$; $\cot\theta = -\frac{1}{2}$
27.

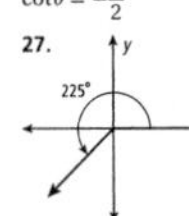

29. 750°
35. 50° 37. 20° 39. 85° 41. 35°
43. $\sin\theta = -\frac{2\sqrt{29}}{29}$; $\cos\theta = \frac{5\sqrt{29}}{29}$; $\tan\theta = -\frac{2}{5}$; $\csc\theta = -\frac{\sqrt{29}}{2}$; $\sec\theta = \frac{\sqrt{29}}{5}$; $\cot\theta = -\frac{5}{2}$
45. $\sin\theta = \frac{3}{5}$; $\cos\theta = \frac{4}{5}$; $\tan\theta = \frac{3}{4}$; $\csc\theta = \frac{5}{3}$; $\sec\theta = \frac{5}{4}$; $\cot\theta = \frac{4}{3}$
47. $\sin\theta = -\frac{2\sqrt{5}}{5}$; $\cos\theta = \frac{\sqrt{5}}{5}$; $\tan\theta = -2$; $\csc\theta = -\frac{\sqrt{5}}{2}$; $\sec\theta = \sqrt{5}$; $\cot\theta = -\frac{1}{2}$
49. $\sin\theta = \frac{4\sqrt{41}}{41}$; $\cos\theta = \frac{5\sqrt{41}}{41}$; $\tan\theta = \frac{4}{5}$; $\csc\theta = \frac{\sqrt{41}}{4}$; $\sec\theta = \frac{\sqrt{41}}{5}$; $\cot\theta = \frac{5}{4}$ 51. 1364°/s 53. $(-2, 2\sqrt{3})$
55a. 402 ft b. 5 s c. 215 ft d. 29 ft
57a. 7.5 min b. 68 rotations
59. −0.643 61. 30°, 150°, 210°, 330°
63. 82°, 98°, 262°, 278° 67. F
69. $\sin\theta = \frac{b\sqrt{a^2+b^2}}{a^2+b^2}$; $\cos\theta = \frac{a\sqrt{a^2+b^2}}{a^2+b^2}$; $\tan\theta = \frac{b}{a}$
71. $\sin\theta = \frac{b\sqrt{a^2+b^2}}{a^2+b^2}$; $\cos\theta = \frac{a\sqrt{a^2+b^2}}{a^2+b^2}$; $\tan\theta = \frac{b}{a}$
73. sine and cosine: none; tangent and secant: for $\theta = 90°$ for $\theta = 270°$ and all angles coterminal with these angles; cosecant and cotangent: for $\theta = 0°$ for $\theta = 180°$ and all angles coterminal with these angles 75. 3 77. $g(f(4)) = 37$
79. $\sin\theta = \frac{5}{13}$; $\cos\theta = \frac{12}{13}$; $\tan\theta = \frac{5}{12}$

13-3

Check It Out! 1a. $\frac{4\pi}{9}$ radians b. 40° c. $-\frac{\pi}{5}$ radians d. 720°
2a. $-\frac{\sqrt{2}}{2}$ b. 0 c. $-\frac{1}{2}$
3a. $\sin 270° = -1$; $\cos 270° = 0$; $\tan 270°$: undefined
b. $\sin\frac{11\pi}{6} = -\frac{1}{2}$; $\cos\frac{11\pi}{6} = \frac{\sqrt{3}}{2}$; $\tan\frac{11\pi}{6} = -\frac{\sqrt{3}}{3}$
c. $\sin(-30°) = -\frac{1}{2}$; $\cos(-30°) = \frac{\sqrt{3}}{2}$; $\tan(-30°) = -\frac{\sqrt{3}}{3}$ 4. 1.5 ft
Exercises 1. 1 unit; 2π units
3. $-\frac{5\pi}{12}$ radians 5. $\frac{3\pi}{4}$ radians
7. −112.5° 9. 80° 11. −1 13. $-\frac{1}{2}$
15. $\sin 120° = \frac{\sqrt{3}}{2}$; $\cos 120° = -\frac{1}{2}$; $\tan 120° = -\sqrt{3}$
17. $\sin\frac{\pi}{3} = \frac{\sqrt{3}}{2}$; $\cos\frac{\pi}{3} = \frac{1}{2}$; $\tan\frac{\pi}{3} = \sqrt{3}$ 19. $\frac{4\pi}{3}$ radians
21. $-\frac{5\pi}{36}$ radians 23. −20°
25. 630° 27. $-\sqrt{3}$ 29. $-\frac{\sqrt{3}}{2}$
31. $\sin 225° = -\frac{\sqrt{2}}{2}$; $\cos 225° = -\frac{\sqrt{2}}{2}$; $\tan 225° = 1$
33. $\sin\frac{11\pi}{6} = -\frac{1}{2}$; $\cos\frac{11\pi}{6} = \frac{\sqrt{3}}{2}$; $\tan\frac{11\pi}{6} = -\frac{\sqrt{3}}{3}$ 35. about 2793 mi
37. reference angle: $\frac{\pi}{4}$
39. 600 revolutions/min
41a. 45° b. 28 ft 51. C
53. $\sin\theta = -\frac{\sqrt{3}}{2}$; $\csc\theta = -\frac{2\sqrt{3}}{3}$; $\sec\theta = 2$; $\cot\theta = -\frac{\sqrt{3}}{3}$
55. $(-5\sqrt{3}, -5)$ 59. D: $\{x \mid x \geq -4\}$; R: $\{y \mid y \geq 0\}$ 61. D: $\{x \mid x \geq 0\}$; R: $\{y \mid y \leq 0\}$ 63. 25,165,824
65. 45° 67. 5°

13-4

Check It Out! 1. $\frac{\pi}{4} + (2\pi)n$ or $\frac{5\pi}{4} + (2\pi)n$, where n is an integer
2a. $-\frac{\pi}{4}$ or −45° b. $\frac{\pi}{2}$ or 90°
3. 37° north of east 4a. $\theta = -63.4°$
b. $\theta = 116.6°$
Exercises 3. $\frac{\pi}{6} + (2\pi)n$ and $\frac{7\pi}{6} + (2\pi)n$, where n is an integer
5. $\frac{\pi}{6}$; 30° 7. undefined 9. $\frac{\pi}{4}$; 45°
11. 5° 13. $\theta = 234.5°$ 15. $\theta = 255.5°$
17. $\frac{\pi}{3} + (2\pi)n$ and $\frac{2\pi}{3} + (2\pi)n$, where n is an integer 19. $\frac{\pi}{3}$; 60°
21. $-\frac{\pi}{6}$; −30° 23. $\frac{\pi}{3}$; 60° 25. 75°
27. $\theta = 228.6°$ 29. $\theta = 275.7°$
31a. style A: 7.5°; style B: 9.1°; style C: 5.1° b. style B c. 9.5°
33a. 84.0° b. 121 ft 35. 0.7
39. A 41. C 43. $\frac{\pi}{3} \leq \theta \leq \frac{5\pi}{3}$
45. $\frac{\pi}{8} \leq \theta < \frac{\pi}{4}$ or $\frac{5\pi}{8} \leq \theta < \frac{3\pi}{4}$ or $\frac{9\pi}{8} \leq \theta < \frac{5\pi}{4}$ or $\frac{13\pi}{8} \leq \theta < \frac{7\pi}{4}$
47. linear; translation 5 units up (or 5 units left) 49. $f^{-1}(x) = 4x - 4$; function; D: ℝ; R: ℝ 51. $\frac{4\pi}{3}$ radians
53. $\frac{7\pi}{3}$ radians

13-5

Check It Out! 1. 47.9 ft²
2a. m∠K = 31°; $k \approx 6.5$; $h \approx 8.4$
b. m∠N = 18°; $m \approx 4.7$; $p \approx 4.0$
3. 1 triangle; m∠B ≈ 35.4°; m∠C ≈ 39.6°; $c \approx 6.6$ cm
Exercises 1. 4.9 cm² 3. 6900.5 m²
5. m∠Z = 40°; $x \approx 36.1$; $y \approx 18.3$
7. m∠C = 65°; $a \approx 2.0$; $b \approx 2.9$
9. m∠R = 55°; $s \approx 38.8$; $t \approx 18.3$
11. 1 triangle; m∠B ≈ 20.3°; m∠C ≈ 39.7°; $c \approx 7.4$ m
13. 1 triangle; m∠B ≈ 37.3°; m∠C ≈ 97.7°; $c \approx 9.8$ m
15. 1376.6 yd² 17. m∠D = 61°; $c \approx 9.9$; $d \approx 8.7$ 19. m∠K = 38°; $\ell \approx 9.4$; $m \approx 7.6$ 21. 0 triangles
23. 1 triangle; m∠B ≈ 22.5°; m∠C ≈ 27.5°; $c \approx 4.2$ in.
25. m∠C = 64°; $b \approx 15.3$; $c \approx 15.6$
27. m∠A = 59°; $a \approx 21.8$; $c \approx 16.7$
29. 21 ft 31. 1 triangle; m∠A ≈ 16.9°; m∠C ≈ 28.1°; $a \approx 4.9$ 33. 1 triangle; m∠A = 90°; m∠C = 60°; $c \approx 5.2$
35a. distance from tower 1 to tower 2: 4.2 mi; distance from tower 2 to tower 3: 4.9 mi b. 8.9 mi²
37. 16.7 cm 39. B is incorrect.
43. B 45b. no 47. 0° < m∠A < 60°
49. y-intercept: 5; x-intercept: 5
51. y-intercept: 2; x-intercept: 6
53. $x = \frac{1}{3}$ 55. 135°; $\frac{3\pi}{4}$ radians
57. 30°; $\frac{\pi}{6}$ radians

13-6

Check It Out! 1a. $a \approx 40.9$; m∠B ≈ 3.9°; m∠C ≈ 3.1°
b. m∠A ≈ 43.4°; m∠B ≈ 55.6°; m∠C ≈ 81.0° 2. 34 mi 3. 367 m²

Exercises **1.** $q \approx 9.1$; $m\angle P \approx 40.5°$; $m\angle R \approx 59.5°$ **3.** $r \approx 11.6$; $m\angle P \approx 40.3°$; $m\angle R \approx 50.7°$ **5.** $m\angle P \approx 43.2°$; $m\angle Q \approx 86.5°$; $m\angle R \approx 50.3°$ **7.** 9 min **9.** $f \approx 55.5$; $m\angle G \approx 53.1°$; $m\angle H \approx 61.9°$ **11.** $f \approx 21.2$; $m\angle G \approx 59.2°$; $m\angle H \approx 40.8°$ **13.** $m\angle F \approx 54°$; $m\angle G \approx 59.6°$; $m\angle H \approx 66.4°$ **15.** 3.8 mi **17.** $m\angle B \approx 26.3°$; $m\angle C \approx 33.7°$; $a \approx 31.2$ **19.** $m\angle A \approx 51.3°$; $m\angle B \approx 32.7°$; $c \approx 16.6$ **21.** $m\angle A \approx 38.6°$; $m\angle B \approx 92.9°$; $m\angle C \approx 48.5°$ **23.** 74°, 46°, and 60° **25a.** 89 mi **b.** 38° **27a.** $m\angle A = 43°$; $m\angle B = 44°$ **b.** $m\angle A = 28°$; $m\angle B = 41°$ **29.** 524.6 cm^2 **31.** 7.3 ft^2 **33.** 1.2 km **39.** H **41.** No, Abby did not make an error. A triangle cannot be formed from sides that measure 2 units, 3 units, and 5 units. **43.** $x = 9.9$ **45.** $x = \pm 4i$ **47.** x-intercept of f: 4; y-intercept of f: −8; x-intercept of g: 4; y-intercept of g: −4 **49.** x-intercept of f: −12; y-intercept of f: 6; x-intercept of g: −4; y-intercept of g: 6 **51.** $m\angle C = 48°$; $b \approx 8.5$; $c \approx 13.8$

Study Guide: Review

1. radian **2.** cosecant **3.** standard position **4.** $\sin\theta = \frac{3}{5}$; $\cos\theta = \frac{4}{5}$; $\tan\theta = \frac{3}{4}$; $\csc\theta = \frac{5}{3}$; $\sec\theta = \frac{5}{4}$; $\cot\theta = \frac{4}{3}$ **5.** $\sin\theta = \frac{2}{3}$; $\cos\theta = \frac{\sqrt{5}}{3}$; $\tan\theta = \frac{2\sqrt{5}}{5}$; $\csc\theta = \frac{3}{2}$; $\sec\theta = \frac{3\sqrt{5}}{5}$; $\cot\theta = \frac{\sqrt{5}}{2}$ **6.** $x = 12\sqrt{3}$ **7.** $x = \frac{9\sqrt{2}}{2}$ **8.** 18 ft **9.** 178 m

10.

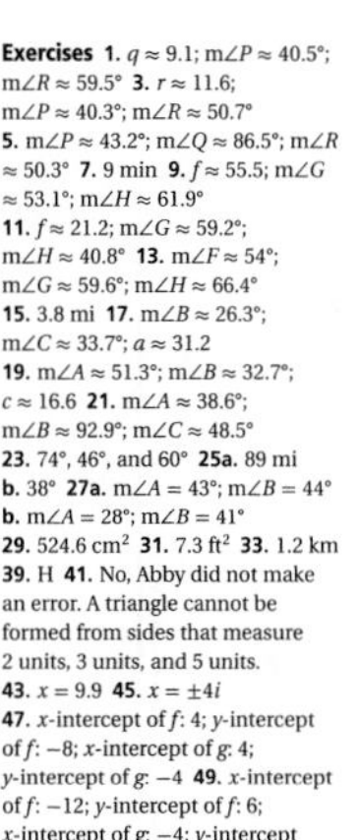

11.

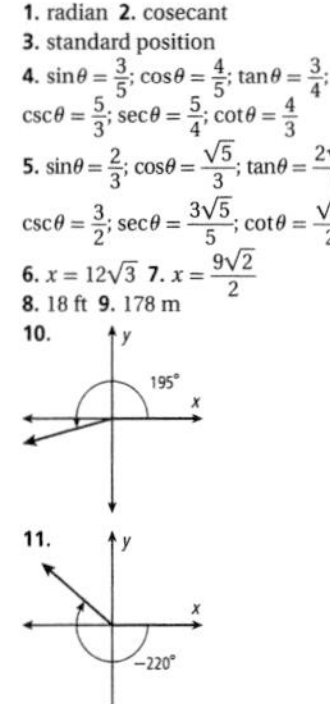

12.

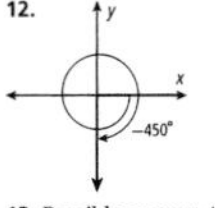

13. Possible answer: 475°; −245° **14.** Possible answer: 22°; −338° **15.** Possible answer: 225°; −495° **16.** 84° **17.** 53° **18.** 75° **19.** $\sin\theta = \frac{3}{5}$; $\cos\theta = -\frac{4}{5}$; $\tan\theta = -\frac{3}{4}$; $\csc\theta = \frac{5}{3}$; $\sec\theta = -\frac{5}{4}$; $\cot\theta = -\frac{4}{3}$ **20.** $\sin\theta = \frac{12}{13}$; $\cos\theta = \frac{5}{13}$; $\tan\theta = \frac{12}{5}$; $\csc\theta = \frac{13}{12}$; $\sec\theta = \frac{13}{5}$; $\cot\theta = \frac{5}{12}$ **21.** $\sin\theta = -\frac{8}{17}$; $\cos\theta = -\frac{15}{17}$; $\tan\theta = \frac{8}{15}$; $\csc\theta = -\frac{17}{8}$; $\sec\theta = -\frac{17}{15}$; $\cot\theta = \frac{15}{8}$ **22.** $\sin\theta = -\frac{3\sqrt{73}}{73}$; $\cos\theta = \frac{8\sqrt{73}}{73}$; $\tan\theta = -\frac{3}{8}$; $\csc\theta = -\frac{\sqrt{73}}{3}$; $\sec\theta = \frac{\sqrt{73}}{8}$; $\cot\theta = -\frac{8}{3}$ **23.** $\sin\theta = -\frac{\sqrt{82}}{82}$; $\cos\theta = -\frac{9\sqrt{82}}{82}$; $\tan\theta = \frac{1}{9}$; $\csc\theta = -\sqrt{82}$; $\sec\theta = -\frac{\sqrt{82}}{9}$; $\cot\theta = 9$ **24.** $\sin\theta = \frac{2\sqrt{5}}{5}$; $\cos\theta = -\frac{\sqrt{5}}{5}$; $\tan\theta = -2$; $\csc\theta = \frac{\sqrt{5}}{2}$; $\sec\theta = -\sqrt{5}$; $\cot\theta = -\frac{1}{2}$ **25.** $\frac{3\pi}{2}$ radians **26.** $-\frac{2\pi}{3}$ radians **27.** $\frac{20\pi}{9}$ radians **28.** 30° **29.** −20° **30.** 405° **31.** $-\frac{1}{2}$ **32.** −1 **33.** 2 **34.** $\sin\frac{7\pi}{6} = -\frac{1}{2}$; $\cos\frac{7\pi}{6} = -\frac{\sqrt{3}}{2}$; $\tan\frac{7\pi}{6} = \frac{\sqrt{3}}{3}$ **35.** $\sin 300° = -\frac{\sqrt{3}}{2}$; $\cos 300° = \frac{1}{2}$; $\tan 300° = -\sqrt{3}$ **36.** $\sin\left(-\frac{\pi}{3}\right) = -\frac{\sqrt{3}}{2}$; $\cos\left(-\frac{\pi}{3}\right) = \frac{1}{2}$; $\tan\left(-\frac{\pi}{3}\right) = -\sqrt{3}$ **37.** 22 in. **38a.** $\frac{\pi}{3}$ radians **b.** 1.6 m

39. $\frac{\pi}{3} + (2\pi)n$ and $\frac{4\pi}{3} + (2\pi)n$, where n is an integer **40.** $\frac{5\pi}{6} + (2\pi)n$ and $\frac{7\pi}{6} + (2\pi)n$, where n is an integer **41.** $\frac{5\pi}{4} + (2\pi)n$ and $\frac{7\pi}{4} + (2\pi)n$, where n is an integer **42.** $\frac{5\pi}{6} + (2\pi)n$ and $\frac{11\pi}{6} + (2\pi)n$, where n is an integer **43.** −30°; $-\frac{\pi}{6}$ radians **44.** 30°; $\frac{\pi}{6}$ radians **45.** 180°; π radians **46.** 45°; $\frac{\pi}{4}$ radians **47.** 34° **48.** 41° **49.** 17.5° **50.** 162.5° **51.** 65.6° **52.** 245.6° **53.** 5.4 m^2 **54.** 4953.1 ft^2 **55.** 24.0 $in.^2$ **56.** 112.5 cm^2 **57.** $m\angle F = 97°$; $d \approx 26.3$; $e \approx 37.0$ **58.** $m\angle B = 75°$; $b = 15$; $c \approx 7.8$ **59.** $m\angle P = 113°$; $p \approx 10.0$; $q \approx 4.9$ **60.** $m\angle Y = 64°$; $w = 4.8$; $x = 8.0$ **61.** 2 triangles; $m\angle B_1 \approx 69.4°$; $m\angle C_1 \approx 55.6°$; $c_1 \approx 14.1$ cm; $m\angle B_2 \approx 110.6°$; $m\angle C_2 \approx 14.4°$; $c_2 \approx 4.3$ cm **62.** $m\angle A \approx 20.9°$; $m\angle B \approx 130.1°$; $c \approx 19.0°$ **63.** $m\angle B \approx 43.0°$; $m\angle C \approx 27.0°$; $a \approx 24.8$ **64.** $m\angle A \approx 125.7°$; $m\angle B \approx 11.7°$; $m\angle C \approx 42.6°$ **65.** $m\angle A \approx 39.4°$; $m\angle B \approx 54.7°$; $m\angle C \approx 85.9°$ **66a.** 40.0 km **b.** 1.4 h **67.** 60 ft^2 **68.** 95 $in.^2$

Chapter 14

14-1

Check It Out! **1a.** not periodic **b.** periodic; 3 **2.** amplitude: $\frac{1}{3}$; period: π **3.** frequency: 250 Hz

4.

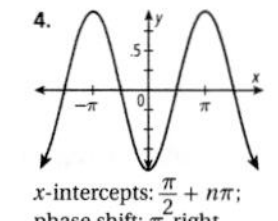

x-intercepts: $\frac{\pi}{2} + n\pi$; phase shift: π right

5a. b. 40 ft

Exercises **1.** periods **3.** not periodic **5.** amplitude: $\frac{1}{4}$; period: 2π **7.** frequency: 100 Hz **9.** x-intercepts: πn; phase shift: $\frac{\pi}{2}$ right **11.** 4 ft **13.** periodic; 2π **15.** amplitude: $\frac{3}{2}$; period: 2π **17.** amplitude: 6; period: 6π **19.** x-intercepts: πn; phase shift: π left **21.** x-intercepts: $\frac{\pi}{4} + \pi n$; phase shift: $\frac{3\pi}{4}$ left **23.** max.: 24.5 ft; min.: 21.5 ft **25.** amplitude: 1; period: 2π; phase shift $\frac{\pi}{4}$ left and vertical shift 1 down **27.** amplitude: 1; period: 1; horizontal compression and vertical shift 2 down **29.** ≈0.3 **31.** ≈0.25 **33.** $f(x) = 6\sin 2x$; $f(x) = 6\cos 2x$ **35.** $f(x) = -4\sin 2x$; $g(x) = 4\cos 2\left(x + \frac{\pi}{4}\right)$ **37a.** period: 12.2; amplitude: 1.5; max.: 3; min.: 0 **b.** $h(0) = 3$; $h(6.1) = 0$ **c.** $h(t) = 1.5\cos\frac{2\pi}{12.2}t + 1.5$ **39.** The period decreases for $b > 1$ and increases for $b < 1$ because the period is given by $\frac{2\pi}{b}$. **41.** H **43.** phase shift π right, horizontal compression, vertical stretch, and reflection across the x-axis amplitude: 4; period: π; x-intercepts $0, \frac{\pi}{2}, \pi, \frac{3\pi}{2}$, and 2π; max.: 4, min.: −4 **45.**

47. $76° < \theta < 256°$ **49.** $(-\infty, -2]$ or $[1, 13)$ **51a.** $6r + 2l + 4c = 100$

b.

Roses	6	4	3	7
Lilies	10	8	5	3
Carnations	11	15	18	13

53. $m\angle A = 10°$; $m\angle B = 12.4°$; $m\angle C = 157.6°$

14-2

Check It Out!

1. period: 2π; x-intercepts: $2\pi n$; asymptotes: $\pi + 2\pi n$

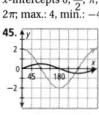

2. period: $\frac{\pi}{2}$; x-intercepts: $\frac{\pi}{4} + \frac{\pi}{2}n$; asymptotes: $\frac{\pi}{2}n$

3.

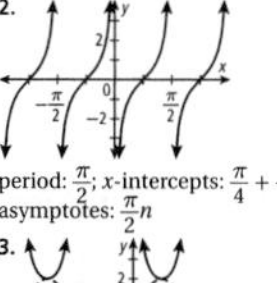

period: 2π; asymptotes: πn

Exercises **1.** period: $\frac{\pi}{3}$; x-intercepts: $\frac{\pi}{3}n$; asymptotes: $\frac{\pi}{6} + \frac{\pi}{3}n$ **3.** period: $\frac{1}{2}$; x-intercepts: $\frac{1}{2}n$; asymptotes: $\frac{1}{4} + \frac{1}{2}n$ **5.** period: $\frac{\pi}{2}$; x-intercepts: $\frac{\pi}{4} + \frac{\pi}{2}n$; asymptotes: $\frac{\pi}{2}n$ **7.** period: 2π; asymptotes: $\frac{\pi}{2} + \pi n$ **9.** period: 2π; asymptotes: πn **11.** period: π; x-intercepts: $\frac{3\pi}{4} + \pi n$; asymptotes: $\frac{\pi}{4} + \pi n$ **13.** period: 2; x-intercepts: $2n$; asymptotes: $1 + 2n$ **15.** period: 4π; x-intercepts: $2\pi + 4\pi n$; asymptotes: $4\pi n$ **17.** period: 2π; asymptotes: $\frac{\pi}{2} + \pi n$ **19.** period: 2π; asymptotes: πn **21.** $\frac{\pi}{2}; \frac{3\pi}{2}; -\frac{\pi}{2}; \frac{5\pi}{2}$ **23.** $\frac{\pi}{2}; \frac{3\pi}{2}; -\frac{\pi}{2}; \frac{5\pi}{2}$

25a. 3 s **c.** $t = \frac{3}{4}$ and $t = \frac{9}{4}$ **27.** increasing; decreasing; decreasing; increasing **29.** decreasing; decreasing; increasing; increasing **31.** increasing; increasing; increasing; increasing **37.** G **39.** H **41.** period: 2; local maximum: 1; local minimum: 7; phase shift: 1 right **47.** D: $\{x \mid x \le -1 \text{ or } x \ge 1\}$; R: $\left\{y \mid 0 \le y \le \pi \text{ and } y \ne \frac{\pi}{2}\right\}$ **49.** D: $\{x \mid x \le -1 \text{ or } x \ge 1\}$; R: $\left\{y \mid -\frac{\pi}{2} \le y \le \frac{\pi}{2} \text{ and } y \ne 0\right\}$ **51.** $\frac{1}{10}$; −10 **53.** $3\sqrt{5}$; $-\frac{\sqrt{5}}{15}$ **55.** 11 pages **57.** 135° **59.** −60°

14-3

Check It Out!

1a. $\sin\theta\cot\theta = \sin\theta\left(\frac{\cos\theta}{\sin\theta}\right) = \cos\theta$

b. $1 - \sec(-\theta) = 1 - \frac{1}{\cos(-\theta)} = 1 - \frac{1}{\cos\theta} = 1 - \sec\theta$

2a. $1 + \sin\theta$ **b.** $\frac{1}{\sin^2\theta} - 1$ **3.** $\theta \approx 22°$

Exercises

1. $\sin\theta\sec\theta = \sin\theta\left(\frac{1}{\cos\theta}\right) = \frac{\sin\theta}{\cos\theta} = \tan\theta$

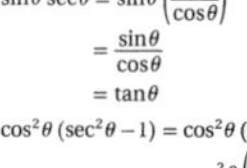

3. $\cos^2\theta(\sec^2\theta - 1) = \cos^2\theta(\tan^2\theta) = \cos^2\theta\left(\frac{\sin\theta}{\cos\theta}\right)^2 = \cos^2\theta\left(\frac{\sin^2\theta}{\cos^2\theta}\right) = \sin^2\theta$

5. $1 + \cos^2\theta$ **7.** $\theta \approx 43°$

9. $\frac{\sin\theta - \cos\theta}{\sin\theta} = \frac{\sin\theta}{\sin\theta} - \frac{\cos\theta}{\sin\theta} = 1 - \cot\theta$

11. $\sec^2\theta(1 - \cos^2\theta) = \left(\frac{1}{\cos^2\theta}\right)(\sin^2\theta) = \frac{\sin^2\theta}{\cos^2\theta} = \tan^2\theta$

13. $\frac{\sin^2\theta}{1 - \sin^2\theta}$ **15.** $\sin^2\theta$ **17.** 1 **19.** $\sec\theta$ **21.** $\cot\theta$ **23.** $\sin\theta$ **25.** $\csc\theta$ **27.** 1 **29.** $\sec^2\theta$ **31.** $\tan\theta$

33. $\sin^2\theta(\csc^2\theta - 1) = \sin^2\theta\cot^2\theta = \sin^2\theta\left(\frac{\cos^2\theta}{\sin^2\theta}\right) = \cos^2\theta$

35. $\frac{\cos\theta}{1 - \sin^2\theta} = \frac{\cos\theta}{\cos^2\theta} = \frac{1}{\cos\theta} = \sec\theta$

39. $\cot\theta = \frac{x}{y} = \frac{r\cos\theta}{r\sin\theta} = \frac{\cos\theta}{\sin\theta}$

43. $x^2 + y^2 = r^2$; $\frac{x^2}{x^2} + \frac{y^2}{x^2} = \frac{r^2}{x^2}$; $1 + \left(\frac{y}{x}\right)^2 = \left(\frac{r}{x}\right)^2$; $1 + \tan^2\theta = \sec^2\theta$

45. no **47.** yes **49.** no **51a.** $r = \ell\sin\theta$ **b.** $\ell = \frac{g}{\omega^2}\sec\theta$ **55.** an infinite number of equivalent forms **57.** D **59.** A **63.** $\frac{1}{\sin\theta\cos\theta}$ **65.** $\frac{1}{1 - \cos^2\theta}$ **67.** $\sin\theta + \cos\theta$ **69.** $\frac{\sin\theta}{\sin\theta + 1}$ **71.** $\frac{1}{36}$ **73.** $\frac{\pi}{2}, \frac{3\pi}{2}, -\frac{\pi}{2}, -\frac{3\pi}{2}$ **75.** $0, \pi, -\pi, 2\pi$

14-4

Check It Out! **1a.** $-2 - \sqrt{3}$ **b.** $\frac{\sqrt{2} - \sqrt{6}}{4}$

2. $\cos\left(\frac{\pi}{2} + x\right) = \cos\left(\frac{\pi}{2}\right)\cos x - \sin\left(\frac{\pi}{2}\right)\sin x = (0)\cos x - (1)\sin x = -\sin x$

3. $\frac{24}{25}$ **4.** $A'(-\sqrt{3}, 1)$, $B'(-2\sqrt{3}, 2)$, $C'(0, 2)$, $D'(-\sqrt{3}, -1)$

Exercises **1.** A rotation matrix assumes a counterclockwise rotation about the origin. **3.** $\frac{\sqrt{6} - \sqrt{2}}{4}$ **5.** $\frac{\sqrt{6} - \sqrt{2}}{4}$

7. $\tan(\pi + x) = \frac{\tan\pi + \tan x}{1 - \tan\pi\tan x} = \frac{0 + \tan x}{1 - 0} = \tan x$

9. $\frac{16}{65}$ **11.** $\frac{16}{63}$ **13.** $A'(-1.73, -1)$, $B'(-0.87, 0.5)$, $C'(-1.5, 2.60)$ **15.** $\sqrt{3} - 2$ **17.** $\frac{-\sqrt{2} - \sqrt{6}}{4}$

19. $\sin\left(\frac{3\pi}{2} + x\right) = \sin\frac{3\pi}{2}\cos x + \cos\frac{3\pi}{2}\sin x = (-1)\cos x + (0)\sin x = -\cos x$

21. $\frac{63}{65}$ **23.** $-\frac{16}{65}$ **25.** $A'(-1.41, 1.41)$, $B'(-0.71, 2.12)$, $C'(-0.71, 0.71)$ **27.** $2 + \sqrt{3}$ **29.** $\frac{\sqrt{2} - \sqrt{6}}{4}$ **31.** $2 + \sqrt{3}$ **33.** $2 - \sqrt{3}$ **35.** $\theta = 90°$ **37.** $\theta = 30°$ or 150° **39.** $\frac{204}{253}, \frac{253}{325}, \frac{36}{325}$

41a. $\begin{bmatrix} 0 & -1 \\ 1 & 0 \end{bmatrix}$ $\begin{bmatrix} -1 & 0 \\ 0 & -1 \end{bmatrix}$ $\begin{bmatrix} 0 & 1 \\ -1 & 0 \end{bmatrix}$

b. $P'(0, 0)$, $Q'(-1, 1)$, $R'(0, 4)$, $S'(1, 1)$; $P''(0, 0)$, $Q''(-1, -1)$, $R''(-4, 0)$, $S''(-1, 1)$; $P'''(0, 0)$, $Q'''(1, -1)$, $R'''(0, -4)$, $S'''(-1, -1)$

43a. 4.2; 3 **b.** $y(t) = -4.2\cos\frac{2\pi}{3}t$ **c.** 2.1 **45.** $A'(-2.60, 1.5)$, $B'(-2.96, 2.87)$, $C'(-1.60, 3.23)$, $D'(1, 1.73)$ **47.** $A'(1.50, 2.60)$, $B'(2.87, 2.96)$, $C'(3.23, 1.60)$, $D'(1.73, -1)$ **49.** A **51.** A **57.** 45° **59.** 30° **61.** $\frac{x - 1}{x + 2}$ **63.** parabola **65.** $\frac{1}{\cos\theta - \cos^3\theta}$ **67.** $\sin^2\theta$

14-5

Check It Out! **1.** $\frac{4\sqrt{2}}{7}$; $-\frac{7}{9}$

2a. Possible answer: $\cos^4\theta - \sin^4\theta = (\cos^2\theta + \sin^2\theta)(\cos^2\theta - \sin^2\theta) = (1)(\cos 2\theta) = \cos 2\theta$

b. Possible answer: $\frac{2\tan\theta}{1 + \tan^2\theta} = \frac{2\left(\frac{\sin\theta}{\cos\theta}\right)}{\sec^2\theta} = \frac{2\left(\frac{\sin\theta}{\cos\theta}\right)}{\frac{1}{\cos^2\theta}} \cdot \frac{\left(\frac{\cos^2\theta}{1}\right)}{\left(\frac{\cos^2\theta}{1}\right)} = 2\left(\frac{\sin\theta}{\cos\theta}\right)\left(\frac{\cos^2\theta}{1}\right) = 2\sin\theta\cos\theta = \sin 2\theta$

3a. $\sqrt{7 + 4\sqrt{3}}$ **b.** $-\frac{\sqrt{2 - \sqrt{2}}}{2}$

4. $\frac{\sqrt{5}}{5}, \frac{2\sqrt{5}}{5}$

Exercises **1.** $-\frac{120}{169}, -\frac{119}{169}, \frac{120}{119}$

3. $2\cos 2\theta = 2(2\cos^2\theta - 1) = 4\cos^2\theta - 2$

5. $\frac{1 + \cos 2\theta}{\sin 2\theta} = \frac{1 + (2\cos^2\theta - 1)}{(2\sin\theta\cos\theta)} = \frac{2\cos^2\theta}{2\sin\theta\cos\theta} = \frac{\cos\theta}{\sin\theta} = \cot\theta$

7. $\frac{\sqrt{2 - \sqrt{2}}}{2}$ **9.** $\sqrt{\frac{2 + \sqrt{2}}{2 - \sqrt{2}}}$ **11.** $\frac{4}{5}, -\frac{3}{5}, -\frac{4}{3}$ **13.** $-\frac{336}{625}, -\frac{527}{625}, \frac{336}{527}$

15. $\frac{\sin 2\theta}{\sin\theta} = \frac{(2\sin\theta\cos\theta)}{\sin\theta} = 2\cos\theta$

17. $\frac{1 - \cos 2\theta}{\sin 2\theta} = \frac{1 - (1 - 2\sin^2\theta)}{2\sin\theta\cos\theta} = \frac{2\sin^2\theta}{2\sin\theta\cos\theta} = \frac{\sin\theta}{\cos\theta} = \tan\theta$

19. $\frac{\sqrt{2 + \sqrt{3}}}{2}$ **21.** $\frac{\sqrt{2 - \sqrt{2}}}{2}$ **23.** $\frac{\sqrt{37}}{37}, \frac{6\sqrt{37}}{37}, -\frac{1}{6}$ **25.** $3\sin\theta\cos^2\theta - \sin^3\theta$ **27.** $\cos\theta(1 - 4\sin^2\theta)$ **29.** 1 **31.** $2\tan\theta$ **33.** $\sin\theta$ **35a.** $y(t) = 6.2\sin t\cos t$ **b.** about 0.66 s **c.** about 3.00 m **37.** $\frac{4\sqrt{5}}{9}, \frac{1}{9}, 4\sqrt{5}$; $\frac{\sqrt{18 + 6\sqrt{5}}}{6}$; $-\frac{\sqrt{18 - 6\sqrt{5}}}{6}$; $-\frac{\sqrt{3} + \sqrt{5}}{\sqrt{3} - \sqrt{5}}$ **39.** $-\frac{4}{5}, \frac{3}{5}, -\frac{4}{3}$; $\sqrt{\frac{5 - 2\sqrt{5}}{10}}$; $-\sqrt{\frac{5 + 2\sqrt{5}}{10}}$; $-\sqrt{\frac{5 - 2\sqrt{5}}{5 + 2\sqrt{5}}}$ **41.** $\frac{\sqrt{2 - \sqrt{3}}}{2}$ **43.** $-\frac{\sqrt{2 - \sqrt{3}}}{2}$ **49a.** $d(\theta) = \frac{v_0^2\sin 2\theta}{32}$ **b.** 100 ft; ≈ 173 ft; 200 ft; ≈ 173 ft; 100 ft **c.** 45° **d.** $30.52° < \theta < 59.48°$ **53.** F **55.** G **59.** $\sqrt{\frac{2 - \sqrt{2 + \sqrt{3}}}{2 + \sqrt{2 + \sqrt{3}}}}$ **61.** $\frac{1}{2}\sqrt{2 - \sqrt{2 + \sqrt{3}}}$ **65.** no **67.** $\frac{5x + 12}{x + 7}$; $x \ne 7$ **69.** $\frac{2x^2 - 30x - 20}{(x + 1)(x - 3)}$; $x \ne 1, 3$ **71.** $\frac{\sqrt{2} - \sqrt{6}}{4}$ **73.** $\frac{\sqrt{2} - \sqrt{6}}{4}$

14-6

Check It Out! **1.** 150° + 360n°, 210° + 360n° **2a.** 0 **b.** ≈ 21.9°, ≈ 158.1° **3a.** 60°, 300° **b.** 90°, 210°, 270°, 330° **4.** late March and late September

Exercises **1.** 60° + 360n°, 300° + 360n° **3.** 30° + 360n°, 330° + 360n° **5.** ≈ 74.5° or 285.5° **7.** π **9.** 60° + 360n°, 300° + 360n° **11.** 150° + 360n°, 210° + 360n° **13.** $\frac{\pi}{3}$, π, or $\frac{5\pi}{3}$ **15.** 90°, 120°, 240°, 270° **17a.** 10:00 A.M. and 6:00 P.M. **19.** 30°, 150°, 270° **21.** 30°, 90°, 150° **23.** 0°, 180°, 210°, 330° **25.** π **27.** $\frac{7\pi}{6}, \frac{11\pi}{6}$ **29.** no solution **31.** $0, \frac{\pi}{3}, \pi, \frac{4\pi}{3}$ **33a.** $\approx \frac{\pi}{2}$; 4 sets **b.** $\approx \frac{2\pi}{5}$; 5 sets **35.** B is incorrect **37.** $x \approx -4.165, -1.797, 1.395, 5.464, 6.831$ **39.** ≈ 84.8°, ≈ 264.8° **41.** 60°, 150°, 240°, 330° **43.** 38.5°, 141.5° **47.** J **49.** J **51.** $\theta \approx 38.7°$ or 321.3° **53.** 90°, 270°, 120°, 240°, 60°, 300° **55.** 210°, 330° **57.** 30°, 150°, 210°, 330° **59.** $2\sqrt{5}, 4.47, \sqrt{21}, \frac{19}{4}, \frac{\pi}{0.65}$ **61.** −1 **63.** $\cos^2\theta$

Study Guide: Review

1. cycle **2.** frequency **3.** period **4.** phase shift **5.** amplitude: 1; period: $\frac{2\pi}{3}$ **6.** amplitude: 1; period: 4π **7.** amplitude: $\frac{1}{3}$; period: 2π **8.** amplitude: 2; period: 2 **9.** amplitude: $\frac{1}{2}$; period: π **10.** amplitude: $\frac{\pi}{2}$; period: 2 **11.** x-intercepts: $\frac{\pi}{2} + \pi n$; phase shift: π left **12.** x-intercepts: $\frac{3\pi}{4} + \pi n$; phase shift: $\frac{\pi}{4}$ left **13.** x-intercepts: $\frac{\pi}{2} + \pi n$; phase shift: $\frac{3\pi}{2}$ right **14.** x-intercepts: πn; phase shift: $\frac{3\pi}{2}$ left **15.**

16. 24 h **17.** 8.2; noon **18.** period: π; x-intercepts: πn; asymptotes: $\frac{\pi}{2} + \pi n$ **19.** period: 1; x-intercepts: n; asymptotes: $\frac{1}{2} + n$ **20.** period: 2; x-intercepts: $2n$; asymptotes: $1 + 2n$ **21.** period: π; x-intercepts: $\frac{\pi}{2} + \pi n$; asymptotes: πn **22.** period: π; x-intercepts: $\frac{\pi}{2} + \pi n$; asymptotes: πn **23.** period: 1; x-intercepts: $\frac{1}{2} + n$; asymptotes: n **24.** period: 2π; asymptotes: $\frac{\pi}{2} + \pi n$ **25.** period: π; asymptotes: $\frac{\pi}{2}n$ **26.** period: 2π; asymptotes: πn **27.** period: 2π; asymptotes: $\frac{\pi}{2} + \pi n$ **28.** period: 2π; asymptotes: $\frac{\pi}{2} + \pi n$ **29.** period: 2π; asymptotes: $\pi + \pi n$

30. $\sec\theta\sin\theta\cot\theta = \left(\frac{1}{\cos\theta}\right)\sin\theta\left(\frac{\cos\theta}{\sin\theta}\right) = \left(\frac{\cos\theta}{\cos\theta}\right)\left(\frac{\sin\theta}{\sin\theta}\right) = 1$

31. $\frac{\sin^2(-\theta)}{\tan\theta} = \frac{(-\sin\theta)(-\sin\theta)}{\frac{\sin\theta}{\cos\theta}} = (\sin\theta)(\sin\theta)\left(\frac{\cos\theta}{\sin\theta}\right) = \sin\theta\cos\theta$

32. $(\sec\theta + 1)(\sec\theta - 1) = \sec^2\theta - 1 = \tan^2\theta$

33. $\cos\theta\sec\theta + \cos^2\theta\csc^2\theta = 1 + \cos^2\theta\frac{1}{\sin^2\theta} = 1 + \cot^2\theta = \csc^2\theta$

34. $(\tan\theta + \cot\theta)^2 = \tan^2\theta + 2\tan\theta\cot\theta + \cot^2\theta = \tan^2\theta + 2 + \cot^2\theta = (\tan^2\theta + 1) + (1 + \cot^2\theta) = \sec^2\theta + \csc^2\theta$

35. $\tan\theta + \cot\theta = \frac{\sin\theta}{\cos\theta} + \frac{\cos\theta}{\sin\theta} = \frac{\sin^2\theta + \cos^2\theta}{\sin\theta\cos\theta} = \frac{1}{\sin\theta\cos\theta} = \sec\theta\csc\theta$

36. $\sin^2\theta\tan\theta = (1 - \cos^2\theta)\tan\theta = \tan\theta - \cos^2\theta\tan\theta = \tan\theta - \cos^2\theta\left(\frac{\sin\theta}{\cos\theta}\right) = \tan\theta - \sin\theta\cos\theta$

37. $\frac{\tan\theta}{1 - \cos^2\theta} = \frac{\left(\frac{\sin\theta}{\cos\theta}\right)}{(\sin^2\theta)} = \left(\frac{\sin\theta}{\cos\theta}\right)\left(\frac{1}{\sin^2\theta}\right) = \left(\frac{1}{\cos\theta}\right)\left(\frac{1}{\sin\theta}\right) = \sec\theta\csc\theta$

38. $\csc\theta$ **39.** $\tan^2\theta$ **40.** $-\tan^2\theta$ **41.** $\sin\theta$ **42.** $\frac{-\sqrt{2} - \sqrt{6}}{4}$ **43.** $\frac{-\sqrt{2} - \sqrt{6}}{4}$ **44.** $\frac{\sqrt{6} + \sqrt{2}}{4}$ **45.** $2 - \sqrt{3}$ **46.** $-\frac{16}{65}$ **47.** $-\frac{63}{65}$ **48.** $\frac{56}{33}$ **49.** $\frac{16}{63}$ **50.** $-\frac{56}{65}$ **51.** $-\frac{33}{65}$ **52.** $\frac{36 - 5\sqrt{7}}{52}$ **53.** $\frac{-15 - 12\sqrt{7}}{52}$ **54.** $\frac{5\sqrt{7} + 36}{15 - 12\sqrt{7}}$ **55.** $\frac{5\sqrt{7} - 36}{15 + 12\sqrt{7}}$ **56.** $\frac{-36 - 5\sqrt{7}}{52}$ **57.** $\frac{-15 + 12\sqrt{7}}{52}$

58. $\approx \begin{bmatrix} 0 & 2.60 & 2.46 & -0.13 \\ 0 & 1.50 & 3.73 & 2.23 \end{bmatrix}$ **59.** $\approx \begin{bmatrix} 0 & 2.12 & 1.41 & -0.71 \\ 0 & 2.12 & 4.24 & 2.12 \end{bmatrix}$ **60.** $\approx \begin{bmatrix} 0 & 1.5 & 0.27 & -1.23 \\ 0 & 2.60 & 4.46 & 1.87 \end{bmatrix}$ **61.** $\begin{bmatrix} 0 & 0 & -2 & -2 \\ 0 & 3 & 4 & 1 \end{bmatrix}$ **62.** $\approx \begin{bmatrix} 0 & -4.23 & -3.46 & 0.77 \\ 0 & 3.33 & -2 & -5.33 \end{bmatrix}$ **63.** $\begin{bmatrix} 0 & -5 & 0 & 5 \\ 0 & -2 & -4 & -2 \end{bmatrix}$ **64.** $\approx \begin{bmatrix} 0 & -0.77 & 3.46 & 4.23 \\ 0 & -5.33 & -2 & 3.33 \end{bmatrix}$ **65.** $\begin{bmatrix} 0 & 2 & 4 & 2 \\ 0 & -5 & 0 & 5 \end{bmatrix}$ **66.** $\frac{24}{25}$

67. $-\frac{7}{25}$ **68.** $\frac{1}{2}$ **69.** $\frac{\sqrt{5}}{5}$ **70.** $-3\sqrt{7}$ **71.** $\frac{1}{8}$ **72.** $-\frac{\sqrt{14}}{4}$ **73.** $\frac{\sqrt{2}}{4}$ **74.** $\frac{\sqrt{2 - \sqrt{3}}}{2}$ **75.** $\frac{\sqrt{2 - \sqrt{3}}}{2}$ **76.** 135° + 360n°, 225° + 360n° **77.** 180° + 360n° **78.** 0° + 180n°, 135° + 180n° **79.** 60° + 180n°, 120° + 180n° **80.** $\frac{2\pi}{3}, \frac{4\pi}{3}$ **81.** 0 **82.** $\frac{\pi}{2}, \frac{3\pi}{2}$ **83.** $\frac{3\pi}{2}$ **84.** $0, \frac{2\pi}{3}, \frac{4\pi}{3}$ **85.** $\frac{\pi}{2}, \frac{7\pi}{6}, \frac{3\pi}{2}, \frac{11\pi}{6}$ **86a.** 900 min; late June **b.** 540 min; late December

Graphic Organizer Answers

Chapter 1

Lesson 1-1

Set	Roster Notation	Interval Notation	Set-Builder Notation
1, 2, 3, 4, and 5	{1, 2, 3, 4, 5}	Cannot be notated	$\{x \mid 1 \le x \le 5 \text{ and } x \in \mathbb{N}\}$
$-2 \le n \le 2$	Cannot be notated	$[-2, 2]$	$\{n \mid -2 \le n \le 2\}$
Whole numbers less than 3	{0, 1, 2}	Cannot be notated	$\{x \mid x < 3 \text{ and } x \in \mathbb{W}\}$

Lesson 1-2

Property	Addition	Multiplication
Identity	$5 + 0 = 5$	$5 \cdot 1 = 5$
Inverse	$5 + (-5) = 0$	$5 \cdot \frac{1}{5} = 1$
Commutative	$5 + 10 = 10 + 5$	$5 \cdot 10 = 10 \cdot 5$
Associative	$(5 + 1) + 2 = 5 + (1 + 2)$	$(5 \cdot 1) \cdot 2 = 5 \cdot (1 \cdot 2)$
Distributive	$5(1 + 2) = 5 \cdot 1 + 5 \cdot 2$	

Lesson 1-3

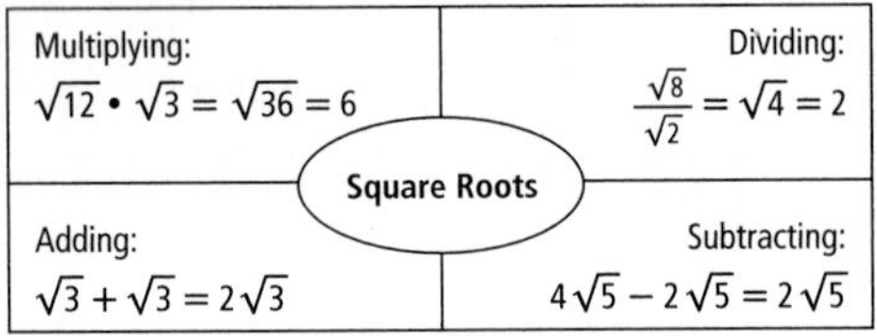

Multiplying:
$\sqrt{12} \cdot \sqrt{3} = \sqrt{36} = 6$
Dividing:
$\frac{\sqrt{8}}{\sqrt{2}} = \sqrt{4} = 2$
Square Roots
Adding:
$\sqrt{3} + \sqrt{3} = 2\sqrt{3}$
Subtracting:
$4\sqrt{5} - 2\sqrt{5} = 2\sqrt{5}$

Lesson 1-4

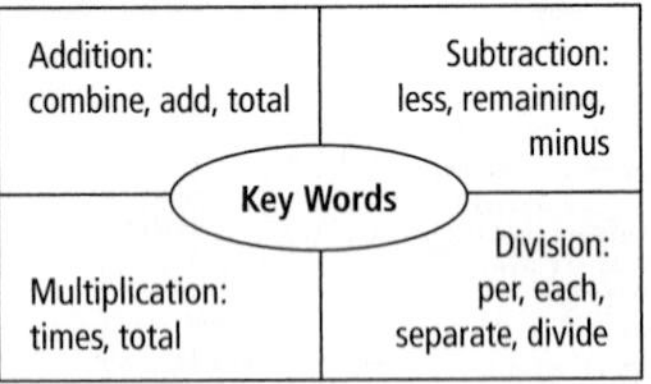

Lesson 1-5

Property	Numerical Example	Algebraic Example
Product of Powers	$4^3 \cdot 4^2 = 4^{3+2} = 4^5$	$a^m \cdot a^n = a^{m+n}$
Quotient of Powers	$\frac{3^7}{3^2} = 3^{7-2} = 3^5$	$\frac{a^m}{a^n} = a^{m-n}$, for $a \neq 0$
Power of a Power	$(4^3)^2 = 4^{3 \cdot 2} = 4^6$	$(a^m)^n = a^{m \cdot n}$
Power of a Product	$(3 \cdot 4)^2 = 3^2 \cdot 4^2$	$(ab)^m = a^m b^m$
Power of a Quotient	$\left(\frac{3}{5}\right)^2 = \frac{3^2}{5^2}$	$\left(\frac{a}{b}\right)^m = \frac{a^m}{b^m}$, for $b \neq 0$

Lesson 1-6

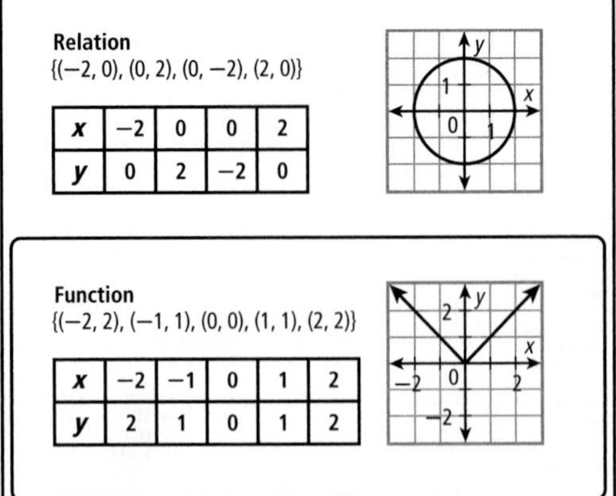

Relation
{(−2, 0), (0, 2), (0, −2), (2, 0)}
x | −2 | 0 | 0 | 2
y | 0 | 2 | −2 | 0
Function
{(−2, 2), (−1, 1), (0, 0), (1, 1), (2, 2)}
x | −2 | −1 | 0 | 1 | 2
y | 2 | 1 | 0 | 1 | 2

Lesson 1-7

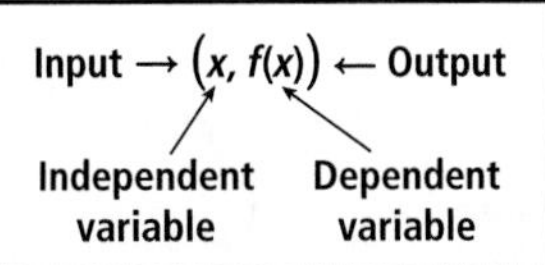

Lesson 1-8

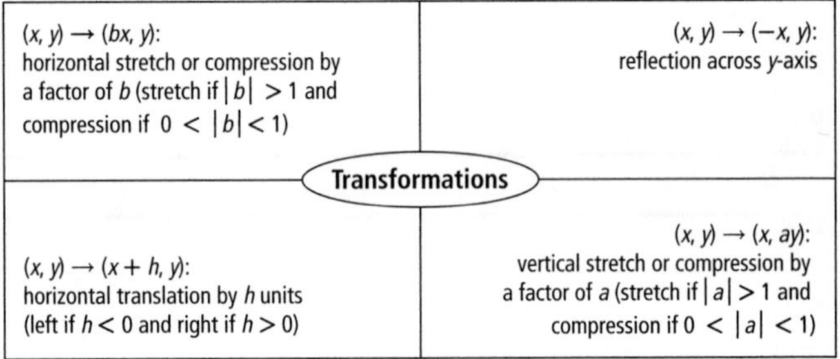

(x, y) → (bx, y): horizontal stretch or compression by a factor of b (stretch if |b| > 1 and compression if 0 < |b| < 1)
(x, y) → (−x, y): reflection across y-axis
Transformations
(x, y) → (x + h, y): horizontal translation by h units (left if h < 0 and right if h > 0)
(x, y) → (x, ay): vertical stretch or compression by a factor of a (stretch if |a| > 1 and compression if 0 < |a| < 1)

Lesson 1-9

Transformed Parent Functions			
Family	Linear	Quadratic	Square root
Rule	$f(x) = x + 3$	$f(x) = x^2 + 3$	$f(x) = \sqrt{x} + 3$
Graph			
Domain	$\mathbb{R}$	$\mathbb{R}$	$x \ge 0$
Range	$\mathbb{R}$	$y \ge 3$	$y \ge 3$
Intersects y-axis	(0, 3)	(0, 3)	(0, 3)

Chapter 2

Lesson 2-1

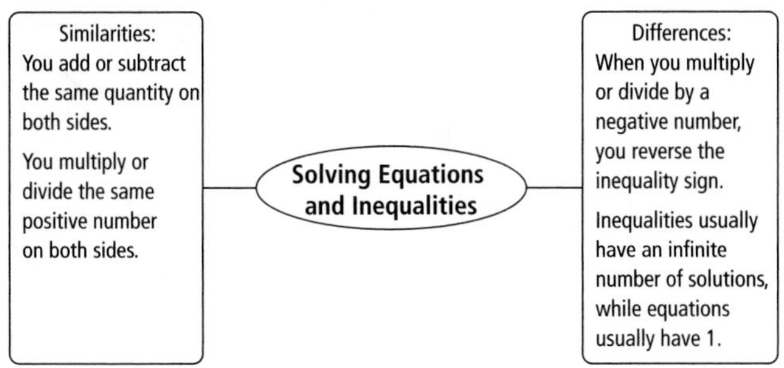

Similarities:
You add or subtract the same quantity on both sides.
You multiply or divide the same positive number on both sides.
Solving Equations and Inequalities
Differences:
When you multiply or divide by a negative number, you reverse the inequality sign.
Inequalities usually have an infinite number of solutions, while equations usually have 1.

Lesson 2-2

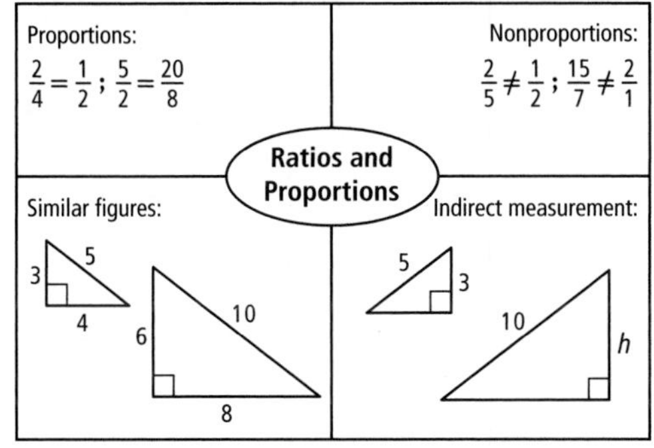

Lesson 2-3

Definition: A function that can be written in the form $y = mx + b$, where x is the independent variable and m and b are real numbers.	Characteristics: The graph is a nonvertical line. x and y are to the first power.
Linear Function	
Examples: $y = 2x + 7$ $y = -3x - 4$ $2x + 5y = 10$ $\frac{x-y}{2} = 1$	Nonexamples: $y = 2x^2$ $y = \frac{1}{x} - 4$ $\sqrt{x} = y + 1$ $2^x = 8$

Lesson 2-4

Slope-intercept form: $y = mx + b$ $y = -2x + 1$	Point-slope form: $y - y_1 = m(x - x_1)$ $y - 5 = 2(x - 4)$
Lines	
Parallel: $y = 4x + 7$ and $y = 4x + 2$	Perpendicular: $y = 4x + 7$ and $y = -\frac{1}{4}x + 2$

Lesson 2-5

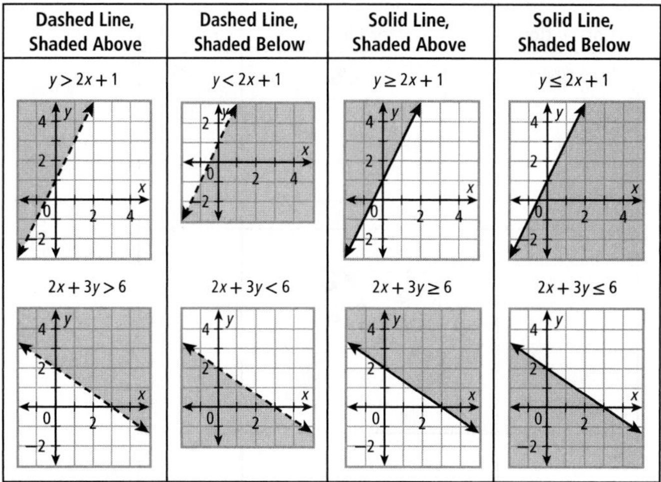

Dashed Line, Shaded Above
Dashed Line, Shaded Below
Solid Line, Shaded Above
Solid Line, Shaded Below
$y > 2x + 1$
$y < 2x + 1$
$y \geq 2x + 1$
$y \leq 2x + 1$
$2x + 3y > 6$
$2x + 3y < 6$
$2x + 3y \geq 6$
$2x + 3y \leq 6$

Lesson 2-6

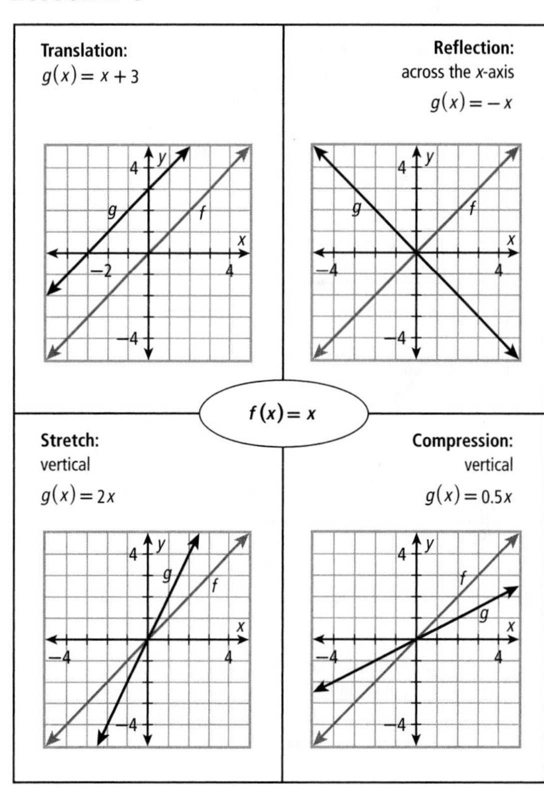

Additional Answers

Lesson 2-7

Correlation	Scatter Plot	Estimated r-value
Strong positive		0.95
Weak positive		0.6
No correlation		0
Weak negative		−0.6
Strong negative		−0.95

Lesson 2-8

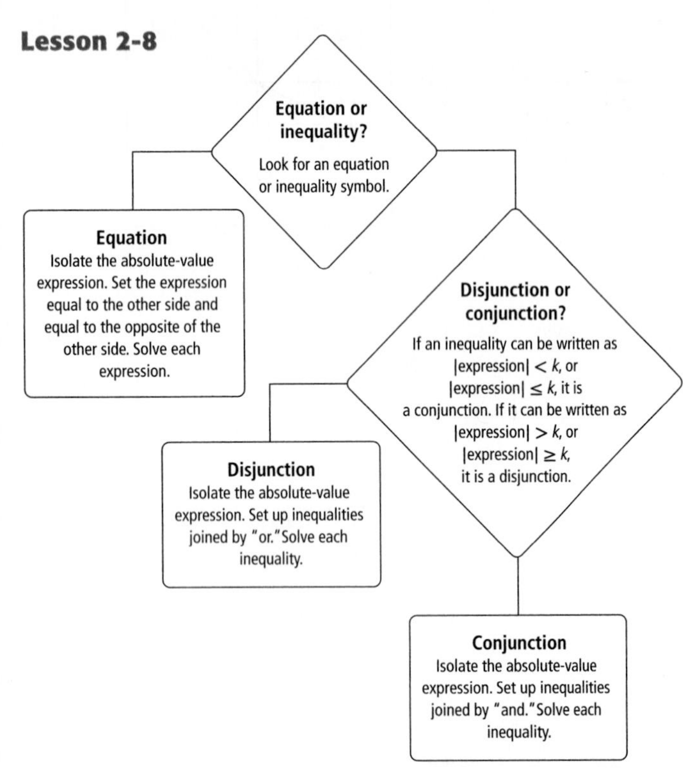

Equation or inequality?
Look for an equation or inequality symbol.
Equation
Isolate the absolute-value expression. Set the expression equal to the other side and equal to the opposite of the other side. Solve each expression.
Disjunction or conjunction?
If an inequality can be written as |expression| < k, or |expression| ≤ k, it is a conjunction. If it can be written as |expression| > k, or |expression| ≥ k, it is a disjunction.
Disjunction
Isolate the absolute-value expression. Set up inequalities joined by "or." Solve each inequality.
Conjunction
Isolate the absolute-value expression. Set up inequalities joined by "and." Solve each inequality.

Lesson 2-9

Transformation	Absolute-value Function	Transformed Function	Graph
Vertical translation	$f(x) = \|x\|$	$f(x) = \|x\| + 1$	
Horizontal translation	$f(x) = \|x\|$	$f(x) = \|x - 1\|$	
(h, k) translation	$f(x) = \|x\|$	$f(x) = \|x - 1\| + 1$	
Vertical stretch	$f(x) = \|x\|$	$f(x) = 2\|x\|$	
Vertical compression	$f(x) = \|x\|$	$f(x) = 0.5\|x\|$	
Reflection	$f(x) = \|x\|$	$f(x) = -\|x\|$	

Chapter 3

Lesson 3-1

	Exactly One Solution	Infinitely Many Solutions	No Solution
Example	$y = 2x + 1$ $y = -x + 2$	$y = 2x + 1$ $y = 2x + 1$	$y = 2x + 1$ $y = 2x + 4$
Graph			
Slopes	Different	Same	Same
***y*-intercepts**	Either	Same	Different

Lesson 3-2

Graphing: $\begin{cases} y = 2x + 1 \\ y = x + 3 \end{cases}$

$x = 2, y = 5$

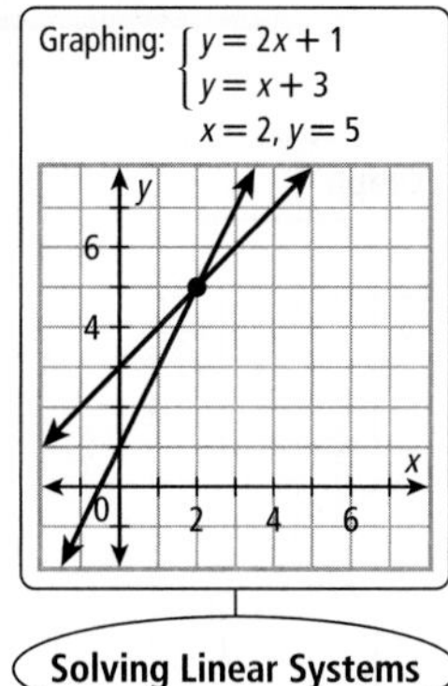

Solving Linear Systems

Substitution:	Elimination:
$\begin{cases} y = 2x + 1 \\ 3x + 2y = 2 \end{cases}$	$\begin{cases} y = 2x + 1 \\ y = -2x + 1 \end{cases}$
$3x + 2(2x + 1) = 2$	$2y = 2$
$3x + 4x + 2 = 2$	$y = 1, x = 0$
$7x = 0$	
$x = 0, y = 1$	

Lesson 3-3

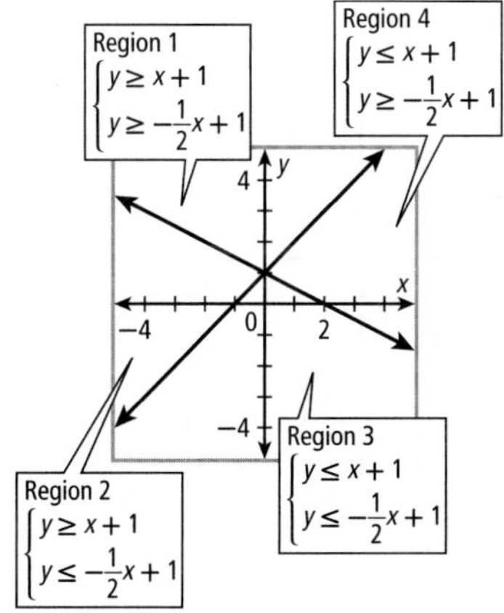

Lesson 3-4

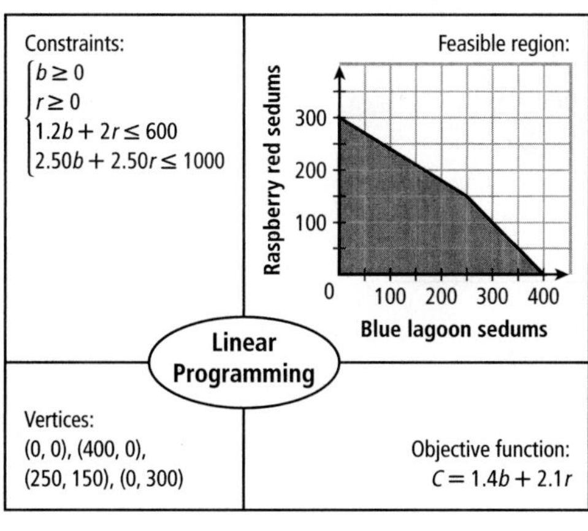

Constraints:
$\begin{cases} b \geq 0 \\ r \geq 0 \\ 1.2b + 2r \leq 600 \\ 2.50b + 2.50r \leq 1000 \end{cases}$
Feasible region:
Raspberry red sedums
300
200
100
0
100 200 300 400
Blue lagoon sedums
Linear Programming
Vertices:
(0, 0), (400, 0),
(250, 150), (0, 300)
Objective function:
$C = 1.4b + 2.1r$

Lesson 3-5

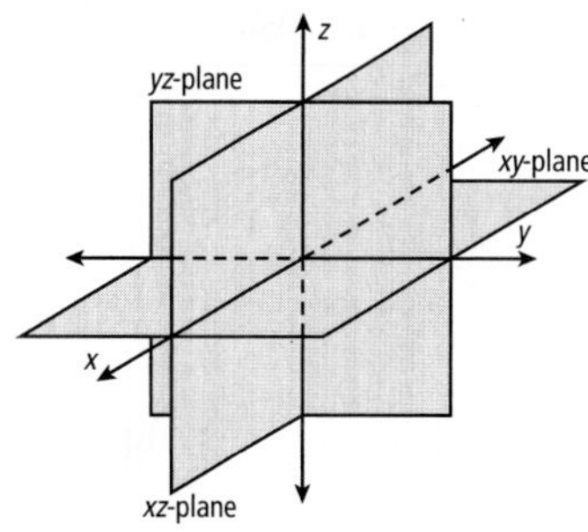

Lesson 3-6

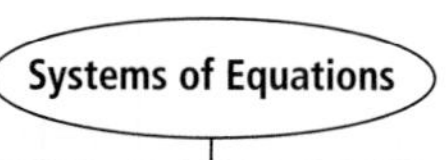

2-by-2: 2 variables; solve by graphing, substitution, or elimination; one, zero, or infinitely many solutions	3-by-3: 3 variables; solve by graphing, substitution, or elimination; one, zero, or infinitely many solutions

Chapter 4

Lesson 4-1

Operation	Real Numbers	Matrices
Addition	$5 + 3 = 8$	$\begin{bmatrix} 3 & 4 \\ 2 & -4 \end{bmatrix} + \begin{bmatrix} 1 & 2 \\ -3 & -5 \end{bmatrix} = \begin{bmatrix} 4 & 6 \\ -1 & -9 \end{bmatrix}$
Subtraction	$5 - 3 = 2$	$\begin{bmatrix} 3 & 4 \\ 2 & -4 \end{bmatrix} - \begin{bmatrix} 1 & 2 \\ -3 & -5 \end{bmatrix} = \begin{bmatrix} 2 & 2 \\ 5 & 1 \end{bmatrix}$
Multiplication by a number	$-2(5) = -10$	$-2\begin{bmatrix} 3 & 4 \\ 2 & -4 \end{bmatrix} = \begin{bmatrix} -6 & -8 \\ -4 & 8 \end{bmatrix}$

Lesson 4-2

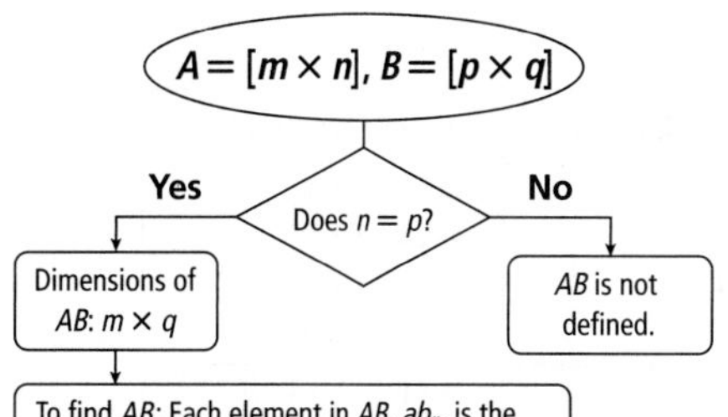

Dimensions of AB: $m \times q$
AB is not defined.

To find AB: Each element in AB, ab_{ij}, is the sum of the products of corresponding entries in row i in matrix A and column j in matrix B.

Lesson 4-3

Transformation	Matrix Operation
Translate Q vertically.	$Q + \begin{bmatrix} 0 & 0 & 0 \\ -2 & -2 & -2 \end{bmatrix}$
Translate Q horizontally.	$Q + \begin{bmatrix} 3 & 3 & 3 \\ 0 & 0 & 0 \end{bmatrix}$
Enlarge or reduce Q.	$4Q$, or $0.5Q$
Reflect Q across the x-axis or y-axis.	$\begin{bmatrix} 1 & 0 \\ 0 & -1 \end{bmatrix}Q$, or $\begin{bmatrix} -1 & 0 \\ 0 & 1 \end{bmatrix}Q$
Rotate Q 90° clockwise or counterclockwise.	$\begin{bmatrix} 0 & 1 \\ -1 & 0 \end{bmatrix}Q$, or $\begin{bmatrix} 0 & -1 \\ 1 & 0 \end{bmatrix}Q$

Additional Answers

Lesson 4-4

	2 × 2 Matrix	3 × 3 Matrix
Determinant	$\det\begin{bmatrix} a & b \\ c & d \end{bmatrix} = ad - cb$	$\det\begin{bmatrix} a_1 & b_1 & c_1 \\ a_2 & b_2 & c_2 \\ a_3 & b_3 & c_3 \end{bmatrix} =$ $a_1b_2c_3 + b_1c_2a_3 + c_1a_2b_3 - (a_3b_2c_1 + b_3c_2a_1 + c_3a_2b_1)$
Cramer's Rule	$x = \dfrac{\begin{vmatrix} c_1 & b_1 \\ c_2 & b_2 \end{vmatrix}}{D}$, and $y = \dfrac{\begin{vmatrix} a_1 & c_1 \\ a_2 & c_2 \end{vmatrix}}{D}$, where $D = \begin{vmatrix} a_1 & b_1 \\ a_2 & b_2 \end{vmatrix}$.	$x = \dfrac{\begin{vmatrix} d_1 & b_1 & c_1 \\ d_2 & b_2 & c_2 \\ d_3 & b_3 & c_3 \end{vmatrix}}{D}$, $y = \dfrac{\begin{vmatrix} a_1 & d_1 & c_1 \\ a_2 & d_2 & c_2 \\ a_3 & d_3 & c_3 \end{vmatrix}}{D}$, and $z = \dfrac{\begin{vmatrix} a_1 & b_1 & d_1 \\ a_2 & b_2 & d_2 \\ a_3 & b_3 & d_3 \end{vmatrix}}{D}$, where $D = \begin{vmatrix} a_1 & b_1 & c_1 \\ a_2 & b_2 & c_2 \\ a_3 & b_3 & c_3 \end{vmatrix}$ and $D \neq 0$.

Lesson 4-5

Multiplicative Inverses		
	Real Numbers	**Matrices**
Notation and Example	For 5, 5^{-1}; The reciprocal of the real number	for a square matrix A^{-1}; $A = \begin{bmatrix} 1 & 3 \\ 2 & 7 \end{bmatrix}$, $A^{-1} = \begin{bmatrix} 7 & -3 \\ -2 & 1 \end{bmatrix}$
How to Show That It Is the Muliplicative Inverse	Show that the product of a real number and its multiplicative inverse is equal to 1. $5 \cdot 5^{-1} = 1$	Show that the product of the matrix and its multiplicative inverse is equal to an identity matrix. $AA^{-1} =$ $\begin{bmatrix} 1 & 3 \\ 2 & 7 \end{bmatrix}\begin{bmatrix} 7 & -3 \\ -2 & 1 \end{bmatrix} = \begin{bmatrix} 1 & 0 \\ 0 & 1 \end{bmatrix}$
Commutative Property	Yes; $5^{-1} \cdot 5 = 1$	Yes; $\begin{bmatrix} 7 & -3 \\ -2 & 1 \end{bmatrix}\begin{bmatrix} 1 & 3 \\ 2 & 7 \end{bmatrix} = \begin{bmatrix} 1 & 0 \\ 0 & 1 \end{bmatrix}$

Lesson 4-6

	System of Equations	Augmented Matrix
Interchange rows or equations.	❶ $x + 3y = 5$ ❷ $2x + y = 8$ ❷ $2x + y = 8$ ❶ $x + 3y = 5$	❶❷ $\left[\begin{array}{cc:c} 1 & 3 & 5 \\ 2 & 1 & 8 \end{array}\right]$ ❷❶ $\left[\begin{array}{cc:c} 2 & 1 & 8 \\ 1 & 3 & 5 \end{array}\right]$
Replace a row or equation with a multiple.	❶ $x + 3y = 5$ ❷ $2x + y = 8$ 2❶ → $2x + 6y = 10$ $2x + y = 8$	❶❷ $\left[\begin{array}{cc:c} 1 & 3 & 5 \\ 2 & 1 & 8 \end{array}\right]$ 2❶ → $\left[\begin{array}{cc:c} 2 & 6 & 10 \\ 2 & 1 & 8 \end{array}\right]$
Replace a row or equation with a sum or difference.	❶ $2x + 6y = 10$ ❷ $2x + y = 8$ $2x + 6y = 10$ ❶ − ❷ → $5y = 2$	❶❷ $\left[\begin{array}{cc:c} 2 & 6 & 10 \\ 2 & 1 & 8 \end{array}\right]$ ❶ − ❷ → $\left[\begin{array}{cc:c} 2 & 6 & 10 \\ 0 & 5 & 2 \end{array}\right]$
Combine the above.	❶ $x + 3y = 5$ ❷ $2x + y = 8$ $x + 3y = 5$ 2❶ − ❷ → $0x + 5y = 2$	❶❷ $\left[\begin{array}{cc:c} 1 & 3 & 5 \\ 2 & 1 & 8 \end{array}\right]$ 2❶ − ❷ → $\left[\begin{array}{cc:c} 1 & 3 & 5 \\ 0 & 5 & 2 \end{array}\right]$

Chapter 5

Lesson 5-1

Transformation	Equation	Graph
Vertical translation	$f(x) = x^2 + 2$	
Horizontal translation	$f(x) = (x - 2)^2$	
Reflection	$f(x) = -x^2$	
Vertical stretch	$f(x) = 2x^2$	
Vertical compression	$f(x) = \frac{1}{2}x^2$	

Lesson 5-2

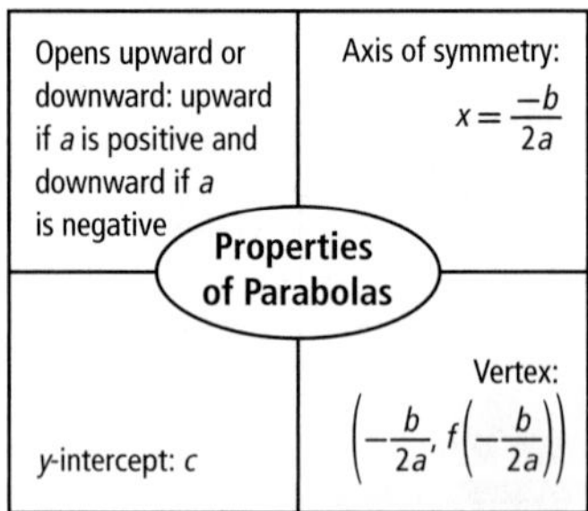

Opens upward or downward: upward if a is positive and downward if a is negative
Axis of symmetry: $x = \frac{-b}{2a}$
Properties of Parabolas
y-intercept: c
Vertex: $\left(-\frac{b}{2a}, f\left(-\frac{b}{2a}\right)\right)$

Additional Answers

Lesson 5-3

Name	Rule	Example	Graph
Difference of Two Squares	$a^2 - b^2 = (a + b)(a - b)$	$x^2 - 9 = (x + 3)(x - 3)$	(−3, 0); (3, 0); 4; −4; 0; x; y
Perfect-Square Trinomial	$a^2 + 2ab + b^2 = (a + b)^2$	$x^2 + 4x + 4 = (x + 2)^2$	(−2, 0); 4; −4; 0; 2; −2; x; y
	$a^2 - 2ab + b^2 = (a - b)^2$	$x^2 - 4x + 4 = (x - 2)^2$	(2, 0); 4; 2; −2; 0; x; y

Lesson 5-4

Using Square-Root Property vs. Completing the Square

Similarities: Both involve taking the square root of each side of an equation. Both may involve writing an expression as a binomial squared.

Differences: The Square-Root Property is useful for expressions that are perfect squares. Completing the square is useful for expressions that are not perfect squares.

Lesson 5-5

Complex Numbers

Definition: numbers that can be written in the form $a + bi$, where a and b are real numbers and $i = \sqrt{-1}$

Examples: $11, \sqrt{-21}, 5 - 2i, 1.75i$

Real Numbers

Definition: all rational and irrational numbers

Examples: $5, \sqrt{3}, -4.\overline{2}, \pi$

Imaginary Numbers

Definition: numbers that can be written in the form bi, where b is a real number and $i = \sqrt{-1}$

Examples: $12i, 0.25i, -i$

Lesson 5-6

Value of Discriminant	Type of Solutions	Possible Solution Methods
Negative	2 distinct complex nonreal	Quadratic Formula, completing the square, square roots
Zero	1 distinct real	Quadratic Formula, completing the square, square roots, factoring, graphing
Positive	2 distinct real	Quadratic Formula, completing the square, square roots, factoring, graphing

Lesson 5-7

	Equation (=)	"Less Than" Inequality (< or ≤)
Example	$x^2 - 4 = 0$	$x^2 - 4 < 0$
Graph	−3 −2 −1 0 1 2 3	−3 −2 −1 0 1 2 3
Solution Set	$x = \pm 2$	$-2 < x < 2$

	"Greater Than" Inequality (> or ≥)
Example	$x^2 - 4 > 0$
Graph	−3 −2 −1 0 1 2 3
Solution Set	$x < -2$ or $x > 2$

Lesson 5-8

Quadratic Model	When Appropriate	Procedure
Exact model	3 noncollinear points	Set up and solve a system of 3 equations to find a, b, and c in $f(x) = ax^2 + bx + c$.
Approximate model	4 or more points from a set of real data	Use the quadratic regression feature on a graphing calculator.

Lesson 5-9

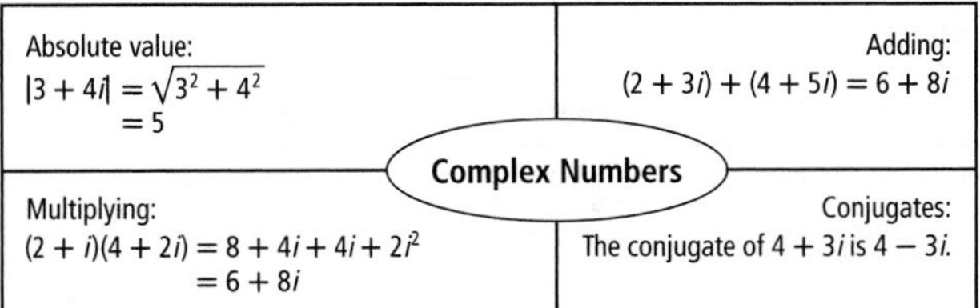

Absolute value:
|3 + 4i| = √(3² + 4²) = 5
Adding:
(2 + 3i) + (4 + 5i) = 6 + 8i
Complex Numbers
Multiplying:
(2 + i)(4 + 2i) = 8 + 4i + 4i + 2i² = 6 + 8i
Conjugates:
The conjugate of 4 + 3i is 4 − 3i.

Chapter 6

Lesson 6-1

Polynomial

Characteristics: no variables in the denominator or exponents; no absolute values; whole-number exponents only

Definition: monomial or sum or difference of monomials

Examples: $3x^2 + 2x + 1$; $5x^5 - x^4 + 9$

Nonexamples: $\sqrt{x}$; $\frac{1}{x}$; $|x|$

Additional Answers

Lesson 6-2

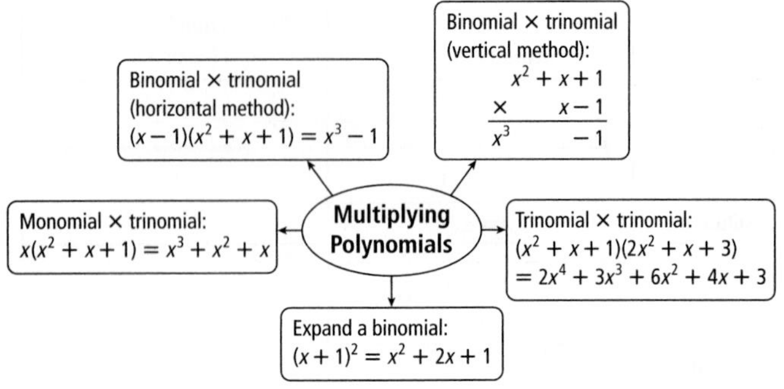

Binomial × trinomial (vertical method):
$x^2 + x + 1$
$\times \quad x - 1$
$x^3 \quad - 1$
Binomial × trinomial (horizontal method):
$(x-1)(x^2 + x + 1) = x^3 - 1$
Monomial × trinomial:
$x(x^2 + x + 1) = x^3 + x^2 + x$
Multiplying Polynomials
Trinomial × trinomial:
$(x^2 + x + 1)(2x^2 + x + 3)$
$= 2x^4 + 3x^3 + 6x^2 + 4x + 3$
Expand a binomial:
$(x+1)^2 = x^2 + 2x + 1$

Lesson 6-3

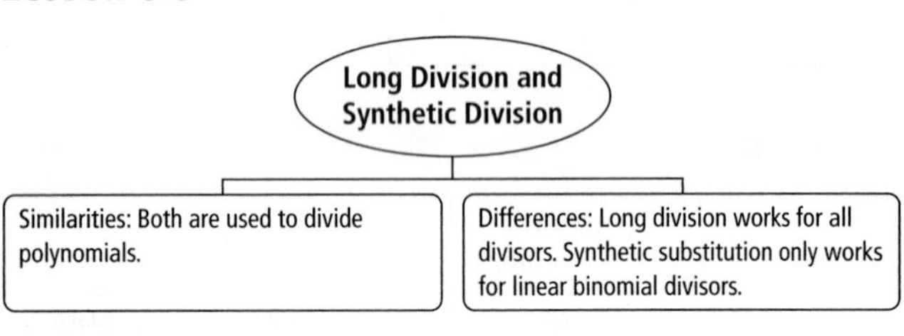

Long Division and Synthetic Division
Similarities: Both are used to divide polynomials.
Differences: Long division works for all divisors. Synthetic substitution only works for linear binomial divisors.

Lesson 6-4

Method	Polynomial	Factored Form
Difference of two squares	$(s^2 - t^2)$	$(s + t)(s - t)$
Difference of two cubes	$(s^3 - t^3)$	$(s - t)(s^2 + st + t^2)$
Sum of two cubes	$(s^3 + t^3)$	$(s + t)(s^2 - st + t^2)$

Lesson 6-5

Theorem	Roots	Polynomial
Rational Root Theorem	1, 2, 3	$(x-1)(x-2)(x-3)$
Irrational Root Theorem	$1, \pm\sqrt{2}$	$(x-1)(x^2-2)$

Lesson 6-6

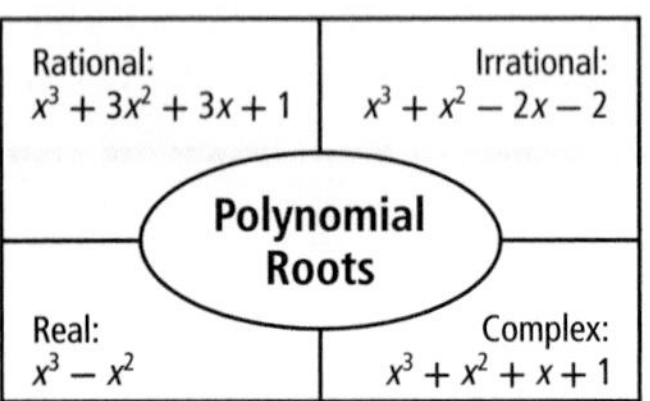

Lesson 6-7

Leading Coefficient	Odd Degree	Even Degree
Positive		
Negative		

Lesson 6-8

Transformation	Vertical shift	Horizontal shift	Vertical stretch	Horizontal compression
Example	$f(x) + 2$	$f(x - 2)$	$2f(x)$	$f(2x)$

Lesson 6-9

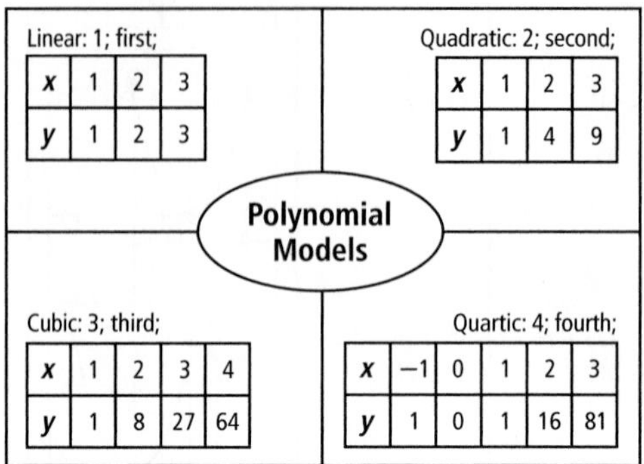

Linear: 1; first;
x 1 2 3
y 1 2 3
Quadratic: 2; second;
x 1 2 3
y 1 4 9
Polynomial Models
Cubic: 3; third;
x 1 2 3 4
y 1 8 27 64
Quartic: 4; fourth;
x −1 0 1 2 3
y 1 0 1 16 81

Chapter 7

Lesson 7-1

Exponential Functions $f(x) = ab^x$, where $a > 0$	Growth	Decay
Value of b	$b > 1$	$0 < b < 1$
General shape of the graph		
What happens to $f(x)$ as x increases?	$f(x)$ increases.	$f(x)$ decreases.
What happens to $f(x)$ as x decreases?	$f(x)$ decreases.	$f(x)$ increases.

Lesson 7-2

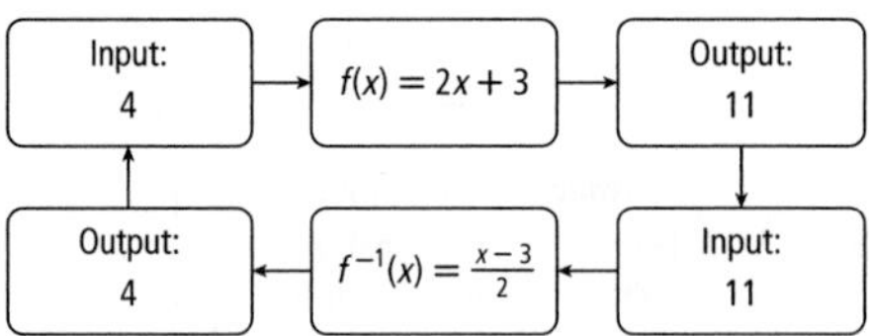

Lesson 7-3

Logarithmic Function

Definition:
the exponent to which a specified base is raised to obtain a given value

Characteristics:
- the inverse of an exponential function
- logarithm can be any real number
- has a positive base not equal to 1
- written $f(x) = \log_b x$
- if the base is 10, $f(x) = \log x$

Examples:
$3^2 = 9$, so $\log_3 9 = 2$.
$4^{-3} = \frac{1}{64}$, so $\log_4 \frac{1}{64} = -3$.
$10^0 = 1$, so $\log 1 = 0$.

Nonexamples:
polynomial functions: $f(x) = x$, $f(x) = x^2$
exponential functions: $f(x) = 2^x$
root functions: $f(x) = \sqrt{x}$

Additional Answers

Lesson 7-4

Property of Exponents	Property of Logarithms
$b^m b^n = b^{m+n}$	$\log_b mn = \log_b m + \log_b n$
$\frac{b^m}{b^n} = b^{m-n}$	$\log_b \frac{m}{n} = \log_b m - \log_b n$
$(b^a)^p = b^{ap}$	$\log_b a^p = p \log_b a$
$b^{\log_b x} = x$	$\log_b b^x = x$
	$\log_b x = \frac{\log_a x}{\log_a b}$

Lesson 7-5

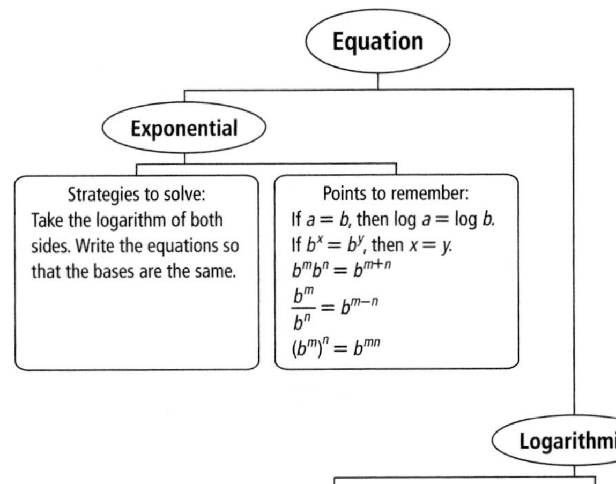

Equation
Exponential
Strategies to solve: Take the logarithm of both sides. Write the equations so that the bases are the same.
Points to remember:
If $a = b$, then $\log a = \log b$.
If $b^x = b^y$, then $x = y$.
$b^m b^n = b^{m+n}$
$\frac{b^m}{b^n} = b^{m-n}$
$(b^m)^n = b^{mn}$

Logarithmic

Strategies to solve: Use the properties of logarithms to solve.

Points to remember:
If $\log_b x = \log_b y$, then $x = y$.
$\log_b mn = \log_b m + \log_b n$
$\log_b \frac{m}{n} = \log_b m - \log_b n$
$\log_b a^p = p \log_b a$
$\log_b b^x = x$

Lesson 7-6

	Natural Logarithms	Common Logarithms
Base	$e = 2.718\ldots$	10
Logarithmic Form	$\ln x = y$ $\ln 100 \approx 4.6$	$\log x = y$ $\log 100 = 2$
Exponential Form	$x = e^y$ $100 \approx e^{4.6}$	$x = 10^y$ $100 = 10^2$
$\log_b 1$	$\ln 1 = 0$	$\log 1 = 0$
$\log_b b$	$\ln e = 1$	$\log 10 = 1$
$\log_b b^x$	$\ln e^x = x$	$\log 10^x = x$
$b^{\log_b x}$	$e^{\ln x} = x$	$10^{\log x} = x$

Lesson 7-7

Transformation	$f(x) = 5^x$ $f(x) = e^x$	$f(x) = \log_b x$ $f(x) = \ln x$
Vertical translation	$5^x + 2$ $e^x + 2$	$\log_2 x + 2$ $\ln x + 2$
Horizontal translation	5^{x+2} e^{x+2}	$\log_2 (x + 2)$ $\ln (x + 2)$
Reflection	-5^x $-e^x$	$-\log_2 x$ $-\ln x$
Vertical stretch	$2e^x$ $2(5^x)$	$2 \log_2 x$ $2 \ln x$
Vertical compression	$\frac{1}{2}(5^x)$ $\frac{1}{2}e^x$	$\frac{1}{2}\log_2 x$ $\frac{1}{2}\ln x$

Lesson 7-8

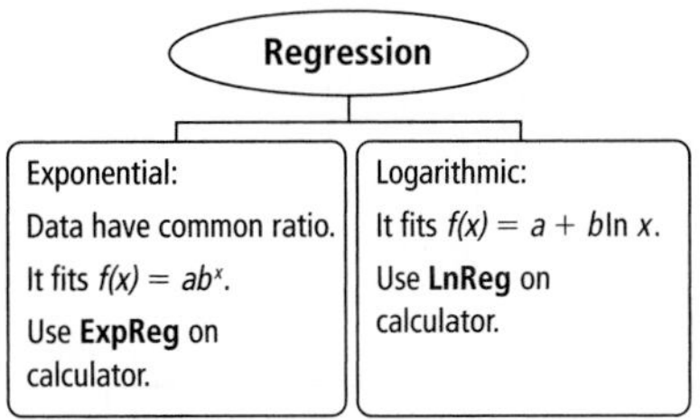

Regression
Exponential: Data have common ratio. It fits $f(x) = ab^x$. Use **ExpReg** on calculator.
Logarithmic: It fits $f(x) = a + b\ln x$. Use **LnReg** on calculator.

Chapter 8

Lesson 8-1

Type of Variation	Equation	Graph	Example
Direct	$y = kx$		$d = rt$
Joint	$y = kxz$		$I = Prt$
Inverse	$y = \frac{k}{x}$		$I = \frac{V}{R}$

Lesson 8-2

	Fractions	Rational Expressions
Simplifying	$\frac{4}{16} = \frac{4}{16} = \frac{1}{4}$	$\frac{3x^2y^3}{12xy^6} = \frac{3x^2y^3}{12xy^6} = \frac{x}{4y^3}$
Multiplying	$\frac{15}{7} \cdot \frac{3}{25} = \frac{15}{7} \cdot \frac{3}{25} = \frac{9}{35}$	$\frac{5x^3}{4y^5} \cdot \frac{3y^8}{20x} = \frac{5x^3}{4y^5} \cdot \frac{3y^8}{20x} = \frac{3x^2y^3}{16}$
Dividing	$\frac{2}{3} \div \frac{8}{9} = \frac{2}{3} \cdot \frac{9}{8} = \frac{3}{4}$	$\frac{2x}{3y^5} \div \frac{4x}{15y} = \frac{2x}{3y^5} \cdot \frac{15y}{4x} = \frac{5}{2y^4}$

Additional Answers

Lesson 8-3

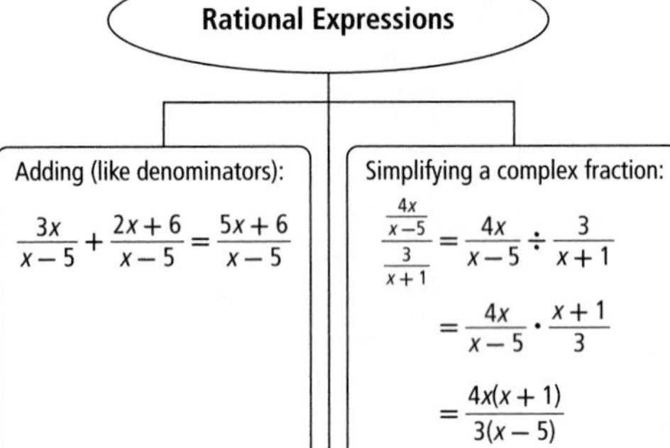

Rational Expressions
Adding (like denominators):
$\frac{3x}{x-5} + \frac{2x+6}{x-5} = \frac{5x+6}{x-5}$
Simplifying a complex fraction:
$\frac{\frac{4x}{x-5}}{\frac{3}{x+1}} = \frac{4x}{x-5} \div \frac{3}{x+1}$
$= \frac{4x}{x-5} \cdot \frac{x+1}{3}$
$= \frac{4x(x+1)}{3(x-5)}$

Subtracting (unlike denominators):

$$\frac{2x}{x-3} - \frac{4}{x} = \frac{2x}{x-3}\left(\frac{x}{x}\right) - \frac{4}{x}\left(\frac{x-3}{x-3}\right)$$
$$= \frac{2x(x) - 4(x-3)}{(x-3)x}$$
$$= \frac{2x^2 - 4x + 12}{x(x-3)}$$
$$= \frac{2(x^2 - 2x + 6)}{x(x-3)}$$

Lesson 8-4

$$f(x) = \frac{p(x)}{q(x)}$$

Zeros: at each real value of x for which $p(x) = 0$	Vertical asymptotes: at each real value of x for which $q(x) = 0$
Horizontal asymptotes: none if degree of $p >$ degree of q; the line $y = 0$ if degree of $p <$ degree of q; the line $y = \frac{\text{leading coefficient of } p}{\text{leading coefficient of } q}$ if degree of $p =$ degree of q	Holes: at any point where $x = b$ if $x - b$ is a factor of both p and q and the line $x = b$ is not a vertical asymptote

Lesson 8-5

Rational Equations

Definition: equations that contain rational expressions	Characteristics: can be solved by multiplying both sides by the LCD of all the terms in the equation; may generate extraneous solutions when solved
Examples: $\frac{1}{x} = 5$, $\frac{x+3}{x-4} = \frac{x}{x-3}$	Nonexamples: $\sqrt{x+2} = 6$, $\lvert x \rvert = 5$

Lesson 8-6

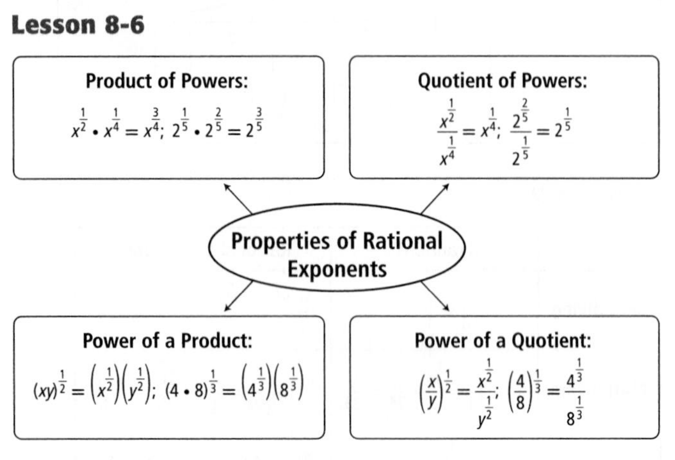

Product of Powers:
$x^{\frac{1}{2}} \cdot x^{\frac{1}{4}} = x^{\frac{3}{4}}$; $2^{\frac{1}{5}} \cdot 2^{\frac{2}{5}} = 2^{\frac{3}{5}}$
Quotient of Powers:
$\frac{x^{\frac{1}{2}}}{x^{\frac{1}{4}}} = x^{\frac{1}{4}}$; $\frac{2^{\frac{2}{5}}}{2^{\frac{1}{5}}} = 2^{\frac{1}{5}}$
Properties of Rational Exponents
Power of a Product:
$(xy)^{\frac{1}{2}} = \left(x^{\frac{1}{2}}\right)\left(y^{\frac{1}{2}}\right)$; $(4 \cdot 8)^{\frac{1}{3}} = \left(4^{\frac{1}{3}}\right)\left(8^{\frac{1}{3}}\right)$
Power of a Quotient:
$\left(\frac{x}{y}\right)^{\frac{1}{2}} = \frac{x^{\frac{1}{2}}}{y^{\frac{1}{2}}}$; $\left(\frac{4}{8}\right)^{\frac{1}{3}} = \frac{4^{\frac{1}{3}}}{8^{\frac{1}{3}}}$

Lesson 8-7

Transformation	Equation	Graph
Vertical translation	$g(x) = \sqrt{x} + 2$	
Horizontal translation	$g(x) = \sqrt{x - 2}$	
Reflection	$g(x) = -\sqrt{x}$	
Vertical stretch	$g(x) = 2\sqrt{x}$	

Lesson 8-8

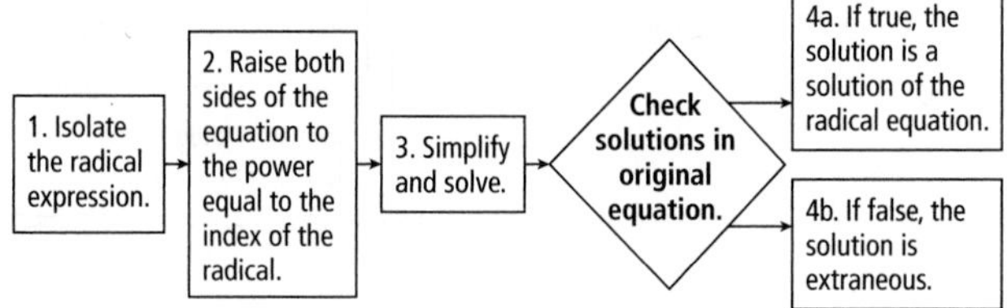

1. Isolate the radical expression.
2. Raise both sides of the equation to the power equal to the index of the radical.
3. Simplify and solve.
Check solutions in original equation.
4a. If true, the solution is a solution of the radical equation.
4b. If false, the solution is extraneous.

Chapter 9

Lesson 9-1

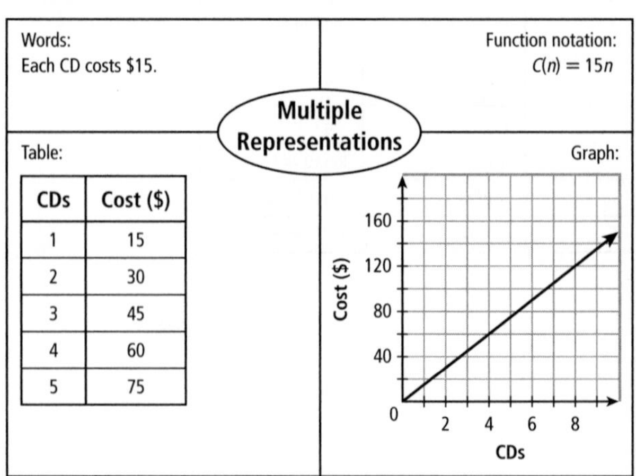

CDs	Cost ($)
1	15
2	30
3	45
4	60
5	75

Lesson 9-2

Function	Domain	Range	Example
Piecewise	Separated into at least 2 intervals	Depends on each piece of the function	$f(x) = \begin{cases} -8x & \text{if } x < 0 \\ 8x & \text{if } x \geq 0 \end{cases}$
Step	Separated into at least 2 and often infinite intervals	A set of discrete values	$f(x) = \begin{cases} 5 & \text{if } 0 \leq x < 1 \\ 10 & \text{if } x \geq 1 \end{cases}$

Lesson 9-3

Transformation	*x*-intercepts	*y*-intercept
Horizontal stretch or compression by a factor of b	Multiplied by b	Stays the same
Vertical stretch or compression by a factor of a	Stay the same	Multiplied by a
Reflection across y-axis	Negated	Stays the same
Reflection across x-axis	Stay the same	Negated

Lesson 9-4

Operation	Notation
Addition	$(f + g)(x) = f(x) + g(x)$
Subtraction	$(f - g)(x) = f(x) - g(x)$
Multiplication	$(fg)(x) = f(x) \bullet g(x)$
Division	$\left(\frac{f}{g}\right)(x) = \frac{f(x)}{g(x)}$
Composition	$f(g(x))$ or $(f \circ g)(x)$

Lesson 9-5

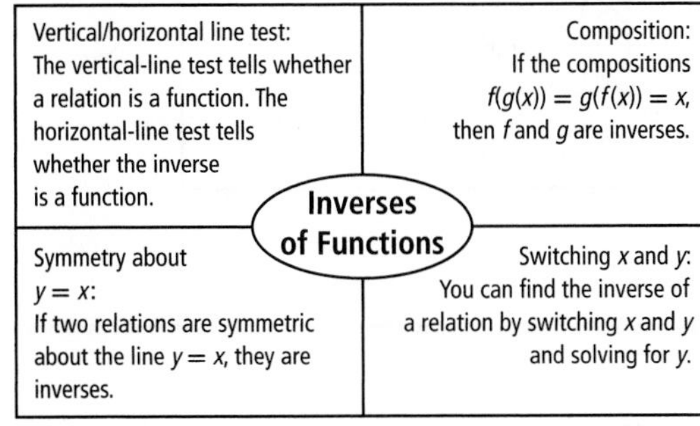

Vertical/horizontal line test:
The vertical-line test tells whether a relation is a function. The horizontal-line test tells whether the inverse is a function.
Composition:
If the compositions $f(g(x)) = g(f(x)) = x$, then f and g are inverses.
Inverses of Functions
Symmetry about $y = x$:
If two relations are symmetric about the line $y = x$, they are inverses.
Switching x and y:
You can find the inverse of a relation by switching x and y and solving for y.

Lesson 9-6

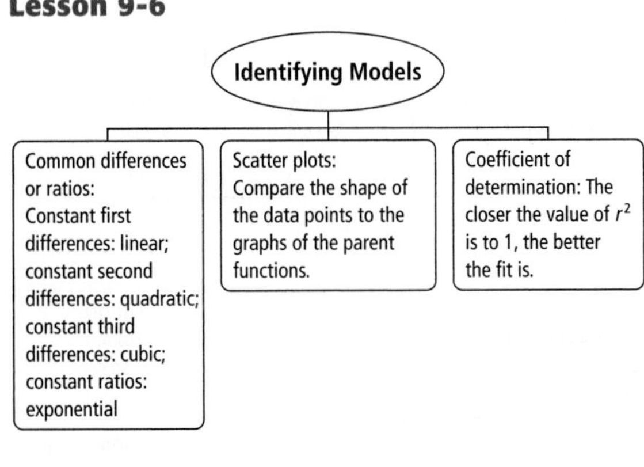

Identifying Models
Common differences or ratios:
Constant first differences: linear; constant second differences: quadratic; constant third differences: cubic; constant ratios: exponential
Scatter plots:
Compare the shape of the data points to the graphs of the parent functions.
Coefficient of determination: The closer the value of r^2 is to 1, the better the fit is.

Chapter 10

Lesson 10-1

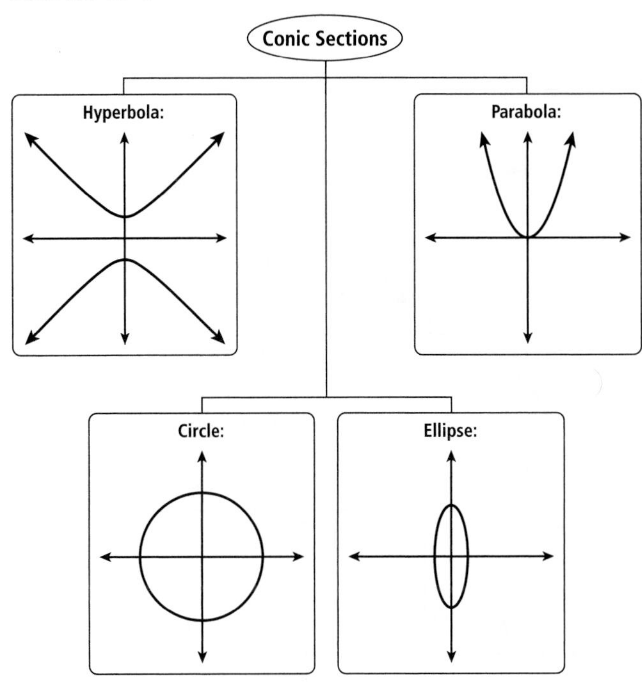

Lesson 10-2

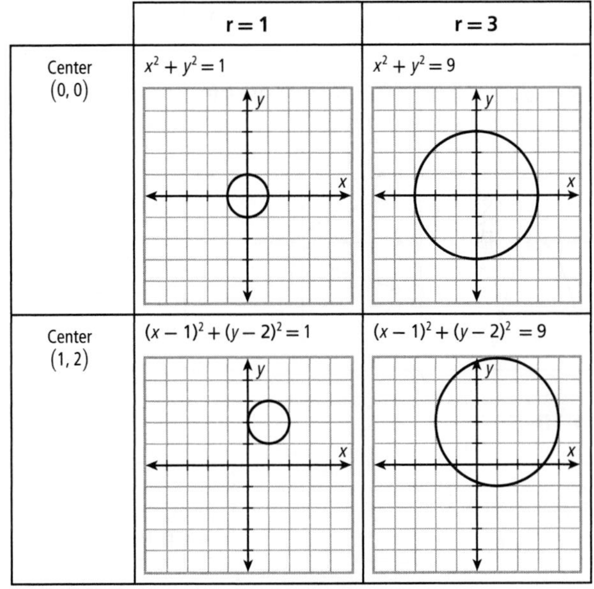

r = 1
r = 3
Center (0, 0)
$x^2 + y^2 = 1$
$x^2 + y^2 = 9$
Center (1, 2)
$(x - 1)^2 + (y - 2)^2 = 1$
$(x - 1)^2 + (y - 2)^2 = 9$
y
x

Lesson 10-3

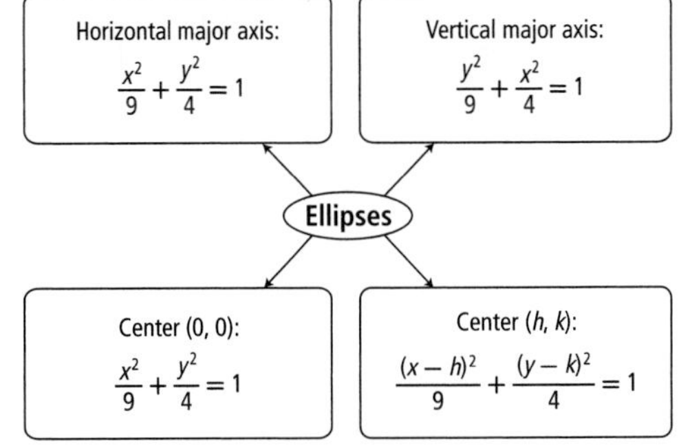

Lesson 10-4

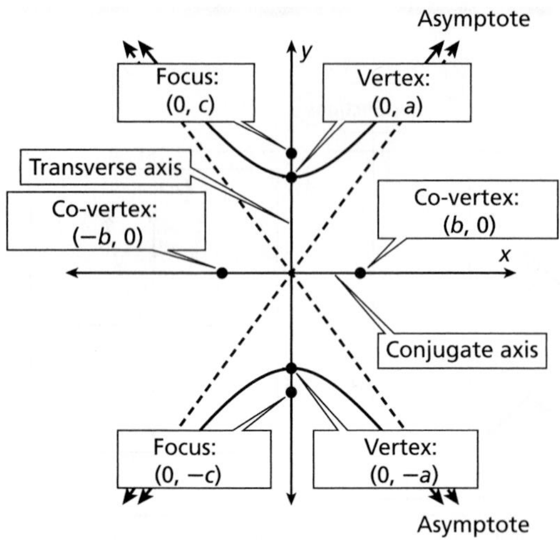

Lesson 10-5

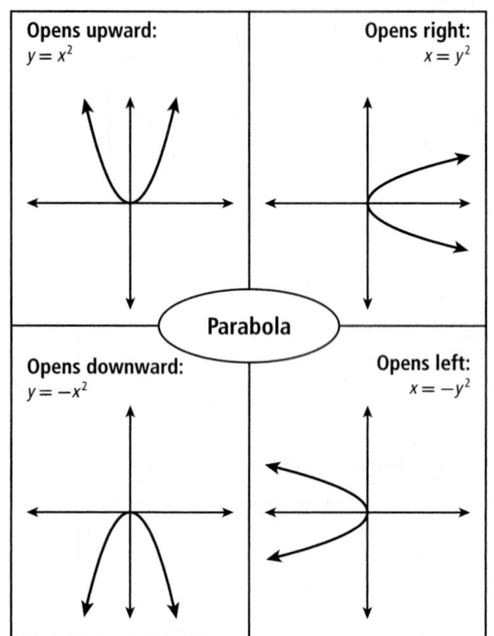

Lesson 10-6

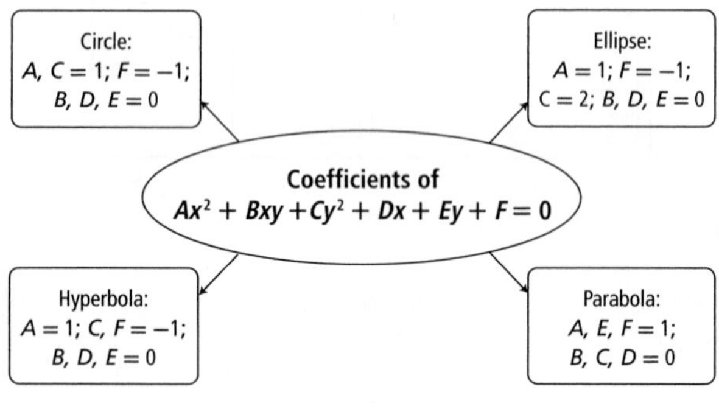

Lesson 10-7

	Graph	Example
No Solutions		$\begin{cases} x^2 + y^2 = 1 \\ \frac{y^2}{4} - x^2 = 1 \end{cases}$
One Solution		$\begin{cases} x^2 + (y-1)^2 = 1 \\ \frac{y^2}{4} - x^2 = 1 \end{cases}$
Two Solutions		$\begin{cases} x^2 + y^2 = 1 \\ y^2 - x^2 = 1 \end{cases}$
Three Solutions		$\begin{cases} x^2 + (y-1)^2 = 9 \\ \frac{y^2}{4} - x^2 = 1 \end{cases}$
Four Solutions		$\begin{cases} x^2 + y^2 = 4 \\ y^2 - x^2 = 1 \end{cases}$

Chapter 11

Lesson 11-1

	Fundamental Counting Principle	Permutation	Combination
Formula	$m_1 \cdot m_2 \cdot \ldots \cdot m_n$	$\frac{n!}{(n-r)!}$	$\frac{n!}{r!(n-r)!}$
Examples	5 shirts × 3 skirts × 4 pairs of shoes = 5 × 3 × 4 outfits	Permutations of 8 items taken 3 at a time $\frac{8!}{(8-3)!} = \frac{8!}{5!} = 336$	3 items chosen from 8 $\frac{8!}{3!(8-3)!} = \frac{8!}{3!5!} = 56$

Lesson 11-2

Probability

Experimental
The experimental probability of rolling a 5 on a number cube that was rolled 30 times and landed on 5 7 times is $\frac{7}{30}$.

Theoretical
There are 6 equally-likely outcomes when rolling a number cube, so each has a theoretical probability of $\frac{1}{6}$

Complement
The complement of the experimental probability above is $1 - \frac{7}{30}$, or $\frac{23}{30}$, which is the experimental probability of not rolling a 5.

Geometric
If a circle of radius 3 is inside a square with side length 10 and any point inside the square is equally likely, the probability of a random point being in the circle is $\frac{\pi(3)^2}{10^2} \approx 0.28$

Lesson 11-3

Probability of Independent Events vs. Probability of Dependent Events

Similarities	Differences
Probabilities are multiplied using the Fundamental Counting Principle. Probability within [0, 1] range	Probability of a previous event does not affect probability for independent events but does for dependent events.

Lesson 11-4

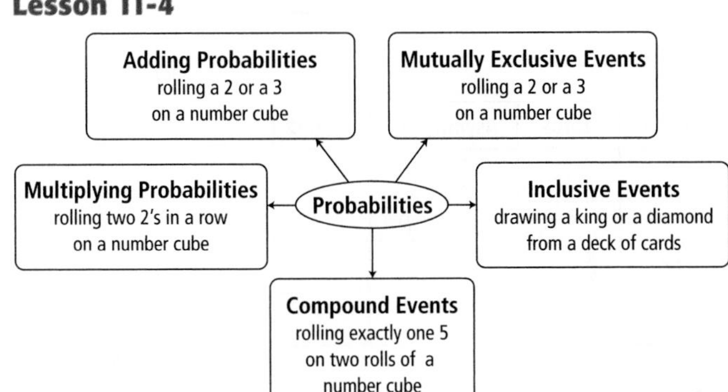

Lesson 11-5

Measures of Variability

Range
the difference between the maximum and minimum value For {1, 2, 3, 4, 5}, the range is 5 − 1, or 4.

Variance
the average of the squared differences from the mean. For {1, 2, 3, 4, 5}, the variance is $\frac{2^2+1^2+0^2+1^2+2^2}{5} = 2$

Interquartile Range
the difference between the third and first quartiles. For {1, 2, 3, 4, 5}, the interquartile range is 4.5 − 1.5, or 3.

Standard Deviation
the square root of the variance. For {1, 2, 3, 4, 5}, the variance is $\sqrt{2} \approx 1.4$

Lesson 11-6

Binomial Experiments	
Probability	**Example**
Probability of r successes in n trials	2 successes in 5 trials, where $p = 0.9$ $= {}_5C_2(0.9)^2(0.1)^3 \approx 0.0081$
Probability of at least r successes	at least 4 successes in 5 trials, where $p = 0.9$ $= {}_5C_4(0.9)^4(0.1)^1 + {}_5C_5(0.9)^5(0.1)^0 \approx 0.9185$
Probability of at most r successes	at most 1 success in 5 trials, where $p = 0.9$ $= {}_5C_0(0.1)^5 + {}_5C_1(0.9)^1(0.1)^4 \approx 0.00046$
Probability using a complement	at least 2 successes in 5 trials, where $p = 0.9$ $= 1 - p$(0 or 1 success) $= 1 - 0.00046 \approx 0.99954$

Chapter 12

Lesson 12-1

Sequences

Definition: A sequence is an ordered set of numbers.	Two types of sequences: • finite—has a last term • infinite—without end
Examples: 1, 1, 2, 3, 5, 8, 13, 21,... (Fibonacci) −3, 6, −12, 24, −36,... (alternating) 2, 5, 10, 17, 26,... (increasing) $1, \frac{1}{2}, \frac{1}{3}, \frac{1}{4}, \frac{1}{5}, \ldots$ (fractions)	Two possible formulas: • recursive—one or more previous terms used to generate the next term • explicit—defines the *n*th term, or general term, of a sequence

Lesson 12-2

	Sequence	Series
Notation	a_1, a_2, a_3, a_4	$a_1 + a_2 + a_3 + a_4$
Example	2, 4, 8, 16	2 + 4 + 8 + 16

Lesson 12-3

Arithmetic Sequences

Definition: a sequence whose successive terms differ by the same number *d*, called the common difference	Characteristics: constant *common difference, d*; linear function with a restricted domain of the natural numbers; increases or decreases linearly; can calculate partial sums
Examples: 0.37, 0.60, 0.83, 1.06,... (increasing) 32, 25, 18, 11, 4,... (decreasing) −3, −5, −7, −9,... (negative) $\frac{2}{5}, \frac{3}{5}, \frac{4}{5}, 1, \ldots$ (fractions)	Formulas: recursive: a_1 is given, $a_n = a_{n-1} + d$ explicit: $a_n = a_1 + (n-1)d$ sum: $S_n = n\left(\frac{a_1 + a_n}{2}\right)$

Lesson 12-4

Geometric Sequences

Definition: a sequence in which the ratio of successive terms is the same number *r*, the *common ratio*	Characteristics: constant *common ratio, r*; exponential function with a restricted domain of the natural numbers; can calculate partial sums;
Examples: −320, −80, −20, −5,... (increasing) −16, −8, −4, −2,... (decreasing) 2, 0.2, 0.002,... (decimals) $\frac{1}{2}, \frac{1}{10}, \frac{1}{50}, \frac{1}{250}, \frac{1}{1250}, \ldots$ (fractions)	Formulas: recursive: a_1 is given, $a_n = a_{n-1}r$ explicit: $a_n = a_1 r^{n-1}$ sum: $S_n = a_1\left(\frac{1-r^n}{1-r}\right)$

Lesson 12-5

	Example	Common Ratio	Sum
Convergent Series	2 + 0.2 + 0.02 + ⋯	$r = \frac{1}{10}$	$\frac{20}{9}$
Divergent Series	2 + 20 + 200 + ⋯	$r = 10$	No limit

Chapter 13

Lesson 13-1

	sin	cos	tan
Function Name	sine	cosine	tangent
Side Length Ratio	$\frac{\text{opp.}}{\text{hyp.}}$	$\frac{\text{adj.}}{\text{hyp.}}$	$\frac{\text{opp.}}{\text{adj.}}$
Reciprocal Function	cosecant	secant	cotangent

Lesson 13-2

Angle θ

Standard position: Draw the angle with its vertex at the origin and one ray along the positive x-axis.	Reference angle: Find the acute angle formed by the terminal side of θ and the x-axis.
Positive coterminal angle: Add or subtract integer multiples of 360° to the measure of θ so that the resulting angle measure is greater than 0°.	Negative coterminal angle: Add or subtract integer multiples of 360° to the measure of θ so that the resulting angle measure is less than 0°.

Lesson 13-3

	Acute Angle of Right Triangle	Angle of Rotation with $P(x, y)$	Angle with $P(x, y)$ on Unit Circle
$\sin\theta$	$\frac{\text{opp.}}{\text{hyp.}}$	$\frac{y}{r}$	y
$\cos\theta$	$\frac{\text{adj.}}{\text{hyp.}}$	$\frac{x}{r}$	x
$\tan\theta$	$\frac{\text{opp.}}{\text{adj.}}$	$\frac{y}{x}$	$\frac{y}{x}$

Lesson 13-4

Inverse Trigonometric Functions

Symbols: $\text{Sin}^{-1}a$: inverse sine $\text{Cos}^{-1}a$: inverse cosine $\text{Tan}^{-1}a$: inverse tangent	Domains: $\text{Sin}^{-1}a$: $\{a\mid -1 \le a \le 1\}$ $\text{Cos}^{-1}a$: $\{a\mid -1 \le a \le 1\}$ $\text{Tan}^{-1}a$: $\{a\mid -\infty < a < \infty\}$
Associated quadrants: $\text{Sin}^{-1}a$: I and IV $\text{Cos}^{-1}a$: I and II $\text{Tan}^{-1}a$: I and IV	Ranges: $\text{Sin}^{-1}a$: $\left\{\theta \mid -\frac{\pi}{2} \le \theta \le \frac{\pi}{2}\right\}$ $\text{Cos}^{-1}a$: $\{\theta \mid 0 \le \theta \le \pi\}$ $\text{Tan}^{-1}a$: $\left\{\theta \mid -\frac{\pi}{2} < \theta < \frac{\pi}{2}\right\}$

Lesson 13-5

SSA: Given a, b, and $m\angle A$			
Angle A	**0 triangles**	**1 triangle**	**2 triangles**
Obtuse	$a \le b$	$a > b$	Not possible
Acute	$a < h$	$a = h$ or $a \ge b$	$h < a < b$

Lesson 13-6

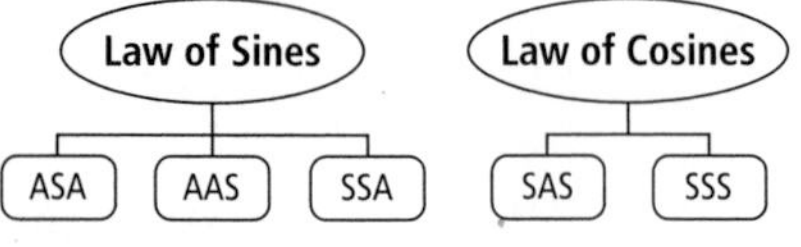

Chapter 14

Lesson 14-1

Cosine Graphs

Vertical compression: $y = \frac{1}{2}\cos x$ period: 2π	Horizontal stretch: $y = \sin\left(\frac{1}{2}x\right)$ period: 4π
Reflection: $y = -\cos x$ period: 2π	Phase shift: $y = \sin(x + \pi)$ period: 2π

Lesson 14-2

Function	Zeros	Asymptotes	Period
$y = \sec x$	none	$\frac{\pi}{2} + \pi n$	2π
$y = \csc x$	none	πn	2π
$y = \cot x$	$\frac{\pi}{2} + \pi n$	πn	π
$y = \tan x$	πn	$\frac{\pi}{2} + \pi n$	π

Lesson 14-3

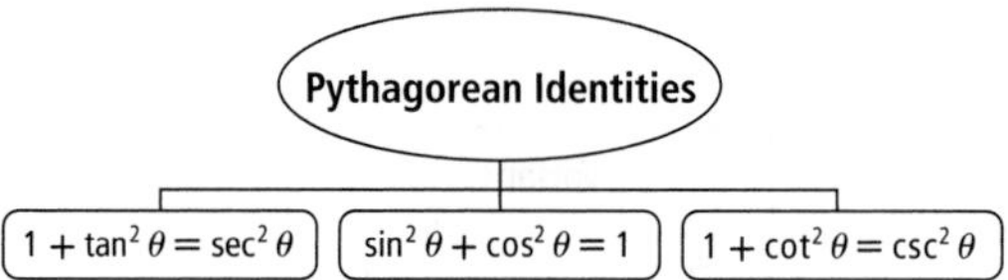

Lesson 14-4

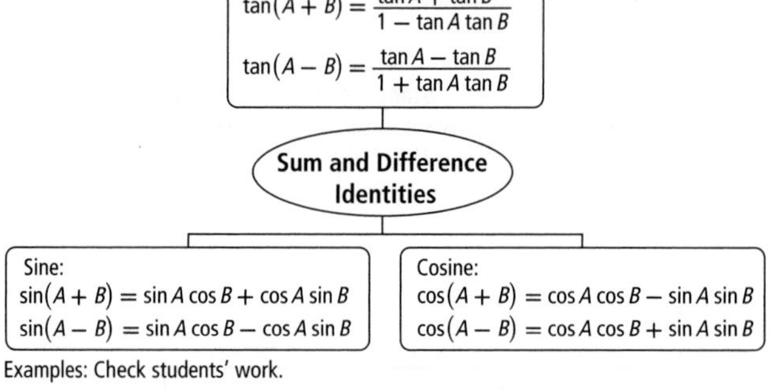

Tangent:
$\tan(A + B) = \frac{\tan A + \tan B}{1 - \tan A \tan B}$
$\tan(A - B) = \frac{\tan A - \tan B}{1 + \tan A \tan B}$
Sum and Difference Identities
Sine:
$\sin(A + B) = \sin A \cos B + \cos A \sin B$
$\sin(A - B) = \sin A \cos B - \cos A \sin B$
Cosine:
$\cos(A + B) = \cos A \cos B - \sin A \sin B$
$\cos(A - B) = \cos A \cos B + \sin A \sin B$

Examples: Check students' work.

Lesson 14-5

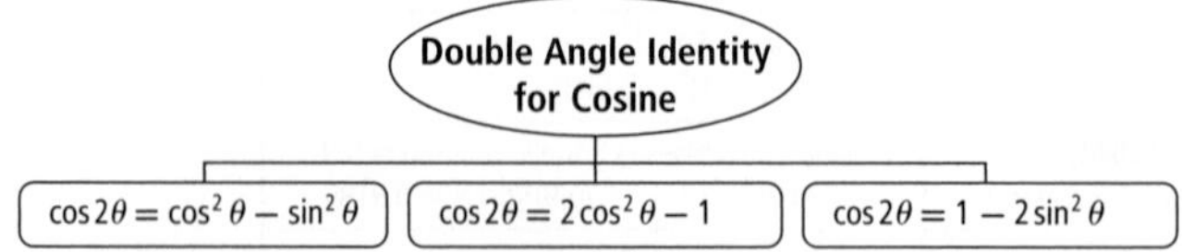

Double Angle Identity for Cosine
$\cos 2\theta = \cos^2\theta - \sin^2\theta$
$\cos 2\theta = 2\cos^2\theta - 1$
$\cos 2\theta = 1 - 2\sin^2\theta$

Lesson 14-6

Method	Most useful when...	Example
Graphing	approximate solutions are okay or only practical solution method	$\cos(2.1\theta) = 0.25$
Solving linear equations	equation has one function in terms of θ	$2\sin\theta = 1$
Factoring	equation has degree of 2	$\sin^2\theta + \sin\theta - 2 = 0$
Quadratic Formula	equation has degree of 2	$\sin^2\theta + \sin\theta - 5 = 0$
Identity substitution	equation contains two different trigonometric functions	$\cos 2\theta + 3\sin\theta + 2 = 0$

Additional Answers

Additional Answers

Chapter 1

1A *Ready to Go On?*

1. $-3\frac{1}{3}$; $-\frac{4}{5}$, $0.\overline{75}$, $\sqrt{5}$, 2.5; $-3\frac{1}{3}$: $\mathbb{R}$, $\mathbb{Q}$; $-\frac{4}{5}$: $\mathbb{R}$, $\mathbb{Q}$; $0.\overline{75}$: $\mathbb{R}$, $\mathbb{Q}$; $\sqrt{5}$: $\mathbb{R}$, irrational; 2.5: $\mathbb{R}$, $\mathbb{Q}$

2. -2, $-\frac{\pi}{2}$, $-1.\overline{15}$, $\frac{5}{6}$, $\sqrt{3}$; -2: $\mathbb{R}$, $\mathbb{Q}$, $\mathbb{Z}$; $-\frac{\pi}{2}$: $\mathbb{R}$, irrational; $-1.\overline{15}$: $\mathbb{R}$, $\mathbb{Q}$; $\frac{5}{6}$: $\mathbb{R}$, $\mathbb{Q}$; $\sqrt{3}$: $\mathbb{R}$, irrational

5. Distributive Property

6. Additive Identity Property

7. Associative Property of Multiplication

8. \$30; (12%)\$250 = (0.10 + 0.02)(\$250) = 0.10(\$250) + $\frac{1}{5}$(0.10)(\$250) = \$25 + $\left(\frac{1}{5}\right)$\$25 = \$30

9. 8.7 ft by 8.7 ft, 11.2 ft by 11.2 ft, and12.2 ft by 12.2 ft; The 75 ft^2 dance floor is the largest that would fit in an 11 ft by 13 ft room.

1-7 *Exercises*

48.

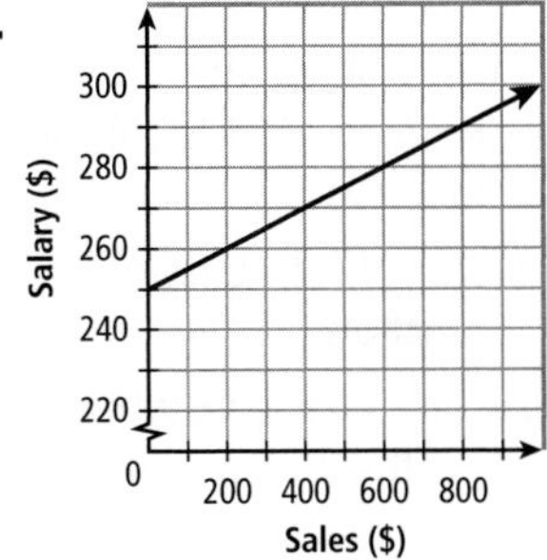

1-8 *Algebra Lab*

3. b4, b8, c5, and c7

4. a1, a2, a3, b1, b2, b3, c1, c2, c3, d1, d2, and d3

5. a7, a8, b2, b3, b4, b5, b6, b7, b8, c1, c2, c3, c4, c5, c6, c7, c8, d6, d7, d8, e1, e2, e3, e4, e5, e6, e7, e8, f6, f8, g6, g8, h6, and h8

6. a2, a4, a6, a8, b3, b5, b7, c2, c6, d3, e4, e6, and e8

7. b4, b6, c3, c7, e3, e7, f4, and f6

8. Possible answer: Both use a horizontal and vertical coordinate, and the horizontal coordinate is listed first. But the coordinate plane uses numbers for both coordinates, and the coordinate plane has an infinite number of points, while the chessboard has only 64 squares.

1-8 *Exercises*

11. vertical compression by a factor of $\frac{1}{2}$

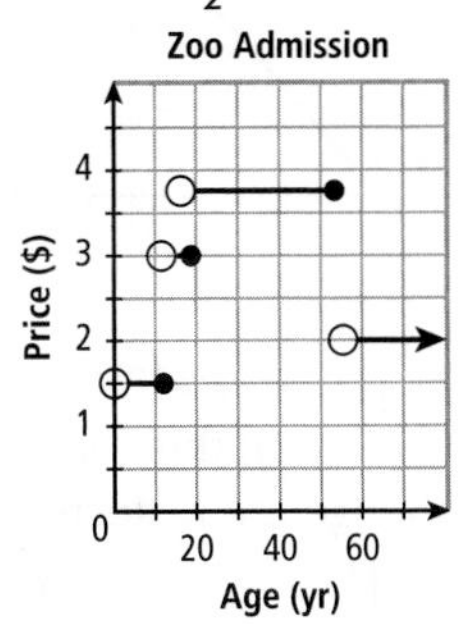

12. vertical shift up 1.5 units

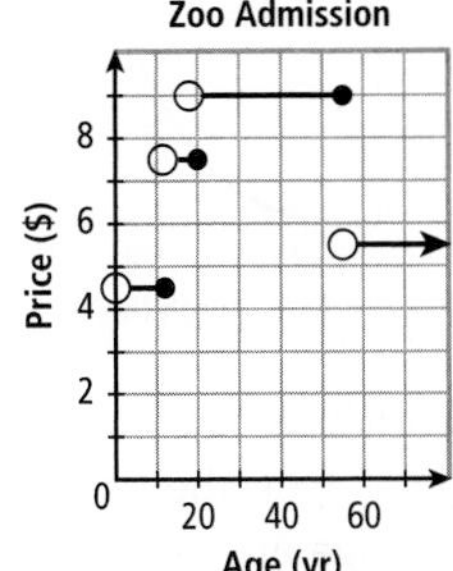

13. horizontal shift right 5 units

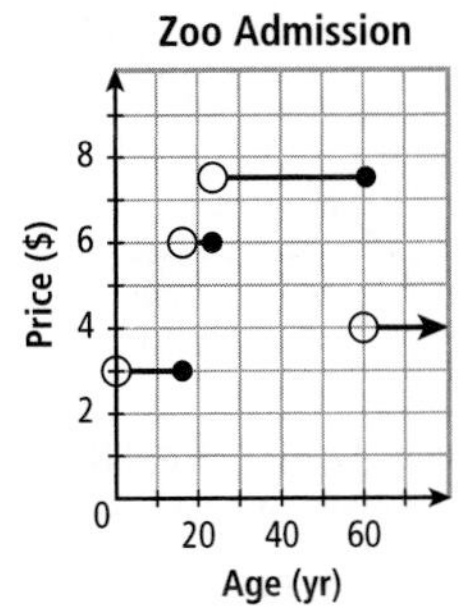

17. Table values will vary.

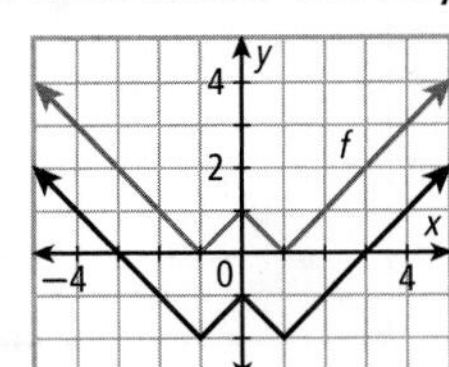

18. Table values will vary.

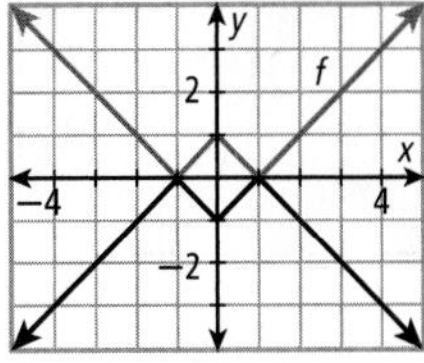

19. Table values will vary.

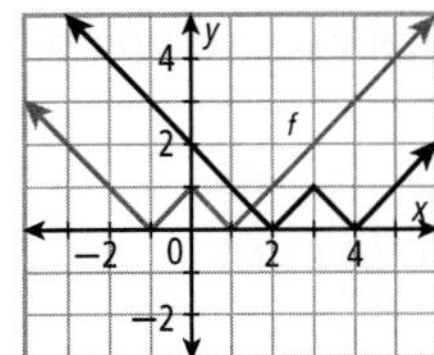

20. Table values will vary.

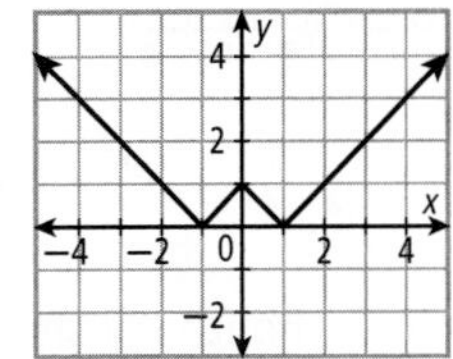

21. Table values will vary.

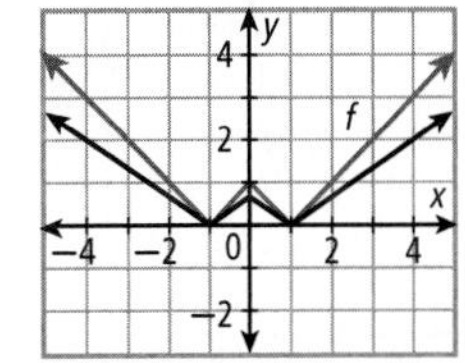

22. Table values will vary.

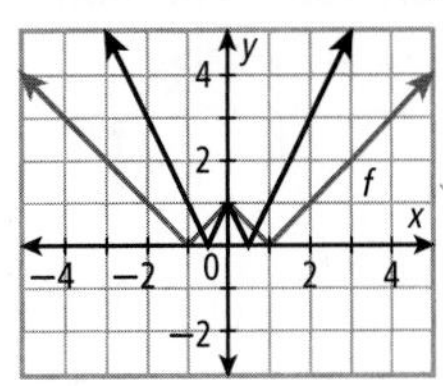

23. Table values will vary.

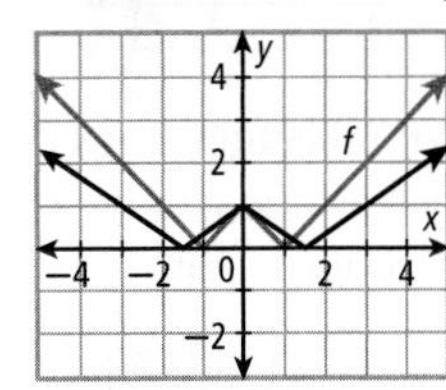

24. Table values will vary.

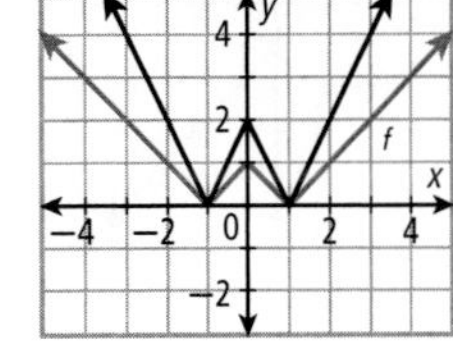

25. vertical shift down 5 units

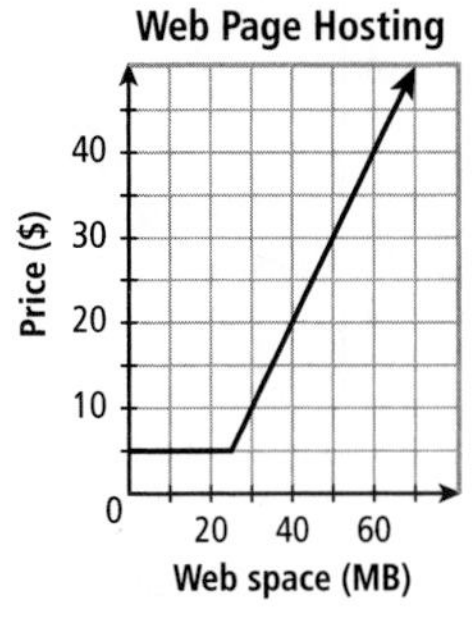

26. vertical compression by a factor of $\frac{3}{4}$

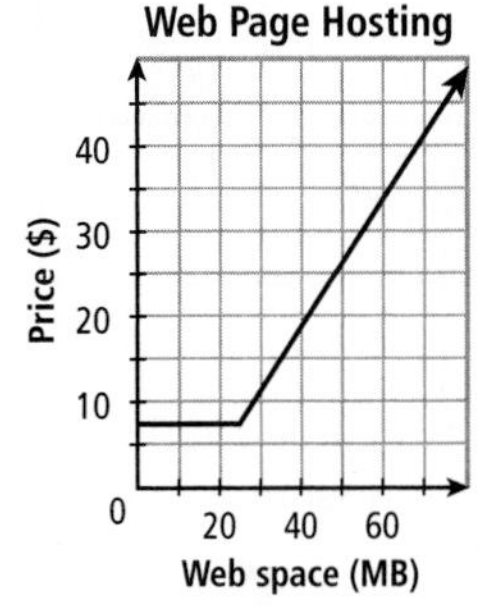

27. horizontal stretch by a factor of 2

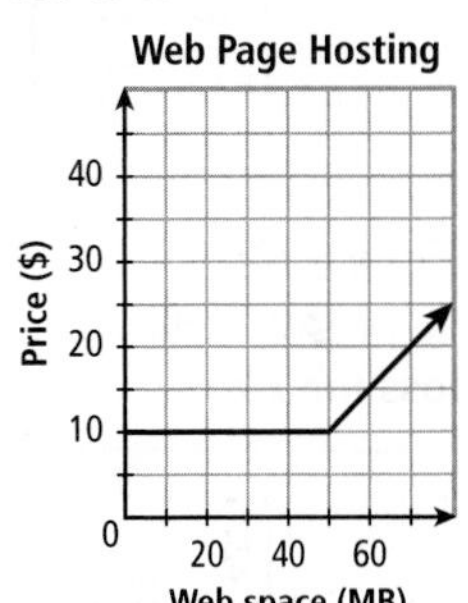

38a. They are both linear graphs.

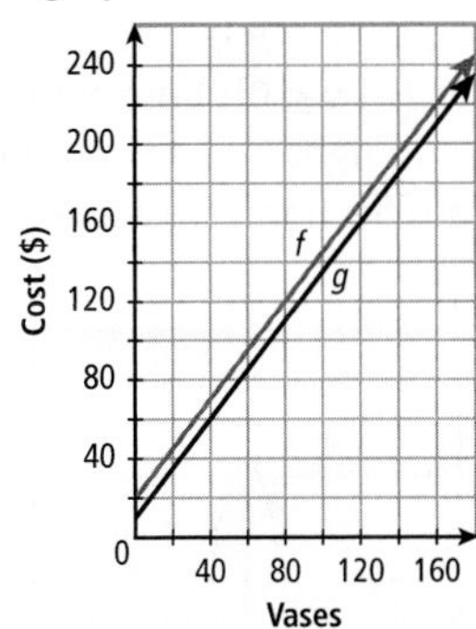

b. The graphs are parallel lines.

c. Add 10 to *f* or subtract 10 from *g*.

d. The graph is 10 units above until $x = 150$, then 10 below.

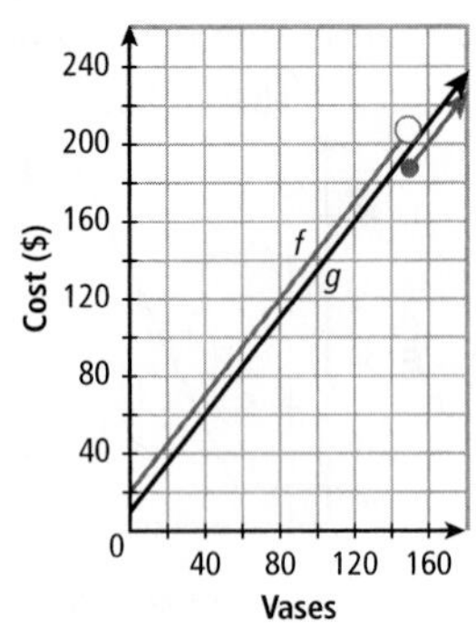

1-9 *Exercises*

18.

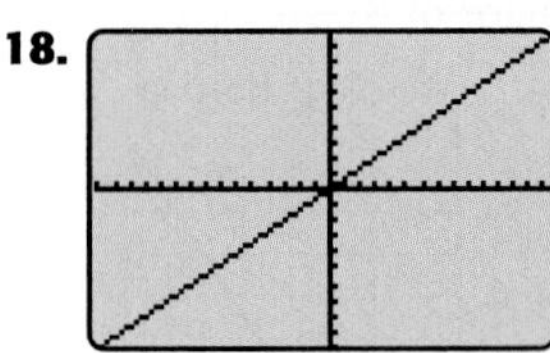

D: $\{x \mid x \in \mathbb{R}\}$;
R: $\{y \mid y \in \mathbb{R}\}$; vertical compression by a factor of $\frac{2}{3}$

19.

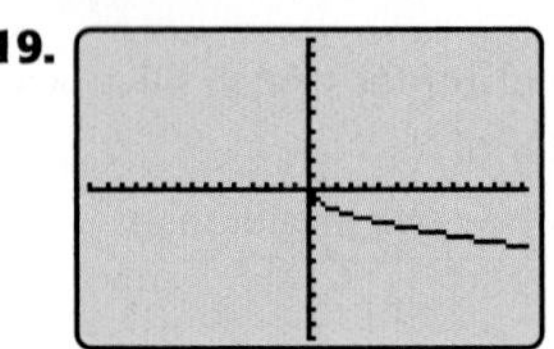

D: $\{x \mid x \geq 0\}$;
R: $\{y \mid y \leq 0\}$; reflection across the x-axis

20.

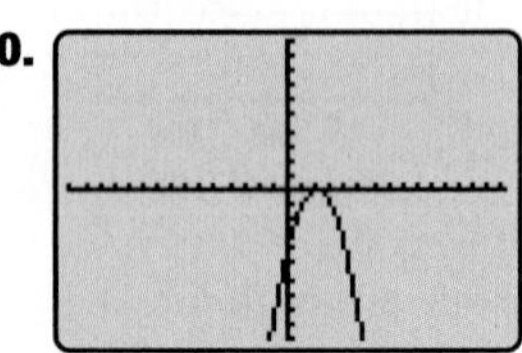

D: $\{x \mid x \in \mathbb{R}\}$;
R: $\{y \mid y \leq 0\}$; horizontal shift right 2 units and then a reflection across the x-axis

21.

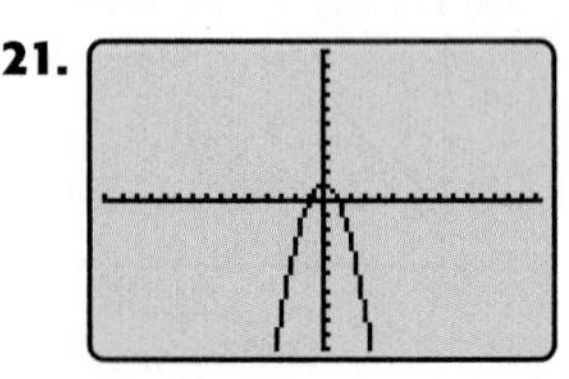

D: $\{x \mid x \in \mathbb{R}\}$;
R: $\{y \mid y \leq 1\}$; reflection across the x-axis and then a vertical shift up 1 unit

22.

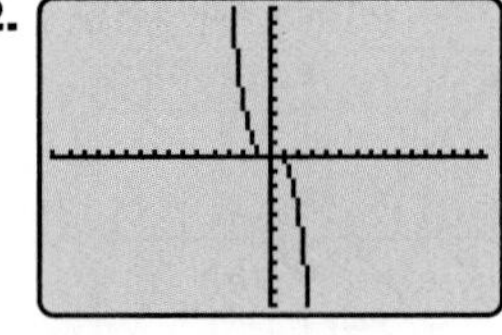

D: $\{x \mid x \in \mathbb{R}\}$;
R: $\{y \mid y \in \mathbb{R}\}$; reflection across the x-axis and a vertical compression by a factor of $\frac{1}{2}$

24. cubic; reflection across the x-axis or y-axis

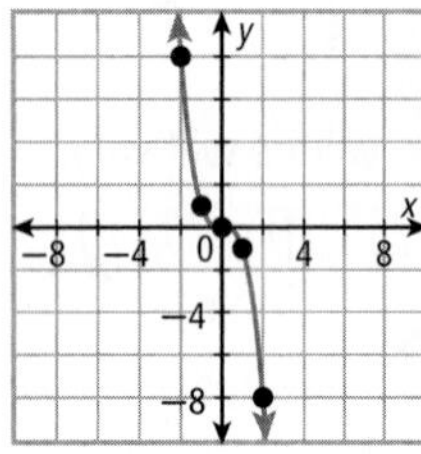

25. quadratic; horizontal shift right 7 units

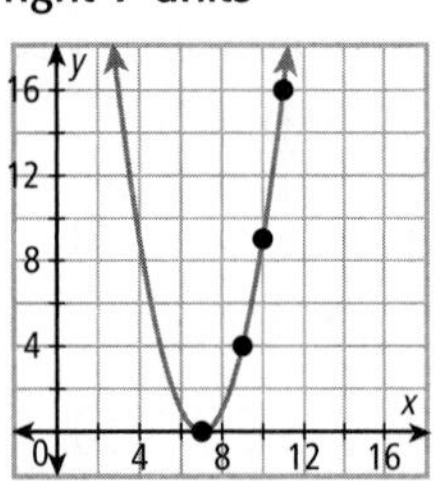

26. square root; reflection across the y-axis

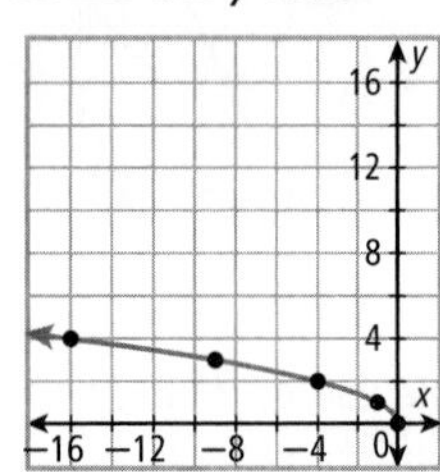

27. linear; reflection across the y-axis and a vertical shift down 1 unit

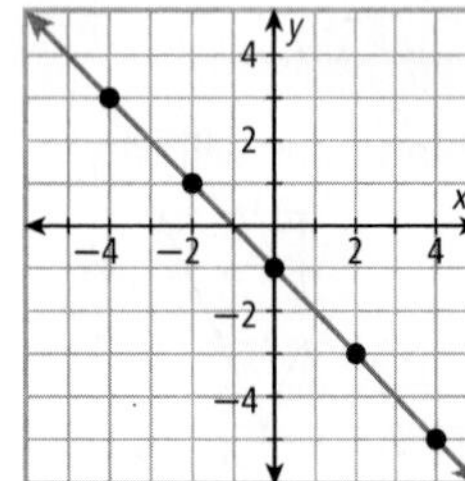

31.

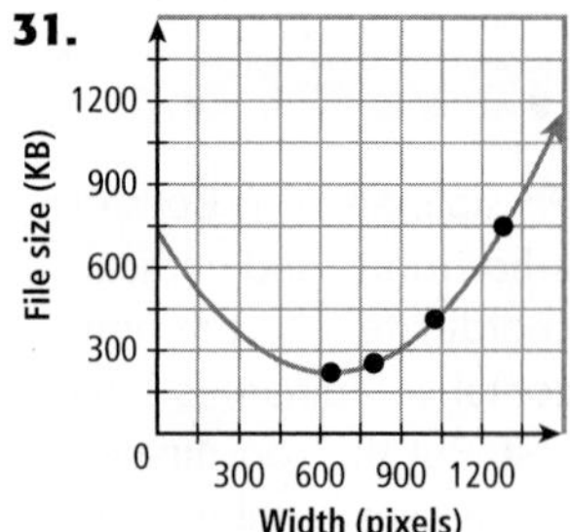

32. Linear; D: $\{h \mid h \geq 0\}$;
R: $\{y \mid y \geq 0\}$; the domain and range are restricted.

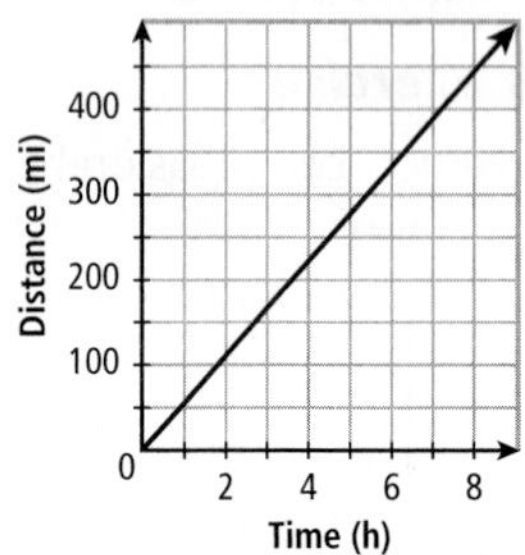

33. Cubic; D: $\{\ell \mid \ell \geq 0\}$;
R: $\{y \mid y \geq 0\}$; the domain and range are restricted.

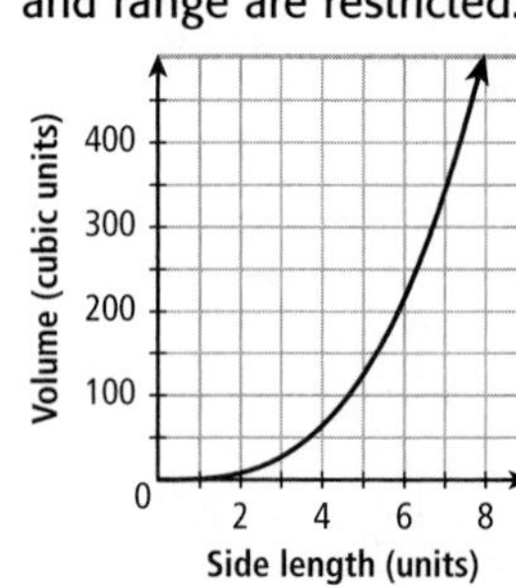

34. Linear; D: $\{w \mid w \geq 0\}$;
R: $\{y \mid y \geq 0\}$; the domain and range are restricted.

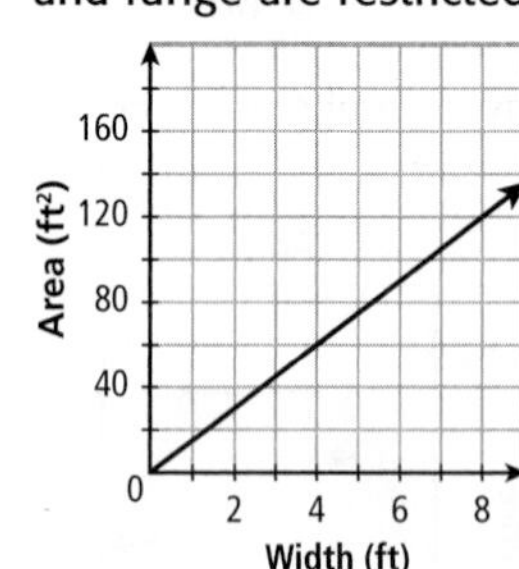

35. Linear; D: $\{n \mid n \in \mathbb{N}\}$; R: $\{y \mid y \in \mathbb{N}\}$; the domain and range are restricted.

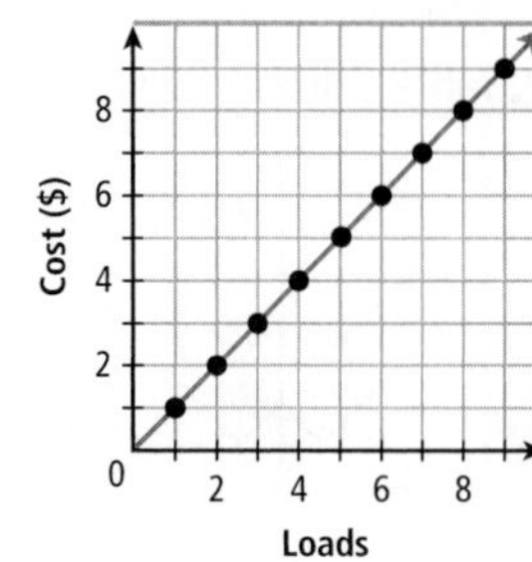

36. Linear; D: $\{p \mid p > 0\}$;
R: $\{y \mid y > 0\}$; the domain and range are restricted.

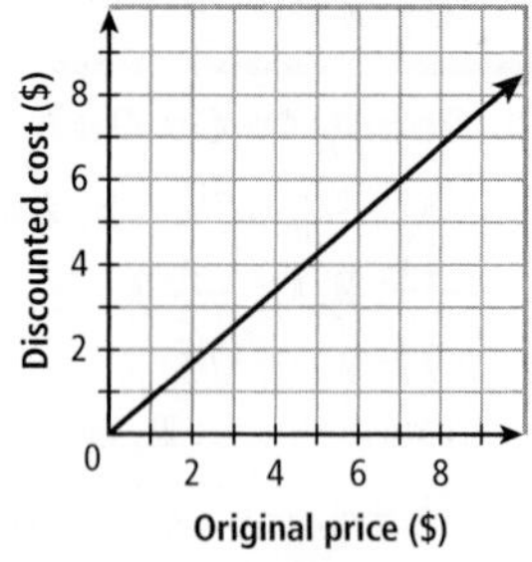

37. Square root; D: $\{a \mid a \geq 0\}$;
R: $\{y \mid y \geq 0\}$; the domain and range are the same.

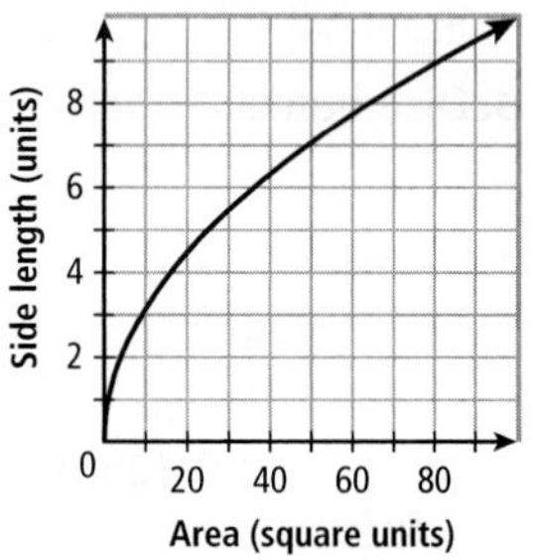

1B *Multi-Step Test Prep*

3. No; the input values −39.4, −10.3, and 0 are each paired with two different output values.

1B *Ready to Go On?*

1. D: [−3, 3]; R: [−1, 2]; not a function

2. D: {0, 2, 4, 6};
R: {5, 8, 10, 12, 20}; not a function

3. D: [−1, 3]; R: [0, 4]; function

7a. $c = 1.75 + m$, where c is the cost per mile in dollars and m is the distance driven in miles

b.

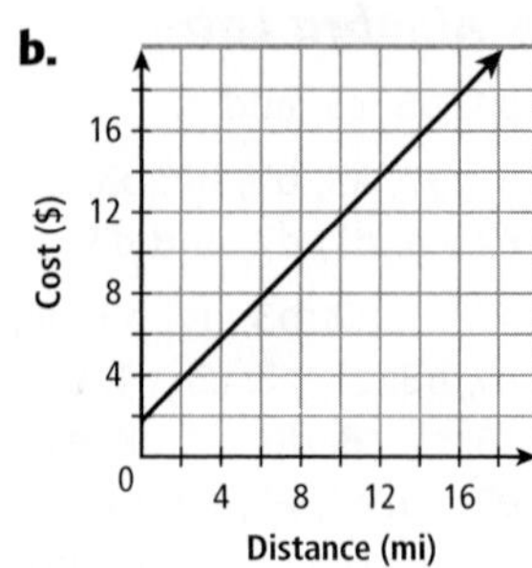

c. $c(5.5) = 7.25$; it represents the cost in dollars for a taxi ride of 5.5 miles.

8. vertical translation up by \$15

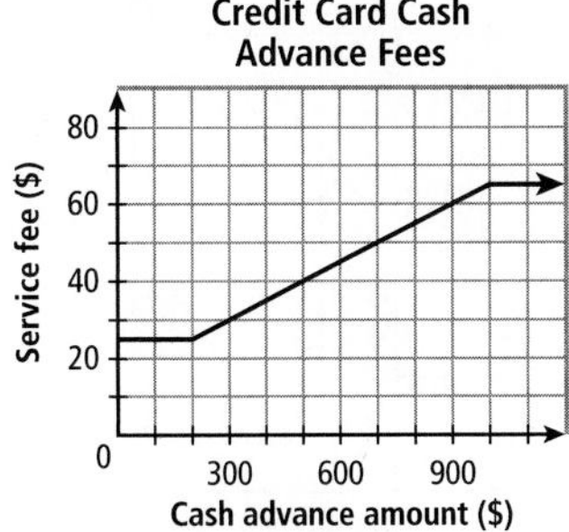

9. vertical compression by a factor of 0.6

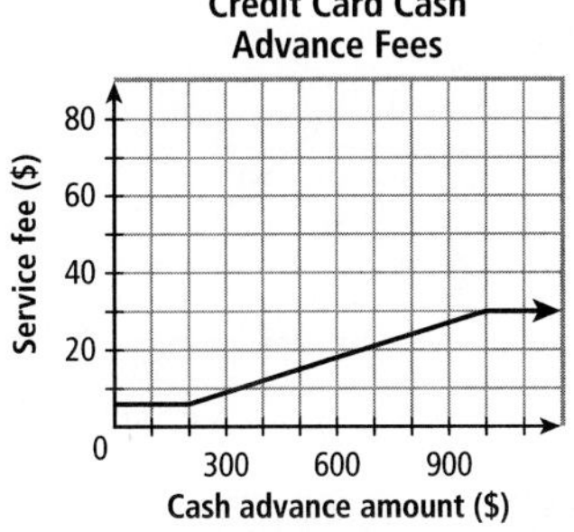

10. quadratic function

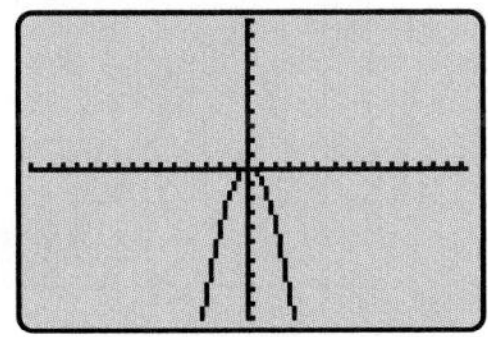

reflection over the x-axis

11. square-root function

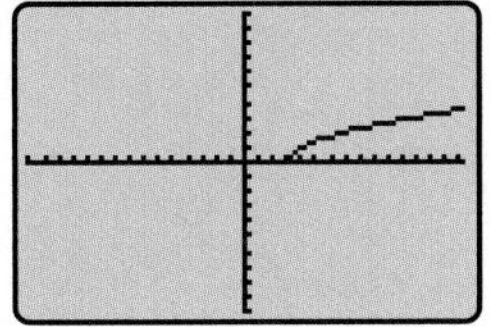

horizontal translation 3 units right

12. linear function

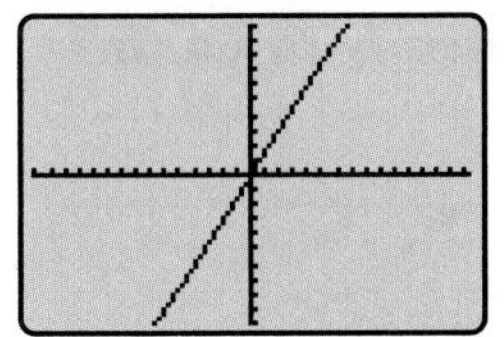

vertical stretch by a factor of 1.5

13. quadratic function; $\approx$ 17.5 mm

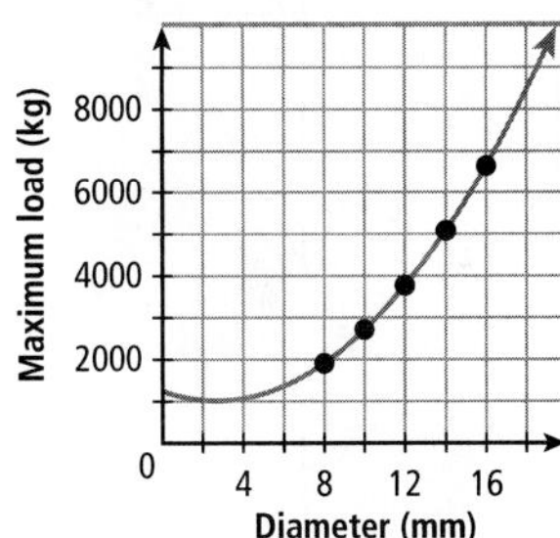

Chapter 2

2-3 *Exercises*

1. y-intercept: y-value of the point on the y-axis where x is 0; function value when x is 0

x-intercept: x-value of the point on the x-axis where y is 0; the input value when the function value is 0

11.

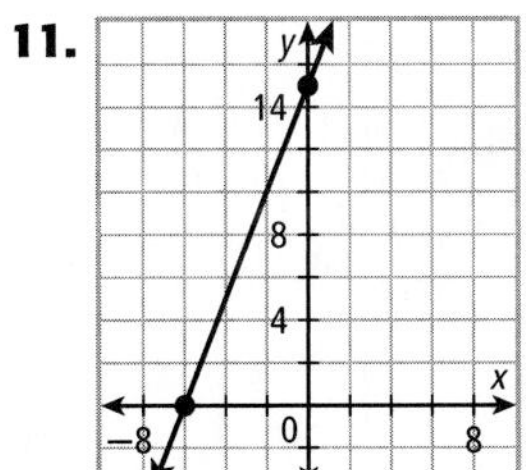

12.

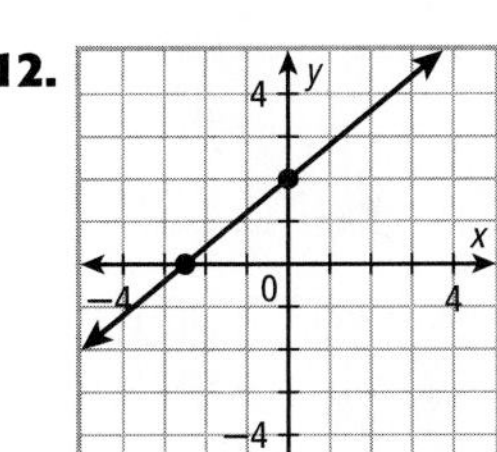

13.

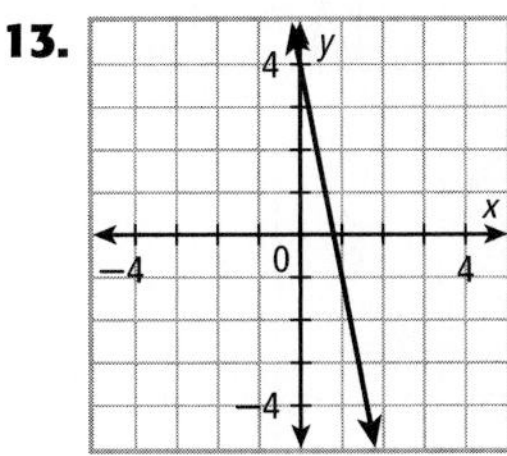

14.

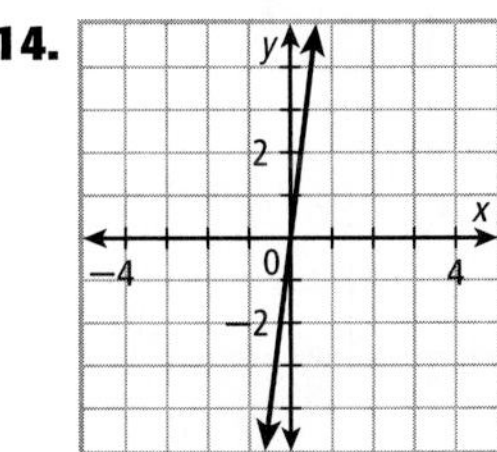

15.

16.

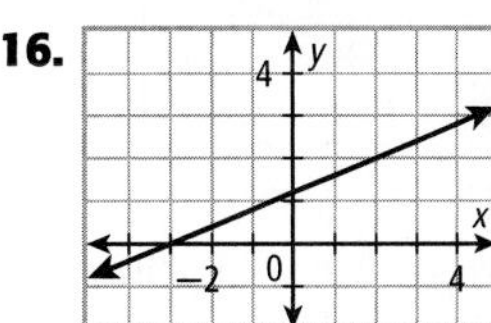

17.

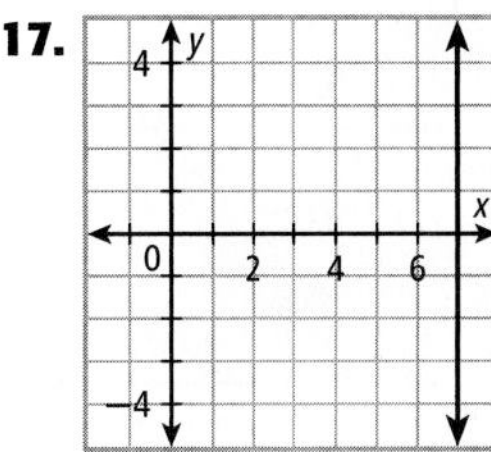

18.

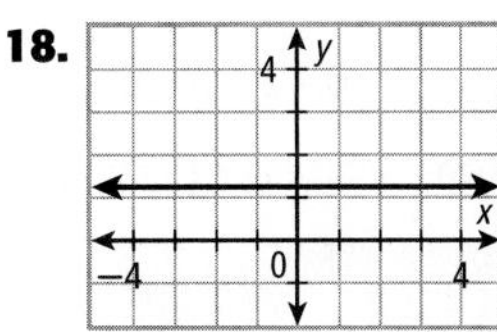

19.

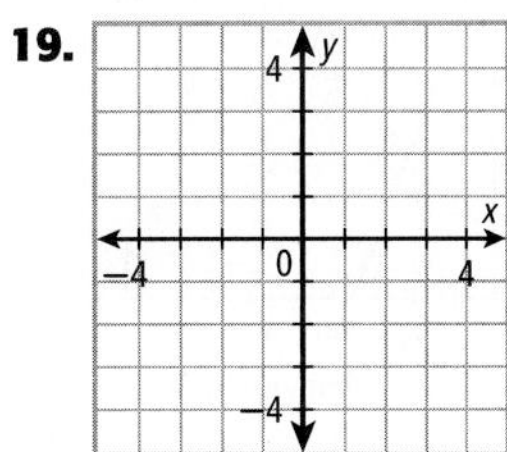

20.

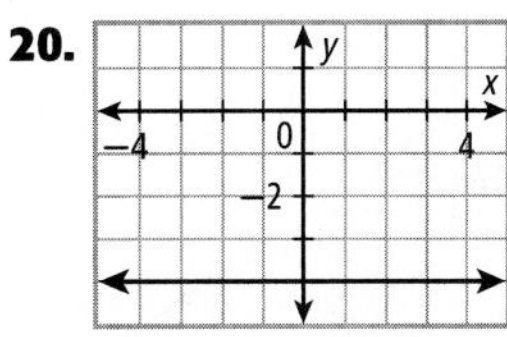

21.

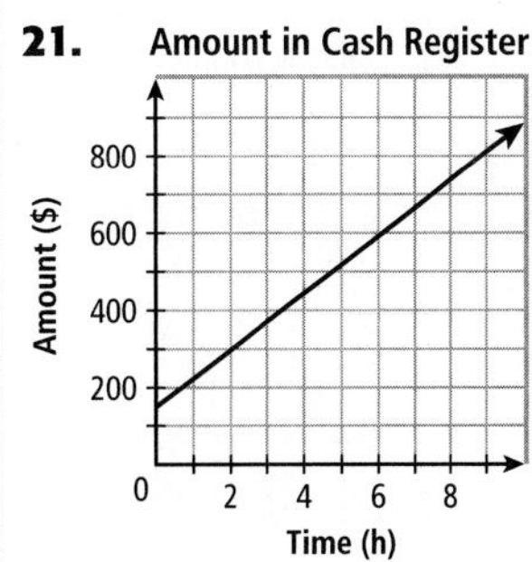

31.

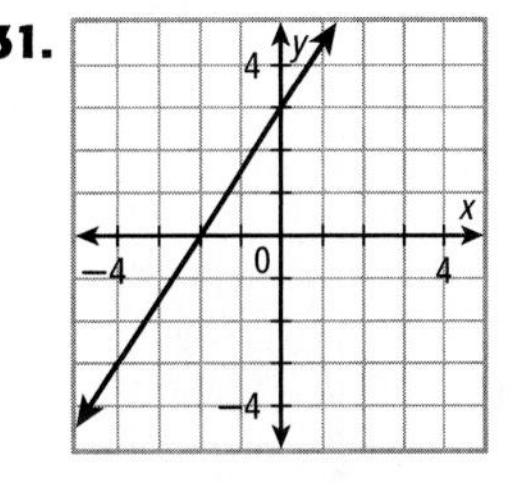

32.

33.

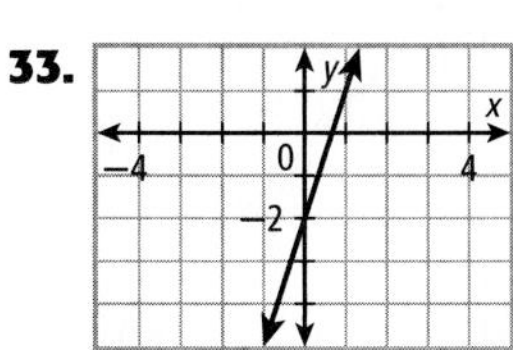

34.

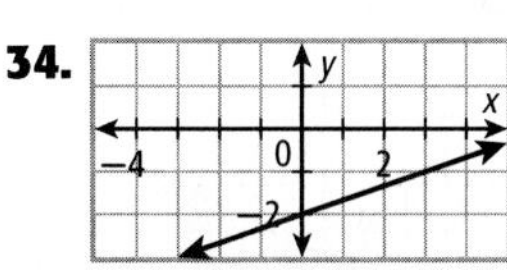

35.

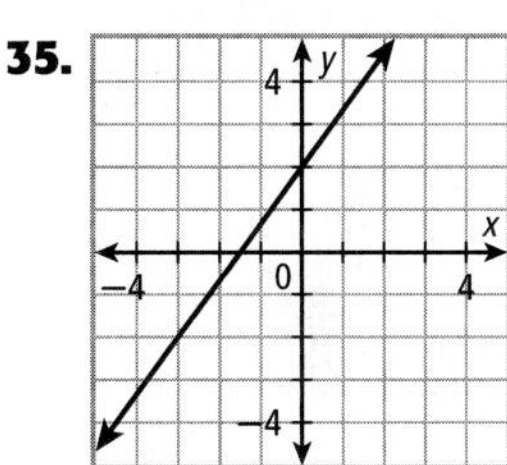

36.

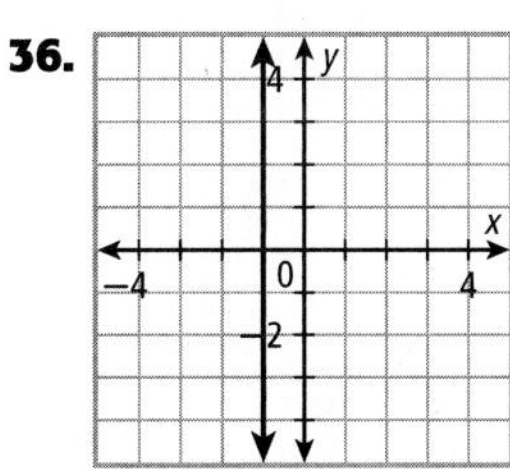

37.

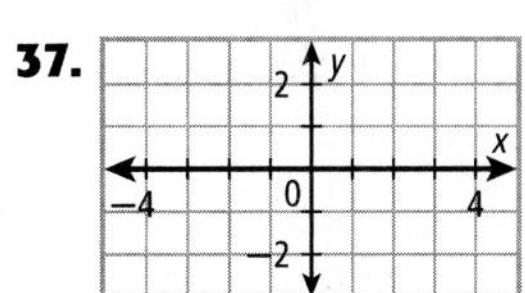

38.

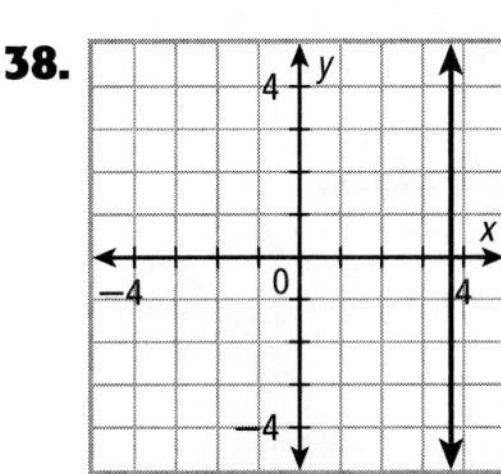

39.

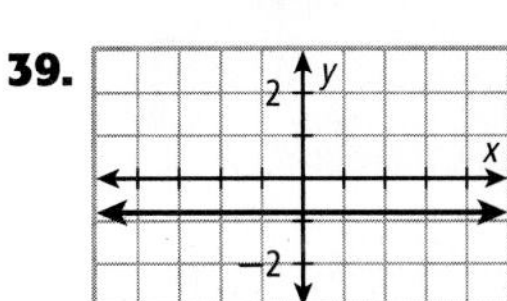

40a.

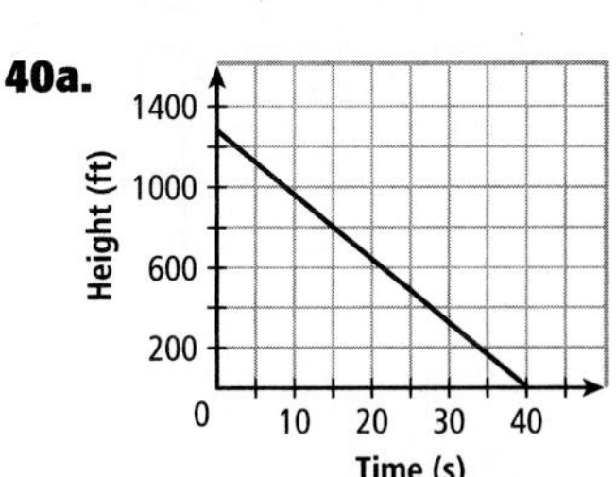

Additional Answers

41.

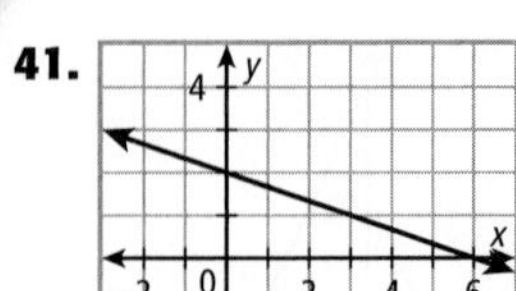

42.

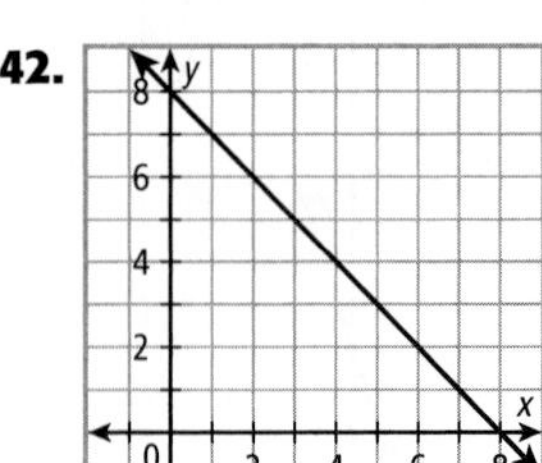

43.

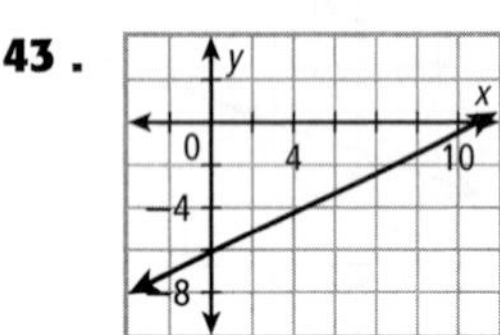

44.

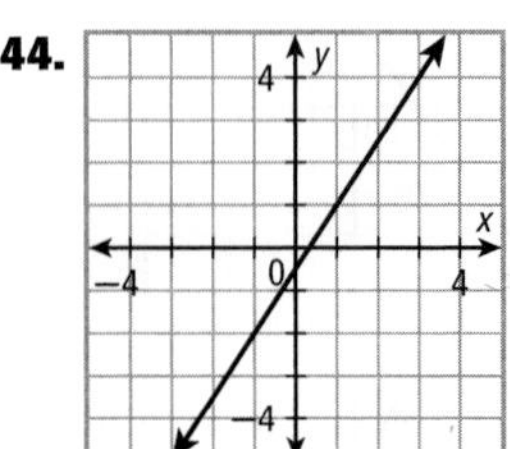

45.

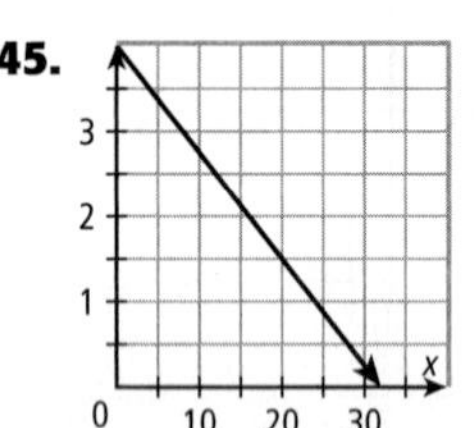

46.

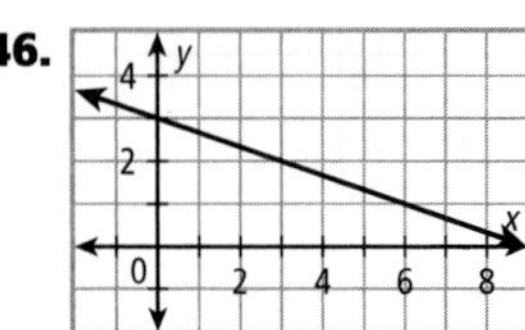

2-5 *Exercises*

15.

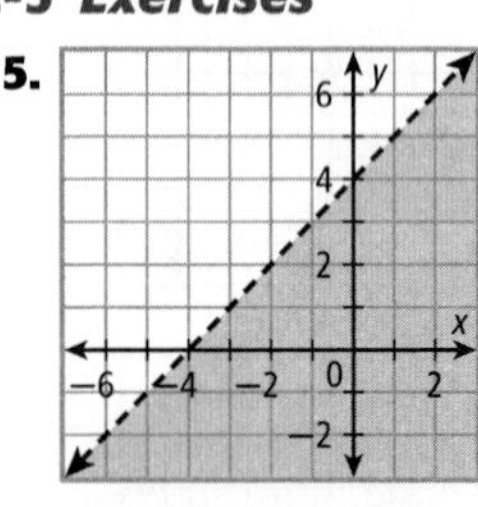

16.

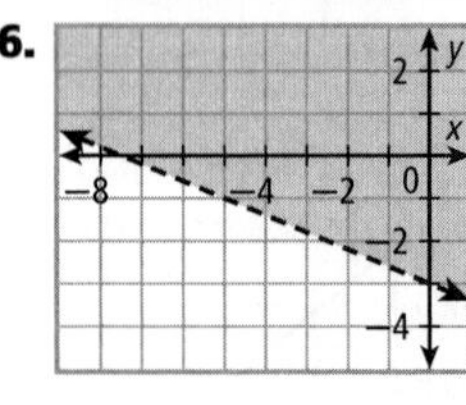

17.

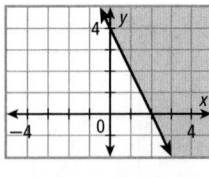

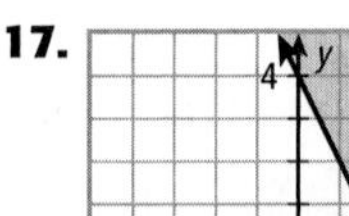

18.

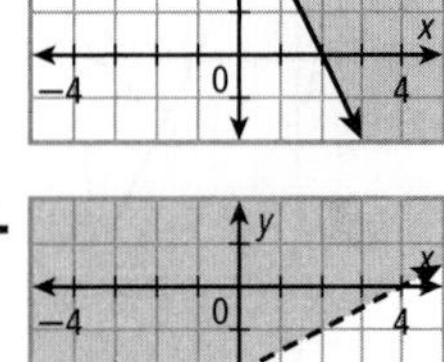

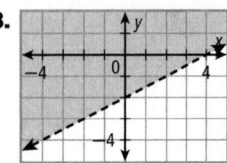

19. $200x + 500y \leq 10{,}000$;

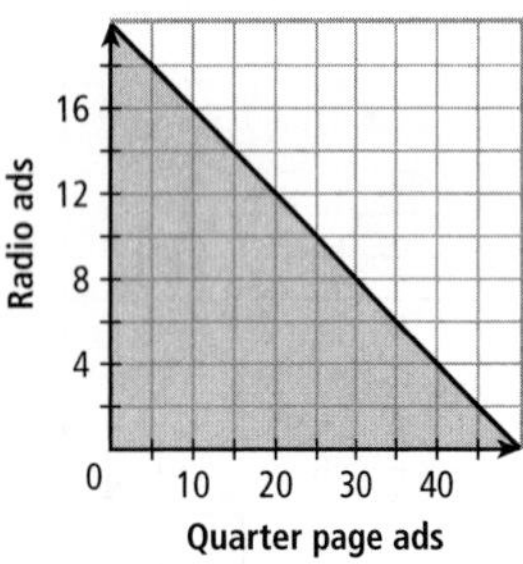

20a. $0.78x + 0.32y \geq 56$;

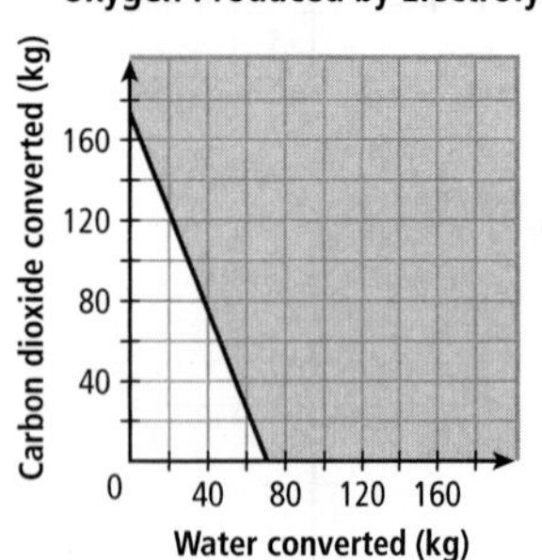

b. Yes

21.

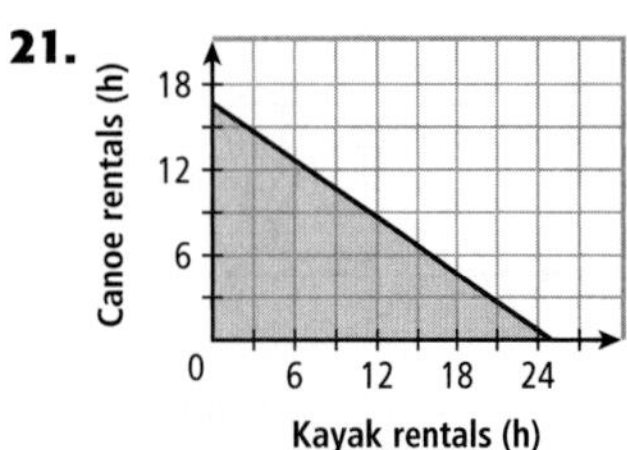

22. $y > -3x + 5$

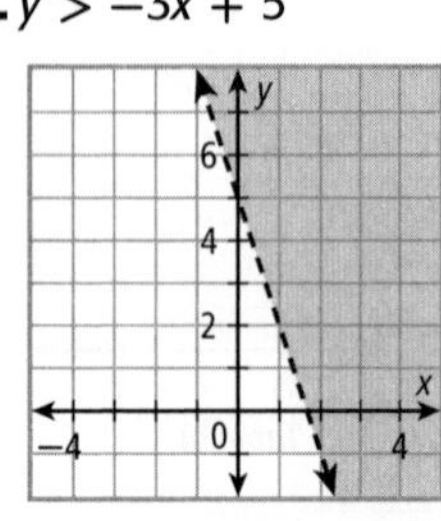

23. $y \leq 5x - 4$

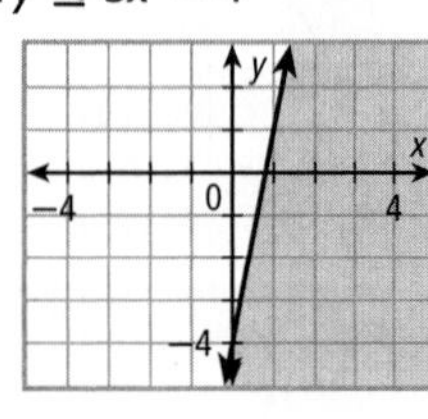

24. $y \leq \frac{5}{3}x - 5$

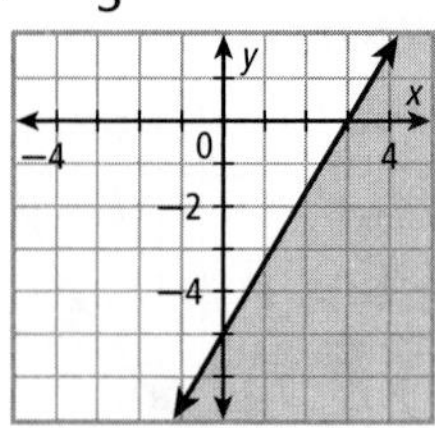

25.

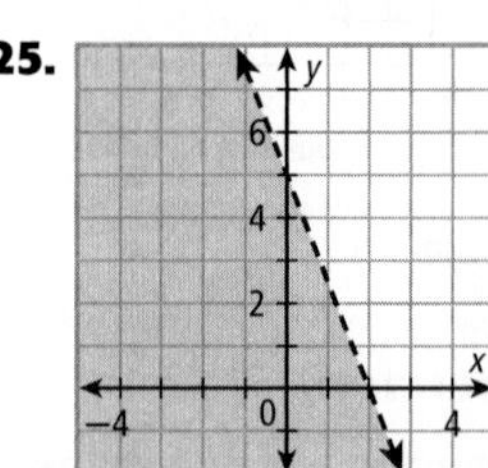

26.

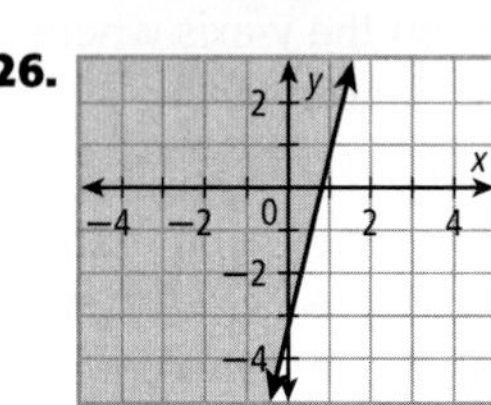

27.

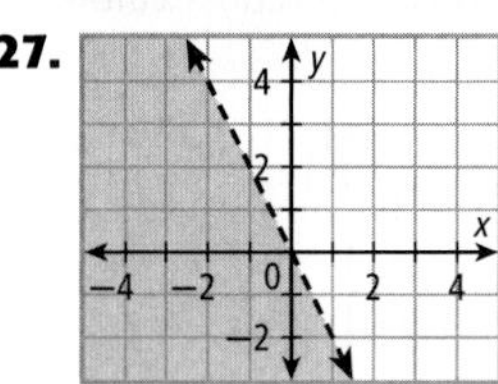

28.

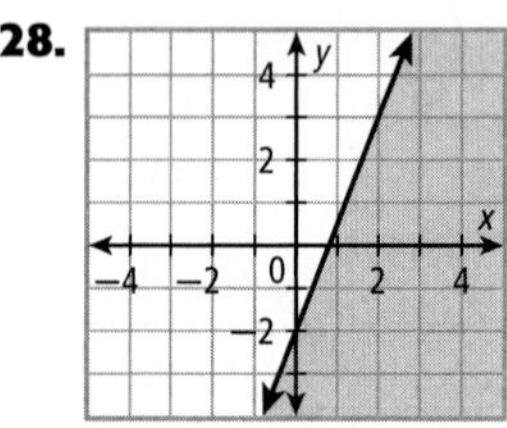

29.

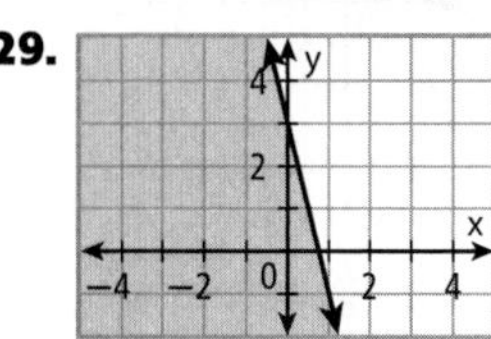

30.

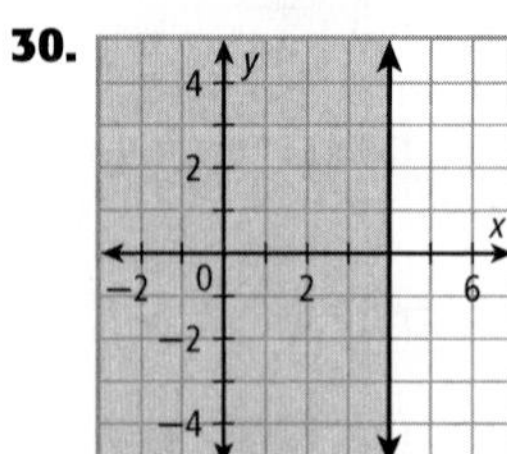

31.

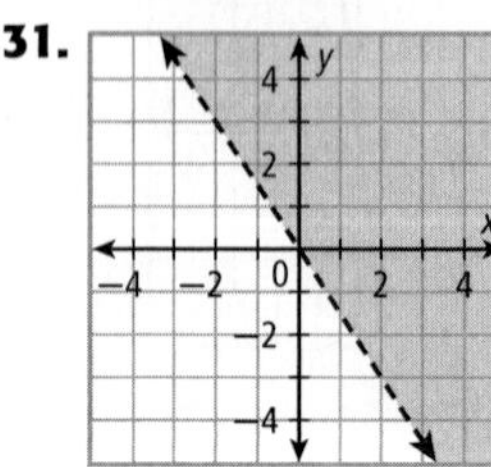

32.

33.

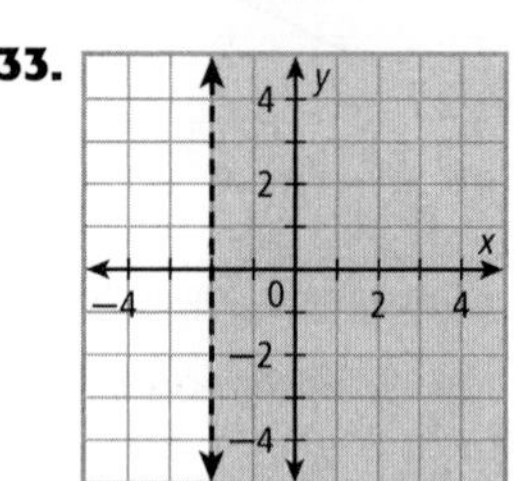

34a.

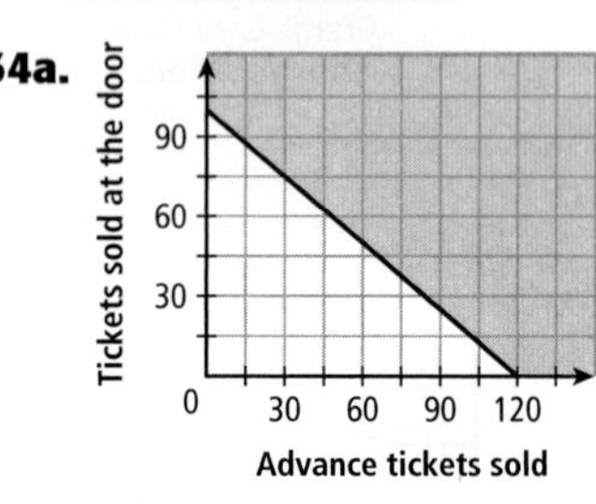

35a.

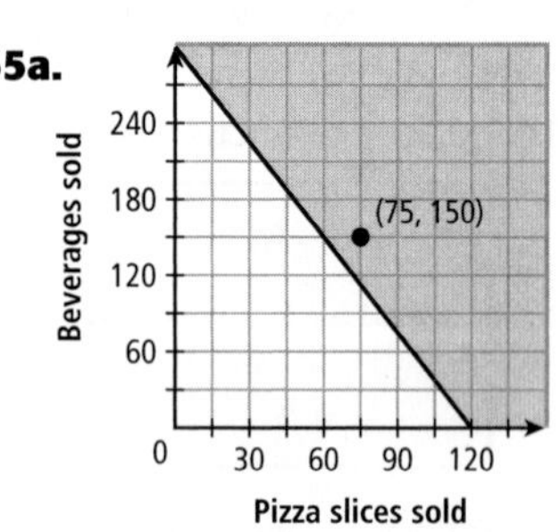

37b.

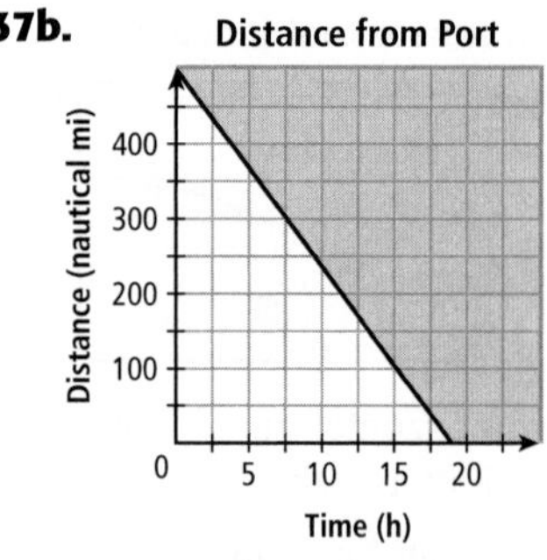

2A *Ready To Go On?*

15.

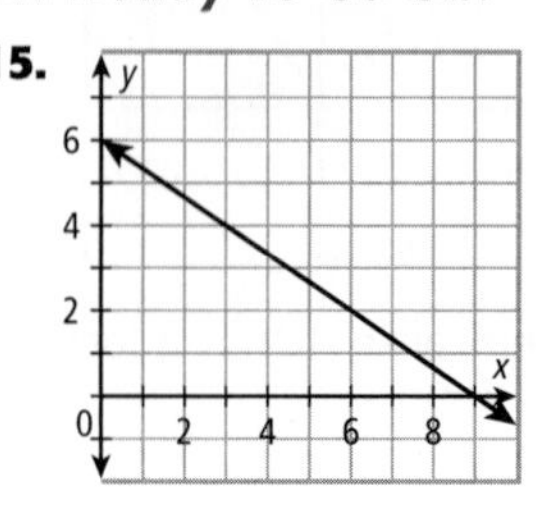

16.

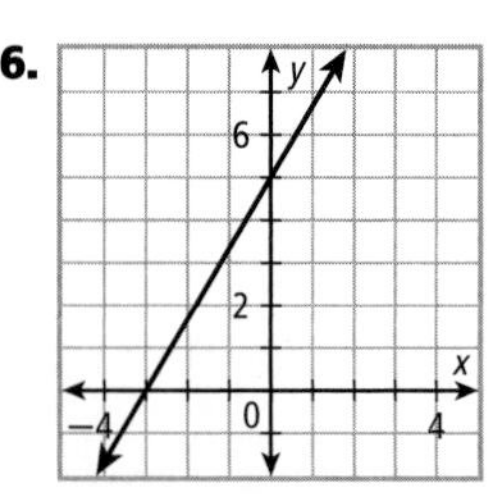

17.

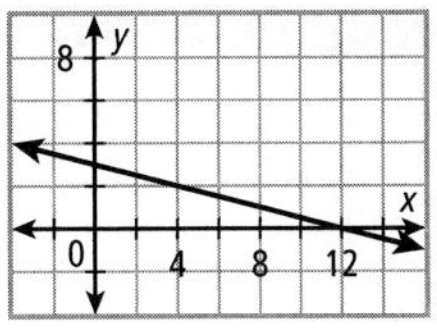

18. 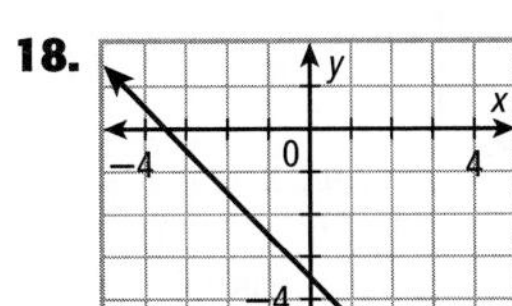

19. 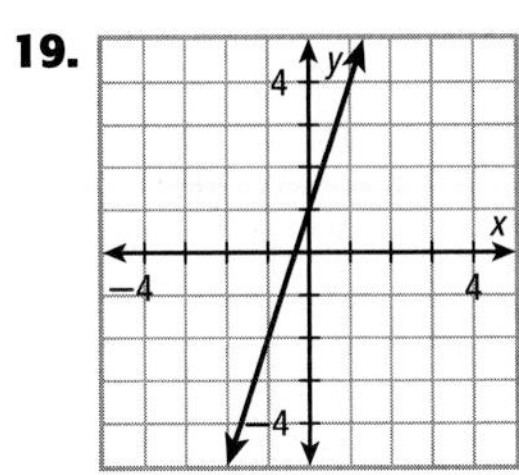

20. 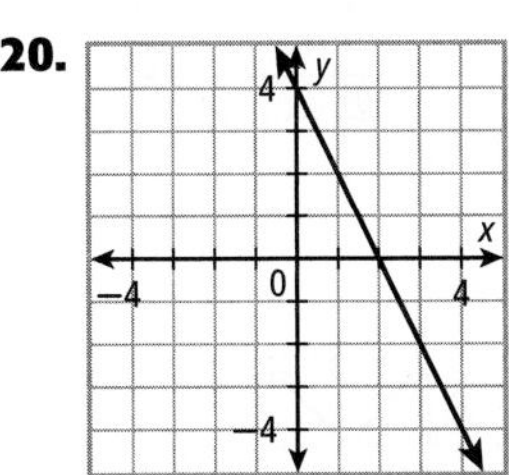

21. 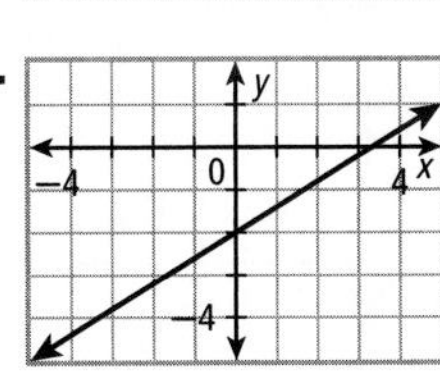

22. 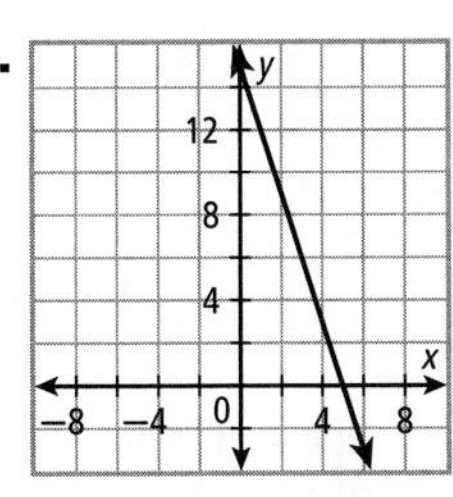

27. 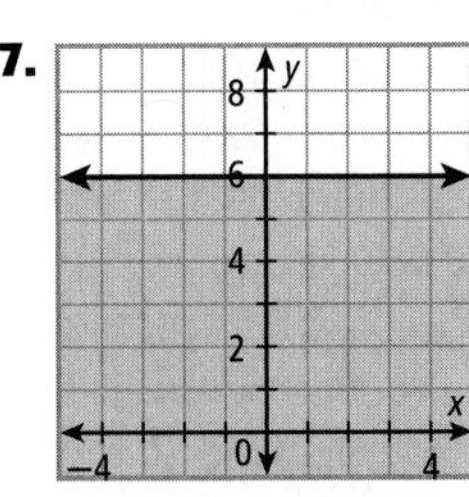

28. 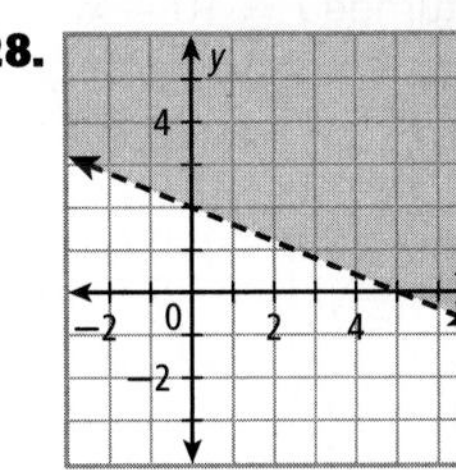

29. 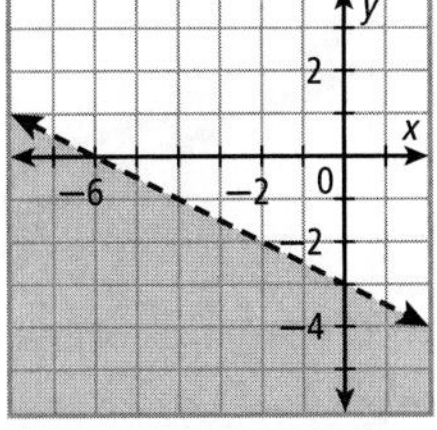

30. 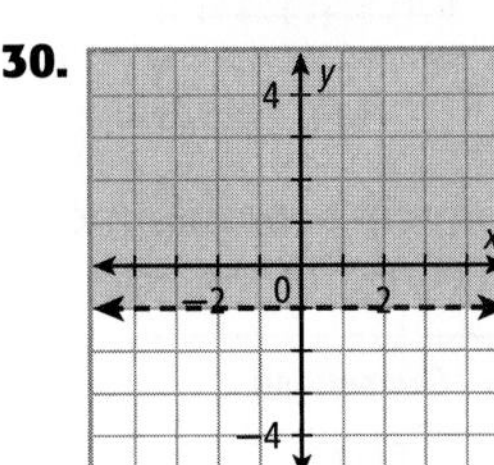

31. 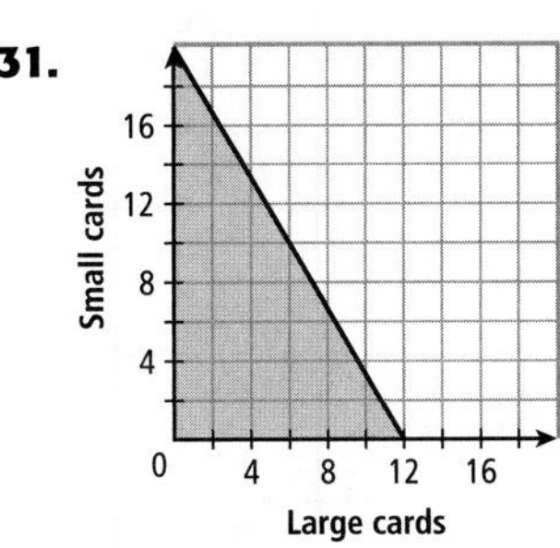

2-6 *Exercises*

22. Possible answer: Stretches, compressions, and reflections affect slope. Translations affect the y-intercept. Vertical stretches/compressions and reflections across the x-axis change a nonzero y-intercept.

36. 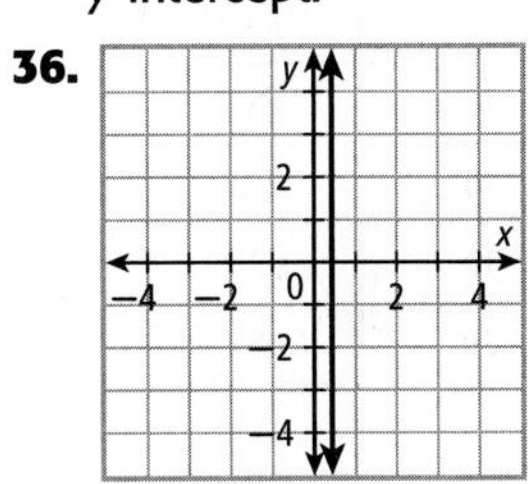

37. 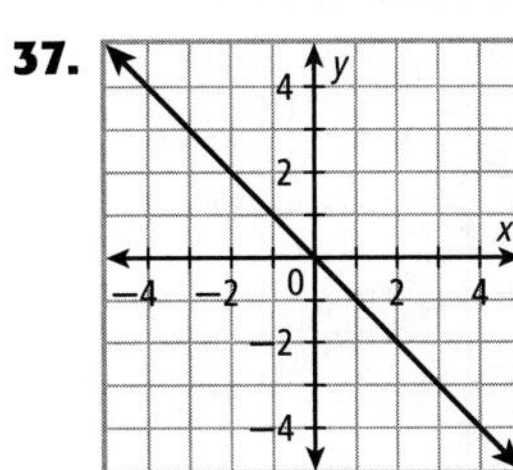

38. 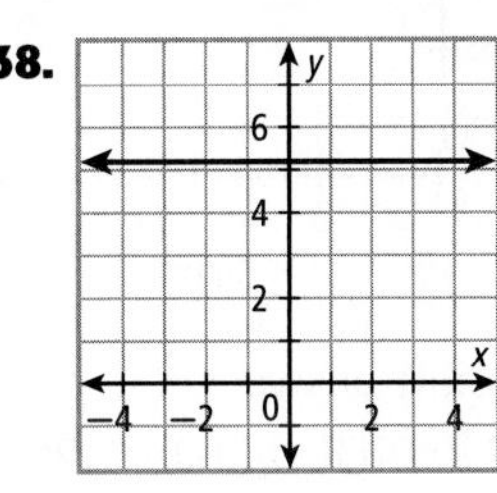

2-7 *Exercises*

17. Possible answer: Yes; if the person walks from 27 ft at a constant rate in 6 s, the distance $d \approx 27 - 4.5t$.

22. 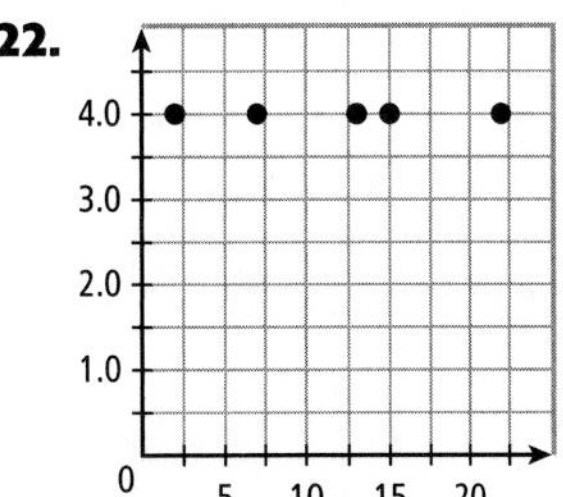

$r = 0$; although the graph forms a line, the value of x has no effect on y, so there is no linear relationship between the variables.

23. 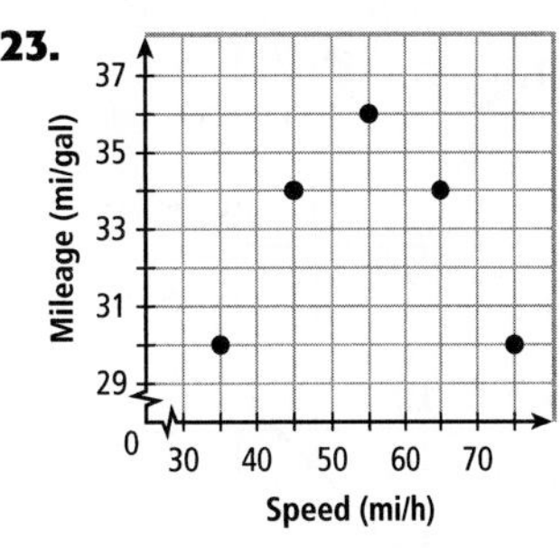

$r = 0$; the data appear related, but not linearly. r measures the strength of the linear relationship between two variables.

24. 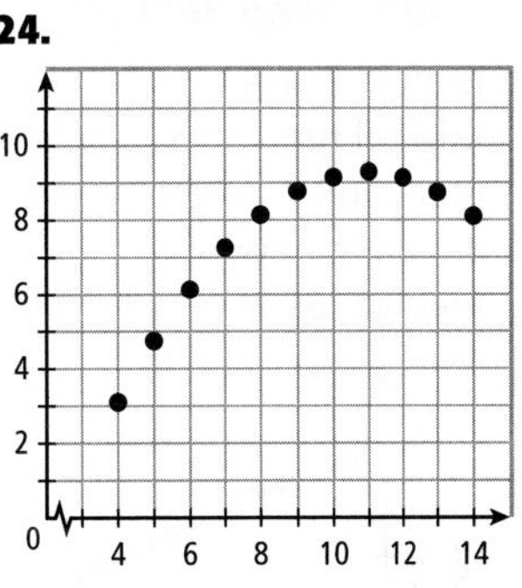

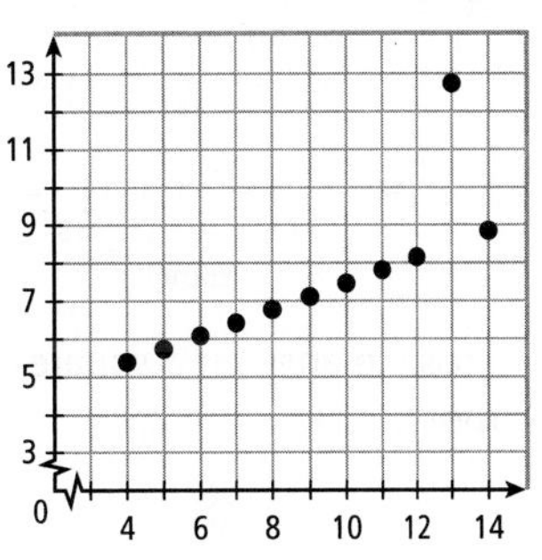

$r = 0.816$ and $y = 0.5x + 3$ for both sets. Possible answer: There may be a better model or an outlier.

32. $f(x) = 3x + 1$;
$g(x) = 3x - 5$;
$g(x) = f(x) - 6$; vertical translation 6 units down.

33. $f(x) = x + 6$;
$g(x) = -x - 6$;
$g(x) = -f(x)$; reflection across the x-axis

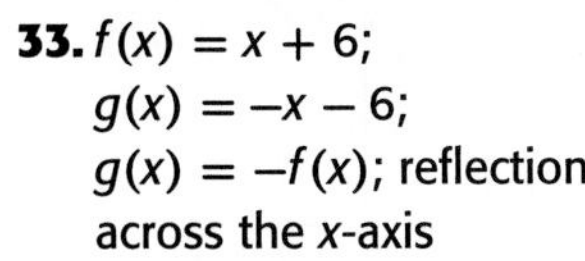

2-8 *Exercises*

14. 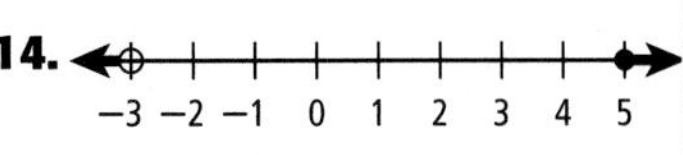

15. 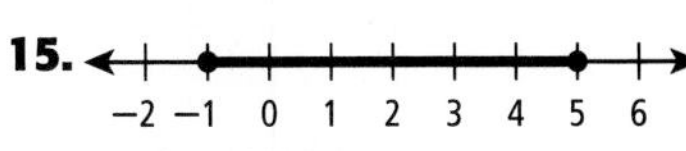

20. 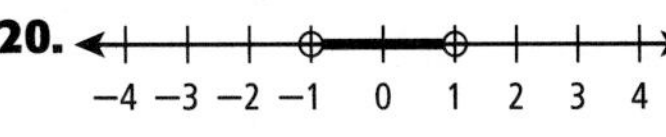

21. 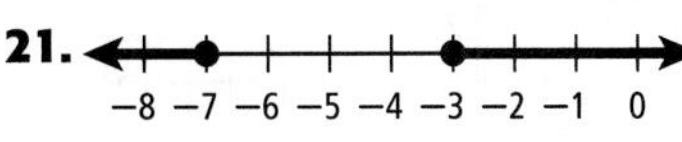

22. 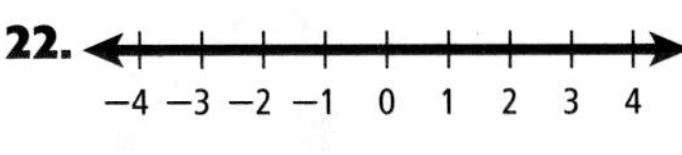

23. 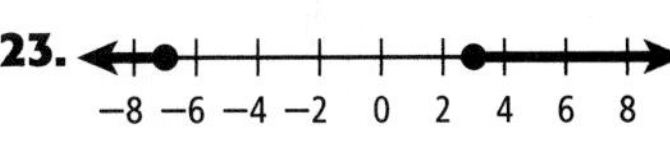

24. 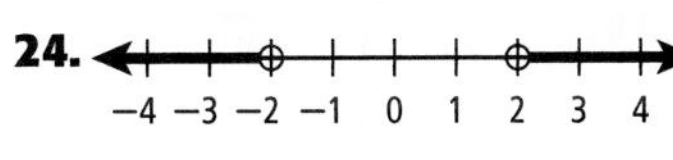

25. 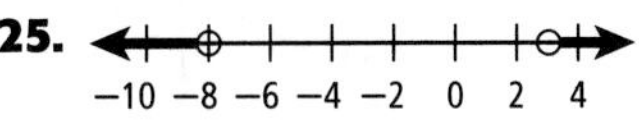

27. 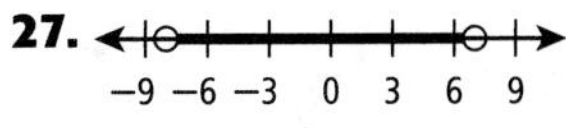

32. 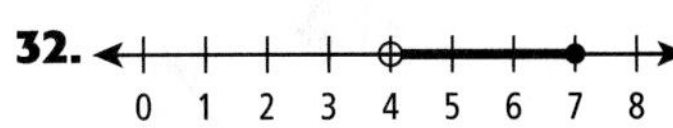

33. 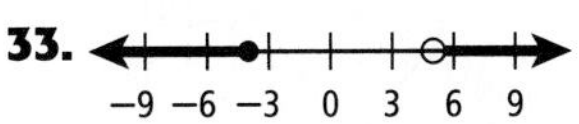

34.

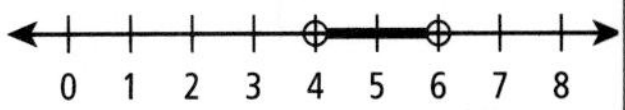

35.

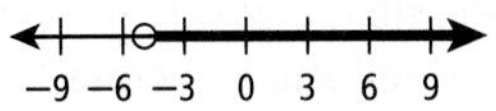

54a. 45 lb; 55 lb; 66.5 lb

b. $|w - 45| \le 5$;
$|w - 55| \le 5$;
and $|w - 66.5| \le 6.5$

c. Possible answer: No, the weight classes overlap, so there is not a specific class for goats that weigh exactly 50 or 60 pounds.

d. Both numbers in the expression would increase by 0.5 lb.

2-9 *Exercises*

13.
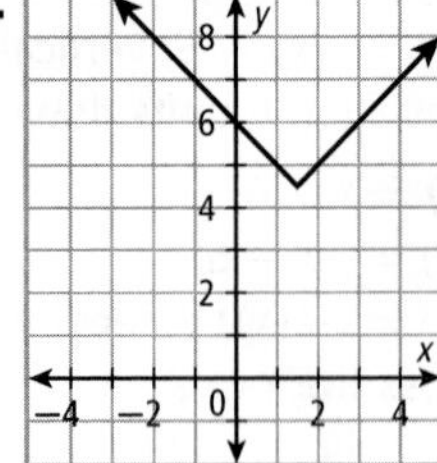

14.
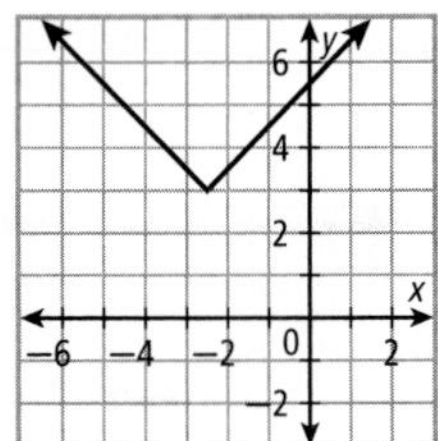

15.
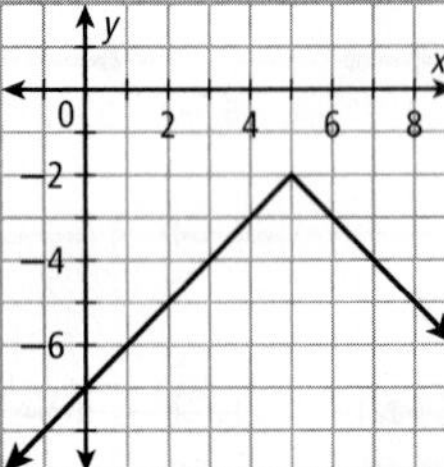

16.
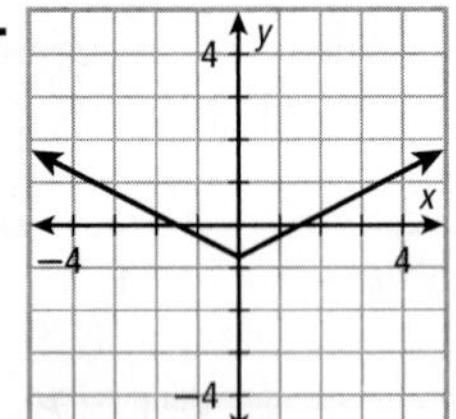

17.
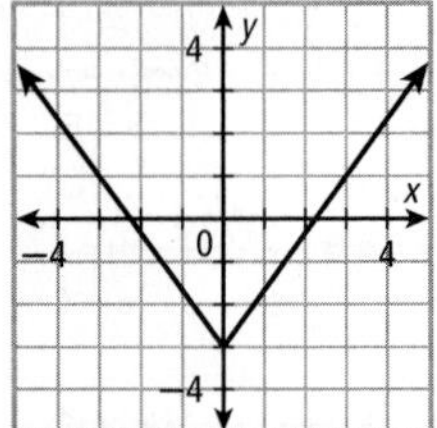

25. They are opposites. Possible answer: The parts are reflections across the vertical line through the vertex; the parts of $f(x) = |2x - 3|$ have slope -2 and 2.

32c.
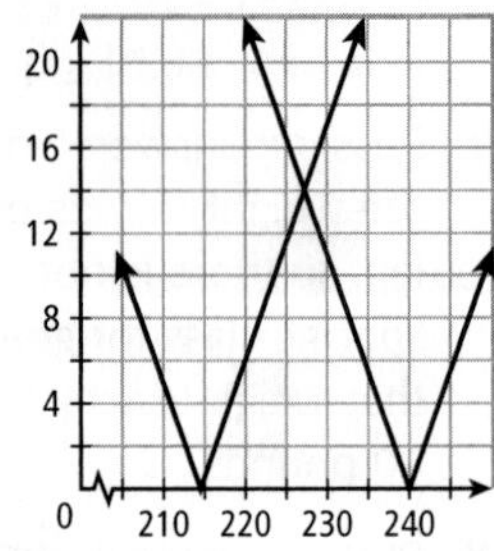

38.
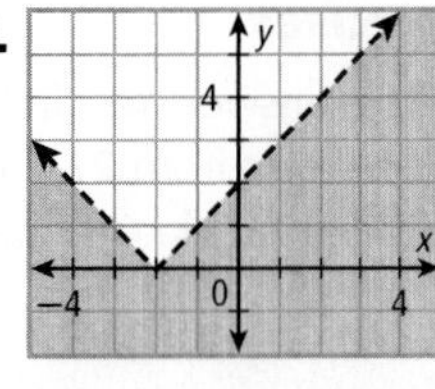

39.
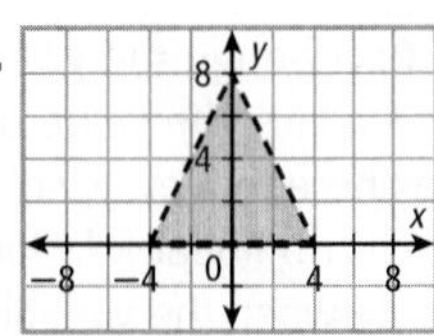

40.
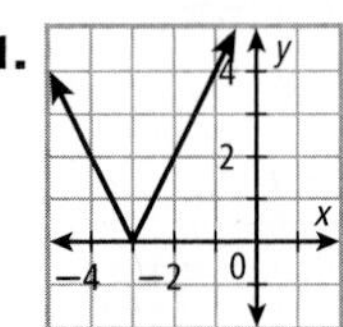

41.
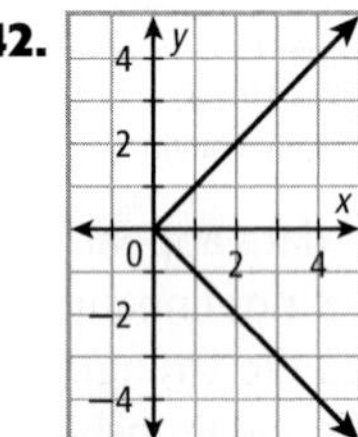

42.

2B *Multi-Step Test Prep*

1. Both increase by 5; original mean: 83.7; new mean: 88.7; original median: 84.5; new median: 89.5.

2.
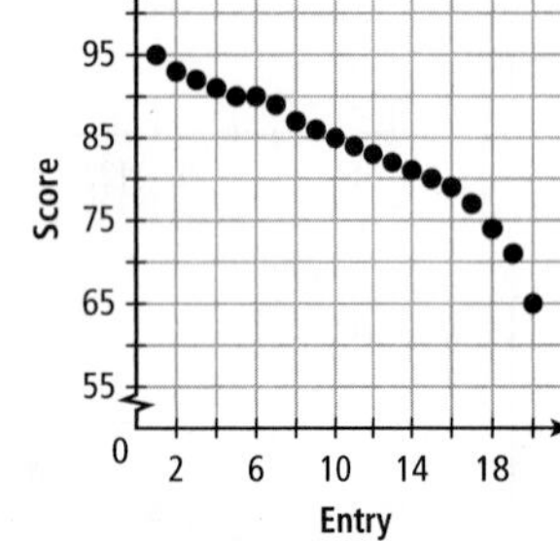

Possible answer: a square-root function

3.

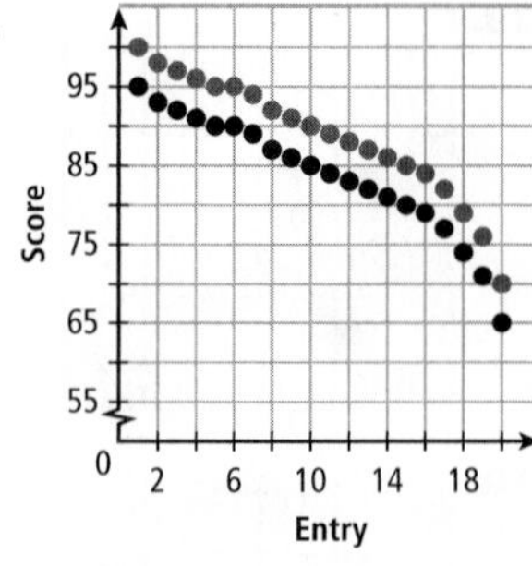

Each point is transformed 5 units up.

6.

Competition Results	
Entry	**Score**
1	100
2	97.9
3	96.8
4	95.8
5	94.7
6	94.7
7	93.7
8	91.6
9	90.5
10	89.5
11	88.4
12	87.4
13	86.3
14	85.3
15	84.2
16	83.2
17	81.1
18	77.9
19	74.7
20	68.4

7. Each point is stretched vertically by a factor of $\frac{100}{95}$; $y = \frac{100}{95}f(x)$

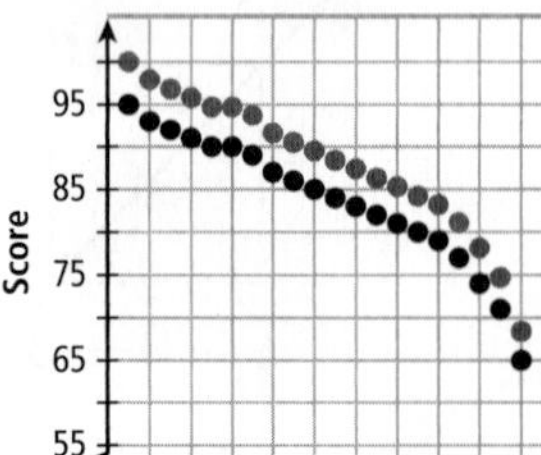

8. Possible answer: The translation; it may be fairer for lower scores.

2B *Ready To Go On?*

5a.
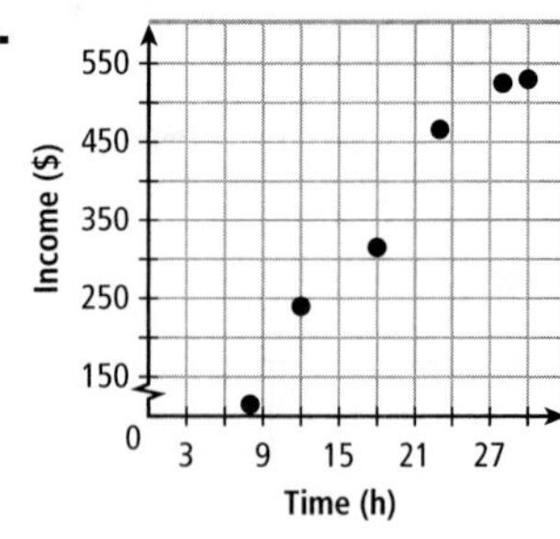

10.
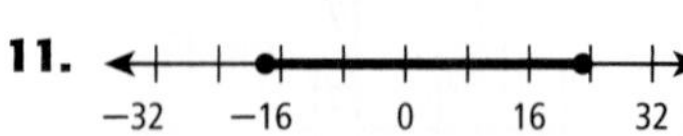

11.
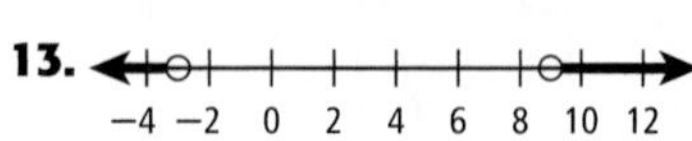

13. −4 −2 0 2 4 6 8 10 12

14.
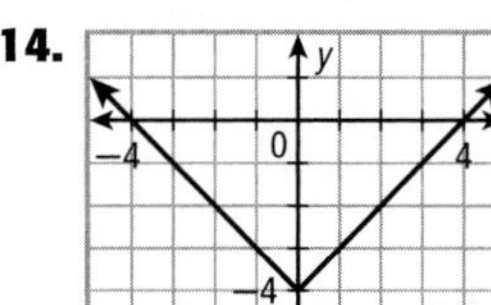

15.
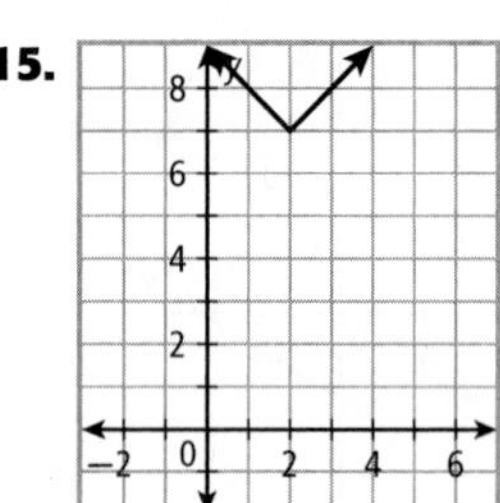

16.
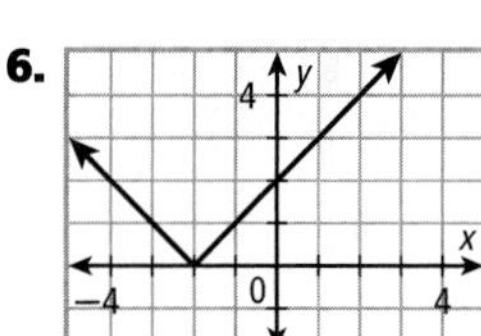

17a. $d = 2|x - 5|$ (or $d = 2|5 - x|$, $d = |2x - 10|$, $d = |10 - 2x|$), where x is the cost of the food in dollars and $d = |x - r|$ is the difference between the cost x and the change returned $r = 10 - x$.

b.
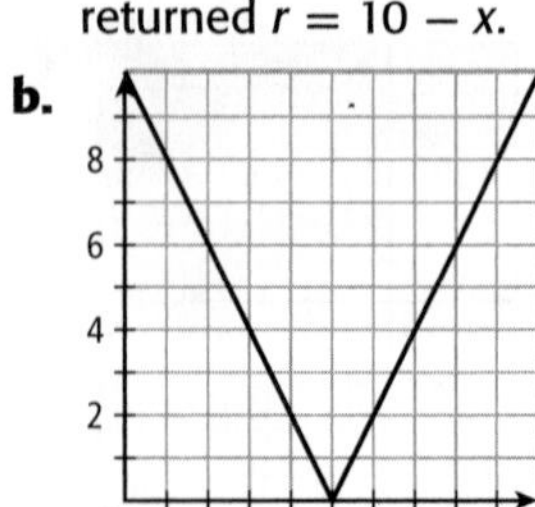

Chapter 3

3-3 *Exercises*

2. 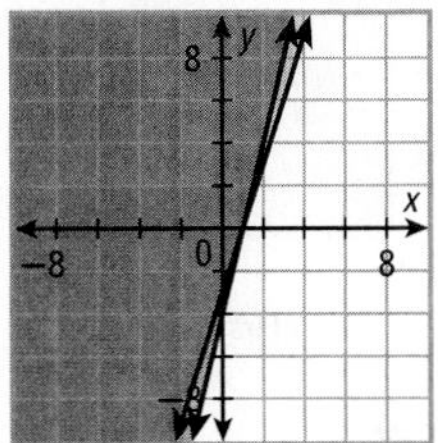

3. 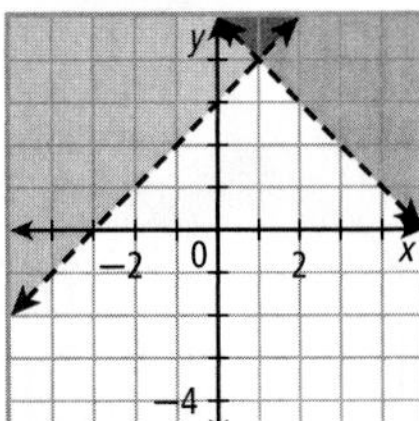

4. 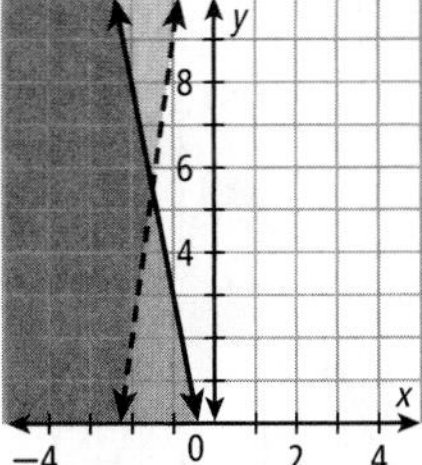

5. 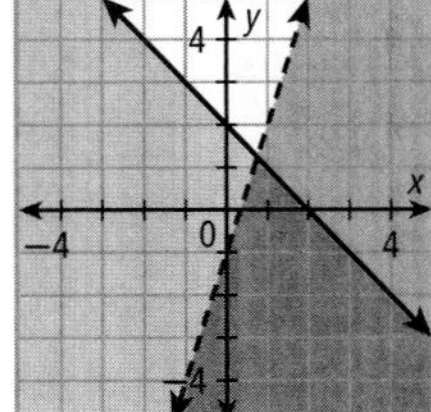

6. 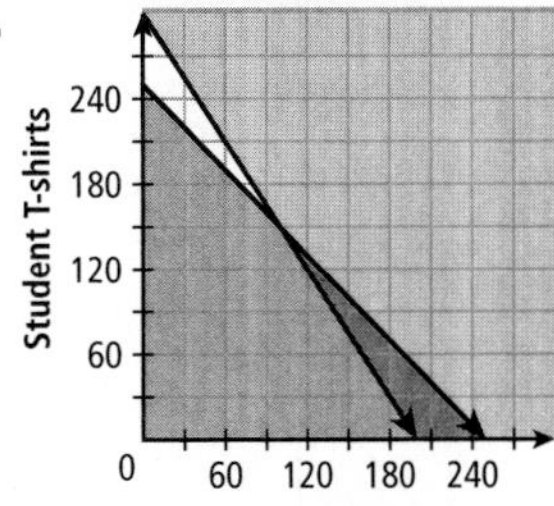

7. 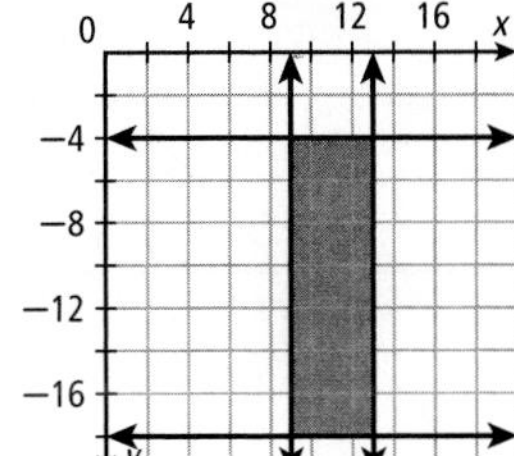

8. 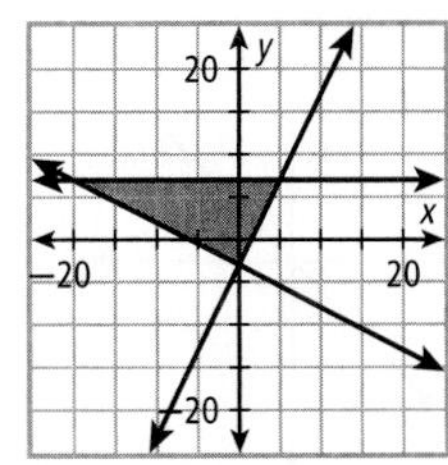

9. 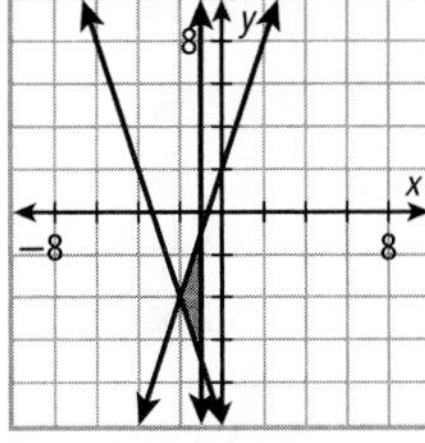

10. 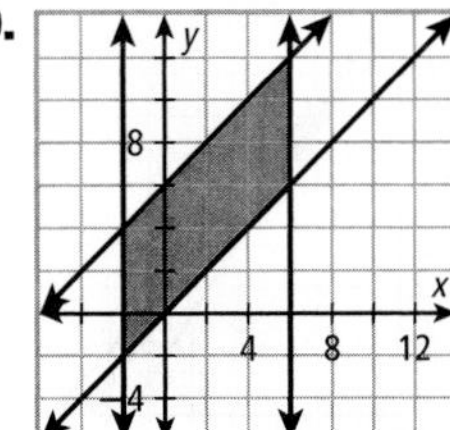

11. 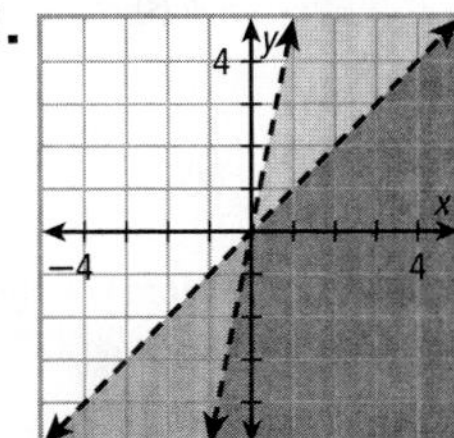

12. 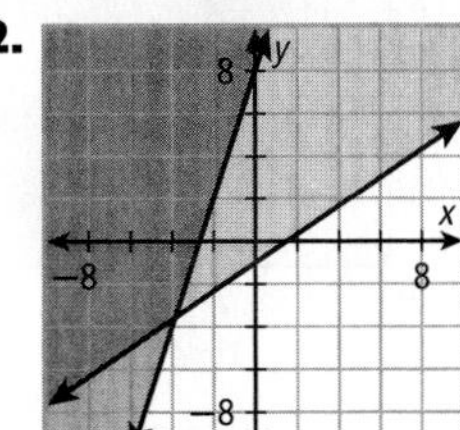

13. 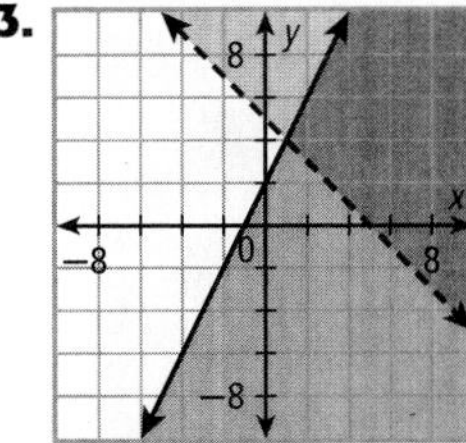

14. 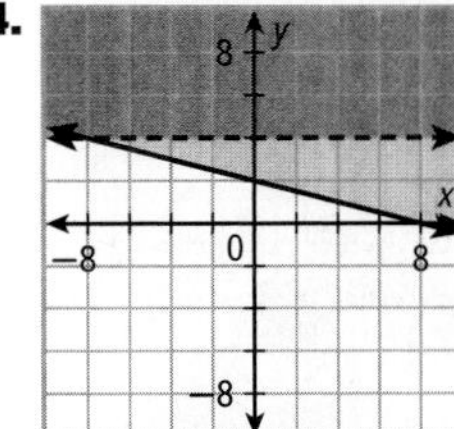

15. 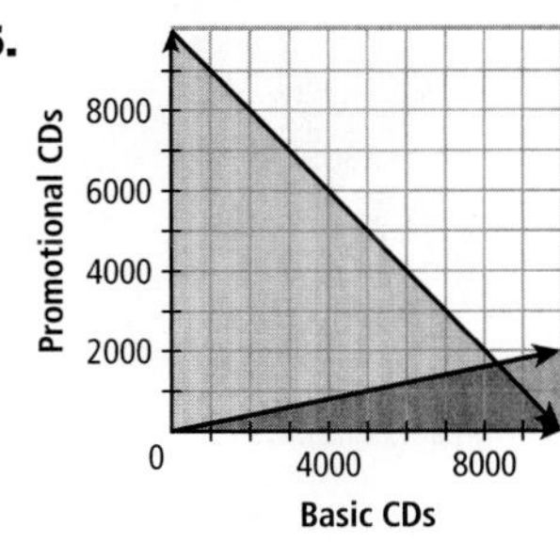

16. 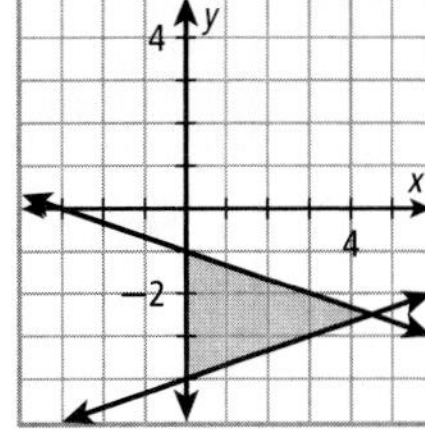

17. 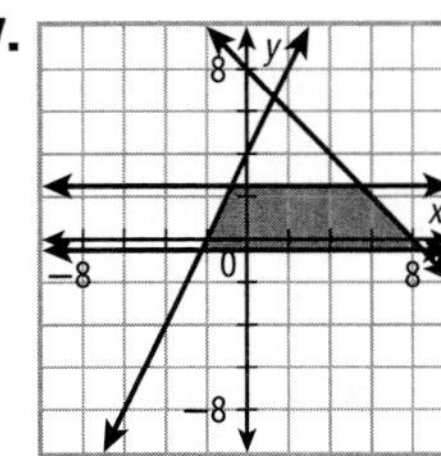

18. 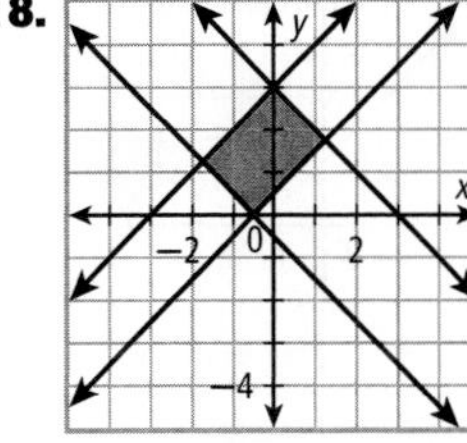

19. 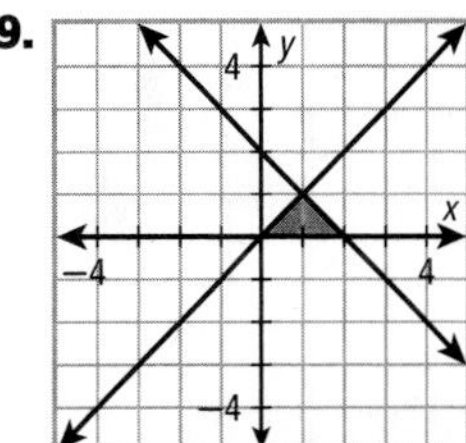

20. 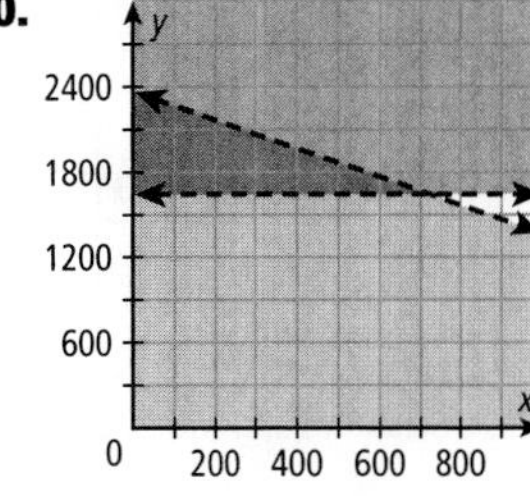

21. Possible answer:

$$\begin{cases} y \le 2x \\ y \ge 2x - 1 \\ y \le -\frac{1}{2}x \\ y \ge -\frac{1}{2}x + 3 \end{cases}$$

22. Possible answer:

$$\begin{cases} y \le x + 2 \\ y \ge x - 3 \\ y \le -x \\ y \ge -x - 5 \end{cases}$$

23. Possible answer:

$$\begin{cases} y \le 3 \\ x \ge 1 \\ y \ge x - 1 \end{cases}$$

24. Possible answer:

$$\begin{cases} y \le 4 \\ y \ge 0 \\ y \le \frac{1}{2}x \\ y \le -3x + 12 \end{cases}$$

27.

$$\begin{cases} x \ge 0 \\ y \ge 0 \\ x + y \le 114{,}650 \\ x + y \ge 56{,}801 \\ y \ge x + 2000 \end{cases}$$

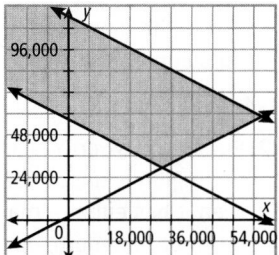

28. 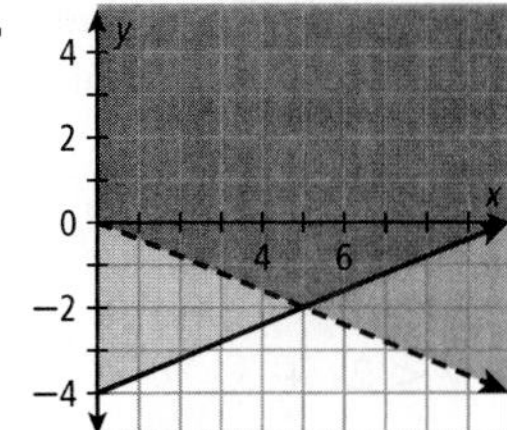

Possible answer: (3, 1), (5, −1), (10, 5)

29. 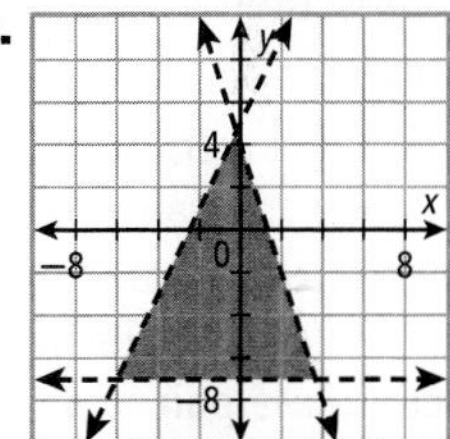

Possible answer: (0, 0), (−1, 2), $\left(1, -\frac{1}{2}\right)$

30. 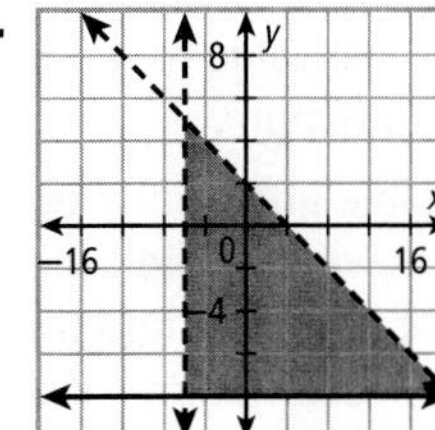

Possible answer: (−2, −3), (−1, 1), (10, −4)

Additional Answers

31.

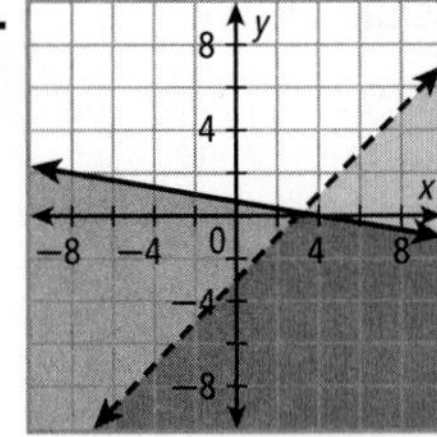

Possible answer: (0, −5), (3, −2), (−6, −10)

32. Possible answer: There are four possible regions: between the two lines, above the upper line, below the lower line, and no solution.

3-4 *Exercises*

22. Possible answer: Yes; if the region is unbounded, then it has either a maximum or minimum, but not both, and the problem may not have a solution. For example, maximize $P = x + y$ for

$$\begin{cases} y \geq 2x \\ x \geq 0 \\ y \leq 2x + 3 \end{cases}$$

24. Possible answer: The problem situation involves profit and loss where loss is represented by negative values.

25. Possible answer: Substitute the values from every vertex of the feasible region into the objective function one pair at a time. Depending on the problem statement, look for the greatest value of the objective function to identify the maximum or the least value to identify the minimum.

26. Possible answer: Once you have identified the feasible region, find the intersection points of the lines that form that region. The coordinates of the intersections are the coordinates of the vertices.

30a.

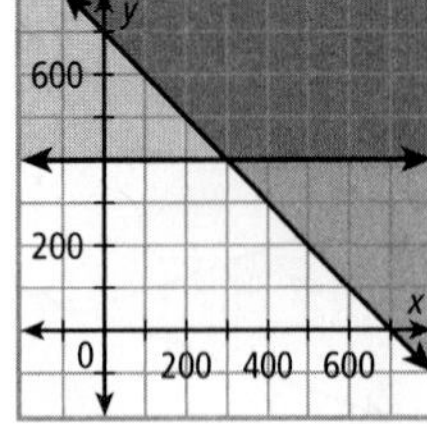

31. $f(7) = \frac{1}{11}; f\left(-\frac{1}{2}\right) = -\frac{1}{4}$

32. $f(7) = 3.5; f\left(-\frac{1}{2}\right) = -\frac{1}{4}$

33. $f(7) = 8; f\left(-\frac{1}{2}\right) = \frac{1}{2}$

34.

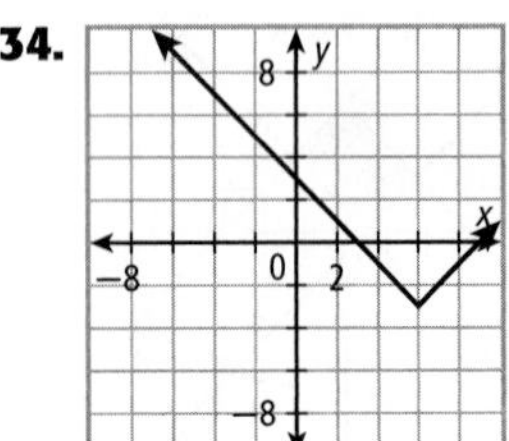

35.

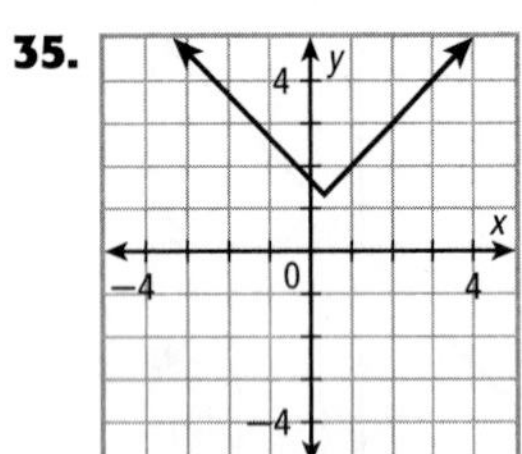

36.

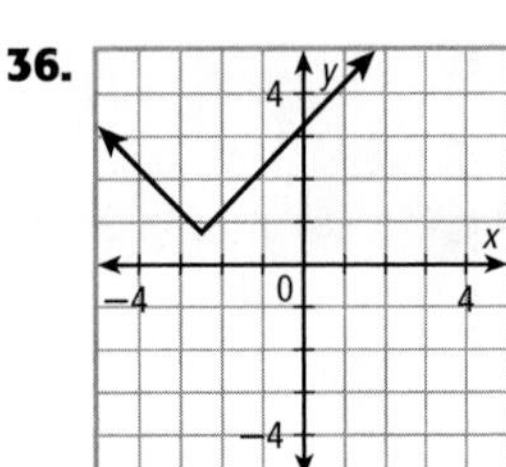

37.

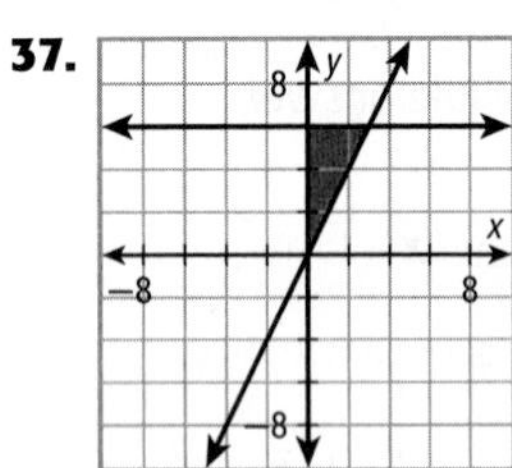

38.

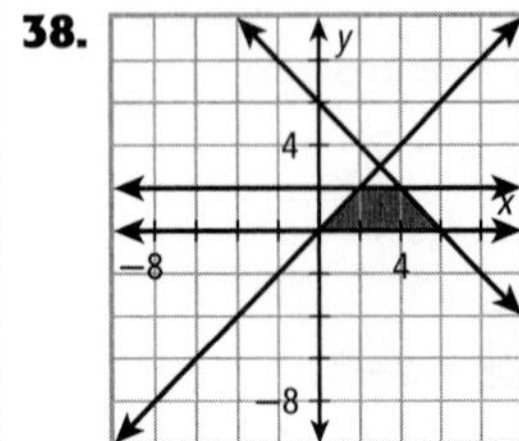

3A *Multi-Step Test Prep*

2. $\begin{cases} f = 18 - 2.33s \\ f = 20 - 2.68s \\ f = 18 - 2.14s \\ f = 20 - 3.06s \end{cases}$

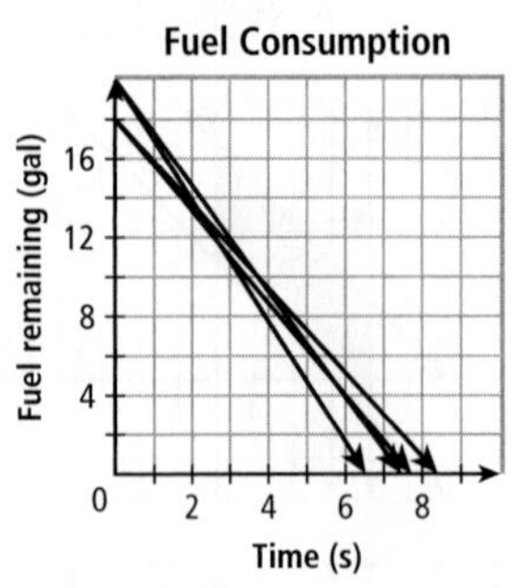

5. $\begin{cases} d \leq 288t \\ d \geq 1000 - 302t \end{cases}$

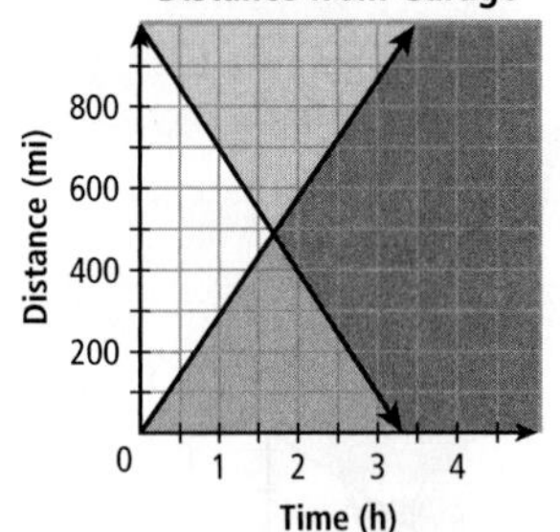

3A *Ready to Go On?*

13.

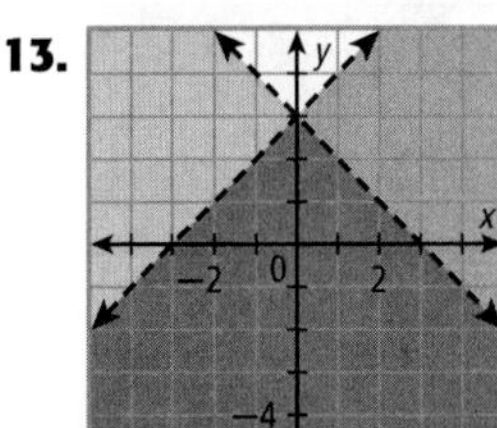

14.

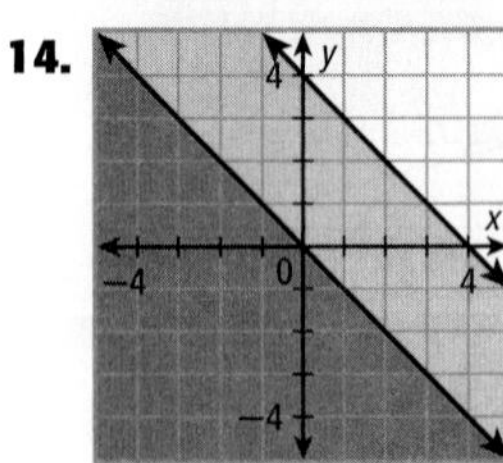

15.

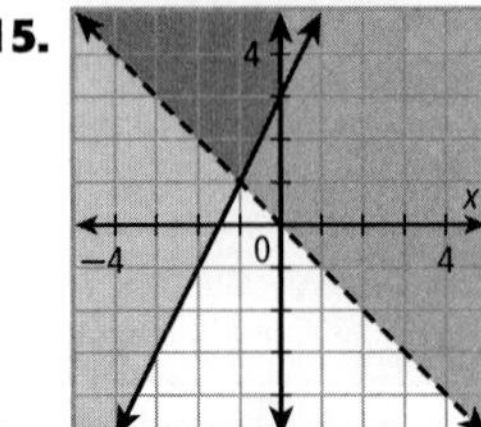

16.

17. $P = 4$

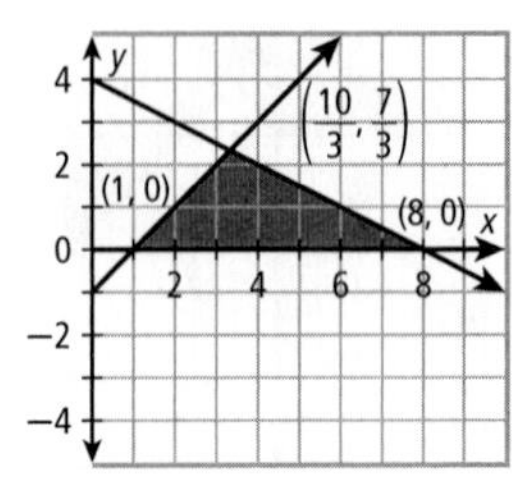

18. $P = 34$

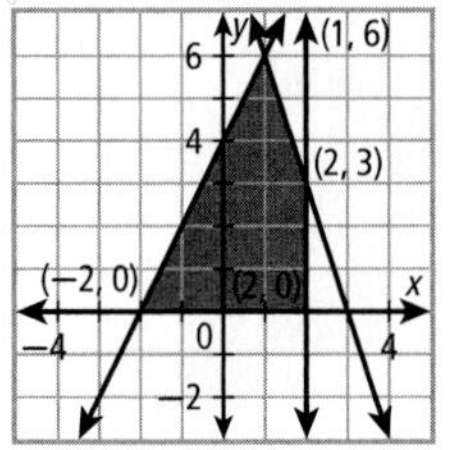

3-5 *Exercises*

2.

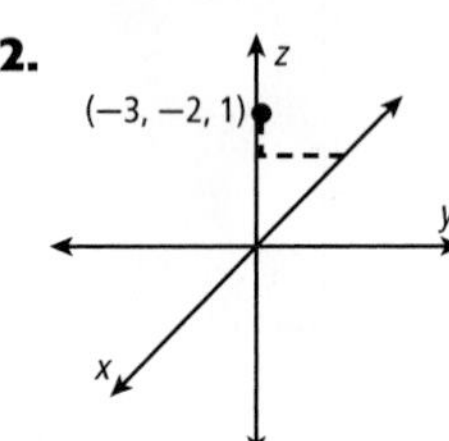

3.

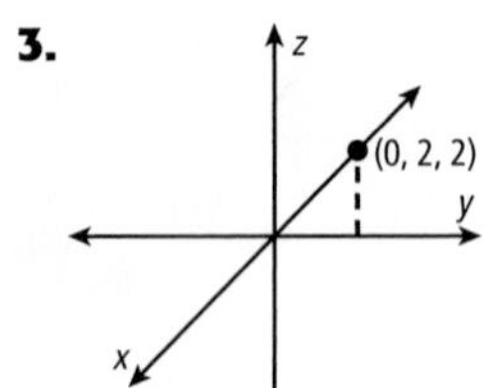

4.

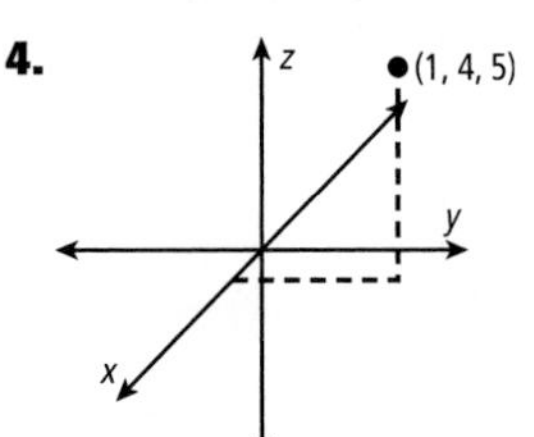

5.

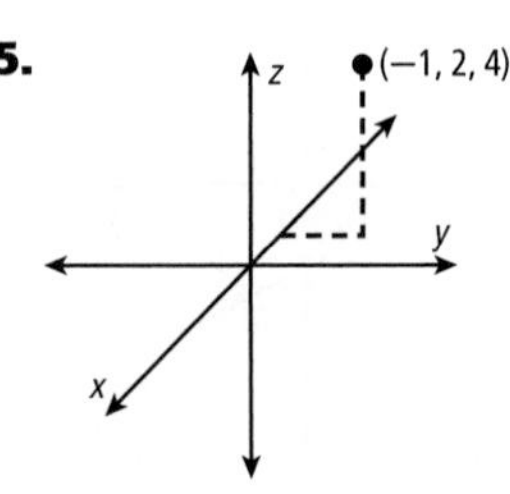

6.

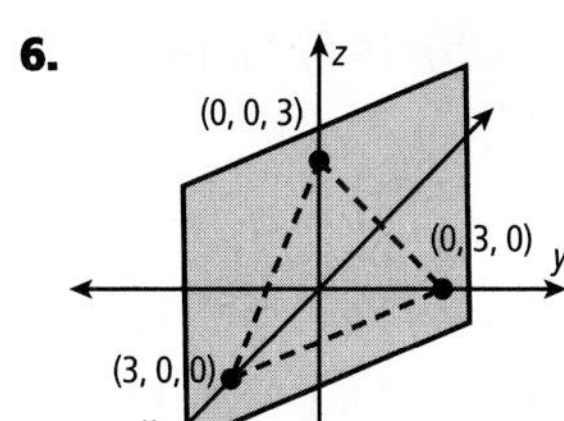

7.

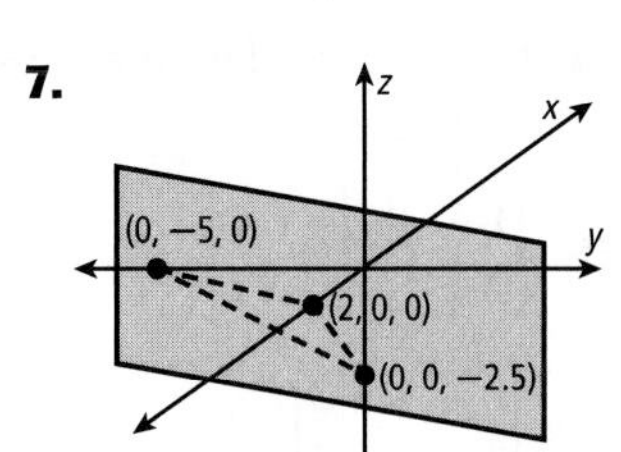

8.

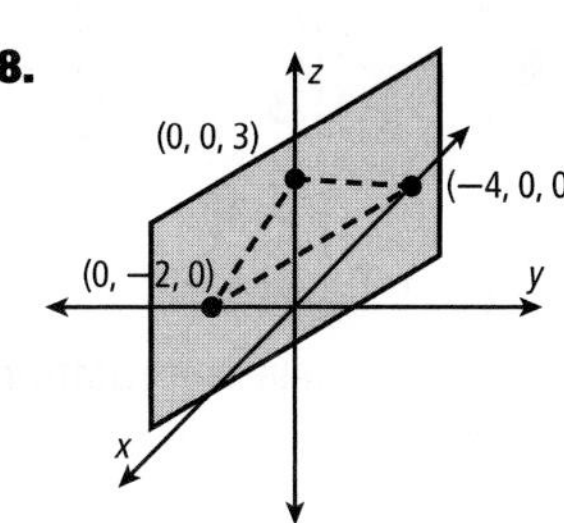

10.

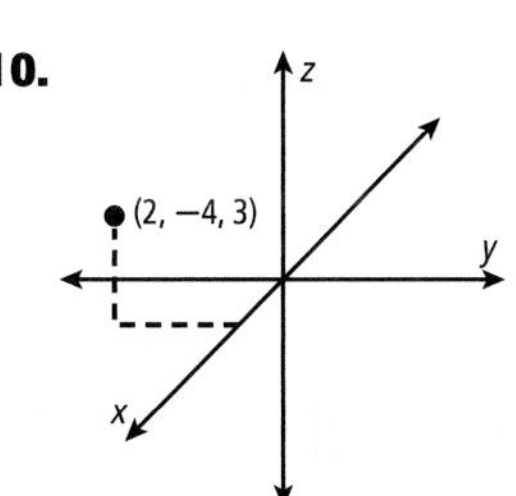

11.

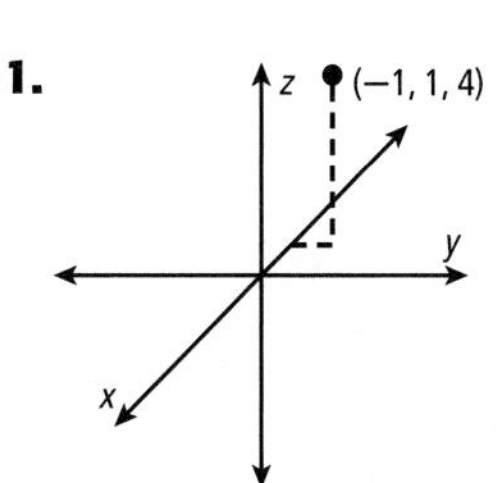

12.

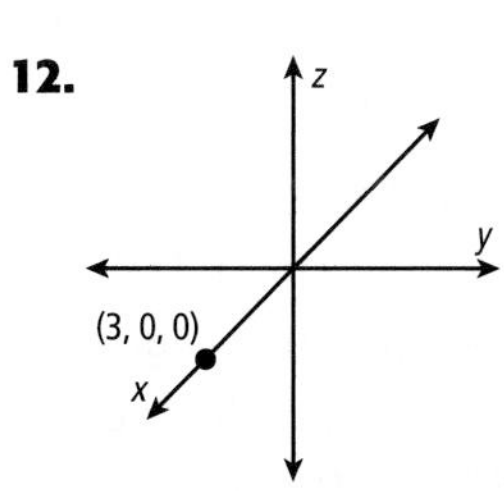

13.

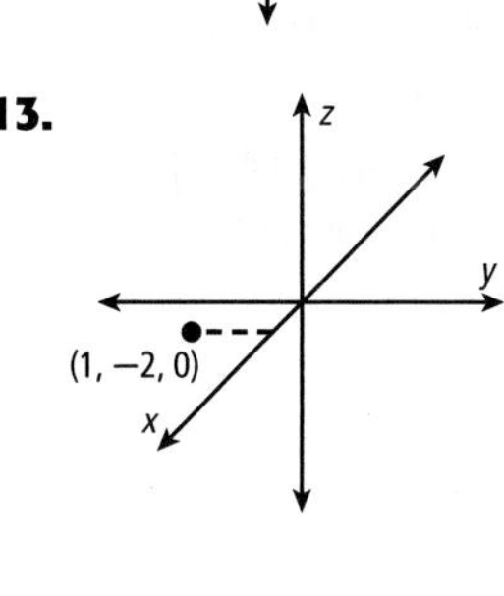

14.

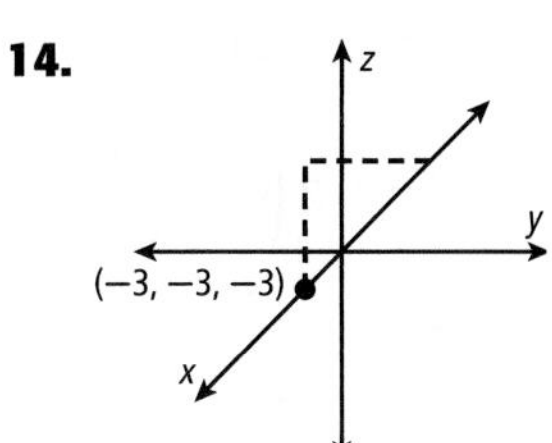

15.

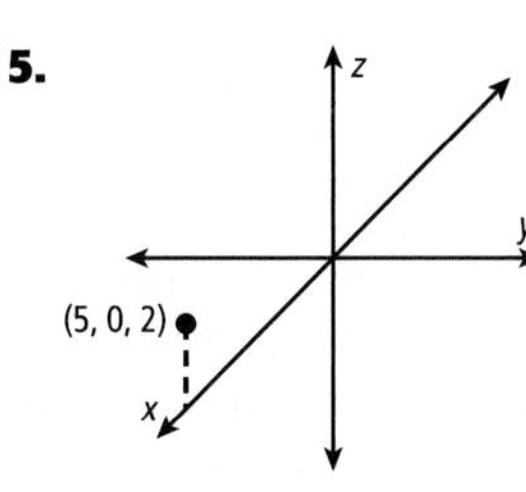

16.

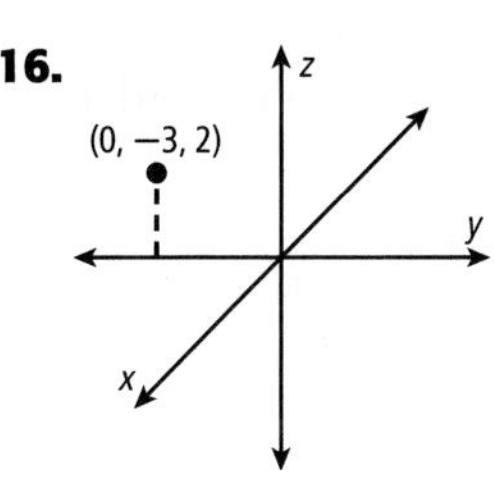

17.

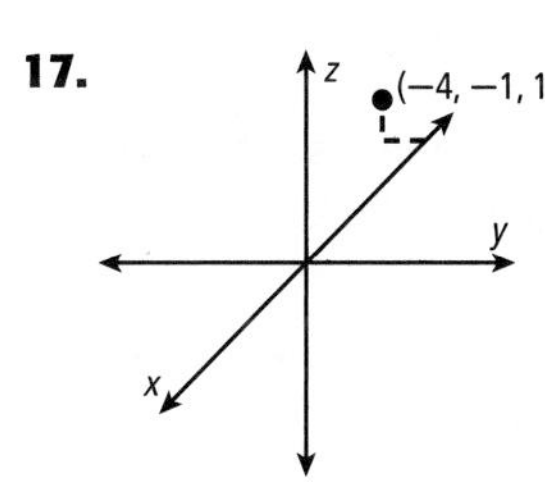

18.

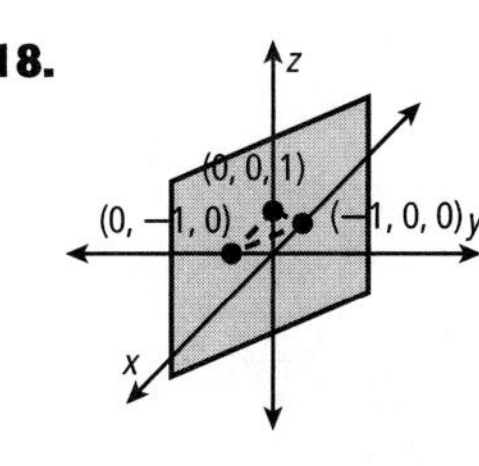

19.

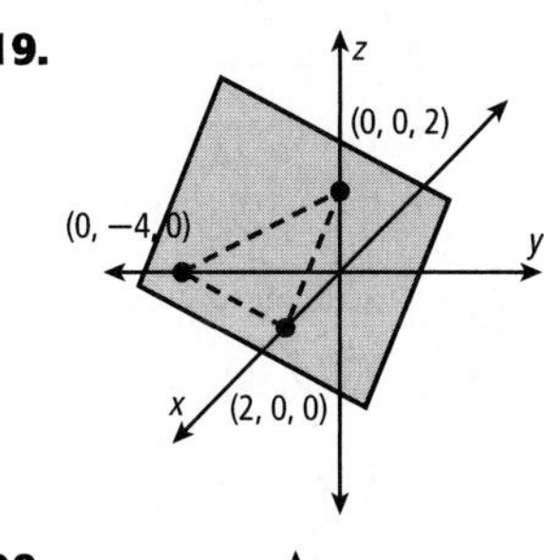

20.

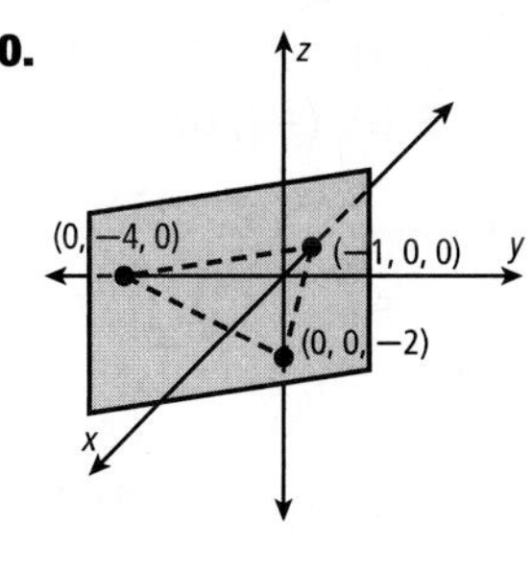

21.

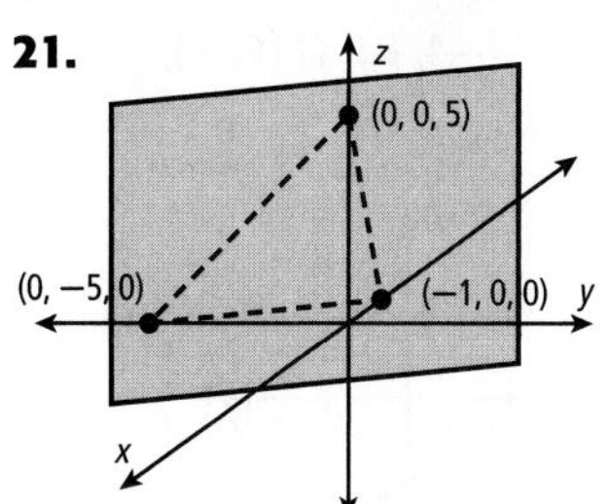

22.

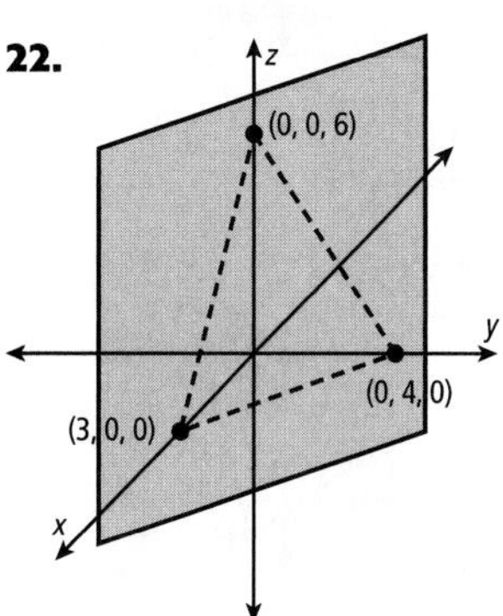

23.

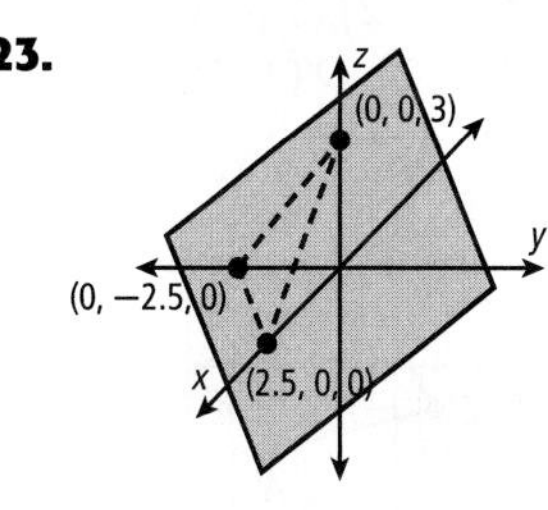

3-6 *Technology Lab*

1a.

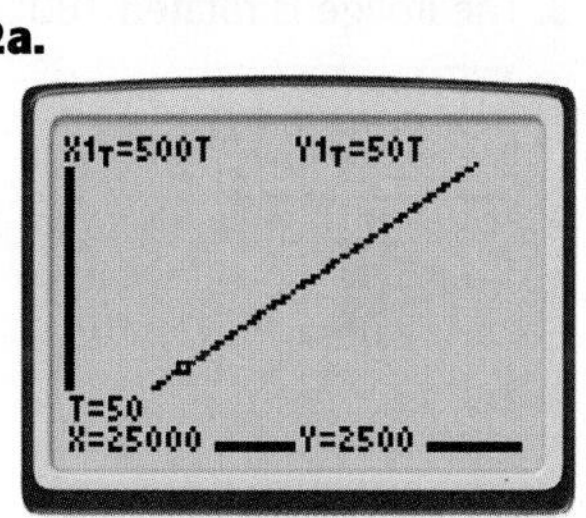

2a.

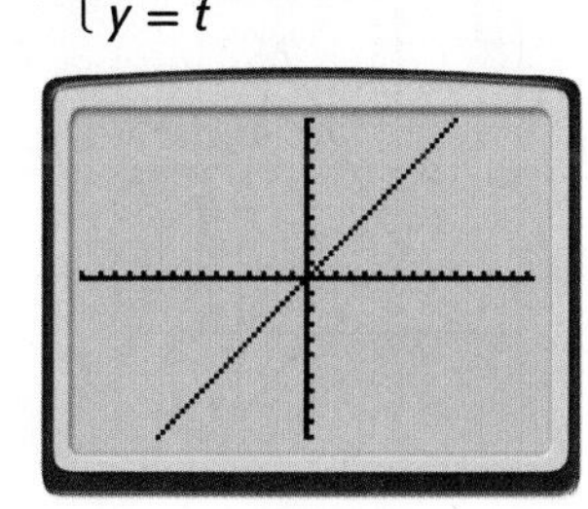

3. $\begin{cases} x = t \\ y = t \end{cases}$

4a.

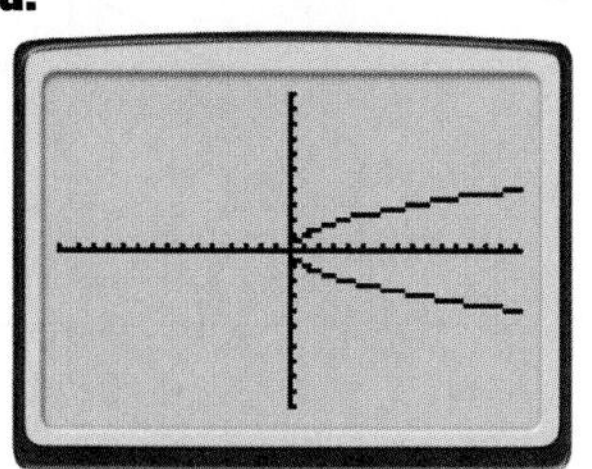

b. Possible answer: The relation is a parabola that opens to the right; $x = y^2$; no.

3B *Multi-Step Test Prep*

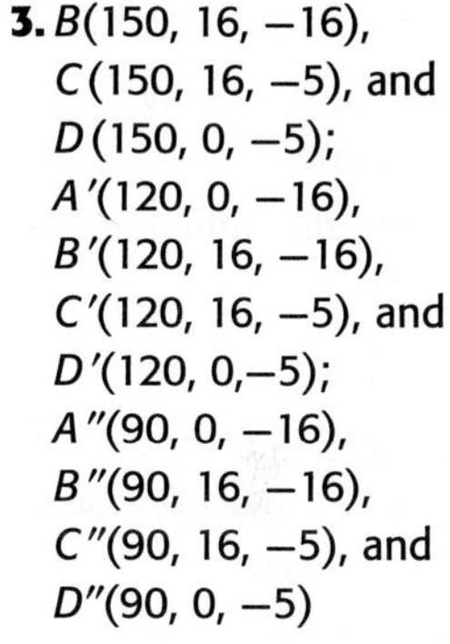

3. $B(150, 16, -16)$, $C(150, 16, -5)$, and $D(150, 0, -5)$; $A'(120, 0, -16)$, $B'(120, 16, -16)$, $C'(120, 16, -5)$, and $D'(120, 0, -5)$; $A''(90, 0, -16)$, $B''(90, 16, -16)$, $C''(90, 16, -5)$, and $D''(90, 0, -5)$

3B *Ready To Go On?*

1–3.

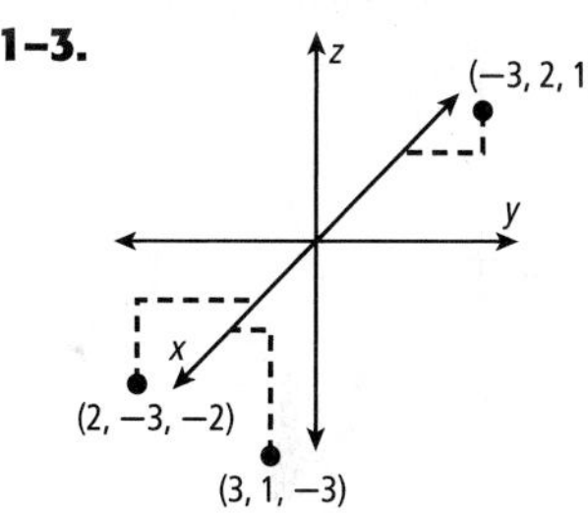

4.

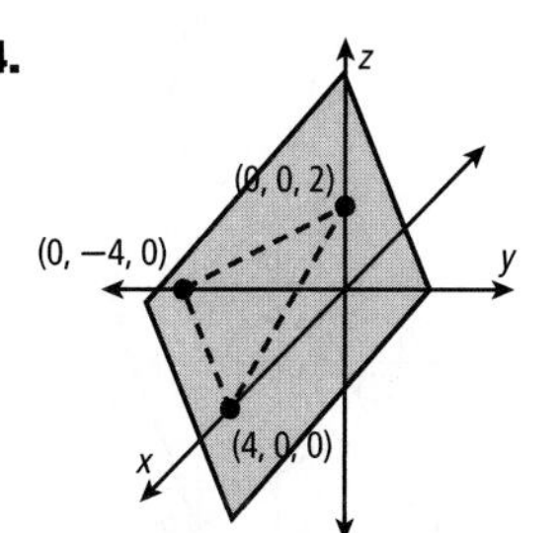

5.

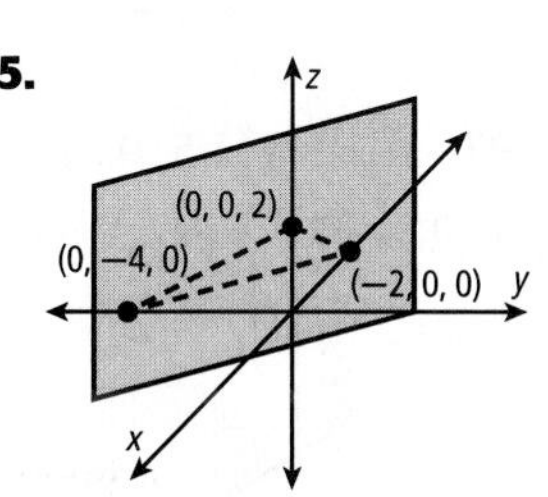

6.

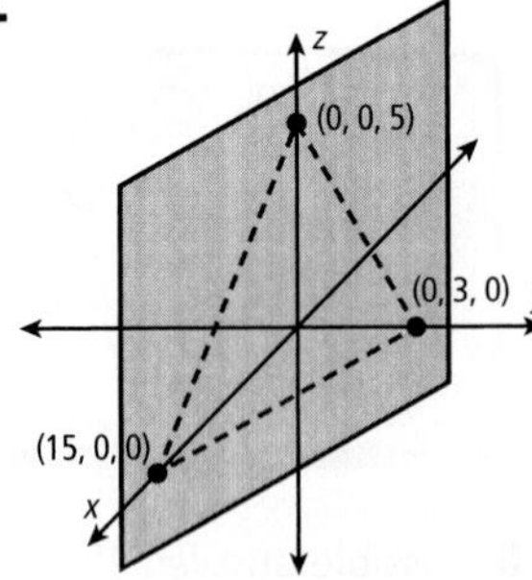

12. $\begin{cases} 6x + 8y + 14z = 65 \\ 10x + 10y + 15z = 80 \\ 12x + 6y + 9z = 60 \end{cases}$

14. inconsistent; no solution

15. consistent; exactly 1 solution

16. dependent; infinitely many solutions

Chapter 4

4-3 *Exercises*

2. $P'(-4, 5)$, $Q'(1, 2)$, $R'(-1, -3)$, $S'(-4, -1)$,

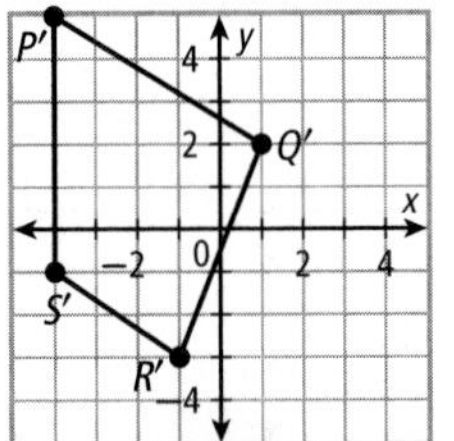

3. $P'(-1, 4)$, $Q'(4, 1)$, $R'(2, -4)$, $S'(-1, -2)$,

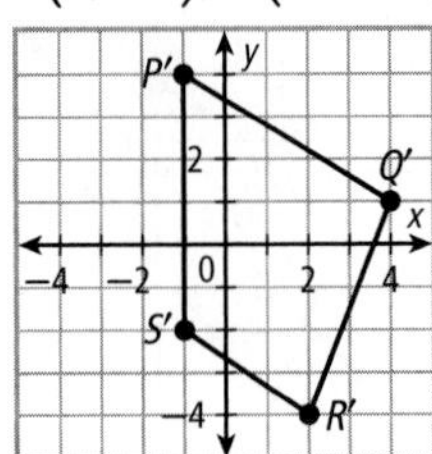

4. $P'(-1, 2)$, $Q'(1.5, 0.5)$, $R'(0.5, -2)$, $S'(-1, -1)$

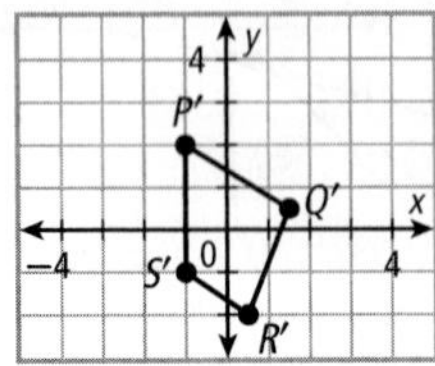

5. $P'(-4, 8)$, $Q'(6, 2)$, $R'(2, -8)$, $S'(-4, -4)$

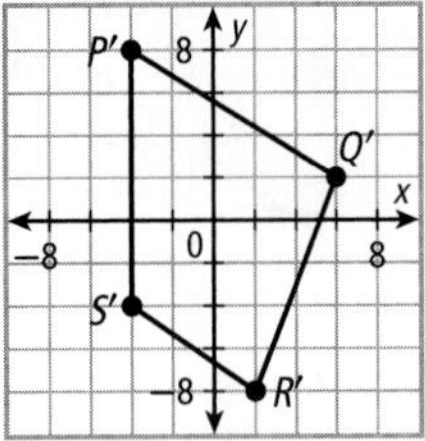

6. $A'(2, 3)$, $B'(0, 4)$, $C'(-2, 3)$, $D'(-2, 1)$, $E'(1, -1)$

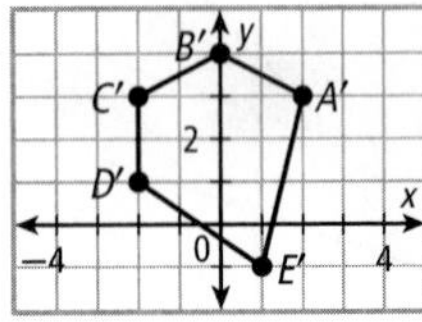

7. $A'(3, -2)$, $B'(4, 0)$, $C'(3, 2)$, $D'(1, 2)$, $E'(-1, -1)$

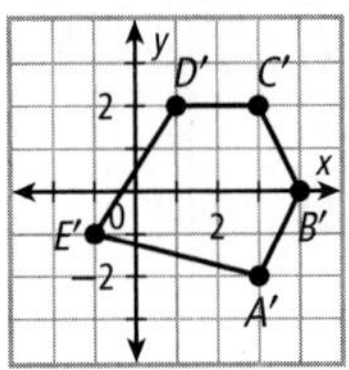

8. The image is rotated 90° clockwise.

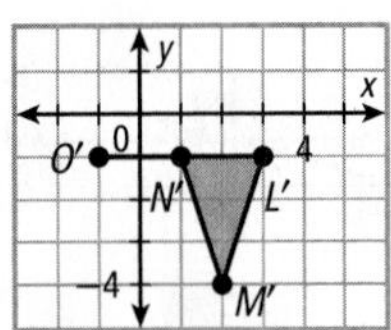

9. The image is rotated 180°.

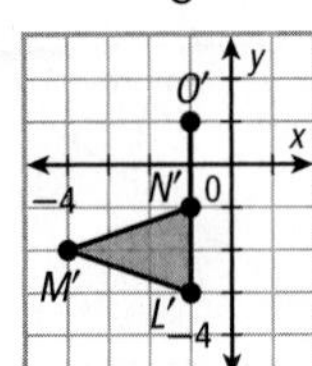

10. $D'(3, 7)$, $E'(0, 2)$, $F'(4, -2)$, $G'(4, 3)$

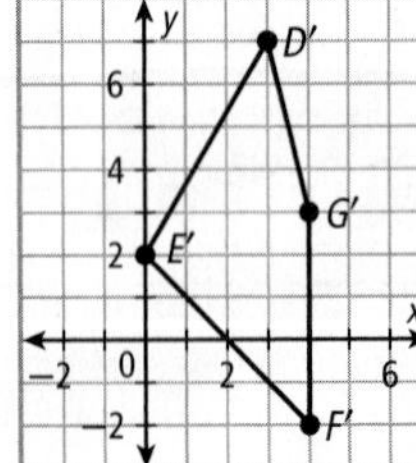

11. $W'\left(\frac{3}{2}, 3\right)$, $X'\left(-3, \frac{9}{2}\right)$, $Y'\left(-\frac{9}{2}, 6\right)$, $Z'\left(-6, \frac{3}{2}\right)$

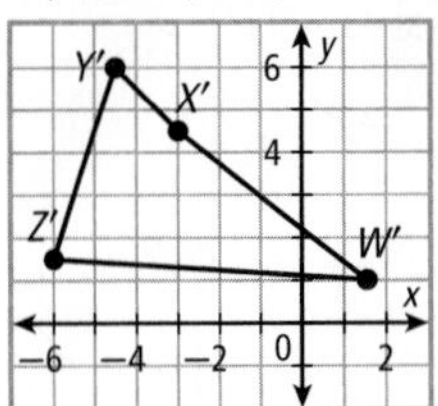

12. The image is a reflection of *ABCDE* across the *x*-axis. The vertices of the image have the same *x*-coordinates of *ABCDE* but opposite *y*-coordinates.

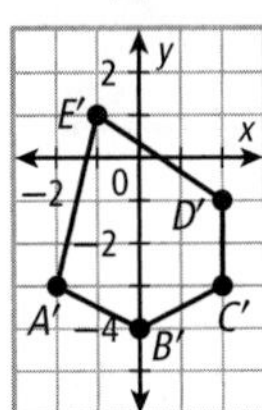

13. The image is rotated 90° counterclockwise.

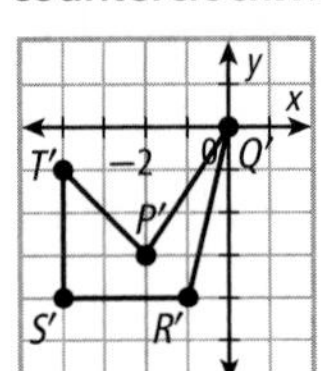

14. The image is rotated 90° clockwise.

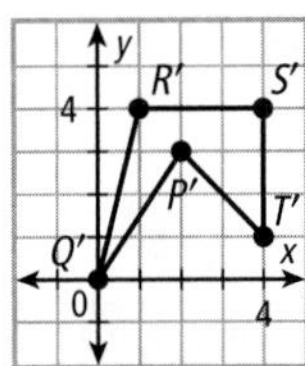

18. $(-5, 6)$, $(-3, 6.5)$, $(-1, 6)$, $(1, 5.5)$, $(5, 6)$, $(4.5, 3)$, $(2, 3)$

19. $(-8, 3)$, $(-6, 3.5)$, $(-4, 3)$, $(-2, 2.5)$, $(2, 3)$, $(1.5, 0)$, $(-1, 0)$

20. $(-10, 8)$, $(-6, 9)$, $(-2, 8)$, $(2, 7)$, $(10, 8)$, $(9, 2)$, $(4, 2)$

21. $(-5, -4)$, $(-3, -4.5)$, $(-1, -4)$, $(1, -3.5)$, $(5, -4)$, $(4.5, -1)$, $(2, -1)$

22. $(4, 5)$, $(4.5, 3)$, $(4, 1)$, $(3.5, -1)$, $(4, -5)$, $(1, -4.5)$, $(1, -2)$

23. $(-4, -5)$, $(-4.5, -3)$, $(-4, -1)$, $(-3.5, 1)$, $(-4, 5)$, $(-1, 4.5)$, $(-1, 2)$

24. It reflects the figure across the line $y = x$.

25. $\begin{bmatrix} 1 & 0 \\ 0 & -1 \end{bmatrix}; \begin{bmatrix} -1 & 0 \\ 0 & 1 \end{bmatrix}$

26a. $\begin{bmatrix} 0 & -1 & -3 \\ 3 & 1 & 1 \end{bmatrix}$

b. $\begin{bmatrix} -1 & 0 \\ 0 & -1 \end{bmatrix}\begin{bmatrix} 0 & -1 & -3 \\ 3 & 1 & 1 \end{bmatrix} =$

$\begin{bmatrix} 0 & 1 & 3 \\ -3 & -1 & -1 \end{bmatrix}$

c. The triangle is a rotation about the origin.

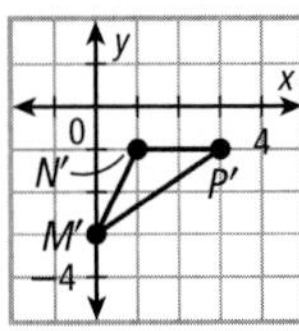

d. $\begin{bmatrix} -1 & 0 \\ 0 & -1 \end{bmatrix}\begin{bmatrix} 0 & 1 & 3 \\ -3 & -1 & -1 \end{bmatrix} =$

$\begin{bmatrix} 0 & -1 & -3 \\ 3 & 1 & 1 \end{bmatrix}$

The triangle is the same as the original.

31. Possible answer: $J(-2, 0)$, $K(0, 2)$, $L(4, 0)$

a. Rotate $\triangle JKL$ by 90° three times either clockwise or counterclockwise.

b. $N(0, 4)$, $E(4, 0)$, $S(0, -4)$, $W(-4, 0)$

32. Possible answer: $\triangle ABC$ has vertices $A(0, 0)$, $B(0, 3)$, and $C(6, 0)$; $\triangle A'B'C'$ has vertices $A'(0, 0)$, $B'\left(0, \frac{9}{2}\right)$, and $C'(-4, 0)$.
The image is a 90° counterclockwise rotation. In addition, one dimension of the figure is enlarged and one dimension is reduced. If the transformation is repeated, the rotated images will become longer and narrower.

4A *Multi-Step Test Prep*

1. $\begin{bmatrix} 0 & 0 & 1 & 3 & 5 \\ 0 & 2 & 1 & 1 & 0 \end{bmatrix}$

2. a vertical shift up 4 units;
$\begin{bmatrix} 0 & 0 & 1 & 3 & 5 \\ 0 & 2 & 1 & 1 & 0 \end{bmatrix} + \begin{bmatrix} 0 & 0 & 0 & 0 & 0 \\ 4 & 4 & 4 & 4 & 4 \end{bmatrix} = \begin{bmatrix} 0 & 0 & 1 & 3 & 5 \\ 4 & 6 & 5 & 5 & 4 \end{bmatrix}$

3. a reflection across the y-axis;
$\begin{bmatrix} -1 & 0 \\ 0 & 1 \end{bmatrix}$
$\begin{bmatrix} 0 & 0 & 1 & 3 & 5 \\ 0 & 2 & 1 & 1 & 0 \end{bmatrix} = \begin{bmatrix} 0 & 0 & -1 & -3 & -5 \\ 0 & 2 & 1 & 1 & 0 \end{bmatrix}$

4. a reflection across the x-axis;
$\begin{bmatrix} 1 & 0 \\ 0 & -1 \end{bmatrix}$
$\begin{bmatrix} 0 & 0 & 1 & 3 & 5 \\ 0 & 2 & 1 & 1 & 0 \end{bmatrix} = \begin{bmatrix} 0 & 0 & 1 & 3 & 5 \\ 0 & -2 & -1 & -1 & 0 \end{bmatrix}$

5. a reflection about the origin;
$\begin{bmatrix} -1 & 0 \\ 0 & -1 \end{bmatrix}$
$\begin{bmatrix} 0 & 0 & 1 & 3 & 5 \\ 0 & 2 & 1 & 1 & 0 \end{bmatrix} = \begin{bmatrix} 0 & 0 & -1 & -3 & -5 \\ 0 & -2 & -1 & -1 & 0 \end{bmatrix}$

6. The transformations are equivalent.

7. Multiplication by the scalar $\frac{1}{2}$; the ratio of the areas will be $\frac{1}{2}$.

4A *Ready To Go On?*

1. $M = \begin{bmatrix} 1.25 & 1.25 & 1 \\ 7.5 & 7.5 & 90 \\ 19.65 & 18.30 & 18.45 \end{bmatrix}$

3. 18.30; hours of handicrafting to make a silver medal

17. $W'(-1, -2)$, $X'(0, 2)$, $Y'(2, 3)$, $Z'(3, 0)$

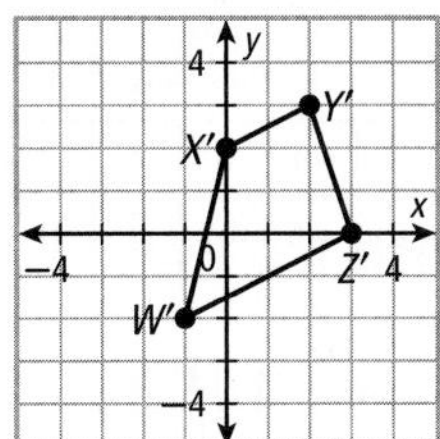

18. $W'(0, 0)$, $X'\left(\frac{2}{3}, 2\frac{2}{3}\right)$, $Y'\left(2, 3\frac{1}{3}\right)$, $Z'\left(2\frac{2}{3}, 1\frac{1}{3}\right)$

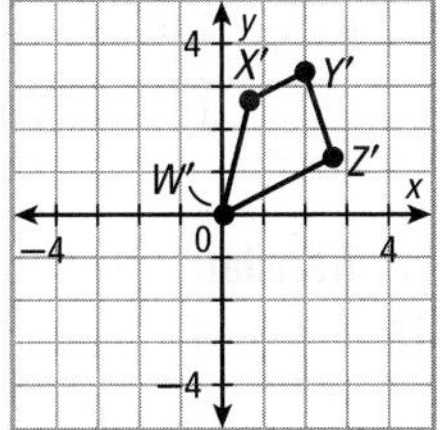

19. $W'(0, 0)$, $X'(1, -4)$, $Y'(3, -5)$, $Z'(4, -2)$

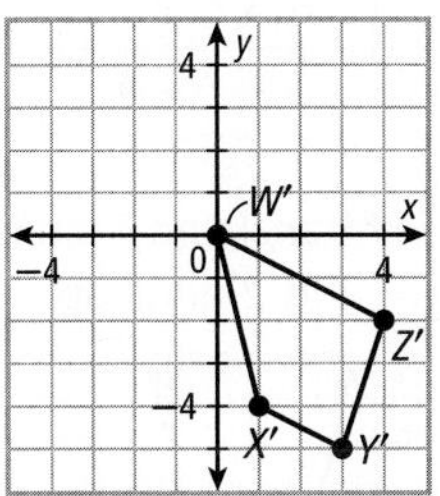

The polygon is reflected across the x-axis.

20. $W'(0, 0)$, $X'(4, -1)$, $Y'(5, -3)$, $Z'(2, -4)$

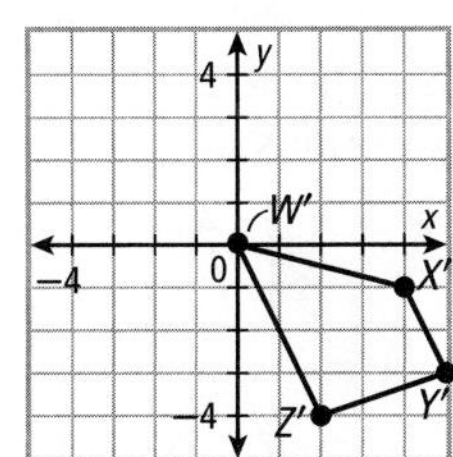

The polygon is rotated 90° clockwise.

4-6 *Exercises*

27a. Possible answer:

$$\begin{cases} 319x + 204y + 116z = 1481 \\ 253x + 233y + 128z = 1353 \\ 95x + 132y + 161z = 710 \end{cases}$$

b. $\left[\begin{array}{ccc|c} 319 & 204 & 116 & 1481 \\ 253 & 233 & 128 & 1353 \\ 95 & 132 & 161 & 710 \end{array}\right]$; $\left[\begin{array}{ccc|c} 1 & 0 & 0 & 3 \\ 0 & 1 & 0 & 2 \\ 0 & 0 & 1 & 1 \end{array}\right]$;
a first-place vote is worth 3 points, a second-place vote is worth 2 points, and a third-place vote is worth 1 point.

28. A coefficient matrix is a square matrix that includes the coefficients of variables in a system of equations. An augmented matrix is a nonsquare matrix that includes the constant terms for each equation in a system.

32. A dependent system has a row of all 0's, an inconsistent system has a row with all 0's but the constant.

38. Possible answer:
$\left[\begin{array}{ccc|c} 1 & 1 & 1 & 10 \\ 2 & -1 & 1 & 2 \\ -1 & 2 & -1 & 5 \end{array}\right]$;
the best first step is to switch the first two rows. Then the second and third rows can be added to yield a row that means $0 + 3y + 0 = 15$. This equation includes only one variable, so it is easy to solve.

4B *Multi-Step Test Prep*

2. The Mombo Combo costs a total of \$29.00, \$5.00 admission plus \$24.00 for tickets. Possible answer: The Mombo Combo is the better buy for Travis, who spent a total of \$31.00, and Kaitlyn, who spent a total of \$29.50. The Pick-ur-Tix is a better buy for Karsyn, who spent a total of \$25.50.

3. No; possible answer: the coefficient matrix has 3 rows and 4 columns. It is not square and does not have an inverse.

4B *Ready To Go On?*

8. $\begin{bmatrix} -\frac{1}{10} & \frac{2}{5} \\ \frac{3}{10} & -\frac{1}{5} \end{bmatrix}$

10. $\begin{bmatrix} \frac{1}{3} & \frac{1}{3} & -\frac{1}{3} \\ \frac{1}{2} & -\frac{1}{2} & 1 \\ \frac{1}{6} & \frac{1}{6} & \frac{1}{3} \end{bmatrix}$

11. $\begin{bmatrix} 2 & -1 \\ 1 & -1 \end{bmatrix} \begin{bmatrix} x \\ y \end{bmatrix} = \begin{bmatrix} 1.5 \\ -0.5 \end{bmatrix}$;
(2, 2.5)

12. $\begin{bmatrix} 10 & 8 \\ 15 & 12 \end{bmatrix} \begin{bmatrix} x \\ y \end{bmatrix} = \begin{bmatrix} 13 \\ 8 \end{bmatrix}$;
no solution

13. $\begin{bmatrix} 5 & 7 & -3 \\ 3 & 4 & 2 \\ 1 & 3 & -5 \end{bmatrix} \begin{bmatrix} x \\ y \\ z \end{bmatrix} = \begin{bmatrix} 3 \\ 6 \\ -7 \end{bmatrix}$;
(4, −2, 1)

14. $\begin{bmatrix} 2 & 1 & 3 \\ 1 & 3 & 2 \\ 3 & 2 & 1 \end{bmatrix} \begin{bmatrix} x \\ y \\ z \end{bmatrix} = \begin{bmatrix} 23{,}650 \\ 20{,}450 \\ 24{,}600 \end{bmatrix}$;
climbing wall \$5200; combination slide \$2750; adventure maze \$3500

15. $\left[\begin{array}{cc|c} 2 & 5 & 5 \\ 50 & -30 & 1 \end{array}\right]$; $\left(\frac{1}{2}, \frac{4}{5}\right)$

16. $\left[\begin{array}{cc|c} 5 & -4 & 6 \\ 10 & -8 & 12 \end{array}\right]$; the system is dependent.

17. $\left[\begin{array}{cc|c} 6 & 5 & -8 \\ 1 & -1 & \frac{1}{2} \end{array}\right]$;
$\left(-\frac{1}{2}, -1\right)$,

Extension

2b. $\begin{bmatrix} 2 & 1 & 1 & 1 & 2 & 1 \\ 1 & 0 & 1 & 1 & 0 & 0 \\ 1 & 0 & 2 & 0 & 0 & 1 \\ 1 & 0 & 0 & 1 & 0 & 0 \\ 0 & 1 & 0 & 0 & 2 & 0 \\ 0 & 0 & 1 & 1 & 0 & 2 \end{bmatrix}$; 1

c. $\begin{bmatrix} 3 & 1 & 4 & 2 & 2 & 4 \\ 2 & 0 & 2 & 1 & 0 & 1 \\ 3 & 1 & 1 & 2 & 2 & 1 \\ 1 & 0 & 2 & 0 & 0 & 1 \\ 0 & 0 & 1 & 1 & 0 & 2 \\ 1 & 2 & 1 & 1 & 4 & 0 \end{bmatrix}$; 4

5. For vertex *A*, one 1-step roundtrip is possible. For vertices *A*, *C*, *D*, *E*, and *F*, at least one 2-step roundtrip is possible. For vertices *A* and *C*, at least one 3-step roundtrip is possible. Look at the main diagonal (from upper left to lower right) of the matrix. A nonzero entry on the main diagonal of an adjacency matrix shows that a roundtrip is possible.

7. Possible answer: Make a square *n* x *n* matrix where *n* is equal to the number of network vertices. Each row represents a starting vertex, and each column represents an ending vertex. Each entry in the matrix represents the number of paths from the starting vertex to the ending vertex.

8. An entry in the cube of an adjacency matrix shows the number of 3-step paths from the row vertex to the column vertex. A zero entry shows that no 3-step path exists from the row vertex to the column vertex.

10. Possible answer:

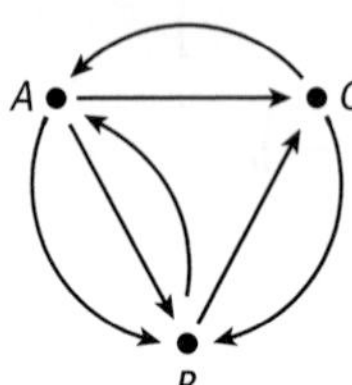

11. Possible answer:

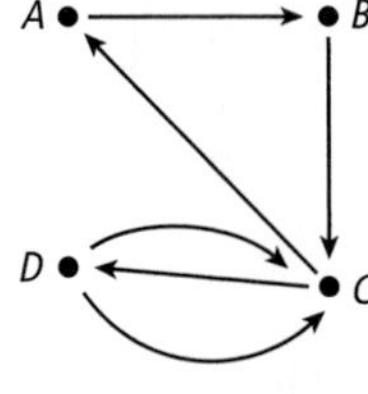

12. Possible answer:

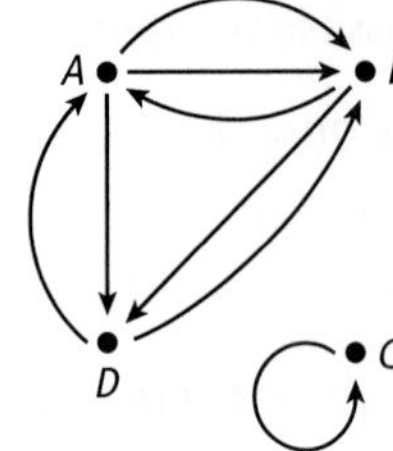

Chapter 4 Test

25. $\begin{bmatrix} 6 & 1 \\ 3 & -2 \end{bmatrix}\begin{bmatrix} x \\ y \end{bmatrix} = \begin{bmatrix} 2 \\ -1 \end{bmatrix}$; $\left(\frac{1}{5}, \frac{4}{5}\right)$

26. $\begin{bmatrix} 5 & -2 \\ 2.5 & -1 \end{bmatrix}\begin{bmatrix} x \\ y \end{bmatrix} = \begin{bmatrix} 3 \\ 1.5 \end{bmatrix}$; infinitely many solutions

27. $\begin{bmatrix} 1 & 2 \\ 3 & -1 \end{bmatrix}\begin{bmatrix} x \\ y \end{bmatrix} = \begin{bmatrix} 3.5 \\ 2.7 \end{bmatrix}$; $(\approx 1.27, \approx 1.11)$

28. $\begin{bmatrix} 2 & -1 & -1 \\ 1 & -1 & 0 \\ 1 & 1 & 4 \end{bmatrix}\begin{bmatrix} x \\ y \\ z \end{bmatrix} = \begin{bmatrix} 3 \\ 3 \\ 1 \end{bmatrix}$; $\left(\frac{2}{3}, -\frac{7}{3}, \frac{2}{3}\right)$

29. $\begin{bmatrix} 5 & 1 & 2 \\ 3 & 5 & 1 \\ 3 & 1 & 4 \end{bmatrix}\begin{bmatrix} x \\ y \\ z \end{bmatrix} = \begin{bmatrix} 41 \\ 42 \\ 29 \end{bmatrix}$; 7 points; 4 points; 1 point

Chapter 5

5A Are You Ready?

21.

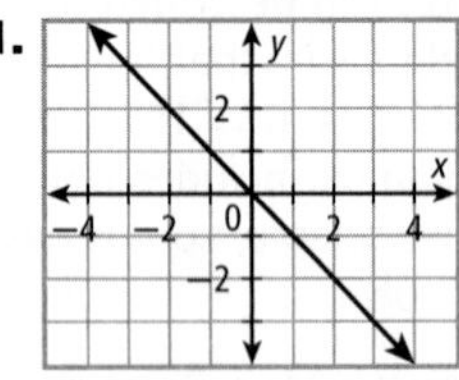

22.

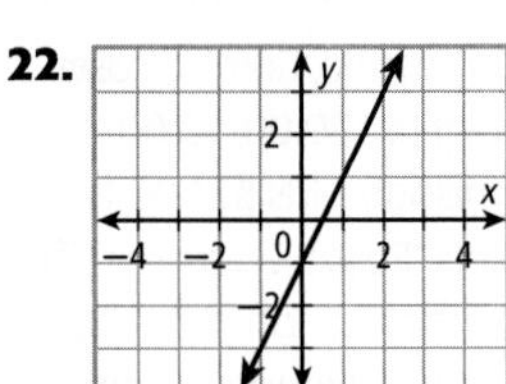

23.

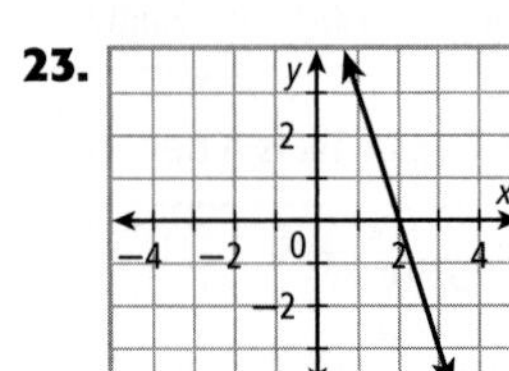

24.

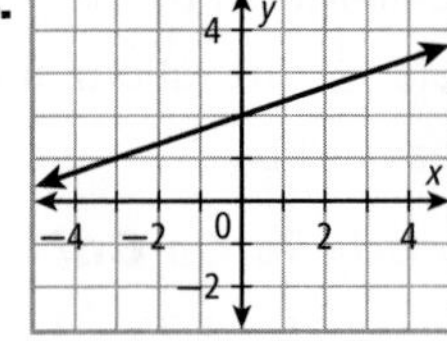

5-1 Exercises

3.

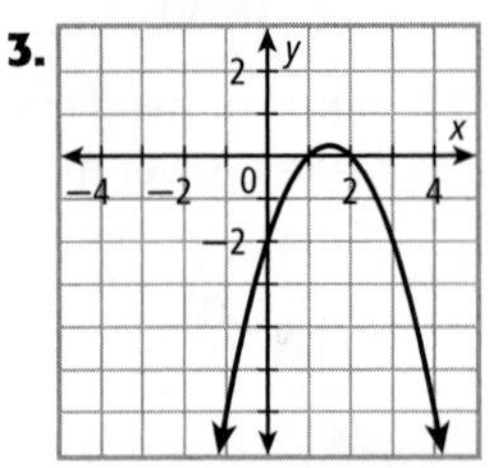

x	−1	0	1	2	3
$g(x)$	−6	−2	0	0	−2

4.

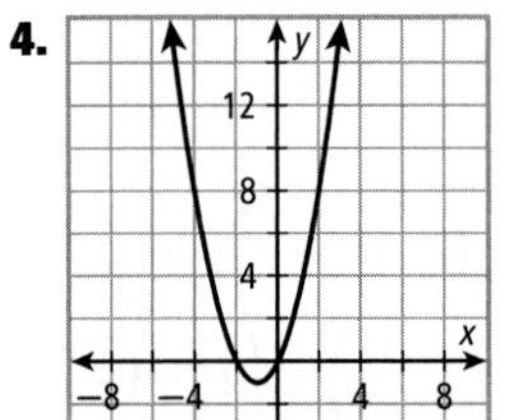

x	−2	−1	0	1	2
$h(x)$	0	−1	0	3	8

5. *d* is *f* translated 4 units right.

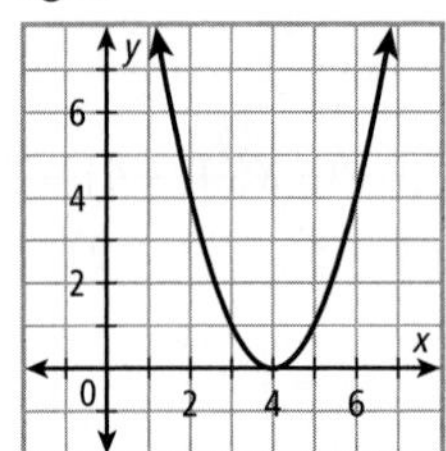

6. *g* is *f* translated 3 units right and 2 units up.

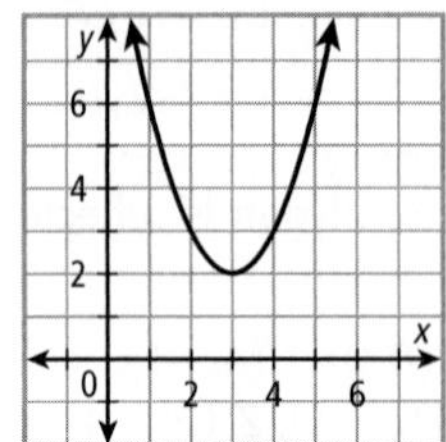

7. *h* is *f* translated 1 unit left and 3 units down.

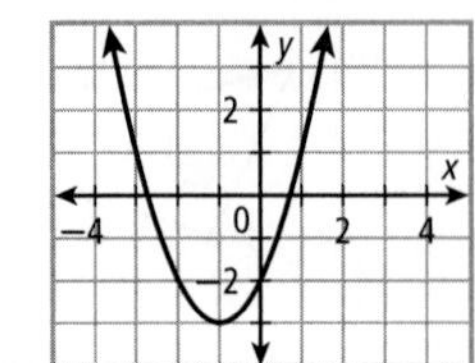

8. *g* is a vertical stretch of *f* by a factor of 3.

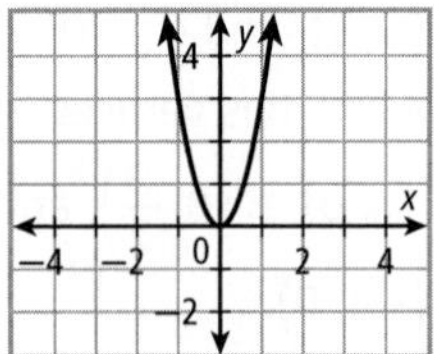

9. *h* is a horizontal stretch of *f* by a factor of 8.

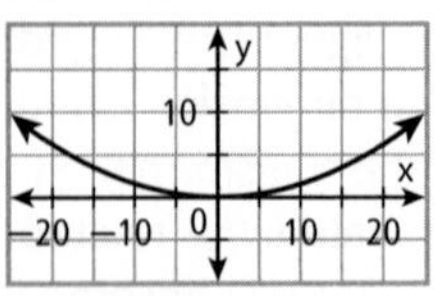

10. *p* is a vertical compression of *f* by a factor of 0.25.

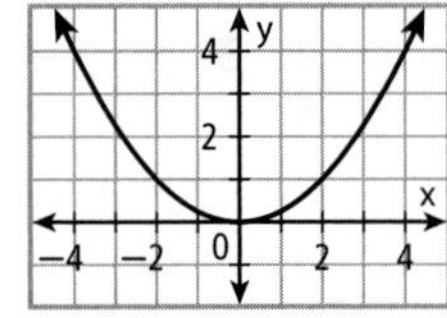

11. *h* is *f* reflected across the *x*-axis and horizontally compressed by a factor of $\frac{1}{5}$.

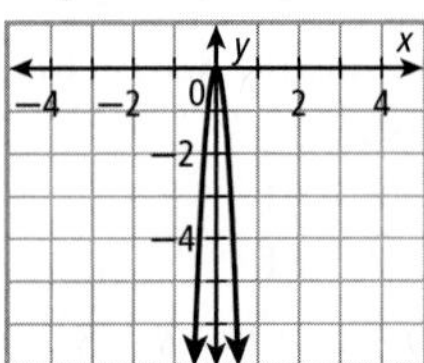

12. *g* is a vertical stretch of *f* by a factor of 4.2.

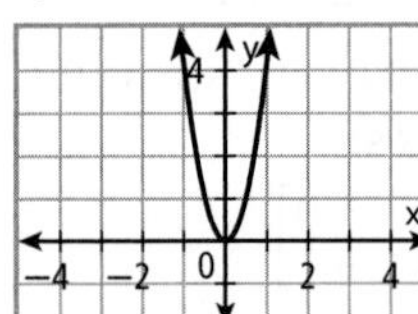

13. *d* is *f* reflected across the *x*-axis and vertically compressed by a factor of $\frac{2}{3}$.

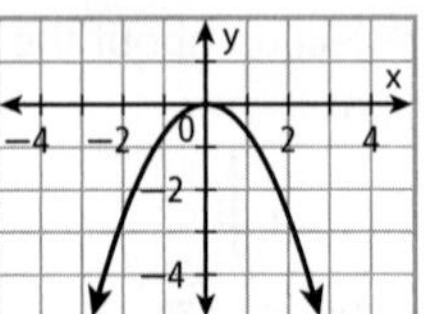

17.

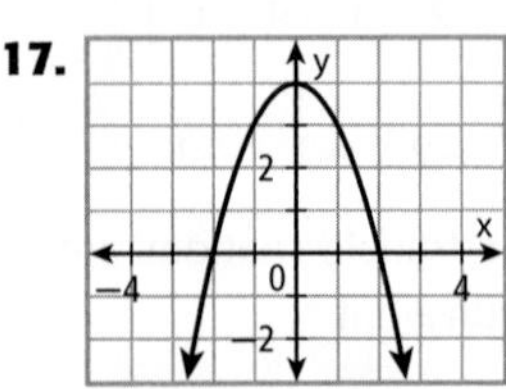

x	−2	−1	0	1	2
$f(x)$	0	3	4	3	0

18.

x	−2	−1	0	1	2
$g(x)$	9	4	1	0	1

19.

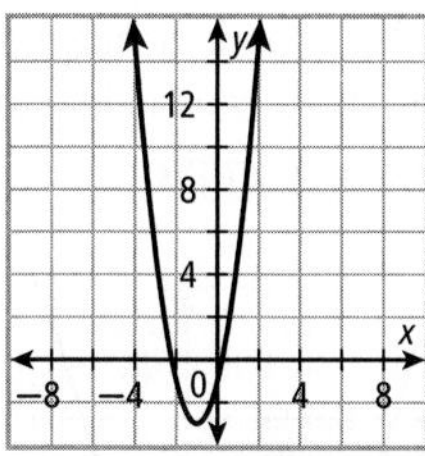

x	−2	−1	0	1	2
$h(x)$	−1	−3	−1	5	15

20. g is f translated 2 units down.

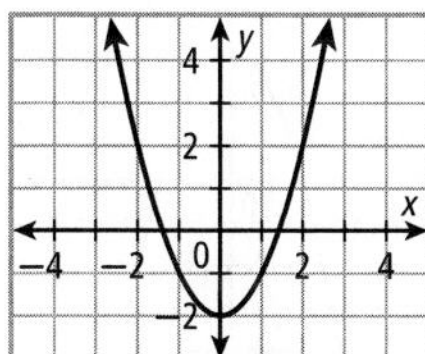

21. h is f translated 5 units left.

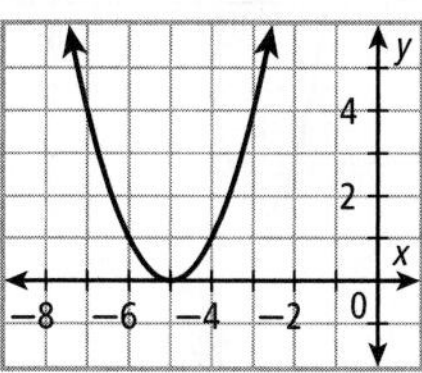

22. j is f translated 1 unit right.

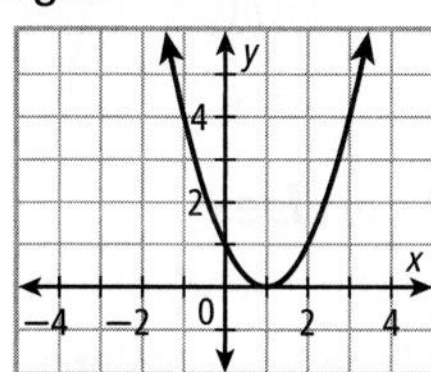

23. g is f translated 4 units left and 3 units down.

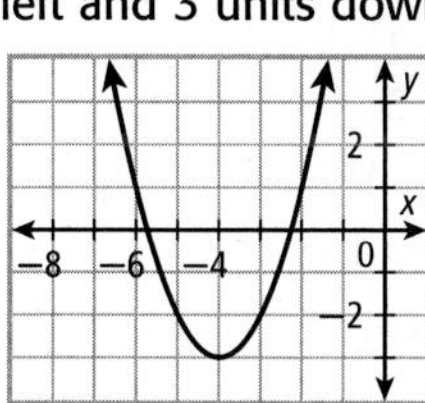

24. h is f translated 2 units left and 2 units up.

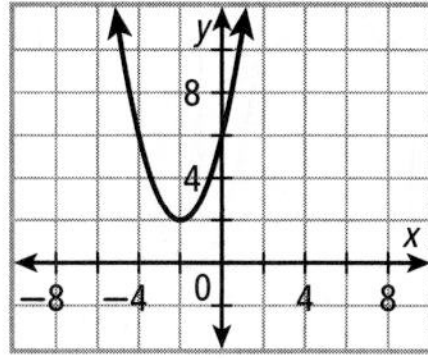

25. j is f translated 4 units right and 9 units down.

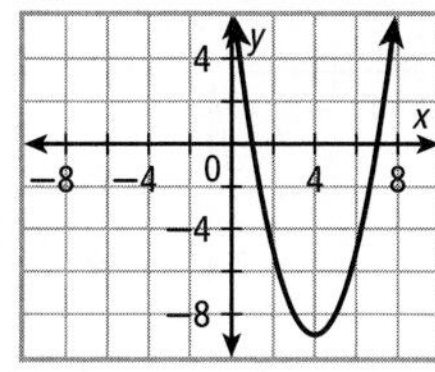

26. g is a vertical compression of f by a factor of $\frac{4}{7}$.

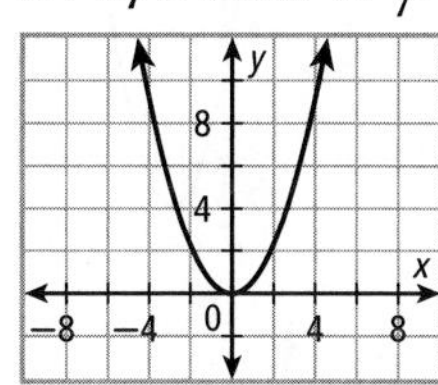

27. h is f reflected across the x-axis and vertically stretched by a factor of 20.

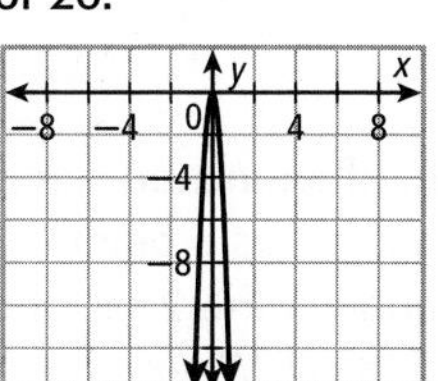

37. g is f horizontally compressed by a factor of $\frac{1}{3}$ and translated 1 unit up.

38. h is f reflected across the x-axis and horizontally stretched by a factor of 3.

42a. $B(r) = 25 - \pi r^2$

b. B is A reflected across the x-axis and translated 25 units up.

c. A: D: $\{r \mid 0 \leq r \leq 2.5\}$; R: $\{A \mid 0 \leq A \leq 6.25\pi\}$; B: D: $\{r \mid 0 \leq r \leq 2.5\}$; R: $\{B \mid (25 - 6.25\pi) \leq B \leq 25\}$; possible answer: the radius of the circle cannot be less than 0 or greater than half the side length of the square.

43. horizontal line; linear or constant function

45a. vertical compression by a factor of 0.38 and translation 2.5 units right and 59 units up

b. $y = -6.08(t - 4)^2 + 95$

5-2 *Exercises*

5e.

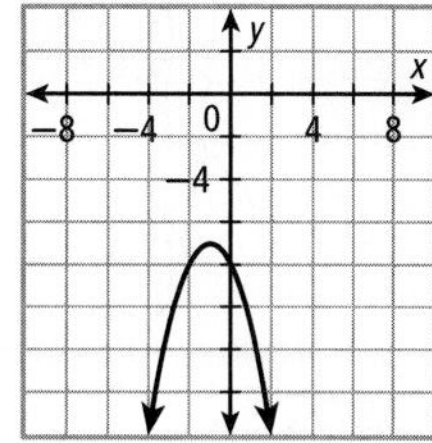

6e.

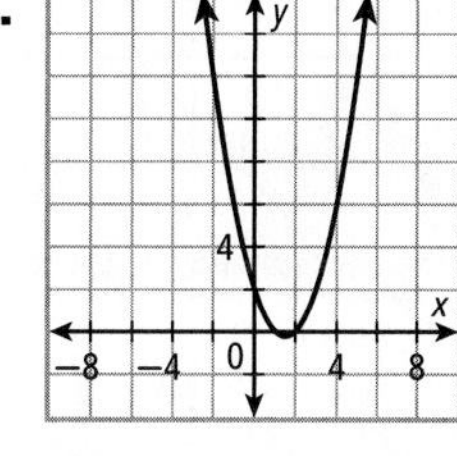

7e.

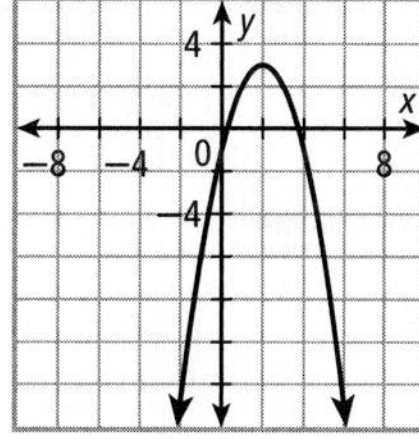

15e.

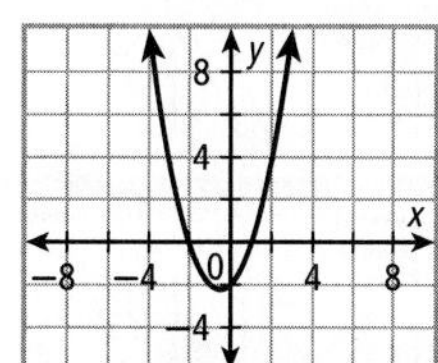

16e.

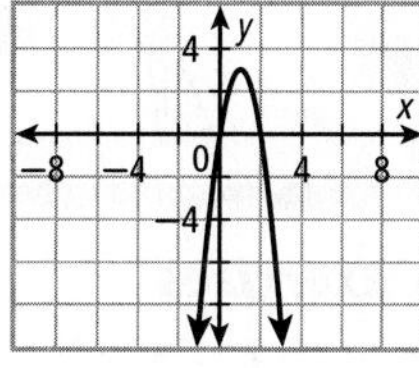

17e.

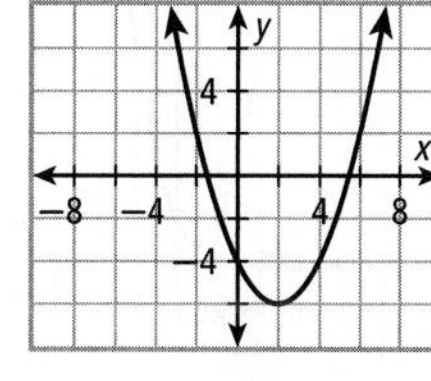

18e.

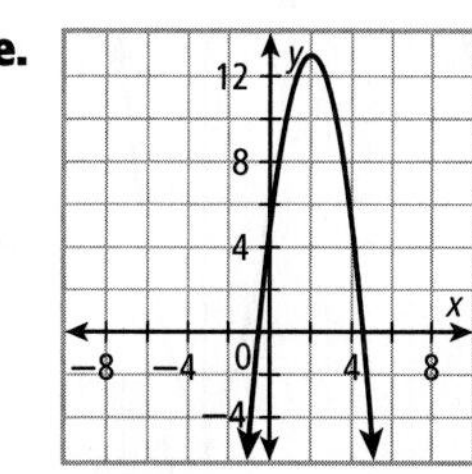

19a. upward

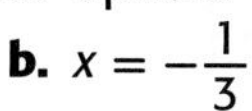

b. $x = -\frac{1}{3}$

c. $\left(-\frac{1}{3}, -\frac{25}{3}\right)$

d. −8

e.

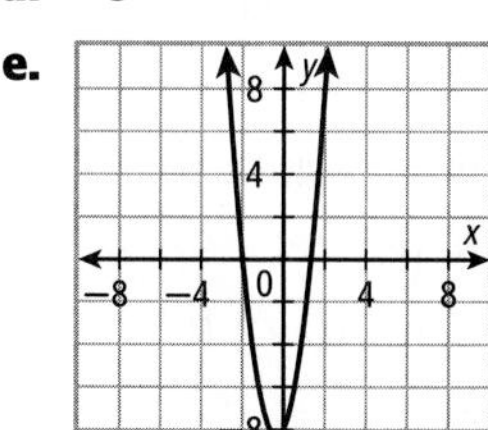

20a. upward

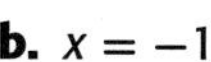

b. $x = -1$

c. $(-1, -2)$

d. −1

e.

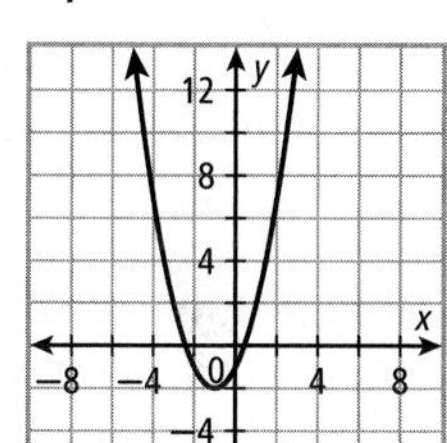

21a. downward

b. $x = 0$

c. $(0, -2)$

d. −2

e.

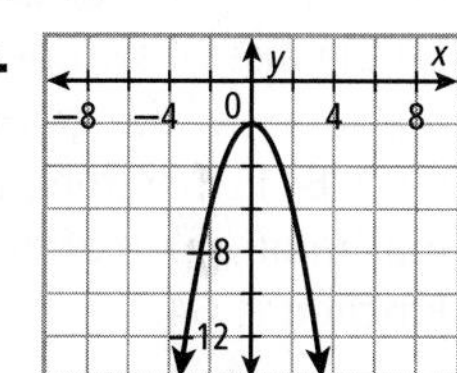

22a. upward

b. $x = -3$

c. $(-3, -9.5)$

d. −5

e.

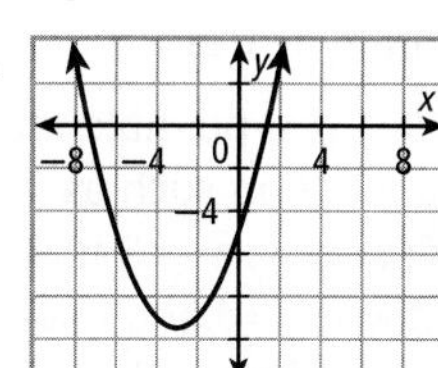

23a. upward

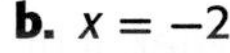

b. $x = -2$

c. $(-2, 1)$

d. 2

e.

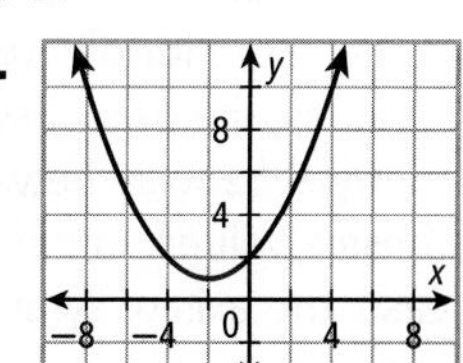

Additional Answers

24. max.: 3.125; D: $\mathbb{R}$; R: $\{y \mid y \leq 3.125\}$

25. max.: 9; D: $\mathbb{R}$; R: $\{y \mid y \leq 9\}$

26. min.: −1; D: $\mathbb{R}$; R: $\{y \mid y \geq -1\}$

27. max.: −4; D: $\mathbb{R}$; R: $\{y \mid y \leq -4\}$

28. max.: 10; D: $\mathbb{R}$; R: $\{y \mid y \leq 10\}$

29. min.: 0; D: $\mathbb{R}$; R: $\{y \mid y \geq 0\}$

31.

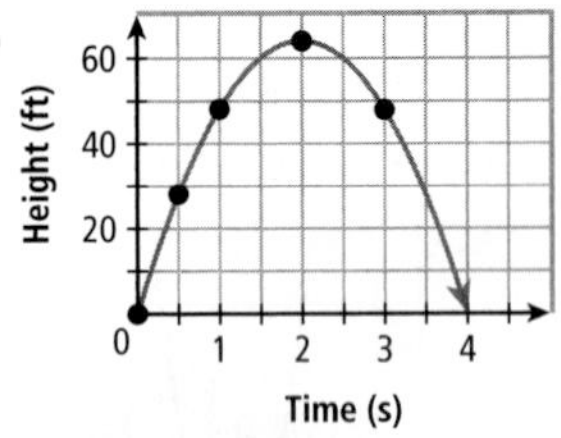

Height (ft)

Time (s)

64 ft; possible answer: the axis of symmetry is halfway between any 2 points with the same y-value. Because the points $(1, 48)$ and $(3, 48)$ have the same y-value, the axis of symmetry is $x = 2$. Because the vertex lies on the axis of symmetry, the vertex of the graph is $(2, 64)$. Therefore, the maximum value of the function is 64.

39. The axis of symmetry is halfway between any 2 points with the same y-value. Halfway between −7 and 3 is −2. Therefore, the axis of symmetry is $x = -2$.

40. Yes; yes; possible answer: a function such as $f(x) = -x^2 - 5$ may open downward and have a vertex below the x-axis. A function such as $f(x) = x^2 + 2$ may open upward and have a vertex above the x-axis.

50. If the value of the function is the same for different x-values, the axis of symmetry is halfway between these x-values. In this case, the axis of symmetry is $x = \frac{1}{2}$.

5-3 *Technology Lab*

2.

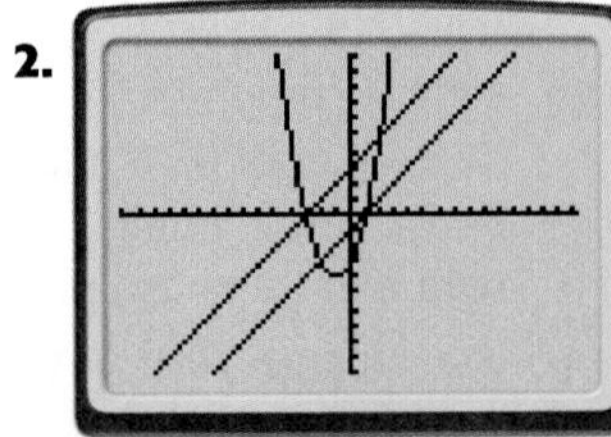

3.

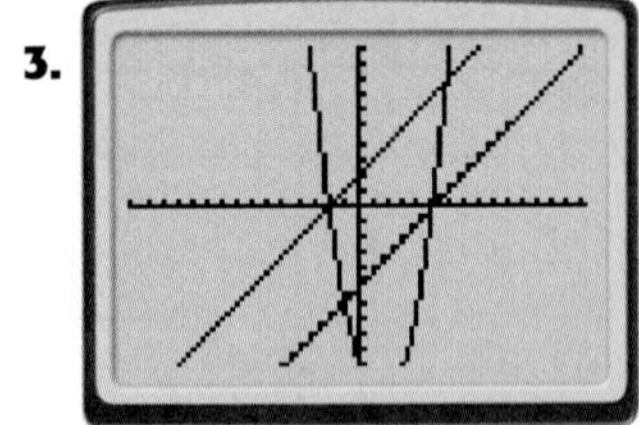

4.

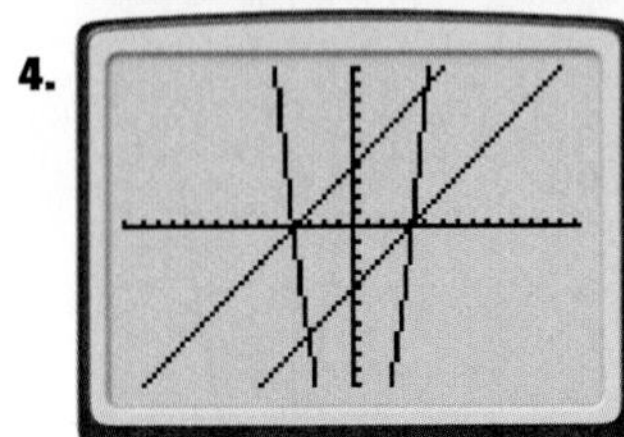

5.

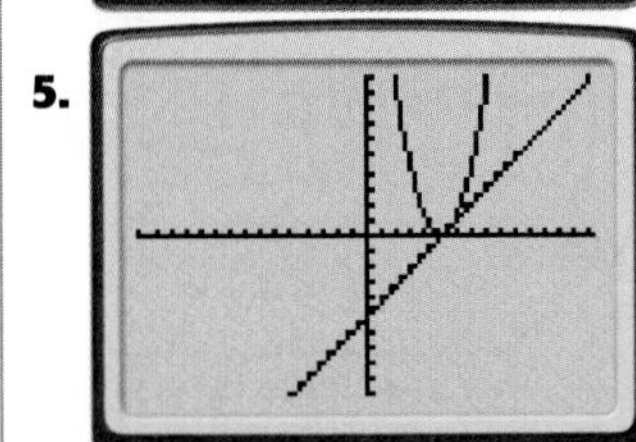

6.

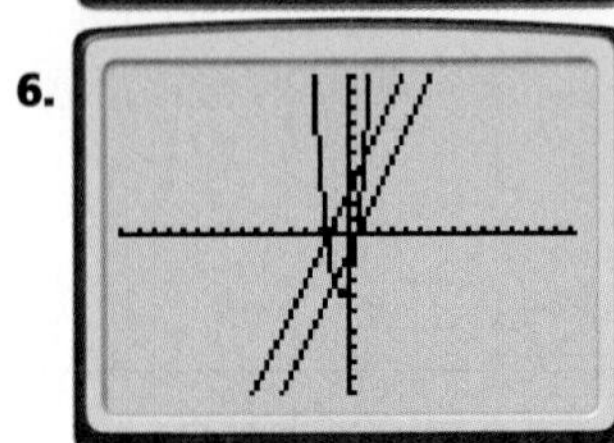

7.

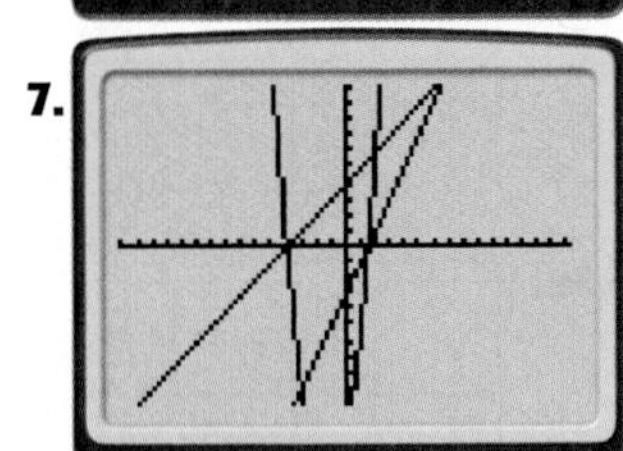

5-3 *Exercises*

54d.

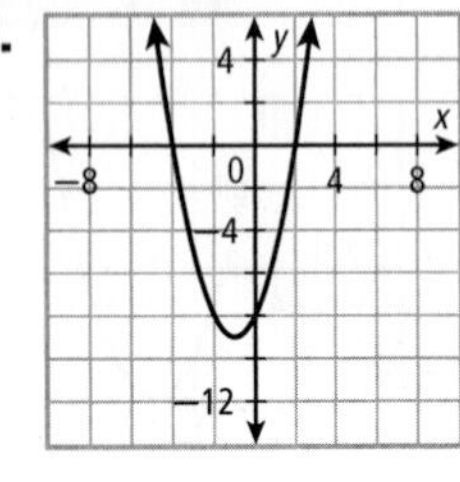

55d.

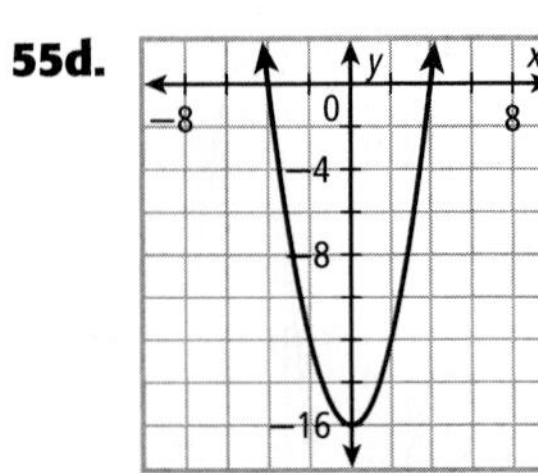

56d.

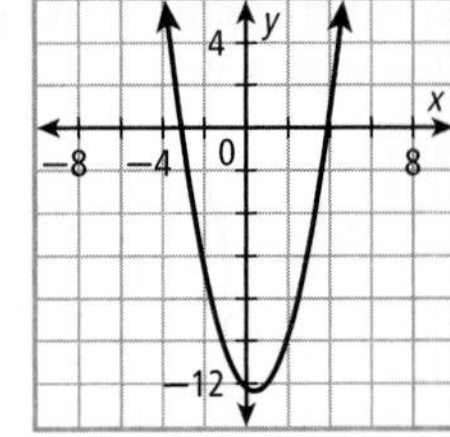

57d.

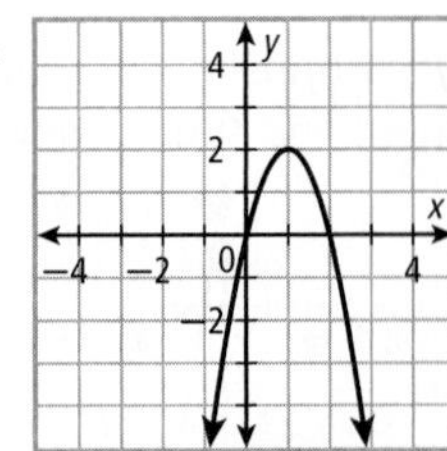

58d.

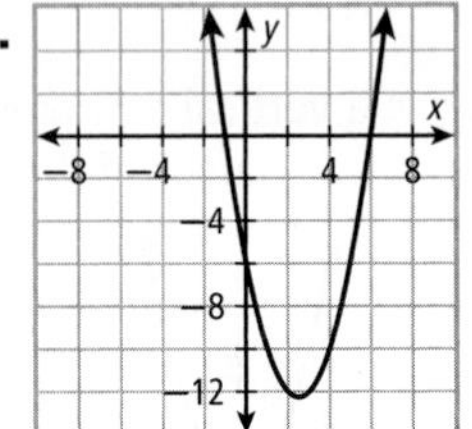

59d.

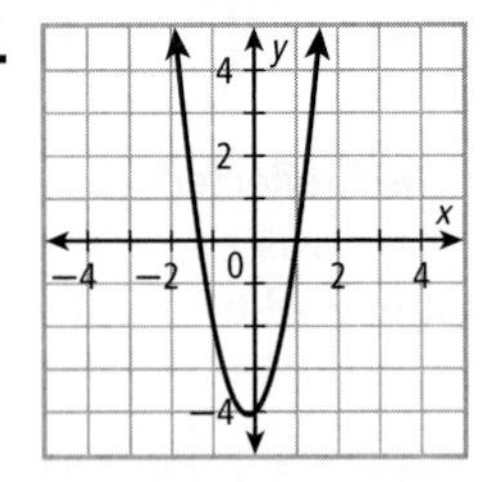

64. No; if a function can be factored as a binomial squared, the 2 factors are identical. When each factor is set equal to 0, each equation will have the same solution. Therefore, the function has only 1 distinct zero.

65. Possible answer: The Zero Product Property states that if a product equals 0, then at least one of the factors must equal 0. The zeros of a function can be found by writing the function rule as a product of factors and setting it equal to 0. You can then determine the value that makes each factor equal to 0. These values are the zeros of the function.

5-5 *Exercises*

83. Possible answer: A quadratic equation can have a single distinct real root. For example, the only distinct root of $(x - 1)^2 = 0$ is $x = 1$. A quadratic equation cannot have a single imaginary root because imaginary roots occur only as conjugate pairs. Because a quadratic equation can have a single distinct real number root and because real numbers are complex, a quadratic equation can have a single distinct complex root.

89e.

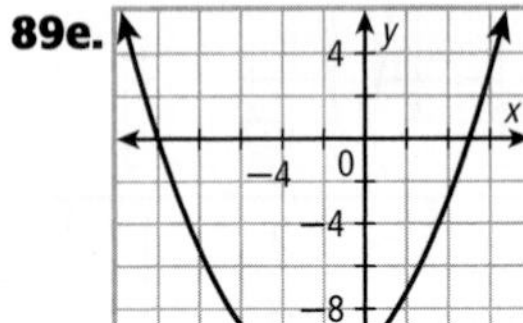

90e.

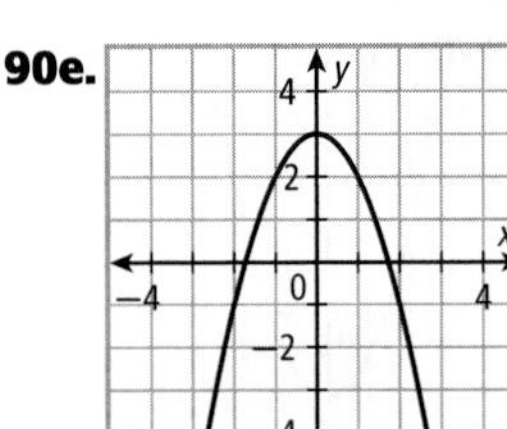

91e.

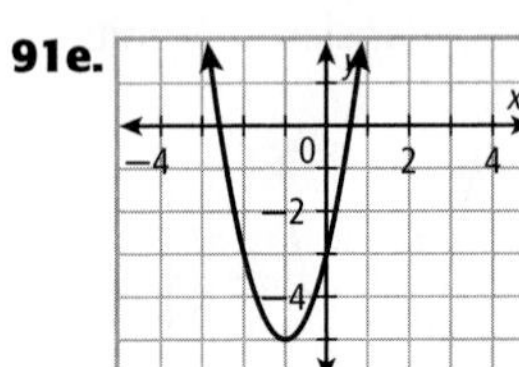

92e.

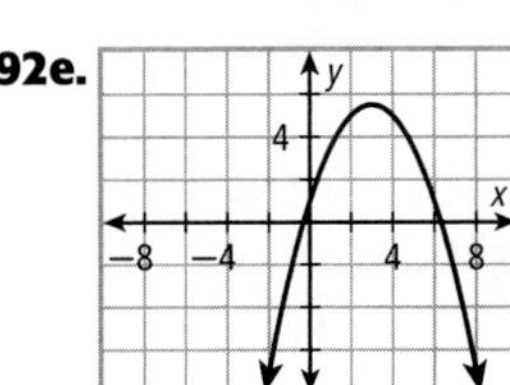

5-6 *Exercises*

14. 1 distinct real solution

15. 2 distinct real solutions

16. 2 distinct nonreal complex solutions

18. $3, \frac{1}{3}$

19. −6, 0

20. −1, 4

21. $-1 \pm \sqrt{10}$

22. $\frac{7 \pm \sqrt{113}}{4}$

23. $\pm\frac{\sqrt{21}}{7}$

Additional Answers

24. $\dfrac{-1 \pm i\sqrt{3}}{2}$

25. $\dfrac{-1 \pm i\sqrt{3}}{2}$

26. $\pm 2i$

27. $\dfrac{-7 \pm 3\sqrt{17}}{4}$

28. $\dfrac{1 \pm \sqrt{21}}{2}$

29. $\dfrac{2 \pm 2i\sqrt{2}}{3}$

30. 2 distinct nonreal complex solutions

31. 2 distinct real solutions

32. 1 distinct real solution

38. 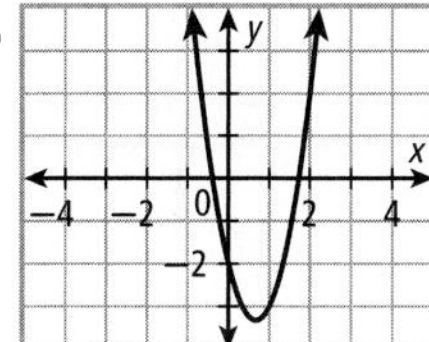

39. 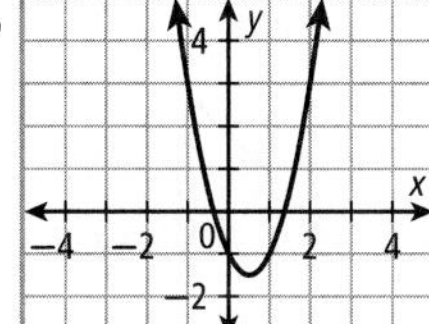

40. 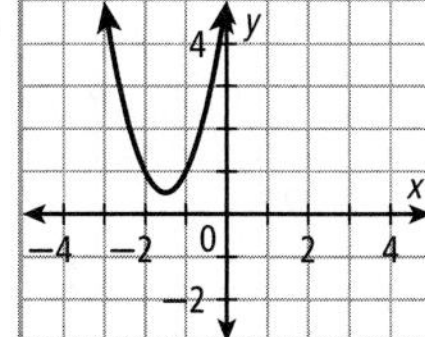

41. 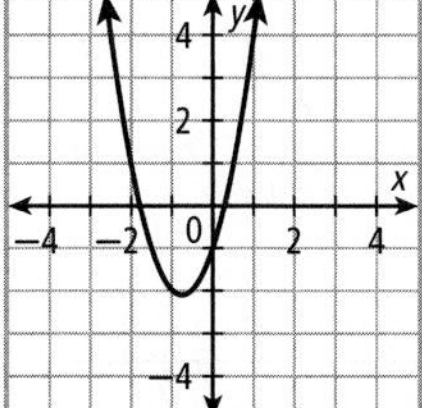

42. 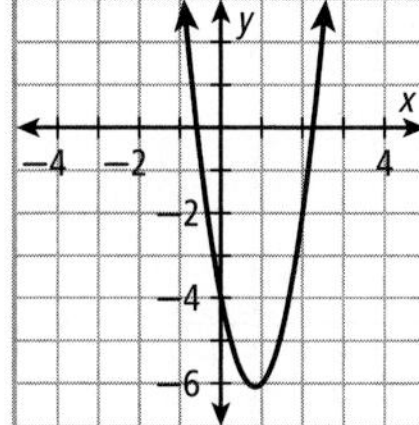

43. 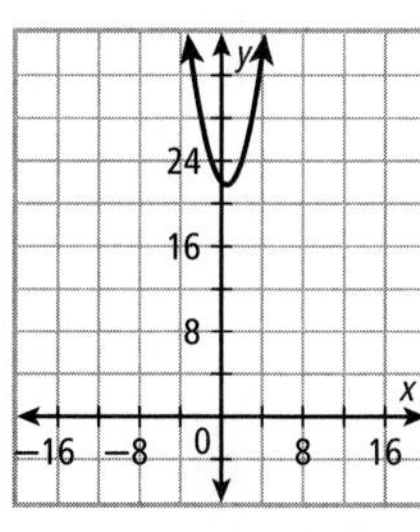

60b. No, the ball will reach third base before the runner. Possible answer: When the ball reaches third base, the runner will have been running for about 2.4 s. The runner will have traveled only about 65 ft in this amount of time.

73. $\left[\begin{array}{cc|c} 2 & -3 & -7 \\ 1 & -6 & 1 \end{array}\right]$;

$x = -5; y = -1$

74. $\left[\begin{array}{cc|c} 2 & 3 & 12 \\ 1 & 1 & 14 \end{array}\right]$;

$x = 30; y = -16$

75. $\left[\begin{array}{cc|c} 4 & 5 & -1 \\ 2 & -7 & 9 \end{array}\right]$;

$x = 1; y = -1$

5A *Multi-Step Test Prep*

5. Yes; possible answer: based on the ball's initial height and vertical velocity, it will reach home plate in about 1.8 s. Because the runner started 3 s before the ball was thrown, he has 4.8 s to reach home plate. However, he only needs 3.6 s, so he will reach home plate well before the ball.

5A *Ready To Go On?*

2. *g* is *f* reflected across the *x*-axis, vertically streched by a factor of 4, and translated 1 unit right.

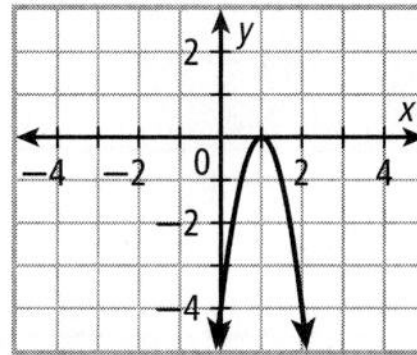

3. *g* is *f* vertically compressed by a factor of $\frac{1}{2}$ and translated 1 unit up.

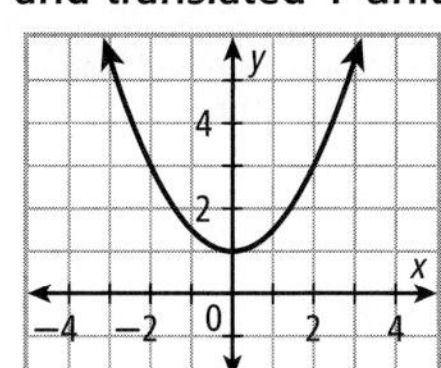

6. upward; $x = 2$; $(2, -1)$; 3

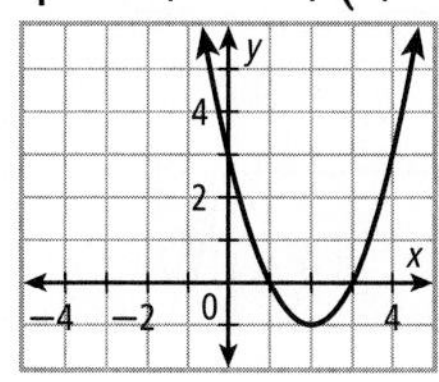

7. downward; $x = 1$; $(1, 0)$; -1

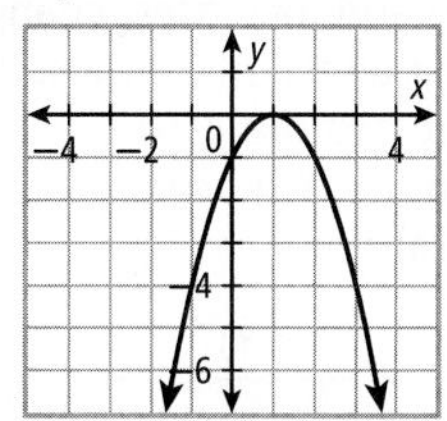

8. upward; $x = 3$; $(3, -9)$; 0

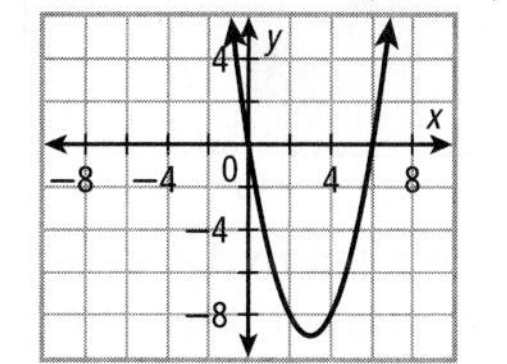

5-7 *Exercises*

2. 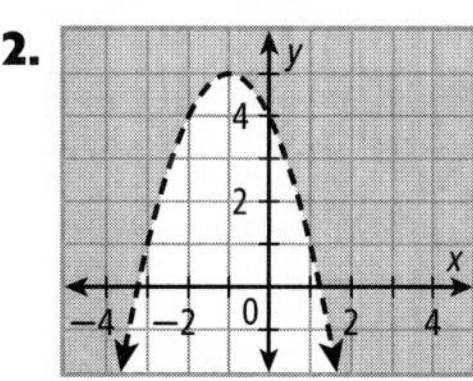

3.

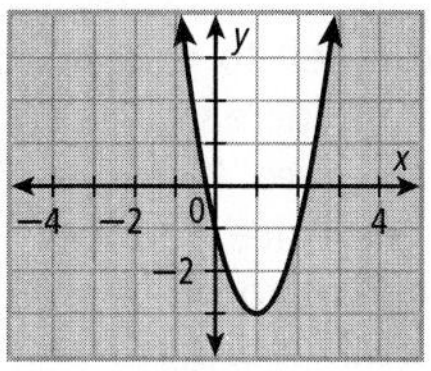

4. 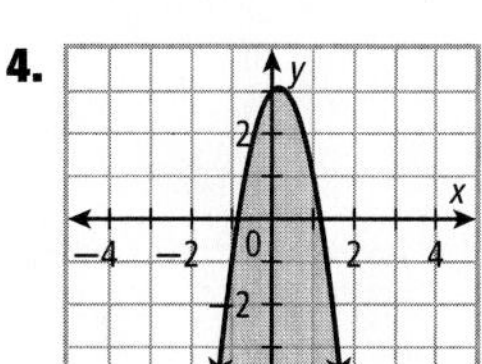

12. 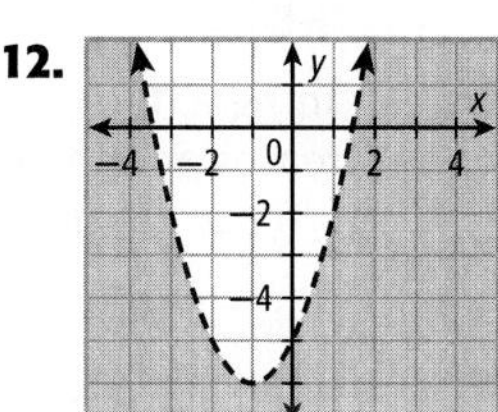

13. 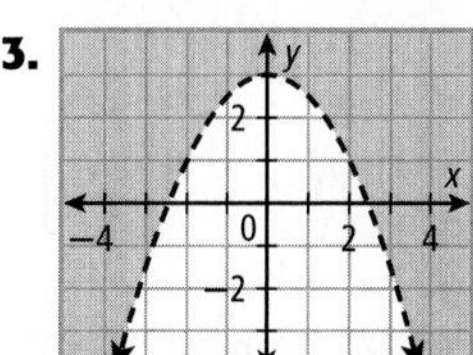

14. 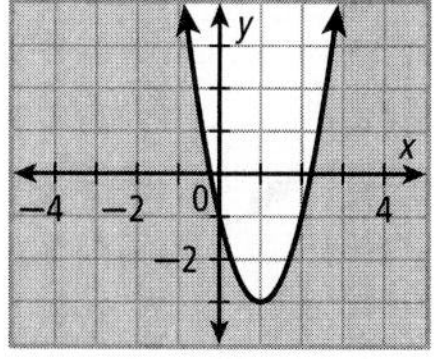

15. 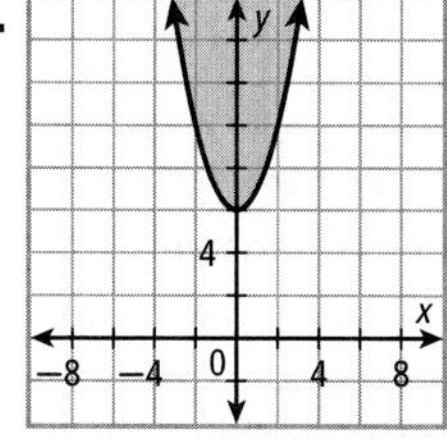

16. 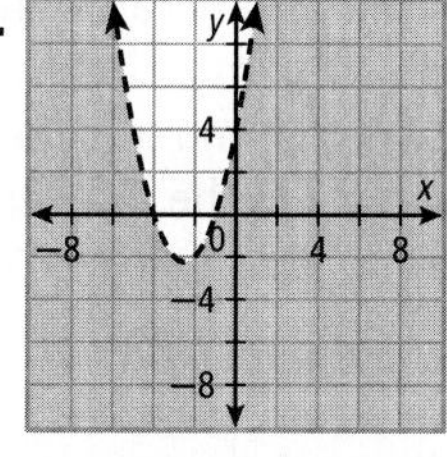

17. 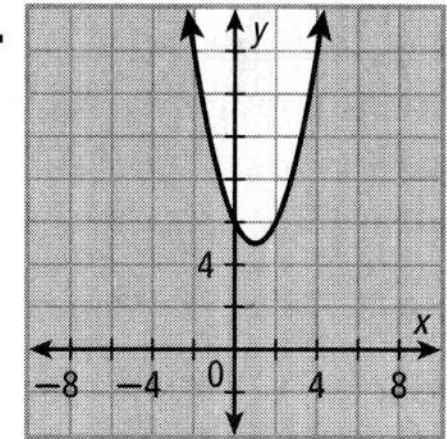

5B *Multi-Step Test Prep*

1.

Area of Tile (cm^2)	*y*
225	0.5625
225	0.5625
240.25	0.600625
240.25	0.600625
256	0.64
256	0.64
289	0.7225
289	0.7225
324	0.81
324	0.81
361	0.9025
361	0.9025
400	1

2. $y \approx 0.005x^2 - 0.1x + 1$; yes; possible answer: the data points lie on or very close to the graph of the quadratic model. In addition, the value of R^2 is very close to 1.

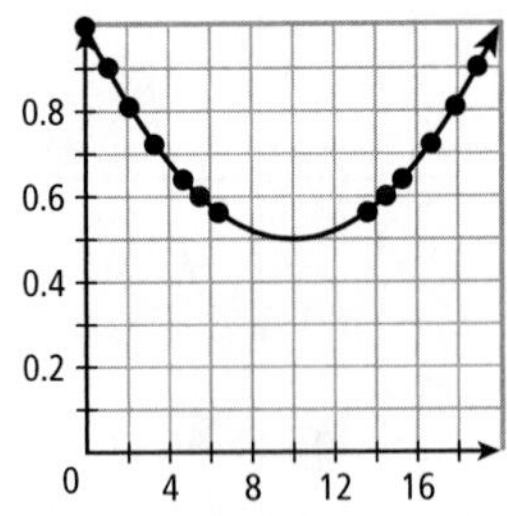

3. D: $\{x \mid 0 < x \leq 20\}$; possible answer: The domain of the model is all real numbers. The domain for the problem situation is restricted because the distance x must be greater than 0 cm and less than or equal to the side length of the grid square.

5B *Ready To Go On?*

2.

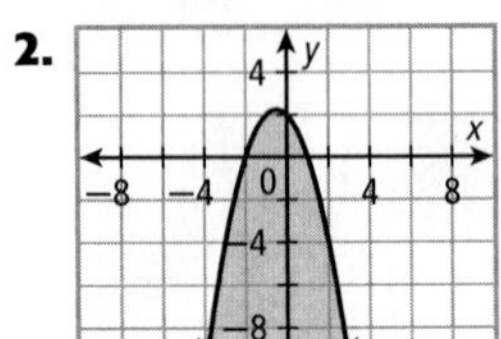

8. Quadratic function; the second differences of the function values are constant for equally spaced x-values.

9. Not a quadratic function; the second differences of the function values are not constant for equally spaced x-values.

Chapter 6

6-1 *Exercises*

15.

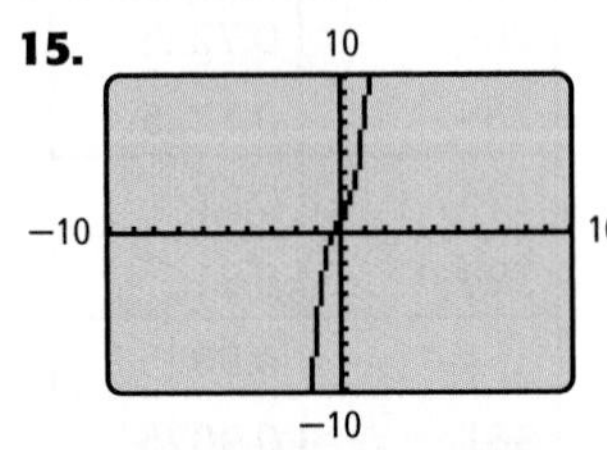

From left to right, the graph increases. It crosses the x-axis once, so there appears to be 1 real zero.

16.

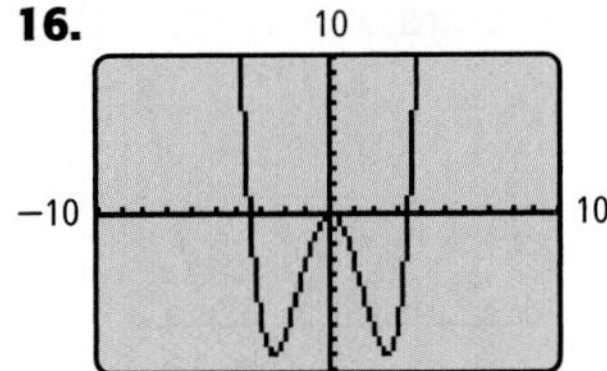

From left to right, the graph alternately decreases and increases, changing direction 3 times. It crosses the x-axis 3 times, so there appear to be 3 real zeros.

17.

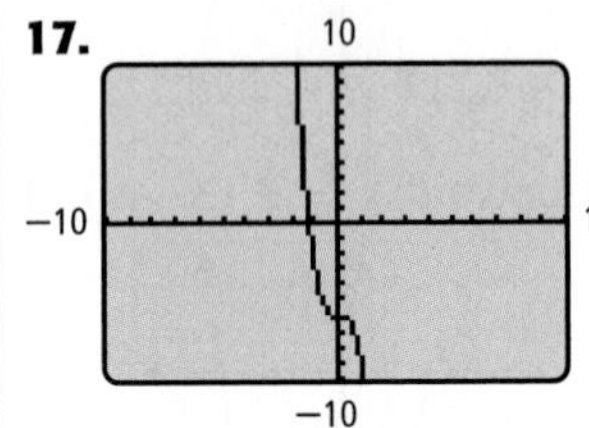

From left to right, the graph decreases. It crosses the x-axis once, so there appears to be 1 real zero.

18.

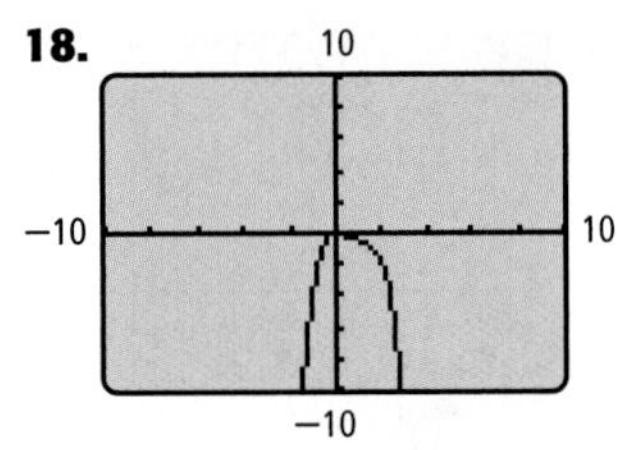

From left to right, the graph increases and then decreases. It crosses the x-axis once, so there appears to be 1 real zero.

32.

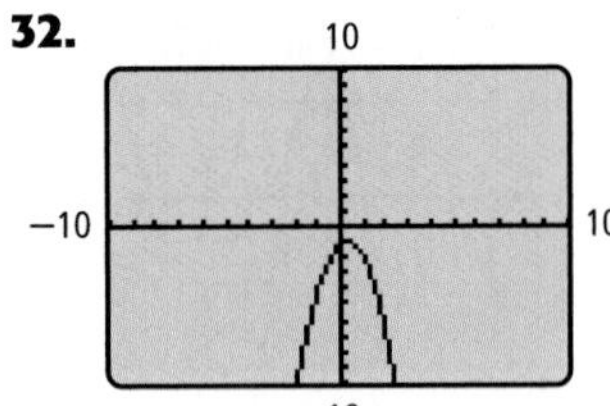

From left to right, the graph increases and then decreases. There are no real zeros.

33.

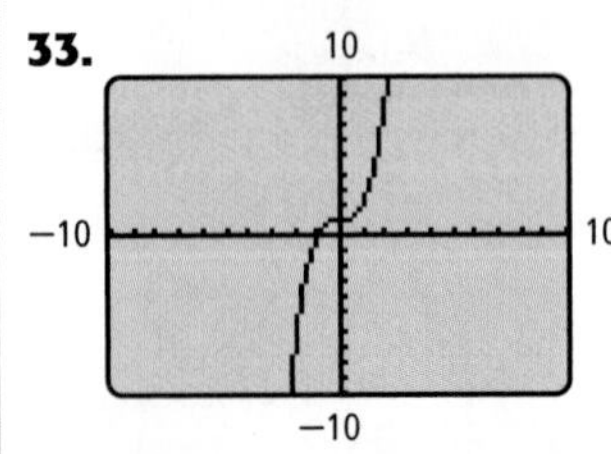

From left to right, the graph increases. There is 1 real zero.

34.

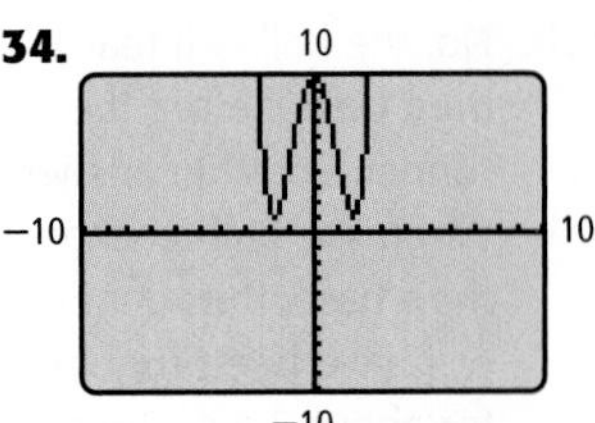

From left to right, the graph decreases, increases, decreases and then increases again. There are no real zeros.

35.

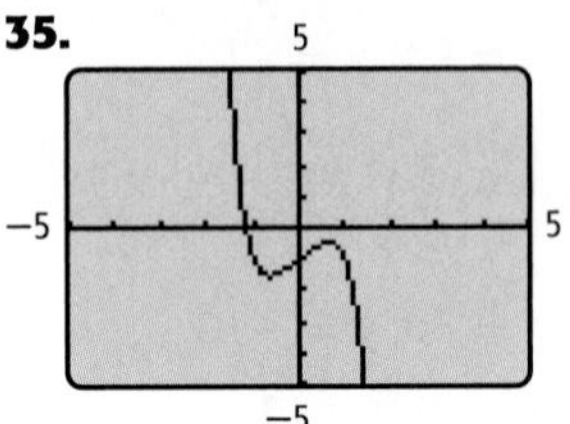

The graph decreases, increases, and then decreases. There is 1 real zero.

51. a.

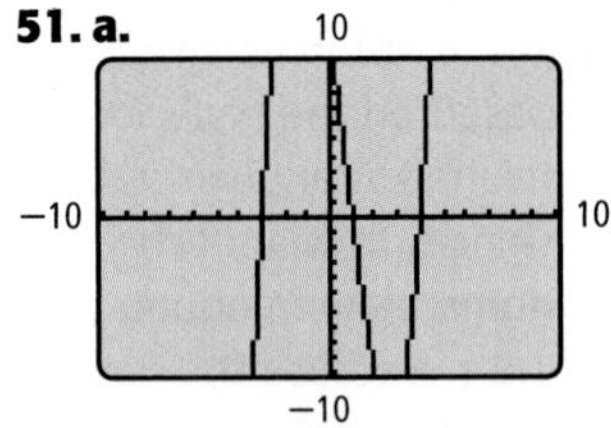

b.

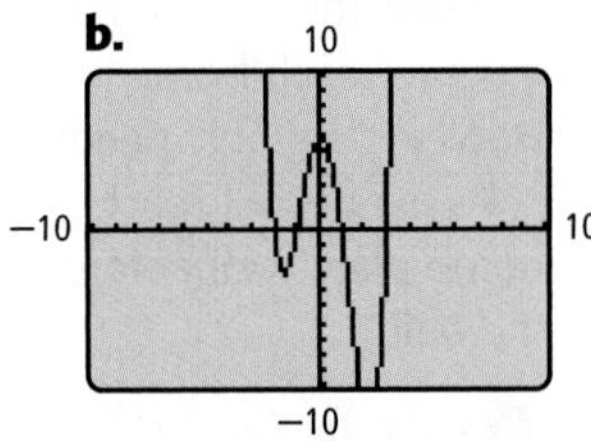

c.

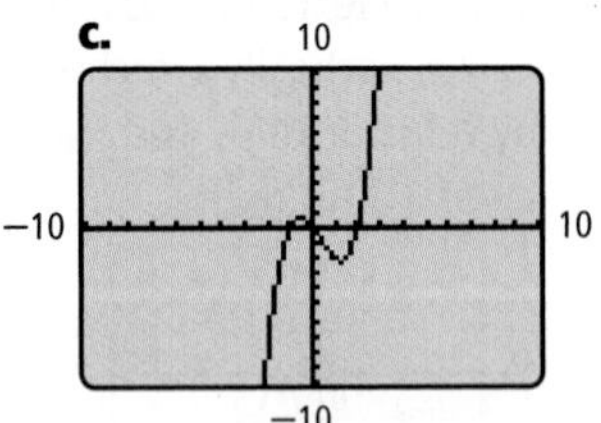

d.

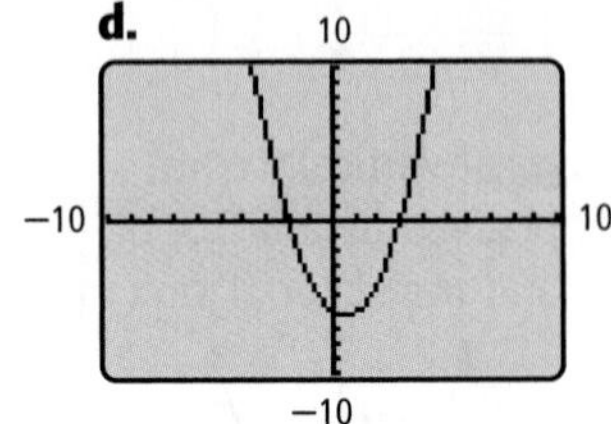

e.

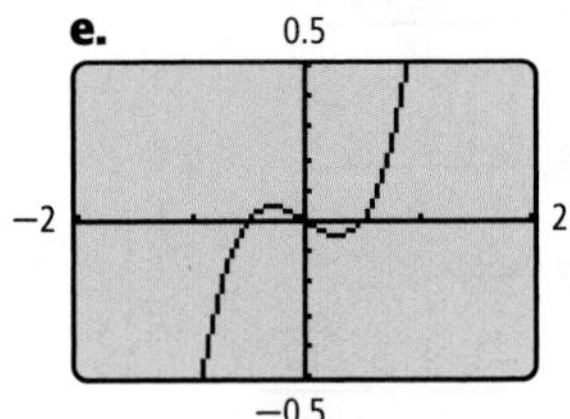

64.

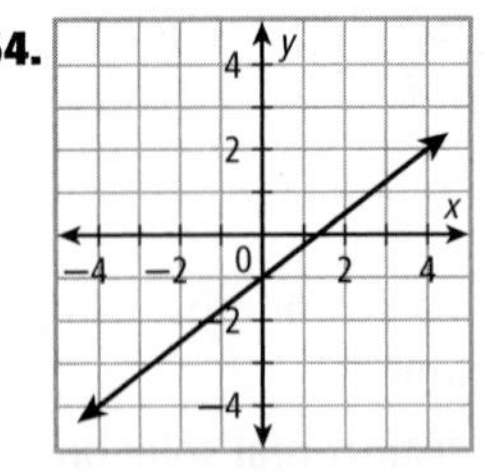

65.

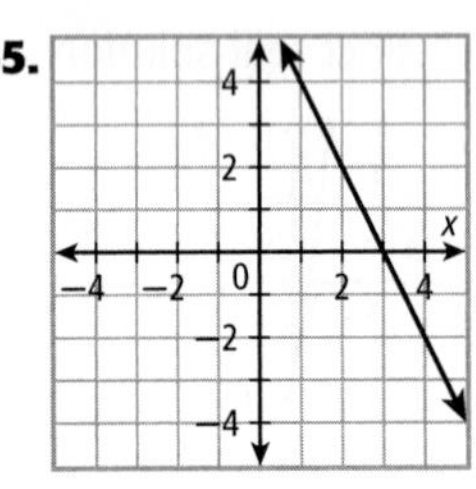

66.

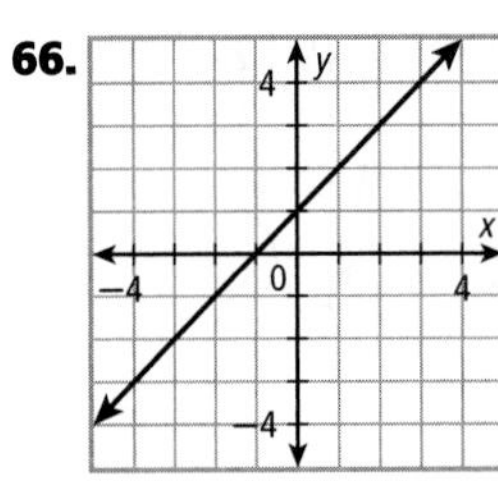

67.

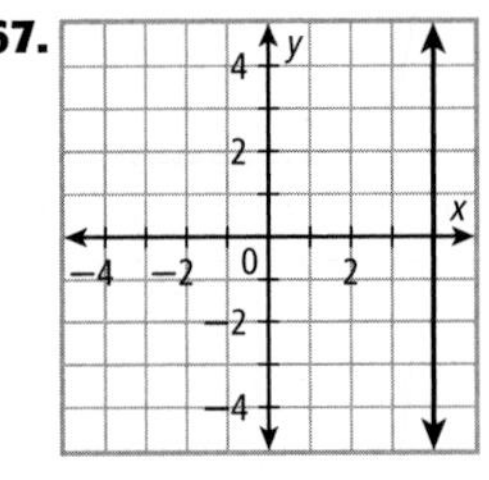

68.

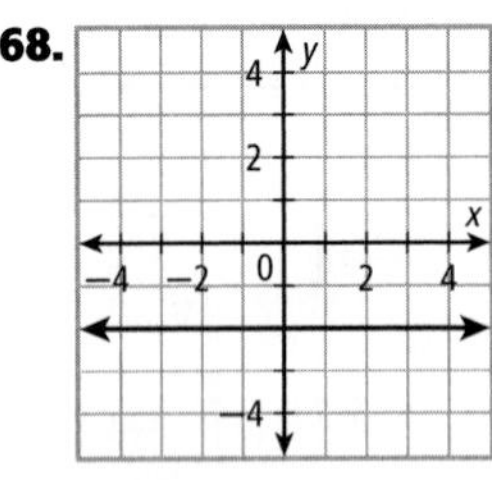

69.

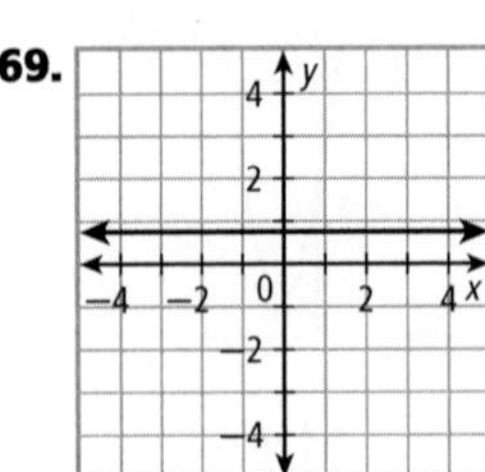

Additional Answers

70.

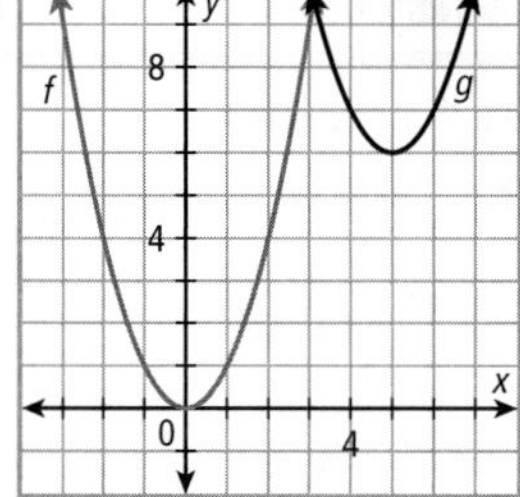

71.

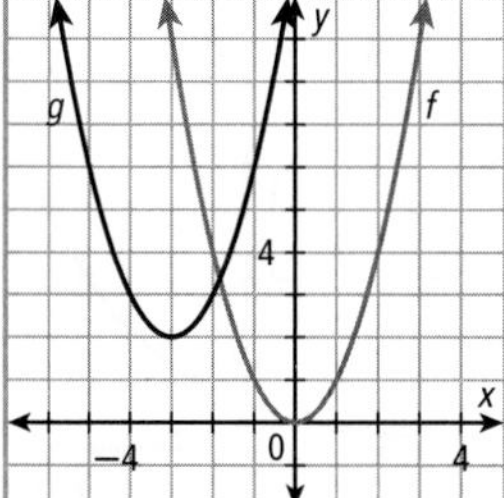

72.

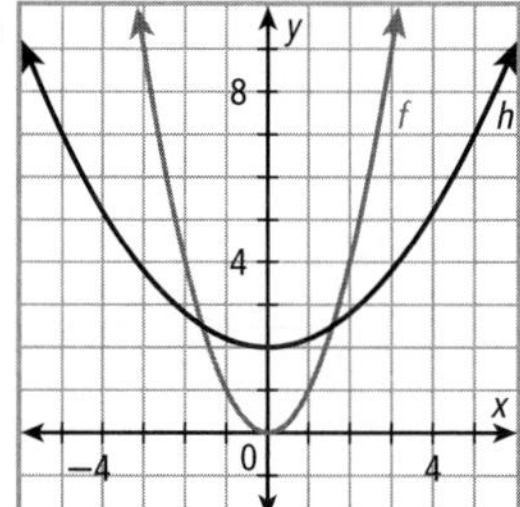

6A *Ready To Go On?*

1. $3x^5 + 4x^2 - 5$; 3; 5; 3; quintic trinomial

2. $13x + 7$; 13; 1; 2; linear binomial

3. $5x^3 + x^2 - 3x + 1$; 5; 3; 4; cubic polynomial with 4 terms

4. $2x^4 - 5x^3 + 8x$; 2; 4; 3; quartic trinomial

10.

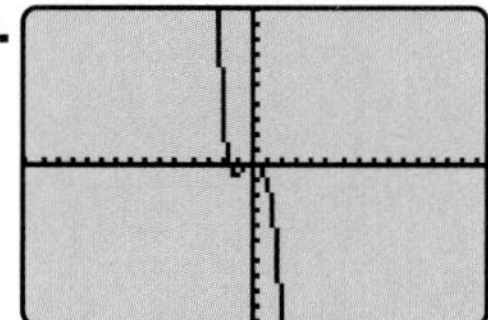

From left to right, it alternately increases and decreases, changing directions twice and crossing the x-axis twice. There appear to be 2 real zeros.

11.

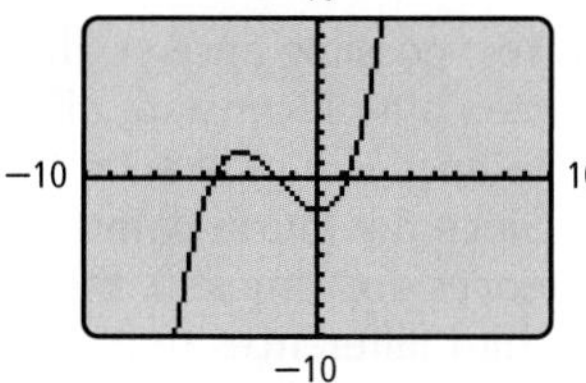

From left to right, it alternately increases and decreases, changing direction twice and crossing the x-axis 3 times. There appear to be 3 real zeros.

12.

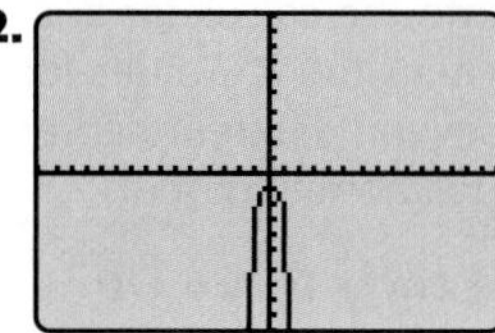

From left to right, it increases then decreases, and never crosses the x-axis. There appear to be no real zeros.

17. $x^4 - 12x^3 + 54x^2 - 108x + 81$

18. $x^3 + 6x^2y + 12xy^2 + 8y^3$

19. $256x^4 - 256x^3 + 96x^2 - 16x + 1$

6A *Technology Lab*

1a. Possible answer: They are all polynomials of degree 3 with positive leading coefficients.

b. Possible answer: The functions have the same end behavior, rising for positive x-values and falling for negative x-values.

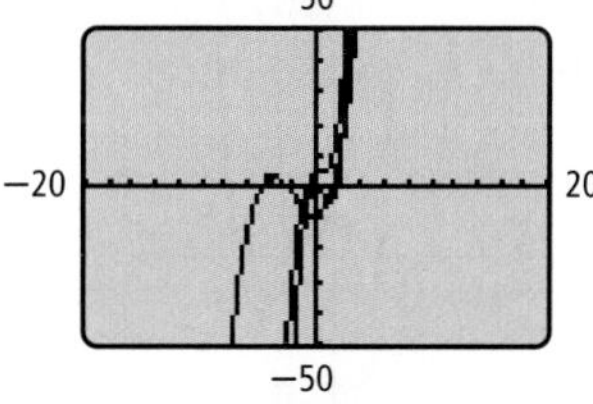

c. Possible answer: The end behavior will be the same as $g(x)$, $h(x)$, and $k(x)$, rising for positive x-values and falling for negative x-values.

2a. Possible answer: They are all polynomials of degree 3 with negative leading coefficients

b. Possible answer: The functions have the same end behavior, rising for negative x-values and falling for positive x-values.

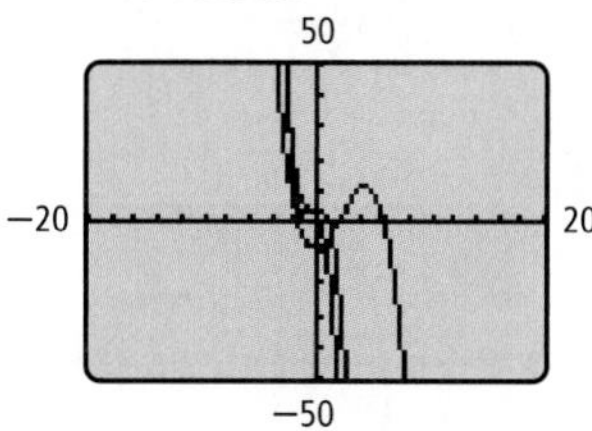

c. Possible answer: The end behavior will be the same as $a(x)$, $b(x)$, and $c(x)$, rising for negative x-values and falling for positive x-values.

3a. Possible answer: They are all polynomials of degree 4 with positive leading coefficients.

b. Possible answer: The functions have the same end behavior, rising for both positive and negative x-values.

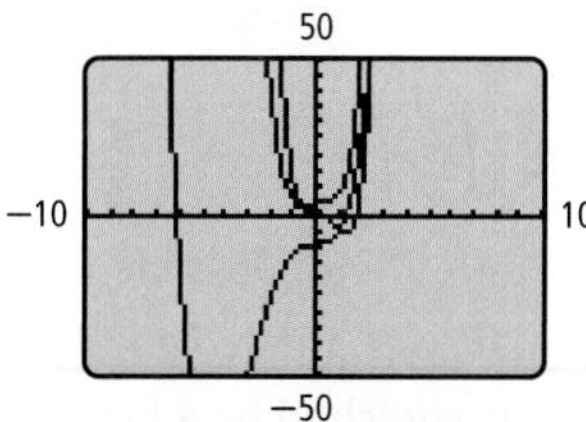

c. Possible answer: The end behavior will be the same as $p(x)$, $r(x)$, and $s(x)$, rising for both positive and negative x-values.

4. Possible answer: The degree of the polynomial and sign of the leading coefficient affect end behavior.

6-7 *Exercises*

25.

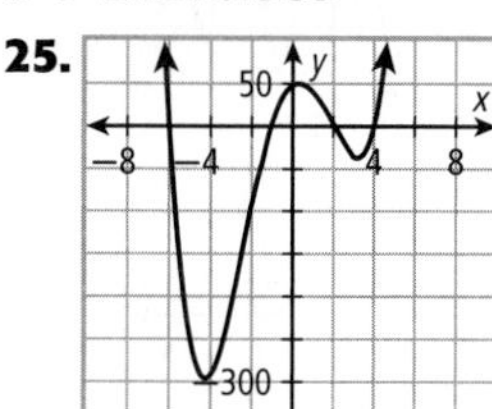

26.

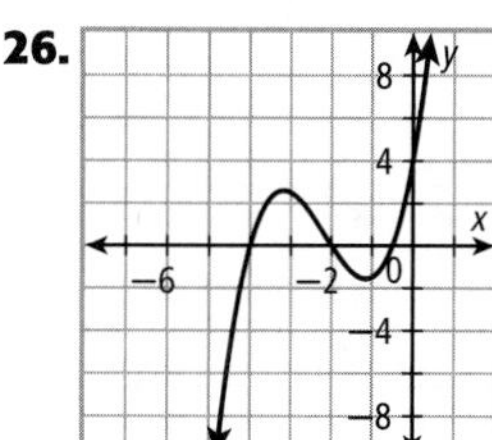

29.

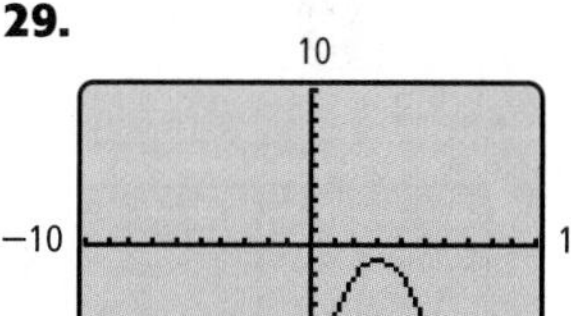

30.

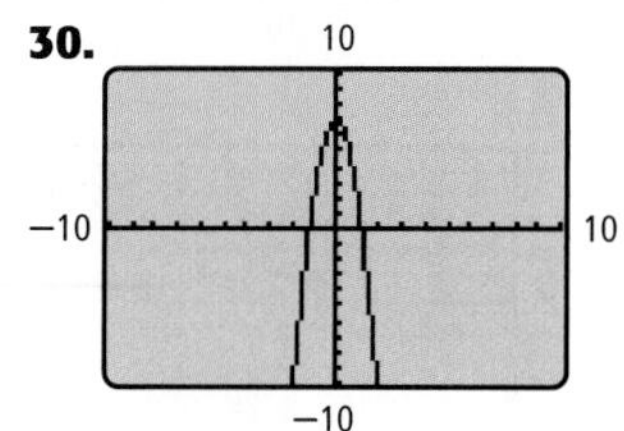

47. Possible answer: Identify possible rational roots and use them to factor the polynomial. Plot the zeros of the function and a few other points as guidelines. Determine the end behavior, and graph.

53.

x	$f(x)$	$g(x)$	$\frac{f(x)}{g(x)}$
5	125	–25	–5
10	1,000	420	2.3810
50	125,000	110,180	1.1345
100	1,000,000	940,380	1.0634
500	125,000,000	123,501,980	1.0121
1000	1,000,000,000	994,003,980	1.0060
5000	1.25×10^{11}	1.2485×10^{11}	1.0012

6-8 *Exercises*

7.

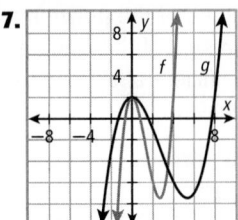

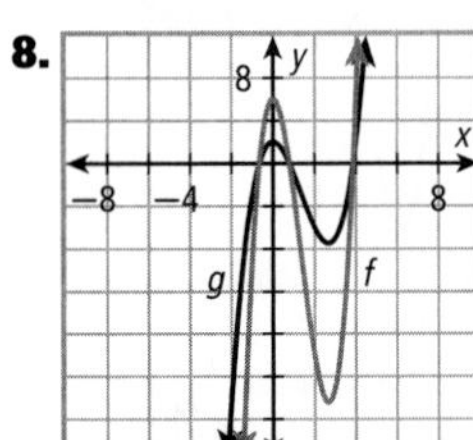

8.

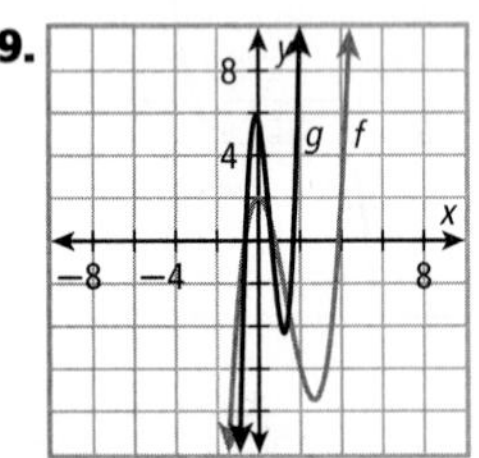

9.

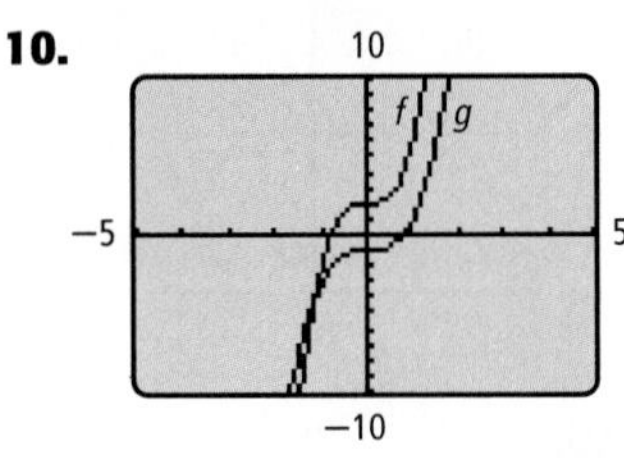

10.

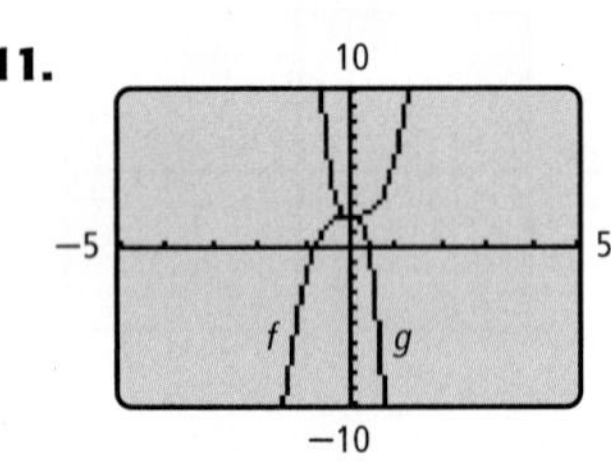

11.

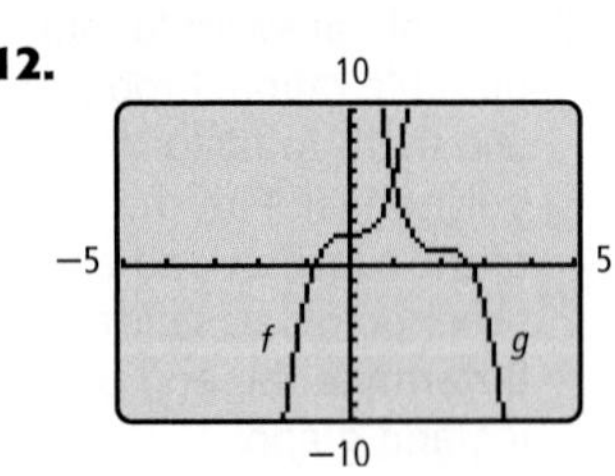

12.

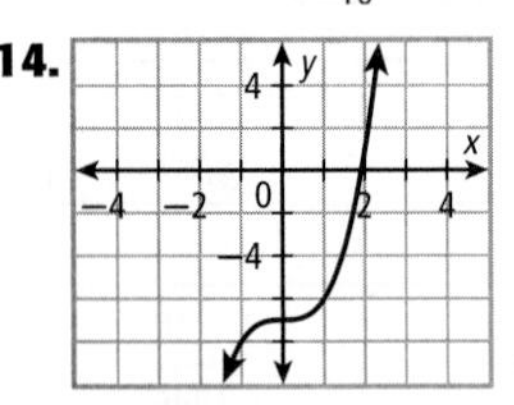

14.

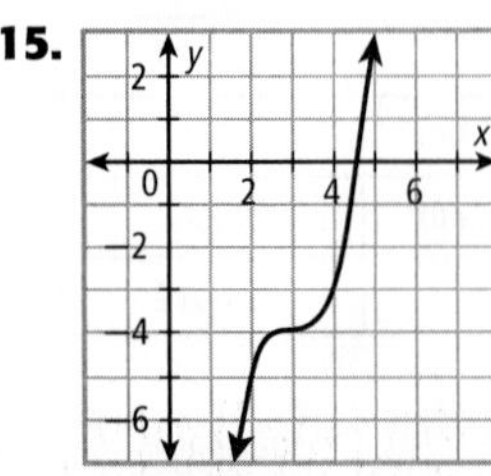

15.

16.

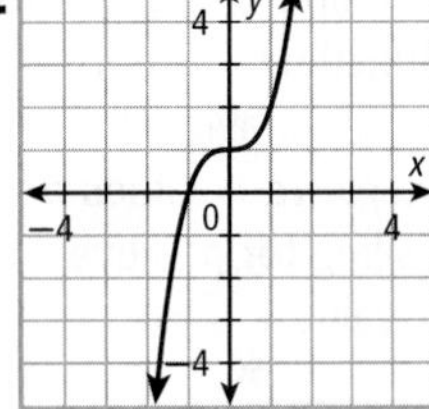

22.

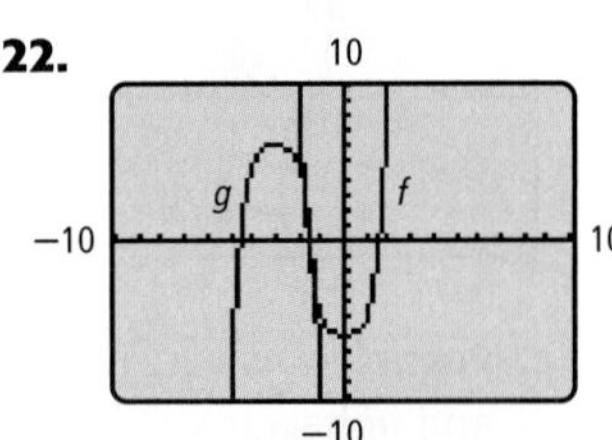

23.

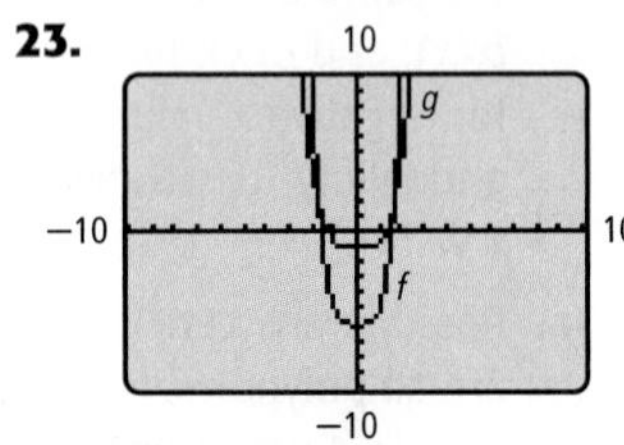

24.

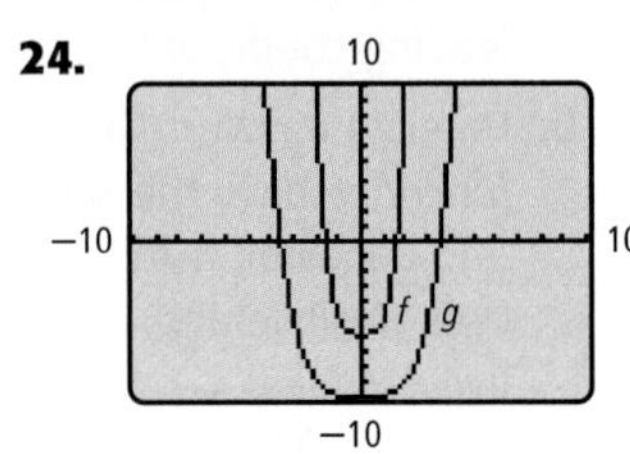

25. $V\left(\frac{2}{3}x\right) = \frac{8}{27}x^3 + \frac{4}{3}x^2 + \frac{2}{3}x + 8$; possible answer: the length of x is stretched by a factor of of $\frac{3}{2}$.

27a.

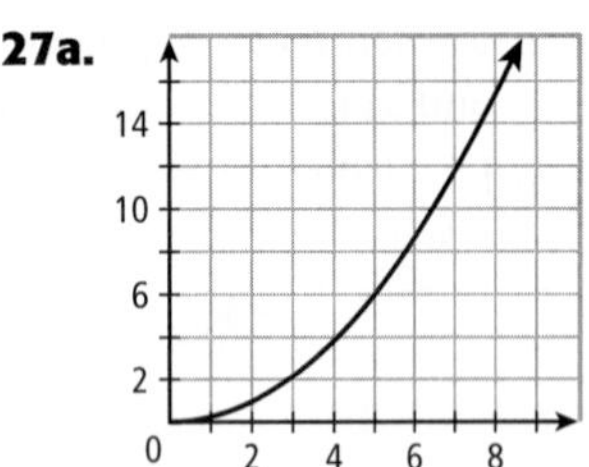

28. Possible answer: 2 real solutions for $k < 0$, no real solution for $k > 0$; negative k shifts the graph down, so it crosses the x-axis; positive k shifts it up and will never cross.

29. Possible answer: The portion of the graph above the x-axis is flipped below the axis, and the portion below is flipped above.

6-9 *Exercises*

15. Yes; possible answer: the step after a constant difference is 0 difference. Since the fourth differences are almost 0, the third differences must be nearly constant, so a cubic polynomial is an appropriate model.

16. Possible answer: Compute finite differences until the values are approximately constant, or enter the data into the calculator and check the R^2-values for several different degree polynomial models.

6B *Ready to Go On?*

8.

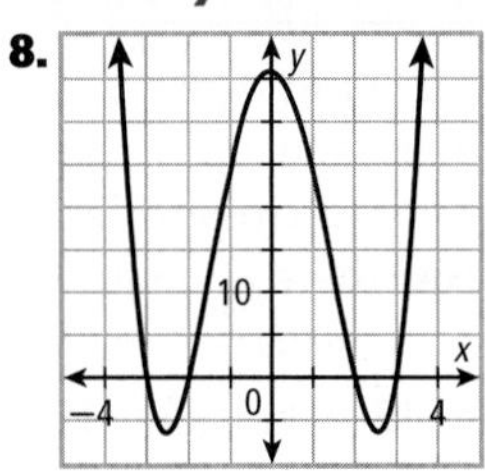

9.

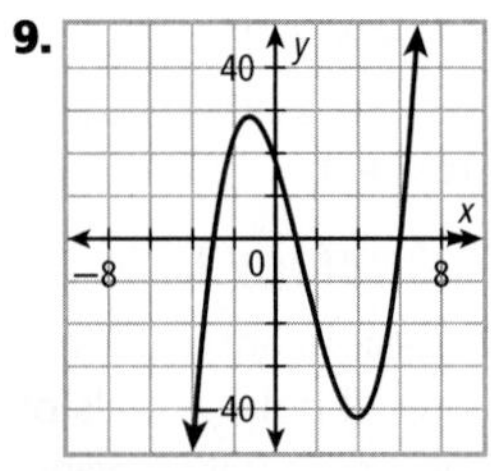

15.

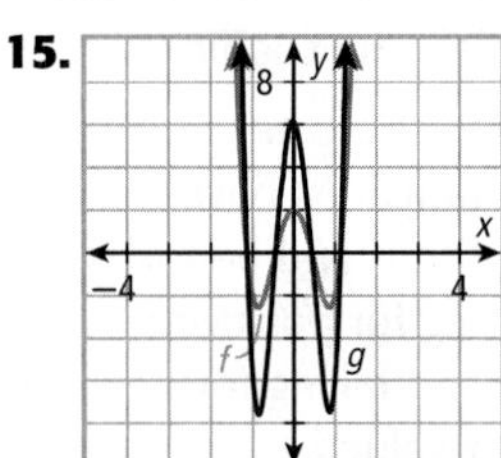

16.

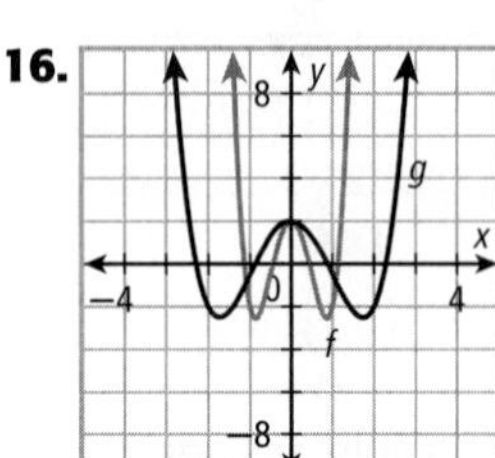

17.

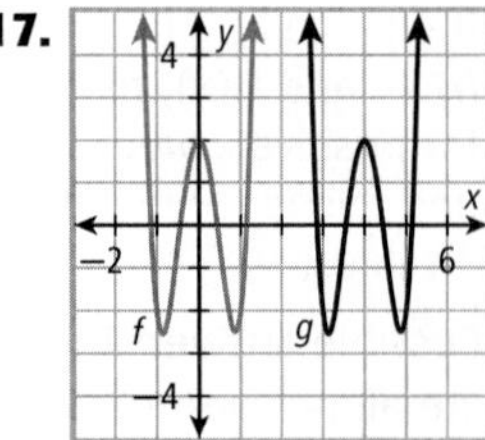

Chapter 7

7-1 *Exercises*

2.

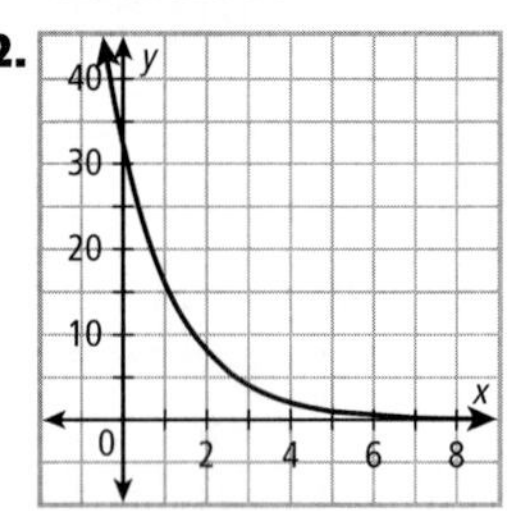

3.

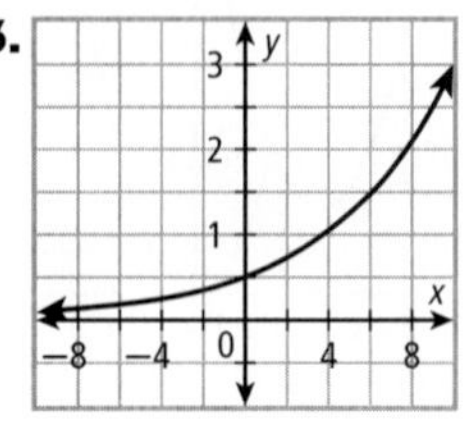

4.

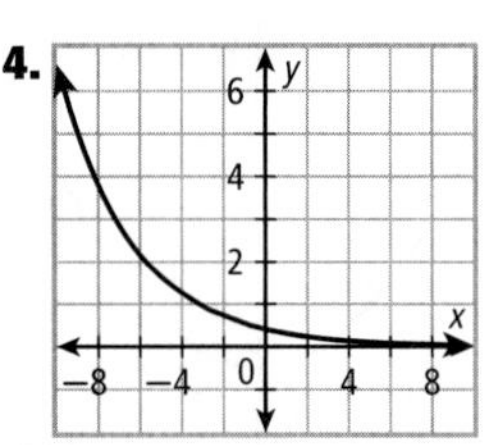

5b.

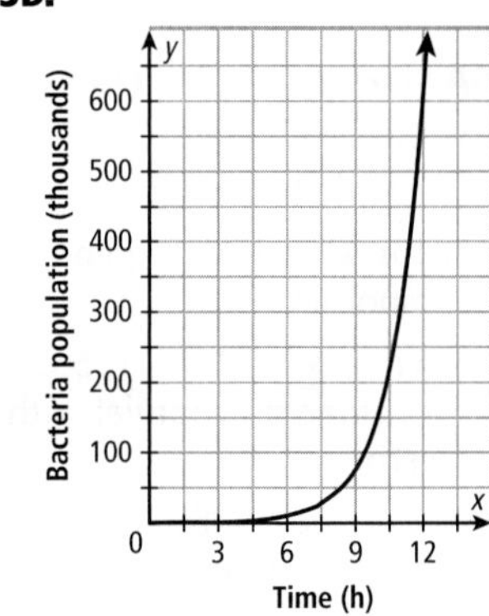

6b.

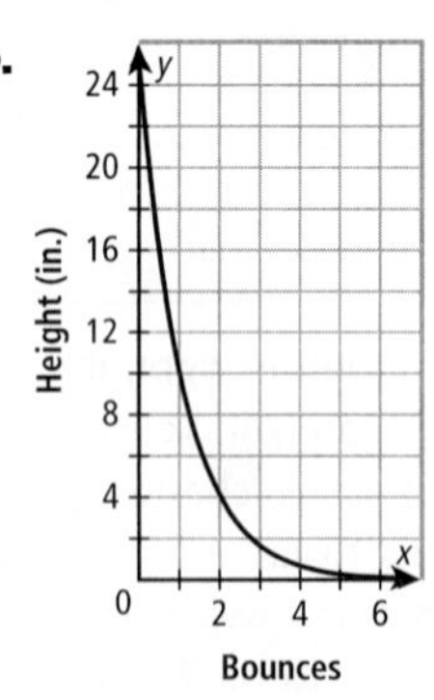

7.

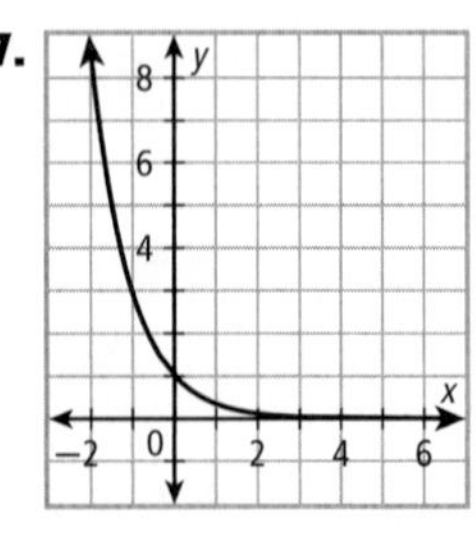

8. 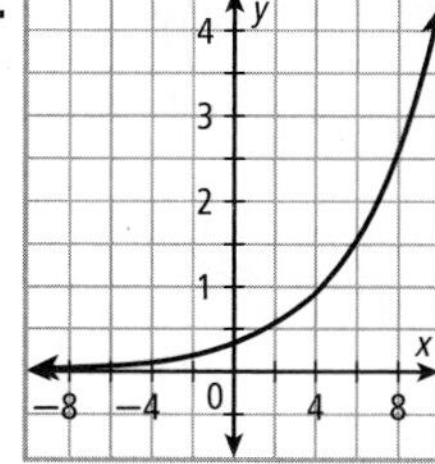

9. 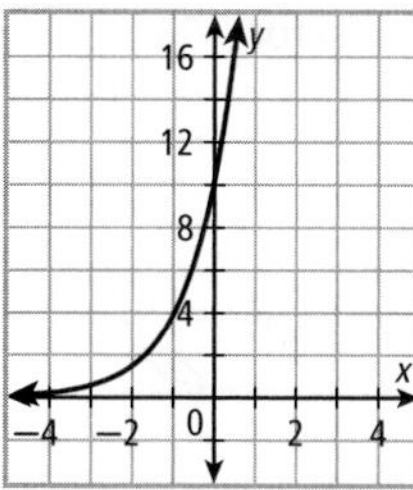

16. $N(t) = 2.5(2)^{\frac{t}{3}}$ exabytes in t yr

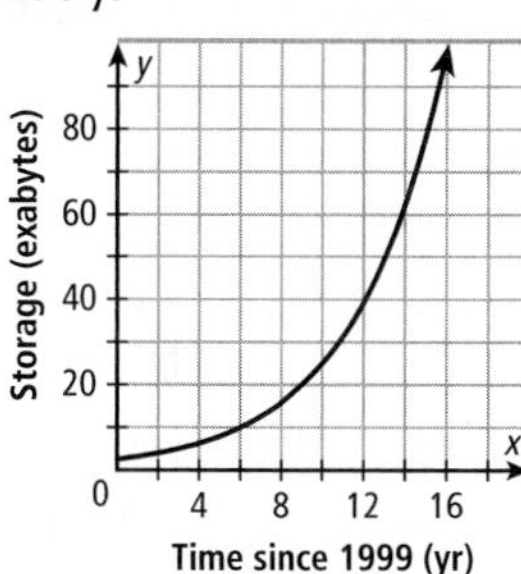

20a. 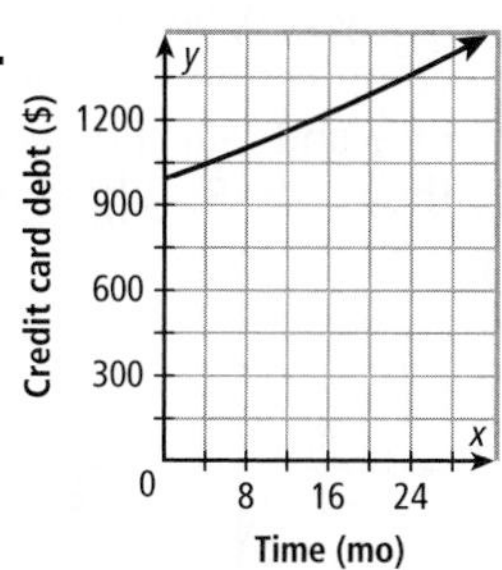

42. 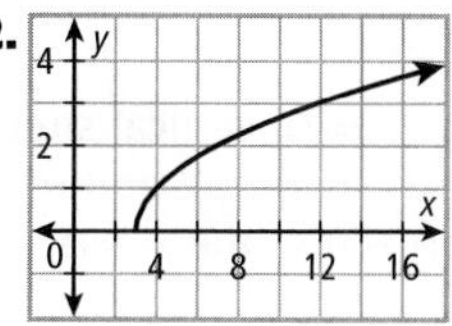

D: $\{x \mid x \geq 3\}$;

R: $\{y \mid y \geq 0\}$

$f(x) = \sqrt{x}$ shifted 3 units right

43. 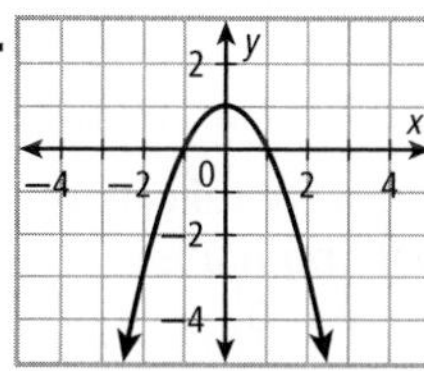

D: $\mathbb{R}$;

R: $\{y \mid y \leq 1\}$;

$f(x) = x^2$ reflected across x-axis and shifted 1 unit up

44. 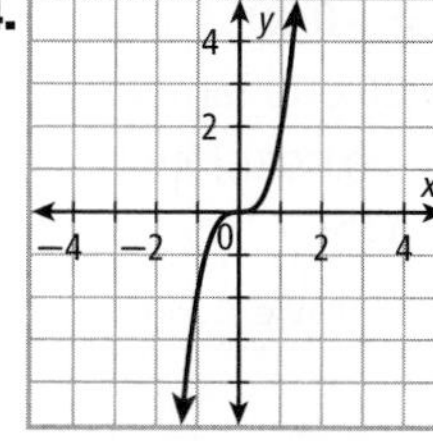

D: $\mathbb{R}$; R: $\mathbb{R}$; $f(x) = x^3$ stretched vertically by a factor of 2

45. 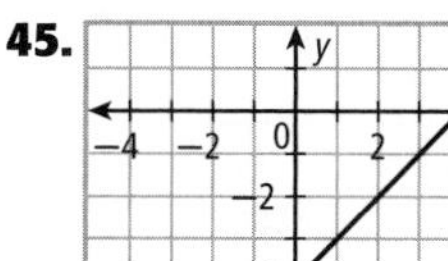

D: $\mathbb{R}$; R: $\mathbb{R}$; $f(x) = x$ shifted 4 units down

7-2 *Exercises*

14. 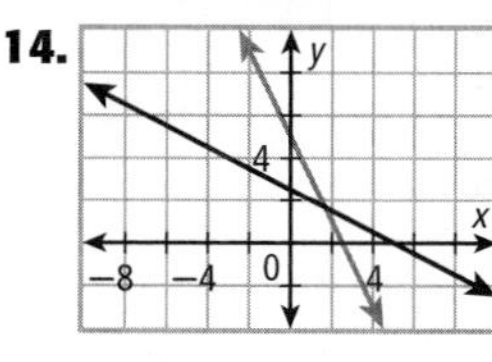

$f^{-1}(x) = -\frac{1}{2}x + \frac{5}{2}$

15. 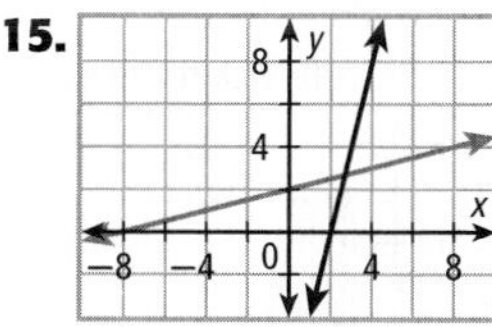

$f^{-1}(x) = 4(x - 2)$

16. 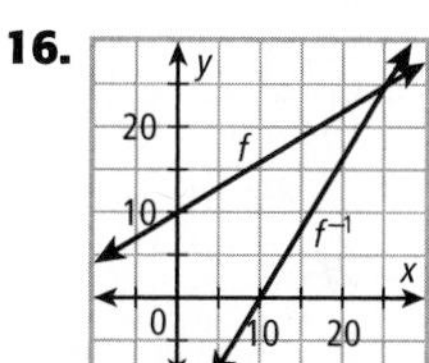

$f^{-1}(x) = \dfrac{x - 10}{0.6}$

18. 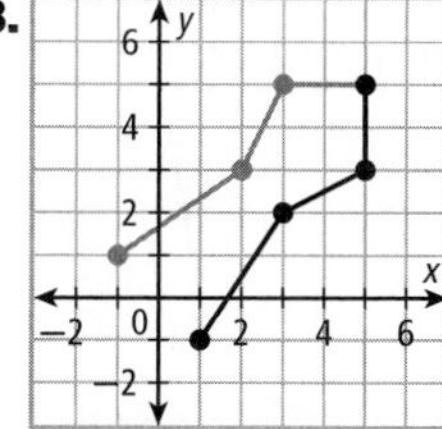

relation:

D: $\{-1 \leq x \leq 5\}$;

R: $\{1 \leq y \leq 5\}$

inverse: D: $\{1 \leq x \leq 5\}$;

R: $\{-1 \leq y \leq 5\}$

19. 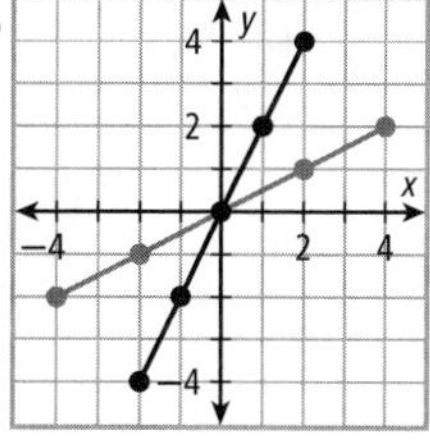

relation:

D: $\{-4 \leq x \leq 4\}$;

R: $\{-2 \leq y \leq 2\}$ inverse:

D: $\{-2 \leq x \leq 2\}$;

R: $\{-4 \leq y \leq 4\}$

65. 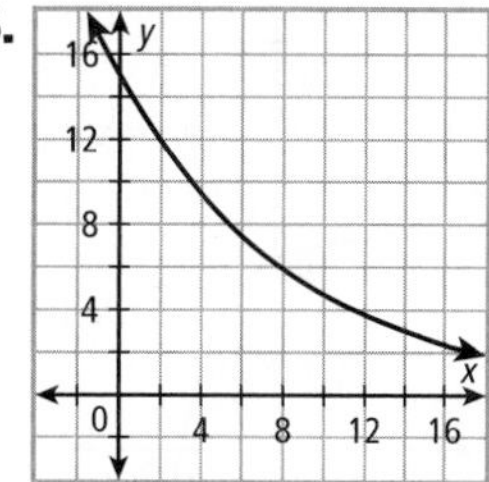

66. 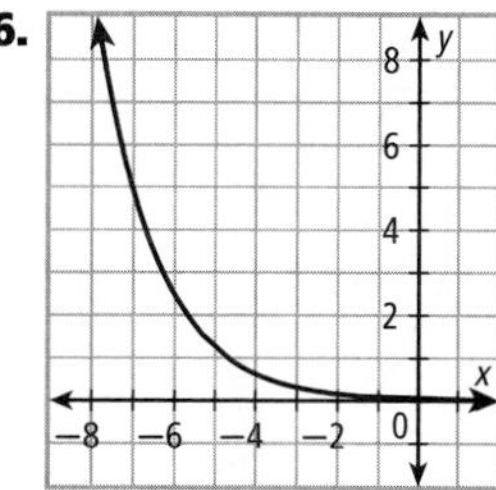

67. 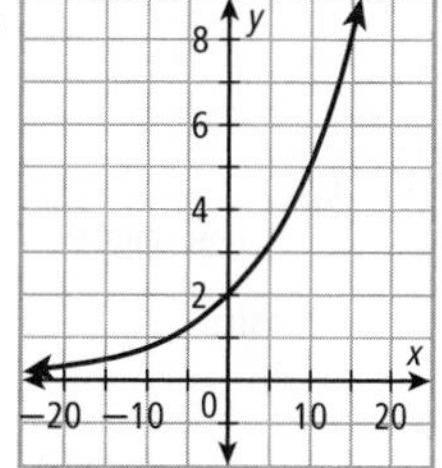

68. 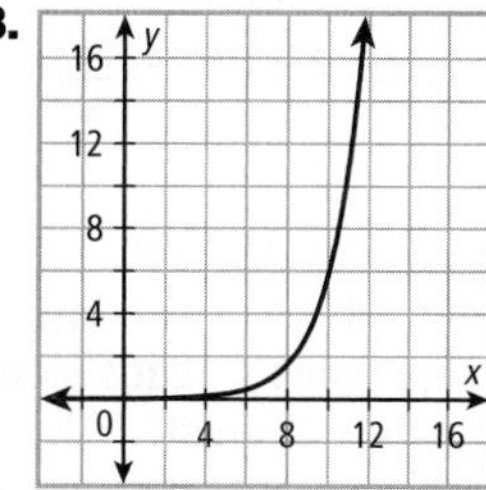

7A *Ready to Go On?*

1. 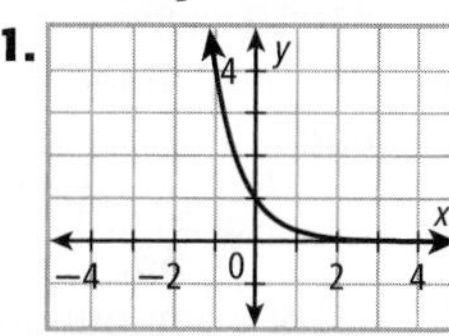

2. 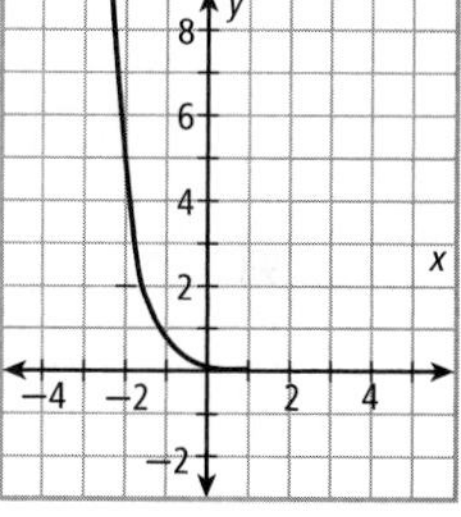

3. 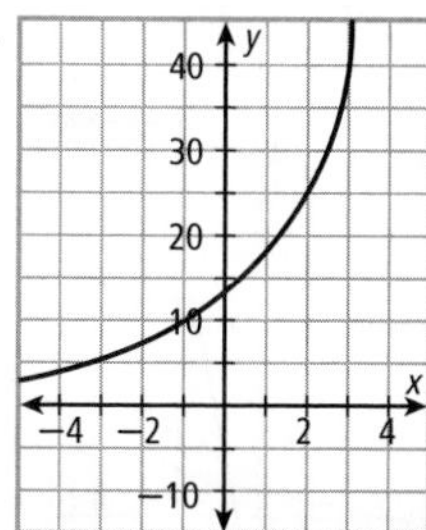

4. 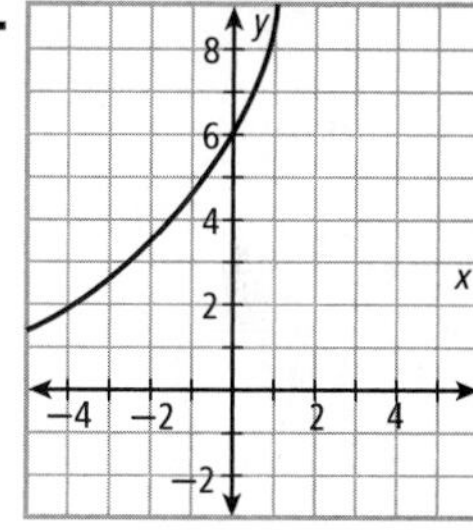

5b. 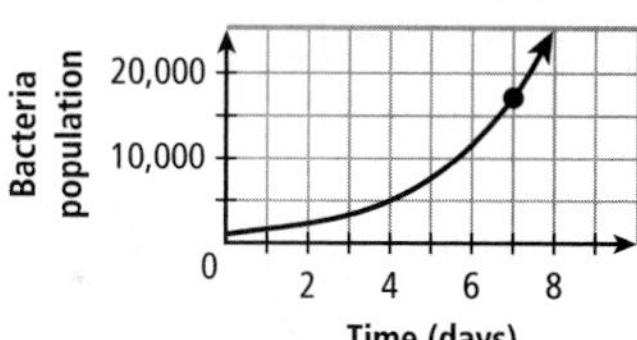

6. 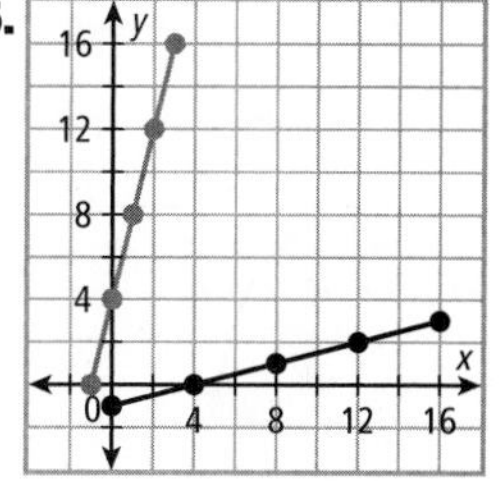

7.

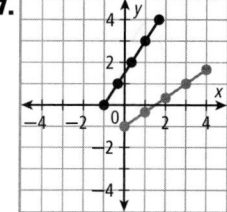

8. 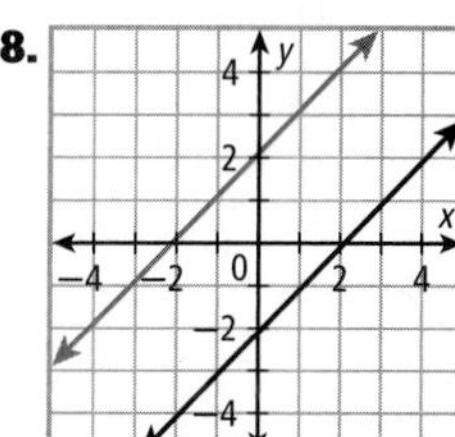

Additional Answers

9. 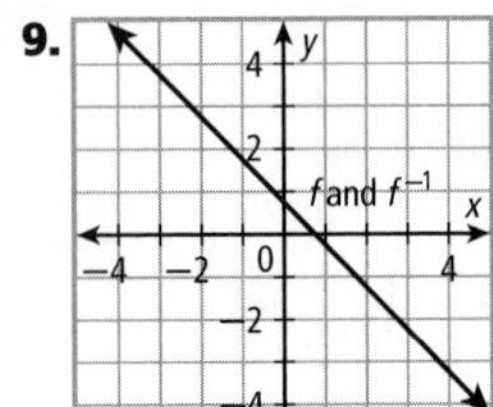

10. 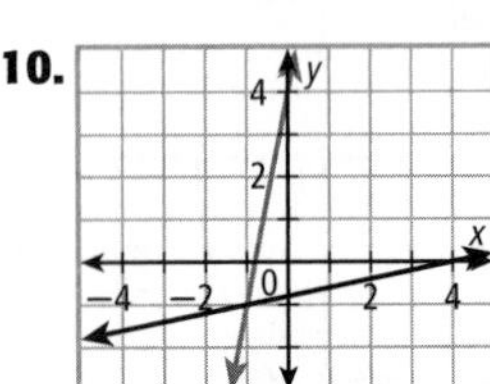

11. 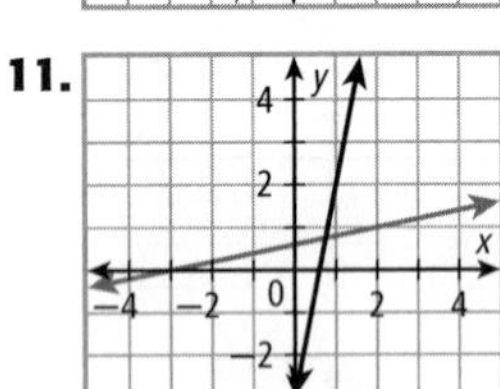

21. 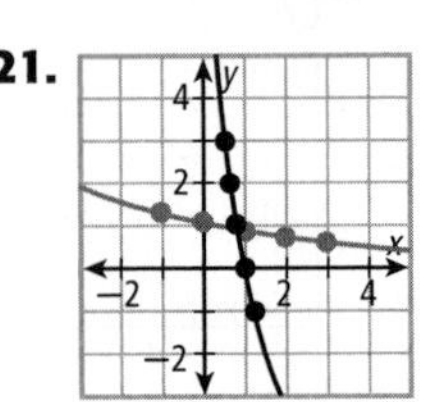

7-6 *Exercises*

2. 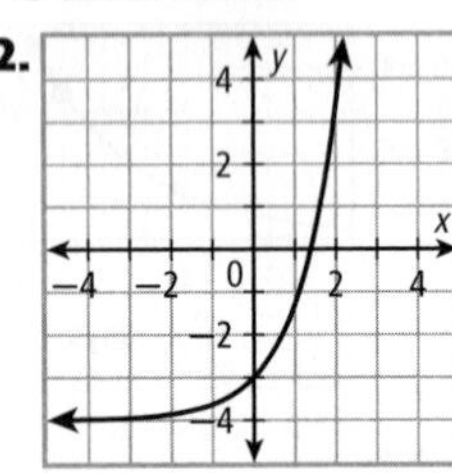

3. 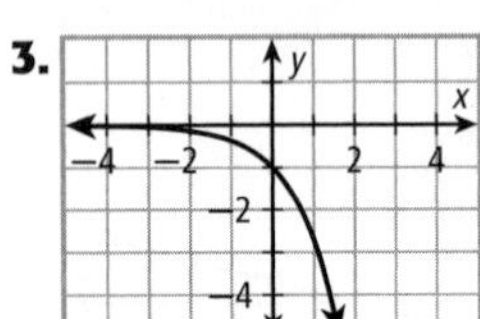

4. 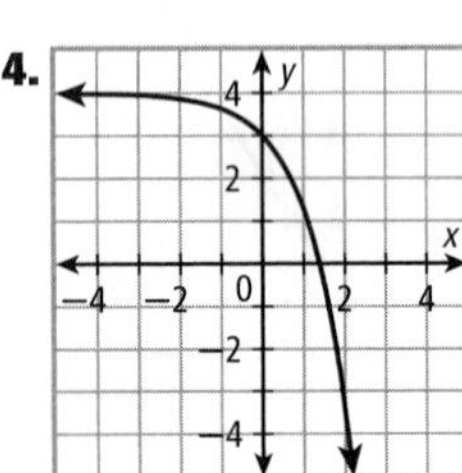

5. 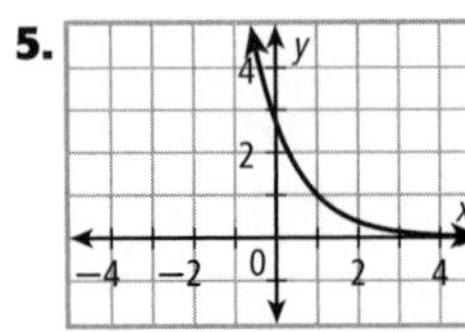

13. 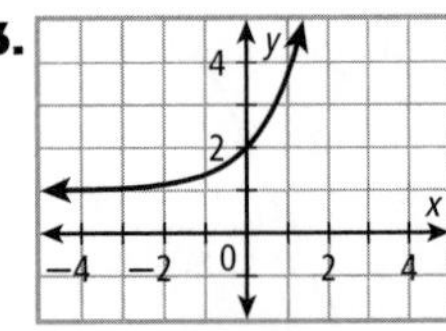

14. 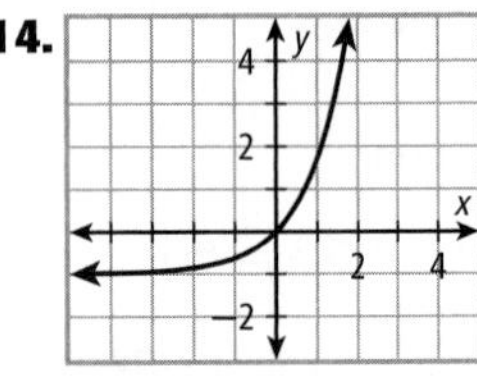

15. 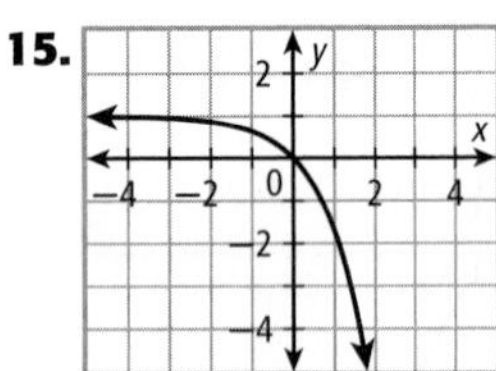

16. 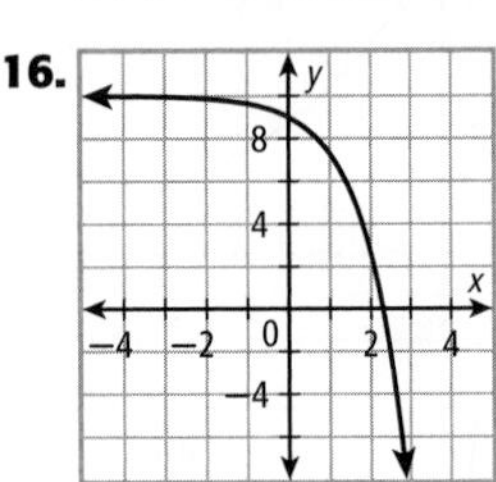

25c. 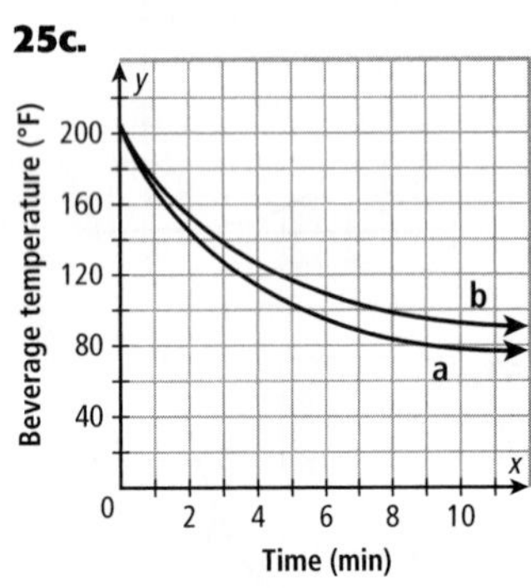

≈ 17.4 min

37a. 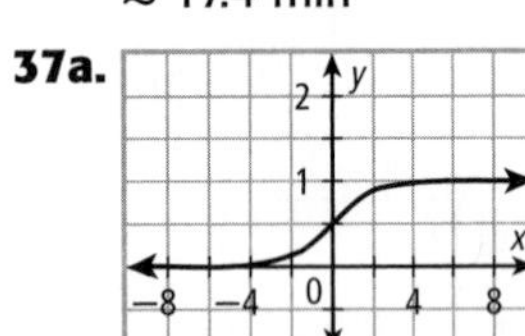

b. 2: $y = 0$ and $y = 1$

c. Possible answer: The epidemic spreads slowly at first, then steadily, and then it tapers off slowly at the end.

39. Possible answer: a little more; \$1000 at 8% interest compounded daily for 1 year:

$$A = 1000\left(1 + \frac{0.08}{365}\right)^{365}$$

$\approx \$1083.28$; compounded continuously: $A = 1000\, e^{0.08} \approx \$1083.29$

40a. $k = -0.0084$

b. $\approx 28{,}000$ farms

c. $k = 0.0056$; $A(t) = A_0 e^{kt}$ ≈ 1350 acres

48a. Movie Ticket Prices

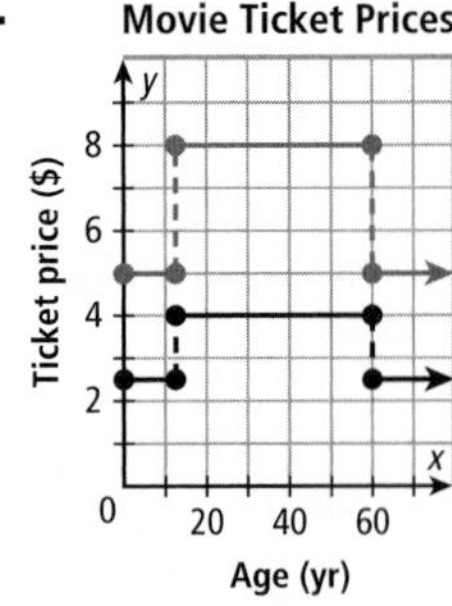

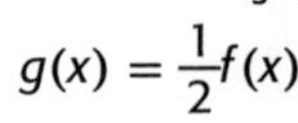

$g(x) = \frac{1}{2}f(x)$

b. Movie Ticket Prices

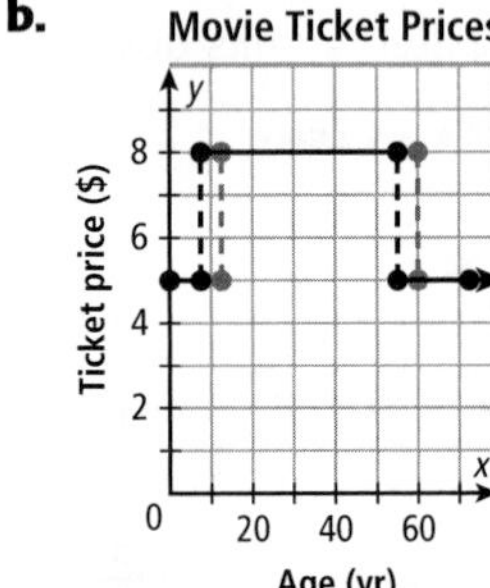

$g(x) = f(x + 3)$

c. Movie Ticket Prices

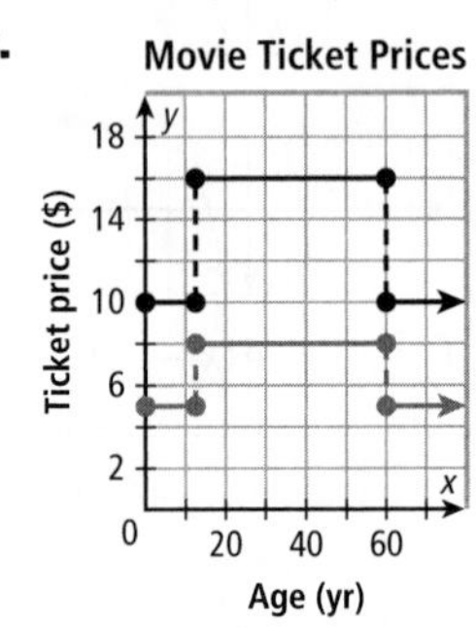

$g(x) = 2f(x)$

7-7 *Exercises*

3.

x	-3	-2	-1	0	1
$j(x)$	0.11	0.33	1	3	9

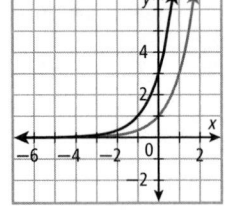

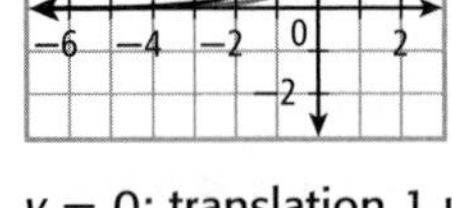

$y = 0$; translation 1 unit left

4.

3; $y = 0$; vertical stretch by a factor of 3

5. 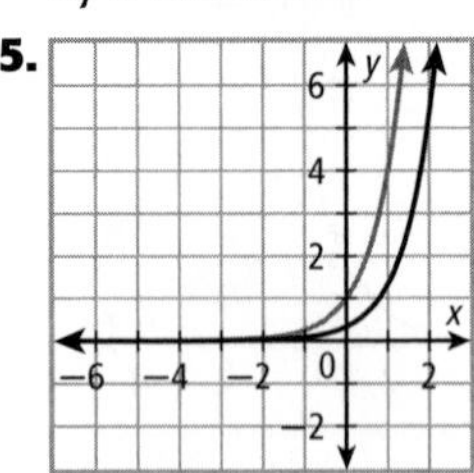

$\frac{1}{3}$; $y = 0$; vertical compression by a factor of $\frac{1}{3}$

6. 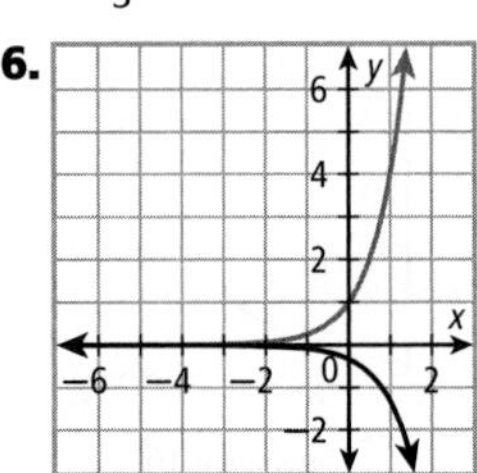

$-\frac{1}{3}$; $y = 0$; vertical compression by a factor of $\frac{1}{3}$ and reflection across the x-axis; R: $\{y \mid y < 0\}$

7. 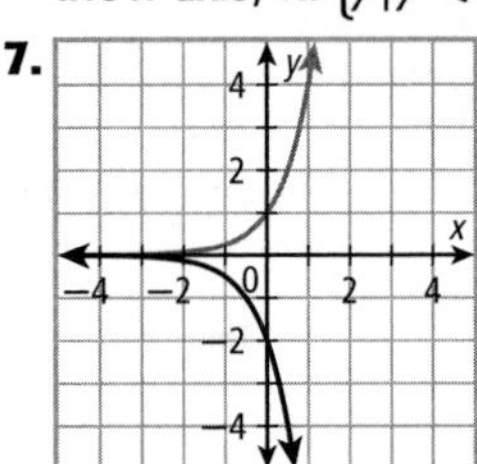

-2; $y = 0$; vertical stretch by a factor of 2 and reflection across the x-axis; R: $\{y \mid y < 0\}$

8. 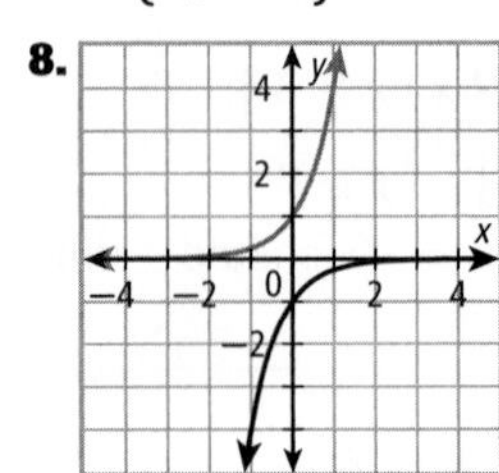

-1; $y = 0$; reflection across both axes; R: $\{y \mid y < 0\}$

9.

1; $y = 0$; horizontal compression by a factor of $\frac{1}{2}$

10.

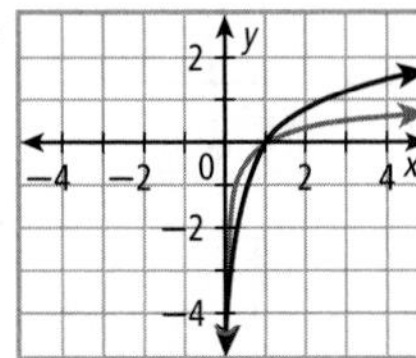

$x = 0$; vertical stretch by a factor of 2.5

11.

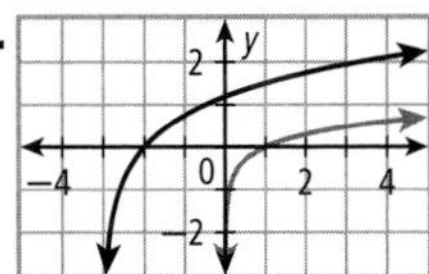

$x = -3$; translation 3 units left and vertical stretch by a factor of 2.5; D: $\{x \mid x > -3\}$

12.

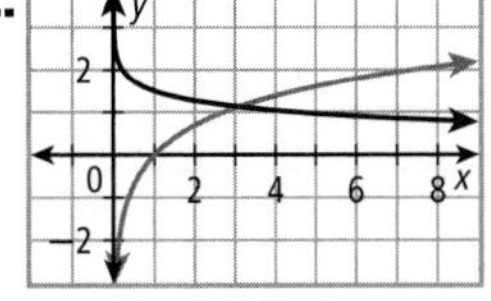

$x = 0$; reflection across the y-axis, vertical compression by a factor of $\frac{1}{3}$, and translation 1.5 units down

16.

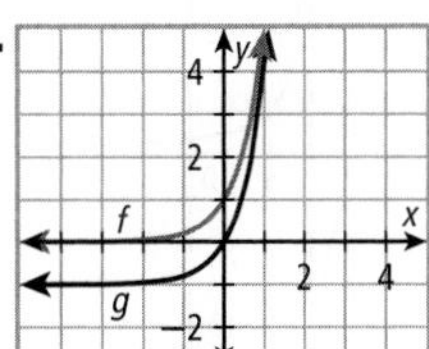

17.

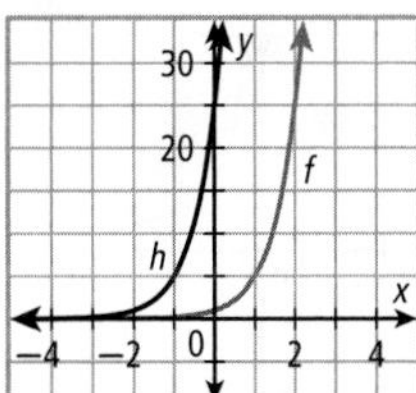

18.

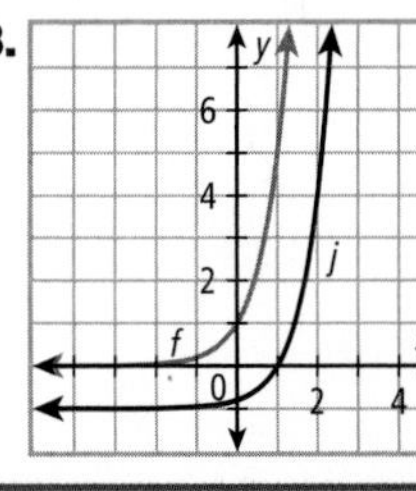

19.

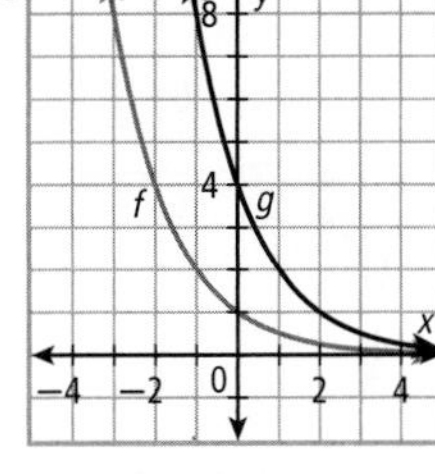

20.

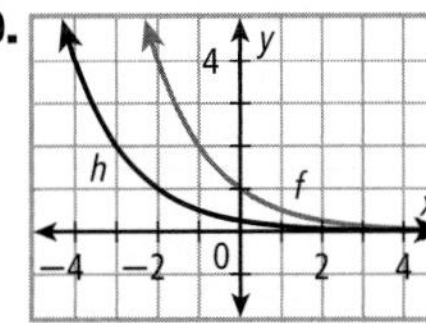

21.

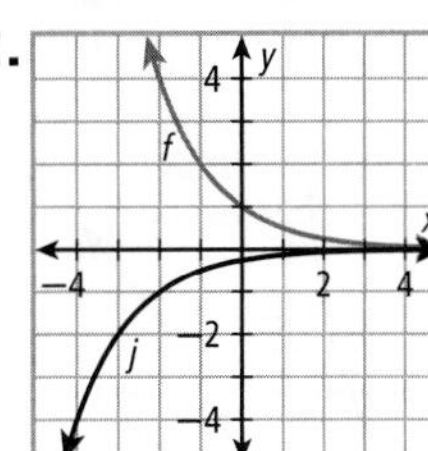

22.

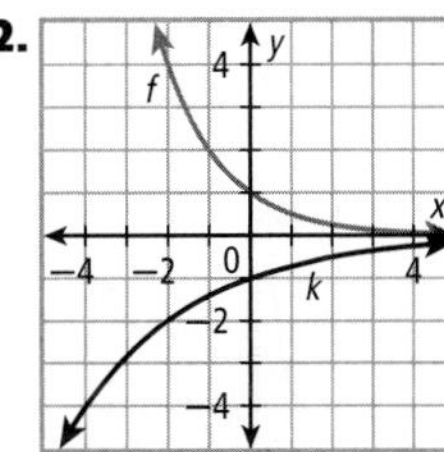

23.

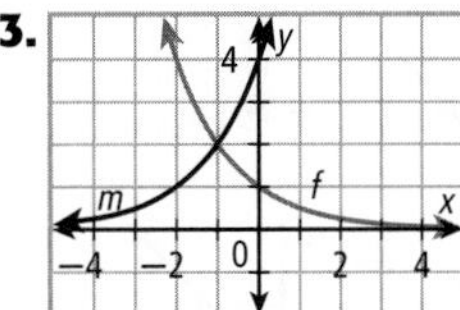

24.

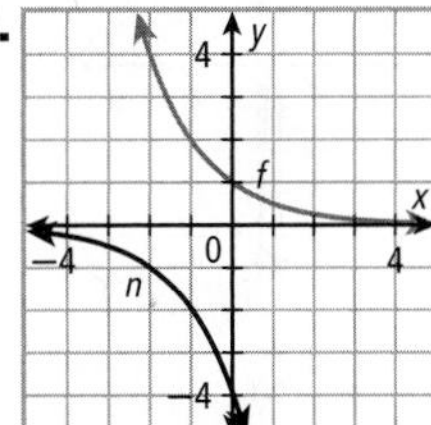

25.

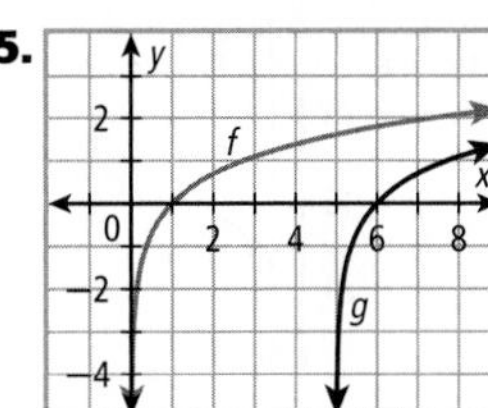

26.

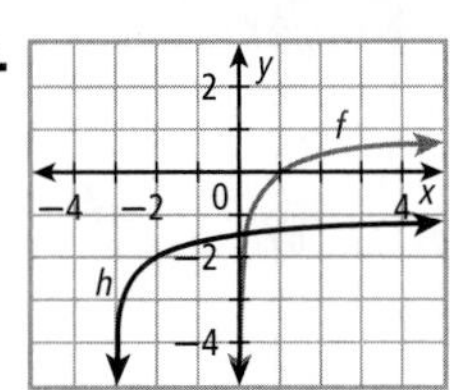

27.

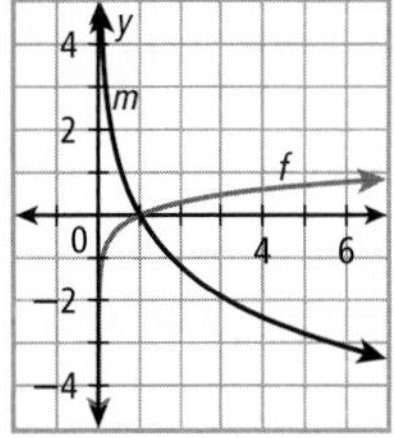

7B *Ready to Go On?*

10.

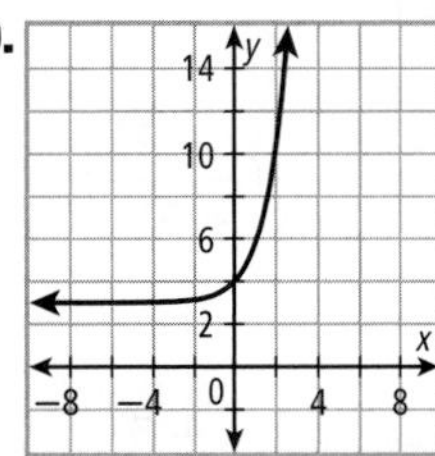

11.

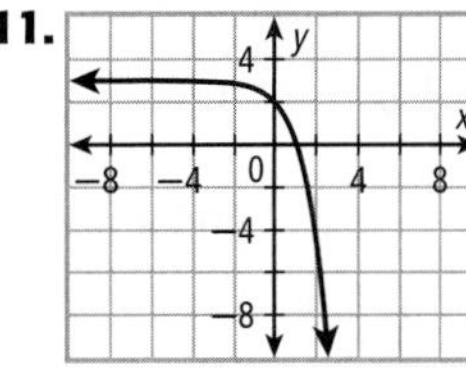

12.

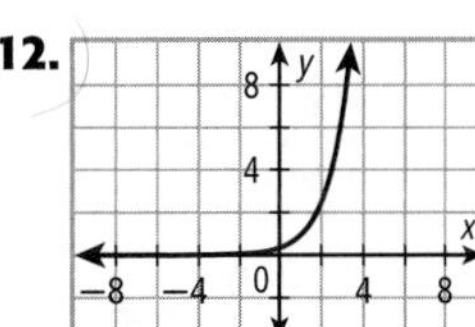

13.

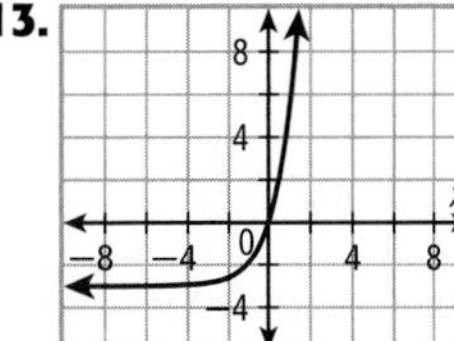

19.

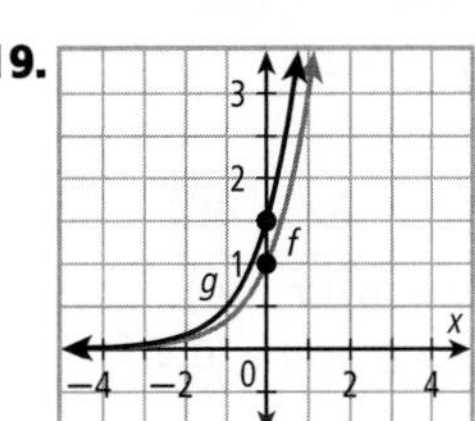

1.5; $y = 0$; The graph is stretched vertically by a factor of 1.5.

20.

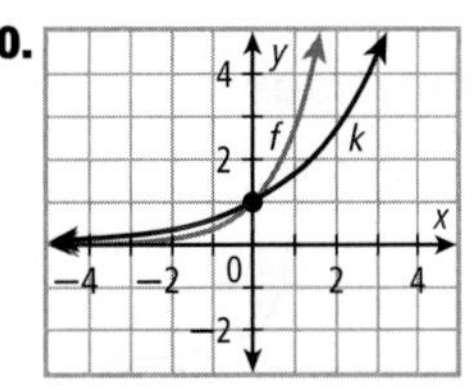

1; $y = 0$; The graph is stretched horizontally by a factor of 2.

21.

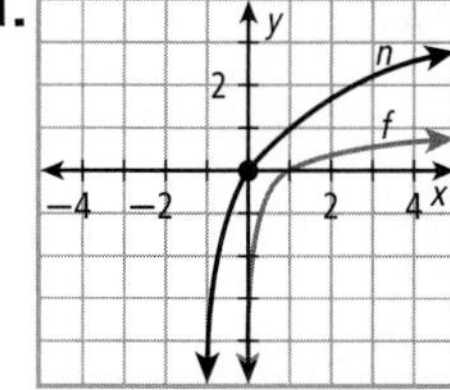

0; $x = -1$; The graph is shifted 1 unit left and stretched vertically by a factor of 3.5; D: $\{x \mid x > -1\}$

22.

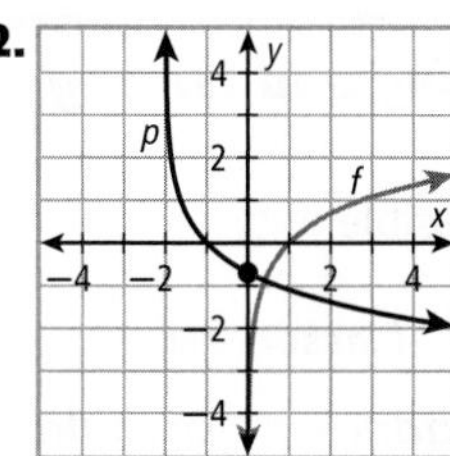

≈ -0.69; $x = -2$; The graph is shifted 2 units left and reflected across the x-axis; D: $\{x \mid x > -2\}$

Chapter 7 Test

8.

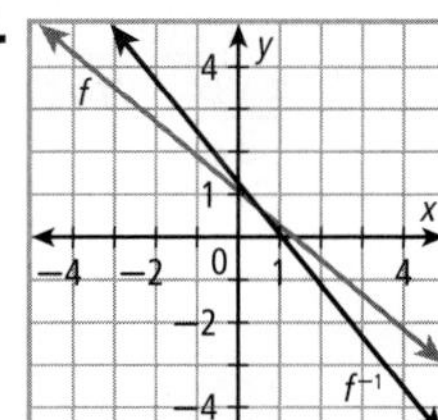

9.

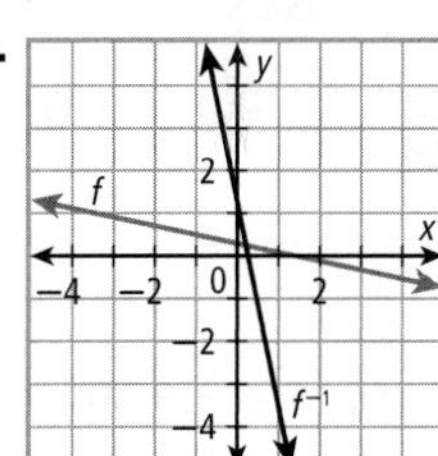

14.

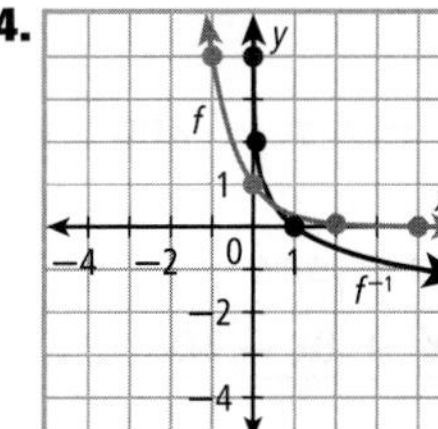

D: $\{x \mid x > 0\}$; R: $\mathbb{R}$

15.

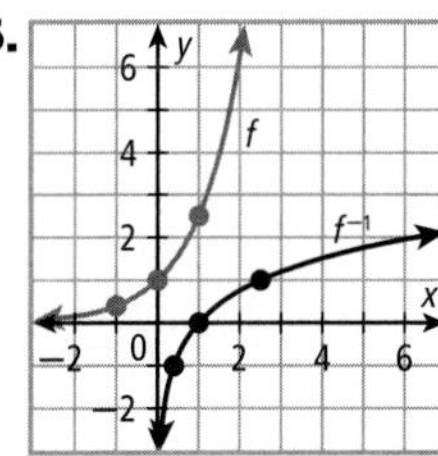

D: $\{x \mid x > 0\}$; R: $\mathbb{R}$

Additional Answers

16. 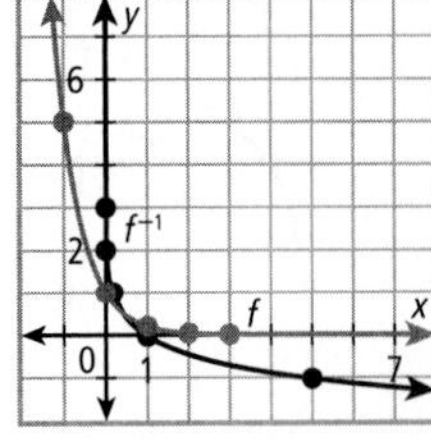

D: $\{x \mid x > 0\}$; R: $\mathbb{R}$

Chapter 8

Reading and Writing Math

2. Possible answer:

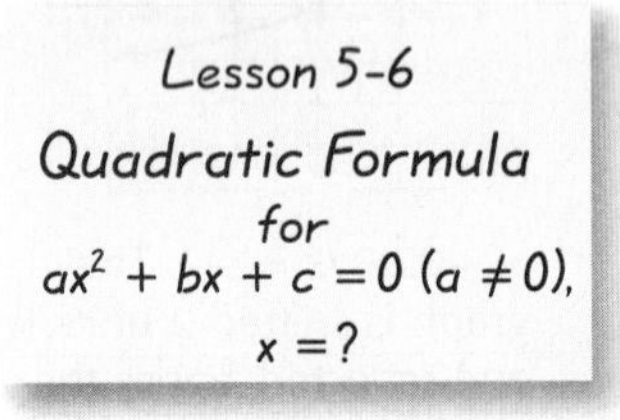

Lesson 5-6
Quadratic Formula
for
$ax^2 + bx + c = 0\ (a \neq 0)$,
$x = ?$

Front

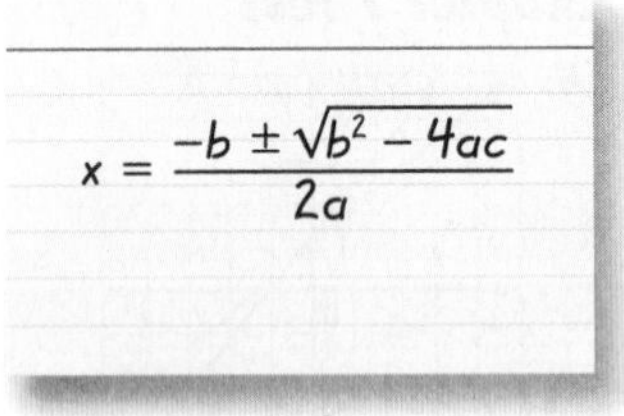

$x = \dfrac{-b \pm \sqrt{b^2 - 4ac}}{2a}$

Back

8-2 *Exercises*

3. $\dfrac{(2x+5)}{(2x-7)}$; $x \neq \frac{1}{3}$ and $x \neq \frac{7}{2}$

4. $\dfrac{1}{3x-1}$; $x \neq -4$ and $x \neq \frac{1}{3}$

5. $\dfrac{-1}{x-5}$; $x \neq -4$ and $x \neq 5$

8-3 *Exercises*

10. $\dfrac{5x^2 + 8x - 30}{(2x-5)(3x+1)}$; $x \neq -\frac{1}{3}$ and $x \neq \frac{5}{2}$

17. $\dfrac{2(2x-3)}{4x-7}$; $x \neq \frac{7}{4}$

18. $\dfrac{-2x}{3x+4}$; $x \neq -\frac{4}{3}$

19. $\dfrac{x^2 - 2x + 2}{2x+7}$; $x \neq -\frac{7}{2}$

22. $\dfrac{14x^2 - 7x + 2}{(x+2)(4x-1)}$; $x \neq -2$ and $x \neq \frac{1}{4}$

23. $\dfrac{7(2x-3)}{3(x-2)}$; $x \neq 2$

24. $\dfrac{33x + 5}{4x(x+1)}$; $x \neq -1$ and $x \neq 0$

25. $\dfrac{-(2x+3)(x-2)}{(x-3)(x+3)}$; $x \neq \pm 3$

26. $\dfrac{-(2x^2 + 11x + 3)}{(2x+3)(2x-3)}$; $x \neq \pm\frac{3}{2}$

27. $\dfrac{1}{x-2}$; $x \neq 2$ and $x \neq 4$

28. $\dfrac{2x-5}{(x-3)(3x-1)}$

29. $\dfrac{(3x-2)(x+3)}{(5x+1)(x+2)}$

37. $\dfrac{2x^2 - 13x + 9}{(x-1)(x-2)}$; $x \neq 1$ and $x \neq 2$

38. $\dfrac{5x+9}{3(3x+4)}$; $x \neq -\frac{4}{3}$

39. $\dfrac{2(4x^3 - 6x^2 - 3x - 4)}{(3x+4)(2x-3)}$; $x \neq -\frac{4}{3}$ and $x \neq \frac{3}{2}$

40. $\dfrac{-(x^2 + 3x - 46)}{(x+8)(x-4)}$; $x \neq -8$ and $x \neq 4$

41. $\dfrac{-9x^2 - 52x + 7}{(x+7)(x+6)(x+1)}$; $x \neq -7$, $x \neq -6$, and $x \neq -1$

8-4 *Exercises*

2. 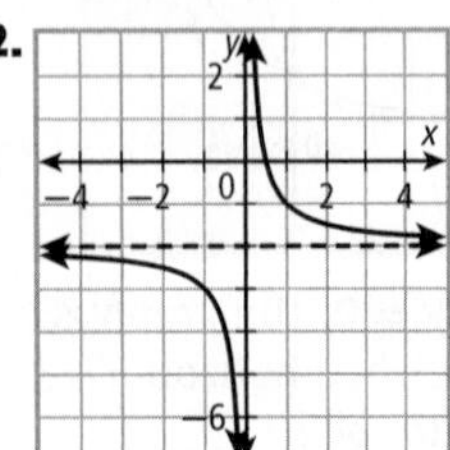

3. 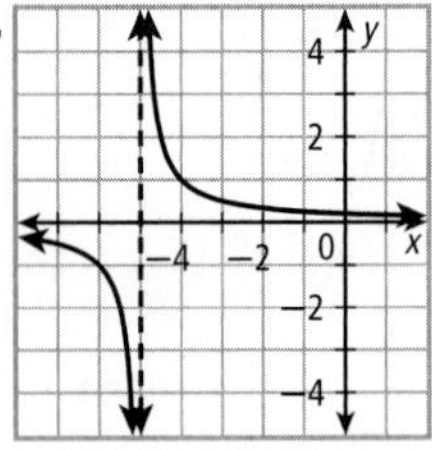

4. 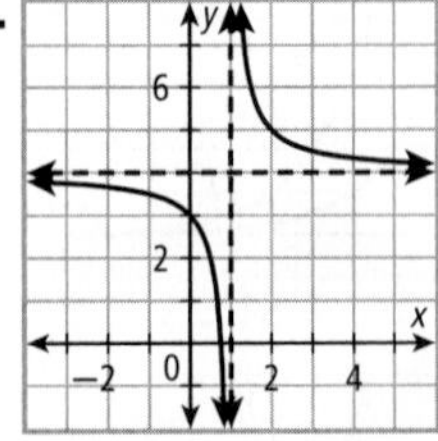

8. 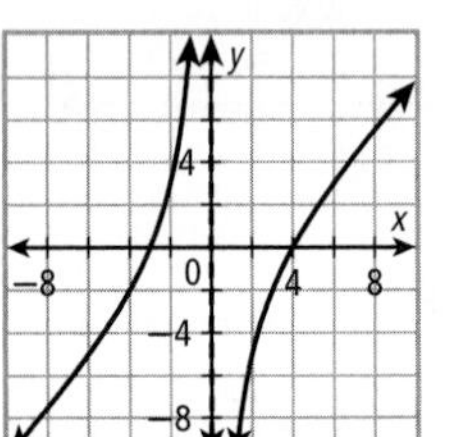

9.

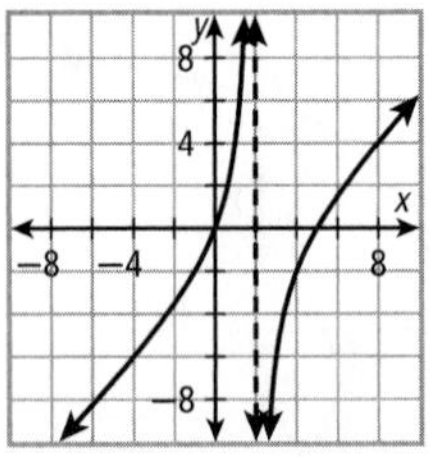

10.

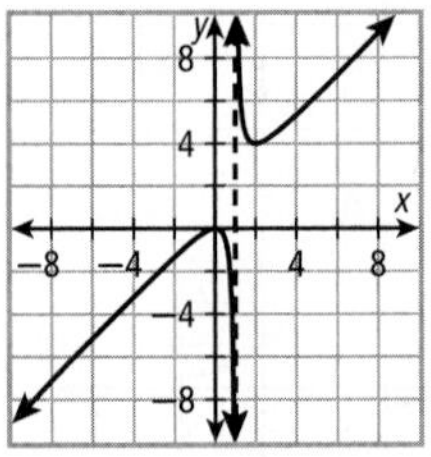

11.

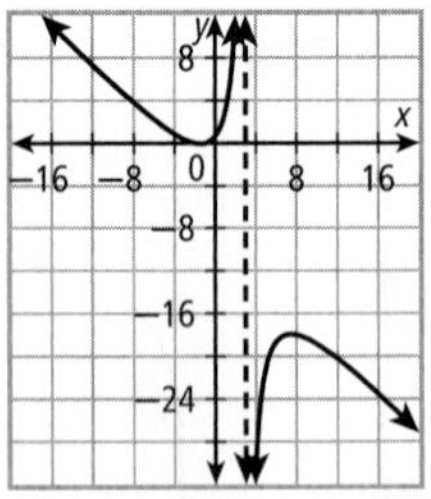

12.

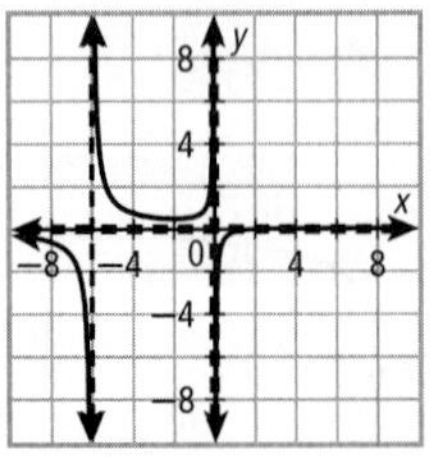

13.

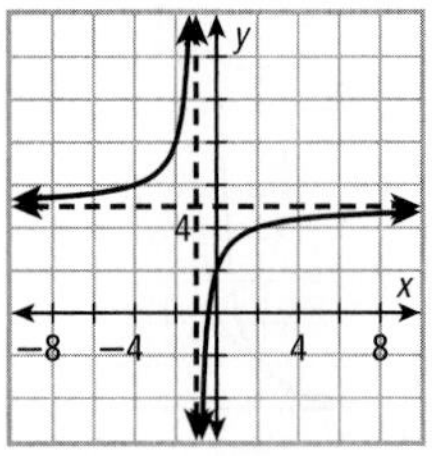

14. Hole at $x = 3$

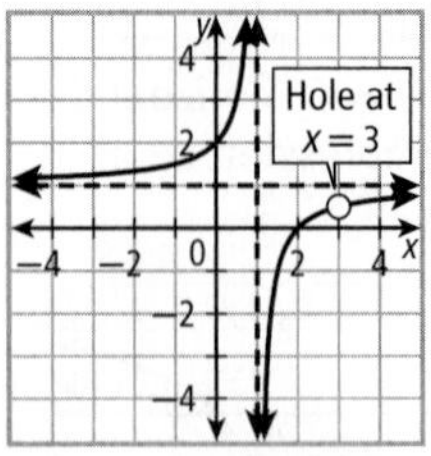

15. Hole at $x = 2$

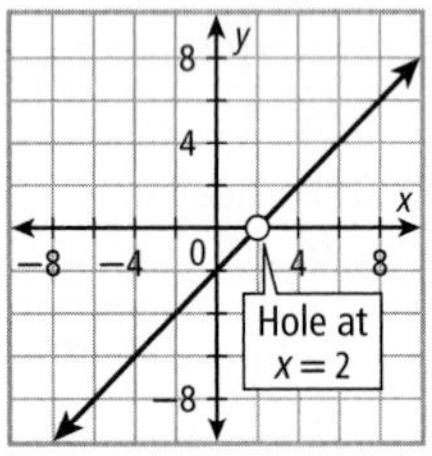

16. 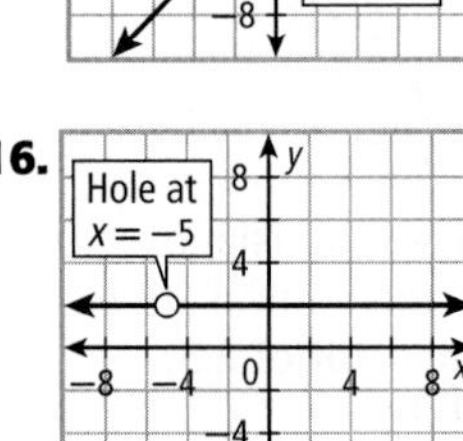

17. 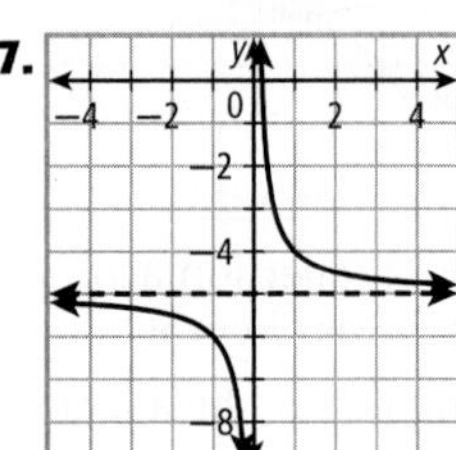

18. 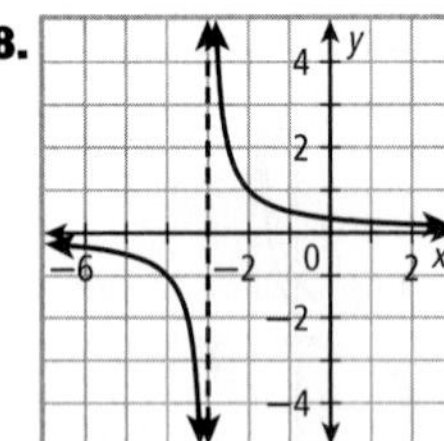

19. 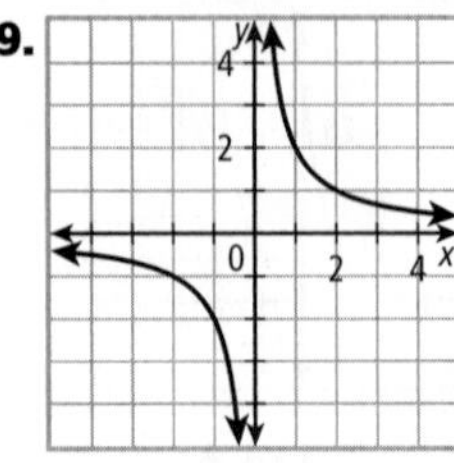

23.

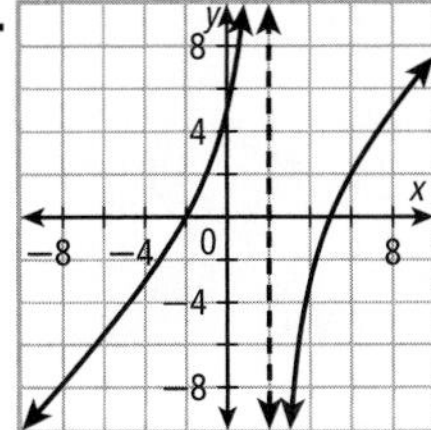

24.

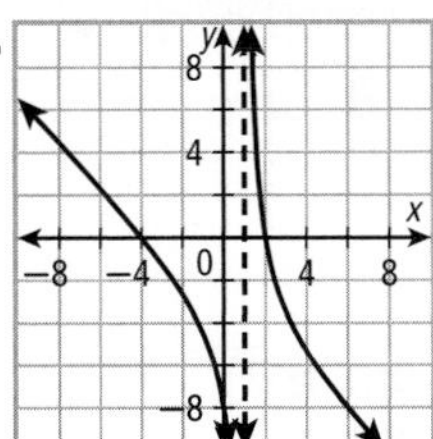

25.

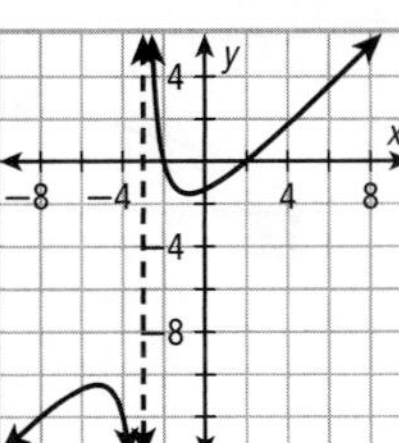

26.

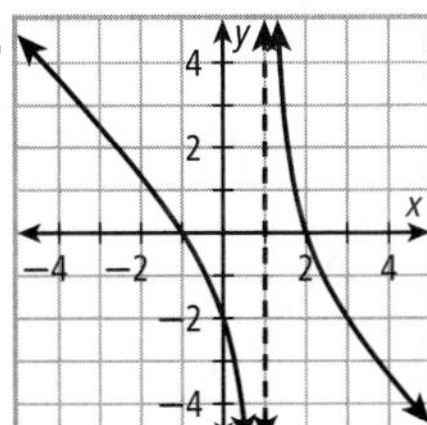

27.

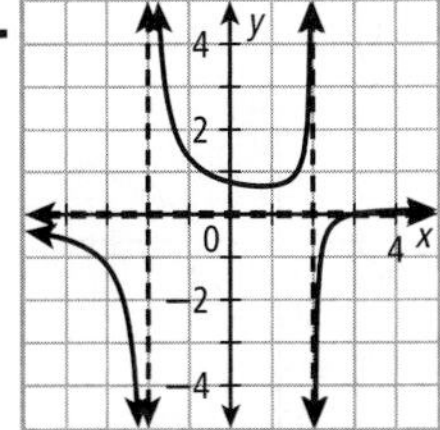

28.

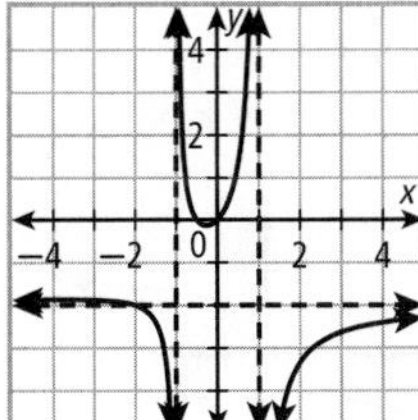

29.

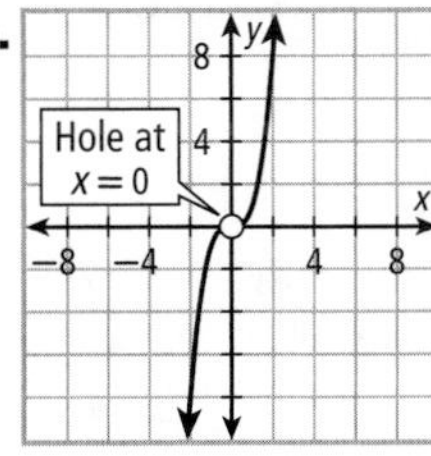

30.

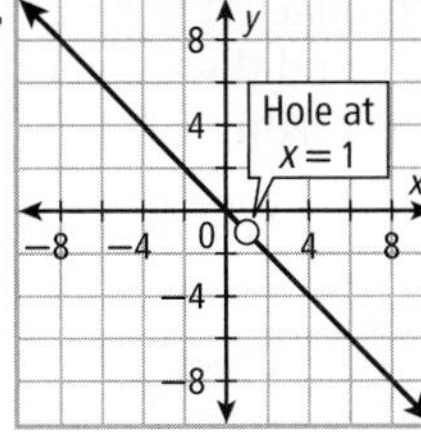

31.

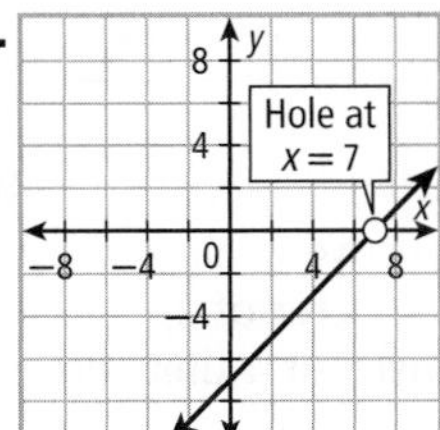

32b.

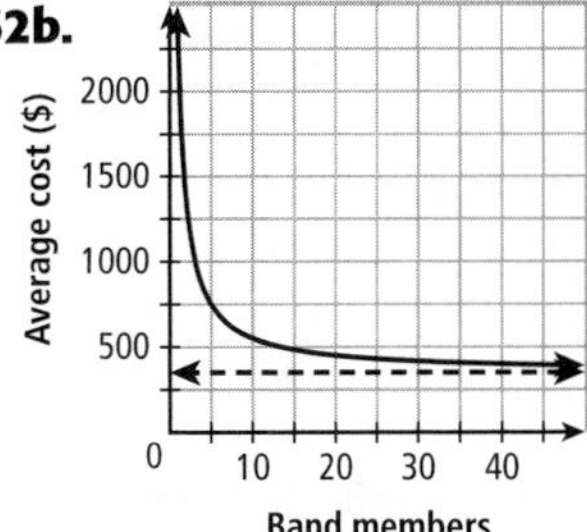

41. Possible answer:
$$f(x) = \frac{(x-2)(x+3)}{(x+3)(x+1)}$$

42a.

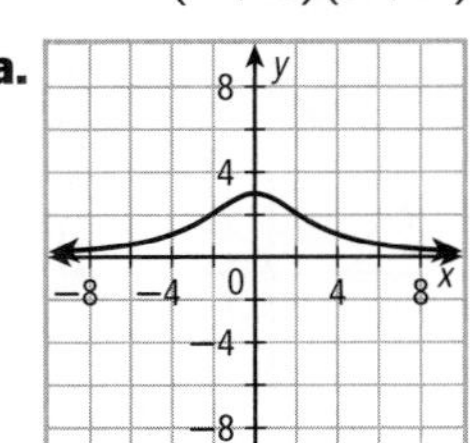

43a.

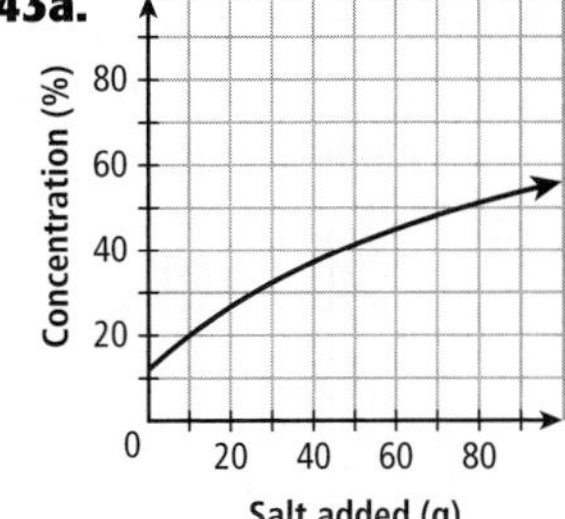

44a.

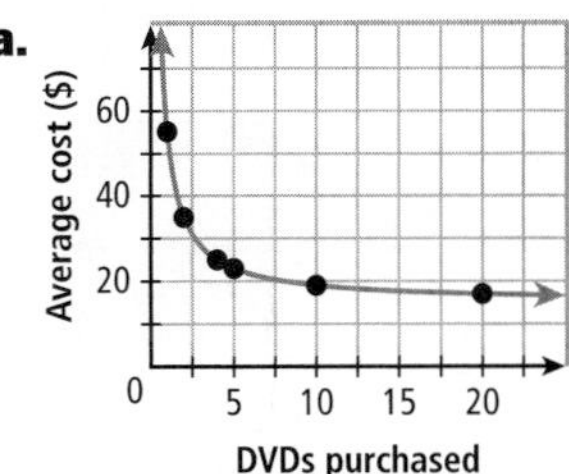

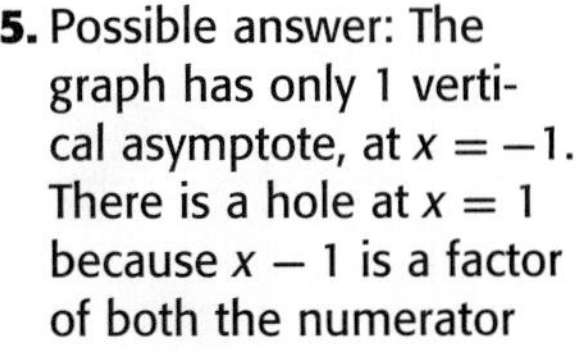

45. Possible answer: The graph has only 1 vertical asymptote, at $x = -1$. There is a hole at $x = 1$ because $x - 1$ is a factor of both the numerator and denominator.

46. Possible answer: Yes; a rational function with a denominator that is never equal to zero will have no vertical asymptotes (for example: $f(x) = \frac{x-3}{x^2+1}$).

47a.

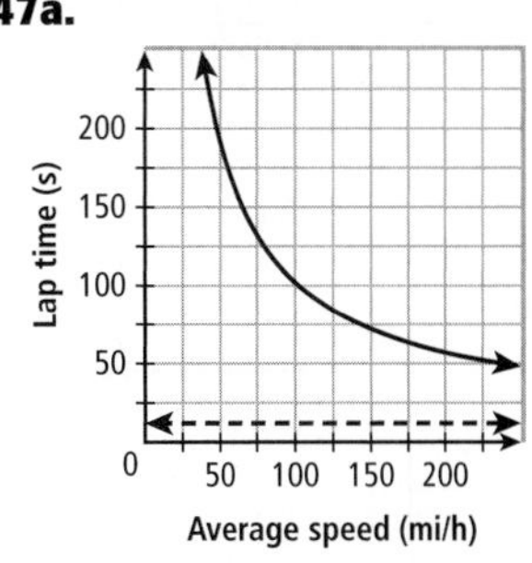

b. $t = 12$; the number of seconds the driver spent at the pit stop

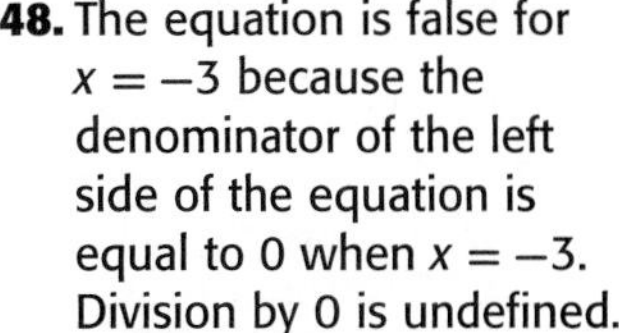

48. The equation is false for $x = -3$ because the denominator of the left side of the equation is equal to 0 when $x = -3$. Division by 0 is undefined.

53. holes at $x = 1$, $x = 2$, $x = 3$

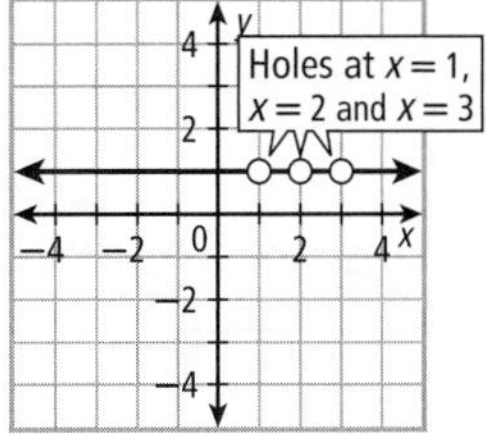

54. zeros: $-3, -\frac{2}{3}$; asymptotes: $x = -2$, $x = 2$, $y = 3$; hole at $x = 3$

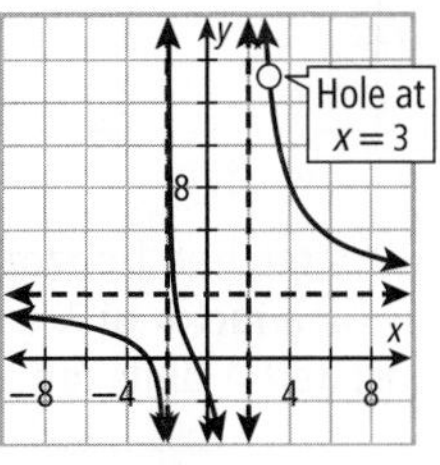

56. Possible answer:
$$f(x) = \frac{x^2+1}{x^2+2}$$

57. Possible answer:
$$f(x) = \frac{x(x^2-1)}{(x^2-1)(x^2-9)}$$

8A *Ready To Go On?*

10. $\frac{x-3}{x-5}$; $x \neq -5$ and $x \neq 5$

11. $\frac{x^2+2x+3}{(x-3)(x+3)}$; $x \neq -3$ and $x \neq 3$

13.

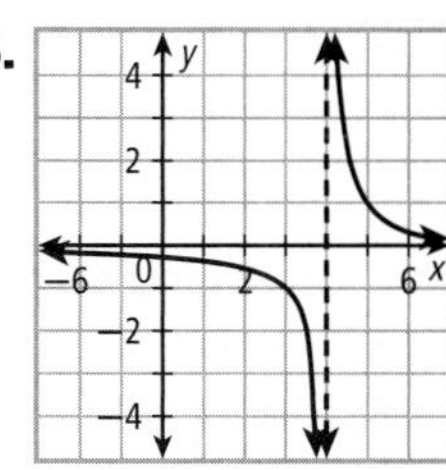

14.

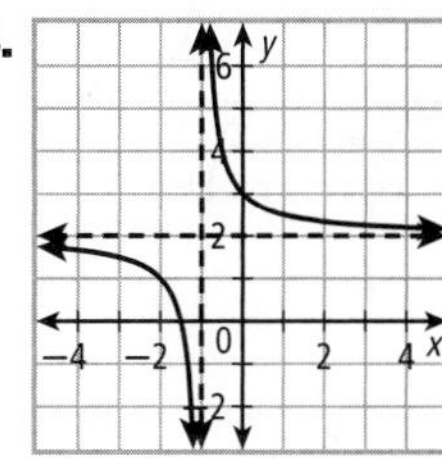

15.

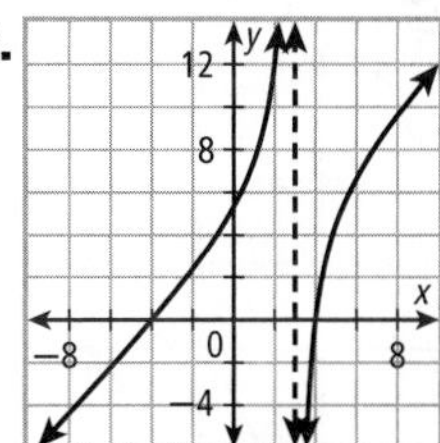

16.

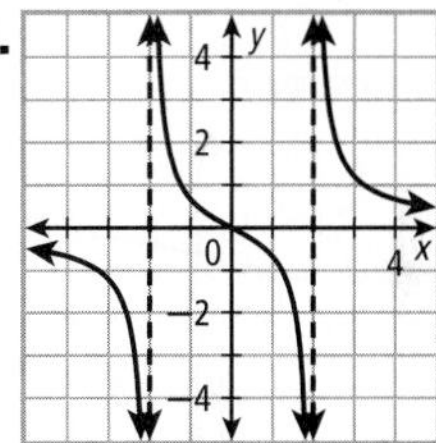

8-6 *Exercises*

92. $1^3 = 1 \cdot 1 \cdot 1 = 1$;
$$\left(\frac{-1+i\sqrt{3}}{2}\right)^3$$
$$= \frac{(-2-2i\sqrt{3})(-1+i\sqrt{3})}{8}$$
$$= \frac{8}{8} = 1; \left(\frac{-1-i\sqrt{3}}{2}\right)^3$$
$$= \frac{(-2+2i\sqrt{3})(-1-i\sqrt{3})}{8}$$
$$= \frac{8}{8} = 1$$

Additional Answers

98. zeros: ± 2; asymptote: $x = -5$

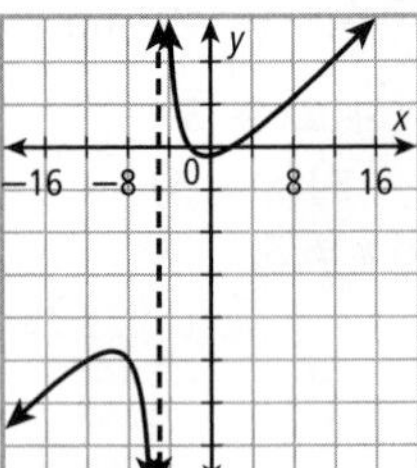

99. zero: -3; asymptotes: $x = -5$, $x = -1$, $y = 0$

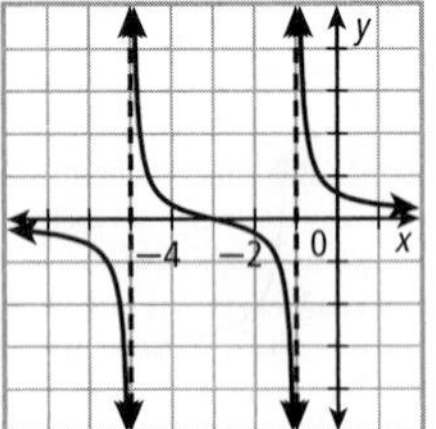

100. zero: $\frac{3}{4}$; asymptotes: $x = -6$, $y = 4$

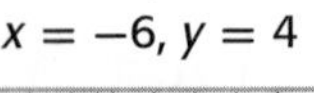

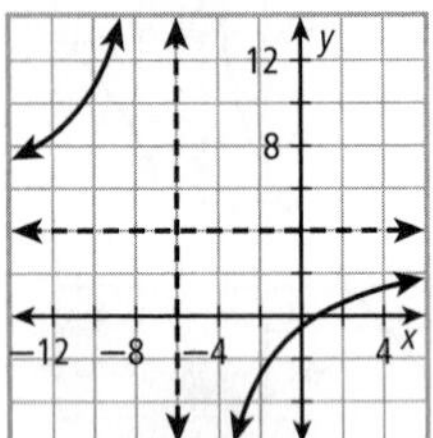

8-7 *Exercises*

2.

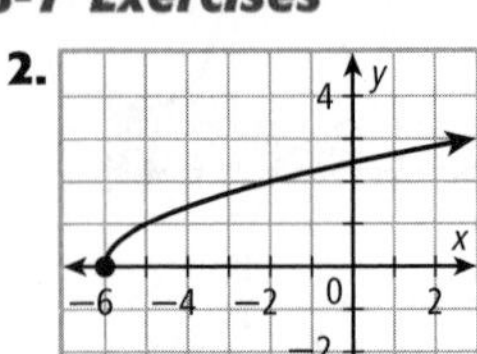

3.

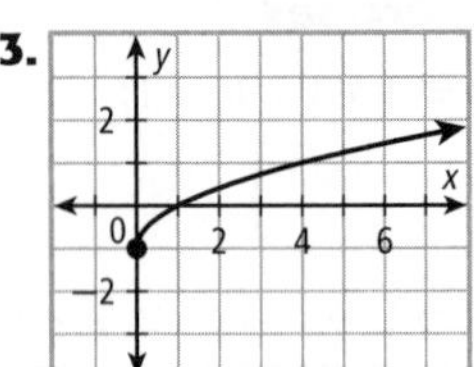

4.

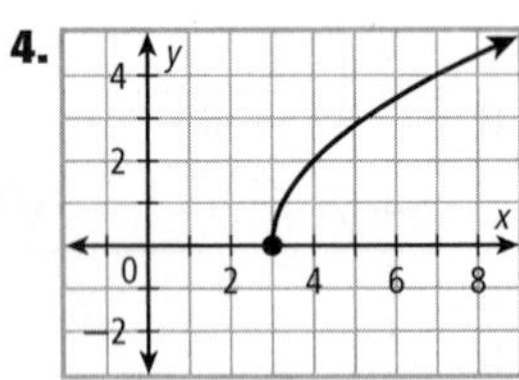

5.

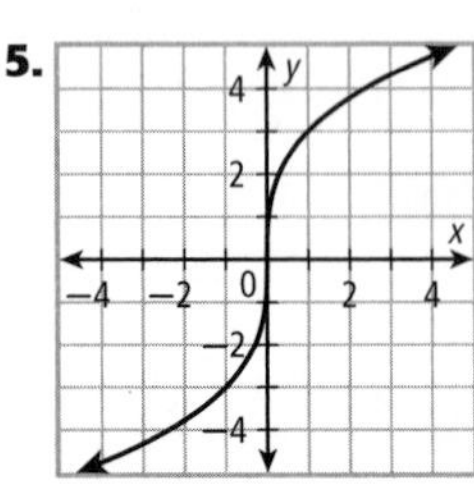

6.

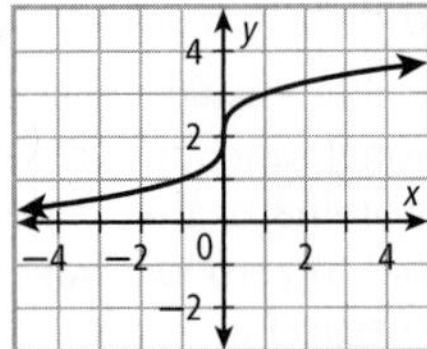

7.

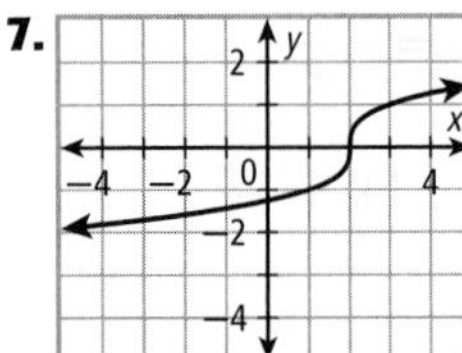

8.

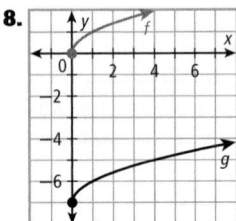

9.

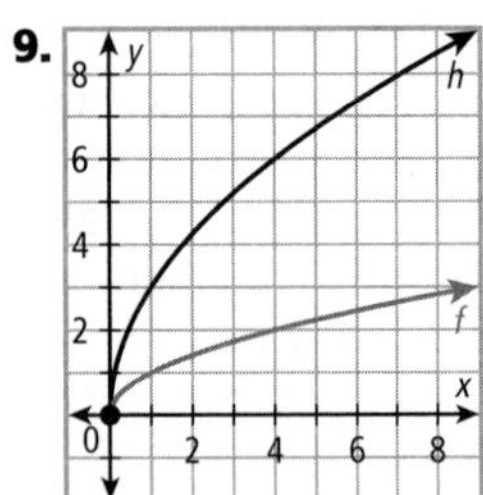

10.

11.

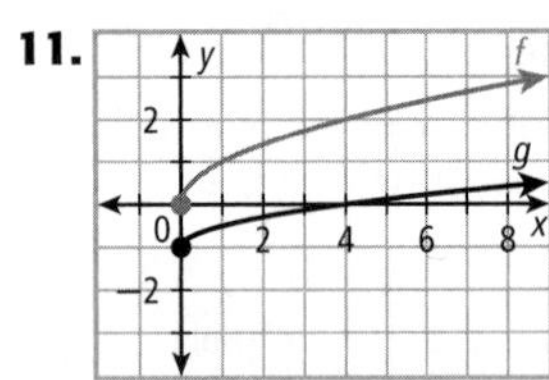

12. h is f stretched horizontally by a factor of 3 and translated 4 units left.

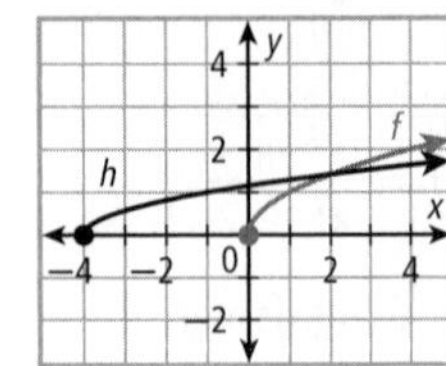

13. j is f reflected across the y-axis and then translated 3 units right.

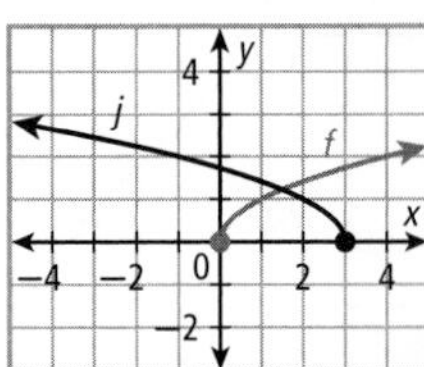

14. g is f reflected across the x-axis, vertically stretched by a factor of 2, and then translated 4 units down.

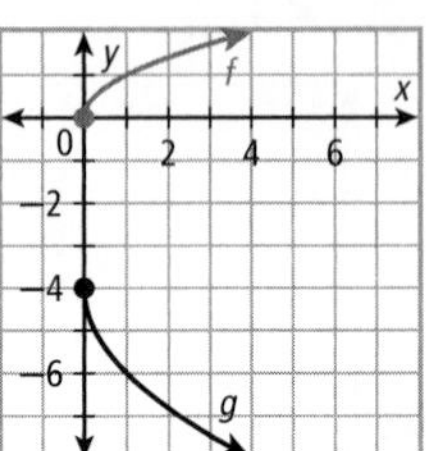

15. h is f reflected across the y-axis, horizontally compressed by a factor of $\frac{1}{2}$, and then translated 2 units left.

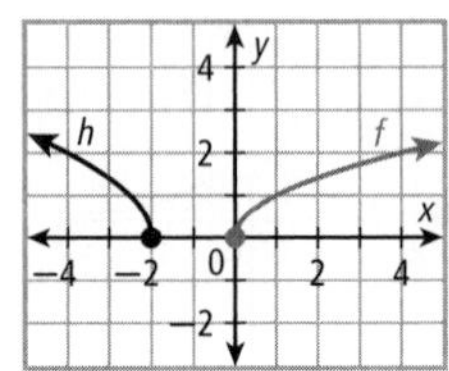

16. j is f vertically stretched by a factor of 3 and then translated 3 units up and 3 units left.

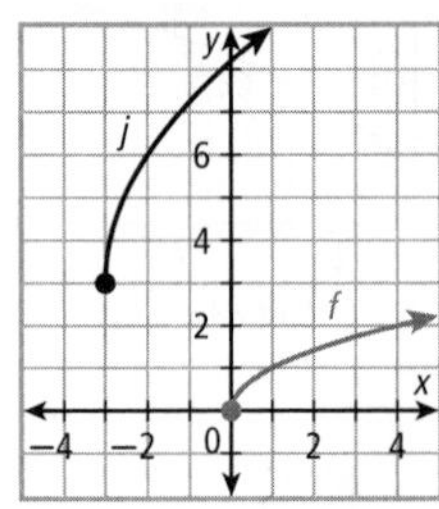

20.

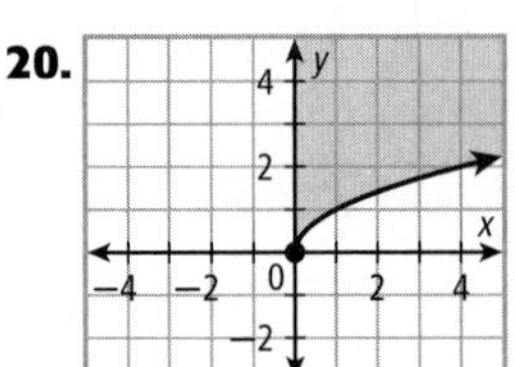

21.

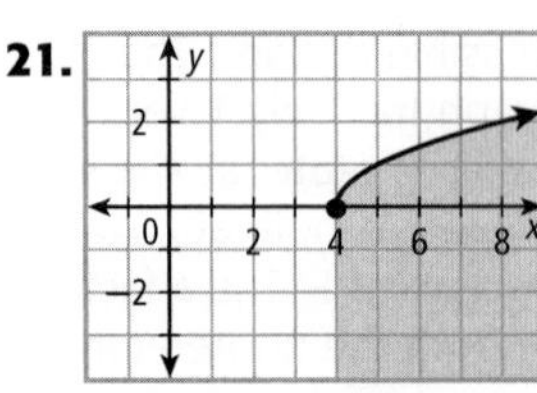

22.

23.

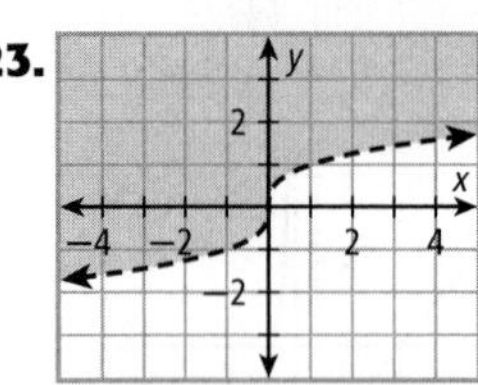

24. D: $\{x \mid x \geq 2\}$; R: $\{y \mid y \geq 0\}$

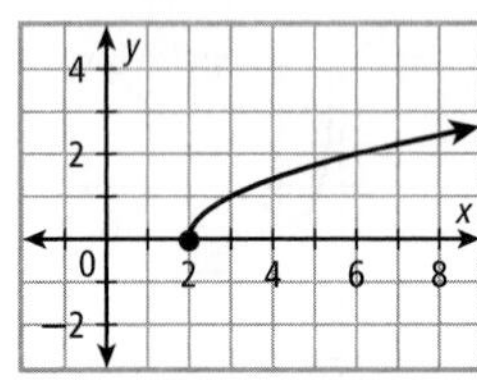

25. D: $\{x \mid x \geq 0\}$; R: $\{y \mid y \leq 0\}$

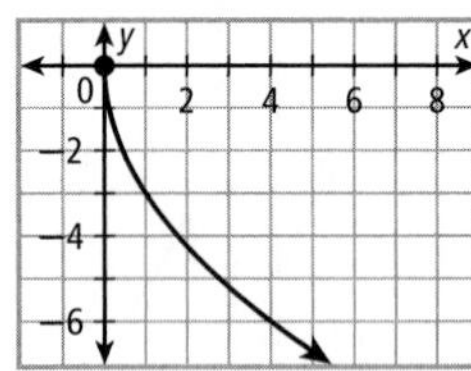

26. D: $\{x \mid x \geq -1\}$; R: $\{y \mid y \geq -3\}$

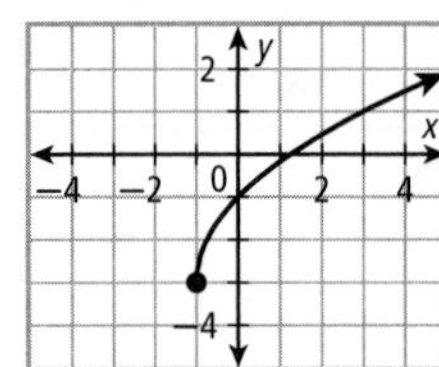

27. D: $\{x \mid x \in \mathbb{R}\}$; R: $\{y \mid y \in \mathbb{R}\}$

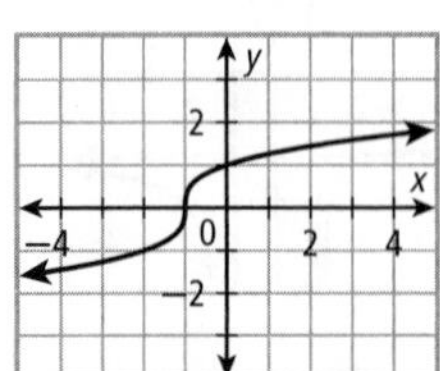

28. D: $\{x \mid x \in \mathbb{R}\}$; R: $\{y \mid y \in \mathbb{R}\}$

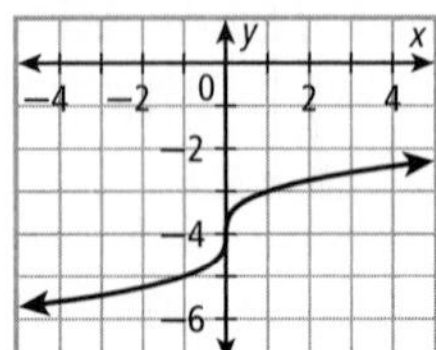

29. D: $\{x \mid x \in \mathbb{R}\}$;
R: $\{y \mid y \in \mathbb{R}\}$

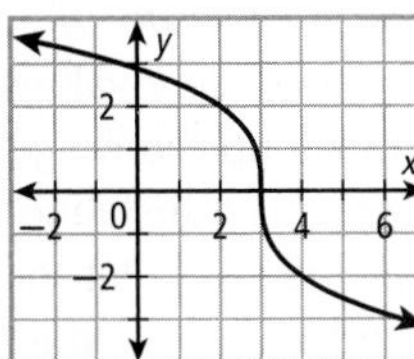

30. g is f translated 2 units up.

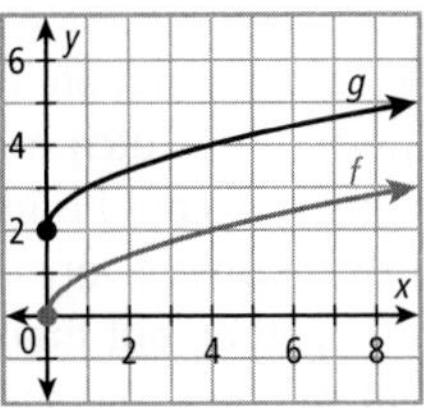

31. h is f translated 4 units right.

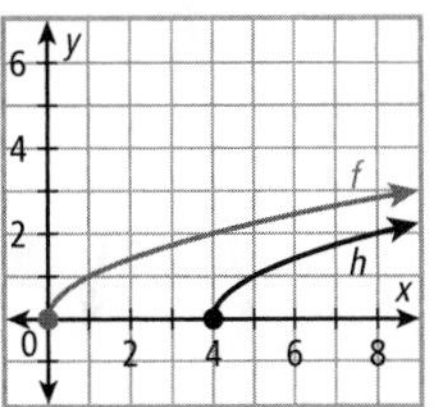

32. j is f vertically compressed by a factor of 0.5.

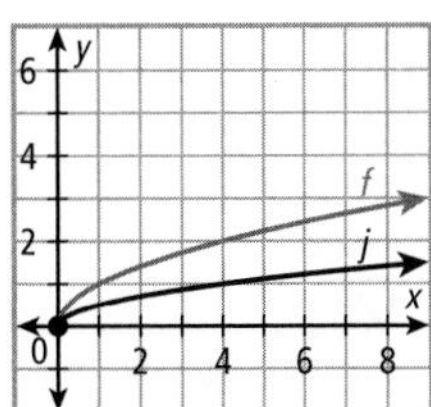

33. g is f horizontally compressed by a factor of $\frac{1}{3}$ and then translated 5 units left.

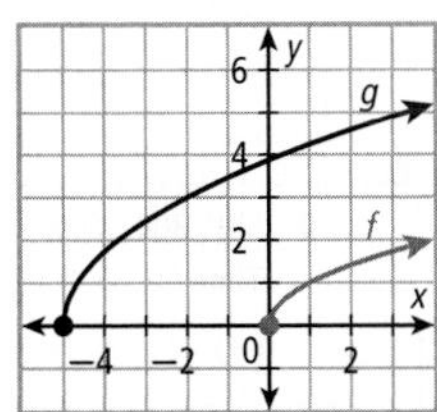

34. h is f vertically compressed by a factor of $\frac{1}{4}$ and then reflected across the y-axis.

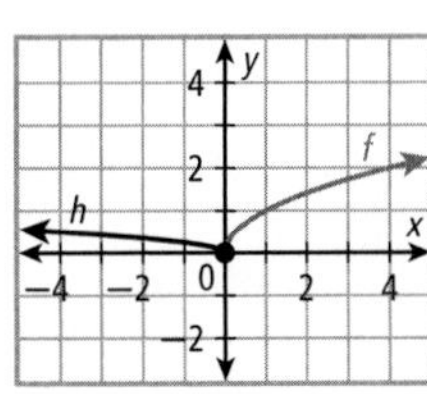

35. j is f translated 4 units left and 1 unit down.

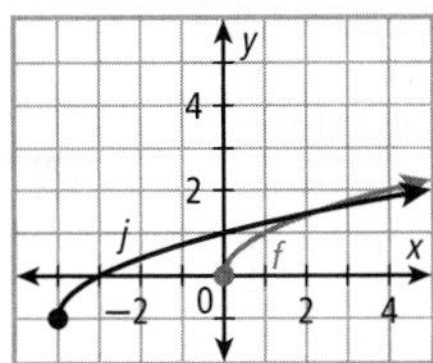

36. g is f reflected across the x-axis, vertically stretched by a factor of 4, and then translated 1 unit up.

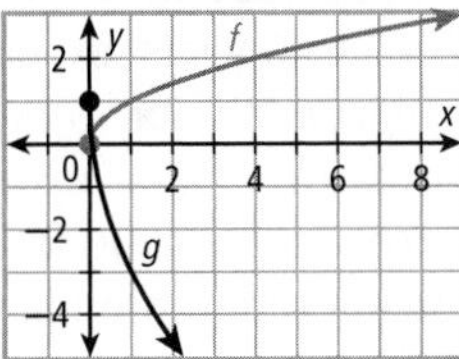

37. h is f reflected across the y-axis, vertically stretched by a factor of 3, and then translated 2 units up.

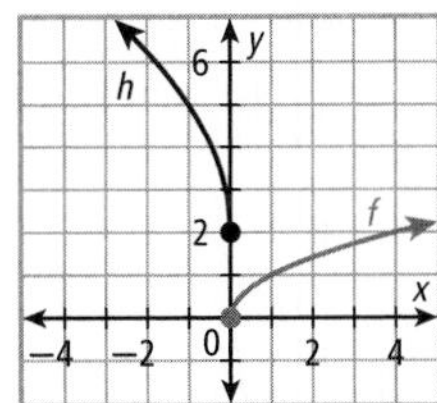

65.

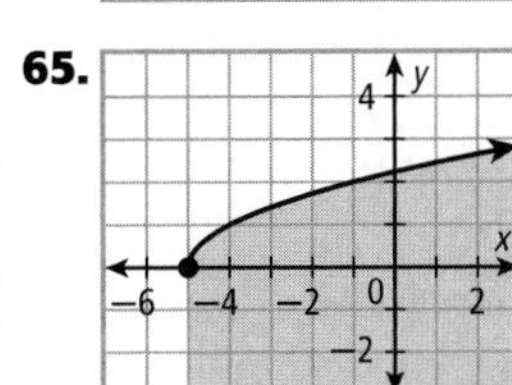

66.

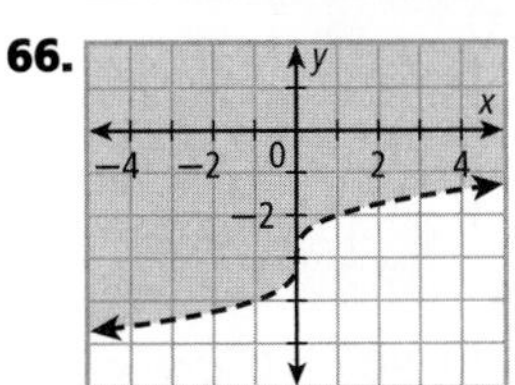

71. Possible answer: Only nonnegative radicands have real square roots; therefore, the domain of square-root functions is limited to values of x that make the radicand nonnegative. By contrast, all real radicands have cube roots; therefore, the domain of cube-root functions is not limited.

72. Possible answer: A horizontal translation affects the domain, but not the range. The domain of the translated function is $x \geq h$, where h is the number of units the function is translated horizontally. A vertical translation affects the range, but not the domain. The range of the translated function is $f(x) \geq k$, where k is the number of units the function is translated vertically.

77. Possible answer: The graph was reflected across the y-axis and then translated 4 units right; $g(x) = \sqrt{-(x-4)}$.

80.
−1 0 1 2 3 4 5

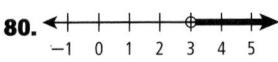

81.

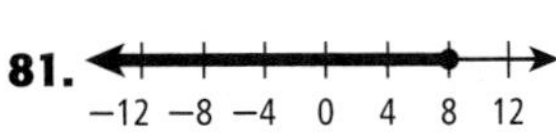

82.

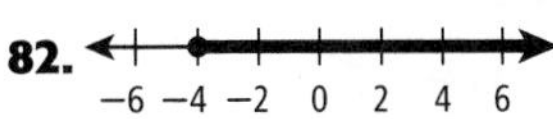

8B *Multi-Step Test Prep*

1.

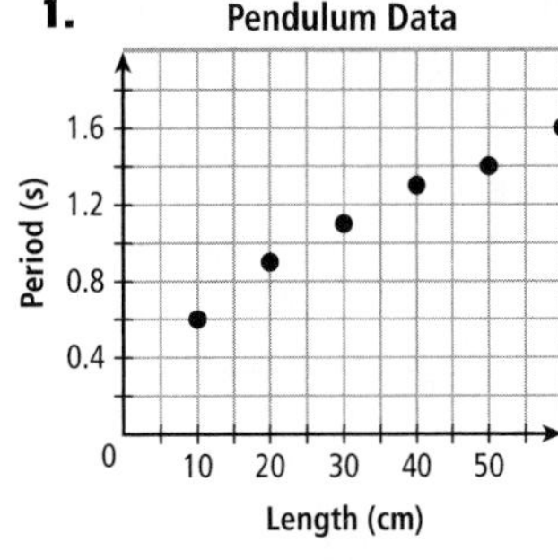

6. Possible answer: Yes, the function is a reasonable model because each of the data points lies close to its graph.

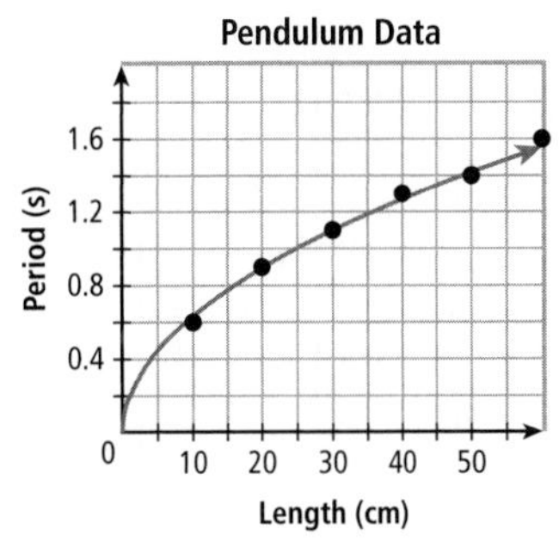

8B *Ready To Go On?*

11. D: $\{x \mid x \geq 0\}$;
R: $\{y \mid y \leq 4\}$

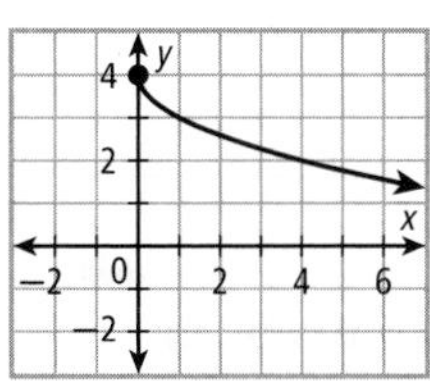

12.

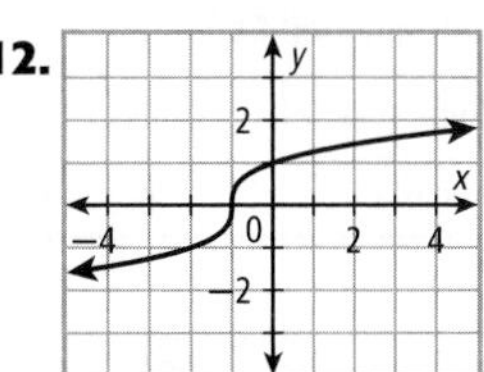

15.

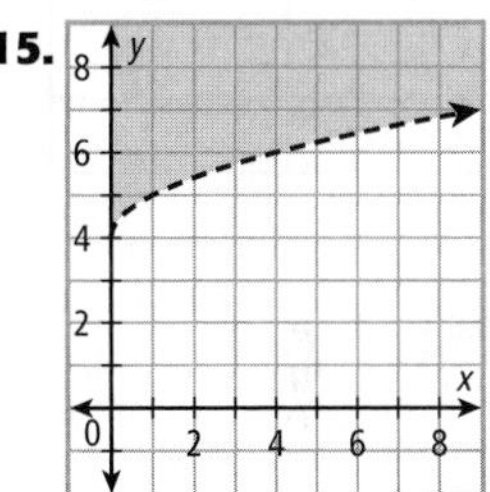

16.

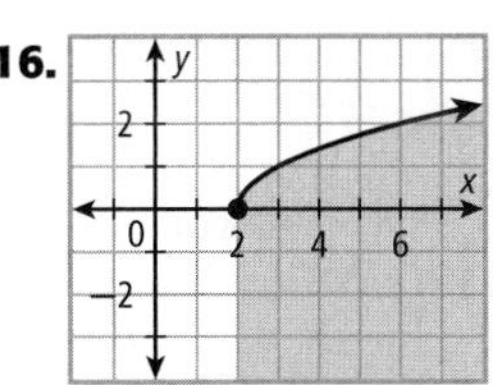

Chapter 9

9-1 *Exercises*

5.

Enrollment Costs	
Credit Hours	**Cost ($)**
1	397.75
2	616.15
3	834.55
4	1053.00
5	1271.40

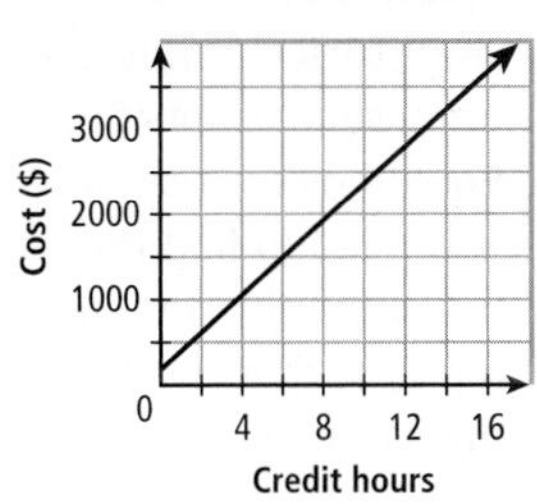

6.

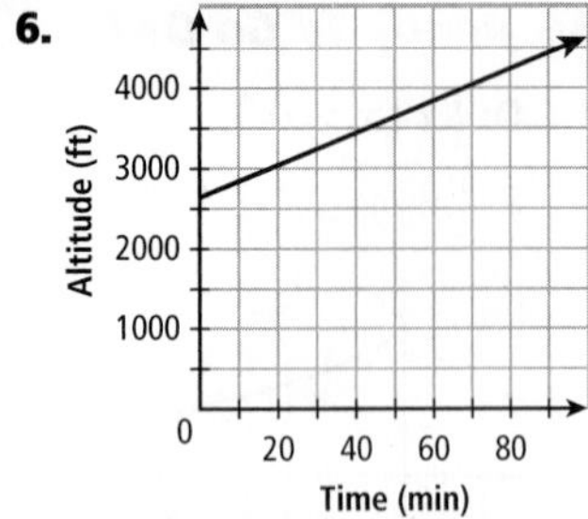

$A = 20t + 2640$

20.

Time (yr)	Dolls
0	6
1	12
2	24
3	48
4	96
5	192

Antique Doll Collection

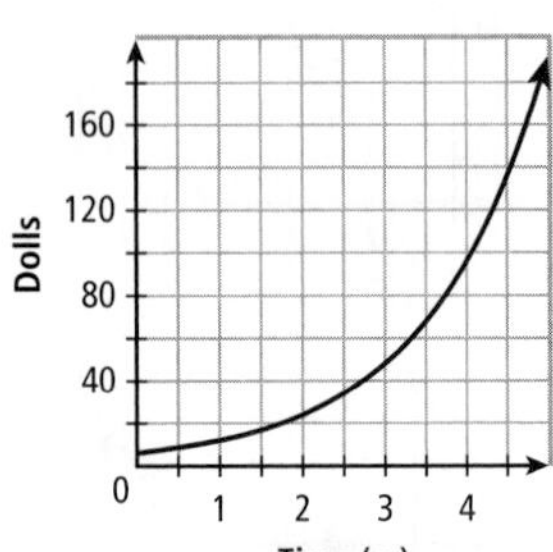

21a.

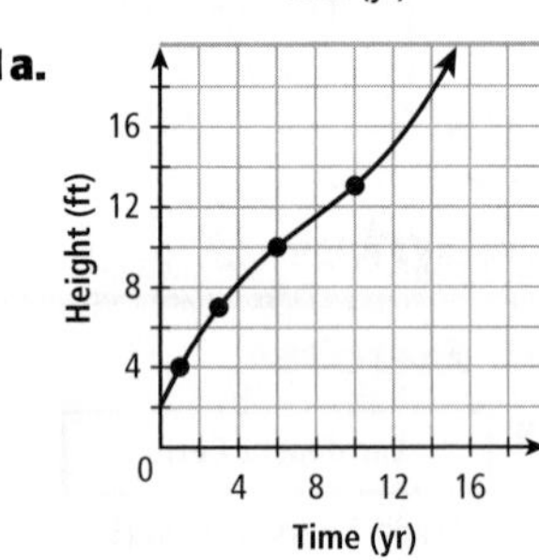

22. Possible answer: A table would be useful when you need exact function values for commonly used inputs, such as in tax tables. A graph is useful when you want to see trends over time, such as inflation. Equations are useful when you need to find the exact function value for any input, such as when finding sales tax.

23. Possible answer: Graphs help you see an overall trend, especially when it is a very recognizable shape such as a straight line. Tables help you see the change between individual values, such as a cost increasing by a certain amount.

24a.

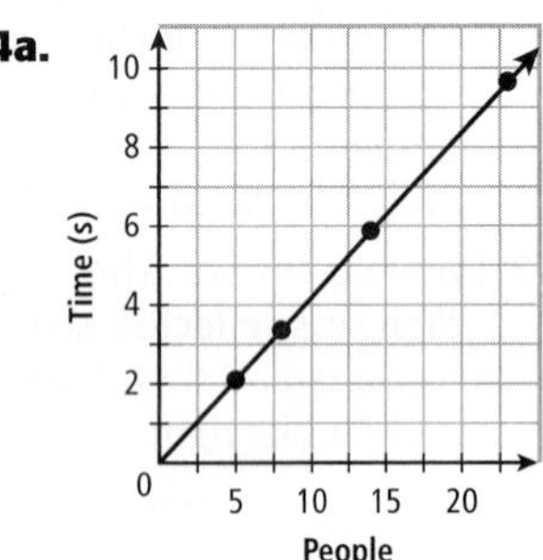

28.

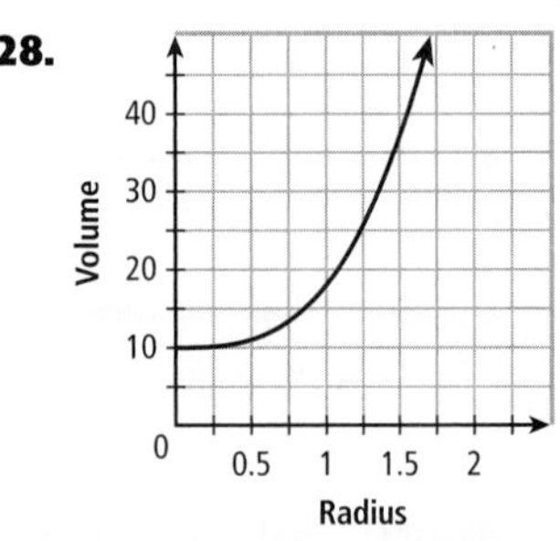

29.

34.

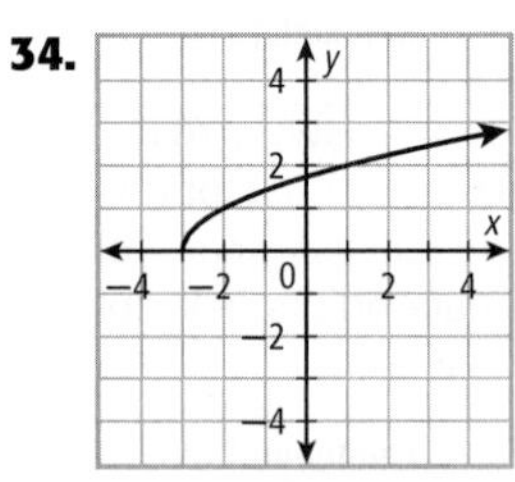

35.

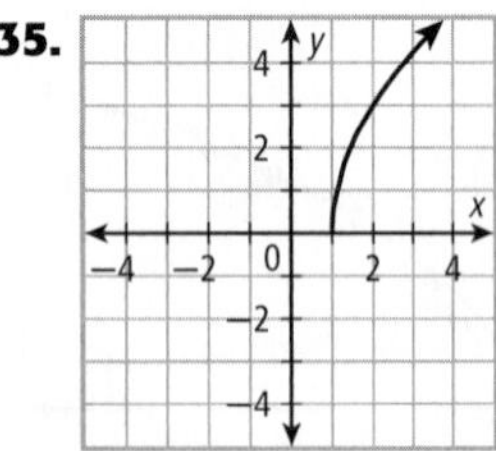

9-2 *Exercises*

10.

Salary (thousand $)	Experience (yr)
45	$0 \le x < 3$
55	$3 \le x < 6$
68	$6 \le x < 11$
73	$x \ge 11$

Salaries in Technology

The average salary is \$45,000 for workers with less than 3 years' experience, \$55,000 for workers with 3 to 6 years' experience, \$68,000 for workers with 6 to 11 years' experience, and \$73,000 for workers with more than 11 years' experience.

25.

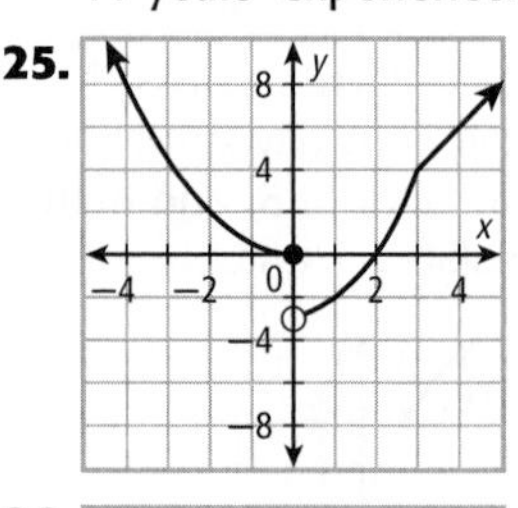

26.

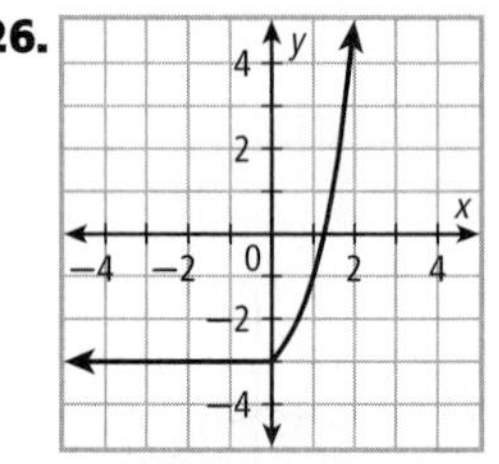

9-3 *Exercises*

22a. $f(x) = \begin{cases} 6 & \text{if } x \le 200 \\ 0.03x & \text{if } x > 200 \end{cases}$

b. $f(x) = \begin{cases} 6.90 & \text{if } 0 < x \le 200 \\ 0.0345x & \text{if } x > 200 \end{cases}$

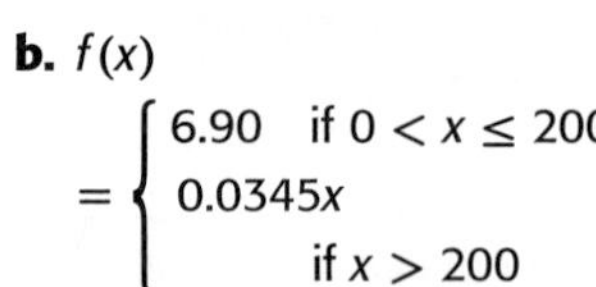

23a. $T(n) = \begin{cases} 2.8n & \text{if } n \le 8 \\ 3.6n - 6.4 & \text{if } n > 8 \end{cases}$

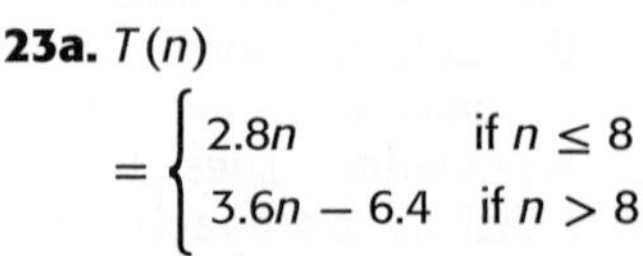

b. The graph has the same basic shape, but the slopes of both pieces of the graph are less steep because it takes less time for the phrase to move through the line.

30. Possible answer: A vertical translation moves the graph up or down, which affects only the y-values that make up the range. A horizontal translation moves the graph left or right, which affects the x-values that make up the domain.

31. No; if a graph is not continuous there are at least 2 points that are not connected. A stretch or compression could bring 2 of those points very close together, but there would still be some space between them.

35a, b.

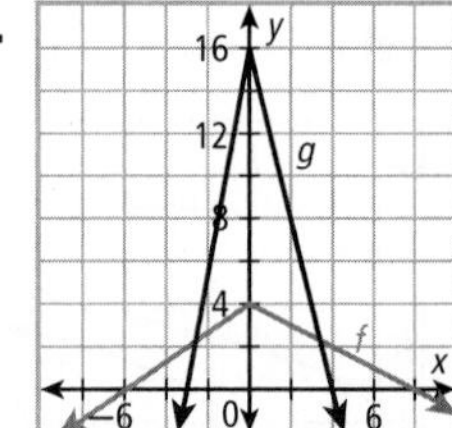

9A *Multi-Step Test Prep*

5.

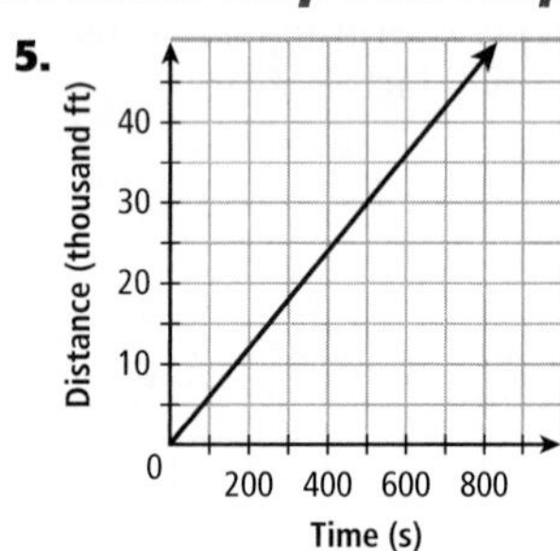

6.

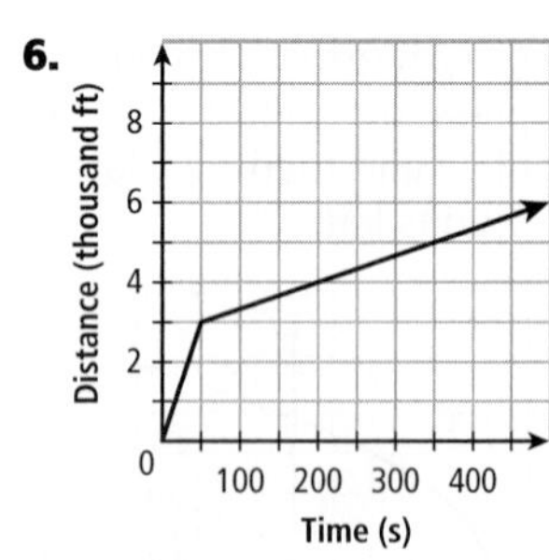

$d(t) = \begin{cases} 60t & \text{if } 0 \le t \le 50 \\ 6.67(t - 50) + 3000 & \text{if } 50 < t < 500 \end{cases}$

where t is time in seconds

9A *Ready To Go On?*

1.

Time (h)	Pages
0	294
1	252
2	210
3	168
4	126
5	84
6	42
7	0

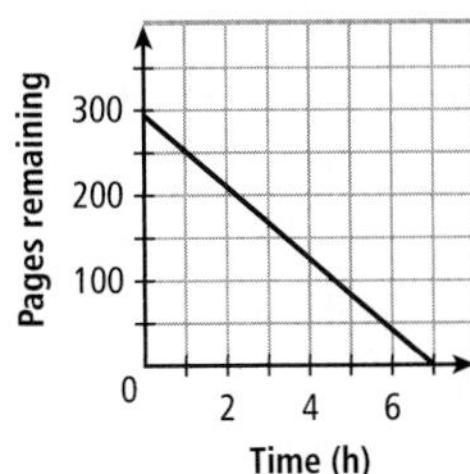

3.

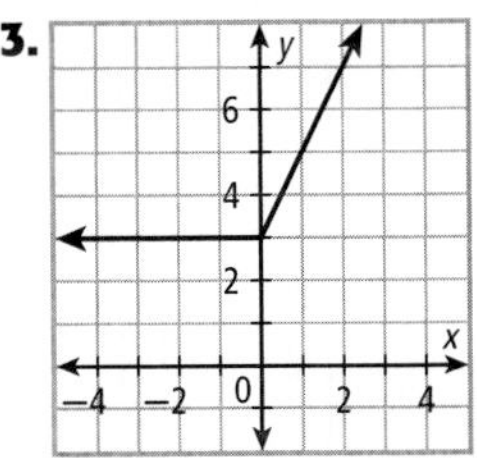

4.

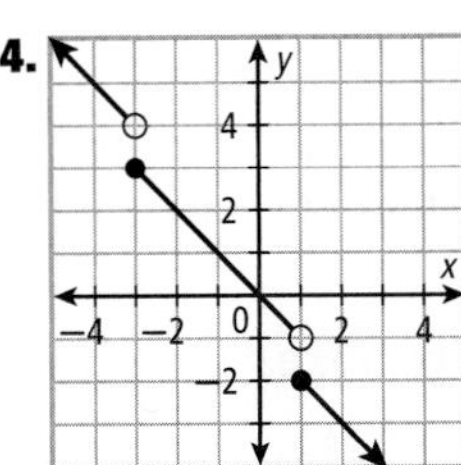

5. Rental Prices

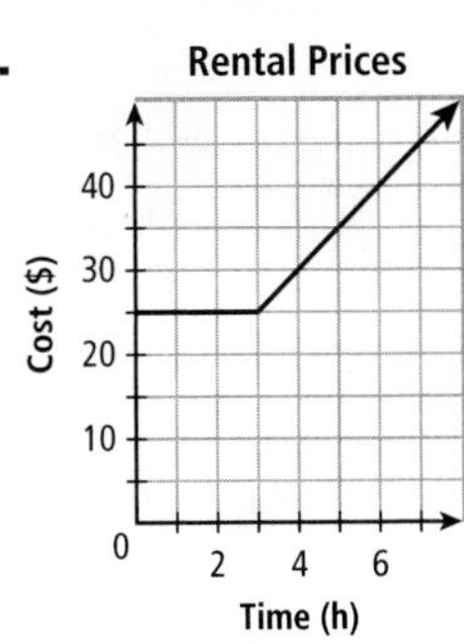

$f(x) = \begin{cases} 25 & \text{if } 0 < x \le 3 \\ 25+5(x-3) & \text{if } x > 3 \end{cases}$

6. $f(x) = \begin{cases} -4 & \text{if } x \le 0 \\ x+1 & \text{if } x > 0 \end{cases}$

7. $f(x) = \begin{cases} 3x+6 & \text{if } x < -3 \\ -2x+1 & \text{if } x \ge -3 \end{cases}$

8. $f(x) = \begin{cases} 4 & \text{if } x < -2 \\ x^2 & \text{if } -2 \le x < 2 \\ x+2 & \text{if } x \ge 2 \end{cases}$

9. $f(x)$: x-int. = 1, y-int. = −2; $g(x)$: x-int. = 2, y-int. = 2

10. $f(x)$: x-int. = −2 and 2, y-int. = −4; $g(x)$: x-int. = −2 and 2, y-int. = −8

11.

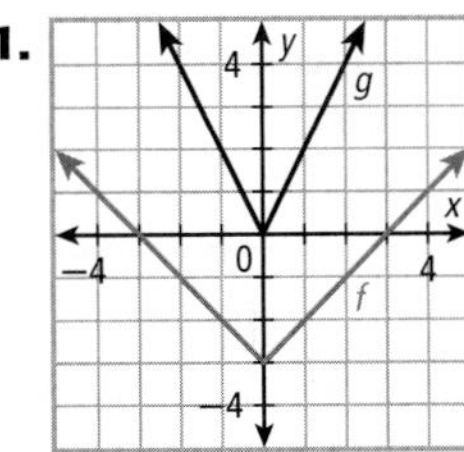

12.

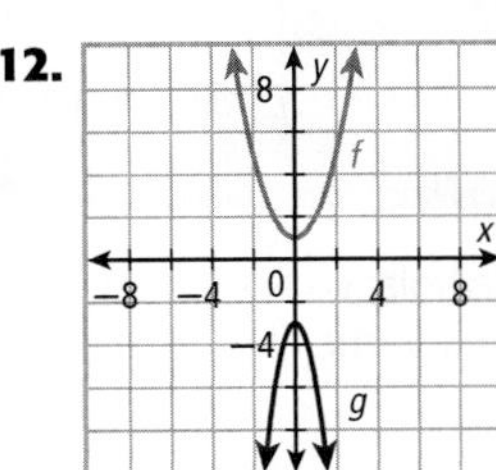

Chapter 9 Test

1.

Sales ($)	Earnings ($)
0	300
2,000	360
4,000	420
6,000	480
8,000	540
10,000	600

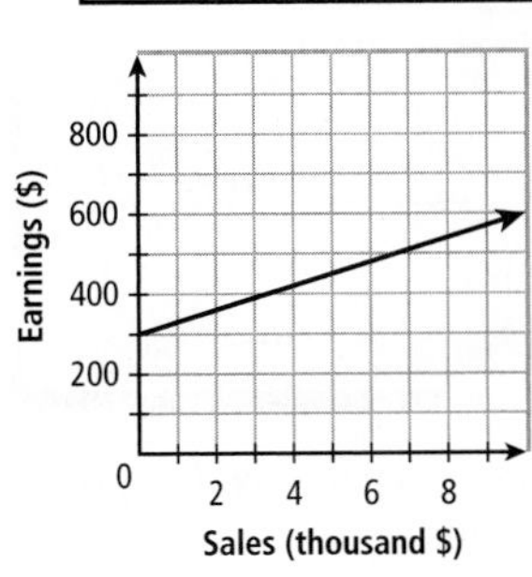

$E = 0.03s + 300$

Chapter 10

10-1 *Exercises*

2.

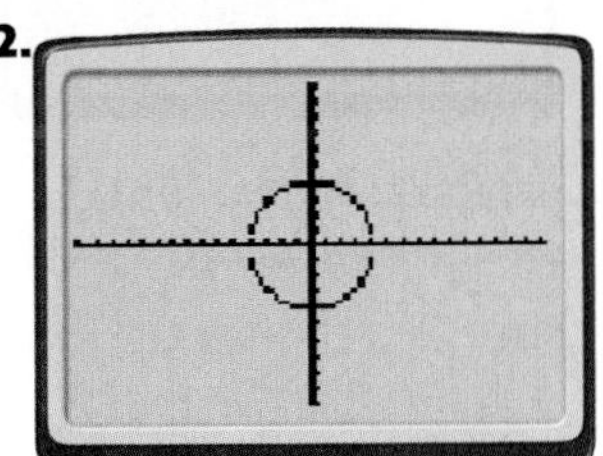

circle; center: (0, 0); intercepts: (0, ±4), (±4, 0)

3.

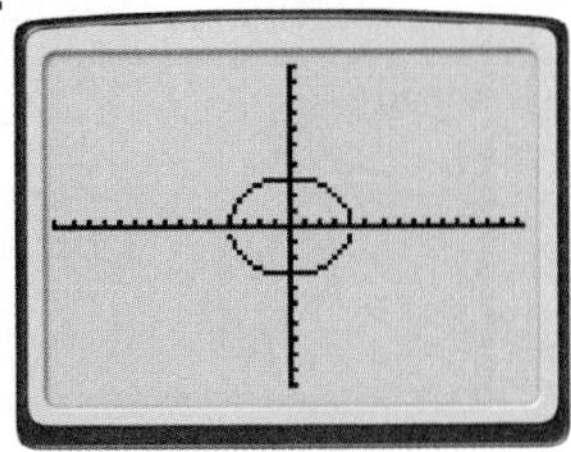

ellipse; center: (0, 0); intercepts: (0, ±3), (±4, 0)

4.

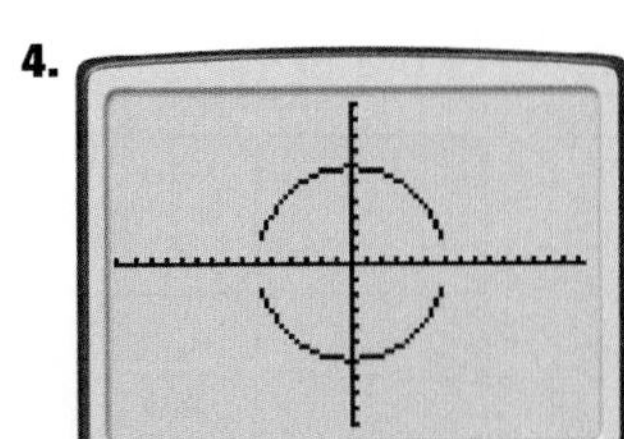

circle; center: (0, 0); intercepts: (0, ±6), (±6, 0)

5.

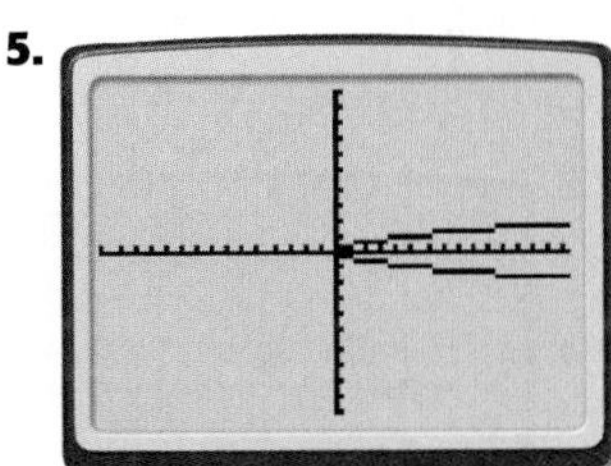

parabola; vertex: (0, 0); opens right

6.

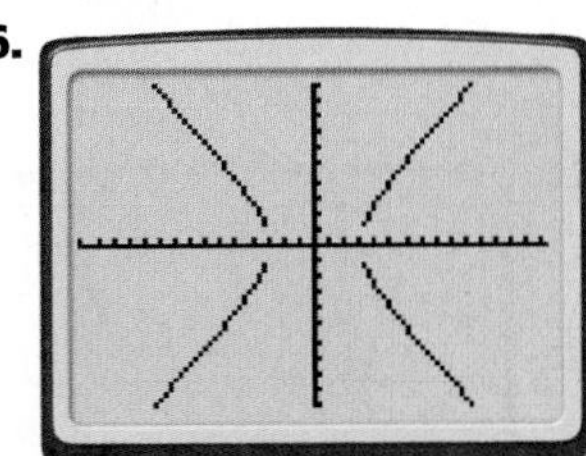

hyperbola; vertices: (±3, 0); opens horizontally

7.

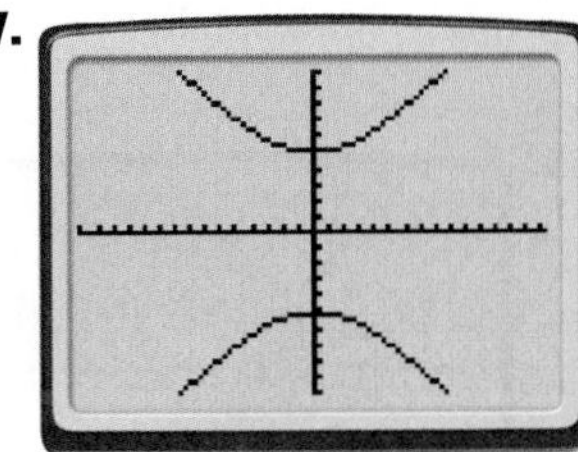

hyperbola; vertices: (0, ±5); opens vertically

8.

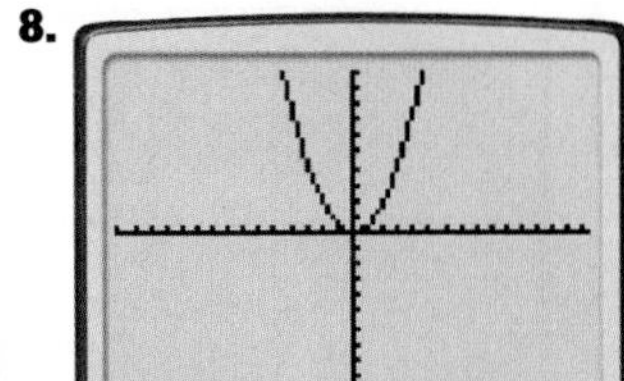

parabola; vertex: (0, 0); opens upward

9.

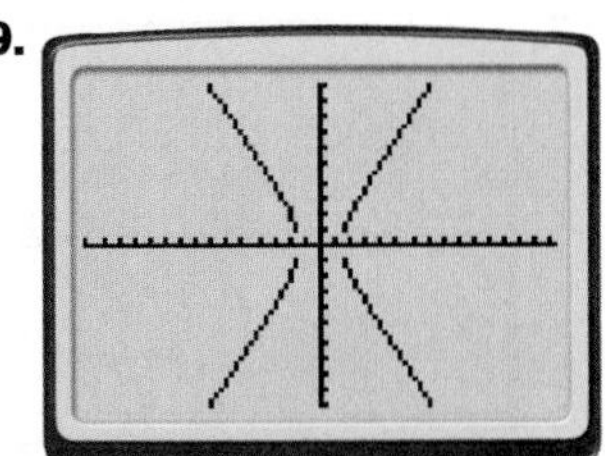

hyperbola; vertices: $(\pm\sqrt{2}, 0)$; opens horizontally

10.

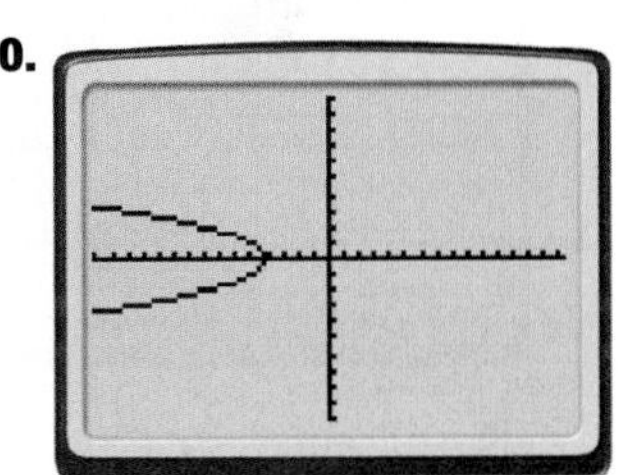

parabola; vertex: (−4, 0); opens left

14.

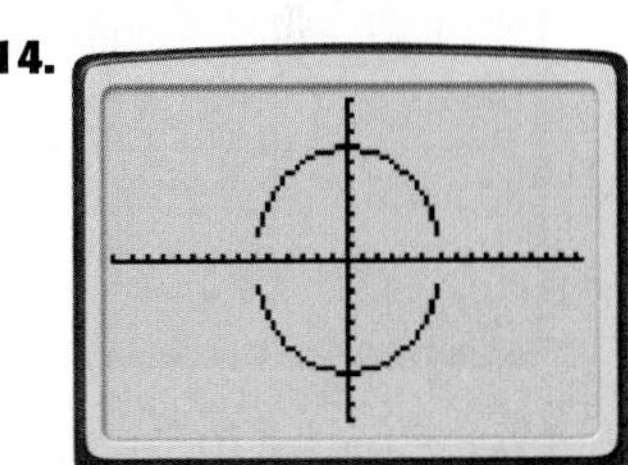

ellipse; center: (0, 0); intercepts: (0, ±7), (±6, 0)

15.

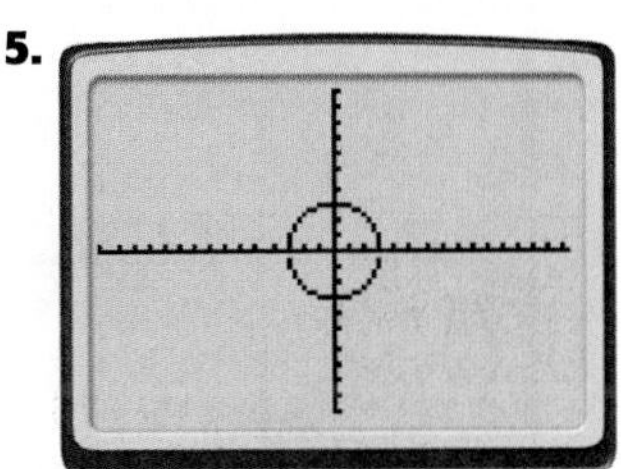

circle; center: (0, 0); intercepts: (0, ±3), (±3, 0)

16.
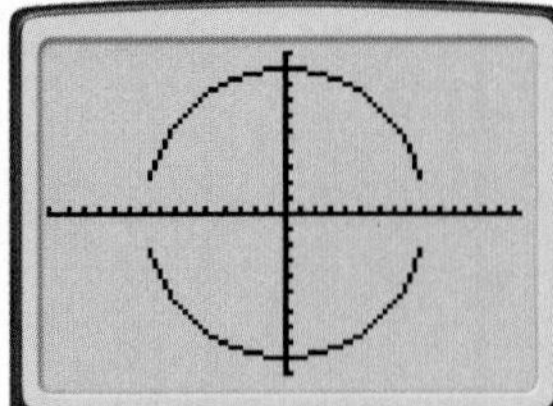

circle; center: (0, 0); intercepts: (0, ±9), (±9, 0)

17.
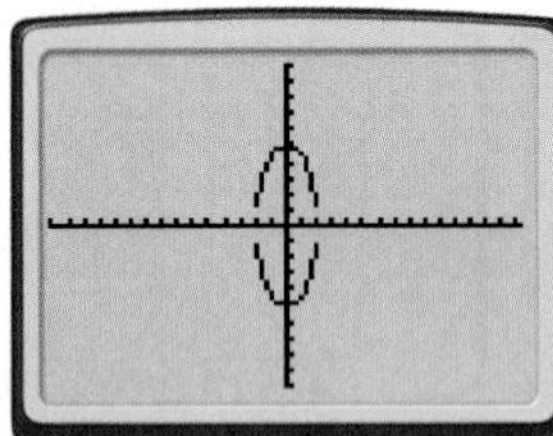

ellipse; center: (0, 0); intercepts: (0, ±5), (±2, 0)

18.
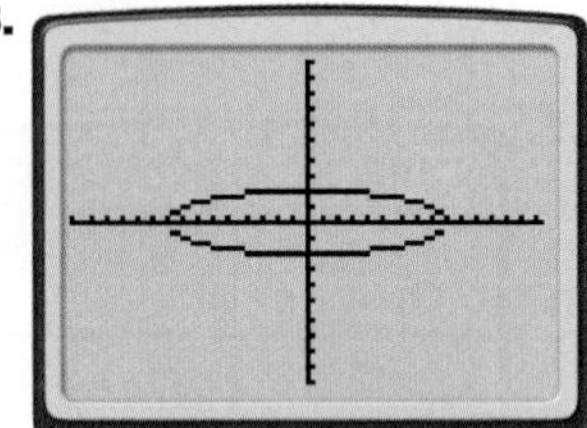

ellipse; center: (0, 0); intercepts: (0, ±2), (±9, 0)

19.
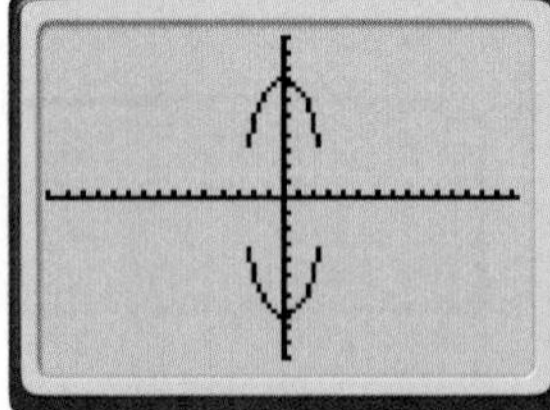

ellipse; center: (0, 0); intercepts: $\left(0, \pm\frac{15}{2}\right)$, $\left(\pm\frac{5}{2}, 0\right)$

20.
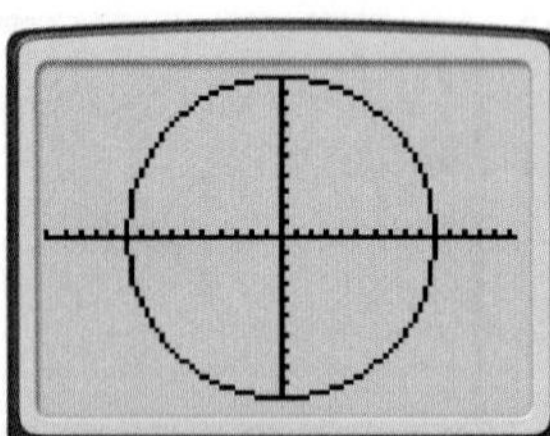

circle; center: (0, 0); intercepts: (0, ±10), (±10, 0)

21.
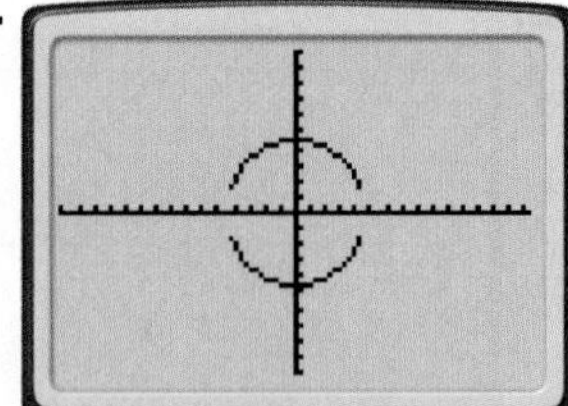

circle; center: (0, 0); intercepts: $\left(0, \pm\frac{9}{2}\right)$, $\left(\pm\frac{9}{2}, 0\right)$

22.
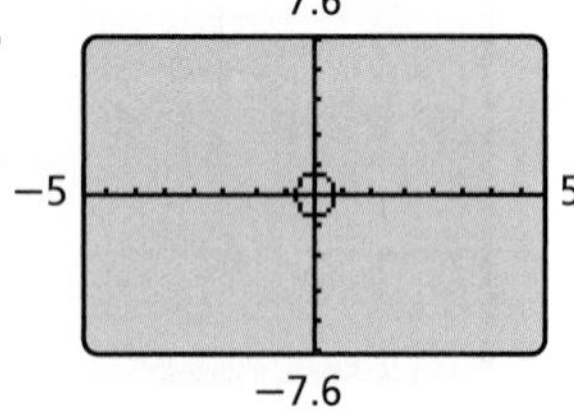

circle; center: (0, 0); intercepts: $\left(0, \pm\frac{2}{3}\right)$, $\left(\pm\frac{2}{3}, 0\right)$

23.
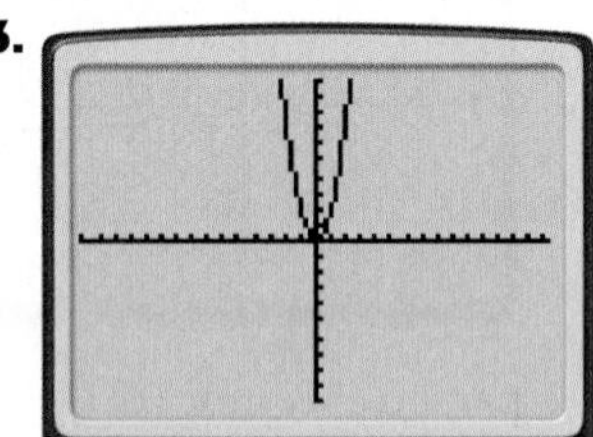

parabola; vertex: (0, 0); opens upward

24.
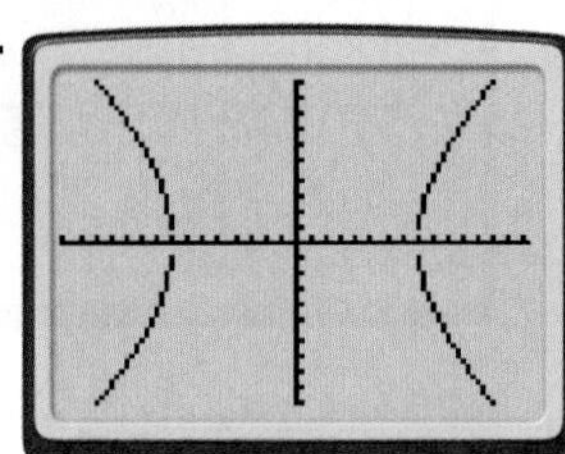

hyperbola; vertices: (±8, 0); opens horizontally

25.
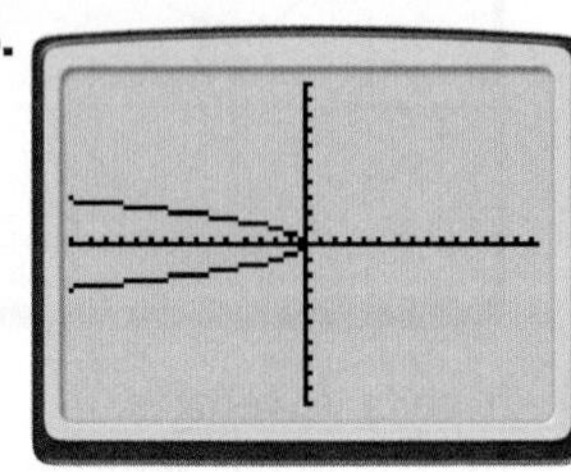

parabola; vertex: (0, 0); opens left

26.
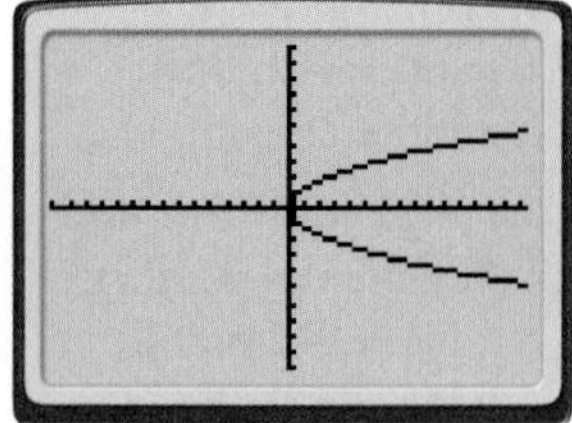

parabola; vertex: (0, 0); opens right

27.
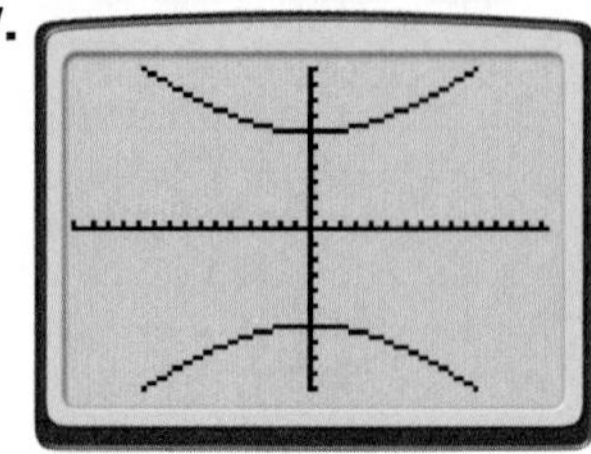

hyperbola; vertices: (0, ±6); opens vertically

28.
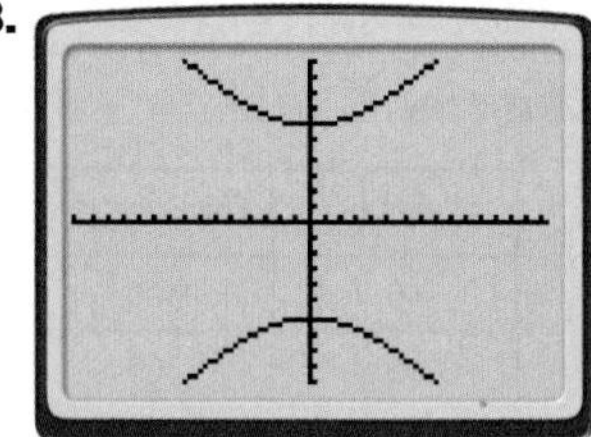

hyperbola; vertices: (0, ±6); opens vertically

29.
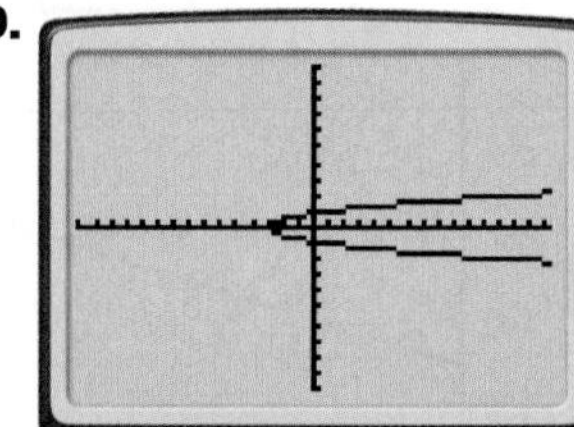

parabola; vertex: (−3, 0); opens right

30.
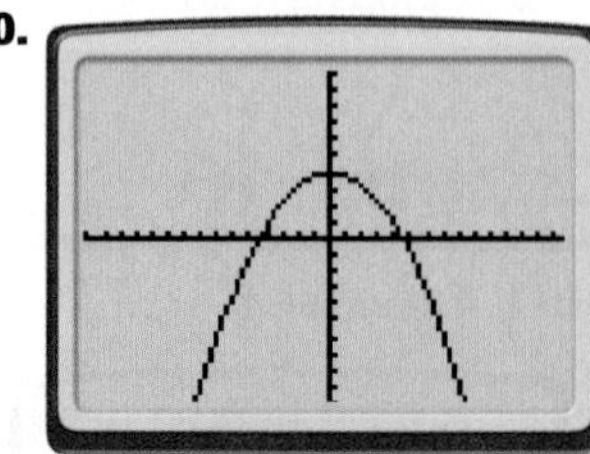

parabola; vertex: (0, 4); opens downward

31.
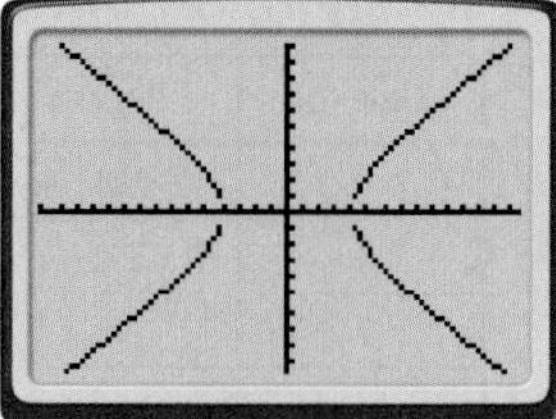

hyperbola; vertices: (±4, 0); opens horizontally

66.
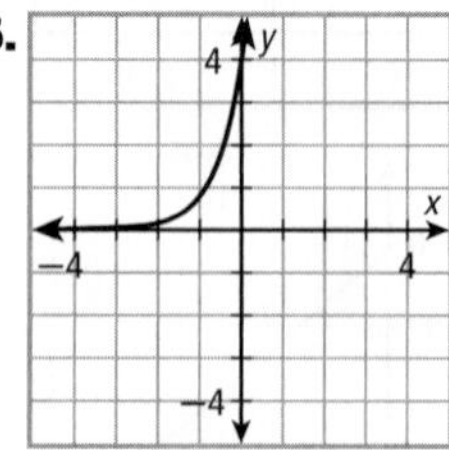

y-int.: 4; asymptote: $y = 0$; vertical stretch by a factor of 4

67.
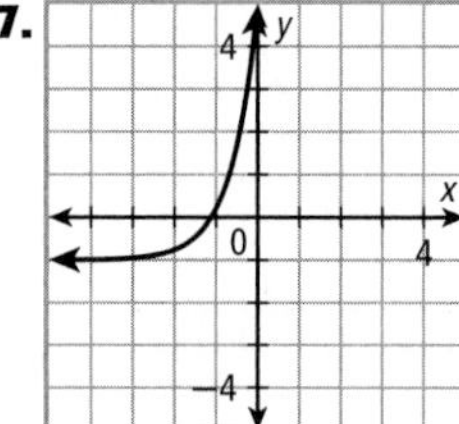

y-int.: 5; asymptote: $y = -1$; vertical stretch by a factor of 6, shift 1 unit down

10-2 *Exercises*

38.
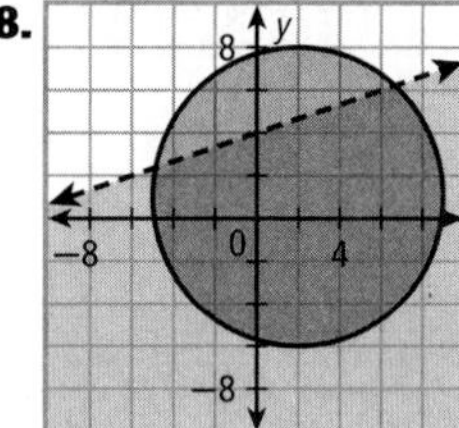

39.
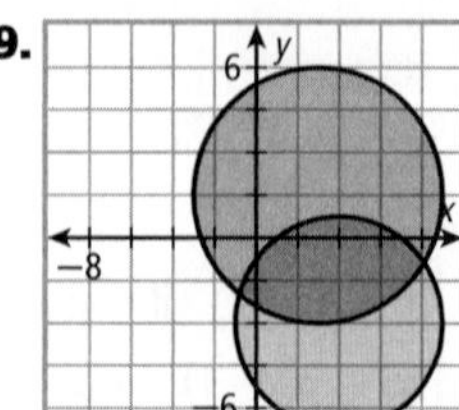

43b.
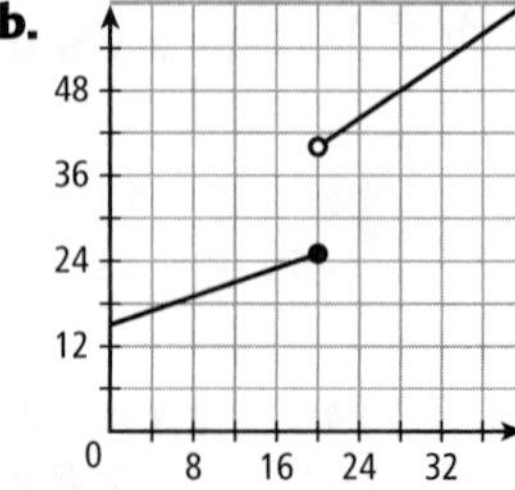

44.

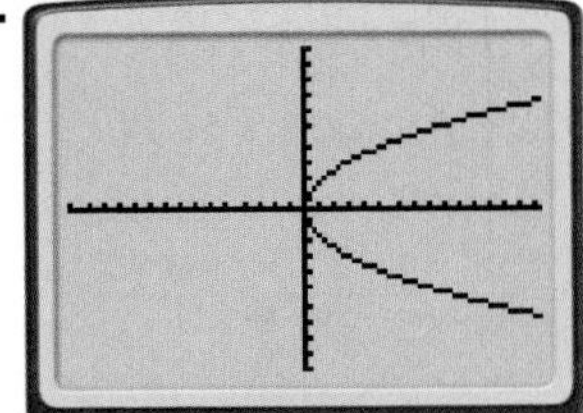

45.

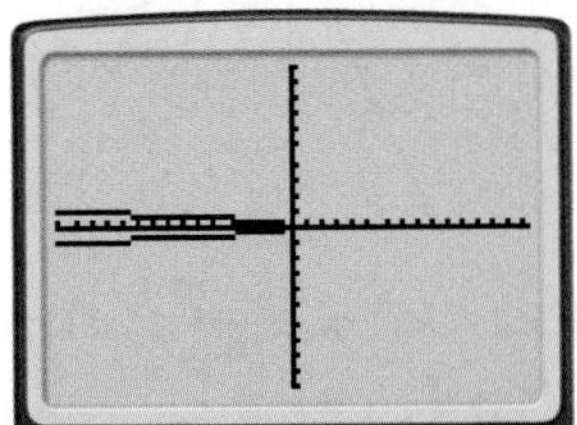

46.

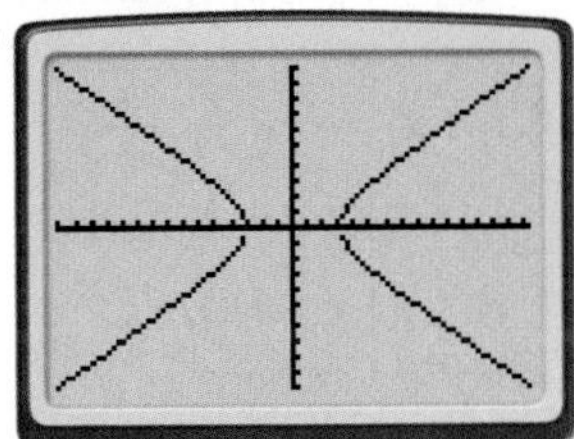

10-3 *Exercises*

8.

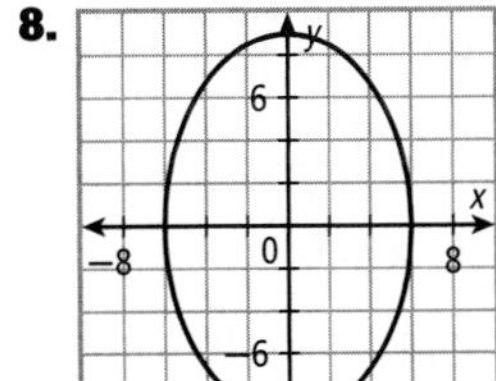

9.

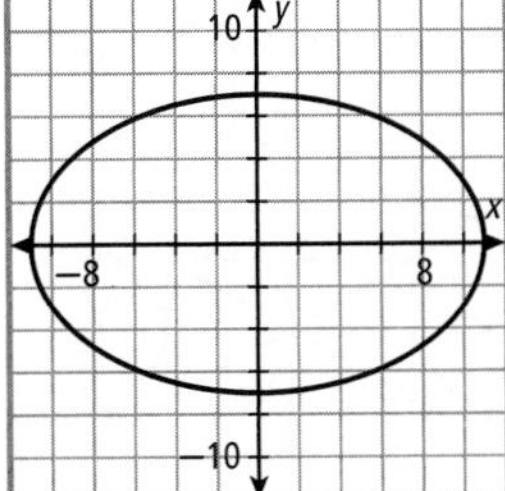

10.

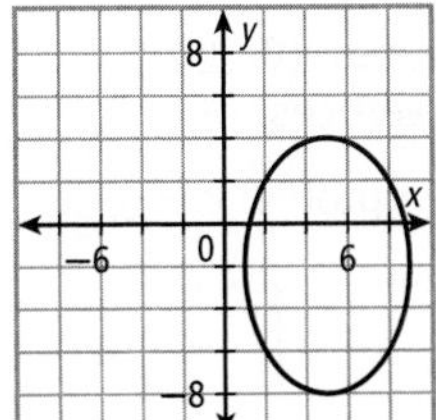

11.

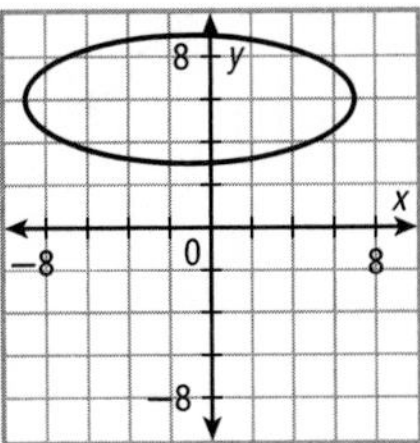

19.

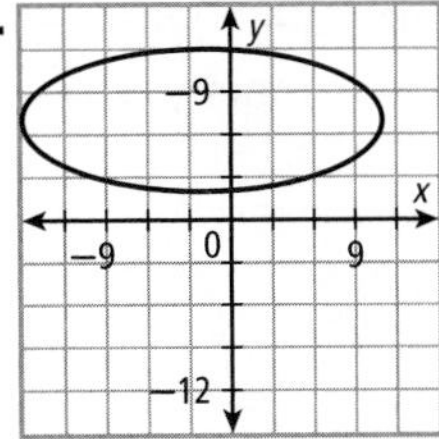

20.

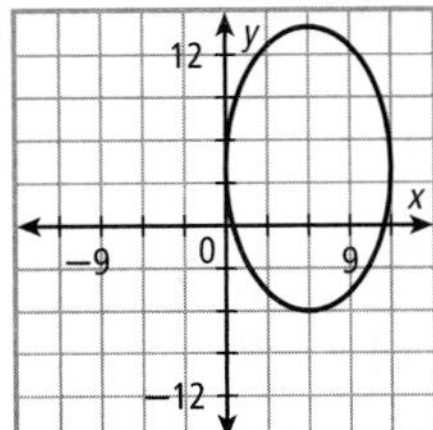

21.

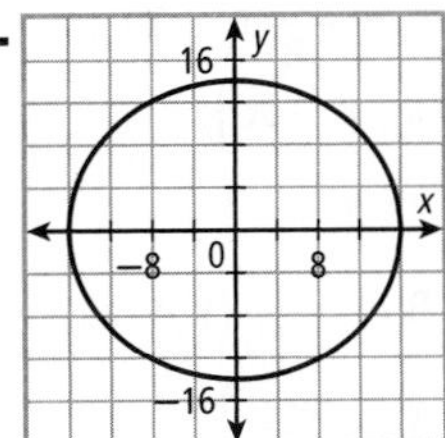

22.

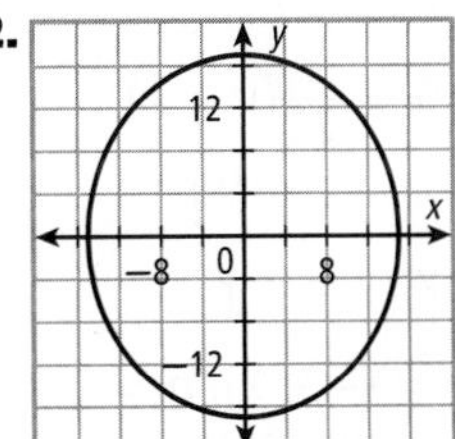

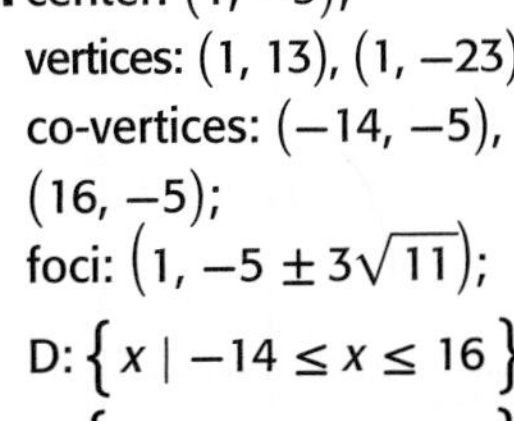

32. center: $(1, -5)$;
vertices: $(1, 13)$, $(1, -23)$;
co-vertices: $(-14, -5)$, $(16, -5)$;
foci: $\left(1, -5 \pm 3\sqrt{11}\right)$;
D: $\left\{x \mid -14 \leq x \leq 16\right\}$;
R: $\left\{y \mid -23 \leq y \leq 13\right\}$

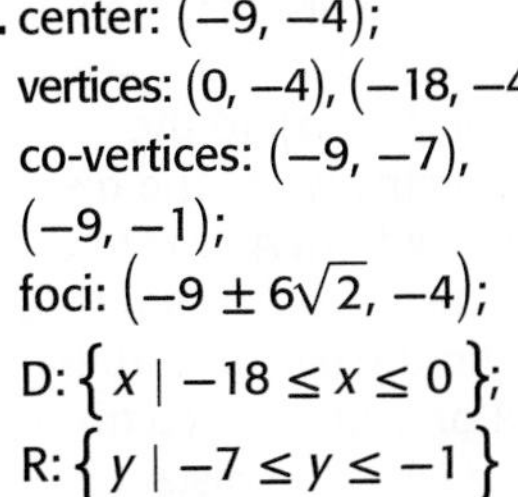

33. center: $(-9, -4)$;
vertices: $(0, -4)$, $(-18, -4)$;
co-vertices: $(-9, -7)$, $(-9, -1)$;
foci: $\left(-9 \pm 6\sqrt{2}, -4\right)$;
D: $\left\{x \mid -18 \leq x \leq 0\right\}$;
R: $\left\{y \mid -7 \leq y \leq -1\right\}$

34. Yes; possible answer: the foci are not on the ellipse, so the distance between them is always less than *d*.

10-4 *Exercises*

8.

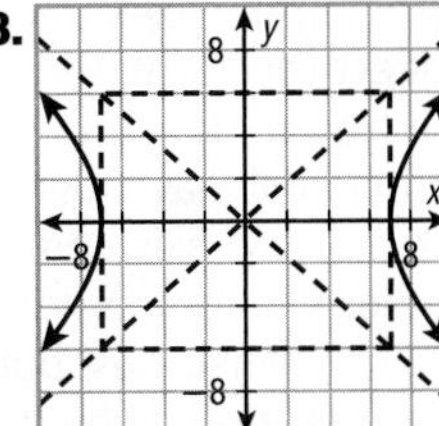

9.

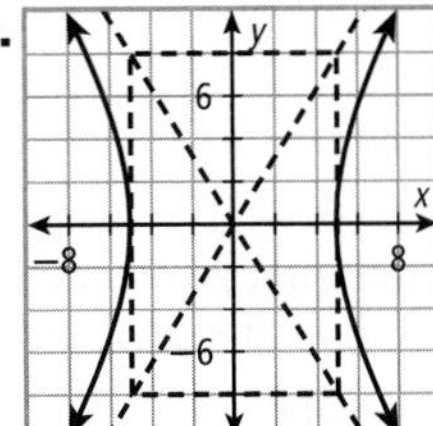

10.

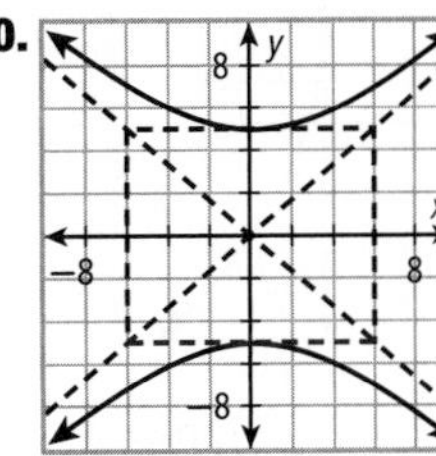

11.

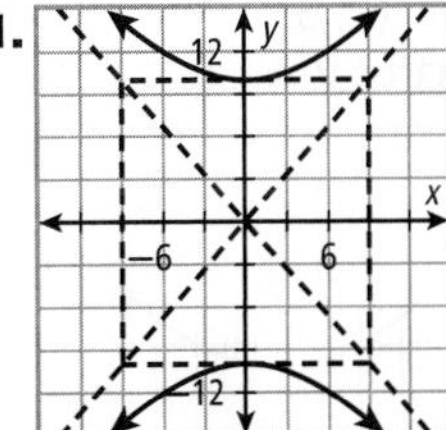

12.

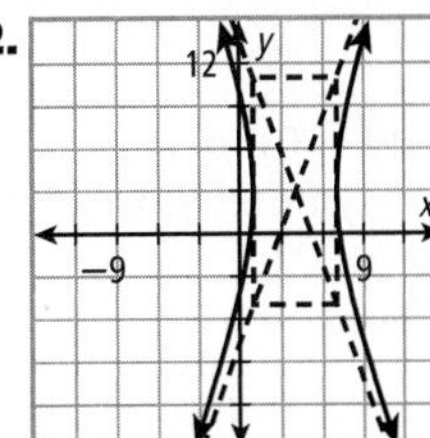

13.

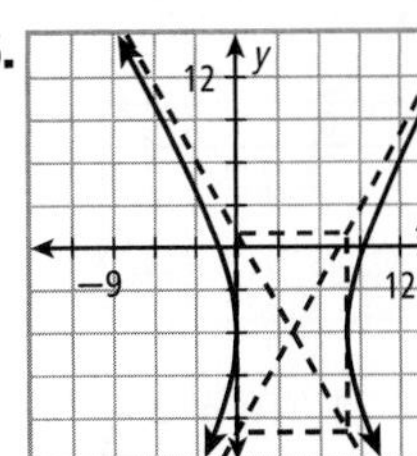

14.

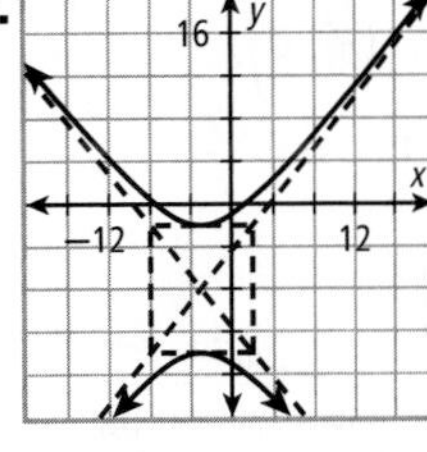

15.

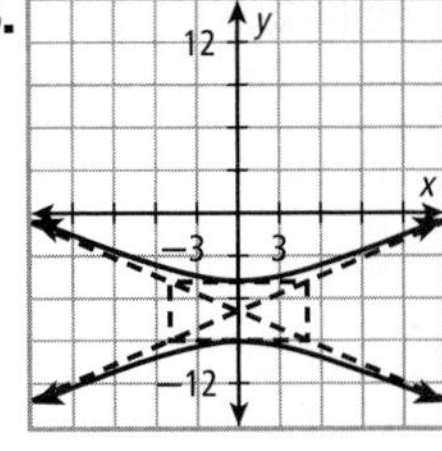

22. vertices: $(\pm 8, 0)$;
co-vertices: $(0, \pm 6)$;
asymptotes: $y = \pm\frac{3}{4}x$

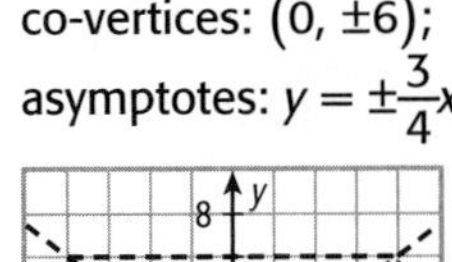

23. vertices: $(0, \pm 5)$;
co-vertices: $(\pm 9, 0)$;
asymptotes: $y = \pm\frac{5}{9}x$

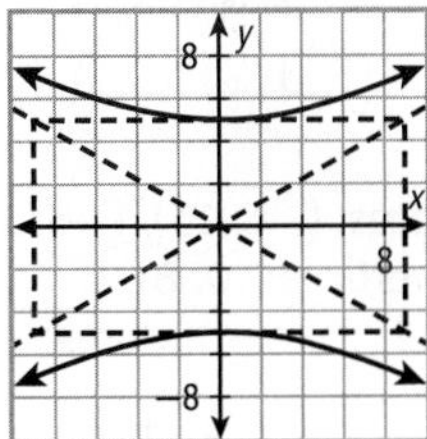

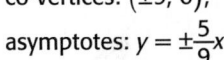

24. vertices: $(0, \pm 9)$;
co-vertices: $(\pm 4, 0)$;
asymptotes: $y = \pm\frac{9}{4}x$

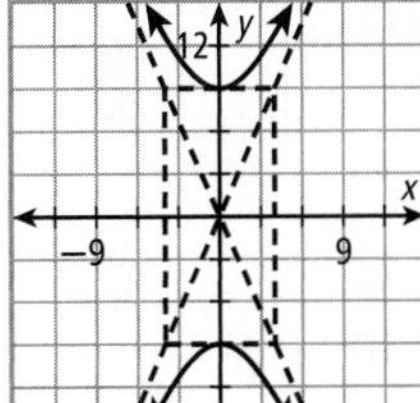

25. vertices: $(\pm 2, 0)$;
co-vertices: $(0, \pm 11)$;
asymptotes: $y = \pm\frac{11}{2}x$

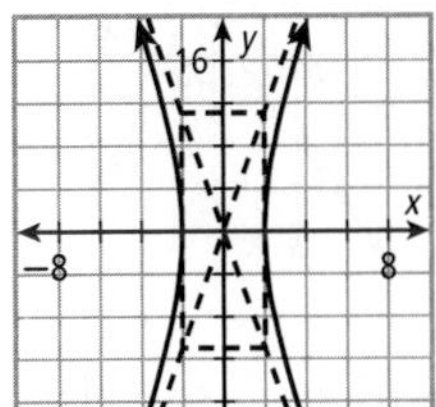

26. vertices: $(-2, 9)$, $(-2, -7)$; co-vertices: $(4, 1)$, $(-8, 1)$; asymptotes: $y = \pm\frac{4}{3}(x + 2) + 1$

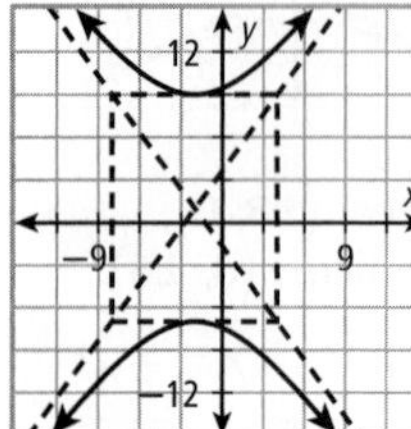

27. vertices: $(0, 3)$, $(-10, 3)$; co-vertices: $(-5, 7)$, $(-5, -1)$; asymptotes: $y = \pm\frac{4}{5}(x + 5) + 3$

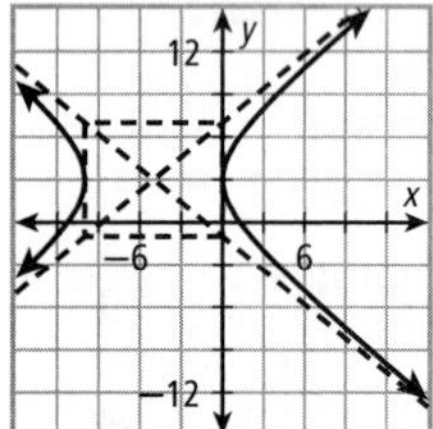

28. vertices: $(-6, 13)$, $(-6, 3)$; co-vertices: $(0, 8)$, $(-12, 8)$; asymptotes: $y = \pm\frac{5}{6}(x + 6) + 8$

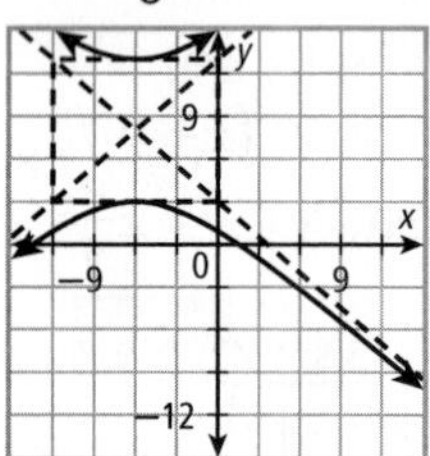

29. vertices: $(9, 2)$, $(3, 2)$; co-vertices: $(6, 6)$, $(6, -2)$; asymptotes: $y = \pm\frac{4}{3}(x - 6) + 2$

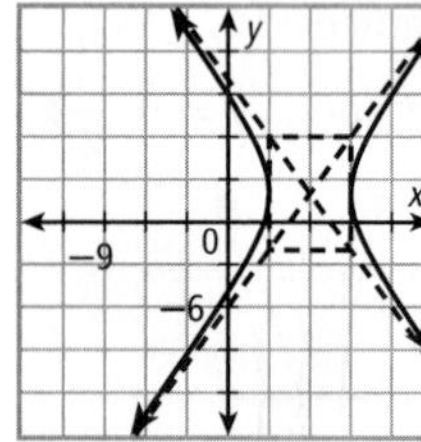

35. $c^2 = a^2 + b^2$, so c always has the greatest value. There is not enough information given to determine whether a or b has the least value.

36. Possible answer: Exchanging the axes does not affect the asymptotes of the hyperbolas. One hyperbola will have a vertical transverse axis and the other will have a horizontal transverse axis, but the asymptotes will be the same for both.

10-5 *Exercises*

11. vertex: $(0, 4)$; $p = 6$; axis of symmetry: $y = 4$; focus: $(6, 4)$; directrix: $x = -6$

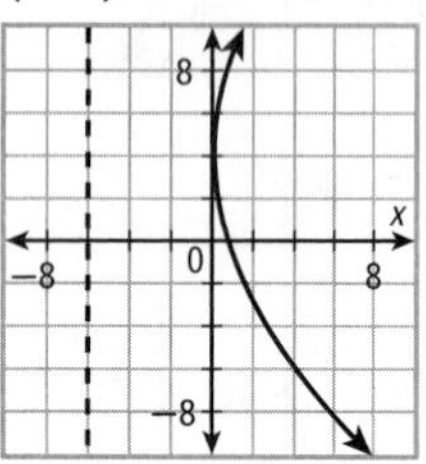

12. vertex: $(2, -1)$; $p = 4$; axis of symmetry: $x = 2$; focus: $(2, 3)$; directrix: $y = -5$

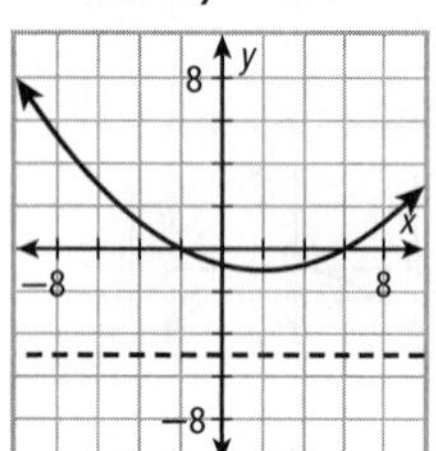

22. vertex: $(1, 0)$; $p = 2$; axis of symmetry: $x = 1$; focus: $(1, 2)$; directrix: $y = -2$

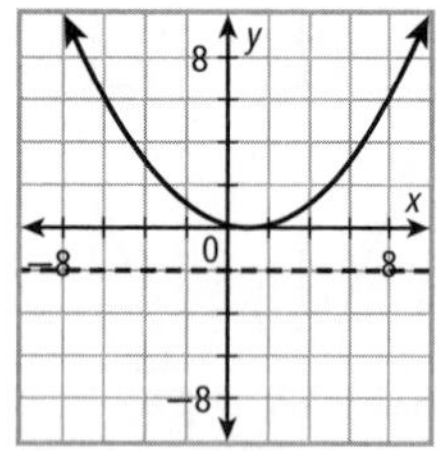

23. vertex: $(1, 0)$; $p = \frac{1}{8}$; axis of symmetry: $y = 0$; focus: $\left(\frac{9}{8}, 0\right)$; directrix: $x = \frac{7}{8}$

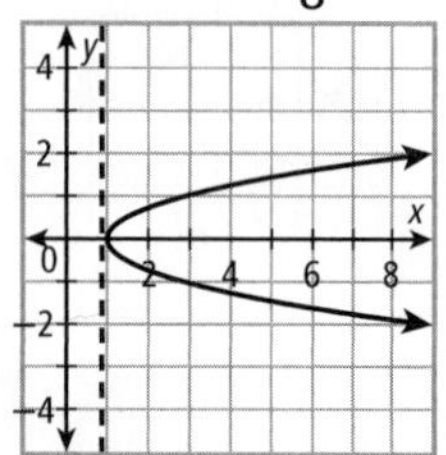

24. vertex: $(2, -1)$; $p = \frac{1}{2}$; axis of symmetry: $y = -1$; focus: $(2.5, -1)$; directrix: $x = 1.5$

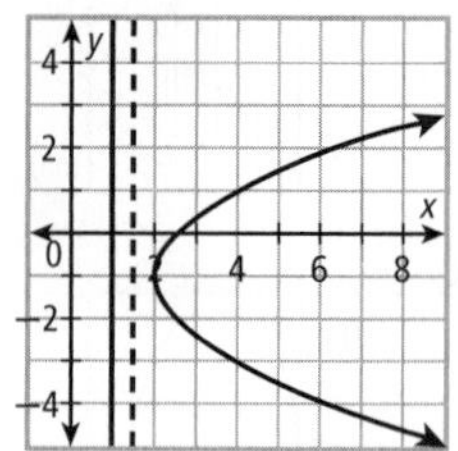

31. $y - 5 = -\frac{1}{20}x^2$; D: $\{x \mid x \in \mathbb{R}\}$; R: $\{y \mid y \leq 5\}$

32. $y + 1 = \frac{1}{28}(x - 2)^2$; D: $\{x \mid x \in \mathbb{R}\}$; R: $\{y \mid y \geq -1\}$

33. $x - 8 = -\frac{1}{16}(y + 5)^2$; D: $\{x \mid x \leq 8\}$; R: $\{y \mid y \in \mathbb{R}\}$

34. $x + 9 = \frac{1}{24}(y - 1)^2$; D: $\{x \mid x \geq -9\}$; R: $\{y \mid y \in \mathbb{R}\}$

41. vertex: $(-3, 2)$; $p = 2$; axis of symmetry: $y = 2$; focus: $(-1, 2)$; directrix: $x = -5$

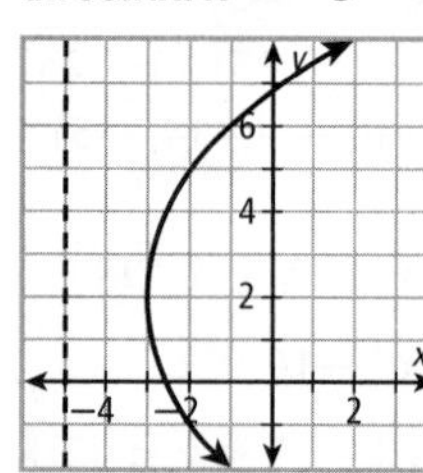

42. *2p;* The distance from the focus *F*, located at the point $(0, p)$, to the directrix is $2p$. The distance from *A* or *B* to the directrix must also be $2p$, and the distance from *A* or *B* to the directrix is equal to the distance from *A* or *B* to the focus.

52. $\begin{cases} y \geq -\frac{1}{2}x + 2 \\ y \leq 2x + 2 \\ y \leq -3x + 7 \end{cases}$

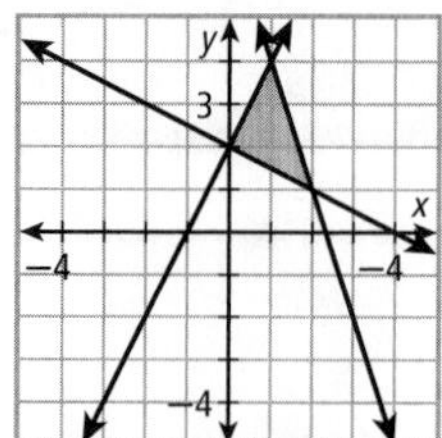

53. $f^{-1}(x) = \frac{x - 22}{4}$; D: $\{x \mid x \in \mathbb{R}\}$; R: $\{y \mid y \in \mathbb{R}\}$; function

54. $f^{-1}(x) = \pm\sqrt{\frac{x - 1}{3}}$; D: $\{x \mid x \geq 1\}$; R: $\{y \mid y \in \mathbb{R}\}$; not a function

55. $f^{-1}(x) = 3x + 2$; D: $\{x \mid x \in \mathbb{R}\}$; R: $\{y \mid y \in \mathbb{R}\}$; function

56. $f^{-1}(x) = \frac{1 + x}{x}$; D: $\{x \mid x \neq 0\}$; R: $\{y \mid y \neq 1\}$; function

57. vertices: $(\pm 9, 0)$; co-vertices: $(0, \pm 5)$; asymptotes: $y = \pm\frac{5}{9}x$

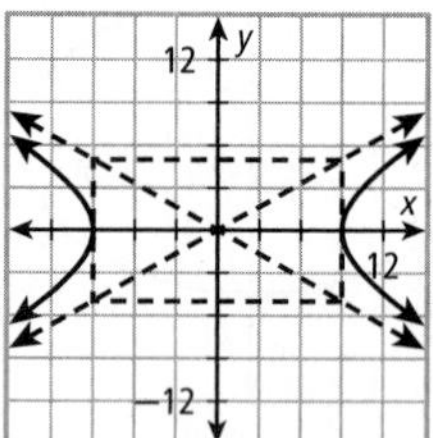

58. vertices: $(0, \pm 3)$; co-vertices: $(\pm 4, 0)$; asymptotes: $y = \pm\frac{3}{4}x$

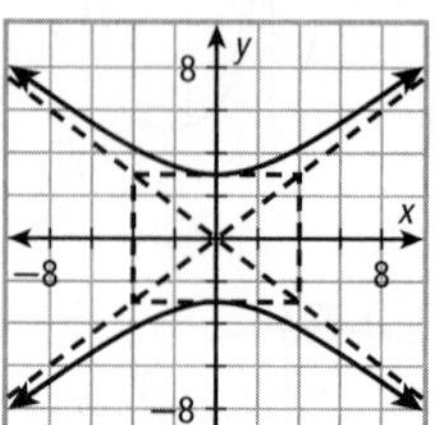

Additional Answers

59. vertices: $(0, \pm 8)$; co-vertices: $(\pm 2, 0)$; asymptotes: $y = \pm 4x$

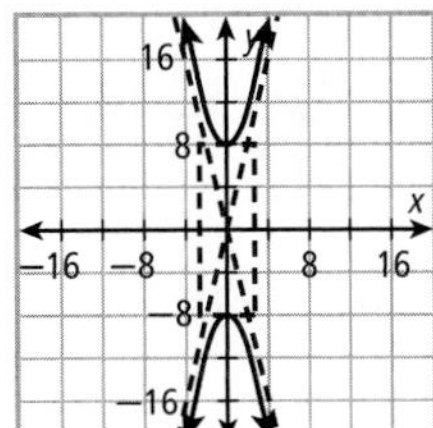

60. vertices: $(\pm 7, 0)$; co-vertices: $(0, \pm 6)$; asymptotes: $y = \pm\frac{6}{7}x$

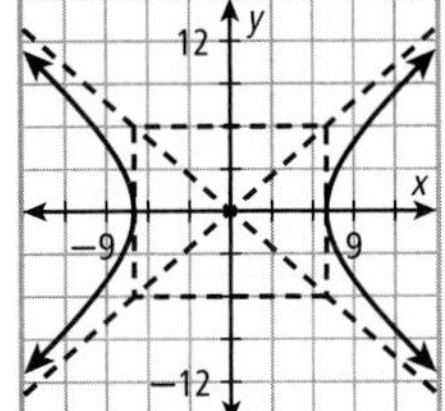

10A *Ready to Go On?*

9.

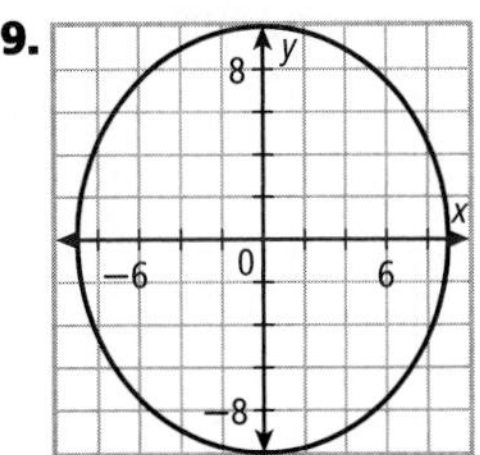

center: $(0, 0)$; vertices: $(0, \pm 10)$; co-vertices: $(\pm 9, 0)$; foci: $(0, \pm\sqrt{19})$

10.

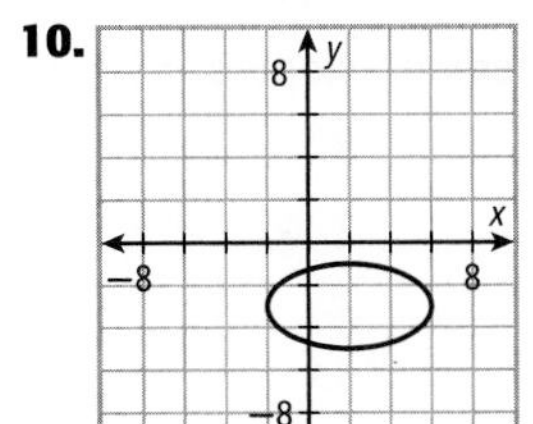

center: $(2, -3)$; vertices: $(6, -3)$, $(-2, -3)$; co-vertices: $(2, -1)$, $(2, -5)$; foci: $(2 \pm 2\sqrt{3}, -3)$

13.

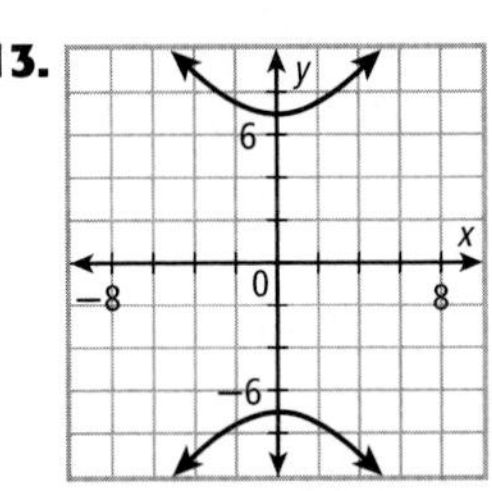

center: $(0, 0)$; vertices: $(0, \pm 7)$; co-vertices: $(\pm 5, 0)$; foci: $(0, \pm\sqrt{74})$; asymptotes: $y = \pm\frac{7}{5}x$

14.

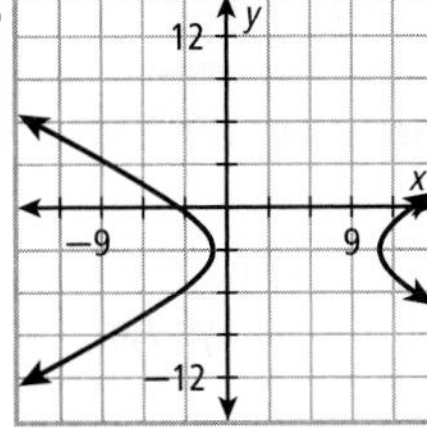

center: $(5, -3)$; vertices: $(11, -3)$, $(-1, -3)$; co-vertices: $(5, 0)$, $(5, -6)$; foci: $(5 \pm 3\sqrt{5}, -3)$; asymptotes: $y + 3 = \pm\frac{1}{2}(x - 5)$

16.

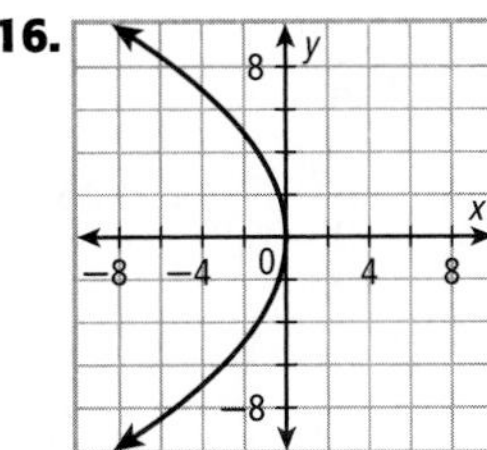

vertex: $(0, 0)$; $p = -3$; axis of symmetry: $y = 0$; focus: $(-3, 0)$; directrix: $x = 3$

17.

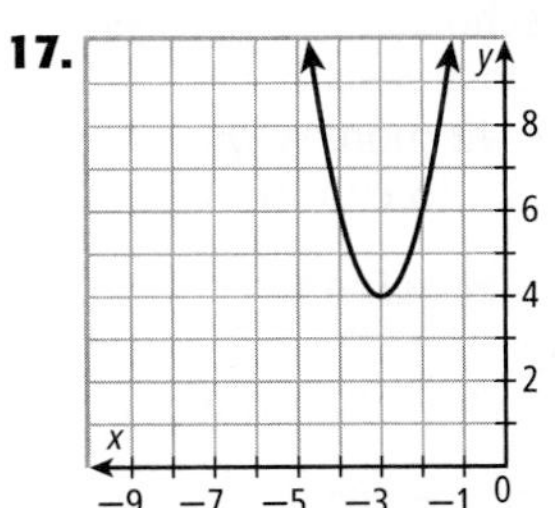

vertex: $(-3, 4)$; $p = \frac{1}{8}$; axis of symmetry: $x = -3$; focus: $\left(-3, 4\frac{1}{8}\right)$; directrix: $y = 3\frac{7}{8}$

10-6 *Exercises*

9.

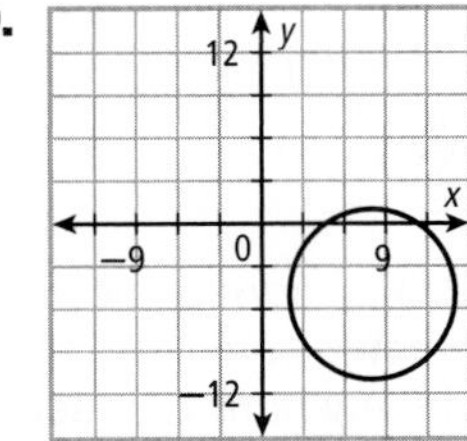

10.

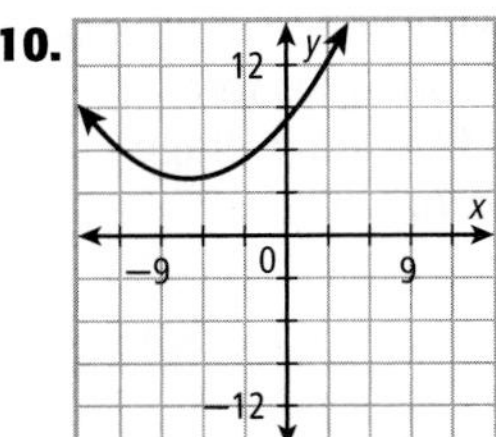

11.

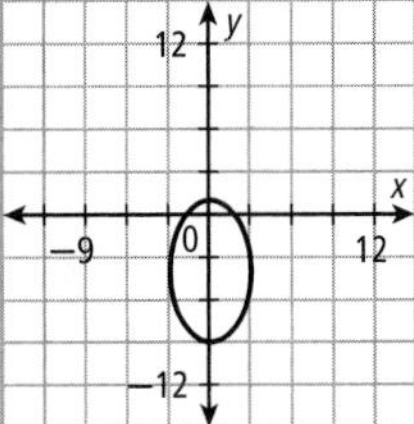

12.

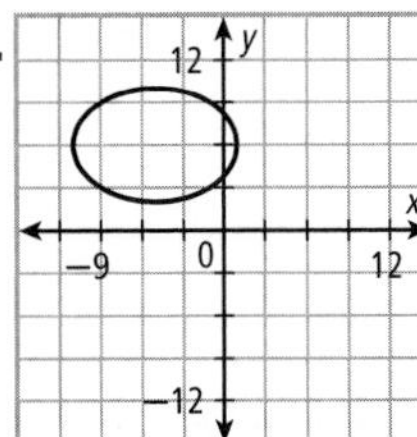

22.

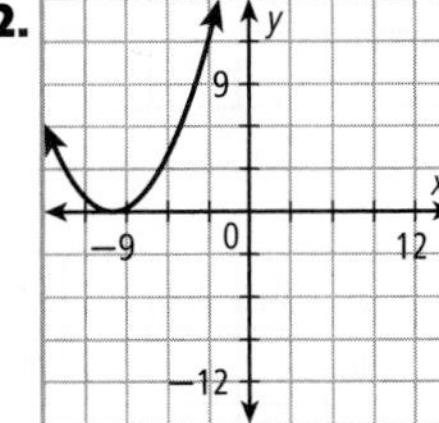

23.

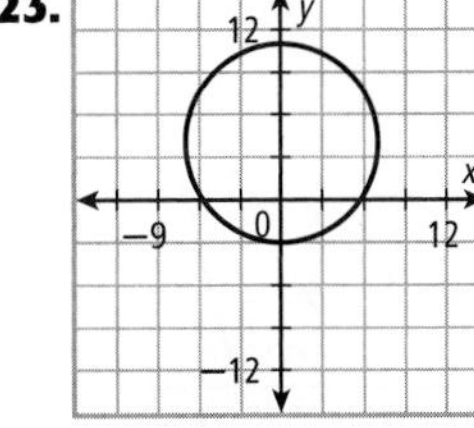

24. $\frac{(x - 4)^2}{36} + \frac{y^2}{9} = 1$; ellipse

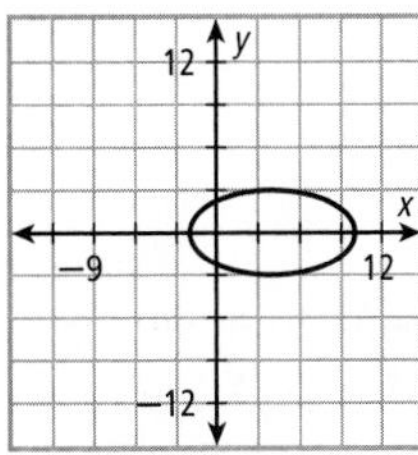

25. $\frac{x^2}{4} - \frac{(y + 9)^2}{25} = 1$; hyperbola

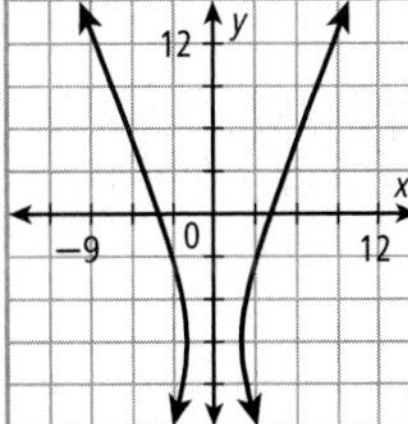

26. $y + 4 = \frac{1}{20}(x - 1)^2$; parabola

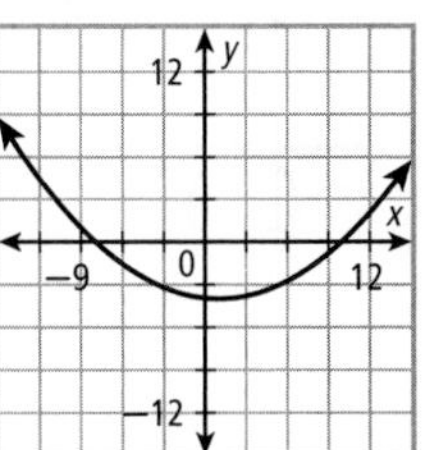

27. $(x + 5)^2 + (y + 2)^2 = 20$; circle

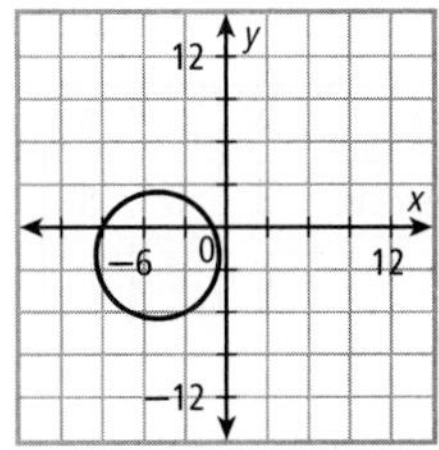

28. $\frac{(x + 2)^2}{49} + \frac{(y - 2)^2}{64} = 1$; ellipse

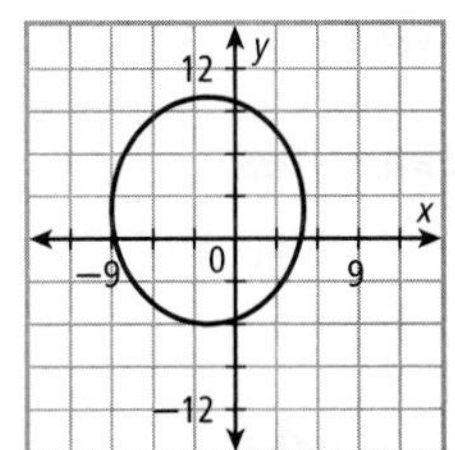

29. $\frac{(x + 1)^2}{4} - \frac{(y - 7)^2}{9} = 1$; hyperbola

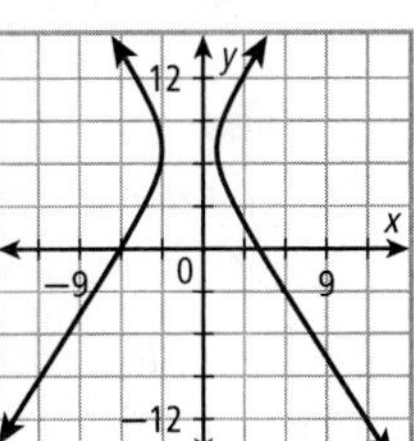

30. $x - 7 = -\frac{1}{6}(y + 6)^2$; parabola

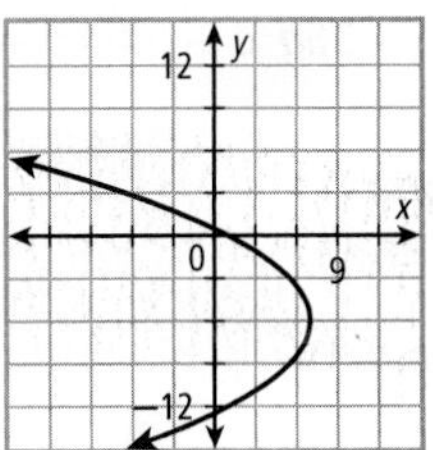

Additional Answers

31. $(x - 2.5)^2 + (y + 4.5)^2 = 16$; circle

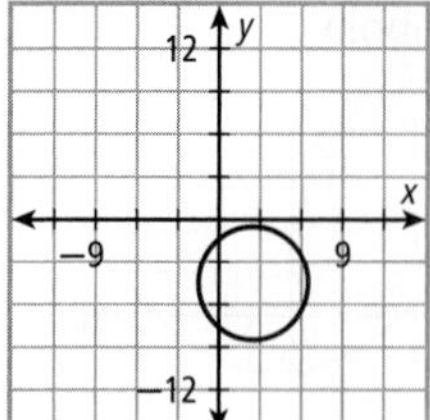

Chapter 11

11-1 *Exercises*

33a.

President	A	A	A	A	A	A	A	A	A	A	A	A
Vice President	B	B	B	C	C	C	D	D	D	E	E	E
Secretary	C	D	E	B	D	E	B	C	E	B	C	D

33b.

President	B	B	B	B	B	B	B	B	B	B	B	B
Vice President	A	A	A	C	C	C	D	D	D	E	E	E
Secretary	C	D	E	A	D	E	A	C	E	A	C	D

60 ways

11-4 *Exercises*

44.

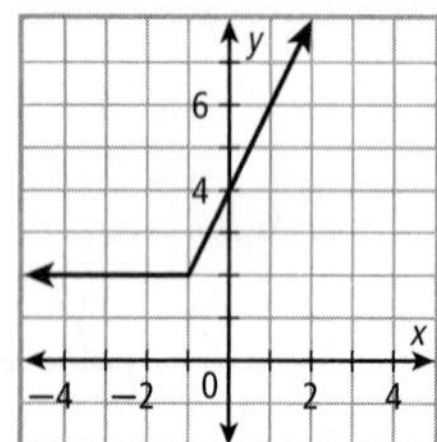

45.

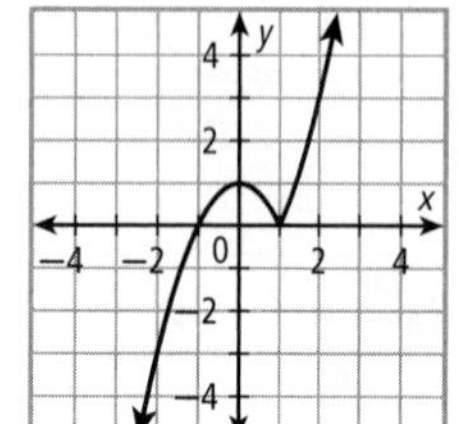

11-6 *Exercises*

2. $x^4 + 12x^3 + 54x^2 + 108x + 81$

3. $27x^3 + 135x^2 + 225x + 125$

4. $p^6 - 12p^5 + 60p^4 - 160p^3 + 240p^2 - 192p + 64$

5. $x^6 + 6x^5y + 15x^4y^2 + 20x^3y^3 + 15x^2y^4 + 6xy^5 + y^6$

9. $y^4 + 20y^3 + 150y^2 + 500y + 625$

10. $8m^3 - 12m^2 + 6m - 1$

11. $1024 + 3840x + 5760x^2 + 4320x^3 + 1620x^4 + 243x^5$

12. $8a^3 + 36a^2c + 54ac^2 + 27c^3$

49. $\dfrac{n!}{r!(n-r)!} + \dfrac{n!}{(r+1)![(n-r-1)]!} =$

$$\frac{n!}{r!(n-r)(n-r-1)!} + \frac{n!}{(r+1)r!(n-r-1)!} =$$

$$\left(\frac{r+1}{r+1}\right)\frac{n!}{r!(n-r)(n-r-1)!} + \left(\frac{n-r}{n-r}\right)\frac{n!}{(r+1)r!(n-r-1)!} =$$

$$\frac{n!(r+1)}{(r+1)!(n-r)(n-r-1)!} + \frac{n!(n-r)}{(r+1)r!(n-r)!} =$$

$$\frac{n!(r+1+n-r)}{(r+1)!(n-r)!} = \frac{n!(n+1)}{(r+1)!(n-r)!} = \frac{(n+1)!}{(r+1)!(n-r)!} =$$

$${}_{n+1}C_{r+1}$$

Chapter 12

Reading and Writing Math

2. Step 1: Compare the number of ways Aidan can choose 3 out of 9 schools with the number of ways he can choose 4 out of 9 schools. Step 2: The answer is the difference in the number of choices. Step 3: Use the combination formula with $n = 9$ and $r = 4$ and then with $r = 3$.

$${}_nC_r = \frac{n!}{r!\,(n-r)!}$$

$$= \frac{9!}{4!(9-4)!} = 126$$

$${}_nC_r = \frac{n!}{r!(n-r)!}$$

$$= \frac{9!}{3!(9-3)!} = 84$$

Subtract the results: 126 − 84 = 42. Step 4: There are 126 ways to choose 4 schools and 84 ways to choose 3 schools, so there are 42 more ways for Aidan to choose 4.

12-2 *Exercises*

59. $\sum_{k=1}^{n} ca_k = ca_1 + ca_2 + \cdots + ca_n = c(a_1 + a_2 + \cdots + a_n) = c\sum_{k=1}^{n} a_k$

60. $\sum_{k=1}^{n} (a_k + b_k) = (a_1 + b_1) + (a_2 + b_2) + \cdots + (a_n + b_n) = (a_1 + a_2 + \cdots + a_n) + (b_1 + b_2 + \cdots + b_n) = \sum_{k=1}^{n} a_k + \sum_{k=1}^{n} b_k$

61. Possible answer: The sum alternates from 1 to 0 as each new term is added to the partial sum. Thus the sum of the sequence that continues forever could be the average value of 0.5.

62. *x*-int.: 4; *y*-int.: −3

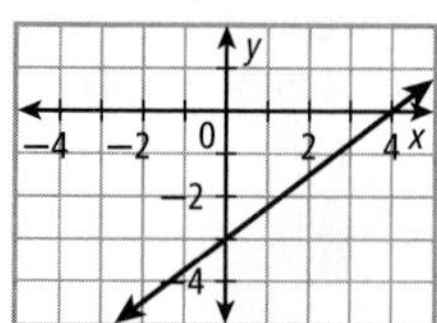

63. *x*-int.: 3; *y*-int.: −6

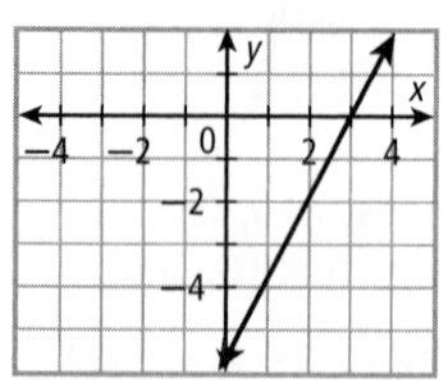

64. *x*-int.: $-\frac{1}{2}$; *y*-int.: $-\frac{1}{3}$

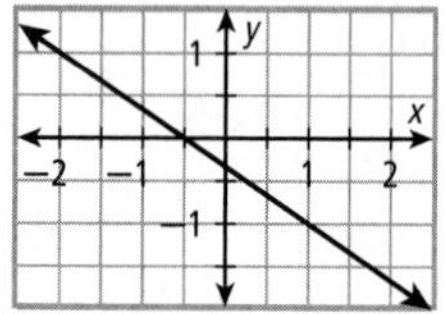

12A *Ready to Go On?*

9. mile marker 238;

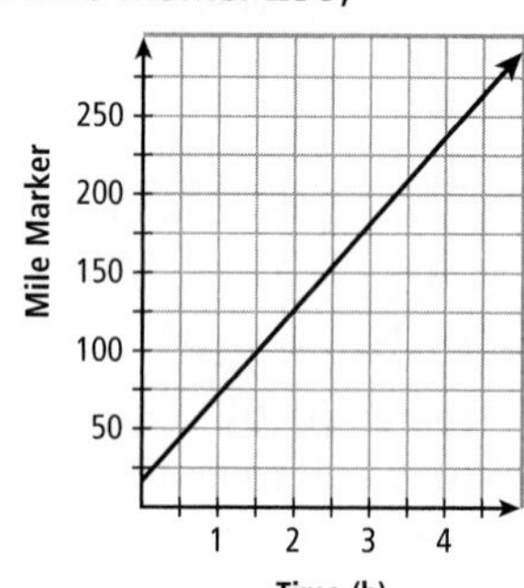

linear with slope of 55

12-5 *Exercises*

47. 1. $1^2 = \frac{1(1+1)(2(1)+1)}{6} = 1$

2. $1^2 + \cdots + k^2 = \frac{k(k+1)(2k+1)}{6}$

3. $1^2 + \cdots + k^2 + (k+1)^2$

$= \frac{k(k+1)(2k+1)}{6} + (k+1)^2$

$= \frac{k(k+1)(2k+1) + 6(k+1)^2}{6}$

$= \frac{(k+1)[k(2k+1) + 6(k+1)]}{6}$

$= \frac{(k+1)(2k^2 + 7k + 6)}{6}$

$= \frac{(k+1)(k+2)(2k+3)}{6}$

$= \frac{(k+1)(k+1+1)(2(k+1)+1)}{6}$

48. 1. $1(1+1) = \frac{1(1+1)(1+2)}{3} = 2$

2. $1(2) + \cdots + k(k+1) = \frac{k(k+1)(k+2)}{3}$

3. $1(2) + \cdots + k(k+1) + (k+1)(k+2)$

$= \frac{k(k+1)(k+2)}{3} + (k+1)(k+2)$

$= \frac{k(k+1)(k+2) + 3(k+1)(k+2)}{3}$

$= \frac{(k+1)(k+2)(k+3)}{3}$

49. 1. $\left(\frac{1}{2}\right)^1 = 1 - \left(\frac{1}{2}\right)^1 = \frac{1}{2}$

2. $\frac{1}{2} + \cdots + \left(\frac{1}{2}\right)^k = 1 - \left(\frac{1}{2}\right)^k$

3. $\frac{1}{2} + \cdots + \left(\frac{1}{2}\right)^k + \left(\frac{1}{2}\right)^{k+1}$

$= 1 - \left(\frac{1}{2}\right)^k + \left(\frac{1}{2}\right)^{k+1}$

$= 1 - \left[\left(\frac{1}{2}\right)^k - \left(\frac{1}{2}\right)^{k+1}\right]$

$= 1 - \left[\left(\frac{1}{2}\right)^k - \left(\frac{1}{2}\right)^k\left(\frac{1}{2}\right)^1\right]$

$= 1 - \left[\left(\frac{1}{2}\right)^k\left(1 - \frac{1}{2}\right)\right]$

$= 1 - \left(\frac{1}{2}\right)^k\left(\frac{1}{2}\right)$

$= 1 - \left(\frac{1}{2}\right)^{k+1}$

Chapter 13

13-1 *Exercises*

28. Possible answer:

$$\frac{\sin\theta}{\cos\theta} = \frac{\frac{\text{opp.}}{\text{hyp.}}}{\frac{\text{adj.}}{\text{hyp.}}}$$

$$= \frac{\text{opp.}}{\text{hyp.}} \div \frac{\text{adj.}}{\text{hyp.}}$$

$$= \frac{\text{opp.}}{\text{hyp.}} \cdot \frac{\text{hyp.}}{\text{adj.}}$$

$$= \frac{\text{opp.}}{\text{adj.}} = \tan\theta$$

29. Possible answer: (1) Use the cosine ratio to find the length of the hypotenuse. (2) Use the tangent ratio to find the length of the opposite leg. Then use the Pythagorean Theorem to find the length of the hypotenuse.

33. Possible answer: The sine ratio of an acute angle is determined by the measure of the angle. Because the sine ratios of the acute angles are equal, the angles are congruent. The right angles of the triangles are also congruent. Therefore, the triangles are similar by angle-angle similarity.

34. Both the cosecant and secant ratios are ratios of the length of the hypotenuse to the length of a leg. Because the hypotenuse is always longer than either leg, these ratios are greater than 1. Both the sine and cosine ratios are ratios of the length of a leg to the length of the hypotenuse. Because the legs are always shorter than the hypotenuse, these ratios are less than 1.

36. Possible answer: The acute angles of a right triangle are complementary because the sum of their measures is 90°. The sine of one of the acute angles is equal to the ratio of the length of the opposite leg to the length of the hypotenuse. The cosine of the other acute angle is equal to the length of the adjacent leg to the length of the hypotenuse. Because the leg opposite the first angle is adjacent to the second angle, the sine of the first angle is equal to the cosine of the second angle.

13-2 *Check It Out*

1a.

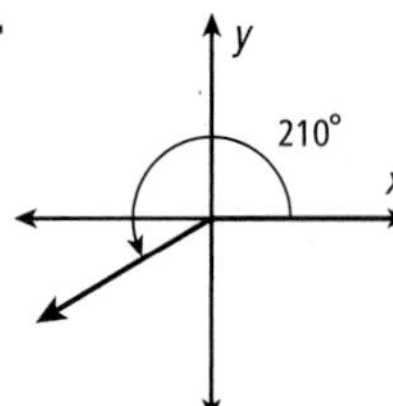

b.

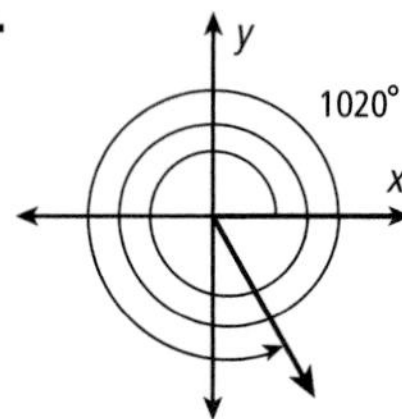

c.

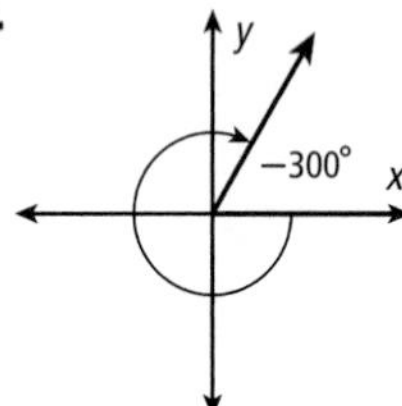

13-2 *Exercises*

19. $\sin\theta = -\frac{\sqrt{5}}{5}$; $\cos\theta = \frac{2\sqrt{5}}{5}$; $\tan\theta = -\frac{1}{2}$; $\csc\theta = -\sqrt{5}$; $\sec\theta = \frac{\sqrt{5}}{2}$; $\cot\theta = -2$

20. $\sin\theta = -1$; $\cos\theta = 0$; $\tan\theta$ is undefined; $\csc\theta = -1$; $\sec\theta$ is undefined; $\cot\theta = 0$.

21. $\sin\theta = -\frac{4}{5}$; $\cos\theta = -\frac{3}{5}$; $\tan\theta = \frac{4}{3}$; $\csc\theta = -\frac{5}{4}$; $\sec\theta = -\frac{5}{3}$; $\cot\theta = \frac{3}{4}$

22. $\sin\theta = -\frac{3\sqrt{34}}{34}$; $\cos\theta = \frac{5\sqrt{34}}{34}$; $\tan\theta = -\frac{3}{5}$; $\csc\theta = -\frac{\sqrt{34}}{3}$; $\sec\theta = \frac{\sqrt{34}}{5}$; $\cot\theta = -\frac{5}{3}$

23. $\sin\theta = \frac{6\sqrt{37}}{37}$; $\cos\theta = \frac{\sqrt{37}}{37}$; $\tan\theta = 6$; $\csc\theta = \frac{\sqrt{37}}{6}$; $\sec\theta = \sqrt{37}$; $\cot\theta = \frac{1}{6}$

24. $\sin\theta = -\frac{5\sqrt{61}}{61}$; $\cos\theta = -\frac{6\sqrt{61}}{61}$; $\tan\theta = \frac{5}{6}$; $\csc\theta = -\frac{\sqrt{61}}{5}$; $\sec\theta = -\frac{\sqrt{61}}{6}$; $\cot\theta = \frac{6}{5}$

25. $\sin\theta = \frac{2\sqrt{5}}{5}$; $\cos\theta = -\frac{\sqrt{5}}{5}$; $\tan\theta = -2$; $\csc\theta = \frac{\sqrt{5}}{2}$; $\sec\theta = -\sqrt{5}$; $\cot\theta = -\frac{1}{2}$

26.

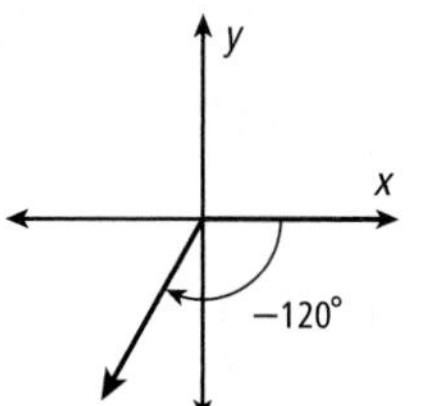

27.

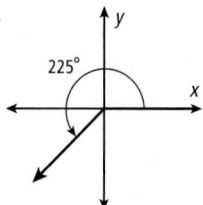

y
225°
x

28.

y
x
−570°

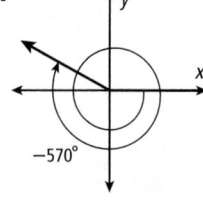

29.

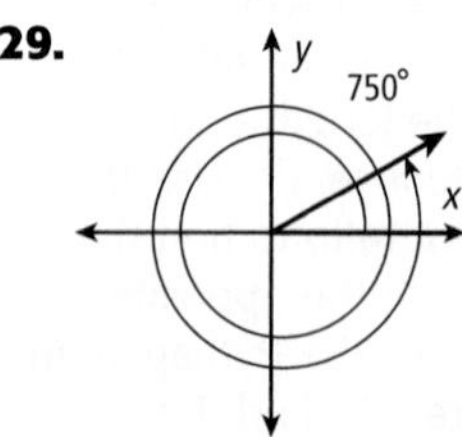

30. Possible answer: 614°; −106°

31. Possible answer: 300°; −60°

32. Possible answer: 195°; −525°

33. Possible answer: 110°; −250°

42. $\sin\theta = -\frac{5\sqrt{29}}{29}$; $\cos\theta = \frac{2\sqrt{29}}{29}$; $\tan\theta = -\frac{5}{2}$; $\csc\theta = -\frac{\sqrt{29}}{5}$; $\sec\theta = \frac{\sqrt{29}}{2}$; $\cot\theta = -\frac{2}{5}$

43. $\sin\theta = -\frac{2\sqrt{29}}{29}$; $\cos\theta = \frac{5\sqrt{29}}{29}$; $\tan\theta = -\frac{2}{5}$; $\csc\theta = -\frac{\sqrt{29}}{2}$; $\sec\theta = \frac{\sqrt{29}}{5}$; $\cot\theta = -\frac{5}{2}$

44. $\sin\theta = \frac{5\sqrt{41}}{41}$; $\cos\theta = -\frac{4\sqrt{41}}{41}$; $\tan\theta = -\frac{5}{4}$; $\csc\theta = \frac{\sqrt{41}}{5}$; $\sec\theta = -\frac{\sqrt{41}}{4}$; $\cot\theta = -\frac{4}{5}$

45. $\sin\theta = \frac{3}{5}$; $\cos\theta = \frac{4}{5}$; $\tan\theta = \frac{3}{4}$; $\csc\theta = \frac{5}{3}$; $\sec\theta = \frac{5}{4}$; $\cot\theta = \frac{4}{3}$

46. $\sin\theta = \frac{\sqrt{10}}{10}$; $\cos\theta = -\frac{3\sqrt{10}}{10}$; $\tan\theta = -\frac{1}{3}$; $\csc\theta = \sqrt{10}$; $\sec\theta = -\frac{\sqrt{10}}{3}$; $\cot\theta = -3$

47. $\sin\theta = -\frac{2\sqrt{5}}{5}$; $\cos\theta = \frac{\sqrt{5}}{5}$; $\tan\theta = -2$; $\csc\theta = -\frac{\sqrt{5}}{2}$; $\sec\theta = \sqrt{5}$; $\cot\theta = -\frac{1}{2}$

48. $\sin\theta = -\frac{2\sqrt{5}}{5}$; $\cos\theta = \frac{\sqrt{5}}{5}$; $\tan\theta = -2$; $\csc\theta = -\frac{\sqrt{5}}{2}$; $\sec\theta = \sqrt{5}$; $\cot\theta = -\frac{1}{2}$

49. $\sin\theta = \frac{4\sqrt{41}}{41}$; $\cos\theta = \frac{5\sqrt{41}}{41}$; $\tan\theta = \frac{4}{5}$; $\csc\theta = \frac{\sqrt{41}}{4}$; $\sec\theta = \frac{\sqrt{41}}{5}$; $\cot\theta = \frac{5}{4}$

64. Possible answer: The tangent of an angle in standard position is equal to $\frac{y}{x}$, where $P(x, y)$ is a point on the terminal side of the angle. The slope of the terminal side of the angle in standard position is also equal to $\frac{y}{x}$, where $P(x, y)$ is a point on the terminal side of the angle.

65. Possible answer: The sine of 225° is equal to $\frac{y}{r}$, where $P(x, y)$ is a point on the terminal side of the angle and $r = \sqrt{x^2 + y^2}$. The value of r is always positive. In this case, the value of y is negative because the terminal side of a 225° angle in standard position is in Quadrant III. Therefore, the ratio $\frac{y}{r}$ is negative, and sin 225° is negative.

69. $\sin\theta = \frac{b\sqrt{a^2 + b^2}}{a^2 + b^2}$; $\cos\theta = \frac{a\sqrt{a^2 + b^2}}{a^2 + b^2}$; $\tan\theta = \frac{b}{a}$

70. $\sin\theta = \frac{a^2\sqrt{a^4 + 1}}{a^4 + 1}$; $\cos\theta = \frac{\sqrt{a^4 + 1}}{a^4 + 1}$; $\tan\theta = a^2$

71. $\sin\theta = \dfrac{b\sqrt{a^2+b^2}}{a^2+b^2}$;

$\cos\theta = \dfrac{a\sqrt{a^2+b^2}}{a^2+b^2}$;

$\tan\theta = \dfrac{b}{a}$

73. sine and cosine: none; tangent and secant: for $\theta = 90°$ or $\theta = 270°$ and all angles coterminal with these angles; cosecant and cotangent: for $\theta = 0°$ or $\theta = 180°$ and all angles coterminal with these angles

80. $\sin\theta = \dfrac{2\sqrt{13}}{13}$;

$\cos\theta = \dfrac{3\sqrt{13}}{13}$; $\tan\theta = \dfrac{2}{3}$

13-3 *Exercises*

36. reference angle: $\dfrac{\pi}{3}$

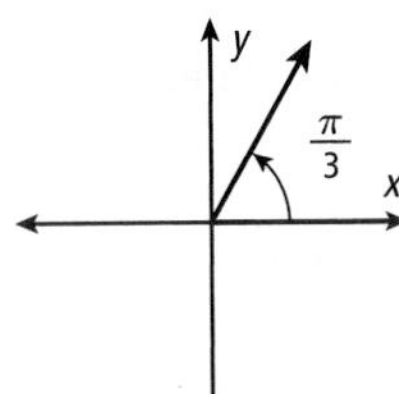

37. reference angle: $\dfrac{\pi}{4}$

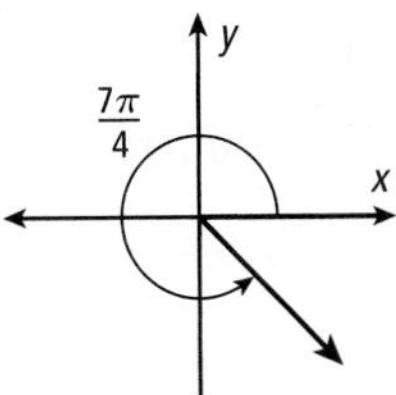

38. reference angle: $\dfrac{\pi}{6}$

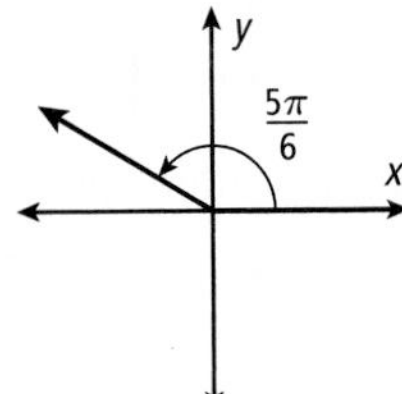

47. Possible answer: If $\theta = 0$, then the terminal side of θ passes through the point $P(1, 0)$ on the unit circle. Therefore, $\sin\theta = \frac{0}{1} = 0$. If $\theta = \frac{\pi}{2}$, then the terminal side of θ passes through the point $P(0, 1)$ on the unit circle. Therefore, $\sin\theta = \frac{1}{1} = 1$. If $\theta = \pi$, then the terminal side of θ passes through the point $P(-1, 0)$on the unit circle. Therefore, $\sin\theta = \frac{0}{1} = 0$. If $\theta = \frac{3\pi}{2}$, then the terminal side of θ passes through the point $P(0, -1)$ on the unit circle. Therefore, $\sin\theta = \frac{-1}{1} = -1$.

50. Possible answer: The reference angle for both θ and $-\theta$ is the same. If the terminal side of θ lies in a quadrant for which the sine function is positive, the terminal side of $-\theta$ lies in a quadrant for which the sine function is negative. Likewise, if the terminal side of θ lies in a quadrant for which the sine function is negative, the terminal side of $-\theta$ lies in a quadrant for which the sine function is positive. Therefore, $\sin(-\theta)$ has the same absolute value but the opposite sign of $\sin\theta$.

53. $\sin\theta = -\frac{\sqrt{3}}{2}$;

$\csc\theta = -\frac{2\sqrt{3}}{3}$;

$\sec\theta = 2$;

$\cot\theta = -\frac{\sqrt{3}}{3}$; possible answer: The cosine of θ is equal to x for a point $P(x, y)$ on the unit circle, the sine of θ is equal to y, and the tangent of θ is equal to $\frac{y}{x}$.

$$\tan\theta = \frac{y}{x} = \frac{\sin\theta}{\cos\theta}$$
$$\tan\theta(\cos\theta) = \sin\theta$$
$$-\sqrt{3}\left(\tfrac{1}{2}\right) = \sin\theta$$
$$-\frac{\sqrt{3}}{2} = \sin\theta$$

The cosecant is the reciprocal of the sine, the secant is the reciprocal of the cosine, and the cotangent is the reciprocal of the tangent.

57. Possible answer: about 81,800 m^2; I used the range of the searchlight to determine the area of a circle with this radius. Then I multiplied this area by the fraction of a circle represented by a central angle of 150°.

58. $\{\sin\theta \mid -1 < \sin\theta < 1\}$;
$\{\cos\theta \mid 0 < \cos\theta \le 1\}$;
$\{\tan\theta \mid -\infty < \tan\theta < \infty\}$;
$\{\csc\theta \mid -\infty < \csc\theta < -1$ or $1 < \csc\theta < \infty\}$;
$\{\sec\theta \mid 1 \le \sec\theta < \infty\}$;
$\{\cot\theta \mid -\infty < \cot\theta < 0$ or $0 < \cot\theta < \infty\}$

59. D: $\{x \mid x \ge -4\}$;
R: $\{y \mid y \ge 0\}$

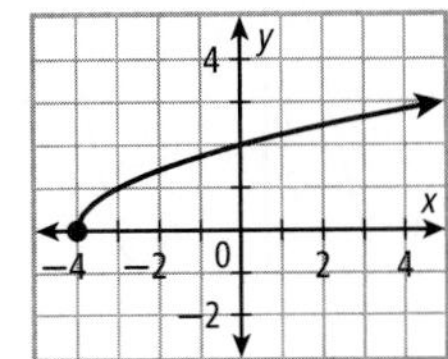

60. D: ℝ; R: ℝ

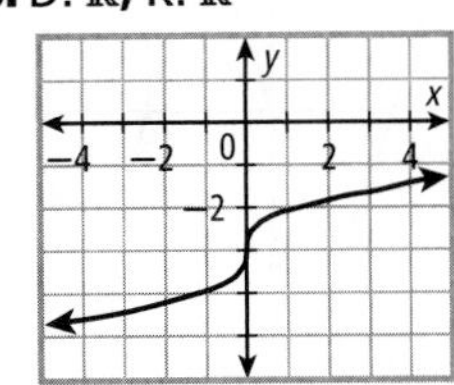

61. D: $\{x \mid x \ge 0\}$;
R: $\{y \mid y \le 0\}$

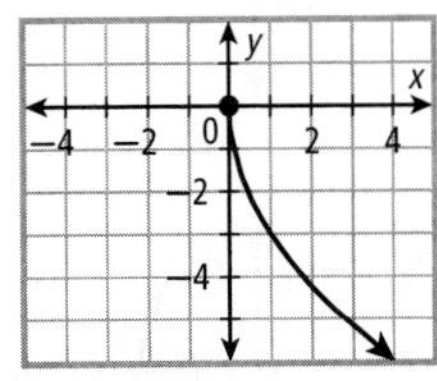

13-4 *Exercises*

37. Possible answer: The domain of the Cosine function is $0 \le \theta \le \pi$. This domain produces Cosine function values that range from -1 to 1 without any function value being repeated. As a result, the Cosine function can be used to define the inverse cosine function. If the domain of the Cosine function were the same as that of the Sine function, the Cosine function values would range from 0 to 1, and all function values except 0 would be repeated. As a result, the Cosine function could not be used to define an inverse cosine function.

46.

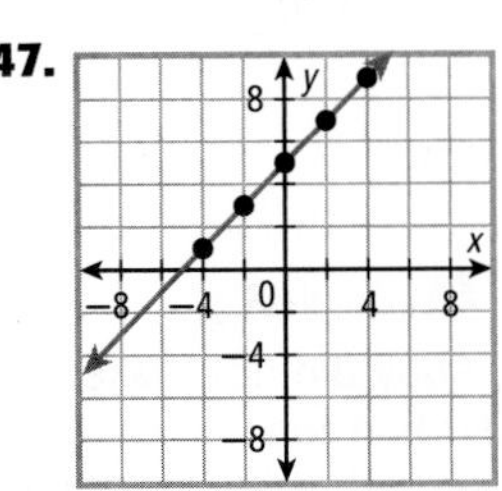

47.

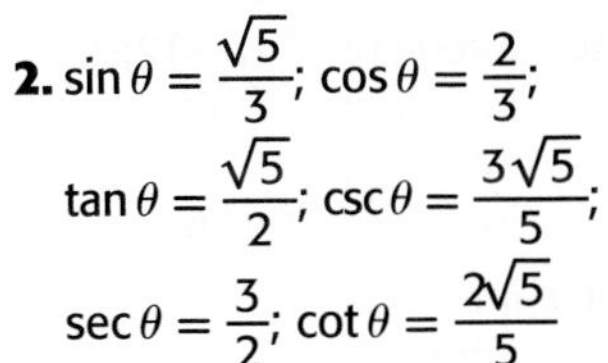

49. $f^{-1}(x) = 4x - 4$; function; D: ℝ; R: ℝ

50. $f^{-1}(x) = \pm\sqrt{\dfrac{x-5}{-2}}$; not a function;
D: $\{x \mid x \le 5\}$; R: ℝ

13A *Ready To Go On?*

2. $\sin\theta = \dfrac{\sqrt{5}}{3}$; $\cos\theta = \dfrac{2}{3}$;
$\tan\theta = \dfrac{\sqrt{5}}{2}$; $\csc\theta = \dfrac{3\sqrt{5}}{5}$;
$\sec\theta = \dfrac{3}{2}$; $\cot\theta = \dfrac{2\sqrt{5}}{5}$

6.

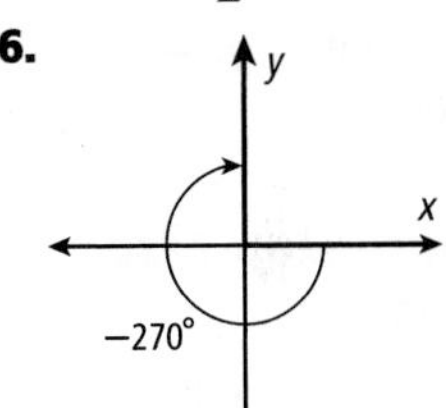

7.

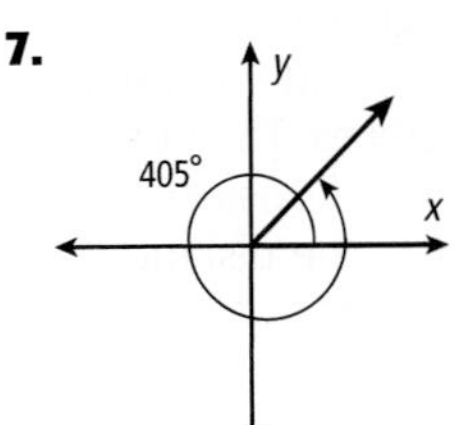

8. $\sin\theta = -\dfrac{5}{13}$; $\cos\theta = \dfrac{12}{13}$;
$\tan\theta = -\dfrac{5}{12}$;
$\csc\theta = -\dfrac{13}{5}$;
$\sec\theta = \dfrac{13}{12}$; $\cot\theta = -\dfrac{12}{5}$

9. $\sin\theta = \frac{7\sqrt{53}}{53}$;

$\cos\theta = -\frac{2\sqrt{53}}{53}$;

$\tan\theta = -\frac{7}{2}$;

$\csc\theta = \frac{\sqrt{53}}{7}$;

$\sec\theta = -\frac{\sqrt{53}}{2}$;

$\cot\theta = -\frac{2}{7}$

13-6 *Exercises*

41. No, Abby did not make an error. A triangle cannot be formed from sides that measure 2 units, 3 units, and 5 units.

47. x-intercept of f: 4; y-intercept of f: −8; x-intercept of g: 4; y-intercept of g: −4

48. x-intercepts of f: −2, 2; y-intercept of f: −4; x-intercepts of g: −2, 2; y-intercept of g: 4

49. x-intercept of f: −12; y-intercept of f: 6; x-intercept of g: −4; y-intercept of g: 6

50. x-intercept of f: −1; y-intercept of f: 1; x-intercept of g: −1; y-intercept of g: −4

13B *Multi-Step Test Prep*

5. About 1.4 mi; possible answer: draw and label a triangle with tower 1, tower 3, and the fire at the vertices. Then use the Law of Cosines to estimate the distance between tower 3 and the fire.

Chapter 14

14-1 *Exercises*

11.

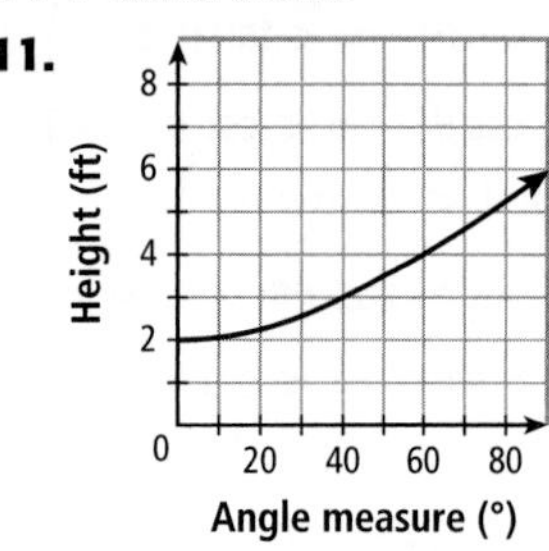

14.

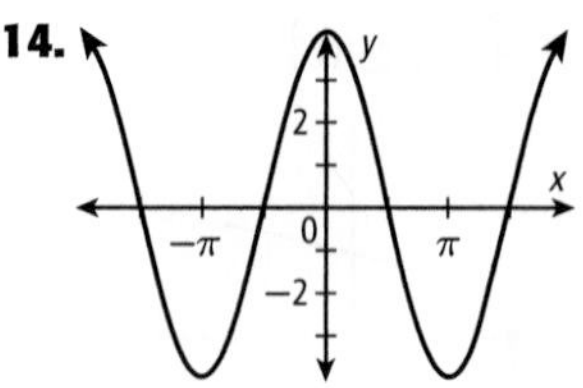

15.

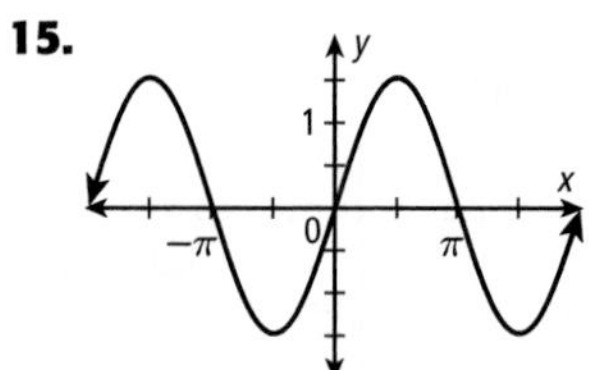

16.

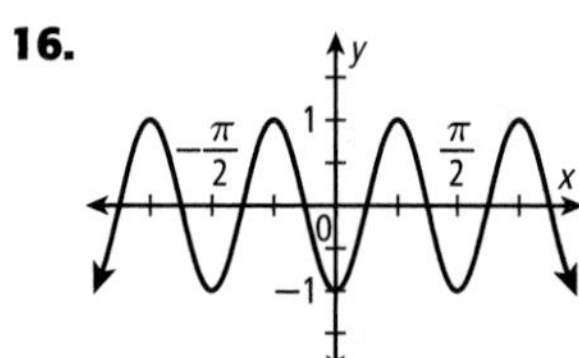

17.

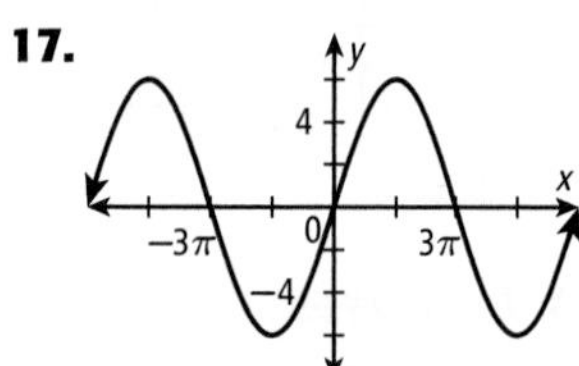

18.

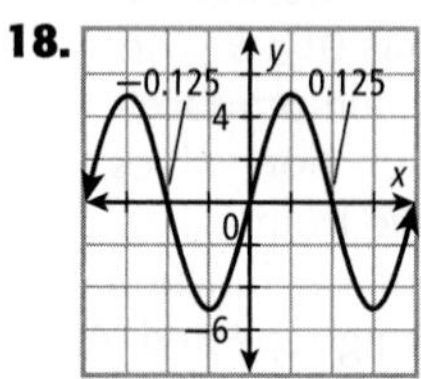

19.

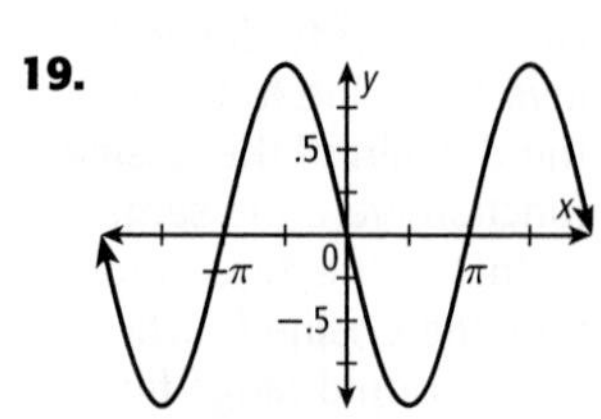

x-intercepts: πn; phase shift: π left

20.

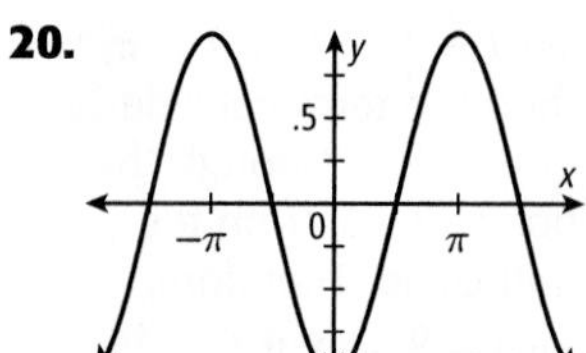

x-intercepts: $\frac{\pi}{2} + \pi n$; phase shift: π right

21.

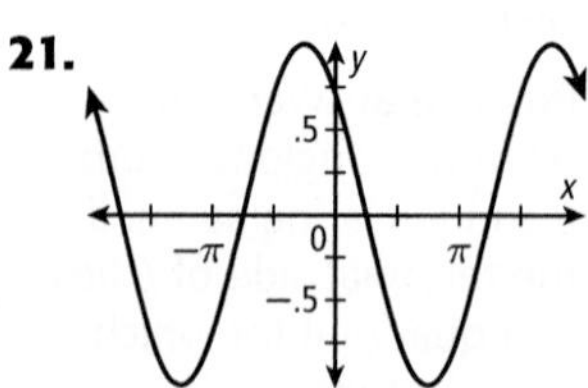

x-intercepts: $\frac{\pi}{4} + \pi n$; phase shift: $\frac{3\pi}{4}$ left

22.

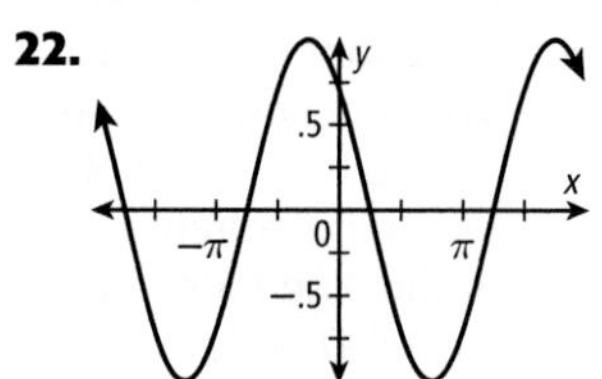

x-intercepts: $\frac{\pi}{4} + \pi n$; phase shift: $\frac{\pi}{4}$ left

25. amplitude: 1; period: 2π; phase shift $\frac{\pi}{4}$ left and vertical shift 1 down

26. amplitude: $\frac{3}{4}$; period: 8; vertical compression and horizontal stretch

27. amplitude: 1; period: 1; horizontal compression and vertical shift 2 down

28. amplitude: 3; period: $\frac{2\pi}{3}$; horizontal compression, vertical stretch, and reflection across the x-axis

44.

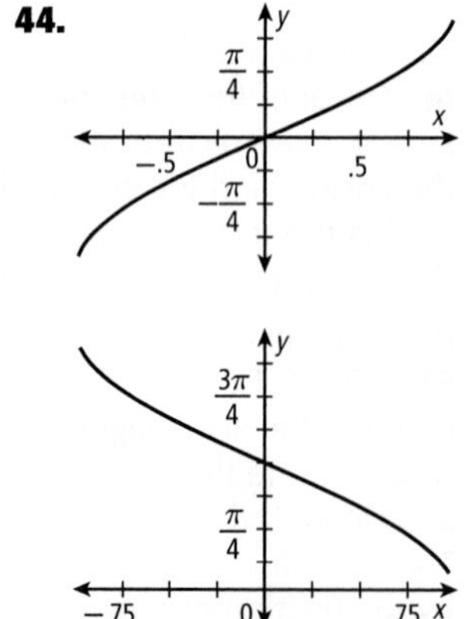

45.

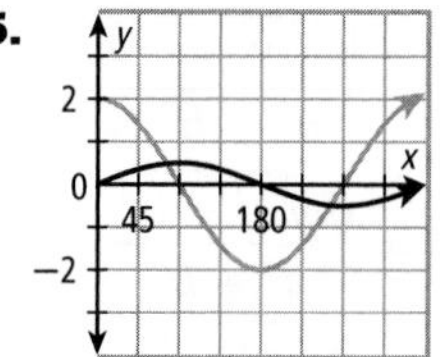

14-2 *Exercises*

1.

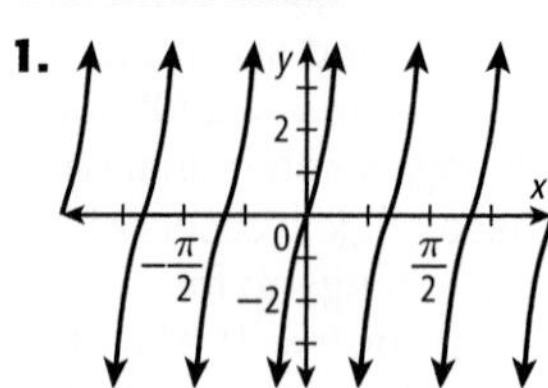

period: $\frac{\pi}{3}$; x-intercepts: $\frac{\pi}{3}n$; asymptotes: $\frac{\pi}{6} + \frac{\pi}{3}n$

2.

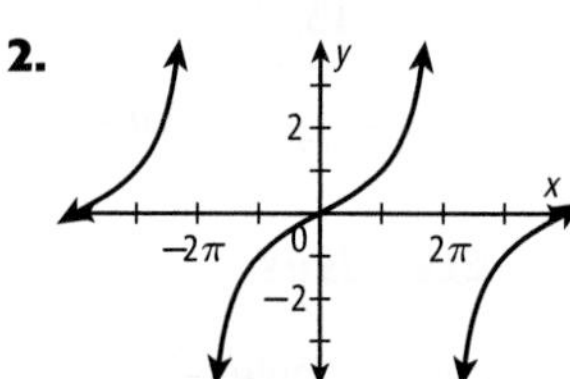

period: 4π; x-intercepts: $4\pi n$; asymptotes: $2\pi + 4\pi n$

3.

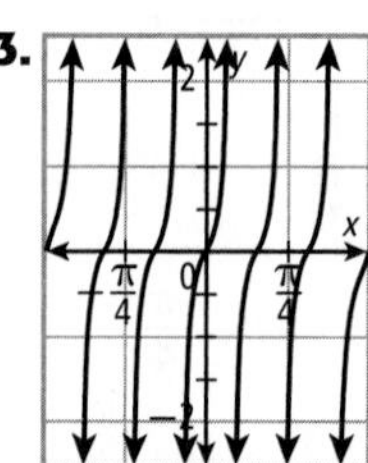

period: $\frac{1}{2}$; x-intercepts: $\frac{1}{2}n$; asymptotes: $\frac{1}{4} + \frac{1}{2}n$

4.

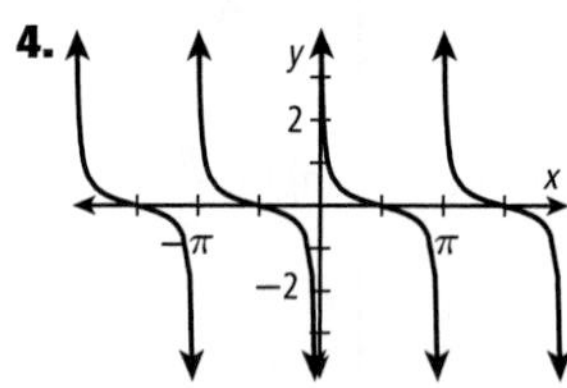

period: π; x-intercepts: $\frac{\pi}{2} + \pi n$; asymptotes: πn

5.

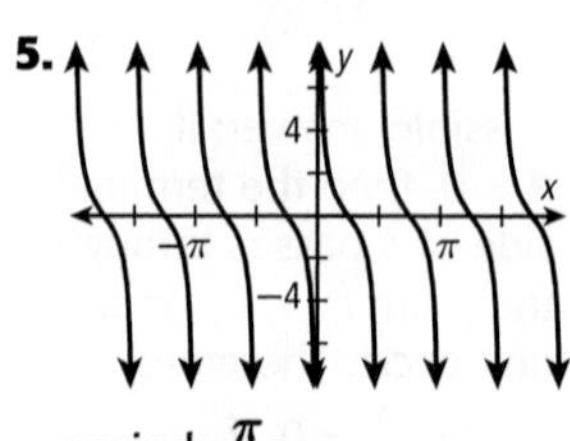

period: $\frac{\pi}{2}$; x-intercepts: $\frac{\pi}{4} + \frac{\pi}{2}n$; asymptotes: $\frac{\pi}{2}n$

Additional Answers

6.

period: π;
x-intercepts: $\frac{\pi}{2} + n\pi$;
asymptotes: $n\pi$

7.

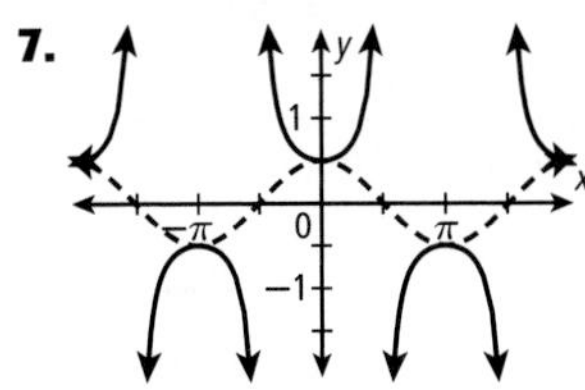

period: 2π;
asymptotes: $\frac{\pi}{2} + \pi n$

8.

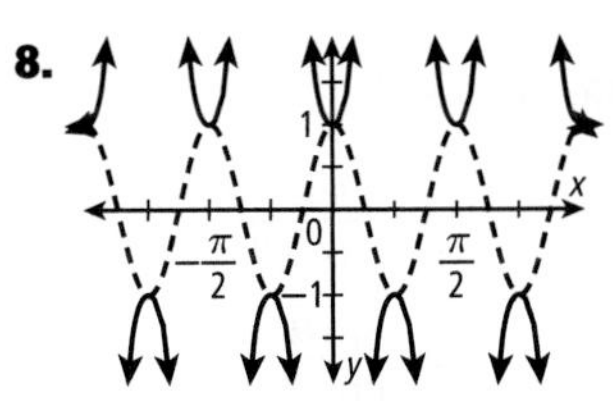

period: $\frac{\pi}{2}$;
asymptotes: $\frac{\pi}{8} + \frac{\pi}{4}n$

9.

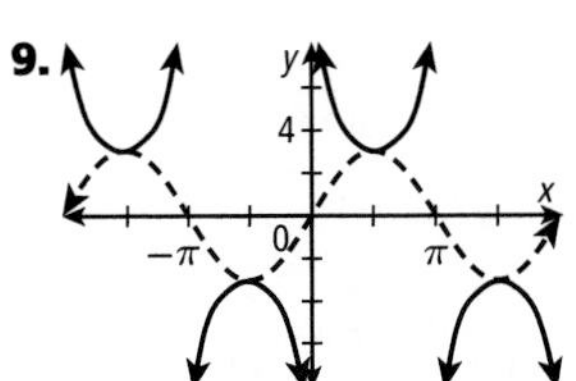

period: 2π;
asymptotes: πn

10.

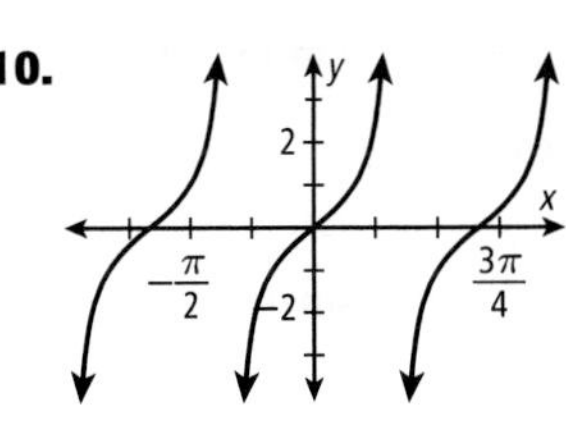

period: $\frac{2\pi}{3}$;
x-intercepts: $\frac{2\pi}{3}n$;
asymptotes: $\frac{\pi}{3} + \frac{2\pi}{3}n$

11.

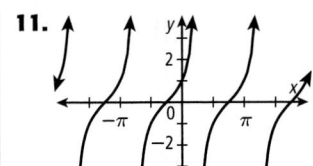

period: π;
x-intercepts: $\frac{3\pi}{4} + \pi n$;
asymptotes: $\frac{\pi}{4} + \pi n$

12.

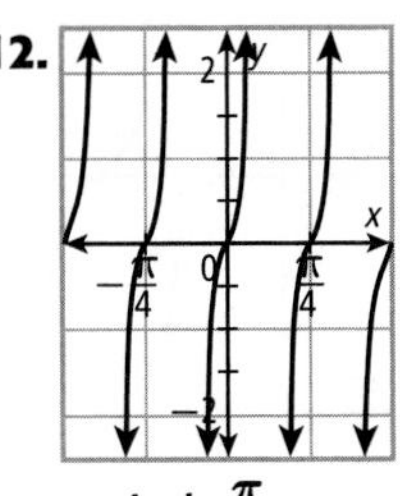

period: $\frac{\pi}{4}$;
x-intercepts: $\frac{\pi}{4}n$;
asymptotes: $\frac{\pi}{8} + \frac{\pi}{4}n$

13.

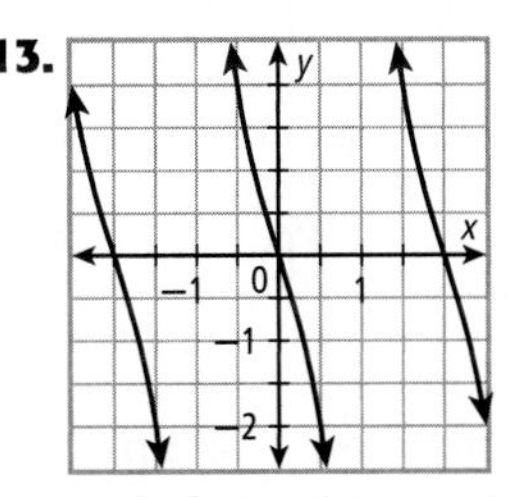

period: 2; x-intercepts: $2n$;
asymptotes: $1 + 2n$

14.

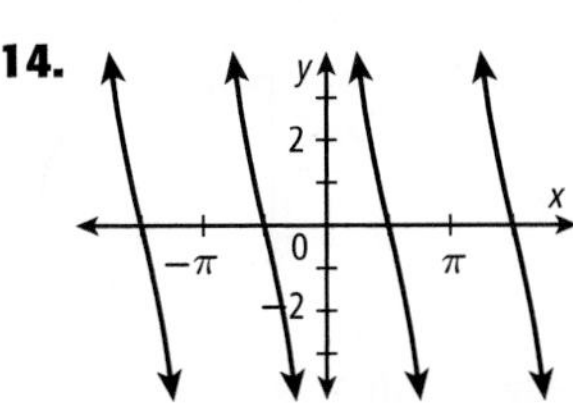

period: π;
x-intercepts: $\frac{\pi}{2} + \pi n$;
asymptotes: πn

15.

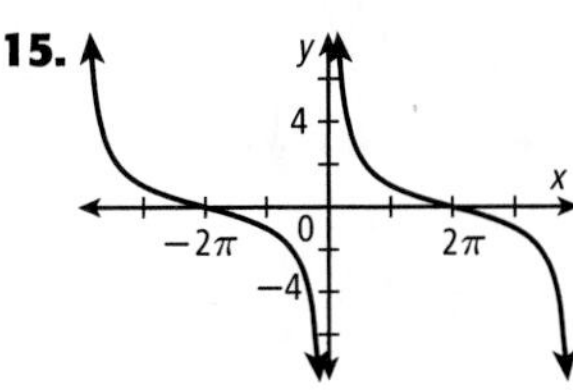

period: 4π;
x-intercepts: $2\pi + 4\pi n$;
asymptotes: $4\pi n$

16.

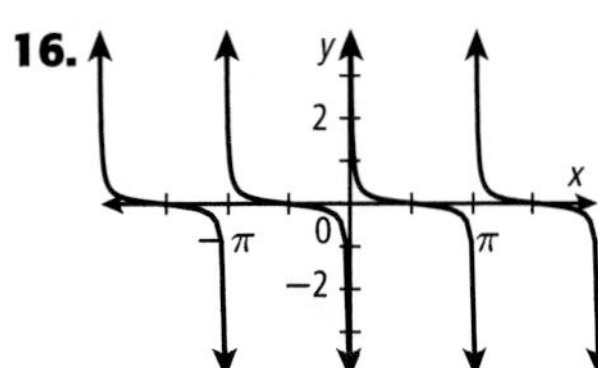

period: π;
x-intercepts: $\frac{\pi}{2} + \pi n$;
asymptotes: πn

17.

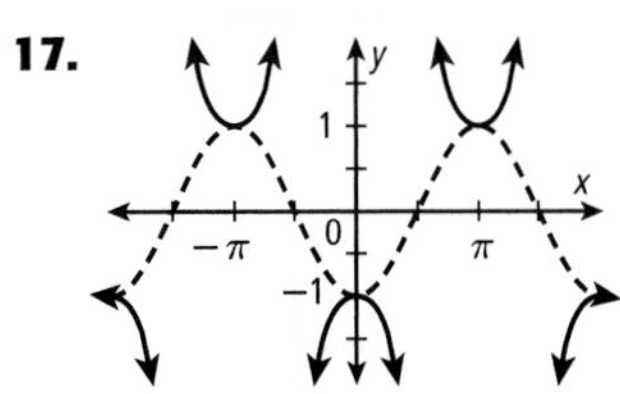

period: 2π;
asymptotes: $\frac{\pi}{2} + \pi n$

18.

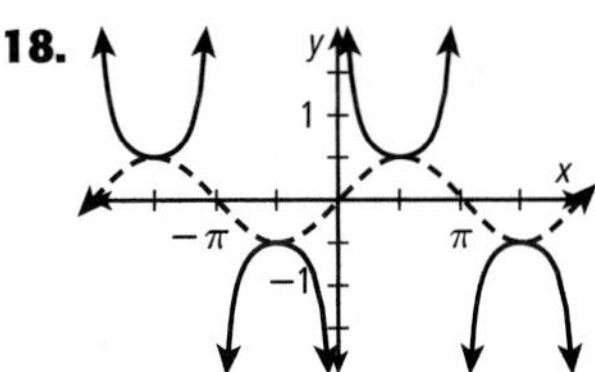

period: 2π;
asymptotes: πn

19.

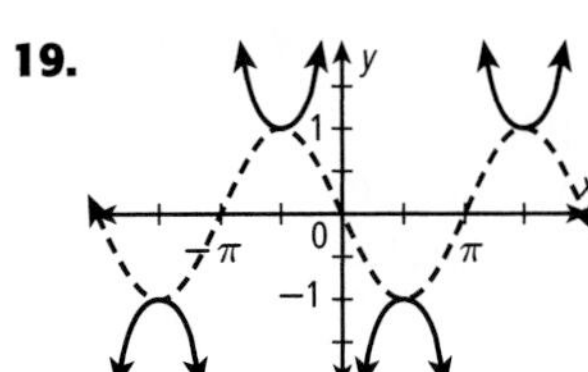

period: 2π;
asymptotes: πn

34. Possible answer: For reciprocal pairs of trigonometric functions, the signs are always the same.

35. Possible answer: First, graph $g(x) = 3\cos 4x$ and draw vertical asymptotes through the zeros of g. Then start at the maximum value of g and draw upward toward the asymptotes on either side. Repeat this step for the minimum value, drawing downward.

41. period: 2; local maximum: 1; local minimum: 7; phase shift: 1 right

42. period: 2π; local maximum: none; local minimum: none; phase shift: $\frac{\pi}{2}$ right

43. period: π; local maximum: -0.5; local minimum: 0.5; phase shift: $\frac{\pi}{4}$ left

44. period: $\frac{\pi}{3}$; local max.: none; local min.: none; phase shift: π left

45. period: 2π; local max.: -0.14; local min.: 1.38; phase shift: none

46. period: 4; local max.: -1; local min.: 1; phase shift: $\frac{5}{7}$ left

47.

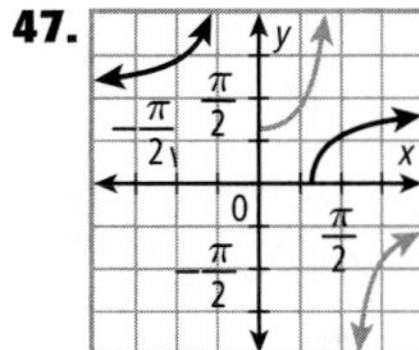

D: $\{x \mid x \le -1 \text{ or } x \ge 1\}$;
R: $\{y \mid 0 \le y \le \pi \text{ and } y \ne \frac{\pi}{2}\}$

48.

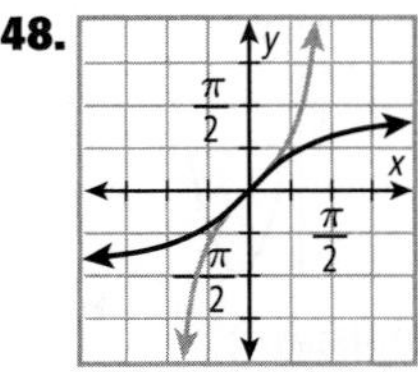

D: $\{x \mid x \in \mathbb{R}\}$;
R: $\{y \mid -\frac{\pi}{2} < y < \frac{\pi}{2}\}$

49.

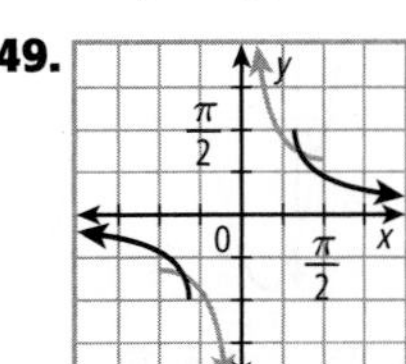

D: $\{x \mid x \le -1 \text{ or } x \ge 1\}$;
R: $\{y \mid -\frac{\pi}{2} \le y \le \frac{\pi}{2} \text{ and } y \ne 0\}$

50.

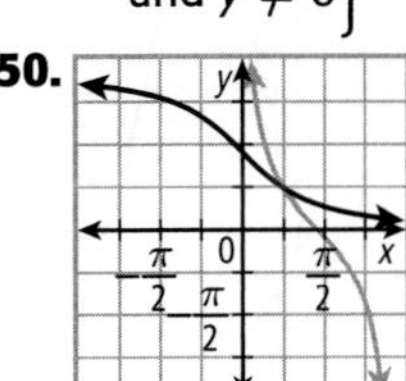

D: $\{x \mid x \in \mathbb{R}\}$;
R: $\{y \mid 0 \le y \le \pi\}$

14A *Ready to Go On?*

5.

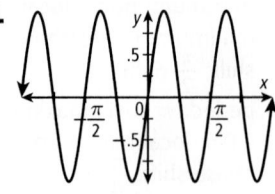

amplitude: 1; period: $\frac{\pi}{2}$

6. 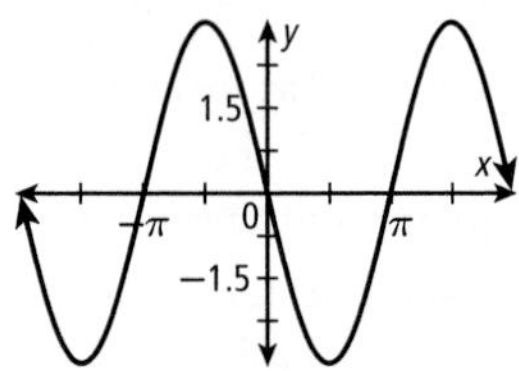

amplitude: −3; period: 2π

7. 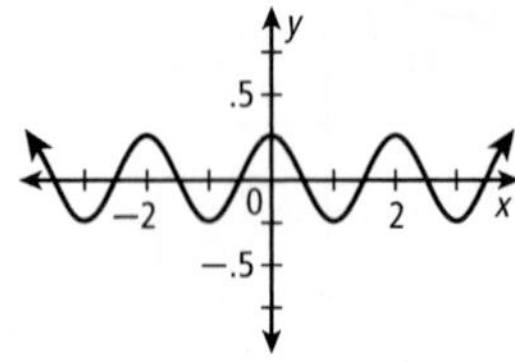

amplitude: $\frac{1}{4}$; period: 2

8. 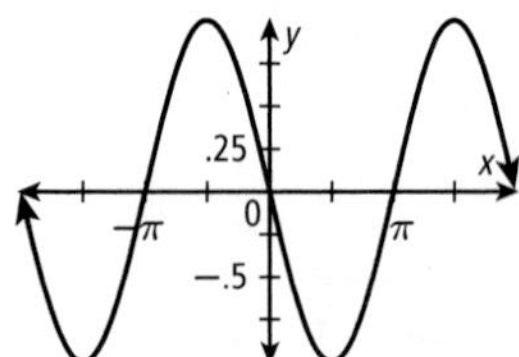

x-intercepts: πn;

phase shift: $\frac{3\pi}{2}$ right

9. 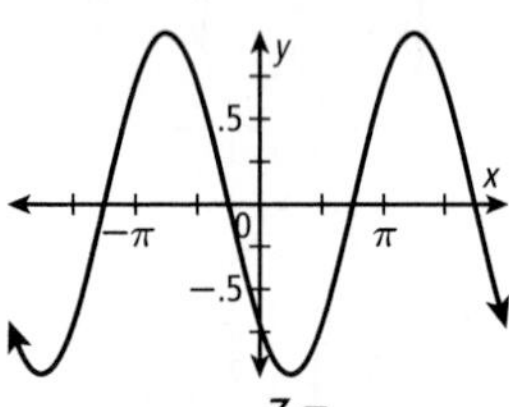

x-intercepts: $\frac{3\pi}{4} + \pi n$;

phase shift: $\frac{3\pi}{4}$ right

10. 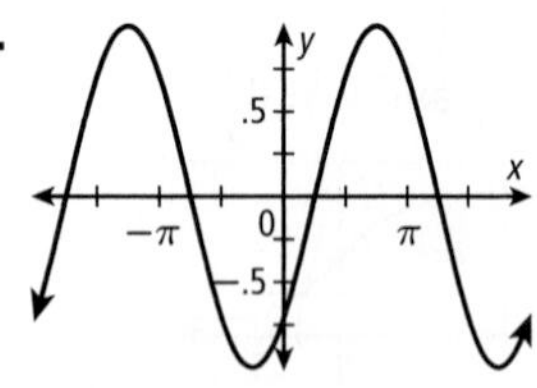

x-intercepts: $\frac{\pi}{4} + \pi n$;

phase shift: $\frac{5\pi}{4}$ left

11. 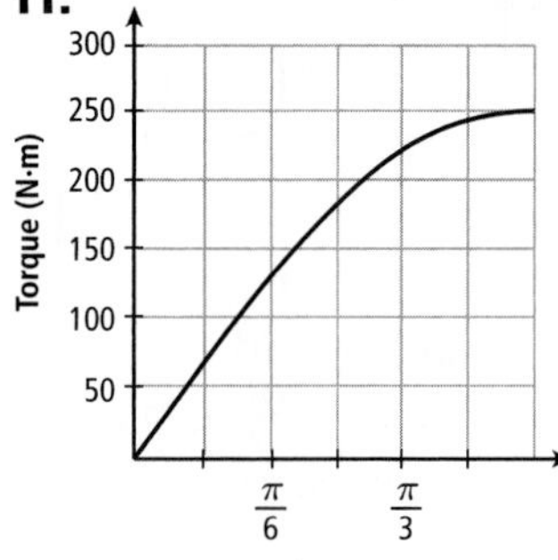

≈ 216.5 Nm

12.

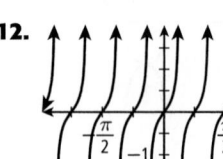

period: $\frac{\pi}{4}$;

x-intercepts: $\frac{\pi}{4}n$;

asymptotes: $\frac{\pi}{8} + \frac{\pi}{4}n$

13. 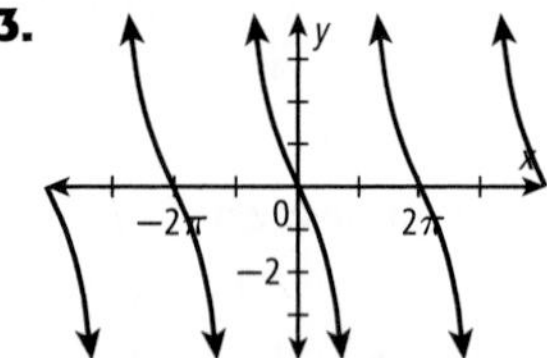

period: 2π;

x-intercepts: $2\pi n$;

asymptotes: $\pi + 2\pi n$

14. 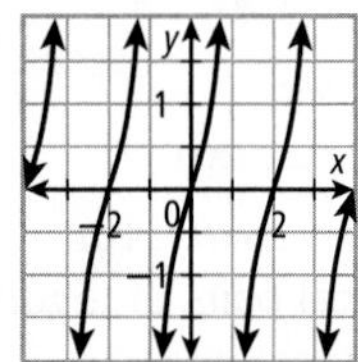

period: 2; x-intercepts: $2n$;

asymptotes: $1 + 2n$

15. 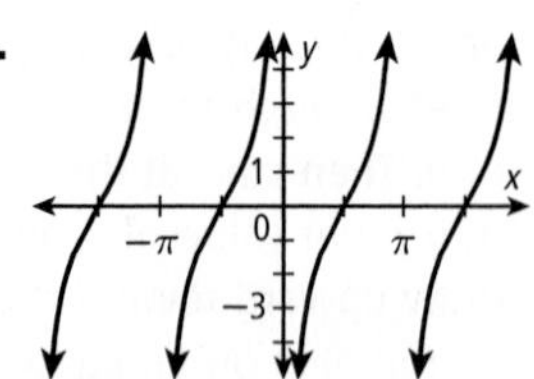

period: π;

x-intercepts: $\frac{\pi}{2} + \pi n$;

asymptotes: πn

16. 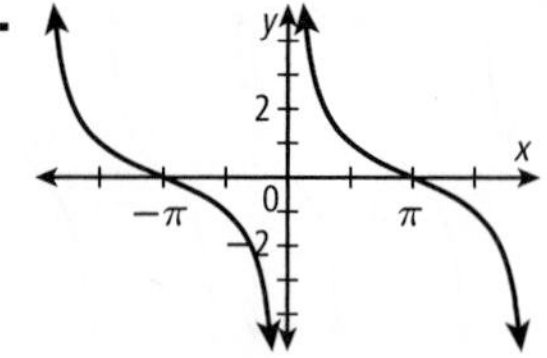

period: 2π;

x-intercepts: $\pi + 2\pi n$;

asymptotes: $2\pi n$

17. 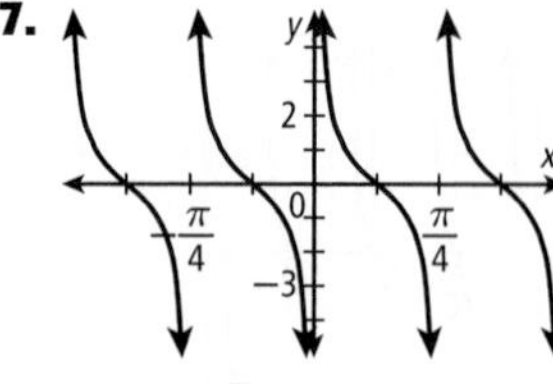

period: $\frac{\pi}{4}$;

x-intercepts: $\frac{\pi}{8} + \frac{\pi}{4}n$;

asymptotes: $\frac{\pi}{4}n$

18. 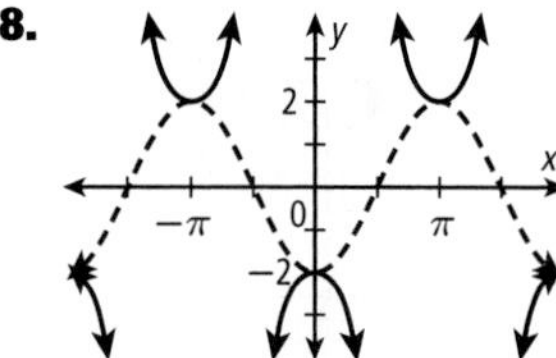

period: 2π;

asymptotes: $\frac{\pi}{2} + \pi n$

19. 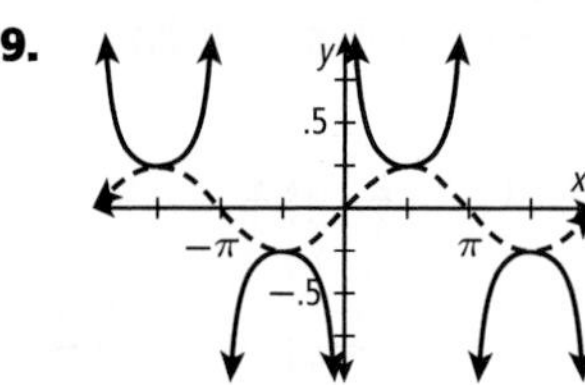

period: 2π;

asymptotes: πn

20. 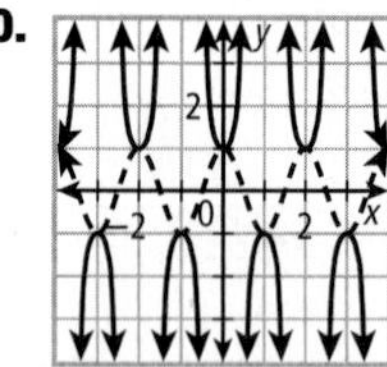

period: 2;

asymptotes: $\frac{1}{2} + n$

14-3 *Exercises*

35. $\frac{\cos\theta}{1 - \sin^2\theta} = \frac{\cos\theta}{\cos^2\theta}$

$= \frac{1}{\cos\theta}$

$= \sec\theta$

35. $\frac{\cos\theta}{1 - \sin^2\theta} = \frac{\cos\theta}{\cos^2\theta}$

$= \frac{1}{\cos\theta}$

$= \sec\theta$

36. $\frac{1 - \cos^2\theta}{\tan\theta} = \frac{\sin^2\theta}{\frac{\sin\theta}{\cos\theta}}$

$= \sin^2\theta\left(\frac{\cos\theta}{\sin\theta}\right)$

$= \sin\theta\cos\theta$

37. $\frac{\csc^2\theta}{1 + \tan^2\theta} = \frac{\csc^2\theta}{\sec^2\theta}$

$= \frac{\frac{1}{\sin^2\theta}}{\frac{1}{\cos^2\theta}}$

$= \frac{\cos^2\theta}{\sin^2\theta}$

$= \cot^2\theta$

38. $\tan\theta = \frac{y}{x}$

$= \frac{r\sin\theta}{r\cos\theta}$

$= \frac{\sin\theta}{\cos\theta}$

39. $\cot\theta = \frac{x}{y}$

$= \frac{r\cos\theta}{r\sin\theta}$

$= \frac{\cos\theta}{\sin\theta}$

40. $x^2 + y^2 = r^2$

$\frac{x^2}{y^2} + \frac{y^2}{y^2} = \frac{r^2}{y^2}$

$\left(\frac{x}{y}\right)^2 + 1 = \left(\frac{r}{y}\right)^2$

$\cot^2\theta + 1 = \csc^2\theta$

$1 + \cot^2\theta = \csc^2\theta$

41. $\csc\theta = \frac{r}{y}$

$= \frac{r}{r\sin\theta}$

$= \frac{1}{\sin\theta}$

42. $\sec\theta = \frac{r}{x}$

$= \frac{r}{r\cos\theta}$

$= \frac{1}{\cos\theta}$

43. $x^2 + y^2 = r^2$

$\frac{x^2}{x^2} + \frac{y^2}{x^2} = \frac{r^2}{x^2}$

$1 + \left(\frac{y}{x}\right)^2 = \left(\frac{r}{x}\right)^2$

$1 + \tan^2\theta = \sec^2\theta$

14-4 *Exercises*

19. $\sin\left(\frac{3\pi}{2}+x\right)$

$= \sin\frac{3\pi}{2}\cos x$

$+ \cos\frac{3\pi}{2}\sin x$

$= (-1)\cos x + (0)\sin x$

$= -\cos x$

20. $\tan(x - 2\pi)$

$= \frac{\tan x - \tan 2\pi}{1 + \tan x \tan 2\pi}$

$= \frac{\tan x + 0}{1 + 0}$

$= \tan x$

44. $A'(-2.12, 2.12)$, $B'(-2.12, 3.54)$, $C'(-0.71, 3.54)$, $D'(1.41, 1.41)$

45. $A'(-2.60, 1.5)$, $B'(-2.96, 2.87)$, $C'(-1.60, 3.23)$, $D'(1, 1.73)$

46. $A'(-2.60, -1.5)$, $B'(-3.96, -1.13)$, $C'(-3.60, 0.23)$, $D'(-1, 1.73)$

47. $A'(1.50, 2.60)$, $B'(2.87, 2.96)$, $C'(3.23, 1.60)$, $D'(1.73, -1)$

48. In general, $\sin(A + B) \neq \sin A + \sin B$; $\sin(45° + 45°) \neq \sin 45° + \sin 45°$, which results in $\sin(90°) \neq \frac{\sqrt{2}}{2} + \frac{\sqrt{2}}{2}$, or $1 \neq \sqrt{2}$.

52. Possible answer:

$\sin(-15°)$

$= \sin(45° - 60°)$

$= \sin 45° \cos 60° - \cos 45° \sin 60°$

$= \frac{\sqrt{2}}{2} \cdot \frac{1}{2} - \frac{\sqrt{2}}{2} \cdot \frac{\sqrt{3}}{2}$

$= \frac{\sqrt{2} - \sqrt{6}}{4}$

53. The rotation matrix for $-\theta$ is

$\begin{bmatrix} \cos(-\theta) & -\sin(-\theta) \\ \sin(-\theta) & \cos(-\theta) \end{bmatrix}$

$= \begin{bmatrix} \cos\theta & \sin\theta \\ -\sin\theta & \cos\theta \end{bmatrix}$.

The inverse of this rotation matrix is

$\frac{1}{\cos^2\theta + \sin^2\theta}\begin{bmatrix} \cos\theta & -\sin\theta \\ \sin\theta & \cos\theta \end{bmatrix}$

$= \begin{bmatrix} \cos\theta & -\sin\theta \\ \sin\theta & \cos\theta \end{bmatrix}$,

which is equivalent to the rotation matrix for θ.

54. $\tan(A + B)$

$= \frac{\sin(A + B)}{\cos(A + B)}$

$= \frac{\sin A \cos B + \cos A \sin B}{\cos A \cos B - \sin A \sin B}$

$= \frac{(\sin A \cos B + \cos A \sin B)}{(\cos A \cos B - \sin A \sin B)} \cdot \frac{\left(\frac{1}{\cos A \cos B}\right)}{\left(\frac{1}{\cos A \cos B}\right)}$

$= \frac{\frac{\sin A}{\cos A} + \frac{\sin B}{\cos B}}{1 - \frac{\sin A \sin B}{\cos A \cos B}}$

$= \frac{\tan A + \tan B}{1 - \tan A \tan B}$

55. $x' = r\cos(\alpha + \theta)$

$= r\cos\alpha(\cos\theta) - r\sin\alpha(\sin\theta)$

$= x(\cos\theta) - y(\sin\theta)$

$y' = r\sin(\alpha + \theta)$

$= r\sin\alpha(\cos\theta) + r\cos\alpha(\sin\theta)$

$= y(\cos\theta) + x(\sin\theta)$

$\begin{bmatrix} \cos\theta & -\sin\theta \\ \sin\theta & \cos\theta \end{bmatrix}\begin{bmatrix} x \\ y \end{bmatrix} = \begin{bmatrix} x' \\ y' \end{bmatrix}$

14-5 *Exercises*

6. $\frac{2\tan\theta}{1 + \tan^2\theta} = \frac{2\tan\theta}{\sec^2\theta}$

$= 2\left(\frac{\sin\theta}{\cos\theta}\right)\cos^2\theta$

$= 2\sin\theta\cos\theta$

$= \sin 2\theta$

15. $\frac{\sin 2\theta}{\sin\theta} = \frac{(2\sin\theta\cos\theta)}{\sin\theta}$

$= 2\cos\theta$

16. $\frac{1}{2}(1 + \cos 2\theta) = \frac{1 + \cos 2\theta}{2}$

$= \frac{1 + 2\cos^2\theta - 1}{2}$

$= \frac{2\cos^2\theta}{2} = \cos^2\theta$

17. $\frac{1 - \cos 2\theta}{\sin 2\theta}$

$= \frac{1 - (1 - 2\sin^2\theta)}{2\sin\theta\cos\theta}$

$= \frac{2\sin^2\theta}{2\sin\theta\cos\theta}$

$= \frac{\sin\theta}{\cos\theta} = \tan\theta$

18. $\frac{\sin 2\theta}{1 + \cos 2\theta}$

$= \frac{2\sin\theta\cos\theta}{1 + 2\cos^2\theta - 1}$

$= \frac{2\sin\theta\cos\theta}{2\cos^2\theta}$

$= \frac{\sin\theta}{\cos\theta} = \tan\theta$

45. Possible answer:

$\cos^2\frac{\theta}{2} = \left(\cos\frac{\theta}{2}\right)^2$

$= \left(\sqrt{\frac{1 + \cos\theta}{2}}\right)^2$

$= \left(\frac{1 + \cos\theta}{2}\right)\left(\frac{1 - \cos\theta}{1 - \cos\theta}\right)$

$= \frac{1 - \cos^2\theta}{2(1 - \cos\theta)}$

$= \frac{\sin^2\theta}{2(1 - \cos\theta)}$

46. Possible answer:

$\frac{1 - \tan^2\theta}{1 + \tan^2\theta} = \frac{1 - \frac{\sin^2\theta}{\cos^2\theta}}{\sec^2\theta}$

$= \frac{1 - \left(\frac{\sin^2\theta}{\cos^2\theta}\right)}{\left(\frac{1}{\cos^2\theta}\right)} \cdot \frac{\cos^2\theta}{\cos^2\theta}$

$= \cos^2\theta - \sin^2\theta$

$= \cos 2\theta$

47. Possible answer:

$\frac{\tan\theta + \sin\theta}{2\tan\theta}$

$= \frac{\left(\frac{\sin\theta}{\cos\theta}\right) + \sin\theta\left(\frac{\cos\theta}{\cos\theta}\right)}{2\left(\frac{\sin\theta}{\cos\theta}\right)}$

$= \frac{\left(\frac{1}{\cos\theta}\right)(\sin\theta + \sin\theta\cos\theta)}{\left(\frac{1}{\cos\theta}\right)(2\sin\theta)}$

$= \frac{\sin\theta + \sin\theta\cos\theta}{2\sin\theta}$

$= \frac{\sin\theta(1 + \cos\theta)}{2\sin\theta}$

$= \frac{1 + \cos\theta}{2}$

$= \left(\sqrt{\frac{1 + \cos\theta}{2}}\right)^2$

$= \left(\cos\frac{\theta}{2}\right)^2 = \cos^2\frac{\theta}{2}$

48.

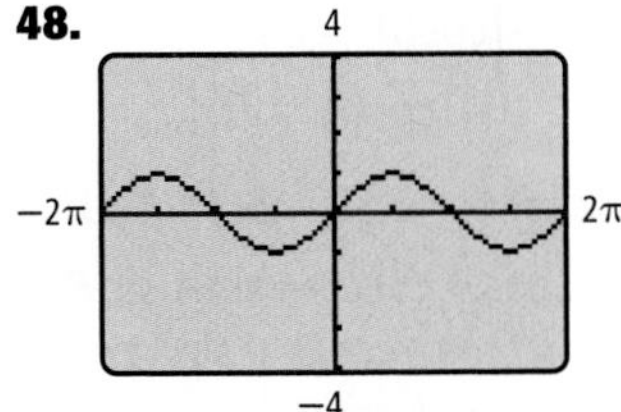

$\frac{(\cos x)(1 - \cos 2x)}{\sin 2x}$

$= \frac{(\cos x)\left[1 - (1 - 2\sin^2 x)\right]}{2\sin x\cos x}$

$= \frac{2\sin^2 x}{2\sin x}$

$= \sin x$

57. Possible answer:

$\tan 2\theta = \frac{\sin 2\theta}{\cos 2\theta}$

$= \frac{2\sin\theta\cos\theta}{1 - 2\sin^2\theta}$

$= \frac{2\sin\theta\cos\theta}{1 - 2\sin^2\theta}\frac{\left(\frac{1}{\cos^2\theta}\right)}{\left(\frac{1}{\cos^2\theta}\right)}$

$= \frac{2\frac{\sin\theta}{\cos\theta}}{\frac{1}{\cos^2\theta} - 2\left(\frac{\sin^2\theta}{\cos^2\theta}\right)}$

$= \frac{2\tan\theta}{\sec^2\theta - 2\tan^2\theta}$

$= \frac{2\tan\theta}{1 - \tan^2\theta}$

58. $\tan\frac{\theta}{2} = \frac{\sin\frac{\theta}{2}}{\cos\frac{\theta}{2}}$

$= \frac{\pm\sqrt{\frac{1 - \cos\theta}{2}}}{\pm\sqrt{\frac{1 + \cos\theta}{2}}}$

$= \pm\sqrt{\frac{1 - \cos\theta}{2}}\left(\sqrt{\frac{2}{1 + \cos\theta}}\right)$

$= \pm\sqrt{\frac{1 - \cos\theta}{1 + \cos\theta}}$

64. $\cos(A - B) - \cos(A + B)$
$= (\cos A \cos B + \sin A \sin B)$
$- (\cos A \cos B - \sin A \sin B)$
$= 2 \sin A \sin B$

$\sin A \sin B$
$= \frac{1}{2}\left[\cos(A - B) - \cos(A + B)\right];$

$\cos(A + B) + \cos(A - B)$
$= (\cos A \cos B - \sin A \sin B)$
$+ (\cos A \cos B + \sin A \sin B)$
$= 2 \cos A \cos B$

$\cos A \cos B$
$= \frac{1}{2}\left[\cos(A + B) + \cos(A - B)\right]$

14B *Ready to Go On*

1. $\sin^2\theta \sec\theta \csc\theta$
$= \sin^2\theta\left(\frac{1}{\cos\theta}\right)\left(\frac{1}{\sin\theta}\right)$
$= \frac{\sin\theta}{\cos\theta} = \tan\theta$

2. $\sin(-\theta)\sec\theta\cot\theta$
$= -\sin\theta\left(\frac{1}{\cos\theta}\right)\left(\frac{\cos\theta}{\sin\theta}\right)$
$= -1$

3. $\frac{\cot^2\theta - 1}{\cot^2\theta + 1}$
$= \frac{(\csc^2\theta - 1) - 1}{\csc^2\theta}$
$= \frac{\csc^2\theta - 2}{\csc^2\theta}$
$= 1 - 2\left(\frac{1}{\csc^2\theta}\right)$
$= 1 - 2\sin^2\theta$

Extra Practice

Chapter 1 Skills

1. 2.3, $2.\overline{4}$, $\frac{5}{2}$, $\sqrt{10}$, $2\sqrt{3}$; 2.3: $\mathbb{R}$, $\mathbb{Q}$; $2.\overline{4}$: $\mathbb{R}$, $\mathbb{Q}$; $\frac{5}{2}$: $\mathbb{R}$, $\mathbb{Q}$; $\sqrt{10}$: $\mathbb{R}$, irrational; $2\sqrt{3}$: $\mathbb{R}$, irrational

2. -2π, $-\sqrt{12}$, $-\pi$, -3, $\frac{2}{5}$; -2π: $\mathbb{R}$, irrational; $-\sqrt{12}$: $\mathbb{R}$, irrational; $-\pi$: $\mathbb{R}$, irrational; -3: $\mathbb{R}$, $\mathbb{Q}$, $\mathbb{Z}$; $\frac{2}{5}$: $\mathbb{R}$, $\mathbb{Q}$

3. $\sqrt{9}$, $3.0\overline{2}$, $3\frac{1}{16}$, $3\frac{2}{30}$, π; $\sqrt{9}$: $\mathbb{R}$, $\mathbb{Q}$, $\mathbb{Z}$, $\mathbb{W}$, $\mathbb{N}$; $3.0\overline{2}$: $\mathbb{R}$, $\mathbb{Q}$; $3\frac{2}{30}$: $\mathbb{R}$, $\mathbb{Q}$; $3\frac{1}{16}$: $\mathbb{R}$, $\mathbb{Q}$; π: $\mathbb{R}$, irrational

14. sometimes true; possible answer: true when $a = 2$ and $b = 2$; false when $a = 2$ and $b = 3$

15. always true by the Distributive Property and the Associative Property of Multiplication: $6b + 6b = 6(b + b) = 6(2b) = (6 \cdot 2)b = 12b$

16. sometimes true; possible answer: true when $a = 0$, $b = 1$, and $c = 4$; false when $a = 2$, $b = 1$, and $c = 4$

47.

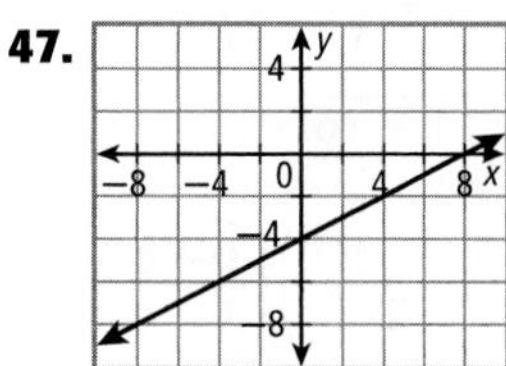

48.

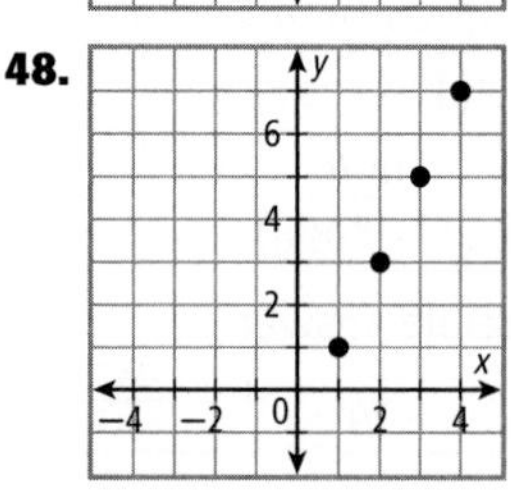

49.

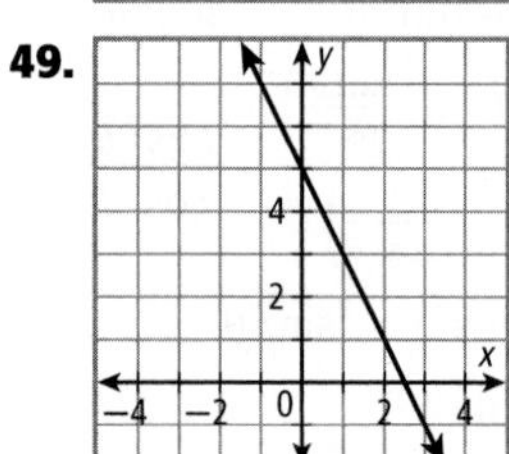

53.

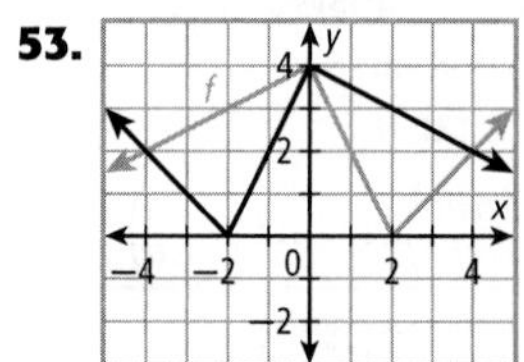

54.

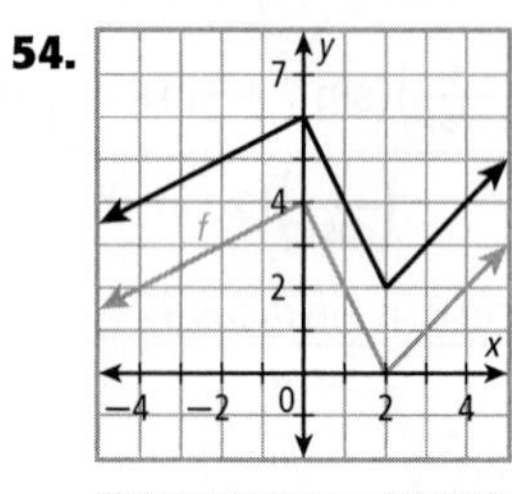

55.

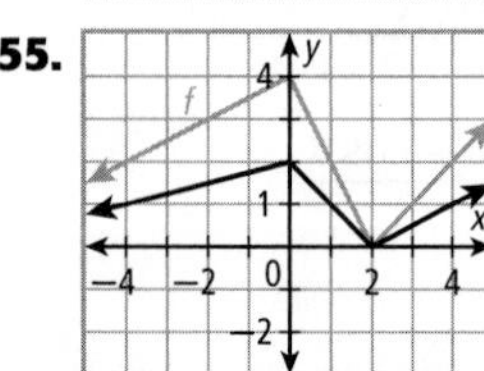

59.

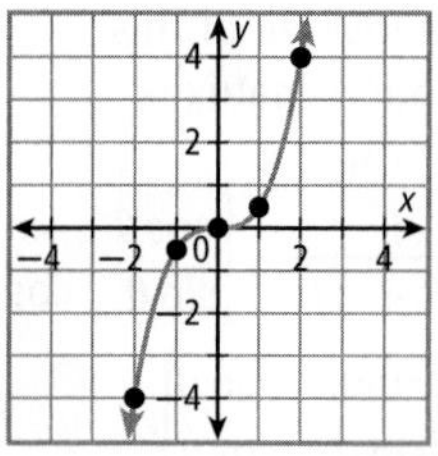

60.

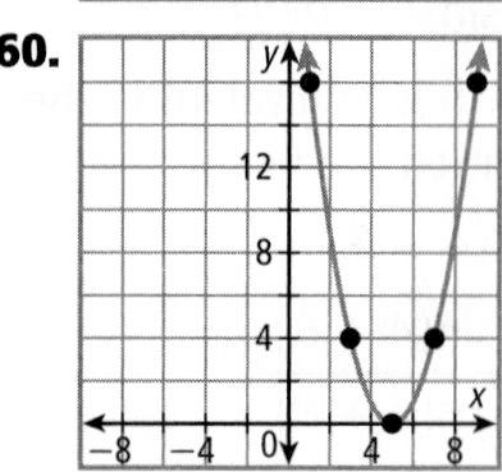

Chapter 2 Skills

7.

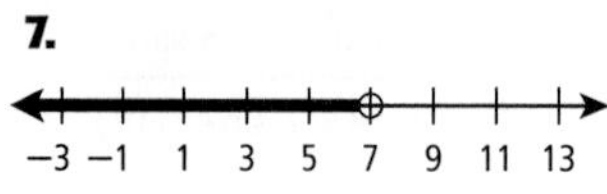

8.

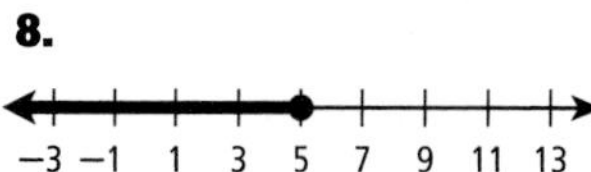

9.

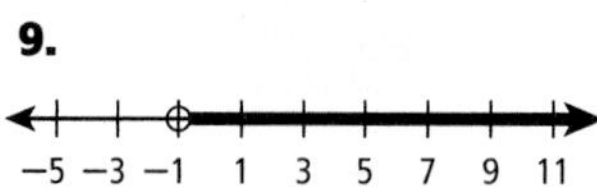

18.

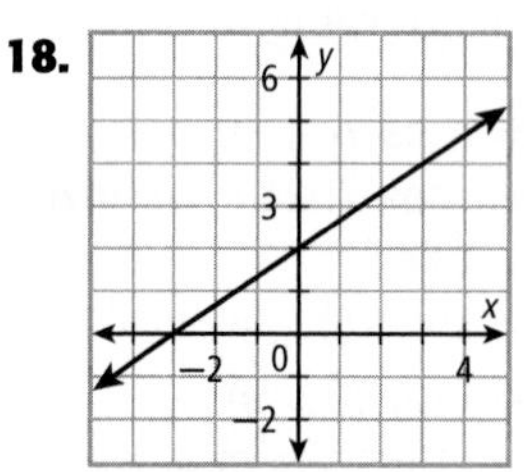

19.

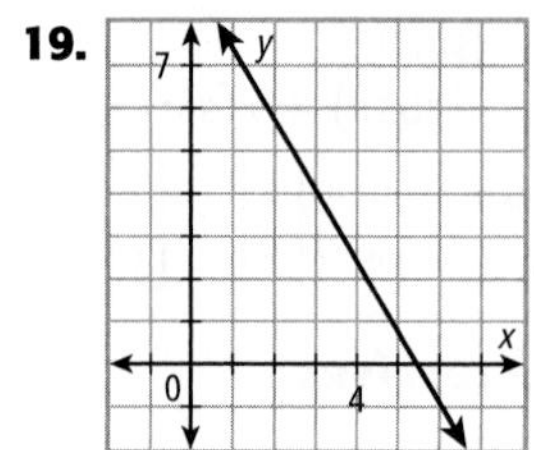

20.

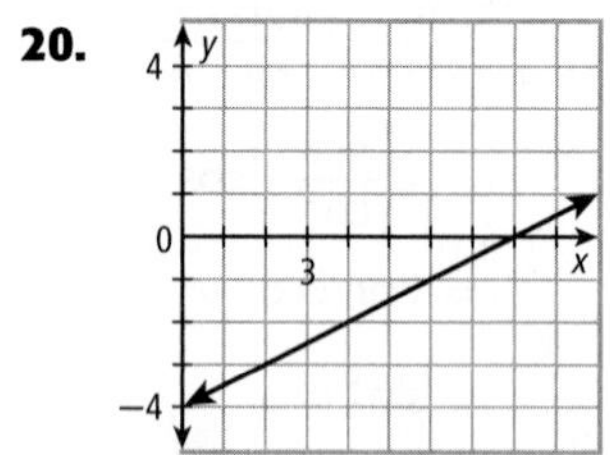

21.

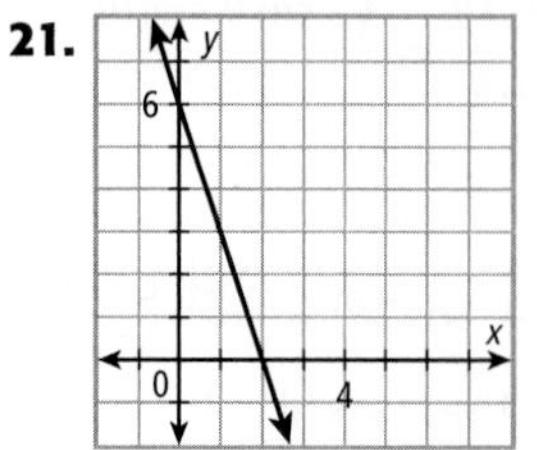

22.

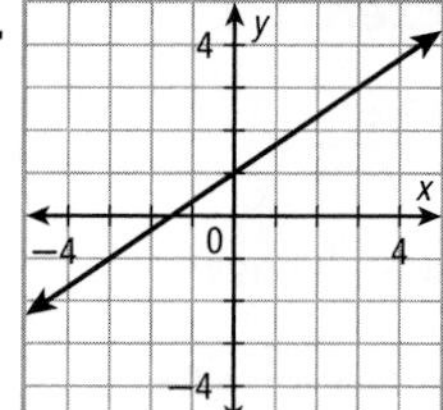

23.

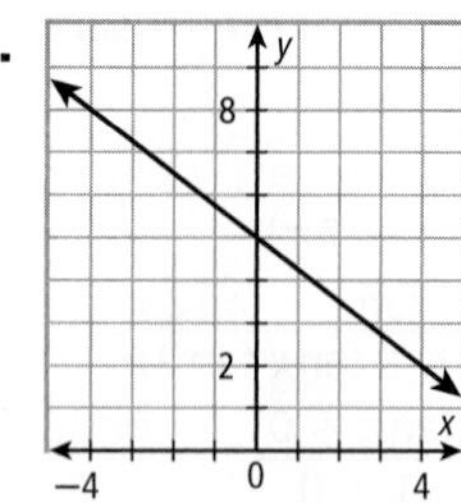

32.

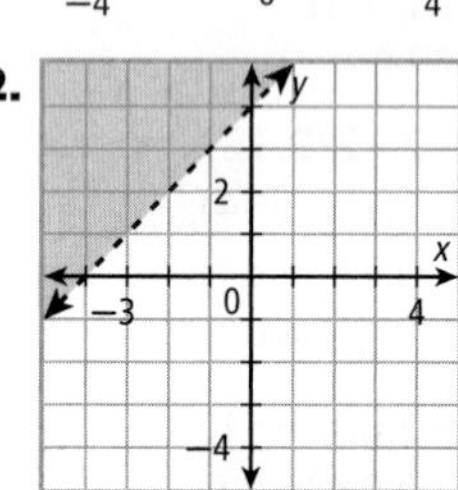

33.

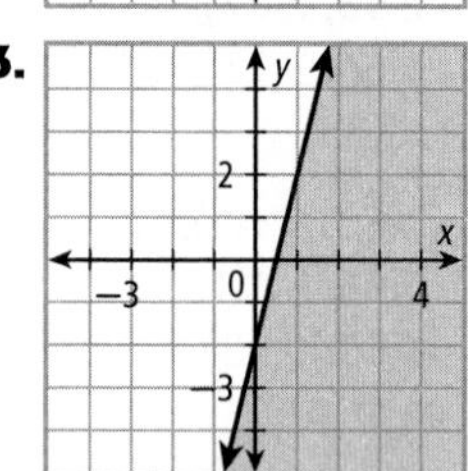

34.

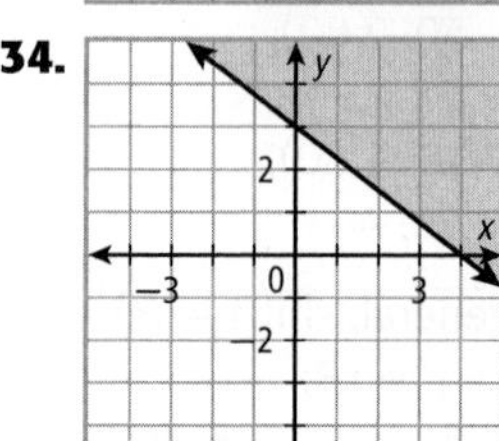

35.

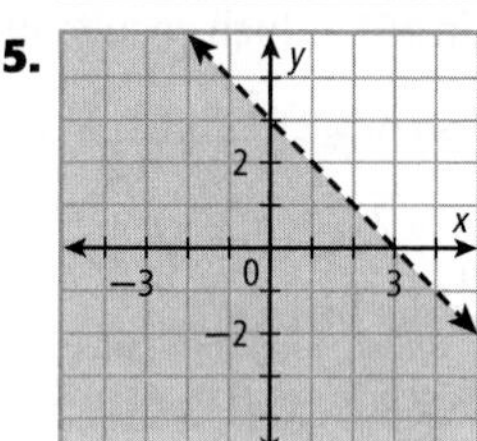

36.

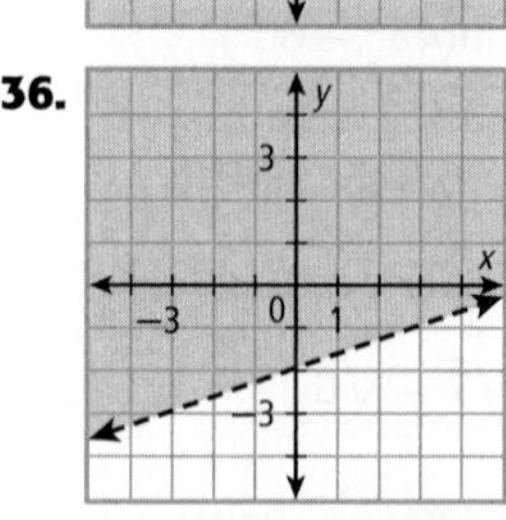

37.

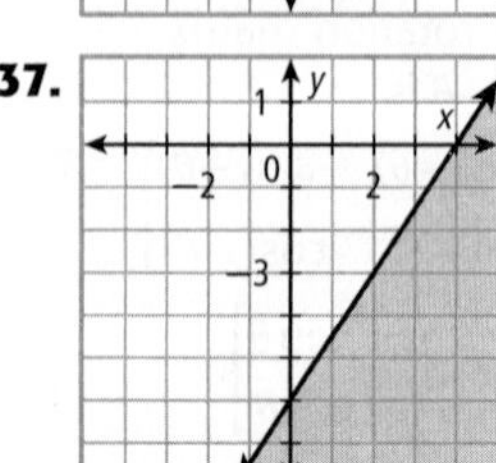

45. 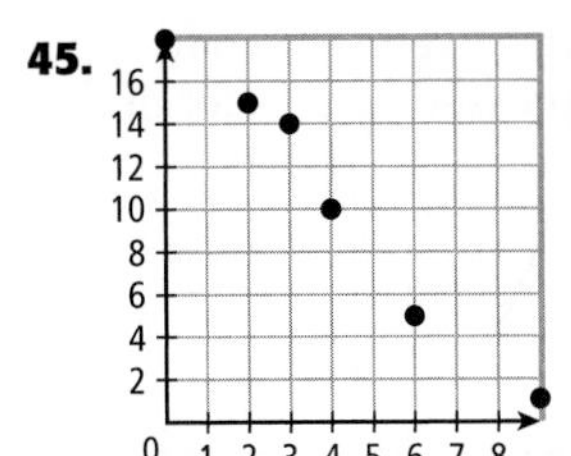

46. 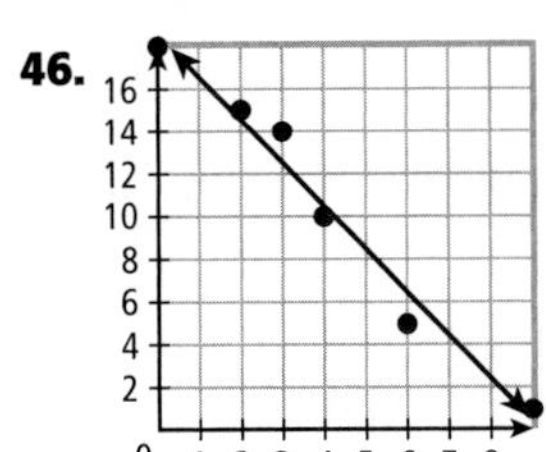

47. 

48. 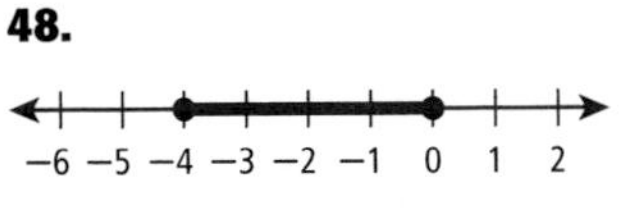

52. 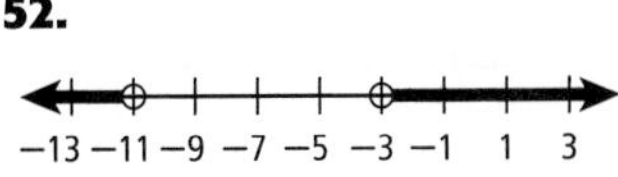

53. 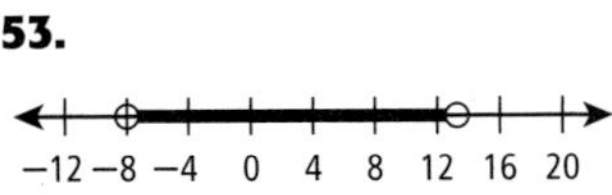

54. 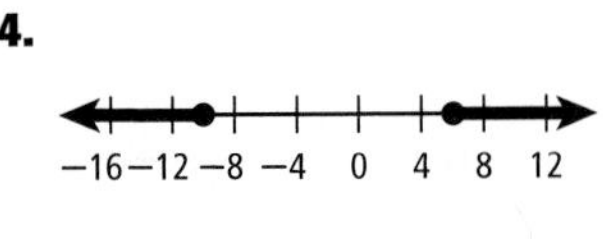

57. 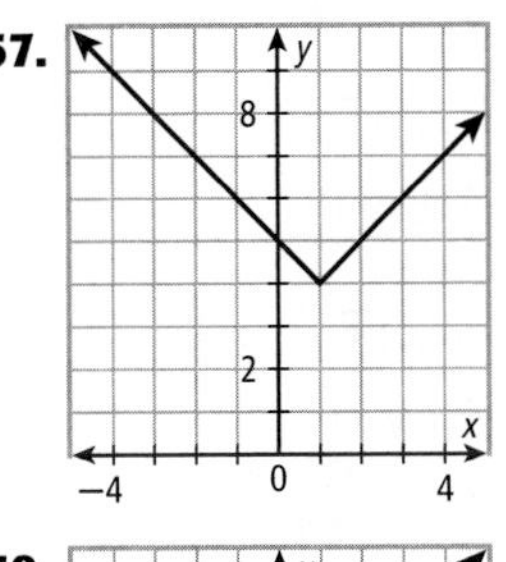

58. 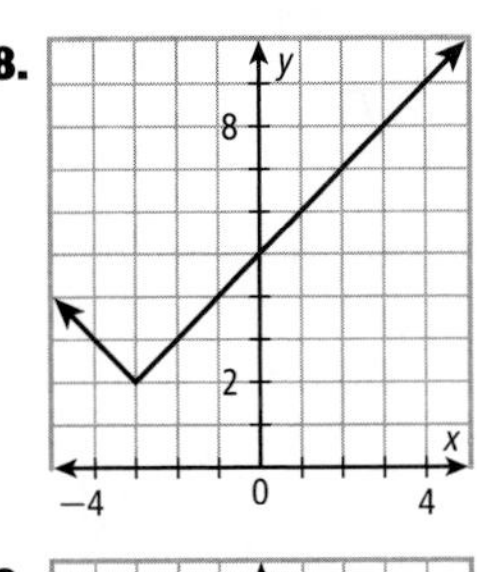

59. 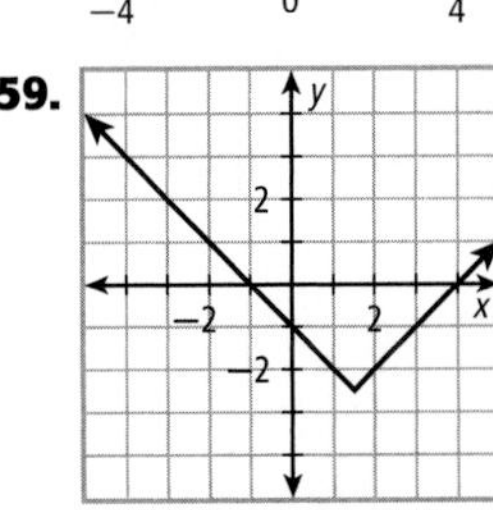

60. 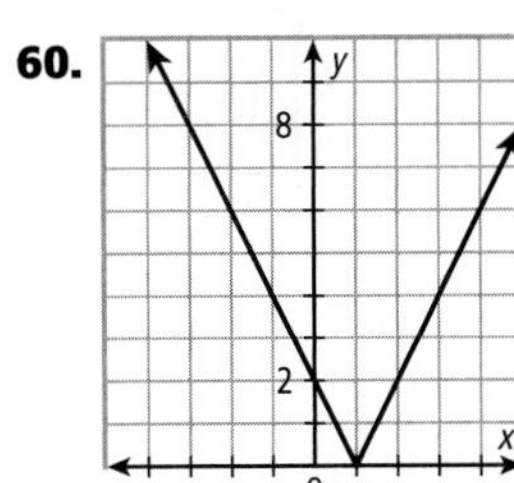

61. 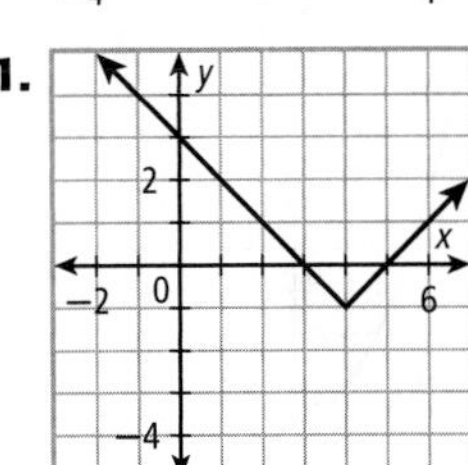

Chapter 3 Skills

9. inconsistent; no solutions

10. consistent, independent; 1 solution

11. consistent, dependent; infinite solutions

12. consistent, dependent; infinite solutions

21. consistent, independent; 1 solution

22. inconsistent; no solutions

23. consistent, dependent; infinite solutions

24. inconsistent; no solutions

25. 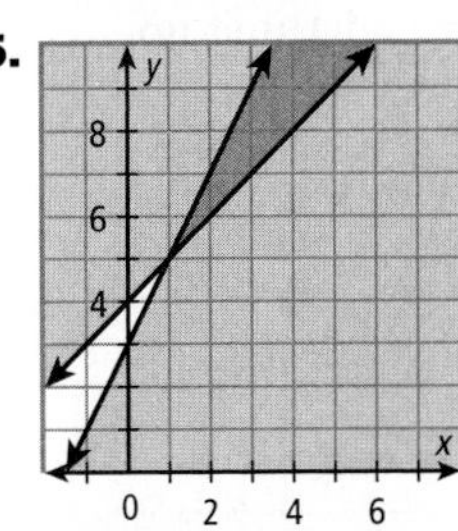

26. 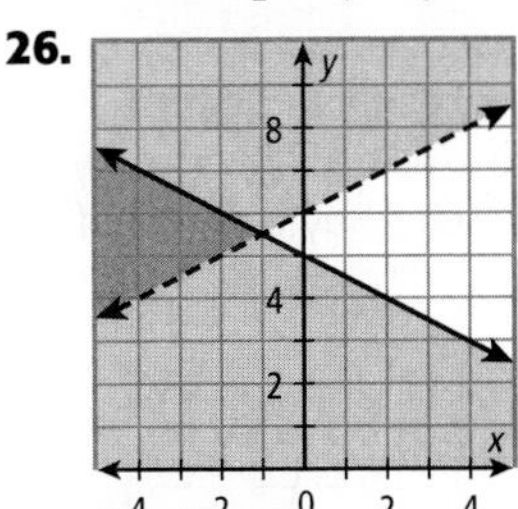

27. 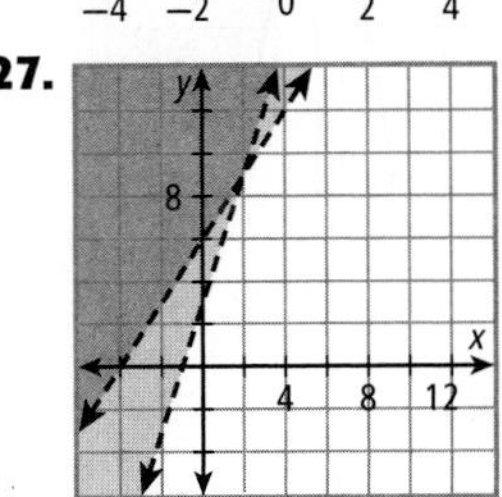

28. 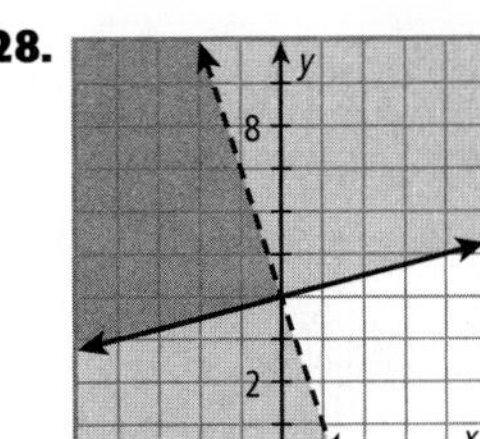

29. 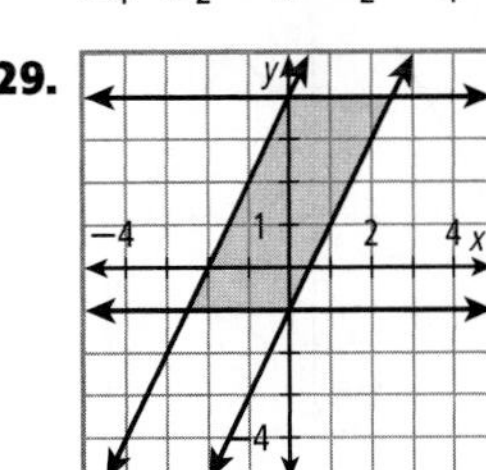

30. 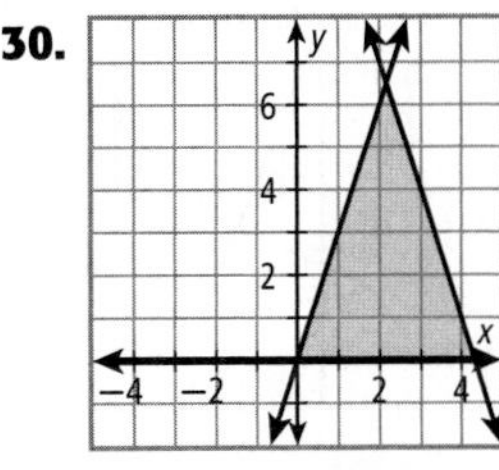

31. 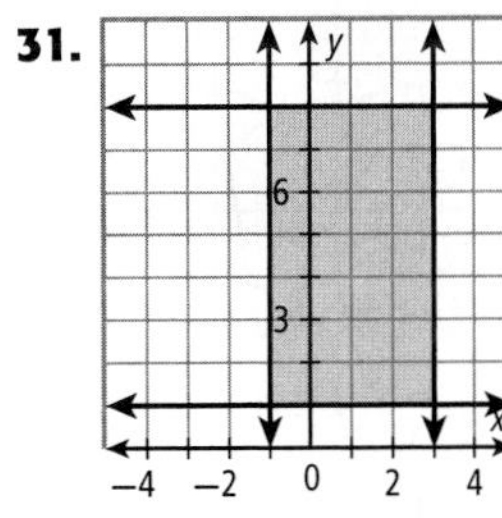

32. 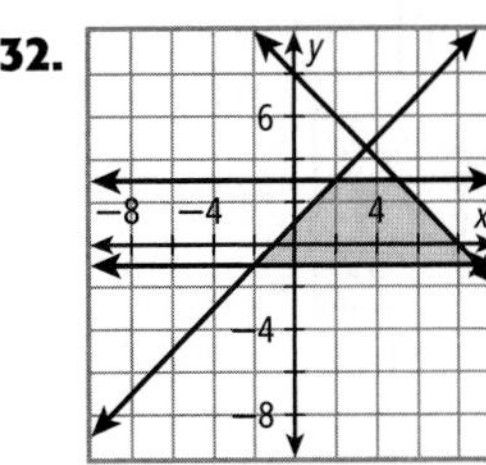

34. 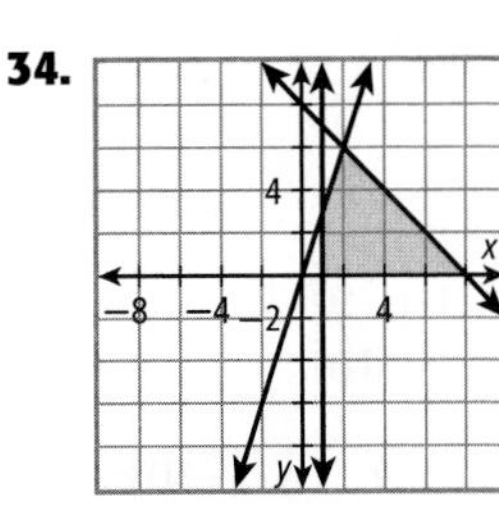

35. 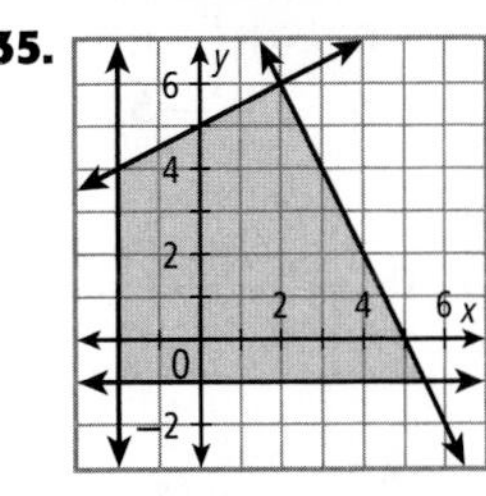

36. 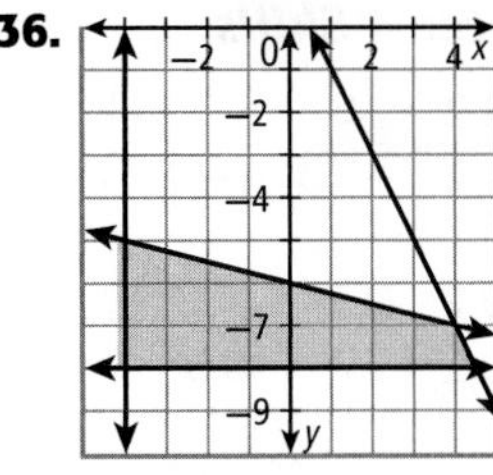

37. 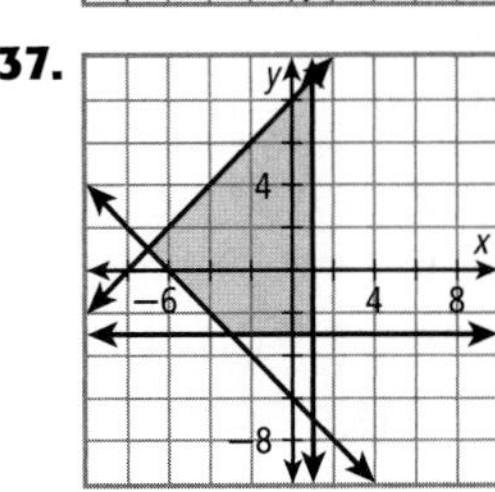

47. 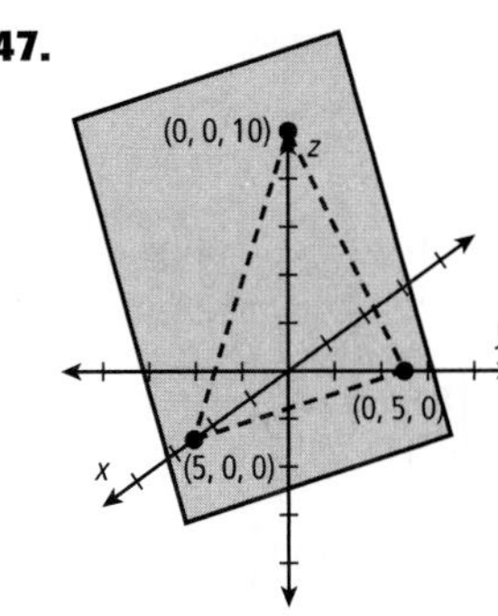

48. 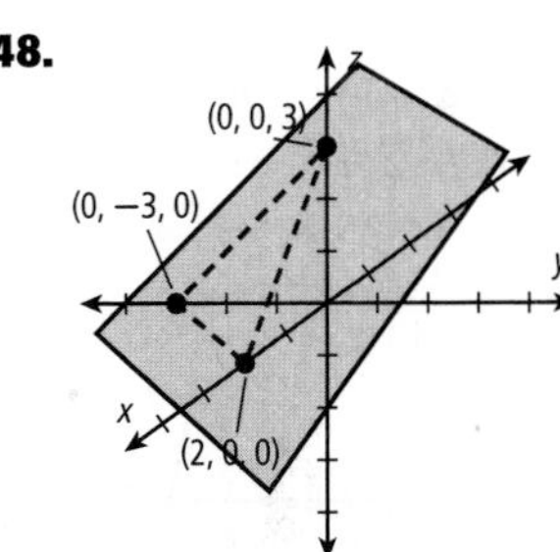

49. 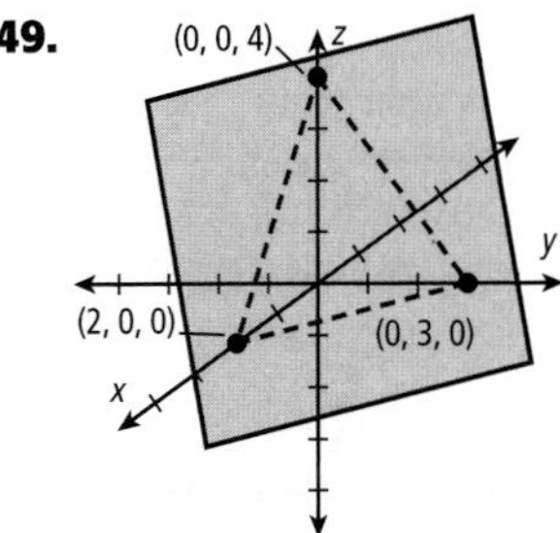

50. 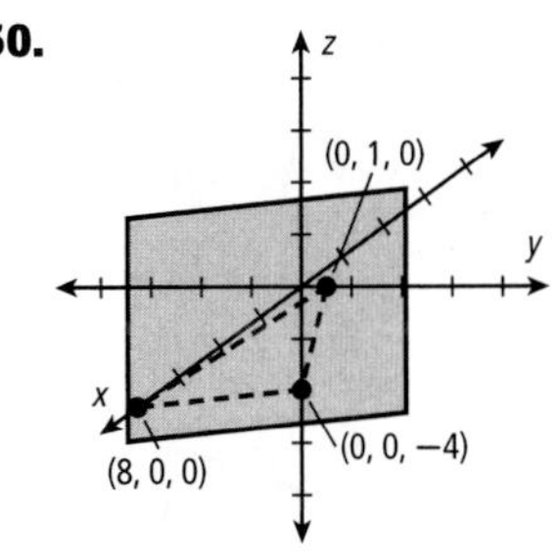

Additional Answers

Chapter 4 Skills

1. $\begin{bmatrix} 2.2 & 6.5 & 10 \\ 4.2 & -2.3 & -0.5 \end{bmatrix}$

3. $\begin{bmatrix} 0.2 & 0.5 & -2 \\ 0.2 & 7.7 & -0.5 \end{bmatrix}$

5. $\begin{bmatrix} 16 & 28 & 12 \\ 8 & 48 & -16 \end{bmatrix}$

6. $\begin{bmatrix} -32 & -16 \\ 6 & -4 \\ -42 & 0 \end{bmatrix}$

7. $\begin{bmatrix} -1 & 13.5 & -7.5 \\ 3 & 6 & -8 \end{bmatrix}$

12. $\begin{bmatrix} 5 & 13 \\ 40 & -16 \end{bmatrix}$

13. $\begin{bmatrix} 56 & 34 & -8 \\ 99 & 57 & -15 \end{bmatrix}$

16. $\begin{bmatrix} 81 & 42 \\ 0 & 4 \end{bmatrix}$

17. $\begin{bmatrix} 729 & 402 \\ 0 & -8 \end{bmatrix}$

18. $\begin{bmatrix} 14 & 40 & 120 \\ 6 & 4 & 0 \\ 9 & 25 & 74 \end{bmatrix}$

20.

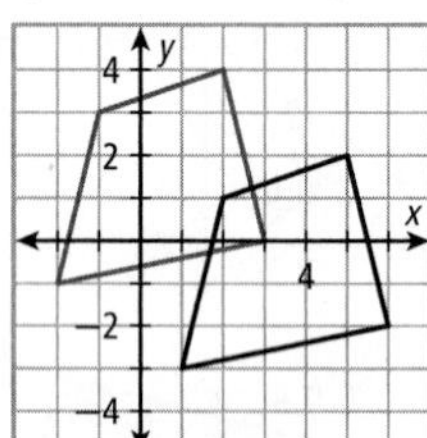

21.

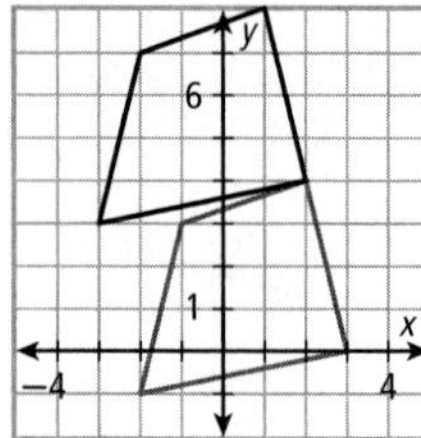

22.

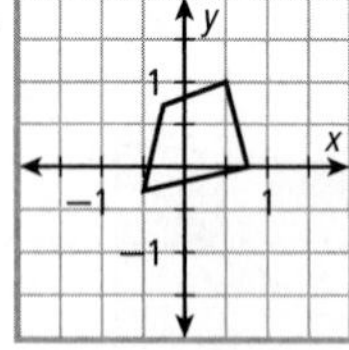

23.

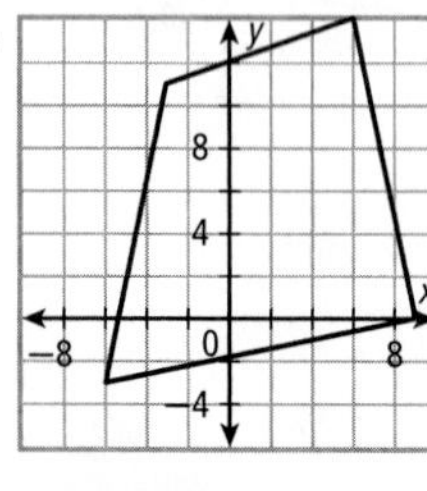

24.

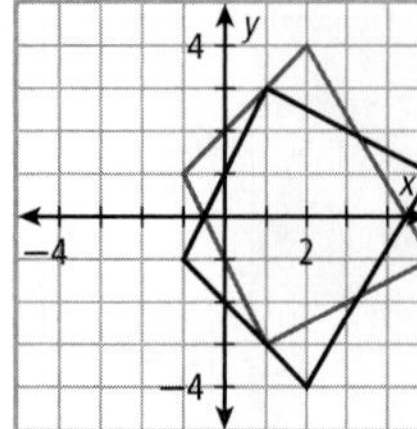

25.

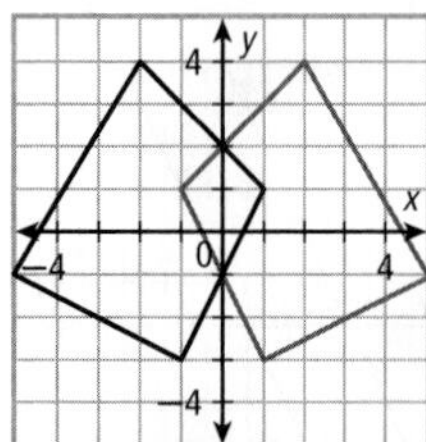

26.

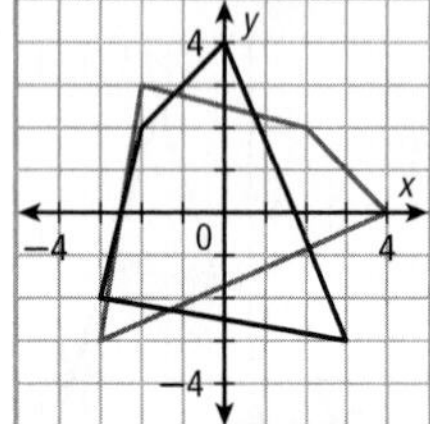

27.

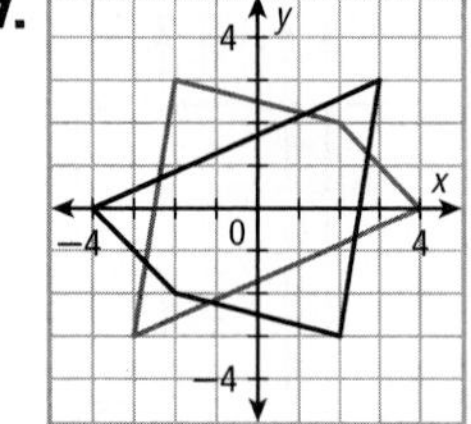

43. $\begin{bmatrix} 1 & 2 \\ 2 & 1 \end{bmatrix}$

44. $\begin{bmatrix} -\frac{1}{6} & -\frac{1}{6} \\ \frac{1}{4} & \frac{1}{12} \end{bmatrix}$

46. $\begin{bmatrix} 3 & 4 \\ \frac{1}{2} & 1 \end{bmatrix}$

50. $\left[\begin{array}{cc:c} 2 & -5 & -8 \\ -12 & 3 & 7 \end{array}\right]$

51. $\left[\begin{array}{cc:c} 2 & 1 & 9 \\ 0 & 3 & 18 \end{array}\right]$

52. $\left[\begin{array}{ccc:c} 2 & 9 & 0 & 10 \\ 3 & 0 & -1 & 8 \\ 0 & -13 & 5 & -5 \end{array}\right]$

53. $\left[\begin{array}{ccc:c} 8 & 5 & 0 & 4 \\ 13 & 0 & -1 & -12 \\ 0 & -2 & 4 & 0 \end{array}\right]$

54. $\left[\begin{array}{cc:c} 4 & -2 & 26 \\ 1 & 6 & -13 \end{array}\right]$; $(5, -3)$

55. $\left[\begin{array}{cc:c} 8 & 3 & \frac{1}{2} \\ 4 & -4 & -8 \end{array}\right]$; $(-0.5, 1.5)$

56. $\left[\begin{array}{cc:c} 6 & \frac{1}{2} & 6 \\ 14 & 1 & 12 \end{array}\right]$; $(0, 12)$

57. $\left[\begin{array}{cc:c} 12 & 1 & -6 \\ -2 & 2 & 14 \end{array}\right]$; $(-1, 6)$

Chapter 5 Skills

1.

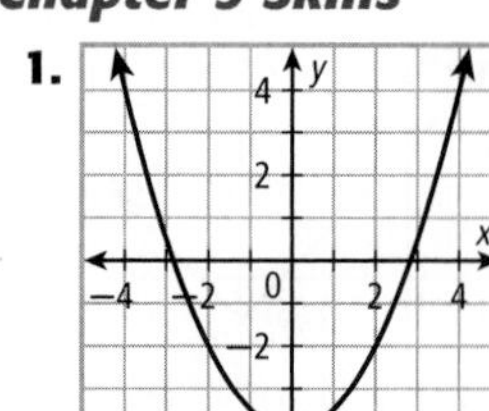

2.

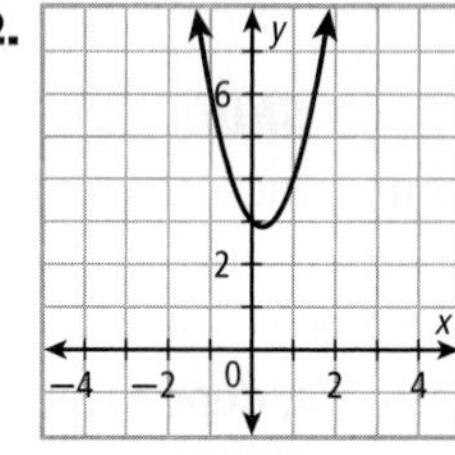

3.

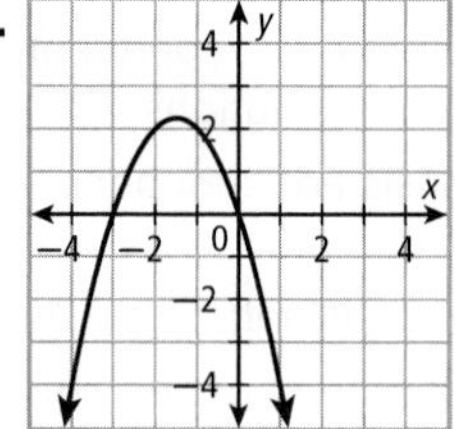

4. g is f translated 2 units left and 1 unit up.

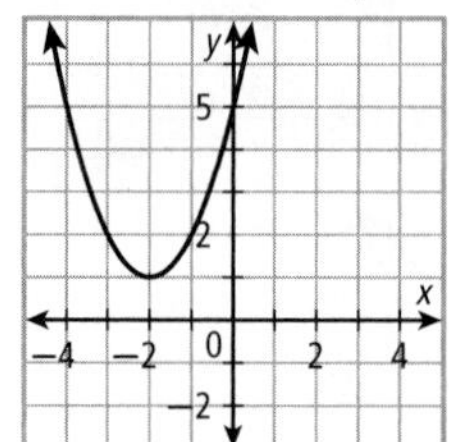

5. g is f reflected across the x-axis and vertically stretched by a factor of 2.

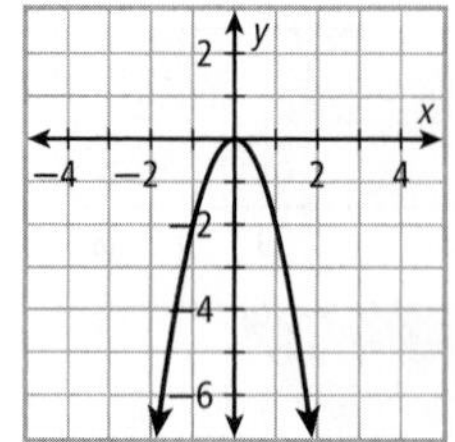

6. g is f vertically compressed by a factor of $\frac{1}{4}$.

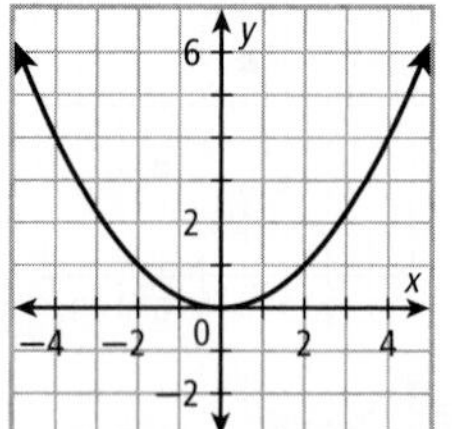

12. upward; $x = 1$; $(1, 3)$; 5

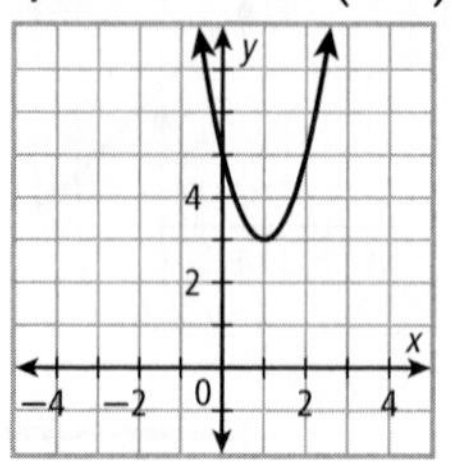

13. downward; $x = -2$; $(-2, 5)$; 3

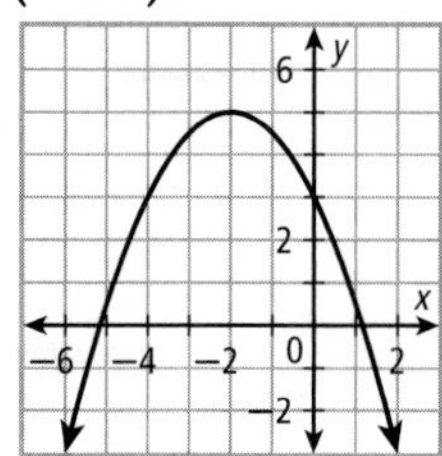

14. downward; $x = -4$; $(-4, 10)$; -6

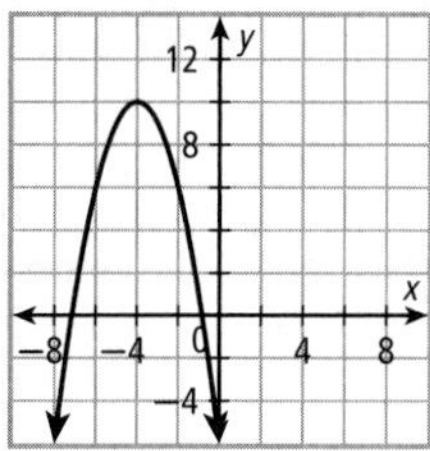

60. $5 \pm \sqrt{22}$

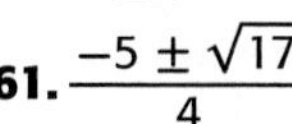

61. $\dfrac{-5 \pm \sqrt{17}}{4}$

62. $4 \pm \sqrt{13}$

63. $3 \pm i\sqrt{31}$

64. $-\frac{7}{2} \pm \frac{\sqrt{3}}{2}i$

65. $\frac{9}{4} \pm \frac{\sqrt{119}}{4}i$

70.

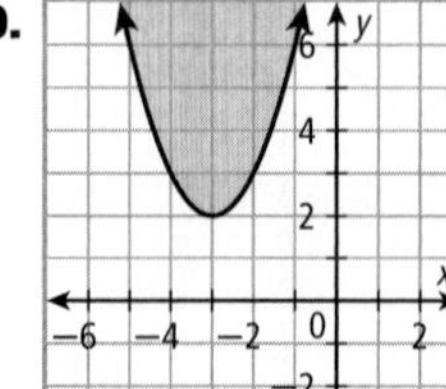

71. 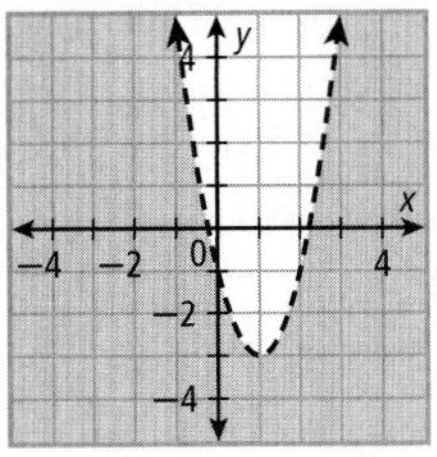

72. 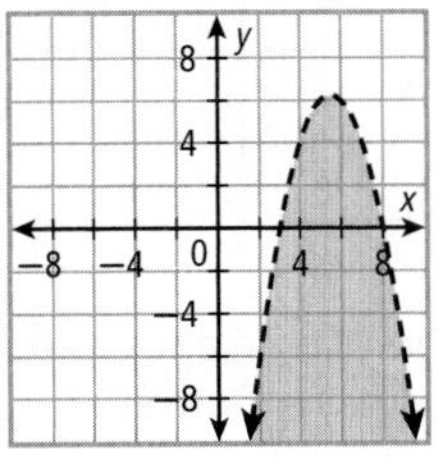

79. Quadratic; second differences are constant for equally spaced x-values.

80. Not quadratic; second differences are not constant for equally spaced x-values.

81. Quadratic; second differences are constant for equally spaced x-values.

84–87.

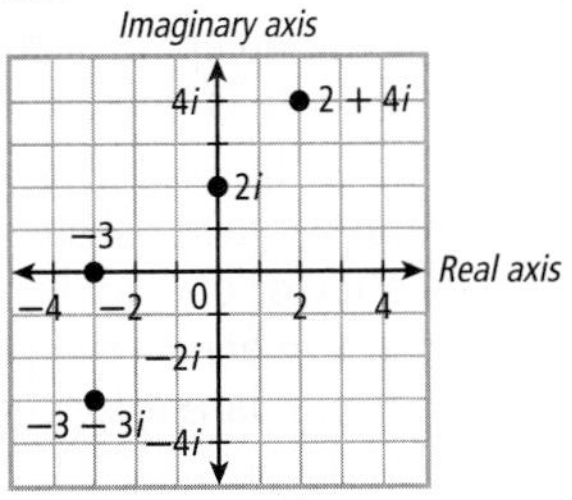

Chapter 6 Skills

5. $-10x^3 + 5x^2 + 9x + 6$; -10; 3; 4; cubic polynomial with 4 terms

6. $-12x^4 - 6x^2 + 3$; -12; 4; 3; quartic trinomial

7. $15x^5 + 14x$; 15; 5; 4; quintic binomial

10. From left to right, the graph increases. It crosses the x-axis once, so there appears to be one real zero.

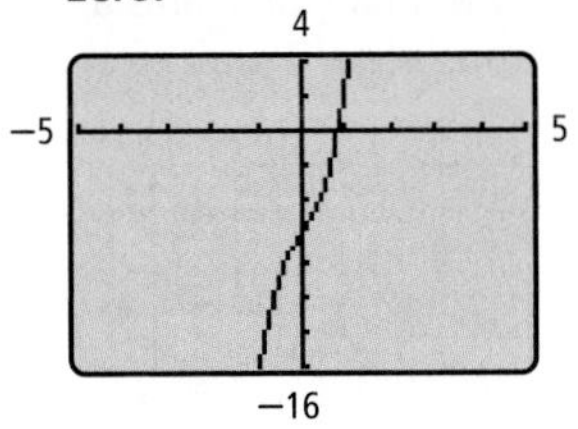

11. From left to right, the graph decreases and then increases. It crosses the x-axis twice, so there appear to be two real zeros.

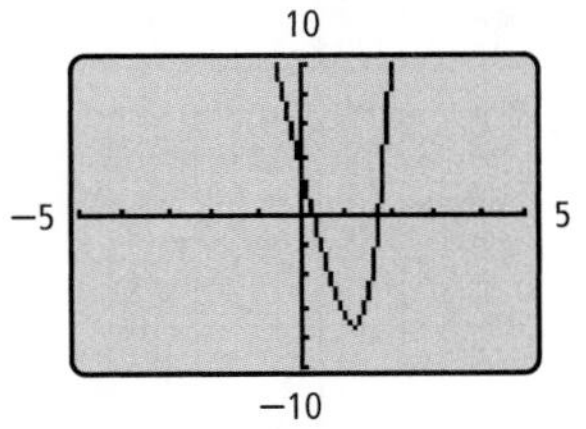

12. From left to right, the graph increases, decreases slightly, and then increases again. It crosses the x-axis three times, so there appear to be three real zeros.

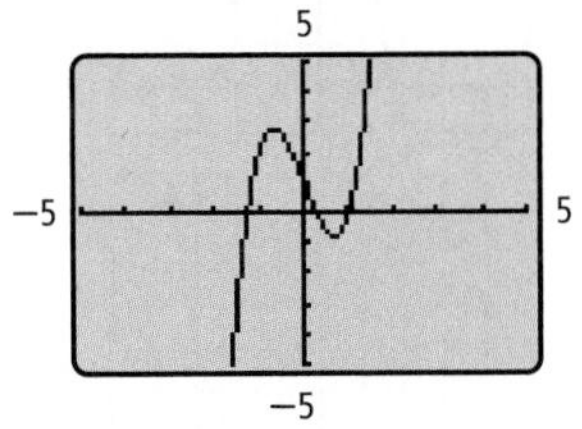

19. $x^5 - 5x^4y + 10x^3y^2 - 10x^2y^3 + 5xy^4 - y^5$

20. $y^4 + 16y^3 + 96y^2 + 256y + 256$

21. $32x^5 + 80x^4y + 80x^3y^2 + 40x^2y^3 + 10xy^4 + y^5$

22. $x^4 - 8x^3y + 24x^2y^2 - 32xy^3 + 16y^4$

33. $2(x^2 - 2)(x + 6)$

34. $(2x + 5)(x + 3)(x - 3)$

35. $4(x + 3)(x^2 + 3)$

36. $(a + 3)(a^2 - 3a + 9)$

37. $2b(4 - b)(16 + 4b + b^2)$

38. $4c^2(c + 2)(c^2 - 2c + 4)$

41. $x = -5$ with multiplicity 3

42. $x = -6$ with multiplicity 1; $x = 4$ with multiplicity 2

43. $x = \frac{1}{2}$ with multiplicity 3

44. $x = -4, -\frac{5}{2}, \frac{5}{2}$ each with multiplicity 1

45. $x = -2, -1, \frac{1}{2}, 3$

46. $x = -\frac{2}{3}, -\frac{1}{2}, 3$

47. $P(x) = x^3 - 4x^2 - x + 4$

48. $P(x) = x^3 + \frac{13}{6}x^2 - \frac{7}{3}x + \frac{1}{2}$

49. $P(x) = x^3 + \frac{4}{3}x^2 - \frac{13}{3}x + 2$

50. $P(x) = x^3 + 2x^2 - 13x + 10$

53. $P(x) = x^3 - 3x^2 - 5x + 15$

54. $P(x) = x^3 - 4x^2 + 6x - 4$

55. $P(x) = x^3 + 2x^2 + 4x + 8$

56. $P(x) = x^5 - x^4 - x^3 + x^2 - 2x + 2$

57. 7; 3; as $x \to -\infty$, $P(x) \to -\infty$, as $x \to +\infty$, $P(x) \to +\infty$

58. -3; 5; as $x \to -\infty$, $P(x) \to +\infty$, as $x \to +\infty$, $P(x) \to -\infty$

62. 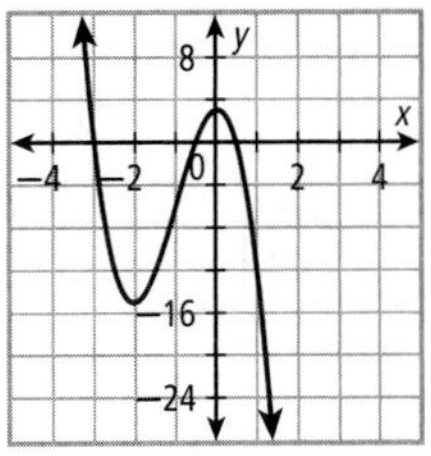

63. 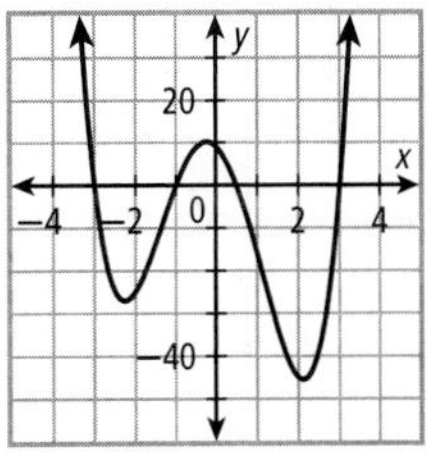

66. 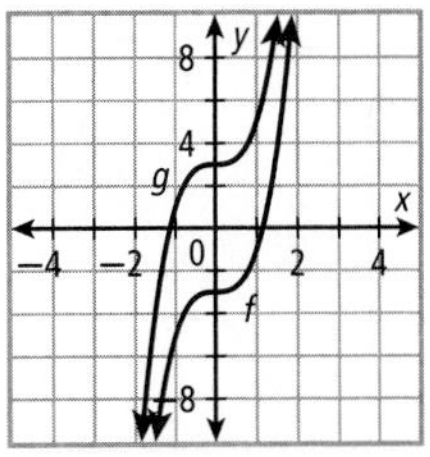

67. 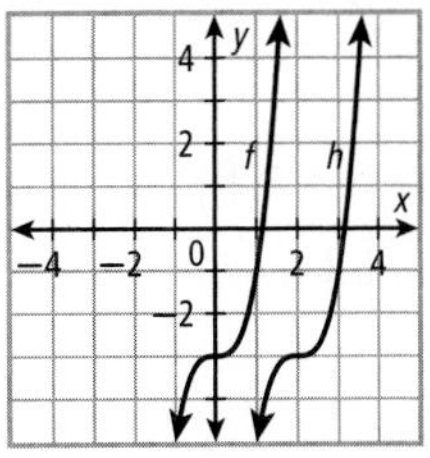

68. 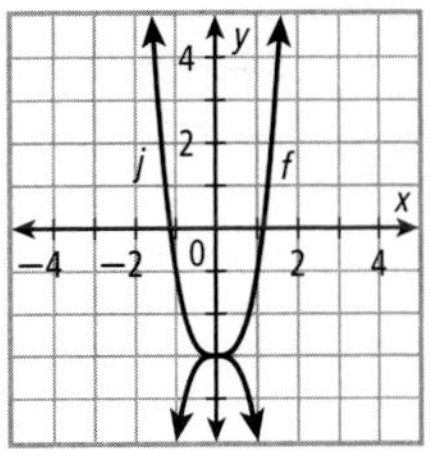

69. 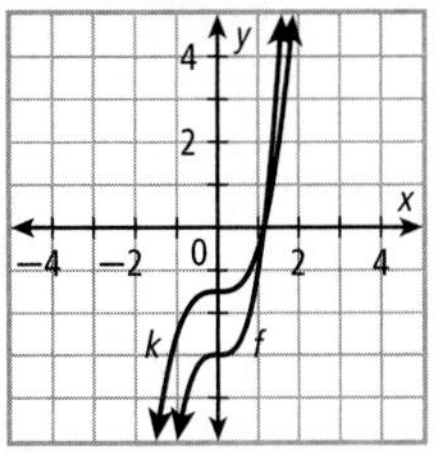

72. horizontal translation

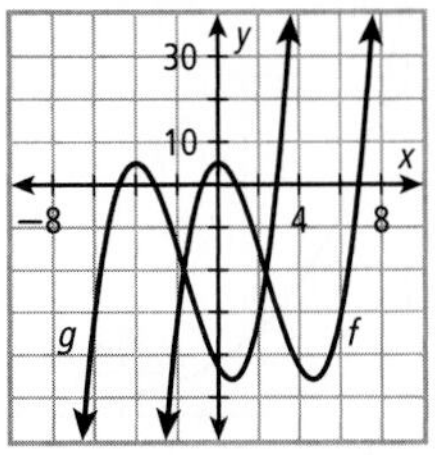

73. vertical stretch and reflection across the x-axis

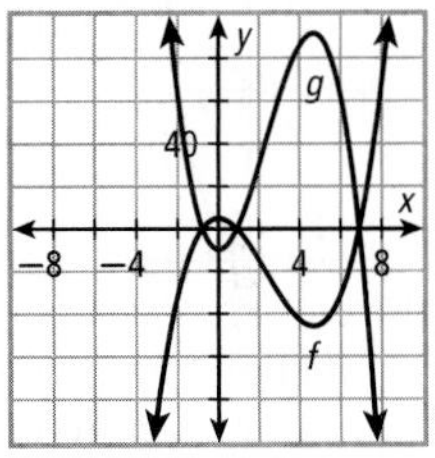

74. reflection across the y-axis and vertical translation

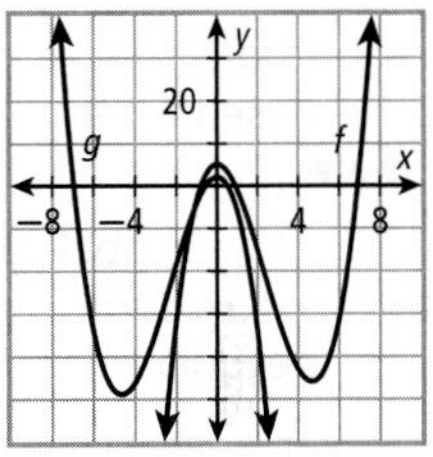

75. $g(x) = 9(x - 1)^3 - 15(x - 1)^2 + 3(x - 1) + 3$

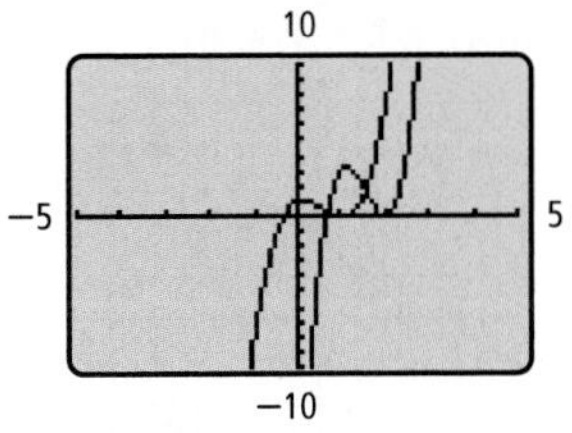

76. $g(x) = -3x^3 - 5x^2 - x$

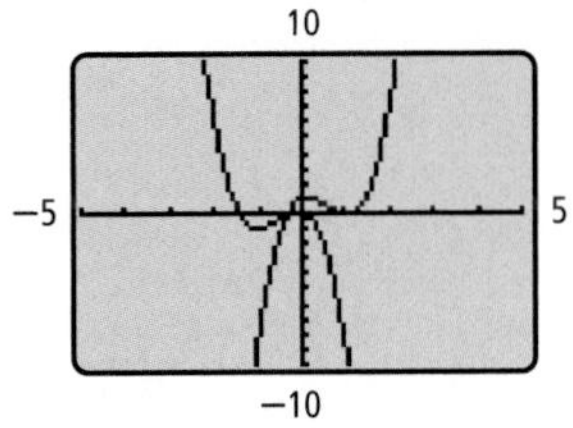

Chapter 7 Skills

1. 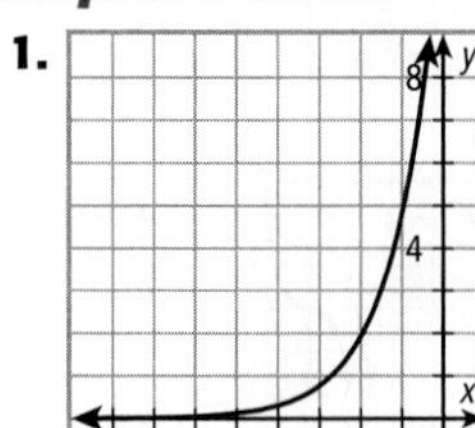

2. 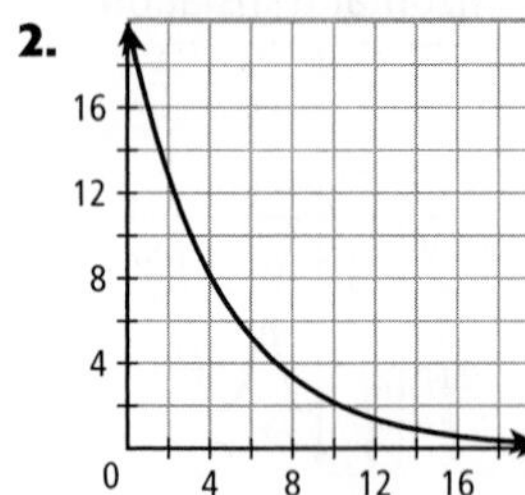

3. 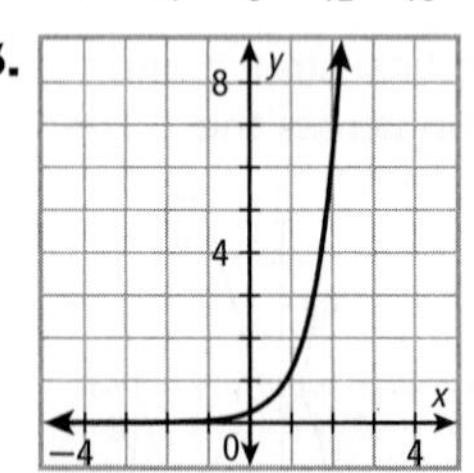

4. The function is polynomial but not exponential, because the variable is in the base and not the exponent.

5. The function is exponential because the variable is in the exponent.

6. The function simplifies to $y = 0$, so it is constant and not exponential.

7. $f(x)$: D: $\{x \mid 1 \leq x \leq 4\}$; R: $\{y \mid -1 \leq y \leq 4\}$
$f^{-1}(x)$: D: $\{x \mid -1 \leq x \leq 4\}$; R: $\{y \mid 1 \leq y \leq 4\}$

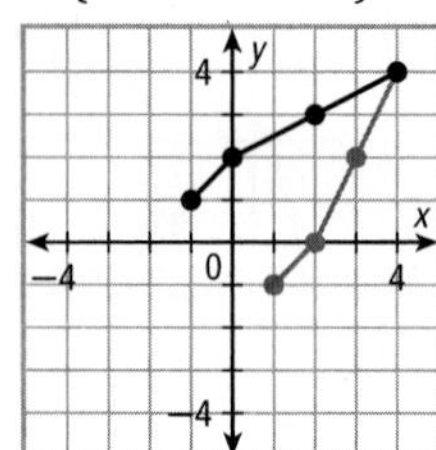

8. $f(x)$: D: $\{x \mid -3 \leq x \leq 4\}$; R: $\{y \mid -3 \leq y \leq -1\}$
$f^{-1}(x)$: D: $\{x \mid -3 \leq x \leq -1\}$; R: $\{y \mid -3 \leq y \leq 4\}$

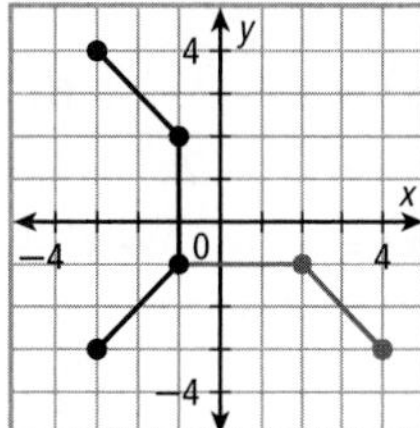

15. $f^{-1}(x) = \frac{x - 4}{2}$

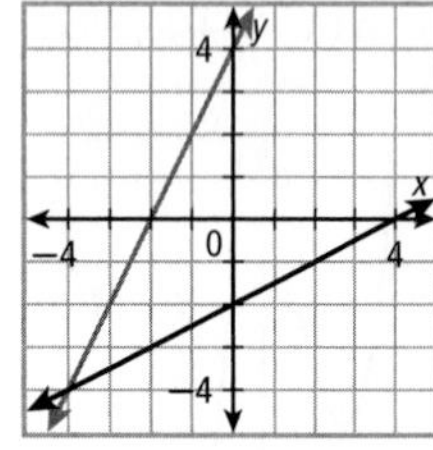

16. $f^{-1}(x) = \frac{5}{4}(x - 1)$

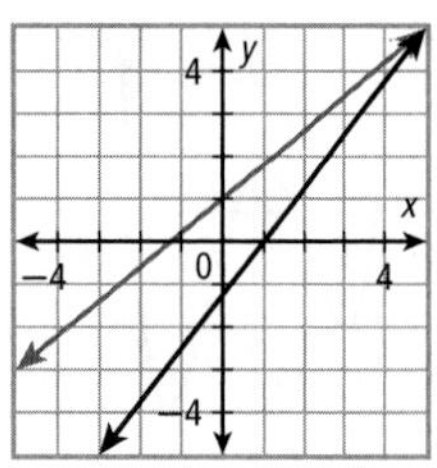

17. $f^{-1}(x) = \frac{3x + 5}{4}$

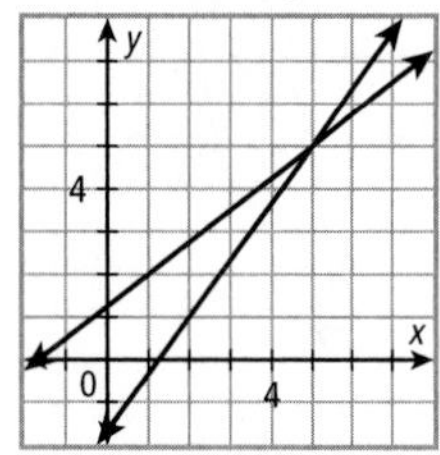

30. D: $\{x \mid x > 0\}$; R: $\mathbb{R}$

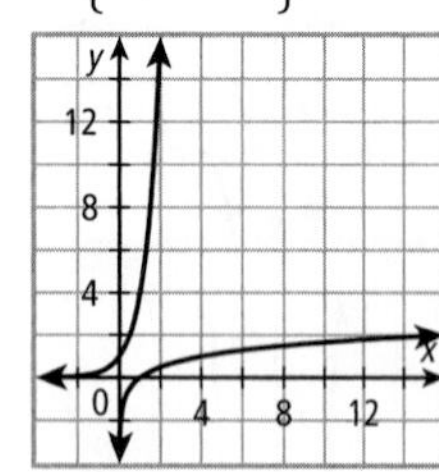

31. D: $\{x \mid x > 0\}$; R: $\mathbb{R}$

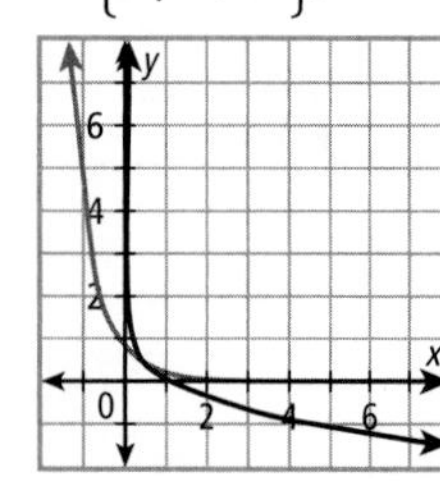

62. 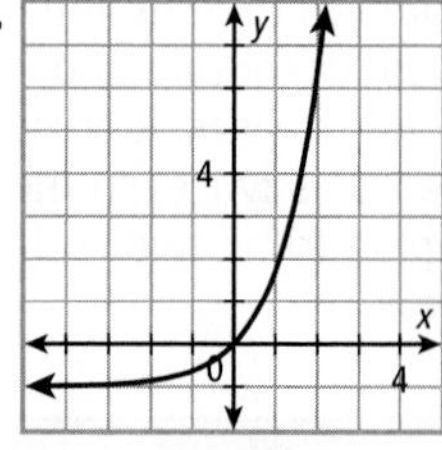

63. 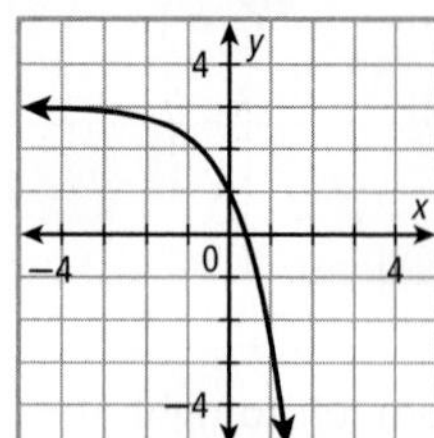

64. 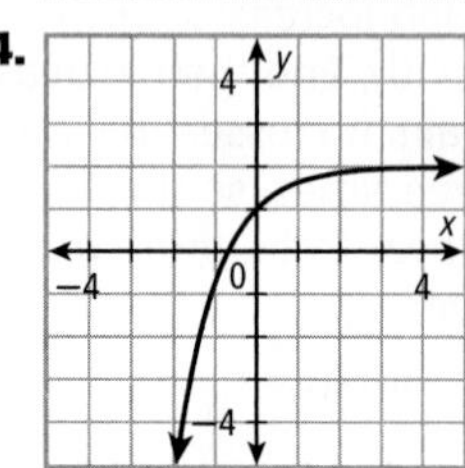

65. 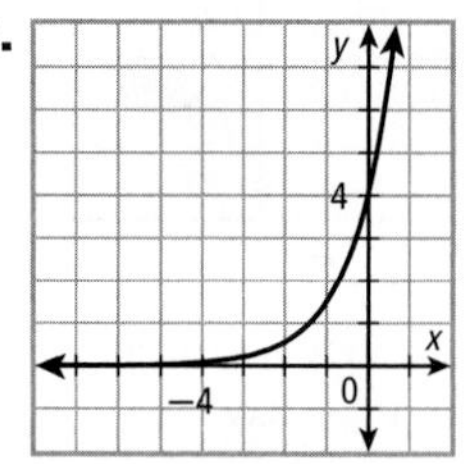

70. The asymptote is $y = -2$; D: $\mathbb{R}$; R: $\{y \mid y > -2\}$; the graph is a translation 2 units down.

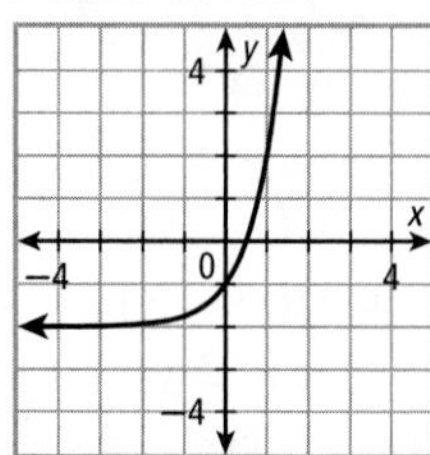

71. The asymptote is $y = 0$; D: $\mathbb{R}$; R: $\mathbb{R}$; the graph is a translation 2 units left.

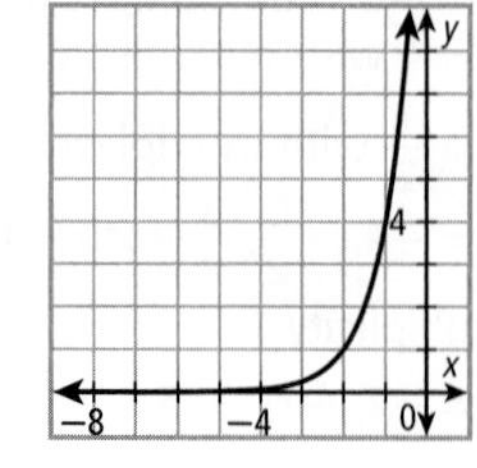

72. The asymptote is $y = -4$; D: $\mathbb{R}$; R: $\{y \mid y > -4\}$; the graph is a translation 4 units down and 1 unit right.

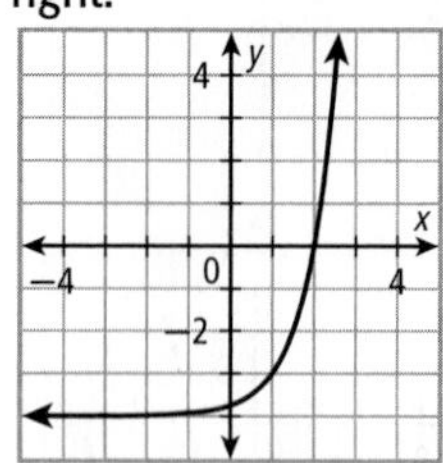

73. The y-intercept is -0.5; the asymptote is $y = 0$; D: $\mathbb{R}$; R: $\{y \mid y < 0\}$; the graph is a vertical compression by a factor of $\frac{1}{2}$ and a reflection across the x-axis from the parent function.

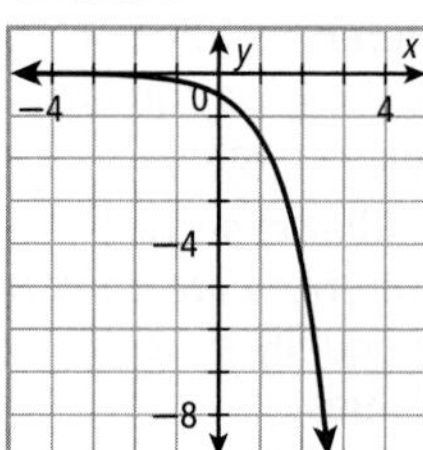

74. The y-intercept is 3; the asymptote is $y = 0$; D: $\mathbb{R}$; R: $\{y \mid y > 0\}$; the graph is a vertical stretch by a factor of 3 and a reflection across the y-axis from the parent function.

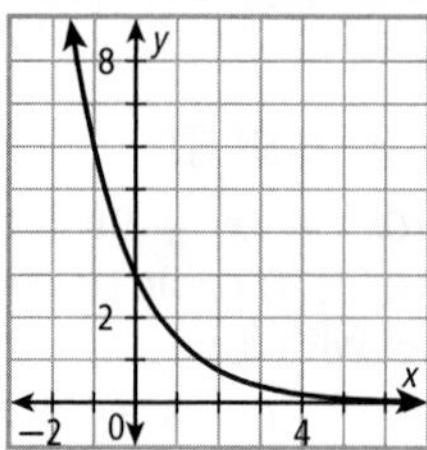

75. The y-intercept is approximately 13.59; the asymptote is $y = 0$; D: $\mathbb{R}$; R: $\{y \mid y > 0\}$; the graph is a vertical stretch by a factor of 5 and a translation 1 unit to the left.

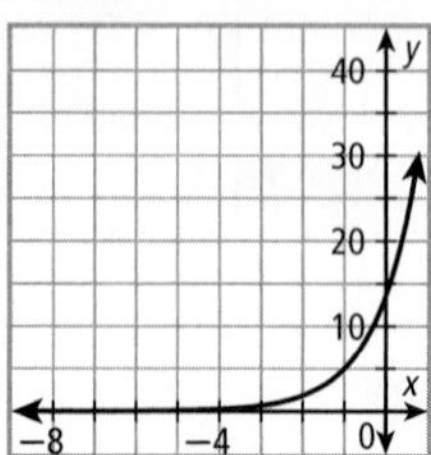

76. The asymptote is $x = 0$. The graph is vertically stretched by a factor of 4 and reflected across the x-axis.

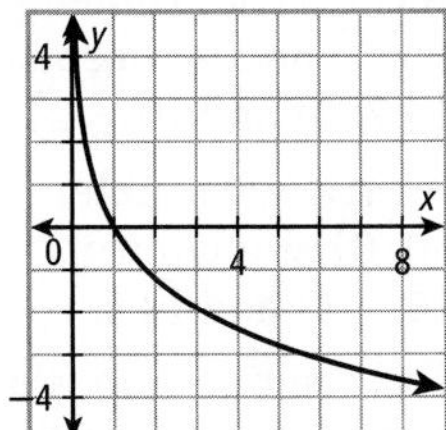

77. The asymptote is $x = 3$. The graph is stretched vertically by a factor of 3, reflected across the y-axis, and translated 3 units right.

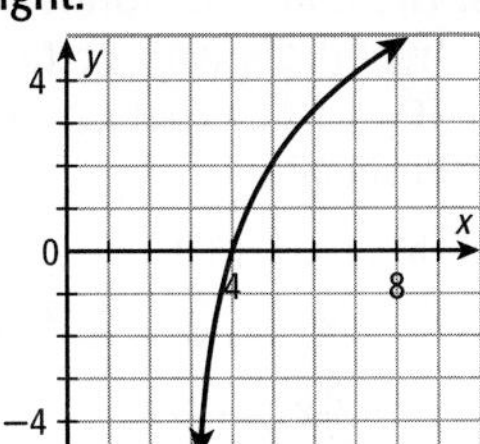

78. The asymptote is $x = 0$, The graph is a horizontal stretch by a factor of 2 and a translation 3 units down.

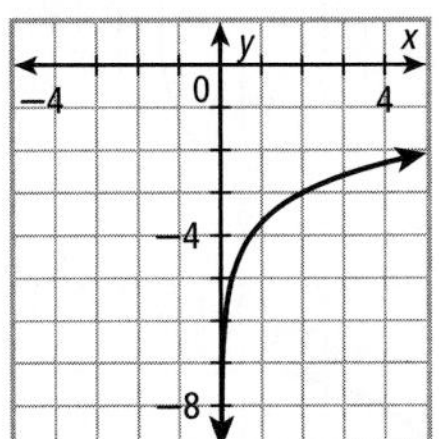

Chapter 8 Skills

1.

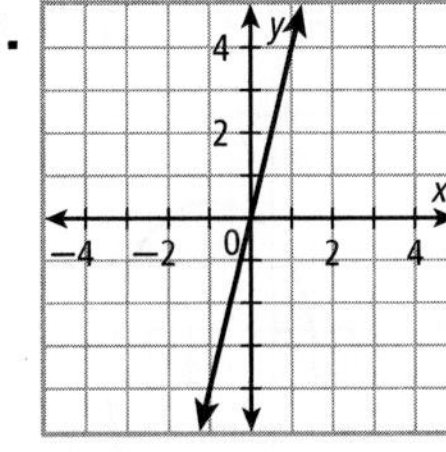

2.

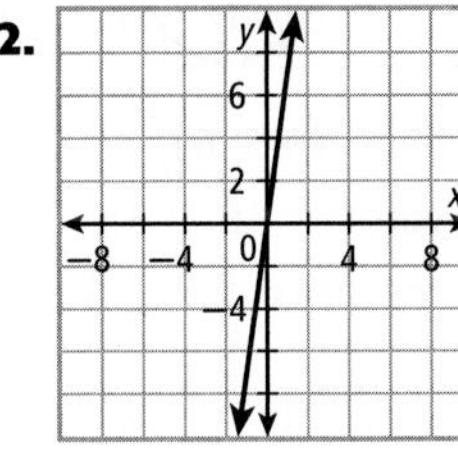

3.

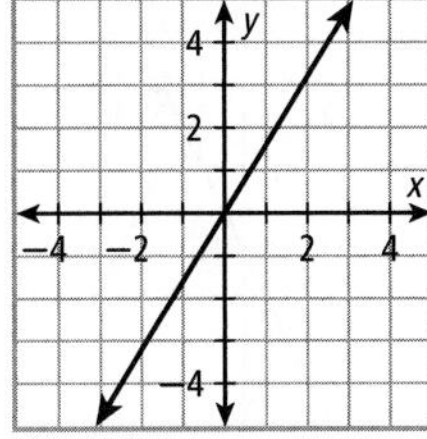

4.

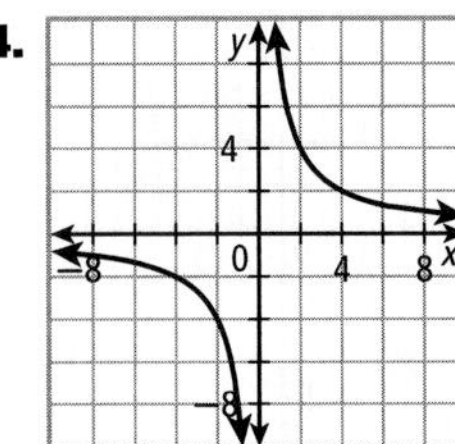

5.

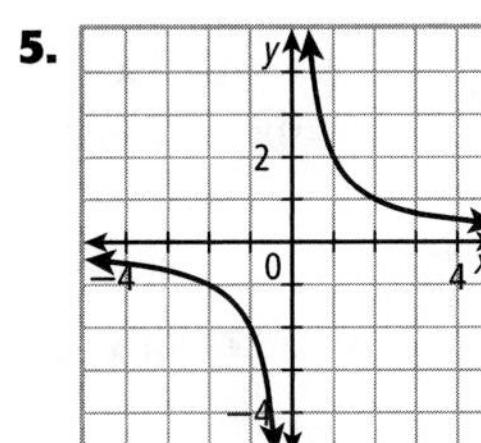

6.

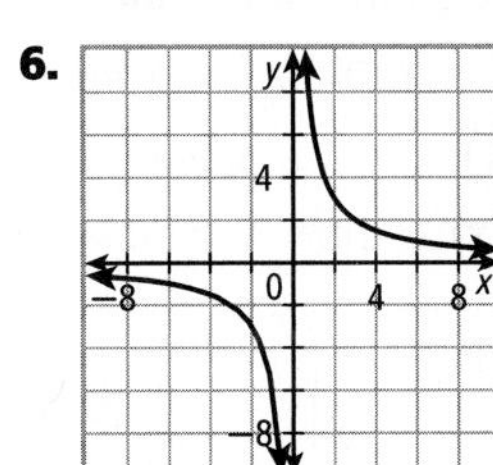

10. $\dfrac{2x^2}{9x + 4}$; $x \neq 0, x \neq -\dfrac{4}{9}$

11. $\dfrac{x + 1}{3}$; $x \neq 2$

12. $\dfrac{x - 4}{x + 5}$; $x \neq -5, x \neq -4$

22. $\dfrac{4x + 15}{2x + 1}$; $x \neq -\dfrac{1}{2}$

23. $\dfrac{6(x - 1)}{(x - 3)(x + 3)}$; $x \neq \pm 3$

24. $\dfrac{2(x - 2)}{(x-8)(x + 2)(x + 4)}$; $x \neq -4, x \neq -2, x \neq 8$

25. $\dfrac{-7x - 13}{x + 5}$; $x \neq -5$

26. $\dfrac{x^2 + x - 3}{(x + 1)(x + 4)}$; $x \neq -4, x \neq -1$

27. $\dfrac{5x - 22}{(x - 9)(x - 4)}$; $x \neq 4$, $x \neq 9$

31. g is f translated 4 units right.

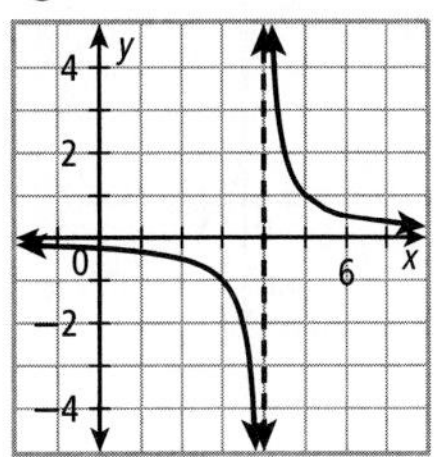

32. g is f translated 6 units up.

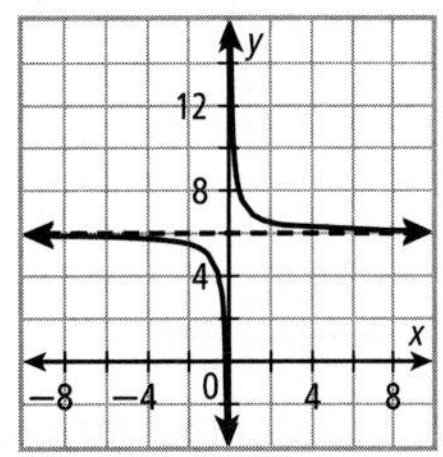

33. g is f translated 2 units left and 5 units down.

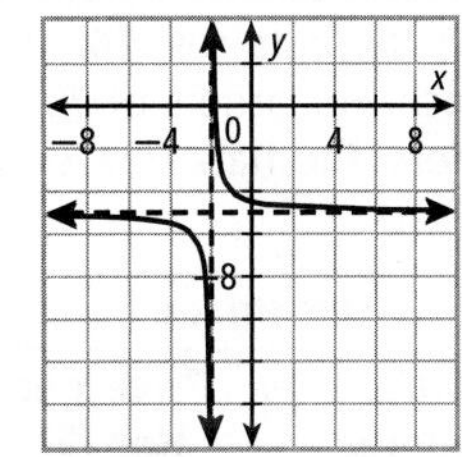

34. zeros: -3 and 8; asymptote: $x = -\dfrac{1}{2}$

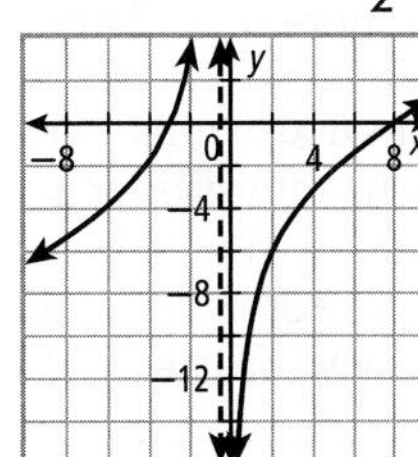

35. zeros: 2 and $-\dfrac{1}{2}$; asymptote: $x = 4$

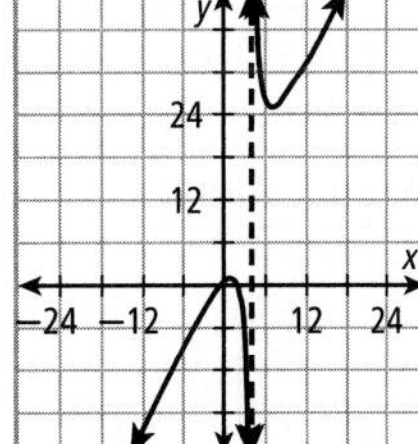

36. zeros: $-\dfrac{2}{3}$, 2; asymptotes: $x = -5$, $x = 5$, $y = -3$

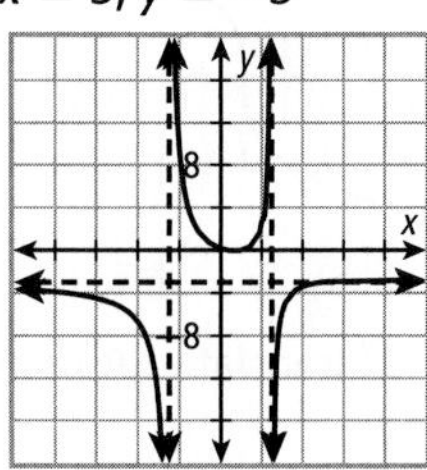

37. hole at $x = -3$

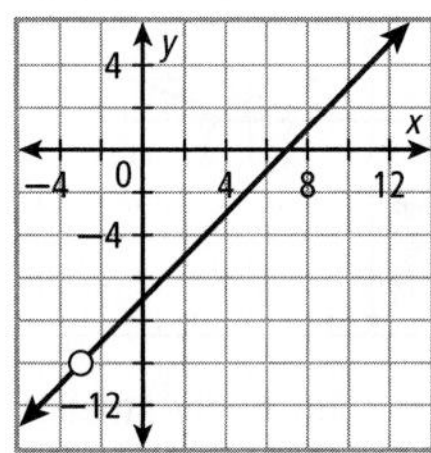

38. hole at $x = 5$

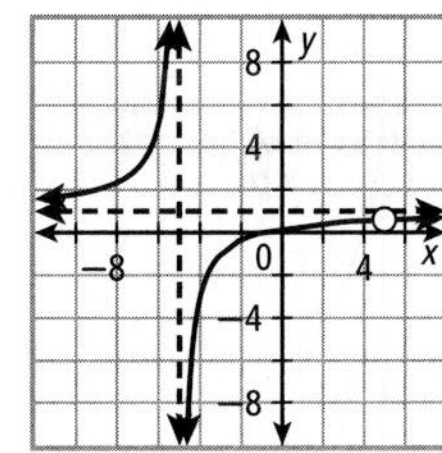

39. hole at $x = 3$

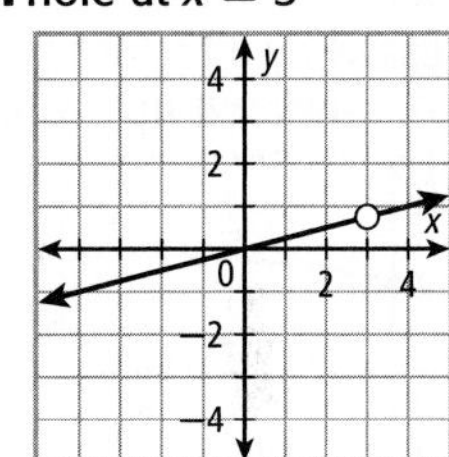

64. D: $\{x \mid x \geq 4\}$; R: $\{y \mid y \geq 1\}$

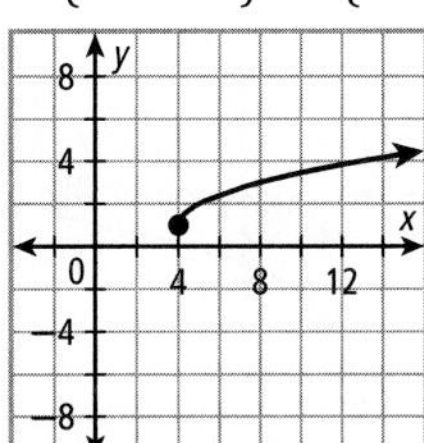

65. D: $\{x \mid x \geq 0\}$; R: $\{y \mid y \leq 0\}$

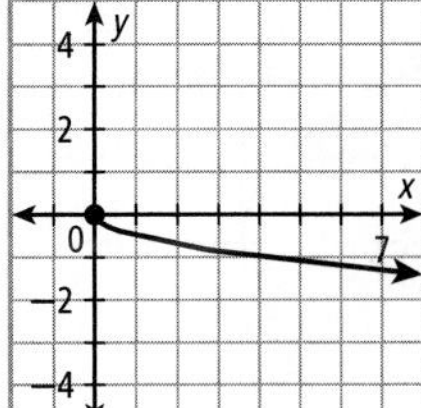

66. D: $\mathbb{R}$; R: $\mathbb{R}$

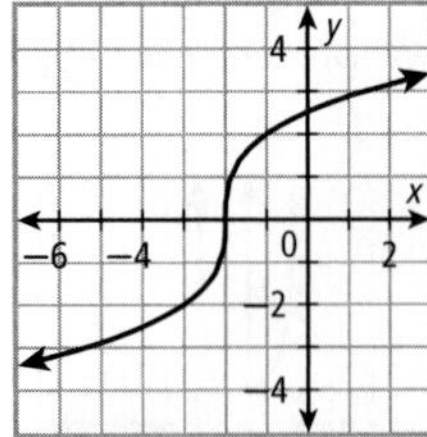

67. g is f translated 8 units right.

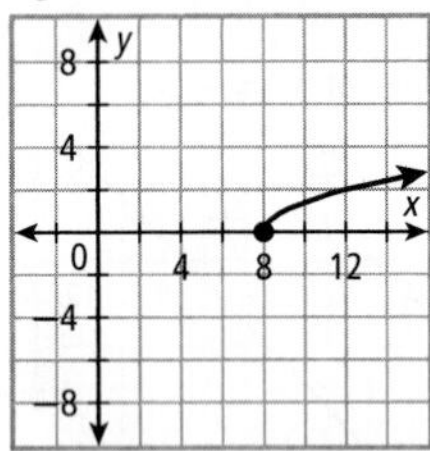

68. g is f vertically stretched by a factor of 6 and reflected across the x-axis.

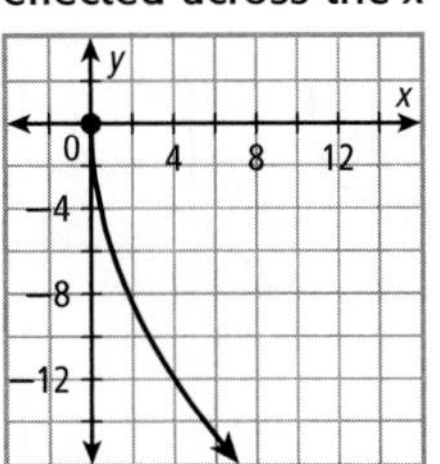

69. g is f vertically compressed by a factor of $\frac{1}{3}$ and translated up 2 units.

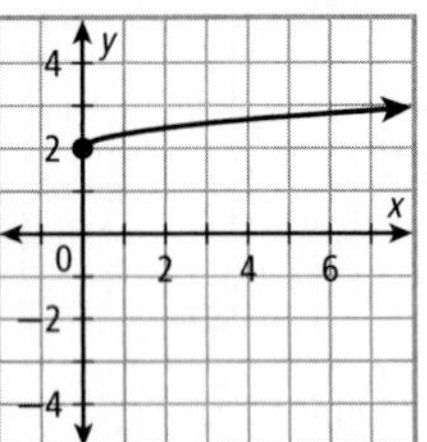

70.

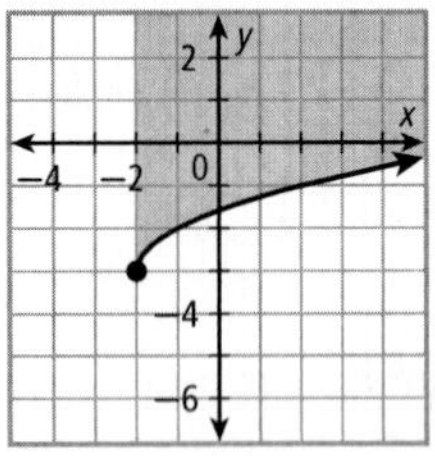

71.

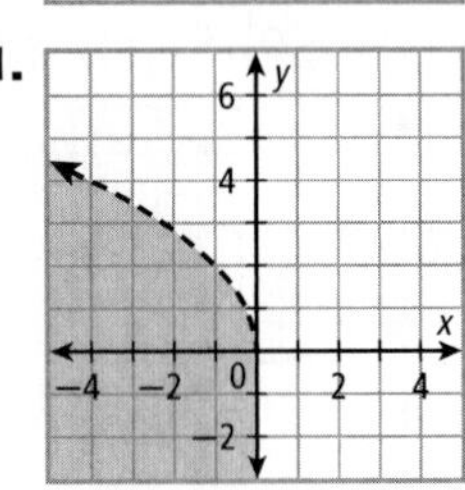

72.

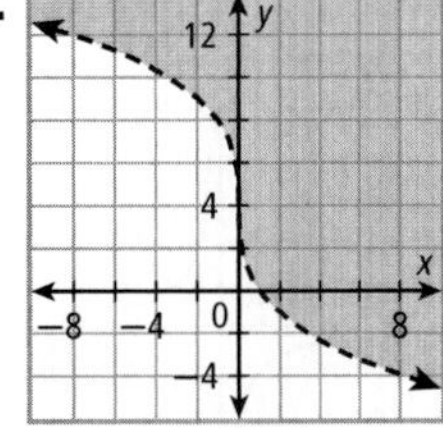

Chapter 9 Skills

3.

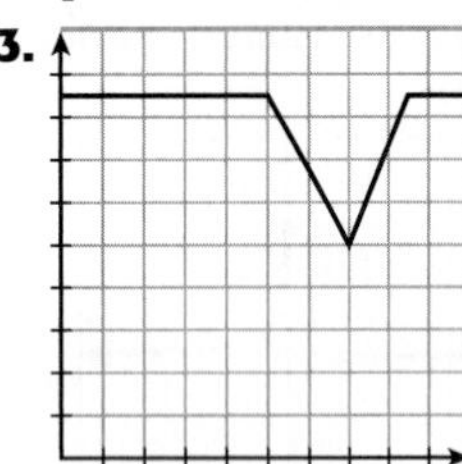

5. For orders of fewer than 30 hats, the hats cost \$5.50 each. For orders of at least 30 but fewer than 70, the hats cost \$4.50 each. For orders of 70 or more, the hats cost \$4.00 each.

Hat Prices	
Hats Ordered	Price per Hat (\$)
0–29	\$5.50
30–69	\$4.50
70 or more	\$4.00

6. From 8 A.M. until before noon, admission is \$3.50. From noon until before 5 P.M., admission is \$2.50. At 5 P.M. or later, it is free.

Pool Admission	
Time	Price (\$)
8 A.M. to before noon	\$3.50
Noon to before 5 P.M.	\$2.50
5 P.M. and after	Free

10.

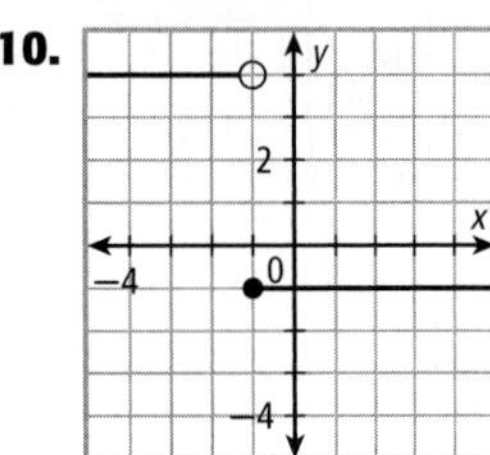

11.

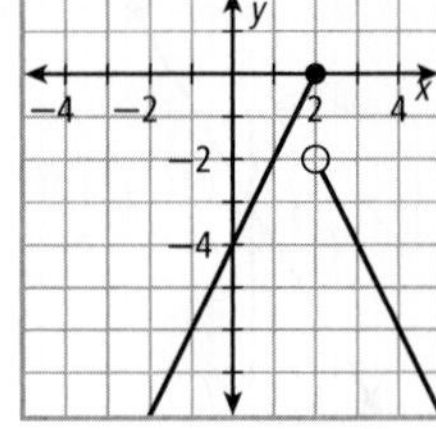

12.

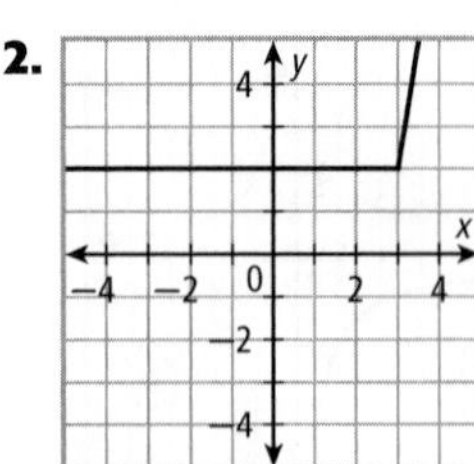

13. $g(x) = \begin{cases} 6x - 6 & \text{if } x < 1 \\ -9x & \text{if } x \geq 1 \end{cases}$

14. $h(x) = \begin{cases} -2x - 2 & \text{if } x > -1 \\ 3x & \text{if } x \leq -1 \end{cases}$

15. $f(x)$: x-int. = 2, y-int. = 6; $g(x)$: x-int. = -1, y-int. = 6

16. $f(x)$: x-int. = 3, y-int. = 9; $g(x)$: x-int. = 3, y-int. = -18

17.

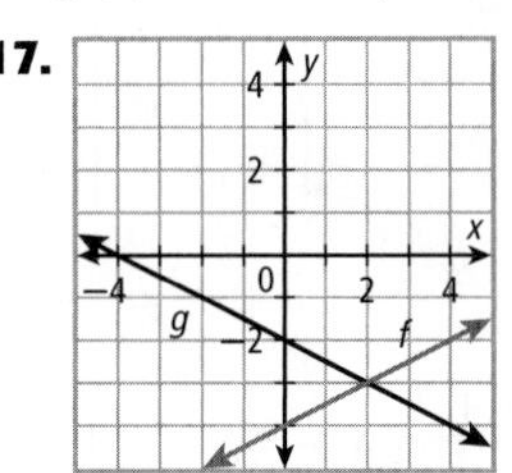

18.

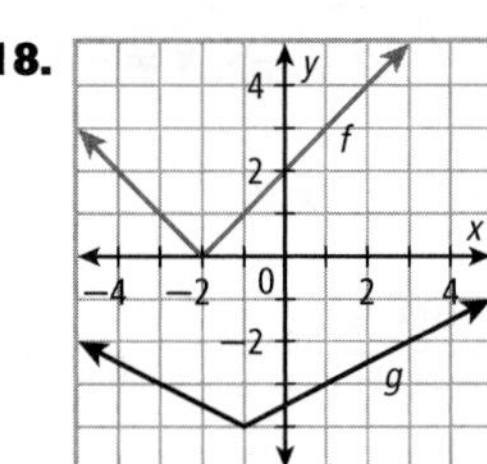

28. $f(g(x)) = \sqrt{2x + 3}$; $\left\{x \mid x \geq -\frac{3}{2}\right\}$

29. $g(f(x)) = 2\sqrt{x} + 3$; $\{x \mid x \geq 0\}$

30. $g(h(x)) = 2x^2 + 43$; $\mathbb{R}$

34. $f^{-1}(x) = 2x + 14$; function; D: $\mathbb{R}$; R: $\mathbb{R}$

35. $y = \pm\sqrt{10 - x}$; not a function; D: $\{x \mid x \leq 10\}$; R: $\mathbb{R}$

36. $h^{-1}(x) = \frac{3}{x} - 4$; function; D: $\{x \mid x \neq 0\}$; R: $\{y \mid y \neq -4\}$

Chapter 10 Skills

1. An ellipse with center $(0, 0)$ and intercepts $(\pm4, 0)$ and $(0, \pm2)$

2. A circle with center $(0, 0)$ and intercepts $(\pm2, 0)$ and $(0, \pm2)$

3. A circle with center $(0, 0)$ and intercepts $(0, \pm5)$ and $(\pm5, 0)$

4. The conic section is a hyperbola with vertices $(\pm4, 0)$ that opens horizontally.

5. The conic section is a parabola that opens to the left with vertex $(0, 0)$.

6. The conic section is a hyperbola with vertices $(0, \pm1.58)$ that opens vertically.

10. $(x + 4)^2 + (y - 3)^2 = 9$

11. $(x - 4)^2 + (y - 6)^2 = 81$

14. $y = \frac{3}{4}x + \frac{15}{4}$

15. $y = -\frac{3}{4}x + \frac{31}{2}$

20.

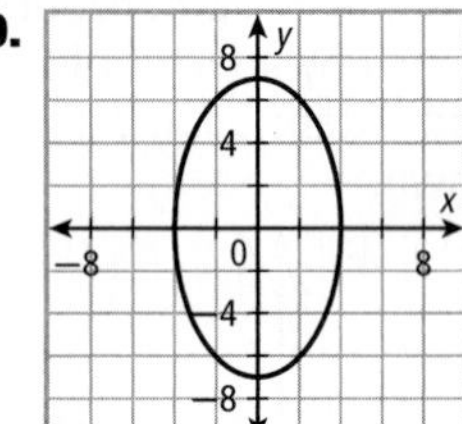

21.

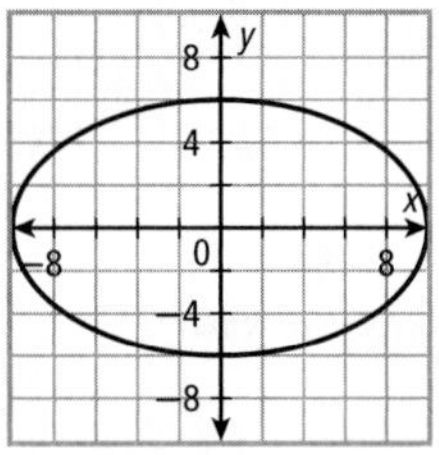

22.

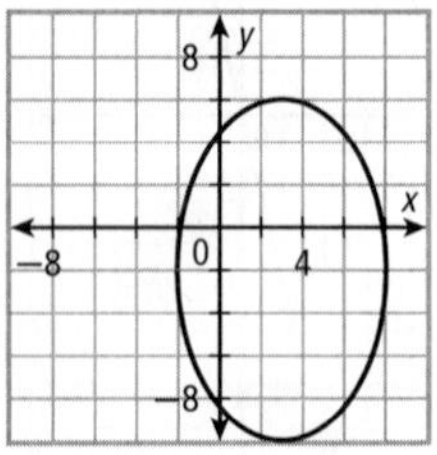

27. vertices: $(\pm5, 0)$; co-vertices: $(0, \pm3)$; asymptotes: $y = \pm\frac{3}{5}x$

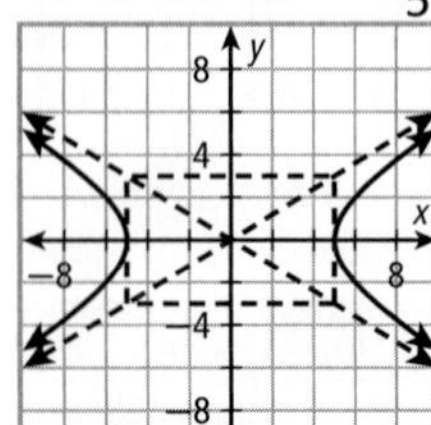

28. vertices: $(0, -2)$ and $(8, -2)$; co-vertices: $(4, 0)$ and $(4, -4)$; asymptotes:
$y = \pm\frac{1}{2}(x - 4) - 2$

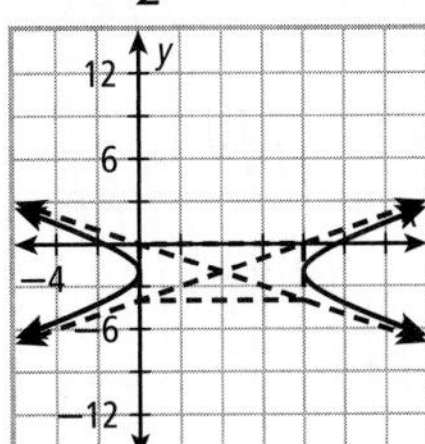

29. vertices: $(2, 5)$ and $(2, -1)$; co-vertices: $(3, 2)$ and $(1, 2)$; asymptotes:
$y = \pm 3(x - 2) + 2$

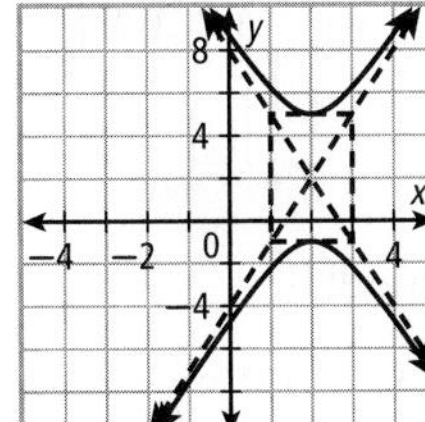

33. $x = -\frac{1}{14}y^2$

34. $y = \frac{x^2}{18}$

35. $x - 3 = \frac{y^2}{20}$

36. vertex: $(1, 0)$; $p = 5$; axis of symmetry: $x = 1$; focus: $(1, 5)$; directrix: $y = -5$

37. vertex: $(0, -4)$; $p = -3$; axis of symmetry: $y = -4$; focus: $(-3, -4)$; directrix: $x = 3$

38. vertex: $(-3, 5)$; $p = 6.5$; axis of symmetry: $x = -3$; focus: $(-3, 11.5)$; directrix: $y = -1.5$

44. $\frac{(x-1)^2}{9} + \frac{(y+4)^2}{4} = 1$; ellipse

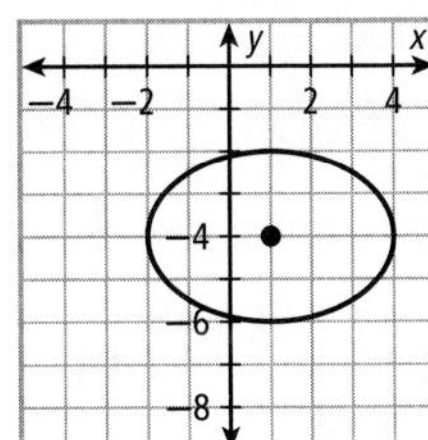

45. $\frac{(y-2)^2}{16} - \frac{(x-2)^2}{4} = 1$; hyperbola

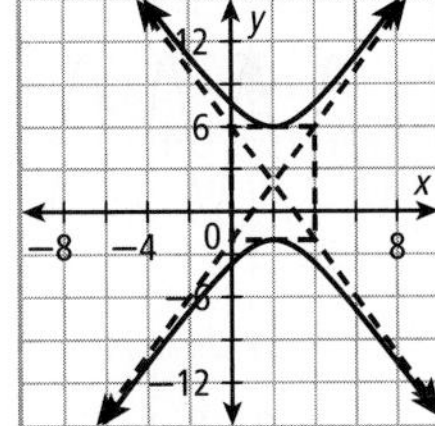

Chapter 11 Skills

21. The events "yellow cube is even" and "sum is 7" are dependent because $P(\text{sum} = 7)$ is different when it is known that the yellow cube must be even. $P(\text{sum is 7} \mid \text{yellow even}) = \frac{1}{12}$.

31. mean: $5\frac{1}{3}$; median: 5.5; mode: 8

32. mean: ≈12.14; median: 12; mode: 12

33. mean: 17.6; median: 18; mode: none

35.

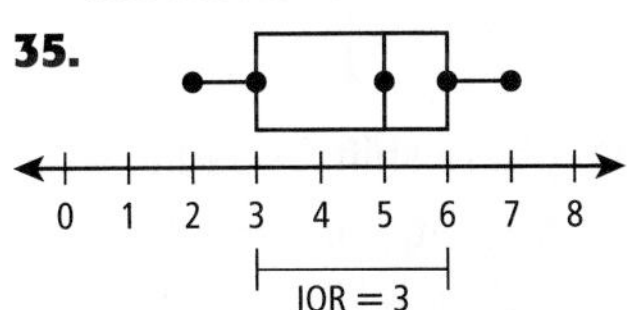

36.

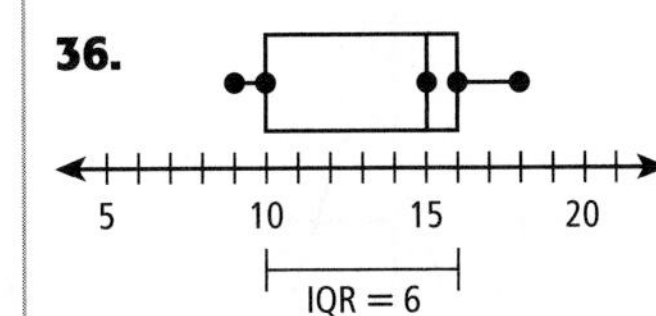

40. $x^5 + 20x^4 + 160x^3 + 640x^2 + 1280x + 1024$

41. $16x^4 - 96x^3 + 216x^2 - 216x + 81$

42. $8a^3 + 84a^2b + 294ab^2 + 343b^3$

Chapter 12 Skills

15. $[12(1) - 7] + [12(2) - 7] + [12(3) - 7] + [12(4) - 7] + [12(5) - 7] = 145$

16. $\frac{[2(1)]^2}{2} + \frac{[2(2)]^2}{2} + \frac{[2(3)]^2}{2} + \frac{[2(4)]^2}{2} = 60$

17. $\frac{1-2}{1+1} + \frac{2-2}{2+1} + \frac{3-2}{3+1} + \frac{4-2}{4+1} + \frac{5-2}{5+1} = \frac{13}{20}$

Chapter 13 Skills

1. $\sin\theta = \frac{5}{13}$; $\cos\theta = \frac{12}{13}$; $\tan\theta = \frac{5}{12}$

2. $\sin\theta = \frac{6\sqrt{61}}{61}$; $\cos\theta = \frac{5\sqrt{61}}{61}$; $\tan\theta = \frac{6}{5}$

3. $\sin\theta = \frac{\sqrt{3}}{2}$; $\cos\theta = \frac{1}{2}$; $\tan\theta = \sqrt{3}$

4. $x = \frac{3\sqrt{2}}{2}$

5. $x = \frac{25}{2}$

6. $x = \frac{10\sqrt{3}}{3}$

7. $\sin\theta = \frac{5\sqrt{89}}{89}$; $\cos\theta = \frac{8\sqrt{89}}{89}$; $\tan\theta = \frac{5}{8}$; $\csc\theta = \frac{\sqrt{89}}{5}$; $\sec\theta = \frac{\sqrt{89}}{8}$; $\cot = \frac{8}{5}$

8. $\sin\theta = \frac{5\sqrt{34}}{34}$; $\cos\theta = \frac{3\sqrt{34}}{34}$; $\tan\theta = \frac{5}{3}$; $\csc\theta = \frac{\sqrt{34}}{5}$; $\sec\theta = \frac{\sqrt{34}}{3}$; $\cot\theta = \frac{3}{5}$

9. $\sin\theta = \frac{\sqrt{30}}{6}$; $\cos\theta = \frac{\sqrt{6}}{6}$; $\tan\theta = \sqrt{5}$; $\csc\theta = \frac{\sqrt{30}}{5}$; $\sec\theta = \sqrt{6}$; $\cot\theta = \frac{\sqrt{5}}{5}$

10.

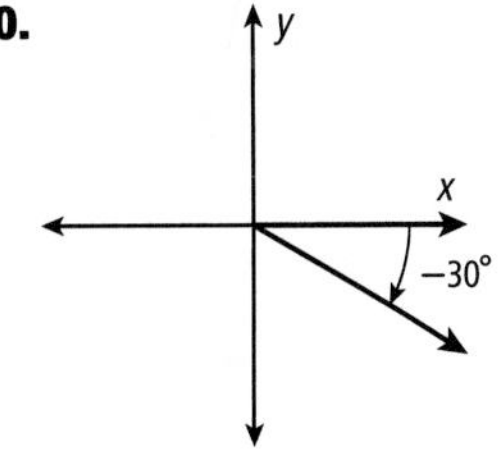

11.

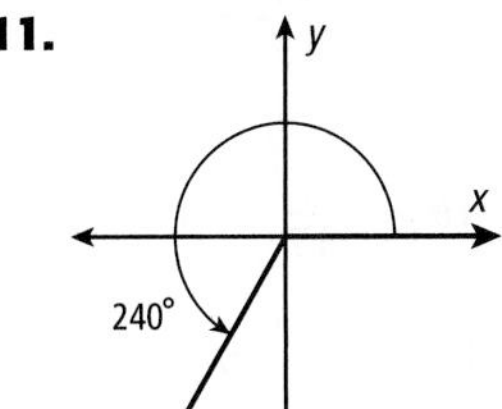

12.

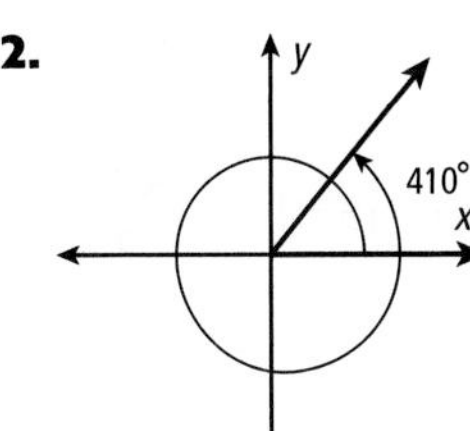

13.

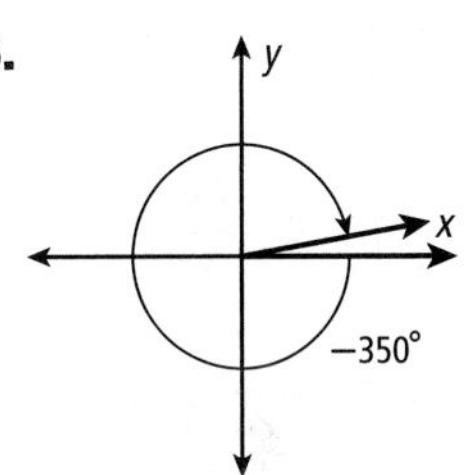

14. Possible answer: 380°; –340°

15. Possible answer: 40°; –320°

16. Possible answer: 235°; –485°

17. Possible answer: 335°; –25°

22. $\sin\theta = \frac{3\sqrt{13}}{13}$; $\cos\theta = \frac{2\sqrt{13}}{13}$; $\tan\theta = \frac{3}{2}$; $\csc\theta = \frac{\sqrt{13}}{3}$; $\sec\theta = \frac{\sqrt{13}}{2}$; $\cot\theta = \frac{2}{3}$

23. $\sin\theta = \frac{4\sqrt{17}}{17}$; $\cos\theta = -\frac{\sqrt{17}}{17}$; $\tan\theta = -4$; $\csc\theta = \frac{\sqrt{17}}{4}$; $\sec\theta = -\sqrt{17}$; $\cot\theta = -\frac{1}{4}$

24. $\sin\theta = -\frac{\sqrt{2}}{2}$; $\cos\theta = -\frac{\sqrt{2}}{2}$; $\tan\theta = 1$; $\csc\theta = -\sqrt{2}$; $\sec\theta = -\sqrt{2}$; $\cot\theta = 1$

Additional Answers

25. $\sin\theta = -\frac{4\sqrt{17}}{17}$; $\cos\theta = \frac{\sqrt{17}}{17}$; $\tan\theta = -4$; $\csc\theta = -\frac{\sqrt{17}}{4}$; $\sec\theta = \sqrt{17}$; $\cot\theta = -\frac{1}{4}$

42. $\sin(-150°) = -\frac{1}{2}$; $\cos(-150°) = -\frac{\sqrt{3}}{2}$; $\tan(-150°) = \frac{\sqrt{3}}{3}$

43. $\sin 210° = -\frac{1}{2}$; $\cos 210° = -\frac{\sqrt{3}}{2}$; $\tan 210° = \frac{\sqrt{3}}{3}$

44. $\sin 315° = -\frac{\sqrt{2}}{2}$; $\cos 315° = \frac{\sqrt{2}}{2}$; $\tan 315° = -1$

45. $\sin 330° = -\frac{1}{2}$; $\cos 330° = \frac{\sqrt{3}}{2}$; $\tan 330° = -\frac{\sqrt{3}}{3}$

46. $\sin\frac{\pi}{4} = \frac{\sqrt{2}}{2}$; $\cos\frac{\pi}{4} = \frac{\sqrt{2}}{2}$; $\tan\frac{\pi}{4} = 1$

47. $\sin\left(-\frac{7\pi}{6}\right) = \frac{1}{2}$; $\cos\left(-\frac{7\pi}{6}\right) = -\frac{\sqrt{3}}{2}$; $\tan\left(-\frac{7\pi}{6}\right) = -\frac{\sqrt{3}}{3}$

48. $\sin\frac{5\pi}{4} = -\frac{\sqrt{2}}{2}$; $\cos\frac{5\pi}{4} = -\frac{\sqrt{2}}{2}$; $\tan\frac{5\pi}{4} = 1$

49. $\sin\frac{5\pi}{3} = -\frac{\sqrt{3}}{2}$; $\cos\frac{5\pi}{3} = \frac{1}{2}$; $\tan\frac{5\pi}{3} = -\sqrt{3}$

50. $\frac{2\pi}{3} + (2\pi)n$ and $\frac{5\pi}{3} + (2\pi)n$, where n is an integer

51. $\frac{\pi}{3} + (2\pi)n$ and $\frac{5\pi}{3} + (2\pi)n$, where n is an integer

52. $\frac{4\pi}{3} + (2\pi)n$ and $\frac{5\pi}{3} + (2\pi)n$, where n is an integer

63. $m\angle P = 83°$; $q \approx 3.7$; $r \approx 6.4$

64. $m\angle J = 48°$; $j \approx 18.9$; $k \approx 25.0$

65. $m\angle B = 29°$; $a \approx 1.8$; $c \approx 3.9$

66. $m\angle U = 55°$; $u \approx 7.6$; $w \approx 7.1$

67. $m\angle D = 77°$; $d \approx 13.8$; $e \approx 9.3$

68. $m\angle T = 47°$; $r \approx 4.0$; $s \approx 7.6$

69. $a \approx 7.5$; $m\angle B \approx 59.9°$; $m\angle C \approx 74.1°$

70. $n \approx 7.0$; $m\angle M \approx 79.0°$; $m\angle L \approx 39.0°$

71. $d \approx 12.2$; $m\angle F \approx 51.1°$; $m\angle E \approx 18.9°$

72. $m\angle F \approx 35.9°$; $m\angle G \approx 38.9°$; $m\angle H \approx 105.2°$

73. $m\angle M \approx 59.1°$; $m\angle N \approx 48.3°$; $m\angle P \approx 72.6°$

74. $m\angle X \approx 93.7°$; $m\angle Y \approx 37.2°$; $m\angle Z \approx 49.1°$

Chapter 14 Skills

7. amplitude: $\frac{1}{2}$; period: π

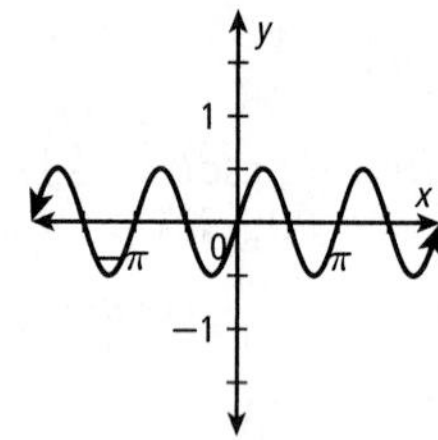

8. amplitude: 3; period: 4π

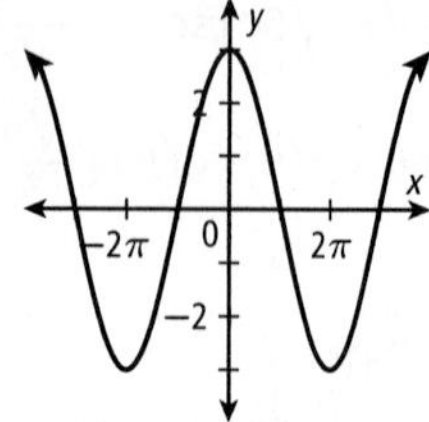

9. amplitude: 2; period: 2

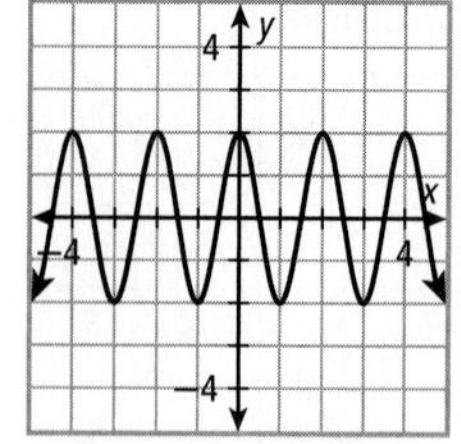

10. phase shift: $\frac{\pi}{2}$ radians to the left; x-intercepts: πn

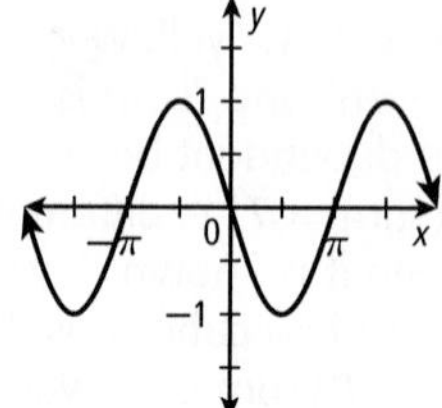

11. phase shift: π radians to the right; x-intercepts: πn

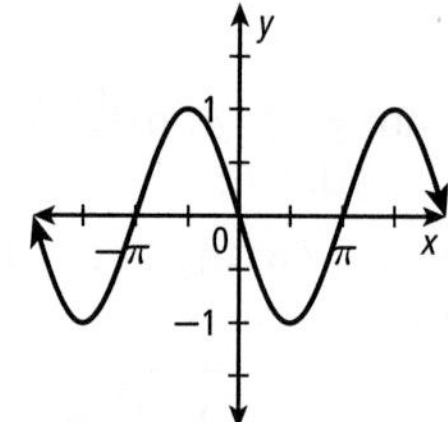

12. phase shift: $\frac{\pi}{4}$ radians to the left; x-intercepts: $-\frac{\pi}{4} + \pi n$

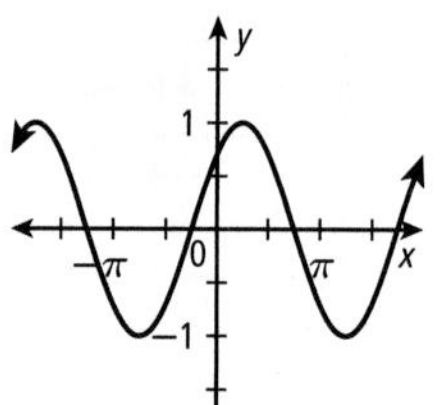

13. period: $\frac{\pi}{2}$; x-intercepts: $\frac{\pi}{2}n$; asymptotes: $x = \frac{\pi}{4} + \frac{\pi}{2}n$

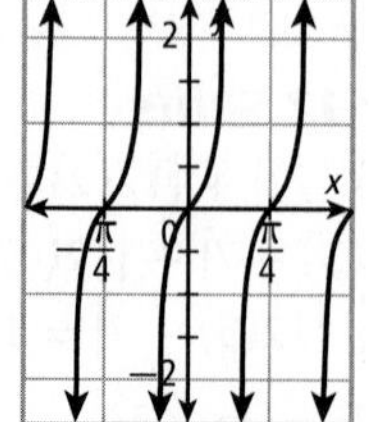

14. period: $\frac{\pi}{3}$; x-intercepts: $\frac{\pi}{3}n$; asymptotes: $x = \frac{\pi}{6} + \frac{\pi}{3}n$

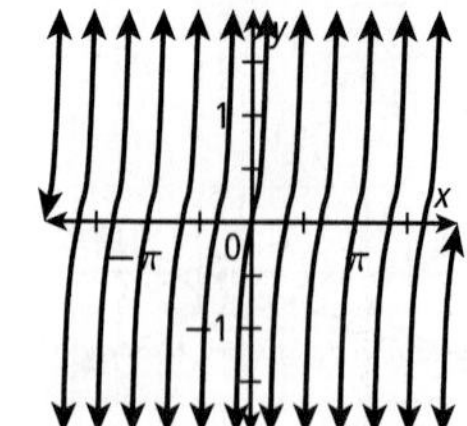

15. period: 1; x-intercepts: n; asymptotes: $x = \frac{1}{2} + n$

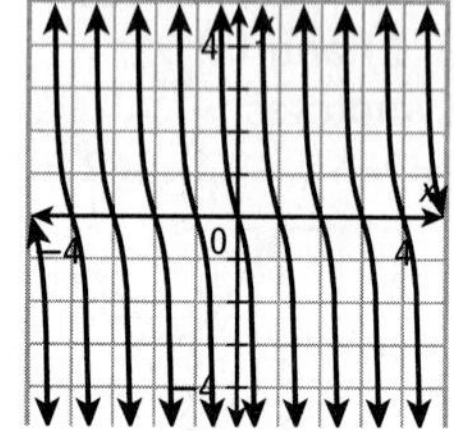

16. period: $\frac{\pi}{2}$; x-intercepts: $\frac{\pi}{4} + \frac{\pi}{2}n$; asymptotes: $x = \frac{\pi}{2}n$

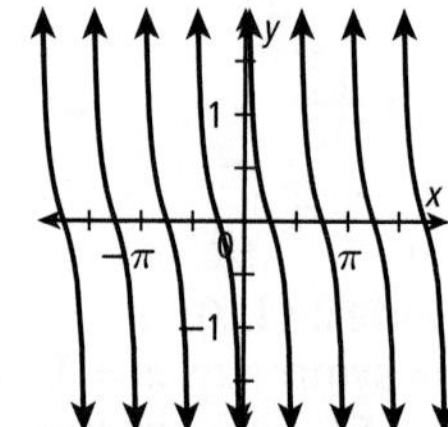

17. period: 2π; x-intercepts: $\pi + 2\pi n$; asymptotes: $x = 2\pi n$

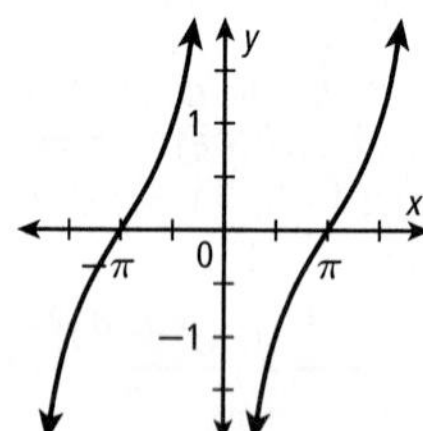

18. period: $\frac{\pi}{3}$; x-intercepts: $\frac{\pi}{6} + \frac{\pi}{3}n$; asymptotes: $x = \frac{\pi}{3}n$

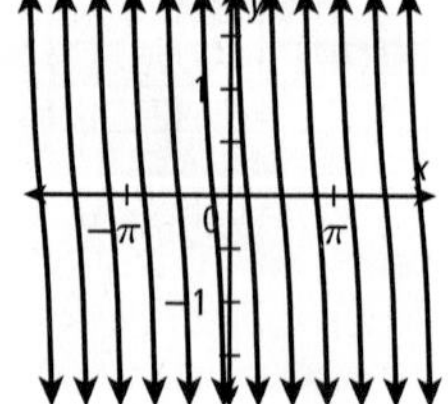

Additional Answers

19. period: 4π; asymptotes: $x = \pi + 2\pi n$

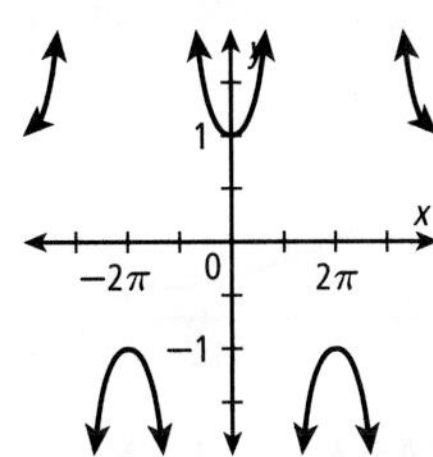

20. period: π; asymptotes: $x = \frac{\pi}{2}n$

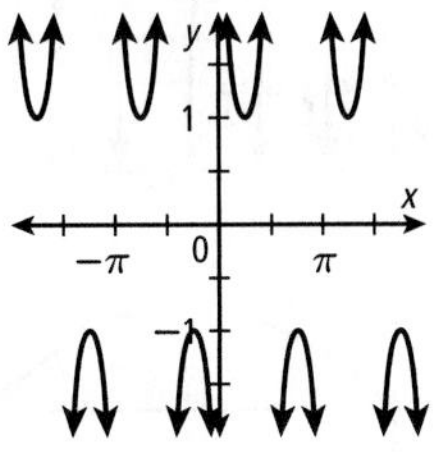

21. period: 2π; asymptotes: $x = \frac{\pi}{2} + \pi n$

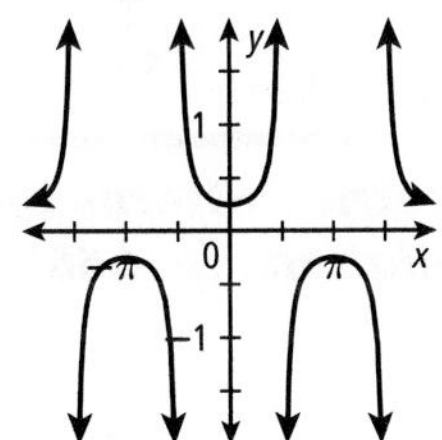

22. $\sec(-\theta) = \frac{1}{\cos(-\theta)}$

$= \frac{1}{\cos\theta} = \sec\theta$

23. $\frac{1 - \cos\theta}{\sin\theta}$

$= \frac{1 - \cos\theta}{\sin\theta} \cdot \frac{1 + \cos\theta}{1 + \cos\theta}$

$= \frac{1 - \cos^2\theta}{\sin\theta(1 + \cos\theta)}$

$= \frac{\sin^2\theta}{\sin\theta(1 + \cos\theta)}$

$= \frac{\sin\theta}{1 + \cos\theta}$

24. $\tan^2\theta(1 - \sin^2\theta)$

$= \frac{\sin^2\theta}{\cos^2\theta}\cos^2\theta = \sin^2\theta$

25. $\sec\theta(1 - \sin^2\theta)$

$= \frac{1}{\cos\theta}(\cos^2\theta) = \cos\theta$

26. $\frac{\sin^2\theta}{1 + \cos\theta} = \frac{1 - \cos^2\theta}{1 + \cos\theta}$

$= \frac{(1 - \cos\theta)(1 + \cos\theta)}{1 + \cos\theta}$

$= 1 - \cos\theta$

27. $\frac{\csc\theta - \sin\theta}{\cot\theta}$

$= \frac{\frac{1}{\sin\theta} - \sin\theta}{\frac{\cos\theta}{\sin\theta}}$

$= \frac{1 - \sin^2\theta}{\cancel{\sin\theta}} \cdot \frac{\cancel{\sin\theta}}{\cos\theta}$

$= \frac{\cos^2\theta}{\cos\theta} = \cos\theta$

28. $\frac{\tan\theta + 1}{\sec\theta + \csc\theta}$

$= \frac{\frac{\sin\theta}{\cos\theta} + 1}{\frac{1}{\cos\theta} + \frac{1}{\sin\theta}}$

$= \frac{\frac{\sin\theta}{\cos\theta} + \frac{\cos\theta}{\cos\theta}}{\frac{\sin\theta}{\sin\theta\cos\theta} + \frac{\cos\theta}{\sin\theta\cos\theta}}$

$= \frac{\frac{\sin\theta + \cos\theta}{\cos\theta}}{\frac{\sin\theta + \cos\theta}{\sin\theta\cos\theta}}$

$= \frac{\cancel{\sin\theta + \cos\theta}}{\cancel{\cos\theta}} \cdot \frac{\sin\theta\cancel{\cos\theta}}{\cancel{\sin\theta + \cos\theta}}$

$= \sin\theta$

29. $\frac{\cot\theta}{\csc\theta} = \frac{\frac{\cos\theta}{\sin\theta}}{\frac{1}{\sin\theta}}$

$= \frac{\cos\theta}{\sin\theta} \cdot \sin\theta = \cos\theta$

30. $1 - \cot\theta\cos\theta\sin\theta$

$= 1 - \frac{\cos\theta}{\sin\theta}\cos\theta\sin\theta$

$= 1 - \cos^2\theta = \sin^2\theta$

36. $\frac{120}{169}; \frac{119}{169}; \frac{120}{119}$

37. $\frac{24}{25}; -\frac{7}{25}; -\frac{24}{7}$

38. $-\frac{12}{13}; -\frac{5}{13}; \frac{12}{5}$

39. $-\frac{4\sqrt{2}}{9}; \frac{7}{9}; -\frac{4\sqrt{2}}{7}$

40. $\frac{\cos 2\theta}{\cos\theta + \sin\theta}$

$= \frac{\cos^2\theta - \sin^2\theta}{\cos\theta + \sin\theta}$

$= \frac{(\cos\theta + \sin\theta)(\cos\theta - \sin\theta)}{\cos\theta + \sin\theta}$

$= \cos\theta - \sin\theta$

41. $\frac{\cos\theta\sin 2\theta}{1 + \cos 2\theta}$

$= \frac{\cos\theta \bullet 2\sin\theta\cos\theta}{1 + (2\cos^2\theta - 1)}$

$= \frac{2\sin\theta\cos^2\theta}{2\cos^2\theta} = \sin\theta$

42. $\cos 2\theta + 2\sin^2\theta$

$= (1 - 2\sin^2\theta)$

$+ 2\sin^2\theta = 1$

43. $(\sin\theta - \cos\theta)^2$

$= \sin^2\theta - 2\sin\theta\cos\theta + \cos^2\theta$

$= 1 - 2\sin\theta\cos\theta$

$= 1 - \sin 2\theta$

44. $\frac{3\sqrt{10}}{10}; \frac{\sqrt{10}}{10}; 3$

45. $\frac{\sqrt{2}}{10}; -\frac{7\sqrt{2}}{10}; -\frac{1}{7}$

46. $\frac{\sqrt{30}}{6}; \frac{\sqrt{6}}{6}; \sqrt{5}$

47. $\frac{\sqrt{10}}{5}; \frac{\sqrt{15}}{5}; \frac{\sqrt{6}}{3}$

Chapter 1 Applications

1. Bantamweight, Featherweight, Super Lightweight, Welterweight, Jr. Middleweight, Middleweight

4. \$48; possible answer: 10% of \$60 is \$6, so 20% of \$60 is \$12. Subtracting \$12 from \$60 gives the sale price of \$48.

9. Yes; for each weight, there is only one corresponding cost. No; for each cost, there is more than one possible weight.

11. 10.49; the charge in dollars for sending 450 text messages in one month

Chapter 2 Applications

3.

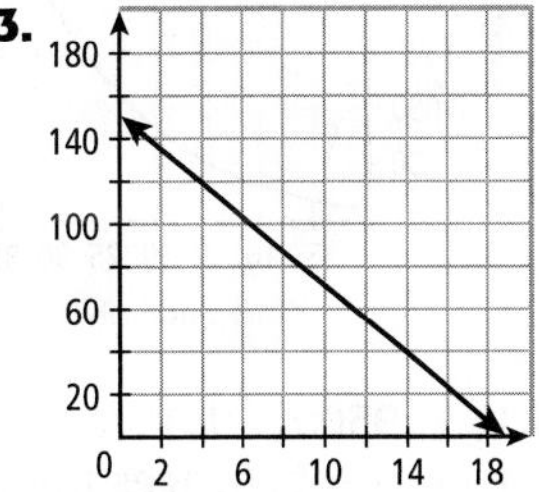

4. (0, 150) means that he initially owes \$150 and (18.75, 0) means that he will have repaid his debt after doing 18.75 hours of chores.

5. $0.75 + 0.15x$; the slope represents the cost per minute, and the y-intercept represents the initial cost of each call.

6.

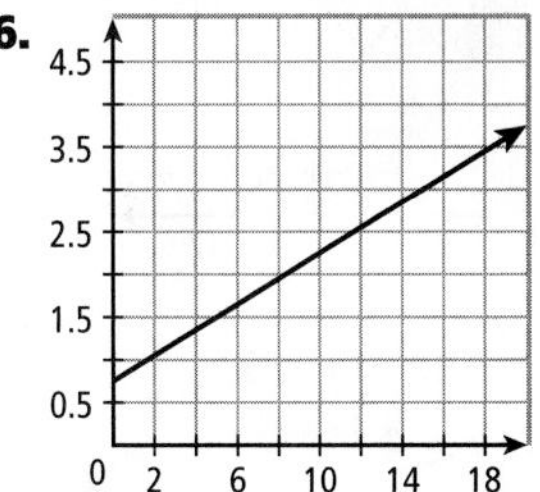

9.

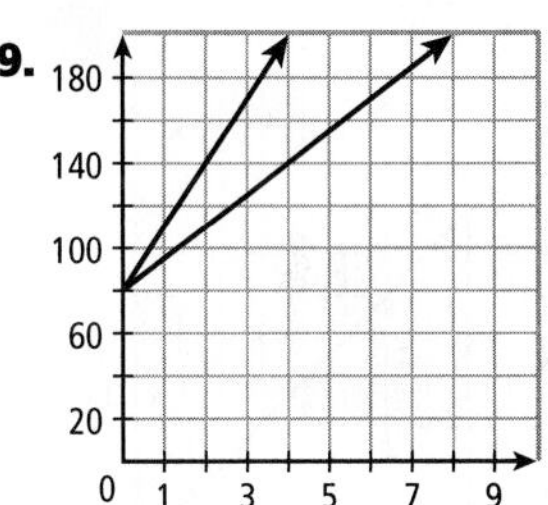

10.

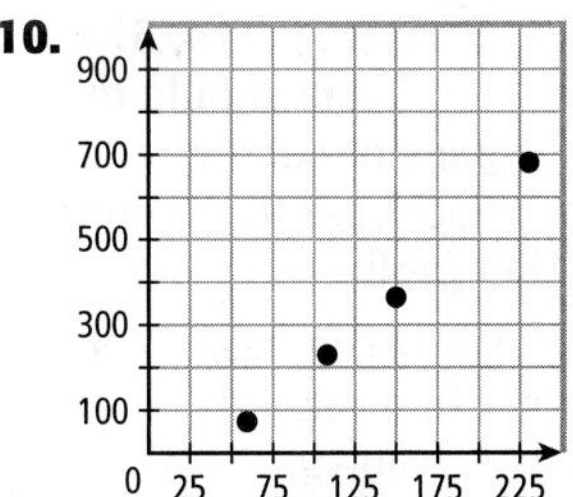

Chapter 3 Applications

1. $\begin{cases} y = 88 - 10.7x \\ y = 100 - 12.2x \end{cases}$

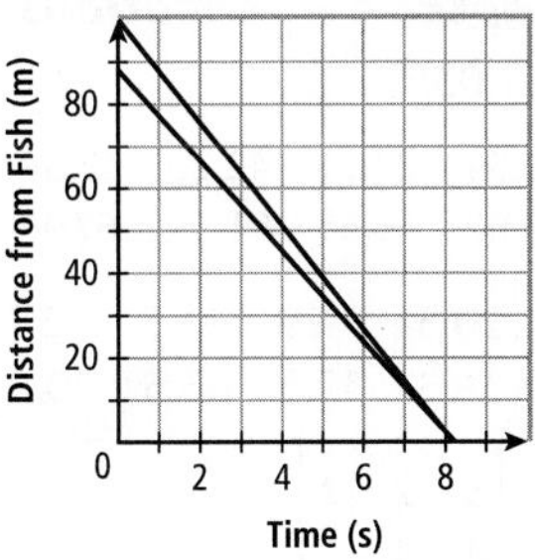

6. Let x = CDs and y = DVDs.

$x \geq 0$

$y \geq 0$

$14x + 12y \leq 150$

$y \geq x$

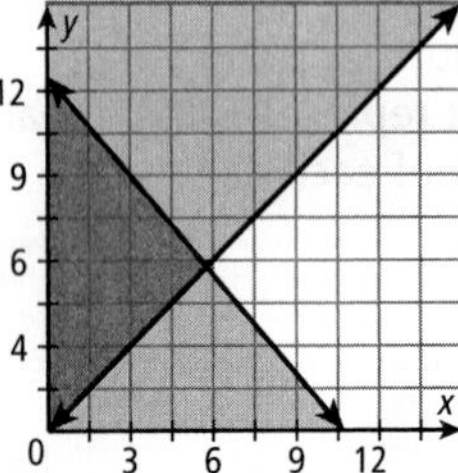

8. $\begin{cases} 0.5x + y \leq 7 \\ x \geq 4 \\ y \geq 0 \end{cases}$

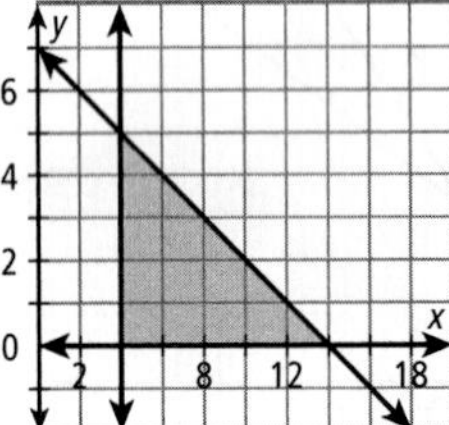

9. $P = 3x + 7y$; $P(4, 5) = 47$; Leora should make 4 pairs of earrings and 5 necklaces to maximize her profit.

10. Let c = candles, f = frames, and p = pillows.
$\frac{20}{3}c + 15f + 25p = 150$

12. cycling: 5 Cal/min; weight lifting: 3.5 Cal/min; swimming: 10 Cal/min

Chapter 4 Applications

1. $1.03B =$

$$\begin{bmatrix} 18.54 & 24.21 & 42.23 & 35.54 \\ 35.02 & 46.35 & 81.37 & 67.98 \end{bmatrix}$$

2. $\begin{bmatrix} 20.5 & 26 & 43.5 & 37 \\ 38.5 & 49.5 & 83.5 & 70.5 \end{bmatrix}$

5. $\begin{bmatrix} 3 & 2 & 2 \\ 4 & 4 & 1 \end{bmatrix}$

7. $\begin{bmatrix} 2 & 1 & 1 \\ 1 & 2 & 1 \\ 3 & 1 & 2 \end{bmatrix} \begin{bmatrix} x \\ y \\ z \end{bmatrix} = \begin{bmatrix} 0.55 \\ 0.75 \\ 0.70 \end{bmatrix}$

8. $\begin{bmatrix} 1.5 & -0.5 & -0.5 \\ 0.5 & 0.5 & -0.5 \\ -2.5 & 0.5 & 1.5 \end{bmatrix}$

9. Stepping out of bounds is a 0.1 point deduction, a heavy brush of hands or feet is a 0.3 point deduction, and being out of sync with the music is a 0.05 point deduction.

10. $\left[\begin{array}{ccc|c} 10 & 12 & 8 & 4468 \\ 7 & 15 & 10 & 5068 \\ 20 & 9 & 5 & 4298 \end{array}\right]$

11. Small boxes use 94 in^2 of wood, medium boxes use 142 in^2 of wood, and large boxes use 228 in^2 of wood.

Chapter 6 Applications

4. $T(4) = 1973.76$; Mr. Schwartz made a profit of \$1973.76 in his fourth year of business.

6. The zeros of the function are 0, 3, and 6. The third and sixth games of the season ended in a tie.

10.

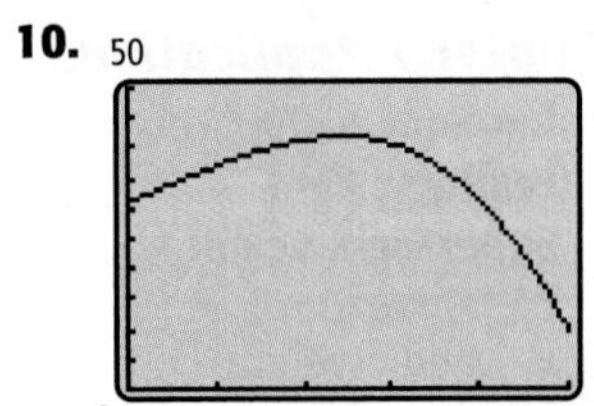

11. The maximum value is \$41.81 and occurs on the twelfth day.

12. The y-intercept is 31.25, which signifies that Sharon paid \$31.25 for the stock when she bought it.

13. $T(x) = -0.005x^5 + 0.07x^4 - 0.5x^2 + 228$

Chapter 7 Applications

2.

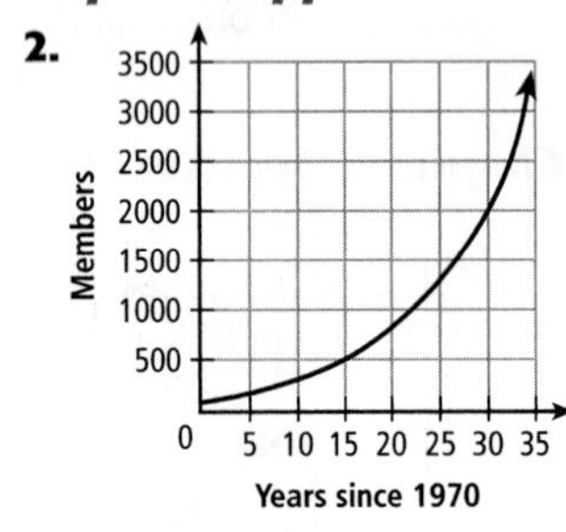

14. $V_2 = 9500(1.03)^x$; the y-intercept changes from 10,500 to 9500, and the graph is compressed vertically.

Chapter 9 Applications

1. The data closely fit the equation $f(x) = 112(1.1^x)$. In 2010 there should be approximately 290 penguins in the colony.

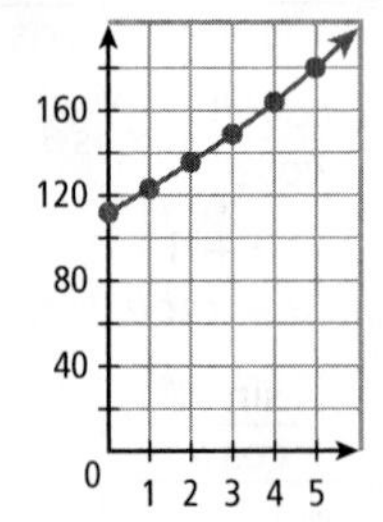

2.

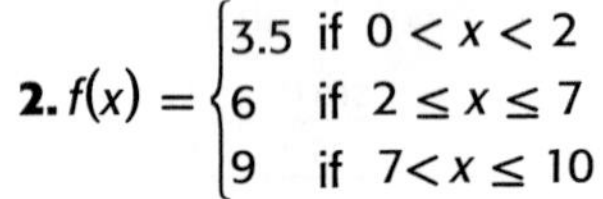

$f(x) = \begin{cases} 3.5 & \text{if } 0 < x < 2 \\ 6 & \text{if } 2 \leq x \leq 7 \\ 9 & \text{if } 7 < x \leq 10 \end{cases}$

3.

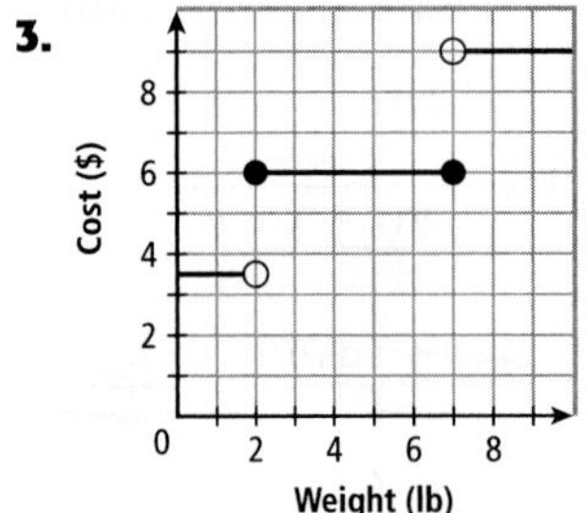

5. $g(x) = \begin{cases} 7x & \text{if } 0 < x < 20 \\ 6x + 15 & \text{if } x \geq 20 \end{cases}$

for x-values less than 20, the graph remains the same. For x-values greater than or equal to 20, the graph is translated 5 units up.

Chapter 14 Applications

1.

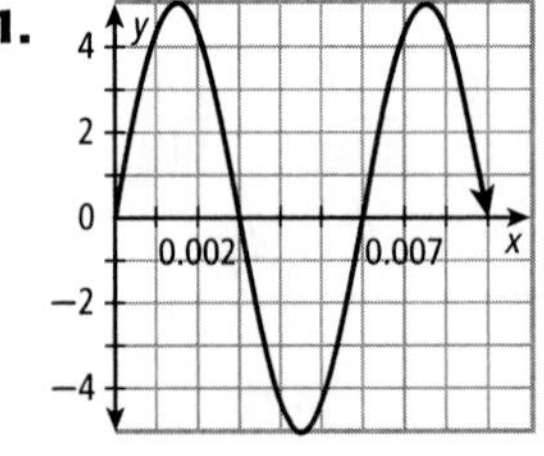

2.

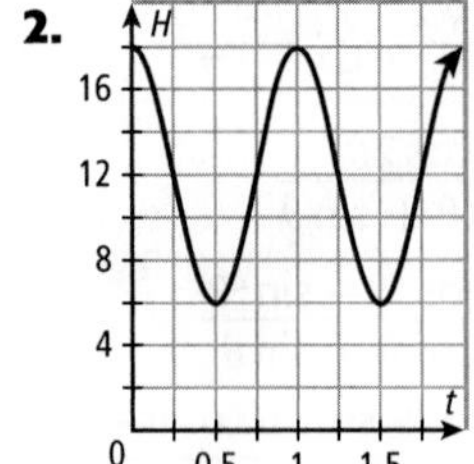

5.

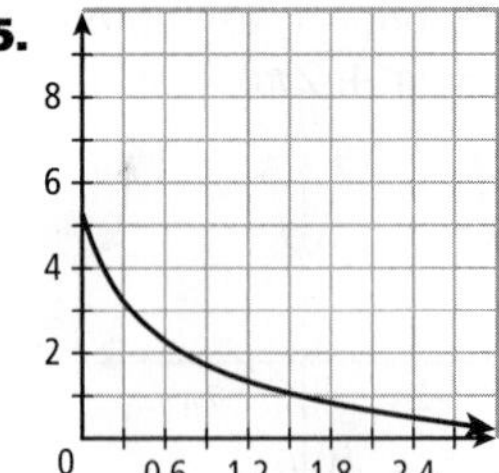

7.

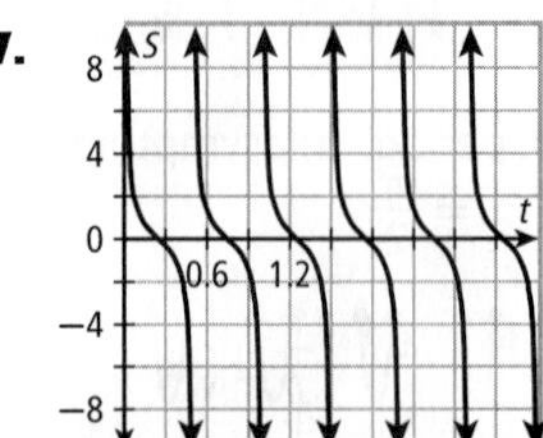

13.

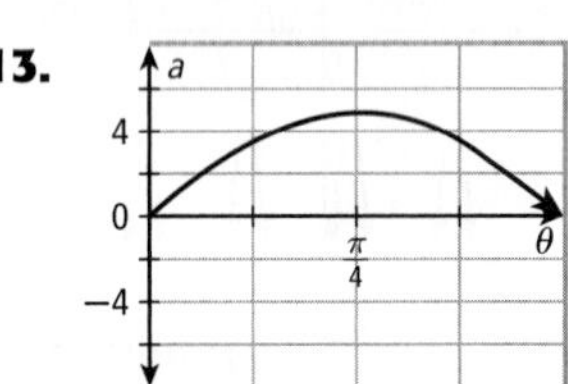

Skills Bank

Geometric Patterns and Tessellations (p. S66)

1.

Stage	1	2	3	4
Dots	1	4	7	10

The terms of the sequence increase by 3 at each stage. The fifth stage probably contains 13 dots.

2.

Stage	1	2	3	4
Dots	1	3	6	10

The terms of the sequence appear to be the sum of the first n whole numbers, where n is the term number. The fifth stage probably contains 15 dots.

3.

Stage	1	2	3	4
Squares	1	4	9	16

The terms of the sequence appear to be the squares of the term numbers. The fifth stage probably contains 25 squares.

4.

Stage	1	2	3
Triangles	1	4	16

Each term of the sequence except the first term appears to be equal to the previous term multiplied by 4. The fourth stage probably contains 64 triangles.

5.

Stage	1	2	3	4
Squares	1	5	9	13

The terms of the sequence increase by 4 at each stage. The fifth stage probably contains 17 squares.

6.

Stage	1	2	3	4
Dots	4	6	8	10

The terms of the sequence increase by 2 at each stage. The fifth stage probably contains 12 dots.

Data Displays (p. S68)

1.

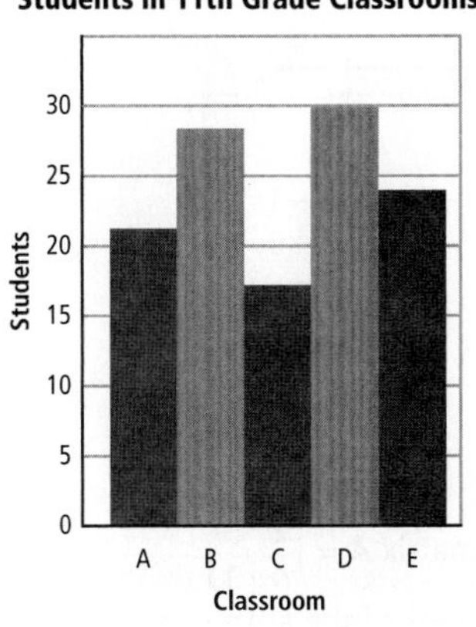

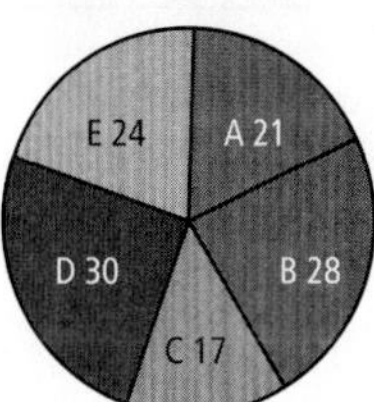

Proofs (p. S71)

Possible answers:

7.

Left Side	Right Side
$(x+2)(x+8)$	$(x+5)^2-9$
$x^2+10x+16$	$x^2+10x+16$

Possible answers:

8. $(x+1)(x-6)(x+7)$

$= (x^2-5x-6)(x+7)$

$= x^3+2x^2-41x-42$

Glossary/Glosario

A

ENGLISH	SPANISH	EXAMPLES
absolute value of a complex number (p. 382) The absolute value of $a + bi$ is the distance from the origin to the point (a, b) in the complex plane and is denoted $\lvert a + bi \rvert = \sqrt{a^2 + b^2}$.	**valor absoluto de un número complejo** El valor absoluto de $a + bi$ es la distancia desde el origen hasta el punto (a, b) en el plano complejo y se expresa $\lvert a + bi \rvert = \sqrt{a^2 + b^2}$.	$\lvert 2 + 3i \rvert = \sqrt{2^2 + 3^2} = \sqrt{13}$
absolute value of a real number (p. 151) The absolute value of x is the distance from zero to x on a number line, denoted $\lvert x \rvert$. $\lvert x \rvert = \begin{cases} x & \text{if } x \geq 0 \\ -x & \text{if } x < 0 \end{cases}$	**valor absoluto de un número real** El valor absoluto de x es la distancia desde cero hasta x en una recta numérica y se expresa $\lvert x \rvert$. $\lvert x \rvert = \begin{cases} x & \text{si } x \geq 0 \\ -x & \text{si } x < 0 \end{cases}$	$\lvert 3 \rvert = 3$ $\lvert -3 \rvert = 3$
absolute-value function (p. 158) A function whose rule contains absolute-value expressions.	**función de valor absoluto** Función cuya regla contiene expresiones de valor absoluto.	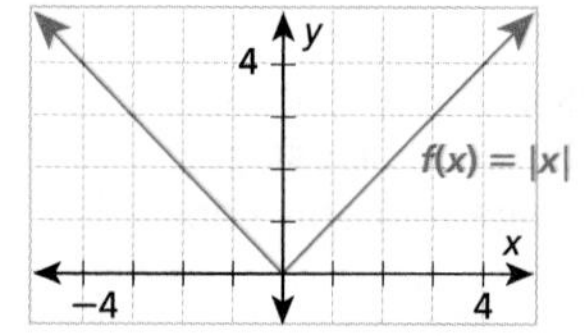
acute angle (p. 960) An angle that measures greater than 0° and less than 90°.	**ángulo agudo** Ángulo que mide más de 0° y menos de 90°.	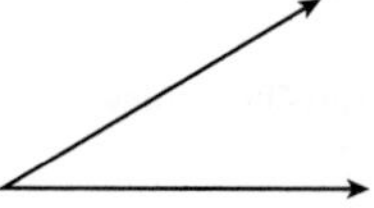
additive inverse of a matrix (p. 249) A matrix where each entry is the opposite of each entry in another matrix. Two matrices are additive inverses if their sum is the zero matrix.	**inverso aditivo de una matriz** Matriz en la cual cada entrada es el opuesto de cada entrada en otra matriz. Dos matrices son inversos aditivos si su suma es la matriz cero.	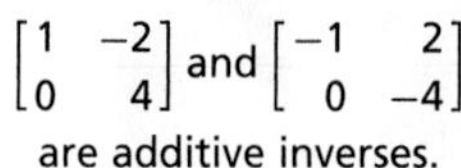 $\begin{bmatrix} 1 & -2 \\ 0 & 4 \end{bmatrix}$ and $\begin{bmatrix} -1 & 2 \\ 0 & -4 \end{bmatrix}$ are additive inverses.
address (p. 246) The location of an entry in a matrix, given by the row and column in which the entry appears. In matrix A, the address of the entry in row i and column j is a_{ij}.	**dirección** Ubicación de una entrada en una matriz, indicada por la fila y la columna en las que aparece la entrada. En la matriz A, la dirección de la entrada de la fila i y la columna j es a_{ij}.	In the matrix $A = \begin{bmatrix} 2 & 3 \\ 4 & 1 \end{bmatrix}$, the address of the entry 2 is a_{11}, the address of the entry 3 is a_{12}.
algebraic expression (p. 27) An expression that contains at least one variable.	**expresión algebraica** Expresión que contiene por lo menos una variable.	$2x + 3y$
amplitude (p. 991) The amplitude of a periodic function is half the difference of the maximum and minimum values (always positive).	**amplitud** La amplitud de una función periódica es la mitad de la diferencia entre los valores máximo y mínimo (siempre positivos).	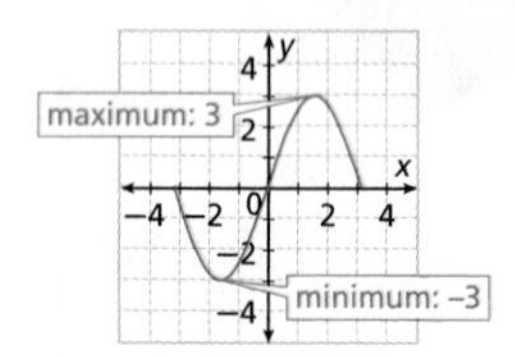 amplitude $= \frac{1}{2}\left[3 - (-3)\right] = 3$

ENGLISH	SPANISH	EXAMPLES
angle of depression (p. 931) The angle formed by a horizontal line and a line of sight to a point below.	**ángulo de depresión** Ángulo formado por una recta horizontal y una línea visual a un punto inferior.	
angle of elevation (p. 931) The angle formed by a horizontal line and a line of sight to a point above.	**ángulo de elevación** Ángulo formado por una recta horizontal y una línea visual a un punto superior.	
angle of rotation (p. 936) An angle formed by a rotating ray, called the terminal side, and a stationary reference ray, called the initial side.	**ángulo de rotación** Ángulo formado por un rayo en rotación, denominado lado terminal, y un rayo de referencia estático, denominado lado inicial.	Terminal side, 45°, 135°, y, x, 0, Initial side
arc (p. 943) An unbroken part of a circle consisting of two points on the circle, called the endpoints, and all the points on the circle between them.	**arco** Parte continua de un círculo formada por dos puntos del círculo denominados extremos y todos los puntos del círculo comprendidos entre éstos.	R, S
arc length (p. 943) The distance along an arc measured in linear units.	**longitud de arco** Distancia a lo largo de un arco medida en unidades lineales.	10 ft, D, 90°, C $m\widehat{CD} = 5\pi$ ft
arithmetic sequence (p. 879) A sequence whose successive terms differ by the same nonzero number d, called the *common difference.*	**sucesión aritmética** Sucesión cuyos términos sucesivos difieren en el mismo número distinto de cero d, denominado *diferencia común.*	4, 7, 10, 13, 16, ... +3 +3 +3 +3 $d = 3$
arithmetic series (p. 882) The indicated sum of the terms of an arithmetic sequence.	**serie aritmética** Suma indicada de los términos de una sucesión aritmética.	$4 + 7 + 10 + 13 + 16 + \ldots$
asymptote (p. 490) A line that a graph approaches as the value of a variable becomes extremely large or small.	**asíntota** Línea recta a la cual se aproxima una gráfica a medida que el valor de una variable se hace sumamente grande o pequeño.	y, 4, Asymptote, −4, 0, 4, x
augmented matrix (p. 287) A matrix that consists of the coefficients and the constant terms in a system of linear equations.	**matriz aumentada** Matriz formada por los coeficientes y los términos constantes de un sistema de ecuaciones lineales.	System of equations: $3x + 2y = 5$, $2x - 3y = 1$ Augmented matrix: $\left[\begin{array}{cc\|c} 3 & 2 & 5 \\ 2 & -3 & 1 \end{array}\right]$
axis of symmetry (p. 323) A line that divides a plane figure or a graph into two congruent reflected halves.	**eje de simetría** Línea que divide una figura plana o una gráfica en dos mitades reflejadas congruentes.	Axis of symmetry, $y = \|x\|$, y, 4, 2, x, −4, −2, 0, 2, 4, −2

Glossary/Glosario

ENGLISH	SPANISH	EXAMPLES

B

base of a power (p. 34) The number in a power that is used as a factor.

base de una potencia Número de una potencia que se utiliza como factor.

$3^4 = 3 \cdot 3 \cdot 3 \cdot 3 = 81$ (base: 3)

base of an exponential function (p. 490) The value of b in a function of the form $f(x) = ab^x$, where a and b are real numbers with $a \neq 0$, $b > 0$, and $b \neq 1$.

base de una función exponencial Valor de b en una función del tipo $f(x) = ab^x$, donde a y b son números reales con $a \neq 0$, $b > 0$, y $b \neq 1$.

$f(x) = 5(2)^x$ (base: 2)

binomial (pp. 336, 406) A polynomial with two terms.

binomio Polinomio con dos términos.

$x + y$

$2a^2 + 3$

$4m^3n^2 + 6mn^4$

binomial experiment (p. 837) A probability experiment consists of n identical and independent trials whose outcomes are either successes or failures, with a constant probability of success p and a constant probability of failure q, where $q = 1 - p$ or $p + q = 1$.

experimento binomial Experimento de probabilidades que comprende n pruebas idénticas e independientes cuyos resultados son éxitos o fracasos, con una probabilidad constante de éxito p y una probabilidad constante de fracaso q, donde $q = 1 - p$ o $p + q = 1$.

A multiple-choice quiz has 10 questions with 4 answer choices. The number of trials is 10. If each question is answered randomly, the probability of success for each trial is $\frac{1}{4} = 0.25$ and the probability of failure is $\frac{3}{4} = 0.75$.

binomial probability (p. 838) In a binomial experiment, the probability of r successes $(0 \le r \le n)$ is $P(r) = {}_nC_r \cdot p^r q^{n-r}$.

probabilidad binomial En un experimento binomial, la probabilidad de r éxitos $(0 \le r \le n)$ es $P(r) = {}_nC_r \cdot p^r q^{n-r}$.

In the binomial experiment above, the probability of randomly guessing 6 problems correctly is $P = {}_{10}C_6\,(0.25)^6\,(0.75)^4 \approx 0.016$.

Binomial Theorem (p. 837) For any positive integer n, $(x + y)^n = {}_nC_0\, x^n y^0 + {}_nC_1\, x^{n-1} y^1 + {}_nC_2\, x^{n-2} y^2 + \cdots + {}_nC_{n-1}\, x^1 y^{n-1} + {}_nC_n\, x^0 y^n$

Teorema de los binomios Dado un entero positivo n, $(x + y)^n = {}_nC_0\, x^n y^0 + {}_nC_1\, x^{n-1} y^1 + {}_nC_2\, x^{n-2} y^2 + \cdots + {}_nC_{n-1}\, x^1 y^{n-1} + {}_nC_n\, x^0 y^n$

$$(x + 2)^4 = {}_4C_0\, x^4 2^0 + {}_4C_1\, x^3 2^1 + {}_4C_2\, x^2 2^2 + {}_4C_1\, x^1 2^3 + {}_4C_4\, x^0 2^4 = x^4 + 8x^3 + 24x^2 + 32x + 16$$

boundary line (p. 124) A line that divides a coordinate plane into two half-planes.

línea de límite Línea que divide un plano cartesiano en dos semiplanos.

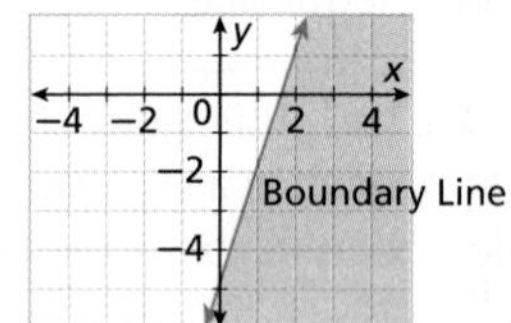

box-and-whisker plot (p. 829) A method of showing how data is distributed by using the median, quartiles, and minimum and maximum values; also called a *box plot*.

gráfica de mediana y rango Método para demostrar la distribución de datos utilizando la mediana, los cuartiles y los valores mínimos y máximos; también llamado *gráfica de caja*.

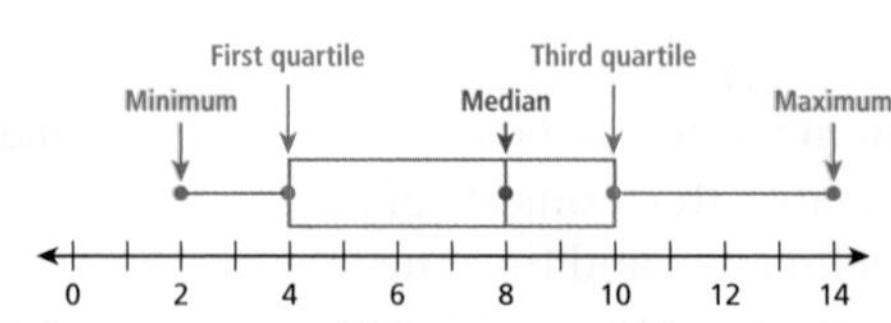

branch of a hyperbola (p. 744) One of the two symmetrical parts of the hyperbola.

rama de una hipérbola Una de las dos partes simétricas de la hipérbola.

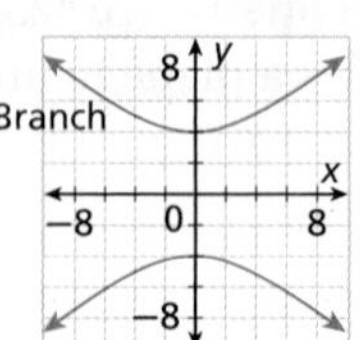

ENGLISH	SPANISH	EXAMPLES
C		
circle (p. 729) The set of points in a plane that are a fixed distance from a given point called the center of the circle.	**círculo** Conjunto de puntos en un plano que se encuentran a una distancia fija de un punto determinado denominado centro del círculo.	A, Chord, B
circumference (p. 943) The distance around a circle.	**circunferencia** Distancia alrededor del círculo.	Circumference
closure (p. 15) A set of numbers is said to be closed, or to have closure, under a given operation if the result of the operation on any two numbers in the set is also in the set.	**cerradura** Se dice que un conjunto de números es cerrado, o tiene cerradura, respecto de una operación determinada, si el resultado de la operación entre dos números cualesquiera del conjunto también está en el conjunto.	The natural numbers are closed under addition because the sum of two natural numbers is always a natural number.
coefficient (p. 47) A number multiplied by a variable.	**coeficiente** Número multiplicado por una variable.	In the expression $2x + 3y$, 2 is the coefficient of x and 3 is the coefficient of y.
coefficient matrix (p. 271) The matrix of the coefficients of the variables in a linear system of equations.	**matriz de coeficientes** Matriz de los coeficientes de las variables en un sistema lineal de ecuaciones.	System of equations: $2x + 3y = 11$, $5x - 4y = 16$; Coefficient matrix: $\begin{bmatrix} 2 & 3 \\ 5 & -4 \end{bmatrix}$
coefficient of determination (p. 376) The number R^2, with $0 \le R^2 \le 1$, that shows the fraction of the data that are close to the curve of best fit and, thus, how well the curve fits the data.	**coeficiente de determinación** El número R^2, con $0 \le R^2 \le 1$, que muestra la fracción de los datos cercanos a la línea de mejor ajuste y, por lo tanto, cuánto se ajusta la línea de mejor ajuste a los datos.	QuadReg y=ax²+bx+c a=1.013528963 b=7.485785061 c=73.78780488 R²=.9852725622
combination (p. 796) A selection of a group of objects in which order is *not* important. The number of combinations of *r* objects chosen from a group of *n* objects is denoted $_nC_r$.	**combinación** Selección de un grupo de objetos en la cual el orden *no* es importante. El número de combinaciones de *r* objetos elegidos de un grupo de *n* objetos se expresa así: $_nC_r$.	For 4 objects *A, B, C,* and *D,* there are $_4C_2 = 6$ different combinations of 2 objects: *AB, AC, AD, BC, BD, CD.*
combined variation (p. 572) A relationship containing both direct and inverse variation.	**variación combinada** Relación que contiene variaciones directas e inversas.	$y = \frac{kx}{z}$, where k is the constant of variation
common difference (p. 879) In an arithmetic sequence, the nonzero constant difference of any term and the previous term.	**diferencia común** En una sucesión aritmética, diferencia constante distinta de cero entre cualquier término y el término anterior.	In the arithmetic sequence 3, 5, 7, 9, 11, ..., the common difference is 2.
common logarithm (p. 506) A logarithm whose base is 10, denoted $\log_{10}$ or just log.	**logaritmo común** Logaritmo de base 10, que se expresa $\log_{10}$ o simplemente log.	$\log 100 = \log_{10}100 = 2$, since $10^2 = 100$.

Glossary/Glosario

ENGLISH	SPANISH	EXAMPLES
common ratio (p. 879) In a geometric sequence, the constant ratio of any term and the previous term.	**razón común** En una sucesión geométrica, la razón constante r entre cualquier término y el término anterior.	In the geometric sequence 32, 16, 18, 4, 2 ..., the common ratio is $\frac{1}{2}$.
complement of an event (p. 803) All outcomes in the sample space that are not in an event E, denoted $\overline{E}$.	**complemento de un suceso** Todos los resultados en el espacio muestral que no están en el suceso E y se expresan $\overline{E}$.	In the experiment of rolling a number cube, the complement of rolling a 3 is rolling a 1, 2, 4, 5, or 6.
completing the square (p. 342) A process used to form a perfect-square trinomial. To complete the square of $x^2 + bx$, add $\left(\frac{b}{2}\right)^2$.	**completar el cuadrado** Proceso utilizado para formar un trinomio cuadrado perfecto. Para completar el cuadrado de $x^2 + bx$, hay que sumar $\left(\frac{b}{2}\right)^2$.	$x^2 + 6x + \blacksquare$ Add $\left(\frac{6}{2}\right)^2 = 9$. $x^2 + 6x + 9$ $(x + 3)^2$ *is a perfect square.*
complex conjugate (p. 352) The complex conjugate of any complex number $a + bi$, denoted $\overline{a + bi}$, is $a - bi$.	**conjugado complejo** El conjugado complejo de cualquier número complejo $a + bi$, expresado como $\overline{a + bi}$, es $a - bi$.	$\overline{4 + 3i} = 4 - 3i$ $\overline{4 - 3i} = 4 + 3i$
complex fraction (p. 586) A fraction that contains one or more fractions in the numerator, the denominator, or both.	**fracción compleja** Fracción que contiene una o más fracciones en el numerador, en el denominador, o en ambos.	$\dfrac{\frac{1}{2}}{1 + \frac{2}{3}}$
complex number (p. 351) Any number that can be written as $a + bi$, where a and b are real numbers and $i = \sqrt{-1}$.	**número complejo** Todo número que se puede expresar como $a + bi$, donde a y b son números reales e $i = \sqrt{-1}$.	$4 + 2i$ $5 + 0i = 5$ $0 - 7i = -7i$
complex plane (p. 382) A set of coordinate axes in which the horizontal axis is the real axis and the vertical axis is the imaginary axis; used to graph complex numbers.	**plano complejo** Conjunto de ejes cartesianos en el cual el eje horizontal es el eje real y el eje vertical es el eje imaginario; se utiliza para representar gráficamente números complejos.	*Imaginary axis* $2i$ $0 + 0i$ *Real axis* -2 2 $-2i$
composite figure (p. 349) A plane figure made up of triangles, rectangles, trapezoids, circles, and other simple shapes, or a three-dimensional figure made up of prisms, cones, pyramids, cylinders, and other simple three-dimensional figures.	**figura compuesta** Figura plana compuesta por triángulos, rectángulos, trapecios, círculos y otras formas simples, o figura tridimensional compuesta por prismas, conos, pirámides, cilindros y otras figuras tridimensionales simples.	18 in. 12 in.
composition of functions (p. 683) The composition of functions f and g, written as $(f \circ g)(x)$ and defined as $f(g(x))$ uses the output of $g(x)$ as the input for $f(x)$.	**composición de funciones** La composición de las funciones f y g, expresada como $(f \circ g)(x)$ y definida como $f(g(x))$ utiliza la salida de $g(x)$ como la entrada para $f(x)$.	If $f(x) = x^2$ and $g(x) = x + 1$, the composite function $(f \circ g)(x) = (x + 1)^2$.
compound event (p. 819) An event made up of two or more simple events.	**suceso compuesto** Suceso formado por dos o más sucesos simples.	In the experiment of tossing a coin and rolling a number cube, the event of the coin landing heads and the number cube landing on 3.

ENGLISH	SPANISH	EXAMPLES
compression (p. 61) A transformation that pushes the points of a graph horizontally toward the y-axis or vertically toward the x-axis.	**compresión** Transformación que desplaza los puntos de una gráfica horizontalmente hacia el eje y o verticalmente hacia el eje x.	
conditional probability (p. 812) The probability of event B, given that event A has already occurred or is certain to occur, denoted $P(B \mid A)$; used to find probability of dependent events.	**probabilidad condicional** Probabilidad del suceso B, dado que el suceso A ya ha ocurrido o es seguro que ocurrirá, expresada como $P(B \mid A)$; se utiliza para calcular la probabilidad de sucesos dependientes.	
congruent (p. 60) Having the same size and shape, denoted by $\cong$.	**congruente** Que tiene el mismo tamaño y forma, expresado por $\cong$.	Q R P S $\overline{PQ} \cong \overline{RS}$
conic section (p. 722) A plane figure formed by the intersection of a double right cone and a plane. Examples include circles, ellipses, hyperbolas, and parabolas.	**sección cónica** Figura plana formada por la intersección de un cono regular doble y un plano. Algunos ejemplos son círculos, elipses, hipérbolas y parábolas.	Circle Ellipse Parabola Hyperbola
conjugate axis (p. 744) The axis of symmetry of a hyperbola that separates the two branches of the hyperbola.	**eje conjugado** Eje de simetría de una hipérbola que separa las dos ramas de la hipérbola.	Conjugate axis
conjunction (p. 150) A compound statement that uses the word *and*.	**conjunción** Enunciado compuesto que contiene la palabra *y*.	3 is less than 5 AND greater than 0.
consistent system (p. 183) A system of equations or inequalities that has at least one solution.	**sistema consistente** Sistema de ecuaciones o desigualdades que tiene por lo menos una solución.	$\begin{cases} x + y = 6 \\ x - y = 4 \end{cases}$ solution: $(5, 1)$
constant function (p. 67) A function of the form $f(x) = c$, where c is a constant.	**función constante** Función del tipo $f(x) = c$, donde c es una constante.	$y = 3$
constant matrix (p. 279) The matrix of the constants in a linear system of equations.	**matriz de constantes** Matriz de las constantes de un sistema lineal de ecuaciones.	System of equations $\begin{cases} 2x + 3y = 11 \\ 5x - 4y = 16 \end{cases}$ Constant matrix $\begin{bmatrix} 11 \\ 16 \end{bmatrix}$
constant of variation (p. 569) The constant k in direct, inverse, joint, and combined variation equations.	**constante de variación** La constante k en ecuaciones de variación directa, inversa, conjunta y combinada.	$y = 5x$ ↑ constant of variation

ENGLISH	SPANISH	EXAMPLES
constant term (p. 28, 569) A term in a function or expression that does not contain variables.	**término constante** Término de una función o expresión que no contiene variables.	$f(x) = 3x + 5$ Constant term
constraint (p. 205) One of the inequalities that define the feasible region in a linear-programming problem.	**restricción** Una de las desigualdades que definen la región factible en un problema de programación lineal.	Constraints: $x > 0$ $y > 0$ $x + y \leq 8$ $3x + 5y \leq 30$ Feasible region
continuous data (p. 846) Data that can take on any real-value measurement within an interval.	**datos continuos** Datos obtenidos por medición que pueden asumir cualquier valor real dentro de un intervalo.	The quantity of water in a glass as the water evaporates is continuous data.
continuous function (p. 593) A function whose graph is an unbroken line or curve with no gaps or breaks.	**función continua** Función cuya gráfica es una línea recta o curva continua, sin espacios ni interrupciones.	
contradiction (p. 92) An equation that has no solutions.	**contradicción** Ecuación que no tiene soluciones.	$x + 1 = x$ $1 = 0$ ✗
converge (p. 900) An infinite series converges when the partial sums approach a fixed number.	**convergir** Una sucesión o serie infinita converge cuando las sumas parciales se aproximan a un número fijo.	$\frac{1}{2} + \frac{1}{4} + \frac{1}{8} + \frac{1}{16} + \ldots$ converges to 1.
conversion factor (p. S57) The ratio of two equal quantities, each measured in different units.	**factor de conversión** Razón entre dos cantidades iguales, cada una medida en unidades diferentes.	$\frac{12 \text{ inches}}{1 \text{ foot}}$
correlation (p. 142) A measure of the strength and direction of the relationship between two variables or data sets.	**correlación** Medida de la fuerza y dirección de la relación entre dos variables o conjuntos de datos.	Positive correlation; No correlation; Negative correlation

ENGLISH	SPANISH	EXAMPLES
correlation coefficient (p. 143) A number r, where $-1 \leq r \leq 1$, that describes how closely the points in a scatter plot cluster around the least-squares line.	**coeficiente de correlación** Número r, donde $-1 \leq r \leq 1$, que describe a qué distancia de la recta de mínimos cuadrados se agrupan los puntos de un diagrama de dispersión.	An r-value close to 1 describes a strong positive correlation. An r-value close to 0 describes a weak correlation or no correlation. An r-value close to −1 describes a strong negative correlation.
cosecant (p. 932) In a right triangle, the cosecant of angle A is the ratio of the length of the hypotenuse to the length of the side opposite A. It is the reciprocal of the sine function.	**cosecante** En un triángulo rectángulo, la cosecante del ángulo A es la razón entre la longitud de la hipotenusa y la longitud del cateto opuesto a A. Es la inversa de la función seno.	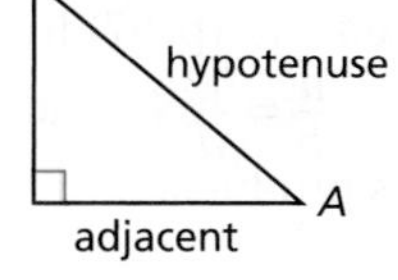 $\csc A = \frac{\text{hypotenuse}}{\text{opposite}} = \frac{1}{\sin A}$
cosine (p. 929) In a right triangle, the cosine of angle A is the ratio of the length of the side adjacent to angle A to the length of the hypotenuse. It is the reciprocal of the secant function.	**coseno** En un triángulo rectángulo, el coseno del ángulo A es la razón entre la longitud del cateto adyacente al ángulo A y la longitud de la hipotenusa. Es la inversa de la función secante.	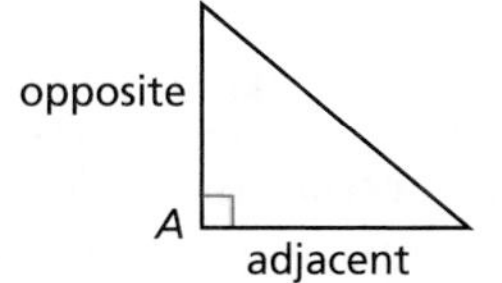 $\cos A = \frac{\text{adjacent}}{\text{hypotenuse}} = \frac{1}{\sec A}$
cotangent (p. 932) In a right triangle, the cotangent of angle A is the ratio of the length of the side adjacent to A to the length of the side opposite A. It is the reciprocal of the tangent function.	**cotangente** En un triángulo rectángulo, la cotangente del ángulo A es la razón entre la longitud del cateto adyacente a A y la longitud del cateto opuesto a A. Es la inversa de la función tangente.	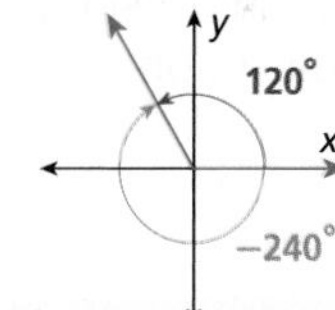 $\cot A = \frac{\text{adjacent}}{\text{opposite}} = \frac{1}{\tan A}$
coterminal angles (p. 937) Two angles in standard position with the same terminal side.	**ángulos coterminales** Dos ángulos en posición estándar con el mismo lado terminal.	
counterexample (p. 903) An example that proves that a conjecture or statement is false.	**contraejemplo** Ejemplo que demuestra que una conjetura o enunciado es falso.	
co-vertices of a hyperbola (p. 744) The endpoints of the conjugate axis.	**co-vértices de una hipérbola** Extremos de un eje conjugado.	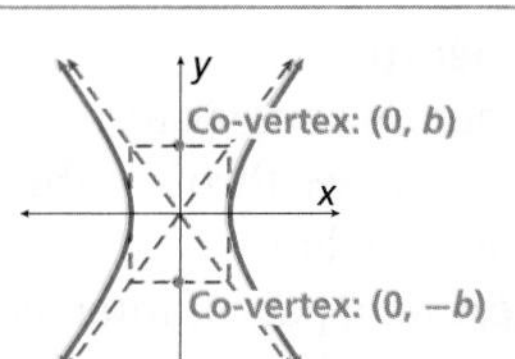
co-vertices of an ellipse (p. 736) The endpoints of the minor axis.	**co-vértices de una elipse** Extremos del eje menor.	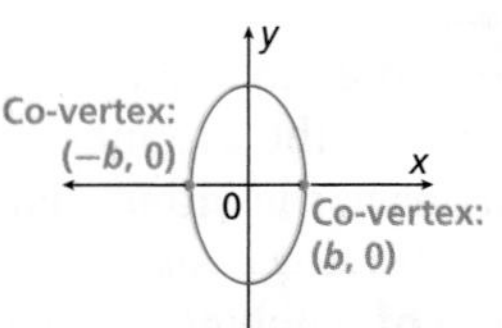

ENGLISH	SPANISH	EXAMPLES
Cramer's rule (p. 271) A method of solving systems of linear equations by using determinants.	**regla de Cramer** Método para resolver sistemas de ecuaciones lineales utilizando determinantes.	For the system $\begin{cases} x - y = 3 \\ 2x - y = -1 \end{cases}$, $D = \begin{vmatrix} 1 & -1 \\ 2 & -1 \end{vmatrix} = 1(-1) - 2(-1) = 1$ $x = \dfrac{\begin{vmatrix} c_1 & b_1 \\ c_2 & b_2 \end{vmatrix}}{D} = \dfrac{\begin{vmatrix} 3 & -1 \\ -1 & -1 \end{vmatrix}}{1} = \dfrac{-3 - 1}{1} = -4$ $y = \dfrac{\begin{vmatrix} a_1 & c_1 \\ a_2 & c_2 \end{vmatrix}}{D} = \dfrac{\begin{vmatrix} 1 & 3 \\ 2 & -1 \end{vmatrix}}{1} = \dfrac{-1 - 6}{1} = -7$
critical values (p. 367) Values that separate the number line into intervals that either contain solutions or do not contain solutions.	**valores críticos** Valores que separan la recta numérica en intervalos que contienen o no contienen soluciones.	
cross products (p. 97) In the statement $\frac{a}{b} = \frac{c}{d}$, bc and ad are the cross products.	**productos cruzados** En el enunciado $\frac{a}{b} = \frac{c}{d}$, bc y ad son los productos cruzados.	$\frac{1}{2} = \frac{3}{6}$ Cross products: $2 \cdot 3 = 6$ and $1 \cdot 6 = 6$
cube-root function (p. 619) The function $f(x) = \sqrt[3]{x}$.	**función de raíz cúbica** La función $f(x) = \sqrt[3]{x}$.	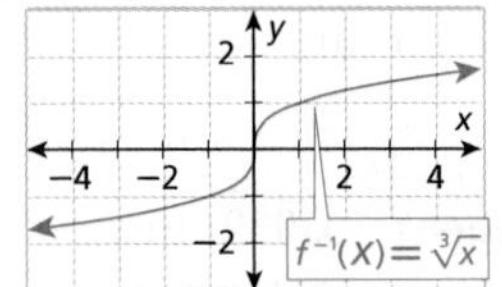
cubic function (p. 67) A polynomial function of degree 3.	**función cúbica** Función polinomial de grado 3.	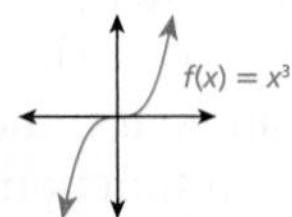
cycle of a periodic function (p. 990) The shortest repeating part of a periodic graph or function.	**ciclo de una función periódica** La parte repetida más corta de una gráfica o función periódica.	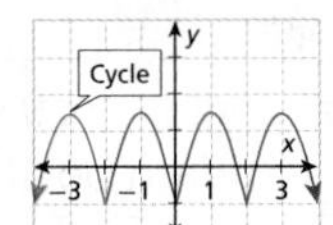

D

ENGLISH	SPANISH	EXAMPLES
decay factor (p. 481) The base $1 - r$ in an exponential expression.	**factor decremental** Base $1 - r$ en una expresión exponencial.	$2(0.93)^t$ ↑ decay factor (representing 1 − 0.07)
degenerate conic (p. 728) A degenerate conic is formed when a plane passes through the vertex of a hollow double cone. A point, a line, and a pair of intersecting lines are all degenerate conics.	**cónica degenerada** Una cónica degenerada se forma cuando un plano atraviesa el vértice de un cono doble hueco. Un punto, una línea y un par de líneas secantes son cónicas degeneradas.	A point is a circle with no radius.
degree of a monomial (p. 406) The sum of the exponents of the variables in the monomial.	**grado de un monomio** Suma de los exponentes de las variables del monomio.	$4x^2y^5z^3$ Degree: $2 + 5 + 3 = 10$ 5 Degree: 0 $(5 = 5x^0)$
degree of a polynomial (p. 406) The degree of the term of the polynomial with the greatest degree.	**grado de un polinomio** Grado del término del polinomio con el grado máximo.	$3x^2y^2 + 4xy^5 - 12x^3y^2$ Degree 6 ↑ Degree 4, ↑ Degree 6, ↑ Degree 5

ENGLISH	SPANISH	EXAMPLES
dependent events (p. 812) Events for which the occurrence or nonoccurrence of one event affects the probability of the other event.	**sucesos dependientes** Dos sucesos son dependientes si el hecho de que uno de ellos se cumpla o no afecta la probabilidad del otro.	From a bag containing 3 red marbles and 2 blue marbles, drawing a red marble, and then drawing a blue marble without replacing the first marble.
dependent system (p. 184) A system of equations that has infinitely many solutions.	**sistema dependiente** Sistema de ecuaciones que tiene infinitamente muchas soluciones.	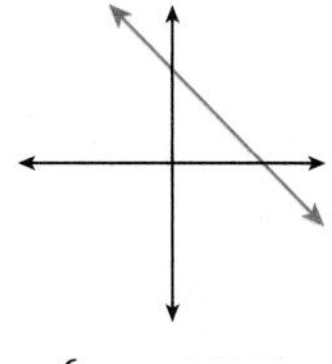 $\begin{cases} x + y = 3 \\ 2x + 2y = 6 \end{cases}$
dependent variable (p. 52) The output of a function; a variable whose value depends on the value of the input, or independent variable.	**variable dependiente** Salida de una función; variable cuyo valor depende del valor de la entrada, o variable independiente.	$y = 2x + 1$ ↑ dependent variable.
determinant (p. 270) A real number associated with a square matrix. The determinant of $A = \begin{bmatrix} a & b \\ c & d \end{bmatrix}$ is $\|A\| = ad - bc$.	**determinante** Número real asociado con una matriz cuadrada. El determinante de $A = \begin{bmatrix} a & b \\ c & d \end{bmatrix}$ es $\|A\| = ad - bc$.	$\begin{vmatrix} 2 & -1 \\ 3 & 4 \end{vmatrix} = 2(4) - (-1)(3) = 11$
difference of two squares (p. 336) A polynomial of the form $a^2 - b^2$, which may be written as the product $(a + b)(a - b)$.	**diferencia de dos cuadrados** Polinomio del tipo $a^2 - b^2$, que se puede expresar como el producto $(a + b)(a - b)$.	$x^2 - 4 = (x + 2)(x - 2)$
dimensions of a matrix (p. 246) A matrix with m rows and n columns has dimensions $m \times n$, read "m by n."	**dimensiones de una matriz** Una matriz con m filas y n columnas tiene dimensiones $m \times n$, expresadas "m por n".	$\begin{bmatrix} -3 & 2 & 1 & -1 \\ 4 & 0 & -5 & 2 \end{bmatrix}$ Dimensions 2×4
direct variation (p. 569) A linear relationship between two variables, x and y, that can be written in the form $y = kx$, where k is a nonzero constant.	**variación directa** Relación lineal entre dos variables, x e y, que puede expresarse en la forma $y = kx$, donde k es una constante distinta de cero.	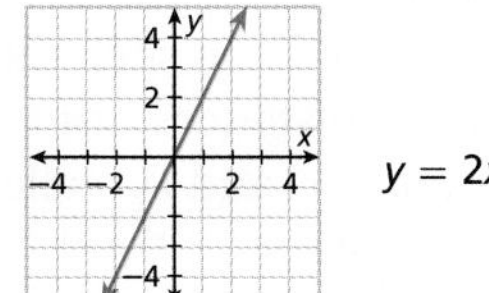 $y = 2x$
directrix (p. 751) A fixed line used to define a *parabola*. Every point on the parabola is equidistant from the directrix and a fixed point called the *focus*.	**directriz** Línea fija utilizada para definir una *parábola*. Cada punto de la parábola es equidistante de la directriz y de un punto fijo denominado *foco*.	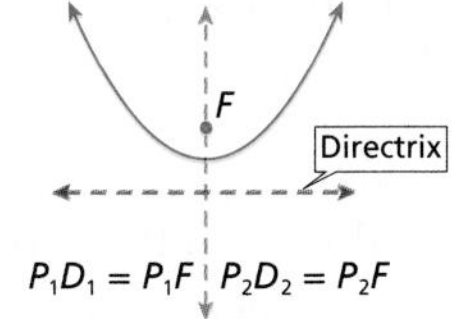
discontinuous function (p. 593) A function whose graph has one or more jumps, breaks, or holes.	**función discontinua** Función cuya gráfica tiene uno o más saltos, interrupciones u hoyos.	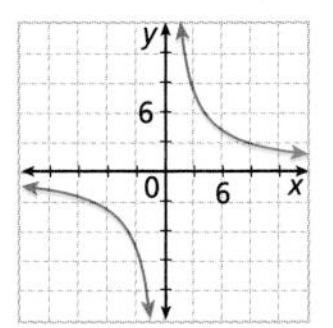
discrete data (p. 846) Data that cannot take on any real-value measurement within an interval.	**datos discretos** Datos que no admiten cualquier medida de valores reales dentro de un intervalo.	the number of pennies in a jar over time

ENGLISH	SPANISH	EXAMPLES
discriminant (p. 357) The discriminant of the quadratic equation $ax^2 + bx + c = 0$ is $b^2 - 4ac$.	**discriminante** El discriminante de la ecuación cuadrática $ax^2 + bx + c = 0$ es $b^2 - 4ac$.	The discriminant of $2x^2 - 5x - 3$ is $(-5)^2 - 4(2)(-3) = 25 + 24 = 49$.
disjunction (p. 150) A compound statement that uses the word *or*.	**disyunción** Enunciado compuesto que contiene la palabra *o*.	John will walk to work OR he will stay home.
Distance Formula (p. 724) In a coordinate plane, the distance from (x_1, y_1) to (x_2, y_2) is $d = \sqrt{(x_2 - x_1)^2 + (y_2 - y_1)^2}$.	**Fórmula de distancia** En un plano cartesiano, la distancia desde (x_1, y_1) hasta (x_2, y_2) es $d = \sqrt{(x_2 - x_1)^2 + (y_2 - y_1)^2}$.	The distance from (2, 1) to (6, 4) is $d = \sqrt{(6-2)^2 + (4-1)^2}$ $= \sqrt{4^2 + 3^2} = \sqrt{9 + 16} = 5$.
diverge (p. 900) An infinite series diverges when the partial sums do not approach a fixed number.	**divergir** Una serie infinita diverge cuando las sumas parciales no se aproximan a un número fijo.	$1 + 2 + 4 + 8 + 16 + \ldots$ diverges.
domain (p. 44) The set of all possible input values of a relation or function.	**dominio** Conjunto de todos los posibles valores de entrada de una función o relación.	The domain of the function $f(x) = \sqrt{x}$ is $\{x \mid x \geq 0\}$.

E

ENGLISH	SPANISH	EXAMPLES
element of a set (p. 6) An item in a set.	**elemento de un conjunto** Componente de un conjunto.	4 is an element of the set of even numbers. $4 \in \{\text{even numbers}\}$
elimination (p. 191) A method used to solve systems of equations in which one variable is eliminated by adding or subtracting two equations of the system.	**eliminación** Método utilizado para resolver sistemas de ecuaciones por el cual se elimina una variable sumando o restando dos ecuaciones del sistema.	
ellipse (p. 736) The set of all points *P* in a plane such that the sum of the distances from *P* to two fixed points F_1 and F_2, called the foci, is constant.	**elipse** Conjunto de todos los puntos *P* de un plano tal que la suma de las distancias desde *P* hasta los dos puntos fijos F_1 y F_2, denominados focos, es constante.	P, y, x, 0, Foci
empty set (p. 6, 153) A set with no elements.	**conjunto vacío** Conjunto sin elementos.	The solution set of $\lvert x \rvert < 0$ is the empty set, $\{\ \}$, or $\varnothing$.
end behavior (p. 453) The trends in the *y*-values of a function as the *x*-values approach positive and negative infinity.	**comportamiento extremo** Tendencia de los valores de *y* de una función a medida que los valores de *x* se aproximan al infinito positivo y negativo.	End behavior: $f(x) \to \infty$ as $x \to \infty$; $f(x) \to -\infty$ as $x \to -\infty$
entry (p. 246) Each value in a matrix; also called an element.	**entrada** Cada valor de una matriz; también denominado elemento.	3 is the entry in the first row and second column of $A = \begin{bmatrix} 2 & 3 \\ 0 & 1 \end{bmatrix}$, denoted a_{12}.

Glossary/Glosario

ENGLISH	SPANISH	EXAMPLES

equally likely outcomes (p. 802) Outcomes are equally likely if they have the same probability of occurring. If an experiment has n equally likely outcomes, then the probability of each outcome is $\frac{1}{n}$.

resultados igualmente probables Los resultados son igualmente probables si tienen la misma probabilidad de ocurrir. Si un experimento tiene n resultados igualmente probables, entonces la probabilidad de cada resultado es $\frac{1}{n}$.

If a coin is tossed, and heads and tails are equally likely, then $P(\text{heads}) = P(\text{tails}) = \frac{1}{2}$.

---

equation (p. 90) A mathematical statement that two expressions are equivalent.

ecuación Enunciado matemático que indica que dos expresiones son equivalentes.

$x + 4 = 7$
$2 + 3 = 6 - 1$
$(x - 1)^2 + (y + 2)^2 = 4$

---

evaluate (p. 28) To find the value of an algebraic expression by substituting a number for each variable and simplifying by using the order of operations.

evaluar Calcular el valor de una expresión algebraica sustituyendo cada variable por un número y simplificando mediante el orden de las operaciones.

Evaluate $2x + 7$ for $x = 3$.
$2x + 7$
$2(3) + 7$
$6 + 7$
13

---

event (p. 802) An outcome or set of outcomes in a probability experiment.

suceso Resultado o conjunto de resultados en un experimento de probabilidad.

In the experiment of rolling a number cube, the event "an odd number" consists of the outcomes 1, 3, and 5.

---

expected value (p. 828) The weighted average of the numerical outcomes of a probability experiment.

valor esperado Promedio ponderado de los resultados numéricos de un experimento de probabilidad.

The table shows the probability of getting a given score by guessing on a three-question quiz.

Score	0	1	2	3
Probability	0.42	0.42	0.14	0.02

The expected value is a score of $0(0.42) + 1(0.42) + 2(0.14) + 3(0.02) = 0.76$.

---

experiment (p. 805) An operation, process, or activity in which outcomes can be used to estimate probability.

experimento Una operación, proceso o actividad cuyo resultado se puede usar para estimar la probabilidad.

Tossing a coin 10 times and noting the number of heads.

---

experimental probability (p. 805) The ratio of the number of times an event occurs to the number of trials, or times, that an activity is performed.

probabilidad experimental Razón entre la cantidad de veces que ocurre un suceso y la cantidad de pruebas, o veces, que se realiza una actividad.

Kendra made 6 of 10 free throws. The experimental probability that she will make her next free throw is

$P(\text{free throw}) = \frac{\text{number made}}{\text{number attempted}} = \frac{6}{10}$.

---

explicit formula (p. 863) A formula that defines the nth term a_n, or general term, of a sequence as a function of n.

fórmula explícita Fórmula que define el enésimo término a_n, o término general, de una sucesión como una función de n.

Sequence: 4, 7, 10, 13, 16, 19, ...

Explicit formula: $a_n = 1 + 3n$

---

exponent (p. 34) The number that indicates how many times the base in a power is used as a factor.

exponente Número que indica la cantidad de veces que la base de una potencia se utiliza como factor.

$3^4 = 3 \cdot 3 \cdot 3 \cdot 3 = 81$
exponent

---

exponential decay (p. 490) An exponential function of the form $f(x) = ab^x$ in which $0 < b < 1$. If r is the rate of decay, then the function can be written $y = a(1 - r)^t$, where a is the initial amount and t is the time.

decremento exponencial Función exponencial del tipo $f(x) = ab^x$ en la cual $0 < b < 1$. Si r es la tasa decremental, entonces la función se puede expresar como $y = a(1 - r)^t$, donde a es la cantidad inicial y t es el tiempo.

y
x
$y = 3\left(\frac{1}{2}\right)^x$

ENGLISH	SPANISH	EXAMPLES
exponential equation (p. 522) An equation that contains one or more exponential expressions.	**ecuación exponencial** Ecuación que contiene una o más expresiones exponenciales.	$2^{x+1} = 8$
exponential function (p. 490) A function of the form $f(x) = ab^x$, where a and b are real numbers with $a \neq 0$, $b > 0$, and $b \neq 1$.	**función exponencial** Función del tipo $f(x) = ab^x$, donde a y b son números reales con $a \neq 0$, $b > 0$ y $b \neq 1$.	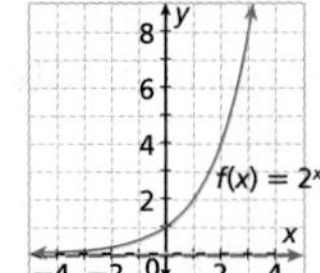
exponential growth (p. 490) An exponential function of the form $f(x) = ab^x$ in which $b > 1$. If r is the rate of growth, then the function can be written $y = a(1 + r)^t$, where a is the initial amount and t is the time.	**crecimiento exponencial** Función exponencial del tipo $f(x) = ab^x$ en la que $b > 1$. Si r es la tasa de crecimiento, entonces la función se puede expresar como $y = a(1 + r)^t$, donde a es la cantidad inicial y t es el tiempo.	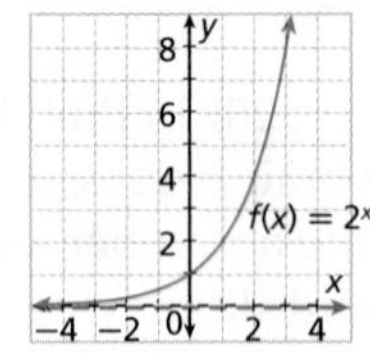
exponential regression (p. 546) A statistical method used to fit an exponential model to a given data set.	**regresión exponencial** Método estadístico utilizado para ajustar un modelo exponencial a un conjunto de datos determinado.	
extraneous solution (p. 524, 600) A solution of a derived equation that is not a solution of the original equation.	**solución extraña** Solución de una ecuación derivada que no es una solución de la ecuación original.	To solve $\sqrt{x} = -2$, square both sides; $x = 4$. ***Check*** $\sqrt{4} = -2$ is false; so 4 is an extraneous solution.

F

ENGLISH	SPANISH	EXAMPLES
Factor Theorem (p. 430) For any polynomial $P(x)$, $(x - a)$ is a factor of $P(x)$ if and only if $P(a) = 0$.	**Teorema del factor** Dado el polinomio $P(x)$, $(x - a)$ es un factor de $P(x)$ si y sólo si $P(a) = 0$.	$(x - 1)$ is a factor of $P(x) = x^2 - 1$ because $P(1) = 1^2 - 1 = 0$.
factorial (p. 795) If n is a positive integer, then n factorial, written $n!$, is $n \cdot (n-1) \cdot (n-2) \cdot \ldots \cdot 2 \cdot 1$. The factorial of 0 is defined to be 1.	**factorial** Si n es un entero positivo, entonces el factorial de n, expresado como $n!$, es $n \cdot (n-1) \cdot (n-2) \cdot \ldots \cdot 2 \cdot 1$. Por definición, el factorial de 0 será 1.	$7! = 7 \cdot 6 \cdot 5 \cdot 4 \cdot 3 \cdot 2 \cdot 1 = 5040$ $0! = 1$
factoring (p. 334) The process of writing a number or algebraic expression as a product.	**factorización** Proceso por el que se expresa un número o expresión algebraica como un producto.	$x^2 - 4x - 21 = (x - 7)(x + 3)$
family of functions (p. 67) A set of functions whose graphs have basic characteristics in common. Functions in the same family are transformations of their parent function.	**familia de funciones** Conjunto de funciones cuyas gráficas tienen características básicas en común. Las funciones de la misma familia son transformaciones de su función madre.	Some members of the family of quadratic functions with the parent function $f(x) = x^2$ are: $f(x) = 3x^2$ $f(x) = x^2 + 1$ $f(x) = (x - 2)^2$ 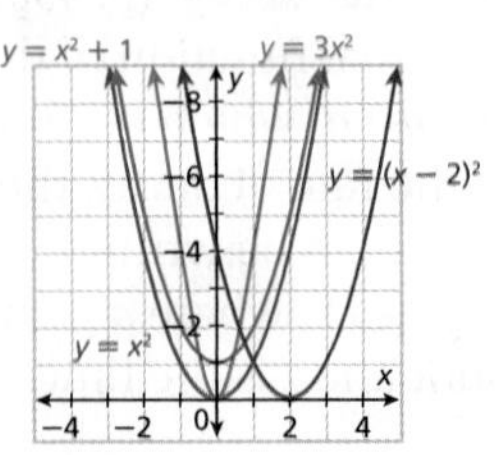

ENGLISH	SPANISH	EXAMPLES
favorable outcome (p. 802) The occurrence of one of several possible outcomes of a specified event or probability experiment.	**resultado favorable** Cuando se produce uno de varios resultados posibles de un suceso específico o experimento de probabilidad.	In the experiment of rolling an odd number on a number cube, the favorable outcomes are 1, 3, and 5.
feasible region (p. 205) The set of points that satisfy the constraints in a linear-programming problem.	**región factible** Conjunto de puntos que cumplen con las restricciones de un problema de programación lineal.	Constraints: $x > 0$, $y > 0$, $x + y \leq 8$, $3x + 5y \leq 30$ — Feasible region
Fibonacci sequence (p. 862) The infinite sequence of numbers beginning with 1, 1 such that each term is the sum of the two previous terms.	**sucesión de Fibonacci** Sucesión infinita de números que comienza con 1, 1 de forma tal que cada término es la suma de los dos términos anteriores.	1, 1, 2, 3, 5, 8, 13, 21, ...
finite sequence (p. 862) A sequence with a finite number of terms.	**sucesión finita** Sucesión con un número finito de términos.	1, 2, 3, 4, 5
finite set (p. 7) A set with a definite, or finite, number of elements.	**conjunto finito** Conjunto con un número de elementos definido o finito.	$\{2, 4, 6, 8, 10\}$
first differences (p. 105) The differences between y-values of a function for evenly spaced x-values.	**primeras diferencias** Diferencias entre los valores de y de una función para valores de x espaciados uniformemente.	x: 0, 1, 2, 3; y: 3, 7, 11, 15; first differences +4 +4 +4
first quartile (p. 829) The median of the lower half of a data set, denoted Q_1. Also called *lower quartile.*	**primer cuartil** Mediana de la mitad inferior de un conjunto de datos, expresada como Q_1. También se llama *cuartil inferior.*	Lower half: 18, (23), 28, — Upper half: 49, 36, 42 — First quartile
focus (pl. foci) of a hyperbola (p. 744) One of two fixed points F_1 and F_2 that are used to define a hyperbola. For every point P on the hyperbola, $PF_1 - PF_2$ is constant.	**foco de una hipérbola** Uno de los dos puntos fijos F_1 y F_2 utilizados para definir una hipérbola, Para cada punto P de la hipérbola, $PF_1 - PF_2$ es constante.	Focus: $(-c, 0)$; Focus: $(c, 0)$; x; y
focus (pl. foci) of an ellipse (p. 736) One of two fixed points F_1 and F_2 that are used to define an ellipse. For every point P on the ellipse, $PF_1 + PF_2$ is constant.	**foco de una elipse** Uno de los dos puntos fijos F_1 y F_2 utilizados para definir una elipse. Para cada punto P de la elipse, $PF_1 + PF_2$ es constante.	Focus: $(0, c)$; Focus: $(0, -c)$; 0; x; y
focus (pl. foci) of a parabola (p. 751) A fixed point F used with a *directrix* to define a *parabola.*	**foco de una parábola** Punto fijo F utilizado con una *directriz* para definir una *parábola.*	Focus; F
frequency of a data value (p. 828) The number of times the value appears in the data set.	**frecuencia de un valor de datos** Cantidad de veces que aparece el valor en un conjunto de datos.	In the data set 5, 6, 6, 6, 8, 9, the data value 6 has a frequency of 3.

Glossary/Glosario

ENGLISH	SPANISH	EXAMPLES
frequency of a periodic function (p. 992) The number of cycles per unit of time. Also the reciprocal of the period.	**frecuencia de una función periódica** Cantidad de ciclos por unidad de tiempo. También es la inversa del periodo.	The function $y = \sin(2x)$ has a period of π and a frequency of $\frac{1}{\pi}$.
function (p. 45) A relation in which every input is paired with exactly one output.	**función** Una relación en la que cada entrada corresponde exactamente a una salida.	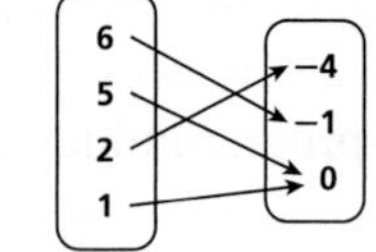
function notation (p. 51) If x is the independent variable and y is the dependent variable, then the function notation for y is $f(x)$, read "f of x," where f names the function.	**notación de función** Si x es la variable independiente e y es la variable dependiente, entonces la notación de función para y es $f(x)$, que se lee "f de x", donde f nombra la función.	equation: $y = 2x$ function notation: $f(x) = 2x$
function rule (p. 53) An algebraic expression that defines a function.	**regla de función** Expresión algebraica que define una función.	$f(x) = 2x^2 + 3x - 7$ ↑ function rule
Fundamental Counting Principle (p. 794) For n items, if there are m_1 ways to choose a first item, m_2 ways to choose a second item after the first item has been chosen, and so on, then there are $m_1 \cdot m_2 \cdot \ldots \cdot m_n$ ways to choose n items.	**Principio fundamental de conteo** Dados n elementos, si existen m_1 formas de elegir un primer elemento, m_2 formas de elegir un segundo elemento después de haber elegido el primero, y así sucesivamente, entonces existen $m_1 \cdot m_2 \cdot \ldots \cdot m_n$ formas de elegir n elementos.	If there are 4 colors of shirts, 3 colors of pants, and 2 colors of shoes, then there are $4 \cdot 3 \cdot 2 = 24$ possible outfits.

ENGLISH	SPANISH	EXAMPLES
general form of a conic section (p. 761) $Ax^2 + Bxy + Cy^2 + Dx + Ey + F = 0$, where A and B are not both 0.	**forma general de una sección cónica** $Ax^2 + Bxy + Cy^2 + Dx + Ey + F = 0$, donde A y B no son los dos 0.	A circle with a vertex at $(1, 2)$ and radius 3 has the general form $x^2 + y^2 - 2x - 4y - 4 = 0$.
geometric mean (p. 892) In a geometric sequence, a term that comes between two given nonconsecutive terms of the sequence. For positive numbers a and b, the geometric mean is $\sqrt{ab}$.	**media geométrica** En una sucesión geométrica, un término que se encuentra entre dos términos no consecutivos dados de la sucesión. Dados los números positivos a y b, la media geométrica es $\sqrt{ab}$.	The geometric mean of 4 and 9 is $\sqrt{4(9)} = \sqrt{36} = 6$.
geometric probability (p. 804) A form of theoretical probability determined by a ratio of geometric measures such as lengths, areas, or volumes.	**probabilidad geométrica** Una forma de la probabilidad teórica determinada por una razón de medidas geométricas, como longitud, área o volumen.	 The probability of the pointer landing on red is $\frac{2}{9}$.

Glossary/Glosario

ENGLISH	SPANISH	EXAMPLES
geometric sequence (p. 890) A sequence in which the ratio of successive terms is a constant r, called the common ratio, where $r \neq 0$ and $r \neq 1$.	**sucesión geométrica** Sucesión en la que la razón de los términos sucesivos es una constante r, denominada razón común, donde $r \neq 0$ y $r \neq 1$.	1, 2, 4, 8, 16, ... $\cdot 2$ $\cdot 2$ $\cdot 2$ $\cdot 2$ $r = 2$
geometric series (p. 893) The indicated sum of the terms of a geometric sequence.	**serie geométrica** Suma indicada de los términos de una sucesión geométrica.	$1 + 2 + 4 + 8 + 16 + \dots$
glide reflection (p. 261) A composition of a translation and a reflection across a line parallel to the translation vector.	**deslizamiento con inversión** Composición de una traslación y una reflexión sobre una línea paralela al vector de traslación.	$\vec{v}$ First translate the preimage along $\vec{v}$. J K L ℓ K′ L′ J′ Then reflect the image across line ℓ.
grade (p. 102) A measure of the steepness of surfaces, expressed as a percent.	**grado** Medida de la inclinación de las superficies, expresada como un porcentaje.	A ramp that rises 1 foot for every 5 feet of the horizontal distance has a grade of 20%.
greatest common factor (GCF) (p. 331) The product of the greatest integer and the greatest power of each variable that divides evenly into each term.	**máximo común divisor (MCD)** Producto del entero mayor y la potencia mayor de cada variable que divide exactamente cada término.	The GCF of $4x^3y$ and $6x^2y$ is $2x^2y$. The GCF of 27 and 45 is 9.
greatest-integer function (p. 669) A function denoted by $f(x) = [x]$ or $f(x) = \lfloor x \rfloor$ in which the number x is rounded down to the greatest integer that is less than or equal to x.	**función de entero mayor** Función expresada como $f(x) = [x]$ o $f(x) = \lfloor x \rfloor$ en la cual el número x se redondea hacia abajo hasta el entero mayor que sea menor que o igual a x.	$\lfloor 4.98 \rfloor = 4$ $\lfloor -2.1 \rfloor = -3$
growth factor (p. 491) The base $1 + r$ in an exponential expression.	**factor de crecimiento** La base $1 + r$ en una expresión exponencial.	$12{,}000(1 + 0.14)^t$ growth factor

ENGLISH	SPANISH	EXAMPLES
half-life (p. 532) The half-life of a substance is the time it takes for one-half of the substance to decay into another substance.	**vida media** La vida media de una sustancia es el tiempo que tarda la mitad de la sustancia en desintegrarse y transformarse en otra sustancia.	Carbon-14 has a half-life of 5730 years, so 5 g of an initial amount of 10 g will remain after 5730 years.
half-plane (p. 124) The part of the coordinate plane on one side of a line, which may include the line.	**semiplano** Parte del plano cartesiano de un lado de una línea, que puede incluir la línea.	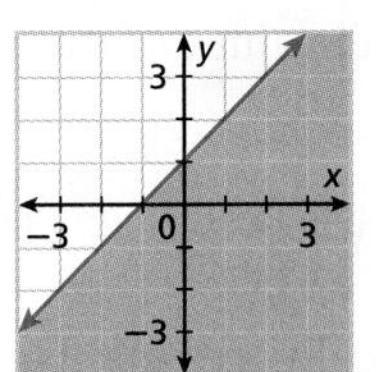

ENGLISH	SPANISH	EXAMPLES
Heron's Formula (p. 969) A triangle with side lengths a, b, and c has area $A = \sqrt{s(s-a)(s-b)(s-c)}$, where s is one-half the perimeter, or $s = \frac{1}{2}(a+b+c)$.	**fórmula de Herón** Un triángulo con longitudes de lado a, b y c tiene un área $A = \sqrt{s(s-a)(s-b)(s-c)}$, donde s es la mitad del perímetro ó $s = \frac{1}{2}(a+b+c)$.	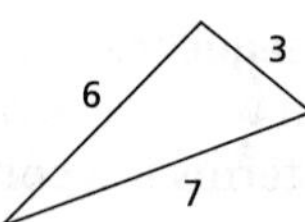 $s = \frac{1}{2}(3+6+7) = 8$ $A = \sqrt{8(8-3)(8-6)(8-7)}$ $= \sqrt{80} = 4\sqrt{5}$ square units
hole (in a graph) (p. 596) An omitted point on a graph. If a rational function has the same factor $x - b$ in both the numerator and the denominator, and the line $x = b$ is not a vertical asymptote, then there is a hole in the graph at the point where $x = b$.	**hoyo (en una gráfica)** Punto omitido en una gráfica. Si una función racional tiene el mismo factor $x - b$ tanto en el numerador como en el denominador, y la línea $x = b$ no es una asíntota vertical, entonces hay un hoyo en la gráfica en el punto donde $x = b$.	$f(x) = \frac{(x-2)(x+2)}{(x+2)}$ has a hole at $x = -2$. 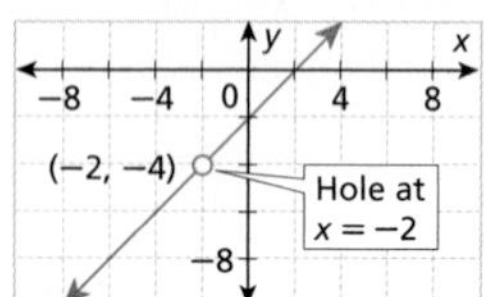
horizontal line (p. 108) A line described by the equation $y = b$, where b is the y-intercept.	**línea horizontal** Línea descrita por la ecuación $y = b$, donde b es la intersección con el eje y.	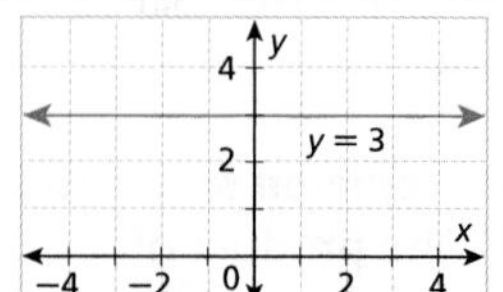
horizontal line test (p. 690) If a horizontal line crosses the graph of a function f at more than one point, then the inverse is not a function.	**prueba de la línea horizontal** Si una línea horizontal cruza la gráfica de una función f en más de un punto, entonces la inversa no es una función.	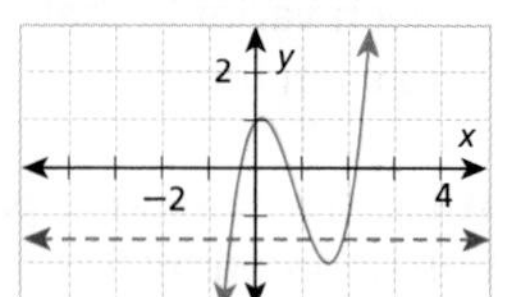 The inverse is not a function.
hyperbola (p. 744) The set of all points P in a plane such that the difference of the distances from P to two fixed points F_1 and F_2, called the foci, is a constant $d = \lvert PF_1 - PF_2 \rvert$.	**hipérbola** Conjunto de todos los puntos P en un plano tal que la diferencia de las distancias de P a dos puntos fijos F_1 y F_2, llamados focos, es una constante $d = \lvert PF_1 - PF_2 \rvert$.	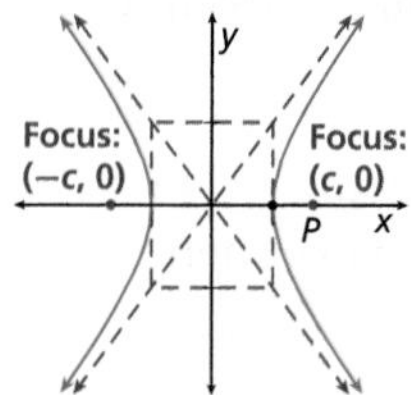
hypotenuse (p. 20) The side opposite the right angle in a right triangle.	**hipotenusa** Lado opuesto al ángulo recto de un triángulo rectángulo.	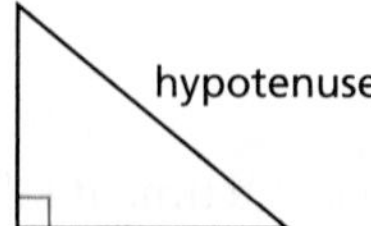

I

ENGLISH	SPANISH	EXAMPLES
identity (p. 92) An equation that is true for all values of the variables.	**identidad** Ecuación verdadera para todos los valores de las variables.	$3 = 3$ $2(x-1) = 2x - 2$
imaginary axis (p. 382) The vertical axis in the complex plane, it graphically represents the purely imaginary part of complex numbers.	**eje imaginario** Eje vertical de un plano complejo. Representa gráficamente la parte puramente imaginaria de los números complejos.	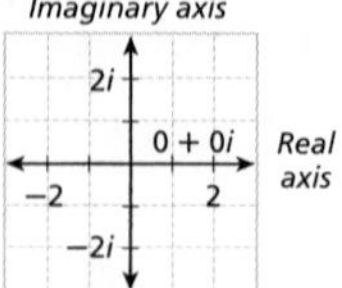

ENGLISH	SPANISH	EXAMPLES
imaginary number (p. 350) The square root of a negative number, written in the form *bi*, where *b* is a real number and *i* is the imaginary unit, $\sqrt{-1}$. Also called a *pure imaginary number*.	**número imaginario** Raíz cuadrada de un número negativo, expresado como *bi*, donde *b* es un número real e *i* es la unidad imaginaria, $\sqrt{-1}$. También se denomina *número imaginario puro*.	$\sqrt{-16} = \sqrt{16} \cdot \sqrt{-1} = 4i$
imaginary part of a complex number (p. 351) For a complex number of the form $a + bi$, the real number *b* is called the imaginary part, represented graphically as *b* units on the imaginary axis of a complex plane.	**parte imaginaria de un número complejo** Dado un número complejo del tipo $a + bi$, el número real *b* se denomina parte imaginaria y se representa gráficamente como *b* unidades en el eje imaginario de un plano complejo.	$5 + 6i$ real part → 5; imaginary part → $6i$
imaginary unit (p. 350) The unit in the imaginary number system, $\sqrt{-1}$.	**unidad imaginaria** Unidad del sistema de números imaginarios, $\sqrt{-1}$.	$\sqrt{-1} = i$
inclusive events (p. 820) Events that have one or more outcomes in common.	**sucesos inclusivos** Sucesos que tienen uno o más resultados en común.	In the experiment of rolling a number cube, rolling an even number and rolling a number less than 3 are inclusive events because the outcome 2 is both even and less than 3.
inconsistent system (p. 183) A system of equations or inequalities that has no solution.	**sistema inconsistente** Sistema de ecuaciones o desigualdades que no tiene solución.	$\begin{cases} y = 2.5x + 5 \\ y = 2.5x - 5 \end{cases}$ is inconsistent.
independent events (p. 811) Events for which the occurrence or non-occurrence of one event does not affect the probability of the other event.	**sucesos independientes** Dos sucesos son independientes si el hecho de que se produzca o no uno de ellos no afecta la probabilidad del otro suceso.	From a bag containing 3 red marbles and 2 blue marbles, drawing a red marble, replacing it, and then drawing a blue marble.
independent system (p. 184) A system of equations that has exactly one solution.	**sistema independiente** Sistema de ecuaciones que tiene exactamente una solución.	$\begin{cases} y = -x + 4 \\ y = x + 2 \end{cases}$ Solution: (1, 3)
independent variable (p. 52) The input of a function; a variable whose value determines the value of the output, or dependent variable.	**variable independiente** Entrada de una función; variable cuyo valor determina el valor de la salida, o variable dependiente.	$y = 2x + 1$ independent variable → x
index (p. 610) In the radical $\sqrt[n]{x}$, which represents the *n*th root of *x*, *n* is the index. In the radical $\sqrt{x}$, the index is understood to be 2.	**índice** En el radical $\sqrt[n]{x}$, que representa la enésima raíz de *x*, *n* es el índice. En el radical $\sqrt{x}$, se da por sentado que el índice es 2.	The radical $\sqrt[3]{8}$ has an index of 3.

ENGLISH	SPANISH	EXAMPLES
indirect measurement (p. 99) A method of measurement that uses formulas, similar figures, and/or proportions.	**medición indirecta** Método para medir objetos mediante fórmulas, figuras semejantes y/o proporciones.	
inequality (p. 92) A statement that compares two expressions by using one of the following signs: $<, >, \le, \ge$, or $\ne$.	**desigualdad** Enunciado que compara dos expresiones utilizando uno de los siguientes signos: $<, >, \le, \ge$, ó $\ne$.	−4 −3 −2 −1 0 1 2 $x \ge -2$
infinite geometric series (p. 900) A geometric series with infinitely many terms.	**serie geométrica infinita** Serie geométrica con una cantidad infinita de términos.	$\frac{1}{10} + \frac{1}{100} + \frac{1}{1000} + \frac{1}{10,000} + \dots$
infinite sequence (p. 862) A sequence with infinitely many terms.	**sucesión infinita** Sucesión con infinitos términos.	1, 3, 5, 7, 9, 11, ...
infinite set (p. 7) A set with an unlimited, or infinite, number of elements.	**conjunto infinito** Conjunto con un número de elementos ilimitado o infinito.	The set of all integers is an infinite set.
initial side (p. 936) The ray that lies on the positive x-axis when an angle is drawn in standard position.	**lado inicial** El rayo que se encuentra en el eje positivo x cuando se traza un ángulo en la posición estándar.	
integer (p. 6) A member of the set of whole numbers and their opposites.	**entero** Miembro del conjunto de números cabales y sus opuestos.	... −3, −2, −1, 0, 1, 2, 3 ...
interquartile range (IQR) (p. 829) The difference of the third (upper) and first (lower) quartiles in a data set, representing the middle half of the data.	**rango entre cuartiles** Diferencia entre el tercer cuartil (superior) y el primer cuartil (inferior) de un conjunto de datos, que representa la mitad central de los datos.	Lower half Upper half 18, (23), 28, | 29, (36), 42 First quartile Third quartile Interquartile range: 36 − 23 = 13.
interval notation (p. 7) A way of writing the set of all real numbers between two endpoints. The symbols [and] are used to include an endpoint in an interval, and the symbols (and) are used to exclude an endpoint from an interval.	**notación de intervalo** Forma de expresar el conjunto de todos los números reales entre dos extremos. Los símbolos [y] se utilizan para incluir un extremo en un intervalo y los símbolos (y) se utilizan para excluir un extremo de un intervalo.	Interval notation — Set-builder notation (a, b) — $\{x \mid a < x < b\}$ $(a, b]$ — $\{x \mid a < x \le b\}$ $[a, b)$ — $\{x \mid a \le x < b\}$ $[a, b]$ — $\{x \mid a \le x \le b\}$
inverse cosine function (p. 951) If the domain of the cosine function is restricted to $[0, \pi]$, then the function $\text{Cos}\,\theta = a$ has an inverse function $\text{Cos}^{-1} a = \theta$, also called *arccosine*.	**función coseno inverso** Si el dominio de la función coseno se restringe a $[0, \pi]$, entonces la función $\text{Cos}\,\theta = a$ tiene una función inversa $\text{Cos}^{-1} a = \theta$, también llamada *arco coseno*.	$\text{Cos}^{-1}\frac{1}{2} = \frac{\pi}{3}$

Glossary/Glosario

ENGLISH	SPANISH	EXAMPLES
inverse function (p. 499) The function that results from exchanging the input and output values of a one-to-one function. The inverse of $f(x)$ is denoted $f^{-1}(x)$.	**función inversa** Función que resulta de intercambiar los valores de entrada y salida de una función uno a uno. La función inversa de $f(x)$ se expresa $f^{-1}(x)$.	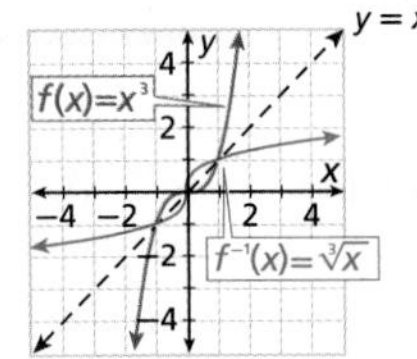
inverse relation (p. 498) The inverse of the relation consisting of all ordered pairs (x, y) is the set of all ordered pairs (y, x). The graph of an inverse relation is the reflection of the graph of the relation across the line $y = x$.	**relación inversa** La inversa de la relación que consta de todos los pares ordenados (x, y) es el conjunto de todos los pares ordenados (y, x). La gráfica de una relación inversa es el reflejo de la gráfica de la relación sobre la línea $y = x$.	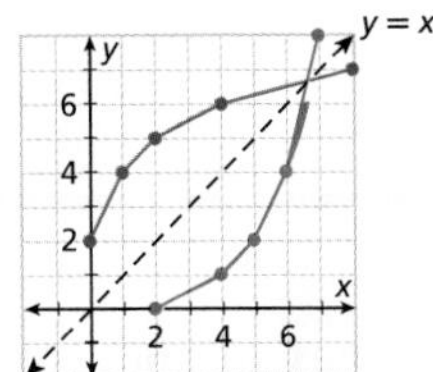
inverse sine function (p. 951) If the domain of the sine function is restricted to $\left[-\frac{\pi}{2}, \frac{\pi}{2}\right]$, then the function $\text{Sin}\,\theta = a$ has an inverse function, $\text{Sin}^{-1} a = \theta$, also called *arcsine.*	**función seno inverso** Si el dominio de la función seno se restringe a $\left[-\frac{\pi}{2}, \frac{\pi}{2}\right]$, entonces la función $\text{Sen}\,\theta = a$ tiene una función inversa, $\text{Sen}^{-1} a = \theta$, también llamada *arco seno.*	$\text{Sin}^{-1}\frac{\sqrt{3}}{2} = \frac{\pi}{3}$
inverse tangent function (p. 951) If the domain of the tangent function is restricted to $\left(-\frac{\pi}{2}, \frac{\pi}{2}\right)$, then the function $\text{Tan}\theta = a$ has an inverse function, $\text{Tan}^{-1} a = \theta$, also called *arctangent.*	**función tangente inversa** Si el dominio de la función tangente se restringe a $\left(-\frac{\pi}{2}, \frac{\pi}{2}\right)$, entonces la función $\text{Tan}\theta = a$ tiene una función inversa, $\text{Tan}^{-1} a = \theta$, también llamada *arco tangente.*	$\text{Tan}^{-1}\sqrt{3} = \frac{\pi}{3}$
inverse variation (p. 570) A relationship between two variables, x and y, that can be written in the form $y = \frac{k}{x}$, where k is a nonzero constant and $x \neq 0$.	**variación inversa** Relación entre dos variables, x e y, que puede expresarse en la forma $y = \frac{k}{x}$, donde k es una constante distinta de cero y $x \neq 0$.	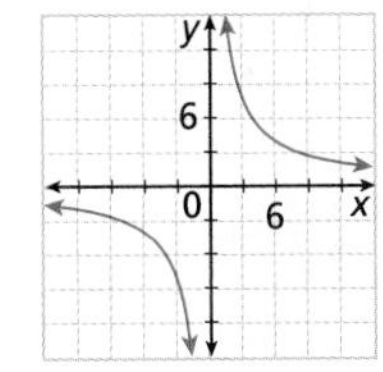 $y = \frac{24}{x}$
irrational number (p. 6) A real number that cannot be expressed as the ratio of two integers.	**número irracional** Número real que no se puede expresar como una razón de enteros.	$\sqrt{2}$, π, e
iteration (p. 864) The repetitive application of the same rule.	**iteración** Aplicación repetitiva de la misma regla.	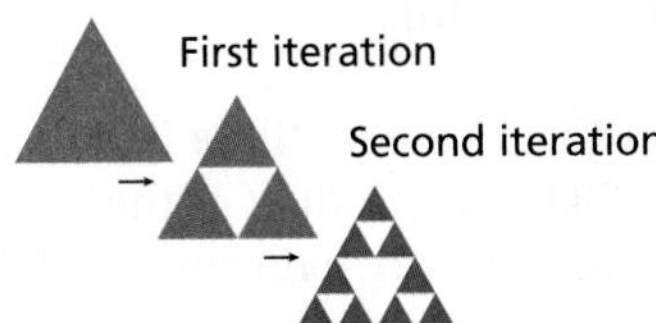

ENGLISH	SPANISH	EXAMPLES

joint variation (p. 570) A relationship among three variables that can be written in the form $y = kxz$, where k is a nonzero constant.	**variación conjunta** Relación entre tres variables que se puede expresar de la forma $y = kxz$, donde k es una constante distinta de cero.	$y = 3xz$

Law of Cosines (p. 966) For $\triangle ABC$ with side lengths a, b, and c, $a^2 = b^2 + c^2 - 2bc \cos A$ $b^2 = a^2 + c^2 - 2ac \cos B$ $c^2 = a^2 + b^2 - 2ab \cos C$.	**Ley de cosenos** Dado $\triangle ABC$ con longitudes de lado a, b y c, $a^2 = b^2 + c^2 - 2bc \cos A$ $b^2 = a^2 + c^2 - 2ac \cos B$ $c^2 = a^2 + b^2 - 2ab \cos C$.	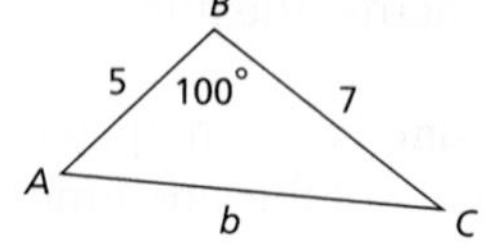 $b^2 = 7^2 + 5^2 - 2(7)(5) \cos 100°$ $b^2 \approx 86.2$ $b \approx 9.3$
law of large numbers (p. 809) The tendency of experimental probability to approach theoretical probability as the number of trials gets very large.	**Ley de los números grandes** Tendencia de la probabilidad experimental a acercarse a la probabilidad teórica cuando el número de pruebas es muy grande.	The more times you toss a coin, the closer the experimental probability will be to $\frac{1}{2}$.
Law of Sines (p. 959) For $\triangle ABC$ with side lengths a, b, and c, $\frac{\sin A}{a} = \frac{\sin B}{b} = \frac{\sin C}{c}$.	**Ley de senos** Dado $\triangle ABC$ con longitudes de lado a, b y c, $\frac{\text{sen } A}{a} = \frac{\text{sen } B}{b} = \frac{\text{sen } C}{c}$.	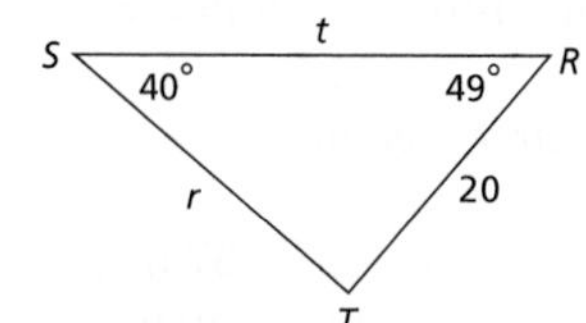 $\frac{\sin 49°}{r} = \frac{\sin 40°}{20}$ $r = \frac{20 \sin 49°}{\sin 40°} \approx 23.5$
leading coefficient (p. 406) The coefficient of the first term of a polynomial in standard form.	**coeficiente principal** Coeficiente del primer término de un polinomio en forma estándar.	$3x^2 + 7x - 2$ ↑ Leading coefficient
least common denominator (LCD) (p. 583) The least common multiple of two or more given denominators.	**mínimo común denominador (mcd)** Mínimo común múltiplo de dos o más denominadores dados.	The LCD of $\frac{3}{4}$ and $\frac{5}{6}$ is 12.
least common multiple (LCM) (p. 583) The product of the smallest positive number and the lowest power of each variable that divides evenly into each term.	**mínimo común múltiplo (mcm)** El producto del número positivo más pequeño y la potencia más baja de cada variable que divide exactamente cada término.	The LCM of 10 and 18 is 90. The LCM of $2x^2$ *and* $5x^3$ *is* $10x^3$.
leg of a right triangle (p. 20) One of the two sides of the right triangle that form the right angle.	**cateto de un triángulo rectángulo** Uno de los dos lados de un triángulo rectángulo que forman el ángulo recto.	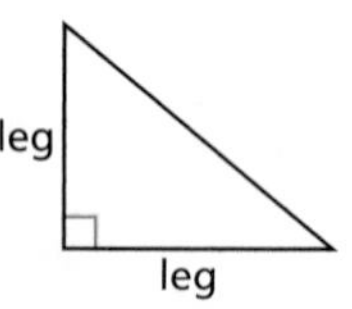

ENGLISH	SPANISH	EXAMPLES
like radical terms (p. 23) Radical terms having the same radicand and index.	**radicales semejantes** Términos radicales que tienen el mismo radicando e índice.	$3\sqrt{2x}$ and $\sqrt{2x}$ Like radicals $\sqrt{3x}$ and $\sqrt{2x}$ Unlike radicals
like terms (p. 28) Terms with the same variables raised to the same exponents.	**términos semejantes** Términos con las mismas variables elevadas a los mismos exponentes.	$3a^3b^2$ and $7a^3b^2$ Like terms $4xy^2$ and $6x^2y$ Unlike terms
limit (p. 900) A number (or infinity) that the terms of an infinite sequence or series approach as the term number increases.	**límite** Número (o infinito) al que se aproximan los términos de una sucesión o serie infinita a medida que aumenta el número de términos.	The series $\frac{1}{2}+\frac{1}{4}+\frac{1}{8}+\frac{1}{16}+\dots$ has a limit of 1.
line of best fit (p. 142) The line that comes closest to all of the points in a data set.	**línea de mejor ajuste** Línea que más se acerca a todos los puntos de un conjunto de datos.	150, 120, 90, 60, 30, 0, 30, 60, 90, 120, 150
linear equation in one variable (p. 90) An equation that can be written in the form $ax = b$, where a and b are constants and $a \neq 0$.	**ecuación lineal en una variable** Ecuación que puede expresarse en la forma $ax = b$, donde a y b son constantes y $a \neq 0$.	$x + 1 = 7$
linear function (p. 105) A function that can be written in the form $f(x) = mx + b$, where x is the independent variable and m and b are real numbers. Its graph is a line.	**función lineal** Función que puede expresarse en la forma $f(x) = mx + b$, donde x es la variable independiente y m y b son números reales. Su gráfica es una línea.	$y=\frac{2}{3}x-2$; y; x; 4, 2, 0, −2, 4, 6, −4
linear inequality in two variables (p. 124) An inequality that can be written in one of the following forms: $y < mx + b$, $y > mx + b$, $y \leq mx + b$, $y \geq mx + b$, or $y \neq mx + b$, where m and b are real numbers.	**desigualdad lineal en dos variables** Desiqualdad que puede expresarse de una de las siguientes formas: $y < mx + b$, $y > mx + b$, $y \leq mx + b$, $y \geq mx + b$, o $y \neq mx + b$, donde m y b son números reales.	$2x + 3y \leq 6$ $y > \frac{1}{2}x - 7$
linear programming (p. 205) A method of finding a maximum or minimum value of a linear function, called the *objective function*, that satisfies a given set of conditions, called *constraints*.	**programación lineal** Método para calcular un valor máximo o mínimo de una función lineal, denominada *función objetiva*, que cumple con una serie dada de condiciones, denominadas *restricciones*.	Constraints $\begin{cases} x \geq 0 \\ 40x + 60y \leq 1440 \\ y \geq \frac{1}{3}x \\ y \leq 16 \end{cases}$ Feasible Region: 30, 20, 10, 0, 10, 20, 30; (12, 16), (24, 8), (0, 16), (0, 0) For the given constraints, the objective function $P = 18x + 25y$ is maximized at (24, 8).
linear regression (p. 143) A statistical method used to fit a linear model to a given data set.	**regresión lineal** Método estadístico utilizado para ajustar un modelo lineal a un conjunto de datos determinado.	LinReg y=ax+b a=2.753883892 b=71.97383483 r²=.9825297615 r=.9912263927

Glossary/Glosario

ENGLISH	SPANISH	EXAMPLES
linear system (p. 182) A system of equations containing only linear equations.	**sistema lineal** Sistema de ecuaciones que contiene sólo ecuaciones lineales.	$\begin{cases} y = 2x + 1 \\ x + y = 8 \end{cases}$
local maximum (p. 455) For a function *f*, *f*(*a*) is a local maximum if there is an interval around *a* such that $f(x) < f(a)$ for every *x*-value in the interval except *a*.	**máximo local** Dada una función *f*, *f*(*a*) es el máximo local si hay un intervalo en *a* tal que $f(x) < f(a)$ para cada valor de *x* en el intervalo excepto *a*.	Local maximum
local minimum (p. 455) For a function *f*, *f*(*a*) is a local minimum if there is an interval around *a* such that $f(x) > f(a)$ for every *x*-value in the interval except *a*.	**mínimo local** Dada una función *f*, *f*(*a*) es el mínimo local si hay un intervalo en *a* tal que $f(x) > f(a)$ para cada valor de *x* en el intervalo excepto *a*.	Local minimum
logarithm (p. 505) The exponent that a specified base must be raised to in order to get a certain value.	**logaritmo** Exponente al cual debe elevarse una base determinada a fin de obtener cierto valor.	$\log_2 8 = 3$, because 3 is the power that 2 is raised to in order to get 8; or $2^3 = 8$.
logarithmic equation (p. 523) An equation that contains a logarithm of a variable.	**ecuación logarítmica** Ecuación que contiene un logaritmo de una variable.	$\log x + 3 = 7$
logarithmic function (p. 507) A function of the form $f(x) = \log_b x$, where $b \neq 1$ and $b > 0$, which is the inverse of the exponential function $f(x) = b^x$.	**función logarítmica** Función del tipo $f(x) = \log_b x$, donde $b \neq 1$ y $b > 0$, que es la inversa de la función exponencial $f(x) = b^x$.	$f(x) = \log_4 x$
logarithmic regression (p. 546) A statistical method used to fit a logarithmic model to a given data set.	**regresión logarítmica** Método estadístico utilizado para ajustar un modelo logarítmico a un conjunto de datos determinado.	LnReg y=a+blnx a=2.003115892 b=.2904046914 r²=.9999625511 r=.9999812754
logistic function (p. 535) An exponential growth function that tapers off at an asymptote.	**función logística** Función de crecimiento exponencial que disminuye en una asíntota.	

M

ENGLISH	SPANISH	EXAMPLES
main diagonal (of a matrix) (p. 255) The diagonal from the upper left corner to the lower right corner of a matrix.	**diagonal principal (de una matriz)** Diagonal que se extiende desde la esquina superior izquierda hasta la esquina inferior derecha de una matriz.	$\begin{bmatrix} 3 & 1 & 2 \\ 5 & 0 & 1 \\ 2 & 7 & 6 \end{bmatrix}$
major axis (p. 736) The longer axis of an ellipse. The foci of the ellipse are located on the major axis, and its endpoints are the *vertices of the ellipse*.	**eje mayor** El eje más largo de una elipse. Los focos de la elipse se encuentran sobre el eje mayor y sus extremos son los *vértices de la elipse*.	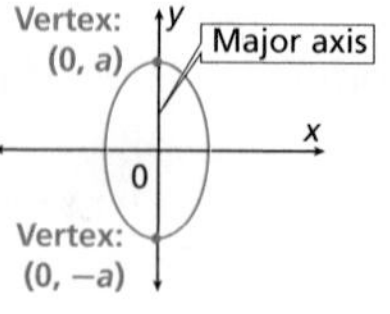

Glossary/Glosario

ENGLISH	SPANISH	EXAMPLES
mapping diagram (p. 44) A diagram that shows the relationship of elements in the domain to elements in the range of a relation or function.	**diagrama de correspondencia** Diagrama que muestra la relación entre los elementos del dominio y los elementos del rango de una función.	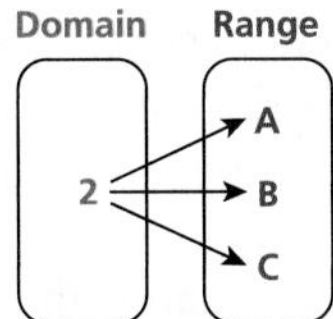
mathematical induction (p. 902) A type of mathematical proof. To prove that a statement is true for all natural numbers n, first show that the statement is true for $n = 1$; then assume it is true for some number k and prove that it is true for $k + 1$. It follows that the statement is true for all values of n.	**inducción matemática** Tipo de demostración matemática. Para demostrar que un enunciado se cumple para todos los números naturales n, primero se demuestra que el enunciado se cumple para $n = 1$; luego se supone que se cumple para un número k y se demuestra que se cumple para $k + 1$. Por lo tanto, el enunciado se cumplirá para todos los valores de n.	
matrix (p. 246) A rectangular array of numbers.	**matriz** Arreglo rectangular de números.	$\begin{bmatrix} 1 & 0 & 3 \\ -2 & 2 & -5 \\ 7 & -6 & 3 \end{bmatrix}$
matrix equation (p. 279) An equation of the form $AX = B$, where A is the coefficient matrix, X is the variable matrix, and B is the constant matrix of a system of equations.	**ecuación matricial** Ecuación del tipo $AX = B$, donde A es la matriz de coeficientes, X es la matriz de variables y B es la matriz de constantes de un sistema de ecuaciones.	System of equations: $\begin{matrix} 2x + 3y = 7 \\ 4x - 6y = 5 \end{matrix}$ Matrix equation: $\begin{bmatrix} 2 & 3 \\ 4 & -6 \end{bmatrix}\begin{bmatrix} x \\ y \end{bmatrix} = \begin{bmatrix} 7 \\ 5 \end{bmatrix}$
matrix product (p. 253) The product of two matrices, where each entry in P_{ij} is the sum of the products of consecutive entries in row i in matrix A and column j in matrix B.	**producto matricial** Producto de dos matrices, donde cada entrada de P_{ij} es la suma de los productos de las entradas consecutivas de la fila i de la matriz A y de la columna j de la matriz B.	$\begin{bmatrix} 1 & 2 \\ 3 & 4 \end{bmatrix}\begin{bmatrix} 5 & 6 \\ 7 & 8 \end{bmatrix} = \begin{bmatrix} 1(5) + 2(7) & 1(6) + 2(8) \\ 3(5) + 4(7) & 3(6) + 4(8) \end{bmatrix}$ $= \begin{bmatrix} 19 & 22 \\ 43 & 50 \end{bmatrix}$
maximum value of a function (p. 326) The y-value of the highest point on the graph of the function.	**máximo de una función** Valor de y del punto más alto en la gráfica de la función.	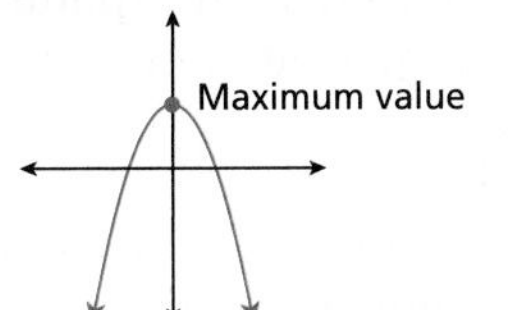
mean (p. 828) The sum of all the values in a data set divided by the number of data values. Also called the *average*.	**media** Suma de todos los valores de un conjunto de datos dividida entre el número de valores de datos. También llamada *promedio*.	Data set: 4, 6, 7, 8, 10 Mean: $\frac{4 + 6 + 7 + 8 + 10}{5} = \frac{35}{5} = 7$
measure of central tendency (p. 828) A measure that describes the center of a data set.	**medida de tendencia dominante** Medida que describe el centro de un conjunto de datos.	the mean, median, or mode
measure of variation (p. 830) A measure that describes the spread of a data set.	**medida de variación** Medida que describe la amplitud de un conjunto de datos.	the range, variance, standard deviation, or interquartile range

ENGLISH	SPANISH	EXAMPLES
median of a data set (p. 828) For an ordered data set with an odd number of values, the median is the middle value. For an ordered data set with an even number of values, the median is the average of the two middle values.	**mediana de un conjunto de datos** Dado un conjunto de datos ordenados con un número impar de valores, la mediana es el valor del medio. Dado un conjunto de datos ordenados con un número par de valores, la mediana es el promedio de los dos valores del medio.	8, 9, (9), 12, 15 — Median: 9 4, 6, (7, 10), 10, 12 — Median: $\frac{7+10}{2} = 8.5$
midpoint (p. 724) The point that divides a segment into two congruent segments.	**punto medio** Punto que divide un segmento en dos segmentos congruentes.	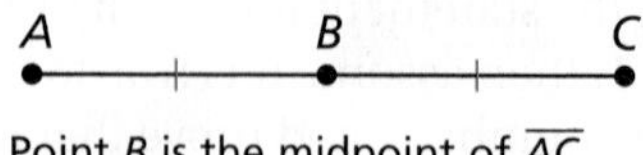 Point B is the midpoint of $\overline{AC}$.
minimum value of a function (p. 326) The y-value of the lowest point on the graph of the function.	**mínimo de una función** Valor de y del punto más bajo en la gráfica de la función.	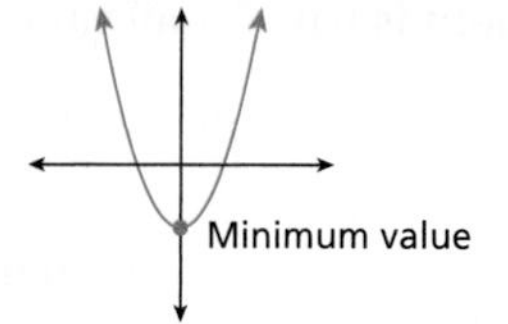
minor axis (p. 736) The shorter axis of an ellipse. Its endpoints are the *co-vertices of the ellipse.*	**eje menor** El eje más corto de una elipse. Sus extremos son los *co-vértices de la elipse.*	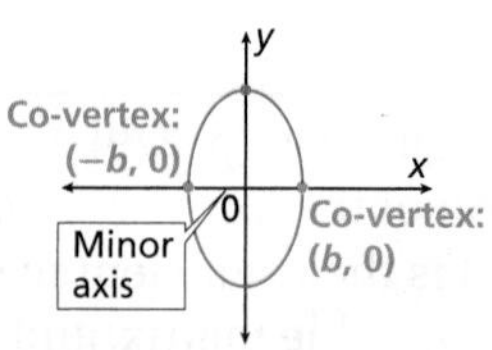
mode (p. 828) The value or values that occur most frequently in a data set; if all values occur with the same frequency, the data set is said to have no mode.	**moda** El valor o los valores que se presentan con mayor frecuencia en un conjunto de datos. Si todos los valores se presentan con la misma frecuencia, se dice que el conjunto de datos no tiene moda.	Data set: 3, 6, (8, 8), 10 — Mode: 8 Data set: 2, (5, 5), (7, 7) — Modes: 5 and 7 Data set: 2, 3, 6, 9, 11 — No mode
monomial (p. 406) A number or a product of numbers and variables with whole-number exponents, or a polynomial with one term.	**monomio** Número o producto de números y variables con exponentes de números cabales, o polinomio con un término.	$8x$, 9, $3x^2y^4$
multiple root (p. 439) A root r is a multiple root when the factor $(x - r)$ appears in the equation more than once.	**raíz múltiple** Una raíz r es una raíz múltiple cuando el factor $(x - r)$ aparece en la ecuación más de una vez.	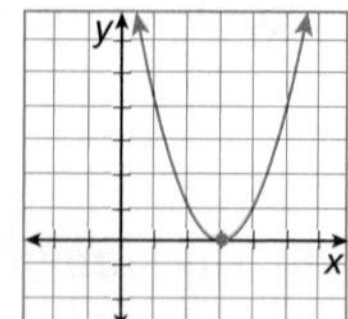 3 is a multiple root of $P(x) = (x - 3)^2$.
multiplicative identity matrix (p. 255) A square matrix with 1 in every entry of the main diagonal and 0 in every other entry.	**matriz de identidad multiplicativa** Una matriz cuadrada que contiene 1 en cada entrada de la diagonal principal y 0 en las demás entradas.	$\begin{bmatrix} 1 & 0 \\ 0 & 1 \end{bmatrix}, \begin{bmatrix} 1 & 0 & 0 \\ 0 & 1 & 0 \\ 0 & 0 & 1 \end{bmatrix}$

ENGLISH	SPANISH	EXAMPLES

multiplicative inverse of a square matrix (p. 278) The multiplicative inverse of square matrix A, if it exists, is notated A^{-1}, where the product of A and A^{-1} is the identity matrix.

inverso multiplicativo de una matriz cuadrada El inverso multiplicativo de una matriz cuadrada A, si existe, se escribe A^{-1}, donde el producto de A y A^{-1} es la matriz de identidad.

The multiplicative inverse of $A = \begin{bmatrix} -2 & 5 \\ 1 & -3 \end{bmatrix}$ is $A^{-1} = \begin{bmatrix} -3 & -5 \\ -1 & -2 \end{bmatrix}$, because $AA^{-1} = A^{-1}A = \begin{bmatrix} 1 & 0 \\ 0 & 1 \end{bmatrix}$.

multiplicity (p. 439) If a polynomial $P(x)$ has a multiple root at r, the multiplicity of r is the number of times $(x - r)$ appears as a factor in $P(x)$.

multiplicidad Si un polinomio $P(x)$ tiene una raíz múltiple en r, la multiplicidad de r es la cantidad de veces que $(x - r)$ aparece como factor en $P(x)$.

For $P(x) = (x - 3)^2$, the root 3 has a multiplicity of 2.

mutually exclusive events (p. 819) Two events are mutually exclusive if they cannot both occur in the same trial of an experiment.

sucesos mutuamente excluyentes Dos sucesos son mutuamente excluyentes si ambos no pueden ocurrir en la misma prueba de un experimento.

In the experiment of rolling a number cube, rolling a 3 and rolling an even number are mutually exclusive events.

N

natural logarithm (p. 532) A logarithm with base e, written as ln.

logaritmo natural Logaritmo con base e, que se escribe ln.

$\ln 5 = \log_e 5 \approx 1.6$

natural logarithmic function (p. 532) The function $f(x) = \ln x$, which is the inverse of the natural exponential function $f(x) = e^x$. Domain is $\{x \mid x > 0\}$; range is all real numbers.

función logarítmica natural Función $f(x) = \ln x$, que es la inversa de la función exponencial natural $f(x) = e^x$. El dominio es $\{x \mid x > 0\}$; el rango es todos los números reales.

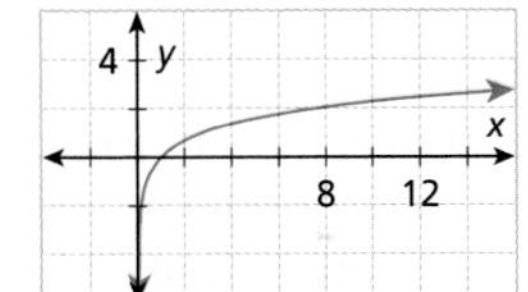

natural number (p. 6) A counting number.

número natural Número que sirve para contar.

1, 2, 3, 4, 5, 6, ...

negative exponent (p. 35) A base raised to a negative exponent is equal to the reciprocal of that base raised to the opposite exponent: $b^{-n} = \frac{1}{b^n}$.

exponente negativo Una base elevada a un exponente negativo es igual al recíproco de dicha base elevado al exponente opuesto: $b^{-n} = \frac{1}{b^n}$.

$5^{-3} = \frac{1}{5^3} = \frac{1}{125}$

net (p. S65) A diagram of the faces of a three-dimensional figure arranged in such a way that the diagram can be folded to form the three-dimensional figure.

plantilla Diagrama de las caras de una figura tridimensional que se puede plegar para formar la figura tridimensional.

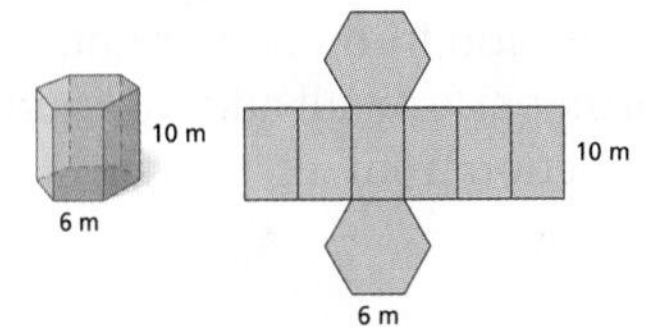

nonlinear system of equations (p. 768) A system in which at least one of the equations is not linear.

sistema no lineal de ecuaciones Sistema en el cual por lo menos una de las ecuaciones no es lineal.

$\begin{cases} y = 2x^2 \\ y = -3x^2 + 5 \end{cases}$

ENGLISH	SPANISH	EXAMPLES
***n*th root** (p. 610) The *n*th root of a number a, written as $\sqrt[n]{a}$ or $a^{\frac{1}{n}}$, is a number that is equal to a when it is raised to the nth power.	**enésima raíz** La enésima raíz de un número a, que se escribe como $\sqrt[n]{a}$ o $a^{\frac{1}{n}}$, es un número igual a a cuando se eleva a la enésima potencia.	$\sqrt[5]{32} = 2$, because $2^5 = 32$.

O

objective function (p. 206) The function to be maximized or minimized in a linear programming problem.	**función objetiva** Función que se debe maximizar o minimizar en un problema de programación lineal.	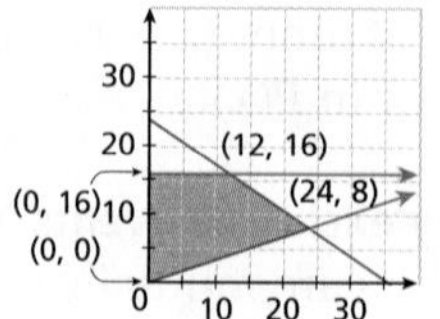 The objective function $P = 18x + 25y$ is maximized at $(24, 8)$.
obtuse angle (p. 198) An angle that measures greater than 90° and less than 180°.	**ángulo obtuso** Ángulo que mide más de 90° y menos de 180°.	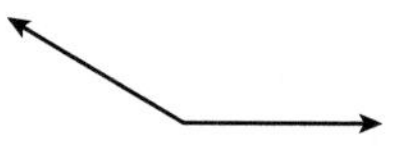
one-to-one function (p. 691) A function in which each y-value corresponds to only one x-value. The inverse of a one-to-one function is also a function.	**función uno a uno** Función en la que cada valor de y corresponde a sólo un valor de x. La inversa de una función uno a uno es también una función.	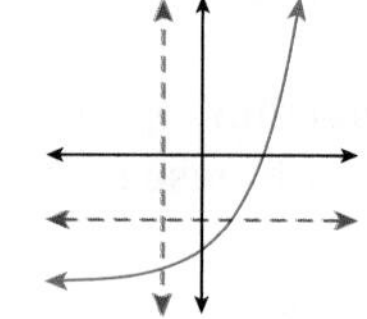
opposite (p. 14) The opposite of a number a, denoted $-a$, is the number that is the same distance from zero as a, on the opposite side of the number line. The sum of opposites is 0.	**opuesto** El opuesto de un número a, expresado $-a$, es el número que se encuentra a la misma distancia de cero que a, del lado opuesto de la recta numérica. La suma de los opuestos es 0.	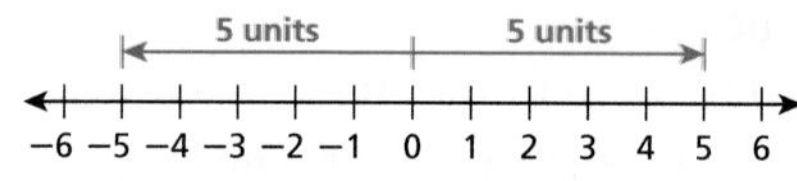 5 and −5 are opposites.
order of operations (p. 28) A process for evaluating expressions: First, perform operations in parentheses or other grouping symbols. Second, evaluate powers and roots. Third, perform all multiplication and division from left to right. Fourth, perform all addition and subtraction from left to right.	**orden de las operaciones** Proceso para evaluar las expresiones: Primero, realizar las operaciones entre paréntesis u otros símbolos de agrupación. Segundo, evaluar las potencias y las raíces. Tercero, realizar todas las multiplicaciones y divisiones de izquierda a derecha. Cuarto, realizar todas las sumas y restas de izquierda a derecha.	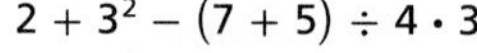 $2 + 3^2 - (7 + 5) \div 4 \cdot 3$ $2 + 3^2 - 12 \div 4 \cdot 3$ Add inside parentheses. $2 + 9 - 12 \div 4 \cdot 3$ Evaluate the power. $2 + 9 - 3 \cdot 3$ Divide. $2 + 9 - 9$ Multiply. $11 - 9$ Add. 2 Subtract.
ordered triple (p. 214) A set of three numbers that can be used to locate a point (x, y, z) in a three-dimensional coordinate system.	**tripleta ordenada** Conjunto de tres números que se pueden utilizar para ubicar un punto (x, y, z) en un sistema de coordenadas tridimensional.	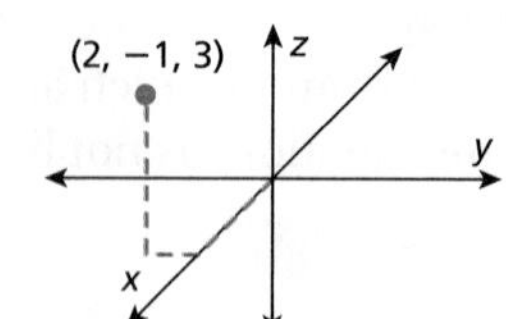

Glossary/Glosario

ENGLISH	SPANISH	EXAMPLES
origin (p. 3) The intersection of the x- and y-axes in a coordinate plane. The coordinates of the origin are $(0, 0)$.	**origen** Intersección de los ejes x e y en un plano cartesiano. Las coordenadas de origen son $(0, 0)$.	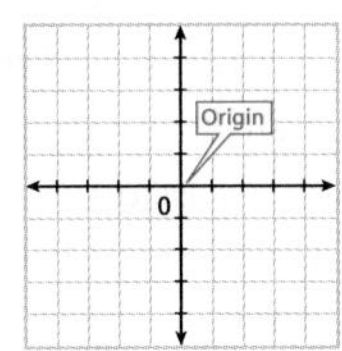
outcome (p. 802) A possible result of a probability experiment.	**resultado** Resultado posible en un experimento de probabilidad.	In the experiment of rolling a number cube, the possible outcomes are 1, 2, 3, 4, 5, and 6.
outlier (p. 831) A data value that is far removed from the rest of the data. A value less than $Q_1 - 1.5(\text{IQR})$ or greater than $Q_3 + 1.5(\text{IQR})$ is considered to be an outlier.	**valor extremo** Valor de datos que está muy alejado del resto de los datos. Un valor menor que $Q_1 - 1.5(\text{IQR})$ o mayor que $Q_3 + 1.5(\text{IQR})$ se considera un valor extremo.	

P

ENGLISH	SPANISH	EXAMPLES
parabola (p. 315) The shape of the graph of a quadratic function. Also, the set of points equidistant from a point F, called the *focus*, and a line d, called the *directrix*.	**parábola** Forma de la gráfica de una función cuadrática. También, conjunto de puntos equidistantes de un punto F, denominado *foco*, y una línea d, denominada *directriz*.	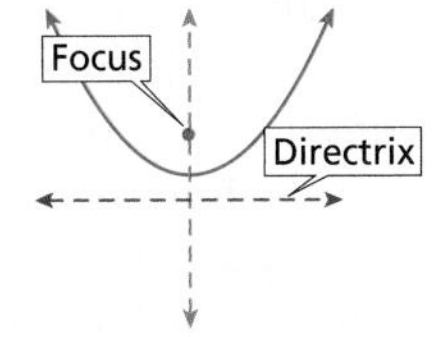
parameter (p. 230) One of the constants in a function or equation that may be changed. Also the third variable in a set of parametric equations.	**parámetro** Una de las constantes en una función o ecuación que se puede cambiar. También es la tercera variable en un conjunto de ecuaciones paramétricas.	$y = (x - h)^2 + k$ parameters
parametric equations (p. 230) A pair of equations that define the x- and y-coordinates of a point in terms of a third variable called a parameter.	**ecuaciones paramétricas** Par de ecuaciones que definen las coordenadas x e y de un punto en función de una tercera variable denominada parámetro.	$x(t) = t + 1$ $y(t) = -2t$
parent function (p. 67) The simplest function with the defining characteristics of the family. Functions in the same family are transformations of their parent function.	**función madre** La función más básica con las características de la familia. Las funciones de la misma familia son transformaciones de su función madre.	$f(x) = x^2$ is the parent function for $g(x) = x^2 + 4$ and $h(x) = 5(x + 2)^2 - 3$.
partial sum (p. 870) Indicated by $S_n = \sum_{i=1}^{n} a_i$, the sum of a specified number of terms n of a sequence whose total number of terms is greater than n.	**suma parcial** Expresada por $S_n = \sum_{i=1}^{n} a_i$, la suma de un número específico n de términos de una sucesión cuyo número total de términos es mayor que n.	For the sequence $a_n = n^2$, the fourth partial sum of the infinite series $\sum_{k=1}^{\infty} k^2$ is $\sum_{k=1}^{4} k^2 = 1^2 + 2^2 + 3^2 + 4^2 = 30$.

ENGLISH	SPANISH	EXAMPLES
Pascal's triangle (p. 416) A triangular arrangement of numbers in which every row starts and ends with 1 and each other number is the sum of the two numbers above it.	**triángulo de Pascal** Arreglo triangular de números en el cual cada fila comienza y termina con 1 y cada uno de los demás números es la suma de los dos números que están encima de él.	1 1 1 1 2 1 1 3 3 1 1 4 6 4 1
perfect square (p. 21) A number whose positive square root is a whole number.	**cuadrado perfecto** Número cuya raíz cuadrada positiva es un número cabal.	36 is a perfect square because $\sqrt{36} = 6$.
perfect-square trinomial (p. 336) A trinomial whose factored form is the square of a binomial. A perfect-square trinomial has the form $a^2 - 2ab + b^2 = (a - b)^2$ or $a^2 + 2ab + b^2 = (a + b)^2$.	**trinomio cuadrado perfecto** Trinomio cuya forma factorizada es el cuadrado de un binomio. Un trinomio cuadrado perfecto tiene la forma $a^2 - 2ab + b^2 = (a - b)^2$ o $a^2 + 2ab + b^2 = (a + b)^2$.	$x^2 + 6x + 9$ is a perfect-square trinomial, because $x^2 + 6x + 9 = (x + 3)^2$.
period of a periodic function (p. 990) The length of a cycle measured in units of the independent variable (usually time in seconds). Also the reciprocal of the frequency.	**periodo de una función periódica** Longitud de un ciclo medido en unidades de la variable independiente (generalmente el tiempo en segundos). También es la inversa de la frecuencia.	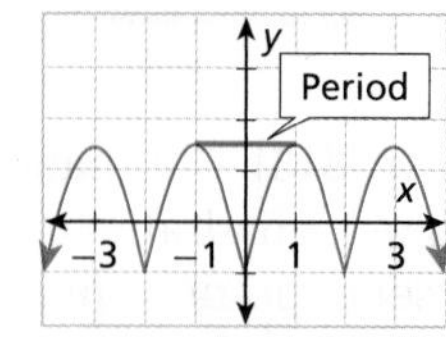
periodic function (p. 990) A function that repeats exactly in regular intervals, called *periods*.	**función periódica** Función que se repite exactamente a intervalos regulares denominados *periodos*.	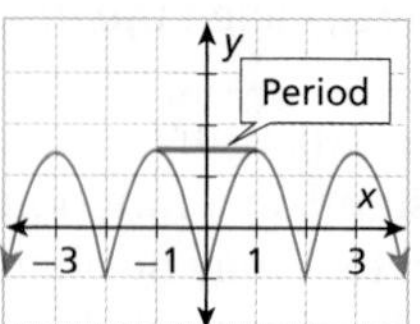
permutation (p. 795) An arrangement of a group of objects in which order is important. The number of permutations of r objects from a group of n objects is denoted ${}_nP_r$.	**permutación** Arreglo de un grupo de objetos en el cual el orden es importante. El número de permutaciones de r objetos de un grupo de n objetos se expresa ${}_nP_r$.	For 4 objects *A, B, C,* and *D,* there are ${}_4P_2 = 12$ different permutations of 2 objects: *AB, AC, AD, BC, BD, CD, BA, CA, DA, CB, DB,* and *DC.*
phase shift (p. 993) A horizontal translation of a periodic function.	**cambio de fase** Traslación horizontal de una función periódica.	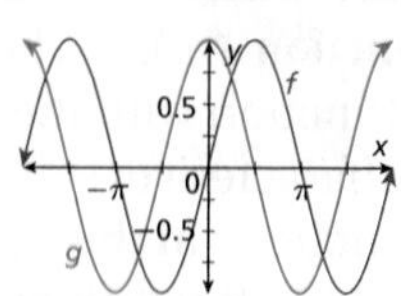 *g* is a phase shift of *f* $\frac{\pi}{2}$ units left.
piecewise function (p. 662) A function that is a combination of one or more functions.	**función a trozos** Función que es una combinación de una o más funciones.	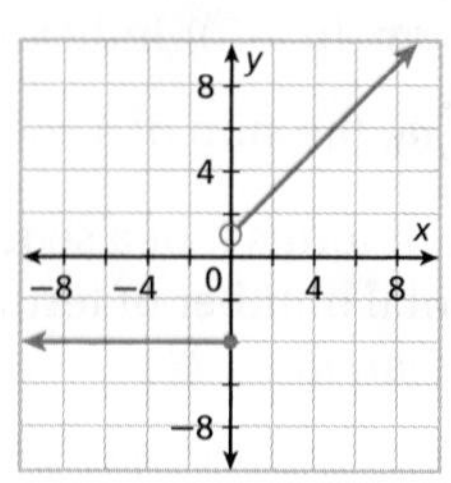 $f(x) = \begin{cases} -4 & \text{if } x \le 0 \\ x + 1 & \text{if } x > 0 \end{cases}$

ENGLISH	SPANISH	EXAMPLES

point-slope form (p. 116) The point-slope form of a linear equation is $y - y_1 = m(x - x_1)$, where m is the slope and (x_1, y_1) is a point on the line.

forma de punto y pendiente La forma de punto y pendiente de una ecuación lineal es $y - y_1 = m(x - x_1)$, donde m es la pendiente y (x_1, y_1) es un punto en la línea.

The equation of the line through (2, 1) with slope 3 is $y - 1 = 3(x - 2)$.

---

polynomial (p. 406) A monomial or a sum or difference of monomials.

polinomio Monomio o suma o diferencia de monomios.

$2x^2 + 3x - 7$

---

polynomial function (p. 408) A function whose rule is a polynomial.

función polinomial Función cuya regla es un polinomio.

$f(x) = x^3 - 8x^2 + 19x - 12$

---

power (p. 34) An expression written with a base and an exponent or the value of such an expression.

potencia Expresión escrita con una base y un exponente o el valor de dicha expresión.

$2^3 = 8$, so 8 is the third power of 2.

---

principal root (p. 21) The positive root of a number, indicated by the radical sign.

raíz principal Raíz cuadrada positiva de un número, expresada por el signo de radical.

$\sqrt{36} = 6$

---

probability (p. 802) A number from 0 to 1 (or 0% to 100%) that is the measure of how likely an event is to occur.

probabilidad Número entre 0 y 1 (o entre 0% y 100%) que describe cuán probable es que ocurra un suceso.

A bag contains 3 red marbles and 4 blue marbles. The probability of choosing a red marble is $\frac{3}{7}$.

---

probability distribution for an experiment (p. 828) The function that pairs each outcome with its probability.

distribución de probabilidad para un experimento Función que asigna a cada resultado su probabilidad.

A number cube is rolled 10 times. The results are shown in the table.

Outcome	1	2	3	4	5	6
Probability	$\frac{1}{10}$	$\frac{1}{5}$	$\frac{1}{5}$	0	$\frac{3}{10}$	$\frac{1}{5}$

---

proportion (p. 97) A statement that two ratios are equal; $\frac{a}{b} = \frac{c}{d}$.

proporción Enunciado que establece que dos razones son iguales; $\frac{a}{b} = \frac{c}{d}$.

$\frac{2}{3} = \frac{4}{6}$

---

pure imaginary number (p. 351) *See* imaginary number.

número imaginario puro *Ver* número imaginario.

$3i$

Q

quadratic equation (p. 334) An equation that can be written in the form $ax^2 + bx + c = 0$, where a, b, and c are real numbers and $a \neq 0$.

ecuación cuadrática Ecuación que se puede expresar como $ax^2 + bx + c = 0$, donde a, b y c son números reales y $a \neq 0$.

$x^2 + 3x - 4 = 0$
$x^2 - 9 = 0$

ENGLISH	SPANISH	EXAMPLES
Quadratic Formula (p. 356) The formula $x = \frac{-b \pm \sqrt{b^2 - 4ac}}{2a}$, which gives solutions, or roots, of equations in the form $ax^2 + bx + c = 0$, where $a \neq 0$.	**fórmula cuadrática** La fórmula $x = \frac{-b \pm \sqrt{b^2 - 4ac}}{2a}$, que da soluciones, o raíces, para las ecuaciones del tipo $ax^2 + bx + c = 0$, donde $a \neq 0$.	The solutions of $2x^2 - 5x - 3 = 0$ are given by $x = \frac{-(-5) \pm \sqrt{(-5)^2 - 4(2)(-3)}}{2(2)}$ $= \frac{5 \pm \sqrt{25 + 24}}{4} = \frac{5 \pm 7}{4}$; $x = 3$ or $x = -\frac{1}{2}$.
quadratic function (p. 315) A function that can be written in the form $f(x) = ax^2 + bx + c$, where a, b, and c are real numbers and $a \neq 0$, or in the form $f(x) = a(x - h)^2 + k$, where a, h, and k are real numbers and $a \neq 0$.	**función cuadrática** Función que se puede expresar como $f(x) = ax^2 + bx + c$, donde a, b y c son números reales y $a \neq 0$, o como $f(x) = a(x - h)^2 + k$, donde a, h y k son números reales y $a \neq 0$.	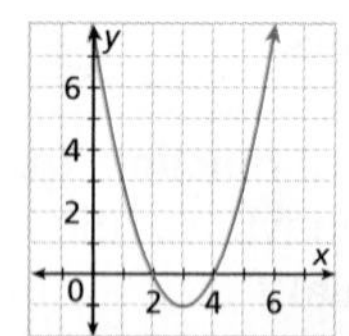 $f(x) = x^2 - 6x + 8$
quadratic inequality in two variables (p. 366) An inequality that can be written in one of the following forms: $y < ax^2 + bx + c$, $y > ax^2 + bx + c$, $y \leq ax^2 + bx + c$, $y \geq ax^2 + bx + c$, or $y \neq ax^2 + bx + c$, where a, b, and c are real numbers and $a \neq 0$.	**desigualdad cuadrática en dos variables** Desigualdad que puede expresarse de una de las siguientes formas: $y < ax^2 + bx + c$, $y > ax^2 + bx + c$, $y \leq ax^2 + bx + c$, $y \geq ax^2 + bx + c$, o $y \neq ax^2 + bx + c$, donde a, b y c son números reales y $a \neq 0$.	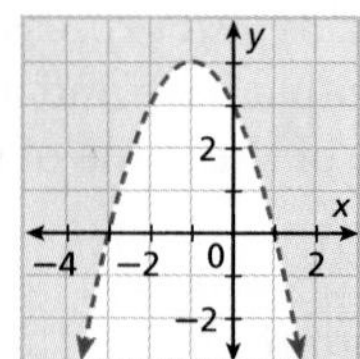 $y > -x^2 - 2x + 3$
quadratic model (p. 376) A quadratic function used to represent a set of data.	**modelo cuadrático** Función cuadrática que se utiliza para representar un conjunto de datos.	see table below
quadratic regression (p. 376) A statistical method used to fit a quadratic model to a given data set.	**regresión cuadrática** Método estadístico utilizado para ajustar un modelo cuadrático a un conjunto de datos determinado.	

Quadratic model example:

x	4	6	8	10
$f(x)$	27	52	89	130

A quadratic model for the data is $f(x) = x^2 + 3.3x - 2.6$.

R

ENGLISH	SPANISH	EXAMPLES
radian (p. 943) A unit of angle measure based on arc length. In a circle of radius r, if a central angle has a measure of 1 radian, then the length of the intercepted arc is r units. 2π radians $= 360°$; 1 radian $\approx 57°$	**radián** Unidad de medida de un ángulo basada en la longitud del arco. En un círculo de radio r, si un ángulo central mide 1 radián, entonces la longitud del arco abarcado es r unidades. 2π radianes $= 360°$; 1 radián $\approx 57°$	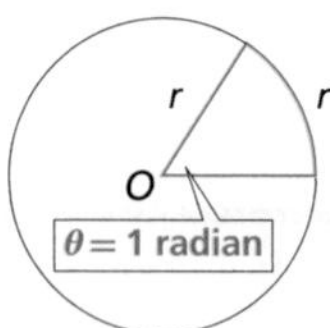
radical (p. 21) An indicated root of a quantity.	**radical** Raíz indicada de una cantidad.	$\sqrt{36} = 6$, $\sqrt[3]{27} = 3$

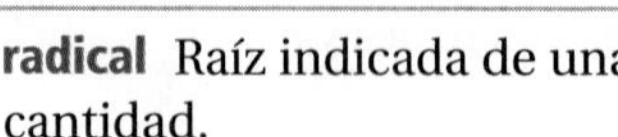

ENGLISH	SPANISH	EXAMPLES
radical equation (p. 628) An equation that contains a variable within a radical.	**ecuación radical** Ecuación que contiene una variable dentro de un radical.	$\sqrt{x+3}+4=7$
radical function (p. 619) A function whose rule contains a variable within a radical.	**función radical** Función cuya regla contiene una variable dentro de un radical.	 $f(x)=\sqrt{x}$
radical inequality (p. 630) An inequality that contains a variable within a radical.	**desigualdad radical** Desigualdad que contiene una variable dentro de un radical.	$\sqrt{x+3}\le 7$
radical symbol (p. 21) The symbol $\sqrt{\ }$ used to denote a root. The symbol is used alone to indicate a square root or with an index, $\sqrt[n]{\ }$, to indicate the nth root.	**símbolo de radical** Símbolo $\sqrt{\ }$ que se utiliza para expresar una raíz. Puede utilizarse solo para indicar una raíz cuadrada, o con un índice, $\sqrt[n]{\ }$, para indicar la enésima raíz.	$\sqrt{36}=6,\ \sqrt[3]{27}=3$
radicand (p. 21) The expression under a radical sign.	**radicando** Número o expresión debajo del signo de radical.	$\sqrt{x+3}-2$ Radicand
random sample (p. S69) A sample selected from a population so that each member of the population has an equal chance of being selected.	**muestra aleatoria** Muestra seleccionada de una población tal que cada miembro de ésta tenga igual probabilidad de ser seleccionado.	Mr. Hansen chose a random sample of the class by writing each student's name on a slip of paper, mixing up the slips, and drawing five slips without looking.
range of a data set (p. 830) The difference of the greatest and least values in the data set.	**rango de un conjunto de datos** La diferencia del mayor y menor valor en un conjunto de datos.	The data set $\{3, 3, 5, 7, 8, 10, 11, 11, 12\}$ has a range of $12-3=9$.
range of a function or relation (p. 44) The set of output values of a function or relation.	**rango de una función o relación** Conjunto de los valores de salida de una función o relación.	The range of $y=x^2$ is $\{y \mid y\ge 0\}$.
rate (p. 98) A ratio that compares two quantities measured in different units.	**tasa** Razón que compara dos cantidades medidas en diferentes unidades.	$\frac{55\text{ miles}}{1\text{ hour}}=55\text{ mi/h}$
ratio (p. 97) A comparison of two quantities by division.	**razón** Comparación de dos cantidades mediante una división.	$\frac{1}{2}$ or 1:2
rational equation (p. 600) An equation that contains one or more rational expressions.	**ecuación racional** Ecuación que contiene una o más expresiones racionales.	$\frac{x+2}{x^2+3x-1}=6$
rational exponent (p. 611) An exponent that can be expressed as $\frac{m}{n}$ such that if m and n are integers, then $b^{\frac{m}{n}}=\sqrt[n]{b^m}=\left(\sqrt[n]{b}\right)^m$.	**exponente racional** Exponente que se puede expresar como $\frac{m}{n}$ tal que, si m y n son números enteros, entonces $b^{\frac{m}{n}}=\sqrt[n]{b^m}=\left(\sqrt[n]{b}\right)^m$.	$4^{\frac{3}{2}}=\sqrt{4^3}=\sqrt{64}=8$ $4^{\frac{3}{2}}=\left(\sqrt{4}\right)^3=2^3=8$

Glossary/Glosario

ENGLISH	SPANISH	EXAMPLES
rational expression (p. 577) An algebraic expression whose numerator and denominator are polynomials and whose denominator has a degree ≥ 1.	**expresión racional** Expresión algebraica cuyo numerador y denominador son polinomios y cuyo denominador tiene un grado ≥ 1.	$\frac{x+2}{x^2+3x-1}$
rational function (p. 592) A function whose rule can be written as a rational expression.	**función racional** Función cuya regla se puede expresar como una expresión racional.	$f(x) = \frac{x+2}{x^2+3x-1}$
rational inequality (p. 603) An inequality that contains one or more rational expressions.	**desigualdad racional** Desigualdad que contiene una o más expresiones racionales.	$\frac{x+2}{x^2+3x-1} \geq 6$
rational number (p. 6) A number that can be written in the form $\frac{a}{b}$, where a and b are integers and $b \neq 0$.	**número racional** Número que se puede expresar como $\frac{a}{b}$, donde a y b son números enteros y $b \neq 0$.	$3, 1.75, 0.\overline{3}, -\frac{2}{3}, 0$
rationalizing the denominator (p. 22) A method of rewriting a fraction by multiplying by another fraction that is equivalent to 1 in order to remove radical terms from the denominator.	**racionalizar el denominador** Método que consiste en escribir nuevamente una fracción multiplicándola por otra fracción equivalente a 1 a fin de eliminar los términos radicales del denominador.	$\frac{1}{\sqrt{2}}\left(\frac{\sqrt{2}}{\sqrt{2}}\right) = \frac{\sqrt{2}}{2}$
real axis (p. 382) The horizontal axis in the complex plane; it graphically represents the real part of complex numbers.	**eje real** Eje horizontal de un plano complejo. Representa gráficamente la parte real de los números complejos.	Imaginary axis; $2i$; $0 + 0i$; Real axis; -2; 2; $-2i$
real number (p. 6) A rational or irrational number. Every point on the number line represents a real number.	**número real** Número racional o irracional. Cada punto de la recta numérica representa un número real.	$-5, 0, \frac{2}{3}, \sqrt{2}, 3.1, \pi$
real part of a complex number (p. 351) For a complex number of the form $a + bi$, a is the real part.	**parte real de un número complejo** Dado un número complejo del tipo $a + bi$, a es la parte real.	$5 + 6i$ — Real part (5); Imaginary part (6)
reciprocal (p. 14) For a real number $a \neq 0$, the reciprocal of a is $\frac{1}{a}$. The product of reciprocals is 1.	**recíproco** Dado el número real $a \neq 0$, el recíproco de a es $\frac{1}{a}$. El producto de los recíprocos es 1.	$\frac{1}{2}$ is the reciprocal of 2. $\frac{5}{3}$ is the reciprocal of $\frac{3}{5}$.
recursive formula (p. 862) A formula for a sequence in which one or more previous terms are used to generate the next term.	**fórmula recurrente** Fórmula para una sucesión en la cual uno o más términos anteriores se utilizan para generar el término siguiente.	For the sequence 5, 7, 9, 11, ..., a recursive formula is $a_1 = 5$ and $a_n = a_{n-1} + 2$.
reduced row-echelon form (p. 288) A form of an augmented matrix in which the coefficient columns form an identity matrix.	**forma escalonada reducida por filas** Forma de matriz aumentada en la que las columnas de coeficientes forman una matriz de identidad.	$\left[\begin{array}{cc\|c} 1 & 0 & -1 \\ 0 & 1 & 3 \end{array}\right]$

Glossary/Glosario

ENGLISH	SPANISH	EXAMPLES
reference angle (p. 937) For an angle in standard position, the reference angle is the positive acute angle formed by the terminal side of the angle and the x-axis.	**ángulo de referencia** Dado un ángulo en posición estándar, el ángulo de referencia es el ángulo agudo positivo formado por el lado terminal del ángulo y el eje x.	y; 135°; 45°; 0; x
reflection (p. 60) A transformation that reflects, or "flips," a graph or figure across a line, called the line of reflection, such that each reflected point is the same distance from the line of reflection but is on the opposite side of the line.	**reflexión** Transformación que refleja, o invierte, una gráfica o figura sobre una línea, llamada la línea de reflexión, de manera tal que cada punto reflejado esté a la misma distancia de la línea de reflexión pero que se encuentre en el lado opuesto de la línea.	
reflection matrix (p. 263) A matrix used to reflect a figure across a specified *line of symmetry*.	**matriz de reflexión** Matriz utilizada para reflejar una figura sobre un *eje de simetría* específico.	J′; J; K′; K; L′; L; y; x; 4; 2; −4; 0; 4 Matrix $\begin{bmatrix} -1 & 0 \\ 0 & 1 \end{bmatrix}$ was used to reflect the figure across the y-axis.
regression (p. 142) The statistical study of the relationship between variables.	**regresión** Estudio estadístico de la relación entre variables.	
relation (p. 44) A set of ordered pairs.	**relación** Conjunto de pares ordenados.	$\{(0, 5), (0, 4), (2, 3), (4, 0)\}$
replacement set (p. 55) A set of numbers that can be substituted for a variable.	**conjunto de reemplazo** Conjunto de números que pueden sustituir una variable.	The solution set of $y = x + 3$ for the replacement set $\{1, 2, 3\}$ is $\{4, 5, 6\}$.
right angle (p. 960) An angle that measures 90°.	**ángulo recto** Ángulo que mide 90°.	
right triangle (p. 20) A triangle with one right angle.	**triángulo rectángulo** Triángulo con un ángulo recto.	
rigid transformation (p. 261) A transformation that does not change the size or shape of a figure.	**transformación rígida** Transformación que no cambia el tamaño o la forma de una figura.	Reflections, rotations, and translations are rigid transformations.
root of an equation (p. 334) Any value of the variable that makes the equation true.	**raíz de una ecuación** Cualquier valor de la variable que transforme la ecuación en verdadera.	The roots of $(x - 2)(x + 1) = 0$ are 2 and -1.
roster notation (p. 7) A way of representing a set by listing the elements between braces, { }.	**notación de lista** Forma de representar un conjunto enumerando los elementos entre llaves, { }.	The first 5 positive odd numbers are $\{1, 3, 5, 7, 9\}$.

Glossary/Glosario

ENGLISH	SPANISH	EXAMPLES
rotation (p. 261) A transformation that rotates or turns a figure about a point called the center of rotation.	**rotación** Transformación que hace rotar o girar una figura sobre un punto llamado centro de rotación.	
rotation matrix (p. 264) A matrix used to rotate a figure about the origin.	**matriz de rotación** Matriz utilizada para rotar una figura sobre el origen.	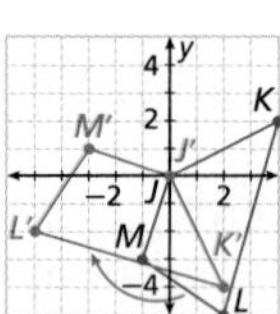 Matrix $\begin{bmatrix} 0 & 1 \\ -1 & 0 \end{bmatrix}$ was used to rotate the figure 90° clockwise.
row operation (p. 288) An operation performed on a row of an augmented matrix that creates an equivalent matrix.	**operación por filas** Operación realizada en una fila de una matriz aumentada que crea una matriz equivalente.	$\left[\begin{array}{cc\|c} 2 & 0 & -2 \\ 0 & 1 & 3 \end{array}\right] = \left[\begin{array}{cc\|c} \frac{1}{2}(2) & \frac{1}{2}(0) & \frac{1}{2}(-1) \\ 0 & 1 & 3 \end{array}\right] = \left[\begin{array}{cc\|c} 1 & 0 & -1 \\ 0 & 1 & 3 \end{array}\right]$
row-reduction method (p. 288) The process of performing elementary row operations on an augmented matrix to transform the matrix to reduced row echelon form.	**método de reducción por filas** Proceso por el cual se realizan operaciones elementales de filas en una matriz aumentada para transformar la matriz en una forma reducida de filas escalonadas.	$\left[\begin{array}{cc\|c} 2 & 0 & -2 \\ 0 & 1 & 3 \end{array}\right] = \left[\begin{array}{cc\|c} \frac{1}{2}(2) & \frac{1}{2}(0) & \frac{1}{2}(-1) \\ 0 & 1 & 3 \end{array}\right] = \left[\begin{array}{cc\|c} 1 & 0 & -1 \\ 0 & 1 & 3 \end{array}\right]$

S

ENGLISH	SPANISH	EXAMPLES
sample space (p. 802) The set of all possible outcomes of a probability experiment.	**espacio muestral** Conjunto de todos los resultados posibles en un experimento de probabilidades.	In the experiment of rolling a number cube, the sample space is $\{1, 2, 3, 4, 5, 6\}$.
scalar (p. 248) A number that is multiplied by a matrix.	**escalar** Número que se multiplica por una matriz.	$3\begin{bmatrix} 1 & -2 \\ 2 & 3 \end{bmatrix} = \begin{bmatrix} 3 & -6 \\ 6 & 9 \end{bmatrix}$ (3 = scalar)
scale factor (p. 99) The multiplier used on each dimension to change one figure into a similar figure.	**factor de escala** El multiplicador utilizado en cada dimensión para transformar una figura en una figura semejante.	$A'(4, 6)$, $A(2, 3)$, $B'(0, 2)$, $B(0, 1)$, $C(3, 0)$, $C'(6, 0)$
scatter plot (p. 142) A graph with points plotted to show a possible relationship between two sets of data.	**diagrama de dispersión** Gráfica con puntos que se usa para demostrar una relación posible entre dos conjuntos de datos.	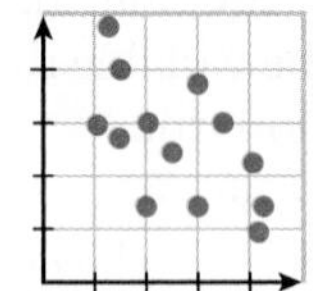

ENGLISH	SPANISH	EXAMPLES
scientific notation (p. 36) A method of writing very large or very small numbers, by using powers of 10, in the form $m \times 10^n$, where $1 \le m < 10$ and n is an integer.	**notación científica** Método que consiste en escribir números muy grandes o muy pequeños utilizando potencias de 10 del tipo $m \times 10^n$, donde $1 \le m < 10$ y n es un número entero.	$1.256\ 10^{13} = 12{,}560{,}000{,}000{,}000$ $7.5 \times 10^{-6} = 0.0000075$
secant of an angle (p. 932) In a right triangle, the ratio of the length of the hypotenuse to the length of the side adjacent to angle A. It is the reciprocal of the cosine function.	**secante de un ángulo** En un triángulo rectángulo, la razón entre la longitud de la hipotenusa y la longitud del cateto adyacente al ángulo A. Es la inversa de la función coseno.	hypotenuse A adjacent leg $\sec A = \frac{\text{hypotenuse}}{\text{adjacent}} = \frac{1}{\cos A}$
second differences (p. 374) Differences between first differences of a function.	**segundas diferencias** Diferencias entre las primeras diferencias de una función.	x: 0, 1, 2, 3; y: 1, 4, 9, 16 first differences +3 +5 +7 second differences +2 +2
sequence (p. 862) A list of numbers that often form a pattern.	**sucesión** Lista de números que generalmente forman un patrón.	1, 2, 4, 8, 16, ...
series (p. 870) The indicated sum of the terms of a sequence.	**serie** Suma indicada de los términos de una sucesión.	$1 + 2 + 4 + 8 + 16 + \ldots$
set (p. 6) A collection of items called elements.	**conjunto** Grupo de componentes denominados elementos.	$\{1, 2, 3\}$
set-builder notation (p. 8) A notation for a set that uses a rule to describe the properties of the elements of the set.	**notación de conjuntos** Notación para un conjunto que se vale de una regla para describir las propiedades de los elementos del conjunto.	$\{x \mid x > 3\}$ is read, "The set of all x such that x is greater than 3."
Sierpinski triangle (p. 864) A fractal formed from a triangle by removing triangles with vertices at the midpoints of the sides of each remaining triangle.	**triángulo de Sierpinski** Fractal formado a partir de un triángulo al cual se le recortan triángulos cuyos vértices se encuentran en los puntos medios de los lados de cada triángulo restante.	
similar (p. 99) Two figures are similar if they have the same shape but not necessarily the same size.	**semejantes** Dos figuras son semejantes si tienen la misma forma pero no necesariamente el mismo tamaño.	
simple event (p. 819) An event consisting of only one outcome.	**suceso simple** Suceso que contiene sólo un resultado.	In the experiment of rolling a number cube, the event consisting of the outcome 3 is a simple event.
simplify (p. 28) To perform all indicated operations.	**simplificar** Realizar todas las operaciones indicadas.	$3(4) + 7$ $12 + 7$ 19

Glossary/Glosario

ENGLISH	SPANISH	EXAMPLES

simulation (p. 810) A model of an experiment, often one that would be too difficult or time-consuming to actually perform.

simulación Modelo de un experimento; generalmente se recurre a la simulación cuando realizar dicho experimento sería demasiado difícil o llevaría mucho tiempo.

A random number generator is used to simulate the roll of a number cube.

---

sine (p. 929) In a right triangle, the ratio of the length of the side opposite $\angle A$ to the length of the hypotenuse.

seno En un triángulo rectángulo, razón entre la longitud del cateto opuesto a $\angle A$ y la longitud de la hipotenusa.

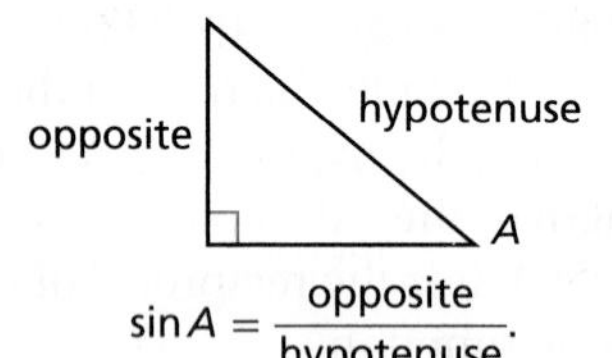

$\sin A = \dfrac{\text{opposite}}{\text{hypotenuse}}$.

---

slope (p. 106) A measure of the steepness of a line. If (x_1, y_1) and (x_2, y_2) are any two points on the line, the slope of the line, known as m, is represented by the equation $m = \dfrac{y_2 - y_1}{x_2 - x_1}$.

pendiente Medida de la inclinación de una línea. Dados dos puntos (x_1, y_1) y (x_2, y_2) en una línea, la pendiente de la línea, denominada m, se representa con la ecuación $m = \dfrac{y_2 - y_1}{x_2 - x_1}$.

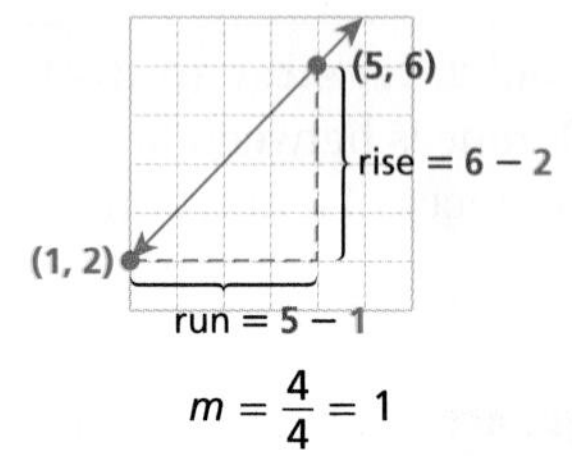

$m = \dfrac{4}{4} = 1$

---

slope-intercept form (p. 107) The slope-intercept form of a linear equation is $y = mx + b$, where m is the slope and b is the y-intercept.

forma de pendiente-intersección La forma de pendiente-intersección de una ecuación lineal es $y = mx + b$, donde m es la pendiente y b es la intersección y.

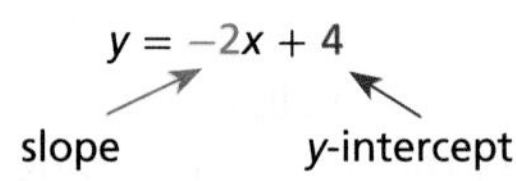

---

solution set of an equation (p. 90) The set of values that make an equation true.

conjunto solución de una ecuación Conjunto de valores que hacen verdadero un enunciado.

The solution set of $x^2 = 9$ is $\{-3, 3\}$.

---

solving a triangle (p. 959) Using given measures to find unknown angle measures or side lengths of a triangle.

resolución de un triángulo Utilizar medidas dadas para hallar las medidas desconocidas de los ángulos o las longitudes de los lados de un triángulo.

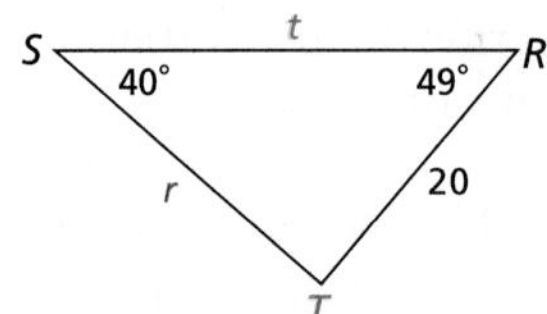

$49° + 40° + m\angle T = 180°$

$m\angle T = 91°$

$\dfrac{\sin 49°}{r} = \dfrac{\sin 40°}{20}$ $\quad$ $\dfrac{\sin 91°}{t} = \dfrac{\sin 40°}{20}$

$r \approx 23.5$ $\quad$ $t \approx 31.1$

---

special right triangle (p. 928) A 45°-45°-90° triangle or a 30°-60°-90° triangle.

triángulo rectángulo especial Triángulo de 45°-45°-90° o triángulo de 30°-60°-90°.

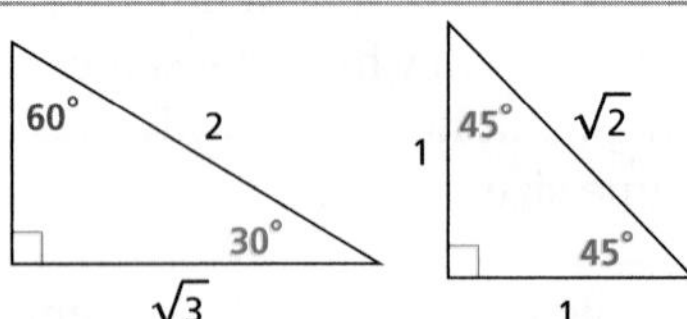

---

square matrix (p. 255) A matrix with the same number of rows as columns.

matriz cuadrada Matriz con el mismo número de filas y columnas.

$\begin{bmatrix} 1 & 2 \\ 0 & -3 \end{bmatrix}, \begin{bmatrix} 1 & -3 & 1 \\ 2 & 0 & -2 \\ 0 & 1 & 3 \end{bmatrix}$

---

square root (p. 21) A number that is multiplied by itself to form a product is called a square root of that product.

raíz cuadrada El número que se multiplica por sí mismo para formar un producto se denomina la raíz cuadrada de ese producto.

-4 and 4 are square roots of 16 because $(-4)^2 = 16$ and $4^2 = 16$.

ENGLISH	SPANISH	EXAMPLES
square-root function (p. 619) A function whose rule contains a variable under a square-root sign.	**función de raíz cuadrada** Función cuya regla contiene una variable bajo un signo de raíz cuadrada.	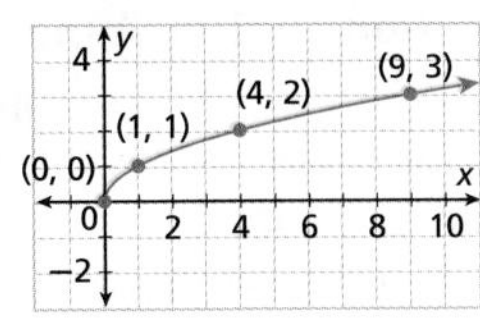 $f(x) = \sqrt{x}$
standard deviation (p. 830) A measure of dispersion of a data set. The standard deviation σ is the square root of the variance.	**desviación estándar** Medida de dispersión de un conjunto de datos. La desviación estándar σ es la raíz cuadrada de la varianza.	Data set: $\{6, 7, 7, 9, 11\}$ Mean: $\frac{6+7+7+9+11}{5} = 8$ Variance: $\frac{1}{5}(4+1+1+1+9) = 3.2$ Standard deviation: $\sigma = \sqrt{3.2} \approx 1.8$
standard form of a linear equation (p. 111) $Ax + By = C$, where A, B, and C are real numbers.	**forma estándar de una ecuación lineal** $Ax + By = C$, donde A, B y C son números reales.	$2x + 3y = 6$
standard form of a polynomial (p. 406) A polynomial in one variable is written in standard form when the terms are in order from greatest degree to least degree.	**forma estándar de un polinomio** Un polinomio de una variable se expresa en forma estándar cuando los términos se ordenan de mayor a menor grado.	$3x^3 - 5x^2 + 6x - 7$
standard form of a quadratic equation (p. 324) $ax^2 + bx + c = 0$, where a, b, and c are real numbers and $a \neq 0$.	**forma estándar de una ecuación cuadrática** $ax^2 + bx + c = 0$, donde a, b y c son números reales y $a \neq 0$.	$2x^2 + 3x - 1 = 0$
standard position (p. 936) An angle in standard position has its vertex at the origin and its initial side on the positive x-axis.	**posición estándar** Ángulo cuyo vértice se encuentra en el origen y cuyo lado inicial se encuentra sobre el eje x.	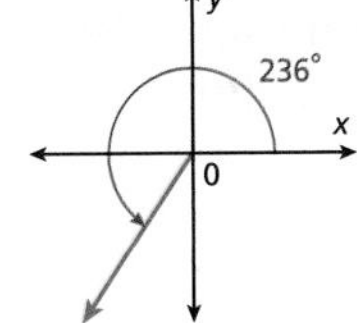
step function (p. 663) A piecewise function that is constant over each interval in its domain.	**función escalón** Función a trozos que es constante en cada intervalo en su dominio.	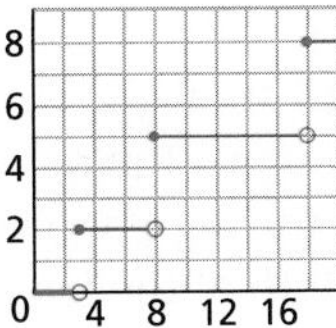
stretch (p. 61) A transformation that pulls the points of a graph horizontally away from the y-axis or vertically away from the x-axis.	**estiramiento** Transformación que desplaza los puntos de una gráfica en forma horizontal alejándolos del eje y o en forma vertical alejándolos del eje x.	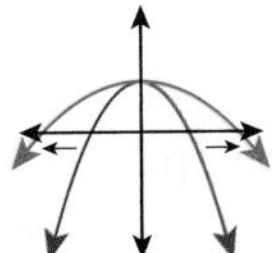
subset (p. 6) A set that is contained entirely within another set. Set B is a subset of set A if every element of B is contained in A, denoted $B \subset A$.	**subconjunto** Conjunto que se encuentra dentro de otro conjunto. El conjunto B es un subconjunto del conjunto A si todos los elementos de B son elementos de A; se expresa $B \subset A$.	The set of integers is a subset of the set of rational numbers, denoted $\mathbb{Z} \subset \mathbb{Q}$.

Glossary/Glosario

ENGLISH	SPANISH	EXAMPLES
substitution (p. 190) A method used to solve systems of equations by solving an equation for one variable and substituting the resulting expression into the other equation(s).	**sustitución** Método utilizado para resolver sistemas de ecuaciones resolviendo una ecuación para una variable y sustituyendo la expresión resultante en las demás ecuaciones.	$\begin{cases} 2x + 3y = -1 \\ x - 3y = 4 \end{cases}$ Solve for x. $x = 4 + 3y$ Substitute into the first equation and solve. $2(4 + 3y) + 3y = -1$ $y = -1$ Then solve for x. $x = 4 + 3(-1) = 1$
summation notation (p. 870) A method of notating the sum of a series using the Greek letter $\sum$ (capital *sigma*).	**notación de sumatoria** Método de notación de la suma de una serie que utiliza la letra griega $\sum$ (SIGMA mayúscula).	$\sum_{k=1}^{5} 3k = 3 + 6 + 9 + 12 + 15 = 45$
synthetic division (p. 423) A shorthand method of dividing by a linear binomial of the form $(x - a)$ by writing only the coefficients of the polynomials.	**división sintética** Método abreviado de división que consiste en dividir por un binomio lineal del tipo $(x - a)$ escribiendo sólo los coeficientes de los polinomios.	$(x^3 - 7x + 6) \div (x - 2)$ $\begin{array}{r\|rrrr} 2 & 1 & 0 & -7 & 6 \\ & & 2 & 4 & 6 \\ \hline & 1 & 2 & -3 & \boxed{0} \end{array}$ $(x^3 - 7x + 6) \div (x - 2) = x^2 + 2x - 3$
system of equations (p. 182) A set of two or more equations that have two or more variables.	**sistema de ecuaciones** Conjunto de dos o más ecuaciones que contienen dos o más variables.	$\begin{cases} 2x + 3y = -1 \\ x^2 = 4 \end{cases}$
system of linear equations (p. 182) *See* linear system.	**sistema de ecuaciones lineales** *Ver* sistema lineal.	
system of linear inequalities (p. 199) A system of inequalities in two or more variables in which all of the inequalities are linear.	**sistema de desigualdades lineales** Sistema de desigualdades en dos o más variables en el que todas las desigualdades son lineales.	$\begin{cases} 2x + 3y \ge -1 \\ x - 3y < 4 \end{cases}$

T

tangent of an angle (p. 929) In a right triangle, the ratio of the length of the leg opposite $\angle A$ to the length of the leg adjacent to $\angle A$.	**tangente de un ángulo** En un triángulo rectángulo, razón entre la longitud del cateto opuesto a $\angle A$ y la longitud del cateto adyacente a $\angle A$.	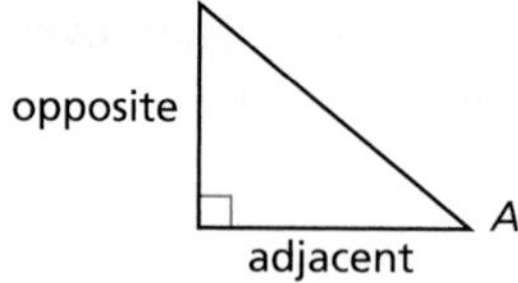 $\tan A = \frac{\text{opposite}}{\text{adjacent}}$
tangent line (p. 731) A line that is in the same plane as a circle and intersects the circle at exactly one point.	**línea tangente** Línea que está en el mismo plano que un círculo y corta al círculo en exactamente un punto.	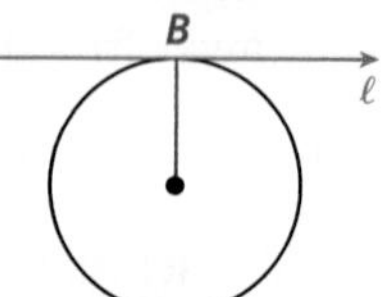
term of an expression (p. 28) The parts of the expression that are added or subtracted.	**término de una expresión** Partes de la expresión que se suman o se restan.	$3x^2 + 6x - 8$ Term Term Term

Glossary/Glosario

ENGLISH	SPANISH	EXAMPLES
term of a sequence (p. 862) An element or number in the sequence.	**término de una sucesión** Elemento o número de una sucesión.	5 is the third term in the sequence 1, 3, 5, 7, ...
terminal side (p. 936) For an angle in standard position, the ray that is rotated relative to the positive x-axis.	**lado terminal** Dado un ángulo en una posición estándar, el rayo que rota en relación con el eje positivo x.	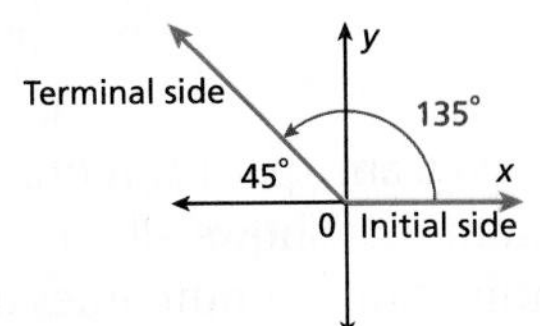
theoretical probability (p. 802) The ratio of the number of equally likely outcomes in an event to the total number of possible outcomes.	**probabilidad teórica** Razón entre el número de resultados igualmente probables de un suceso y el número total de resultados posibles.	The theoretical probability of rolling an odd number on a number cube is $\frac{3}{6} = \frac{1}{2}$.
third quartile (p. 829) The median of the upper half of a data set. Also called *upper quartile*.	**tercer cuartil** La mediana de la mitad superior de un conjunto de datos. También se llama *cuartil superior.*	Lower half Upper half  Third quartile
three-dimensional coordinate system (p. 214) A space that is divided into eight regions by an x-axis, a y-axis, and a z-axis. The locations, or coordinates, of points are given by ordered triples.	**sistema de coordenadas tridimensional** Espacio dividido en ocho regiones por un eje x, un eje y y un eje z. Las ubicaciones, o coordenadas, de los puntos son dadas por tripletas ordenadas.	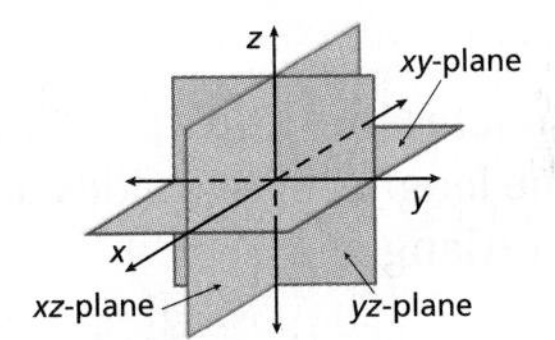
transformation (p. 59) A change in the position, size, or shape of a figure or graph.	**transformación** Cambio en la posición, tamaño o forma de una figura o gráfica.	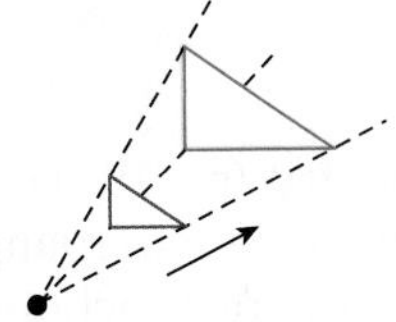
translation (p. 59) A transformation that shifts or slides every point of a figure or graph the same distance in the same direction.	**traslación** Transformación en la que todos los puntos de una figura se mueven la misma distancia en la misma dirección.	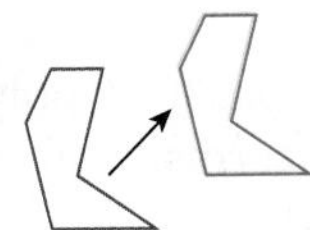
translation matrix (p. 262) A matrix used to translate points on the coordinate plane.	**matriz de traslación** Matriz utilizada para trasladar puntos en el plano cartesiano.	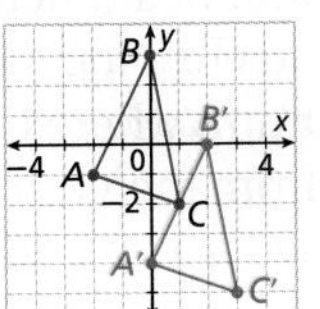 Matrix $\begin{bmatrix} -2 & -2 & -2 \\ 3 & 3 & 3 \end{bmatrix}$ is used to translate the figure 2 units left and 3 units up.
transpose (p. 260) A matrix that reverses the rows and columns of a matrix.	**transposición** Matriz que invierte las filas y columnas de una matriz.	$\begin{bmatrix} 1 & 2 \\ 3 & 4 \\ 5 & 6 \end{bmatrix}$ is the transpose of $\begin{bmatrix} 1 & 3 & 5 \\ 2 & 4 & 6 \end{bmatrix}$.

ENGLISH | **SPANISH** | **EXAMPLES**

transverse axis (p. 744) The axis of symmetry of a hyperbola that contains the vertices and foci.

eje transversal Eje de simetría de una hipérbola que contiene los vértices y focos.

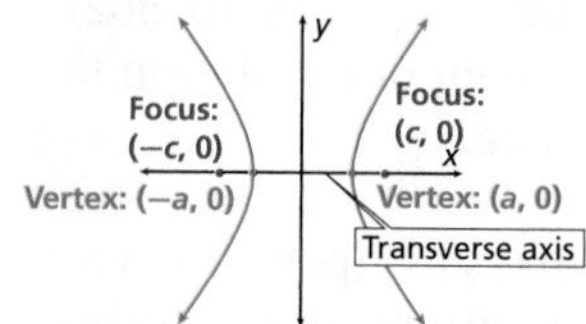

tree diagram (p. 812) A branching diagram that shows all possible combinations or outcomes of an experiment.

diagrama de árbol Diagrama con ramificaciones que muestra todas las combinaciones o resultados posibles de un experimento.

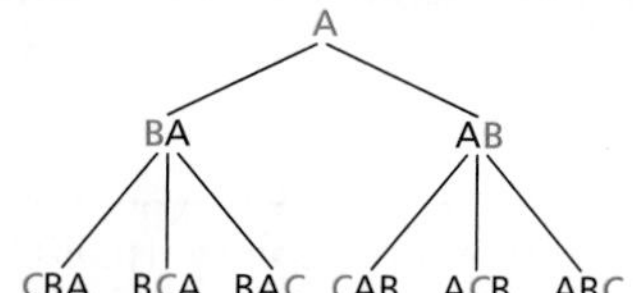

trial (p. 805) In probability, a single repetition or observation of an experiment.

prueba En probabilidad, una sola repetición u observación de un experimento.

In the experiment of rolling a number cube, each roll is one trial.

trigonometric function (p. 929) A function whose rule is given by a trigonometric ratio.

función trigonométrica Función cuya regla es dada por una razón trigonométrica.

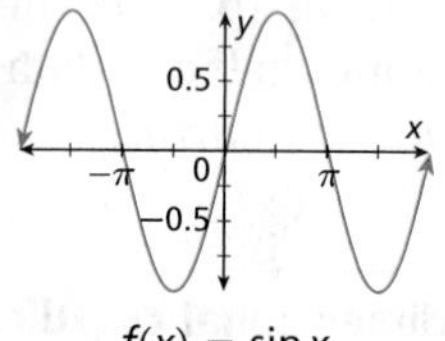

$f(x) = \sin x$

trigonometric ratio (p. 929) Ratio of the lengths of two sides of a right triangle.

razón trigonométrica Razón entre dos lados de un triángulo rectángulo.

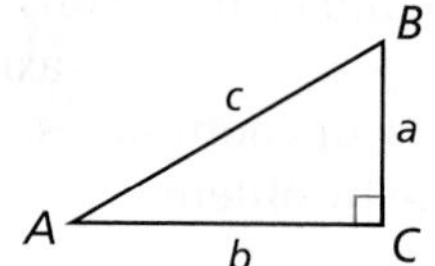

$\sin A = \frac{a}{c}$, $\cos A = \frac{b}{c}$, $\tan A = \frac{a}{b}$

trigonometry (p. 929) The study of the measurement of triangles and of trigonometric functions and their applications.

trigonometría Estudio de la medición de los triángulos y de las funciones trigonométricas y sus aplicaciones.

trinomial (p. 336) A polynomial with three terms.

trinomio Polinomio con tres términos.

$4x^2 + 3xy - 5y^2$

turning point (p. 455) A point on the graph of a function that corresponds to a local maximum (or minimum) where the graph changes from increasing to decreasing (or vice versa).

punto de inflexión Punto de la gráfica de una función que corresponde a un máximo (o mínimo) local donde la gráfica pasa de ser creciente a decreciente (o viceversa).

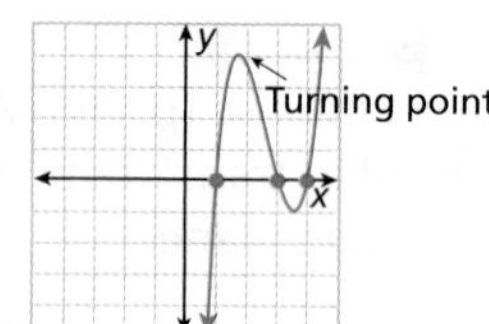

unit circle (p. 944) A circle with a radius of 1, centered at the origin.

círculo unitario Círculo con un radio de 1, centrado en el origen.

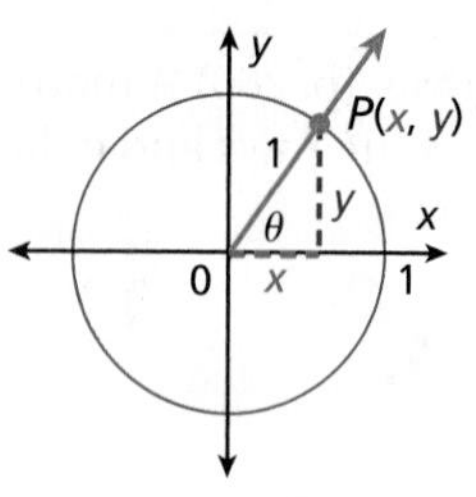

Unit circle

Glossary/Glosario

ENGLISH	SPANISH	EXAMPLES

V

variable (p. 3) A symbol used to represent a quantity that can change.

variable Símbolo utilizado para representar una cantidad que puede cambiar.

$2x + 3$ ← variable

variable matrix (p. 279) The matrix of the variables in a linear system of equations.

matriz de variables Matriz de las variables de un sistema lineal de ecuaciones.

System of equations: $\begin{cases} 2x + 3y = -1 \\ x - 3y = 4 \end{cases}$

Variable matrix: $\begin{bmatrix} x \\ y \end{bmatrix}$

variance (p. 830) The average of squared differences from the mean. The square root of the variance is called the *standard deviation.*

varianza Promedio de las diferencias cuadráticas en relación con la media. La raíz cuadrada de la varianza se denomina *desviación estándar.*

Data set: is $\{6, 7, 7, 9, 11\}$

Mean: $\frac{6 + 7 + 7 + 9 + 11}{5} = 8$

Variance: $\frac{1}{5}(4 + 1 + 1 + 1 + 9) = 3.2$

Venn diagram (p. S72) A diagram used to show relationships between sets.

diagrama de Venn Diagrama utilizado para mostrar la relación entre conjuntos.

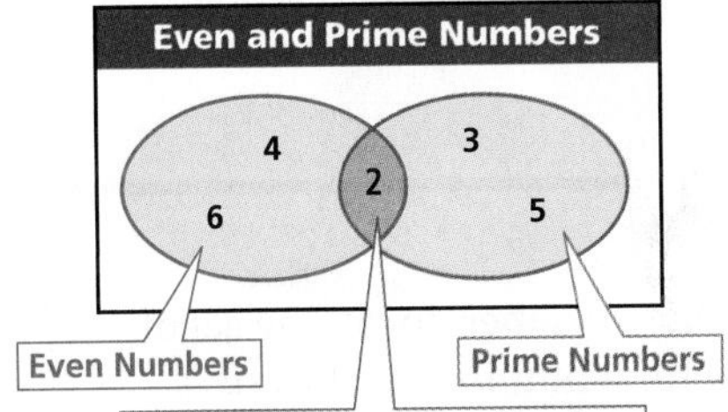

vertex form of a quadratic function (p. 318) A quadratic function written in the form $f(x) = a(x - h)^2 + k$, where a, h, and k are constants and (h, k) is the vertex.

forma en vértice de una función cuadrática Una función cuadrática expresada en la forma $f(x) = a(x - h)^2 + k$, donde a, h y k son constantes y (h, k) es el vértice.

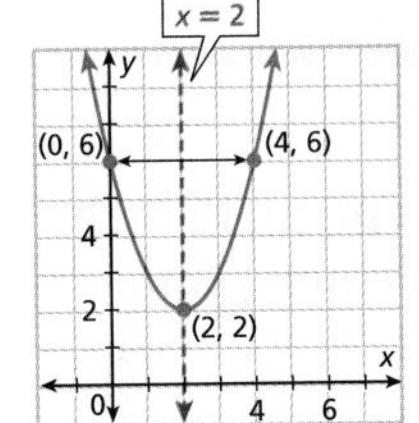

$f(x) = (x - 2)^2 + 2$

vertex of a hyperbola (vertices) (p. 744) The endpoints of the transverse axis of the hyperbola.

vértice de una hipérbola Extremos del eje transversal de la hipérbola.

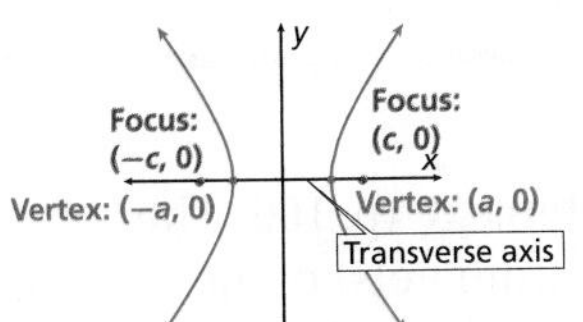

vertex of an absolute-value graph (p. 158) The point where the axis of symmetry intersects the graph.

vértice de una gráfica de valor absoluto Punto donde en el eje de simetría interseca la gráfica.

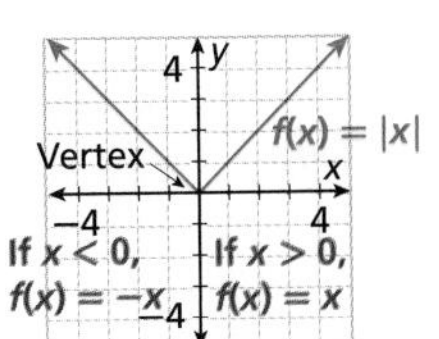

vertex of an ellipse (vertices) (p. 736) The endpoints of the major axis of the ellipse.

vértice de una elipse Extremos del eje mayor de la elipse.

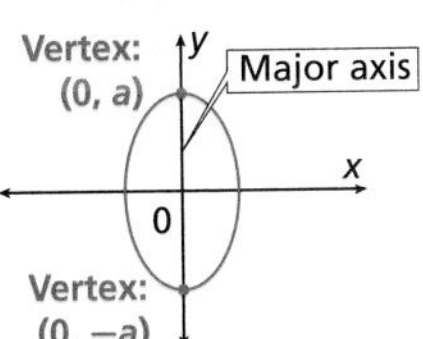

ENGLISH	SPANISH	EXAMPLES
vertex of a parabola (p. 318) The highest or lowest point on the parabola.	**vértice de una parábola** Punto más alto o más bajo de una parábola.	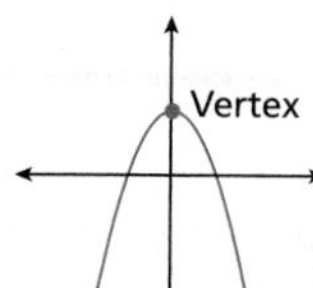
vertical line (p. 108) A line whose equation is $x = a$, where a is the x-intercept. The slope of a vertical line is undefined.	**línea vertical** Línea cuya ecuación es $x = a$, donde a es la intersección con el eje x. La pendiente de una línea vertical es indefinida.	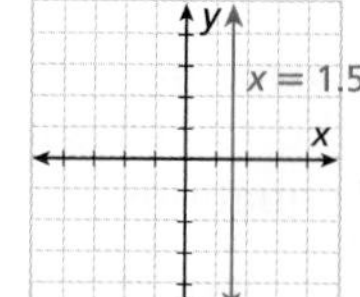
vertical-line test (p. 46) A test used to determine whether a relation is a function. If any vertical line crosses the graph of a relation more than once, the relation is not a function.	**prueba de la línea vertical** Prueba utilizada para determinar si una relación es una función. Si una línea vertical corta la gráfica de una relación más de una vez, la relación no es una función.	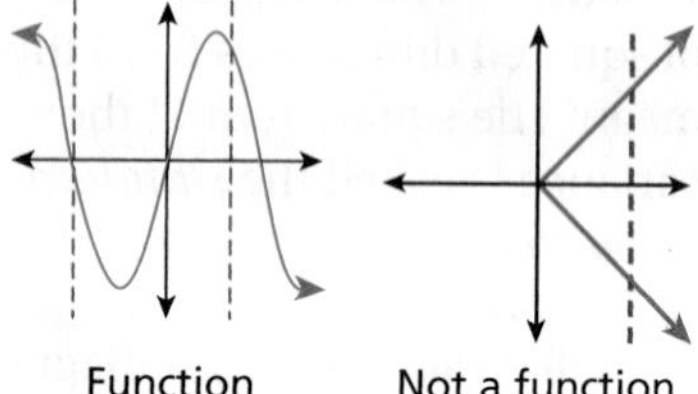

W

whole number (p. 6) The set of natural numbers and zero.	**número cabal** Conjunto de los números naturales y cero.	0, 1, 2, 3, 4, 5, …

X

x-intercept (p. 106) The x-coordinate(s) of the point(s) where a graph intersects the x-axis.	**intersección con el eje x** Coordenada(s) x de uno o más puntos donde una gráfica corta el eje x.	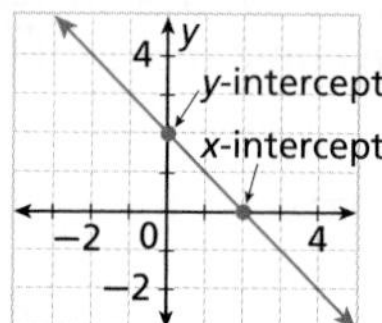

Y

y-intercept (p. 106) The y-coordinate(s) of the point(s) where a graph intersects the y-axis.	**intersección con el eje y** Coordenada(s) y de uno o más puntos donde una gráfica corta el eje y.	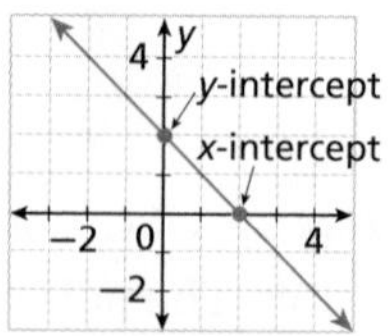

Glossary/Glosario

ENGLISH	SPANISH	EXAMPLES

Z

***z*-axis** (p. 214) The third axis in a three-dimensional coordinate system.	**eje *z*** Tercer eje en un sistema de coordenadas tridimensional.	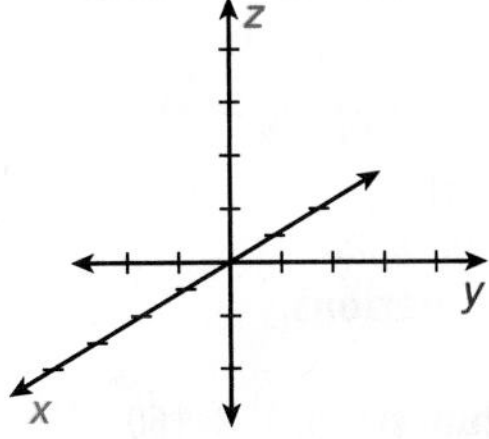
zero exponent (p. 35) For any nonzero real number x, $x^0 = 1$.	**exponente cero** Dado un número real distinto de cero x, $x^0 = 1$.	$5^0 = 1$
zero of a function (p. 333) For the function f, any number x such that $f(x) = 0$.	**cero de una función** Dada la función f, todo número x tal que $f(x) = 0$.	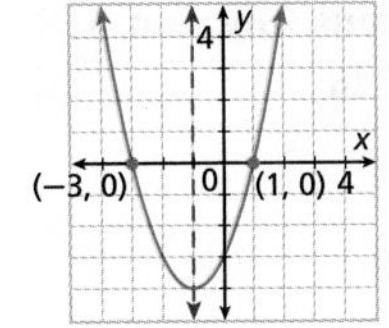 The zeros of $f(x) = x^2 + 2x - 3$ are −3 and 1.

Index

A

Index

Index

Index

D

Index

G

Index

I

J

K

L

M

Index

Index

Index

Index

S

Index

Index

Index

Credits

Abbreviations used: (t) top, (c) center, (b) bottom, (l) left, (r) right, (bkgd) background

Staff Credit

Bruce Albrecht, Angela Beckmann, Lorraine Cooper, Marc Cooper, Jennifer Craycraft, Martize Cross, Nina Degollado, Lydia Doty, Sam Dudgeon, Kelli R. Flanagan, Mary Fraser, Stephanie Friedman, Jeff Galvez, Pam Garner, Diannia Green, Tom Hamilton, Tracie Harris, Liz Huckestein, Jevara Jackson, Kadonna Knape, Cathy Kuhles, Jill M. Lawson, Peter Leighton, Christine MacInnis, Jonathan Martindill, Erin Miller, Stacey Murray, Susan Mussey, Kim Nguyen, Matthew Osment, Manda Reid, Patrick Ricci, Michael Rinella, Michelle Rumpf-Dike, Beth Sample, Annette Saunders, Kay Selke, Robyn Setzen, Patricia Sinnott, Victoria Smith, Jeannie Taylor, Ken Whiteside, Sherri Whitmarsh, Aimee F. Wiley, Glenn P. Worthman, Jill Zarestky

Photo Credits

All images by HRW Photo unless otherwise noted.

Master Icons: teens, authors, (all), Sam Dudgeon/HRW Photo

Front Matter: vi (l), © Masa Ushioda/SeaPics.com; vii (r), Cai Yuhao/Imaginechina/ZUMA Press; viii (l), Tom & Pat Leeson; ix (r), Reuters/CORBIS; ix (bkgd), Martin Sasse/laif/Aurora; x (l), Ezra O. Shaw/Allsport/Getty Images; xi (r), Glasswork by Dave Davidson/Image by Jeff Clarke Photography; xii (l), Robert Glusic/Photodisc Green/gettyimages; xiii (r), Lester Lefkowitz/CORBIS; xiv (l), CORBIS; xv (r), Bert Wiklund; xvii (r), SIME s.a.s/eStock Photo; xviii (l), © The Studio Dog/PhotoDisc Green/gettyimages; xix (r), Martin Rogers/Getty Images; xx (t), © PunchStock; xx (b), Stewart Cohen/Photodisc Red/gettyimages; xx (c) LWA-Dann Tardif/CORBIS; xxi (l), NASA; xxi (t), L. Hammel/A. van der Voort/Bildarchiv Monheim GmbH/Alamy Photos; xxi (c), James L. Amos/CORBIS; xxi (r), © Kevin Lamarque/Reuters/CORBIS; xxii (b), Victoria Smith/HRW.

Chapter One: 2–3 (all), © Masa Ushioda/SeaPics.com; 6 (tr), Gary Rhijnsburger/Masterfile; 6 (bl), NASA Kennedy Space Center; 11 (t, inset), Victoria Smith/HRW; 12 (l), Mark A. Schneider/Photo Researchers, Inc.; 14 (tr), on-page credit; 17 (br, inset), Sam Dudgeon/HRW; 18 (cl), Dinodia Picture Agency; 18 (bl), NASA Kennedy Space Center; 21 (tr), © Royalty Free/CORBIS; 25 (tr), Chase Swift/CORBIS; 25 (bl), NASA Kennedy Space Center; 25 (cl), Jason Hawkes Photo Library; 27 (tr), Don Emmert/AFP/Getty Images; 27 (tr), Cartoon copyrighted by Mark Parisi, printed with permission.; 29 (tr), Orlin Wagner/AP/Wide World Photos; 31 (cl), Mike Elicson/AP/Wide World Photos; 31 (bl), NASA Kennedy Space Center; 34 (tr), NASA; 37 (l), NASA/JPL/University of Arizona; 38 (r), Cornell University; 39 (l), James Martin/Getty Images; 40 (tl), NASA Kennedy Space Center; 42 (tl), NASA Kennedy Space Center; 42 (tr), NASA; 44 (tr), Bananastock; 45 (t, tc, bc, b), Victoria Smith/HRW; 48 (tr), United States Mint Image; 49 (tl), Victoria Smith/HRW; 49 (br), Sam Dudgeon/HRW; 51 (tr), Adastra/Getty Images; 53 (tr), Dallas and John Heaton/PictureQuest; 55 (tl), © Royalty Free/CORBIS; 56 (tl), Victoria Smith/HRW; 57 (cl), Len Rubenstein/Index Stock Imagery, Inc.; 60 (t), © PunchStock; 64 (bl), Victoria Smith/HRW; 64 (cl), Terry I. Husebye/workbookstock.com; 67 (t), Alex Rosenfield/Science Photo Library; 71 (bl), Victoria Smith/HRW; 72 (l), NASA; 72 (c), Copyright © Image Source Limited ; 72 (cr), Photodisc/Getty Images; 74 (tl), Victoria Smith/HRW; 74 (br), George H. H. Huey/CORBIS.

Chapter Two: 86–87 (all), Cai Yuhao/Imaginechina/ZUMA Press; 90 (tr), Corel Royalty Free; 91 (tl), Boccon-Gibod Thierry/Gamma; 95 (cl), © CORBIS SYGMA; 95 (bl), AbleStock.com; 97 (tr), Brad Wrobleski/Masterfile; 98 (br), Mike Dobel/Alamy Photos; 102 (tl), AbleStock.com; 102 (inset), PictureNet/CORBIS; 102 (bl), D. Hurst/Alamy Photos; 102 (cr), Andrew Brown; Ecoscene/CORBIS; 105 (tr), NASA/Science Photo Library; 110 (cr), Patrick Beckers; 111 (tl), AbleStock.com; 111 (cl), © Image State/Alamy; 115 (tr), Ray Stubblebine/Reuters/CORBIS; 117 (bl), Digital Vision; 118 (inset), Sam Dudgeon/HRW; 118 (inset), Sam Dudgeon/HRW; 118 (inset), Sam Dudgeon/HRW; 121 (cl), Erich Lessing/Art Resource, NY; 121 (tl), AbleStock.com; 124 (tr), Photo by 20th Century Fox/ZUMA Press; 128 (bl), Detlev Van Ravenswaay/Science Photo Library; 129 (tr), ©Alamy Photos; 129 (bl), AbleStock.com; 130 (tr), Andy Christiansen/HRW; 132 (tl), AbleStock.com; 132 (br), ©Onne van der Wal/CORBIS; 134 (tr), © CORBIS; 137 (tr), Sam Dudgeon/HRW; 139 (bl), Steve Vidler/SuperStock; 139 (cl), Russell C. Poole; 142 (tr), Annie Griffiths Belt/CORBIS; 144 (tl), Carlos Lopez-Barillas/Corbis; 147 (tl), Tim Zurowski/CORBIS; 148 (br), James L. Amos/CORBIS; 148 (tl), Steve Vidler/SuperStock; 150 (tr), Courtesy of the Louisville Slugger Museum; 155 (cl), Patrick Hertzog/AFP/Getty Images; 155 (bl), Steve Vidler/SuperStock; 158 (tr), Morton Beebe & Associates; 161 (br), Photodisc/gettyimages; 162 (bl), Steve Vidler/SuperStock; 162 (cr), © PunchStock; 164 (br), Kim Christensen; 164 (tl), Steve Vidler/SuperStock; 174 (br), Bob Krist/CORBIS; 176 (cr), Bob Krist/CORBIS; 177 (b), Jim Wark/Airphoto; 177 (cr), Michael Townsend/Getty Images.

Chapter Three: 178–179 (all), Tom & Pat Leeson; 182 (tr), Richard Price/Getty Images; 186 (tl), © Royalty Free/CORBIS; 187 (tl), Michael Melford/Getty Images; 190 (tr), Eric Vandeville/Gamma; 193 (tl), Jesse Cohen; 193 (bl), Comstock Royalty Free; 195 (br), Frank Herholdt/Alamy Photos; 195 (tl), Phil Kember/Index Stock Imagery, Inc.; 195 (tr), Javier Pierini/gettyimages; 195 (bl), Jules Frazier/Photodisc Green/gettyimages; 196 (tl), © Royalty Free/CORBIS; 199 (tl), VAN HASSELT JOHN/CORBIS SYGMA; 200 (cl), Galen Rowell/CORBIS; 203 (tl), © Royalty Free/CORBIS; 210 (tl), © Royalty Free/CORBIS; 210 (cl), CORBIS; 212 (tl), © Royalty Free/CORBIS; 212 (br), Paltera Stefano/Gamma; 214 (tr, inset), Gilles Mingasson/Getty Images; 217 (inset), David B. Fleetham/Photolibrary; 220 (tr), Al Tielemans/SI/Newsport/CORBIS; 222 (tl), Ralph Freso/East Valley Tribune/AP/Wide World Photos; 225 (bl), ACE STOCK LIMITED/Alamy; 227 (bl), ACE STOCK LIMITED/Alamy; 227 (br), Dean/Alamy; 228 © Mark Peterson/CORBIS; 228 (tl), ACE STOCK LIMITED/Alamy.

Chapter Four: 242–243 (all), Reuters/CORBIS; 242–243 (bkgd), Martin Sasse/laif/Aurora; 244 (tr), United Press International/NewsCom; 248 (cr), © Paul A. Souders/CORBIS; 251 (bl), Photodisc/gettyimages; 253 (tr), ZUMA Press; 255 (tr), Victoria Smith/HRW; 258 (cl), Itar-Tass Photos/NewsCom; 258 (bl), Photodisc/gettyimages; 259 (tl), Jeff Cooper/Salina Journal/AP/Wide World Photos; 262 (tr), The Granger Collection, New York; 266 (tl) © 2005 The M.C. Escher Company-Holland. All rights reserved. www.mcescher.com; 266 (bl), Photodisc/gettyimages; 268 (b), Brian Summers/Veer Images; 268 (tl), Photodisc/gettyimages; 270 (tr), Rosemary Weller/Getty Images; 273 (cr), Sam Dudgeon/HRW; 275 (cl), James L. Amos/CORBIS; 276 (tl), Purestock/SuperStock; 277 (bl), LWA-Dann Tardif/CORBIS; 284 (tl), Purestock/SuperStock; 285 (tr), Artville/gettyimages; 287 (tr), © Royalty Free/CORBIS; 289 (bl), © Royalty Free/CORBIS; 292 (tl), Victoria Smith/HRW; 292 (cr), ADAM NADEL/AFP/Getty Images; 292 (bl), Purestock/SuperStock; 293 (t), Victoria Smith/HRW; 294 (br), Stone/Getty Images; 294 Purestock/SuperStock; 307 Copyright © Image Source Limited ; 308 (bl), Courtesy James Island County Park; 308 (cr), Copyright © Image Source Limited ; 309 (tr), Paul Franklin.

Chapter Five: 310–311 (all), Ezra O. Shaw/Allsport/Getty Images; 315 (tr), Bill Brooks/Masterfile; 321 (tl), © Royalty Free/CORBIS; 321 (bl), Andy Christiansen/HRW; 323 (tr), Robert Holland/Image Bank/Getty Images; 329 (tl), James Robinson/Animals Animals/Earth Scenes; 329 (bl), Andy Christiansen/HRW; 333 (tr), Aflo Foto; 339 (bl), Andy Christiansen/HRW; 339 (tl), David Mendelsohn/Masterfile; 341 (tr), David Welling/Nature Picture Library; 346 (br), Peter Guttman/CORBIS; 347 (tl), Andy Christiansen/HRW; 350 (tr), on-page credit; 354 (cl), The Granger Collection, New York; 356 (tr), Reuters/CORBIS; 358 (bl), © BananaStock Ltd.; 362 (tl), Scaled Composites/SPL/Photo Researchers, Inc.; 362 (bl), Andy Christiansen/HRW; 362 (inset), Steve Bloom Images; 364 (tl), Andy Christiansen/HRW; 364 (br), Ray Stubblebine/Reuters/CORBIS; 366 (tr), David M. Dennis/Animals Animals/Earth Scenes; 372 (tl), Andy Christiansen/HRW; 374 (tr), The Granger Collection, New York; 378 (bl), Andy Christiansen/HRW; 380 (l), Science Photo Library/Photo Researchers, Inc.; 382 (tr), Gregory Sams/SPL/Photo Researchers, Inc.; 387 (r), Mehau Kulyk/Photo Researchers, Inc.; 387 (l), A. Pasieka/Photo Researchers, Inc.; 388 (bl), Andy Christiansen/HRW; 390 (tl), Andy Christiansen/HRW; 390 (b), Jennifer Shephard, The Truth/AP/Wide World Photos; 390 (r), Andy Christiansen/HRW.

Chapter Six: 402–403 (all), Glasswork by Dave Davidson/Image by Jeff Clarke Photography; 406 (tr), Dan Lim/Masterfile; 411 (bl), © Hans Neleman/The Image Bank/Getty Images; 414 (tr), Digital Vision/eStock Photo; 417 (tl), © LWA-Dann Tardif/CORBIS; 419 (bl), © Hans Neleman/The Image Bank/Getty Images; 419 (tl), © Bettman/CORBIS; 422 (tr), © Cartoon Stock; 425 (l), Theater of Electricity at the Museum of Science, Boston; 427 (bl), © Hans Neleman/The Image Bank/Getty Images; 427 (tl), © Bettman/CORBIS; 428 (tr), © PhotoDisc/gettyimages; 428 (br), © PhotoDisc/gettyimages; 430 (tr), Ian Lloyd/Masterfile; 434 (tl), © Hans Neleman/The Image Bank/Getty Images; 435 (bl), Zuma Press/NewsCom; 436 (tl), © Hans Neleman/The Image Bank/Getty Images; 436 (br), © Neal Preston/CORBIS; 438 (tr), Sam Dudgeon/HRW; 443 (bl), Neil Beer/CORBIS; 443 (cl), © 2005 Busch Entertainment Corporation. All rights reserved; 445 (tr), © Mark M. Lawrence/CORBIS; 450 (tl), Neil Beer/CORBIS; 450 (cl), © James Randklev/CORBIS; 453 (tr), © Craig Lovell/CORBIS; 458 (bl), Neil Beer/CORBIS; 458 (tl), PHOTOTAKE Inc./Alamy

Credits

Photo

All Teacher-to-Teacher photos courtesy of the teachers.

Chapter One TE wrap: 2 (tl), NASA Kennedy Space Center; 2 (cl), Victoria Smith/HRW.

Chapter Two TE wrap: 86 (tl), AbleStock; 86 (cl), Steve Vidler/SuperStock.

Chapter Three TE wrap: 178 (tl), © Royalty Free/CORBIS; 178 (cl), ACE STOCK LIMITED/Alamy.

Chapter Four TE wrap: 242 (tl), PhotoDisc/gettyimages; 242 (cl), Purestock/SuperStock.

Chapter Five TE wrap: 310 (tl, cl), Andy Christiansen/HRW.

Chapter Six TE wrap: 402 (tl), Hans Neleman/The Image Bank/Getty Images; 402 (cl), Burke Triolo/Brand X Pictures/gettyimages.

Chapter Seven TE wrap: 486 (cl), age fotostock/Imagestate.

Chapter Eight TE wrap: 546 (tl), Stockdisc/gettyimages; 546 (cl), Comstock Images/Alamy.

Chapter Nine TE wrap: 650 (cl), © Royalty Free/CORBIS.

Chapter Ten TE wrap: 718 (cl), Victoria Smith/HRW.

Chapter Eleven TE wrap: 794 (tl), Sam Dudgeon/HRW; 794 (cl), © ThinkStock LLC/Index Stock Imagery, Inc.

Chapter Twelve TE wrap: 858 (tl), © Anthony Lysson; 858 (cl), © 2005 Marvel/CORBIS.

Chapter Thirteen TE wrap: 924 (tl), Norbert Wu/Minden Pictures; 924 (cl), D. Hurst/Alamy.

Chapter Fourteen TE wrap: 986 (tl), Eckhard Slawik/SPL/Photo Researchers, Inc.; 986 (cl), Sam Dudgeon/HRW.

Photos; 460 (tr), © Black Star/Alamy Photos; 462 (r), Pixonnet.com/Alamy Photos; 464 (bl), Neil Beer/CORBIS; 464 (cl), Tom Stack/Tom Stack & Associates; 466 (tr), Getty Images; 469 (bl, bc, br), Victoria Smith/HRW; 470 (r), Worldsat International/SPL/Photo Researchers, Inc.; 472 (b), © Richard T. Nowitz/CORBIS; 484 (b), Grace Davies/Omni-Photo Communications; 484 (cr), Courtesy Adventure Aquarium; 485 (r), © Bettman/CORBIS.

Chapter Seven: 486–487 (all), Robert Glusic/Photodisc Green/gettyimages; 490 (tr), Richard Lewis/AP/Wide World Photos; 491 (b), © PunchStock; 493 (r), M. Kalab/Custom Medical Stock Photo; 494 (l), Bettmann/CORBIS; 496 (l), CDC/PHIL/CORBIS; 498 (tr), Cartoon copyrighted by Mark Parisi, printed with permission.; 502 (cl), Vandystadt-Didier Givois/TIPS Images; 503 (l), © PunchStock; 505 (t), Peter Van Steen/HRW; 509 (br), The Garden Picture Library/Alamy Photos; 509 (bc), Steve Satushek/Getty Images; 509 (bl), jack sparticus/Alamy Photos; 512 (tr), Simon Kwong/CORBIS; 517 (tr), Fred Espenak/Photo Researchers, Inc.; 517 (cl), George Bernard/Photo Researchers, Inc.; 518 (l), Randy Allbritton/Photodisc Green/gettyimages; 518 (r), Christie's Images/CORBIS; 519 (c, inset), Sam Dudgeon/HRW; 520 (b), Jerry King/eToon.com; 522 (tr), Philippe Petit-Mars/CORBIS; 527 (bl), age fotostock/ImageState; 527 (inset), Sam Dudgeon/HRW; 527 (cl), © photographer/Alamy Photos; 531 (t), D. Schwimmer/Bruce Coleman, Inc.; 533 (t), R.A. Mittermeir/Bruce Coleman, Inc.; 535 (cl), franc Lukasseck/Picture Press/photolibrary; 535 (bl), age fotostock/Imagestate; 537 (t), Scott Bodell/Phototake; 540 (all images), © Royalty Free/CORBIS; 542 (cl), David Ducros/Photo Researchers, Inc.; 543 (bl), age fotostock/ImageState; 543 (cl), Susumu Nishinf/SPL/Photo Researchers, Inc; 545 (t), Steve Taylor/Getty Images; 549 (cl), © PunchStock; 550 (t), age fotostock/Imagestate; 551 (bl), © PunchStock; 552 (b), Jim Wark/Airphotona.

Chapter Eight: 546–547 (all), Letser Lefkowitz/CORBIS; 568 (tl, tr, c, b), Andy Christiansen/HRW; 569 (t), Steve Gates/AP/Wide World Photos; 571 (b), Andy Christiansen/HRW; 574 (cl), Robbie Jack/CORBIS; 574 (tr), Sam Dudgeon/HRW; 575 (t), Stockdisc/gettyimages; 577 (t), Design Pics Inc/Alamy; 581 (cl), Dr. E. Strouhal/Werner Forman/Art Resource, NY; 581 (r), PhotoDisc/gettyimages; 581 (bl), Stockdisc/gettyimages; 583 (t), Digital Vision/gettyimages; 587 (t), BananaStock/age fotostock; 589 (cl), L. Hammel/A. van der Voort/Bildarchiv Monheim GmbH/Alamy Photos; 589 (tl), Stockdisc/gettyimages; 592 (t), Simon Hayter/Toronto Star/NewsCom; 598 (tl), The Granger Collection, New York; 598 (bl), Stockdisc/gettyimages; 600 (tr), © Skip Brown/Getty Images; 602 (tr), Photodisc Blue/Getty Images; 606 (r), Ezra Shaw/Getty Images; 606 (t), Stockdisc/gettyimages; 606 (tl), © William Sallaz/Duomo/CORBIS; 608 (l), Stockdisc/gettyimages; 608 (b), Michael Kim/CORBIS; 608 (r), Bettmann/CORBIS; 610 (t), Paul Sancya/AP/Wide World Photos; 615 (cl), Chris Johnsr/National Geographic Image Collection; 616 (cl), Breck P. Kent/Animals Animals/Earth Scenes; 616 (tl), Comstock Images/Alamy; 619 (t), NASA; 622 (b), NASA; 625 (l), John Boyd/photolibrary.com; 626 (cl), John Gay/Ensign/AP/Wide World Photos; 626 (tl), Comstock Images/Alamy; 626 (br), © Eastcott Momatiuk/Photographer's Choice/Getty Images; 628 (t), The New Yorker Collection, 2002, Leo Cullum from Cartoonbank.com. All rights reserved.; 633 (l), Don Lloyd/The Reporter/AP/Wide World Photos; 634 (t), Comstock Images/Alamy; 636 (t), Comstock Images/Alamy Photos; 636 (b), Bob Krist/CORBIS; 640 (b), Thomas Mangelsen/Minden Pictures; 648 (cl), Michael Quinton/Minden Pictures; 649 (inset), Bettmann/CORBIS; 649 (t), Bruce Ando/Stone/Getty Images.

Chapter Nine: 650–651 (all), CORBIS; 654 (tr), Alan Schein Photography/CORBIS; 659 (cl), Phillip Colla/Oceanlight; 660 (tl, tc, tr), Sam Dudgeon/HRW; 662 (tr), ©Mike Finn-Kelcey/Reuters/CORBIS; 664 (bl), © PunchStock; 667 (l), Victoria Smith/HRW; 672 (t), Mike Baldwin/www.cartoonstock.com; 677 (cl), eye35.com/Alamy ; 678 (tl, tr), Digital Vision/gettyimages; 680 (b), Wernher Krutein; 682 (t, tl), Sam Dudgeon/HRW; 687 (cl), © PunchStock; 690 (t), Sam Dudgeon/HRW; 694 (l), © PunchStock; 695 (t), CORBIS Royalty free; 698 (t), Bruce Ayres/Getty Images; 700 CORBIS Royalty Fee Photographs; 700 (t), Tim Fitzharris/Minden Pictures; 703 SPL/Photo Researchers, Inc.; 704 (bl), Stuart Westmorland/Getty Images; 704 (tl), CORBIS Royalty Free; 706 (c), PhotoDisc/ gettyimages; 706 (b), Gerard Vandystadt/TIPS Images; 706 (tl), Carl & Ann Purcell/CORBIS.

Chapter Ten: 718–719 (all), Bert Wiklund; 727 (l), Jeremy Woodhouse/Digital Vision/gettyimages; 729 (t), Adam Crowley/Photodisc Green/gettyimages; 733 (cl), Jason Hawkes/CORBIS; 736 (tr), Scott Brownell/Museum of Science and Industry, Chicago; 740 (b), Lani Howe/Photri-Microstock; 741 (cl), Free Agents Limited/CORBIS; 744 (t), David Fleetham/Getty Images; 749 (cl), Paul Katz/Index Stock Imagery, Inc.; 751 (t), © David Madison Sports Images, Inc.; 755 (l), Kevin Taylor/Alamy; 756 (t), AFP/Getty Images; 757 (cl), Sheila Terry/Photo Researchers, Inc.; 758 (b), Mehau Kulyk/SPL/Photo Researchers, Inc.; 760 (t), Jim Sugar/CORBIS; 761 (t), © PunchStock; 764 (b), NOAO/AURA/NSF/PHOTO RESEARCHERS, INC; 765 (tl), Victoria Smith/HRW; 768 (t), Travel Ink/Digital Vision/gettyimages; 773 (cl), Bruno Fert/CORBIS; 773 (b), Victoria Smith/HRW; 775 (b), Copyright © Image Source Limited ; 776 (t), Victoria Smith/HRW; 776 (b), Randy Faris/CORBIS; 788 (cl), ©CORBIS; 788 (b), Bettmann/CORBIS; 789 (t), Jim Wark/Airphoto; 789 (b), John Gress/Reuters/CORBIS.

Chapter Eleven: 794 (t), Sam Dudgeon/HRW/Artwork by Teri Jonas, Courtesy Wally Workman Gallery, Austin, TX; 796 (l, cl, cr, r), ©The Andy Warhol Foundation for the Visual Arts/Corbis; 797 (r), Japack Photo Library/Photolibrary; 799 (bl), Sam Dudgeon/HRW; 799 (cl), Jacek Bednarczyk/EPA Photos/NewsCom; 799 (br), Sam Dudgeon/HRW; 802 (t), Sam Dudgeon/HRW; 803 (r), Sam Dudgeon/HRW; 805 (r), Sam Dudgeon/HRW; 808 (tl, tr), Sam Dudgeon/HRW; 811 (t), Adey Bryant/www.CartoonStock.com; 813 (r), Jason Reeves/Reuters; 813 (l), Jim Young/Reuters; 814 (t), Sam Dudgeon/HRW; 816 (l), © Kevin Lamarque/Reuters/CORBIS; 816 (bl, br), Sam Dudgeon/HRW; 818 (t), Sam Dudgeon/HRW; 819 (b), Sam Dudgeon/HRW; 820 (r), Sam Dudgeon/HRW; 821 (t), Sam Dudgeon/HRW/The Isahinkai Foundation; 823 (l), CBS/Landov; 824 (l, tr, all inset), Sam Dudgeon/HRW; 826 (all photos), Sam Dudgeon/HRW; 828 (t), Republished with permission of Globe Newspaper Company, Inc./Stan Grossfeld; 829 (b), © Comstock Images/Alamy Photos; 834 (t), © Lester Lefkowitz/CORBIS; 835 (t), © ThinkStock LLC/Index Stock Imagery, Inc.; 836 (t), © ThinkStock LLC/Index Stock Imagery, Inc.; 836 (b), © Ron Sherman/Getty Images; 841 (l), Werner Layer/Animals Animals/Earth Scenes; 841 (b), © ThinkStock LLC/Index Stock Imagery, Inc.; 842 (l), The Granger Collection, New York; 844 (b), © Wolfgang Kaehler/CORBIS.

Chapter Twelve: 858–859 (all); SIME s.a.s/eStock Photo; 862 (t), The Image Bank/Getty Images; 866 (l), The Granger Collection, New York; 866 (bl, br), Sam Dudgeon/HRW; 867 (tl), Anthony Lysson; 870 (t), Jim Barcus/Kansas City Star/KRT Photos/NewsCom; 872 (b), Blow Up/Getty Images; 875 (l), The Granger Collection, New York; 876 (tl), Anthony Lysson; 877 (b), Stewart Cohen/Photodisc Red/gettyimages; 879 (tl, tr), United States Mint Image; 879 (tc), ™ Rachel Robinson by CMG Worldwide/www.JackieRobinson.com; Stamp Designs: © 1982, United States Postal Service. Displayed with permission. All rights reserved. Written authorization from the Postal Service is required to use, reproduce, post, transmit, distribute, or publicly display these images.; 880 (b), Lucca DiCecco/Alamy; 882 (t), Anthony Lysson; 885 (t), Chuck Pefley/Alamy Photos; 885 (cr), David Noton/Getty Images; 886 (tl), Anthony Lysson; 888 (b), STEPHANE/Gamma; 890 (tl), Reuters/CORBIS; 890 (cl), PhotoDisc green/gettyimages; 894 (t), REUTERS/Ian Hodgson/CORBIS; 896 (t), Bettman/CORBIS; 897 (t), Ingram Publishing/Alamy; 900 (t), Vaughan Fleming/David Parkeker/Photo Researchers, Inc.; 905 (t), Victoria Smith/HRW; 906 (t), Ingram Publishing/Alamy; 908 (t), Ingram Publishing/Alamy; 908 (b), Sony Pictures/ZUMA; 922 (b), Lester Lefkowitz/CORBIS; 922 (cr), Lake County Museum/CORBIS; 923 (r), Digital Vision/gettyimages; 923 (b), ImageState/Alamy Photos; 923 (c), Don Farrall/Photodisc Green/getty images.

Chapter Thirteen: 924–925 (all), © The Studio Dog/PhotoDisc Green/gettyimages; 929 (t), © John Elk III/Lonely Planet Images; 934 (tl), © Larry Lee Photography/CORBIS; 934 (b), NORBERT WU/Minden Pictures; 936 (t), Photo by Rick Wilking/Reuters; 940 (t), © Steve Allen/Brand X Pictures/Alamy Photos; 940 (b), NORBERT WU/Minden Pictures; 943 (t), NASA Marshall Space Flight Center (NASA-MSFC); 948 (t), NORBERT WU/Minden Pictures; 949 (b), © Michael Keller/CORBIS; 950 (t), Jimmy Chin/National Geographic Image Collection; 953 (b), © GOODSHOOT/Alamy Photos; 954 (l), © DAVID LOH/Reuters/CORBIS; 955 (t, tl), NORBERT WU/Minden Pictures; 956 (b), © Amos Nachoum/CORBIS; 958 (t), © Ron Watts/CORBIS; 964 (t), © D. Hurst/Alamy Photos; 964 (l), © Jay Ireland & Georgienne E. Bradley; 966 (t), © VALLON FABRICE/CORBIS KIPA; 967 (b), © Michael A. Keller/CORBIS; 970 (b), Jim Wark/Airphoto; 972 (t), © D. Hurst/Alamy Photos; 972 (l), © Charles and Josette Lenars/CORBIS; 974 (t), © D. Hurst/Alamy Photos; 974 (b), George Hall/Check Six.

Chapter Fourteen: 986–987 (all), Martin Rogers/Getty Images; 990 (t), Thinkstock/Alamy Photos; 992 (r), Charles D. Winters; 994 (t), Index Stock Imagery/Photo Library; 996 (t), Brand X Pictures/Alamy Photos; 996 (b), Eckhard Slawik/SPL/Photo Researchers, Inc.; 998 (t), Richard Gaul/Getty Images; 1002 (t), Eckhard Slawik/SPL/Photo Researchers, Inc.; 1002 (cl), Allan H Shoemake/Getty Images; 1004 (t), Eckhard Slawik/SPL/Photo Researchers, Inc.; 1004 (bl), Paul A. Souders/CORBIS; 1004 (br), Buddy Mays/CORBIS; 1008 (t), Duomo/CORBIS; 1009 (b), Ken Weingart/SuperStock/Alamy; 1012 (t), Sam Dudgeon/HRW; 1018 (b), Donald Miralle/Getty Images; 1020 (t), Donald Miralle/Getty Images; 1025 (t), Sam Dudgeon/HRW; 1025 (cl), Kevin Fleming/CORBIS; 1027 (t), Cosmo Condina/TIPS Images; 1032 (tl), Yuriko Nakao/Reuters/CORBIS; 1032 (b), Sam Dudgeon/HRW; 1034 (t, b), Sam Dudgeon/HRW; 1046 (cr), Brooks Kraft/CORBIS; 1046 (b), Brownie Harris/CORBIS; 1047 (t), Tom Till/Alamy Photos; 1047 (b), Jeff Greenberg/Index Stock/Photo Library.

Backmatter: 1060, Bettmann/Corbis, S2 (t), John Langford/HRW; S3 (b), John Langford/HRW.

Credits